# MAMMALS OF THE WORLD

VOLUME III

*A Classified Bibliography*

BY ERNEST P. WALKER

FLORENCE WARNICK
KENNETH I. LANGE
HOWARD E. UIBLE
SYBIL E. HAMLET
MARY A. DAVIS
PATRICIA F. WRIGHT

THE JOHNS HOPKINS PRESS, BALTIMORE
1964

*Material for these books was prepared under the project*
*"Genera of Recent Mammals of the World,"*
*begun by the author prior to 1933.*
*The last seven years and three months of the project were*
*financed by THE NATIONAL INSTITUTES OF HEALTH*
*under Research Grant 5140 and were sponsored*
*by the New York Zoological Society.*


Printed in the United States of America
Library of Congress Catalog No. 64-23218
*Second Printing, 1965*
*Third Printing, 1967*

# CONTENTS

## *Volume III*

### *A Classified Bibliography of Literature Regarding Mammals*

PAGE

PAGE

GEOGRAPHICAL



GENERAL

PAGE

# INTRODUCTION

This is one of the three volumes prepared under a National Institutes of Health grant and sponsored by the New York Zoological Society for the purpose of bringing together basic information regarding the genera of recent mammals in such form that it can be understood by laymen and students as well as advanced workers.

This volume contains only bibliographic citations which were assembled and put into book form to supplement Volumes I and II. The first two volumes are complete in themselves. This volume can be used as a separate unit or in association with the other two.

To produce this volume and the Selected Bibliography in Volume I, about 70,000 bibliographic cards of mammal literature were assembled from the Recent Literature section of the Journal of Mammalogy from its beginning in 1918 to the end of 1960, from the Author Index File of the Division of Mammals of the U.S. National Museum, from the Library of Congress, from the Library of the U.S. Department of Agriculture, from the Library of the U.S. Fish and Wildlife Service, from *Wildlife Review*, published by the Fish and Wildlife Service of the U.S. Department of Interior, and from a few other minor sources. The cards were sorted for filing under the classifications used herein, and duplicates were eliminated when detected. It is entirely possible that some duplicates may have inadvertently been included, and a few titles are meant to appear in more than one location because of the nature of the contents. It has not been possible to verify the titles, so they have been used as they appeared on the cards unless there was an obvious error. The titles and other data were not uniformly written on the cards, resulting in many inconsistencies. For our purposes we wished to place the title first, instead of the author's name as is usual. Foreign titles have been translated into English, accurately, we hope. The English title appears first in parentheses, followed by the original foreign title, permitting the user to request the publication under the proper name and to translate it himself.

The titles in this volume and in the Selected Bibliography in Volume I are classified by subjects to facilitate locating articles or books when the author's name is not known to the searcher. There are four main groupings:

1. **Orders.** All titles that pertain to only one order are in this group. (Names of a few publications that treat different orders in different volumes or parts sometimes appear under more than one order.) There are various subdivisions under the orders to treat the *families* and other appropriate subdivisions which will give the greatest assistance in the search for articles regarding various subjects.

2. **Geographical.** In this section, titles pertaining to mammals of given geographical areas are grouped according to the areas. These are subdivided also.

3. **General.** Titles that do not readily fall into either of the other major classifications are included in this group—natural histories, zoologies, and many other books and papers of a general character.

4. **Periodicals.** In addition to the list of books and articles, there is a list of periodicals that regularly or occasionally publish articles regarding mammals. Some of the publications have been discontinued and some are to be found only in a few large, specialized libraries. The list contains both technical and popular publications, for the latter often contain articles that supply basic information that was not previously,

or is not generally, known. Publications are listed that are issued by institutions such as museums as parts of series and may be published at irregular intervals.

Perhaps the most important periodical is the *Proceedings* of the Zoological Society of London. In 1830 the Zoological Society of London began issuing its *Proceedings.* This remarkable work is still continuing and is the longest series of any publication dealing with such a wide variety of animal life. Throughout its entire life, it has maintained a high standard and yet has not become too technical for the layman. It is profusely illustrated, and the superb pictures, some in color, that appear in it are often the only visual record of the appearance of certain animals. In some years as many as 1,108 pages were issued.

The *Transactions* of the Society are quarto volumes and are somewhat more technical in character, but they are well illustrated and almost invariably understandable to the layman. These two sets, together with the remarkably good collections of living animals maintained by the organization in the Zoo in Regents Park, London, and in large enclosures at Whipsnade, are a very outstanding contribution, if not the world's finest, by a single organization privately financed.

Many of the titles listed herein could be placed in two or more locations under our system, so if titles are not found in one location, it is possible that a search of other related topics may reveal them.

Volumes I and II contain:

1. Pictures of one or more representatives of the 1,044 genera so far as they have been obtainable;
2. Text regarding the orders, families, and genera;
3. A selected bibliography of about 4,500 titles; and
4. An index to Volumes I and II, which lists in bold-face type the orders, families, and genera which are considered valid; many synonyms of the generic names and vernacular names are also listed.

# MAMMALS OF THE WORLD

MONOTREMATA

STRAY NOTES ON MONOTREMES. Charles Barrett. Victorian Nat., vol.51, no.1, pp.22-24, pl.5, May, 1934.

THE RED BLOOD CORPUSCLES OF PRIMITIVE MAMMALS. E. A. Briggs. Nature, London, vol.138, no.3496, p.762, Oct.31, 1936.

FIELD NOTES ON THE LIFE HISTORY OF THE MONOTREMES. Harry Burrell. Australian Zool., vol.1, pt.8, pp.231-240, figs.1-6, July 30, 1920.

MISCELLANEOUS NOTES ON MONOTREMES. Harry Burrell. Australian Zoologist, vol.6, pt. 4, pp.387-392, Feb.13, 1931.

ON THE DEVELOPMENT OF THE EXTERNAL OCULAR, MASTICATORY, AND HYOID MUSCLES OF MONOTREMATA. F. H. Edgeworth. Proc. Zool. Soc. Lond., 1931, pt. 3, pp.809-815, pls.13, Sept.30, 1931.

ON MAMMALS FROM THE LAKE EYRE BASIN. PART IV. THE MONODELPHIA. H. H. Finlayson. Trans. Roy. Soc. S. Australia, Adelaide, vol.63, no.1, pp.88-118, July 28, 1939.

THE DEVELOPMENT OF THE MONOTREMATA. PT.6. THE LATER STAGES OF CLEAVAGE AND THE FORMATION OF THE PRIMARY GERM-LAYERS. T. T. Flynn, J. P. Hill. Trans. Zool. Soc. Lond., vol.26, pt.1, pp.1-151, pls.27, July, 1947.

THE DEVELOPMENT OF THE MONOTREMATA. PART IV. GROWTH OF THE OVARIAN OVUM, MATURATION, FERTILIZATION, AND EARLY CLEAVAGE. T. Thomson Flynn, J. P. Hill. Trans. Zool. Soc. Lond., vol.24, pt.6, pp.445-622, figs. 6, pls.21, Dec. 1939.

THE GROWTH OF THE OOCYTE, MATURATION, FERTILIZATION, AND EARLY CLEAVAGE IN THE MONOTREMATA. T. T. Flynn, J. P. Hill. Bio-Morphosis, Leipzig, vol.1, nos.3-4, pp.327-329, 1938.

THE LATER STAGES OF CLEAVAGE AND THE FORMATION OF THE PRIMARY GERM-LAYERS IN THE MONOTREMATA. T. T. Flynn, J. P. Hill. Proc. Zool. Soc. Lond., vol.111, ser.A, 1941, pts.3-4, pp.233-253. Feb., 1942.

(ON THE BLOOD SYSTEM OF THE BLASTODERMAL VESICLE, CERTAIN STRUCTURAL CHARACTERISTICS AND THE ORIGIN OF THE MONOTREMES.) Notes sur les mammifères. XIV. Du système vasculaire de la vésicule blastodermique, de certains caractères structuraux et de l'origine des Monotrèmes. Serge Frechkop. Bull. Mus. Roy. d'Hist. Nat. Belgique, Bruxelles, vol.9, no.8, pp. 13, figs., April, 1933.

ORIGIN OF THE NAME MONOTREMES. Theodore Gill. Science, n.s., vol.17, no. 428, pp.433-434, Mar.13, 1903.

THE MONOTREMES AND THE PALIMPSEST THEORY. William King Gregory. Bull. Amer. Mus. Nat. Hist., New York, vol.88, art.1, pp.1-52, figs.1-17, pls.1-2, Jan.27, 1947.

A MICROLOGICAL INVESTIGATION OF THE HAIR STRUCTURE OF THE MONOTREMATA. Leon A. Hausman. Amer. Jour. Anat., vol.27, pp.463-495, Sept., 1920.

THE DEVELOPMENT OF THE MONOTREMATA. PART V. FURTHER OBSERVATIONS ON THE HISTOLOGY AND THE SECRETORY ACTIVITIES OF THE OVIDUCT PRIOR TO AND DURING GESTATION. C. J. Hill. Trans. Zool. Soc. Lond., vol.25, pt.1, pp.1-31, pls.5, May, 1941.

THE SECRETORY ACTIVITIES OF THE OVIDUCT IN THE MONOTREMES. C. J. Hill. Bio-Morphosis, Leipzig, vol.1, nos.3-4, pp.329-331, 1938.

DEVELOPMENT OF THE MONOTREMATA, PART 7. THE DEVELOPMENT AND STRUCTURE OF THE EGG-TOOTH AND THE CARUNCLE IN THE MONOTREMES, AND ON THE OCCURRENCE OF VESTIGES OF THE EGG-TOOTH AND CARUNCLE IN MARSUPIALS. J. P. Hill, G. R. de Beer. Trans. Zool. Soc. Lond., vol.26, pt.6, pp. 503-539, pls.10, Mar., 1950.

STUDIES ON THE ORGANIZATION OF THE MONOTREMES, CONTRASTED WITH THE MARSUPIALS AND PLACENTALS. Ernst Huber. Morphol. Jahrbuch, Leipzig, vol.66, pp.46-64, figs.7, 1931.

THE FOREBRAIN ARTERIES IN PLAGIOSTOMES, REPTILES, BIRDS, AND MONOTREMES. C. U. Ariens Kappers. Proc. Koninklijke Akad. Van Wetenschappen te Amsterdam, vol.36, no.1, pp.52-62, 1933.

CONTRIBUTIONS TO THE DEVELOPMENT OF THE PELVIC GIRDLE. 3. THE PELVIC GIRDLE AND ITS RELATED MUSCULATURE IN MONOTREMES. James W. Low. Proc. Zool. Soc. Lond., 1929, pt.2, pp.245-265, figs.1-9, Aug., 1929.

(NOTES ON THE MORPHOLOGY AND PHYLOGENY OF THE VERTEBRATES. 9. ON SOME PECULIARITIES OF THE MONOTREMATA SKULL AND ITS PHYLOGENIC SIGNIFICANCE.) Notizen zur Morphologie und Stammesgeschichte der Wirbeltiere. 9. Ueber einige Besonderheiten des Monotremenschaedels und ihre stammesgeschichtliche Bedeutung. A. Naef. Biol. Zentralblatt, vol.46, pp.161-176, 3 figs., 1926.

MAMMALS THAT LAY EGGS. Maynard Shipley. Evolution, vol.2, no.3, p.7, illus., 1929.

SKELETONS OF THE MONOTREMES IN THE COLLECTION OF THE ARMY MEDICAL MUSEUM AT WASHINGTON. R. W. Shufeldt. Roy. Soc. Tasmania, Papers and Proc., 1921, pp.99-110, 5 pls., Oct.28, 1921.

OSTEOGRAPHY OF THE EAR REGION IN MONOTREMES. George Gaylord Simpson. Amer. Mus. Novitates, no.978, pp.1-15, figs. 7, May 9, 1938.

THE EGG-LAYING FURRED ANIMALS OF AUSTRALIA. Ellis L. Troughton. Australian Mus. Mag., vol.4, no.10, pp.327-334, figs., Apr.-June, 1932.

THE EGG-LAYING FURRED ANIMALS OF AUSTRALIA. Ellis G. Troughton. Mid-Pacific Mag. Honolulu, vol.45, no.4, pp. 358-364, Apr., 1933.

MAMMALIAN PARADOXES. Frederick A. Ulmer, Jr. Fauna, Philadelphia, vol.4, no. 4, p.109, illus., Dec., 1942.

THE MONOTREME SKULL: A CONTRIBUTION TO MAMMALIAN MORPHOGENESIS. D. M. S. Watson. Philos. Trans. Roy. Soc. of Lond., ser.B, vol.207, pp.311-374, pls. 23-25, 1916.

THE HAIRS OF THE MONOTREMATA, WITH SPECIAL REFERENCE TO THEIR CUTICULAR-SCALE PATTERN. A. B. Wildman, J. Manby. Trans. Roy. Soc. Edinburgh, vol.59, pt.2, sess. 1937-38, pp.333-349, figs.1-2, pls.1-7, June 3, 1938.

DEVELOPMENT IN THE MONOTREMES. Nature, London, vol.146, no.3697, pp. 339-340, Sept. 7, 1940.

Tachyglossidae

ZAGLOSSUS. Glover M. Allen. Mem. Mus. Com. Zool., vol.40, no.5, pp.253-307, pls. 2, Oct., 1912.

THE ECHIDNA UNDER DOMESTICATION. Edith Coleman. Victorian Nat., vol.51, no. 1, pp.12-21, pl.4, figs., May, 1934.

THE ECHIDNA UNDER DOMESTICATION. Edith Coleman. Victorian Nat., vol.52, no. 8, pp.151-154, pl.17, Dec., 1935.

ECHIDNA IN A SYDNEY SUBURB. Alec Costin. Victorian Nat., Melbourne, vol. 64, no.12, p.245, Apr., 1948.

AUSTRALIAN WITH MANY PRICKLES. ECHIDNA OR SPINY ANTEATER FROM DOWN UNDER. Joyce Burns Glen. Our Dumb Animals, Norwood, vol.77, no.12, p.225, illus., Dec., 1944.

LETTER FROM, RELATING TO THE DISCOVERY OF AN EXTINCT SPECIES OF ECHIDNA IN AUSTRALIA. Gerard Krefft. Proc. Zool. Soc. Lond., p.49, 1868.

QUEER FACTS ABOUT THE ECHIDNA. Geoffrey Morey. Field, London, vol.158, no.4106, p.365, illus., Sept.5, 1931.

OBSERVATIONS ON THE LIVING ECHIDNA EXHIBITED AT THE MENAGERIE OF THE SOCIETY IN MAY, 1845. R. Owen. Proc. Zool. Soc. Lond., pt.3, pp.80-82.

THE ECHIDNA--A MAMMALIAN THROWBACK. George H. Pournelle. Zoonooz, San Diego Zool. Soc., 30 (6): 6-7, illus., June, 1957.

ON THE OCCURRENCE OF ACANTHOGLOSSUS IN BRITISH NEW GUINEA. Oldfield Thomas. Ann. & Mag. Nat. Hist. (7), vol.20, no.117, pp.293-294, Sept., 1907.

DIGGER FROM DOWN UNDER. Anim. Kingdom, New York, vol.50, no.5, pp.151-153, illus., Sept.-Oct. (Oct.1), 1947.

Anatomy

THE BRAIN-STEM AND CEREBELLUM OF ECHIDNA ACULEATA. A. A. Abbie. Philos. Trans. Roy. Soc. Lond., ser.B, vol.224, no. 509, pp.1-74, figs.1-22, Oct. 30, 1934.

THE HISTOLOGY OF THE SPLEEN AND SUPRARENALS OF ECHIDNA. M. A. Basir. Jour. Anat., Cambridge, vol.66, pt.4, pp. 628-648, pls.1-3, figs.6, July, 1932.

CONTRIBUTIONS TO THE MYOLOGY OF TACHYGLOSSA HYSTRIX (AUCT.) J. Walter Fewkes. Bull. Essex Inst., vol.9, nos.7-8, pp.111-137, pls.1-2, July-Sept., 1877.

ON THE OPTIC LOBES OF THE BRAIN OF THE ECHIDNA. W. H. Flower. Proc. Zool. Soc. Lond., pp.18-20, figs.2, 1864.

(THE ELBOW JOINT OF ECHIDNA ACULEATA SHAW.) Das Ellbogengelenk von Echidna aculeata Shaw. Wilhelm Freudenberg. Zeitschr. F. Saeugetierkunde, vol.9, nos.1-3, pp.424-428, figs.7, Dec.12, 1934.

AN EXPERIMENTAL INVESTIGATION OF THE MOTOR CORTEX AND PYRAMIDAL TRACT OF ECHIDNA ACULEATA. F. Goldby. Jour. Anat., Cambridge, vol.73, pt. 4, pp.509-524, figs.11, July, 1939.

THE EYE OF THE MONOTREME, ECHIDNA HYSTRIX. E. B. Gresser, C. V. Noback. Jour. Morph., vol.58, no.1, pp.279-284. figs.3, Sept. 5, 1935.

ON SOME POINTS IN THE ANATOMY OF ECHIDNA HYSTRIX. St. George Mivart. Trans. Linn. Soc. Lond., vol.25, pp.379-403, pls.52-53, 1866.

(THE "EPISTERNUM" OF ECHIDNA.) Das "Episternum" von Echidna. E. T. Nauck. Anat. Anzeiger, vol.67, pp.144-148, 3 figs., Apr.20, 1929.

(ON THE GENITAL TRACT OF PROECHIDNA BRUYNII.) Ueber den Genitaltrakt von Proechidna bruynii. T. Okmura. Zeitschr. f. Anat. u. Entwicklungsgesch., vol.84, pp.175-191, 14 figs., Oct. 8, 1927.

ON THE MAMMARY GLAND OF ECHIDNA HYSTRIX, CUV. R. Owen. Proc. Comm. Sci. & Corres. Zool. Soc. Lond., pt.2, pp. 179-181, 1832.

NOTES ON THE CHARACTERS OF THE DIFFERENT RACES OF ECHIDNA. Oldfield Thomas. Proc. Zool. Soc., Lond., pp.329-339, pl.23-24, vol.1, no.29, Apr.21, 1885.

A LEFT-SIDED INFERIOR VENA CAVA IN ECHIDNA ACULEATA. Rupert A. Willis. Jour. Mam., vol.13, no.1, pp.55-58, Feb., 1932.

Habits and Behavior

CLIMBING HABITS AND FURTHER NOTES ON HIBERNATION OF THE ECHIDNA. Edith Coleman. Victorian Nat., vol.53, no.7, pp. 124-128, pl.13, Nov., 1936.

FURTHER NOTES ON HIBERNATION OF THE ECHIDNA. Edith Coleman. Victorian Nat., Melbourne, vol.54, no.11, pp.178-179, illus., March, 1938.

HIBERNATION AND OTHER HABITS OF THE ECHIDNA UNDER DOMESTICATION. Edith Coleman. Victorian Nat., Melbourne, vol.52, no.4, pp.55-61, illus., Aug., 1935.

NOTES ON HIBERNATION, ECDYSIS, AND SENSE OF SMELL OF THE ECHIDNA UNDER DOMESTICATION. Edith Coleman. The Victorian Naturalist, Melbourne, vol.55, no.6, pp.105-107, illus., Oct., 1938.

Taxonomy

TASMANIAN SPINY ANTEATER WITHSTAND LOW TEMPERATURE. Alfred M. Bailey. Jour. Mam., vol.32, no.1, pp.116-117, Feb. 15, 1951.

BEHAVIOUR OF YOUNG ECHIDNA. Charles Barrett. Victorian Naturalist, vol. 45, no.5, p.146, Sept., 1928.

FIELD NOTES ON NATURAL HABITS OF ECHIDNA (TACHYGLOSSUS ACULEATUS). Harry Burrell. Australian Zool., vol.4, 1 pl., June 14, 1925.

THE GENERIC NAMES OF THE THREE-TOED ECHIDNA. T. S. Palmer. Science, N.S. vol.1, no.19, pp.518-519, May 10, 1895.

A NEW ACANTHOGLOSSUS FROM THE ISLAND OF SALAWATTI. Oldfield Thomas. Ann. & Mag. Nat. Hist. (7), vol.20, no.120, pp.498-499, Dec., 1907.

ON A NEW SUBSPECIES OF ZAGLOSSUS, WITH REMARKS ON OTHER SPECIES OF THE GENUS. Oldfield Thomas, Lord Rothschild. Ann. & Mag. Nat. Hist. (9), vol.10, no.55, pp.129-131, July, 1922.

Ornithorhynchidae

THE WORLD'S WONDER ANIMAL, THE PLATYPUS. Charles Barrett. Robertson & Mullens, Melbourne, Australia, pp.64, illus., 1944.

NOTES ON THE DUCK-BILL (ORNITHORHYNCHUS ANATINUS). George Bennett. Proc. Zool. Soc., London, pt.27, pp.213-218, pl.LXXI, 1859.

MORE DETAILS ON CECIL AND PENELOPE. John Blair. Animal Kingdom, New York Zool. Soc., vol.55, no.1, pp.23-65, illus., Jan.-Feb., 1952. (Platypus)

FACTS AND FANCIES PERTAINING TO PLATYPUS. Harry Burrell. Australian Zool., vol.7, no.2, pp.110-118, Feb.5, 1932.

THE PLATYPUS: ITS DISCOVERY, ZOOLOGICAL POSITION, FORM, AND CHARACTERISTICS, HABITS, LIFE HISTORY, ETC. Harry Burrell. Sydney: Angus and Robertson, ltd., 8 vol., 227 pp., 35 pls. 1 colored. April, 1927.

(Review by H. H. T. Jackson of) THE PLATYPUS: ITS DISCOVERY, ZOOLOGICAL POSITION, FORM AND CHARACTERISTICS, HABITS, LIFE HISTORY, ETC. Harry Burrell. Jour. Mam., vol.8, no.3, pp.252-254, 256, Aug.9, 1927.

BABY PLATYPUS INTERESTS THE WORLD. A. H. Chisholm. Victorian Nat., Melbourne, vol.60, no.10, p.158, Feb., 1944.

THE PLATYPUS AT HOME. A. H. Chisholm. Nat. Mag., Washington, vol.40, no.9, pp. 461-463, illus., Nov., 1947.

DUCK-BILLED PLATYPUS. Lee S. Crandall. Zoo Life, London, vol.9, no.2, pp.73-76, illus., Summer, 1954.

A NOTE ON THE FIRST EXHIBITION OF THE DUCK-BILLED PLATYPUS. Lee S. Crandall. Animal Kingdom, New York Zool. Soc., vol.55, no.2, pp.62-63, Mar.-Apr., 1952.

THE PLATYPUS IN CAPTIVITY. Robert Eadie. Victorian Nat., vol.51, no.1, pp. 3-11, pls.1-3, May, 1934.

HOW THE DUCK-BILLED PLATYPUSES CAME TO NEW YORK. David Fleay. Anim. Kingdom, New York, vol.50, no.3, pp.66-80, illus., May-June, 1947.

REFLECTIONS ON DR. WEATHERHEAD'S COMMUNICATION RESPECTING THE ORNITHORHYNCHUS. Geoffroy M. Saint Hilaire. Proc. Zool. Soc. Lond., pt.1, p.15, 1833.

CONCERNING THE PLATYPUS. Thomas S. Hart. Victorian Nat., Melbourne, vol. 58, no.10, p.155, Feb., 1942.

THE DUCK-BILLED PLATYPUS. Carl G. Hartman. Nature Mag., vol.22, no.3, pp. 107-109, illus., Sept., 1933.

NEW YORK'S DUCK-BILLED PLATYPUS. W. T. Hornsday. Zool. Soc. Bull., vol.25, pp.99-105, 16 figs., Sept., 1922.

AN ANIMAL THAT LAYS EGGS. V. T. Johnson. Our Dumb Animals, Norwood, vol. 74, no.2, p.27, Feb., 1941.

MY EXPERIENCES WITH THE PLATYPUS IN CAPTIVITY. Ellis S. Joseph. Zool. Soc. Bull., vol.25, pp.105-111, 9 figs., Sept., 1922.

THE FIRST WHAT-IS-IT. Willie Ley. Frontiers, Philadelphia, vol.5, no.2, pp. 39-43, illus., Dec., 1940.

THE WORLD'S QUEEREST BEAST. HOME LIFE OF THE DUCK-BILLED PLATYPUS. Geoffrey Morey. Field, Lond., vol.158, no. 4099, p.100, figs.2, July 18, 1931.

ON THE YOUNG OF THE ORNITHORHYNCHUS PARADOXUS, BLUM. R. Owen. Proc. Zool. Soc. London, pt.2, pp.43-44, 1834.

THE DUCK-BILLED PLATYPUS--A PATCHWORK OF PAST AND PRESENT. W. P. Pycraft. Illus. London News, vol.198, no. 5307, p.30, figs.3, Jan. 4, 1941.

THE DUCK-BILLED PLATYPUS. Edward Samuel. Discovery, Cambridge, n.s., vol. 11, no.13, p.186, photo., Apr., 1939.

THE PLATYPUS GROUP. LIFE HISTORY EXHIBIT IN THE AUSTRALIAN MUSEUM. Ellis L. Troughton. Australian Mus. Mag., Sydney, vol.6, no.11, pp.363-367, July-Sept., 1938.

ON TWO YOUNG SPECIMENS OF ORNITHORHYNCHUS. J. H. Weatherhead. Proc. Zool. Soc. Lond., pt.2, pp.22-23, 1834.

THE ONLY DUCK-BILLED PLATYPUS IN CAPTIVITY: A SPECIMEN THAT HAS BROKEN THE RECORD BY LIVING FOR A YEAR. Illus. London News, vol.189, no.5092, pp.904-905, Nov.21, 1936.

Anatomy

ANATOMY OF THE PLATYPUS SNOUT. R. Broom. S. African Jour. Sci., vol.32, pp.322-328, figs.3, Nov., 1935.

DENTITION OF ORNITHORHYNCHUS. R. Broom. Nature, Lond., vol.136, no. 3432, p.219, figs.2, Aug.10, 1935.

X-RAY PHOTOGRAPHS OF AUSTRALIAN MAMMALS. F. S. Fergus. Victorian Nat., vol.53, no.5, p.83, pl.10, Sept., 1936.

NEW OBSERVATIONS ON THE NATURE OF THE ABDOMINAL GLANDS OF THE ORNITHORHYNCHUS. Geoffroy Saint-Hilaire. Proc. Zool. Soc. Lond., pt.1, pp.91-95, 1833.

ON THE ABDOMINAL GLANDS OF THE ORNITHORHYNCHUS. Geoffroy Saint-Hilaire. Proc. Zool. Soc. Lond., pt.1, pp.28-30, 1833.

THE MUSCULATURE OF THE ANTEBRACHIUM AND MANUS IN THE PLATYPUS. A. Brazier Howell. Amer. Jour. Anat., vol.59, no.3, pp.425-432, figs.2, Sept.15, 1936.

THE SWIMMING MECHANISM OF THE PLATYPUS. A. Brazier Howell. Jour. Mam., vol.18, no.2, pp.217-222, figs.2, May 14, 1937.

ON THE INTERPRETATION OF CERTAIN FEATURES OF AN EMBRYONIC SKULL OF PLATYPUS. H. Leighton Kesteven. Proc. Linnean Soc. New South Wales, Sydney, vol.65, nos.287-288, pp.144-154, figs.9, 1940.

ON THE TOPOGRAPHY OF HERBST'S AND GRANDRY'S CORPUSCLES IN THE ADULT AND EMBRYONIC DUCK-BILL. Anna Krogis. Acta Zoologica, vol.12, pp. 241-263, 1931.

ON THE MAMMARY GLANDS OF THE ORNITHORHYNCHUS. R. Owen. Proc. Zool. Soc. Lond., pt.1, pp.30-31, 95, 1833.

PELVIC AND THIGH MUSCLES OF ORNITHORHYNCHUS. Helga S. Pearson. Jour. Anat., vol.60, pp.152-163, Jan., 1926.

THE STRUCTURE OF THE BILL AND HAIRS OF ORNITHORHYNCHUS PARADOXUS: WITH A DISCUSSION OF THE HOMOLOGIES AND ORIGIN OF MAMMALIAN HAIR. Edward B. Poulton. Quart. Jour. Microscop. Sci., Lond, n.s., vol.36, pp.143-200, pls.14-15a, June, 1894.

THE TRUE TEETH AND THE HORNY PLATES OF ORNITHORHYNCHUS. Edward B. Poulton. Quart. Jour. Microscop. Sci., Lond., n.s., vol.29, pp.9-48, pls.2-4, July, 1888.

TRUE TEETH IN THE YOUNG ORNITHORHYNCHUS PARADOXUS. Edward B. Poulton. Proc. Roy. Soc. Lond., vol.43, pp.353-356, illus., 1888.

THE DENTITION OF ORNITHORHYNCHUS AS EVIDENCE OF ITS AFFINITIES. George G. Simpson. Amer. Mus. Nov., no. 390, pp.1-15, figs.2, Dec.6, 1929.

ON THE DENTITION OF ORNITHORHYNCHUS. Oldfield Thomas. Proc. Roy. Soc., Lond., vol.46, pp.126-131, pl.2, 1890.

Geographical

PLATYPUS TRANSFERRED TO KANGAROO ISLAND. David Fleay. Victorian Nat., Melbourne, vol.57, no.12, pp.214-215, Apr., 1941.

THE PLATYPUS ON WILSON'S PROMONTORY. J. A. Kershaw. Victorian Nat., Melbourne, vol.57, no.11, pp.194-195, pl. 20, Mar., 1941.

THE RANGE OF THE PLATYPUS. Edgar R. Waite. Proc. Linnean Soc. New South Wales, pt.4, pp.500-502, Sept.30, 1896.

Habits and Behavior

ON THE NATURAL HISTORY AND HABITS OF THE ORNITHORHYNCHUS PARADOXUS, BLUM. G. Bennett. Proc. Zool. Soc. Lond., pt.2, pp.141-143, 1834.

BURROWING HABITS OF ORNITHORHYNCHUS. Harry Burrell. Proc. Linnean Soc. New South Wales, vol.1, pt.2, pp.167-170, July 1, 1925.

PRACTICAL OBSERVATIONS OF ORNITHORHYNCHUS BENEATH WATER. Harry Burrell. Australian Zool., vol.4, pt.1, 4 pp., 1 pl., June 14, 1925.

HIBERNATION OF THE PLATYPUS. Robert Eadie. Victorian Nat., Melbourne, vol.52, no.4, pp.71-72, Aug., 1935.

THE LIFE AND HABITS OF THE PLATYPUS WITH SIDELIGHTS ON "SPLASH" THE TAME PLATYPUS. Robert Eadie. Stillwell & Stephens Pty. Ltd., Melbourne, pp.78, illus., 1935.

BIGGEST WORM FARM CATERS TO PLATYPUSES. W. H. Nicholas. Nat. Geogr. Mag., Washington, vol.95, no.2, pp.269-280, illus., Feb., 1949.

NOTES ON ORNITHORHYNCHUS PARADOXUS. BY GEORGE FREDERIC BENNETT, IN A LETTER FROM DR. GEORGE BENNETT, F.L.S., F.Z.S., TO PROFESSOR OWEN, C.B., F.R.S., & C., WITH REMARKS BY THE LATTER. Richard Owen. Proc. Zool. Soc. Lond., pt.2, pp.161-166, 1877.

OBSERVATIONS OF THE PLATYPUS IN CAPTIVITY. Robert A. Patten. Parks and Recreation, Rockford, vol.23, no.9, pp.413-418, May, 1940.

ON THE HABITS AND ECONOMY OF THE ORNITHORHYNCHUS. Dr. Weatherhead. Proc. Comm. Sci. & Corres. Zool. Soc. Lond., pt.2, p.145, 1832.

A DIET OF WORMS AT THE NEW YORK ZOO: BREEDING THE STAPLE FOOD OF THE CAPTIVE DUCK-BILLED PLATYPUS. Illus. London News, vol.213, no.5701, p. 103, illus., July 24, 1948.

Reproductive Biology

OBSERVATIONS ON THE PLATYPUS (ORNITHORHYNCHUS ANATINUS). THE EGG-LAYING PERIODS. Harry Burrell. Australian Zool., vol.6, pt.3, pp.301-304, Aug.20, 1930.

THE PLATYPUS "ORNITHORYNCHUS PARADOXUS." Harry Burrell. The Koala Mag., Sydney, pp.16-17, illus., Oct., 1937.

PRELIMINARY NOTE ON THE BREEDING OF ORNITHORHYNCHUS IN 1920. Harry Burrell. Australian Zool., vol.2, pt.2, pp. 20-23, 2 pls., Apr.11, 1921.

A PLATYPUS ROMANCE. A. H. Chisholm. Victorian Nat., Melbourne, vol.58, no.9, p. 148, Jan., 1942.

THE PLATYPUS--A GOOD TRY. Lee S. Crandall. Animal Kingdom, New York Zool. Soc., vol.54, no.6, p.172, Nov.-Dec.,1951.

WE ARE ATTEMPTING TO BREED THE PLATYPUSES. Lee S. Crandall. Animal Kingdom, New York, vol.54, no.3, pp. 89-91, illus., May-June, 1951.

THE BIRTH OF A BABY PLATYPUS. David Fleay. Animal Kingdom, New York, vol.47, no.3, pp.51-69, illus., May-June, 1944.

OBSERVATIONS ON THE BREEDING OF PLATYPUS IN CAPTIVITY. David Fleay. Victorian Nat., 61:8-14, 29-37, 54-57, 74-78, 1944.

ON AN OVUM OF ORNITHORHYNCHUS EXHIBITING POLAR BODIES AND POLYSPERMY. J. B. Gatenby, J. P. Hill. Quart. Jour. Micros. Sci., vol.68, pp.229-238, 1 fig., pl.10, July 1, 1924.

NO BABY PLATYPUS! Robert M. McClung. Animal Kingdom, New York Zool. Soc., vol. 56, no.6, pp.162-166, illus., Nov.-Dec.,1953.

THE UNPREDICTABLE PLATYPUSES. Robert M. McClung. Animal Kingdom, New York Zool. Soc., vol.57, no.4, pp.110-111, illus., Aug., 1954.

## MARSUPIALIA

SOME OBSERVATIONS ON THE MAJOR SUBDIVISIONS OF THE MARSUPIALIA WITH ESPECIAL REFERENCE TO THE POSITION OF THE PERAMELIDAE AND CAENOLESTIDAE. A. A. Abbie. Jour. Anat., Lond., vol. 71, pt.4, pp.429-436, figs.3, July, 1937.

THE ZOO'S PIONEER EXPEDITION. T. N. Faulconer. San Diego Zoonooz, vol.16, no. 8, pp.3-7, illus., Aug., 1943.

(NOTES ON THE MAMMALS. II DISTINCTIVE CHARACTERS AND PHYLOGENY OF THE WOMBAT (PHASCOLYMYS) AND KOALA (PHASCOLARCTUS).) Notes sur les mammiferes. II. Caracteres distinctifs et phylogenie du Wombat (Phascolymys) et du Koala (Phascolarctus). Serge Frechkop. Bull. Mus. Roy. d'Hist. Nat. de Belgique, vol.6, no.12, pp.1-34, figs.9, Aug., 1930.

THE PROBLEM OF EXTINCTION, WITH SPECIAL REFERENCE TO AUSTRALIAN MARSUPIALS. Edmund D. Gill. Evolution, Lancaster, vol.9, no.1, pp.87-92, Mar., 1955.

CHARACTERS OF A NEW SPECIES OF PERAMELES, AND A NEW SPECIES OF DASYURUS. J. Gould. Proc. Zool. Soc. Lond., pt.10, pp.41-42, 1842.

AN EARLY RECORD OF A MARSUPIAL IN CEYLON. David H. Johnson. Jour. Mam., 37 (2): 274, June 9, 1956.

THE ZOOGEOGRAPHY OF MARSUPIALS. WITH NOTES ON THE ORIGIN OF THE AUSTRALIAN FAUNA. Heber A. Longman. Mem. Queensland Mus., vol.8, pt.1, pp.1-15, Jan.30, 1924.

OUTLINES OF A CLASSIFICATION OF THE MARSUPIALIA. R. Owen. Proc. Zool. Soc. Lond., 7: 3-19, 1839.

NOTES ON THE BLOOD SYSTEM OF THE MARSUPIALIA. Joseph Pearson. Papers and Proc. Roy. Soc. Tasmania for 1939, Hobart, pp.77-94, figs.32, 1940.

FROM REPTILES TO MARSUPIALS IN 180,000,000 YEARS. George H. Pournelle. Zoonooz, Zool. Soc. San Diego, 31 (1): 10-14, illus., Jan., 1958.

ON THE MYOLOGY AND CLASSIFICATION OF THE WOMBAT, KOALA, AND PHALANGERS. Charles F. Soontag. Proc. Zool. Soc. Lond., 1922, pt.4, pp.863-896, Feb., 1923.

NEW OR LITTLE-KNOWN MARSUPIALS: A NEW SPECIES OF PHASCOGALINAE, WITH NOTES UPON ACROBATES PULCHELLUS ROTHSCHILD. G. H. H. Tate. Novitates Zoologicae, vol.41, no.1, pp.58-60, 1938.

RESULTS OF THE ARCHBOLD EXPEDITIONS. NO.55. NOTES ON THE SQUIRREL-LIKE AND MOUSE-LIKE POSSUMS (MARSUPIALIA). G. H. H. Tate. Amer. Mus. Novitates, New York, no.1305, pp.12, Dec. 29, 1945.

A SELECTION OF LECTOTYPES OF THE AUSTRALIAN MARSUPIALS IN THE BRITISH MUSEUM COLLECTION. Oldfield Thomas. Ann. and Mag. Nat. Hist., ser.9, vol.10, pp.127-128, July, 1922.

NEW MARSUPIAL GROUPS IN THE AUSTRALIAN MUSEUM. E. Le G. Troughton. Australian Museum Mag., Sydney, vol.6, no.8, pp.255-259, illus., Oct.-Dec., 1937.

A NATURAL HISTORY OF THE MAMMALIA. G. R. Waterhouse. Vol.1, Marsupiata, or Pouched Animals. 1846.

A PRELIMINARY STUDY OF MARSUPIAL RELATIONSHIPS AS INDICATED BY THE PRECIPITIN TEST. Courtney T. Wemyss, Jr. Zoologica, New York Zool. Soc., vol. 38, pt.4, pp.173-181, illus., Dec.31, 1953.

THE POSITION OF THE "SPARASSODONTS": WITH NOTES ON THE RELATIONSHIPS AND HISTORY OF THE MARSUPIALIA. Horace Elmer Wood, II. Bull. Amer. Mus. Nat. Hist., vol.51, pp.77-101, figs.1-57, Sept. 19, 1924.

MARSUPIALS. R. Ramsey Wright. Natural History of Mammals, pp.33-45, illus.

### Anatomy

A MASTICATORY ADAPTATION PECULIAR TO SOME DIPROTODONT MARSUPIALS. A. A. Abbie. Proc. Zool. Soc. Lond., vol. 109, ser.B, Syst. and Morphol., pt.2, pp. 261-279, figs.9, Aug., 1939.

THE HAIR TRACTS OF MARSUPIALS. PART I. DESCRIPTION OF SPECIES. W. Boardman. Proc. Linnean Soc. New South Wales, Sydney, vol.68, pts.3-4, pp.95-113, figs.25, Sept.15, 1943.

THE HAIR TRACTS OF MARSUPIALS. PART II. DESCRIPTION OF SPECIES, CONTINUED. W. Boardman. Proc. Linnean Soc. New South Wales, Sydney, vol.70, pts.5-6, pp.179-202, figs.43, July 15, 1946.

THE HAIR TRACTS IN MARSUPIALS. PART IV. DIRECTION CHARACTERISTICS OF WHORLS AND MERISTIC REPETITION OR RADIAL FIELDS. W. Boardman. Proc. Linnean Soc. New South Wales, Sydney, vol. 75, pts.1-2, pp.89-95, June 6, 1950.

THE HAIR TRACTS OF MARSUPIALS. PART V. A CONTRIBUTION ON CAUSATION. PART VI. EVOLUTION AND GENETICS OF TRACT PATTERN. PART VII. A SYSTEM OF NOMENCLATURE. W. Boardman. Proc. Linnean Soc. New South Wales, vol.75, pts.5-6, pp. 254-278, illus., Dec.21, 1950.

THE HAIR TRACTS OF SOME AMERICAN MARSUPIALS. W. Boardman. Proc. Zool. Soc. Lond., vol.121, pt.4, pp.845-850, illus., Feb.8, 1952.

ON THE EXTERNAL CHARACTERS OF THE POUCH YOUNG OF SOME AUSTRALIAN MARSUPIALS. W. Boardman. Australian Zoologist, Sydney, vol.10, pt.2, pp.138-160, figs. 13, Apr.30, 1943.

REPORT ON SOME POINTS IN THE ANATOMY OF THE THYLACINE (THYLACINUS CYNOCEPHALUS), CUSCUS (PHALANGISTA MACULATA), AND PHASCOGALE (PHASCOGALE CALURA), COLLECTED DURING THE VOYAGE OF H.M.S. CHALLENGER IN THE YEARS 1873-1876; WITH AN ACCOUNT OF THE COMPARATIVE ANATOMY OF THE INTRINSIC MUSCLES AND THE NERVES OF THE MAMMALIAN PES. Daniel John Cunningham. Challenger office. Report on the scientific results of the voyage of H.M.S. Challenger during the years 1873-1876, Edinburgh, 1880-95, Zoology, vol.5, (1882), no.II, 192 pp. illus., XIII pl.

(THE MASTICATING MECHANISM OF THE MARSUPIALS.) L'Appareil masticateur des Marsupiaux. X. J. Dubeco. Etude morphophysiologique. Bull. Sta. Biol. D'Arachon, Bordeaux, vol.30, pp.129-166, figs.1-14, 1933.

FUNCTIONAL ADAPTATIONS OF THE PELVIS IN MARSUPIALS. Herbert Oliver Elftman. Bull. Amer. Mus. Nat. Hist., vol.58, pp.189-232, pls.9-14, Mar.5, 1929.

ON THE DEVELOPMENT AND SUCCESSION OF THE TEETH IN THE MARSUPIALIA. William Henry Flower. Philos. Trans. Lond., pp.631-641, pls.29-30, 1867.

ON THE DEVELOPMENT AND SUCCESSION OF THE TEETH IN THE MARSUPIALIA. William Henry Flower. Proc. Roy. Soc. Lond., no.93, pp.1-4, 1867.

SYNDACTYLY IN MARSUPIALS. Edwin S. Goodrich. Proc. Zool. Soc. Lond., pt.1, pp.175-178, Apr.,1935.

EXHIBITION AND CHARACTER OF A NUMBER OF ANIMALS TRANSMITTED FROM AUSTRALIA BY MR. GILBERT. John Gould. Proc. Zool. Soc. Lond., pt.12, pp.103-107, 1844.

THE DEVELOPMENT OF THE PALATINE TONSIL IN THE MARSUPIALS TRICHOSURUS AND DASYURUS, WITH NOTES ON TONSIL DEVELOPMENT IN THE RABBIT. Mary L. Hett. Proc. Zool. Soc. Lond., pt.4, pp.941-968, figs.1-25, Dec., 1933.

OBSERVATIONS ON MARSUPIALS IN THE ROYAL SCOTTISH MUSEUM, WITH SPECIAL REFERENCE TO THE FOETAL MATERIAL. W. C. Osman Hill. Trans. Roy. Soc. Edinburgh, vol.62, pt.1, pp.145-167, Oct.30, 1951.

THE EXTERNAL CHARACTERS OF POUCH EMBRYOS OF MARSUPIALS. Frederic Wood Jones. Trans. Roy. Soc. South Australia, vol.47, 1923.

ON THE SPECIALIZED INCISOR TEETH OF SOME OF THE DIDACTYLOUS MARSUPIALS. Frederic Wood Jones. Trans. Roy. Soc. S. Australia, vol.48, pp.187-191, figs.1-5, 1924.

(ON THE MORPHOLOGY OF POUCH BONES.) Zur Morphologie der Beutelknochen. Wilhelm Leche. Biol. Ver. Stockholm, vol.3, no.7, pp.120-126, illus., 1891.

ON SOME REMARKABLE DIGESTIVE ADAPTATIONS IN DIPROTODONT MARSUPIALS. Einar Loennberg. Proc. Zool. Soc. Lond., pp.12-13, figs.,4-6, Jan.14, 1902.

(THE MECHANICS OF THE SYNDACTYL TOES OF MACROPUS AND OTHER MARSUPIALIA AND THEIR APPLICATION AS CLEANING ORGANS.) Die Mechanik der syndactylen Zehen von Macropus und anderen Beuteltieren und ihre Verwendung als Putz organ. R. J. Mueller. Zeitschr. Morph. u. Oekol. Tiere, vol.17, pp.154-218, 95 figs., Feb.20, 1930.

A PRELIMINARY NOTE ON THE PRESENCE OF DOUBLE CONES AND OIL DROPLETS IN THE RETINA OF MARSUPIALS. Kevin O'Day. Jour. Anat., Cambridge, vol.70, pt.4, pp. 465-467, figs.2, July, 1936.

FOETAL MEMBRANES OF THE MARSUPIALS. Henry F. Osborn. Jour. Morphol. Boston, vol.1, no.2, pp.373-382, figs.4, pl.17, Dec., 1887.

NOTICE OF A FIFTH MEMOIR ON THE OSTEOLOGY OF THE MARSUPIALIA. R. Owen. Proc. Zool. Soc. Lond., p.325, 1874.

ON THE OSTEOLOGY OF THE MARSUPIALIA. R. Owen. Proc. Zool. Soc. Lond., pt.6, pp.120-147, 1838.

NOTE ON THE HOMOLOGY OF THE TYMPANIC BONE. William Peters. Proc. Zool. Soc. Lond., p.953, 1867.

ON THE TONGUES OF MARSUPIALIA. Edward B. Poulton. Proc. Zool. Soc. Lond., pp.599-628, pls.54-55, Apr.1, 1884.

(ON ANAL AND CIRCUMANAL GLANDS. THIRD COMMUNICATION: MARSUPIALS.) Ueber Anal-und Circumanaldruesen. 3. Mitteilung: Marsupialier. J. Schaffer, H. Hamperl. Zeitschr. fuer Wiss. Zoologie, vol.147, pp.529-569, 15 figs., Apr.24, 1926.

CONTRIBUTIONS TO THE VISCERAL ANATOMY AND MYOLOGY OF THE MARSUPIALIA. Charles F. Sonntag. Proc. Zool. Soc. Lond., 1921, pt.4, pp.851-882, Jan., 1922.

Australia and Tasmania

PALAEONTOLOGICAL NOTES NO. 1. MACROPUS TITAN AND THYLACOLEO CARNIFEX OWEN. Charles Anderson. Records Australian Mus., Sydney, vol.17, no. 1, pp.35-49, pls.17-23, June 20, 1929.

COMMENTS ON GILBERT'S NOTE-BOOK ON MARSUPIALS. J. H. Calaby. West. Australian Nat., Perth, vol.4, no.6, pp.147-148, Sept.15, 1954.

TASMANIA'S VANISHING MARSUPIALS. Anthony DeVos. Nature Mag., Washington, vol.39, no.9, pp.482-484, illus., Nov., 1946.

SOME AUSTRALIAN MARSUPIALS. Raymond L. Ditmars. Bull. New York Zool. Soc., vol. 34, no.2, pp.51-61, figs.10, Mar.-Apr., 1931.

NOTES ON SOME SOUTH AND CENTRAL AUSTRALIAN MAMMALS. PART I. PETAURUS BREVICEPS, THALACOMYS LAGOTIS, PETROGALE LATERALIS. H. H. Finlayson. Trans. Roy. Soc. South Australia, vol.54, pp.177-180, 1930.

GIANT MARSUPIAL REMAINS AT BREWARRINA, NEW SOUTH WALES. H. O. Fletcher. Australian Mus. Magazine, 11 (8): 247-251, Dec.15, 1954.

ON THE AFFINITIES AND PROBABLE HABITS OF THE EXTINCT AUSTRALIAN MARSUPIAL, THYLACOLEO CARNIFEX (OWEN). William Henry Flower. Quart. Jour. Geol. Soc., vol., no., pp.307-319, Aug., 1868.

AUSTRALIAN TERTIARY MARSUPIALS. Edmund D. Gill. Australian Jour. Sci., vol. 16, no.3, pp.106-108, Dec., 1953.

THE STRATIGRAPHICAL OCCURRENCE AND PALAEOECOLOGY OF SOME AUSTRALIAN TERTIARY MARSUPIALS. Edmund D. Gill. Mem. Nat. Mus. Victoria, Melbourne, 21: 135-203, Aug.6, 1957.

THE DEVELOPMENT OF OUR KNOWLEDGE OF THE MARSUPIALS OF WESTERN AUSTRALIA. L. Glauert. Jour. Roy. Soc. West. Australia, Perth, vol.34, pp.115-134, Apr.6, 1950.

THE DISTRIBUTION OF THE MARSUPIALS IN WESTERN AUSTRALIA. L. Glauert. Jour. Roy. Soc. Western Australia, vol.19, pp.17-32, (1932-33) 1934.

A RE-EXAMINATION OF SKELETAL CHARACTERS OF WYNYARDIA BASSIANA, AN EXTINCT TASMANIAN MARSUPIAL. Frederic Wood Jones. Roy. Soc., Tasmania, Papers and Proc.1930, pp.96-115, figs.10, pl.5, Dec.31, 1930.

THE MARSUPIALS OF QUEENSLAND. Heber A. Longman. Mem. Queensland Mus., vol.10, pt.1, pp.55-64, Aug.28, 1930.

A NEW GENUS OF FOSSIL MARSUPIALS. Heber A. Longman. Mem. Queensland Mus., vol.7, pt.2, pp.65-80, pls.4-7, fig.1, Feb.11, 1921.

RESTORATION OF EURYZYGOMA DUNENSE. Heber A. Longman. Mem. Queensland Mus., vol.10, pt.4, pp.201-202, pls.30-31, June 30, 1934.

SOUTH QUEENSLAND MARSUPIALS. Heber A. Longman. Mem. Queensland Mus., vol.7, pp.297-300, Dec.19, 1922.

EXISTING TASMANIAN MARSUPIALS. Clive Lord. Papers and Proc. Roy. Soc. Tasmania year 1927, pp.17-24, Feb.29, 1928.

REMARKS ON SOME MARSUPIALS FROM THE INTERIOR OF NEW SOUTH WALES. W. Ogilby. Proc. Zool. Soc. Lond., pt.3, p.191, 1835.

MARSUPIAL MASQUERADE. TASMANIA'S TROOP OF STRANGE AUSTRALIAN MAMMALS. Harold C. Reynolds. Pacific Discovery, California Acad. Sci., 9 (5): 22-26, illus., Sept.-Oct., 1956.

IN THE AUSTRALIAN BUSH. Joseph R. Slevin. Nature Mag., Washington, D.C., vol.35, no.9, pp.473-476, illus., Nov., 1942.

CONTRIBUTIONS TO THE VISCERAL ANATOMY AND MYOLOGY OF THE MARSUPIALIA. Charles F. Sonntag, Proc. Zool. Soc. Lond., 1921, pt.4, pp.851-882, Jan., 1922.

LATE MARSUPIALS FROM SOUTH AUSTRALIA. R. A. Stirton. Rec. South Australian Mus., vol.11, no.3, pp.247-268, illus., Feb.28, 1955.

TERTIARY MARSUPIALS FROM VICTORIA, AUSTRALIA. R. A. Stirton. Mem. Nat. Mus. Victoria, Melbourne, 21: 121-134, Aug.6, 1957.

NOTES ON AUSTRALIAN MARSUPIALS RARE OR LITTLE-KNOWN IN THE UNITED STATES. G. H. H. Tate. Amer. Mus. Novitates, New York, no.1528, pp.1-6, July 17, 1951.

ON SOME KANGAROOS AND BANDICOOTS FROM BARROW ISLAND, N.W. AUSTRALIA, AND THE ADJOINING MAINLAND. Oldfield Thomas. Novitates Zoologicae, vol.8, pp.294-296, Dec., 1901.

ON TWO SPECIES OF MARSUPIAL ANIMALS FROM SOUTH AUSTRALIA. G. R. Waterhouse. Proc. Zool. Soc. Lond., pt.10, p.47, 1842.

JOHN GILBERT'S NOTEBOOK ON MARSUPIALS. H. M. Whittell. West. Australian Nat., Perth, vol.4, no.5, pp.104-114, June 30, 1954.

THE SKULL OF THYLACOLEO CARNIFEX. Jack T. Woods. Mem. Queensland Mus., 12 (2): 125-140, illus., Apr.26, 1956.

Cytology

THE MALE MEIOTIC PHASE IN TWO GENERA OF MARSUPIALS. W. E. Agar. Quart. Journ. Microscopical Sci., vol.67, pp.183-202, pls.12-14, July, 1923.

THE CHROMOSOMES OF FOUR SPECIES OF MARSUPIALS. Stella C. A. Altmann. Quart. Jour. Micro. Sci., vol.69, pp.463-469, pls.37, and 38, 1925.

(NOTES ON MAMMALS. III. ON CHROMOSOME NUMBER IN MARSUPIALS.) Notes sur les mammifères. III. Au sujet du nombre des chromosomes chez les Marsupiaux. Serge Frechkop. Bull. Mus. Roy. d'Hist. Nat. de Belgique, vol.6, no.18, pp.1-11, Oct., 1930.

MARSUPIAL SPERMATOGENSIS. A. W. Greenwood. Quart. Jour. Microscopical Sci., vol.67, pp.203-218, pls.15, 16, July, 1923.

ON THE BLOOD-CORPUSCLES OF MARSUPIAL ANIMALS. G. Gulliver. Proc. Zool. Soc. Lond., pt.9, p.49, 1841.

THE GENETICAL AND MECHANICAL PROPERTIES OF THE SEX-CHROMOSOMES. P. C. Koller. Jour. Genetics, vol.32, no.3, pp.451-472, figs.17, July, 1936.

THE CHROMOSOMES OF SOME SPECIES OF MARSUPIALS. A. S. McIntosh, G. B. Sharman. Jour. Morphol., Phila., vol.95, no.3, pp.509-532, Nov., 1953.

THE CELLULAR STRUCTURE OF THE MARSUPIALIAN CORTEX. W. Riese. Naturaliste Canadienne, Quebec, vol.70 (ser.3, vol.14), nos.5-6, pp.139-144, figs. 4, May-June, 1943.

Diseases and Parasites

THE SUSCEPTIBILITY TO YELLOW FEVER OF THE VERTEBRATES OF EASTERN COLOMBIA. John C. Bugher, Jorge Boshell-Manrique, Manuel Roca-Garcia, Raymond M. Gilmore. Amer. Jour. Tropical Med., Balto., vol.21, no.2, pp.309-333, fig.1, Mar., 1941.

ON A COLLECTION OF NEMATODES FROM AUSTRALIAN MARSUPIALS. T. Harvey Johnston, Patricia M. Mawson. Records Australian Mus., Sydney, vol.20, no.5, pp.360-366, figs.12, Mar.15, 1940.

TUBERCULOSIS IN MARSUPIALS. H. Harold Scott. Proc. Zool. Soc. Lond., 1928, pt.1, pp.249-256, pls.1-3, Apr.,1928.

THE ECTOPARASITES OF AUSTRALIAN BIRDS AND MAMMALS. II. NOTES ON THE MAMMOPHAGA PARASITIC ON AUSTRALIAN MARSUPIALS. Gordon B. Thompson. Ann. & Mag. Nat. Hist., Lond., ser. 11, vol.3, no.18, pp.602-608, June, 1939.

Fossils

THE DISCOVERY OF FOSSIL MARSUPIALS IN NEW GUINEA. C. Anderson. Rpt.23rd meeting Australian and New Zealand Assoc. Adv. Sci., Auckland meeting January, 1937, Wellington, vol.23, p.98, 1937.

THE FOOD HABITS OF THYLACOLEO. C. Anderson. Rept. Australian Assoc. Adv. Sci., vol.19, pp.243-344. (1928) 1929.

PALAEONTOLOGICAL NOTES. NO.IV. FOSSIL MARSUPIALS FROM NEW GUINEA. C. Anderson. Rec. Australian Mus., Sydney, vol.20, no.2, pp.73-76, 1 map, 1 table, pl.8, Aug.27, 1937.

A MARSUPIAL FROM THE FLORISSANT BEDS (TERTIARY) OF COLORADO. C. Lewis Gazin. Jour. Paleont., vol.9, no.1, pp.57-62, pl.12, Jan., 1935.

A MARSUPIAL FROM THE BELLY RIVER CRETACEOUS. WITH CRITICAL OBSERVATIONS UPON THE AFFINITIES OF THE CRETACEOUS MAMMALS. W. D. Matthew. Bull. Amer. Mus. Nat. Hist., New York, vol. 35, art.25, pp.477-500, figs.4, pls.2-6, July 24, 1916.

SYNONYMY OF EUTEMNODUS AMERICANUS BURMEISTER. Bryan Patterson. Trans. Amer. Philos. Soc., n.s., vol.24, pt.1, pp.31-32, Apr., 1934.

FOSSIL MAMMALS FROM THE BEGINNING OF THE CENOZOIC IN BRAZIL. Carlos De. Paula Couto. Amer. Mus. Novitates, New York, no.1559, pp.27, illus., May 6, 1952.

A NEW MARSUPIAL SABER-TOOTH FROM THE PLIOCENE OF ARGENTINA AND ITS RELATIONSHIPS TO SOUTH AMERICA PREDACIOUS MARSUPIALS. Elmer S. Riggs. Trans. Amer. Philo. Soc., N.S. vol.24, pt.1, pp.1-32, pls.1-8, 1934.

A PRELIMINARY DESCRIPTION OF A NEW MARSUPIAL SABERTOOTH FROM THE PLIOCENE OF ARGENTINA. Elmer S. Riggs. Geol. Ser. Field Mus. Nat. Hist., vol.6, pp. 61-66, Dec.11, 1933.

NEW PLIOCENE REMAINS OF DIPROTODONT MARSUPIALS FROM ARGENTINA. Carlos Rusconi. Jour. Mam., vol.14, no.3, pp.244-250, Aug., 1933.

NOTOTHERIA AND ALLIED ANIMALS --A REJOINDER. H. H. Scott, Clive E. Lord. Papers of the Roy. Soc. Tasmania, pp.5, pls. 3, issued separately, May 14, 1921.

STUDIES IN TASMANIAN MAMMALS, LIVING AND EXTINCT. NUMBER I. NOTOTHERIUM MITCHELLI (A MARSUPIAL RHINOCEROS). H. H. Scott, Clive E. Lord. Roy. Soc. Tasmania, Pap. and Proc., pp.13-15, May 29, 1920.

STUDIES IN TASMANIAN MAMMALS, LIVING AND EXTINCT. NUMBER II. SECTION 1. THE HISTORY OF THE GENUS NOTOTHERIUM. SECTION 2. THE OSTEOLOGY OF THE CERVICAL VERTEBRAE OF NOTOTHERIUM MITCHELLI. H. H. Scott, Clive E. Lord. Roy. Soc. Tasmania, Pap. and Proc., pp.17-32, July 24, 1920.

STUDIES IN TASMANIAN MAMMALS, LIVING AND EXTINCT. ITS EVOLUTIONARY TREND--THE SKULL, AND SUCH STRUCTURES AS RELATED TO THE NASAL HORN. H. H. Scott, Clive E. Lord. Roy. Soc. Tasmania, Pap. and Proc., pp.76-96, pls.13-21, Sept.28, 1920.

STUDIES IN TASMANIAN MAMMALS, LIVING AND EXTINCT. NOTOTHERIUM MITCHELLI. NUMBER IV. APPENDICULAR SKELETON, INCLUDING THE MANUS AND PES (HITHERTO UNKNOWN). H. H. Scott, Clive E. Lord. Roy. Soc. Tasmania, Pap. and Proc., pp.97-113, pls. 22-23, Oct.29, 1920.

TASMANIAN GIANT MARSUPIALS. H. H. Scott, Clive E. Lord. Pap. and Proc. Roy. Soc. Tasmania, pp.1-4, 1925.

THE AFFINITIES OF THE BORHYAENIDAE. George Gaylord Simpson. Amer. Mus. Novitates, New York, no.1118, pp.1-6, June 5, 1941.

AFFINITIES OF THE POLYDOLOPIDAE. George Gaylord Simpson. Amer. Mus. Novitates, New York, no.323, 13 pp., figs.7, July 14, 1928.

A NEW EOCENE MARSUPIAL FROM BRAZIL. George Gaylord Simpson. Amer. Mus. Novitates, New York, no.1357, pp.1-7, illus., 1947.

A NEW MARSUPIAL FROM THE EOCENE OF PATAGONIA. George Gaylord Simpson. Amer. Mus. Novitates, no.989, pp.1-5, fig. 1, May 24, 1938.

POST-MESOZOIC MARSUPIALIA. George Gaylord Simpson. Fossilium Catalogus. 1: Animalia, pt.47, W. Junk: Berlin, p.87, Sept.10, 1930.

THE SUPPOSED FOSSIL MARSUPIAL FROM AFRICA. George Gaylord Simpson. Nat. Hist., New York, vol.33, no.1, pp. 106-107, Jan.-Feb., 1933.

THE MARSUPIAL FAUNA OF THE SANTA CRUZ BEDS. William J. Sinclair. Proc. Amer. Philos. Soc. vol.49, no.179, pp.73-81, pls.2, 1905.

NEW CARNIVOROUS MARSUPIALS FROM THE DESEADO FORMATION OF PATAGONIA. William J. Sinclair. Field Mus. Nat. Hist., Geol. Mem., vol.1, no.1, pp. 35-39, pl.8, 1930.

THE POSITION OF THE "SPARASSODONTS": WITH NOTES ON THE RELATIONSHIPS AND HISTORY OF THE MARSUPIALIA. Elmer Horage Wood, II. Bull. Amer. Mus. Nat. Hist., vol.51, art.4, pp. 77-101, figs.57, 1 fold chart, Sept.19, 1924.

New Guinea and Celebes

A NEW MARSUPIAL FROM NETHERLAND NEW GUINEA. Thomas Barbour, Glover M. Allen. Proc. N. Eng. Zool. Club, vol.4, pp. 43-46, July, 1909.

(NEW MARSUPIALS FROM THE HUON GULF (GERMAN NEW GUINEA.) Neue Marsupialia vom Huongolf-Inland (Deutsch-Neuguinea). F. Foerster. Zool. Anzeiger, 42: 177-180.

(THE DISTRIBUTION OF MARSUPIALS IN NEW GUINEA, WITH SOME REMARKS ON THEIR DIVISION INTO SUBGENERA.) Die Verbreitung der Beuteltiere auf Neuguinea mit einigen Bemerkungen ueber ihre Einteilung in Untergattungen. Paul Matschie. Mitteilungen aus dem Zoologischen Museum in Berlin, vol.8, pt.2, pp. 259-308, map , June, 1916.

ON A WALLABY AND A PHALANGER BROUGHT BY MR. WILFRED FROST FROM THE ISLANDS WEST OF NEW GUINEA. WITH NOTES ON THE EVOLUTION OF COAT, COLOUR, AND PATTERN IN THE GENUS PHALANGER. Ernst Schwartz. Proc. Zool. Soc. Lond., pt.1, pp. 87-91, Apr., 1934.

(SOME NEW MARSUPIALS FROM NEW GUINEA.) Einige neue Beuteltiere aus Neuguinea. George Stein. Zeitschrift f, Saeugetierkunde, vol.7, no.6, pp.254-257, Dec.15, 1932.

RESULTS OF THE ARCHBOLD EXPEDITIONS NO.8. FOUR APPARENTLY NEW POLYPROTODONT MARSUPIALS FROM NEW GUINEA. G. H. H. Tate, Richard Archbold. Amer. Mus. Novitates no.823, pp.4, Mar.9, 1936.

RESULTS OF THE ARCHBOLD EXPEDITIONS. NO.16. SOME MARSUPIALS OF NEW GUINEA AND CELEBES. G. H. H. Tate, Richard Archbold. Bull. Amer. Mus. Nat. Hist., vol.73, art.4, pp.331-476, figs. 12, June 11, 1937.

NEW PSEUDOCHIRUS AND PHASCOGALE FROM N.W. NEW GUINEA. Oldfield Thomas. Ann. and Mag. Nat. Hist. (9), vol.8, no.45, pp.357-359, Sept., 1921.

Reproductive Biology

NOTES ON CERTAIN REPRODUCTIVE PHENOMENA IN SOME TASMANIAN MARSUPIALS. T. Thomson Flynn. Ann. and Mag. Nat. Hist., ser.9, vol.10, pp. 225-231, 1 fig., Aug., 1922.

MARSUPIAL REPRODUCTION. Heber A. Longman. Queensland Nat., vol.8, no.1, pp.1-2, Oct., 1931.

SOME ASPECTS OF MARSUPIAL REPRODUCTION. G. B. Sharman. Proc. Zool. Soc. Lond., 127 (1): 141-143, Sept.28, 1956.

THE MYSTERY OF MARSUPIAL BIRTH AND TRANSFERENCE TO THE POUCH. Ellis Troughton. Australian Mus. Mag., vol.2, pp.387-391, illus., July, 1926.

THE TRUTH ABOUT MARSUPIAL BIRTH. Ellis Troughton. Australian Mus. Mag., Sydney, vol.8, no.2, pp.40-44, illus., Nov. 20, 1942.

South America

THE DEVELOPMENT OF MARSUPIALS IN SOUTH AMERICA. George Gaylord Simpson. Physis, Buenos Aires, vol.14, no.46, pp.373-398, Mar., 1939.

(MARSUPIALS OF SAO PAULO STATE.) Xenartrose Marsupiais do Estado de Sao Paulo. C. Vieira. Arquivos de Zoologia do Estado de Sao Paulo, vol.7, pp.325-362, 1951.

Taxonomy

CLASSIFICATION OF SOUTH AMERICAN MARSUPIAL GENERA. Raymond M. Gilmore. Amer. Jour. Tropical Med., Baltimore, vol.21, no.2, pp.314-319, Mar., 1941.

ANOTHER NEW GENERIC NAME FOR A SOUTH AMERICAN MARSUPIAL. Paul H. Oehser. Jour. Mam., vol.15, no.3, p.240, Aug., 1934.

NEW GENERIC NAMES FOR TWO SOUTH AMERICAN MARSUPIALS. G. H. H. Tate. Jour. Mam., vol.15, no.2, p.154, May 15, 1934.

Didelphidae

THE FOOL OF THE FOREST. Roy L. Abbott. Frontiers, Lancaster, vol.8, no. 5, pp.136-137, 146, illus., June, 1944.

BANANA STOWAWAYS. L. A. Adams. Science, n.s., vol.67, p.218, Feb.24, 1928.

NOBODY LOVES THE 'POSSUM. Durward L. Allen. Mich. Cons. 9(6): 5, 10, Mar., 1940.

BR'ER POSSUM, HERMIT OF THE LOWLANDS. Agnes Akin Atkinson. Nat. Geogr. Mag., Washington, vol.103, no.3, pp.405-418, illus., Mar., 1953.

PASSIVE 'POSSUM. Elizabeth Bachmann. Conserv. Volunteer, St. Paul, vol.11, no. 67, pp.21-23, Nov.-Dec., 1948.

JACKING FOR YAPOCKS. William Beebe. Zool. Soc. Bull., vol.26, pp.150-156, 3 figs., Nov., 1923.

STUDIES ON REARING THE OPOSSUM (DIDELPHIS VIRGINIANA). G. E. Coghill. Ohio J. Sci., 39(5): 239-249, Sept., 1939.

CINNAMON AND ALBINO OPOSSUMS FOUND AT AUSTIN, TEXAS. Kenneth W. Cuyler. Jour. Mam., vol.5, no.1, p.130, May, 1934.

THE PRIMITIVE OPOSSUM. J. C. Darsie. North Carolina Wildlife Conserv., Raleigh, vol.8, no.1, pp.10, 15, Jan., 1944.

THE OPOSSUM, PROPHET WITHOUT HONOR. Dwight D. Davis. Chicago Nat., vol.2, no.4, pp.99-104, Dec., 1939.

OL' MISTER 'POSSUM IS QUALITY FOLKS. Les Duck. Oklahoma Game and Fish News, Oklahoma City, vol.3, no.11, pp.6-7, 12-13, illus., Nov., 1947; Texas Game and Fish, Austin, vol.6, no.1, pp.12, 29, illus., Dec., 1947.

OPOSSUMS GET ABOUT. Claire Dumond. Nature Mag., Washington, vol.37, no.3, pp. 154-155, illus., Mar., 1944.

POSSUMS ARE DUDS. Ben East. Field and Stream, New York, vol.49, no.12, pp. 14-15, 65-71, illus., Apr., 1945.

BANANA STOWAWAYS AGAIN. R. K. Enders. Science, vol.71, no.1843, pp.438-439, Apr.25, 1930.

TROPICAL OPOSSUMS. (ABSTRACT OF DEMONSTRATION.) Edmond J. Farris. Anat. Record, Philadelphia, vol.82, no.3, pp.493-494, Mar.25, 1942.

'POSSUM WAYS. James S. Findley. Explorer, Bull. Cleveland Mus. Nat. Hist., no.75, pp.3-4, illus., Summer, 1943.

ZOOLOGICAL HISTORY OF THE OPOSSUMS. P. Gervais. L'Histoire zoologique des Sarigues, pp.95-103, 3 pls., 1855.

LITTLE DIDELPHIS. L. Robinson Gleason. Nat. Hist., New York, vol.53, no.4, p.192, illus., Apr., 1944.

(THE LITTLE OPOSSUM DROMICIOPS AUSTRALIS AUSTRALIS (F. PHILIPPI.) La comadrejita enana Dromiciops australis australis (F. Philippi). Jose Santos Gollan. Holmbergia, Buenos Aires, vol.4, no.9, pp. 191-195, pls.3, Oct.28, 1946.

SO! YOU BELIEVE IT, EH! Phil Goodrum. Texas Game and Fish, Austin, vol.2, no.4, pp.9, 18, Mar., 1944.

INCREDIBLE "BROTHER 'POSSUM." James Nelson Gowanloch. Iowa Conservationist, Des Moines, vol.9, no.11, pp.81, 84, illus., Nov.15, 1950.

A BROWN MUTATION IN THE OPOSSUM (DIDELPHIS VIRGINIANA) WITH REMARKS UPON THE GRAY AND THE BLACK PHASES IN THIS SPECIES. Carl Hartman. Jour. Mam., vol.3, no.3, pp.146-149, Aug., 1922.

POSSUMS. Carl G. Hartman. Austin, Univ. Texas Press, XIII plus.174 pp., 104 illus., 1952.

(Review by Wm. J. Hamilton of) POSSUMS. Carl G. Hartman. Jour. Mam., vol.34, no. 2, pp.274-275, May 14, 1953.

HOW ABOUT THESE QUINTS? John J. Hayes. Nat. Notes, Peoria, vol.6, no.10, pp.201-202, Oct., 1939.

(ON A CASE OF TAMENESS AS REGARDS DIDELPHYS.) Ueber einen Fall von Zahmheit bei Didelphys. H. Hediger. Zool. Garten N. F., Leipzig, vol.7, nos. 1-3, pp.28-44, May, 1934.

OPOSSUM. Charles Hjelte. Colorado Outdoors Mag., 5 (4): 8-10, illus., July-Aug., 1956.

MOUSE OPOSSUM STOWAWAYS ON BANANAS. Walter C. Kraatz. Science, vol. 71, no.1837, p.288, Mar.14, 1930.

OPOSSUM IN CAPTIVITY. John B. Lewis. Jour. Mam., vol.10, no.2, pp.167-168, May, 1929.

A BIOGRAPHY OF A BACKYARD VISITOR, THE FRIENDLY AND ADVENTUROUS 'POSSUM. Joseph W. Lippincott. Frontiers, vol. 1, no.3, pp.89-91, Jan., 1937.

WHY THE 'POSSUM THRIVES. Joseph W. Lippincott. Nat. Mag., vol.4, pp.273-277, 319, illus., Nov., 1924.

THE OPOSSUM PEST AND ITS FRIENDLY PREDATOR, THE TRAPPER. Joey Longtail. Forest and Bird, Wellington, no.75, pp.2-3, Feb., 1945.

MRS. OPOSSUM. AN AIR-MINDED SMALL FUR-BEARING ANIMAL. Francis X. Lueth. Illinois Conservation, Springfield, vol.8, no. 2, pp.6, 20, Summer, 1943.

(MOUNTAIN OPOSSUM (DROMICIOPS AUSTRALIS.) Monito del monte Dromiciops australis Philippi. Guillermo Mann. Investig. Zool. Chilenas, Santiago, vol.2, fasc.9-10, pp.159-166, illus., Oct., 1955.

SEXUAL DIFFERENTIATION IN THE OPOSSUM AFTER EARLY GONADECTOMY. Carl R. Moore. Jour. Exper. Zool. Phila., vol.94, no.3, pp.415-461, illus., Dec.,1943.

BILE CONSTITUENTS OF THE OPOSSUM DIDELPHYS MARSUPIALIS VIRGINIANA. F. Nakayama, C. G. Johnston. Proc. Soc. Exper. Biol. & Med. 95 (4): 690-693, Aug.-Sept., 1957.

A METHOD FOR INDUCING OVULATION IN THE ANOESTROUS OPOSSUM (DIDELPHYS VIRGINIANA). Olin E. Nelsen, Elizabeth Lloyd White. Anat. Record, Phila., vol.81, no.4 and suppl., pp.529-535, Dec., 1941.

REMARKS UPON CHIRONECTES YAPOCK, DESM. W. Ogilby. Proc. Zool. Soc. Lond., pt.4, p.56, 1836.

SEX AND AGE DETERMINATION IN THE OPOSSUM. George A. Petrides. Jour. Mam., vol.30, no.4, pp.364-378, pls.2, illus., Nov.17, 1949.

MARMOSA AS A STOWAWAY AGAIN. G. E. Potter. Science, vol.72, no.1856, p.91, July 25, 1930.

THE OPOSSUM. H. C. Reynolds. Scientific American, New York, vol.188, no.6, pp.88-95, June, 1953.

'POSSUMS: DUMB BUT NUMEROUS. Frank Sampson. Missouri Conservationist, Jefferson City, vol.11, no.12, pp.4-5, 12, illus., Dec., 1950; also in Texas Game & Fish, Austin, vol.9, no.3, pp.17-19, illus., Feb., 1951.

FACTS ABOUT 'POSSUMS. Charles W. Schwartz. Missouri Conservationist, Jefferson City, vol.6, no.8, p.17, illus., Aug., 1945.

OPOSSUM. Charles W. Schwartz, Elizabeth R. Schwartz. Nature, Washington, D.C., vol.34, no.3, pp.149-150, 4 illus., Mar., 1941.

OPOSSUM. Charles Schwartz, Elizabeth Schwartz. Mo. Cons. 14 (7): 11-13, illus., July, 1953.

A STUDY OF THE VIRGINIA OPOSSUM (DIDELPHIS VIRGINIANA KERR: FAMILY DIDELPHYIDAE). Henry W. Sheak. Bull. Wagner Free Inst. Sci. Philadelphia, vol.1, no.5, pp.39-45, Dec., 1926.

THE OPOSSUMS. R. W. Shufeldt. Amer. Forestry, vol.26, pp.96-101, 7 figs., Feb., 1920.

ALBINISM IN THE OPOSSUM. Dorothy M. Smith. Jour. Heredity, Washington, D.C., vol.31, no.8, p.342, fig.1, Aug., 1940.

(SOME REMARKS ON LUTREOLINA CRASSICAUDATA DESM.) Einige Bemerkungen ueber Lutreolina crassicaudata Desm. W. Stichel. Zeit f. Saeugetierkunde, bd.4, heft 1, pp.57-63, July 6, 1929.

REMARKS ON ABUNDANCE AND RANGE OF THE OPOSSUM. Dayton Stoner. Jour. Mam., vol.20, no.2, pp.250-251, May 14, 1939.

BANANA STOWAWAYS. George Wagner. Science, n.s., vol.67, p.422, Apr.20, 1928.

ELECTROCARDIOGRAPHIC STUDIES ON THE OPOSSUM. Charles G. Wilber. Jour. Mam., 36 (2): 284-286, 3 tables, May 26, 1955.

THE WATER OPOSSUM - CHIRONECTES PANAMENSIS GOLDMAN. James Zetek. Jour. Mam., vol.11, no.4, pp.470-471, pl. 20, Nov., 1930.

AMERICAN WITH A POUCH. Jour. Nat. Hist. Mag., New York, vol.7, no.10, pp. 8-9, illus., Dec., 1942.

HISTORY OF THE OPOSSUM (DIDELPHIS VIRGINIANA VIRGINIANA). Iowa Conservationist, Des Moines, vol.3, no.8, p.63, illus., Aug.15, 1944.

THE OPOSSUM. U. S. Fish and Wildl. Serv., Wildl. Leafl., 359, 2 p., illus., Mar., 1955.

OUR ONLY MARSUPIAL. Fauna, Phila., vol.8, no.3, pp.80-81, illus., Sept., 1946.

THE PROFESSOR ENTERTAINS 'POSSUMS. Maryland Conservationist, vol.19, no.4, pp. 3-4, Fall, 1942.

## Anatomy

VITALITY OF THE VIRGINIA OPOSSUM AS EXHIBITED IN THE SKELETON. J. D. Black. Jour. Mam., vol.16, no.3, p.223, Aug., 1935.

THE REPRODUCTIVE SYSTEM OF THE MALE OPOSSUM DIDELPHIS VIRGINIANA KERR AND ITS EXPERIMENTAL MODIFICATION. Elizabeth Brown Chase. Jour. Morph., Philadelphia, vol.65, no.2, pp. 215-239, Sept.1, 1939.

THE DEVELOPMENT OF THE SHOULDER REGION OF THE OPOSSUM DIDELPHYS VIRGINIANA, WITH SPECIAL REFERENCE TO THE MUSCULATURE. Cze-Ching Cheng. Jour. Morphology, Philadelphia, vol. 97, no.3, pp.415-472, Nov., 1955.

PANNICULUS CARNOSUS AND FORMATION OF THE POUCH IN DIDELPHIDS. Robert Kendall Enders. Jour. Morph., vol. 61, no.1, pp.1-26, 1937.

THE PREMANDIBULAR HEAD CAVITIES IN THE OPOSSUM DIDELPHIS VIRGINIANA. Perry W. Gilbert. Jour. Morphol., Phila., vol.95, no.1, pp.47-76, July, 1954.

THE MOTOR CORTEX OF THE OPOSSUM. P. A. Gray, Jr., E. L. Turner. Jour. Comp. Neur., vol.36, pp.376-386, 3 figs., Apr.15, 1924.

THE CORTICAL LAMINATION PATTERN OF THE OPOSSUM, DIDELPHYS VIRGINIANA. Percival Allen Gray. Jour. Comp. Neur., vol.37, pp.221-264, 31 figs., Aug. 15, 1924.

HYSTERECTOMY AND THE OESTROUS CYCLE IN THE OPOSSUM. Carl G. Hartman. Amer. Jour. Anat., vol.35, pp.25-29, Mar.15, 1925.

OBSERVATIONS ON THE MOTILITY OF THE OPOSSUM GENITAL TRACT AND THE VAGINAL PLUG. Carl G. Hartman. Anat. Record, vol.27, pp.293-303, 5 figs., May, 1924.

POLYNUCLEAR OVA AND POLYOVULAR FOLLICLES IN THE OPOSSUM AND OTHER MAMMALS WITH SPECIAL REFERENCE TO THE PROBLEM OF FECUNDITY. Carl G. Hartman. Amer. Jour. Anat., vol.37, pp.1-51, illus., Mar., 1926.

DESCRIPTION OF A SEX-INTERGRADE OPOSSUM WITH AN ANALYSIS OF THE CONSTITUENTS OF ITS GONADS. Carl G. Hartman, Bessie League. Anat. Record, vol. 29, pp.283-292, 2 pls., Feb.25, 1925.

THE GONADS OF A SEX-INTERGRADE OPOSSUM. Carl G. Hartman, Bessie League. Anat. Record, vol.29, p.114, Dec.25, 1924.

THE NUCLEUS OLFACTORIUS ANTERIOR OF THE OPOSSUM. Judson C. Herrick. Jour. Comp. Neur., vol.37, pp.317-359, 16 figs., Aug.15, 1924.

THE CEREBRUM AND OLFACTORIES OF THE OPOSSUM, DIDELPHYS VIRGINICA. C. L. Herrick. Bull. Sci. Lab. Denison Univ., vol.6, pt.2, pp.75-94, Jan., 1892.

SOME OBSERVATIONS ON THE FEMALE UROGENITAL ORGANS OF DIDELPHYIDAE. J. P. Hill, Elizabeth A. Fraser. Proc. Zool. Soc. Lond., pt.1, pp.189-219, 7 pls., 1925.

NOTES ON THE DISSECTION OF AZARA'S OPOSSUM (DIDELPHIS AZAROE, TEMM.) R. Jones. Proc. Zool. Soc. Lond., pt.2, p. 101, 1834.

THE MICROSCOPIC ANATOMY OF THE EPIPHYSIS OF THE OPOSSUM. H. E. Jordan. Anat. Record, Philadelphia, vol.5, no.7, pp.325-338, figs.18, July, 1911.

(THE DEVELOPMENT OF THE SCROTUM IN DIDELPHIS AURITA WEID.) Die entwicklung des scrotums bei didelphis aurita weid. Walter Kaiser. Morphologisches Jahrbuch, bd.68, Heft 3/4, pp.391-433, figs. 19, 1931.

THE PANNICULUS CARNOSUS AND POUCH MUSCULATURE OF THE OPOSSUM, A MARSUPIAL. Orthello R. Langworthy. Jour. Mam., vol.13, no.3, pp.241-251, Aug., 1932.

THE DEVELOPMENT AND MORPHOLOGY OF THE CEREBELLUM IN THE OPOSSUM. PT. 1. EARLY DEVELOPMENT. O. Larsell. Jour. Comp. Neur., vol.63, no.1, pp.65-94, figs.54, Dec.15, 1935.

THE DEVELOPMENT AND MORPHOLOGY OF THE CEREBELLUM IN THE OPOSSUM. PT. 2. LATER DEVELOPMENT AND ADULT. O. Larsell. Jour. Comp. Neur., vol.63, no.2, pp.251-289, fig.10, pls.2, Feb. 15, 1936.

MORPHOLOGICAL AND FUNCTIONAL DEVELOPMENT OF THE MEMBRANOUS LABYRINTH IN THE OPOSSUM. O. Larsell, E. McCrady, Jr., A. A. Zimmerman. Jour. Comp. Neur. vol.63, no.1, pp.95-118, figs. 10, Dec.15, 1935.

THE FOREBRAIN OF THE OPOSSUM, DIDELPHIS VIRGINIANA. PART 1. GROSS ANATOMY. Y. T. Loo. Jour. Comp. Neur., vol.51, no.1, pp.13-64, figs.31, Oct., 1930.

CORRELATIONS OF CERTAIN PONDERAL AND LINEAR SKELETAL MEASUREMENTS WITH SKULL WEIGHT AND SKULL LENGTH IN THE OPOSSUM. E. W. Lowrance. Anat. Record, Philadelphia, 128 (1): 69-76, May, 1957.

VARIABILITY AND GROWTH OF THE OPOSSUM SKELETON. E. W. Lowrance. Jour. Morphol., Phila., vol.85, no.3, pp. 569-593, Nov., 1949.

THE DEVELOPMENT OF THE AUDITORY OSSICLES OF THE OPOSSUM (DIDELPHYS VIRGINIANA). John A. McClain. Jour. Morphol., Philadelphia, vol.64, no.2, pp. 211-266, Mar., 1939.

A CONTRIBUTION TO THE ANATOMY AND DEVELOPMENT OF THE VENOUS SYSTEM OF DIDELPHYS MARSUPIALIS (L). PT. II, DEVELOPMENT. Charles F. W. McClure. Amer. Jour. Anat., vol.5, no.2, pp.163-226, May 31, 1906.

(PHYLOGENY AND FUNCTION IN THE MARMOSA ELEGANS MUSCULATURE MARSUPIALIA, DIDELPHYDAE). Filogena y funcion de la musculatura de Marmosa elegans (Marsupialia, Didelphydae). F. Guillermo Mann. Investig. Zool. Chilenas, Santiago, vol.1, fasc.9, pp.1-15, illus., Mar., 1953.

PHYLOGENY AND FUNCTION IN THE MARMOSA ELEGANS SKELETON MARSUPIALIA, DIDELPHIDAE.) Filogenia y funcion en el esqueleto de Marmosa elegans (Marsupialia, Didelphidae). F. Guillermo Mann. Investig. Zool. Chilenas, Santiago, vol.1, fasc.6, pp.6-16, May, 1952.

OBSERVATIONS ON THE HISTOLOGY OF THE OPOSSUM OVARY. Pedro Martinez-Esteve. Carnegie Inst. Washington (Contrib. Embryol., vol.30, no.189), publ.541, pp.17-26, pls.7, Dec.31, 1942.

PROSTATE GLAND INDUCTION IN THE FEMALE OPOSSUM BY HORMONES AND THE CAPACITY OF THE GLAND FOR DEVELOPMENT. Carl R. Moore. Amer. Jour. Anat., Phila., vol.76, no.1, pp.1-31, pls.1-2, Jan., 1945.

THE ROLE OF SEX HORMONES IN THE ORIGIN AND DEVELOPMENT OF UTERINE GLANDS IN THE OPOSSUM. Carl R. Moore, Elizabeth A. Failor. Jour. Exper. Zool., Philadelphia, vol.102, no.2, pp.209-235, illus., July, 1946.

OBSERVATIONS UPON THE FOETAL MEMBRANES OF THE OPOSSUM AND OTHER MARSUPIALS. Henry F. Osborn. Quart. Jour. Microscop. Sci., Lond., vol.23, pp.473-484, pl.33, July, 1883.

STRUCTURE AND FUNCTION OF THE BRAIN OF THE OPOSSUM (DIDELPHIS VIRGINIANA) AT THE TIME OF BIRTH. W. Riese. Jour. Mam., vol.26, no.2, pp. 148-153, pl.1, May, 1945.

THE EFFECTS OF ESTRADIOL AND PROGESTERONE ON THE REPRODUCTIVE TRACT OF THE OPOSSUM, AND THEIR POSSIBLE RELATION TO PARTURITION. George C. Risman. Jour. Morph., Philadelphia, vol.81, no.3, pp.343-397, Nov., 1947.

ON THE SO-CALLED INTERPLEURAL OPENING IN THE OPOSSUM, DIDELPHYS VIRGINIANA (KERR). Alice M. Russell. Anat. Record, Philadelphia, vol.82, no.4, pp.587-592, figs.2, Apr.25, 1942.

THE FUNCTIONAL SIGNIFICANCE OF THE CAPILLARY BED IN THE BRAIN OF THE OPOSSUM. Ernst Scharrer. Anat. Record, Philadelphia, vol.75, no.3, pp. 319-340, Nov.25, 1939.

EXHIBITION OF, AND REMARKS UPON A SKIN OF THE WATER-OPOSSUM (CHIRONECTES VARIEGATUS). Philip Lutley Sclater. Proc. Zool. Soc. Lond., p.702, 1871.

DEGENERATIVE CHANGES IN THE UNFERTILIZED UTERINE EGGS OF THE OPOSSUM, WITH REMARKS ON THE SO-CALLED PARTHENOGENESIS OF MAMMALS. Septima C. Smith. Amer Jour. Anat., vol.35, pp.81-96, pls.1-4, Mar.15, 1925.

THE DESCENDING TRACTS OF THE THALAMUS AND MIDBRAIN OF THE OPOSSUM, DIDELPHIS VIRGINIANA. Chiao Tsai. Jour. Comp. Neur., vol.39, pp.217-248, 15 figs., Oct.15, 1925.

THE OPTIC TRACTS AND CENTERS OF THE OPOSSUM, DIDELPHIS VIRGINIANA. Chiao Tsai. Jour. Comp. Neur., vol.39, pp.173-216, 4 figs., Oct.15, 1925.

THE PYRAMIDAL TRACT OF THE VIRGINIAN OPOSSUM. E. L. Turner. Jour. Comp. Neur., vol.36, pp.387-398, 6 figs., Apr.15, 1924.

THE HINDBRAIN OF THE OPOSSUM, DIDELPHIS VIRGINIANA. H. H. Voris, N. L. Hoerr. Jour. Comp. Neur., vol.54, pp.277-356, figs.41, 1932.

UNUSUAL FEATURES IN THE LUMBAR PLEXUS OF THE OPOSSUM. Otis Wade, Ernest William Hancock. Nat. Hist. Miscellanea, Chicago Acad. Sci., no.50, pp. 1-2, fig.1, June 29, 1949.

THE HEART AND ATTACHED VESSELS OF THE OPOSSUM, A MARSUPIAL. Otis Wade, Patricia Neely. Studies Dept. Zool. Univ. Nebraska, Lincoln, no.240, pp.111-116, illus., 1949; also in Jour. Mam., Balto., vol.30, no.2, pp.111-116, figs.1, pl.1, May 23, 1949.

NOTES ON THE RETINAE OF TWO OPOSSUM GENERA. G. L. Walls. Jour. Morphol., Philadelphia, vol.64, no.1, pp.67-87, Jan., 1939.

THE SEQUENCE OF EPIPHYSIAL UNION IN THE OPOSSUM. S. L. Washburn. Anat. Record, Philadelphia, vol.95, no.3, pp.353-363, July, 1946.

NORMAL DEVELOPMENT OF THE PITUITARY IN THE OPOSSUM AND ITS RESPONSES TO HORMONAL TREATMENTS. Robert S. Wheeler. Jour. Morphol., Philadelphia, vol.73, no.1, pp.43-87, illus., July, 1943.

PECULIARITIES OF THE CEREBRAL BLOOD VESSELS OF THE OPOSSUM: DIENCEPHALON, AREA POSTREMA AND RETINA. G. B. Wislocki. Anat. Record, Philadelphia, vol.78, no.1, pp.119-137, 3 pls., Sept.25, 1940.

THE UNUSUAL MANNER OF VASCULARIZATION OF THE BRAIN OF THE OPOSSUM (DIDELPHYS VIRGINIANA). G. B. Wislocki, A. C. P. Campbell. Anat. Record, vol.67, no.2, pp.177-189, figs.6, pl.1, Jan.25, 1937.

BIG POSSUM PARTICULARS. Ohio Conserv. Bull., Columbus, vol.11, no.3, p.1, Mar., 1947.

LARGE OPOSSUMS. Ohio Conserv. Bull., Columbus, vol.11, no.1, p.27, illus., Jan., 1947.

## Cytology

THE SOMATIC CHROMOSOMES OF THE OPOSSUM (DIDELPHIS VIRGINIANA). W. E. Hoy, Jr., W. C. George. Jour. Morphol. and Physiol., vol.47, pp.201-215, 1 text fig. and 5 pls., 1929.

THE SPERMATOGENESIS OF THE OPOSSUM (DIDELPHYS VIRGINIANA) WITH SPECIAL REFERENCE TO THE ACCESSORY CHROMOSOME AND THE CHONDRIOSOMES. H. E. Jordan. Archiv f. Zellforsch., Leipzig, vol.7, no.1, pp.41-86, figs.2, pls. 3, 1911.

STUDIES IN MAMMALIAN SPERMATOGENESIS. III. THE FATE OF THE CHROMATIN-NUCLEOLUS IN THE OPOSSUM. Theophilus S. Painter. Jour. Exper. Zool., vol.39, pp.197-227, Apr.5, 1924.

THE CHROMOSOMES OF THE SOUTH AMERICAN OPOSSUM, DIDELPHIS PARAGUAYENSIS. Francisco A. Saez. Amer. Nat., vol.65, no.698, pp.287-288, May-June, 1931.

## Diseases and Parasites

EXPERIMENTS WITH THE VIRUS OF YELLOW FEVER IN MARSUPIALS, WITH SPECIAL REFERENCE TO BROWN AND GREY MASKED OPOSSUMS. Martson Bates. Amer. Jour. Trop. Med., Baltimore, vol.24, no.2, pp.91-103, figs.3., Mar., 1944.

SUSCEPTIBILITY OF THE OPOSSUM (DIDELPHIS VIRGINIANA) TO THE VIRUS OF ENDEMIC TYPHUS FEVER. George D. Brigham. Pub. Health Rep. 51 (13): 333-337, Mar.27, 1936.

THE SUSCEPTIBILITY TO YELLOW FEVER OF THE VERTEBRATES OF EASTERN COLOMBIA. I. MARSUPIALIA. John C. Bucher, Jorge Boshell-Manrique, Manuel Roca-Garcia, Raymond M. Gilmore. Amer. Jour. Trop. Med., Baltimore, vol.21, no.2, pp.309-333, fig.1, Mar., 1941.

THE ANATOMY OF A LUNG FLUKE FROM THE OPOSSUM (DIDELPHIS VIRGINIANA KERR). Elon E. Byrd, Robert J. Reiber. Jour. Tennessee Acad. Sci., Nashville, vol. 17, no.1, pp.116-129, pls.2, Jan., 1942.

MAMMALIAN TREMATODES. I. TREMATODES FROM THE OPOSSUM, DIDELPHIS VIRGINIANA KERR. Elon E. Byrd, Robert J. Reiber. Rep. Reelfoot L. Biol. Sta. 6: 130-142, 1942.

THE ANATOMY OF A LUNG FLUKE FROM THE OPOSSUM (DIDELPHIS VIRGINIANA KERR). Elon E. Byrd, Robert J. Reiber, Malcolm V. Parker. Rep. Reelfoot L. Biol. Sta. 6: 116-129, 1942.

MAMMALIAN TREMATODES. I. TREMATODES FROM THE OPOSSUM, DIDELPHIS VIRGINIANA KERR. Elon E. Byrd, Robert J. Reiber, Malcolm V. Parker. Jour. Tennessee Acad. Sci., Nashville, vol.17, no.1, pp. 130-142, pls.4, Jan., 1942.

OBSERVATIONS ON THE SEGMENTAL ANATOMY OF THE TAPEWORM, MESOCESTOIDES VARIABILIS MUELLER 1928, FROM THE OPOSSUM. Elon E. Byrd, James W. Ward. Jour. Parasitol., Lancaster, vol.29, no.3, pp.217-226, illus., June, 1943.

THE OCCURRENCE OF EURYTREMA ALLENTOSHI (FOSTER, 1939) IN THE OPOSSUM IN TEXAS. J. Fred Denton. Proc. Helminth. Soc. Wash. 11 (2): 54-55, July, 1944.

THE OCCURRENCE OF VIANNAIA VIANNAIA TRAVASSOS (NEMATODA: HELIGMOSOMIDAE) IN OPOSSUMS IN NORTH AMERICA. G. Dikmans. Proc. Helminth. Soc. Wash. 10 (1): 6-7, Jan., 1943.

SOME HELMINTHS OF THE WOOLLY OPOSSUM IN PANAMA. A. O. Foster. Trans. Amer. Microscopical Soc., vol.58, no.2, pp.185-198, Apr., 1939.

SPIROCERCA LONGISPICULATA N. SP. William C. Hill. Am. Midland Nat. 21 (3): 636-640, May, 1939.

TULAREMIA FROM OPOSSUMS. J. A. Mease. Jour. Amer. Med. Asso., vol.92, p.1042, Mar.30, 1929.

TWO NEW PARASITIC WORMS OF DIDELPHYS AURITA: SKRJABINOFILARIA PRICEI N. SP. AND GONGYLONEMA MARSUPIALIS N. SP. Zeferino Vaz, Clemente Pereir. Jour. Washington Acad. Sci., vol.24, no.1, pp.54-56, Jan.15, 1934.

ISOSPORA BOUGHTONI N. SP. FROM THE AMERICAN OPOSSUM, DIDELPHIS VIRGINIANA. Joseph J. Volk. J. Parasitology 24 (6): 547-548, Dec., 1938.

## Ecology, Habits, Behavior

MATERNAL BEHAVIOR OF THE POUCHLESS MARSUPIAL MARMOSA CINEREA. Frank A. Beach. Jour. Mam., vol.20, no. 3, pp.315-322, figs.3, Aug.14, 1939.

AN OPOSSUM DIES OF COLD AND HUNGER. Frank W. Blair. Jour. Mam., vol. 17, no.4, p.410, Nov., 1936.

EARLY MOVEMENTS OF THE OPOSSUM WITH SPECIAL REFERENCE TO THE WALKING GAIT. G. E. Coghill. Proc. Soc. Exper. Biol. and Med., New York, vol. 39, no.1, pp.31-35, Oct., 1938.

DRAMA IN THE WOODS. L. E. Crawford. Oklahoma Game and Fish News, Oklahoma City, vol.4, no.4, p.11, illus., May, 1948.

THE SWIMMING OF THE OPOSSUM, DIDELPHIS MARSUPIALIS VIRGINIANA. Kenneth J. Doutt. Jour. Mam. 35(4): 581-583, Nov., 1954.

ECOLOGY OF THE OPOSSUM ON A NATURAL AREA IN NORTHEASTERN KANSAS. Henry S. Fitch, Lewis L. Sandidge. Univ. Kansas Publ., Mus. Nat. Hist., vol.7, no.2, pp.305-338, Aug.24, 1953.

THE FOOD OF THE OPOSSUM IN NEW YORK STATE. W. J. Hamilton, Jr. Jour. Wildl. Mgt. 15 (3): 258-264, July, 1951.

(ON A CASE OF TAMENESS IN DIDELPHYS.) Ueber einen Fall von Zahmheit bei Didelphys. H. Hediger. Zool. Garten, n. F., vol.7, nos. 1-3, pp.28-44, 9 figs., May, 1934.

ON THE FOOD HABITS OF MARMOSA. George E. Hudson. Jour. Mam., vol.13, no.2, p.159, May, 1932.

ECOLOGY OF THE OPOSSUM IN EASTERN TEXAS. Daniel W. Lay. Jour. Mam. 23 (2): 147-159, May, 1942.

THE USE OF THE TAIL BY AN OPOSSUM. James N. Layne. Jour. Mam., vol.32, no.4, pp.464-465, Nov.19, 1951.

OPOSSUM TAKING REFUGE UNDER WATER. Joseph Curtis Moore. Jour. Mam., 36 (4): 559, Dec.14, 1955.

POSSUM MAKES A NEST. Peter Payne. Everglades Nat. Hist., Homestead, Fla., vol. 2, no.3, p.101, June, 1954.

OPOSSUM CARRIES LEAVES WITH ITS TAIL. Leon L. Pray. Jour. Mam., vol.2, no. 2, pp.109-110, May, 1921.

A CASE OF MATRICIDE IN THE OPOSSUM. H. C. Raven. Jour. Mam., vol.10, no.2, p. 168, May, 1929.

A CONTRIBUTION TO THE LIFE HISTORY AND ECOLOGY OF THE OPOSSUM, DIDELPHIS VIRGINIANA (KERR), IN CENTRAL MISSOURI. Harold C. Reynolds. AM thesis, Univ. Mo., 1942.

SOME ASPECTS OF THE LIFE HISTORY AND ECOLOGY OF THE OPOSSUM IN CENTRAL MISSOURI. Harold C. Reynolds. Jour. Mam., vol.26, no.4, pp.361-379, illus., Feb.12, 1946.

FOODS AND DENS OF THE OPOSSUM (DIDELPHIS VIRGINIANA) IN NORTHEASTERN KANSAS. Lewis L. Sandidge. Trans. Kansas Acad. Sci. Topeka, vol.56, no.1, pp.97-109, 1953.

AN OPOSSUM IN NEW YORK STATE FEELS THE EFFECTS OF WINTER. Daniel Smiley, Jr. Jour. Mam., vol.19, no.4, p.499, Nov.14, 1938.

AN OBSERVATION ON THE NEST-BUILDING BEHAVIOR OF THE OPOSSUM. Luther Smith. Jour. Mam., vol.22, no.2, pp.201-202, May 14, 1941.

FOOD HABITS OF MICHIGAN OPOSSUMS. Clarence M. Taube. Jour. Wildl. Mgt. 11 (1): 97-103, Jan., 1947.

STUDIES ON THE OCCURRENCE, GROWTH, AND FOOD HABITS OF THE OPOSSUM IN MICHIGAN. Clarence M. Taube. MS thesis, Mich. State Coll., 1942.

FOOD HABITS OF THE OPOSSUM IN SUMTER COUNTY, ALABAMA. Robert J. Wheeler. MS thesis, Ala. Polytechnic Inst., 1939.

NOTES ON THE LIFE HISTORY AND ECOLOGY OF THE OPOSSUM IN SOUTHEAST IOWA. George L. Wiseman, George O. Hendrickson. Jour. Mam. 31 (3): 331-337, Aug., 1950.

WINTER DAYTIME DENS OF OPOSSUMS. Lee E. Yeager. Jour. Mam., 17 (4): 410-411, Nov., 1936.

## Economic Importance

OPOSSUM POUCH YOUNG AS EXPERIMENTAL MATERIAL. Carl R. Moore, David

Bodian. Anat. Rec., Philadelphia, vol.76, no. 3, pp.319-327, Fig.1, table 1, Mar.25, 1940.

A NEW EXPERIMENTAL ANIMAL FOR PSYCHIATRIC RESEARCH: THE OPOSSUM, DIDELPHIS VIRGINIANA. William S. Wiedom. Science, vol.119, no.3090, pp.360-361, Mar. 19, 1954.

Embryology

BISEXUAL DIFFERENTIATION OF THE SEX DUCTS IN OPOSSUMS AS A RESULT OF TREATMENT WITH ANDROGEN. Robert K. Burns. Jour. Exper. Zool. Phila., vol.100, no.1, pp.119-140, Oct., 1945.

THE DIFFERENTIATION OF SEX IN THE OPOSSUM (DIDELPHYS VIRGINIANA) AND ITS MODIFICATION BY THE MALE HORMONE TESTOSTERONE PROPIONATE. Robert K. Burns, Jr. Jour. Morph., Phila., vol.65, no.1, pp.79-113, pls.3, July 1,1939.

EFFECT OF TESTOSTERONE PROPIONATE ON SEX DIFFERENTIATION IN POUCH YOUNG OF OPOSSUM. Robert K. Burns, Jr. Proc. Soc. Exper. Biol. and Med., New York, vol.41, no.1, pp.60-62, May, 1939.

THE ORIGIN AND DIFFERENTIATION OF THE EPITHELIUM OF THE URINOGENITAL SINUS IN THE OPOSSUM, WITH A STUDY OF THE MODIFICATIONS INDUCED BY ESTROGENS. Robert K. Burns, Jr. Carnegie Inst. Washington (Contrib. Embryol., vol.30, no.191), publ.541, pp.63-83, figs.2, pls.10, Dec.31, 1942.

SEX DIFFERENTIATION DURING THE EARLY POUCH STAGES OF THE OPOSSUM (DIDELPHYS VIRGINIANA) AND A COMPARISON OF THE ANATOMICAL CHANGES INDUCED BY MALE AND FEMALE SEX HORMONES. Robert K. Burns, Jr. Jour. Morph., Philadelphia, vol.65, no.3, pp.497-535, 6 pls., Nov.1, 1939.

STUDIES IN THE DEVELOPMENT OF THE OPOSSUM DIDELPHYS VIRGINIANA L. Carl G. Hartman. Jour. Morphology, vol.27, no.1, pp.1-62, pls.1-11, Mar., 1916.

THE DEVELOPMENT OF THE PHARYNGEAL DERIVATIVES OF THE OPOSSUM (DIDELPHYS VIRGINIANA), WITH SPECIAL REFERENCE TO THE THYMUS. B. F. Kingsbury. Amer. Jour. Anat., Philadelphia, vol.67, no.3, pp.393-435, 5 pls., Nov.15, 1940.

THE EMBRYOLOGY OF THE OPOSSUM. Edward McCrady, Jr. Amer. Anat. Memoirs, no.16, 234 pp., illus., Oct., 1938.

NOTE ON THE BLASTODERMIC VESICLE OF THE OPOSSUM. Charles S. Minot. Anat. Record, Philadelphia, vol.5, no.6, pp.295-300, figs.2, June, 1911.

EMBRYONIC DIFFERENTIATION OF OPOSSUM PROSTATE FOLLOWING CASTRATION, AND RESPONSES OF THE JUVENILE GLAND TO HORMONES. Carl R. Moore. Anat. Record, Philadelphia, vol.80, no.3, pp.315-327, 1 pl., July 25, 1941.

THE FORMATION OF THE EARLY GENITAL RUDIMENT AND DIFFERENTIATION OF SEX IN THE OPOSSUM. Olin E. Nelson. Jour. Morphol., Philadelphia, vol.75, no.2, pp.303-319, pls.1-7, Sept., 1944.

OSSIFICATION CENTERS AND SKELETAL DEVELOPMENT IN THE POSTNATAL VIRGINIA OPOSSUM. Carlita L. Nesslinger. Jour. Mam., 37 (3): 382-394, illus., Sept.11, 1956.

NORMAL DEVELOPMENT AND EXPERIMENTAL TREATMENT OF THE OPOSSUM MAMMARY GLAND PRIMORDIUM. Dorothy Wells Plagge. Proc. Soc. Exper. Biol. and Med., Utica, vol.51, no.2, pp.219-220, fig. 1, Nov., 1942.

THE EARLY POSTNATAL DEVELOPMENT OF THE BRAIN OF THE OPOSSUM (DIDELPHIS VIRGINIANA). W. Riese. Jour. Mam., vol.29, no.2, pp.150-155, pl.1, May 14, 1948.

EMBRYONIC DIFFERENTIATION OF COWPER'S AND BARTHOLIN'S GLANDS OF THE OPOSSUM FOLLOWING CASTRATION AND OVARIOTOMY. David Rubin. Jour. Exper. Zool., Philadelphia, vol.94, no. 3, pp.463-475, illus., Dec., 1943.

THE RELATION OF HORMONES TO THE DEVELOPMENT OF COWPER'S AND BARTHOLIN'S GLANDS IN THE OPOSSUM (DIDELPHYS VIRGINIANA). David Rubin. Jour. Morphol., Philadelphia, vol.74, no.2, pp.213-285, pls.1-3, Mar., 1944.

THE DEVELOPMENT OF THE CORTICOSPINAL TRACT IN THE POUCH YOUNG OF THE VIRGINIA OPPOSUM DIDELPHYS VIRGINIANA. J. W. Ward. Jour. Comp. Neur., Philadelphia, vol.101, no.2, pp.483-494, Oct., 1954.

Fossils

NANODELPHYS, AN OLIGOCENE DIDELPHINE. Paul O. McGrew. Geol. Ser. Field Mus. Nat. Hist., Chicago, vol.6, no.26 (no.455), pp.393-400, fig.1, Oct.,1939.

NEW MARSUPIALS FROM THE TERTIARY OF NEBRASKA. Paul O. McGrew. Jour. Geol., vol.45, no.4, pp.448-455, figs.4, May-June, 1937.

FOSSIL MAMMALS FROM THE BEGINNING OF THE CENOZOIC IN BRAZIL. MARSUPIALIA: DIDELPHIDAE. Carlos De Paula Couto. Amer. Mus. Novitates, New York, no. 1567, pp.26, illus., June 5, 1952.

(OBSERVATIONS ON NOTICITIS ORTIZI AMEGH.) Observaciones sobre Notictis ortizi Amegh. Osvaldo A. Reig. Ann. Soc. Cienc. Argentina, vol.104, pp.3-9, illus., July, 1952.

DIDELPHIIDAE FROM THE LANCE BEDS OF WYOMING. Loris S. Russell. Jour. Mam., vol.9, no.3, pp.229-232, Aug., 1928.

AMERICAN EOCENE DIDELPHIDS. George Gaylord Simpson. Amer. Mus. Novitates, New York, no.307, 7 pp., figs.5, Apr.14, 1928.

A NEW MARSUPIAL FROM THE EOCENE OF PATAGONIA. George Gaylord Simpson. Amer. Mus. Novitates, no.989, pp.1-5, fig. 1, May 24, 1938.

A NEW SPECIMEN OF EODELPHIS CUTLERI FROM THE BELLY RIVER FORMATION OF ALBERTA. George Gaylord Simpson. Bull. no.63, Canada Dept. Mines, Geol. Ser., no.51, pp.29-32, pl.1, 1930.

SESPE EOCENE DIDELPHIDS. Chester Stock. Proc. Nat. Acad. Sci., vol.22, no.2, pp.122-124, pl.1, Feb., 1936.

Mexico and Central America

DESCRIPTION OF A NEW SPECIES OF OPOSSUM FROM THE ISTHMUS OF TEHUANTEPEC, MEXICO. Joel Asaph Allen. Amer. Mus. Nat. Hist., Bull. New York, vol.5, pp.235-236, 1893.

A NEW MARSUPIAL FROM EL SALVADOR. Donald R. Dickey. Proc. Biol. Soc. Washington, vol.41, pp.15-16, Feb.4, 1928.

DESCRIPTIONS OF TWO NEW MURINE OPOSSUMS FROM MEXICO. Hart C. Merriam. Proc. Biol. Soc., Washington, vol.11, pp.43-44, Mar.16, 1897.

TWO NEW MOUSE OPOSSUMS FROM YUCATAN. Wilfred H. Osgood. Proc. Biol. Soc. Washington, vol.26, pp.175-176, Aug. 8, 1913.

North America

A PRELIMINARY STUDY OF THE NORTH AMERICAN OPOSSUMS OF THE GENUS DIDELPHIS. J. A. Allen. Bull. Amer. Mus. Nat. Hist., vol.14, pp.149-188, pls.22-25, June 15, 1901.

THE OPOSSUM. Rod Amundson. Wildlife in North Carolina, Raleigh, vol.13, no.4, pp.4-6, illus., Apr., 1949.

WISCONSIN WILDLIFE FOR BOYS AND GIRLS--ANIMALS. OPOSSUM (DIDELPHIS VIRGINIANA VIRGINIANA). N. R. Barger. Wisconsin Conserv. Bull., Madison, vol.12, no.3, pp.24-25, Mar., 1947.

POSSUMS...AND POINTS WEST. Richard G. Beidleman. Colo. Cons. 1 (4): 2-5, illus., July-Aug., 1952.

RECORDS OF OPOSSUMS FROM SAN DIEGO COUNTY, CALIFORNIA. Jack C. von Bloeker. Jour. Mam., vol.9, no.1, p. 62, Feb., 1928.

OPOSSUM--INVADER FROM THE SOUTH. G. W. Bradt. Mich. Cons. 16 (3): 4, Mar.-Apr., 1947.

THE FLORIDA OPOSSUM ON THE COAST OF SOUTH CAROLINA. E. B. Chamberlain. Jour. Mam., vol.9, no.3, p.247, Aug., 1928.

OPOSSUM IN THE LOWER HUDSON VALLEY, NEW YORK. Robert H. Coleman. Jour. Mam., vol.10, no.3, Aug., 1929, p.250.

THE OPOSSUM. Art Cook. New York Conserv., Albany, vol.3, no.1, p.25, illus., Aug.-Sept., 1948.

OPOSSUMS IN ONTARIO. J. L. Cull. Rod & Gun in Canada, Montreal, vol.49, no.5, p. 24, 1947.

VIRGINIA OPOSSUM IN VERMONT. George W. Davis. Jour. Mam., vol.19, no.4, p.499, Nov.14, 1938.

THE TENNESSEE POSSUM HAS ARRIVED IN CALIFORNIA. Joseph Grinnell. Cal. Fish and Game, vol.1, no.3, pp.3, fig.29, Apr.10, 1915.

THE NORTHWARD SPREAD OF THE OPOSSUM IN NEW YORK. W. J. Hamilton, Jr. Jour. Mam., vol.14, no.2, pp.151-152, May, 1933.

THE OPOSSUM IN ARIZONA. Raymond J. Hock. Jour. Mam., 33 (4): 464-470, map, Nov., 1952.

THE VIRGINIA OPOSSUM IN OREGON. Stanley G. Jewett, Harold W. Dobyns. Jour. Mam., vol.10, no.4, p.351, nov., 1929.

THE VIRGINIA OPOSSUM IN MASSACHUSETTS AND NEW HAMPSHIRE. Fred H. Kennard. Jour. Mam., vol.6, no.3, p.196, Aug., 1925.

ANOTHER OPOSSUM TAKEN IN VERMONT. George L. Kirk. Jour. Mam., vol.3, no.2, p.115, May, 1922.

OPOSSUM IN VERMONT. George L. Kirk. Jour. Mam., vol.2, no.2, p.109, May, 1921.

OCCURRENCE OF THE VIRGINIA OPOSSUM IN SOUTHERN CENTRAL NEW YORK. J. Alden Loring. Science, n.s., vol.9, no. 211, p.71, Jan.13, 1899.

DISTRIBUTIONAL RECORDS OF THE OPOSSUM IN ONTARIO. Randolph L. Peterson, S. C. Downing. Jour. Mam., 37 (3): 431-435, Sept.11, 1956.

THE OPOSSUM SETTLES IN WASHINGTON STATE. Victor B. Scheffer. Murrelet, Seattle, vol.24, no.2, pp.27-28, Aug.15, 1943.

VIRGINIA ANIMALS EVERYONE SHOULD KNOW: THE OPOSSUM. C. H. Shaffer. Virginia Wildlife, Richmond, vol.9, no.1, pp.19-20, illus., Jan., 1948.

THE OPOSSUM IN KENT COUNTY, ONTARIO. J. H. Smith. Canadian Field-Nat., vol.49, no.6, p.109, Sept., 1935.

FURTHER REMARKS ON THE OPOSSUM IN NEW YORK. Dayton Stoner. Jour. Mam., vol.26, no.2, pp.192-193, July 15, 1945.

OPOSSUM'S COMEBACK. Lewis Wayne Walker. Nature Mag., vol.21, no.6, p.299, June, 1933.

AN OPOSSUM IN KENT COUNTY, ONTARIO. A. A. Wood. Canadian Field-Nat., Ottawa, vol.6, no.6, p.199, Feb.13, 1948.

OPOSSUM, MOST PRIMITIVE OF MARYLAND MAMMALS. Rally Sheet, League of Maryland Sportsmen, Baltimore, vol.3, no.10, p.6, illus., Oct., 1945.

Physiology

PERISTALSIS OF THE COMMON BILE DUCT IN THE OPOSSUM. Franklin S. Dubois, Eleanor A. Hunt. Anat. Record, vol.53, no.3, pp.387-393, pls.2, Aug.25, 1932.

CHARACTER OF THE BLOOD-CLOT IN THE THYROIDECTOMIZED ADULT OPOSSUM. Mamie Gray. Amer. Jour. Physiol., vol.68, pp.149-152, 1 fig., Apr., 1924.

THE INTERRUPTION OF PREGNANCY BY OVARIECTOMY IN THE APLACENTAL OPOSSUM: A STUDY IN THE PHYSIOLOGY OF IMPLANTATION. Carl Hartman. Amer. Jour. Physiol., vol.71, pp.436-454, illus., Jan., 1925.

OBSERVATIONS ON THE FUNCTIONAL COMPENSATORY HYPERTROPHY OF THE OPOSSUM OVARY. Carl Hartman. Amer. Jour. Anat., vol.35, pp.1-24, Mar.15, 1925.

VITAMIN-A AND EXERCISE IN RELATION TO FOLLICULAR ATRESIA IN THE OPOSSUM. Carl Hartman. Amer. Jour. Physiol., vol.68, pp.97-101, Mar., 1924.

TEMPERATURE REGULATION IN THE VIRGINIA OPPOSUM. A. C. Higginbotham, W. E. Koon. Amer. Jour. Physiol., Wash., vol.181, no.1, pp.69-71, Apr., 1955.

SEXUAL RHYTHMS IN THE REPRODUCTIVE TRACT OF THE ADULT FEMALE OPOSSUM AND EFFECTS OF HORMONAL TREATMENTS. Charles F. Morgan. Amer. Jour. Anat., Philadelphia, vol.78, no.3, pp. 411-463, figs.1-2, pls.1-5, May, 1946.

ELECTROCARDIOGRAM OF OPOSSUM DURING EXPOSURE TO COLD. R. M. Nardone, C. G. Wilber, X. J. Musacchia. Amer. Jour. Physiol., vol.181, no.2, pp. 325-329, May, 1955.

AN EXPERIMENTAL STUDY OF THE CEREBRAL PHYSIOLOGY OF THE VIRGINIA OPOSSUM. Fred T. Rogers. Jour. Comp. Neur., vol.37, pp.265-316, 6 pls., Aug.15, 1924.

THE ARTERIAL SUPPLY OF THE BRAIN AND SPINAL CORD IN THE VIRGINIAN OPOSSUM (DIDELPHIS VIRGINIANA). H. C. Voris. Jour. Comp. Neur., vol.44, pp. 403-423, illus., 1927.

REGULATION OF BODY TEMPERATURE IN OPOSSUMS OF THE GENUS MARMOSA. Otis Wade. Science, vol.72, no.1867, pp. 365-366, Oct.10, 1930.

Reproductive Biology

OBSERVATIONS ON THE BREEDING OF THE AMERICAN OPOSSUM IN FLORIDA. R. K. Burns, Lucille M. Burns. Rev. Suisse Zool., 64 (32): 595-605, Dec., 1957.

STUDIES ON REARING THE OPOSSUM (DIDELPHYS VIRGINIANA). G. E. Coghill. Ohio Jour. Sci., Columbus, vol.39, no.5, pp.239-249, figs.11, Sept., 1939.

OBSERVATIONS ON PARTURITION IN THE OPOSSUM DIDELPHYS VIRGINIANA. L. M. Dickerson. Science, n.s., vol.68, pp.111-112, Aug.3, 1928.

BIRTH IN THE OPOSSUM FAMILY. W. J. Hamilton, Jr. Pa. Game News 13 (11): 4-5, Feb., 1943.

BREEDING HABITS, DEVELOPMENT, AND BIRTH OF THE OPOSSUM. Carl G. Hartman. Ann. Rep. Smithsonian Inst., 1921, pp.347-363, 10 plates, 1923.

THE OESTROUS CYCLE IN THE OPOSSUM. Carl G. Hartman. Amer. Jour. Anat., vol.32, pp.353-421, 13 pls., Nov., 1923.

THE STORY OF THE BABY OPOSSUM. Carl G. Hartman. American Fur Breeder, vol.3, no. 4, pp.4-8. Oct., 1930.

STUDIES IN THE DEVELOPMENT OF THE OPOSSUM DIDELPHYS VIRGINIANA L. V. THE PHENOMENA OF PARTURITION. Carl G. Hartman. Anat. Record, vol.19, no.5, pp. 1-11 (of separate), Oct. (Sept.13), 1920.

SOME OLD AND FORGOTTEN OBSERVATIONS UPON THE BREEDING HABITS OF THE OPOSSUM. Chester H. Heuser, Carl G. Hartman. Jour. Mam., vol.9, no.1, pp.61-62, Feb., 1928.

MEMOIR ON THE REPRODUCTION OF THE OPOSSUM. DIDELPHIS VIRGINIANA. Ch. D. Meigs. Trans. Amer. Philos. Soc., vol.10, pp.155-166, 1853.

(DIDELPHIA OR MAMMALIA OVOVIVIPARA). Didelphia ou Mammalia-Ovovivipara. Alipio de Miranda-Ribeiro. Revista Mus. Paulista, vol.20, pp.245-427, figs.8, tables, illus., 1936.

(Review by Robert K. Enders of) DIDELPHIA OU MAMMALIA-OVOVIVIPARA. Alipio de Miranda-Ribeiro. Jour. Mam., vol.18, no.1, pp.108-109, Feb., 1937.

STUDIES ON REPRODUCTION IN THE OPOSSUM (DIDELPHIS VIRGINIANA VIRGINIANA). Harold C. Reynolds. Univ. California Publ. Zool., vol.52, no.3, pp. 223-284, illus., nov.13, 1952.

South America

A PRELIMINARY STUDY OF THE SOUTH AMERICAN OPOSSUMS OF THE GENUS DIDELPHIS. J. A. Allen. Bull. Amer. Mus. Nat. Hist., vol.16, pp.249-279, Aug.18, 1902.

IS THE YAPOK OR WATER OPOSSUM FOUND IN TRINIDAD? Arthur M. Greenhall. Jour. Trinidad Field Nat. Club, 1956: 27, 1956.

A NEW SPECIES OF MURINE OPOSSUM (GENUS MARMOSA) FROM PERU. Charles O. Handley, Jr. Jour. Washington Acad. Sci., vol.46, no.12, pp.402-404, Feb.13, 1957.

THE TRINIDAD OPOSSUM ON MARTINIQUE. Ned Hollister. Proc. Biol. Soc. Wash., vol. 25, p.93, May 4, 1912.

(OBSERVATIONS ON ARGENTINIAN OPOSSUMS.) Beobachtungen an argentinischen Beutelratten. Hans Kreig. Zeitschr. Wissensch. Biologie, Abteil.A, vol.1, pp.637-659, 14 figs., Sept.22, 1924.

(VOYAGES IN SOUTH AMERICA FOR THE PURPOSE OF BIOLOGICAL STUDY. III. CHILEAN OPOSSUMS.) Biologische Reisestudien in Suedamerika. III. Chilenische Beutelratten. Hans Krieg. Zeitschr. Wissensch. Biologie, Abteil.A, vol.3, pp.169-176, 6 figs., Dec.3, 1924.

SOUTH AMERICAN MARSUPIALS. Alipio Miranda-Ribeiro. Revista do Museu Paulista, Sao Paula, Brasil, vol.20, pp.245-427, illus., June 20, 1936.

A NEW MURINE OPOSSUM FROM ARGENTINA. H. Harold Shamel. Jour. Washington Acad. Sci., vol.20, no.5, pp.83-84, Mar. 4, 1930.

BRIEF DIAGNOSES OF TWENTY-SIX APPARENTLY NEW FORMS OF MARMOSA (MARSUPIALIA) FROM SOUTH AMERICA. G. H. H. Tate. Amer. Mus. Novitates 493, pp.1-14, Sept.26, 1931.

A NEW GENUS OF OPOSSUM FROM SOUTHERN PATAGONIA. Oldfield Thomas. Ann. and Mag. Nat. Hist., ser.9, vol.8, pp.136-139, July, 1921.

A NEW SHORT-TAILED OPOSSUM FROM ARGENTINA. Oldfield Thomas. Ann. and Mag. Nat. Hist., ser.9, vol.13, p.586, June, 1924.

A NEW SHORT-TAILED OPOSSUM FROM BRAZIL. Oldfield Thomas. Ann. and Mag. Nat. Hist., ser.9, vol.8, pp.441-442, Oct., 1921.

A NEW SHORT-TAILED OPOSSUM FROM MARAJO AMAZONIA. Oldfield Thomas. Ann. and Mag. Nat. Hist., ser.9, vol.12, p.157, July, 1923.

THREE NEW SPECIES OF MARMOSA WITH A NOTE ON DIDELPHYS WATERHOUSEI, TOMES. Oldfield Thomas. Ann. and Mag. Nat. Hist., ser.9, vol.7, pp.519-523, June, 1921.

ADDITIONAL NOTE ON DIDELPHYS WATERHOUSII. Robert F. Tomes. Proc. Zool. Soc. Lond., pt.28, pp.303-304, figs. 2, 1860.

DESCRIPTION OF A NEW SPECIES OF OPOSSUM, OBTAINED BY MR. FRASER IN ECUADOR. Robert F. Tomes. Proc. Zool. Soc. Lond., pt.28, pp.58-60, 1860.

NOTICE OF A NEW AMERICAN FORM OF MARSUPIAL. Robert F. Tomes. Proc. Zool. Soc. Lond., pt.31, pp.50-51, 1863.

("COLORED OPOSSUMS" OF ARGENTINA.) Las "comadrejas coloradas" de la Argentina (Didelphidae). Jose Yepes. Physis Buenos Aires, vol.16, no.48, p.293, May, 1939.

Taxonomy

DESCRIPTIONS OF NEW AMERICAN MARSUPIALS. J. A. Allen. Bull. Amer. Mus. Nat. Hist., vol.13, pp.191-199, Oct.23, 1900.

NOTE ON THE GENERIC NAMES DIDELPHIS AND PHILANDER. J. A. Allen. Bull. Amer. Mus. Nat. Hist., vol.13, pp.185-190, Oct.12, 1900.

(THE TYPE OF PHILANDER LANIGER IN THE MUSEUM OF NATURAL SCIENCE IN MADRID.) El tipo de Philander laniger Desm. en el Museo de Ciencias Naturales de Madrid. Angel Cabrera. Bol. Real Soc. Espanola Hist. Nat. Madrid, vol.16, no.10, pp.514-517, Dec., 1916.

GENERIC NAMES OF THE FOUR-EYED POUCH OPOSSUM AND THE WOOLLY OPOSSUM (DIDELPHIDAE). Philip Hershkovitz. Proc. Biol. Soc. Washington, vol.62, pp. 11-12, Mar.17, 1949.

ON DIDELPHIS CAUDIVOLVULA KERR AND DIDELPHIS VULPECULA KERR. Fredericus Anna Jentink. Notes, Leyden Mus., vol.7, no.4, pp.21-28, nov., 1884.

THE APPLICATION OF DIDELPHIS MARSUPIALIS LINNAEUS. James A. G. Rehn. Amer. Nat., Boston, vol.35, no.410, pp. 147-149, Feb., 1901.

A NEW NAME FOR MARMOSA MUSCULA SHAMEL. H. H. Shamel. Jour. Mam., vol. 11, no.3, p.311, Aug., 1930.

NOTE ON THE CLASSIFICATION OF RECENT AND FOSSIL OPOSSUMS. George Gaylord Simpson. Jour. Mam., vol.16, no. 2, pp.134-137, May, 1935.

A SYSTEMATIC REVISION OF THE MARSUPIAL GENUS MARMOSA. G. H. H. Tate. Bull. Amer. Mus. Nat. Hist., vol.66, art. 1, pp.1-250, figs.29, pls.26, 1 table (9 Sections), Aug.10, 1933.

DIAGNOSES OF FOUR NEW SPECIES OF DIDELPHYS. Oldfield Thomas. Ann. and Mag. Nat. Hist. (6), vol.1, no.2, pp.158-159, Feb., 1888.

THE GEOGRAPHICAL RACES OF LUTREOLINA CRASSICAUDATA. Oldfield Thomas. Ann. and Mag. Nat. Hist., ser.9, vol.11, pp.583-585, May, 1923.

THE GEOGRAPHICAL RACES OF THE WOOLLY OPOSSUM. Oldfield Thomas. Ann. and Mag. Nat. Hist. (8), vol.12, no. 70, pp.358-361, Oct., 1913.

ON A NEW SPECIES OF MARMOSA. Oldfield Thomas. Ann. and Mag. Nat. Hist. (7), vol.3, no.13, pp.44-45, Jan., 1899.

ON MARMOSA MARMOTA AND ELEGANS, WITH DESCRIPTIONS OF NEW SUBSPECIES OF THE LATTER. Oldfield Thomas. Ann. and Mag. Nat. Hist. (7), vol.10, no.56, pp.158-163, Aug., 1902.

ON MICOUREUS GRISEUS, DESM., WITH THE DESCRIPTION OF A NEW GENUS AND SPECIES OF DIDELPHYIDAE. Oldfield Thomas. Ann. and Mag. Nat. Hist. (6), vol.14, no.81, pp.184-188, Sept.1894.

THE SUBSPECIES OF METACHIRUS. Oldfield Thomas. Ann. and Mag. Nat. Hist., ser.9, vol.11, pp.602-607, May, 1923.

THREE NEW SPECIES OF MARMOSA, WITH A NOTE ON DIDELPHYS WATERHOUSEI, TOMES. Oldfield Thomas. Ann. and Mag. Nat. Hist. (9), vol.7, no.42, pp. 519-523, June, 1921.

Dasyuridae

NOTES ON THE FAT-TAILED MARSUPIAL MOUSE (SMINTHOPSIS CRASSICAUDATA). M. A. Alexander. Mem. Queensland Mus., vol.7, pp.295-296, Dec. 19, 1922.

BRUSH-TAILED RAIDERS. Charles Barrett. Victorian Nat., vol.44, no.4, p.100, Aug., 1927.

NOTES ON NATIVE CATS. F. J. Buckland. Victorian Nat., Melbourne, vol.70, no.11, pp.210-211, Mar., 1954.

AUSTRALIA'S MARSUPIAL "TIGER CAT." David Fleay. Animal Kingdom, New York, vol.51, no.2, pp.36-41, illus., Mar.-Apr. (April 1), 1948.

AUSTRALIA'S YELLOW-FOOTED MARSUPIAL MOUSE. David Fleay. Animal

Kingdom, New York, vol.53, no.1, pp. 20-24, illus., Jan.-Feb., 1950.

THE BRUSH-TAILED PHASCOGALE. David Fleay. Victorian Nat., vol.46, no.6, pp. 135-136, fig.1, Oct., 1929.

EXPERIENCES WITH AUSTRALIA'S BRUSH-TAILED TUAN. David Fleay. Animal Kingdom, New York, vol.53, no.5, pp.152-157, illus., Sept.-Oct., 1950.

THE RARE DASYURES (NATIVE CATS). David Fleay. Victorian Nat., vol.49, no.3, pp.63-68, figs.3, pls.3, July, 1932.

SWAINSON'S PHASCOGALE (THE "BUSH-MOUSE"). David Fleay. Victorian Nat., vol.49, no.5, pp.132-134, fig.1, Sept., 1932.

LETTER RELATING TO TWO LIVING SPECIMENS OF THYLACINUS CYNOCEPHALUS, PRESENTED TO THE SOCIETY BY HIMSELF AND DR. JAMES GRANT OF LAUNCESTON. Ronald C. Gunn. Proc. Zool. Soc. Lond., pt.18, pp.90-91, 1850.

THE STUDY OF A GENERALIZED MARSUPIAL (DASYCERCUS CRISTICAUDA KREFFT). Frederic Wood Jones. Trans. Zool. Soc. Lond., vol.26, pt.5, pp.409-501, figs.99, pls.2, Nov., 1949.

RESULTS OF THE ARCHBOLD EXPEDITIONS. NO.56. ON THE ANATOMY AND CLASSIFICATION OF THE DASYURIDAE MARSUPIALIA. G. H. H. Tate. Bull. Amer. Mus. Nat. Hist., New York, vol.88, art.3, pp.97-156, fig.1, Feb.20, 1947.

DESCRIPTION OF A NEW PHASCOLOGALE FROM BRITISH NEW GUINEA, OBTAINED BY DR. L. LORIA. Oldfield Thomas. Annali del Museo Civico di Storia Naturale di Genova (2), vol.20, pp.191-192, July 21, 1899.

NOTES ON PHASCOGALE AND CHAETOCERCUS. Oldfield Thomas. Ann. and Mag. Nat. Hist. (8), vol.9, no.49, pp.91-92, Jan., 1912.

Anatomy

THE GROWTH STAGES OF THE POUCH YOUNG OF THE NATIVE CAT (DASYURUS VIVERRINUS) TOGETHER WITH OBSERVATIONS ON THE ANATOMY OF THE NEW BORN YOUNG. J. P. Hill, W. C. Osman Hill. Trans. Zool. Soc. Lond., vol.28, pt. 5, pp.349-452, pls.13, Mar., 1955.

THE ORIGIN AND BEHAVIOUR OF CHIASMATA. XI. DASYURUS AND SARCOPHILUS. P. C. Koller. Cytologia, Tokyo, vol.7, nos. 1-2, pp.82-103, figs.23, tables 6, May, 1936.

NOTES OF A DISSECTION OF A LONG-TAILED DASYURUS (DASYURUS MACROURUS, GEOFF.) R. Owen. Proc. Zool. Soc. Lond., pt.3, p.7, 1835.

ON THE RUDIMENTAL MARSUPIAL BONES IN THE THYLACINUS. R. Owen. Proc. Zool. Soc. Lond., pt.11, pp.148-149, 1843.

THE FEMALE UROGENITAL SYSTEM OF ANTECHINUS (MARSUPIALIA). J. Pearson, J. M de Bavay. Proc. Roy. Soc. Tasmania, Hobart, pp.137-142, Dec.15, 1951.

THE UROGENITAL SYSTEM OF THE DASYURINAE AND THYLACININAE. J. Pearson, J. M. de Bavey. Pap. and Proc. Roy. Soc. Tasmania, vol.87, pp.175-199, 1953.

THE EXTERNAL CHARACTERS OF THYLACINUS, SARCOPHILUS, AND SOME RELATED MARSUPIALS. R. I. Pocock. Proc. Zool. Soc. Lond., 1926, pt.4, pp.1037-1084, illus., Dec., 1928.

ON THE HOMOLOGIES AND SUCCESSION OF THE TEETH IN THE DASYURIDAE, WITH AN ATTEMPT TO TRACE THE HISTORY OF THE EVOLUTION OF MAMMALIAN TEETH IN GENERAL. Oldfield Thomas. Philos. Trans. Roy. Soc., Lond., (B), vol.178, pp.443-462, pls.27-28, 1887.

ON THE HOMOLOGIES AND SUCCESSION OF THE TEETH IN THE DASYURIDAE, WITH AN ATTEMPT TO TRACE THE HISTORY OF THE EVOLUTION OF THE MAMMALIAN TEETH IN GENERAL. Oldfield Thomas. Proc. Roy. Soc. Lond., vol.42, pp.310-312, Apr.28, 1887.

Australia and Tasmania

THE TASMANIAN TIGER. THE PRESERVATION OF THE TASMANIAN TIGER OR MARSUPIAL WOLF (THYLACINUS). E. P. Andrewartha. Jour. Soc. Preservation Fauna of Empire, Hertford, n.s., pt.34, pp.87-88, Aug., 1938.

THE SUPPOSED "TIGER-CAT" OF QUEENSLAND. Maurice Burton. Oryx, Hertford, vol.1, no.7, pp.321-326, Nov., 1952.

ON MAMMALS FROM THE LAKE EYRE BASIN. I.--THE DASYURIDAE. H. H. Finlayson. Trans. and Proc. Roy. Soc. South Australia, vol.57, pp.195-202, Dec. 23, 1933.

ON THE TRAIL OF THE MARSUPIAL WOLF. (TRACKING AND TRAPPING IN THE WILD AND PICTURESQUE WEST OF TASMANIA.) David Fleay. Victorian Nat., Melbourne, vol.63, no.6, pp.129-135, pl.10; no.7, pp. 154-159, pl.11; no.8, pp.174-177, Oct.-Nov., Dec., 1946.

THE THYLACINE. REPORTS ON TWO EXPEDITIONS IN SEARCH OF THE THYLACINE (TASMANIAN TIGER, OR TASMANIAN WOLF). A. L. Fleming. Jour. Soc. Preservation Fauna of Empire, Hertford, n.s., pt.38, pp.20-25, Dec., 1939.

EXHIBITION OF SPECIMENS OF ANTECHINUS MINUTISSIMUS, FROM ROCKHAMPTON, AUSTRALIA. Albert Gunther. Proc. Zool. Soc. Lond., p.274, 1876.

A NEW MARSUPIAL OF THE GENUS ANTECHINUS FROM NORTHERN AUSTRALIA. (NEW: ANTECHINUS BILARNI.) David H. Johnson. Proc. Biol. Soc. Washington, 67: 77-80, Mar.22, 1954.

A PREHISTORIC BEAST STILL LIVING--THE STRIPED WOLF OF TASMANIA. G. W. Morey. Field, London, vol.158, no.4118, p. 822, illus., Nov.28, 1931.

TASMANIAN ENVOYS. George H. Pournelle. Zoonooz, Zool. Soc. San Diego, vol.28, no. 12, pp.3-4, illus., Dec., 1955.

THE FATE OF THE THYLACINE. W. P. Pycraft. Illus. London News, vol.196, no. 5271, p.564, illus., Apr.27, 1940.

THE THYLACINE. Graham Renshaw. Jour. Soc. Preservation Fauna of Empire, Hertford, n.s., pt.35, pp.47-49, illus., Dec., 1938.

LETTER FROM, ADDRESSED TO THE SECRETARY, RESPECTING THE SUPPOSED "NATIVE TIGER" OF QUEENSLAND. Walter J. Scott. Proc. Zool. Soc. Lond., p.355, Fig.1, 1872.

SECOND LETTER FROM, ON THE EXISTENCE OF A "NATIVE TIGER" IN QUEENSLAND. Walter J. Scott. Proc. Zool. Soc. Lond., p.796, 1872.

IN SEARCH OF THE THYLACINE. M.S.R. Sharland. Proc. Roy. Soc., N.S.W., pp. 20-38, pls.8, map, Aug.24, 1939.

TASMANIAN RARE "TIGER". M. S. R. Sharland. Bull. New York Zool. Soc., vol.44, no.3, pp.84-88, figs.2, May-June, 1941.

A NEW POUCHED MOUSE (PHASCOGALE) FROM NORTHERN NEW SOUTH WALES. Oldfield Thomas. Ann. and Mag. Nat. Hist., ser.9, vol.14, pp.528-529, Nov., 1924.

DESCRIPTION OF A NEW PHASCOGALE FROM NORTH WESTERN AUSTRALIA. E. R. Waite. Records Australia Mus., vol. 5, no.2, pp.120-124, Jan.28, 1904.

Habits

LETTER FROM, ANNOUNCING THE SHIPMENT OF LIVING THYLACINES, WITH REMARKS ON THEIR HABITS. Ronald Gunn. Proc. Zool. Soc. Lond., pt.31, pp.103-104, 1863.

THE TASMANIAN OR MARSUPIAL DEVIL--ITS HABITS AND FAMILY LIFE. David Fleay. Australian Mus. Mag., Sydney, vol. 10, no.9, pp.275-280, Mar.15, 1952.

Reproductive Biology

BREEDING OF DASYURUS VIVERRINUS AND GENERAL OBSERVATIONS ON THE SPECIES. D. H. Fleay. Jour. Mam., vol. 16, no.1, pp.10-16, pls.1-2, Feb., 1935.

BREEDING OF THE TIGER-CAT. David Fleay. Victorian Nat., Melbourne, vol.56, no.10, pp.159-163, illus., Feb., 1940.

THE BRUSH-TAILED PHASCOGALE--FIRST RECORD OF BREEDING HABITS. David Fleay. Victorian Nat., vol.51, no.4, pp.89-150, pls.18-20, Aug., 1934.

NOTES ON THE BREEDING OF TASMANIAN DEVILS. David Fleay. Victorian Nat., vol. 52, no.6, pp.100-105, pls.8-9, Oct., 1935.

NOTE ON THE NIDIFICATION OF PHASCOGALE FLAVIPES. (A FEMALE POUCHED MOUSE AND HER EIGHT YOUNG ONES.) Edgar R. Waite. Proc. Linn. Soc. New South Wales, vol.21, pp.349-350, 1896.

Taxonomy

(ON THE STRUCTURE OF DASYUROIDES BYRNEI AND ITS RELATIONSHIPS TO THE OTHER DASYURIDAE.) Ueber den bau des Dasyuroides byrnei und seine Beziehungen zu den uebrigen Dasyuridae. Albertina Carlsson. Acta Zoologica (Stockholm), vol. 7, pts.2-3, pp.249-275, 7 figs., 1926.

ON THE CLASSIFICATION OF THE SMALL DASYURIDAE OF AUSTRALIA, WITH DESCRIPTIONS OF TWO NEW GENERA AND ONE NEW SPECIES. Gerard Krefft. Proc. Zool. Soc. Lond., pp.431-435, pl.36, 1866.

DIAGNOSIS OF A NEW SPECIES OF PHASCOLOGALE. Oldfield Thomas. Annali del Museo Civico di Storia Naturale di Genova (2), vol.4, p.208, Nov.25, 1886.

THE LOCAL RACES OF DASYURUS HALLUCATUS. Oldfield Thomas. Ann. and Mag. Nat. Hist., ser.9, vol.18, pp.543-544, 1926.

NOTE ON THE TECHNICAL NAME OF THE TASMANIAN DEVIL. Oldfield Thomas. Ann. and Mag. Nat. Hist. (7), vol.11, no.63, p. 289, Mar., 1903.

ON THE SPECIMENS OF PHASCOLOGALE IN THE MUSEO CIVICO, GENOA, WITH NOTES ON THE ALLIED SPECIES OF THE GENUS. Oldfield Thomas. Annali del Museo Civico di Storia Naturale di Genova (2), vol. 4, pp.1-10, Apr.8, 1887.

THE TECHNICAL NAME OF THE TASMANIAN DEVIL. Oldfield Thomas. Proc. Biol. Soc. Washington, vol.25, p.116, June 29, 1912.

A NEW SPECIES OF FAT-TAILED MARSUPIAL MOUSE, AND THE STATUS OF ANTECHINUS FROGGATTI RAMSAY. Ellis LeG. Troughton. Records Australian Mus., vol.18, no.6, pp.349-353, fig.1, Apr.20, 1932.

A NEW GENUS, SPECIES, AND SUBSPECIES OF MARSUPIAL MICE (FAMILY DASYURIDAE). Ellis LeG. Troughton. Records Australian Mus., vol.16, no.6, pp.281-288, pl.39, June 11, 1928.

A NEW SPECIES OF FAT-TAILED MARSUPIAL MOUSE, AND THE STATUS OF ANTECHINUS FROGGATI RAMSAY. Ellis LeG. Troughton. Records Australian Mus., vol.18, no.6, pp.349-353, fig.1, Apr.20, 1932.

## Myrmecobiidae

ON THE EREMIAN REPRESENTATIVE OF MYRMECOBIUS FASCIATUS (WATERHOUSE). H. H. Finlayson. Trans. and Proc. Roy. Soc. South Australia, vol.57, pp.203-205, Dec.23, 1933.

THE NUMBAT IN VICTORIA. David Fleay. Victorian Nat., Melbourne, vol.59, no.1, pp.3-7, pls.2, May 8, 1942.

THE NUMBAT ... RELIC OF THE EARTH'S EARLY FURRED ANIMALS. David Fleay. Illus. London News, vol.221, no.5907, pp. 32-33, illus, July 5, 1952.

THE PECULIAR LITTLE NUMBAT. David Fleay. Animal Kingdom, New York, vol.52, no.5, pp.144-148, illus., Sept.-Oct., 1949.

AN EXTINCT MARSUPIAL FROM THE FORT UNION WITH NOTES ON THE

MYRMECOBIDAE AND OTHER FAMILIES OF THIS GROUP. James W. Gidley. Proc. U. S. Nat. Mus, vol.48, no.2077, pp.395-402, pl.23, Jan.28, 1915.

LETTERS BEGGING THE SOCIETY'S ACCEPTANCE OF TWO AUSTRALIAN QUADRUPEDS WHICH HAVE BEEN DESCRIBED IN THE SOCIETY'S PROCEEDINGS. A. Gordon. Proc. Zool. Soc. Lond., pt.6, p. 149, 1838.

(CONTRIBUTIONS ON THE ANATOMY OF MYRMECOBIUS FASCIATUS.) Beitraege zur Anatomie des Myrmecobius fasciatus. Wilhelm Leche. Biol. Foereningens Foerhandlingar, Verhandl. Biol. Ver. Stockholm, vol.3, no.8, pp.136-154, May, 1891.

THE BANDED ANTEATER, MYRMECOBIUS WATERHOUSE (MARSUPIALIA). G. H. H. Tate. Amer. Mus. Novitates, New York, no.1521, pp.1-8, June 18, 1951.

DESCRIPTION OF A NEW GENUS (MYRMECOBIUS) OF MAMMIFEROUS ANIMALS FROM NEW HOLLAND, PROBABLY BELONGING TO THE MARSUPIAL TYPE. G. G. Waterhouse. Proc. Zool. Soc. Lond., pt.4, p.69, 1836.

ON A SECOND SPECIMEN OF MYRMECOBIUS. G. R. Waterhouse. Proc. Zool. Soc. Lond., pt.4, p.131, 1836.

## Notoryctidae

A RARE MARSUPIAL (NOTORYCTES TYPHLOPS). Guy Dollman. Proc. Linnaean Soc. Lond., 145th session, pp.15-16, Jan.20, 1933.

THE EXTERNAL CHARACTERS OF POUCH EMBRYOS OF MARSUPIALS. NO.2.--NOTORYCTES TYPHLOPS. F. Wood Jones. Trans. Roy. Soc. South Australia, vol.14, 1921.

(AUSTRALIAN OPOSSUM, NOTORYCTES TYPHLOPS.) Australischen Beutelthiers Notoryctes typhlops. Wilhelm Leche. Verhandl. Biol. Ver. Stockholm, vol.4, pp.1-2, May, 1892.

ON THE GENUS NOTORYCTES, STIRLING. J. Douglas Ogilby. Catalogue Australian Mus., Sydney, no.16, pp.5-7, 1892.

NOTORYCTES IN NORTH-WEST AUSTRALIA. Oldfield Thomas. Ann. and Mag. Nat. Hist., ser.9, vol.6, pp.111-113, July, 1920.

## Peramelidae

(THE PAPUAN SPECIES OF PERAMELES.) Die papuasischen Perameles-Arten. L. Cohn. Zool. Anzeiger, 35: 718-728, 3 figs., 1910.

(PERAMELES.) Peramele. R. P. Lesson. Dict. Class. Hist. nat., 13: 197-200, 1828.

STUDIES IN THE EPIDEMIOLOGY OF Q FEVER. 10. THE TRANSMISSION OF Q FEVER BY THE TICK IXODES HOLOCYCLUS (WITH NOTES ON TICK-PARALYSIS IN BANDICOOTS). D. J. W. Smith. Australian Jour. Exper. Biol. and Med. Sci., Adelaide, vol.20, pt.3, pp.213-217, Sept., 1942.

RESULTS OF THE ARCHBOLD EXPEDITIONS, NO.60. STUDIES IN THE PERAMELIDAE (MARSUPIALIA). G. H. H. Tate. Bull. Amer. Mus. Nat. Hist., New York, vol.92, pp.313-346, fig.1, Nov.25, 1948.

BANDICOOTS--RARE AND OTHERWISE. Ellis Troughton. Australian Mus. Mag., Sydney, vol.10, no.4, pp.113-117, Dec.15, 1950.

### Anatomy

THE YOLK-SAC AND ALLANTOIC PLACENTA IN PERAMELES. T. Thomson Flynn. Quart. Jour. Microscopical Sci., vol.67, pp.123-182, pls.9-11, Apr., 1923.

(NOTES ON MAMMALS. I. ON CERTAIN CORRELATIVE CHARACTERISTICS IN THE PERAMELIDAE (MARSUPIALIA). Serge Frechkop. Bull. Mus. Roy. d'Hist. Nat. de Belgique, vol.6, no.5, pp.1-20, figs.4, May, 1930.

THE EXTERNAL CHARACTERS OF POUCH EMBRYOS OF MARSUPIALS. NO.3 ISOODON BARROWENSIS. F. Wood Jones. Trans. Roy. Soc. South Australia, vol.46, pp.39-45, 11 figs., 1922.

THE DEVELOPMENT AND REPLACEMENT OF PELAGE HAIRS IN THE BANDICOOT PERAMELES NASUTA GEOFFROY (MARSUPIALIA: PERAMELIDAE). A. G. Lyne. Australian Jour. Biol. Sci., 10 (2): 197-216, May, 1957.

NOTES ON EXTERNAL CHARACTERS OF THE BARRED BANDICOOT (PERAMELES GUNNII GRAY), WITH SPECIAL REFERENCE TO THE POUCH YOUNG. A. G. Lyne. Proc. Zool. Soc. Lond., vol.121, pt.3, pp.587-598, pls.3, Nov.19, 1951.

NOTES ON EXTERNAL CHARACTERS OF THE POUCH YOUNG OF FOUR SPECIES OF BANDICOOTS. A. G. Lyne. Proc. Zool. Soc. Lond., vol.122, pt.3, pp.625-649, illus., pls.2, Nov., 1952.

THE MYSTERY OF THE BANDICOOT'S TOE. Crosbie Morrison. Victorian Nat., Melbourne, vol.63, no.1, pp.8-11, pls.1-2, May, 1946.

(ON DENTAL DEVELOPMENT IN PERAMELES.) Ueber die Zahnentwicklung bei Perameles. K. Mueller. Morphol. Jahrb., vol.61, pp.457-488, 18 text figs., 1929.

THE TONGUE OF PERAMELES NASUTA, WITH SOME SUGGESTIONS AS TO THE ORIGIN OF TASTE BULBS. Edward B. Poulton. Quart. Jour. Microsc. Sci., Lond., n.s., vol.23, pp.69-86, pl.1, Jan., 1883.

### Australia and Tasmania

ON MAMMALS FROM THE LAKE EYRE BASIN. PT.2. THE PERAMELIDAE. H. H. Finlayson. Trans. and Proc. Roy. Soc. S. Australia, Adelaide, vol.59, pp.227-236, fig.1, Dec.23, 1935.

A QUEENSLAND RABBIT-BANDICOOT. Heber A. Longman. Queensland Nat., vol. 3, no.3, pp.52-53, Feb., 1922.

ON A NEW SPECIES OF MARSUPIAL ANIMAL FOUND BY MAJOR MITCHEL ON THE BANKS OF THE RIVER MURRAY IN NEW SOUTH WALES. W. Ogilby. Proc. Zool Soc. Lond., pt.6, p.25, 1838.

AUSTRALIA'S BANDICOOTS. Tarlton Rayment. Victorian Nat., Melbourne, vol. 70, no.11, pp.194-196, Mar., 1954.

THE BANDICOOTS OF NUYTS ARCHIPELAGO, S. AUSTRALIA, AND OF CAPE YORK, N. QUEENSLAND. Oldfield Thomas. Ann. and Mag. Nat. Hist., ser.9, vol.9, pp.677-679, June, 1922.

### Habits and Behavior

NOTE ON THE FOOD OF A BANDICOOT. Keith C. McKeown. Proc. Roy. Zool. Soc. New South Wales, pp.42-43, for the year 1949-1950, Apr.2, 1951.

### Taxonomy

MEMOIR ON A NEW GENUS OF MAMMALIA WITH POUCHES, NAMED PERAMELES. E. Geoffroy. Philos. Mag., Lond., vol.21, no. 81, pp.28-34, pls.2, Feb., 1805.

ON A NEW SPECIES OF PERAMELES. J. E. Gray. Proc. Zool. Soc. Lond., pt.6, p.1, 1838.

THE MARSUPIAL GENUS THALACOMYS. A REVIEW OF THE RATTIT-BANDICOOTS; WITH THE DESCRIPTION OF A NEW SPECIES. Frederic Wood Jones. Rec. S. Australian Mus., vol.2, no.3, pp.333-352, figs.9, June 30, 1923.

NOTES ON ZOOLOGY OF THE MACLAY-COAST IN NEW GUINEA. I. ON A NEW SUB-GENUS OF PERAMELIDAE: BRACHYMELIS. N. de Miklouho-Maclay. Proc. Linn. Soc. New South Wales, Sydney, vol. 9, pt.3, pp.713-720, 1885.

ON THYLACOMYS, OWEN. T. S. Palmer. Ann. and Mag. Nat. Hist., Lond., ser.7, vol.4, pp.302, Oct., 1899.

DESCRIPTION OF A NEW SPECIES OF THE GENUS PERAMELES (P. LAGOTIS). James Reid. Proc. Zool. Soc. Lond., pt.4, p.129, 1836.

(WHAT ARE PEROCYTES ROTHSCHILDI AND PEROCYTES MAINOIS?) Was sind Peroryctes rothschildi und Peroryctes mainois? Georg. Stein. Zeitschr. f. Saugetierkunde, Berlin, vol.8, nos.3-6, pp.282-283, Dec.20, 1933.

DESCRIPTION OF A SECOND SPECIES OF RABBIT-BANDICOOT (PERAGALE). Oldfield Thomas. Ann. and Mag. Nat. Hist. (5), vol. 19, no.114, pp.397-399, June, 1887.

ON BANDICOOTS ALLIED TO PERAMELES BOUGAINVILLEI. Oldfield Thomas. Ann. and Mag. Nat. Hist., ser.9, vol.10, pp.143-145, July, 1922.

A REVISION OF THE RABBIT-BANDICOOTS. FAMILY PERAMELIDAE, GENUS MACROTIS. Ellis LeG. Troughton. Australian Zoologist, vol.7, no.3, pp.219-236, map, Sept.15, 1932.

THE GENERIC NAME THYLACOMYS. Edgar R. Waite. Ann. Mag. Nat. Hist., ser.7, vol.5, pp.222-223, Feb., 1900.

(Remarks by Oldfield Thomas on) THE GENERIC NAME THYLACOMYS. Edgar R. Waite. Ann. and Mag. Nat. Hist., (7), vol. 5, no.26, p.223, Feb., 1900.

NOTES ON THE CLASSIFICATION OF THE BANDICOOTS. R. C. Wroughton. Jour. Bombay Nat. Hist. Soc., vol.18, no.4, pp. 736-752, Nov.15, 1908.

## Caenolestidae

ON THE FEMALE GENITAL TRACT IN THE CAENOLESTIDS (MARSUPIALIA). James S. Baxter. Proc. Zool. Soc. Lond. for 1935, pt.1, pp.157-162, figs.3, Apr., 1935.

(THE HINDFOOT OF CAENOLESTES.) Der Hinterfuss von Caenolestes. J. E. V. Boas. Det Kgl. Danske Videnskabernes Selskab. Biol. Meddel., vol.10, no.6, pp.8, pl.1, 1933.

ON THE ORGAN OF JACOBSON AND SOME OTHER STRUCTURES IN THE NOSE OF CAENOLESTES. R. Broom. Proc. Zool. Soc. Lond., 1926, pp.419-424, 1 pl., July, 1926.

ON THE "HABITUS" AND "HERITAGE" OF CAENOLESTES. William K. Gregory. Jour. Mam., vol.3, no.2, pp.106-114, May, 1922.

THE BRAIN OF CAENOLESTES OBSCURUS. C. Judson Herrick. Field Mus. Nat. Hist., Zool. Ser., vol.14, no.1, pp.157-162, pls. 21-22, May, 1921.

THE BRAINS OF THE SOUTH AMERICAN MARSUPIALS CAENOLESTES AND OROLESTES. Jeannette Brown Obenchain. Field Mus. Nat. Hist., publ.224, zool. series vol.14, no.3, pp.175-232, pls.24-36, Jan.26, 1925.

A MONOGRAPHIC STUDY OF THE AMERICAN MARSUPIAL, CAENOLESTES. Wilfred H. Osgood. Field Mus. Nat. Hist., Pub. 207, Zool. Series, vol.14, no.1, pp.1-162, pls.22, Chicago, May, 1921.

(Review by N. Hollister of) A MONOGRAPHIC STUDY OF THE AMERICAN MARSUPIAL, CAENOLESTES. Wilfred H. Osgood. Jour. Mam., vol.2, no.4, pp.241-242, Nov., 1921.

REVIEW OF LIVING CAENOLESTIDS WITH DESCRIPTION OF A NEW GENUS FROM CHILE. Wilfred H. Osgood. Field Mus. Nat. Hist., publ.222, zool. ser. vol.14, no. 2, pp.165-172, pl.23, Oct.20, 1924.

ON CAENOLESTES, A STILL EXISTING SURVIVOR OF THE EPANORTHIDAE OF AMEGHINO, AND THE REPRESENTATIVE OF A NEW FAMILY OF RECENT MARSUPIALS. Oldfield Thomas. Proc. Zool. Soc. Lond., pp.870-878, pl.50, Dec.17, 1895.

## Phalangeridae

THE KOALA OR "NATIVE BEAR" OF AUSTRALIA. Arthur L. Anderson. China Jour., vol.26, no.1, p.43, illus., Jan., 1937.

DIATASE IN THE OPOSSUM (TRICHOSURUS VULPECULA). Doris Anderson. Australian Jour. Exper. Biol. and Med. Sci., vol.16, pt. 2, pp.117-125, June, 1938.

THE INFLUENCE OF THE LIVER AND THE PANCREAS ON THE BLOOD AND URINARY DIASTASE OF THE OPOSSUM. Doris Anderson. Australian Jour. Exper. Biol. and

Med. Sci., vol.16, pt.2, pp.127-132, June, 1938.

STUDIES ON THE OPOSSUM (TRICHOSURUS VULPECULA). I. BLOOD ANALYSES AND LIPOID GLANDULAR CONSTITUENTS IN NORMAL AND LACTATING OPOSSUMS. Doris Anderson. Australian Jour. Exper. Biol. and Med. Sci., vol.15, pt.1, pp.17-23, Mar., 1937.

STUDIES ON THE OPOSSUM (TRICHOSURUS VULPECULA). 2. THE EFFECTS OF SPLENECTOMY, ADRENALECTOMY AND INJECTIONS OF CORTICAL HORMONE. Doris Anderson. Australian Jour. Exper. Biol. and Med. Sci., vol.15, pt.1, pp.24-32, Mar., 1937.

TRANSMISSION OF KALA-AZAR TO THE POUCH YOUNG OF THE COMMON AUSTRALIAN POSSUM (TRICHOSURUS VULPECULA). J. E. Armytage, A. Bollinger. Nature, Lond., vol.155, no.3927, pp.145-146, Feb.3, 1945.

KOALA: NATIVE BEAR. Charles Barrett. Bull. New York Zool. Soc., vol.34, no.2, pp.61-70, figs.9, Mar.-Apr., 1931.

THE STORY OF AUSTRALIA'S NATIVE BEAR. Charles Barrett. Robertson and Mullens, Melbourne, Australia, 31 pp., 15 pls., 1937.

KOALAS! Belle J. Benchley. San Diego Zoonooz, vol.25, no.3, pp.2-4, illus., Mar., 1952.

THE STORY OF "TWINKLE." J. M. Bocking. Victorian Nat., Melbourne, vol.56, no.8, pp. 134-135, illus., Dec., 1939.

THE RESPONSE OF THE STERNAL INTEGUMENT OF TRICHOSURUS VULPECULA TO CASTRATION AND TO SEX HORMONES. Adolph Bolliger. Jour. and Proc. Roy. Soc. New South Wales, Sydney, vol.78, pt.4, pp. 234-238, pl.14, Mar.8, 1946.

SPERMATORRHOEA IN MARSUPIALS, WITH SPECIAL REFERENCE TO THE ACTION OF SEX HORMONES ON SPERMATOGENESIS OF TRICHOSURUS VULPECULA. Adolph Bolliger. Jour. and Proc. Roy. Soc. New South Wales, Sydney, vol.76, pt.1, pp.86-92, fig. 1, Oct.15, 1942.

FIELD NOTES ON THE YELLOW-BELLIED FLYING PHALANGER. PETAURUS AUSTRALIS SHAW. C. W. Brazenor. Australian Zoologist, Sydney, vol.8, no.1, pp.54-55, pl.1, May 9, 1934.

A RE-EXAMINATION OF GYMNOBELIDEUS LEADBEATERI MCCOY. C. W. Brazenor. Australian Zool., Sydney, vol.7, pt.2, pp. 106-109, pl.6, Feb.5, 1932.

A NEW RECORD OF THE SCALY-TAILED POSSUM (WYULDA SQUAMICAUDATA ALEXANDER). J. H. Calaby. Western Australian Nat., 5 (7): 186-191, Mar.8, 1957.

"JIM" AND "TIP", THE FLYING PHALANGERS. B. E. Carthew. Victorian Nat., Melbourne, vol.59, no.7, pp.119-120, illus., Nov., 1942.

THE OPOSSUM MOUSE (DROMICIA NANA). Norman Chaffer. Australian Zool., vol.6, no.2, p.109, pl.1, 1930; and Victorian Nat., vol.47, no.1, pp.18-19, fig.1, 1930.

THE LIFE OF "BLUEY." Kathleen Conway. Victorian Nat., Melbourne, vol.56, no.8, pp.133-134, Dec., 1939.

AUSTRALIAN "BEARS," SLAUGHTERED BY MAN, THE KOALAS MAKE A LAST STAND. Winifred Duncan. Nature Magazine, vol.20, no.1, pp.13-16, figs.4, July, 1932.

A LIVE-TRAPPING STUDY OF THE BRUSH-TAILED POSSUM. TRICHOSURUS VULPECULA KERR (MARSUPIALIA). G. M. Dunnet. Wildlife Res., Commonwealth Scientific & Industrial Research Organization, Melbourne, 1 (1): 1-18, Sept., 1956.

A SECOND SPECIMEN OF WYULDA SQUAMICAUDATA ALEXANDER. H. H. Finlayson. Trans. Roy. Soc. S. Australia, Adelaide, vol.66, no.2, pp.255-261, (1942) 1943.

AUSTRALIA'S SQUIRREL GLIDERS. David Fleay. Animal Kingdom, New York Zool. Soc., vol.57, no.6, pp.187-190, illus., Dec., 1954.

AUSTRALIA'S VIVACIOUS SUGAR GLIDER. (PETAURUS BREVICEPS). David Fleay. Animal Kingdom, New York, vol.52, no.3, pp.70-76, 96, illus., June 1, 1949.

A BEAUTIFUL PHALANGER. David Fleay. Victorian Naturalist, vol.50, no.2, pp.35-40, 1 fig., 4 pls., June, 1933.

THE EASTERN AUSTRALIAN RING-TAILED OPOSSUM. David Fleay. Victorian Nat., vol.44, no.10, pp.279-282, 2 figs., Feb., 1928.

GLIDERS OF THE GUM TREES: THE MOST BEAUTIFUL AND ENCHANTING AUSTRALIAN MARSUPIALS. David Fleay. Bread and Cheese Club, Melbourne, 113 pp., illus., 1947.

THE GREATER FLYING PHALANGER. David Fleay. Victorian Naturalist, vol. 50, no.6, pp.135-142, figs.2, pls.5, Oct., 1933.

THE LESSER FLYING PHALANGER ("SUGAR SQUIRREL"). David Fleay. Victorian Naturalist, vol.49, no.4, pp.97-101, 2 pls., Aug., 1932.

THE ODOROUS AND CURIOUSLY-NAMED CUSCUS. David H. Fleay. Illus. London News, vol.214, no.5742, pp.638-639, illus., May 7, 1949.

THE PIGMY FLYING POSSUM; David Fleay. Victorian Nat., vol.49, no.7, pp.165-171, 1 fig., 3 pls., Nov., 1932.

THE REMARKABLE STRIPED POSSUM. David Fleay. Victorian Nat., Melbourne, vol.58, no.10, pp.151-155, illus., Feb., 1942.

THE SQUIRREL GLIDER. David Fleay. Victorian Nat., Melbourne, vol.70, no. 11, pp.208-210, Mar., 1954.

THAT CURIOUS MARSUPIAL, THE CUSCUS. David Fleay. Animal Kingdom, New York, vol.52, no.1, pp.22-25, illus., Feb.15, 1949.

THE AUSTRALIAN OPOSSUM. Walter W. Froggatt. Agric. Gazette, N.S. Wales, Sydney, Misc. Pub.796, pls.2, 1904.

LIVING TEDDY BEAR. Joyce Burns Glen. Our Dumb Animals, Norwood, vol.77, no.8, p.147, illus., Aug., 1944.

THE AUSTRALIAN KOALA. Kilroy Harris. Nat. Mag., vol.4, p.176, Sept., 1924.

GLUCURONURIA IN A HERBIVOROUS MARSUPIAL TRICHOSURUS VULPECULA. W. T. Hinks, A. Bollinger. Australian Jour. Exp. Biol. & Med. Sci., Adelaide, 35 (1): 37-44, Feb., 1957.

TEDDY BEAR MUST HOLD ON TIGHT. Julian S. Huxley. Zoo, vol.1, no.1, pp.32-33, illus., June, 1936.

"MIRRAM"--"LITTLE HAPPY ONE." Florence M. Irby. Australian Zool., vol.7, pt.1, pp.11-14, Aug.24, 1931.

THE KOALA ON WILSON'S PROMONTORY. James A. Kershaw. Victorian Nat., vol.51, no.3, pp.76-77, pl.15, July, 1934.

(ON THE QUESTION OF ALBINISM IN PHALANGER ORIENTALIS.) Zur Frage des Albinismus dei Phalanger orientalis. P. F. Kopstein. Treuba, vol.8, pp.381-383, 1926.

THE KOALA IN VICTORIA. F. Lewis. Victorian Nat., vol.51, no.3, pp.73-76, pls.13-14, July, 1934.

THE REHABILITATION OF THE KOALA IN VICTORIA. F. Lewis. Victorian Nat., Melbourne, vol.70, no.11, pp.197-200, Mar., 1954.

THE TWO-THUMBED "TEDDY BEAR." Willy Ley. Nat. History, New York, vol. 57, no.7, pp.328-332, illus., Sept., 1948.

A FIELD SURVEY OF A KOALA POPULATION. J. McNally. Proc. Roy. Zool. Soc. New South Wales, 1955-56: 18-27, May 8, 1957.

A SANCTUARY FOR AUSTRALIA'S "TEDDY BEARS." M. B. Neilson. Field, London, vol. 159, no.4144, p.809, illus., May 28, 1932.

BEARS OF A SORT. Florence Nelson. Our Dumb Animals, Norwood, vol.79, no.11, p. 205, Nov., 1946.

KOALAS ON THE LOWER GOULBURN. Harry S. Parris. Victorian Nat., Melbourne, vol.64, no.10, pp.192-193, Feb., 1948.

OBSERVATIONS ON THE KOALA. R. A. Patten. Parks and Recreation, vol.22, no. 3, pp.125-126, illus., Nov., 1938.

SAVING THE WORLD'S RAREST ANIMAL. E. K. Patterson. Canadian Geogr. Jour., vol.17, no.1, pp.41-43, illus., July, 1938.

THE CALL OF THE KOALA. Ambrose Pratt. Robertson & Mullens Ltd., Melbourne, pp.120, figs.2, pls.18, 1937.

(Review by Erna Mohr of) THE CALL OF THE KOALA. Ambrose Pratt. Robertson and Mullens, Melbourne, pp.120, figs.24, 1937. Zool. Garten, Leipzig, n. F., vol. 10, nos.5-6, pp.242-245, illus., 1 table, Jan., 1939.

AUSTRALIA'S GLIDING 'POSSUMS. Edward Samuel. Discovery, London, vol.18, no.216, pp.363-365, figs.4, Dec., 1937.

THE KOALA AND THE KOOKABURRA. Arthur de Carle Sowerby. China Jour., vol. 25, no.6, pp.344-345, illus., Dec., 1936.

FURTHER NOTES ON THE KOALA. WITH SPECIAL REFERENCE TO SOME RECENT DISCUSSIONS. David G. Stead. Australian Wild Life, Sydney, vol.1, no.5, pp.45-56, Apr., 1939.

THE KOALA, OR NATIVE BEAR. David G. Stead. Australian Wild Life, Sydney, vol. 1, no.1, pp.13-22, illus., Nov., 1934.

TRAGEDY OF THE POSSUM. David G. Stead. Australian Wild Life, Sydney, vol. 1, no.3, pp.24-37, illus., Jan., 1937.

AUSSIE AMBASSADORS. Ken Stott, Jr. Pacific Discovery, San Francisco, vol.5, no.4, pp.14-17, July-Aug., 1952.

THE "HONEY MOUSE," TARSIPES SPENCERAE GRAY. Ellis LeG. Troughton. Australian Zool., vol.3, pt.4, pp.148-156, pl.23, Aug.15, 1923.

THE KOALA. Ellis Troughton. Australian Mus. Mag., Sydney, vol.11, no.12, pp.396-401, illus., Dec., 1955.

THE LARGEST GLIDERS OR "FLYING POSSUMS." Ellis LeG. Troughton. The Australian Mus. Mag., vol.5, no.9, pp.314-319, figs.2, Jan.16, 1935.

MARSUPIAL GLIDERS OR "FLYING POSSUMS." Ellis LeG. Troughton. Australian Mus. Mag., vol.5, no.8, pp.257-264, illus., Oct.16, 1934.

NOTES ON STRIPED OPOSSUMS OF THE GENUS DACTYLOPSILA. Ellis LeG. Troughton. Australian Zool., vol.6, pt.2, pp.169-174, Jan.14, 1930.

THE STRIPED POSSUM OF AUSTRALIA AND NEW GUINEA. Ellis LeG. Troughton. Australian Mus. Mag., Sydney, vol.7, no.12, pp.431-434, illus., Mar.16, 1942.

OBSERVATIONS ON THE REPRODUCTION AND ECOLOGY OF THE BRUSH-TAILED POSSUM, TRICHOSURUS VULPECULA KERR (MARSUPIALIA), IN NEW ZEALAND. C. H. Tyndale-Biscoe. Australian Jour. Sci., Melbourne, vol.3, no.2, pp.162-184, illus., 1955.

THE EARLY HISTORY OF THE KOALA. Gilbert Whitley, Tom Iredale. Victorian Nat., vol.51, no.3, pp.62-72, figs.1-4, July, 1934.

THE AUSTRALIAN KOALA--TO BE PROTECTED AND TO APPEAR ON A STAMP. Illus., London News, vol.192, no.5154, p. 167, Jan.29, 1938.

A BABY ALBINO KOALA IN SYDNEY'S ZOO. Illus. London News, vol.218, no.5835, p. 259, illus., Feb.17, 1951.

FLYING PHALANGER. Life, Chicago, vol. 28, no.20, pp.75, 76, illus., May 15, 1950.

KOALA ROUNDUP IN AUSTRALIA. Animal Kingdom, New York Zool. Soc., 60 (5): 142-147, illus., Oct., 1957.

Anatomy

THE CAROTID SINUS COMPLEX "PARA-THYROID" III AND THYMOPARATHYROID BODIES, WITH SPECIAL REFERENCE TO THE AUSTRALIAN OPOSSUM TRICHOSURUS VULPECULA. W. E. Adams. Amer. Jour. Anat., vol.97, no.1, pp.1-58, July, 1955.

NOTES ON THE FEMALE UROGENITAL SYSTEM OF TARSIPES SPENSERAE (MARSUPIALIA). J. M. de Babay. Proc. Roy. Soc. Tasmania, Hobart, pp.137-142, Dec. 15, 1951.

THE EFFECT OF GONADOTROPIN OBTAINED FROM HUMAN PREGNANCY URINE ON THE POUCH OF TRICHOSURUS VULPECULA. Adolph Bollinger. Jour. and Proc. Roy. Soc. New South Wales, Sydney, vol. 76, pt.3, pp.137-141, fig.1, pl.1, May 26, 1943.

EXPERIMENTAL PRODUCTION OF A POUCH IN THE MALE OF TRICHOSURUS VULPECULA. Adolph Bollinger. Nature, Lond., vol.150, no.3815, pp.688-689, Dec.12, 1942.

FUNCTIONAL RELATIONS BETWEEN SCROTUM AND POUCH AND THE EXPERIMENTAL PRODUCTION OF A POUCH-LIKE STRUCTURE IN THE MALE OF TRICHOSURUS VULPECULA. Adolph Bollinger. Jour. and Proc. Roy. Soc. New South Wales, Sydney, vol.76, pt.4, pp.283-293, pls.16-18, Dec.17, 1943.

THE ACTION OF PROGESTERONE ON THE POUCH OF THE MARSUPIAL TRICHOSURUS VULPECULA. Adolph Bollinger, Arthur Carrodus. Jour. and Proc. Roy. Soc. New South Wales, Sydney, vol.73, pt.4, pp.228-232, pls.15-17, Apr.12, 1940.

EFFECT OF OESTROGENS ON THE POUCH OF THE MARSUPIAL TRICHOSURUS VULPECULA. Adolph Bollinger, Arthur Carrodus. Nature, Lond., vol.144, no.3660, p. 1049, Dec.23, 1939; also in Jour. and Proc. Roy. Soc. New South Wales, Sydney, vol. 73, pt.4, pp.218-227, pls.12-14, Apr.12, 1940.

THE STERNAL INTEGUMENT OF TRICHOSURUS VULPECULA. Adolph Bollinger, Margaret H. Hardy. Jour. and Proc. Roy. Soc. New South Wales, Sydney, vol.78, pt. 3, pp.122-133, pls.4-7, Dec.3, 1945.

ON SOME POINTS IN THE ANATOMY OF THE KOALA (PHASCOLARCTOS CINEREUS). W. A. Forbes. Proc. Zool. Soc. Lond., pp.180-195, figs.6, Jan.18, 1881.

A STUDY ON THE DEVELOPMENT OF THE SKIN AND HAIR OF THE AUSTRALIAN OPOSSUM, TRICHOSURUS VULPECULA. Helena F. Gibbs. Proc. Zool. Soc. Lond., vol.108, ser.B, Syst. and Morph. pt.3, pp. 611-648, figs.9, table 1, pls.5, Oct., 1938.

AN EXPERIMENTAL INVESTIGATION OF THE MOTOR CORTEX AND ITS CONNEXIONS IN THE PHALANGER, TRICHOSURUS VULPECULA. F. Goldby. Jour. Anat., Cambridge, vol.74, pt.1, pp.12-33, figs.11, Oct., 1939.

THE EXTERNAL CHARACTERS OF POUCH EMBRYOS OF MARSUPIALS. NO. I--TRICHOSURUS VULPECULA, VAR. TYPICUS. F. Wood Jones. Trans. Roy. Soc. South Australia, vol.44, pp.360-373, pls.14, 15, 1920.

THE EXTERNAL CHARACTERS OF POUCH EMBRYOS OF MARSUPIALS. NO.4.--PSEUDOCHIROPS DAHLI. F. Wood Jones. Trans. Roy. Soc. South Australia, vol.46, pp.119-130; 1 pl.; 13 figs., 1922.

COMPARATIVE ANATOMY AND THE KOALA. Colin MacKenzie. Victorian Nat., vol.51, no. 3, pp.58-61, pls.11-12, July, 1934.

NOTES OF THE DISSECTION OF A VULPINE OPOSSUM (PHALANGISTA VULPINA, CUV.) Mr. W. Martin. Proc. Zool. Soc. Lond., pt.4, pp.2-3, 1836.

NOTES ON THE ANATOMY OF THE KOALA (PHASCOLARCTOS FUSCUS, DESM.). Mr W. Martin. Proc. Zool. Soc. Lond., pt.4, p.109, 1836.

ON THE DENTITION OF THE KOALA (LIPURUS CINEREUS, GOLDF.). R. Owen. Proc. Zool. Soc. Lond., pt.6, pp.154-156, 1838.

AN EXPERIMENTAL INVESTIGATION OF THE VISUAL SYSTEM IN THE PHALANGER, TRICHOSURUS VULPECULA. A. D. Packer. Jour. Anat., Cambridge, vol.35, pt.3, pp. 309-329, figs.10, Apr., 1941.

THE EXTERNAL CHARACTERS OF THE KOALA (PHASCOLARETOS) AND SOME RELATED MARSUPIALS. R. I. Pocock. Proc. Zool. Soc. Lond., 1921, pt.3, pp.591-607, Sept., 1921.

THE COMPARATIVE ANATOMY OF THE KOALA (PHASCOLARCTOS CINEREUS) AND THE VULPINE PHALANGER (TRICHOSURUS VULPECULA). Charles Sonntag. Proc. Zool. Soc. Lond., pt.3, pp.547-577, pls.5-6, Sept., 1921.

ON THE MILK-DENTITION OF THE KOALA. Oldfield Thomas. Proc. Zool. Soc., Lond., pp.338-339, fig., Mar.15, 1887.

ON THE DENTITION OF THE FLYING OPOSSUMS. G. R. Waterhouse. Proc. Zool. Soc. Lond., pt.6, pp.149-156.

Fossils

ON A SMALL FOSSIL MARSUPIAL WITH LARGE GROOVED PREMOLARS. R. Broom. Proc. Linn. Soc., N.S.W., 10:563, 1896.

FOSSIL REMAINS OF THE KOALA AND ITS RELATIVES. F. Chapman. Victorian Nat., vol.51, no.3, p.61, July, 1934.

A RE-EXAMINATION OF THE SKELETAL CHARACTERS OF WYNYARDIA BASSIANA, AN EXTINCT TASMANIAN MARSUPIAL. Frederic Wood Jones. Papers and Proc. Roy. Soc. Tasmania, Hobart, 1930, pp.96-115, pl.5, figs.10, Dec.31, 1930.

THE AFFINITIES OF BURRAMYS PARVUS BROOM, A FOSSIL PHALANGEROID MARSUPIAL. W. D. L. Ride. Proc. Zool. Soc. Lond., vol.127, no.3, pp.413-429, pls.1-2, Nov.29, 1956.

A NEW KOALA FROM THE PLIOCENE PALANKARINNA FAUNA OF SOUTH AUSTRALIA. R. A. Stirton. Records South Australian Mus., Adelaide, 13 (1): 71-82, Apr.30, 1957.

RECENT MAMMAL BONES IN THE BUCHAN DISTRICT. N. A. Wakefield. Victorian Nat., 77: 164-78, 1960.

Habits

GLIDERS OF THE GUM TREES: THE MOST BEAUTIFUL AND ENCHANTING AUSTRALIAN MARSUPIALS. David Fleay. Bread and Cheese Club, Melbourne, 113 p., 1947.

ON THE HABITS OF TRICHOSURUS VULPECULA. Frederic Wood Jones. Jour. Mam., vol.2, no.4, pp.187-193, Nov., 1921.

THE OPOSSUM IN NEW ZEALAND (HABITS AND TRAPPING). L. T. Pracy, R. I. Kean. New Zealand Dept. Internal Affairs, Wellington, Wildlife Branch Bull., no.1, pp.19, illus., 1949.

RESULTS OF THE ARCHBOLD EXPEDITIONS. NO.17. SOME ORIGINAL OBSERVATIONS ON THE HABITS OF DACTYLOPSILA TRIVIRGATA GRAY. A. L. Rand. Amer. Mus. Novitates, no.957, pp.1-7, Nov.1, 1937.

THE KOALA'S FOOD TREES. C. S. Sutton. Victorian Nat., vol.51, no.3, pp.78-80, July, 1934.

Reproductive Biology.

REMARKS ON E. A. BOWLEY'S NOTE CONCERNING ALLEGED DELAYED FERTILIZATION IN DROMICIA. Carl G. Hartman. Jour. Mam., vol.21, no.2, p.213, May 14, 1940.

NOTES ON THE WEANING OF A YOUNG KOALA (PHASCOLARCTUS CINEREUS). A. Keith Minchin. Rec. S. Austral. Mus., vol. 6, no.1, pp.1-3, pls.1-2, Nov.30, 1937.

THE NEST OR DREY OF THE RING-TAILED OPOSSUM (PSEUDOCHIRUS PEREGRINUS, BODD). E. R. Waite. Records Australian Mus., vol.3, pt.5, pp.93-94, pl.19, Apr. 17, 1899.

Taxonomy and Distribution

A NOTE ON PHALANGER ATRIMACULATUS TATE (MAMMALIA, MARSUPIALIA). A. C. V. van Bemmel. Treubia, Buitenzorg, vol. 20, pt.1, pp.55-56, 1949.

ON A NEW GENUS OF MARSUPIAL ANIMALS TARSIPES ROSTRATUS. M. P. Gervais, M. J. Verreaux. Proc. Zool. Soc. Lond., pt.10, p.1, 1842.

ADDITIONAL OBSERVATIONS OF THE GENUS CUSCUS. John Gray. Proc. Zool. Soc. Lond., pt.29, pp.314-322, figs.4, 1861.

OBSERVATIONS ON THE GENUS CUSCUS, WITH THE DESCRIPTION OF A NEW SPECIES. John E. Gray. Proc. Zool. Soc. Lond., pt.26, pp.100-105, pls.61-62, 1858.

DISTRIBUTION OF THE BRUSH POSSUM IN TASMANIA. Eric R. Guiler. Nature Lond., vol.172, no.4389, pp.1091-1093, Dec.12, 1953.

A FURTHER EXAMINATION OF THE DISTRIBUTION OF THE BRUSH POSSUM TRICHOSURUS VULPECULA IN TASMANIA. Eric R. Guiler, Doris M. Banks. Ecology, 39 (1): 89-97, Jan., 1958.

ON THE SPECIES OF THE PHALANGER-GENUS PSEUDOCHIRUS. F. A. Jentink. Notes Leyden Mus., 6: 108-110.

A NEW SOUTH AUSTRALIAN DORMOUSE OPOSSUM. Frederic Wood Jones. Trans. Roy. Soc. S. Australia, vol.49, pp.96-98, 1925.

DESCRIPTION OF A NEW SPECIES OF THE GENUS DROMICIA DISCOVERED IN THE NEIGHBOURHOOD OF SYDNEY. Gerard Krefft. Proc. Zool. Soc. Lond., pt.31, pp. 49-50, 1863.

A NEW PHALANGER FROM NORTH QUEENSLAND. Heber A. Longman. Mem. Queensland Mus., vol.3, pp.22-23, Jan.28, 1915.

A NEW PHALANGER FROM CELEBES. Gerrit S. Miller, Jr., N. Hollister. Proc. Biol. Soc. Washington, vol.35, pp.115-116, Oct.17, 1922.

ON A NEW PHALANGER (PHALANGISTA VIVERRINA), FROM VAN DIEMEN'S LAND. W. Ogilby. Proc. Zool. Soc. Lond., pt.5, p.131, 1837.

ON TWO NEW SPECIES OF PHALANGISTA, CUV. W. Ogilby. Proc. Comm. Sci. & Corres. Zool. Soc. Lond., pt.1, p.135, 1830-1831.

THE TASMANIAN BRUSH OPOSSUM: ITS DISTRIBUTION AND COLOUR VARIATIONS. Joseph Pearson. Papers and Proc. Roy. Soc. Tasmania for 1937, pp.21-29, 1938.

THE KOALA'S WESTERN RANGE. J. D. Somerville. Victorian Nat., vol.54, no.12, p.195, Apr., 1938.

RESULTS OF THE ARCHBOLD EXPEDITIONS. NO.52. THE MARSUPIAL GENUS PHALANGER. G. H. H. Tate. Amer. Mus. Novitates, New York, no.1283, pp.41, figs.9, Apr.27, 1945.

RESULTS OF THE ARCHBOLD EXPEDITIONS. NO.54. THE MARSUPIAL GENUS PSEUDOCHEIRUS AND ITS SUBGENERA. G. H. H. Tate. Amer. Mus. Novitates, New York, no.1287, pp.30, figs.5, June 11, 1945.

RESULTS OF THE ARCHBOLD EXPEDITIONS. NO.55. NOTES ON THE SQUIRREL-LIKE AND MOUSE-LIKE POSSUMS (MARSUPIALIA). G. H. H. Tate. Amer. Mus. Novitates, New York, no.1305, pp.12, Dec. 29, 1945.

RESULTS OF THE ARCHBOLD EXPEDITIONS. NO.5. SEVEN APPARENTLY NEW FORMS OF PHALANGERIDAE FROM THE NEW GUINEA REGION. G. H. H. Tate, Richard Archbold. Amer. Mus. Novitates, no.810, pp.1-8, July 19, 1935.

(FIRST MONOGRAPH. ON THE GENUS

PHALANGER.) Premiere Monographie. Sur le genre Phalanger. C. J. Temminck. Monographies de Mammalogie, 1: 1-28, pls. 1-4, 1824.

DESCRIPTION OF A NEW PAPUAN PHALANGER. Oldfield Thomas. Ann. and Mag. Nat. Hist. (5), vol.19, no.110, pp.146-147, Feb., 1887.

DESCRIPTIONS OF TWO NEW CUSCUSES (PHALANGER) OBTAINED BY DR. LORIA IN BRITISH NEW GUINEA. Oldfield Thomas. Viaggio di Lamberto Loria nella Papuasia Orientale. Annali del Museo Civico di Storia Naturale di Genova (2), vol.19, pp. 5-8, May 28, 1898.

DESCRIPTIONS OF TWO NEW CUSCUSES (PHALANGER). Oldfield Thomas. Novitates Zoologicae, vol.5, pp.433-434, Aug., 1898.

A NEW GENUS FOR DACTYLOPSILA PALPATOR. Oldfield Thomas. Ann. and Mag. Nat. Hist. (8), vol.6, no.36, p.610, Dec., 1910.

NEW PSEUDOCHIRUS AND PHASCOGALE FROM N.W. NEW GUINEA. Oldfield Thomas. Ann. and Mag. Nat. Hist., ser. 9, vol.8, pp.357-359, Sept., 1921.

ON SOME NEW PHALANGERS OF THE GENUS PSEUDOCHIRUS. Oldfield Thomas. Annali del Museo Civico di Storia Naturale di Genova. (2), vol.18, pp.142-146, June 28, 1897.

ON SOME QUEENSLAND PHALANGERIDAE. Oldfield Thomas. Ann. and Mag. Nat. Hist., ser.9, vol.11, pp.246-250, Feb., 1923.

THE SPECIES OF THE GENUS DACTYLOPSILA. Oldfield Thomas. Ann. and Mag. Nat. Hist. (8), vol.1, no.1, pp.122-124, Jan., 1908.

TWO NEW SUBSPECIES OF PHALANGER ORIENTALIS. Oldfield Thomas. Ann. and Mag. Nat. Hist., ser.9, vol.9, pp.680-681, June, 1922.

THE SOUTHERN RACE OF THE KOALA. E. LeG. Troughton. Australian Nat., Sydney, vol.9, pt.6, pp.137-140, Sept., 1935.

A NEW SPECIES OF RING-TAILED PHALANGER (PS. LANIGINOSUS GROUP) FROM THE BUNYA MOUNTAINS, S.E. QUEENSLAND. E. LeG. Troughton, A. S. LeSouef. Records Australian Mus., vol.17, no.6, pp. 291-296, fig.1, pl.40, Nov.28, 1929.

ZOOLOGICAL RESULTS OF THE DENISON-CROCKETT SOUTH PACIFIC EXPEDITION FOR THE ACADEMY OF NATURAL SCIENCES OF PHILADELPHIA, 1937-38. PART VI--A NEW RACE OF THE NEW GUINEA SHORT-HEADED FLYING PHALANGER FROM BIAK ISLAND. Frederick A. Ulmer, Jr. Notulae Naturae, Philadelphia, no.52, pp.3, Sept.6, 1940.

ON A NEW GENUS OF MARSUPIAL ANIMALS, (TARSIPES ROSTRATUS). M. Jules Verreaux, M. Gervais. Proc. Zool. Soc. Lond., pt.10, pp.1-5, 1842.

DESCRIPTION OF A RING-TAILED OPOSSUM, REGARDED AS A VARIETY OF PSEUDOCHIRUS HERBERTENSIS, COLLETT. E. R. Waite. Records Australian Mus., vol.3, pt. 5, pp.91-93, Apr.17, 1899.

## Phascolomidae

NOTES ON THE BROAD-FRONTED WOMBAT OF SOUTH AUSTRALIA (PHASCOLOMYS LATIFRONS, OWEN). George French Angas. Proc. Zool. Soc. Lond., pt.29, pp.268-271, 1861.

(CRANIUM AND BRAIN OF PHASCOLOMYS LATIFRONS OWEN.) Schädel und Gehirn von Phascolomys latifrons (Owen). J. Draseke. Zool. Garten, Leipzig, n. F. vol. 4, nos.10-12, pp.364-370, figs.2, Dec.16, 1931.

GROWING UP WITH WOMBATS. Rosemary Fleay. Animal Kingdom, New York Zool. Soc., 60 (4): 107-110, illus., Aug., 1957.

A CENTRAL QUEENSLAND WOMBAT. H. A. Longman. Mem. Queensland Mus., vol.11, pt.3, pp.283-297, pl.26, Mar.17, 1939.

OBSERVATIONS ON THE SKULL OF PHASCOLOMYS VOMBATUS. John E. Gray. Proc. Zool. Soc. Lond., pt.15, p.41, 1847.

LETTER FROM, ON THE SPECIES OF WOMBAT (PHASCOLOMYS). Gerard Krefft. Proc. Zool. Soc. Lond., pp.795-796, 1872.

ON THE GENERIC IDENTITY OF SCEPARNODON AND PHASCOLONUS. R. Lydekker. Proc. Roy. Soc. Lond., vol.49, pp.60-64, pl.1, 1890.

NOTES ON A SPECIMEN OF THE BROAD-HEADED WOMBAT (PHASCOLOMYS LATIFRONS). Alexander Macalister. Proc. Zool. Soc. Lond., pp.497-502, figs.2, 1872.

(SOME DATA ON WOMBAT FORMS AND MARSUPIALIA POUCHES.) Einiges uber Wombat-Formen und Marsupialia-Beutel. Erna Mohr. Zool. Garten, vol.14, nos.1-2, pp.55-68, illus., 1942.

ON THE IDENTITY OF THE HAIRY-NOSED WOMBAT (PHASCOLOMYS LASIORHINUS, GOULD) WITH THE BROAD-FRONTED WOMBAT (P. LATIFRONS, OWEN, WITH FURTHER OBSERVATIONS ON THE SEVERAL SPECIES OF THE GENUS. James Murie. Proc. Zool. Soc. Lond., pp.838-854, figs. 3, pl. XLVII, 1865.

ON THE PLATYRHINE WOMBAT (PHASCOLOMYS PLATYRHINUS, OWEN). James Murie. Proc. Zool. Soc. Lond., pp.798-815, figs.6, pl.XXXV, 1867.

NOTES ON THE ANATOMY OF THE WOMBAT (PHASCOLOMYS WOMBAT PER.). R. Owen. Proc. Zool. Soc. Lond., pt.4, p.49, 1836.

NOTICE OF HIS FOURTH MEMOIR ON THE OSTEOLOGY OF THE MARSUPIALIA. R. Owen. Proc. Zool. Soc. Lond., p.865, 1872.

ON THE EXISTENCE OF TWO SPECIES OF WOMBAT (PHASCOLOMYS). R. Owen. Proc. Zool. Soc. Lond., pt.13, pp.82-83, 1845.

THE EXISTING SPECIES OF THE GENUS PHASCOLOMYS. Baldwin Spencer. Melbourne, J. Kemp, 1910.

THE WOMBATS (MARSUPIALIA, PHASCOLOMYIDAE). G. H. H. Tate. Amer. Mus. Novitates, New York, no.1525, pp.1-18, July 13, 1951.

PRONOUNCED PARAMERAL DIFFERENTIATION IN THE WOMBAT (LASIORHINUS). Richard Tucker. Proc. Roy. Soc. Queensland, vol.65, pp.71-74, 1954.

## Macropodidae

KANGAROO FIGURES ON COINS. Charles Barrett. Victorian Nat., vol.43, no.12, p. 364, Apr., 1927.

KANGAROOS AND THEIR KIN. Charles Barrett. Bull. New York Zool. Soc., vol. 34, no.1, pp.3-48, figs.50, Jan.-Feb., 1931.

TEMPERATURE REGULATION IN THE MACROPOD MARSUPIAL, SETONIX BRACHYURUS. George A. Bartholomew. Physiological Zoology, Chicago, vol.29, no. 1, pp.26-49, Jan., 1956.

KANGAROOS ON SPERM WHALE HEAD. Fred Barton, Jr. Victorian Nat., vol.44, no.6, p.168, Oct., 1927.

NEW WALLABIES. Belle J. Benchley. Zoonooz, San Diego, vol.12, no.3, pp.1-4, Mar., 1940.

OBSERVATIONS ON THE BUSH-TAILED KANGAROO (MACROPUS PENICILLATUS, GRAY). E. T. Bennett. Proc. Zool. Soc. Lond., pt.3, pp.1-2, 1835.

SOME ASPECTS OF THE WATER METABOLISM OF AN AUSTRALIAN MARSUPIAL SETONYX BRACHYURUS. P. J. Bentley. Jour. Physiol., Cambridge, England, vol. 127, no.1, pp.1-10, Jan., 1955.

(KANGAROOS IN THE WILD IN GERMANY.) Kanguruhs in Deutschland in freier Wildbahn. Caesar R. Boettger. Natur und Volk, 73, pp. 331-336, Nov., 1943.

(ON THE KANGAROO.) Vom Kanguruh. Gustav Brandes. Naturforscher, Berlin, vol. 12, no.5, pp.152-157, illus., Aug., 1935.

OLD BOOMER FROM DOWN UNDER. Alan Devoe. Nature Mag., Washington, vol.45, no.1, pp.8-12, illus., Jan., 1952.

POST-NATAL DEVELOPMENT OF KANGAROOS. Guy Dollman. Proc. Linnean Soc. Lond., 151st sess., pt.1, pp.19-23, pls.1-2, Feb.3, 1939.

A POPULATION STUDY OF THE QUOKKA, SETONIX BRACHYURUS QUOY AND GAIMARD (MARSUPIALIA). I. TECHNIQUES FOR TRAPPING AND MARKING. C.S.I.R.O. G. M. Dunnet. Wildlife Res., Melbourne, 1 (2): 73-78, Dec., 1956.

CALOPRYMNUS CAMPESTRIS, ITS RECURRENCE AND CHARACTERS. H. H. Finlayson. Trans. & Proc. Roy. Soc. South Australia, vol.56, pp.148-167, figs.5, pls.7-9, Feb.16, 1932.

OBSERVATIONS ON THE SOUTH AUSTRALIAN MEMBERS OF THE SUBGENUS "WALLABIA." H. H. Finlayson. Trans. Roy. Soc. S. Australia, vol.51, pp.363-377, pls. 16-18, 1927.

OBSERVATIONS ON THE SOUTH AUSTRALIAN SPECIES OF THE SUBGENUS "WALLABIA." PT.2. H. H. Finlayson. Trans. & Proc. Roy. Soc. South Australia, vol.54, pp. 47-56, pls.3, Dec.20, 1930.

REDISCOVERY OF CALOPRYMNUS CAMPESTRIS (MARSUPIALIA). H. H. Finlayson. Nature, Lond., vol.129, no.3267, p.871, June 11, 1932.

ON THE CAUSE OF DEATH IN A BLACK-FACED KANGAROO (MACROPUS MELANOPS). Alfred Henry Garrod. Proc. Zool. Soc. Lond., pp.202-203, 1873.

MUSCLE DYSTROPHY IN TREE KANGAROOS ASSOCIATED WITH FEEDING OF COD LIVER OIL AND ITS RESPONSE TO ALPHA-TOCOPHEROL. Leonard J. Goss. Zoologica, Sci. Contrib. New York Zool. Soc., New York, vol.25, pt.4, no.32, pp.523-524, Dec.31, 1940.

REMARKS ON A KANGAROO LIVING IN THE SOCIETY'S GARDEN. John Gould. Proc. Zool. Soc. Lond., pt.28, p.373, 1860.

THE GREAT GREY KANGAROO. Langton Gould-Marks. Zoo Life, London, vol.9, no. 2, pp.55-57, illus., Summer, 1954.

LONGEVITY IN THE WILD POTOROO, POTOROUS TRIDACTYLUS (KERR). Eric R. Guiler. Australian Jour. Sci., 20 (1): 26, July, 1957.

OLD MAN KANGAROO. Kilroy Harris. Sportsman, vol.5, no.4, pp.72-73, illus., Apr., 1929.

OLD MAN KANGAROO. AUSTRALIA'S THREE-LEGGED QUADRUPED AS A SPORTING POSSIBILITY. Kilroy Harris. The Sportsman, Boston, Mass., vol.5, no.4, pp.72-73, illus., Apr., 1929.

NOTE ON THE TAXONOMY AND THE HABITS OF DENDROLAGUS URSINUS TEMMINCK AND D. LEUCOGENYS MATSCHIE (MAMMALIA: MARSUPIALIA). A. M. Husson, F. W. Rappard. Nova Guinea, new ser., vol.9, pt.1, pp.9-15, pls.1-4, July 15, 1958.

CAPTAIN COOK'S KANGAROO. Tom Iredale, Ellis LeG. Troughton. Australian Zool., vol.3, pt.8, pp.311-316, pl.41, Jan.14, 1925.

THE IDENTITY OF COOK'S KANGAROO. Tom Iredale, E. LeG. Troughton. Records Australian Mus., vol.20, no.1, pp.67-71, May 15, 1937.

THE INCREDIBLE KANGAROO. David H. Johnson. Nat. Geogr. Mag., Washington, vol.108, no.4, pp.487-500, illus., Oct., 1955.

KANGAROO. Osa Johnson. Frontiers, Lancaster, vol.8, no.4, pp.105-106, 126, Apr., 1944.

OCCASIONAL NOTES. ALTERATION IN CHARACTER OF WALLABIES ACCLIMATISED ON KAWAU ISLAND, NEW ZEALAND. A. S. LeSouef. Australian Zool., vol.6, no.2, p.111, 1930.

IS THE KANGAROO DOOMED? Heber A. Longman. Australian Zool. vol.3, pt.3, pp.103-107, June 7, 1923.

KANGAROOS. "THOSE BIZARRE ANIMALS FROM THE LAND DOWN UNDER." Donald Marcy. Popular Ser. no.8, Dept. Education New York Zool. Soc., pp.8 (not numbered), illus., 1944.

THOSE BIZARRE ANIMALS FROM DOWN UNDER. Donald Marcy. Animal Kingdom, New York, vol.47, no.1, pp.2-8, illus., Jan.-Feb., 1944.

STUDIES ON MARSUPIAL NUTRITION. I. RUMINANT-LIKE DIGESTION IN A HERBIVOROUS MARSUPIAL (SETONIX BRACHYURUS QUOY AND GAIMARD). R. J. Moir, M. Somers, H. Waring. Australian Jour. Biol. Sci., 9 (2): 293-304, May, 1956.

THE IDENTITY OF CAPTAIN COOK'S KANGAROO. T. C. S. Morrison-Scott, F. C. Sawyer. Bull. Brit. Mus. (Nat. Hist.), Zool., vol.1, no.3, pp.45-50, pls.3-5, Mar., 1950.

(THE IMPRESSION OF THE HIND FEET OF THE RECENT KANGAROO.) Der abdruck der Hinterfusse des rezenten Kanguruhs. Fritz Noetling. Centralblatt f. Mineral. geol. and Paleontol, Stuttgart, no.23, pp. 725-728, figs.2, 1908.

ON HYPSIPRYMNODON, RAMSAY, A GENUS INDICATIVE OF A DISTINCT FAMILY (PLEOPODIDAE) IN THE DIPROTODONT SECTION OF A MARSUPIAL. R. Owen. Zoology, second series, vol.1, pp.573-582, figs.3, pls.71-72, 1878.

THE TREE-KANGAROO. W. P. Pycraft. Illus. London News, vol.182, no.4891, p.44, illus., Jan.14, 1933.

THE IDENTITY OF CAPTAIN COOK'S KANGAROO. H. C. Raven. Jour. Mam., vol. 20, no.1, pp.50-57, figs.3, Feb.14, 1939.

ADAPTIVE BRANCHING OF THE KANGAROO FAMILY IN RELATION TO HABITAT. H. C. Raven, William K. Gregory. Amer. Mus. Novitates, New York, no.1309, pp.33, figs. 22, Mar.8, 1946.

THE GENUS DENDROLAGUS. Lord L. W. Rothschild, Guy Dollman. Trans. Zool. Soc. Lond., vol.21, pt.6, no.1, pp.477-551, pls.35-57, Mar.31, 1936.

(Review by P. Rode of) THE GENUS DENDROLAGUS. Lord L. W. Rothschild, Guy Dollman. Mammalia, Paris, 1 (1): 30, Sept., 1936.

DENDROLAGUS MAXIMUS. Walter Rothschild. Novitates Zoologicae, Tring, vol.6, no.2, pp.2,17, pl.1, Aug., 1899.

BOUNCING POCKETBOOKS. Jacqueline Schermerhorn. San Diego Zoonooz, vol.18, no.3, pp.4-5, illus., Mar., 1945.

(ON THE TREE KANGAROO (DENDROLAGUS LEUCOGENYS MATSCHIE ).) Vom Baumkanguruh (Dendrolagus Leucogenys Matschie). Karl Max Schneider. Zool. Garten, Leipzig, vol.21, nos.1-2, pp.63-106, illus., Mar., 1955.

(SEX DICHROMISM IN THE KANGAROO AND THE INFLUENCE THEREON OF CASTRATION.) Geschlechtsdichromismus bei Kanguruhs und seine Beeinflussung durch Kastration. Ernst Schwarz. Biol. Zentralbl., vol.51, no.11, pp.652-656, figs.4, 1931.

OBSERVATIONS ON DENSITY OF THE WESTERN GREY KANGAROO. Bruce Shipway. West. Australian Nat., Perth, vol.1, no.1, pp.18-19, June 18, 1947.

WALLAROOS, MOUNTAIN COUSINS. Homer F. Snow. Nature Magazine, Washington, D. C., vol.37, no.1, pp.20-21, 50, illus., Jan., 1944.

RESULTS OF THE ARCHBOLD EXPEDITIONS. NO.59. STUDIES ON THE ANATOMY AND PHYLOGENY OF THE MACROPODIDAE (MARSUPIALIA). G. H. H. Tate. Bull. Amer. Mus. Nat. Hist., New York, vol.91, art.2, pp.233-325, figs.3, Nov.1, 1948.

THE KANGAROO FAMILY. Ellis Troughton. Australian Mus. Mag., Sydney, vol.8, no.5, pp.171-175, pls.3, Sept.30, 1943.

THE KANGAROO FAMILY. Ellis Troughton. Australian Mus. Mag., 12 (7): 230-237, Sept. 15, 1957.

THE KANGAROO FAMILY. ORIGIN AND EARLIEST DISCOVERIES. Ellis Troughton. Australian Mus. Mag., Sydney, vol.8, no.1, pp.17-22, illus., July 20, 1942.

THE KANGAROO FAMILY. THE PADEMELONS OR SCRUB-WALLABIES. Ellis Troughton. Australian Mus. Mag., Sydney, vol.10, no.7, pp.218-222; no.8, pp.261-264, Sept.-Dec., 1951.

OBSERVATIONS ON DENDROLAGUS BENNETTIANUS DE VIS. Edgar R. Waite. Proc. Linnean Soc. New South Wales, ser.2, vol.9, pp.571-582, pls.42-43, Sept.26, 1894.

DISCOVERY OF THE TOOLACH, OR GREY'S WALLABY (WALLABIA GREYI) (J. E. GRAY, 1843; WATERHOUSE, 1846). H. M. Whittell, J. D. Somerville. South Australian Nat., Adelaide, vol.23, no.3, pp.11-13, Feb.15, 1946.

MR. WINSTON CHURCHILL AT THE LONDON ZOO. Illus. London News, vol.211, no. 5657, p.310, illus., Sept.20, 1947.

QUOKKAS ARE QUAINT. Zoonooz, Zool. Soc. San Diego, 30 (10): 12, Oct., 1957.

## Anatomy

ON THE ANATOMY AND FUNCTIONAL ADAPTATION OF THE THORAX AND PECTORAL GIRDLE IN THE WALLAROO (MACROPUS ROBUSTUS). W. Boardman. Proc. Linnean Soc. New South Wales, Sydney, vol. 66, nos.297-298, pts.5-6, pp.349-387, figs. 9, pl.12, 1941.

THE BLOOD VESSELS IN THE CENTRAL NERVOUS SYSTEM OF THE KANGAROO. E. Horne Craigie. Science, n.s., vol.88, no.2285, pp.359-360, fig.1, Oct.14, 1938.

ON SOME POINTS IN THE ANATOMY OF THE UROGENITAL ORGANS IN FEMALES OF CERTAIN SPECIES OF KANGAROOS. PT.I. J. J. Fletcher. Proc. Linn. Soc. New South Wales, vol.7, pp.640-659, 1883.

EXHIBITION OF SKULLS OF A NEW SPECIES OF KANGAROO. J. Gould. Proc. Zool. Soc. Lond., pt.9, p.77, 1841.

VASCULAR PATTERNS IN THE TESTIS, WITH PARTICULAR REFERENCE TO MACROPUS. R. G. Harrison. Nature, Lond., vol.161, no.4089, pp.399-400, illus., Mar. 13, 1948.

THE HAIR PATTERN OF A KANGAROO, A STUDY OF CAUSE AND EFFECT. F. Wood Jones. Jour. Mam., vol.6, no.1, pp.13-17, Feb., 1925.

POUCH EMBRYOS OF MARSUPIALS. NO.8. DENDROLOGUS MATSCHIEI. F. Wood Jones. Trans. Roy. Soc. S. Australia, vol. 48, pp.79-82, figs.1-7, 1924.

(ON OSSIFIED MACROPUS TENDONS.) Ueber verknoecherte Sehnen bei Macropus. W. Koch. Anat. Anzeiger, vol.62, pp.138-144, illus., Dec.4, 1926.

A NOTE ON THE FEMALE REPRODUCTIVE TRACT IN THE TREE KANGAROOS (DENDROLAGUS). L. Harrison Matthews. Proc. Zool. Soc. Lond., vol.117, pts.2-3, pp.313-333, Oct.30, 1947.

(CHROMOSOME FORMULA IN THE KANGAROO.) La formule chromosomiale du Kangourou. Robert Matthey. Societe de Biologie, vol.117, pp.406-407, Oct.27, 1934.

ON THE MOVEMENT OF THE SYMPHSIS OF THE LOWER JAW IN THE KANGAROO. James Murie. Proc. Zool. Soc. Lond., pp. 28-34, figs.2, 1866.

EXHIBITION OF A FOETAL KANGAROO, PROVING THE EXISTENCE OF AN ALLANTOIS. R. Owen. Proc. Zool. Soc. Lond., pt.5, p.82, 1837.

NOTES ON THE ANATOMY OF A NEW SPECIES OF KANGAROO (MACROPUS PARRYI, BENN.). R. Owen. Proc. Zool. Soc. Lond., pt.2, p.152, 1834.

NOTES ON THE ANATOMY OF THE TREE-KANGAROO (DENDROLAGUS INUSTUS, GOULD). R. Owen. Proc. Zool. Soc. Lond., pt.20, pp.103-107, 1852.

ON THE ORGANS OF GENERATION OF THE FEMALE KANGAROO (MACROPUS MAJOR, SHAW). R. Owen. Proc. Comm. Sci & Corres. Zool. Soc. Lond., pt.1, pp.159-160, 1830-1831.

A FURTHER NOTE ON THE FEMALE UROGENITAL SYSTEM OF HYPSIPRYMNODON MOSCHATUS (MARSUPIALIA). Joseph Pearson. Pap. & Proc. Roy. Soc. Tasmania, 1949, pp.203-210, Sept.15, 1950.

EXHIBITION OF A DRAWING OF A SPECIES OF ROCK-KANGAROO JUST RECEIVED BY THE SOCIETY FROM SOUTH AUSTRALIA. Philipp Scater. Proc. Zool. Soc. Lond., pt. 28, pp.323-324, 1860.

AN EXAMPLE OF "PRELACTEAL INCISORS" IN ADVANCE POUCH YOUNG OF MACROPUS. G. H. H. Tate. Jour. Mam., vol.28, no.4, pp.399-400, pl.1, Nov.26, 1947.

A DESCRIPTION OF MACROPUS ISABELLINUS, GOULD. Edgar R. Waite. Records Australian Mus., vol.4, no.3, July 29, 1901. pp.131-134, pls.18-19.

THE SKULL OF DENDROLAGUS DORIANUS, RAMSAY. Edgar R. Waite. Records Australian Mus. vol.2, no.6, pp.85-87, pls.18-19, 1896.

ON THE STRUCTURE OF THE MUCOUS MEMBRANE OF THE STOMACH IN THE KANGAROOS. D. James Williams. Proc. Zool. Soc. Lond., pp.165-177, figs.2, 1876.

## Australia and Tasmania

RECENT CAPTURE OF THE QUOKKA (SETONIX BRACHYURUS) ON THE MAINLAND. S. Barker, A. R. Main, R. M. Sadleir. Western Australian Naturalist, 6 (2): 53-55, Aug.15, 1957.

ON A NEW SPECIES OF POTOROUES (MARSUPIALIA) FROM A CAVE DEPOSIT ON KANGAROO ISLAND, SOUTH AUSTRALIA. H. H. Finlayson. Trans. Roy. Soc. S. Australia, Adelaide, vol.62, pt.1, pp.132-140, pls.5-7, 1 table, July 22, 1938.

ON A NEW SPECIES OF HYPSIPRYMNUS FROM KING GEORGE'S SOUND. J. Gould. Proc. Zool. Soc. Lond., pt.9, p.14, 1841.

THE STATUS OF THE KANGAROO ISLAND KANGAROO (MACROPUS FULIGINOSUS DESM.). Frederic Wood Jones. Proc. Zool. Soc. Lond., pp.451-460, figs.1-4, July 9, 1924.

DESCRIPTION OF A NEW SPECIES OF ROCK-KANGAROO FROM NEW SOUTH WALES. Gerard Krefft. Proc. Zool. Soc. Lond., pp.324-325, 1865.

KANGAROOS IN VICTORIA. F. Lewis. Victorian Nat., vol.45, no.2, p.51, June, 1928.

OBSERVATIONS UPON SOME RECENT COMMUNICATIONS OF MR. J.E. GRAY, OF THE BRITISH MUSEUM, TO THE ANNALS OF NATURAL HISTORY; WITH DESCRIPTIONS OF TWO NEW KANGAROOS FROM VAN DIEMEN'S LAND. W. Ogilby. Ann. Nat. Hist., Lond., vol.1, no.2, pp.216-221, May, 1838.

A NEW KANGAROO FROM THE NORTHERN TERRITORY OF WESTERN AUSTRALIA. Oldfield Thomas. Ann. and Mag. Nat. Hist. (8), vol.7, no.42, pp.609-610, June, 1911.

A NEW ROCK-KANGAROO (PETROGALE) OBTAINED IN NORTHERN QUEENSLAND. Oldfield Thomas. Proc. Zool. Soc. Lond., pp.177-178, Apr., 1923.

A NEW ROCK-WALLABY (PETROGALE) FROM THE ISLANDS OFF SOUTH AUSTRALIA. Oldfield Thomas. Ann. and Mag. Nat. Hist., ser.9, vol.9, pp.681-683, June, 1922.

ON A KANGAROO FROM QUEENSLAND OR NORTH AUSTRALIA. Oldfield Thomas. Proc. Zool. Soc. Lond., pp.112-113, Feb. 20, 1900.

ON A KANGAROO FROM WESTERN AUSTRALIA. Oldfield Thomas. Proc. Zool. Soc. Lond., p.113, Feb.20, 1900.

ON A NEW ROCK-WALLABY FROM NORTH-WEST AUSTRALIA. Oldfield Thomas. Novitates Zoologicae, vol.11, pp.365-366, Mar., 1904.

TWO NEW ROCK-WALLABIES (PETROGALE) DISCOVERED BY CAPT. G. W. WILKINS IN NORTHERN AUSTRALIA. Oldfield Thomas. Ann. and Mag. Nat. Hist., ser.9, vol.17, pp.184-187, Jan., 1926.

THE REDISCOVERY OF THE ROCK-WALLABY IN VICTORIA. N. A. Wakefield. Victorian Naturalist, Melbourne, vol.70, no.11, pp.202-206, Mar., 1954.

Diseases and Parasites

(FATAL SICKNESS AND RARE HEALING OF A MALE KANGAROO (MACROPUS RUFUS DESM.). Toedliche Erkrankung und seltene Heilung eines Kaenguruhbockes (Macropus rufus Desm.). Kurt Ehlers. Zool. Garten, Leipzig, vol.22, no.1, pp.110-112, 1955.

A LISTROPHORID PARASITE OF THE WALLABY, FROM NEW GUINEA. Carl E. M. Gunther. Proc. Linn. Soc. New South Wales, Sydney, vol.45, pts.3-4 (nos.289-290), pp. 353-354, figs.5, Sept.16, 1940.

AN ERYTHRAEID MITE FROM NEW GUINEA (ACARINA: ERYTHRAEIDAE). Carl E. M. Gunther. Proc. Linnean Soc. New South Wales, Sydney, vol.66, nos.295-296, pts.3-4, p.156, figs.4, 1941.

PENTATRICHOMONAS MACROPI TANABE FROM KANGAROOS. Carlton M. Herman. Zoologica, New York, vol.24, pt.3, pp. 293-295, fig.1, nov.2, 1939.

FILARINEMA FLAGRIFER N. GEN., N. SP., A TRICHOSTRONGYLID PARASITE OF THE KANGAROO. H. O. Monnig. 15th annual report Director Veterinary Services and Animal Industry, Union South Africa, pp.307-310, figs.5, Oct., 1929.

HYPODONTUS MACROPI, N. GEN., N. SP., A HOOKWORM OF THE KANGAROO. H. O. Monnig. 15th Annual report Director Veterinary Services and Animal Industry, Union South Africa, pp.303-306, figs.5, Oct., 1929.

A STREPTOTHRIX DISEASE OF WALLABIES. H. Harold Scott. Proc. Zool. Soc. Lond., 1925, pt.3, pp.799-814, 5 pls., Oct., 1925.

TOXOPLASMOSIS IN A SWAMP WALLABY. Samuel W. Thompson, Theodore H. Reed. Jour. Amer. Vet. Med. Assoc., 131 (12): 545-549, illus., Dec.15, 1957.

Fossils

PALAEONTOLOGICAL NOTES. NO. III. THE SKULL OF STHENURUS OCCIDENTALIS GLAUERT. C. Anderson. Records Australian Mus., Sydney, vol.18, no.7, pp. 383-387, pls.45-46, June 21, 1932.

PALORCHESTES--AUSTRALIA'S EXTINCT GIANT KANGAROO. H. O. Fletcher. Australian Mus. Mag., Sydney, vol.8, no.11, pp.361-365, illus., May 31, 1945.

ON A NEW SPECIES OF STHENURUS, WITH REMARKS ON THE RELATION OF THE GENUS TO DORCOPSIS, MUELLER. Richard Owen. Proc. Zool. Soc. Lond., pt.2, pp.352-361, fig.1, pls.37-38, 1877.

Habits, Behavior

VOCAL POWERS AND EYES OF KANGAROOS. James W. Barrett. Nature, Lond., vol.129, no.3262, p.689, May 7, 1932.

VOCAL POWERS OF KANGAROOS. H. H. Finlayson. Nature, Lond., vol.129, no.3247, p.131, Jan.23, 1932.

(THE PROBLEM OF THROWING IN THE KANGAROO.) Das problem des Werfens beim Kaenguruh. H. Hediger. Zool. Garten, n.F., vol.4, nos.6-7, pp.244-246, July, 1931.

NOTE ON THE HABITS OF THE KANGAROOS. Sir R. Heron. Proc. Zool. Soc. Lond., pt. 3, p.187, sec.4, 1835.

NOTE ON THE HABITS OF THE BUSH-TAILED KANGAROO (MACROPUS PENICILLATUS, GRAY). Capt. Sir E. W. Parry. Proc. Zool. Soc. Lond., pt.3, p.1, 1835.

A NEW USE FOR TAILS. W. P. Pycraft. Illus. London News, vol.194, no.5221, p. 825, figs.3, May 13, 1939.

(THE EXCHANGE OF KANGAROO BABIES.) Babyverwisseling bij Kangeroes. Artis, Amsterdam, vol.1, no.3, pp.69-70, illus., Oct., 1955.

THE KANGAROO AND ITS EXTRA "LEG": A JUMP FROM START TO FINISH. Illus London News, vol.192, no.5159, p.402, illus., Mar.5, 1938.

New Guinea

(TWO NEW RACES OF THE RED TREE KANGAROO OF GERMAN NEW GUINEA.) Zwei neue Rassen des roten Baumkaenguruhs aus Deutsch-Neuguinea. Paul Matschie. Sitz. Ger. Gesell. Naturf. Freunde, Berlin, Jahrg. 1912, no.10, pp.568-572, Dec., 1912.

A NEW TREE-KANGAROO FROM THE WONDIWOI MOUNTAINS, DUTCH NEW GUINEA. Lord Rothschild, Guy Dollman. Proc. Zool. Soc. Lond., pt.2, 1933, pp.540-541, June 30, 1933.

EXTRACT FROM A LETTER ADDRESSED TO HIM BY M. LUIGI M. D'ALBERTIS, C. M.Z., CONTAINING AN ACCOUNT OF A NEW SPECIES OF KANGAROO (HALMATURUS LUCTUOSUS) FROM NEW GUINEA. Philip Lutley Sclater. Proc. Zool. Soc. Lond., p.110, 1874.

RESULTS OF THE ARCHBOLD EXPEDITIONS. NO.4. AN APPARENTLY NEW RACE OF WALLABIES FROM SOUTHERN NEW GUINEA. G. H. H. Tate, Richard Archbold. Amer. Mus. Nov., No.804, p.2, May 21, 1935.

A NEW TREE-KANGAROO, FROM BRITISH NEW GUINEA. Oldfield Thomas. Ann. and Mag. Nat. Hist. (8), vol.2, no.11, pp.452-453, Nov., 1908.

A NEW TREE-KANGAROO FROM SOUTH-EASTERN PAPUA. E. LeG. Troughton, A. S. Le Souef. Records Australian Mus., vol. 19, no.6, pp.388-390, Oct.7, 1936.

TWO NEW TREE KANGAROOS FROM PAPUA, WITH NOTES ON ALLIED FORMS. E. LeG. Troughton, A. S. Le Souef. Australian Zool., Sydney, vol.8, pt.3, pp.193-197, June 29, 1936.

RESULTS OF THE ARCHBOLD EXPEDITIONS. NO.76. A NEW SPECIES OF WALLABY (GENUS DORCOPSIS) FROM GOODENOUGH ISLAND, PAPUA. Hobart Merritt Van Deusen. Amer. Mus. Novitates, New York, 1826: 1-25, Apr.3, 1957.

Reproductive Biology

(HOW DOES THE NEWLY BORN KANGAROO GET INTO THE POUCH?) Wie kommt das eben geborne Kaegaruh in den Brutbeutel? G. Brandes. Zool. Garten, Leipzig, n.F., vol.3, nos.1-3, pp.68-69, May, 1930.

(A NEW OBSERVATION OF THE ACT OF BIRTH IN THE KANGAROO.) Eine neue Beobachtung des Kanguruhgeburtsaktes. Heinrich Dathe. Zool. Garten N.F., Leipzig, vol.7, nos.7-9, pp.223-224, Nov., 1934.

(NEW OBSERVATIONS OF A KANGAROO BIRTH.) Neuerliche Beobachtung einer Kaenguruhgebart. Heinrich Dathe. Verhandl. Deutschen Zoologen in Mainz, 1949, (Zool. Anzeiger, 14 Supplementband), Leipzig, pp. 341-343, 1950.

OBSERVATIONS ON THE BIRTH OF A WALLABY. David Fleay. Australian Zool. Soc., Sydney, vol.8, pt.3, pp.153-155, pl.1, June 29, 1936.

OBSERVATIONS ON THE BIRTH OF A WALLABY. David Fleay. Proc. Roy. Zool. Soc. Lond., pp.25-27, pls.3, 4, Aug.25, 1936.

THE UTERINE CYCLE OF PREGNANCY AND PSEUDO-PREGNANCY AS IT IS IN THE DIPROTODONT MARSUPIAL BETTONGIA CUNICULUS, WITH NOTES ON OTHER REPRODUCTIVE PHENOMENA IN THIS MARSUPIAL. T. Thomas Flynn. Proc. Linn. Soc. New South Wales, vol.55, pt.5, no.231, pp.506-531, pls.19-21, Dec.15, 1930.

ON THE PASSAGE OF THE YOUNG TO THE POUCH IN THE KANGAROOS (MACROPUS AND HELMATURUS). COMMUNICATED, WITH REMARKS BY PROF. OWEN. E. S. Hill. Proc. Zool. Soc. Lond., pp.475-476, 1867.

HOW BABY KANGAROOS GET INTO THE POUCH. L. Harrison Matthews. Animal Kingdom, New York, vol.47, no.5, p.121, Sept.-Oct., 1944.

PARTURITION IN THE KANGAROO. L. Harrison Matthews. Proc. Zool. Soc. Lond., ser.A, vol.113, 1943, pts.3-4, pp.117-120, figs.2, Feb., 1944.

ON THE PERIOD OF UTERINE GESTATION, AND THE CONDITION OF THE NEW-BORN FOETUS IN THE KANGAROO (MACROPUS MAJOR, SHAW). R. Owen. Proc. Zool. Soc. Lond., pt.1, p.128, 1833.

NOTE ON SOME KANGAROO HYBRIDS. Walter Rothschild. Novitates Zoologicae, vol.5, no.1, p.4, Mar., 1898.

(A KANGAROO HYBRID "MACROPUS HAGENBECKI ROTHSCHILD".) Ein Kaenguruhbastard "Macropus hagenbecki Rothschild." Ernst Schwarz. Zool. Garten, Leipzig, n. F., vol.4, nos.6-7, pp.197-203, figs.5, July, 1931.

KANGAROOS AND THEIR YOUNG. W. Henry Sheak. Natural History, vol.32, no. 1, pp.98-100, figs.2, Jan.-Feb., 1932.

THE MYSTERY OF MARSUPIAL BIRTH AND TRANSFERENCE TO THE POUCH. Ellis LeG. Troughton. Australian Mus. Mag. July-Sept., 1926, vol.2, no.11, July-Sept., 1926.

(ON THE BREEDING OF KANGAROOS.) Zur Fortpflanzung des Kaeguruhs. J. Vosseler. Unter Benutzung von Beobachtungen A. Goerlings. Zool. Garten, Leipzig, n. F., vol.3, nos.1-3, pp.1-11, 3 figs., May, 1930.

Taxonomy

PRELIMINARY DESCRIPTION OF TWO NEW FORMS OF BETTONGIA (MARSUPIALIA). H. H. Finlayson. Ann. and Mag. Nat. Hist., ser.12, 10 (115): 552-554, July, 1957.

ON THE KANGAROO CALLED HALMATURUS LUCTUOSUS BY D'ALBERIS, AND ITS AFFINITIES. Alfred Henry Garrod. Proc. Zool. Soc. Lond., pp.48-58, pls.7-9, 1875.

DESCRIPTIONS OF FOUR NEW SPECIES OF KANGAROOS. John Gould. Proc. Zool. Soc. Lond., pt.9, pp.80-83, 1841.

DESCRIPTIONS OF THREE NEW SPECIES OF HALMATURUS AND LAGORCHESTES. John Gould. Proc. Zool. Soc. Lond., pt.12, p.31, 1844.

ON A NEW SPECIES OF KANGAROO, OF THE GENUS HALMATURUS. John Gould. Proc. Zool. Soc. Lond., pt.28, p.375.

ON A NEW SPECIES OF KANGAROO RAT. John Gould. Proc. Zool. Soc. Lond., pt. 11, p.81, 1843.

ON A NEW SPECIES OF PETROGALE,--P. INORNATA. John Gould. Proc. Zool. Soc. Lond., pt.10, pp.5-6, 1842.

ON FIVE NEW SPECIES OF KANGAROOS. John Gould. Proc. Zool. Soc. Lond., pt. 8, p.92, 1840.

ON TWO NEW SPECIES OF KANGAROO (PETROGALE CONCINNA AND HALMATURUS BINOE). John Gould. Proc. Zool. Soc. Lond., pt.10, p.57, 1842.

DESCRIPTION OF A NEW SPECIES OF PETROGALE. Dr. John Edward Gray. Proc. Zool. Soc. Lond., pt.22, p.249.

DESCRIPTION OF A NEW SPECIES OF KANGAROO. Albert Gunther. Proc. Zool. Soc. Lond., p.653, 1874.

THE GREAT GREY KANGAROO (MACROPUS GIGANTEUS) AND ITS ALLIES. A. S. Le Souef. Australian Zool., vol.3, pt.4, pp.145-147, 2 plates, Aug.15, 1923.

THE MACROPUS ROBUSTUS GROUP OF KANGAROOS. A. S. Le Souef. Aust. Zool., vol. 5, pt.3, pp.247-256, pl.30, Aug.17, 1928.

NOTES ON FOUR LITTLE-KNOWN SPECIES OF KANGAROOS. A. S. Le Souef. Proc. Linn. Soc. New South Wales, vol.53, pt.4, Oct.15, 1928.

NOTES ON SOME ROCK WALLABIES, GENUS PETROGALE, WITH DESCRIPTIONS OF TWO NEW SPECIES. A. S. Le Souef. Australian Zoologist, vol.3, pp.272-276, Oct.7, 1924.

DESCRIPTION OF VARIOUS SPECIES OF THE GENUS HYPSIPRYMNUS. W. Ogilby. Proc. Zool. Soc. Lond., pt.6, p.62, 1838.

ON A NEW SPECIES OF KANGAROO. W. Ogilby. Proc. Zool. Soc. Lond., pt.6, p. 23, 1838.

ON A NEW SPECIES OF KANGAROO (MACROPUS PARRYI, BENN.) Capt. Sir. E. W. Parry. Proc. Zool. Soc. Lond., pt.2, pp. 151-152, 1834.

THE RELATIONSHIPS OF THE POTOROIDAE TO THE MACROPODIDAE (MARSUPIALIA). Joseph Pearson. Pap. and Proc. Roy. Soc. Tasmania, 1949, pp.211, 229, Sept.15, 1950.

PROTEMNODON PARMA (WATERHOUSE) AND THE CLASSIFICATION OF RELATED WALLABIES (PROTEMNODON, THYLOGALE, AND SETONIX). W. D. L. Ride. Proc. Zool. Soc. Lond., 128 (3): 327-346, pl.1, June 6,

DESCRIPTIONS OF THREE NEW KANGAROOS, AND NOTES ON THE SKULL OF DENDROLAGUS BENNETTIANUS DE VIS. Walter Rothschild, N. C. Rothschild. Novitates Zoologicae Tring, vol.5, no.4, pp.511-513, Dec., 1898.

THE RELATIONSHIPS OF THE QUOKKA (SETONIX BRACHYURUS). G. B. Sharman. West. Australian Nat., Perth, vol.4, no. 7, pp.159-168, illus., Dec.24, 1954.

EXHIBITION OF A NEW ROCK-KANGAROO. Oldfield Thomas. Abstr. Proc. Zool. Soc. Lond., no.235, p.13, Feb.6, 1923.

ON THE WALLABY COMMONLY KNOWN AS LAGORCHESTES FASCIATUS. Oldfield Thomas. Proc. Zool. Soc., Lond., pp.544-547, pl.59, Dec.7, 1886.

## INSECTIVORA

MONOGRAPH OF THE INSECTIVORA. G. E. Dobson. Brit. Natl. Mus. Publ., vol. 3.

INSECTIVORA. Theodore Gill. Natural History of Mammals, pp.134-158, illus.

INSECTIVORA. Theodore Gill. The Standard Natural History. Mammals. (Edited by John Sterling Kingsley), Boston, vol.5, pp. 134-158, 1886.

SYNOPSIS OF INSECTIVOROUS MAMMALS. Theodore Gill. Dept. Int. Bull. Geol. Geog. Surv. Territories, no.2, 2nd ser., p.32, May 14, 1875.

INSECTS AND INSECT-EATERS. W. P. Pycraft. Illus. London News, Lond., vol. 190, no.5115, p.758, figs.3, May 1, 1937.

MOLES AND SHREWS. Charles Ripper. New York, Morrow, 1957.

(CATALOG OF TYPES OF MAMMALS OF THE NATIONAL MUSEUM OF NATURAL HISTORY. III. ORDER INSECTIVORA.) Catalogue des types de mammifères du Muséum National d'Histoire Naturelle, III. Ordre des Insectivores. P. Rode. Bull. Mus. Nat. Hist. Nat., Paris, ser.2, vol. 14, no.5, pp.307-314; no.6, pp.382-387, 1942.

(THE MAMMALS OF THE MOTTAZ COLLECTION. I. THE INSECTIVORES.) Les mammifères de la collection Mottaz. I. Les insectivores. P. Rode, P. Cantuel. Bull. Mus. Nat. Hist. Nat., Paris, ser.2, vol.1, no.2, pp.228-233, 1939.

### Africa

(ON SOME INSECTIVORES FROM ST. JOSEPH DE LULUABOURG (BELGIAN CONGO). Sobre algunos insectívoros de Saint Joseph de Luluabourg (Congo Belga). E. Morales Agacino. Bol. Soc. Española Hist. Nat., Madrid, vol.35, nos.1-2, pp. 17-23, fig.1, Mar.5. 1935.

THE AMERICAN MUSEUM CONGO EXPEDITION: INSECTIVORA. J. A. Allen. Bull. Amer. Mus. Nat. Hist., vol. 47, art. 1, pp. 1-38, 4 pls., 1 fig., July 20, 1922.

(GLANDS PRESENT IN THE ANAL REGION OF INSECTIVORES.) Zur Kenntniss der in der Analgegend bei Insectivoren vorkommenden Druesen. H. Hamperl. Verhandl. Anat. Gesellsch., Anat. Anzeiger., Ergaenzungsheft zum vol.57, pp.233-247, Dec., 1923.

(ON ANAL AND CIRCUMANAL GLANDS. FOURTH COMMUNICATION: INSECTIVORES.) Ueber Anal-und Circumanaldruesen. 4. Mitteilung: Insektivoren. H. Hamperl. Zeitschr. fuer Wiss. Zoologie, vol.147, pp. 570-589, 10 figs., Apr.24, 1926.

THE PITUITARY IN SWEDISH INSECTIVORA. Bertil Hanstrom. Arkiv Zool., Stockholm, vol.38A, pt.2, no.7, pp.1-20, figs.23, Sept. 30, 1946.

(ANATOMY OF THE PELVIC REGION OF INSECTIVORES, WITH SPECIAL CONSIDERATION OF ITS MORPHOLOGICAL RELATIONSHIPS TO THAT OF THE OTHER MAMMALS.) Zur Anatomie Der Beckenregion Bei Insectivora, Mit Besonderer Beruecksichtigung Ihrer Morphologischen Beriehunger Zu Derjenigen Anderer Saeugethiere. Wilhelm Leche. Kongl. Svenska Vetenskaps-Akademiens Handlingar, vol.20, no.4, pp.3-113, pls.10, Stockholm, 1883.

(ON THE MORPHOLOGY OF THE DENTAL SYSTEM OF THE INSECTIVORES (I).) Zur Morphologie des Zahnsystems der Insectivoren. I. William Leche. Anat. Anz. Jena, vol.13, nos.1-2, pp.1-11, figs.1-10, 1897.

(ON THE MORPHOLOGY OF THE DENTAL SYSTEM OF THE INSECTIVORES (II).) Zur Morphologie des Zahnsystems der Insectivoren. II. Anat. Anz., Jena, vol.13, nos. 19-20, pp.513-529, figs.1-7, 1897.

(ON THE MORPHOLOGY OF THE PELVIC REGION IN INSECTIVORA.) Zur Morphologie der Beckenregion bei Insectivora. Wilhelm Leche. Morphologischen Jarbuch, Leipzig, vol.6, no.4, pp.8, June, 1880,

NOTES ON THE OSTEOLOGY OF THE INSECTIVORA. St. George Mivart. Jour. Anat and Physiol., vol.1, pp.281-312 (1-32), 1867.

NOTES ON THE OSTEOLOGY OF THE INSECTIVORA. St. George Mivart. Jour. Anat. and Physiol., vol.2, pp.117-154, 1868.

ON THE STRUCTURE AND DEVELOPMENT OF THE SKULL IN THE MAMMALIA. PART III. INSECTIVORA. W. K. Parker. Proc. Roy. Soc. Lond., vol.38, no.235, pp.129-138, 1885.

THE CRANIAL DEVELOPMENT OF CERTAIN ETHIOPIAN "INSECTIVORES" AND ITS BEARING ON THE MUTUAL AFFINITIES OF THE GROUP. G. H. Roux. Acta Zoologica, Stockholm, vol.28, nos.2-3, pp. 165-397, figs.69, 1947.

(THE STRUCTURE OF THE ESOPHAGUS IN INSECTIVORES.) Der Bau der Speiseroehre bei Insektivoren. H. Scholtyssek. Anat. Anz., vol.70, nos.1-4, pp.22-59, 15 figs., June 30, 1930.

(ANATOMY AND MORPHOLOGICAL AND SYSTEMATIC SIGNIFICANCE OF THE MIDDLE EAR AND OF THE STRUCTURE CONNECTED TO IT IN SOME INSECTIVORA (SUNCUS, TALPA, CHRYSOCHLORIS.) Anatomia e significato morfologico e sistematice dell 'orecchio medio e delle strutture ad esso connesse in alcuni insettivori (Suncus, Talpa, Chrysochloris). Alberto Simonetta. Arch. Italiano Anat. and Embriol., Firenze, vol.62, no.1, pp.55-94, 1957.

(ON THE EXISTENCE OF KINETIC JOINTS IN THE CRANIUM OF SOME INSECTIVORA (MYOSORES, TALPA) AND ON THEIR POSSIBLE SIGNIFICANCE.) Sull 'esistenza di giunti cinetici nel cranio di alcuni insettivori (Myosorex, Talpa) e sul loro possibile significate. Alberto Simonetta. Monitere Zool. Italiano, Firenze, vol.64, no.4, pp. 172-180, June 10. 1957.

THE HYOID REGION IN THE INSECTIVORA. James M. Sprague. Amer. Jour. Anat., Philadelphia, vol.74, no.2, pp.175-216, figs. 11, Mar., 1944.

NEW SPECIES OF INSECTIVORES FROM BRITISH EAST AFRICA, UGANDA, AND THE SUDAN WITH ONE PLATE. Edmund Heller. Washington, Smithsonian institution, 1910.

NEW INSECTIVORES, ELEPHANTULUS AND CROCIDURA, FROM ANGOLA, AFRICA. John Eric Hill, T. Donald Carter. Amer. Mus. Novitates no.937, pp.4, July 13, 1937.

(STUDY OF ZOOLOGICAL GEOGRAPHY ON THE BARBARY: THE INSECTIVORES.) Etudes de geographie zoologique sur la Berberie: Les Insectivores. L. Joleaud. Assoc. Franc. Avanc. Sci., Constantine, 51 sess., pp.523-526, 1927.

THE INSECT EATERS OF NIGERIA. D. R. Rosevear. Nigerian Field, London, vol.10, pp.98-103, Oct., 1941.

THE HEDGEHOGS AND SHREWS (INSECTIVORA) OF EGYPT. Henry W. Setzer. Jour. Egyptian Publ. Health Assoc., Cairo, 32 (1): 1-17, Mar.28, 1957.

### Americas

NOTES ON AMERICAN INSECTIVOROUS MAMMALS, WITH DESCRIPTIONS OF NEW SPECIES. Elliott Coues. Bull. U.S. Geol. and Geogr. Sur., vol.3, no.3, pp. 631-653, May 15, 1877.

NOTE ON THE DERIVATION AND DISTRIBUTION OF THE INSECTIVORA OF THE NEW WORLD. G. E. Dobson. Proc. Zool. Soc. Lond., no.24, pp.349-351, June 2, 1891.

MAMMALS OF WEST VIRGINIA. I--SHREWS AND MOLES. L. Wayne Wilson. West Virginia Conserv., Charleston, vol. 9, no.11, pp.10, 20-21, Feb., 1946.

MOLES AND SHREWS. Virginia Wildlife, Richmond, vol.9, no.9, pp.9-10, illus., Sept., 1948.

### Anatomy

CORPORA AMYLACEA IN THE PROSTATIC SECRETION AND EXPERIMENTS ON THE FORMATION OF A COPULATORY PLUG IN SOME INSECTIVORES. William Robert Eadie. Anat. Record, Philadelphia, vol.102, no.2, pp.259-271, 1948.

THE DEVELOPMENT OF THE AUDITORY OSSICLES IN THE ELEPHANT SHREW, THE TENREC AND THE GOLDEN MOLE. G. H. Findlay. Proc. Zool. Soc. Lond., vol.114, pts.1-2, pp.91-99, figs.6, Aug., 1944.

(NOTES ON MAMMALS. VIII. ON THE FORM OF MOLARS IN INSECTIVORES.) Notes sur les Mammifères. VIII.--De la forme des Molaires chez les Insectivores. Serge Frechkop. Bull. Mus. Roy. Hist. Nat., Belgique, Bruxells, vol.8, no.6, pp. 23, figs.14, Feb., 1932.

MORPHOLOGY OF NASAL CAVITY IN INSECTIVORA. (IN RUSSIAN, WITH ENGLISH SUMMARY). L. V. Ganeshina, N. N. Vorontsov, V. I. Chabovsky. Zool. Zhurnal, Moscow, 36 (1): 122-127, 1957.

A COMPARATIVE STUDY OF THE OSTEOLOGY AND MYOLOGY OF THE CRANIAL AND CERVICAL REGIONS OF BLARINA BREVICAUDA KIRTLANDI AND SCALOPUS AQUATICUS MACHRINUS. George R. L. Gaughran. Ph. D. thesis, U. Mich., 191 pp., 1952.

A COMPARATIVE STUDY OF THE OSTEOLOGY AND MYOLOGY OF THE CRANIAL AND CERVICAL REGIONS OF THE SHREW, BLARINA BREVICAUDA, AND THE MOLE, SCALOPUS AQUATICUS. George R. L. Gaughran. Misc. Publ. Mus. Zool. Univ. Mich., Ann Arbor, no.80, pp.82, pls.23, Feb.26, 1954.

A COMPARISON OF THE DEVELOPMENT OF THE RUDIMENTARY EYE OF EREMITALPA GRANTI (BROOM) WITH THAT OF THE NORMAL EYE OF ELEPHANTULUS MYURUS JAMESONI (CHUBB). V. Gubbay. South African Jour. Sci., vol.52, no.8, pp. 182-186, 193-195, 198, Mar., 1956.

THE ANATOMY OF THE HAND OF CERTAIN INSECTIVORES. R. Wheeler Haines. Proc. Zool. Soc. Lond., vol.125, pts.3-4, pp.761-777, illus., Nov.23, 1955.

(COMPARATIVE EVALUATION OF PLACENTATION IN INSECTIVORES.) Vergleichende Beurteilung der Placentation bei den Insektivoren. Fritz Strauss. Rev. Suisse Zool., Bern, vol.49, no.19, pp.269-282, figs.11, Sept., 1942.

THE CHROMOSOMES OF TWO SPECIES OF INSECTIVORA. Shinkichi Tateishi. Annot. Zool. Japonenses, vol.17, nos.3-4, pp.516-521, fig.1, pl.28, Nov.18, 1938.

AIDS TO THE IDENTIFICATION OF MOLE AND SHREW HAIRS WITH GENERAL COMMENTS ON HAIR STRUCTURE AND HAIR DETERMINATION. Cecil S. Williams. Jour. Wildlife Management, vol.2, no.4, pp.239-250, figs.9, pl.23, Oct., 1938.

ON SOME HITHERTO UNRECOGNIZED REPTILIAN CHARACTERS IN THE SKULL OF THE INSECTIVORA AND OTHER MAMMALS. Jacob Lawson Wortman. U. S. Nat. Mus. Proc. Washington, vol.57, p.1-52, illus., 1921.

Behavior

BEHAVIOR OF THE MOLE (SCALOPUS) AND THE SHREW (BLARINA). John J. Christian. Jour. Mam., vol.31, no.3, pp.281-287, Aug. 21, 1950.

(THE BEHAVIOR OF INSECTIVORES.) Das Verhalten der Insektivoren. Konrad Herter. Handbuch der Zoologie, Berlin, Bd.8, Teil 10, no.10 (Lief. 9), pp.1-48, illus., Apr., 1957.

Diseases and Parasites

TWO NEW LARVAL NEMATODES BELONGING TO THE GENUS PORROCACUM FROM MAMMALS OF THE ORDER INSECTIVORA. Benjamin Schwartz. Proc. U.S. Nat. Mus., vol.67, art.17, pp.1-8, pl.1, 1925.

NIGERIAN INSECTIVORA (HEDGEHOGS AND SHREWS)--THEIR REACTION TO NEUROTROPIC YELLOW FEVER VIRUS. E. C. Smith. Trans. Roy. Soc. Trop. Medicine and Hygiene, vol.29, no.4, pp.413-416, pls. 4, Jan., 1936.

KEY-CATALOGUE OF PARASITES REPORTED FOR INSECTIVORA (MOLES, SHREWS, ETC.) WITH THEIR POSSIBLE PUBLIC HEALTH IMPORTANCE. C. W. Stiles, Samuel F. Stanley. Nat. Inst. Health Bull.159, pp.I-IV, 791-911, June, 1932.

Eurasia

NEW CHINESE INSECTIVORES. Glover M. Allen. Amer. Mus. Nov., no.100, 11 pp., Dec.28, 1923.

(FAUNA OF ABBRUZZI AND MOLISE, MAMMALS, I. INSECTIVORA.) Fauna dell' Abruzzi e del Molise, Mammiferi, I. Insectivora. G. Altobello. 36 pp., 1920.

KEY TO THE MAMMALS OF U.S.S.R. (INSECTIVORA.) N. A. Bobrinskii, A. P. Kuzyakin. pp.35-58, 1944.

THREE NEW SPANISH INSECTIVORES. Angel Cabrera. Ann. Mag. Nat. Hist., ser.7, vol.20, pp.212-215, Sept., 1907.

(MAMMALOGY NOTES: THE ITALIAN INSECTIVORA.) Note di mammalogia: Gli insettivori Italiani. Giuseppe Gulino. Boll. Mus. Zool. e Anat. Comp. Univ. Torino, vol.47, ser.3, no.96, pp.25, 1939.

(INSECTIVOROUS MAMMALS OF BULGARIA.) Nasekomoyadite bozainitsi v. Bulgariya. Georgi Markov. Bulgarska Akad. Nauk Zool. Inst., Sofia, Fauna na Bulgariya, no.3, pp. 287, 1957.

(CONTRIBUTION TO THE CLASSIFICATION OF THE MAMMALIAN INSECTIVORES OF RUSSIA.) Contribution à la classification des mammifères insectivores de la Russie. S. I. Ognev. Yearbook Zool. Mus., Russian Acad. Sci., 1921, pp.311-350, (1922).

A GUIDE TO THE MAMMALS OF CEYLON. PART III. INSECTIVORA. W. W. A. Phillips. Spolia Zeylanica (Ceylon), vol.13, pt. 2, pp.185-193, July 31, 1925.

THE INSECTIVORES OF CHINA AND NEIGHBORING REGIONS. Arthur De Carle Sowerby. The China Journal, Shanghai, vol. 33, no.3, pp.116-125, illus., Sept., 1940.

(ANIMALS OF SIBERIA: INSECTIVORA.) Zveri Sibiri: nasekomoyadnyye. S. U. Stroganov. Moscow, Academy of Sciences USSR Publishing House, 1957, 267 pp., illus., maps, 1957.

INSECTIVORE MAMMALS OF THE FAUNA OF THE USSR. S. U. Stroganov. Doklady Akad. Nauk USSR, Moscow, n.s., vol.33, no.3, pp.270-272, 1941.

ON THE INSECTIVOROUS FAUNA IN TAIWAN, JAPAN. Ryo Tanaka. Trans. Nat. Hist. Soc. Formosa, vol.26, nos.155-156, pp.310-313, Sept., 1936.

(THE WILD MAMMALS OF CRETE. 2) CRETAN INSECTIVORES.) Die Wildsaeuger von Kreta. 2) Die Insectivora von Kreta. Otto v. Wettstein. Zeitschr. Saeugetierk., Berlin, vol.17, no.1, pp.4-13, pl.2, Feb. 19, 1953.

(ATTEMPT TO PROVIDE FOR THE DESMAN (MYOGALE MOSCHATA PALL.) IN THE HUNTING DISTRICT OF THE CENTRAL BIOLOGICAL AND HUNTING STATION OF MOSCOW.) Versuch der Unterbringung der Desmane (Myogale moschata Pall.) im Gehege der Zentralen Station fuer Biologie und Jagdwesen (Moskau). D. Wjashlinsky, L. Schaposchnikov. Zoologitscheskij Journal (vormals "Revue Zool. Russe"), Moscow, vol.12, pt.1, pp.69-85, 1933.

Fossils

INSECTIVORES OF THE REXROAD FAUNA, UPPER PLIOCENE OF KANSAS. Claude W. Hibbard. Jour. Paleontol., vol.27, no.1, pp.21-32, Jan., 1953.

A NEW INSECTIVORE FROM THE OLIGOCENE OF THE WIND RIVER BASIN, WYOMING, WITH NOTES ON THE TAXONOMY OF THE OLIGOCENE TENRECOIDEA. Jean Hough. Jour. Paleontol., 30 (3): 531-541, illus., May, 1956.

AFFINITIES OF THE PATAGONIAN FOSSIL MAMMAL NECROLESTES. Bryan Patterson. Harvard University, Museum of Comparative Zoology, Braviora, no.94, 14 pp., illus., 1958.

A SORICID AND TWO ERINACEIDS FROM THE WHITE RIVER OLIGOCENE. Bryan Patterson, Paul O. McGrew. Geol. Ser., Field Mus. Nat. Hist., vol.6, no.18, pp. 245-272, figs.60-74, Dec.28, 1937.

A NEW SPECIES OF THE FOSSORIAL MAMMAL ARCTORYCTES FROM THE OLIGOCENE OF COLORADO. Charles A. Reed. Fieldiana, Geol., Chicago Nat. Hist. Mus., 10 (24): 305-311, illus., Apr.24, 1956.

NEW INSECTIVORES FROM THE LOWER PALEOCENE. T. Emmett Reynolds. Bull. Geol. Soc. America, vol.42, no.1, p.368, Mar., 1931.

TWO NEW INSECTIVORES FROM THE LOWER PALEOCENE OF NEW MEXICO. T. Emmett Reynolds. Jour. Paleontology, vol.10, no.3, pp.202-209, figs.2, pl.25, Apr., 1936.

A DETAILED STUDY OF THE STRUCTURE AND RELATIONSHIPS OF A NEW ZALAMBDODONT INSECTIVORE FROM THE MIDDLE OLIGOCENE. Erich M. Schlaikjer. Bull. Mus. Comp. Zool. Harvard College, vol. 76, no.1, pp.1-27, figs.8, pl.1, Nov., 1933.

A NEW FOSSIL ZALAMBDODONT INSECTIVORE. Erich Schlaikjer. Amer. Mus. Novitates, no.698, pp.1-8, figs.3, Mar.8, 1934.

AFFINITIES OF THE MONGOLIAN CRETACEOUS INSECTIVORES. George Gaylord Simpson. Amer. Mus. Novitates, no.330, pp.1-11, Oct.30, 1928.

AMERICAN CRETACEOUS INSECTIVORES. George Gaylord Simpson. Amer. Mus. Novitates, New York, no.1541, pp.1-19, illus., Dec.3, 1951.

A NEW INSECTIVORE FROM THE OLIGOCENE, ULAN GOCHU HORIZON, OF MONGOLIA. George Gaylord Simpson. Amer. Mus. Novit., no.505, pp.22, figs. 5, Nov.25, 1931.

INSECTIVORA FROM THE SESPE UPPERMOST EOCENE, CALIFORNIA. Chester Stock. Proc. Nat. Acad. Sci., vol.21, no. 4, pp.214-219, pl.1, Apr., 1935.

ON THE GENUS PSEUDICTOPS--AN UNUSUAL INSECTIVORE FROM LOWER TERTIARY DEPOSITS IN MONGOLIA. B. A. Trofimov. Proc. Paleo. Inst., Acad. Sci. U.S.S.R., vol.41, pp.7-12, illus., 1952.

Islands

(DESCRIPTION OF TWO NEW INSECTIVOROUS MAMMALS FROM MADAGASCAR.) Description de deux nouveaux mammifères insectivores de Madagascar. M. G. Grandidier. Bull. Mus. Hist. Nat. Paris, vol.34, pp.8, illus., 1928.

THE GREATER ANTILLEAN INSECTIVORES. Samuel Booker McDowell. Bull. Amer. Mus. Nat. Hist., vol.115, art.3, 1958.

DESCRIPTION OF A NEW GENUS AND TWO NEW SPECIES OF INSECTIVORA FROM MADAGASCAR. Oldfield Thomas. Jour. Linnean Soc., Lond., Zool., vol.16, pp. 319-322, figs., Mar., 1882.

Taxonomy

THE SKULL OF ICTOPS AND THE CLASSIFICATION OF THE INSECTIVORA. P. M. Butler. Proc. Zool. Soc. Lond., 126 (3): 453-481, illus., May 31, 1956.

ON THE NAMES OF TWO GENERA OF INSECTIVORA. A. Cabrera. Jour. Mam., vol.5, no.2, pp.131-132, May, 1924.

ON THE CLASSIFICATION OF THE INSECTIVOROUS MAMMALS. Theodore Gill. Bull. Philos. Soc. Washington, vol.5, pp.118-120, 1882.

(CATALOGUE OF TYPES OF MAMMALS FROM THE MUSEUM OF NATURAL HISTORY. III. ORDER OF INSECTIVORES.) Catalogue des types de mammifères du Museum National d'Histoire Naturelle. III. Ordre des insectivores. P. Rode. Bull. Mus. Nat. Hist. Nat., Paris, ser.2, vol. 14, no.5, pp.307-314, May; no.6, pp.382-387 (reprint pp.109-127), June, 1942.

UNACHINIA, NEW NAME FOR APATOR SIMPSON, NOT SEMENOW. George Gaylord Simpson. Jour. Paleont., vol.11, no.1, p. 78, Jan., 1937.

(REVIEW OF THE RELATIONSHIP OF THE INSECTIVORES.) Udsigt over Insektaedernes indbyrdes Slaegtskab. H. Winge. Vidensk. Medd. Dansk Naturh. Foren. Kjbenhavn, vol.68, pp.83-196, 1917.

Solenodontidae

SOLENODON PARADOXUS. Glover M. Allen. Mem Mus. Com. Zool., vol.40, no. 1, pp.5-53, pls.9, June, 1910.

NOTES ON SOLENODON PARADOXURUS BRANDT. J. A. Allen. Bull. Amer. Mus. Nat. Hist., vol.24, pp.305-517, pls.28-33, text figs.1-9, June 8, 1908.

ON A SUPPOSED CONTINENTAL SPECIMEN OF SOLENODON. Outram Bangs. Proc. Biol. Soc. Wash., vol.17, pp.165-167, Dec. 27, 1904.

THE SOLENODONS OF CUBA. Thomas Barbour. Proc. New England Zool. Club, Boston, vol.23, pp.1-8, pls.3, Mar.7, 1944.

THE HAITIAN SOLENODON. William Bridges. Bull. New York Zool. Soc., vol.39, no.1, pp. 13-18, illus., Jan.-Feb., 1936.

THE STRATIGRAPHY AND PALEONTOLOGY OF THE CHADRON FORMATION IN THE BIG BADLANDS OF SOUTH DAKOTA. John Clark. Ann. Carnegie Mus., vol.25, pp. 261-350, figs.12, pls.21-26, Dec.31, 1937.

THE CUBAN SOLENODON--UNPREPOSSESSING BUT A ZOOLOGICAL RARITY. L. S. Crandall. Animal Kingdom, New York, vol. 52, no.3, p.95, June 1, 1949.

NOTICE OF A SPECIMEN OF SOLENODONTA, OBTAINED BY HIM IN HAITI. J. Hearne. Proc. Zool. Soc. Lond., pt.3, p. 105, 1835.

(ON THE PECULIAR INSECTIVORE SOLENODON PARADOXUS, FROM HAITI.) Några ord om den egendomliga insektaetaren, Soleodon paradoxus Brandt, från Haiti.

Einar Loennberg. Fauna och Flora, popular Tidskrift foer Biologi, Uppsala, pp.193-198, pl., 1931.

(BIOLOGICAL OBSERVATIONS OF SOLENODON PARADOXUS BRANDT IN CAPTIVITY. I.) Biologische Beobachtungen an Solenodon paradoxus Brandt in Gefangenschaft. I. Erna Mohr. Zool. Anz., vol. 113, nos.7-8, pp.177-188, figs.17, Feb.15, 1936.

(BIOLOGICAL OBSERVATIONS OF SOLENODON PARADOXUS BRANDT IN CAPTIVITY III.) Biologische Beobachtungen an Solenodon paradoxus Brandt in Gefangenschaft III. Erna Mohr. Zool. Anz., vol.117, nos. 9-10, pp.233-241, figs.36-41, Mar.1, 1937.

(BIOLOGICAL OBSERVATIONS OF SOLENODON PARADOXUS BRANDT IN CAPTIVITY IV.) Biologische Beobachtungen an Solenodon paradoxus Brandt in Gefangenschaft. IV. Erna Mohr. Zool. Anz., vol.122, nos. 5-6, pp.132-143, figs.9, May 1, 1938.

(DEATH FROM AGE, AND DENTAL CHARACTERS IN THE AGOUTA, SOLENODON PARADOXUS BRANDT.) Alterstod und Zahnverhaeltnisse beim Schlitzruessler, Solendon paradoxus Brandt. Erna Mohr. Zool. Anz., Leipzig, vol.141, nos. 11-12, pp.264-268, fig.1, Mar.31, 1943.

(ON THE MAMMALIAN GENUS SOLENODON.) Uber die Saeugethiere--Gattung Solenodon. Wilhelm Peters. Abh. der Konigl. Akad. der Wissensch. zu Berlin, pp.1-22, pls.2, 1863.

CONTRIBUTIONS TO THE STRATIGRAPHY AND PALAEONTOLOGY OF THE GOSHEN HOLE AREA, WYOMING. I. A DETAILED STUDY OF THE STRUCTURE AND RELATIONSHIPS OF A NEW ZALAMBDODONT INSECTIVORE FROM THE MIDDLE OLIGOCENE. Erich M. Schlaikjer. Bull. Mus. Comp. Zool. at Harvard College, vol.76, no.1, pp.1-27, figs.7, pl.1, Nov., 1933.

THE ALMIQUI. F. W. True. Science, vol.8, no.190, p.282, Sept.24, 1886.

THE PLACENTATION OF SOLENODON PARADOXUS. George B. Wislocki. Amer. Jour. Anat., Philadelphia, vol.66, no.3, pp. 497-531, figs.1, pls.7, May 15, 1940.

OUR HAITIAN SOLENODON PROSPECTING FOR INSECTS IN AN OLD STUMP. New York Zool. Soc. School News, New York, vol.4, no.2, pp.1-2, photo., June, 1939.

## Tenrecidae

(ON THE ONTOGENY OF THE CENTEDID DENTITION. SUMMARY. INAUGURAL DISSERTATION OF THE MEDICAL DEPARTMENT OF BERNE UNIVERSITY.) Zar Ontogenie des Centetes-Gebisses. Zusummenfassing. Inaugural-Dissertation der medisinischen Fakultaet der Univ. Bern. Peter Althaus. Anat. Inst. Univ. Bern, pp.4, fig. 29, pls.1-15, July 13, 1938.

(THE EARLY DEVELOPMENT OF A CENTETID (HEMICENTETES SEMISPRINOSUS CUV.) Die Fruehentwicklung eines Centetinen (Hemicentetes semispinosus Cuv.). H. Bluntschli. Revue Suisse Zool., Genève, vol. 44, no.2, pp.271-282, figs.7, Apr., 1937.

(EMBEDDING OF THE EGG IN HEMICENTETES.) Die Einbettung des Eies bei Hemicentetes. H. Bluntschli. Bio-Morphosis, Leipzig, vol.1, nos.3-4, pp.332-333, 1938.

(THE PRIMARY DEVELOPMENT AND FORMATION OF A VERY COMPLICATED PERFORATED PLACENTA OF THE LABYRINTH TYPE IN HEMICENTETES.) Le développement primaire et la formation d'un placenta perforé très compliqué et du type labyrinthe chez Hemicentetes. H. Bluntschli. Bull. Acad. Malgache, Tananarive, n.s., vol.20, pp.73-75, (1937) 1938.

(PRIMARY DEVELOPMENT AND IMPLANTATION IN A CENETID (HEMICENTETES.) Le développement primaire et l'implantation chez un centetiné (Hemicentetes). H. Bluntschli. Comptes Rendus Assoc. Anat., Bâle, pp.1-8, figs.4, Apr.10-14, 1938.

STUDIES OF THE MAMMALIAN DENTITION. I. THE TEETH OF CENTETES ECAUDATUS AND ITS ALLIES. P. M. Butler. Proc. Zool. Soc. Lond., 1937, vol.107, ser.B, Syst. and Morphol., pt.1, pp.103-132, figs. 28, pls.3, Apr., 1937.

DESCRIPTION OF AN APPARENTLY NEW SUBSPECIES OF MICROGALE FROM MADAGASCAR. D. G. Elliot. Proc. Biol. Soc. Washington, vol.18, pp.237-238, Dec. 9, 1905.

(CONTRIBUTION TO THE FEMALE GENITAL CYCLE OF THE MADAGASCAR CENTETIDS. ) Beitrag zum weiblichen Genitalzyklus der madagassischen Centetinen. Kurt Feremutsch, F. Strauss. Rev. Suisse Zool., Geneva, vol.56, fasc. suppl. no.1, pp.110, illus., 1949.

(ON THE MORPHOLOGY OF QUILLS IN ERICULINAE, INSECTIVORES OF MADAGASCAR.) Sur la morphologie des piquants chez des Ericulinae, insectivores malgaches. M. Friant. Bull. Soc. Zool. France, Laval, vol.72, no.3, p.113, 1948.

(A NEW TYPE OF INSECTIVORE OF MADAGASCAR.) Un nouveau type de mammifère insectivore de Madagascar. G. Grandidier. Bull. Acad. Malgache, vol. 11, pp.85-90, pls.2, figs.9, (1928) 1929.

(TWO NEW INSECTIVORE MAMMALS OF MADAGASCAR, MICROGALE DROUHARDI AND M. PARVULA.) Deux nouveaux mammiferes insectivores de Madagascar Microgale et M. parvula. G. Grandidier. Bull. Mus. Nat. Hist. Nat., Paris, ser.2, vol. 6, no.6, pp.474-477, 1934.

(DESCRIPTION OF A NEW SPECIES OF MADAGASCAR INSECTIVORES, FOLLOWED BY CRITICAL REMARKS ON THE GENUS ORYZORYCTES.) Description d'une espece nouvelle d'insectivore Malgache, suivie de remarques critiques sur le genre Oryzoryctes. G. Grandidier, G. Petit. Bull. Mus. Nat. Hist. Nat., Paris, vol.2, no.5, pp. 498-504, 1930.

(A NEW TYPE OF MADAGASCAR CENTETID, PARAMICROGALE OCCIDENTALIS.) Un type nouveau de Centetide Malgache, Paramicrogale occidentalis. G. Grandidier, G. Petit. Bull. Soc. Zool. France, 56: 126-139, 2 figs., 1931.

(THE PLACENTA OF CENTETES AND WHAT IT HAS TAUGHT US CONCERNING ABSORPTION IN THE PLACENTA.) Die Placenta von Centetes und ihre Lehren betreffs der Stoffaufnahme in der Placenta. O. Grosser. Zeitschr. f. Anat. u. Entwickges, vol.88, pp.509-521, 10 figs., 1929.

(CONTRIBUTION TO THE STUDY OF THE NEOFORMATION OF OVULES IN PRIMITIVE ADULT MAMMALS. INVESTIGATION OF THE OVARY OF ERICULUS SETOSUS.) Contribution a l'étude de la néoformation d'ovules chez les mammifères primitifs adultes. Recherches sur l'ovaire d'Ericulus setosus. Leopold Kon. Rev. Suisse Zool., vol.53, no.29, pp.597-623, figs.23, Oct., 1946.

ON THE CHANGE AND FORM OF THE TEETH IN THE CENTETIDAE, A MALAGASY FAMILY OF INSECTIVORA. C. I. Forsyth Major. Ann. and Mag. Nat. Hist., ser.6, vol.20, pp.525-544, Dec., 1897.

ON A NEW GENUS OF INSECTIVOROUS MAMMALIA. W. Martin. Proc. Zool. Soc. Lond., pt.6, p.17, 1838.

(CHEWING MUSCLES IN THE TENREC. A CONTRIBUTION TO THE QUESTION OF THE CAUSES OF LOSS OF THE ZYGOMATIC ARCH IN INDIVIDUAL MAMMALS.) Das Kaumuskelverhalten bei Centetes. Ein Beitrag zur Frage nach den Ursachen des Jochbogenverlustes bei einzelnen Saeugetieren. Gertrud Mathys. Zusammenfassung. Inaugural-Dissertation der medizinischen Fakultaet der Univ. Bern, Anat. Inst. Univ. Bern, pp.4, July 13, 1938.

ON HEMICENTETES, A NEW GENUS OF INSECTIVORA, WITH SOME ADDITIONAL REMARKS ON THE OSTEOLOGY OF THAT ORDER. St. George Mivart. Proc. Zool. Soc. Lond., pp.58-79, figs.9, pl.5, 1871.

THE INSECTIVOROUS GENERA MICROGALE AND NESOGALE (MADAGASCAR). T. C. S. Morrison-Scott. Proc. Zool. Soc. Lond., vol.118, pt.3, pp.817-822, Nov., 1948.

(THE SET OF MILK AND SECONDARY DENTITION IN CENTETES ECAUDATUS, SCHR.) Maelketandsaettet og Tandskiftningen hos Centetes ecaudatus (Schr.). J. Reinhardt. Vidensk. Medd. Naturhist. Foren. Kjbenhavn, no.3, pp.1-8, 1869.

(THE SET OF MILK TEETH AND SECONDARY DENTITION IN CENTETES ECAUDALUS, SCHR.) Maekletandsaettet og Tandskiftningen hos Centetes ecaudatus (Schr.). J. Reinhardt. Vidensk. Medd. naturhist. Foren Kjobenhavn, nos.6-8, pp.1-4, 1869.

ON THE FORM OF THE PLACENTA IN THE TENREC. George Rolleston. Proc. Zool. Soc. Lond., pt.31, p.237, 1863.

(AN ATTEMPT TO EXPLAIN THE UTERINE CYCLE OF ERICULUS.) Ein Deutungsversuch des uterinen Zyklus von Ericulus. Fritz Strauss. Rev. Suisse Zool., Geneva, vol.53, fasc.3, no.21, pp.511-517, figs.9, July, 1946.

(FERTILIZATION AND THE PROCESS OF OVULATION IN ERICULUS OF THE FAMILY CENTETIDAE.) Die Befruchtung und der Vorgang der Ovulation bei Ericulus aus der Familie der Centetiden. Fritz Strauss. Bio-Morphosis, Leipzig, vol.1, nos.3-4, pp.281-312, figs.16, 1938.

(THE FORMATION OF THE CORPUS LUTEUM IN CENTEDIDS. Die Bildung des Corpus luteum bei Centetiden. Fritz Strauss. Biomorphis, Basel, vol.1, no.6, pp.488-544, figs.28, Dec., 1939.

(THE PLACENTATION OF ERICULUS SETOSUS.) Die placentation von Ericulus setosus. Fritz Strauss. Rev. Suisse Zool., Geneva, vol.50, fasc.1, no.2, pp.17-87, figs.49, Feb., 1943.

LETTERS ON THE SOKINAH, AND UNDESCRIBED SPECIES OF TENREC (CENTENTES, ILLIG.). C. Telfair. Proc. Zool. Soc. Lond., pt.1, p.81, 1833.

DESCRIPTION OF A NEW SPECIES OF MICROGALE. Oldfield Thomas. Ann. and Mag. Nat. Hist. (5), vol.14, no.83, pp.337-338, Nov., 1884.

ON THE ARRANGEMENT OF THE SMALL TENRECIDAE HITHERTO REFERRED TO ORYZORICTES AND MICROGALE. Oldfield Thomas. Ann. and Mag. Nat. Hist. (9), vol. 1, no.4, pp.302-307, Apr., 1918.

ON THE INSECTIVOROUS GENUS ECHINOPS, MARTIN, WITH NOTES ON THE DENTITION OF THE ALLIED GENERA. Oldfield Thomas. Proc. Zool. Soc. Lond., pp.500-505, June 14, 1892.

QUEER BEASTS OF MADAGASCAR. THE TENREC. Field, London, vol.154, no.4015, p.861, Dec.7, 1929.

## Potamogalidae

ON THE CHARACTERS AND AFFINITIES OF POTAMOGALE, A GENUS OF INSECTIVOROUS MAMMALS RECENTLY DISCOVERED IN WESTERN AFRICA. Prof. Allman. Proc. Zool. Soc. Lond., p.467, 1865.

SUPPLEMENTARY NOTE ON POTAMOGALE VELO. Prof. Allman. Proc. Zool. Soc. Lond., pp.256-258, 1867.

THE OTTER SHREW. A. B. Cozens. Nigerian Field, vol.15, no.2, pp.76-83, illus., Apr., 1950.

(AN UNDESCRIBED AND UNEXPECTED GENUS OF MAMMALS (INSECTIVORE TENRECIDAE) OF WEST AFRICA.) Un genre inedit et inattendu de mammifere (Insectivore Tenrecidae) d'Afrique Occidentale. Henri Heim de Balsac. Comptes Rendus Acad. Sci., Paris, vol.239, no.1, pp.102-104, July 5, 1954.

THE MACROSCOPIC FEATURES OF THE PLACENTATION OF THE WATER-SHREW (POTAMOGALE VELOX). J. P. Hill. Bio-Morphosis, Leipzig, vol.1, nos.3-4, pp. 331-332, 1938.

ON POTAMOGALE VELOX DU CHAILLU. F. A. Jentink. Notes Leyden Mus., vol.16, no.27, pp.234-236, 1895.

(ON AN UNKNOWN SPECIES OF AFRICAN MAMMAL.) Sur une espece encore inconnue de mammifere africain, Potamogale ruwenzorii, sp. n. Gaston-Francois de Witte, Serge Frechkop. Bull. Inst. Roy. Sci. Nat. Belgique, 31 (84): 1-11, Dec., 1955.

Chrysochloridae

THE MOLE TROUBLE. H. J. Bishop. Farming in South Africa, Apr., 1948.

ON TWO PLEISTOCENE GOLDEN MOLES. R. Broom. Ann. Transvaal Mus., Cambridge, vol.20, pt.3, pp.215-216, 1 fig., Sept.12, 1941.

SOME FURTHER ADVANCES IN OUR KNOWLEDGE OF THE CAPE GOLDEN MOLES. R. Broom. Ann. Transvaal Mus., Pretoria, vol.21, p.3, pp.234-241, illus., May 9, 1950.

SOME NEW AND SOME RARE GOLDEN MOLES. R. Broom. Ann. Transvaal Mus., Cambridge, vol.20, pt.2, pp.329-35, figs. 3, Oct.18, 1946.

ON THE EAR REGION OF CERTAIN OF THE CHRYSOCHLORIDAE. C. Forster Cooper. Philos. Trans. Roy. Soc. Lond., (B), vol.216, pp.265-283, pls.15-17, figs. 4, Mar.21, 1928.

CONTRIBUTION TO THE KNOWLEDGE OF THE PLACENTATION OF THE CAPE GOLDMOLE (CHRYSOCHLORIS). Dan de Lange, Jr. Bijdragen tot de Dierkunde, Amsterdam, vol.20, Feest-number, pp.165-173, pls.4-7, Leiden, 1919.

(CONTRIBUTIONS TO KNOWLEDGE OF THE INSECTIVORE FAMILY CHRYSOCHLORIDAE.) Beitraege zur Kentniss der Insectivorenfamilie Chrysochloridae. L. Forcart. Rev. Suisse Zool., Geneva, vol. 49, no.1, pp.1-6, figs.2, Feb., 1942.

A REVISION OF THE SPECIES OF GOLDEN MOLE (CHRYSOCHLORIS). John Edward Gray. Proc. Zool. Soc. Lond., pp.678-680, 1865.

A NEW PARASITIC MITE FROM THE GOLDEN MOLE. R. F. Lawrence. Proc. Zool. Soc. Lond., vol.114, pt.3, pp.302-306, figs.4, Dec., 1944.

A NEW GOLDEN MOLE FROM SPITZKOP, SABIE. J. Meester. South African Jour. Sci., vol.49, no.6, pp.207-208, Jan., 1953.

(A NEW CHRYSOCHLORE FROM THE SOUTH CAMEROONS.) Ein neuer Chrysochloris aus Sud-Kamerun. Robert Mertens. See: Schwarz, Ernst and Mertens, Robert. 1922.

A NEW GOLDEN MOLE (CHLOROTALPA) FROM MT. ELGON, UGANDA. J. St. Leger. Ann. and Mag. Nat. Hist., ser.10, vol.8, pp.605-607, Dec., 1931.

(A NEW CHRYSOCHLORE FROM THE SOUTH CAMEROONS.) Ein neuer Chrysochloris aus Sued-Kamerun. Ernst Schwarz, Robert Mertens. Senckenbergiana, Band 4, Heft 5, pp.151-152, Nov., 1922.

(CHONDRO-CRANIUM AND DERMASKELETON OF "CHRYSOCHLORIS ASIATICA", LINNAEUS).) Condrocranio e dermascheletro di "Chrysochloris asiatica" (Linnaeus). Monitore Zool. Italianio, 65 (1-2): 28-47, Sept., 1957.

ON A NEW GOLDEN MOLE. Oldfield Thomas. Proc. Zool. Soc., Lond., vol.2, p.57, Oct.17, 1905.

Erinaceidae

MATERIALS ON THE BIOLOGY OF THE HEDGEHOG. I. S. Bashkirov, V. A. Popov. Raboty Volzhsko-Kamskoi Zonal'noi Okhotnich'epromyslonoi Biologischeskoi Stantsii, Kazan, no.3 (Uchen'ie Zapiski Kazanskogo Gosudarstvennogo Universiteta im V. I. Ul'ianova-Lenina, vol.94, no.8), pp.67-92, tables 6, 1934. (In Russian with English summary.)

(A TAME HEDGEHOG SPECIES.) Eine zahme Igelart. Arvid Behning. Natur und volk, vol.64, no.4, p.139, illus., Apr., 1934.

HEDGEHOG DEATHS ON THE ROAD. Maurice Burton. Illus. London News, vol. 211, no.5656, p.300, illus., Sept.13, 1947.

HEDGEHOGS' WEIGHTS AND ECSTATIC MEASURES. Maurice Burton. Illus. London News, vol.137, no.3575, p.774, illus., Oct.29, 1955.

ON THE EVOLUTION OF THE SKULL AND TEETH IN THE ERINACEIDAE, WITH SPECIAL REFERENCE TO FOSSIL MATERIAL IN THE BRITISH MUSEUM. P. M. Butler. Proc. Zool. Soc. Lond., vol.118, pt.2, pp.446-500, figs.28, Aug.18, 1948.

NOTES ON ECHINOSOREX GYMNURUS (RAFFLES). F. N. Chasen. Bull. Raffles Mus., Singapore, Straits Settlements, no. 9, pp.86-89, Dec., 1934.

A HEDGEHOG ROAD MORTALITY INDEX. J. L. Davies. Proc. Zool. Soc. Lond., 128 (4): 606-608, July 24, 1957.

(CONTRIBUTION TO THE BIOLOGICAL STUDY OF PARAECHINUS AETHIOPICUS EHRENB.) Contribution a l'étude biologique de Paraechinus aethiopicus Ehrenb. M. Eisentraut. Mammalia, Paris, vol.16, no. 4, pp.232-252, Dec., 1952.

(THE NATURAL FAMILY OF THE HEDGEHOG (ERINACEI) ACCORDING TO THE PRESENT-DAY LEVEL OF SCIENCE.) Die natuerliche Familie der Igel (Erinacei) nach dem gegenwaertigen Stande der Wissenschaft. L. J. Fitzinger. Sitzb. Akad. Wissensch. Wien, Abth., vol.56, pp.47, Nov., 1867.

ON THE EVOLUTION OF THE TEETH IN THE ERINACEIDAE. Madeline Friant. Proc. Zool. Soc. Lond., vol.119, pt.4, p. 821, Feb., 1950.

(THE BIOLOGY OF THE EUROPEAN HEDGEHOG.) Die Biologie der europaeischen Igel. K. Herter. Leipzig. Monographie der Wildsaeugetiere, no.5, 222 pp., 1938.

(ON THE DISTRIBUTION AND BEHAVIOR OF THE EUROPEAN HEDGEHOG.) Ueber die Verbreitung und das Verhalten europaeischer Igel. K. Herter. Sitz.-Ber. Gesell. Naturf. Freunde, Berlin, Jahrg. 1933, nos.8-10, pp.340-344, Dec., 1934.

(ON THE NATURAL HISTORY OF THE HEDGEHOG ERINACEUS EUROPAEUS.) Zur Naturgeschichte des Igels, Erinaceus europaeus. Viktor Hornung. Zool. Garten, n.F., vol.18, nos.3-4, p.152, 1951.

THE HEDGEHOG. T. Hyde-Parker. Naturalist, London, no.785, pp.291-294, Dec., 1940.

ON GYMNURA ALBA GIEBEL. F. A. Jentink. Notes Leyden Mus., vol.17, no.4, pp.19-20, May, 1895.

ON GYMNURA CANDIDA. F. A. Jentink. Notes Leyden Mus., vol.3, no.33, pp.166-168, June, 1881.

THE HEDGEHOG. Phyllis Kelway. Game and Gun and Angler's Monthly, London, vol. 16, no.163, pp.223-226, illus., Apr., 1939.

THE HEDGEHOG AND ITS LORE. Frank W. Lane. Nature Mag., Washington, vol.39, no.2, pp.90-93, Feb., 1946.

(REMARKS ON THE GENEALOGY OF ERINACEIDAE.) Bemerkungen ueber Die Genealogie Der Erinaceidae. Wilhelm Leche. Fetskrift fuer Lilljeborg, pp.139-145, Upsala, 1896.

NOTES ON THE EUROPEAN HEDGEHOG. J. Alden Loring. Jour. Mam., vol.2, no.2, pp.110-111, May, 1921.

REMARKS ON THE INSECTIVORES OF THE GENUS GYMNURA. Marcus Ward Lyon, Jr. Proc. U.S. Nat. Mus., vol.36, pp.449-456, pls.34-37, May 27, 1909.

NOTES ON HARDWICKE'S HEDGEHOG. C. McCann. Jour. Bombay Nat. Hist. Soc., vol.39, no.3, p.616, Sept.25, 1937.

(ON THE BIOLOGY OF THE HEDGEHOG (ERINACEUS EUROPAEUS L.) Sur la biologie du hérisson (Erinaceus europaeus L.). P. Mathias. Bull. Soc. Zool. France, vol. 45, no.5, pp.463-466, June, 1929.

(CONTRIBUTION TO THE STUDY OF THE INSECTIVORES. I. INSECTIVORES WITH QUILLS.) Contribution à l'étude des insectivores. I. Les Insectivores à piquants. P. Mathias, P. Rode. Bull. Soc. Zool. France, vol.55, pp.429-437, figs.2, 1930.

(EASTERN EUROPEAN AND MIGRATING HEDGEHOG IN CAPTIVITY.) Osteuropaeischer und Wanderigel in Gefangenschaft. Erna Mohr. Zeitschr. f. Saeugetierkunde, vol.11, no.2, pp.242-246, pl.58, Dec.15, 1936.

(HEDGEHOGS AS PREY OF MARTENS.) Igel als Marderfrass. D. Mueller-Using. Saeugetierk. Mitteil., Stuttgart, 3(2): 83, Apr.1, 1955.

(NEW BIOLOGICAL NOTES ON THE DESERT HEDGEHOG.) Nouvelle note biologique sur le herisson du desert. F. Petter. Mammalia, Paris, vol.18, no.2, pp.220-221, June, 1954.

AN INTERESTING HEDGEHOG. R. I. Pocock. Field, London, vol.150, p.472, illus., Sept.22, 1927.

THE HEDGEHOG AND ITS COUSINS. W. P. Pycraft. Illus. London News, vol.193, no. 5194, p.832, figs.3, Nov.5, 1938.

NEW LABORATORY ANIMALS FROM WILD SPECIES BREEDING A LABORATORY STOCK OF HEDGEHOGS (ERINACEUS EUROPAEUS L.). R. M. Ranson. Jour. Hygiene, vol. XLI, no.2, pp.131-138, fig.1, Sept.30, 1941.

DENIZENS OF THE UNDERBRUSH. Jacqueline Schermerhorn. San Diego Zoonooz, vol.19, no.11, p.3, illus., Nov., 1946.

(THORNY, ROUGH--BUT A STERLING CREATURE. A VINDICATION OF THE HEDGEHOG.) Stachelig, grob-aber doch von echtem schrot und Korn. Eine Ehrenrettung des Igels. Heinrich Schutz. Kosmos, handweiser fuer Naturfreunde (Gesell. der Naturfreunde), Stuttgart, Jahrg., no.10, pp.335-338, figs.3, Oct., 1932.

(DATA ON ERINACEUS ROUMANICUS B. HAMILT.) Zur Kenntnis von Erinaceus roumanicus B. Hamilt. G. Stein. Zeitschrift f, Saeugetierkunde, vol.4, nos.4-6, pp.240-250, Feb.10, 1930.

(ALBINIC HEDGEHOGS (ERINACEUS EUROPAEUS L.) Albinotische Igel (Erinaceus europaeus, L.). R. Stohler. Zool. Anzeiger, vol.79, pp.123-127, Nov.1, 1928.

(ON THE HIBERNATION OF THE HEDGEHOG, WITH SPECIAL CONSIDERATION OF ENZYME ACTIVITY AND BROMINE METABOLISM.) Ueber den Winterschlaf des Igels mit besonderer Berucksichtigung der Enzymataetigkeit und des Bromstoffwechsels. Paavo Suomalainen. Ann. Acad. Sci., Fennicae, Helsinki, ser.A., vol.45, pp.1-115, 1937.

(LIVING AND FOSSIL HEDGEHOGS.) Les Erinacéidés actuels et fossiles. Jean Viret. Bull. Soc. Linnéenne Lyon, 7 Année, no.5, pp.142-144, May, 1938.

ON THE OCCURRENCE OF PARAECHINUS DORSALIS (ANDERSON & DE WINTON) IN SOUTH SINAI, WITH A NOTE ON THE OSTEOLOGY OF THE ANIMAL. Kamal Wassif. Bull. Faculty Sci. Fouad I Univ., Cairo, no.25, pp.201-211, figs.3, pls.3, 1945.

THE LONG-EARED HEDGEHOG. China Jour., vol.11, no.2, p.105, 1929.

Africa

A NEW HEDGEHOG FROM AFRICA. Henry W. Setzer. Jour. Washington Acad. Sci., vol.43, no.7, pp.237-238, July 23, 1953.

A NEW HEDGEHOG FROM THE ISLAND OF DJERBA, TUNIS. Oldfield Thomas. Ann. and Mag. Nat. Hist., ser.9, vol.8, p.570, Nov., 1921.

ON THE OCCURRENCE OF HEDGEHOGS OF THE GENUS PARAECHINUS IN THE EL TAHREER PROVINCE OF EGYPT. Kamal Wassif. Bull. Zool. Soc. Egypt, Cairo, vol.11, pp.40-47, 1953.

Anatomy

ON THE ANTERIOR COMMISSURE OF THE FOREBRAIN IN THE HEDGE-HOG (ERINACEUS EUROPEUS). Y. Appajee. Half-yearly Jour. Mysore Univ., Bangalore City, n.s., sect.B, vol.3, no.1, pp.1-7, figs.2, Sept., 1942.

THE HYPOGLOSSAL NERVE IN AN EMBRYO OF ERINACEUS EUROPAEUS. H. Berkelbach van der Sprenkel. Jour. Comp. Neur., vol. 36, pp.219-272, 2 pls., Feb.15, 1924.

(ON THE PRESENCE OF GLIAL ELEMENTS IN THE ADENO-HYPOPHYSIS OF ERINACEUS EUROPEAUS.) Sulla presenza di elementi gliali nelladenoipofsi di Erinaceus europaeus. P. Contu. Monitore Zool. Italiano, vol.61, no.1, pp.33-35, 1953.

AN EXTRA MOLAR IN THE EASTERN HEDGEHOG, ERINACEUS ROUMANICUS. Julius Ehik. Jour. Mam., vol.9, no.2, pp. 148-149, May, 1928.

(PERSISTENCE OF AN ANCIENT FUNDAMENTAL CHARACTERISTIC IN THE UPPER MOLARS IN THE PRESENT-DAY HEDGEHOG.) Persistance d'un caractère archaique fondamental des molaires supérieures chez le Hérisson actuel. M. Friant. Sci. Nat., Paris, vol.1, no.5, pp.134-140, 1939.

(THE PRIMITIVE TYPE OF MOLAR IN INSECTIVORES.) Le type primitif des molaires chez les Insectivores (Erinacéidés). M. Friant. Archiv. Mus. Nat. d'Hist. Nat., Paris, ser.6, vol.11, pp.125-145, figs.14, pl.1, 1934.

PLACENTATION OF A PRIMITIVE INSECTIVORE ECHINOSOREX GYMNURA. Waldemar Meister, D. Dwight Davis. Fieldiana: Zoology, Chicago, Nat. Hist. Mus., vol.35, no.2, pp.11-26, pls.4-9, Oct.7, 1953.

(STRIATE MUSCULATURE OF THE HEDGEHOG (ERINACEUS EUROPAEUS).) Die Hautmuskulatur des Igels (Erinaceus europaeus). G. Michelsson. Morphol. Jahrb., vol.51, pp.147-229, 1921.

(ON ALBINISM IN THE COMMON HEDGEHOG ERINACEUS EUROPAEUS L.) Sur un cas d'albinisme chez le hérisson commun Erinaceus europaeus L. R. Poisson, R. Godet. Bull. Soc. Sci. Bretagne, Rennes, vol.25, pp.48-49, May 20, 1952.

HOW DID THE HEDGEHOGS GET THEIR SPINES? W. P. Pycraft. Illus. London News, vol.189, no.5089, p.786, illus., Oct.31, 1936.

(BEHAVIOR OF TESTIS AND EPIDIDYMIS IN THE HEDGEHOG (ERINACEUS EUROP. ET ROM. L.) DURING ANESTRUS.) Das Verhalten des Hodens und Nebenhodens beim Igel (Erinaceus europ. et rom. L.) waehrend des Anoestrus. Helga Schuetz. Anat. Anz. Jena, vol.103, nos.1/4, pp.66-78, Mar., 1956.

Diseases and Parasites

THE SUSCEPTIBILITY OF NIGERIAN HEDGEHOGS TO YELLOW FEVER. G. M. Findlay, A. F. Mahaffy. Trans. Roy. Soc. Trop. Medicine and Hygiene, vol.29, no.4, pp. 417-424, Jan., 1936.

NOTES ON AFRICAN HAEMAPHYSALIS TICKS. I. THE MEDITERRANEAN-LITTORAL HEDGEHOG PARASITE H. ERINACEI PAVESI, 1884 (IXODOIDEA, IXODIDAE). Harry Hoogstraal. Jour. Parasitol., 41 (3): 221-233, June, 1955.

A NEW NEMATODE (RICTULARIA AETHECHINI, SP. NOV.) A PHYSALOPTERA AND AN ACANTHOCEPHALA FROM THE HEDGEHOG (AETHECHINUS FRONTALIS). P. L. Leroux. 16th Report Director Veterinary Serv. and Anim. Industry, Union S. Africa, pp.217-227, figs. 18, Aug., 1930.

THE OCCURRENCE OF FOOT-AND-MOUTH DISEASE IN THE HEDGEHOG UNDER NATURAL CONDITIONS. J. C. McLaughlan, W. M. Henderson. Jour. Hygiene, Lond., vol. 45, no.4, pp.474-479, pls.11, Feb., 1948.

NEMATODES AND HEDGEHOG MORTALITY. Ishwar Prakash, S. C. Sharma. Jour. Bombay Nat. Hist. Soc., vol.53, no.1, p. 123, Aug., 1955.

INFECTION WITH NUTTALLIA NINENSE AMONG HEDGEHOGS IN THE NORTH-WEST FRONTIER PROVINCE, INDIA. J. A. Sinton. Indian Jour. Med. Research, vol.9, pp.359-363, 2 pls., 1921.

THE PARASITES OF BRITISH BIRDS AND MAMMALS. VII. RECORDS OF IXODOIDEA FROM HEDGEHOGS AND THEIR NESTS. Gordon B. Thompson. Entom. Monthly Mag., vol.72, no.254, pp.116-118, May, 1936.

Ecology, Habits and Behavior

THE REACTION OF ANOESTROUS HEDGEHOGS TO EXPERIMENTAL CONDITIONS. M. Allanson, R. Deanesly. Proc. Roy. Soc. Lond., ser.B., vol.116, no.797, pp.170-185, Oct.1, 1934.

REACTIONS OF HEDGEHOGS, HIBERNATING AND NONHIBERNATING, TO THE INHALATION OF OXYGEN, CARBON DIOXIDE AND NITROGEN. G. Bioerck, B. Johansson, H. Schmid. Acta Physiologica Scandinavica, Stockholm, 27 (1): 71-82, 1956.

SOME LABORATORY DATA ON HEDGEHOGS, HIBERNATING AND NONHIBERNATING. G. Bioerck, B. Johansson, S. Veige. Acta Physiologica Scandinavica, Stockholm, 37 (4): 281-294, Nov., 1956.

HEDGEHOG SELF-ANOINTING. Maurice Burton. Proc. Zool. Soc. Lond., 129 (3): 452-453, pl.2, Nov.11, 1957.

THE PALATABILITY OF THE EGGS OF BIRDS: ILLUSTRATED BY EXPERIMENTS ON THE FOOD PREFERENCES OF THE HEDGEHOG (ERINACEUS EUROPAEUS). Hugh B. Cott. Proc. Zool. Soc. Lond., vol. 121, pt.1, pp.1-42, illus., May 22, 1951.

(OBSERVATIONS ON CAPTIVE EUROPEAN HEDGEHOGS.) Gefangenschaftsbeobachtungen an europaeischen Igeln II. Konrad Herter. Zeitschrift f. Saeugetierkunde, vol.8, no.4, pp.195-218, pl.21-23, Dec.20, 1933.

(ON FEEDING IN THE HEDGEHOG.) Zum Nahrungserwerb des Igels. Viktor Hornung. Zool. Garten, vol.14, nos.1-2, p.103, 1942.

HEDGEHOGS OF THE DESERT OF RAJASTHAN. PART II. FOOD AND FEEDING HABITS. Daya Krishna. Jour. Bombay Nat. Hist. Soc., 53 (3): 362-366, Apr., 1956.

HEDGEHOGS OF THE DESERT OF RAJASTHAN. Daya Krishna, Ishwar Prakash. Jour. Bombay Nat. Hist. Soc., vol.53, no.1, pp. 38-43, illus., Aug., 1955.

NOTES ON THE FOOD OF CHINESE HEDGEHOGS. Ch'eng-chao Liu. Jour. Mam., vol. 18, no.3, pp.355-357, 1 table, Aug.14, 1937.

(THE HEDGEHOG (ERINACEUS EUROPAEUS L.) IN MID-WINTER.) Igel (Erinaceus europaeus L.) im Mittwinter. Detlev Muehler-Using. Saeugetierk. Mitteil., 5 (1): 27-28, Jan.1, 1957.

DO HEDGEHOGS SUCK COWS? P. Talbot. Field, Lond., vol.154, p.255, Aug.17, 1929.

(ON THE ABILITY OF THE HEDGEHOG TO CATCH MICE.) Ueber die Befaehigung des igels zum Maeusefang. A. Wahlstroem. Zeitschr. f. Saeugetierkunde, Berlin, vol. 8, nos.1-2, pp.100-107, Apr.24, 1933.

(ON THE QUESTION AS TO WHETHER THE HEDGEHOG CAN CATCH MICE.) Zur Frage, ob der Igel Maeuse fangen kann. A. Wahlstroem. Zeitschr. f. Saeugetierkunde, vol. 10, no.1, pp.73-77, Dec.31, 1935.

Eurasia

NOTES ON THE OCCURRENCE OF THE HEDGEHOG IN OUR COUNTIES. J. S. Ash. Vasculum (Substitute), Newcastle upon Tyne, vol.29, no.1, p.5, Feb., 1944.

(THE LONG HAIRED HEDGEHOG (HEMIECHINUS AURITUS GM.) IN THE VICINITY OF MARIUPOL, UKRAINE.) Der langohrige Igel (Hemiechinus auritus Gm.) in der Gegend von Mariupol. W. Golizinsky. Acad. Sci. Ukraine, Mém. Cl. Sci. Phys. et Math., (Trav. Mus. Zool. no.7), vol.13, no.1, pp. 25-26, 1929.

(STUDIES ON THE DISTRIBUTION OF THE EUROPEAN HEDGEHOG (ERINACEIDAE).) Studien zur Verbreitung der europaeischen Igel (Erinaceidae). Konrad Herter. Archiv. Naturgesch. (Zeitschr. Wiss. Zool. Abt.B), Leipzig, n.F., vol.3, no.3, pp.313-382, figs.10, 1934.

SOME REMARKS ABOUT EASTERN HEDGEHOGS. Einar Loennberg. Ann. and Mag. Nat. Hist., ser.9, vol.9, pp.620-629, May, 1922.

(A NEW HEDGEHOG FROM VARDAR PROVINCE.) Novi jez iz Vardarske banovine. E. Martino, V. Martino. Prirodoslovne Razprave, vol.2, no.1, pp.56-57, Apr. 13, 1933.

ON TWO FORMS OF THE KOREAN HEDGEHOG. T. Mori. Ann. and Mag. Nat. Hist., ser.9, vol.10, pp.614-616, Dec., 1922.

(ON THE SYSTEMATICS AND DISTRIBUTION OF THE EUROPEAN HEDGEHOG IN WESTERN SIBERIA.) Zur Systematik und Verbreitung des europaeischen Igels in West-Sibirien. W. N. Skalon. Zool. Anzeiger, vol.78, pp.67-76, 1 fig., 1 map, Aug.15, 1928.

THE HEDGEHOG OF PALESTINE AND ASIA MINOR. Oldfield Thomas. Ann. and Mag. Nat. Hist. (9), vol.2, no.9, pp.211-213, Sept., 1918.

A NEW HEDGEHOG FROM ADEN. Oldfield Thomas. Ann. and Mag. Nat. Hist., ser.9, vol.10, pp.307-308, Sept., 1922.

ON SOME INTERESTING HEDGEHOGS FROM THE PERSIAN GULF. Oldfield Thomas. Ann. and Mag. Nat. Hist., ser.9, vol.9, pp.142-144, Jan., 1922.

HEDGEHOG IN ARGYLL. George Waterston. Scottish Naturalist, no.193, p.19, Jan.-Feb., 1932.

Fossils

A NEW FOSSIL HEDGEHOG FROM PALESTINE. Dorthea M. A. Bate. Ann. and Mag. Nat. Hist., ser.10, vol.10, no.60, pp.575-585, figs.13, Dec., 1932.

STATUS OF THE OLIGOCENE INSECTIVORE GENUS METACODON. John Clark. Jour. Paleont., Menasha, Wisc., vol.13, no.1, pp.139-140, Jan., 1939.

A SECOND NEW GENUS OF HEDGEHOG FROM THE PLIOCENE OF NEVADA. E. Raymond Hall. Univ. California Publ., Bull. Dept. Geol. Sci., vol.18, no.8, pp. 227-231, illus., Mar.19, 1929.

A FOSSIL HEDGEHOG FROM THE AMERICAN OLIGOCENE. W. D. Matthew. Bull. Amer. Mus. Nat. Hist., New York, vol.19, art.7, pp.227-229, fig.1, May 9, 1903.

A NEW AND REMARKABLE HEDGEHOG FROM THE LATER TERTIARY OF NEVADA. W. D. Matthew. Univ. California Publ. Geol., vol.18, no.4, pp.93-102, pls.7-8, Jan.29, 1929.

A NEW ERINACEID FROM THE LOWER MIOCENE. Grayson E. Meade. Geol. Ser., Field Mus. Nat. Hist., Chicago, vol.8, no. 7, pp.43-47, Figs.15, Sept.30, 1941.

Islands

THE HEDGEHOG POPULATION AND INVERTEBRATE FAUNA OF THE WEST COAST SAND DUNES. R. E. Brockie. Proc. New Zealand Ecol. Soc., no.5, pp.27-29, Dec., 1957.

(NEW SHREW, GYMNURA ALBA, OF BORNEO.) Neue Spitzratte, Gymnura alba, von Borneo. C. Giebel. Zeitschr. Natur., Halle, vol.22, pp.277-294, pls.1-2, 1863.

Physiology

TEMPERATURE CHANGES IN HIBERNATING HEDGEHOGS. Elsie Proctor. Nature, London, vol.163, no.4133, pp.108-109, Jan. 15, 1949.

OBSERVATIONS ON THE ELECTROCARDIOGRAPHIC ALTERATIONS IN THE HIBERNATING HEDGEHOG. H. S. Samuli Sarajas. Acta. Physiologica Scandinavica, Stockholm, vol.32, fasc.1, pp.28-38, Oct., 1954.

(ON THE HIBERNATION OF THE HEDGEHOG.) Zum Winterschlaf des Igels. Ludwig Schuster. Zool. Garten, Leipzig, n.F., vol. 4, nos.8-9, p.298, 1931.

THE HIBERNATING GLAND AND THE ALARM REACTION. Paavo Suomalainen,

Auma-Maija Herleir. Soc. Zool. Bot. Fennicae 'Vanamo', vol.5, no.2, pp.72-73, 1950.

NEUROSECRETION IN THE HIBERNATING HEDGEHOG. Paavo Suomalainen, Paula Nyholm. Bertil Hanstroem, Zoological Papers in Honour of his Sixty-fifth Birthday, Zoological Institute, Lund, Sweden, pp.269-277, 1956.

THE HEART RATE IN THE HIBERNATING HEDGEHOG. Paavo Suomalainen, Samuli Sarajas. Ann. Zool. Soc. 'Vanamo' Helsinki, vol.14, no.2, pp.1-8, 4 figs., 4 tables, 1951.

STUDIES ON THE PHYSIOLOGY OF THE HIBERNATING HEDGEHOG. I. THE BODY TEMPERATURE. Paavo Suomalainen, Irene Suvanto. Ann. Acad. Sci. Fennicae, ser.A, no.20, pp.20, 1953.

(HIBERNATION OF THE HEDGEHOG (ERINACEUS ERINACEUS L.). K zimnímu spánku ježka (Erinaceus erinaceus L.). M. Zalesky. Véda Přírodni Měs. pro Šíř. a Pěst. Věd Přír., Prague, vol.7, no.9, p.285, 1926.

Reproductive Biology

THE REPRODUCTIVE PROCESSES OF CERTAIN MAMMALS. PART 7. SEASONAL VARIATION IN THE REPRODUCTIVE ORGANS OF THE MALE HEDGEHOG. Marjorie Allanson, Philos. Trans. Roy. Soc. Lond., ser.B, vol.223, no.B 500, pp. 277-303, pls.34-37, 1934.

MY HEDGEHOG AND HER FAMILY. H. Mortimer Batten. Field, London, vol.155, no.4019, p.13, Jan.4, 1930.

THE REPRODUCTIVE PROCESSES OF CERTAIN MAMMALS. PART 6. THE REPRODUCTIVE CYCLE OF THE FEMALE HEDGEHOG. Ruth Deanesly. Philos. Trans. Roy. Soc. Lond., ser.B, vol.223, no.B 499, pp.239-276, pls.27-33, 1934.

(ON THE REPRODUCTIVE BIOLOGY OF THE HEDGEHOG.) Zur Fortpflanzungsbiologie des Igels. Konrad Herter. Zeitschr. f. Saeugetierkunde, Berlin, vol.7, nos.1-6, pp.251-253, figs.2, pl.21, Dec.15, 1932.

NUMBER OF YOUNG HEDGEHOGS HAVE AT A BIRTH. C. McCann. Jour. Bombay Nat. Hist. Soc., vol.41, no.1, p.171, 1939.

MOTHER HEDGEHOG AND HER YOUNG. Nat. Hist., New York, vol.54, no.5, p.199, illus., May, 1945.

Taxonomy

THE TYPE SPECIMEN OF ERINACEUS ALBIVENTRIS WAGNER. Glover M. Allen. Jour. Mam., vol.17, no.1, pp.62-64, Feb., 1936.

NOTE ON THE COMMON HEDGEHOG (ERINACEUS EUROPAEUS, LINNAEUS) AND ITS SUBSPECIES OR LOCAL VARIATIONS. G. E. H. Barrett-Hamilton. Ann. and Mag. Nat. Hist., ser.7, vol.5, pp.360-368, Apr., 1900.

(THE GEOGRAPHIC FORMS OF AETHECINUS ALGIRUS.) Las formas geográficas de Aethecinus algirus. A. Cabrera. Bol. Real Soc. Espanola Hist. Nat., Madrid, vol.28, no.9, pp.453-455, 1928.

(ON THE QUESTION OF THE SYSTEMATIC POSITION OF SOME REPRESENTATIVES OF THE GENUS PARAECHINUS TROUESSART.) Zur Frage ueber die systematische Stellung einiger Vertreter der Gattung Paraechinus Trouessart. S. I. Ognev. Zool. Anzieger, vol.69, no.9-10, pp.209-218, Jan.1, 1927.

ERINACEUS ECAUDATUS DESIGNATED TYPE OF SETIFER 1800. C. W. Stiles, Samuel F. Stanley. Jour. Mam., vol.11, no.2, p.226, May, 1930.

FOUR NEW SPECIES OF HEDGEHOG. Oldfield Thomas. Ann. and Mag. Nat. Hist. (9), vol.1, no.3, pp.230-233, Mar., 1918.

THE GENERIC DIVISION OF THE HEDGEHOGS. Oldfield Thomas. Ann. and Mag. Nat. Hist. (9), vol.1, no.2, pp.193-196, Feb., 1918.

NEOTETRACUS SINENSIS, A NEW INSECTIVORE OF THE FAMILY ERINACEIDAE. E. L. Trouessart. Ann. and Mag. Nat. Hist., ser.8, vol.4, pp.389-391, Oct., 1909.

ON THE NOMENCLATURE OF THE INDIAN HEDGEHOGS. R. C. Wroughton. Jour. Bombay Nat. Hist. Soc., vol.20, no. 1, pp.80-82, June 13, 1910.

Macroscelididae

NOTE ON THE PREMOLARS OF THE ELEPHANT SHREWS. R. Broom. Ann. Transvaal Mus., vol.2, pt.2, pp.251-252, fig.1, Oct.31, 1938.

(THE MACROSCELIDIDAE AND THEIR RELATIONSHIP TO OTHER INSECTIVORES.) Die Macroscelididae und ihre Beziehungen zu den uebrigen Insectivoren. Albertina Carlsson. Zool. Jahrbuecher, Abt. Syst., Geog. Biol., vol.28, no.4, pp.349-400, figs. A-E, 1909.

THE OSTEOLOGY AND RELATIONSHIPS OF THE ELEPHANT SHREWS (MACROSCELIDIDAE). Francis Gaynor Evans. Bull. Amer. Mus. Nat. Hist., New York, vol.80, art.4, pp.85-125, figs.16, Oct.7, 1942.

(NOTES ON THE MAMMALS. V. PRELIMINARY COMMUNICATION ON THE DENTITION AND SYSTEMATIC POSITION OF MACROSCELIDIDAE.) Notes sur les Mammifères. V. Note préliminaire sur la dentition et la position systématique des Macroscelididae. Serge Frechkop. Bull. Mus. Roy. d'Hist. Nat. de Belgique, vol.6, no.6, pp.1-11, figs.5, Feb., 1931.

(STUDY OF THE MODIFICATIONS OF THE UTERUS DURING GESTATION IN NASILIO BRACHYRHYNCHUS (SMITH). Etude sur les modifications de l'uterus pendant la gestation chez Nasilio brachyrhynchus (Smith). Pol Gerard. Arch. de Biol., vol.33, pp.197-227, 2 pls., 1923.

NOTES ON THE DENTITION OF A JUMPING SHREW (NASILIO BRACHYRHYNCHA). John Eric Hill. Jour. Mam., vol.19, no.4, pp.465-467, fig.1, Nov.14, 1938.

A MALARIAL PARASITE OF THE AFRICAN ELEPHANT SHREW, ELEPHANTULUS RUFESCENS DUNDASI DOLLMAN. Henry Hoogstreal, Clay G. Huff, Deaner K. Lawless. Jour. Nat. Malaria Soc., vol.9, no. 4, pp.293-306, Dec., 1950.

A CASE OF INTERSTITIAL IMPLANTATION IN ELEPHANTULUS. C. J. van der Horst. South African Jour. Sci., Johannesburg, vol. 47, no.6, pp.164-166, illus., Jan., 1951.

ELEPHANTULUS GOING INTO ANOESTRUS, MENSTRUATION AND ABORTION. C. J. van der Horst. Philos. Trans. Roy. Soc. Lond., vol.238, no.653, pp.27-61, Dec., 1954.

A HUMAN-LIKE EMBRYO OF ELEPHANTULUS. C. J. van der Horst. Proc. Zool. Soc. Lond., vol.117, pts.2-3, pp.334-344, figs.6, Oct.30, 1947.

THE MAMMALIAN TROPHOBLAST AS INTERPRETED BY THE DEVELOPMENT OF ELEPHANTULUS. C. J. van der Horst. Proc. Zool. Soc. Lond., vol.115, pts.1, 2, pp.14-18, figs.2, Oct., 1945.

REMARKS ON THE SYSTEMATICS OF ELEPHANTULUS. C. J. van der Horst. Jour. Mam., vol.25, no.1, pp.77-82, figs. 5, Feb., 1944.

SOME REMARKS ON THE BIOLOGY OF REPRODUCTION IN THE FEMALE OF ELEPHANTULUS, THE HOLY ANIMAL OF SET. C. J. van der Horst. Trans. Roy. Soc. South Africa, Cape Town, vol.31, pt. 2, pp.181-199, figs.1-7, June, 1946.

ACUTE INHIBITION OF THE CORPUS LUTEUM EXCITED BY THE ONSET OF ANOESTRUS IN ELEPHANTULUS. C. J. van der Horst. Nature, Lond., vol.149, no. 3777, pp.329-330, illus., Mar.21, 1942.

SOME OBSERVATIONS ON THE DEVELOPMENT OF THE TOOTH IN ELEPHANTULUS MYURUS JAMESONI. Maertha Kindahl. Arkiv foer Zoologi, Stockholm, 11 (2): 21-29, Feb.5, 1958.

ON THE DEVELOPMENT OF THE TYMPANIC REGION OF THE SKULL IN THE MACROSCELIDIDAE. C. J. van der Klaauw. Proc. Zool. Soc. Lond., pp.491-560, 25 figs., 1 pl., Oct.16, 1929.

CAUDAL AND PECTORAL GLANDS OF AFRICAN ELEPHANT SHREWS (ELEPHANTULUS). Herbert Lang. Jour. Mam., vol.4, no.4, pp.261-263, Nov., 1923.

(DETERMINATION OF THE WEIGHT OF ADULT MACROSCELIDES.) Détermination du poids du Macroscelide adulte. P. Laurent. Mammalia, Paris, vol.3, no.2, pp.55-56, fig.1, June, 1939.

(THE CHROMOSOMES OF MACROSCELIDES ROZETI DUVERNOY (MAMMALIA, INSECTIVORA). DOES A SERIES OF POLYPLOIDS EXIST IN THE MACROSCELIDAE?) Les chromosomes de Macroscelides rozeti Duvernoy (Mammalia--Insectivora). Existe-t-il une serie polyploide chez les Macroscelidae? Robert Matthey. Rev. Suisse, Zool., vol.61, no.33, pp.669-677, Dec., 1954.

THE LACTATION CYCLE OF ELEPHANTULUS MYURUS JAMESONI (CHUBB). Muriel J. McKerrow. Philos. Trans. Roy. Soc. Lond., vol.238, no.653, pp.62-98, Dec., 1954.

THE MALE GENITAL SYSTEM AND REPRODUCTIVE CYCLE OF ELEPHANTULUS MYURUS JAMESONI (CHUBB). Zelda G. Stoch. Philos. Trans. Roy. Soc. Lond., vol.238, no.653, pp.99-126, Dec., 1954.

A NEW RHYNCHOCYON FROM NYASALAND. Oldfield Thomas. Ann. and Mag. Nat. Hist. (7), vol.10, no.59, pp.403-404, Nov., 1902.

DESCRIPTIONS OF TWO NEW SPECIES OF MACROSCELIDES. Oldfield Thomas. Ann. and Mag. Nat. Hist. (6), vol.13, no.73, pp. 67-70, Jan., 1894.

NOTES ON PETRODROMUS AND EHYNCHOCYON. Oldfield Thomas. Ann. and Mag. Nat. Hist. (9), vol.1, no.5, pp.364-370, May, 1918.

Soricidae

SHORTY, THE SHREW. Vernon Bailey. Nature Magazine, Washington, D.C., vol. 32, no.1, pp.12-14, illus., Jan., 1939.

SHREWS ARE SMALL AND VICIOUS BUT THEY'RE MAN'S FRIENDS. Jack H. Berryman. Utah Fish and Game Bull., Salt Lake City, vol.6, no.1, pp.6-8, illus., Sept., 1948.

(DATA ON THE BIOLOGY OF THE SORICIDAE.) Materialy do biologii Soricidae. Stanislaw Borowski, August Dehnel. Ann. Univ. Mariae Curie-Sklodowska, Lublin, vol.7, no.6, pp.305-448, Oct., 1, 1952.

(THE MASKED SHREW MOUSE, CIRCUMBOREAL SPECIES.) La musaraigne masquée, espèce circum-boréale. F. H. van den Brink. Mammalia, Paris, vol.17, no.2, pp. 96-125, illus., June, 1953.

THE HERO SHREW. Maurice Burton. Illus. London News, vol.219, no.5874, p.812, illus., Nov.17, 1951.

LIGHT ON THE LEGEND OF THE SHREW. Maurice Burton. Illus. London News, vol. 217, no.5803, p. 68, illus., July 8, 1950.

(CONTRIBUTION TO THE STUDY OF THE GENUS SOREX LINNE 1758.) Contribution à l'étude du genre Sorex Linne 1758. P. Cantuel. Mammalia, Paris, vol.14, nos.1-2, pp.14-19, Mar.-June, 1950.

(SORICIDAE WITH PIGMENTED TEETH.) Les Soricidés à dente pigmentées. P. Cantuel. Mammalia, Paris, vol.12, no.4, pp.152-154, fig.1, Dec., 1948.

A CONTRIBUTION ON THE LIFE HISTORY OF THE WATER SHREW (SOREX PALUSTRIS NAVIGATOR BAIRD). Clinton H. Conaway. MA Thesis, Mont. State Univ., 1949.

LIFE HISTORY OF THE WATER SHREW (SOREX PALUSTRIS NAVIGATOR). Clinton H. Conaway. Amer. Midland Nat., Notre Dame, vol.48, no.1, pp.219-248, July, 1952.

NOTES ON THE LIFE-HISTORY OF THE LITTLE SHORT-TAILED SHREW. William B. Davis, Leonard Joeris. Jour. Mam., vol. 26, no.2, pp.136-138, July 15, 1945.

NOTES ON THE WATER SHREW. Fred Dean. Naturalist, London, no.829, pp.75-76, Apr.-June, 1949.

(CONCERNING SUNCUS ETRUSCUS.) A propos de la Pachyure étrusque. Ed Dechambre. Mammalia, Paris, vol.3, no. 1, pp.17-18, Mar., 1939.

STUDIES ON THE GENUS SOREX L. August Dehnel. Ann. Universitatis Mariae Curie-Sklodowska, vol.4, no.2, sec.C, 1949.

NOTES ON A NORTHERN SHORT-TAILED SHREW. Richard A. Edgren, Jr. Nat. Hist. Miscellanea, Chicago, no.25, pp.2, Sept. 25, 1948.

(CONTRIBUTION TO THE QUESTION OF GEOGRAPHICAL RACES OF THE COMMON WOOD SHREW MOUSE (SOREX ARANEUS L.) IN SLOVAKIA AND COMMENTS TO ITS ECOLOGY.) Prispevok k otázke geografiskych rás piskora obyčajného (Sorex araneus L.) na Slovensku a poznámky k jeho ekologii. O. Ferianc. Věstnik Československé Zool. Společnosti, Acta Soc. Zool., vol.16, nos.3-4, pp.218-236, 1952.

AN UNUSUAL ABUNDANCE OF SHORT-TAILED SHREWS, BLARINA BREVICAUDA. C. David Fowle, R. Y. Edwards. Jour. Mam. 36 (1): 36-41, Feb., 1955.

THE TAMING OF A SHREW. George C. Goodwin. Nat. Hist., New York, vol.49, no.5, pp.282-285, illus., May, 1942.

APPEAL FOR THE COLLECTION OF SHREWS. Morris M. Green. Jour. Mam., vol.12, no.2, pp.186-187, May, 1931.

(THE WATER SHREW (NEOMYS FODIENS).) Die Wasserspitzmaus (Neomys fodiens). M. Grueber. Blaetter fuer Aquarienund Terrarienkunde, Jahrg.35, no.2, pp.40-41, Feb., 1924.

THE BIOLOGY OF THE LITTLE SHORT-TAILED SHREW, CRYPTOTIS PARVA. W. J. Hamilton, Jr. Jour. Mam., vol.25, no.1, pp.1-7, pl.1, Feb.15, 1944.

THE BIOLOGY OF THE SMOKY SHREW (SOREX FUMEUS FUMEUS MILLER). W. J. Hamilton, Jr. Zoologica, Sci. Contrib. New York Zool. Soc., New York, vol.25, pt.4, no.29, pp.473-492, figs.8, Dec.31, 1940.

(THE GEOGRAPHICAL VARIABILITY OF DIPLOMESODON PULCHELLUM LICHT.) Sur la variabilité géographique de Diplomesodon pulchellum Licht. V. G. Heptner. Bull. Soc. Nat. Moscou, Sect. Biol., vol. 47, no.2, pp.165-166, 1938.

THE TURKESTAN DESERT SHREW, ITS BIOLOGY AND ADAPTIVE PECULIARITIES. V. G. Heptner. Jour. Mam., vol.20, no.2, pp.139-149, figs.5, May 14, 1939.

SHREW LORE. Phyllis Kelway. Discovery, London, vol.18, no.215, pp.332-334, Nov., 1937.

THE WATER SHREW. Phyllis Kelway. Game and Gun and the Angler's Monthly, London, vol.17, no.172, pp.26-29, Jan., 1940.

PRESENTING BLARINA. A. Brooker Klugh. Nature Magazine, vol.15, no.4, pp.241-243, figs.3, Apr., 1930.

ANALYSIS OF THE PULAWY POPULATION OF SOREX ARANEUS ARANEUS L. AND SOREX MINUTUS MINUTUS L. Jerzy Kubick. Ann. Univ. Mariae Curie-Sklodowska, vol. 5, no.11, pp.335-372, Oct.5, 1951.

CONTRIBUTION TO THE BIOLOGY OF THE COMMON SHREW. N. P. Lavrov. Zool. Jour. USSR, Moscow, vol.22, no.6, pp.361-365, tables 3, 1943.

(OBSERVATIONS ON A CAPTIVE WATER SHREW (NEOMYS FODIENS SCHREBER).) Beobachtungen an einer gefangenen Wasserspitzmaus (Neomys fodiens (Schreber). Wolfgang Luther. Zool. Garten, N.F., Leipzig, vol.8, nos.10-12, pp.303-307, Sept., 1936.

OBSERVATIONS ON THE GREY MUSK SHREW. C. McCann. Jour. Bombay Nat. Hist. Soc., vol.39, no.2, p.380, Apr.15, 1937.

TIGER OF THE GRASS ROOTS. Tom McHugh. Nat. Hist., New York, vol.59, no.9, pp.400-401, Nov., 1950.

(ZOOLOGICAL CONCEPTS: SORICIDS.) Zoologische-Begriffe: Spitzmause. Paul Matschie. Handworterbuch der Zoologie, Anthropologie und Ethnologie, Breslau, Lief., vol.7 (Encyklopaedie der Naturwissenschaften, Abt., Lief.), pp.366-368, 1895.

A WATER SHREW. H. G. Maurice. Jour. Soc. Preservation Fauna Empire, Hertford, n.s., pt.46, pp.25-27, Dec., 1942.

A CONTRIBUTION TO THE BIOLOGY OF THE COMMON SHREW, SOREX ARANEUS LINNAEUS. A. D. Middleton. Proc. Zool. Soc. Lond., pt.1, pp.133-143, figs.4, Apr., 1931.

A CONTRIBUTION TO THE NATURAL HISTORY OF THE FLORIDA SHORT-TAILED SHREW. Joseph C. Moore. Proc. Florida Acad. Sci., vol.6, nos.3-4, pp. 155-166, Dec., 1943.

THE METABOLISM OF A VERY SMALL MAMMAL. Peter R. Morrison, Oliver P. Pearson. Science, Lancaster, vol.104, no. 2700, pp.287-289, Sept.27, 1946.

(DATA ON THE SYSTEMATICS, MORPHOLOGY, AND GEOGRAPHICAL DISTRIBUTION OF THE SORICIDS.) Materialien zur Systematik, Morphologie und Geographischen Verbreitung der Soriciden. S. Ognev. Zoologitscheskij Journal (Vormals "Revue Zool. Russe"), Moskau, vol.12, pt. 4, pp.8-16, 1933.

(DATA ON THE TAXONOMY, MORPHOLOGY AND ZOOGEOGRAPHY OF PALAEARCTIC SHREWS.) Materialien zur Systematik, morphologie und Zoogeographie der palaearktischen Spitzmaeuse. S. Ognev. Zool. Anzeiger, Leipzig, vol.105, nos.3-4, pp. 77-85, Dec.15, 1933.

SHREWS. Oliver P. Pearson. Scientific American, New York, vol.191, no.2, pp. 66-68, 70, Aug., 1954.

SUNCUS MURINUS, A RECENT INTRODUCTION TO GUAM. George D. Peterson. Jour. Mam., 37 (2): 278-279, June 9, 1956.

THE SHREWS. Richard Stuart Phillips. Field and Stream, New York, vol.62, no. 12, pp.167-169, illus., Apr., 1948.

THE BROWN SHREW. H. H. Pittman. Nature Mag., Washington, vol.42, no.3, pp.125-126, illus., Mar., 1949.

NEWS AND VIEWS ON SHREWS. Ralph Pogue. Missouri Conservationist, Jefferson City, vol.11, no.11, pp.13-14, illus., Nov., 1950.

A SURVEY OF THE MAMMALIAN FAMILY SORICIDAE (SHREWS). William Pruitt, Jr. Saeugetierk, Mitteil., 5 (1): 18-27, Jan.1, 1957.

SHREWS, ANCIENT AND MODERN. W. P. Pycraft. Illus. London News, vol.194, no. 5204, p.63, figs.4, Jan.14, 1939.

LOCOMOTION AND APPENDICULAR ANATOMY IN THREE SORICOID INSECTIVORES. Charles A. Reed. Amer. Midland Nat., Notre Dame, vol.45, no.3, pp.513-671, illus., May, 1951.

(ON THE GEOGRAPHICAL DISTRIBUTION OF SUNCUS ETRUSEUS.) Sur la repartition géographique de la Pachyure etrusque. P. Rode. Bull. Soc. Zool. France, vol.63, no. 1, pp.20-23, 1938.

POPULATION VARIATION AND HYBRIDIZATION IN SOME CALIFORNIA SHREWS. Robert L. Rudd. Systematic Zool. Wash., vol.4, no.1, pp.21-34, Mar., 1955.

NOTES ON THE WATER SHREW. F. E. Sawyer. Jour. Soc. Preservation Fauna Empire, Hertford, pt.L, pp.47-48, Dec., 1944.

(DATA ON THE WATER SHREW (NEOMYS FODIENS PALL.) Einiges ueber die Wasserspitzmaus (Neomys fodiens Pall.) Wilhelm Schreitmueller. Zeitschr. Saeugetierk., Berlin, vol.17, no.3, pp.149-151, Feb.19, 1953.

(THE WATER SHREW.) Die Wasserspitzmaus. Heinrich Schuetz. Kosmos, handweiser fuer Naturfreunde (Gesell. der Naturfreunde), Stuttgart, Jahrg., no.3, pp. 83-86, fig.1, Mar., 1932.

SHORT-TAILED SHREW. Charles Schwartz, Elizabeth Schwartz. Mo. Cons. 14 (8): 15-17, illus., Aug., 1953.

MORPHOLOGICAL AND ECOLOGICAL INVESTIGATIONS ON POLISH SPECIES OF THE GENUS SOREX L. (INSECTIVORA, SORICIDAE). Wlodzimierz Serafinski. Acta Theriologica, Inst. Zool. Polska Akad. Nauk, Warsaw, vol.1, no.3, pp.27-86, Mar.30, 1955.

SHREWS ARE LIKE THAT. George Smokey. South Dakota Conserv. Digest, Pierre, vol. 11, no.3, pp.7, 11, Mar., 1944.

ON CROCIDURA MINUTA OTTEN AND SUNCUS MURINA LINNAEUS. H. J. V. Sody. Mededeeligen van den Dienst der Volksgezondheit in Ned.-Indie, pt.22, Anno 1932, pp. 37-40, 1932.

ON CROCIDURA MINUTA AND SUNCUS MURINA. H. J. V. Sody. Mededeelingen van den Dienst der Volksgezondheit in Ned.-Indie Aftevering 1, pp.13-16, 1933.

THE LOWLY SHREWS, DIMINUTIVE CREATURES OF THE SURFACE-STRATUM. T. Surber. Conservation Volunteer, St. Paul, vol.5, no.30, pp.32-35, Mar., 1943.

THE MOUNTAIN WATER SHREW. Arthur Svihla. The Murrelet, vol.15, no.2, pp.44-45, May, 1934.

(CONTRIBUTIONS TO THE BIOLOGY OF CROCIDURA LEUCODON (HERM).) Beiträge zur Biologie von Crocidura leucodon (Herm.). A. Wahlstrom. Zeits. f. Saeugetierkunde, 4:157-185, 1928.

(CONTRIBUTIONS TO THE BIOLOGY OF SOREX VULGARIS L.) Beitraege zur Biologie von Sorex vulgaris L. A. Wahlstrom. Zeitsch. f. Saeugetierkunde, vol.3, pp.284-294, June 11, 1928.

SHREWS IS SHREWS. Ernest P. Walker. Nature Mag., Washington, vol.47, no.3, pp.125-128, Mar., 1954.

THE SHREW'S PLACE IN THE WORLD. National Nature News, Washington, D.C., vol.2, no.17, p.4, Apr.25, 1938.

Africa

A NEW SHREW FROM NORTHERN RHODESIA. Edgar N. Barclay. Ann. and Mag. Nat. Hist., ser.10, vol.10, no.58, p.440, Oct., 1932.

ON THE GENUS MYOSOREX, WITH DESCRIPTION OF A NEW SPECIES FROM THE RIO DEL REY (CAMEROONS) DISTRICT. G. E. Dobson. Proc. Zool. Soc. Lond., pp. 575-578, illus., Nov.15, 1887.

(DIAGNOSIS OF UNDESCRIBED CROCIDURA OF WESTERN AFRICA.) Diagnoses de Crocidura inedites d'Afrique Occidentale. H. Heim de Balsac. Mammalia, 20 (2): 131-139, illus., June, 1956.

(INSECTIVORE SORICIDAE OF MONT CAMEROUN.) Insectivores Soricidae du Mont Cameroun. H. Heim de Balsac. Zool. Jahrb., 85 (6): 607-618, Dec.18, 1957.

(INSECTIVORES OF THE FAMILY OF SORICIDAE OF EAST AFRICA.) Insectivores de la famille des Soricidae de l'Afrique orientale. H. Heim de Balsac. Zool. Anzeiger, 158 (7-8): 143-153, Apr., 1957.

THREE NEW AFRICAN SHREWS OF THE GENUS CROCIDURA. N. Hollister. Smithsonian Misc. Coll., vol.66, no.8, pp.1-3, May 22, 1916.

SHREWS COLLECTED BY THE CONGO EXPEDITION OF THE AMERICAN MUSEUM. N. Hollister. Bull. Amer. Mus. Nat. Hist., New York, vol.35, art.35, pp.663-680, pls. 7-11, Oct.21, 1916.

(EVOLUTION AND PHYLOGENY OF AFRICAN SORICIDS.) Evolution et phylogénie des soricidés africains. M. Lamotte. 1957.

THE GENERA OF AFRICAN SHREWS. J. Meester. Ann. Transvaal Mus., vol.22, pt.2, pp.205-213, Nov.25, 1953.

(DESCRIPTION OF A NEW SHREW OF THE GENUS "CROCIDURA" WAGLER FROM THE RIO DE ORO.) Descripción de un nuevo sorícido del género "Crocidura" Wagler procedente del Rio de Oro. Agacino E. Morales. Bol. Soc. Española Hist. Nat., Madrid, vol.34, pp.93-95, fig.1, 1934.

SUNCUS ETRUSCUS (SAVI) IN AFRICA. T. C. S. Morrison-Scott. Mammalia, Paris, vol.10, nos.3-4, p.145, Sept.-Dec., 1946 (issued in 1947).

TWO NEW AFRICAN SHREWS. Wilfred H. Osgood. Ann. and Mag. Nat. Hist., Lond., ser.8, vol.5, pp.369-370, Apr., 1910.

NOTE ON CROCIDURA DENTI ST. L. J. St. Leger. Ann. and Mag. Nat. Hist., Lond., ser.10, vol.10, no.59, p.487, Nov., 1932.

ON A NEW SPECIES OF SHREW FROM MERIFANO, EAST AFRICA. J. St. Leger. Ann. and Mag. Nat. Hist., Lond., ser.10, vol.13, no.77, pp.559-560, May, 1934.

DESCRIPTION OF FIVE NEW AFRICAN SHREWS. Oldfield Thomas. Ann. and Mag. Nat. Hist. (6), vol.16, no.91, p.51-55, July, 1895.

ON SHREWS OF BRITISH EAST AFRICA. Oldfield Thomas. Ann. and Mag. Nat. Hist. (7), vol.14, no.81, pp.236-241, Sept., 1904.

Age, Longevity

ON THE LIFE SPAN OF THE COMMON SHREW (SOREX ARANEUS L.). Peter Crowcroft. Proc. Zool. Soc. Lond., 127(2): 285-292, Oct.29, 1956.

(GREAT AGE IN A EUROPEAN FIELD SHREW (CROCIDURA L. LEUCODON HERMANN 1780.) Hohes Alter bei der europaeischen Feldspitzmaus, Crocidura l. leucodon (Hermann, 1780). Fritz Frank. Saeugetierk, Mitteil., Stuttgart, 4 (1): 31, Jan.1, 1956.

LONGEVITY OF THE SHORT-TAILED SHREW. Oliver P. Pearson. Amer. Midland Nat., Notre Dame, vol.34, no.2, pp. 531-546, Sept., 1945.

AGING IN THE MASKED SHREW, SOREX CINEREUS CINEREUS KERR. William C. Pruitt. Jour. Mam., vol.35, no.1, pp.35-39, Feb.10, 1954.

AGE, SEX, AND WEIGHT COMPARISONS IN THREE SPECIES OF SHREWS. Robert L. Rudd. J. Mamm. 36 (3): 323-339, illus., Aug., 1955.

Anatomy

THE SKELETAL CHARACTERS OF SCUTISOREX THOMAS. J. A. Allen. Bull. Amer. Mus. Nat. Hist., vol.37, no. 28, pp.769-784, Nov.26, 1917.

(ON DETERMINATION OF SPECIES AND SEX BY THE PELVIS OF GERMAN SHREWS (SORICIDAE). Ueber Art-und Geschlechtsunterschiede am Becken einheimischer Spitzmaeuse (Soricidae). Kurt Becker. Zeitschr. Saeugetierk., Berlin, vol.20, no.2-3, pp. 78-88, illus., Aug.3, 1955.

ANATOMICAL AND HISTOLOGICAL STUDIES OF AN INTERSEXUAL LESSER SHREW (SOREX MINUTUS L.), WITH SPECIAL REFERENCE TO THE EFFECTS OF THE MALE HORMONES ON THE UTERUS AND VAGINA. F. Brambell, W. Rogers, Kathleen Hall. Jour. Anat., Cambridge, vol.70, pt.3, pp.339-348, pls.4, Apr., 1936.

THE DEVELOPMENT OF THE EMBRYONIC MEMBRANES OF THE SHREWS, SOREX ARANEUS LINN. AND SOREX MINUTUS LINN. F. Brambell, W. Rogers, J. S. Perry. Proc. Zool. Soc. Lond., vol.115, pts.1, 2, pp.251-278, figs.18, pls.9, Oct., 1945.

(ON THE OSTEOLOGY OF THE SHREWS 2: NEOMYS, BEREMENDIA, PACHYURA.) Zur Osteologie der Spitzmaeuse 2: Neomys, Beremendia, Pachyura. Georg Brunner. Zeitschr. Saeugetierk., vol.17, no.2, pp. 93-101, illus., Feb.19, 1953.

(INVESTIGATION OF THE SEASONAL VARIABILITY OF THE BRAIN OF THE SMALL SHREW (SOREX MINUTUS MINUTUS L.).) Untersuchungen ueber die saisonale Veraenderlichkeit des Gehirnes beider kleinen Spitzmaus (Sorex minutus minutus L.). Krystyna Cabon. Ann. Univ. Mariae Curie Sklodowska, Lublin, sec.C, 10 (5): 93-115, July, 1956.

THE OUTER EAR OF BLARINA BREVICAUDA. Elliott Coues. Amer. Jour. Otology., vol.1, pp.3-4, July, 1879.

(SEASONAL VARIABILITY OF THE THYROID GLAND IN THE WATER SHREW NEOMYS FODIENS SCHREB.) Die saisonale Veraenderlichkeit der Schilddruese bei der Wasserspitzmaus (Neomys fodiens Schreb.). Irena Dzierzykraj-Rogalska. Ann. Univ. Mariae Curie-Sklodowska, Lublin, sec.C, 10 (12): 295-310, Mar.15, 1957.

THE DERMAL GLANDS OF SHREWS. W. Robert Eadie. Jour. Mam., vol.19, no.2, pp.171-174, fig.1, May 14, 1938.

THE TEMPOROMANDIBULAR JOINT OF SHREWS. R. W. Fearnhead, C.C.D. Shute, A.d'A Bellairs. Proc. Zool. Soc. Lond., vol.125, pts.3-4, pp.795-806, 1 pl., Nov. 23, 1955.

THE FUNCTIONAL ANATOMY OF THE PENIS OF THE SHREW. R. H. Gibbs. Anat. Record, Philadelphia, vol.121, no.2, pp. 298-299, Feb., 1955.

EXTRA TEETH IN A SHREW. Emmett T. Hooper. Jour. Mam., vol.27, no.4, p.394, Nov.25, 1946.

A COMPARATIVE STUDY OF CERTAIN TRIGEMINAL COMPONENTS IN TWO SORICID SHREWS, BLARINA BREVICAUDA AND SOREX CINEREUS. J. B. Hyde. Jour. Comp. Neurol., Philadelphia, 107 (3): 339-352, June, 1957.

ON THE DENTITION AND OTHER CHARACTERS OF THE BRITISH SHREWS, WITH REFERENCE TO M. DUVERNOY'S RECENT RESEARCHES INTO THE STRUCTURE OF THIS GENUS OF ANIMALS. Leonard Jenyns. Mag. of Zool. and Bot., vol.2, pp.24-42, pl. 1, 1838.

A DENTAL ABNORMALITY IN THE SHREW, CROCIDURA LASIURA. J. Knox Jones, Jr. Trans. Kansas Acad. Sci., vol.60, no.1, pp.88-89, illus., 1957.

THE OCCURRENCE OF CERTAIN FORAMINA IN THE FRONTAL BONES OF SHREWS (SORICIDAE). Stuart O. Landry, Jr. Ann. and Mag. Nat. Hist., ser.12, vol. 10, pp.17-24, Jan., 1957.

(WEIGHT OF THE WOOD SHREW (SOREX ARANEUS LINNE 1758) DURING THE COURSE OF THE YEAR.) Das Gewicht der Waldspitzmaus, Sorex araneus Linne, 1758, im Jahreslauf. Jochen Niethammer. Saeugetierk. Mitteil., 4 (4): 160-165, Oct. 1, 1956.

BRONCHIAL DIVERTICULA IN BLARINA BREVICUADA. Wesley W. Parke. Jour. Mam., 37 (2): 236-245, illus., June 9, 1956.

SCENT GLANDS OF THE SHORT-TAILED SHREW. Oliver P. Pearson. Anatomical Record 94 (4): 615-629, Apr., 1946.

(INVESTIGATIONS OF THE VARIABILITY OF THE SKULL IN THE LIFE CYCLE OF SOREX ARANEUS ARANEUS L.) Untersuchungen ueber die Veraenderlichkeit des Schaedels im Lebenszyklus von Sorex araneus araneus L. Zdzislaw Pucek. Ann. Univ. Mariae Curie-Sklodowska, Lublin, sec.C, 9 (4): 163-205, Oct.4, 1955.

SOME REMARKABLE BACKBONES. W. P. Pycraft. Illus. London News, vol.182, no. 4898, p.320, illus., Mar.4, 1933.

UNILATERAL DISPLACEMENT OF THE INNOMINATE BONE IN SOREX. Charles A. Reed. Jour. Mam., vol.24, no.3, pp.396-397, fig.1, Aug.17, 1943.

ORGANIZATION OF THE CEREBRAL CORTEX. III. THE CORTEX OF SOREX PACIFICUS. M. Ryzen, B. Campbell. Jour. Comp. Neurology, Philadelphia, vol.102, no.2, pp. 365-424, Apr., 1955.

EARLY DEVELOPMENT AND PLACENTATION OF THE INDIAN MUSK-SHREW (CROCIDURA CAERULEA). G. S. Sansom. Bio-Morphosis, Leipzig, vol.1, nos.3-4, pp.321-322, 1938.

THE PLACENTATION OF THE INDIAN MUSK-SHREW (CROCIDURA CAERULEA). G. S. Sansom. Trans. Zool. Soc. Lond., vol.23, pt.5, pp.267-314, pls.20-32, Dec., 1937.

THE CAUDAL AND PERINEAL MUSCULATURE OF THE HOUSE SHREW SUNCUS MURINUS LINN. D. R. Sharma. Ann. and Mag. Nat. Hist., ser.12, 10 (118): 713-718, Oct., 1957.

THE PLACENTATION OF THE AMERICAN SHREWS, BLARINA BREVICAUDA AND SOREX FUMEUS. William A. Wimsatt, George B. Wislocki. Amer. Jour. Anat., Philadelphia, vol.80, no.3, pp.361-435, figs.54, May, 1947.

CHEMICAL CYTOLOGY OF THE PLACENTA OF TWO NORTH AMERICAN SHREWS (BLARINA BREVICAUDA AND SOREX FUMEUS). George B. Wislocki, William A. Wimsatt. Amer. Jour. Anat., Philadelphia, vol.8, no.2, pp.269-296, pls.5, 1947.

(THE DEVELOPMENT OF THE SEX ORGANS IN THE LIFE CYCLE OF SOREX ARANEUS.) Rozwoj aparatu plciowego w cyklu zyciowym Sorex araneus L. Janina Wolska. Ann. Univ. Mariae Curie-Sklodowska, Lublin, vol.7, no. 8, pp.497-539, Oct.20, 1952.

Asia

ON THE SPECIES AND DENTITION OF THE SOUTHERN ASIATIC SHREWS, PRELIMINARY TO A MONOGRAPH OF THE GROUP. John Anderson. Proc. Zool. Soc. Lond., pp.227-238, 1873.

NEOMYS FODIENS BRACHYOTIS OGNEV IN THE MARITIME PROVINCE OF THE FAR EASTERN REGION. A. A. Emelianof. Bull. Far. Eastern Branch Acad. Sci. USSR., Vladivostok, no.22, p.120, 1937.

A NEW SPECIES OF SHREW FROM EASTERN SIBERIA. George G. Goodwin. Amer. Mus. Novitates no.657, pp.2, Sept. 8, 1933.

SOME MALAYAN SHREWS. J. L. Harrison. Malayan Nature Jour., vol.5, no.1, pp.21-24, Illus., Mar., 1950.

A NEW WHITE-TOOTHED SHREW FROM FUKIEN, CHINA. A. Brazier Howell. Jour. Mam., vol.9, no.1, p.60, Feb.9, 1928.

NEW SPECIES AND SUBSPECIES OF SOREX FROM JAPAN (MAMMALIA: INSECTIVORA). Yoshinori Imaizumi. Bull. Nat. Sci. Mus. Tokyo, n.s., vol.1, no.2, (no.35), pp.94-102, illus., Sept., 1954.

NOTES ON SOREX HAWKERI TSCHERSKII OGNEV FROM SOUTH SAKHALIN. Yoshinori Imaizumi. Trans. Mam. Soc. Japan, no.9, pp.73-75, illus., Apr., 1954.

TWO UNDESCRIBED SHREWS FROM MOUNT PANGERANGO, JAVA. F. A. Jentink. Notes Leyden Mus., vol.32, pp.197-198, July, 1910.

ON A NEW SHREW FROM THE INDIAN ARCHIPELAGO. F. A. Jentink. Notes Leyden Mus., vol.11, no.41, pp.213-214, Aug., 1889.

ON TWO NEW PYGMY SHREWS FROM THE MALAY PENINSULA. C. Boden Kloss. Jour. Fed. Malay States Mus., vol.7, pt. 3, pp.127-128, Sept., 1917.

(THE SORICIDS OF THE ZOOLOGICAL MUSEUM IN BUITENZORG, JAVA.) Die Soriciden des zoologischen Museums in Buitenzorg auf Java. Otto Koller. Treubia, vol.11, no.3, pp.313-324, Feb., 1930.

ON THE SYNONYMY OF THE NORTH KOREAN MUSK-SHREW. Nagamichi Kuroda. Dobutsugaku Zasshi, Zool. Soc. Japan, Tokyo, vol.47, p.327, May 15, 1935.

SCIENTIFIC RESULTS FROM THE MAMMAL SURVEY. NO.48. INDIAN SHREWS. Helen M. Lindsay. Journ. Bombay Nat. Hist. Soc., vol.33, no.2, pp.326-340, Feb.15, 1929.

DESCRIPTIONS OF THREE NEW ASIATIC SHREWS. Gerrit S. Miller, Jr. Proc. Biol.

Soc. Washington, vol.14, pp.157-159, Aug. 9, 1901.

A NEW SHREW FROM BALTISTAN. Gerrit S. Miller, Jr. Proc. Biol. Soc. Washington, vol.26, pp.113-114, May 3, 1913.

A NEW SHREW FROM EASTERN TURKESTAN. Gerrit S. Miller. Proc. Washington Acad. Sci., vol.2, pp.39-40, Mar.30, 1900.

TWO NEW SHREWS FROM KASHMIR. Gerrit S. Miller, Jr. Proc. Biol. Soc., Washington, vol.24, pp.241-242, Nov.28, 1911.

ADDITIONS TO THE FAUNA OF CEYLON. NO.3. A NEW PIGMY SHREW FROM THE MOUNTAINS OF CENTRAL CEYLON. W. W. A. Phillips. Ceylon Jour. Sci., Sect.B., Zool. and Geol. Spolia Zeylanica, vol.17, pt.2, pp.123-126, fig.1, pl.27, Nov.3, 1932.

CEYLON SHREWS. W. W. A. Phillips. Ceylon Jour. Sci., Section B.-Zool. and Geol., Spolia Zeylanica, vol.14, pt.2, pp. 295-332, pls.19-20, Mar.12, 1928.

NEW AND RARE CEYLON SHREWS. W. W. A. Phillips. Ceylon Jour. Sci., Sect.B., Zool. and Geol. Spolia Zeylanica, vol.15, no.2, pp.113-118, figs.3, May 20, 1929.

A NEW SPECIES OF SHREW FROM THE SHANGHAI AREA. Arthur de Carle Sowerby. Musee Heude, Notes de Mammalogie, no.3, pp.2, Apr.1, 1945.

ON A NEW SPECIES OF SHREW FROM KOREA. Arthur de Carle Sowerby. Ann. and Mag. Nat. Hist., London, ser.8, vol. 20, pp.317-319, Oct., 1917.

DESCRIPTION OF A NEW SPECIES OF SOREX FROM INDIA. R. Templeton. Proc. Zool. Soc. Lond., pt.21, p.100, 1853.

A NEW GENUS AND SPECIES OF SHREW FROM CEYLON. Oldfield Thomas. Spolia Zeylanica, vol.13, pp.93-95, Sept. 16, 1924.

A NEW SHREW FROM THE ANDAMAN ISLANDS. Oldfield Thomas. Ann. and Mag. Nat. Hist. (8), vol.11, no.65, pp.468-469, May, 1913.

A NEW SHREW OF THE GENUS BLARINELLA FROM UPPER BURMA. Oldfield Thomas. Ann. and Mag. Nat. Hist. (8), vol.15, no. 87, pp.335-336, Mar., 1915.

A NEW SORICULUS FROM MISHMI HILLS. Oldfield Thomas. Jour. Bombay Nat. Hist. Soc., vol.22, no.4, p.683, Mar.31, 1914.

ON A MINUTE SHREW FROM LAKE BAIKAL. Oldfield Thomas. Ann. and Mag. Nat. Hist. (8), vol.15, no.89, pp.499-500, May, 1915.

THE WHITE-TOOTHED SHREW OF PALESTINE. Oldfield Thomas. Ann. and Mag. Nat. Hist. (9), vol.3, no.13, p.32, Jan., 1919.

Diseases and Parasites

A NEW NEMATODE, LONGISTRIATA CAUDABULLATA, N. SP. (NEMATODA: VIANAIINAE), FROM THE SHORT-TAILED SHREW, BLARINA BREVICAUDA. G. Dikmans. Proc. Helminth. Soc. Wash., 13 (1): 14-16, Jan., 1946.

MYONYSSUS JAMESONI, A NEW LIPONYSSID MITE (ACARINA: LAELAPTIDAE) FROM BLARINA BREVICAUDA (SAY). H. E. Ewing, Edward W. Baker. J. Parasitology 33(4): 376-379, Aug., 1947.

A NEW SPECIES OF TICK FOUND ON SHREWS. J. D. Gregson. Can. Ent. 74(8): 137-139, Aug., 1942.

THE EXTERNAL PARASITES OF THE SHORT-TAILED SHREW, BLARINA BREVICAUDA (SAY). E. W. Jameson, Jr. Jour. Mam., vol.31, no.2, pp.138-145, illus., May 25, 1950.

MYOBIID MITES (ACARINA: MYOBIIDAE) FROM SHREWS (MAMMALIA: SORICIDAE) OF EASTERN NORTH AMERICA. E. W. Jameson, Jr. Jour. Parasitol., Lancaster, vol.34, no.4, pp.336-342, Aug., 1948.

DIORCHIS REYNOLDSI N. SP., A HYMENOLEPIDID CESTODE FROM THE SHREW. Arthur W. Jones. Trans. Am. Micros. Soc. 63 (1): 46-49, Jan., 1944.

PROTOGYNELLA BLARINAE N.G., N. SP., A NEW CESTODE FROM THE SHREW, BLARINA BREVICAUDA SAY. Arthur W. Jones. Trans. Am. Micros. Soc. 62 (2): 169-173, Apr., 1943.

TULAREMIA: SPONTANEOUS OCCURRENCE IN SHREWS. Glen M. Kohls. U.S. Public Health Repts., Washington, D.C., vol.58, no.22, p.842, May 28, 1943.

SOME CESTODES FROM OREGON SHREWS, WITH DESCRIPTIONS OF FOUR NEW SPECIES OF HYMENOLEPIS WEINLAND, 1858. Betty Locker, Robert Rausch. J. Wash. Acad. Sci. 42 (1): 26-31, illus., Jan., 1952.

Europe

NOTES ON SUBSPECIES OF EUROPEAN SHREWS (SOREX AND NEOMYS). G.E.H. Barrett-Hamilton. Ann. and Mag. Nat. Hist., ser.7, vol.15, pp.505-508, 1905.

SHREWS (CROCIDURA CASSITERIDUM) ON THE SCILLY ISLES. Y. Spencer Booth. Proc. Zool. Soc. Lond., vol.126, pt.1, pp. 167-170, Jan.11, 1956.

(THE ALPINE SHREW (SOREX ALPINUS SCHINZ 1837) FROM THE LOWER AREA IN THE BORDER REGION OF THE BAVARIAN FOREST.) Die Alpenspitzmaus (Sorex alpinus schinz, 1837) aus niedriger Hoehenlage im Randgebiet des Bayerischen Waldes. Elmar Bothschafter. Saeugetierk. Mitteil., 5 (1): 28-30, Jan.1, 1957.

(A NEW SHREWMOUSE IN THE NETHERLANDS.) Une nouvelle Musaraigne dans les Pays-Bas. F. H. van den Brink. Proc. Roy. Netherlands Acad. Sci., Amsterdam, ser.C, 55, no.4, pp.370-374, 1952.

(THE SMALLEST MAMMAL OF EUROPE.) Le plus petit mammifère d'Europe. J. de la Cerisaie. La Nature, Paris, no.3025, p. 322, illus., May 15, 1938.

(TWO NEW SMALL VERTEBRATES OF SWITZERLAND (SOREX PYGMAEUS). SEVERAL INTERESTING VARIETIES.) Deux petits vertébrés nouveaux pour la Suisse. (Sorex pygmaeus Pall. et Rana graeca Boul.) Quelques interessantes varietes. Victor Fatio. Rev. Suisse Zool. (Ann. Soc. Zool. Suisse et Mus. Hist. Nat. Genève) vol.8, no.3, pp.467-476, 1900.

ON A NEW SPECIES OF CROCIDURA FROM SICILY. Martin A. C. Hinton. Ann. and Mag. Nat. Hist., ser.9, vol.14, pp.509-510, Oct., 1924.

(THE SHREW SUNCUS ETRUSCUS SAVI 1832 ON CORSICA AND ITS CIRCUM-MEDITERRANEAN DISTRIBUTION.) Die Wimperspitzmaus, Suncus etruscus (Savi, 1832), auf der Insel Korsika und ihre circummediterrane Verbreitung. Herman Kahmann, Helmut Altner. Saeugetierk. Mitteil., Stuttgart, 4 (2): 72-81, Apr.1, 1956.

(THE SHREW-MOUSE OF CORSICA.) La musaraigne de Corse. Herman Kahmann, Elizabeth Kahmann. Mammalia, Paris, vol.18, no.2, pp.129-158, illus., June, 1954.

(THE PEARL-TOOTHED SHREW (SOREX MARGARITODON KORM.) AND THE ADAPTATION PROBLEM.) Die perlzaehnige Spitzmaus (Sorex margaritodon Korm.) und das Anpassungs-problem. Th. Kormos. Allattani Koezlemenyek, Budapest, vol.32, nos.1-2, pp.61-79, figs.3, Apr.20, 1935.

(SOREX ALPINUS HERCYNICUS MELL. IN PRUSSIAN UPPER LUSATIA .) Sorex alpinus hercynicus Mell. in der preussischen Oberlausitz. Herbert Kramer. Zool. Anzeiger, vol.73, p.244, 1 fig., Sept.20, 1927.

(CONTRIBUTIONS TO THE KNOWLEDGE OF MAMMALS (SHREWS) OF JESENIKY MOUNTAINS.) Příspěvky k poznání ssávai zvířeny Jeseníkü. J. Kratochvil, Ivo Grulich. Přírodovedecky Sbornik, vol.11, nos.2, 3, pp.202-243, 1950.

(A NEW RACE OF SHREWMOUSE FROM CZECHOSLOVAKIA (SOREX, ALPINUS TATRICUS SSP. N).) Nová rasa rejska z ČSR (Sorex alpinus tatricus ssp. n.). J. Kratochvil, B. Rosicky. Věstník Československé Zool. Společnosti, Acta Soc. Zool., vol.16, nos.1-2, pp.51-65, 1952.

(IS THERE MORE THAN ONE RACE OF THE WATER-SHREW, NEOMYS FODIENS, IN THE SCANDINAVIAN COUNTRIES?) Finns det mera aen en ras av vattennaebbmusen, Neomys fodiens, i. de nordiska laenderna? Einar Lonnberg. Fauna och Flora, pp.75-79, 1934.

THE WATER SHREW (NEOMYS FODIENS) ON PLADDA ISLAND. J. M. McWilliam. Scottish Nat., no.208, pp.99-100, July-Aug., 1934.

NOTE ON A NEW SHREW FROM BOSNIA. V. Martino, E. Martino. Ann. Hist. Nat. Mus. Nat. Hungarici, Budapest, vol.27, p. 158, 1930.

(SOREX, A NEW DIURNAL ANIMAL FOUND IN NORTH SWEDEN.) Lappnaebbmusen, ett nytt daeggdjur funnet i norra Sverige. Yngve Melander. Fauna och Flora, Uppsala, haeft.5, pp.193-202, figs.4, 1941.

FIVE NEW SHREWS FROM EUROPE. Gerrit S. Miller, Jr. Proc. Biol. Soc., Wash., vol.14, pp.41-45, Apr.25, 1901.

A NEW SHREW FROM SWITZERLAND. Gerrit S. Miller, Jr. Proc. Biol. Soc., Wash., vol.14, pp.95-96, fig.1, June 27, 1901.

ON THE GUERNSEY CROCIDURA. Ivor G. S. Montagu, Grace Pickford. Proc. Zool. Soc. Lond., pp.1043-1044, Dec., 1923.

(DESCRIPTION OF TWO NEW SHREW MICE OF WESTERN FRANCE.) Description de deux muscaraignes nouvelles de France occidentale. Charles Mottaz. Bull. Soc. Zool. Geneve, vol.1, fasc.7, pp.118-120, Apr.30, 1908.

(A SHREWMOUSE NEW TO ITALY, CROCIDURA MIMULA MIMULA MILLER.) Une musaraigne nouvelle pour l'Italie, Crocidura mimula mimula Miller. Charles Mottaz. Bull. Soc. Zool. Geneve, vol.1, pp.39-40, Dec., 1907.

(ON THE OCCURRENCE OF SOREX TETRAGONURUS HERMANN IN LOIRE-INFERIEURE.) Sur la présence en Loire-Inferieure de Sorex tetragonurus Hermann. P. L. Niort. Mammalia, Paris, vol.13, nos.1-2, pp.38-48, figs.2, Mar.-June, 1949.

(DATA ON THE SYSTEMATICS, MORPHOLOGY, AND ZOOGEOGRAPHY OF THE PALAEARCTIC SHREWS.) Materialien zur Systematik, Morphologie und Zoogeographie der palaearktischen Spitzmaeuse. S. I. Ognev. Zool. Anz., vol.105, nos.3-4, pp.77-85, Dec.15, 1933.

(MAMMOLOGICAL NOTES. A SURVEY OF THE DISTRIBUTION OF THE GENUS NEOMYS IN THE UKRAINE.) Mammologische Notizen. Uebersicht der Verbreitung der Gattung Neomys in der Ukraine. I. G. Pidoplitshka. Acad. Sci. Ukraine, Mem. Cl. Sci. Phys. et Math., (Trav. Mus. Zool. no.7), vol.13, no.1, pp.65-83, pl.1, 1929.

(NEW DATA ON THE DISTRIBUTION OF DIPLOMESODON PULCHELLUM LICHT. BETWEEN THE VOLGA AND URAL (MAMMALIA, INSECTIVORA.) Neues ueber Verbreitung von Diplomesodon pulchellum Licht. zwischen den fluessen Wolga und Ural (Mammalia, Insectivora). G. Rall. Comptes Rendus (Doklady) Acad. Sci. URSS, Moscou, vol.3, (8), no.8, (68), pp.377-378, 1935.

(SOREX ALPINUS IN THE SILESIAN PLAIN.) Sorex alpinus in der schlesischen Ebene. Helmut Schaefer. Zool. Anz., vol.91, nos. 1-4, p.66, Sept.25, 1930.

MORPHOLOGICAL AND ECOLOGICAL INVESTIGATIONS ON POLISH SPECIES OF THE GENUS SOREX L. (INSECTIVORA, SORICIDAE). Wkodzimierz Serafiński. Acta Theriologica, Inst. Zool. Polska Akad. Nauk, Warsaw, vol.1, no.3, pp.27-86, Mar. 30, 1955.

(CROCIDURA MIMULA MILLER (SORICIDAE) IN POLAND.) Zebielek karliczek (Crocidura mimula Miller) w Polsce. K. Simm. Polska Akad. Umiejetnosci, Cracow, no.31, pp.1-11, Mar.19, 1952.

CROCIDURA MIMULA MIMULA G.S. MILLER (1901) IN POLAND. K. Simm. Bull. Soc. Sci. and Lettres Poznan, ser.B, vol.12, pp.189-195, 1953.

(THE WOOD SHREW (SOREX ARANEUS L.) IN ITS RELATIONSHIP TO THE FORM TETRAGONURUS HERM. IN NORTHERN AND CENTRAL EUROPE.) Die Waldspitzmaus (Sorex araneus L.) in ihrer Beziehung zur Form tetragonurus Herm. in Nord- und Mitteleuropa. Karl Zalesky. Sitzber. Oesterreichische Akad. Wissensch., Math.-Natur. Kl., Vienna, Abt. I, vol.157, nos. 6-10, pp.129-185, 1948.

Food Habits

FOOD HABITS OF THE VAGRANT SHREW. Harold E. Broadbooks. Murrelet, Seattle, vol.20, no.3, Sept.-Dec., pp.62-66, Dec. 16, 1939.

REFECTION IN THE COMMON SHREW. Peter Crowcroft. Nature 170 (4328): 627, Oct.11, 1952.

PREDATION ON SOREX BY BLARINA. W. Robert Eadie. Jour. Mam., vol.30, no.3, pp.308-309, Aug.17, 1949.

THE FOOD OF THE SORICIDAE. W. Y. Hamilton. Jour. Mam., vol.11, no.1, pp. 26-39, Feb., 1930.

FEEDING HABITS OF THE LEAST SHREW. Robert T. Hatt. Jour. Mam., vol.51, no. 2, pp.247-248, May 14, 1938.

(ON THE DIET OF SORICIDS.) Zur Nahrung der Soriciden. Werner Herold. Saeugetierk Mitteil., Stuttgart, 4 (3): 127, July 1, 1956.

SNAIL ASSOCIATES OF BLARINA BREVICAUDA TALPOIDES (SAY). William M. Ingram. Jour. Mam 23 (3): 255-256, Aug., 1942.

SHREWS AS TREE SEED EATERS IN THE DOUGLAS FIR REGION. Rudolph Kangur. Oreg. State Board For., Res. Note no.17, ii 23 p., illus., Dec., 1954.

A NOTE ON THE PREDACEOUS HABIT OF THE WATER SHREW. Ben Hur Lampman. Jour. Mam. 28 (2): 181, May, 1947.

FOOD OF THE GREY MUSK SHREW (CROCIDURA CAERULEA). W. S. Millard. Jour. Bombay Nat. Hist. Soc., vol.27, p.164, July 1, 1920.

SHREWS AS A CHECK ON DOUGLAS FIR REGENERATION. A. W. Moore. Jour. Mam. 23 (1): 37-41, Feb., 1942.

FEEDING A SHORT-TAILED SHREW. E. L. Moseley. Jour. Mam., vol.11, no.2, pp.224-225, May, 1930.

SHREW PREYING ON RIBBON SNAKE. R. A. O'Reilly. Jour. Mam., vol.30, no.3, p.309, Aug.17, 1949.

A NOTE ON THE FOOD HABITS OF CAPTIVE SHREWS, CRYPTOTIS FLORIDANA. Paul G. Pearson. Quarterly Jour. Florida Acad. Sci., vol.14, no.1, pp.49-50, Mar., 1951.

(DOES THE FOOD OF SORICIDS CONSIST EXCLUSIVELY OF ANIMAL MATERIAL?) Besteht die Nahrung der Soriciden ausschliesslich aus tierischen Stoffen? Edwin Reinwaldt. Saeugetierk. Mitteil., Stuttgart, 3 (3): 124-125, July 1, 1955.

(DESTRUCTION OF THE BLOSSOMS OF SPOTTED CUCKOOPINT (ARUM MACULATUM L.) BY WOOD SHREWS (SOREX VULGARIS L.).) Zerstoerung der Blueten des gefleckten Aronstabes (Arum maculatum L.) durch Waldspitzmaeuse (Sorex vulgaris L.). W. Schreitmuller. Zool. Anz., Leipzig, vol.111, nos.11-12, p.335, Sept.15, 1935.

(DESTRUCTION OF THE BLOSSOMS OF SPOTTED CUCKOOPINT BY WOOD SHREWS.) Zerstoerung der Blueten des gefleckten Aronstabes durch Waldspitzmaeuse Zeitschr. f. Saeugetierkunde, Berlin, vol.13, no.2, p. 338, 1939.

Fossils

PLEISTOCENE SHREWS FROM THE LARGER WESTERN MEDITERRANEAN ISLANDS. Dorthea M. A. Bate. Ann. and Mag. Nat. Hist., Lond., ser.11, vol.11, no.83, pp.738-769, figs.8, Nov., 1944.

SHREWS FROM THE PLEISTOCENE OF THE RANCHO LA BREA ASPHALT. Lawrence V. Compton. Univ. Calif. Publ., Bull. Dept. Geol. Sci., vol.24, no.5, pp.85-90, figs.2, Feb.3, 1937.

PLEISTOCENE SORICIDAE FROM SAN JOSECITO CAVE, NUEVO LEON, MEXICO. James S. Findley. Univ. Kansas Publ., Mus. Nat. Hist., Lawrence, vol.5, no.36, pp.633-639.

A NEW SHREW FROM THE UPPER PLIOCENE OF IDAHO. C. Lewis Gazin. Jour. Mam., vol.14, no.2, pp.142-144, fig.1, May, 1933.

ON A NEW INSECTIVORE FROM THE UPPER KUZUUE FORMATION IN JAPAN. Yoshikazu Hasegawa. Sci. Rept. Yokohama Nat. Univ., sec.2, 6: 65-69, 1 pl. Oct., 1957.

(THE ALGERIAN HEDGEHOG, AETHECHINUS ALGIRUS, PLIOCENE RELIC IN FRANCE.) Le hérisson d'Algérie, Aethechinus algirus, relique pliocène en France. Balsac H. de Heim. Bull. Mus. Nat. d'Hist. Nat., Paris, ser.2, vol.8, no.4, pp.322-326, June, 1936.

NOTES ON LATE CENOZOIC SHREWS. Claude W. Hibbard. Trans. Kansas Acad. Sci., 60 (4): 327-336, illus., Feb., 1958.

A NEW SHREW FROM THE NIOBRARA RIVER UPPER MIOCENE OF NEBRASKA. J. R. Macdonald. Amer. Jour. Sci., New Haven, vol.245, no.2, pp.123-126, Feb., 1947.

FOSSIL SHREWS OF SOUTH AFRICA. J. Meester. Ann. Transvaal Mus., vol.22, no.3, pp.271-278, table, Jan.24, 1955.

(ON THE PRESENCE IN THE LOWER LOIRE BEDS OF SOREX TETRAGONURUS HERMANN.) Sur la presence en Loire-Inferieure de Sorex tetragonurus Hermann. Paul-Leon Niort. Mammalia, Paris, vol.13, nos.1-2, pp.38-44, Mar.-June, 1949.

A NEW OLIGOCENE INSECTIVORE. George Gaylord Simpson. Amer. Mus. Novitates, New York, no.1150, 3 pp., 1 fig., Oct.28, 1941.

A NEW GENUS OF SORICIDAE FROM THE BARSTOW MIOCENE OF CALIFORNIA. R. A. Stirton. Univ. Calif. Pub., Bull. Dept. Geol. Sci., vol.19, no.8, pp.217-229, figs.2, May 5, 1930.

FOSSIL SHREW FOUND IN GREEN RIVER BASIN OF WESTERN WYOMING. Life, Chicago, vol.30, no.18, p.55, illus., Apr. 30, 1951.

General Habits, Behavior, Ecology

ON THE HABITS OF THE WATER-SHREW (CROSSOPUS FODIENS). N. L. Austen. Proc. Zool. Soc. Lond., pp.519-521, 1865.

NOTES ON HOME RANGES AND POPULATIONS OF THE SHORT-TAILED SHREW. W. Frank Blair. Ecology 21 (2): 284-288, Apr., 1940.

A PAIR OF LONG-TAILED SHREWS (SOREX CINEREUS CINEREUS) IN CAPTIVITY. Philip M. Blossom. Jour. Mam., vol. 13, no.2, pp.136-143, May, 1932.

NEST AND BEHAVIOR OF A SHORT-TAILED SHREW, CRYPTOTIS PARVA. Harold E. Broadbrooks. Jour. Mam., vol. 33, no.2, pp.241-243, pl.1, May 16, 1952.

NOTES ON THE ACTIVITY OF SHREWS ALONG THE YUKON RIVER. Tom Cade. Jour. Mam., vol.34, no.1, pp.120-121, Feb. 19, 1953.

THE SHORT-TAILED SHREW AS A TREE CLIMBER. T. D. Carter. Jour. Mam., vol. 17, no.3, p.285, Aug., 1936.

BEHAVIOR OF THE LEAST SHREW. E. B. Chamberlain. Jour. Mam., vol.10, no.3, pp.250-251, Aug., 1929.

THE DAILY CYCLE OF ACTIVITY IN BRITISH SHREWS. Peter Crowcroft. Proc. Zool. Soc. Lond., vol.123, pt.4, pp.715-729, illus., Feb.10, 1954.

KEEPING BRITISH SHREWS IN CAPTIVITY. Peter Crowcroft. Jour. Mam., vol.32, no. 3, pp.354-355, Aug.23, 1951.

NOTES ON THE BEHAVIOR OF SHREWS. Peter Crowcroft. Behavior 8 (1): 63-80, 1955.

NOTES ON THE LIFE HISTORY OF THE GRAY SHREW. Joseph Dixon. Jour. Mam., vol.5, no.1, pp.1-6, pl.1, Feb., 1924.

(PECULIAR SLEEPING POSITION OF A WOOD SHREW (SOREX ARANEUS L.) Eigenartige Schlafstellung einer Waldspitzmaus (Sorex araneus L.). M. Eisentraut. Zeitschr. f. Saeugetierkunde, Berlin, vol. 8, nos.3-6, pp.277-278, Dec.20, 1933.

NOTES ON SHREWS OF THE GENUS NOTIOSOREX. Harvey I. Fisher. Jour. Mam., vol. 22, no.3, pp.263-269, figs.2, pl.1, Aug.14, 1941.

"TAMING THE SHREW." Richard W. Fyfe. Blue Jay, Saskatchewan Nat. Hist. Soc., 15 (3): 120 illus., Sept., 1957.

A GRAY SHREW IN A WOOD RAT'S NEST. Frank F. Gander. Jour. Mam., vol.9, no. 3, pp.247-248, Aug., 1928.

A CONJECTURE AS TO THE HABITS OF SOME WEST AMERICAN SHREWS. Morris M. Green. Jour. Mam., vol.7, no.4, p.331, Nov., 1926.

HABITS OF CRYPTOTIS PARVA IN NEW YORK. W. J. Hamilton, Jr. Jour. Mam., vol.15, no.2, pp.154-155, May 15, 1934.

HABITS OF THE SHORT-TAILED SHREW, BLARINA BREVICAUDA (SAY). W. J. Hamilton, Jr. The Ohio Hour. Sci., Columbus, vol.31, no.2, pp.97-106, Mar., 1931.

SOME HABITS OF A GRAY SHREW IN CAPTIVITY. Laurence M. Huey. Jour. Mam., vol.17, no.2, pp.143-145, May, 1936.

COW-PASTURE NESTS OF CRYPTOTIS PARVA PARVA. Lawrence Kilham. Jour. Mam., vol.35, no.2, p.252, May 26, 1954.

MOTHER AND YOUNG OF SOREX CINEREUS FONTINALIS IN CAPTIVITY. Lawrence Kilham. Jour. Mam., vol.32, no.1, p.115, Feb.15, 1951.

NOTES ON THE HABITS OF BLARINA BREVICAUDA. A. Brooker Klugh. Jour. Mam., vol.2, no.1, p.35, Feb., 1921.

(GATHERING INSTINCT IN THE SHREW SOREX ARANEUS LINNE 1758.) Sammeltrieb bei der Waldspitzmaus, Sorex araneus Linne, 1758. H. Loehri. Saeugetierk. Mitteil., Stuttgart, 3 (4): 171, Oct.1, 1955.

ACTIVITY OF THE SHORT-TAILED SHREW. P. M. Mann, R. H. Stinson. Canadian Jour. Zool., Ottawa, 35 (2): 171-178, Apr., 1957.

KEEPING SHORT-TAILED SHREWS IN CAPTIVITY. Peter M. Mann. Jour. Mam., 37 (2): 274-275, June 9, 1957.

OBSERVATIONS ON THE HERERO MUSK SHREW, CROCIDURA FLAVESCENS HERERO ST. LEGER, IN CAPTIVITY. B. J. G. Marlow. Proc. Zool. Soc. Lond., vol. 124, pt.4, pp.803-808, Feb.22, 1955.

A NOTE ON THE DUSKY SHREW IN CAPTIVITY. Frederic W. Miller. Jour. Mam., vol.11, no.3, pp.311-312, Aug., 1930.

NOTES ON THE HABITS OF BLARINA. D. G. Nichols. Jour. Mam., vol.17, no.4, p.412, Nov., 1936.

(ON CARE OF YOUNG AND ORIENTATION IN THE DOMESTIC SHREW (CROCIDURA RUSSULA HERM.).) Zur Jungenpflege und Orientierung der Huasspitzmaus (Crocidura russula Herm.). Guenther Niethammer. Bonner Zool. Beitraege, vol.1, nos.2-4, pp.117-125, Mar., 1951.

DEATH FROM FRIGHT IN LONG-TAILED SHREWS. Robert T. Orr. Jour. Mam., Baltimore, vol.30, no.2, pp.195-196, May 23, 1949.

NOTES ON A CAPTIVE SHORT-TAILED SHREW. Richard Stuart Phillips. Jour. Mam., 37 (4): 543, Jan.9, 1957.

MASS MOVEMENT OF THE WATER SHREW, NEOMYS FODIENS. Frances Pitt. Nature, Lond., vol.156, no.3956, p.247, Aug.25, 1945.

NOTES ON THE HABITS OF THE PIGMY SHREW (MICROSOREX HOYI) IN CAPTIVITY.

Leslie A. Prince. Canadian Nat., Ottawa, vol.54, no.7, pp.97-100, Oct., 1940.

RESTING NEST OF THE SHORT-TAILED SHREW. Janet L.C. Rapp, William F. Rapp, Jr. Jour. Mam., vol.26, no.3, p.307, Aug., 1945.

ECOLOGY AND DISTRIBUTION OF THE SHREW SOREX DISPAR IN PENNSYLVANIA. Neil D. Richmond, William C. Grimm. Ecology 31 (2): 279-282, Apr., 1950.

NOTES ON MAINTENANCE AND BEHAVIOR OF SHREWS IN CAPTIVITY. Robert L. Rudd. Jour. Mam. 34 (1): 118-120, Feb., 1953.

(CONTRIBUTION TO KNOWLEDGE OF THE ETRUSCAN SHREW IN CAPTIVITY.) Contribution à la connaissance de la pachyure étrusque en captivite. M. C. Saint Girons. Mammalia, Paris, 21 (1): 69-76, Mar., 1957.

HABITS OF THE SHORT-TAILED SHREW, BLARINA BREVICAUDA (SAY). A. Franklin Shull. Amer. Nat., Lancaster, vol.41, no. 488, pp.495-522, figs.5, Aug., 1907.

SHREW IN A HOUSE IN PERTHSHIRE. John B. Simpson. The Scottish Naturalist, no. 182, p.36, Mar.-Apr., 1930.

THE NEST OF CRYPTOTIS FLORIDANA. Clarence F. Smith. Jour. Mam., vol.19, no.3, pp.372-373, Aug., 1938.

(ON THE ECOLOGY OF GARDEN SHREWS (CROCIDURA SUAVEOLENS MIMULA MILLER 1917) OF NORTHERN GERMANY.) Zur Oekologie norddeutscher Gartenspitzmaeuse, Crocidura suaveolens mimula, Miller, 1917. Georg Stein. Saeugetierk. Mitteil., Stuttgart, 4 (3): 130, July 1, 1956.

CLIMBING OF THE WATER SHREW. F. J. Stubbs. Essex Nat., vol.19, 1923.

OBSERVATIONS ON THE BIG-TAILED SHREW (SOREX DISPAR BATCHELDER). G. H. H. Tate. Jour. Mam., vol.16, no. 3, pp.213-215, Aug., 1935.

(OBSERVATIONS OF FREE-LIVING AND CAPTIVE SOREX ARANEUS L.) Freilands- und Gefangenschaftsbeobachtungen an Sorex araneus L. Gerhard Wilcke. Zeitschr. f. Saeugetierkunde, Berlin, vol.12, no.3, pp. 332-335, July 15, 1938.

(SHREWS IN THE NESTS OF PYGMY MICE.) Spitzmaeuse in Zwergmausnestern. Wilhelm Wolf. Saeugetierk. Mitteil., Stuttgart, vol. 2, no.1, pp.33-34, Jan.1, 1954.

Mexico and Central America

A NEW CRYPTOTIS FROM COSTA RICA. George G. Goodwin. Amer. Mus. Novitates, New York, no.1267, pp.2, Dec.10, 1944.

A NEW SHORT-TAILED SHREW FROM WESTERN PANAMA. George G. Goodwin. Amer. Mus. Novitates, New York, no.1677, pp.1-2, June 28, 1954.

FIVE NEW SHREWS OF THE GENUS CRYPTOTIS FROM MEXICO AND GUATEMALA. Hartley H. T. Jackson. Proc. Biol. Soc. Washington, vol.46, pp.79-82, Apr.27, 1933.

A NEW SHREW (GENUS SOREX) FROM COAHUILA. Hartley H. T. Jackson. Proc. Biol. Soc. Washington, vol.60, pp.131-32, Oct.9, 1947.

DESCRIPTIONS OF FIVE NEW SHREWS FROM MEXICO, GUATEMALA, AND COLOMBIA. C. Hart Merriam. Proc. Biol. Soc., Washington, vol.11, pp.227-230, July 15, 1897.

TWO NEW SHREWS OF THE GENUS CRYPTOTIS FROM PANAMA. Henry W. Setzer. Jour. Washington Acad. Sci., vol.40, no.9 pp.299-300, Sept.29, 1950.

North America

THE WATER SHREW OF NOVA SCOTIA. Glover M. Allen. Proc. Biol. Soc. Washington, vol.28, no. pp.15-18, Feb.12, 1915.

NORTH AMERICAN SHREWS. J. A. Allen. Science, N.S., vol.3, pp.411-413, Mar.13, 1896.

SOREX PALUSTRIS BROOKSI, A NEW WATER SHREW FROM VANCOUVER ISLAND. R. M. Anderson. Canadian Field-Nat., vol.48, no. 8, p.134, Nov.1, 1934.

THE WATER SHREW (SOREX PALUSTRIS) IN ONTARIO. R. M. Anderson. Canadian Field Nat., vol.43, pp.136-137, Sept.3, 1929.

A NEW FORM OF DUSKY SHREW FROM THE PRAIRIE PROVINCES OF CANADA. R. M. Anderson, A. L. Rand. Canadian Field-Nat., Sutton West, vol.59, no.2, pp.47-48, (Mar.-Apr.) Oct.16, 1945.

A NEW SHREW FROM ARCTIC NORTH AMERICA. R. M. Anderson, A. L. Rand. Canadian Field-Nat., Sutton West, vol.59, no.2, pp.62-64, (Mar.-Apr.) Oct.16, 1945.

A NEW SPECIES OF SHREW FROM THE GASPE PENINSULA. H. E. Anthony, G. G. Goodwin. Amer. Mus. Nov., no.109, pp. 1-2, Mar.10, 1924.

THE PIGMY SHREW NEAR OTTAWA. D. Baker, A. La Rocque. Canadian Field-Nat., vol.44, p.20, Jan.2, 1930.

FIRST RECORD OF THE SHORT-TAILED SHREW (BLARINA BREVICAUDA MANITOBENSIS ANDERSON) IN SASKATCHEWAN. M. E. Baker. Canadian Field-Nat., Ottawa, vol.61, no.6, p.199, Feb.13, 1948.

SOREX VAGRANS FIRST REPORTED FROM SOUTH DAKOTA. Rollin H. Baker, James S. Findley. Jour. Mam., vol.34, no.3, p. 382, Aug.14, 1954.

THE SECOND RECORD OF THE LITTLE SHORT-TAILED SHREW IN SOUTHERN ONTARIO. A. W. F. Banfield. Canadian Field-Nat., Ottawa, vol.62, no.5, pp.163-164, Sept.-Oct., 1948.

SHORT-TAILED SHREW (BLARINA BREVICAUDA BREVICAUDA). N. R. Barger. Wisconsin Conserv. Bull., Madison, vol. 14, no.11, p.33, Nov., 1949.

AN UNDESCRIBED SHREW OF THE GENUS SOREX. Charles F. Batchelder. Proc. Biol. Soc. Washington, vol.10, pp.133-134, figs. 26-28, Dec.8, 1896.

THE CINEREOUS SHREW BELOW 6000 FEET IN NORTH CENTRAL COLORADO. R. C. Beidleman. Jour. Mam., vol.31, no.4, p. 459, Nov.21, 1950.

A COLORADO MASKED SHREW. R. C. Beidleman. Life, Chicago, vol.30, no.21, p.10, illus., May 21, 1951.

NEW LOCALITY RECORDS FOR SOME WEST AMERICAN SHREWS. Jack C. von Bloeker. Jour. Mam., vol.25, no.3, pp.311-312, Sept.8, 1944.

A NEW SHREW FROM SANTA CATALINA ISLAND, CALIFORNIA. Jack C. von Bloeker. Bull. Southern California Acad. Sci., Los Angeles, vol.40, no.3, pp.163-164, Sept.-Dec., 1941.

ANOTHER RECORD OF CRYPTOTIS PARVA FOR MICHIGAN. Philip M. Blossom. Jour. Mam., vol.12, no.4, p.429, Nov., 1931.

NOTIOSOREX IN ARIZONA. Philip M. Blossom. Jour. Mam., vol.14, no.1, p.70, Feb., 1933.

SOREX FONTINALIS IN VIRGINIA. Robert S. Bray. Jour. Mam., vol.20, no.1, p.102, Feb.14, 1939.

SOREX LONGIROSTRIS LONGIROSTRIS IN AUGUSTA COUNTY, VIRGINIA. James A. Bruce. Jour. Mam., vol.18, no.4, pp.513-514, Nov., 1937.

A NEW WATER-SHREW (SOREX PALUSTRIS) FROM LABRADOR. William Henry Burt. Occas. Papers Mus. Zool. Univ. Michigan, no.383, pp.1-2, Aug.27, 1938.

GREY SHREW, NOTIOSOREX, FROM EASTERN OKLAHOMA. William K. Clark. Jour. Mam., vol.34, no.1, pp.117-118, Feb. 19, 1953.

CONTRIBUTION TO THE LIFE HISTORY OF SOREX VAGRANS IN MONTANA. Ronald Clothier. Jour. Mam. 36 (2): 214-221, May, 1955.

TAXONOMY OF THE SOREX VAGRANS-OBSCURUS GROUP IN WESTERN MONTANA. Ronald Clothier. Proc. Montana Acad. Sci., vol.10, pp.11-12, 1951.

SOREX LONGIRESTRIS NEAR THE TYPE LOCALITY. Robert H. Coleman. Jour. Mam., vol.21, no.1, pp.89, Feb.14, 1940.

SOREX LONGIROSTRIS LONGIROSTRIS IN MISSISSIPPI. Fannye A. Cook. Jour. Mam., vol.23, no.2, p.218, May 14, 1942.

A NEW RECORD FOR MICROSOREX IN NEW YORK. Manton Copeland. Proc. Biol. Soc. Washington, vol.25, pp.93-96, May 4, 1912.

INSULARITY IN THE GENUS SOREX ON THE NORTH COAST OF BRITISH COLUMBIA. Ian McTaggart Cowan. Proc. Biol. Soc. Washington, vol.54, pp.95-108, July 31, 1941.

A NEW SHREW (SOREX) FROM FLORIDA. Joseph A. Davis. Amer. Mus. Nat. Hist., New York, p.9, map, tables, 1957.

ADDITIONAL RECORDS OF NOTIOSOREX CRAWFORDI FROM TEXAS. William B. Davis. Jour. Mam., vol.22, no.3, pp.319-320, fig.1, Aug.14, 1941.

A NEW SHREW (GENUS BLARINA) FROM TEXAS. William B. Davis. Jour. Mam., Vol.22, no.3, pp.317-318, Aug.14, 1941.

THE SHORT-TAILED SHREWS (CRYPTOTIS) OF TEXAS. William B. Davis. Jour. Mam., vol.22, no.4, pp.411-418, figs.4, Nov.14, 1941.

A NEW COUNTY RECORD FOR THE OHIO SHREW. Ralph W. Dexter. Jour. Mam., vol.27, no.2, p.177, May 14, 1946.

WATER SHREW IN ALLEGANY STATE PARK, NEW YORK. Theodore H. Eaton, Jr. Jour. Mam., vol.26, no.2, p.194, July 15, 1945.

DISTRIBUTION AND HABITAT OF SOREX LONGIROSTRIS IN NORTH CAROLINA. William L. Engels. Jour. Mam., vol.22, no.4, p.447, Nov.14, 1941.

LONG-TAILED SHREWS IN NORTHERN INDIANA. William L. Engels. Jour. Mam., vol.12, no.3, p.312, Aug., 1931.

MERRIAM SHREW IN NEW MEXICO. James S. Findley. Jour. Mam., 37 (2): 277, June 9, 1956.

TAXONOMY AND DISTRIBUTION OF SOME AMERICAN SHREWS. James S. Findley. Univ. Kansas Publ., Mus. Nat. Hist., Lawrence, vol.7, no.14, pp.613-618, June 10, 1955.

SHORT-TAILED SHREW IN SOUTH DAKOTA. James S. Findley, Richard G. Van Gelder. Jour. Mam., 36 (3): 452, Aug.30, 1955.

DWARF SHREW FIRST REPORTED IN SOUTH DAKOTA. James S. Findley, Rollin H. Baker. Jour. Mam., 37 (4): 543, Jan.9, 1957.

RECENT OCCURRENCES OF THE SMOKY SHREW IN THE TORONTO REGION. George Francis. Ontario Field Biologist, Toronto, no.9, pp.19-20, illus., May, 1955.

A LOCALITY RECORD FOR SOREX ORNATUS. Frank F. Gander. Jour. Mam., vol. 9, no.4, p.334, Nov., 1928.

A SECOND NOTIOSOREX FROM OKLAHOMA. Bryan P. Glass. Jour. Mam., vol.34, no.1, p.118, Feb.19, 1953.

CRYPTOTIS PARVA IN CONNECTICUT. George G. Goodwin. Jour. Mam., vol.23, no.3, p.336, Aug.14, 1942.

CONCERNING SOME SHREWS OF THE MAINLAND OF SOUTHWESTERN BRITISH COLUMBIA. Morris M. Green. Canadian Field-Nat., vol.42, pp.165-166, Oct., 1928.

A DELAWARE RECORD OF THE MASKED SHREW. Morris M. Green. Jour. Mam., vol.6, no.4, p.280, Nov., 1925

NOTES ON A FAT WATER SHREW FROM QUEBEC. Morris M. Green. Canadian Field-Nat., Sutton West, vol.59, no.2, p. 68, Mar.-Apr., 1945.

AN UNRECOGNIZED SHREW FROM NEW JERSEY. Morris M. Green. Univ. Calif Publ. in Zool., vol.38, no.7, pp.387-388, June 9, 1932.

THE SPECIES OF THE MAMMALIAN GENUS SOREX OF WEST-CENTRAL CALIFORNIA WITH A NOTE ON THE VERTEBRATE PALUSTRINE FAUNAS OF THE REGION. Joseph Grienell. Univ. Cal. Publ. Zool., vol.10, no.9, pp.179-195, figs.6, Mar.20, 1913.

WATER SHREW IN WESTCHESTER COUNTY, NEW YORK. Stanley Oliver Grierson. Jour. Mam., vol.29, no.1, p.77, Feb.13, 1948.

A RELIC SHREW FROM CENTRAL CALIFORNIA. Joseph Grinnell. Univ. Calif Publ. in Zool., vol.38, no.8, pp.389-390, June 9, 1932.

INDIVIDUAL AND GEOGRAPHIC VARIATION IN BLARINA BREVICAUDA FROM PENNSYLVANIA. John E. Guilday. Ann. Carnegie Mus., vol.35, no.5, pp.41-68, Dec.16, 1957.

A NEW SHREW OF THE SOREX MERRIAMI GROUP FROM ARIZONA. E. Raymond Hall. Jour. Mam., vol.13, no.3, pp.259-262, pl. 13, Aug.9, 1932.

SOREX LEUCOGENYS IN ARIZONA. E. Raymond Hall. Jour. Mam., vol.14, no. 2, pp.153-154, May 15, 1933.

CRYPTOTIS PARVA IN CENTRAL NEW YORK. W. J. Hamilton, Jr. Jour. Mam., vol.9, no.4, pp.334-335, Nov., 1928.

A NEW SUBSPECIES OF BLARINA BREVICAUDA FROM FLORIDA. W. J. Hamilton, Jr. Proc. Biol. Soc. Washington, vol.68, pp.37-40, May 20, 1955.

THE OCCURRENCE AND BREEDING OF THE MARYLAND SHREW (SOREX FONTINALIS) IN THE PATAPSCO STATE PARK. Irving E. Hampe. Bull. Nat. Hist. Soc. Maryland, Baltimore, vol.7, no.4, pp.17-18, Dec., 1936.

THE SHREW SOREX DISPAR IN VIRGINIA. Charles O. Handley, Jr. Jour. Mam., 37 (3): 435, Sept.11, 1956.

A THIRD SPECIMEN OF THE SHREW NOTIOSOREX FROM OKLAHOMA. Charles O. Handley, Jr. Jour. Mam., 37 (2): 278, June 9, 1956.

OUR SMALLEST CITIZEN. Robert T. Hatt. News-letter, Cranbrook Inst. Sci., Bloomfield Hills, vol.5, no.6, p.2, Feb., 1936.

SHREWS. Caroline A. Heppenstall. Pa. Game News, 17 (1): 12, 29, Apr., 1946.

NOTES ON AN ABUNDANCE OF SHREWS (SOREX CINEREUS CINEREUS) AND OTHER SMALL MAMMALS IN THE UNGAVA BAY REGION OF FAR NORTHERN QUEBEC. Henry Hildebrand. Jour. Mam., vol.30, no. 3, pp.309-311, Aug. 17, 1949.

REMARKS ON THE LONG-TAILED SHREWS OF THE EASTERN UNITED STATES, WITH DESCRIPTION OF A NEW SPECIES. Ned Hollister. Porc. U.S. Nat. Mus., vol.40, pp.377-381, Apr.17, 1911.

ADDITIONAL RECORDS OF THE MERRIAM SHREW IN MONTANA. Emmet T. Hooper. Jour. Mam., vol.25, no.1, p.92, Feb., 1944.

THE WATER SHREW (SOREX PALUSTRIS) OF THE SOUTHERN ALLEGHENY MOUNTAINS. Emmet T. Hooper. Occas. Papers Univ. Michigan Mus. Zool., Ann Arbor, no. 463, pp.4, Sept.15, 1942.

MICROSOREX HOYI, A NEW MAMMAL FOR THE TORONTO REGION. C. E. Hope. Canadian Field-Nat., vol.43, no.7, p.168, Oct.1, 1929.

MICROSOREX HOYI HOYI AT TORONTO, ONTARIO. C. E. Hope. Canadian Field-Nat., vol.46, no.8, p. 190, Nov., 1932.

NEW RECORDS OF SOREX MERRIAMI FOR EASTERN WASHINGTON. George E. Hudson, Marion Bacon. Jour. Mam., 37 (3): 436-438, Sept.11, 1956.

NOTES ON THE RANGE OF THE LABRADOR SHREW, SOREX CINEREUS MISCIX. C. F. Jackson. Canadian Field-Nat., Ottawa, vol. 53, no.1, pp.7-8, Jan., 1939.

A NEW SHREW FROM NOVA SCOTIA. Hartley H. T. Jackson. Proc. Biol. Soc. Wash., vol.30, pp.149-150, July 27, 1917.

NEW SPECIES AND SUBSPECIES OF SOREX FROM WESTERN AMERICA. Hartley H. T. Jackson. Jour. Washington Acad. Sci., vol. 12, no.11, pp.262-264, June 4, 1922.

A NOTE ON TWO SPECIES OF SHREWS. Hartley H. T. Jackson. Jour. Mam., vol. 12, no.2, p.163, May, 1931.

PRELIMINARY DESCRIPTIONS OF SEVEN SHREWS OF THE GENUS SOREX. Hartley H. T. Jackson. Proc. Biol. Soc. Wash., vol.38, pp.127-130, Nov.13, 1925.

THE SOREX ARCTICUS AND SOREX ARCTICUS CINEREUS OF KERR. Hartley H. T. Jackson. Jour. Mam., vol.6, no.1, pp.55-56, Feb., 1925.

A TAXONOMIC REVIEW OF THE AMERICAN LONG-TAILED SHREWS (GENERA SOREX AND MICROSOREX). Hartley H. T. Jackson. North Amer. Fauna no.51, U.S. Dept. Agric., pp. VI, 238, pls.13, July 24, 1928.

TWO NEW PIGMY SHREWS OF THE GENUS MICROSOREX. Hartley H. T. Jackson. Proc. Biol. Soc. Washington, vol.38, pp.125-126, Nov.13, 1925.

TWO NEW SHREWS FROM OREGON. Hartley H. T. Jackson. Proc. Biol. Soc. Wash., vol.31, pp.127-130, Nov.29, 1918.

TWO UNRECOGNIZED SHREWS FROM CALIFORNIA. Hartley H. T. Jackson. Jour. Mam., vol.2, no.3, pp.161-162, Aug.19, 1921.

AN UNRECOGNIZED SHREW FROM WARREN ISLAND, ALASKA. Hartley H. T. Jackson. Proc. Biol. Soc. Wash., vol.32, pp.23-24, Apr.11, 1919.

AN UNRECOGNIZED WATER SHREW FROM WISCONSIN. Hartley H. T. Jackson. Jour. Mam., vol.7, no.1, pp.57-58, Feb.15, 1926.

WATER-SHREW IN CONNECTICUT. Hartley H. T. Jackson. Jour. Mam., vol.12, no.3, p.312, Aug., 1931.

SOREX FONTINALIS ON THE EASTERN SHORE OF MARYLAND. Ralph W. Jackson. Jour. Mam., vol.10, no.3, p.250, Aug., 1929.

THE MERRIAM SHREW IN WASHINGTON STATE. William B. James. Jour. Mam., vol.34, no.1, p.121, Feb.19, 1953.

OBSERVATIONS ON THE BIOLOGY OF SOREX TROWBRIDGEI IN THE SIERRA NEVADA, CALIFORNIA. E. W. Jameson, Jr. Jour. Mam., 36 (3): 339-345, 3 figs., 1 table, Aug.30, 1955.

THE WATER SHREWS OF THE LABRADOR PENINSULA. David H. Johnson. Proc. Biol. Soc. Washington, vol.64, pp.109-116, Aug. 24, 1951.

NATURAL HISTORY OF SOREX MERRIAMI IN WASHINGTON STATE. Murray L. Johnson, C. Wesley Clanton. Murrelet 35 (1): 1-4, graph., Jan.-Apr., 1954.

GEOGRAPHIC DISTRIBUTION OF THE SHORT-TAILED SHREW, BLARINA BREVICAUDA, IN THE GREAT PLAINS. J. Knox Jones, James S. Findley. Trans. Kansas Acad. Sci., vol.57, no.2, pp.208-211, 1954.

RECORDS OF THE SHORT-TAILED SHREW AND LEAST SHREW FROM COLORADO. J. Knox Jones, Jr., Richard B. Loomis. Jour. Mam., vol.35, no.1, pp.110, Feb.10, 1954.

CRYPTOTIS PARVA IN CENTRAL NEW YORK. John C. Jones. Jour. Mam., vol. 18, no.4, p.514, Nov., 1937.

DISTRIBUTION OF SOREX CINEREUS CINEREUS IN ILLINOIS. E. J. Koestner. Amer. Midland Nat., Notre Dame, vol.27, no.3, pp.610-612, fig.1, May (July), 1942.

MICROSOREX HOYI WASHINGTONI IN MONTANA. Carl B. Koford, Jour. Mam., vol.19, no.3, p.372, Aug., 1938.

THE DWARF SHREW, SOREX NANUS, IN MEXICO. William J. Koster, Ronald R. Clothier. Jour. Mam., vol.33, no.2, pp. 250-251, May 16, 1952.

NOTES ON THE BACHMAN SHREW. John B. Lewis. Jour. Mam., vol.24, no.1, pp.97-98, Feb.20, 1943.

SOREX DISPAR IN NEW HAMPSHIRE. Alexander Lincoln, Jr. Jour. Mam., vol. 16, no.3, p.223, Aug., 1935.

NEW RECORD OF THE SMALL SHORT-TAILED SHREW IN INDIANA. Marcus Ward Lyon, Jr. Proc. Indiana Acad. Sci., vol. 34, 1924, p.391, 1925.

NORTH AMERICA'S SMALLEST MAMMAL. Romeo Mansuetti. Nat. Mag., Washington, vol.41, no.2, pp.79-80, Feb., 1948.

LONG-TAILED SHREW (SOREX DISPAR IN MARYLAND. Romeo Mansuetti, Vagn F. Flyger. Jour. Mam., vol.33, no.2, p.250, May 16, 1952.

GRAY LONG-TAILED SHREW FROM NEW HAMPSHIRE. Deane W. Mather. Jour. Mam., vol.14, no.1, p.70, Feb., 1933.

A NEW GENUS AND SPECIES OF THE SORECIDAE. C. Hart Merriam. Trans. Linnaean Soc. of New York, vol.11, pp.217-225, illus., Aug.28, 1884.

REVISION OF THE SHREWS OF THE AMERICAN GENERA BLARINA AND NOTIOSOREX. C. Hart Merriam. North American Fauna, no.10, pp.34, figs.2, pls.3, Dec.31, 1895.

SYNOPSIS OF THE AMERICAN SHREWS OF THE GENUS SOREX. C. Hart Merriam. North American Fauna, no.10, pp.57-100, pls.12, Dec.31, 1895.

TWO NEW SHREWS OF THE SOREX TENELLUS GROUP FROM CALIFORNIA. C. Hart Merriam. Proc. Biol. Soc. Wash., vol.15, pp.75-76, Mar.2?, 1902.

A RECORD OF THE SHREW SOREX NANUS FOR WYOMING. Arthur B. Mickey. Jour. Mam., vol.29, no.3, pp.294-295, Aug.31, 1948.

A RECORD OF SOREX MERRIAMI MERRIAMI FOR SOUTHEASTERN WYOMING. Arthur B. Mickey, Charles N. Steele, Jr. Jour. Mam., vol.28, no.3, p.293, Aug.19, 1947.

THE RANGE OF CRYPTOTIS PARVA (SAY). F. W. Miller. Jour. Mam., vol.5, no.3, p.199, Aug., 1924.

THE LONG-TAILED SHREWS OF THE EASTERN UNITED STATES. Gerrit S. Miller, Jr. U.S. Dept. Agric., Div. Orinth. and Mam., North Amer. Fauna no.10, pp. 35-56, pls.12, Dec.31, 1895.

THREE NEW SHREWS OF THE GENUS CRYPTOTIS. Gerrit S. Miller, Jr. Proc. Biol. Soc., Washington, vol.24, pp.221-224, Oct.31, 1911.

BACHMAN'S SHREW EAST OF ST. JOHNS RIVER, FLORIDA. Joseph C. Moore. Jour. Mam., vol.24, no.3, pp.404-405, Aug.17, 1943.

NOTES ON THE SHREW, SOREX CINEREUS IN THE SOUTHERN APPALACHIANS. Joseph C. Moore. Ecology 30 (2): 234-237, Apr., 1949.

A NOTE ON THE DISTRIBUTION OF THE TWO SHREWS FOUND IN JERSEY. T. C. S. Morrison-Scott. Jour. Animal Ecology, vol. 6, no.2, pp.284-285, Nov., 1937.

LOW ELEVATION RECORDS OF THE DUSKY SHREW. Vincent Mowbray. Yosemite Nat. Notes, Yosemite, vol.20, no.3, pp.23-24, Mar., 1941.

ADDITIONAL RECORDS OF THE SHORT-TAILED SHREW IN SASKATCHEWAN. R. W. Nero. Blue Jay, 14 (2): 45-46, illus., June, 1956.

EXTENSION OF THE RANGE OF THE SHORT-TAILED SHREW. R. W. Nero. Blue Jay, Saskatchewan, Nat. Hist. Soc., 15 (4): 177-178, Dec., 1957.

SHORT-TAILED SHREW RECORDS. R. W. Nero. Blue Jay, Saskatchewan Nat. Hist. Soc., 15 (3): 121, Sept., 1957.

MASKED SHREW, SOREX CINEREUS, IN UTAH. J. Paul Newey. See: Durrant, Stephen D., and J. Paul Newey, 1953.

SOREX LONGIROSTRIS AT MOUNTAIN LAKE, VIRGINIA. Eugene P. Odum. Jour. Mam., vol.25, no.2, p.196, May 25, 1944.

EXTENSION OF THE RANGE OF SOREX TUNDRENSIS. Robert T. Orr. Jour. Mam., Baltimore, vol.20, no.2, p.251, May 14, 1939.

FOUR VERMONT RECORDS OF THE BIG-TAILED SHREW. F. L. Osgood. Jour. Mam., vol.16, no.2, p.146, May, 1935.

NORTHERN SMOKY SHREW IN VERMONT. F. L. Osgood. Jour. Mam., vol.19, no.2, p.247, May 14, 1938.

THE STATUS OF SOREX MERRIAMI, WITH DESCRIPTION OF AN ALLIED NEW SPECIES FROM UTAH. Wilfred H. Osgood. Proc. Biol. Soc. Washington, vol.22, pp.51-53, Apr.17, 1909.

NOTES ON SOME MAINE SHREWS. Ralph S. Palmer. Jour. Mam., vol.28, no.1, pp. 13-16, pl.1, Feb.15, 1947.

CRYPTOTIS PARVA IN WESTERN NEW YORK. C. Bernard Peterson. Jour. Mam., vol.17, no.3, pp.284-285, Aug., 1936.

PENNSYLVANIA RECORDS OF SOREX CINEREUS FONTALIS. L. Poole. Jour. Mam., vol.18, no.1, p.96, Feb.14, 1937.

A NEW MICROSOREX FROM THE VICINITY OF WASHINGTON, D.C. Edward A. Preble. Proc. Biol. Soc. Wash., vol.23, pp.101-102, June 24, 1910.

ADDITIONAL RECORDS OF THE PIGMY SHREW IN NEW HAMPSHIRE. Norman A. Preble. Jour. Mam., vol.19, no.3, pp.371-372, Aug., 1938.

A NOVA SCOTIAN SMOKY SHREW IN NEW HAMPSHIRE. Norman A. Preble. Jour. Mam., vol.18, no.4, p.513, Nov., 1937.

PIGMY SHREW IN NEW HAMPSHIRE. Norman A. Preble. Jour. Mam., vol.18, no.3, pp.362-363, Aug.14, 1937.

SOREX DISPAR IN NEW HAMPSHIRE. Norman A. Preble. Jour. Mam., vol.18, no.1, p.95, Feb.14, 1937.

GEOGRAPHIC RANGE EXTENSIONS OF THE SMOKY SHREW (SOREX FUMEUS) IN ONTARIO AND QUEBEC. Leslie A. Prince. Canadian Field-Nat., Ottawa, vol.55, no.7, p.103, Oct., 1941.

AN ANALYSIS OF SOME PHYSICAL FACTORS AFFECTING THE LOCAL DISTRIBUTION OF THE SHORTTAIL SHREW (BLARINA BREVICAUDA KIRTLANDI) IN NORTHERN LOWER MICHIGAN. William O. Pruitt, Jr. Ph.D. thesis, U. Mich., 133 pp., 1952.

AN ANALYSIS OF SOME PHYSICAL FACTORS AFFECTING THE LOCAL DISTRIBUTION OF THE SHORTTAIL SHREW (BLARINA BREVICAUDA) IN THE NORTHERN PART OF THE LOWER PENINSULA OF MICHIGAN. William O. Pruitt, Jr. Misc. Publ. Mus. Zool. Univ. Michigan, Ann Arbor, no.79, pp.39, July 30, 1953.

NOTES ON THE SHORTTAIL SHREW (BLARINA BREVICAUDA KIRTLANDI) IN NORTHERN LOWER MICHIGAN. William O. Pruitt, Jr. Amer. Midland Nat., Notre Dame, vol.52, no.1, pp.236-241, July, 1954.

ECOLOGY AND DISTRIBUTION OF THE SHREW SOREX DISPAR IN PENNSYLVANIA. Neil D. Richmond, William C. Grimm. Ecology, Lancaster, vol.31, no.2, pp.279-282, Apr., 1950.

HOY'S PYGMY SHREW IN ILLINOIS. Colin Campbell Sanborn, Douglas Tibbitts. Nat. Hist. Misc., Chicago Acad. Sci., no.36, pp.2, Feb.18, 1949.

THE SADDLE-BACKED SHREW IN RIDING MOUNTAIN NATIONAL PARK. W. E. Saunders. Canadian Field-Nat., vol.49, no. 4, p.76, Apr., 1935.

THE SMOKY SHREW AT LONDON, ONTARIO. W. E. Saunders. Canadian Field-Nat., vol. 43, p.42, Feb., 1929.

THE WATER SHREW AT SCOTIA JUNCTION, ONTARIO. W. E. Saunders. Canadian Field-Nat., vol.43, p.108, May 1, 1929.

A NEW SUBSPECIES OF THE LONGTAIL SHREW (SOREX DISPAR BATCHELDER) FROM THE SOUTHERN APPALACHIAN MOUNTAINS. Albert Schwartz. Jour. Elisha Mitchell Soc., 72 (1): 24-30, May, 1956.

PIGMY SHREW, MICROSOREX, IN MONTANA. Henry W. Setzer. Jour. Mam., vol.33, no.3, p.398, Aug.19, 1952.

A FLORIDA RECORD OF SOREX LONGIROSTRIS. Harley B. Sherman. Jour. Mam., vol.9, no.2, p.148, May, 1928.

A NEW RACE OF SOREX ARCTICUS FROM NOVA SCOTIA. Ronald W. Smith. Jour. Mam., vol.20, no.2, pp.244-245, May, 1939.

CRYPTOTIS PARVA, A NEW SHREW FOR THE CANADIAN LIST. L. L. Snyder. Jour. Mam., vol.10, no.1, pp.79-80, Feb., 1929.

NOTES ON THE LARGE SHORT-TAILED SHREW AT FORT GARRY, MANITOBA. J. Dewey Soper. Canadian Field-Nat., Sutton West, vol.58, no.3, p.104, May-June, 1944.

LONGTAIL SHREW, SOREX DISPAR, IN MAINE. A. Starrett. Jour. Mam., vol.35, no.4, pp.583-584, Nov.29, 1956.

MERRIAM SHREW, SOREX MERRIAMI, IN COLORADO. A. Starrett, P. Starrett. Jour. Mam., 37 (2): 276-277, June 9, 1956.

ADDITIONAL RECORDS FOR WATER SHREWS SOREX PALUSTRIS, IN NEW ENGLAND. A. Starrett, P. Starrett, P. M. Youngman. Jour. Mam., vol.33, no.3, p. 398, Aug.19, 1952.

NOTICE OF A SPECIES OF NEOSOREX FROM MASSACHUSETTS AND OF SOREX THOMPSONI FROM MAINE. A. E. Verrill. Proc. Boston Soc. Nat. Hist., vol.9, pp.164-173, Feb., 1863.

A RECORD FOR SOREX FONTINALIS. Alexander Wetmore. Jour. Mam., vol.9, no.3, p.247, Aug., 1928.

WATER SHREW FROM POTTER COUNTY, PENNSYLVANIA. Mary Wible. Jour. Mam., vol.27, no.1, p.89, Mar.14, 1946.

AN EXTENSION OF THE KNOWN RANGE OF NOTIOSOREX CRAWFORDI. G. Willett. Jour. Mam., vol.20, no.1, p.102, Feb.14, 1939.

OUR SMALLEST MAMMAL--THE SHREW. Colorado Conserv. Comments, Denver, vol. 10, no.1, pp.10-11, Mar., 1947.

## Pelage, Molts

AN ALBINO SHREW. Glover M. Allen. Jour. Mam., vol.16, no.3, pp.223-224, Aug., 1935.

(SEASONAL CHANGES IN THE HAIR COVER OF THE SORCIDAE.) Saisonale Veraenderungen der Behaarung der Soricidae. Stanislaw Borowski. Ann. Univ. Mariae Curie-Sklodowska, vol.7, no.2, pp.65-117, July 25, 1952.

REMARKS ON THE PELAGE OF THE COMCOM SHREW (SOREX ARANEUS L.). Peter Crowcroft. Proc. Zool. Soc. Lond., vol. 125, pt.2, pp.309-315, illus., Aug.31, 1955.

THE MOLTING OF THE WANDERING SHREW. Walter W. Dalquest. Jour. Mam., vol.25, no.2, pp.146-148, fig., May 25, 1944.

POSSIBLE HIMALAYAN COLOR PATTERN IN THE MASKED SHREW. James S. Findley. Jour. Mam., 37 (2): 275-276, June 9, 1956.

MOLT OF THE SHORT-TAILED SHREW, BLARINA BREVICAUDA. James S. Findley, J. Knox Jones, Jr. Amer. Midland Nat., 56(1): 246-249, 1956.

A CASE OF PARTIAL ALBINISM IN THE SHORT-TAILED SHREW. Joseph Gentile. Maryland Nat., Baltimore , vol.10, no.1, pp.11-12, Winter, 1949.

THE THREE PELAGES OF THE SMOKY SHREW. Morris M. Green. Canadian Field-Nat., Sutton West, vol.57, nos.3-4, p.96, Apr.-May, 1943.

HAS SOREX CINEREUS A DISTINCTIVE NESTLING PELAGE? Morris M. Green. Jour. Mam., vol.22, no.3, pp.322-323, Aug.14, 1941.

ALBINO BLARINAS. W. J. Hamilton, Jr. Jour. Mam., vol.20, no.2, p.252, May 14, 1939.

THE MOLT OF BLARINA BREVICAUDA. W. J. Hamilton, Jr. Jour. Mam., Baltimore, vol.21, no.4, pp.457-458, Nov.14, 1940.

AN UNUSUAL COLOR PHASE OF THE SHORT-TAILED SHREW. Irving E. Hampe. Maryland, A journal of natural history, Baltimore, vol.14, no.3, p.73, July, 1944.

ALBINISM IN THE CINEREOUS SHREW. John Pearce. Jour. Mam., vol.15, no.1, p.67, Feb., 1934.

A TECHNIQUE FOR THE AUTOMATIC COLOR MARKING OF SHREWS. W. B. Quay. Jour. Mam., vol.29, no.3, pp. 225-234, figs.2, illus., Aug.31, 1948.

ALBINO SHORT-TAILED SHREWS FROM CONNECTICUT. P. R. Sime. Jour. Mam., vol.21, no.2, p.214, May 14, 1940.

ALBINISM IN BLARINA. Frederick A. Ulmer, Jr. Jour. Mam., vol.21, no.1, pp.88-90, Feb.14, 1940.

## Predators

SHREWS FROM MICHOACAN, MEXICO, FOUND IN BARN OWL PELLETS. Rollin H. Baker, Albert A. Alcorn. Jour. Mam., vol.34, no.1, p.116, Feb.19, 1953.

ROUGH-LEGGED HAWK FEEDS ON SHREWS. James B. Cope. Jour. Mam., vol.30, no.4, p.432, Nov.17, 1949.

ANOTHER HEAVY CONCENTRATION OF CRYPTOTIS IN TEXAS. William B. Davis. Jour. Mam., 21 (2): 213-214, May, 1940.

A HEAVY CONCENTRATION OF CRYPTOTIS. William B. Davis. Jour. Mam., vol. 19, no.4, pp.499-500, Nov.14, 1938.

WEASELS EAT SHREWS. W. J. Hamilton, Jr. Jour. Mam., vol.9, no.3, pp.249-250, Aug., 1928.

THE SHORT-TAILED SHREW (BLARINA) AS A SOURCE OF FOOD FOR THE GREEN SUNFISH. Melvin T. Huish, Donald F. Hoffmeister. Copeia, Ann Arbor, no.3, p.198, Sept.12, 1947.

THREE SHREWS, CRYPTOTIS PARVA, EATEN BY A FERAL HOUSE CAT. Frank B. McMurry. Jour. Mam., vol.26, no.1, p.94, Feb.23, 1945.

PREDATION ON SHREWS BY FROGS. William H. Marshall. Jour. Mam., vol.32, no.2, p.219, May 21, 1951.

SHREW ON BOX TURTLE MENU. Joseph Curtis Moore. Everglades Nat. Hist., Homestead, Florida, vol.1, no.3, p.129, Sept., 1953.

THE IMPORTANCE OF THE COMMON SHREW (SOREX ARANEUS L.) AND SOME OTHER MAMMALS IN THE DIET OF THE GRAYLING (THYMALLUS THYMALLUS L.). V. P. Teplov. Zool. Zh. 22 (6): 366-368, 1943.

## Reproductive Biology

REPRODUCTION IN THE COMMON SHREW (SOREX ARANEUS LINNAEUS). I. THE OESTROUS CYCLE OF THE FEMALE. II. SEASONAL CHANGES IN THE REPRODUCTIVE ORGANS OF THE MALE. F. Brambell, W. Rogers. Philos. Trans. Roy. Soc. Lond., ser.B., vol.225, no.518, pp.1-9, May 22, 1935.

REPRODUCTION OF THE LESSER SHREW. F. Brambell, W. Rogers, Kathleen Hall. Proc. Zool. Soc., Lond., for 1936, pt.4, pp.957-969, figs.5, tables 8, pls.3, Jan., 1937.

THE BIOLOGY OF BREEDING OF COMMON SHREW S. ARANEUS L. IN LABORATORY CONDITIONS. August Dehnel. Ann. Univ. Mariae Curie-Sklodowska, vol.6, no.11, p. 359-377, Apr.1, 1952.

(CONTRIBUTION TO THE BIOLOGY, PARTICULARLY THE REPRODUCTIVE BIOLOGY, OF THE FIELD SHREW (CROCIDURA LEUCODON).) Beitrag zur Biologie, insbesondere Paarungsbiologie der Feldspitzmaus, (Crocidura leucodon). Fritz Frank. Bonner Zool. Beitraege, Jahrg.4, Heft 3-4, pp.187-194, Dec.15, 1953.

A PREGNANT WATER SHREW. Kenneth Gordon. Jour. Mam., vol.12, no.4, p.429, Nov., 1931.

BREEDING HABITS OF THE SHORT-TAILED SHREW, BLARINA BREVICAUDA. William

J. Hamilton, Jr. Jour. Mam., vol.10, no.2, pp.125-134, pls.10-12, May, 1929.

BREEDING OF CRYPTOTIS PARVA IN TEXAS. Tom Hunt. Jour. Mam., vol.32, no.1, pp.115-116, Feb.15, 1951.

NEST AND YOUNG OF SOREX VAGRANS VAGRANS. Stanley J. Jewett, Jr. Jour. Mam., vol.12, no.2, p.163, May, 1931.

(A FEMALE IN GESTATION (SUNCUS ETRUSCUS).) Une femelle en gestation de Suncus etruscus. P. L. Niort. Mammalia, Paris, vol.14, no.3, pp.99-102, Sept., 1950.

REPRODUCTION IN THE SHREW (BLARINA BREVICAUDA SAY). Oliver P. Pearson. Amer. Jour. Anat., Philadelphia, vol.75, no.1, pp.39-93, pls.6, July, 1944.

THE REPRODUCTIVE CYCLE OF THE WATER SHREW, NEOMYS FODIENS BICOLOR SHAW. Myfanwy Price. Proc. Zool. Soc. Lond., vol.123, pt.3, pp.599-621, pls. 1-4, Nov.20, 1953.

NOTES ON A LITTER OF YOUNG MASKED SHREWS. William O. Pruitt, Jr. Jour. Mam., vol.35, no.1, pp.109-110, Feb.10, 1954.

NUMBER OF FETUSES IN THE HOY PIGMY SHREW. Thomas G. Scott. Jour. Mam., vol.20, no.2, p.251, May, 1939.

IMMATURE WATER SHREWS FOUND IN A BEAVER LODGE. Hilbert R. Siegler. Jour. Mam., 37 (2): 277-278, June 9, 1956.

NEST AND YOUNG OF THE OLYMPIC DUSKY SHREW. John W. Slipp. Jour. Mam., vol.23, no.2, pp.211-212, May 14, 1942.

STUDIES ON REPRODUCTION AND PRENATAL MORTALITY OF THE COMMON-SHREW (SOREX ARANEUS L.). PART I. FOETAL REGRESSION. Andrzej Krzysztof Tarkowski. Ann. Univ. Mariae Curie-Sklodowska, Lublin, sec.C, 9(9): 387-425, Sept. 12, 1956.

STUDIES ON REPRODUCTION AND PRENATAL MORTALITY OF THE COMMON-SHREW (SOREX ARANEUS L.). PART II. REPRODUCTION UNDER NATURAL CONDITIONS. Andrzej Krzysztof Tarkowski. Ann. Univ. Mariae Curie-Sklodowska, Lublin, sec. C, 10 (8): 177-244, Feb.15, 1957.

PREGNANCY RECORDS OF THE DSINEZUMI, CROCIDURA RUSSULA CHISAI (THOMAS). Michiya Tashiro. Trans. Mamm. Soc. Japan, no.9, p.77, Apr., 1954.

A LATE BREEDING RECORD FOR BLARINA. Monty Wood. Intermediate Naturalist, Toronto, no.8, p.29, 1953.

Shrew Poison

POSSIBLE ANTI-ADRENALIN ACTION OF SHREW VENOM. Donald H. DeMeules. Jour. Mam., 35 (3): 425, Aug., 1954.

BRIEF COMPARISON OF SHORT-TAILED SHREW AND REPTILE POISONS. Barbara Lawrence. Jour. Mam., 26 (4): 393-396, Nov., 1945.

ON THE CAUSE AND NATURE OF A POISONOUS ACTION PRODUCED BY THE BITE OF A SHREW (BLARINA BREVICAUDA). Oliver P. Pearson. Jour. Mam., vol.23, no. 2, pp.159-166, May 14, 1942.

A TOXIC SUBSTANCE FROM THE SALIVARY GLANDS OF A MAMMAL (SHORT-TAILED SHREW). Oliver P. Pearson. Venoms, Publ. no.44, Amer. Asso. Adv. Sci., Wash., pp. 55-58, 1956.

South America

A NEW SHREW FROM COLOMBIA. Glover M. Allen. Proc. New England Zool. Club, vol.8, pp.37-38, Feb.12, 1923.

DISTRIBUTION OF THE SOUTH AMERICAN SHREWS. G. H. H. Tate. Jour. Mam., vol. 13, no.3, pp.223-228, Aug., 1932.

Taxonomy, Phylogeny, Evolution

(A NEW GENUS OF THE SORICIDAE FAMILY.) Un Nuovo genere della Famiglia Soricidae. G. Altobello. Rev. Franc Mamm. vol.1, pp.6-9, fig.1, Dec.7, 1927.

A NEW NAME FOR SOREX MACRURUS BATCHELDER. Charles F. Batchelder. Proc. Biol. Soc. Wash., vol.24, pp.97-100, May 15, 1911.

CROCIDURA SAMARITANA BATE: A CORRECTION. Dorothea M. A. Bate. Ann. and Mag. Nat. Hist. Lond., ser.11, vol.1, no.1, pp.78-79, Jan., 1938.

NOTES ON SOREX MERRIAMI DOBSON. Seth B. Benson, Richard M. Bond. Jour. Mam., vol.20, no.3, pp.348-351, figs. 2, Aug.14, 1939.

(A NEW SHREW?) Eine neue Spitzmaus? G. von Burg. Der Weidmann, Jahrg., no.3, p. 6, Jan.20, 1921.

A SYNOPSIS OF THE GENERA OF THE FAMILY SORICIDAE. G. E. Dobson. Proc. Zool. Soc., Lond., vol., no.4, pp.49-51, Feb.4, 1890.

SPECIATION OF THE WANDERING SHREW. James S. Findley. Univ. Kansas Publ., Mus. Nat. Hist., vol.9, no.1, pp.1-68, Dec.10, 1955.

REVISION OF THE GENUS SOREX, LINN. J. E. Gray. Proc. Zool. Soc. Lond., pt. 5, p.123, 1837.

SOREX MELANOGENYX HALL, A SYNONYM OF SOREX VAGRANS MONTICOLA MERRIAM. Raymond E. Hall. Jour. Mam., vol. 15, no.2, p.155, May 15, 1934.

(EVOLUTION AND PHYLOGENY OF AFRICAN SORICIDS.) Evolution et phylogenie des soricides africains. H. Heim de Balsac, M. Lamotte. Mammalia, 20 (2): 140-167, illus., June, 1956.

SOREX MYOPS, A SYNONYM OF SOREX TENELLUS. Donald V. Hemphill. Jour. Mam., vol.23, no.2, p.219, May 14, 1942.

NOTE ON SORICULUS NIGRESCENS AND ITS SUBSPECIES. Martin A. C. Hinton. Jour. Bombay Nat. Hist. Soc., vol.28, pp. 1052-1055, Dec.20, 1922.

ON THE CHARACTERS OF SOREX EXIGUUS VAN DEN BRINK AS COMPARED WITH THOSE OF SOREX MINUTUS L. L. van Leeuwen. Proc. Kon. Ned. Akad. Weten., ser. C, vol.57, no.3, pp.332-338, May-June, 1954.

ON THE STATUS OF THE SHREW GENUS MYSOREX. J. Meester. Ann. Mag. Nat. Hist., ser.12, vol.7, no.84, pp.947-950, Dec., 1954.

(PRELIMINARIES OF NOTES TO OUR "STUDIES OF MICROMAMMALOGY." DESCRIPTION OF NEOMYS MILLERI SP. NOVA.) Preliminaires a nos "Etudes de micrommalogie." Description du Neomys milleri, sp. nova. Charles Mottaz. Mem. Soc. Zool. France, Paris, vol.20, pp.20-32, Sept.20, 1907.

(ON A TOPOTYPE OF SOREX TETRAGONURUS HERMANN.) A propos d'un topotype de Sorex tetragonurus Hermann. P. L. Niort. Bull. Assoc. Philomathique, vol.19, no.1, pp.29-30, 1950.

CLASSIFICATION MATERIAL ON THE PALEARTIC SHREW-MOUSE. S. I. Ognev. The Empire Medical Publication, Moscow, Leningrad, pp.2-7, 1933.

MATERIALS CONCERNING THE SYSTEMATICS OF PALEARCTIC SORICIDAE. S. I. Ognev. Bull. Nauchnoissledovatel' skogo instituta Zoologii Moskovskogo Gosudarstvennogo Universiteta im. M.N. Pokrovskogo (Abstracts Works Zool. Inst. Moscou State Univ.), Sektor Nauki Narkomprose RSFSR, Medgiz, pp.57-63, 1933.

A NEW AND REMARKABLE SPECIES OF SHREW (SOREX MIRABILIS SP. NOVA.). S. I. Ognev. Bull. Soc. Nat. Moscou, sect. biol., n.s., vol.46, no.5, pp.268-271, figs. 4, 1937.

NEOMYS FODIENS STRESEMANNI STEIN. NEOMYS FODIENS FODIENS SCHREBER. Hermann Pohle. Zeitschr. f. Saeugetierkunde, Berlin, vol.7, nos.1-6, p.264, Dec. 15, 1932.

(NOTES ON A SPECIMEN OF CROCIDURA GIFFARDI WINTON.) Note sur un exemplaire de Crocidura giffardi de Winton. P. Rode. Bull. Mus. Nat. Hist. Nat., Paris, ser.2, vol.12, no.7, pp.379-381, fig.1, 1940.

(THE CROSSOPS OF WESTERN EUROPE. A CONTRIBUTION TO THE CLASSIFICATION OF THE NEOMYS KAUP SPECIES.) Les Crossopes de l'Europe occidentale, contribution à la systématique du genre Neomys Kaup. P. Rode, P. Cantuel. Mammalia, Paris, vol.9, no.1, pp.20-30, figs.3, Mar., 1945.

(ON THE PHYLOGENY OF THE SORICIDS.) Zur Stammesgeschichte der Soriciden. H. G. Stehlin. Ecologae Geol. Helvetiae, Basel, vol.33, no.2, pp.298-306, figs.5, 1940.

A NOTE ON CROCIDURA FULIGINOSA BLYTH. G. H. H. Tate. Jour. Mamm., vol.26, no.3, p.316, Aug., 1945.

FOUR NEW SHREWS. Oldfield Thomas. Ann. and Mag. Nat. Hist. (8), vol.11, no. 62, pp.214-218, Feb., 1913.

ON THE PROPER SPECIFIC NAMES OF THE COMMON SHREWS OF ENGLAND AND THE CONTINENT. Oldfield Thomas. The Zoologist (3), vol.19, pp.62-64, Feb., 1895.

Trapping

A SIMPLE PERMANENT LIVETRAP PLOT FOR SHREWS. C. H. Buckner. Jour. Mam. 36 (2),: 286, May, 1955.

LIVE-TRAPPING BRITISH SHREWS. Peter Crowcroft. Jour. Mam., vol.32, no.3, pp. 355-356, Aug.23, 1951.

TECHNIQUES IN TRAPPING SHREWS. C. Arthur Foster. Jour. Mam., vol.26, no. 2, p.197, July 15, 1945.

WATER TRAPS CAPTURE THE PIGMY SHREW (MICROSOREX HOYI) IN ABUNDANCE. Leslie A. Prince. Canadian Field-Nat., Ottawa, vol.55, no.5, p.72, May, 1941.

## Talpidae

A CONTRIBUTION TO OUR KNOWLEDGE OF THE MOLE (TALPA EUROPAEA). Lionel R. Adams. Mam. and Proc., Manchester Lit. and Philos. Soc., vol.47 (1903), no.4, Separately paged, 2-39, figs.28, 1903.

STAR-NOSED MOLE (CONDYLURA CRISTATA). N. R. Barger. Wisconsin Conserv. Bull., Madison, vol.16, no.3, pp.29-30, Mar.-Aprl., 1951.

MOLES: AN ANCIENT BELIEF DISCUSSED. Maurice Burton. Illus. London News, vol. 218, no.5839, p.428, illus. Mar.17, 1951.

THE BIOLOGY OF THE LEAST SHREW-MOLE, NEUROTRICHUS GIBBSII MINOR. Walter W. Dalquest, Donald R. Orcutt. Am. Midland Nat. 27(2): 387-401, Mar.,1942.

A CONTRIBUTION TO THE BIOLOGY OF PARASCALOPS BREWERI. W. Robert Eadie. Jour. Mam. 20(2): 150-173, May, 1939.

THE LIFE HISTORY AND ECOLOGY OF THE HAIRY-TAILED MOLE PARASCALOPS BREWERI BACHMAN. W. Robert Eadie. PhD Thesis, Cornell Univ., 1939.

(THE NATURAL FAMILY OF MOLES (TALPAE) AND THEIR SPECIES, ACCORDING TO CRITICAL INVESTIGATION.) Dis natuerliche Familie der Maulwuerfe (Talpae) und ihre Artan, nach kritischen Untersuchungen. Leop. Jos. Fitzinger. Sitz. Akad. Wissensch, Wien, vol.59, Abth.1, pp.80, Mar., 1869.

THE BIOLOGY OF THE STAR-NOSED MOLE, CONYLURA CRISTATA (LINNAEUS). William John Hamilton, Jr. Abstract of Thesis, Graduate School Cornell Univ., Ithaca, May, 1930.

NOTES ON THE MOLES OF LOWER CALIFORNIA, MEXICO. Lawrence M. Huey. Jour. Mam., vol.17, no.2, pp.166-167, May, 1936.

A LIVE MOLE TRAP. A. W. Moore. Jour. Mam., vol.21, no.2, pp.223-225, illus., May 14, 1940.

SOME NOTES ON THE MOLE. T. Hyde-Parker. Naturalist, London, no.967, pp. 185-187, Aug., 1937.

THE MOLE. Phyllis Kelway. Game and Gun and Angler's Monthly, London, vol. 16, no.106, pp.419-421, illus., July, 1939.

(INVESTIGATIONS OF THE SENSORY PHYSIOLOGY, BIOLOGY, AND SURROUNDINGS OF THE MOLE (TALPA EUROPAEA L.) Untersuchungen zur Sinnesphysiologie, Biologie und Umwelt des Maulwurfs (Talpa europaea L.). Georg Krizat. Zeitsch Morphol. und Oekologie der Tiere, Berlin, vol.36, no.3, pp.446-556, 1940.

NOTES ON THE UROTRICHUS. J. D. Lord. Proc. Zool. Soc. Lond., pp.161-163, 1864.

THE MOLE. ITS LIFE HISTORY, HABITS, AND ECONOMIC IMPORTANCE. R. Stewart MacDougall. Trans. Highland and Agric. Soc. Scotland, Edinburgh, 5th ser., vol.54, pp.80-106, figs.9-16, 1942.

BIOLOGY OF DESMANS. A. A. Paramonov. Contrib. to Study of Conservation, Moscow, no.9, pp.3-34, map, pls.2, figs.5, 1928.

THE MOLE SHREW. Samuel N. Rhoads. The American Friend, p.1149, Nov.26, 1896.

DEALING WITH THE MOLE. Theo. H. Scheffer. W. Wash. Exp. Sta., Mimeo. Cir., 146, 4 p., May, 1949.

(A MOLE ATTACKS A RINGED SNAKE.) Eine Schermaus ueberfaellt eine Ringelnatter. Wilhelm Schreitmueller. Zeitschr. Saeugetierk., Berlin, vol.17, no.3, pp.170-171, Feb.19, 1953.

THE MOLE. G. I. R. Scott. Game and Gun, vol.4, p.440, Sept., 1927.

VARIATIONS OF THE ABUNDANCE OF MOLES (TALPA EUROPAEA L.). L. V. Shaposhnikov. Zool. Jour., Moscow, vol. 25, fasc.4, pp.367-371, Aug.5, 1946.

CONTRIBUTION TO THE KNOWLEDGE OF THE USSURI MOLE, MOGERA ROBUSTA NEHRING. V. N. Stark. Far Eastern Branch. Acad. Sci. USSR, Vladivostok, no.31, pp. 133-144, tables 2, 1938.

(ON THE BIOLOGY OF THE MOLE.) Zur Biologie des Maulwurfs, Talpa europaea L. Georg H. W. Stein. Bonner Zool. Beitraege, Bonn, vol.1, nos.2-4, pp.97-116, Mar.15, 1951.

(THE ORIGIN OF THE DIGGING ADAPTATION IN TALPA EUROPAEA.) Die Entstehung der Grabanpassungen bei Talpa europaea. Zdrawa Todorowa. Gegenbaur's Morph. Jahrb., vol.57, pp.381-409, illus., 1927.

(OBSERVATIONS ON MOLES.) Beobachtungen an Schermaeusen. A. Wahlstroem. Zool. Garten, Leipzig, n.F., vol.9, no.5, pp.225-229, Oct., 1937.

(OBSERVATIONS OF MOLES.) Beobachtungen an Schermaeusen. (Pt.4-8). A. Wahlstrom. Zool. Garten, N.F., Leipzig, vol.9, no.6, pp.285-290, Dec., 1937.

ON THE COMMON SHREW-MOLE (SCALOPUS AQUATICUS MACHRINUS RAFINESQUE). Frank Elmer Wood. Bull. Illinois State Lab. Nat. Hist., vol.9, Art.1, pp.13, Oct., 1910.

## Anatomy

(CONTRIBUTION TO THE ANATOMY OF THE PELVIS OF TALPA EUROPAEA.) Contribution à l'anatomie du bassin de la Talpa europaea L. E. Aburel. Bull. Mus. Nat. Hist. Paris, ser.2, vol.1, no.5, pp. 292-297, figs.2, June, 1929.

(INVESTIGATIONS OF THE OVARY OF TALPA EUROPAEA WITH SPECIAL CONSIDERATION OF ITS CYCLICAL CHANGES.) Untersuchungen ueber das Ovarium von Talpa europaea mit besonderer Beruecksichtigung seiner cyclischen Veraenderungen. F. Altmann. Zeitschr. f. Anat. u. Entwicklungsgesch., vol.82, pp.482-569, illus., Mar.8, 1927.

(RELATION BETWEEN THE WEIGHT OF THE LIVER AND BODY WEIGHT IN TALPA EUROPEA L.) Rapporto trapeso del fegato e peso corporeo in Talpa europea L. Antonio Balli. Att. Soc. Nat. and Math. Modena, vol.71, pp.165-185, tables 13, 1940.

THE SHOULDER ANATOMY OF THE MOLES. A STUDY IN PHYLOGENY AND ADAPTATION. Berry Campbell. Amer. Jour. Anat., Phila., vol.64, no.1, pp.1-39, figs.62, table 1, Jan. 15, 1939.

THE ACCESSORY REPRODUCTIVE GLANDS OF PARASCALOPS WITH NOTES ON HOMOLOGIES. W. Robert Eadie. Anat. Record, Philadelphia, vol.97, no.2, pp.239-251, pls. 2, Feb., 1947.

A COMPARATIVE STUDY OF THE MALE ACCESSORY GENITAL GLANDS OF NEUEROTRI. W. Robert Eadie. Jour. Mam., vol.32, no.1, pp.36-43, figs.3, Feb. 15, 1951.

THE PELVIC GIRDLE OF PARASCALOPS. W. Robert Eadie. Jour. Mam., vol.26, no. 1, pp.94-95, Feb.23, 1945.

MORPHOLOGY OF THE FORELIMB OF THE MOLE (SCALOPS AQUATICUS L.) IN RELATION TO ITS FOSSORIAL HABITS. Linden F. Edwards. Ohio Jour. Sci., Columbus, vol. 37, no.1, pp.20-41, figs.16, Jan., 1937.

THE OLFACTORY CENTERS AND CONNECTIONS IN THE CEREBRAL HEMISPHERE OF THE MOLE (SCALOPUS AQUATICUS MACHRINUS). T. N. Johnson. Jour. Comp. Neurol., Philadelphia, 107 (3): 379-426, June, 1957.

THE SUPERIOR AND INFERIOR COLLICULI OF THE MOLE (SCALOPUS AQUATICUS MACHRINUS). T. N. Johnson. Jour. Comp. Neurol., Philadelphia, vol.101, no. 3, pp.765-800, Dec., 1954.

NOTES ON THE TOOTH DEVELOPMENT IN TALPA EUROPAEA. Maertha Kindahl. Arkiv foer Zoologi, Stockholm, 11 (13): 187-191, Feb.5, 1958.

THE MOLE CLAVICLE. Albert D. Kistin. Jour. Mam., vol.10, no.4, pp.305-313, Nov., 1929.

STUDIES ON THE SENSORY STRUCTURES OF THE PROBOSCIS AND TONGUE OF THE GROUND MOLE, SCALOPUS AQUATICUS (L.). Anna Catherine Lawler. Catholic Univ. America, Washington, D.C., biol. ser., no. 23, pp. xii, 52, pls.43, 1937.

THE EPITHELIO-CHORIAL PLACENTA OF AN AMERICAN MOLE, SCALOPUS AQUATICUS. H. W. Mossman. Proc. Zool. Soc. Lond., ser.B, vol.109, pts.3-4, pp.373-375, Dec.29, 1939.

VARIABLE DENTITION IN A CHINESE INSECTIVORE. Wilfred H. Osgood. Zool. Ser. Field Mus. Nat. Hist., Chicago, vol. 20, no.27, pp.365-368, Dec.28, 1937.

THE EPITHELIOCHORIAL PLACENTA OF THE AMERICAN MOLES. M. R. N. Prasad, H. W. Mossman. Anat. Record, Philadelphia, 27 (2): 477-478, Feb., 1957.

THE EYE OF THE COMMON MOLE. James Rollin Slonaker. Science, Lancaster, n.s., vol.15, no.380, p.574, Apr.11, 1902.

THE EYE OF THE COMMON MOLE, SCALOPS AQUATICUS MACHRINUS. James Rollin Slonaker. Jour. Compar. Neurol., vol.12, no.4, pp.335-366, pls.18-20, 1902.

A PRELIMINARY REPORT ON THE EYE OF THE MOLE (SCALOPS AQUATICUS MACHRINUS). James Rollin Slonaker. Rept. Indiana Acad. Sci., (Contrib. Zool. Lab. Indiana Univ., no.40 ), pp.146-149, figs.5, 1899.

SOME MORPHOLOGICAL CHANGES FOR ADAPTATION IN THE MOLE. James Rollin Slonaker. Jour. Morphology, vol.34, pp. 335-373, Sept.20 (October), 1920.

MORPHOLOGICAL CHARACTERS OF THE AUDITORY OSSICLES OF RECENT TALPIDAE. S. U. Stroganov. Jour. Mam., vol. 26, no.4, pp.412-420, illus., Feb.12, 1946.

THE ATTACHMENTS OF THE AUDITORY OSSICLES OF THE COMMON MOLE (TALPA EUROPAEA). H. C. Wilkie. Proc. Zool. Soc. Lond., pt.1, pp.61-65, illus., Apr., 1929.

THE AUDITORY APPARATUS OF THE COMMON MOLE, TALPA EUROPAEA. H. C. Wilkie. Proc. Zool. Soc. Lond., pt.4, pp. 1281-1292, illus., Jan., 1926.

## Diseases and Parasites

A REDESCRIPTION OF PHYSALOPTERA LIMBATA LEIDY, 1856 (NEMATODA PHYSALOPTERINAE). Banner Bill Morgan. Jour. Parasitol., Lancaster, vol.32, no.1, pp.69-71, pl.1, Feb., 1946.

SOME PARASITES OF THE PRAIRIE MOLE, SCALOPUS AQUATICUS MACHRINUS (RAFINESQUE). John R. Olive. Ohio Jour. Sci. 50 (6): 263-266, Nov., 1950.

THE MOLE AS A POSSIBLE RESERVOIR OF POLIOMYELITIS. L. E. Rector. Arch. Pathol. Chicago, vol.47, no.4, pp.366-377, Apr., 1949.

COCCIDIOMYCOSIS IN THE SALIVARY GLAND OF THE TOWNSEND MOLE. L. E. Rector, E. J. Rector. Amer. Jour. Trop. Med., Balto., vol.28, no.5, pp.707-720, Sept., 1948.

HYMENOLEPIS SCALOPI N. SP. Richard L. Schultz. Am. Midland Nat. 21 (3): 641-645, May, 1939.

## Economic Importance, Control

MOLES AND THEIR CONTROL IN IOWA. J. E. Guthrie. Agric. Exper. Station, Iowa State College Agric. and Mechanic Arts, Ames, circular 137, pp.7, figs.6, Apr., 1932.

(ECOLOGICAL AND BIOLOGICAL STUDIES OF THE ECONOMIC IMPORTANCE OF THE MOLE (TALPA EUROPAEA).) Oekologisch-biologische Studien ueber die wirtschaftliche Bedeutung des Maulwurfs (Talpa europaea). F. Hauchecorne. Zeitschr. f. Morph. u. Oekologie der Tiere, vol.9, pp.439-571, 6 figs., Nov.23, 1927.

(STUDIES OF THE ECONOMIC IMPORTANCE OF THE MOLE (TALPA EUROPAEA).) "Studien ueber die wirtschaftliche Bedeutung des Maulwurfes (Talpa Europaea)." F. Hauchecorne. Zeits. f. Morphol. Oekol. Tiere, 9: 439-571, 1927.

STUDIES IN CONTROL OF THE PRAIRIE MOLE SCALOPUS AQUATICUS MACHRINUS (RAFINESQUE). Willard L. Henning. Jour. Wildlife Management, Ithaca, vol.16, no.4, pp.419-424, Oct., 1952.

ANIMAL CULTIVATORS. John Eric Hill. Nat. Hist., New York, vol.55, no.5, p.233, May, 1946.

ANIMAL CULTIVATORS. John Eric Hill. Pennsylvania Game News, Harrisburg, vol. 18, no.5, p.34, Aug., 1947.

MOLE CONTROL IN EASTERN UNITED STATES. John C. Jones. Pests and Their Control, Cleveland, vol.16, no.10, pp.23-28, illus., Oct., 1948.

MOLE DESTRUCTION EXPERIMENTS. W. W. Ling, C. A. MacEacharn, E. C. Read. Univ. Bristol Dept. Agric. and Hort., Bull. 4, pp.1-14, 1 fig., 1930.

MOLE CONTROL IS A CINCH! Maurice H. Naggiar. Pest Control. 22 (8): 9-10, 12, 14, illus., Aug., 1954.

ECONOMIC IMPORTANCE OF MOLES. John R. Olive. Ohio Cons. Bull. 10 (12): 4-5, Dec., 1946.

ON THE CONSERVATION OF DESMANS. A. A. Paramonov. Contrib. to Study of Conservation, Moscow, no.9, pp.35-51, map, 1928.

MOLE-CATCHING IN WESTERN SIBERIA. A. P. Razorenova. Zool. Jour. USSR., vol. 11, no.2, pp.89-96, 5 figs., 1932.

VALUE OF THE MOLE TO AGRICULTURE. S. N. Rhoads. Forest and Stream, New York, vol.20, no.10, p.183, Mar.5, 1898.

AMERICAN MOLES AS AGRICULTURAL PESTS AND AS FUR PRODUCERS. Theo. H. Scheffer. U.S. Dept. Agric., Farm Bull. 1247, 23 pp., 16 figs., Mar., 1922.

THE VALUE OF MOLES. Ernest Thompson Seton. Jour. Mam., vol.4, no.1, p.51, Feb., 1923.

MOLE CONTROL. James Silver, A. W. Moore. U.S. Dept. Agric., Farmers' Bull. no.1716, pp. ii, 17, figs.14, Nov., 1933.

CONTROL OF MOLES. A. N. Tissot. Press. Bull. Florida Agr. Expt. Sta., Gainesville, no.643, pp.4, 1948.

A FIRST LESSON IN GOVERNMENT MOLES. (RE: TRUE, FREDERICK W. A REVISION

OF THE AMERICAN MOLES.) New York Sun, p.1, Mar.1, 1897.

MIGHTY MINERS. Ohio Conservation Bull., Columbus, vol.10, no.6, p.2, illus., June, 1946.

Embryology, Development

THE DEVELOPMENT OF THE MOLE (TALPA EUROPEA). THE FORMATION OF THE GERMINAL LAYERS AND EARLY DEVELOPMENT OF THE MEDULLARY GROOVE AND NOTOCHORD. Walter Heape. Quart. Jour. Microscop. Sci., Lond., vol. 23, pp.1-41, pls.28-31, July, 1883.

THE DEVELOPMENT OF THE MOLE (TALPA EUROPEA), THE OVARIAN OVUM, AND SEGMENTATION OF THE OVUM. Walter Heape. Studies from the Morphological Lab., Univ. of Cambridge, vol.2, pt. 2, pp.201-218, pl.18, 1886.

"ON THE GERMINAL LAYERS AND EARLY DEVELOPMENT OF THE MOLE." Walter Heape. Proc. Roy. Soc. Lond., no.217, pp. 1-9, Nov.30, 1881.

(THE POSTEMBRYONIC DEVELOPMENT OF TALPA EUROPAEA L.) Die postembryonale Entwicklung von Talpa europaea L. Erna Mohr. Vidensk. Medd. fra Dansk. naturh. Foren., vol.94, pp.249-272, figs. 6, May 2, 1933.

Eurasia

ON THE BIOLOGY AND TRAPPING OF THE MOLE IN TARTARY. I. S. Bashkirov, I. V. Zharkov. Raboty Volzhsko-Kamskoi Zonal'noi Okhotnich'epromyslonoi Biologischeskoi Stants ii, Kazan, no.3 (Uchen'ie Zapiski Kazanskogo Gosudarstvennogo Universiteta im V.I. Ul'ianova-Lenina, vol.94, no.8), pp. 1-66, figs.18, 1934.

THE DISTRIBUTION AND BIOLOGY OF THE MOLE (TALPA EUROPAEA BRAUNERI SATUN.) AND MOLE CATCHING IN UKRAINE. S. Folitarek. Bull. Moscow Soc. Nat. 41: 235-302, 1932.

DESCRIPTION OF A NEW GENUS OF INSECTIVOROUS MAMMALIA OR TALPIDAE FROM BORNEO. J. E. Gray. Proc. Zool. Soc. Lond., pt.16, pp.23-24, 1848.

A DESMAN FROM PORTUGAL. Martin A. C. Hinton. Nat. Hist. Mag., Lond., vol. 2, no.10, pp.49-50, fig.1, 1929.

TAXONOMIC STUDIES ON THE JAPANESE MOUNTAIN MOLE (TALPA MIZURA), WITH DESCRIPTIONS OF TWO NEW SUBSPECIES. Yoshinori Imaizumi. Bull.Nat. Sci. Mus., Tokyo, vol.2, no.1, pp.26-38, Mar., 1955.

(ON THE ECOLOGY AND AGRICULTURAL IMPORTANCE OF THE MOLE IN THE FOREST PLAINS WEST OF THE DNIEPER AND IN THE UKRAINIAN FOREST REGION.) Zur Oekologie und Landwirtschaftlichen Bedeutung des Maulwurfs in der Waldsteppe westlich vom Dnepr und im Ukrainischen Waldegebiet. A. F. Kryschtal. Zoologicheskii Zhurnal (Zool. Jour. USSR), Moscou, vol.13, no.2, pp.292-310, 1934.

A NEW NAME FOR THE LESSER JAPANESE MOLE. Nagamichi Kuroda. Jour. Mam. Soc. Japan, vol.1, no.4, p.74, June, 1957.

MATERIAL ON THE BIOLOGY OF THE MOLE (TALPA EUROPEA L.) OF TULA DECIDUOUS FOREST. A. P. Kuzyakin. Bull. Moscow Soc. Nat. 44: 230-239, 1935.

A NEW FORM OF MOLE FROM YUGOSLAVIA. V. Martino, E. Martino. Jour. Mam., vol.12, no.1, p.53, Feb., 1931.

A NEW MOLE FROM ANNAM. Gerrit S. Miller, Jr. Jour. Mam., vol.21, no.2, pp. 203-204, May 14, 1940.

NOTES ON SOME MOLES FROM SOUTHEASTERN ASIA. Gerrit S. Miller, Jr. Jour. Mam., Baltimore, vol.21, no.4, pp. 442-444, Nov.14, 1940.

BRIEF ACCOUNT OF THE EXPEDITION TO STUDY DESMANA MOSCHATA IN THE KOZLOW DISTRICT (CENTRAL RUSSIA), IN THE FALL OF 1929. L. V. Shaposchnikov. Zool. Zhurn. Moscow, vol.11, no.1, pp.61-81, map, figs.10, 1932.

DESCRIPTION OF A NEW SPECIES OF MOLE FROM CHINA. Oldfield Thomas. Ann. and Mag. Nat. Hist. (5), vol.7, pp. 469-471, June, 1881.

A NEW CHINESE MOLE OF THE GENUS SCAPTOCHIRUS. Oldfield Thomas. Ann. and Mag. Nat. Hist. (8), vol.5, no.28, pp. 350-351, Apr., 1910.

A NEW MOLE FROM WESTERN SIAM. Oldfield Thomas. Ann. and Mag. Nat. Hist., ser.10, vol.3, pp.206-207, Feb., 1929.

ON THE MOLE OF THE ROMAN DISTRICT. Oldfield Thomas. Ann. and Mag. Nat. Hist., (7), vol.10, no.60, pp.516-517, Dec., 1902.

DESCRIPTION OF A NEW GENUS AND SPECIES OF MOLE, DYMECODON PILIROSTRIS, FROM JAPAN. Frederick W. True. U.S. Nat. Mus. Proc., Washington, vol.9, pp.97-98, Sept.2, 1886.

Food Habits

MOLES DESTROY WASPS' NESTS. Fred E. Brooks. Jour. Mam., vol.4, no.3, p.183, Aug., 1923.

DO MOLES (TALPA EUROPAEA L.) STORE UP WORMS? Magnus Degerbol. Videnska beliga Meddelelser fra Dansk Naturhist. Forening, vol.84, pp.195-200, Oct., 1927.

THE IDENTITY OF EARTHWORMS STORED BY MOLES. A. C. Evans. Proc. Zool. Soc. Lond., vol.118, pt.2, pp.356-359, Aug.18, 1948.

QUANTITATIVE EXPERIMENTS ON THE FOOD CONSUMPTION OF PARASCALOPS BREWERI. Francis H. Fay. Jour. Mam., vol.35, no.1, pp.107-109, Feb.10, 1954.

(STOMACH STONES CONSISTING OF PLANT PARTS IN THE MOLE.) Magensteinbildungen aus Pflanzenteilien im Magen des Maulwurfs (Talpa europaea, L.). F. Hauchecorne. Zool. Anzeiger, vol.62, pp.27-31, 12 figs., Jan.20, 1925.

MOLES: A CHANGE OF DIET? Ernest Heath. Field, London, vol.159, no.4123, p. 15, Jan.2, 1932.

(ON THE DIET OF THE MOLE TALPA EUROPAEA FRISIUS MUELLER 1776.) Zur Nahrung des Maulwurfs, Talpa europaea frisius Mueller, 1776. H. Loehrl. Saeugetierk. Mitteil., Stuttgart, 4 (1): 30, Jan.1, 1956.

FOOD HABITS OF TOWNSEND AND COAST MOLES. A. W. Moore. Jour. Mam., vol. 14, no.1, pp.36-40, pl.2, Feb., 1933.

(INVESTIGATIONS OF THE FOOD OF THE MOLE.) Untersuchungen ueber die Nahrung des Maulwurfs. Hans Sachtleben. Arbeit aus der Biol. Reichsanstalt fuer Land-und Forstwirtschaft, Band 14, Heft.1, pp.77-96, 1925.

A STUDY OF THE FOOD OF MOLES IN ILLINOIS. James A. West. Bull. Illinois State Lab. Nat. Hist., vol.9, Art.2, Oct., 1910, pp.13-22., Oct., 1910.

FOOD HABITS OF TOWNSEND'S MOLE, SCAPANUS TOWNSENDII (BACHMAN). H. M. Wight. Jour. Mam., vol.9, no.1, pp.19-33, Feb., 1928.

Fossils

THE PLEISTOCENE MOLE OF SARDINIA. Dorothea M. A. Bate. Ann. and Mag. Nat. Hist., London, ser.11, vol.12, no.91, pp. 448-461, Feb.20, 1946.

IDENTITY OF THE PLEISTOCENE MOLE FROM GIBRALTAR. Charles A. Reed. Jour. Mam., 35 (4): 583, Nov.29, 1954.

A REVISION OF THE FOSSIL WATER-MOLES (DESMANINAE). A. Schreuder. Archiv. Néerlandaises Zool. Haarlem, vol. 4, livr.3-4, pp.201-333, figs.99, pls.11, 1940.

General Habits, Ecology, Behavior

AN ECOLOGICAL STUDY OF THE MOLE. A. V. Arlton. Jour. Mam., 17 (4): 349-371, Nov., 1936.

ON NOMADIC HABITS OF THE MUSK RAT (DESMANA MOSCHATA L.) IN RELATION TO THE PROBLEM OF ITS AREA OF DISTRIBUTION. I. I. Barabash-Nikiphorov. Zool. Jour. USSR, Moscow, vol.24, no.6, pp.379-383, map 1, 1945.

MOLE POPULATIONS, AND DEEP NESTING. Maurice Burton. Illus. London News, vol. 217, no.5821, pp.785-787, illus., Nov.11, 1950.

MOLES AND OPEN SPACES. Maurice Burton. Illus. London News, 228 (6099): 416, illus., Apr.28, 1956.

MOLES. Wm. Christie. Gardeners' Chronicle, Pangbourne, ser.3, vol.113, no. 2939, p.164, Apr.24, 1943.

FIELD OBSERVATION OF THE MOLE, TALPA EUROPAEA. Peter Crowcroft. Proc. Zool. Soc. Lond., 128 (4): 592, July 24, 1957.

THE STAR-NOSED MOLE AMPHIBIOUS. A. K. Fisher. Amer. Nat. Extra, vol.19, p.895, Sept., 1885.

A SWIMMING HAIRY-TAILED MOLE. Leonard E. Foote. Jour. Mam., vol.22, no.4, p.452, Nov.14, 1941.

A PRELIMINARY INVESTIGATION ON THE ECOLOGY OF THE COMMON MOLE (TALPA EUROPEA). John Ford. Jour. Anim. Ecol., London, vol.4, no.1, pp.88-89, May, 1935.

ON THE REACTION OF MOGERA WOGURA WOGURA TO METALIC MATERIALS IN THE UNDERGROUND LIFE. Eiji Fujiwara. Trans. Mamm. Soc. Japan, no.9, pp.78-79, illus., Apr., 1954.

(CONTRIBUTION TO THE ETHOLOGY OF THE MOLE.) "Contribution a l'ethologie de la taupe (Talpa europaea)." R. Godet. Bull. Soc. Zool. France, 75:107-128, 1951.

AGGRESSIVE BEHAVIOUR IN THE MOLE. G. K. Godfrey. Proc. Zool. Soc. London, 128 (4): 602-604, July 24, 1957.

A FIELD STUDY OF THE ACTIVITY OF THE MOLE (TALPA EUROPAEA). G. K. Godfrey. Ecology, vol.36, no.4, pp.678-685, illus., 1955.

OBSERVATIONS OF THE MOVEMENTS OF MOLES (TALPA EUROPAEA L.) AFTER WEANING. G. K. Godfrey. Proc. Zool. Soc. Lond., 128 (2): 287-295, pl.1, Apr.18, 1957.

THE VOYAGE OF A DRY-LAND SUBMARINE. A. Lee Haines. Yosemite Nat. Notes, Yosemite, vol.19, no.9, p.68, Sept., 1940.

ACTIVITY OF BREWER'S MOLE (PARASCALOPS BREWERI). W. J. Hamilton, Jr. Jour. Mam., 20 (3): 307-309, Aug., 1939.

HABITS OF THE STAR-NOSED MOLE, CONDYLURA CRISTATA. W. J. Hamilton, Jr. Jour. Mam., vol.12, no.4, pp.345-355, pl.13, Nov., 1931

HABITS OF THE COMMON MOLE. F. A. Hanawalt. Ohio Jour. Sci., vol.22, pp.164-169, Apr., 1922.

MOLES. W. M. Hornsey. Gardeners' Chronicle, Pangbourne, ser.3, vol.113, no. 2946, p.239, June 12, 1943.

(THE MOLE AS A DAY ANIMAL.) Der Maulwurf als Tagtier. Viktor Hornung. Zool. Garten, vol.14, nos.1-2, p.104, 1942.

(ON THE VORACITY OF THE MOLE.) Zur Gefraessigkeit des Maulwurfs. Viktor Hornung. Zool. Garten, vol.14, no.3, p.156, 1942.

(SOUNDS OF THE MOLE TALPA EUROPAEA L.) Lautaeusserungen des Maulwurfs, Talpa europaea L. Viktor Hornung. Zool. Garten, Leipzig, NF, vol.16, no.5, p.208, 1950.

THE MOLE--SKILLFUL BURROWER. Eric Hosking, Harold Bastin. Canadian Nat., Toronto, vol.11, no.2, p.62, illus., Mar. Apr., 1949.

MOLE NOTES. A. Brazier Howell. Jour. Mam., vol.4, no.4, p.253, Nov.1, 1923.

SOME HABITS OF THE PRAIRIE MOLE, SCALOPUS AQUATICUS MACHRINUS. Hartley H. T. Jackson. Jour. Mam., vol. 3, no.2, p.115, May 9, 1922.

(ON THE VORACITY OF THE MOLE.) Zur Gefraessigkeit des Maulwurfs. Harald

Kuenzl. Garten, Leipzig, (N.F.), vol.20, nos.4/5, pp.314-315, 1954.

THE LOWLY MOLE, A BLIND BURROWER. Hamilton M. Laing. Illus. Canadian Forest and Outdoors, vol.25, pp.475-476, 493, illus., Aug., 1929.

OBSERVATIONS ON NEUROTRICHUS GIBBSII GIBBSII. Kenneth Racey. Murrelet, Seattle (mimeographed), vol.10, no.3, pp. 61-62, 1 fig., Sept., 1929.

BEHAVIOR OF A SHREW-MOLE IN CAPTIVITY. Charles A. Reed. Jour. Mam., vol.25, no.2, pp.196-198, May, 1944.

SWIMMING, FEEDING AND LOCOMOTION OF A CAPTIVE MOLE. Charles A. Reed, Thane Riney. Amer. Midland Nat., Notre Dame, vol.30, no.3, pp.790-791, Nov., 1943.

ECOLOGICAL COMPARISONS OF THREE GENERA OF MOLES. Theo. H. Scheffer. Trans. Kansas Acad. Sci., 52 (1): 30-37, Mar., 1949.

(MY OBSERVATIONS OF THE MOLE (TALPA VULGARIS L.) IN CAPTIVITY.) Meine Beobachtungen am Maulwurf (Talpa vulgaris, L.) in der Gefangenschaft. W. Schreitmueller. Archiv f. Nat., Abt. A, vol.89, Heft 8, pp.112-118, 1923.

MOST SECRETIVE MAMMALS. George Smokey. South Dakota Conserv. Digest, Pierre, vol.11, no.7, p.10, July, 1944.

METHODOLOGY OF THE MIGRATION OF MUSK-RATS (MYOGALE MOSCHATA L.) V. I. Tikhvinsky. Raboty Volzhsko-Kamskoi Zonal'noi Okhotnich'epromyslonoi Biologischeskoi Stantsii, Kazan, no.2, (Uchen'ie Zapiski Kazanskogo Gosudarstvennogo Universiteta im V.I. Ul'ianova-Lenina, vol.92, nos.7-8), pp.125-137, 1932.

ON THE STUDY OF MOLE TUNNELS. N. P. Voronov. Zool. Zhurnal, Moscow, 36 (10): 1530-1539, 1957.

(OBSERVATIONS OF MOLES.) Beobachtungen an Schermaeusen. A. Wahlstrom. Zool. Garten, N.F., Leipzig, vol.9, no.5, pp. 225-229, Oct., 1937.

(OBSERVATIONS OF MOLES (PARTS 4-8).) Beobachtungen an Schermaeusen. (Pt. 4-8). A. Wahlstrom. Zool. Garten, N.F., Leipzig, vol.9, no.6, pp.285-290, Dec., 1937.

OBSERVATIONS ON THE EASTERN MOLE IN CAPTIVITY. Ernest P. Walker. Jour. Mam., vol.26, no.2, p.192, July 15, 1945.

PARASCALOPS TUNNEL IN USE AFTER EIGHT YEARS. Philip L. Wright. Jour. Mam., vol.26, no.4, pp.438-439, Feb.12, 1946.

THE STAR-NOSED MOLE: A STRANGE NORTH AMERICAN CREATURE WITH ITS MUZZLE SURROUNDED BY A RING OF TENTACLES WHICH PROBABLY AID IT TO FIND WORMS DURING ITS SUBTERRANEAN WANDERINGS. Illus. London News, vol. 190, no.5102, p.187, illus., Jan.30, 1937.

Methods, Techniques

METHOD FOR KEEPING THE EASTERN MOLE IN CAPTIVITY. Willard Loren Henning. Jour. Mam., vol.33, no.3, pp. 392-395, Aug.19, 1952.

MARKING THE EUROPEAN MOLE (TALPA EUROPAEA L.) IN THE URAL MOUNTAINS. V. N. Pavlinine. Zool. Zjur., 27: 555-62, 1948.

METHODS FOR MAKING A MOLE CENSUS AND OBTAINING COEFFICIENTS FOR PLANNING MOLE CATCHING. V.K. Popov, B. Yu. Fal-kenshtein. Problems Ecol. and Biocenology, 4: 26-35, 1934.

(KEEPING AND CARING FOR THE MOLE (TALPA EUROPAEA L.).) Haltung und Pfiege des Maulwurfs (Talpa europaea L.). B. Schaerffenberg. Zool. Garten, 11: 107-9, 1939.

North America

THE STAR-NOSED MOLE IN EASTERN NORTH CAROLINA. C. S. Brimley. Jour. Mam., vol.4, no.3, pp.183-184, Aug., 1923.

DISTRIBUTION OF THE NORTHERN PLAINS MOLE IN COLORADO. W. L. Burnett. Jour. Mam., vol.5, no.4, p.264, Nov., 1924.

A MOLE FROM IDAHO. Edwin B. Caswell. Murrelet, vol.34, no.1, p.9, 1953.

THE SHREW-MOLE OF WESTERN WASHINGTON. Walter W. Dalquest, Robert L. Burnger. Murrelet, Seattle, vol.22, no.1, pp.12-14, Apr.30, 1941.

A NEW MOLE FROM WASHINGTON STATE. Walter W. Dalquest, Victor B. Scheffer. Murrelet, Seattle, vol.25, no.2, pp.27-28, May-Aug. (Sept.19), 1944.

THE MOLES (GENUS SCALOPUS) OF TEXAS. William B. Davis. Amer. Midland Nat., Notre Dame, vol.27, no.2, pp.380-386, fig.1, Mar., 1942.

THE COMMON GARDEN MOLE IN IOWA. E. E. Dunnam. Iowa Agric. Exper. Station, Circular 88, 4 pp., 5 figs., Jan., 1924.

SHREW MOLE AT BAKER LAKE. J. M. Edson. Murrelet, Seattle, vol.20, no.1, p. 10, Jan.-Apr., 1939.

CONDYLURA CRISTATA FROM THE COASTAL PLAIN OF SOUTH CAROLINA. William C. Grimm. Jour. Mam., 36 (2): 288, May 26, 1955.

THE MOLE OF SOUTHERN CALIFORNIA. J. Grinnell, H. S. Swarth. Univ. Cal. Pub. Zool., vol.10, nos.3-4, pp.131-136, figs.2, tables, Apr.13, 1912.

MOLES. Caroline A. Heppenstall. Pennsylvania Game News, Harrisburg, vol.16, no. 12, pp.10, 25, Mar., 1946.

NEW MOLES OF THE GENUS SCALOPUS. Hartley H. T. Jackson. Proc. Biol. Soc. Wash., vol.27, pp.19-22, Feb.2, 1914.

NEW MOLES OF THE GENUS SCAPANUS. Hartley H. T. Jackson. Proc. Biol. Soc. Wash., vol.27, pp.55-56, Mar.20, 1914.

A REVIEW OF THE AMERICAN MOLES. Hartley H. T. Jackson. N. Amer. Fauna, no.38, pp.1-100, figs.1-24, pls.1-6, Sept. 30, 1915.

CANADA'S BLIND TUNNELLERS. William MacMillan. Canadian Nature, Toronto, vol. 5, no.3, pp.108-109, illus., May-June, 1943.

TWO NEW MOLES FROM CALIFORNIA AND OREGON. C. Hart Merriam. Proc. Biol. Soc., Washington, vol.11, pp.101-102, Apr. 26, 1897.

AN EXTENSION OF RANGE OF THE HAIRY-TAILED MOLE, PARASCALOPS BREWERI BACHMAN. John R. Olive. Jour. Mam., vol.31, no.4, pp.458-459, Nov.21, 1950.

BREWER MOLE IN ONTARIO. W. Saunders. Canadian Field-Nat., vol.43, p.42, Feb., 1929.

A MOLE, SCALOPUS AQUATICUS (LINNAEUS) FROM TARRANT COUNTY, TEXAS. William B. Stallcup. Field and Laboratory, Dallas, 24 (3): 104, June, 1956.

A NOTE ON THE DISTRIBUTION OF THE STAR-NOSED MOLE. Dayton Stoner. Jour. Mam., vol.6, no.2, p.125, May, 1925.

A REVISION OF THE AMERICAN MOLES. Frederick W. True. Proc. U.S. Nat. Mus., vol.19, pub.1101, pp.1-112, pls.1-4, figs.45, Dec.21, 1896.

ADDITIONAL RECORDS OF THE EASTERN MOLE IN WEST VIRGINIA. L. Wayne Wilson. Jour. Mam., vol.25, no.2, pp.201-202, May 25, 1944.

Pelage, Molts

ALBINO MOLES. (Miss) Christie. Scottish Naturalist, no.172, p.125, Aug., 1928.

ABNORMAL COLORATION IN THE PRAIRIE MOLE. E. Lendell Cockrum, Norman A. Meinkoth. Jour. Mam., vol.23, no.4, p. 451, Nov.14, 1942.

AN ABNORMALLY COLORED MOLE FROM MARYLAND. John E. Cooper. Maryland Naturalist, vol.23, nos.1-2, pp.78-79, 1953.

SKIN GLAND ACTIVITY AND PELAGE DESCRIPTIONS IN MOLES. W. Robert Eadie. Jour. Mam., 35 (2): 186-196, graphs., May, 1954.

(ABNORMALLY COLORED MOLES.) Abnorm gefaerbte Maulwuerfe. H. Erhard. Zeitschr. f. Saeugetierkunde, bd.4, heft 1, pp.47-48, July 6, 1929.

(A CASE OF RARE ALBINISM OBSERVED IN THE COMMON MOLE.) Un cas d'albinisme rare observé chez la taupe commune. Emile Genevoix. Mem Soc. Sci. Nat. et Archeol. Creuse, vol.23, nos.2, 3, pp.43-44, 1926.

OCCURRENCE OF AN ALBINO TOWNSEND MOLE. Margaret Klein. Murrelet, Seattle, vol.25, no.1, p.10, June 27, 1944.

IRIDESCENCE IN THE OREGON MOLE. C. Hart Merriam. Amer. Nat. Extra, p. 895, Sept., 1885.

THE COAT COLOR OF MOLES. Loye Miller. Jour. Mam., Baltimore, vol.2, no.3, pp. 163-166, Aug.19, 1921.

THE PROBLEM OF VARIATION IN THE COLOUR OF THE MOLE. A. M. Stewart. Scottish Nat., no.200, pp.39-44, Mar.-Apr., 1933.

OCCURRENCE OF AN ALBINO MOLE. Arthur Svihla. Murrelet, Seattle, vol.20, no.3, Sept.-Dec., p.70, Dec.16, 1939.

OCCURRENCE OF ANOTHER ALBINO MOLE. Arthur Svihla. Murrelet, Seattle, vol.22, no. 2, p.36, May-Aug., 1941.

EXHIBITION OF FOUR EXAMPLES OF A CURIOUSLY COLOURED VARIETY OF THE COMMON MOLE (TALPA EUROPAEA). F. H. Wilson. Proc. Zool. Soc. Lond., pt.28, p.206, 1860.

Predators

EASTERN MOLES EATEN BY COTTONMOUTH AND GRAY FOX. W. B. Davis. Jour. Mam., vol.32, no.1, pp.114-115, Feb. 15, 1951.

RAT EATING MOLE. V. R. Garrett. The Field (London), vol.148, p.205, July 29, 1926.

BREWER'S MOLE AS FOOD OF THE BULLFROG. John A. Heller. Copeia, no.165, p. 116, Dec.23, 1927.

Reproductive Biology

NOTES ON REPRODUCTION IN THE STAR-NOSED MOLE. W. Robert Eadie, W. J. Hamilton, Jr. Jour. Mam., 37 (2): 223-231, June 9, 1956.

REPRODUCTION OF TALPA EUROPAEA IN SUFFOLK. Gillian K. Godfrey. Jour. Mam., 37 (3): 438-440, Sept.11, 1956.

A STAR-NOSED MOLE'S NEST AT NEWTON CENTRE, MASSACHUSETTS. Fred H. Kennard. Jour. Mam., vol.10, no.1, pp.77-78, Feb.11, 1929.

THE OESTROUS CYCLE AND INTERSEXUALITY IN THE FEMALE MOLE (TALPA EUROPAEA LINN.). L. Harrison Matthews. Proc. Zool. Soc. London for 1935, pt.2, pp. 347-383, figs.29, July, 1935.

A NOTE ON THE REPRODUCTION OF THE MOLE (TALPA EUROPAEA BRAUNERI SATUN.). N. G. Milyutin. Zool. Zh., 20 (3): 482-484, 1941.

(YOUNG MOLES.) Junge Maulwuerfe. Erna Mohr. Freude am Leben, Berlin, vol.17, nos.4-5, pp.70-72, illus., July-Aug., 1940.

(YOUNG MOLES.) Nestjunge Maulwuerfe. Erna Mohr. Zool. Anz., vol.109, nos.5-6, pp.158-159, Feb., 1935.

THE NEST AND YOUNG OF THE STAR-NOSED MOLE (CONDYLURA CRISTATA). Sutherland Eric Simpson. Jour. Mam., vol. 4, no.3, pp.167-171, pls.17-20, Aug., 1923.

Taxonomy

TWO NEW MOLES (GENUS SCALOPUS) FROM MEXICO AND TEXAS. Rollin H. Baker. Univ. Kansas Publ., Mus. Nat. Hist., vol.5, no.2, pp.17-24, Feb.28, 1951.

GEOGRAPHIC VARIATION IN THE MOLE SCAPANUS LATIMANUS. Fletcher G. Palmer. Jour. Mam., vol.18, no.3, pp.280-314, pls.2, tables 2, Aug., 1937.

REVISION OF THE OLD-WORLD MOLES OF THE GENUS TALPA LINNAEUS. Ernst Schwarz. Proc. Zool. Soc. Lond., vol.118, pt.1, pp.36-48, May 20, 1948.

(SIZE VARIABILITY AND RACE FORMATION IN TALPA EUROPAEA.) Grossenvariabilitaet und Rassenbildung bei Talpa europaea. G.H.W. Stein. Zool. Jahrb., (Syst.), 79: 321-49, 1950.

THE PROPER SCIENTIFIC NAME FOR BREWER'S MOLE. Frederick W. True. Science, N.S., vol.1, no.4, p.101, Jan.25, 1895.

Nesophontidae

PRELIMINARY DIAGNOSIS OF AN APPARENTLY NEW FAMILY OF INSECTIVORA. H. E. Anthony. Bull. Amer. Mus. Nat. Hist., vol.35, art.41, pp.725-728, pls.23, Nov.16, 1916.

## DERMOPTERA

### Cynocephalidae

THE FLYING LEMUR. C. William Beebe. Bull. New York Zool. Soc., vol.16, no.55, pp.952-954, illus., Jan., 1913.

NOTES ON THE FLYING LEMURS (GALEOPTERUS). F. N. Chasen, C. Boden Kloss. Bull. Raffles Mus., Singapore, no.2, pp.12-22, July, 1929.

TWO NEW RACES OF GALEOPTERUS. F. N. Chasen, C. Boden Kloss. Bull. Raffles Mus., Singapore, Straits Settlements, no. 2, pp.11-12, July, 1929.

(ON THE MAMMAL GENUS GALEOPITHECUS: A MORPHOLOGICAL INVESTIGATION.) Ueber Die Saeugethiergattung Galeopithecus. Eine Morphologische Untersuchung. Wilhelm Leche. Kongl. Svenska Vetenskaps-Akademiens Bandlingar, vol.21, no.2, pp.3-92, pl. 5, Stockholm, 1886.

THE NOMENCLATURE OF THE FLYING-LEMURS. Gerrit S. Miller, Jr. Proc. Biol. Soc., Wash., vol.19, p.41, Feb.26, 1906.

THE EXTERNAL CHARACTERS OF THE FLYING LEMUR (GALEOPTERUS TEMMINCKII). R. I. Pocock. Proc. Zool. Soc., Lond., pt.2, pp.429-444, figs.16-23, July 15, 1926.

THE SKELETON IN THE FLYING LEMURS, GALEOPTERIDAE. Robert W. Shufeldt. Philippine Jour. Sco., Manila, vol.6, nos. 3-4, (Section D, General Biology, Ethnology and Anthropology), pp.139-211, pls.6, Bur. Sci., Philippine Gov., Manila, P.I., June, Aug., 1911.

A CASE OF POLYDACTYLY IN THE COLUGO, CYNOCEPHALUS. C. C. D. Shute, A. d'A. Bellairs. Jour. Mam., 36 (1): 131-132, illus., Feb.25, 1955.

THE NOMENCLATURE OF THE FLYING-LEMURS. Oldfield Thomas. Ann. and Mag. Nat. Hist. (8), vol.1, no.3, pp.252-255, Mar., 1908.

ON THE FLYING LEMURS (GALEOPITHECUS). G. R. Waterhouse. Proc. Zool. Soc. Lond., pt.6, pp.119-120, 1838.

NOTES ON THE LIFE HISTORY OF THE FLYING LEMUR. Charles H. Wharton. Jour. Mam., vol.31, no.3, pp.269-273, Aug.21, 1950.

HABITS OF THE FLYING LEMUR (GALEOPTERUS PENINSULAE). W. S. Wood. Jour. Bombay Nat. Hist. Soc., vol.32, p.372, Oct.20, 1927.

## CHIROPTERA

BATS. G. M. Allen. Cambridge, Harvard University Press, 368 pp., 1939.

BATS, STRANGEST OF MAMMALS. G. M. Allen. Science Digest, Chicago, vol.6, no. 3, pp.54-58, Sept., 1939.

ON THE EMBRYOS OF BATS. Allen Harrison. Contrib. Zool. Lab. Univ. Pennsylvania, vol.1, no.2, pp.3-42, 1895.

THE BAT. H. E. Anthony. Nat. Hist., vol. 25, no.6, pp.560-570, Dec., 1925.

BATS--MAMMALIAN PURSUIT PLANES. G. W. Bradt. Michigan Conserv., Lansing, vol.17, no.5, pp.4-5, illus., May, 1948.

SOME BAT-OLOGY. John F. Breen. All-Pets Mag., Fond du Lac, vol.19, no.10, pp. 67, 69-70. Oct., 1948.

CONCOURSE OF BATS. P. J. Burton. Trans. Suffolk Nat. Soc., Norwich, vol.4, pt.4, p. 287, Dec., 1941.

THE FLYING MAMMALS. Marion B. Carr. Jour. Nat. Hist. Mag., New York, vol.6, no.8, pp.11-13, illus., Oct., 1941.

FANNIE WAS A BAT. Richard L. Cassell. Nature Mag., Washington, vol.37, no.9, pp.457-460, 497, illus., Nov., 1944.

BATS. H. F. Cofer. Yosemite Nat. Notes, Yosemite, vol.21, no.11, p.91, Nov., 1942.

THE CHARMING FLITTERMOUSE. Edith Coleman. Victorian Nat., Melbourne, vol. 63, no.12, pp.251-255, illus., Apr., 1947.

BATS, CLOVER, WATER LETTUCE AND MALARIA. G. Covell. Trop. Disease Bull., Lond., vol.45, no.9, p.757, Sept., 1948.

BATS. Freda Davies. Canadian Nature, Toronto, vol.10, no.2, pp.44-46, illus., Mar.-Apr., 1948.

(OBSERVATIONS ON THE BIOLOGY OF FLYING FOXES.) Observations sur la biologie des Rousettes. Ed Dechambre. Bull. Soc. Nat. Acclim. France, Paris, 82 annee, no.3, pp.65-71, Mar., 1935.

A BAT COLONY. Albert De Lestang. Australian Zool., vol.6, pt.1, pp.106-107, Aug.13, 1929.

THE LIFE OF THE BAT. Charles Derennes. Translated from the French by Louise Collier Wilcox, 183 pp., 1924.

(BATS OF THE MADAGASCAN FAUNA.) Les chauves-souris de la faune Malgache. Jean Dorst. Mus. Nat. d'Hist. Nat., Paris, ser.2, vol.19, no.4, pp.306-313, Sept., 1947.

FLYING MAMMALS. Eugene H. Dustman. Ohio Conservation Bull., Columbus, vol.15, no.3, pp.13, 28, Mar., 1951.

A BAT REPORTS. Ruth Elwonger. Frontiers, Philadelphia, vol.9, no.2, pp.46-47, 54, Dec., 1944.

(FLYING FOXES AND VAMPIRE BATS.) Von Flughunden und Vampiren. Heinz Felten. Natur und Volk, Frankfurt, vol. 82, no.3, pp.65-73, Mar.1, 1952.

(MAMMALS. II. CHIROPTERS.) Mammiferi. II. Chirotteri. Enrico Festa. Boll. Mus. Zool. and Anat. Comp., Univ. Torino, vol.21, no.524, pp.8, Mar.15, 1906.

(CONTRIBUTION TO THE NATURAL HISTORY OF BATS.) Beitrag zur Naturgeschichte der Fledermaeuse. G. von Frauenfeld. Mittheilungen Freuden Naturwissenschaften in Vienna, vol.4, 5 pp., Mar., 1848.

FLYING SHADOWS OF THE NIGHT. G. G. Goodwin. Nat. Hist., vol.28, pp.515-522, illus., Oct., 1928.

MYSTERY MAMMALS OF THE TWILIGHT. Donald R. Griffin. Nat. Geogr. Mag., Washington, vol.90, no.1, pp.117-134, illus., July, 1946.

WINGS WITHOUT FEATHERS. Donald R. Griffin. New England Naturalist, Boston, no.4, pp.11-13, illus., Sept., 1939.

NOTES ON THE SEASONAL MOVEMENTS AND HABITS OF SOME CAVE BATS. Mary J. Guthrie. Jour. Mam., vol.14, no.1, pp. 1-19, pl.1, Feb., 1933.

INSECT-EATING BATS. J. L. Harrison. Malayan Nature Jour., vol.7, no.5, pp.191-195, Mar., 1953.

INTRODUCING BATS. J. L. Harrison. Malayan Nature Jour., vol.7, no.2, pp.56-63, June, 1952.

THE MUCH MALIGNED BAT. Paul Griswold Howes. Scientific American, vol.138, pp. 130-131, illus., Feb., 1928.

(BIOLOGICAL OBSERVATIONS ON BATS.) Biologische Beobachtungen an Fledermaeusen. Anton Kolb. Saeugetierk. Mitteil., Stuttgart, vol.2, no.1, pp.15-26, illus., Jan.1, 1954.

(MALE ASSOCIATIONS AND CHANGES OF QUARTERS IN BATS.) Maennchengesellschaften und Quartierwechsel bei Fledermaeusen. Hans Loehrl. Saeugetierk. Mitteil., Stuttgart, 3 (3): 103-104, July 1, 1955.

(Review by Glover Morrill Allen of) BATS. Marcus Ward Lyon, Jr. Amer. Midland Nat., Notre Dame, vol.22, no.2, pp.478-479, Sept., 1939.

(CONTRIBUTION TO KNOWLEDGE OF BATS.) Contribucion al conocimiento de los murcielagos. Liborio Martinez, Bernardo Villa Ramirez. III. Anales Inst. Biol., Mexico City, vol.12, no.1, pp.401-419, figs.3, 1941.

(CONTRIBUTION TO KNOWLEDGE OF THE BIOLOGY OF BATS. Contribution à la connaissance de la biologie des Chauves-Souris. P. Mathias, J. Séguéla. Mammalia, Paris, vol.4, no.1, pp.15-19, Mar., 1940.

(ON THE LIFE OF THE COMMON BAT.) Vom Leben der gemeinen Fledermaus. Juerg Mathis. Zeitschr. Morph. und Oekol., der Tiere, vol.13, pp.706-721, fig., Feb.25, 1929.

BATS: MAMMALS THAT FLY. Gerrit S. Miller, Jr. The World is Yours, Smithsonian Inst., Radio Program, vol.1, no.37, pp.1-13, June 17, 1940.

THE NEW CATALOGUE OF CHIROPTERA IN THE BRITISH MUSEUM. Gerrit S. Miller, Jr. Science, n.s., vol.36, no.929, pp.525-527, Oct.18, 1912.

CAVES. Charles E. Mohr. Audubon Nat. Bull., New York, ser.no.18, Bull.no.5, 4 pp., Jan., 1948.

CREATURES OF DARKNESS. Charles E. Mohr. Nat. Hist., vol.38, no.3, pp.260-264, illus., 1936.

THESE BATS! Charles E. Mohr. Fauna, Philadelphia, vol.1, no.3, pp.42-45, Sept., 1939.

(FROM THE LIFE OF OUR BATS.) Aus dem Leben unserer Fledermaeuse. F. P. Mohres. Kosmos, Stuttgart, vol.46, no.7, pp.291-297, July, 1950.

BATS: NAVIGATORS OF THE NIGHT. Robert T. Orr. Pacific Discovery, San Francisco, vol.1, no.1, pp.15-18, illus., Jan.-Feb., 1948.

THE BAT: CHILD OF NIGHT. Donald Culross Peattie. Frontiers, Lancaster, vol. 11, no.3, pp.77-78, 87, 91, Feb., 1947.

BATS. Oliver G. Pike. Nature, Lond., vol.155, no.3926, p.122, illus., Jan.27, 1945.

BATS. Charles L. Ripper. Wm. Morrow and Co., New York, 1954.

(CATALOG OF THE TYPES OF MAMMALS OF THE NATIONAL MUSEUM OF NATURAL HISTORY. II. ORDER CHIROPTERA. Catalogue des types de mammifères du Muséum National d'Histoire Naturelle. II. Ordre des Chiropteres. P. Rode. Bull. Mus. Nat. Hist., Paris, ser.2, vol.13, no.4, pp.227-252, 1941.

(THE MAMMALS OF THE MOTTAZ COLLECTION (CONTINUATION). II. THE CHIROPTERS.) Les mammifères de la collection Mottaz (suite). II.--Les chiroptères. P. Rode, P. Cantuel. Bull. Mus. Nat. Hist., Paris, ser.2, vol.11, no.3, pp.274-278, 1939.

THE DETECTION AND EVASION OF BATS BY MOTHS. K. D. Roeder, A. E. Treat. Smithsonian Institution, Publ.4493, 6 pls., 1962.

(BATS.) Fladdermoessen. Olof Ryberg. Svenska Djur. Daeggdjuren, P. A. Norstedt and Soener Uddevalla, pp.555-575, illus., 1949.

STUDIES ON BATS AND BAT PARASITES. Olof Ryberg. Univ. Lund and Zool. Lab. Agr., Dairy, and Hort. Inst. of Alnarp, Stockholm, Sweden, 330 pp., 1947.

(ORGANIZATION AND BIONOMICS OF THE CHIROPTERS.) Organización y bionomía de los quirópteros. Castellarnau de Sala, P. Ignacio. Revista "Ibérica," Barcelona, no. 101, pp.3-8, figs.5, Jan.4, 1947.

DESCRIPTIONS AND RECORDS OF NEO-TROPICAL BATS. Colin Campbell Sanborn. Papers on Mammalogy, Zool. Ser., Field Mus. Nat. Hist., Chicago, vol.27, pp.371-387, Dec.8, 1941.

NEOTROPICAL BATS IN THE CARNEGIE MUSEUM. Colin Campbell Sanborn. Ann. Carnegie Mus., vol.21, no.3, pp.171-183, Sept., 1932.

NOTES ON NEOTROPICAL BATS. Colin Campbell Sanborn. Occas. Papers, Mus. Zool. Univ. Michigan, no.373, pp.5, May 26, 1938.

RECORDS AND MEASUREMENTS OF NEO-TROPICAL BATS. Colin Campbell Sanborn. Zool. Ser. Field Mus. Nat. Hist., vol.20, no.13, pp.93-106, Aug.15, 1936.

(BATS IN POPULAR BELIEF AND REALITY.) Fledermaeuse in Volksglauben und Wirklichkeit. M. Schlott. Naturforscher, vol.10, no.1, 1942.

(INFORMATION ON DOMESTIC BATS.) Zur Kenntnis heimischer Fledermaeuse. M. Schlott. Zool. Garten, vol.14, nos.1-2, pp. 35-48, illus., 1942.

THE BAT. George Smokey. South Dakota Conservation Digest, Pierre, vol.9, no.9, pp.8, 11, Sept., 1942.

(CHIROPTER ACQUISITIONS.) Die Chiropternausbeute. Dr. Karl Toldt. Denkschr. math.-naturw. kl. kais. Akad. Wiss., Wein, vol.76, pp.43-53, 1-11, figs.3, 1908.

NOTES ON BATS. Frederick W. True. Science Record, Boston, vol.2, no.3, pp.52-53, Jan.15, 1884.

BATS ARE MY BEST FRIENDS. Ernest P. Walker. Saturday Evening Post, Philadelphia, vol.222, no.32, pp.26-27, 97-98, illus., Feb.4, 1950.

BATS. W. A. Wimsatt. Scientific American, New York, 197 (5): 105, Nov., 1957.

THE BATS. John Sumner Wiseman. Wyoming Wildlife, Cheyenne, vol.13, no.2, pp. 26-30, illus., Feb., 1949.

BATS ON THE WING. Iowa Conservationist, Des Moines, vol.5, no.6, p.47, June 15, 1946.

"WHAT IS A BAT?"--NEW EXHIBIT TELLS PRINCIPAL FACTS ABOUT ODD FLYING MAMMALS. Field Mus. News, Chicago, vol.14, no.3, pp.4-5, Mar., 1943.

DWELLERS IN DARKNESS. Texas Game and Fish, Austin, vol.1, no.9, pp.7, 14, illus., Aug., 1943.

### Africa

(CONTRIBUTION TO THE STUDY OF THE BATS OF CAMEROUN.) Contribution à l'étude des Chiroptères du Cameroun. V. Aellen. Neuchâtel, Impr. Paul Attinger S.A., 121 pp., illus., maps, 1952.

(NATIONAL PARK OF NIOKOLO-KOBA. II. CHIROPTERA.) Le Parc National du Niokolo-Koba. II. Chiroptera. V. Aellen. Mem. Inst. Afrique Francais Noire, 48:23-34, 1956.

BATS FROM BRITISH EAST AFRICA. Glover M. Allen. Bull. Mus. Comp. Zool., Harvard College, vol.54, no.9, pp.321-331, Dec., 1911.

THE AMERICAN MUSEUM CONGO EXPEDITION COLLECTION OF BATS. J. A. Allen. Bull. Amer. Mus. Nat. Hist., vol.37, no.18, pp.405-563, Sept.29, 1917.

(CAVE BATS OF UPPER KATANGA. BELGIAN CONGO.) Chiropteres des grottes du Haut-Katange (Congo Belge). Felix Anciaux de Faveaux. Bull. Inst. Francais Afrique Nord, ser.A, 20 (1): 263-275, 1958.

(CAVE BATS OF FRENCH GUINEA.) Les chauves-souris cavernicles de la Guinee Francaise. M. Eisentraut, H. Knorr. Mammalia, Paris, 21 (4): 321-335, Dec., 1957.

TWO BATS (MICROCHIROPTERA) NEW TO THE FAUNA OF TANGANYIKA TERRITORY. D. L. Harrison. Durban Mus. Nov., 5 (7): 95-98, Feb.15, 1958.

NOTES ON THE BATS (MICROCHIROPTERA) FROM A CAVE IN THE PIETERMARITZ-BURG DISTRICT OF NATAL. D. L. Harrison, P. A. Clancey. Ann. Natal Mus., vol. 12, pt.2, pp.177-181, Apr., 1952.

(NOTES ON A NEW BAT OF THE FRENCH SUDAN.) Note sur un Chéiroptere nouveau du Soudan Francais. Robert T. Hatt. Bull. Soc. Zool. France, vol.53, pp.374-376, 1928.

NOTES ON SOME AFRICAN BATS, MAINLY FROM THE BELGIAN CONGO. R. W. Hyman. Rev. Zool. and Bot. Africaine, vol. 50, nos.3-4, pp.277-295, Dec.30, 1954.

TWO NEW BATS, EPTESICUS AND MOPS, FROM ANGOLA. John Eric Hill. Amer. Mus. Novitates, no.916, pp.1-3, fig.1, Apr.17, 1937.

(ATTEMPT AT A DICHOTOMOUS KEY TO THE BATS OF THE BARBARY.) Essai e'une clef dichotomique des chéiroptéres dela Barbarie. P. Laurent. Mammalia, Paris, vol.1, no.4, pp.133-159, June, 1937.

NOTES ON THE GENITALIA AND REPRODUCTION OF SOME AFRICAN BATS. L. Harrison Matthews. Proc. Zool. Soc. Lond., ser.B, vol.111, pp.289-346, figs.20, pls.9, 1942.

A NEW BAT FROM GERMAN EAST AFRICA. Gerrit S. Miller, Jr. Proc. Biol. Soc., Washington, vol.18, pp.227-228, Dec.9, 1905.

(CONTRIBUTION TO STUDY OF THE BATS OF MOROCCO: PIPISTRELLUS SAVII AND BARBASTELLA BARBASTELLUS.) Contribution a l'etude des chauves souris du Maroc: Pipistrellus savii et Barbastella barbastellus. Jean B. Panouse. Bull. Soc. Sci. Nat. and Phys. Maroc, 35 (3): 259-263, 1955.

(OBSERVATIONS OF THE BATS OF MOROCCO AND THE ADDITION OF A NEW SPECIES, MYOTIS MYSTACINUS (KUHL 1819), TO THE MOROCCAN FAUNA.) Observations sur les chauves-souris du Moroc et addition d'une nouvelle espece Myotis mystacinus (Kuhl 1819) a la faune marocaine. Jean B. Panouse. Bull. Soc. Sci. Nat. and Phys. Maroc, vol.33, pp.89-107, 1953.

CHIROPTERA FROM DUNDO, LUNDA, NORTHEASTERN ANGOLA. Colin Campbell Sanborn. Publicacões Culturais da Companhia de Diamantes de Angola, Lisbon, no.10, pp.53-62, figs.1-5, Nov.29, 1950.

DESCRIPTIONS AND RECORDS OF AFRICAN BATS. Colin Campbell Sanborn. Zool. Ser. Field Mus. Nat. Hist., vol.20, no.14, pp.107-114, Aug.15, 1936.

THE IDENTIFICATION OF EGYPTIAN BATS. Colin Campbell Sanborn, Harry Hoogstraal. Jour. Egyptian Publ. Health Assoc., 30 (4): 103-121, 1955.

(BATS FROM WESTERN AND CENTRAL AFRICA. RESULTS OF THE SECOND GERMAN CENTRAL AFRICA EXPEDITION. (1910-11) VOL. 1: ZOOLOGY.) Fledermaeuse aus West - und Zentralafrika. Ergebnisse der Zweiten Deutschen Zentral-Afrika-Exped. Ernest Schwarz. 1910-11, vol.1, Zoologie, pp.1045-1062, June, 1920.

(WITH REFERENCE TO SOME SPECIES OF MICRO-BATS OF ANGOLA.) A Proposito de algumas especies de Microchiropteros d'Angola. A. F. de Seabra. Ann. Sci. Nat., Oporto, vol.10, pp.81-82, 1906.

(NOTE ON THE BATS OF MOROCCO.) Note sur les chauves-souris de Maròc. P. Strinati. Mammalia, Paris, vol.15, nos.1-2, pp.23-31, Mar.-June, 1951.

(SECOND NOTE ON THE BATS OF MOROCCO.) Deuxieme note sur les chauves-souris du Maroc. P. Strinati. Mammalia, Paris, vol.17, no.3, pp.189-193, Sept., 1953.

DESCRIPTION OF A NEW BAT FROM GAMBIA. Oldfield Thomas. Ann. and Mag. Nat. Hist. (6), vol.3, no.16, pp.362-364, figs. Apr., 1889.

A NEW BAT FROM NORTHERN NIGERIA. Oldfield Thomas. Ann. and Mag. Nat. Hist. (8), vol.16, no.95, pp.447-448, Nov., 1915.

NEW BATS FROM BRITISH EAST AFRICA COLLECTED BY MRS. HINDE, AND FROM THE CAMEROONS BY MR. G. L. BATES. Oldfield Thomas. Ann. and Mag. Nat. Hist. (7), vol.13, no.75, pp.206-210, Mar., 1904.

ON BATS FROM OLD CALABAR. Oldfield Thomas. Ann. and Mag. Nat. Hist. (5), vol.6, no.32, pp.164-167, figs.2, Aug., 1880.

ON THREE NEW BATS OBTAINED BY MR. WILLOUGHBY LOWE IN THE SUDAN. Oldfield Thomas. Ann. and Mag. Nat. Hist. (8), vol.15, no.90, pp.557-562, June, 1915.

THREE NEW BATS FROM THE CAMEROONS, DISCOVERED BY MR. G.L. BATES. Oldfield Thomas. Ann. and Mag. Nat. Hist. (7), vol.12, no.72, pp.633-635, Dec., 1903.

NOTES ON A COLLECTION OF BATS MADE BY MR. ANDERSON IN THE DAMARA COUNTRY, SOUTH-WESTERN AFRICA, WITH NOTICES OF SOME OTHER AFRICAN SPECIES. Robert F. Tomes. Proc. Zool. Soc. Lond., pp.31-40, 1861.

(CONTRIBUTION TO CONGOLESE SPELEOLOGY. THE CAVES OF THE HOMAS MOUNTAINS.) Contribution à la spéléologie conglaise. Les grottes des monts des Homas. M. Van den Abeele. Bull. Séances Inst. Royal Colonial Belge, Brussels, vol. 17, no.1, pp.358-363, pls.2, 1946.

(NOTES ON THE MICROCHIROPTERS OF PORTUGUESE GUINEA.) Notes acerca dos Microquiropteros da Guine Portugesa. Maria Corinta Veign-Ferreira. Annais, Estudos de Zoologica, Lisbon, vol.4, pp. 189-207, 1949.

(ECOLOGY, BIOLOGY AND CLASSIFICATION OF THE CHIROPTERS.) Ecologie, biologie et systematique des chiropteres. Jacques Verschuren. Exploration du Parc National de la Garamba, Mission H. De Saeger, Inst. Parcs Nat. Congo Belge, fasc.7, pp.473, pl. Mar., 1957.

### Age, Longevity

ON THE DETERMINATION OF AGE IN BATS. Knud Andersen. Jour. Bombay Nat. Hist. Soc., vol.25, no.2, pp.249-259, 1 pl., Sept.15, 1917.

NOTES ON BANDED BATS. Roger W. Barbour. Jour. Mam., vol.31, no.3, p.350, Aug.21, 1950.

LONGEVITY OF BATS. William Bridges. Animal Kingdom, New York, vol.46, no.2, p.45, Mar.-Apr., 1943.

(THE LONGEVITY OF CHIROPTERS.) La longévite des Chiroptères. Jean Dorst. Mammalia, Paris, vol.18, no.3, pp.231-236, Sept., 1954.

LONGEVITY IN BATS. P. F. Heerdt, J. W. Sluiter. Natuurhist. Maandblad, vol.44, nos.3-4, pp.35-36, Apr., 1955.

(LONGEVITY OF CHIROPTERS IN BELGIUM. ELEMENTS AND DISCUSSION.) La longevite des cheiropteres en Belgique. Elements et discussion. Jacques Verschuren. Bull. Inst. Royal Sci. Nat. Belgique, 32 (11): 1-8, Feb., 1956.

### Anatomy

THE ETHMOID BONE IN THE BATS. Harrison Allen. Bull. Mus. of Comp. Zool., Harvard College, vol.6, no.5, 1880.

ON THE TARSUS OF BATS. Harrison Allen. Amer. Nat., vol.20, no.25, pp.175-177, Feb., 1886.

ON THE WINGS OF BATS. Harrison Allen. Proc. Philadelphia Acad. Nat. Sci., pp.336, 1891.

ON INTERMEDIATE FORMS AMONG CHIROPTERA. Augusta Arnback-Christie-Linde. Zool. Anz. Vol.34, no.18, 19, July 27, 1909.

(A NOTE ON THE NERVOUS TERMINATIONS OF THE TACTILE HAIRS OF THE BAT.) Nota acerca de las terminaciones nerviosas de los pelos tactiles o cavernosos de dos especies de murcielagos. Amelia Samano Bishop. Anal. Inst. Biol., Mexico, D.F., vol.14, no.1, pp.291-301, figs.8, 1943.

VASCULAR CHANGES IN THE WINGS OF BATS. Raymond B. Cowles. Science, Lancaster, vol.105, no.2727, pp.362-363, Apr.4, 1947.

HISTOLOGICAL ASPECTS OF THE FACES OF NORTH AMERICAN BATS. Walter W.

Dalquest, Henry J. Werner. Jour. Mam., vol.35, no.2, pp.147-160, illus., May 26, 1954.

(REMARKS ON THE DECIDUOUS DENTITION OF THE CHIROPTERS.) Remarques sur la dentition de lait des Chiroptères. J. Dorst. Mammalia, Paris, vol.13, nos.1-2, pp.45-48, figs.2, Mar.-June, 1949.

DEVELOPMENT OF FETAL MEMBRANES IN TWO SPECIES OF MICROCHIROPTERA. A. Gopalakrishna. Anat. Record, Philadelphia, 27 (2): 467, Feb., 1957.

(IMPLANTATION AND THE EMBRYONIC SHEATH IN TWO SOUTH AMERICAN BATS.) Implantation und Embryonalhuellen bei zwei suedamerikanschen Fledermaeusen. G.W.D. Hamlett. Anat. Anz., vol.79, nos.7-9, pp. 146-149, figs.2, Nov.22, 1934.

A NOTE ON SOME EPITHELIAL STRUCTURES IN MICROCHIROPTERA. B. A. Harrison, D. V. Davies. Proc. Zool. Soc. Lond., vol.119, pt.2, pp.351-357, pl.1, Aug.17, 1949.

THE CRANIAL VAULT IN CHIROPTERA. D. L. Harrison. Bull. British Ornithol. Club, Lond., vol.69, no.7, pp.67-70, May 11, 1949.

A NOTE ON SOME EPITHELIAL STRUCTURES IN MICROCHIROPTERA. D. L. Harrison, D. V. Davies. Proc. Zool. Soc. Lond., vol.119, pt.2, pp.351-357, pl.1, Aug.17, 1949.

SOME DEVELOPMENTAL PECULIARITIES IN THE SKULLS OF BIRDS AND BATS. J. G. Harrison. Bull. British Ornithol. Club, Lond., vol.69, no.7, pp.61-69, May 11, 1949.

(MEASUREMENTS AND WEIGHTS OF NATIVE BATS.) Masse und Gewichte eincheimischer Fledermaeuse. H. Havekost. Zeitschr. Saeugetierk., 22 (1-2): 101-102, 1957.

THE NORMAL HISTOLOGY OF BROWN FAT OF CERTAIN ARKANSAS BATS. P. M. Johnston, J. A. Sealander. Proc. Arkansas Acad. Sci., vol.7, pp.50-54, illus., 1955.

ADDITIONAL DATA ON THE BACULA OF NORTH AMERICAN BATS. Philip H. Krutzsch, Terry A. Vaughan. Jour. Mam., 36 (1): 96-100, 1 fig., Feb.25, 1955.

THE CHARACTERS OF SEVEN GENERA OF BATS WITH FOLIACEOUS APPENDAGES TO THE NOSE. William Elford Leach. Trans. Linn. Soc. Lond., vol.13, pp.73-82, pl.7, 1820.

THE CHARACTERS OF THREE NEW GENERA OF BATS WITHOUT FOLIACEOUS APPENDAGE TO THE NOSE. William Elford Leach. Trans. Linn. Soc. Lond., vol.13, pt.1, pp.69-72, 1821.

(DATA ON DECIDUOUS DENTITION AND DENTAL HOMOLOGUES IN CHIROPTERS.) Zur Kenntniss des Milchgebisses und der Zahnhomologien bei Chiroptera. Wilhelm Leche. Lund, vol.2, 37 pp., 2 pls., 1878.

A STUDY OF CHROMOSOMES IN TWO SPECIES OF BATS (CHIROPTERA). Sajiro Makino. Biol. Bull., Lancaster, vol.94, no. 3, pp.275-282, June, 1948.

THE FORM OF THE PENIS IN THE BRITISH RHINOLOPHOID BATS, COMPARED WITH THAT IN SOME OF THE VESPERTILIONID BATS. L. Harrison Matthews. Proc. Zool. Soc. Lond., Abstracts, vol.107, ser.C, no. 3, p.8, Mar.2, 1937.

THE FORM OF THE PENIS IN THE BRITISH RHINOLOPHID BATS, COMPARED WITH THAT IN SOME OF THE VESPERTILIONIS BATS; AND THE FEMALE SEXUAL CYCLE IN THE BRITISH HORSE-SHOE BATS, RHINOLOPHUS FERRUM-EQUINIM INSULANUS BARRETT-HAMILTON AND R. HIPPOSIDEROS MINUTUS MONTAGU. L. Harrison Matthews. Trans. Zool. Soc. Lond., pt.4, no.1, pp.213-255, figs.20, pls.15-19, Aug., 1937.

ON THE MORPHOGENESIS OF THE YOLK-SAC GLAND IN CHIROPTERA. Sindhu Moghe. Proc. Nat. Inst. Sci. India, pt.B, 22 (1): 34-40, Feb.26, 1956.

THE HEART AND ITS VESSELS IN SOME NEW WORLD BATS. Helen Park. Trans. Kansas Acad. Sci., vol.57, no.2, pp.197-199, illus., 1954.

THE GROSS ANATOMY OF THE TONGUES AND STOMACHS OF EIGHT NEW WORLD BATS. Helen Park, E. Raymond Hall. Trans. Kansas Acad. Sci., Lawrence, vol.54, no.1, pp.64-72, illus., 1951.

(THE STRUCTURAL CHARACTERS OF THE SPINAL CORD IN CHIROPTERS.) Die Struktureigentuemlichkeiten des Rueckenmarks bei den Chiropteren. S. Poljak. Zeitschr. Gesammte Anat., I. Abteil., vol. 74, pp.509-576, 28 figs., Oct.31, 1924.

RELATIVE WING RATIOS OF BATS AND BIRDS. Earl L. Poole. Jour. Mam., vol. 17, no.4, pp.412-413, Nov., 1936.

(MORPHOLOGICAL INVESTIGATIONS OF CHIROPTER BRAINS.) Morphologische Untersuchungen am Gehirn der Chiroptera. Rolf Schneider. Zeitschr. Saeugetierk., Berlin, 21 (3-4): 182-183, Feb.28, 1957.

THE HYOID REGION OF PLACENTAL MAMMALS WITH ESPECIAL REFERENCE TO THE BATS. James M. Sprague. Amer. Jour. Anat., Philadelphia, vol.72, no.3, pp.385-472, figs.8, May, 1943.

THE MISSING PREMOLAR OF THE CHIROPTERA. Oldfield Thomas. Ann. and Mag. Nat. Hist. (8), vol.1, no.3, pp.346-348, Apr., 1908.

(ON THE SKIN STRUCTURE OF CHIROPTERS.) Ueber die Hautgebilde der Chiropteren. Karl Toldt. Verhandl. Zool.-bot. Gesell Wien, Jahrg., 1907.

A STUDY IN THE VARIATIONS OF PROPORTIONS IN BATS, WITH BRIEF NOTES ON SOME OF THE SPECIES MENTIONED. Henry L. Ward. Trans. Wisconsin Acad. Sci., Art, and Letters, vol.14, pp.630-654, pls.50-55, Aug., 1904.

THE PROCESSUS MUSCULARIS AND THE TENSOR TYMPANI MUSCLE OF BATS. K. Wassif. Nature, vol.157, pp.877, June 29, 1946.

THE TENSOR TYMPANI MUSCLE OF BATS. K. Wassif. Annals and Magazine of Nat. Hist., ser.12, vol.3, pp.811-812, Sept., 1950.

## Asia

A NEW BAT FROM TONKIN. Glover M. Allen. Proc. Biol. Soc. Washington, vol. 26, pp.213-214, Dec.20, 1913.

NEW CHINESE BATS. Glover M. Allen. Amer. Mus. Novit., no.85, pp.1-8, Aug. 28, 1923.

TWO NEW RACES OF INDIAN BATS. Glover M. Allen. Records Indian Mus., vol.38, pt.3, pp.343-346, Sept., 1936.

BATS OF CENTRAL ASIA. N. Bobrinskoy. Ann. Mus. Zool. Acad. Sci. URSS., pp. 217-249, figs.1-5, 1929.

PRELIMINARY NOTE ON THE CHIROPTERA OF CENTRAL ASIA. N. Bobrinskoy. Comptes Rendus Acad. Sci. U.R.S.S., pp.95-98, 1926.

NEW AND NOTEWORTHY BATS FROM THE MALAY PENINSULA. F. N. Chasen. Bull. Raffles Mus., no.12, pp.133-134, May, 1936.

MONOGRAPH OF THE ASIATIC CHIROPTERA, AND CATALOGUE OF THE SPECIES OF BATS IN THE INDIAN MUSEUM. G. E. Dobson. 8 vo, wrs., 228 pp., Lond., 1876.

FISH-EATING BATS OF INDIA AND BURMA. E. W. Gudger. Jour. Bombay Nat. Hist. Soc., vol.43, no.4, pp.635-640, figs.4, pl.1, Apr., 1943.

A KEY TO THE IDENTIFICATION OF THE BATS (CHIROPTERA) OF THE ARABIAN PENINSULA. David L. Harrison. Proc. Zool. Soc. Lond., 127 (4): 447-452, Dec. 21, 1956.

NOTES ON SOME BATS (MICROCHIROPTERA) FROM IRAQ. David L. Harrison. Bonner Zool. Beitraege, 7 (1-3): 1-7, 1956.

MALAYAN BATS. J. L. Harrison. Malayan Museum Popular Pamphlets, Singapore, 8: 1-17, 1956.

EXPEDITION TO SOUTH-WEST ARABIA. I. MAMMALIA: CHIROPTERA. R. W. Hayman. British Mus. Nat. Hist., vol.1, nos.1-8, pp.1-2, Feb.22, 1941.

ON BATS OF THE NORTH-WESTERN HIMALAYAS. WITH NOTES AND CORRECTIONS IN NOMENCLATURE BY PROF. W. PETERS. Thomas Hutton. Proc. Zool. Soc. Lond., pp.690-714, 1872.

TAXONOMIC STUDIES ON SOME INDIAN CHIROPTERA. H. Khajuria. Records Indian Mus., vol.50, pt.1, pp.113-128, 1953.

A LIST OF THE BATS OCCURRING IN THE PENINSULAR REGION, WITH A KEY TO THE GENERA. C. Boden Kloss. Jour. Fed. Malay States Mus., vol.2, pp.151-161, Sept., 1908.

THE BATS FROM TASHKENT AND SYSTEMATIC REMARKS ON SOME CHIROPTERA FROM CAUCASUS, BUCHARIA AND TURKMENIA. A. P. Kuzjakin. Bull. Soc. Nat. Moscou, sect. Biol. vol.40, no.2, pp.316-330, tables 2, 1934.

LIST OF BATS COLLECTED BY DR. W. L. ABBOTT IN SIAM. G. S. Miller, Jr. Proc. Acad. Nat. Sci. Phila., vol.50, pp.316-325, July 25, 1898.

SEVEN NEW MALAYAN BATS. G. S. Miller, Jr. Proc. Biol. Soc., Washington, vol.19, pp.61-66, May 1, 1906.

ON THE KOREAN BATS. T. Mori. Zool. Soc. of Japan, Tokyo, pp.284-303, pl.3, 1928.

ON TWO NEW BATS FROM KOREA. T. Mori. Jour. Chosen Nat. Hist. Soc., no.16, pp.4-5, July 31, 1933.

ON THE BATS OF THE NORTH-WESTERN HIMALAYAS. BY CAPT. THOMAS HUTTON, C.M.Z.S. WITH NOTES AND CORRECTIONS OF NOMENCLATURE BY PROF. W. PETERS. William Peters. Proc. Zool. Soc. Lond., pp.690-714, 1872.

ON THE BATS COLLECTED BY MR. F. DAY IN BURMA. William Peters. Proc. Zool. Soc. Lond., pp.513-514, figs.3, 1871.

ADDITIONS TO THE FAUNA OF CEYLON. NO. 2. SOME NEW AND INTERESTING BATS, FROM THE HILLS OF THE CENTRAL PROVINCE. W.W.A. Phillips. Spolia Zeylanica, Ceylon Jour. Sci., vol. 16, pt.3, pp.329-335, pl.66, Mar.18, 1932.

A GUIDE TO THE MAMMALS OF CEYLON. PART I. CHIROPTERA. W.W.A. Phillips. Spolia Zeylanica (Ceylon), vol.13, pt.1, pp. 1-63, Sept.16, 1924.

BATS FROM SZECHWAN AND KWEICHOW, CHINA. Colin Campbell Sanborn. Proc. Biol. Soc. Washington, vol.46, pp.55-56, Mar.24, 1933.

A COLLECTION OF BATS FROM THAILAND. H. Harold Shamel. Jour. Mam., vol.23, no. 3, pp.317-328, Aug.14, 1942.

THE BATS OF CHINA. Arthur de C. Sowerby. China Jour., vol.17, no.6, pp. 299-305, figs.4, Dec., 1932.

ON A NEW BAT FROM MANCHURIA. Arthur de C. Sowerby. Jour. Mam., vol.3, no.1, pp.46-47, Feb., 1922.

DESCRIPTION OF A NEW BAT FROM SELANGORE. Oldfield Thomas. Ann. and Mag. Nat. Hist. (7), vol.1, no.5, pp.360-362, May, 1898.

LIST OF MICROCHIROPTERA OTHER THAN LEAF-NOSE BATS, IN THE COLLECTION OF THE FEDERATED MALAY STATES MUSEUMS. Oldfield Thomas. Malay States Museums, vol.7, pt.1, pp.1-6, Aug., 1916.

ON SOME BATS OBTAINED IN THE SURAT AND THANA DISTRICTS BY MR. R. C. WROUGHTON. Oldfield Thomas. Jour. Bombay, Nat. Hist. Soc., vol.11, pp.274-276, 1897.

SCIENTIFIC RESULTS FROM THE MAMMAL SURVEY. XIII. B. TWO NEW INDIAN BATS.

Oldfield Thomas. Jour. Bombay Nat. Hist. Soc., vol.24, no.3, pp.416-417, June 20, 1916.

TWO NEW ASIATIC BATS OF THE GENERA TADARIDA AND DYACOPTERUS. Oldfield Thomas. Ann. and Mag. Nat. Hist., ser. 9, vol.5, pp.283-285, Mar., 1920.

DESCRIPTIONS OF FOUR UNDESCRIBED SPECIES OF BATS. Robert F. Tomes. Proc. Zool. Soc. Lond., pt.25, pp.50-54, 1857.

(BATS OF AFGHANISTAN.) Fledermaeuse aus Afghanistan. K. Zimmerman. Zeitschr. Saeugetierk., Berlin, 21 (3-4): 195-196, Feb. 28, 1957.

Australia and Various Islands

A BAT NEW TO THE JAPANESE FAUNA. Glover M. Allen. Jour. Mam., vol.1, no. 3, p.139, May, 1920.

BATS FROM PALAWAN, PHILIPPINE ISLANDS. Glover M. Allen. Occ. Pap. Mus. Zool., Univ. Michigan, no.110, pp.1-5, Feb.25, 1922.

NOTES ON BAHAMA BATS. Glover M. Allen. Proc. Biol. Soc. Washington, vol.18, pp.65-72, Feb.21, 1905.

TWO NEW BATS FROM AUSTRALIA. Glover M. Allen. Jour. Mam., vol.14, no. 2, pp.149-151, May, 1933.

TWO UNDESCRIBED WEST INDIAN BATS. Glover M. Allen. Proc. Biol. Soc. Washington, vol.30, pp.165-170, Oct.23, 1917.

NOTES ON BATS FROM THE BAHAMAS. Glover M. Allen, Colin Campbell Sanborn. Jour. Mam., vol.18, no.2, pp.226-228, fig. 1, May 14, 1937.

NOTES ON A SMALL COLLECTION OF WEST INDIAN BATS, WITH DESCRIPTION OF AN APPARENTLY NEW SPECIES. J. A. Allen. Bull. Amer. Mus. Nat. Hist., vol.3, pp.169-173, Nov.14, 1890.

A COLLECTION OF BATS FROM FORMOSA. Augusta Arnback-Christie-Linde. Ann. and Mag. Nat. Hist., ser.8, vol.2, pp.235-238, Sept., 1908.

THE SEASONS IN A TROPICAL RAIN-FOREST (NEW HEBRIDES). PT. 4. INSECTIVOROUS BATS (VESPERTILIONIDAE AND RHINOLOPHIDAE). John R. Baker, T. F. Bird. Jour. Linn. Soc. Lond., Zool., vol. 40, no.269, pp.143-161, pl.4, Nov.30, 1936.

NOTES ON SOME SOUTH AUSTRALIAN BATS. E. F. Boehm. No. 1. South Australian Nat., Adelaide, vol.21, no.3, p.15, July 14, 1942.

NOTES ON SOME SOUTH AUSTRALIAN BATS. E. F. Boehm. No. 2. South Australian Nat., Adelaide, vol.23, no.3, pp.10-11, Feb.15, 1946.

ON BATS FROM THE LIMESTONE CAVES OF NORTH BORNEO. F. N. Chasen. Bull. Raffles Mus., Singapore, Straits Settlements, no.5, pp.107-114, Aug., 1931.

(A NEW BAT FROM MADAGASCAR.) Une nouvelle chauve-souris de Madagascar. G. Grandidier. Bull. Museum, Paris, pp. 8-9, 1912.

LETTER FROM J. E. GRAY, ON SOME NEW SPECIES OF BATS FROM JAMAICA. J. E. Gray. Proc. Zool. Soc. Lond., pt.11, p.50, 1843.

NOTES ON JAMAICAN NATURAL HISTORY. THE BATS OF JAMAICA. P. W. Jarvis. Jamaica Post, July 6, 1897.

ON A COLLECTION OF BATS FROM THE WEST-INDIES. F. A. Jentink. Notes Leyden Mus., vol.15, no.41, pp.278-283, Sept., 1893.

BAT RECORDS FROM THE ISLANDS OF GRENADA AND TOBAGE, BRITISH WEST INDIES. T. S. Jones. Jour. Mam., vol.32, no.2, pp.223-224, May 21, 1951.

BAT CAVERNS. Tokio Kaburaki. Report on the survey of the natural monuments, Sect. Zool. no.4, Dept. Interior, Tokyo, pp.5, pl.1, Jan., 1938.

FORMOSAN BATS. Nagamichi Kuroda. Syokukutu oyobi Dobutu (Botany and Zool.), vol.6, no.6, pp.113-116, June 1, 1938.

JAMAICA BATS--A NEW GENUS AND SPECIES. Gerrit S. Miller, Jr. Jour. Inst. Jamaica, vol.2, pp.625-627, figs.2-5, Aug.31, 1899.

A NEW BAT FROM CUBA. Gerrit S. Miller, Jr. Proc. Biol. Soc., Washington, vol.27, pp.225-226, Dec.29, 1914.

A NEW BAT FROM THE CAROLINE ISLANDS. Gerrit S. Miller, Jr. Proc. Biol. Soc., Washington, vol.24, pp.161-162, June 16, 1911.

A NEW BAT FROM THE ISLAND OF DOMINICA. Gerrit S. Miller, Jr. Proc. Biol. Soc., Washington, vol.15, pp.243-244, Dec.16, 1902.

A NEW GENUS OF BATS FROM SUMATRA. Gerrit S. Miller, Jr. Proc. Biol. Soc., Washington, vol.18, pp.229-230, Dec.9, 1905.

NOTES ON THE BATS COLLECTED BY WILLIAM PALMER IN CUBA. Gerrit S. Miller, Jr. Proc. U.S. Nat. Mus., vol.27, pp.337-348, pl.9, Jan.23, 1904.

THREE NEW BATS FROM HAITI AND SANTO DOMINGO. Gerrit S. Miller, Jr. Proc. Biol. Soc., Washington, vol.31, pp. 39-40, May 16, 1918.

NOTES ON THE CHIROPTERA OF JAMAICA. COMMUNICATED BY THE SECRETARY. W. Osburn. Proc. Zool. Soc. Lond., pp. 61-85, 1865.

NOTE ON A BAT FROM THE AZORES. W. Peters. Proc. Zool. Soc. Lond., p.558, 1866.

(ON THE CHIROPTERS COLLECTED BY DR. F. HILGENDORF IN JAPAN.) Ueber die von Hrn. Dr. F. Hilgendorf in Japan gesammelten Chiropteren. W. Peters. Monatsber. Akad. Wissensch. Berlin, pp. 23-25, pl.1, Jan.5, 1880.

(ON THE CHIROPTERS OF BOUGAINVILLE.) Ueber die Fledertiere von Bougainville. Hermann Pohle. Zeitschr. Saeugetierk, Berlin, vol.17, no.2, pp.127-137, Feb.19, 1953.

BATS FROM POLYNESIA, MELANESIA, AND MALAYSIA. C. C. Sanborn. Field Mus. Nat. Hist. Publ. 286, Zool. ser., vol.8, no.2, pp.7-29, Feb.12, 1931.

BATS FROM NEW CALEDONIA, THE SOLOMON ISLANDS, AND NEW HEBRIDES. C. C. Sanborn, A. J. Nicholson. Fieldiana, Zoology, Chicago, vol.31, no.36, pp.313-338, illus., Aug.31, 1950.

BATS FROM THE BAHAMAS. Harold H. Shamel. Jour. Washington Acad. Sci., vol. 21, no.11, pp.251-253, June 4, 1931.

THE INSECTIVOROUS BATS COLLECTED BY H. C. RAVEN IN CELEBES. H. Harold Shamel. Jour. Mam., vol.21, no.3, pp.352-354, Aug.14, 1940.

A NEW BAT FROM DOMINICA. H. Harold Shamel. Proc. Biol. Soc. Washington, vol. 41, pp.67-68, Mar.16, 1928.

ON A NEW BAT FROM BORNEO. R. Shelford. Ann. and Mag. Nat. Hist. Lond., ser. 7, vol.8, pp.113-114, Aug., 1901.

(NOTES ON THE BATS COLLECTED IN JAMAICA AND HAITI DURING THE CUBANA SCIENTIFIC EXPEDITION IN 1951.) Notas sobre los murcielagos colectados en Jamaica y Haiti durante le Expedicion Cientifica Cubana--1951. Gilberto Silva Taboada. Rev. Arqueol. and Etnol., Havana, ser.2, ano 7, nos.15-16, pp.203-214, illus., 1952.

(A LIST OF JAVANESE BATS.) Naamlijst van de Vleermuizen van Java. H.J.V. Sody. Natuurk. Tijdsch., vol.89, no.1, pp.28-66, 1929.

BATS FROM THE PACIFIC ISLANDS, INCLUDING A NEW FRUIT BAT FROM GUAM. G. H. H. Tate. Amer. Mus. Novitates, no. 713, pp.1-3, Apr.11, 1934.

GEOGRAPHICAL DISTRIBUTION OF THE BATS IN THE AUSTRALASIAN ARCHIPELAGO. G. H. H. Tate. Amer. Mus. Novitates, New York, no.1323, pp.21, figs. 2, July 15, 1946.

DESCRIPTION OF A NEW BAT FROM NORTH BORNEO. Oldfield Thomas. Ann. and Mag. Nat. Hist. (7), vol.1, no.3, p. 243, Mar., 1898.

A NEW BAT FROM THE KEY ISLANDS. Oldfield Thomas. Ann. and Mag. Nat. Hist. (7), vol.5, no.25, p.145, Jan., 1900.

NOTE ON THE NOMENCLATURE OF THE SHORT-EARED NEW ZEALAND BAT. Oldfield Thomas. Ann. and Mag. Nat. Hist. (6), vol.4, no.24, p.462, Dec., 1889.

ON SOME SMALL MAMMALS, CHIEFLY BATS, FROM THE EAST INDIAN ARCHIPELAGO. Oldfield Thomas. Ann. and Mag. Nat. Hist. (9), vol.11, no.62, pp.250-255, Feb., 1923.

ON THE BATS COLLECTED BY MR. C.M. WOODFORD IN THE SOLOMON ISLANDS. Oldfield Thomas. Proc. Zool. Soc., Lond., pp.320-328, pls.25-26, Mar.15, 1887.

NOTES ON FIVE SPECIES OF BATS IN THE COLLECTION OF L. L. DILLWYN, COLLECTED IN LABUAN BY MR. JAMES MOTLEY. Robert F. Tomes. Proc. Zool. Soc. Lond., pt.26, pp.536-540, 1858.

ON TWO SPECIES OF BATS INHABITING NEW ZEALAND. Robert F. Tomes. Proc. Zool. Soc. Lond., pt.25, pp.134-138, pl.53, 54, 1857.

THE BATS OF AUSTRALIA AND NEW GUINEA. E. LeG. Troughton. Included in "The Wild Animals of Australia" by A.S. Le Souef and Harry Burwell.

SIX NEW BATS (MICROCHIROPTERA) FROM THE AUSTRALASIAN REGION. E. LeG. Troughton. Australian Zool., Sydney, vol. 8, pt.4, pp.274-281, Mar.12, 1937.

THREE NEW BATS OF THE GENERA PTEROPUS, NYCTIMENE, AND CHAEREPHON FROM MELANESIA. E. LeG. Troughton. Proc. Linn. Soc. N.S. Wales, vol.56, pt.3, pp.204-209, 1931.

ON NEW SPECIES OF BATS COLLECTED IN THE PHILIPPINE ISLANDS, AND PRESENTED TO THE SOCIETY BY HUGH CUMING. G. R. Waterhouse. Proc. Zool. Soc. Lond., pt.13, p.3-10, 1845.

ON VARIOUS SPECIES OF BATS COLLECTED BY H. CUMING, ESQ. IN THE PHILIPPINE ISLANDS. George R. Waterhouse. Proc. Zool. Soc. Lond., pt.11, pp.66-69, 1843.

ON NEW BATS FOUND IN POLYNESIAN REGION (JAPANESE MANDATE). Yoshimaro Yamashina. Trans. Nat. Hist. Soc. Formosa, vol.22, no.121, pp.240-241, 1932.

Banding, Ringing, and Marking

BANDING BATS. A. A. Allen. Jour. Mam., vol.2, no.2, pp.53-57, pls.2, May, 1921.

FIFTEEN YEARS OF BAT BANDING IN THE NETHERLANDS. L. Bels. Publ. Nat. Genootschap in Limburg, vol.5, pp.99, Feb. 15, 1952.

A PRELIMINARY REPORT ON BAT BANDING IN INDIANA. James B. Cope. Proc. Indiana Acad. Sci., vol.64, pp.284-286, 1955.

(MARKING EXPERIMENTS WITH BATS.) Markierungsversuche bei Fledermaeusen. M. Eisentraut. Zeitschr. Wissenschaft. Biol., Abt. A, Zeitschr. Morphol. u. Ökol Tiere, Berlin, vol.28, no.5, pp.553-560, fig.1, Aug.11, 1934.

(RESULTS OF BAT RINGING AFTER A THREE-YEAR EXPERIMENT.) Ergebnisse der Fledermaus-beringung nach dreijaehriger Versuchszeit. M. Eisentraut. Zeitschr. Morphol. u. Oekol. Tiere, vol. 31, no.1, pp.1-26, Feb.29, 1936.

(TEN YEARS OF BAT RINGING.) Zehn Yahre Fledermausberingung. M. Eisentraut. Zool. Anzeiger, Leipzig, vol.144, nos.1-2, pp.20-32, Oct.15, 1943.

BAT BANDING. Donald R. Griffin. Jour. Mam., vol.17, no.3, pp.235-239, Aug., 1936.

(Comments by A. Brazier Howell on) BANDING BATS. Donald R. Griffin. Jour. Mam., vol.17, no.2, p.195, May, 1936.

MARKING BATS. Donald R. Griffin. Jour. Mam., vol.15, no.3, pp.202-207, Aug., 1934.

RINGING BATS IN DENBIGHSHIRE. G. E. Hesketh. Naturalist, Lond., no.839, pp. 177-181, Dec., 1951.

EXTENDING TECHNIQUE OF BIRD STUDY TO BATS: BANDING AND WEIGHING HORSESHOE BATS IN DEVON CAVES. J.H.D. Hooper. Illus. London News, vol.216, no. 5801, pp.990-991, illus., June 24, 1950.

(DATA ON THE RECOVERY OF RINGED BATS.) Wiederfundzahlen beringter Fledermaeuse. W. Issel. Saeugetierk. Mitteil., Stuttgart, vol.2, no.3, p.127, July 1, 1954.

REPORT ON BAT BANDING IN POLAND IN THE YEARS 1939-1953. Kazimierz Kowalski, Adam Krzanowski, Roman J. Wojtusiak. Acta Theriologica, Inst. Zool. Polska Akad. Nauk, Warsaw, 1 (5): 109-158, Jan.10, 1957.

BAT TAGGING IN PENNSYLVANIA TURNPIKE TUNNELS. Charles E. Mohr. Jour. Mam., vol.23, no.4, pp.375-379, Nov.14, 1942.

RESULTS OF TEN YEARS' BAT MARKING IN PENNSYLVANIA. Charles E. Mohr. Proc. Pennsylvania Acad. Sci., Philadelphia, vol.16, pp.32-36, 1942.

A SURVEY OF BAT BANDING IN NORTH AMERICA, 1932-1951. Charles E. Mohr. American Caver, Bull. Nat. Speleol. Soc., no.14, pp.3-13, illus., Sept., 1952.

UNDERGROUND--WITH A BAT-BANDER. Charles E. Mohr. Frontiers, Lancaster, vol.7, no.2, pp.48-51, illus., Dec., 1942.

BAT BANDING IN INDIANA CAVES. Russell E. Mumford. Outdoor Indiana, vol.20, no. 1, pp.7-10, illus., Jan., 1953.

(APPLICATION OF THE BIOMETRICAL METHOD AND RINGING IN THE ECOLOGICAL STUDY OF BATS.) Application de la methode biometrique et du baguage dans l'etude ecologique des cheiropteres. Edmond Nerincx. Bull. Mus. Roy. Hist. Nat. Belgique, Brussels, vol.19, no.62, pp. 16, figs.4, Dec., 1943.

BANDED BATS. Arthur Palme. Life, vol. 2, no.4, p.66, illus., Jan.23, 1937.

TEN THOUSAND BATS. Clay Perry. Nature Magazine, Washington, D.C., vol. 31, no.3, pp.149-151, Mar., 1938.

(BAT RINGING DONE IN 1937.) Baguages de chauves-souris effectures in 1937. A. Reeb. Bull. Soc. Hist. Nat. Colmar, vol. 43, ser.3 (1937), vol.1, pp.139-141, 1939.

(BAT RINGING.) Le baguage des chauves-souris. P. Rode. Sci. Nat., Paris, vol.1, no.3, pp.65-70, Mar., 1939.

(RINGING BATS, ANALYSIS OF THE WORK OF DONALD R. GRIFFIN.) Le baguage des chauves-souris (Analyse du travail de Donald R. Griffin). P. Rode. Mammalia, Paris, vol.1, no.2, pp.70-72, Dec., 1936.

THE WING BANDING METHOD IN THE STUDY OF THE TRAVELS OF BATS. Harold Trapido, Peter E. Crowe. Jour. Mam., vol.27, no.3, pp.224-226, pl.1, Aug.14, 1946.

THE RESULTS OF BAT-BANDING IN THE NETHERLANDS IN 1952 AND 1953. P. F. Van Heerdt. Natuur-hist. Maanblad, Utrecht, vol.42, no.11, pp.101-104, Nov.30, 1953.

### Care in Captivity

(NOTES ON RAISING BATS IN CAPTIVITY.) Notes sur l'élevage de chauves-souris en captivité. P. Albisson, J. Dorst. Mammalia, Paris, vol.15, no.4, pp.170-174, Dec., 1951.

KEEPING BATS IN CAPTIVITY. William H. Gates. Jour. Mam., vol.17, no.3, pp.268-273, Aug., 1936.

BATS AS PETS. Robert H. McCauley, Jr. Nature Mag., vol.27, no.5, pp.270-271, illus., May, 1936.

NOTES ON KEEPING BATS IN CAPTIVITY. Mary C. Ramage. Jour. Mam., vol.28, no. 1, pp.60-62, Feb.15, 1947.

### Collecting

(COMPLEMENTARY NOTES ON A NEW APPARATUS FOR CAPTURING CHIROPTERS.) Note complementaire sur un nouvel appareil pour la capture de chiropteres. E. Morales Agacino. Mammalia, Paris, vol.2, no.3, pp.137-139, figs.2, Sept., 1938.

A NEW METHOD OF COLLECTING BATS. Adrey E. Borell. Jour. Mam., vol.18, no. 4, pp.478-480, Nov., 1937.

AN AUTOMATIC BAT-COLLECTING DEVICE. Denny G. Constantine. Jour. Wildlife Management, 22 (1): 17-22, illus., Jan., 1958.

CATCHING BATS WITH GILL-NETS. Hartley H. T. Jackson. Jour. Mam., vol.7, no.3, p.231, Aug.9, 1926.

(A METHOD OF CATCHING FLYING BATS.) Eine Methode zum Fang fliegender Fledermaeuse. Konrad Klemmer. Saeugetierk. Mitteil., 5 (3): 118-120, Aug.1, 1957.

A METHOD OF COLLECTING BATS. E. J. Koestner. Jour. Tennessee Acad. Sci., Nashville, vol.17, no.3, p.301, July, 1942.

COLLECTING BATS WITH A NET. Storrs H. Lyman. Jour. Mam., vol.1, no.3, pp. 230-231, Aug., 1926.

NOTES ON BAT NETTING. F. L. Osgood. Jour. Mam., vol.16, no.3, p.228, Aug., 1935.

THE TRAMMEL NET AS A MEANS OF COLLECTING BATS. Josselyn Van Tyne. Jour. Mam., vol.14, no.2, pp.145-146, May, 1933.

### Control

HOW TO CONTROL BATS. John C. Jones. Pests and Their Control, Cleveland, vol.16, no.12, pp.7-8, illus., Dec., 1948.

ELIMINATING BATS FROM BUILDINGS. James Silver. Leaflet no.109, U.S. Dept. Agric., pp.5, figs.2, Sept., 1935; USDI, FWS, Wildl. Leaflet 260, pp.4, Sept., 1944.

(Comments by A. Brazier Howell on) ELIMINATING BATS FROM BUILDINGS. James Silver. Jour. Mam., vol.17, no.1, p.86, Feb., 1936.

CONTROL OF BATS. James Silver, John C. Jones. US FWS, Wildl. Leaflet 333, pp.1-4, Jan., 1951.

GUIDE FOR BAT BATTLERS. Norman York. Pest Control 21 (6): 38-39, June, 1953.

### Ecology

(ECOLOGICAL NOTES ON SOME BRAZILIAN CHIROPTERS.) Notas ecologicas sobre algunos quirópteros del Brasil. Eduardo F. Acosta y Lara. Comunicaciones Zool Mus. Hist. Nat. Montevideo, vol.3, no.65, pp.1-2, Sept.20, 1951.

(ECOLOGICAL OBSERVATIONS OF SARDINIAN BATS.) Oekologische Beobachtungen an sardischen Fledermaeusen. H. Frick, H. Felten. Zool. Jahrbuecher, Jena, vol.81, no.3, pp.175-189, Aug.8, 1952.

(NOTES ON THE ETIOLOGY AND ECOLOGY OF THE CHIROPTERS OF BELGIUM.) "Notes sur l'ethologie et l'ecologie des Cheiropteres de Belgique." E. Nerincx. Bull. Mus. Roy. Hist. Nat. Belgique, 20, art.19, 24 pp., 1944.

### Economic Importance

BATS, MOSQUITOES, AND DOLLARS. Charles A. R. Campbell. Boston: The Stratford Co., 12 mo., pp.1-viii, 1-262, with unnumbered plates, 1925.

(Review by E. A. Goldman of) BATS, MOSQUITOES, AND DOLLARS. Charles A. R. Campbell. Jour. Mam., vol.7, no. 2, pp.136-138, May, 1926.

(Comments by Tracy I. Storer on) BATS, MOSQUITOES AND DOLLARS. Charles A. R. Campbell. Science, n.s., vol.43, no. 1630, pp.337-338, Mar.26, 1926.

BATS AS A SOLUTION OF INSECT PROBLEMS. Charles H. Gable. Better Fruit, vol.23, no.4, pp.5-7, 2 figs., Oct., 1928.

BATS AS DESIRABLE CITIZENS. Joseph Grinnell. Pacific Rural Press, vol.85, no. 11, pp.344-345, Mar.15, 1913.

BATS AS DESIRABLE CITIZENS. Cal. Fish and Game Commiss., Teachers' Bull., no.6, pp.4, fig.1, Apr., 1916.

(THE PROTECTION OF BATS.) La proteccion de los murcielagos. Carlos Lizer y Trelles. Rev. Argentina Zoogeogr., Buenos Aires, vol.1, no.3, pp.181-188, 1942.

BAT OIL FOR RHEUMATISM. Marcus Ward Lyon. Jour. Mam., vol.12, no.3, p. 313, Aug., 1931.

BAT CAVES AND BAT BOMBS. Walter G. Moore. Turtox News, Chicago, vol.26, no. 11, pp.262-265, Nov., 1948.

BATS IN RELATION TO THE PRODUCTION OF GUANO AND THE DESTRUCTION OF INSECTS. E. W. Nelson. U.S. Dept. Agric., Dept. Bull. no.1395, pp.1-12, Mar. 24, 1926.

(Comments by A. Brazier Howell on) BATS IN RELATION TO THE PRODUCTION OF GUANO AND THE DESTRUCTION OF INSECTS. E. W. Nelson. Jour. Mam., vol.17, no.1, p.86, Feb., 1936.

BATS ARE BIG AID TO LANDOWNER. Ray Osborne. Texas Game, Fish, and Oyster Comm., Monthly Bull., Austin, vol.3, no. 1, p.5, Dec., 1939.

(THE PROTECTION OF BATS IN THE NETHERLANDS.) Bescherming van vleermuizen in Nederland. J. W. Sluiter, P. F. van Heerdt, J. Th. de Smidt. De Levende Natuur, Arnhem, pp.51, illus., 1956.

BATS, BAT TOWERS AND MOSQUITOES. Tracy I. Storer. Jour. Mam., vol.7, no. 2, pp.85-90, pl.11, May, 1926.

USEFULNESS OF BATS. Frank Thone. Science News Letter, Washington, vol.51, no.10, p.157, Mar.8, 1947.

FURRED AERONAUTS OF NIGHT. LITTLE BATS AS FRIENDS OF MAN. Ellis Troughton. Australian Mus. Mag., Sydney, vol.7, no.6, pp.206-211, figs.6, Sept.2, 1940.

### Europe

(OBSERVATIONS ON THE CHIROPTERS OF THE CAVE OF BAUME-GRANAT AT ROQUEFORT-LES-PINS (ALPES-MARITIMES).) Observations sur les chiropteres de la grotte de la Baume-Granat a Roquefort-les-Pins (Alpes-Maritimes). Dom F. Anciaux de Faveaux. Mammalia, Paris, vol.16, no. 3, pp.148-156, illus., Sept., 1952.

(MASS BAT MIGRATION NEAR NEUSIEDL (BURGENLAND).) Fledermaus-Massenzug bei Neusiedl (Burgenland). Kurt Bauer. Saeugetierk. Mitteil., Stuttgart, 3 (4): 154-156, Oct.1, 1955.

(THE COLONY OF CHIROPTERS OF THE DUCAL CASTLE OF NANTES.) La Colonie de Chiropteres du Chateau des ducs de Nantes. J. C. Beaucournu. Mammalia, Paris, vol.20, no.1, pp.66-74, Mar., 1956.

NOTES ON THE HISTORY OF THE BRITISH AND IRISH BATS. Bryan P. Beirne. Irish Naturalists' Jour., Belfast, vol.9, no.6, pp. 153-155, Apr., 1948.

EXPERIENCES WITH BATS IN DEVONSHIRE. Michael Blackmore. Trans. and Proc. Torquay Nat. Hist. Soc., vol.7, pt.1, pp.57-61, 1935.

FIELD RESEARCH ON BRITISH BATS. Michael Blackmore. Oryx, vol.2, no.3, pp.193-196, Nov., 1953.

CREATURES OF THE TWILIGHT. BATS AND THEIR HABITS--HOW TO RECOGNIZE OUR COMMON SPECIES. Michael Blackmore, G. Seccombe-Hett. Country Life, London, vol.78, no.2020, pp.347-349, figs. 12, Oct.5, 1935.

(NEW DATA ON THE GEOGRAPHICAL DISTRIBUTION OF THE BATS (CHIROPTERA) OF RUSSIA.) Neue Angaben ueber die geographische Verbeitung der Fledermaeuse (Chiroptera) Russlands. N. Bobrinskoi. Zool. Anzeiger, vol.96, nos.9-10, pp.265-268, Nov.1, 1931.

NEW DATA ON DISTRIBUTION OF BATS OF USSR. N. Bobrinskoi, A. Kusiakin. Bull. Soc. Nat. Moscou, sect. biol., n.s., vol.46, no.5, pp.265-267, 1937.

SOME RANDOM OBSERVATIONS ON BATS. George Bolam. Northwestern Nat. (Scotland), vol.8, no.1, pp.33-36, Mar., 1933.

(OBSERVATIONS ON THE CHIROPTERS OF VAUD CANTON AND BORDERING REGIONS.) Observations sur les chiropteres du canton de vaud et des regions voisines. Rene Bovey. Bull. Soc. Vaudoise Sci. Nat., Lausanne, vol.66, no.286, pp.1-18, 1954.

(MONOGRAPH ESSAY ON THE BATS OF SPAIN.) Ensayo monográfico sobre los Quirópteros de España. Angel Cabrera. Mem. Soc. Española Hist. Nat., Madrid, vol.2, art. mem.5, pp.249-287, pls.1-5, 1904.

(NEW OBSERVATIONS ON THE BATS OF SPAIN.) Neuvas observaciones sobre los quirópteros de Espana. Angel Cabrera. Bol. Real Soc. Espanola Hist. Nat., Madrid, vol.8, no.10, pp.447-449, Dec., 1908.

(THE CHIROPTER SWARM OF THE CAVES OF QUEIRE, BIERT COMMUNE (ARIEGE).) L'essaim de chiropteres des grottes du Queire, commune de Biert (Ariege). B. Caubere, R. Caubere. Mammalia, Paris, vol.12, no.3, pp.94-99, Sept., 1948.

(THE CHIROPTERS OF THE CAVES OF QUEIRE IN 1948.) Les Chiroptères des grottes du Queire en 1948. B. Caubère, E. Caubère. Mammalia, Paris, vol.12, no. 4, pp.136-139, Dec., 1948.

(ON A CHIROPTER SPECIES NEW FOR ITALY AND ANOTHER NEW FOR TRIDENTINE VENICE.) Sopra una specie di chirottero nuova per l'Italia ed un'altra nuova per Venezia Tridentina. Gian Battista Dal Piaz. Studi Trentini, ser.2, Sci. Nat. ed Econ., vol.7, pp.49-50, 1926.

(ON SOME DALMATIAN CHIROPTERA.) Sopra alcuni chirotteri Dalmati. Gian Battista Dal Piaz. Atti dell'Accad. Veneto-Trentino-Istriana, vol.16, pp.1-3, 1925.

(BIOLOGICAL NOTES ON DOMESTIC BATS, PARTICULARLY FROM THE ENVIRONS OF BERLIN.) Biologische notizen ueber heimische Fledermaeuse, insbesondere aus der umgebung Berlins. M. Eisentraut. Sitz-Ber. Gesell. Naturforschender Freunde Berlin, pt.2, pp.193-206, Oct.15, 1932.

(GERMAN BATS: A BIOLOGICAL STUDY.) Die deutschen Fledermaeuse, eine biologische Studie. M. Eisentraut. Leipzig, Monographie der Wildsaeugetiere, no.2, 184 pp., 1937.

(A NEW SWISS CHIROPTER.) Un nouveau cheiroptere suisse. Victor Fatio. Arch. Sci. Phys. et Nat., vol.24, pp.509-512, Nov., 1890.

(ECOLOGICAL AND SYSTEMATIC REVIEW OF THE CHIROPTER FAUNA OF SWITZERLAND.) Oekologische und systematische Uebersicht ueber die Chiropteren-fauna der Schweiz. Martin Furrer. Inaugural-Dissertation Univ. Zuerich, pp.1-87, 1957.

(THE BATS OF CZECHOSLOVAKIA. A KEY DESCRIPTION, AND REMARKS ABOUT THEIR OCCURRENCE.) Netopýři Československa. Určovací klíče, popisy a poznámky o výskytu. J. Gaisler, V. Hanak, M. Klima. Acta Universitatis Carolinae, Prague, Biologica, pp.1-65, 1957.

THE BATS OF HELMSLEY, NORTH YORKSHIRE. Adam Gordon. Northwestern Nat., Arbroath, vol.13, no.1, pp.19-21, illus., Mar., 1938.

(BATS FROM ALSACE AND LORRAINE.) Chauves-Souris d'Alsace et de Lorraine. F. Gouin. Bull. Assoc. Philomathique, vol. 19, no.1, pp.17-18, 1950.

(STUDY OF THE CAVE BATS OF MAINE-ET-LOIRE.) Etudes sur les Chauves-souris troglodytes du Maine-et-Loire. M. Gruet, Y. Dufour. Mammalia, Paris, vol. 13, no.3, pp.69-75, figs.2, Sept., 1949.

(THE CHIROPTERS OF PIEDMONT.) I Chirotteri del Piemonte. Guiseppe Gulino. Boll. Mus. Zool. e Anat. Comp. Univ. Torino, ser.3, vol.46, no.83, pp.1-56, figs.11, tables, 1937-1938.

(LIST OF SPECIES WITH NOTES ON THEIR GEOGRAPHIC DISTRIBUTION AND FREQUENCY ON THE PENINSULA.) I Chirotteri Italiani. Elenco delle specie con annotazioni sulla loro distribuzione geografica e frequenza nella penisola. Giuseppe Gulino, Giambattista Dal Piaz. Boll. Mus. Zool. Anat. Comp. Torino, vol.47, ser.3, no.91, pp.43, figs.8, 1939.

THE BATS OF THE SEGEBERG-GIPSHOEHLE IN SCHLESWIG-HOLSTEIN. David L. Harrison. Bonner Zool. Beitraege, Bonn, vol.1-2, pp.9-16, Aug.15, 1951.

BATS IN THE BISHOP'S STORTFORD AREA. J. Hayden, P. Kirby. Oryx, vol.2, no.5, pp.325-328, Aug., 1954.

BRITISH BATS. G. Seccombe Hett, Guy Dollman. Nat. Hist. Mag., British Mus., vol.5, no.37, pp.193-201, figs.6, Jan., 1936.

SOME OBSERVATIONS ON THE DISTRIBUTION AND MOVEMENTS OF CAVE-DWELLING BATS IN DEVONSHIRE. Winfred M. Hooper, John H. D. Hooper, Trevor R. Shaw. Naturalist, Lond., no.835, pp.149-157, illus., Oct.-Dec., 1950.

(BAVARIAN CHIROPTERS: A CONTRIBUTION TO KNOWLEDGE OF THE LIVING HABITS AND GEOGRAPHICAL DISTRIBUTION OF GERMAN BATS.) Die bayerischen Chiroptern, Ein beitrag zur Kenntniss der Lebenweise und der geographischen Verbreitung der deutschen Fledermaeuse. Andreas Johannes Jackel. Regensburg, Abhandl. Zool., vol.8, no.1, pp.1-109, 1860.

(THE PICTURE OF THE BAT WORLD ON CORSICA.) Das Bild der Fledermauslebwelt auf der Insel Korsika. Herman Kahmann, Anton Brotzler. Saeugetierk. Mitteil., Stuttgart, 3 (2): 53-66, Apr.1, 1955.

(CHIROPTERS OF CORSICA.) Les Chiropteres de Corse. Herman Kahmann, Peter Goerner. Mammalia, Paris, 20 (4): 333-389, pls.3-4, Dec., 1956.

(CONTRIBUTIONS TO THE BAT FAUNA OF MECKLENBURG.) Beitrag zur Fledermausfauna Mecklenburgs. Hans-Alfred Kirchner. Archiv. Ver. Freunde Naturgesch. Mecklenburg, Rostock, n.F., vol.11, pp.70-72, 1937.

(EUROPE'S CHIROPTERS.) Europas Chiroptern. Friederico A. Kolenati. Allg. deutsche Naturhist. Zietung. n.p., II, pp. 121-192, 1856.

(BAT INVESTIGATION IN POLAND.) Fledermausforschung in Polen. Kazimierz Kowalski. Bioloski Glasnik, vol.10, nos. 3-4, pp.209-215, pls.1-4, 1957.

CAVE DWELLING BATS IN POLAND AND THEIR PROTECTION. Kazimierz Kowalski. Ochrona Przyrody 21: 58-77, illus., 1953.

MATERIAL RELATING TO THE DISTRIBUTION AND ECOLOGY OF CAVE BATS IN POLAND. Kazimierz Kowalski. Fragmenta Faunistica Mus. Zool. Polonici, Warsaw, vol.6, no.21, pp.541-567, Nov.13, 1953.

(OUR BATS AND THEIR PROTECTION.) Nasze nietoperse i ich ochrona. Kazimierz Kowalski. Polska Akad. Nauk. Zaklad Ochrony Przyrody, Krakow, pp.110, no.11, illus., 1955.

THE BATS (CHIROPTERA) OF PUTAWY. LIST OF SPECIES WITH BIOLOGICAL OBSERVATIONS. Adam Krzanowski. Acta Theriologica, Inst. Zool. Polska Akad. Nauk, Warsaw, 1 (4): 87-108, Oct.15, 1956.

(GERMAN BATS.) Die deutschen fledermaeuse. Heinrich Kuhl. Privately printed at Hanau, pp.67, pls.22, 25, 1817.

(GERMAN BATS.) Die deutschen fledermaeuse. Heinrich Kuhl. Pt.1, pp.11-55, pt.2, pp.185-215, pls.12, 13, 1818.

(DATA ON THE BATS OF THE EASTERN BALTIC REGION.) Zur Kenntnis der Fledermaeuse des Ostbaltischen Gebiets. Karl Reinhold Kupffer. Korrespondenzblatt Naturforsch.-Vereins, Riga, vol.62, pp. 65-79, 1937.

(NEW DATA ON THE SYSTEMATICS AND GEOGRAPHICAL DISTRIBUTION OF THE BATS (CHIROPTERA) OF THE USSR.) Neue Angaben ueber Systematik und geographische Verbreitung der Fledermaeuse (Chiroptera) der U.d.S.S.R. A. P. Kusjakin. Bull. Soc. Nat. Moscou, sec. Biol., n.s., vol. 44, nos.7-8, pp.428-438, 1935.

(THE DETERMINATION OF DUTCH CHIROPTERA.) Het determieeren van de Nederlandsche Chiroptera. H. Landsman. Naturrhistorisch Museum te Rotterdam, no. 2, pp.21-31, 1933.

(OBSERVATIONS OF CHIROPTERS OF SOUTHERN FRANCE BELONGING TO THE SIEPI COLLECTION.) Observations sur les cheiroptères du Midi de la France appartenant à la collection siepi. P. Laurent. Bull. Mus. Hist. Nat. Marseille, vol.1, no.4, pp. 290-305, Oct., 1941.

(THE CHIROPTERS OF SOUTHERN ITALY.) I chirotteri del mezzogiorno d'Italia. Fr. Sav Monticelli. Atti Soc. Italiano Sci. Nat., Milano, vol.28, pp.169-214, pls.3, 1886.

A KEY TO THE BRITISH BATS. T.C.S. Morrison-Scott. The Naturalist, Lond., no.985, pp.33-36, figs.4, Feb., 1939.

(NOTES ON THE ETHOLOGY AND ECOLOGY OF THE CHIROPTERS OF BELGIUM.) Notes sur l'ethologie et l'ecologie des cheiropteres de Belgique. Edmond Nerincx. Bull. Mus. Roy. Hist. Nat. Belgique, Brussels, vol.20, no.19, pp.24, fig.1, July, 1944.

(THE CAVES OF ALPES-MARITIMES AND THEIR FAUNA.) Les grottes de Alpes-Maritimes et leur faune cavernicole. J. Ochs. Riviera Scientifique, 14th year, no. 1, pp.17-20, 1927.

A SYNOPSIS OF THE RUSSIAN BATS. S. I. Ognev. Jour. Mam., vol.8, no.2, pp.140-157, May, 1927.

JUG HOLES CAVE AND ITS BATS. A. L. Pill. Naturalist, London, no.836, pp.7, Jan.-Mar., 1951.

(THE WILD MAMMALS OF CRETE. 3) CRETAN CHIROPTERS.) Die Wildsaeuger von Kreta. 3) Ueber Fledertiere von Kreta. Herman Pohle. Zeitschr. Saeugetierk., vol.17, no.1, pp.14-20, Feb.19, 1953.

THE BATS OF OUR COUNTRYSIDE. W. P. Pycraft. Illus. London News, vol.194, no. 5223, p.928, figs.4, (2 photos, 2 drawings), May 27, 1939.

(DATA ON SILESIAN BATS.) Zur Kenntnis schlesischer Fledermaeuse. J. Seidel. Abhandl. Naturforsch. Ges. Goerlitz, vol. 30, no.1, pp.1-39, pls.2, 1927.

(DATA ON THE BAT FAUNA OF THE ZAMOYSKI ESTATE.) Materialy do fauny nietoperzy Ordynacji Zamoyskich. Materialien zur Chiropteren-Fauna des Zamoyski-Majorats. Waclaw Skuratowicz. Fragmenta Faunistica Mus. Zool. Polonici, Warsaw, vol.4, no.13, pp.227-235, July 13, 1939.

NOTES ON BRITISH BATS--WITH SPECIAL REFERENCE TO THOSE OF THE MIDLAND PLATEAU. C.W.K. Wallis. Proc. Birmingham Nat. Hist. and Philos. Soc., vol.16, no.1, pp.1-12, 1930.

(PROVISIONAL RESULTS OF THE POPULATION INVESTIGATION OF BATS IN THE BETUWE.) Vorlaeufige Ergebnisse der Populations-untersuchung an Feldmaeusen in der Betuwe. A. van Wijngaarden. Zeitschr. Saeugetierk., Berlin, vol.20, nos. 2-3, pp.61-69, illus., Aug.3, 1955.

BATS IN BELFRIES AND ELSEWHERE. Nature, London, vol.137, no.3463, pp.427-428, Mar.14, 1936.

(THE ESSENTIALS OF THE CHIROPTERS, WITH SPECIAL DESCRIPTION OF THE BATS OCCURRING IN THE DUCHY OF NASSUA AND BORDERING REGIONS.) Das Wesentiliche der Chiropteren mit besonderer Beschreibung der in dem Herzogthum

Nassua und den angeanzen den Landestheilen vorkommenden Fledermause. Nat. Hist. Mammals, vol.58.

Flight

HOW BATS FLY. Richard L. Cassell. Nat. Hist., New York, vol.59, no.10, pp.460-463, illus., Dec., 1950.

(CONTRIBUTION TO THE MECHANICS OF BAT FLIGHT.) Beitrag zur Mechanik des Fledermausfluges. M. Eisentraut. Zeitschr. f. Wissen. Zool., Abt.A., Leipzig, vol.148, no.2, pp.159-188, figs.18, Oct., 1936.

THE AVOIDANCE OF OBSTACLES BY FLYING BATS: SPALLANZANI'S IDEAS (1794) AND LATER THEORIES. Robert Galambos. Isis, Burlington, vol.34, pt.2, no.94, Aug., 1942.

FLIGHT IN THE DARK: A STUDY OF BATS. Robert Galambos. Sci. Monthly, Lancaster, vol.56, no.2, whole no.329, pp.155-162, Feb., 1943.

OBSTACLE AVOIDANCE BY FLYING BATS: THE CRIES OF BATS. Robert Galambos, Donald R. Griffin. Jour. Exper. Zool., Philadelphia, vol.89, no.3, pp.475-490, figs.6, Apr.6, 1942.

THE FLIGHT OF ANIMALS. James Gray. Ann. Rept. Smithsonian Inst., Washington, 1954, pp.285-303, pls.1-10, 1955.

THE NAVIGATION OF BATS. Donald R. Griffin. Scientific American, New York, vol.183, no.2, pp.52-55, illus., Aug., 1950.

THE SENSORY BASIS OF OBSTACLE AVOIDANCE BY FLYING BATS. Donald R. Griffin, Robert Galambos. Jour. Exper. Zool., Philadelphia, vol.86, no.3, pp.481-506, Apr. 5, 1941.

ACOUSTIC CONTROL IN THE FLIGHT OF BATS. H. Hartridge. Nature, Lond., vol. 156, no.3965, pp.490-494, Oct.27, 1945.

NON-STOP FLIGHT. John Eric Hill. Nat. Hist., New York, vol.56, no.2, p.67, Feb., 1947.

(HOW FAST DOES A BAT FLY?) Wie schnell fliegt eine Fledermaus? A. Kolb. Saeugetierk. Mitteil., Stuttgart, 3 (4): 176-177, Oct.1, 1955.

AVOIDANCE OF OBSTACLES BY BATS. A. K. McIntyre. Nature, Lond., vol.155, no.3944, p.672, June 2, 1945.

HOW BATS IN FLIGHT AVOID OBSTACLES. A. L. Rand. Canadian Field-Nat., Sutton West, vol.57, nos.3-4, p.94, Apr.-May, 1943.

(ON FLIGHT ADAPTATION IN THE MICROCHIROPTERANS.) A propos de l'adaptation au vol chez les Microchiropteres. P. Revilliod. Verhand. Naturfors. Gesell. Basel, vol.27, no. pp.156-183, 1916.

THE IMPORTANCE OF THE NERVOUS SYSTEM IN THE EVOLUTION OF ANIMAL FLIGHT. Maynard J. Smith. Evolution, Lancaster, vol.6, no.1, pp.127-129, Mar., 1952.

(CONTRIBUTIONS TO KNOWLEDGE OF THE FLIGHT OF BATS AND OF THE ONTOGENETIC DEVELOPMENT OF THEIR FLIGHT APPARATUS.) Beitraege zur Kenntniss des Fluges der Fledermaeuse und der ontogenetischen Entwicklung ihres Flugapparats. Fr. Spillman. Acta Zoologica, vol.6, pp. 217-222, 1 pl., 1925.

THE BATS "CLOISTERED FLIGHT" ARRESTED BY HIGH-SPEED PHOTOGRAPHY. Illus. London News, vol.191, no.5134, p.443, Sept.11, 1937.

"ON LEATHERN WING": BATS IN FLIGHT PHOTOGRAPHED BY THEMSELVES. Illus. London News, vol.213, no.5711, p.388, illus., Oct.2, 1948.

Food Habits

THE DIET OF THE BAT. Maurice Burton. Illus. London News, vol.219, no.5860, pp. 226, 227, illus., Aug.11, 1951.

(THE NUTRITION OF BATS.) Die Ernaehrung der Fledermaeuse (Microchiroptera). M. Eisentraut. Zool. Jahrb., 79:114-77, 1950.

BATS TAKING MOTHS AT SUGAR. B. Vesey Fitzgerald. Entomologist, Lond., vol.76, pp.173-174, 1943.

THE FEEDING EFFICIENCY OF INSECTIVOROUS BATS. Edwin Gould. Jour. Mam., 36 (3): 399-407, Aug.30, 1955.

BATS FEEDING ON MOTHS AT SALLOW. S. B. Hodgson. Entomologist, London, vol. 76, pp.147-148, 1943.

MOTHS EATEN BY BATS. C. Nicholson. Entomologist, vol.68, p.61, 1935.

REMARKS ON POLLINATION BY BATS IN THE GENERA FREYCINETIA, DUBANGA AND HAPLOPHRAGMA, AND ON CHIROPTEROPHILY IN GENERAL. L. van der Pijl. Acta Botanica Neerlandica, 5 (2): 135-144, pls.1-2, Aug., 1956.

(CRESCENTIA, A BAT BLOSSOM.) Crescentia, eine Fledermausblume. O. Porsch. Oesterr. Bot. Zeits., 80:31-44, pls.9-10, 1932.

BRITISH INSECTIVOROUS BATS AND THEIR PREY. Edward B. Poulton. Proc. Zool. Soc., Lond., pt.2, pp.277-303, Aug., 1929.

THE EATING HABITS OF BATS. W. P. Pycraft. Illus. London News, vol.197, no. 5282, p.60, illus., July 13, 1940.

NOTES ON THE FOOD OF SOME FLORIDA BATS. H. B. Sherman. Jour. Mam., vol. 20, no.1, pp.103-104, table, Feb.14, 1939.

BATS AND BIRDS COMPETING FOR FOOD. Richard G. Van Gelder, Woodrow W. Goodpaster. Jour. Mam., vol.33, no.4, p.491, Nov.19, 1952.

(HONEY SPECIALISTS AMONG BATS.) Honigspezialisten unter Fledermaeusen. C. Zimmer. Sitz.-Ber. Gesell. Naturf. Fr. Berlin, Jahrg., 1936, pt.2, pp.249-252, 1937.

Fossils

A PLEISTOCENE BAT FROM FLORIDA. Glover M. Allen. Jour. Mam., vol.13, no. 3, pp.256-259, Aug., 1932.

A SUBFOSSIL BAT'S SKULL FROM RODRIGUEZ ISLAND. Knud Andersen. Records Indian Mus., vol.9, pp.337-340, 1913.

TWO NEW FOSSIL BATS FROM PORTO RICO. H. E. Anthony. Bull. Amer. Mus. Nat. Hist., vol.37, art.19, pp.565-568, Sept.7, 1917.

(NATURAL ENDOCRANIAL MOLDS OF FOSSIL MICROCHIROPTERS.) Moulages endocraniens naturels de Microchiropteres fossiles. Colette Dechaseaux. Ann. Paleontologie, 42: 117-137, 1956.

A NEW GENUS OF BAT FROM THE LATER TERTIARY OF NEVADA. E. Raymond Hall. Bull. Dept. Geol. Sci., Univ. Calif., vol. 19, no.14, pp.319-320, pl.38, Nov.25, 1930.

FOSSIL BATS FROM THE BAHAMAS. Karl F. Koopman. Jour. Mam., vol.32, no.2, p.229, May, 1951.

FOSSIL CHIROPTERA COLLECTED BY H. E. ANTHONY IN JAMAICA, 1919-1920. Karl F. Koopman, Ernest E. Williams. Amer. Mus. Novitates, New York, no.1519, pp.29, figs.6, June 6, 1951.

MIOCENE BAT REMAINS FROM FLORIDA, WITH NOTES ON THE GENERIC CHARACTERS OF THE HUMERUS OF BATS. Barbara Lawrence. Jour. Mam., vol.24, no.3, pp.359-369, figs.2, Aug., 1943.

A PALEOCENE BAT. W. D. Matthew. Bull. Amer. Mus. Nat. Hist., New York, vol.37, art.20, pp.569-571, fig.1, Sept.7, 1917.

(FOSSILS OF BATS FROM BRAZIL.) Os chiropteros fosseis do Brasil. Carlos de Paula Couto. Acad. Colombiana Cienc. Exactas, Fis. y Nat. Bogota, vol.2, no.7, pp.464-465, illus., Sept.-Oct., 1938.

(CONTRIBUTION TO STUDY OF THE CHIROPTERS OF TERTIARY TERRAINS.) Contribution à l'Etude des Chiroptères des Terrains Tertiares. P. Revilliod. Mém. Soc. Paléont. Suisse, vol.44 (1919), pp.63-128, 2 pls., 1920.

(ON ARCHAEONYCTERIS DENTITION.) A propos de la dentition d'Archaeonycteris. P. Revilliod. Actes Soc. Helvétique Sci. Nat., no.109, pt.2, pp.222-223, 1928.

(THE PRESENT STATE OF OUR KNOWLEDGE OF FOSSIL CHIROPTERS (PRELIMINARY COMMUNICATION).) L'etat actuel de nos connaissances sur les Chiropteres fossiles (Note preliminaire). P. Revilliod. Compte Rendu Soc. Phys. et Hist. Nat. Geneve, (Suppl. Archiv. Sci. Phys. et Nat.), vol.36, no.3, pp.93-96, Aug.-Dec., 1919.

ADDITIONAL NOTES ON FOSSIL AND SUBFOSSIL BATS FROM JAMAICA. Ernest E. Williams. Jour. Mam., vol.33, no.2, pp. 171-179, May 16, 1952.

General Habits, Behavior

BATS AND ARTIFICIAL LIGHT. Fred Allen. Northwestern Nat., Arbroath, vol.11, no.2, pp.153-154, June, 1936.

BATS AND THEIR HABITS. Glover M. Allen. Bull. Boston Soc. Nat. Hist., no.40, pp.3-6, July, 1926.

A PECULIAR ROOSTING HABIT OF BATS. T. Barbour. From Quart. Rev. Biol., vol. 7, no.3, pp.307-312, figs.4, Sept., 1932.

THE EFFECT OF AIR ACTIVITY ON BIRDS AND BATS. A. G. Bennett. Ibis, London, vol.86, p.408, July, 1944.

ON THE HABITS AND ECONOMY OF TWO BRITISH SPECIES OF BATS. G. Daniell. Proc. Zool. Soc. Lond., pt.2, p.129, 1834.

(DAY QUARTERS OF BATS ACCORDING TO OBSERVATIONS IN EL SALVADOR.) Tagesquartiere von Fledermaeusen nach Beobachtungen in El Salvador. Heinz Felten. Natur und Volk, Frankfurt a. M., vol.85, no.10, pp.315-321, illus., Oct.1, 1955.

AN ACCOUNT OF A REMARKABLE ACCUMULATION OF BATS. M. Figanierre e Morao. Smithsonian Inst. Ann. Rept., Washington, 1863, pp.407-409, 1864.

ACTIVITY RHYTHMS IN BATS UNDER CONSTANT EXTERNAL CONDITIONS. Donald R. Griffin, John H. Welsh. Jour. Mam., vol.18, no.3, pp.337-342, figs.3, Aug.14, 1937.

SOME HABITS AND SENSORY ADAPTATIONS OF CAVE-INHABITING BATS. Walter Louis Hahn. Biological Bulletin, vol.15, no.3, pp. 135-193, Aug., 1908.

BAT FISHERMEN. John Eric Hill. Nat. Hist., New York, vol.51, no.4, p.197, illus., Apr., 1943.

HABITS AND MOVEMENTS OF CAVE-DWELLING BATS IN DEVONSHIRE. J.H.D. Hooper, W.M. Hooper. Proc. Zool. Soc. Lond., 127 (1): 1-26, pls.1-6, Sept.28, 1956.

SOME CALIFORNIAN EXPERIENCES WITH BAT ROOSTS. A. Brazier Howell. Jour. Mam., vol.1, no.4, pp.169-177, pl.9, Aug. 24, 1920.

ACCIDENTS OF BATS. Paul B. Johnson. Jour. Mam., vol.14, no.2, pp.156-157, May, 1933.

ROBIN AND BAT. Haven Kolb. Maryland Conservation, Baltimore, vol.18, no.3, pp. 50-51, Summer, 1948.

BATS AND ARTIFICIAL LIGHT. A. K. Lawson. Northwestern Nat., Arbroath, vol.11, no.1, p.43, Mar., 1936.

BATS CAUGHT IN BURDOCKS. Marcus W. Lyon, Jr. Jour. Mam., vol.6, no.4, p.280, Nov.14, 1925.

NOTES ON THE HABITS OF AUSTRALIAN BATS. A. J. Marshall. Australian Zool., Sydney, vol.8, pt.2, pp.81-86, June 28, 1935.

BATS AND VIBRATIONS. A.H.E. Mattingley. Victorian Nat., Melbourne, vol.61, no.11, pp.202-203, Mar., 1945.

I EXPLORE CAVES. Charles E. Mohr. Natural History, New York, vol.43, no.4, pp.190-204, illus., Apr., 1939.

OBSERVATIONS ON THE YOUNG OF CAVE-DWELLING BATS. Charles E. Mohr. Jour. Mam., vol.14, no.1, pp.49-53, Feb., 1933.

(THE "LYING-IN ROOMS" OF BATS.) Die Wochenstuben der Fledermaeuse. Franz Peter Moehres. Die Umschau, Frankfurt am Main, vol.21, pp.658-659, Nov.1, 1951.

FURTHER NOTES ON SOME CEYLON BATS. W.W.A. Phillips. Jour. Bombay Nat. Hist. Soc., vol.29, pp.154-156, 2 pls., Apr.20, 1923.

NOTES ON THE HABITS OF SOME CEYLON BATS. W.W.A. Phillips. Jour. Bombay Nat. Hist. Soc., vol.28, pp.448-452, Mar. 25, 1922.

THE DISPERSAL OF PLANTS BY BATS. L. van der Pijl. Acta Botanica Neerlandica, 6: 291-315, 1957.

BATS FLYING IN SUNLIGHT. R. Lloyd Praeger. Irish Naturalists' Jour., vol.2, no.4, p.73, July, 1928.

BATS KILLED BY SEVERE STORM. G. N. Rysgaard. Jour. Mam., vol.22, no.4, pp. 452-453, Nov.14, 1941.

SUMMER OUTINGS OF BATS DURING FOURTEEN SEASONS. Althea R. Sherman. Jour. Mam., vol.10, no.4, pp.319-326, Nov., 1929.

ASPECTS OF A POPULATION STUDY OF CAVERN-DWELLING BATS. John W. Twente, Jr. Jour. Mam., 36 (3): 379-390, 1 fig., 2 tables, Aug.30, 1955.

SOME ASPECTS OF HABITAT SELECTION AND OTHER BEHAVIOR OF CAVERN-DWELLING BATS. J. W. Twente, Jr. Ecology, Durham, vol.36, no.4, pp.706-732, illus., Oct., 1955.

(THE ACTIVITY AND WINTER DISPLACEMENTS OF THE CHIROPTERS OF BELGIUM.) L'Activite et les desplacements hivernaux des cheiropteres en Belgique. Jacques Verschuren. Bull. Inst. Roy. Sci. Nat. Belgique, vol.25, no.3, pp.1-7, Jan., 1949.

### Hibernation

BATS HIBERNATE IN THE CENTER OF A LARGE CITY. Theodor G. Ahrens. Jour. Mam., vol.18, no.2, p.238, May 14, 1937.

BATS HIBERNATING IN THE DISTRICT OF THUNDER BAY, ONTARIO. A. E. Allin. Canadian Field-Nat., Ottawa, vol.56, no. 6, pp.90-91, Sept., 1942.

TEMPERATURE CHANGES AND WINTER SLEEP OF BATS. R. C. Burbank, J. Z. Young. Jour. Physiol., Lond., vol.82, no. 4, pp.459-467, Nov.12, 1934.

(THE HIBERNATION OF BATS, WITH SPECIAL CONSIDERATION OF WARMTH REGULATION.) Der Winterschlaf der Fledermaeuse mit besonderer Beruecksichtigung der Waermeregulation. M. Eisentraut. Zeits. f. Morphol. Oekol. Tiere, 29:231-67, 1934.

OBSERVATIONS ON HIBERNATING BATS WITH ESPECIAL REFERENCE TO REPRODUCTION AND SPLENIC ADAPTATION. Charles A. Evans. Amer. Nat., Lancaster, Pa., vol.72, no.742, pp.480-484, Sept.-Oct., 1938.

(OBSERVATIONS ON HIBERNATING BATS IN THE RHINE-MAIN REGION.) Beobachtungen an winterschlafender Fledermaeusen im Rhein-Main-Gebiet. H. Felten. Saeugertierk. Mitteil., Stuttgart, vol.1, no. 1, pp.8-13, Jan.10, 1953.

MUSEUM EXPEDITION UNDERGROUND. Richard W. Fyfe. Blue Jay, Saskatchewan Nat. Hist. Soc., 15 (2): 65-69, June, 1957.

(INVESTIGATIONS OF THE POTENTIALITY OF THE DEVELOPMENT OF EGGS OBTAINED BY PRODUCING OVULATION IN THE BAT IN HIBERNATION.) Recherches sur les potentialités de développement des oeufs obtenus par ovulation provoquée chez la chauve-souris en hibernation. M. Herlant. Bull. Acad. Roy. Belgique, (5), 20: 359-66, 1934.

HIBERNATION OF BATS IN SOUTHEASTERN ONTARIO AND ADJACENT QUEBEC. Harold B. Hitchock. Canadian Field-Nat., vol.63, no.2, pp.47-59, fig.1, Mar.-Apr., 1949.

A PRELIMINARY NOTE ON THE BATS HIBERNATING IN THE CASEMATES OF THE TOWN OF LUXEMBOURG. A.M. Husson. Archives Inst. Grand-Ducal Luxembourg, vol.21, n.s., pp.65-70, illus., 1954.

WHAT ARE PROPER HIBERNATING CONDITIONS FOR BATS. Charles E. Johnson. Jour. Mam., vol.14, no.4, pp.366-368, Nov., 1933.

CHANGES IN SPLENIC WEIGHT ASSOCIATED WITH HIBERNATION IN BATS. W. Z. Lidicker, W. H. Davis. Proc. Soc. Exper. Biol. and Med., New York, vol.89, no.4, pp.640-642, Aug.-Sept., 1955.

EXPERIMENTAL EVIDENCE ON THE BODY TEMPERATURES OF HIBERNATING BATS. M. S. Mahalev, Jr. Bios, vol.25, no.2, pp.107-110, May, 1954.

HIBERNATION OF BATS. C. Hart Merriam. Science, vol.8, no.190, p.281, 1886.

CHANGES IN THE ISLETS OF LANGERHANS ASSOCIATED WITH AGE AND HIBERNATION. L. Mosca. Quart. Jour. Exper. Physiol., Edinburgh, 41 (4): 433-441, Oct., 1956.

NOTES ON HIBERNATING BATS. James W. Sprague. Jour. Mam., Baltimore, vol.19, no.4, p.500, Nov.14, 1938.

THE HIBERNATION OF CERTAIN BATS IN SOUTHERN MINNESOTA. Gustav Swanson, Charles Evans. Jour. Mam., vol.17, no.1, pp.39-43, Feb., 1936.

(OBSERVATIONS ON THE HIBERNATION OF BATS.) Waarnemingen betreffende de Winterslaa van Vleermiuzen. J. de Wilde, P.J. van Nieuwenhoven. Publ. Nat. Genootschap Limburg, vol.7, pp.51-83, 1954.

WHERE THE BATS SLEEP. A GLIMPSE INTO A HIDDEN WORLD OF LIFE IN WINTER. Field, London, vol.165, no.4286, pp.330-331, figs.7, Feb.16, 1933.

### Mexico and Central America

BATS FROM THE PANAMA REGION. Glover M. Allen. Jour. Mam., vol.16, no. 3, pp.227-228, Aug., 1935.

A NEW BAT FROM MEXICO. Glover M. Allen. Proc. Biol. Soc. Washington, vol. 27, pp.109-112, July 10, 1914.

DESCRIPTION OF A NEW MEXICAN BAT. Harrison Allen. Proc. Acad. Nat. Sci. Philadelphia, pp.359-361, 1861.

EXTENSIONS OF KNOWN RANGES OF MEXICAN BATS. Sydney Anderson. Univ. Kansas Publ., Mus. Nat. Hist., 9(9): 347-351, Aug.15, 1956.

DESCRIPTIVE ECOLOGY OF LA CUEVA CHICA, WITH ESPECIAL REFERENCE TO THE BLIND FISH, ANOPTICHTYS. C. M. Breder. Zoologica, New York, vol.27, pt. 1, no.3, pp.7-15, fig.1, pls.3, Apr.30, 1942.

BATS OF THE MEXICAN STATE OF MORELOS. William B. Davis, Robert J. Russell, Jr. Jour. Mam., vol.33, no.2, pp.234-239, May 16, 1952.

(BATS (MAMMALIA, CHIROPTERA) OF EL SALVADOR.) Fledermaeuse (Mammalia, Chiroptera) aus El Salvador. Heinz Felten. Senckenbergiana Biologica, Frankfurt am Main, 36 (5-6): 271-285, pl.25, Dec.1, 1955; 37 (1-2): 69-86, pls.7-8, Feb.15, 1956; 37 (3-4): 179-212, pls.24-27, Apr.15, 1956; 37 (5-6): 342-367, pls.45-48, Sept.15, 1956; 38 (1-2): 1-22, pls.1-2, Jan.15, 1957.

A NEW GENUS OF BAT FROM COSTA RICA. George G. Goodwin. Amer. Mus. Novitates, New York, no.976, pp.2, May 4, 1938.

THREE NEW BATS FROM HONDURAS AND THE FIRST RECORD OF ENCHISTHENES HARTI (THOMAS) FOR NORTH AMERICA. George G. Goodwin. Amer. Mus. Novitates, New York, no.1075, pp.3, June 27, 1940.

THE FISH-EATING BATS OF THE GULF OF CALIFORNIA. E. W. Gudger. California Fish and Game, San Francisco, vol.29, no. 2, pp.79-81, figs.27-28, Apr., 1943.

A NEW BAT FROM MEXICO. Walter L. Hahn. Proc. Biol. Soc. Washington, vol. 18, pp.247-248, Dec.9, 1905.

SEVENTEEN SPECIES OF BATS RECORDED FROM BARRO COLORADO ISLAND, PANAMA CANAL ZONE. E. Raymond Hall, William B. Jackson. Univ. Kansas Publ., Mus. Nat. Hist., Lawrence, vol.5, no.37, pp.641-646, Dec.1, 1953.

NOTES ON THE CAPTURE OF TROPICAL BATS AT CUEVO EL PACHON, TAMAULIPAS, MEXICO. Marian Martin, Paul S. Martin. Jour. Mam., vol.35, no.4, pp. 584-585, Nov.29, 1954.

(CONTRIBUTIONS TO KNOWLEDGE OF MEXICAN BATS.) Contribuciones al conocimiento de los Murcielagos de Mexico. Liborio Martinez, Bernardo Villa. Anal. Inst. Biol., Mexico City, vol.9, nos.3-4, pp.339-360, figs.10, 1938.

(SECOND CONTRIBUTION TO KNOWLEDGE OF MEXICAN BATS. STATE OF GUERRERO.) Segunda contribucion al conocimiento de los Murcielagos Mexicanos. Liborio Martinez, Bernardo Villa. Anal. Inst. Biol., Mexico, vol.11, no.1, pp.291-361, illus., 1940.

DESCRIPTION OF A NEW BAT FROM LOWER CALIFORNIA. Gerrit S. Miller, Jr. Ann. and Mag. Nat. Hist., ser.7, vol.2, pp.124-125, Aug., 1898.

A SMALL COLLECTION OF BATS FROM PANAMA. Gerrit S. Miller, Jr. Proc. U. S. Nat. Mus., vol.42, pp.21-26, 1912.

SOME BATS FROM LOWER CALIFORNIA. Gerrit S. Miller, Jr. Amer. Nat., vol.36, pp.75-77, Jan., 1897.

TWO TROPICAL BATS NEW TO THE FAUNA OF PANAMA. Gerrit S. Miller, Jr. Proc. Biol. Soc. Washington, vol.45, p.149, Sept. 9, 1932.

TWO GENERA OF BATS NEW TO MIDDLE AMERICA. E. W. Nelson. Proc. Biol. Soc. Washington, vol.25, p.93, May 4, 1912.

RECORDS OF BATS FROM HONDURAS. Frederick H. Test. Jour. Mam., vol.15, no.4, p.316, Nov., 1934.

DESCRIPTION OF A NEW MEXICAN BAT. Oldfield Thomas. Ann. and Mag. Nat. Hist. (6), vol.10, no.60, pp.477-478, Dec., 1892.

BATS FROM GUERRERO, JALISCO AND OAXACA, MEXICO. Luis de la Torre. Fieldiana: Zoology, Chicago Nat. Hist. Mus., vol.37, pp.695-704, illus., 2 pls., June 19, 1955.

BATS FROM SOUTHERN TAMAULIPAS, MEXICO. Luis de la Torre. Jour. Mam., vol.35, no.1, pp.113-116, 1 table, Feb.10, 1954.

(NOTES ON THE BATS OF THE ALFREDO DUGES MUSEUM.) Nota acerca de los murcielagos del Museo Alfredo Duges. R. Bernardo Villa. Rev. Soc. Mexicana Hist. Nat., 14 (1-4): 151-155, Dec., 1953.

DESCRIPTIONS OF THREE NEW SPECIES OF MEXICAN BATS. Henry L. Ward. American Naturalist, vol.25, pp.743-753, figs.6, Aug., 1891.

### Migration

THE BAT AS TRAVELLER. SOME NEW OBSERVATIONS. Michael Blackmore. Country Life, London, vol.82, no.2119, pp. 228-229, figs.4, Aug.28, 1937.

(BAT MIGRATION.) Flagermusetraek. F. W. Braestrup. Naturens Verden, Aargang 21, no.6, pp.269-279, figs.4, June-July, 1937.

(BATS MIGRATE LIKE MIGRATING BIRDS.) Die Fledermaeuse ziehen wie die Zugvoegel. I. Buresch. Schr. Bulgar. Akad. Wiss., 61: 51-72, 1941.

(OBSERVATIONS ON A COLONY OF MIGRATORY BATS.) Observations sur une colonie de chauves-souris. Norbert Casteret. Mammalia, Paris, vol.2, no.1, pp.29-34, Mar., 1938.

(BAT MIGRATION AND BAT RINGING.) Fledermauszug und Fledermausberingung. M. Eisentraut. Ornith. Monatsber., vol. 43, no.1, pp.22-25, Jan.-Feb., 1935.

(BAT TRAVELS.) Fledermaus-Wanderungen. M. Eisentraut. Natur und Volk, vol. 67, no.8, pp.361-371, figs.6, Aug.1, 1937.

(DIURNAL BAT MIGRATION.) Fledermauszug am Tage. H. Graf Finck von Finckenstein, Helmut Schaefer. Zool. Anz., vol. 106, nos.1-2, pp.46-48, Mar.5, 1934.

BATS MIGRATE TOO. Donald R. Griffin. New England Nat., Boston, no.5, pp.1-4, illus., Dec., 1939.

MIGRATIONS OF NEW ENGLAND BATS. Donald R. Griffin. Bull. Mus. Comp. Zool. Harvard College, Cambridge, vol. 86, no.6, pp.217-246, figs.3, tables 4, pls.5, Jan., 1940.

TRAVELS OF BANDED CAVE BATS. Donald R. Griffin. Jour. Mam., vol.26, no.1, pp.15-23, figs.4, Feb.23, 1945.

NOTES ON THE SEASONAL MOVEMENTS OF SOME CAVE BATS. Mary J. Guthrie. Anat. Rec., vol.54, no.3, suppl., pp.112-113, Nov.25, 1932.

MASS MIGRATION OF BATS, CLARENCEVILLE, P.Q., 1931. Geo. H. Hammond. Canadian Field-Nat., Ottawa, vol.62, no. 4, p.124, July-Aug., 1948.

NOTES ON THE DIURNAL MIGRATIONS OF BATS. Arthur H. Howell. Proc. Biol. Soc., Washington, vol.21, pp.35-38, Jan. 23, 1908.

(BATS AND THEIR WANDERINGS IN THE RHINE-MAIN REGION.) Fledermaeuse und ihre Wanderungen im Rhein-Main-Gebiet. Konrad Klemmer. Natur und Volk, vol.84, nos.1-2, pp.413-421, illus., 1954.

(MIGRATING BATS.) Ziehende Fledermaeuse. H. Loehrl. Saeugetierk. Mitteil., Stuttgart, 3 (3): 128, July 1, 1955.

DO ANY CANADIAN BATS MIGRATE? EVIDENCE IN THE AFFIRMATIVE. C. Hart Merriam. Trans. Roy. Soc. Canada, sect.4, pp.85-87, May 25, 1887.

(MIGRATING BATS.) Ziehende Fledermaeuse. F. Neubaur. Saeugetierk. Mitteil., Stuttgart, vol.2, no.1, p.31, Jan.1, 1954.

BATS ON MIGRATION. Oldfield Thomas. Jour. Mam., vol.2, no.3, p.167, Aug., 1921.

ECHO-LOCATION FAILURE IN MIGRATORY BATS. Richard G. van Gelder. Trans. Kansas Acad. Sci., vol.59, no.2, pp.220-222, 1956.

North America

NOTES ON THE WINTER OCCURRENCE OF BATS IN NEVADA. J. R. Alcorn. Jour. Mam., vol.25, no.3, pp.308-310, Sept.8, 1944.

BATS FROM MOUNT WHITNEY, CALIFORNIA. Glover M. Allen. Jour. Mam., vol.1, no.1, pp.1-5, Nov., 1919.

BATS FROM NEW MEXICO AND ARIZONA. Glover M. Allen. Jour. Mam., vol.3, no. 3, pp.156-162, Aug., 1922.

MONOGRAPH OF THE BATS OF NORTH AMERICA. Harrison Allen. Smithsonian Misc. Coll. no.165, pp.85, illus., 1864.

MONOGRAPH OF THE BATS OF NORTH AMERICA. Harrison Allen. New ed., Washington, Govt. Print. Off., 1893.

BATS OF CARLSBAD CAVERN. Vernon Bailey. Nat. Geog. Mag., vol.48, pp.321-331, Sept., 1925.

BATS OF THE EDWARDS PLATEAU IN CENTRAL TEXAS. W. Frank Blair. Texas Jour. Sci., San Marcos, vol.4, no.1, pp. 95-98, Mar.30, 1952.

EXTENSIONS OF RANGE FOR THREE BATS IN CALIFORNIA. Jack C. von Bloeker, Jr. Jour. Mam., vol.24, no.3, pp.403-404, Aug.17, 1943.

NEW BATS FOUND IN YOSEMITE. A. E. Borell. Yosemite Nature Notes, vol.14, no. 7, pp.58-59, July, 1935.

BATS ON THE COLORADO DESERT. Berry Campbell. Jour. Mam., vol.12, no.4, p. 430, Nov., 1931.

NOTES ON BATS COLLECTED IN ARIZONA DURING THE SUMMER OF 1933. Berry Campbell. Jour. Mam., vol.15, no.3, pp. 241-242, Aug., 1934.

THE BATS OF CARLSBAD CAVERNS. Ernst Christensen. Animal Kingdom, New York, vol.49, no.3, pp.98-102, illus., June., 1946.

FURTHER NOTES ON THE WINTER OCCURRENCE OF BATS IN BRITISH COLUMBIA. I. McT. Cowan. Murrelet, Seattle, vol.25, no.3, p.45, Sept.-Dec. (Dec.20), 1944.

NOTES ON THE WINTER OCCURRENCE OF BATS IN BRITISH COLUMBIA. I. McT. Cowan. Murrelet, Seattle, vol.23, no.2, p.61, Aug.14, 1942.

BATS IN THE SAN JUAN ISLANDS, WASHINGTON. Walter W. Dalquest. Murrelet, Seattle, vol.21, no.1, pp.4-5, Jan.-Apr., 1940.

BATS IN THE STATE OF WASHINGTON. Walter W. Dalquest. Jour. Mam., vol.19, no.2, pp.211-213, May 14, 1938.

TEXAS BATS. William B. Davis. Texas Game and Fish 3(2): 4-5, 12-13, Jan., 1945.

A BAT NEW FOR CALIFORNIA. Donald R. Dickey. Jour. Mam., vol.3, no.2, p.116, May, 1922.

MODERN INHABITANTS OF PREHISTORIC CASA GRANDE. Natt N. Dodge. Nat. Parks Mag., Washington, no.80, pp.15-18, illus., Jan.-March, 1945.

NEW LOCALITY RECORDS FOR TEXAS BATS. R. B. Eads, G. C. Menzies, J. S. Wiseman. Jour. Mam., 37 (3): 440, Sept. 11, 1956.

BATS OF INDIAN KEY, TAMPA BAY, FLORIDA. William G. Fargo. Jour. Mam., vol.10, no.3, pp.203-205, Aug., 1929.

SOME OF THE BATS OF WESTCHESTER CO., N.Y. A. K. Fisher. Forest and Stream, New York, vol.16, no.25, pp.490-491, July 21, 1881.

RECENT ADDITIONS TO THE CHECKLIST OF FAUNA FROM CAVES EXPLORED BY THE NATIONAL SPELEOLOGICAL SOCIETY. J. A. Fowler. Bull. Nat. Speleol. Soc., Washington, D.C., no.3, pp.34-35, Jan., 1942.

A LIST OF MARYLAND MAMMALS. PART II. BATS. Marshall C. Gardner. Proc. Biol. Soc. Washington, vol.63, pp.111-114, Dec.29, 1950.

THE BAT....ONE OF OUR MOST INTERESTING MAMMALS. William H. Gates. Louisiana Conservation Rev., New Orleans, vol.9, no.4, pp.40, 60, photo.1, Winter, 1940-1941.

NEW RECORDS FOR BATS IN OKLAHOMA. Bryan P. Glass. Jour. Mam., 36 (1): 128, Feb.25, 1955.

BATS IN THE BELFRY. (A PICTORIAL ACCOUNT OF A RECENT SURVEY MADE BY H.B. HITCHCOCK, UNIVERSITY OF WESTERN ONTARIO, LONDON, CANADA.) Arthur Gleason. MacLean's Magazine, Toronto, vol.53, no.6, p.17, Mar.15, 1940.

NOTES ON SOME BATS FROM ALASKA AND BRITISH COLUMBIA. Hilda Wood Grinnell. Berkeley, University of California press, 1918.

A SYNOPSIS OF THE BATS OF CALIFORNIA. Hilda Wood Grinnell. Univ. Cal. Publ. Zool., vol.17, no.12, pp.223-404, figs.2-4, pls.14-24, Jan.31, 1918.

SOME NOTES ON UTAH BATS. Ross Hardy. Jour. Mam., Baltimore, vol.22, no.3, pp. 289-295, Aug.14, 1941.

NOTES ON THREE GENERA OF BATS FROM ARIZONA. Lyndon L. Hargrave. Jour. Mam. vol.25, no.3, pp.312-313, Sept.8, 1944.

VIEW OF THE BAT CAVE IN MAQUOKETA CAVE STATE PARK. BATS FAIL TO RETURN. James R. Harlan. Iowa Conserv. Notes, Des Moines, 2 pp. mimeogr. Dec.16, 1943.

BATS. Caroline A. Heppenstall. Pennsylvania Game News, Harrisburg, vol.16, no. 11, pp.13, 27, Feb., 1946.

NOTES ON SOME CAVE BATS OF KANSAS. Claude W. Hibbard. Trans. Kansas Acad. Sci., vol.37, pp.235-238, 1934.

TWO NEW BATS FROM THE SOUTHWESTERN UNITED STATES. Ned Hollister. Proc. Biol. Soc. Wash., vol.22, pp.43-44, Mar.10, 1909.

DESCRIPTION OF A NEW BAT FROM NICKAJACK CAVE, TENNESSEE. Arthur H. Howell. Proc. Biol. Soc. Wash., vol.22, pp.45-48, Mar.10, 1909.

CAVE FAUNA WITH ESPECIAL REFERENCE TO ECOLOGICAL FACTORS. J. D. Ives. Jour. Elisha Mitchell Sci. Soc., vol.43, nos. 1-2, pp.84-90, Nov. (Dec.), 1927.

NEW RECORDS OF BATS FROM NORTHEASTERN KANSAS, WITH NOTES ON THE BAT CHIGGER, EUSCHONGASTIA PIPISTRELLI (ACARINA, TROMBICULIDAE). Knox J. Jones, Jr., Richard B. Loomis, Philip H. Krutzsch, Olin L. Webb. Trans. Kansas Acad. Science, vol.55, no.3, pp. 312-314, 1952.

A KEY TO THE BATS OF WESTERN NORTH AMERICA NORTH OF MEXICO. Philip H. Krutzsch. Nat. Hist. Misc., Chicago Acad. Sci., no.133, pp.1-6, Apr.20, 1954.

ADDITIONAL DISTRIBUTIONAL RECORDS OF BATS IN UTAH. Philip H. Krutzsch, Caroline A. Heppenstall. Jour. Mam., 36 (1): 125-127, Feb.25, 1955.

THE BATS OF LOUISIANA. George H. Lowery, Jr. Louisiana Conservation Rev., New Orleans, vol.9, no.4, pp.41-42, 60 illus., Winter, 1940-41.

A BAT NEW TO THE UNITED STATES. Gerrit S. Miller, Jr. Proc. Biol. Soc., Washington, vol.19, p.96, June 4, 1906.

BATS OF FLORIDA AND SOUTHERN GEORGIA. Gerrit S. Miller, Jr. Proc. Boston Soc., Nat. Hist., vol.28, pp.213-218, Mar., 1898.

TWENTY NEW AMERICAN BATS. Gerrit S. Miller, Jr. Proc. Acad. Nat. Sci. Philadelphia, pp.389-412, Sept.12, 1902.

TWO NEW NORTH AMERICAN BATS. Gerrit S. Miller, Jr. Proc. Biol. Soc. Washington, vol.27, pp.211-212, Oct.31, 1914.

AUDUBON'S BATS. Charles E. Mohr. Audubon Mag., New York, vol.54, no.3, pp.172-177, May-June, 1952.

EXPLORING CAVES IN PENNSYLVANIA. Charles E. Mohr. Frontiers, Philadelphia, vol.1, no.3, pp.80-83, illus., Jan., 1937.

THE SEASONAL DISTRIBUTION OF BATS IN PENNSYLVANIA. Charles E. Mohr. Proc. Pennsylvania Acad. Sci., vol.6, pp. 1-6, 1932.

SEX RATIOS OF BATS IN PENNSYLVANIA. Charles E. Mohr. Proc. Pennsylvania Acad. Sci., Philadelphia, vol.19, pp.65-69, 1945.

TEXAS CAVE BATS. THE CAVES OF TEXAS. Charles E. Mohr. Bull. Nat. Speleol. Soc., Washington, no.10, pp.103-105, illus., Apr., 1948.

THE CAVES OF TEXAS. Charles E. Mohr, and others. Natl. Speleological Soc., Bul. 10, 136 pp., Apr., 1948.

RANGE EXTENSIONS OF TWO BATS IN FLORIDA. Joseph Curtis Moore. Quart. Jour. Florida Acad. Sci., Gainesville, vol. 11, no.1, p.50, Mar.22, 1949.

A NEW BAT FROM THE EASTERN UNITED STATES. E. W. Nelson. Proc. Biol. Soc. Washington, vol.26, pp.183-184, Aug.8, 1913.

NOTES ON LONG ISLAND, NEW YORK, BATS. D. G. Nichols, J. T. Nichols. Jour. Mam., vol.15, no.2, p.156, May, 1934.

CREATURES OF PERPETUAL NIGHT. AN ACCOUNT OF THE AMERICAN MUSEUM'S EXPEDITION TO THE CAVES OF THE OZARKS IN SEARCH OF THE BLIND SALAMANDER. G. Kingsley Noble. Nat. Hist., vol.27, pp.405-419, illus., Sept.-Oct., 1927. (January, 1928).

SOME BATS FROM OKLAHOMA. A. I. Ortenburger. Proc. Oklahoma Acad. Sci., vol.6, p.129, Jan., 1927.

NOTES ON SOME BATS FROM NEBRASKA AND WYOMING. W. B. Quay. Jour. Mam., vol.29, no.2, pp.181-182, May 14, 1948.

ON SOME BRITISH COLUMBIA BATS. A. L. Rand. Murrelet, Seattle, vol.23, no.3, pp. 83-84, Feb.15, 1943.

COLLECTING BATS IN OHIO. Robert Rausch. Jour. Mam., vol.27, no.3, pp. 275-276, Aug.14, 1946.

THREE NEW AMERICAN BATS. James A. G. Rehn. Proc. Acad. Nat. Sci. Phila., pp. 638-641, Dec.12, 1902.

BATS OF MINNESOTA. G. N. Rysgaard. Conservation Volunteer, St. Paul, vol.2, no.8, pp.15-18, May, 1941.

BATS OF THE UNITED STATES. Colin Campbell Sanborn. Public Health Repts., U.S. Public Health Service, Washington, vol.69, no.1, pp.17-28, illus., Jan., 1954.

WHAT MAMMAL IS THAT? PT.2. THE BATS. Thomas G. Scott. Iowa Conservationist, Des Moines, vol.5, no.9, pp.65, 68-69, 71, Sept.15, 1946.

PRELIMINARY OBSERVATIONS ON THE CAVE BATS OF ARKANSAS. John A. Sealander, Howard Young. Proc. Arkansas Acad. Sci., vol.7, pp.21-31, illus., 1955.

STUDIES ON THE LIFE HISTORY OF NON-CAVE-DWELLING BATS IN NORTHEASTERN OHIO. Elizabeth Smith. Ohio Jour. Sci., vol.54, no.1, pp.1-12, Jan., 1954.

BATS IN WINTER. P. A. Tayerner. Canadian Field-Nat., vol.38, p.76, Apr., 1924.

WINTER OCCURRENCE OF BATS AT HOPE, B.C. T. L. Thacker. Murrelet, Seattle, vol.25, no.1, p.10, Jan.-Apr., 1944.

PENNSYLVANIA'S UNDERWORLD. Bill Wolf. Pennsylvania Game News, Harrisburg, vol.20, no.5, pp.13-15, illus., Aug., 1949.

AN ANNOTATED CHECKLIST OF NEBRASKAN BATS. Olin L. Webb, J. Knox Jones, Jr. Univ. Kansas Publ., Mus. Nat. Hist., Lawrence, vol.5, no.21, pp.269-279, May 31, 1952.

BAT BLITZ. THE CAVES OF TEXAS. Patrick J. White. Bull. Nat. Speleol. Soc. Washington, no.10, p.101, Apr., 1948.

MAMMALS OF WEST VIRGINIA. 2 BATS. L. Wayne Wilson. West Virginia Conserv., Charleston, vol.9, no.12, pp.8-9, 15-16, Mar., 1946.

NOTES ON BATS FROM EASTERN WEST VIRGINIA. L. Wayne Wilson. Jour. Mam., vol.27, no.1, pp.85-86, Mar.14, 1946.

### Orientation

THE BAT KNEW IT FIRST. Rachel L. Carson. Iowa Conserv., Des Moines, vol. 7, no.4, pp.33, 39, illus., May 15, 1948.

COCHLEAR POTENTIALS ELICITED FROM BATS BY SUPERSONIC SOUNDS. Robert Galambos. Jour. Acoustical Soc. Amer., Lancaster, vol.14, no.1, pp.41-49, figs.12, July, 1942.

BAT SOUNDS UNDER NATURAL CONDITIONS, WITH EVIDENCE FOR ECHOLOCATION OF INSECT PREY. Donald R. Griffin. Jour. Exp. Zool. 123 (3): 435-465, illus., Aug., 1953.

MEASUREMENTS OF THE ULTRASONIC CRIES OF BATS. Donald R. Griffin. Jour. Acoustical Soc. Amer., New York, vol.22, no.2, pp.247-255, figs.13, Mar., 1950.

PROBLEMS CONCERNING ACOUSTIC ORIENTATION IN BATS. Donald R. Griffin. Proceedings of a Conference on Orientation in Animals, Office of Naval Research, Washington, pp.139-148, 1954.

SUPERSONIC CRIES OF BATS. Donald R. Griffin. Nature, London, vol.158, no.4002, pp.46-48, July 13, 1946.

ABILITY OF BATS TO DISCRIMINATE ECHOES FROM LOUDER NOISE. Donald R. Griffin, Alan D. Grinnell. Science, vol. 128, no.3316, July 18, 1958.

SUPERSONIC CRIES OF BATS. H. Hartridge. Nature, London, vol.158, no.4004, p.135, July 27, 1946.

BAT RADAR. John Eric Hill. Current Sci., Bangalore, vol.14, no.11, p.296, illus., Nov., 1945.

BAT 'RADAR.' Richard H. Knight. New Biology, Penguin Books, Lond., no.2, pp. 116-120, 147.

HOMING EXPERIMENTS ON BATS. PART I. K. Kowalski, R. J. Wojtusiak. Bull. Acad. Polonaise Sci. and Lettres, Krakow, Classe Sci. Math. and Nat., ser.B, Sci. Nat. (II), 1951, pp.33-56, pls.3-4, 1952.

(ON THE ORIENTATION OF BATS.) Ueber die Orientierung der Fledermaeuse. E. Kulzer. Naturwiss. Monats. "Aus der Heimat," vol.65, nos.7-8, pp.132-139, 9 pls., 1957.

(EXPERIMENTS IN CONNECTION WITH ORIENTATION TO IMMEDIATE SURROUNDINGS AND HOMING IN BATS.) Versuche ueber die Nahorientierung und das Heimfindvermogen der Fledermaeuse. Franz Peter Mohres. Verhandl. Deutschen Zool. Mainz, 1949, pp.248-252, 1949.

(ON THE ORIENTATION OF THE BATS.) Zur Orientierung der Fledermaeuse. Franz Peter Mohres. Natur and Volk, Frankfurt am Main, vol.80, nos.5-6, pp.153-161, illus., June 30, 1950.

(INVESTIGATIONS OF THE SUPERSONIC ORIENTATION OF FOUR AFRICAN BAT FAMILIES.) Untersuchungen ueber die Ultraschallorientierung von vier afrikanischen Fledermausfamilien. Franz Peter Moehres, Erwin Kulzer. Zool. Anz., Verh. Deutschen Zool. Gesell., suppl.19, pp.59-65, 1956.

(A NEW, COMBINED TYPE OF ULTRASONIC ORIENTATION IN BATS.) Ein neuer, kombinierter Typ der Ultraschallorientierung bei Fledermaeusen. Franz Peter Moehres, Erwin Kulzer. Die Naturwissenschaften, vol.42, no.5, pp.131-132, 1955.

(EXPERIMENTS IN CONNECTION WITH ORIENTATION TO IMMEDIATE SURROUNDINGS AND HOMING IN BATS.) Versuche ueber die Nahorientierung und das Heimfindevermoegen der Fledermaeuse. Franz Peter Moehres, Therese zu Oettingen-Spielberg. Verhandl. Deutschen Zoologen in Mainz, 1949, (Zool. Anzeiger, 14 Supplementband), Leipzig, pp.248-252, 1950.

HOMING IN BATS. H. C. Mueller, J. T. Emlen, Jr. Science, 126: 307-308, Aug.16, 1957.

ORIENTATION IN PALEOTROPICAL BATS. I. MICROCHIROPTERA. Alvin Novick. Jour. Exper. Zool., 138 (1): 81-153, 1958.

EXPERIMENTAL DETERMINATION OF SUPERSONIC NOTES EMITTED BY BATS. G. W. Pierce, Donald R. Griffin. Jour. Mam., vol.19, no.4, pp.454-455, Nov.14, 1938.

(ORIENTATION AND DERMIC AND ACOUSTIC SENSIBILITY OF THE CHIROPTERS.) Orientación, sensibilidad dermica y acústica de los quirópteros. P. Ignacio Sala de Castellarnau. Revista "Ibérica," Barcelona, no.102, pp.3-8, figs.5, Jan.11, 1947.

HOW BATS "SEE" IN THE DARK. AFTER NEARLY 150 YEARS OF EXPERIMENTING, SCIENCE SOLVES THE RIDDLE OF NIGHT FLYING. Edwin Teale. Popular Sci. Monthly, New York, vol.138, no.3, pp.102-104, figs.7, Mar., 1941.

### Parasites

THE IXODES TICKS OF CHIROPTERA (IXODOIDEA, IXODIDAE). Don R. Arthur. Jour. Parasitol., 42 (2): 180-196, Apr., 1956.

TROMBICULID MITES INFESTING BATS IN MALAYA, WITH DESCRIPTIONS OF THREE NEW SPECIES. J. R. Audy. Bull. Raffles Mus., Singapore, no.24, pp.132-158, Aug., 1952.

NEW SPECIES OF CHIGGERS (ACARINA, TROMBICULIDAE) FROM BATS OF THE NEARCTIC REGION. James M. Brennan. Jour. Parasitol., Lancaster, vol.33, no.3, pp.245-52, June, 1947.

MAMMALIAN TREMATODES. III. CERTAIN SPECIES FROM BATS. Elon E. Byrd. Rep. Reelfoot L. Biol. Sta 6: 149-156, 1942.

MAMMALIAN TREMATODES. III. CERTAIN SPECIES FROM BATS. Elon E. Byrd, Ralph W. Macy. Jour. Tennessee Acad. Sci., Nashville, vol.17, no.1, pp.149-156, fig.1, pl.1, Jan., 1942.

(DESCRIPTION OF PARALLINTOSHIUS TADARIDAE N. SP. ON THE BATS OF MEXICO.) Descripcion de Parallintoshius tadaridae n. sp. (Nematoda: Trichostrongylidae) de los murcielagos de Mexico. C. Eduardo Cabellero y. Anales Inst. Biol., Univ. Nac. Mexico, Mexico, D.F., vol.13, no.1, pp.105-109, fig.1, 1942.

(TREMATODES OF THE BATS OF MEXICO. II. REDESCRIPTION AND SYSTEMATIC POSITION OF DISTOMUM TUBIPORUM.) Trematodos de los murcielagos de Mexico. II. Rediscripcion y posicion sistematica de Distomum tubiporum Braun, 1900. C. Eduardo Caballero y, Christina Cerecero. Anales Inst. Biol., Univ. Nac. Mexico, Mexico, D.F., vol.13, no.1, pp.97-104, figs.3, 1942.

FURTHER NEW SPECIES OF ORNITHODOROS FROM BATS (ACARINA: ARGASIDAE). R. A. Cooley, Glen M. Kohls. Pub. Health Rep. 56 (17): 910-914, Apr.25, 1941.

ON A SCHIZOTRYPANUM FROM A BAT OF BRAZIL. Emmanuel Dias. Mem. Inst. Oswaldo Cruz, Rio de Janeiro, vol.27, no.2, pp.143-146, pls.29-30, 1933.

SUSCEPTIBILITY OF BATS TO INFECTION WITH THE HORSE TRYPANOSOME, TRYPANOSOMA HIPPICUM DARLING, IN PANAMA. Lawrence H. Dunn. Jour. of Preventive Medicine, vol.6, no.3, pp.155-160, May, 1932.

TWO UNUSUAL RECORDS OF MALLOPHAGA FROM BATS. Eugene J. Gerberg, Frans C. Goble. Jour. Mam., vol.22, no.4, p.454, Nov.14, 1941.

STUDIES OF THE TREMATODES FROM CERTAIN MID-WESTERN BATS. James H. Gilford. Master's thesis, U. Ill., 1952.

NEMA PARASITES IN EMBRYO BATS. G.W. D. Hamlett. Biol. Bull., vol.66, no.3, pp. 357-360, June, 1934.

TYPE HOSTS OF THE BAT TREMATODES, PROSTHODENDRIUM OLIGOLECITHUM MANTER AND DEBUS, 1945, AND ACANTHATRIUM MACYI SOGANDARES-BERNAL, 1956. Knox J. Jones, Jr. Jour. Parasitol., 43 (2): 185, Apr., 1957.

ECTOPARASITES AND OTHER ARTHROPODS OCCURRING IN TEXAS BAT CAVES. THE CAVES OF TEXAS. Glen M. Kohls, William L. Jellison. Bull. Nat. Speleol. Soc., Washington, no.10, pp.116-117, Apr., 1948.

ECTOPARASITES FROM SOME SPECIES OF BATS FROM WESTERN NORTH AMERICA. Philip H. Krutzsch. Jour. Mam., 36 (3): 457-458, Aug.30, 1955.

DESCRIPTION OF THREE NEW TREMATODES WITH NOTES ON OTHER SPECIES OF ACANTHATRIUM (LECITHODENDRIIDAE), AND A KEY TO THE GENUS. Ralph W. Macy. Jour. Parasitol., 26 (4): 279-286, Aug., 1940.

TWO TREMATODES FROM A HIBERNATING BAT, MYOTIS CALIFORNICUS. H. W. Manter, Jeanette S. Debus. Trans. Am. Micros. Soc. 64(4): 297-299, Oct., 1945.

A HAEMOSPORIDIAN OF BATS. G. G. Mer, N. Goldblum. Nature, Lond., vol.159, no. 4039, p.444, Mar.29, 1947.

TRYPANOSOMA VESPERTILIONIS FROM SOME SOUTHERN CALIFORNIAN BATS. Ormond G. Mitchell. Jour. Mam., 37 (3): 443-444, Sept.11, 1956.

DESCRIPTION OF A NEW BAT-BUG FROM INDIA. G. Orvath. Records Indian Mus. (Calcutta), vol.27, pp.191-192, May, 1925.

TICKS (ORNITHODOROS SPP.) IN ARIZONA BAT "CAVES". Cornelius B. Philip. Pub. Health Rep. 55 (16): 680-682, Apr.19, 1940.

TWO NEW SPECIES OF TROMBICULID MITES FROM MALAYAN BATS. Cornelius B. Philip, Robert Traub. Jour. Parasitol., Lancaster, vol.36, no.1, pp.29-33, Feb., 1950.

ECTO-PARASITES OF CEYLON BATS. W. W. A. Phillips. Spolia Zeylanica (Ceylon Jour. Sci.), vol.13, pt.1, pp.65-70, Sept. 16, 1924.

A NEW PARASITIC NEMATODE FROM AN UNKNOWN SPECIES OF BAT. Benjamin Schwartz. Proc. U.S. Nat. Mus., vol.71, art.5, pp.1-4, Mar., 1927.

SOME GENERAL REMARKS ON THE BAT-PARASITES OF THE FAMILY NYCTERIBIIDAE. Hugh Scott. Proc. Linn. Soc. Lond., 148th Sess., pt.3, pp.119-120, Aug.3, 1936.

KEY CATALOGUE OF PARASITES REPORTED FOR CHIROPTERA (BATS) WITH THEIR POSSIBLE PUBLIC HEALTH IMPORTANCE. C. W. Stiles, M. O. Nolan. U.S. Public Health Service, Nat. Inst. Health Bull.155, pp.603-742, 1930.

THE PARASITES OF BRITISH BIRDS AND MAMMALS. VIII. SOME ADDITIONAL RECORDS OF BAT PARASITES. Gordon B. Thompson. Entom. Monthly Mag., vol.72, no.258, pp.133-136, June, 1936.

SOME YORKSHIRE BAT PARASITES. Geo. B. Walsh. Naturalist (London), no.857, p. 170, June, 1928.

A NEW LOCALITY FOR TRYPANOSOMA VESPERTILIONIS (T. CRUZI?) IN BATS IN THE UNITED STATES. Sherwin F. Wood. J. Parasitology 29 (5): 363, Oct., 1943.

OF BATS AND BUGS. Pacific Discovery, San Francisco, vol.1, no.1, p.19, illus., Jan.-Feb., 1948.

Pelage, Coloration

HAIR STRUCTURE AS A GENERIC CHARACTER IN BATS. Frances A. Benedict. Univ. California Publ. Zool., 59 (8): 285-548, Oct.10, 1957.

MORPHOLOGY OF HAIR OF EASTERN NORTH AMERICAN BATS. Eileen Sinclair Nason. Amer. Midland Nat., Notre Dame, vol.39, no.2, pp.345-361, figs.2, Mar., 1948.

ALBINISM IN BATS. Henry W. Setzer. Jour. Mam., vol.31, no.3, p.350, Aug.21, 1950.

COLOR ABNORMALITIES IN THREE GENERA OF NORTHEASTERN CAVE BATS. Harold Trapido, Peter E. Crowe. Jour. Mam., Baltimore, vol.23, no.3, pp.303-305, pl.1, Aug.14, 1942.

(MORPHOLOGY OF THE FUR IN OUR BATS.) Morfología del pelo en nuestros murciélagos. Jose Yepes, Angela Chiarelli. Physis, Buenos Aires, vol.16, no.48, p.297, May, 1939.

Physiology

STUDIES ON THE ENERGY SOURCES OF THE BAT. C. L. Dodgen. Ph.D. thesis, Vanderbilt U., 116 pp., 1955.

ENERGY SOURCES IN THE BAT. C. L. Dodgen, F. R. Blood. Amer. Jour. Physiol., Washington, 187 (1): 151-154, Oct., 1956.

(THE INFLUENCE OF LOW TEMPERATURES ON THE EMBRYONAL DEVELOPMENT OF BATS.) Die Wirkung niedriger Temperaturen auf die Embryonalentwicklung bei Fledermaeusen. M. Eisentraut. Biol. Zentralblatt, Leipzig, vol.57, nos. 1-2, pp.59-74, figs.3, 1937.

(HISTOPHYSIOLOGICAL INVESTIGATIONS OF THE FOETAL APPENDAGES OF CHIROPTERS (VESPERUGO NOCTULA, SCHREB.).) Recherches histophysiologiques sur les annexes foetales des Cheiroptères (Vesperugo noctula, Schreb.). P. Gerard. Archives de Biologie, vol.38, pp.327-354, 4 figs., 1 pl., 1928.

THE METABOLIC RATES AND BODY TEMPERATURES OF BATS. Raymond J. Hock. Biol. Bull., Lancaster, vol.101, no. 3, pp.289-299, Dec., 1951.

ANABIOSIS OF ANIMALS AT A TEMPERATURE BELOW $0^{0}$1. ON THE INFLUENCE OF LOW TEMPERATURES ON BATS--CHIROPTERA. N. I. Kalabuchov. Moscou Univ. Sbornik Nauchno issledovatel's kogo inst. Zool. (Abstracts Works Zool. Inst. Moscou State Univ.), no.3, pp.181-182, 1936. (In Russian)

(CONTRIBUTION TO THE STUDY OF THE SENSES OF THE CHIROPTERS.) Contribution a l'etude des sens chez les cheiropteres. Ed Nerincx. Mammalia, Paris, vol.7, no. 3-4, pp.110-114, Sept.-Dec., 1943.

BLOOD CIRCULATION IN THE SUBCUTANEOUS TISSUE OF THE LIVING BAT'S WING.

Paul A. Nicoll, Richard L. Webb. Ann. New York Acad. Sci., vol.46, art.8, pp. 297-711, fig.1, Sept.16, 1946.

SOME RADIATION RESPONSES OF TWO SPECIES OF BATS EXPOSED TO WARM AND COLD TEMPERATURES. G. K. Osborn, D. S. Kimeldorf. Jour. Exper. Zool., Philadelphia, 134 (1): 159-170, Feb., 1957.

ASPECTS OF THE THERMOREGULATION IN BATS. William G. Reeder, Raymond B. Cowles. Jour. Mam., vol.32, no.4, pp. 389-403, figs.2, pls.2, Nov.19, 1951.

THE SENSES OF BATS. Brian Vesey-Fitzgerald. Endeavor, Lond., vol.6, no. 21, pp.36-41, figs.8, Jan., 1947.

THE DEVELOPMENT OF THE SENSES IN BATS. Arthur Whitaker. Naturalist, pp. 145-151, figs.5, May, 1906. (p.151 missing.)

REACTIVITY OF ARTERIOLES FOLLOWING DENERVATION OF SUBCUTANEOUS AREAS OF THE BAT WING. Mary P. Wiedeman. Amer. Jour. Physiol., Wash., vol.177, no.2, pp.308-314, May, 1954.

Predators

BATS AS PREY FOR MINK IN KENTUCKY CAVE. Woodrow Goodpaster, Donald F. Hoffmeister. Jour. Mam., vol.31, no.4, p.457, Nov.21, 1950.

BAT PREDATION BY THE CUBAN BOA, EPICRATES ANGULIFER BIBRON. Jerry D. Hardy, Jr. Copeia, no.2, pp.151-152, July 15, 1957.

GULL ATTACKING BAT. Nicol Hopkins, John Paterson. Scottish Nat., no.163, p.16, Jan.-Feb., 1927.

BATS EATEN BY SHORT-EARED OWL. Laurence M. Huey. Auk, vol.43, pp.96-97, Jan., 1926.

COOPER'S HAWK OBSERVED CATCHING A BAT. A. Starker Leopold. Wilson Bull., Ann Arbor, vol.56, no.2, p.116, June, 1944.

OPOSSUM AND SKUNK EAT BATS. Charles C. Sperry. Jour. Mam., vol.14, no.2, pp. 152-153, May, 1933.

PREDATION ON BATS BY HAWKS AND OWLS. John W. Twente, Jr. Wilson Bull., 66 (2): 135-136, June, 1954.

Reproductive Biology

RELATIVE EFFECTS OF ANDROGEN UPON THE MATING BEHAVIOR OF MALE BATS SUBJECTED TO FOREBRAIN INJURY OR CASTRATION. Frank A. Beach. Jour. Exper. Zool., Philadelphia, vol.97, no.3, pp.259-295, illus., Dec., 1944.

(REMARKS ON THE BEHAVIOR OF CHIROPTERS DURING THE REPRODUCTION PERIOD.) Remarques sur le comportement des Chiropteres pendant la période de reproduction. A. Brosset. Mammalia, vol. 17, no.2, pp.85-88, June, 1953.

REPRODUCTION IN NORTH AMERICAN BATS. E. Lendell Cockrum. Trans. Kansas Acad. Sci., vol.58, no.4, pp.487-511, Jan.23, 1956.

(ON THE REPRODUCTIVE BIOLOGY OF THE BAT.) Zur Fortpflanzungsbiologie der Fledermause. M. Eisentraut. Zeitschr. Morphol. u Oekol. Tiere, vol.31, no.1, pp. 27-63, figs.9, Feb.29, 1936.

(REPRODUCTIVE HABITS OF OUR NATIVE BATS.) Fortpflanzungsgewohnheiten unserer heimeschen Fledermaeuse. M. Eisentraut. Naturforscher, Berlin, vol.11, no.8, pp.265-270, figs.6, Nov., 1934.

(CONTRIBUTIONS TO THE REPRODUCTIVE BIOLOGY AND ONTOGENY OF THE BATS.) Beitraege zur Fortpflanzungsbiologie und Ontogenese der Fledermaeuse. Hans Englaender. Bonner Zool. Beitraege, Jahrgang 3, Heft 3-4, pp.221-230, Feb.20, 1953.

THE REPRODUCTIVE CYCLES OF SOME CAVE BATS. Mary J. Guthrie. Jour. Mam., vol.14, no.3, pp.199-216, Aug., 1933.

BREEDING HABITS OF THE PHYLLOSTOMID BATS. G.W.D. Hamlett. Jour. Mam., vol.16, no.2, pp.146-147, May, 1935.

ON THE SURVIVAL OF SPERMATOZOA IN THE FEMALE GENITAL TRACT OF THE BAT. Carl G. Hartman. Quart. Review Biol., Baltimore, vol.8, no.3, pp.185-193, June, 1933.

(COMPARATIVE STUDY OF THE GENITAL ACTIVITY OF CHIROPTERS.) Etude comparative sur l'activite genitale des cheiropteres. Marc Herlant. Ann. Soc. Roy. Zool. Belgique, vol.85, no.1, pp.87-116, 1953.

UNUSUAL STATE AT BIRTH OF A BAT. T. S. Jones. Nature, London, vol.156, no. 3960, p.365, Sept.22, 1945.

HEAD PRESENTATION IN INDIAN CHIROPTERA. P. A. Ramakrishna. Nature, Lond., vol.163, no.4135, p.176, Jan.29, 1949.

PARTURITION IN CERTAIN INDIAN BATS. P. A. Ramakrishna. Jour. Mammal., 31: 274-8, 1950.

(ON THE REPRODUCTION OF CHIROPTERS.) Sur la reproduction des Chiropteres. R. Rollinat, E. L. Trouessart. Comptes rendus Soc. Biol., pp.1-2, Jan.20, 1895.

(SECOND COMMUNICATION ON CHIROPTER REPRODUCTION.) Deuxième note sur la reproduction des chiroptères. R. Rollinat, E. L. Trouessart. Comptes Rendus Soc. Biol., Paris, ser.10, vol.2, no.24, pp. 534-536, July 12, 1895.

A BOTTLE BABY. Horace Trout. Nature Magazine, vol.18, no.5, p.290, Nov., 1931.

BATS AND THEIR YOUNG. Burt G. Wilder. Popular Science Monthly, vol.7, no.42, pp. 12, figs.11, Oct., 1875.

SURVIVAL OF SPERMATOZOA IN THE FEMALE REPRODUCTIVE TRACT OF THE BAT. William A. Wimsatt. Anat. Record, Philadelphia, vol.83, no.2, pp.299-307, pl.1, June 25, 1942.

South America

(CHIROPTERS FROM URUGUAY.) Quirópteros del Uruguay. Eduardo F. Acosta y Lara. Comunicaciones Zool. Mus. Hist. Nat. Montevideo, vol.3, no.58, pp.1-71, July 1, 1950.

(A NEW CHIROPTER FOR URUGUAY.) Un neuvo quiroptero para el Uruguay. Eduardo F. Acosta y Lara. Comunicaciones Zool. Mus. Hist. Nat. Montevideo, vol.3, no.64, pp.1-4, Apr.28, 1951.

(SOME UNPUBLISHED PAGES OF FELIX DE AZARA ON CHIROPTERA OF PARAGUAY.) Unas páginas ineditas de Félix de Azara sobre quirópteros del Paraguay. E. Morales Agacino. Notas Mus. La Plata, vol.6, Zool., no.49, pp.215-223, July 16, 1941.

LIST OF BATS COLLECTED BY MR. H.H. SMITH IN THE SANTA MARTA REGION OF COLOMBIA, WITH DESCRIPTIONS OF NEW SPECIES. J. A. Allen. Bull. Amer. Mus. Nat. Hist., vol.13, pp.87-94, May 12, 1900.

A NEW BAT FROM COLOMBIA. Outram Bangs. Proc. New England Zool. Club, vol.1, pp.73-74, Nov.24, 1899.

(ON NEW BATS FROM ARGENTINA.) Sobre dos Murcielagos nuevos para la Argentina. Angel Cabrera. Inst. Mus. Univ. Nac., La Plata, Buenos Aires (Notas Mus. La Plata), vol.3, Zool. no.8, pp.14, figs.2, 1938.

(SYNOPSIS OF THE CHILEAN BATS.) Sinopsis de los Quiropteros chilenos. Angel Cabrera. Revista Chilena de Hist. Nat., vol.7, pp.278-308, figs.10-14, 1903.

BATS FROM THE ISLAND OF TRINIDAD. Walter W. Dalquest. Louisiana Acad. Sci., Shreveport, vol.14, pp.26-33, Nov.30, 1951.

(STUDY OF A CHIROPTER COLLECTION OF UCAYALI RIVER, PERU.) Etude d'une collection de chiroptères du Rio Ucayali, Perou. Jean Dorst. Bull. Mus. Nat. Hist. Nat., Paris, ser.2, vol.25, pp.269-271, May, 1953.

(STUDY OF A COLLECTION OF CHIROPTERS OF ECUADOR.) Étude d'une collection de Chiroptères d'Ecuador. Jean Dorst. Bull. Mus. Nat. Hist. Nat., Paris, ser.2, vol.23, no.6, pp.602-606, Dec., 1951.

(ZOOLOGIC DOCUMENTS TO BE USED IN THE MONOGRAPH OF SOUTH AMERICAN BATS.) Documents zoologiques pour servir a la monographie des cheiropteres sud-americains, (Montpellier, Boehm, 1857?) Paul Gervais. 20 pp., 1857.

THREE NEW BATS FROM TRINIDAD. George G. Goodwin. Amer. Mus. Novitates, 1877: 1-6, Feb.28, 1958.

OBSERVATIONS ON SOME BRAZILIAN BATS, WITH THE DESCRIPTION OF A NEW GENUS. J. E. Gray. Proc. Zool. Soc. Lond., pt.16, pp.57-58, 1848.

BATS OF TRINIDAD. Arthur M. Greenhall. Jour. Trinidad Field Nat. Club, 1956: 16-18, 1956.

NEW TRINIDAD RECORDS OF BATS. R. W. Hayman. Jour. Mam., vol.19, no.1, pp.103-104, Feb.14, 1938.

MAMMALS OF NORTHERN COLOMBIA: PRELIMINARY REPORT NO.5; BATS. Philip Hershkovitz. Proc. U.S. Nat. Mus., vol.99, no.3246, pp.429-454, May 10, 1949.

THE BATS OF SURINAME. A.M. Husson. Zoologische Verhandelingen, Rijksmuseum van Natuurlijke Historie, Leiden, 1962.

(STUDIES ON THE FAUNA OF CHILE. II. NOTES ON THE BATS.) Etudes Sur La Faune Chilienne. II. Note Sur Les Chauves-souris. (Ordre des Chiroptères). Fernand Lataste. Actas. Soc. Sci. Chili, vol.1, pp. 70-91, 1892.

DESCRIPTION OF A NEW BAT FROM COLOMBIA. Marcus W. Lyon, Jr. Proc. Biol. Soc. Washington, vol.15, pp.151-152, June 20, 1902.

DESCRIPTION OF A NEW BAT FROM MARGARITA ISLAND, VENEZUELA. Gerrit S. Miller, Jr. Proc. Biol. Soc. Washington, vol.11, p.139, May 13, 1897.

A SECOND COLLECTION OF BATS FROM THE ISLAND OF CURACAO. Gerrit S. Miller, Jr. Proc. Biol. Soc. Washington, vol.8, pp.159-162, Oct.31, 1900.

THREE NEW BATS FROM THE ISLAND OF CURACAO Gerrit S. Miller, Jr. Proc. Biol. Soc. Washington, vol.8, pp.123-127, Apr.6, 1900.

TWO NEW SOUTH AMERICAN BATS. Gerrit S. Miller, Jr. Jour. Mam. Baltimore, vol.12, no.4, pp.411-412, Nov.11, 1931.

(MONOGRAPHIC STUDY OF THE CHIROPTERS OF LIMA AND SURROUNDINGS.) Estudio monografico de los quiropteros de Lima y alrededores. Javier Ortiz de la Puente. Publ. Mus. Hist. Nat. "Javier Prado," Univ. Nac. Mayor de San Marcos, Lima, ser.A, Zool., no.7, pp.48, pls.9, Dec., 1951.

NOTE ON A COLLECTION OF BATS FROM TRINIDAD. William Peters. Proc. Zool. Soc. Lond., pp.430-431, 1866.

(ON BATS OF SAO PAULO.) Ueber Fledermaeuse von saeo Paulo. Adolf Pira. Zool. Anzeiger, vol.28, no.1, pp.12-19, figs.2, Aug.23, 1904.

(CONTRIBUTIONS TO KNOWLEDGE OF THE BATS OF PARAGUAY.) Contribuciones al conocimiento de los murcielagos del Paraguay. B. Podtiaguin. Rev. Soc. Cient. Paraguay, Asuncion, vol.6, no.4, pp.25-62, Aug.15, 1944.

BATS FROM CHIMANTA-TEPUI, VENEZUELA, WITH REMARKS ON CHOERONISCUS. Colin Campbell Sanborn. Fieldiana, Zool., Chicago, vol.34, no.27, pp.289-293, July 23, 1954.

A NEW BAT FROM COLOMBIA. H. Harold Shamel. Proc. Biol. Soc. Washington, vol. 40, pp.129-130, Sept.26, 1927.

A RECORD OF LASIURUS AND OF VAMPYROPS FROM PARAGUAY. H. B. Sherman. Jour. Mam., 36 (1): 130, Feb.25, 1955.

ON A COLLECTION OF BATS FROM PARA. Oldfield Thomas. Ann. and Mag. Nat. Hist. (7), vol.8, no.45, pp.189-193, Sept., 1901.

ON A COLLECTION OF BATS FROM PARAGUAY. Oldfield Thomas. Ann. and Mag. Nat. Hist. (7), vol.8, no.47, pp.435-443, Nov., 1901.

NOTES ON SOME TRINIDAD BATS. F. W. Urich, Ludolf Wehekind. Jour. Trinidad Field Nat. Club, 1956: 18-21, 1956.

(MONOGRAPHIC ESSAY ON THE BATS OF BRAZIL.) Ensaio monográfico sobre os quirópteros do Brasil. Carlos O. da Cunha Vieira. Arquiv. Zool. Estado São Paulo, vol.3, art.8, pp.219-471, figs.42, pls.4, Aug., 1942.

Taxonomy

NOTES ON CHIROPTERA. Glover M. Allen. Bull. Mus. Comp. Zool., Harvard College, vol.52, no.3, pp.25-62, pl.1, fig.1-7, July, 1908.

ON THE TAXONOMIC VALUES OF THE WING MEMBRANES AND OF THE TERMINAL PHALANGES OF THE DIGITS IN THE CHEIROPTERA. Harrison Allen. Proc. Acad. Nat. Sci., Philadelphia, pp.313-340, pl.10, 1889.

THE FAMILIES AND GENERA OF BATS. J. A. Allen. Amer. Nat., vol.41, pp.671-672, Oct., 1907.

NEW BATS FROM TROPICAL AMERICA, WITH NOTE ON SPECIES OF OTOPTERUS. J. A. Allen. Bull. Amer. Mus. Nat. Hist., vol.20, pp.227-237, June 29, 1904.

CHARACTERS OF SIX NEW GENERA OF BATS NOT HITHERTO DISTINGUISHED. John E. Gray. Proc. Zool. Soc. Lond., pt.15, p.14, 1847.

NOMENCLATURE OF SOME TERTIARY CHIROPTERA. Charles O. Handley, Jr. Jour. Mam., 36 (1): 128-130, Feb.25, 1955.

SOME OBSERVATIONS RELATING CYNOPTERUS BRACHYOTIS MUELLER AND KERIVOULA PELLUCIDA WATERHOUSE. F. A. Jentink. Notes from Leyden Museum, vol. 13, pp.202-206, 1891.

(DESCRIPTION OF A NEW OR LITTLE KNOWN BAT SPECIES.) Description d'une espèce nouvelle ou mal connue de chauve-souris. Fernand Lataste. Ann. Mus. Civico Storia Nat. Genova, ser.2a, vol.10, pp.658-664, figs.1-3, Apr.11, 1891.

THE FAMILIES AND GENERA OF BATS. Gerrit S. Miller, Jr. Smithsonian Inst., U.S. Nat. Museum, bull.57, pp.282, pls. 14, figs.49, 1907.

THE GENERIC NAME NYCTERIS. Gerrit S. Miller, Jr. Proc. Biol. Soc., Washington, vol.22, p.90, Apr.17, 1909.

NOMENCLATURE OF SOME EUROPEAN BATS. Gerrit S. Miller, Jr. Ann. and Mag. Nat. Hist., ser.6, vol.20, pp.379-385, Oct., 1897.

TWELVE NEW GENERA OF BATS. Gerrit S. Miller, Jr. Proc. Biol. Soc. Washington, vol.19, pp.83-86, June 4, 1906.

TWO NEW TROPICAL OLD WORLD BATS. Gerrit S. Miller, Jr. Proc. Biol. Soc. Washington, vol.15, pp.245-246, Dec.16, 1902.

RANDOM NOTES ON THE NOMENCLATURE OF THE CHIROPTERA. T. S. Palmer. Proc. Biol. Soc. Washington, vol.12, pp. 109-114, Apr.30, 1898.

(ON NEW CHIROPTERS (PHYLLORHINA MICROPUS, HARPYIOCEPHALUS HUTTONII, MURINA GRISEA, VESPERUGO MICROPUS, VESPERUS (MARSIPOLOEMUS) ALBIGULARIS, VESPERUS PROPINQUUS, VTENIPINNIS).) Ueber neue Flederthiere (Phyllorhina micropus, Harpyiocephalus Huttonii, Murina grisea, Vesperugo micropus, Vesperus (Marsipoloemus) albigularis, Vesperus propinquus, Vtenipinnis). W. Peters. Monatsbericht der Koenigl. Akad. der Wiss. zu Berlin, vol., pp.256-264, 1872.

(ON NEW CHIROPTERS (VESPERUS, VAMPYROPS).) Ueber neue Flederthiere (Vesperus, Vanpyrops). W. Peters. Monatsber. K. Preuss. Akad. Wiss. Berlin, Jahrg., pp. 258-259, fig.1, Mar., 1880.

(ON THE CHIROPTERS BELONGING TO THE GENERA MIMON AND SACCOPTERYX.) Ueber die zu den Gattungen Mimon and Saccopteryx gehoeri gen Flederthiere. W. Peters. Monatsber. K. Preuss. Akad. Wiss. Berlin, Jahrg., pp.469-482, pl.1, 1867.

(BATS OF THE BERLIN MUSEUM OF NATURAL SCIENCE.) Plates of "Die Fledermaeuse des Berliner Museums fuer Naturkunde". W. Peters. A projected monograph of the bats. 81 plates, no text, 1880.

NOTES ON CHIROPTERA. James A. G. Rehn. Proc. Acad. Nat. Sci. Phila., pp. 755-759, Feb.9, 1901.

(CATALOGUE OF TYPES OF MAMMALS IN THE NATIONAL MUSEUM OF NATURAL HISTORY. II. ORDER OF CHIROPTERS.) Catalogue des types de mammiferes du Museum National d'Histoire Naturelle. II. Ordre des chiropteres. P. Rode. Bull. Mus. Nat. Hist. Nat., Paris, ser.2, vol. 13, no.4, pp.227-252, (reprint pp.73-105), Apr., 1941.

DESCRIPTIONS OF THREE NEW BATS IN THE BRITISH MUSEUM COLLECTION. Oldfield Thomas. Ann. and Mag. Nat. Hist. (6), vol.7, no.42, June, 1891, pp.527-530, June, 1891.

A NEW GENUS AND TWO NEW SPECIES OF BATS. Oldfield Thomas. Ann. and Mag. Nat. Hist. (7), vol.16, no.95, pp.572-576, Nov., 1905.

THREE NEW BATS, AFRICAN AND ASIATIC. Oldfield Thomas. Ann. and Mag. Nat. Hist. (7), vol.13, no.77, pp.384-388, May, 1904.

TWO NEW EASTERN BATS. Oldfield Thomas. Ann. and Mag. Nat. Hist. (8), vol.8, no.45, pp.378-380, Sept., 1911.

DESCRIPTION OF SIX HITHERTO UNDESCRIBED SPECIES OF BATS. R. F. Tomes. Proc. Zool. Soc. Lond., pt.27, pp.68-79, 1859.

ON A NEW GENUS AND SPECIES OF LEAF-NOSED BATS IN THE MUSEUM AT FORT PITT. R. F. Tomes. Proc. Zool. Soc. Lond., pt.31, pp.71-84, pl. XII, 1863.

ON THREE GENERA OF VESPERTILIONIDAE, FURIPTERUS, NATALUS, AND HYONYCTERIS, WITH THE DESCRIPTIONS OF TWO NEW SPECIES. R. F. Tomes. Proc. Zool. Soc. Lond., pt.24, pp.172-181, pls.42-43, 1856.

(ATTEMPT TO DETERMINE THE CLAIMED NEW SPECIES OF BATS DESCRIBED BY CRESPON IN HIS "MERIDIONAL FAUNA".) Essai de détermination des prétendues espèces nouvelles de Chauve-Souris décrites par Crespon dans sa Faune Meridionale. E. L. Trouseeart. Bull. Soc. Sci. Nat. Mines, vol.7, no.2, pp.7 (pp.35- ), Feb., 1879.

(OBSERVATIONS RELATIVE TO DR. E. L. TROUESSART'S ATTEMPT TO DETERMINE THE BATS DESCRIBED AS NEW BY CRESPON.) Observations relatives a l 'essai de détermination du Dr. E. L. Trouessart de Chauves-Souris décrites comme nouvelles par Crespon. E. L. Trouessart. Le Naturaliste, Paris, 1879.

Virus Diseases

CHIROPTERAN RABIES IN MONTANA. J. Frederick Bell, W. J. Hadlow, William L. Jellison. Public Health Repts., U. S. Public Health Service, Washington, vol.70, no.10, pp.991-994, Oct., 1955.

A SURVEY OF CHIROPTERAN RABIES IN WESTERN MONTANA. J. Frederick Bell, W. J. Hadlow, William L. Jellison. U. S. Public Health Service, Washington, 72 (1): 16-18, Jan., 1957.

RABIES IN NONSANGUIVOROUS BATS OF TEXAS. K. F. Burns, J. Farinacci. Jour. Infectious Dis., 97 (2): 211-218, illus., Sept.-Oct., 1955.

VIRUS OF BATS ANTIGENICALLY RELATED TO ST. LOUIS ENCEPHALITIS. K. F. Burns, C. J. Farinacci. Science, Lancaster, vol. 123, no.3189, p.227, Feb.10, 1956.

BAT RABIES. Robert D. Courter. U. S. Public Health Service, Washington, vol.69, no.1, pp.9-16, Jan., 1954.

A FURTHER ACCOUNT OF THE TRINIDAD OUTBREAK OF ACUTE RABIC MYELITIS: HISTOLOGY OF THE EXPERIMENTAL DISEASE. E. Weston Hurst, J. L. Pawan. Jour. Pathology and Bacteriology, vol.35, pp.301-321, pls.31-37, 1932.

AN OUTBREAK OF RABIES IN TRINIDAD WITHOUT HISTORY OF BITES AND WITH THE SYMPTOMS OF ACUTE ASCENDING MYELITIS. E. Weston Hurst, J. L. Pawan. The Lancet, pp.622-639, Sept.19, 1931.

(EXPERIMENTAL INVESTIGATIONS REGARDING PARALYTIC RABIES IN VENEZUELA AND ITS TRANSMISSION THROUGH HEMATOPHAGOUS BATS.) Investigaciones experimentales acerca de la rabia paralitica en Venezuela y su trasmision por los murcielagos hematofagos. Juan Iturbe, P. Gallo. Proc. 8th Amer. Sci. Congr., Wash., D.C., vol.3, pp.431-443, Aug.3, 1942.

FRUIT-EATING BATS AND PARALYTIC RABIES IN TRINIDAD. J. L. Pawan. Ann. Trop. Med. and Parasitol., Liverpool, vol. 42, no.2, pp.173-177, Sept., 1948.

BAT RABIES IN FLORIDA. James E. Scatterday. Jour. Am. Vet. Med. Assn., 124 (923): 125, Feb., 1954.

THE ROLE OF BATS IN THE TRANSMISSION OF RABIES. C. R. Schroeder. Essays in Natural Sciences in Honor of Captain Allen Hancock, Univ. Southern California, Los Angeles, pp.221-232, illus., July 26, 1955.

RECOVERY OF RABIES VIRUS FROM COLONIAL BATS IN TEXAS. Thelma D. Sullivan, J. E. Grimes, R. B. Eads, G. C. Menzies, J. V. Irons. Public Health Repts., U.S. Public Health Service, Washington, vol.69, no.8, pp.766-768, Aug., 1954.

HEALTHY BATS SUSPECTED AS RABIES CARRIERS. Public Health Repts., U. S. Public Health Service, Washington, vol.70, no.2, pp.165-167, Feb., 1955.

LOCATE POSITIVE EVIDENCE OF BAT RABIES IN FLORIDA. Public Health Repts., U. S. Public Health Service, Washington, vol.69, no.2, pp.186-187, Feb., 1954.

Pteropodidae

CATALOGUE OF THE CHIROPTERA IN THE COLLECTION OF THE BRITISH MUSEUM. I. MEGACHIROPTERA. K. Andersen. London, iii-ci, 1-854 pp., 97 figs., 1912.

FLYING FOXES ON A HILL TEA GARDEN. T. A. Baldry. Jour. Bengal Nat. Hist. Soc., Darjeeling, vol.17, no.4, p.142, Apr., 1943.

A NEW ASCARID FROM A BAT. H. A. Baylis. Ann. and Mag. Nat. Hist., Lond., ser.10, vol.17, no.99, pp.360-365, Mar., 1936.

(BIOLOGICAL NOTES ON FRUIT BATS IN CAPTIVITY.) Notes biologiques sur les rousettes en captivite. Robert Didier. La Terre et La Vie, 8 Annee, no.4, pp.101-106, illus., July-Aug., 1938.

(BIOLOGY OF FRUIT BATS (MEGACHIROPTERA).) Biologie der Flederhunde (Megachiroptera). M. Eisentraut. Giologia Generalis, 18: 327-435, 1945.

(GHOST BAT AND TUBE-NOSED FLYING FOX.) Gespenstfledermaus und Roehrennasen-Flughund. Heinz Felten. Natur und Volk, Band 88, Heft 11, pp.361-369, 10 figs., illus., Nov.1, 1958.

FRUIT BATS. J. L. Harrison. Malayan Nature Jour., vol.7, no.4, pp.125-132, Dec., 1952.

THE UNILATERAL ENDOMETRIAL REACTION IN THE GIANT FRUIT-BAT (PTEROPUS GIGANTEUS BRUENNICH). A. J. Marshall. Jour. Endocrinol., London, vol. 9, no.1, pp.42-44, Jan., 1953.

ON AN EXTINCT UNDESCRIBED FRUIT-BAT OF THE GENUS PTEROPUS FROM THE MASCARENES. George E. Mason. Ann. and Mag. Nat. Hist., ser.7, vol. 20, pp.220-222, Sept., 1907.

(CONTINUATION AND CONCLUSION OF A SURVEY OF THE FLYING FOXES.) Die Fortsetzung und den Schluss einer Uebersicht der Flederhunde. W. Peters. Monatsber. K. Preuscischer Akad. Wiss. Berlin, Jahrg., 1867, pp.864-872, 1867.

THE FOX WHO FLIES. Ken Stott, Jr. San Diego Zoonooz, vol.18, no.1, pp.5-6, illus., Jan., 1945.

(MONOGRAPHS ON MAMMALOGY. FRUIT BATS.) Monographies de Mammalogie Cheiropteres Frugivores. C. J. Temminck. 1835.

Africa

DESCRIPTIONS OF NEW PTEROPINE BATS FROM AFRICA. Harrison Allen. Proc. Acad. Nat. Sci. Philadelphia, pp.156-160, July, 1861.

ON A REMARKABLE PTEROPINE BAT FROM THE GAMBIA. E. T. Bennett. Proc. Zool. Soc. Lond., pt.3, p.149, 1835.

A NEW RACE OF SCOTONYCTERIS ZENKERI FROM THE GOLD COAST. R. W. Hayman. Ann. Mag. Nat. Hist., London, ser. 11, vol.13, no.103, pp.503-4, June 25, 1947.

A NEW SCOTONYCTERIS, WITH NOTES ON OTHER GOLD COAST BATS. R. W. Hayman. Ann. and Mag. Nat. Hist., London, ser., vol.12, no.95, pp.766-775, Sept.19, 1946.

DESCRIPTION OF A NEW AFRICAN BAT, LEIPONYX BUETTIKOFERI. Fredericus Anna Jentink. Notes Leyden Mus., vol.3, no.15, pp.59-62, Jan., 1881.

(CONTRIBUTIONS TO KNOWLEDGE OF HYPSIGNATHUS MONSTROSUS ALLEN.) Beitrage zur Kenntnis von Hypsignathus monstrosus Allen. Paul Matschie. Sitz. Ber. Gesell. Naturf. Freunde, Berlin, Jahrg., no.2, pp.28-30, 1 fig., Feb.21, 1899.

(ZOOLOGICAL IMPRESSIONS OF A CAMEROON TRIP.) Zoologische Eindruecke von einer Kamerun-Reise. Robert Mertens. Natur und Volk, Frankfurt a. M., vol.68, no.12, pp.594-597, Dec.1, 1938.

DESCRIPTION OF SPHYROCEPHALUS LABROSUS, A NEW BAT FROM OLD CALABAR RIVER, WESTERN AFRICA. Andrew Murray. Proc. Zool. Soc. Lond., pt.30, pp.8-12, 1862.

NOTES ON AN ADDITIONAL EXAMPLE OF THE FRUIT BAT, SCOTONYCTERIS OPHIODON POHLE. Alvin Novick. Postilla, Yale Peabody Mus. Nat. Hist., 34: 1-5, Mar.7, 1958.

(THE FRUIT BATS OF THE SUDAN.) Les roussetes du Soudan. R. Rousselot. Premiere Conférence Internationale des Africanistes de l'Ouest, Dakar, vol.1, pp.233-238, 1950.

A NEW FRUIT-BAT FROM SIERRA LEONE. Oldfield Thomas. Ann. and Mag. Nat. Hist. (8), vol.2, no.10, pp.375-376, Oct., 1908.

ON A NEW SPECIES OF FRUIT-BAT FROM FERNANDO PO. Oldfield Thomas. Proc. Zool. Soc., Lond., pt.1, pp.371-372, Aug. 2, 1904.

(NOTES ON THE MEGACHIROPTERS OF PORTUGUESE GUINEA.) Notas acerca dos Megaquiropteros da Guine Portuguesa. Maria Corinta Veign-Ferreira. Conferencia Internacional dos Africanistas Ocidentais, Lisbon, vol.3, pp.291-294, Aug., 1951.

Anatomy

THE INTERSCAPULAR GLAND OF A TROPICAL FRUIT BAT. Walter W. Dalquest, Henry J. Werner. Anat. Record, vol.111, no.3, pp.345-353, illus., Nov., 1951.

THE BACULA OF SOME FRUIT BATS. D. Dwight Davis. Fieldiana, Zool., Chicago, vol.31, no.16, pp.125-31, figs.19-20, May 14, 1947.

(NOTE ON A FRUIT BAT FOETUS.) Note sur un foetus de rousette. Robert Didier. Mammalia, Paris, vol.2, no.3, pp.135-136, pl.11, Sept., 1938.

THE SEASONAL MODIFICATION OF THE INTERSTITIAL TISSUE OF THE TESTIS IN THE FRUIT BAT. J. R. Groome. Proc. Zool. Soc. Lond., vol.110, ser.A, pts.1-2, pp.37-42, figs.2, Sept.19, 1940.

DEVELOPMENT AND PLACENTATION OF THE INDIAN FRUIT BAT, PTEROPUS GIGANTEUS GIGANTEUS (BRUENNICH). M. A. Moghe. Proc. Zool. Soc., Lond., vol.121, pt.3, pp.703-721, pls.1-5, Nov., 1951.

ON THE DEVELOPMENT AND PLACENTATION OF A MEGACHIROPTERAN BAT--CYNOPTERUS SPHINX GANGETICUS (ANDERSON). M. A. Moghe. Proc. Nat. Inst. Sci. India, pt.B, 22 (1): 48-55, Feb. 26, 1956.

(STRUCTURAL DIFFERENCES IN THE DIAPHYSES OF THE CARPALS AND TARSALS IN TWO FLYING ANIMALS (PTEROPUS NEOHIBERNICUS PET. AND ARDEA CINEREA L.).) Strukturverschiedenheiten in den Diaphysen der karpalen und tarsalen knochen bei zwei Flugtieren (Pteropus neohibernicus Pet. und der Ardea cinerea L.). M. E. Nedbal. Zeitschr. f. Anat. u. Entwickl. gesch., vol.97, pp.210-250, 2 figs., 6 pls., 1932.

THE MALE GENITAL TRACT OF THE INDIAN MEGACHIROPTERAN BAT CYNOPTERUS SPHINX GANGETICUS AND. S. A. Vamburkar. Proc. Zool. Soc. Lond., 130 (1): 57-77, pls.1-2, Jan.23, 1958.

Asia

THE OCCURRENCE OF THE FLYING FOX (PTEROPUS GIGANTEUS) IN THE PUNJAB. C. Breadon. Jour. Bombay Nat. Hist. Soc., vol.35, no.3, p.670, Feb.15, 1932.

EXHIBITION OF SOME ARTICLES SOLD AS FOOD IN THE MARKET OF OLD CALABAR. Andrew Murray. Proc. Zool. Soc. Lond., p.530, 1869.

THE SHORT-NOSED FRUIT BATS (CYNOPTERUS) OF CEYLON. W. W. A. Phillips. Ceylon Jour. Sci., Sec.B., Zool. and Geol., Spolia Zeylanica, Colombo, vol.18, pt.2, pp.237-248, May 22, 1934.

DESCRIPTION OF A NEW SPECIES OF FRUIT BAT, PTEROPYS ALDABRENSIS, FROM ALDABRA ISLAND. Frederick W. True. Proc. U.S. Nat. Mus., vol.16, publ. 948, pp.533-534, Advance sheets July 14, 1893, Regular edition Oct.21, 1893.

NOTE ON FRUIT-BATS FROM THE MALAY PENINSULA. M.W.F. Tweedie. Bull. Raffles Mus., no.8, p.101, pl.4, Dec., 1933.

Australia and Pacific Islands

A FRUIT BAT, DOBSONIA, NEW TO AUSTRALIA. Glover M. Allen. Australian Zool., Sydney, vol.8, pt.2, p.151, June 28, 1935.

A NEW PYGMY FRUIT BAT FROM BORNEO. Glover M. Allen. Jour. Mam., vol.19, no. 4, pp.496-498, Nov.14, 1938.

THE SEASONS IN A TROPICAL RAINFOREST (NEW HEBRIDES). PT.3. FRUIT-BATS (PTEROPIDAE). John R. Baker, Zita Baker. Jour. Linn. Soc. Lond., Zool., vol. 40, no.269, pp.123-141, Nov.30, 1936.

OBSERVATIONS ON THE PTEROPUS OF AUSTRALIA. J.K.E. Fairhoime. Proc. Zool. Soc. Lond., pt.24, pp.311-312, 1856.

NOTICE OF NOTOPTERIS, A NEW GENUS OF PTEROPINE BAT FROM THE FEEJEE ISLANDS. John E. Gray. Proc. Zool. Soc. Lond., pt.27, pp.36-38, pl.LXVII, 1859.

TWO NEW PHILIPPINE FRUIT BATS. N. Hollister. Proc. Biol. Soc. Washington, vol.26, pp.111-112, May 3, 1913.

NOTES ON THE HYPOMELANUS FRUIT-BATS OF THE STRAITS OF MALACCA, WITH THE DESCRIPTION OF A NEW RACE PTEROPUS HYPOMELANUS FRETENSIS. C. B. Kloss. Jour. Fed. Malay States Mus., vol.6, pt.4, pp.245-248, Feb., 1916.

A REVISION OF THE GENUS PTEROPUS FOUND IN THE ISLANDS OF THE RIU KIU CHAIN, JAPAN. Nagamicri Kuroda. Jour. Mam., vol.14, no.4, pp.312-316, Nov.13, 1933.

THREE NEW PTEROPUS FROM NEW CALEDONIA AND THE SOLOMONS. Barbara Lawrence. Proc. New England Zooel. Club, Cambridge, vol.23, pp.59-69, Mar.26, 1945.

A NEW NYCTIMENE FROM SOUTH QUEENSLAND. Heber A. Longman. Mem. Queensland Mus., vol.7, pp.179-181, Nov.4, 1921.

(A SPECIES OF THE GENUS PTEROPUS FROM PEMBA ISLAND.) Eine Art der Gattung Pteropus von der Insel Pemba. Paul Matschie. Sitz. Ber. Gesell. Naturf. Freunde Berlin, Jahrg., no.8, pp.482-486, Jan.8, 1909.

A NEW PTEROPINE BAT FROM LUZON. Gerrit S. Miller, Jr. Proc. Biol. Soc., Washington, vol.26, pp.73-74, Mar.22, 1913.

HUNTING FLYING FOXES IN THE PACIFIC AREA. A. J. Nicholson. Texas Game and Fish, Austin, vol.4, no.1, pp.4-5, 22, illus., Dec., 1945.

ON A NEW SPECIES OF PTEROPINE BAT FROM THE NEW BRITAIN GROUP. E. Pierson Ramsay. Records Australian Mus., vol.1, no.6, pp.105-106, Mar., 1891.

THE FLYING FOX (PTEROPUS) IN AUSTRALIA. F. Ratcliffe. Commonwealth Australia Council Science and Industries Res. Bull. 53, pp.81, pls.2, map 1, 1931.

NOTES ON THE FRUIT BATS (PTEROPUS SP.) OF AUSTRALIA. F. Ratcliffe. Jour. Anim. Ecology, vol.1, no.1, pp.32-57, pls. 1-4, May, 1932.

NEW PHILIPPINE FRUIT BATS. C. C. Sanborn. Proc. Biol. Soc. Washington, vol.63, pp.189-190, Dec.29, 1950.

TWO NEW FRUIT BATS COLLECTED BY THE WHITNEY SOUTH SEA EXPEDITION. C. C. Sanborn. Amer. Mus. Nov. no.435, pp.3, Oct.16, 1930.

REPORT ON THE ADDITIONS TO THE SOCIETY'S MENAGERIE IN JANUARY 1873. Philip Lutley Sclater. Proc. Zool. Soc. Lond., pp.193-194, pl.XXII, illus., 1873.

(NOTE ON SOME SPECIES OF THE GENUS "PTEROPUS" FROM THE ISLAND OF TIMOR.) Noticia sobre algumas especies do genero "Pteropus" provenientes da ilha de Timor. A. F. de Seabra. Jor. Sci. Math., Phys. e Nat., Lisboa, ser.2, vol. 5, no.18, pp.117-125, 1897.

AN APPARENTLY NEW FRUIT BAT OF THE PTEROPUS HYPOMELANUS GROUP FROM GOWER ISLAND, SOLOMON ISLANDS. G.H.H. Tate. Amer. Mus. Novitates, no. 718, pp.1-2, May 4, 1934.

AN APPARENTLY UNDESCRIBED MEMBER OF THE PTEROPUS PSELAPHON GROUP FROM NEW CALEDONIA. G.H.H. Tate. Amer. Mus. Novitates, New York, no.1213, pp.2, Dec.8, 1942.

DESCRIPTION OF A NEW FRUIT-BAT FROM NEW GUINEA. Oldfield Thomas. Ann. and Mag. Nat. Hist. (7), vol.5, no.26, pp.216-217, Feb., 1900.

DESCRIPTION OF TWO NEW SPECIES OF PTEROPUS FROM THE CAROLINE ISLANDS. Oldfield Thomas. Proc. Zool. Soc., Lond., pp.755-757, pls.54-55, Dec.2, 1882.

DIAGNOSES OF TWO NEW FRUIT-EATING BATS FROM THE SOLOMON ISLANDS. Oldfield Thomas. Ann. and Mag. Nat. Hist. (5), vol.19, no.110, p.147, Feb., 1887.

DIAGNOSIS OF A NEW CYNOPTERUS FROM BORNEO. Oldfield Thomas. Ann. and Mag. Nat. Hist. (6), vol.5, no.27, pp.235-236, Mar., 1890.

DIAGNOSIS OF A NEW PTEROPUS FROM THE ADMIRALTY ISLANDS. Oldfield Thomas. Ann. and Mag. Nat. Hist. (6), vol.13, no.75, p.293, Mar., 1894.

EXHIBITION OF THE SKULL OF A PIGMY FRUIT-BAT FROM SUMATRA. Oldfield Thomas. Abstr. Proc. Zool. Soc. Lond., no.235, p.13, Feb.6, 1923.

ON SOME PTEROPINE BATS FROM VULCAN AND DAMPIER ISLANDS, OFF THE N.E. COAST OF NEW GUINEA. Oldfield Thomas. Ann. and Mag. Nat. Hist. (8), vol.15, no. 88, pp.387-389, Apr., 1915.

FIXATION OF THE HABITAT, AND EXTENDED DESCRIPTION OF PTEROPUS TUBERCULATUS, PETERS. E. LeG. Troughton. Records Australian Mus., vol. 15, no.5, pp.355-359, fig.1, Apr.6, 1927.

A NEW FRUIT BAT (PTEROPUS RAYNERI GROUP) FROM THE SOLOMONS. E. LeG. Troughton. Rec. Australian Mus., vol.17, no.4, pp.193-198, Sept.4, 1929.

A NEW SPECIES AND SUB-SPECIES OF FRUIT-BATS (PTEROPUS) FROM THE SANTA CRUZ GROUP. E. LeG. Troughton. Records Australian Mus., vol.18, no.1, pp. 1-4, Nov.10, 1930.

NOTE ON THE OCCURRENCE OF A SECOND SPECIES OF FRUIT-BAT (PTEROPUS SCAPULATUS) IN NEW SOUTH WALES. E. LeG. Troughton, Australian Zool., vol. 6, no.1, pp.104-106, Aug.13, 1929.

LETTER FROM, CONCERNING SOME BIRDS AND A PAIR OF BATS SENT TO THE SOCIETY FROM SAMOA. S. J. Whitmee. Proc. Zool. Soc., pp.666-667, 1874.

### Control

NOTES ON POISONING FRUIT BATS (EPIMORPHUS WAHLBERGEI). G. J. Jex-Blake. Jour. East Africa and Uganda Nat. Hist. Soc., nos.42-43, pp.179-182, July, 1932.

WAR ON FLYING FOXES. Ewen K. Patterson. Game and Gun and the Angler's Monthly, Lond., vol.18, no.185, pp.54-55, Feb., 1941.

THE FLYING FOX PEST IN AUSTRALIA. A.C.D. Rivett. Nature, no.3014, vol.120, pp.189-190, Aug.6, 1927.

THE GREY-HEADED FLYING FOX OR FRUIT BAT: AN AUSTRALIAN PEST. Otho Webb. Field London, vol.152, p.368, illus., Aug.30, 1928.

### Habits and Behavior

ROOSTS OF FLYING FOX. H. G. Acharya. Jour. Bombay Nat. Hist. Soc., vol.38, no. 4, pp.812-813, Aug., 1936.

BAT, BAT, COME UNDER MY HAT. Pacific Discovery, California Acad. Sci., 8 (6): 10-15, illus., Nov.-Dec., 1955.

LOCAL MIGRATION OF THE FLYING-FOX (PTEROPUS GIGANTEUS) IN THE PUNJAB. G. Breadon. Jour. Bombay Nat. Hist. Soc., vol.35, no.2, p.439, Oct.15, 1931.

DAILY FLIGHTING OF FLYING FOXES (PTEROPUS GIGANTEUS BRUNN.). M. L. Ferrar. Jour. Bombay Nat. Hist. Soc., vol.37, no.1, pp.214-215, Apr.15, 1934.

FURTHER OBSERVATIONS ON THE FLYING-FOX (PTEROPUS GIGANTEUS BRUNN.) AND THE FULVOUS FRUIT-BAT (ROUSETTUS LESCHENAULTI DESM.). Charles McCann. Jour. Bombay Nat. Hist. Soc., vol.42, no. 3, pp.587-592, 1 photo, 1 fig., Aug., 1941.

NOTES ON THE FLYING-FOX (PTEROPUS GIGANTEUS BRUENN.). Charles McCann. Jour. Bombay Nat. Hist. Soc., vol.37, no. 1, pp.143-149, pl.1, Apr.15, 1934.

NOTES ON THE FULVOUS FRUIT BAT (ROUSETTUS LESCHENAULTI DESM.). Charles McCann. Jour. Bombay Nat. Hist. Soc., vol.41, no.4, pp.805-816, figs.2, Aug., 1940.

THE SHORT-NOSED FRUIT-BAT (CYNOPTERUS SPHINX) AS AN AGENT OF SEED DISPERSAL IN THE WILD DATE (PHOENIX SYLVESTRIS L.). Charles McCann. Jour. Bombay Nat. Hist. Soc., vol.42, no.1, pp. 184-185, Dec., 1940.

LETTER ON A PTEROPINE BAT LATELY LIVING IN THE SOCIETY'S MENAGERIE. William Peters. Proc. Zool. Soc. Lond., p.531, 1868.

### Orientation

(FLYING FOXES PRODUCE ORIENTATION SOUNDS BY CLICKING THE TONGUE.) Flughunde erzeugen Orientierungslaute durch Zungenschlag. Erwin Kulzer. Die Naturwissenschaften, 43 (5): 117-118, 1956.

(ON THE ORIENTATION OF FLYING FOXES (CHIROPTERA-PTEROPOPIDAE). Ueber die Orientierung der Flughunde (Chiroptera-Pteropodidae). F. P. Moehres, E. Kulzer. Zeitschr. Vergleich. Physiol., vol.38, pp. 1-29, illus., 1956.

ORIENTATION IN PALEOTROPICAL BATS. II. MEGACHIROPTERA. Alvin Novick. Jour. Exper. Zool., 137 (3): 443-462, 1958.

### Reproductive Biology

ON THE MATING OF FLYING-FOXES (PTEROPUS GIGANTEUS). J. R. Bhatt. Jour. Bombay Nat. Hist. Soc., vol.43, no. 3, pp.514-516, Dec., 1942.

(NOTE ON A FRUIT BAT FOETUS (PTEROPUS EDULIS TEMMINCK).) Note sur un foetus de roussette (Pteropus edulis Temminck). Robert Didier. Mammalia, Paris, vol.2, no.3, pp.135-136, pl.11, Sept., 1938.

(A NEWBORN PTEROPUS.) Un neonato di Pteropus. Giulio Levi. Boll. Zool. dall 'Unione Zool. Italiana, Torino, vol.6, nos. 5-6, pp.301-309, figs.2, 1935.

POST-PARTUM OESTRUS IN THE INDIAN SHORT-NOSED FRUIT BAT, CYNOPTERUS SPHINX (VAHL.). P. A. Ramakrishna. Current Sci., Bangalore, vol.16, no.6, p. 186, 1947.

### Taxonomy

DESCRIPTION OF A NEW SPECIES OF PTEROPUS. Harrison Allen. Proc. Amer. Philos. Soc., vol.28, no.132, pp.70-72, Feb.25, 1890.

NOTES ON THE GENUS ACERODON, WITH A SYNOPSIS OF ITS SPECIES AND SUB-SPECIES, AND DESCRIPTIONS OF FOUR NEW FORMS. Knud Andersen. Ann. and Mag. Nat. Hist., ser.8, vol.13, pp.20-29, Jan., 1909.

ON PTEROCYON, ROUSETTUS, AND MYCAYETERIS. Knud Andersen. Ann. and Mag. Nat. Hist., ser.7, vol.10, pp.501-515, June, 1907.

ON SOME SPECIES OF THE GENUS EPOMOPS. Knud Andersen. Ann. and Mag. Nat. Hist. (8), vol.5, pp.99-106, 1910.

ON THE CHARACTERS AND AFFINITIES OF DESMALOPEX AND PTERALOPEX. Knud Andersen. Ann. and Mag. Nat. Hist. ser.8, vol.3, pp.213-222, Feb., 1909.

ON THE FRUIT-BATS OF THE GENUS DOBSONIA. Knud Andersen. Ann. and Mag. Nat. Hist. (8), vol.4, pp.528-533, 1909.

PRELIMINARY DESCRIPTION OF A NEW GENUS OF EPOMOPHORINE BATS. Knud Andersen. Ann. and Mag. Nat. Hist. (8), vol.5, pp.97-99, 1910.

TEN NEW FRUIT-BATS OF THE GENERA NYCTIMENE, CYNOPTERUS, AND EONYCTERIS. Knud Andersen. Ann. and Mag. Nat. Hist. (8), vol.6, pp.621-625, 1910.

REMARKS ON SOME RACES OF CYNOPTERUS. Knud Andersen, C. Boden Kloss. Jour. Fed. Malay States Mus., vol.5, no. 4, pp.220-222, Mar., 1915.

(MAMMALS RECENTLY ENTERED IN THE COLLECTIONS OF THE ZOOLOGICAL LABORATORY OF THE HIGHER SCHOOL OF SCIENCES. DESCRIPTION OF A NEW VARIETY.) Mammiferes récemment entres dans les collections du laboratoire de Zoologie de l'Ecole supérieure des sciences. Description d'une variété nouvelle. R. Bourret. Notes and Travaux Ecole Superieure Sci., Univ. Indochinoise, Hanoi, no.3, pp.1-17, Mar., 1944.

(TWO NEW FRUGIVOROUS BATS.) Dos nuevos murcielagos frugıvorous. Angel Cabrera. Bol. Real Soc. española Hist. nat., vol.20, pp.106-108, Mar., 1920.

(CRITICAL SUMMARY OF ORDER OF BATS (CHIROPTERA). FAMILY OF FLYING FOXES (CYNOPTERI). SECTION I.) Kritische Durchsicht der Ordnung der Flatterthiere oder Handfluegler (Chiroptera). Familie der Flughunde (cynopteri). I. Abtheilung. Leop. Jos. Fitzinger. Sitz. Akad. Wissensch, Abth.11, pp.90, Oct., 1869.

(CRITICAL SUMMARY OF THE ORDER OF BATS (CHIROPTERA). FAMILY OF FLYING FOXES (CYNOPTERI). SECTION II. Kritische Durchsicht der Ordnung der Flatterthiere oder Handfluegler (Chiroptera). Familie der Flughunde (Cynopteri). II. Abtheilung. Leop. Jos. Fitzinger. Sitzb. Akad. Wissensch., Wien, vol.60, Abth.1, pp.58, Nov., 1869.

(NEW SPECIES OF FRUIT BAT.) Nouvelle espece de chauve-souris frugivore. G. Grandidier. Bull. Acad. Malgache, vol.11, pp.91-93, pl.1, figs.4, (1928) 1929.

A REVISION OF THE GENERA OF PTEROPINE BATS (PTEROPIDAE) AND THE DESCRIPTIONS OF SOME APPARENTLY UNDESCRIBED SPECIES. John Edward Gray. Proc. Zool. Soc. Lond., pp.62-67, figs.2, 1866.

ON A NEW GENUS AND A NEW SPECIES IN THE MACROGLOSSINE-GROUP OF BATS. F. A. Jentink. Notes Leyden Mus., vol.11, no.40, pp.209-212, pl.9, Aug., 1889.

REVISION OF THE GENERA MACROGLOSSUS AND SYNCONYCTERIS AND DESCRIPTION OF A NEW GENUS AND SPECIES, ODONTONYCTERIS MEIJERI. F. A. Jentink. Notes Leyden Mus., vol.23, no. 18, pp.131-142, Apr.24, 1902.

(THE MEGACHIROPTERA OF THE BERLIN MUSEUM OF NATURAL SCIENCE.) Die Megachiroptera des Berliner Museums fuer Naturkunde. Paul Matschie. 1899.

A SECOND SPECIMEN OF ODONTONYCTERIS MEYERI JENTINK. Gerrit S. Miller, Jr. Proc. Biol. Soc., Washington, vol.18, p.253, Dec.9, 1905.

THE TECHNICAL NAME OF THE INDIAN FLYING FOX. Gerrit S. Miller, Jr. Proc. Biol. Soc., Washington, vol.6, p.50, Mar. 19, 1903.

ON THE STANDING OF PTEROPUS HALDEMANI HALOWELL. James A.G. Rehn. Amer. Nat., Boston, vol.36, no.423, pp. 201-202, Mar., 1902.

HARPYIONYCTERIS, A GENUS OF RARE FRUIT BATS. G.H.H. Tate. Amer. Mus. Novitates, New York, no.1522, pp.1-9, June 18, 1951.

RESULTS OF THE ARCHBOLD EXPEDITIONS. NO. 46. A NEW GENUS AND SPECIES OF FRUIT BATS, ALLIED TO NYCTIMENE. G.H.H. Tate. Amer. Mus. Novitates, New York, no.1204, pp.2, Oct. 23, 1942.

RESULTS OF THE ARCHBOLD EXPEDITIONS. NO.48. PTEROPODIDAE (CHIROPTERA) OF THE ARCHBOLD COLLECTIONS. G.H.H. Tate. Bull. Amer. Mus. Nat. Hist., New York, vol.80, art.9, pp.331-347, Dec. 31, 1942.

NEW GENERIC NAME FOR THE PIGMY FRUIT BAT. Oldfield Thomas. Proc. Zool. Soc., Lond., p.178, Apr., 1923.

ADDITIONS TO THE MONOGRAPH OF THE GENUS EPOMOPHORUS. Robert F. Tomes. Proc. Zool. Soc. Lond., pt.29, pp.11-12, 1861.

A MONOGRAPH OF THE GENUS EPOMOPHORUS, WITH THE DESCRIPTION OF A NEW SPECIES. Robert F. Tomes. Proc. Zool. Soc. Lond., pt.28, pp.45-59, pl. LXXV, 1860.

## Rhinopomatidae

(AN ADDITION TO THE MAMMALIA FAUNA OF NORTH AFRICA: RHINOPOMA CYSTOPS ARABIUM THOMAS.) Une addition a la faune mammalogique Nord-Africaine: Rhinopoma cystops arabium Thomas. P. Laurent. Mammalia, Paris, 5 (1): 11-17, Mar., 1941.

(THE TUNISIAN RHINOPOME.) A propos de la Rhinopome Tunisienne. P. Laurent. Mammalia, Paris, 5 (3-4): 99-100, Sept.-Dec., 1941.

THE SO-CALLED MARSUPIAL BONE IN A MICROCHIROPTERAN. Himadri Kumar Mookerjee. Nature, Lond., vol.130, no. 3277, p.278, fig.1, Aug.20, 1932.

(RHINOPOMA MICROPHYLLUM IN TUNISIA.) Rhinopoma microphyllum en Tunisie. E. Oliver. Bull. Soc. Zool. France, Paris, vol.34, nos.7-8, p.148, Aug.14, 1909.

ON THE SPECIES OF THE GENUS RHINOPOMA. Oldfield Thomas. Ann. and Mag. Nat. Hist. (7), vol.11, no.65, pp.496-499, May, 1903.

SCIENTIFIC RESULTS FROM THE MAMMAL SURVEY. NO.XXII. (A) A NEW BAT OF THE GENUS RHINOPOMA FROM S.E. PERSIA. Oldfield Thomas. Jour. Bombay Nat. Hist. Soc., vol.27, no.1, p.25, July 1, 1920.

## Emballonuridae

A SOUTHERN RECORD OF THE YELLOW-BELLIED BAT. E. F. Boehm. South Australian Nat., Adelaide, vol.21, no.2, p.5, Dec.22, 1941.

A NEW BAT (BALANTIOPTERYX) FROM SONORA, MEXICO. William H. Burt. Occas. Papers Mus. Zool., Univ. Michigan, no.515, pp.1-2, Oct.30, 1948.

OBSERVATIONS ON THE SHARP-NOSED BAT, RHYNCHISCUS NASO (MAXIMILIAN). Walter W. Dalquest. Texas Jour. Sci., vol. 9, no.2, pp.219-226, June, 1957.

A NORTHERN RECORD FOR CENTRONYCTERIS MAXIMILIANI CENTRALIS WITH A KEY TO THE SKULLS OF THE NORTH AMERICAN EMBALLONURINE BATS. Walter W. Dalquest, W. Gene Frum, E. Raymond Hall. Anales Inst. Biol., Mexico, vol.21, no.2, pp.431-433, Mar.6, 1951.

OBSERVATIONS ON THE BREEDING HABITS AND OVARIAN CYCLE IN THE INDIAN SHEATH-TAILED BAT, TAPHOZOUS LONGIMANUS (HARDWICKE). A. Gopalakrishna. Proc. Nat. Inst. Sci. India, Calcutta, vol. 21, pt. B, no.1, pp.29-41, illus., Feb.26, 1955.

TWO NEW BATS OF THE GENUS TAPHOZOUS. N. Hollister. Proc. Biol. Soc. Washington, vol.26, pp.157-158, June 30, 1913.

BATS FROM SAN LUIS POTOSI WITH A NEW RECORD FOR BALANTIOPTERYX PLICATA. Karl F. Koopman. Jour. Mam., vol.37, no. 4, pp.547-548, Nov., 1956.

NOTES ON THE LONG-TAILED BAT TAPHOZOUS LONGIMANUS, HARDW. C. McCann. Jour. Bombay Nat. Hist. Soc., vol.31, pp. 1030-1031, illus., Feb.20, 1927.

REPLY TO MR. PHILLIPS' NOTE ON P. 371, VOL.XXXII RE COLOR OF THE LONG-ARMED SHEATH-TAILED BAT (TAPHOZOUS LONGIMANUS). C. McCann. Jour. Bombay Nat. Hist. Soc., vol.32, p.791, May 31, 1928.

A NEW GENUS OF SAC-WINGED BATS. Gerrit S. Miller, Jr. Proc. Biol. Soc., Washington, vol.19, pp.59-60, May 1, 1906.

ON TAPHOZOUS FLAVIVENTRIS, GOULD, A NEW SPECIES OF BAT FROM AUSTRALIA. William Peters. Proc. Zool. Soc. Lond., pp.430, 1866.

THE COLOR CHANGE, AND SEXUAL DIFFERENCES IN COLOR IN THE LONG-ARMED SHEATH-TAILED BAT (TAPHOZOUS LONGIMANUS). W.W.A. Phillips. Jour. Bombay Nat. Hist. Soc., vol.32, pp.371-372, Oct.30, 1927.

AMERICAN BATS OF THE SUBFAMILY EMBALLONURINAE. Colin Campbell Sanborn. Zool. Ser., Field Mus. Nat. Hist., vol.20, no.24, pp.321-354, figs.37-48, Dec.28, 1937.

NOTES ON THE CAROLINE SHEATH-TAILED BAT (EMBALLONURA SULCATA MILLER). Colin Campbell Sanborn. Nat. Hist. Misc., Chicago Acad. Sci., no.48, pp.2, May 10, 1949.

THE SHEATH-TAILED BATS OF THE PALAU AND MARSHALL ISLANDS. Colin Campbell Sanborn. Fieldiana, Zool., Chicago, vol.31, no.8, pp.59-62, Jan.20, 1947.

RESULTS OF THE ARCHBOLD EXPEDITIONS, NO. 37. NOTES ON ORIENTAL TAPHOZOUS AND ALLIES. G.H.H. Tate. Amer. Mus. Novitates, New York, no.1141, pp.1-5, Aug.20, 1941.

RESULTS OF THE ARCHBOLD EXPEDITIONS. NO.23. A REVISION OF THE GENUS EMBALLONURA (CHIROPTERA). G.H.H. Tate, Richard Archbold. Amer. Mus. Novitates no.1035, pp.14, figs.2, July 31, 1939.

THE GENERIC CLASSIFICATION OF THE TAPHOZOUS GROUP. Oldfield Thomas. Ann. and Mag. Nat. Hist., ser.9, vol.9, pp.266-267, Mar., 1922.

A NEW TAPHOZOUS FROM THE SUDAN. Oldfield Thomas. Ann. and Mag. Nat. Hist., ser.9, vol.5, pp.142-144, Jan., 1920.

NOTES ON BATS OF THE GENUS COLEURA. Oldfield Thomas. Ann. and Mag. Nat. Hist., (8), vol.15, no.90, pp.576-579, June, 1915.

NOTES ON EMBALLONURA WITH DESCRIPTIONS OF NEW SPECIES. Oldfield Thomas. Ann. and Mag. Nat. Hist. (8), vol.15, no. 85, pp.137-140, Jan., 1915.

SCIENTIFIC RESULTS FROM THE MAMMAL SURVEY. XI. K. NOTES ON TAPHOZOUS AND SACCOLAIMUS. Oldfield Thomas. Jour. Bombay Nat. Hist. Soc., vol.24, no. 1, pp.57-63, Sept.30, 1915.

A REVISION OF THE GENERA TAPHOZOUS AND SACCOLAIMUS (CHIROPTERA) IN AUSTRALIA AND NEW GUINEA, INCLUDING A NEW SPECIES, AND A NOTE ON TWO MALAYAN FORMS. Ellis LeG. Troughton. Rec. Australian Mus., vol.14, no.4, pp. 313-341, pls.47-48, Apr.9, 1925.

(THE WHITE BAT, GENUS DICLIDURUS FOUND FOR THE FIRST TIME IN MEXICO.) El murcielago blanco, genero Diclidurus, hallado por primera vez en Mexico. Bernardo Villa R. Anales Inst. Biol., Mexico, vol.21, no.2, pp.435-437, illus., Mar.6, 1951.

## Noctilionidae

SEX DICHROMATISM IN NOCTILIO. Glover M. Allen. Jour. Mam., vol.18, no.4, p.514, Nov., 1937.

NOTES ON THE FEEDING HABITS OF NOCTILIO. J. E. Benedict. Jour. Mam., vol.7, no.1, pp.58-59, Feb., 1926.

FISHERMEN BATS OF THE CARIBBEAN REGION. E. W. Gudger. Jour. Mam., vol.26, no.1, pp.1-15, figs.3, pl., Feb.23, 1945.

NOTES ON THE LITTLE BULLDOG BAT, DIRIAS ALBIVENTER MINOR (OSGOOD), IN PANAMA. Lawrence H. Dunn. Jour. Mam., vol.15, no.2, pp.89-99, May, 1934.

OBSERVATIONS ON NOCTILIO. George G. Goodwin. Jour. Mam., vol.9, no.2, pp. 104-113, May, 1928.

BRIEF NOTES ON THE HABITS OF NOCTILIO MASTIVUS. P. H. Gosse. Proc. Zool. Soc. Lond., pt.15, pp.105-110, 1847.

OCCURRENCE OF MEXICAN BULLDOG BAT IN PANAMA. Laurence M. Huey. Jour. Mam., vol.13, no.2, pp.159-160, May, 1932.

A NEW SOUTH AMERICAN BAT. A. Cabrera Latorre. Proc. Biol. Soc. Wash., vol.20, pp.57-58, Apr.18, 1907.

## Nycteridae

(NOTE ON THE MILK TEETH OF NYCTERIS CAPENSIS (CHIROPTERA, NYCTERIDAE).) Note sur la dentition de lait de Nycteris capensis (Chiropteres, Nycterides). Jean Dorst. Bull. Mus. Nat. Hist. Nat., Paris, ser.2, vol.24, no.6, pp.515-518, Dec., 1952.

(BATS EAT SCORPIONS.) Fledermaeuse fressen Skorpione, Heinz Felten. Natur und Volk 86, Heft 2, 53-57, Frankfurt a.M., 1.2, 1956.

(A CASE OF COMPLETE ALBINISM IN A CHIROPTER: NYCTERIS NANA (ANDERSEN).) Un cas d'albinisme complet chez un cheiroptere: Nycteris nana (Andersen). Jaques Verschuren. Inst. Roy. Sci. Nat. Belgique, Bull., vol.31, no.34, 4 pp., July, 1955.

Megadermatidae

ON THE BATS OF THE FAMILY MEGADERMATIDAE. Knud Andersen, R. C. Wroughton. Ann. and Mag. Nat. Hist., ser.7, vol.19, pp.129-145, Feb., 1907.

NOTICE OF THE PREDATORY AND SANGUIVOROUS HABITS OF THE BATS OF THE GENUS MEGADERMA WITH SOME REMARKS ON THE BLOOD-SUCKING PROPENSITIES OF OTHER VESPERTILIONIDAE. Edward Blyth. Jour. Asiatic Soc. Bengal, vol.11, pp.255-262, 1842.

(NOTE ON THE DENTITION OF A LAVIA FRONS FOETUS (CHIROPTERA, MEGADERMATIDAE).) Note sur dentition d'un foetus de Lavia frons (chiroptères, mégadermatidés). Jean Dorst. Mammalia, Paris, vol.17, no.2, pp.83-84, June, 1953.

STUDIES ON THE EMBRYOLOGY OF MICROCHIROPTERA, PART VI. STRUCTURE OF THE PLACENTA IN THE INDIAN VAMPIRE BAT, LYRODERMA LYRA LYRA (GEOFFROY)--(MEGADERMATIDAE). A. Gopalakrishna. Proc. Nat. Inst. Sci. India, Delhi, vol.16, no.2, pp.93-98, pl.6, Mar.-Apr., 1950.

THE INDIAN VAMPIRE (MEGADERMA LYRA) FEEDING ON A PIPISTREL. Charles C. McCann. Jour. Bombay Nat. Hist. Soc., vol.37, no.2, p.479, Aug.15, 1934.

DOES THE GHOST BAT STILL FLY? Crosbie Morrison. Victorian Nat., Melbourne, vol.58, no.1, pp.3-5, fig.1, May, 1941.

ON THE FOOD OF THE VAMPIRE BAT (LYRODERMA LYRA). A.H.E. Mosse. Jour. Bombay Nat. Hist. Soc., vol.34, no. 4, pp.1052-1053, Mar.2, 1931.

RECURRENCE OF MEGADERMA GIGAS, DOBSON. E. R. Waite. Records Australian Mus., vol.3, no.7, pp.188-189, June 15, 1900.

ON A NEW SPECIES OF MEGADERMA. George R. Waterhouse. Proc. Zool. Soc. Lond., pt.11, p.69, 1843.

Rhinolophidae

(RHINOLOPHUS BLASII PETERS (1866), A BAT NEW FOR NORTH AFRICA.) Rhinolophus blasii Peters (1866), chave-souris nouvelle pour l'Afrique du Nord. Villy Aellen. Mammalia, Paris, vol.19, no.3, pp.361-366, illus., Sept., 1955.

(SOME DATA ON THE SPANISH REHINOLOPHIDS.) Algunos datos sobre Rinolófidos españoles. E. Morales Agacino. Bol. Soc. Española Hist. Nat., Madrid, vol.35, no.8, pp.437-441, fig.1, Oct.31, 1935.

A LIST OF THE SPECIES AND SUBSPECIES OF THE GENUS RHINOLOPHUS, WITH SOME NOTES ON THEIR GEOGRAPHICAL DISTRIBUTION. Knud Andersen. Ann. and Mag. Nat. Hist., ser.7, vol.16, pp.648-662, Dec., 1905.

ON SOME BATS OF THE GENUS RHINOLOPHUS, COLLECTED BY DR. W.L. ABBOTT IN THE ISLANDS OF NIAS AND EGANO. Knud Andersen. Proc. U.S. Nat. Mus., vol.29, pp.657-659, no.1440, Mar.7, 1906.

ON SOME BATS OF THE GENUS RHINOLOPHUS WITH REMARKS ON THEIR MUTUAL AFFINITIES, AND DESCRIPTION OF TWENTY-SIX NEW FORMS. Knud Andersen. Proc. Zool. Soc. Lond., vol.2, pls. 3-4. pp.75-145, 1905.

ON SOME NEW OR LITTLE-KNOWN BATS OF THE GENUS RHINOLOPHUS, IN THE COLLECTION OF THE MASCO CIVICO, GENOA. Knud Andersen. Ann. Mus. Civ. di Stori. Nat. Genova, ser.3a, vol.2, pp. 175-195, pls.3, figs.1-7, May 10, 1906.

ON THE GEOGRAPHICAL RACES OF THE LESSER HORSESHOE BAT (RHINOLOPHUS HIPPOSIDERUS). Knud Andersen. Ann. and Mag. Nat. Hist., ser.7, vol.20, pp. 384-389, Nov., 1907.

ON THE SO-CALLED COLOUR PHASE OF THE RUFOUS HORSESHOE-BAT OF INDIA (RHINOLOPHUS ROUXI, TEMM.). Knud Andersen. Jour. Bombay Nat. Hist. Soc., vol.25, no.2, pp.260-273, pls.1-2, Sept. 15, 1917.

ON VON KOUGLIN'S, RUEPPELL'S, AND SUNDEVALL'S TYPES OF AFRICAN RHINELOPHI. Knud Andersen. Ann. and Mag. Nat. Hist., ser.7, vol.14, pp.451-458, Dec., 1904.

(SURVEY OF SOME GEOGRAPHICAL FORMS OF THE SUBGENUS EURYALUS.) Ueberscht einiger geographischen Formen der Untergattung Euryalus. Knud Andersen, Paul Matschie. Siz. Ber. Gesell. Naturf. Freunde Berlin, Jahrg., no.5, pp.71-83, May 10, 1904.

(A POPULATION OF RHINOLOPHUS EURYALE IN THE CAVE OF SAINT-MARCEL D'ARDECHE.) Un peuplement de Rhinolophus euryale dans la grotte de Saint-Marcel d'Ardeche. Theodorides J. Balazug. Bull. Soc. Zool. France, Laval, vol.72, no.2, p.87, 1947.

(NOTE ON THE DISTRIBUTION OF RHINOLOPHUS EURYALE (BLASIUS) IN WESTERN FRANCE.) Note sur la repartition de Rhinolophus euryale (Blasius) dans l'ouest de la France. J. C. Beaucournu. Mammalia, Paris, 21 (1): 90-95, Mar., 1957.

(NOTE ON THE PRESENCE OF RHINOLOPHUS EURYALE IN MAYENNE.) Note sur la presence de Rhinolophus euryale dans la Mayenne. J. C. Beaucournu. Mammalia, Paris, vol.19, no.4, pp.478-481, Dec., 1955.

(RHINOLOPHUS BLASII, PET., IN THE TRE VENEZIE AND IN ITALY.) Il Rhinolophus blasii, Pet. nelle Tre Venezie ed in Italia. O. de Beaux, G. B. Dal Piaz. Studi Trentini, a. VI, Fasc. II, pp.3, 1925.

(A NEW BAT FROM TONKIN.) Une nouvelle chauve-souris du Tonkin. Rene Bourret. Bull. Mus. Nat. Hist. Nat., Paris, ser.2, vol.23, no.6, pp.607-609, Dec., 1951.

NOTES ON THE GREATER HORSESHOE BAT, RHINOLOPHUS FERRUM-EQUINUM (SCHREBER) IN CAPTIVITY. T. A. Coward. Mem. and Proc. Manchester Lit. and Phil. Soc., vol.52, pt.2, no.11, pp.12, pl.1, Apr. 21, 1908.

ON SOME HABITS OF THE LESSER HORSESHOE BAT (RHINOLOPHUS HIPPOSIDERUS). T. A. Coward. Proc. Zool. Soc., Lond., pp.849-855, Apr.11, 1907.

ON THE WINTER HABITS OF THE GREATER HORSESHOE, RHINOLOPHUS FERRUM-EQUINUM (SCHREBER), AND OTHER CAVE-HAUNTING BATS. T. A. Coward. Proc. Zool. Soc., Lond., pp.312-324, Aug.1, 1907.

(OBSERVATIONS OF SMALL HORSESHOE BATS (RHINOLOPHUS HIPPOSIDEROS BECHST.) IN CAPTIVITY.) Beobachtungen an Kleinen Hufeisennasen (Rhinolophus hipposideros (Bechst.) in Gefangenschaft. Hans Englaender. Zool. Garten, Leipzig, n.F., vol.10, nos.5-6, pp.221-224, Jan., 1939.

(CRITICAL REVIEW OF ORDER CHIROPTERA, FAMILY RHINOLOPHI. SECTION I.) Kritische Durchsicht der Ordung der Flatterthiere oder Randfluegler (Chiroptera). Familie des Kammanasen (Rhinolophi). I. L. J. Fitzinger. Sitz.-Ber. math-naturw. cl. Akad. Wiss., Wien, vol.60, pt.1, pp. 823-890, 1870.

(CRITICAL REVIEW OF ORDER CHIROPTERA, FAMILY RHINOLOPHI. SECTION II.) Kritische Durchsicht der Ordnung der Flatterthiere oder Handfluegler (Chiroptera). Familie der Kammnasen (Rhinolophi). II. Abtheilung. L. J. Fitzinger. Sitzb. Akad. Wissensch., Wien, vol.61, Abth.1, pp.76, Feb., 1870.

THE LESSER HORSE-SHOE BAT (RHINOLOPHUS HIPPOSIDEROS) IN CO. CORK. J. E. Flynn. Irish Nat. Jour., vol.5, no.9, p. 228, May, 1935.

ON A NEW RHINOLOPHUS, AND FOUR NEW SPECIES OF BIRDS FROM WESTERN AFRICA. L. Fraser. Proc. Zool. Soc., Lond., pt.11, pp.25-26, 1843.

(NOTES ON MAMMALS. XXVII. ON THE OCCURRENCE IN BELGIUM OF RHINOLOPHUS EURYALE, WITH REMARKS ON THE NASAL TISSUE OF RHINOLOPHIDS.) Notes sur les mammifères. XXVII. Sur la presence en Belgique de Rhinolophus euryale, avec remarques sur la feuille nasale des rhinolophidés. Serge Frechkop. Bull. Mus. Roy. Hist. Nat. Belgique, Brussels, vol.19, no.37, pp.1-8, July, 1943.

CHARACTERS OF A NEW SPECIES OF BAT RHINOLOPHUS, GEOFFREY FROM NEW HOLLAND. J. E. Gray. Proc. Zool. Soc. Lond., pt.2, p.53, 1834.

A REVISION OF THE GENERA OF RHINOLOPHIDAE, OR HORSESHOE BATS. J. E. Gray. Proc. Zool. Soc. Lond., pp.81-83, 1866.

(CONTRIBUTION TO THE KNOWLEDGE OF THE VARIABILITY OF RHINOLOPHUS HIPPOSIDEROS BECHST.) Přispěvek k pozáni variability vrapence malěko Rhinolophus hipposideros bechst. Ivo Grulich. Pracé Moravskoslezskė Akad. Přirodnich, Brno, vol.21, no.5, pp.60, 1949.

A NEW BAT OF THE RHINOLOPHUS PHILIPPINENSIS GROUP FROM MOUNT RUWENZORI, AFRICA. John Eric Hill. Amer. Mus. Novitates, New York, no.1180, p.2, fig.1, July 28, 1942.

TWO NEW NOSE-LEAF BATS FROM BURU. Martin A. C. Hinton. Ann. and Mag. Nat. Hist., ser.9, vol.16, pp.255-257, Aug., 1925.

THE HORSESHOE BATS. J. H. D. Hooper. Discovery, Norwich, vol.10, no.4, pp.107-111, Apr., 1949.

HORSESHOE BATS AND THEIR YOUNG IN DEVONSHIRE CAVES. J. H. D. Hooper. Illus. London News, vol.219, no.5874, pp. 808-809, illus., Nov.17, 1951.

(ECOLOGICAL INVESTIGATIONS OF THE SMALL HORSESHOE BAT (RHINOLOPHUS HIPPOSIDEROS BECHSTEIN) IN THE CENTRAL RHINELAND AND LOWER ALTMUHL VALLEY.) Okologische Untersuchungen an der Kleinen Hufeisennase (Rhinolophus hipposideros (Bechstein)) im mittleren Rheinland und unteren Altmuhltal. W. Issel. Zool. Jahrbucher, Jena, vol.79, nos.1-2, pp.71-86, July 25, 1950.

(RHINOLOPHUS FERRUM-EQUINUM (SCHREBER) IN THE RHINELAND.) Rhinolophus ferrum-equinum (Schreber) im Rheinland. W. Issel. Decheniana, Bonn, vol.97B, Biol. Abt., pp.19-20, May, 1938.

(OCCURRENCE IN MOROCCO (TANGIER) OF AN IBERIAN BAT, RHINOLOPHUS MEHELYI CARPETANUS.) Presence, au Maroc, d'une chave-souris iberique: Rhinolophus mehelyi carpetanus, a Tanger. P. Laurent. Bull. Soc. Sci. Nat. Maroc, vol. 17, nos.3-4, pp.151-153, illus., tables, Dec.31, 1937.

LIBERATION OF GREATER HORSESHOE BATS IN CO. MONOGHAN, AND OTHER BAT NOTES. John Leslie. Irish Nat. Jour., vol.3, pp.222, July, 1931.

THE FEMALE SEXUAL CYCLE IN THE BRITISH HORSE-SHOE BATS, RHINOLOPHUS FERRUM-EQUINUM INSULANS BARRETT-HAMILTON AND R. HIPPOSIDEROS MINUTUS MONTAGU. L. Harrison Matthews. Proc. Zool. Soc. Lond., Abstracts, vol.107, ser.C., no.3, pp.7-8, Mar.2, 1937.

A NEW NAME FOR RHINOLOPHUS MINUTUS MILLER. Gerrit S. Miller, Jr. Proc. Biol. Soc., Wash., vol.19, p.41, Feb.26, 1906.

(SOME DATA ON THE SPANISH RHINOLOPHIDS.) Algunos datos sobre Rinolofidos españoles. E. Morales Agacino. Bol. Soc. Española Hist. Nat., Madrid, vol.35, pp. 437-441, fig.1, 1935.

(ON THE REPRODUCTION OF BATS. II) THE RHINOLOPHIDS AND THEIR EPIZOOTIC PARASITES.) Sur la reproduction des Chauves-souris. II. Les rhinolophes et note sur leurs parasites épizoieques. R. Rollinat, E. L. Trouessart. Mem. Soc. Zool. France, Paris, vol.10, pp.114-138, 1897.

LESSER HORSE-SHOE BAT (RHINOLOPHUS HIPPOSIDERUS) IN CO. MAYO. Robert F. Ruttledge. Irish Nat. Jour., Belfast, vol. 5, no.3, pp.77, Mar., 1943.

EIGHT NEW BATS OF THE GENUS RHINOLOPHUS. Colin Campbell Sanborn. Zool. Ser. Field Mus. Nat. Hist., Chicago, vol.24, no. 5, (447), pp.37-43, Sept.19, 1939.

(NOTES ON THE OCCURRENCE OF THE GREATER HORSESHOE BAT (RHINOLOPHUS FERRUM EQUINUM) IN THE NETHERLANDS.) Over het voorkomen van de Groote Hoefijzerneus (Rhinolophus ferrum equinum) in Nederland. Ir. D. v. Schaik. Natuurhist. Maandblad, Maastricht, 27 Jaargang, no.3, pp.22-24, illus., Mar.31, 1938.

LETTER RESPECTING SOME BATS OBTAINED IN CHINA. Robert Swinhoe. Proc. Zool. Soc. Lond., pp.500-501, 1874.

RESULTS OF THE ARCHBOLD EXPEDITIONS. NO.49. FURTHER NOTES ON THE RHINOLOPHUS PHILIPPINENSIS GROUP (CHIROPTERA). G.H.H. Tate. Amer. Mus. Novitates, New York, no.1219, pp.7, Feb. 17, 1943.

RESULTS OF THE ARCHBOLD EXPEDITIONS. NO.67. A NEW RHINOLOPHUS FROM QUEENSLAND (MAMMALIA, CHIROPTERA). G.H.H. Tate. Amer. Mus. Novitates, New York, no.1578, pp.1-3, July 30, 1952.

RESULTS OF THE ARCHBOLD EXPEDITIONS. NO.24. ORIENTAL RHINOLOPHUS, WITH SPECIAL REFERENCE TO MATERIAL FROM THE ARCHBOLD COLLECTIONS. G.H.H. Tate, Richard Archbold. Amer. Mus. Novitates, New York, no.1036, pp.12, tables, Aug.11, 1939.

## Hipposideridae

(DESCRIPTION OF A NEW HIPPOSIDEROS (CHIROPTERA) FROM THE IVORY COAST.) Description d'un nouvel Hipposideros (Chiroptera) de la Cote d'Ivoire. V. Aellen. Rev. Suisse Zool., vol.61, no.3, pp.473-483, Sept., 1954.

ON HIPPOSIDERUS CAFFER, SUND., AND ITS CLOSEST ALLIES; WITH SOME NOTES ON H. FULIGINOSTS, TEMM. Knud Andersen. Ann. and Mag. Nat. Hist., ser.7, vol. 17, pp.269-282, 1906.

ON HIPPOSIDERUS DIADEMA AND ITS CLOSEST ALLIES. Knud Andersen. Ann. and Mag. Nat. Hist., ser.7, vol.16, pp. 492-507, 1905.

ON THE BATS OF THE HIPPOSIDERUS ARMIGER AND COMMERSONI TYPES. Knud Andersen. Ann. and Mag. Nat. Hist., ser.7, vol.17, pp.35-47, Jan., 1906.

(CHIROPTERS OF THE GENUS TRIAENOPS DOBSON (HIPPOSIDERIDAE).) Les Chiropteres du genre Triaenops Dobson (Hipposiderines). Jean Dorst. Mammalia, Paris, vol.12, nos.1-2, pp.15-21, figs.3, Mar.-June, 1948.

(A NEW BAT FROM FRENCH INDO-CHINA PARASCOELOPS MEGALOTIS.) Une nouvelle chauve-souris de l'Indochine francaise. Jean Dorst. Bull. Mus. Nat. Hist. Nat., Paris, ser.2, vol.19, no.6, pp.436-437, Nov., 1947.

(NOTE ON THE SYSTEMATIC POSITION OF "TRIAENOPS" WHEELERI OSGOOD (CHIROPTERA, HIPPOSIDERIDAE).) Note sur la position systematique de "Triaenops" wheeleri Osgood (Chiropteres, Hipposiderines). Jean Dorst. Bull. Mus. Nat. Hist. Nat., Paris, ser.2, vol.23, no.5, pp.489-492, illus., Oct., 1951.

(A NEW BAT FROM MADAGASCAR, TRIAENOPS AURITA.) Une nouvelle chauve-souris de Madagascar, le Triaenops aurita G. G. G. Grandidier. Bull. Mus. Hist. Nat. Paris, no.1, art.3, pp.2, illus., 1912.

SOME SYSTEMATIC NOTES ON THE TRIDENT BATS (ASELLIA TRIDENS E. GEOFFROY) OF ARABIA. David L. Harrison. Mammalia, Paris, 21 (1): 1-8, pl.1, Mar., 1957.

A NEW HIPPOSIDEROS FROM SIERRA LEONE. R. W. Hayman. Ann. and Mag. Nat. Hist., Lond., ser.11, vol.14, no.109, pp.71-73, Jan. (Nov.19), 1947.

A NOTE ON HIPPOSIDEROS CYCLOPS TEMMINCK AND ITS SYNONYM HIPPOSIDEROS LANGI ALLEN. R. W. Hayman. Ann. and Mag. Nat. Hist., Lond., ser.10, vol.15, no.85, pp.47-50, Jan., 1935.

(A NEW FORM OF THE GENUS "ASELLIA: A TRIDENS PALLIDA" SUBSP. NOV.) Une forme nouvelle du genre "Asellia: A. tridens pallida" subsp. nov. P. Laurent. Mammalia, Paris, vol.1, no.3, pp.111-116, figs.8, tables, Mar., 1937.

A NEW BAT OF THE GENUS COELOPS. Gerrit S. Miller, Jr. Proc. Biol. Soc., Washington, vol.41, pp.85-86, Mar.16, 1928.

THE STATUS OF "TRIAENOPS WHEELERI" OSGOOD. Colin Campbell Sanborn. Nat. Hist. Misc., Chicago Acad. Sci., no.97, pp.1-3, Feb.8, 1952.

RESULTS OF THE ARCHBOLD EXPEDITIONS, NO. 35. A REVIEW OF THE GENUS HIPPOSIDEROS WITH SPECIAL REFERENCE TO INDO-AUSTRALIAN SPECIES. G. H. H. Tate. Bull. Amer. Mus. Nat. Hist., New York, vol.78, art.5, pp.353-393, figs.5, Aug.19, 1941.

RESULTS OF THE ARCHBOLD EXPEDITIONS, NO. 36. REMARKS ON SOME OLD WORLD LEAF-NOSED BATS. G. H. H. Tate. Amer. Mus. Novitates, New York, no.1140, pp.1-11, Aug.20, 1941.

A NEW HIPPOSIDERUS FROM BORNEO. Oldfield Thomas. Ann. and Mag. Nat. Hist. (7), vol.9, no.52, pp.271-272, Apr., 1902.

TRIDENT BATS (ASELLIA TRIDENS) IN THE EGYPTIAN OASIS OF KHARGA. Kamal Wassif. Bull. Zool. Soc. Egypt, no.8, pp. 9-12, 1949.

## Phyllostomidae

OBSERVATIONS ON THE SHARP-NOSED BAT, RHYNCHISCUS NASO (MAXIMILIAN). Walter W. Dalquest. Texas Jour. Sci., 9 (2): 219-226, June, 1957.

NOTES ON THE EMBRYOLOGY OF A PHYLLOSTOMID BAT. G. W. D. Hamlett. Amer. Jour. Anat., vol.56, no.2, pp.327-349, pls. 2, 17 figs., Mar.15, 1935.

A NOTE ON THE FEEDING HABITS OF THE CUBAN RACER, ALSOPHIS ANGULATUS (BIBRON). Jerry D. Hardy, Jr. Copeia, 1957 (1): 49-50, Apr.5, 1957.

A MIOCENE PHYLLOSTOMATID BAT FROM COLOMBIA, SOUTH AMERICA. Donald E. Savage. Univ. California Publ., Bull. Dept. Geol. Sci., Berkeley, vol.28, no.12, pp. 357-366, figs.15, July 18, 1951.

### Anatomy

REMARKS ON SPECIMENS OF CHILONYCTERIS RUBIGINOSUS FROM WESTERN MEXICO, AND ON THE COLOR PHASES OF PTERONOTUS DAVYI GRAY. J. A. Allen. Bull. Amer. Mus. Nat. Hist., vol. 6, pp.247-248, Aug.3, 1894.

(NOTES ON THE MILK TEETH OF TONATIA AMBLYOTIS (CHIROPTERA, PHYLLOSTOMIDAE).) Note sur la dentition lacteale de Tonatia amblyotis (Chiropteres, Phyllostomidés). Jean Dorst. Mammalia, Paris, 21 (3): 302-304, Sept., 1957.

THE EXTERNAL CHARACTERS OF BRACHYPHYLLA PUMILA MILLER. G. G. Goodwin. Jour. Mam., vol.14, no.2, pp.154-155, May, 1933.

THE CRANIAL AND DENTAL CHARACTERS OF CHILOPHYLLA. Gerrit S. Miller, Jr. Proc. Biol. Soc., Washington, vol.25, p. 117, June 29, 1912.

THE EXTERNAL CHARACTERS OF BRACHYPHYLLA NANA MILLER. Gerrit S. Miller, Jr. Proc. Biol. Soc., Washington, vol.15, p.249, Dec.16, 1902.

(THE EPITHELIUM OF THE ESOPHAGUS MUCOUS MEMBRANE OF THE NECTAR-FEEDING BAT GLOSSOGHAGA SORICINA IN COMPARISON WITH INSECT-EATING CHIROPTERA.) Das Epithel der Speiseroehren-schleimhaut der bluetenbesuchenden Fledermaus Glossophaga soricina im Vergleich zu insektenfressenden Chiropteren. Walter Moller. Jahrb. Morph. u. Mikrosk. Anat. Abt.2, Zeitschr. Mikroskopisch-Anat. Forsch., Leipzig, vol.29, no.4, pp. 637-653, figs.6, May, 1932.

EXTERNAL CHARACTERS OF THE BATS OF THE SUBFAMILY GLOSSOPHAGINAE. Colin Campbell Sanborn. Zool. Ser. Field Mus. Nat. Hist., Chicago, vol.24, no.25, pp.271-277, fig.25, Jan.6, 1943.

DECIDUOUS TEETH IN THE HOGNOSE BAT, CHOERONYCTERIS MEXICANA. Howard J. Stains, R. H. Baker. Jour. Mam., vol.35, no.3, 1954.

MUSCULAR ADAPTATION OF THE NECTAR-EATING BATS (SUBFAMILY GLOSSOPHAGINAE). Alvaro Wille. Trans. Kansas Acad. Sci., vol.57, no.3, pp.315-325, illus., 1954.

ON THE NATURE OF THE INTERSCAPULAR GLAND OF THE TROPICAL AMERICAN FRUIT BAT ARTIBEUS JAMAICENSIS LEACH. W. A. Wimsatt. Anat. Record, Phila., vol.121, no.3, pp.549-564, Mar., 1955.

THE PLACENTATION OF THE JAMAICAN BAT (ARTIBEUS JAMAICENSIS PARVIPES). George B. Wislocki, Don W. Fawcett. Anat. Record, Phila., vol.81, no.3, pp.307-317, 1 fig., 2 pls., Nov.25, 1941.

### Antilles

A THIRD SPECIES OF CHILONYCTERIS FROM CUBA. Glover M. Allen. Proc. New England Zool. Club, vol.6, pp.1-7, Feb.8, 1916.

COLLECTING BATS IN TRINIDAD. FOUR SPECIMENS OF VAMPYRUS SPECTRUM ARE EXHIBITED FOR THE FIRST TIME. Raymond L. Ditmars. Bull. New York Zool. Soc., vol.38, no.6, pp.213-218, illus., Nov.-Dec., 1935.

ON VAMPYRODES CARACCIOLAE (THOMAS) AND SOME OTHER BATS FROM THE ISLAND OF TOBAGO (BRITISH WEST INDIES). A. M. Husson. Zool. Mededel. Rijkmsu. Nat. Hist. Leiden, vol.33, no.10, pp.63-67, Dec.13, 1954.

TWO NEW GLOSSOPHAGINE BATS FROM THE WEST INDIES. Gerrit S. Miller, Jr. Proc. Biol. Soc., Washington, vol.13, pp. 33-37, May 29, 1899.

(A NEW GENUS OF CHIROPTERS OF CUBA, PHYLLONYCTERIS, DESCRIBED BY DR. GUNDLACH.) Eine neue von Hrn. Dr. Gundlach beschriebene Gattung von Flederthieren aus Cuba, Phyllonycteris. W. Peters. Auszug Monatsber Koen. Akad. Wiss. Berlin, vol., no., pp.817-819, Dec. 13, 1860.

DESCRIPTION OF A NEW BAT OF THE GENUS ARTIBEUS FROM TRINIDAD. Oldfield Thomas. Ann. and Mag. Nat. Hist. (6), vol.10, no.59, pp.408-410, Nov., 1892.

DESCRIPTION OF A NEW BAT OF THE GENUS STENODERMA FROM MONTSERRAT. Oldfield Thomas. Proc. Zool. Soc., Lond., pp.132-133, Feb.6, 1894.

DESCRIPTION OF A NEW STENODERMATOUS BAT FROM TRINIDAD. Oldfield Thomas. Ann. and Mag. Nat. Hist. (6), vol.4, no.20, pp.167-170, figs.3, Aug., 1889.

### Central America

THE RANGE OF CHIRODERMA ISTHMICUM MILLER. Glover M. Allen. Jour. Mam., vol.8, no.2, p.158, May, 1927.

NEW RECORDS OF THE BAT, ANOURA GEOFFROYI LASIOPYGA. Sydney Anderson. Nat. Hist. Misc., Chicago Acad. Sci., no.159, pp.1-3, Oct.28, 1957.

A NEW BAT OF THE GENUS TRACHOPS FROM GUATEMALA. E. A. Goldman. Proc. Biol. Soc. Washington, vol.38, pp. 23-24, Mar.12, 1925.

A NEW GENUS OF BAT FROM COSTA RICA. George G. Goodwin. Amer. Mus. Novitates, no.976, pp.1-2, May 4, 1938.

NEW PTERONOTUS FROM NICARAGUA. George G. Goodwin. Jour. Mam., vol.23, no.1, p.88, Feb.14, 1942.

DESCRIPTION OF A NEW PHYLLOSTOME BAT FROM THE ISTHMUS OF PANAMA. Marcus W. Lyon, Jr. Proc. Biol. Soc. Washington, vol.15, pp.83-84, Apr.25, 1902.

TWO NEW GLOSSOPHAGINE BATS FROM CENTRAL AMERICA. Oldfield Thomas. Ann. and Mag. Nat. Hist. (7), vol.11, no. 63, pp.286-289, Mar., 1903.

Diseases and Parasites

A NEW PARASITIC FLY FROM BATS (DIPTERA: PUPIPARA). G. F. Augustson. Bull. S. Calif. Acad. Sci. 42 (1): 52-53, Jan.-Apr., 1943.

(REGARDING A "SCHIZOTRYPANUM" OF THE BAT "PHYLLOSTOMUS ELONGATUM" OF VENEZUELA.) Sobre um "Schizotrypanum" do morcego "Phyllostomus elongatum" da Venezuela. Emmanuel Dias, Felix Pifano C. Rev. Brasileira Biol., Rio de Janeiro, vol.2, no.1, pp.95-97, figs.4, Mar., 1942.

A NEW TRYPANOSOMA OF THE VAMPIROPS LINEATUS. Juan Iturbe, Eudoro Gonzalez. Lab. of Juan Iturbe, Caracas, Venezuela, pp.8, illus., 1916.

FRUIT EATING BATS AND PARALYTIC RABIES IN TRINIDAD. J. L. Pawan. Liverpool School of Tropical Medicine, Univ. Press of Liverpool. Annals of Tropical Medicine and Parasitology, vol.42, no.2, pp.173-177, Sept., 1948.

(STUDIES ON THE "SCHIZOTRYPANUM" OF THE BAT "PHYLLOSTOMUS HASTATUS".) Investigacoes sobre o "Schizoyrypanum" do morcego "Phyllostomus hastatus". Felix Pifano C., Emmanuel Dias. Rev. Brasileira Biol., Rio de Janeiro, vol.2, no.1, pp.99-102, Mar., 1942.

(ATHESMIA PARKERI N. SP. (TREMATODA DICROCOELIIDAE), PARASITE OF THE INTESTINE OF ARTIBEUS JAMAICENSIS.) Athesmia parkeri n. sp. (Trematoda, Dicrocoeliidae) parasito del intestino de Artibeus jamaicensis parvipes (Chiroptera). I. Perez Vigueras. Mem. Soc. Cubana Hist. Nat. "Felipe Poey," Havana, vol.16, no.1, pp.67-69, pl.7, May, 1942.

Habits and Behavior

A PECULIAR ROOSTING HABIT OF BATS. T. Barbour. Quart. Review Biol., Baltimore, vol.7, no.3, pp.307-312, figs.4, Sept., 1932.

A HOME-MAKING BAT. Frank M. Chapman. Natural History, New York, vol.32, no.6, p.555, illus., Nov.-Dec., 1932.

OBSERVATIONS ON THE CARNIVOROUS HABITS OF THE SPEAR-NOSED BAT, PHYLLOSTOMUS HASTATUS PANAMENSIS ALLEN, IN PANAMA. Lawrence H. Dunn. Jour. Mam., vol.14, no.3, pp.188-199, Aug., 1933.

THE FOOD OF SOME TRINIDAD FRUIT BATS (ARTIBEUS AND CAROLLIA). Arthur M. Greenhall. Jour. Agric. Soc. Trinidad and Tobago, 56 (3): 424-447, Sept., 1956.

NOTES ON THE BEHAVIOUR OF THE CALIFORNIA LEAF-NOSED BAT. Donald M. Hatfield. Jour. Mam., vol.18, no.1, pp.96-97, Feb., 1937.

FOOD OF THE CALIFORNIA LEAF-NOSED BAT. Laurence M. Huey. Jour. Mam., vol.6, no.3, pp.196-197, Aug., 1925.

(STRANGE AND SEVERE MORTALITY AMONG MORMOOPS MEGALOPHYLLA BATS IN THE NORTH OF MEXICO.) Una extrana y severa mortalidad de murcielagos Mormoops megalophylla en el norte de Mexico. Bernardo Villa R. Anales Inst. Biol., 26 (2): 547-552, 1955.

THE LEGENDARY "DRACULA" OF THE BAT-WORLD: VAMPYRUS SPECTRUM. Illus. London News, vol.192, no.5155, pp. 202-203, illus., Feb.5, 1938.

North America

CALIFORNIA WINTER RECORDS OF MACROTUS CALIFORNICUS BAIRD. Lee W. Arnold. Jour. Mam., vol.24, no.1, p.103, Feb.20, 1943.

MEXICAN BATS OF THE GENUS ARTIBEUS. Walter W. Dalquest. Proc. Biol. Soc. Washington, vol.66, pp.61-66, Aug.10, 1953.

A NEW BAT OF THE GENUS MIMON FROM MEXICO. E. A. Goldman. Proc. Biol. Soc. Washington, vol.27, pp.75-76, May 11, 1914.

CHOERONYCTERIS MEXICANA FROM SOUTHERN CALIFORNIA AND BAJA CALIFORNIA, MEXICO. Laurence M. Huey. Jour. Mam., vol.35, no.3, pp. 436-437, Aug.20, 1954.

ON THE OCCURRENCE OF A BAT OF THE GENUS MORMOOPS IN THE UNITED STATES. Edgar A. Mearns. Proc. Biol. Soc. Washington, vol.13, p.166, Oct.31, 1900.

FIRST RECORD OF CHOERONYCTERIS MEXICANA IN CALIFORNIA. Andrew C. Olson, Jr. Jour. Mam., vol.28, no.2, pp. 183-184, May 19, 1947.

ARTIBEUS LITURATUS IN MORELOS, MEXICO. Robert J. Russell. Jour. Mam., 37 (2): 283-284, June 9, 1956.

A NEW BAT (GENUS LEPTONYCTERIS) FROM COAHUILA. Howard J. Stains. Univ. Kansas Publ., Mus. Nat. Hist., 9 (10): 353-356, Jan.21, 1957.

NOTE ON MEXICAN EXAMPLES OF CHILONYCTERIS DAVYI, GRAY. Oldfield Thomas. Ann. and Mag. Nat. Hist. (6), vol.10, no.59, p.410, Nov., 1892.

AN ADDITIONAL RECORD OF THE BAT, STURNIRA LUDOVICI, IN MEXICO. Luis de la Torre. Nat. Hist. Misc., Chicago Acad. Sci., no.105, pp.2, May 2, 1952.

Reproductive Biology

A VAMPYRUS SPECTRUM IS BORN. R. L. Ditmars. Bull. New York Zool. Soc., vol. 39, no.4, p.162, July-Aug., 1936.

BREEDING HABITS OF THE PHYLLOSTOMID BATS. G. W. D. Hamlett. Jour. Mam., vol.16, no.2, pp.146-147, May, 1935.

UTERINE BLEEDING IN A BAT, GLOSSOPHAGA SORICINA. G. W. D. Hamlett. Anat. Rec., vol.60, no.1, pp.9-13, pls.2, Aug.25, 1934.

PARTURITION IN A WEST INDIAN FRUIT BAT (PHYLLOSTOMIDAE). T. S. Jones. Jour. Mam., vol.27, no.4, pp.327-330, Nov.25, 1946.

South America

(A NEW SUBSPECIES OF TRACHOPS CIRRHOSUS (MAMMALIA, CHIROPTERA) OF BRAZIL.) Eine neue Unterart von Trachops cirrhosus (Mammalia, Chiroptera) aus Brasilien. Heinz Felten. Senckenbergiana Biologica, Frankfurt am Main, 37 (5-6): 369-370, Sept.15, 1956.

A BAT OF THE GENUS LICHONYCTERIS IN SOUTH AMERICA. Gerrit S. Miller, Jr. Proc. Biol. Soc., Washington, vol.8, p.156, June 13, 1900.

A NEW BAT FROM COLOMBIA. H. Harold Shamel. Proc. Biol. Soc., Washington, vol. 40, pp.129-130, Sept.26, 1927.

A NEW GENUS OF GLOSSOPHAGINE BAT FROM COLOMBIA. Oldfield Thomas. Ann. and Mag. Nat. Hist. (8), vol.12, no.69, pp. 270-271, Sept., 1913.

OBSERVATIONS ON THE GENUS VAMPYRUS AND ITS ALLIES. Robert F. Tomes. Proc. Zool. Soc., Lond., pt.29, pp.102-109, pl. 18, 1861.

Taxonomy

THE TYPE LOCALITY OF AMETRIDA MINOR H. ALLEN. Glover M. Allen. Proc. Biol. Soc., Washington, vol.15, pp. 88-89, Apr.25, 1902.

DESCRIPTION OF A NEW SPECIES OF BAT OF THE GENUS CAROLLIA, AND REMARKS ON CAROLLIA BREVICAUDA. Harrison Allen. Proc. Amer. Philos. Soc., vol.28, no.132, pp.19-26, Feb.25, 1890.

DESCRIPTION OF A NEW SPECIES OF BAT OF THE GENUS GLOSSOPHAGA. Harrison Allen. Proc. U.S. Nat. Mus., vol.18, no. 1100, pp.779-781, Oct.27, 1896.

DESCRIPTION OF A NEW SPECIES OF MACROTUS. Harrison Allen. Proc. Amer. Philos. Soc., vol.28, no.132, pp.72-74, Feb.25, 1890.

DESCRIPTION OF A NEW SPECIES OF WAMPYROPS. Harrison Allen. Proc. Acad. Nat. Sci., Phila., pp.400-405, 1891.

ON A NEW SPECIES OF AMETRIDA. Harrison Allen. Proc. Boston Soc. Nat. Hist., vol.26, pp.240-246, figs.4, June 23, 1894.

ON A NEW SUBFAMILY OF PHYLLOSTOME BATS. DESCRIPTION OF A NEW GENUS OF PHYLLOSTOME BATS. ON TEMMINCK'S BAT, SCOTOPHILUS TEMMINCKII. Harrison Allen. Proc. U.S. Nat. Mus., vol.15, pp. 437-444, 1892.

A MONOGRAPH OF THE CHIROPTERAN GENERA URODERMA, ENCHISTHENES, AND ARTIBEUS. Knud Andersen. Proc. Zool. Soc., Lond., no.14, pp.204-319, figs.40-59, Sept., 1908.

ON THE BATS OF THE GENERA MICRONYCTERIS AND GLYPHONYCTERIS. Knud Andersen. Ann. and Mag. Nat. Hist., ser. 7, vol.18, pp.50-65, July, 1906.

AMERICAN BATS OF THE GENUS MIMON. Walter W. Dalquest. Proc. Biol. Soc., Washington, 70: 45-48, June 28, 1957.

THE BAT GENUS PTERONOTUS RENAMED DERMONOTUS. Theodore Gill. Proc. Biol. Soc., Washington, vol.14, p.177, Sept.25, 1901.

A SUMMARY OF RECOGNIZABLE SPECIES OF TONATIA, WITH DESCRIPTIONS OF TWO NEW SPECIES. George G. Goodwin. Jour. Mam., vol.23, no.2, pp.204-209, May, 1942.

CHARACTERS OF A NEW GENUS OF BATS (BRACHYPHYLLA) OBTAINED BY THE SOCIETY FROM THE COLLECTION OF THE LATE REV. LANSDOWN GUILDING. J. E. Gray. Proc. Zool. Soc., Lond., pt. 1, p.122, 1833.

REVISION OF THE GENERA OF PHYLLOSTOMIDAE, OR LEAF-NOSED BATS. J. E. Gray. Proc. Zool. Soc., Lond., pp.111-118, figs.1, 1866.

A REVIEW OF THE BATS OF THE GENUS HEMIDERMA. Walter L. Hahn. Proc. U. S. Nat. Mus., vol.32, pp.103-118, no.1514, 1907.

THE STATUS OF THE BAT GENUS REITHRONYCTERIS. Karl F. Koopman. Jour. Mam., vol.33, no.2, pp.255-258, May 16, 1952.

LOPHOSTOMA VENEZUELAE CHANGED TO TONATIA VENEZUELAE. Marcus W. Lyon, Jr. Proc. Biol. Soc., Washington, vol.15, p.248, Dec.16, 1902.

NOTE ON THE TYPE SPECIMEN OF THE BAT MICRONYCTERIS MICROTIS, MILLER. Marcus W. Lyon, Jr. Ann. and Mag. Nat. Hist., ser.7, vol.18, pp.371-373, Nov., 1906.

THE BATS OF THE GENUS MONOPHYLLUS. Gerrit S. Miller, Jr. Proc. Washington Acad. Sci., vol.2, pp.31-38, Mar.30, 1900.

DESCRIPTIONS OF FIVE NEW PHYLLOSTOME BATS. Gerrit S. Miller, Jr. Proc. Acad. Nat. Sci., Phila., pp.326-337, figs. 5, July 25, 1898.

A NEW NAME FOR THE GENUS RHYNCHONYCTERIS PETERS. Gerrit S. Miller, Jr. Proc. Biol. Soc., Washington, vol.20, p. 65, June 12, 1907.

NOTE ON MICRONYCTERIS BRACHYOTIS (DOBSON) AND M. MICROTIS MILLER. Gerrit S. Miller, Jr. Proc. Biol. Soc., Washington, vol.8, pp.154-155, June 13, 1900.

NOTE ON THE CHILONYCTERIS DAVYI FULVUS OF THOMAS. Gerrit S. Miller,

Jr. Proc. Biol. Soc., Washington, vol.15, p.155, June 20, 1902.

NOTES ON THE GENERIC NAMES PTERONOTUS AND DERMONOTUS. Gerrit S. Miller, Jr. Proc. Biol. Soc., Washington, vol.18, pp.223-226, Oct.17, 1905.

AN OVERLOOKED SPECIMEN OF CHILONYCTERIS PSILOTIS. Proc. Biol. Soc., Washington, vol.15, p.249, Dec.16, 1902.

REVISION OF THE BATS OF THE GENUS GLOSSOPHAGA. Gerrit S. Miller, Jr. Proc. U.S. Nat. Mus., vol.46, pp.413-429, illus., tables, 1914.

(ON CHIROPTERS BELONGING TO THE GROUP MORMOOPS.) Ueber die zu der Gruppe der Mormopes gehoerigen Flederthiere. W. Peters. Monatsber. K. Preussischan Akad. Wiss. Berlin Jahrg. pp.358-361, 1872.

(ON STERNODERMA GEOFFROY AND A RELATED NEW CHIROPTER GENUS, PELTORHINUS.) Ueber Sternoderma Geoffroy und eine damit verwandte neue Flederthier-Gattund Pelthorhinus. W. Peters. Monatsber. K. Preussischan Akad. Wiss. Berlin, Jahrg., 1876, pp.429-434, pls.1-2, July, 1876.

(ON THE CHIROPTER GENERA MORMOOPS AND PHYLLOSTOMUS.) Ueber die Chiropterengattungen mormoops und Phyllostoma. W. Peters. Abhand. K. Akad. Wiss. Berlin, 1856, pp.287-310, 1857.

A NEW BAT OF THE GENUS GLOSSOPHAGA. James A. G. Rehn. Proc. Acad. Nat. Sci., Phila., pp.37-38, Apr.23, 1902.

A REVISION OF THE GENUS MORMOOPS. James A. G. Rehn. Proc. Acad. Nat. Sci. Phila., pp.160-172, June 11, 1902.

A REVISION OF THE MAMMALIAN GENUS MACROTUS. James A. G. Rehn. Proc. Acad. Nat. Sci. Phila., pp.427-446, June 29, 1904.

A STUDY OF THE BATS OF THE GENUS DERMONOTUS (PTERONOTUS AUCT.). James A. G. Rehn. Proc. Acad. Nat. Sci. Phila., pp.250-256, Apr.7, 1904.

A STUDY OF THE GENUS CENTURIO. James A. G. Rehn. Proc. Acad. Nat. Sci. Phila., pp.295-302, June 7, 1901.

A STUDY OF THE MAMMALIAN GENUS CHILONYCTERIS. James A. G. Rehn. Proc. Acad. Nat. Sci. Phila., pp.181-207, Mar.26, 1904.

BATS OF THE GENERA ANOURA AND LONGOGLOSSA. Colin Campbell Sanborn. Field Mus. Nat. Hist., Zool. Ser., vol.20, pp.23-28, Dec.11, 1933.

BATS OF THE GENUS MICRONYCTERIS AND ITS SUBGENERA. Colin Campbell Sanborn. Fieldiana Zool., Chicago Nat. Hist. Mus., vol.31, no.27, pp.215-233, figs.41-49, Apr.29, 1949.

REMARKS ON THE BATS OF THE GENUS VAMPYROPS. Colin Campbell Sanborn. Fieldiana: Zoology, Chicago Nat. Hist. Mus., vol.37, pp.403-413, June 19, 1955.

FURTHER NOTES ON THE GENUS CHIRODERMA. Oldfield Thomas. Ann. and Mag. Nat. Hist. (6), vol.11, no.62, pp.186-187, Feb., 1893.

A NEW GENUS AND SPECIES OF GLOSSOPHAGINE BAT, WITH A SUBDIVISION OF THE GENUS CHOERONYCTERIS. Oldfield Thomas. Ann. and Mag. Nat. Hist., ser. 10, vol.1, pp.120-123, Jan., 1928.

NOTE ON CHIRODERMA VILLOSUM, PETERS, WITH THE DESCRIPTION OF A NEW SPECIES OF THE GENUS. Oldfield Thomas. Annali del Museo Civico di Storia Naturale di Genova (2), vol.10, pp. 881-883, June 25, 1891.

NOTES ON THE PHYLLOSTOMATOUS GENERA MIMON AND TONATIA. Oldfield Thomas. Ann. and Mag. Nat. Hist. (7), vol.10, no.55, pp.53-54, July 1902.

ON THE GENUS MONOPHYLLUS OF LEACH. Robert F. Tomes. Proc. Zool. Soc., Lond., pt.29, pp.87-92, pl.15, 1861.

THE CORRECT TYPE LOCALITY OF THE BAT TRACHOPS COFFINI. Luis de la Torre. Proc. Biol. Soc. Washington, vol.69, pp. 189-190, Dec.31, 1956.

## Desmodontidae

NOTES ON THE VAMPIRE BAT (DIPHYLLA ECAUDATA), WITH SPECIAL REFERENCE TO ITS RELATIONSHIPS WITH DESMODUS RUFUS. Harrison Allen. Proc. U.S. Nat. Mus., vol.18, no.1099, pp.769-777, illus., Oct.27, 1896.

VAMPIRE RESEARCH. R. L. Ditmars. Bull. New York Zool. Soc., vol.38, no.1, pp.29-31, illus., Jan.-Feb., 1935.

PROFILE OF A VAMPIRE. Arthur M. Greenhall. Pageant, vol.8, no.6, pp.52-57, illus., Dec., 1952.

LES VAMPIRES. A. Guillon. La Terre et la Vie, Rev. d'Hist. Nat., vol.4, no.2, pp. 131-133, illus., Feb., 1934.

THE VAMPIRE BAT. Marcus Ward Lyon, Jr. Science, vol.73, publ.1883, pp.124-125, Jan.30, 1931.

(BIOLOGY OF THE VAMPIRE.) Biologia del vampiro. Guillermo Mann F. Biologica, Trabajos Inst. Biol. "Juan Noe" Univ. Chile, Santiago, fasc. 12-13, pp.3-24, illus., July-Dec., 1951.

THE MYSTERY OF THE VAMPIRE BAT. Willard Price. Nature Mag., Washington, vol.43, no.4, pp.176-179, illus., Apr., 1950.

VAMPIRE BATS. Ellis Troughton. Australian Mus. Mag., Sydney, vol.7, no.7, pp.244-248, figs.3, Dec., 1940-Feb., 1941.

THE REAL VAMPIRE: THE LITTLE BAT THAT HAS "DEPOSED" VAMPYRUS. Illus. London News, vol.191, no.5139, p.653, Oct. 16, 1937.

### Anatomy

ON THE STRUCTURE OF THE STOMACH IN DESMODUS RUFUS. Thomas Henry Huxley. Proc. Zool. Soc., Lond., pp.386-390, fig.1, 1865.

NOTE ON THE MILK DENTITION OF DESMODUS. Gerrit S. Miller, Jr. Proc. Biol. Soc., Washington, vol.9, pp.113-114, figs.2, July 22, 1896.

THE DENTAL FORMULA OF THE BATS OF THE GENUS DIAEMUS. Luis de la Torre. Proc. Biol. Soc., Washington, vol.69, pp. 191-192, Dec.31, 1956.

### Habits, Behavior

THE VAMPIRE'S BITE. William Beebe. Bull. New York Zool. Soc., vol.30, pp.113-115, Aug., 1927.

(THE BAT THAT BITES HORSES.) El murcielago que muerde a los caballos. Angel Cabrera. El Caballo, Buenos Aires, anos. 5, no.18, pp.65-75, illus., July, 1938.

THE VAMPIRE BAT: A PRESENTATION OF UNDESCRIBED HABITS AND REVIEW OF ITS HISTORY. Raymond L. Ditmars, Arthur M. Greenhall. Zoologica, Sci. Contrib. New York Zool. Soc., vol.19, no. 2, pp.53-74, figs.3, pls.5-7, Apr.3, 1935.

KILLER BATS. G. M. Dyott. Outdoor Life, vol.75, no.6, pp.16-17, 85, 99, illus., June, 1935.

SOME OBSERVATIONS ON THE FEEDING METHODS OF THE VAMPIRE BATS. Barry G. King, Robert Saphir. Zoologica, Sci. Contrib. N.Y. Zool. Soc., vol.22, pt.3, pp.281-287, pls.3, Oct.7, 1937.

(BLOOD SUCKING BY DESMODUS.) Succion de sangre por Desmodus. Guillermo F. Mann. Investigaciones Zool. Chilenas, Santiago, fasc. 1, pp.7-8, illus., July, 1950.

OBSERVATIONS ON THE VAMPIRE BAT WITH SPECIAL REFERENCE TO LONGEVITY IN CAPTIVITY. Harold Trapido. Jour. Mam., vol.27, no.3, pp.217-219, Aug. 14, 1946.

### North America

NATURAL HISTORY OF THE VAMPIRE BATS OF EASTERN MEXICO. Walter W. Dalquest. Amer. Midland Nat., Notre Dame, vol.53, no.1, pp.79-87, Jan., 1955.

GEOGRAPHIC RANGE OF THE HAIRY-LEGGED VAMPIRE IN EASTERN MEXICO. Walter W. Dalquest, E. Raymond Hall. Trans. Kansas Acad. Sci., vol.5, nos.3, 4, pp.315-317, Dec., 1947.

(THE VAMPIRE OF THE TROPICS.) El Vampiro de Tierra Caliente. A. Duges, A. L. Herrera. Comis. de Parasitologia Agricola, Mexico, circ., no.34, pp.1-9, figs.18, 1906.

WHAT ABOUT VAMPIRE BATS? THE CAVES OF TEXAS. Charles E. Mohr. Bull. Nat. Speleol. Soc., Washington, no.10, pp. 106-107, illus., Apr., 1948.

(DISTRIBUTION IN MEXICO OF THE VAMPIRE BATS, FAMILY DESMODONTIDAE.) Distribución en México de los murciélagos vampiros familia Desmodontidae. Bernardo Villa R. Boletin Oficina Sanitaria Panamericana, vol.35, no.4, pp.426-432, Oct., 1953.

### Parasites

EXPERIMENTS IN THE TRANSMISSION OF TRYPANOSOMA HIPPICUM DARLING WITH THE VAMPIRE BAT, DESMODUS ROTUNDUS MURINUS WAGNER, AS A VECTOR IN PANAMA. Lawrence H. Dunn. Jour. Preventive Medicine, vol.6, no.5, pp.415-424, Sept., 1932.

A NATURAL INFECTION OF TRYPANOSOMA HIPPICUM DARLING IN THE VAMPIRE BAT DESMODUS ROTUNDUS MURINUS WAGNER. Carl M. Johnson. Amer. Jour. Tropical Medicine, vol.16, no.1, pp. 59-62, Jan., 1936.

### Rabies

(IMMUNOLOGICAL REACTION IN THE VIRUS OF DERRIENGUE (CEPA DESMODUS) AND RABIES.) Reaction immunologica entre los virus del derriengue (cepa Desmodus) y el de la rabia. Alfredo Tellez Giron. Rev. Soc. Mexicana Hist. Nat., México, D.F., vol.6, nos.3-4, pp.179-195, Dec., 1945.

DERRIENGUE: VAMPIRE BAT RABIES IN MEXICO. Harald V. Johnson. Amer. Jour. Hygiene, Baltimore, vol.47, no.2, pp.189-204, Mar., 1948.

VAMPIRE BAT AS A CARRIER OF RABIES. Aurelio Málaga-Alba. Am. Jour. Public Health and Nation's Health, 44 (7): 909-918, illus., July, 1954.

RABIES IN THE VAMPIRE BAT OF TRINIDAD, WITH SPECIAL REFERENCE TO THE CLINICAL COURSE AND THE LATENCY OF INFECTION. J. L. Pawan. Liverpool School of Tropical Medicine, Univ. Press of Liverpool. Annals of Tropical Medicine and Parasitology, vol.30, no.4, pp.401-422, Dec.23, 1936.

THE TRANSMISSION OF PARALYTIC RABIES IN TRINIDAD BY THE VAMPIRE BAT (DESMODUS ROTUNDUS MURINUS WAGNER, 1840). J. L. Pawan. Liverpool School of Tropical Medicine, Univ. Press of Liverpool, Reprinted from the Annals of Tropical Medicine and Parasitology, vol. 30, no.1, pp.101-128, pl.4, Apr.8, 1936.

MALAGA-ALBA DESCRIBES VAMPIRE BAT RABIES. Public Health Repts., U.S. Public Health Service, Washington, vol.69, no.2, pp.185-186, illus., Feb., 1954.

## Natalidae

THE GENERA OF THE CHIROPTERAN FAMILY NATALIDAE. Walter W. Dalquest. Jour. Mam., vol.31, no.4, pp.436-443, Nov.21, 1950.

A NEW SUBSPECIES OF FUNNEL-EARED BAT (NYCTALUS MEXICANUS) FROM EASTERN MEXICO. Walter W. Dalquest, E. Raymond Hall. Proc. Biol. Soc. Washington, vol.62, pp.153-154, Aug.23, 1949.

HISTORY AND CHARACTERS OF THE FAMILY NATALIDAE. Gerrit S. Miller, Jr. Amer. Mus. Nat. Hist., vol.12, art. 18, pp.245-253, pl.10, Dec.23, 1899.

A NEW NATALINE BAT FROM THE BAHAMAS. Gerrit S. Miller, Jr. Proc. Biol. Soc., Washington, vol.16, pp.119-120, Sept.30, 1903.

A NEW BAT FROM DOMINICA. Harold H. Shamel. Proc. Biol. Soc. Washington, vol. 41, pp.67-68, Mar.16, 1928.

Thyropteridae

A NEW DISC-WINGED BAT FROM PANAMA. Glover M. Allen. Proc. New England Zool. Club, vol.9, pp.1-2, Dec.10, 1923.

THE DISK-WINGED BAT (THYROPTERA) IN PANAMA. E. R. Dunn. Jour. Mam., vol.12, no.4, pp.429-430, Nov., 1931.

Myzopodidae

ON THE OSTEOLOGY AND SYSTEMATIC POSITION OF THE RARE MALAGASY BAT MYZOPODA AURITA. Oldfield Thomas. Proc. Zool. Soc., Lond., pt.2, pp.2-6, pl. 1, Oct.1, 1904.

Vespertilionidae

BATS OF THE GENUS CORYNORHINUS. Glover M. Allen. Bull. Mus. Comp. Zool., Harvard College, vol.60, no.9, pp.333-356, 1 pl., Apr., 1916.

NOTES ON THE VESPERTILIONIDAE OF TROPICAL AMERICA. Harrison Allen. Proc. Acad. Nat. Sci. Phila., pp.279-288, Aug., 1866.

SURVIVAL AND MOVEMENTS OF BANDED BIG BROWN BATS. James R. Beer. Jour. Mam., 36 (2): 242-248, May, 1955.

(LIFE AND MIGRATION OF THE BROWN BAT (NYCTALUS NOCTULA SCHREB).) Leven en Trek van de Rosse Vleermuis (Nyctalus noctula Schreb). L. Bels. De Levende Natuur, pp.289-299, 1939.

NOTES ON A SUMMER COLONY OF MYOTIS LUCIFUGUS LUCIFUGUS. Fred R. Cagle, Lendell Cockrum. Jour. Mam., vol. 24, no.4, pp.474-492, figs.7, pl.1, Nov.17, 1943.

THE NATURAL HISTORY OF A SUMMER AGGREGATION OF EPTESICUS FUSCUS FUSCUS. John J. Christian. Naval Med. Res. Inst., Memo. Rep. 53-16, 161-193 pp., illus., Aug., 1953.

THE NATURAL HISTORY OF A SUMMER AGGREGATION OF THE BIG BROWN BAT, EPTERICUS FUSCUS. John J. Christian. Amer. Mid. Nat., Notre Dame, vol.55, no.1, pp.66-95, illus., Jan., 1956.

LIFE HISTORY NOTES AND GROWTH STUDIES ON THE LITTLE BROWN BAT, MYOTIS LUCIFUGUS LUCIFUGUS. J. R. Dymond. Canadian Field Nat., vol.50, no. 7, pp.114-116, fig.1, Oct., 1936.

(OUR BATS--THEIR SIGNIFICANCE TO FORESTRY.) Die forstwirtschaftliche Bedeutung unserer Fledermaeuse. M. Eisentraut. Aus der Natur (Der Naturforscher), vol.15, no.9, pp.295-300, illus., Dec., 1938.

(NOTES ON MAMMALS; REMARKS CONCERNING MYOTIS WELWITSCHI (GRAY).) Notes sur les mammiferes--Remarque concernant le Myotis welwitschi (Gray). Serge Frechkop. Bull. Mus. Roy Hist. Belgique, Bruxelles, vol.15, no.29, pp.1-3, May, 1939.

(REMARKS ON M. RODE'S "ABOUT FRENCH NOCTULES.") Remarques sur la note de M. Rode 'A propos des noctules de France." H. Heim de Balsac. Bull. Mus. Nat. Hist. Nat., Paris, vol.4, no.5, pp.484-486, 1932.

MYOTIS LUCIFUGUS LUCIFUGUS MISTAKEN FOR MYOTIS KEENI SEPTENTRIONALIS. Harold B. Hitchcock. Canadian Field Nat., Ottawa, vol.63, no.5, p.209, Oct.25, 1949.

(DISTRIBUTION AND LIVING HABITS OF THE EMARGINATE BAT, MYOTIS EMARGINATUS GEOFFROY 1806.) Zur verbreitung und Lebensweise der Gewimperten Fledermaus, Myotis emarginatus (Geoffroy, 1806). B. Issel, W. Issel. Saeugetierk. Mitteil., Stuggart, vol.1, no.4, pp.145-148, illus., Oct.1, 1953.

NOTES ON THE HABITS OF THE BAT, MYOTIS CALIFORNICUS. Philip H. Krutzsch. Jour. Mam., vol.35, no.4, pp.539-545, Nov.29, 1954.

(THE BROWN BAT.) Der Abendsegler. Wilhelm Meise. Die neue Brehm-Buecherei das Leben der Tiere und Pflanzen in Einzeldarstellungen, Leipzig, Heft 42, pp.43 illus., 1951.

DAUBENTON'S BAT. C. B. Moffat. Irish Naturalist's Jour., vol.4, no.2, pp.26-28, Mar., 1932.

THE HABITS OF THE LONG-EARED BAT. C. B. Moffat. Irish Naturalist, vol.31, pp. 105-111, Oct., 1922.

THE HAIRY-ARMED BAT. C. B. Moffat. Irish Naturalist's Jour., vol.3, no.3, pp. 50-54, May, 1930.

THE LONG-EARED BAT. C. B. Moffat. Irish Naturalist's Jour., vol.3, pp.182-185, May, 1931.

THE PIPISTRELLE. C. B. Moffat. Irish Naturalist's Jour., vol.3, no.2, pp.26-29, Mar., 1930.

THE WHISKERED BAT. C. B. Moffat. Irish Naturalist's Jour., vol.4, no.6, pp. 106-109, Nov., 1932.

NOTES ON THE LEAST BROWN BAT MYOTIS SUBULATUS LEIBII. Charles E. Mohr. Proc. Penn. Acad. Sci., pp.62-65, vol. 10, maps, 2, 1936.

(BEHAVIOR AND BREEDING OF THE BROWN BAT (NYCTALUS NOCTULA SCHREB.).) Haltung und Aufzucht des Abendseglers (Nyctalus noctula Schreb.). Erna Mohr. Zool. Garten, Leipzig, n.F., vol.5, nos.4-6, pp.106-120, figs.1-9, Aug., 1932.

(SOME FACTS ABOUT THE HABITS OF PIPISTRELLUS PIPISTRELLUS (SCHREBER).) Algunos datos sobre las costumbres del Pipistrellus pipistrellus (Schreber). Agacino E. Morales. Rev. Ciencias, Madrid, vol.1, no.2, pp.1-8, figs.3, 1934.

NATURAL HISTORY OF THE PALLID BAT, ANTROZOUS PALLIDUS (LE CONTE). Robert T. Orr. Proc. California Acad. Sci., San Francisco, ser.4, vol.28, no.4, pp.165-246, illus., Jan.7, 1954.

A QUEST FOR SEAFARING BATS. Robert T. Orr. Pacific Discovery, vol.6, no.1, pp.14-15, illus., Feb., 1953.

SOME NOTES ON MYOTIS LUCIFUGUS. Robert C. Patterson. Proc. W. Virginia Acad. Sci., (W. Va. Univ. Bull., ser.35, no.15), vol.8, no.1, pp.52-54, Mar.15, 1935.

LASIURUS CINEREUS. S. E. Perkins, III. Proc. Indiana Acad. Sci., vol.47, p.229, fig., 1938.

CONCERNING BATS. W. P. Pycraft. Illus. London News, vol.185, no.4979, p.428, figs. 3, Sept.22, 1934.

(OBSERVATIONS OF BATS.) Beobachtungen an Fledermaeusen. Walter Rammner. Zool. Anz., Leipzig, vol.125, nos.9-10, pp.271-272, Mar.15, 1939.

DISTRIBUTION, TYPE LOCALITY, AND HABITS OF THE FISH-EATING BAT, PIZONYX VIVESI. William G. Reeder, Kenneth S. Norris. Jour. Mam., vol.35, no.1, pp.81-87, illus., Feb.19, 1954.

NOTES ON HOMING AND HIBERNATION IN EPTESICUS FUSCUS. Keith Reynolds. Canadian Field-Nat., Ottawa, vol.55, no.9, p.132, Dec., 1941.

THE EMBRYOLOGY OF THE THYROID, PARATHYROID AND THYMUS OF THE PACIFIC PALLID BAT (ANTROZOUS PACIFICUS MERRIAM). Raymond Martin Louis Selle. Amer. Jour. Anat., vol.56, no.2, pp.161-190, 1 pl., Mar.15, 1935.

(CONTRIBUTION TO THE STUDY OF THE NOCTULES (NYCTALUS NOCTULA SCHREB) IN THE WILD AND IN CAPTIVITY.) Contribution à l'étude des noctules (Nyctalus noctula Schreb.) en liberté et en captivité. Nicolas Skreb, Beatrice Gjulic. Mammalia, Paris, vol.19, no.2, pp.335-343, June, 1955.

SEXUAL MATURITY IN BATS OF THE GENUS MYOTIS. II. FEMALES OF M. MYSTACINUS AND SUPPLEMENTARY DATA ON FEMALE M. MYOTIS AND M. EMARGINATUS. J. W. Sluiter. Proc. Kon. Nederlandse Akad. Weten., Amsterdam, ser.c, vol.57, no.5, pp. 696-700, Nov.-Dec., 1954.

POPULATION STATISTICS OF THE BAT MYOTIS MYSTACINUS, BASED ON THE MARKING-RECAPTURE METHOD. J. W. Sluiter, P. F. van Heerdt, J. J. Bezem. Arch. Néerlandaises Zool., 12 (1): 63-88, 1956.

BLOOD CLOTTING TIME AND TISSUE MAST CELL NUMBER OF THE BAT (MYOTIS LUCIFUGUS) IN DIFFERENT PHYSIOLOGICAL STATES. Douglas E. Smith, Yevette S. Lewis, George Svihla. Proc. Soc. Exper. Biol. and Med., New York, vol.86, no.3, pp.473-475, July, 1954.

NOTES ON THE DEVELOPMENT OF THE LITTLE BROWN BAT MYOTIS LUCIFUGUS LUCIFUGUS. Le Roy C. Stegeman. Jour. Mam., vol.35, no.3, pp.432-433, Aug.20, 1954.

ON THE CHARACTERS OF FOUR SPECIES OF BATS INHABITING EUROPE AND ASIA, AND THE DESCRIPTION OF A NEW SPECIES OF VESPERTILIO INHABITING MADAGASCAR. Robert F. Tomes. Proc. Zool. Soc. Lond., pt.26, pp.78-90, pl.60, 1858.

THE NOCTULE. Brian Vesey-Fitzgerald. Naturalist, London, no.792, pp.157-161, July, 1941; no.793, pp.189-198, Aug., 1941.

THE NOCTULE. (CONTINUED.) Brian Vesey-Fitzgerald. Naturalist, London, no. 795, pp.233-239, Oct., 1941.

Africa

A SECOND SPECIMEN OF AN AFRICAN BAT, PLEROTES ANCHIETAE (SEABRA). Glover M. Allen. Annals of the Carnegie Museum, vol.30, art.10, pp.93-95, Pittsburgh, 1945.

ON THE REDISCOVERY OF THE BAT KERIVOULA BRUNNEA, DOBS. E. C. Chubb. Ann. Transvaal Mus., vol.3, no.1, Dec.22, 1910.

(A NEW BAT FOR TUNISIA: OTONYCTERIS HEMPRICHI PETERS 1860.) Une nouvelle chauve-souris pour la Tunisie: Otonycteris hemprichi Peters 1860. R. Deleuil. Mammalia, Paris, 21 (2): 190, June, 1957.

NOTICE OF A NEW BAT (SCOTOPHILUS WELWITSCHII) FROM ANGOLA. John Edward Gray. Proc. Zool. Soc. London, p.211, pl.24, 1866.

A NOTE ON THE OCCURRENCE OF THE WOOLLY BAT, KERIVOULA CUPROSA THOMAS IN KENYA. David L. Harrison. Rev. Zool. and Bot. Africaine, 55 (1-2): 47-48, Mar.27, 1957.

SOME SYSTEMATIC NOTES ON THE LONG-FINGERED BATS OF THE GENUS MINIOPTERUS BONAPARTE OCCURRING IN SOUTH AFRICA AND MADAGASCAR. David L. Harrison. Durban Mus. Novitates, vol.4, p.5, pp.65-75, June 30, 1953.

A NEW RACE OF GLAUCONYCTERIS SUPERBA FROM WEST AFRICA. R. W. Hayman. Ann. Mag. Nat. Hist., Lond., ser.11, vol.13, no.104, pp.547-50, Aug.7, 1947.

(A SAHARIAN FORM OF THE GENUS PLECTOTUS, P. AURITUS SAHARAE SUBSP. NOV.) Uhe forme Saharienne du Genre Plecotus, P. auritus saharæ subsp. nov. P. Laurent. Bull. Soc. d'Hist. Nat. Afrique du Nord, Alger, vol.29, no.9, pp.408-412, figs.3, Dec., 1936.

(VESPERTILIO VENUSTUS MTSCH., A NEW BAT FROM GERMAN-EAST-AFRICA.) Vespertilio venustus Mtsch., eine neue fledermaus aus Deutsch-Ost-Afrika. Paul Matschie. Sitz. Gesell. Naturf. Freunde Berlin, Jahrg., 1899, no.4, pp.74-76, Apr. 18, 1899.

DESCRIPTION OF A NEW SCOTOPHILUS FROM THE GAMBIA, WITH REMARKS ON SOME OF THE ALLIED SPECIES. Oldfield Thomas. Annali del Museo Civico di Storia Naturali di Genova (2), vol.9, pp.1-7, Feb., 1890.

A NEW BAT OF THE GENUS MYOTIS FROM ABYSSINIA. Oldfield Thomas. Ann. and Mag. Nat. Hist., ser.9, vol.19, pp.554-555, May, 1927.

A NEW SCOTOPHILINE BAT FROM BRITISH EAST AFRICA, WITH THE DESCRIPTION OF A NEW GENUS OF THE GROUP. Oldfield

Thomas. Ann. and Mag. Nat. Hist. (7), vol. 7, no.39, pp.263-265, Mar., 1901.

A NEW VESPERTILIONINE BAT FROM ANGOLA. Oldfield Thomas. Ann. and Mag. Nat. Hist. (8), vol.10, no.56, pp.204-206, Aug., 1912.

ON A NEW GENUS AND SPECIES OF VESPERTILIONINE BAT FROM EAST AFRICA. Oldfield Thomas. Ann. and Mag. Nat. Hist. (7), vol.7, no.41, pp.460-462, May, 1901.

ON SOME SPECIMENS OF GLAUCONYCTERIS FROM THE CAMEROONS. Oldfield Thomas. Ann. and Mag. Nat. Hist. (8), vol.11, no.61, pp.144-145, Jan., 1913.

Age, Longevity

A FURTHER NOTE ON THE LONGEVITY OF THE BIG BROWN BAT. A. W. F. Banfield. Jour. Mam., vol.31, no.4, p.455, Nov.21, 1950.

LONGEVITY OF THE BIG BROWN BAT. A. W. F. Banfield. Jour. Mam., vol.29, no.4, p.418, Dec.31, 1948.

NOTES ON BANDED BATS. Roger W. Barbour. Jour. Mam., vol.31, no.3, p.350, Aug.21, 1950.

NOTES ON LONGEVITY IN MYOTIS LUCIFUGUS LUCIFUGUS. Fred R. Cagle. Jour. Mam., vol.26, no.3, p.307, Aug., 1945.

LONGEVITY IN THE LITTLE BROWN BAT, MYOTIS LUCIFUGUS LUCIFUGUS. E. Lendell Cockrum. Jour. Mam., vol.30, no. 4, pp.433-434, Nov.17, 1949.

LONGEVITY IN THE PIPISTRELLE, PIPISTELLUS SUBFLAVUS SUBFLAVUS. E. Lendell Cockrum. Jour. Mam., vol.33, no. 4, pp.491-492, Nov.19, 1952.

(FINDINGS REACHED THROUGH THE USE OF RINGING METHODS REGARDING LIFE SPAN AND ANNUAL LOSS FIGURES IN THE CASE OF MYOTIS MYOTIS BORKH.) Die mit Hilfe der Beringungsmethode erzielten Ergebnisse ueber Lebensdauer und jaehrliche Verlustziffern bei Myotis myotis Borkh. M. Eisentraut. Experientia, 3:157, 1947.

Anatomy

ABNORMALITY IN DENTITION OF MYOTIS LUCIFUGUS. W. Gene Frum. Jour. Mam., vol.27, no.2, p.176, May 14, 1946.

(CONTRIBUTION TO THE MORPHOLOGICAL STUDY OF THE UMBILICAL VESICLE IN CHIROPTERS (VESPERUGO NOCTULA SCHREIB).) Contribution à l'Etude Morphologique de la vésicule ombilicale chez les Cheiroptères (Vesperugo noctula Schreib). P. Gerard. Archives de Biologie, vol.38, pp.203-217, 9 figs., 1 pl., 1928.

A CYTOLOGICAL STUDY OF THE OVARIES OF THE BATS MYOTIS LUCIFUGUS LUCIFUGUS AND MYOTIS GRISESCENS. Mary Jane Guthrie, Katharine Rosetta Jeffers. Jour. Morph., vol.62, no.3, pp.523-557, figs.6, pls.1-4, May, 1938.

GROWTH OF FOLICLES IN THE OVARIES OF THE BAT MYOTIS LUCIFUGUS LUCIFUGUS. Mary Jane Guthrie, Katharine Rosetta Jeffers. Anat. Rec., vol.71, no.4, pp.477-496, figs.5, table 1, Aug.25, 1938.

THE OVARIES OF THE BAT MYOTIS LUCIFUGUS LUCIFUGUS AFTER INJECTION OF HYPOPHYSEAL EXTRACT. Mary Jane Guthrie, Katharine Rosetta Jeffers. Anat. Rec., vol.72, no.1, pp.11-36, figs.6, tables 4, Sept.25, 1938.

CERTAIN OSTEOLOGICAL FEATURES OF EUDERMA MACULATUM. E. Raymond Hall. Jour. Mam., vol.15, no.1, pp.68-70, Feb.15, 1934.

THE BACULA OF SOME NORTH AMERICAN VESPERTILIONID BATS. W. J. Hamilton, Jr. Jour. Mam., vol.30, no.2, pp.97-102, May 23, 1949.

THE CYTOLOGY OF THE MAMMARY GLAND OF THE BAT MYOTIS GRISESCENS. Katharine R. Jeffers. Amer. Jour. Anat., Philadelphia, vol.67, no.1, pp.1-18, pl.1, July 15, 1940.

(SOME MORPHOLOGICAL PECULIARITIES IN COMMON MYOTIS MYOTIS (BORKHAUSEN) 1797, FROM MORAVIA.) Některé morfologické zajimavosti u netopýrců obecných Myotis myotis (Borkhausen) 1797 z Moravy. Karel Kostroň. Zvláštní otisk z Čas Vlast. spolku musejniho v Olomouci, vol.58, pp.1-9, figs.3, 1949.

(ON THE PRESENCE OF A SPECIAL BUCCAL EPITHELIAL FORMATION IN PIPISTRELLUS.) Sulla presenza in Pipistrellus di una speciale formazione epiteliale buccale. Benedetto Lanza. Mon. Zool. Italiano, vol.63, no.4, pp.285-292, 1956.

THE DEVELOPMENT OF THE CEREBELLUM IN THE BAT (CORYNORHINUS SP.) AND CERTAIN OTHER MAMMALS. O. Larsell, Robert S. Dow. Jour. Comp. Neurol., vol.62, no.2, pp.443-463, pls. 3, figs.5, Oct., 1935.

(DECIDUOUS DENTITION IN NYCTALUS LEISLERI KUEHL.) La dentition de lait chez Nyctalus Leisleri (Kuehl). L. Harrison Mathews. Mammalia, vol.14, no. 1-2, pp.12-13, figs.2, Mar.-June, 1950.

(STUDIES OF THE DEVELOPMENT OF THE FEMALE GENITAL TRACT IN MAMMALS. IV. THE DEVELOPMENT OF THE VAGINA AND THE SINUS UROGENITALIS IN PIPISTRELLUS TRALATITIUS.) Studien ueber die Entwicklung des weiblichen Genitaltractus bei den Saeugern. IV. Die Entwicklung der Vagina und des Sinus urogenitalis beim Pipistrellus tralatitius. W. A. Mijsberg. Zeitschr. f. Anat. u. Entwicklungs., vol. 96, pp.183-214, figs.15, 1931.

THE HEMORRHAGIC AND HEMOPOIETIC NODULES IN THE ALAR AND INTERFEMORAL MEMBRANES OF PIZONYX VIVESI (CHIROPTERA). W. B. Quay, W. G. Reeder. Jour. Morphol., Philadelphia, vol.94, no.3, pp.439-472, May, 1954.

THE DECIDUOUS DENTITION OF THE FISH-EATING BAT, PIZONYX VIVESI. William G. Reeder. Occas. Papers Mus. Zool. Univ. Michigan, Ann Arbor, no.545, pp.3, pl.1, Mar.25, 1953.

THE CYTOLOGY OF THE HYPOPHYSIS CEREBRI OF THE BAT. Elizabeth L. Sawyer. Jour. Morph., vol.60, no.1, pp. 127-151, 2 figs., Dec.5, 1936.

CYTOCHEMICAL AND HISTOPHYSIOLOGICAL OBSERVATIONS ON THE BASOPHILS OF THE ANTERIOR PITUITARY OF THE BAT MYOTIS LUCIFUGUS LUCIFUGUS. J. H. Siegel. Jour. Morphol., Philadelphia, vol.96, no.2, pp.223-264, Mar., 1955.

THE REPRODUCTIVE ORGANS OF FEMALE BATS (MYOTIS MYOTIS) FOLLOWING ADMINISTRATION OF LARGE DOSES OF GONADOTROPHINS DURING THE HIBERNATION PERIOD. J. W. Sluiter, L. Bels, G. J. van Oordt. Acta endocrinol. 9, 258-270, 1952.

AN ABNORMAL EAR IN LASIONYCTERIS NOCTIVAGANS. LeRoy C. Stegeman. Jour. Mam., vol.14, no.4, p.366, Nov., 1933.

TOOTH DEVELOPMENT AND WEAR IN MYOTIS. LeRoy C. Stegeman. Jour. Mam., 37 (1): 58-63, illus., Feb.28, 1956.

THE EFFECT OF TEMPERATURE CHANGES AND ADRENALECTOMY ON THE LIVER GLYCOGEN OF THE HIBERNATING LITTLE BROWN BAT. J. Robert Troyer. Anat. Record, Philadelphia, 27 (2): 378-379, Feb., 1957.

OBSERVATIONS ON THE STRUCTURE OF THE GUSTATORY ORGANS OF THE BAT VESPERTILIO SUBULATUS. Frederick Tuckerman. Jour. Morph., vol.2, no.1, pp.1-6, pl.1, July, 1888.

AN ANALYSIS OF IMPLANTATION IN THE BAT, MYOTIS LUCIFUGUS LUCIFUGUS. William A. Wimsatt. Amer. Jour. Anat., Philadelphia, vol.74, no.3, pp.355-411, pls. 1-7, May, 1944.

THE NATURE AND DISTRIBUTION OF LIPOIDS IN THE PLACENTA OF THE BAT MYOTIS LUCIFUGUS LUCIFUGUS, WITH OBSERVATIONS ON THE MITOCHONDRIA AND GOLGI APPARATUS. William A. Wimsatt. Amer. Jour. Anat., Philadelphia, vol.82, no.3, pp.393-468, pls.1-7, May, 1948.

THE PLACENTATION OF A VESPERTILIONID BAT, MYOTIS LUCIFUGUS LUCIFUGUS. William A. Wimsatt. Amer. Jour. Anat., Philadelphia, vol.77, no.1, pp.1-51, figs.1-2, pls.1-7, July, 1945.

THE UNIQUE MATURATION RESPONSE OF THE GRAAFIAN FOLLICLES OF HIBERNATING VESPERTILIONID BATS AND THE QUESTION OF ITS SIGNIFICANCE. William A. Wimsatt, Frank C. Kallen. Anat. Rec., Philadelphia, 129 (1): 115-131, Sept., 1957.

Antilles

THE RED BAT IN BERMUDA. Glover M. Allen. Jour. Mam., vol.4, no.1, p.61, Feb., 1923.

DASYPTERUS INTERMEDIUS H. ALLEN IN CUBA. L. F. de Beaufort. Jour. Mam., vol.15, no.4, p.316, Nov., 1934.

A NEW BAT FROM PUERTO RICO. Hartley H. T. Jackson. Proc. Biol. Soc. Wash., vol.29, pp.37-38, Feb.24, 1916.

THE RED BATS OF THE GREATER ANTILLES. Gerrit S. Miller, Jr. Jour. Mam., Baltimore, vol.12, no.4, pp.409-410, Nov.11, 1931.

THE SYSTEMATIC NAME OF THE CUBAN RED BAT. Gerrit S. Miller, Jr. Proc. Biol. Soc., Washington, vol.8, p.155, June 13, 1900.

A NEW EPTESICUS FROM JAMAICA. H. Harold Shamel. Proc. Biol. Soc. Washington, vol.58, pp.107-110, July 18, 1945.

DETERMINATION OF VESPERUGO VAGANS DOBSON FROM BERMUDA. Oldfield Thomas. Proc. Biol. Soc. Washington, vol.28, p.69, Mar.12, 1915.

Asia

ON A HABITAT OF MINIOPTERUS SCHREIBERSII JAPONIAE IN NARA PREF. Ikkan Akita. Trans. Mam. Soc. Japan, no.9, pp. 76-77, Apr., 1954.

MATERIALS ON THE BAT FAUNA OF TURKESTAN (RUSSIAN TURKESTAN WITH THE REGIONS OF SEMIRETCHIE AND OF TRANSCASPIA, KHIVA AND BOUCHARA). N. A. Bobrinskoy. Bull. Soc. Nat. Moscow, sect. biol., year 1925, new ser., vol.34, pp.330-374, 1925.

MINIOPTERUS MEDIUS IN THE MALAY PENINSULA. F. N. Chasen. Jour. Royal Asiatic Soc., Malayan Branch, vol.4, pt.1, p.156, July, 1926.

MYOTIS LUCIFUGUS IN KAMCHATKA. Walter L. Hahn. Proc. Biol. Soc. Washington, vol.18, p.254, Dec.9, 1905.

OBSERVATIONS ON TWO SPECIES OF BATS, FROM MADRAS, ONE OF THEM NEW, PRESENTED BY MR. HEATH. T. Horsfield. Proc. Comm. Sci. and Corres. Zool. Soc. London, pt.1, p.113, 1830-1831.

SYSTEMATIC NOTES ON THE KOREAN AND JAPANESE BATS OF PIPISTRELLUS SAVII GROUP. Yoshinori Imaizumi. Bull. Nat. Sci. Mus., Tokyo, vol.2, no.2, pp. 52-63, pls.8-9, Sept., 1955.

TAXONOMIC STUDIES ON JAPANESE MYOTIS WITH DESCRIPTIONS OF THREE NEW FORMS (MAMMALIA: CHIROPTERA). Yoshinori Imaizumi. Bull. Nat. Sci. Mus. Tokyo, n.s., vol.1, no.1 (no.34), pp.40-58, Mar., 1954.

NOTE ON A JAPANESE BAT MURINA HILGENDORFI (PETERS, 1880). Kyukichi Kishida. Zool. Mag., Tokyo, vol.53, no. 12, pp.585-586, 1941.

MURINA USSURIENAIS OBTAINED IN PROV. KAI HONDO, IN DECEMBER. N. Kuroda. Reprint from Botany and Zoology, vol.3, no. 2, pp.103-104, 1935.

FOUR NEW SPECIES OF BATS (VESPERTILIONIDAE) FROM KOREA. T. Mori. Annotat. Zool. Japonenses, Tokyo, vol.11, no.4, pp.389-395, Dec.20, 1928.

ON THE COREAN BATS. T. Mori. The Zool. Soc. of Japan, Tokyo, pp.284-303, pl.3, 1928.

A NOTE ON THE DISCOVERY OF PIPISTRELLUS MORDAX (PETERS) THE GRIZZLED BAT IN CEYLON. W. A. A. Phillips. Jour. Bombay Nat. Hist. Soc., vol.38, no.1, p.177, Aug.15, 1935.

A NEPAL RECORD OF THE LONG-EARED BAT (PLECOTUS HOMOCHROUS HODGSON). Colin Campbell Sanborn. Nat. Hist. Misc., Chicago Acad. Sci., no.69, pp.1-2, Oct.18, 1950.

REMARKS ON A JAPANESE BAT, VESPERTILIO MACRODACTYLUS TEMMINCK. Colin Campbell Sanborn. Nat. Hist. Misc., Chicago Acad. Sci., no.118, pp.1-3, Mar. 13, 1953.

A NEW MYOTIS FROM FORMOSA. H. Harold Shamel. Jour. Mam., vol.25, no. 2, pp.191-192, May, 1944.

A NEW MYOTIS FROM MANCHURIA. H. Harold Shamel. Proc. Biol. Soc. Washington, vol.55, pp.103-104, Aug.13, 1942.

DESCRIPTION OF A NEW SPECIES OF VESPERTILIO FROM CHINA. Oldfield Thomas. Ann. and Mag. Nat. Hist. (6), vol.14, pp.300-301, Oct., 1894.

A NEW LONG-EARED BAT FROM CENTRAL ASIA. Oldfield Thomas. Ann. and Mag. Nat. Hist., ser.9, vol.18, pp. 306-307, Sept., 1926.

A NEW MYOTIS FROM LADAK. Oldfield Thomas. Ann. and Mag. Nat. Hist., ser. 9, vol.17, pp. 609-610, May, 1926.

SCIENTIFIC RESULTS FROM THE MAMMAL SURVEY. XIV. (A) A NEW BAT OF THE GENUS MURINA FROM DARJILING. Oldfield Thomas. Jour. Bombay Nat. Hist. Soc., vol.24, pp.639-640, Oct.25, 1916.

SCIENTIFIC RESULTS FROM THE MAMMAL SURVEY. X. THE INDIAN BATS ASSIGNED TO THE GENUS MYOTIS. Oldfield Thomas. Jour. Bombay Nat. Hist. Soc., vol.23, pp.607-613a, May 25, 1915.

SCIENTIFIC RESULTS FROM THE MAMMAL SURVEY. XI. A. ON PIPISTRELS OF THE GENERA PIPISTRELLUS AND SCOTOZOUS. Oldfield Thomas. Jour. Bombay Nat. Hist. Soc., vol.24, pp.29-36, Sept. 30, 1915.

SCIENTIFIC RESULTS OF THE MAMMAL SURVEY. IX. A NEW PIPISTRELLE BAT FROM TENASSERIM. Oldfield Thomas. Jour. Bombay Nat. Hist. Soc., vol.23, pp. 413-416, Feb.2, 1915.

SCIENTIFIC RESULTS FROM THE MAMMAL SURVEY. NO.XXIII. A NEW BAT OF THE GENUS MYOTIS FROM SIKKIM. Oldfield Thomas. Jour. Bombay Nat. Hist. Soc., vol.27, no.2, pp.248-249, Dec.20, 1920.

SCIENTIFIC RESULTS FROM THE MAMMAL SURVEY. XXVII. THE GEOGRAPHICAL RACES OF SCOTOMANES ORNATUS. Oldfield Thomas. Jour. Bombay Nat. Hist. Soc., vol.27, pp.772-773, 1921.

SCIENTIFIC RESULTS FROM THE MAMMAL SURVEY. NO.XLI. ON THE FORMS CONTAINED IN THE GENUS HARPIOCEPHALUS. Oldfield Thomas. Jour. Bombay Nat. Hist. Soc., vol.29, no.1, pp.88-89, Apr.20, 1923.

A SPECIAL GENUS FOR THE HIMALAYAN BAT KNOWN AS MURINA GRISEA. Oldfield Thomas. Ann. and Mag. Nat. Hist. (8), vol.16, no.94, pp.309-310, Oct., 1915.

A NEW SPECIES OF KERIVOULA FROM N.W. MYSORE. R. G. Wroughton, Kathleen V. Ryley. Jour. Bombay Nat. Hist. Soc., vol.22, no.1, pp.14-15, Apr. 21, 1913.

SCIENTIFIC RESULTS FROM THE MAMMAL SURVEY. A NEW SPECIES OF MYOTIS FROM KANARA. R. C. Wroughton, Kathleen V. Ryley. Jour. Bombay Nat. Hist. Soc., vol.22, no.1, pp.13-14, Apr. 21, 1913.

Australia and Pacific Islands

A SECOND RECORD OF BALSTON'S BROAD-NOSED BAT IN SOUTH AUSTRALIA. E. F. Boehm. South Australian Nat., Adelaide, vol.21, no.1, p.4, May 31, 1941.

DESCRIPTION OF A NEW BAT FROM JAVA, OF THE GENUS KERIVOULA. Oldfield Thomas. Ann. and Mag. Nat. Hist. (5), vol.5, no.30, pp.472-473, June 1880.

A NEW BAT OF THE GENUS MINIOPTERUS FROM N. AUSTRALIA. Oldfield Thomas. Ann. and Mag. Nat. Hist., ser.9, vol.10, pp.616-617, Dec., 1922.

A NEW SCOTEINUS FROM QUEENSLAND. Oldfield Thomas. Ann. and Mag. Nat. Hist., ser.9, vol.13, p.540, May, 1924.

ON A NEW GENUS OF VESPERTILIONINE BAT FROM NEW GUINEA. Oldfield Thomas. Ann. and Mag. Nat. Hist. (7), vol.9, no.51, pp.220-222, Mar., 1902.

A NEW GENUS AND SPECIES OF BAT (KERIVOULINAE) FROM THE SOLOMONS, WITH A REVIEW OF THE GENERA OF THE SUB-FAMILY. Ellis Le G. Troughton. Records Australian Mus., vol.17, no.2, pp. 85-99, June 26, 1929.

NOTES ON AUSTRALIAN BATS, AND THE OCCURRENCE OF CHALINOLOBUS GOULDII, GRAY AT NORFOLK ISLAND. Ellis Le G. Troughton. Australian Zool., vol.3, pt.1, pp.39-41, Sept.15, 1922.

Banding

BANDING AS AN AID IN STUDYING THE ACTIVITIES OF THE LITTLE BROWN BAT, MYOTIS LUCIFUGUS LUCIFUGUS. Harold B. Hitchcock. Papers Michigan Acad. Sci., Arts and Letters, vol.29 (1943), pp.277-279, 1944.

KEEPING TRACK OF BATS. Harold B. Hitchcock. Canadian Field-Naturalist, Ottawa, vol.54, no.4, pp.55-56, Apr., 1940.

Diseases, Parasites

A BEDBUG ON A LITTLE BROWN BAT. A. W. F. Banfield. Canadian Field-Nat., Ottawa, vol.62, no.4, p.126, July-Aug., 1948.

A NEW SPECIES OF TREMATODE FROM NYCTICEIUS PALLIDUS, WITH A KEY TO THE SPECIES OF LECITHODENDRIUM. G. D. Bhalerao. Ann. and Mag. Nat. Hist., ser.9, vol.18, pp.299-304, 1 fig., Sept., 1926.

A NEW TREMATODE (ACANTHATRIUM NYCTERIDIS) NOV. GEN. NOV. SPEC., FROM THE LITTLE BROWN BAT. Ernest Carroll Faust. Trans. Amer. Micr. Soc., vol.38, pp.209-215, 1 pl., July (Oct.), 1919.

A NEW CESTODE FROM A BAT. S. L. Loewen. Trans. Kansas Acad. Sci., vol. 37, pp.257-258, pl.7, 1934.

PARASITES IN CERTAIN OREGON BATS WITH DESCRIPTION OF A NEW CESTODE, HYMENOLEPIS GERTSCHI. Ralph W. Macy. Am. Midland Nat. 37 (2): 375-378, Mar., 1947.

TWO TREMATODES FROM A HIBERNATING BAT, MYOTIS CALIFORNICUS. H. W. Manter, Jeanette Smith Debus. Studies Zool. Lab. Univ. Nebraska, Lincoln, no.223, pp. 297-299, illus, 1945; Trans. American Microscopical Soc., Manhattan, vol.64, no.4, pp.297-299, Oct., 1945.

TRANSMISSION OF A STRAIN OF RABIES VIRUS TO THE LARGE BROWN BAT (EPTESICUS FUSCUS) AND TO THE CAVE BAT (MYOTIS LUCIFUGUS). R. L. Reagan, A. L. Brueckner. Cornell Vet. 41 (3): 295-298, July, 1951.

(DISCOVERY OF TRYPANOSOMES IN BATS IN VILLA ANA (SANTA FE).) Hallazgo de Tripanosomas de Murciélagos en Villa Ana (Santa Fe). Cecilio Romana. Novena Reunión Soc. Argentina de Patalogia Regional Filiales y Afiliadas, Buenos Aires, vol.1, pp.232-234, 1936.

A NEW SPECIES OF PROSTHODENDRIUM FROM THE LARGE BROWN BAT. Aaron Seamster, A. L. Stevens. Jour. Parasitol., Lancaster, vol.34, no.2, pp.108-110, Apr., 1948.

SOME PARASITES OF THE HOARY BAT LASIURUS CINEREUS (BEAUVOIS). Francis G. Tromba. Jour. Mam., vol.35, no.2, pp.253-254, May 26, 1954.

A NEW LOCALITY FOR TRYPANOSOMA VESPERTILIONIS (T. CRUZI?) FROM BATS IN THE UNITED STATES. Sherwin F. Wood. Jour. Parasitol., Lancaster, vol. 29, no.5, p.363, Oct., 1943.

Europe

(NOTE ON A NEW BAT FOR THE CANTON OF NEUCHATEL: MYOTIS BECHSTEINII (KUHL).) Note sur une chauve-souris nouvelle pour le Canton de Neuchatel: Myotis bechsteinii (Kuhl). Villy Aellen. Bull. Soc. Neuchateloise Sci. Nat., vol.76, pp. 93-97, 1953.

(ON A NEW LOCALITY OF NYCTALUS SICULUS PALUMBO (CHIROPTERA) IN THE USSR.) Sur une localité nouvelle du Nyctalus siculus Palumbo (Chiroptera) dans l' URSS. A. I. Argiropulo. Ann. Mus. Zool. Acad. Sci., URSS., pp.131-132, 1929.

(ON THE ECOLOGY AND DISTRIBUTION OF THE BICOLORED BAT (VESPERTILIO DISCOLOR NATTERER) IN AUSTRIA.) Zu Oekologie und Verbreitung der Zweifarbigen Fledermaus (Vespertilio discolor Natterer) in Oesterreich. Kurt Bauer. Zool. Anzeiger, Leipzig, vol.152, nos.11-12, pp.274-279, June, 1954.

BECHSTEIN'S BAT IN SHROPSHIRE. M. Blackmore. Oryx, vol.2, no.3, pp.196-197, Nov., 1953.

AN OCCURRENCE OF THE MOUSE-EARED BAT MYOTIS MYOTIS (BORKHAUSEN) IN ENGLAND. M. Blackmore. Proc. Zool. Soc. Lond., 127 (2): 201-203, pl.1, Oct.29, 1956.

(CONTRIBUTION TO STUDY OF PIPISTRELLUS PIPISTRELLUS SCHREBER AND PIPISTRELLUS KUEHLI NATT. IN WESTERN FRANCE.) Contribution à l'étude des Pipistrelles communes (Pipistrellus pipistrellus Schreber) et des Pipistrelles de Kuehl (Pipistrellus Kuehli Natt.) dans l'Ouest de las France. A. Brosset. Mammalia, Paris, vol.15, no.4, pp.152-156, Dec., 1951.

AN OCCURRENCE OF LEISLER'S BAT IN ESSEX. Kenneth F. Burtsal. Naturalist, London, no.832, pp.19-20, Jan.-Mar., 1950.

(MYOTIS NATTERERI KUHL IN CANTAL.) Myotis nattereri Kuhl dans le Cantal. P. Cantuel. Mammalia, Paris, vol.15, no.4, pp.210-211, Dec., 1951.

(MIMIOPTERUS SCHREIBERSI (NATTERER) IN THE LOIR-ET-CHER.) Mimiopterus Schreibersi (Natterer) dans le Loire-et Cher. B. Caubere. Mammalia, Paris, vol.16, no.4, pp.257-258, Dec., 1952.

(A CHIROPTER NEW TO FRENCH FAUNA: NYCTALUS MAXIMUS (FATIO) REPRESENTED IN THE MUSEUM COLLECTIONS.) Un Chéiroptère nouveau pour la faune française: Nyctalus maximus (Fatio), représenté dans les collections du Muséum. H. Heim de Balsac. Bull. Mus. Nat. Hist. Nat., Paris, ser.2, vol.4, no.2, pp.162-164, Feb., 1932.

THE NOCTULE AND SEROTINE BATS IN KENT. George Dowker. The Zoologist, London, vol.15, no.176, pp.305-306, Aug., 1891.

THE WHISKERED BAT (VESPERTILIO MYSTACINUS LEISL.) IN EAST LOTHIAN. William Evans. Ann. Scottish Nat. Hist., Edinburgh, no.7, p.146, pl.1, July, 1893.

(NOTES ON THE MAMMALS. XXIV. REMARKS CONCERNING THE MYOTIS WELWITSCHI (GRAY).) Notes sur les mammifères. XXIV. Remarque concernant le Myotis welwitschi (Gray). Serge Frechkop. Bull. Mus. Roy. Hist. Nat. Belgique, Bruxelles, vol.15, no.29, pp.3, May, 1939.

(THE FINDING OF THE BAT MYOTIS OXYGNATHUS MONTICALLI 1885 IN CZECHOSLOVAKIA.) Nález netopýra Myotis oxygnathus Monticelli 1885 na území Csr. J. Gaisler, V. Hanak. Acta Soc. Zool. Bohemoslovenicae, vol.20, no. 4, pp.364-365, illus., 1956.

AN EXTENSION OF THE DISTRIBUTION OF LEISLER'S BAT (NYCTALUS LEISLERI KUHL.) IN GREAT BRITAIN. David L. Harrison. Naturalist, London, no.819, pp. 147-148, Oct.-Dec., 1946.

AN OCCURRENCE OF SAVI'S PIPISTRELLE (PIPISTRELLUS SAVII BONAPARTE) IN THE FRENCH PYRENEES, WITH NOTES ON THE BATS OF FABIAN. David L. Harrison. Ann. and Mag. Nat. Hist., London, ser.12, vol.2, no.24, pp.962-964, Dec.14, 1949.

(THE VESPERTILION (NATTERER MYOTIS NATTERERI KUHL), WITH THE GARD.) Le Vespertilion de natterer Myotis Nattereri (kuhl), dans le Gard. Albert Hugues. Rev. Franc Mamm., vol.1, no.1, pp.42-43, Dec.7, 1927.

(DATA ON THE EMARGINATE BAT, MYOTIS EMARGINATUS GEOFFROY, IN CENTRAL EUROPE.) Zur Kenntnis der gewimperten Fledermaus, Myotis emarginatus (Geoffroy), in Mitteleuropa. Willi Issel. Bonner Zool. Beitraege, Bonn, vol. 1, no.1, pp.2-10, Aug., 1950.

THE DISTINCTIVE CHARACTERS OF TWO BRITISH SPECIES OF PLECOTUS, SUPPOSED TO HAVE BEEN CONFOUNDED UNDER THE NAME OF LONG-EARED BAT. Leonard Jenyns. Trans. Linn. Soc. London, vol.16, pp.53-60, pl.1, 1833.

(EPTESICUS SEROTINUS, A NEW BAT FOR CORSICA.) Eptesicus serotinus, Chauve-souris nouvelle pour la Corse. Herman Kahmann. Mammalia, Paris, vol.19, no.4, pp.459-463, Dec., 1955.

(PROOF OF THE BAT BARBASTELLA BARBASTELLUS SCHREBER 1774 ON THE ISLAND OF SICILY.) Der Nachweis der Fledermaus Barbastella barbastellus, Schreber 1774 auf der Insel Sizilien. Herman Kahmann. Zool. Anzeiger, 158 (7-8): 139-143, Apr., 1957.

(DISTRIBUTION OF THE BROWN BAT, NYCTALUS NOCTULA SCHREBER 1774, ON THE TYRRHENIAN ISLANDS AND SICILY.) Die Verbreitung des Abendseglers, Nyctalus noctula (Schreber, 1774), auf den Tyrrhenischen Inseln and Sizilien. Herman Kahmann, Helmut Altner. Saeugetierk Mitteil, 5 (3): 120-121, Aug.1, 1957.

(THE EMARGINATE BAT (MYOTIS EMARGINATUS GEOFFROY 1806)--ALSO IN THE PALATINATE.) Die Wimperfledermaus Myotis emarginatus (Geoffroy, 1806), auch in der Pfalz. Claus Koenig, August Epple. Saeugetierk. Mitteil., 5 (3): 123-124, Aug.1, 1957.

(MYOTIS EMARGINATUS GEOFFROY CHIROPTERA VESPERTILIONIDAE) A NEW BAT IN POLISH FAUNA.) Nocek orze Myotis emarginatus Geoffroy (Chiroptera, Vespertilionidae) nowy ssak dla fauny Polski. Kazimierz Kowalski. Fragmenta Faunistica Mus. Zool. Polonici, Warsaw, vol.6, no.9, pp.165-167, June 8, 1951.

(ON SOME CHIROPTERA OF THE BALKAN PENINSULA. PRESENCE OF "EPTESICUS NILSSONI NILSSONI" (KEYSERLING AND BLASIUS, 1839) IN JUGOSLAVIA.) Su alcuni chirotteri della Penisola Balcanica. Presenza di "Eptesicus nilssoni nilssoni" (Keyserling e Blasius, 1839), in Jugoslavia. Bendetto Lanza. Monitore Zool. Italianio, 65 (1-2): 3-6, Sept., 1957.

(THE EXISTENCE IN FRANCE OF NYCTALUS LEISLERI KUHL.) A propos de la présence en France du Vespérien de Leisler (Nyctalus leisleri Kuhl). P. Laurent. Bull. Mus. Nat. Hist. Nat., Paris, ser.2, vol.10, no.5, pp.482-484, June, 1938.

DESCRIPTION OF THE VESPERTILIO PYGMAEUS, A NEW SPECIES, RECENTLY DISCOVERED IN DEVONSHIRE BY DR. LEACH. William E. Leach. Zool. Jour., vol.1, pp.559-561, pl.22, 1825.

A NEW HERTFORDSHIRE MAMMAL: NATTERER'S BAT. Bertram Lloyd. Trans. Hertfordshire Nat. Hist. Soc. and Field Club, Hertford, vol.21, pt.5, p.316, Feb., 1942.

LONG-EARED BAT IN ORKNEY. James G. Marwick. Scottish Naturalist, 1931, no.189, pp.88-89, May-June, 1931.

THE SYSTEMATIC NAME OF THE LARGE NOCTULE BAT OF EUROPE. Gerrit S. Miller, Jr. Proc. Biol. Soc., Washington, vol.8, p.156, June 13, 1900.

SEROTINE BAT, VESPERTILIO SEROTINUS SCHREBER, HERTFORDSHIRE. Charles Oldham. Trans. Hertfordshire Nat. Hist. Soc. and Field Club, vol.18, no.4, p.194, Apr., 1929.

(THE BARBASTELLE BAT--A BAT NEW TO THE UKRAINE (BARBASTELLA BARBASTELLA SCHREB.).) Eine fuer Ukraine neue Fledermaus--Breitohr (Barbastella barbastella Schreb). I. G. Pidoplitshka. Trav. Mus. Zool., Kiev, vol.3, pp.61-63, fig.1, 1927.

(THE ALPINE BAT--PREVIOUSLY UNKNOWN IN GERMANY.) Die Alpenfledermaus bisher nicht fuer Deutschland nachgewiesen. Helmut Richter. Zeitschr. Saeugetierk., Berlin, 21 (3-4): 195, Feb.28, 1957.

A LONG FLIGHT--THE EUROPEAN PARTI-COLOURED BAT (VESPERTILIO MURINUS) IN SCOTLAND. James Ritchie. Scottish Nat., no.166, pp.101-103, July-Aug., 1927.

(ABOUT THE FRENCH NOCTULES.) A propos des noctules de France. P. Rode. Bull. Mus. Nat. Hist. Nat., Paris, ser.2, vol.4, no.5, pp.222-227, Apr., 1932.

LEISLER'S BAT IN CO. MAYO. Robert F. Ruttledge. Irish Naturalist's Jour., Belfast, vol.9, no.11, pp.307-308, July, 1949.

DISTRIBUTION AND DECLINE OF BAT POPULATIONS IN S. LIMBURG FROM 1942 TILL 1957. J. W. Sluiter, P. F. van Heerdt. Overdruk uit het Natuurhistorisch Maanblad, 46e Jrg. no.11-12, 31-12-1957.

(NEW FINDS IN THE USSR OF MYOTIS BECHSTEINII KUEHL, MAMMALIA, CHIROPTERA.) Novie nakhodki v SSSR dlinnoukhoi nochnitsi (Myotis bechsteinii Kuehl, Mammalia, Chiroptera ). K. A. Tatarinov. Zool. Zhurnal, Moscow, vol. 32, no.6, pp.1276-1280. 1953.

NATTERER'S BAT. A NEW MANX MAMMAL. R. Wagstaffe. Peregrine, vol.1, no.3, p.1, 1945.

(PRESENCE OF A BARBASTELLE BAT IN BRITTANY.) Présence de la barbastelle en Bretange. J. J. Walling. Mammalia, Paris, 21 (4): 455, Dec., 1957.

Flight, Orientation

A NEW HOMING RECORD FOR THE LARGE BROWN BAT (EPTESICUS FUSCUS FUSCUS). Ellas Cohen. Maryland, A journal of natural history, Baltimore, vol.14, no.3, pp.65-67, figs.2, July, 1944.

(EVALUATION OF THE FLIGHT SPEED OF MINIOPTERUS.) Evaluation de la vitesse de vol des miniopteres. Pierre Constant, Bernard Cannonge. Mammalia, Paris, 21 (3): 301-302, Sept., 1957.

(HOW FAST DOES A BAT FLY?) Wie schnell fliegt eine Fledermaus? A. Kolb. Saugetierkundliche Mitteilungen, Band 3, Heft 4, p.176, Oct.1, 1955.

EVENING FLIGHT OF THE PIPISTRELLE BAT. L. C. Lloyd. Trans. Caradoc and Severn Valley Field Club, Shrewsbury, vol. 11, pp.259-264, 1945.

A HOMING RECORD IN THE BAT, MYOTIS LUCIFUGUS LUCIFUGUS. Elizabeth Smith, Kelley Hale. Jour. Mam., vol.34, no.1, p. 122, Feb.19, 1953.

A FLYING LESSON FROM THE BAT: HIGH-SPEED PHOTOGRAPHS OF ZIGZAGS BY "FILMY SHAPES THAT HAUNT THE DUSK." Illus. London News, vol.191, no.5139, pp. 650-651, figs.9, Oct.16, 1937.

Food Habits

FEEDING HABITS OF THE PALLID BAT. A. E. Borell. Jour. Mam., 23 (3): 337, Aug., 1942.

THE FISH-EATING HABITS OF PIZONYX VIVESI (MENEGAUX). William Henry Burt. Jour. Mam., vol.13, no.4, pp.363-365, Nov., 1932.

CARNIVOROUS ACTIVITIES OF BIG BROWN AND PALLID BATS. Carl H. Engler. Jour. Mam., vol.24, no.1, pp.96-97, Feb.20, 1943.

THE INSECT FOOD OF THE BIG BROWN BAT. W. J. Hamilton, Jr. Jour. Mam., vol.14, no.2, pp.155-156, May 15, 1933.

FOOD HABITS OF THE PACIFIC PALLID BAT. Robert T. Hatt. Jour. Mam., vol.4, no.4, pp.260-261, Nov., 1923.

FOOD OF THE CALIFORNIA LEAF-NOSED BAT. Laurence M. Huey. Jour. Mam., vol. 6, no.3, pp.196-197, Aug., 1925.

HUNTING HABITS OF THE BAT, MYOTIS EVOTIS. Lloyd G. Ingles. Jour. Mam., Baltimore, vol.30, no.2, pp.197-198, May 23, 1949.

CARNIVOROUS BEHAVIOR IN THE BIG BROWN BAT. Philip H. Krutzsch. Jour. Mam., vol.31, no.1, p.96, Feb.21, 1950.

(ON THE DIURNAL RHYTHM OF THE HUNTING PERIOD IN THE BEARDED BAT (MYOTIS MYSTACINUS KUHL.) DURING THE SUMMER.) Ueber der Tagesrhythmus der Nahrungsjagdzeit bei der Bartfledermaus Myotis mystacinus Kuhl., waehrend des Sommers. Erik S. Nyholm. Arch. Soc. Zool. Bot. Fennicae "Vanamo," 12 (1): 53-58, 1957.

NOTES ON THE FEEDING HABITS OF THE LITTLE BROWN BAT (MYOTIS LUCIFUGUS). H. H. Pittman. Jour. Mam., vol.5, no.4, pp.231-232, pl.23, Nov., 1924.

(PIPISTRELLUS PIPISTRELLUS BECHST. AND NYCTALUS NOCTULA SCHREB. EAT GLOW-WORMS.) Pipistrellus pipistrellus Bechst. und Nyctalus noctula Schreb. fressen Gluewuermchen. Wilhelm Schreitmueller. Zeitschr. Saeugetierk., Berlin, vol. 17, no.3, pp.151-152, Feb.19, 1953.

FOOD HABITS OF THE SEMINOLE BAT. H. B. Sherman. Jour. Mam., vol.16, no. 3, p.224, Aug., 1935.

Fossils

A NEW GENUS OF BAT FROM THE LATER TERTIARY OF NEVADA. E. Raymond Hall. Univ. Calif. Publ., Bull. Dept. Geol. Sci., vol.19, no.14, pp.319-320, pl.38, Nov.25, 1930.

A NEW PLEISTOCENE BAT (CORYNORHINUS) FROM MEXICO. Charles O. Handley. Jour. Washington Acad. Sci., 45 (2): 48-49, Mar.16, 1955.

A NEW GENUS OF THE FAMILY VESPERTILIONIDAE FROM THE SAN PEDRO PLIOCENE OF ARIZONA. R. A. Stirton. Univ. Calif. Publ., Dept. Geol. Sci., vol.20, no. 4, pp.27-30, figs.2, Apr.21, 1931.

General Habits, Behavior

A RECORD OF THE HOARY BAT FROM A CAVE. James R. Beer. Jour. Mam., vol. 35, no.1, pp.116, Feb.10, 1954.

(BIRDS WARN OF FLYING BATS.) Voegel warnen vor fliegenden Fledermaeusen. Rudolf Berndt. Ornithologische Monatsber., Berlin, Jahrg.48, no.6, pp.192-193, Nov.-Dec., 1940.

CURIOUS BEHAVIOR OF A HOARY BAT. Sherman C. Bishop. Jour. Mam., vol.28, no.3, pp.293-294, Aug.19, 1947.

THE ROOSTING-PLACE OF PIPISTRELLUS HESPERUS. Jack C. von Bloeker, Jr. Jour. Mam., vol.13, no.3, p.273, Aug., 1932.

THE TIMES OF EMERGENCE OF THE PIPISTRELLE. H. F. Church. Proc. Zool. Soc. London, 128 (4): 600-602, July 24, 1957.

ON SOME HABITS OF NATTERER'S BAT. T. A. Coward. The Zoologist, London, ser.4, vol.9, no.98, pp.51-57, Feb.15, 1905.

A WEST VIRGINIA CAVE RECORD FOR THE SILVER-HAIRED BAT. Wayne H. Davis. American Caver Bull. Nat. Speleol. Soc., no.14, p.63, Sept., 1952.

(OBSERVING MYOTIS NATTERERI KUHL IN CAPTIVITY.) Gefangenschaft-Beobachtungen an Myotis nattereri Kuhl. G. Duncker. Zool. Garten, n.F., vol.4, nos. 1-2, pp.17-27, figs.1-4, Feb., 1931.

(OBSERVATIONS ON SOME HABITS OF VESPERTILIO MURINUS L.) Osservazioni sopra alcuni costumi del Vespertilio murinus L. G. B. Ercolani. 1879.

TREE ROOSTING OF THE EASTERN PIPISTRELLE. James S. Findley. Jour. Mam., vol.35, no.3, p.433, Aug.20, 1954.

OBSERVATIONS ON HOARY BATS IN A STORM. Harry H. Goehring. Jour. Mam., 36 (1): 130-131, Feb.25, 1955.

THE FISH-EATING BATS OF THE GULF OF CALIFORNIA. E. W. Gudger. California Fish and Game, San Francisco, vol. 29, no.2, pp.79-81, figs.27-28, Apr., 1943.

BAT VERSUS ANT. Charles O. Handley, Jr. Jour. Mam., 37 (2): 279, June 9, 1956.

DESERT PALLID BATS CAUGHT IN MOUSE TRAPS. Laurence M. Huey. Jour. Mam., vol.17, no.3, pp.285-286, Aug., 1936.

THE BROWN BAT ACTIVE IN WINTER AT WASHINGTON, D.C. Hartley H. T. Jackson. Jour. Mam., vol.3, no.1, p.52, Feb. 8, 1922.

A SUMMER AGGREGATION OF LUMP-NOSED BATS AT LAKE PEND OREILLE, IDAHO. Gardiner F. Jones. Murrelet, Seattle, vol.29, no.3, p.48, Mar.1, 1949.

NOTES ON EPTESICUS FUSCUS. A. Brooker Klugh. Jour. Mam., vol.5, no.1, pp.42-43, Feb., 1924.

(DAILY RHYTHM OF ACTIVITY OF THE BAT "MYOTIS MYOTIS" BORKHAUSEN.) Rytmika dobowa aktywnosci nietoperza "Myotis myotis" Borkhausen. Kazimierz Kowalski. Folia Biologica, vol.3, pt.1, pp. 55-64, 1955.

(PLECOTUS AURITUS L. IN CAPTIVITY.) Plecotus auritus L. in der Gefangenschaft. H. Kummerloewe. Der Zoologische Garten, Leipzig (N.F.), vol.2, pts.4/6, pp.106-113, 1929.

SUMMER ACTIVITIES OF BATS (GENUS LASIURUS) IN IOWA. H. Elliott McClure. Jour. Mam., vol.23, no.4, pp.430-434, fig.1, Nov.14, 1942.

A STUDY OF THE ROOSTING HABITS, AND OF THE ENVIRONMENTAL FACTORS CONCURRENT WITH TIME OF EVENING FLIGHT, OF LITTLE BROWN BATS (MYOTIS LUCIFUGUS) IN NORTHERN LOWER MICHIGAN. Jerome S. Miller. Ph. D. Thesis, U. Mich., 97 pp., 1955.

A CAVE RECORD FOR THE RED BAT, LASIURUS B. BOREALIS. Charles E. Mohr. American Caver, Bull. Nat. Speleol. Soc., no.14, pp.62-63, Sept., 1952.

(PLECOTUS AURITUS L. IN CAPTIVITY.) Plecotus auritus L. in der Gefangenschaft. Erna Mohr. Zeitschr. f. Saeugetierkunde, vol.2, no.1, pp.87-92, Oct.15, 1927.

HOARY BAT SKULL IN AN INDIANA CAVE. Russell E. Mumford. Jour. Mam., vol.34, no.1, p.121, Feb.19, 1953.

WINTER ACTIVITY OF THE BROWN BAT, VESPERTILIO FUSCUS (BEAUVOIS), AT BROOKLYN, N.Y. Robert Cushman Murphy. Science, Lancaster, n.s., vol. 45, no.1170, pp.565-566, June 1, 1917.

(ECOLOGY OF PIPISTRELS: AN INTERESTING POPULATION OBSERVED IN LOIRE-INFÉRIEURE.) Ecologie des Pipistrelles. Une intéressante population observée en Loire-Inférieure. P. L. Niort. Mammalia, Paris, vol.14, nos.1-2, pp.29-36, Mar.-June, 1950.

BEHAVIOUR OF A NEWLY-BORN SILVER-HAIRED BAT. L. T. S. Norris-Elye. Jour. Mam., vol.32, no.2, pp.221-222, May 21, 1951.

UNUSUAL BEHAVIOR AND OCCURRENCE OF A HOARY BAT. Robert T. Orr. Jour. Mam., vol.31, no.4, pp.456-457, Nov.21, 1950.

SWIMMING ABILITY OF THE LITTLE BROWN BAT. Bernard C. Patten, Jr., Marie A. Patten. Jour. Mam., 37 (3): 440-441, Sept.11, 1956.

THE MATERNAL INSTINCT IN THE DWARF PIPISTRELLE, (P. MIMUS MIMUS). W. W. A. Phillips. Jour. Bombay Nat. Hist. Soc., vol.32, pp.211-213, Aug.1, 1927.

OCCURRENCE OF THE RED BAT, LASIURUS BOREALIS, IN CAVES. W. B. Quay, Jerome S. Miller. Jour. Mam., 36 (3): 454-455, Aug.30, 1955.

TWO SILVER-HAIRED BATS, LASIONYCTERIS NOCTIVAGANS, FOUND IN A VIRGINIA CAVE. Nancy Rogers. American Caver, Bull. Nat. Speleol. Soc., no.14, p.63, Sept., 1952.

(DOMESTIC SPARROWS AND PYGMY BATS IN THE SAME BOX.) Haussperlinge und Zwergfledermaeuse in demselben Starkasten. W. Schreitmueller. Zeitschr. f. Saeugetierkunde, Berlin, vol.13, no.2, p. 240, 1939.

A ROVING BAND OF SAY'S BATS. Ernest Thompson Seton. Jour. Mam., vol.3, no.1, p.52, Feb., 1922.

ADJACENT ROOSTS OF EPTESICUS AND MYOTIS. Elizabeth Smith, Woodrow Goodpaster. Jour. Mam., 37 (3): 441-442, Sept. 11, 1956.

WINTER ACTIVITY OF BATS. L. L Snyder. Canadian Field-Nat., vol.38, p.95, May, 1924.

ON THE OCCURRENCE AND HABITS OF VESPERTILIO EMARGINATUS. R. F. Tomes. Proc. Zool. Soc. London, pt.16, pp.112-114, 1848.

HABITAT SELECTION OF CAVERN-DWELLING BATS AS ILLUSTRATED BY FOUR VESPERTILIONIDS. John W. Twente, Jr. Ph. D. Thesis, U. Mich., 163 pp., 1954.

UNUSUAL CONCENTRATION OF HOARY BATS. Terry A. Vaughan. Jour. Mam., vol.34, no.2, p.256, May 14, 1953.

SOME HABITS OF PIPISTRELLE COLONIES. Tom Warwick. Scottish Naturalist, Edinburgh, no.237, pp.68-70, May-June, 1939.

Hawaii

OCCURRENCE AND BEHAVIOR OF THE HAWAIIAN BAT. Paul H. Baldwin. Jour. Mam., vol.31, no.4, pp.455-456, Nov.21, 1950.

NOTICE OF A NEW SPECIES OF LASIURUS SENT FROM THE SANDWICH ISLANDS BY MR. W. H. PEASE. John Edward Gray. Proc. Zool. Soc. London, pt.30, p.143, 1862.

Hibernation

HIBERNATION OF THE BIG BROWN BAT. James R. Beer, A. Glenn Richards. Jour. Mam., 37 (1): 31-41, illus., Feb.28, 1956.

SOME NOTES ON THE HIBERNATION OF LASIONYCTERIS NOCTIVAGANS. I. McTaggart Cowan. The Canadian Field-Nat., vol.47, no.4, pp.74-75, Apr., 1933.

HIBERNATING BATS IN MINNESOTA. Charles A. Evans. Jour. Mam., vol.15, no.3, pp.240-241, Aug., 1934.

PIPISTRELLUS SUBFLAVUS OBSCURUS, MYOTIS KEENII, AND EPTESICUS FUSCUS FUSCUS HIBERNATING IN A STORM SEWER IN CENTRAL MINNESOTA. Harry H. Goehring. Jour. Mam., vol.35, no.3, pp.434-435, Aug.20, 1954.

(ON THE HIBERNATION OF PIPISTRELLUS P. PIPISTRELLUS SCHREBER 1774.) Zur Uberwinterung von Pipistrellus p. pipistrellus (Schreber, 1774). Gisela Haagen, Joachim Arnold. Saeugetierk. Mitteil., Stuttgart, 3 (3): 122, July 1, 1955.

MYOTIS SUBULATUS LEIBII AND OTHER BATS HIBERNATING IN ONTARIO AND QUEBEC. Harold B. Hitchcock. Canadian Field-Nat., Ottawa, vol.55, no.3, p.46, Mar.27, 1941.

PIPISTRELLUS HIBERNATING IN ONTARIO. Harold B. Hitchcock, Keith Reynolds. Canadian Field-Nat., Ottawa, vol.54, no. 6, p.89, Sept., 1940.

(HIBERNATION OF NYCTALUS NOCTULA SCHREB. ON THE BASIS OF OBSERVATIONS AT THE HIBERNATION PLACE.) Der Winterschlaf von Nyctalus noctula Schreb. auf Grund von Beobachtungen am Winterschlafplatz. Hans Loehrl. Zeitschr. Morphol. u Oekol. der Tiere, Berlin, vol. 32, no.1, pp.47-66, figs.3, 1937.

HIBERNATING TEMPERATURE OF THE BAT, MYOTIS CALIFORNICUS PALLIDUS. William G. Reeder. Jour. Mam., Baltimore, vol.30, no.1, pp.51-53, illus., Feb.14, 1949.

THE HIBERNATION OF CERTAIN BATS IN SOUTHERN MINNESOTA. Gustav Swanson, Charles Evans. Jour. Mam., vol.17, no.1, pp.39-43, Feb., 1936.

A NOTE ON EPTESICUS FUSCUS. G. C. Toner. Jour. Mam., vol.16, no.2, p.147, May, 1935.

HIBERNATION OF THE BROWN BAT. Alexander Wetmore. Jour. Mam., vol.17, no.2, pp.130-131, May, 1936.

HIBERNATION OF EPTESICUS FUSCUS IN A NEW HAMPSHIRE BUILDING. R. M. Whelden. Jour. Mam., vol.22, no.2, p. 203, May 14, 1941.

In Captivity

FAMILY PET. C. M. Breeder, Jr. Bull. New York Zool. Soc., vol.43, no.6, pp. 198-200, Fig.1, Nov.-Dec., 1940.

RAISING THE YOUNG OF RED BATS ON AN ARTIFICIAL DIET. W. H. Gates. Jour. Mam., vol.19, no.4, pp.461-464, Nov.14, 1938.

Mexico and Central America

A NEW BAT (GENUS PIPISTRELLUS) FROM NORTHEASTERN MEXICO. Rollin H. Baker. Univ. Kansas Publ., Mus. Nat. Hist., vol.7, no.10, pp.583-586, Nov.15, 1954.

A NEW SPECIES OF BAT (GENUS MYOTIS) FROM COAHUILA, MEXICO. Rollin H. Baker. Proc. Biol. Soc. Washington, vol. 68, pp.165-166, illus., Dec.31, 1955.

A NEW LONG-EARED MYOTIS (MYOTIS-EVOTIS) FROM NORTHEASTERN MEXICO. Rollin H. Baker, Howard J. Stains. Univ. Kansas Publ., Mus. Nat. Hist., vol.9, no. 3, pp.81-84, Dec.10, 1955.

DESCRIPTION OF A SUBSPECIES OF MYOTIS YUMANENSIS FROM BAJA CALIFORNIA, MEXICO. Seth B. Benson. Proc. Biol. Soc. Washington, vol.60, pp.45-46, May 19, 1947.

A NEW BAT (GENUS MYOTIS) FROM MEXICO. Walter W. Dalquest, E. Raymond Hall. Univ. Kansas Publ., Mus. Nat. Hist., Lawrence, vol.1, no.12, pp.237-244, figs. 6, Dec.10, 1947.

PIPISTRELLUS CINNAMOMEUS REDISCOVERED. Walter W. Dalquest, E. Raymond Hall. Jour. Mam., vol.29, no. 2, p.180, May 14, 1948.

THE STATUS OF THE COSTA RICAN RED BAT. E. A. Goldman. Proc. Biol. Soc. Washington, vol.45, p.148, Sept.9, 1932.

EPTESICUS ALBIGULARIS (PETERS) FROM HONDURAS. George G. Goodwin. Amer. Mus. Novitates, New York, no.1199, pp.2, Oct.9, 1942.

A NEW NAME FOR THE MEXICAN RED BAT. E. Raymond Hall. Univ. Kansas Publ., Mus. Nat. Hist., Lawrence, vol.5, no.14, pp.223-226, Dec.15, 1951.

TAXONOMIC NOTES ON MEXICAN BATS OF THE GENUS RHOGEEESSA. E. Raymond Hall. Univ. Kansas Publ., Mus. Nat. Hist., Lawrence, vol.5, no.15, pp. 227-232, Apr.10, 1952.

PIPISTRELLUS CINNAMOMEUS MILLER 1902 REFERRED TO THE GENUS MYOTIS. E. Raymond Hall, Walter W. Dalquest. Univ. Kansas Publ., Mus. Nat. Hist., Lawrence, vol.1, no.25, pp.581-590, figs. 5, Jan.20, 1950.

PIZONYX VIVESI ON ISLA PARTIDA, GULF OF CALIFORNIA. M. E. McLellan. Jour. Mam., vol.8, no.3, p.243, Aug., 1927.

NOTES ON THE MEXICAN BATS OF THE GENUS DASYPTERUS. Gerrit S. Miller, Jr. Proc. Biol. Soc. Washington, vol.24, pp.227-228, Oct.21, 1911.

A BAT (PIPISTRELLUS) FROM HONDURAS. George C. Rinker. Jour. Mam., vol.29, no.2, pp.179-180, May 14, 1948.

(THE SEMINOLA RED-BAT, LASIURUS BORALIS SEMINOLUS (RHOADS), IN MEXICO.) El murciélago colorado de Seminola (Lasiurus borealis seminolus (Rhoads) en México. Bernardo Villa R. Anales Inst. Biol., Mexico, vol.26, no.1, pp.237-238, Sept.26, 1955.

THE FISH BATS OF PESCADORA. Lewis Wayne Walker. Audubon Mag., New York, vol.52, no.5, pp.294-299, illus., Sept.-Oct., 1950.

Migration

ON THE MIGRATION OF THE RED BAT, LASIURUS BOREALIS BOREALIS. T. Donald Carter. Jour. Mam., vol.31, no.3, pp.349-350, Aug.21, 1950.

(NOTES ON THE MIGRATIONS OF BATS (CHIROPTERA, VESPERTILIONIDAE).) Note sur les passages des chauves-souris. (Chiroptera, Vespertilionidae.) A. N. Formozov. Comptes Rendus Acad. Sci. URSS., A. no.17, pp.272-274, 1927.

BATS MIGRATE TOO. Donald R. Griffin. New England Naturalist, Boston, no.5, pp. 1-4, photos 4, Dec., 1939.

MIGRATIONS OF NEW ENGLAND BATS. Donald R. Griffin. Bull. Mus. Comp. Zool., Harvard College, Cambridge, vol.86, no. 6, pp.217-246, figs.3, pls.5, Jan., 1940.

TRAVELS OF BANDED CAVE BATS. Donald R. Griffin. Jour. Mam., 26 (1): 15-23, Feb., 1945.

RED BAT AT SEA. A. K. Haagner. Jour. Mam., vol.2, no.1, p.36, Feb., 1921.

OCEANIC RECORDS OF LASIONYCTERIS NOCTIVAGANS AND LASIURUS BOREALIS. John Mackiewicz, Richard H. Backus. Jour. Mam., 37 (3): 442-443, Sept.11, 1956.

MIGRATION OF BATS ON CAPE COD, MASSACHUSETTS. Gerrit S. Miller, Jr. Science, N.S., vol.5, no.118, pp.541-543, Apr.2, 1897.

MARKING BATS FOR LATER RECOGNITION. Charles E. Mohr. Proc. Pennsylvania Acad. Sci., Harrisburg, vol.8, pp.26-30, fig.1, 1934.

A RED BAT AT SEA. Arthur H. Norton. Jour. Mam., vol.11, no.2, pp.225-226, May, 1930.

MIGRATION RECORDS OF THE RED BAT, LASIURUS BOREALIS. John K. Terres. Jour. Mam., 37 (3): 442, Sept.11, 1956.

BATS ON MIGRATION. (LASIONYCTERIS NOCTIVAGANS AND LASIURUS BOREALIS). Oldfield Thomas. Jour. Mam., vol.2, no. 3, p.167, Aug., 1921.

MIGRATION OF LITTLE BROWN BATS. Fred R. Zimmerman. Jour. Mam., vol. 18, no.3, p.363, Aug.14, 1937.

Pelage, Coloration

A COLOR PATTERN ABERRATION IN PIPISTRELLUS SUBFLAVUS SUBFLAVUS. W. Frank Blair. Jour. Mam., vol.29, no.2, pp.178-179, May 14, 1948.

(ABNORMAL COLORING OF A MINIOPTERUS SCHREIBER.) Coloration anormale chez un minioptere de Schreibers. Jean Dorst. Mammalia, Paris, 21 (2): 191, June, 1957.

A BAT WITH WHITE WING TIPS. Robert Goslin. Jour. Mam., vol.28, no.1, p.62, Feb.15, 1947.

A NOTE ON PATTERN VARIATION IN THE VESPERTILIONID BAT GLAUCONYCTERIS POENSIS (GRAY). R. W. Hayman, T. S. Jones. Ann. and Mag. Nat. Hist., London, ser.12, vol.3, no.33, pp.761-763, Sept., 1950.

SCALE STRUCTURE OF THE HAIR OF THE BAT. J. Manby. Nature, London, vol.132, no.3328, pp.244-245, fig.1, Aug.12, 1933.

PARTIAL ALBINISM IN MYOTIS SODALIS. Brice Metzger. Jour. Mam., 37 (4): 546, Jan.9, 1957.

MELANISTIC PIPISTRELLES. F. L. Osgood. Jour. Mam., vol.17, no.1, p.64, Feb., 1936.

Predators

BLUE JAY ATTACKS RED BATS. Philip F. Allan. Jour. Mam., vol.28, no.2, p.180, May 19, 1947.

THE SCREECH OWL AS PREDATOR ON THE BIG BROWN BAT. James R. Beer. Jour. Mam., vol.34, no.3, p.384, Aug.14, 1953.

FOOD HABITS OF HORNED OWLS IN THE PAHRANAGAT VALLEY, NEVADA. R. M. Bond. Condor, Berkeley, vol.42, no.3, pp. 164-165, May-June, 1940.

PILOT BLACK-SNAKE FEEDING ON THE BIG BROWN BAT. James Silver. Jour. Mam., vol.9, no.2, p.149, May, 1928.

EASTERN SPARROW HAWK FEEDING ON BIG BROWN BAT. Dayton Stoner. Auk, Cambridge, vol.56, no.4, p.474, Oct., 1939.

Reproductive Biology

A HOARY BAT FAMILY. Alfred M. Bailey. Jour. Mam., vol.18, no.4, pp.514-515, Nov., 1937.

(THE LONG-EARED BAT WITH YOUNG.) Langoret flaggermus med unge. Aug Brinkmann. Naturen, Bergen, vol.53, pp. 27-28, illus., Jan., 1929.

OBSERVATIONS ON PREGNANCY IN THE COMMON BAT (PIPISTRELLUS PIPISTRELLUS). R. Deanesly, T. Warwick. Proc. Zool. Soc. London, vol.109, ser.A, pt.1, pp.57-60, May, 1939.

MISCELLANEOUS NOTES. Ned Dearborn. Jour. Mam., vol.27, no.2, p.178, illus., May 14, 1946.

NOTES ON THE YOUNG OF THE RED BAT (NYCTERIS BOREALIS BOREALIS). L. R. Dice. Jour. Mam., vol.8, no.3, pp.243-244, Aug., 1927.

INVESTIGATION OF BIRTH PRODUCTIVITY IN MYOTIS. Charles H. Farr. Oklahoma Acad. Sci., vol.33, pp.29-30, Jan., 1954.

REPRODUCTION IN TWO SPECIES OF MYOTIS IN JACKSON HOLE, WYOMING. James S. Findley. Jour. Mam., vol.35, no.3, p. 434, Aug.20, 1954.

THE LONGEVITY OF SPERM IN THE FEMALE BAT. G. Edgar Folk, Jr. Anat. Record, Philadelphia, vol.76, no.1, pp. 103-108, 1 pl., Jan.25, 1940.

FOUR RED BATS IN ONE LITTER. Doris B. Gates, Jeanne Wolcott. Jour. Mam., vol.27, no.1, pp.84-85, Mar.14, 1946.

NOTES ON THE BIG BROWN BAT. William H. Gates. Jour. Mam., vol.18, no.1, pp. 97-98, Feb.14, 1937.

(OBSERVATION OF A PARTURITION IN MYOTIS EMARGINATUS.) Observation d'une parturition chez Myotis emarginatus. G. Goguyer, M. Gruet. Mammalia, Paris, 21 (2): 97-110, pls.2-4, June, 1957.

STUDIES ON THE EMBRYOLOGY OF MICROCHIROPTERA. PT.I. REPRODUCTION AND BREEDING SEASONS IN THE SOUTH INDIAN VESPERTILIONID BAT--SCOTOPHILUS WROUGHTONI (THOMAS). A. Gopalkrishna. Proc. Indian Acad. Sci., Bangalore City, sect.B., vol.26, no.6, pp.219-231, figs.3, Dec., 1947.

LITTLE BROWN BATS COPULATING IN WINTER. John E. Guilday. Jour. Mam., vol.29, no.4, pp.416-417, Dec.31, 1948.

WINTER FETUS IN THE LITTLE BROWN BAT, MYOTIS LUCIFUGUS. John E. Guilday. Jour. Mam., vol.31, no.1, pp. 96-97, Feb.21, 1950.

A MATERNITY COLONY OF BATS. John Hendrickson. Malayan Nat. Jour., 11 (4): 121-125, May, 1957.

A SUMMER COLONY OF THE LEAST BAT, MYOTIS SUBULATUS LEIBII (AUDUBON AND BACHMAN). Harold B. Hitchcock. Canadian Field-Nat., vol.69, no.2, p.31, Apr.-June, 1955.

NOTES ON THE SEX RATIO IN NYCTICEIUS HUMERALIS. Emmett T. Hooper. Jour. Mam., vol.20, no.3, pp.369-370, Aug.14, 1939.

A BAT NURSERY. T. H. E. Jackson. Jour. East Africa and Uganda Nat. Hist. Soc., London, vol.14, no.3 (64), p.180, June, 1939.

NOTES ON A FAMILY OF RED BATS IN CAPTIVITY. Charles E. Johnson. Jour. Mam., vol.13, no.2, pp.132-135, May, 1932.

BREEDING COLONIES OF BATS, PIPISTRELLUS HESPERUS AND MYOTIS SUBULATUS MELANORHINUS. Carl B. Koford, Mary R. Koford. Jour. Mam., vol.29, no.4, pp. 417-418, Dec.31, 1948.

NOTES ON PIPISTRELLUS SUBFLAVUS SUBFLAVUS (F. CUVIER) DURING THE SEASON OF PARTURITION. Harry K. Lane. Proc. Pennsylvania Acad. Sci., Myerstown, vol.20, pp.57-61, 1946.

OBSERVATIONS ON THE NUMBER OF YOUNG OF THE LASIURINE BATS. Marcus W. Lyon, Jr. Proc. U. S. Nat. Mus., vol.26, no.1314, pp.425-426, pl.17, Jan.26, 1903.

THE REPRODUCTIVE CYCLE IN MALE BATS OF THE SPECIES MYOTIS LUCIFUGUS LUCIFUGUS (SIC) AND MYOTIS GRISESCENS. Roland E. Miller. Jour. Morph., Philadelphia, vol.64, no.2, pp.267-296, Mar., 1939.

THE NUMBER OF YOUNG RED BATS IN ONE LITTER. E. L. Moseley. Jour. Mam., vol.9, no.3, p.249, Aug., 1928.

RED BAT AS A MOTHER. E. L. Moseley. Jour. Mam., vol.9, no.3, pp.248-249, Aug., 1928.

AN OBSERVATION ON QUADRUPLETS IN THE RED BAT. Ross L. Packard. Jour. Mam., 37 (2): 279-280, June 9, 1956.

REPRODUCTION OF THE LUMP-NOSED BAT CORYNORHINUS RAFINESQUEI IN CALIFORNIA. Oliver P. Pearson, Mary R. Koford, Anita K. Pearson. Jour. Mam., vol.33, no.3, pp.273-320, Aug.19, 1952.

BREEDING OF THE HOARY BAT IN PENNSYLVANIA. Earl L. Poole. Jour. Mam., vol.13, no.4, pp.365-367, Nov., 1932.

NOTES ON THE BREEDING OF LASIURUS AND PIPISTRELLUS IN PENNSYLVANIA. Earl L. Poole. Jour. Mam., vol.19, no.2, p.249, May 14, 1938.

NOTES ON A NORTHERN RED BAT AND HER YOUNG. Don Quimby. Jour. Mam., vol.23, no.4, pp.448-449, Nov.14, 1942.

(ON THE REPRODUCTION OF BATS. THE VESPERTILIO (VESPERTILIO MURINUS SCHREBER).) Sur la reproduction des Chauves-souris. Le Vespertilion murin (Vespertilio murinus Schreber). R. Rollinat, E. L. Trouessart. Mem. Soc. Zool. France, Paris, vol.9, pp.214-240, 1896.

BIRTH OF THE YOUNG OF MYOTIS AUSTRORIPARIUS. H. B. Sherman. Jour. Mam., vol.11, no.4, pp.495-503, Nov., 1930.

PREGNANCY IN THE LITTLE BROWN BAT. Elizabeth Smith. Amer. Jour. Physiol., 185 (1): 61-64, Apr., 1956.

A COLONY OF PACIFIC PALLID BATS. Tracy I. Storer. Jour. Mam., vol.12, no. 3, pp.244-247, Aug., 1931.

A RECORD OF RED BATS MATING. Frederick W. Stuewer. Jour. Mam., vol. 29, no.2, pp.180-181, May 14, 1948.

THE NUMBER OF YOUNG OF THE RED BAT. Henry L. Ward. Bull. Wisconsin Nat. Hist. Soc., vol.3, no.4, pp.181-182, 1905.

FURTHER STUDIES ON THE SURVIVAL OF SPERMATOZOA IN THE FEMALE REPRODUCTIVE TRACT OF THE BAT. William A. Wimsatt. Anat. Record, Philadelphia, vol. 88, no.2, pp.193-204, Feb., 1944.

GROWTH OF THE OVARIAN FOLLICLE AND OVULATION IN MYOTIS LUCIFUGUS LUCIFUGUS. William A. Wimsatt. Amer. Jour. Anat., Philadelphia, vol.74, no.2, pp. 129-173, pls.7, Mar., 1944.

NOTES ON BREEDING BEHAVIOR, PREGNANCY, AND PARTURITION IN SOME VESPERTILIONID BATS OF THE EASTERN UNITED STATES. W. A. Wimsatt. Jour. Mam., 26: 23-33, 1945.

South America

A NEW BAT FROM PERU. Gerrit S. Miller, Jr. Ann. and Mag., Nat. Hist., ser.7, vol.6, pp.570-574, 1 fig., Dec., 1900.

(ON THE CHILEAN CHIROPTERS RELATED TO HISTIOTUS VELATUS.) Ueber die mit Histiotus velatus verwandten Flederthiere aus Chile. W. Peters. Monatsbar, Koen., Wiss. Berlin, pp.785-792, Dec.6, 1875.

TWO SOUTH AMERICAN FORMS OF RHOGEEESSA. Oldfield Thomas. Ann. and Mag. Nat. Hist. (7), vol.11, no.64, pp.382-383, Apr., 1903.

Taxonomy

(REGARDING THE TYPE AND LOCALITY OF MYOTIS ALBESCENS (E. GEOFFREY).) Sobre el tipo y la localidad tipica del Myotis albescens (E. Geoffrey). E. Agacino Morales. Bol. Soc. Espanola Hist. Nat. Madrid, vol.37, pp.17-19, 1938.

THE STATUS OF VESPERTILIO PILOSUS PETERS. Glover M. Allen. Jour. Mam., vol.17, no.2, pp.168-169, May, 1936.

DESCRIPTION OF A NEW SPECIES OF BAT, ATALAPHA SOMOTA. Harrison Allen. U.S. Nat. Mus., Proc., Washington, 1891, vol.13, 1890, p.173-175.

DESCRIPTIONS OF TWO NEW SPECIES OF VESPERTILIONIDES AND SOME REMARKS ON THE GENUS ANTROZOUS. Harrison Allen. Proc. Acad. Nat. Sci. Phila., pp. 246-248, Apr., 1862.

A NEW GENUS OF VESPERTILIONIDAE. Harrison Allen. Proc. Acad. Nat. Sci. Phila., pp.467-470, 1891.

ON A NEW SPECIES OF ATALAPHA. Harrison Allen. Proc. Amer. Phil. Soc., vol.29, pp.1-3, Apr.10, 1891.

THE STATUS OF THE SEMINOLE BAT, LASIURUS SEMINOLUS (RHOADS). Frederick S. Barkalow, Jr. Jour. Mam., vol.29, no.4, pp.415-416, Dec.31, 1948.

DESCRIPTIONS OF TWO NEW SPECIES OF PTERYGISTES. G. E. H. Barrett-Hamilton. Ann. and Mag. Nat. Hist., ser.7, vol.17, pp.98-100, Jan., 1906.

THE BAT NAME MYOTIS RUDDI SILLIMAND AND VON BLOEKER, A SYNONYM OF MYOTIS VOLANS LONGICRUS (TRUE). Seth B. Benson. Jour. Mam., Baltimore, vol.30, no.1, pp.48-50, Feb.14, 1949.

THE STATUS OF LASIURUS BOREALIS SEMINOLUS (RHOADS). Robert H. Coleman. Jour. Mam., vol.31, no.2, pp.190-192, May 25, 1950.

A NEW NAME FOR THE DESERT RACE OF THE BAT, MYOTIS CALIFORNICUS. Walter W. Dalquest. Proc. Biol. Soc. Washington, vol.59, pp.67-68, Mar.11, 1946.

THE SYSTEMATIC STATUS OF THE RACES OF THE LITTLE BIG-EARED BAT MYOTIS EVOTIS H. ALLEN. Walter W. Dalquest. Proc. Biol. Soc. Washington, vol.56, pp.1-2, Feb.25, 1943.

THE STATUS OF THE SEMINOLE BAT, LASIURUS SEMINOLUS (RHOADS). Wayne H. Davis. Proc. Biol. Soc. Washington, 70: 181-182, Dec.31, 1957.

(MAMMALS. SYSTEMATIC STUDY OF SPECIES. MINIOPTERUS SCHREIBERSI (NATTERER) 1819.) Mammiferès. Étude systematique par espeçes. Miniopterus schreibersi (Natterer) 1819. Robert Didier, Paul Rode. Paul Lechevalier, Paris, pp. 1-12, figs.1-8, pls.3, 1937.

(THE SYSTEMATIC POSITION OF THE NOCTULE.) De la position systematique de la noctule. Serge Frechkop. Mammalia, Paris, vol.16, no.4, pp.216-222, illus., Dec., 1952.

A REVISION OF THE GENERA OF BATS VESPERTILIONIDAE AND THE DESCRIPTION OF SOME NEW GENERA AND SPECIES. John E. Gray. Mag. Zool. and Bot. vol.2, no.12, pp.484-505, 1838.

A SYNOPSIS OF THE AMERICAN BATS OF THE GENUS PIPISTRELLUS. E. Raymond Hall, Walter W. Dalquest. Univ. Kansas Publ., Mus. Nat. Hist., Lawrence, vol.1, no.26, pp.591-602, fig.1, Jan.20, 1950.

NEW BATS OF THE GENUS CORYNORHINUS. Charles O. Handley, Jr. Jour. Washington Acad. Sci., vol.45, no.5, pp. 147-149, May 23, 1955.

A REVISION OF THE AMERICAN BATS OF THE GENERA EUDERMA AND PLECOTUS. Charles O. Handley, Jr. Ph.D. Thesis, U. Mich., 247 pp., 1955.

THE TAXONOMIC STATUS OF THE BATS CORYNORHINUS PHYLLOTIS G. M. ALLEN AND IDIONYCTERIS MEXICANUS ANTHONY. Charles O. Handley, Jr. Proc. Biol. Soc. Washington, 69: 53-54, May 21, 1956.

A REVISION OF THE PIPISTRELLUS HESPERUS GROUP OF BATS. Donald M. Hatfield. Jour. Mam., vol.17, no.3, pp. 257-262, fig.1, Aug., 1936.

NOTE ON THE COTYPES OF VESPERTILIO HARPIA TEMMINCK, 1840 (MAMMALIA, CHIROPTERA, GENUS HARPIOCEPHALUS). A. M. Husson. Zool. Mededel. Rijksmus, Nat. Hist. Leiden, vol.33, no.16, pp.121-125, June 23, 1955.

(LASIURUS BOREALIS (MULLER): A NEW BAT SPECIES.) Lasiurus borealis (Muller) A propos D'une nouvelle espece de chauve-souris. G. Maheux. Naturaliste Canadien, vol.57, no.10, pp.185-186, Oct., 1930.

NOTE ON THE LECTOTYPE OF LASIURUS SEMOTUS ( H. ALLEN). Gerrit S. Miller, Jr. Jour. Mam., vol.20, no.3, p.369, Aug. 14, 1939.

NOTE ON THE VESPERTILIO INCAUTUS OF J. A. ALLEN. Gerrit S. Miller, Jr. Proc. Biol. Soc. Washington, vol.15, p.155, June 20, 1902.

NOTE ON THE VESPERTILIO OXYGNATHUS OF MONTICELLI. Gerrit S. Miller, Jr. Ann. Mus. Zool. R. Univ. Napoli, n.s., vol.3, pp.1-2, Apr.26, 1909.

NOTES ON THE VESPERITILIO BLYTHII OF TOMES. Gerrit S. Miller, Jr. Proc. Biol. Soc. Wash., vol.13, p.155, June 13, 1900.

THE SCOTOPHILUS PACHYOMUS OF TOMES A VALID SPECIES. Gerrit S. Miller, Jr. Proc. Biol. Soc. Washington, vol.8, pp.155-156, June 13, 1900.

A SECOND SPECIMEN OF PTERYGISTES AZOREUM THOMAS. Gerrit S. Miller, Jr. Proc. Biol. Soc., Washington, vol.15, p. 250, Dec.16, 1902.

THE VESPERTILIO CONCINNUS OF HARRISON ALLEN. Gerrit S. Miller, Jr. Proc. Biol. Soc., Washington, vol.8, p.154, June 13, 1900.

THE AMERICAN BATS OF THE GENERA MYOTIS AND PIZONYX. Gerrit S. Miller, Jr., Glover M. Allen. U.S. Nat. Mus. bull.144, pp.viii, 218, pl.1, May 25, 1928.

(Review by Francis Harper of) AMERICAN BATS OF THE GENERA MYOTIS AND PIZONYX. Miller, Allen. Bull. Boston Soc. Nat. Hist., no.49, pp.13-14, illus., Oct., 1928.

NOTE ON EPTESICUS PROPINQUUS. Wilfred H. Osgood. Proc. Biol. Soc. Wash., vol.27, p.101, May 11, 1914.

(ON VESPERTILIO CALCARATUS PRINCE ZU WIED AND A NEW GENUS OF CHIROPTERS, TYLONYCTERIS.) Ueber den Vespertilio calcaratus Prinz zu Wied und eine neue Gattung der Flederthiere, Tylonycteris. W. Peters. Monatsber. K. Wiss. Berlin, Jahrg., 1872, pp.699-706, 1872.

(THE WHITE BAT (LASIURUS CINEREUS) AND ITS SUB-SPECIES.) El murcielago blanquizco (Lasiurus cinereus) y sus subespecies. Colin Campbell Sanborn, Jorge A. Crespo. Bol. Mus. Argentino Cienc. Nat. "Bernardino Rivadavia", Buenos Aires, no.4, pp.1-13, 1957.

RESULTS OF THE ARCHBOLD EXPEDITIONS. NO.39. A REVIEW OF THE GENUS MYOTIS (CHIROPTERA) OF EURASIA, WITH SPECIAL REFERENCE TO SPECIES OCCURRING IN THE EAST INDIES. G. H. H. Tate. Bull. Amer. Mus. Nat. Hist., vol.78, art.8, pp.537-565, Dec.29, 1941.

RESULTS OF THE ARCHBOLD EXPEDITIONS, NO.40. NOTES ON VESPERTILIONID BATS. G. H. H. Tate. Bull. Amer. Mus. Nat. Hist., New York, vol.78, pp. 567-597, figs.4, Dec.31, 1941.

RESULTS OF THE ARCHBOLD EXPEDITIONS. NO.47. REVIEW OF THE VESPERTILIONINE BATS, WITH SPECIAL ATTENTION TO GENERA AND SPECIES OF THE ARCHBOLD COLLECTIONS. G. H. H. Tate. Bull. Amer. Mus. Nat. Hist., New York, vol.80, art.7, pp.221-297, Nov.27, 1942.

DESCRIPTION OF A NEW BAT OF THE GENUS NYCTOPHILUS. Oldfield Thomas. Ann. and Mag. Nat. Hist. (6), vol.2, no.9, p.226, Sept., 1888.

DESCRIPTION OF A THIRD SPECIES OF THE GENUS NYCTOPHILUS. Oldfield Thomas. Ann. and Mag. Nat. Hist. (6), vol.9, no.53, pp.405-406, May, 1892.

DESCRIPTIONS OF TWO NEW BATS OF THE GENUS KERIVOULA. Oldfield Thomas. Ann. and Mag. Nat. Hist. (6), vol.14, no. 84, pp.460-462, Dec., 1894.

A NEW BAT OF THE GENUS SCOTAECUS. Oldfield Thomas. Ann. and Mag. Nat. Hist. (8), vol.19, no.111, pp.280-281, Mar., 1917.

A NEW GENUS OF BATS ALLIED TO NYCTOPHILUS. Oldfield Thomas. Ann. and Mag. Nat. Hist. (8), vol.14, no.83, pp. 381-383, Nov., 1914.

NOTE ON THE NAME CORYNORHINUS MEGALOTIS. Oldfield Thomas. Proc. Biol. Soc. Washington, vol.29, p.127, June 6, 1916.

NOTES ON BATS OF THE GENUS HISTIOTUS. Oldfield Thomas. Ann. and Mag. Nat. Hist. (8), vol.17, no.99, pp.272-276, Mar., 1916.

NOTES ON THE GENUS NYCTOPHILUS. Oldfield Thomas. Ann. and Mag. Nat. Hist. (8), vol.15, no.89, pp.493-499, May, 1915.

ON AZARA'S "CHAUVE-SOURIS ONZIEME" (MYOTIS RUBER, GEOFF.) AND A NEW SPECIES ALLIED TO IT. Oldfield Thomas. Ann. and Mag. Nat. Hist. (7), vol.10, no. 60, pp.493-494, Dec., 1902.

ON BATS OF THE GENERA NYCTALUS, TYLONYCTERIS, AND PIPISTRELLUS. Oldfield Thomas. Ann. and Mag. Nat. Hist. (8), vol.15, no.86, pp.225-232, Feb., 1915.

ON NEOTROPICAL BATS OF THE GENUS EPTESICUS. Oldfield Thomas. Ann. and Mag. Nat. Hist., ser.9, vol.5, pp.360-367, Apr., 1920.

TWO NEW SPECIES OF LEUCONOE. Oldfield Thomas. Ann. and Mag. Nat. Hist. (8), vol.15, no.85, pp.170-172, Jan., 1915.

MONOGRAPH OF THE GENUS LASIURUS. Robert F. Tomes. Proc. Zool. Soc. London, pt.25, pp.34-45, 1857.

A MONOGRAPH OF THE GENUS KERIVOULA. Robert F. Tomes. Proc. Zool. Soc. London, pt.26, pp.322-338, pl.66, 1858.

A MONOGRAPH OF THE GENUS MINIOPTERIS. Robert F. Tomes. Proc. Zool. Soc. London, pt.26, pp.115-128, pl.65, 1858.

A MONOGRAPH OF THE GENUS NYCTOPHILUS. Robert F. Tomes. Proc. Zool. Soc. London, pt.26, pp.25-37, 1858.

ON THE VESPERTILIO SUILLUS OF TEMMINCK, THE TYPE OF THE GENERA MURINA (GRAY) AND OCYPETES (LESSON). Robert F. Tomes. Proc. Zool. Soc. London, pt.26, pp.367-372, 1858.

A NOTE ON VESPERUGO HESPERUS ALLEN. Frederick W. True. Proc. U.S. Nat. Mus., vol.10, publ.659, p.515, Aug.6, 1887.

United States and Canada

MYOTIS SUBULATUS LEIBII IN NORTH CAROLINA. David A. Adams. Jour. Mam., vol.31, no.1, pp.97-98, Feb.21, 1950.

THE HOARY BAT AT MARSHALL, MISSOURI. Gordon Alexander. Jour. Mam., vol.5, no.1, pp.68-69, Feb., 1924.

INTRODUCTION TO A MONOGRAPH OF THE NORTH AMERICAN BATS. NOTES ON THE GENERA OF VESPERTILIONIDAE. Harrison Allen. Proc. U.S. Nat. Mus., vol.16, pp.1-31, 1893.

DESCRIPTION OF A NEW SPECIES OF BIG-EARED BAT, OF THE GENUS HISTIODUS, FROM SOUTHERN CALIFORNIA. J. A. Allen. Bull. Amer. Mus. Nat. Hist., vol. 3, pp.195-198, Feb.20, 1891.

TWO SPECIES OF BATS ADDED TO THE LIST OF QUEBEC MAMMALS. Rudolph Martin Anderson. Rapport Annuel Soc. Provancher d'Hist. Nat. du Canada, 1940, Quebec, pp.23-29, pls.3, 1941.

THE THIRD RECORD OF THE SPOTTED BAT (EUDERMA MACULATA) FOR CALIFORNIA. Granville P. Ashcraft. Jour. Mam., vol.13, no.2, pp.162-163, May, 1932.

A HOARY BAT FROM NORTHWESTERN KANSAS. Rollin H. Baker. Trans. Kansas Acad. Sci., vol.57, no.2, p.196, 1954.

LITTLE BROWN BAT (MYOTIS LUCIFUGUS LUCIFUGUS). N. R. Barger. Wisconsin Conserv. Bull. Madison, vol.12, no.6, pp. 27-28, illus., June, 1947.

A RECORD OF THE BAT, PIPISTRELLUS SUBFLAVUS, IN NORTHWESTERN ILLINOIS. James R. Beer, Frederick Greeley. Nat. Hist. Miscellanea, Chicago Acad. Sci., no. 14, p.1, Mar.15, 1948.

MYOTIS LUCIFUGUS PHASMA IN CALIFORNIA. Seth B. Benson. Jour. Mam., Baltimore, vol.21, no.3, p.354, Aug.14, 1940.

RECORDS OF THE SPOTTED BAT (EUDERMA MACULATA) FROM CALIFORNIA AND UTAH. Seth B. Benson. Jour. Mam., vol.35, no.1, pp.117, Feb.10, 1954.

MYOTIS GRISESCENS AND MYOTIS SODALIS IN ARKANSAS. J. D. Black. Jour. Mam., vol.15, no.1, pp.67-68, Feb., 1934.

MYOTIS AUSTRORIPARIUS IN TENNESSEE. B. P. Bole, Jr. Jour. Mam., vol.24, no.3, p.403, Aug.17, 1943.

MYOTIS THYSANODES IN SOUTH DAKOTA. B. P. Bole, Jr. Jour. Mam., vol.16, no.2, pp.147-148, May, 1935.

CORYNORHINUS IN NORTHEASTERN OREGON. Ernest S. Booth. Murrelet, Seattle, vol.26, no.2, p.26, May-Aug. (Aug.10), 1945.

THE HOARY BAT IN MAINE. Charles P. Brown. Jour. Mam., vol.25, no.3, pp. 310-331, Sept.8, 1944.

HOARY BAT TAKEN AT WESTPORT, WASHINGTON. D. E. Brown. Murrelet, vol.16, no.3, p.72, Sept., 1935.

THE BUNKER BAT IN OKLAHOMA. William Henry Burt. Jour. Mam., vol.26, no.3, p.309, Aug., 1945.

THE RAFINESQUE BAT IN MICHIGAN. William Henry Burt. Jour. Mam., vol.20, no.1, p.103, Feb.14, 1939.

LARGE BROWN BAT IN MICHIGAN. Victor H. Cahalane. Jour. Mam., vol.13, no.1, pp.70-71, Feb., 1932.

MYOTIS KEENII SEPTENTRIONALIS, A NEW BAT RECORD FOR ALABAMA. Ralph L. Chermock, Jesse S. White. Jour. Alabama Acad. Sci., vol.25, p.24, Dec., 1953.

MYOTIS KEENII SEPTENTRIONALIS (TROUESSART) IN MARYLAND. Elias Cohen. Jour. Mam., vol.23, no.1, p.96, Feb.14, 1942.

DASYPTERUS FLORIDANUS IN SOUTH CAROLINA. Robert H. Coleman. Jour. Mam., vol.21, no.1, p.90, Feb.14, 1940.

A RECORD OF DASYPTERUS EGA XANTHINUS FROM PALM SPRINGS, CALIFORNIA. D. G. Constantine. Bull. Southern California Acad. Sci., Los Angeles, vol.45, pt.2, p. 107, May-Aug., 1946.

SECOND RECORD OF THE HOARY BAT IN FLORIDA. R. Cooley. Jour. Mam., vol. 35, no.1, pp.116-117, Feb.10, 1954.

PIPISTRELLUS IN MAINE. Morton Copeland. Proc. Biol. Soc. Washington, vol. 27, p.227, Dec.29, 1914.

A SECOND HOARY BAT RECORD FOR WESTERN WASHINGTON. Leo K. Couch. Murrelet, vol.15, no.1, p.26, Jan., 1934.

NOTES ON THE NATURAL HISTORY OF THE BAT CORYNORHINUS RAFINESQUII IN CALIFORNIA. Walter W. Dalquest. Jour. Mam., 28 (1): 17-30, Feb., 1947.

NOTES ON THE NATURAL HISTORY OF THE BAT, MYOTIS YUMANENSIS, IN CALIFORNIA, WITH A DESCRIPTION OF A NEW RACE. Walter W. Dalquest. Amer. Midland Nat., Notre Dame, vol.38, no.1, pp.224-47, figs.4, July, 1947.

SEASONAL DISTRIBUTION OF THE HOARY BAT ALONG THE PACIFIC COAST. Walter W. Dalquest. Murrelet, Seattle, vol.24, no.2, pp.20-24, figs.2, Aug., 1943.

NOTES ON THE LONG-LEGGED BAT (MYOTIS VOLANS) AT OLD PORT TEJON AND VICINITY, CALIFORNIA. Walter W. Dalquest, Mary C. Ramage. Jour. Mam., vol.27, no.1, pp.60-93, Feb., 1946.

FIRST CANADIAN RECORD OF LEAST BROWN BAT. Eli Davis. Canadian Field-Nat., vol.45, no.5, pp.118-119, May, 1931.

ANOTHER RECORD OF THE RED BAT IN ARIZONA. W. B. Davis. Jour. Mam., vol.27, no.3, p.278, Aug.14, 1946.

THE RED BAT IN ARIZONA. W. B. Davis. Jour. Mam., vol.26, no.2, p.194, July 15, 1945.

STATUS OF MYOTIS SUBULATUS IN TEXAS. W. B. Davis. Jour. Mam., vol.25, no.2, p.201, May 25, 1944.

A NEW SUBSPECIES OF THE EASTERN PIPISTRELLE FROM FLORIDA. Wayne H. Davis. Proc. Biol. Soc. Washington, 70: 213-216, Dec.31, 1957.

A NEW BAT FOR THE TORONTO REGION LIST. O. E. Devitt. Canadian Field-Nat., vol.52, no.1, p.14, Jan., 1938.

CONCERNING THE SUBSPECIFIC STATUS OF BIG BROWN BATS IN WASHINGTON. Ford Dicks. Murrelet, vol.16, no.2, pp. 41-42, May, 1935.

SECOND ONTARIO RECORD FOR THE PIPISTRELLE. Stuart C. Downing. Jour. Mam., vol.19, no.1, p.103, Feb.14, 1938.

OCCURRENCE OF THE SPOTTED BAT IN UTAH. Stephen D. Durrant. Jour. Mam., vol.16, no.3, p.226, Aug., 1935.

SOME LITTLE BROWN BATS FROM ONTARIO. J. R. Dymond. Canadian Field-Nat., vol.43, p.137, Sept.3, 1929.

BIG-EARED BAT IN ILLINOIS. W. H. Elder. Jour. Mam., vol.26, no.4, pp.433-434, Feb.12, 1946.

DISTRIBUTION OF RACES OF THE BROWN BAT (EPTESICUS) IN WESTERN NORTH AMERICA. William L. Engels. Amer. Midland Nat., vol.17, no.3, pp.653-660, fig.1, May, 1936.

HOARY BAT TAKEN IN SEATTLE, WASHINGTON. Martha R. Flahaut. Murrelet, vol.14, no.3, p.77, Sept., 1933.

SECOND LOCALITY RECORD OF BIG BROWN BAT IN WESTERN WASHINGTON. Martha R. Flahaut. The Murrelet, vol.12, no.2, p.56, May, 1931.

THE BATS OF WEST VIRGINIA, IDENTIFICATION, MEASUREMENTS, DISTRIBUTION. W. Gene Frum. MS thesis, W. Va. Univ., 1947.

CORYNORHINUS MACROTIS, BIG-EARED BAT, IN WEST VIRGINIA. W. Gene Frum. Jour. Mam., vol.29, no.4, p.418, Dec.31, 1948.

PIPISTRELLUS SUBFLAVUS OBSCURUS IN WEST VIRGINIA. W. Gene Frum. Jour. Mam., vol.25, no.2, p.195, May 25, 1944.

SILVER-HAIRED BAT, LASIONYCTERIS NOCTIVAGANS, IN WEST VIRGINIA. W. Gene Frum. Jour. Mam., vol.34, no.4, pp.499-500, Nov.13, 1953.

THE STATUS OF CERTAIN AMERICAN SPECIES OF MYOTIS. E. A. Goldman. Proc. Biol. Soc. Washington, vol.27, pp.99-102, May 11, 1914.

EASTERN BIG-EARED BAT IN OHIO. Robert M. Goslin. Jour. Mam., vol.35, no.3, pp.430-431, Aug.20, 1954.

THE PIPISTREL (PIPISTRELUS SUBFLAVUS) IN NORTHERN WISCONSIN. Frederick Greeley, James R. Beer. Jour. Mam., Baltimore, vol.30, no.2, p.198, May 23, 1949.

OCCURRENCE OF THE HOARY BAT AT HOT SPRINGS NATIONAL PARK, ARKANSAS. H. R. Gregg. Jour. Mam., vol.18, no.1, p.98, Feb.14, 1937.

NOTES ON THE LIFE HISTORIES OF NEW ENGLAND CAVE BATS. Donald R. Griffin. Jour. Mam., vol.21, no.2, pp.181-187, May 14, 1940.

A NEW BAT OF THE GENUS MYOTIS FROM THE HIGH SIERRA NEVADA OF CALIFORNIA. Hilda Wood Grinnell. Univ. Cal. Pub. Zool., vol.17, no.2, pp.9-10, Aug.23, 1916.

THREE NEW RACES OF VESPERTILIONID BATS FROM CALIFORNIA. Hilda Wood Grinnell. Univ. Cal. Publ. Zool., vol.12, no.10, pp.317-320, Dec.4, 1914.

MYOTIS ORINOMUS ELLIOT, A BAT NEW TO CALIFORNIA. Joseph Grinnell. Berkeley, University of California press, pp.137-142, 2 illus., 1912.

A SECOND RECORD OF THE SPOTTED BAT (EUDERMA MACULATUM) FOR CALIFORNIA. Joseph Grinnell. Univ. Cal. Publ. Zool., vol.5, no.10, pp.317-318, pl. 30, Feb.24, 1910.

OCCURRENCE OF THE HOARY BAT AT LAWRENCE, KANSAS. E. Raymond Hall. Jour. Mam., vol.4, no.3, pp.192-193, Aug., 1923.

OCCURRENCE OF THE SPOTTED BAT AT RENO, NEVADA. E. Raymond Hall. Jour. Mam., vol.16, no.2, p.148, May, 1935.

THE SPOTTED BAT IN KERN COUNTY, CALIFORNIA. E. Raymond Hall. Jour. Mam., vol.20, no.1, p.103, Feb.14, 1939.

THE HOARY BAT IN LAKE TOWNSHIP, HASTINGS COUNTY, ONTARIO. G. H. Hammond. Canadian Field-Nat., Sutton West, vol.59, no.1, p.44, Jan.-Feb., 1946.

A RECORD OF LASIURUS BOREALIS TELIOTIS FROM ARIZONA. Lyndon L. Hargrave. Jour. Mam., vol.25, no.4, p. 414, Dec.12, 1944.

ANTROZOUS BUNKERI, A NEW BAT FROM KANSAS. Claude W. Hibbard. Jour. Mam., vol.15, no.3, pp.227-228, Aug., 1934.

HOARY BAT, LASIURUS CINEREUS, AT SOUTHAMPTON ISLAND, N.W.T. Harold B. Hitchcock. Canadian Field-Nat., Sutton West, vol.57, nos.3-4, p.86, Apr.-May, 1943.

A NEW SUBSPECIES OF MYOTIS EVOTIS (H. ALLEN) FROM SOUTHEASTERN ARIZONA AND MEXICO. Donald F. Hoffmeister, Philip H. Krutzsch. Nat. Hist. Misc., Chicago Acad. Sci., no.151, pp.4, Dec.28, 1955.

HOARY BAT AT TORONTO (ONTARIO) IN SUMMER. Clifford E. Hope. Canadian Field-Nat., vol.45, no.6, p.147, figs.1, Sept., 1931.

THE HOARY BAT IN OHIO. L. S. Hopkins. Ohio Jour. Science, vol.20, no.2, pp.35-37, Dec., 1919.

THE GEORGIAN BAT, PIPISTRELLUS SUBFLAVUS, IN WISCONSIN. Hartley H. T. Jackson. Jour. Mam., vol.1, no.1, p.38, Nov., 1919.

MYOTIS SUBULATUS LEIBII IN VIRGINIA. David H. Johnson. Jour. Mam., vol.31, no. 2, p.197, May, 1950.

HOARY BAT IN MINNESOTA. Maynard S. Johnson. Fins, Feathers and Fur, no.44, p.64, Dec., 1925.

FALL AND WINTER RECORD OF SILVER-HAIRED BAT FOR WASHINGTON STATE. Murray L. Johnson. Murrelet, Seattle, vol.34, no.2, p.32, Oct.5, 1953.

MYOTIS THYSANODES THYSANODES IN IDAHO. Knox J. Jones, Olin L. Webb. Jour. Mam., vol.34, no.1, p.122, Feb.19, 1953.

A LONG ISLAND HOARY BAT. Heathcote M. H. Kimball, John T. Nichols. Jour. Mam., vol.21, no.2, pp.214-216, May 14, 1940.

HOARY BAT IN VERMONT. George L. Kirk. Jour. Mam., vol.3, no.3, p.185, Aug., 1922.

SOME OBSERVATIONS ON THE BIG BROWN BAT IN SAN DIEGO COUNTY, CALIFORNIA. Philip H. Krutzsch. Jour. Mam., vol.27, no.3, pp.240-242, Aug.14, 1946.

SEMINOLE BAT, LASIURUS SEMINOLUS, IN CENTRAL NEW YORK. James N. Layne. Jour. Mam., 36 (3): 453, Aug.30, 1955.

ADDITIONAL RECORDS OF NYCTICEIUS IN INDIANA. Dwight M. Lindsay. Jour. Mam., 37 (2): 282, June 9, 1956.

SOME BAT RECORDS FROM SOUTHEASTERN INDIANA. Dwight M. Lindsay. Jour. Mam., 37 (4): 543-545, Jan.9, 1957.

BIG-EARED BAT IN THE GRAND CANYON. Edwin D. McKee. Jour. Mam., vol.13, no. 1, p.71, Feb., 1932.

FRINGED-TAILED BAT IN BRITISH COLUMBIA. T. P. Maslin, Jr. Jour. Mam., vol. 19, no.3, p.373, Aug., 1938.

DESCRIPTION OF A NEW SPECIES OF BAT FROM THE WESTERN UNITED STATES. C. Hart Merriam. Proc. Biol. Soc., Washington, vol.4, 1886-87, pp.4, Dec., 1886.

A NEW BAT OF THE GENUS ANTROZOUS FROM CALIFORNIA. C. Hart Merriam. Proc. Biol. Soc. Washington, vol.11, pp. 179-180, July 1, 1897.

REVISION OF THE NORTH AMERICAN BATS OF THE FAMILY VESPERTILIONIDAE. Gerrit S. Miller, Jr. North American Fauna, no.13, pp.140, figs.40, pls.3, Oct.16, 1897.

A SECOND SPECIMEN OF EUDERMA MACULATUM. Gerrit S. Miller, Jr. Proc. Biol. Soc., Washington, vol.16, pp.165-166, fig. 1, Nov.30, 1903.

MYOTIS GRISECENS AND MYOTIS SODALIS IN TENNESSEE AND ALABAMA. Charles E. Mohr. Jour. Mam., vol.13, no.3, pp.272-273, Aug., 1932.

MYOTIS SUBULATUS LEIBII AND MYOTIS SODALIS IN PENNSYLVANIA. Charles E. Mohr. Jour. Mam., vol.13, no.2, pp.160-161, May, 1932.

PENNSYLVANIA BATS OF THE GENUS MYOTIS. Charles E. Mohr. Proc. Pennsylvania Acad. Sci., Harrisburg, vol.7, pp. 39-43, 1933.

MYOTIS VOLANS INTERIOR IN SOUTH DAKOTA. Philip N. Moulthrop. Jour. Mam., vol.17, no.4, pp.413-414, Nov., 1936.

STATUS OF MYCTICEIUS HUMERALIS IN INDIANA. Russell E. Mumford. Jour. Mam., vol.34, no.1, pp.121-122, Feb.19, 1953.

A FLORIDA SPECIMEN OF LE CONTE'S LUMP-NOSED BAT. Wilfred Neill. Jour. Mam., vol.34, no.3, pp.382-383, Aug.14, 1953.

ADDITIONAL REPORTS ON SILVER-HAIRED BATS. R. W. Nero. Blue Jay, Saskatchewan Nat. Hist. Soc., 15 (2): 86, June, 1957.

NEW SILVER-HAIRED BAT RECORDS. R. W. Nero. Blue Jay, Saskatchewan Nat. Hist. Soc., 15 (3): 121, Sept., 1957.

SASKATCHEWAN SILVER-HAIRED BAT RECORDS. R. W. Nero. Blue Jay, Saskatchewan Nat. Hist. Soc., 15 (1): 38-41, 46, Mar., 1957.

A RECORD OF THE SPOTTED BAT (EUDERMA MACULATA) FOR MONTANA. A. J. Nicholson. Jour. Mam., vol.31, no. 2, p.197, May 25, 1950.

THE DISTRIBUTION OF MYOTIS THYSANODES IN CALIFORNIA. Robert T. Orr. Jour. Mam., 37 (4): 545-546, Jan.9, 1957.

NOTES ON THE SEASONAL OCCURRENCE OF RED BATS IN SAN FRANCISCO. Robert T. Orr. Jour. Mam., vol.31, no.4, pp.457-458, Nov.21, 1950.

TWO NEW RECORDS OF THE SPOTTED BAT IN CALIFORNIA. Harry C. Parker. Jour. Mam., vol.33, no.4, pp.480-482, 1 pl., Nov.19, 1952.

THE BATS OF ILLINOIS. Paul W. Parmalee, Philip W. Smith. Living Museum, Springfield, vol.16, no.6, pp.523-526, Oct., 1954.

NATURE NOTELET. G. A. Petrides. Yosemite Nat. Notes, Yosemite, vol.19, no.12, p.96, Dec., 1940.

LASIURUS SEMINOLUS IN PENNSYLVANIA. E. L. Poole. Jour. Mam., vol.13, no.2, p.162, May, 1932.

A SECOND PENNSYLVANIA SPECIMEN OF LASIURUS SEMINOLUS (RHOADS). E. L. Poole. Jour. Mam., vol.30, no.1, p.80, Feb.14, 1949.

THE HOARY BAT IN EASTERN KANSAS. Norman A. Preble. Jour. Mam., 37 (1): 111, Feb.28, 1956.

A NEW NORTHERMOST RECORD OF THE YELLOW BAT, DASYPTERUS FLORIDANUS. R. H. Rageot. Jour. Mam., vol.36, no.3, p.456, Aug.30, 1955.

EARLY SEASONAL RECORD OF THE RED BAT IN KANSAS. Dennis G. Rainey, Howard J. Stains. Trans. Kansas Acad. Sci., Topeka, vol.57, no.1, p.85, 1954.

ON SOME BRITISH COLUMBIA BATS. A. L. Rand. Murrelet, Seattle, vol.23, no.3, pp.83-84, Feb.15, 1943.

A NEW SOUTHEASTERN RACE OF THE LITTLE BROWN BAT. Samuel N. Rhoads. Proc. Acad. Nat. Sci. Philadelphia, pp.227-228, May 22, 1897.

ON THE COMMON BROWN BATS OF PENINSULAR FLORIDA AND SOUTHERN CALIFORNIA. Samuel N. Rhoads. Proc. Acad. Nat. Sci., Philadelphia, pp.618-619, 1901.

MYOTIS KEENII IN FLORIDA. Dale W. Rice. Jour. Mam., 36 (4): 567, Dec.14, 1955.

A NEW RACE OF MYOTIS AUSTRORIPARIUS FROM THE UPPER MISSISSIPPI VALLEY. Dale W. Rice. Jour. Florida Acad. Sci., vol.18, no.1, pp.67-68, Mar., 1955.

STATUS OF MYOTIS GRISESCENS IN FLORIDA. Dale W. Rice. Jour. Mam., 36 (2): 289-290, May 26, 1955.

A STUDY OF THE CAVE BATS OF MINNESOTA WITH SPECIAL REFERENCE TO THE LARGE BROWN BAT, EPTESICUS FUSCUS FUSCUS (BEAUVOIS). G. N. Rysgaard. Am. Midland Nat. 28 (1): 245-267, July, 1942.

APRIL RECORD OF SILVER-HAIRED BAT IN OREGON. Colin Campbell Sanborn. Murrelet, Seattle, vol.34, no.2, p.32, Oct.5, 1953.

BAT MATTERS. Theo. H. Scheffer. Murrelet, vol.11, no.2, pp.11-13, illus., May, 1930.

A SECOND RECORD OF MYOTIS SUBULATUS LEIBI IN NORTH CAROLINA. Albert Schwartz. Jour. Elisha Mitchell Sci. Soc., vol.70, no.2, p.222, Dec., 1954.

LUMP-NOSED BAT IN ARKANSAS. John A. Sealander, Jr. Jour. Mam., vol.32, no.4, p.465, Nov.19, 1951.

OCCURRENCE OF THE SEMINOLE BAT IN ARKANSAS. John A. Sealander, Arnold J. Hoiberg. Jour. Mam., vol.35, no.4, p.585, Nov.29, 1954.

THE FLORIDA YELLOW BAT, DASYPTERUS FLORIDANUS. H.B.Sherman. Proc. Florida Acad. Sci., Gainesville, vol.7, nos.2-3, pp.193-197, 1944 (1945).

THE OCCURRENCE OF MYOTIS GRISESCENS IN FLORIDA. H. B. Sherman. Jour. Mam., vol.15, no.2, p.156, May, 1934.

THIRD RECORD OF THE HOARY BAT IN FLORIDA. H. B. Sherman. Jour. Mam., 37 (2): 281-282, June 9, 1956.

A NEW BAT, GENUS MYOTIS, FROM WEST-CENTRAL CALIFORNIA. O. P. Silliman, J. C. von Bloeker, Jr. Proc. Biol. Soc. Washington, vol.51, pp.167-168, Aug.23, 1938.

STUDIES ON THE LIFE HISTORY OF NON-CAVE-DWELLING BATS IN NORTHEASTERN OHIO. Elizabeth Smith. Ohio J. Sci., 54 (1): 1-12, Jan., 1954.

THREE TORONTO RECORDS OF THE HOARY BAT. L. L. Snyder. Canadian Field-Nat., vol.41, no.7, p.155, 1927.

RECORD OF A FEMALE HOARY BAT, LASIURUS CINEREUS, AND YOUNG IN SYRACUSE, NEW YORK. LeRoy C. Stegeman. Jour. Mam., 36 (3): 455-456, 1 table, Aug.30, 1955.

SAY'S BAT IN NEBRASKA. T. C. Stephens. Jour. Mam., vol.26, no.1, p.92, Feb.23, 1945.

OCCURRENCE OF THE LUMP-NOSED BAT IN EASTERN WASHINGTON. Arthur Svihla. Murrelet, vol.18, nos.1-2, pp.18-19, Jan.-May, 1938.

A NEW BAT FROM THE UNITED STATES, REPRESENTING THE EUROPEAN MYOTIS (LEUCONOE) DAUBENTONI. Oldfield Thomas. Ann. and Mag. Nat. Hist. (7), vol.13, no.77, pp.382-384, May, 1904.

THE LEAST BROWN BAT, MYOTIS SUBULATUS LEIBII, IN NEW YORK. Harold Trapido. Jour. Mam., vol.23, no.2, p. 218, May 14, 1942.

THE ACADIAN BAT IN NEW JERSEY. Harold Trapido, James Kezer. Jour. Mam., vol.22, no.4, pp.449-450, Nov.14, 1941.

DESCRIPTION OF A NEW SPECIES OF BAT, VESPERTILIO LONGICRUS, FROM PUGET SOUND. Frederick W. True. Proc. U.S. Nat. Mus., vol.10, publ.602, pp.6-7, Apr.25, 1887.

A NEW BAT FROM PUGET SOUND. Frederick W. True. Science, vol.8, no. 203, p.588 , Dec.24, 1886.

A NEW SUBSPECIES OF BAT (MYOTIS VELIFER) FROM SOUTHEASTERN CALIFORNIA AND ARIZONA. Terry A. Vaughan. Univ. Kansas Publ., Mus. Nat. Hist., vol.7, no.8, pp.507-512, July 23, 1954.

SEASONAL DISTRIBUTION OF THE HOARY BAT IN SOUTHERN CALIFORNIA. Terry A. Vaughan, Philip H. Krutzsch. Jour. Mam., 35 (3): 431-432, Aug.20, 1954.

THE ARIZONA SPECIMEN OF EUDERMA MACULATUM. Charles T. Vorhies. Jour. Mam., vol.16, no.3, pp.224-226, Aug., 1935.

THE FRINGED BAT IN OREGON. Alex Walker. Murrelet, Seattle, vol.23, no.2, p.62, Aug.14, 1942.

THE RED BAT IN THE WASHINGTON REGION IN WINTER. Alexander Wetmore. Jour. Mam., vol.14, no.2, pp.157-158, May, 1933.

(A NEW CHIROPTER OF QUEBEC.) Un Chéiroptère nouveau a Québec. Edmond

Yourans. Le Naturaliste Canadien, vol. 57, no.3, pp.65-66, Mar., 1930.

LASIURUS BOREALIS (MUELLER). Naturaliste Canadien, vol.57, no.10, pp. 185-186, 1930.

Variation

GEOGRAPHIC VARIATION IN THE BIG BROWN BAT (EPTESICUS FUSCUS). Glover M. Allen. Canadian Field-Nat., vol.47, no.2, pp.31-32, Feb., 1933.

VARIATION IN A COLONY OF LITTLE BROWN BATS. Le Roy C. Stegeman. Jour. Mam., 35 (1): 111-113, graph., Feb., 1954.

## Molossidae

Migration

COMMENTS ON MIGRATION AND HIBERNATION IN TADARIDA MEXICANA. Seth B. Benson. Jour. Mam., vol.28, no.4, pp. 407-408, Nov.26, 1947.

NOTES ON THE POCKETED FREE-TAILED BAT. Seth B. Benson. Jour. Mam., vol.21, no.1, pp.26-29, Feb.14, 1940.

A COLONY OF RARE FREE-TAILED BATS. Adrey E. Borell. Jour. Mam., vol.20, no. 1, pp.65-68, 1 table, Feb.14, 1939.

ON THE TAXONOMIC VALUE OF THE SUBGENUS LOPHOMOPS (NYCTINOMINE BATS) WITH REMARKS ON THE BREEDING TIMES OF AFRICAN BATS. F. W. Braestrup. Ann. and Mag. Nat. Hist., London, ser.10, vol.11, no.63, pp.269-274, Mar., 1933.

MIGRATION OR HIBERNATION OF TADARIDA MEXICANA. Ernst Christensen. Jour. Mam., vol.28, no.1, pp.59-60, Feb. 15, 1947.

A PROGRAM FOR MAINTAINING THE FREE-TAIL BAT IN CAPTIVITY. Denny G. Constantine. Jour. Mam., vol.33, no.3, pp.395-397, Aug.19, 1952.

BANDING MEXICAN FREE-TAILED BATS. R. B. Eads, J. S. Wiseman, G. C. Menzies. Jour. Mam., 36 (1): 120-121, Feb.25, 1955.

EXHIBITION OF A DRAWING OF MOLOSSUS AUSTRALIS OF GRAY. John Gould. Proc. Zool. Soc. London, pt.26, p.372, 1858.

THE WHITE-STRIPED BAT, NYCTINOMUS AUSTRALIS GRAY. J. A. Kershaw. Victorian Nat., vol.44, no.4, p.110, Aug., 1927.

OBSERVATIONS ON A COLONY OF MOLOSSIDS. Philip H. Krutzsch. Jour. Mam., vol.26, no.2, p.196, July 15, 1945.

OBSERVATIONS ON THE CALIFORNIA MASTIFF BAT. Philip H. Krutzsch. Jour. Mam., 36 (3): 407-414, Aug.30, 1955.

OBSERVATIONS ON THE MEXICAN FREE-TAILED BAT, TADARIDA MEXICANA. Philip N. Krutzsch. Jour. Mam., 36 (2): 236-242, May 26, 1955.

CHIQUITO, A GUANO BAT. Mary Louise Perry. Nat. Hist., New York, vol.56, no. 4, pp.178-83, illus., Apr., 1947.

BREEDING HABITS OF THE FREE-TAILED BAT. H. B. Sherman. Jour. Mam., vol.18, no.2, pp.176-187, figs.5, May 14, 1937.

Africa

DESCRIPTION OF A NEW GENUS OF MOLOSSINE BATS FROM WEST AFRICA. Guy Dollman. Ann. and Mag., Nat. Hist., London, ser.8, vol.7, pp.210-212, Feb., 1911.

A NEW FLAT-HEADED BAT OF THE GENUS PLATYMOPS THOMAS FROM S.E. SUDAN. David L. Harrison. Ann. and Mag. Nat. Hist., ser.12, 9: 549-552, Aug., 1956.

NOTES ON AFRICAN BATS. I. SOME SYSTEMATIC AND ANATOMICAL NOTES ON THE AFRICAN BATS OF THE GENUS OTOMOPS THOMAS. David L. Harrison. Durban Mus. Nov., 5 (2): 17-26, Sept.1, 1957.

(NOTES ON A NEW CHIROPTER OF THE FRENCH SUDAN.) Note sur un cheiroptere nouveau du Soudan Francais. Robert T. Hatt. Bull. Soc. Zool. de France, vol. 53, pp.374-376, 1928.

A NEW AFRICAN MOLOSSID BAT. R. W. Hayman. Rev. Zool and Bot. Africaine, vol.45, nos.1-2, pp.82-83, Dec.22, 1951.

A NEW GENUS OF FREE-TAIL BAT FROM N.E. AFRICA. Oldfield Thomas. Ann. and Mag. Nat. Hist. (7), no.101, pp.499-501, May, 1906.

NOTES ON BATS OF THE GENUS NYCTINOMUS FOUND IN AFRICA, ETC. W. E. de Winton. Ann. Mag. Nat. Hist., ser.7, vol.7, pp.36-42, Jan., 1901.

Anatomy

VARIATION IN THE LOWER INCISORS OF THE MEXICAN FREETAIL BAT, TADARIDA MEXICANA (SAUSSURE). Bryan P. Glass. Proc. Oklahoma Acad. Sci., vol. 34, (for 1953), pp.73-74, Jan., 1955.

NOTES ON SOME EARLY BLASTOCYSTS OF THE SOUTH AMERICAN BAT MOLOSSUS. G. S. Sansom. Proc. Zool. Soc. London, 1932, pt.1, pp.113-118, pls.2, Mar., 1932.

HISTOLOGICAL ASPECTS OF THE GLANDS OF THE BAT, TADARIDA CYNOCEPHALA (LECONTE). H. J. Werner, W. W. Dalquest, H. H. Roberts. Jour. Mam., vol.31, no.4, pp.395-399, pls.2, Nov.21, 1950.

Diseases, Parasites

ISOLATION OF RABIES VIRUS FROM AN INSECTIVOROUS BAT (TADARIDA MEXICANA) IN CALIFORNIA. John B. Enright. Proc. Soc. Exp. Biol. and Med., 89 (1): 94-96, May, 1955.

(FIRST CONTRIBUTION REGARDING THE HEMATOMETRY OF THE MEXICAN BATS.) Primera contribucion acerca de la hematometria de los murcielagos Mexicanos. Liborio Martinez. Anal. Inst. Biol., Mexico City, vol.10, nos.1-2, pp.103-108, 1939.

(TRYPANOSOMES IN BATS IN THE CITY OF JUJUY.) Tripanosomas en murciélagos de la ciudad de Jujuy. Salvador Mazza. Univ. Buenos Aires, Mision de Estudios de Patologia Regional Argentina Jujuy. Novena Réunion Soc. Argentina de Patologia Regional Filiales y Afiliadas, Buenos Aires, vol.1, pp.172-173, illus., 1936.

ROLE OF BROWN FAT IN PATHOGENESIS OF RABIES IN INSECTIVOROUS BATS (TADARIDA B. MEXICANA). S. E. Sulkin, P. H. Krutzsch, C. Wallis, R. Allen. Proc. Soc. Exper. Biol. and Med., Philadelphia, 96 (2): 461-464, Nov., 1957.

Ecology, Habits, Behavior

EVENING BAT FLIGHT FROM CARLSBAD CAVERNS. Vernon C. Allison. Jour. Mam., vol.18, no.1, pp.80-82, Feb.14, 1937.

THE DAYTIME RETREAT OF A CALIFORNIA MASTIFF BAT. Walter W. Dalquest. Jour. Mam., vol.27, no.1, pp. 86-88, pl.1, Mar.14, 1946.

THE WING POUCHES OF THE NAKED BULLDOG BAT. J. L. Harrison. Malayan Nature Jour., vol.9, no.2, pp.66-67, Sept., 1954.

A NAKED BULLDOG BAT. H. J. Kitchener. Malayan Nature Jour., Kuala Lumpur, vol. 8, no.4, pp.165-166, pl.31, Mar., 1954.

NOTES ON THE LITTLE KNOWN POCKETED BAT. Philip H. Krutzsch. Jour. Mam., vol.25, no.2, p.201, May 25, 1944.

ECOLOGICAL OBSERVATIONS ON A COLONY OF TADARIDA MEXICANA. John W. Twente, Jr. Jour. Mam., 37 (1): 42-47, Feb.28, 1956.

Economic Importance

ECONOMIC VALUE OF THE MEXICAN FREE-TAILED BAT. E. Raymond Hall. California Fish and Game, vol.12, pp.135-137, July, 1926.

TEXAS BAT CAVES SERVED IN THREE WARS. THE CAVES OF TEXAS. Charles E. Mohr. Bull. Nat. Speleol. Soc., Washington, no.10, pp.89-96, illus., Apr., 1948.

Eurasia

(NYCTINOMOUS TAENIOTIS (RAF.) IN PIEDMONT.) Il Nyctinomus taeniotis (Raf.) in Piemonte. E. Festa. Boll. Mus. Zool. Anat. comp. R. Univ. Torino, vol.35, no. 735, pp.1-2, Nov.15, 1920.

ON A REMARKABLE NEW FREE-TAILED BAT FROM SOUTHERN BOMBAY. Oldfield Thomas. Jour. Bombay, Nat. Hist. Soc., vol.22, no.1, pp.87-91, pl., Apr.21, 1913.

SCIENTIFIC RESULTS FROM THE MAMMAL SURVEY. XX. (D). ON THE GENUS TADARIDA. (WRINKLE-LIP BATS). R. C. Wroughton. Jour. Bombay Nat. Hist. Soc., vol.26, no.3, pp.731-733, Oct.20, 1919.

Flight

SOME NOTES CONCERNING THE MASTIFF BAT. Luther Little. Jour. Mam., vol.1, no.4, p.182, Aug., 1920.

HOW FAST DO BATS FLY? THE CAVES OF TEXAS. Charles E. Mohr. Bull. Nat. Speleol. Soc., Washington, no.10, p.108, Apr., 1948.

Islands

A NEW NAME FOR THE JAMAICAN BAT MOLOSSUS FULIGINOSUS GRAY. David H. Johnson. Proc. Biol. Soc. Washington, vol. 65, pp.197-198, Nov.5, 1952.

A NEW BAT, OTOMOPS, FROM PAPUA. Barbara Lawrence. Jour. Mam., vol.29, no.4, pp.413-414, Dec.31, 1948.

THE COMMON NYCTINOMUS OF THE GREATER ANTILLES. Gerrit S. Miller, Jr. Proc. Biol. Soc. Washington, vol.15, p.248, Dec.16, 1902.

North America

BATS OF THE CARLSBAD CAVERN. Vernon Bailey. Nat. Geog. Mag., vol.48, no.3, pp.321-330, illus., Sept., 1925.

EUMOPS UNDERWOODI SORONIENSIS IN ARIZONA. Rollin H. Baker. Jour. Mam., vol.37, no.1, pp.111-112, Feb., 1956.

EUMOPS IN FLORIDA. Thomas Barbour. Jour. Mam., vol.17, no.4, p.414, Nov., 1936.

THE LECONTE FREE-TAILED BAT IN ALABAMA. Fred S. Barkalow, Jr. Jour. Mam., vol.20, no.3, p.370, Aug.14, 1939.

A SECOND RECORD OF TADARIDA MACROTIS FROM UTAH. William H. Behle. Jour. Mam., vol.19, no.4, p.500, Nov.14, 1938.

DESCRIPTION OF A MASTIFF BAT (GENUS EUMOPS) FROM SONORA, MEXICO. Seth B. Benson. Proc. Biol. Soc. Washington, vol.60, pp.133-34, Dec.31, 1947.

TADARIDA MEXICANA FROM CASTLE ROCK, KANSAS. J. D. Black. Jour. Mam., vol.16, no.2, p.147, May, 1935.

SUMMER RECORDS OF EUMOPS CALIFORNICUS (MERRIAM). Jack C. von Bloeker. Jour. Mam., vol.13, no.3, p.274, Aug., 1932.

MILLIONS OF BATS. Harold J. Brodrick. Natl. Park Serv., Region Three Quart., 3(3): 2-6, July, 1941.

A TEXAS COLONY OF BATS, TADARIDA MEXICANA. Fred B. Cagle. Jour. Mam., vol.31, no.4, pp.400-402, Nov.21, 1950.

THE BATS OF CARLSBAD CAVERNS. Ernst Christensen. Animal Kingdom, 49 (3): 98-102, June, 1946.

THE BIG FREE-TAILED BAT IN OKLAHOMA. E. Lendell Cockrum. Jour. Mam., vol.33, no.4, p.492, Nov.19, 1952.

THE FREE-TAILED BAT, TADARIDA MACROTIS, IN BRITISH COLUMBIA. Ian McTaggart Cowan. Canadian Field-Nat., Sutton West, vol.59, no.4, p.149, July-Aug., 1945.

TADARIDA FEMOROSACCA (MERRIAM) IN TAMAULIPAS, MEXICO. Walter W. Dalquest, E. Raymond Hall. Univ. Kansas Publ., Mus. Nat. Hist., Lawrence, vol.1, no.13, pp.245-248, fig.1, Dec.10, 1947.

NOTES ON TADARIDA MACROTIS IN UTAH. Stephen D. Durrant, Henry W. Setzer. Jour. Mam., vol.24, no.4, p.501, Nov.17, 1943.

OBSERVATIONS CONCERNING THE MEXICAN FREE-TAILED BAT, TADARIDA

MEXICANA, IN TEXAS. R. B. Eads, J. S. Wiseman, G. C. Menzies. Texas Jour. Sci., 9 (2): 227-242, June, 1957.

ESTABLISHED COLONIES OF THE MEXICAN FREE-TAILED BAT IN KANSAS. Claude W. Hibbard. Jour. Mam., vol.17, no.2, pp.167-168, May, 1936.

CONTRIBUTIONS TO THE LIFE-HISTORY OF THE CALIFORNIA MASTIFF BAT. A. Brazier Howell. Jour. Mam., vol.1, no.3, pp.111-117, pls.5-6, May, 1920.

ADDITIONAL NOTES ON CALIFORNIA BATS; WITH OBSERVATIONS UPON THE YOUNG OF EUMOPS. A. Brazier Howell, Luther Little. Jour. Mam., 5:261-263, 1924.

THE LARGE-EARED FREE-TAILED BAT IN SAN DIEGO. Laurence M. Huey. Jour. Mam., vol.13, no.2, p.160, May, 1932.

SECOND RECORD OF TADARIDA MOLOSSA FROM SAN DIEGO, CALIFORNIA. Laurence M. Huey. Jour. Mam., vol.35, no.3, p.435, Aug.20, 1954.

FOURTH RECORD OF THE POCKETED BAT IN CALIFORNIA. Philip H. Krutzsch. Jour. Mam., vol.25, no.4, pp.413-414, Dec.12, 1944.

DESCRIPTION OF A NEW SPECIES OF FREE-TAILED BAT FROM THE DESERT REGION OF SOUTHERN CALIFORNIA. NYCTINOMUS FEMOROSACCUS SP. NOV. C. Hart Merriam. North American Fauna, no.2, p.23, Oct., 1889.

DESCRIPTION OF A NEW SPECIES OF FREE-TAILED BAT FROM THE LOWER COLORADO RIVER IN ARIZONA. C. Hart Merriam. North American Fauna, no.2, p.25, Oct., 1889.

DESCRIPTION OF A NEW SPECIES OF MOLOSSUS FROM CALIFORNIA (MOLOSSUS CALIFORNICUS). C. Hart Merriam. North American Fauna, no.4, pp.31-32, Oct., 1890.

THE MEXICAN FREE-TAILED BAT IN TARRANT COUNTY, TEXAS. F. W. Miller. Jour. Mam., vol.29, no.4, pp. 418-419, Dec.31, 1948.

ANOTHER RARE BAT IN YOSEMITE. C. C. Presnall. Yosemite Nat. Notes, vol.12, no. 6, p.64, June, 1933.

SECOND COLORADO RECORD OF TADARIDA MACROTIS. J. L. Smead. Jour. Mam., vol.19, no.1, p.104, Feb.14, 1938.

A NEW FREE-TAILED BAT FROM TEXAS. Kenneth E. Stager. Bull. Southern California Acad. Sci., Los Angeles, vol.41, pt. 1, pp.49-50, May 31, 1942.

WHAT IS THE NORTHWARD LIMIT OF RANGE FOR THE MASTIFF BAT? Tracy I. Storer. Jour. Mam., vol.7, no.2, p.131, May, 1926.

ON THE OCCURRENCE OF NYCTINOMUS MOHAVENSIS IN THE SANTA CLARA VALLEY. J. M. Stowell. ZOE, vol.4, no.4, pp.362-364, Feb.7, 1894.

A RECORD OF TADARIDA MACROTIS FROM UTAH. A. M. Woodbury. Jour. Mam., vol.18, no.4, p.515, Nov., 1937.

Pelage, Coloration

ABERRANT COLORATION IN TADARIDA MEXICANA. Bryan P. Glass. Amer. Midland Nat., vol.52, no.2, pp.400-402, pl.1, Oct., 1954.

(THE SPOON-SHAPED HAIRS OF THE MOLOSSI DAE.) Die loeffelfoermigen haare der Molossi. J. Jablonowski. Abhandl. Ber. Koen. Zool. Anthropol. Ethno. Mus. Dresden, vol.7, no.7, pp.32-55, pls.10-11, 1898-1899.

Predators

GREAT BAT COLONIES ATTRACT PREDATORS. THE CAVES OF TEXAS. Denny G. Constantine. Bull. Nat. Speleol. Soc., Washington, no.10, p.100, Apr., 1948.

BAT, MOLOSSUS NIGRICANS, EATEN BY THE RAT SNAKE, ELAPHO LAETA. W. B. Davis. Jour. Mam., vol.32, no.2, p.219, May 21, 1951.

CALIFORNIA LYRE SNAKE FEEDING ON THE POCKETED BAT. Philip H. Krutzsch. Jour. Mam., vol.25, no.4, pp.410-412, Dec.12, 1944.

A CORRECTION. TADARIDA MEXICANA INSTEAD OF T. CYNOCEPHALA. Ralph W. Macy. Jour. Mam., vol.20, no.3, p.382, Aug.14, 1939.

HAWKS AS ENEMIES OF BATS. Ruby M. Macy, Ralph W. Macy. Jour. Mam., vol. 20, no.2, p.252, May, 1939.

OCCURRENCE OF MASTIFF BAT REMAINS IN A PELLET OF THE BARN OWL. W. G. Reeder. Condor, Berkeley, vol.48, no.6, p.282, Nov.-Dec., 1946.

FALCONS PREY ON NEY CAVE BATS. THE CAVE OF TEXAS. Kenneth E. Stager. Bull. Nat. Speleol. Soc. Washington, no.10, pp.97-99, fig.1, Apr., 1948.

A GROUP OF BAT-EATING DUCK HAWKS. Kenneth E. Stager. Condor, Berkeley, vol. 43, no.3, pp.137-139, May 15, 1941.

South and Central America

A NEW SPECIES OF FREE-TAILED BAT (GENUS EUMOPS) FROM BRAZIL. Charles O. Handley, Jr. Proc. Biol. Soc. Washington, vol.68, pp.177-178, Dec.31, 1955.

A NEW SPECIES OF FREE-TAILED BAT (GENUS MORMOPTERUS) FROM PERU. Charles O. Handley, Jr. Proc. Biol. Soc. Washington, 69: 197-202, Dec.31, 1956.

A NEW FREE-TAILED BAT FROM CENTRAL AMERICA. Gerrit S. Miller, Jr. Ann. and Mag. Nat. Hist., ser.7, vol.6, pp.471-472, Nov., 1900.

A NEW BAT OF THE GENUS PROMOPS FROM PERU. Oldfield Thomas. Ann. and Mag. Nat. Hist., ser.9, vol.8, p.139, July, 1921.

A NEW FREE-TAILED BAT FROM THE LOWER AMAZONS. Oldfield Thomas. Ann. and Mag. Nat. Hist. (7), vol.7, no. 38, pp.190-191, Feb., 1901.

Taxonomy

DESCRIPTION OF TWO NEW SPECIES OF BATS NYCTINOMUS EUROPS AND N. ORTHOTIS. Harrison Allen. U. S. Nat. Mus., Proc. Washington, vol.12, pp.635-640, 1889.

ON THE GENUS NYCTINOMUS AND DESCRIPTION OF TWO NEW SPECIES. Harrison Allen. Proc. Amer. Philos. Soc. vol.26, pp.1-6, Dec.3, 1889.

THE TYPE LOCALITY OF TADARIDA MEXICANA SAUSSURE. Seth B. Benson. Jour. Washington Acad. Sci., vol.34, no.5, p.159, May 15, 1944.

(CONSIDERATIONS ON THE GENUS "OTOMOPS" AND DESCRIPTION OF A NEW SPECIES OF MADAGASCAR.) Considérations sur le genre "Otomops" et description d'une espèce nouvelle de Madagascar. Jean Dorst. Mem. Inst. Sci. Madagascar, ser.A, vol.8, pp.235-240, pl.31, 1953.

A NEW CRESTED BAT (CHAEREPHON). R. W. Hayman. Ann. and Mag. Nat. Hist., London, ser.11, vol.1, pp.383-386, Apr., 1938.

TADARIDA RAFINESQUE VERSUS NYCTINOMUS GEOFFROY. Marcus W. Lyon, Jr. Proc. Biol. Soc. Washington, vol.27, pp. 217-218, Oct.31, 1914.

DESCRIPTIONS OF THREE NEW FREE-TAILED BATS. Gerrit S. Miller, Jr. Amer. Mus. Nat. Hist., vol.12, art.12, pp.173-181, figs.3, Oct.20, 1899.

THE GENERIC POSITION OF NYCTINOMUS ORTHOTIS H. ALLEN. Gerrit S. Miller, Jr. Proc. Biol. Soc. Washington, vol.15, p.250, Dec.16, 1902.

NOTES ON THE BATS OF THE GENUS MOLOSSUS. Gerrit S. Miller, Jr. Proc. U.S. Nat. Mus., vol.46, no.2013, pp.85-92, Aug.23, 1913.

THE STATUS OF NYCTINOMUS NEVADENSIS (H. ALLEN). Gerrit S. Miller, Jr. Proc. Biol. Soc. Washington, vol.15, p.250, Dec.16, 1902.

(ON THE CHIROPTERAN GENUS MORMOPTERUS AND ITS SPECIES.) Ueber die Chiropterengattung Mormopterus und die dahin gehoerigen Arten. W. Peters. Monatsber. K. Preussischen Akad. Wiss. Berlin, Jahrg., pp.482-485, pl.1, May, 1881.

NOTES ON THE AMERICAN BATS OF THE GENUS TADARIDA. H. Harold Shamel. Proc. U.S. Nat. Mus., vol.78, art.19, no.2862, pp.1-27, May 6, 1931.

RESULTS OF THE ARCHBOLD EXPEDITIONS, NO. 38. MOLOSSID BATS OF THE ARCHBOLD COLLECTIONS. G. H. H. Tate. Amer. Mus. Novitates, New York, no.1142, pp.1-4, Aug.20, 1941.

A NEW SUBSPECIES OF NYCTINOMUS AUSTRALIS. Oldfield Thomas. Ann. and Mag. Nat. Hist., ser.9, vol.14, pp.455-456, Oct., 1924.

ON BATS OF THE GENUS PROMOPS. Oldfield Thomas. Ann. and Mag. Nat. Hist. (8), vol.16, no.91, pp.61-64, July, 1915.

THREE NEW SPECIES OF NYCTINOMUS. Oldfield Thomas. Ann. and Mag. Nat. Hist. (7), vol.12, no.71, pp.501-505, Nov., 1903.

THE STATUS OF MORMOPTERUS PERUANUS J. A. ALLEN. Luis de la Torre. Proc. Biol. Soc. Washington, 69: 187-188, Dec.31, 1956.

PRIMATES

RELATION BETWEEN BODY-SIZE, WAKING ACTIVITY, SIZE OF EYEBALLS AND THE ORIGIN OF SOCIAL LIFE IN THE PRIMATES. M. F. Ashley Montagu. Nature, London, vol.152, no.3863, pp.573-574, Nov.13, 1943.

RARE MONKEYS. Belle J. Benchley. Zoonooz, San Diego, vol.12, no.11, pp.1-5, illus., Nov., 1940.

APES AND MONKEYS. E. G. Boulenger. Publ. by George G. Harrap and Co. Ltd., London, 1936.

WHO'S WHO IN THE MONKEY WORLD (16 PORTRAITS IN COLOR FROM LIFE). Elie Cheverlange. Nat. Geogr. Mag., vol.73, no.5, pls.1-16, May, 1938.

HISTORY OF THE PRIMATES. W. E. LeGros Clark. British Mus. (Nat. Hist.), London, 117 pp., illus., 1950.

THE MONKEY LEGION. Raymond L. Ditmars. Bull. New York Zool. Soc., vol. 31, no.3, pp.63-69, 27 pls., 1928.

TROUBLE WITH MONKEYS. Raymond L. Ditmars. Science Digest, Chicago, vol.6, no.1, pp.27-30, July, 1939.

A REVIEW OF THE PRIMATES. D. G. Elliot. 27 color plates, 110 crania, and 25 other plates, 3 vols., New York, 1912.

(Review by Robert C. Murphy of) A REVIEW OF THE PRIMATES. D.G. Elliot. New York Times Book Review, p.164, Apr. 5, 1914.

(Comments by Gerrit S. Miller, Jr. on) ELLIOTT'S REVIEW OF THE PRIMATES. D.G. Elliot. Science, n.s., vol.39, no. 992, pp.28-31, Jan. 2, 1914.

A HAND-BOOK TO THE PRIMATES. Henry C. Forbes. Lloyd's Natural History, vol. I-II, 1896-1897.

APES AND MONKEYS: THEIR LIFE AND LANGUAGE. R. L. Garner. Boston, 1900.

(DESCRIPTION OF MAMMALS. FIRST REPORT. THE MONKEY FAMILY.) Description des Mammiferes. Premier memoire. Famille des Singes. I. Geoffroy Saint-Hilaire. Archives du Museum, vol.2, pp.485-592, 6 pls., 1843.

(DESCRIPTION OF MAMMALS. THIRD REPORT. THE MONKEY FAMILY; SUPPLEMENT.) Description des Mammifères. Troisième mémoire. Famille des Singes; Supplément. I. Geoffroy Saint-Hilaire. Archives du Museum, vol.5, pp.529-584, pls.6, 1852.

(DESCRIPTION OF MAMMALS. FOURTH REPORT. THE MONKEY FAMILY. Description des Mammifères. Quatreième mémoire. Famille des Singes. Second supplement. I. Geoffroy Saint-Hilaire. Archives du Museum, vol.10, pp.1-102.

TWO RARE MONKEYS. L. Heck. Popular Science Monthly, New York, vol.41, no.3, pp.389-395, figs.1-3, July, 1892.

PRIMATES: COMPARATIVE ANATOMY AND TAXONOMY. W. C. Osman Hill. Vol. I: Strepsirhini, Edinburgh University Press, XXIII plus 798 pp., 34 pls., 199 figs., 1953.

(Review by G.E. Erikson of) PRIMATES: COMPARATIVE ANATOMY AND TAXONOMY. VOL. I. STEPSIRHINI. W. C. Osman Hill. Jour. Mamm., vol.35, no.4, pp.601-603, Nov. 29, 1954.

PRIMATES: COMPARATIVE ANATOMY AND TAXONOMY. II. HAPLORHINI: TARSIOIDEA. W. C. Osman Hill. Univ. Press, Edinburgh; Interscience, New York, pp.347, illus., 1955.

(PRIMATOLOGIA. HANDBOOK OF PRIMATOLOGY. I. SYSTEMATICS, PHYLOGENY, ONTOGENY.) Primatologia. Handbook of Primatology. I. Systematik, Phylogenie, Ontogenie. H. Hofer, A. H. Schultz, D. Starck. S. Karger, Basel and New York, pp. xxii, 1063, illus., 1956.

MAN'S POOR RELATIONS. Earnest Albert Hooton. Doubleday, Doran and Co., Inc., New York, pp. xl, 412, illus., 1942.

(Review by Adolph H. Schultz of) MAN'S POOR RELATIONS. Earnest Albert Hooton. Sci. Monthly, Lancaster, vol.56, no.5, pp.473-474, May, 1943.

(Review by William L. Straus, Jr. of) MAN'S POOR RELATIONS. Earnest Albert Hooten. Amer. Jour. Phys. Anthropol., Philadelphia, n.s., vol.1, no.2, pp.215-218, June, 1943.

(KNOWLEDGE OF ANTHROPOIDS IN THE MIDDLE AGES.) Zur Kenntnis der Menschenaffen im Mittelalter. S. Killermann. Zeitschr. fuer Saeugetierkunde, Berlin, vol.6, no.6, pp.227-229, pl.24, Dec.15, 1931.

MONKEYS. R. Lydekker. Allen's Naturalist's Library, vol.1.

NOTES ON CERTAIN MONKEYS NOW LIVING IN THE ZOOLOGICAL SOCIETY'S MENAGERIE. R. Lydekker. Novitates Zool., vol.9, pp.138-140, Apr., 1902.

THE APE IN ANTIQUITY. William Coffman McDermott. Baltimore, Johns Hopkins Press, pp. xi, 338, pls.10, 1938.

MONKEY FOLK. WITH (16) PAINTINGS FROM LIFE BY ELIE CHEVERLANGE. William M. Mann. Nat. Geogr. Mag., vol.73, no.5, pp.615-656, illus., May, 1938.

MAN-EATING MONKEYS AND POISONOUS LOCUSTS. A. C. Miller. Jour. Bombay Nat. Hist. Soc., vol.27, p.629, Mar.31, 1921.

(BIOLOGICAL NOTES ON THE MADAGASCAR LEMURIDS.) Notes biologiques sur les lemuriens Malgaches. J. Millot. Le Naturaliste Malgache, vol.4, no.2, pp.109-121, 1952.

MAMMALIA PRIMATES. Philipp Ludwig Statius Mueller. Muller's Linnaeus - Supplement and Register - Vollst. Natursystem, ed. 12, pp.62, pls.3, 1776.

PRIMITIVE PRIMATES. George H. Pournelle. Zoonooz, Zool. Soc. San Diego, vol.28, no.8, pp.1-4, illus., Aug., 1955.

(THE DEFINITIVE NATURAL HISTORY OF MONKEYS.) Die vollsandigste Naturgeschichte der Affen, Les singes. H. G. L. Reichenbach. Leipzig, 204 pp., 38 pls., 1862.

SOME REMARKS ON DR. D. G. ELLIOT'S REVIEW OF THE PRIMATES. Herbert C. Robinson, C. Boden Kloss. Ann. and Mag. Nat. Hist., London, ser.8, vol.13, pp.389-399, Apr., 1914.

(SOME INTERESTING PHOTOS OF MONKEYS.) Quelques photos interessantes de Singes. H. Schouteden. Rev. Zool. Bot. Afric., vol.24, Suppl., pp.86-87, figs.2, Bull. Cercle Zool. Congol., vol.10, no.4, Aug.25, 1934.

VARIABILITY IN MAN AND OTHER PRIMATES. Adolph H. Schultz. Amer. Jour. Phys. Anthropol., Phila., n.s., vol.5, no. 1, pp.1-14, fig. 1, Mar., 1947.

(MAMMALOGICAL NOTES. PROSIMIAE.) Notes mammalogiques. Prosimiae. A. F. de Seabra. Bull. Soc. Portugaise Sci. Nat., Lisbonne, vol.4, fusc.1, pp.11-22, 1910.

(ON THE DEVELOPMENT OF THE APES.) Zur Entwickelung der Affen. Emil Selenka. Sitz. Ber. Akad. Wiss. Berlin, pp.1257-1262, 1890.

MAMMALOGY--AN ANATOMICAL AND TAXONOMIC CONSIDERATION OF THE GROUP TO WHICH MAN BELONGS. (Pt.1) R. W. Shufeldt. Med. Record, New York, vol.98, no.11, (whole no.2601), pp.421-431, figs.1-8, Sept.11, 1920.

MAMMALOGY--AN ANATOMICAL AND TAXONOMIC CONSIDERATION OF THE GROUP TO WHICH MAN BELONGS. PT.2. R. W. Shufeldt. Med. Record, New York, vol.98, no.17, pp.673-683, figs.9-14, Oct. 23, 1920.

MONOGRAPH OF THE PREHENSILE-TAILED QUADRUMANA. J. H. Slack. Proc. Acad. Nat. Sci. Phila., vol.16, pp.1-13, Nov., 1862.

(BIOLOGICAL RECORDS OF CAPTIVE MONKEYS AND LEMURS.) Biologische Aufzeichnungen ueber in Gefangenschaft gehaltene Affen und Halbaffen. R. Stadie. Zool. Garten, Leipzig, n.F. vol.4, nos. 3-5, pp.132-140, May, 1931.

PRIMATE BABIES. Ken Stott, Jr. San Diego Zoonooz, vol.19, no.11, pp.6-7, illus., Nov., 1946.

PRIMATES. William L. Straus, Jr. Anthropology Today (Univ. Chica. Press, 1953), pp.77-92, 1953.

(THE ANTHROPOID APES.) Les singes anthropoides. Achille Urbain, Paul Rode. Presses Universitaires de France, Paris, pp.127, figs.20, 1946.

(NATURAL HISTORY OF KNOWLEDGE IN THE LOWER MONKEYS.) Histoire naturelle de la connaissance chez le singe inferieur. Louis Verlaine. Actualites Scientifiques et Industrielles, Paris, pp.1-49, 4 pls., 1935.

THE MONKEY BOOK. Ernest P. Walker. The Macmillan Company, New York, 153 pp., 51 pls., 1 fig., 1954.

(Review by Robert W. Eadie of) THE MONKEY BOOK. Ernest P. Walker. Jour. Mam., vol.35, no.4, pp.603-604, Nov.29, 1954.

PORTRAITS OF MY MONKEY FRIENDS. Ernest P. Walker. Natl. Geogr. Mag., Washington, vol.109, no.1, pp.105-119, illus., Jan., 1956.

MONKEYS. Alfred R. Wallace. Contemporary Review, pp.417-430, 1882.

(Review by W. M. Krogman of) APES, GIANTS AND MAN. Franz Weidenreich. Science, Lancaster, vol.104, no.2709, p. 516, Nov.29, 1946.

(Review by Richard S. Lull of) APES, GIANTS AND MAN. Franz Weidenreich. Amer. Jour. Sci., New Haven, vol.244, no. 10, pp.740-742, Oct., 1946.

JUST MONKEYS. Maurice Wilson. Country Life Ltd. London and Charles Scrinbers's Sons, New York, 88 pages, illus., 1937.

PROVISION FOR THE STUDY OF MONKEYS AND APES. Robert M. Yerkes. Science, Lancaster, n.s., vol.43, no.1103, pp.231-234, Feb.18, 1916.

YALE LABORATORIES OF PRIMATE BIOLOGY, INCORPORATED. Robert M. Yerkes. Science, n.s., vol.82, no.2139, pp.618-620, Dec.27, 1935.

SOCIAL BEHAVIOR IN INFRAHUMAN PRIMATES. Robert M. Yerkes, Ada W. Yerkes. Chapter 21 (pp.973-1033, figs.13) of: A handbook of social psychology (24 contributors, pp. xii, 1195), edited by Carl Murchison. Clark Univ. Press, Worcester, Mass., 1935.

FUNCTIONAL AFFINITIES OF MAN, MONKEYS AND APES. A STUDY OF THE BEARINGS OF PHYSIOLOGY AND BEHAVIOR ON THE TAXONOMY AND PHYLOGENY OF LEMURS, MONKEYS, APES AND MAN. S. Zuckerman. New York: Harcourt, Brace and Company, pp.xviii, 203, figs.24, Dec. 1, 1933.

(Review by G.S. Miller of) FUNCTIONAL AFFINITIES OF MAN, MONKEYS, AND APES. S. Zuckerman. Amer. Anthrop., vol.36, no.3, pp.471-473, July-Sept., 1934.

(THE SOCIAL AND SEXUAL LIFE OF MONKEYS.) La vie sexuelle et sociale des singes. S. Zuckerman. Mammalia, Paris, vol.2, no.2, p.105, June, 1938.

THE SOCIAL LIFE OF MONKEYS AND APES. S. Zuckerman. International Library of Psychology, Philosophy and Scientific Method. Kegan Paul, Trench, Trubner, and Co., London, pp. XII, 375, pls.24, (Dec., 1931), 1932.

(Review by Gerrit S. Miller, Jr. of) THE SOCIAL LIFE OF MONKEYS AND APES. S. Zuckerman. Jour. Mamm., Baltimore, vol.13, no.1, pp.83-84, Feb.9, 1932.

(THE WANDEROO-MANDRILL HYBRIDS OF THE FRANKFURT ANIMAL GARDEN.) Die Wanderu-Schweinsaffen-Mischlinge des Frankfurter Tier gartens. Ludwig Zukowsky. Zool. Garten, Leipzig, vol.19, no.1, pp.1-26, illus., 1952.

MONKEYS FIRST. National Nature News, Washington, D.C., vol.2, no.17, p.4, Apr.25, 1938.

PORTRAITS OF FOUR PRIMATES. Animal Kingdom, New York, vol.46, no.3, pp.59-62, illus., May, 1943.

PORTRAITS OF FOUR PRIMATES. III. Animal Kingdom, New York, vol.46, no.4, pp.83-86, illus., Aug.6, 1943.

PORTRAITS OF FOUR PRIMATES. IV. Animal Kingdom, New York, vol.46, no.5, pp.107-110, Sept.-Oct., 1943.

PUBLICATIONS FROM THE YALE LABORATORIES OF PRIMATE BIOLOGY, INC. School of Medicine, Yale Univ., New Haven, 14 pp., 1940 (1925-1939).

Africa

PRIMATES COLLECTED BY THE AMERICAN MUSEUM CONGO EXPEDITION. J. A. Allen. Bull. Amer. Mus. Nat. Hist., vol. 47, art.4, pp.283-499, pls.79-167, Feb.6, 1925.

TWO NEW EAST AFRICAN PRIMATES. N. Hollister. Smithsonian Misc. Coll., vol.72, no.2, pp.1-2, Jan.22, 1920.

(NOTE ON AN AFRICAN ANTHROPOID. THE KOULA-NGUIA.) Note sur un anthropoide africain: Le Koula-Nguia. Raingeard. Mammalia, Paris, vol.2, no.2, pp.81-83, tables, pl.10, June, 1938.

(BIOLOGICAL AND BIOGEOGRAPHICAL CONSIDERATIONS ON THE PRIMATES OF AFRICA.) Considerations biologique et biogeographiques sur les primates de l'Afrique. P. Rode. Scientia, Bologna, 64: 27-36, 1938.

(THE PRIMATES OF AFRICA.) Les primates de l'Afrique. P. Rode. Mammalia, Paris, vol.1, no.5, pp.219-220, Sept., 1937.

THE MONKEYS AND BABOONS OF NIGERIA. D. R. Rosevear. Nigerian Field, Lond., vol.3, no.4, pp.138-151, illus., Oct., 1934.

Age Changes

AGE CHANGES IN DIMENSIONAL DIFFERENCES BETWEEN THE SKULLS OF MALE AND FEMALE APES. E. H. Ashton. Proc. Zool. Soc. Lond., 128 (2): 259-265, Apr.18, 1957.

AGE CHANGES IN SOME BODILY DIMENSIONS OF APES. E. H. Ashton. Proc.

Zool. Soc. Lond., vol.124, pt.3, pp.587-594, Nov.15, 1954.

AGE CHANGES IN THE BASICRANIAL AXIS OF THE ANTHROPOIDEA. E. H. Ashton. Proc. Zool. Soc. Lond., 129 (1): 61-74, Sept.9, 1957.

AGE CHANGES IN THE CRANIAL CAPACITY AND FORAMEN MAGNUM OF HOMINOIDS. E. H. Ashton, T. F. Spence. Proc. Zool. Soc. Lond., 130 (2): 169-181, Mar.13, 1958.

AGE CHANGES IN THE POSITION OF THE FORAMEN MAGNUM IN HOMINOIDS. E. H. Ashton, S. Zuckerman. Proc. Zool. Soc. Lond., 126 (2): 315-325, Apr.6, 1956.

(PHENOMENA INCIDENT TO OLD AGE IN THE BRAIN OF MONKEYS AND MAN.) Alterserscheinungen im Hirn von Affen und Menschen. J. W. Harms. Zool. Anzeiger, vol.74, pp.249-256, 3 figs., Dec.5, 1927.

The Americas

(THE MONKEYS OF ARGENTINA.) Los monos de la Argentina. Angel Cabrera. Physis (Rev. Soc. Argentina Cienc. Nat.) Buenos Aires, vol.16, pp.29, figs.3, pls. 2, 1939.

(DESCRIPTION OF THE MAMMALS: AMERICAN MONKEYS.) Description des Mammifères. Second mémoire. Singes Américains. I. Geoffroy Saint-Hilaire. Archives du Museum, vol.4, pp.5-42, pls. 3, 1845.

MAMMALS OF NORTHERN COLOMBIA. PRELIMINARY REPORT NO.4: MONKEYS (PRIMATES), WITH TAXONOMIC REVISIONS OF SOME FORMS. Philip Hershkovitz. Proc. U.S. Natl Mus. Washington, vol.98, no.3232, pp.323-427, figs.52-59, pls.15-17, May 10, 1949.

(REPORTS ON THE MONKEYS OF THE AMAZON AND NEW GRANADA REGIONS.) Memorias sobre los monos de las regiones Amazonicas y de Nueva Granada. Alexander de Humboldt. Revista Acad. Colombiana Cienc. Exactas, Fisicas y Naturales, Bogota, vol.5, no.20, pp.506-527, 4 col. pls., Aug., 1944.

NOTES ON THE PRIMATES OF SURINAME. A. M. Husson. Studies on the Fauna of Suriname and other Guyanas. 1(2): 13-40, pls.1-8, 1957.

(REMARKS ON THE EVOLUTION OF SOUTH AMERICAN PRIMATES. ON THE GREAT MONKEY OF VENEZUELA.) Remarques sur l'evolution des primates Sud-Americains. A propos du grand singe du Venezuela. L. Joleaud. Revue Scientifique, 67 année, no.9, pp.269-273, figs.131-134, May 11, 1929.

MAMMALS OF AMAZONIA. VOL. I, GENERAL INTRODUCTION AND PRIMATES. Eladio da Cruz Lima. Contrib. Mus. Paraense Emilio Goeldi Hist. Nat. e Etnografia, Belem do Para and Rio de Janeiro, pp.1-274, pls.42, 1945.

COMMENTARIES ON SOUTH AMERICAN PRIMATES. Alipio de Miranda Ribeiro. Memorias Instituto Oswaldo Cruz, Rio de Janeiro, vol.35, no.4, pp.779-851, pls.18, 1940.

EXTRACTS FROM LETTERS RECEIVED FROM MR. E. BARTLETT. Philip Lutley Sclater. Proc. Zool. Soc. Lond., p.2, 1867.

(MONKEYS FROM SAO PAULO STATE.) Os Símios do estado de Sao Paulo. C. C. Vierira. Papéis Avulsos do Dept. Zool., Brasil, vol.4, no.1, pp.1-31, Oct.3, 1944.

Anatomy

(DACTYLOSCOPIC IDENTIFICATION OF THE PRIMATES.) Identificación Dactiloscópica de los Primates. Luis Reyna Almandos. Revista de Identificación y Ciencias Penales, vol.2, no.10, pp.1-11, figs.1-13, May-June, 1929.

(EXCEPTIONAL DISPOSITION OF THE SULCUS ARCUATUS ON THE FRONTAL LOBE OF A PLATYRRHINE MONKEY.) Disposition exceptionnelle du Sulcus arcuatus sur le lobe frontal d'un atele Singes Platyrhiniens. J. Anthony. Mammalia, Paris, vol.16, no.3, pp.157-159, Sept., 1952.

(EXTERNAL MORPHOLOGY OF THE BRAIN OF PLATYRRHINE MONKEYS.) Morphologie externe du cerveau des Singes Platyrhiniens. J. Anthony. Anal. Sci. Nat., Paris, ser.11, vol.8, pp.1-149, 1946.

THE MESETHMOID-PRESPHENOID RELATIONSHIPS IN THE PRIMATES. M. F. Ashley-Montagu. Amer. Jour. Phys. Anthropol., Phila., n.s., vol.1, no.2, pp. 129-141, pl.1, June, 1943.

NOTE ON THE EXTERNAL GENITALIA IN THREE FEMALE OLD WORLD PRIMATES. M. F. Ashley-Montague. Anat. Record, vol.69, no.4, pp.389-405, figs.6, Nov.25, 1937.

THE PREMAXILLA IN THE PRIMATES. M. F. Ashley-Montagu. Quart. Rev. Biol., vol.10, no.1, pp.32-59, figs.3, Mar., 1935.

THE PREMAXILLA IN THE PRIMATES (CONCLUDED). M. F. Ashley-Montagu. Quart. Review Biol., vol.10, no.2, pp. 181-208, figs.11, June, 1935.

SOME EFFECTS OF FIXATION AND OTHER INSULTS ON UTERINE EPITHELIAL CELLS IN PRIMATES. G. W. Bartelmez. Anat. Record, Phila., vol.77, no.4, pp.509-527, illus., Aug.26, 1940.

(CHRONOLOGY OF THE DENTITION OF ANTHROPOIDS.) La chronologie de la dentition chez les anthropoides. Charles Bennejeant. Mammalia, Paris, vol.4, no. 2, pp.41-45, figs.2, pl.3, June, 1940.

(DISCUSSION OF THE OBSERVATIONS OF MLLE. M. FRIANT (ON THE INTERPRETATION OF THE PREMOLARS OF PRIMATES).) Discussion sur les observations de Mlle. M. Friant (de l'interpretation des premolars chez les Primates). Charles Bennejeant. Bull. Mus. Nat. d 'Hist. Nat., Paris, ser.2, vol.7, no.6, pp.343-348, figs.3, Nov., 1935.

(NUMERICAL DENTAL VARIATIONS AND PROGRESSIVE DENTAL REDUCTION IN THE PRIMATES.) Les variations dentaires numeriques et la reduction dentaire progressive chez les Primates. Charles Bennejeant. Assoc. Franc. l'Avanc. Sci. Compte rendu de la 59 Session, Nantes, pp.459-464, figs.3, 1935.

(MORPHOLOGICAL CHANGE OF THE PRIMATE SKULL AND ITS RELATION TO THE ONTOGENETIC DEVELOPMENT AND PHYLOGENETIC SPECIALIZATIONS OF THE ORGANS OF THE HEAD.) Der Formwandel des Primatenschaedels und seine Beziehungen zur ontogenetischen Entwicklung und den phylogenetischen Sepzialisationen der Kopforgane. J. Biegert. Mor. Jahrbuch., Leipzig, 98 (1): 77-199, 1957.

(MAMMALIAN OSTEOGRAPHY.) Osteographie des Mammiferes. H. M. de Blainville. vol.1 and 2. Atlas only. Vol. 1, Primates, Sept.7, 1951.

(A PECULIAR NAIL CHARACTER, REMINISCENT OF PROSIMIAE FIND, ON THE FOOT OF PLATYRRHINE MONKEYS.) Ein eigenartiges an Prosimierbefunde erinnerndes Nagelverhalten am Fuss von platyrrhinen Affen. Hans Bluntschli. Roux' Archiv. f. Entwicklungsmechanik der Organismen, Berlin, vol.118, pp.1-10, figs.11, 1929.

(CONTRIBUTION TO KNOWLEDGE OF THE GLOSSOPHARYNGEAL NERVE IN THE PRIMATES.) Contribution a la connaissance du nerf glossopharyngien chez les primates. F. Bolonyi. Bull. Mus. Nat. Hist. Nat., Paris, ser.2, vol.20, no.2, pp.136-146, illus., Feb., 1948.

THE AXIS OF THE FOREBRAIN IN MACAQUE AND MAN. G.von Bonin. Amer. Jour. Phys. Anthropol., Phila., vol.29, no. 1, pp.41-46, figs.3, Mar.30, 1942.

(ON THE STRUCTURE OF THE NERVES OF THE INTERCAROTID GLAND (GLOMUS CAROTICUM) IN THE ANTHROPOID MONKEYS.) Sur la structure des nerfs de la glande intercarotidienne (glomus caroticum) chez les singes anthropoides. J. Botar. Archiv. Mus. Nat. d'Hist. Nat., Paris, ser.6, vol.12, pp.243-249, figs.7, June, 1935.

THE PRENATAL DEVELOPMENT OF THE HAIR TRACTS IN PRIMATES. Walter Brandt. Human Biology, Baltimore, vol.12, no.2, pp.203-231, figs.21, pls.3, May, 1940.

A COMPARATIVE CYTOARCHITECTONIC STUDY OF THE MOTOR AND PREMOTOR AREAS IN THE PRIMATE CORTEX. Paul C. Bucy. Jour. Comp. Neurology, vol.62, no.2, pp.293-311, pls.10, Oct., 1935.

CRANIOMETRIC MEMOIRS. NO. 5. THE INFERIOR GNATHIC TRIANGLE. A NEW CRANIAL TRIANGLE. ITS SIGNIFICANCE IN MODERN AND FOSSIL MAN, THE ANTHROPOIDS AND LOWER MAMMALS. John Cameron. Jour. Anat., vol.67, pt.2, pp.318-330, figs.3, Jan., 1933.

(MORPHOLOGICAL VARIATION OF THE HARD PART OF THE TEMPORAL BONE OF THE HIGHER PRIMATES.) La variation morphologique du rocher chez les primates superieurs. Mm. Carette-Pillot. Mammalia, Paris, vol.11, no.4, pp.153-159, Dec., 1947.

ARTERIAE CORONARIAE (CORDIS) IN THE HIGHER PRIMATES. Ralph E. Chase, Charles F. De Garis. Amer. Jour. Phys. Anthrop., Phila., vol.24, no.3, pp.427-448, figs.4, table 1, Jan.-Mar., 1939.

THE PROBLEM OF THE CLAW IN PRIMATES. W. E. Le Gros Clark. Proc. Zool. Soc. Lond., pt.1, pp.1-24, figs.13, pl.1, Apr., 1936.

EXTERNAL MORPHOLOGY OF THE PRIMATE BRAIN. Cornelius Connolly. Charles C. Thomas, Springfield, pp.xiii, 378, illus., 1950.

THE FISSURAL PATTERN OF THE PRIMATE BRAIN. Cornelius Connolly. Amer. Jour. Phys. Anthrop., vol.21, no.3, pp.301-422, figs.67, July-Sept., 1936.

CHROMOSOMES OF MONKEYS AND MEN. C. D. Darlington, Ashraful Haque. Nature, Lond., vol.175, no.4444, p.32, Jan.1, 1955.

SUPRA-STERNAL OSSICLES IN PRIMATES OTHER THAN MAN. D. V. Davies. Nature, London, vol.176, no.4493, p.1130, illus., Dec.10, 1955.

(REMARKS ON THE CIRCLE OF WILLIS IN THE PRIMATES.) Remarques a propos du cercle de Willis des Primates. J. L. Decerisy. Mammalia, Paris, vol.16, no.4, pp.213-215, Dec., 1952.

THE AORTIC ARCH IN PRIMATES. Charles F. De Garis. Amer. Jour. Phys. Anthrop., Phila., vol.28, no.1, pp.41-74, figs.2, Mar.31, 1941.

(MORPHOLOGICAL ANALYSIS OF THE SPLANCHNOCRANIUM IN THE PRIMATES AND ITS RELATION TO PROGNATHISM.) Analyse morphologique du splanchnocrane chez les Primates et ses rapports avec la prognathisme. A. Delattre, R. Fenart. Mammalia, 20 (2): 168-214, illus., June, 1956.

(STUDY OF THE ONTOGENSIS OF THE CRANIUM OF THE ANTHROPOIDS OF THE BELGION CONGO.) Etude de l'ontogénèse du crane des anthropoides du Congo Belge. A. R. Delattre. Ann. Mus. Roy. Congo Belge, Tervuren, Sci. Zool., 47: 121, 1956.

SIMILARITY IN CERVIX OF RHESUS MONKEY AND WOMAN. Robert L. Dickinson, Carl G. Hartman. Amer. Jour. Obstetrics and Gynecology, St. Louis, vol.32, no.5, pp.813-822, illus., Nov., 1936.

(TO WHAT EXTENT IS THE VERMIFORM PROCESS ON THE HUMAN CAECUM A RUDIMENTARY STRUCTURE?) Inwieweit ist der Wurmfortsatz am Menschlichen Blinddarm ein rudimentaeres Gebilde? H. Eggeling. Anatom. Anz., vol.53, pp.401-428, 1920.

FUNCTIONAL ANATOMY OF THE HAND IN NEW WORLD PRIMATES. G. E. Erikson. Anat. Record, Phila., 27 (2): 290, Feb., 1957.

(NOTES ON THE MAMMALS. XXIII. ARE THERE BUT TWO PHALANGES IN THE THUMB AND GREAT TOE OF THE PRIMATE?) Notes sur les mammiferes. XXIII. Noy a-t-il que deux phalanges dans le pouce et le gros orteil des Primates? Serge Frechkop. Bull. Mus. Roy. Hist. Nat. Belgique, vol. 13, no.40, pp.1-21, illus., Oct., 1937.

(NOTES ON THE MAMMALS. XL. THE BEARING OF THE HEAD AND THE FORM OF THE CRANIUM IN THE MONKEYS.) Notes sur les mammifères. XL. Le port de la tête et la forme du crâne chez les singes. Serge Frechkop. Bull. Inst. Roy. Sci. Nat. Belgique, vol.30, no.12, pp.11, Apr., 1954.

(THE NUMBER OF LOWER INCISORS IN THE PRIMATES.) Le nombre des incisives inferieures chez les Primates. Madeleine Friant. Bull. Soc. Zool. France, Paris, vol.60, pp.447-450, figs.6, 1935.

(ON THE INTERPRETATION OF THE PREMOLARS IN THE PRIMATES.) De l'interpretation des premolaires chez les Primates. Madeleine Friant. Bull. Mus. Nat. d'Hist. Nat., Paris, ser.2, vol.7, no.6, pp.340-342, fig.1, Nov., 1935.

(THE PHYLOGENESIS OF THE COELIAC ARTERY OF THE PRIMATES.) La phylogénèse de l'artère coeliaque chez les primates. Jozef Grzybowski. Comptes Rendus Séances Soc. Sci. et Lettr. de Varsovie, pp.165-282, 1926.

(STRUCTURE AND FUNCTION OF THE MONKEY FOOT. A CONTRIBUTION TO JOINT AND MUSCLE MECHANICS. I. THE ANTHROPOIDS.) Bau und Funktion des Affenfusses. Ein Beitrag zur Gelenk- und Muskelmechanik. I. Die Anthropoiden. Anton Hafferi. Ztschr. f. Anat. u. Entwickgesch. vol.88, pp.749-783, 11 figs., 1929.

(CONTRIBUTION TO THE STUDY OF THE DEVELOPMENT OF THE CEREBRAL LOBES OF THE PRIMATES.) Contribution a l'étude du développement des lobes cérébraux des primates. T. E. Hamy. Revue d' Anthropologie., vol.1, pp.424-431, 1872.

MULTIOVULAR FOLLICLES IN THE OVARIES OF LOWER PRIMATES. R. J. Harrison. Nature, London, vol.164, no. 4166, pp.409-410, Sept.3, 1949.

(CONTRIBUTIONS ON THE DEVELOPMENT OF THE PRIMATE HAND.) Beitraege zur Entwicklung der Primatenhand. K. O. Henckel. I. Zur Entwicklung der Makakenhand. Morphol. Jahrb., vol.61, pp.43-48, 1 text fig., 1929.

OBSERVATIONS ON THE STRUCTURE AND MECHANISM OF THE EXTERNAL EAR IN THE LORISOIDS AND TARSIUS. W. C. Osman Hill. Ceylon Jour. Sci., sect.B, Zool. and Geol., Spolia Zeylanica, Colombo, vol.22, pt.1, pp.135-139, figs.2, June 12, 1940.

THE HEART AND GREAT VESSELS IN THE STREPSIRHINI. W. C. Osman Hill, D. V. Davies. Trans. Roy. Soc. Edinburgh, 63 (1): 115-128, 1957.

THE CAECUM OF PRIMATES. ITS APPENDAGES, MESENTERIES AND BLOOD SUPPLY. W. C. Osman Hill, R. E. Rewell. Trans. Zool. Soc. Lond., vol.26, pt.3, pp.199-256, pls.6, Dec., 1948.

THE BRACHIAL FLEXOR MUSCLES IN PRIMATES. A. Brazier Howell, Wm. L. Straus, Jr. Proc. U.S. Nat. Mus., vol. 80, art.13, pp.1-31, pls.1-2, Nov.21, 1931.

(AN M. MANDIBULO-AURICULARIS IN PRIMATES, WITH CONTRIBUTIONS TO KNOWLEDGE OF THE PHYLOGENESIS OF THE AURAL MUSCULATURE OF MAN.) Ein M. mandibulo-auricularis bei Primaten, nebst Beitraegen zur Kenntniss der Phylogenese der menschlichen Ohrmuskulatur. Ernst Huber. Anat. Anzeiger, vol.60, pp. 11-21, illus., July 9, 1925.

(REMARKS CONCERNING THE REGIO OLFACTORIA OF THE ANTHROPOIDS.) Bemerkungen ueber die Regio olfactoria der Anthropoiden. W. Kilmer. Zeitschr. f. Anat. u. Entwicklungsgesch., vol.84, pp.160-170, 8 figs., Oct.8, 1927.

(ON THE MORPHOLOGY OF THE PRIMATE SPLEEN.) Zur Morphologie der Primatenmilz. Christian Krogh. Anthrop. Anz., Stuttgart, Jahrg., 13, nos.1-2, pp.89-100, figs.20, 1936.

(ON THE RELATIONSHIPS BETWEEN BRAIN AND SKULL IN MONKEYS.) Ueber Beziehungen zwischen Gehirn und Schaedel bei den Affen. Wilhelm Leche. Zool. Jahrb., suppl.15, vol.2, pp.1-106, pls.1-4, figs.1-45, 1912.

THE FACIAL MUSCULATURE OF SOME LESSER PRIMATES AND A TUPAIA. A COMPARATIVE STUDY. G. S. Lightoller. Proc. Zool. Soc. Lond., pt.2, pp.259-309, pls.1-9, July, 1934.

THE HOMOLOGIES OF THE INCISORS OF THE HIGHER PRIMATES IN THE LIGHT OF SOME "ANOMALIES" IN THE DENTITION OF GIBBONS. Einar Loennberg. Arkiv. Zool., Stockholm, vol.22A, no.6, pp.1-6, figs.4, Dec.24, 1930.

FORM OF HAND AND FOOT IN PRIMATES. Charles Midlo. Amer. Jour. Phys. Anthrop., vol.19, no.3, pp.337-389, figs.61, Oct.-Dec., 1934.

PALMAR AND PLANTAR DERMATOGLYPHICS IN PRIMATES. Charles Midlo, Harold Cummins. Wistar Inst. Anat. and Biol., Amer. Anat. Memoirs, Phila., no. 20, pp.198, figs.602, Oct., 1942.

(Review by G.S. Miller, Jr. of) PALMAR AND PLANTAR DERMATOGLYPHICS IN PRIMATES. Charles Midlo, Harold Cummins. Amer. Jour. Phys.Anthropol., Philadelphia, n.s., vol.1, no.2, p.218, June, 1943.

HUMAN HAIR AND PRIMATE PATTERNING. G. S. Miller, Jr. Smithson. Misc. Coll., vol.85, no.10, pp.13, pls.5, Dec.19, 1931.

THE ISCHIAL CALLOSITIES OF PRIMATES. Ruth A. Miller. Amer. Jour. Anat., Phila., vol.76, no.1, pp.67-91, figs.1-3, pls.1-2, Jan., 1945.

CONTRIBUTIONS TOWARDS A MORE COMPLETE KNOWLEDGE OF THE AXIAL SKELETON IN THE PRIMATES. St. George Mivart. Proc. Zool. Soc. Lond., pp.545-592, figs.13, 1865.

CONTRIBUTIONS TOWARDS A MORE COMPLETE KNOWLEDGE OF THE SKELETON OF THE PRIMATES. St. George Mivart. Trans. Zool. Soc. Lond., vol.6, pt.4, pp.175-225, pls.35-42, 1866.

ON THE APPENDICULAR SKELETON OF THE PRIMATES. St. George Mivart. Nat. Hist., vol.73, 1866.

ON THE APPENDICULAR SKELETON OF THE PRIMATES. St. George Mivart. Philos. Trans. Lond., pp.299-429, pls.11-14, 1867.

MEMOIR ON THE ANATOMY OF THE LEMUROIDEA. James Murie. Proc. Zool. Soc. Lond., p.168, 1866.

ON THE ANATOMY OF THE LEMUROIDEA. James Murie. Trans. Zool. Soc. Lond., vol.7, pt.1, pp.1-113, pls.6, 1866.

(THE LARYNX OF THE PRIMATES.) Das Stimmorgan der Primaten. J. Nomai. Anatom. Hefte, Abt., pp.257-292, 1920.

THE MAXILLARY NERVE IN THE CEBOIDEA. C. E. Oxnard. Proc. Zool. Soc. Lond., 128 (1): 113-117, Feb.14, 1957.

STUDIES IN MAMMALIAN SPERMATOGENESIS. IV. THE SEX CHROMOSOMES OF MONKEYS. Theophilus S. Painter. Jour. Exper. Zool., vol.39, pp.433-462, May 5, 1924.

THE EXTERNAL CHARACTERS OF THE CATARRHINE MONKEYS AND APES. R. I. Pocock. Proc. Zool. Soc. Lond., 1925, pt.4, pp.1479-1579, Jan.14, 1926.

PECTORAL GLAND IN APES AND MONKEYS. R. I. Pocock. Nature, London, vol.153, no. 3882, p.381, Mar.25, 1944.

(ON CRYSTALLOIDS IN THE OVA OF MACACUS RHESUS.) Ueber Kristalloide in Eizellen von Macacus rhesus. W. Pollak. Anat. Anzeiger, vol.61, pp.202-204, illus., June 9, 1926.

THE PRIMATE COLON. Norman Reider. Proc. Zool. Soc. Lond., 1936, pt.2, pp. 438-453, pls.1-10, July, 1936.

(ON THE BASICRANIAL MORPHOGENESIS OF SOME PRESENT-DAY AND FOSSIL PRIMATES.) Sobre morfogénesis basicraneana de algunos primates actuales y fósiles. Carlos Rusconi. Rev. Argentina de Paleont. y Antrop. Ameghinia, Buenos Aires, vol.1, no.1, pp.3-23, July 15, 1935.

(ROENTGENOLOGICAL INVESTIGATIONS OF THE HAND ROOT OF MONKEYS.) Roentgenologische Untersuchungen an der Handwurzel der Affen. Hans Schreiber. Anat. Anz., vol.78, nos.20-24, pp.369-429, 19 figs., 1 pl., Sept.24, 1934.

CONDITIONS FOR BALANCING THE HEAD IN PRIMATES. Adolph H. Schultz. Amer. Jour. Phys. Anthrop., Phila., vol.29, no.4, pp.483-497, figs.3, Dec.30, 1942.

THE DENSITY OF HAIR IN PRIMATES. Adolph H. Schultz. Human Biology, vol.3, no.3, pp.303-317, tables 1-4, Sept., 1931.

THE NASAL CARTILAGES IN HIGHER PRIMATES. Adolph H. Schultz. Amer. Jour. Phys. Anthrop., vol.20, no.2, pp.205-212, figs.6, July-Sept., 1935.

THE PALATINE RIDGES OF PRIMATES. Adolph H. Schultz. Carnegie Inst. Washington Publ.583, Contrib. to Embryology no. 215, pp.43-66, figs.7, Feb.28, 1949.

THE RELATIVE LENGTH OF THE REGIONS OF THE SPINAL COLUMN IN OLD WORLD PRIMATES. Adolph H. Schultz. Amer. Jour. Phys. Anthrop., vol.24, no.1, pp.1-22, fig.1, tables 10, July-Sept., 1938.

THE RELATIVE WEIGHT OF THE TESTES IN PRIMATES. Adolph H. Schultz. Anat. Rec., vol.72, no.3, pp.387-394, Nov.25, 1938.

THE SKELETON OF THE TRUNK AND LIMBS OF HIGHER PRIMATES. Adolph H. Schultz. Human Biology, vol.2, no.3, pp.303-438, figs.23, Sept., 1930.

THE TECHNIQUE OF MEASURING THE OUTER BODY OF HUMAN FETUSES AND OF PRIMATES IN GENERAL. Adolph H. Schultz. Carnegie Inst. Washington, publ. 394, pp.213-257, illus., Jan., 1929.

THE NUMBERS OF VERTEBRAE IN PRIMATES. Adolph H. Schultz, William L. Straus, Jr. Proc. Amer. Philos. Soc., Phila., vol.89, no.4, pp.601-626, figs.3, Dec., 1945.

ON THE OSTEOLOGY OF THE GENERA LASIOPYGA AND CALLITHRIX WITH NOTES UPON THE OSTEOLOGY OF THE GENERA SENIOCEBUS AND AOTUS. R. W. Shufeldt. Ann. Carnegie Mus. Pittsburgh, vol.9, nos.1-2, pp.58-85, pls.12-21, Aug. 17, 1914.

THE COMPARATIVE ANATOMY OF THE TONGUES OF THE MAMMALIA. IV. FAMILIES 3 AND 4. CEBIDAE AND HAPALIDAE. Charles F. Sonntag. Proc. Zool. Soc. Lond., pt.3, pp.497-524, Sept., 1921.

THE COMPARATIVE ANATOMY OF THE TONGUES OF THE MAMMALIA. V. LEMUROIDEA AND TARSIOIDEA. Charles F. Sonntag. Proc. Zool. Soc. Lond., 1921, pt.4, pp.741-755, Jan., 1922.

THE COMPARATIVE ANATOMY OF THE TONGUES OF THE MAMMALIA. VI. SUMMARY AND CLASSIFICATION OF THE TONGUES OF THE PRIMATES. Charles F. Sonntag. Proc. Zool. Soc. Lond., 1921, pt.4, pp.757-767, Jan., 1922.

ACCESSORY SACRO-ILIAC ARTICULATIONS IN THE HIGHER PRIMATES AND THEIR SIGNIFICANCE. T. D. Stewart. Amer. Jour. Anthrop., vol.24, no.1, pp. 43-55, tables, July-Sept., 1938.

THE MUSCULATURE OF THE ANTHROPOIDS. 1. NECK AND TRUNK. T. D. Stewart. Amer. Jour. Phys. Anthrop., vol.21, no.2, pp.141-204, figs.9, Apr.-June, 1936.

THE FORM OF THE TRACHEAL CARTILAGES OF PRIMATES, WITH REMARKS ON THE SUPPOSED TAXONOMIC IMPORTANCE. William L. Straus, Jr. Jour. Mam., vol.12, no.3, pp.281-285, pl.12, Aug., 1931.

RUDIMENTARY DIGITS IN PRIMATES. William L. Straus, Jr. Quart. Rev. Biol., Baltimore, vol.17, no.3, pp.228-243, figs. 11, Sept., 1942.

THE STRUCTURE OF THE PRIMATE KIDNEY. William L. Straus, Jr. Jour. Anat., vol.69, no.1, pp.93-108, figs.5, Oct., 1934.

STUDIES ON PRIMATE ILIA. William L. Straus, Jr. Amer. Jour. Anat., vol.43, pp.403-460, May 15, 1929.

SUPRASTERNAL OSSICLES. William L. Straus, Jr. Science, Lancaster, vol.123, no.3192, p.366, Mar.2, 1956.

SOME UNIFORM CHARACTERISTICS OF THE PRIMATE EAR. George L. Streeter. Anat. Record, vol.23, pp.335-341, June, 1922.

COMPARATIVE ANATOMY OF MUSCULUS ABDOMINIS OBLIQUUS INTERNUS IN MAN AND PRIMATES. Z. S. Sztajnfeld. Bull. Acad. Poloaniase Sci., et Lettres Cl. Medecine, Cracovie, pp.197-201, figs.2, 1936.

(ON THE VARIATIONS OF SUPERFICIAL ARTERIES OF THE FACE IN MAN AND IN PRIMATES.) Sur les variations des arteres superficielles de la face chez l'homme et chez primates. S. Tokarski. Z Zakladu Anatomji Prawidlowej Uniwersytetu J. Pilsudskiego w Warzwae, Folia Morphologica, vol.6, pp.58-64, figs.8, 1936.

A COMPARATIVE STUDY OF THE ANTERIOR CEREBRAL ARTERY AND THE CIRCLE OF WILLIS IN PRIMATES. James W. Watts. Jour. Ana., Cambridge, vol. 68, pt.4, pp.534-550, figs.1-13, July, 1934.

(SUPERNUMERARY INCISORS IN MONKEYS.) Ueberzaehlige Incisiven bei affen. Richard N. Wegner. Zeitschrift fur Morphol., und Anthrop., vol.12, no.2, pp.353-358, pls.12, 1909.

THE HISTOLOGY AND CYTOLOGY OF THE HUMAN AND MONKEY PLACENTA, WITH SPECIAL REFERENCE TO THE TROPHOBLAST. George B. Wislocki, H. Stanley Bennett. Amer. Jour. Anat., Phila., vol. 73, no.3, pp.335-449, fig.1, pls.1-13, Nov., 1943.

ON THE NATURE OF MODIFICATIONS OF THE SKIN IN THE STERNAL REGION OF CERTAIN PRIMATES. George B. Wislocki, Adolph H. Schultz. Jour. Mam., vol.6, no. 4, pp.236-243, pl.22, Nov., 1925.

A COMPARATIVE STUDY OF THE FORM AND DERMATOGLYPHS OF THE EXTREMITIES OF PRIMATES. Charlotte Wolff. Proc. Zool. Soc. Lond., vol.108, ser.A, pt.1, pp.143-161, pls.1-7, Apr., 1938.

(ANTHROPOMORPHOLOGY OF THE M. GLUTAEUS MAXIMUS.) Anthropomorphologie des M. glutaeus maximus. H. Zielinska. Bull. Acad. Polonaise Sci. et Lettres Cl. Medecine Cracovie, pp.203-210, figs.5, 1936.

OBSERVATIONS ON THE STRUCTURE OF THE UTERUS MASCULINUS IN VARIOUS PRIMATES. S. Zuckerman, A. S. Parkes. Jour. Anat., Lond., vol.69, pt.4, pp.484-496, pls.1-5, July, 1935.

## Asia

ASIA AND THE DISPERSAL OF PRIMATES. Davidson Black. Bull. Geol. Soc. China, vol.4, no.2, pp.133-183, 9 pls., 1 table, 1925.

MAMMAL AND BIRD COLLECTIONS OF THE ASIATIC PRIMATE EXPEDITION. Harold J. Coolidge, Jr. Bull. Mus. Comp. Zool., Cambridge, vol.87, no.3, pp.121-130, Dec., 1940.

THE PRIMATES OF TRAVANCORE. W. C. O. Hill. Proc. Zool. Soc., Lond., vol. 107, ser.B, Syst. and Morphol., pt.2, pp. 205-216, figs.2, pl.1, July 15, 1937.

ON SOME VARIETIES OF THE MONKEYS OF CEYLON, CERCOPITHECUS PILEATUS AND LORIS GRACILIS. Roy Templeton. Proc. Zool. Soc. Lond., pt.12, p.3, 1844.

## Bibliographies

BIBLIOGRAPHICA PRIMATOLOGICA. A CLASSIFIED BIBLIOGRAPHY OF PRIMATES OTHER THAN MAN. PART 1. ANATOMY, EMBRYOLOGY AND QUANTITATIVE MORPHOLOGY; PHYSIOLOGY, PHARMACOLOGY AND PSYCHOBIOLOGY; PRIMATE PHYLOGENY AND MISCELLANEA. WITH AN INTRODUCTION BY JOHN F. FULTON. Theodore C. Ruch. Yale Medical Library, Historical Library, Publ. no.4 (Charles C. Thomas, Springfield), pp.xxvii, 241, 1941.

(Review by C.E. McClung of) PRIMATOLOGICA--A CLASSIFIED BIBLIOGRAPHY OF PRIMATES OTHER THAN MAN. Theodore C. Ruch. Science, Lancaster, n.s., vol.95, no.2466, pp.358-359, Apr. 3, 1942.

(Review by P. Rode of) BIBLIOGRAPHIA PRIMATOLOGICA--A CLASSIFIED BIBLIOGRAPHY OF PRIMATES OTHER THAN MAN. J. F. Ruch. Mammalia, Paris, 11 (1-2): 62, Mar.-June, 1947.

GROWTH OF PRIMATE LITERATURE SINCE 1800. T. C. Ruch, J. F. Fulton. Science, Lancaster, n.s., vol.95, no.2454, pp.47-48, fig.1, Jan.9, 1942.

PUBLICATIONS FROM THE YALE LABORATORIES OF PRIMATE BIOLOGY, INC. 1925-1936. Robert M. Yerkes. School of Medicine, Yale Univ., New Haven, Conn., pp. 1-9, 1937.

## Blood and Circulation

NEW OBSERVATIONS ON THE BLOOD GROUP FACTORS IN SIMIIDI AND CERCOPITHECIDAE. P. B. Candela, A. S. Wiener, J. L. Goss. Zoologica, Sci. Contrib. New York Zool. Soc., New York, vol.25, pt.4, no.31, pp.513-521, Dec.31, 1940.

BLOOD GROUPS OF ANTHROPOIDS. J. B. S. Haldane. Nature, London, vol.146, no. 3707, p.652, Nov.16, 1940.

SEROLOGICAL OBSERVATIONS ON THE RELATIONSHIP OF THE BLOODS OF MAN AND THE ANTHROPOID APES. K. Landsteiner, C. Philip Miller, Jr. Science, n.s., vol.61, pp.492-493, May 8, 1925.

SEROLOGICAL STUDIES ON THE BLOOD OF PRIMATES. I. THE DIFFERENTIATION OF HUMAN AND ANTHROPOID BLOODS. K. Landsteiner, C. Philip Miller, Jr. Jour. Exper. Med., vol.42 no.6, pp.841-852, Dec.1, 1925.

SEROLOGICAL STUDIES ON THE BLOOD OF THE PRIMATES. III. DISTRIBUTION OF SEROLOGICAL FACTORS RELATED TO HUMAN ISOGGLUTINOGENS IN THE BLOOD OF LOWER MONKEYS. K. Landsteiner, C. Philip Miller, Jr. Jour. Exper. Med., vol.42, no.6, pp.863-872, Dec.1, 1925.

HAEMATOLOGY OF THE PRIMATES. Eric J. Ponder, Franklin Yeager, Harry A. Charipper. Sci. Contrib. New York, Zool. Soc., vol.11, no.2, pp.9-18, Feb.28, 1929.

CIRCULATION IN THE MATERNAL PLACENTA OF THE RHESUS MONKEY AND MAN, WITH OBSERVATIONS ON THE MARGINAL LAKES. Elizabeth Mapelsden Ramsey. Amer. Jour. Anat., Phila., 98 (2): 159-190, Mar., 1956.

(ON THE CHRONOLOGICAL SUCCESSION OF THE GENESIS OF THE VITELLINE AND PLACENTAL CIRCULATION IN PRIMATES.) Ueber die zeitliche Folge der Entstehung der Dotter-und Plazentarkreislaeufe bei Primaten. Chr. van Gelderen. Zool. Anzeiger, vol.66, pp.103-114, 3 figs., Mar.20, 1926.

## Care in Captivity

(THE NEW MONKEY HOUSE OF THE ZOO AT DUESSELDORF.) Das neue Affenhaus im Duesseldorfer Zoo. G. Aulmann. Zool. Garten, Leipzig, n.F., vol.6, nos.1-3, pp. 48-56, figs.7, May, 1933.

IMPROVED CAGE DESIGNS FOR USE IN HANDLING MONKEYS. Howard F. Brubach. Science, Lancaster, vol.106, no.2740, pp. 18-19, figs.2, July 4, 1947.

(KEEPING MONKEYS FREE IN THE ZOO.) Affenfreihaltung im Zoo. Bernhard Grzimek. Zool. Garten, Leipzig, n.F., vol.18, nos. 3-4, pp.138-140, 1951.

ON THE MANAGEMENT OF VARIOUS SPECIES OF MONKEYS IN CONFINEMENT. Professor Percy. Proc. Zool. Soc. Lond., pt.12, p.81, 1844.

AN ALBINO MONKEY AT THE ZOOLOGICAL GARDENS. R, I. Pocock. The Field (London), vol.148, p.1154, Dec.30, 1926.

A DIET FOR CHIMPANZEES AND MONKEYS IN CAPTIVITY. O. L. Tinklepaugh. Jour. Mam., vol.12, no.4, pp.400-404, Nov., 1931.

CORRECTIONS TO "A DIET FOR CHIMPANZEES AND MONKEYS IN CAPTIVITY." O. L. Tinklepaugh. Jour. Mam., vol.14, no.1, pp.68-69, Feb., 1933.

(KEEPING AND CARING FOR SOME NEW WORLD MONKEY SPECIES.) Zur Haltung und Pflege einiger Neuweltaffenarten. Ludwig Zukowsky. Zool. Garten, Leipzig, n.F., vol.12, nos.2-3, pp.92-110, figs.9, July, 1940.

## Collections

(THE COLLECTION OF PRIMATES OF THE MENAGERIE OF THE MUSEUM OF NATURAL HISTORY.) La collection de primates de la menagerie du Museum National d' Histoire Naturelle. E. Bourdelle. Bull. Mus. Nat. d'Hist. Nat., Paris, vol.1, no. 4, pp.234-238, 1929.

PRIMATES IN THE ROYAL SCOTTISH MUSEUM. PT. 2. PLATYRRHINI. W. C. Osman Hill. Proc. Royal Physical Soc. Edinburgh, vol.24, pt.3, pp.49-62, pls.4, Dec., 1955.

CATALOGUE OF MAMMALS IN THE ZOOLOGICAL SURVEY OF INDIA. I. PRIMATES; HOMINOIDEA. H. Khajuria. Records Indian Mus., vol.50, pt.2, pp.129-145, 1953.

(THE PRIMATE COLLECTION OF THE MENAGERIE OF THE NATIONAL MUSEUM OF NATURAL HISTORY.) La collection de primates de la Menagerie du Museum National d'Histoire Naturelle. A. Mouquet. See: Bourdelle, E., Mouquet, A., and Mathias, P. 1929.

NOTICE OF SOME RARE SPECIES OF QUADRUMANA, NOW LIVING IN THE SOCIETY'S MENAGERIE. Philip Lutley Sclater. Proc. Zool. Soc. Lond., pt.28, pp.419-422, pl. lxxxii, 1860.

(CATALOG OF PRIMATES IN THE COLLECTIONS OF THE ZOOLOGICAL MUSEUM OF COIMBRA.) Catalogue des primates existants dans les collections du Museum Zoologique de Coimbra. Antonio Armando Themido. Mem. e Est. do Museu Zoologico da Univ. de Coimbra, ser.1, no.19, pp. 1-30, 1928.

(MONKEY PAVILION AND ITS INHABITANTS IN THE PRAGUE ZOO.) Pavilon opic a jeho obyvatelé v pražském zoo. A. Turek, J. Volf. Ziva, Prague, vol.41, no. 3, pp.221-227, illus., 1955.

PRIMATE ACCESSIONS IN THE PHILADELPHIA ZOOLOGICAL SOCIETY FROM THE ABREU COLLECTION. Carroll S. Tyson, Jr. Bull. Zool. Soc. Phila., vol.6, no.1, pp.4, illus., Apr.-May, 1931.

## Diseases

PRIMATE MALARIA. S. D. Aberle, MD. Pub. by Natl. Research Council Div. of Med. Sciences.

(THE TREATMENT OF EPILEPTIC-LIKE SEIZURES IN MONKEYS.) Zur Behandlung epileptiformer Anfaelle bei Affen. Horst-Joachim Christoph. Zool. Garten, Leipzig, 23 (1-3): 65-67, 1957.

ENTERIC INFECTIONS IN CHIMPANZEES AND SPIDER MONKEYS WITH SPECIAL REFERENCE TO A SULFADIAZINE RESISTANT SHIGELLA. M. M. Galton, R.B.

Mitchell, George Clark, A. H. Riesen. Jour. Infectious Diseases, Chicago, vol.83, no.2, pp.147-154, Sept.-Oct., 1948.

(CAECUM INFLAMMATION AS CAUSE OF DEATH IN GORILLA YOUNG.) Blinddarmentzuendung als Todersursache bei Gorilla-Kleinkind. B. Grzimek. Zool. Garten, Garten, Leipzig, 23 (1-3): 249, 1957.

(WORM DISEASES IN MONKEYS, WITH SOME REMARKS ON A NEW TYPE OF TREATMENT.) Wurmkrankheiten bei Affen nebst einigen Bemerkungen ueber eine neuartige Behandlung. H. Mendheim. Saeugetierk. Mitteil., Stuttgart, vol.1, no.4, pp.167-170, illus., Oct.1, 1953.

(TUBERCULOSIS IN MONKEYS.) Zur kenntniss der Affentuberkulose. A. Meyn. Zool. Garten, Leipzig, NF, vol.91-101, 1950.

OUTBREAK OF SHIGELLA SCHMITZII INFECTION IN MEN AND APES. R. E. Rewell. Lancet, Lond., vol.256, no.6545, pp.220-221, 1949.

A DIAGNOSTIC TEST FOR THE RECOGNITION OF TUBERCULOSIS IN PRIMATES; A PRELIMINARY REPORT. Charles R. Schroeder. Zoologica, vol.23, pt.4, nos. 17-21, pp.397-400, pls.2, Dec.31, 1938.

A REGIONAL RECONNAISSANCE OF YELLOW FEVER IN THE SUDAN WITH SPECIAL REFERENCE TO PRIMATE HOSTS. R. M. Taylor, M. A. Haseeb, T. H. Work. Bull. World Health Organization, Geneva, 12: 711-725, 1955.

(TWO CASES OF CEREBRAL TUBERCULOSIS IN MONKEYS AT A ZOOLOGICAL PARK.) Deux cas de Tuberculose cérébrale des Singes du Parc zoologique. Ach. Urbain, W. Riese, J. Nouvel. Bull. Mus. Nat. Hist. Nat., Paris, ser.2, vol.10, no. 6, pp.560-566, figs.2, Nov., 1938.

(PSEUDO-TUBERCULOSIS IN THE MONKEY.) Pseudo-tuberculose chez le singe. J. Verge, L. Placidi. Compt. Rend. Soc. Biol., Paris, vol.136, nos.13-14, pp.483-484, July, 1942.

## Economic Importance

THE USE OF THE MONKEY AND APE IN THE STUDIES OF HUMAN BIOLOGY, WITH SPECIAL REFERENCE TO PRIMATE AFFINITIES. Carl G. Hartman. Amer. Naturalist, vol.73, pp.139-155, figs.5, table 1, Mar.-Apr., 1939.

WHY WE STUDY APES AND MONKEYS. Earnest A. Hooton. Fauna, Philadelphia, vol.5, no.1, pp.2-6, illus., Mar., 1943.

## Evolution, Phylogeny

(THE ORANG FROM NEWLY-BORN TO YOUNG.) Buschi: Vom Orang-Saeugling zum Backenwuelster. Gustav von Brandes. Quelle and Meyer, Leipzig, 135 pp., 155 figs., Mar., 1939.

PRIMATE EVOLUTION FROM THE VIEWPOINT OF COMPARATIVE ANATOMY. D. Dwight Davis. Human Biology, 26 (3): 211-219, Sept., 1954.

(THE EVOLUTION OF THE PRIMATES AND THE THEORY OF FOETALIZATION.) L 'évolution des Primates et la théorie de la foetalisation. Ed Dechambre. Mammalia, Paris, vol.12, nos.1-2, pp.27-41, fig.1, Mar.-June, 1948.

(THE EVOLUTION OF THE PRIMATES AND THE THEORY OF FOETALIZATION.)L'evol ution des primates et la theorie de la foetalisation (conclusion). Ed. Dechambre. Mammalia, Paris, vol.12, no.3, pp.100-117, figs.2, Sept., 1948.

THE EVOLUTION OF THE PELVIC FLOOR OF PRIMATES. Herbert Oliver Elftman. Amer. Jour. Anat., vol.51, no.2, pp.307-339, pls.1-7, Nov.15, 1932.

(NOTES ON THE MAMMALS. XXVI. PRELIMINARY CONSIDERATIONS ON THE EVOLUTION OF THE DENTITION OF THE PRIMATES.) Notes sur les mammifères. XXVI. Considérations préliminaires sur l'évolution de la dentition des Primates. Serge Frechkop. Bull. Mus. Roy. Hist. Nat. Belgique, Bruxelles, vol.16, no.11, pp. 22, figs.14, Feb., 1940.

ENCEPHALIZATION OF MOTOR FUNCTIONS DURING THE EVOLUTION OF THE PRIMATE NERVOUS SYSTEM. John Fulton. Ohio Jour. Sci., Columbus, vol.41, no.3, pp.173-182, May, 1941.

THE SIGN OF BABINSKI. A STUDY OF THE EVOLUTION OF CORTICAL DOMINANCE IN PRIMATES. John F. Fulton, Allen D. Keller. Charles C. Thomas, Springfield, Illinois, pp.XI, 165, figs.65, frontisplate, July 1, 1932.

A CRITIQUE OF PROFESSOR FREDERIC WOOD-JONES'S PAPER: "SOME LANDMARKS IN THE PHYLOGENY OF THE PRIMATES". William K. Gregory. Human Biology, vol.2, no.1, Feb., 1930, pp.99-108.

STUDIES ON THE EVOLUTION OF THE PRIMATES. PT. 1. THE COPE-OSBORN "THEORY OF TRITUBERCULY" AND THE ANCESTRAL MOLAR PATTERNS OF THE PRIMATES. PT. 2. PHYLOGENY OF RECENT AND EXTINCT ANTHROPOIDS WITH SPECIAL REFERENCE TO THE ORIGIN OF MAN. William K. Gregory. Bull. Amer. Mus. Nat. Hist., vol.35, art. 19, pp.239-355, figs.37, pl.1, June 16, 1916.

THE DENTITION OF DRYOPITHECUS AND THE ORIGIN OF MAN. William K. Gregory, Milo Hellman. Anthrop. Papers Amer. Mus. Nat. Hist., vol.28, pt.1, pp.1-123, pls.1-25, text figs.1-21, 1926.

THE EVOLUTIONARY SIGNIFICANCE OF THE PROTOZOAN PARASITES OF MONKEYS AND MAN. Robert Hegner. Quart. Rev. Biol., vol.3, pp.225-244, illus., June, 1928.

REMARKS ON THE PAPERS BY PROFESSOR F. WOOD JONES AND PROFESSOR W. K. GREGORY CONCERNING THE PHYLOGENY OF PRIMATES. K. O. Henckel. Human Biology, vol.2, pp.555-557, Dec., 1930.

THE DEVELOPMENTAL HISTORY OF THE PRIMATES. J. P. Hill. Philos. Trans. Roy. Soc. Lond., ser.B, vol.221, B 475, pp.45-178, figs.17, pls.21, 1932.

DOUBTS AND SUSPICIONS CONCERNING CERTAIN FUNCTIONAL THEORIES OF PRIMATE EVOLUTION. Earnest A. Hooton. Human Biology, vol.2, no.2, pp. 223-249, May, 1930.

THE DESCENT OF THE PRIMATES. A. W. Hubrecht. 1897.

(SEROLOGICAL INVESTIGATIONS OF THE PHYLOGENIC POSITION OF SOME PRIMATES.) Serologische Untersuchungen ueber die stammesgeschichtliche Stellung einiger Primaten. Chr. von Krogh. Anthropol. Anz., Stuttgart, vol.13, nos.3-4, pp.240-247, figs.8, 1937.

(SOME TRAITS OF THE EVOLUTION OF THE ENDO-AND EXOCRANIAL CIRCULATION OF THE PRIMATES.) Quelques traits de l'evolution de la circulation endo- et exocranienne chez les Primates. Ch. Lamberton. Bull. Acad. Malgache, Tananarive, n.s., vol.26, Annees, 1944-45, pp. 141-142, 1947.

THE EVOLUTION OF "BALDNESS" IN MONKEYS, APES AND MEN. Edward Lawrence. II. The Hairdressers' Weekly Jour., vol. 51, no.2630, pp.3368-3369, figs.1-2, Sept. 17, 1932; III. vol.51, no.2634, pp.3871-3872, figs.3, Oct.15, 1932; IV. vol.51, no.2636, pp.4092-4093, figs.4-6, Oct.29, 1932.

GOD--OR GORILLA: HOW THE MONKEY THEORY OF EVOLUTION EXPOSES ITS OWN PRINCIPLES, DENIES ITS OWN INFERENCES, DISPROVES ITS OWN CASE. Alfred Watterson McCann. pp. i-xiii; 1-340, 27 plates, New York, The Devin-Adair Co., 1922.

EVOLUTION OF THE PECTORAL GIRDLE AND FORE LIMB IN THE PRIMATES. Ruth A. Miller. Amer. Jour. Phys. Anthrop., vol.17, no.1, pp.1-56, pls.1-10, July-Sept., 1932.

PROBLEMS OF MENTAL EVOLUTION IN THE PRIMATES. Henry W. Nissen. Human Biology, 26 (3): 277-287, Sept., 1954.

THE EVOLUTION OF THE PRIMATES. C. Tate Regan. Ann. and Mag. Nat. Hist., 10, Ser., vol.6, no.34, pp.383-392, Oct., 1930.

(PALEONTOLOGY AND EVOLUTION OF THE PRIMATES, PARTICULARLY THE NONHOMINOIDS.) A. Remane. Palaeontologie und Evolution der Primaten. Besonders der Nicht-Hominoiden. Primatologia. Handbook of Primatology. I. Systematic Phylogenie, Ontogenie, pp.267-378, illus., 1956.

STUDIES ON THE EVOLUTION OF THE PELVIS OF MAN AND OTHER PRIMATES. Harriet Cutler Waterman. Bull. Amer. Mus. Nat. Hist., vol.LVIII, art.XII, pp. 585-642, figs.10, pl.22, Dec.7, 1929.

ONTOGENY AND PHYLOGENY OF THE NASAL CARTILAGES IN PRIMATES. I. Chuan Wen. Contributions To Embryology, no.130, Carnegie Inst. Wash. Pub. no.414, pp.109-134, text figs.12, pl.1, Nov., 1930.

DESCENT AND DIVERGENCE. Arthur Willey. Nature, vol.120, p.840, Dec.10, 1927.

ON THE PLACENTATION OF PRIMATES, WITH A CONSIDERATION OF THE PHYLOGENY OF THE PLACENTA. George B. Wislocki. Contrib. to Embryol. Carnegie Instit. Washington, Publ. no.394, vol.20, no.111, pp.51-80, 7 pls., 1 text fig., 1929.

## Fossils

(TABULAR SYNOPSIS OF A GENERIC CLASSIFICATION OF RECENT AND FOSSIL PRIMATES.) Tableau résumé d'une classification générique des Primates fossiles et actuels. M. R. Anthony, F. Coupin. Bull. Mus. Nat. Hist. Nat., Paris, ser.2, vol.3, no.7, pp.566-569, Nov., 1931.

(DISCUSSION ON THE INTERPRETATION OF THE LOWER DENTAL SERIES OF STEHLINIUS UINTAHENSIS MATTH.) Discussion sur l'interprétation de la série dentaire inférieure du Stehlinius uintahensis Matth. R. Anthony. Bull. Mus. Hist. Nat. Paris, vol.34, no.6, pp.416-421, figs.2, 1928.

SOME QUANTITATIVE DENTAL CHARACTERS OF FOSSIL ANTHROPOIDS. E. H. Ashton, S. Zuckerman. Philos. Trans. Royal Soc. Lond., ser.B., Biol. Sci., vol. 234, no.617, pp.485-520, 1950.

(A REVISION OF THE FOSSIL MAMMAL FAUNA OF THE CLAY STRATA OF TEGELEN. III. MACACUS OF FLORENTINUS COCCHI.) Eine Revision der fossilen Saeugetierfauna aus den Tonen von Teglen. III. Macacus cf. florentinus Cocchi. J. J. A. Bernsen. Natuurhist. Maandblad., Limburg, vol.20, no.5, pp.67-71, pl.1, May 21, 1931.

AN ANAPTOMORPHID PRIMATE FROM THE OLIGOCENE OF MONTANA. John Clark. Jour. Palaeont., Menasha, vol.15, no.5, pp. 562-563, fig.1, Sept., 1941.

AFRICAN FOSSIL PRIMATES DISCOVERED DURING 1947. W. E. LeGros Clark. Nature, London, vol.161, no.4096, pp. 667-669, May 1, 1948.

THE MIOCENE HOMINOIDEA OF EAST AFRICA. FOSSIL MAMMALS OF AFRICA. NO.1. W. E. LeGros Clark. British Mus. (Nat. Hist.), Lond., pp.vi, 117, figs.28, pls.9, 1951.

NEW PALEONTOLOGICAL EVIDENCE BEARING ON THE HOMINOIDEA. W. E. LeGros Clark. Quart. Jour. Geol. Soc. Lond., vol.105, pp.225-264, pls.11-15, 1950.

ON THE SKULL STRUCTURE OF PRONYCTIBUS GUADRYI. W. E. LeGros Clark. Proc. Zool. Soc. Lond., pt.1, pp.19-27, figs.3, Apr., 1934.

REPORT ON FOSSIL HOMINOID MATERIAL COLLECTED BY THE BRITISH-KENYA MIOCENE EXPEDITION, 1949-1951. W. E. LeGros Clark. Proc. Zool. Soc. Lond., vol.122, pt.2, pp.273-286, illus., Aug.15, 1952.

(THE FIRST PRIMATE FINDS OF BAMMENTAL NEAR MAUER A.D. ELSENZ FROM PRE-GLACIAL NECKAR GRAVEL.) Die ersten Primatenfunde von Bammental bei Mauer a.d. Elsenz aus praeglacialen Neckarkiesen. Wilhelm Freudenberg. Verhandl. Ges Phys. Anthrop., vol.3, pp.68-82, 2 pl., 1 fig., 1929.

(PRIMATES AND HUMAN FOSSILS IN SOUTH AMERICA.) Les Primates et l'homme fossiles en Amérique du Sud. M. Friant. La Terre et la Vie, Rev. d'Hist. Nat., vol.3, no.5, pp.276-281, figs.1-8, May, 1933.

ON THE PRIORITY OF SPECIFIC NAMES FOR THE UPPER BRIDGER NOTHARCTUS. C. Lewis Gazin. Jour. Mam., vol.15, no. 1, p.71, Feb., 1934.

PALEOCENE PRIMATES OF THE FORT UNION, WITH DISCUSSION OF RELATIONSHIPS OF EOCENE PRIMATES. James Williams Gidley. Proc. U.S. Nat. Mus., vol.63, art.1, pp.1-38; 5 pls, 4 text-figs., 1923.

ON THE RELATIONSHIP OF THE EOCENE LEMUR NOTHARCTUS TO THE ADAPIDAE AND TO OTHER PRIMATES. W. K. Gregory. Bull. Geol. Soc. Amer., vol.26, pp.419-425, Nov.24, 1915.

ON THE STRUCTURE AND RELATIONS OF NOTHARCTUS, AN AMERICAN EOCENE PRIMATE. W. K. Gregory. Mem. Amer. Mus. Nat. Hist., n.s., vol.3, pt.2, pp.49-243, pls.23-59, Sept., 1920.

NOTES ON THE TYPE OF HESPEROPITHECUS HAROLDCOOKII OSBORN. W. K. Gregory, Milo Hellman. Amer. Mus. Novitates, no.53, pp.16, figs.5, Jan.6, 1923.

ON THREE INCOMPLETE ANTHROPOID JAWS FROM THE SIWALIKS, INDIA. W. K. Gregory, Milo Hellman, Barnum Brown. Amer. Mus. Novitates, no.150, pp.8, figs. 5, table, Sept.22, 1924.

FOSSIL ANTHROPOIDS OF THE YALE-CAMBRIDGE INDIA EXPEDITION OF 1935. W. K. Gregory, Milo Hellman, G. Edward Lewis. Carnegie Inst. Washington, publ. 495, pp.27, pls.8, Mar.30, 1937.

(THE FOSSIL HISTORY OF THE HOMINOIDEA.) Die Fossilgeschichte der Hominoidea. Gerhard Heberer. Primatologia. Handbook of Primatology. I. Systematic Phylogenie, Ontogenie. pp.379-560, illus., 1956.

PREHISTORIC TEETH OF MAN AND OF THE ORANG-UTAN FROM CENTRAL SUMATRA, WITH NOTES ON THE FOSSIL ORANG-UTAN FROM JAVA AND SOUTHERN CHINA. D. A. Hooijer. Zoologische Mededeelingen, vol.29, pp.175-301, pls.9, 1948.

MIOCENE PRIMATES FROM BRITISH EAST AFRICA. A. Tindell Hopwood. Ann. and Mag. Nat. Hist., ser.10, vol.11, no. 61, pp.96-98, Jan., 1933.

MIOCENE PRIMATES FROM KENYA. A. Tindell Hopwood. Jour. Linn. Soc. Lond., vol.38, no.260, pp.437-464, pl.6, Nov.7, 1933.

FOSSIL PRIMATES IN THE NEW WORLD. G. L. Jepsen. Human Biology, 26 (3): 189-190, Sept., 1954.

A REVISION OF THE AMERICAN APATEMYIDAE AND THE DESCRIPTION OF A NEW GENUS, SINCLAIRELLA, FROM THE WHITE RIVER OLIGOCENE OF SOUTH DAKOTA. G. L. Jepsen. Proc. Amer. Philos. Soc., vol.74, no.4, pp.287-305, figs.4, pls.1-3, Aug., 1934.

MIOCENE ANTHROPOID MANDIBLE FROM RUSINGA, KENYA. L. S. B. Leakey. Nature, Lond., vol.152, no.2855, pp.320-321, illus., Sept.18, 1943.

TAXONOMIC SYLLABUS OF SIWALIK FOSSIL ANTHROPOIDS. G. Edward Lewis. Amer. Jour. Sci., vol.34, no.200, pp.139-147, Aug., 1937.

THE DENTITION OF NOTHODECTES. W. D. Matthew. Mus. Nat. Hist., New York, vol.37, art.33, pp.831-839, pls. 99-102, Dec.5, 1917.

STEHLINIUS, A NEW EOCENE INSECTIVORE. W. D. Matthew. Amer. Mus. Novitates, New York, no.14, pp.5, figs.2, Sept.7, 1921.

A NOTE ON THE FOOT OF NOTHARCTUS. Gerrit S. Miller, Jr. Jour. Mam., vol.18, no.4, pp.515-516, Nov., 1937.

FOSSIL MAMMALS FROM THE MAKAPAN VALLEY, POTGIETERSRUST. I. PRIMATES. O. D. van der Spuyt Mollett. South African Jour. Sci., Johannesburg, vol.43, pp.295-303, figs.6, July, 1946.

HESPEROPITHECUS, THE FIRST ANTHROPOID PRIMATE FOUND IN AMERICA. Henry Fairfield Osborn. Amer. Mus. Nov. New York, no.37, pp.5, figs.3, Apr.25, 1922.

THE GEOLOGIC HISTORY OF NON-HOMINID PRIMATES IN THE OLD WORLD. Bryan Patterson. Human Biology, 26 (3): 191-209, Sept., 1954.

A SIVAPITHECUS PALATE AND OTHER FOSSIL PRIMATES FROM INDIA. Guy E. Pilgrim. Mem. Geol. Surv. India, vol.14, pp.1-24, pl.1, 1927.

(Review by G. S. Miller of) A SIVAPITHECUS PALATE AND OTHER PRIMATE FOSSILS FROM INDIA. Guy E. Pilgrim. Amer. Jour. Phys. Anthrop., Phila., vol. 11, no.2, pp.362-363, Apr., 1928.

THE SPECIES OF NOTHARCTUS FROM THE MIDDLE EOCENE. Peter Robinson. Postilla, Yale Peabody Mus. Nat. Hist., 28: 1-27, illus., Jan.21, 1957.

TWO NEW PRIMATES FROM THE LOWER EOCENE OF WYOMING. Henry Seton. Proc. New England Zool. Club, Cambridge, vol.18, pp.39-42, pl.8, Aug.14, 1940.

AN APATEMYID FROM THE EARLY EOCENE OF NEW MEXICO. George Gaylord Simpson. Amer. Mus. Novitates, New York, no.1654, pp.4, Jan.22, 1954.

THE PHENACOLEMURIDAE, NEW FAMILY OF EARLY PRIMATES. George Gaylord Simpson. Bull. Amer. Mus. Nat. Hist., vol.105, art.5, pp.417-441, pls.30-35, Mar.21, 1955.

STUDIES ON THE EARLIEST PRIMATES. George Gaylord Simpson. Bull. Amer. Mus. Nat. Hist., New York, vol.77, pp. 185-212, figs.8, July 31, 1940.

THE TIFFANY FAUNA, UPPER PALEOCENE. II. STRUCTURE AND RELATIONSHIPS OF PLEISIADAPIS. George Gaylord Simpson. Amer. Mus. Novitates no.816, pp.30, figs.11, Aug.16, 1935.

ON SUB-FOSSIL PRIMATES FROM MADAGASCAR. Trans. Zool. Soc. Lond., vol. 18, p.59, 1908.

AN EOCENE PRIMATE FROM CALIFORNIA. Chester Stock. Proc. Nat. Acad. Sci., vol. 19, pp.954-959, pl.1, 1933.

EOCENE PRIMATES FROM CALIFORNIA. Chester Stock. Science, Lancaster, n.s., vol.78, no.2031, p.524, Dec.1, 1933.

A SECOND EOCENE PRIMATE FROM CALIFORNIA. Chester Stock. Proc. Nat. Acad. Sci., vol.20, no.3, pp.150-154, pl., Mar., 1934.

FOSSIL ANTHROPOIDS OF INDIA: A LIST OF THE FOSSIL MATERIAL HITHERTO DISCOVERED FROM THE TERTIARY DEPOSITS OF INDIA. D. N. Wadia, N. K. N. Aiyengar. Rec. Geol. Surv. India, Calcutta, vol.72, pt.4, pp.467-494, 1938.

WEST INDIAN FOSSIL MONKEYS. Ernest E. Williams, Karl F. Koopman. Amer. Mus. Novitates, New York, no.1546, pp. 16, illus., Mar.3, 1952.

NEW MATERIALS OF THE EARLIEST PRIMATE KNOWN IN CHINA. Ju-kang Woo, Minchen Chow. Vertebrata Palasiatica, 1 (4): 267-272, illus., Dec., 1957.

STUDIES OF EOCENE MAMMALIA IN THE MARSH COLLECTION, PEABODY MUSEUM. PART II. PRIMATES. J. L. Wortman. Amer. Jour. Sci., vols.15-17, pp.147-250, figs.100-146, pls.11-12, 1903-1904.

SOUTH AFRICAN FOSSIL ANTHROPOIDS. S. Zuckerman. Nature, London, vol.165, no.4199, p.652, Apr.22, 1950.

Habits, Behavior

(ON SEEKING INVISIBLE FOOD IN MONKEYS AND LEMURS.) Ueber das Suchen nach unsichtbarem Futter bei Affen und Halbaffen. J. A. Bierens de Haan. Zugleich ein Beitrag zu der Frage nach dem Konkreten Verstaendniss dieser Tiere. Zeitschr. f. vergleich. Physiologie, vol. 11, pp.650-655, May 19, 1930.

(THE SINGING OF OLD MALE ORANGS.) Das Singen der alten Orangmaenner. Gustav Brandes. Zool. Garten, N.F., Leipzig, vol.10, nos.1-2, pp.31-33, May, 1938.

CHARACTERISTICS OF SOCIAL BEHAVIOR IN NON-HUMAN PRIMATES. C. R. Carpenter. Trans. New York Acad. Sci., ser.2, vol.4, no.8, pp.248-258, June, 1942.

SOCIAL BEHAVIOR OF NON-HUMAN PRIMATES . C. R. Carpenter. In Structure et physiologie des societes animales. Paris, Mar., 1950 (1952), pp.227-245, pls.VIII-XIII, 1950.

SOCIETIES OF MONKEYS AND APES. C. R. Carpenter. Biol. Symposia, Lancaster, vol.8, pp.177-204, 1942.

TENTATIVE GENERALIZATIONS ON THE GROUPING BEHAVIOR OF NON-HUMAN PRIMATES. C. R. Carpenter. Human Biology, 26 (3): 269-276, Sept., 1954.

MONKEYS' TRUCE--A STUDY IN ANIMAL BEHAVIOR. William H. Carr. Natural History, vol.32, no.4, pp.417-423, figs.5, July-Aug., 1932.

(Review by S. Zuckerman of) THE SOCIAL LIFE OF MONKEYS AND APES. Carl G. Hartman. Anat. Record, vol.54, no.1, pp. 129-133, Sep., 1932.

BEHAVIOR AND ADAPTATIONS OF THE PRIMATES. W. C. Osman Hill. Proc. Roy. Soc. Edinburgh, Sec.B (Biology), 66 (1): 94-110, May 31, 1956.

A CURIOUS HABIT COMMON TO LORISOIDS AND PLATYRRHINE MONKEYS. W. C. Osman Hill. Ceylon Jour. Sci., sect.B, Zool. and Geol., Spolia Zeylanica, vol.21, pt.1, p.65, Feb.10, 1938.

SOME PROBLEMS CONCERNING THE FEEDING BEHAVIOUR OF MONKEYS. David Katz, Rosa Katz. Proc. Zool. Soc. Lond., pt.2, pp.579-582, July, 1936.

BEHAVIOR MECHANISMS IN MONKEYS. Heinrich Kluever. Univ. Chicago Press, pp.xi, 387, 52 figs., Apr., 1933.

(THE SOCIAL BEHAVIOR OF THE LOWER AND HIGHER MONKEYS.) Das soziale verhalten der niederen und hoeheren Affen. von A. H. Maslow. Sonderabdruck von Heft 1, pp.14-25, 1936.

(MONKEYS PLAY.) Affen spielen. Bastian Schmid. Frankfurt, 39 Jahrg., no.4, pp.70-73, figs.1-7, Jan.20, 1935.

ACROBATS OF THE MONKEY WORLD. W. Henry Sheak. Nat. Hist., vol.29, pp. 307-311, illus., May, 1929.

(COPROPHAGY--A PHENOMENON OCCURRING IN CAPTIVE ANTHROPOMORPHS.) Die Koprophagie, eine Gefangenschaftserscheinung bei den Anthropomorphen. Carl Stemmler-Morath. Zool. Garten, N.F., Leipzig, vol.9, nos.3-4, pp.159-161, May, 1937.

(ON THE QUESTION OF THE BEHAVIOR OF PRIMATES IN EUROPEAN CAPTIVITY.) Zur Frage der Haltung von Primaten in europaeischer Gefangenschaft. Edmund Vermes, Alfred Weidholz. Zool. Garten, Leipzig, n.F., vol.2, nos.10-12, pp.314-338, figs.1-10, Mar., 1930.

GENETIC ASPECTS OF GROOMING, A SOCIALLY IMPORTANT PRIMATE BEHAVIOR PATTERN. Robert M. Yerkes. Jour. Social Psychol., Worcester, Mass., vol.4, no.1, pp.3-23, Feb., 1933.

Man and the Great Apes

(GROWTH IN ANTHROPOIDS IN COMPARISON WITH THAT IN MAN (REPRESENTED

IN CURVES).) Das wachstum der Menschenaffen im Vergleich zu dem des Menschen in Kurven dargestellt. Gustav Brandes. Zool. Garten, Leipzig, n.F., vol.4, nos.10-12, pp.339-347, figs.4, Dec.16, 1931.

APE OR MAN? R. Broom, J. T. Robinson. Nature, Lond., vol.166, no.4229, pp.843-844, illus., Nov.18, 1950.

(ON THE RELATIONSHIP OF THE SURFACE OF THE FRONTAL LOBE TO THAT OF THE ENTIRE BRAIN IN THE HIGHER APES AND MAN.) Ueber das Verhaeltnis der Oberflaeche des Frontalhirns zu derjenigen des ganzen Gehirnes bei hoeheren Affen und Menschen. R. Brummelkamp. Proc. Kon. Nederl. Akad. Wetensch., Amsterdam, vol.41, no.10, pp.1127-1133, figs.4, Dec., 1938.

DERMATOGLYPHICS IN THE CHIMPANZEE; DESCRIPTION AND COMPARISON WITH MAN. Harold Cummins, S. D. Shirley Spragg. Human Biology, Baltimore, vol.10, no.4, pp.457-510, figs.41, tables 25, Dec., 1938.

CHIMPANZEE AND HUMAN FEET IN BIPEDAL WALKING. Herbert Elftman, John Manter. Amer. Jour. Phys. Anthrop., vol. 20, no.1, pp.69-79, figs.6, July, 1935.

COMPARATIVE ANATOMY OF NEW WORLD PRIMATES AND ITS BEARING ON THE PHYLOGENY OF ANTHROPOID APES AND MAN. G. E. Erikson. Human Biology, 26 (3): 210, Sept., 1954.

(MODERN VIEWS ON THE ORIGIN OF MAN.) Die modernen Anschauungen ueber die Abstammung des Menschengeschlechts. H. Friedenthal. Sitz.-Ber. Gesell. Naturforsch. Freunde Berlin, pt.1, pp.3-23, pls. 1-3, July 15, 1931.

DAWN-MAN OR APE. William K. Gregory. Scientific American, 3 pages, illus., Sept., 1927.

REPLY TO PROFESSOR WOOD-JONES'S NOTE: "MAN AND THE ANTHROPOIDS". William K. Gregory. Amer. Jour. Phys. Anthrop., vol.12, no.2, pp.253-256, pl.1, Oct.-Dec., 1928.

(COMPARATIVE ANATOMICAL INVESTIGATION OF THE QUESTION OF THE ORIGIN OF MAMMILLAE IN MAN AND THE ANTHROPOIDS.) Vergleichend-anatomische Untersuchung zur Frage der Entstehung des Warzenfortsatzes beim Menschen und den Menschenaffen. Werner Groth. Gegenbaurs Morphol. Jahbuch, Leipzig, vol.79, no.4, pp.547-597, figs.8, tables 8, 1937.

APES, MEN AND TEETH. Ernest A. Hooten. Sci. Monthly, vol.38, pp.24-34, Jan., 1934.

(Review by Adolph H. Schultz of) UP FROM THE APE. Ernest A. Hooten. Amer. Jour. Phys. Anthropol., Phila., n.s. vol.5, no.1, pp.87-91, Mar., 1947.

APING THE MAN, OR MANNING THE APE. (REVIEW OF "WHY MEN BEHAVE LIKE APES AND VICE VERSA, OR BODY AND BEHAVIOR", BY ERNEST A.HOOTEN.) Ellsworth Huntington. Jour. Heredity, Washington, D.C., vol.33, no.2, pp.44-80, Feb., 1942.

FORM AND CHARACTER. (REVIEW OF WHY MEN BEHAVE LIKE APES AND VICE VERSA OR BODY AND BEHAVIOR, BY ERNEST A. HOOTEN.) S. Zuckerman. Nature, Lond., vol.149, no.3778, pp.340-341, Mar.28, 1942.

THE APE AND THE CHILD: A STUDY OF THE ENVIRONMENTAL INFLUENCE UPON EARLY BEHAVIOR. W. N. Kellogg, L. A. Kellogg. Whittlesey House, McGraw-Hill Book Co., New York, 341 pp., 100 figs., 1933.

THE PROBLEM OF GROWTH CHANGES IN THE FACE AND SKULL AS VIEWED FROM A COMPARATIVE STUDY OF ANTHROPOIDS AND MAN. W. M. Krogman. Dental Cosmos, pp.1-7, June, 1930.

(SIMULTANEOUS COMPARISON OF SEEN QUANTITIES IN THE RHESUS MONKEY.) Simultanvergleich gesehener Mengen beim Rhesusaffen. Erich Kuehn. Zeitschr. f. Tierpsychol., vol.10, no.2, pp.268-296, 1953.

MAN AND APES. St. George Mivart. New York, 6, 200 pp., 1874.

(THE CORRESPONDENCE OF THE MAXILLARY JOINT OF THE NEWBORN CHILD WITH THAT OF THE ANTHROPOIDS.) Die Uebereinstimmung des Kiefergelenkes des Neugebornen Kindes mit dem Kiefergelenk der Anthropoiden. L. Petrovits. Anat. Anz., vol.69, nos.4-6, pp.145-155, 1930.

INVESTIGATIONS ON THE PARS INTERMEDIA OF THE HYPOPHYSIS IN ANTHROPOID APES AND MAN. Alfred Plaut. Jour. Ana., Cambridge, vol.70, pt.1, pp. 242-249, Oct., 1935.

GORILLAS, MEN AND SLEEPING SICKNESS. CHAPTER XIII OF GREGORY, WILLIAM KING, "IN QUEST OF GORILLAS." H. C. Raven. Sci. Monthly, vol.43, no.6, pp.522-540, illus., Dec., 1936.

CHARACTERS COMMON TO HIGHER PRIMATES AND CHARACTERS SPECIFIC FOR MAN. Adolph H. Schultz. Quart. Review Biol., vol.11, no.3, pp.259-283, figs.9, Sept., 1936; no.4, pp.425-455, figs.10-21, Dec., 1936.

PROPORTIONS, VARIABILITY AND ASYMMETRIES OF THE LONG BONES OF THE LIMBS AND THE CLAVICLES IN MAN AND APES. Ernst Schwarz. Human Biology, vol.9, no.3, pp.281-328, figs.6, Sept., 1937.

SOME OBSERVATIONS ON MONKEYS. STRIKING AFFINITIES APPARENT BETWEEN HOMO AND SIMIA, BOTH MENTALLY AND MORPHOLOGICALLY. R. W. Shufeldt. Jour. Heredity, Washington, D.C., vol.9, no.4, pp.182-186, figs.11-15, Apr., 1918.

THE MORPHOLOGY AND EVOLUTION OF THE APES AND MAN. Charles F. Sonntag. John Bale Sons and Danielsson, Ltd., Lond., pp.I-XI, 1-364, figs.1-57, 1924.

(THE HIGHLAND REGIONS OF THE EARTH AND THE QUESTION OF THE ORIGIN OF MAN.) Die Hochlandgebiete der Erde und die Frage ueber den ursprung des Menschen. P. P. Suschkin. Palaeobiologica, vol.5, pp.275-306, 1933.

THE BRAIN FROM APE TO MAN. Frederick Tilney. Paul B. Hoever, Inc., New York, 8 vols., 2, pp.XXVII, pls.1120, figs.539, 1928.

(Review by G. S. Miller of) THE BRAIN FROM APE TO MAN. Frederick Tilney. Jour. Mam., Baltimore, vol.9, no.4, pp. 340-341, Nov.13, 1928.

APES, GIANTS, AND MAN. Franz Weidenreich. Univ. Chicago Press, pp.viii, 122, figs.90, 1946.

MAN OR APE? Franz Weidenreich. Nat. Hist., New York, vol.45, no.1, illus., Jan., 1940.

OBSERVATIONS ON THE FORM AND PROPORTIONS OF THE ENDOCRANIAL CASTS OF SINANTHROPUS PEKINENSIS, OTHER HOMINIDS AND THE GREAT APES: A COMPARATIVE STUDY OF BRAIN SIZE. Franz Weidenreich. Palaeontologica Sinica, ser.D, vol.7, no.4, pp.50, figs.21, 1936.

(THE GAIT OF THE GIBBON IN RELATION TO THE HUMAN FOOT.) Der Gang des Gibbon in Beziehung zum Menschenfuss. M. Westenhofer. Zeitschrift f. Saeugetierkunde, vol.3, pp.278-283, pl.17, June 11, 1928.

(THE POSTERIOR TARSUS OF MAN AND THE GORILLA.) Die hintere Fusswurzel von Mensch und Gorilla. M. Westenhoefer. Zeit. f. Saeugetierkunde, Bd.4, heft 3, pp. 186-192, 2 pls., Sept.18, 1929.

EXHIBITION OF DIAGRAMS OF THE BRAINS AND MEDISECTED HEADS OF MAN AND A CHIMPANZEE. Burt G. Wilder. Proc. Amer. Assoc. Adv. Sci., vol.39, p.375, 1890.

AMONG PYGMIES AND GORILLAS WITH THE SWEDISH ZOOLOGICAL EXPEDITION TO CENTRAL AFRICA 1921. Prince William of Sweden. Gyldendal, London, 269 pp., 40 pls., 2 maps, 1923.

(Review by N. Kohts of) INFANT APE AND HUMAN CHILD (INSTINCTS, EMOTIONS, PLAY, HABITS). Robert M. Yerkes. Science, Moscow, n.s., vol.83, no.2159 pp.466-467, May 15, 1936.

MAN VERSUS CHIMPANZEE. Animal Kingdom, New York, vol.47, no.2, p.32, Mar-Apr., 1944.

Parasites

SOME NEW GENERA AND SPECIES OF NEMATODE WORMS, FILARIOIDEA, FROM ANIMALS DYING IN THE CALCUTTA ZOOLOGICAL GARDEN. Asa C. Chandler. Proc. U.S. Nat. Mus., vol.75, art.6, pp.1-10, pls.1-3, 1929.

LICE FROM HUMAN MUMMIES. H. E. Ewing. Science, n.s., vol.60, pp.389-390, Oct.24, 1924.

A REVISION OF THE AMERICAN LICE OF THE GENUS PEDICULUS, TOGETHER WITH A CONSIDERATION OF THE SIGNIFICANCE OF THEIR GEOGRAPHICAL AND HOST DISTRIBUTION. H. E. Ewing. Proc. U.S. Nat. Mus., vol.68, art.19, pp.1-30, pls.1-3, June, 1926.

NOTE ON BACTERIUM MORGANI OBTAINED FROM ANIMALS THAT HAD DIED IN THE SOCIETY'S GARDENS. Reginald Lovell. Proc. Zool. Soc. Lond., pt.3, pp.777-778, Sept., 1928.

KEY-CATALOGUE OF PARASITES REPORTED FOR PRIMATES (MONKEYS AND LEMURS) WITH THEIR POSSIBLE PUBLIC HEALTH IMPORTANCE AND KEY-CATALOGUE OF PRIMATES FOR WHICH PARASITES ARE REPORTED. C. W. Stiles, Albert Hassall, M. O. Nolan. Bull.152, Hygienic Laboratory, U.S. Treasury Dept., Washington, D.C., pp.iv, 409-601, Nov., 1929.

Physiology

STARVATION KETOSIS OF THE PRIMATES. Theodore E. Friedemann. Science, n.s., vol.67, pp.221-222, Feb.24, 1928.

CONTROL OF MOVEMENTS BY THE CEREBRAL CORTEX IN PRIMATES. Marion Hines. Biol. Rev. Cambridge Philos. Soc., vol.18, no.1, pp.1-31, Jan., 1943.

AN EXPERIMENTAL ANALYSIS OF THE FUNCTIONS OF THE FRONTAL ASSOCIATION AREAS IN PRIMATES. Carlyle F. Jacobsen, J. B. Wolfe, T. A. Jackson. Jour. Nervous and Mental Disease, vol. 82, no.1, pp.14, figs.4, July, 1935.

A COMPARATIVE FUNCTION ANALYSIS OF PRIMATE SKULLS BY THE SPLIT-LINE TECHNIQUE. N. C. Tappen. Human Biology, 26 (3): 220-238, Sept., 1954.

(THE "ARM-SWINGING" REFLEX OF THE GIBBON.) Der "Hangelreflex" des Gibbons. M. Westenhofer. Zeitschrift f. Saeugetierkunde, vol.2, no.3, p.201, 1929.

Psychology

CURIOSITY IN MONKEYS. Robert A. Butler. Scientific American, New York, vol.190, no.2, pp.70-75, Feb., 1954

THE INTELLIGENCE OF MONKEYS. Charles Coltar. Forest and Stream, vol. 90, pp.15, 34, Jan., 1920.

(COMPUTING REFLECTION IN THE CHIMPANZEE.) Berechnende Ueberlegung beim Schimpansen. Paul Eipper. Natur und Volk, vol.64, no.4, pp.127-129, Apr., 1934.

SPEECH OF MONKEYS. R. L. Garner. New York, 1898.

MONKEYS TRAINED AS HARVESTERS. E. W. Gudger. Nat. Hist., vol.23, no.3, pp.272-279, 1923.

(NEW RESEARCH IN THE PSYCHOLOGY OF MONKEYS.) Nouvelles recherches sur la psychologie des singes. P. Hachet-Souplet. Revue Sci., Paris, Annee 73, no. 17, pp.561-568, figs.4, Sept.14, 1935.

(ON THE PSYCHOLOGY OF VARIATION APPERCEPTION IN THE LOWER APES.) Zur Psychologie der Veraenderungsauffassung bei niederen Affen. Heinrich Kluver. Zeitschr. Angewandte Psych. Leipzig, no.59, pp.131-156, fig.1, 1931.

(ON THE PSYCHOLOGY OF MONKEYS.) Zur Psychologie der Affen. Bastian Schmid. Naturforscher, vol.10, no.7, pp. 234-239, pl.20, figs.1-6, Oct., 1933.

(COMPARATIVE BIOLOGICAL AND PSYCHOLOGICAL OBSERVATIONS AND EXPERIMENTS ON THREE CERCOPITHECIDAE AND A BLACK ALOUATTA CARAYA HUMBOLDT.) Vergleichend biologische und psychologische Beobachtungen und Versuche an drei Meerkatzenartigen (Cercopithecidae) und einem schwarzen Bruellaffen (Alouatta caraya Humboldt). Bastian Schmid. Zeitschr. f. Saeugetierkunde, Berlin, vol.9, nos.1-3, pp.164-187, pls.9-22, Dec.30, 1934.

(SITUATION INSIGHT IN MONKEYS.) Situationseinsicht bei Affen. Georg Steinbacher. Saeugetierk. Mitteil., Stuttgart, vol.1, no.4, pp.178-179, illus., Oct.1, 1953.

MULTIPLE DELAYED REACTION WITH CHIMPANZEES AND MONKEYS. O. L. Tinklepaugh. Jour. Comp. Psych., vol.13, no.2, pp.207-243, 1932.

IMITATION IN MONKEYS. John B. Watson. Psychol. Bull., Lancaster, vol.5, no.6, pp. 169-178, June 15, 1908.

THE MENTALITY OF PRIMATES. Leslie A. White. Sci. Monthly, vol.34, no.1, pp.69-72, Jan., 1932.

ON THE USE OF TOOLS BY PRIMATES. Leslie A. White. Jour. Comp Psychol., Baltimore, vol.34, no.3, pp.369-374, Dec., 1942.

THE MENTAL LIFE OF MONKEYS AND APES: A STUDY OF IDEATIONAL BEHAVIOR. Robert M. Yerkes. Behavior Monographs, vol.3, no.1, ser. no.12, pp.145, pls.VI, figs.20, 1916.

PRIMATE COOPERATION AND INTELLIGENCE. Robert M. Yerkes. Amer. Jour. Psychol., Golden Jubilee Volume, vol.50, pp.154-270, Nov., 1937.

COMPARATIVE BEHAVIOR OF PRIMATES. V. DELAYED REACTIONS IN PRIMATES IN HORIZONTAL AND VERTICAL PLANES. H. C. Yudin, H. F. Harlow. Jour. Comp. Psych., vol.16, no.1, pp.143-146, pl.1, Aug., 1933.

Reproductive Biology

SEX BEHAVIOR IN PRIMATES. William E. Galt. Ann. New York Acad. Sci., vol.47, art.5, pp.617-30, May 9, 1947.

A STUDY OF SEXUAL TENDENCIES IN MONKEYS AND BABOONS. G. V. Hamilton. Jour. Animal Behavior, vol.4, no.5, pp. 295-318, Sept.-Oct., 1914.

ON THE BREEDING AND REARING OF CERTAIN SPECIES OF PRIMATES IN CAPTIVITY. W. C. O. Hill. Ceylon Jour. Sci., sec.B, Zool and Geol., Spolia Zeylanica, vol.20, no.3, pp.369-389, fig.1, pls.17-19, Aug.14, 1937.

OBSERVATIONS UPON OVULATION IN PRIMATES. Arthur H. Morse, G. van Wagenen. Amer. Jour. Obstetrics and Gynecology, vol.32, no.5, pp.823-832, 1936.

(THE THREE BIRTHS IN THE MONKEY HOUSE OF THE PASTEUR INSTITUTE OF TUNIS.) A propos de trois naissances dans la singerie de l' Institut Pasteur de Tunis. C. Nicolle, L. Wetterle. Bull. Soc. Path. Exot. Paris, vol.23, no.6, pp.596-599, June 11, 1930.

NOTES UPON MENSTRUATION, GESTATION, AND PARTURITION OF SOME MONKEYS THAT HAVE LIVED IN THE SOCIETY'S GARDENS. R. I. Pocock. Proc. Zool. Soc. Lond., pp.558-570, Oct.10, 1906.

FETAL GROWTH OF MAN AND OTHER PRIMATES. Adolph H. Schultz. Quart. Rev. Biol., vol.1, pp.465-521, illus., Oct. (Nov.), 1926.

(OBSERVATIONS OF THE SEXUAL CYCLE, GESTATION, AND BIRTH IN JAVA MACAQUES(MACACA IRUS MORDAX THOMAS AND WROUGHTON (CYNOMOLGUS L.).) Beobachtungen ueber den sexualzyklus, die graviditaet und die geburt bei Javamakaken (Macaca irus mordax Thomas and Wroughton (cynomolgus L.). Arnold Spiegel. Archiv. f. Gynaekol. vol.142, pp.561-591, 1930.

(OBSERVATIONS ON THE NURSING BEHAVIOR OF THE GIBBON, AND ON A PREMATURE FOETUS IN THE CASE OF CROSS-BREEDING WITH HYLOBATES.) Beobachtungen ueber das brutbiologische Verhalten des Gibbons und an einem fruehgeborenen Foetus bei einer Bastardzucht von Hylobates. Hans Steiner. Archiv Julius Klaus-Stiftung Verebungsforschung, Sozialanthropologie und Rassenhygiene, Zurich, vol.24, pp.217-236, figs.6, pls. 2, 1949.

SOME REMARKS ON THE POLYOESTRUS OF PRIMATES. M. A. Van Herwenden. Anat. Record, vol.30, pp.221-224, 1 fig., June 25, 1925.

OBSERVATIONS ON THE DESCENT OF THE TESTES IN THE MACAQUE AND IN THE CHIMPANZEE. George B. Wislocki. Anat. Rec., vol.57, no.2, pp.133-148, figs.7, Sept.25, 1933.

THE DURATION AND PHASES OF THE MENSTRUAL CYCLE IN PRIMATES. S. Zuckerman. Proc. Zool. Soc. Lond., ser. A, vol.107, pt.3, pp.315-329, tables 3, Sept., 1937.

THE MENSTRUAL CYCLE OF THE PRIMATES.--PART I. GENERAL NATURE AND HOMOLOGY. S. Zuckerman. Proc. Zool. Soc. Lond., no.45, pt.3, pp.691-754, illus., 2 pls., Oct.22, 1930.

THE MENSTRUAL CYCLE OF THE PRIMATES.--PART 4. OBSERVATIONS ON THE LACTATION PERIOD. S. Zuckerman. Proc. Zool. Soc. Lond., pt.2, pp.593-602, pls.2, June 29, 1931.

THE MENSTRUAL CYCLE OF THE PRIMATES.--PART VI. FURTHER OBSERVATIONS ON THE BREEDING OF PRIMATES, WITH SPECIAL REFERENCE TO THE SUBORDERS LEMUROIDEA AND TARSIOIDEA. S. Zuckerman. Proc. Zool. Soc. Lond., pt.4, pp.1059-1075, figs.1-9, Jan. 6, 1933.

THE MENSTRUAL CYCLE OF THE PRIMATES. VIII. THE OESTRIN-WITHDRAWAL THEORY OF MENSTRUATION. S. Zuckerman. Proc. Roy. Soc., Lond., ser.B., vol.118, no.807, pp.13-21, July 1, 1935.

THE MENSTRUAL CYCLE OF THE PRIMATES. IX. THE EFFECT OF OESTRIN ON THE DENERVATED SEXUAL SKIN. S. Zuckerman. Proc. Roy. Soc., Lond., ser.B., vol.118, no.807, pp.22-33, figs.10, July 1, 1935.

Skull and Teeth

CRANIAL CRESTS IN THE ANTHROPOIDEA. E. H. Ashton, S. Zuckerman. Proc. Zool. Soc. Lond., 126 (4): 581-634, pls.11, July 31, 1956.

(THE CHRONOLOGY OF THE DENTITION OF THE ANTHROPOIDS.) La chronologie de la Dentition chez les Anthropoides. Charles Bennejeant. Mammalia, Paris, 4 (2): 41-45, illus., pl.3, June, 1940.

(NUMERICAL DENTAL VARIATIONS AND PROGRESSIVE DENTAL REDUCTION IN THE PRIMATES.) Les variations dentaires numeriques et la reduction dentaire progressive chez les primates. Charles Bennejeant. Assoc. Francaise Av. Sci., 59 Sess. Nantes, Paris, pp.459-464, figs. 3, 1935.

(THE TRANSFORMATION OF THE PRIMATE SKULL AND ITS RELATIONSHIP TO ONTOGENETIC DEVELOPMENT AND THE PHYLOGENIC SPECIALIZATIONS OF THE CEPHALIC ORGANS.) Der Formwandel des Primatenschaedels und seine Beziehungen zur ontogenetischen Entwicklung und den phylogenetischen Spezialisationen der Kopforgane. J. Biegert. Morphol. Jahrbuch, Leipzig, vol.98, no.1, pp.77-109, 1957.

THE EMISSARY FORAMINA OF THE CRANIUM IN PRIMATES. G. I. Boyd. Jour. Anat., Cambridge, vol.69, pt.1, pp.113-117, Oct., 1934.

ON THE STRUCTURE OF THE ENAMEL IN THE PRIMATES AND SOME OTHER MAMMALS. J. Thornton Carter. Proc. Zool. Soc. Lond., pp.599-608, 7 pls., Sept., 1922.

(MORPHOLOGICAL ANALYSIS OF THE SPLANCHNOCRANIUM IN THE PRIMATES AND ITS AFFINITIES WITH PROGNATHISM (CONTINUATION AND CONCLUSION.).) Analyse morphologique du splanchnocrane chez les primates et ses rapports avec le prognathisme (suite et fin). A. Delattre, R. Fenart. Mammalia, Paris, 20 (3): 276-325, pl.2, Sept., 1956.

(STUDIES OF THE DENTAL EVOLUTION OF PRIMATES. THE EVOLUTION OF THE PRIMITIVE TYPE OF UPPER MOLARS IN ADAPIDAE.) Etudes sur l'evolution dentaire des Primates. L'evolution du type primitif des molaires superieures chez les Adapides. M. Friant. Revue anthropologique, Paris, vol.52, nos.1-2, pp.31-46, figs.13, Jan.-Mar., 1935.

(SKULL CAPACITY OF THE ANTHROPOIDS.) Schaedelkapazitat der Anthropomorphen. A. Hagedoorn. Anat. Anzeiger, vol.60, pp.417-427, Jan.20, 1926.

THE SKULL, THE FACE, AND THE TEETH OF PRIMATES, WITH SPECIAL REFERENCE TO DOLICHOCEPHALY AND THE CENTRES OF GROWTH IN THE FACE. PT. 1. H. A. Harris. Proc. Zool. Soc. Lond., pt.3, pp.491-502, 6 pls., Sept., 1927.

(ON THE RELATIVE POSITION OF THE JAW JOINT IN THE CRANIUM OF THE PRIMATES.) Ueber die relative Lage des Kiefergelenkes am Schaedel der Primaten. H. O. von Haussen. Zeitschr. f. Morphol. u. Anthropol., vol.29, pp.465-497, figs. 9, 1931.

VARIATIONS IN THE DIMENSIONS OF LOWER MOLARS IN MAN AND ANTHROPOID APES. Ales Hrdlicka. Amer. Jour. Phys. Anthropol., Washington, D.C., vol.6, no.4, pp.423-438, Oct.-Dec., 1923.

ON THE STRUCTURE OF THE SKULL OF MAN, THE GORILLA, THE CHIMPANZEE, AND THE ORANG-UTAN, DURING THE PERIOD OF THE FIRST DENTITION. T. H. Huxley. Proc. Zool. Soc. Lond., p.586, 1864.

THE PROBLEM OF GROWTH CHANGES IN THE FACE AND SKULL AS VIEWED FROM A COMPARATIVE STUDY OF ANTHROPOIDS AND MAN. W. M. Krogman. Dental Cosmos, Phila., pp.1-7, figs.1-7, June, 1930.

STUDIES IN GROWTH CHANGES IN THE SKULL AND FACE OF ANTHROPOIDS. I. THE ERUPTION OF THE TEETH IN ANTHROPOIDS AND OLD WORLD APES. W. M. Krogman. Amer. Jour. Anat., vol.46, no.2, pp.303-313, Sept.15, 1930.

STUDIES IN GROWTH CHANGES IN THE SKULL AND FACE OF ANTHROPOIDS. II. ECTOCRANIAL AND ENDOCRANIAL SUTURE CLOSURE IN ANTHROPOIDS AND OLD WORLD APES. W. M. Krogman. Amer. Jour. Anat., vol.46, no.2, pp.315-353, Sept.15, 1930.

(AN ANOMALOUS LAST PREMOLAR (P4) IN MEGALADAPIS GRANDIDIERI MAMMALIA.) Une Derniere Premolarie Anomale (P4) Chez Megaladapis grandidieri. Lamberton. Mammalia, vol.3, pp.53-54, 1939.

ON SOME CHARACTERS OF THE SKULL IN THE LEMURS AND MONKEYS. C. I. Forsyth Major. Proc. Zool. Soc. Lond., vol.1, pp.129-153, pls.11-13, figs.26-46, June 1, 1901.

(SUPERNUMERARY MILK MOLARS AND PREMOLARS IN THE JAW OF THE SIAMANG

AND MAN.) Ueberzaehlige Milchmolaren und Praemolaren im Gebiss des Siamangs und des Menschen. W. A. Mijsberg. Zeitschr. f. Anat. u. Entwicklungs., vol. 96, pp.98-118, figs.15, 1931.

CATALOGUE OF SKULLS OF MAN AND THE INFERIOR ANIMALS. Samuel Geo. Morton. 3rd Ed., Philadelphia, illus., 1849.

ON THE CAPACITY OF THE CRANIUM IN THE NEGRO, THE ORANG, AND THE GORILLA (WHICH WILL BE PUBLISHED IN THE TRANSACTIONS.) P. Owen. Proc. Zool. Soc. Lond., pt.19, p.264, 1851.

ERUPTION AND DECAY OF THE PERMANENT TEETH IN PRIMATES. Adolph H. Schultz. Amer. Jour. Phys. Anthrop., vol.19, no.4, pp.489-581, figs.21, tables 27, Jan.-Mar., 1935.

THE RELATIVE SIZE OF THE CRANIAL CAPACITY IN PRIMATES. Adolph H. Schultz. Amer. Jour. Phys. Anthrop., Phila., vol.28, no.3, pp.273-287, figs.3, Sept.30, 1941.

(THE LACKING INCISOR OF THE PRIMATES.) Der fehlende Schneidezahn der Primaten. Ernst Schwarz. Zool. Anzeiger, vol.89, nos.1-2, pp.37-38, 1930.

PULP CAVITIES OF MOLARS IN PRIMATES. Muzaffer Sueleyman Senyuerek. Amer. Jour. Phys. Anthrop., Phila., vol.5, no.1, pp. 119-130, pl.1, Apr.-June, 1939.

A STUDY OF THE PULP CAVITIES AND ROOTS OF THE LOWER PREMOLARS AND MOLARS OF PROSIMII, CEBOIDEA AND CERCOPITHECOIDEA. Muzaffer Sueleyman Senyuerek. Belleten, Ankara, vol.17, no.67, pp.321-365, pls., July, 1953.

COMPARATIVE STUDY OF CERTAIN CRANIAL SUTURES IN THE PRIMATES. R. W. Shufeldt. Anat. Record, Phila., vol.9, no.1, pp.121-124, Jan.20, 1915.

(FURTHER OBSERVATIONS OF THE TIME OF TEETHING AND LATER TEETHING DEVELOPMENT IN JAVA MACAQUES.) Weitere Beobachtungen ueber den zeitlichen Ablauf der Bezahnung u. des Zahnwechsels bei Javamakaken. Arnold Spiegel. Zeitsch. Saeugetierk, vol.18, no.2, pp.125-135, Sept.28, 1952.

(DENTITION OF PRIMATES.) Uzbienie Naczelnych. Wanda Steślicka. Ann. Univ. Mariae Curie-Sklodowska, Lublin, vol.1, no.8, pp.183-276, pls.8-12, Oct.10, 1947.

Taxonomy

(ANALYTIC KEY FOR THE GENERIC DETERMINATION OF AMERICAN MONKEYS BY THE CHARACTERS OF THE CRANIUM.) Clef analytique pour la détermination générique des singes américains par les caractères de la tête osseuse. J. Anthony. Bull. Mus. Nat. Hist. Nat., Paris, ser.2, vol.19, no.1, pp.47-50, figs.2, Jan., 1947.

(THE SCIENTIFIC NAMES OF SOME AMERICAN MONKEYS.) Los nombres cientificos de algunos monos americanos. Angel Cabrera. Cienca, Revista hispanoamericana de Ciencias puras y aplicadas, Mexico, D.F., vol.1, no.9, pp.402-405, Nov.1, 1940.

THE CLASSIFICATION OF THE PRIMATES. W. E. LeGros Clark. Nature, London, vol.125, no.3146, pp.236-237, Feb.15, 1930.

DESCRIPTIONS OF APPARENTLY NEW SPECIES AND SUBSPECIES OF MAMMALS BELONGING TO THE FAMILIES LEMURIDAE, CEBIDAE, CALLITRICHIDAE, AND CERCOPITHECIDAE IN THE COLLECTION OF THE NATURAL HISTORY MUSEUM. D. G. Elliot. Ann. and Mag. Nat. Hist., ser.7, vol.20, pp.185-195, Sept., 1907.

DESCRIPTIONS OF APPARENTLY NEW SPECIES AND SUBSPECIES OF MONKEYS OF THE GENUS CALLICEBUS, LAGOTHRIX, PAPIO, PITHECUS, CERCOPITHECUS, ERYTHROCEBUS, AND PRESBYTIS. D. G. Elliot. Ann. and Mag. Nat. Hist. ser.8, vol.4, pp.243-274, Sept., 1909.

DESCRIPTIONS OF NEW SPECIES OF MONKEYS OF THE GENERA GALAGO, CEBUS, ALOUATTA, AND CERCOPITHECUS. D. G. Elliot. Ann. and Mag. Nat. Hist., Lond., ser.8, vol.5, pp.77-83, Jan., 1910.

ON SOME NEW OR LITTLE KNOWN SPECIES OF MONKEYS. J. E. Gray. Proc. Zool. Soc. Lond., pt.17, pp.7-10, 1849.

ON THE CLASSIFICATION AND PHYLOGENY OF THE LEMUROIDEA. W. K. Gregory. Bull. Geol. Soc. Amer., vol.26, pp.426-446, Nov.24, 1915.

(TWO NEW MONKEYS (CERCOPITHECUS STUHLMANNI AND HAPALE SANTAREMENSIS.) Zwei neue Affen (Cercopithecus stuhlmanni und Hapale santaremensis). Paul Matschie. Sitz. Ber. Gesell, Naturf. Freunde Berlin, Jahrg., no.9, pp.225-228, Nov.21, 1893.

THE CLASSIFICATION OF THE PRIMATES. C. Tate Regan. Nature, London, vol.125, no.3143, pp.125-126, 1930.

(CATALOGUE OF THE MAMMAL TYPES OF THE NATIONAL MUSEUM OF NATURAL HISTORY. I. ORDER PRIMATES. B. SUBORDER LEMURIDS.) Catalogue des types de mammiferes du Museum National d'Histoire Naturelle. I. Ordre des Primates. B. Sousordre des Lemuriens. P. Rode. Bull. Mus. Nat. Hist. Nat., Paris, ser.2, vol.11, no.5, pp.434-449, 1939.

THE SUBDIVISIONS OF THE ORDER PRIMATES. G. Elliot Smith. Nature, Lond., vol.124, no.3136, pp.876-877, Dec.7, 1929.

THE NOMENCLATURE FOR MAN, THE CHIMPANZEE, THE ORANG-UTAN AND THE BARBARY APE. Ch. Wardell Stiles, Mabelle B. Orleman. Treasury Dept., U.S. Pub. Health Serv., Hygienic Lab. Bull., no.145, pp.1-66, figs.16, 1927.

THE NOMENCLATURE OF PRIMATES COMMONLY USED IN LABORATORY WORK. S. Zuckerman, J. F. Fulton. Privately printed by the Tuttl, Morehouse & Taylor Co., New Haven, Conn., pp.14, July, 1934.

Vision and the Eye

(THE RELATIVE VALUE OF FORM AND COLOR CHARACTERS IN THE PERCEPTION OF MONKEYS.) Der relative Wert von Form - und Farbenmerkmalen in der Wahrnehmung des Affen. J. A. Bierens de Haan. Biol. Zentralblatt, vol.45, pp.727-734, 1925.

COMPARATIVE STUDIES UPON THE EYES OF NOCTURNAL LEMUROIDS, MONKEYS AND MAN. S. R. Detwiler. Anat. Record, Phila., vol.74, pp.129-145, 1 pl., June 25, 1939.

A COMPARISON OF HUMAN AND CHIMPANZEE SPECTRAL HUE DISCRIMINATION CURVES. Walter F. Grether. Jour. Exper. Psychol., Balto., vol.26, no.4, pp.394-403, figs.2, Apr., 1940.

STRUCTURE OF THE RETINA IN PRIMATES. S. Poljak. Acta Ophthalmologica, Copenhagen, vol.13, nos.1-2, pp.52-60, figs.1-2, 1935.

THE SIZE OF THE ORBIT AND OF THE EYE IN PRIMATES. Adolph H. Schultz. Amer. Jour. Phys. Anthrop., Phila., vol. 26, pp.389-408, figs.3, Mar.30, 1940.

NEW LIGHT ON VISION. G. Elliot Smith. Nature, Lond., vol.125, no.3161, pp.820-824, figs.6, May 31, 1930.

THE DIFFERENTIATION OF THE RETINA IN THE PRIMATES. H. H. Woollard. Proc. Zool. Soc. Lond., pt.1, pp.1-17, 4 pls., Apr.6, 1927.

Tupaiidae

THE MYOLOGY OF THE TREE-SHREW (TUPAIA MINOR). W. E. LeGros Clark. Proc. Zool. Soc. Lond., pp.461-497, 24 figs., July, 1924.

ON THE ANATOMY OF THE PEN-TAILED TREE-SHREW (PTILOCERCUS LOWII). W. E. LeGros Clark. Proc. Zool. Soc. Lond., pt.4, pp.1179-1309, 5 pls., 62 text figs., Dec., 1926.

ON THE BRAIN OF THE TREE-SHREW (TUPAIA MINOR). W. E. LeGros Clark. Proc. Zool. Soc. Lond., pt.4, pp.1053-1074, 3 pls., 1925.

ON THE SKULL OF TUPAIA. W. E. LeGros Clark. Proc. Zool. Soc. Lond., pt.2, pp. 559-567, July, 1925.

THE TREE-SHREW, TUPAIA MINOR. W. E. LeGros Clark. Proc. Zool. Soc. Lond., pt.1, pp.254-256, 1 pl., Apr.6, 1927.

A NEW TREE SHREW OF THE GENUS TANA FROM MOUNT KINABALU, NORTH BORNEO. Harold J. Coolidge, Jr. Proc. New England Zool. Club, vol.17, pp.45-47, May 6, 1938.

NOTES ON THE ANATOMY OF THE TREE-SHREW DENDROGALE. D. Wright Davis. Field Mus. Nat. Hist., Zool. ser., vol.20, no.31, pp.383-404, figs.49-56, May 27, 1938.

(NOTES ON MAMMALS. IV. ON THE SKULLS OF THE TUPAIIDAE (INSECTIVORES).) Notes sur les mammiferes. IV. Au sujet des cranes des Tupaiidae (Insectivores). Serge Frechkop. Bull. Mus. Roy. d'Hist. Nat. de Belgique, vol.6, no.21, pp. 108, Dec., 1930.

NOTICE OF A SPECIES OF TUPAIA FROM BORNEO, IN THE COLLECTION OF THE BRITISH MUSEUM. John Edward Gray. Proc. Zool. Soc. Lond., p.322, pl.12, 1865.

ABSTRACT OF LYON'S "TREESHREWS: AN ACCOUNT OF THE MAMMALIAN FAMILY TUPAIIDAE". N. Hollister. Jour. Washington Acad. Sci., vol.4, no.12, pp. 330-331, June 19, 1914.

THE TENASSERIM TREE-SHREW (TUPAIA BELANGERI). C. Imrose. Jour. Bombay Nat. Hist. Soc., vol.28, pp.796-798, June 30, 1922.

ON THE DEVELOPMENT OF THE TOOTH IN TUPAIA JAVANICA. Maertha Kindahl. Arkiv. foer zoologi, Stockholm, 10 (11): 463-479, Apr.15, 1957.

THE MALAYAN TREE-SHREW. C. W. Leister. Bull. New York Zool. Soc., vol. 41, no.1, pp.37-39, illus., Jan.-Feb., 1938.

THE FACIAL MUSCULATURE OF SOME LESSER PRIMATES AND A TUPAIA. A COMPARATIVE STUDY. G. G. Lightoller. Proc. Zool. Soc. Lond., pt.2, pp.259-309, pls.8, figs.1-40, July, 1934.

DESCRIPTION OF FOUR NEW TREE-SHREWS. Marcus W. Lyon, Jr. Proc. Biol. Soc. Washington, vol.24, pp.167-170, June 16, 1911.

TREE-SHREWS: AN ACCOUNT OF THE MAMMALIAN FAMILY TUPAIIDAE. Marcus W. Lyon, Jr. Proc. U.S. Nat. Mus., vol.45, no.1976, pp.1-88, figs.1-15, pls. 1-11, Nov.29, 1913.

PLACENTATION OF THE PIGMY TREE-SHREW TUPAIA MINOR. Waldemar Meister, D. Dwight Davis. Fieldiana Zool., Chicago, 34 (4): 71-84, pls.10-14, Sept.14, 1956.

DERMATOGLYPHICS IN TUPAIA LACERNATA LACERNATA. Charles Midlo. Jour. Mam., vol.16, no.1, pp.35-37, Feb., 1935.

DESCRIPTION OF DENDROGALE MURINA. G. S. Miller, Jr. Proc. U.S. Nat. Mus., vol.45, no.1976, p.129, Nov.29, 1913.

NOTES ON DENDROGALE MURINA IN THE LEYDEN MUSEUM. G. S. Miller, Jr. Proc. U.S. Nat. Mus., vol.45, no.1976, p. 129, Nov.24, 1913.

TREE SHREWS. R. I. Pocock. Field, Lond., vol.152, p.242, illus., Aug.9, 1928.

THE LIVING DEAD. LITTLE RAT-LIKE PATRIARCHS FROM THE JUNGLES OF THE FAR EAST THAT CREEP BEFORE US AS LIVING IMAGES OF OUR FORE-FATHERS. Erich M. Schlaikjer. Nat. Hist., New York, vol.41, no.3, pp.203-211, illus., Mar., 1938.

(OBSERVATIONS OF THE SQUIRREL SHREW (TUPAIA TANA RAFFL.).) Beobachtungen an Tanas (Tupaia tana Raffl.). Martin Schlott. Zool. Garten, Leipzig, n.F., vol.12, nos.2-3, pp.153-157, figs.2, July, 1940.

"FLYING" SNAKES, TREE SHREWS AND MIMICRY. E. O. Shebbeare. Malayan Nature Jour., Kuala Lumpur, vol.1, no.4, pp.157-162, 1 figs., 1 map, July, 1941.

BREEDING OF THE PHILIPPINE TREE SHREW, UROGALE EVERETTI THOMAS. Robert Snedigar. Jour. Mam., Balto., vol. 30, no.2, pp.194-195, May 23, 1949.

OCCURRENCE OF THE TREE SHREW (ANATHANA WROUGHTONI) AT KHANDALLA, POONA DISTRICT. M. Suter. Jour. Bombay Nat. Hist. Soc., vol.28, p.537, Mar.25, 1922.

DESCRIPTION OF A NEW BORNEAN TUPAIA. Oldfield Thomas. Ann. and Mag. Nat. Hist. (6), vol.12, no.67, pp.53-54, July, 1893.

ON THE PALAWAN REPRESENTATIVE OF TUPAIA FERRUGINEA. Oldfield Thomas. Ann. and Mag. Nat. Hist. (6), vol.13, no. 76, p.367, Apr., 1894.

SCIENTIFIC RESULTS FROM THE MAMMAL SURVEY. XVI. A. THE TUPAIAS OF SOUTH TENASSERIM. Oldfield Thomas. Jour. Bombay Nat. Hist. Soc., vol.25, pp. 199-201, Sept.15, 1917.

SCIENTIFIC RESULTS FROM THE MAMMAL SURVEY. NO. XXXVII. ON TREE-SHREWS FROM THE MERGUI ARCHIPELAGO. Oldfield Thomas. Jour. Bombay Nat. Hist. Soc., vol.29, no.1, p.84, Apr. 20, 1923.

THE TREE-SHREWS OF THE TUPAIA-BELANGERI-CHINENSIS GROUP. Oldfield Thomas. Ann. and Mag. Nat. Hist. (8), vol.13, no.74, pp.243-245, Feb., 1914.

DESCRIPTION OF A NEW SPECIES OF TUPAIA, DISCOVERED IN CONTINENTAL INDIA BY W. ELLIOTT. G. R. Waterhouse. Proc. Zool. Soc. Lond., pt.17, pp.106-108, 1849.

NOTES ON THE PHILIPPINE TREE-SHREW, UROGALE EVERETTI THOMAS. Charles H. Wharton. Jour. Mam., vol.31, no.3, pp.352-354, Aug.21, 1950.

SCIENTIFIC RESULTS FROM THE MAMMAL SURVEY. XXVI. (A) A NEW TREE-SHREW. R. C. Wroughton. Jour. Bombay Nat. Hist. Soc., vol.27, no.3, pp.599-600, 1921.

## Lemuridae

(THE CUTANEOUS BRACHIAL ORGANS OF HAPALEMUR GRISEUS.) May Affolter. Les organes cutanes brachiaux d'Hapalemur griseus. Bull. Acad. Malgache, Tananarive, n.s., vol.20, pp.77-100, fig.1, pls. 1-5, 1937.

A NEW LEMUR FROM MADAGASCAR. Richard Archbold. Amer. Mus. Novit., no.518, p.1, Mar.26, 1932.

(EARLY DEVELOPMENTAL STAGES IN MICROCEBUS MURINUS.) Fruehe Entwicklungsstadien von Microebus murinus. H. Bluntschli. Bio-Morphosis, Leipzig, vol.1, nos.3-4, pp.333-334, 1938.

(VARIABILITY OF CENTRAL TEMPERATURE IN THE LEMURIDAE.) Variabilite de la temperature centrale chez les lemuriens. F. J. J. Bourliere, A. Petter-Rousseaux. Mem. Inst. Sci. Madagascar, ser.A, 10: 303-304, 1956.

LEMURS AND CROCODILES. Alice Carleton. Jour. Anat., Lond., vol.72, pt. 1, pp.167-168, Oct., 1937.

THE LIMB-BONES AND VERTEBRAE OF THE EXTINCT LEMURS OF MADAGASCAR. Alice Carleton. Proc. Zool. Soc., Lond., pt.1, pp.281-307, pls.9, Apr., 1936.

ON THE OSTEOLOGY OF CERTAIN EXTINCT LEMURIDS OF MADAGASCAR. Alice Carleton. Proc. Zool. Soc. Lond., 1937, ser.B, vol.107, pt.4, pp.553-556, pls.1-2, Jan., 1938.

THE BRAIN OF MICROCEBUS MURINUS. W. E. LeGros Clark. Proc. Zool. Soc. Lond., pt.2, pp.463-486, figs.7, pls.1-8, June, 1931.

(ON THE SUPPOSED AFFINITIES OF LEMURIDS.) Sur les prétendues affinités des lémuriens. L. Clerget. Riviera Scientifique, 13th year, no.4, pp.65-68, 1926.

THE ABDOMINAL PORTION OF THE ALIMENTARY SYSTEM IN HAPALEMUR AND LEPILEMUR. D. V. Davies, W. C. Osman Hill. Proc. Roy. Soc. Edinburgh, vol.65, pt.2, pp.182-203, July, 1954.

(OBSERVATIONS ON THE LEMURS OF THE MENAGERIE OF THE JARDIN DES PLANTES.) Observations sur les Makis de la Menagerie du Jardin des Plantes. Ed Dechambre. Bull. Mus. Nat. Hist. Nat., Paris, ser.2, vol.7, no.6, pp.315-318, 1935.

THE LEMURS AS ANCESTORS OF THE APES. C. Earl. Natural Science, Lond., vol.10, no.63, pp.309-313, May, 1897.

(OBSERVATIONS ON SOME POINTS OF THE EMBRYOLOGY OF THE LEMURIDAE, AND ON THE ZOOLOGICAL AFFINITIES OF THESE ANIMALE.) Observations sur quelques points de l'embryologie des lémuriens et sur les affinités zoologiques de ces animaux. Alph Milne Edwards. Bibl. l'École Hautes Études, sec. Sci. Nat., Paris, vol. 4, no.5, pp.7, 1871.

BREEDING SEASON OF LEMURS. S. S. Flower. Proc. Zool. Soc. Lond., pt.2, p. 317, June, 1933.

(GENERIC CLASSIFICATION OF THE CHIROGALINAE, MADAGASCAN GROUP OF LEMURIDS.) Classification generique des Chirogalinae, groupe malgache de lemuriens. M. Friant. Bull. Mus. Nat. Hist., Paris, ser.2, vol.19, no.3, pp.257-260, 1947.

(ON THE PRESENCE OF A SUPERNUMERARY INCISOR IN A FEMALE LEMUR CATTA L.).) Sur la presence d'une incisive surnumeraire chez une Lemur catta L. J. K. Gan. Bull. Mus. Nat. Hist. Nat., Paris, ser.2, vol.10, no.6, pp.558-559, fig.1, Nov., 1938.

NOTE ON A NEW SPECIES OR VARIETY OF LEMUR IN THE SOCIETY'S GARDENS. J. E. Gray. Proc. Zool. Soc. Lond., p. 596, pl.XXXI, 1867.

NOTES ON HAPALEMUR SIMUS, A NEW SPECIES LATELY LIVING IN THE GARDENS OF THE SOCIETY. J. E. Gray. Proc. Zool. Soc. Lond., pp.828-831, figs. 4, pl.LII, 1870.

ON THE RAT OF MADAGASCAR. J. E. Gray. Ann. and Mag. Nat. Hist. Lond., ser.4, vol.11, no.66, pp.465-466, June, 1873.

REVISION OF THE SPECIES OF LEMUROID ANIMALS, WITH THE DESCRIPTION OF SOME NEW SPECIES. J. E. Gray. Proc. Zool. Soc. Lond., pt.31, pp.129-152, figs. 7, pls.XVII, XVIII, XIX, 1863.

(LEMUR HYBRIDS.) Halbaffenbastarde. Ludwig Heck. Zool. Garten, Leipzig, n.F., vol.1, nos.7-9, p.332, Feb., 1929.

DO LEMURS COMB THEIR FUR WITH THEIR TEETH? W. C. Osman Hill. Loris, Ceylon, vol.2, no.3, pp.179-181, illus., Dec., 1940.

DEAMER THE LEMUR. Harry Hoogstraal. Animal Kingdom, New York, vol.53, no.4, pp.102-109, illus., July-Aug., 1950.

MAKEE, A LEMUR FROM MADAGASCAR, LIKES CIVILIZED LIFE. Harry Hoogstraal. Bull. Chicago Nat. Hist. Mus., vol.20, no. 4, pp.6-7, Apr., 1949.

CONTRIBUTION TO THE MYOLOGY OF LEMUR BRUNEUS. G. S. Huntington. Trans. N. Y. Acad. Sci., vol.16, pp. 335-363, pls.28-35, 1897-98.

THE "MYTH" OF THE LEMUR'S COMB. Frederic Wood Jones. Amer. Nat., vol. 71, no.732, pp.95-96, Jan.-Feb., 1937.

(CONTRIBUTIONS ON THE DEVELOPMENT OF THE PRIMATE HAND. II. ON THE DEVELOPMENT OF THE LEMUR CATTA HAND.) Beitraege zur Entwicklung der Primatenhand. II. Zur Entwicklung der Hand von Lemur catta. H. Koblick. Morphol. Jahrb., vol.61, pp.452-456, 1 text fig., 1929.

(NOTES ON THE GENERA CHEIROGALEUS AND MICROCEBUS.) Notes sur les genres Chirogale et Microcebus. M. Kollman. Bull. Museum, Paris, pp.301-304, 1910.

(ON THE PRESENCE OF THE PLANUM BONE IN THE LEMURIDS.) Sur la presence de l'os planum chez les Lemuriens. M. Kollmann. Bull. Mus. Hist. Nat., no.5, pp.321-323, 1919.

(STUDIES ON THE LEMURIDS. II. SYSTEMATIC RESEARCH ON SOME SPECIES BELONGING TO THE GENERA CHEIROGALEUS AND MICROCEBUS.) Etudes sur les Lemuriens. II. Recherches systematique sur quelques especes appartenant aux genres Chirogale et Microcebus. M. Kollmann. Mem. Soc., Zool., Paris, 26:155-189, figs., 1914.

(A LAST IRREGULAR PREMOLAR (P4), IN MEGALADAPIS GRANDIDIERI.) Une dernière premolaire anormale (P4) chez Megaladapis grandidieri. C. Lamberton. Mammalia, Paris, vol.3, no.2, pp.53-54, figs.2, pl.4, June, 1939.

(MILK TEETH OF SOME SUBFOSSIL MADAGASCAN LEMURIDS.) Dentition de lait de quelques lémuriens subfossiles malgaches. C. Lamberton. Mammalia, Paris, vol.2, no.2, pp.57-80, pls.3-9, June, 1938.

(A NEW PROPITHECAN OF MADAGASCAR (PROPITHECUS PERRIERI SP. N.).) Un nouveau propitheque de Madagascar (Propithecus perrieri sp. n.) L. Lavauden. C. R. Acad. Sci., Paris, 193: 77-79, 1931.

(INVESTIGATIONS ON THE DENTAL SYSTEM OF LIVING AND FOSSIL LEMURS.) Untersuchungen ueber das Zahnsystem Lebender Und Fossiler Halbaffen. Wilhelm Leche. Festschrift Fur Carl Gegenbaur, vol.3, pp.127-166, text figs.29, pl.1, Leipzig, 1896.

(SOME OF THE MADAGASCAN LEMURS.) Nagra av Madagaskars halvapor. B. Ljungqvist. Fauna och Flora, Stockholm, pt.1, pp.25-33, illus., 1931.

THE MECHANISM OF THE LEMURINE FOOT. D. W. MacKenzie, Jr. Trans. Roy. Soc. Canada, ser.3, vol.25, sec.5, pp.45-57, figs.7, May, 1931.

ON LEMUR MONGOZ AND LEMUR RUBRIVENTER. C. E. Forsyth Major. Proc. Zool. Soc. Lond., vol.1, pp.248-268, pl. 22, figs.61-70, Aug.1, 1901.

NOTES OF THE DISSECTION OF A SMALL NOCTURNAL LEMUR (MICROCEBUS MURINUS, GEOFF.). W. Martin. Proc. Zool. Soc. Lond., pt.3, p.125, 1835.

(OBSERVATIONS ON SOME POINTS OF THE EMBRYOLOGY OF LEMURIDS AND ON THE ZOOLOGICAL AFFINITIES OF THESE ANIMALS.) Observations sur quelques points de l'embryologie des Lemuriens et sur les affinites zoologiques de ces Animaux. Alphonse Milne-Edwards. Nat. Hist., vol.21, 1871.

ADDITIONAL NOTES ON THE OSTEOLOGY OF THE LEMURIDAE. St. George Mivart. Proc. Zool. Soc. Lond., pp.960-975, Dec. 12, 1867.

NOTES ON THE CRANIA AND DENTITION OF THE LEMURIDAE. St. George Mivart. Proc. Zool. Soc. Lond., pp.611-648, figs. 2, illus., 1864.

ON LEPILEMUR AND CHEIROGALEUS, AND ON THE ZOOLOGICAL RANK OF THE LEMUROIDEA. St. George Mivart. Proc. Zool. Soc. Lond., pp.484-510, figs.18, pl. XLIII, 1873.

LEMURS. Richard Johannes Muller. Mus. News, Brooklyn, vol.8, no.2, pp.17-23, Nov., 1912.

(DESCRIPTION OF A FOETUS OF LEPIDOLEMUR RUFICAUDATUS A. GRANDIDIER.) Description d'un foetus de Lepidolemur ruficaudatus A. Grandidier. G. Petit. La Terre et la Vie, Paris, vol.4, no.8, pp.497-499, illus., Aug., 1934.

(THE GENUS "LEPIDOLEMUR" AND ITS GEOGRAPHICAL DISTRIBUTION. PRELIMINARY NOTE.) Le genre "Lepidolemur" et sa repartition geographique. (Note preliminaire.) G. Petit. Compte Rendu Som. Seances Soc. Biogeogr., annee 10, no.82, pp.33-37, 1933.

(ON THE MADAGASCAN LEMURID CHEIROGALEUS TRICHOTIS.) A propos du Lémurien malgache Cheirogaleus trichotis. J. J. Petter, A. Petter-Rousseaux. Mammalia, Paris, vol.20, no.1, pp.46-48, Mar., 1956.

(ON THE CHEWING MUSCULATURE OF MICROCEBUS MURINUS AND THE CORRELATIONS BETWEEN ITS DEVELOPMENT AND THAT OF THE SKULL AND THE TOOTH ARRANGEMENT.) Ueber die Kaumuskeln von Microcebus murinus und die Korrelationen zwischen ihrer Entwicklung und jener des Schaedels und der Zahnanlagen. Heinrich Pfenninger. Zusammenfassung. Inaugural-Dissertation der medizinischen Fakultaet der Univ. Bern. Anat. Inst. Univ. Bern, pp.4, July 13, 1938.

(THE BRAIN OF THE LEMURID HADROPITHECUS SUBFOSSIL OF MADAGASCAR.) L'encéphale de l'Hadropithecus lémurien subfossile de Madagascar. Jean Piveteau. Ann. Paleontologie, 42: 141-150, 1956.

THE LEMURS OF THE HAPALEMUR GROUP. R. I. Pocock. Ann. and Mag. Nat. Hist., Lond., ser.8, vol.19, pp. 343-352, Apr., 1917.

ON A RING-TAILED LEMUR AND YOUNG. R. I. Pocock. Proc. Zool. Soc. Lond., pp.124-125, fig.4, June 7, 1906.

PECULIARITIES OF THE LEMURS. W. P. Pycraft. Illus. London News, vol.191, no. 5132, p.336, figs.3, Aug.28, 1937.

THE TOOTH-COMB OF THE LEMURS. W. P. Pycraft. Illus. London News, vol. 194, no.5224, p.974, figs.4, June 3, 1939.

(CATALOG OF THE TYPES OF MAMMALS OF THE NATIONAL MUSEUM OF NATURAL HISTORY. ORDER PRIMATES. B. SUBORDER OF LEMURIDS.) Catalogue des Types de Mammifères du Muséum National d'Histoire Naturelle. Ordre des Primates. B. Sous-ordre des Lémuriens. P. Rode. Bull. Mus. Nat. Hist. Nat., Paris, ser.2, vol.11, no.5, pp.434-449, June, 1939.

(THE TEMPORAL BONE AND ITS AFFINITIES WITH THE SUBFOSSIL LEMURIDS OF MADAGASCAR. I. TYPE A QUADRITUBERCULATED MOLARS. PRIMITIVE FORMS.) L'os temporal et ses rapports chez les lemuriens suffossiles de Madagascar. I. Type A molaires quadrituberculees. Formes archaiques. R. Saban. Mem. Inst. Sci. Madagascar, ser.A, 10: 251-297, 1956.

(STUDIES OF THE NUMBER OF VERTEBRAE AND BODY PROPORTIONS OF LEMURS.) Studien ueber die Wirbelzahlen und die Koerperproportionen von Halbaffen. Adolph H. Schultz. Vierteljahrsschrift Naturf. Gesell. Zuerich, vol.99, no.1, pp. 39-75, Mar.31, 1954.

(THE DENTITION OF THE LEMURID GENUS LEPILEMUR J. GEOFFROY AND ITS SIGNIFICANCE FOR THE DENTAL FORMULA OF THE PRIMATES.) Das Gebiss der Lemuridengattung Lepilemur J. Geoffroy und seine Bedeutung fuer die Gebissformel der Primaten. Ernst Schwarz. Zool. Anzeiger vol.87, nos. 1-2, pp.47-48, 3 figs., 1930.

(ON THE "LEMUR MACACO" LINNAEUS.) A propos du "Lemur macaco" Linnaeus. Ernst Schwarz. Mammalia, Paris, vol.1, no.1, pp.24-25, Sept., 1936.

A REVISION OF THE GENERA AND SPECIES OF MADAGASCAR LEMURIDAE. Ernst Schwarz. Proc. Zool. Soc. Lond., pt.2, pp.399-428, June, 1931.

NOTE ON LEMUR MACACO, AND THE WAY IN WHICH IT CARRIES ITS YOUNG. P. L. Sclater. Proc. Zool. Soc. Lond., pp.672-673, fig.1, June 16, 1885.

REMARKS ON LEMUR LEUCOMYSTAX, BARTLETT. P. L. Sclater. Proc. Zool. Soc. Lond., pp.1-2, 1866.

A FEW NOTES ON FOUR SPECIES OF LEMURS, SPECIMENS OF WHICH WERE BROUGHT ALIVE TO ENGLAND IN 1878. George A. Shaw. Proc. Zool. Soc. Lond., pp.132-136, 1879.

NOTES ON THE CRANIAL ANATOMY OF NECROLEMUR. E. L. Simons, D. E. Russell. Cambridge, Mass., Harvard Univ., Mus. of Comp. Zool., 14 pp., illus., 1960.

THE MYTH OF THE LEMUR'S COMB. M. Russell Stein. Amer. Nat., vol.70, no. 726, pp.19-28, figs.7, Jan.-Feb., 1936.

LEAST KNOWN PRIMATES. Ken Stott, Jr. San Diego Zoonooz, vol.15, no.6, pp.5-7, illus., June, 1942.

(ABOUT THE CONFORMATION OF THE MIDDLE EAR OF THE LEMURIDAE AND THE CONNECTION BETWEEN THE FOSSIL LEMURIDAE OF FRANCE AND THOSE OF MADAGASCAR.) Sur la conformation de l'oreille moyenne des Lémuriens et sur les rapports des Lémuriens fossile des France avec ceux de Madagascar. E. L. Trouessart. Comptes rendus Soc. Biol., Paris, vol.61, pp.712-715, figs., Dec., 1906.

(REMARKS ON THE SUMMER SLEEP OF PYGMY LEMURS.) Bemerkungen zum Sommerschlaf der Zwerglemuren. Alfred Weidholz. Zool. Garten, Leipzig, n.F., vol.5, nos.10-12, pp.282-285, figs.4, Dec., 1932.

## Indridae

NOTE ON THE OSTEOLOGY OF PALAEOPROPITHECUS. Alice Carleton. Proc. Zool. Soc. Lond., vol.107, ser.B, Syst. and Morphol., pt.2, pp.295-297, fig.1, July, 1937.

NOTES ON PROPITHECUS, INDRIS, AND OTHER LEMURS (LEMURINA) IN THE BRITISH MUSEUM. J. E. Gray. Proc. Zool. Soc. Lond., pp.846-859, fig.6, pls. LXIX, LXXI, 1872.

(CONTRIBUTION TO KNOWLEDGE OF THE SUBFOSSIL FAUNA OF MADAGASCAR. NOTE XVI. BRADYTHERIUM OR PALEOPROPITHECUS?) Contribution à la connaissance de la faune subfossile de Madagascar. Note XVI. Bradytherium ou palaeopropithèque? C. Lamberton. Bull. Acad. Malgache Tananarive, n.s., vol.26, Annees 1944, pp.89-140, pls.14, 1947.

(NEW FOSSIL LEMURIDS OF THE PROPITHECUS GROUP.) Nouveaux Lemuriens Fossiles du Groupes des Propithecus. C. Lamberton. Men. Acad. Malgache, vol. 27, pp.1-203, 1939.

(A NEW PROPITHECAN OF MADAGASCAR (PROPITHECUS PERRIERI SP. NOV.).) Un nouveau Propithèque de Madagascar (Propithecus perrieri, sp. nov.). L. Lavauden. Comptes Rendus Acad. Sci., Paris, vol. 193, no.1, pp.77-79, July 6, 1931.

ON THE SKULL OF INDRIS DIADEMA. St. George Mivart. Proc. Zool. Soc. Lond., pp.247-256, figs.3, pl.XVIII, 1867.

PLATE OF PROPITHECUS MAJORI. Walter Rothschild. Novitates Zoologicae, Tring., vol.1, no.4, pl.14, Sept., 1894.

EXHIBITION OF A SPECIMEN OF A NEWLY DESCRIBED LEMUR (PROPITHECUS DEMANUS). P. L. Sclater. Proc. Zool. Soc. Lond., p.112, 1870.

(ON THE ONTOGENY OF THE DENTITION OF INDRIS.) Zur Ontogenie des Indrisinengebisses. Hans Spreng. Zusammenfassung. Inaugural-Dissertation der medizinischen Fakultaet der Univ. Bern. Anat. Inst. Univ. Bern, pp.4, July 13, 1938.

SOME MADAGASCAN ANIMALS. C. S. Webb. Zoo Life, vol.1, no.2, pp.57-58, Summer, 1946.

(THE PRIMORDIAL CRANIUM OF AN AVAHIS LANIGER FETUS.) Das Primordialcranium eines Fetus von Avahis laniger. Inaugural Dissertation of the Medical Department of the Univ. of Berne, Anat. Inst. Univ. Bern, pp.6, 1938.

## Daubentoniidae

(ONE PRESENT AND ONE NEW VARIETY OF CHEIROMYS MADAGASCARIENSIS.) Une variète du Cheiromys madagascariensis actuel et un nouveau. G. Grandidier.

ON THE MUSCULAR SHEATH OF THE CARDIAC END OF THE ESOPHAGUS OF THE AYE-AYE (CHIROMYS MADAGASCARIENSIS). George Gulliver. Proc. Zool. Soc. Lond., pp.249-250, 1869.

THE FETAL MEMBRANES AND PLACENTATION OF CHIROMYS MADAGASCARIENSIS. J. P. Hill, R. H. Burne. Proc. Zool. Soc. Lond., pt.4, pp.1145-1165, pls.6, Feb., 1923.

(THE GROOVES OF THE CEREBRAL CORTEX OF DAUBENTONIA MADAGASCARIENSIS GMELIN 1788 AND THEIR MORPHOLOGICAL SIGNIFICANCE.) Das Furchenbild der Hirnrinde von Daubentonia madagascariensis (Gmelin, 1788) und seine Morphologische Bedeutung. H. Hofer. Zool. Anz., Leipzig, vol.156, nos.5-6, pp.177-196, Mar., 1956.

(ON THE GLANDULAE VESICULARES IN CHIROMYS MADAGASCARIENSIS.) Ueber die Glandulae vesiculares bei Chiromys madagascariensis. Walter Kaudern. Arkiv. Zool., vol.9, no.7, pp.1-4, figs.1-4, 1915.

THE ARTICULATIONS OF THE CARPUS IN CHIROMYS MADAGASCARENSIS WITH REFERENCE TO CERTAIN OTHER LEMURS. U. V. Nayak. Jour. Anat., Cambridge, vol.68, pt.1, pp.109-115, Oct., 1933.

(THE AYE-AYE.) Le Aye-aye. L. Lavauden. Terre et Vie, 3: 142-152, 1933.

ON THE ANATOMY OF THE AYE-AYE. PART I. (ABSTRACT) Richard Owen. Proc. Zool. Soc. Lond., pt.30, pp.11-12, 1862.

ON THE EXTERNAL CHARACTERS OF A FOETAL CHIROMYS. R. I. Pocock. Proc. Zool. Soc. Lond., pt.4, pp.1165-1170, Feb., 1923.

EXHIBITION OF A CAST OF THE SKULL OF THE AYE-AYE (CHIROMYS MADAGASCARIENSIS). P. L. Sclater. Proc. Zool. Soc. Lond., pt.29, pp.306-307, 1861.

NOTICE OF A LIVING AYE-AYE (CHIROMYS MADAGASCARIENSIS) IN THE SOCIETY'S MENAGERIE. P. L. Sclater. Proc. Zool. Soc. Lond., pt.30, pp.222-223, 1862.

HABITS OF THE AYE-AYE. G. A. Shaw. American Nat. Lancaster, vol.17, no.12, p.1301, Dec., 1883.

## Lorisidae

THE SLOW LORIS AS A PET. R. S. Butterfield. Malayan Nature Jour., vol.9, no.2, pp.43-49, Sept., 1954.

THE LESSER BUSH BABIES. G. S. Cansdale. Nat. Hist., New York, vol.55, no.1, pp.33-37, illus., Jan., 1946.

THE LESSER BUSH BABY. GALAGO DEMIDOVII DEMIDOVII G. FISCH. G. S. Cansdale. Jour. Soc. Preservation Fauna Empire, Hertford, pt.1, pp.7-12, pls.3, Dec., 1944.

THE SLENDER LORIS. Guy Dollman. Nat. Hist. Mag., British Mus., vol.5, no. 33, pp.1-4, illus., Jan., 1935.

EXHIBITION OF A SPECIMEN OF THE GALAGO SENEGALENSIS SHREW FROM FERNANDO PO. L. Fraser. Proc. Zool. Soc. Lond., pt.10, p.200, 1842.

EXPERIMENTS ON THE LEARNING AND PROBLEM SOLVING OF NYCTICEBUS TARDIGRADUS L. F. J. Gorter. Archiv. Neerlandaises de Zool., vol.2, no.1, pp. 95-111, 1935.

(OBSERVATIONS ON NYCTICEBUS TARDIGRADUS, THE CLUMSY LORIS.) Waarnemingen bij Nycticebus tardigradus, de plompe lori. F. J. Gorter. Tropische Natuur, vol.23, no.2, pp.21-25, figs.2, Feb., 1934.

(ON THE POTTO.) Ueber den Potto. Bernhard Grzimek. Zool. Garten, Leipzig, (N.F.), vol.20, nos.2-3, pp.67-73, illus., 1953.

THE AFFINITIES OF THE LORISOIDS. W. C. Osman Hill. Spolia Zeylanica, Ceylon Jour. Sci., Colombo, sec. B, Zool.

and Geol., vol.19, pt.3, pp.287-314, Feb. 18, 1936.

BODY ODOUR IN LORISES. W. C. Osman Hill. Proc. Zool. Soc. Lond., 127 (4): 580, Dec.21, 1956.

LORIS. W. C. Osman Hill. Ceylon, vol. 1, no.1, pp.7-9, illus., Nov., 1936.

A MONOGRAPH ON THE GENUS LORIS. WITH AN ACCOUNT OF THE EXTERNAL, CRANIAL AND DENTAL CHARACTERS OF THE GENUS: A REVISION OF THE KNOWN FORMS: AND THE DESCRIPTION OF A NEW FORM FROM NORTHERN CEYLON. W. C. Osman Hill. Ceylon Jour. Sci., sect. B, Zool. and Geol., vol.18, pt.1, pp.89-132, figs.8, pls.7-11, Dec.22, 1933.

RETINOSCOPY OF LORIS. W. C. Osman Hill. Nature, London, vol.135, no.3415, p.584, Apr.13, 1935.

A CONTRIBUTION TO A NORMAL TABLE OF THE DEVELOPMENT OF LORIS LYDEKKERIANUS. Frances E. Ince. Trans. Zool. Soc. Lond., vol.23, pt.2, pp.43-62, pls.8-13, Mar., 1937.

PRELIMINARY NOTICE OF A NEW GENUS OF LEMUROID FROM THE SIWALIKS. G. Edward Lewis. Amer. Jour. Sci., vol.26, no.152, pp.134-138, figs.1-2, Aug., 1933.

BUSH BABIES, WILD AND TAME. A. Loveridge. Nat. Hist., New York, vol.51, no.2, pp.76-77, 106, illus., Feb., 1943.

A STUDY OF THE ACTIVITIES OF A PAIR OF GALAGO SENEGALENSIS MOHOLI IN CAPTIVITY, INCLUDING THE BIRTH AND POSTNATAL DEVELOPMENT OF TWINS. Florence De L. Lowther. Zoologica, Sci. Contrib. New York Zool. Soc., New York, vol.25, pt.4, no.27, pp.433-462, pls. 1-6, Dec.31, 1940.

OBSERVATIONS ON THE HABITS OF LORIS LYDEKKERIANUS. C. R. Narayan Rao. Half-Yearly Jour. Mysore Univ., vol.1, no. 1, pp.57-62, Jan., 1927.

EXHIBITION OF, AND REMARKS UPON, SOME SPECIMENS OF THE POTTO (PERODICTICUS POTTO). P. L. Sclater. Proc. Zool. Soc. Lond., pp.1-2, 1869.

SOME OBSERVATIONS ON THE HABITS OF THE SLENDER LORIS, LORIS TARDIGRADUS (LINNAEUS). Swarna Subramoniam. Jour. Bombay Nat. Hist. Soc., 54 (2): 387-398, Apr., 1957.

THE PRIMATE AFFINITIES OF THE BLOOD SERUM OF THE LEMURS PERODICTICUS AND GALAGO. S. Zuckerman. Proc. Zool. Soc. Lond., pt.3, pp.609-612, Sept., 1934.

"BUSH BABIES" AT HOME. Field, London, vol.163, no.4240, p.697, illus., Mar.31, 1934.

Africa

(CONTRIBUTION TO THE KNOWLEDGE OF THE POTTO OF BOSMAN IN SOUTH TOGO.) Contribution a la connaissance du Potto de Bosman dans le Togo-sud. P. Baudenon. Mammalia, Paris, vol.13, no.3, pp.76-99, Sept., 1949.

THE ANGWANTIBO OF CALABAR. Maurice Burton. Illus. London News, vol.219, no. 5859, p.188, illus., Aug.4, 1951.

NOTICE OF A NEW VARIETY OF GALAGO FROM QUILLIMANE (OTOGALE CRASSICAUDATA, VAR. KIRKII). J. E. Gray. Proc. Zool. Soc. Lond., pp.456-458, 1864.

ON LEMURS AT MOROGORO, G.E.A. Arthur Loveridge. Jour. East Africa and Uganda Nat. Hist. Soc., no.14, pp.401-403, July, 1919.

(NOTE ON THE POTTO OF BOSMAN OR PERODICTICUS POTTO.) Note sur le potto de Bosman ou Perodicticus potto. Alphonse Milne Edwards. Bull. Nouvelles Archives Museum, Paris, vol.10, pp.111-114, pls.3-4, 1874.

ON THE GENUS GALAGO, WITH DESCRIPTION OF AN APPARENTLY NEW SPECIES (GALAGO MURINUS) FROM OLD CALABAR. Andrew Murray. Edin. Philos. Jour. N.S., pp.3-11, pl.11, Oct., 1859.

THE MAHOLI BUSH-BABY. W. P. Pycraft. Illus. London News, vol.193, no.5199, p. 1104, figs.3, Dec.10, 1938.

THE LEMURS OF NIGERIA. D. R. Rosevear. Nigerian Field, Lond., vol.4, no.1, pp.16-21, pls.2, Jan., 1935.

(A PROSIMIAN FROM SPANISH GUINEA, PERODICTICUS EDWARDSI.) Un prosimio de la Guinea Española, Perodicticus edwardsi. P. Ignacio Sala de Castellarnau. Revista Brotéria, ser. Ciênc. Nat., Lisbon, vol.16, (43), fasc.3, pp.122-126, figs.2, 1947.

THE GALAGO. H. Schmidt-Schaumberg. Discovery, vol.18, no.206, p.59, Feb., 1937.

(A NEW GALAGO FROM LAKE ALBERT.) Ein neuer Galago vom Albert-See. Ernst Schwarz. Rev. Zool. et Bot. Africaines, vol.19, nos.3-4, pp.391-392, Oct.1, 1930.

ON A NEW GALAGO FROM SOUTH-EAST AFRICA, WITH A NOTE ON OTOLICNUS GARNETTII, OGILBY. Ernst Schwarz. Ann. and Mag. Nat. Hist., Lond., (10), vol.5, no.25, pp.48-50, 1930.

ON THE AFRICAN LONG-TAILED LEMURS OR GALAGOS. Ernst Schwarz. Ann. and Mag. Nat. Hist. (10), vol.7, no.37, pp.41-66, Jan., 1931.

ON THE AFRICAN SHORT-TAILED LEMURS OR POTTOS. Ernst Schwarz. Ann. and Mag. Nat. Hist., ser.10, vol.8, no.45, pp.249-256, Sept., 1931.

A NEW POTTO FROM BRITISH EAST AFRICA. Oldfield Thomas. Proc. Zool. Soc. Lond., pp.536-537, Aug., 1910.

Anatomy

THE CARDIOVASCULAR SYSTEM OF THE SLOW LORIS (NYCTICEBUS TARDIGRADUS MALAIANUS). D. V. Davies. Proc. Zool. Soc. Lond., vol.117, nos.2-3, p.377, 1947.

THE EYE OF NYCTICEBUS TARDIGRADA. S. R. Detwiler. Anat. Rec., Phila., vol. 76, no.3, pp.295-301, figs.7, Mar.25, 1940.

ON THE ORGAN OF JACOBSON AND THE NASAL-FLOOR CARTILAGES IN THE CHONDROCRANIUM OF GALAGO SENEGALENSIS. F. C. Eloff. Proc. Zool. Soc. Lond., vol.121, pt.3, pp.651-655, illus., Nov., 1951.

MEMOIR ON THE BRAIN OF THE JAVAN LORIS (STENOPS JAVANICUS). W. H. Flower. Proc. Zool. Soc. Lond., pt.30, pp.103-105, 1862.

NOTES ON THE DISSECTION OF A SPECIES OF GALAGO. W. H. Flower. Proc. Zool. Soc. Lond., pt.20, pp.73-75, 1852.

(REMARKS ON THE FOOT RETICULUM OF THE GENUS GALAGO.) Bemerkungen zum Fussgeruest der Gattung Galago. Wilhelm Freudenberg. Zeitschr. fuer Saeugetierkunde, Berlin, vol.6, no.6, pp. 233-235, pl.25, Dec.15, 1931.

NYCTICEBUS MALAIANUS. A DISSECTION OF THE ABDOMINO-PELVIC VISCERA. Gordon Harrower. Spolia Zeylanica, Ceylon Jour. Sci., sec.B, vol.18, pt.1, pp.73-87, figs.9, pl.6, Dec.22, 1933.

THE DEVELOPMENT OF THE FOETAL MEMBRANES IN LORIS, WITH SPECIAL REFERENCE TO THE MODE OF VASCULARISATION OF THE CHORION IN THE LEMUROIDEA AND ITS PHYLOGENETIC SIGNIFICANCE. J. P. Hill, Frances E. Ince, A. Subba Raev. Proc. Zool. Soc. Lond., pt.3, pp.699-716, pl.1, Sept., 1928.

THE ALIMENTARY SYSTEM OF THE ANGWANTIBO, ARCTOCEBUS C. CALABARENSIS (SMITH). W. C. Osman Hill. Proc. Zool. Soc. Lond., vol.120, pt.1, pp.49-72, figs.5, pls.3, May 16, 1950.

THORACIC TRANSPEDICULAR FORAMINA IN THE LORISIDAE. W. C. Osman Hill. Proc. Zool. Soc. Lond., vol.116, pts.3-4, pp.525-530, figs.4, Feb.28, 1947.

THE INTRINSIC MUSCLES OF THE HAND IN THE SLENDER LORIS. R. Kanagasuntheram, F. L. W. Jayawardene. Proc. Zool. Soc. Lond., 128 (3): 301-312, June 6, 1957.

NOTES OF THE DISSECTION OF A SLENDER LORIS (LORIS GRACILIS, GEOFFR.). W. Martin. Proc. Zool. Soc. Lond., pt.1, p.22, 1833.

(THE CHROMOSOMES OF GALAGO SENEGALENIS GEOFFROY (PROSIMII-LORISIDAE GALAGINAE).) Les chromosomes de Galago senegalensis Geoffroy (Prosimii--Lorisidae--Galaginae). Robert Matthey. Rev. Suisse Zool., Geneva, vol.62, pp. 190-197, Nov., 1955.

FUNCTIONAL AND MORPHOLOGICAL ADAPTATIONS IN THE FORELIMBS OF THE SLOW LEMURS. Ruth A. Miller. Amer. Jour. Anat., Phila., vol.73, no.2, pp.153-183, figs.1-3, Sept., 1943.

OBSERVATIONS ON THE ANATOMY OF NYCTICEBUS TARDIGRADUS. St. George Mivart, James Murie. Proc. Zool. Soc. Lond., pp.240-256, figs.7, 1865.

ON THE STRUCTURE OF THE OVARY AND THE OVARIAN OVUM OF LORIS LYDEKKERIANUS, CABR. C. R. N. Rao. Quart. Jour. Micro. Sci., vol.71, pp.57-74, 2 pls., 2 figs., May, 1927.

CONTRIBUTIONS TO OUR KNOWLEDGE OF THE ANATOMY OF LEMUROIDEA. PART VI. DIGESTIVE SYSTEM OF LORIS LYDEKKERIANUS. A. Subba Rua, S. Hiriyannaiya. Half-Yearly Jour. Mysore Univ., n.s., sect. B, vol.3, no.2, pp.171-194, figs.15, Mar., 1943.

Asia

THE QUEEREST LITTLE MONKEY IN THE WORLD. W. G. Adam. Field, London, vol.159, no.4130, p.259, figs.2, Feb.20, 1932.

AN UNKNOWN LEMUR FROM THE LUSHAI HILLS, ASSAM. N. Annandale. Proc. Zool. Soc. Lond., pp.888-889, Apr., 1909.

EARLY RECORDS OF THE SLENDER LORIS AND ITS ALLIES. W. C. Osman Hill. Proc. Zool. Soc. Lond., vol.123, pt. 1, pp.43-47, June 10, 1953.

THE SLENDER LORIS OF THE HORTON PLAINS, CEYLON, LORIS TARDIGRADUS NYCTICEBOIDES, SUBSP. NOV. W. C. Osman Hill. Jour. Bombay Nat. Hist. Soc., vol.43, no.1, pp.73-78, pl.1, Apr., 1942.

A NEW RACE OF SLENDER LORIS FROM THE HIGHLANDS OF CEYLON. W. C. Osman Hill. Ceylon Jour. Sci., Sect. B, Zool. and Geol., Spolia Zeylanica, vol.17, pt.2, pp.109-122, pls.25-26, Nov.3, 1932.

(NOTE ON A NEW SPECIES OF THE GENUS NYCTICEBUS FROM SIAM AND COCHINCHINE.) Note sur une nouvelle espece du genre Nycticebus provenent de Siam et de Cochinchine. Alphonse Milne Edwards. Bull. Nouv. Arch. Mus. Hist. Nat. Paris, vol.3, pp.9-13, pl.3, 1867.

THE SLENDER LORIS OF MALABAR. R. C. Wroughton. Jour. Bombay Nat. Hist. Soc., vol.25, no.1, pp.45-46, Mar.20, 1917.

Habits

OLFACTORY MARKING OF TERRITORY IN TWO YOUNG MALE LORIS, LORIS TARDIGRADUS LYDEKKERIANUS, KEPT IN CAPTIVITY IN POONA. D. R. Ilse. British Jour. Animal Behaviour, Lond., vol. 3, no.3, pp.118-120, illus., July, 1955.

THE FEEDING AND GROOMING HABITS OF THE GALAGO. Florence de L. Lowther. Zoologica, New York, vol.24, pt.4, nos. 27-31, pp.477-480, pl.1, Dec.22, 1939.

FOOD OF THE SLOW LORIS (NYCTICEBUS COUCANG). J. M. D. Mackenzie. Jour. Bombay Nat. Hist., vol.33, no.4, p.971, Oct.15, 1929.

NIGHT LIFE OF THE BUSH BABY. Donald Marcy. Animal Kingdom, New York, vol. 46, no.5, pp.99-103, illus., Sept.-Oct., 1943.

THE FOOD OF THE CEYLON SLENDER LORIS (LORIS TARDIGRADUS) IN CAPTIVITY. W. W. A. Phillips. Spolia Zeylanica, vol.16, pt.2, pp.205-208, pl.1, Aug.8, 1931.

Reproductive Biology

THE BREEDING CYCLE OF THE SENEGAL GALAGO, GALAGO SENEGALENSIS SENEGALENSIS. H. Butler. Proc. Zool. Soc. Lond., 129 (1): 147-149, Sept.9, 1957.

IMPLANTATION OF THE BLASTOCYST IN GALAGO DEMIDOFFI. J. P. Hill. Bio-Morphosis, Leipzig, vol.1, nos.3-4, p.333, 1938.

BREEDING OF LORIS IN CAPTIVITY. W. C. O. Hill. Nature, London, vol.136, no.3429, pp.107-108, July 20, 1935.

MAHOLI GALAGOS BREED IN CAPTIVITY. Florence deL. Lowther. Science, Lancaster, n.s., vol.89, no.2322, p.604, June 30, 1939.

PERIOD OF GESTATION OF LORIS. Lucius Nicholls. Nature, London, vol.143, no. 3615, p.246, Feb.11, 1939.

(ON RAISING AND BREEDING THE PYGMY GALAGO (GALAGO ZANZIBARICUS MTSCH.) Ueber Haltung und Zucht des Zwerggalagos (Galago zanzibaricus Mtsch.). Karl Peter. Zool. Garten N.F., Leipzig, vol.6, nos.7-9, pp.165-173, Oct., 1933.

Taxonomy

A NOTE ON GALAGO SENEGALENSIS INUSTUS SCHWARZ. R. W. Hayman. Ann. and Mag. Nat. Hist., Lond., ser.10, vol.20, no. 115, pp.149-151, figs.4, July, 1937.

THE STATUS OF NYCTICEBUS COUCANG BRACHYCEPHALUS SODY. David H. Johnson. Jour. Mam., vol.33, no.1, pp. 115-116, Feb., 1952.

A NEW EASTERN RACE OF GALAGO DEMIDOVII. Barbara Lawrence, Sherwood L. Washburn. Occas. Papers Boston Soc. Nat. Hist., vol.8, pp.255-266, Jan.8, 1936.

THE AUTHORITY FOR THE NAME NYCTICEBUS MENAGENSIS. Marcus W. Lyon, Jr. Proc. Biol. Soc. Washington, vol.22, p.87, Apr.17, 1909.

NOTES ON THE SLOW LEMURS. Marcus W. Lyon, Jr. Proc. U.S. Nat. Mus., vol. 31, no.1494, pp.527-538, pl.13, Nov.9, 1906.

ON GALAGO MURINUS, MURRAY. Andrew Murray. Proc. Zool. Soc. Lond., pp.560-562, 1866.

SUPPLEMENTARY REMARKS ON THE GENUS GALAGO. Andrew Murray. Edin. Philos. Jour., N.S., pp.1-4, pl.5, Jan., 1860.

ON A NEW SPECIES OF GALAGO. W. Ogilby. Proc. Zool. Soc. Lond., pt.6, p. 6, 1838.

REMARKS ON GALAGO CRASSICAUDATA AND G. CRASSICAUDATA VAR KIRKII. P. L. Sclater. Proc. Zool. Soc. Lond., pp.60-61, 1865.

THE GEOGRAPHICAL RACES OF GALAGO CRASSICAUDATUS. Oldfield Thomas. Ann. and Mag. Nat. Hist. (8), vol.20, no. 115, pp.47-50, July, 1917.

A NEW SPECIES OF DWARF POTTO. Oldfield Thomas. Ann. and Mag. Nat. Hist. (8), vol.12, no.70, pp.387-388, Oct., 1913.

THE NOMENCLATURE OF CERTAIN LORISES. Oldfield Thomas. Ann. and Mag. Nat. Hist. (8), vol.1, no.6, pp.467-469, June, 1908.

NOTE ON THE NOMENCLATURE OF THE NORTHERN SLOW LORIS. Oldfield Thomas. Jour. Bombay Nat. Hist. Soc., vol.28, no.2, p.433, Mar.25, 1922.

TWO NEW SPECIES OF SLOW-LORIS. Oldfield Thomas. Ann. and Mag. Nat. Hist., ser.9, vol.8, pp.627-682, Dec., 1921.

Tarsiidae

OBSERVATIONS ON TARSIUS FUSCUS. Harrison Allen. Proc. Acad. Nat. Sci. Phila., pp.34-55, figs.1-4, Jan., 1897.

ON THE IDENTIFICATION OF SIMIA SYRICHTA LINNAEUS. Angel Cabrera. Jour. Mam., no.4, pp.89-91, May 9, 1923.

TARSIERS IN CAPTIVITY. Hubert R. Catchpole, John F. Fulton. Nature, Lond., vol.144, no.3646, p.514, Sept.16, 1939.

NOTES ON THE LIVING TARSIER (TARSIUS SPECTRUM). W. E. LeGros Clark. Proc. Zool. Soc. Lond., pp.217-223, pl., 1924.

NOTES ON CAPTIVE TARSIUS CARBONARIUS. Norman Cook. Jour. Mam., vol.20, no.2, pp.173-178, May 14, 1939.

ON THE AFFINITIES OF TARSIUS: A CONTRIBUTION TO THE PHYLOGENY OF THE PRIMATES. C. Earle. Amer. Nat., vol. 31, pp.569-689, July, 1897.

A TRIP TO BOHOL IN QUEST OF TARSIUS. John F. Fulton. Yale Jour. Biol. and Med., New Haven, vol.11, no.5, pp.561-573, figs.6, May, 1939.

(ON THE DEVELOPMENTAL HISTORY OF THE FOOT SKELETON OF TARSIUS SPECTRUM L.) Zur Entwicklungsgeschichte des Fussskeletts von Tarsius spectrum L. K. O. Henckel. Gegenbaurs morphol. Jahrbuch, Leipzig, vol.64, pp.636-650, figs.9, July, 1930.

THE TARSIER'S PLACE IN THE FAMILY TREE. Lilo Hess. Nat. Hist., New York, vol.56, no.10, p.467, illus., Dec., 1947.

THE BLOOD-VASCULAR SYSTEM OF TARSIUS. W. C. Osman Hill. Proc. Zool. Soc. Lond., vol.123, pt.3, pp.655-694, pls. 1-3, Nov.20, 1953.

CAUDAL CUTANEOUS SPECIALIZATIONS IN TARSIUS. W. C. Osman Hill. Proc. Zool. Soc. Lond., vol.123, pt.1, pp.17-26, pls.1-3, June 10, 1953.

EPIGASTRIC GLAND OF TARSIUS. W. C. Osman Hill. Nature, London, vol.167, p. 994, June 16, 1951.

THE FEMALE REPRODUCTIVE ORGANS OF TARSIUS, WITH OBSERVATIONS ON THE PHYSIOLOGICAL CHANGES THEREIN. W. C. Osman Hill. Proc. Zool. Soc. Lond., vol.123, pt.3, pp.589-598, illus., Nov.20, 1953.

NOTE ON THE TAXONOMY OF THE GENUS TARSIUS. W. C. Osman Hill. Proc. Zool. Soc. Lond., vol.123, pt.1, pp.13-16, June 10, 1953.

THE NATURAL HISTORY, ENDOPARASITES AND PSEUDO-PARASITES OF THE TARSIERS (TARSIUS CARBONARIUS) RECENTLY LIVING IN THE SOCIETY'S MENAGERIE. W. C. Osman Hill, Annie Porter, Margaret D. Southwick. Proc. Zool. Soc. Lond., vol. 122, pt.1, pp.79-119, pls.1-4, May 16, 1952.

THE INSIDE STORY OF THE TARSIER. Harry Hoogstraal. Chicago Nat. Hist. Mus. Bull., Chicago, vol.18, no.11, pp.7-8, illus., Nov., 1947; no.12, pp.4-5, illus., Dec., 1947.

THE EXTERNAL CHARACTERS OF A FOETAL TARSIER. F. Wood Jones. Proc. Zool. Soc. Lond., vol.120, no.2, pp.723-730, figs.10, Feb., 1951.

NOTES ON A PAIR OF TARSIERS FROM MINDANAO. George Chase Lewis. Jour. Mam., vol.20, no.1, pp.57-61, Feb.14, 1939.

(A NEW TARSIUS SPECIES.) Eine neue Tarsius-art. A. B. Meyer. Abhandl. Ber. K. Zool. Anthrop. Athno. Mus. Dresden, no.1, pp.1-2, 1894-1895.

AN EXAMPLE OF TARSIUS FROM SARAWAK. G. Elliot Smith. Proc. Zool. Soc., Lond., pp.184-186, 1 pl., Mar., 1921.

A CLINICAL REPORT ON THE EYE OF THE TARSIER. Arnold Sorsby. Proc. Zool. Soc. Lond., vol.119, pt.2, pp.359-361, pl.1, Aug.17, 1949.

THE CURIOUS BUT PRACTICAL PECULIARITIES OF THE TARSIER--A LONG-JUMP CHAMPION--SHOWN BY HIGH-SPEED PHOTOGRAPHY. Ernest P. Walker. Illus. London News, vol.213, no.5723, pp.738-739, illus., Dec.25, 1948.

THE TARSIER IN CAPTIVITY. Charles H. Wharton. Jour. Mam., vol.31, no.3, pp. 260-268, Aug.21, 1950.

THE ANATOMY OF TARSIUS SPECTRUM. H. H. Woollard. Proc. Zool. Soc. Lond., pt.3, pp.1071-1184, illus., Oct., 1925.

THE TARSIER'S PLACE IN THE FAMILY TREE. Nat. Hist., New York, vol.56, no. 10, p.467, illus., Dec., 1947.

Cebidae

MONKEYS AS HUMAN FOOD. Ernest G. Holt. Jour. Mam., vol.4, no.3, pp.193-194, Aug., 1923.

(STRUCTURAL INVESTIGATIONS OF NEW WORLD MONKEYS (CEBUS APELLA L. AND ALOUATTA CARAYA HUMBOLDT).) Gefuegegesetzliche Untersuchungen an Neuweltaffen (Cebus apella L. und Alouatta caraya Humboldt). Friedrich Kuehlhorn. Zeitschr. Saeugetierk., Berlin, vol.20, no. 1, pp.13-36, July 30, 1954.

NOTES ON A SPIDER MONKEY (ATELES CUCULLATUS, GRAY) LATELY LIVING IN THE SOCIETY'S MENAGERIE. James Murie. Proc. Zool. Soc. Lond., pp.739-740, 1865.

LETTERS ON THE CHARACTERS AND HABITS OF A SPECIMEN OF THE PITHECIA SAGULATA, PRESENTED BY HIM TO THE SOCIETY. R. K. Porter. Proc. Zool. Soc. Lond., pt.2, p.41, 1834.

LETTER FROM, ON THE LOCALITY AND IDENTITY OF THE SPIDER MONKEY (ATELES) OF MEXICO. J. Reinhardt. Proc. Zool. Soc. Lond., pp.797-798, 1872.

(THE STERNAL GLAND IN THE SPIDER MONKEYS (ATELES).) Die Sternaldruese bei den Klammeraffen, Ateles. Willy Schwarz. Gegenbaurs Morphol. Jahrbuch, Leipzig, vol.79, no.4, pp.600-633, figs. 22, 1937.

EXHIBITION OF A SPECIMEN OF ATELES VARIEGATUS. P. L. Sclater. Proc. Zool. Soc. Lond., p.39, 1871.

NOTICE OF A RARE AMERICAN MONKEY (PITHECIA LEUCOCEPHALA) LATELY ADDED TO THE SOCIETY'S MENAGERIE. P. L. Sclater. Proc. Zool. Soc. Lond., p.305, 1866.

REMARKS ON THE MEXICAN SPIDER MONKEY (ATELES) IN THE BERLIN MUSEUM. P. L. Sclater. Proc. Zool. Soc. Lond., p.798, 1872.

A VERY STRANGE MONKEY. D. Seth-Smith. Field, Lond., vol.159, no.4134, p.410, fig.1, Mar.19, 1932.

THE SPIDER MONKEY. Ken Stott, Jr. Nature Magazine, Washington, D.C., vol. 31, no.4, p.205, Apr., 1938.

IN QUEST OF THE HOWLING MONKEY. Nature, Mag., vol.6, pp.339-342, 4 figs., Dec., 1925.

Anatomy

(COMPLEMENTARY NOTE ON THE EXTERNAL MORPHOLOGY OF THE BRAIN IN THE GENUS ALOUATTA.) Note complémentaire sur la morphologie externe du cerveau dans le genre Alouatta. J. Anthony. Bull. Mus. Nat. Hist. Nat., Paris, ser.2, vol.22, no.1, pp.60-62, Jan., 1950.

(EXCEPTIONAL DISPOSITION OF THE SULCUS ARCUATUS ON THE FRONTAL LOBE OF THE SPIDER MONKEY.) Disposition exceptionnelle du sulcus arcuatus sur le lobe frontal d'un atele (singes platyrhiniens). J. Anthony. Mammalia, Paris, vol.16, no. 3, pp.157-159, illus., Sept., 1952.

BRAIN-WEIGHT AND BODY-WEIGHT IN THE RED SPIDER MONKEY. George Clark. Science, Lancaster, n.s., vol.100, no. 2603, pp.455-456, Nov.17, 1944.

(THE ARTERIES OF THE BULB AND OF THE PROTUBERANCE IN CERTAIN MONKEYS OF THE NEW WORLD.) Les arteres du bulbe et de la protuberance chez certains singes du Nouveau Monde. J. L. Decerisy. Bull. Mus. Nat. Hist. Nat., Paris, ser.2, vol.22, no.4, pp.431-437, June, 1950.

NOTES ON THE ANATOMY OF PITHECIA MONACHUS (GEOFF.). W. H. Flower. Proc. Zool. Soc. Lond., pt.30, pp.326-333, figs.4, pl.37, 1862.

ON THE BRAIN OF THE RED HOWLING MONKEY (MYCOTES SENICULUS, LINN.). W. H. Flower. Proc. Zool. Soc. Lond., pp.335-338, pl.29, 1864.

ON THE EXTERNAL CHARACTERS AND ANATOMY OF THE RED UAKARI MONKEY (BRACHYURUS RUBICUNDUS); WITH REMARKS ON THE OTHER SPECIES OF THAT GENUS. W. A. Forbes. Proc. Zool. Soc. Lond., pp.627-647, figs.11, pl.41-43, Nov.30, 1880.

THE REPRESENTATION OF THE TAIL IN THE MOTOR CORTEX OF PRIMATES, WITH SPECIAL REFERENCE TO SPIDER MONKEYS. J. F. Fulton, J. G. Dusser de Barenne. Jour. Cell. and Comp Physiol., vol.2, no.4, pp.399-426, figs.12, Feb.20, 1933.

ANATOMY OF CALLIMICO GOELDII (THOMAS). W. C. Osman Hill. American Philos. Soc. Phila., 116 pp., 1959.

OBSERVATIONS ON THE GENITALIA OF THE WOOLLY MONKEY (LAGOTHRIX). W. C. Osman Hill. Proc. Zool. Soc. Lond., vol.122, pt.4, pp.973-984, illus., Feb., 1953.

ON THE BRAIN OF ATELES PANISCUS. Thomas H. Huxley. Proc. Zool. Soc. Lond., pt.29, pp.247-260, figs.2, pl.29, 1961.

THE ILEO-CAECAL REGION OF CALLICEBUS PERSONATUS, WITH SOME OBSERVATIONS ON THE MORPHOLOGY OF THE MAMMALIAN CAECUM. T. B. Johnston. Jour. Anat. Lond., vol.54, pt.1, pp.66-78, 1919.

NOTES ON THE DISSECTION OF A SQUIRREL MONKEY. W. Martin. Proc. Zool. Soc. Lond., pt.1, pp.88-89, 1833.

THE TEETH OF A MONKEY FOUND IN CUBA (WITH ONE PLATE). Gerrit S. Miller, Jr. Smith. Misc. Coll., vol.66, no.13, publ.2430, 1916.

ADDITIONAL NOTES ON THE EXTERNAL CHARACTERS OF SOME PLATYRRHINE MONKEYS. R. I. Pocock. Proc. of the Zool. Soc. Of Lond., text-figs.6-12, pp. 27-47, Apr.3, 1925.

ANATOMY OF THE SOUTH AMERICAN WOOLLY MONKEY (LAGOTHRIX). PART I. THE FORELIMB. Donald Ford Robertson. Zoologica (Sci. Contrib. New York Zool. Soc.), vol.29, pt.4, no.16, pp.169-192, pls.5, Dec.30, 1944.

(TOTAL BIPARTITION OF THE PARIETAL BONE IN TWO CEBUS, PARTIAL BIPARTITION IN THE HUMAN CRANIUM.) Biparticao total do osso parietal em dois Cebus; biparticao parcial num craneo humano. Paulo Sawaya. Ann. Faculdade Med. Univ. S. Paulo, vol.10, fasc.2, pp.209-217, figs. 6-9, 1934.

EXHIBITION OF, AND REMARKS ON, A SKIN OF ATELES VARIEGATUS. P. L. Sclater. Proc. Zool. Soc. Lond., pp.651-652, 1871.

(THE INTERMEDIARY POSTERIOR TUBERCLE OF THE UPPER MOLARS IN THE GENUS ALOUATTA LAC (PLATYRRHINE MONKEYS).) Le tubercule intermediaire posterieur des molaires superieures, ou metaconule, dans le genre Alouatta Lac. (Singes Platyrhiniens). O. Della Serra. Mammalia, Paris, vol.14, no.4, pp.159-164, illus.. Dec.. 1950.

(VARIATIONS ON ARTICULATIONS OF MACAQUE INCISORS IN THE GENUS ALOUATTA LAC, 1799.) Variacoes do articulado dos dentes incisivos nos macacos de genero Alouatta Lac., 1799. O. Della Serra. Papeis Avulsos Dept. Zool., Sec. Agric., Sao Paulo vol.10, no.7, pp.139-146, illus., Aug.25, 1951.

(THE INTERMEDIARY POSTERIOR TUBERCLE OF THE UPPER MOLARS OF THE MACAQUES OF THE GENUS CALLICEBUS THOMAS, 1903.) O tuberculo intermediario posterior (metaconule) dos molares superiores nos macacos do genero Callicebus Thomas, 1903. O. Della Serra, Milton Picosse. Papeis Avulsos Dept. Zool., Sec. Agric., São Paulo, vol.10, no.5, pp.127-131, illus., Aug.25, 1951.

ON THE PRESENCE OF PERMANENT COMMUNICATIONS BETWEEN THE LYMPHATIC AND THE VENOUS SYSTEM AT THE LEVEL OF THE RENAL VEINS IN ADULT SOUTH AMERICAN MONKEYS. Charles F. Silvester. Amer. Jour. Anat., vol.12, no.4, pp.447-458, pls.10, Jan., 1912.

ON THE PRESENCE OF PERMANENT LYMPHATICO-VENOUS COMMUNICATIONS AT THE LEVEL OF THE RENAL VEINS IN ADULT SOUTH AMERICAN MONKEYS. Charles F. Silvester. Verhandl. Anat. Gesell. auf der vierundzwanzigsten Versammlung in Bruessel, pp.111-113, Aug.7-11, 1910.

(DESCRIPTIVE ANATOMY OF THE SKULL IN THE GENUS CEBUS.) Anatomia descriptiva de la cabeza osea, en el genero Cebus. Miguel Fernando Soria. Buenos Aires, Estab. Gráfico, E.G.L.H., pp.465-468, illus., 1957.

CERVICAL RIBS IN THE WOOLLY MONKEY. William L. Straus, Jr. Jour. Mam., vol. 18, no.2, pp.241-242, May 14, 1937.

REMARKS ON THE PLACENTATION OF A PLATYRRHINE MONKEY (ATELES GEOFFROYI). G. B. Wislocki. Amer. Jour. Anat. vol.36, no.3, pp.467-487, figs.5, pls.2, Jan.15, 1926.

Care in Captivity

MONKEYS AS PETS. John F. Breen. All-Pets Mag., Fond du Lac, vol.19, no.6, pp. 62-63; no.7, pp.63-64, June-July, 1948.

(ON THE KEEPING AND CARE OF SOME NEW WORLD MONKEYS.) Zur Haltung und Pflege einiger Neuweltaffenarten. Ludwig Zukowsky. Zool. Garten, N.F., vol.12, nos.2-3, pp.92-110, illus., July, 1940.

Central America

CONCERNING ATELES GRISESCENS. T. Barbour. Jour. Mam., vol.13, no.4, pp. 367-368, Nov., 1932.

A NEW SPIDER MONKEY FROM PANAMA. E. A. Goldman. Proc. Biol. Soc. Wash., vol.28, pp.101-102, Apr.13, 1915.

THE BLACK HOWLERS OF BARRO COLORADO. Charles H. Southwick. Animal Kingdom, New York Zool. Soc., vol.58, no.4, pp.104-109, illus., July-Aug., 1955.

Coloration

(ON CHANGE IN COLORATION IN A MONKEY OF THE GENUS CEBUS.) Sobre el cambio de coloracion en un mono del genero Cebus. Angel Cabrera. Bol. R. Soc. Espanola Hist. Nat., vol.24, pp.130-131, Mar., 1924.

A BLACK SAKI MONKEY. Guy Dollman. Nat. Hist. Mag., British Mus., vol.5, no. 35, pp.132-133, illus., July, 1935.

ONCE IN A THOUSAND. Zoonooz, San Diego, vol.17, no.2, pp.6-7, illus., Feb., 1944.

Diseases and Parasites

(REGARDING THE PARASITISM OF SAIMIRIS SCIUREUS BY GONGILONEMA AND THE POSSIBILITIES OF HUMAN INFECTION.) Sobre o parasitismo do Saimiris sciureus por um Gongilonema (G. saimirisi n. sp.) e as possibilidades de infestacao humana. Paulo Artigas. Rev. Soc. Paulista Med. Vet., vol.3, nos.3-4, pp.83-88, figs.6, May-Aug., 1933.

THE NATURAL HISTORY OF YELLOW FEVER IN COLOMBIA. Marston Bates. Sci. Monthly, Lancaster, vol.63, no.1, pp. 42-52, illus., July, 1946.

THE SAIMIRI MONKEY AS AN EXPERIMENTAL HOST FOR THE VIRUS OF YELLOW FEVER. Marston Bates. Amer. Jour. Trop. Med., Balto., vol.24, no.2, pp.83-89, figs.2, Mar., 1944.

THE DOUROUCOULI (AOTUS) IN LABORATORY CYCLES OF YELLOW FEVER. Marston Bates, Manuel Roca-Garcia. Amer. Jour. Trop. Med., Balto., vol.25, no.5, pp.387-389, Sept., 1945.

STUDIES ON SOUTH AMERICAN YELLOW FEVER. 2. IMMUNITY OF RECOVERED MONKEYS TO AFRICAN VIRUS. Nelson C. Davis. Jour. Exper. Med., vol.49, no.6, pp.985-991, June 1, 1929.

SUSCEPTIBILITY OF CAPUCHIN (CEBUS) MONKEYS TO YELLOW FEVER VIRUS. Nelson C. Davis. Amer. Jour. Hygiene, vol.11, no.2, pp.321-334, Mar., 1930.

THE TRANSMISSION OF YELLOW FEVER. EXPERIMENTS WITH THE "WOOLLY MONKEY" (LAGOTHRIX LAGOTRICHA HUMBOLDT), THE "SPIDER MONKEY" (ATELEUS ATER F. CUVIER) AND THE "SQUIRREL MONKEY" (SAIMIRI SCIREUS LINNAEUS). Nelson C. Davis. Jour. Exper. Med., vol.51, no.5, pp.703-720, pls.2, May 1, 1930.

THE TRANSMISSION OF YELLOW FEVER. FURTHER EXPERIMENTS WITH MONKEYS OF THE NEW WORLD. Nelson C. Davis. Amer. Jour. Trop. Med., vol.11, no.2, pp. 113-125, Mar., 1931.

STUDIES ON SOUTH AMERICAN YELLOW FEVER. 3. TRANSMISSION OF THE VIRUS TO BRAZILIAN MONKEYS PRELIMINARY OBSERVATIONS. Nelson C. Davis, Raymond C. Shannon. Jour. Exper. Med., vol.50, no.1, pp.81-85, July 1, 1929.

(BEHAVIOR OF THE MONKEY ALOUATTA FUSCA HUMBOLDT WITH YELLOW FEVER VIRUS.) Comportamento do bugio Alouatta fusca Humboldt inoculado com virus amarilico asibi. Flavio da Fonseca. Mem. Inst. Butantan, vol.13, pp.363-370, 1 fig., Jan., 1940.

(INVESTIGATION OF THE SUSCEPTIBILITY OF CEBUS CIRRIFER TO YELLOW FEVER VIRUS.) Inquerito sobre a sensibilidade de Cebus cirrifer ao virus amarilico. Flavio da Fonseca, Paulo Artigas. Mem. Inst. Butantan, vol.13, 1939, pp.373-380, 1 fig., Jan., 1940.

FILARIAL PARASITES OF THE MONKEYS OF PANAMA. O. R. McCoy. Amer. Jour. Trop. Med., vol.16, no.4, pp.383-399, pls. 2, July, 1936.

(EXPERIMENTAL LEPROSY IN MONKEYS.) Lepra experimental em macacos. H. C. de Souza-Araujo. Mem. Inst. Oswaldo Cruz, Rio de Janeiro, 52 (3-4): 619-673, pl.1, 1955.

ON THE STRUCTURE, OCCURRENCE AND SIGNIFICANCE OF ATHESMIA FOXI, A LIVER FLUKE OF AMERICAN MONKEYS. Horace W. Stunkard. Jour. Parasitology, vol.10, pp.71-79, pl.8, Dec., 1923.

THE TRANSMISSION OF PLASMODIUM FALCIPARUM TO THE HOWLER MONKEY, ALOUATTA SP. 1. GENERAL NATURE OF THE INFECTIONS AND MORPHOLOGY OF THE PARASITES. William H. Taliaferro, Lucy G. Taliaferro. Amer. Jour. Hygiene, vol.19, no.2, pp.318-334, figs.3, Mar., 1934.

THE TRANSMISSION OF PLASMODIUM FALCIPARUM TO THE HOWLER MONKEY, ALOUATTA SP. 2. CELLULAR REACTIONS. William H. Taliaferro, Paul R. Cannon. Amer. Jour. Hygiene, vol.19, no.2, pp.335-342, pls.3, Mar., 1934.

(EFFECTS OF DIET ON THE COURSE OF EXPERIMENTAL PALUDISM IN MONKEYS.) Efectos de la dieta en el curso del paludismo experimental de los monos. Ciencia, Mexico, D.F., vol.3, no.1, pp.31-32, Jan.25, 1942.

Fossils

(CONTRIBUTIONS TO KNOWLEDGE OF THE FOSSIL PRIMATES OF PATAGONIA.) Contribuciones al conocimiento de los primates fosiles de la Patagonia. Jorge Lucas Kraglievich. Com. Mus. Argentino Cien. Nat., vol.2, no.5, pp.55-82, illus., Sept., 1951.

(ON THE TEETH OF A PREHISTORIC MONKEY FROM CUBA, MONTANEIA ANTHOLOMORPHA.) Sur les dents d'un singe pre-historique, Montaneia antholomorpha, de Cuba. Montane. L'Anthropologie, Paris, vol.32, pp.276-277, 1922.

(NEW REMAINS OF FOSSIL MONKEYS OF THE ANCIENT TERTIARY OF PATAGONIA.) Nuevos Restos de Monos Fosiles del Terciario Antiguo de la Patagonia. Carlos

Rusconi. Anal. Soc. Cient. Argentina, Buenos Aires, vol.116, pp.286-289, 1933.

(THE PRIMATE SPECIES OF THE OLIGOCENE OF PATAGONIA (GEN. HOMUNCULUS).) Las especies de primates del Oligoceno de Patagonia (gen. Homunculus). Carlos Rusconi. Rev. Argentina Paleontol. y Antropol. Ameghinia, vol.1, no.3, pp.71-100, figs.13-41, Sept.15, 1935.

CEBOID MONKEYS FROM THE MIOCENE OF COLOMBIA. R. A. Stirton. Univ. California Publ., Bull. Dept. Geol. Sci., Berkeley, vol.28, no.11, pp.315-356, figs. 2, pls.7-14, Apr.24, 1951.

A NEW MONKEY FROM THE LA VENTA MIOCENE OF COLOMBIA. R. A. Stirton, Donald E. Savage. Compilacion de los Estudios Geologicos Oficiales en Colombia, Servicio Geol. Nac., Ministerio de Minas y Petroleos, Bogota, vol.8, pp.345-356, pls.91-97, 1950.

Habits, Behavior, Ecology

MONKEYSHINES. TRIX AND HER TRICKS. Franklin H. Avers. Fauna, Phila., vol.5, no.2, pp.48-49, illus., June, 1943.

BEHAVIOR OF RED SPIDER MONKEYS IN PANAMA. C. R. Carpenter. Jour. Mam., 16: 171-180, 1935.

A FIELD STUDY OF THE BEHAVIOR AND SOCIAL RELATIONS OF HOWLING MONKEYS. C. R. Carpenter. Comparative Psychology Monographs, Baltimore, vol.10, no.2, ser. no.48, pp.1-168, figs.3, pls.16, May, 1934.

(Review by Robert K. Enders of) A FIELD STUDY OF THE BEHAVIOR AND SOCIAL RELATIONS OF THE HOWLING MONKEYS. C.R. Carpenter. Jour. Mamm., vol.15, no. 4, p.324, Nov., 1934.

THE HOME RANGE OF BRAZILIAN CEBUS MONKEYS IN A REGION OF SMALL RESIDUAL FORESTS. O. R. Causey, H. W. Laemmert, Jr., G. S. Hayes. Amer. Jour. Hygiene, vol.47, no.3, pp.304-314, figs.3, May, 1948.

THE CONQUEST OF CLAUDIA. Frank M. Chapman. Nat. Hist., vol.29, pp.369-379, illus., Aug., 1929.

MY MONKEY NEIGHBORS ON BARRO COLORADO--THE UNBELIEVABLE ACROBATIC FEATS THEY PERFORM HIGH UP IN THEIR JUNGLE HIGHWAY; THEIR FAMILY LIFE; AND THE UNCONTROLLABLE HATRED THAT A GROUP OF FREE MONKEYS SHOWED TOWARD THEIR CAPTIVE BROTHERS. Frank M. Chapman. Nat. Hist., New York, vol.40, no.2, pp.471-479, figs.12, Sept., 1937.

A FIELD STUDY OF POPULATION DENSITY AND SOCIAL ORGANIZATION IN HOWLING MONKEYS. Nicholas Collias, Charles Southwick. Proc. Amer. Philos. Soc., Lancaster, vol.96, no.2, pp.143-156, illus., Apr., 1952.

THE MYTH OF THE MONKEY CHAIN. E. W. Gudger. Nat. Hist., New York, vol.19, no.2, pp.216-221, illus., 1919.

RE-EXAMINATION OF IMPLEMENT-USING BEHAVIOR IN A CEBUS MONKEY AFTER AN INTERVAL OF THREE YEARS. Heinrich Kluever. Acta Psychol., The Hague, vol.2, no.3, pp.347-397, figs.3, 1937.

(TWO TYPES OF PITHECOID GALLOPS.) Les deux formes du galop pithécoide. Paul Magne de la Croix. Anales Soc. Cient. Argentina, Buenos Aires, vol.113, pt.4, pp.150-154, figs.5, Apr., 1932.

BLUEPRINT FOR SPIDERS. Jacqueline Schermerhorn. San Diego Zoonooz, vol. 19, no.3, pp.3-5, illus., Mar., 1946.

THE FLIRT. Jacqueline Schermerhorn. San Diego Zoonooz, vol.18, no.7, pp.3-4, illus., Aug., 1945.

LETTERS FROM, RELATING TO THE MANNERS WHILST IN CONFINEMENT OF A BLACK SPIDER MONKEY (ATELES ATER). Lady Shelley. Proc. Zool. Soc. Lond., pt. 7, p.169, 1839.

A FIELD STUDY OF POPULATION DENSITY AND SOCIAL ORGANIZATION IN HOWLING MONKEYS. Charles Southwick. See: Collias, Nicholas, Charles Southwick., 1952.

HOWLERS' ACROBATICS IN THE TREE-TOPS: SPECTACULAR MONKEY-LEAPS. A HOWLER'S FOREST BRIDGE FOR HER BABY: MONKEY RESOURCEFULNESS. Illus. London News, vol.192, no.5151, pp. 58-59, Jan.8, 1938.

Reproductive Biology

THE REPRODUCTIVE CYCLE OF NEW WORLD MONKEYS. Edward W. Dempsey. Amer. Jour. Anat., Phila., vol.64, no.3, pp.381-406, figs.2, pls.1-4, May 15, 1939.

NOTES ON THE BREEDING OF A DOUROUCOULI (AOTUS TRIVIRGATUS) IN CAPTIVITY. W. L. English. Proc. Zool. Soc. Lond., pt.1, pp.143-144, pl.1, Apr., 1934.

CYCLICAL UTERINE BLEEDING IN A NEW WORLD MONKEY (ATELES GEOFFROYI). Leroy Goodman, George B. Wislocki. Anat. Record, vol.61, no.4, pp.379-385, pl.1, Mar.25, 1935.

CAPTIVE BORN FOETUS OF WOOLLY MONKEY (LAGOTHRIX LAGOTRICHA). W. C. Osman Hill. Proc. Zool. Soc. Lond., 129 (3): 447-449, pl.1, Nov.11, 1957.

FETUSES OF THE GUIANA HOWLING MONKEY. Adolph H. Schultz. Zoologica, vol. 3, no.12, pp.243-262, 6 figs., Dec.24, 1921.

TWINNING IN HOODED CAPUCHIN. Ken Stott, Jr. Jour. Mam., vol.34, no.3, p. 385, Aug.14, 1953.

ON A SERIES OF PLACENTAL STAGES OF A PLATYRRHINE MONKEY (ATELES GEOFFROYI) WITH SOME REMARKS UPON AGE, SEX AND BREEDING PERIOD IN PLATYRRHINES. George B. Wislocki. Contributions to Embryology, no.133, Carnegie Inst. Wash. Pub., no.414, pp.173-192, pls. 5, Nov., 1930.

South America

NEW SOUTH AMERICAN MONKEYS. J. A. Allen. Bull. Amer. Mus. Nat. Hist., vol. 33, pp.647-655, Dec.14, 1914.

THE DISCOVERY OF A NEW ANTHROPOID APE IN SOUTH AMERICA. Francis M. Ashley-Montagu. Sci. Monthly, vol.29, pp. 275-279, illus., Sept., 1929.

(THE MONKEYS OF ARGENTINA.) Los monos de la Argentina. Angel Cabrera. Physis (Rev. Soc. Argentina Cienc. Nat.), Buenos Aires, vol.16, pp.29, figs.3, pls.2, Apr.3-11, 1937.

(ON THE SUPPOSED ANTHROPOID FROM VENEZUELA.) Sobre el supuesto antropoideo de Venezuela. Angel Cabrera. Revista Soc. Argentina Cienc. Nat., vol. 10, pp.204-209, July 12, 1930.

PRESENCE OF THE REDDISH HOWLING MONKEY (ALOUATTA GUARIBA CLAMITANS CABRERA) IN ARGENTINA. Jorge A. Crespo. Jour. Mam., vol.35, no.1, pp. 117-118, Feb.10, 1954.

TWO RARE SOUTH AMERICAN MONKEYS. Guy J. Dollman. Nat. Hist. Mag. (British Museum), vol.4, no.29, pp.186-187, figs. 1-2, Jan., 1934.

DESCRIPTIONS OF NEW SPECIES OF MONKEYS OF THE GENERA SENIOCEBUS AND AOTUS FROM COLOMBIA SOUTH AMERICA. D. G. Elliot. Bull. Amer. Mus. Nat. Hist., N. Y., vol.32, art.12, pp.251-253, July 14, 1913.

DESCRIPTION OF ATELAS BARTLETTII, A NEW SPIDER MONKEY FROM THE RIVER AMAZON. J. E. Gray. Proc. Zool. Soc. Lond., pp.992-993, pl.XLVII, 1867.

NOTES ON AMERICAN MONKEYS OF THE GENUS CEBUS. Philip Hershkovitz. Jour. Mam., vol.36, no.3, pp.449-452, Aug., 1955.

(NOTES ON THE MONKEYS IN THE AMAZON AND NEW GRANADA REGIONS.) Memorias sobre los monos de las regiones Amazonicas y de Nueva Granada. Alexander de Humboldt. Revista Acad. Colombiana Cienc. Exactas, Fisicas y Naturales, Bogota, vol.5, no.20, pp.506-527, 4 color pls., Aug., 1944.

THE MONKEYS OF DUTCH GUIANA. August Kappler. Popular Sci. Monthly, New York, vol.32, no.3, pp.396-400, Jan., 1888.

THE ALLEGED DISCOVERY OF AN ANTHROPOID APE IN SOUTH AMERICA. Arthur Keith. Man, London, vol.29, no. 8, pp.135-137, 1929.

(JOURNEYS IN SOUTH AMERICA FOR THE PURPOSE OF BIOLOGICAL STUDY: XVI. THE MONKEYS OF THE GRAN CHACO AND BORDERING REGIONS.) Biologische Reisestudien in Suedamerika. XVI. Die Affen des Gran Chaco und seiner Grenzgebiete. Hans Krieg. Zeitschr. fuer Morphologie und Oekologie der Tiere (Abt. A. der Zeitschr. fuer wissenschaftliche Biologie), vol.18, pt. 4, pp.760-785, figs.14, July 18, 1930.

REMARKS ON SOME MEMBERS OF THE GENERA PITHECIA AND CACAJAO FROM BRAZIL. Einar Loennberg. Arkiv. f. Zool., vol.30A, no.18, pp.1-25, figs.2, tables, June 16, 1938.

ENGLISH EXPLORER DISCOVERS HUGE, TAILLESS ANTHROPOID APE IN SOUTH AMERICA, UPSETTING ACCEPTED THEORIES OF THE EVOLUTION OF MAN. Francis de Loys. Washington Post, p.14, Nov.24, 1929.

(DATA ON THE PITHECIA FORMS OF THE CENTRAL AMAZON REGION.) Zur Kenntnis der Pithecia-Formen des mittleren Amazonenstrom-Gebietes. Robert Mertens. Senckenbergiana, Bd. 7, Heft 1-2, pp.17-18, Feb.12, 1925.

(FURTHER REMARKS ON PITHECANS OF THE CENTRAL AMAZON RIVER REGION.) Weitere Bemerkungen ueber Pithecien des mittleren Amazonenstrom-Gebietes. Robt. Mertens. Senckenbergiana, Franfurt, vol. 7, no.3-4, pp.74-75, Apr.20, 1925.

WINGS ON BRAZILIAN APES. Gerrit S. Miller, Jr. Science, N.S., vol.II, no.50, pp.3, Dec.13, 1895.

(AN ANTHROPOIDAL MONKEY IN AMERICA.) Un singe anthropoide actuel en Amérique. George Montandon. Revue Scientifique, Paris, 67 année, no.9, pp.268-269, fig.130, May 11, 1929.

(AN ANTHROPOIDAL MONKEY IN SOUTH AMERICA.) Un singe d'apparence anthropoide en Amérique du Sud. George Montandon. Compt. Rend. Acad. Sci., Paris, vol. 188, pp.815-817, 1929.

(AN ANTHROPOIDAL MONKEY IN SOUTH AMERICA.) Un Singe d'Apparence Anthropoide en Amerique du Sud. George Montandon. La Nature, pp.439-440, May 15, 1929.

(DISCOVERY IN SOUTH AMERICA OF AN ANTHROPOIDAL MONKEY.) Decouverte d'un singe d'apparence anthropoide en Amerique du Sud. George Montandon. Jour. Soc. Americanistes Paris, n.s., vol.21, pp.183-195, pls.5, 1929.

NOTES ON THE MONKEYS OF EASTERN PERU. P. L. Sclater. Proc. Zool. Soc. Lond., pp.217-220, pl.13, 1871.

ON THE SPECIES OF QUADRUMANA COLLECTED BY MR. BUCKLEY IN ECUADOR. P. L Sclater. Proc. Zool. Soc. Lond., pp. 663-664, pl.LIV, 1872.

FOUR NEW AMAZONIAN MONKEYS. Oldfield Thomas. Ann. and Mag. Nat. Hist. (8), vol.2, no.7, pp.88-91, July, 1908.

DESCRIPTION OF THE NEW MONKEY. Oldfield Thomas. Report Peru-Bolivia Boundary Commission, 1911-1913, Cambridge, Appendix, pp.241-242, May 31, 1919.

A REMARKABLE NEW MONKEY FROM PERU. Oldfield Thomas. Ann. and Mag. Nat. Hist. (9), vol.19, no.109, pp.156-157, Jan., 1927.

ON THE MONKEYS OF THE AMAZON. Alfred B. Wallace. Proc. Zool. Soc. Lond., pt.20, pp.107-110, 1852.

Taxonomy

DESCRIPTION OF AN APPARENTLY NEW SPECIES OF MONKEY OF THE GENUS CEBUS. D. G. Elliot. Ann. and Mag. Nat.

Hist., Lond., ser.7, vol.20, pp.292-293, Sept.1907.

DESCRIPTIONS OF APPARENTLY A NEW SPECIES AND SUBSPECIES OF CEBUS, WITH REMARKS ON THE NOMENCLATURE OF LINNAEUS'S SIMIA APELLA AND SIMIA CAPUCINA. D. G. Elliot. Bull. Amer. Mus. Nat. Hist., vol.36, art.15, pp.227-231, Apr.17, 1909.

NEW SPECIES OF MONKEYS OF THE GENERA SENIO CEBUS, ALOUATTA, AND AOTUS. Bull. Amer. Mus. Nat. Hist. New York, vol.31, art.2, pp.31-33, Mar.4, 1912.

THE STATUS OF CEBUS IMITATOR THOMAS. E. A. Goldman. Proc. Biol. Soc. Washington, vol.27, pp.99-102, May 11, 1914.

NOTE ON THE SPECIES OF THE GENUS PITHECIA, WITH DESCRIPTION OF A NEW SPECIES, P. ALBICANS. J. E. Gray. Proc. Zool. Soc. Lond., pt.28, pp.228-232, pl.LXXXI, 1860.

NOTICE OF SOME NEW SPECIES OF SPIDER MONKEYS (ATELES) IN THE COLLECTION OF THE BIRITISH MUSEUM. J. E. Gray. Proc. Zool. Soc. Lond., pp. 732-733, 1865.

NOTICE OF SOME APPARENTLY UNDESCRIBED SPECIES OF SAPAJOUS (CEBUS) IN THE COLLECTION OF THE BRITISH MUSEUM. J. E. Gray. Proc. Zool. Soc. Lond., pp.824-828, figs.4, pl.XLV, 1865.

THE SYSTEMATIC NAME OF THE MEXICAN SPIDER MONKEY. N. Hollister. Proc. Biol. Soc. Washington, vol.28, p.142, June 29, 1915.

REVIEW OF THE SPIDER MONKEYS. Remington Kellogg, E. A. Goldman. Proc. U.S. Nat. Mus., vol.96, publ.3186, pp.1-45, figs.2, Nov.2, 1944.

HOWLER MONKEYS OF THE PALLIATA GROUP. Barbara Lawrence. Bull. Mus. Comp. Zool., vol.75, no.8 pp.315-354, Nov., 1933.

NOTES ON MEMBERS OF THE GENERA ALOUATTA AND AOTUS. Einar Loennberg. Arkiv foer Zoologi, Stockholm, vol.33A, no.10, pp.44, pls.3, Dec.20, 1941.

NOTES ON SOME MEMBERS OF THE GENERA LAGOTHRIX AND ATELES. Einar Loennberg. Arkiv foer Zoologi, Stockholm, vol.32A, no.25, pp.14, July 18, 1940.

NOTES ON SOME MEMBERS OF THE GENUS CALLICEBUS. Einar Loennberg. Arkiv. f. Zool., Stockholm, vol.31A, no. 13, pp.1-18, pl.1, Mar.9, 1939.

NOTES ON SOME MEMBERS OF THE GENUS SAIMIRI. Einar Loennberg. Arkiv Zool., Stockholm, vol.32A, no.21, pp.18, 1 table, Apr.30, 1940.

A REMARKABLE SPECIES OF LAGOTHRIX. Einar Loennberg. Arkiv. Zool., Stockholm, vol.22B, no.2, pp.1-3, Feb.4, 1931.

REMARKS ON SOME MEMBERS OF THE GENUS CEBUS. Einar Loennberg. Arkiv f. Zool., Stockholm, vol.31A, no.23, pp. 1-24, tables, Aug.1, 1939.

(THE VALIDITY OF THE CEBUS ROBUSTUS KUHL AND ITS RELATIONS TO SOME RELATED FORMS.) Da validez de Cebus robustus Kuhl e de suas relacoes com as formas mais affins. Oliverio Pinto. Papens Avulsos Dept. Zool., Secretaria Agric., Sao Paulo, vol.1, art.15, pp.111-120, figs. 4, Mar.11, 1941.

ON CEBUS APELLA (LINNAEUS), WITH A NOTE ON CEBUS CAPUCINUS (LINNAEUS). George H. H. Tate. Jour. Mam., 35 (3): 414-418, illus., Aug., 1954.

ON FURTHER MONKEYS OF THE CALLICEBUS TORQUATUS GROUP. Oldfield Thomas. Ann. and Mag. Nat. Hist., ser. 9, vol.20, p.287, Sept., 1927.

ON THE TITI MONKEYS OF THE CALLICEBUS TORQUATUS GROUP. Oldfield Thomas. Ann. and Mag. Nat. Hist., ser. 9, vol.19, pp.509-510, Apr., 1927.

## Callithricidae

THE ANATOMY OF THE COMMON MARMOSET. J. Beattie. Proc. Zool. Soc. Lond., pt.3, pp.593-718, illus., Sept., 1927.

MARMOSETS. Belle J. Benchley. Zoonooz, Zool. Soc. San Diego, vol.11, no.6, pp.4-6, June, 1939.

THE MARMOSET MONKEY. John F. Breen. All-Pets Mag., Fond du Lac, vol.19, no.1, p.65, Jan., 1948.

(ON IDENTIFICATION OF SIMIA LEONINA HUMBOLDT (MAMMALIA, PRIMATES).) Sobre la identificacion de Simia leonina Humboldt (Mammalia, Primates. Angel Cabrera. Neotropica, Notas Zool. Sudamer., 2 (8): 49-53, Aug.1, 1956.

EXPERIMENTAL TRANSMISSION TO MAN OF A RELAPSING FEVER SPIROCHETE IN A WILD MONKEY OF PANAMA--LEONTOCEBUS GEOFFROYI (PUCHERAN). Herbert C. Clark, Lawrence H. Dunn, Joaquin Benavides. Amer. Jour. Trop. Med., vol.11, no.4, pp.243-257, July, 1931.

THOSE "FOREST SPRITES" CALLED MARMOSETS. Lee S. Crandall. Animal Kingdom, New York Zool. Soc., vol.54, no.6, pp.178-184, illus., Nov.-Dec., 1951.

(ON THE ACCLIMATIZATION OF THE MARMOSET (CALLITHRIX PENICILLATA.) Zur Akklimatisation des Schwarzpinselaffen (Callithrix penicillata). Karl David. Zool. Garten (NF), vol.13, nos.1-2, pp.131-132, Feb., 1941.

THE SUSCEPTIBILITY OF MARMOSETS TO YELLOW FEVER VIRUS. Nelson C. Davis. Jour. Exper. Med., vol.52, no.3, pp.405-415, pls.1, Sept.1, 1930.

DEVELOPMENT OF THE SILKY MARMOSET. Raymond L. Ditmars. Bull. New York Zool. Soc., vol.36, no.6, pp.175-176, Nov.-Dec., 1933.

MARMOSETS AND TAMARINS OF THE FAMILY HAPALIDAE. Guy Dollman. Abstract--Proc. Zool. Soc., Lond., ser. C, vol.107, no.13, pp.64-65, Dec.30, 1937.

DESCRIPTION OF A NEW SPECIES OF OEDIPOMIDAS. D. G. Elliot. Bull. Amer. Mus. Nat. Hist. New York, vol.31, art.15, p.137, July 23, 1912.

THE GENERA OEDIPOMIDAS AND SENIOCEBUS. D. G. Elliot. Bull. Amer. Mus. Nat. Hist., N. Y., vol.33, art.42, pp.643-645, Nov.26, 1914.

THE STATUS OF CALLITHRIX LUGENS (HUMBOLDT) AND CALLITHRIX AMICTUS E. GEOFFROY. D. G. Elliot. Bull. Amer. Mus. Nat. Hist. New York, vol.33, art.39, pp.599-601, Oct.30, 1914.

REARING MARMOSETS IN CAPTIVITY. Alice Fitzgerald. Jour. Mam., vol.16, no.3, pp.181-188, pl.4, Aug., 1935.

ON SOME NEW AND INSUFFICIENTLY KNOWN SPECIES OF MARMOSET MONKEYS FROM THE AMAZONIAN REGION. Emil A. Goeldi. Proc. Zool. Soc. Lond., pp.88-99, figs.20-23, June 12, 1907.

NOTICE OF AN INTERESTING AMERICAN MONKEY LIVING IN THE SOCIETY'S GARDENS. J. E. Gray. Proc. Zool. Soc. Lond., pp.256-257, pl.24, 1868.

NOTICE ON SOME NEW SPECIES OF MARMOSET MONKEYS (HAPALE AND MIDAS). J. E. Gray. Proc. Zool. Soc. Lond., pp. 733-735, 1865.

THE SYSTEMATIC POSITION OF THE MARMOSET, SIMIA LEONINA HUMBOLDT (PRIMATES). Philip Hershkovitz. Proc. Biol. Soc. Washington, vol.70, pp.17-20, Mar.8, 1957.

PRIMATES: COMPARATIVE ANATOMY AND TAXONOMY. 3. PITHECOIDEA: PLATYRRHINI (FAMILIES HAPALIDAE AND CALLIMICONIDAE). W. C. Osman Hill. A monograph. University Press, Edinburgh, and Interscience Publishers, New York, pp.xix, 354, pls.27, 1957.

(LETHARGY CONDITION OF A JACCHUS (CALLITHRIX JACCHUS, LINNE, 1766).) Lethargie-Zustand eines Weisspinselaeffchens, Callithrix jacchus (Linne, 1766). Helmut Kraft. Saeugetierk. Mitteil., 5(4): 175-176, Dec.1, 1957.

A NEW MARMOSET, MYSTAX PLUTO, N. SP. Einar Loennberg. Arkiv foer Zool., vol.18B, no.9, pp.1-3, May 3, 1926.

NOTES ON MARMOSETS. Einar Loennberg. Arkiv. foer Zool., Stockholm, vol.32A, no. 10, pp.1-22, 1940.

ON THE BREEDING OF THE COMMON MARMOSET (HAPALE JACCHUS LINN.) IN CAPTIVITY WHEN IRRADIATED WITH ULTRA-VIOLET RAYS. N. S. Lucas, E. Margaret Hume. Proc. Zool. Soc. Lond., pt.2, pp. 447-451, 2 pls., July, 1927.

ON THE BREEDING OF THE COMMON MARMOSET (HAPALE JACCHUS LINN.) IN CAPTIVITY WHEN IRRADIATED WITH ULTRA-VIOLET RAYS. II. A TEN YEAR'S FAMILY HISTORY. N. S. Lucas, E. Margaret Hume, H. Henderson Smith. Proc. Zool. Soc., Lond., vol.107, ser.A, Gen and Exper., pt.2, pp.205-211, table 1, July, 1937.

BRIGHT EYES--A MARMOSET PET. C. B. Manning. Nature Mag., vol.7, pp.87-88, 2 figs., Feb., 1926.

(OBSERVATIONS ON THE REPRODUCTIVE BIOLOGY OF THE MARMOSET (CALLITHRIX JACCHUS L.).) Beobachtungen zur Fortpflanzungsbiologie der Uistiti (Callithrix jacchus L.). Margarethe Marik. Zool. Garten, Leipzig, n.F., vol.4, nos.10-12, pp.347-349, Dec.16, 1931.

THE GENERA OF HAPALIDAE (MARMOSETS). R. I. Pocock. Ann. and Mag. Nat. Hist., Lond., ser.8, vol.20, pp.247-258, figs.2, Sept., 1917.

EMILY POST AND THE MARMOSETS. Fletcher Pratt. Harper's Mag., Albany, vol.198, no.1189, pp.65-69, illus., June, 1949.

(SOME FACTS AND TWO NEW MONKEYS OF OUR FAUNA.) Alguns factos e mais dois simios novos da nossa fauna. A. deM. Ribeiro. Bol. Mus. Nac. Rio de Janeiro, vol.1, pp.211-215, Mar., 1924.

(DESIGNATION OF A LECTOTYPE OF CALLITHRIX PENICILLA (E. GEOFFROY).) Designation d'un lectotype de Callithrix penicillatus (E. Geoffroy). P. Rode, Ph. Hershkovitz. Bull. Mus. Nat. Hist. Nat., Paris, ser.2, vol.17, no.3, pp.221-222, 1945.

NOTE ON THE REARING OF A JACCHUS MONKEY (JACCHUS PENICILLATUS, GEOFF.). Lady Rolle. Proc. Zool. Soc. Lond., pt.3, p.21, 1835.

A "SEXUAL SKIN" IN A MARMOSET. A. E. Russell, S. Zuckerman. Jour. Anat., Lond., vol.69, pt.3, pp.356-362, figs.2, pl.1, Apr., 1935.

(INFECTIOUS STREPTOCOCCUS INFECTION IN MARMOSETS.) Seuchenhafte Streptokokkeninfektion bei Meerkatzen. Fritz Schmidt-Hoensdorf. Zool. Garten, n.F., vol.4, no.1-2, pp.43-47, Feb., 1931.

REMARKS ON TWO SPECIES OF MAMMALS DESCRIBED FROM SPECIMENS RECENTLY LIVING IN THE SOCIETY'S GARDENS. P. L. Sclater. Proc. Zool. Soc. Lond., pp.592-596, pl. XLVI, 1869.

(DIVISION OF THE GENUS LEONTOCEBUS INTO TWO SUBGENERA BASED ON DENTO-MORPHOLOGICAL CHARACTERS.) Divisao do genero Leontocebus (macacos platyrrhina) em dois sub-generos sob bases de caracteres dento-morfologicos. Octavio Della Serra. Papeis Avulsos Dept. Zool. Sec. Agric., Sao Paulo, vol.10, no.8, pp.147-154, illus., Aug.25, 1951.

A NEW MARMOSET FROM THE LOWER AMAZONS. Oldfield Thomas. Ann. and Mag. Nat. Hist., ser.9, vol.9, pp.265-266, Mar., 1922.

A NEW MARMOSET FROM THE PERUVIAN AMAZONS. Oldfield Thomas. Ann. and Mag. Nat. Hist., ser.9, vol.5, p.144, Jan., 1920.

ON THE SYSTEMATIC ARRANGEMENT OF THE MARMOSETS. Oldfield Thomas. Ann. and Mag. Nat. Hist., ser.9, vol.9, pp.196-199, Feb., 1922.

OBSERVATIONS ON TWINNING IN MARMOSETS. George B. Wislocki. Amer. Jour. Anat., Phila., vol.64, no.3, pp.445-483, figs.5, pls.6, May 15, 1939.

PLACENTATION IN THE MARMOSET (OEDIPOMIDAS GEOFFROYI), WITH REMARKS ON TWINNING IN MONKEYS. George B. Wislocki. Anat. Record, vol. 52, no.4, pp.381-392, pls.1-3, May 25, 1932.

A STUDY ON SCENT GLANDS IN THE MARMOSETS, ESPECIALLY OEDIPOMIDAS GEOFFROYI. George B. Wislocki. Jour. Mam., vol.11, no.4, pp.475-483, pls.3, Nov., 1930.

MARMOSETS BRED IN CAPTIVITY--A RARE EVENT: DELICATE PETS WHOSE REGIMEN INCLUDES RAW BEEF, APPLE SAUCE, AND SUN-RAY TREATMENT! Illus. London News, vol.191, no.5149, p. 1159, illus., Dec.25, 1937.

## Cercopithecidea

(MORE ON THEROPITHECUS GELADA RUEPP.) Noch einige Worte ueber Theropithecus gelada Ruepp. F. J. Appelman. Zool. Garten, Leipzig, 23 (1-3): 246-247, 1957.

(ON THEROPITHECUS GELADA RUEPP.) Ueber Theropithecus gelada Ruepp. F. J. Appelman. Zool. Garten, Leipzig, (N.F.), vol.20, nos.2-3, pp.95-98, illus., 1953.

THE BEARDED BABY. Belle J. Benchley. San Diego Zoonooz, vol.19, no.1, p.7, illus., Jan., 1946.

(REMARKS ON SEMNOPITHECUS ALBOCINEREUS.) Bemerkungen ueber Semnopithecus albocinereus. J. K. Berthold. Zool. Garten, Leipzig, n.F., vol.4, nos. 3-5, p.172, May, 1931.

MAIMON. D. S. Blondheim. Romania, Paris, vol.41, no.162, pp.260-265, Apr., 1912.

OBSERVATIONS ON THE NATURAL HISTORY OF THE OLIVE COLOBUS MONKEY, PROCOLOBUS VERUS (VAN BENEDEN). A. H. Booth. Proc. Zool. Soc. Lond., 129 (3): 421-430, Nov.11, 1957.

THE IRASCIBLE BABOON. E. G. Boulenger. Science Digest, Chicago, vol.7, no.2, pp. 8-14, Feb., 1940.

(ON SEVERAL SPECIES OF CERCOPITHEQUES OF THE MONAS GROUP AND IN PARTICULAR, OF CERCOPITHECUS ERXLEBENI, GRAYI AND POGONIAS. A propos de quelques especes de Cercopitheques du groupe des Mones et, en particulier, de Cercopithecus erxlebeni, grayi et pogonias. E. Bourdelle, P. Mathias. Bull. Mus. Nat. d'Hist. Nat., Paris, vol. 34, no.5, pp.306-310, 1928.

(ON THE ORIGIN OF BABOONS.) Sur l'origene des babouins. P. L. Dekeyser. Notes Africaines, Dakar, no.54, pp.60-63, Apr., 1952.

AN EFFECTIVE BABOON TRAP. V. FitzSimons. Fauna and Flora, Transvaal, 6 (for 1955): 78-83, 1957.

PHOTOGRAPH OF MANDRILL. Russell Froelich. Science Illus., Louisville, vol. 1, no.9, p.55, Dec., 1946.

FIELD AND LABORATORY STUDIES ON AN AFRICAN MONKEY, CERCOPITHECUS ASCANIUS SCHMIDTI. A. J. Haddow. Matschie. Proc. Zool. Soc. Lond., 122: 297-394, 3 pls., 1952.

MUTATION AND THE RHESUS REACTION. J. B. S. Haldane. Nature, Lond., vol.153, no.3873, p.106, Jan.22, 1944.

SOME OBSERVATIONS ON THE BONNET MACAQUE. Carl G. Hartman. Jour. Mam., vol.19, no.4, pp.468-474, pls.1-2, table, Nov.14, 1938.

A MONOGRAPH ON THE PURPLE-FACED LEAF-MONKEYS (PITHECUS VETULUS). W. C. Osman Hill. Ceylon Jour. Sci., Sect.B. Zool. and Geol., vol.19, pt.1, pp. 23-88, pls.5-9, Sept.10, 1934.

NOTE ON BARBE'S LEAF-MONKEY (TRACHYPITHECUS BARBEI (BLYTH) ). W. C. Osman Hill. Proc. Zool. Soc. Lond., pt.1, pp.105-109, fig.1, Apr.16, 1936.

SUPPLEMENTARY OBSERVATIONS ON PURPLE-FACED LEAF-MONKEYS (GENUS KASI). W. C. Osman Hill. Ceylon Jour. Sci., sect.B, Zool. and Geol., vol.20, pt. 1, pp.115-133, pl.2, Aug.5, 1936.

VOICE AND LARYNX IN AFRICAN AND ASIATIC COLOBIDAE. W. C. Osman Hill, A. H. Booth. Jour. Bombay Nat. Hist. Soc., 54 (2): 309-321, Apr., 1957.

(THE PROBOSCIS MONKEY, NASALIS LARVATUS GEOFFR.) De Neusaap, Nasalis larvatus Geoffr. Edward Jacobson. Tropische Natuur, Buitenzorg, vol.22, no. 9, p.164, fig.1, Sept., 1933.

LETTER ON CERCOPITHECUS ATERRIMUS. F. A. Jentink. Proc. Zool. Soc. Lond., pp.338-339, May 7, 1895.

ON THE "DIANA" AND THE ROLOWAY". F. A. Jentink. Notes Leyden Mus., vol. 20, note 35, pp.233-239, 1898.

MACAQUES. Remington Kellogg. S. D. Aberle, "Primate Malaria", Office of Medical Information, Div. Medical Sci., Nat. Research Council, Washington, pp. 3, 171, pls.12, Mar., 1945.

THE HEART OF A JUNGLE MONKEY. Julie Closson Kenly. Nature Magazine, Washington, D.C., vol.33, no.4, pp.193-196, Apr., 1940.

BANDARLOG. Winifred E. King. San Diego Zoonooz, vol.18, no.7, pp.4-5, illus., Aug., 1945.

NOTE ON TWO MANGABEY-LIKE MONKEYS (CERCOCEBUS HAGENBECKI AND SEMNOCEBUS ALBIGENA KOTHSCHILDI), NOW LIVING IN THE MENAGERIE OF THE ZOOLOGICAL SOCIETY. R. Lydekker. Novit. Zool. Tring, vol.7, pp.593-596, Dec., 1900.

PLATE TO ACCOMPANY ARTICLE BY LYDEKKER DESCRIBING TWO MONKEYS IN THE ZOOL. SOC. GARDENS IN LONDON, CERCOCEBUS HAGENBECKI AND SEMNOCEBUS ALBIGENA ROTHSCHILDI. R. Lydekker. Novit. Zool. vol.8, pl.1, pp. 593-596, Feb., 1901.

OBSERVATIONS ON THE SOOTY AND WHITE-EYED MONKEYS (CERCOPITHECUS FULIGINOSUS AND C. AETHIOPS). W. Martin. Proc. Zool. Soc. Lond., pt.6, p.117, 1838.

(ON SOME SPECIES OF CERCOPITHECIDS OF THE MONES GROUP AND, IN PARTICULAR, OF CERCOPITHECUS ERXLEBENI, GRAYI AND POGONIAS. E. P. Mathias. Bull. Mus. Nat. d'Hist. Nat. Paris, no.5, pp.306-310, 1928.

A NEW RHESUS ANTIBODY. A. E. Mourant. Nature, London, vol.155, no.3940, p.542, May 5, 1945.

OBSERVATIONS UPON PRESBYTES ALBIGENA, GRAY, AND COLOBUS GUEREZA, RUEPP. James Murie. Proc. Zool. Soc. Lond., pp.740-745, 1865.

SUPPLEMENTARY NOTES ON THE RED-BELLIED MONKEY (CERCOPHITHECUS ERYTHROGASTER, GRAY). James Murie. Proc. Zool. Soc. Lond., pp.380-382, 1866.

(ON THE BEARDED LONG-TAILED MONKEY.) Ueber die Bartmeerkatzen. Oscar Neumann. Sitz. Ber. Gesell. Naturf. Freunde, Berlin, no.4, pp.22-25, 1899.

ON THE MORBID APPEARANCES OF A MANDRILL (CYNOCEPHALUS MAIMON). R. Owen. Proc. Comm. Sci. and Corres. Zool. Soc. Lond., pt.2, p.17, 1832.

NOTES ON THE CERCOPITHECINE GENERA RHINOSTIGMA AND MIOPITHECUS. R. I. Pocock. Ann. and Mag. Nat. Hist., ser.9, vol.16, pp.264-268, Aug., 1925.

THE PIG-TAILED MACAQUES (MACACA NEMESTRINA). R. I. Pocock. Jour. Bombay Nat. Hist. Soc., vol.35, no.2, pp. 297-311, Oct.15, 1931.

THE RHESUS MACAQUES (MACACA MULATTA). R. I. Pocock. Jour. Bombay Nat. Hist., Soc., vol.35, no.3, pp.530-551, figs.2, pl.1, Feb.15, 1932.

BABOONS--MONKEYS WHICH HAVE ABANDONED TREES FOR LIFE ON THE GROUND. Colin Campbell Sanborn. Field Mus. News, vol.9, no.5, pl.1, May, 1938.

JUST PLAIN HAM. Jacqueline Schermerhorn. San Diego Zoonooz, vol.18, no.1, pp.3-4, illus., Jan., 1945.

(SOME MONKEYS.) Quelques singes. H. Schouteden. Rev. Zool. Bot. Afr., vol.26, (Suppl. Bull. Cercle Zool. Congo., vol.11, nos.3-4), pp.69-70, Mar.-May, 1935.

NOTE ON CERCOPITHECUS PICTURATUS SANTOS. Ernst Schwarz. Bull. Soc. Portugaise Sci. Nat., vol.12, no.5, pp.27-28, Jan., 1937.

ADDITIONAL NOTES ON THE MONKEYS OF THE GENUS CERCOPITHECUS. P. L. Sclater. Proc. Zool. Soc. Lond., pt.3, pp.441-444, fig.1, pl.33 (missing), Oct.2, 1893.

(MAMMALOGICAL NOTES. II. SEMNOPITHECUS. III. COLOBES.) Notes mammalogiques. II. Semnopithecus. III. Colobes. A. F. de Seabra. Bull. Soc. Portugaise Sci. Nat. Lisbonne, vol.1, fasc. 4, pp.155-162, 1907.

(MAMMALOGICAL NOTES. IV. CERCOPITHECUS.) Notes mammalogiques. IV. Cercopithecus. A. F. de Seabra. Bull. Soc. Portugaise Sci. Nat. Lisbonne, vol.2, fasc.1-2, pp.25-40, Nov., 1908.

(MAMMALOGICAL NOTES. V. CERCOCEBUS. VI. CYNOMALGUS, THEROPITHECUS, VETULUS AND MACACUS. VII. PAPIO. A. F. de Seabra. Bull. Soc. Portugaise Sci. Nat. Lisbonne, vol.2, fasc.1, pp.125-138, 1908.

STUDIES WITH MONKEYS FED ARMY COMBAT RATIONS. Eugene Sporn, W. R. Ruegamer, C. A. Elvehjem. Jour. Nutrition, Phila., vol.35, no.5, pp.559-575, May 10, 1948.

SAA COMES OF AGE--LIFE STORY OF A MANDRILL. G. H. H. Tate. Nat. Hist., New York, vol.47, no.2, pp.70-72, fig.1, Feb., 1941.

EXTRACT OF A LETTER RELATING TO COLOBUS FULIGINOSUS AND MACACUS SPECIOSUS. M. Temminck. Proc. Zool. Soc. Lond., pt.7, p.49, 1839.

COMMUNICATION, ACCOMPANIED WITH DRAWINGS OF SEMNOPITHECUS LEUCOPRYMNUS NESTOR, BENN. Roy Templeton. Proc. Zool. Soc. Lond., pt.12, p.1, 1844.

(DESCRIPTION OF NEW OR IMPERFECTLY KNOWN MAMMALS IN THE COLLECTION OF THE NATIONAL MUSEUM OF NATURAL HISTORY. ORDER OF PRIMATES. FAMILY CERCOPITHECIDS.) Description des Mammiferes nouveaux ou imparfaitment connus de la collection du Museum National D'Histoire Naturelle. Ordre des primates. Famille des Cercopithecides. E. L. Trouessart. Nouv. Archiv. du Mus. Paris, ser.5, vol.4, fasc.2, pp.267-284, pls.1-5, 1912.

THEORETICAL AND PRACTICAL PROBLEMS OF MEDICINE AND BIOLOGY IN EXPERIMENTS ON MONKEYS. I. A. Utkin. Published on behalf of the Pergamon Inst. Translated and published with the aid of a grant from the National Institutes of Health, Bethesda, Md.

(ON THE OREOPITHECID.) A propos de l'Oreopitheque. Jean Viret. Mammalia, Paris, vol.19, no.2, pp.320-324, June, 1955.

THE BEARDED BABY. San Diego Zoonooz, vol.18, no.10, p.7, Oct., 1945.

THE COLOBUS FAMILY ALBUM. Nat. Hist., New York, vol.54, no.1, pp.42-43, illus., Jan., 1945.

YOUNG OF ZOO ANIMALS ON DISPLAY. News Bull. Staten Island Zool. Soc., New York, vol.9, no.3, p.4, illus., May, 1942.

Africa

"J.T. JR." THE BIOGRAPHY OF AN AFRICAN MONKEY. Delia J. Akeley. Macmillan Co., N.Y., 1928.

THE CERCOPITHECIDAE OF THE GOLD AND IVORY COASTS: GEOGRAPHIC AND SYSTEMATIC OBSERVATIONS. A. H. Booth. Ann. and Mag. Nat. Hist., ser.12, 9 (103): 476-480, July, 1956.

(INVESTIGATION OF THE GEOGRAPHICAL DISTRIBUTION OF THE RED AND GREEN MONKEYS OF WEST AFRICA.) Enquete sur la repartition geographique du singe rouge et des singes verts dans l'Ouest Africain. Pierre-L Dekeyser. Notes Africaines (Bull. Inst. Francaise d'Afrique Noire), Dakar, no.31, pp.28-29, figs.13-14, July, 1946.

DESCRIPTION OF A NEW BABOON FROM BRITISH EAST AFRICA. D. G. Elliot. Ann. and Mag. Nat. Hist. Lond., ser.7, vol.20, pp.497-498, Dec., 1907.

DESCRIPTION OF A NEW SUBSPECIES OF AFRICAN MONKEY OF THE GENUS CERCOPITHECUS. D. G. Elliot. Smiths. Misc. Coll., publ.1937, vol.56, no.7, pp. 1, June 11, 1910.

NOTICE OF A NEW WEST-AFRICAN MONKEY LIVING IN THE GARDENS OF THE SOCIETY (PLATE XVI). J. E. Gray. Proc. Zool. Soc. Lond., pp.168-169, pl.XVI, 1866.

NOTICE OF A NEW SPECIES OF COLOBUS AND OF ANOTHER MONKEY FROM ZANZIBAR. J. E. Gray. Proc. Zool. Soc. Lond., pp.180-182, pl.XV, 1868.

ON A NEW SPECIES OF MONKEY FROM ANGOLA. J. E. Gray. Proc. Zool. Soc. Lond., pt.16, pp.56-57, 1848.

THE RHODESIAN BABOON (CHORIOPITHECUS RHODESIAE, HAAGNER). A. K. Haagner. South African Jour. Nat. Hist., vol.1, pp.172, 173: pls.10, 11, 1919.

DESCRIPTION OF A NEW SUBSPECIES OF MONKEY FROM BRITISH EAST AFRICA. Ned Hollister. Smithsonian Misc. Coll., vol.59, no.3, pp.1-2, Mar.2, 1912.

TWO NEW EAST AFRICAN PRIMATES. Ned Hollister. Smithsonian Misc. Coll., vol.72, no.2, publ.2582, 1 p., 1876.

(THE BABOON OF BARBARY.) Le magot de berberie. L. Joleaud. Bull. Soc. Nat. Acclimat. France, vol.78, no.5, pp.153-155, May, 1931.

(THE ROLE OF MONKEYS IN THE COMMON NORTH AFRICAN TRADITIONS.) Le role des singes dans les traditions populaires Nord-Africaines. L. Joleaud. Jour. Soc. Africanistes, Paris, vol.1, no.1, pp.117-150, 1931.

A NEW GENUS OF AFRICAN MONKEY, ALLENOPITHECUS. Herbert Lang. Amer. Mus. Nov., no.87, pp.1-5, figs.1-3, Sept.12, 1923.

CONTRIBUTIONS TO THE KNOWLEDGE ABOUT THE MONKEYS OF BELGIAN CONGO. Einar Loennberg. Rev. Zool. Africaine, Brussels, vol.7, pp.107-154, 1919.

(BABOONS OF GERMAN EAST AFRICA.) Paviane von Deutsch-Ost-Afrika. Paul Matschie. Sitz. Ber. Gesell. Naturf. Freunde Berlin, Jahrg. 1897, no.9, pp.158-161, Nov.16, 1897.

(A MONKEY, APPARENTLY NEVER BEFORE DESCRIBED, OF CENTRAL AFRICA.) Ueber einen anscheinend noch nicht beschreibenen Affen aus Mittel-Afrika. Paul Matschie. Zool. Anzeiger, no.390, pp.161-163, May 2, 1892.

(ON MONKEYS FROM THE BELGIAN CONGO.) Ueber Affen aus dem Belgischen Congo. Paul Matschie. Rev. Zool. Africaine, Brussels, vol.2, fasc.2, pp.203-212, Feb., 1913.

(THE MONKEY COLLECTION OF THE SECOND GERMAN CENTRAL AFRICA EXPEDITION.) Die Affensammlung der Zweiten Deutschen Zentral-Afrika-Expedition. Robert Mertens. Zeitschr. f. Saeugetierkunde, vol.4, no.3, pp.129-141, Sept.18, 1929.

REMARKS ON AN AFRICAN MONKEY, CERCOPITHECUS WOLFI. A. B. Meyer. Proc. Zool. Soc. Lond., pt.1, pp.83-84, pl.7, June, 1894.

(GEOGRAPHICAL DISTRIBUTION OF COLOBUS MONKEYS IN EAST AFRICA AND THEIR LIVING HABITS.) Geographische Verbreitung der Colobusaffen in Ost-Afrika und deren Lebensweise. Oskar Neumann. Sitz. Ber. Gesell. Naturf. Freunde Berlin, no.9, pp.151-156, Nov.17, 1896.

THE INFLUENCE OF THE BELGIAN CONGO ON THE DISTRIBUTION OF UGANDA'S PRIMATES, AND SOME OF THEIR CHARACTERISTICS. Charles R. S. Pitman. Ann. Mus. Royal Congo Belge, Tervuren, n.s., Sci. Zool., vol.1, pp.47-55, 1954.

(ON SOME AFRICAN MONKEYS BELONGING TO THE GENERA COLOBUS AND CERCOPITHECUS.) Sur quelques singes africains appartenant aux genres Colobus et Cercopithecus. E. de Pousargues. Ann. Sci. Nat., Paris, ser.8, Zool. et Paleantol, vol. 1, pp.245-276, figs.6, 1896.

(THE GOLDEN MONKEY FOUND NEAR ASTRIDA.) Le Singe dore trouve pres d'Astrida. H. Schouteden. Rev. Zool. Bot. Afr., vol.26 (Suppl. Bull. Cercle Zool. Congo., vol.11, nos.1-2), pp.43-44, illus., Nov.-Dec., 1934.

(A MONKEY FROM THE ISLAND OF IDJWI.) Un Singe provenant de l'ile Idjwi. H. Schouteden. Rev. Zool. Bot. Afr., vol. 26 (Suppl. Bull. Cercle Zool., Congo., vol. 11, nos.1-2), pp.42-43, Nov.-Dec., 1934.

A NEW BLACK-AND-WHITE GUEREZA FROM THE IVORY COAST. Ernst Schwarz. Ann. and Mag. Nat. Hist., ser.9, vol.19, p. 155, Jan., 1927.

ON THE LOCAL RACES AND DISTRIBUTION OF THE BLACK AND WHITE COLOBUS MONKEY. Ernst Schwarz. Proc. Zool. Soc., Lond., pp.585-598, with 1 map, Oct.16, 1929.

ON A NEW AFRICAN MONKEY OF THE GENUS CERCOPITHECUS, WITH A LIST OF THE KNOWN SPECIES. P. L. Sclater. Proc. Zool. Soc. Lond., pt.2, pp.243-258, fig.1, pl.16-17, (missing), Aug.1, 1893.

(REMARKS ON THREE ABYSSINIAN MONKEYS.) Bemerkungen ueber drei Affen aus Abyssinien. Embrik Strand. Folia Zool. et Hydrobiol., Univ. Lettlands, Riga, vol. 3, no.2, pp.191-198, 1931.

DESCRIPTION OF A NEW BABOON FROM EAST AFRICA. Oldfield Thomas. Ann. and Mag. Nat. Hist. (6), vol.11, no.61, pp. 46-47, Jan., 1893.

A NEW MONKEY FROM THE ITURI FOREST. Oldfield Thomas. Abstract of Proc. Zool. Soc. Lond., no.38, p.1, Jan. 15, 1907.

ON A NEW MONKEY FROM NYASALAND. Oldfield Thomas. Ann. and Mag. Nat. Hist. (7), vol.10, no.57, pp.243-244, Sept., 1902.

ON A NEW MONKEY FROM THE ITURI FOREST. Oldfield Thomas. Proc. Zool. Soc. Lond., pp.2-3, pl.1, June 12, 1907.

TWO NEW GUENONS FROM THE IVORY COAST, WEST AFRICA. Oldfield Thomas. Ann. and Mag. Nat. Hist. (9), vol.11, no. 65, pp.607-608, May, 1923.

(THE DRILL OF FERNANDO PO.) Der Dril von Fernando Po. Ludwig Zukowsky. Archiv f. Nat., 88 Jahrg., Abt.A, 3 Heft, pp.184-192, pl., 1922.

(THE MANDRILL OF FERNANDO PO.) Der Mandrill von Fernando Po. Ludwig Zukowsky. Archiv. f. Naturgeschichte, vol.91, pp.132-136, illus., July, 1926.

(PRELIMINARY COMMUNICATION ON A NEW BABOON SPECIES OF THE WEBBE BASIN.) Vorlaeufige Mitteilung Ueber eine neue Pavianart aus dem Webbibecken. Ludwig Zukowsky. Zool. Garten, vol.14, no.4, pp.261-263, illus., 1942.

A RARE APE IN SIERRA LEONE. Nigerian Field, vol.14, no.4, pp.157-158, Oct., 1949.

Anatomy

(STUDY OF THE SINUSES OF MONKEYS.) Etude des sinus chez les singes. Edmond Aubert. Ann. Mus. Hist. Nat. Marseilles, vol.22, no.1, pp.3-27, 12 figs., 1929.

THE EXTERNAL MORPHOLOGY OF THE BRAIN OF SEMNOPITHECUS ENTELLUS (A COMPARATIVE STUDY). A. A. Ayer. Proc. Indian Acad. Sci., Bangalore City, vol.15, no.1, pp.43-57, figs.5, Jan., 1942.

THE MUSCLE ILIACUS MINOR IN THE INDIAN LANGUR, SEMNOPITHECUS ENTELLUS. A. A. Ayer. Anat. Record, Phila., vol.79, no.1, pp.79-82, fig.1, Jan.25, 1941.

A STUDY OF THE PARATHYROID GLANDS OF THE NORMAL HYPOPHYSECTOMIZED MONKEY (MACACA MULATTA). Burton Lowell Baker. Anat. Record, Phila., vol. 83, no.1, pp.47-73, fig.1, pls.2, May 25, 1942.

THE VISCERAL LYMPHATIC CHANNELS OF THE CATARRHINAE. (ILLUSTRATED BY THE DIRECTION OF THE SPREAD OF TUBERCULOSIS.) J. Beattie. Proc. Zool. Soc. Lond., pt.2, pp.459-470, July, 1927.

THE NEOCORTEX OF MACACA MULATTA. Herhardt von Bonin, Percival Bailey. Illinois Monographs in Medical Sci., Univ. Illinois Press, Urbana, vol.5, no.4, pp.x, 163, figs.40, pls.62, 1947.

(STUDIES OF THE THORACIC COLLATERAL TRUNK OF THE SYMPATHETIC SYSTEM IN MONKEYS.) Études sur le tronc collatéral thoracique du sympathique chez les Singes. J. Botar. Bull. Mus. Nat. Hist. Nat., Paris, ser.2, vol.3, no.7, pp. 579-585, figs.4, Nov., 1931.

PRELIMINARY INVESTIGATION CONCERNING THE REPRESENTATION OF THE FOVEA IN THE EXTERNAL GENICULATE BODY OF THE MONKEY. S. Brody. Proc. Kon. Akad. Wet. Amsterdam, vol.37, no. 9, pp.724-731, figs.9, pls.4, Nov., 1934.

(THE PRESENCE OF A MONILIA ON THE TONGUE OF ALGERIAN MONKEYS.) Présence d'un Monilia sur la langue de singes d'Algérie. A. Catanei. Comptes Rendus des Séances Soc. Biol., vol.93, no. 21, pp.92-94, June, 1925.

THE CORONARY ARTERIES IN 266 HEARTS OF RHESUS MONKEY. Ralph E. Chase. Amer. Jour. Phys. Anthropol., vol.23, no. 3, pp.299-320, figs.6, Jan.-Mar., 1938.

LUNG LOBATION IN RHESUS MONKEY, COMPARED WITH MAN. Ralph E. Chase. Amer. Jour. Phys. Anthropol., Phila., vol. 29, no.2, pp.267-286, figs.5, June 30, 1942.

THE BRACHIAL PLEXUS IN MACACUS RHESUS, COMPARED WITH MAN. Ralph E. Chase, Charles F. DeGaris. Amer. Jour. Phys. Anthrop., Phila., vol.27, no. 2, pp.223-254, figs.15, Sept.30, 1940.

THE CRANIAL SUTURE CLOSURE IN MONKEYS. S. R. K. Chopra. Proc. Zool. Soc. Lond., 128 (1): 67-112, Feb.14, 1957.

THE THALAMIC CONNECTIONS OF THE PARIETAL AND FRONTAL LOBES OF THE BRAIN IN THE MONKEY. W. E. LeGros Clark, R. H. Boggon. Philos. Trans. Roy. Soc. Lond., ser.B, vol.224, no.515, pp. 313-359, pls.23-27, Feb.27, 1935.

THE SENSORY INNERVATION OF THE SPINAL ACCESSORY AND TONGUE MUSCULATURE IN THE RHESUS MONKEY. Kendall B. Corbin, Frank Harrison. Brain, Lond., pt.2, vol.62, pp.191-197, June, 1939.

(CONCERNING A CRANIUM OF THEROPITHECUS.) A proposito de un cranio di Theropithecus. Oscar de Beaux. Giorn. Morfologio dell' Uomo e dei Primati, vol. 4, fasc.1, pp.24-29, 1 fig., 1923.

THE EYE OF THE OWL MONKEY (NYCTIPITHECUS). S. R. Detwiler. Anat. Record,

Phila., vol.80, no.2, pp.233-239, figs.4, pl.1, June 25, 1941.

(THE DEVELOPMENT OF THE BRAIN IN A MONKEY, (SEMNOPITHECUS PRIAMUS BLYTH), AND THE CHARACTERISTICS OF THE CEREBRAL DEVELOPMENT OF SEMNOPITHECIDAE.) Le developpement du cerveau chez un singe, le Semnopitheque (Semnopithecus priamus Blyth), et les caracteristiques du developpement cerebral des Semnopithecidae. Madeleine Friant. Ann. Soc. Roy. Zool. Belgique, vol.85, no. 1, pp.39-60, 1953.

PATTERNS OF THE AORTIC ARCH IN A SERIES OF 133 MACAQUES. Charles F. de Garis. Jour. Anat. Cambridge, vol.70, pt.1, pp.149-158, Oct., 1935.

THE CRANIAL CHARACTERS OF SOME SOUTH AFRICAN BABOONS. I. Goldblatt. South Afr. Jour. Sci., Pretoria, vol.23, pp.764-783, pls.16, Dec., 1926.

DENTAL VARIATIONS IN THE GENUS MANDRILLUS RITGEN. W. C. Osman Hill. Mammalia, Paris, vol.17, no.3, pp.208-218, pls.7-9, Sept., 1953.

THE EXTERNAL AND VISCERAL ANATOMY OF THE OLIVE COLOBUS MONKEY. W. C. Osman Hill. Proc. Zool. Soc. Lond., vol. 122, pt.1, pp.127-186, pls.1-6, May 16, 1952.

ONTOGENTIC CHANGES IN THE MESOGASTRIC VISCERA OF THE COLOBIDAE. W. C. Osman Hill. Proc. Zool. Soc. Lond., vol.124, pt.1, pp.163-183, pls.1-3, May 27, 1954.

SPINA BIFIDA IN A SACRED BABOON (PAPIO HAMADRYAS). W. C. Osman Hill. Ceylon Jour. Sci., Colombo, ser.D, vol.5, pt.1, pp.9-15, pls.2-4, Feb.11, 1939.

THE SUPRARENAL CORTEX IN MONKEYS OF THE GENUS PITHECUS. W. C. Osman Hill. Jour. Anat., Cambridge, vol.68, pt. 1, pp.19-38, figs.1-8, Oct., 1933.

NOTES ON THE DENTITION OF THE GOLDEN MONKEY, RHINOPITHECUS. D. A. Hooijer. Jour. Mam., vol.33, no.2, pp.258-260, May 16, 1952.

ON SOME POINTS IN THE FORMATION AND DISTRIBUTION OF THE CERVICAL PLEXUS IN CYNOMORPHOUS MONKEYS. G. S. Huntington. Trans. N. Y. Acad. Sci., vol.16, pp.83-95, pls.7-8, Mar.3, 1897.

BASIC DATA ON THE EMERGENCE OF DECIDUOUS TEETH IN THE MONKEY (MACACA MULATTA). V. O. Hurme, G. van Wegenen. Proc. Amer. Philos. Soc. Phila., vol.97, no.3, pp.291-315, illus., June 30, 1953.

A SIMIAN DEEPLY CLEFT, BILOBED GALL BLADDER WITH A "PHRYGIAN CUP". Hadley Kirkman. Anat. Record, Phila., vol.95, no.4, pp.423-447, figs.37, Aug., 1946.

CYTOPLASMIC INCLUSIONS IN PERIPHERAL AUTONOMIC GANGLION CELLS OF THE MONKEY. Edwin H. Lennette, Ernst Scharrer. Anat. Record, Phila., vol.94, no.1, pp.85-92, figs.2, Jan., 1946.

THE EFFERENT FIBERS OF THE FRONTAL LOBE OF THE MONKEY, MACACA MULATTA. Paul M. Levin. Jour. Comp. Neur., vol.63, no.3, pp.360-419, figs.32, Apr.15, 1936.

RETROGRADE DEGENERATION OF THE SUPRAOPTIC NUCLEI AFTER SECTION OF THE INFUNDIBULAR STALK IN THE MONKEY. H. W. Magoun, S. W. Ranson. Anat. Record, Phila., vol.75, no.1, pp.107-123, Sept.25, 1939.

NOTES ON THE ANATOMY OF THE PROBOSCIS MONKEY (SIMIA NASALIS). W. Martin. Proc. Zool. Soc. Lond., pt.5, pp. 70-73, 1837.

BRAIN OF PITHECUS RHESUS (M. RHESUS). Fred A. Mettler. Amer. Jour. Phys. Anthrop., vol.17, no.3, pp.309-331, figs.4, Jan.-Mar., 1933.

CORTICIFUGAL FIBER CONNECTIONS OF THE CORTEX OF MACACA MULATTA. THE FRONTAL REGION. Fred A. Mettler. Jour. Comp. Neur., vol.61, no.3, pp.509-542, figs.10, June 15, 1935.

CORTICIFUGAL FIBER CONNECTIONS OF THE CORTEX OF MACACA MULATTA. THE TEMPORAL REGION. Fred A. Mettler. Jour. Comp. Neur., vol.63, no.1, pp.25-47, figs.8, Dec.15, 1935.

NOTES ON THE MYOLOGY OF A SPECIMEN OF CERCOPITHECUS SABAEUS. St. George J. Mivart. Proc. Zool. Soc. Lond., pp.43-46, figs.2, 1865.

OBSERVATION UPON A SPECIMEN OF COLOBUS TEMMINCKII, PRESENTED TO THE SOCIETY BY P. L. STRACHAN. W. Ogilby. Proc. Zool. Soc. Lond., pt.8, p. 20, 1840.

OBSERVATIONS UPON THE SKULL OF CERCOPITHECUS AETHIOPS, AUCT. W. Ogilby. Proc. Zool. Soc. Lond., pt.8, p. 1, 1840.

(THE CLAVICLE OF THE LANGUR.) La Clavicule du Semnopitheque. Georges Olivier. Mammalia, Paris, vol.17, no.3, pp.173-186, illus., Sept., 1953.

(THE SACRUM OF THE LANGUR.) La sacrum du Semnopitheque. Georges Olivier. Mammalia, Paris, vol.16, no.3, pp.122-136, illus., Sept., 1952.

(THE SHOULDER BLADE OF THE LANGUR.) L'omoplate du semnopithèque. Georges Olivier, Robert Depreux. Mammalia, Paris, vol.18, no.2, pp.181-211, illus., June, 1954.

(THE LEG BONES OF THE LANGUR.) Les os de la jambe du Semnopithèque. Georges Olivier, Raphael Fenart. Mammalia, Paris, vol.20, no.3, pp.248-275, illus., Sept., 1956.

(THE FOOT BONES OF THE LANGUR.) Les os du pied du Semnopithèque. Georges Olivier, Michel Fontaine. Mammalia, Paris, 21 (2): 142-189, pl.6, June, 1957.

(THE COXAL BONE AND THE PELVIS OF THE LANGUR.) L'os coxal et le bassin du Semnopithèque. Georges Olivier, Claude Libersa. Mammalia, Paris, vol.18, no.3, pp.287-328, illus., Sept., 1954.

(THE LANGUR SKULL (SUMMARY).) Le Crane du Semnopithèque (Sommaire). Georges Olivier, Claude Libersa, Raphael Fenart. Mammalia, Paris, vol.19, no.1, pp.1-292, illus., Mar., 1955.

(THE FEMUR OF THE LANGUR.) Le fémur du Semnopithèque. Georges Olivier, Guy Piganiol. Mammalia, Paris, 21 (4): 430-451, pl.12, Dec., 1957.

DESCRIPTION OF THE STOMACH OF THE COLOBUS URSINUS, OGILBY. R. Owen. Proc. Zool. Soc. Lond., pt.9, pp.84-85, 1841.

ON THE ANATOMY OF THE CERCOPITHECUS ALBOGULARIS, SYKES. R. Owen. Proc. Comm. Sci. and Corres. Zool. Soc. Lond., pt.2, p.18, 1832.

ON THE STOMACH OF SEMNOPITHECUS MANRUS, F. CUV. R. Owen. Proc. Zool. Sci. Lond., pt.2, p.6, 1834.

ON THE STOMACHS OF TWO SPECIES OF SEMNOPITHECUS, F. CUV. R. Owen. Proc. Zool. Soc. Lond., pt.1, pp.74-75, 1833.

THE SEX CHROMOSOMES OF THE MONKEY. Theophilus S. Painter. Science, vol. 56, pp.286-287, Sept.8, 1922.

THE MYOLOGY OF RHINOPITHECUS ROXELLANAE AND CYNOPITHECUS NIGER. E. L. Patterson. Proc. Zool. Soc. Lond., vol.112, ser.B, pts.1-2, pp. 31-104, figs.26, Oct., 1942.

ENDOMETRIAL VASCULAR REACTIONS AND THE MECHANISM OF NIDATION. Doris Phelps. Amer. Jour. Anat., Phila., vol.79, no.2, pp.167-197, figs.38, Sept., 1946.

THE EXTERNAL CHARACTERS OF A FEMALE RED COLOBUS MONKEY (PROCOLOBUS BADIUS WALDRONI.). R. I. Pocock. Proc. Zool. Soc. Lond., pt.4, pp.939-944, figs.2, Jan.10, 1936.

(ON SOME DIFFERENTIAL CHARACTERS OF THE SKULL OF LANGURS AND MANGABEYS.) Sur quelques caracteres differentiels de la tete osseuse des cercopitheques et des cercoebes. P. Rode. Mammalia, Paris, vol.1, no.2, pp.56-64, figs. 2, tables 2, pl.2, Dec., 1936.

CYCLIC CHANGES IN THE ENDOMETRIAL LIPINS OF THE RHESUS MONKEY. I. Rossman. Amer. Jour. Anat., Phila., vol. 69, no.2, pp.187-228, illus., Sept.15, 1941.

(CONTRIBUTION TO THE STUDY OF THE ORIGIN AND GROWTH OF THE TEMPORAL BONE IN THE MACAQUE.) Contribution a l'etude de la genese et de la croissance de l'os temporal chez le macaque. R. Saban. Mammalia, Paris, vol.19, no.4, pp.447-458, illus., Dec., 1955.

CRANIAL AND DENTAL VARIABILITY IN COLOBUS MONKEYS. Adolph H. Schultz. Proc. Zool. Soc. Lond., 130 (1): 79-105, pl.1, Jan.23, 1958.

EXHIBITION OF, AND REMARKS UPON, A MOUNTED SPECIMEN OF CERCOPITHECUS ALBIGULARIS FROM THE LEYDEN MUSEUM. P. L. Sclater. Proc. Zool. Soc. Lond., pt.4, p.691, Apr.2, 1894.

(OBSERVATIONS ON THREE CASES OF ABNORMAL DENTITION IN HYLOBATES.) Osservazioni su tre casi di dentiione anormale in ilobatini. Alberto Simonetta. Monitore Zool. Italiano, Firenze, vol.63, no.3, pp.1-6, 1955.

ON THE ANATOMY OF THE DRILL (MANDRILLUS LEUCOPHAEUS). Charles F. Sonntag. Proc. Zool. Soc. Lond., pp.429-453, June, 1922.

THE INNERVATION OF THE PHARYNX IN THE RHESUS MONKEY, AND THE FORMATION OF THE PHARYNGEAL PLEXUS IN PRIMATES. James M. Sprague. Anat. Record, Phila., vol.90, no.3, pp.197-208, figs.2, Nov., 1944.

(ON THE MORPHOLOGY AND TOPOGRAPHY OF THE LIVER OF COLOBUS POLYCOMOS ABYSSINICUS OKEN.) Zur Morphologie und Topographie der Leber von Colobus polycomos abyssinicus (Oken). Dietrich Starck. Mitt. Naturf. Gesell. Bern, n.F., 14: 21-32, Feb., 1957.

THE NERVE SUPPLY OF THE VERTEBRAL COLUMN AND ITS ASSOCIATED STRUCTURES IN THE MONKEY. Donald L. Stillwell. Anat. Record, Phila., 125 (2): 139-170, June, 1956.

THE COAGULATING FUNCTION OF THE CRANIAL LOBE OF THE PROSTATE GLAND IN THE MONKEY. G. Van Wagenen. Anat. Rec., vol.66, no.4, pp.411-421, figs.5, Nov.25, 1936.

THE SEQUENCE OF EPIPHYSIAL UNION IN OLD WORLD MONKEYS. Sherwood L. Washburn. Amer. Jour. Anat., Phila., vol.72, no.3, pp.339-360, May, 1943.

VARIATIONS IN THE SKULL OF CERCOPITHECUS AETHIOPS PYGERYTHRUS. Clara Weinbrenn. South African Jour. Sci., vol.27, pp.501-520, Nov., 1930.

A NOTE ON TWO BABOON CRANIA FROM CATHKIN PEAK FOREST RESERVE, NATAL. L. H. Wells. South African Jour. Sci., vol.29, pp.647-650, Oct., 1932.

A PERONEUS TERTIUS MUSCLE IN A CHACMA BABOON (PAPIO PORCARIUS). L. H. Wells. Jour. Anat., Lond., vol.69, pt.4, pp.508-514, figs.2, July, 1935.

THE CHEMICAL CYTOLOGY OF THE CHORIOID PLEXUS AND BLOOD BRAIN BARRIER OF THE RHESUS MONKEY (MACACA MULATTA). George B. Wislocki, Edward W. Dempsey. Jour. Comp. Neurol. Phila., vol.88, no.3, pp.319-345, pls.1-3, June, 1948.

REMARKS ON THE LYMPHATICS OF THE REPRODUCTIVE TRACT OF THE FEMALE RHESUS MONKEY (MACACA MULATTA). George B. Wislocki, Edward W. Dempsey. Anat. Record, Phila., vol.75, no.3, pp.341-363, pl.1, Nov.25, 1939.

OBSERVATIONS ON THE AUTONOMIC SYSTEM AND ON VERTEBRAL AND NEURAL SEGMENTATION IN MONKEYS. S. Zuckerman. Trans. Zool. Soc. Lond., vol.23, pt.6, pp.315-378, figs.8, tables 5, pl.33, Jan., 1938.

### Asia and Japan

(NOTE ON A NEW SPECIES OF SEMNOPITHECAN FROM COCHIN CHINA.) Note sur une Nouvelle espece de Semnopitheque provenant de la Cochinchine. Milne A. Edwards. Bull. Nouv. Archiv. du Mus., Paris, vol.6, pp.7-10, pls.2, 1870.

ON THE EXISTENCE OF A LARGE APE UNKNOWN TO SCIENCE IN SIKKIM. H. J. Elwes. Proc. Zool. Soc. Lond., p.294, June, 1915.

NOTICE OF MACACUS LASIOTUS, A NEW SPECIES OF APE FROM CHINA, IN THE COLLECTION OF THE SOCIETY. John E. Gray. Proc. Zool. Soc. Lond., pp.60-61, pl.6, 1868.

THE HIGHLAND MACAQUE OF CEYLON. W. C. Osman Hill. Jour. Bombay Nat. Hits. Soc., vol.43, no.3, pp.402-406, fig. 1, Dec., 1942.

THE SYNONYMIES, CHARACTERS AND DISTRIBUTION OF THE MACAQUES INCLUDED UNDER THE NAMES RHESUS AND ASSAMENSIS IN BLANFORD'S MAMMALS. M. A. C. Hinton, R. C. Wroughton. Jour. Bombay Nat. Hist. Soc., vol.27, pp. 665-672, 1921.

ON THE GEOGRAPHICAL RANGE OF SEMNOPITHECUS ENTELLUS. T. Hutton. Proc. Zool. Soc. Lond., pp.944-952, 1867.

THE HABITAT OF THE JAPANESE MONKEY (MACACA FUSCATA) ON KOSIMA, MIYAZAKI PREFECTURE. Tokio Kaburaki. Report on the survey of the natural monuments, Sect. Zool. no.4, Dept. Interior, Tokyo, pp.3, pl.1, Jan., 1938.

A NEW LANGUR (PRIMATES: COLOBIDAE) FROM GOALPARA DISTRICT, ASSAM. H. Khajuria. Ann. and Mag. Nat. Hist., (12) 9 (98): 86-88, Feb., 1956.

NOTES ON THE AUTOCHTHONY AND ENDEMICITY OF THE JAPANESE MACAQUE WITH A DESCRIPTION OF ITS PRESENT HAUNTS IN JAPAN AND OF THE BEARING UPON HUMAN LIFE. Kyukichi Kishida. Ornithol. and Mammal. Rept., Forestry Agency, Ministry Agr. and Forestry, Tokyo, no.14, pp.1-92, illus., July, 1953.

DESCRIPTION OF A NEW MACAQUE FROM SIAM. C. Boden Kloss. Jour. Nat. Hist. Soc., Siam, vol.2, pp.247-249, May, 1917.

A NEW RACE OF MONKEY FROM ANNAM. C. Boden Kloss. Ann. and Mag. Nat. Hist., ser.9, vol.18, p.214, Aug., 1926.

(A NEW LANGUR FROM SIAM.) Ein neuer Schlankaffe aus Siam. Theodor Knottnerus-Meyer. Zool. Garten, Leipzig, n.F., vol. 6, nos.10-12, p.259, Dec., 1933.

NOTES ON SOME INDIAN MACAQUES. C. McCann. Jour. Bombay Nat. Hist. Soc., vol.36, no.4, pp.796-810, pls.1-5, Dec.15, 1933.

NOTES ON THE COMMON INDIAN LANGUR (PITHECUS ENTELLUS). C. McCann. Jour. Bombay Nat. Hist. Soc., vol.33, no.1, pp. 192-194, pl.1, Sept.30, 1928.

OBSERVATIONS ON SOME OF THE INDIAN LANGURS. C. McCann. Jour. Bombay Nat. Hist. Soc., vol.36, no.3, pp.618-628, pls.1-2. Aug.15, 1933.

(CONTRIBUTIONS TO KNOWLEDGE OF THE SOUTHERN CHINA SHORT-TAILED MACAQUES.) Zur Kenntnis der Suedchinesischen Kurzschwanz-Makaken. Paul Matschie. Sitz. Ber. Gesell. Naturf. Freunde Berlin, Jahrg. 1912, no.5, pp.305-310, May, 1912.

OBSERVATIONS ON THE MACAQUES. II. BELANGER'S MONKEY. James Murie. Proc. Zool. Soc. Lond., pp.770-771, 1872.

OBSERVATIONS ON THE MACAQUES. III. THE FORMOSAN OR ROUND-FACED MONKEY. James Murie. Proc. Zool. Soc. Lond., pp.771-780, figs.2, 1872.

OBSERVATIONS ON THE MACAQUES. IV. THE JAPANESE MONKEY. James Murie. Proc. Zool. Soc. Lond., pp.780-787, figs., 1872.

A FURTHER NOTE UPON THE WHITE (ALBINO) LANGUR IN CEYLON. W. W. A. Phillips. Ceylon Jour. Sci. Sect.B, Zool. and Geol., Spolia Zeylanica, vol.14, no.2, pp.335-337, pl.1, 1928.

A GUIDE TO THE MAMMALS OF CEYLON. PART IV. THE MONKEYS. W. W. A. Phillips. Ceylon Jour. Sci., Sect.B, Zool. and Geol., Spolia Zeylanica, vol.13, pt.3, pp.261-283, pls.10-13, Mar.31, 1926.

A NEW PITHECUS MONKEY FROM CEYLON, PITHECUS PHILBRICKI SP. N. W. W. A. Phillips. Ceylon Jour. Sci., Sect.B, Zool. and Geol., Spolia Zeylanica, Colombo, vol.14, pt.1, pp.57-59, Apr.30, 1927.

THE WHITE LANGUR OR WANDEROO IN CEYLON. W. W. A. Phillips. Ceylon Jour. Sci., Sect.B, Zool. and Geol., Spolia Zeylanica, Colombo, vol.13, pt.3, pp.291-294, Mar.31, 1926.

THE LANGURS OR LEAF MONKEYS OF BRITISH INDIA. R. I. Pocock. Jour. Bombay Nat. Hist. Soc., vol.32, pp.472-504, 660-677, pls.4 (1 col.), many text figs., 1928.

THE LONG-TAILED MACAQUE MONKEYS (MACACA RADIATA AND M. SINICA) OF SOUTHERN INDIA AND CEYLON. R. I. Pocock. Jour. Bombay Nat. Hist. Soc., vol.35, no.2, pp.276-288, Oct.15, 1931.

THE MAMMAL SURVEY OF THE EASTERN GHATS. REPORT ON THE MONKEYS. R. I. Pocock. Jour. Bombay Nat. Hist. Soc., vol.35, no.1, pp.51-59, June 15, 1931.

THE MONKEYS OF THE GENERA PITHECUS (OR PRESBYTIS) AND PYGATHRIX FOUND TO THE EAST OF THE BAY OF BENGAL. R. I. Pocock. Proc. Zool. Soc. Lond. for 1934, pt.4, pp.895-961, figs.5, pls.2, Jan.14, 1935.

NEW BABOON FROM ADEN. Oldfield Thomas. Proc. Zool. Soc. Lond., p.929, Nov.28, 1899.

A NEW MONKEY FROM THE MALAY PENINSULA. Oldfield Thomas. Proc. Zool. Soc. Lond., pp.634-635, Oct., 1910.

ON A NEW CHINESE MONKEY. Oldfield Thomas. Proc. Zool. Soc. Lond., pp.224-225, pl.21, Aug.6, 1903.

A NEW LEAF MONKEY FROM THE SHAN STATES. R. C. Wroughton. Jour. Bombay Nat. Hist. Soc., vol.25, no.1, pp.46-48, illus., Mar.20, 1917.

SCIENTIFIC RESULTS FROM THE MAMMAL SURVEY. XI. A NEW MONKEY FROM THE CHINDWIN RIVER. R. C. Wroughton. Jour. Bombay Nat. Hist. Soc., vol.24, no.1, pp.55-57, Sept.30, 1915.

SCIENTIFIC RESULTS FROM THE MAMMAL SURVEY. XIV. THE LANGURS OF ASSAM. R. C. Wroughton. Jour. Bombay Nat. Hist. Soc., vol.24, pp.653-655, Oct. 25, 1916.

THE SHAN STATES LANGUR. A CORRECTION. SCIENTIFIC RESULTS FROM THE MAMMAL SURVEY. NO. XVII. R. C. Wroughton. Jour. Bombay Nat. Hist. Soc., vol.25, no.3, pp.361, Jan.15, 1918.

THE WORLD'S RAREST MONKEY FOR THE ZOO: THE GOLDEN SNUB-NOSED MONKEY FROM SOUTH-WESTERN CHINA. Illus. London News, vol.194, no.5205, p. 103, illus., Jan.21, 1939.

### Care in Captivity

(ON KEEPING SEMNOPITHECUS IN CAPTIVITY IN EUROPE.) Ueber die Haltung von Semnopithecus in europaeischer Gefangenschaft. P. Chalmers Mitchell. Zool. Garten, Leipzig, n.F., vol.4, nos.8-9, p. 298, Oct., 1931.

(BIRTH AND RAISING OF A YELLOW-GREEN MARMOSET (CERCOPITHECUS CALLITRICHUS H. GEOFFR.).) Geburt und Aufzucht einer Gelbgruenen Meerkatze, Cercopithecus callitrichus H. Geoffr. Gustav Moog. Zool. Garten, Leipzig, 23 (1-3): 220-223, 1957.

CARE AND DISEASES OF THE RESEARCH MONKEY. Robert M. Sauer. New York Acad. of Sci., vol.85, art., 1960.

FEEDING AND BREEDING OF LABORATORY ANIMALS. A COMPARED DIET FOR MONKEYS. D. J. Short, A. S. Parkes. Jour. Hyg., Cambridge, vol.47, no.2, pp.209-212, June, 1949.

### Diseases and Parasites

A RARE CASE OF OSTEOMALACIA WITH SEVERE CARIES OF THE MAXILLARY CANINE TEETH IN A CAPTIVE BABOON. Montague Francis Ashley-Montagu. Internat. Jour. Orthodontia and Dent. for children, St. Louis, vol.21, no.7, pp.672-681, figs. 11, July, 1935.

ON A NEW SPECIES OF HYMENOLEPIS FROM A MONKEY. J. G. Baer. Jour. Parasitology, vol.14, pp.48-50, illus., 1927.

THE SUSCEPTIBILITY OF AFRICAN MONKEYS TO YELLOW FEVER. Johannes H. Bauer, Alexander F. Mahaffy. Amer. Jour. Hygiene, vol.12, no.1, pp.155-174, July, 1930.

POLIOMYELITIS IN AN UNINOCULATED RHESUS MONKEY, AND IN ORALLY INOCULATED MONKEYS, RECEIVING DESOXYPYRIODOXINE. David Bodian. Amer. Jour. Hygiene, Lancaster, vol.48, no.1, pp.87-93, July, 1948.

ACTIVE IMMUNIZATION IN MONKEYS AGAINST POLIOMYELITIS WITH GERMICIDALLY INACTIVATED VIRUS. Maurice Brodie. Science, n.s., vol.79, no.2061, pp.594-595, June 29, 1934.

EFFECT OF REPEATED SUPERINFECTION UPON THE POTENCY OF IMMUNE SERUM OF MONKEYS HARBORING CHRONIC INFECTIONS OF PLASMODIUM KNOWLESI. L. T. Coggeshall, Henry W. Kumm. Jour. Exper. Medicine, vol.68, no.1, pp.17-27, July 1, 1938.

INFECTION IN MONKEYS WITH STRAINS OF TRYPANOSOMA CRUZI IN THE UNITED STATES. U.S. Public Health Repts., Washington, D.C., vol.58, no.27, pp.1006-1010, pl.1, July 2, 1943.

RESEARCHES ON THE INTESTINAL PROTOZOA OF MONKEYS AND MAN. V. THE ENDOMILAX OF MACAQUES. Clifford Dobell. Parasitology, vol.25. no. 4, pp.436-467, Dec., 1933.

SPIORCHETES IN GASTRIC GLANDS OF MACACUS RHESUS AND HUMANS WITHOUT DEFINITE HISTORY OF RELATED DISEASE. James L. Doenges. Proc. Soc. Exper. Biol. and Med., New York, vol.38, no.4, pp.536-538, May, 1938.

THE CULTURE AND THE STUDY OF THE STRAINS OF TUBERCULAR BACILLI FROM MONKEYS. A. V. Dolinin. Proc. Moscou Zool. Park, vol.1, pp.305-310.

SARCOCYSTIS IN MACACA MULATTA. I. N. Dubin, Aimee Wilcox. Jour. Parasitology, Lancaster, vol.33, no.2, pp.151-153, 1947.

A SIMPLE METHOD FOR COLLECTING ADULT FILARIAL PARASITES FROM MUSCLE TISSUES OF MONKEYS. Lawrence H. Dunn. Jour. Parasitology, vol.18, pp.111-112, Dec.7, 1931.

MULTICEPS SERIALIS INFESTATION IN A BABOON. REPORT OF A CASE EXHIBITING MULTIPLE CONNECTIVE TISSUE CYSTIC MASSES. Stephen R. Elek, Leonard E. Finkelstein. Zoologica, New York, vol.24, pt.3, pp.323-328, pls.1-2, Nov.2, 1939.

TETRATHYRIDIUM SP. IN SYKES' MONKEY (CERCOPITHECUS ALBIGULARIS) FROM GIZA ZOOLOGICAL GARDENS, EGYPT. M. A. E. Ezzat, S. M. Gaafar. Jour. Parasitol., Lancaster, vol.37, no.4, pp.392-394, Aug., 1951.

POLIOMYELITIS IN THE CYNOMOLGUS MONKEY. H. K. Faber, R. J. Silverberg, Luther Dong. Jour. Exper. Med., Balto., vol.88, no.1, pp.65-72, July 1, 1948.

SPONTANEOUS YELLOW FEVER IN RHESUS MONKEYS IN THE ABSENCE OF MOSQUITOES. G. M. Findlay, F. O. MacCallum. Nature, Lond., vol.144, no. 3642, p.332, Aug.19, 1939.

IMMUNIZATION OF RHESUS MONKEYS AGAINST MALARIAL INFECTION (P. KNOWLESI) WITH KILLED PARASITES AND ADJUVANTS. Jules Freund, K. J. Thomson, Harriet E. Sommer, Annabel W. Walter, Edna L. Schenkein. Science, Lancaster, n.s., vol.102, no.2643, pp. 202-204, Aug.24, 1945.

MONKEYS IN RELATION TO YELLOW FEVER IN BWAMBA COUNTY, UGANDA. A. J. Haddow, K. C. Smithburn, A. F. Mahaffy, J. C. Bugher. Roy. Soc. Trop. Med. and Hygiene, Lond., vol.40, no.5, pp.677-700, figs.4, May, 1947.

POLIOMYELITIS IN THE CYNOMOGLUS MONKEY FOLLOWING ORAL INOCULATION. H. A. Howe, David Bodian. Amer. Jour. Hygiene, Lancaster, vol.98, no.1, pp.99-106, July, 1948.

EXPERIMENTAL YELLOW FEVER IN THE MACACUS RHESES. N. Paul Hudson. Amer. Jour. Pathology, vol.4, no.5, pp. 395-429, pls.20, Sept., 1928.

DENTAL LESIONS IN BABOONS FROM THE SOCIETY'S GARDENS. W. Warwick James, N. A. Barnicot. Proc. Zool. Soc. Lond., vol.119, pt.3, pp.743-753, fig.1, pl.5, Nov.22, 1949.

STUDIES ON ACUTE DISSEMINATED ENCEPHALOMYELITIS PRODUCED EXPERIMENTALLY IN RHESUS MONKEYS. III. Elvin A. Kabat, Abner Wolf, Ada A. Bezer. Jour. Exper. Med., Balto., vol. 88, no.4, pp.417-426, pls.22, Oct.1, 1948.

INTESTINAL PROTOZOA OF MONKEYS. John F. Kessel. Univ. California Publ. Zool., vol.31, pp.275-306, pls.12-13, Aug. 11, 1928.

THE ORAL AMOEBA OF MONKEYS. Chas. A. Kofoid, Herbert G. Johnstone. Univ. California Publ. Zool., vol.33, no.18, pp. 379-382, pls.41-42, Aug.26, 1930.

YELLOW FEVER VIRUS ENCEPHALITIS IN AFRICAN AND ASIATIC MONKEYS. Wray Lloyd, A. F. Mahaffy. Amer. Jour. Trop. Med., vol.16, no.1, pp.73-75, Jan., 1936.

YELLOW FEVER VIRUS ENCEPHALITIS IN AFRICAN AND ASIATIC MONKEYS. O. R. McCoy. Amer. Jour. Trop. Med., vol.16, no.1, pp.73-75, Jan., 1936.

COMPARATIVE SUSCEPTIBILITY OF CYNOMOLGUS AND OTHER MONKEY SPECIES TO POLIOMYELITIS VIRUS BY THE INTRACEREBRAL AND ORAL ROUTES. J. L. Melnick, Herdis von Magnus. Amer. Jour. Hygiene, Lancaster, vol.48, no.1, pp.107-112, July, 1948.

IMMUNIZATION OF MONKEYS WITH FORMALIN INACTIVATED POLIOMYELITIS VIRUSES. Isabel M. Morgan. Amer. Jour. Hygiene, Lancaster, vol.48, no.3, pp.381-393, Nov., 1948.

EXPERIMENTAL PERTUSSIS IN THE MONKEY (MACACA MULATTA). E. A. North, E. V. Keogh, R. Christie, G. Anderson. Australian Jour. Exper. Biol. and Med. Sci., Adelaide, vol.18, pt.2, pp.125-129, June, 1940.

EVIDENCE OF HEALED HUNGEROSTEOMALACIA (LATE RICKETS) IN A GREEN MONKEY, CERCOPITHECUS SABAEUS. Joseph Pick. Zoologica, New York, vol. 28, pt.3, nos.15-19, pp.145-148, pl.1, Dec.6, 1943.

EFFECT OF BLOOD AND OXYGEN ON PLASMODIUM KNOWELESI INFECTION IN MONKEYS. R. H. Rigdon. Amer. Jour. Hygiene, Lancaster, vol.48, no.2, pp.147-157, Sept., 1948.

STUDIES ON THE MORPHOLOGY OF THE E. HISTOLYTICA-LIKE AMOEBAE FOUND IN MONKEYS. Herbert Salis. Jour. Parasitology, Lancaster, vol.27, no.4, pp.327-341, pls.2, Aug., 1941.

NOTES ON DISEASES AND HEALED FRACTURES OF WILD APES AND THEIR BEARING ON THE ANTIQUITY OF PATHOLOGICAL CONDITIONS IN MAN. Adolph H. Schultz. Bull. Hist. Med., Balto., vol. 7, no.6, pp.571-582, pls.3, June, 1939.

MATERIALS ON COMPARATIVE PATHOLOGY OF OSSEOUS TUBERCULOSIS IN MONKEYS. W. H. Stefko. Proc. Moscou Zool. Park, vol.1, pp.293-304, 1940.

THE TRANSMISSION OF YELLOW FEVER TO MACACUS RHESUS. Adrian Stokes, J. H. Bauer, N. Paul Hudson. Amer. Med. Assoc., vol.90, pp.253-254, Jan.28, 1928.

(ON ASCARIASIS IN MONKEYS.) Zur Spulwurmkrankheit der Affen. Lothar Szidat. Der Zoologische Garten, Leipzig (N.F.), vol.2, pt.4-6, pp.127-130, 1929.

A SEXUAL REPRODUCTION OF PLASMODIUM KNOWLESI IN RHESUS MONKEYS. William H. Taliaferro, Lucy Graves Taliaferro. Jour. Inf. Disease, Chicago, vol.85, no.2, pp.107-125, Sept.-Oct., 1949.

DENTAL LESIONS IN BABOONS FROM THE SOCIETY'S GARDENS. James W. Warwick, N. A. Banicot. Proc. Zool. Soc. Lond., vol.119, pt.3, pp.743-753, pls.1-5, Nov.22, 1949.

Economic Importance

RHESUS MONKEYS (MACACA MULATTA) FOR AMERICAN LABORATORIES. C. R. Carpenter. Science, Lancaster, n.s., vol. 92, no.2387, pp.284-286, Sept.27, 1940.

BOTANICAL MONKEYS. E. J. H. Corner. Annual Report of Director of Gardens, Straits Settlements, Singapore for year 1937, pp.5-7, 1938.

BABOONS AS MARAUDERS. THEIR HAVOC NEVER ENDS IN SOUTH AFRICA, WHERE THE GOVERNMENT HAS SET A BOUNTY ON THEIR HIDES. Lawrence G. Green. New York Times, p.25, Nov.27, 1938.

MONKEYS TRAINED AS HARVESTERS. INSTANCES OF A PRACTICE EXTENDING FROM REMOTE TIMES TO THE PRESENT. E. W. Gudger. Nat. Hist., vol.23, pp.272, 279, 4 figs., May-June, 1923.

MONKEYS AS COCONUT PICKERS. Carl D. La Rue. Science, n.s., vol.50, p.187, Aug.22, 1919.

Embryology

AN UNFERTILIZED TUBAL OVUM FROM MACACUS RHESUS. Edgar Allen. Anat. Rec., vol.37, pp.351-356, Feb.25, 1928.

FURTHER EXPERIMENTS WITH AN OVARIAN HORMONE IN THE OVARIECTOMIZED ADULT MONKEY, MACACUS RHESUS, ESPECIALLY THE DEGENERATIVE PHASE OF THE EXPERIMENTAL MENSTRUAL CYCLE. Edgar Allen. Amer. Jour. Anat., vol.42, pp.467-487, illus., Nov.15, 1928.

THE FATE OF THE CORPORA LUTEA AND THE NATURE OF THE CORPORA ABERRANTIA IN THE RHESUS MONKEY. George W. Corner. Carnegie Inst. Washington (Contrib. Embryol., vol.30, no.192), publ. 541, pp.85-96, figs.5, pls.7, Dec.31, 1942.

FURTHER ATTEMPTS TO CAUSE OVULATION BY MEANS OF GONADOTROPES IN THE ADULT RHESUS MONKEY. Carl G. Hartman. Carnegie Inst. Washington (Contrib. Embryol., vol.30, no.194), publ.541, pp.111-126, pls.2, Dec.31, 1942.

THE FIRST MATURATION DIVISION OF THE MACAQUE OVUM. Carl G. Hartman, George W. Corner. Carnegie Inst. Wash. Publ.538 (Contrib. to Embryology, no.179), pp.1-6, pls.2, 1941.

THE FOLLICLE-STIMULATING EFFECT OF PIG ANTERIOR LOBE ON THE MONKEY OVARY. Carl G. Hartman, R. R. Squier. Anat. Record, vol.50, no.3, pp. 267-272, illus., Sept., 1931.

THE FETAL HEART RATE IN THE MONKEY (MACACUS RHESUS). C. G. Hartman, R. R. Squier, O. L. Tinklepaugh. Proc. Soc. Exper. Biol. and Med., vol.28, pp. 285-288, table, 1930.

DEVELOPMENT OF THE MACAQUE EMBRYO. Chester H. Heuser, George L. Streeter. Carnegie Inst. Washington Publ. 538 (Contrib. to Embryology, no.181), pp. 15-55, pls.33, 5 figs., 1941.

THE PRE-NATAL DEVELOPMENT OF THE GREY LANGUR, SEMNOPITHECUS PRIAM THERSITES. W. C. Osman Hill. Spolia Zeylanica, Ceylon Jour. Sci., sec.B, Zool. and Geol., vol.20, pt.2, pp.211-251, figs. 6, pls.8-12, Apr.15, 1937.

ORGANIZATION, HISTOLOGY, AND CIRCULATORY PATTERN OF THE NEAR-TERM PLACENTA OF THE GUINEA BABOON, PAPIO CYNOCEPHALUS, DEMAREST. Howard H. Hillemann. Oregon State Monographs, Zool., no.9, pp.20, pls.13, June, 1955.

EARLY CLEAVAGE STAGES OF THE EGG OF THE MONKEY (MACACUS RHESUS). Warren H. Lewis, Carl G. Hartman. Carnegie Inst. Washington, Publ. 443, Contr. to Embryol., vol.24, pp.189-201, pls.2, figs.6, 1933.

TUBAL OVA OF THE RHESUS MONKEY. Warren H. Lewis, Carl G. Hartman. Washington Publ.538 (Contrib. to Embryol., no.180), pp.7-14, pl.1, 1941.

ON THE LIPIN AND PIGMENT IN THE CORPUS LUTEUM OF THE RHESUS MONKEY. I. Rossman. Carnegie Inst. Washington (Contrib. Embryol., vol.30, no.193), publ.541, pp.97-110, pls.3, Dec.31, 1942.

FETAL GROWTH AND DEVELOPMENT OF THE RHESUS MONKEY. Adolph H. Schultz. Carnegie Inst. Washington Publ.538 (Contrib. to Embryol., no.155) pp.71-97, figs.5, pls.2, 1941.

OBSERVATIONS ON COLOBUS FETUSES. Adolph H. Schultz. Bull. Amer. Mus. Nat. Hist., vol.49, pp.443-457, 5 figs., Sept. 5, 1924.

(POSITION OF THE PLACENTA OF SEMNOPITHECUS PRUINOSUS OF BORNEO.) Placentaranlage des Lutung (Semnopithecus pruinosus, von Borneo). Emil Selenka. Sitzungsber. Math. Phys. Cl., Kgl. Bayer Akad. Wiss., vol.1, pp.3-14, pls.2, figs. 12, 1901.

EMBRYO. George L. Streeter. Bio-Morphosis, Leipzig, vol.1, nos.3-4, pp.325-326, 1938.

ON THE PLACENTATION OF THE MACAQUE (MACACA MULATTA), FROM THE TIME OF IMPLANTATION UNTIL THE FORMATION OF THE DEFINITIVE PLACENTA. George B. Wislocki, George L. Streeter. Carnegie Inst. Washington Publ. 538 (Contrib. to Embryol., no.160), pp. 1-66, fig.1, pls.13, 1941.

EMBRYOLOGY OF THE RHESUS MONKEY. S. Zuckerman. Nature, Lond., vol.149, no.3787, p.592, May 30, 1942.

Europe

THE BARBARY APES OF GIBRALTAR. D. England. Zoo Life, Lond., vol.10, no.3, pp.67-69, illus., Autumn, 1955.

THE "APES" OF GIBRALTAR. W. T. Hornaday. Zool. Soc. Bull., vol.23, pp. 102-103, Sept., 1920.

Experimental Biology, Biochemistry

PRECOCIOUS SEXUAL DEVELOPMENT FROM ANTERIOR HYPOPHYSIS IMPLANTS IN A MONKEY. Edgar Allen. Anat. Rec., vol.39, pp.315-323, illus., Aug.25, 1928.

(AN OBSERVATION ON CASTRATED MONKEYS IN SCHOENBRUNN.) Eine Beobachtung an Affenkastraten in Schoenbrunn. Otto Antonius. Der Zoologische Garten, Leipzig (N.F.), vol.2, pts.4-6, pp.134-135, 1929.

THE EFFECTS OF PROLONGED OESTRIOL ADMINISTRATION UPON THE SEX SKIN OF MACACA MULATTA. Carl Bachman, J. B. Collip, Hans Selye. Proc. Roy. Soc.,

Lond., ser.B, vol.117, no.802, pp.16-21, pls.1-4, Feb.4, 1935.

THE USE OF GONADOTROPIC HORMONES IN THE ADULT RHESUS MONKEY. Carl G. Hartman. Bull. Johns Hopkins Hospital, vol.63, no.6, pp.351-371, tables 4, pls.3, Dec., 1938.

NON-EFFECT OF IRRADIATION OF THE HYPOPHYSIS IN STERILE MONKEY FEMALES. Carl G. Hartman, Charles Smith. Proc. Soc. Exper. Biol. and Med., vol.39, pp.330-332, table 1, 1938.

ASSAYS OF URINE FROM RHESUS MONKEYS FOR PREGNANDIOL AND OTHER STEROIDS. R. E. Marker, Carl G. Hartman. Jour. Biol. Chemistry, Balto., vol.133, no.2, pp.529-537, table 1, Apr., 1940.

OBSERVATIONS ON THE BIOCHEMISTRY OF THE GENITAL TRACT OF THE FEMALE MACAQUE PARTICULARLY DURING THE MENSTRUAL CYCLE. H. B. Van Dyke, Graham Ch'en. Amer. Jour. Anat., vol.58, no.2, pp.473-492, pls.1-3, Mar.15, 1936.

THE SENSITIVITY OF THE NEW-BORN MONKEY TO OESTRIN. S. Zuckerman, G. van Wagenen. Jour. Anat. Lond., vol. 69, pt.4, pp.497-500, pl.1, July, 1935.

Fossils

A NEW FOSSIL BABOON FROM THE TRANSVAAL. R. Broom. Ann. Transvaal Mus., vol.18, no.4, pp.393-396, figs.2, May 25, 1936.

THE SOUTH AFRICAN PLEISTOCENE CERCOPITHECID APES. R. Broom. Ann. Transvaal Mus., Cambridge, England, vol.20, pt.2, pp.89-100, figs.6, Apr.22, 1940.

A NEW FOSSIL BABOON FROM THE CAVES AT POTGIETERSRUST. R. Broom, J. S. Jensen. Ann. Transvaal Mus., Cambridge, vol.20, pt.4, pp.337-340, figs.2, Oct.18, 1946.

A NEW SUBFOSSIL BABOON FROM KROMDRAAI, TRANSVAAL. R. Broom, J. T. Robinson. Ann. Transvaal Mus., Pretoria, vol.21, pt.3, pp.242-243, May 9, 1950.

A NEW TYPE OF FOSSIL BABOON GORGOPITHECUS MAJOR. R. Broom, J. T. Robinson. Proc. Zool. Soc., Lond., vol. 119, pt.2, pp.379-386, pl.1, Aug.17, 1949.

OREOPITHECUS: HOMUNCULUS OR MONKEY? Loren C. Eiseley. Sci. American, 194 (6): 91-100, illus., June, 1956.

THE FOSSIL CERCOPITHECOIDEA OF SOUTH AFRICA. Leonard Freedman. Ann. Transvaal Mus., 23 (2): 121-262, illus., Nov.29, 1957.

A PRELIMINARY ACCOUNT OF THE BABOON REMAINS FROM TAUNGS. J. H. S. Gear. South Afr. Jour. Sci., Pretoria, vol. 23, pp.731-747, Dec., 1926.

OREOPITHECUS BAMBOLII GERVAIS. Johannes Huerzeler. Verh. Naturf. Ges. Basel, 69 (1): 1-48, Jan., 1958.

A NEW FOSSIL PRIMATE FROM STERKFONTEIN, KRUGERSDORP, TRANSVAAL. Trevor R. Jones. South Afr. Jour. Sci., Johannesburg, vol.33, pp.709-728, figs.4, Mar., 1937.

A NEW SPECIES OF FOSSIL BABOON FROM POTGIETERSRUST. J. W. Kitching. South Afr. Jour. Sci., vol.50, no.3, pp. 66-69, Oct., 1953.

NOTES ON SIMOPITHECUS OSWALDI FROM THE TYPE SITE. L. S. B. Leakey. Jour. East Africa Nat. Hist. Soc., Nairobi, vol. 17, nos.1-2 (75-76), pp.39-44, pls.9-13, Mar., 1943.

Habits, Behavior

REACTIONS OF A RHESUS MONKEY TO EMBALMED CORPSES. John E. Bauman. Jour. Mam., vol.26, no.4, pp.437-438, Feb.12, 1946.

LEAF EATERS. MONKEYS WITH HYSTERICAL RESPONSES AND POCKETS IN THEIR STOMACHS. Nancy Bode. San Diego Zoonooz, vol.24, no.12, pp.2-3, illus., Dec., 1951.

BEHAVIOUR OF MONKEYS WHEN ATTACKED. A. A. Dunbar Brander. Jour. Bombay Nat. Hist. Soc., vol.41, no.1, p. 165, 1939.

NOTE ON KIDNAPPING BY BONNET MONKEY. Robert Bullerman. Jour. Mam., vol. 31, no.1, pp.93-94, Feb.21, 1950.

FURTHER OBSERVATIONS OF THE NIGHT-RESTING HABITS OF MONKEYS IN A SMALL AREA ON THE EDGE OF THE SEMLIKI FOREST, UGANDA. A. P. Buxton. Jour. Animal Ecol., Lond., vol.20, no.1, pp.31-32, May, 1951.

OBSERVATIONS ON THE DIURNAL BEHAVIOR OF THE REDTAIL MONKEY (CERCOPITHECUS ASCARNIUS SCHMIDTI) IN A SMALL FOREST IN UGANDA. A. P. Buxton. Jour. Animal Ecol., 21: 25-58, 1952.

FRIENDLY ENEMIES. THE STORY OF TWO EAST INDIAN MONKEYS THAT LED AN EXCITING LIFE FAR FROM THEIR NATIVE HOME. William H. Carr. Junior Nat. Hist. Mag., vol.3, no.5, pp.4-7, illus., July, 1938.

SOCIAL STRUCTURE OF A COLONY OF MACACA MULATTA. M. R. A. Chance. British Jour. Animal Behaviour, vol.4, no. 1, pp.1-13, Jan., 1956.

(NOTE ON THE BEHAVIOR OF TWO LONG-TAILED MONKEYS FROM HOEST IN CAPTIVITY.) Note sur le comportement de deux Cercopithèques de l'Hoest en captivité. P. Dandelot. Mammalia, Paris, vol.20, no.3, pp.330-331, illus., Sept., 1956.

A DAY WITH KENNETH. Sam Dunton. Animal Kingdom, New York Zool. Soc., vol.57, no.6, pp.180-181, Dec., 1954.

SPEED IN THE LANGUR. Robert K. Enders. Jour. Mam., vol.27, no.2, pp. 174-175, May 14, 1946.

SHAM LOUSE-PICKING, OR GROOMING, AMONG MONKEYS. H. E. Ewing. Jour. Mam., vol.16, no.4, pp.303-306, Nov., 1935.

A BUNCH OF BABOONS THAT WERE TOO MUCH FOR A LEOPARD. G. S. F. Fitzpatrick. Field, Lond., vol.156, no.4061, p.588, Figs.2, Oct.25, 1930.

SOME FACTS CONCERNING THE SOCIAL LIFE OF CHACMA BABOONS IN CAPTIVITY. Joseph Gillman. Jour. Mam., vol.20, no.2, pp.178-181, May, 1939.

TOE-SUCKING IN BABOONS: A CONSIDERATION OF SOME OF THE FACTORS RESPONSIBLE FOR THIS HABIT. Joseph Gillman. Jour. Mam., vol.22, no.4, pp. 395-402, 1 pl., Nov.14, 1941.

TOE SUCKING IN THE BABOON. Joseph Gillman. S. African Jour. Sci., Johannesburg, vol.37, p.250, Feb., 1941.

SOCIAL BEHAVIOR OF PRIMATES. I. SOCIAL FACILITATION OF FEEDING IN THE MONKEY AND ITS RELATION TO ATTITUDES OF ASCENDANCE AND SUBMISSION. H. F. Harlow, H. C. Yudin. Jour. Comp. Psychol., vol.16, no.1, pp. 171-185, Aug., 1933.

THE MODE OF CARRYING THE TAIL IN LEAF-MONKEYS. W. C. Osman Hill. Ceylon Jour. Sci., sect.B, Zool. and Geol., Spolia Zeylanica, vol.21, pt.1, pp.66-67, figs.1, Feb.10, 1938.

BEHAVIOUR OF MONKEYS UNDER LIGHT OF POOR VISIBILITY. David Katz. Proc. Zool. Soc., Lond., vol.107, ser.A, Gen. and Exper., pt.2, pp.183-186, July, 1937.

ADAPTIVE MOTOR HABITS OF THE MACACUS RHESUS UNDER EXPERIMENTAL CONDITIONS. N. Kohts. Sci. Mem. Mus. Darwinianum, Moscow, 368 pp., 24 pls., 1928.

ALARM CALL OF LANGOORS. W. M. Logan-Home. Jour. Bombay Nat. Hist. Soc., vol.33, no.4, p.971, Oct.15, 1929.

MONKEY BUSINESS. A. Loveridge. Nat. Hist., New York, vol.51, no.4. pp.176-177, 196, illus., Apr., 1943.

THE NIGHT-RESTING HABITS OF MONKEYS IN A SMALL AREA ON THE EDGE OF THE SEMLIKI FOREST, UGANDA. A STUDY IN RELATION TO THE EPIDEMIOLOGY OF SYLVAN YELLOW FEVER. W. H. R. Lumsden. Jour. Animal Ecol., Lond., vol.20, no.1, pp.11-30, May, 1951.

FIGHTING CAPACITY OF THE GREY LANGUR. Alyson Minchin. Field, Lond., vol.168, no.4375, p.1086, Oct.31, 1936.

MONKEYS AND THE FEAR OF SNAKES. P. Chalmers Mitchell. Proc. Zool. Soc. Lond., pp.347-348, June, 1922.

LETTER ON THE HABITS OF CYNOCEPHALUS ANUBIS. L. A. Monteiro. Proc. Zool. Soc. Lond., pt.31, p.238, 1863.

FIELD OBSERVATIONS ON THE DAILY ROUTINE AND SOCIAL BEHAVIOUR OF COMMON INDIAN MONKEYS, WITH SPECIAL REFERENCE TO THE BONNET MONKEY (MACACA RADIATA GEOFFROY). Angela Nolte. Jour. Bombay Nat. Hist. Soc., vol.53, no.2, pp.177-184, Dec., 1955.

BABOONS ATTACKING CHILDREN. G. A. S. Northcote. Jour. East Africa and Uganda Nat. Hist. Soc., no.16, pp.60-61, Feb., 1921.

CONCERNING BABOONS. A. Blayney Percival. Jour. East Africa and Uganda Nat. Hist. Soc., no.14, p.415, July, 1919.

BEHAVIOUR OF MONKEYS WHEN ATTACKED. E. G. Phythian-Adams. Jour. Bombay Nat. Hist. Soc., vol.41, no. 3, p.653, Apr., 1940.

FUR-PICKING IN MONKEYS AS AN ACT OF ADORNMENT. O. L. Tinklepaugh. Jour. Mam., vol.12, no.4, pp.430-431, Nov., 1931.

THE SELF-MUTILATION OF A MALE MACACUS RHESUS MONKEY. O. L. Tinklepaugh. Jour. Mam., vol.9, no.4, pp.293-300, Nov., 1928.

BEHAVIOR AND MATERNAL CARE OF THE NEWBORN MONKEY (MACACA MULATTA--"M. RHESUS"). O. L. Tinklepaugh, C. G. Hartman. Jour. Genetic Psych., vol.40, no.2, pp.257-286, pls.1-3, June, 1932.

HANDEDNESS IN THE RHESUS MONKEY. J. M. Warren. Science, vol.118, no.3073, pp.622-623, illus., Nov.20, 1953.

ISCHIAL CALLOSITIES VS. SLEEPING ADAPTATIONS. S. L. Washburn. Amer. Jour. Phys. Anthropol., n.s., 15 (2): 269-276, June, 1957.

TAKING THE SUN, YOUNG SOUTH AFRICAN HUSSAR MONKEY. . . BASKS IN HER CAGE. Life, New York, vol.27, no.6, p. 61, illus., Aug.8, 1949.

Hematology

(MORPHOLOGY OF THE BLOOD OF THE LOWER CATARRHINE MONKEYS OF THE SUBFAMILY CERCOPITHECINAE.) Morfologiia krovi nizshikh uzkononosykh obez' ian iz podsemeistva martyshkovykh (Cercopithecinae). O. P. Grigorova, M. F. Nesturkh. Trudy Moskovskogo Zooparka (Proc. Moscow Zool. Park), vol.3, pp.95-124, illus., 1946.

BLOOD GROUPS IN PHILIPPINE MONKEYS. Hayashi Hirano. Philippine Jour. Sci., vol. 47, no.4, pp.449-462, 1932.

THE CIRCULATION IN THE TAIL OF A MONKEY (CERCOPITHECUS PYGERYTHRUS). T. T. Hongo, C. P. Luck. Jour. Physiol., Cambridge, England, vol.122, no.3, pp.570-581, Dec., 1953.

(ON THE SPECIFIC WEIGHT OF MONKEY BLOOD.) Ueber das spezifische Gewicht des Affenblutes. B. M. Solowiev. Biol. Zentralblatt, vol.50, pp.116-119, 1930.

(NEW BLOOD-GROUP EXPERIMENTS ON MONKEYS IN THE YEAR 1932.) Neue Blutgruppenuntersuchungen an Affen im Jahre 1932. Hans Weinert. 3. Mitteilung. Zeitschr. f. Rassenphysiologie, Munich, vol.6, no.2, pp.75-81, Aug.15, 1933.

SERUM RELATIONSHIPS WITHIN THE FAMILY CERCOPITHECIDAE. S. Zuckerman, Ann E. Sudermann. Jour. Exper.

Biol., Lond., vol.12, no.3, pp.222-228, July, 1935.

Islands

(THE NEWLY DISCOVERED ORANG PENDEK.) De nieuw-ontdekte orang pendek. K. W. Dammerman. Tropische Natuur, Buitenzorg, vol.21, no.8, pp.123-131, figs. 3, Aug., 1932.

THE ORANG PENDEK OR APE-MAN OF SUMATRA. K. W. Dammerman. Proc. Fourth Pacific Sci. Congress Java, Batavia-Bandoeng, 1929, vol.3, Biol. Papers, pp. 121-126, figs.2, 1930.

THE MONA MONKEY ON THE ISLAND OF ST. KITTS. Ned Hollister. Proc. Biol. Soc. Wash., vol.25, p.93, May 4, 1912.

A NEW RACE OF THE LEAF MONKEY PRESBYTIS AYGULA (L.) FROM DELI, NORTH-EASTERN SUMATRA. D. A. Hooijer. Proc. Koninklijke Nederl. Akad. Wetenschappen, Amsterdam, vol.51, no.2, pp.234-237, 1948.

THE PROBOSCIS-MONKEY FROM BORNEO. F. A. Jentink. Leyden Mus., vol.23, no. 16, pp.113-122, pls.1-5, Feb., 1902.

SOME OBSERVATIONS RELATING TWO SEMNOPITHECUS SPECIES FROM THE MALAYAN ARCHIPELAGO. F. A. Jentink. Notes Leyden Mus., vol.11, no.42, pp.215-218, pl.9, Sept., 1889.

A MYTH! THE APE-MAN OF SUMATRA. Arthur Keith. The Illustrated London News, p.9, figs.4, July 2, 1932.

A NEW MACAQUE FROM AN ISLAND OFF THE EAST COAST OF BORNEO. Remington Kellogg. Proc. Biol. Soc. Wash., vol.57, pp.75-76, Oct.31, 1944.

A NOTE ON JAVANESE MONKEYS. C. Boden Kloss. Ann. and Mag. Nat. Hist., ser.10, vol.6, no.36, p.697, Dec., 1930.

(BRIEF COMMUNICATIONS: THE DISTRIBUTION OF MONKEYS ON CELEBES.) Kleinere Mitteilungen. Die Verbreitung der Affen auf Celebes. Paul Matschie. Naturwissenschaftliche, n.F., vol.1 (vol. 17), no.12, pp.141-142, Dec., 1901.

A NEW MONKEY FROM DUTCH NORTH-EAST BORNEO. Gerrit S. Miller, Jr. Proc. Biol. Soc. Wash., vol.47, pp.15-18, Feb.9, 1934.

OBSERVATIONS ON THE MACAQUES. I. THE BORNEAN APE. James Murie. Proc. Zool. Soc. Lond., pp.721-728, figs.5, 1872.

REMARKS ON SOME MONKEYS RECEIVED FROM ST. KITTS, WEST INDIES. P. L. Sclater. Proc. Zool. Soc. Lond., pp.79-80, 1866.

(BIOLOGICAL OBSERVATIONS ON JAVA MACAQUES, MACACUS IRUS F. CUV. (CYNOMOLOGUS L.).) Biologische Beobachtungen an Javamakaken, Macacus irus F. Cuv. (cynomologus L.). A. Spiegel. Zool. Anzeiger., vol.81, pp.37-65, figs.1-10, Apr.1, 1929.

(OBSERVATIONS AND INVESTIGATIONS OF JAVA MACAQUES.) Beobachtungen und Untersuchungen an Javamakaken. A. Spiegel. Zool. Garten, Leipzig, (N.F.), vol.20, nos. 4-5, pp.227-270, illus., 1954.

DESCRIPTION OF A NEW BORNEAN MONKEY BELONGING TO THE GENUS SEMNOPITHECUS. Oldfield Thomas. Proc. Zool. Soc. Lond., pp.159-160, pl.16, May 19, 1889.

DESCRIPTION OF A NEW MONKEY OF THE GENUS SEMNOPITHECUS FROM NORTHERN BORNEO. Oldfield Thomas. Proc. Zool. Soc. Lond., pp.582-583, pl. 41, Nov.15, 1892.

DESCRIPTION OF A REMARKABLE NEW SEMNOPITHECUS FROM SARAWAK. Oldfield Thomas. Ann. and Mag. Nat. Hist. (6), vol.10, no.60, pp.475-477, Dec., 1892.

TWO NEW MACAQUES FROM W. JAVA. Oldfield Thomas, R. C. Wroughton. Ann. and Mag. Nat. Hist. (8), vol.3, no.16, pp. 380-381, Apr., 1909.

(THE DISCOVERY OF THE ORANG PENDEK.) De vondst van den Orang Pendek. De Sumatra Post, Medan, figs., June 7, 1932.

(PHOTOGRAPHS OF THE ORANG LETJO.) Foto's van den orang letjo. De onbekende bewoner der wildernis. De Deli Courant, Medan, figs., June 9, 1932.

Pelage, Skin, Coloration

EXHIBIT OF A WHITE OR SEMI-ALBINO COLOBUS MONKEY FROM MOUNT KENYA. Guy Dollman. Proc. Linnean Soc. Lond., Sess.150, 1937-38, pt.2, pp.115-116, Mar., 1938.

SOME NOTES ON THE COLORATION OF BABOON SKIN. James Forbes. Anat. Rec., vol.65, no.1, pp.51-54, illus., Apr.25, 1936.

ALBINISM IN CEYLON MACAQUES. W. C. Osman Hill. Spolia Zeylanica, Ceylon Jour. Sci., vol.17, pt.3, pp.248-250, pl. 39, May 19, 1933.

A NOTE ON INTEGUMENTAL COLOURS WITH SPECIAL REFERENCE TO THE GENUS MANDRILLUS. W. C. Osman Hill. Saeugetierk. Mitteil., Stuttgart 3(4): 145-151, Oct.1, 1955.

(THE HAIR COLOR OF THE BLACK LANGUR.) De haarkleur van den zwarten loetoeng. W. Keers. Tropische Natuur, vol.23, no.11, pp.225-226, Nov., 1934.

COLOR EVOLUTION IN GUEREZA MONKEYS. R. Lydekker. Proc. Zool. Soc. Lond., vol.2, pp.325-329, figs.54-58, Apr.5, 1906.

THE COLORATION OF THE NEWLY-BORN YOUNG OF THE CAPPED LANGUR (TRACHYPITHECUS PILEATUS (BLYTH) ). C. McCann. Jour. Bombay Nat. Hist. Soc., vol.43, no.3, pp.513-514, Dec., 1942.

ALBINISM IN A MALE VERVET MONKEY, CERCOPITHECUS PYGERYTHRUS. G. W. H. Schepers. South African Jour. Sci., Johannesburg, vol.36, pp.351-358, figs.2, Dec., 1939.

ERYTHRISM IN MONKEYS OF THE GENUS CERCOPITHECUS. STUDIES OF VARIATION IN MAMMALS. Ernst Schwarz. Ann. and Mag. Nat. Hist., ser.9, vol.19, pp. 151-155, Jan., 1927.

EXHIBITION OF, AND REMARKS UPON, A SKIN OF CERCOPITHECUS STAIRSI FROM MOMBASA. P. L. Sclater. Proc. Zool. Soc. Lond., pt.3, p.609, Oct.1, 1896.

OBSERVATIONS UPON SOME MONKEY SKINS FROM FERNANDO PO. G. R. Waterhouse. Proc. Zool. Soc. Lond., pt. 9, p.71, 1841.

ON SOME SKINS OF TWO SPECIES OF MONKEYS FROM SIERRA LEONE. G. R. Waterhouse. Proc. Zool. Soc. Lond., pt. 6, p.61, 1838.

AN UNUSUAL ARRANGEMENT OF HAIR IN A RHESUS MONKEY (MACACA MULATTA). S. Zuckerman. Proc. Zool. Soc. Lond. for 1934, pt.4, pp.727-729, pl.1, Jan., 1935.

Physiology

PUBERTY AND ADOLESCENCE IN A BABOON (PAPIO PORCARIUS). Joseph Gillman. South African Jour. Sci., Johannesburg, vol.36, pp.406-407, Dec., 1939.

THE ENDOCRINE BASIS FOR THE BODY WEIGHT CHANGES AND THE METABOLISM OF WATER IN THE ADULT FEMALE BABOON (PAPIO URSINUS). Joseph Gillman, Christine Gilbert. Amer. Jour. Anat., Phila., 98 (2): 231-272, Mar., 1956.

LONGEVITY IN A MACAQUE. W. C. Osman Hill. Spolia Zeylanica, Ceylon Jour. Sci., ser.B, Zool. and Geol., vol.20, pt.2, pp. 255-256, Apr.15, 1937.

SOME OBSERVATIONS ON THE MECHANISM OF DOUBLE VISION. A PRELIMINARY PAPER. P. Lineback. Anat. Rec., vol.38, pp.193-201, illus., Apr.25, 1928.

RELATIVE GROWTH OF THE LIMB SEGMENTS AND TAIL IN THE MACAQUES. Hyman Lumer, Adolph H. Schultz. Human Biol., Balto., vol.13, no.3, pp.283-305, figs.8, Sept., 1941.

MENSTRUATION IN INTRAOCULAR ENDOMETRIAL TRANSPLANTS IN THE RHESUS MONKEY. J. Eldridge Markee. Carnegie Inst. Washington publ.518 (Contrib. to Embryology, vol.28, no.177), pp.219-308, fig.1, pls.7, Aug.15, 1940.

(SOME OBSERVATIONS ON THE CEREBRAL TRUNK OF THE BABOON; PHYSIOLOGICAL INTERPRETATION.) Quelques observations sur le tronc cérébral du babouin; interprétation physiologique. Walther Riese. Archiv. Suisses Neurol. et Psychiat., Zurich, vol. 66, pp.377-379, 1950.

EARLY PHASES IN THE DEVELOPMENT OF THE MOTOR MECHANISMS OF THE SOUTH AFRICAN BABOON, PAPIO PORCARIUS. G. W. H. Schepers. South African Jour. Sci., Johannesburg, vol.37, pp.228-238, figs.2, Feb., 1941.

(NOTES ON THE YOUNG DEVELOPMENT OF THE YELLOW-GREEN MARMOSET (CERCOPITHECUS CALLITRICHUS IS. GEOFFR.).) Notizen zur Kenntnis der Jugendentwicklung der Gelbgruenen Meerkatze (Cercopithecus callitrichus Is. Geoffr.). M. Schlott. Zool. Garten, Leipzig, 21 (4): 270-274, 1956.

GROWTH AND DEVELOPMENT OF THE PROBOSCIS MONKEY. Adolph H. Schultz. Bull. Mus. Comp. Zool., Cambridge, vol. 89, no.6, pp.279-314, fig.7, pls.4, Mar., 1942.

GROWTH OF THE BRAIN IN THE RHESUS MONKEY. S. Zuckerman, R. B. Fisher. Proc. Zool. Soc. Lond., vol.107, ser.C., no.11, p.49, Oct.26, 1937; ser.B., pt.4, pp. 529-538, tables 9, Jan., 1938.

GROWTH-CHANGES IN THE SKULL OF THE BABOON, PAPIO PORCARIUS. S. Zuckerman. Proc. Zool. Soc. Lond., vol.55, pt.3, pp.843-873, 1 pl., 1926.

Psychology

(ON IMITATION IN THE MONKEYS (MACACUS RHESUS). Ueber die Nachahmung bei den Affen (Macacus rhesus). G. Aronowitsch, B. Chotin. Zeitschr. Morph. u. Oekol. Tiere., vol.16, pp.1-25, 6 figs., Dec.17, 1929.

(ON PERCEPTION COMPLEXES AND ELEMENTS IN A LOWER APE (NEMESTRINUS NEMESTRINUS), ALSO AN EXPERIMENT REGARDING SIGHT IN MONKEYS, II.) Ueber Wahrnehmungskomplexe und Wahrnehmungselemente bei einem niederen Affen (Nemestrinus nemestrinus) (zugleich ein Versuch ueber das Sehen der Affen, II). J. A. Bierens de Haan. Zool. Jahrbuecher, Abt. fuer allgemeine Zool. und Physiol. der Tiere, vol.42, pp.272-306, 5 figs., 1925.

(TRAINING ATTEMPTS WITH A STRONGLY MOTOR MONKEY.) Dressurversuche an einem stark motorischen Affen. J. A. Bierens de Haan, J. Th. Meyknecht. Biol. Zentralbl., Leipzig, vol.54, nos.3-4, pp. 185-195, 1934.

(ON SELECTION ACCORDING TO RELATIVE AND ABSOLUTE CHARACTERISTICS (EXPERIMENTS WITH MONKEYS AND BEES).) Ueber Wahl nach relativen und absoluten Merkmalen (Versuche an Affen und Bienen). J. A. Bierens de Haan. Zeitschr. f. Vergleichende Physiologie, vol.7, pp.462-487, 4 figs., May 25, 1928.

THE LIMITS OF LEARNING IN RHESUS MONKEYS. Harriett Anderson Fjeld. Genetic Psychology Monographs, Clark Univ., Worcester, Mass., vol.15, nos.5-6, tables 1-30, pp.369-537, May-June, 1934.

THE DEVELOPMENT AND REGRESSION OF REFLEXES, POSTURES, AND PROGRESSION IN YOUNG MACAQUE. Marion Hines. Carnegie Inst. Wash.(Contrib. Embryol., vol.30, no.196), publ.541, pp. 153-210, figs.9, pls.4, Dec.31, 1942.

THE MATURATION OF "EXCITABILITY" IN THE PRECENTRAL GYRUS OF THE YOUNG MONKEY (MACACA MULATTA). Marion Hines, E. P. Boynton. Carnegie

Inst. Wash., publ.518 (Contrib. to Embryology, vol.28, no.178), pp.311-451, figs.31, Aug.15, 1940.

STUDIES OF CEREBRAL FUNCTION IN PRIMATES. IV. THE EFFECTS OF FRONTAL LOBE LESIONS ON THE DELAYED ALTERNATION HABIT IN MONKEYS. C. F. Jacobsen, H. W. Nissen. Jour. Comp. Psychology, vol.23, no.1, pp.101-112, figs.4, Feb., 1937.

THE EQUIVALENCE OF STIMULI IN THE BEHAVIOR OF MONKEYS. Heinrich Kluever. Jour. Genetic Psych., vol.39, pp.3-27, figs.1-5, 1931.

ON THE COUNTING ABILITY OF A MONKEY (MACACUS CYNOMOLGUS). Ryo Kuroda. Jour. Comp. Psychol., vol.12, no.2, pp.171-180, Aug., 1931.

(A CONTRIBUTION TO THE INTELLIGENCE TESTING OF THE LOWER APES.) Ein Beitrag zur Intelligenzpruefung niederer Affen. H. Nellman, W. Trendelenburg. Zeitschr. f. vergleichende Physiol., vol. 4, pp.142-200, illus., July 31, 1926.

EXPERIMENTAL STUDY IN ABSTRACTION IN MONKEYS. G. Revesz. Jour. Comp. Psych., vol.5, pp.293-343, 1925.

A PRELIMINARY EXPERIMENT ON ABSTRACTION IN A MONKEY. E. W. Robinson. Jour. Comp. Psychol., vol.16, no.1, pp.231-236, Aug., 1933.

(DOES THE MACAQUE GRASP LOGICAL CONNECTIONS?) Le macaque saisit-il le rapport logique? M. Tellier. Bull. Soc. Roy. Sci. Liége, no.11, pp.227-231, 1932.

AN EXPERIMENTAL STUDY OF REPRESENTATIVE FACTORS IN MONKEYS. O. L. Tinklepaugh. Jour. Comp. Psych., vol.8, pp.197-236, illus., 1928.

(BEHAVIOR OF THE BABOON (MACACA SYLVANUS L.) RELATIVE TO AN ELECTRIC CLOSURE SYSTEM.) Comportement du magot (Macaca sylvanus L.) vis-à-vis d'un système de clôture électrique. A. Urbain, P. Bullier, J. Weill. Mammalia, Paris, vol.14, nos.1-2, pp.7-10, Mar.-June, 1950.

(THE ANALYTIC CHARACTER OF PERCEPTION IN THE MACAQUE.) Le caractère analytique de la perception chez le Macaque. L. Verlaine. Bull. Cl. Sci. Acad. Roy. Belgique, ser.5, vol.21, no.7, pp.744-758, 1935.

(INTELLIGENCE OF LOWER MONKEYS.) L'intelligence des Singes inférieurs. L. Verlaine, P. Gallis. Mém. Soc. Roy. Sci. de Liége, ser.3, vol.17, fasc.3, pp.1-48, 1932.

DISCRIMINATION BY THE MONKEY OF TEMPORAL SEQUENCES OF VARYING NUMBER OF STIMULI. H. Woodrow. Jour. Comp. Psych., vol.9, pp.123-157, 3 figs., Apr., 1929.

TEMPORAL DISCRIMINATION IN THE MONKEY. H. Woodrow. Jour. Comp. Psych., vol.8, pp.395-427, 3 figs., Dec., 1928.

Reproductive Biology

THE TIME OF OVULATION IN THE MENSTRUAL CYCLE OF THE MONKEY, MACACUS RHESUS. E. Allen. Soc. Exper. Biol. and Med. Proc., vol.23, pp.381-383, 1926.

SEXUAL EXCITABILITY AS RELATED TO THE MENSTRUAL CYCLE IN THE MONKEY. Josephine Ball, Carl G. Hartman. Amer. Jour. of Obstetrics and Gynecology, St. Louis, vol.29, no.1, pp.1-4, Jan., 1935.

INTERBREEDING AMONG SOME BORNEAN 'LEAF-MONKEYS OF THE GENUS PITHECUS. E. Banks. Proc. Zool. Soc. Lond. for 1929, pt.4, pp.693-695, Feb., 1930.

THE FOLLICULAR PHASE OF THE MENSTRUAL CYCLE IN THE RHESUS MONKEY. George W. Bartelmez. Science, Lancaster, vol.111, no.2887, p.454, Apr.28, 1950.

SEXUAL BEHAVIOR OF FREE RANGING RHESUS MONKEYS (MACACA MULATTA). I. SPECIMENS, PROCEDURES AND BEHAVIORAL CHARACTERISTICS OF ESTRUS. C. R. Carpenter. Jour. Comp. Psychol., Balto., vol.33, no.1, pp.113-142, Feb., 1942.

SEXUAL BEHAVIOR OF FREE RANGING RHESUS MONKEYS (MACACA MULATTA). II. PERIODICITY OF ESTRUS, HOMOSEXUAL, AUTOEROTIC AND NONCONFORMIST BEHAVIOR. C. R. Carpenter. Jour. Comp. Psychol., Balto., vol.33, no. 1, pp.143-162, Feb., 1942.

IN THE RHESUS MONKEY OVULATION IS SPONTANEOUS. G. W. Corner. Proc. Soc. Exper. Biol. and Med., vol.29, pp. 598-599, 1932.

THE MENSTRUAL CYCLE OF THE MALAYAN MONKEY, MACACA IRUS. G. W. Corner. Anat. Record, vol.52, no.4, pp.401-410, figs.1-3, May 25, 1932.

OVULATION AND MENSTRUATION IN MACACUS RHESUS. G. W. Corner. Carnegie Inst. Washington, publ.332, Contribution to Embryology, no.75, 29 pp., 6 pls., 2 figs., 1924.

THE RELATION BETWEEN MENSTRUATION AND OVULATION IN THE MONKEY. ITS POSSIBLE SIGNIFICANCE FOR MAN. G. W. Corner. Jour. Amer. Med. Assoc., vol.89, no.22, pp.1838-1840, Nov.26, 1927.

THE REPRODUCTIVE CYCLE OF THE RHESUS MONKEY. G. W. Corner. Amer. Scientist, Easton, vol.39, no.1, pp.50-73, illus., Jan., 1951.

THE TIME OF OVULATION IN THE MONKEY. Edmond J. Farris. Anat. Record, Phila., vol.95, no.3, pp.337-345, July, 1946.

THE OESTROUS CYCLE OF THE BABOON. H. S. Gear. South African Jour. Sci., Pretoria, vol.23, pp.706-712, Dec., 1926.

ON HYBRIDISM BETWEEN MACACUS NEMESTRINUS AND M. CYNOMOLGUS. Thomas G. Gentry. Proc. Acad. Nat. Sci. Phila., p.122, 1872.

ALLEGED BIRTH OF TRIPLETS IN THE RHESUS MONKEY. Carl G. Hartman. Science, n.s., vol.87, no.2268, p.552, June 17, 1938.

BIRTH OF A TWO-HEADED MONSTER IN THE RHESUS MONKEY. Carl G. Hartman. Science, Lancaster, n.s., vol.98, no.2551, p.449, Nov.19, 1943.

THE BREEDING SEASON IN MONKEYS, WITH SPECIAL REFERENCE TO PITHECUS (MACACUS) RHESUS. Carl G. Hartman. Jour. Mam., vol.12, no.2, pp. 129-142, May, 1931.

PELVIC (RECTAL) PALPATION OF THE FEMALE MONKEY, WITH SPECIAL REFERENCE TO THE ASCERTAINMENT OF OVULATION TIME. Carl G. Hartman. Amer. Jour. Obstetrics and Gynecology, vol.26, no.4, pp.600-608, figs.5, Oct., 1933.

THE PERIOD OF GESTATION IN THE MONKEY, MACACUS RHESUS. Carl G. Hartman. Science, n.s., vol.67, p.15, Jan.6, 1928.

THE PERIOD OF GESTATION IN THE MONKEY, MACACUS RHESUS, FIRST DESCRIPTION OF PARTURITION IN MONKEYS, SIZE AND BEHAVIOR OF THE YOUNG. Carl G. Hartman. Jour. Mam., vol.9, no.3, pp.181-194, pls.2, Aug., 1928.

A READILY DETECTABLE SIGN OF OVULATION IN THE MONKEY. Carl G. Hartman. Science, n.s., vol.68, pp.452-453, Nov.9, 1928.

STUDIES IN THE REPRODUCTION OF THE MONKEY MACACUS (PITHECUS) RHESUS, WITH SPECIAL REFERENCE TO MENSTRUATION AND PREGNANCY. Carl G. Hartman. Publ.433, Carnegie Inst. Wash., pp.1-161, figs.39, pls.6, Aug., 1932.

STUDIES ON REPRODUCTION IN THE MONKEY AND THEIR BEARING ON GYNECOLOGY AND ANTHROPOLOGY. Carl G. Hartman. Endocrinology, Los Angeles, vol.25, no.5, pp.670-682, figs.12, table 1, Nov., 1939.

(FURTHER OBSERVATIONS ON BIRTH IN THE MONKEY MACACUS RHESUS.) Weitere Beobachtungen ueber die Geburt beim Affen Macacus rhesus. Carl G. Hartman, O. L. Tinklepaugh. Archiv fuer Gynaekologie, Berlin, vol.149, no.1, pp.21-37, figs.3, 1932.

THE MENSTRUAL CYCLE OF THE TOQUE MACAQUE (MACACA SINICA LINN.), WITH OBSERVATIONS ON ITS UTERINE STRUCTURE, COMPARED WITH THAT OF OTHER MACAQUES. W. C. Osman Hill. Ceylon Jour. Sci., Colombo, sect.D, Med. Sci., vol.5, pt.2, pp.21-36, figs.2, pls.3, Sept. 4, 1939.

A NEW LEAF-MONKEY HYBRID (TRACHYPITHECUS OBSCURUS FLAVICAUDA MALE X SEMNOPITHECUS PRIAM THERSITES FEMALE). W. C. Osman Hill. Ceylon Jour. Sci., sect.B, Zool. and Geol., Spolia Zeylanica, Colombo, vol.21, pt.3, pp.265-275, figs.3, tables 2, pls.32-33, Oct.24, 1939.

ON A HYBRID LEAF-MONKEY; WITH REMARKS ON THE BREEDING OF LEAF-MONKEYS IN GENERAL. W. C. Osman Hill. Ceylon Jour. Sci., sect.B, Zool and Geol., vol.20, pt.1, pp.135-148, fig.1, pl.3, Aug.5, 1936.

THE CONTRACTIONS OF THE MONKEY UTERUS AT TERM. A. C. Ivy, Carl G. Hartman, Arthur Koff. Amer. Jour. Obstetrics and Gynecology, St. Louis, vol.22, no.3, pp.388-399, illus., Sept., 1931.

THE MENSTRUAL CYCLE OF THE PRIMATES. PART II. SOME EFFECTS OF OESTRIN ON BABOONS AND MACAQUES. A. S. Parkes, S. Zuckerman. Jour. Anat., Cambridge, vol.65, pt.2, pp.272-276, pls. 1-2, Jan., 1931.

(RESEARCH ON THE MENSTRUAL CYCLE OF HAMADRYAS PAPION L.) Recherche du cycle menstruel de l'Hamadryas papion L. Jean Seguy, Paul Bullier. Archiv. Mus. Nat. Hist. Nat., Paris, ser.6, vol.12, pp. 309-311, June, 1935.

TWINS IN GREEN GUENON. Ken Stott, Jr. Jour. Mam., vol.27, no.4, p.394, Nov.25, 1946.

BEHAVIORAL ASPECTS OF PARTURITION IN THE MONKEY (MACACUS RHESUS). O. L. Tinklepaugh, Carl G. Hartman. Jour. Comp. Psychology, vol.11, no.1, pp. 63-98, figs.1-3, Oct., 1930.

MENSTRUAL BLEEDING AND GENITAL SWELLING IN MIOPITHECUS (CERCOPITHECUS) TALAPOIN. Michael Tomilin. Proc. Zool. Soc. Lond., ser.A, vol.110, pp.43-45, pl.1, 1940.

THE DISTRIBUTION OF LIPOIDS IN THE GENITAL TRACT OF THE MONKEY AT DIFFERENT STAGES OF THE MENSTRUAL CYCLE. H. B. van Dyke, Graham Chen. Amer. Jour. Ana., Phila., vol.66, no.3, pp.411-423, 2 pls., May 15, 1940.

EARLY MATING AND PREGNANCY IN THE MONKEY. G. Van Wagenen. Endocrinology, Los Angeles, vol.40, no.1, pp. 37-43, 1947.

THE MENSTRUAL CYCLE OF THE PRIMATES. PART III. THE ALLEGED BREEDING-SEASON OF PRIMATES, WITH SPECIAL REFERENCE TO THE CHACMA BABOON (PAPIO PORCARIUS). S. Zuckerman. Proc. Zool. Soc. Lond., pt.1, pp. 325-343, Apr.14, 1931.

THE MENSTRUAL CYCLE OF THE PRIMATES. PART V. THE CYCLE OF THE BABOON. S. Zuckerman, A. S. Parkes. Proc. Zool. Soc. Lond., pt.1, pp.139-191, pls.18, figs.3, Mar., 1932.

Reproductive Organs

THE CERVIX UTERI OF THE RHESUS MONKEY. Orlo H. Clark, George W. Corner. Anat. Record, vol.63, no.3, pp.247-252, figs.6, Oct., 1935.

THE CYCLICAL CHANGES IN THE EXTERNAL GENITAL ORGANS OF THE BABOON, (P. PORCARIUS). Joseph Gillman. South African Jour. Sci., Johannesburg, vol.32, pp.342-355, figs.3, pl.1, Nov., 1935.

A CASE OF SUPERNUMERARY NIPPLE IN MACACUS RHESUS, WITH REMARKS UPON THE BIOLOGY OF POLYMASTIA AND POLYTHELIA. Carl G. Hartman. Jour. Mam., vol.8, no.2, pp.96-106, pl.10, May, 1927.

SUPERNUMERARY NIPPLE IN A MACAQUE. W. C. Osman Hill. Spolia Zeylanica, Ceylon Jour. Sci., ser.B, Zool. and Geol., vol.20, pt.2, p.257, Apr.15, 1937.

THE SEXUAL SKIN OF THE GELADA BABOON (THEROPITHECUS GELADA). L. Harrison Matthews. Trans. Zool. Soc. Lond., 28 (7): 543-545, illus., Sept., 1956.

AN ABNORMAL BABOON SACRUM FOUND AT LINDEQUES DRIFT. J. J. Prag. South African Jour. Sci., Johannesburg, vol.32, pp.356-359, fig.1, Nov., 1935.

CYCLIC VARIATIONS IN THE SPONTANEOUS CONTRACTIONS OF THE FALLOPIAN TUBE OF MACACUS RHESUS. Daniel L. Seckinger, George W. Corner. Anat. Record, Phila., vol.26, no.4, pp. 299-301, Nov., 1923.

SUPERNUMERARY MAMMAE, WITH SPECIAL REFERENCE TO THE RHESUS MONKEY. Harold Speert. Quart. Rev. Biol., Balto., vol.17, no.1, pp.59-68, figs. 6, Mar., 1942.

STUDIES ON THE INNERVATION OF THE REPRODUCTIVE ORGANS OF MACACUS RHESUS. Lawrence R. Wharton. Anat. Record, vol.68, no.1, suppl. 1, pp.43-61, figs.7, Apr.25, 1937.

THE REPRODUCTIVE SYSTEMS. George B. Wislocki. Chapter 11 (pp. 231-247) of: The Anatomy of the Rhesus Monkey (19 Contributors, pp. ix, 383 illus.), edited by Carl G. Hartman and William L. Straus, Jr. Baltimore: The Williams and Wilkins Co., Dec.1, 1933.

SUPERNUMERARY NIPPLES IN MONKEYS. S. Zuckerman. Jour. Mam., vol.16, no.3, pp.229-230, Aug., 1935.

THE SEXUAL SKIN OF THE RHESUS MONKEY. S. Zuckerman, C. van Wagenen, R. H. Gardiner. Proc. Zool. Soc. Lond., vol. 108, ser.A, Gen and Exper., pt.2, pp.385-401, pls.1-6, July, 1938.

Taxonomy

(RECTIFICATION, DESCRIPTION, AND DEDUCTION ON THE GENUS CYNOPITHECUS IS. GEOFFR.) Rettifica, descrizioni sul genere Cynopithecus Is. Geoffr. Oscar De Beaux. Boll. Mus. Zool. e Anat. Comp. Univ. Genova, vol.9, no.28, pp.1-35, 1 pl., 1929.

(ON THE CLASSIFICATION AND NOMENCLATURE OF THE LASIOPYGIDAE.) Sobre la clasificacion y nomenclatura de los Lasiopygidae. Angel Cabrera. Revista Real Acad. Cienc. Exactas, Fisicas y Nat. Madrid, pp.1-7, Dec., 1914.

(MAMMALS. SYSTEMATIC STUDY BY SPECIES. MACACA SYLVANUS.) Mammifères. Étude systématique par spèces. Macaca sylvanus. Robert Didier, Paul Rode. Paul Lechevalier, Paris, no.3, pp.1-13, pls.4, 1936.

DESCRIPTION OF A NEW SPECIES OF MONKEY OF THE GENUS CERCOPITHECUS. D. G. Elliot. Ann. and Mag. Nat. Hist. Lond., ser.8, vol.4, pp.274-275, Sept., 1909.

DESCRIPTION OF NEW SPECIES OF MONKEY OF THE GENERA CERCOPITHECUS AND PAPIO. D. G. Elliot. Ann. and Mag. Nat. Hist. Lond., ser.8, vol.4, pp. 305-306, Sept., 1909.

DESCRIPTIONS OF SOME NEW SPECIES OF MONKEYS OF THE GENERA PITHECUS AND PYGATHRIX COLLECTED BY DR. W. L. ABBOTT AND PRESENTED TO THE UNITED STATES NATIONAL MUSEUM. D. G. Elliot. Proc. U.S. Nat. Mus., vol. 38, no.1751, pp.343-352, Aug.6, 1910.

THE GENERIC NAME CERCOPITHECUS. D. G. Elliot. Bull. Amer. Mus. Nat. Hist. N. Y., vol.30, art.14, pp.341-342, Dec.21, 1911.

ON SIMIA SPHINX LINNAEUS. D. G. Elliot. Ann. and Mag. Nat. Hist. Lond., ser.8, vol.4, pp.417-418, Nov., 1909.

THE STATUS OF PAPIO RHODESIAE (HAAGNER) 1918. L. Freedman. Ann. Transvaal Mus., 22 (3): 267-270, pl.22, Jan.24, 1955.

AN ANNOTATED SYSTEMATIC LIST OF THE LEAF-MONKEYS. W. C. Osman Hill. Ceylon Jour. Sci., sect.B, Zool. and Geol., Spolia Zeylanica, Colombo, vol.21, pt.3, pp.277-305, figs.2, pls.34-38, Oct.24, 1939.

THE TYPE OF SEMNOPITHECUS THERSITES BLYTH. W. C. Osman Hill. Spolia Zeylanica, Ceylon Jour. Sci., sec.B, Zool. and Geol., vol.20, pt.2, pp.207-209, pl. 7, Apr.15, 1937.

THE NOMENCLATURE AND SUBSPECIES OF THE PURPLE-FACED LANGUR, WITH NOTES ON THE OTHER LANGURS INHABITING CEYLON. Martin A. C. Hinton. Ann. and Mag. Nat. Hist., ser.9, vol.11, pp.506-515, Apr., 1923.

ON THE NOMENCLATURE OF THE SOUTH INDIAN LONG-TAILED MACAQUES. M. A. C. Hinton, R. C. Wroughton. Jour. Bombay Nat. Hist. Soc., vol.27, pp.813-815, 1921.

ON THE CAPPED LANGUR (PITHECUS PILEATUS, BLYTH) AND ITS ALLIES. Martin A. C. Hinton. Jour. Bombay Nat. Hist. Soc., vol.29, pp.73-83, Apr.20, 1923.

THE GENERIC NAME OF THE MANDRILL AND BABOONS WITH NOTES ON SOME OF THE GENERA OF BRISSON, 1792. A. T. Hopwood. Proc. Zool. Soc. Lond., vol. 117, nos.2-3, p.533, 1947.

ON THE SEMNOPITHECUS PYRRHUS HORSFIELD. F. A. Jentink. Notes Leyden Mus., vol.14, no.20, pp.119-121, pls.3-4, Jan., 1892.

ON TWO NEW SPECIES OF CERCOPITHECUS. F. A. Jentink. Notes Leyden Mus., vol.8, no.11, pp.55-57, Dec., 1885.

TAXONOMIC STATUS OF THE CELEBES ASHY-BLACK MONKEY--A REMARKABLE CASE OF CONVERGENCE. H. Khajuria. Records Indian Mus., vol.50, pts.3-4, pp.301-305, 1953.

ON A NEW GUEREZA (COLOBUS ANGOLENSIS SANDBERGI) AND REMARKS ON OTHER BLACK AND WHITE GUEREZAS. Einar Loennberg. Arkiv. Zool. Upsala, vol.4, no.15, pp.1-13, figs.1-3, Apr.28, 1908.

LASIOPYGA (CERCOPITHECUS) WEIDHOLZI SP. NOV. Ludwig Lorenz-Liburnau. Ann. Nat. Mus. Wien., vol.36, separate, pp.1-3, 1 pl., 1922.

AN UNDESCRIBED GUEREZA. R. Lydekker. Ann. and Mag. Nat. Hist., ser.7, vol.16, Oct., 1905.

MACACA VERSUS PITHECUS AS THE GENERIC NAME OF THE MACAQUES. Marcus W. Lyon, Jr. Proc. Biol. Soc. Wash., vol.28, p.179, Nov.29, 1915.

(SOME SPECIES OF THE GENUS COLOBUS.) Einige Formen der Gattung Colobus. Paul Matschie. Sitz. Ber. Gesell. Naturf. Freunde, Berlin, Jahrg.1900, no.8, pp.181-189, Oct.16, 1900.

CERCOPITHECUS WOLFI. A. B. Meyer. Notes Leyden Mus., vol.13, no.3, pp.63-64, 1890.

THE GROUPS AND NAMES OF MACAQUES. Gerrit S. Miller, Jr. Chapter 1 (pp.1-9) of: The Anatomy of the Rhesus Monkey (19 contributors, pp. ix, 383, illus), edited by Carl G. Hartman and William L. Straus, Jr. Balto: The Williams and Wilkins Co., Dec. 1, 1933.

THE LANGURS OF THE PRESBYTIS FEMORALIS GROUP. Gerrit S. Miller, Jr. Jour. Mam., Balto., vol.15, no.2, pp. 124-137, May 15, 1934.

THE MONKEYS OF THE MACACA NEMESTRINA GROUP. Gerrit S. Miller, Jr. U.S. Nat. Mus. Proc., Wash., vol.29, p. 555-563, pl.13-22, 1906.

DESCRIPTION OF A NEW SPECIES OF CERCOPITHECUS (C. TANTALUS). W. Ogilby. Proc. Zool. Soc. Lond., pt.9, p. 33, 1841.

ON A NEW SPECIES OF MONKEY (PAPIO MELANOTUS). W. Ogilby. Proc. Zool. Soc. Lond., pt.7, p.31, 1839.

ON TWO NEW SPECIES OF BABOON. W. Ogilby. Proc. Zool. Soc. Lond., pt.11, pp.10-12, 1843.

DESCRIPTION OF A NEW SPECIES OF MONKEY OF THE GENUS CERCOPITHECUS. R. I. Pocock. Proc. Zool. Soc. Lond., pp.158-160, pl.10, Sept., 1908.

A MONOGRAPHIC REVISION OF THE MONKEYS OF THE GENUS CERCOPITHECUS. R. I. Pocock. Proc. Zool. Soc. Lond., pp.677-746, Oct.8, 1907.

A NEW GENUS OF MONKEYS. R. I. Pocock. Proc. Zool. Soc. Lond., pt.1, pp.330-331, Mar., 1924.

THE SYSTEMATIC VALUE OF THE GLANS PENIS IN MACAQUE MONKEYS. R. I. Pocock. Ann. and Mag. Nat. Hist., ser.9, vol.7, pp.224-229, 2 figs., Mar., 1921.

(ON A NEW SPECIES OF APE (CERCOPITHECUS ALBOTORQUATUS).) Sur une Guenon d'espece nouvelle (Cercopithecus albotorquatus). E. Pousargues. Bull. Mus. Hist. Nat. Paris, vol.12, no.2, pp.55-58, 1896.

(ON THE AFFINITIES OF CERCOPITHECUS ERYTHROGASTER (GRAY).) Sur les affinites du Cercopithecus erythrogaster (Gray). E. Pousargues. Mem. Soc. Zool. France, Paris, vol.7, pp.69-72, 1894.

NOTES ON CERCOPITHECUS HAMLYNI POCOCK. Henry C. Raven, John Eric Hill. Amer. Mus. Novitates, New York, no.1177, pp.6, figs.3, July 27, 1942.

ON A NEW SPECIES OF MONKEY (SEMNOPITHECUS OBSCURUS). J. Reid. Proc. Zool. Soc. Lond., pt.5, p.14, 1837.

(CATALOG OF MAMMAL TYPES OF THE NATIONAL MUSEUM OF NATURAL HISTORY. ORDER PRIMATES, SUBORDER OF SIMIANS.) Catalogue des types de mammifères du Muséum National d'Histoire Naturelle. Ordre des Primates, sous-ordre des Simiens. P. Rode. Bull. Mus. Nat. Hist. Mus. Paris, vol.10, pp.201-251, 1938.

DESCRIPTION OF A NEW BABOON. Lord Rothschild. Ann. and Mag. Nat. Hist., ser.9, vol.10, p.232, Aug., 1922.

(CERCOPITHECUS MITIS WOLF FOR SIMIA LEUCAMPYX FISCHER.) Cercopithecus mitis Wolf fuer Simia leucampyx Fischer. E. Schwartz. Zeitschr. f. Saeugetierkunde, Berlin, vol.8, nos.3-6, p.279, Dec.20, 1933.

(THE FORMS OF THE GENUS ERYTHROCEBUS.) Die formen der Gattung Erythrocebus. E. Schwarz. Sitz.-Ber. Gesellsch. naturforsch. Freunde. Berlin, nos.1-10, pp.24-31, (1926) 1927.

NOTES ON THE CLASSIFICATION OF THE AFRICAN MONKEYS IN THE GENUS CERCOPITHECUS, ERXLEBEN. E. Schwarz. Ann. and Mag. Nat. Hist., Lond., ser.10, vol.1, no.6, pp.649-663, June, 1928.

EXHIBITION OF, AND REMARKS UPON, THE TYPICAL SPECIMEN OF CERCOPITHECUS GRAYI, GRASER. P. L. Sclater. Proc. Zool. Soc. Lond., pt.3, pp.484-485, Oct.1, 1894.

PITHECUS AYGULA FREDERICAE N. SUBSP. H. J. V. Sody. Tropische Natuur, vol.19, no.4, p.68, 1930.

RETENTION OF CERCOPITHECUS, TYPE DIANA, FOR THE GUENONS. C. W. Stiles, Mabelle B. Orleman. Jour. Mam., vol.7, no.1, pp.48-53, Feb., 1926.

CHARACTERS OF A NEW SPECIES OF MONKEY (SEMNOPITHECUS). W. H. Sykes. Proc. Comm. Sci. and Corres. Zool. Soc. Lond., pt.1, pp.105-106, 1830-1831.

ON THE GENERIC NAMES OF CERTAIN OLD-WORLD MONKEYS. Oldfield Thomas. Ann. and Mag. Nat. Hist. (8), vol.17, no. 98, pp.179-181, Feb., 1916.

(CONTRIBUTION TO THE SPECIFIC DISTINCTION OF THE CERCOPITHICANS OF THE DIANE GROUP.) Contribution a la distinction specifique des Cercopitheques du groupe de la Diane. E. L. Trouessart. Bull. Mus. d'Hist. Nat., Paris, no.2, pp. 97-101, figs.2, 1908.

(SYNOPTIC REVISION OF THE GENUS SEMNOPITHECUS AND DESCRIPTION OF SOME RARE OR LITTLE KNOWN SPECIES.) Revision synoptique du genre Semnopitheque (Semnopithecus) et description de quelques especes rares ou peu connues. E. L. Trouessart. Revue et Magasin de Zoologie, pp.12. Rev. et Mag. Zool., Paris, ser.3, vol.7, fasc.1, pp.48-59, 1879.

THE GENERA OF MALAYSIAN LANGURS. Sherwood L. Washburn. Jour. Mam., vol. 25, no.3, pp.289-294, Sept.8, 1944.

A NOTE ON THE SPECIFIC NAME OF THE CHACMA BABOON. L. H. Wells, W. C. Osman Hill. Ann. and Mag. Nat. Nist., Lond., ser.12, vol.6, no.72, pp.955-956, Dec., 1953.

Pongidae

GORILLAS--REAL AND MYTHICAL. Carl E. Akeley. Nat. Hist., vol.23, pp.428-447, 16 figs., Sept.-Oct., 1923.

ON THE GORILLA AND THE CHIMPANZEE. C. R. Aschemeier. Jour. Mam., vol.2, no.2, pp. 90-92, May, 1921.

(STUDIES ON THE NATURAL HISTORY OF THE GORILLA.) Studien zur Naturgeschichte des Gorillas. J. F. Babor, Z. Frankenberger. Biologia Generalis, vol. 6, no.4, pp.553-632, figs.17, pls.38-40, 1930.

CHIMPANZEE NOTES. Belle J. Benchley. Zoonooz, vol.4, no.28, pp.5-6, Apr., 1938.

GORILLA NOTES. Belle J. Benchley. Zoonooz, San Diego, vol.12, no.3, pp.4-5, Mar., 1940.

GORILLAS AGAIN. Belle J. Benchley. Zoonooz, San Diego, vol.22, no.10, pp.3-4, illus., Oct., 1949.

THE IMPOSSIBLE CAN HAPPEN. Belle J. Benchley. Zoonooz, San Diego, vol.13, no. 10, pp.5-7, illus., Oct., 1941.

MY FRIENDS, THE APES. Belle J. Benchley. Little, Brown and Co., Boston, pp. x, 296, illus., 1942.

NEWS NOTES OF INTEREST. Belle J. Benchley. Zoonooz, San Diego, vol.15, no.11, pp.5-7, illus., Nov., 1942.

SOMETHING NEW ABOUT GORILLAS. Belle J. Benchley. Zoonooz, San Diego, vol.17, no.4, pp.3-4, illus., Apr., 1944.

THE LOWLAND GORILLA. Lucien Blancou. Animal Kingdom, New York Zool. Soc., vol.58, no.6, pp.162-169, illus., Dec., 1955.

AMONG GORILLAS. Mary Hastings Bradley. Liberty, New York, vol.2, no.43, pp.29-31, 32, Feb.27, 1926.

HOW TO WEIGH A GORILLA. William Bridges. Animal Kingdom, New York, vol. 49, no.6, pp.200-203, illus., Dec.16, 1946.

(THE HIGHER APES AND THEIR EXPANSION IN THE GEOLOGICAL PAST.) De hoogere apen en hun verspreiding in het geologisch verleden. L. D. Brongersma. Mensch en Maatschappij, Tweemaandelijksh Tijdschrift, Amsterdam, vol.18, nos.3-4, pp.130-140, figs.2, May-July, 1942.

CHIMPANZEES AS WE SEE THEM--A GUIDE TO IDENTIFICATION. Lee S. Crandall. Animal Kingdom, New York Zool. Soc., vol.59, no.1, pp.18, 30-31, Feb., 1956.

AN OBSERVATIONAL STUDY OF TWO CAPTIVE MOUNTAIN GORILLAS (GORILLA BERINGEI). C. R. Carpenter. Human Biology, vol.9, no.2, pp.175-196, pls.3, May, 1937.

THE MANLIKE APES OF JUNGLE AND MOUNTAIN. Elie Cheverlange. Nat. Geog. Mag., Wash., D.C., vol.78, no.2, pp.221-228, pls.1-8, Aug., 1940.

BAMBOO. Roger Conant. Fauna, Phila., vol.1, no.1, pp.7-9, illus., Mar., 1939.

MEET THE CHAMPIONS. Roger Conant. Fauna, Phila., vol.3, no.2, pp.43-49, illus., June, 1941.

THE APES IN ANIMAL SOCIOLOGY. Harold Jefferson Coolidge, Jr. Harvard Alumni Bull., vol.36, no.13, pp.363-366, Dec.22, 1933.

THE ORANG UTAN. K. W. Dammerman. Dutch East Indies, Department van landbouw, nijverheid en handel (Nature Protection in the Netherlands Indies), Dept. Econ. Affairs, Batavia, pp.1-6, illus., 1938.

JOHN HUNTER AND THE EARLY KNOWLEDGE OF THE ANTHROPOID APES. Jessie Dobson. Proc. Zool. Soc. Lond., vol.123, pt.1, pp.1-12, pls.1-4, June 10, 1953.

THE EASTERN OR KIVU GORILLA. J. G. Dollman. Nat. Hist. Mag., Lond., vol.1, no.6, pp.213-216, illus., Apr., 1928.

(ANTHROPOIDS.) Menschen-Affen. Paul Eipper. Natur und Volk, Frankfurt a.M., vol.68, no.7, pp.310-315, illus., July, 1938.

METHODS OF ANESTHETIZING CHIMPANZEES. J. H. Elder. Jour. Pharmacology and Exper. Therapeutics, vol.60, no.3, pp.347-357, fig.1, table 1, July, 1937.

HOME LIFE OF THE HIGHLAND GORILLA. H. F. Fenn. Field, Lond., vol.154, no. 4006, p.509, Oct.5, 1929.

(A CHIMPANZEE PICTURE FROM THE MIDDLE AGES.) Ein Schimpansenbild aus dem Mittelalter. Wilhelm Freudenberg. Zeitschr. f. Saeugetierkunde, vol.4, no. 1, p.64, 1 fig., July 6, 1929.

INTRODUCING SUMAILI. Leonard J. Goss. Animal Kingdom, New York, vol.52, no.4, pp.115-117, illus., Aug.13, 1949.

(Review by Francis Petter of) THE LIFE OF THE ANTHROPOIDS. GORILLAS AND CHIMPANZEES.) La Vie des Anthropoides. Gorilles et Chimpanzes. E. Gromier. Mammalia, Paris, vol.17, no. 1, pp.52-53, Mar., 1953.

(GORILLAS OUTSIDE AFRICA.) Die Gorillas ausserhalb Afrikas. Bernhard Grzimek. Zool. Garten, Leipzig (N.F.), vol.20, nos.2-3, pp.173-185, illus., 1952.

THE CAMEROONS MOUNTAIN. A GENERAL CONSPECTUS. E. F. G. Haig. The Nigerian Field, vol.6, no.3, pp.118-128, pls.2, July, 1937.

ANTHROPOID APES. Robert Hartmann. The International Scientific Series, pp.326, figs.63, 1886.

GORILLA NOTES. PART 5. Edalee Harwell. San Diego Zoonooz, vol.23, no.7, pp.3-5, illus., July, 1950.

(ON THE TRACES OF THE MOUNTAIN GORILLA.) Auf den Spruen des Berg-Gorillas. Arnold Heim. Mitt. Naturf. Gesell. Bern, n.F., 14, 87-96, Feb., 1957.

OBSERVATIONS ON A GIANT SUMATRAN ORANG. W. C. Osman Hill. Amer. Jour. Phys. Anthrop., Phila., vol.24, no.3, pp. 449-510, figs.5, pls.1-5, tables 8, Jan.-Mar., 1939.

JOHN DANIEL OF THE JUNGLE. Ross L. Holman. Fauna, Phila., vol.2, no.4, pp. 82-84, illus., Dec., 1940.

THE SIMIAN BASIS OF HUMAN MECHANICS OR APE TO ENGINEER. Earnest A. Hooten. Antiquity, Gloucester, vol.12, no. 46, pp.196-209, June, 1938.

(GORILLAS.) Les Gorilles. Pierre Ichac. La Nature, no.3025, pp.300-305, illus., May 15, 1938.

(OBSERVATIONS ON THE GIBBON AND OTHER ANIMALS.) Waarnemingen betreffende gibbons en andere dieren. Edward Jacobson. De Tropische Natuur., Buitenzorg, vol.22, no.9, pp.161-164, Sept., 1933.

SOME REMARKS CONCERNING THE ORANG-UTAN. F. A. Jentink. Notes Leyden Mus., vol.17, no.3, pp.17-18, May, 1895.

MAN'S NEAREST KIN IN THE ANIMAL WORLD. Arthur Keith. In J. A. Hammerton, Wonders of Animal Life, London, Waverly Book Co., Ltd., vol.1, pp.1-456, 1930.

GORILLA "TWENTY QUESTIONS." Joan Morton Kelly. Zoonooz, Zool. Soc. San Diego, vol.28, no.6, pp.3-6, illus., June, 1955.

(ANTHROPOID APES IN THE MIDDLE AGES.) Zur Kenntnis der Menschenaffen im Mittelalter. S. Killermann. Zeitschrift f. Saeugetierkunde, vol.6, no.6, pp.227-229, Dec.15, 1931.

(CONTRIBUTIONS TO THE NATURAL HISTORY OF ANTHROPOID APES.) Beitraege zur Naturgeschichte der Menschenaffen. Otto Kleinschmidt. Berajah, Zoographia infinita, Halle a.S., pp.16, figs.10, pl.4, 1934.

(THE MOVEMENT OF THE GIBBON.) Der Gang des Gibbons. Johannes Kuehlhorn. Zeitschrift fuer Saeugetierkunde, Berlin, vol.19, no.3, p.180, Dec.31, 1954.

(GORILLAS.) Les Gorilles. L. Lavauden. La Terre et la Vie (Revue d'Hist. Nat.), vol.2, no.7, pp.395-403, illus., July, 1932.

THE LARGEST AND MOST IMPRESSIVE OF THE MANLIKE APES. Claude W. Leister. New York Zool. Soc., Popular Ser. no.4, pp.7, 1944.

PEOPLING AN ISLAND WITH GIBBON MONKEYS: AN AMBITIOUS WEST INDIAN EXPERIMENT IN BIOLOGY. Constance M. Locke. Illus. London News, vol.193, no. 5182, pp.290-291, illus., Aug.13, 1938.

MAN'S CLOSEST COUNTERPARTS. HEAVYWEIGHT OF MONKEYDOM IS THE "OLD MAN" GORILLA, BY FAR THE LARGEST OF THE FOUR GREAT APES. William M. Mann. Nat. Geog., Wash., D.C., vol.78, no.2, pp.213-220, 229-236, 10 illus., Aug., 1940.

(ABOUT A GORILLA, GORILLA GORILLA REX PYGMAEORUM SCHWARZ, KILLED BY M. BABAULT.) A propos d'un Gorille, Gorilla gorilla rex pygmaeorum Schwarz, tue par M. Babault. P. Mathias. Bull. Mus. Nat. d'Hist. Nat., Paris, vol.34, no.6, pp. 434-436, 1928.

ANTHROPOPITHECUS ERECTUS EUG. DUBOIS. Paul Matschie. Naturwisschaftliche Wochenschrift, Berlin, vol.9, no.10, pp.122-123, Mar. 11, 1894.

(NEW FINDINGS OF CHIMPANZEE INVESTIGATIONS.) Neue Ergebnisse Der Schimpansenforschung. Paul Matschie. Zeitschr. f. Ethnol., vol.51, pp.62-82, 1919.

(REMARKS ON THE GENUS GORILLA.) Bemerkungen ueber die gattung Gorilla. Paul Matschie. Sitz. Ber. Gesell. Naturf. Freunde, Berlin, Jahrg.1904, no.3, pp.45-53, Mar.8, 1904.

(SOME REMARKS ON THE ANTHROPOPITHECUS SPECIMENS KEPT IN BERLIN.) Einige bemerkungen ueber die in Berlin aufbewahrten Exemplare von Anthropopithecus. Paul Matschie. Sitz. Ber. Gesell. Naturf. Freunde, Berlin, Jahrg.1900, no. 2, pp.77-85, Feb.20, 1900.

(SOME REMARKS ON THE CHIMPANZEES.) Einige Bemerkungen ueber die Schimpansen. Paul Matschie. Sitz. Ber. Gesell. Naturf. Freunde, Berlin, Jahrg.1904, no.4, pp.55-69, Apr.12, 1904.

NOTES ON THE COLOURATION AND HABITS OF THE WHITE-BROWED GIBBON OR HOOLOCK (HYLOBATES HOOLOCK HARL.). Charles McCann. Jour. Bombay Nat. Hist. Soc., vol.36, no.2, pp.395-405, pls.2, Apr.15, 1933.

THE GREAT APES. Gerrit S. Miller, Jr. The World is Yours, Listener Aid no.7, Smithsonian Inst. Radio Program, pp.1-10, illus., Broadcast of Nov.12, 1939.

A HYBRID GIBBON. M. F. Ashley Montagu. Jour. Mam., vol.31, no.2, pp.150-153, May 25, 1950.

(A CUBAN CHIMPANZEE. NOTES ON A CHIMPANZEE BORN IN CUBA.) Un chimpancé cubano. Notas sobre un chimpancé nacido en Cuba. Louis Montané. Imprenta "El Siglo XX", Habana, pp.17, figs.4, 1915.

RIVERS AS BARRIERS TO THE DISTRIBUTION OF GIBBONS. R. C. Morris. Jour. Bombay Nat. Hist. Soc., vol.43, no.4, p. 656, Apr., 1943.

EXHIBITION OF SOME SPECIMENS OF YOUNG ANTHROPOID APES. James Murie. Proc. Zool. Soc. Lond., p.157, 1868.

THE APE COLONY IN FLORIDA. Henry W. Nissen. Animal Kingdom, New York, vol.47, no.6, pp.137-142, illus., Nov.-Dec., 1944.

GORILLA NOTES. Edalee Orcutt. San Diego Zoonooz, vol.28, no.3, pp.4-5, Mar., 1950.

ON THE GORILLA (TROGLODYTES GORILLA, SAV.). R. Owen. Proc. Zool. Soc. Lond., pt.27, pp.1-23, 1859.

(A CHIMPANZEE UNLIKE THE OTHERS: PAN PANISCUS.) Un chimpanze pas comme les autres: le Pan paniscus. M. Palmans. Zoo, Antwerp, vol.21, no.3, pp.80-84, illus., Jan., 1956.

RIVERS AS BARRIERS TO THE DISTRIBUTION OF GIBBONS. R. E. Parsons. Jour. Bombay Nat. Hist. Soc., vol.42, no.4, p. 926, Dec., 1941.

(SOME OBSERVATIONS ON CHIMPANZEES.) Quelques observations sur les chimpanzés. E. Passemard. Jour. Psych. Normale et Pathologique, Paris, vol.24, pp.243-253, May 15, 1927.

THE GREAT APES. Wallace Patterson. Smithsonian Inst. Radio Program, The World is Yours, Wash., D.C., no.7, pp. 3-14, Nov.12, 1939.

A FAMILY OF ORANG-UTANS. R. I. Pocock. Field, Lond., vol.151, p.244, illus., Feb.9, 1928.

THE GIBBONS OF THE GENUS HYLOBATES. R. I. Pocock. Proc. Zool. Soc. Lond., pt.3, pp.719-741, illus., Sept., 1927.

THE SIAMANG GIBBON. R. I. Pocock. Field, Lond., vol.151, p.344, illus., Mar. 1, 1928.

GORILLA: THE GREATEST OF ALL APES. H. C. Raven. Natural History, vol.31, no. 3, pp.231-242, figs.12, May-June, 1931.

THE BEHAVIOR OF TWO CAPTIVE SPECIMENS OF THE LOWLAND GORILLA, GORILLA GORILLA (SAVAGE AND WYMAN). B. F. Riess, Sherman Ross, S. B. Lyerly, H. B. Birch. Zoologica, New York Zool. Soc., vol.34, pt.3, no.13, pp.111-118, pls. 1-2, Nov.30, 1949.

(THE GEOGRAPHIC RACES OF THE CHIMPANZEE (PAN SATYRUS L.). OBSERVATIONS ON FACE PIGMENTATION IN PAN SATYRUS VERUS SCHWARZ.) Les races géographiques du chimpanzé (Pan satyrus L.). Observations sur la pigmentation de la face chez Pan satyrus verus Schwarz. P. Rode. Mammalia, Paris, vol.1, no.4, pp.165-177, figs.2, June, 1937.

(STUDY OF AN ADOLESCENT PYGMY CHIMPANZEE (PAN SATYRUS PANISCUS SCHWARZ).) Etude d'un Chimpanze Pygmée adolescent (Pan satyrus paniscus Schwarz). P. Rode. Mammalia, Paris, 5 (2): 50-68, pls.2, 3, 4, June, 1941.

FURTHER NOTES ON ANTHROPOID APES. Walter Rothschild. Proc. Zool. Soc. Lond., pp.465-468, Oct.10, 1906.

ANIMATED DISHMOPS. Jacqueline Schermerhorn. San Diego Zoonooz, vol. 18, no.2, pp.6-7, illus., Feb., 1945.

(EXTREMITY MOVEMENTS OF THE CHIMPANZEE HAND.) Die Extrembewegungen der Schimpansenhand. Hans Schreiber. Gegenbaurs Morphol. Jahrbuch, Leipzig, vol.77, no.1, pp.22-60, figs.11, Feb., 1936.

OBSERVATIONS ON THE GROWTH, CLASSIFICATION AND EVOLUTIONARY SPECIALIZATION OF GIBBONS AND SIAMANGS. Adolph H. Schultz. Human Biol., vol.5, no.2, pp.212-255, figs.9, pl.1, May, 1933; no.3, pp.385-428, figs.10, pls. 2-3, Sept., 1933.

(REMARKS ON THE VARIABILITY AND SYSTEMATICS OF THE CHIMPANZEES.) Bemerkungen zur Variabilitaet und Systematik der Schimpansen. Adolph H. Schultz. Saeugetierk. Mitteil., Stuttgart, vol.2, no. 4, pp.159-163, illus., Oct.1, 1954.

(THE KOULA-NGUIA.) A propos du Koulanguia. Ernst Schwarz. Mammalia, Paris, vol.3, no.2, pp.57-58, June, 1939.

(MAMMALOGICAL NOTES. I. SIMIA.) Notes mammalogiques. I. Simia. A. F. de Seabra. Bull. Soc. Portugaise Sci. Nat., Lisbon, vol.1, fasc.3, pp.115-121, 1907.

A LARGE CHIMPANZEE. D. Seth-Smith. Field, Lond., vol.150, p.818, illus., Nov. 17, 1927.

ANTHROPOID APES I HAVE KNOWN. W. Henry Sheak. Nat. Hist., vol.23, pp.44-55, 5 figs., Jan.-Feb., 1923.

SOME FURTHER OBSERVATIONS ON THE CHIMPANZEE. W. Henry Sheak. Jour. Mam., vol.5, no.2, pp.122-129, May, 1924.

ON THE ANATOMY, PHYSIOLOGY, AND PATHOLOGY OF THE CHIMPANZEE. Charles F. Sonntag. Proc. Zool. Soc. Lond., pt.2, pp.323-429, 3 pls., July, 1923.

ON THE ANATOMY, PHYSIOLOGY, AND PATHOLOGY OF THE ORANG-OUTAN. Charles F. Sonntag. Proc. Zool. Soc. Lond., pp.349-350, 30 text figs., 4 pls., July, 1924.

A IS FOR APES. Ken Stott, Jr. San Diego Zoonooz, vol.23, no.6, pp.3-5, illus., June, 1950.

KERJEUNG. Ken Stott, Jr. San Diego Zoonooz, vol.20, no.5, pp.4-5, illus., May, 1947.

(ON "GOLIATH," THE DRESDEN ORANG.) Ueber den Dresdener Orang "Goliath." C. Strauch, G. Brandes. Zeitschr. f. Saeugetierkunde, vol.2, no.1, pp.78-82, 2 figs., Oct.15, 1927.

THE POSTURE OF THE GREAT APE HAND IN LOCOMOTION, AND ITS PHYLOGENETIC IMPLICATIONS. William L. Straus, Jr. Amer. Jour. Phys. Anthrop., Phila., vol.27, no.2, pp.199-207, fig.1, Sept.30, 1940.

A CHIMP AND HIS WORLD. THE STORY OF WAU, WHICH MEANS CHIMPANZEE IN GREBO DIALECT. G. H. H. Tate. Nature Mag., Washington, D.C., vol.34, no.9, pp.485-488, Nov., 1941.

OUR MOST APE-LIKE RELATIVE. Pierre Teilhard de Chardin. Nat. Hist., New York, vol.40, no.2, pp.514-517, figs.8, Sept., 1937.

(CHRONOLOGY OF RESEARCH ON AND BEHAVIOR IN CAPTIVITY OF THE GORILLA.) Chronologie der Erforschung und Gefangenhaltung des Gorillas. Eduard Paul Tratz. Zool. Garten, Leipzig (N.F.), vol.20, nos.2-3, pp.163-170, 1953.

SKIPPER DISCOVERS THE APES. Irve Tunick. Smithsonian Inst. Radio Program, The World is Yours, no.7, pp.12-14, Nov. 12, 1939.

GEORGE, THE SIAMANG. Frederick A. Ulmer, Jr. Fauna, Phila., vol.1, no.3, pp.51-53, Sept., 1939.

"MAN OF THE WOODS." Frederick A. Ulmer, Jr. Fauna, Phila., vol.8, no.4, pp.98-103, illus., Dec., 1946.

(OBSERVATIONS MADE ON A YOUNG ORANGUTAN BORN IN THE MENAGERIE OF THE JARDIN DES PLANTES.) Observations faites sur un jeune Orang-outan né a la ménagerie du Jardin des Plantes. Ach Urbain, Ed. Dechambre, P. Rode. Mammalia, Paris, vol.5, nos.3-4, pp.82-85, pl.6, Sept.-Dec., 1941.

THE GORILLA--LARGEST LIVING PRIMATE. David P. Willoughby. Sci. Monthly, Lancaster, vol.70, no.1, pp.48-57, figs.7, Jan., 1950.

HE'S AFTER THE REAL KING KONG. A MULAHU? FEW WILL GRANT THE MONSTER EXISTS, BUT GATTI, BAGGER OF BONGO AND OKAPI, FEELS SURE IT DOES, IS NOW AFTER ONE. George Witten. The Family Circle, New York, pp.10, 11, 18, illus., Sept.16, 1938.

ALMOST HUMAN. R. M. Yerkes. The Century Co., pp.278, illus., 1925.

CHIMPANZEES: A LABORATORY COLONY. R. M. Yerkes. Yale Univ. Press, New Haven, pp.xv, 321, figs.24, pls.63, 1943.

(Review by W. C. Allee of) CHIMPANZEES: A LABORATORY COLONY. R. M. Yerkes. Yale University Press, New Haven, 1943, 321 pp., Ecology, Lancaster, vol.25, no.1, pp.122-123, Jan., 1944.

GORILLA CENSUS AND STUDY. R. M. Yerkes. Jour. Mam., vol.32, no.4, pp. 429-436, illus., Nov.19, 1951.

LABORATORY CHIMPANZEES. R. M. Yerkes. Science, Lancaster, n.s., vol. 91, no.2362, pp.336-337, Apr.5, 1940.

THE LIFE HISTORY AND PERSONALITY OF THE CHIMPANZEE. R. M. Yerkes. Amer. Naturalist, Lancaster, Pa., vol. 73, pp.97-112, Mar.-Apr., 1939.

THE GREAT APES: A STUDY OF ANTHROPOID LIFE. R. M. Yerkes, A. W. Yerkes. New Haven, Yale University Press, xix, 652 pp., 1929.

(Review by Gerrit S. Miller, Jr. of) THE GREAT APES: A STUDY OF ANTHROPOID LIFE. R. M. Yerkes, Ada W. Yerkes. Jour. Mam., Balto., vol.10, no.4, pp.360-362, Nov.11, 1929.

LIFE AND MENTALITY OF THE CHIMPANZEE. S. Zuckerman. Nature, Lond., vol. 153, no.3872, pp.65-66, Jan.15, 1944.

MBONGO--MOUNTAIN GORILLA. San Diego Zoonooz, vol.15, no.4, pp.3-4, illus., Apr., 1942.

NOTES ON GORILLA. Nigerian Field, Lond., vol.3, no.3, pp.92-102, July, 1934.

OBSERVATION OF CHIMPANZEES. Nature, Lond., vol.145, no.3684, p.890, June 8, 1940.

Africa

GORILLAS IN A NATIVE HABITAT. W. C. Allee. Ecology., vol.14, no.3, pp.319-320, July, 1933.

(NOTE ON THE BIOLOGY AND HABITAT OF THE GORILLA OF BERINGE.) Note sur la biologie et l'habitat du Gorille de Béringé. Guy Babault. Rev. Francaise Mammal., ser.1, no.2, pp.61-63, pl.1, Dec.7, 1928.

A CHIMPANZEE NEAR AUCHI. J. A. Bey. Nigerian Field, vol.15, no.2, p.94, Apr., 1950.

GORILLAS IN A NATIVE HABITAT. REPORT OF THE JOINT EXPEDITION OF 1929-1930 OF YALE UNIVERSITY AND CARNEGIE INSTITUTION OF WASHINGTON FOR PSYCHOBIOLOGICAL STUDY OF MOUNTAIN GORILLAS (GORILLA BERINGEI) IN PARC NATIONAL ALBERT, BELGIAN CONGO, AFRICA. Harold C. Bingham. Carnegie Inst. Washington, no.426, pp.1-66, figs.5, pls.1-22, Aug., 1932.

(NOTES ON THE MAMMALS OF FRENCH EQUATORIAL AFRICA. THE GORILLA (WITH A PLATE).) Notes sur les mammifères de l'Equateur africain francais. Le Gorille (avec une planche). L. Blancou. Mammalia, Paris, vol.15, no.4, pp.143-151, illus., Dec., 1951.

THE MOUNTAIN GORILLA AND ITS HABITAT IN THE BIRUNGA VOLCANOES. John Blower. Oryx, 3 (6): 287-297, Nov., 1956.

ON THE GORILLA TRAIL. Mary Hastings Bradley. 270 pp., 47 pls., map, D. Appleton and Co., New York, 1922.

STALKING THE MOUNTAIN GORILLA WITH THE CAMERA IN ITS NATURAL HAUNTS: LADY BOUGHTON'S REMARKABLE PHOTOGRAPHS OF BEASTS AND NATIVES IN THE CONGO FORESTS.--I, II. Lady Broughton. Illus. London News, vol. 181, nos.4881-4882, pp.710-713, 756-759, illus., Nov.5, Nov.12, 1932.

GORILLA: TRACKING AND CAPTURING THE APE-MAN OF AFRICA. Ben Burbridge. George G. Harrap and Co., Ltd., Lond., pp.285, pls.32, 1928.

GORILLAS AT HOME. Maurice Burton. Illus. London News, vol.137, no.3580, p. 968, illus., Dec.3, 1955.

THE BLACK DEVIL OF THE ITURI FOREST. Bernard Carp. African Wild Life, Johannesburg, vol.9, no.4, pp.275-280, illus., Dec., 1955.

ON THE TRAIL OF THE MOUNTAIN GORILLA. Kenneth Carr. Field and Stream, New York, vol.47, no.1, pp.34-35, 65, illus., May, 1942.

NOTES ON THE GORILLA. THE AFRICAN REPUBLIC OF LIBERIA AND THE BELGIAN CONGO. BASED ON THE OBSERVATIONS MADE AND MATERIAL COLLECTED DURING THE HARVARD AFRICAN EXPEDITION 1926-1927. Harold J. Coolidge. Cambridge, Harvard Univ. Press, pp.623-635, figs.454-461, map 8, 1930.

PIGMY CHIMPANZEE FROM SOUTH OF THE CONGO RIVER. Harold J. Coolidge, Jr. Amer. Jour. Phys. Anthrop., vol.18, no.1, pp.1-57, figs.4, pls.2, July-Sept., 1933.

ZOOLOGICAL RESULTS OF THE GEORGE VANDERBILT AFRICAN EXPEDITION OF 1934. PT. 4. NOTES ON FOUR GORILLAS FROM THE SANGA RIVER REGION. Harold J. Coolidge, Jr. Proc. Acad. Nat. Sci. Phila., vol.88, pp.479-501, pls.2, fig.1, Oct.23, 1936.

(NOTES ON THE GORILLAS OF THE KIVU VOLCANOES (ALBERT NATIONAL PARK).) Notes sur les Gorilles des Volcans di Kivu (Parc National Albert). J. M. Derscheid. Ann. Soc. Roy. Zool. Belgique, vol.58, pp. 147-159, 1927.

THE OCCURRENCE OF THE CHIMPANZEE IN TANGANYIKA TERRITORY. Guy J. Dollman. Proc. Linn. Soc. Lond., 148th sess. (1935-36), pt.1, pp.15-16, Dec.23, 1935.

ON THE OCCURRENCE OF A LARGE APE IN THE VICINITY OF FERNANDO PO. Louis Fraser. Proc. Zool. Soc. Lond., pt.21, p.13, 1853.

(NOTES ON THE MAMMALS. XVII. ON A CHIMPANZEE OF THE LEFT BANK OF THE CONGO.) Notes sur les mammiferes. XVII. A propos du Chimpanze de la rive gauche du Congo. Serge Frechkop. Bull. Mus. Roy. Hist. Nat. Belgique, Bruxelles, vol.11, no.2, pp.43, figs.24, Mar., 1935.

GORILLA--A HUNT FOR THE MOST POWERFUL AND INTERESTING OF ALL THE BIG APES. Attilio Gatti. Field and Stream, vol.37, no.6, pp.18-20, 66-67, 73, fig.1, Oct., 1932.

FERNANDO PO AS AN APE RESERVE. H. Gifford. Jour. Mam., vol.8, no.4, p.312, Nov., 1927.

GORILLA-LAND. A. I. Good. Nat. Hist., New York, vol.56, no.1, pp.36-37, 44-46, illus., Jan., 1947.

IN QUEST OF GORILLAS. I. ON OUR WAY TO GORILLA-LAND. William K. Gregory. Sci. Monthly, vol.41, no.5, pp. 385-395, illus., Nov., 1935.

IN QUEST OF GORILLAS. II. TANGANYIKA SNAPSHOTS. William K. Gregory. Sci. Monthly, vol.41, pp.505-529, figs. 19, Dec., 1935.

IN QUEST OF GORILLAS. III. KIVU, LAND OF OLYMPIAN CLOUDS. William K. Gregory. Sci. Monthly, vol.42, no.1, pp. 47-61, illus., Jan., 1936.

IN QUEST OF GORILLAS. IV. JOYOUS DAYS IN KIVU COUNTRY. William K. Gregory. Sci. Monthly, vol.42, no.2, pp.111-128, illus., Feb., 1936.

IN QUEST OF GORILLAS. V. ELUSIVE GIANTS OF THE MOUNTAINS. William K. Gregory. Sci. Monthly, vol.42, no.3, pp. 258-279, illus., Mar., 1936.

IN QUEST OF GORILLAS. VI. FAREWELL TO THE GREAT LAKES. William K. Gregory. Sci. Monthly, vol.42, no.2, pp. 325-338, illus., Apr., 1936.

IN QUEST OF GORILLAS. VII. THE LUALABA SHOW-BOAT. William K. Gregory. Sci. Monthly, vol.42, no.5, pp.403-420, illus., May, 1936.

IN QUEST OF GORILLAS. VIII. DRUMS IN THE FOREST. William K. Gregory. Sci. Monthly, vol.42, no.6, pp.517-531, illus., June, 1936.

IN QUEST OF GORILLAS. IX. CONGO QUEER 'UNS. William K. Gregory. Sci. Monthly, vol.43, no.1, pp.23-32, illus., July, 1936.

IN QUEST OF GORILLAS. X. CAMEROON FOLKS. William K. Gregory. Sci. Monthly, vol.43, no.2, pp.130-147, illus., Aug., 1936.

IN QUEST OF GORILLAS. XI. GORILLA CHILDREN. William K. Gregory. Sci. Monthly, vol.43, no.3, pp.211-223, illus., Sept., 1936.

IN QUEST OF GORILLAS. William K. Gregory, Henry G. Raven. The Darwin Press, New Bedford, Mass., pp.241, illus., 1937.

IN THE LAND OF THE GORILLA. William K. Gregory. Evolution, vol.3, no.3, pp. 3-4, illus., June, 1931.

(OBSERVATIONS OF GORILLAS AND CHIMPANZEES IN SPANISH GUINEA.) Boebachtungen an Gorillas und Schimpansen in Span.-Guinea. B. Grzimek. Zool. Garten, Leipzig, 23 (1-3): 249, 1957.

(OBSERVATIONS OF CHIMPANZEES (PAN TR. TROGLODYTES BLUMENBACH 1775) IN THE NIMBA MOUNTAINS.) Beobachtungen an Schimpansen, Pan tr. troglodytes (Blumenbach, 1775) in den Nimbabergen. B. Grzimek. Saeugetierk. Mitteil., vol.1, no.1, pp.1-5, illus., Jan.10, 1953.

GORILLAS OF EASTERN NIGERIA. E. W. March. Oryx, 4 (1): 30-34, Apr., 1957.

(ON A GORILLA FROM GERMAN EAST AFRICA.) Einen Gorilla aus Deutsch-Ostafrika. Paul Matschie. Sitz. Gesell. Naturf. Freunde Berlin, Jahrg. no.6, pp. 253-259, June 9, 1903.

(SOME CHIMPANZEES FROM THE CONGO STATE.) Einige Schimpansen aus dem Kongo-Staate. Paul Matschie. Rev. Zool. Africaine, Brussels, vol.2, fasc.1, pp.115-124, Sept., 1912.

THE HOME OF THE EASTERN GORILLA. Marius Maxwell. Jour. Bombay Nat. Hist. Soc., vol.32, pp.436-444, pls.10, map, Jan., 1928.

A FIELD STUDY OF THE CHIMPANZEE. OBSERVATIONS OF CHIMPANZEE BEHAVIOR AND ENVIRONMENT IN WESTERN FRENCH GUINEA. Henry W. Nissen. Compar. Psychol. Monographs, vol.8, no. 1, pp.vi, 105, pls.17, 1931.

(THE CHIMPANZEE OF THE LEFT BANK OF THE CONGO.) La Chimpanze de la rive Gauche du Congo. G. Petit. La Terre et la Vie (Revue d'Hist. Nat.), vol.1, no. 10, pp.629-631, illus., Nov., 1931.

GORILLAS IN THE EMPIRE. A TROOP WHICH NEVER LEAVES BRITISH TERRITORY. Tracy Phillips. Field, Lond., vol 160, no.4149, p.23, figs.2, July 2, 1932.

THE GORILLAS OF THE KAYONSA REGION, WESTERN KIGEZI, SOUTHWEST UGANDA. C. R. S. Pitman. Proc. Zool. Soc. Lond., pt.3, pp.477-494, pls.7, Sept., 1935.

THE GORILLAS OF THE KAYONSA REGION, WESTERN KIGEZI, SOUTHWEST UGANDA. C. R. S. Pitman. Smithsonian Report, 1936, publ.3426, pp.253-275, figs. 2, pl.1-6, 1937.

HUNTING GORILLAS IN WEST AFRICA. H. C. Raven. Sci. Monthly, vol.43, no.4, pp.313-334, illus., Oct., 1936.

HUNTING THE GORILLA. H. C. Raven. Evolution, vol.3, no.3, pp.4-5, illus., June, 1931.

(THE CHIMPANZEE OF THE LEFT BANK OF THE CONGO.) Le Chimpanze de la rive gauche du Congo. H. Schouteden. Bull. Cercle Zool. Congolais (Suppl. Rev. Zool. Bot. Afr.), vol.20, no.4, pp.114-119, figs. 4, June 15, 1931.

(CONGOLESE GORILLAS.) Les Gorilles Congolais. H. Schouteden. Rev. Zool. et Bot. Africaines, vol.19, no.2, pp.298-302, July 30, 1930.

(SOME NOTES ON THE CHIMPANZEE OF THE LEFT BANK OF THE CONGO.) Quelques notes sur le Chimpanze de la rive gauche du Congo, Pan satyrus paniscus. H. Schouteden. Rev. Zool.-Bot. Africaines, vol.20, no.3, pp.310-314, figs.2, Mar.1, 1931.

(THE OCCURRENCE OF THE CHIMPANZEE ON THE LEFT BANK OF THE CONGO.) Das Vorkommen des Schimpansen auf den linken Kongo-Ufer. E. Schwarz. Rev. Zool. Bot. Afr., vol.16, no.4, pp.425-426, Apr.1, 1929.

THE CAMEROON GORILLA. N. A. Dyce Sharp. Nature, vol.123, no.3101, p.525, Apr.6, 1929.

(THE LIFE OF THE GORILLA OF GABON.) La vie du gorille au Gabon. Abbe A. Valker. Bull. Mus. Nat. Hist. Nat., Paris, vol.3, no.5, pp.393-398, 1931.

THE KING OF THE APES IN HIS NATIVE JUNGLE: SCENES FROM "CONGORILLA"--A WONDERFUL SOUND-FILM OF FOREST LIFE IN AFRICA. Illus. London News, vol. 181, no.4866, pp.132-133, illus., July 23, 1932.

THE MOUNTAIN GORILLA IN ITS NATIVE WILD IN THE CONGO FORESTS: THE FINEST PHOTOGRAPH OF A YOUNG FEMALE EVER TAKEN AT CLOSE RANGE. Illus. London News, vol.181, no.4881, p. 701, photo., Nov.5, 1932.

## Anatomy

SUPRA-STERNAL OSSICLES IN PRIMATES OTHER THAN MAN: SOME ISOLATED CASES IN GORILLA AND CHIMPANZEE. G. T. Ashley. Nature, Lond., vol.176, no.4482, pp.608-609, illus., Sept.24, 1955.

THE MUSCULATURE OF THE INFERIOR EXTREMITY OF THE ORANG-UTAN SIMIA SATYRUS. Esther L. Boyer. Amer. Jour. Anat., vol.56, no.2, pp.193-256, 15 figs., Mar.15, 1935.

(THE IMPORTANCE OF THE ORANG'S LARYNGEAL SAC.) Die Bedeutung des Orang-Kehlsackes. G. Brandes. Zeit f. Saeugetierkunde, vol.4, heft 2, pp.81-83, Aug.6, 1929.

NOTES ON THE NASAL FOSSA OF A YOUNG CHIMPANZEE. A. J. E. Cave. Proc. Zool. Soc. Lond., vol.119, pt.1, pp.61-63, fig.1, May 16, 1949.

THE PARANASAL SINUSES OF THE ANTHROPOID APES. A. J. E. Cave, R. Wheeler Haines. Jour. Anat., Cambridge, vol.74, pt.4, pp.493-523, figs.21, July, 1940.

ANOMALIES OF VENAE CAVAE SUPERIORES IN AN ORANG. Ralph E. Chase, Charles F. DeGaris. Amer. Jour. Phys. Anthrop., Phila., vol.24, no.1, pp.61-65, fig.1, July-Sept., 1938.

(MANIFESTATION OF TWO ATLOIDEAN VERTEBRAE IN A CHIMPANZEE.) Manifestation des deux vertebres atloidiennes d'un Chimpanze. E. G. Dehaut. Bull. Mus. Nat. Hist. Nat., Paris, vol.19, ser. 2, no.5, p.378, Oct., 1947.

(BRIEF REPORT ON MY INVESTIGATIONS OF THE VERTEBRAE OF ANTHROPOIDS.) Kurzer Bericht ueber meine Unter suchungen an der Wirbelsaeule der Menschenaffen. R. Fick. Zeitschr. f. Saeugetierkunde, vol. 11, no.3, pp.261-271, pls.59-61, Dec.30, 1936.

(INVESTIGATIONS OF THE VERTEBRAE OF ANTHROPOIDS.) Untersuchungen an der Wirbelsaeule der Menschenaffen. R. Fick. Sitz.-Ber. preuss. Akad. Wiss. Phys.-math, Kl., Berlin, pp.167-239, figs. 25, Mar.16, 1933.

(OBSERVATIONS ON THE MUSCLES OF SOME CHIMPANZEES.) Beobachtungen an den Muskeln einiger Chimpansen. R. Fick. Zeitschr. fuer Anatomie und Entwicklungsgeschichte, vol.76, pp.117-141, Apr. 5, 1925.

(ON THE BODY MEASUREMENTS AND THE LARYNGEAL SAC OF AN ADULT ORANGUTAN.) Ueber die Koerpermasse und den Kehlsack eines erwachsenen Orangs. R. Fick. Zeitschr. f. Saeugetierkunde, vol. 4, no.2, pp.65-80, 5 pls., Aug.6, 1929.

ON THE OSTEOLOGY OF THE ACTIVE GIBBON (HYLOBATES AGILIS). Edward Fry. Proc. Zool. Soc. Lond., pt.14, pp. 11-18, 1846.

ARTERIES OF THE CHIMPANZEE (PAN SPEC?). Evelyn M. Glidden, Charles F. DeGaris. Amer. Jour. Anat., vol.58, no. 2, pp.501-527, figs.1-7, Mar.15, 1936.

THE ANATOMY OF THE GORILLA. William K. Gregory. Henry Cushier Raven Memorial Volume, pp.1-12, 1950.

THE GORILLA'S FOOT. William K. Gregory. Nature, vol.112, p.758, Nov.24, 1923; p.933 Dec.29, 1923; vol.113, pp.421-423, 7 figs., Mar.22, 1924.

WEIGHT NORMS AND RELATIONS FOR CHIMPANZEE. Walter F. Grether, R. M. Yerkes. Amer. Jour. Phys. Anthrop., Phila., vol.27, no.2, pp.181-197, figs.5, Sept.30, 1940.

(SIZE AND WEIGHT OF LEVEL-REGION GORILLAS.) Masse und Gewichte von Flachland-Gorillas. B. Grzimek. Zeitschr. Saeugetierk., Berlin, 21 (3-4): 192-194, pl. 10, Feb.28, 1957.

NOTES ON TWO GORILLA SKELETONS. Rodgers D. Hamilton. Jour. Mam., vol. 26, no.3, pp.313-314, Aug., 1945.

EXTERNAL FORM OF THE MAN-LIKE APE. Robert Hartmann. The Popular Science Monthly, pp.736-754, figs.9, Apr. , 1886.

(DATA ON THE TONSILLA PALATINA OF THE ORANGUTAN.) Zur Kenntnis der Tonsilla palatina des Orang-Utan. H. O. von Haussen. Morphol. Jahrb., vol.69, pp.98-109, 6 figs., 1932.

SOME POINTS IN THE ENTERIC ANATOMY OF THE GREAT APES. W. C. Osman Hill. Proc. Zool. Soc. Lond., vol.119, pt.1, pp. 19-32, figs.4, May 16, 1949.

ACCOUNT OF A SKELETON OF A GORILLA REMARKABLE BECAUSE SHOWING RECOVERY FROM GUNSHOT WOUNDS. W. J. Holland. Ann. Carnegie Mus., vol.15, pp. 293-298, 2 pls., July 3, 1924.

(MUSCULAR PECULIARITIES OF THE UPPER ARM AND HAND IN THE CHIMPANZEE (PAN TROGLODYTES OWEN).) Particularites musculaires de l'avant-bras et de la main chez un Chimpanze, Pan troglodytes (Owen). F. K. Jouffroy, J. Lessertisseur. Bull. Mus. Nat. Hist. Nat., Paris, 29: 121-126, Mar., 1957.

OBSERVATIONS ON THE ANATOMY OF THE HOOLOCK GIBBON. K. Kanagasuntheram. Ceylon Jour. Sci., sec.G, vol.5, pt.1, pp.11-64, illus., Sept., 1952; vol.5, pt.2, pp.69-122, illus., June, 1954.

THE ANATOMICAL BASIS OF PHONATION IN THE CHIMPANZEE. George Kelemen. Jour. Morphol., Phila., vol.82, no.2, pp. 229-256, Mar., 1948.

DIVERTICULUM OF THE LARYNX. Harry H. Kerr, Thomas Bradley. Surgery, St. Louis, vol.2, no.4, pp.3-11 (598-606), figs.4, Oct., 1937.

THE GORILLA'S FOOT. E. Ray Lankester. Nature, vol.112, pp.758-759, 2 figs., Nov. 24, 1923; vol.113, pp.10-11, 6 figs., Jan.5, 1924.

POLYTHELIA IN A CHIMPANZEE. L. Harrison Matthews, James S. Baxter. Proc. Zool. Soc. Lond., vol.118, pt.1, pp.144-145, pl.1, illus., May 20, 1948.

THE LARYNGEAL SACS OF AN INFANT AND AN ADULT GORILLA. Ruth A. Miller. Amer. Jour. Anat., Phila., vol.69, no.1, pp.1-17, figs.4, July 15, 1941.

THE MUSCULATURE OF PAN PANISCUS. Ruth A. Miller. Amer. Jour. Anat., Phila., vol.91, no.2, pp.183-232, Sept., 1952.

MEMOIR ON THE "APPENDICULAR SKELETON OF THE ORANG (SIMIA)". St. George J. Mivart. Proc. Zool. Soc. Lond., p.558, 1866.

A STUDY BY SERIAL SECTIONS OF THE STRUCTURE OF THE LARYNX OF HYLOBATES SYNDACTYLUS (SIAMANG GIBBON). Frederick Mott. Proc. Zool. Soc. Lond., 1924, pt.4, pp.1161-1170, 5 pls., 1925.

(THE VOCAL ORGAN OF THE ORANGUTAN.) Das Stimmorgan des Orang-Utan. Josef Nemai, George Kelemen. Zeitschr. f. Anat. u. Entwickges., vol.88, pp.697-709, figs.11, 1929.

DIGITAL EPIPHYSES AND CARPAL BONES IN THE GROWING INFANT FEMALE GORILLA WITH SITTING HEIGHT, WEIGHT AND ESTIMATED AGE. Charles V. Noback. Zoologica, New York, vol.11, no.5, pp.117-151, figs.57-72, Dec.30, 1930.

(THE TONGUE OF THE ORANG-UTAN.) Die Zunge des Orang-Utan. W. Oppenheimer. Morphol. Jahrb., vol.69, pp.62-97, figs.19, 1932.

DISSECTION OF A FEMALE ORANG-UTAN. R. Owen. Proc. Zool. Soc. Lond., pt.11, pp.123-124, 1843.

NOTES ON THE DISSECTION OF A FEMALE CHIMPANZEE (TROGLODYTES NIGER). R. Owen. Proc. Zool. Soc. Lond., pt.14, pp.2-3, 1846.

ON THE ANATOMY OF THE ORANG-UTAN (SIMIA SATYRUS, L.). R. Owen. Proc. Comm. Sci. and Corres. Zool. Soc. Lond., pt.1, pp.4-5, 9-28, 67-69, 70-71, 1830-1831.

ON THE MORBID APPEARANCES OBSERVED IN THE DISSECTION OF THE CHIMPANZEE (SIMIA TROGLODYTES, LINN.). R. Owen. Proc. Zool. Soc. Lond., pt.4, p.41, 1836.

ON THE SKELETON OF TROGLODYTES GORILLA. R. Owen. Proc. Zool. Soc. Lond., pt.19, p.263, 1851.

OSTEOLOGICAL CONTRIBUTIONS TO THE NATURAL HISTORY OF THE CHIMPANZEES AND ORANGS (TROGLODYTES PITHECUS), NO.6. R. Owen. Proc. Zool. Soc. Lond., pt.24, p.369, 1856.

THE GORILLA'S FOOT. R. I. Pocock. Nature, vol.112, p.827, Dec.8, 1923.

THE ANATOMY OF THE GORILLA. Henry Cushier Raven. Columbia Univ. Press, New York, pp.259, pls.109, 1950.

(Review by George C. Rinker of) THE ANATOMY OF THE GORILLA. Henry Cushier Raven. Jour. Mamm., vol.33, no.1, pp.119-120, Feb. 18, 1952.

(THE BODY PROPORTIONS OF FULLY GROWN CATARRHINE PRIMATES, WITH SPECIAL CONSIDERATION OF ANTHROPOIDS.) Die Koerperproportionen der erwachsenen catarrhinen Primaten, mit spezieller Berueckschtigung der Menschenaffen. Adolph H. Schultz. Anthropologischer Anzeiger, Muenchen, Jahrg.10, nos. 2-3, pp.154-185, figs.5-8, pl.1, Sept., 1933.

MORPHOLOGICAL OBSERVATIONS ON A GORILLA AND AN ORANG OF CLOSELY KNOWN AGES. Adolph H. Schultz. Amer. Jour. Phys. Anthropol., Phila., vol.29, no. 1, pp.1-21, figs.4, Mar., 1942.

THE MALLEUS (OSSICULUM AUDITUS) OF THE ANTHROPOID APES. Walter Segall. Chicago Nat. Hist. Mus., vol.31, no.14, pp.113-120, Apr.11, 1947.

THE COMPARATIVE ANATOMY OF THE TONGUES OF THE MAMMALIA. II. FAMILY 1, SIMIIDAE. Charles F. Sonntag. Proc. Zool. Soc. Lond., pp.1-29, Mar., 1921.

ANATOMICAL OBSERVATIONS IN A GORILLA GORILLA. Paul E. Steiner. Amer. Jour. Phys. Anthropol., n.s., vol. 12, no.2, pp.145-165, June, 1954.

THE FOOT MUSCULATURE OF THE HIGHLAND GORILLA (GORILLA BERINGEI). W. L. Straus, Jr. Quart. Review Biol., vol.5, no.3, pp.261-317, figs.27, Sept., 1930.

THE STRUCTURE OF THE CROWN-PAD OF THE GORILLA AND OF THE CHEEK-PAD OF THE ORANG-UTAN. W. L. Straus, Jr. Jour. Mam., vol.23, no.3, pp.276-281, pl.1, Aug.14, 1942.

THE THORACIC AND ABDOMINAL VISCERA OF PRIMATES, WITH SPECIAL REFERENCE TO THE ORANG-UTAN. W. L. Straus, Jr. Proc. Amer. Philos. Soc., vol.71, no.1, pp. 1-85, figs.16, 1936.

THE VISCERAL ANATOMY OF AN INFANT CHIMPANZEE. W. L. Straus, Jr. Jour. Mam., vol.18, no.4, pp.501-507, Nov., 1937.

ON THE ARTICULAR PROCESSES OF THE VERTEBRAE IN THE GORILLA COMPARED WITH THOSE IN MAN, AND ON COSTO-VERTEBRAL VARIATION IN THE GORILLA. John Struthers. Jour. Anat. and Phys., vol. 27, pp.131-138, 1892.

THE FACIALIS MUSCULATURE OF THE ORANG SIMIA SATYRUS. W. E. Sullivan, C. W. Osgood. Anat. Record, vol.29, pp. 195-243, 6 figs., Jan.25, 1925.

DISSECTION OF THE THYROID AND PARATHYROID GLANDS IN AN ADULT MOUNTAIN GORILLA. John H. Venable, Allan L. Grafflin. Jour. Mam., vol.21, no.1, pp. 71-73, fig.1, Feb.14, 1940.

THORACIC VISCERA OF THE GORILLA. S. L. Washburn. The Anatomy of the Gorilla. Henry Cushier Raven Memorial Volume, pp.189-196, pls.97-99, 1950.

(MORE ON THE FRONTAL CAVITIES OF THE ORANG-UTAN.) Nochmals die Stirnhohlen beim Orang-Utan. Hans Weinert. Zeitschrift f. Saeugetierkunde, vol.8, no.6, pp.284-286, Dec.20, 1933.

CONTRIBUTIONS TO THE COMPARATIVE MYOLOGY OF THE CHIMPANZEE. Burt G. Wilder. Boston, Jour. Nat. Hist., vol.7, pp.353-384, Apr.17, 1861.

THE FORM AND DERMATOGLYPHS OF THE HANDS AND FEET OF CERTAIN ANTHROPOID APES. Charlotte Wolff. Proc. Zool. Soc. Lond., ser.A, vol.107, pt.3, pp.347-350, pls.1-5, Sept., 1937.

THE CHROMOSOMES OF THE CHIMPANZEE. C. H. Yeager, T. S. Painter, R. M. Yerkes. Science, Lancaster, n.s., vol. 91, no.2351, pp.74-75, figs.1a-2b, Jan.19, 1940.

(THE CHEEK BONE AND THE "OS MALARE BIPARTIUM" OF THE ORANGUTAN.) Das Jochbein und das "Os Malare bipartium: des Orang-Utan. A. Zimmermann, A. Hassko. Anat. Anz., vol.69, nos.1-3, pp.1-11, figs. 4, 1930.

Asia

A SURVEY OF WILD LIFE CONDITIONS AT ATJEH, NORTH SUMATRA. WITH SPECIAL REFERENCE TO THE ORANG-UTAN. C. R. Carpenter. Communications No.12, Netherlands Comm. Internat. Nature Protection, Amsterdam, pp.34, maps 2, 1 photo., 1938.

THE LIVING ASIATIC APES. Harold J. Coolidge, Jr. Harvard Alumni Bull., pp. 1-12, illus., May 27, 1938.

(INDOCHINESE GIBBONS.) Les gibbons indochinois. J. Delacour. La Terre et la Vie, Rev. d'Hist. Nat., vol.4, no.1, pp. 3-12, illus., Jan., 1934.

ON THE INDOCHINESE GIBBONS (HYLOBATES CONCOLOR). J. Delacour. Jour. Mam., vol.14, no.1, pp.71-73, Feb., 1933.

(THE GIBBONS OF INDOCHINA.) Les gibbons d'Indochine. Francois Edmond-Blanc. La Terre et la Vie, Rev. d'Hist. Nat., vol. 2, no.6, pp.363-365, illus., June, 1932.

ON THE SPECIES OF BORNEAN ORANGS, WITH NOTES ON THEIR HABITS. W. T. Hornaday. Proc. Amer. Assoc. Adv. Sci., vol.28, pp.1-20, 1880.

(NOTE ON A NEW SPECIES OF GIBBON FROM HAUT-TONKIN.) Sur un Gibbon d'espece nouvelle provenant du Haut-Tonkin. E. Pousargues. Bull. Mus. d'Hist. Nat., Paris, vol.2, no.8, pp.367-369, 1896.

(PICTURES OF JAVANESE GIBBONS (HYLOBATES MOLOCH).) Bij eenige afbeeldingen van Javaansche gibbons (Hylobates moloch). H. J. V. Sody. De Tropische Natuur, Batavia, vol.29, no.1, pp.15-19, illus., Jan., 1940.

THE ORANG UTAN OF MALAYA. Arthur deC Sowerby. China Jour., vol.12, no.3, p.170, Mar., 1930.

A NEW GIBBON FROM ANNAM. Oldfield Thomas. Ann. and Mag. Nat. Hist. (8), vol.4, no.20, pp.112-113, Aug., 1909.

NOTE ON THE GIBBON OF THE ISLAND OF HAINAN (HYLOBATES HAINANUS, SP. N.). Oldfield Thomas. Ann. and Mag. Nat. Hist. (6), vol.9, no.50, pp.145-146, Feb., 1892.

(ON THE DISTRIBUTION OF SOME ANTHROPOID APES ON SUMATRA.) Ueber die Verbreitung einiger anthropoider Affen in Sumatra. Walter Volz. Biol. Control, vol. 24, no.14, pp.415-476, July 15, 1904.

Brain

(STUDIES ON THE NATURAL HISTORY OF THE GORILLA. III. CONTRIBUTION TO THE MORPHOLOGY AND MORPHOGENESIS OF THE CEREBRUM OF THE GORILLA.) Studien zur Naturgeschichte des Gorillas. III. Beitrag zur Morphologie und Morphogenese des Grosshirns des Gorillas. J. F. Babor. Zeitschr. fuer Anatomie und Entwicklungsgeschichte, vol.97, no.6, pp.780-793, figs.7, 1932.

DESCRIPTION OF THE CEREBRAL HEMISPHERES OF THE BRAIN OF A GORILLA. W. E. LeGros Clark. Jour. Anat., vol.61, pp.469-475, 1927.

THE BRAIN OF A MOUNTAIN GORILLA, OKERO (G. BERINGEI). C. J. Connolly. Amer. Jour. Phys. Anthrop., vol.17, no.3, pp.291-307, figs.7, Jan.-March, 1933.

(STUDIES IN RELATION TO THE NATURAL HISTORY OF THE GORILLA. III. CONTRIBUTION ON THE MORPHOLOGY AND MORPHOGENESIS OF THE CEREBRUM OF THE GORILLA.) Studien zur Naturgeschichte des Gorillas. III. Beitrag zur Morphologie und Morphogenese des Grosshirns des Gorillas. Z. Frankenberger, J. F. Babor. Zeitsch. fuer Anatomie und Entwicklungsgeschichte, vol.97, no.6, pp. 780-793, figs.7, 1932.

(THE CEREBRAL ARTERIES OF THE CHIMPANZEE.) Die Hirnarterien des Schimpansen. B. Hindze. Zeitschr. f. Morphol. u. Anthropol., vol.27, no.3, pp. 468-491, 6 figs., and 8 pls., 1930.

(ON THE CEREBRAL FURROWS OF A "SYMPHALANGUS SYNDACTYLUS.") Sui solchi cerebrali di un "Symphalangus syndactylus." Jole Pastore. Atti R. Accad. Sci. di Torino, vol.68, pp.570-587, pls.3, 1933.

(THE HYPOPHYSIS OF AN ORANGUTAN.) Die Hypophysis eines Orang-Utan. A. Plant. Anat. Anz., vol.68, pp.408-415, 15 text figs., 1930.

THE BRAIN OF THE CHIMPANZEE AT THE TIME OF BIRTH (MYELOGENESIS). W. Riese. Jour. Mam., 36 (1): 78-83, 1 pl., Feb.25, 1955.

THE CEREBRAL CORTEX OF THE CHIMPANZEE AT THE TIME OF BIRTH. W. Riese. Jour. Mam., vol.30, no.3, pp.270-273, pl.1, Aug.17, 1949.

(PROBLEMS OF BRAIN FORM. THIRD COMMUNICATION: ON THE SIMILARITY OF THE ORANG BRAIN TO THAT OF MAN.) Formprobleme des Gehirns. Dritte Mitteilung: Ueber die Menschenahulichkeit des Oranggehirnes. W. Riese. Anat. Anzeiger, vol.60, pp.533-536, 1 pl., Mar.6, 1926.

THE ARTERIES OF THE BRAIN OF THE ORANG-UTAN. J. L. Shellshear. Jour. Anat., vol.61, pp.167-197, 1927.

THE BRAIN OF A CHIMPANZEE. S. Zuckerman. Proc. Zool. Soc. Lond., pt. 3, pp.1079-1081, illus., Sept.10, 1932.

Captivity

AROUND THE WORLD IN 60 MINUTES. Belle J. Benchley. Zoonooz, vol.4, no.29, pp.1-5, May, 1938.

MBONGO AND NGAGI. TWO GORILLAS WHO LIVE FAR FROM THEIR NATIVE MOUNTAINS. Belle J. Benchley. Nature Mag., vol.21, no.5, pp.217-222, illus., May, 1933.

MOUNTAIN GORILLAS IN SAN DIEGO ZOO. Belle J. Benchley. Parks and Recreation, Rockford, vol.24, no.1, pp.19-27, illus., Sept., 1940.

THE STORY OF TWO MAGNIFICENT GORILLAS. SAN DIEGO'S MBONGO AND NGAGI HAVE DEVELOPED WITH A MINIMUM OF HUMAN INTERFERENCE AND NOW HOLD THE RECORD FOR SIZE. Belle J. Benchley. Bull. New York Zool. Soc., vol.48, no.4, pp.105-116, illus., July-Aug., 1940.

(GORILLAS IN THE ZOO AT ZURICH AND SCHOENBRUNN.) Gorillas im Zoo Zuerich und Schoenbrunn. G. Brandes. Zool. Garten, n.F., vol.4, nos.6-7, p.246, July, 1931.

(ON THE DEATH OF OUR MALE ORANG, "PETER".) Zum Tode unseres Orangmannes "Peter." G. Brandes. Zool.Garten, Leipzig, n.F., vol.3, nos.1-3, pp. 12-18, pls.1-5, May, 1930.

BAMBOO. Roger Conant. Parks and Recreation, Rockford, Ill., vol.22, no.9, pp. 481-484, illus., May, 1939.

A GORILLA'S LIFE IN CIVILIZATION. Alyse Cunningham. Zool. Soc. Bull., vol. 24, pp.118-124, 9 illus., Sept., 1921.

IN THE BAG WITH ANDY. Sam Dunton. Animal Kingdom, New York Zool. Soc., vol.58, no.6, pp.176-178, illus., Dec., 1955.

A NEW WORLD FOR MAMBO. Sam Dunton. Animal Kingdom, New York Zool. Soc., vol.56, no.2, pp.48-50, illus., Apr., 1953.

ORANG-UTANS IN THE LONDON ZOO. Tom Harrison. Sarawak Mus. Jour., Kuching, 7: 226-228, June, 1956.

ZOO STARS--MOK AND MOINA. Julian S. Huxley. Zoo, vol.1, no.1, pp.12-13, illus., June, 1936.

TWO HEALTHY BABY GORILLAS. Claude W. Leister. Animal Kingdom, New York Zool. Soc., vol.46, no.6, pp.123-128, illus., Nov.-Dec., 1943.

THE ZOOLOGICAL PARK'S YOUNG FEMALE GORILLA, JANET PENSEROSA. WITH NOTES CONCERNING HER COMPANION, A YOUNG FEMALE CHIMPANZEE, ELLEN ALLEGRA. Charles V. Noback. Bull. New York Zool. Soc., vol.34, no.3, pp.75-104, figs.42, May-June, 1931.

TWO ORANG UTANS. R. I. Pocock. Field, Lond., vol.151, p.921, illus., May 31, 1928.

("TOTO," THE GORILLA, IN THE FRANKFURT ZOO.) Der Gorilla "Toto" im Frankfurter Zoo. Kurt Preimel. Zool. Garten, Leipzig, n.F., vol.5, nos.1-3, pp.58-59, June, 1932.

(A VISIT TO JIMMIE AND HELEN, THE LAST ACQUISITIONS OF THE ZOOLOGICAL GARDEN OF NEW YORK.) Une visite a Jimmie et Hélène, les dernières acquisitions du Jardin Zoologique de New York. Quentz. La Terre et la Vie Rev. d'Hist. Nat., vol.2, no.5, pp.302-305, illus., May, 1932.

FURTHER ADVENTURES OF MESHIE. A CHIMPANZEE THAT HAS LIVED MOST OF HER LIFE IN A NEW YORK SUBURBAN HOME. H. C. Raven. Nat. Hist. New York, vol.33, no.6, pp.607-617, figs.12, Nov.-Dec., 1933.

MESHIE--THE CHILD OF A CHIMPANZEE. H. C. Raven. Natural History, vol.32, no. 2, pp.158-166, figs.16, Mar.-Apr., 1932.

BOBBY. A GORILLA FROM THE WEST AFRICAN CAMEROONS. Ernst Schwarz. Nature Mag., vol.31, no.6, pp.341-342, illus., June-July, 1938.

LONDON'S FIRST BABY CHIMPANZEE. D. Seth-Smith. Field, Lond., vol.165, no. 4290, p.576, illus., Mar.16, 1935.

(A PYGMY CHIMPANZEE (PAN SATYRUS PANISCUS SCHWARZ) OF THE ZOOLOGICAL PARK OF THE BOIS DE VINCENNES.) Un chimpanzé pygmée (Pan satyrus paniscus Schwarz) au Parc Zoologique du Bois de Vincennes. Ach. Ubain, P. Rode. Mammalia, Paris, vol.4, no.1, pp.12-14, pl.1, Mar., 1940.

THE LARGEST GORILLA IN CAPTIVITY. "ALFRED'S" UPBRINGING IN THE BRISTOL ZOO. F. L. Vanderplank. Field, Lond., vol.167, no.4355, p.1437, illus., June 13, 1936.

"BUSHMAN," THE GORILLA AT LINCOLN PARK ZOO. Floyd S. Young. Parks and Recreation, Rockford, vol.23, no.7, pp. 305-308, illus., Mar., 1940.

THE "ALMOST HUMAN" GORILLA: 524 POUND BOBBY, OF THE BERLIN ZOO. Illus. London News, vol.187, no.5023, p. 161, July 27, 1935.

CINDERELLA AND IVY, THE TWO YOUNG ORANG-UTANS. Fauna, Phila., vol.4, no. 1, p.31, illus., Mar., 1942.

CLAIMED TO BE THE LARGEST IN CAPTIVITY: A PAIR OF ORANG-UTANS IN SURABAYA (JAVA) ZOO. Illus. London News, vol.218, no.5841, p.499, illus., Mar.31, 1951.

DROWNING AT THE BRONX PARK ZOO. Life, Chicago, vol.30, no.28, p.30, illus., May 28, 1951.

THE GREATEST "ZOO" ATTRACTION SINCE JUMBO; JUBILEE GIVEN AS MUCH CARE AS A PRINCESS--AND TAUGHT TO PLAY. Illus. London News, vol.186, no. 5506, pp.514-515, Mar.30, 1935.

LORDS OF THE FOREST IN CAPTIVITY; GIANT GORILLAS IN AMERICAN ZOOS. Illus. London News, vol.210, no.5623, p. 120, illus., Jan.25, 1947.

A "MAN OF THE WOODS" AT THE ZOO. Illus. London News, vol.211, no.5659, p. 386, illus., Oct.4, 1947.

THE MOTHER AND HER CHILD: BOO-BOO AND THE INFANT JUBILEE RECEIVE. Illus. London News, vol.186, no.5004, pp. 408-409, Mar.16, 1935.

THE NEW BABY GORILLA AT THE ZOO: A YOUNG MALE OF THE MOUNTAIN SUB-SPECIES FROM LAKE KIVU. Illus. London News, vol.193, no.5183, p.321, photos., Aug.20, 1938.

THE NEW PAIR OF GORILLAS NOW THE "ZOOS" MOST POPULAR ATTRACTION. Illus. London News, vol.181, no.4872, p. 335, illus., Sept.3, 1932.

THE PASSING OF "MO-KOUMDJE," THE CHIEF; KNOWN TO LONDONERS AS MOK: DRAWINGS OF THE ZOO'S "UNIQUE" GORILLA, BY NINA SCOTT-LANGLEY. Illus. London News, vol.192, no.5153, p. 127, illus., Jan.22, 1938.

WHO'S WHO IN THE ZOO--GUARINA, MOTHER ORANGUTAN. Fauna, Phila., vol.6, no.1, p.31, Mar., 1944.

THE ZOO'S BABY ORANG-UTANS. Illus. London News, vol.211, no.5660, p.413, illus., Oct.11, 1947.

Diseases, Parasites

A NEW SUCKING LOUSE FROM THE CHIMPANZEE. H. E. Ewing. Proc. Biol. Soc. Wash., vol.45, pp.117-118, July 30, 1932.

(MOUTH SCURVY IN CHIMPANZEES.) Mundfaeule bei Schimpansen. Bernhard

Grzimek. Zool. Garten, Leipzig, (N.F.), vol.20, nos.2-3, p.197, 1953.

THREE ILL GORILLAS. Edalee Harwell. Zoonooz, Zool. Soc. San Diego, vol.24, no.11, pp.3-4, Nov., 1951.

APPENDICITIS IN GIBBONS. W. C. Osman Hill. Proc. Zool. Soc. Lond., vol.124, pt. 1, pp.13-16, pls.1-2, May 27, 1954.

ACUTE COCCIDIOMYCOSIS IN A MOUNTAIN GORILLA (GORILLA BERINGERI) WITH ANATOMICAL NOTES. Frank D. McKenney, J. Traum, Aileen E. Bonestell. Jour. Amer. Veterin. Assoc., New York, vol.104, no.804, pp.136-141, Mar., 1944.

EXPERIMENTAL ATTEMPTS TO TRANSMIT PHLEBOTOMUS (SANDFLY, PAPPATACI) AND DENGUE FEVERS TO CHIMPANZEES. J. R. Paul, J. L. Melnick, A. B. Sabin. Proc. Soc. Exper. Biol. Med., Utica, vol.68, no.1, pp.193-198, May, 1948.

AN ADDITIONAL NOTE ON THE FILARIAL WORMS OF THE CHIMPANZEES. E. Peel, M. Chardome. Trop. Disease Bull., Lond., vol.45, no.9, p.809, Sept., 1948.

SUSCEPTIBILITY OF THE CHIMPANZEE TO P. MALARIAE OF HUMAN ORIGIN. J. Rodhain. Amer. Jour. Trop. Med., Balto., vol.28, no.5, pp.629-631, Sept., 1948.

THE ILLNESS OF THE CHIMPANZEE "BELLA". W. H. Stefko. Proc. Moscou Zool. Park, vol.1, pp.277-284, 1940.

OSTEOARTHRITIS OF THE HIP IN GORILLAS. REPORT OF TWO CASES. H. W. Y. Taylor, J. B. King, Robert M. Stecher. Clinical Orthopaedics, 6: 149-157, 1955.

CONVALESCENT YOUNG CHIMPANZEES. Illus. London News, vol.216, no.5783, p. 269, illus., Feb.18, 1950.

Economic Importance

DATED CHIMPANZEES. YALE'S APE COLONY, IN FLORIDA, IS A LABORATORY IN WHICH DISCOVERIES DIRECTLY APPLICABLE TO MAN ARE BEING MADE ON MAN'S CLOSEST RELATIVE, THE APE. Barclay Moon Newman. Scientific American, Lancaster, Pa., vol.160, no.2, pp. 71-73, illus., Feb., 1939.

A GIBBON THAT RAIDED FRENCH COTTAGES. D. Seth-Smith. Field, London, vol.156, no.4062, p.619, figs.2, Nov.1, 1930.

YALE LABORATORIES OF COMPARATIVE PSYCHOBIOLOGY: PLAN AND PROVISION FOR SCIENTIFIC USE OF ANTHROPOID APES. R. M. Yerkes. Comp. Psychology Monographs, ser.no.38, vol.6, no.3, pp. 23, pls.10, Feb., 1932.

GORILLAS FOR RESEARCH? Jour. Soc. Preservation Fauna Empire, Hertford, n.s., pt.45, pp.20-22, Aug., 1942.

Embryology

(STUDIES ON THE NATURAL HISTORY OF THE GORILLA. II. ON THE FETAL GROWTH OF THE GORILLA.) Studien zur Naturgeschichte des Gorillas. II. Ueber das fetale Wachstum des Gorillas. J. F. Babor, Z. Frankenberger. Biologia Generalis, vol.7, no.3, pp.367-406, pls.9-11, 1931.

NOTES ON A LATE GORILLA FOETUS. R. Broom. Ann. Transvaal Mus., Cambridge, vol.20, pt.4, pp.347-350, fig.1, pl.13, Oct.18, 1946.

A TEN AND ONE-HALF DAY CHIMPANZEE EMBRYO, "YERKES A." J. H. Elder, Carl G. Hartman, C. H. Heuser. Jour. Amer. Med. Assoc., vol.111, no.13, pp. 1156-1159, figs.1, Sept.24, 1938.

THE FETUS OF AN ORANG-UTAN. Herbert Fox. Report of the Laboratory and Museum of Comparative Pathology of the Zoological Society of Philadelphia, 1933.

(STUDIES ON THE NATURAL HISTORY OF THE GORILLA. I. INTRODUCTION: SUPERFICIAL DESCRIPTION OF A NEW GORILLA FETUS FROM WEST AFRICA.) Studien zur Naturgeschichte des Gorillas. I. Einleitung. Aeussere Beschreibung eines neuen Gorillenfetus aus Westafrika. Z. Frankenberger, J. F. Babor. Biologia Generalis, vol.6, pt.4, pp.553-632, figs. 17, pls.38-40, 1930.

(STUDIES ON THE NATURAL HISTORY OF THE GORILLA. II. ON THE FETAL DEVELOPMENT OF THE GORILLA.) Studien zur Naturgeschichte des Gorillas. II. Ueber das fetale Wachstum des Gorillas. Z. Frankenberger, J. F. Babor. Biologia Generalis, vol.7, no.2, pp.367-406, pls. 9-11, 1931.

OVARIES OF GORILLA, CHIMPANZEE, ORANG-UTANG AND GIBBON. Saim Saglik. Carnegie Inst. Washington, publ.496 (Contrib. Embryol. no.165), pp.181-189, table 1, pls.1-5, May 31, 1938.

CHIMPANZEE FETUSES. Adolph H. Schultz. Amer. Jour. Phys. Anthrop., vol.18, no.1, pp.61-79, figs.3, July-Sept., 1933.

NOTES ON THE FETUS OF AN ORANG-UTAN WITH SOME COMPARATIVE OBSERVATIONS. Adolph H. Schultz. Report Laboratory and Mus. Compar. Pathology, Zool. Sec., Phila., pp.28-39, fig.1, pl., 1933.

Exhibits, Collections

THE MOUNTAIN GORILLA GROUP. H. E. Anthony. Natural History, New York, vol. 37, no.1, pp.11-15, illus., Jan., 1936.

ANTHROPOID APE MATERIALS IN AMERICAN COLLECTIONS. Wilton M. Krogman, Adolph H. Schultz. Amer. Jour. Phys. Anthrop., vol.24, no.2, pp.199-234, tables 23, Oct.-Dec., 1938.

NEW HABITAT GROUP OF GIBBONS INSTALLED IN HALL OF ASIATIC MAMMALS. Wilfred H. Osgood. Field Mus. News, Chicago, vol.14, no.11, pp.1-2, illus., Nov., 1943.

Fossils

(AUSTRALOPITHECUS AND ITS POSITION RELATIVE TO ANTHROPOIDS AND HOMINIDS.) Ueber Australopithecus und seine Stellung zu den Anthropoiden und Hominiden. Wolfgang Abel. Verhandl. Zool.-Bot. Gesellschaft, Wien, vol.80, pts.3-4, pp.92-100, May 12, 1931.

(THE DENTITION OF AUSTRALOPITHECUS AFRICANUS DART. SOME SUPPLEMENTARY REMARKS ON THE CORNER-TOOTH PROBLEM.) Das Gebiss von Australopithecus africanus Dart. Einige ergaenzende Bemerkungen zum Eckzahnproblem. Adloff. Zeitschr. f. Anat. u. Entwickl. gesch., vol.97, pp.145-156, 7 figs., 1932.

THE ENDOCRANIAL CAPACITIES OF THE AUSTRALOPITHECINAE. E. H. Ashton. Proc. Zool. Soc. Lond., vol.120, pt.4, pp.715-721, Feb.6, 1951.

(THE DENTITION OF AUSTRALOPITHECUS AFRICANUS (DART).)La dentition de l'Australopithecus africanus (Dart). Ch. Bennejeant. Mammalia, Paris, vol.1, no.1, pp.8-14, figs.6, pl.1, Sept., 1936.

AGE OF THE SOUTH AFRICAN APE-MAN. R. Broom. Nature, London, vol.155, no. 3935, pp.389-390, Mar.31, 1945.

AN ANKLE BONE OF THE APE-MAN, PARANTHROPUS ROBUSTUS. R. Broom. Nature London, vol.152, no.3867, pp.689-690, Dec. 11, 1943.

AUSTRALOID ELEMENT IN THE KORANNAS. R. Broom. Nature, London, vol.124, no.3127, p.507, fig.1, Oct.5, 1929.

THE DENTITION OF AUSTRALOPITHECUS. R. Broom. Nature, London, vol.138, no. 3495, p.719, Oct.24, 1936.

THE DENTITION OF THE TRANSVAAL PLEISTOCENE ANTHROPOIDS, PLESIANTHROPUS AND PARANTHROPUS. R. Broom. Ann. Transvaal Mus., Cambridge, vol.19, pt.3, pp.303-314, figs.4, May 24, 1939.

DISCOVERY OF A LOWER MOLAR OF AUSTRALOPITHECUS. R. Broom. Nature, London, vol.140, no.3546, pp.681-682, fig. 1, Oct.16, 1936.

DISCOVERY OF A NEW SKULL OF THE SOUTH AFRICAN APE-MAN, PLESIANTHROPUS. R. Broom. Nature, London, vol.159, no.4046, p.672, figs.2, May 17, 1947.

FINDING THE MISSING LINK. R. Broom. Watts and Co., London, pp.vi, 104, illus., 1950.

FURTHER EVIDENCE ON THE STRUCTURE OF THE SOUTH AFRICAN PLEISTOCENE ANTHROPOIDS. R. Broom. Nature, London, vol.142, no.3603, pp.897-899, figs., Nov.19, 1938.

THE HAND OF THE APE-MAN, PARANTHROPUS ROBUSTUS. R. Broom. Nature, London, vol.149, no.3784, pp.513-514, figs.10, May 9, 1942.

THE ILLUSTRATIONS OF THE AUSTRALOPITHECINAE. R. Broom. Nature, London, vol.158, no.4020, p.714, Nov.16, 1946.

THE MISSING LINK NO LONGER MISSING? A NEW TYPE OF FOSSIL APE VERY NEAR TO MAN: THE KROMDRAAI SKULL (PARANTHROPUS ROBUSTUS) RECENTLY FOUND IN THE TRANSVAAL AND STRENGTHENING AFRICA'S CLAIM TO BE THE ANCESTRAL HOME OF THE HUMAN RACE. R. Broom. Illu. London News, vol.193, no.5183, pp. 310-311, figs.5, Aug.20, 1938.

MORE DISCOVERIES OF AUSTRALOPITHECUS. R. Broom. Nature, London, vol.141, no.3575, pp.828-829, illus., May 7, 1938.

A NEW ANCESTRAL LINK BETWEEN APE AND MAN. AN IMPORTANT DISCOVERY IN SOUTH AFRICA: THE BRAIN-CAST AND PARTS OF THE SKULL OF AN ANTHROPOID APE WITH HUMAN CHARACTERISTICS, AKIN TO THE TAUNGS APE, BUT A MORE ADULT SPECIMEN. R. Broom. Illus. London News, vol.189, no.5083, pp. 476-477, illus., Sept.19, 1936.

A NEW FOSSIL ANTHROPOID SKULL FROM SOUTH AFRICA. R. Broom. Nature, London, vol.138, no.3490, pp.486-488, figs.4, Sept.19, 1936.

NEW LIGHT ON HUMAN ORIGINS: APE-MAN DISCOVERIES IN TRANSVAAL. R. Broom. Illus. London News, vol.217, no. 5809, pp.290-291, illus., Aug.19, 1950.

A NEW MISSING-LINK SKULL FROM SOUTH AFRICA. R. Broom. Nat. Hist., New York, vol.56, no.7, pp.320-323, illus., Sept., 1947.

NOTE ON AUSTRALOPITHECUS. R. Broom. Natural History, New York, vol.30, no.1, p.111, Jan.-Feb., 1930.

NOTE ON THE MILK DENTITION OF AUSTRALOPITHECUS. R. Broom. Proc. Zool. Soc. Lond., pp.85-88, figs.1-5, 1929.

(Review by Gerrit S. Miller, Jr. of) NOTE ON THE MILK DENTITION OF AUSTRALOPITHECUS. R. Broom. Jour. Mam., Balto., vol.11, no.1, p.92, Feb.11, 1930.

AUSTRALOPITHECUS AND ITS AFFINITIES. R. Broom. Early Man, edited by G. G. MacCurdy, Lippincott and Co., Lond., pp. 285-292, figs.46-48, 1937.

ON THE AFFINITIES OF THE SOUTH AFRICAN PLEISTOCENE ANTHROPOIDS. R. Broom. S. African Jour. Sci., Johannesburg, vol.36, pp.408-411, Dec., 1939.

ON THE FOSSIL REMAINS ASSOCIATED WITH AUSTRALOPITHECUS AFRICANUS. R. Broom. S. African Jour. Sci., vol.31, pp.471-480, figs.7, Nov., 1934.

ON THE NEWLY DISCOVERED SOUTH AFRICAN MAN-APE. R. Broom. Nat. Hist., vol.25, pp.409-418, July-Aug., 1925.

THE PLEISTOCENE ANTHROPOID APES OF SOUTH AFRICA. R. Broom. Nature, London, vol.142, no.3591, pp.377-379, figs. 6, Aug.27, 1938.

(REVIEW BY E. HENNIG OF) THE PLEISTOCENE ANTHROPOID APES OF SOUTH AFRICA. R. Broom. Zentralbl. f. Mineral. Geol. u. Palaeont., Stuttgart, Abt.B, no.10, pp.383-384, 1938.

A RESTORTATION OF THE KROMDRAAI SKULL. R. Broom. Ann. Transvaal Mus.,

Cambridge, 19 pt.3, pp.327-329, figs.3, May 24, 1939.

SOME POINTS IN THE ANATOMY OF THE AUSTRALOPITHECINES. R. Broom. South African Biol. Soc. Pamphlet, Pretoria, no. 11, pp.59-60, 1942.

THE STERCKFONTEIN APE. R. Broom. Nature, London, vol.139, no.3512, p.326, Feb.20, 1937.

STRUCTURE OF THE STERKFONTEIN APE. R. Broom. Nature, London, vol.147, no.3716, p.86, Jan.18, 1941.

THE UPPER MILK MOLARS OF THE APE-MAN, PLESIANTHROPUS. R. Broom. Nature, London, vol.159, no.4044, p.602, illus., May 3, 1947.

JAW OF THE MALE STERKFONTEIN APE-MAN. R. Broom, J. T. Robinson. Nature, London, vol.160, no.4057, p.153, illus., Aug.2, 1947.

THE LOWER END OF THE FEMUR OF PLESIANTHROPUS. R. Broom, J. T. Robinson. Ann. Transvaal Mus., Cambridge, vol.21, pt.2, pp.181-182, illus., May 12, 1949.

SWARTKRANS APE-MAN, PARANTHROPUS CRASSIDENS. R. Broom, J. T. Robinson. Transvaal Museum, Pretoria, Union of South Africa, pp.ix, 123, illus., 1952.

SIGNIFICANCE OF THE AUSTRALOPITHECINAE. W. E. Clark. Nature, London, vol.157, no.4000, pp.863-865, June 29, 1946.

A NEW PRIMATE FROM THE UPPER EOCENE PONDAUNG FORMATION OF BURMA. Edwin H. Colbert. Amer. Mus. Novitates, no.951, pp.18, figs.3, Oct.1, 1937.

CULTURAL STATUS OF SOUTH AFRICAN MAN-APES. R. A. Dart. Ann. Rept. Smithsonian Inst., Wash., 1955: 317-338, pls.1-4, 1956.

THE FIRST AUSTRALOPITHECINE FRAGMENT FROM THE MAKAPANSGAT PEBBLE CULTURE STRATUM. R. A. Dart. Nature, London, vol.176, no.4473, pp.170-171, July 23, 1955.

A NOTE ON THE TAUNGS SKULL. R. A. Dart. S. Afr. Jour. Sci., vol.26, pp.648-658, pl.8, Dec., 1929.

TAUNGS AND ITS SIGNIFICANCE. R. A. Dart. Nat. Hist., vol.26, pp.315-327, May-June, 1926.

SOME PALEONTOLOGICAL INFERENCES AS TO THE LIFE-HABITS OF THE AUSTRALOPITHECINES. Loren C. Eiseley. Sci., Lancaster, n.s., vol.98, no.2533, pp.61-62, July 16, 1943.

THE DATING OF THE AUSTRALOPITHECINAE: FAUNAL EVIDENCE. R. F. Ewer. South African Archaeol. Bull., 11 (42): 41-45, June, 1956.

THE EXTINCT ANTHROPOID APE PARANTHROPUS. E. N. Fallaize. Science, n.s., Suppl., vol.88, no.2293, pp.6-7, Dec.9, 1938.

THE DENTITION OF THE EXTINCT SOUTH AFRICAN MAN-APE AUSTRALOPITHECUS (PLESIANTHROPUS) TRANSVAALENSIS BROOM. A COMPARATIVE AND PHYLOGENETIC STUDY. William K. Gregory, Milo Hellman. Annals Transvaal Mus., Cambridge, England, vol.19, pt.4, pp.339-373, figs.14, tables 8, June 6, 1920.

EVIDENCE OF THE AUSTRALOPITHECINE MAN-APES ON THE ORIGIN OF MAN. William K. Gregory, Milo Hellman. Sci., n.s., vol.88, no.2296, pp.615-616, Dec. 30, 1938.

FOSSIL MAN-APES OF SOUTH AFRICA. William K. Gregory, Milo Hellman. Nature, London, vol.143, no.3610, pp.25-26, illus., Jan.7, 1939.

QUESTIONS RELATING TO A NEW LARGE ANTHROPOID APE FROM THE MIO-PLIOCENE OF THE SIWALIKS. D. A. Hooijer. Amer. Jour. Phys. Anthrop., Phila., n.s., vol.9, no.1, pp.79-96, pl.1, Mar., 1951.

SOME NOTES ON THE GIGANTOPITHECUS QUESTION. D. A. Hooijer. Amer. Jour. Phys. Anthrop., n.s., vol.7, no.4, pp.513-518, Dec., 1949.

THE YALE FOSSILS OF ANTHROPOID APES. Ales Hrdlicka. Amer. Jour. Sci., ser.5, vol.29, no.169, pp.34-40, Jan., 1935.

(CONTRIBUTION TO THE ODONTOLOGY AND PHYLOGENESIS OF THE GENUS PLIOPITHECUS GERVAIS.) Contribution a l'odontologie et la phylogénèse du genre Pliopithecus Gervais. J. Huerzeler. Ann. Paléontol., Paris, vol.40, pp.1-63, illus., 1954.

HAND OF THE STERKFONTEIN APE. Arthur Keith. Nature, London, vol.147, no.3718, p.146, Feb.1, 1941.

A NEW LINK BETWEEN NEANDERTHAL MAN AND PRIMITIVE MODERN RACES: PALAEANTHROPUS OF PALESTINE. Arthur Keith. Illus. London News, vol. 181, no.4864, pp.33-35, illus., July 9, 1932.

(NEW PITHECANTHROPUS DISCOVERIES IN CENTRAL JAVA.) Nieuwe Pithecanthropus-vondsten uit Midden-Java. G. H. R. von Koenigswald. Natuurkundig Tijdschrift v. Nederlandsch-Indie, Batavia, vol.98, pt.4, pp.195-207, figs.3, Sept., 1938.

SKULL OF PROCONSUL FROM RUSINGA ISLAND. L. S. B. Leakey. Nature, London, vol.162, no.4122, p.688, Oct.30, 1948.

A NEW SPECIES OF SUGRIVAPITHECUS. G. Edward Lewis. Amer. Jour. Sci., ser. 5, vol.31, no.186, pp.450-452, fig.1, June, 1936.

PRELIMINARY NOTICE OF NEW MAN-LIKE APES FROM INDIA. G. Edward Lewis. Amer. Jour. Sci., vol.27, pp.161-179, pls.2, Mar., 1934.

PRELIMINARY NOTE ON THE DISCOVERY OF A NEW JAW OF MEGANTHROPUS VON KOENIGSWALD IN THE LOWER MIDDLE PLEISTOCENE OF SANGIRAN, CENTRAL JAVA. P. Marks. Madjalah Ilmu Alam Untuk Indonesia, Indonesian Jour. Nat. Sci., Bandung, vol.109, nos.1-3, pp.26-33, illus., Jan.-June, 1953.

CONCERNING SOME REMAINS OF A NEW STERKFONTEIN PRIMATE. Shaw J. C. Middleton. Ann. Transvaal Mus., Cambridge, vol.20, pt.2, pp.145-156, Apr.22, 1940.

(THE TEETH OF PARANTHROPOIDS.) Les dents des Paranthropiens. George Montandon. Rev. Scientifique Rev. Rose illus., Paris 7th Année, vol.77, nos.11-12, pp.635-649, figs.18, Nov.-Dec., 1939.

IS THE APE-MAN A MYTH? Henry Fairfield Osborn. Human Biology, vol.1, no.1, pp.4-9, Jan., 1929.

DISCOVERY OF GIGANTOPITHECUS MANDIBLES AND OTHER MATERIAL IN LIU-CHENG DISTRICT OF CENTRAL KWANGSI IN SOUTH CHINA. W. C. Pei. Vertebrata Palasiatica, 1 (2): 65-72, 3 pls., June 1957.

NEW MATERIALS OF GIGANTOPITHECUS TEETH FROM SOUTH CHINA. W. C. Pei, Ju-kang Woo. Acta Palaeont. Sin., 4 (4): 477-490, illus., 1956.

THE AUSTRALOPITHECINE-BEARING DEPOSITS OF THE STERKFONTEIN AREA. J. T. Robinson. Ann. Transvaal Mus., vol.22, pt.1, pp.1-19, pls.1-2, Nov.4, 1952.

NUCHAL CRESTS IN AUSTRALOPITHECUS. J. T. Robinson, S. Zuckerman. Nature, London, vol.174, no.4443, pp.1197-1198, Dec.25, 1954.

AUSTRALOPITHECUS NOT A CHIMPANZEE. Alfred S. Romer. Science, vol.71, no.1845, pp.482-483, May 9, 1930.

THE STERCKFONTEIN APE. Ernst Schwarz. Nature, London, vol.138, no.3501, p.969, Dec.5, 1936.

THE DENTITION OF PLESIANTHROPUS AND PARANTHROPUS. Muzaffer Sueleyman Senyuerek. Ann. Transvaal Mus., Cambridge, vol.20, pt.3, pp.293-302, fig.1, Sept.12, 1941.

FURTHER REMAINS OF A STERKFONTEIN APE. J. C. Middleton Shaw. Nature, London, vol.143, no.3612, p.117, Jan.21, 1939.

THE HUMERUS OF PARANTHROPUS ROBUSTUS. William L. Straus, Jr. Amer. Jour. Phys. Anthropol., Phila., n.s., vol. 6, no.3, pp.285-312, figs.25, Sept.,1948.

ON THE ZOOLOGICAL STATUS OF TELANTHROPUS CAPENSIS. William L. Straus, Jr. Amer. Jour. Phys. Anthrop., Phila., n.s., vol.8, no.4, pp.495-498, Dec., 1950.

(ON THE SYSTEMATIC POSITION OF AUSTRALOPITHECUS AFRICANUS DART.) Ueber die systematische Stellung des Australopithecus africanus Dart. Franz Weidenreich. Natur. u. Mus., Frankfurt a.M., vol.61, no.5, pp.229-234, figs.6, May, 1931.

DRYOPITHECUS TEETH FROM KEIYUAN, YUNNAN PROVINCE. Ju-kang Woo. Vertebrata Palasiatica, 1 (1): 25-32, 1 pl., Mar., 1957.

THE PLESIANTHROPUS SKULL. F. Wood-Jones. Nature, London, vol.159, no.4052, p.883, June 28, 1947.

DENTITION OF AUSTRALOPITHECUS (PLESIANTHROPUS) Nature, London, vol. 144, no.3644, pp.451-452, Sept.2, 1939.

MIOCENE APE SKULL (SPECIES PROCONSUL). Illus. London News, vol.213, no. 5717, p.554, illus., Nov.13, 1948.

Growth and Development

AGE CHANGES IN THE POSITION OF THE OCCIPITAL CONDYLES IN THE CHIMPANZEE AND GORILLA. E. H. Ashton, S. Zuckerman. Jour. Phys. Anthropol., Phila., vol.10, no.3, pp.277-288, Sept., 1952.

ONE HUNDRED AND ONE MONTHS IN THE GROWTH AND DEVELOPMENT OF MOUNTAIN GORILLAS. Belle J. Benchley. Zoonooz, San Diego, vol.12, no.5, pp.3-10, illus., May, 1940.

OBSERVATIONS ON GROWTH AND DEVELOPMENT OF CHIMPANZEES. Harold C. Bingham. Amer. Jour. Phys. Anthrop., vol.13, no.3, pp.433-468, illus., Oct.-Dec., 1929.

(ANOTHER ACCOUNT OF THE GROWTH OF THE GORILLA.) Noch einmal zum Heranwachsen des Gorilla. G. Brandes. Zool. Garten, n.F., vol.3, nos.4-8, pp. 222-223, Aug.11, 1930.

(THE CHANGES IN THE YOUNG ORANG.) Die Veraenderungen des Orangkindes. G. Brandes. Zool. Garten, Leipzig, n.F., vol.3, nos.9-10, pp.286-289, figs.7, Oct., 1930.

(THE GROWTH OF THE CHIMPANZEE.) Das Heranwachsen des Schimpansen. G. Brandes. Zool. Garten, Leipzig, n.F., vol.4, nos.3-5, pp.115-132, pls.1-19, May, 1931.

(IMPORTANT DATA ON THE GROWTH OF THE GORILLA.) Wichtige Daten ueber das Heranwachsen des Gorilla. G. Brandes. Zool. Garten, Leipzig, vol.3, nos.4-8, pp. 104-116, 13 figs., 1930.

(THE YOUNG DEVELOPMENT OF AN ARTIFICIALLY RAISED CHIMPANZEE.) Aus der Jugendentwicklung einer kuenstlich aufgezogenen Schimpansin. Werner V. Catel. Zool. Garten, Leipzig, N.F., vol. 18, nos.1-2, pp.19-47, 1951.

EFFECTS OF THEELIN INJECTIONS IN NORMAL PRE-PUBESCENT CHIMPANZEES. James Harlan Elder. Anat. Rec., Phila., vol.72, no.1, pp.37-42, fig.1, pl.1, Sept., 1938.

THE GROWTH OF THE INFANT CHIMPANZEE BORN IN THE SOCIETY'S GARDENS AND A COMPARISON WITH THAT OF A CHIMPANZEE BORN IN FLORIDA. Julian S. Huxley. Proc. Zool. Soc. Lond., pt.2, pp.587-589, July, 1936.

DEVELOPMENT OF AN INFANT CHIMPANZEE DURING HER FIRST YEAR. Carlyle F. Jacobsen, Marion M. Jacobsen, Joseph G. Yoshioka. Comparative Psychology Monographs, Johns Hopkins Press, Balto., vol.9, no.1, ser. no.41, pp.1-94, pls.4, Sept., 1932.

STUDIES IN GROWTH CHANGES IN THE SKULL AND FACE OF ANTHROPOIDS. II. ECTOCRANIAL AND ENDOCRANIAL SUTURE CLOSURE IN ANTHROPOIDS AND OLD WORLD APES. W. M. Krogman. Amer. Jour. Anatomy, vol.46, no.2, pp. 315-353, figs.1-6, Sept.15, 1930.

STUDIES IN GROWTH CHANGES IN THE SKULL AND FACE OF ANTHROPOIDS. III. GROWTH CHANGES IN THE SKULL AND FACE OF THE GORILLA. W. M. Krogman. Amer. Jour. Anat., vol.47, no. 1, pp.89-115, Jan.15, 1931.

STUDIES IN GROWTH CHANGES IN THE SKULL AND FACE OF ANTHROPOIDS. IV. GROWTH CHANGES IN THE SKULL AND FACE OF THE CHIMPANZEE. W. M. Krogman. Amer. Jour. Anat., vol.47, no. 2, pp.325-342, Mar.15, 1931.

STUDIES IN GROWTH CHANGES IN THE SKULL AND FACE OF ANTHROPOIDS. V. GROWTH CHANGES IN THE SKULL AND FACE OF THE ORANG-UTAN. W. M. Krogman. Amer. Jour. Anat., vol.47, no. 2, pp.343-365, figs.9, Mar.15, 1931.

RELATIVE GROWTH OF THE LIMB BONES IN THE ANTHROPOID APES. Hyman Lumer. Human Biology, Balto., vol.11, no.3, pp. 379-392, figs.7, Sept., 1939.

GORILLA GROWTH-CHART. C. V. Noback. Bull. New York Zool. Soc., vol.35, no.4, pp.139-140, fig.1, July-Aug., 1932.

GROWTH OF INFANT FEMALE GORILLA. C. V. Noback. Amer. Jour. Phys. Anthrop., vol.14, no.2, pp.165-176, 1930.

THE POSTURAL DEVELOPMENT OF INFANT CHIMPANZEES. Austin H. Riesen, Elaine F. Kinder. New Haven and London, Yale University Press and Geoffrey Cumberlge, Oxford Univ. Press, XXI plus. 204 pp., 34 numbered tables, 6 pls., 1952. (Review by Walter Riese of) POSTURAL DEVELOPMENT OF INFANT CHIMPANZEES. Austin H. Riesen, Elaine F. Kinder. Jour. Mamm., vol.34, no.2, p. 275, May 14, 1953.

AGE CHANGES AND VARIABILITY IN GIBBONS. A MORPHOLOGICAL STUDY ON A POPULATION SAMPLE OF A MAN-LIKE APE. Adolph H. Schultz. Amer. Jour. Phys. Anthrop., Phila., n.s., vol.2, no.1, pp.1-129, figs.30, Mar., 1944.

GROWTH AND DEVELOPMENT OF THE CHIMPANZEE. Adolph H. Schultz. Carnegie Inst., Wash., publ.518 (Contrib. to Embryology, vol.28, no.170), pp.1-63, figs.11, pls.3, Aug.15, 1940.

GROWTH AND DEVELOPMENT OF THE ORANG-UTAN. Adolph H. Schultz. Carnegie Inst., Wash., publ.525 (Contrib. to Embryology, no.182), pp.57-110, 14 figs., 1 pl., Oct.23, 1941.

STUDIES ON THE GROWTH OF GORILLA AND OF OTHER HIGHER PRIMATES WITH SPECIAL REFERENCE TO A FETUS OF GORILLA, PRESERVED IN THE CARNEGIE MUSEUM. Adolph H. Schultz. Mem. Carnegie Mus., vol.11, no.1, pp.1-86, pls.1-8, Nov.14, 1927.

WEIGHT, GROWTH AND AGE IN CHIMPANZEE. Kenneth W. Spence, Robert M. Yerkes. Amer. Jour. Phys. Anthrop., vol 22, no.2, pp.229-246, figs.4, Jan.-Mar., 1937.

(THE ORANGUTAN YOUNG, "BOBBY".) Das Orang-Utan-Kind "Bobby." Karl Thaeter. Zool. Garten, Leipzig, 21 (5-6), 371-374, illus., 1956.

SEX CYCLES AND OTHER CYCLIC PHENOMENA IN A CHIMPANZEE DURING ADOLESCENCE, MATURITY, AND PREGNANCY. O. L. Tinklepaugh. Jour. Morph., vol.54, no.3, pp.521-546, figs.4, pl.1, June 5, 1933.

GROWTH AND DENTITION OF AN INFANT CHIMPANZEE AT THE BRISTOL ZOO. F. L. Vanderplank. Proc. Zool. Soc. Lond., vol.107, ser.B, Syst. and Morphol., pt.1, pp.175-176, tables 2, Apr., 1937.

AGE-CHANGES IN THE CHIMPANZEE, WITH SPECIAL REFERENCE TO GROWTH OF BRAIN, ERUPTION OF TEETH, AND ESTIMATION OF AGE; WITH A NOTE ON THE TAUNGS APE. S. Zuckerman. Proc. Zool. Soc. Lond., pt.1, pp.1-42, pls.1-4, Apr., 1928.

TWELVE HUNDRED POUNDS OF TWO YOUNG GORILLAS. Field, London, vol. 160, no.4159, p.372, figs.2, Sept.10, 1932.

Habits, Behavior

A NOTE ON THE BEHAVIOR OF AN ORANG-UTAN. M. F. Ashley-Montagu. Jour. Mam., vol.11, no.2, pp.231-232, May, 1930.

A NOTE ON THE BEHAVIOR OF THE CHIMPANZEE. Harry Beatty. Jour. Mam., vol.32, no.1, p.118, Feb.15, 1951.

PARENTAL PLAY OF CHIMPANZEES. Harold C. Bingham. Jour. Mam., vol.8, no.2, pp.77-89, pls.2, May, 1927.

HORMONAL MODIFICATION OF SOCIAL BEHAVIOR. II. THE EFFECTS OF SEX-HORMONES ADMINISTRATION ON THE SOCIAL DOMINANCE STATUS OF THE FEMALE CASTRATE CHIMPANZEE. H. G. Birch, G. Clark. Psychosom. Med., Wash., D.C., vol.8, no.5, pp.320-331, 1946.

(NOTES ON A YOUNG ORANG (PONGO PYGMAEUS HOPPIUS) BORN IN THE MENAGERIE OF THE JARDIN DES PLANTES.) Notes à propos d'un jeune orang (Pongo pygmaeus Hoppius) né a la Ménagerie du Jardin des Plantes. E. Bourdelle, P. Rode. Bull. Mus. Nat. Hist. Nat., Paris, ser.2, vol.4, no.5, pp.472-477, June, 1932.

MISS CONGO. Juanita Cassil Burbridge. Nat. Mag., vol.8, no.2, pp.113-115, illus., Aug., 1926.

THE NEST OF A CHIMPANZEE. Harry Burrell. Jour. Mam., vol.4, no.3, pp.178-180, pls.2, Aug., 1923.

BEHAVIOR AND SOCIAL RELATIONS OF FREE-RANGING PRIMATES. C. R. Carpenter. Scientific Monthly, Lancaster, Pa., vol.48, no.4, pp.319-325, illus., Apr., 1939.

BEHAVIOR RESEARCH ON FREE RANGING PRIMATES. C. R. Carpenter. Jour. Siam Soc., Nat. Hist. Suppl., Bangkok, vol.10, no.3, pp.47-52, Nov., 1937.

A FIELD STUDY IN SIAM OF THE BEHAVIOR AND SOCIAL RELATIONS OF THE GIBBON (HYLOBATES LAR). C. R. Carpenter. Comp. Psychology Monographs, Balto., vol.16, no.5, ser.no.83, pp.1-212, Dec., 1940.

THE CAREFREE LIFE OF A BABY GIBBON. Lee S. Crandall. Animal Kingdom, New York, vol.49, no.2, pp.70-72, illus., Mar.-Apr., 1946.

FAMILY AFFAIRS ON GIBBON ISLAND. Lee S. Crandall. Animal Kingdom, New York, vol.48, no.6, pp.165-167, Nov.-Dec., 1945.

GIBBONS--THE SMALLEST APES. THEIR SCIENTIFIC NAME MEANS "DWELLERS IN THE TREES," AND THEY PROVE THAT IT IS AN APT DESIGNATION. Jean Delacour. Animal Kingdom, New York, vol.45, no.2, pp.35-39, illus., Mar.-Apr., 1942.

THE BIPEDAL WALKING OF THE CHIMPANZEE. Herbert Elftman. Jour. Mam., vol.25, no.1, pp.67-71, fig.1, Feb., 1944.

CHIMPANZEE HANDEDNESS. Glen Finch. Science, Lancaster, n.s., vol.94, no.2431, pp.117-118, fig.1, Aug.1, 1941.

ON THE HABITS OF THE GORILLA AND OTHER TAILLESS LONG-ARMED APES. John E. Gray. Proc. Zool. Soc. Lond., pt.29, pp.212-213, 1861.

(OBSERVATIONS OF CHIMPANZEES (PAN TROGLODYTES BLUMENBACH 1775) IN THE NIMBA MOUNTAINS.) Beobachtungen an Schimpansen, Pan troglodytes (Blumenbach, 1775) in den Nimbabergen. Bernhard Grzimek. Saeugetierk. Mitteil., Stuttgart, vol.1, no.1, pp.1-5, illus., Jan.10, 1953.

(OBSERVATIONS OF THE BEHAVIOR OF A GREY GIBBON (HYLOBATES LEUCISCUS).) Beobachtungen ueber das Benehmen eines grauen Gibbons (Hylobates leuciscus). B. J. Krijgsman, J. Krijgsman-Tiessen. Archiv. Neerlandaises Zool., vol.2, no.4, pp.414-431, pl.3, June 30, 1937.

(OBSERVATIONS OF THE BEHAVIOR OF A GIBBON FAMILY IN THE ZURICH ZOOLOGICAL GARDEN.) Beobachtungen ueber das Verhalten einer Gibbonfamilie im Zuericher Zoologischen Garten. Monika Meyer-Holzapfel. Zool. Garten, Leipzig, N.F., vol.17, nos.1-5, pp.10-27, illus., 1950.

(DESCRIPTION OF AN ORANG-UTAN NEST.) Beschreibung eines Orang-Utan Nestes. K. Moebius. Sitz. Ber. Akad. Wissensch. Berlin, Math.-Phys. Classe, Jahg. 1893, pp.833-834, Nov.2, 1893.

STUDIES OF INFANT CHIMPANZEES. Henry W. Nissen. Science, Lancaster, n.s., vol.95, no.2459, pp.159-161, Feb. 13, 1942.

THE BEHAVIOR AND SOCIAL RELATIONS OF THE GIBBON (HYLOBATES LAR) OBSERVED UNDER RESTRICTED FREE-RANGE CONDITIONS. Bernard F. Riess. Zoologica, New York Zool. Soc., 41 (3): 89-99, Nov.23, 1956.

(CAN THE CHIMPANZEE BEAT ITS BREAST?) Kann der Schimpanse "brusttrommeln"? Karl Max Schneider. Zool. Garten, N.F., Leipzig, vol.9, nos.3-4, pp.161-165, May, 1937.

CHIMPANZEE TWINS: BEHAVORIAL RELATIONS AND DEVELOPMENT. Michael I. Tomilin, R. M. Yerkes. Jour. Genetic Psychol., vol.46, pp.239-263, figs.8, 1935.

(LEAPING BEHAVIOR OF THE CHIMPANZEE PAN TR. TROGLODYTES BLUMENBACH 1799.) Das Verhalten des Schimpansen, Pan tr. Troglodytes (Blumenbach, 1799), beim Sprung. W. Ullrich. Saeugetierk. Mitteil., Stuttgart, vol.2, no.3, pp.124-126, illus., July 1, 1954.

(OBSERVATIONS CONDUCTED ON A YOUNG ORANG-UTAN BORN IN THE MENAGERIE OF THE JARDIN DES PLANTES.) Observations faites sur un jeune orang-outan ne a la Menagerie du Jardin des Plantes. Ach. Urbain, Ed. Dechambre, P. Rode. Mammalia, Paris, vol.5, no.3-4, pp.82-85, pl. 6, Sept.-Dec., 1941.

THE ZOO'S FIRST BABY CHIMPANZEE AND SOME NOTES ON THE CHILDHOOD OF HER HALF-BROTHER "ADAM." F. L. Vanderplank. Field, London, vol.165, no. 4287, p.381, illus., Feb.23, 1935.

ANTHROPOID BEHAVIOR. R. M. Yerkes, Margaret Sykes Child. Quart. Rev. Biol., vol.2, pp.37-57, pls.1-2, Mar., 1927.

Hematology

NEW DATA ON THE SEROLOGY OF THE ANTHROPOID APES. P. B. Candella. Amer. Jour. Phys. Anthrop., Phila., vol.27, no.2, pp.209-221, Sept.30, 1940.

PUERPERAL HEMORRHAGE IN CHIMPANZEES. James H. Elder. Amer. Jour. Obstetrics and Gynecology, St. Louis, vol. 37, no.2, pp.327-329, table 1, Feb., 1939.

IMMUNIZATION OF CHIMPANZEES WITH HUMAN BLOOD. K. Landsteiner, Philip Levine. Jour. Immunol., vol.22, no.6, pp.397-400, 1932.

SEROLOGICAL STUDIES ON THE BLOOD OF THE PRIMATES. II. THE BLOOD GROUPS IN ANTHROPOID APES. K. Landsteiner, C. Philip Miller, Jr. Jour. Exper. Med., vol.42, no.6, pp.853-862, Dec.1, 1925.

BLOOD GROUP FACTORS IN ANTHROPOID APES AND MONKEYS. I. STUDIES ON A CHIMPANZEE, "PAN." Alexander S. Wiener. Jour. Phys. Anthropol., Phila., vol.10, no.3, pp.372-375, Sept., 1952.

Longevity

(THE DEATH OF "GOLIATH," OUR GIANT ORANG.) Der Tod unseres Riesenorangs

"Goliath." G. Brandes. Zool. Garten, Leipzig, vol.1, nos.10-12, pp.396-400, figs. 2, 1929.

(HOW LONG DOES THE ORANGUTAN LIVE?) Wie alt wird der Orang-Utan? G. Brandes. Zool. Garten, Leipzig, n.F., vol.4, nos.1-2, pp.1-9, figs.1-2, Feb., 1931.

DEATH OF THE OLDEST CHIMPANZEE IN CAPTIVITY. Michael I. Tomilin. Science, n.s., vol.83, no.2144, pp.103-104, Jan.31, 1936.

BUSHMAN, GORILLA OF LINCOLN PARK, CHICAGO, 22 YEARS OLD. Illus. London News, vol.216, no.5791, p.569, illus., Apr. 15, 1950.

Pelage, Skin, Coloration

(THE HAIR COVER OF A CHIMPANZEE FETUS.) Das Haarkleid eines Fetus von Schimpanse. L. Bolk. Bijdragen tot de Dierkunde, Amsterdam, vol.20, Feest-no., pp.57-65, with 8 figs., Leiden, 1919.

NOTES ON THE COLOURATION OF THE WHITE-BROWED GIBBON (H. HOOLOCK HARL.). J. F. Peart. Jour. Bombay Nat. Hist. Soc., vol.37, no.1, p.214, Apr.15, 1934.

(DEVIATION OF COLORS IN FLATLAND GORILLAS, GORILLA G. GORILLA WYMAN, 1847.) Abweichende Faerbungen bei Flachland-Gorillas, Gorilla g. Gorilla (Wyman, 1847). Hans Petzsch. Saeugetierk Mitteil., vol.1, no.3, p.124, July 1, 1953.

(GEOGRAPHICAL RACES OF THE CHIMPANZEE (PAN SATYRUS L.). OBSERVATIONS ON THE PIGMENTATION OF THE FACE IN PAN SATYRUS VERUS SCHWARZ.) Les races geographiques du chimpanze (Pan satyrus L.). Observations sur la pigmentation de la face chez Pan satyrus verus Schwarz. P. Rode. Mammalia, Paris, vol.1, no.4, pp.165-177, figs.2, June, 1937.

(ANOTHER YOUNG BROWN CHIMPANZEE.) Ein weiterer junger brauner Schimpanse. Karl Max Schneider. Zool. Garten, N.F., vol.1, pp.182-195, figs.1-9, 1928.

THE COLOUR OF THE FACE AND SKIN IN UPPER GUINEA CHIMPANZEE. Ernst Schwarz. Proc. Zool. Soc. Lond., pt.1, p.333, Apr., 1936.

THE MICROSCOPIC ANATOMY OF THE SKIN OF THE GORILLA. William L. Straus, Jr. The Anatomy of the Gorilla. Henry Cushier Raven Memorial Volume, pp.213-337, pls.106-109, 1950.

Psychology

PAYDAY FOR PRIMATES. Frank A. Beach. Nat. Hist., New York, vol.56, no.10, pp. 448-451, illus., Dec., 1947.

CHIMPANZEE TRANSLOCATION BY MEANS OF BOXES. Harold C. Bingham. Comp. Psych. Monographs, vol.5, no.3, Serial no. 25, pp.1-91, pls.1-4, Feb., 1929.

SELECTIVE TRANSPORTATION BY CHIMPANZEES. Harold C. Bingham. Comp. Psych. Monographs, vol.5, no.4, serial no. 26, pp.1-45, pls.1-4, May, 1929.

SEX DEVELOPMENT IN APES. Harold C. Bingham. Comp. Psychol. Monographs, vol.5, no.1, serial no.23, pp.1-165, 1 pl., Balto: The Johns Hopkins Press.

FOUR LITTLE FACES AND FOUR LITTLE TEMPERAMENTS. William Bridges. Animal Kingdom, New York Zool. Soc., vol.16, no.3, pp.90-91, illus., June, 1953.

FOOD-TOKENS AS INCENTIVES FOR LEARNING BY CHIMPANZEES. John T. Cowles. Comp. Psychol. Monographs, vol. 14, no.5, serial no.71, pp.1-96, figs.9, tables 19, Sept., 1937.

THE COOPERATIVE SOLVING OF PROBLEMS BY YOUNG CHIMPANZEES. Meredith P. Crawford. Comp. Psychol. Monographs, vol.14, no.2, serial no.68, pp.1-88, figs.4, June, 1937.

CHIMPANZEE: A PSYCHO-BIOLOGICAL REVIEW. J. Gray. Discovery, Norwich, vol.5, no.4, pp.121-124, figs.6, Apr., 1944.

THE CULTURAL CAPACITY OF CHIMPANZEE. Keith J. Hayes, Catherine Hayes. Human Biology, 26 (3): 288-303, Sept., 1954.

THE INTELLECTUAL DEVELOPMENT OF A HOME-RAISED CHIMPANZEE. Keith J. Hayes, Catherine Hayes. Proc. Amer. Philos. Soc., Phila., vol.95, no.2, pp.105-109, illus., Apr.30, 1951.

(THE INTELLIGENCE OF THE HIGHER APES.) L'intelligence des singes supérieurs. W. Koehler. Transl. from 2nd ed (German) by P. Guillaume, vol.1, pp.XIX, 319, 7 pls., 19 figs., Bibliothèque de Philosophie contemporaine. Félix Alcan: Paris, 1927.

AFFECTIVE RESPONSES OF AN INFANT CHIMPANZEE REARED IN ISOLATION FROM ITS KIND. T. L. McCulloch, George M. Haslerud. Jour. Comp. Psychol., Balto., vol.28, no.3, pp.437-445, table 1, Dec., 1939.

EQUATED AND NON-EQUATED STIMULUS IN DISCRIMINATION LEARNING BY CHIMPANZEES. 1. COMPARISON WITH UNLIMITED RESPONSE. 2. COMPARISON WITH LIMITED RESPONSE. 3. PREPOTENCY OF RESPONSE TO ODDITY THROUGH TRAINING. T. L. McCulloch, H. W. Nissen. Jour. Comp. Psychology, vol.23, no.1, pp.165-189, Feb., 1937; vol. 23, no.2, pp.365-381, Apr., 1937.

THE INFLUENCE OF AMOUNT OF INCENTIVE ON DELAYED RESPONSE PERFORMANCES OF CHIMPANZEES. H. W. Nissen. J. H. Elder. Jour. Genetic Psychol., vol. 47, pp.49-72, figs.1, tables 8, 1935.

DELAYED REWARD IN DISCRIMINATION LEARNING BY CHIMPANZEES. Austin H. Riesen. Comp. Psychol. Monographs, Balto., vol.15, no.5, ser.77, pp.54, figs. 9, tables 9, Feb., 1940.

(DO YOU SPEAK CHIMPANZEE?) Sprechen Sie Schimpansisch? Georg Schwidetzky. Verlag der Deutsche Gesellschaft fuer Tier-und Ursprachenforschung, Leipzig, pp.vii, 80, 1931.

DO YOU SPEAK CHIMPANZEE? AN INTRODUCTION TO THE STUDY OF THE SPEECH OF ANIMALS AND OF PRIMITIVE MEN. Georg Schwidetsky. London, George Routledge and Sons, Ltd., pp.141, 1932.

DISPOSITION AND INTELLIGENCE OF THE ORANG-UTAN. W. Henry Sheak. Jour. Mam., vol.3, no.1, pp.47-51, Feb., 1922.

SOME OBSERVATIONS AND EXPERIMENTS OF THE INTELLIGENCE OF THE CHIMPANZEE AND OURANG. W. T. Shepherd. Amer. Jour. Psychol., vol.34, pp.590-591, 1923.

THE SOLUTION OF MULTIPLE CHOICE PROBLEMS BY CHIMPANZEES. Kenneth W. Spence. Compar. Pshcyol. Monogr., Balto., vol.15, no.3, serial no.75, pp.1-54, figs.2, Apr., 1939.

MORPHINE ADDICTION IN CHIMPANZEES. S. D. S. Spragg. Comp. Psychol. Monogr., Balto., Md., vol.15, no.7, ser.79, pp.132, figs.11, tables 10, Apr., 1940.

(CHARACTERISTICS OF CHIMPANZEE PSYCHOLOGY.) Grundzuege der Schimpansen-Psychologie. Guenter Tembrock. Verlag Naturkundliche Korrespondenz, Berlin, pp.96, pls.4, 1949.

A CHIMPANZEE HYPNOTIZED LIKE A HUMAN BEING: EXPERIMENTS INDICATING THAT APES DO NOT RESPOND TO HYPNOTIC METHODS USED WITH LOWER ANIMALS, BUT ONLY TO THOSE APPLIED TO MEN AND WOMEN. Leopold Thoma. Illus. London News, vol.189, no.5083, pp. 488-489, illus., Sept.19, 1936.

(OBSERVATIONS OF THE MENTAL CAPACITY OF PRESENT-DAY "MAN-APES.") Beobachtungen geistiger Leistungen an heutigen Menschenaffen. H. Weinert. Freude am Leben, Berlin, vol.17, no.7, pp.109-113, illus., Oct., 1940.

EXPERIMENTS WITH AN INFANT CHIMPANZEE. Ada W. Yerkes. Jour. Genetic Psychol., vol.46, pp.171-181, 1935.

A CHIMPANZEE FAMILY. R. M. Yerkes. Jour. Genetic Psych., vol.48, no.2, pp. 362-370, June, 1936.

CONJUGAL CONTRASTS AMONG CHIMPANZEES. R. M. Yerkes. Jour. Abnormal and Social Psychol., pp.175-199, Apr., 1941.

(MEASUREMENT OF ADAPTIVE RESPONSE IN THE CHIMPANZEES.) La mesure du comportement adapte chez les chimpanzes. R. M. Yerkes. Jour. Psychol. Normale et Patholog., Paris, vol.34, nos.5-8, pp.449-474, fig.1, tables 6, May 15 - Oct.15, 1937.

THE MIND OF A GORILLA. R. M. Yerkes. Genetic Psychology Monographs, vol.2, nos. 1-2, Clark Univ., Worcester, Mass., pp. 193, 9 pls., Dec., 1926.

(Review by Hartley H.T. Jackson of) THE MIND OF A GORILLA. R. M. Yerkes. Jour. Mam., vol.8, no.2, p.168, May, 1927.

THE MIND OF A GORILLA. PART III. MEMORY. R. M. Yerkes. Comp. Psychology Monographs, serial no.24, vol. 5, no.2, pp.92, illus., Dec., 1928.

MODES OF BEHAVIORAL ADAPTATION IN CHIMPANZEE TO MULTIPLE-CHOICE PROBLEMS. R. M. Yerkes. Comp. Psychol. Mongr., vol.10, no.1, pp.108, May, 1934.

SOCIAL BEHAVIOR OF CHIMPANZEES: DOMINANCE BETWEEN MATES, IN RELATION TO SEXUAL STATUS. R. M. Yerkes. Jour. Comp. Psychology, vol.30, no.1, pp.147-186, Aug., 1940.

SOCIAL DOMINANCE AND SEXUAL STATUS IN THE CHIMPANZEE. R. M. Yerkes. Quart. Rev. Biol., Balto., vol. 14, no.2, pp.115-136, figs.2, tables 2, June, 1939.

SUGGESTIBILITY IN CHIMPANZEE. R. M. Yerkes. Jour. Social Psychology, vol.5, pp.271-282, 1934.

CHIMPANZEE INTELLIGENCE AND ITS VOCAL EXPRESSIONS. R. M. Yerkes, Blanche W. Learned. 12 mo., pp.1-157, 1 pl., Balto: The Williams and Wilkins Co., Apr., 1925.

PRE-LINGUISTIC SIGN BEHAVIOR IN CHIMPANZEE. R. M. Yerkes, Henry W. Nissen. Science, Lancaster, n.s., vol.89, no.2321, pp.585-587, June 23, 1939.

MOTHER-INFANT RELATIONS IN CHIMPANZEE. R. M. Yerkes, Michael I. Tomilin. Jour. Comparative Psychol., vol. 20, no.3, pp.321-348, pls.1-6, Dec., 1935.

NATURE AND CONDITIONS OF AVOIDANCE (FEAR) RESPONSE IN CHIMPANZEE. R. M. Yerkes, Ada W. Yerkes. Jour. Comp. Psychol., Balto., vol.21, no.1, pp.53-66, Feb., 1936.

CONCERNING MEMORY IN THE CHIMPANZEE. R. M. Yerkes, D. N. Yerkes. Jour. Comp. Psych., vol.8, pp.237-271, illus., 1928.

CAN A GORILLA BE MADE TO LAUGH? EXPRESSIONS OF ESEKA OF BERLIN. Illus. London News, vol.189, no.5087, p. 667, illus., Oct.17, 1936.

LONDON APE MAKES SKETCH. SIMIAN ARTISTS IN ENGLAND AND INDIA GIVE HINTS OF POSSIBLE ORIGIN OF HUMAN ART. COMPANIONS SHOW INTEREST IN OUTLINE DRAWINGS MADE WITH TWIG OR FINGER-TIP. Science News Letter, Wash., D.C., vol.42, no.9, p.135, Aug.29, 1942.

Reproductive Biology

ANALYSES OF URINE OF THE CHIMPANZEE FOR ESTROGENIC CONTENT DURING VARIOUS STAGES OF THE MENSTRUAL CYCLE. Edgar Allen, A. W. Diddle, T. H. Burford, J. H. Elder. Endocrinology, Los Angeles, vol.20, no.4, pp.546-549, table, July, 1936.

NOTES ON THE BIRTH OF AND INFANCY OF A GIBBON. Belle J. Benchley. Parks and Recreation, Rockford, Ill., vol.22, no. 2, pp.67, 71, illus., Oct., 1938.

NOTES ON THE BIRTH OF A CHIMPANZEE. W. Reid Blair. Zool. Soc. Bull., vol.23, pp.104-111, Sept., 1920.

(THE NURSING PERIOD OF THE ORANG-UTAN.) Die Stillzeit des Orang. G. Brandes. Zool. Garten, Leipzig, n.F., vol.10, nos. 3-4, pp.139-141, Sept., 1938.

(ORANG COPULATION.) Die Begattung der Orangs. G. Brandes. Zool. Garten, Leipzig, n.F., vol.3, nos.4-8, pp.216-217, Aug.11, 1930.

ON THE BIRTH AND UPBRINGING OF THE FEMALE CHIMPANZEE "JACQUELINE." A. Budd, L. G. Smith, F. W. Shelley. Proc. Zool. Soc. Lond., vol.113, ser.A, pts.1, 2, pp.1-20, pls.1, 2, figs.2, June, 1943.

THE MENSTRUAL CYCLE AND BODY TEMPERATURE IN TWO GIBBONS (HYLOBATES LAR). C. R. Carpenter. Record, Phila., vol.79, no.3, suppl., no.2, pp.291-296, Mar.25, 1941.

THE FAILURE OF ESTROGEN TO INDUCE CHANGES IN THE SEX SKIN OF THE MALE CHIMPANZEE. George Clark. Yale Jour. Biol. Med., New Haven, vol.21, no.3, pp. 245-247, Jan., 1949.

OBSERVATIONS ON THE SEX SKIN AND SEX CYCLE WITH A CHIMPANZEE. George Clark, H. G. Birch. Endocrinology, Boston, vol.43, no.4, pp.218-231, Oct., 1948.

NOTES ON BIRTH OF A CHIMPANZEE IN THE CLIFTON ZOOLOGICAL GARDENS, BRISTOL. R. C. Clarke. Proc. Zool. Soc., Lond., pt.4, pp.731-732, Jan., 1935.

NOTES ON A FAMILY OF BREEDING GIBBONS. H. J. Coolidge, Jr. Human Biol., vol.5, no.2, pp.288-294, figs.4, May, 1933.

OUR FIRST BABY GIBBON IS BORN AND SEEMS TO BE DOING WELL. Lee S. Crandall. Animal Kingdom, New York, vol.48, no.5, pp.158-159, illus., Oct.8, 1945.

THE TIME OF OVULATION IN CHIMPANZEES. J. H. Elder. Yale Jour. Biol. and Med., vol.10, no.4, pp.347-364, figs.3, table 1, Mar., 1938.

USE OF THE FRIEDMAN TEST FOR PREGNANCY WITH CHIMPANZEES. J. H. Elder, John M. Bruhn. Yale Jour. Biol. and Med., New Haven, vol.12, no.2, pp.155-160, fig. 1, Dec., 1939.

CHIMPANZEE BIRTHS IN CAPTIVITY; A TYPICAL CASE HISTORY AND REPORT OF SIXTEEN BIRTHS. J. H. Elder, R. M. Yerkes. Proc. Roy. Soc. London, ser.B, no.819, vol.120, pp.409-421, July, 1936.

THE SEXUAL CYCLE OF THE CHIMPANZEE. J. H. Elder, R. M. Yerkes. Anat. Record, vol.67, no.1, pp.119-143, Dec.25, 1936.

BODILY ELECTRICAL POTENTIAL CHANGES ASSOCIATED WITH OVULATION AND EARLY PREGNANCY IN THE CHIMPANZEE. Glen Finch, R. M. Yerkes, James H. Elder. Proc. Soc. Exper. Biol. and Med., vol.37, pp.560-563, figs.2, 1937.

THE BIRTH OF TWO ANTHROPOID APES. Herbert Fox. Jour. Mam., vol.10, no.1, pp.37-51, pls.4-7, Feb., 1929.

(REPORT ON A GIBBON BIRTH IN THE ZOOLOGICAL GARDEN OF AARHUS, DENMARK.) Bericht ueber eine Gibbon-Geburt im Zoologischen Garten von Aarhus (Daenemark). Hubert B. Hutzelsider. Zool. Garten, n.F., vol.9, nos.3-4, pp. 113-122, figs.6, May 2, 1937.

MANNER OF COPULATION OF GIBBONS. (IN: COOLIDGE, HAROLD J., JR., NOTES ON A FAMILY OF BREEDING GIBBONS.) Gerrit S. Miller, Jr. Human Biology, vol. 5, no.2, p.291, May, 1933.

(HISTORY OF A CHIMPANZEE FAMILY.) Histoire d'une famille de Chimpanzés. L. Momyane. pp.1-21, pls.1-4 (not original), Bull et Mém. Soc. Anthrop., Paris, 1928.

REPRODUCTION IN THE CHIMPANZEE: REPORT ON FORTY-NINE BIRTHS. H. W. Nissen, R. M. Yerkes. Anat. Record, Phila., vol.86, no.4, pp.567-578, Aug., 1943.

(ON THE DURATION OF GESTATION AMONG THE GIBBONS.) A propos de la durés de gestation chez les gibbons. P. Rode. Mammalia, Paris, vol.6, no.1, pp. 46-47, pl.4, Mar., 1942.

(OUR PRESENT KNOWLEDGE OF THE MENSTRUAL CYCLE OF THE SIMIANS.) Nos connaissances actuelles sur le cycle menstruel chez les Simiens. P. Rode. Mammalia, Paris, 2 (2): 95-98, June, 1938.

OBSERVATIONS ON REPRODUCTION IN THE CHIMPANZEE. A. H. Schultz, F. F. Snyder. Bull. Johns Hopkins Hospital, vol. 57, no.4, pp.193-205, Oct., 1935.

GORILLA BORN IN CAPTIVITY. William L. Straus, Jr. Science, vol.125, no.3241, pp. 227-228, Feb.8, 1957.

PARTURITION AND PUERPERAL SEPSIS IN A CHIMPANZEE. O. L. Tinklepaugh. Anat. Record, vol.53, no.2, pp.193-202, pl.1, July 25, 1932.

BREEDING OF ORANG-UTANS. Frederick A. Ulmer. Zool. Garten, Leipzig, 23 (1-3): 57-65, illus., 1957.

A CAPTIVE-BORN CHIMPANZEE. Bessie A. White. Scientific Monthly, vol.29, no. 6, pp.558-565, 2 pls., 1929.

ON THE BIRTH OF A CHIMPANZEE RECENTLY BORN IN THE SOCIETY'S GARDENS. J. M. Wyatt, G. M. Vevers. Proc. Zool. Soc. Lond., pt.1, pp.195-197, Apr., 1935.

MULTIPLE BIRTHS IN ANTHROPOID APES. R. M. Yerkes. Science, n.s., vol.79, no. 2054, pp.430-431, May 11, 1934.

A SECOND-GENERATION CAPTIVE-BORN CHIMPANZEE. R. M. Yerkes. Science, n.s., vol.81, no.2109, pp.542-543, May 31, 1935.

SEXUAL BEHAVIOR IN THE CHIMPANZEE. R. M. Yerkes. Human Biology, Balto., vol.11, no.1, pp.78-111, figs.5, tables 10, Feb., 1939.

CONCERNING REPRODUCTION IN THE CHIMPANZEE. R. M. Yerkes, James H. Elder. Yale Jour. Biol. and Med., vol. 10, no.1, pp.41-48, table 1, Oct., 1937.

OESTRUS, RECEPTIVITY, AND MATING IN CHIMPANZEE. R. M. Yerkes, James H. Elder. Comp. Psychol. Monog., vol.13, no.5, pp.39, Oct., 1936.

THE SEXUAL AND REPRODUCTIVE CYCLES OF CHIMPANZEE. R. M. Yerkes, James H. Elder. Proc. Nat. Acad. Sci., U.S. Amer., vol.22, no.5, pp.276-283, May, 1936.

THE ASCHEIM-ZONDEK DIAGNOSIS OF PREGNANCY IN THE CHIMPANZEE. S. Zuckerman. Amer. Jour. Phys., vol. 110, no.3, pp.597-601, Jan., 1935.

THE MENSTRUAL CYCLE OF THE PRIMATES. PART 7. THE SEXUAL SKIN OF THE CHIMPANZEE. S. Zuckerman, J. F. Fulton. Jour. Anat., Cambridge, vol.69, pt.1, pp.38-46, pl.1, figs.2, Oct., 1934.

Reproductive Organs

THE BACULUM OF THE GORILLA. D. Dwight Davis. Fieldiana, Zoology, Chicago, Nat. Hist. Mus., vol.31, no.54, pp.645-647, illus., Oct.12, 1951.

THE STRUCTURE OF THE REPRODUCTIVE TRACT IN THE FEMALE GIBBON. Edward W. Dempsey. Amer. Jour. Anat., Phila., vol.67, no.2, pp.229-253, figs.2, pls.4, Sept.16, 1940.

REPORT OF A CASE OF INHERITED POLYMASTIA IN CHIMPANZEE. J. H. Elder. Anat. Record, vol.65, no.1, pp. 83-87, pl.1, Apr.25, 1936.

THE EXTERNAL GENITALIA OF THE GORILLA, GORILLA GORILLA GORILLA (SAVAGE AND WYMAN). Leonard J. Goss. Zoologica, New York, vol.32, pt.2, pp.97-100, pls.1-5, July 31, 1947.

THE EXTERNAL GENITALIA OF THE FEMALE CHIMPANZEE; WITH OBSERVATIONS ON THE MAMMARY APPARATUS. W. C. Osman Hill. Proc. Zool. Soc. Lond., vol. 121, pt.1, pp.133-145, illus., May, 1951.

NOTE ON THE MALE EXTERNAL GENITALIA OF THE CHIMPANZEE. W. C. Osman Hill. Proc. Zool. Soc. Lond., vol. 116, pt.1, pp.129-132, figs.2, pl.1, May, 1946.

THE MALE EXTERNAL GENITALIA OF THE GORILLA, WITH REMARKS ON THE OS PENIS OF OTHER HOMINOIDEA. W. C. Osman Hill, L. Harrison Matthews. Proc. Zool. Soc. Lond., vol.119, pt.2, pp.363-378, figs.6, pls.4, Aug.17, 1949.

SUPPLEMENTARY NOTE ON THE MALE EXTERNAL GENITALIA OF GORILLA. W. C. Osman Hill, L. Harrison Matthews. Proc. Zool. Soc. Lond., vol.120, pt.2, pp. 311-316, figs.3, pl.1, Aug.30, 1950.

NOTES ON THE GENITAL ANATOMY AND PHYSIOLOGY OF THE GIBBON (HYLOBATES). L. Harrison Matthews. Proc. Zool. Soc. Lond., vol.116, pt.2, pp.339-364, figs.8, Nov., 1946.

GENITAL SWELLING IN A FEMALE GORILLA. H. C. Raven. Jour. Mam., vol.17, no.4, p.416, Nov., 1936.

ON THE PELVIC MUSCLES AND GENERATIVE ORGANS IN THE MALE CHIMPANZEE. Charles F. Sonntag. Proc. Zool. Soc. Lond., pp.1001-1011, Dec., 1923.

OCCURRENCE OF VAGINAL PLUG IN A CHIMPANZEE. O. L. Tinklepaugh. Anat. Record, vol.46, no.4, pp.329-332, fig.1, Sept.25, 1930.

THE EXTERNAL GENITALIA OF THE SIMIAN PRIMATES. George B. Wislocki. Human Biology, vol.8, no.3, pp.309-347, figs.34, Sept., 1936.

GRAVID REPRODUCTION TRACT AND PLACENTA OF THE CHIMPANZEE. George B. Wislocki. Amer. Jour. Phys. Anthrop., vol.18, no.1, pp.81-92, pls.2, July-Sept., 1933.

ON THE FEMALE REPRODUCTIVE TRACT OF THE GORILLA, WITH A COMPARISON OF THAT OF OTHER PRIMATES. George B. Wislocki. Publ. 433 Carnegie Inst. Wash., pp.163-204, figs.4, pls.12, Aug., 1932.

SIZE, WEIGHT, AND HISTOLOGY OF THE TESTES IN THE GORILLA. George B. Wislocki. Jour. Mam., vol.23, no.3, pp. 281-287, pls.2, Aug.14, 1942.

Senses

OBSERVATIONS ON SENSE OF SMELL IN CHIMPANZEES. Thos. M. Blackman. Amer. Jour. Phys. Anthropol., Phila., vol.5, no.3, pp.283-294, 1947.

AUDITORY ACUITY OF THE CHIMPANZEE. James Harlan Elder. Jour. Comp. Psychol., vol.17, no.2, pp.157-183, figs.4, Apr., 1934.

TASTE-TESTING THE ANTHROPOID APES. R. A. Fisher, E. B. Ford, Julian Huxley. Nature, Lond., vol.144, no.3652, p.750, Oct.28, 1939.

CHIMPANZEE COLOR VISION. I. HUE DISCRIMINATION AT THREE SPECTRAL POINTS. Walter F. Grether. Jour. Comp. Psychol., Balto., vol.29, no.2, pp.167-177, figs.2, table 1, Apr., 1940.

CHIMPANZEE COLOR VISION. II. COLOR MIXTURE PROPORTIONS. Walter F. Grether. Jour. Comp. Psychol., Balto., vol.29, no.2, pp.179-186, figs.2, tables 2, Apr., 1940.

CHIMPANZEE COLOR VISION. III. SPECTRAL LIMITS. Walter F. Grether. Jour. Comp. Psychol., Balto., vol.29, no.2, pp. 187-192, fig.1, Apr., 1940.

ANALYSIS OF THE FORMATION OF VISUAL DISCRIMINATION HABITS IN CHIMPANZEES. Kenneth W. Spence. Jour. Comp. Psychology, vol.23, no.1, pp.77-100, figs.3, tables 4, Feb., 1937.

Skull and Teeth

(AN ASPECT OF THE DEVELOPMENT OF THE PREMAXILLARY IN THE GORILLA.) Un aspect du developpement du premaxillaire chez le Gorille. J. Anthony. Mammalia, Paris, vol.11, no.4, pp.160-164, figs.2, (Dec., 1947), 1948.

ON A POST-FRONTAL AND ORBITAL ELEMENTS IN A YOUNG GORILLA SKULL. F. M. Ashley-Montagu. Jour. Anat., Cambridge, vol.65, pt.4, pp.446-456, figs. 6, July, 1931.

A UNIQUE DEVELOPMENT OF THE PREMAXILLA IN THE GORILLA. M. F. Ashley-Montagu. Amer. Jour. Phys. Anthrop., Phila., vol.29, no.3, pp.417-423, pls.2, Sept.30, 1942.

AN ACCESSORY CUSP ON THE LOWER FIRST PERMANENT MOLAR OF THE CHIMPANZEE AND GORILLA. E. H. Ashton. Proc. Zool. Soc. Lond., vol.123, pt.1, pp.27-32, pl.1, June 10, 1953.

SEXUAL DIFFERENCES IN THE DIMENSIONS OF THE MILK TEETH OF THE CHIMPANZEE AND GORILLA. E. H. Ashton. Proc. Zool. Soc. Lond., vol. 126, pt.1, pp.121-125, Jan.11, 1956.

SOME QUANTITATIVE DENTAL CHARACTERISTICS OF THE CHIMPANZEE, GORILLA, AND ORANG-OUTANG. E. H. Ashton, S. Zuckerman. Philos. Trans. Roy. Soc. Lond., Ser.B, Biol. Sci., vol. 234, no.616, pp.471-484, 1950.

A FEMALE ORANG SKULL WHICH SHOWS WHAT APPEAR TO BE IMPERFECTLY FORMED ADDITIONAL ANTERIOR PREMOLARS. R. Broom. Ann. Transvaal Mus., Cambridge, vol.20, pt.4, pp.341-342, fig.1, Oct.18, 1946.

(COMPARATIVE MORPHOLOGICAL STUDIES OF THE MOLARS OF THE ORANGUTAN AND THE GIBBON. Vergleichende morphologische Studien an den Molaren des Orangutan und des Gibbon. H. Eckardt. Zeitschr. f. Morphol. u. Anthropol., u. vol.27, pp.225-338, 21 figs., 6 pls., 1929.

EXHIBITION OF THE SKULL OF A GORILLA. Louis Fraser. Proc. Zool. Soc. Lond., pt.31, p.372, 1863.

(CRANIOLOGICAL STUDIES OF THE CHIMPANZEE.) Studii craniologici sui cimpanze. Enrico Hillyer Giglioli. Ann. Mus. Civ. Nat. Genova, vol.3, pp.3-127, pls.7-8, Dec., 1872.

CRANIAL ALLOMETRY IN THE GREAT APES. Eugene Giles. Human Biology, 28 (1): 43-58, Feb., 1956.

A CRITICAL REVIEW OF COOLIDGE'S MEASUREMENTS OF GORILLA SKULLS. A. J. Haddow, R. W. Ross. Proc. Zool. Soc. Lond., vol.121, pt.1, pp.43-54, May 22, 1951.

OBSERVATIONS ON THE FORM OF THE DENTAL ARCH OF THE ORANG. Milo Hellman. Int. Jour. Orthodontia, vol.4, no.2, pp.1-15, figs.1-19, Feb., 1918.

A NOTE ON SEXUAL DIFFERENCES IN THE SKULL OF GIBBONS. D. A. Hooijer. Proc. Kon. Nederl. Akad. Wetenschappen, Amsterdam, ser.C, vol.55, no.4, pp.375-381, 1952.

NOTES ON SOME ANOMALOUS GIBBON SKULLS. A. Tindell Hopwood. Jour. Anat., vol.67, pt.3, pp.475-479, figs.12, Apr., 1933.

ANATOMICAL OBSERVATIONS ON A COLLECTION OF ORANG SKULLS FROM WESTERN BORNEO; WITH A BIBLIOGRAPHY. Ales Hrdliceka. Proc. U. S. Nat. Mus., vol.31, no.1495, pp.539-568, figs.1-8, Nov.17, 1906.

A BILATERAL DIVISION OF THE PARIETAL BONE IN A CHIMPANZEE; WITH SPECIAL REFERENCE TO THE OBLIQUE SUTURES IN THE PARIETAL. Ales Hrdliceka. Bull. Amer. Mus. Nat. Hist., vol.13, art.21, pp.281-295, figs.1-6, Dec.31, 1900.

SOME REMARKS ON PROGNATHISM WITH SPECIAL REFERENCE TO THE SKULL OF PONGO PYGMAEUS (HOPPIUS). A. M. Husson. Koninklijke Nederlandse Akademie Van Wetenschappen, Amsterdam, vol.53, no.2, pp.14, figs.2, 1950.

AN ACCOUNT OF FIVE UNPUBLISHED HUXLEYAN PLATES ILLUSTRATING THE CRANIOLOGY OF YOUNG ANTHROPOID APES. Arthur Keith. Proc. Zool. Soc. Lond., vol.119, pt.4, pp.839-860, pls.5, Feb.1, 1950.

CRANIAL CHARACTERISTICS OF GORILLAS AND CHIMPANZEES. Arthur Keith. Nature, no.3034, vol.120, pp.914-915, Dec.24, 1927.

(THE CRANIUM OF HYLOBATES CONCOLOR, THE CYCLE OF VARIATION AND TOOTH STRUCTURE.) Der Schaedel des Hylobates concolor, sein Variationskreis und Zahnban. G. Kirchner. Inaugural-Dissertation, Konigl. Friedrich-Alexander-Univ., Berlin, pp.1-55, pls.1-3, 1895.

(ON FRONTAL BONE SOCKETS AND BONE SIEVE CELLS IN THE ORANG.) Ueber Stirnbeinhoehlen und Siebbeinzellen beim Orang. Otto Kleinschmidt. Zeitschrift f. Saeugetierkunde, vol.8, no.2, pp.70-72, Apr.24, 1933.

THE HOMOLOGIES OF THE INCISORS OF THE HIGHER PRIMATES IN THE LIGHT OF SOME "ANOMALIES" IN THE DENTITION OF GIBBONS. Einar Loennberg. Arkiv. Zool., Upsala, vol.22 A, no.6, pp. 1-6, figs.1-4, Dec.24, 1930.

REMARKS UPON THE CRANIUM OF AN ORAN UTAN (SIMIA WURMBII). R. Owen. Proc. Zool. Soc. Lond., pt.5, p.82, 1837.

(THE DENTITION OF THE ORANGUTAN.) Das Gebiss des Orang-Utans. L. Petrovits. Anat. Anz., vol.68, pp.1-15, 5 text figs., 1929.

(NOTE ON A CHIMPANZEE CRANIUM.) Note sur un crane de Chimpanze. P. Rode. Bull. Soc. Anthrop., Paris, ser.9, vol.2, pp.13-15, fig.1, 1941.

ON THE SKULL OF GORILLA GORILLA HALLI ROTHSCHILD. Lionel W. Rothschild. Ann. and Mag. Nat. Hist., ser.9, vol.19, p.512, Apr., 1927.

NOTES ON THE GROWTH OF ANTHROPOID APES, WITH ESPECIAL REFERENCE TO DECIDUOUS DENTITION. A. H. Schultz. Report of the Lab. and Mus. of Comp. Pathol., Zool. Soc., Phila., pp.34-45, 1930.

METRIC AND MORPHOLOGIC VARIATIONS IN THE DENTITION OF THE LIBERIAN CHIMPANZEE. E. L. Schuman, C. L. Brace. Human Biology, 26 (3): 239-268, Sept., 1954.

(OBSERVATIONS ON THREE CASES OF ABNORMAL DENTITION IN HYLOBATINES.) Osservazioni su tre casi di dentiione anormale in ilobatini. Alberto Simonetta. Monitore Zool. Italiano, Firenze, vol.63, no.3, pp.1-6 (reprint), 1955.

GORILLA SKULLS IN THE BRISTOL MUSEUM. H. Tetley. Nature, London, vol.136, no.3442, p.642, Oct.19, 1935.

A GORILLA SKULL WITH ABNORMAL DENTURE. Wilson D. Wallis. Amer. Nat., vol.68, no.715, pp.179-183, figs.5, Mar.-Apr., 1934.

(A SUPERNUMERARY PREMOLAR IN THE SIAMANG (SYMPHALANGUS SYNDACTYLUS DESMAREST).) Ein ueberzaehliger Praemolar beim Siamang (Symphalangus syndactylus Desmarest). R. N. Wegner. Zeitschrift fuer Ethnologie, no.1, pp.86-88, fig.1, 1908.

Taxonomy

A NEW SPECIES OF GORILLA (GORILLA MAYEMA). Edmond Alix, Aime Bouvier. Amer. Naturalist, vol.12, no.11, pp.750-751, 1878.

A NOTE ON THE NAME OF THE JAVANESE GIBBON. Angel Cabrera. Proc. Zool. Soc. Lond., pt.1, p.257, May, 1930.

A REVISION OF THE GENUS GORILLA. Harold J. Coolidge, Jr. Mem. Mus. Compar. Zool. (Harvard Coll.), vol.50, no.4, pp. 293-381, figs.19, pls.21, maps 2, Cambridge, Mass., Aug., 1929.

(Review by Gerrit S. Miller, Jr. of) A REVISION OF THE GENUS GORILLA. Harold J. Coolidge, Jr. Mem. Mus. Comp. Zool., vol.50, pp.293-381, figs.19, pls.21, maps 2, Aug., 1929.

(THE SYSTEMATICS OF INDOCHINESE GIBBONS.) La systematique des gibbons Indochinois. J. Delacour. Mammalia, Paris, vol.15, no.4, pp.118-123, illus., Dec., 1951.

SOME REMARKS ON THE GIBBONS, WITH THE DESCRIPTION OF A NEW SUBSPECIES. C. Boden Kloss. Proc. Zool. Soc. Lond., pt.1, pp.113-127, Apr., 1929.

(A NEW CHIMPANZEE.) Ein neuer Schimpanse. Walter Koch. Zool. Garten, Leipzig, n.F., vol.5, nos.4-6, pp.98-106, figs.1, Aug., 1932.

THE SPECIES OF ORANGS. F. A. Lucas. Proc. Boston Soc. Nat. Hist., vol.21, pp. 228-232, Oct.5, 1881.

(A GORILLA, GORILLA GORILLA REX PUGMAEORUM SCHWARZ, KILLED BY M. BABAULT.) A propos d'un gorille Gorilla gorilla rex pygnaeorum Schwarz, tue par M. Babault. P. Mathias. Bull. Mus. Nat. Hist. Nat., Paris, vol.34, no.6, pp.434-436, 1928.

THE CLASSIFICATION OF THE GIBBONS. Gerrit S. Miller, Jr. Jour. Mam., Balto., vol.14, no.2, pp.158-159, May 15, 1933.

(CLASSIFICATION OF GORILLAS.) La classification des gorilles. H. Neuville. L'Anthropologie, Paris, vol.42, nos.3-4, pp.330-337, map, 1932.

ON A NEW SPECIES OF GIBBON (HYLOBATES LEUCOGENYS). W. Ogilby. Proc. Zool. Soc. Lond., pt.8, p.20, 1840.

ON A NEW ORANG (SIMIA MORIO). R. Owen. Proc. Zool. Soc. Lond., pt.4, pp. 91-96, 1836.

ON A NEW SPECIES OF CHIMPANZEE. R. Owen. Proc. Zool. Soc. Lond., pt.16, pp. 27-35, 53-56, 1848.

(CATALOG OF THE MAMMAL TYPES OF THE NATIONAL MUSEUM OF NATURAL HISTORY. I. ORDER PRIMATES. A. SUBORDER OF SIMIANS.) Catalogue des types de mammifères du Muséum National d'Histoire Naturelle. I. Ordre des Primates. A. Sous-ordre des Simiens. P. Rode. Bull. Mus. Nat. Hist. Nat., Paris, ser.2, vol.10, no.3, pp.202-251, 1938.

(CONSIDERATIONS ON THE CLASSIFICATION OF AFRICAN SIMIANS.) Considérations sur la systématique des Simiens Africains. P. Rode. Mammalia, Paris, 2 (4): 182-186, 1938.

(ON THE NOMENCLATURE OF THE ANTHROPOID APES: AN ANSWER. Zur nomenklatur der Menschenaffen. Eine Erwiderung. Walter Rothschild. Sitz. Ber. Gesell. Naturfor. Freunde Berlin Jahrg., pt.3, pp.85-87, Mar.13, 1906.

ON THE LOCAL RACES OF THE CHIMPANZEE. Ernst Schwarz. Ann. and Mag. Nat. Hist., Lond., ser.10, vol.13, no.78, pp. 576-583, June, 1934.

(THE PLURALITY OF GORILLA SPECIES.) La pluralite des especes de gorille. E. L. Trouessart. Bull. Mus. d'Hist. Nat., pp. 102-108, 191-196 (1-13 of reprint), 9 figs., 1920.

Hominidae

(VERY PRIMITIVE CHARACTERS AND PRESENT-DAY MAN.) Caracteres tres primitifs presentes par des de l'homme actuel. Dr. Ampoulange. Mammalia, Paris, vol.19, no.4, pp.491-497, Dec., 1955.

THE ANTHROPOLOGICAL SIGNIFICANCE OF THE PTERION IN THE PRIMATES. M. F. Ashley-Montagu. Amer. Jour. Phys. Anthrop., vol.18, no.2, pp.159-336, figs. 48, Oct.-Dec., 1933.

HUMAN BIOLOGY. G. A. Baitsell. 2nd. ed. New York, McGraw-Hill Book Co., Inc., xvii, 730 pp., 361 figs., 1950.

AN INTRODUCTION TO ANTHROPOLOGY. R. L. Beals, Harry Hoijer. New York, The Macmillan Co., xxi, 658 pp., illus., 1953.

THE STORY OF MAN. Elsie Bramell. Australian Mus. Mag., Sydney, vol.7, no. 12, pp.403-407; vol.8, no.1, pp.13-16 illus., Mar.16, July 20, 1942.

THE STATURE OF MEN. Laurence B. Chenoweth. Science, Lancaster, n.s., vol.95, no.2478, pp.648-649, June 26, 1942.

DEAD VERSUS LIVING MEN. Austin H. Clark. The Scientific Monthly, vol.29, pp. 255-264, Sept., 1929.

STORY OF MAN FROM THE FIRST HUMAN TO PRIMITIVE CULTURE. C. S. Coon. New York, A. A. Knopf, Inc., xxii, 437 pp., illus., 1954.

ANTHROPOLOGY AT A GLANCE. Will Cuppy. Condensed from "How to tell your friends from the Apes." Reader's Digest, vol.20, no.120, pp.34-36, Apr., 1932.

THE IMPORTANCE OF COOPERATIVE STUDIES OF THE BIOLOGY OF MAN. Lee R. Dice. Science, Lancaster, n.s., vol.99, no.2580, pp.457-461, June 9, 1944.

A SHORT COURSE ON PHYSICAL ANTHROPOLOGY. M. R. Drennan. Mercantile-Atlas Printing Co. Ltd., Cape Town, pp. 69, figs.24, 1937.

THE "BABOON BOY" OF SOUTH AFRICA. John P. Foley, Jr. Science, Lancaster, n.s., vol.91, no.2360, pp.291-292, Mar. 22, 1940.

SOME OBSERVATIONS ON COMPARATIVE CONSTITUTION IN MAN AND THE LOWER MAMMALS. Herbert Fox. Proc. Amer. Philos. Soc., Phila., vol.68, no.1, pp.27-51, 1929.

THE POSSIBLE IMPROVEMENT OF THE HUMAN BREED UNDER THE EXISTING CONDITIONS OF LAW AND SENTIMENT. Francis Galton. Smithsonian Inst., Ann. Rept., 1901, pp.523-538, illus., 1902.

THE BIOGRAPHY OF A WOLF-CHILD. Arnold Gesell. Harper's Mag., New York, vol.182, no.1088, pp.183-193, Jan., 1941.

FROM FISH TO MAN. THE NATURAL HISTORY OF MAN. William K. Gregory. Natural History, New York, vol.32, no.4, pp.440-442, figs., July-Aug., 1932.

NATURE'S UPSTART: HOMO SAPIENS. William K. Gregory. The Teaching Biologist, vol.5, no.2, pp.22-25, 30, 31, illus., Nov., 1935.

SPEAKING OF MAN. A BIOLOGIST LOOKS AT MAN. Michael F. Guyer. Harper and Bros., New York and Lond., pp.321, 1942.

ZOOLOGICAL SUBSPECIES OF MAN AT THE PEACE TABLE. E. Raymond Hall. Jour. Mam., vol.27, no.4, pp.358-364, Nov., 1946.

THE PEOPLE WHICH SAT IN DARKNESS SAW GREAT LIGHT. Oliver P. Hay. Anthropologic Scraps, no.5, pp.17-20, Dec. 5, 1921.

(ON THE HERITAGE OF MAN.) Zur Herkunft des Menschen. E. Hennig. Naturwissenschaftliche Monatsschrift aus der Heimat, Jahrg.42, no.9, pp.257-270, figs. 16, Sept., 1929.

MAN AS AN ANIMAL. W. C. Osman Hill. Pub. Hutchinson, London, 176 pp., 1957.

THE IMPORTANCE OF PRIMATE STUDIES IN ANTHROPOLOGY. Earnest Hooten. Human Biology, 26 (3): 179-188, Sept., 1954.

THE DISTRIBUTION OF MAN IN RELATION TO THE INVENTION OF FIRE-MAKING METHODS. Walter Hough. Amer. Anthrop., n.s., vol.18, no.2, pp.257-263, Apr.-June, 1916.

DIRECTIONS FOR COLLECTING INFORMATION AND SPECIMENS FOR PHYSICAL ANTHROPOLOGY. Ales Hrdlicka. Bull. U.S. Nat. Mus., no.39, pt.R, pp.1-25, pls.1-8, 1904.

THE BIOLOGIST LOOKS AT MAN. Julian Huxley. Fortune, New York, vol.26, no.6, pp.138-141, 146, 148, 150, 152, illus., Dec., 1942.

THE BONES OF RAFINESQUE. David Starr Jordan. Science, n.s., vol.59, pp. 553-554, June 20, 1924.

(GENUS HOMO SAPIENS (L.). A NATURAL HISTORICAL MONOGRAPH OF MAN.) Realgattung Homo Sapiens (L.). Eine naturgeschichtliche Monographie des Menschen. Otto Kleinschmidt. Berajah, Zoographia infinita, Halle a.S., 1922, pp. 1-30; 1927, pp.31-38; pp.1-6, pls.1-8, 1928.

ANTHROPOLOGY. A. L. Kroeber. New York, Harcourt, Brace and Co., Inc., xii, 856, xxxix pp., 42 figs., 1948.

THE HUMAN ANIMAL. Weston LaBarre. Univ. Chicago Press, p.xv, 372, illus., 1954.

NOMAD DWARFS AND CIVILIZATION. Herbert Lang. Nat. Hist. New York, vol. 19, no.6, pp.696-713, illus., 1919.

HUMAN EVOLUTION AND SCIENCE. Francis P. LeBuffe. New York, America Press, 7th ed., pp.1-48, 1931.

EDUCATIONAL ANTHROPOLOGY. Arthur MacDonald. Jour. Education, 2 pp.

(ON SCIENTIFIC ANTHROPOLOGICAL PHOTOGRAPHY.) Zur Wissenschaftlich-anthropologischen Photographie. R. Martin. Anatomischer Anzeiger, Java, Bd.59, pp. 529-538, 1925.

(ANTHROPOMETRICAL AND MEDICAL INVESTIGATIONS OF MUNICH STUDENTS.) Anthropometrische und Arztliche Untersuchungen an Muenchenger Studierenden. R. Martin, A. Alexander. Muencherner medizinischen Wochenschr, nr.11, pp.321-325, (separate paged 1-16), 1924.

HANDBOOK OF BIOLINGUISTICS. C. L. Meader, J. H. Muyskens. Pt.1, Sect.A., Toledo, 1950.

PLEISTOCENE LUXATIONS. Roy L. Moodie. Amer. Jour. Surgery n.s., vol.9, no.2, pp. 348-362, figs.14, Aug., 1930.

ABOUT OURSELVES. A SURVEY OF HUMAN NATURE FROM THE ZOOLOGICAL STANDPOINT. James G. Needham. Jaques Cattell Press, Lancaster, 276 pp., illus., 1941.

(REMARKS ON ANTHROPOLOGICAL METHODICS AND TECHNICS.) Anmerkungen zur anthropologischen Methodik und Technik. Bruno Oetteking. Anthrop. Anzeiger, Stuttgart, Jahrg.3, no.4, pp.257-261, figs.2, 1926.

THE INFLUENCE OF BODILY LOCOMOTION IN SEPARATING MAN FROM THE MONKEYS AND APES. Henry Fairfield Osborn. Sci. Monthly, vol.26, pp.385-399, illus., May, 1928.

THE CURVE OF POPULATION GROWTH. Raymond Pearl. Proc. Amer. Philos. Soc., Phila., vol.63, no.1, pp.10-17, figs. 5, 1924.

MAN AND THE BIOLOGICAL WORLD. J. Speed Rogers, Theodore H. Hubbell, C. Francis Byers. McGraw-Hill Book Co., Inc., New York, pp.x, 607, figs.180, 1942.

MAN AND THE VERTEBRATES. Alfred Sherwood Romer. Univ. Chicago Press, pp.viii, 405, illus., Nov., 1941.

(Review by R.S. Lull of) MAN AND THE VERTEBRATES. Alfred Sherwood Romer. Univ. Chicago Press, 1941. Amer. Jour. Sci., New Haven, vol.240, no.5, pp. 381-382, May, 1942.

(CONSTITUTION AND RACE IN MAN.) Konstitution und Rasse beim Menschen. K. Saller. Ztschr. f. ges. Anat., III. Ergeb. d. Anat. u. Entwickges., vol.28, pp.251-423, 21 figs., 1929.

MAN AS A PRIMATE. Adolph H. Schultz. The Scientific Monthly, vol.33, pp.385-412, figs.31, Nov., 1931.

ATLAS OF MEN. William H. Sheldon. Harper and Bros., New York, pp.xvi, 357, illus., 1954.

INDIAN TYPES OF BEAUTY. Robert W. Shufeldt. Amer. Field, Chicago, vol.36, nos.23-25, pp.3-24, figs.8, 1891.

WOLF-CHILDREN AND FERAL MAN. J. A. L. Singh, Robert M. Zingg. Harper and Brothers, New York, pp.xli, 379, illus., 1942.

PRIMATES. William L. Straus, Jr. Anthropology Today (Univ. Chicago Press, 1953), pp.77-92, 1953.

PATHOLOGY AND THE POSTURE OF NEANDERTHAL MAN. William L. Strauss, Jr., A. J. E. Cave. Quarterly Review Biol., vol.32, no.4, pp.348-363, illus., Dec., 1957.

HEREDITY, ENVIRONMENT, AND RESPONSIBILITY. Francis B. Sumner. Bull. Scripps Inst. Biol. Research, La Jolla, no. 10, pp.1-12, July 2, 1921.

"LEGALISED MURDER." Oldfield Thomas. Evening Standard and St. James Gazett. Mar.27, 1906.

AN ANTHROPOLOGIST'S STUDY OF NEGRO LIFE. T. Wingate Todd. Brush Foundation Pub., no.8, pp.8, Oct., 1930.

ASSESSING THE HAZARDS OF CHILDHOOD. T. Wingate Todd. Jour. Medicine, Cin., Ohio, Oct., 1931.

THE BASIS OF PERSONALITY. T. Wingate Todd. Brush Foundation Publ., no.11, pp.8, Feb., 1931.

LIFE'S IMPACT AND YOUTH'S ADJUSTMENT. T. Wingate Todd. Brush Foundation Publ. no.13, pp.19, Mar.22, 1931.

PHYSICAL ANALYSIS IN THE ADOLESCENT PROBLEM. T. Wingate Todd. Amer. Jour. Diseases Children, vol.43, pp.533-546, Mar., 1932.

SAFEGUARDING HUMANITY. T. Wingate Todd. Brush Foundation Publ., no.9, pp. 13, Nov., 1930.

(ANTHROPOLOGICAL NOMENCLATURE.) Nomenclature anthropologique. Henri V. Vallois. Rev. Sci. (Revue Rose Illus.), Paris, no.3, pp.181-183, Mar., 1941.

HOMINIDAE. H. Weinert. Fortschr. der Palaeont., Berlin, vol.2, pp.363-368, 1939.

FERAL MAN AND EXTREME CASES OF ISOLATION. Robert M. Zingg. Amer. Jour. Psychology, Ithaca, vol.53, no.4, pp.487-517, Oct., 1940.

MORE ABOUT THE 'BABOON BOY' OF SOUTH AFRICA. Robert M. Zingg. Amer. Jour. Psychology, Ithaca, vol.53, no.3, pp. 455-462, July, 1940.

MAN. London, vol.29, no.8, pp.135-136, 1929.

## Africa and Near East

THE FOSSIL HUMAN REMAINS FROM THE PALEOLITHIC SITE OF SIDI ABDERRAHMAN (MOROCCO). C. Arambourg, P. Biberson. Amer. Jour. Anthropol., n.s., 14 (3): 467-490, illus., Sept., 1956.

MAKAPANSGAT. George B. Barbour. Sci. Monthly, Lancaster, vol.69, no.3, pp.141-147, figs.8, Sept., 1949.

SYMPOSIUM ON HUMAN SKELETAL REMAINS FROM THE CAPE COAST. I. FOSSIL REMAINS FROM KEURBOOMS RIVER. Ralph E. Bernstein. S. African Jour. Sci., vol.32, pp.603-607, figs.2, Nov., 1935.

SYMPOSIUM ON HUMAN SKELETAL REMAINS FROM THE NORTHERN AND EASTERN TRANSVAAL. I. HUMAN SKELETAL REMAINS FROM SMITSDORP. G. F. Berry. S. African Jour. Sci., vol. 32, pp.616-621, fig.1, Nov., 1935.

(Review by David H. Johnson of) FOREST LORE OF THE MAORI. Elsdon Best. Jour. Mamm., vol.27, no.3, pp.284-285, Aug., 1946.

THE TRANSVAAL FOSSIL HUMAN SKELETON. Robert Broom. Nature, Lond., vol. 123, no.3098, pp.415-416, figs.3, Mar.16, 1929.

SUMMARY OF MY FINDINGS ON PREHISTORIC SKELETAL MATERIAL FROM

RHODESIA. M. R. Drennan. Proc. and Trans. Rhodesia Sci. Assoc., Salisbury, vol.37, pp.167-169, fig.1, pl.1, Sept., 1939.

FLAKED FLINTS FROM THE BONE BEDS OF BETHLEHEM. D. A. E. Garrod. Nature, Lond., vol.140, no.3549, p.808, Nov.6, 1937.

NOTE ON A DEFORMED SKULL FROM SIWAH OASIS. E. A. Hooten. Harvard African Studies, vol.2, pp.101-104, Cambridge, 1918.

RHODESIAN MAN AND ASSOCIATED REMAINS. A. Tindell Hopwood. Mammalia, London, British Mus., pp.70-73, Aug.18, 1928.

THE FEMUR OF PLESIANTHROPUS TRANSVAALENSIS. Howard M. Kern, Jr., William L. Straus, Jr. Amer. Jour. Phys. Anthrop., n.s., vol.7, no.1, pp.53-78, Mar., 1949.

PREHISTORIC MAN IN PALESTINE. George G. MacCurdy. Proc. Amer. Philos. Soc., vol.76, no.4, pp.523-541, pls.16, 1936.

(THE NEW RHODESIAN SKULL FIND.) Der neue Schaedelfund von Rhodesia. Rud Martin. Mannus, Leipzig, Bd.14, Heft 1-2, pp.141-147, 1922.

HUMAN REMAINS FROM THE HOLE-IN-THE-WALL, MQANDULI, TRANSKEI. K. Barbara Meaker. S. African Jour. Sci., vol.32, pp.609-612, Nov., 1935.

THE EVIDENCE FOR THE AGE OF HOMO RHODESIENSIS. F. P. Mennell. S. Afr. Jour. Sci., vol.26, pp.659-664, Dec., 1929.

NATURE AND MAN IN ETHIOPIA. Wilfred H. Osgood. Nat. Geog. Mag., vol.54, no. 2, pp.121-176, illus., Aug., 1928.

A CONTRIBUTION TO THE STUDY OF PREHISTORIC MAN IN ALGERIA, NORTH AFRICA; BEING A DESCRIPTION OF SOME EXCAVATIONS IN THE HABITATION SITE AT MECHTA EL ARBI, CONSTANTINE, ALGERIA. Alonzo William Pond. Beloit, Wisc., The Logan Mus., Beloit College, 1928.

RHODESIAN MAN. DESCRIPTION OF THE SKULL AND OTHER HUMAN REMAINS FROM BROKEN HILL. William P. Pycraft. Rhodesian Man and Associated Remains, British Mus. Nat. Hist., pp.1-70, pls.1-5, Aug.18, 1928.

FOSSIL MAN IN TANGIER. Muzaffer Sueleyman Senyuerek. Peabody Museum of American Archaeology and Ethnology, Harvard Univ., vol.16, no.3, pp.1-27, figs.3, 1940.

NEANDERTHAL MEN IN THE HEART LAND OF HUMAN EVOLUTION; DISCOVERIES AT SHANIDAR CAVE IN NORTHERN IRAQ. Ralph S. Solecki. Illus. London News, May 7, 1960.

Anatomy

THE DEVELOPMENTAL ANATOMY OF THE HUMAN STAPES. Barry J. Anson, Earl W. Cauldwell. Ann.Otology, Rhinology and Laryngology, St. Louis, vol.51, no.4, pp. 891-903, pls.6, Dec., 1942.

THE HUMAN STAPES: A NONCOMFORMIST AMONG BONES. Barry J. Anson, Earl W. Cauldwell, Arthur F. Reinmann. Quart.Bull., Northwestern Univ. Med. School, Chicago, vol.18, no.1, pp.33-40, pls.4, Feb., 1944.

TERMINAL STAGES IN THE DEVELOPMENT OF THE HUMAN STAPES. Barry J. Anson, Earl W. Cauldwell, Arthur F. Reimann. Annals Otol., Rhinol. and Laryngol., St. Louis, vol.53, no.1, pp.12, figs.7, Mar., 1944.

ON THE CEPHALIZATION STAGE OF PITHECANTHROPUS ERECTUS AND SINANTHROPUS PEKINENSIS. R. Brummelkamp. Proc. K. Nederlandsche Akad. Wetensch., Amsterdam, vol.43, no.6, pp.741-752, figs.1-3, June, 1940.

CRANIOMETRIC MEMOIRS. NO.4. HORIZONTAL ZONES OF THE FACIAL NORMA IN MODERN AND FOSSIL MAN. John Cameron. Jour. Anat., Cambridge, vol.66, pt.1, pp.114-122, pls.1-4, Oct., 1931.

SUPERNUMERARY BREAST. Tibor de Cholnoky. Archives of Surgery, Chicago, vol.39, pp.926-941, figs.10, Dec., 1939.

THE CRANIO-FACIAL UNION IN MAN. W. Montague Cobb. Amer. Jour. Phys. Anthropol., Phila., vol.26, pp.87-111, figs.20, Mar.30, 1940.

THE OSSA SUPRASTERNALIA IN WHITES AND AMERICAN NEGROES AND THE FORM OF THE SUPERIOR BORDER OF THE MANUBRIUM STERNI. W. Montague Cobb. Jour. Anat., Cambridge, vol.71, pt.2, pp.245-291, figs.7, Jan., 1937.

WIDTH OF HEAD AND PELVIS IN HOMO. T. D. A. Cockerell. Nature, London, vol.125, no.3143, p.131, 1930.

THE CRURAL INDES. C. B. Davenport. Amer. Jour. Phys. Anthrop., vol.17, no.3, pp.333-353, figs.6, Jan.-Mar., 1933.

POST-NATAL DEVELOPMENT OF THE HUMAN OUTER NOSE. C. B. Davenport. Proc. Amer. Philos. Soc., Phila., vol.80, no.2, pp.175-355, figs.84, A, B, C, tables 4, pls.1-18, Jan.31, 1939.

(ANLAGE AND DEVELOPMENT OF THE MAXILLAE AND PREMAXILLAE IN MAN.) Anlage und Entwicklung des maxillare und praemaxillare beim Menschen. Paul Felber. Inaugural Dissertation der Med. Fakultaet Univ. Zurich. Morphologischen, Jahrbuch, vol.50, no.4, pp.53, figs.41, 1917.

HUMAN PROPORTION IN ART AND ANTHROPOMETRY. Robert Fletcher. Cambridge, Mass., pp.37, figs.4, 1883.

VARIATIONS IN HUMAN SCAPULAE. D. J. Gray. Amer. Jour. Phys. Anthropol., Phila., vol.29, no.1, pp.57-72, Mar.30, 1942.

ORIGIN OF HUMAN LIMB PROPORTIONS THROUGH CHANGE OF FUNCTION. William K. Gregory. Bull. New York Acad. Medicine, ser.2, vol.4, pp.239-242, 1928.

INTRODUCTION TO HUMAN ANATOMY. GUIDE TO SECTION I OF THE HALL OF NATURAL HISTORY OF MAN. William K. Gregory, Marcelle Roigneau. Publ. Amer. Mus. Nat. Hist., pp.82, figs.28, 1934.

A STUDY OF PELVIC TYPE AND ITS RELATIONSHIP TO BODY BUILD IN WHITE WOMEN. William W. Greulich, Thomas Herbert. Jour. Amer. Med. Assoc., Chicago, vol.112, no.6, pp.485-493, figs. 1-10, Feb.11, 1939.

HERMAPHRODITISMUS VERUS IN MAN. J. F. Gudernatsch. Amer. Jour. Anat., Phila., vol.11, no.3, pp.267-278, pls.3, Mar., 1911.

A PROVISIONAL MAP OF A HUMAN CHROMOSOME. J. B. S. Haldane. Science, n.s., vol.137, no.3462. pp.398-400, Mar. 7, 1936.

ON THE RELATIONSHIP BETWEEN STATURE AND THE LENGTH OF THE APPENDAGES IN MAN. J. Arthur Harris. Amer. Nat., vol.58, no.656, pp.254-271, 4 figs., May-June, 1924.

GROSS ANATOMY; A BRIEF SYSTEMATIC PRESENTATION OF THE MACROSCOPIC STRUCTURE OF THE HUMAN BODY. A. Brazier Howell. D. Appleton-Century, New York and London, pp.vii, 403, figs. 56, Mar.25, 1939.

THE ADULT SCAPULA. ADDITIONAL OBSERVATIONS AND MEASUREMENTS. Ales Hrdlicka. Amer. Jour. Phys. Anthrop. Phila., vol.29, no.3, pp.363-415, figs.6, Sept.30, 1942.

DESCRIPTION OF AN ANCIENT ANOMALOUS SKELETON FROM THE VALLEY OF MEXICO; WITH SPECIAL REFERENCE TO SUPERNUMERARY AND BICIPITAL RIBS IN MAN. Ales Hrdlicka. Bull. Amer. Mus. Nat. Hist., vol.12, art.5, pp.81-107, figs.1-10, pls.1-5, May 13, 1899.

HUMAN TYPOGENY. Ales Hrdlicka. Proc. Amer. Philos. Soc. Phila., vol.78, no.1, pp.79-95, figs.5, Oct., 1937.

THE SCAPULA: VISUAL OBSERVATIONS. Ales Hrdlicka. Amer. Jour. Phys. Anthro-Phila., vol.29, no.1, pp.73-94, figs.5, Mar.30, 1942.

(AN M. MANDIBULO-AURICULARIS IN THE PRIMATES, AND CONTRIBUTIONS TO KNOWLEDGE OF THE PHYLOGENESIS OF THE HUMAN AURAL MUSCULATURE.) Ein M. mandibulo-auricularis bei Primaten, nebst Beitraegen zur Kenntnis der Phylogenese der menschlichen Ohrmuskulatur. Ernst Huber. Anat. Anzeiger, vol.60, pp. 11-21, 1925-1926.

PHYSICAL CHARACTERISTICS OF THE COPPER ESKIMOS. D. Jenness. Rep. Canadian Arctic Exped., 1913-1918, vol.12, pt.B, pp.1-89, pls.1-12, May, 1923.

THE QUESTION OF A LATERAL THYROID IN MAMMALS WITH SPECIAL REFERENCE TO MAN. B. F. Kingsbury. Amer. Jour. Anat., Phila., vol.65, no.2, pp.333-359, 3 pls., Sept.15, 1939.

ABORIGINAL PHYSICAL TYPES IN THE WESTERN HEMISPHERE. Wilton Marion Krogman. Ciba Symposia (Ciba Pharmaceutical Products Inc.,), vol.3, no.1, pp.804-812, figs.10, Apr., 1941.

THE CEPHALIC TYPE OF THE FULL-BLOODED AND MIXED-BLOOD SEMINOLE INDIANS OF OKLAHOMA. Wilton Marion Krogman. Zeitschrift fur Rassenkunde, vol.3, no.2, pp.176-190, figs. 9, tables 3, 1936.

THE MEASUREMENT OF THE HUMAN BODY. Wilton Marion Krogman. Ciba Symposia, Ciba Pharmaceutical Products, Inc., Summit, New Jersey, vol.5, nos.1-2, pp.1467-1477, illus., Apr.-May, 1943.

(ANTHROPOMETRY.) Anthropometrie. Rudolf Martin. Muenchener medizinischen Wochenschr., nr.11, pp.383-389, 1922.

STEATOPYGY AND ACROMEGALY. Gerrit S. Miller, Jr. Amer. Jour. Phys. Anthrop., vol.14, no.1, pp.79-80, pl.1, Jan.-Mar., 1930.

STEATOPYGY IN HOTTENTOT WOMEN. Gerrit S. Miller, Jr. Amer. Jour. Phys. Anthrop., vol.2, pp.200-202, Oct.9, 1919.

(CERTAIN CHARACTERS OF THE HUMAN FORM AND THEIR CAUSES.) De certains caracteres de la forme humaine et leurs causes. H. Neuville. L'Anthropologie, Paris, vol.37, pp.305-328; 491-515, figs. 15, 1927.

(THE TRANSVERSAL CANAL OF THORACIC AND LUMBAR VERTEBRAE AND SOME RARE VARIATIONS OF HUMAN VERTEBRAE.) Zagadniente kanau wyrostkow poprzecznych kregow piersiowych i ledzwiowych i kilka razadkich odmian kregow ludzkich. M. Orowski. Kosmos, Jour. Soc. Polonaise Nat. Kopernik, vol.50, fasc.4, pp.1226-1241, figs.2, pls.3, 1925.

COMMUNICATION BETWEEN LYMPHATIC AND VENOUS SYSTEM AT RENAL LEVEL IN MAN. James W. Pick, Barry J. Anson, Harry W. Burnett, Jr. Quarterly Bull. Northwestern Univ. Med. School, Chicago, vol.18, no.4, pp.307-316, figs.2, Winter, 1944.

CHEVRON BONES IN ADULT MAN. Adolph H. Schultz. Amer. Jour. Phys. Anthrop., Phila., vol.28, no.1, pp.91-97, Mar.31, 1941.

ANTHROPOMETRIC NOMENCLATURE: II. THE INDICES OF HEAD HEIGHT. T. D. Stewart. Amer. Jour. Phys. Anthropol., Phila., vol.29, no.1, pp.23-39, Mar.30, 1942.

THE HUMAN ILIUM: SEX AND STOCK. William L. Straus, Jr. Amer. Jour. Phys. Anthrop., vol.11, no.1, 28 pp., figs. 6, Oct.-Dec., 1927.

THE UPPER END OF THE FEMUR. William J. Tobin, T. Dale Stewart. Amer. Acad. Orthopaedic surgeons Instructional Course Lectures, Ann Arbor, vol.10, pp.213-223, illus., 1953.

FACIAL GROWTH AND MANDIBULAR ADJUSTMENT. T. W. Todd. Internat. Jour.

Orthodontia, Oral Surg., and Radiography, St. Louis, vol.16, no.12, pp.3-27, figs.19, Dec., 1930.

HEREDITARY AND ENVIRONMENTAL FACTORS IN FACIAL DEVELOPMENT. T. W. Todd. Internat. Jour. Orthodontia, Oral Surg., and Radiography, St. Louis, vol.18, no.8, pp.799-808, Aug., 1932.

THE ORTHODONTIC VALUE OF RESEARCH AND OBSERVATIONS IN DEVELOPMENTAL GROWTH OF THE FACE. T. W. Todd. Angle Orthodontist, New York, 4 pp., figs. 2, July, 1931.

RECENT STUDIES IN THE DEVELOPMENT OF THE FACE. T. W. Todd. Internat. Jour. Orthodontia, Oral Surgery and Radiography, vol.15, no.12, pp.2-20, 1929.

REPORT ON THE HUMAN CRANIA AND OTHER BONES OF THE SKELETONS COLLECTED DURING THE VOYAGE OF H. M. S. CHALLENGER IN THE YEARS 1873-1876. William Turner. Gt. Brit. Challenger Office, Report on the Scientific Results of the Voyage of H. M. S. Challenger during the years 1873-1876. Edinburgh, 1880-1895. Zoology, vol.10, no.4, 1884; vol.16, no.4, 1886.

(THE FORMATION OF THE HUMAN SHOULDER BLADE.) La formation de L'omoplate Humaine. Henri M. V. Vallois. Bull. Mus. Nat. D'Hist. Nat., Paris, no.1, pp.65-68, figs.2, 1927.

THE EXTERNAL TUBERCLE OF THE HUMAN TUBER CALCANEI. Franz Weidenreich. Amer. Jour. Phys. Anthrop., Phila., vol.26, pp.473-486, figs.9, pl.1, Mar.30, 1940.

(THE HUMAN CHIN AND ITS ORIGIN. A STUDY AND CRITIQUE.) Das Menschenkinn und seine Entstehung. Eine Studie und Kritik. Franz Weidenreich. Ergebnisse Anat. u. Entwicklungsgeschichte, Berlin, vol.31, pp.1-124, figs.89, 1934.

Australia

THE ANTIQUITY OF MAN IN VICTORIA. J. W. Gregory. Proc. Roy. Soc. Victoria, vol.17, pt.1, pp.120-144, Sept., 1904.

AUSTROMELANESIAN MIGRATIONS ONCE MORE. Dirk Albert Hooijer. Southwestern Jour. Anthropol., Albuquerque, vol.8, no. 4, pp.472-477, 1952.

THE ANTIQUITY OF MAN IN AUSTRALIA. F. Wood Jones. Nature, London, vol.153, no.3877, pp.211-212, Feb.19, 1944.

Blood

THE RHESUS FACTOR--A STUDY IN SCIENTIFIC METHOD. R. A. Fisher. Amer. Scientist, Burlington, Vt., vol.35, no.1, pp.95-102, Jan., 1947.

GEOGRAPHY OF HUMAN BLOOD GROUPS (A, B, O, SYSTEM). Bertil Lundman. Evolution, Lancaster, vol.2, no.3, pp. 231-237, figs.5, Sept., 1948.

POTENCY OF SOME OLD HUMAN ISOHEMAGGLUTINATING SERUMS. Marcus W. Lyon, Jr. Jour. Amer. Med. Assoc., vol. 75, pp.1002-1003, Oct.9, 1920.

THE RH FACTOR AND RACIAL ORIGINS. Alexander S. Wiener. Science, Lancaster, n.s., vol.96, no.2496, pp.407-408, Oct.30, 1942.

Brain

INTELLIGENCE OF INFANTS AND ITS MEASUREMENT. Psyche Cattell. Trans. New York Acad. Sci., New York, ser.2, vol.3, no.6, pp. 162-171, Apr., 1941.

THE SHAPE AND SIZE OF THE BRAIN IN SINANTHROPUS AND IN PITHECANTHROPUS. Eugene Dubois. Proc. Koninklijke Akad. van Wetenschappen te Amsterdam, vol.36, no.4, pp.415-423, pls.1-4, 1933.

(FOSSIL HUMAN BRAINS FROM THE ICE AGE?) Versteinerte Menschenhirne aus der Eiszeit? T. Edinger. Natur and Museum, Frankfurt a.M., vol.57, no.7, pp. 311-318, 4 figs., July, 1927.

AN ESKIMO BRAIN. Ales Hrdlicka. New York, the Knickerbocker Press, pp.1-49, figs.2, pls.1-4, 1901.

DAWN MAN'S BRAIN. E. O. James. Sci. News-Letter, p.196, Mar.30, 1929.

THE CEREBRAL CORTEX IN THE VERY OLD HUMAN BRAIN. W. Riese. Jour. Neuropathol. and Exper. Neurol., vol.5, no.2, pp.160-164, figs.3, Apr., 1946.

CEREBRAL CORTEX OF A MAN WITH SENILE DEMENTIA BELIEVED TO BE 107 YEARS OLD. W. Riese, I. S. Zfass. Arch. Neu. and Psych., vol.51, pp.78-83, figs.4, Jan., 1944.

CASTS OBTAINED FROM THE BRAIN CASES OF FOSSIL MEN. G. Elliot Smith. Nat. Hist., vol.26, pp.294-299, May-June, 1926.

THE BRAIN AND ITS ROLE IN THE PHYLOGENETIC TRANSFORMATION OF THE HUMAN SKULL. Franz Weidenreich. Trans. Amer. Philos. Soc., Phila., n.s., vol.31, pt.5, pp.321-442, figs.56, Aug., 1941.

THE HUMAN BRAIN IN THE LIGHT OF ITS PHYLOGENETIC DEVELOPMENT. Franz Weidenreich. Sci. Monthly, Lancaster, Pa., vol.67, no.2, pp.103-109, figs.7, Aug., 1948.

A BRAIN OF ABOUT ONE-HALF THE AVERAGE WEIGHT FROM AN INTELLIGENT WHITE MAN. Burt G. Wilder. Proc. Amer. Philos. Soc., vol.49, pp.188-190, 1910.

Diseases and Parasites

MICROSPORUM OF CATS CAUSING RINGWORM IN MAN. Vera K. Charles, Aline Fenner Kempton. Jour. Wash. Acad. Sci., vol.24, no.5, pp.222-227, May 15, 1934.

EXPERIMENTAL EFFORTS TO TRANSFER MONKEY MALARIA TO MAN. Herbert C. Clark, Lawrence H. Dunn. Amer. Jour. Trop. Med., vol.11, no.1, pp.1-13, 1932.

SOURCES OF INFECTION AND SEASONAL INCIDENCE OF TULAREMIA IN MAN. Edward Francis. Public Health Reports, Washington, D.C., vol.52, no.4, pp.103-113, Jan. 22, 1937.

ACUTE STREPTOCOCCUS INFECTION OF THE SKIN AND SUBCUTANEOUS TISSUES OF THE HEAD. John R. Gorham. Fur of Canada, Winnipeg, vol.15, no.6, pt.4, Mar., 1950.

TULAREMIA IN MAN FROM A DOMESTIC RURAL WATER SUPPLY. W. L. Jellison, Deane C. Epler, Edith Kuhns, Glen M. Kohls. U.S. Public Health Repts., Wash., vol.65, no.38, pp.1219-1226, Sept.22, 1950.

STUDIES IN PALEOPATHOLOGY, XXIII. AN UNUSUAL SKULL FROM PRE-COLUMBIAN PERU. Roy L. Moodie. Amer. Jour. Surgery, Kansas City, vol.8, no.4, pp.903-904, fig.1, Apr., 1930.

STUDIES IN PALEOPATHYOLOGY, XXIV. PREHISTORIC SURGERY IN NEW MEXICO. Roy L. Moodie. Amer. Jour. Surgery, Kansas City, vol.8, no.4, pp.905-908, figs.2, Apr., 1930.

ANIMAL PARASITES IN MAN. Nicholas H. Swellengrebel, Max M. Sterman. 640 pp., illus., D. Van Nostrand Co., Inc.

Ecology

ECOLOGY AND THE PROTOHOMINIDS. George A. Bartholomew, Jr., Joseph B. Birdsell. Amer. Anthropologist, vol.55, no.4, pp.481-498, Oct., 1953.

FOREST LORE OF THE MOARI. Elsdon Best. Dominion Museum, Wellington, New Zealand, bull. no.14, 503 pp., 31 figs., 1942.

THE ECOLOGICAL RELATIONS OF THE POLAR ESKIMO. W. Elmer Ekslaw. Ecology, vol.2, pp.132-144, Apr., 1921.

THE APPLICATION OF ECOLOGICAL RULES TO THE RACIAL ANTHROPOLOGY OF THE ABORIGINAL NEW WORLD. Marshall T. Newman. Amer. Anthrop., vol.55, no.3, pp.311-327, illus., Aug., 1953.

DECIDUOUS FOREST MAN AND THE GRASSLAND FAUNA. II. V. E. Shelford. Science, Lancaster, n.s., vol.100, no.2591, pp.160-162, Aug.25, 1944.

DECIDUOUS FOREST MAN IN THE GRASSLAND OF NORTH AMERICA. V. E. Shelford. Proc. 8th Amer. Sci. Congr., Wash., pp.203-204, 1940.

"MAN AND NATURE"--A CONTEMPORARY VIEW. Walter P. Taylor. Scientific Monthly, vol.41, pp.350-362, Oct., 1935.

Embryology

THE EARLY RELATION OF THE AUDITORY VESICLE TO THE ECTODERM IN HYMAN EMBRYOS. Barry J. Anson, William T. Black, Jr. Anat. Record, Phila., vol.58, no.2, pp.127-134, pls.2, Jan., 1934.

A HUMAN OVUM IN ITS EARLY PHASES OF DEVELOPMENT. C. Lordy. Ann. Fac. Med. Sao Paulo, vol.6, pp.29-35, pls.5, 1931.

THE DEVELOPMENT AND GROWTH OF THE EXTERNAL DIMENSIONS OF THE HUMAN BODY IN THE FETAL PERIOD. Richard E. Scammon, Leroy A. Calkins. Univ. Minnesota Press, pp.XXIII, 367, 180 tables, 73 figs., 70 field graphs., 1929.

Erect Posture of Man

ON THE MECHANISM OF THE INTERVERTEBRAL SUBSTANCE, AND ON SOME EFFECTS OF THE ERECT POSITION OF MAN. Alfred Henry Garrod. Proc. Zool. Soc. Lond., pt.1, pp.48-50, figs.6, 1877.

THE UPRIGHT POSTURE OF MAN: A REVIEW OF ITS ORIGIN AND EVOLUTION. William K. Gregory. Proc. Amer. Philos. Soc., vol.67, pp.339-374, figs.1-15, 1928.

PSYCHIC AND ECONOMIC RESULTS OF MAN'S PHYSICAL UPRIGHTNESS. T. W. Heineman. Privately printed, Pasadena, California, pp.103, 1906.

MAN THE ERECT AND CANCEROUS. R. C. Kelsey. Medical Sentinel, Portland, pp.3, Sept., 1922.

EVOLUTION OF MAN'S ERECT POSTURE. Dudley Joy Morton. Jour. Morph. and Phys., vol.43, no.1, pp.147-179, figs.6, Dec.5, 1926.

THE EVOLUTION OF THE HUMAN PELVIS IN RELATION TO THE MECHANICS OF THE ERECT POSTURE. Edward Reynolds. Papers Peabody Mus. Amer. Arch. and Ethnol., Harvard Univ., vol.11, no.5, pp. 255-334, figs.10, pls.3, 1931.

Eurasia

FOSSIL MAN OF PEKING (SINANTHROPUS PEKINENSIS). El hombre fosil de Pekin (Sinanthropus pekinensis). Teresa Gurri Aguilera. Memor. Soc. Cubana Hist. Nat., vol.10, no.3, pp.173-194, pl.8, July, 1936.

DISCOVERY OF FURTHER HOMINID REMAINS OF THE LOWER QUATERNARY AGE FROM THE CHOU KOU TIEN DEPOSIT. Davidson Black. Science, n.s., vol.67, pp.135-136, Feb.3, 1928.

EVIDENCES OF THE USE OF FIRE BY SINANTHROPUS. Davidson Black. Bull. Geol. Soc. China, Peiping, vol.11, no.3, pp.107-108, 1931.

GEOLOGY OF FOSSIL MAN IN CHINA. Davidson Black. Pan-Amer. Geol., vol. 62, no.4, pp.267-272, fig.1, Nov., 1934.

THE LOWER MOLAR HOMINID TOOTH FROM THE CHOU KOU TIEN DEPOSIT. Davidson Black. Palaeontologia Sinica, ser.D, vol.7, fasc.1, pp.1-28, pls.1-2, 1927.

ON THE DISCOVERY, MORPHOLOGY, AND ENVIRONMENT OF SINANTHROPUS PEKINENSIS. Davidson Black. Philos. Trans. Roy. Soc. Lond., ser.B, vol.223, pp.57-120, pls.6-15, Feb.7, 1934.

PRELIMINARY NOTE ON ADDITIONAL SINANTHROPUS MATERIAL DISCOVERED IN CHOU KOU TIEN DURING 1928. Davidson Black. Bull. Geol. Soc. China, vol.8, no.1, pp.15-33, illus., May, 1929.

SINANTHROPUS PEKINENSIS: A FURTHER NOTE ON THE NEW MATERIAL RECOVERED AT CHOU KOU TIEN IN 1928 AND ITS ZOOGEOGRAPHICAL SIGNIFICANCE. Davidson Black. Proc. Fourth Pacific Sci. Congress Java, Batavia-Bandoeng, 1929, vol.3, biol. papers, pp.105-112, figs.2, 1930.

SINANTHROPUS PEKINENSIS: THE RECOVERY OF FURTHER FOSSIL REMAINS

OF THIS EARLY HOMINID FROM THE CHOU KOU TIEN DEPOSIT. Davidson Black. Science, n.s., vol.69, pp.674-676, June 28, 1929.

SKELETAL REMAINS OF SINANTHROPUS OTHER THAN SKULL PARTS. Davidson Black. Bull. Geol. Soc. China, vol.11, no. 4, pp.365-369, pls.1, 2, 1932.

TERTIARY MAN IN ASIA--THE CHOU KOU TIEN DISCOVERY. Davidson Black. Science, n.s., vol.64, pp.586-587, Dec. 17, 1926.

FOSSIL MAN IN CHINA. THE CHOUKOUTIEN CAVE DEPOSITS WITH A SYNOPSIS OF OUR PRESENT KNOWLEDGE OF THE LATE CENOZOIC IN CHINA. Davidson Black, Teilhard de Chardin, C. C. Young, W. C. Pei. Geol. Mem., Geol. Surv. China, Peiping, ser.A, no.11, pp.x, 166, figs.82, with 6 maps, May, 1933.

(A NEW PREHISTORIC-MAN FIND IN GERMANY (HOMO VISURGENSIS).) Ein neuer Fund des Urmenschen in Deutschland (Homo visurgensis). H. von Buttel-Reepen. Mannus, Leipzig, vol.22, pp.169-170, figs.2, 1930.

PEKING MAN--GREAT NEW DISCOVERIES. A. J. E. Cave. London Illus. News, vol. 190, no.5099, pp.42-43, illus., Jan.9, 1937.

HOW AND WHERE TO SEARCH THE OLDEST MAN IN CHINA. P. Teilhard de Chardin. Bull. Geol. Soc. China, Peking, vol.5, nos.3-4, pp.201-206, 1927.

EARLY MAN IN JAVA AND PITHECANTHROPUS ERECTUS. Eugene Dubois. Early Man, edited by G. G. MacCurdy, Lippincott and Co., Lond., pp.315-322, figs.49-52, 1937.

THE FOSSIL HUMAN REMAINS DISCOVERED IN JAVA BY DR. G. H. R. VON KOENIGSWALD AND ATTRIBUTED BY HIM TO PITHECANTHROPUS ERECTUS IN REALITY REMAINS OF HOMO SAPIENS SOLOENSIS. Eugene Dubois. Proc. K. Nederlandsche Akad. Wetenschappen, Amsterdam, vol.43, no.4, pp.494-496, pls.1-2; no.7, pp.842-851, pls.1-4; no. 10, pp.1268-1275, 1940.

NEW EVIDENCE OF THE DISTINCT ORGANIZATION OF PITHECANTHROPUS. Eugene Dubois. Proc. Koninklijke Akad. van Wetenschappen to Amsterdam, vol.37, no.3, pp.139-145, Mar., 1934.

(ON PITHECANTHROPUS ERECTUS.) Over den Pithecanthropus erectus. Eugene Dubois. Natuurhist. Maandblad, Maastricht vol.27, no.9, pp.92-95, illus., Sept.30, 1938.

NEANDERTHAL (MOUSTERIAN) MAN. Oliver C. Farrington, Henry Field. Field Mus. Nat. Hist., Geol. Leaflet no.11, pp. 1-14, pls.8, map, 1929.

(NEW REMAINS OF THE NEANDERTHAL AND HEIDELBERG MAN IN SOUTHERN GERMANY AND AUSTRIA.) Neue Reste des Neandertalers und des Heidelberger Urmenschen in Sueddeutschland und Oesterreich. W. Freudenberg. Palaeont Zeitschr., Berlin, vol.8, pp.153-158, June 30, 1926.

JAVANTHROPUS SOLOENSIS. Rene Herrera Fritot. Mem. Soc. Cubana Hist. Nat., Havana, vol.10, no.5, pp.317-324, pl.22, Dec., 1936.

(PREHISTORIC HUMAN FIND.) Forhistoriske menneskefunn. Anatol Heintz. Naturen, Copenhagen, vol.63, no.3, pp. 83-94, figs.9-13, Mar., 1939.

(PREHISTORIC HUMAN FIND. 3. NEANDERTHAL MAN OF EUROPE.) Forhistoriske menneskefunn. 3. Neandertal-mannen fra Europa. Anatol Heintz. Naturen, Copenhagen, vol.63, nos.7-8, pp.215-229, figs.25-29, July-Aug., 1939.

(PREHISTORIC HUMAN FIND. 4. THE OLDEST NEANDERTHAL MAN FROM EUROPE.) Forhistoriske menneskefunn. 4. De eldste Neandertalere fra Europa. Anatol Heintz. Naturen, Bergen, vol.63, no.11, pp.321-328, figs.30-32, Nov., 1939.

(PREHISTORIC HUMAN FIND.) Forhistoriske menneskefunn. Anatol Heintz. Naturen, Copenhagen, vol.63, no.12, pp. 353-365, figs.33-35, Dec., 1939.

THE GEOLOGICAL AGE OF PITHECANTHROPUS, MEGANTHROPUS AND GIGANTOPITHECUS. D. A. Hooijer. Amer. Jour. Phys. Anthropol., Phila., n.s., vol. 9, no.3, pp.265-281, Sept., 1951.

THE LOWER BOUNDARY OF THE PLEISTOCENE IN JAVA AND THE AGE OF PITHECANTHROPUS. D. A. Hooijer. Quaternaria. 3: 5-10, 1956.

ON THE SUPPOSED EVIDENCE OF EARLY MAN IN THE MIDDLE PLEISTOCENE OF SOUTHWEST CHINA. D. A. Hooijer. Southwestern Jour. Anthrop., Albuquerque, vol.7, no.1, pp.77-81, pls.2, 1951.

(PITHECANTHROPUS ERECTUS.) Le Pithecanthropus erectus. E. Houze. Rev. Univ. Bruxelles, vol.1, pp.1-42, figs.4, 1896.

(FIRST COMMUNICATION ON A FOSSIL HOMINID FROM THE OLD PLEISTOCENE OF EAST JAVA.) Erste Mitteilung ueber einen fossilen Hominiden aus dem Altpleistocaen Ostjavas. G. H. R. von Koenigswald. Proc. Koninklijke Akad. van Wetenschappen te Amsterdam, vol.39, no. 8, pp.1-12, pl.1, map 1, 1936.

(NEW PITHECANTHROPUS FINDS.) Neue Pithecanthropus Funde. G. H. R. von Koenigswald. Forschungen und Fortschritte, Berlin, vol.14, no.19, pp.218-219, figs.2, July 1, 1938.

(THE PRESENT STAND OF THE PITHECANTHROPUS PROBLEM.) Der gegenwaertige Stand des Pithecanthropus Problems. G. H. R. von Koenigswald. Handelingen v/h. 7th Ned.-Ind. Natuurwetenschappelijk Congress, pp.724-732, figs.8, 1936.

A REVIEW OF THE STRATIGRAPHY OF JAVA AND ITS RELATIONS TO EARLY MAN. G. H. R. von Koenigswald. Early Man, edited by G. G. MacCurdy, Lippincott and Co., Lond., pp.23-32, pls.1-2, 1937.

ON A PRESUMABLY PLEISTOCENE HUMAN TOOTH FROM THE SJARA-OSSO-GOL (SOUTH-EASTERN ORDOS) DEPOSITS. E. Licent, Teilbard de Chardin, Davidson Black. Bull. Geol. Soc. China, vol.5, no.3-4, pp.285-290, pl.1, 1927.

PROFESSOR O. C. MARSH AND PITHECANTHROPUS. Edwin Linton. Science, vol.62, pp.51-52, July 17, 1925.

NEW LIGHT ON PREHISTORIC MAN IN ASIA. George G. MacCurdy. Proc. Amer. Philos. Soc., vol.34, no.3, pp.185-191, pls.1-6, July, 1934.

RECENT STUDIES ON THE SKULL AND BRAIN OF PITHECANTHROPUS. J. H. McGregor. Nat. Hist., vol.25, no.6, pp. 544-559, Nov.-Dec., 1925 (Jan., 1926).

RESTORING NEANDERTHAL MAN. J. H. McGregor. Nat. Hist., vol.26, pp.288-293, May-June, 1926.

ON PITHECANTHROPUS ERECTUS. L. Manouvrier. (Translated from the French, by George G. MacCurdy.) Amer. Jour. Sci., New Haven, ser.4, vol.4, no.21, pp. 213-234, Sept., 1897.

(CRITICAL CONSIDERATIONS DIRECTED AGAINST PITHECANTHROPUS ERECTUS DUBOIS.) Kritische Bedenken gegen den Pithecanthropus erectus Dubois. R. Martin. Globus, vol.67, no.14, pp.1-5, Braunschweig, Mar., 1895.

BRIEF NOTES ON THE RACIAL TYPES OF THE FOSSIL TO SUBFOSSIL HUMAN SKELETONS IN JAPAN. Hikoshichiro Matsumoto. Sci. Reports Tohoku Imp. Univ. (2), Geol., vol.13, no.3, pp.111-114, 1930.

THE APE-MAN OF JAVA. W. D. Matthew. Nat. Hist., vol.28, pp.577-588, illus., Dec., 1928.

REPORT ON A FOSSIL FOUND AT TRINIL IN 1926, AND ERRONEOUSLY CONSIDERED AS THE REMAINS OF A SKULL OF PITHECANTHROPUS. W. A. Mijsberg, H. J. T. Bijimer. Proc. Kon. Acad. Wetensch. Amsterdam, Sec. Sci., vol.30, pp.126-133, figs.3, 1927.

EARLY MAN AND PLEISTOCENE STRATIGRAPHY IN SOUTHERN AND EASTERN ASIA. Hallam L. Movius, Jr. Papers Peabody Mus. Amer. Archaeol. and Ethnol., Harvard Univ., Cambridge, vol.19, no.3, pp.ix, 125, figs.47, 1944.

HUMAN REMAINS IN THE BOULDER-CLAY AT SALTNEY. Robert Newstead. Proc. Chester Soc. Nat. Sci., Lit. and Art., pp.26-29, pl.1, 1899-1900.

(NEW INVESTIGATIONS OF THE OLDEST HUMAN TYPES.) Nyere Undersogelser af de aeldste Mennesketyper. V. Nordmann. Naturens Verden, Copenhagen, vol.23, no. 7, pp.289-303, figs.9, 1939.

(HOMO (JAVANTHROPUS) SOLOENSIS, A PLEISTOCENE MAN OF JAVA.) Homo (Javanthropus) soloensis een Plistoceene Mensch van Java. W. F. F. Oppenoorth, Jr. Wetenschappelijke Mededeelingen no. 20 van den Dienst van den Mijnbouw in Ned-Indiee, Batavia, pp.49-63, figs.2, pls.6, 1932.

OLD AND NEW STANDARDS OF PLEISTOCENE DIVISION IN RELATION TO THE PREHISTORY OF MAN IN EUROPE. Henry Fairfield Osborn, Chester A. Reeds. Bull. Geol. Soc. Amer., Wash., D.C., vol.33, no.2, pp.411-490, figs.14, July 3, 1922.

THE PLIOCENE MAN OF FOXHALL IN EAST ANGLIA. Henry Fairfield Osborn. Nat. Hist., New York, vol.21, no.6, pp. 565-576, illus., Nov.-Dec., 1921.

NOTICE OF THE DISCOVERY OF QUARTZ AND OTHER STONE ARTIFACTS IN THE LOWER PLEISTOCENE HOMINID-BEARING SEDIMENTS OF THE CHOUKOUTIEN CAVE DEPOSIT. W. C. Pei. Bull. Geol. Soc. China, Peiping, vol.11, no.2, pp.109-146, figs.15, pls.3, 1931.

PEKING MAN. W. C. Pei. Nature, Lond., vol.138, no.3503, p.1056, Dec.19, 1936.

(REGARDING THE PHYLETIC POSITION OF PITHECANTHROPUS ERECTUS. CAN IT BE CONSIDERED A GIANT GIBBON?) A propos de la position phyletique du Pithecanthropus erectus. Peutil etre considere comme un gibbon geant? Eugene Pittard. Compte Rendu Soc. Phys. et Hist. Nat. Geneve, vol.60, no.1, pp.32-36, Jan.-Mar., 1943.

EARLY MAN IN CHINA. G. Elliot Smith. Nature, London, vol.125, no.3151, pp.448-449, figs.2, Mar.22, 1930.

MORE ABOUT THE PEKING MAN. G. Elliot Smith. Scientific American, New York, pp.188-190, illus., Sept., 1930.

THE PEKING MAN. G. Elliot Smith. China Jour., vol.13, no.5, pp.266-269, Nov., 1930.

ANTHROPOMETRY IN CHINA: AN EXTENDED OUTLINE OF RESEARCH. Paul H. Stevenson. China Medical Jour., vol. 40, no.2, pp.1-33 (of reprint), Feb., 1926.

RELATIONSHIPS OF THE UPPER PALAEOLITHIC RACES OF EUROPE. Louis R. Sullivan. Nat. Hist., New York, vol.24, no.6, pp.682-696, 1924.

NOTES ON THE "PEKING MAN." THE AGE OF THE "LOESS" DEPOSITS AND THEIR EMBEDDED FOSSILS. TRUTH OF THE GREAT DELUGE. Tse Tsan Tai. South China Morning Post, Sept.2, 1930.

CENOZOIC CYCLES IN ASIA AND THEIR BEARING ON HUMAN PREHISTORY. Hellmut de Terra. Proc. Amer. Philos. Soc., vol.77, no.3, pp.289-308, pls.1-6, Mar., 1937.

THE SIWALIKS OF INDIA AND EARLY MAN. Hellmut de Terra. Early Man, edited by G. G. MacCurdy, Lippincott and Co., Lond., pp.257-268, figs.43-45, 1937.

(DEVELOPMENTAL AND RACIAL TYPES OF HOMO PRIMIGENIUS.) Entwicklungs- und Rassetypen des Homo primigenius Natur und Museum, vol.58, no.1, pp.1-13, Jan.; no.2, pp.51-62, 18 figs., Feb., 1928.

DISCOVERY OF THE FEMUR AND THE HUMERUS OF SINANTHROPUS PEKINENSIS. Franz Weidenreich. Nature, London, vol. 141, no.3570, pp.614-617, figs.3, Apr.2, 1938.

THE DISCOVERY OF THE FEMUR OF SINANTHROPUS PEKINENSIS. Franz Weidenreich. Science, n.s., vol.87, no.2258, pp.322-323, Apr.8, 1938.

THE EXTREMITY BONES OF SINANTHROPUS PEKINENSIS. Franz Weidenreich. Palaeontologia Sinica, Peking n.s.D, no.5 (whole ser. no.116), pp.1-150, pls.1-34, 1941.

GIANT EARLY MAN FROM JAVA AND SOUTH CHINA. Franz Weidenreich. Science, Lancaster n.s., vol.99, no.2581, pp.479-482, June 16, 1944; Anthropol. Papers Amer. Mus. Nat. Hist., New York, vol.40, pt.1, pp.1-134, figs.28, pls.12, 1945.

MAN OR APE? Franz Weidenreich. Natural History, New York, vol.45, no.1, pp.32-37, illus., Jan., 1940.

(A NEW PITHECANTHROPUS FIND IN CHINA.) Ein neuer Pithecanthropus-Fund in China. Franz Weidenreich. Ber. Senckenberg Naturforsch. Ges. Natur. u. Mus., vol.60, no.12, pp.546-551, figs.3, Dec., 1930.

ON THE EARLIEST REPRESENTATIVES OF MODERN MANKIND RECOVERED ON THE SOIL OF EAST ASIA. Franz Weidenreich. Nat. Hist. Bull., Peking, vol.13, pt.3, pp.161-174, pls.6, Mar., 1939.

PITHECANTHROPUS AND SINANTHROPUS. Franz Weidenreich. Nature, London, vol. 141, no.3565, pp.378-379, Feb.26, 1938.

SINANTHROPUS PEKINENSIS--A DISTINCT PRIMITIVE HOMINID. Franz Weidenreich. Proc. Joint Meeting Anthrop. Soc. Tokyo, and Japanese Soc. Ethnol., 1st session, Tokyo, pp.13-37, figs.13, 1936.

THE SINANTHROPUS POPULATION OF CHOUKOUTIEN (LOCALITY 1) WITH A PRELIMINARY REPORT ON NEW DISCOVERIES. Franz Weidenreich. Bull. Geol. Soc. China, vol.14, no.4, pp.427-461, pls.3, 1935.

THE SITE AND TECHNIQUE OF THE EXCAVATIONS OF FOSSIL MAN IN CHOUKOUTIEN, CHINA. Franz Weidenreich. Trans. New York Acad. Sci., ser.2, vol. 4, no.1, pp.23-31, Nov., 1941.

SIX LECTURES ON SINANTHROPUS PEKINENSIS AND RELATED PROBLEMS. Franz Weidenreich. Bull. Geol. Soc. China, Peiping, vol.19, no.1, pp.4, 1-110, pls.9, Mar., 1939.

(HOMO SAPIENS IN THE OLD PALEOLITHIC DILUVIUM?) Homo sapiens im altpalaeolithischen Diluvium? Hans Weinert. Zeitschr. f. Morphol. u. Anthrop., Stuttgart, vol.34 (Festband Eugen Fischer), pp.459-468, fig.1, 1934.

A FOSSILIZED HUMAN FEMUR FROM EAST LONDON, C.P. L. H. Wells. S. African Jour. Sci., vol.32, pp.596-600, Nov., 1935.

PLEISTOCENE MAN IN ITALY AND GERMANY. F. E. Zeuner. Man, no.80, pp.1-2, 1954.

THE ANIMALS CONTEMPORARY WITH "PEKING MAN." China Jour., vol.12, no.3, pp.164-166, Mar., 1930.

BONE AND STONE INDUSTRIES OF EARLY MAN IN CHINA. Nature, London, vol.145, no.3684, pp.904-905, June 8, 1940.

EARLY MAN IN JAVA. Nature, London, vol.139, no.3511, p.294, Feb.13, 1937.

FOSSIL MAN OF MONTE CIRCEO, ITALY. Nature, London, vol.145, no.3677, p.629, Apr.20, 1940.

PALAEOLITHIC MAN IN THE NORTH MIDLANDS. Nature, London, vol.145, no.3663, pp.78-79, Jan.13, 1940.

PITHECANTHROPUS AND PEKING MAN. Nature, London, vol.141, no.3565, pp.361-362, Feb.26, 1938.

RECENT RESEARCHES ON EARLY MAN IN CHINA. I. Nature, London, vol.144, no.3660, pp.1054-1056, Dec.23, 1939.

Evolution

(THE POSITION OF MAN WITHIN THE FRAMEWORK OF THE VERTEBRATES.) Die Stellung des Menschen im Rahmen der Wirbeltiere. Othenio Abel. Gustav Fischer, Jena: pp.xvi, 398, figs.276, 1931.

(THE RELATIONSHIP BETWEEN MAN AND THE HIGHER FOSSIL PRIMATES.) Das Verwandtschaftsverhaeltnis zwischen dem Menschen und den hoeheren fossilen Primaten. Othenio Abel. Zeitschr. Morphol. u. Anthrop., Stuttgart, vol.34 (Festbd. Eugen Fischer), pp.1-14, fig.1, Apr., 1935.

THE TAUNGS PUZZLE. A BIOLOGICAL ESSAY. Paul Alsberg. Man, London, vol. 34, no.179, pp.154-159, Oct., 1934.

MEET YOUR ANCESTORS. A BIOGRAPHY OF PRIMITIVE MAN. Roy Chapman Andrews. Viking Press, New York, pp. xii, 259, illus., 1946.

THE TARSIAN HYPOTHESIS AND THE DESCENT OF MAN. F. M. Ashley-Montagu. Jour. Roy. Anthrop. Inst., London, vol.60, pp.335-362, pls.9-10, Dec., 1930.

ORIGIN OF RACIAL CHARACTERISTICS IN MAN. Louis Bolk. Amer. Jour. Phys. Anthrop., vol.13, no.1, pp.1-28, Apr.-June, 1929.

TALES THAT DEAD MEN TELL. John Hodgdon Bradley. Sci. Monthly, vol.28, pp.527-538, June, 1929.

THE ORIGIN OF THE HUMAN SKELETON. R. Broom. London, H. F. & G. Witherby, pp.164, figs.46, 1930.

(ENDOCRINAL INFLUENCE IN HUMAN MORPHOGENESIS.) La influencia endocrina en la morfogenesis humana. Alfredo Castellanos. Revista de Medicina de Rosario, nos.63-64, pp.35, 1932.

THE ANTECEDENTS OF MAN. W. E. LeGros Clark. Edinburgh Univ. Press, Edinburgh, 1959; Quadrangle Books, Chicago, 1960.

EARLY FORERUNNERS OF MAN. A MORPHOLOGICAL STUDY OF THE EVOLUTIONARY ORIGIN OF THE PRIMATES. W. E. LeGros Clark. Balto: William Wood and Co., pp.xvi, 296, figs. 89, 1934.

FOSSIL EVIDENCE FOR HUMAN EVOLUTION. W. E. LeGros Clark. Chicago, Univ. of Chicago Press, 180 pp., illus., 1955.

MAN'S PLACE AMONG THE PRIMATES. W. E. LeGros Clark. Man, vol.35, nos. 1-20, pp.1-6, Jan., 1935.

PALAEONTOLOGICAL EVIDENCE BEARING ON HUMAN EVOLUTION. W. E. LeGros Clark. Biol. Reviews, Cambridge, England, vol.15, no.2, pp.202-230, figs.12, Apr., 1940.

THE RELATIONSHIP BETWEEN PITHECANTHROPUS AND SINANTHROPUS. W. E. LeGros Clark. Nature, London, vol.145, no.3663, pp.70-71, Jan.13, 1940.

SOME PALEONTOLOGICAL PRINCIPLES SIGNIFICANT IN HUMAN EVOLUTION. Edwin H. Colbert. Studies in Physical Anthropology, no.1, Early Man in the Far East, Phila., pp.103-148, figs.5, 1949.

SOME PROBLEMS OF HUMAN RACIAL DEVELOPMENT AND MIGRATION. Fay-Cooper Cole. Amer. Nat., Lancaster, vol.79, no.780, pp.5-13, Jan.-Feb., 1945.

(PLACE OF HOMO NEANDERTHALENSIS IN HUMAN PHYLOGENY.) Lugar que ocupa el Homo neanderthalensis en la filogenia humana. Juan Comas. Rev. Mexicana Estudios Antropologicos, Mexico, D.F., vol.4, no.3, pp.225-254, figs.11, Sept.-Dec., 1940.

THE SEARCH FOR MAN'S ANCESTORS. H. B. S. Cooke. S. African Sci., Johannesburg, vol.2, no.2, pp.34-36, Sept., 1948.

RACE, CLASS, AND MATING IN THE EVOLUTION OF MAN. C. D. Darlington. Nature, London, vol.152, no.3855, pp. 315-319, Sept.18, 1943.

(Review by Cyrus Thomas of) THE DESCENT OF MAN, AND SELECTION IN RELATION TO SEX. Charles Darwin. Appleton and Co., New York, 2 vols., 1871; Quart. Review Evangelical Luthern Church, n.s., vol.2, no.2, pp.213-241, Apr., 1872.

(CAN INDIVIDUAL CALLOSITIES BECOME HEREDITARY?) Les callosités individuelles peuvent-elles devenir héréditaires? Ed Dechambre. Mammalia, vol.17, no.2, pp.89-95, June, 1953.

A PROPOSED LABORATORY FOR THE STUDY OF HUMAN HEREDITY IN MICHIGAN. Lee R. Dice. Thirty-eighth Annual Report Michigan Acad. Sci. Arts and Letters, pp.84-87, 1937.

ON THE GIBBON-LIKE APPEARANCE OF PITHECANTHROPUS ERECTUS. Eugene Dubois. Proc. Kon. Akad. Wetensch. te Amsterdam, vol.38, no.6, pp.578-585, 1935.

THE BIRTHPLACE OF MAN. George S. Duncan. Scientific Monthly, vol.29, no.9, pp.359-362, Oct., 1929.

THE SIGNIFICANCE OF PEKING MAN. E. N. Fallaize. Discovery, vol.18, no. 208, pp.116-118, figs.2, Apr., 1937.

THE ORIGIN OF THE HUMAN RACES. A. B. Drogleever Fortuyn. Science, Lancaster, n.s., vol.90, no.2337, pp. 352-354, Oct.13, 1939.

(ANTHROPOLOGY AND MUTATIONS.) Anthropologie et mutations. Charles Fraipont. Revue anthropologique, Paris, année 43, nos.1-3, pp.37-43, Jan.-Mar., 1933.

(CEREBRAL EVOLUTION OF THE PRIMATES, PARTICULARLY OF THE HOMINIDS.) L'evolution cérébrale des primates et en particulier des hominiens. Charles Fraipont. Archiv. Inst. Paléont. Humaine (Fondation Albert 1, Prince de Monaco), Paris, Mem.8, pp.86, figs.112, pls.1-4, Mar., 1931.

(PRECURSORS AND SUCCESSORS OF HOMO HEIDELBERGENSIS: NEW FINDS FROM THE ENVIRONS OF HEIDELBERG.) Vorlaeufer und Nachfolger des Homo Heidelbergensis, neue Funde aus Heidelbergs Umgebung, Heidelberg. Wilhelm Freudenberg. Beitraege zur Natur-und Urgeschichte Westdeutschlands, Leif.2, pt.2, pp.3-56, figs.9, pls.4, 1938.

HUMAN ANCESTRY FROM A GENETICAL POINT OF VIEW. Ruggles R. Gates. Harvard University Press, Cambridge, XVI, 422 pp., illus., Jan.26, 1948.

ANCESTORLESS MAN: THE ANTHROPOLOGICAL DILEMMA. J. M. Gillett. Scientific Monthly, Wash., D.C., vol.57, no.6, whole no.339, pp.533-545, Dec., 1943.

ASIA AND THE EVOLUTION OF MAN. A. W. Grabau. China Jour., vol.12, no.3, pp.152-163, Mar., 1930.

THE AGE-INCIDENCE PRINCIPLE OF INVESTIGATION IN EVALUATING THE BIOLOGICAL SIGNIFICANCE OF INHERITED VARIATIONS IN THE PROBLEMS OF HUMAN CONSTITUTION. William Washington Graves. Amer. Jour. Psych., vol.93, no.5, pp.1109-1117, pl.16, Mar., 1937.

A CRITIQUE OF PROFESSOR OSBORN'S THEORY OF HUMAN ORIGIN. W. K. Gregory. Amer. Jour. Phys. Anthrop., vol.14, no.2, pp.133-161, pls.1-3, Apr.-June, 1930.

DID MAN ORIGINATE IN CENTRAL ASIA? W. K. Gregory. Scientific Monthly, vol. 24, pp.385-401, photos, May, 1927.

THE EVOLUTION OF THE HUMAN FACE. W. K. Gregory. Amer. Mus. Jour., vol. 17, no.6, pp.377-388, illus., Oct., 1917; Nat. Hist., vol.19, pp.421-425, Apr.-May, 1919.

FACTS AND THEORIES OF EVOLUTION, WITH SPECIAL REFERENCE TO THE ORIGIN OF MAN. W. K. Gregory. Dental Cosmos, pp.19, figs.6, Mar., 1920.

HOW NEAR IS THE RELATIONSHIP OF MAN TO THE CHIMPANZEE-GORILLA STOCK? W. K. Gregory. Quart. Rev. Biol., vol.2, pp.549-560, illus., Dec., 1927.

IS SIVAPITHECUS PILGRIM AN ANCESTOR OF MAN? W. K. Gregory. Science, n.s., vol.42, no.1080, pp.341-342, Sept.10, 1915.

THE LINEAGE OF MAN. W. K. Gregory. Reprinted from "Creation by Evolution," New York, pp.270-292, 1928.

(Review by C. Tate Regan of) MAN'S PLACE AMONG THE ANTHROPOIDS. W. K. Gregory. Ann. and Mag. Nat. Hist., Lond., ser.10, vol.13, no.76, pp.479-480, Apr., 1934.

MAN'S PLACE AMONG THE PRIMATES. W. K. Gregory. Palaeobiologica, Wien u. Leipzig, vol.6, no.2, pp.208-213, 1938.

THE ORIGIN OF MAN FROM A BRACHIATING ANTHROPOID STOCK. W. K. Gregory. Science, vol.71, no.1852, pp.645-650, June 27, 1930.

THE ORIGIN OF MAN FROM THE ANTHROPOID STEM: WHEN AND WHERE? PART I. W. K. Gregory. Evolution, vol.2, no.2, pp.3-4, Mar., 1929.

THE ORIGIN OF MAN FROM THE ANTHROPOID STEM: WHEN AND WHERE? PART II. W. K. Gregory. Evolution, vol.2, no.3, pp.3-4, illus., Apr., 1929.

THE ORIGIN OF THE HUMAN FACE: A STUDY IN PALEOMORPHYOLOGY AND EVOLUTION. W. K. Gregory. pp.16, figs. 8, 1935.

THE ORIGIN, RISE AND DECLINE OF HOMO SAPIENS. W. K. Gregory. Scientific Monthly, vol.39, pp.481-486, figs.18, Dec., 1934.

THE ROLES OF UNDEVIATING EVOLUTION AND TRANSFORMATION IN THE ORIGIN OF MAN. W. K. Gregory. Amer. Nat., vol.69, no.724, pp.385-404, figs.12, Sept.-Oct., 1935.

THE STUDY OF HUMAN EVOLUTION: A PLEA FOR A MORE SYNTHETIC APPROACH. W. K. Gregory. Bull. School Medicine, Univ. Maryland, vol.20, no.1, pp.31-33, July, 1935.

TWO VIEWS OF THE ORIGIN OF MAN. W. K. Gregory. Science, vol.65, no.1695, pp.601-605, June 24, 1927.

WERE THE ANCESTORS OF MAN PRIMITIVE BRACHIATORS? W. K. Gregory. Proc. Amer. Philos. Soc., vol.67, pp. 129-130, illus., 1928.

EVIDENCE OF THE AUSTRALOPITHECINE MAN-APES ON THE ORIGIN OF MAN. W. K. Gregory, Milo Hellman. Science, n.s., vol.88, no.2296, pp.615-616, Dec.30, 1938.

(THE FIRST HUMAN MIGRATIONS.) Le prime migrazione umane. V. Giuffrida-ruggeri. Scientia, Riv. Sci., Bologna, ser.2, vol.27, anno 14, no.XCV-3, pp.201-209, Mar., 1920.

THE NEANDERTHAL CONTROVERSY: NINETEENTH-CENTURY VERSION. Jacob W. Gruber. Sci. Monthly, Lancaster, vol.67, no.6, pp.436-439, Dec., 1948.

(ON OUR PRESENT KNOWLEDGE OF THE ORIGIN OF MAN.) Ueber unsere gegenwaertige Kenntniss vom Ursprung des Menschen. Ernst Haeckel. Emil Strauss, Bonn, pp.53, 1899.

THE ASCENT OF MAN: A HANDBOOK TO THE CASES ILLUSTRATING THE STRUCTURE OF MAN AND THE GREAT APES. H. S. Harrison. The Horniman Museum and Library, London County Council, no. 13, pp.1-74, 1920.

(ON THE ORIGIN OF MAN.) Zur Herkunft des Menschen. E. Hennig. Naturwissenschaftliche Monatsschrift, aus der Heimat, vol.42, no.9, pp.257-270, figs.1-17, Sept., 1929.

(HISTORICAL AND CRITICAL REMARKS ON BOLK'S PROBLEM OF ANTHROPOGENESIS.) Historisches und Kritisches zu Bolks Problem der Menschwerdung. Max Hilzheimer. Anat. Anzeiger, vol.62, pp. 110-121, 1927.

HOMO SAPIENS--WHENCE AND WHITHER. E. A. Hooton. Science, n.s., vol.82, no. 2115, pp.19-31, July 12, 1935.

MAN'S DEBT TO THE APE. E. A. Hooton. Frontiers, Phila., vol.2, no.3, pp.71-76, figs.6, Feb., 1938.

UP FROM THE APE. E. A. Hooton. Rev. ed. New York, The Macmillan Co., xxii, 788 pp., 41 pls., 68 figs., 1947.

THE WAGES OF BIOLOGICAL SIN. E. A. Hooton. Atlantic Monthly, Boston, vol.164, no.4, pp.435-445, Oct., 1939.

THE AGE OF HOMO SAPIENS. W. Howells. Scientific Monthly, Lancaster, vol.54, no.6, (whole no.321), pp.552-554, June, 1942.

BACK OF HISTORY; THE STORY OF OUR OWN ORIGINS. W. Howells. New York, Doubleday and Co., 384 pp., illus., 1954.

MANKIND SO FAR. W. Howells. Amer. Mus. Nat. Hist., New York, Doubleday Doran and Co., Garden City, Sci. ser., vol.5, pp.xii, 319, illus., 1944.

THE NEANDERTHAL PHASE OF MAN. Ales Hrdlicka. Ann. Rept. Board Regents Smithson. Inst. for 1928, publ.2981, pp. 593-621, pls.4, figs.6, Nov.18, 1929.

THE PROBLEM OF HUMAN EVOLUTION. Ales Hrdlicka. Science and Man, Harcourt Brace and Co., New York, pp.17-43, 1942.

THE INHERITANCE OF EYE COLOR IN MAN--BROWN AND NONBROWN. Byron O. Hughes. Contrib. Lab. Vert. Biol., Univ. Mich., Ann Arbor, no.27, pp.10, Apr., 1944.

THE ANCESTRY OF MAN. F. W. Jones. Douglas Price Memorial Lecture, no.3, 35 pp., R. G. Gillies and Co., Brisbane, 1923.

(Review by William L. Straus of) MAN'S PLACE AMONG THE MAMMALS. F.W. Jones. Jour. Mamm., vol.12, no.2, pp. 171-173, May, 1931.

CONCEPTIONS OF MAN'S ANCESTRY. Arthur Keith. Nature, London, vol.135, no.3418, pp.705-708, May 4, 1935.

THE CONSTRUCTION OF MAN'S FAMILY TREE. Arthur Keith. The Forum Series, London, no.18, pp.1-54, figs.10, 1934.

DARWIN'S THEORY OF MAN'S DESCENT AS IT STANDS TODAY. Arthur Keith. Science, n.s., vol.66, pp.201-208, Sept. 2, 1927.

EVOLUTION OF MODERN MAN (HOMO SAPIENS). Arthur Keith. Nature, London, vol.153, no.3894, p.742, June 17, 1944.

NEW DISCOVERIES RELATING TO THE ANTIQUITY OF MAN. Arthur Keith. W. W. Norton and Co., Inc., New York, pp. 512, figs.186, 1931.

A NEW THEORY OF HUMAN EVOLUTION. Arthur Keith. Philosophical Library, New York, pp.x, 451, 1949.

THE ORIGIN AND AGE OF MAN: NEW LIGHT ON A DEEP RIDDLE. Arthur Keith. New York Times, p.4, Sept.18, 1932.

OUR NEW ANCESTOR: SOLO MAN--"A DISCOVERY OF THE HIGHEST INTEREST TO THOSE WHO FOLLOW THE UNFOLDING OF MAN'S LONG PAST HISTORY." Arthur Keith. Illus. London News, vol.180, no.4859, pp.915-917, illus., June 4, 1932.

MOUNT CARMEL MAN. HIS BEARING ON THE ANCESTRY OF MODERN RACES. Arthur Keith, Theodore D. McCown. Amer. School of Prehistoric Research, Old Lyme, Conn., Bull.13, pp.5-15, pls. 5, May, 1937.

ANTHROPOLOGICAL AND HISTORICAL STUDIES RELATING TO THE EARLIEST EVIDENCE OF MAN. G. H. R. von Koenigswald. Year Book no.36, Carnegie Inst. Wash., pp.349-352, 1937.

THE RELATIONSHIP BETWEEN PITHECANTHROPUS AND SINANTHROPUS. G. H. R. von Koenigswald. Nature, London, vol.144, no.3657, pp.926-929, illus., Dec.2, 1939.

SUB-HUMAN CULTURE BEGINNINGS. A. L. Kroeber. Quart. Rev. Biol., vol.3, pp. 325-342, Sept., 1928.

THE HUMAN FAMILY TREE. Wilton M. Krogman. Ciba Symposia, Ciba Pharmaceutical Products Inc., Summit, N.J., vol.3, no.1, pp.790-803, figs.16, Apr., 1941.

(THE FORERUNNERS OF FOSSIL MAN.) Az Oesember eloedei. K. Lambrecht. Budapest: Dante Kiadas, 1927.

ADAM'S ANCESTORS; OLD STONE AGE AND MAN'S EVOLUTION. L. S. B. Leakey. 4th ed. London, Methuen and Co., Ltd., 235 pp., illus., 1953.

HUMAN EVOLUTION AND SCIENCE. Francis P. LeBuffe, S.J. 7th ed. revised, with 5 pages of bibliography, 75th thousand, pp.48, The America Press, New York City, 1931.

THE COMING OF MAN, PRE-MAN AND PREHISTORIC MAN. George G. MacCurdy. Prehistoric Anthropology, The Univ. Soc., New York, pp.x, 157, figs.58, pl.1, 1932.

FACTS AND THEORIES RELATING TO THE ANCESTRY OF MAN. W. D. Matthew. Amer. Mus. Jour., New York, vol.12, no. 7, pp.255-256, Nov., 1912.

THE PLACE OF PITHECANTHROPUS AMONG PRIMATES. W. A. Mijsberg. Proc. Fourth Pacific Sci. Congress Java, Batavia-Bandoeng, vol.3, Biol. Papers, pp.369-373, 1929.

CONFLICTING VIEWS ON THE PROBLEM OF MAN'S ANCESTRY. Gerrit S. Miller, Jr. Amer. Jour. Phys. Anthr., vol.3, pp. 213-245, 2 pls., 1920.

THE CONTROVERSY OVER HUMAN MISSING LINKS. Gerrit S. Miller, Jr. Ann. Rept. Smithsonian Inst., Wash., D.C.,1928, publ.2996, pp.413-465, pls.5, 1929.

(Review by Gerrit S. Miller, Jr. of) THE ORIGIN AND MAINTENENCE OF DIVERSITY IN MAN. M. I. Newbigin. Amer. Jour. Phys. Anthrop., vol.2, pp. 207-209, Oct.9, 1919.

(THE FIRST STEPS OF THE DEVELOPMENT OF MAN. AN INTUITIVE REPRESENTATION OF HUMAN PHYLOGENY AND A CRITICAL OBSERVATION OF ITS GENERAL HYPOTHESES.) Die Vorstufen der Menschwerdung. Eine anschauliche Darstellung der Menschlichen Stammesgeschichte und eine kritische Betrachtung ihrer allgemeinen Voraussetzungen. Adolf Naef. Jena: Verlag von Gustav Fischer, pp. viii, 232, figs.129, 1933.

LIVING RACES OF MAN. Bruno Oetteking. New Intern Encycl., New York, vol.14, pp.760-764 (reprint of 8 pp.), 1914-1915.

THE PLACE OF HOMO SOLOENSIS AMONG FOSSIL MEN. W. F. F. Oppenoorth. Early Man, edited by G. G. MacCurdy, Lippincott and Co., London, pp. 349-360, pls.25-26, 1937.

THE EVOLUTION OF HUMAN RACES. Henry F. Osborn. Nat. Hist., New York, vol.26, no.1, pp.1-13, illus., Jan.-Feb., 1926.

INFLUENCE OF THE GLACIAL AGE ON THE EVOLUTION OF MAN. Henry F. Osborn. Bull. Geol. Soc. Amer., vol. 40, pp.489-496, figs.3, Dec.31, 1929.

THE ORIGIN AND ANTIQUITY OF MAN; A CORRECTION. Henry Fairfield Osborn. Science, Lancaster, n.s., vol.65, no. 1694, p.597, June 17, 1927.

PRESENT STATUS OF THE PROBLEM OF HUMAN ANCESTRY. Henry F. Osborn. Proc. Amer. Philos. Soc., vol.67, pp. 151-155, 1928.

RECENT DISCOVERIES RELATING TO THE ORIGIN AND ANTIQUITY OF MAN. Henry F. Osborn. Proc. Amer. Phil. Soc., vol. 66, pp.373-389, 1927; Science, n.s., vol. 65, pp.471-488, May 20, 1927; Palaeobiol., vol.1, no.1, pp.189-202, 1928.
WHY CENTRAL ASIA? Henry F. Osborn. Nat. Hist., vol.26, pp.263-269, May-June, 1926.

THE NEW HERESY OF MAN'S DESCENT. R. I. Pocock. Conquest, London, vol.1, no.4, pp.151-157, illus., Feb., 1920.

THE ANTIQUITY OF MAN. A. R. Radcliffe-Brown. Australian Mus. Mag., vol. 4, no.1, pp.28-36, figs.7, Jan.-Mar., 1930.

EMBRYOLOGICAL EVIDENCE OF THE EVOLUTION OF MAN. Adolph H. Schultz. Jour. Wash. Acad. Sci., vol.15, pp.247-263, June 19, 1925.

VARIATIONS IN MAN AND THEIR EVOLUTIONARY SIGNIFICANCE. Adolph H. Schultz. Amer. Nat., vol.60, pp.297-323. July-Aug., 1926.

THE VERO FINDS IN THE LIGHT OF PRESENT KNOWLEDGE. E. H. Sellards. Early Man, edited by G. G. MacCurdy, Lippincott and Co., Lond., pp.193-210, figs.27-30, pls.16-17, 1937.

THE GENESIS OF MAN. Leonard R. Sillman. Evolution, Lancaster, vol.9, no. 1, pp.94-99, Mar., 1955.

SOME PRINCIPLES OF HISTORICAL BIOLOGY BEARING ON HUMAN ORIGINS. George G. Simpson. Cold Spring Harbor Symposia on Quantitative Biology, vol.15, pp.55-66, 1950.

THE ANCESTRY OF MAN. G. Elliot Smith. Bull. Geol. Soc. China, Peiping, vol.9, no. 3, pp.191-194, 1930.

THE CRADLE OF MANKIND. G. Elliot Smith. Scientia, Bologna (3), vol.47, pp. 401-408, 1930.

THE SEARCH FOR MAN'S ANCESTORS. G. Elliot Smith. The Forum Series, no.16, Watts and Co., Lond., pp.viii, 56, figs.6, pls.6, Oct., 1931.

(Review by Gerrit S. Miller, Jr. of) THE SEARCH FOR MAN'S ANCESTORS. G. Elliot Smith. Jour. Mam., Balto., vol. 13, no.4, pp.373-374, Nov.2, 1932.

THE SIGNIFICANCE OF THE PEKING MAN. G. Elliot Smith. The Henderson Trust Lectures, no.11, Univ. Edinburgh, Oliver and Boyd, Edinburgh, pp.20, figs.16, 1931.

A REFUTATION OF THE DARWINIAN CONCEPTION OF THE ORIGIN OF MANKIND. John C. Stallcup. Rev. ed., Tacoma, Wash., Pioneer bindery and printing co., 1913.

THE RIDDLE OF MAN'S ANCESTRY. William L. Straus, Jr. Quart. Rev. Biol., vol.24, no.3, pp.200-223, Sept., 1949.

GEOLOGIC DATING OF HUMAN EVOLUTION IN ASIA. Helmut de Terra. Sci. Monthly, Lancaster, vol.51, no.2, pp.112-124, Aug., 1940.
THE GENESIS OR CREATION OF MAN. Cyrus Thomas. Reformed Church Review, vol.5, no.4, pp.487-508, Oct., 1901.

DOWN FROM THE TREES. Frank Thone. Science News Letter, Wash., vol.50, no. 16, p.254, Oct.19, 1946.

(ARE THERE SEVERAL HUMAN ORIGINS?) Y a-t-il plusieurs souches humaines? Rev. Gen. Sci. Pures et Appl., vol.38, no.7, pp.201-209, Apr.15, 1927.

(THE NEW PITHECANTHROPUS AND THE PROBLEM OF THE ORIGIN OF MAN.) Les nouveaux pithecanthropes et le probleme de l'origine de l'homme. Henri V. Vallois. La Nature, Paris, no.3125, pp.367-370, figs.3, Dec.1, 1946.

DO THE CHARACTERISTICS OF PREHISTORIC HUMAN REMAINS IMPLY A COMMON ANCESTRY FOR MAN AND APES? Wilson D. Wallis. Amer. Nat., vol.59, no.660, pp.62-69, Jan.-Feb., 1925.

AFRICA AND THE ORIGIN OF MAN. D. M. S. Watson. Amer. Scientist, Burlington, vol.41, no.3, pp.427-438, illus., July, 1953.

THE DRIFT OF HUMAN PHYLOGENETIC EVOLUTION. Franz Weidenreich. Nat. Hist. Bull., Peking, vol.13, pt.4, pp.227-230, 1939.

THE FORERUNNER OF SINANTHROPUS PEKINENSIS. Franz Weidenreich. Bull. Geol. Soc. China, Nanking, vol.17, no.2, pp.137-144, June, 1937.

GENERIC, SPECIFIC, AND SUBSPECIFIC CHARACTERS IN HUMAN EVOLUTION. Franz Weidenreich. Jour. Physical Anthropol., Phila., n.s., vol. 4, pp.413-430, Dec., 1946.

THE "NEANDERTHAL MAN" AND THE ANCESTORS OF "HOMO SAPIENS." Franz Weidenreich. Amer. Anthropol., Menasha, n.s., vol.45, no.1, pp.39-48, fig.1, Jan.-Mar., 1943.

THE NEW DISCOVERIES OF SINANTHROPUS PEKINENSIS AND THEIR BEARING ON THE SINANTHROPUS AND PITHECANTHROPUS PROBLEMS. Franz Weidenreich. Bull. Geol. Soc. China, vol.16, pp.439-470, figs. 17, pls.2, Apr., 1937.
NEW DISCOVERIES ON SINANTHROPUS AND PITHECANTHROPUS PROBLEMS (E.A.). Franz Weidenreich. Jour. Anthrop. Soc. Tokyo, vol.52, no.600, pp.398-400, Oct., 1937.

(ON THE PHYLOGENIC GROWTH OF THE HOMINID BRAIN.) Ueber das phylogentische Wachstum des Homindengehirns. Franz Weidenreich. Kaibogaku Zasshi, vol.9, no. 5, Anatomical Inst. of the Imperial Univ., Tokyo, pp.14, figs.14, Aug., 1936.

THE RAMIFICATION OF THE MIDDLE MENINGEAL ARTERY IN FOSSIL HOMINIDS AND ITS BEARING UPON PHYLOGENETIC PROBLEMS. Franz Weidenreich. Palaeontologia Sinica, Peiping, n.s., D, no. 3 (whole ser. no.110), pp.1-16, figs.30, 1938.

THE RELATION OF SINANTHROPUS PEKINENSIS TO PITHECANTHROPUS, JAVANTHROPUS AND RHODESIAN MAN. Franz Weidenreich. Jour. Roy. Anthrop. Inst., London, vol.67, pp.51-65, figs.4, table, pls.8-11, Jan.-June, 1937.

SINANTHROPUS PEKINENSIS AND ITS POSITION IN THE LINE OF HUMAN EVOLUTION. Franz Weidenreich. Peking Nat. Hist. Bull., vol.10, pt.4, pp.281-290, figs.15, June, 1936.

THE TORUS OCCIPITALIS AND RELATED STRUCTURES AND THEIR TRANSFORMATION IN THE COURSE OF HUMAN EVOLUTION. Franz Weidenreich. Bull. Geol. Soc. China, Peiping, vol.19, no.4, pp.479-544, pls.6, 1940.

THE UPPER PALEOLITHIC MAN OF THE UPPER CAVE OF CHOUKOUTIEN AND HIS BEARING ON THE PROBLEM OF THE AMERICAN INDIANS. Franz Weidenreich. Proc. 6th Pacific Sci. Congr., Berkeley, vol.4, pp.165-168, 1940.

(THE CONTEMPORARY MISSING LINK.) Das heutige "missing link." Hans Weinert. Jenaische Zeitschr. Naturwiss., vol.67, pp.245-259, figs.7, 1932.

(THE FAMILY TREE OF MAN IN THE VARIATIONS OF SCIENTIFIC RESEARCH.) Der Stammbaum des Menschen im Wechsel wissenschaftlicher Forschung. Hans Weinert. Kosmos, handweiser fuer Naturfreunde (Gesell. der Naturfreunde), Stuttgart, Jahrg.1932, no.6, pp.209-214, figs.5, June, 1932.

(Review by E. Bourdelle of)(THE PROBLEM OF THE GENESIS OF MAN.) Le problème de la genèse d l'Homme. M. Westenhoefer. (Condensed and annotated.) Mammalia, Paris, vol.17, no.2, pp.127-128, June, 1953.

NEW EVIDENCE OF MAN'S RELATIONSHIP TO THE ANTHROPOID APES. J. Leon Williams. Evolution, no.10, pp.2-3, illus., Nov., 1928.
THE BIRTHPLACE OF MAN (ABSTRACT). Arthur Smith Woodward. Nature, Lond., vol.136, no.3436, pp.384-385, Sept.7, 1935.

CRADLE OF MANKIND SOUGHT IN CENTRAL ASIA. Arthur Smith Woodward. Science, n.s., vol.82, no.2124, suppl., p.7, Sept.13, 1935.

RECENT PROGRESS IN THE STUDY OF EARLY MAN. Arthur Smith Woodward. Brit. Assoc. Adv. Sci. Report Ann. Meeting 1935, Norwich, Sept.4-11, Lond., pp.129-142, 1935.

THE FORERUNNER OF SINANTHROPUS PEKINENSIS. C. C. Young. Bull. Geol. Soc. China, Peking, vol.17, no.2, pp.137-144, 1937.

HORMONES AND EVOLUTION: AN EXAMINATION OF CERTAIN VIEWS ON THE PART PLAYED BY THE ENDOCRINE GLANDS OF HUMAN EVOLUTION. S. Zuckerman. Man, vol.36, art.180, pp.129-135, 1936.

SINANTHROPUS AND OTHER FOSSIL MEN. THEIR RELATIONS TO EACH OTHER AND TO MODERN TYPES. S. Zuckerman. Eugenics Review, vol.24, no.4, pp.273-284, Jan., 1933.

PEKING MAN OUR OLDEST ANCESTOR. China, Jour., vol.12, no.1, p.47, 1930.

PEKING MAN: THE NEW SKULLS AND THE EVOLUTIONARY PROBLEM. Nature, London, vol.139, no.3511, pp.261-262, Feb.13, 1937.

PITHECANTHROPUS AMONG PRIMITIVE MEN: AN ANCESTRAL FAMILY TREE. Illus. London News, vol.191, no.5148, p. 1119, figs.2, Dec.18, 1937.

## Eye and Vision

THE TERMINAL LOOPS OF THE CONES AND RODS OF THE HUMAN RETINA, WITH PHOTOMICROGRAPHS. W. F. Norris. Amer. Ophthalmol. Soc. Trans., Hertford, pp.347-352, figs.7, 1895.

A CONTRIBUTION TO THE ANATOMY OF THE HUMAN RETINA, WITH A SPECIAL CONSIDERATION OF THE TERMINAL LOOPS OF THE RODS AND CONES. W. F. Norris, James Wallace. Univ. Med. Mag., Phila., vol.6, no.6, pp.353-358, illus., Mar., 1894.

ON THE GROWTH OF THE HUMAN EYEBALL AND OPTIC NERVE. Richard E. Scammon, Ellery L. Armstrong. Jour. Comp. Neur., vol.38, pp.165-219, 20 figs., Feb.15, 1925.

## Fossils

FOSSIL MEN: ELEMENTS OF HUMAN PALEONTOLOGY. Marcellin Boule. London: Gurney and Jackson, pp.xxvii, 504, 1923. (Translated from the French.)

(FOSSIL MEN.) Les hommes fossiles. Marcellin Boule, H. V. Vallois. 4th ed. Paris, Masson et Cie., x, 583 pp., 299 figs., 1952.

HISTORY OF THE PRIMATES: AN INTRODUCTION TO THE STUDY OF FOSSIL MAN. W. E. LeGros Clark. British Mus. Nat. Hist., London, pp.117, illus., 1949; ed.4, 119 pp., 1954.

THE OLDEST HUMAN FOSSILS. W. E. LeGros Clark. Discovery, London, vol.6, no.4, pp.102-106, figs.4, Apr., 1945.

PRIMITIVE MAN. Joseph S. Didusch. Bull. Nat. Hist. Soc. Maryland, Balto., vol.11, no.3, pp.1-46, figs.7, Jan.-Feb., 1941.

NEWLY FOUND BONES INDICATE THAT APE WALKED LIKE A MAN. TOE BONE IS LONGER THAN THAT OF A MAN BUT BELONGED TO A FOOT USED TO UPRIGHT WALKING; ARM BONES CONFORM. E. N. Fallaize. Science News Letter, vol.34, no. 24, p.382, Dec.10, 1938.

IS THE PRO-DAWN MAN A MYTH? W. K. Gregory. Human Biology, vol.1, no.2, pp. 153-165, May, 1929.

A DISSENTING OPINION AS TO DAWN MEN AND APE MEN. W. K. Gregory, J. Howard McGregor. Nat. Hist., New York, vol.26, no.3, pp.270-271, 1926.

PLEISTOCENE MAN IN EUROPE AND IN AMERICA. Oliver P. Hey. N. Y. Herald-Tribune, with slight changes, 8 pp., figs.1-8, July 1, 1928.

(PREHISTORIC HUMAN FINDS.) Forhistoriske menneskefunn. Anatol Heintz. Naturen, Copenhagen, vol.63, no.5, pp. 129-140, figs.18-21, May, 1939.

THE MOST ANCIENT SKELETAL REMAINS OF MAN. Ales Hrdlicka. Smithsonian Rep., pp.491-552, figs.1-12, pls. 1-41, 1914; pp.3-63, pls.41, figs.12, 2nd ed., May 13, 1916.

RECENT DISCOVERIES OF FOSSIL MAN. Arthur Keith. Nature, no.3164, pp.935-942, June 21, 1930.

THE SOUTH AFRICAN MAN-APES AND PITHECANTHROPUS. G. H. R. von Koenigswald. Contrib. Paleontol., Carnegie Inst. Wash., Publ.530, pp.205-222, figs.6, pls.10, July 22, 1942.

INTRODUCTORY REMARKS. John C. Merriam. Early Man, edited by G. G. MacCurdy, Lippincott and Co., Lond., pp.19-22, 1937.

THE EVIDENCE FOR THE EXISTENCE OF MAN IN THE TERTIARY PERIOD. Edwin T. Newton. Proc. Geol. Assoc., Lond., vol.15, pt.2, pp.63-82, May, 1897.

PALAEOLITHIC MAN. Edwin T. Newton. Proc. Geol. Assoc., Lond., vol.15, pt.7, pp.246-263, May, 1898.

THE DISCOVERY OF TERTIARY MAN. Henry F. Osborn. Science, vol.71, no.1827, pp.1-7, figs.2, Jan.3, 1930.

IS THE APE-MAN A MYTH? Henry F. Osborn. Human Biology, Balto., vol.1, no.1, pp.4-9, Jan., 1929.

NOTE ON THE GEOLOGIC AGE OF PITHECANTHROPUS AND EOANTHROPUS. Henry F. Osborn. Science, n.s., vol.69, pp.216-217, Feb.22, 1929.

RECENT DISCOVERIES ON THE ANTIQUITY OF MAN. Henry F. Osborn, Chester A. Reeds. Proc. Nat. Acad. Sci., Wash., D.C., vol.8, no.8, pp.246-247, Aug., 1922.

THE FIRST PAN-AFRICAN CONGRESS ON PREHISTORY. Wendell Phillips. Science, Lancaster, vol.105, no.2737, pp.611-613, June 13, 1947.

HOMINIDAE FOSSILES. FOSSILIUM CATALOGUS I: ANIMALIA. W. Quenstedt, A. Quenstedt. Pars 74, pp.456, W. Junk: Verlag fuer Naturwissenschaften, 's-Gravenhage, Apr.15, 1936.

(A CONJECTURE ON A PRIMITIVE HUMAN FORM OF THE OLD TERTIARY.) Una congettura intorno ad una primitiva forma umana del terziario antico. G. Sergi. Rivista Biol., Roma, vol.2, fasc.6, pp. 20, figs.3, 1920.

RECENT PROGRESS IN THE STUDY OF EARLY MAN. Woodward A. Smith. Nature, Lond., vol.136, no.3437, pp.419-423, Sept.14, 1935.

GEOLOGY, 1888-1938. PREHISTORIC ARCHEOLOGY. Chester Stock. Geol. Soc. Amer., 50th Anniversary Vol., pp. 137-158, June, 1941.

SOME PROBLEMS DEALING WITH ANCIENT MAN. Franz Weidenreich. Amer. Anthropologist, Lancaster, vol.42, no.3, pp.375-383, July-Sept., 1940.

(HUMANS OF ANTIQUITY, A SURVEY OF THE HUMAN REMAINS OF THE OLD STONE AGE.) Menschen der Vorzeit. Ein Ueberblick ueber die altsteinzeitlichen Menschenreste. Hans Weinert. Ferdinand Enke, Stuttgart, pp.139, figs.61, 1930.

(FOSSIL MAN.) Der fossile Mensch. E. Werth. Berlin, pp.xii, 898, figs.699, 1928.

(FOSSIL MAN.) Der fossile Mensch. (Prospectus.) E. Werth. Gebrueder Borntraeger, Berlin, Aug., 1928.

A GUIDE TO THE FOSSIL REMAINS OF MAN IN THE DEPARTMENT OF GEOLOGY AND PALAEONTOLOGY IN THE BRITISH MUSEUM (NATURAL HISTORY), CROMWELL ROAD, LONDON, S.W.7. A. Smith Woodward. 3rd. ed., 34 pp., figs.14, pls. 6, 1922.

RECENT PROGRESS IN THE STUDY OF EARLY MAN. A. Smith Woodward. Science, n.s., vol.82, no.2131, pp.390-407, Nov.1, 1935.

TWO TRANSITIONAL FORMS BETWEEN MAN AND APE. PART. I. Matajiro Yokoyama. Jour. Geogr. Tokyo, vol.43, no.506, pp.187-191, figs.4, pl.5; pt.2, no. 507, pp.247-255, pl.1, figs.11, 1931.

HOMO SAPIENS IN AUSTRALIA CONTEMPORARY WITH HOMO NEANDERTHALENSIS IN EUROPE. F. E. Zeuner. Nature, Lond., vol.153, no.3890, pp.622-623, May 20, 1944.

HOMO MODJOKERTENSIS. Nature, Lond., vol.139, no.3511, p.291, Feb.13, 1937.

Future of Man

MAN'S FUTURE IN THE LIGHT OF HIS PAST AND PRESENT. Ales Hrdlicka. Proc. Amer. Philos. Soc., vol.68, no.1, pp.1-11, 1929.

MAN'S BIOLOGICAL OUTLOOK. Gerrit S. Miller, Jr. Science, Lancaster, vol.94, pp.163-164, Aug.15, 1941.

THE SPECIAL CONTRIBUTION OF DEVELOPMENTAL MECHANICS TO THE THOUGHT AND PURPOSE OF THE MAN OF TOMORROW. Oscar Riddle. Proc. Amer. Philos. Soc., vol.68, no.2, pp.107-117, 1929.

MAN--500,000 YEARS FROM NOW. TRENDS AND INFLUENCES NOW AT WORK IN CHANGING OR MODIFYING THE PHYSICAL CHARACTERISTICS OF CIVILIZED MAN--A SCIENTIFIC ATTEMPT TO FORECAST WHAT MAY OCCUR IN THE FUTURE EVOLUTION OF MAN. H. L. Shapiro. Natural History, New York, vol. 33, no.6, pp.582-595, figs.9, Nov.-Dec., 1933.

(Review by J. C. Hardwick of ) THE OUTLOOK FOR HOMO SAPIENS. H. G. Wells. Nature, London, vol.149, no.3777, pp.316-317, Mar. 21, 1942.

Growth

(THE GROWTH OF BODY LENGTH IN MAN.) Das wachstum der Koerper-laenge des Menschen. Gaston Backman. Kungl. Svenska Vetensk. Akad. Handlingar, vol. 14, no.1, pp.1-145, figs.25, 1934.

GROWTH PATTERN OF THE HUMAN PHYSIQUE. (ABSTRACT.) Earl W. Count. Anat. Record, Phila., vol.82, no.3, pp. 405-406, Mar.25, 1942.

THE APPEARANCE OF CENTERS OF OSSIFICATION FROM BIRTH TO 5 YEARS. Carl C. Francis, Peter P. Werle. Amer. Jour. Phys. Anthrop., Phila., vol.24, no.3, pp.272-299, figs.2, tables 4, Jan.-Mar., 1939.

GROWTH DURING ADULT LIFE. Ales Hrdlicka. Proc. Amer. Philos. Soc., vol. 76, no.6, pp.847-897, tables, 1936.

FACTORS AFFECTING HUMAN GROWTH. Wilton M. Krogman. Ciba Symposia, Ciba Pharmaceutical Products, Inc., Summit, New Jersey, vol.5, nos.1-2, pp. 1478-1484, illus., Apr.-May, 1943.

PRINCIPLES OF HUMAN GROWTH. Wilton M. Krogman. Ciba Symposia, Ciba Pharmaceutical Products, Inc., Summit, New Jersey, vol.5, nos.1-2, pp.1458-1466, illus., Apr.-May, 1943.

(THE PHYSICAL DEVELOPMENT OF MUNICH ELEMENTARY SCHOOL CHILDREN IN THE YEARS 1921, 1922 and 1923.) Die Koerperentwicklung Muenchener Volksschulkinder in den Jahren 1921, 1922 und 1923. Rudolf Martin. Anthrop. Anzeiger, Jahrg. 1, Hft.2, pp.76-95, figs. 5, 1924.

(THE PHYSICAL DEVELOPMENT OF MUNICH ELEMENTARY SCHOOL CHILDREN IN 1924.) Die Koerperentwicklung Muenchener Volksschulkinder im Jahre 1924. Rudolf Martin. Anthrop. Anzeiger, Jahrg.2, Hft.1, pp.59-68, 1925.

GROWTH STUDIES ON PRIMATES BEARING UPON MAN'S EVOLUTION. Adolph H. Schultz. Amer. Jour. Phys. Anthr., vol.7, pp.149-164, 9 figs., Apr.-June, 1924.

GROWTH OF WELL CHILDREN: ANALYSIS OF STATURE AND WEIGHT, 3 MONTHS TO 13 YEARS. Katherine Simmons, T. Wingate Todd. Growth, Menasha, vol.2, no.2, 1938, paper 46, pp.93-134, figs.25, Aug., 1938.

THE BODILY EXPRESSION OF HUMAN GROWTH AND WELFARE. T. Wingate Todd. Science, n.s., vol.82, no.2122, pp.181-186, Aug.30, 1935.

THE NATURAL HISTORY OF HUMAN GROWTH. T. Wingate Todd. Brush Foundation Publ. no.12, pp.15, Mar.15, 1931.

THE ROENTGENOGRAPHIC APPRAISEMENT OF SKELETAL DIFFERENTIATION. T. Wingate Todd. Child Development, vol. 1, no.4, pp.298-310, Dec., 1930.

DIFFICULTIES OF DEVELOPMENT AS APPLIED TO MAN. Alfred R. Wallace. Popular Science Monthly, vol.10, no.55, pp.60-72, Nov., 1876.

(FACTS AND PROBLEMS OF HUMAN DEVELOPMENT.) Tatsachen und Probleme der Menschheitsentwicklung. Franz Weidenreich. Bio-Morphosis, Basel, vol. 1, fasc.1, pp.5-29, Apr., 1938.

Habits, Behavior

HOW NEANDERTHAL MAN HUNTED CAVE BEARS. Othenio Abel. Nat. Hist., vol.26, pp.252-256, May-June, 1926.

THE USE OF ANIMAL LIFE BY THE MOUND-BUILDING INDIANS OF ILLINOIS. Frank Collins Baker. Trans. Ill. State Acad. Sci., vol.22, pp.41-64, pls.5, 1930.

(PREBIPEDAL LOCOMOTION OF CHILDREN.) La locomacion prebipedal del nina. Paul Magne De la Croix. Physis., vol.11, no.38, pp.114-120, 1932.

FOOD ANIMALS OF THE NAVAJO. Francis H. Elmore. El Palacio, Santa Fe, vol.44, nos.22-24, pp.149-160, illus., June 1-15, 1938.

ANNOTATED LIST OF FOSSIL MAMMALIA ASSOCIATED WITH HUMAN REMAINS AT MELBOURNE. C. Lewis Gazin. Jour. Washington Acad. Sci., vol.40, no.12, pp.397-404, Dec.22, 1950.

DOES ANYBODY KNOW? (USE BY INDIANS OF BRAINS OF BISON FOR TANNING SKINS.) C. E. Hagie. Southwestern Lore, Gunnison, vol.7, no.4, pp.54-55, fig.1, Mar., 1942.

ANNOTATED LIST OF ANIMALS (MAMMALS). ETHNOZOOLOGY OF THE TEWA INDIANS. Junius Henderson, John Peabody Harrington. Smithsonian Inst., Bur. Amer. Ethnology, bull.56, pp.12-32, 1914.

MAN AND METALS. Walter Hough. Proc. Nat. Acad. Sciences, Wash., D.C., vol. 2, pp.123-129, Mar., 1916.

QUADRUPED PROGRESSION IN THE HUMAN CHILD. Ales Hrdlicka. Amer. Jour. Phys. Anthrop., vol.10, no.3, pp.347-354, figs. 1-5, July-Sept., 1927.

HUNTING CUSTOMS OF THE ORDOS MONGOLS. Joseph Kler. Primitive Man, Wash., D.C., vol.14, no.3, pp.38-48, figs.3, July, 1941.

THE FOOD SUPPLY OF THE ABORIGINES. Frederick D. McCarthy. Australian Mus. Mag., Sydney, vol.7, no.9, pp.300-305, illus., June-Aug., 1941.

RACE RETAINS HORDE INSTINCT. Gerrit S. Miller, Jr. New York Herald Tribune, Sunday, sect.3, p.5, Jan.6, 1929.

MOVEMENT OF THE ARMS IN WALKING. Frederick W. True. Science, vol.1, no.1, p.11, Feb.9, 1883.

OBSERVATIONS ON THE BUTCHERING TECHNIQUE OF SOME ABORIGINAL PEOPLES: I. Theodore E. White. Amer. Antiquity, Menasha, vol.17, no.4, pp.337-338, Apr., 1952.

HUMAN LOCOMOTION: HOW WE STAND, WALK AND RUN. Burt G. Wilder. Sci. Lectures, Amer. Inst., pp.18, figs.15, 1870.

THE BIOLOGICAL BACKGROUND OF HUMAN SOCIAL BEHAVIOR. S. Zuckerman. Proc. Sec. Conf. Soc. Sci., Inst. Sociology, London, pp.1-13, Aug., 1936.

Hair and Skin

NOTES ON NEGRO ALBINISM. William C. Farabee. Science, n.s., vol.19, no.419, pp.75-76, Jan.9, 1903.

PARADOXES AND PUZZLES ABOUT MAN'S HAIR. Edward Lawrence. The Hairdressers' Weekly Jour., vol.51, no.2622, pp.2662-2663, figs.5-6, July 23, 1932.

THE SIZE AND SHAPE OF HUMAN HEAD HAIR ALONG ITS SHAFT. Henri C. Seibert. Jour. Heredity, Wash., D.C., vol.33, no.8, pp.302-304, fig.11, Aug., 1942.

A PEDIGREE OF SKIN-SPOTTING IN MAN. 42 PIEBALDS IN A NORWEGIAN FAMILY. Hans Sundfoer. Jour. Heredity, Wash., D.C., vol.30, no.3, pp.67-77, figs.6, cover, frontispiece, Mar., 1939.

Hand and Foot

RESTORATION OF AN EGYPTIAN MUMMIFIED FOOT. Montague Francis Ashley-Montagu. Amer. Jour. Phys. Anthrop., vol.20, no.1, and suppl., pp.95-101, pls. 2, Apr.-June, 1935.

(INFLUENCE OF PHYSICAL EXERCISE ON THE PROPORTIONS OF THE HUMAN HAND.) Vliyanie fizicheskix uprajnenii na proportzii ruki cheloveka. L. P. Asmanin. Prepoda, Akad. Nauk SSSR, Moscow, vol.6, pp.42-53, 1952.

THE ORIGIN OF THE HUMAN FOOT. R. Broom. Annals Transvaal Mus., vol.18, pt.1, pp.53-54, fig.1, Oct.1, 1935.

FOOT-POSITION IN HOMO SAPIENS. John W. Crist. Jour. Heredity, vol.19, pp.229-234, illus., May, 1928.

A CINEMATIC STUDY OF THE DISTRIBUTION OF PRESSURE IN THE HUMAN FOOT. Herbert Elftman. Anat. Record, vol.59, no.4, pp.481-490, fig.1, pls.2, July 25, 1934.

THE AXIS OF THE HUMAN FOOT. Herbert Elftman, John Manter. Science, n.s., vol.80, no.2082, p.484, fig.1, Nov.23, 1934.

THE EVOLUTION OF THE HUMAN FOOT, WITH ESPECIAL REFERENCE TO THE JOINTS. Herbert Elftman, John Manter. Jour. Anatomy, Cambridge, vol.70, pt.1, pp.56-67, figs.6, Oct., 1935.

(THE FOOT OF MAN (ANTHROPOLOGICAL ESSAY).) Le pied de l'homme (Essai anthropologique). Serge Frechkop. Mem. Mus. Roy. d'Hist. Nat. Belgique, ser.2, fasc.3, pp.319-334, figs.9, Apr.30, 1936.

THE HISTORY OF THE HUMAN FOOT AND ITS BEARING ON ORTHOPAEDIC PRACTICE. Arthur Keith. Jour. Bone and Joint Surgery, Boston, vol.11, no.1, pp.10-32, figs.12, Jan., 1929.

THE EVOLUTION OF THE HUMAN FOOT. J. P. McMurrich. Amer. Jour. Phys. Anthrop., vol.10, pp.165-171, 1927.

EVOLUTION OF THE HUMAN FOOT. D. J. Morton. Amer. Jour. Phys. Anthr., vol.5, pp.305-336, 8 figs., Oct.-Dec., 1922.

EVOLUTION OF THE HUMAN FOOT. PART II. D. J. Morton. Amer. Jour. Phys. Anthrop., vol.7, pp.1-52, 25 figs., Jan.-Mar., 1924.

EVOLUTION OF THE LONGITUDINAL ARCH OF THE HUMAN FOOT. D. J. Morton. Jour. of Bone and Joint Surgery, vol.6, pp. 56-90, 19 figs., Jan., 1924.

FOOT DISORDERS IN GENERAL PRACTICE. D. J. Morton. Jour. Amer. Med. Assoc., vol.109, no.14, pp.1112-1119, Oct.2, 1937.

MECHANISM OF THE NORMAL FOOT AND OF FLAT FOOT. D. J. Morton. Jour. Bone Joint Surgery, Boston, vol.6, no.2, pp.368-406, fig.16, Apr., 1924.

SIGNIFICANT CHARACTERISTICS OF THE NEANDERTHAL FOOT. D. V. Morton. Nat. Hist., vol.26, pp.310-314, May-June, 1926.

THE NATURE AND INHERITANCE OF WEBBED TOES IN MAN. William L. Straus, Jr. Jour. Morphology Phys., vol. 41, no.2, pp.427-439, figs.19, Mar., 1926.

THE THUMB OF MAN. Edward L. Troxell. Sci. Monthly, vol.43, no.2, pp. 148-150, Aug., 1936.

(THE PRIMARY GRASPING CHARACTER OF THE HUMAN HAND AND FOOT AND ITS IMPORTANCE AS REGARDS THE QUESTION OF DERIVATION.) Der primare Greifcharakter der menschlichen Hande und Fuesse und seine Bedeutung fuer das Abstammungs-problem. Franz Weidenreich. Verhandl. Gesellsch. f. Physische Anthrop., pp.97-110, figs.8, 1931.

(AFTERTHOUGHTS ON THE PHYLOGENETIC-MECHANISTIC ATTEMPT TO CLARIFY THE MORPHOLOGY OF THE "CLASSICAL" HUMAN FOOT.) Nachbemerkungen zu dem phylogenetisch-mechanistischen Erklaerungsversuch der Morphologie des "Klassischen" Menschenfusses. "Verhandlungen" Zool. Bot. Gesell. Wien, vol.80, nos.3-4, pp. 139-163, 1931.

Longevity

VITAL STATISTICS. LAW OF HUMAN MORTALITY IN MASSACHUSETTS, WITH PRACTICAL TABLES. E. B. Elliott. Proc. Amer. Assoc. Adv. Sci., Montreal, pp. 51-82, tables 14, Aug., 1857.

LENGTHENING OF HUMAN LIFE IN RETROSPECT AND PROSPECT. Irving Fisher. Smithsonian Inst., Annual Report, Wash., 1927, pp.535-554, diagrs., 1928.

FETAL AGE ASSESSMENT BY CENTERS OF OSSIFICATION. Alfred H. Hill. Amer. Jour. Phys. Anthrop., Phila., vol.24, no.3, pp.251-272, tables 14, Jan.-Mar., 1939.

AGE OF PRESBYOPIC VISION AS AN INDEX OF THE LONGEVITY OF PRIMITIVE MAN. Marcus W. Lyon, Jr. Science, n.s., vol.64, no.1661, p.427, Oct.29, 1926.

DEATH IN MAN. Arthur MacDonald. Western Med. Times, vol., pp.1-22, Apr., 1922.

THE DURATION OF LIFE OF FOSSIL MAN IN CHINA AND THE PATHOLOGICAL LESIONS FOUND IN HIS SKELETON. Franz Weidenreich. Chinese Medical Jour., Shanghai, vol.55, pp.34-44, 1939.

DURATION OF LIFE IN EARLY MAN. Nature, Lond., vol.143, no.3624, p.645, Apr.15, 1939.

New World

THE SPREAD OF ABORIGINAL MAN TO NORTH AMERICA. Ernst Antevs. Geogr. Rev., vol.25, no.2, pp.302-309, Apr., 1935.

ADDITIONAL NOTES ON ANIMAL LIFE ASSOCIATED WITH THE MOUND BUILDERS OF ILLINOIS. Frank Collins Baker. Trans. Illinois State Acad. Sci., vol.23, no.3, pp. 231-235, Mar., 1931.

DID GLACIAL MAN INHABIT NEBRASKA? Erwin Hinckley Barbour, C. Bertrand Schultz. Nebraska Alumnus, vol.32, no.5, pp.4-5, May, 1936.

PALAEONTOLOGIC AND GEOLOGIC CONSIDERATION OF EARLY MAN IN NEBRASKA WITH A NOTICE OF A NEW BONE BED IN THE EARLY PLEISTOCENE OF MORRILL COUNTY, NEBRASKA. Erwin Hinckley Barbour, C. Bertrand Schultz. Nebraska State Mus., vol.1, bull. 45, pp.431-450, figs.9, Apr., 1936.

PLEISTOCENE MAN IN SOUTHERN CALIFORNIA. A. O. Bowden, Ivan A. Lopatin. Science, n.s., vol.84, no.2188, pp.507-508, Dec.4, 1936.

FOLSOM CULTURE; AND OCCURRENCE OF PREHISTORIC MAN WITH EXTINCT ANIMALS NEAR FOLSOM, NEW MEXICO. Barnum Brown. Pan-Amer. Geol., vol.60, no.5, p.378, Dec., 1933.

MINNESOTA MAN--A DISCUSSION OF THE SITE. Kirk Bryan. Science, n.s., vol.82, no.2121, pp.170-171, Aug.23, 1935.

INTERPRETATION OF THE FORMATIONS CONTAINING HUMAN BONES AT VERO, FLORIDA. Rollin T. Chamberlin. Jour. Geol., Chicago, vol.25, no.1, pp.25-39, figs.9, Jan.-Feb., 1917.

AGE OF THE "LOS ANGELES MAN" DEPOSITS. Thomas Clements. Amer. Jour. Sci., New Haven, ser.5, vol.36, no.212, pp.137-141, Aug., 1938.

DEFINITE EVIDENCE OF HUMAN ARTIFACTS IN THE AMERICAN PLEISTOCENE. Harold J. Cook. Science, n.s., vol.62, pp. 459-460, Nov.20, 1925.

FURTHER EVIDENCE CONCERNING MAN'S ANTIQUITY AT FREDERICK, OKLAHOMA. Harold J. Cook. Science, vol.67, no.1736, pp.371-373, Apr.6, 1928.

EARLY MAN IN THE NORTHERN PART OF THE GREAT BASIN OF SOUTH-CENTRAL OREGON. L. S. Cressman. Proc. 6th Pacific Sci. Congr., Berkeley, vol.4, pp. 169-175, 1940.

THE ANTIQUITY OF MAN IN AMERICA. J. D. Figgins. Nat. Hist., vol.27, no.3, pp.229-239, 1927.

NEW WORLD MAN. J. D. Figgins. Proc. Colorado Mus. Nat. Hist., Denver, vol.14, no.1, pp.5, pls.4, July 22, 1935.

ANCIENT MAN IN FLORIDA: FURTHER INVESTIGATIONS. J. W. Gidley. Bull. Geol. Soc. Amer., vol.40, pp.491-502, pls.14-15, June 30, 1929.

FURTHER INVESTIGATIONS ON EVIDENCE OF EARLY MAN IN FLORIDA. J. W. Gidley. Explorations and field-work of the Smithsonian Institution in 1930, publ.3111, pp.41-44, figs.33-36, Mar.26, 1931.

FURTHER STUDY OF THE PROBLEM OF EARLY MAN IN FLORIDA. J. W. Gidley. Explorations and Field-Work of the Smithsonian Institution in 1928, Smithsonian publ.3011, pp.13-20, illus., Apr., 1929.

PALEONTOLOGICAL EVIDENCE BEARING ON THE PROBLEM OF THE ORIGIN OF THE AMERICAN ABORIGINES. J. W. Gidley. Amer. Anthrop., Lancaster, Pa., vol.14, no.1, pp.18-23, Jan.-Mar., 1912.

FOSSIL MAN IN FLORIDA. J. W. Gidley, F. B. Loomis. Amer. Jour. Sci., vol.12, no.69, pp.254-264, 1926.

AGAIN ON PLEISTOCENE MAN AT VERO, FLORIDA. Oliver P. Hay. Jour. Wash. Acad. Sci., vol.18, no.9, pp.233-241, May 4, 1928.

ANTHROPOLOGIC SCRAPS. Oliver P. Hay. Amer. Bureau of Ethnology, bull.60, no.3, pp.9-12, Mar.29, 1920.

DOCTOR ALES HRDLICKA AND THE VERO MAN. Oliver P. Hay. Science, n.s., vol. 48, no.1245, pp.459-462, Nov.8, 1918.

FURTHER CONSIDERATION OF THE OCCURRENCE OF HUMAN REMAINS IN THE PLEISTOCENE DEPOSITS AT VERO, FLORIDA. Oliver P. Hay. Amer. Anthrop., n.s., vol.20, no.1, pp.1-36, Jan.-Mar., 1918.

THE NEWEST DISCOVERY OF "ANCIENT" MAN IN THE UNITED STATES. Oliver P. Hay. Anthropologic Scraps, no.4, pp.13-16, Jan.24, 1921.

ON PLEISTOCENE MAN AT TRENTON, NEW JERSEY. Oliver P. Hay. Anthropologic Scraps, no.2, pp.5-8, Dec.3, 1919.

ON THE RECENT DISCOVERY OF A FLINT ARROW-HEAD IN EARLY PLEISTOCENE DEPOSITS AT FREDERICK, OKLAHOMA. Oliver P. Hay. Jour. Wash. Acad. Sci., vol.19, no.5, pp.93-98, Mar.4, 1929.

A REVIEW OF SOME PAPERS ON FOSSIL MAN AT VERO, FLORIDA. Oliver P. Hay. Science, n.s., vol.47, no.1215, pp.370-371, Apr.12, 1918.

ETHNOZOOLOGY OF THE TEWA INDIANS. Junius Henderson, John Peabody Harrington. Bull. bur. Amer. Ethnology, Smithsonian Inst., no.56, pp.x, 76, 1914.

CAMEL, HORSE, AND BISON ASSOCIATED WITH HUMAN BURIALS AND ARTIFACTS

NEAR FRESNO, CALIFORNIA. Gordon W. Hewes. Science, Lancaster, n.s., vol.97, no.2519, pp.328-329, Apr.9, 1943.

THE ANTIQUITY OF MAN IN AMERICA. E. B. Howard. Sci. Monthly, vol.43, no.4, pp.367-371, figs.3, Oct., 1936.

THE ASSOCIATION OF A HUMAN CULTURE WITH AN EXTINCT FAUNA IN NEW MEXICO. E. B. Howard. Amer. Nat., vol.70, no. 729, pp.314-323, illus., July-Aug., 1936.

EARLY MAN IN AMERICA. E. B. Howard. Proc. Amer. Philos. Soc., vol.76, no.3, pp.327-333, July, 1936.

EVIDENCE OF EARLY MAN IN NORTH AMERICA. E. B. Howard. Mus. Jour., Univ. Pennsylvania, Phila., vol.24, nos.2-3, pp.53-175, pls.14-39, 1935.

THE COMING OF MAN FROM ASIA IN THE LIGHT OF RECENT DISCOVERIES. Ales Hrdlicka. Proc. Amer. Philos. Soc., vol. 71, no.6, pp.393-402, map, 1932.

PHYSICAL ANTHROPOLOGY OF THE LENAPE OR DELAWARES, AND OF THE EASTERN INDIANS IN GENERAL. Ales Hrdlicka. Bur. Amer. Ethnol., bull.62, pp.1-130, pls.1-29, 1916.

PRELIMINARY REPORT ON FINDS OF SUPPOSEDLY ANCIENT HUMAN REMAINS AT VERO, FLORIDA. Ales Hrdlicka. Jour. Geol. Chicago, vol.25, no.1, pp.43-51, figs.2, Jan.-Feb., 1917.

RECENT DISCOVERIES ATTRIBUTED TO EARLY MAN IN AMERICA. Ales Hrdlicka. Bur. Amer. Ethnol., bull.66, pp.1-65, pls. 1-14, figs.1-8, 1918.

(NEOLITHIC INHABITANTS OF THE BUENOS AIRES LAKE.) Habitantes Neoliticos del lago Buenos Aires. Jose Imbelloni. Rev. Mus. La Plata, vol.27, ser.4, no.3, pp.85-160, figs.1-18, pls.1-4, 1923.

MINNESOTA PLEISTOCENE HOMO. (ABSTRACT.) A. E. Jenks. Science, vol. 76, no.1980, pp.546-547, Dec.9, 1932.

PLEISTOCENE MAN IN MINNESOTA. A. E. Jenks. Science, n.s., vol.75, no.1954, pp.607-608, June 10, 1932.

THE LIFE OF THE COPPER ESKIMOS. D. Jenness. Rep. Canadian Arctic Exped. 1913-18, vol.12, pp.1-277, 9 pls., 69 figs., 2 maps, Ottawa, 1922.

THE ANTIQUITY OF MAN AND HIS CULTURE IN THE AMERICAS. Wilton M. Krogman. Ciba Symposia, Ciba Pharmaceutical Products Inc., Summit, N.J., vol. 3, no.1, pp.813-824, figs.12, Apr., 1941.

VITAL DATA ON THE POPULATION OF THE SEMINOLE INDIANS OF FLORIDA AND OKLAHOMA. Wilton M. Krogman. Human Biology, vol.7, no.3, pp.335-349, fig.1, Sept., 1935.

THE FLORIDA MAN. F. B. Loomis. Science, n.s., vol.62, p.436, Nov.13, 1925.

FOSSIL MAN IN THE VICINITY OF LOS ANGELES, CALIFORNIA. Ivan A. Lopatin. Proc. 6th Pacific Sci. Congr., Berkeley, vol.4, pp.177-181, fig.1, 1940.

PLEISTOCENE MAN IN SOUTHERN CALIFORNIA. Ivan A. Lopatin. Science, n.s., vol.84, no.2188, pp.507-508, Dec.4, 1936.

A BROWN MAN IN VENEZUELA. M. W. Lyon, Jr. Brown Alumni Monthly, vol.1, pp.41-42, Oct., 1900.

ARCHAEOLOGICAL EVIDENCES OF MAN'S ANTIQUITY AT VERO, FLORIDA. George Grant MacCurdy. Jour. Geol., Chicago, vol.25, no.1, pp.56-62, figs.6, Jan.-Feb., 1917.

RACE IN THE PACIFIC AREA, WITH SPECIAL REFERENCE TO THE ORIGIN OF THE AMERICAN INDIANS: ANTIQUITY OF OCCUPATION. George Grant MacCurdy. Amer. Anthropol., n.s., vol.17, no.4, pp. 708-711, Oct.-Dec., 1915.

THE GEOLOGIC ANTECEDENTS OF MAN IN THE POTOMAC VALLEY. W. J. McGee. Amer. Anthropol., Wash., D.C., vol.2, no.3, pp.1-8, July, 1889.

PALEOLITHIC MAN IN AMERICA: HIS ANTIQUITY AND ENVIRONMENT. W. J. McGee. Popular Sci. Monthly, New York, vol.34, no.1, pp.20-36, figs.7, Nov., 1888.

ANCIENT DWELLINGS OF THE RIO VERDE VALLEY. Edgar A. Mearns. Popular Sci. Monthly, New York, vol.37, no.6, pp.745-763, figs.16, Oct., 1890.

PRESENT STATUS OF THE PROBLEM OF THE ANTIQUITY OF MAN IN NORTH AMERICA. John C. Merriam. Science, Lancaster, n.s., vol.78, no.2031, p.524, Dec.1, 1933.

A REVIEW OF EVIDENCE RELATING TO THE STATUS OF THE PROBLEM OF ANTIQUITY OF MAN IN FLORIDA. John C. Merriam. Science, Lancaster, n.s., vol. 82, no.2118, p.103, Aug.2, 1935.

PRIMITIVE TRAITS IN THE AMERICAN ABORIGINAL POPULATION. Bruno Oetteking. Inst. Internat. d'Anthropologie, Amsterdam, pp.4, 1928.

THE NEW WORLD PALEO-INDIAN. Frank H. H. Roberts, Jr. Smithsonian Rept., 1944, publ.3794, pp.403-434, pls.12, 1945.

RECENT DISCOVERIES OF THE MATERIAL CULTURE OF FOLSOM MAN. Frank H. H. Roberts, Jr. Amer. Nat., vol.70, no.729, pp.337-345, illus., July-Aug., 1936.

(CATALOGUE OF THE ANTHROPOLOGY DEPARTMENT OF THE JUAN C. MOYANO MUSEUM.) Cataloge del Departmento de Anthropologia del Museo Juan C. Moyano. Carlos Rusconi. Rev. Junta Estudios Hist. Mendoza, vol.13, no.3, pp.15, Dec.31, 1938.

(THE FOSSIL HUMAN REMAINS FROM THE PROVINCE OF SANTIAGO DEL ESTERO.) Restos humanos fósiles procedentes de la provincia de Santiago del Estero. Carlos Rusconi. Rev. Argentina Paleontol. y Anthropol. Ameghinia, Buenos Aires, vol. 1, nos.5-6, pp.135-161, pls.1-8, Nov.15-Dec., 1935.

(PRELIMINARY NOTICE REGARDING PRE-HISPANIC ANTHROPOLOGY AND ARCHEOLOGY IN MENDOZA.) Noticia preliminar sobre la antropologia y arqueologia pre-hispanica de Mendoza. Carlos Rusconi. Acad. Cienc. Buenos Aires, vol.1, pp.61-71, 1940.

(SUBFOSSIL HUMAN REMAINS OF MENDOZA.) Restos humanos subfosiles de Mendoza. Carlos Rusconi. Anales Soc. Cient. Argentina, Buenos Aires, Dec., 1938, entr. 6, vol.126, pp.460-470, figs.4, 1939.

PRELIMINARY REPORT ON THE LIME CREEK SITES: NEW EVIDENCE OF EARLY MAN IN SOUTHWESTERN NEBRASKA. Bertrand C. Schultz, W. D. Frankforter. Bull. Univ. Nebraska State Mus., Lincoln, vol.3, no.4, pt.2, pp.43-62, figs.13, Nov., 1948.

EARLY MAN IN AMERICA. INDEX TO LOCALITIES AND SELECTED BIBLIOGRAPHY, 1940-1945. E. H. Sellards. Bull. Geol. Soc. America, Balto., vol.58, pp. 955-978, fig.1, Oct., 1947.

THE EVOLUTION OF HOUSE BUILDING AMONG THE NAVAJO INDIANS. R. W. Shufeldt. Proc. U.S. Nat. Mus., vol.15, no.902, pp.279-282, pls.41-43, 1892.

CHILDREN OF PATAGONIA. George G. Simpson. Nat. Hist., New York, vol.32, no.2, pp.135-147, illus., Mar.-Apr., 1932.

OCCURRENCE OF HUMAN REMAINS IN CONKLING CAVERN, NEW MEXICO. (ABSTRACT.) Chester Stock. Bull. Geol. Soc. America, vol.42, no.1, p.370, Mar., 1931.

WHAT IS A "PRE-AMERINDIAN"? Wm. Duncan Strong. Science, Lancaster, vol. 91, no.2373, pp.594-596, June 21, 1940.

ON REPORTED PLEISTOCENE HUMAN REMAINS AT VERO, FLORIDA. Thomas W. Vaughan. Jour. Geol., vol.25, no.1, pp.40-42, Jan.-Feb., 1917.

(THE FOSSIL MAN OF CHAPADMALAL.) El Hombre Fósil de Chapadmalal. Milciades A. Vignati. Physis, (Rev. de la Soc. Arg. de Cienc. Nat.), vol.5, pp.80-82, 98-100, illus., Oct.31, 1921.

(SUPPOSED RECOVERY OF FOSSIL HUMAN BONES IN A CERTAIN PLACE IN THE STATE OF COAHUILA.) Pretendido Hallazgo de Hueses Humanos Fosiles, en Cierto Lugar del Estado de Coahuila. Manuel M. Villada. La Naturaleza, ser. 3, vol.1, no.1, pp.45-51, Mexico, 1910.

LAWSON PREHISTORIC VILLAGE SITE, MIDDLESEX COUNTY, ONTARIO. W. J. Wintemberg. Nat. Mus. Canada, Dept. Mines and Resources, Mines and Geol. Br., bull.94 (Anthrop. ser.25), Ottawa, pp.1-104, figs.7, pls.1-18, 1939.

ADDITIONAL EVIDENCE OF EARLY MAN IN AMERICA. Nature, London, vol.143, no. 3613, p.173, Jan.28, 1939.

ARCHAEOLOGICAL EVIDENCES OF MAN'S ANTIQUITY AT VERO, FLORIDA. Jour. Geol., vol.25, no.1, pp.56-62, figs.6, Jan.-Feb., 1917.

INDIANS OF THE AMERICAS. Nat. Geog. Society., 432 pp., illus.

### Physiology

PHYSIOLOGY OF MAN IN THE DESERT. E. F. Adolph. New York, xiii, 357 pp., figs., 1947.

THE EFFECT OF EXERCISE IN HOT ATMOSPHERES UPON THE SALTWATER BALANCE OF HUMAN SUBJECTS. Douglas H. K. Lee, R. E. Murray, W. J. Simmonds, R. G. Atherton. Medical Jour. Australia, pp.249-258, figs.2, Sept.6, 1941.

THE DISTRIBUTION OF IODINE WITH SPECIAL REFERENCE TO GOITER. J. F. McClendon. Physiol. Rev., vol.7, pp. 189-258, 7 figs., Apr., 1927.

(SOME RESULTS OF URINE INVESTIGATIONS OF CHILDREN.) Ueber einige Ergebnisse der Harnuntersuchung bei Kindern. R. W. Raudnitz. Prager Med. Wochenschrift, vol.26, nos.45-50, pp.1-26, 1901.

### Piltdown Man

A CONTRIBUTION TO THE PILTDOWN PROBLEM. M. R. Drennan. Nature, no. 3033, vol.120, p.874, illus., Dec.17, 1927.

(Review by G.S. Miller of) A CONTRIBUTION TO THE PILTDOWN PROBLEM. M. R. Drennan. Amer. Jour. Phys. Anthrop., Phila., vol.11, no.2, pp.363-364, Apr., 1928.

NEW VIEWS ON THE "DAWN MAN" OF PILTDOWN (SUSSEX). Fabio Frassetto. Man, vol.27, pp.121-124, illus., July, 1927.

(Review by G. S. Miller of) NEW VIEWS ON THE "DAWN MAN" OF PILTDOWN (SUSSEX). Fabio Frassetto. Amer.Jour. Phys. Anthrop., Philadelphia, vol.10, no. 3, p.413, Nov. 7, 1927.

(SKULL AND LOWER JAW OF PILTDOWN ("EOANTHROPUS DAWSONI WOODWARD") IN NEW INVESTIGATIONS.) Schaedel und Unterkiefer von Piltdown ("Eoanthropus dawsoni Woodward") in neuer Untersuchung. Heinz F. Friederichs. Zeitschr. f. Anat. u. Entwicklungs., Berlin, vol.98, nos.1-2, pp.199-262, figs.40, 1932.

THE DAWN MAN OF PILTDOWN, ENGLAND. W. K. Gregory. Amer. Mus. Jour., vol.14, pp.189-200, figs.11, May, 1914.

NEW LIGHT ON THE CONTROVERSY OF THE PILTDOWN JAW AND CRANIUM. John I. Hunter. Summary of address given before the Society of Dental Science, N.S.W., pp.1-11, fig.1-5, about 1924.

THE PILTDOWN MAN. G. Evelyn Hutchinson. Amer. Scientist, Burlington, vol.42, no.2, pp.305-307, Apr., 1954.

THE PILTDOWN MAN DISCOVERY. UNVEILING A MONOLITH MEMORIAL. Arthur Keith. Nature, London, vol.142, no.3587, pp.196-197, July 20, 1938.

THE JAW OF THE PILTDOWN MAN. Gerrit S. Miller, Jr. Smithsonian Miscel. Coll., vol.65, no.12, publ.2376, pp.31, pls. 5, Nov.24, 1915.

THE PILTDOWN JAW. Gerrit S. Miller, Jr. Amer. Jour. Phys. Anthrop., vol.1, pp.25-52, pls.1-4, July 9, 1918.

PILTDOWN MAN. Kenneth P. Oakley, J. S. Weiner. Amer. Scientist, vol.43, no.4, pp.573-583, illus., Oct., 1955.

THE DAWN MAN OF PILTDOWN SUSSEX. Henry Fairfield Osborn. Nat. Hist., vol. 21, pp.577-590, 15 figs., Nov.-Dec., 1921.

(THE PILTDOWN FIND.) Der Piltdown-Fund. M. Ramstroem. Bull. Geol. Inst. Upsala, vol.16, pp.261-304, figs.1-12, 1919.

THE GREAT PILTDOWN HOAX. William L. Straus, Jr. Science, vol.119, no.3087, pp. 265-269, Feb.26, 1954.

THE PREHISTORIC FIND AT PILTDOWN. Prof. Waterston. Proc. Roy. Phys. Soc. Edinburgh, sess.1919-20, 1920-21, vol.20, pt.5, pp.211-216, May 6, 1921.

(Abstract by Gerrit S. Miller, Jr. of) FOURTH NOTE ON THE PILTDOWN GRAVEL. A. Smith Woodward. Amer. Jour. Phys.Anthrop., vol.1, pp.442-443, Jan. 2, 1919.

Reproductive Biology

RECOVERY OF HUMAN OVA FROM THE UTERINE TUBES, TIME OF OVULATION IN THE MENSTRUAL CYCLE. Edgar Allen. Jour. Amer. Med. Asso., vol.91, pp.1018-1020, Oct.6, 1928.

ADOLESCENT STERILITY. M. F. Ashley-Montagu. Quart. Review Biol., Balto., vol. 14, no.1, pp.13-34, Mar., 1939.

VIRILISM IN WOMEN CAUSED BY ANDROGENIC THERAPY FOR MENSTRUAL DISTURBANCES. J. P. Greenhill, G. C. Freed. Jour. Amer. Med. Asso., Chicago, vol.112, no.16, pp.1573-1574, Apr.22, 1939.

(Review by Gerrit S. Miller, Jr. of) SEX AND REPRESSION IN SAVAGE SOCIETY. Bronislaw Malinowski. Amer. Anthrop., Lancaster, n.s., vol.31, no.1, pp.145-146, Jan.-Mar., 1929.

MODERN SCIENCE AND THE HUMAN FERTILITY PROBLEM. Richard L. Meier. Univ. of Mich., 263 pp., illus., 1959.

THE PRIMATE BASIS OF HUMAN SEXUAL BEHAVIOR. Gerrit S. Miller, Jr. Quart. Review Biol., Balto., vol.6, no.4, pp.379-410, Dec.16, 1931.

SOME ELEMENTS OF SEXUAL BEHAVIOR IN PRIMATES AND THEIR POSSIBLE INFLUENCE ON THE BEGINNINGS OF HUMAN SOCIAL DEVELOPMENT. Gerrit S. Miller, Jr. Jour. Mam., Balto., vol.9, no.4, pp.273-293, Nov.13, 1928.

(Review by W. Montague Cobb of) FERTILITY AND CONTRACEPTION OF URBAN WHITES AND NEGROES. Pearl Raymond. Jour. Negro Education, vol.6, no.1, pp.93-95, Jan., 1937.

FUNDAMENTALS OF HUMAN REPRODUCTION. Edith L. Potter. McGraw-Hill, New York, pp.xi, 231, illus., 1948.

THE NATURE OF PERIODS OF SEX DESIRE IN WOMAN AND THEIR RELATION TO OVULATION. O. L. Tinklepaugh. Amer. Jour. Obs. and Gyn., vol.26, no.3, pp.2-12, Sept., 1933.

THE QUESTION OF A SEASONAL STERILITY AMONG THE ESKIMOS. Wayne L. Whitaker. Science, n.s., vol. 88, no.2279, pp.214-215, Sept.2, 1938.

Skull and Teeth

INTERIM REPORT ON THE SKULL OF SINANTHROPUS. Davidson Black. Bull. Geol. Soc. China, vol.9, no.1, pp.7-22, pls.1-6, 1930.

NOTICE OF THE RECOVERY OF A SECOND ADULT SINANTHROPUS SKULL SPECIMEN. Davidson Black. Bull. Geol. Soc. China, vol.9, no.2, pp.97-98, 1 pl., 1930.

ON AN ADOLESCENT SKULL OF SINANTHROPUS PEKINENSIS IN COMPARISON WITH AN ADULT SKULL OF THE SAME SPECIES AND WITH OTHER HOMINID SKULLS, RECENT AND FOSSIL. Davidson Black. Palaeontologia Sinica, Peiping, Ser. D, vol.7, fasc.2, pp.111, figs.37, pls.16, 1931.

ON THE ENDOCRANIAL CAST OF THE ADOLESCENT SINANTHROPUS SKULL. Davidson Black. Proc. Roy. Soc. Lond., ser.B, vol.112, no.B 776, pp.263-276, pls. 10-15, figs.1-6, Jan.2, 1933.

PRELIMINARY NOTICE OF THE DISCOVERY OF AN ADULT SINANTHROPUS SKULL AT CHOU KOU TIEN. Davidson Black. Bull. Geol. Soc. China, Peiping, vol. 8, no.3, pp.207-211, pls.9, 1929.

A PRELIMINARY REPORT ON THE DISCOVERY OF A SKULL OF ADULT SINANTHROPUS PEKINENSIS AT CHOU KOU TIEN. Davidson Black. China Jour., vol.12, no.3, pp.163-164, pl.1, 1930.

PRELIMINARY REPORT ON THE SINANTHROPUS LOWER JAW SPECIMENS RECOVERED FROM THE CHOU KOUTIEN CAVE DEPOSIT IN 1930 AND 1931. Davidson Black. Bull. Geol. Soc. China, vol.11, no. 3, pp.241-246, figs.5, Dec., 1931.

A STUDY OF KANSU AND HONAN AENEOLITHIC SKULLS AND SPECIMENS FROM LATER KANSU PREHISTORIC SITES IN COMPARISON WITH NORTH CHINA AND OTHER RECENT CRANIA. PT. I. ON MEASUREMENT AND IDENTIFICATION. Davidson Black. Palaeontologica Sinica, Geol. Surv. China, Peiping (D), vol.6, fasc.1, pp.83, figs.31, tables 21, 1928.

ON A PRIMITIVE HUMAN SKULL FROM MOGORJELO NEAR CAPLJINA (HERCEGOVINA). PRELIMINARY ACCOUNT. St. J. Bolkay. Novit. Mus. Sarajevoensis, no.7, pp.1-3, pls.3, May 5, 1928.

MORSUS HUMANUS, SIXTY CASES OF HUMAN BITES IN NEGROES. Frank K. Boland. Jour. Amer. Med. Assoc., Chicago, vol.116, no.2, pp.127-131, figs.9, Jan.11, 1941.

THE PLEISTOCENE HUMAN SKULL FROM HENGELO. II. ANTHROPOLOGICAL PART. A. J. P. van den Broek. Proc. Sect. Sci., Kon. Akad. Wetensch. Amsterdam, vol.39, no.1, pp.81-82, fig., 1936.

THE LONDON SKULL. C. N. Bromhead. Nature, London, vol.128, no.3220, p.118, July 18, 1931.

FURTHER OBSERVATIONS UPON THE "TALGAI" SKULL, MORE ESPECIALLY WITH REGARD TO THE TEETH. A. N. Burkitt. Rept. Australasian Assoc. Adv. Sci., vol.19, pp.366-371, (1928) 1929.

THE PLEISTOCENE HUMAN SKULL FROM HENGELO. III. ARCHAEOLOGICAL PART. F. C. Bursch. Proc. Sect. Sci., Kon. Akad. Wetensch. te Amsterdam, vol.39, no.1, pp.83-87, figs.9, 1936.

CONTOUR OF ORBITAL APERTURE IN REPRESENTATIVES OF MODERN AND FOSSIL HOMINIDAE. John Cameron. Amer. Jour. Phys. Anthropol., Phila., vol.3, no.4, pp.476-488, figs.6, Oct.-Dec., 1920.

(Review by Gerrit S. Miller, Jr. of) A CONTRIBUTION TO THE EVOLUTION AND MORPHOLOGY OF THE HUMAN SKULL. John Cameron. Amer. Jour. Phys.Anthrop., vol.2, pp.209-210, Oct. 9, 1919.

THE KREFFT TOOTH--IS IT A HUMAN MOLAR? T. D. Campbell. Records Australian Mus., Sydney, vol.22, no.2, pp.200-206, pl.14, Jan.18, 1949.

THE ENDOCRANIAL CAST OF THE SWANSCOMBE BONES. W. E. LeGros Clark. Jour. Roy. Anthropol. Inst., Great Britain and Ireland, London, vol. 68, pp.61-67, figs.17-18, Jan.-June, 1938.

GENERAL FEATURES OF THE SWANSCOMBE SKULL BONES. W. E. LeGros Clark. Jour. Roy. Anthropol. Inst. Great Britain and Ireland, London, vol.68, pp.58-60, pls.4-5, Jan.-June, 1938.

THE HUMAN CHIN AND HUMAN TOOTH CHANGE. Thomas W. Cook. Internat. Jour. Orthodontia and Dentistry for Children, St. Louis, vol.19, no.7, pp.730-734, fig.1, July, 1933.

POST-NATAL DEVELOPMENT OF THE HEAD. C. B. Davenport. Proc. Amer. Philos. Soc., Phila., vol.83, no.1, pp.1-215, 170 figs., 6 pls., July 20, 1940.

ON THE SHEDDING AND ERUPTION OF TEETH AMONG COPENHAGEN SCHOOL CHILDREN, COMPARED WITH THAT OF THE OTHER PRIMATES. Magnus Degerbol. Meddelelser om Danmarks Antrop., vol.3, no.2, pp.238-327, fig.1, tables 1-25 plus 6, 1931.

A HUMAN SKULL FROM FLORISBAD, ORANGE FREE STATE, WITH A NOTE ON THE ENDOCRANIAL CAST BY C. N. ARIENS KAPPERS. J. F. Dreyer. Proc. Sect. Sci. K. Akad. Wetensch. Amsterdam, vol.38, nos.1-5, pp.119-128, text figs.1-7, 1935.

THE MANDIBLE RECENTLY DESCRIBED AND ATTRIBUTED TO THE PITHECANTHROPUS BY G. H. R. VON KOENIGSWALD, COMPARED WITH THE MANDIBLE OF PITHECANTHROPUS ERECTUS DESCRIBED IN 1924 BY EUG. DUBOIS. E. Dubois. Proc. Kon. Nederl. Akad. Wet., vol.41, no.2, pp.139-147, pls.1-2, Feb., 1938.

ON THE FOSSIL HUMAN SKULL RECENTLY DESCRIBED AND ATTRIBUTED TO PITHECANTHROPUS ERECTUS BY G. H.R. VON KOENIGSWALD. E. Dubois. Proc. Kon. Nederl. Akad. Wet. Amsterdam, vol.41, no.4, pp.380-386, pls.1-3, Apr., 1938.

THE SO-CALLED NEW PITHECANTHROPUS SKULL. E. Dubois. Prov. Kon. Akad. Wetensch. Amsterdam, vol.30, pp.134-137, illus., 1927.

(THE SO-CALLED "NEW PITHECANTHROPUS SKULL.") Der sogenannte neue Pithecanthropus Schadel. T. Edinger. Natur und Museum, vol.57, no.12, pp.589-590, 3 figs., Dec., 1927.

(Review by Gerrit S. Miller, Jr. of) (MEASUREMENTS OF THE JAWS OF IDOITS.) Kiefermessungen an idioten. F. Faesch. Amer. Jour. Phys. Anthrop., vol.2, p.437, Mar.15, 1920.

FOSSIL HUMAN SKULL FRAGMENTS OF PROBABLE PLEISTOCENE AGE FROM AITAPE, NEW GUINEA. Frank J. Fenner. Records South Australian Mus., Adelaide, vol.6, no.4, pp.335-356, figs.9, pls.23-24, Feb.28, 1941.

THE IDENTITY OF A SUPPOSED HUMAN MOLAR FROM THE WELLINGTON CAVES OF NEW SOUTH WALES. H. H. Finlayson. Records Australian Mus., Sydney, vol.22, no.2, pp.164-170, pls.12-13, Jan.18, 1949.

THE PLEISTOCENE HUMAN SKULL FROM HENGELO. I. GEOLOGICAL-PALAEONTOLOGICAL PART. F. Florschuetz, I. M. Van der Vlerk. Proc. Sect. Sci., Kon. Akad. Wetensch. te Amsterdam, vol.39, no.1, pp.76-80, figs.5, 1936.

(THE SKULL OF MAN AND THAT OF MAMMAL.) Le crane de l'Homme et tant que crane de mammifere. Serge Frechkop. Bull. Inst. Roy. Sci. Nat. Belgique, Bruxelles, vol.25, no.23, pp.12, figs.7, Aug., 1949.

NEW LIGHT ON MAN'S REMOTE ANCESTRY: THE OLDEST SKULL YET FOUND IN FRANCE. Dorothy Garrod. Illus. London News, vol.214, no.5746, pp. 782-783, illus., June 4, 1949.

(HUMAN HEXACUSPID MOLARS AND THE INDEX OF MOLAR DEVELOPMENT.) I molari umani esacuspidi e l'indice di molarizzione. V. Giuffrida-Ruggeri. Rend R. Accad. Sci. Fis. e Matem. Napoli, ser. 3a, vol.27, pp.14, fig.1, tables 3, 1921.

THE BIOGENETIC LAW AND THE SKULL FORM OF PRIMITIVE MAN. W. K. Gregory. Amer. Jour. Phys. Anthrop. Phila., vol.8, no.4, pp.373-378, Oct.-Dec., 1925.

THE ORIGIN AND EVOLUTION OF THE HUMAN DENTITION (A PALAEONTOLOGICAL REVIEW). W. K. Gregory. Jour. Dental Research, vol.2, nos.1-2-3-4, pp. 89-228, figs.344, 1921.

THE ORIGIN AND EVOLUTION OF THE HUMAN DENTITION. W. K. Gregory.

Balto., Williams and Wilkins Co., pp.i-xviii, 1-548, including pls., 1922.

(Review by J. W. Gidley of) THE ORIGIN AND EVOLUTION OF THE HUMAN DENTITION. W. K. Gregory. Jour. Mam., vol.3, no.4, pp.268-269, Nov., 1922.

THE PALAEOMORPHOLOGY OF THE HUMAN HEAD: TEN STRUCTURAL STAGES FROM FISH TO MAN. PT. I. THE SKULL IN NORMA LATERALIS. W. K. Gregory. Quart. Rev. Biol., vol.2, no.2, pp.267-279, figs.5, June, 1927.

THE PALAEOMORPHOLOGY OF THE HUMAN HEAD. TEN STRUCTURAL STAGES FROM FISH TO MAN. PART II. THE SKULL IN NORMA BASALIS. W. K. Gregory. Quart. Rev. Biol., vol.4, no.2, pp.233-247, figs.3, June, 1929.

PALAEONTOLOGY OF THE HUMAN DENTITION. TEN STRUCTURAL STAGES IN THE EVOLUTION OF THE CHEEK TEETH. W. K. Gregory. Amer. Jour. Phys. Anthrop., vol.9, pp.401-426, illus., Dec., 1926.

SOME NEW MODELS ILLUSTRATING THE EVOLUTION OF THE HUMAN DENTITION. W. K. Gregory. Internat. Jour. Ortho. and Dentistry for Children, St. Louis, vol.20, no.11, pp.1077-1081, Nov., 1934.

THE CROWN PATTERNS OF FOSSIL AND RECENT HUMAN MOLAR TEETH AND THEIR MEANING. W. K. Gregory, Milo Hellman. Nat. Hist., vol.26, pp.300-309, May-June, 1926.

THE DENTITION OF DRYOPITHECUS AND THE ORIGIN OF MAN. W. K. Gregory, Milo Hellman. Anthropol. Papers Amer. Mus. Nat. Hist., vol.28, pt.1, 123 pp., figs.32, tables 50, pls.25, 1926.

THE EVIDENCE OF THE DENTITION ON THE ORIGIN OF MAN. W. K. Gregory, Milo Hellman. Early Man, edited by G. G. MacCurdy, Lippincott and Co., London, pp.243-256, figs.38-42, pls.20-21, 1937.

THE SOUTH AFRICAN FOSSIL MAN-APES AND THE ORIGIN OF THE HUMAN DENTITION. W. K. Gregory, Milo Hellman. Jour. Amer. Dental Assoc., Chicago, vol. 26, pp.558-564, figs.6, Apr., 1939.

RACIAL CHARACTERS IN HUMAN DENTITION. PART I. A RACIAL DISTRIBUTION OF THE DRYOPITHECUS PATTERN AND ITS MODIFICATIONS IN THE LOWER MOLAR TEETH OF MAN. Milo Hellman. Proc. Amer. Philos. Soc., vol.67, pp.157-174, illus., 1928.

HUMAN DENTITION AND TEETH FROM THE EVOLUTIONARY AND RACIAL STANDPOINT. Ales Hrdlicka. Dominion Dental Jour., pp.1-15, 1911.

NEW EXAMPLES OF AMERICAN INDIAN SKULLS WITH LOW FOREHEAD. Ales Hrdlicka. Proc. U.S. Nat. Mus., vol.35, pp.171-175, pl.28, Nov.9, 1908.

THE DESCRIPTION OF A NEANDERTHALOID AUSTRALIAN SKULL, WITH REMARKS ON THE PRODUCTION OF THE FACIAL CHARACTERISTICS OF AUSTRALIAN SKULLS IN GENERAL. John I. Hunter, A. St. N. Burkitt. Reprint, Jour. Anat., vol. 57, pt.1, pp.31-54, Oct., 1922.

INTERPRETING A HUMAN SKULL FRAGMENT. C. T. Hurst. Southwestern Lore, Gunnison, vol.7, no.4, pp.61-63, figs.5-7, Mar., 1942.

OBSERVATIONS ON FOUR THOUSAND OPTIC FORAMINA IN HUMAN SKULLS OF KNOWN ORIGIN. John E. L. Keyes. Archives Opthalmology, vol.13, pp.538-566, figs.23, Apr., 1935.

DISCOVERY OF AN ADDITIONAL PITHECANTHROPUS SKULL. G. H. R. Koenigswald, Franz Weidenreich. Nature, Lond., vol.142, no.3598, p.715, Oct.15, 1938.

MISSING TEETH IN SKULLS AND DENTAL CARIES. Wilton M. Krogman. Amer. Jour. Phys. Anthropol., vol.20, no.1, pp. 43-49, Apr.-June, 1935.

THE MORPHOLOGICAL CHARACTERS OF THE AUSTRALIAN SKULL. Wilton M. Krogman. Jour. Anat., Cambridge, vol. 66, pt.3, pp.399-413, figs.7, Apr., 1932.

THE NAIVASHA FOSSIL SKULL AND SKELETON. L. S. B. Leakey. Jour. E. Africa Nat. Hist. Soc., Nairobi, vol.16, nos.4-5, (73-74), pp.169-177, pls.57-59, June, 1942.

A NEW FOSSIL SKULL FROM EYASSI, EAST AFRICA. L. S. B. Leakey. Nature, London, vol.138, no.3504, pp.1082-1084, figs.3, Dec.26, 1936.

OBSERVATIONS ON THE BONES OF THE SKULL IN WHITE AND NEGRO FETUSES AND INFANTS. Marciano Limson. Publ. 433 Carnegie Inst. Wash., pp.205-222, figs.13, Aug., 1932.

NOTES ON CERTAIN HUMAN CRANIA IN THE QUEENSLAND MUSEUM. Heber A. Longman. Mem. Queensland Mus., vol.6, pp.1-4, pls.1-5, Dec.19, 1918.

NEANDERTHAL MAN IN SPAIN: THE LOWER JAW OF BONOLAS. George G. MacCurdy. Amer. Anthrop., n.s., vol.17, no.4, pp.759-762, figs.128-129, Oct.-Dec., 1915.

A PRIMITIVE CHARACTER OF THE TEMPORAL RIDGES OF THE GALLEY HILL SKELETON. Hikoshichiro Matsumoto. Dobutsugaku Zasshi, Zool. Soc. Japan, Tokyo, vol.47, pp.53-56, Jan.15, 1935.

NOTES ON THE CASTS OF THE PITHECANTHROPUS MOLARS. Gerrit S. Miller, Jr. Bull. Amer. Mus. Nat. Hist., vol.47, pp. 527-530, figs.14-15, Dec.4, 1923.

THE NATURAL HISTORY OF THE HUMAN TEETH, BY JOHN HUNTER: A STUDY. M. F. Ashley Montagu. Jour. Amer. Dent. Assoc., vol.22, pp.1311-1320, Aug., 1935.

THE SIGNIFICANCE OF THE PREMAXILLARY DIASTEMA IN PITHECANTHROPUS ROBUSTUS (SKULL IV). M. F. Ashley Montagu. Amer. Jour. Phys. Anthropol., Phila., n.s., vol.4, no.2, pp.193-198, June, 1946.

A STUDY OF CERTAIN ORIENTAL SERIES OF CRANIA INCLUDING THE NEPALESE AND TIBETAN SERIES IN THE BRITISH MUSEUM (NATURAL HISTORY). G. M. Morant. Biometrika, vol.16, nos. 1-2, pp.1-105, May, 1924.

(NOTES ON THE MORPHOLOGY AND PHYLOGENY OF THE VERTEBRATES. 8. FIRST STAGES OF THE DENTITION OF MAN (THE MOLARS).) Notizen zur morphologie und Stammesgeschichte der Wirbeltiere. 8. Vorstufen des Menschengebisses (Backenzaehne). A. Naef. Biol. Zentralblatt, vol.46, pp.111-128, 3 figs., 1926.

ON A HUMAN SKULL AND LIMB-BONES FOUND IN THE PALAEOLITHIC TERRACE-GRAVEL AT GALLEY HILL, KENT. Edwin T. Newton. Quart. Jour. Geol. Soc., London, vol.51, pt.3, no.203, pp.505-527, figs.2, pl.16, Aug., 1895.

SOLO MAN--A NEW FOSSIL SKULL. William F. F. Oppenoorth. Scientific American, pp.154-155, illus., Sept., 1932.

THE HISTORY AND HOMOLOGIES OF THE HUMAN MOLAR CUSPS. Henry Fairfield Osborn. Anat. Anzieger, Jena, Jahrg.7, nos.23-24, pp.740-747, figs.3, Oct.20, 1892.

THE SKULL OF ROBERT, THE BRUCE, KING OF SCOTLAND, 1274-1329. Karl Pearson. Biometrika, vol.16, pts.3, 4, pp.253-272, 16 pls., Dec., 1924.

ON THE BIOMETRIC CONSTANTS OF THE HUMAN SKULL. Karl Pearson. Biometrika, vol.16, pts.3, 4, pp.328-363, Dec., 1924.

AN ACCOUNT OF THE DISCOVERY OF AN ADULT SINANTHROPUS SKULL IN THE CHOU KOU TIEN DEPOSIT. W. C. Pei. Bull. Geol. Soc. China, Peiping, vol.8, no. 3, pp.203-205, 1929.

THE FIFTH SKULL OF PEKING MAN. W. C. Pei. Nature, London, vol.139, no.3507, pp.109-110, Jan.16, 1937.

NOTES ON CERTAIN HUMAN REMAINS FOUND IN SOUTHERN RHODESIA. A. E. Phaup. Proc. and Trans. Rhodesia Sci. Assoc., Salisbury, vol.37, pp.157-166, fig.1, Sept., 1939.

(DENTAL CARIES OF PRE-HISPANIC NATIVES OF MENDOZA.) Caries dentales en indigenas prehispanicos de Mendoza. Carlos Rusconi. Revista Odontologica, Buenos Aires, vol.26, no.9, pp.388-392, Sept., 1938.

(MULTIPLE PARIETAL BONE IN AN INDIGENOUS SKULL OF MENDOZA.) Parietal múltiple en un cráneo indígena de Mendoza. Carlos Rusconi. Semana Medica, Buenos Aires, no.24, pp.1-7, illus., 1940.

A FOSSILISED HUMAN MANDIBLE FROM KOPJE ENKEL, WESTERN TRANSVAAL. G. W. H. Schepers. S. African Jour. Sci., vol.32, pp.587-596, 6 figs., Nov., 1935.

THE MANDIBLE OF THE TRANSVAAL FOSSIL HUMAN SKELETON FROM SPRINGBOK FLATS. G. W. H. Schepers. Ann. Transvaal Mus., Cambridge, vol.20, pt.3, pp.253-271, figs.7, Sept.12, 1941.

THE HEREDITARY TENDENCY TO ELIMINATE THE UPPER LATERAL INCISORS. Adolph H. Schultz. Human Biol., vol.4, no.1, pp.34-40, figs.5, Feb., 1932.

SOME NOTES UPON A TASMANIAN ABORIGINAL SKULL. H. H. Scott, R. McClinton. Papers and Proc. Roy. Soc. Tasmania, 1925, pp.5-10, 8 pls., 1926.

A COMPARATIVE STUDY OF THE ENDOCRANIAL CAST OF SINANTHROPUS. Joseph L. Shellshear, G. Elliot Smith. Philos. Trans. Roy. Soc. London, ser.B, vol.223, no.B 503, pp.469-487, pls.53-55, 1934.

CONTRIBUTIONS TO THE COMPARATIVE CRANIOLOGY OF THE NORTH-AMERICAN INDIANS: THE SKULL IN THE APACHES. R. W. Shufeldt. Jour. Anat. and Physiol., Cambridge, vol.21, pp.525-535, figs.3, 1887.

A SKULL OF A NAVAJO CHILD. R. W. Shufeldt. Jour. Anat. and Physiol., Cambridge, vol.21, pp.66-71, figs. A-B, 1887.

HISTORY OF THE HUMAN TEETH. AN INTRODUCTION TO COMPARATIVE DENTAL ANATOMY. Cleveland S. Simkins. P. Blakiston's Son and Co., Inc., Phila., pp.viii, 1-329, figs.111, 1937.

THE PEKING SKULL. G. Elliot Smith. Science, vol.72, no.1856, p.92, July 25, 1930.

ACCOUNT OF A COLLECTION OF HUMAN SKULLS FROM TORRES STRAITS. Oldfield Thomas. Jour. Anthropol. Inst., pp.328-343, May, 1885.

RACIAL FEATURES IN THE AMERICAN NEGRO CRANIUM. T. Wingate Todd. Amer. Jour. Phys. Anthrop., vol.15, no.1, pp.53-110, figs.22, Oct.-Dec., 1930.

(ON THE EVOLUTION OF THE MOLARS AND PREMOLARS IN THE PRIMATES AND PARTICULARLY IN MAN.) De l'evolution des molaires et premolaires chez les Primates et en particulier chez l'homme. Paul Topinard. L'Anthropologie, Paris, no.6, pp.641-710 8 figs., Nov.-Dec., 1892.

THE FUNCTIONS OF THE HUMAN SKULL. Wilfred Trotter. Nature, vol.123, no.3101, pp.533-537, Apr.6, 1929.

THE DENTITION OF SINANTHROPUS PEKINENSIS: A COMPARATIVE ODONTOGRAPHY OF THE HOMINIDS. Franz Weidenreich. Palaeontologica Sinica, Peiping, n. ser.D, no.1, (whole ser. no. 101), pp.1-180, tables 1-27; vol.2, pls.1-36, 49 diagrams, 1937.

THE MANDIBLES OF SINANTHROPUS PEKINENSIS: A COMPARATIVE STUDY. Franz Weidenreich. Palaeontologica Sinica, ser.D, vol.7, no.3, pp.162, figs. 100, pls.15, 1936.

THE NEW DISCOVERY OF THREE SKULLS OF SINANTHROPUS PEKINENSIS. Franz

Weidenreich. Nature, London, vol.139, no. 3511, pp.269-272, figs.4, Feb.13, 1937; Science, n.s., vol.85, no.2204, pp.316-317, Mar.26, 1937.

RECONSTRUCTION OF THE ENTIRE SKULL OF AN ADULT FEMALE INDIVIDUAL OF SINANTHROPUS PEKINENSIS. Franz Weidenreich. Nature, London, vol. 140, no.3554, p.1010, figs.3, Dec.11, 1937.

THE SKULL OF SINANTHROPUS PEKINENSIS; A COMPARATIVE STUDY ON A PRIMITIVE HOMINID SKULL. Franz Weidenreich. Palaeontologia Sinica, Lancaster, Pa., n.s.D, no.10, whole ser. no.127, pp.1-298, pls.1-93, 1943.

(Review by M.F. Ashley Montagu of) THE SKULL OF SINANTHROPUS PEKINENSIS; A COMPARATIVE STUDY ON A PRIMITIVE HOMINID SKULL. Franz Weidenreich. Amer. Anthrop., Menasha, n.s., vol.46, no.3, pp. 402-405, July-Sept., 1944.

A DIMINUTIVE SKULL FROM PERU. J. Robert Wells. Amer. Jour. Phys. Anthrop., Phila., vol.29, no.3, pp.425-427, pl.1, Sept.30, 1942.

THE FOSSIL HUMAN SKULL FROM SINGA. FOSSIL MAMMALS OF AFRICA NO. 2. THE PLEISTOCENE FAUNA OF TWO BLUE NILE SITES. L. H. Wells. British Mus. Nat. Hist., Lond., pp.29-42, figs.3, 1951.

THE STATUS OF THE BUSHMAN AS REVEALED BY A STUDY OF ENDOCRANIAL CASTS. L. H. Wells. South African Jour. Sci., Johannesburg, vol.34, pp.365-398, figs.6, Nov., 1937.

THE PREMAXILLA AND THE ANCESTRY OF MAN. F. Wood Jones. Nature, Lond., vol.159, no.4039, p.439, Mar.29, 1947.

A NEW TOOTH OF SINANTHROPUS PEKINENSIS BLACK. Otto Zdansky. Acta Zool., Stockholm, vol.33, pp.189-191, illus., 1952.

THE ADICHANALLUR SKULLS. WITH NOTES BY G. ELLIOT SMITH. S. Zuckerman. Bull. Madras Govern. Mus., N.S., Gen. Sec., vol.2, pt.1, pp.24, pls.3, 1930.

ANATOMICAL FEATURES OF FOSSIL SKULLS. Nature, London, vol.143, no. 3622, p.565, Apr.1, 1939.

MANDIBLES OF PEKING MAN. Nature, London, vol.139, no.3507, pp.120-121, Jan.16, 1937.

MOST PERFECT NEANDERTHAL SKULL IS BEING STUDIED IN ROME. Science News Letter, Wash., D.C., vol.36, no.7, p.108, illus., Aug.12, 1939.

NEW FOUND FOSSILS PROVE PITHECANTHROPUS WAS HUMAN. LOWER JAWBONE CONTAINING WISDOM TOOTH AND MANY FRAGMENTS OF SKULL CAP IDENTIFY AS OLDEST MAN. Science News Letter, vol.32, no.871, p.387, Dec.18, 1937.

REMOVAL OF FRONT TEETH IN MAN. Nature, London, vol.145, no.3677, p.631, Apr.20, 1940.

THE SWANSCOMBE SKULL. Nature, London, vol.143, no.3614, pp.187-188, Feb.4, 1939.

Taxonomy

(THE CLASSIFICATION OF THE PRIMATES, PARTICULARLY THE HOMINIDS.) La classification des Primates et particulierement des Hominiens. C. Arambourg. Mammalia, Paris, vol.12, no.4, pp.123-135, figs.7, Dec., 1948.

THE RACES OF MEN AND THEIR DISTRIBUTION. A. C. Haddon. New York, The Macmillan Co., vii, 201 pp., 10 pls., 1925.

CLASSIFICATION OF HOMINIDAE. W. C. Osman Hill. Nature, London, vol.146, no. 3699, pp.402-403, Sept.21, 1940.

(ON THE PRIMITIVE PLACEMENT OF MAN AMONG THE MAMMALS.) Ueber die primitive Stellung der Menschen unter den Saeugetieren. M. Westenhoefer. Mitteil. Anthropol. Ges. Wien, vol.60, nos.2-3, pp.171-180, 1930.

## EDENTATA

(TWO NEW EDENTATES FOR THE ZOOLOGICAL MUSEUM.) Deux edentes nouveaux pour le Musee Zoologique. H. Blanc. Bull. Societe Vandoise des Sci. Nat., vol.55, no.214, p.269, 1924.

ANT-EATERS, SLOTHS AND ARMADILLOS. Maurice Burton. Zoo Life, London, vol. 10, no.4, pp.100-103, illus., Winter, 1955-1956.

(BIOLOGY OF XENARTHRA.) A proposito de la Biologia de los Xenartros. A. Cabrera. Real Soc. Espanola Hist. Nat., vol.4, no.3, pp.123-126, 1929.

ANIMAL ANTIQUES. T. H. Eaton, Jr. Frontiers, Phila., vol.7, no.1, pp.9-11, illus., Oct., 1942.

EDENTATES. Theodore Gill. Natural History of Mammals, pp.46-67, illus.

THE SLOTHS, ANT-EATERS, AND ARMADILLOS. W. P. Pycraft. In Cornish, Charles John: The Living Animals of the World; a popular natural history, London, vol.1, pp.336-343, figs.10, 1901.

BODY TEMPERATURES OF SLOTHS, ANTEATERS, AND ARMADILLOS. G. B. Wislocki, R. K. Enders. Jour. Mam., vol. 16, no.4, pp.328-329, Nov., 1935.

Anatomy

ON THE STRUCTURE AND DEVELOPMENT OF THE SKULL IN THE MAMMALIA. PART II. EDENTATA. W. K. Parker. 1885.

THE EXTERNAL CHARACTERS OF THE SOUTH AMERICAN EDENTATES. R. I. Pocock. Proc. Zool. Soc. London, 1924, pt.4, pp.983-1031, 1925.

ON THE VAGUS AND SYMPATHETIC NERVES OF THE EDENTATA. Charles F. Sonntag. Proc. Zool. Soc. London, 1922, pt.1, pp.99-108, Apr., 1922.

ON THE GUSTATORY ORGANS OF SOME EDENTATA. Frederick Tuckerman. Internat. Monatsschrift f. Anat. u. Phys., vol.7, no.9, pp.1-5, 1890.

THE TOPOGRAPHY OF THE HYPOPHYSIS IN THE XENARTHRA. George B. Wislocki. Anat. Rec., vol.70, no.4, pp.451-471, figs. 12, pls.4, Mar.25, 1938.

Fossils

(COMPLEMENT TO THE WORK "ON THE FOSSIL EDENTATES ARGENTINA." CRITICAL ANALYSIS, REVISION, AND CORRECTION OF THE WORK OF MR. LYDEKKER, "THE EXTINCT EDENTATES OF ARGENTINA" (BIBLIOGRAPHIC NUMBER: 93).) Complement de l'oeuvre "Sur les edentes fossiles de l'argentine." Examen critique, revision et correction de l'ouvrage de Mr. Lydekker: "The extinct edentates of Argentine" (numero bibliographique:93). Florentino Ameghino. Obras completas y correspondencia cientifica de Florentino Ameghino, La Plata, vol.23, pp.390-429, 1936.

(FOSSILS OF EDENTATES FROM FRANCE AND GERMANY.) Les Edentes fossiles de France et d'Allemagne. Florentino Ameghino. Obras Completas y correspondencia cientifica de Florentino Ameghino La Plata, vol.15, pp.577-685, figs.61, 1934.

(AN EDENTATE IN THE SUB-ANDES TERTIARY OF SALTA.) Un desdentado actual en el Terciario subandino de Salta. Angel Cabrera. Boletin de Informaciones Petroliferas, Buenos Aires, Ano IX, no. 94, pp.8, figs.3, map 1, July, 1932.

AN EDENTATE FROM THE OLIGOCENE OF WYOMING. Edwin H. Colbert. Notulae Naturae, Phila., no.109, pp.16, figs.3, Nov.3, 1942.

FINDING A NEW ANIMAL IN THE LABORATORY. Edwin H. Colbert. Frontiers, Lancaster, vol.7, no.2, pp.41-43, illus., Dec., 1942.

REPORT ON GROUND SLOTH COPROLITE FROM DONA ANA COUNTY, NEW MEXICO. Arthur J. Eames. Amer. Jour. Sci. (5), vol.20, no.119, pp.353-356, Nov., 1930.

EXPLORATION FOR THE REMAINS OF GIANT GROUND SLOTHS IN PANAMA. C. Lewis Gazin. Annual Rept. Smithsonian Institution, Wash., 1956, 341-354, pls.1-7, 1957.

A NEW GROUND SLOTH DEN. M. R. Harrington. The Masterkey, Southwest Mus. Los Angeles, vol.10, no.6, pp.225-227, fig.1, Nov., 1936.

DESCRIPTIONS OF TWO EXTINCT MAMMALS OF THE ORDER XENARTHRA FROM THE PLEISTOCENE OF TEXAS. Oliver P. Hay. Proc. U.S. Nat. Mus., vol.51, pp. 107-123, pls.3-7, Oct.28, 1916.

PLEISTOCENE EXPLORATION AND FOSSIL EDENTATES IN FLORIDA. Walter W. Holmes, George G. Simpson. Bull. Amer. Mus. Nat. Hist., vol.59, art.7, pp.383-418, figs.17, June 13, 1931.

AN EDENTATE FROM THE PLEISTOCENE OF TEXAS. Gideon T. James. Jour. Paleontol., 31 (4): 796-808, July, 1957.

A MEMOIR OF THE EXTINCT SLOTH TRIBE OF NORTH AMERICA. Joseph Leidy. Washington, Smithsonian Institution, 1855.

REMARKABLE GROUND SLOTH. R. S. Lull. Bull. Geol. Soc. Amer., vol.40, no. 1, pp.246-247, Mar., 1929; Memoirs of the Peabody Museum of Yale Univ., vol.3, pt. 2, pp.1-21, figs.5, pls.9, 1929.

GENERA AND NEW SPECIES OF GROUND SLOTHS FROM THE PLEISTOCENE OF CUBA WITH PREFATORY NOTE BY WALTER GRANGER. W. D. Matthew. Amer. Mus. Novitates, New York, no.511, pp.5, Dec.15, 1931.

XENOTHERIUM, AN EDENTATE. W. D. Matthew. Jour. Mam., vol.9, no.1, pp. 70-71, Feb., 1928.

UNIQUE CONSTRUCTION OF AN EXHIBIT OF PLIOCENE EDENTATES. Phil C. Orr. Publ. Field Mus. Nat. Hist., tech. ser. no.5, pp.6, fig.1, Mar.30, 1938.

METACHEIROMYS AND THE EDENTATA. George G. Simpson. Bull. Amer. Mus. Nat. Hist., vol.59, art.6, pp.295-381, figs.1-23, Apr.2, 1931.

SOME EDENTATE-LIKE REMAINS FROM THE MASCALL BEDS OF OREGON. William J. Sinclair. Bull. Dept. Geol., Univ. Cal. Publ., Berkeley, vol.5, no.2, pp.65-66, figs.3, Dec.6, 1906.

CENOZOIC GRAVIGRADE EDENTATES OF WESTERN NORTH AMERICA WITH SPECIAL REFERENCE TO THE PLEISTOCENE MEGALONYCHINAE AND MYLODONTIDAE OF RANCHO LA BREA. Chester Stock. Publ. by the Carnegie Inst., Wash., no. 331, Wash., Jan., 1925.

A GROUND SLOTH IN ALASKA. Chester Stock. Science, Lancaster, n.s., vol.95, no.2474, pp.552-553, May 29, 1942.

SLOTH TRACKS IN THE CARSON PRISON. Chester Stock. Westways, Los Angeles, vol.28, no.7, pp.26-27, figs., July, 1936.

(CONCERNING SOUTH AMERICAN FOSSIL EDENTATES.) A proposito di Edentati fossili Sud Americani. Embrik Strand. Rivista Italiana di paleontologia, vol.37, fasc.3-4, pp.65-70, 1931.

THE STATUS OF MINERVA ANTIQUA, AQUILA FEROX AND AQUILA LYDEKKERI AS FOSSIL BIRDS. Alexander Wetmore. Amer. Mus. Novitates, no.680, pp.1-4, Dec.4, 1933.

(ON THE SYSTEMATIC POSITION OF XENOTHERIUM DOUGLASS.) Ueber die systematische stellung von Xenotherium, Douglass. Otto Zdansky. Bull. Geol. Inst. Upsala, vol.20, pp.231-236, figs.1-3, Feb. 23, 1926.

South America

NOTES ON SOME SOUTH AMERICAN EDENTATES. Einar Loennberg. Arkiv foer zool., vol.20 A, no.10, pp.1-17, pl.1, Oct.25, 1928.

NOTES ON XENARTHRA FROM BRAZIL AND BOLIVIA. Einar Loennberg. Arkiv.

f. Zool., Stockholm, vol.34 A, no.9, pp. 1-58, figs.13, pl.1, 1942.

(FOSSIL AND LIVING EDENTATA FROM LAGOA SANTA MINAS GERAES, BRAZIL.) Jordfundne og nulevende Gumlere (edentata) fra Lagoa Santa, Minas Geraes, Brasilien. Herluf Winge. E. Museo Lundil, Copenhagen, vol.3, pt.1, pp.321, pls.42, 1915.

(THE EDENTATA. ARGENTINA SYSTEMATICS AND DISTRIBUTION.) Los "Edentata." Argentinas Sistematica y Distribucion. Jose Yepes. Rev. Universidad de Buenos Aires, ser.2, sect.5, vol.1, pp.461-515 (1-55 of reprint), pls.1-6, Apr., 1928.

## Taxonomy

CLASSIFICATION OF THE EDENTATES. Theodore Gill. Science, Lancaster, n.s., vol.32, no.810, p.56, July 8, 1910.

A SUGGESTED CLASSIFICATION OF THE EDENTATES. H. H. Lane. State Univ. Oklahoma Research Bull., no.2, pp.21-27, Oct.30, 1909.

NOTES ON TATOUA AND OTHER GENERA OF EDENTATES. T. S. Palmer. Proc. Biol. Soc. Wash., vol.13, pp.71-73, Sept. 28, 1899.

ON THE ARRANGEMENT OF THE EDENTATE MAMMALIA. H. N. Turner. Proc. Zool. Soc. London, pt.19, pp.205-206, 1851.

## Megalonychidae

HAIR OF THE FOSSIL GROUND SLOTH (NOTHROTHERIUM). L. A. Hausman. Amer. Jour. Sci., ser.5, vol.31, no.183, pp.223-228, figs.4, Mar., 1936.

THE "OVATE BODIES" OF THE HAIR OF NOTHROTHERIUM SHASTENSE. L. A. Hausman. Amer. Jour. Sci., ser.5, vol. 18, no.106, pp.331-333, figs.3, Oct., 1929.

(ENUMERATION AND DESCRIPTION OF REMAINS OF THE GENUS MEGALONYX.) Enumeracion y descripcion de restos del genero Megalonyx. J. L. Kraglievich. Obras de Geologia y Paleontologia, Ministerio de Obras Publicas de la Provincia de Buenos Aires, La Plata, vol.3, pp.787-794, 1940.

(OROPHODON AMEGH. AS A REPRESENTATIVE OF A NEW SUPER-FAMILY, THE OROPHONDONTOIDEA (SUB-ORDER XENARTHRA).) Orophodon Amegh. representante de una nueva superfamilia Orophodontoidea del suborden Xenarthra. Jorge Lucas Kraglievich, Santiago Rivas. Com. Mus. Argentino Cien. Nat., vol.2, no.2, pp.9-28, illus., Sept., 1951.

PLANTS IN THE DUNG OF NOTHROTHERIUM FROM GYPSUM CAVE, NEVADA. J. D. Laudermilk, Philip A. Munz. Publ. 453, Carnegie Inst. Wash. (Contrib. Paleont.), pp.29-37, pls.11, Dec.20, 1934.

THE GROUND SLOTH NOTHROTHERIUM. R. S. Lull. Amer. Jour. Sci. (5), vol.20, no.119, pp.344-352, figs.6, Nov., 1930.

A REMARKABLE GROUND SLOTH. R. S. Lull. Mem. Peabody Mus. Yale Univ., vol.3, pt.2, pp.1-38, pls.1-9, text figs.1-2, 1929.

MEGALONYX MILLERI, A NEW PLEISTOCENE GROUND SLOTH FROM SOUTHERN CALIFORNIA. Gretchen M. Lyon. Trans. San Diego Soc. Nat. Hist., vol.9, no.6, pp.15-30, figs.7, pl.1, tables 3, Nov.21, 1938.

GENERA AND NEW SPECIES OF GROUND SLOTHS FROM THE PLEISTOCENE OF CUBA. W. D. Matthew. Amer. Mus. Nov. no.511, pp.1-5, Dec.15, 1931.

ON TWO MOUNTED SKELETONS OF MEGALOCNUS RODENS. Carolos de Paula Couto. Jour. Mam., 37 (3): 423-427, illus., Sept.11, 1956.

(GIANT SLOTH GENUS COELODON.) Kaempedovendyr-slaegten Coelodon. J. Reinhardt. Vidensk. Selsk. naturvid. og math. ser.5, vol.12, no.3, pp.255-349, pls.5, 1878.

NEW TYPE OF GROUND SLOTH FROM LATER CENOZOIC OF MEXICO. Chester Stock. Pan-Amer. Geol., Des Moines, vol.64, no.1, p.78, Aug., 1935.

NOTHROTHERIUM AND MEGALONYX FROM THE PLEISTOCENE OF SOUTHERN CALIFORNIA. Chester Stock. Univ. California Publs., Bull. Dept. Geology, vol.7, no.17, pp.341-358, figs.18, Sept.19, 1913.

A MEGALONYX TOOTH FROM THE NORTHWEST TERRITORIES, CANADA. Chester Stock, Horace G. Richards. Science, Lancaster, vol.110, no.2870, pp. 709-710, illus., Dec.30, 1949.

MEGALONYX HOGANI, A NEW SPECIES OF GROUND SLOTH FROM GOULD, OKLAHOMA. J. Willis Stovall. Amer. Jour. Sci., New Haven, vol.238, pp.140-146, figs.2, pl.1, Feb., 1940.

## Megatheriidae

(ALIMENTATION OF MEGATHERIUM.) Sobre la alimentacion del megaterio. Angel Cabrera. Bol. Real Soc. Espanola Hist. Nat., vol.26, pp.388-391, 1926.

(A NEW SANTA CRUZ REPRESENTATIVE OF FAMILY MEGATHERIIDAE.) Un nuevo representante Santa Cruz de la familia Megatheriidae. Angel Cabrera. Inst. Mus. Univ. Nac. La Plata, Buenos Aires, vol.4, Paleont. no.20, pp.475-483, figs.3, 1939.

MEMOIR ON THE MEGATHERIUM AND OTHER EXTINCT GIGANTIC QUADRUPEDS OF THE COAST OF GEORGIA, WITH OBSERVATIONS ON ITS GEOLOGIC FEATURES. William Brown Hodgson. New York, Bartlett and Welford, 1846.

REMARKS ON A GIANT SLOTH FOUND NEAR HUMBLE, TEXAS. Keith M. Hussey. Trans. Texas Acad. Sci., Houston, vol.26, p.132, 1943.

(THE TYMPANIC REGION OF THE MEGATHERIUM SKULL.) La region tympanique du crane du Megatherium, Tijdschrift der Ned. C. J. van der Klaauw. Dierkunde Vereeniging (3), vol.2, no.2, pp.77-82, 1930.

(MEGATHERIUM LUNDI SEIJORI, NEW SUBSPECIES OF THE PLEISTOCENE OF URUGUAY.) Megatherium lundi seijori, nueva subespecie Pleistocena del Uruguay. Lucas Kraglievich. Revista Soc. "Amigos de la Arqveologia," Montevideo, vol.5, pp. 81-89, figs.2, (1931) 1932.

ON SOME REMAINS OF "NEOMYLODON LISTAI" AMEGHINO BROUGHT HOME BY THE SWEDISH EXPEDITION TO TIERRA DEL FUEGO 1895-1897. Einar Loennberg. Svenska Exped. till Magellanslaenderna, Stockholm, vol.11, no.7, pp.149-170, pls. 12-14, 1899.

SKELETON OF HUGE MEGATHERIUM, GREATEST OF GROUND SLOTHS, EXHIBITED. Elmer S. Riggs. Field Mus. Notes, vol.6, no.7, p.1, fig., Aug., 1935.

AN ADDITIONAL RECORD OF MEGATHERIUM FROM THE PLIOCENE OF FLORIDA. Theodore E. White. Proc. New England Zool. Club, Cambridge, vol. 19, pp.3-6, 1 pl., Dec.4, 1941.

## Mylodontidae

A NEW MYLODON. Glover M. Allen. Mem. Mus. Com. Zool., vol.40, no.7, pp.319-346, pls.4, Sept., 1913.

MYLODONT (GROUND SLOTH) DERMAL OSSICLES FROM COLOMBIA, SOUTH AMERICA. R. Lee Collins. Jour. Wash. Acad. Sci., vol.23, no.9, pp.426-429, fig.1, Sept.15, 1933.

THE SKULL OF MYLODON HARLANI FROM THE LOWER PLEISTOCENE OF WEST TEXAS. C. Stuart Johnston. Amer. Midland Naturalist, vol.18, no.3, pp.465-469, pls.2, May, 1937.

ON THE TYMPANIC REGION OF THE SKULL IN THE MYLODONTINAE. C. J. van der Klaauw. Proc. Zool. Soc. London, pt.3, pp.607-656, figs.1-7, Sept., 1931.

(THE TYMPANIC REGION OF THE CRANIUM OF SCELIDOTHERIUM.) La region tympanique du crane du Scelidotherium C. J. van der Klaauw. Tijdschrift der Ned. Dier kunde Vereeniging (3), vol.2, no.2, pp.83-87, 1930.

ON A PORTION OF MAMMALIAN SKIN, NAMED NEOMYLODON LISTAI, FROM A CAVERN NEAR CONSUELO COVE, LAST HOPE INLET, PATAGONIA. F.P. Moreno. Proc. Zool. Soc. Lond., pp.143-156, pls. 13-15, June 1, 1899.

(A GIANT MYLODON FOUND IN THE VALLEY OF MEXICO.) Sobre un gravigrado gigantesco (Mylodon) encontrado en el Valle de Mexico. Federico K. G. Muellerried. Anales del Instituto de Biologia, Universidad Nacional de Mexico, vol.5, no.3, pp.223-236, 12 figs., 1934.

(CONTRIBUTIONS TO KNOWLEDGE OF THE GIANT SLOTH, LESTODON ARMATUS.) Bidrag til Kundskab om Kjaempedovendyret Lestodon armatus. J. Reinhardt. Vidensk. Selsk. Skr. Naturvid. og Math., ser.5, vol.11, no.1, pp.3-38, pls.3, 1875.

(JUVENILE SPECIMENS OF THE GENUS "SCELIDOTHERIUM.") Sobre ejemplares juveniles del genero "Scelidotherium." Carlos Rusconi. Anales Soc. Cient. Argentina, Buenos Aires, entr.1, vol.126, pp.33-40, figs.5, table., July, 1938.

(NEW SUBSPECIES OF GLOSSOTHERIUM EDENTATA.) Nueva subespecie de Glossotherium (Edentata). Carlos Rusconi. Rev. Argentina Paleontol. y. Antropol. Ameghinia, Buenos Aires, vol.1, nos.5-6, pp.162-171, figs.4, Nov.15-Dec., 1935.

A MIOCENE SLOTH FROM SOUTHERN CHILE. George G. Simpson. Amer. Mus. Novitates, New York, no.1156, pp.1-6, Dec.31, 1941.

ORIGIN OF THE SUPPOSED HUMAN FOOTPRINTS OF CARSON CITY, NEVADA. Chester Stock. Science, n.s., vol.51, p. 514, May 21, 1920.

SKULL AND DENTITION OF THE MYLODONT SLOTHS OF RANCHO LA BREA. Chester Stock. Berkeley, University of California Press, 1914.

## Glyptodontidae

(NOTES AND RECTIFICATIONS ON GENUS GLYPTODON OWEN, AND FAMILY GLYPTODONTINAE.) Anotcoes e retificacoes ao genero Glyptodon Owen e a Family Glyptodontinae. Alfredo Castellanos. An. Acad. Brasil. Cien., vol.25, no.4, pp.391-410, Dec.31, 1953.

GLYPTOTHERIUM TEXANUM, A NEW GLYPTODONT, FROM THE LOWER PLEISTOCENE OF TEXAS. Henry F. Osborn. Bull. Amer. Mus. Nat. Hist., New York, vol.19, art.17, pp.491-494, pl.43, Aug.17, 1903.

A MIOCENE GLYPTODONT FROM VENEZUELA. George G. Simpson. Amer. Mus. Novitates, New York, no.1368, pp.10, illus., Nov.19, 1947.

## Myrmecophagidae

THE GENERIC NAMES MYRMECOPHAGA AND TAMANDUA, AND THE SPECIFIC NAMES OF THE OPOSSUMS OF THE GENUS DIDELPHIS. J. A. Allen. Proc. Biol. Soc. Wash., vol.14, pp.91-93, June 19, 1901.

THE PROPER NAME OF THE MEXICAN TAMANDUA. J. A. Allen. Proc. Biol. Soc. Wash., vol.19, p.200, Dec.31, 1906.

THE TAMANDUA ANTEATERS. J. A. Allen. Bull. Amer. Mus. Nat. Hist., vol. 20, pp.385-398, figs.1-4, Oct.29, 1904.

ANTEATERS BECAME MILK-EGG-MEAT-EATERS IN THE ZOO. William Bridges. Animal Kingdom, New York Zool. Soc., 59 (2): 43-46, illus., Apr., 1956.

CAPTURING A GIANT ANTEATER. William H. Chippendale. Animal Kingdom, New York, vol.47, no.4, pp.100-103, illus., July-Aug., 1944.

THE PAROTID GLAND OF AN ANTEATER, TAMANDUA TETRADACTYLA. W. W. Dalquest, H. J. Warner. Amer. Midland Nat., Notre Dame, vol.48, no.1, pp.250-252, July, 1952.

THE PIGMY ANTEATER. Guy Dollman. Nat. Hist. Mag. British Mus., London, vol. 4, no.27, pp.104-105, 1 fig., July, 1933.

(OBSERVATION ON THE CONFORMATION OF THE PLACENTA IN THE ANTEATER TAMANDUA (TAMANDUA TETRADACTYLA).) Observations sur la conformation du placenta chez le fourmilier Tamandua (Tamandua Tetradactyla). Alph Milne Edwards. Bibl. l'École Hautes Études, Sci. Nat., vol.5, no.6, pp.1-4, pls.5, 1872.

ON THE SIZE OF THE RED CORPUSCLES OF THE BLOOD OF THE GREAT ANT-EATER (MYRMECOPHAGA JUBATA). George Gulliver. Proc. Zool. Soc. Lond., pt.22, p.24, 1854.

A LITTLE SILKY ANTEATER. A RARE LITTLE DWELLER OF THE CENTRAL AMERICAN JUNGLE. V. W. von Hagen. Nature Magazine, Wash., D.C., vol.32, no.4, pp.189-190, illus., Apr., 1939.

NATURAL HISTORY OF TERMITES. II. THEIR SOCIAL ORGANIZATION. V. W. von Hagen. Sci. Monthly, Lancaster, vol. 55, no.1, whole no.322, pp.29-41, illus., July, 1942.

(OBSERVATIONS ON LARGE ANT BEARS (MYRMECOPHAGA TRIDACTYLA L.).) Beobachtungen am Grossen Ameisenbaeren (Myrmecophaga tridactyla L.). Hans Honigmann. Zeitschr. f. Saeugetierkunde, vol.10, no.1, pp.78-104, figs.2, pl.3, Dec. 31, 1935.

THE ANTEATER STRETCHES. C. W. Leister. Bull. New York Zool. Soc., vol. 38, no.6, pp.219-220, illus., Nov.-Dec., 1935.

DESCRIPTIONS OF A NEW SPECIES OF GREAT ANT-EATER FROM CENTRAL AMERICA. Marcus W. Lyon, Jr. U. S. National Museum Proceedings, Wash., vol. 31, pp.569-571, pl.14, 1907.

(OBSERVATIONS ON THE CONFORMATION OF THE PLACENTA IN THE TAMANDUA.) Observations sur la conformation du Placenta chez le Tamandua. Alph Milne Edwards. Nat. Hist., vol.21, 1872.

(THE HYPOPHYSIS OF MYRMECOPHAGA JUBATA L.) Die Hypophyse von Myrmecophaga jubata L. H. Oboussier. Zool. Anzeiger, 157 (9-10): 196-201, Nov., 1956.

THE GREATER ANTEATER GROUP AT THE FIELD MUSEUM. Wilfred H. Osgood. Sci. Monthly, Lancaster, Pa., vol.48, no. 5, pp.484-485, May, 1939.

ON THE ANATOMY OF THE GREAT ANT-EATER (MYRMECOPHAGA JUBATA). R. Owen. Proc. Zool. Soc. Lond., pt.22, pp. 154-157; pt.25, pp.22-29, 1857.

ON THE ANT-BEAR (MYRMECOPHAGA JUBATA, LINN.). R. Owen. Proc. Comm. Sci. and Corres. Zool. Soc. Lond., pt.1, p.149, 1830-1831.

(NOTES ON THE GREAT ANTEATER, MYRMECOPHAGA JUBATA LINNE.) Mémoires sur le grand fourmilier (Myrmecophaga jubata, Linne.). George Pouchet. G. Mason: Paris, pp.218, pls.18, 1874.

THE GREAT ANTEATER. Edward A. Preble. Nat. Mag., vol.4, p.158, illus., Sept., 1924.

RELATIVE GROWTH IN THE SNOUT OF ANTEATERS. A STUDY IN APPLICATION OF QUANTITATIVE METHODS TO SYSTEMATICS. E. C. R. Reeve. Proc. Zool. Soc. Lond., vol.110, ser.A, pt.1-2, pp.47-80, figs.4, Sept.19, 1940.

A STATISTICAL ANALYSIS OF TAXONOMIC DIFFERENCES WITHIN THE GENUS TAMANDUA GRAY (XENARTHRA). E. C. R. Reeve. Proc. Zool. Soc. Lond., vol. 111, ser.A, 1941, pts.3-4, pp.279-302, figs. 4, Feb., 1942.

(PSYCHOLOGY OF THE LARGE ANT BEARS. IS THE ANT BEAR STUPID?) Zur Psychologie des grossen Ameisenbaeren. Ist der Ameisenbaer dumm? Bastian Schmid. Die Umschau, Frankfurt am Main, Jahrg. 43, no.36, pp.836-839, figs.7, Sept.3, 1939.

(ON TAMANDUA TETRADACTYLA LONGICAUDATA WAGN.) Ueber Tamandua tetradactyla longicaudata (Wagn.). Wilhelm Schroeder. Zool. Anz., vol.119, nos.5-6, pp.124-138, figs.6, Aug.1, 1937.

EXHIBITION OF A PHOTOGRAPH OF A YOUNG ANTEATER (MYRMECOPHAGA JUBATA) BORN IN CAPTIVITY. Philip L. Sclater. Proc. Zool. Soc. Lond., pt.1, p.2, fig.1, June 1, 1897.

NOTES ON THE HABITS OF CYCLOPES DORSALIS. Josselyn Van Tyne. Jour.Mamm., vol.10, no.4, pp.314, pl.23, Nov., 1929.

NEMATODE PARASITES IN THE OVARIES OF THE ANTEATER (TAMANDUA TETRADACTYLA). George B. Wislocki. Jour. Mam., vol.9, no.4, pp.318-319, pl.1, Nov., 1928.

ON THE PLACENTATION OF THE TWO-TOED ANT-EATER (CYCLOPES DIDACTYLUS). George B. Wislocki. Anat. Rec. Vol.39, pp.69-83, illus., June 25, 1928.

A LETTER FROM A READER OF ZOONOOZ. Zoonooz, San Diego, vol.12, no.12, pp.4-5, Dec., 1940.

## Bradypodidae

(EXTERNAL MORPHOLOGY OF THE TELENCEPHALON IN THE GENUS BRADYPUS L. (EDENTATA).) Morphologie externe du telencephale dans le genre Bradypus L. (Edentata). J. Anthony. Mammalia, Paris, vol.17, no.3, pp.149-163, illus., Sept., 1953.

ON THE BRADYPUS DIDACTYLUS. R. Ball. Proc. Zool. Soc. Lond., pt.12, pp. 93-94, 1844.

THE JUNGLE SLUGGARD. William Beebe. Ladies Home Journal, vol.42, no.2, pp.12-13, 56, Feb., 1925.

THE LEISURELY SLOTH. William Beebe. Zool. Soc. Bull., vol.26, no.1, pp.12-16, 6 figs., Jan., 1923.

THE THREE-TOED SLOTH, BRADYPUS CUCULLIGER CUCULLIGER WAGLER. William Beebe. Zoologica, vol.7, no.1, pp.1-67, 23 figs., Mar.25, 1926.

(ON THE COURSE OF THE BRONCHUS IN BRADYPUS TRIDACTYLUS.) Ueber den Verlauf der Luftroehre bei Bradypus tridactylus. W. Blume. Anat. Anz., vol.65, no., pp.230-232, 2 figs., 1928.

(SOME BIOLOGICAL OBSERVATIONS OF THE TWO-TOED SLOTH CHOLOEPUS DIDACTYLUS LINNÉ 1766.) Einige biologische Beobachtungen am Zweizehenfaultier, Choloepus didactylus (Linné 1766). Peter Bopp. Saeugetierk. Mitteil., Stuttgart, vol.2, no.3, pp.114-118, illus., July 1, 1954.

FORM AND FUNCTION IN THE SLOTH. S. W. Britton. Quart. Rev. Biol., Balto., vol.16, no.1, pp.13-34, figs.13, Mar., 1941; no.2, pp.190-207, figs.14-19, June, 1941.

POIKILOTHERMISM IN THE SLOTH. S. W. Britton, W. E. Atkinson. Jour. Mam., vol. 19, no.1, pp.94-99, figs.2, table 1, Feb.14, 1938.

ON DESLOTHING THE SLOTH. S. W. Britton, R. F. Kline. Science, Lancaster, n.s., vol.90, no.2323, pp.16-17, July 7, 1939.

TREE SLOTHS: A STUDY IN SLOW MOTION. Maurice Burton. Illus. London News, vol. 211, no.5658, pp.356-357, illus., Sept.27, 1947.

(THE ORGAN OF ACKERKNECHT IN BRADYPODIDAE.) Das Organ von Ackerknecht bei Bradypodidae. H. Coebergh. Anat. Anz., vol.69, nos.1-3, pp.12-18, 5 figs., 1930.

(A REMARKABLE SKELETON OF A GREAT EXTINCT SLOTH.) Ein bemerkenswertes Skelett eines grossen augestorbenen Faultieres. F. Drevermann. Ber. Senckenberg. Naturforsch. Ges. Natur u. Mus., vol. 60, no.12, pp.553-556, 2 figs., Dec., 1930.

OBSERVATIONS ON SLOTHS IN CAPTIVITY AT HIGHER ALTITUDES IN THE TROPICS AND IN PENNSYLVANIA. Robert K. Enders. Jour. Mam., vol.21, no.1, pp.5-7, Feb.14, 1940.

(NOTES ON THE MAMMALS. XXXIX. CONCERNING SOME ADAPTIVE PECULIARITIES OF THE SKELETON OF THE THREE-TOED SLOTH.) Notes sur les mammifères. XXXIX. De quelques particularités adaptatives du squelete des paresseux. Serge Frechkop. Bull. Inst. Roy. Sci. Nat. Belgique, vol.29, no.35, pp.14, illus., July, 1953.

NOTES ON THE SPECIES OF BRADYPODIDAE IN THE BRITISH MUSEUM. John E. Gray. Proc. Zool. Soc. Lond., pp.428-449, figs.6, pls.35-37, 1871.

SLOWFOOT THE SLOTH, A PREHISTORIC THROWBACK, VIEWS HIS UPSIDE-DOWN WORLD. V. W. von Hagen. Frontiers, Phila., vol.4, no.3, pp.66-71, illus., Feb., 1940.

THE SUBSPECIFIC STATUS OF TWO CENTRAL AMERICAN SLOTHS. E. Raymond Hall, Keith R. Kelson. Univ. Kansas Publ., Mus. Nat. Hist., vol.5, no.24, pp.313-317, Nov.21, 1952.

EARLY DEVELOPMENT OF THE SLOTH (BRADYPUS GRISEUS) AND ITS SIMILARITY TO THAT OF MAN. Chester H. Heuser, George B. Wislocki. Publ. no.459, Carnegie Inst. Wash., pp.1-13, fig.1, pls. 1-4, July, 1935.

EXPERIMENTAL STUDIES OF THE RESPIRATION OF SLOTHS. Laurence Irving, P. F. Scholander, S. W. Grinnell. Jour. Cell. and Comp. Physiol., Phila., vol.20, no.2, pp.189-210, figs.13, Oct.20, 1942.

NOTE ON THE TEMPERATURE OF THE SLOTH. Frederick E. Kredel. Jour. Mam., vol.9, no.1, pp.48-51, Feb., 1928.

A PHYSIOLOGICAL STUDY OF THE CEREBRAL MOTOR CORTEX AND THE CONTROL OF POSTURE IN THE SLOTH. Orthello R. Langworthy. Jour. Comp. Neurol., vol.62, no.2, pp.333-348, figs. 5, Oct., 1935.

DIPETALONEMA SPIRALIS (MOLIN, 1860) (NEMATODA, FILARIOIDEA). Herman Lent, J. F. Teixeira de Freitas. Mem. Inst. Oswaldo Cruz, Rio de Janeiro, vol. 37, no.3, pp.383-389, illus., Sept., 1942.

(OBSERVATIONS ON THE "MUSCULUS DIAPHRAGMA" IN BRADYPUS TRIDACTYLUS.) Observations sur le "Musculus diaphragma" chez le Bradypus tridactylus. R. Locchi. Bull. de l'Assoc. des Anatomistes, no.21, pp.203-211, 1930; Ann. Fac. Med. Sao Paulo, vol.6, pp.3-20, pls.3, 1931.

(OBSERVATIONS ON THE SLOTH (BRADYPUS TRIDACTYLUS, L.) IN THE WILD STATE AND IN CAPTIVITY.) Observacões sobre a preguica (Bradypus tridactylus, L.) em liberdade e no captiveiro. H. Luederwaldt. Revista Mus. Paulista, vol.10, pp. 793-812, 1918.

(SOME MORE OBSERVATIONS CONCERNING THE SLOTH BRADYPUS TRIDACTYLUS L.) Mais algumas observacões sobre a preguica Bradypus tridactylus L. H. Luederwaldt. Revista do Museu Paulista, vol.14, pp.393-396, 1926.

(CONTRIBUTION TO STUDY OF PRESENT-DAY EDENTATES.) Contribution à l'étude des Édentés actuels. A. Menegaux. Archiv. Zool. Experimentale Generale, Paris, ser. 5, vol.1, no.3, pp.277-344, pls.3-6, May 10, 1909.

FUNCTIONAL ADAPTATIONS IN THE FORELIMB OF THE SLOTHS. Ruth Miller. Jour. Mam., vol.16, no.1, pp.38-51, Feb., 1934.

ACQUIRED HOMIOTHERMISM IN THE PREGNANT SLOTH. Peter R. Morrison. Jour. Mam., vol.26, no.3, pp.272-275, fig.1, Aug., 1945.,

MEET MISTER SLOWPOKE. Gareth Munro. Our Dumb Animals, Norwood, vol.78, no. 9, p.167, illus., Sept., 1945.

GENUS BRADYPUS, SPECIES BRADYPUS STRIATUS, OR WEASEL SLOTH. G. Perry.

Arcana, or Mus. Nat. Hist., Lond., pt.11, sign.Y, pl.41, pp.3, Nov., 1810.

(ON THE ANATOMY AND THE SYSTEMATIC PLACEMENT OF BRADYPUS TORQUATUS (ILL.).) Ueber die Anatomie und die systematische Stellung von Bradypus torquatus (Ill.). Franz Poche. Zool. Anzeiger, Leipzig, vol.33, no.17-18, pp.567-580, figs.7, Nov.10, 1908.

TWO-TOED SLOTH. Edward A. Preble. Nat. Mag., vol.4, pp.354-382, illus., Dec., 1924.

SLOTH-FUL TACTICS. Jacqueline Schermerhorn. San Diego Zoonooz, vol. 20, no.1, pp.5-6, illus., Jan., 1947.

(ON THE DENTINE OF BRADYPUS TRIDACTYLUS.) Ueber das Dentin von Bradypus tridactylus. W. J. Schmidt. Anat. Anzeiger, vol.58, pp.97-107, 6 figs., Aug. 5, 1924.

(ON THE GAIT OF THE TWO-TOED SLOTH (CHOLOEPUS DIDACTYLUS L.).) Zum Gang des Unaus (Choloepus didactylus L.). Karl M. Schneider. Zool. Garten, Leipzig, n.F., vol.12, nos.4-6, pp.325-330, figs. 10, Dec., 1940.

COUNTERCURRENT HEAT EXCHANGE AND VASCULAR BUNDLES IN SLOTHS. P. F. Scholander, J. Krog. Jour. Applied Physiol., 10 (3): 405-411, May, 1957.

AN UPSIDE-DOWN LIFE. THE SLOTH AND ITS VERY QUEER RELATIONS. D. Seth-Smith. Field, Lond., vol.164, no. 4275, p.1297, illus., Dec.1, 1934.

MASTICATORY APPARATUS OF THE SLOTHS. Harry Sicher. Zool. Ser. Field Mus. Nat. Hist., Chicago, vol.29, no.10, pp.161-168, Mar.28, 1944.

ADVENTURES WITH SLOTHS. Alexander F. Skutch. Nat. Mag., Wash., vol.40, no. 10, pp.521-524, 552, illus., Dec., 1947.

A CONTRIBUTION TO THE ANATOMY OF THE THREE-TOED SLOTH (BRADYPUS TRIDACTYLUS). Charles F. Sonntag. Proc. Zool. Soc. Lond., pp.157-177, 4 pls., Mar., 1921.

NATURE'S STRAP-HANGER. Paul L. Swanson. Fauna, Phila., vol.7, no.4, pp. 104-108, illus., Dec., 1945.

SOME NOTES ON THREE-TOED SLOTHS. Oldfield Thomas. Ann. and Mag. Nat. Hist. (8), vol.19, no.112, pp.352-357, Apr., 1917.

(ON THE DEVELOPMENT AND STRUCTURE OF THE HAND AND FOOT SKELETON OF BRADYPUS TRIDACTYLUS.) Ueber Entwicklung und Bau des Hand-und Fuss-Skeletts bei Bradypus tridactylus. Bjorn Ursing. Lunds Univ. Arsskrift, N.F., Avd.2, vol.28, no.12, pp.108, figs.63, 1932.

FURTHER OBSERVATIONS UPON THE PLACENTATION OF THE SLOTH (BRADYPUS GRISEUS). George B. Wislocki. Anat. Record, vol.32, pp.45-52, Jan.25, 1926.

OBSERVATIONS ON THE GROSS AND MICROSCOPIC ANATOMY OF THE SLOTHS (BRADYPUS GRISEUS GRAY AND CHOLOEPUS HOFFMANNI PETERS). George B. Wislocki. Jour. Morph. and Physiol., vol. 46, no.2, pp.317-378, pls.1-7, Dec.5, 1928.

ON THE PLACENTATION OF THE SLOTH (BRADYPUS GRISEUS). George B. Wislocki. Contributions to Embryology, no.78, Carnegie Inst., Wash., Pub.no.361, pp.5-21, pls.2, 1925.

TOO LAZY TO LEAVE. Life, Chicago, vol. 33, no.17, p.158, illus., Oct.27, 1952.

## Dasypodidae

THE GIANT ARMADILLO. William Beebe. Zool. Soc. Bull., vol.25, pp.117-120, 2 figs., Sept., 1922.

A LIVE GIANT ARMADILLO AT LAST. William Beebe. Zool. Soc. Bull., vol.27, pp.118-120, 5 figs., Sept., 1924.

ZOO NEWS FROM EVERY PLACE. Belle J. Benchley. Zoonooz, San Diego, vol.12, no.4, pp.1-4, Apr., 1940.

IT'S AN ARMADILLO. Frank Dufresne. Nature Mag., Wash., vol.38, no.10, pp. 527-528, 552, Dec., 1945.

(ON THE ARMADILLO TOLYPEUTES CONURUS.) Vom Kuget-Guerteltier (Tolypeutes conurus). M. Eisentraut. Natur und Volk, Frankfurt, vol.82, no.2, pp.43-48, Feb.1, 1952.

ARMADILLO, THE ARMORED GRAVE DIGGER. William L. Finley, Irene Finley. Nature Mag., vol.5, pp.361-363, illus., June, 1925.

(SYSTEMATIC AND ZOOGEOGRAPHIC STUDY OF THE DASYPODOIDS KEPT AT THE INSTITUTE.) Étude systématique et zoogéographique des dasypodidés conservés a l'institut. Serge Frechkop, Jose Yepes. Bull. Inst. Roy. Sci. Nat. Belgique, Brussels, vol.2, no.5, pp.56, figs.20, Apr., 1949.

THE ARMADILLO AND WILD TURKEY. Ramon Graham. Oologist, vol.41, p.90, July, 1924.

THE ARTFUL ARMADILLO. Ethel O. Hill. Nature Mag., vol.20, no.5, pp.218-219, fig.1, Nov., 1932.

(ON MOVEMENT STEROTYPIES IN CAPTIVE MAMMALS. III. COMMUNICATION: ANALYSIS OF THE MOVEMENT STEREOTYPY OF AN ARMADILLO (DASYPUS VILLOSUS DESM.) Ueber Bewegungsstereotypien bei gehaltenen Saeugern. III. Mitteilung: Analyse der Bewegungsstereotypie eines Guerteltieres (Dasypus villosus Desm.). Monika Holzapfel. Zool. Garten, Leipzig, n.F., vol.10, nos.5-6, pp.184-193, figs.3, Jan., 1939.

(AN ARMADILLO AT PONT DU GARD.) Un tatou au Pont du Gard. A. Hugues. Mammalia, Paris, vol.2, no.3, p.157, Sept., 1938.

(ADAPTATION TYPES OF THE ARMADILLOS.) Die anpassungstypen der Guerteltiere. Friedrich Kuhlhorn. Zeitschr. f. Saeugetierkunde, vol.12, pp.245-303, pls. 17-23, July 15, 1938.

(THE GIANT ARMADILLO (PRIODONTES GIGANTEUS E. GEOFFR.).) Das Riesenguerteltier (Priodontes giganteus E. Geoffr.). Friedrich Kuhlhorn. Zool. Garten, Leipzig, N.F., vol.10, nos.3-4, pp.107-114, Sept., 1938.

SOME OBSERVATIONS ON THE HABITS AND PLACENTATION OF TATU NOVEMCINCTUM. H. H. Lane. State Univ. Oklahoma Research Bull., Norman, no.1, pp.1-18, figs.1-3, Oct.30, 1909.

NATURE'S LITTLE TANK. Karl H. Maslowski. Nat. Hist., New York, vol. 57, no.8, pp.371-373, illus., Oct., 1948.

(BRIEF OBSERVATIONS OF LIVING GIANT ARMADILLOS.) Kleine Beobachtungen am lebenden Riesengrueteltier. Erna Mohr. Zool. Garten, Leipzig, N.F., vol.10, nos. 5-6, pp.198-202, figs.6, 1939.

(THE BIGGEST ARMADILLO OF THE WORLD.) El carpincho mas grande del mundo. Carlos Rusconi. Rev. Geog. Americana, Buenos Aires, figs.3, pp.1-4, Jul.24, 1936.

CONTRIBUTION ON THE LIFE HISTORY AND ECOLOGY OF THE NINE-BANDED ARMADILLO. F. Wallace Taber. Jour. Mam., vol.26, no.3, pp.211-226, Aug., 1945; MS. thesis, A. and M. College, Texas, 1940.

THE ARMADILLO (DASYPUS NOVEMCINCTUS). A REVIEW OF ITS NATURAL HISTORY, ECOLOGY, ANATOMY AND REPRODUCTIVE PHYSIOLOGY. Roy V. Talmage, G. Dale Buchanan. Rice Inst. Pamphlet, Monograph in Biology, Houston, vol.41, no.2, pp.viii, 135, July, 1954.

THE ALOOF ARMADILLO. Laura M. Trester. Frontiers, Phila., vol.15, no.1, pp.18-20, illus., Oct., 1950.

AN ANIMAL IN ARMOR. Explorer, Cleveland, no.70, p.5, illus., Spring, 1942.

ARMORED TRAVELERS OF THE DESERT. National Nature News, vol.1, no.27, pp. 3, 5, illus., Sept.27, 1937.

THE VERY RARE GIANT ARMADILLO--ARMED FOR DEFENCE AND ATTACK. Illus. London News, vol.190, no.5102, p. 186, illus., Jan.30, 1937.

### Anatomy

(CRANIOMETRY AND AUDITORY REGION OF CHLAMYTHERIUM TYPUM AMEGHINO.) Craneometria y region auditiva de Chlamytherium typum Ameghino. Alejandro F. Bordas. Physis., Buenos Aires, vol.14, no.46, pp.447-460, figs.3, pls.3, Mar., 1939.

A HISTOLOGICAL STUDY OF THE INTEGUMENT OF THE ARMADILLO, TATUSIA NOVEMCINCTA. Zola K. Cooper. Amer. Jour. Anat., vol.45, no.1, pp.1-38, 4 figs., 2 pls., 1930.

ON THE DEVELOPMENT AND SUCCESSION OF THE TEETH IN THE ARMADILLOS (DASYPODIDAE). William H. Flower. Proc. Zool. Soc. Lond., pp.378-380, 1868.

NOTES ON THE ANATOMY OF TOLYPEUTES TRICINCTUS, WITH REMARKS ON ARMADILLOS. Alfred H. Garrod. Proc. Zool. Soc. Lond., pp.222-230, figs.3, 1878.

ON THE STRUCTURE OF THE PELVIS OF CHLAMYPHORUS TRUNCATUS. John E. Gray. Proc. Zool. Soc. Lond., pt.25, pp. 8-9, figs.3, 1857.

EXTRA-OVARIAL SEX CORDS ON AN ARMADILLO OVARY. G. W. D. Hamlett. Anat. Record, Phila., vol.62, no.2, pp.195-197, pl.1, May 25, 1935.

THE BASAL DIENCEPHALON OF THE ARMADILLO. Howard A. Howe. Jour. Comp. Neurol., vol.58, no.2, pp.311-357, pls.1-9, Oct., 1933.

(THE ADAPTATION TYPES OF ARMADILLOS.) Die Anpassungstypen der Guerteltiere. Friedrich Kuehlhorn. Zeitschr. f. Saeugetierkunde, Berlin, vol.12, no.3, pp. 245-303, pls.17-23, July 15, 1938.

(COMPREHENSIVE REPORT ON THE ORIGIN AND INSERTION OF THE FUNCTIONALLY MOST IMPORTANT NECK AND EXTREMITY MUSCLES IN SOME SPECIES OF ARMADILLOS.) Zusammenfassende Uebersicht ueber ursprung und Insertion der funktionell wichtigaten Hals-und Extremitaetenmuskeln bei einigen Guerteltierarten. Friedrich Kuehlhorn. Morphol. Jahrb., vol.89, pp.629-660, 1937.

(THE GIANT ARMADILLO (PRIODONTES GIGANTEUS E. GEOFFR.) AS ADAPTATION FORM.) Das Riesenguerteltier (Priodontes giganteus E. Geoffr.) als Anpassungsform. Friedrich Kuhlhorn. Zool. Garten, Leipzig, n.F., vol.10, nos.3-4, pp.107-114, figs.10, Sept., 1938.

NOTES ON THE ANATOMY OF A SPECIMEN OF DASYPUS MINUTUS WITHOUT NUCHAL PLATES. Einar Loennberg. Ofversigt Kongl. Vetenskaps-Akad. Forhandl., Stockholm, no.5, pp.297-304, 1898.

INNERVATION OF THE PANNICULUS CARNOSUS IN THE ARMADILLO, DASYPUS NOVEMCINCTUS. Samuel S. Miles. Anat. Record, Phila., vol.78, no.3, pp.273-279, fig.1, Nov.25, 1940.

THE SHOULDER ANATOMY OF THE ARMADILLO. Samuel S. Miles. Jour. Mam., vol.22, no.2, pp.157-169, figs.5, May 14, 1941.

THE DEVELOPMENT OF THE HYPOPHYSIS OF THE ARMADILLO. Frances K. Oldham. Amer. Jour. Anat., Phila., vol. 68, no.2, pp.293-315, pls.3, figs.1-14, Mar.15, 1941.

THE PHARMACOLOGY AND ANATOMY OF THE HYPOPHYSIS OF THE ARMADILLO. Frances K. Oldham. Anat. Record, vol. 72, no.3, pp.265-291, 2 pls., Nov.25, 1938.

ON THE ANATOMY OF THE NINE-BANDED ARMADILLO (DASYPUS PEBA, DESM.). R. Owen. Proc. Comm. Sci. and Corres. Zool. Soc. Lond., pt.1, pp.141-144, 1830-1831.

ON THE ANATOMY OF THE WEASEL-HEADED ARMADILLO (DASYPUS SEXCINCTUS, LINN.). R. Owen. Proc. Comm.

Sci. and Corres. Zool. Soc. Lond., pt.1, p.154, 1830-1831.

ON THE ANATOMY OF TWO SPECIES OF ARMADILLO (DASYPUS, L.). R. Owen. Proc. Comm. Sci. and Corres. Zool. Soc. Lond., pt.2, p.130, 1832.

ON THE OSTEOLOGY OF THE WEASEL-HEADED ARMADILLO (DASYPUS 6-CINCTUS, L.). R. Owen. Proc. Comm. Sci. and Corres. Zool. Soc. Lond., pt.2, p.134, 1832.

ON THE DORSAL GLANDS IN ARMADILLOS. R. I. Pocock. Proc. Zool. Soc. London, pt.4, pp.1099-1103, figs.193-195, Dec.17, 1913.

A POSSIBLE ALBINO ARMADILLO. John K. Strecker. Jour. Mam., vol.8, no.1, p.60, Feb., 1927.

ON THE MALE GENERATIVE ORGANS OF CHLAMYDOPHORUS TRUNCATUS AND DASYPUS SEXCINCTUS. M. Watson. Proc. Zool. Soc. Lond., pp.673-679, pl.XLIII, 1878.

SEASONAL VARIATIONS IN HEMATOPOIESIS IN THE DERMAL BONES OF THE NINE-BANDED ARMADILLO. L. P. Weiss, G. B. Wislocki. Anat. Record, Phila., 126 (2): 143-164, Oct., 1956.

DEVELOPMENT AND HISTOLOGY OF THE INTEGUMENT OF THE NINE-BANDED ARMADILLO (TATUSIA NOVEMCINCTA). Charlie W. Wilson. Austin, Tex., Univ. Texas, 18 pp., 10 pls., 1914.

(DIPHYODONTISM IN THE MULITAS (DASYPODIDAE). (SUMMARY.).) El difiodontismo en la mulitas (Dasypodidae). (Resumen.) Jose Yepes. Physis, Buenos Aires, vol.16, no.48, p.295, May, 1939.

Ecology, Habits, Behavior

MAY FOOD HABITS OF ARMADILLOS IN EASTERN TEXAS. Rollin H. Baker. Amer. Midland Naturalist, vol.29, no.2, pp.379-380, Mar., 1943.

THE PLACE OF THE ARMADILLO IN FLORIDA WILDLIFE COMMUNITIES. Roswell Bushnell. Master's thesis, Stetson U., 1952.

ECOLOGICAL LIFE HISTORY OF THE ARMADILLO IN THE EASTERN EDWARDS PLATEAU REGION. William K. Clark. Am. Midland Nat. 46 (2): 337-358, Sept., 1951.

DAY AND NIGHT IN THE LIFE OF AN ARMADILLO. OUR GIANT SPECIMEN'S KEEPER IS TRYING TO TURN THE HOURS TOPSY-TURVY FOR THE BENEFIT OF VISITORS, BY A CHANGE IN FEEDING TIME. William Cully. Bull. New York Zool. Soc., vol.42, no.6, pp.180-182, figs.3, Nov.-Dec., 1939.

ARMADILLOS INVADING LOUISIANA ARE NOT QUAIL ENEMIES. James N. Gowanloch. La. Cons. Rev. 8 (4): 7, 50, Winter, 1939-1940.

HABITS OF XENURUS UNICINCTUS, OR CABASSOU. John E. Gray. Ann. and Mag. Nat. Hist., Lond., ser.4, vol.11, no.66, pp.463-464, June, 1873.

(REMARKABLE TYPE OF ARMADILLO HUNTING.) Merkwuerdige Jagdart auf Guerteltiere. Hans-Joachim Hahn. Zool. Garten, Leipzig, N.F., vol.16, no.5, pp.207-208, 1950.

THE BLACK PERSIMMON AS A SUMMER FOOD OF THE TEXAS ARMADILLO. W. J. Hamilton, Jr. Jour. Mam., vol.27, no.2, p.175, May 14, 1946.

(THE GIANT ARMADILLO (PRIODONTES GIGANTEUS E. GEOFFR.) AS AN ADAPTATION FORM.) Das Riesenguerteltier (Priodontes giganteus E. Geoffr.) als Anpassungsform. Friedrich Kuhlhorn. Zool. Garten, N.F., Leipzig, vol.10, nos. 3-4, pp.107-114, illus., Sept., 1938.

(SMALL OBSERVATIONS OF LIVING GIANT ARMADILLOS.) Kleine Beobachtungen am lebenden Riesenguerteltier. Erna Mohr. Zool. Garten, Leipzig, N.F., vol.10, nos. 5-6, pp.198-202, figs.6, Jan., 1939.

ARMADILLO EATS YOUNG RABBITS. Coleman C. Newman. Jour. Mam., 23 (4): 450, Nov., 1942.

SELF-DEFENSE EQUIPMENT OF THE TORTOISE-ARMADILLOS. Bryan Patterson. Field Museum News, Chicago, vol.14, no. 11, pp.4-5, illus., Nov., 1943.

RESPIRATION OF THE ARMADILLO WITH POSSIBLE IMPLICATIONS AS TO ITS BURROWING. P. F. Scholander, Laurence Irving, S. W. Grinnell. Jour. Cell. and Comp. Physiol., Phila., vol.21, no.1, pp. 53-63, figs.3, Feb., 1943.

THE VALUE OF ARMADILLOS TO FUR ANIMALS. F. Wallace Taber. Texas Agr. Exp. Sta., Prog. Rep. 723, 3 pp., Jan., 1941.

Economic Importance

IN DEFENSE OF ARMADILLOS. J. Casey. Our Dumb Animals, Norwood, vol.75, no. 4, p.64, illus., Apr., 1942.

THE ARMADILLO: ITS RELATION TO AGRICULTURE AND GAME. E. R. Kalmbach. Texas Game, Fish and Oyster Comm., 61 pp., 1943.

(Review by E. Raymond Hall of) THE ARMADILLO: ITS RELATION TO AGRICULTURE AND GAME. E. R. Kalmbach. Jour. Wildlife Management, Menasha, vol.8, no. 4, pp.342-343, Oct., 1944.

ECCENTRIC ENIGMA. (TEXAS ARMADILLO FARM) People and Places, Chicago, vol.6, no.7, pp.4-5, illus., Mar., 1949.

Embryology and Later Development

(THE DEVELOPMENT OF ORGANS IN THE RUDIMENTARY EMBRYOS OF MULITAS (TATUSIA HYGRIDA DESMAREST).) Sobre el desarrollo de los órganos en los embriones rudimentarios de la mulita (Tatusia hygrida Demarest). Miguel Fernandez. Physis (Rev. Soc. Argentina Cien. Nat.) Buenos Aires, vol.18, pp.1-13, pl.1, 1939.

(ON CELL DEATH AND SO-CALLED "ROUND CELLS" IN RUDIMENTARY EMBRYOS OF TATUSIA HYBRIDA DESM.) Uber Zelluntergang und sog. "Rundzellen" bei rudimentaeren Embryonen von Tatusia Hybrida Desm. Miguel Fernandez. Vierteljahrsschrift Naturforsch. Gesell, Zuerich, Jahrg.83, Beiblatt, pp.197-208, figs.2, pl.1, Nov.3, 1938.

POLYEMBRYONY OF THE ARMADILLO: GENETIC OR PHYSIOLOGICAL? G. W. D. Hamlett. Quart. Rev. Biol., Balto., vol. 8, no.3, pp.348-358, Sept., 1933.

(ON THE GROWTH OF THE MALE BRISTLE ARMADILLO (CHAETOPHRACTUS VILLOSUS FISCH.).) Zum Wachstum maennlicher Borstenguerteltiere (Chaetophractus villosus Fisch.). Erich Kuehn. Zool. Garten, Leipzig, N.F., vol.20, nos. 2-3, pp.82-85, illus., 1953.

SEX DIFFERENTIATION IN THE NINE-BANDED ARMADILLO, DASYPUS NOVEMCINCTUS. Dorothy M. Newfang. Jour. Morph., Phila., vol.81, no.3, pp.283-315, 5 pls., Nov., 1947.

A CASE OF NORMAL IDENTICAL QUADRUPLETS IN THE NINE-BANDED ARMADILLO, AND ITS BEARING ON THE PROBLEMS OF IDENTICAL TWINS AND OF SEX DETERMINATION. H. H. Newman, J. T. Patterson. Biol. Bull., vol.17, no.3, pp.181-187, Aug., 1909.

THE DEVELOPMENT OF THE NINE-BANDED ARMADILLO FROM THE PRIMITIVE STREAK STAGE TO BIRTH; WITH SPECIAL REFERENCE TO THE QUESTION OF SPECIFIC POLYEMBRYONY. H. H. Newman, J. T. Patterson. Jour. Morphol., Phila., vol.21, no.3, pp.359-423, pls.1-6, figs.25, 1910.

THE LIMITS OF HEREDITARY CONTROL IN ARMADILLO QUADRUPLETS: A STUDY OF BLASTOGENIC VARIATION. H. H. Newman, J. T. Patterson. Jour. Mam., vol.22, no.4, pp.855-926, figs.1-24, Dec., 1911.

A REMARKABLE EXPLANATION OF POLYEMBRYONY IN THE ARMADILLO. Charles R. Stockard. Amer. Nat., vol.55, pp.62-68, Feb., 1921.

Fossils

(NOTES ON THE EUTATINAE. NEW EXTINCT SUBFAMILY DASYPODIDAE.) Notas sobre los Eutatinae. Nueva subfamilia extinguida de Dasypodidae. Alejandro F. Bordas. Anal. Mus. Argentino Cienc. Nat. "Bernardino Rivadavia," Buenos Aires, vol.37, pp.583-614, figs.15, pls.57-61, Nov.30, 1933.

AN ARMADILLO FROM THE MIDDLE EOCENE (BRIDGER) OF NORTH AMERICA. Henry F. Osborn. Amer. Mus. Nat. Hist., New York, vol.20, art.12, pp.163-165, May 10, 1904.

(THE LOWER PREMOLAR OF THE GREAT EXTINCT CARPINCHOS.) El premolar inferior de los grandes carpinchos extinguidos. Carlos Rusconi. Anal. Soc. Cient. Argentina, Buenos Aires, vol.128, entr.4, pp.233-239, figs.10, Oct., 1939.

ENAMEL ON THE TEETH OF AN EOCENE EDENTATE. George G. Simpson. Amer. Mus. Novitates no.567, pp.4, fig.1, Sept. 21, 1932.

HOLMESINA SEPTENTRIONALIS, EXTINCT GIANT ARMADILLO OF FLORIDA. George G. Simpson. Amer. Mus. Novitates no.442, pp.1-10, figs.5, Dec.18, 1930.

THE GIANT ARMADILLO, HOLMESINA SEPTENTRIONALIS (LEIDY), NEW TO THE PLEISTOCENE OF OKLAHOMA. J. Willis Stovall, Claude W. Hibbard. Jour. Mam., vol.29, no.4, p.420, Dec.31, 1948.

Mexico and Central America

DESCRIPTION OF A NEW ARMADILLO (DASYPUS NOVEMCINCTUS) FROM MEXICO WITH REMARKS ON GEOGRAPHIC VARIATION OF THE SPECIES. Robert J. Russell. Proc. Biol. Soc. Wash., vol.66, pp.21-26, Mar.30, 1953.

NOTE ON THE OCCURRENCE OF AN ARMADILLO OF THE GENUS XENURUS IN HONDURAS. Frederick W. True. Proc. U.S. Nat. Mus., vol.18, publ.1069, pp.345-347, pls.10-11, July 8, 1896.

North America

THE ARMADILLO IN FLORIDA AND HOW IT REACHED THERE. H. H. Bailey. Jour. Mam., vol.5, no.4, pp.264-265, Nov., 1924.

ANOTHER ARKANSAS ARMADILLO. John D. Black. Jour. Mam., vol.25, no.4, p.415, Dec.12, 1944.

THE NINE-BANDED ARMADILLO IN NORTHEASTERN OKLAHOMA. W. Frank Blair. Jour. Mam., vol.17, no.3, pp.293-294, Aug., 1936.

NINE-BANDED ARMADILLO--INVADER FROM THE SOUTH. G. D. Buchanan. Animal Kingdom, New York Zool. Soc., vol.58, no.3, pp.82-88, June, 1955.

THE GEOGRAPHICAL DISTRIBUTION OF THE ARMADILLO IN THE UNITED STATES. G. D. Buchanan, Roy V. Talmage. Texas Jour. Sci., vol.6, no.2, pp.142-150, June, 1954.

THE ARMADILLO IN THE SOUTHEASTERN UNITED STATES. Henry S. Fitch, Phil Goodrum, Coleman Newman. Jour. Mam., vol.32, no.1, pp.21-37, Feb., 1952.

ANOTHER OKLAHOMA ARMADILLO. Marshall C. Gardner. Jour. Mam., vol. 29, no.1, p.76, Feb.13, 1948.

THE NINE-BANDED ARMADILLO AND THE EASTWARD EXPANSION OF ITS RANGE. F. Max Hardberger. Turtox News 28 (9): 174-177, Sept., 1950.

THE SPREAD OF THE ARMADILLO IN FLORIDA. Wilfred T. Neill. Ecology, New York, vol.33, no.2, pp.282-284, Apr., 1952.

OUR ARMORED INVASION. Coleman Newman. Louisiana Conservationist, New Orleans, vol.2, no.6, pp.14-15, illus., Feb., 1950.

THE ARMADILLO IN FLORIDA. H. G. Sherman. Fla. Ent. 26 (4): 54-59, Dec., 1943.

THE EXTENSION OF RANGE OF THE NINE-BANDED ARMADILLO. John K.

Strecker. Jour. Mam., vol.7, no.3, pp. 206-210, Aug., 1926.

THE NINE-BANDED ARMADILLO IN NORTHEASTERN LOUISIANA. John K. Strecker. Jour. Mam., vol.9, no.1, pp. 69-70, Feb., 1928.

EXTENSION OF THE RANGE OF THE ARMADILLO. F. Wallace Taber. Jour. Mam., 20 (4): 489-493, Nov., 1939.

ARMADILLOS ABUNDANT IN KERR COUNTY, TEXAS. Walter P. Taylor. Jour. Mam., 27 (3): 273, Aug., 1946.

Parasites

HELMINTHS OF ARMADILLOS, DASYPUS NOVEMCINCTUS, IN EASTERN TEXAS. Asa C. Chandler. Jour. Parasitology 32 (3): 237-241, June, 1946.

(CONTRIBUTION TO KNOWLEDGE OF FILARIDS OF ARMADILLOS.) Contribuicão ao conhecimento dos filarídeos de dasipodídeos. Herman Lent, J. F. Teixeira de Freitas. Rev. Brasileira Biol., Rio de Janeiro, vol.2, no.3, pp. 275-280, figs.15, Sept., 1942.

A NEW TRICHOSTRONGYLE GENUS FROM AN ARMADILLO, EUPHRECTUS VILLOSUS. M. A. Ortlepp. Ann. and Mag. Nat. Hist., ser.9, vol.9, pp.413-421, Apr., 1922.

Reproductive Biology

IMPLANTATION IN ARMADILLOS OVARIECTOMIZED DURING THE PERIOD OF DELAYED IMPLANTATION. G. D. Buchanan, A. C. Enders, R. V. Talmage. Jour. Endocrinol., vol.14, pp.121-128, pl. 1, 1956.

THE REPRODUCTIVE CYCLE IN THE ARMADILLO. G. W. D. Hamlett. Zeitschr. fuer wissenschaft. Zool., Abt.A, vol.141, no.1, pp.143-157, 1 pl., 1932.

REPORT ON THE CIRCUMSTANCES ATTENDING THE BIRTH OF TWO ARMADILLOS (DASYPUS SEXCINCTUS, L.). Mr. Miller. Proc. Comm. Sci. and Corres. Zool. Soc. Lond., pt.1, p.48, 1830-1831.

THE PRESENCE OF A FUNCTIONAL CORPUS LUTEUM DURING DELAYED IMPLANTATION IN THE ARMADILLO. R. V. Talmage, G. D. Buchanan, F. W. Kraintz, E. A. Lazo-Wasem, M. X. Zarrow. Jour. Endocrinol., London, vol. 11, no.1, pp.44-49, July, 1954.

South America

(CONTRIBUTION TO KNOWLEDGE OF THE ECOLOGY OF SOME ARMADILLOS (EDENTATA) FROM ARGENTINA.) Contribucion al conocimiento de la ecologia de algunos dasipodidos (Edentata) argentinos. Jorge A. Crespo. Rev. Argentina Zoogeogr. Buenos Aires, vol.4, nos.1-2, pp.7-39, pls.9, 1945.

(OBSERVATIONS OF SOME RARE OR UNKNOWN ARMADILLOS INHABITING THE ARGENTINIAN AND BOLIVIAN "PUNA.") Observations relatives à quelques tatous rares ou inconnus habitant la "Puna" argentine et bolivienne. G. Grandidier, M. Neveu-Lemaire. Bull. Mus. Nat. Hist. Nat., Paris, vol.14, no.1, pp.4-7, pls.1-2, 1908.

(VOYAGES IN SOUTH AMERICA FOR THE PURPOSE OF BIOLOGICAL STUDY. IX. ARMADILLOS.) Biologische Reisestudien in Suedamerika. IX. Guerteltiere. Hans Krieg. Zeitschr. Morph. und Oekol. der Tiere, vol.14, pp.166-190, figs.1-15, Mar. 12, 1929.

ON A NEW SPECIES OF ARMADILLO FROM BOLIVIA. Oldfield Thomas. Ann. and Mag. Nat. Hist. (6), vol.13, no.73, pp.70-72, Jan., 1894.

NOTES ON CHLAMYDOPHORUS TRUNCATUS. E. W. White. Proc. Zool. Soc. Lond., pp.8-11, Jan.6, 1880.

(ARGENTINIAN SPECIES OF GENUS CABASSOUS (DASYPODIDAE).) Las especies Argentinas del genero "Cabassous" (Dasypodidae). Jose Yepes. Rev. Soc. Argentina Cienc. Nat., vol.11, pp.438-44, pls.1-3, Feb.2, 1935.

(A NEW SPECIES OF "MULITA" (DASIPODINAE) FOR NORTHERN ARGENTINA.) Una especie Nueva de "Mulita" (Dasipodinae) para el Norte Argentino. José Yepes. Physis (Revista Soc. Argentina Cien. Nat.), vol.11, pp.225-232, Oct., 1933.

(THE SHORT-EAR PICHICIAGO (ZAEDYUS PICHIY) INTEGRATES ALL PATAGONIA WITH ITS DISTRIBUTION.) El piche de oreja corta (Zaedyus pichiy) integra con su distribucion el total del distrito patagonico. José Yepes. Rev. Argentina Zoogeogr., Buenos Aires, vol.4, nos.1-2, p.83, 1945.

Taxonomy

(NOTE ON A NEW ARMADILLO SPECIES WITH INCOMPLETE CUIRASS (SCLEROPLEURA BRUNETI).) Note sur une Nouvelle espece de Tatou a Cuirasse incomplete (Scleropleura bruneti). Alph Milne Edwards. Mem. Nouv. Archiv. du Mus., Paris, vol. 7, pp.177-179, pl.12, 1871.

ADDITIONAL NOTE ON TOLYPEUTES CONURUS. John E. Gray. Ann. and Mag. Nat. Hist., Lond., ser.4, vol.11, no.66, p.469, June, 1873.

ON THE SHORT-TAILED ARMADILLO (MULETIA SEPTEMCINCTA). John E. Gray. Proc. Zool. Soc. Lond., pp.244-246, pl.41, Apr.21, 1874.

IDENTITY OF DASYPUS SEPTEMCINCTUS LINNAEUS WITH NOTES ON SOME RELATED SPECIES. G. W. D. Hamlett. Jour. Mam., vol.20, no.3, pp.328-336, fig.1, table 1, 1939.

THE SYSTEMATIC NAME OF THE TEXAS ARMADILLO. N. Hollister. Jour. Mam., vol.6, no.1, p.60, Feb.9, 1925.

NOTES ON THE NAKED-TAILED ARMADILLOS. Gerrit S. Miller, Jr. Proc. Biol. Soc., Wash., vol.13, pp.13, figs.2, Jan.31, 1899.

DESCRIPTION OF A NEW ARMADILLO, WITH REMARKS ON THE GENUS MULETIA GRAY. Samuel N. Rhoads. Proc. Acad. Nat. Sciences, Phila., pp.112-114, 1894.,

SIZE-DIFFERENCES IN THE LITTLE "PICHI" ARMADILLOS. Oldfield Thomas. Ann. and Mag. Nat. Hist., ser.10, vol.1, pp.526-527, Apr., 1928.

PHOLIDOTA

Manidae

WHY THE PANGOLIN IS HARD TO KILL. W. G. Adam. Field, London, vol.159, no. 4146, p.882, illus., June 11, 1932.

NOTES ON THE SCALY ANT-EATER (MANIS JAVANICA), TAKEN DURING LIFE AND AFTER DEATH. Arthur Adams. Proc. Zool. Soc. Lond., pt.27, pp.133-135, 1859.

NOTES ON THE PANGOLIN (MANIS CRASSICAUDATA). A. Aiyappan. Jour. Bombay Nat. Hist. Soc., vol.43, no.2, pp.254-257, figs.4, Aug., 1942.

(OBSERVATIONS ON SMUTSIA TEMMINCKII (SMUTS) IN CAPTIVITY.) Beobachtungen an Smutsia temminckii (Smuts) in der Gefangenschaft. R. Bigalke. Zool. Garten. Leipzig, n.F., vol.5, nos.7-9, pp.173-178, figs.4, Oct., 1932.

THE ORGAN OF JACOBSON IN THE SCALY ANTEATER. R. Broom. Ann. Transvaal Mus., Cambridge, vol.19, pt.3, pp.323-325, fig.1, May 24, 1939.

(CONFIRMATION OF THE PRESENCE OF THE GIANT PANGOLIN ON THE IVORY COAST.) Confirmation de la présence du pangolin géant en Basse Côte d'Ivoire. P. Cachan. Mammalia, Paris, 21 (4): 455-457, Dec., 1937.

THE INDIAN PANGOLIN (MANIS PENTADACTYLA L.). N. C. Chatterjee. Jour. Bombay Nat. Hist. Soc., vol.28, pp.273-274, Dec.30, 1921.

(THE JAVANESE PANGOLIN (MANIS JAVANICA DESEN.).) Het javaansche Schubdier (Manis javanica Desen.). L. Coomans de Ruiter. Tropische Natuur, vol.19, nos.5-6, pp.100-102, figs.2, 1930.

THE PANGOLIN OF JAVA. K. W. Dammerman. Dutch East Indies, Department van landbouw, nijverheid en handel (Nature Protection in the Netherlands Indies), Dept. Econ. Affairs, Batavia, pp.36-38, illus., 1938.

(THE PANGOLINS.) Les pangolins. P. L. Dekeyser. Notes Africaines, Dakar, no. 57, pp.27-30, Jan., 1953.

(THE PANGOLIN (MANIS TRICUSPIS RAF.).) Das Weissbauch-Schuppentier (Manis tricuspis Raf.). M. Eisentraut. Zool. Garten, Leipzig, 23 (1-3): 50-54, illus., 1957.

(THE NATURAL FAMILY OF PANGOLINS (MANIS).) Die natuerliche Familie der Schuppenthiere (Manis). Leop. Jos. Fitzinger. Sitz. Akad. Wissensch. Wien, vol.65, Abth.1, pp.75, Jan., 1872.

ON TWO SPECIMENS OF MANIS. L. Fraser. Proc. Zool. Soc. Lond., pt.11, pp.53-54, 1843.

(NOTES ON MAMMALS. VI. SOME OBSERVATIONS ON THE CLASSIFICATION OF PANGOLINS (MANIDAE).) Notes sur les Mammifères. VI. Quelques observations sur la classification des Pangolins (Manidae). Serge Frechkop. Bull. Mus. roy. d'Hist. nat. Belgique, Bruxelles, vol.7, no.22, pp. 1-14, Sept., 1931.

PANGOLIN AND YOUNG. Argenton Fryer. Field, London, vol.166, no.4312, p.437, illus., Aug.24, 1935.

(OBSERVATIONS OF MANIS JAVANICA DESM.) Beobachtungen an Manis javanica Desm. Eberhard Gartner. Zool. Garten, N.F., Leipzig, vol.8, nos.7-9, pp.226-227, June, 1936.

(INFORMATION ON THE PANGOLIN (MANIS JAVANICA DESM.).) Etwas vom Tengiling (Manis javanica Desm.). H. Haenel. Zool. Garten, Leipzig, n.F., vol. 4, nos.3-5, p.173, May, 1931.

PANGOLINS. AN ACCOUNT OF CERTAIN STRANGE ANTEATERS OF AFRICA AND ASIA. Robert T. Hatt. Natural History, New York, vol.34, no.8, pp.725-732, figs. 10, Dec., 1934.

THE PANGOLIN OR SCALY ANT-EATER. G. A. C. Herklots. Hong Kong Nat., vol. 7, no.2, pp.79-83, pls.2, July, 1937.

REMARKS UPON A YOUNG SPECIMEN OF TEMMINCK'S MANIS (MANIS TEMMINCKI). F. Holmwood. Proc. Zool. Soc. Lond., pp.632-633, 1878.

SOME NOTES ON THE PANGOLIN (MANIS PENTADACTYLA) IN BURMA. S. F. Hopwood. Jour. Bombay Nat. Hist. Soc., vol.33, no.2, pp.439-440, pl.1, Feb.15, 1929.

ON THE NOMENCLATURE OF THE FORMOSAN PANGOLIN. (TRANSLATED TITLE.) Yasuichi Horikawa. Trans. Nat. Hist. Soc. Taiwan, Taihoku, vol.33, no.234, pp. 67-70, Mar., 1943. (In Japanese.)

HABITS OF THE SCALY ANTEATER FROM JAVA. A. F. Jentink. Notes, Leyden Mus., vol.23, no.25, pp.183-184, Jan., 1903.

REVISION OF THE MANIDAE IN THE LEYDEN MUSEUM. Fredericus A. Jentink. Notes, Leyden Mus., vol.4, no.25, pp.193-209, May, 1882.

(ON THE STEPPE ARMADILLO (MANIS TEMMINCKII).) Ueber das Steppenschuppentier (Manis temminckii). Ernst M. Lange. Zool. Garten, Leipzig, 21 (4): 225-230, illus., 1956.

PANGOLINS AS PETS. Arthur Loveridge. Natural History, New York, vol.52, no.4, pp.152-155, illus., Nov., 1943.

(MANIS HUNGARICA N. SP., THE FIRST ARMADILLO FROM THE EUROPEAN UPPER PLIOCENE.) Manis hungarica n. sp., das erste Schuppentier aus dem europaeischen Oberpliozaen. Th. Kormos. Folia Zool. et Hydrobiol, Riga, vol.6, no. 1, pp.87-94, pl.1, Aug.31, 1934.

NOTES ON THE CHROMOSOMES OF THE PANGOLIN MANIS PENTADACTYLA (EDENTATA). Sajiro Makino, Shinkichi

Tateishi. Jour. Fac. Sci. Hokkaido Univ., Sapporo, vol.10, nos.3-4, pp.318-323, Dec., 1951.

(THE NATURAL RELATIONSHIP AND DISTRIBUTION OF MANIS SPECIES.) Die natuerliche Verwandtschaft und die Verbreitung der Manis-Arten. Paul Matschie. Sitz. Bern Gesell., Naturf. Freunde Berlin, Jahrg., 1894, no.1, pp.1-13, Jan.16, 1894.

A GUIDE TO THE MAMMALS OF CEYLON. PART V. THE PANGOLIN. W. W. A. Phillips. Ceylon Jour. Sci., Sect.B, Zool. and Geol., Spolia Zeylanica, Colombo, vol. 13, pt.3, pp.285-289, pl.14, Mar.31, 1926.

A NOTE ON THE HABITS OF THE INDIAN PANGOLIN (MANIS CRASSICAUDATA). W. W. A. Phillips. Ceylon Jour. Sci., Sec.B, Zool and Geol., Spolia Zeylanica, vol.14, pt.2, pp.333-334, Mar.12, 1928.

THE EXTERNAL CHARACTER OF AN ADULT FEMALE CHINESE PANGOLIN (MANIS PENTADACTYLA) EXHIBITED IN THE SOCIETY'S GARDENS. R. I. Pocock. Proc. Zool. Soc. Lond., pp.213-220, illus., Apr.29, 1926.

THE EXTERNAL CHARACTERS OF THE PANGOLINS (MANIDAE). R. I. Pocock. Proc. Zool. Soc. Lond., pp.707-723, 8 figs., Sept., 1924.

NOTES ON PANGOLINS OF THE IVORY COAST. U. Rahm. Jour. Mam., 37 (4): 531-537, illus., Jan.9, 1957.

(THE PANGOLINS.) Les Pangolins. H. Schouteden. Rev. Zool. and Bot. Africaines, vol.17, no.4, pp.87-95, figs.3, Feb.15, 1930.

PANGOLIN AND ALLIGATORS IN SHANGHAI. A. deC. Sowerby. China Jour., vol.25, no. 2, pp.110-111, illus., Aug., 1936.

ON THE NAME OF THE INDIAN PANGOLIN (MANIS CRASSICAUDATA GEOFFR.). R. F. Stoney. Jour. Bombay Nat. Hist. Soc., vol.45, no.2, p.233, Apr., 1945.

SOME NOTES ON THE FEEDING HABITS OF THE GROUND PANGOLIN, SMUTSIA TEMMINCKII (SMUTS). R. C. H. Sweeney. Ann. and Mag. Nat. Hist., ser.12, 9 (108): 893-896, Dec., 1956.

ON AN IMMATURE SPECIMEN OF THE LONG-TAILED MANIS (MANIS TETRADACTYLA, LINN.), FROM SIERRA LEONE. W. Thompson. Proc. Zool. Soc. Lond., pt.2, pp.28-29, 1834.

(CONTRIBUTIONS TO THE ANATOMY AND DEVELOPMENT OF THE GENUS MANIS.) Beitraege zur Anatomie und Entwicklung des Genus Manis. Max Weber. Zool. Ergebnisse, II, pp.1-116, pls.9.

A PANGOLIN DISCOVERED IN NANTAO. China Jour., Shanghai, vol.23, no.5, p. 310, figs.2, Nov., 1935.

TEMMINCK'S PANGOLINS: STRANGE SCALY RARITIES, RECENTLY GIVEN TO THE ZOO. Illus. London News, vol.215, no.5756, p.245, illus., Aug.4, 1949.

## LAGOMORPHA

LAGOMORPHS COLLECTED BY THE ASIATIC EXPEDITIONS. Glover M. Allen. Amer. Mus. Novit., no.284, 11 pp., Sept. 13, 1927.

A REVIEW OF THE FOSSIL LAGOMORPHS IN THE PALAEONTOLOGICAL MUSEUM OF UPSULA. B. Bohlin. Bull. Geol. Inst. Univ. Upsula, vol.30, pp.117-154, 1942.

EOCENE LAGMORPHA. J. J. Burke. Science, n.s., vol.77, no.1990, p.191, Feb.17, 1933.

DAMAGE TO MANGOLDS BY RODENTS (LAGOMORPHS). W. Maldwyn Davies. Jour. Min. Agric., Great Britain, vol.37, no.3, pp.269-276, pls.2, 1930.

NOTES ON PACIFIC COAST RABBITS AND PIKAS. L. R. Dice. Univ. Michigan, Occ. Papers Mus. Zool., no.166, 28 pp., Feb. 11, 1926.

THE LAGOMORPHS AN INDEPENDENT ORDER. James W. Gidley. Science, n.s., vol.36, no.922, pp.285-286, Aug.30, 1912.

NOTES ON THE LUNGWORMS OF NORTH AMERICAN LEPORIDAE. Frans C. Goble, E. L. Cheatum. Jour. Parasitol., Lancaster, vol.30, no.2, pp.119-120, Apr., 1944.

A SYNOPSIS OF THE NORTH AMERICAN LAGOMORPHA. E. Raymond Hall. Univ. Kansas Publ., Mus. Nat. Hist., Lawrence, vol.5, no.10, pp.119-202, illus., Dec.15, 1951.

SYSTEMATICS OF AMERICAN LAGOMORPHA. (SUMMARY.) E. Raymond Hall. Proc. XIV Internat. Congr. Zool., Copenhagen, 1953, pp.521-522, 1956.

OCHOTONA H. YOSHIKURAI OF SAGHALIEN IN CAPTIVITY. Nagamichi Kuroda. Syokukutu oyobi Dobutu (Botany and Zool.), vol.6, no.4, pp.137-138, figs.3, Apr.1, 1938. (In Japanese)

ON FOSSIL AND RECENT LAGOMORPHA. C. J. F. Major. Trans. Linn. Soc. Lond., ser.2, vol.7, 1896-1900.

(SIMILARITIES AND DIFFERENCES IN THE EMBRYONIC DEVELOPMENT OF PIKAS AND RABBITS.) Skhodstva i razlichiya v embrionalnom razvitli pishchukh (Ochotona daurica) i krolikov (Oryctolagus cuniculus L.). B. S. Matvyeyev, V. V. Popova. Zool. Zhurnal, Moscow, vol.32, no.4, pp.701-711, 1953.

A FUNDAMENTAL SEX DIFFERENCE BETWEEN LAGOMORPHS AND OTHER PLACENTAL MAMMALS. George A. Petrides. Evolution, Lancaster, vol.4, no.1, p.99, Mar., 1950.

THE EXTERNAL CHARACTERS OF THE LAGOMORPH RODENTS. R. I. Pocock. Proc. Zool. Soc. Lond., pt.2, pp.669-700, figs.13-30, July 21, 1925.

(ON THE POSITION OF LAGOMORPHA IN THE SYSTEM OF MAMMALS.) Ueber die Stellung der Lagomorpha im System der Saeugetiere. Gabor Stohl. Annales Inst. Biol. (Tihany) Hungaricae Acad. Sci., 24: 51-57, 1957.

THE MAMMALIAN FAUNA OF THE WHITE RIVER OLIGOCENE. PART III: LAGOMORPHA. Albert E. Wood. Trans. Amer. Philos. Soc., Phila., n.s., vol.28, pt.3, pp.271-362, figs.71-116, pls.34-35, Apr., 1940.

NOTES ON THE PALEOCENE LAGOMORPH, EURYMYLUS. Albert E. Wood. Amer. Mus. Novitates, New York, no.1162, pp.1-7, 7 figs., Feb.2, 1942.

### Ochotonidae

THE MOUSE-HARES OF THE GENUS OCHOTONA. J. L. Bonhote. Proc. Zool. Soc. Lond., vol.2, pp.205-220, Apr.18, 1905.

PIKAS: ACE MOUNTAINEERS. Maurice Burton. Illus. London News, vol.218, no. 5844, p.626, illus., Apr.21, 1951.

(THE CORRECT INTERPRETATION OF THE DENTAL CUSPS OF TITANOMYS.) A Titanomys fogcsúcsainak helyes értelmezéséröl. Gyula Éhik. Allattani Koezlemények, vol.23, nos.3-4, pp.159-168, figs.7, 1926.

THE WEASEL AS AN ENEMY OF THE PIKE. W. S. Long. Jour. Mam., vol.19, no.2, p. 250, May 14, 1938.

THE GESTATION PERIOD OF THE PIKA (OCHOTONA PRINCEPS). J. Harold Severaid. Jour. Mam., vol.31, no.3, pp. 356-357, Aug.21, 1950.

A DEAD CONY. Lloyd M. Smith. Yosemite Nat. Notes, Yosemite, vol.19, no.4, p.31, Apr., 1940.

#### Capture

TRAPPING OCHOTONA. Walter W. Dalquest. Jour. Mam., vol.20, no.1, pp. 108-109, Feb.14, 1939.

THE HAND CAPTURE OF CONIES. F. W. Miller. Jour. Mam., vol.20, no.3, p.380, Aug.14, 1939.

#### Ecology, Habits, Behavior

THE LABORS OF A CONY. Edward Butts. Yosemite Nature Notes 19 (1): 3-4, Jan., 1940.

THE COLORADO PIKA IN CAPTIVITY. L. R. Dice. Jour. Mam., vol.8, no.3, pp.228-231, Aug., 1927.

PIKAS VERSUS WEASEL. Joseph Dixon. Jour. Mam., vol.12, no.1, p.72, Feb., 1931.

THE PIKA HARVESTERS. John Eric Hill. Nat. Hist., New York, vol.50, no.2, p.75, illus., Sept., 1942.

A FOOD HOARD OF OCHOTONA FROM TAISETSUZAN, THE CENTRAL MOUNTAINS OF HOKKAIDO. T. Inukai. Trans. Sapporo Nat. Hist. Soc., vol.11, pt.4, pp. 210-214, figs.1-3, 1931.

OCHOTONA H. YOSHIKURAI OF SAGHALIEN, IN CAPTIVITY. Nagamichi Kuroda. Botany and Zool., vol.6, no.4, pp.137-138, figs.3, Apr.1, 1938. (In Japanese.)

WINTER MOVEMENTS OF THE CONY. M. P. Skinner. Jour. Mam., vol.6, no.3, p.202, Aug., 1925.

#### Eurasia

SECOND PRELIMINARY REPORT ON THE RESULTS OF THE SECOND DOLAN EXPEDITION TO WEST CHINA AND TIBET: A NEW RACE OF OCHOTONA. Glover M. Allen. Proc. Acad. Nat. Sci. Phila., vol. 89, pp.341-342, Oct.25, 1937.

(DATA ON THE RODENTS OF CENTRAL ASIA. II. THE OCHOTONIDS (OCHOTONA LINK, FAM. OCHOTONIDAE) OF CENTRAL ASIA AND KAZAKHSTAN. PRELIMINARY REVIEW.) Matériaux pour servir à la connaissance des Rongeurs de l'Asie Centrale. II. Les ogotones (Ochotona Link, fam. Ochotonidae) de l'Asie Centrale et du Kazakstan. A. Argyropulo. Revue Préliminaire. Trudy Zool. Inst. Akad. Nauk SSSR (Trav. Inst. Zool. Acad. Sci. URSS), Leningrad, vol.1, no.1, pp.35-57, figs.8, 1932. (In Russian.)

REPRESENTATIVES OF OCHOTONIDAE (DUPLICIDENTATA, MAMMALIA) IN THE PLIOCENE OF THE USSR. A. Argyropulo, I. G. Pidoplichka. Comptes Rendus (Doklady) Acad. Sci. URSS, Moscow, n.s., vol. 24, no.7, pp.723-728, figs.2, 1939.

ON THE TYPE-LOCALITY AND SYNONYMY OF OCHOTONA PUSILLA (PALLAS). J. L. Chaworth-Musters. Ann. and Mag. Nat. Hist., Lond., ser.10, vol.12, no.67, p. 137, July, 1933.

(ON THE OCHOTONA (MAMMALIA, RODENTIA) FROM THE NORTHERN URALS.) Sur l'Ochotona (Mammalia, Rodentia), provenant de l'Oural du Nord. K. K. Flerov. Ann. Mus. Zool. Acad. Sci. 1'Urse, pp.138-144, pl.4, illus., 1927.

DISTRIBUTION OF OCHOTONA SO FAR DISCOVERED IN HOKKAIDO AND SAKHALIN. T. Inukai. Proc. Imp. Acad. Tokyo, vol.8, no.6, pp.255-258, figs.3, June, 1932.

A RECORD OF OCHOTONA FROM SAKHALIN. T. Inukai. Trans. Sapporo Nat. Hist. Soc., vol.12, pt.1, pp.6-8, figs.3, 1931.

ON OCHOTONA, A NEW RODENT UNRECORDED FROM HOKKAIDO. T. Inukai, Kyojiro Shimakura. Trans. Sapporo Nat. Hist. Soc., vol.11, no.2, pp.115-118, figs.4, 1930.

(NOTES ON OCHOTONA OF IRAN.) Notes sur les ochotones de l'Iran. Xavier Misone. Bull. Inst. Roy. Sci. Nat. Belgique, 32 (54): 1-7, Sept., 1956.

A NEW PIKA FROM THE ALTAI. Oldfield Thomas. Ann. and Mag. Nat. Hist., ser. 9, vol.13, pp.163-164, Jan., 1924.

ON SOME NEW FORMS OF OCHOTONA. Oldfield Thomas. Ann. and Mag. Nat. Hist., ser.9, vol.9, pp.187-193, Feb., 1922.

ON A NEW OCHOTONID FROM NORTH SUIYUAN. C. C. Young. Bull. Geol. Soc. China, vol.11, no.3, pp.255-258, fig.1, Dec., 1931.

#### North America

THE DISTRIBUTION OF THE PIKAS (OCHOTONA) IN BRITISH COLUMBIA AND

ALBERTA. I. McT. Cowan. Murrelet 35 (2): 19-24, map, May-Aug., 1954.

A NEW PIKA (GENUS OCHOTONA) FROM BRITISH COLUMBIA. I. McT. Cowan, Kenneth Racey. Canadian Field-Nat., Sutton West, vol.60, no.5, pp.102-104, Sept.-Oct., 1946. (Issued in 1947.)

THREE NEW PIKAS (GENUS OCHOTONA) FROM UTAH. Stephen D. Durrant, M. Raymond Lee. Proc. Biol. Soc. Wash., vol.68, pp.1-10, May 20, 1955.

AN UNDESCRIBED PIKA FROM UTAH. Marshall C. Gardner. Jour. Wash., Acad. Sci., vol.40, no.10, p.344, Oct.15, 1950.

THE YOSEMITE CONY. William C. Godfrey. Yosemite Nature Notes, vol.7, pp.102-104, illus., Dec., 1928.

A NEW CONY FROM THE VICINITY OF MOUNT WHITNEY. J. Grinnell. Univ. Cal. Pub. Zool. vol.10, no.2, pp.125-129, table, Jan.31, 1912.

THE WARNER MOUNTAIN CONY. J. Grinnell. Proc. Biol. Soc. Wash., vol.25, pp.129-130, July 31, 1912.

THE YOSEMITE CONY, A CHAPTER IN THE NATURAL HISTORY OF THE YOSEMITE NATIONAL PARK. J. Grinnell, Tracy I. Storer. Sierra Club Bull., vol. 10, no.2, pp.159-166, pl.161, figs.3, 1917.

A NEW PIKA (MAMMALIAN GENUS OCHOTONA) FROM CENTRAL NEVADA. E. Raymond Hall. Proc. Biol. Soc. Wash., vol.47, pp.103-106, June 13, 1934.

A NEW PIKA (MAMMALIAN GENUS OCHOTONA) FROM SOUTHEASTERN IDAHO WITH NOTES ON NEAR-BY SUBSPECIES. E. Raymond Hall, H. Lorraine Bowlus. Univ. Calif. Publ. Zool., Berkeley, vol. 42, no.6, pp.335-340, fig.1, Oct.12, 1938.

NOTES ON THE PIKAS OF COLORADO. Junius Henderson, D. A. Cockerell. Proc. Biol. Soc. Wash., vol.26, pp.125-128, May 21, 1913.

TWO NEW AMERICAN PIKAS. Ned Hollister. Proc. Biol. Soc. Wash., vol. 25, pp.57-58, Apr.13, 1912.

THE PIKA AT SEA LEVEL. R. Bruce Horsfall. Jour. Mam., vol.6, no.3, pp. 201-202, Aug., 1925.

DESCRIPTIONS OF NINE NEW NORTH AMERICAN PIKAS. Arthur H. Howell. Proc. Biol. Soc. Wash., vol.32, pp.105-110, May 20, 1919.

REVISION OF THE AMERICAN PIKAS (GENUS OCHOTONA). Arthur H. Howell. North Amer. Fauna, no.47, pp.i-iv, 1-57, 6 pls., 4 figs., Aug.21 (distributed Sept. 23), 1924.

THE COLORADO PIKA. Ken Martin. Jour. Mam., 24 (3): 394-396, Aug., 1943.

DESCRIPTION OF A NEW SPECIES OF PIKA (LAGOMYS SCHISTICEPS) FROM THE SIERRA NEVADA MOUNTAINS IN CALIFORNIA. C. Hart Merriam. North American Fauna, no.2, pp.11-13, Oct., 1889.

AN ISOLATED COLONY OF THE GRAY-HEADED PIKA IN NEVADA. Alden H. Miller. Jour. Mam., vol.17, no.2, pp. 174-175, May 14, 1936.

NOTES ON PIKAS FROM THE OREGON CASCADES. Aryan I. Roest. Jour. Mam., vol.34, no.1, pp.132-133, Feb.19, 1953.

Parasites

THE ALLOTYPE OF GEUSIBIA ASHCRAFTI AUGUSTSON 1941. G. F. Augustson. Bull. Southern California Acad. Sci., Los Angeles, vol.40, no.3, pp.157-159, illus., Sept.-Dec., 1941.

SCHIZORCHIS OCHOTONAE N. GEN., N. SP., OF ANOPLOCEPHALID CESTODE. Merle F. Hansen. Amer. Midland Nat., Notre Dame, vol.39, no.3, pp.754-757, figs.7, May, 1948.

SIPHONAPTERA: THE GENERA AMPHALIUS AND CTENOPHYLLUS IN NORTH AMERICA. William L. Jellison. Pub. Health Rep. 56 (49): 2341-2349, Dec., 1941.

AN UNDETERMINED PARASITE IN THE LUNGS OF A ROCK RABBIT, OCHOTONA PRINCEPS RICHARDSON (LAGOMORPHA: OCHOTONIDAE). William L. Jellison. Proc. Helminthol. Soc. Wash., vol.14, no. 2, pp.75-77, figs.3, July, 1947.

A NEW TRICHOSTRONGYLID NEMATODE FROM THE PIKA, OCHOTONA PRINCEPS FIGGINSI. Leland S. Olsen. American Midland Nat., Notre Dame, vol.39, no.3, pp.748-753, figs.9, May, 1948.

Taxonomy

ON THE TYPE-LOCALITY AND SYNONYMY OF OCHOTONA PUSILLA (PALLAS). J. L. Chaworth-Musters. Ann. and Mag. Nat. Hist. Lond., ser.10, vol.12, pp.137-138, July 1, 1933.

ON THE NAMES OF GEOGRAPHICAL FORMS OF OCHOTONA PALLASII GRAY. V. G. Heptner. Jour. Mam., vol.22, no. 3, pp.327-328, Aug.14, 1941.

A NEW NAME FOR OCHOTONA MINIMA. Wilfred H. Osgood. Proc. Biol. Soc. Wash., vol.26, p.80, Mar.22, 1913.

THE NAME OF OGOTONA. Oldfield Thomas. Proc. Biol. Soc. Wash., vol.14, p.24, Apr.2, 1901.

## Leporidae

Differentiation

(ON THE DIFFERENCE BETWEEN HARE AND RABBIT SKULLS.) Ueber den Unterschied zwischen Hasen-und Kaninchenschaedeln. J. F. van Bemmelen. Zool. Lab. Rijsuniver. Groningen, pp.1-134, figs. 107, 1909.

USE OF THE SCAPULA AS A MEANS OF DIFFERENTIATION BETWEEN THE MEARNS COTTON-TAIL AND THE AUSTRALIAN IMPORTED AND DOMESTIC HARE. Fred R. Glenny. Ohio Jour. Sci., Columbus, vol.51, no.5, pp.271-272, illus., Sept., 1951.

SEROLOGICAL DIFFERENCES BETWEEN THE DOMESTIC RABBIT, THE HARE AND THE AMAMI BLACK HARE. Kurasi Moribe. Dobutsugaku Zasshi (Zool. Soc. Japan, Tokyo), vol.40, no.480, pp.407-416, 1928.

Diseases and Parasites

THE COCCIDIA OF WILD RABBITS OF IOWA. I. TAXONOMY AND HOST-SPECIFICITY. Jose C. M. Carvalho. Iowa State Coll. Jour. Sci. 18 (1): 103-135, Oct., 1943.

THE OCCURRENCE OF THE MITE CHEYLETIELLA PARASITIVORAX (MEGNIN) IN NORTH AMERICA, WITH NOTES ON ITS SYNONYMY AND "PARASITIC" HABIT. Kenneth W. Cooper. Jour. Parasitol. Lancaster, vol.32, no.5, pp.480-482, Oct., 1946.

NOTES ON THE LUNGWORMS OF NORTH AMERICAN LEPORIDAE. Frans C. Goble, E. L. Cheatum. Jour. Parasitology 30 (2): 119-120, Apr., 1944.

RABBIT TICK POPULATIONS ON THE LAKE ALEXANDER AREA, 1931-1938. R. G. Green, others. Minn. Wildl. Dis. Invest., Nov., 1938: 80-86, Nov., 1938.

A TEN YEAR POPULATION STUDY OF THE RABBIT TICK HAEMAPHYSALIS LEPORIS PALUSTRIS. R. G. Green, C. A. Evans, C. L. Larson. Am. Jour. Hygiene 38 (3): 260-281, Nov., 1943.

SIPHONAPTERA: NOTES ON SYNONYMY OF NORTH AMERICAN SPECIES OF THE GENUS HOPLOPSYLLUS BAKER. Glen M. Kohls. Pub. Health Rep. 54 (45): 2019-2020, Nov.10, 1939.

SIPHONAPTERA. A STUDY OF THE SPECIES INFESTING WILD HARES AND RABBITS OF NORTH AMERICA NORTH OF MEXICO. Glen M. Kohls. U.S. Publ. Health Serv., bul.175, 26 pp., 1940.

SYPHILIS AS A DISEASE OF WILD RABBITS AND HARES. A. D. Middleton. Jour. Anim. Ecology, vol.1, no.1, pp.84-85, May, 1932.

A NEW LUNGWORM FROM THE LEPORIDAE PROTOSTRONGYLUS SYLVILAGI, N. SP. John W. Scott. Univ. Wyo. Pub. 10 (6): 57-71, July, 1943.

COTTONTAILS AND JACK RABBITS ON THE TURNPIKE. (CENSUS OF MAMMALS KILLED.) Dayton Stoner. Nature Notes, Peoria, vol.9, no.5, pp.50-51, Jan.-Feb., 1943.

STUDIES ON THE LIFE HISTORY OF THE ANOPLOCEPHALINE CESTODES OF HARES AND RABBITS. Horace W. Stunkard. Jour. Parasitology 27 (4): 299-315, Aug., 1941.

Ecology

COACTION OF JACK RABBIT, COTTONTAIL, AND VEGETATION IN A MIXED PRAIRIE. H. Leo Brown. Trans. Kansas Acad. Sci. 50 (1): 28-44, 1947.

BR'ER RABBIT'S WIDESPREAD FAMILY; THE NUMEROUS RABBITS AND HARES THAT DWELL IN SWAMP AND THICKET, ON PLAIN AND DESERT AND MOUNTAIN FROM TIERRA DEL FUEGO TO THE MOUTH OF THE MACKENZIE AND FROM THE ATLANTIC TO THE PACIFIC. Robert T. Hatt. Nat. Hist., vol.28, no.5, pp.477-485, 1928.

(RABBIT, ORYCTOLAGUS CUNICULUS LINNE 1758, AND HARE, LEPUS EUROPAEUS PALLAS 1778, AS MUSHROOM EATERS.) Kaninchen, Oryctolagus cuniculus (Linne, 1758) und Hasen, Lepus europaeus Pallas, 1778, als Pilzfresser. H. Kumerloeve. Saeugetierk. Mitteil., Stuttgart, 4 (3): 125-126, July 1, 1956.

SOME OBSERVATIONS OF THE FOOD COACTIONS OF RABBITS IN WESTERN KANSAS DURING PERIODS OF STRESS. Andrew Riegel. Trans. Kansas Acad. Sci. 45: 369-375, 1942.

ECOLOGIC NICHES OCCUPIED BY RABBITS IN EASTERN TEXAS. Walter P. Taylor, Daniel W. Lay. Ecology 25 (1): 120-121, Jan., 1944.

Economic Importance

STOCKING HARES AND RABBITS IN NEW JERSEY. Jock Francine. N. J. Outdoors 3 (8): 20, Feb., 1953.

UTILITY OF JACK RABBIT AND COTTONTAIL SKINS. Charles E. Kellogg. USDA, Misc. Pub.289, 7 pp., Nov., 1937.

Fossils

MYTONOLAGUS, A NEW LEPORINE GENUS FROM THE UINTA EOCENE SERIES IN UTAH. J. J. Burke. Ann. Carnegie Mus., vol.23, pp.399-420, 1 pl., Nov.19, 1934.

NEW FOSSIL LEPORIDAE FROM MONGOLIA. J. J. Burke. Amer. Mus. Novitates, New York, no.1117, pp.23, figs.9, June 5, 1941.

ALILEPUS, A NEW NAME TO REPLACE ALLOLAGUS DICE, PREOCCUPIED, AND NOTES ON SEVERAL SPECIES OF FOSSIL HARES. Lee R. Dice. Jour. Mam., vol. 12, no.2, pp.159-160, May, 1931.

A STUDY OF THE OLIGOCENE LEPORIDAE IN THE KANSAS UNIVERSITY MUSEUM OF VERTEBRATE PALEONTOLOGY. Morton Green. Trans. Kansas Acad. Sci., Topeka, vol.45, pp.229-247, pls.3, 1942.

NEKROLAGUS, NEW NAME FOR PEDIOLAGUS HIBBARD, NOT MARELLI. Claude W. Hibbard. Amer. Midland Nat., Notre Dame, vol.21, table of contents, p.(2), July, 1939.

A NEW MIOCENE LAGOMORPH (OREOLAGUS NEBRASCENSIS). Paul O. McGrew. Geol. Series Field Mus. Nat. Hist., Chicago, vol.8, no.6, pp.37-41, fig.14, Sept.20, 1941.

THE SKULL OF MEGALAGUS TURGIDUS (COPE). Everett Claire Olson. Amer. Jour. Sci., New Haven, vol.240, no.7, pp. 505-511, figs.2, July, 1942.

HYPOLAGUS FROM THE TEGELEN CLAY; WITH A NOTE ON RECENT NESOLAGUS. A. Schreuder. Archives Neerlandaises de Zool., Leiden, vol.2, nos.2-3, pp.225-239, figs.6, pl.2, Dec.21, 1936.

NOTE ON NORTH AMERICAN FOSSIL LAGOMORPHS. M. V. Walker. The

Aerend, Kansas State Teachers College Quarterly, Hays, vol.2, no.4, pp.227-240, pl.1, 1931.

A NEW GENUS OF LAGOMORPH FROM THE PLIOCENE OF MEXICO. (NOTOLAGUS N. VELOX.) Robert W. Wilson. Bull. Sou. California Acad. Sci., Los Angeles, vol.36, pt.3, pp.98-104, table, pl.43, Sept.-Dec., 1937.

Hybrids

THE HARE-RABBIT, A STUDY IN EVOLUTION BY HYBRIDIZATION. W. E. Castle. Amer. Nat., vol.59, no.662, pp.280-282, May-June, 1925.

(LEPORIDES.) Ueber Leporiden. A. L. Hagedoorn. Verhandl. des I. Internat. Kaninchenzuechter-Kongresses, Leipzig, 1930, pp.66-69, 1931.

ON THE ACTUAL EXISTENCE OF LEPORIDES. K. Kuiper. Genetica, vol.7, pp.471-474, 1926.

(DO LEPORIDES EXIST?) Gibt es Leporiden? H. Nachtsheim. Der Deutsche Pelztierzuechter, Muenchen, 8 Jahrgang, no.3, pp. 69-72, Feb.1, 1933.

(THE LEPORIDE PROBLEM.) Das Leporidenproblem. Hans Nachtsheim. Zeitschr. f. Zuechtung, Reihe B. Tierzuechtung und Zuechtungsbiologie einschliesslich Tierernahrung, Berlin, vol.33, no.3, pp.343-408, figs.17, tables 13, 1935.

ACCOUNT OF A HYBRID BETWEEN THE HARE AND THE RABBIT. R. Thursfield. Proc. Comm. Sci. and Corres. Zool. Soc. Lond., pt.1, p.66, 1830-1831.

North America

HARES AND RABBITS IN NORTH DAKOTA. Charles Hargrave, Leroy Shearey. North Dakota Outdoors, Bismarck, vol.13, no.8, pp.7-8, illus., Feb., 1951.

HARES AND RABBITS. William MacMillan. Canadian Nature, Toronto, vol.4, no.5, pp. 160-161, illus., Nov.-Dec., 1942.

COTTONTAILS, CANE CUTTERS, AND JACK--ALL IN ILLINOIS. Lee E. Yeager. Illinois Conservation, Springfield, vol.10, no.1, pp.7, 37, Winter Issue, 1945.

Taxonomy

A SYNOPSIS OF THE LEPORINE MAMMALS OF JAPAN. Yoshio Abe. Jour. Sci. Hiroshima Univ., Japan, ser.B, div.1, vol. 1, art.4, pp.45-63, pls.1-8, Mar., 1931.

SYNOPSIS OF THE AMERICAN LEPORIDAE. J. A. Allen. Proc. Boston Soc. Nat. Hist., vol.17, pp.430-436, Feb.17, 1875.

THE PHYLOGENY OF THE LEPORIDAE, WITH DESCRIPTION OF A NEW GENUS. Lee R. Dice. Jour. Mam., vol.10, no.4, pp.340-344, fig.1, Nov., 1929.

MORPHO-FUNCTIONAL ANALYSIS OF THE JAW APPARATUS IN LEPORIDAE. N. S. Lebedkina. Zool. Zhurnal Moscow, 36 (10): 1539-1556, 1957.

SYSTEMATICS AND NATURAL HISTORY OF CALIFORNIAN HARES AND RABBITS (FAMILY LEPORIDAE). Robert T. Orr. PhD thesis, Univ. Calif., 1937.

NOTES ON S. AMERICAN LEPORIDAE. Oldfield Thomas. Ann. and Mag. Nat. Hist. (8), vol.11, no.62, pp.209-214, Feb., 1913.

(Hares)

ON THE VARIABLE HARE. G. E. H. Barrett-Hamilton. Proc. Zool. Soc. Lond., pp.87-92, Feb.6, 1900.

THE GEOGRAPHICAL VARIATION OF THE GREENLAND HARES. Magnus Degerbol, F. Wimpffen Braestrup. Vidensk. Medd. fra Dansk naturh. Foren, vol.98, pp.197-206, figs.3, Dec.15, 1934.

LAST CRACK AT SNOWSHOES. Ben East. Field and Stream, New York, vol.49, no. 10, pp.30-32, 78-79, illus., Feb., 1945.

THOSE OF THE FOREST. Wallace B. Grange. Flambeau, 314 pp., 1953.

MARCH MADNESS. (VARYING HARE.) John Eric Hill. Nat. Hist. New York, vol. 51, no.3, p.135, illus., Mar., 1943.

THE ALPINE VARYING HARE. Gerrit S. Miller, Jr. Proc. Biol. Soc., Wash., vol.14, pp.97-98, June 27, 1901.

LEPUS HIBERNICUS. Robert Leslie Ogilby. Proc. Zool. Soc. Lond., pt.11, p.75, 1843.

ON BRINGING UP A HARE. D. R. Rosevear. Nigerian Field, vol.14, no.2, pp.41-47, pls. 4, Apr., 1949.

(LEPUS NIGRICOLLIS, THE BLACKNECKED HARE.) Lepus nigricollis, de Zwartnekhaas. H. J. V. Sody. De Tropische Natuur, Buitenzorg, Jrg.28, aft.10, pp.161-168, figs.3, 1939.

BIOLOGY OF THE VARIABLE HARE. V. G. Stakhrovskii. Zool. Zhurn., Moscow, vol. 11, no.2, pp.70-78, 1 fig., 1932.

NOTES ON THE ARCTIC HARE. Lawrence H. Walkinshaw. Jour. Mam., vol.28, no. 4, pp.353-357, pl.1, Nov.26, 1947.

Africa

(SOME BARBARY HARES.) Sobre algunas liebres berberiscas. Angel Cabrera. Bol. R. Soc. Espanola Hist. Nat., vol.23, pp. 329-333, July, 1923.

DISTRIBUTION OF LEPUS VICTORIAE VICTORIAE THOMAS. C. H. B. Grant. Ann. and Mag. Nat. Hist. (6) 12:268, 1893: Nassa, Speke Gulf, Southeastern Lake Victoria, Tanganyika Territory; Ann. and Mag. Nat. Hist., Lond., ser.11, vol.11, no.76, p.272, Apr., 1944.

(THE HARE OF THE LOWER CONGO.) Le lapin du Bas Congo. (Lepus ansorgei zairensis.) Robert T. Hatt. Rev. Zool. Bot. Afr., vol.26, no.4, pp.423-424, fig. 1, June 15, 1935.

A NEW HARE FROM BRITISH EAST AFRICA. Ned Hollister. Proc. Biol. Soc. Wash., vol.31, pp.35-36, May 16, 1918.

ON LEPUS SALAE, A NEW AFRICAN HARE. Fredericus A. Jentink. Notes, Leyden Mus., vol.2, no.11, pp.57-58, Feb., 1880.

ON A HITHERTO UNRECORDED SUBSPECIES OF SOUTH AFRICAN BUSH HARE (LEPUS SAXATILIS ORGANENSIS N. SUBSP.). F. F. Kolbe. Ann. Transvaal Mus., vol.21, pt.1, pp.71-72, Apr.6, 1948.

A NEW GENUS FOR THE UGANDA HARE (LEPUS MARJORITA). J. St. Leger. Proc. Zool. Soc. Lond., pp.119-123, figs.3, Mar. 30, 1932.

ON A REMARKABLE NEW HARE FROM CAPE COLONY. Oldfield Thomas. Ann. and Mag. Nat. Hist. (7), vol.11, no.61, pp.78-79, Jan., 1903.

Anatomy

MORPHOLOGICAL CHARACTERISTIC OF THE TRANSBAICALIAN HARE (LEPUS TOLAITOLAI PALL.). A. S. Fetisov. Bull. Soc. Nat. Moscow, sect. biol.n.s., vol.46, no.3, pp.145-154, 1937.

ABNORMAL TOOTH PATTERN IN THE LOWER DENTITION OF THE JACKRABBIT, LEPUS CALIFORNICUS (MEARNS). Claude W. Hibbard. Jour. Mam., vol.26, no.1, pp.64-65, fig.1, Feb., 1944.

WEIGHT AND LENGTH OF WHITE-TAILED JACKRABBITS IN BLUE EARTH COUNTY, MINNESOTA. Carl O. Mohr. Jour. Mam., vol.24, no.4, pp.504-506, Nov.17, 1943.

JACKRABBIT WEIGHT. Hunter Robertson. Hunting and Fishing in Canada, vol.13, no. 10, p.44, 1947.

(A CASE OF A DOUBLE GALL BLADDER IN LEPUS CUNICULUS.) Ein Fall von doppelter Gallenblase bei Lepus cuniculus. P. L. Stal, S. J. Ruizeveld. Anat. Anz., vol.69, nos.7-12, pp.210-213, 2 figs., 1930.

(THE PLACENTA OF THE FIELD HARE.) Die Placenta des Feldhasen. Fritz Strauss. Acta Anatomica, Basel, vol.30, pp.815-826, 1957.

(ANATOMY AND MECHANICS OF THE HARE FOOT.) Anatomie und Mechanic des Hasenfusses. Hans Virchow. Zeitsch. f. Saeugetierkunde, vol.3, pp.98-171, 5 pls., 10 figs., June 11, 1928.

Asia

BIOLOGICAL OBSERVATIONS ON THE TRANSBAIKAL TOLAI HARE LEPUS TOLAI TOLAI PALLAS. A. S. Fetisov. Izvestiia Vostochnosibirskogo Sel'skokhoziaistvennoge Instituta (Bull. Inst. Agric. East Siberia), vol.1, pp.138-148, 1935.

A NEW HARE FROM THE MOUNTAINS OF CHINA (LEPUS ARAHAMI). A. Brazier Howell. Proc. Biol. Soc. Wash., vol.41, pp.143-144, Oct.15, 1928.

NOTES ON SOME HARES IN THE INDIAN MUSEUM WITH DESCRIPTIONS OF TWO NEW FORMS. C. Boden Kloss. Records Indian Mus., Calcutta, vol.15, pt.2, no.10, pp.89-96, figs.1-13, Apr., 1918.

ON THE HARES OF NORTHERN MANCHURIA. Anatole S. Loukashkin. Jour. Mam., vol.24, no.1, pp.73-81, figs.2, pl. 1, Feb.20, 1943.

A NEW RACE OF HARE FROM THE PERSIAN FRONTIER OF MESOPOTAMIA. H. C. Robinson. Records Indian Mus., Calcutta, vol.15, pt.2, pp.49-50, figs.3, Apr., 1918.

DIAGNOSIS OF A NEW SUBSPECIES OF HARE FROM THE COREA. Oldfield Thomas. Ann. and Mag. Nat. Hist. (6), vol.9, no.50, pp.146-147, Feb., 1892.

A NEW ARABIAN HARE (LEPUS OMANENSIS CHEESMANI). Oldfield Thomas. Jour. Bombay Nat. Hist. Soc., vol.28, pp.28-29, Dec.30, 1921.

DESCRIPTION OF A NEW SPECIES OF HARE FROM TIBET. G. R. Waterhouse. Proc. Zool. Soc. Lond., pt.9, pp.7-8, 1841.

A NEW INDIAN HARE. R. C. Wroughton. Jour. Bombay Nat. Hist., vol.25, no.3, pp.361-362, Jan.15, 1918.

SCIENTIFIC RESULTS FROM THE MAMMAL SURVEY. XI. D. THE CEYLON HARE. R. C. Wroughton. Jour. Bombay Nat. Hist. Soc., vol.24, pp.41-42, Sept. 30, 1915.

A NEW SPECIES OF HARE FROM THE CENTRAL PROVINCES. R. C. Wroughton, Kathleen V. Ryley. Jour. Bombay Nat. Hist. Soc., vol.22, no.1, pp.15-16, Apr.21, 1913.

INDIAN HARES. Jour. Bomb. Nat. Hist. Soc., vol.18, p.673.

Diseases

A DESCRIPTION OF SHOCK DISEASE IN THE SNOWSHOE HARE. R. G. Green, C. L. Larson. Amer. Jour. Hygiene, vol. 28, no.2, pp.190-212, pl.1, Sept., 1938.

SHOCK DISEASE AND THE SNOWSHOE HARE CYCLE. R. G. Green, C. L. Larson. Science 87 (2257): 298-299, Apr.1, 1938.

SHOCK DISEASE OF WILD SNOWSHOE RABBITS. R. G. Green, C. L. Larson. Amer. Jour. Physiol., Memphis, vol.119, no.2, pp.319-320, June, 1937.

SHOCK DISEASE AS THE CAUSE OF THE PERIODIC DECIMATION OF THE SNOWSHOE HARE. R. G. Green, C. L. Larson, J. F. Bell. Amer. Jour. Hyg., Balto., vol. 30, no.3, sec.B, pp.83-102, figs.2, Nov., 1939.

THE NATURAL OCCURRENCE OF SHOCK DISEASE IN HARES. R. G. Green, C. L. Larson, D. W. Mather. Trans. Third North Amer. Wildlife Conference, 1938, Amer. Wildlife Inst., Wash., D.C., pp.877-881, 1938.

AN EXPERIMENT IN THE CONTROL OF DISEASE IN THE SNOW HARE. Teppo Lampio. Pap. Game Res. 8: 139-142, 1952.

EVIDENCE OF INFECTIOUS DISEASES AND PARASITES IN A PEAK POPULATION OF BLACK-TAILED JACK RABBITS IN NEVADA. Cornelius B. Philip, J. Frederick Bell, Carl L. Larson. Jour. Wildl. Mgt., 19 (2): 225-233, illus., Apr., 1955.

TULAREMIA. FIRST CASE TO BE REPORTED IN ALASKA. Ralph B. Williams. Pub. Health Rep. 61 (24): 875-876, June 14, 1946.

AN ANNUAL CYCLE IN THE DESERT BLACK-TAILED JACK-RABBIT. Angus M.

Woodbury. Symposium on ecology of disease transmission in native animals, Univ. Utah, pp.19-23, 1955.

Ecology

WHITE HARE. MATERIALS ON THE ECOLOGY AND CHASE OF THE WHITE HARE IN THE VOLGA-KAMA REGIONS. D. I. Aspisov. Volzhsko-Kamskaia Zonal' naia Okhotpomyslovaia Biologicheskaia Stantsiia Tsnib Soiuzzagotpushniny, Kazan, no.4, pp.1-179, 1936.

SNOWSHOE RABBITS AND CONIFERS IN THE WASATCH MOUNTAINS OF UTAH. F. S. Baker, C. F. Korstian, N. J. Fetherolf. Ecology, vol.2, pp.304-310, Oct., 1921 (Jan.20, 1922).

VARYING HARE AND FOREST SUCCESSION. David B. Cook, Stacy B. Robeson. Ecology 26 (4): 406-410, Oct., 1945.

A STUDY OF THE WINTER RELATIONSHIPS OF THE SNOWSHOE HARE, LEPUS AMERICANUS VIRGINIANUS HARLAN TO THE HARVARD FOREST. V. A. Gould. MF thesis, Harvard Univ., 1938.

DISTRIBUTION AND ECOLOGY OF THE HARES OF PAMIR (LEPUS TOLAI PAMIRENSIS BLANF.). R. Meklenbursev. Bull. Soc. Nat. Moscow, Sect. Biol., n.s., vol.49, nos.5-6, pp.43-46, 1940.

THE RELATION OF JACK RABBITS TO GRAZING IN SOUTHERN ARIZONA. Walter P. Taylor, Charles T. Vorhies, P. B. Lister. Jour. Forestry, vol.33, no.5, pp. 490-498, May, 1935.

THE DISSEMINATION OF PRICKLY PEAR SEED BY JACK RABBITS. F. L. Timmons. Jour. Amer. Soc. Agronomy, Geneva, N.Y., vol.34, no.6, pp.513-520, figs.2, June, 1942.

THE LIFE HISTORIES AND ECOLOGY OF JACK RABBITS, LEPUS ALLENI AND LEPUS CALIFORNICUS SSP., IN RELATION TO GRAZING IN ARIZONA. Charles T. Vorhies, Walter P. Taylor. Tech. Bull. 49, Univ. Arizona, College Agric., Agric. Exper. Station, Tucson, pp.471-587, figs.5, pls.12, May 31, 1933.

(Review by J. Grinnell and R. T. Orr, of) THE LIFE HISTORIES AND ECOLOGY OF JACK RABBITS, LEPUS ALLENI AND LEPUS CALIFORNICUS SSP., IN RELATION TO GRAZING IN ARIZONA. Charles T. Vorhies, Walter P. Taylor. Jour. Mam., Balto., vol.15, no.3, pp.259-260, Aug.10, 1934.

ECOLOGY OF THE GREAT SALT LAKE DESERT I. AN ANNUAL CYCLE OF THE DESERT JACKRABBIT. Angus M. Woodbury. Ecology, Durham, vol.36, no.2, pp.353-356, illus., Apr., 1955.

Economic Importance

THE SNOWSHOE HARE--A SERIOUS ENEMY OF FOREST PLANTATIONS. C. M. Aldous, Shaler E. Aldous. Jour. Forestry 42 (2): 88-94, Feb., 1944.

A REPELLENT PROTECTING FRUIT TREES AGAINST ATTACKS FROM HARES. Johs Andersen. Viltbiol. Sta. Denmark, Meddel, no.1, 1-12 pp., illus., Dec., 1950.

SNOWSHOE HARE USEFUL IN THINNING FOREST STANDS. W. T. Cox. Jour. Forestry 36 (11): 1107-1109, Nov., 1938.

COOPERATIVE SNOWSHOE HARE CONTROL PROJECT. Therman Deerwester. Wis. Cons. Bul. 6(4): 19-20, Apr., 1941.

(SNOW HARE FARMING.) Jaenistarhaus. Arne Krafft. Suomen Riista, Finnish Foundation for Game Preservation, Helsinki, no.5, pp.82-91, illus., 1950.

SNOWSHOE HARE DAMAGE TO A JACK PINE PLANTATION IN MINNESOTA. Laurits W. Krefting. U.S. For. Serv., Lake States Exp. Sta., Tech. Notes No.402, 1 p., July, 1953.

PLANTING PRACTICE TO REDUCE CROP DAMAGE BY JACKRABBITS. John H. Lewis. Jour. Wildl. Mgt. 10 (3): 277, July, 1946.

REPORT ON THE SNOWSHOE HARE REPELLENT AND POISON STUDIES CONDUCTED ON THE NICOLET NATIONAL FOREST IN 1941 AND 1942. Deane W. Mather, Robert H. Gensch, H. Allen Barton. U.S. Forest Service, Wash., D.C., 36 pp., illus., 1943.

THE JACK RABBIT NUISANCE. Samuel N. Rhoads. The American Friend, p.370, Apr.16, 1896.

THE JACK RABBIT NUISANCE. PART 2. Samuel N. Rhoads. The American Friend, pp.461-462, May 7, 1896.

THE JACK RABBIT NUISANCE. PART 3. Samuel N. Rhoads. The American Friend, pp.479-480, May 14, 1896.

THINNING OVERDENSE JACK PINE SEEDLING STANDS IN THE LAKE STATES. Eugene I. Roe, J. H. Stoeckeler. Jour. Forestry 48 (12): 861-865, Dec., 1950.

THE JACK RABBIT BRINGS MONEY TO NORTH DAKOTA. Stanley Saugstad. N. Dak. Agr. Exp. Sta., Bul. 1 (4): 8-10, Mar., 1939.

HARES AND REPELLENTS. Pertti Seiskari. Suomen Riista 9: 39-40, illus., 1954.

GAME MANAGEMENT IN ONTARIO. D. J. Taylor. Trans. N. A. Wildl. Conf., 7: 361-365, 1942.

(PRODUCTIVITY AND QUALITY OF HARE HARVESTS IN 1953.) Produktivitaet und Qualitaet der Hasenstrecken 1953. D. J. Tilgner. Z. Jagdwissensch., 1 (2): 75-77, 1955.

(HARE DAMAGE AND PROTECTION.) Harskador och harskyddsmedel. Bertil J. O. Wahlin. Svensk Jakt, Stockholm, vol.88, no.12, pp.306-308, illus., Dec., 1950.

SNOWSHOE HARE DAMAGE AND CONTROL. F. G. Wilson. Wis. Cons. Bul., 7 (12):4-7, Dec., 1942.

A METHOD FOR CONTROLLING THE DAMAGE TO ORCHARDS CAUSED BY THE FIELD HARE. Suomen Riista 8: 135, 1953.

SOUTH DAKOTA'S JACK RABBIT BUSINESS. Amer. Fur Breeder, Duluth, vol.14, no.11, p.24, May, 1942.

Europe

ALPINE HARE IN LANCS. Fred Allen. Naturalist London, no.857, p.168, June, 1928.

(DOCUMENTS OF LUCHON GEOLOGY. VII. DOES THE WHITE HARE OF THE PYRENEES CONSTITUTE A RELICT OF GLACIAL EPOCHS?) Documents de géologie Luchonnaise. VII. Le lièvre blanc constituet-il, aux Pyrénées, une relicte des epoques glaciares? Gaston Astre. Bull. Soc. d'Hist. Nat. Toulouse, vol.68, no.1, pp.387-398, Dec.30, 1935.

(WHITE HARE FROM THE PRAT-COMMUNAL (PYRENEES DE L'ARIEGE).) Lievre blanc de Prat-Communal (Pyrénées de l'Ariège). Gaston Astre. Mammalia, Paris, 10 (2): 94-96, June, 1946.

THE HARES OF CRETE AND OF CYPRUS. G. E. H. Barrett-Hamilton. Ann. and Mag. Nat. Hist., ser.7, vol.11, pp.126-127, Jan., 1903.

NOTES ON THE INTRODUCTION OF THE BROWN HARE INTO IRELAND. G. E. H. Barrett-Hamilton. Irish Nat., vol.7, no.3, pp.69-76, Mar., 1898.

THE HARE IN NORTH UIST. George Beveridge. Scottish Nat., no.208, p.94, July-Aug., 1934.

THE HARE IN THE ISLE OF MAN. H. E. Forrest. Irish Nat. Jour., vol.2, no.2, p. 44, Mar., 1928.

ALPINE HARE IN LANCASHIRE. R. Fortune. Naturalist London, no.859, pp. 235-236, Aug., 1928.

THE MOUNTAIN HARE IN ENGLAND AND WALES. R. Hewson. Naturalist, London, no.858, pp.107-109, July-Sept., 1956.

(STOCKING OF WILD ANIMALS: THE WOOD HARE.) Viltutplantering: Skogshare. Nils Hoglund. Svensk Jakt, Stockholm, vol. 89, no.1, pp.12-15, illus., Jan.20, 1951.

(OUR WILD ANIMAL: THE HARE.) Vart villebrad. Haren. Gustav Lundberg. Skogen, vol.16, no.5, pp.144-151, 8 figs., 1929.

A NEW HARE FROM GREECE. Gerrit S. Miller, Jr. Proc. Biol. Soc., Wash., vol. 16, pp.145-146, Nov.12, 1903.

TWO NEW FORMS OF THE SPANISH HARE. Gerrit S. Miller, Jr. Ann. and Mag. Nat. Hist., ser.7, vol.20, pp.398-401, Nov., 1907.

THE HARE IN THE ISLE OF MAN. C. B. Moffat. Irish Naturalists' Jour., vol.2, no.3, p.64, May, 1928.

THE IRISH HARE. C. B. Moffat. Irish Naturalists' Jour., vol.1, no.14, pp.271-273, Nov., 1927.

(THE HARE POPULATION OF THE GREIFSWALD ISLE.) Der Hasenbestand der Greifswalder Oie. Using D. Muller. Zeitschr. f. Saeugetierkunde, Berlin , vol.12, no.3, pp. 335-336, July 15, 1938.

(OBSERVATIONS OF A FIELD HARE LIVING IN A LARGE CITY.) Beobachtungen an einem Feldhasen in der Grosstadtwohnung. Walter Rammer. Zool. Garten, Leipzig, (N.F.), vol.20, nos.4-5, pp.282-293, 1954.

THE SPREAD OF THE MOUNTAIN HARE IN THE SCOTTISH LOWLANDS AND BORDER COUNTRY. James Ritchie. Scottish Nat., no.180, pp.169-175, 1929.

SOME NOTES ON THE EUROPEAN HARE. Stuart L. Thompson. Canadian Field-Nat., vol.45, no.8, pp.192-193, Nov., 1931.

(A NEW HARE RACE OF THE PELOPONNESUS.) Eine neue Hasenrasse vom Peloponnes. Otto V. Wettstein. Zool. Anz., Bd.143, heft 11-12, pp.282-284, Sept.30, 1943.

CHARACTERS OF THE IRISH HARE, A NEW SPECIES OF THE GENUS LEPUS, LINN. W. Yarrell. Proc. Zool. Soc. Lond., pt.1, p.88, 1833.

(FIELD HARE, LEPUS EUROPAEUS TRANSSYLVANICUS MATSCHIE 1901, IN AUSTRIA.) Der Feldhase, Lepus europaeus transsylvanicus Matschie, 1901, in Oesterreich. Karl Zalesky. Saeugetierk. Mitteil., Stuttgart, 3 (3): 108-110, July 1, 1955.

Food Habits

FOOD HABITS OF LEPUS AMERICANUS PHAEONOTUS. C. M. Aldous. Jour. Mam., vol.17, no.2, pp.175-176, May, 1936.

FORAGE REQUIREMENTS OF RANGE VEGETATION BY JACK RABBITS. J. F. Arnold. Ann. Rep. Ariz. Agr. Exp. Sta., 52: 45-46, 1942.

(ON THE QUESTION OF ANIMAL FOOD IN THE FIELD HARE, LEPUS EUROPAEUS PALLAS, 1778.) Zur Frage animalischer Nahrung beim Feldhasen, Lepus europaeus Pallas, 1778. Alfred Willy Boback. Saeugetierk. Mitteil., Stuttgart, 3 (4): 165-167, Oct.1, 1955.

REINGESTION IN THE BLACK-TAILED JACK RABBIT. R. R. Lechleitner. Jour. Mam., vol.38, no.4, pp.481-485, Nov., 1957.

WINTER FOOD HABITS OF THE WHITE HARE (LEPUS TIMIDUS LIN.) S. P. Naumov. Zool. Zhurn. (Zool. Jour. USSR), Moscow, vol.18, pp.1055-1062, 1939.

(DOES THE FIELD HARE, LEPUS EUROPAEUS, EAT ANIMAL FOOD?) Verzehrt der Feldhase, Lepus europaeus, tierische Nahrung? H. Petzsch. Saeugetierk. Mitteil., 5 (2): 74-75, Apr.1, 1957.

WINTER FOOD OF THE SNOW HARE IN FINLAND. Pertti Seiskara. Suomen Riista 9: 181-182, illus., 1954.

THE WHITE-TAILED JACK RABBIT EATS DANDELION STALKS. M. P. Skinner. Jour. Mam., vol.8, no.3, p.249, Aug., 1927.

REINGESTION IN THE HARE LEPUS EUROPAEUS PAL. J. S. Watson, R. H. Taylor. Science, Lancaster, vol.121, no. 3139, p.314, Feb.25, 1955.

THE SEASONAL FOOD HABITS OF THE SNOWSHOE HARE. Forest Res. Dig., May, 1935: 7, May, 1935.

WOODY FOOD PREFERENCES OF THE SNOWSHOE RABBIT IN THE LAKE STATES. USDA, Lake States Forest Exp. Sta., Tech. Note 109, 1 p., Jan., 1936.

Fossils

NOTES ON HYPOLAGUS BROWNI AND LEPUS BENJAMINI, FOSSIL HARES FROM THE PLEISTOCENE OF ARIZONA. Lee R. Dice. Michigan Acad. Sci. Arts Letters, Papers, vol.16, pp.379-382, figs.4, Mar., 1932.

SOME CHARACTERS OF THE SKULL AND SKELETON OF THE FOSSIL HARE, PALAEOLAGUS HAYDENI. Lee R. Dice. Papers Michigan Acad. Sci. Arts. and Letters, vol.18, pp.301-306, 3 figs., 2 pls., 1933.

THE LOWER CHEEK TEETH OF THE FOSSIL HARE PALAEOLAGUS HAYDENI. Lee R. Dice, Dora S. Dice. Papers Michigan Acad. Sci. Arts and Letters, Ann Arbor, vol.20, pp.455-463, figs.7, pl.93, June 24, 1935.

FOSSIL HARES FROM THE LATE PLIOCENE OF SOUTHERN IDAHO (HYPOLAGUS LIMNETUS, H. FURLONGI, AND ALILEPUS? VAGUS). C. Lewis Gazin. Proc. U.S. Nat. Mus., vol.83, no.2976, pp.111-121, figs.5, Nov.14, 1934.

General Habits and Behavior

DO MALE AND FEMALE HARES (LEPUS EUROPAEUS) BEHAVE DIFFERENTLY? Johs Andersen. Viltbiol. Sta. Denmark, Meddel. no.10, 1-8 pp., Apr., 1953.

ON THE MOVEMENTS OF MARKED EUROPEAN HARES (LEPUS EUROPAEUS) IN DENMARK. Johs. Andersen. Viltbiol. Sta. Denmark, Meddel, no.5, pp.1-7, illus., Aug., 1951.

OBSERVATIONS ON THE BEHAVIOUR OF THE EUROPEAN HARE WHEN PURSUED BY HOUNDS. William H. Bennett. Canadian Field-Nat., Ottawa, vol.53, no. 1, pp.6-7, Jan., 1939.

ACTIVITIES OF THE EUROPEAN HARE. R. Delamere Black, Jr. Canadian Field-Nat., vol.44, no.6, p.149, Sept.2, 1930.

(ON THE QUESTION OF "URINE SQUIRTING" IN THE FIELD HARE (LEPUS EUROPAEUS PALLAS, 1778) Zur Frage des "Harnspritzens" beim Feldhasen, Lepus europaeus Pallas, 1778. A. Boback. Saeugetierk. Mitteil., Stuttgart, vol.2, no.2, pp.78-79, Apr.1, 1954.

HARE VOLUNTARILY TAKING TO THE SEA. C. Bourlet. Field, London, vol. 152, p.492, Sept.27, 1928.

ARE HARES UNCLEAN ANIMALS? F. W. Champion. Jour. Bombay Nat. Hist. Soc., vol.39, no.1, pp.163-164, Dec.1, 1936.

JACK RABBIT AS A SPRINTER. Harold J. Cook. Nature Mag., vol.9, p.176, illus., Mar., 1927.

MIGRATIONS OF THE WASHINGTON BLACK-TAILED JACK RABBIT. Leo K. Couch. Jour. Mam., vol.8, no.4, pp.313-314, Nov., 1927.

SNOWSHOE RABBIT MIGRATION, TICK INFESTATION, AND WEATHER CYCLES. W. T. Cox. Jour. Mam., vol.17, no.3, pp.216-221, Aug., 1936.

A STUDY OF THE SNOWSHOE RABBIT. Stuart Criddle. Canadian Field-Nat., vol.52, no.3, pp.31-40, Mar., 1938.

THE JEEPY JACKRABBIT. THE FACTS ALMOST VIE WITH THE AMAZING FOLKLORE THAT HAS GROWN UP ABOUT THIS "LEAN, LANKY SON OF DESERT SAGE." Frank J. Dobie. Nat. Hist., New York, vol.51, no.1, pp.40-45, illus., Jan., 1943.

WHEN ANIMALS SLEEP (SNOWSHOE HARE). Henry H. Graham. Our Dumb Animals, Boston, vol.78, no.11, p.209, Nov., 1945.

OBSERVATIONS ON THE SNOWSHOE HARE, LEPUS AMERICANUS PHAEONOTUS ALLEN. Wallace B. Grange. Jour. Mam., vol.13, no.1, pp.1-9, pls.2, Feb., 1932.

GLIMPSES OF THE SNOWSHOE RABBIT. R. G. Green. Cons. Volunteer 4 (19): 44-49, Apr., 1942.

SNOWSHOES IN WINTER. Tappan Gregory. Jour. Mam., vol.10, no.4, pp.290-293, pls.2, Nov., 1929.

DISLIKE OF WATER BY THE CALIFORNIA JACK RABBIT. Albert C. Hawbecker. Jour. Mam., vol.23, no.1, pp.98-99, Feb. 14, 1942.

STUDIES ON THE MOBILITY OF THE WHITE-TAILED JACKRABBIT, LEPUS TOWNSENDII CAMPANIUS HOLLISTER. Wilber Henry. MS thesis, Iowa State Coll., 1942.

AQUATIC ACTIVITY OF A SNOWSHOE HARE. George S. Hunt. Jour. Mam., vol.31, no.2, pp.193-194, May 25, 1950.

THE JACK AND SNOWSHOE RABBITS AS SWIMMERS. Charles Eugene Johnson. Jour. Mam., vol.6, no.4, pp.245-249, Nov., 1925.

EVIDENCE OF ORIENTATION AND HOMING IN SNOWSHOE HARES. L. B. Keith, J. D. Waring. Canadian Jour. Zool., 34 (6): 579-581, Dec., 1956.

STUDIES ON THE WINTER HABITAT PREFERENCES OF THE SNOW HARE, LEPUS TIMIDUS L. Junka Koskimies. Arch. Soc. Zool. Bot. Fennicae "Vanamo", vol.12, no.1, pp.29-37, 1957.

PETEY, THE JACK RABBIT. HABITS OF A CAPTIVE YOUNG. Edna Maslowski. Fauna, Phila., vol.5, no.1, pp.18-19, illus., Mar., 1943.

(ON THE TIP-TOE GAIT OF THE FIELD HARE LEPUS EUROPAEUS PALLAS, 1778.) Ueber den Zehenspitzengang des Feldhasen , Lepus europaeus Pallas, 1778.

HARES GOING TO GROUND. R. Pack-Beresford. Irish Naturalists' Jour., vol. 2, no.5, p. 104, Sept., 1928.

NOTES ON THE SNOWSHOE RABBIT. J. Dewey Soper. Jour. Mam., vol.2, no.2, pp.101-108, May, 1921.

(INTELLIGENCE OR INSTINCT IN THE HARE.) Intelligence ou instinct chez le Lievre. Jean Tenaille. Mammalia, Paris, 5 (3-4): 101-102, 1 fig., Sept.-Dec., 1941.

SPEED OF THE VARYING HARE. J. Kenneth Terres. Jour. Mam., vol.22, no. 4, pp.453-454, Nov.14, 1941.

Hunting and Trapping

JACKS IN JUNE. SHOOTING JACK RABBITS IN OKLAHOMA. Howard Brisco. Outdoor Life, New York, vol.101, no.4, pp.30-31, 142-143, illus., Apr., 1948.

THE GAMEY JACK. Jim Chapman. Rod and Gun in Canada, Ottawa, vol.50, no.5, pp.12, 34, illus., Oct., 1948.

JACKS ARE BIG GAME! Louis Corbeau. N. Dak. Outdoors 14 (11): 10-11, illus., May, 1952.

A BETTER SNOWSHOE HARE LIVE TRAP. Wilbur L. Libby. Jour. Wildlife Mgt., 21 (4): 452, Oct., 1957.

NEW GAME ANIMAL FOR KENTUCKY HAS BEEN PLANTED. Robert H. Myers. Ky. Happy Hunting Ground 8 (4): 16, 30, illus., July, 1952.

HUNTING ANTELOPE JACKS. A. N. Pack. Nature Mag., vol.6, pp.110-112, 5 figs., Aug., 1925.

Mexico and Central America

A NEW JACK RABBIT FROM WESTERN MEXICO. Outram Bangs. Proc. New England Zool. Club, vol.1, pp.85-86, Feb.23, 1900.

AN UNDESCRIBED JACK-RABBIT, GENUS LEPUS, FROM CARMEN ISLAND, GULF OF CALIFORNIA, MEXICO. William H. Burt. Proc. Biol. Soc. Wash., vol.46, pp. 37-38, Feb.20, 1933.

THE HARES (GENUS LEPUS) OF THE MEXICAN BORDER. Edgar A. Mearns. Science, n.s., vol.1, no.24, pp.698-699, June 21, 1895.

DESCRIPTION OF A NEW JACK-RABBIT FROM SAN PEDRO MARTIR MOUNTAIN, LOWER CALIFORNIA. John M. Stowell. California Acad. Sci., 2nd ser., vol.5, pp. 51-52, pls.3, May 28, 1895.

North America

NOTES ON THE LIFE HISTORY OF THE SNOWSHOE HARE. C. M. Aldous. Jour. Mam., 18 (1): 46-57, Feb., 1937.

EUROPEAN HARE INTRODUCED INTO THE DISTRICT OF THUNDER BAY, ONTARIO. A. E. Allin. Canadian Field-Nat., Ottawa, vol.64, no.3, pp.122-124, May-June, 1950.

FURTHER NOTES ON THE EUROPEAN HARE IN ONTARIO. R. M. Anderson. Canadian Field-Nat., vol.37, pp.75-76, Apr., 1923.

THE EUROPEAN HARE, A NEW MAMMAL FOR TORONTO. Jas. L. Baillie, Jr. Canadian Field-Nat., vol.43, p.64, Mar., 1929.

EUROPEAN HARE AT COLLINGWOOD. Jas. L. Baillie, Jr. Canadian Field-Nat., vol.42, p.179, Oct.1, 1928.

THE GEOGRAPHICAL DISTRIBUTION OF THE EASTERN RACES OF THE COTTONTAIL (LEPUS SYLVATICUS BACH) WITH A DESCRIPTION OF A NEW SUBSPECIES AND WITH NOTES ON THE DISTRIBUTION OF THE NORTHERN HARE (LEPUS AMERICANUS ERXL.) IN THE EAST. Outram Bangs. Proc. Boston Soc., Nat. Hist., vol.26, pp.404-414, Jan.31, 1895.

MINNESOTA VARYING HARE--SNOWSHOE HARE (LEPUS AMERICANUS PHAEONOTUS). N. R. Barger. Wisconsin Conserv., Madison, vol.13, no.9, pp.24-25, illus., Sept., 1948.

WHITE-TAILED JACK RABBIT (LEPUS TOWNSENDI CAMPANIUS). N. R. Barger. Wisconsin Conserv. Bull., Madison, vol. 14, no.4, p.39, Apr., 1939.

SPEED KING OF THE PRAIRIES (JACK-RABBIT). Bennie Bengston. Volunteer, St. Paul, vol.11, no.66, pp.33-36, Sept.-Oct., 1948.

AN ISOLATED POPULATION OF THE VIRGINIA VARYING HARE. Maurice Brooks. Jour. Wildlife Management, Ithaca, vol.19, no.1, pp.54-61, Jan., 1955.

THE DISTRIBUTION OF THE WHITE-TAILED JACK RABBIT (LEPUS TOWNSENDII CAMPANIUS HOLLISTER) IN KANSAS. Leo Brown. Trans. Kansas Acad. Sci., Topeka, vol.43, pp.385-389, 1940.

JACK RABBITS OF EASTERN COLORADO. W. L. Burnett, Sam C. McCampbell. State Entomologist, Colorado Agric. Coll., circ.52, 18 pp., Nov., 1926.

A STUDY IN JACKRABBIT SHIFTS IN RANGE IN WESTERN KANSAS. F. L. Carter. Trans. Kansas Acad. Sci., Topeka, vol.42, pp.431-435, maps 4, tables, 1939.

GHOST RABBITS. (REINTRODUCTION OF SNOWSHOE HARES.) Floyd B. Chapman. Ohio Cons. Bull., 17 (7): 6-7, 32, illus., July, 1953.

THE SNOWSHOE RABBIT ENQUIRY, 1935-36. Dennis Chitty, Charles Elton. Canadian Field-Nat., vol.51, no.5, pp.63-73, figs.1-3, May, 1937.

THE SNOWSHOE RABBIT ENQUIRY, 1936-37. Dennis Chitty, Charles Elton. Canadian Field-Nat., vol.52, no.5, pp.63-72, figs.1-3, May, 1938.

THE SNOWSHOE RABBIT ENQUIRY 1937-38. Dennis Chitty, Charles Elton. Canadian Field-Nat., Ottawa, vol.53, no.5, pp. 63-70, figs.2, tables 2, May, 1939.

THE SNOWSHOE RABBIT ENQUIRY 1938-39. Dennis Chitty, Charles Elton. Canadian Field-Nat., Ottawa, vol.54, no.8, pp. 117-124, figs.2, Nov., 1940.

THE SNOWSHOE RABBIT ENQUIRY, 1939-40. Dennis Chitty, Helen Chitty. Canadian Field-Nat., Ottawa, vol.56, no.2, pp. 17-21, fig.1, Feb., 1942.

THE SNOWSHOE RABBIT ENQUIRY, 1940-41. Dennis Chitty, Mary Nicholson. Canadian Field-Nat., 57 (4-5): 64-68, Apr.-May, 1943.

THE SNOWSHOE RABBIT ENQUIRY, 1941-42. Helen Chitty. Canadian Field-Nat., Sutton West, vol.57, nos.7, 8, pp.136-141, maps 3, Oct.-Nov., 1943.

THE SNOWSHOE RABBIT ENQUIRY, 1942-43. Helen Chitty. Canadian Field-Nat., Sutton West, vol.60, no.3, pp.67-70, figs. 2, May-June, 1946.

THE SNOWSHOE RABBIT ENQUIRY, 1943-46. Helen Chitty. Jour. Animal Ecol., London, vol.17, no.1, pp.39-44, May, 1948.

THE SNOWSHOE RABBIT ENQUIRY, 1946-48. Helen Chitty. Jour. Animal Ecol., London, vol.19, no.1, pp.15-20, May, 1950.

WHITE-TAILED JACK RABBIT IN WASHINGTON. C. Wesley Clanton, Murray L. Johnson. Murrelet 35 (1): 15, Jan.-Apr., 1954.

NOTES ON THE HARES OF BRITISH COLUMBIA WITH THE DESCRIPTION OF A NEW RACE. Ian McT. Cowan. Jour. Mam., vol.19, no.2, pp.240-243, May 14, 1938.

VARIATION IN NORTHWESTERN SNOWSHOE HARES. Walter W. Dalquest. MS thesis, Univ. Wash., 1941; Jour. Mam., vol.23, no.2, pp.166-183, figs.2, May 14, 1942.

SNOWSHOE RABBITS. Joseph Dell. New York State Conservationist, Albany, vol.3, no.4, p.29, illus., Feb.-Mar., 1939.

SNOWSHOE RABBITS. NEW HOMES FOR DISPLACED ANIMALS. Jospeh Dell. New York State Conservationist, 7 (3): 23, illus., Dec.-Jan., 1952-1953.

THE PRESENT RANGE OF THE EUROPEAN HARE IN ONTARIO. J. R. Dymond. Canadian Field-Nat., vol.42, p.95, Apr., 1928.

THE SPREAD OF THE EUROPEAN HARE IN ONTARIO. J. R. Dymond. Roy. Ontario Mus. Zool., bull.no.2, pp.9-11, Jan., 1929.

THE WHITE-TAILED JACK RABBIT IN MANITOBA. J. R. Dymond. Canadian Field-Nat., vol.48, no.6, p.103, Sept., 1934.

THE CANADIAN SNOWSHOE RABBIT ENQUIRY, 1931-32. Charles Elton. The Canadian Field-Nat., vol.47, no.4, pp. 63-69, Apr., 1933; vol.47, no.5, pp.84-86, May, 1933.

THE CANADIAN SNOWSHOE RABBIT ENQUIRY, 1932-33. Charles Elton. Canadian Field-Nat., vol.48, no.5, pp.73-78, figs. 1-3, May, 1934.

THE CANADIAN SNOWSHOE RABBIT ENQUIRY, 1933-34. Charles Elton, G. Swynnerton. Canadian Field-Nat., vol.49, no.5, pp.79-85, figs.3, May, 1935.

THE CANADIAN SNOWSHOE RABBIT ENQUIRY, 1934-35. Charles Elton, G. Swynnerton. Canadian Field-Nat., vol.50, no.5, pp.71-81, figs.4, May, 1936.

NOTES ON THE CATSKILL HARE. Arthur B. Flick. New York State Conservationist, Albany, vol.10, no.3, pp.20-22, illus., Jan., 1956.

THE SIERRA WHITE-TAILED JACKRABBIT. Walter Fry. Calif. Fish and Game, vol.10, pp.172-175, Oct., 1924.

A NEW BLACK-TAILED JACK-RABBIT FROM IDAHO (LEPUS CALIFORNICUS DEPRESSUS). E. Raymond Hall, Wayne B. Whitlow. Proc. Biol. Soc. Wash., vol.45, pp.71-72, Apr.2, 1932.

A NEW HARE (LEPUS ARCTICUS) FROM NORTHERN CANADA. Charles O. Handley, Jr. Proc. Biol. Soc. Wash., vol. 65, pp.199-200, Nov.5, 1952.

A NEW SPECIES OF HARE FROM THE SUMMIT OF WIND RIVER MOUNTAINS. F. V. Hayden. Amer. Nat., pp.1-4, May, 1869.

NATURE'S TURNCOAT (SNOWSHOE HARE). Earl L. Hilfiker. Canadian Nature, Toronto, vol.18, no.1, pp.10-13, illus., Feb., 1956.

A SPECIMEN OF THE WHITE-TAILED JACK RABBIT, LEPUS TOWNSENDII, FROM ILLINOIS. Donald F. Hoffmeister, Lee G. Grebner. Nat. Hist. Miscellanea, Chicago, no.29, pp.1-2, Oct.15, 1948.

A PAIR OF JACKS. J. W. Jackson. Nature Mag., Wash., vol.38, no.9, p.480, illus., Nov., 1946.

PRAIRIE DWELLERS OF THE MIDDLE BORDER (JACK-RABBIT). Wallace R. Labisky. Fur-Fish-Game, Harding's Mag., Columbus, vol.79, no.5, pp.26-27, May, 1945.

SUMMARY OF THE DISSERTATION, "THE BLACK-TAILED JACK RABBIT ON THE GRAY LODGE WATERFOWL AREA, CALIF." Robert R. Lechleitner. Univ. Calif., 1 page, 1956.

THE DISTRIBUTION OF WISCONSIN HARES. Aldo Leopold. Trans Wis. Acad. Sci., Arts and Letters 37: 1-14, 1947.

THE LATE NORMAN CRIDDLE'S RECORD OF THE SNOWSHOE RABBIT (LEPUS AMERICANUS) AT AWEME, MANITOBA. Hoyes Lloyd. Canadian Field-Nat., 50 (8): 129-130, Nov., 1936.

THE VARYING HARE, OR SNOWSHOE RABBIT, IN MARYLAND. Romeo Mansueti. Md. Nat., 23 (1-2): 71-75, illus., 1953.

AMERICAN POLAR HARES: A REPLY TO MR. RHOADS. C. Hart Merriam. Science, n.s., Lancaster, vol.3, no.75, p.845, June 5, 1896.

JACK RABBITS OF THE LEPUS CAMPESTRIS GROUP. C. Hart Merriam. Proc. Biol. Soc. Wash., vol.17, pp.131-134, July 14, 1904.

UNRECOGNIZED JACK RABBITS OF THE LEPUS TEXIANUS GROUP. C. Hart Merriam. Proc. Biol. Soc. Wash., vol. 17, pp.135-138, July 14, 1904.

A NEW POLAR HARE FROM LABRADOR. Gerrit S. Miller, Jr. Proc. Biol. Soc. Wash., vol.13, pp.39-40, May 29, 1899.

NEW SUBSPECIES OF THE AMERICAN ARCTIC HARE. E. W. Nelson. Proc. Biol. Soc. Wash., vol.47, pp.83-86, Mar. 8, 1934.

DESCRIPTION OF A NEW SNOWSHOE RABBIT FROM EASTERN OREGON, WITH NOTES ON ITS LIFE HISTORY. Robert T. Orr. Jour. Mam., Balto., vol.15, no.2, pp.152-154, May 15, 1934.

A NEW RACE OF SNOWSHOE RABBIT FROM CALIFORNIA. Robert T. Orr. Jour. Mam., Balto., vol.14, no.1, pp.54-56, Feb.14, 1933.

THE JACK RABBITS OF THE UNITED STATES. T. S. Palmer. Div. Ornithology and Mammalogy, U.S. Dept. Agric., bull. no.8, pp.84, pls.7, Mar.18, 1896.

THE JACK RABBITS OF THE UNITED STATES. T. S. Palmer. U. S. Dept. Agric., Div. Biol. Surv., bull. no.8, pp. 5-88, revised, figs.3, pls.7, Dec.28, 1897.

NOTES ON THE VARYING HARES OF WASHINGTON AND BRITISH COLUMBIA WITH DESCRIPTION OF A NEW SUBSPECIES. Samuel N. Rhoads. Proc. Acad. Nat. Sciences, Phila., pp.241-243, July 2, 1895.

THE POLAR HARES OF EASTERN NORTH AMERICA, WITH DESCRIPTIONS OF NEW FORMS. Samuel N. Rhoads. Amer. Nat., pp.251-256, Feb.20, 1896.

(Review by C. Hart Merriam of) THE POLAR HARES OF EASTERN NORTH AMERICA, WITH DESCRIPTIONS OF NEW FORMS. Samuel N. Rhoads. Science, n.s., vol.3, no.67, pp.564-565, Apr.10, 1896.

THE POLAR HARES OF EASTERN NORTH AMERICA. AN ANSWER TO DR. C. H. MERRIAM'S CRITICISMS. Samuel N. Rhoads. Science, n.s., vol.3, no.75, pp. 843-845, June 5, 1896.

THE LIFE HISTORY AND ARTIFICIAL PROPAGATION OF THE SNOWSHOE HARE, LEPUS AMERICANUS STRUTHOPUS BANGS. J. H. Severaid. MS thesis, Univ. Maine, 1941.

THE SNOWSHOE HARE, ITS LIFE HISTORY AND ARTIFICIAL PROPAGATION. J. H. Severaid. Maine Dept. Inland Fisheries and Game, 95 pp., 1942.

THE EUROPEAN HARE (LEPUS EUROPAEUS PALLAS) IN NORTH AMERICA. James Silver. Jour. Agric. Research, vol.28, no. 11, pp.1133-1137, June 14, 1924.

THE EUROPEAN HARE IN NEW YORK. Fred Streever. New York State Cons., 1 (4): 11, 29, Feb.-Mar., 1947.

PRAIRIE JACK (WHITE-TAILED JACK-RABBIT (LEPUS TOWNSENDII), C. ALBERTA). Kerry Wood. Fauna, Phila., vol.6, no.2, pp.42-47, illus., June, 1944.

ANOTHER INVASION OF CANADA (LEPUS EUROPAEUS IN ONTARIO). Canadian Field-Nat., vol.39, pp.158-160, Oct., 1925.

WHITE-TAILED JACK RABBIT, LEPUS TOWNSENDII CAMPANIUS. Wyoming Wild Life, Cheyenne, vol.5, no.11, pp. 6-14, Nov., 1940.

Parasites

RINGWORM IN A POPULATION OF SNOWSHOE HARES. Lowell Adams, S. B. Salvin, W. J. Hadlow. Jour. Mam., 37 (10): 94-99, illus., Feb.28, 1956.

(THE HARE AND PULMONARY WORM DISEASE.) Haren och lungmasksjukan. K. Borg. Svensk Jakt. Stockholm, vol.89, no. 2, pp.56-57, illus., Feb.15, 1951.

THE INFLUENCE OF HELMINTH PARASITISM ON THE ABUNDANCE OF THE SNOWSHOE RABBIT IN WESTERN CANADA. R. V. Boughton. Canadian Jour. Research, vol. 7, no.5, pp.524-547, illus., Nov., 1932.

MALIGNANT NEOPLASMS IN VARYING HARES (LEPUS AMERICANUS VIRGINIANUS). E. L. Cheatum, Henry Bunting. Cornell Vet. 41 (2): 136-140, Apr., 1951.

HELMINTH INFECTIONS IN RELATION TO POPULATION FLUCTUATIONS IN SNOWSHOE HARES. Arnold B. Erickson. Jour. Wildl. Mgt., 8(2): 134-153, Apr., 1944.

HELMINTH INFECTIONS IN SNOWSHOE HARES AND THEIR RELATION TO FLUCTUATIONS OF HARE POPULATIONS. Arnold B. Erickson. PhD thesis, Univ. Minn., 1942.

WORMS, CYCLES, AND SNOWSHOE HARES. Arnold B. Erickson. Cons. Volunteer 8 (48): 40-44, Sept.-Oct., 1945.

NOTES ON THE LUNG-WORMS (GENUS PROTOSTRONGYLUS) OF VARYING HARES (LEPUS AMERICANUS) IN EASTERN NORTH AMERICA. Frans C. Goble, Ellsworth C. Dougherty. Jour. Parasitology 29 (6): 397-404, Dec., 1943.

VECTORS, TRANSMISSION, DEVELOPMENT, AND INCIDENCE OF DIROFILARIA SCAPICEPS (LEIDY, 1886) (NEMATODA) FROM THE SNOWSHOE HARE IN MINNESOTA. Paul R. Highby. Jour. Parasitology 29 (4): 253-259, Aug., 1943.

INVESTIGATIONS ON THE LUNG-WORM DISEASE OF THE HARE. G. Lahermaa. Papers on Game Res. 6: 47-59, 1951.

THE LUNG-WORM DISEASE OF THE HARE. G. Lahermaa. Suomen Riista 7: 93-119, illus., 1952.

ON THE OCCURRENCE OF THE BLADDER-WORM (CYSTICERCUS PISIFORMIS) IN FINLAND. Teppo L'ampio. Papers on Game Res. 6: 32-39, 1951.

PARASITES OF THE SNOWSHOE HARE. J. Manweiler. Jour. Mam., vol.19, no.3, p.379, Aug., 1938.

PARASITIC INVASIONS OF LEPUS TIMIDUS L. AND THEIR DEPENDENCY ON LOCAL

CONDITIONS. S. P. Naunov. Proc. Moscou Zool. Park, vol.1, p.201, 1940.

DIROFILARIA SCAPICEPS FROM SNOW-SHOE HARE IN CONNECTICUT. Lawrence R. Penner. Jour. Mam., vol.35, no.3, pp.458-459, Aug.20, 1954.

A PARASITOLOGICAL RECONNAISSANCE IN ALASKA WITH PARTICULAR REFERENCE TO VARYING HARES. I. SOME BIOLOGICAL CONSIDERATIONS. Cornelius B. Philip. Jour. Mam., 20 (1): 82-86, Feb., 1939.

A PARASITOLOGICAL RECONNAISSANCE IN ALASKA WITH PARTICULAR REFERENCE TO VARYING HARES. II. PARASITOLOGICAL DATA. Cornelius B. Philip. Jour. Parasitology 24 (6): 483-488, Dec., 1938.

Pelage, Coloration

A MELANISTIC SNOWSHOE HARE FROM MAINE. C. M. Aldous. Jour. Heredity, Wash., D.C., vol.30, no.1, pp.25-26, Jan., 1939.

ON THE SEASONAL CHANGE OF COLOR IN THE VARYING HARE (LEPUS AMERICANUS ERXL.). J. A. Allen. Bull. Amer. Mus. Nat. Hist., vol.6, pp.107-128, Apr. 14, 1894.

BUFF COLORED COMMON HARE. C. W. Badger. Scottish Nat., no.147, p.68, May-June, 1924.

(THE ALPINE HARE WITH BLUE EARS AND BROWN BACK (LEPUS CYANOTUS NOV. SPEC.).) Le lièvre a oreilles bleues et a dos brun, des Alpes (Lepus cyanotus nov. spec.). Claude Blanchard. Les cahiers de Chasse et de Nature, Paris, fasc.30, pp.7-38, illus., 1957.

(EXTERNAL DIFFERENTIATING CHARACTERS, IN PARTICULAR THOSE OF THE HAIR OF THE SWISS FIELD AND ALPINE HARE (LEPUS EUROPAEUS PALL. AND LEPUS VARRONIS MILLER).) Aussere Unterscheidungsmerkmale, insbesondere solche des Haarkleides der schweizerischen Feld-und Alpenhasen (Lepus europaeus Pall., und Lepus varronis Miller). Hans Bodmer-Giger. Zeitschrift fuer induktive Abstammungs-und Vererbungslehre, vol. 35, pp.1-105, 5 pls., 1924.

SNOWSHOE HARE--TURNCOAT OF THE SNOW LANDS. G. W. Bradt. Mich. Cons. 16 (1): 4, Jan., 1947.

(THE COAT OF THE ALPINE SNOW HARE.) Das Haarkleid Des Alpenschneehasen. M. Couturier. Z. Jagdwissensch. 1(1): 8-21, illus., 1955.

MELANISM IN A MOUNTAIN HARE. A. Bryce Duncan. Scottish Nat., no.167, p. 132, Sept-Oct., 1927.

MELANISM IN THE VARYING HARE, LEPUS AMERICANUS VIRGINIANUS. David C. Gordon. Jour. Mam., vol.35, no.1, p.122, Feb.10, 1954.

THE PELAGES AND COLOR CHANGES OF THE SNOWSHOE HARE, LEPUS AMERICANUS PHAEONOTUS, ALLEN. Wallace B. Grange. Jour. Mam., vol.13, no.2, pp.99-116, pls.6-8, May, 1932.

COLOR CHANGES IN LEPUS AMERICANUS AND OTHER MAMMALS. S. Hadwen. Canadian Jour. Research, Ottawa, vol.1, no.2, pp.189-200, pls.4-8, July, 1929.

COLOUR CHANGES IN SNOWSHOE HARES. S. Hadwen. Canadian Jour. Research, vol. 10, pp.539-556, 1934.

A RECENT RECORD OF AN ALBINO TEXAS JACK RABBIT. Cecil A. Kennedy. Jour. Mam., Balto., vol.30, no.2, p.202, May 23, 1949.

CONTROL OF COAT COLOR IN THE VARYING HARE BY DAILY ILLUMINATION. C. P. Lyman. Proc. New Eng. Zool. Club, 19:75-8, 1942.

CONTROL OF COAT COLOR IN THE VARYING HARE LEPUS AMERICANUS ERXLEBEN. C. P. Lyman. Bull. Mus. Comp. Zool., Cambridge, vol.93, no.3, pp.393-461, pls.1-11, Dec., 1943.

(CONTRIBUTIONS TO KNOWLEDGE OF HAIR COVER OF SOLES IN LAGOMORPHA.) Beitraege zur Kenntnis der Fussohlenbehaarung bei den Lagomorpha. Isolde Meyer. Zool. Anzeiger, Leipzig, 160 (1-2): 7-20, Jan., 1958.

BLACK MOUNTAIN HARES. M. Portal. Field, London, vol.162, no.4218, p.1101, Oct.28, 1933.

CHINCHILLA MUTATION IN THE WILD HARE. R. Prawochenski. Jour. Heredity, vol.26, no.4, pp.145-146, figs.9, Apr., 1935.

WINTER EXAMPLE OF BLACK VARIETY OF MOUNTAIN HARE. James Ritchie. Scottish Nat., nos.139-140, p.125, July-Aug., 1923.

PELAGE CHANGES IN THE SNOWSHOE HARE (LEPUS AMERICANUS STRUTHOPUS BANGS). Joye Harold Severaid. Jour. Mam., vol.26, no.1, pp.41-63, figs.16, Feb.23, 1945.

THE VARYING HARE (LEPUS AMERICANUS VIRGINIANUS) IN CHANGING PELAGE. Wendell P. Smith. Jour. Mam., vol.14, no.1, p.77, Feb., 1933.

OBSERVATIONS ON LEPUS AMERICANUS, ESPECIALLY WITH REFERENCE TO THE MODIFICATIONS IN THE FUR CONSEQUENT ON THE ROTATION OF THE SEASONS, AND THE CHANGE OF COLOR ON THE ADVENT OF WINTER; BASED ON SPECIMENS OBTAINED IN THE PROVINCE OF NEW BRUNSWICK, NORTH AMERICA. Francis H. Welch. Proc. Zool. Soc. London, pp.228-236, figs.3, 1869.

ON THE GROWING OF FUR AND THE AUTUMN SHEDDING OF THE WHITE HARE. I. V. Zharkov (Jarkov). Roboty Volzhsko-Kamskoi Krajevoi Promyslovoi Biologischeskoi Stantsii (Works of Volga-Kama Region Industrial Biological Station), Kazan, no.1, pp.153-167, 1931.

Population Dynamics

FLUCUTATIONS IN THE FIELD HARE POPULATION IN DENMARK COMPARED WITH CERTAIN CLIMATIC FACTORS. Johs Andersen. Pap. Game Res. 8: 41-43, graphs, 1952.

STUDIES IN DANISH HARE POPULATIONS. I. POPULATION FLUCTUATIONS. Johs Andersen. Danish Rev. Game Biol., 3 (2): 85-131, 1957.

DROPPINGS OF ARIZONA AND ANTELOPE JACK RABBITS AND THE "PELLET CENSUS." Joseph F. Arnold, Hudson G. Reynolds. Jour. Wildlife Mgt., Menasha, vol.7, no.3, pp.322-327, July, 1943.

READING RABBIT POPULATION CYCLES FROM PINES. Robert A. Bailey. Wis. Cons. Bul. 11 (7): 14-17, July, 1946.

SCARCITY OF JACK RABBITS IN EASTERN WASHINGTON. J. Hooper Bowles. Murrelet, vol.11, no.2, p.18, May, 1930.

WHY HAS THE WHITE-TAILED JACK RABBIT (LEPUS TOWNSENDII CAMPANIUS HOLLISTER) BECOME SCARCE IN KANSAS? H. Leo Brown. Trans. Kansas Acad. Sci. 49(4): 455-456, 1947.

SNOWSHOE RABBIT MIGRATION, TICK INFESTATION, AND WEATHER CYCLES. W. T. Cox. Jour. Mam., 17 (3): 216-221, Aug., 1936.

PRESENT STATUS OF THE SNOWSHOE HARE CYCLE INVESTIGATION. R. G. Green. Univ. Minn., 3 pp., Jan., 1937.

STUDIES ON A POPULATION CYCLE OF SNOWSHOE HARES ON THE LAKE ALEXANDER AREA. I. GROSS ANNUAL CENSUSES, 1932-1939. R. G. Green, C. A. Evans. Jour. Wildlife Mgt., Menasha, vol. 4, no.2, pp.220-238, Apr., 1940.

STUDIES ON A POPULATION CYCLE OF SNOWSHOE HARES ON THE LAKE ALEXANDER AREA. II. MORTALITY ACCORDING TO AGE GROUPS AND SEASONS. R. G. Green, C. A. Evans. Jour. Wildlife Mgt., Menasha, vol.4, no.3, pp. 267-278, July, 1940.

STUDIES ON A POPULATION CYCLE OF SNOWSHOE HARES ON THE LAKE ALEXANDER AREA. III. EFFECT OF REPRODUCTION AND MORTALITY OF YOUNG HARES ON THE CYCLE. R. G. Green, C. A. Evans. Jour. Wildlife Mgt., Menasha, vol.4, no.4, pp.347-358, Oct., 1940.

WESTERN HIGHWAY HAZARD FOR JACK RABBITS. A. O. Larson, D. E. Fox. Science, n.s., vol.85, no.2195, p.101, Jan.22, 1937.

ARCTIC HARES IN SCOTLAND--AMAZING INCREASE WITHIN LIVING MEMORY. Dugald Macintyre. Field, London, vol. 159, no.4129, p.223, Feb.13, 1932.

FLUCTUATIONS IN NUMBERS OF VARYING HARES. D. A. MacLulich. Science, n.s., vol.83, no.2146 , p.162, Feb.14, 1936.

FLUCTUATIONS IN THE NUMBER OF SNOWSHOE RABBITS. D. A. MacLulich. Forestry Chronicle, vol.11, no.4, pp.283-286, Dec., 1935.

FLUCTUATIONS IN THE NUMBERS OF THE VARYING HARE (LEPUS AMERICANUS). D. A. MacLulich. Univ. Toronto Studies, Biol. Ser.43, 136 pp., 1937.

RUFFED GROUSE AND SNOWSHOE HARE POPULATIONS ON THE CLOQUET EXPERIMENTAL FOREST, MINNESOTA. William H. Marshall. Jour. Wildlife Mgt., Ithaca, vol.18, no.1, pp.109-112, Jan., 1954.

(SOME REGULARITIES OF CHANGES IN THE NUMBER OF HARES (LEPUS EUROPEUS PALL.) IN THE UKRAINIAN SSR.) Einige Gesetzmaessigkeiten der Aenderungen in der Anzahl der Hasen (Lepus europeus Pall.) in der Ukr. SSR. A. Migulin. Acad. Sci. RSS Ukraine, Travaux Mus. Zool., Kiev, vol.18, no.20, pp.103-113, 1937.

RECENT JACK RABBIT POPULATIONS AT RAPIDAN, MINN. W. P. Mohr, Carl O. Mohr. Jour. Mam., 17 (2): 112-114, May, 1936.

A LOCAL STUDY OF PREDATION UPON HARES AND GROUSE DURING THE CYCLIC DECIMATION. Marius Morse. Jour. Wildlife Mgt., 3 (3): 203-214, July, 1939.

METHODS FOR FORECASTING POPULATION CHANGES IN THE WHITE HARE (LEPUS TIMIDUS L.). S. P. Naumov. Trans. Cent. Lab. Game-Indus, 5: 46-60, 1941.

INCREASE OF THE MOUNTAIN HARE IN THE SCOTCH LOWLANDS. James Ritchie. Scottish Nat., no.152, pp.47-48, Mar.-Apr., 1925.

THE CORRELATION BETWEEN THE FLUCTUATIONS OF PARTRIDGE AND EUROPEAN HARE POPULATIONS AND THE CLIMATIC CONDITIONS OF WINTERS IN SOUTHWEST FINLAND DURING THE LAST THIRTY YEARS. Lauri Siivonen. Papers on Game Research, Finnish Game Foundation, Helsinki 17 : 1-30, 1956.

(WHAT DOES THE FLYING ENEMY OF THE HARE LOOK LIKE?) Wie sieht der fliegende Feind des Hasen aus? L. G. Tirala. Biol. Zentralbl., Leipzig, vol.55, nos.9-10, pp.526-528, 1935.

NOTES ON A METHOD FOR CENSUSING SNOWSHOE HARE POPULATIONS. William L. Webb. Jour. Wildlife Mgt., 6 (1): 67-69, Jan., 1942.

NOTES ON THE SEX RATIO OF THE SNOWSHOE RABBIT. William L. Webb. Jour. Mam., 18 (3): 343-347, Aug., 1937.

1939, HIGHWAY MORTALITY OF RABBITS IN IDAHO. Cecil S. Williams, Marcus C. Nelson. Jour. Mam., vol.20, no.3, pp. 380-382, Aug.14, 1939.

PERIODIC ABUNDANCE AND SCARCITY OF VARYING HARES. Bull. 7, Roy. Ontario Mus. Zool., pp.12-14, Jan., 1938.

Reproductive Biology

(PROBLEMS OF THE PROPAGATION OF FIELD HARE.) Probleme der Fortpflanzung des Feldhasen. S. Bloch, H. Hediger, C. Mueller, F. Strauss. Revue Suisse de Zoologie, Neuchatel, vol.61, no.26, pp. 485-490, Sept., 1954.

GROWTH,DEVELOPMENTAL FOOD REQUIREMENTS, AND BREEDING ACTIVITY OF THE CALIFORNIA JACK RABBIT. Horace S. Haskell. Jour. Mam., 28 (2): 129-136, May, 1947.

(REARING THE FIELD HARE (LEPUS EUROPAEUS PALLAS) IN CAPTIVITY.) Die Zucht des Feldenhasen (Lepus europaeus Pallas) in Gefangenschaft (Rearing field Hares in captivity). H. Hediger. Physiologia Comparata et Oecologia 1(1): 46-62, Apr., 1948.

DETERMINING THE SEX OF YOUNG HARES. Nils Hoeglund, Johan Viklund. Suomen Riista 8: 175-176, illus., 1953.

REPRODUCTIVE BIOLOGY OF THE COMMON HARE (LEPUS EUROPAEUS PALL.). A. M. Kolosov. Zool. Zh. 20 (1): 154-172, 1941.

ON HYBRID HARES BETWEEN LEPUS TIMIDUS L. AND LEPUS EUROPAEUS PALL. FROM SOUTHERN SWEDEN. Einar Loennberg. Proc. Zool. Soc. Lond., vol.1, pp. 278-287, figs.53-54, Aug.10, 1905.

BREEDING HARES IN CAPTIVITY. L. Harrison Matthews. Proc. Zool. Soc. Lond., vol.126, pt.1, pp.161-163, 1 pl., Jan.11, 1956.

SEXUAL CYCLE AND FERTILITY IN LEPUS TIMIDUS L. S. P. Naumov. Narodnii Komissariat Zagotovok SSSR, Trudy Tsentralnoi Naucho-Issledovatelskoi Laboratorii Biologii, Oxotnichego Promysla i Tovarovedeniia Zhivotnogo Syria, Moscow, no.6, pp.4-44, figs.1-9, 1944.

OBSERVATIONS ON THE REPRODUCTION OF LEPUS EUROPAEUS PALLAS IN ONTARIO. Keith Reynolds. MS thesis, Univ. W. Ont., 1950.

REPRODUCTIVE POTENTIAL AND SEX RATIOS OF SNOWSHOE HARES IN NORTHERN ALBERTA. William Rowan, L. B. Keith. Canadian Jour. Zool., 34 (4): 273-281, Aug., 1956.

BREEDING OF THE WASHINGTON VARYING HARE. Theo. H. Scheffer. Murrelet, vol.14, no.3, pp.77-78, Sept., 1933.

BREEDING POTENTIAL AND ARTIFICIAL PROPAGATION OF THE SNOWSHOE HARE. Joye Harold Severaid. Jour. Wildlife Mgt., Menasha, vol.9, no.4, pp.290-295, Oct., 1945.

LATE-BREEDING SNOWSHOE HARE. Hilbert R. Siegler. Jour. Mam., vol.35, no.1, p.122, Feb.10, 1954.

(ON THE REPRODUCTION BIOLOGY OF THE EUROPEAN FIELD HARE (LEPUS EUROPAEUS PALLAS).) Zur Fortpflanzungsbiologie des europaeischen Feldhasen (Lepus europaeus Pallas). H. Stieve. Zool. Anzeiger, Leipzig, vol.148, pp.101-114, Mar.-Apr., 1952.

(NEW INVESTIGATIONS ON THE PROPAGATION OF THE FIELD HARE.) Neue Untersuchungen Ueber die Fortpflanzung des Feldhasen. Fritz Strauss. Seitschrift Jager, Fischer and Freunde Natur Verlag J. J. Hort, Lausanne, pp.1-8, 1954.

BREEDING HABITS OF JACK RABBITS. Walter P. Taylor. Jour. Mam., vol.5, no.3, p.216, Aug., 1924.

CAESARIAN OPERATION ON LEPUS ALLENI, AND NOTES ON THE YOUNG. Charles T. Vorhies. Jour. Mam., vol.2, no.2, pp.114-116, May, 1921.

MATERNAL INSTINCT IN THE HARE. W. Wallace. Field, London, vol.153, p. 761, May 9, 1929.

YOUNG OF EUROPEAN HARE BORN IN WINTER. H. L. Yack. Canadian Field-Nat., vol.45, no.7, p.179, Oct., 1931.

Taxonomy

DESCRIPTIONS OF A NEW SPECIES AND A NEW SUBSPECIES OF THE GENUS LEPUS. Joel Asaph Allen. Amer. Mus. Nat. Hist., New York, Bull., vol.111, pp.159-160, 1891.

A NEW SUBSPECIES OF SNOWSHOE RABBIT FROM WYOMING (LEPUS AMERICANUS SECLUSUS). Rollin H. Baker, Robert M. Hankins. Proc. Biol. Soc. Wash., vol.63, pp.63-64, May 25, 1950.

A REVISION OF THE AMERICAN ARCTIC HARES. Arthur H. Howell. Jour. Mam., vol.17, no.4, pp.315-337, figs.4, Nov., 1936.

CLASSIFICATION OF THE HARES AND THEIR ALLIES. Marcus W. Lyon, Jr. Smithsonian Misc. Coll., Wash., vol.XLV (Quarterly issue, vol.1), pp.321-447, illus., pl.LXXIV-C, 1903.

PRELIMINARY DESCRIPTION OF A NEW SUBGENUS AND SIX NEW SPECIES AND SUBSPECIES OF HARES, FROM THE MEXICAN BORDER OF THE UNITED STATES. Edgar A. Mearns. Proc. U.S. Nat. Mus., vol.18, no.1081, pp.551-565, June 24, 1896.

A NEW SUBGENUS FOR LEPUS IDAHOENSIS. Gerrit S. Miller, Jr. Proc. Biol. Soc., Wash,, vol.8, p.157, June 13, 1900.

ON THE SYSTEMATICS OF THE RUSSIAN HARES. S. I. Ognev. Yearbook Zool. Mus. Russian Acad. Sci., vol.23, pp.474-496, 1922.

(ON THE SYSTEMATICS OF THE RUSSIAN HARES.) Zur Systematik der russischen Hasen. S. I. Ognev. Zool. Anzeiger, Leipzig, vol.84, nos.1-4, pp.69-83, 1929.

TAXONOMIC STATUS OF THE EUROPEAN HARE IN ONTARIO. Randolph L. Peterson, J. K. Reynolds. Contrib. Roy. Ontario Mus. Zool. and Palaeontol., Toronto, no. 38, pp.1-7, Jan.31, 1954.

SYNOPSIS OF THE POLAR HARES OF NORTH AMERICA. Samuel N. Rhoads. Proc. Acad. Nat. Sciences, Phila., pp.351-376, pls.6-10, 1896.

THE SUBGENERIC POSITION OF THE LEPUS CALIFORNICUS GROUP OF HARES. H. Harold Shamel. Proc. Biol. Soc. Wash., vol.55, pp.25-26, May 12, 1942.

ON TWO NEW HARES ALLIED TO ORYCTOLAGUS CRASSICAUDATUS. Oldfield Thomas. Ann. and Mag. Nat. Hist. (7), vol.10, no.57, pp.244-246, Sept., 1902.

Africa

NEW KIND OF RABBIT. (Poalagus majorita larkeni; also an unnamed species called "namangia" in the Sudan.) P.M. Larken. Field, London, vol.167, no.4356, p.1509, illus., June 20, 1936.

A NEW PRONOLAGUS FROM NATAL. Austin Roberts. Nat.Ann.Transvaal Mus., Cambridge, vol.21, pt.2, pp.179-180, May 12, 1949.

NEW GENUS FOR THE UGANDA HARE (Lepus marjorita). J. St.Leger.Proc. Zool. Soc.London, 1932, pt.1, pp.119-123, figs. 3, 1932.

NEW RACE OF POELAGUS FROM THE BAHR-EL-GHAZAL. J. St.Leger. Ann. Mag.Nat.Hist., London, ser.10, vol.16, no.96, pp.598-600, Dec., 1935.

Aging

AGE CHANGES IN THE TEETH OF THE COTTONTAIL RABBIT, Sylvilagus floridanus. Lee R. Dice, Dora S. Dice. Papers Michigan Acad.Sci.Arts Letters, Ann Arbor, vol.26, pp.219-228, figs.8, pl.1, 1941.

AGING COTTONTAIL RABBITS BY BONE GROWTH. James B. Hale. MS thesis, Univ.Wis., 1947; Jour.Wildl.Mgt., vol. 13, no.2, pp.216-225, Apr., 1949.

BONE GROWTH AS AN AGE CRITERION IN THE COTTONTAIL RABBIT. Hans Peter Thomsen, Otto A. Mortensen. Jour. Wildl.Mgt., vol.10, no.2, pp.171-174, Apr., 1946.

APOPHYSEAL LINE AS AN AGE INDICATOR FOR THE WILD RABBIT, ORYCTOLAGUS CUNICULUS (L). J.S.Watson, C.H.Tyndale-Biscoe. New Zealand Jour.Sci. & Tech. sec. B, vol.34, no.6, pp.427-435, May, 1953.

Anatomy

OBSERVATIONS ON THE FOLLICULAR ATRESIA IN THE RABBIT OVARY. Goichi Asomi. Anat.Rec., vol.18, no.4, pp.323-343, May 20 (June), 1920.

NOTES ON THE BRANCHES OF THE AORTA (AREUS AORTAE) AND THE SUBCLAVIAN ARTERY OF THE RABBIT. Francis Marsh Baldwin. Anat.Rec., vol.19, pp.173-183, figs.11, July 20, 1920.

FAMILIAL VARIATIONS IN THE PATTERN OF RIB OSSIFICATION IN THE RABBIT. Inez M. Baumgartner, P.B. Sawin. Anat. Rec., Philadelphia, vol.86, no.4, pp.473-489, fig.1, pl.1, Aug., 1943.

BENSLEY'S PRACTICAL ANATOMY OF THE RABBIT. Benjamin Arthur Bensley. Blakiston Co., Philadelphia, pp.391, illus., 1948.

ANATOMIC AND HISTOLOGIC STUDIES OF THE SEX ACCESSORIES OF THE MALE RABBIT. H.A. Bern. Univ.Calif. Publ.Zool., vol.47, no.7, pp.175-196, illus., 1943.

VESICULA SEMINALIS OF THE RABBIT. Edna B. Carr. Proc.Zool.Soc.London, vol. 124, pt.3, pp.675-683, pl.1, Nov. 15, 1954.

MICROSCOPIC STUDIES OF THE NEW FORMATION OF FAT IN LIVING ADULT RABBITS. Eliot R. Clark, Eleanor Linton Clark. Amer.Jour.Anat., Philadelphia, vol. 67, no.2, pp.255-285, figs.6, pls.3, Sep. 16, 1940.

LABORATORY GUIDE TO THE ANATOMY OF THE RABBIT. E. Horne Craigie. Univ. Toronto Press, pp.vii-113, illus., 1951.

PRACTICAL ANATOMY OF THE RABBIT. E. Horne Craigie. Blakiston, Philadelphia, pp.xii-391, illus., 1948.

COMPARATIVE HISTOLOGICAL STUDY OF THE ADRENAL GLAND IN NATIVE RABBITS. I.E. Gonzalez. Anat. Rec., Philadelphia, vol.121, no.2, pp.397-398, Feb., 1955. (Abstract).

PERILOBULAR SPACES IN THE RABBIT PANCREAS. H. Hughes. Nature, London, vol.158, no.4012, pp.418-419, figs.3, Sep. 21, 1946.

(ANATOMY OF THE RABBIT IN TOPOGRAPHICAL AND FUNCTIONAL OBSERVATION (SECOND EDITION).) Anatomie des Kaninchens in Topographischer und Operativer Ruecksicht. Zweite Auflage. W. Krause. 1884.

HISTOLOGIC ANALYSIS OF UTERINE GROWTH DURING PREGNANCY IN THE RABBIT. Boris Krichesky. Anat. Rec., Philadelphia, vol.82, no.4, pp.551-564, fig.1, Apr. 25, 1942.

DISTRIBUTION OF BODY WEIGHT IN THE ORGANS AND TISSUES OF THE RABBIT. Charles J. Levine, Walter Mann, Harold C. Hodge, I.Ariel, O.DuPont. Proc.Soc. Exper.Biol.and Med., New York, vol.47, no.2, pp.318-321, June, 1941.

FORM AND FUNCTION OF THE AURICULOVENTRICULAR BUNDLE IN THE RABBIT. Wray Lloyd. Amer. Jour. Anat., vol. 45, no.3, pp.379-410, figs.17, May 15, 1930.

DEVELOPMENT OF THE CARDIAC LOOP IN THE RABBIT, WITH ESPECIAL REFERENCE TO THE BULBOVENTRICULAR GROOVE AND ORIGIN OF THE INTERVENTRICULAR SEPTUM. Henry A.Murray, Jr. Amer. Jour. Anat., vol.26, pp.29-39, Sep. 15, 1919.

CELL SIZE AND BODY SIZE IN RABBITS. T.S. Painter. Jour. Exp. Zool., vol.50, no.3, pp.441-454, 1928.

TRANSPARENT CHAMBER OF THE RABBIT'S EAR, GIVING A COMPLETE DESCRIPTION OF IMPROVED TECHNIC OF CONSTRUCTION AND INTRODUCTION, AND GENERAL ACCOUNT OF GROWTH AND BEHAVIOR OF LIVING CELLS AND

TISSUES AS SEEN WITH THE MICROSCOPE. J.C. Sandison. Amer. Jour.Anat., vol.41, pp.447-473, illus., July 15, 1928.

INTRACELLULAR BILE CANALICULI IN THE RABBIT LIVER. M.Wachstein, F.G. Zak. Proc. Soc. Exp.Biol.Med., Utica, vol.72, no.1, pp.234-236, Oct., 1949.

RELATIONSHIP BETWEEN PAUNCHED AND DEAD WEIGHTS OF RABBITS. J.S. Watson, R.M. Williams. New Zealand Jour.Sci. & Technol., sec.B, vol.37, no.1, pp.54-58, July, 1955.

Anomalies

ARTIFICIAL PRODUCTION OF MONSTROSITIES IN THE RABBIT. M.C.Chang. Nature, London, vol.154, no.3900, p.150, illus., July 29, 1944.

QUEER KINDS OF RABBITS. Henry H. Graham. Our Dumb Animals, Boston, vol. 76, no.10, p.185, Oct., 1943.

INCISOR MALOCCLUSION IN A COTTONTAIL RABBIT. Joseph T. Gregory. Jour. Mamm., vol.34, no.3, pp.393-394, Aug. 14, 1953.

OVERGROWTH OF TEETH IN RABBITS. Tom Hare. Field, London, vol.167, no. 4338, p.348, illus., Feb. 15, 1936.

SOME ANOMALOUS BLOOD VESSELS IN THE RABBIT. Joan E. Heriot, Sylvia M. Weston. Proc.Zool.Soc.London, vol.120, no.2, pp.737-741, figs.5, Feb., 1951.

ON TWO CASES OF ABNORMALITIES IN THE VENOUS CIRCULATORY SYSTEM OF THE COMMON RABBIT (Lepus cunicula) WITH OBSERVATIONS ON THEIR DEVELOPMENTAL SIGNIFICANCE. J.H. Lloyd. Zool.Anzeiger, vol.77, pp.137-142, June 1, 1928.

ON ABNORMAL TEETH IN CERTAIN MAMMALS, ESPECIALLY IN THE RABBIT. W. C. M'Intosh. Trans.Royal Soc.Edinburgh, vol.56, no.16, pp.51, 334-407, figs.103, 1930.

A FIVE LEGGED RABBIT. Adolph Murie. Jour. Mamm., vol.15, no.2, p.162, May, 1934.

(ABNORMAL GROWTH OF THE INCISORS IN RABBITS.) Anormale accrescimento degli incisivi nei conigli. C. Parona. Bol. Mus.Zool. & Anat. Comp., R. Univ. Genova, no.33, pp.6, pls.7, 1895.

ABNORMAL RABBIT'S SKULL. Alvin L. Throne. Milwaukee Public Mus., Yearbook, vol.5, 1925, pp.184-185, illus., Mar. 10, 1927.

Australia

RABBITS AND NATIVE FLORA. Fred C.W. Barton. Victorian Nat., vol.50, no.7, p.170, Nov., 1930.

RABBIT IN AUSTRALIA. David G. Stead. Winn & Co., Sydney, pp.108, 1935.

RABBITS, RABBITS AND RABBITS. Robert Strother. Nature Mag., Washington, vol.43, no.6, pp.314-316, 331, illus., June-July, 1950.

RABBIT IN AUSTRALIA. Nature, London, vol.137, no.3472, pp.806-807, May 16, 1936.

Blood and Blood Cells

PHAGOCYTOSIS IN THE APPENDIX OF THE RABBIT. Frank Baker, John Enticknap. Nature, London, vol.151, no.3836, pp.532-533, May 8, 1943.

STATISTICAL STUDY OF THE NUMBER OF WHITE BLOOD CELLS IN THE BLOOD OF THE RABBIT. Anne Haynes, R.H. Rigdon. Anat.Rec., Philadelphia, vol.83, no.4, pp.587-594, Aug. 25, 1942.

RATE OF RENEWAL OF THE ACID SOLUBLE ORGANIC PHOSPHORUS COMPOUNDS IN THE ORGANS AND THE BLOOD OF THE RABBIT WITH A NOTE ON THE DURATION OF LIFE OF THE RED BLOOD CORPUSCLES. G.Hevesy, L. Hahn. Kgl.Danske Videnskab.Selskab., Biol.Meddel., Copenhagen, vol.15, no.7, pp.36, Sep. 21, 1940.

GLOMERULAR CONTROL OF THE KIDNEY BLOOD FLOW. J.M. O'Connor. Jour.Physiol., vol.59, pp.200-212, Oct., 1924.

(ON THE BLOOD SUPPLY OF WHITE AND RED RABBIT MUSCLES.) Ueber die Blutversorgung von weissen und roten Kaninchenmuskeln. G. Stoel. Zeitschr. f. Zellforschung und Mikroskopische Anat., vol. 3, pp.91-98, figs.3, Dec. 18, 1925.

BLOOD COUNTING OF NORMAL AND MIXOMATOUS RABBITS. Alvaro Emery Trindade. Mem.Inst.Oswaldo Cruz, Rio de Janeiro, vol.52, no.2, pp.397-403, June 1954. (In Portuguese with English translation.)

Control

MYXOMATOSIS AS A METHOD OF BIOLOGICAL CONTROL AGAINST THE AUSTRALIAN RABBIT. Frank MacFarlane Burnet. Amer. Jour. Public Health, Albany, vol.42, no.12, pp.1522-1526, Dec., 1952.

HUMANE RABBIT-TRAPPING--THE END OF A 30 YEAR QUEST. Maurice Burton. Illus.London News, vol.216, no.5781, p. 184, illus., Feb. 4, 1950.

PEN TESTS OF RABBIT REPELLENTS. H.A. Cardinell, D.W. Hayne. Michigan Agric.Exper.Sta., East Lansing, Quart. Bull., vol.29, no.4, pp.303-315, May, 1947.

WHAT IS THE BEST FREE-FEEDING SYSTEM FOR FURROW-POISONING THE RABBIT? R. Carrick. C.S.I.R.O. Wildl. Res., vol.2, no.2, pp.76-84, 1957.

TOXICITY STUDY OF RABBIT FUMIGANTS. J.P. Gleeson, F.S. Maguire. C.S.I.R.O. Wildl.Res., Canberra, Australia, vol.2, no.2, pp.71-77, 1957.

OBJECTIONS TO POISON AS A METHOD OF RABBIT CONTROL. Wallace Grange. Trans.20th Amer. Game Conf., 1934, Amer. Game Assoc., New York, pp.340-354, 1934.

FRUIT TREE COATING EFFECTIVE AGAINST COTTONTAILS. D.W. Hayne. Michigan Exper.Sta.Quart.Bull., vol.24, no.1, pp.65-68, Aug., 1941.

FURTHER TEST OF COTTONTAIL REPELLENTS FOR GARDEN USE. D.W. Hayne. Michigan Agr.Exp.Sta.Quart. Bull., vol.32, no.3, pp.373-377, Feb., 1950.

TESTS OF REPELLENTS FOR PROTECTING GARDENS AGAINST COTTONTAIL RABBITS. D.W. Hayne. Michigan Agric.Exper. Sta.Quart.Bull., vol.31, no.4, pp.434-440, May, 1949.

REVIEW OF EXPERIMENTS IN BIOLOGICAL CONTROL OF RABBITS IN AUSTRALIA. Carlton M. Herman. Jour. Wildl.Mgt., Ithaca, vol.17, no.4, pp.482-486, Oct., 1953.

PROTECTING TREES AND SHRUBS FROM RABBIT DAMAGE. NATURE OF DAMAGE, REPELLENTS, PREPARATION, APPLICATION. A.C. Hildreth, G.B.Brown. U.S. Dept. Agric., Leafl.no.396, 1 sheet folder, illus., Sep., 1955.

CONTROLLING COTTONTAILS. John C. Jones. Pest Control, vol.20, no.10, pp. 32, 34, 68, illus., Oct., 1952.

TOXICITY AND RELATIVE ACCEPTABILITY OF SOME POISONS TO THE WILD RABBIT, ORYCTOLAGUS CUNICULUS (L). Marian Lazarus. C.S.I.R.O. Wildl.Res., Melbourne, vol.1, no.2, pp.96-100, Dec., 1956.

AUSTRALIA'S WAR AGAINST THE RABBIT. Douglas Liversidge. Discovery, London, vol.13, no.6, pp.190-195, June, 1952.

SOME EXPERIMENTS IN RABBIT CONTROL. R.M. Lockley. Nature, vol.145, no.3681, pp.767-769, May 18, 1940.

USE OF SODIUM FLUOROACETAE (COMPOUND 1080) FOR THE CONTROL OF THE RABBIT IN TASMANIA. G.K.Meldrum and others. Australian Vet. Jour., vol.33, no. 8, pp.186-196, 1957.

CONTROL AND EXTERMINATION OF WILD RABBITS. A.D.Middleton. Bur. Animal Population, pp.27, Sep., 1940.

RABBIT CONTROL IN AUSTRALIA: PROBLEMS AND POSSIBILITIES. J.E.Nichols. Nature, vol.168, no.4283, pp.932-934, Dec. 1, 1951.

TEST OF HUNTING AS COTTONTAIL CONTROL. Miles D. Pirnie. Quart.Bull. vol.31, no.3, pp.304-308, Feb., 1949.

MYXOMATOSIS IN AUSTRALIA, A STEP TOWARDS THE BIOLOGICAL CONTROL OF THE RABBIT. F.N. Ratcliffe, and others. Nature, vol.170, no.4314, pp.7-11, map, July 5, 1952.

PAINLESS RABBIT TRAP. F.E.Sawyer. Field, London, vol.168, no.4361, p.237, illus., July 25, 1936.

BOX TRAPPING RABBITS PAYS. Chas. F. Stambaugh. Pennsylvania Game News, Harrisburg, vol.17, no.3, pp.8, 27, June, 1946.

POWER GASSING OF RABBITS. Harry V. Thompson, C.J. Armour. Jour.Ministry Agr., vol.60, pp.383-386, illus., 1953.

DIRECTIONS FOR ORGANIZING AND CONDUCTING RABBIT DRIVES. U.S. Dept.Agric., Biol.Survey, Wildl.Leaflet 59, pp.2, June, 1936.

INDIRECT RABBIT CONTROL. Forest Res. Dig., Feb., 1935.

Coprophagy

COPROPHAGY IN THE RABBIT. A.Eden. Nature, London, vol.145, no.3662, pp. 36-37, Jan. 6, 1940.

COPROPHAGY IN THE RABBIT: ORIGIN OF THE "NIGHT" FAECES. A. Eden. Nature, London, vol.145, no.3577, pp. 628-629, Apr. 20, 1940.

COPROPHAGY IN THE SWAMP RABBIT. W.J. Hamilton, Jr. Jour. Mamm., vol. 36, no.2, pp.303-304, May, 1955.

COPROPHAGY IN THE COTTONTAIL. Charles M. Kirkpatrick. Jour.Mamm., vol.37, no.2, p.300, June 9, 1956.

DOES THE RABBIT CHEW THE CUD? (Coprophagy a Normal and Regular Physiological Process.) Holger Madsen. Nature, London, vol.143, no.3632, pp.981-982, June 10, 1939.

COPROPHAGY IN THE EUROPEAN RABBIT (ORYCTOLAGUS CUNICULUS) IN AUSTRALIA. K. Myers. Australian Jour. Zool., Melbourne, vol.3, no.3, pp.336-345, illus., Oct., 1955.

COPROPHAGY IN THE RABBIT, ORYCTOLAGUS CUNICULUS (L.), IN TASMANIA. Ian Rowley. C.S.I.R.O. Wildl.Res., Melbourne, vol.1, no.2, p.133, Dec., 1956.

COPROPHAGY IN THE WILD RABBIT. H.N. Southern. Nature, London, vol.145, no. 3668, p.262, Feb. 17, 1940.

PERIODICITY OF REFECTION IN THE WILD RABBIT. (Swallowing Fecal Pellets.) H.N. Southern. Nature, London, vol. 149, no.3785, pp.553-554, May 16, 1942.

DOES THE RABBIT CHEW THE CUD?(Feces Produced at Night are Swallowed and Redigested.)E.L. Taylor. Nature, London, vol.143, no.3632, pp.981-983, June 10, 1939.

PSEUDO-RUMINATION IN THE RABBIT. E.L. Taylor. Proc.Zool.Soc.London, ser. A, vol.110, pts.3-4, pp.159-163, Mar., 1941.

REINGESTION IN THE WILD RABBIT, ORYCTOLAGUS CUNICULUS (L.). J.S. Watson. Proc.Zool.Soc.London, vol.124, no.3, pp.615-624, graphs, pl.1, Nov., 1954.

Diseases

WORD TO THE COTTONTAIL HUNTER. B.Randolph Allen. Va.Wildl., vol.7, no.4, pp.6-7, Oct., 1946.

RABBIT FEVER OR TULAREMIA. Will C. Barnes. Sci. Monthly, vol.27, pp.463-469, Nov., 1928.

BUNNIES CAN HIT BACK. (Tularemia.) Bert Benowitz. Field and Stream, New York, vol.49, no.6, pp.19, 89, 101, Oct., 1944.

NOTE REGARDING THE TREATMENT OF EAR CANKER IN RABBITS. Frank E. Blaisdell, Sr. Science, n.s., vol.60, pp.429-430, Nov.7, 1924.

(INSULIN AND EXPERIMENTAL CANCER IN THE RABBIT.) Insuline et cancer expérimental du lapin. Andre Boivin. Comptes

Rendus des Séances de la Soc.de Biol., vol. 97, pp.809-811, Aug. 26, 1927.

INITIAL SPREAD OF MYXOMATOSIS IN AUSTRALIA. John L. Brereton. Nature, vol.172, no.4368, pp.108-110, map, July 18, 1953.

TULARAEMIA. WHO'S AFRAID OF THE BIG BAD RABBIT? T.W.M. Cameron. Rod & Gun in Canada, Montreal, vol.4, pp.12, 45, 1947.

LYMPHADENITIS IN NEW YORK COTTONTAILS. E.L. Cheatum. Jour. Wildl.Mgt., Menasha, vol.5, no.3, pp.304-308, illus., July, 1941.

PRIMARY TULAREMIC PNEUMONIA TREATED WITH STREPTOMYCIN. Richard B. Cohen, Richard Lasser. Jour. Amer. Vet.Med.Assoc., vol.131, no.14, pp.1126-1127, Aug. 3, 1946.

FREAK RABBIT WITH HORNY GROWTH FROM WHILBY ISLAND, WASHINGTON. Leo K. Couch. The Murrelet, vol.15, no.2, p.54, May, 1934.

STUDIES ON RABBITS AND SPOTTED FEVER. David E. Davis. Trans. 18th N.Amer. Wildl.Conf., pp.188-190, 1953.

RELAPSING FEVER: THE TICK ORNITHODOROS TURICATA AS SPIROCHETAL RESERVOIR. Gordon E. Davis. U.S.Public Health Repts., Washington, D.C., vol. 58, no.22, pp.839-842, May 28, 1943.

FACTORS INFLUENCING THE TRANSMISSIBILITY OF MYXOMA VIRUS BY MOSQUITOES. M.F. Day. Jour.Australian Inst.Agr.Sci., vol.21, no.3, pp.145-151, Sep., 1955.

INCIDENCE AND TRANSMISSION OF SARCOCYSTIS IN COTTONTAILS. Arnold B.Erickson. Jour. Wildl.Mgt., vol.10, no. 1, pp.44-46, Jan., 1946.

CHANGES IN THE MORTALITY-RATE DUE TO MYXOMATOSIS IN THE AUSTRALIAN WILD RABBIT. Frank Fenner. Nature, vol.172, no.4371, pp.228-230, Aug. 8, 1953.

CHANGES IN THE VIRULENCE OF MYXOMA VIRUS ASSOCIATED WITH ITS NATURAL TRANSMISSION IN POPULATIONS OF THE RABBIT ORYCTOLAGUS CUNICULUS. Frank Fenner. Jour.Australian Inst.Agric.Sci., vol.21, no.3, pp.137-144, Sep., 1955.

RABBIT PLAGUE. Frank F. Fenner. Scientific American, New York, vol.190, no.2, pp. 30-35, Feb., 1954.

EXPERIMENTAL TRANSMISSION OF TULARAEMIA IN RABBIT LOUSE, MAEMODIPSUS VENTRICOSUS (DENNY). Edward Francis, G.C. Lake. U.S. Public Health Serv., Hygiene Lab., Bull.no.130, pp. 17-23, Mar., 1922. (Reprinted from Public Health Rep., vol.36, pp.1747-1753, 1921.)

OCCURRENCE OF ATTENUATED STRAINS OF MYXOMA VIRUS IN EUROPE. Frank Fenner, I.D. Marshall. Nature, vol.176, no.4486, pp.782-783, Oct. 22, 1955.

STUDIES IN THE EPIDEMIOLOGY OF INFECTIOUS MYXOMATOSIS OF RABBITS. VI. THE EXPERIMENTAL INTRODUCTION OF THE EUROPEAN STRAIN OF MYXOMA VIRUS INTO AUSTRALIAN WILD RABBIT POPULATIONS. Frank Fenner, W.E.Poole, I.D. Marshall, A.L.Dyce. Jour.Hygiene, vol.55, no.2, pp.192, 206, pls.4, June, 1957.

BLOOD HISTAMINE, LEUKOCYTES AND PLATELETS IN EXPERIMENTAL SERUM DISEASE IN RABBITS. Carolyn Forman, E. Mertens, M.Craub, W.Ehrich. Proc.Soc. Exp.Biol.Med., Utica, vol.72, no.2, pp. 439-443, Nov., 1949.

CONCERNING TULAREMIA. Richard Gerstell. Penn.Game News, vol.6, no.10, p.6, Jan., 1936.

EXPERIMENTAL RICKETS IN RABBITS. H.Goldblatt, A.R.Moritz. Jour.Exper. Med., vol.42, no.4, pp.499-506, illus., 1925.

RABBIT AS USED IN DISEASE RESEARCH. A SELECTED BIBLIOGRAPHY INCLUDING THE SPONTANEOUS DISEASES OF RABBITS. Carlton M. Herman. U.S.Dept. Interior, Fish and Wildl.Serv., pp.519, 1942.

RABBITS AND THE PREVENTION OF TULAREMIA IN OHIO. Lawrence E. Hicks. Ohio Wildl.Res.Sta., Release 176, pp.13, Dec., 1942.

INFECTIOUS MYXOMATOSIS IN MALNOURISHED RABBITS. Ralph B. Houlihan, E.Ansell Derrick. Science, Lancaster, vol. 101, no.2623, p.364, Apr. 6, 1945.

GEOGRAPHICAL DISTRIBUTION OF ROCKY MOUNTAIN SPOTTED FEVER AND NUTTALL'S COTTONTAIL IN THE WESTERN UNITED STATES. William L.Jellison.U.S. Publ.Health Repts., Washington, vol.60, no.33, pp.958, 961, Aug. 17, 1945.

HOST-VIRUS-MOSQUITO RELATIONSHIPS OF SHOPE FIBROMAS IN COTTONTAIL RABBITS. Lawrence Kilham, Herbert T. Dalmat. Amer. Jour. Hyg., vol.61, no.1, pp.45-54, illus., Jan., 1955.

TULAREMIA: THE RABBIT DISEASE. Robert Page Lincoln. Southern Sportsman, Austin, vol.7, no.3, pp.8, 23-24, Dec., 1943.

HISTORY OF EPIZOOTICS OF MYXOMATOSIS IN RABBITS OF S. AUSTRALIA DURING 1951-52. E.W.L. Lines. Jour. Dept.Agr. S.Australia, vol.56, pp.232-238, Dec., 1952.

PLAGUE EPIZOOTIC IN COTTONTAIL RABBITS. Vernon B. Link. Pub.Health Rep., vol. 65, no.21, p.696, May 26, 1950.

HEMORRHAGIC SEPTICEMIA OF DOMESTIC RABBITS. CONTAGIOUS NASAL CATARRH (SNUFFLES), SUBCUTANEOUS ABSCESSES (BOILS) AND OTHER FORMS. F.D.McKenney. U.S.Dept.Agric., Wildl.Res.&Mgt., Leaflet BS-90, pp.1-5, May, 1937.

INFECTIOUS MYXOMATOSIS OF DOMESTIC RABBITS. (Mosquito Disease; Big-Head Disease.) F.D.McKenney, J.E.Shillinger. U.S. Dept.Agric., Wildl.Res. & Mgt., Leaflet BS-89, pp.2, May, 1937.

TRANSMISSION OF PASTEURELLA CUNICULICIDA IN RABBITS BY BREEDING. F.D. McKenney, J.E.Shillinger. Jour.Amer.Vet. Med.Assoc., vol.93, pp.161-164, Sep., 1938.

VENT DISEASES OF DOMESTIC RABBITS. F.D.McKenney, J.E.Shillinger. U.S.Dept. Agric., Widl.Res. & Mgt., Leaflet BS-79, pp.4, Jan., 1937.

INFECTIOUS MYXOMATOSIS OF DOMESTIC RABBITS. F.D.McKenney, E.L.Vail. U.S. Dept.Int., Fish and Wildl.Ser., Leaflet 166, pp.2, July, 1940.

CURE AND PREVENTION OF EAR CANKER IN RABBITS. David Marine. Science, n.s., vol.60, p.158, Aug. 15, 1924.

STUDIES IN THE EPIDEMIOLOGY OF INFECTIOUS MYXOMATOSIS OF RABBITS. IV. OBSERVATIONS OF DISEASE BEHAVIOUR IN TWO LOCALITIES NEAR THE NORTHERN LIMIT OF RABBIT INFESTATION IN AUSTRALIA, MAY 1952 TO APRIL 1953. I.D.Marshall, A. L.Dyce, W.E.Poole, Frank Fenner. Jour. Hygiene, vol.53, no.1, pp.12-25, Mar., 1955.

(INFECTIOUS DISEASES IN THE RABBIT.) Infektionskrankheiten beim Kaninchen. A. Meyn. Verhandl.des I.Internat.Kaninchenzuechter-Kongresses, Leipzig, 1930, pp. 243-253, 1931.

TULAREMIA IN WISCONSIN. B.B.Morgan. Trans.Wis.Acad.Sci., Arts & Letters, vol. 39, pp.1-19, 1949.

STUDIES IN THE EPIDEMIOLOGY OF INFECTIOUS MYXOMATOSIS OF RABBITS. II. FIELD EXPERIMENTS, AUGUST-NOVEMBER 1950, AND THE FIRST EPIZOOTIC OF MYXOMATOSIS IN THE RIVERINE PLAIN OF SOUTHEASTERN AUSTRALIA. K. Myers. Jour.Hygiene, vol. 52, no.1, pp.47-59, illus., Mar., 1954.

STUDIES IN THE EPIDEMIOLOGY OF INFECTIOUS MYXOMATOSIS OF RABBITS. III. OBSERVATIONS ON TWO SUCCEEDING EPIZOOTICS IN AUSTRALIAN WILD RABBITS ON THE RIVERINE PLAIN OF SOUTHEASTERN AUSTRALIA 1951-1953. K. Myers, I.D.Marshall, Frank Fenner. Jour.Hygiene, vol.52, no.3, pp. 337-360, pls.12-13, Sep., 1954.

TRANSMISSION OF MYXOMATOSIS BY SIMULIUM MELATUM WHARTON (DIPTERA: SIMULIIDAE). R. Mykytowycz. C.S.I.R.O. Wildl.Res., Canberra, Australia, vol.2, no.1, pp.1-4, 1957.

(TOXIC ACTION OF PARAMECIUM ON THE SERUM OF ANIMALS WITH MALIGNANT TUMORS.) O.K. Nastiukova. Zool. Jour. USSR, Moscow, vol.21, no.3, pp. 94-101, figs.3, tbls.4, 1942. (English summary.)

PRIMARY TULAREMIA OF THE EYE. (Epidemic Among Rabbits, Thought to be Tularemia.) M.C.Pfunder. Jour. Amer. Med.Assoc., vol.85, no.14, p.1061, 1925.

TULAREMIA SPELLS RABBIT FEVER. Lonsdale J. Raper. Virginia Wildl., Richmond, vol.9, no.12, pp.10-11, illus., Dec., 1948.

DISEASES AND PARASITES OF THE COTTONTAIL RABBIT. James R. Reilly, Joseph Dell. N.Y.State Cons., vol.9, no. 3, pp.8-10, illus., Dec.-Jan., 1954-1955.

MYXOMATOSIS. J.N.Ritchie, J.R.Hudson, H.V.Thompson. Vet.Rec., vol.66, pp. 796-804, (repr. pp.1-9), Dec., 1954.

NOTE OF A "HORNED" COTTONTAIL FROM NORTHWEST MISSOURI. Kenneth C. Rowe. Jour. Mamm., vol.28, no.4, p.405, Nov. 26, 1947.

CHANGES IN THE INNATE RESISTANCE OF RABBITS TO MYXOMATOSIS. W.R.Sobey. Jour.Australian Inst.Agric.Sci., vol.21, no.3, pp.135-136, Sep., 1955.

ECOLOGISTS ARE EXCITED BY ENGLAND'S "RABBIT DISEASE." H.N.Southern. Animal Kingdom, New York Zool.Soc., vol.59, no. 4, pp.116-123, Aug., 1956.

FATAL FORM OF SEPTICAEMIA IN THE RABBIT PRODUCED BY THE SUBCUTANEOUS INJECTION OF HUMAN SALIVA. George M. Sternberg. Nat.Board of Health Bull., Baltimore, pp.1-22, pl.1, Apr.30, 1881.

MYXOMATOSIS: RECENT DEVELOPMENTS. Harry V.Thompson. Jour. Ministry Agr., vol.61, pp.317-321, 1954.

MYXOMATOSIS OF RABBITS. Harry V. Thompson. Jour.Ministry Agr., vol.60, pp.503-508, illus., 1954.

RABBIT DISEASE: MYXOMATOSIS. Harry V. Thompson. Ann.Applied Biol., vol.41, no.2, pp.358-366, map, June, 1954.

EXPERIMENTAL AMOEBIASIS IN THE RABBIT. Margaret Dora Thompson. Univ. Calif. Publ.Zool., vol.29, no.2, pp.9-23, illus., June 23, 1926.

SUGGESTIONS FOR CONTROL OF COCCIDIOSIS IN RABBITS. Edward L. Vail. U.S.Biol.Surv.Wildl.Res. and Mgt., Leaflet BS-116, p.1, June, 1938.

DISEASES OF DOMESTIC RABBITS. Edward L. Vail, F.D.McKenny. U.S.Dept.Interior, Fish and Wildl.Serv., Conservation Bull.31, pp.1-28, figs.4, 1943.

STUDY OF RABBIT SPIROCHETOSIS. Alfred Warthin, Estella Buffington, Ruth Wanstrom. Jour.Infect.Diseases, vol.32, pp.315-332, pls.1-12, 1923.

TULAREMIA (RABBIT FEVER). M.Morris Whitehurst. Md.Cons., vol.17, no.1, pp. 20-22, Winter, 1940.

RESPONSE TO YELLOW FEVER VIRUS IN THE NONSUSCEPTIBLE RABBIT. Loring Whitman. Jour.Immunology, vol.29, no.2, pp.99-110, Aug., 1935.

COTTONTAILS, TULAREMIA AND WEATHER. Ralph E. Yeatter, David H. Thompson. Ill.Cons., vol.8, no.4, pp.6-7, 36, Winter, 1943.

TULAREMIA, WEATHER, AND RABBIT POPULATIONS. Ralph E.Yeatter, David H.Thompson. Bull.Ill.Nat.Hist.Survey, vol.25, art.6, pp.351-382, illus., June, 1952.

(BENEFITS FROM MYXOMATOSIS IN FRANCE.) IUPN Bull., vol.4, no.1, p. 3, 1955.

HORNED RABBIT. Ill.Cons., Springfield, vol.9, no.1, p.37, Spring, 1944.

LITTLE KNOWLEDGE--A DANGEROUS THING. Jour.Amer.Vet.Med.Assoc., vol. 123, no.920, p.456, Nov., 1953.

LOOK UPON EVERY RABBIT AS CARRIER OF TULAREMIA. Texas Game and Fish, Austin, vol.5, no.1, pp.7, 30, Dec., 1946.

MYXOMATOSIS IN EUROPE. Sports Afield, vol.131, no.3, p.142, Mar., 1954.

RABBIT AND THE BUBONIC PLAGUE. Md. Conservationist, Baltimore, vol.27, no.2, pp.11-12, illus., Summer, 1950.

RABBITS. (Diseases and Parasites.) Nat. Mag., Wash., D.C., vol.37, no.1, p.53, Jan., 1944.

REPORT OF THE ADVISORY COMMITTEE ON MYXOMATOSIS. Great Brit. Ministry Agr. & Fisheries; Scotland Dept.Agr., pp. iv-14, 1954.

TULAREMIA--"RABBIT FEVER." Wyoming Wild Life, Cheyenne, vol.5, no.6, pp.1-2, 16, June, 1940.

Ecology

ECOLOGICAL INVESTIGATION OF THE MARSH RABBIT OF THE REGION OF GAINESVILLE, FLORIDA. W. Frank Blair. MS thesis, Univ.Fla., 1935.

COTTONTAIL RABBIT (SYLVILAGUS AUDUBONI BAILEYI) POPULATIONS IN RELATION TO PRAIRIE DOG (CYNOMYS LUDOVICIANUS LUDOVICIANUS) TOWNS. Lee E. Dano. MS thesis, Colo.A.& M. Coll., 1952.

CHECK YOUR SOIL FOR RABBITS. (Average Weights of Rabbits Tend to Vary Directly with Fertility of Soil.) Arthur H. Denny. Mo.Cons., vol.4, no.2, pp.12, 16, May, 1943.

ECOLOGY OF A COTTONTAIL RABBIT (SYLVILAGUS AUDUBONI) POPULATION IN CENTRAL CALIFORNIA. Henry S. Fitch. Calif. Fish and Game, vol.33, no. 3, pp.159-184, July, 1947.

RABBITS KILLED ON AN IDAHO HIGHWAY. Kenneth Gordon. Jour. Mamm., vol.13, no.2, p.169, May, 1932.

COTTONTAIL AND THE WEATHER. (Live Catches Positively Correlated with Barometric Pressure.) Harold C. Hanson. Trans.Wis. Acad.Sci., Arts & Letters, vol.35, pp.91-97, 1944.

RABBIT VERSUS REPTILE. James W.Kimball. Nature Mag., Wash., vol.37, no.7, p.373, illus., Aug.-Sep., 1944.

REACTIONS OF THE RABBIT TO HOT ATMOSPHERES. Douglas H.K.Lee, Kathleen Robinson, H.J.G.Hines. Proc. Roy. Soc.Queensland, Brisbane, vol.53, no.8, pp.129-144, figs.6, Dec. 12, 1941.

SURVIVAL OF NATIVE TRAPPED RABBITS RELEASED ON AGRICULTURAL LANDS. Robert D. McDowell. MS thesis, Pa. State Coll., June 1952.

OLD ORCHARDS HELP RABBITS. Tom Osmer. Mich.Cons., vol.20, no.5, pp.9-10, 29, Sep.-Oct., 1951.

MAGPIE AS SENTINEL FOR RABBITS. Ernest Thompson Seton. Jour. Mamm., vol.3, no.2, p.119, May, 1922.

PIGMY RABBIT (SYLVILAGUS IDAHOENSIS) IN MONO COUNTY, CALIFORNIA. (Ecology and Behavior.) J.H. Severaid. Jour.Mamm., vol.31, no.1, pp.1-4, Feb., 1950.

RABBIT ATTACKING STOAT. E.Scot Skirving. Field, London, vol.153, p.228, Feb. 7, 1929.

RABBIT MORTALITY ALONG AN IDAHO HIGHWAY. Clarence F. Smith. Jour.Mamm., vol.24, no.2, pp.262, 264-265, May, 1943.

ECOLOGY AND POPULATION DYNAMICS OF THE WILD RABBIT (ORYCTOLAGUS CUNICULUS). H.N. Southern. Ann.Applied Biol., vol.27, no.4, pp.509-526, Nov., 1940.

HIGHWAY MORTALITY OF RABBITS IN IDAHO. Charles C. Sperry. Jour.Mamm., vol.14, no.3, p.260, Aug., 1933.

ECOLOGIC NICHES OCCUPIED BY RABBITS IN EASTERN TEXAS. Walter P. Taylor, Daniel W. Lay. Ecology, Lancaster, vol.25, no.1, pp.120-121, Jan., 1944.

RELATION OF THE EASTERN COTTONTAIL TO WEATHER AND CLIMATE. Donald R. Thompson. Thesis, Univ.Ill., 1942.

Economic Importance

PREPARING RABBITS FOR MARKET. Frank G. Ashbrook. Fur of Canada, Winnipeg, vol. 9, no.2, p.9, Nov., 1943.

RABBIT RAISING IN THE UNITED STATES. Frank G. Ashbrook. Verhandl.des I.Internat.Kaninchenzuechter-Kongresses, Leipzig, 1930, pp.146-151, 1931.

RABBIT-HOUSE CONSTRUCTION. Frank G. Ashbrook. U.S.Dept.Agric., Leaflet no.15, pp.6, illus., Dec., 1927.

FUR BEARING ANIMALS OF THE UNITED STATES. THE RABBIT. Frank G. Ashbrook, Horace J. McMullen. Fur Jour., vol.2, no.4, pp.30, 40-42, illus., Apr., 1928.

IS IT PROFITABLE TO STOCK IMPORTED RABBITS? Daniel R. Atzenhoefer. Ohio Conserv.Bull., Columbus, vol.15, no.2, pp.10-11, illus., Feb., 1951.

IS YOUR RABBIT HUNTING DOOMED? Logan J. Bennett. Outdoorsman, vol.91, no.6, pp.4, 6-7, Dec., 1949.

PENNSYLVANIA'S COTTONTAIL PROBLEM. John D. Beule. Pa.Game News, vol.18, no. 2, pp.10-13, 34-37, May, 1947.

SAN JUAN RABBIT... AN ARM LOAD OF TROUBLE. Robert R. Bowers. W.Va. Conserv., vol.19, no.2, pp.3-5, 23, illus., Apr., 1955.

COTTONTAIL RABBIT--BIG GAME OF THE SMALL BOY. G.W.Bradt. Michigan Conserv., Lansing, vol.15, no.9, pp.4-5, illus., Oct., 1946.

RABBIT, BIG GAME OF THE SMALL BOY. G.W.Bradt. Texas Game and Fish, Austin, vol.6, no.2, pp.5, 15, Jan., 1948.

THE RABBIT PEST. PROBLEMS BEFORE THE HOUSE OF LORDS COMMITTEE. Broadleaze. Field, London, vol.168, no. 4379, p.1351, illus., Nov. 28, 1936.

RABBIT FUR PRODUCTION IN ENGLAND. W. Brumwell. Verhandl.des I.Internat. Kaninchenzuechter-Kongresses, Leipzig, 1930, pp.138-143, 1931.

DAMAGE BY RABBITS. W.H.Buckley. Field, London, vol.167, no.4355, p.1444, June 13, 1936.

ASSET AND NUISANCE. SOME REFLECTIONS ON THE RABBIT. Patrick R. Chalmers. Field, London, vol.162, no.4214, p.826, figs., Sep. 30, 1933.

SURVEYS OF RABBIT DAMAGE TO WHEAT IN ENGLAND AND WALES, 1950-52. B.M. Church, F.H.Jacob, H.V.Thompson. Plant. Path., vol.2, no.4, pp.107-112, pl.1, Dec., 1953.

SAN JUAN RABBITS: WANT 'EM ON YOUR FARM? Richard C. Davids. Farm.Jour., p.33, 150, illus., May, 1955.

TAMING A COTTONTAIL. Agnes Dobryoden. Blue Jay, Saskatchewan Nat.Hist.Soc., vol. 15, no.2, p.79, June, 1957.

FUR RABBITS. Guy Dollman. Nat.Hist.Mag., London, vol.2, no.12, pp.118-123, pls.3, Oct., 1929.

RABBIT MENACE. (Destructiveness of Rabbit in Australia and Great Britain.) Guy Dollman. Nat.Hist.Mag., vol.5, no.39, pp. 297-311, July, 1936.

RABBITS WILL EAT YOUR GRASS. W.S. Foster. Prog.Farmer, vol.56, no.2, p.71, Feb., 1941.

RABBITS IN RELATION TO CROPS. F.E. Garlough, J.F.Welch, H.J.Spencer. U.S. Dept.Interior, Cons.Bull.11, pp.20, 1942.

RABBIT DAMAGE TO OAK REPRODUCTION AT THE KELLOGG BIRD SANCTUARY. Aelred D. Geis. Jour.Wildl.Mgt., vol.18, no.3, pp.423-424, July, 1954.

HOW TO GET MORE RABBITS. Arthur Grahame. W.Va.Conserv., Charleston, vol.14, no.2, pp.15-17, 29-30, May, 1950.

CHINCHILLA RABBITS FOR FOOD AND FUR. D.Munroe Green. U.S.Dept.Agric., Leaflet no.22, pp.6, illus., May, 1928.

RABBIT SKINS FOR FUR. D.Monroe Green. U.S.Dept.Agric., Farmers' Bull.1519, pp. 13, figs.7, Jan., 1927.

CARE OF RABBITS. W.J.Hamilton, Jr. Cornell Extension Bull., no.284, Ithaca, pp.24, figs.8, May, 1949.

GARDEN PROTECTION FROM RABBITS. George O. Hendrickson. Iowa Conserv., Des Moines, vol.4, no.5, pp.131-133, May 15, 1945.

(DEVELOPMENT OF THE INSURANCE OF THE SWISS RABBIT BREEDING ASSOCIATION.) Der Werdegang der Versicherung des Schweizer Kaninchenzuchtverbandes. E. Horisberger. Verhandl.des I.Internat.Kaninchenzuechter-Kongresses, Leipzig, 1930, pp.280-283, 1931.

SURVEY OF THE 1940 RABBIT HUNTING SEASON. David T. Katz. Ohio Wildl. Res.Sta., Release 171, pp.37, Dec., 1941.

FUTURE OF COMMERCIAL RABBIT PRODUCTION. Charles E. Kellogg. Nat. Fur News, Denver, vol.17, no.2, p.8, Mar., 1945.

RABBIT INDUSTRY AIDED BY EDUCATIONAL ACTIVITIES. Charles E. Kellogg. Nat. Fur News, Denver, vol.16, no.5, pp.5, 18-19, June, 1944; Fur of Canada, Winnipeg, vol.9, no.9, pp.16-17, June, 1944.

COTTONTAIL RABBITS IN RELATION TO TREES AND FARM CROPS. David E. Lantz. U.S.Dept.Agric., Farmers' Bull.702, pp.1-12, figs.5, Jan.17, 1916.

RABBIT AS A FARM AND ORCHARD PEST. David E. Lantz. Yearbook of U.S.Dept. Agric., 1907, pp.329-342, fig.34, pls. 37-38, 1908.

RAISING BELGIAN HARES AND OTHER RABBITS. David E. Lantz. U.S.Dept.Agric., Famers' Bull.496, pp.1-16, figs.1-5, May 7, 1912.

CONTROVERSIAL SAN JUAN RABBIT. Roger M. Latham. Trans. 20th N.Amer.Wildl. Conf., pp.406-414, 1955.

SAN JUAN RABBIT. Roger M. Latham. Pa. Game News, vol.25, no.9, pp.20-25, illus., Sep., 1954.

ALIAS: SAN JUAN RABBIT. C.W.Lemke. Wis.Cons.Bull., vol.20, no.11, pp.9-11, 40, illus., Nov., 1955.

SANITATION IN DOMESTIC RABBITRIES. Frank D. McKenney. U.S.Dept.Agric. Wildl.Research & Mgt. Leaflet BS-86, pp. 1-4, Apr., 1937.

SANITATION IS IMPORTANT FACTOR IN FINANCIAL SUCCESS OF RABBITRIES. Frank D. McKenney. Amer.Nat.Fur and Market Jour., Wausau, vol.25, no.12, pp. 13, 14, July, 1947.

COUNT YOUR COTTONTAILS. (Rabbit Damage and Repellent.) William F. Mann, Jr., H.J. Derr. U.S.For.Serv., S.Exp.Sta., S.For.Notes no.89, Jan., 1954.

(RAISING RABBITS IN BELGIUM.) L'Elevage du Lapin en Belgique. J.Marcq. Verhandl.des I.Internat.Kaninchenzuechter-Kongresses, Leipzig, 1930, pp.117-120, 1931.

STANDARD OF PERFECTION FOR AMERICAN DOMESTIC RABBITS. Marcellus W. Meek. American Rabbit Assoc., 447 S. Hewitt St., Los Angeles, Calif., pp.174, illus., Jan., 1928.

(REX RABBIT AND ITS IMPORTANCE TO THE BREEDING OF FUR ANIMALS AND THE FUR TRADE.) Rexkaninchen und seine Bedeutung fuer Pelztierzucht und Rauchwaren-wirtschaft. Hans Nachtsheim. Verhandl. des I.Internat.Kaninchenzuechter-Kongresses, Leipzig, 1930, pp.70-79, 1931.

MISSOURI RABBITS FAIL TO SOLVE PENNSYLVANIA'S COTTONTAIL PROBLEM. Werner O. Nagel. Missouri Conserv., Jefferson City, vol.5, no.6, p.11, June, 1944.

RABBIT FEEDING ON HARDWOODS. John Pearce, L.H.Reineke. U.S.Dept.Agric., Northeastern Forest Exp.Sta., Tech.Note 35, pp.3, June, 1940.

(INDUSTRIAL RAISING OF THE FUR RABBIT IN FRANCE.) L'Elevage industriel du Lapin à Fourrure en France. Maxime Petit. Verhandl. des I.Internat.Kaninchenzuechter-Kongresses, Leipzig, 1930, pp.114-116, 1931.

BICOLOR--A BUSHY LESPEDEZA FOR QUAIL AND OTHER WILDLIFE. (Cottontail Rabbits.) Chester F. Phelps. Va. Wildl., Richmond, vol.7, no.3, pp.9-11, 22, illus., Sep., 1946.

MENACE OF THE RABBIT. SOME PROBLEMS OF EXTERMINATION. Horace Phillips. Field, London, vol.172, no.4486, p. 1494, illus., Dec. 17, 1938.

ANGORA RABBITS AND ANGORA RABBIT WOOL PRODUCTION IN GREAT BRITAIN. James N. Pickard. Verhandl. des I.Internat. Kaninchenzuechter-Kongresses, Leipzig, 1930, pp.96-102, 1931.

RABBIT PROBLEM--A SURVEY OF RESEARCH NEEDS AND POSSIBILITIES. F.N. Ratcliffe. Commonwealth Sci. and Industrial Res.Organ., Melbourne, Australia, pp.17, 1951.

RABBITS--A MILLION DOLLAR CROP. Kenneth C. Rowe. Mo. Cons., vol.9, no. 3, pp.13-14, Mar., 1948.

(WORLD PRODUCTION OF RABBIT SKINS.) Weltproduktion an Kaninfellen. Paul Schops. Verhandl.des I.Internat.Kaninchenzuechter-Kongresses, Leipzig, 1930, pp.260-279, 1931.

CASE FOR EXTERMINATING THE RABBIT. Rowland Sperling. Countryman, Idbury, Kingham, Oxfordshire, vol.17, no.1, pp.55-58, illus., Apr.-June, 1938.

RABBIT MENACE IN AUSTRALIA IN 1933 AND THE WAY OUT. David G. Stead. F.E.Moore & Co., Ltd., Sydney, pp.28, illus., Dec., 1932.

CARE OF RABBITS DURING WARM WEATHER. George S.Templeton. U.S.Biol.Surv. Wildl.Research & Mgt. Leaflet BS-114, pp. 1-3, May, 1938.

RABBIT PRODUCTION. George S.Templeton, Frank G.Ashbrook, Chas.E.Kellogg. U.S. Dept.Agric., Farmers Bull., Wash.,D.C., no.1730, pp.1-50, figs.31, June, 1939.

RABBIT RAISING. George S. Templeton, Frank G.Ashbrook, Charles E.Kellogg. U.S.Dept.Interior, Fish and Wildl.Serv. Conserv.Bull., no.25, pp.63, figs.35, 1942.

WILD EUROPEAN RABBIT AND POSSIBLE DANGERS OF ITS INTRODUCTION INTO THE U.S.A. Harry V. Thompson. Jour. Wildl.Mgt., Ithaca, vol.19, no.1, pp.8-13, Jan., 1955.

DIGESTIBLE NUTRIENTS OF FEEDING STUFFS OF THE DOMESTIC RABBIT. LeRoy Voris, L.F.Marcy, Edward J. Thacker, Walter W.Wainio. Jour.Agric.Res., vol.61, no. 9, pp.673-683, Nov., 1940.

FRISKY COTTONTAIL ENJOYS FRIENDLY FEELING AMONG COUNTRY FOLK AS PIONEER OF GAME. Earl Wallace.Kentucky Happy Hunting Ground, Frankfort, vol.1, no. 4, p.17, July, 1946.

TABLE RABBIT PRODUCTION. PRACTICAL BOOKLET IN WHICH EVERY DEPARTMENT OF TABLE RABBIT FARMING IS DISCUSSED IN CONCISE, SIMPLE AND PRACTICAL LANGUAGE. P.E. Wilson. Newport, Salop, (Eng.) P.E.Wilson, pp.46, illus., 1911.

(ON THE QUESTION OF INTERNATIONAL EVALUATION DETERMINATIONS FOR JUDGING RABBITS.) Zur Frage internationaler Bewertungsbestimmungen fuer die Beurteilung von Kaninchen. Max Wischer. Verhandl.des I.Internat.Kaninchenzuechter-Kongresses, Leipzig, 1930, pp.178-183, 1931.

BUNNY BUSINESS. (San Juan Rabbits.) Washington State Game Commission Bull., vol.7, no.1, pp.2, 6, Jan., 1955.

COTTONTAIL PROVIDES PLENTY OF SPORT. Outdoor Indiana, Indianapolis, vol.11, no.10, p.12, illus., Nov., 1944.

DAMAGE FROM RABBITS--CONSIDERATION IN SHELTERBELT PLANTING. U.S. Dept.Agric., Lake State Forest Exp.Sta., Tech.Note 121, p.1, Jan., 1937.

LIVE RABBIT SALES REACH HIGH FIGURE. Mo.Conserv., vol.3, no.6, pp.2-3, Jan., 1942.

NEW THREAT TO AMERICAN AGRICULTURE--EUROPEAN RABBITS IN THE UNITED STATES. Dr.H.W.Levi, Univ. Wis.Zool.Dept., p.1, mimeo.

PENNSYLVANIA FARMERS ASK BAN ON SAN JUAN RABBITS. Md.Sportsman, vol. 13, no.3, p.10, Mar., 1955.

PURCHASE OF RABBITS. N.Jersey Dept. Conserv.and Economic Development, N. Jersey Outdoors, vol.5, no.4, p.29, Oct., 1954.

RABBIT DAMAGE IN RELATION TO TIME OF PLANTING. S.Forestry Notes 17, pp. 3-4, Oct., 1936.

RABBIT RAISING IN HAWAII. Hawaii Agric. Ext., Honolulu, Circ.no.177, pp.1-10, illus., Aug., 1945.

RABBITS AGAIN. Md.Dept.of Game and Inland Fish, Md.Conserv., vol.31, no.2, p.31, Mar., 1954.

RABBITS CAUSE GREAT LOSSES TO PLANTATIONS IN BRUSHY AREAS. U.S.Dept. Agric., Lake States Forest Exp.Sta., Tech. Note 116, p.1, May, 1936.

RABBITS MENACE FOOD. (European Rabbits from San Juan Islands.) Sci.News Letter, vol.66, no.20, p.310, Nov. 13, 1954.

RELEASE OF EUROPEAN RABBITS NOT RECOMMENDED. Outdoor News Bull., vol.8, no.22, p.3, Oct. 29, 1954.

STUDY THE RABBITS FOR A DAY OF GREAT SPORT. S.Dakota Conserv.Digest, Pierre, vol.9, no.3, p.11, Mar., 1942.

TREE GIRDLING BY RABBITS. Ohio Conserv. Bull., Columbus, vol.9, no.2, p.27, illus., Feb., 1945.

Embryology

HISTORY OF THE PROCHORDAL PLATE IN THE RABBIT. Y.H.Aasar. Jour.Anat., vol.66, pp.14-45, figs.25, pls.4, 1931.

STUDIES ON STERILITY AND PRENATAL MORTALITY IN WILD RABBITS. 1. THE RELIABILITY OF ESTIMATES OF PRENATAL MORTALITY BASED ON COUNTS OF CORPORA LUTEA IMPLANTATION SITES AND EMBRYOS. Patricia Allen, F.Brambell, W.Rogers, Ivor H.Mills. Jour.Exp.Biol., London, vol.23, nos.3-4, pp.312-331, Apr., 1947.

EXPERIMENTAL INDUCTION OF PRENATAL MORTALITY AND THE SUBSEQUENT ELIMINATION OF THE DEAD EMBRYOS IN RABBITS. F.Brambell, W.Rogers, Ivor H. Mills. Jour.Exp.Biol., London, vol.25, no.3, pp.209-218, Sep., 1948.

STUDIES ON STERILITY AND PRENATAL MORTALITY IN WILD RABBITS. 2. THE OCCURRENCE OF FIBRIN IN THE YOLK-SAC CONTENTS OF EMBRYOS DURING AND IMMEDIATELY AFTER IMPLANTATION. F.Brambell, W.Rogers, Ivor H.Mills. Jour.Exp.Biol., London, vol.23, nos.3-4, pp.332-345, pl.1, Apr., 1947.

STUDIES ON STERILITY AND PRENATAL MORTALITY IN WILD RABBITS. 3. THE LOSS OF OVA BEFORE IMPLANTATION. F.Brambell, W.Rogers, Ivor H.Mills.Jour. Exp.Biol., London, vol.24, nos.1-2, pp. 192-210, Sep., 1947.

STUDIES ON STERILITY AND PRENATAL MORTALITY IN WILD RABBITS. 4. THE LOSS OF EMBRYOS AFTER IMPLANTATION. F.Brambell, W. Rogers, Ivor H.Mills. Jour. Exp.Biol., London, vol.25, no.3, pp.241-269, Sep., 1948.

EFFECTS OF BREED ON EMBRYO SIZE IN THE DOMESTIC FOWL AND THE RABBIT. Theodore Byerly. Science, Lancaster, n.s., vol.74, no.1926, pp.546-547, Nov. 27, 1931.

FATE OF UNBORN RABBIT EMBRYOS. W.E. Castle. Amer. Jour.Anat., vol.42, pp.399-401, illus., Nov. 15, 1928.

TRANSPLANTATION OF RABBIT BLASTOCYSTS AT LATE STAGE: PROBABILITY OF NORMAL DEVELOPMENT AND VIABILITY AT LOW TEMPERATURE. M.C.Chang. Science, n.s., vol.111, pp.544-545, May 19, 1950.

(FIRST STAGES OF DEVELOPMENT OF THE NASAL CHAMBERS AND MOUTH OF THE RABBIT (ORYCTOLAGUS CUNICULUS L.). THE HARELIP OF A RABBIT FOETUS.) Les premiers stades de development des fosses nasales et de la bouche chez le Lapin (Oryctolagus cuniculus L.). Le bec-de-lievre d'un foetus de Lapin. Madeleine Friant. Vierteljahrsschrift Nat.Ges.Zuerich, Jahr.100, no.3, pp.206-211, Sep., 1955.

EARLY EMBRYOLOGY OF THE RABBIT. P.W.Gregory. Contrib.to Embryol.Carnegie Inst.Washington, vol.21, no.125, pls.2, text figs.3, pp.141-168, 1930.

EMBRYOLOGY OF HEREDITARY BRACHYDACTYLY IN THE RABBIT. Ottilie Ruth Inman. Anat. Rec., Philadelphia, vol.79, no.4, pp.483-505, pls.2, Apr.25, 1941.

(DEVELOPMENT OF THE GERM LAYERS OF THE RABBIT.) Entwicklung der Keimblaetter des Kaninchens.A.Koelliker. Zool. Anzeiger, nos.61-62, pp.1-11, 1880.

STUDIES OF NORMAL DEVELOPMENT OF THE NEW ZEALND WHITE STRAIN OF RABBIT. I. OOGENESIS. II. EXTERNAL MORPHOLOGY OF THE EMBRYO. Allyn J. Waterman. Amer. Jour.Anat., Philadelphia, vol.72, no.3, pp.473-515, figs.2, pls.7, May, 1943.

Europe

INTRODUCTION OF THE RABBIT TO THE ISLE OF VALLAY, NORTH UIST. George Beveridge. Scottish Nat., no.194, pp.33-34, Mar.-Apr., 1932.

INQUEST ON RABBITS. Maurice Burton. Illus.London News, vol.137, no.3578, p. 880, illus., Nov. 19, 1955.

STATUS OF THE RABBIT AT ODSEY. W.H. Fordham. Trans.Hertfordshire Nat.Hist.Soc. and Field Club, vol.20, pt.5, p.352, Apr., 1938.

(CONTRIBUTION TO STUDY OF THE RABBIT OF PORTO SANTO (ORYCTOLAGUS CUNICULUS HUXLEYI HAECKEL).) Contribution à l'etude du lapin de Porto Santo (Oryctolagus cuniculus Huxleyi Haeckel). Carlos Franca. Bull.Soc.Portugaise Sci. Nat., Lisbon, vol.6, no.2, pp.14, pl.1, 1913.

(REGARDING THE RABBIT OF PORTO SANTO AND THE VALIDITY OF THE SPECIES.) A proposito del coniglio di Porto Santo e della realta della specie. Ermanno Giglio-Tos. Riv.Biol., Roma, vol.I, no.1, pp.24, 1919.

BELGIAN HARE--PAST, PRESENT AND FUTURE. Ellye Howell. International, Chicago, vol.9, pp.282-286, illus., Oct., 1900.

(DISTRIBUTION OF ORYCTOLAGUS CUNICULUS L. IN NORTH-EAST POLAND.) Rozmieszczenie krolika dzikiego (Oryct. cuniculus L.) w Poln.-Wschodniej Polsce. Józef Goetz. Polska Akad.Umiejetnosci, Cracow, no.29, pp.1-12, Mar. 19, 1952.

(SCIENTIFIC WORKS ON THE BIOLOGY OF RABBITS IN THE U.S.S.R.) Wissenschaftliche Arbeiten zur Biologie des Kaninchens in der U.d.S.S.R. N.Iljin. Verhandl.des I.Internat.Kaninchenzuechter-Kongresses, Leipzig, 1930, pp.161-169, 1931.

THE RABBIT. Phyllis Kelway. Game & Gun and Angler's Monthly, London, vol. 18, no.193, pp.345-347, illus., Oct., 1941.

(WILD RABBITS.) Vom wilden Kaninchen. Friedrich von Lucanus. Naturforscher, Berlin, vol.11, no.9, pp.311-313, figs.3, Dec., 1934.

BELGIAN HARE, A MISLEADING MISNOMER. Marcus W. Lyon, Jr. Science, n.s., vol.43, no.1115, p.686, May 12, 1916.

THE RABBIT. C.B. Moffat. Irish Naturalists' Jour., vol.2, no.2, pp.28-30, Mar., 1928.

ORGANIZATION OF RABBIT EDUCATION AND INVESTIGATION IN GREAT BRITAIN. Raymond T. Parkhurst. Verhandl. des I.Internat.Kaninchenzuechter-Kongresses, Leipzig, 1930, pp.51-54, 1931.

OBSERVATIONS ON THE RABBIT IN WEST WALES. W.M.Phillips, M.N.Stephens, A.N.Worden. Nature, vol.169, no.4308, pp.869-870, May 24, 1952.

(ON THE VARIABILITY OF THE NORMAL DOMESTIC RABBIT.) Zur Variabilitaet des normalen Hauskaninchens. Alfred Ploetz. Jenaische Zeitschr.Naturwiss., vol.67, pp. 493-510, 1932.

SEASONAL OBSERVATIONS ON THE WILD RABBIT (ORYCTOLAGUS CUNICULUS CUNICULUS L.) IN WEST WALES. Marie N. Stephens. Proc.Zool.Soc.London, vol. 122, pt.2, pp.417-434, illus., Aug.15,1952.

(RABBIT OF PORTO SANTO AND THE BLACK RABBIT OF LA CAMARGUE.) Le Lapin de Porto Santo et le Lapin negre de la Camargue. E.L. Trouessart. Bull.Mus.d'Hist.Nat., Paris, no.6, pp.366-373, figs., 1917.

(ISLAND-LIKE OCCURRENCE OF THE WILD RABBIT (ORYCTOLAGUS C. CUNICULUS LINNE 1758) IN SOUTHERN THURINGIA.) Ein inselartiges Auftreten des Wildkaninchens, Oryctolagus c.cuniculus (Linne, 1758), in Suedthueringen. Walter Uloth. Saeugetierk. Mitteil., Stuttgart, vol.4, no.1, p.32, Jan. 1, 1956.

(WILD RABBIT AS A PEST ALONG THE MOSELLE AND IN OTHER GERMAN WINE-GROWING REGIONS.) Wildkaninchen als Rebschaedling an der Mosel und in den uebrigen deutschen Weinbaugebieten. H. Zillig. Anz.Schaedlingsk.zug.Nachrichtenblatt Deutsch.Ges.ang.Ent., vol.10, no.7, pp.80-83, July 15, 1934.

Experimental Biology

TERMINATION OF PREGNANCY IN THE RABBIT BY INTRAVENOUS INJECTION OF ANTERIOR LOBE PITUITARY EXTRACT. C.W. Bellerby. Jour.Exp.Biol., London, vol.12, no.3, pp.286-295, July, 1935.

EFFECTS OF X-RAYS AND NITROGEN MUSTARD ON LYMPHATIC NODULE OF THE RABBIT. P.P.H. Bruyn. R.C. Robertson. Proc.Soc.Exp.Biol.Med., Utica, vol. 72, no.3, pp.717-718, Dec., 1949.

INFLUENCE OF A PREVIOUS INJECTION OF EPHINEPHRINE UPON THE DIABETOGENIC EFFECT OF ALLOXAN IN RABBITS. R. Carrasco-Formigvera, Isabel Escobar. Amer. Jour. Physiol., Baltimore, vol.152, no.3, pp.609-614, Mar. 1, 1948.

FERTILITY AND SEX RATIONS IN THE RABBIT FROM SEMEN TREATED IN VITRO WITH LACTIC ACID AND SODIUM BICARBONATE. L.E.Casida, R.L. Murphree. Jour. Heredity, Wash., D.C., vol.33, no.12, pp.434-438, Dec., 1942.

(CHANGED COLORATION OF FUR IN THE YOUNG OF RABBITS SUBJECTED TO X-RADIATION.) Veraenderte Fellfarbung bei Nachkommen roentgenbestrahlter Kaninchen. Rolf Danneel, Ernst Lubnov. Biol.Zentralblatt, Leipzig, vol.59, nos.11-12, pp.588-597, figs.9, 1939.

NOTE ON ARTERIOSCLEROSIS IN RABBITS CAUSED BY SOME SAMPLES OF URANIUM NITRATE. R.Dominguez. Science, n.s., vol.64, pp.407-408, Oct. 22, 1926.

RESPIRATORY ARREST IN RABBITS EXPOSED TO HYPOXIA AFTER DIBENAMINE. Eben Dustin, George Maison. Proc.Soc. Exp.Biol.Med., Utica, vol.67, no.4, pp. 435-437, Apr., 1948.

ON THE PRODUCTION AND SUPPRESSION OF GLYCOSURIA IN RABBITS THROUGH ELECTROLYTES. (A PRELIMINARY COMMUNICATION.) Martin H. Fischer. Univ. Calif.Publ., Physiology, vol.1, no.9, pp. 77-79, Dec. 24, 1903.

ON THE PRODUCTION AND SUPPRESSION OF GLYCOSURIA IN RABBITS THROUGH ELECTROLYTES. (SECOND COMMUNICATION.) Martin H. Fischer. Univ.Calif. Publ.Physiology, vol.1, no.12, pp.87-113, Feb. 15, 1904.

STUDIES ON CYTOLYSINS. II. TRANSMISSION OF INDUCED EYE DEFECTS. (Transmission through Successive Generations of Eye Defects in Rabbits Originally Induced by Lens-Sensitized Fowl Serum.) M.F.Guyer, E.A.Smith. Jour.Exp.Zool., vol.31, pp.171-215, pls.1-4, Aug. 20,1920.

EFFECT OF ATROPINE AND ESTROGENS ON INTRAOCULAR UTERINE TRANSPLANTS IN THE RABBIT. Irwin H. Kaiser. Bull.Johns Hopkins Hosp., Baltimore, vol. 82, no.4, pp.429-445, Apr., 1948.

CYTOLOGY OF THE SYNOVIAL FLUID OF NORMAL JOINTS. (Experiments on Rabbits.) J.Albert Key. Anat.Rec., vol.40, pp.193-211, illus., Oct. 25, 1928.

SEXUAL GLANDS AND METABOLISM. II. INFLUENCE OF EMULSIONS OF TESTIS AND PROSTATE UPON THE NITROGEN METABOLISM OF RABBITS. V. Korenchevsky, M.Carr. British Jour.Path., vol.6, no.2, pp.74-83, 1925.

EFFECT OF LIVER EXTRACT ON GROWTH OF RABBITS. H.O.Kunkel, R.E.Simpson, P.B.Pearson, O.Olcest, B.S.Schweigert. Proc. Soc.Exp.Biol.Med., Utica, vol.68, no.1, pp.122-124, May, 1948.

POST-ROTATION NYSTAGMUS IN THE RABBIT WITH HEAD FIXED AND WITH HEAD FREE. R.C. Lumpkin. Jour.Comp.Psych., vol.7, pp.181-185, illus., 1927.

ON THE ACTION OF SALINE PURGATIVES IN RABBITS AND THE COUNTERACTION OF THEIR EFFECT BY CALCIUM. John Bruce MacCallum. Univ.Calif.Publ. Physiol., vol.1, no.20, pp.175-185, July 10, 1904.

EFFECT OF HABITUATION ON THE ROTATION-NYSTAGMUS AS COMPARED WITH THE AFTER-NYSTAGMUS IN THE RABBIT. S.S. Maxwell. Amer. Jour.Physiol., vol. 68, pp.125-126, 1924.

(ACTION OF LACRIMAL GLAND EXTRACT ON BLOOD PRESSURE.) Action de l'extrait de glandes lacrymales sur la pression sanguine. D.Michail, P.Vancea. Comptes Rendus des Seances de la Soc.de Biol., vol. 97, pp. 1101-1104, figs.3, Oct. 21, 1927.

(DOES FEEDING THE RABBIT A DIET CONTAINING CHOLESTERIN AND LECITHIN AFFECT THE SEX RATIO OF THE PROGENY?) Hat beim Kaninchen eine Fuetterung mit Cholesterin und Lezithin einen Einfluss auf das Geschlechtsverhaeltniss der Nachkommen? C.A. Mirbt. Zeitschr.f. Ind.Abstammungs- und Vererbungslehre, vol.48, pp.259-304, figs.37, 1928.

MIOTIC ACTIVITY IN THE EPIDERMIS OF THE RABBIT STIMULATED WITH LOCAL APPLICATIONS OF TESTOSTERONE PROPIONATE. William Montagna, Patricia Kenyon, James B.Hamilton. Jour.Exp.Zool., Philadelphia, vol.110, no.3, pp.379-395, pls.4, Apr., 1949.

ON TISSUE CULTURE OF THE PLACENTA OF THE RABBIT. Vladimir Pljesakov. Jour. Exp.Zool., vol.42, pp.315-332, figs.21, 1925.

(A CURIOUS PECULIARITY IN THE RETRACTION OF CERTAIN BLOOD CLOTS WITHOUT PLATELETS.) Une particularité curieuse de la rétraction de certains caillots sans plaquettes. (Experiments on Rabbits.) Jacques Roskam. Comptes Rendus des Séances de la Soc.de Biol., vol.97, pp.730-731, Aug. 26, 1927.

ON THE OBLITERATION OF THE LUMEN OF BLOOD VESSELS. IV. THE ORIGIN AND NATURE OF THE MASS WHICH COMES TO OCCUPY THE LUMEN OF AN ARTERY SEGMENT BETWEEN TWO LIGATURES. (Work on Rabbit.) J.Parsons Schaeffer, H.E.Radasch. Amer. Jour. Anat., vol.33, pp.219-242, pls.6, May 15, 1924.

EFFECT OF LIGHT ON OVARIAN ACTIVITY IN THE RABBIT. G.K.Smelser, Arthur Walton, E.O.Whetham. Jour.Exp.Biol., Edinburgh, vol.11, no.4, pp.352-363, Oct., 1934.

EFFECTS OF CEREBRAL DESTRUCTION ON THE SEXUAL BEHAVIOR OF MALE RABBITS. III. FRONTAL, PARIETAL, AND OCCIPITAL REGIONS. Calvin P. Stone. Jour.Comp.Psych., vol.6, no.6, pp.435-448, 1926.

EFFECTS OF SUB-LETHAL PHOSPHORUS POISONING ON BONE GROWTH IN WILD RABBITS. C.H. Tyndale-Biscoe. New Zealand Jour.Sci.& Technol., sec.B, vol.37, no.3, pp.407-415, illus., Nov., 1955.

Food Habits

RADIOGRAPHIC ANALYSIS OF MASTICATION AND SWALLOWING IN THE DOMESTIC RABBIT: ORYCTOLAGUS CUNICULUS (L). G.M.Ardran, F.H.Kemp, W.D.L. Ride. Proc.Zool.Soc.London, vol.130, no. 2, pp.257-274, pls.1-7, Mar. 13, 1958.

COTTONTAIL RABBITS ARE INSECTIVOROUS. R.D. Bird. Jour. Mamm., vol.11, no.2, p.240, May, 1930.

FOOD HABITS OF THE COTTONTAIL RABBIT IN SOUTHERN ILLINOIS. Edward L. Corder, Jr. M.A.thesis, S.Ill.Univ., pp.v-38, 1955.

FOOD HABITS OF THE EASTERN AND NEW ENGLAND COTTONTAILS. Paul D.Dalke, Palmer R. Sime. Jour.Wildl.Mgt., Menasha, vol.5, no.2, pp.216-228, Apr., 1941.

PLENTY FOOD--PLENTY RABBITS. David E. Davis. Md.Conserv., vol.31, no.4, pp. 22-23, illus., July, 1954.

DOES KUDZU HAVE WILDLIFE VALUE? (Relished Food of Cottontails.) Verne E. Davison. Soil Cons., vol.7, no.10, p.253, Apr., 1942.

SOME WINTER FOODS OF THE COTTONTAIL IN SOUTHERN MICHIGAN. Lee R. Dice. Jour. Mamm., vol.26, no.1, pp.87-88, Feb., 1945.

WINTER FOOD OF THE COTTONTAIL RABBIT IN THE VICINITY OF ITHACA, NEW YORK. H.M. Doremus. MS thesis, Cornell Univ., 1938.

FOOD HABITS OF SOME POPULATIONS OF COTTONTAIL RABBITS IN OHIO. Julian L. Dusi. PhD thesis, Ohio State Univ., 1949; Jour.Widl.Mgt., vol.16, no.2, pp.180-186, illus., Apr., 1952.

UTILIZATION OF WOODY PLANTS AS FOOD BY MEARNS COTTONTAIL, SYLVILAGUS FLORIDANUS MEARNSII (ALLEN), IN WINTER. William Wynn Eakins. MS thesis, Iowa State Coll., 1949.

PLANT LIFE ON EAST ANGLIAN HEATHS, BEING OBSERVATIONAL AND EXPERIMENTAL STUDIES OF THE VEGETATION OF BRECKLAND. (Relation of Rabbits to Vegetation.) E.Pickworth Farrow. Cambridge, Univ.Press, pp.x-108, pls.23, 1925.

(NUTRITION IN THE WILD RABBIT ORYCTOLAGUS CUNICULUS LINNE 1758.) Zur Ernaehrungsweise des Wildkaninchens, Oryctolagus cuniculus (Linné, 1758). G.Gaffrey. Saeugetierk. Mitteil., Stuttgart, vol.2, no.2, p.80, Apr. 1, 1954.

WINTER FOOD AND COVER OF MEARNS COTTONTAIL. George O. Hendrickson. Trans. N.Amer.Wildl.Conf., vol.3, pp. 787-793, 1938.

WINTER RABBIT BROWSE TALLY ON THE UNIVERSITY OF WISCONSIN ARBORETUM. Robert A. McCabe. Trans.Wis.Acad.Sci., Arts & Letters, vol.37, pp.15-33, 1947.

SOME OBSERVATIONS OF THE FOOD COACTIONS OF RABBITS IN WESTERN KANSAS DURING PERIODS OF STRESS. Andrew Riegel. Trans.Kansas Acad.Sci., Lawrence, vol.45, no.49, pp.369-375, figs.4, 1942.

BICOLOR AS A RABBIT FOOD. Walter Rosene, Jr. Jour.Wildl.Mgt., vol.19, no.2, p.324, Apr., 1955.

FURTHER STUDIES OF THE WINTER FEEDING HABITS OF COTTONTAIL RABBITS. Harvey L. Sweetman. Ecology, vol. 30, no.3, pp.371-376, July, 1949.

SELECTION OF WOODY PLANTS AS WINTER FOOD BY THE COTTONTAIL RABBIT. Harvey L. Sweetman. Ecology, vol.25, no.4, pp.467-472, Oct., 1944.

SUPPLEMENTARY NOTE ON THE WINTER FOOD HABITS OF COTTONTAIL RABBITS. Harvey L. Sweetman. Ecology, vol.27, no. 2, pp.185-188, Apr., 1946.

GRAZING BEHAVIOR OF THE WILD RABBIT, ORYCTOLAGUS CUNICULUS (L). Harry V. Thompson. Brit. Jour. Anim.Behaviour, vol.1, no.1, pp.16-19, Jan., 1953.

WINTER FOOD OF COTTONTAIL RABBITS. John B. Todd. Jour.Mamm., vol.8, no.3, pp.222-228, Aug., 1927.

FOOD RELATIONSHIPS OF THE COTTONTAIL RABBIT IN SOUTHERN MICHIGAN. R.E. Trippensee. Trans.N.Amer.Wildl. Conf., vol.3, pp.794-804, 1938.

(CONTRIBUTION TO THE THEORY OF RABBIT NUTRITION.) Beitraege zur Theorie der Kaninchenernaehrung. G.V. Wendt. Verhandl. des I. Internat. Kaninchenzuechter-Kongresses, Leipzig, 1930, pp.184-190, 1931.

RHUBARB LEAVES AS A FEEDING-STUFF FOR RABBITS. W.King Wilson. Nature, London, vol.158, no.4002, pp.67-68, July 13, 1946.

General Habits, Behavior

RABBIT NESTS ARE DEATH TRAPS... SOMETIMES! Daniel R. Atzenhoefer. Ohio Cons.Bull., vol.17, no.6, pp.10-11, June, 1953.

HABITS OF LOWLY COTTONTAIL DESCRIBED BY DEAN OF WILDLIFE SPECIALISTS. Vernon Bailey. Va.Wildl., Blacksburg, vol.1, no.10, p.7, June, 1938.

NOTES ON ESCAPE BEHAVIOR IN THE FLORIDA MARSH RABBIT. A.F.Carr, Jr. Jour.Mamm., vol.20, no.3, pp.322-325, fig.1, Aug. 14, 1939.

RABBITS' NESTS ABOVE GROUND. G.N. Carter. Northwestern Nat., Arbroath, vol. 11, no.1, p.42, Mar., 1936.

HOME RANGE AND MOBILITY OF BRUSH RABBITS IN CALIFORNIA CHAPARRAL. Joseph H. Connell. Jour. Mamm., vol.35, no.3, pp.392-405, Aug. 20, 1954.

(SWIMMING RABBIT (ORYCTOLAGUS C. CUNICULUS LINNÉ 1758).) Schwimmendes Kaninchen, Oryctolagus c. cuniculus (Linne, 1758). Gerhard Creutz. Saeugetierk.Mitteil., Stuttgart, vol.1, no.1, p.22, Jan.10, 1953.

HOME AND SEASONAL RANGES OF THE EASTERN COTTONTAIL IN CONNECTICUT. Paul D.Dalke, Palmer R. Sime. Trans. N.Amer.Wildl.Conf., vol.3, pp.659-669, 1938.

NOTES ON EMERGENCE BEHAVIOUR OF THE RABBIT, ORYCTOLAGUS CUNICULUS (L.), AND ITS BEARING ON THE VALIDITY OF SIGHT COUNTS FOR POPULATION ESTIMATES. G.M. Dunnet. C.S.I.R.O. Wildl.Res., Canberra, Australia, vol.2, no.2, pp.85-89, 1957.

NOTE ON THE COTTONTAIL RABBIT. Forrest V. Durand. Jour.Mamm., vol.21, no.1, p.95, Feb. 14, 1940.

(CANNIBALISM IN THE RABBIT.) Kanibalismus bei Kaninchen. Heinz F. Friederichs. Pelztierzucht, vol.5, no.10, pp.197-200, 1929.

COVER PREFERENCE OF THE COTTONTAIL RABBIT. Charles E. Friley, Jr. MS thesis, Univ.Conn., 1938.

STUDY OF COTTONTAIL HABITAT PREFERENCES ON A SOUTHERN MICHIGAN FARMING AREA. Charles E. Friley, Jr. Mich. Dept. Cons., Final Rep. Proj. W-48-R, pp.iii-19, appendix pp.18 (maps, graphs, tbls.), Mar., 1955.

FRACTURED LEG NOT FATAL TO A RABBIT. Frank F. Gander. Jour. Mamm., vol. 11, no.2, p.240, May, 1930.

TRAP RESPONSE OF THE COTTONTAIL RABBIT AND ITS EFFECT ON CENSUSING. Aelred D. Geis. Jour.Wildl.Mgt., vol.19, no.4, pp.466-472, Oct., 1955.

VALUE OF GROUNDHOG HOLES AS WINTER RETREATS FOR RABBITS. Richard Gerstell. Penna.Game News, Harrisburg, vol.10, no.6, pp.6-9, figs.6, tbls.3, Sep., 1939.

HOME RANGE OF THE COTTONTAIL RABBIT. Arnold O. Haugen. Ecology, vol.23, no.3, pp.354-367, July, 1942.

NESTING COVER USED BY MEARNS COTTONTAIL. George O. Hendrickson. Trans. N.Amer.Wildl.Conf., vol.5, pp.328-331, 1941.

RABBIT SWIMMERS. (Marsh Rabbit.) John Eric Hill. Nat.Hist., New York, vol.50, no.1, p.27, illus., June, 1942.

STRESS RESPONSE AND SURVIVAL TIME IN THREE WILDLIFE SPECIES. (Cotton - tail Rabbit.) Ruth L. Hine, Kenneth G. Flakas. Jour.Wildl.Mgt., vol.21, no.2, pp.239-240, Apr., 1957.

USE OF REARING COVER BY MEARNS COTTONTAIL IN DECATUR COUNTY, IOWA. Raymond L. Linder. MS thesis, Iowa State Coll., pp.113, illus., 1955.

WINTER DEN STUDIES OF THE COTTONTAIL IN SOUTHERN MICHIGAN. J.P. Linduska. Ecology, vol.28, no.4, pp.448-454, Oct., 1947.

PUGNACIOUS RABBIT. L.B. Nagler. Outdoor Life, vol.67, no.4, p.104, fig.1, Apr., 1931.

FOR HIS SPECIALTY, THE RABBIT NEEDS PRIVACY--SAVE BRUSH PILES AND COVER. Ralph Pogue. Missouri Wildl., Boonville, vol.13, no.2, p.12, Spring Issue, 1951.

ON THE HOME RANGE OF COTTONTAILS. D.H.Salman. Physiologia Comparata et Oecologia, vol.1, no.2, pp.95-109, Feb., 1949.

HOME RANGE OF THE COTTONTAIL IN CENTRAL MISSOURI. Charles W. Schwartz. Jour. Mamm., vol.22, no.4, pp.386-392, Nov., 1941.

HABITS OF SYLVILAGUS AQUATICUS LITTORALIS. Ruth Dowell Svihla. Jour.Mamm., vol.10, no.4, pp.315-319, pl.24, Nov., 1929.

(HABITS OF THE SWAMP RABBITS SYLVILAGUS AQUATICUS LITTORALIS.) Les moeurs du lapin des marais Sylvilagus aquaticus littoralis. Ruth Dowell Svihla. Revue d'Histoire Naturelle, Pt.1, A, Mammiferes, Paris, vol.11, no.1, pp.33-37, Jan., 1930.

SALT REQUIREMENTS OF RABBITS. George S. Templeton. U.S.Dept.Agric., Wildl.Res. and Mgt.Leaflet BS-102, p.1, Jan., 1938.

AQUATIC RABBIT. Ivan R. Tomkins. Nature Mag., vol.27, no.6, pp.333-334, figs., June, 1936.

WINTER COVER OF THE MEARNS COTTONTAIL, SYLVILAGUS FLORIDANUS MEARNSII (ALLEN), IN CENTRAL IOWA. C.G. Trautman. MS thesis, Iowa State Coll., 1942.

NIGHT-STROLLING RABBITS. C.Huber Watson. Nature Mag., Washington, vol. 37, no.1, pp.14-15, illus., Jan., 1944.

Growth and Development

DEVELOPMENT OF THE VAGINA IN THE RABBIT. James S. Baxter. Jour. Anat., vol. 67, pt.4, pp.555-562, pl.1, July, 1933.

EARLY DEVELOPMENT OF THE SKULL OF THE RABBIT. G.R.de Beer, J.H. Woodger. Philos.Trans.Roy.Soc.London, ser.B, vol. 218, pp.373-414, pls.35-43, Aug. 21, 1930.

ON THE TYPE OF POSTEMBRYONIC GROWTH OF THE SKELETON OF A RABBIT (ORYCTOLAGUS CUNICULUS DOM.). V.Y. Brovar. Comptes Rendus (Doklady) Acad.Sci.USSR, Moscow, n.s., vol.29, no.2, pp.160-164, 1940.

TIME AND ORDER OF APPEARANCE OF OSSIFICATION CENTERS AND THEIR DEVELOPMENT IN THE SKULL OF THE RABBIT. Jean A. Bruce. Amer. Jour.Anat., Philadelphia, vol.68, no.1, pp.41-67, Jan. 15, 1941.

GROWTH AND PROPORTIONS OF THE RABBIT'S EAR IN RELATION TO BODY WEIGHT. George Dunlop, John Hammond. Jour.Genetics, London, vol.34, no.3, pp.463-475, figs.6, tbl.1, pls.16, June, 1937.

GROWTH RATE OF YOUNG RABBITS, ORYCTOLAGUS CUNICULUS (L.). G.M. Dunnet. C.S.I. R.O. Wildl.Res., Commonwealth Scientific & Industrial Res. Organization, Melbourne, vol.1, no.1, pp. 66-67, Sep., 1956.

DEVELOPMENT OF THE HEART OF THE RABBIT. A. Girgis. Proc. Zool. Soc. London, 1930, pt.3, pp.755-782, pls.1-11, text figs.1-4, Oct., 1930.

FURTHER CONTRIBUTION ON THE DEVELOPMENT OF THE HEART IN THE RABBIT. A. Girgis. P.Z.S., pt.2, pp.421-450, fig.1, pls.8, June, 1933.

OBSERVATIONS ON THE GROWTH OF YOUNG BRUSH RABBITS. Robert T. Orr. Jour. Mamm., vol.23, no.3, pp.299-302, fig.1, Aug. 14, 1942.

OBSERVATIONS ON THE GROWTH OF BLOOD VESSELS AS SEEN IN THE TRANSPARENT CHAMBER INTRODUCED INTO THE RABBIT'S EAR. J.C. Sandison. Amer. Jour.Anat., vol.41, pp.475-496, illus., July 15, 1928.

Heredity

HISTOPATHOLOGY OF A NEW TYPE OF HEREDITARY LOSS OF COORDINATION IN THE DOMESTIC RABBIT. M.V.Anders. Amer.Jour.Anat., Philadelphia, vol.76, no. 2, pp.183-199, figs.1-3, pls.1-2, Mar., 1945.

POLYPLOIDY IN RABBITS. R.A. Beatty, M. Fischberg. Nature, London, vol.166, no. 4214, p.239, Aug. 5, 1950.

GENETICS OF THE VIENNA WHITE RABBIT. W.E.Castle. Science, n.s., vol.55, pp.269-270, Mar. 10, 1922.

LINKAGE OF DUTCH, ENGLISH, AND ANGORA IN RABBITS. W.E. Castle. Proc. Nat.Acad.Sci., vol.10, no.3, pp.107-109, Mar., 1924.

LINKAGE STUDIES ON CASTORREX RABBITS. W.E. Castle. Zeitschr.f. Ind.Abstammungs und Vererbungslehre, vol.52, pp.53-60, 1929.

REX RABBIT. W.E. Castle. Jour.Heredity, vol.20, pp.193-199, fig.4, May, 1929.

BLOOD GROUP INHERITANCE IN THE RABBIT. W.E. Castle, C.E.Keeler. Proc.Nat. Acad.Sci., vol.19, pp.92-98, Jan., 1933.

TESTS FOR LINKAGE BETWEEN THE BLOOD-GROUP GENES AND OTHER KNOWN GENES OF THE RABBIT. W.E. Castle, C.E. Keeler. Proc.Nat.Acad.Sci., vol.19, pp.98-100, Jan., 1933.

GENETIC LINKAGE IN THE RABBIT. W.E. Castle, P.B. Sawin. Proc.Nat.Acad.Sci., Wash., D.C., vol.27, no.11, pp.519-523, Nov., 1941.

(ON THE TRANSMISSIBILITY OF AN ACQUIRED SOMATIC CHARACTER (RABBIT CATARACTS).) Sur la transmissibilite d'un caractere somatique acquis (cataracte de Lapins). L.R. Cuénot, P. Venier. Compt. Rend.Acad.Sci., Paris, vol.178, pp.1129-1132, 1924.

INHERITANCE OF A RIB VARIATION IN THE RABBIT. Earl L. Green. Anat.Rec., Philadelphia, vol.74, no.1, pp.47-60, May 25, 1939.

HEREDITARY VARIATIONS IN THE SKULL OF THE RABBIT. Harry S. Green, Wade H. Brown. Science, vol.76, no.1975, pp. 421-422, Nov. 4, 1932.

GLUTATHIONE CONCENTRATION AND HEREDITARY BODY SIZE. II. GLUTATHIONE CONCENTRATION IN NON-NURSED YOUNG OF SIX POPULATIONS OF RABBITS DIFFERING IN GENETIC CONSTITUTION FOR

ADULT SIZE.III. BACKCROSS TO THE LARGE PARENT RACE. P.W.Gregory, H. Goss. Jour.Exp.Zool., vol.66, no.1, pp. 155-173, Aug.5, 1933; no.3, pp.335-349, Nov.5, 1933.

RELATION OF SULPHYDRYL CONCENTRATION TO SIZE INHERITANCE IN THE RABBIT. P.W.Gregory, H.Goss. Amer.Nat., vol. 67, no.709, pp.180-185, Mar.-Apr., 1933.

FURTHER STUDIES ON INHERITANCE OF EYE DEFECTS INDUCED IN RABBITS. M.F. Guyer, E.A. Smith. Jour. Exp.Zool., vol.38, pp.449-475, Jan. 5, 1924.

MORPHOGENETIC STUDIES IN THE RABBIT. Inez Baumgartner Hull. Jour.Exp.Zool., Philadelphia, vol.105, no.2, pp.173-197, July, 1947.

PRODUCTION AND INHERITANCE OF EYE DEFECTS IN RABBITS. Heman L.Ibsen, L. D.Bushnell. Amer.Nat., vol.68, no.714, pp.92-95, Jan.-Feb., 1934.

ROLE OF HEREDITY IN RESPONSE TO A DRUG AS DEMONSTRATED BY THE EXPERIMENTAL MOLT OF RABBITS INDUCED BY TOXIC THALLIUM COMPOUNDS. N.A.Iljin. Jour.Heredity, Wash., vol.36, no.3, pp.85-91, figs.6-8, Mar., 1945.

NAKED--A RECESSIVE MUTATION IN THE RABBIT. D.A. Kislovsky. Jour.Heredity, vol. 19, pp.438-439, illus., Oct., 1928.

ON THE INHERITANCE OF WEIGHT IN RABBITS FROM A STUDY OF THE NEW-BORN (trans.title). S. Kopeć. Pam.Państ. Inst.Nauk.Gosp.Wiejsk.Pulawach , vol.4, A, pp.218-243, 1923.

HEREDITARY VARIATIONS IN THE VENA CAVA INFERIOR OF THE RABBIT. C.W. McNutt, P.B.Sawin. Amer.Jour.Anat., Philadelphia, vol.72, no.2, pp.259-289, figs.1-31, pl.1, Mar., 1943.

(GENETIC STUDIES ON THE CHINCHILLA RABBIT.) Etudes génetiques sur le lapin chinchilla. J.O.L.Marco. Zeitschr.f.Ind. Abstammungs- und Vererbungslehre, vol. 47, pp.75-79, 1928.

(ON AN INHERITED NERVOUS DISEASE IN RABBITS (SYRINGOMYELIA). Ueber eine erbliche Nervenkrankheit (Syringomyelie) beim Kaninchen. Hans Nachtsheim. Verhandl. des I.Internat. Kaninchenzuechter-Kongresses, Leipzig, 1930, pp.254-259, 1931.

(REX RABBIT AND ITS GENETICS.) Das Rexkaninchen und seine Genetik. Hans Nachtsheim. Zeitschr.f.Ind.Abstammungs- und Vererbungslehre, vol.52, pp.1-52, figs. 12, tbls.24, 1929.

REXING THE LILAC RABBIT. INHERITANCE OF FUR COAT AND COLOR FACTORS DEMONSTRATED IN THE DOMESTIC RABBIT. Raymond Parkhurst, W.King Wilson. Jour.Heredity, vol.24, no.1, pp.35-39, figs. 9-13, Jan., 1933.

INHERITANCE OF YELLOW FAT IN RABBITS. Michael S. Pease. Verhandl.des I. Internat.Kaninchenzuechter-Kongresses, Leipzig, 1930, pp.91-94, 1931.

MORPHOGENETIC STUDIES OF THE RABBIT. VIII. GENETIC VARIATION IN THE STERNUM AS DETERMINED BY THE INTERACTION OF GENERAL AND OF REGIONALLY SPECIFIC GROWTH FACTORS. Elsie D. Peck, Paul B. Sawin. Jour.Exp.Zool., vol. 114, no.2, pp.335-358, July, 1950.

HEREDITARY VARIATION OF THE CHINCHILLA RABBIT. Paul B.Sawin. Jour.Heredity, vol.23, no.1, pp.39-46, figs.20-24, Jan., 1932.

MORPHOGENETIC STUDIES OF THE RABBIT. Paul B. Sawin. Jour.Exp.Zool., vol. 100, no.2, pp.301-329, Nov., 1945.

PRELIMINARY STUDIES OF HEREDITARY VARIATION IN THE AXIAL SKELETON OF THE RABBIT. Paul B. Sawin. Anat.Rec., vol.69, no.4, pp.407-427, figs.3, Nov.25, 1937.

"ATAXIA," A HEREDITARY NERVOUS DISORDER OF THE RABBIT. Paul B. Sawin, M.V. Anders, R.B.Johnson. Proc.Nat.Acad. Sci., Wash., D.C., vol.28, no.4, pp.123-127, Apr., 1942.

ATROPINESTERASE, A GENETICALLY DETERMINED ENZYME IN THE RABBIT. Paul B.Sawin, David Glick. Proc. Nat.Acad. Sci., Wash., D.C., vol.29, no.2, pp.55-59, Feb., 1943.

GENETIC LINKAGE OF BLOOD TYPES IN THE RABBIT. Paul B. Sawin, M.A.Griffith, C.A.Stuart. Proc.Nat.Acad.Sci., Wash., vol.30, no.9, pp.217-221, Sep., 1944.

MORPHOGENETIC STUDIES OF THE RABBIT. II. EVIDENCE OF REGIONALLY SPECIFIC HEREDITARY FACTORS INFLUENCING THE EXTENT OF THE LUMBAR REGION. Paul B. Sawin, Inez Baumgartner Hull. Jour.Morphol., Philadelphia, vol.78, no.1, pp.1-26, Jan., 1946.

MORPHOGENETIC STUDIES OF THE RABBIT. V. INHERITANCE OF AN ASYMETRICAL VASCULAR PATTERN. Paul B. Sawin, M.A.Nace. Jour.Morphol., Philadelphia, vol. 82, no.3, pp.331-354, May, 1948.

PICTORIAL PRESENTATION OF ANTIGEN AND ANTIBODY RELATIONS ASSOCIATED WITH THE "A" CHARACTER IN THE RABBIT. Paul B. Sawin, C.A. Stuart, K.M. Wheeler. Jour.Heredity, Wash., vol.34, no.6, pp.179-186, figs.13-17, June, 1943.

Management

COTTONTAIL RABBIT AND ITS MANAGEMENT IN OHIO. Daniel R. Atzenhofer, Daniel L. Leedy. Ohio Div.Conserv. and Nat.Resources, Columbus, Wildl.Conserv. Bull., no.2, pp.15, illus., Dec., 1947.

EVALUTION OF COTTONTAIL RABBIT MANAGEMENT IN PENNSYLVANIA. Glenn L. Bowers. Trans. 19th N.Amer. Wildl.Conf., pp.358-367, 1954.

PENNSYLVANIA'S RABBIT TRANSFER PROGRAM. Wilbur M. Cramer. Pa.Game News, vol.11, no.2, pp.6-7, 31, May, 1940; vol.11, no.7, pp.6-7, 27, Oct., 1940.

EVALUATION OF THE RESULTS OF STOCKING IMPORTED COTTONTAIL RABBITS IN NEW YORK STATE. Joseph Dell. N.Y.Fish and Game Jour., vol.4, no.2, pp.121-149, July, 1957.

TRANFER OF GAME AND FUR-BEARING MAMMALS FROM STATE TO STATE, WITH SPECIAL REFERENCE OF THE COTTONTAIL RABBIT. Lee Raymond Dice. Jour.Mamm., vol.8, no.2, pp. 90-96, May, 1927.

MANAGEMENT OF THE COTTONTAIL RABBIT IN PENNSYLVANIA. Richard Gerstell. Penna.Game News, vol.7, no. 12, pp.6-7, 27, 30; vol.8, no.1, pp.15-19, Mar. and Apr., 1937. (1st and 2nd pts.)

MANAGEMENT OF THE COTTONTAIL RABBIT IN PENNSYLVANIA. Richard Gerstell. Penna.Game News, vol.8, no. 2, pp.8-11, 32; vol.8, no.3, pp.12-15, 26, May and June, 1937. (3rd and 4th parts.)

PROGRESS REPORT ON PENNSYLVANIA'S NEW RABBIT PROGRAM. Richard Gerstell. Penna.Game News, vol.10, no.3, pp.4-5, 31, June, 1939.

COTTONTAIL RABBIT MANAGEMENT. C.O. Handley. W.Va.Conservation, Charleston, vol.12, no.8, pp.4, 19, illus., Nov., 1948.

STOCKING COTTONTAIL RABBITS. C.O. Handley. W.Va.Conservation, vol.16, no.1, pp.18-19, Apr., 1952.

TWO BASIC THINGS IN RABBIT AND QUAIL MANAGEMENT. C.O. Handley. W.Va. Conservation, vol.15, no.5, pp.20-24, Aug., 1951.

COTTONTAILS NEED MORE COVER. Arnold O. Haugen. Mich.Conservation, vol.11, no.4, pp.5-9, 11, Apr., 1942.

MANAGEMENT STUDIES OF THE COTTONTAIL RABBIT IN SOUTHWESTERN MICHIGAN. Arnold O. Haugen. Jour. Wildl.Mgt., vol.7, no.1, pp.102-119, Jan., 1943.

COTTONTAIL MANAGEMENT IN IOWA. George O. Hendrickson. Trans. 12th N. Amer. Wildl.Conf., pp.473-477, 1947.

HELPING THE COTTONTAIL. Paul F. Hickie. Mich.Conservation, vol.9, no.3, pp.3, 11-12, Dec., 1939.

RABBITS--AND SOME OF THE COSTLY MYTHS ABOUT RESTOCKING THEM. Paul F. Hickie. Mich.Conservation, vol. 8, no.6, pp.4-5, 8, 10-11, Feb., 1939.

HE SHOWED THE EXPERTS. Ted Janes. Outdoor Life, vol.112, no.3, pp.48-51, 105-107, illus., Sep., 1953.

SO YOU WANT MORE RABBITS? Roger M. Latham. Penna.Game News, vol.23, no.9, pp.9-13, illus., Dec., 1952.

MANAGEMENT OF OHIO COTTONTAILS. Daniel L. Leedy. Ohio Cons.Bull., vol. 10, no.6, pp.12-13, June, 1946.

ABSTRACTS OF COTTONTAIL RABBIT MANAGEMENT PAPERS. Charles W.Lemke. Wis.Cons.Dept., pp.1-14, mimeo., 1953.

HOW CAN WE PRODUCE MORE COTTONTAILS? Charles W. Lemke. Wis.Cons. Bull., vol.17, no.7, pp.22-25, July, 1952.

RESTOCKING WITH "NATIVE" COTTONTAILS. Robert D. McDowell. Jour. Wildl. Mgt., Ithaca, vol.19, no.1, pp.61-65, Jan., 1955.

WANT MORE RABBITS? Robert D. Parlaman. Penna.Game News, vol.26, no.6, p.10, illus., June, 1955.

MANAGMENT OF THE COTTONTAIL RABBIT IN NORTH CAROLINA. C.P. Patton. N.C.Wildl. Cons., vol.5, no.1, pp.3-4, 15-16, Jan., 1941.

WISCONSIN RABBIT-TRAPPING PROGRAM. George W. Resler. Wis.Conservation, Madison, vol.15, no.4, pp.13-15, illus., Apr., 1950.

RABBIT MANAGEMENT. Kenneth C. Rowe. Missouri Conservationist, Jefferson City, vol.10, no.9, pp.4-5, 12, illus., Oct., 1949.

PENNSYLVANIA'S COTTONTAIL RABBIT MANAGEMENT STUDY. C.R. Studholme. Penna.Game News, vol.19, no.8, pp.10-11, 19, Nov., 1948.

RABBITS DOWN THE RAT HOLE! Jim Trefethen, Dan Poole. Va.Wildl., vol.15, no.8, pp.4-7, illus., Aug., 1954. Repr. from Hunting and Fishing Mag., May, 1954.

STACKING THE CARDS FOR COTTONTAILS! Jim Trefethen, Dan Poole. Hunting and Fishing, vol.31, no.7, pp.11-13, 46-47, illus., Aug., 1954.

BIOLOGY AND MANAGEMENT OF THE COTTONTAIL RABBIT, SYLVILAGUS FLORIDANUS MEARNSII ALLEN. R.E. Trippensee. PhD thesis, Univ.Mich., 1934.

COTTONTAILS APLENTY. W.C.Truax. Wis.Cons.Bull., vol.20, no.8, pp.3-8, illus., Aug., 1955.

RABBITS--AND SOME OF THE COSTLY MYTHS ABOUT RESTOCKING THEM. DANGER OF SPREADING TULAREMIA AND GOOD REASON AGAINST IMPORTATION OF RABBITS FOR RESTOCKING PURPOSES. S.C. Whitlock. Michigan Cons., Lansing, vol.8, no.6, pp.5, 7, illus., Feb., 1939.

COTTONTAIL TRANSPLANTING PROJECT. T.J. Wright. Federated Rhode Island Sportsman, Providence, vol.10, no.4, p.7, Apr., 1949.

HOW TO IMPROVE RABBIT HABITAT. Ohio Outdoor News, vol.2, no.6, p.2, Dec., 1926.

Methods, Techniques

RADIOIODINE AS AN INDICATOR OF FREE-FEEDING ACTIVITY OF THE RABBIT, ORYCTOLAGUS CUNICULUS (L.). R.Carrick. C.S.I.R.O. Wildl.Res., Melbourne, vol.1, no.2, pp.106-113, Dec., 1956.

TECHNIQUES IN THE ESTIMATION OF A MEARNS COTTONTAIL POPULATION. Charles W. Crunden. MS thesis, Iowa State Coll., pp.iii-73, 1954.

EVALUATION OF TECHNIQUES IN ESTIMATING A MEARNS COTTONTAIL POPULATION. Charles W. Crunden, George O. Hendrickson. Proc.Iowa Acad.Sci., vol.62, pp.498-501, Dec., 1955.

METHOD OF EVALUATING THE RANGE FOR THE COTTONTAIL RABBIT. R.Franklin Dugan. MS thesis, Univ.Mich., 1941.

TEST OF THE RECAPTURE METHOD OF ESTIMATING THE NUMBER OF RABBITS, ORYCTOLAGUS CUNICULUS (L.), IN A WARREN. G.M. Dunnet. C.S.I.R.O.Wildl. Res., Canberra, Australia, vol.2, no.2, pp.90-100, 1957.

METHOD FOR THE DETERMINATION OF THE FOOD HABITS OF THE COTTONTAIL RABBIT BY USE OF THE PLANT MICROTECHNIQUES AND HISTOLOGY IN FECAL PELLET ANALYSIS. Julian L. Dusi. MS thesis, Ohio State Univ., 1946.

METHODS FOR THE DETERMINATION OF FOOD HABITS BY PLANT MICROTECHNIQUES AND HISTOLOGY AND THEIR APPLICATION TO COTTONTAIL RABBIT FOOD HABITS. Julian L. Dusi. Jour.Wildl. Mgt., Menasha, vol.13, no.3, pp.295-298, pl.10, July, 1949.

DEVICE FOR HOLDING RABBITS DURING X-RAY PHOTOGRAPHY. R.L.Edgar. Jour. Wildl.Mgt., vol.21, no.4, pp.453-454, Oct., 1957.

EVALUATION OF CENSUS METHODS FOR COTTONTAIL RABBITS. Thomas E. Greathouse. MS thesis, Univ.Mich., 1950.

INVENTORY METHODS FOR MEARNS' COTTONTAIL. George O. Hendrickson. Trans. 4th N.Amer.Wildl.Conf., pp.209-215, 1939.

FERRET AS AN AID TO WINTER RABBIT STUDIES. J.P. Linduska. Jour.Wildl.Mgt., Menasha, vol.11, no.3, pp.252-255, July, 1947.

TECHNIC FOR APPRAISING ABILITY TO RESIST GRAVITATIONAL SHOCK IN THE RABBIT. Arthur Locke, R.B.Locke, A.P. McIlroy, L.Chung. Proc.Soc.Exp.Biol. and Med., Utica, vol.51, no.1, pp.184-187, fig.1, Oct., 1942.

OPALESCENCE OF SERUM AFTER TOTAL BODY X-IRRADIATION AS A PROGNOSTIC SIGN OF DEATH. (White New Zealand Rabbits.) Robert L. Rosenthal. Science, Lancaster, vol.110, no.2845, pp.43-44, illus., July 8, 1949.

FIELD ENCLOSURES FOR THE STUDY OF THE WILD RABBIT, ORYCTOLAGUS CUNICULUS (L.). Ian Rowley. C.S.I.R.O. Wildl.Res., Melbourne, vol.2, no.1, pp. 101-105, Dec., 1956.

INDIVIDUAL MARKING OF THE RABBIT ORYCTOLAGUS CUNICULUS (L.). Ian Rowley. C.S.I.R.O.Wildl.Res., Commonwealth Scientific & Industrial Res. Organization, Melbourne, vol.1, no.1, pp. 40-44, Sep., 1956.

METHOD FOR THE MICROSCOPIC STUDY OF THE GROWTH OF TRANSPLANTED BONE IN THE TRANSPARENT CHAMBER OF THE RABBIT'S EAR. J.C. Sandison. Anat.Rec., vol.40, pp.41-49, illus., Sep. 25, 1928.

USE OF PELLET COUNTS FOR ESTIMATING THE DENSITY OF POPULATIONS OF THE WILD RABBIT, ORYCTOLAGUS CUNICULUS (L.). R.H. Taylor, R.M. William. New Zealand Jour. Sci.& Tech., sec.B, vol. 38, no.3, pp.236-256, Nov., 1956.

SELF-FEEDING SYSTEM FOR MARKET RABBITS. George S. Templeton. U.S.Dept. Agric., Bur.Biol.Survey, Wildl.Res. and Mgt., Leaflet BS-85, pp.9, illus., Mar., 1937.

METHODS OF MARKING WILD RABBITS. Harry V. Thompson, C.J.Armour. Jour. Wildl.Mgt., Ithaca, vol.18, no.3, pp.411-414, illus., July, 1954.

METHOD OF MARKING RABBITS FOR FIELD STUDIES. C.H. Tyndale-Biscoe. Jour.Wildl.Mgt., Ithaca, vol.17, no.1, pp.42-45, Jan., 1953.

MECHANICAL DEVICE FOR THE SPREAD OF DISEASE AGENTS AMONGST RABBITS. Jour.Council Sci.and Industrial Research, Melbourne, vol.15, no.1, pp.82-83, figs.2, Feb., 1942.

Mexico

NEW COTTONTAIL (SYLVILAGUS FLORIDANUS) FROM NORTHEASTERN MEXICO. Rollin H. Baker. Univ. Kansas Publ., Mus. Nat.Hist., vol.7, no.13, pp.609-612, Apr. 8, 1955.

NEW COASTAL FORM OF BRUSH RABBIT FROM THE VICINITY OF SAN QUINTIN, LOWER CALIFORNIA, MEXICO. Laurence M. Huey. Trans.San Diego Soc.Nat.Hist., vol.9, no.23, pp.221-224, July 31, 1940.

ROMEROLAGUS NELSONI. A NEW GENUS AND SPECIES OF RABBIT FROM MT. POPOCATEPETL, MEXICO. C.Hart Merriam. Proc.Biol.Soc., Wash., vol.10, pp. 169-174, figs.33-34, Dec. 29, 1896.

VOLCANO RABBIT OF MOUNT IZTACCIHUATL. Gerrit S. Miller, Jr. Proc.Biol. Soc., Wash., vol.24, pp.228-229, Oct. 31, 1911.

DESCRIPTIONS OF SEVEN NEW RABBITS FROM MEXICO. E.W. Nelson. Proc.Biol. Soc., Wash., vol.17, pp.103-110, May 18, 1904.

North America

MICHIGAN COTTONTAILS IN WINTER. Durward L. Allen. Jour.Wildl.Mgt., vol.3, no.4, pp.307-332, Oct., 1939.

COTTONTAIL RABBIT. Rod Amundson. Wildl. in N.Carolina, Raleigh, vol.13, no.2, pp.4-7, illus., Feb., 1949.

SPREAD OF COTTONTAIL RABBITS IN CANADA. R.M. Anderson. Can.Field-Nat., vol.54, no.5, pp.70-72, May, 1940.

CONDENSED REPORT OF RABBIT STUDIES/ NORTH CENTRAL OHIO (ERIE AND HURON COUNTIES, 1936-1940). Daniel R. Atzenhoefer, E.D. Martin. Ohio Div.Wildl., Game Mgt.Leaflet, no.14, pp.20, Nov., 1949.

SOME NOTES ON THE COTTONTAIL IN ONTARIO. James L.Baillie, Jr.Canadian Field-Nat., vol.49, no.4, pp.70-71, Apr., 1935.

MEARN'S COTTONTAIL (SYLVILAGUS FLORIDANUS MEARNSI). N.R. Barger. Wisconsin Conservation Bull., Madison, vol.14, no.9, pp.31-32, illus., Sep., 1949.

CONCERNING THE COTTONTAIL IN WYOMING. Thomas A. Bell. Wyo. Wildl., vol.12, no.11, pp.8-12, 26-27, Dec., 1948.

COTTONTAIL RABBIT IN PENNSYLVANIA. John D. Beule. Penna.Game News, Comm., Final Rep., PR Proj.6-R, pp.58, mimeo., 1946.

FLORIDA MARSH RABBIT. W.Frank Blair. Jour.Mamm., vol.17, no.3, pp.197-207, Aug., 1936.

NEW RACE OF THE EASTERN COTTONTAIL FROM THE TEXAS PANHANDLE. W. Frank Blair. Occas.Papers Mus.Zool. Univ.Michigan, no.380, pp.3, June 17, 1938.

WILD RABBIT MEETING. Kate L. Bloodgood. Nat.Mag., Wash., D.C., vol.37, no.1, p.51, Jan., 1944.

KENTUCKY RABBIT INVESTIGATIONS. Joe F. Bruna. Presented at 5th Ann. Meeting, S.E.Wildl.Conf., pp.1-21, illus., Oct., 1951; Ky.Dept.Fish & Wildl.Resources, Fed. Aid. Proj., pp.1-83, illus., July, 1952.

PRIVATE LIFE OF MR. AND MRS. COTTONTAIL. Joe F. Bruna. Ky.Happy Hunting Ground, vol.8, no.2, pp.30-31, Mar., 1952.

SOME FACTS CONCERNING COTTONTAILS IMPORTED INTO WISCONSIN. T.T.Chaddock. Wis.Cons.Bull., vol.3, no.4, pp.49-52, Apr., 1938.

RANGE EXTENSION OF THE SWAMP RABBIT IN ILLINOIS. E. Lendell Cockrum. Jour.Mamm., vol.30, no.4, pp.427-429, fig.1, Nov.17, 1949.

RABBITS. Fannye A. Cook. Mississippi Game and Fish, Jackson, vol.10, no.4, pp.3-4, Oct., 1946.

INTRODUCED EUROPEAN RABBITS IN THE SAN JUAN ISLANDS, WASHINGTON. Leo K. Couch. Jour.Mamm., vol.10, no.4, pp.334-336, illus., 1929.

OUT WHERE THEY BELONG. (Cottontail Rabbits.) Wilbur M. Cramer. Penna.Game News, Harrisburg, vol.15, no.7, pp.4-5, 26, Oct., 1944.

VIRGINIA ANIMALS EVERYONE SHOULD KNOW: COTTONTAIL RABBITS. R. H. Cross, Jr. Va.Wildl., Richmond, vol.8, no.4, pp.6-8, illus., Apr., 1947.

COTTONTAIL RABBITS IN CONNECTICUT. A REPORT ON THE WORK OF THE CONNECTICUT WILDLIFE RESEARCH UNIT. Paul D. Dalke and others. Conn.Pub.Doc. 47, pp.93, 1942; Conn.State Geol. and Nat.Hist.Surv., Hartford, Bull.no.65, pp. 97, figs.22, 1942.

PRELIMINARY REPORT OF THE NEW ENGLAND COTTONTAIL STUDIES. Paul D. Dalke. Trans. 2nd N.Amer.Wildl. Conf., pp.542-548, 1937.

DISTRIBUTION OF COTTONTAIL RABBITS IN WASHINGTON STATE. Walter W. Dalquest. Jour.Wildl.Mgt., vol.5, no.4, pp. 408-411, Oct., 1941.

COTTONTAIL. Joseph Dell. N.Y.State Conservationist, Albany, vol.5, no.3, pp. 16-17, illus., Dec., 1950-Jan., 1951.

GEOGRAPHICAL AND ECOLOGICAL DISTRIBUTION OF COTTONTAIL RABBITS IN MASSACHUSETTS. Francis H. Fay, Edwin H. Chandler. Jour. Mamm., vol.36, no.3, pp.415-424, illus., Aug. 30, 1955.

RABBITS OF LOUISIANA. James Nelson Gowanloch. Louisiana Conservationist, New Orleans, vol.3, no.3, pp.4-6, 21-23, illus., Nov., 1950.

COTTONTAIL RABBIT INTRODUCTIONS AND DISTRIBUTION IN WESTERN OREGON. William Graf. Jour.Wildl.Mgt., vol.19, no. 2, pp.184-188, Apr., 1955.

COLORADO RABBITS. Frank Gregg, Lyndale Dunn. Colorado Outdoors Mag., vol.5, no. 1, pp.16-17, illus., Jan., 1956.

COTTONTAIL RABBIT IN OHIO. Arthur R. Harper. Ohio Div.Wildl., Educ.Booklet no.1, pp.1-24, illus., 1952.

INDIANA'S SWAMP RABBIT. Thomas Harrison, P.F.Hickie. Jour. Mamm., vol.12, no.3, pp.319-320, Aug., 1931.

LIFE HISTORY AND MANAGEMENT STUDIES OF THE COTTONTAIL RABBIT IN SOUTHWESTERN MICHIGAN. Arnold O. Haugen. PhD thesis, Univ. Mich., 1941.

LIFE HISTORY STUDIES OF THE COTTONTAIL RABBIT IN SOUTHWESTERN MICHIGAN. Arnold O. Haugen. Amer. Midland Nat., vol.28, no.1, pp.204-244, July, 1942.

MEARNS COTTONTAIL INVESTIGATIONS IN IOWA. George O. Hendrickson. Ames Forester, vol.21, pp.59-73, 1943.

STUDIES WITH THE COTTONTAIL RABBIT, SYLVILAGUS FLORIDANUS MEARNSII (ALLEN). George O. Hendrickson. Quart. Rept., Iowa Coop. Wildl.Research Unit, pp. 22-23, Jan-Mar., 1947; pp.41-42, July-Sep., 1948; pp.35-38, Jan.-Mar., 1949; vol. 16, no.1, pp.10-15, July-Sep., 1950.

SUMMER STUDIES ON THE COTTONTAIL RABBIT (SYLVILAGUS FLORIDANUS MEARNSI (ALLEN)). George O. Hendrickson. Iowa State Coll., Jour.Sci., vol.10, no.4, pp.367-371, July, 1936.

STUDIES WITH MEARNS COTTONTAIL. George O. Hendrickson. Iowa Coop.Wildl. Res.Unit.Quart.Rept., pp.79-85 (mimeog.), 1947.

FOUR NEW RABBITS FROM THE UPPER PLIOCENE OF KANSAS. Claude W. Hibbard. Amer.Midland Naturalist, Notre Dame, Indiana, vol.21, no.2, pp.506-513, figs.4, Mar., 1939.

COTTONTAILS IN MICHIGAN. Paul F. Hickie. Mich.Dept.Cons., pp.112, 1940.

INTRODUCTION OF BELGIAN HARES IN COLORADO. A. Brazier Howell. Jour.

Mamm., vol.17, no.1, pp.86-87, Feb., 1936.

COTTONTAIL LORE. J. Hynes. Field and Stream, New York, vol.49, no.7, pp.34-35, 80-82, Nov., 1944.

NATURAL HISTORY OBSERVATIONS ON THE AUDUBON COTTONTAIL. Lloyd G. Ingles. Jour. Mamm., vol.22, no.3, pp. 227-250, Aug., 1941.

COTTONTAIL--MOTHER NATURE'S RABBIT TRICK. Ellsworth Jaeger. Canadian Nat., Toronto, vol.13, no.1, pp.6-7, illus., Jan.-Feb., 1951.

SURVEY OF THE NATIVE RABBITS OF UTAH, WITH REFERENCE TO THEIR CLASSIFICATION, DISTRIBUTION, LIFE HISTORY, AND ECOLOGY. Reuel G. Janson. MS thesis, Utah State Agr.Coll., 1946.

COTTONTAIL RABBIT. E.R. Lamster. S.Dakota Conservation Digest, Pierre, vol. 11, no.12, p.12, Dec., 1944.

PROGRESS REPORT ON COTTONTAIL RABBITS IN PENNSYLVANIA. John R. Langenbach, John D. Beule. Penna.Game News, vol.13, no.8, pp.14-15, 30, Nov., 1942.

STUDY OF THE GENUS SYLVILAGUS IN THE VICINITY OF BATON ROUGE, LOUISIANA. Virgil T. Lapham. MS thesis, La.State Univ., 1950.

DETERMINATION OF THE SPECIES AND SUBSPECIES OF THE RABBITS OF THE GENUS SYLVILAGUS, AND THEIR DISTRIBUTION IN VIRGINIA. Leonard M. Llewellyn. MS thesis, Va.Polytechnic Inst., 1943.

COTTONTAIL IN MARYLAND. Jake Longwell. Md.Cons., vol.29, no.3, pp.4-8, illus., Fall., 1952.

PRESENT STATUS OF THE SAN JUAN RABBIT IN NEW JERSEY. L.G.MacNamara. N.J.Outdoors, vol.5, no.12, pp.4-9, illus., June, 1955.

POPULATION AND LIFE HISTORY STUDIES OF THE COTTONTAIL RABBIT IN LEE AND TALLAPOOSA COUNTIES, ALABAMA. Edward Majors. MS thesis, Ala.Poly, Inst., pp.xvi-119, illus., Aug., 1955.

(RUST COLORED HARE, SYLVILAGUS FLORIDANUS (ALLEN) IN SOUTHWEST QUEBEC.) Le lievre roux, Sylvilagus floridanus (Allen) dans le sud-ouest du Québec. George Maheux. Naturaliste Canadien, vol.59, no.5, pp.131-132, May, 1932.

RABBITS, A SUBJECT BIBLIOGRAPHY. Laura I. Makepeace. Spec.Biblio.no.3, Bibliographical Center for Research, Rocky Mountain Region, pp.xii-81, multigraphed, 1956.

COTTONTAILS. Frank Mauer. Western New York Conservationist, Buffalo, vol. 5, no.6, p.6, June, 1944.

DESCRIPTION OF A NEW RABBIT FROM ISLANDS OFF THE COAST OF VIRGINIA. Edgar A. Mearns. Proc. U.S.Nat.Mus., Wash., D.C., vol.39, no.1784, pp.227-228, Jan. 9, 1911.

LEPUS BAILEYI, A NEW COTTONTAIL RABBIT FROM WYOMING. C.Hart Merriam. Proc.Biol.Soc., Wash., vol.11, pp.147-148, June 9, 1897.

DISTRIBUTION OF SPECIES OF COTTONTAILS IN CENTRE COUNTY, PENNSYLVANIA. Helen Merritts. MS thesis, Penna. State Coll., 1943.

COTTONTAILS IN CENTRAL NEW YORK. Gerrit S. Miller, Jr. Proc. Boston Soc. Nat.Hist., vol.26, p.410, Jan. 31, 1895.

NEW RABBIT FROM SOUTHERN TEXAS. Gerrit S. Miller, Jr. Proc.Biol.Soc., Wash., vol.15, pp.81-82, Apr. 25, 1902.

NEW RABBIT FROM WESTERN FLORIDA. Gerrit S. Miller, Jr. Proc.Biol.Soc., Wash., vol.9, pp.105-108, June 9, 1894.

DESCRIPTIONS OF NEW NORTH AMERICAN RABBITS. E.W.Nelson. Proc. Biol. Soc., Wash., vol.20, pp.81-84, July 22, 1907.

RABBIT OF NORTH AMERICA. E. W. Nelson. N.American Fauna, no.29, pp. 287, figs.19, pls.13, Apr. 17, 1909.

DESCRIPTIONS OF THREE NEW RACES OF BRUSH RABBIT FROM CALIFORNIA. Robert T. Orr. Proc.Biol.Soc. Washington, vol.48, pp.27-30, Feb. 6, 1935.

RABBITS OF CALIFORNIA. Robert T. Orr. Calif.Acad.Sci., Occ.Papers 19, p.227, 1940.

NEW ENGLAND COTTONTAIL IN MAINE. Ralph S. Palmer. Jour.Mamm., vol.25, no.2, pp.193-195, May, 1944.

COTTONTAIL RABBIT IN BRITISH COLUMBIA. Kenneth Racey. Murrelet, Seattle, vol. 34, no.1, pp.9-10, 1953.

COTTONTAIL RABBIT. O.T. Roberts, Jr. Del.Board Game & Fish Comm., pp.1-9, Mar., 1950.

COTTONTAIL RABBIT. Wilford E. Sanderson. School Nat.League Bull., New York, ser.no.15, Bull.no.3, pp.1-4, illus., Nov., 1944.

COTTONTAIL RABBITS (SYLVILAGUS FLORIDANUS) OF PENINSULA FLORIDA. Albert Schwartz. Proc.Biol.Soc. Washington, vol.69, pp.145-152, Sep. 12, 1956.

COTTONTAIL IN MISSOURI. Chas. W. Schwartz. Missouri Conservationist, Jefferson City, vol.6, no.1, pp.8-9, illus., Jan., 1945.

SWAMP RABBIT (SYLVILAGUS AQUATICUS AQUATICUS) IN SOUTH CAROLINA. Franklin Sherman. Jour. Mamm., vol.20, no.2, p.259, May, 1939.

NOTES ON THE FOOD AND PARASITES OF THE RABBITS OF A LOWLAND AREA IN OKLAHOMA. Charles C. Smith. Jour. Wildl.Mgt., vol.4, no.4, pp.429-431, Oct., 1940.

COTTONTAIL RABBIT INVESTIGATIONS. Ralph H. Smith. N.Y.Cons.Dept., Final Rep.PR Proj.1-R, Suppl. B, pp.84, May, 1950.

15, 000, 000 COTTONTAILS. F.W.Stuewer. Michigan Conserv., Lansing, vol.20, no.1, pp.3-5, illus., Jan., 1951.

RABBIT HAVEN. Oadis V. Swigart. Missouri Conservationist, Jefferson City, vol. 12, no.2, pp.7, 15, Feb., 1951.

DISTRIBUTION OF THE MARSH RABBIT IN GEORGIA. Ivan R. Tompkins. Jour. Mamm., vol.36, no.1, pp.144-145, Feb. 25, 1955.

MARSH RABBIT: AN INCOMPLETE LIFE HISTORY. Ivan R. Tomkins. Jour.Mamm., vol.16, no.3, pp.201-205, Aug., 1935.

EXTENSION OF RANGE OF COTTONTAIL RABBITS. Oliver Trafford. Canadian Field-Nat., vol.49, no.3, p.61, Mar., 1935.

COTTONTAIL RABBIT IN MARYLAND. W.Bryant Tyrrell. Nature Mag., Wash., D.C., vol.32, no.5, p.69, photos 2, May, 1939.

IN RE RABBITS. W. Bryant Tyrrell. Nature Mag., Wash., vol.38, no.3, pp.138-139, illus., Mar., 1945.

COTTONTAIL RABBIT. Hans G. Uhlig. West Va.Conserv., Charleston, vol.14, no.5, pp.13-16, illus., Aug., 1950.

ON A NEW SPECIES OF HARE FROM NORTH AMERICA. G.R. Waterhouse. Proc.Zool.Soc.London, pt.6, p.103, 1838.

NO HARES FOR OHIO. Ohio Dept. of Natural Resources, Ohio Cons.Bull., vol. 18, no.8, p.30, Aug., 1954.

ROSIE--THE TALE OF A RABBIT. Michigan Conservation, Lansing, vol.22, no.1, pp. 20-22, Jan., 1953.

"STUDYIN' RABBITS," THE OLD FISHERMAN REPORTS. Outdoor Indiana, Indianapolis, vol.10, no.1, pp.11, 12, Feb., 1943.

Pacific Islands

NOTES ON THE SUMATRAN HARE. E. Jacobson, C.Boden Kloss. Jour. Fed.Malay States Mus., vol.7, pt.4, pp.293-298, pl. 5, fig.2, Dec., 1919.

SIZE VARIATIONS IN TANSMANIAN RABBITS. M.B.Liederman. Pap.& Proc.Roy. Soc.Tasmania, Hobart, vol.89, pp.125-130, illus., 1955.

RABBITS ON LEPER ISLAND (MOKOPUNA). Forest & Bird, Wellington, New Zealand, no.102, p.11, Nov., 1951.

Parasites

LIFE HISTORY OF THE RABBIT STOMACH WORM OBELISCOIDES CUNICULI. Joseph E. Alicata. Jour.Agric.Research, vol.44, no.5, pp.401-419, Mar. 1, 1932.

NEW RABBIT NEMATODE, STUNKARDIONEMA HALLA. John G. Arnold. Trans. Amer.Micros.Soc., vol.60, no.1, pp.65-68, Jan., 1941.

STUDY OF THE ANOCEPHALINE CESTODES OF NORTH AMERICAN RABBITS. John G. Arnold. PhD thesis, N.Y.Univ., 1934; Zoologica, vol.23, no.2, pp.31-54, Mar. 31, 1938.

CHANGING INCIDENCE OF PARASITES IN A DECLINING RABBIT POPULATION. P.C. Bull. Proc. New Zealand Ecol.Soc., no.5, pp.11-12, Dec., 1957.

DISTRIBUTION OF THE NEMATODE TRICHOSTRONGYLUS RETORTAEFORMIS (ZEDER, 1800) IN THE WILD RABBIT, ORYCTOLAGUS CUNICULUS (L.). P.C. Bull. New Zealand Jour.Sci.& Tech., sec. B, vol.34, no.6, pp.449-456, May, 1953.

PARASITES OF THE WILD RABBIT, ORYCTOLAGUS CUNICULUS (L.) IN NEW ZEALAND. P.C. Bull. New Zealand Jour. Sci.& Technol., sec.B, vol.34, no.5, pp. 341-372, Mar., 1953.

INFLUENCE OF HOST AGE IN PARASITISM OF WILD RABBITS. P.C. Bull, R.H.Taylor. Proc. New Zealand Ecol.Soc., no.3, pp.29-30, Mar., 1956.

(STREPTOCOCCAL TOXIN IN THE RABBIT.) La toxine streptococcique chez le lapin. E. Burnet. Comptes Rendus des Seances de la Soc. de Biol., vol.97, pp.688-689, Aug.26, 1927.

COCCIDIA OF WILD RABBITS IN IOWA. I. TAXONOMY AND HOST-SPECIFICITY. Jose C.M. Carvalho. Iowa State Coll.Jour. Sci., Ames, vol.18, no.1, pp.103-135, illus., Oct., 1943; II. EXPERIMENTAL STUDIES WITH EIMERIA NEOLEPORIS CARVALHO, 1942. Iowa State Coll.Jour.Sci., Ames, vol. 18, no.2, pp.177-189, illus., Jan., 1944.

COCCIDIA OF WILD RABBITS OF IOWA, WITH SPECIAL REFERENCE TO EIMERIA NEOLEPORIS CARVALHO, 1942. Jose C.M. Carvalho. PhD thesis, Iowa State Coll., 1943.

EIMERIA NEOLEPORIS N. SP., OCCURRING NATURALLY IN THE COTTONTAIL AND TRANSMISSIBLE TO THE TAME RABBIT. Jose C.M. Carvalho. Iowa State Coll. Jour.Sci., vol.16, no.3, pp.409-410, Apr., 1942.

NEW SPECIES OF TREMATODE WORMS BELONGING TO THE GENUS HASSTILESIA FROM RABBITS IN TEXAS. Asa C.Chandler. Proc. U.S.Nat.Mus., vol.75, art.21, pp.1-5, 1929.

SOME PARASITIC ROUND WORMS OF THE RABBIT WITH DESCRIPTIONS OF TWO NEW SPECIES. Asa C. Chandler. Proc.U.S. Nat.Mus., vol.66, art. 16, pp.1-6, pls.2, Nov., 1924.

INTERNAL PARASITES OF COTTONTAIL RABBITS IN CONNECTICUT. Carl F. Clancy, Erwin Jungherr, Palmer R. Sime. Jour.Wildl.Mgt., Menasha, vol.4, no.2, pp.162-168, Apr., 1940.

MORPHOLOGY AND CULTIVATION OF EMBADOMONOS CUNICULI N. SP. Jane Collier, William C. Boeck. Jour.Parasitology, vol.12, pp.131-140, pl.15, Mar., 1926.

NEW NEMATODE OF THE RABBIT. Bertha L. Danheim. Anat.Record, vol.29, p.124, Dec. 25, 1924.

PARASITES WHICH AFFECT THE FOOD VALUE OF RABBITS. E.Ralph DeOng. California Fish and Game, vol.5, no.3, pp.142-143, July, 1919.

HELMINTH PARASITES OF RABBITS OF THE GENUS SYLVILAGUS. Arnold B. Erickson. Jour.Wildl.Mgt., vol.11, no.3, pp.255-263, July, 1947.

INCIDENCE AND TRANSMISSION OF SARCOCYSTIS IN COTTONTAILS. Arnold B. Erickson. Jour.Wildl.Mgt., Menasha, vol.10, no.1, pp.44-46, Jan., 1946.

INCIDENCE AND EFFECT OF WARBLES ON SOUTHERN MICHIGAN COTTONTAILS. Aelred D. Geis. Jour.Wildl.Mgt., vol.21, no.1, pp.94-95, Jan., 1957.

NEW SPECIES OF ROUND WORM OF THE GENUS TRICHOSTRONGYLUS FROM THE RABBIT. H.W. Graybill. Proc.U.S.Nat. Mus., vol.66, art.11, pp.1-2, pl.1, Oct., 1924.

A TEN-YEAR POPULATION STUDY OF THE RABBIT TICK HAEMAPHYSALIS LEPORIS-PALUSTRIS. R.G.Green, C.A.Evans, C.L. Larson. Amer. Jour. Hygiene, Baltimore, vol.38, no.3, pp.260-281, Nov., 1943.

(MATERIALS FOR THE STUDY OF THE STRUCTURE OF THE COCCID EIMERIA STIEDAE LINDEMANN IN THE RABBIT.) Materialen zum Studium der Struktur des Coccids Eimeria stiedae Lindemann bei Kaninchen. B.M. Gurwitsch. Archiv.f. Protistenkunde, vol.59, pp.369-372, Oct. 17, 1927.

OCCURRENCE AND MORPHOLOGY OF COENURUS SERIALIS IN RABBITS. A.G. Hamilton. Parasitology, Cambridge, vol. 40, nos.1-2, pp.46-49, pls.1-4, Jan., 1950.

PARASITES OF COTTONTAIL RABBITS ON THE SAN JOAQUIN EXPERIMENTAL RANGE, CALIFORNIA. Carlton M.Herman, Harry A.Jankiewicz. Jour.Wildl.Mgt., Menasha, vol.7, no.4, pp.395-400, Oct., 1943.

COCCIDIA INFESTING THE COTTONTAIL RABBIT, SYLVILAGUS NUTTALLII GRANGERI (ALLEN), WITH DESCRIPTIONS OF TWO NEW SPECIES. Ralph F. Honess. Parasitology, vol.31, no.3, pp. 281-284, Sep., 1939.

SOME TAXONOMIC CHARACTERS OF CUTEREBRINE (DIPTERA) LARVAE, WITH LARVAL DESCRIPTIONS OF TWO SPECIES FROM GEORGIA. E.F.Knipling, A.L. Brody. Jour.Parasitology, vol.26, no.1, pp. 33-43, Feb., 1940.

TRANSMISSION OF RABBIT PAPILLOMATOSIS BY THE RABBIT TICK, HEAMAPHYSALIS LEPORIS-PALUSTRIS. C.L. Larson, J.E.Schillinger, G.Green.Proc. Soc.for Exp.Biol.and Med., vol.33,no.4, pp.536-538, Jan., 1936.

CELLULAR PROLIFERATION ASSOCIATED WITH CYSTICERCUS INFESTATIONS IN THE COTTONTAIL RABBIT. A.B.Leonard, Alice E.Leonard. Trans.Kansas Acad.Sci., Topeka, vol.43, pp.429-432, figs.4, 1940.

NOTES ON LARVAE OF CUTEREBRA SP. (DIPTERA:OESTRIDAE) INFESTING THE OKLAHOMA COTTONTAIL RABBIT. A.B. Leonard. Trans.Kansas Acad.Sci., vol. 36, pp.270-274, illus., 1933.

SURVEY OF INTESTINAL PARASITES IN DOMESTIC RABBITS IN SIX COUNTIES IN SOUTHERN CALIFORNIA. Everett E. Lund. Jour. Parasitology, Lancaster, vol. 36, no.1, pp.13-19, Feb., 1950.

HELMINTH PARASITES OF THE COTTONTAIL RABBITS IN THE VICINITY OF AUBURN, ALABAMA. Eugenia R.Moore. MS thesis, Ala.Polytechnic Inst., 1939.

HELMINTH PARASITES OF COTTONTAIL RABBITS IN ALABAMA, WITH NOTES ON THE ARTHROPOD LINGUATULA SERRATA. Eugenia R. Moore, George C. Moore. Jour. Mamm., vol.28, no.3, pp.279-284, Aug., 1947.

SURVEY OF THE PARASITES OF THE IOWA COTTONTAIL (SYLVILAGUS FLORIDANUS MEARNSI). B.B.Morgan, E.F. Waller. Jour. Wildl.Mgt., vol.4, no.1, pp.21-26, Jan., 1940.

METHODS OF SAMPLING WINGED INSECTS FEEDING ON THE RABBIT ORYCTOLAGUS CUNICULUS (L.). K. Myers. C.S.I.R.O. Wildl.Res., Commonwealth Scientific & Industrial Research Organization, Melbourne, vol.1, no.1, pp.45-58, pl.1, Sep., 1956.

SURVEY OF ENDOPARASITES OF THE WILD RABBIT, ORYCTOLAGUS CUNICULUS (L.) IN AUSTRALIA. R. Mykytowycz. C.S.I.R.O. Wildl.Res., Commonwealth Scientific & Industrial Research Organization, Melbourne, vol.1, no.1, pp.19-25, Sep., 1956.

WILD RABBITS AS RESERVOIR HOSTS OF THE COMMON LIVER FLUKE, FASCIOLA HEPATICA, IN SOUTHERN TEXAS. O. Wilford Olsen. Jour.Parasitology, Lancaster, vol.34, no.2, pp.119-123, Apr., 1948.

NOTES ON THE RABBIT TICK, HAEMAPHYSALIS LEPORIS-PALUSTRIS(PACKARD), AND TULAREMIA IN CENTRAL ALASKA. Cornelius B.Philip. Jour.Parasitology, vol. 40, no.4, pp.484-485, Aug., 1954.

WINTER DISTRIBUTION OF TWO ECTOPARASITES OF THE COTTONTAIL RABBIT IN MISSOURI. Roland W.Portman. Jour.Econ.Ent., vol.37, no.4, p.541, Aug., 1944.

STUDIES ON THE INTESTINAL NEMATODES OF THE COTTONTAIL RABBIT. Anthony T. Rozycki. MS thesis, Univ. Minn., 1941.

CUTEREBRA LEPIVORA REARED FROM SYLVILAGUS AUDUBONII SANCTIDIEGI IN SAN BERNARDINO COUNTY, CALIFORNIA. Raymond E. Ryckman, Chester C. Lindt. Jour. Economic Entomol., vol. 47, no.6, pp.1146-1148, Dec., 1954.

RABBIT PARASITES AND DISEASES. Benjamin Schwartz. Amer. Fur Breeder, vol. 1, no.12, pp.21-24, illus., June, 1929.

ROLE OF TICKS IN DECLINE OF AN INSULAR COTTONTAIL POPULATION. R.H. Smith, E.L.Cheatum. Jour.Wildl.Mgt., vol.8, no.4, pp.311-317, Oct., 1944.

(PARASITES AND PARASITIC DISEASES IN THE RABBIT.) Parasiten und parasitaere Krankheiten beim Kaninchen. C. Sprehn. Verhandl. des I.Inter.Kaninchenzuechter-Kongresses, Leipzig, 1930, pp. 218-242, figs.12, 1931.

ISOLATION OF A FILTER-PASSING AGENT FROM THE RABBIT TICK HAEMAPHYSALIS LEPORIS-PALUSTRIS PACKARD. Edward A. Steinhaus, R.R.Parker. Publ.Health Repts., Washington, vol.59, no.47, pp. 1528-1529, Nov. 24, 1944.

PATHOLOGY OF EIMERIA LEPORIS (COCCIDIA) IN THE COTTONTAIL RABBIT. E.F. Waller, B.B.Morgan. Amer.Jour.Hygiene, vol.34, no.2, pp.83-85, Sep., 1941.

INFECTION OF COTTONTAIL RABBITS BY CYSTICERCUS PISIFORMIS (TAENIA PISIFORMIS). S.C. Whitlock. Jour.Wildl.Mgt., vol.3, no.3, pp.258-260, July, 1939.

TAPEWORMS IN RABBITS. S.C.Whitlock, Carl Gower. Mich.Cons., vol.8, no.2, p. 8, Oct., 1938.

Pelage and Coloration

(WHITE RABBIT FROM PRAT-COMMUNAL (ARIEGE PYRENEES).) Lièvre blanc de Prat-Communal (Pyrénées de l'Ariège).Gaston Astre. Mammalia, Paris, vol.10, no.2, pp. 94-96, June, 1946.

GLYCOGEN CONTENT OF RABBIT HAIR. A.Bolliger, Norma D. McDonald.Australian Jour.Exp.Biol.& Med., Adelaide, vol.26, no.5, pp.459-463, Sep., 1948.

FURLESS RABBIT. W.E. Castle. Jour. Heredity, vol.24, no.3, pp.81-86, illus., Mar., 1933.

MOSAIC (INTENSE-DILUTE) COAT PATTERN IN THE RABBIT. W.E. Castle. Jour. Exp.Zool., vol.52, no.3, pp.471-480,1929.

SOME VARIATION OF WHITE RABBITS. W.E.Castle. Jour.Heredity, vol.15, pp.211-219, May, 1924.

STUDY OF THE PIGMENTATION OF THE HIMALAYAN RABBIT. A.C.Chaudhuri. Proc.Roy.Phys.Soc.Edinburgh, vol.21, pt. 4, pp.195-203, pls.2, Feb., 1929.

ANATOMICAL STUDY OF THE FURLESS CONDITION IN RABBITS. Elizabeth East Drapeau. Jour.Morphol., vol.54, no.2, pp.365-385, pls.1-3, Mar., 1933.

(INFLUENCE OF DIFFERENT BEHAVIOR AND FEEDING ON THE QUALITY OF THE RABBIT PELT.) Einfluss verschiedener Haltung und Fuetterung auf die Qualitaet des Kaninchenpelzes. R.Gartner, Breslau Schaube. Verhandl. des I.Internat. Kaninchenzuechter-Kongresses, Leipzig, pp.201-210, 1931.

COLOUR AND GROWTH OF HAIR IN RABBITS. C.W. Hale. Nature, London, vol. 155, no.3944, pp.670-671, June 2, 1945.

MICROSCOPIC STUDY OF COAT VARIATION IN WHITE NEW ZEALAND AND ANGORA RABBITS. Thora M. Hardy, Merle H. Markley. Jour. Heredity, Washington, vol.35, no.6, pp.182-192, figs.6-8, June, 1944.

WILD WHITE RABBIT. G.E. Howard. Field, London, vol.151, p.593, Apr. 5, 1928.

STUDIES OF THE CAUSE OF PARTIAL ALBINISM IN THE HIMALAYAN RABBIT (trans.title). L. Kaufman. Pam.Panst. Inst.Nauk.Gosp.Wiejsk. Pulawach (Mem. Inst.Nat.Polon.Écon.Rurale Pulawy), vol. 4, A, pp.199-217, illus.,1923. (English translation in Biol.Gen., vol.1, no.1, pp. 7-21, 1925.)

(ON THE INHERITANCE AND FORMATION OF PIGMENT IN RACES OF RABBITS.) Ueber die Vererbung und Bildung von Pigment bei Kaninchenrassen. C. Kosswig. Zeitschr.f.Ind.Abstammungs- und Vererbungslehre, vol.45, pp.368-401, figs. 12, 1927.

STUDIES ON SILVERING IN RABBITS III. A FACTOR INHIBITING UNIFORM COLORING. T.Marchlewski. Bull.Internat. Acad. Polonaise Sci. et Lett., Cl.Sci.Math. et Nat., Ser.B, Sci.Nat.(II) (Zool), Cracovie, nos.8-10, pp.263-269, pl.16, Oct.-Dec., 1929.

WHITE WILD RABBIT. Prince Orloff. Field, London, vol.151, p.654, Apr. 19, 1928.

(MODIFICATIONS AND MUTATIONS IN RABBIT COLORATION.) Modifikationen und Mutationen der Kaninchenfaerbung. W. Schultz. Arch.Mikr.Anat.und Entwicklungsmechanik, vol.104, pp.88-108, Feb. 23, 1925.

(UNMODIFIABLE, ABSOLUTELY PURE YELLOW IN THE RABBIT.) Unmodefizierbare absolute Reingelb beim Kaninchen. W. Schultz. Zeitschr.f. induktive Abstammungs- und Vererbungslehre, vol.44, pp. 247-252, 1927.

ANOTHER CASE OF A BLACK-BLUE MOSAIC IN THE DUTCH RABBIT.Sedgwick E. Smith. Jour. Heredity, Washington, vol. 35, no.11, pp.325-326, fig.3, Nov., 1944.

(ANGORA HAIR AND ITS MECHANICAL PROPERTIES.) Angorahaar und seine mechanischen Eigenschaften. Ernst Tanzer. Verhandl. des I. Internat.Kaninchenzuechter-Kongresses, Leipzig, 1930, pp.104-113, 1931.

(FUR OF THE REX RABBIT AND ITS BEHAVIOR IN CROSSING.) Haarkleid des Rexkaninchens und sein Verhalten bei der Kreuzung. Oskar Thiel. Zeitschr.f. Ind.Abstammungs- und Vererbungslehre, vol.48, pp.305-324, figs.19, 1928.

WHITE WILD RABBITS. J. Whitaker. Field, London, vol.151, p.763, May 3, 1928.

HAIR REPLACEMENT IN THE DOMESTIC RABBIT. H.J. Whiteley, F.N. Ghadially. Jour. Anat., Cambridge, England, vol.88, pt.1, pp.13-18, Jan., 1954.

(GENETIC INVESTIGATIONS OF COLOR STREAKS IN THE RABBIT.) Genetische Untersuchungen an Farbenschlaegen des Kaninchens. E. Witschi. Revue Suisse de Zool., vol.32, pp.121-124, illus., July 2, 1925.

Physiology

REPAIR OF BONE. T.R.Bast, W.E.Sullivan, F.D.Geist.Anat.Record, vol.31, pp.255-280, figs.14, Nov. 25, 1925.

(INVESTIGATIONS OF THE NERVES OF THE BLADDER. STUDY OF THE RABBIT IN PARTICULAR.) Recherches sur les nerfs de la vessie. Etude particuliere du Lapin. Victor Bobin. Arch.d'anat.d'histol.et d'embryol., vol.11, fasc.1-4, pp.197-244, figs.15, 1930.

(OPTICALLY INDUCED EYE AND BODY REFLEXES IN THE RABBIT.) Optisch ausgeloeste Augen- und Koerperreflexe am Kaninchen. Gerhard A. Brecher. Zeitschrift f. Vergleich.Physiol., Berlin, vol.23, no.3, pp.374-390, figs.4, July 21, 1936.

INTERRELATION OF PARATHYROIDS, SUPRARENALS AND PANCREAS. (Experiments on Rabbits.) G. A. Clark. Jour. Physiol., vol.58, pp.294-301, Mar., 1924.

GLUCOSE EXCRETION BY THE RABBIT KIDNEY. T.W.T.Dillon. Nature, London, vol.150, no.3808, p.492, Oct. 24, 1942.

MUSCLE ACTIVITY AND MUSCLE PROTEINS. M.Dubuisson. Biol.Reviews, London, vol.25, no.1, pp.46-71, Jan., 1950.

UROGENITAL ORGANS OF THE COTTONTAIL RABBIT (SYLVILAGUS FLORIDANUS). J.G. Elchlepp. Jour. Morph., vol.91, no.1, pp.169-198, illus., July, 1952.

STUDY OF SEASONAL CHANGES IN THE BODY WEIGHT AND ENDOCRINE GLANDS OF THE COTTONTAIL RABBIT SYLVILAGUS FLORIDANUS MEARNSI. William H. Elder. PhD thesis, Univ. Wis., 1942.

NEURAL REGULATION OF THE GONADOTROPIC FUNCTION OF THE PITUITARY IN RABBITS. I.A. Eskin. Bull.Soc.Nat. Moscow, Sect.Biol., n.s., vol.49, nos. 5-6, pp.125-150, figs.8, 1940. (In Russian with English summary.)

EXPERIMENTAL STUDY OF LYMPH NODE REGENERATION IN RABBITS. William J. Furuta. Amer. Jour.Anat., Philadelphia, vol.80, no.3, pp.437-505, figs.23, May, 1947.

EFFECTS OF THYROIDECTOMY ON THE SKULL OF THE DOMESTIC RABBIT. Martha Wright Hunter, P.B.Sawin. Amer. Jour.Anat., Philadelphia, vol.71, no.3, pp.417-449, fig. 1, pls.4, Nov. 16, 1942.

SPECIFICITY OF HEMOLYTIC ANTIBODIES. Roscoe R. Hyde. Anat.Record, vol.29, p. 87, Dec. 25, 1924.

EXCRETION OF 17-KETOSTEROIDS BY MALE RABBITS DURING ALTERED GONADAL FUNCTION. Donald J. Kimeldorf. Endocrinol., Boston, vol.43, no.2, pp.83-88, Aug., 1948.

EXCRETION OF URINARY 17-KETOSTEROIDS BY THE MALE RABBIT. Donald J. Kimeldorf. Amer.Jour.Phys., Baltimore, vol.152, no.3, pp.615-622, Mar. 1, 1948.

VASCULAR CHANGES IN THE RABBIT UTERUS AND IN INTRAOCULAR ENDOMETRIAL TRANSPLANTS DURING PREGNANCY. B. Krichesky. Anat. Record, Philadelphia, vol.87, no.3, pp.221-223, Nov., 1943.

GOLGI APPARATUS IN UTERINE GLAND CELLS DURING PREGNANCY IN THE RABBIT. B. Krichesky, H.Mandel. Univ. California Publ.Zool., Berkeley, vol.47, no.6, pp.169-174, 1943.

(SOME PECULIAR CONDITIONS OF RABBIT DIGESTION.) Nogle ejendommelige forhold ved kaninernes fordojelse. Holger Madsen. Naturens Verden, Copenhagen, 23 Argang, no.5, pp.214-220, figs.2, 1939.

EFFECTS OF THE THYROID, CASTRATION, AND SEASON ON ADRENALS IN THE MALE RABBIT. M.Maqsood. Nature, London, vol.167, no.4243, p.323, Feb. 24, 1951.

MECHANORECEPTORS OF THE RABBIT MANDIBULAR INCISOR. A.R. Ness. Jour. Physiol., Cambridge, England, vol.126, no.3, pp.475-493, Dec., 1954.

LOCALIZATION OF EXCRETION IN THE URINIFEROUS TUBULE. PART II. (Experiments on Rabbits.) J.M.O'Connor, J.A. McGrath. Jour. Physiol., vol.58, pp.338-347, Mar., 1924.

SYNTHESIS OF CERTAIN B VITAMINS BY THE RABBIT. Orlando Olcese, P.B.Pearson, B.S.Schweigert. Jour.Nutrition, Philadelphia, vol.35, no.5, pp.577-590, May 10, 1948.

BODY TEMPERATURE DATA FOR THE COTTONTAIL RABBIT. George A. Petrides. Jour.Mamm., vol.28, no.4, pp.400-401, Nov. 26, 1947.

RELATION OF HYDROSTATIC CONDITIONS IN THE UTERUS TO THE SIZE AND SHAPE OF THE CONCEPTUS DURING PREGNANCY: A CONCEPT OF UTERINE ACCOMMODATION. S.R.M. Reynolds. Anat.Record, Philadelphia, vol.95, no.3, pp.283-296, figs.3, July, 1946.

TEMPERATURE VARIATIONS IN RABBITS. Florence B. Seibert, L.B.Mendel. Amer. Jour.Physiol., vol.67, pp.83-89, 1923.

DORSAL AORTIC PLEXUS: A FACTOR IN THE DEVELOPMENT OF BODY WALL DRAINAGE IN THE RABBIT. Leon H. Strong. Univ.California Publ.Zoo., vol.29, pp.305-319, illus., Jan. 8, 1927.

CHARACTERISTICS AND BEHAVIOR OF LIVING CELLS IN AUTOGENOUS GRAFTS OF ADRENAL CORTEX IN RABBITS. Roy G. Williams. Amer. Jour.Anat., Philadelphia, vol.77, no.1, pp.53-79, figs.1-5, pls.1-2, July, 1945.

ON RABBIT NUTRITION, WITH REFERENCE TO WORK AT HARPER ADAMS COLLEGE. W.King Wilson. Verhandl. des I.Internat. Kaninchenzuechter-Kongresses, Leipzig, 1930, pp.191-199, 1931.

ON A POSSIBLE RELATION BETWEEN THE PANCREAS AND THE PARATHYROIDS. (Experiments on Rabbits.) L.B.Winter, W. Smith. Jour.Physiol., vol.58, pp.108-109, 1923.

### Population Dynamics

COTTONTAIL POPULATION AND MORTALITY STUDY IN CENTRAL PENNSYLVANIA. David A. Arnold. MS thesis, Penna.State Coll., 1950.

POPULATION STUDIES OF THE COTTONTAIL IN NORTHERN OHIO. Daniel R. Atzenhofer. MS thesis, Ohio State Univ., 1940.

OZARK RABBIT DILEMMA. Bill T. Crawford. Mo.Cons., vol.13, no.12, pp.4-5, 12, illus., Dec., 1952.

ROADSIDE RABBIT COUNTS AS AN INDEX TO RABBIT POPULATIONS. Herbert Dahl. W.Va.Cons., vol.17, no.11, pp.10-11, illus., Jan., 1954.

FLUCTUATION IN THE ABUNDANCE OF RABBITS. J.B. Harkin. Canadian Field-Nat., vol.41, p.113, June 17, 1927.

POPULATION STUDIES AND ECOLOGY OF THE COTTONTAIL RABBIT. David T. Katz. MS thesis, Ohio State Univ., 1941.

AUTUMNAL DECIMATION OF MEARNS COTTONTAIL IN DECATUR COUNTY, IOWA, 1952. Paul D. Kline. MS thesis, Iowa State Coll., 1953; Proc.Iowa Acad.Sci., vol.61, pp.524-527, Dec. 4, 1954.

THE 1936 COTTONTAIL SCARCITY IN WISCONSIN. Aldo Leopold, Harry G.Anderson. Jour. Mamm., vol.19, no.1, pp.110-111, Feb., 1938.

POPULATION TRENDS IN WISCONSIN COTTONTAILS. Robert A. McCabe. Jour.Mamm., vol.24, no.1, pp.18-22, Feb., 1943.

WHERE'S HOTFOOT NOW? (Fall decline of rabbits.) John Madson. Iowa Cons., vol. 13, no.11, pp.81, 84-85, illus., Nov., 1954.

RABBITS HAVE THEIR UPS AND DOWNS. E.D.Martin, Daniel Atzenhoefer. Ohio Cons.Bull., vol.16, no.3, pp.10-11, 31, illus., Mar., 1952.

COTTONTAIL POPULATION, MOVEMENT AND MORTALITY STUDY IN CENTRAL PENNSYLVANIA. Richard Keith Neal. MS thesis, Penna.State Coll., 1951.

FACTORS INFLUENCING THE COTTONTAIL RABBIT POPULATION ON REPRESENTATIVE AREAS IN VIRGINA. Frank Page Nelson. MS thesis, Va.Polytechnic Inst., 1950.

POPULATION STUDIES OF COTTONTAILS, SYLVILAGUS FLORIDANUS (ALLEN), IN CENTRAL MISSOURI, AND THE EFFECTS OF COMMERCIAL SHIPPING OF LIVE RABBITS. Kenneth C. Rowe. AM thesis, Univ. Mo., 1947.

ANALYSIS OF COVARIANCE OF COTTONTAIL RABBIT POPULATION DATA. Vincent Schultz, Mitchell A.Byrd. Jour.Wildl.Mgt., vol.21, no.3, pp.315-319, July, 1957.

COTTONTAIL POPULATION AND MORTALITY STUDY IN CENTRAL PENNSYLVANIA. Dale E. Sheffer. MS thesis, Penna.State Coll., Aug., 1952.

24 X 95 YEARS - 2,000,000,000. (San Juan Rabbits.) Howard Smith. Baltimore Sun, p.1, Sect.A, Sunday, Nov. 21, 1954.

ECOLOGY AND POPULATION DYNAMICS OF THE WILD RABBIT(ORYCTOLAGUS CUNICULUS). H.N. Southern. Ann.Appl. Biol., vol.27, pp.509-528, 1940.

POPULATION STUDY OF WILD RABBITS. H.N.Southern. Quart. Jour. Univ. Fed. for Animal Welfare, pp.4-7, July, 1939.

(SECRET DEATH.) Den hemliga doden. Gunnar Svardson. Svensk Jakt, Stockholm, vol.87, no.6, pp.171-175, illus., June 20, 1949.

STUDY OF NATURAL MORTALITY IN A WILD POPULATION OF THE RABBIT, ORYCTOLAGUS CUNICULUS (L.). C.H. Tyndale-Biscoe, R.M. Williams. New Zealand Jour.Sci.and Technol., sec.B, vol.36, no.6, pp.561-580, May, 1955.

POPULATION DYNAMICS OF THE MEARNS COTTONTAIL (SYLVILAGUS FLORIDANUS MEARNSII ALLEN) IN THE IOWA STATE COLLEGE ORCHARD AND ARBORETUM. Herbert S. Wallace. PhD thesis 1106, Iowa State Coll., 1950.

INVESTIGATION OF PERIODIC FLUCTUATIONS IN THE NEW ZEALAND RABBIT POPULATION. P. Whittle. New Zealand Jour.Sci.Tech., Wellington, sec.B, vol. 37, no.2, pp.179-200, illus., Sep., 1955.

### Predators

NEW YORK WEASEL PREYING ON THE COTTONTAIL RABBIT. R.D. Burroughs. Jour. Mamm., vol.20, no.2, p.253, May, 1939.

STOAT AND RABBIT. W.R.P. Henry.Field, London, vol.168, no.4370, p.741, Sep.26, 1936.

GOPHER SNAKE KILLED TRYING TO SWALLOW COTTONTAIL. Walter E. Howard. Copeia, no.4, p.289, Dec. 15, 1949.

SPARROW HAWK PREYS ON COTTONTAIL. Douglas H. Hubbard. Jour. Mamm., vol.22, no.4, p.454, Nov. 14, 1941.

CROW PREDATION UPON NESTLING COTTONTAILS. Charles M. Kirkpatrick. Jour. Mamm., vol.31, no.3, pp.322-327, Aug., 1950.

ADDITIONAL INCIDENT OF CROW ATTACK ON RABBIT. Joseph Curtis Moore. Jour.Mamm., vol.32, no.2, p.223, May 21, 1950.

BOBCATS AID FARMERS BY HELPING CONTROL RABBITS. Science News Letter, Washington, vol.47, no.16, p.248, Apr. 21, 1945.

### Reproductive Biology

BREEDING OF THE COTTONTAIL IN SOUTHERN MICHIGAN. Durward L.Allen. Amer.Midland Nat., vol.20, no.2, pp.464-468, fig.1, tbl.1, Sep., 1938.

COTTONTAIL NESTING STUDY IN PENNSYLVANIA. John D. Beule. Penna.Game News, vol.11, no.2, pp.10-11, 28, May, 1940. Trans. 5th N.Amer. Wildl.Conf., pp. 320-328, 1941.

COTTONTAIL RABBIT NESTS AND NESTLINGS. John D.Beule, Allen T. Studholme. Jour. Wildl.Mgt., vol.6, no.2, pp.133-140, Apr., 1942.

MODIFIED SEXUAL PHOTOPERIODICITY IN COTTONTAIL RABBITS. Thomas Hume Bissonnette, Albert George Csech. Biol. Bull., Lancaster, vol.77, no.3, pp.364-367, Dec., 1939.

UNUSUAL BREEDING OF COTTONTAILS IN PENNSYLVANIA. Glenn L. Bowers. Jour.Mamm., vol.36, no.2, p.303, May, 1955.

REPRODUCTION OF THE WILD RABBIT ORYCTOLAGUS CUNICULUS (L.). F.W. Rogers Brambell. Proc. Zool.Soc.London, vol.114, pts.1-2, pp.1-45, figs.15, Aug., 1944.

DIURNAL MATING ACTIVITY OF THE COTTONTAIL. E.E.Brown. Jour.Mamm., vol.16, no.1, p.69, Feb., 1935.

RABBIT ON HER NEST. Howard H.Cleaves. Forest and Stream, vol.90, p.123, Mar., 1920.

COTTONTAILS BREEDING IN THEIR FIRST SUMMER. Marvin E. Cooley. Jour.Mamm., vol.27, no.3, pp.273-274, Aug., 1946.

YOUNG OF THE BRUSH RABBIT.SYLVILAGUS BACHMANI. William B. Davis. Murrelet, Seattle, Wash., vol.17, nos.2-3, pp. 36-40, illus., Nov. 14, 1936.

PROPAGATING COTTONTAIL RABBITS. Malcolm Dunn. Modern Game Breeding, vol.6, no.4, p.7, Apr., 1936.

REPRODUCTIVE CYCLE OF THE MEARNS COTTONTAIL IN ILLINOIS. Dean H.Ecke. Amer.Midland Nat., vol.53, no.2, pp.294-311, illus., Apr., 1955.

GONADOTROPIC ACTIVITY OF THE PITUITARY GLAND IN RELATION TO THE SEASONAL SEXUAL CYCLE OF THE COTTONTAIL RABBIT (SYLVILAGUS FLORIDANUS MEARNSI). Wm.H.Elder, John C. Finerty. Anat.Record, Philadelphia, vol.85, no.1, pp.1-16, figs.4, Jan., 1943.

BODY WEIGHT AND SEX RATIO OF COTTONTAIL RABBITS. Wm.H.Elder, Lyle K. Sowls. Jour. Wildl.Mgt., vol.6, no.3, pp. 203-207, July, 1942.

PENNSYLVANIA'S EXPERIMENTS IN THE PROPAGATION OF COTTONTAIL RABBITS. Richard Gerstell. Trans. 21st Amer.Game Conf., 1935, Amer.Game Assoc., New York, pp.313-318, 1935.

BREEDING HABITS OF THE COTTONTAIL RABBIT IN NEW YORK STATE. W.J.Hamilton, Jr. Jour. Mamm., vol.21, no.1, pp.8-11, Feb. 14, 1940.

PROCESSES OF REPRODUCTION IN THE RABBIT. John Hammond. Verhandl. des I. Internat.Kaninchenzuechter-Kongresses, Leipzig, 1930, pp.56-63, 1931.

REPRODUCTION IN THE RABBIT; WITH FOREWORD AND CHAPTER ON THE FORMATION OF THE CORPUS LUTEUM BY F.H.A. MARSHALL. John Hammond. Edinburgh and London, Oliver and Boyd, Biological monographs and manuals, no.IV, pp.xxv-210, pls.20, 1925.

COTTONTAIL BREEDING IN ITS FIRST SUMMER. George O. Hendrickson. Jour. Mamm., vol.28, no.1, p.63, Feb. 15, 1947.

(ON THE STATUS OF THE BREEDING OF RABBITS IN THE GRAND DUCHY OF LUXEMBOURG.) Ueber den Stand des Kaninchenzucht im Grossherzogtum Luxembourg. B. Herschbach. Verhandl. des I. Internat. Kaninchenzuechter-Kongresses, Leipzig, 1930, pp.174-177, 1931.

PRODUCTIVITY OF THE COTTONTAIL RABBIT, SYLVILAGUS FLORIDANUS MEARNSII (ALLEN), IN DECATUR COUNTY, IOWA, 1951. Fred H. Hubbard. MS thesis, Iowa State Coll., 1952.

PRODUCTIVITY OF THE COTTONTAIL RABBIT IN DECATUR COUNTY, IOWA, 1951. Fred H. Hubbard, George O. Hendrickson. Iowa Acad.Sci., vol.59, pp.457-460, 1952.

AVERAGE WEIGHT OF RABBITS AT WEANING AGE. Chas. E. Kellogg. U.S. Dept. Agric., Bur.Biol.Surv., Wildlife Research and Management Leaflet, no.BS-31, pp.3, figs.3, Jan., 1936.

RELATIVE WEIGHTS OF YOUNG RABBITS AND DOES DURING THE SUCKLING PERIOD. Chas. E. Kellogg. Wildlife Research and Management Leaflet, no.BS-65, Bur.Biol. Surv., U.S.Dept.Agric., pp.5, Oct., 1936.

RESULTS FROM BREEDING RABBITS THAT ARE SUCKLING YOUNG. Chas. E. Kellogg. U.S.Dept.Agric., Circ.no.410, pp.1-8, illus., Oct., 1936.

(RABBIT BREEDING IN ITALY AND METHODS OF DIFFUSION.) L'allevamento del coniglio in Italia e mezzi di diffusione. Francesco Maiocco. Verhandl.des I.Internat. Kaninchenzuechter-Kongresses, Leipzig, 1930, pp.154-159, 1931.

PHYSIOLOGY OF REPRODUCTION IN THE RABBIT--AGE OF SEXUAL MATURITY, BREEDING SEASON, DURATION OF NORMAL PREGNANCY, AND OVULATION. Miguel Maresa. Philippine Jour.Sci., vol. 51, no.3, pp.323-330, July, 1933.

PRENATAL SEX RATIOS IN WILD RABBITS. I.H. Mills. Jour. Endocrinol., Cambridge, England, vol.12, no.3, pp.ix-xi (proceedings), May, 1955.

(THE RABBIT PLACENTA.) Die Placenta des Kaninchens. Charles S. Minot. Biol. Centralblatt, Erlangen, vol.10, no.4, pp. 114-122, Apr. 1, 1890.

REPRODUCTION OF THE BRUSH RABBIT IN CALIFORNIA. Archie S. Mossman. Jour. Wildl.Mgt., vol.19, no.2, pp.177-184, graphs, Apr., 1955.

COTTONTAIL SUCKLING YOUNG. Russel T.Norris. Jour.Mamm., vol.24, no.4, p. 499, Nov.17, 1943.

CASE OF EXTRAUTERINE PREGNANCY IN THE RABBIT. M-D.Fellows Nutting. Anat. Record, Philadelphia, vol.84, no.2, pp.215-219, fig.1, Oct. 26, 1942.

DETERMINATION OF SEX AND AGE RATIOS IN THE COTTONTAIL RABBIT. George A. Petrides. Amer.Midland Nat., vol.46, no.2, pp.312-336, Sep., 1951.

SCIENTIFIC ASPECTS OF RABBIT BREEDING. James N. Pickard, F.A.E.Crew. Watmoughs Ltd., Idle, Bradford, and London, pp.122, pls.12, 1931.

GENERAL POSITION OF RABBIT BREEDING IN ENGLAND. E.C. Richardson. Verhandl. des I.Internat.Kaninchenzuechter-Kongresses, Leipzig, 1930, pp.133-136, 1931.

OBSERVATIONS ON THE GESTATION PERIOD OF THE RABBIT. Paul D. Rosahn, Harry S.N. Greene, Ch'uan-K'uei Hu. Jour. Exp.Zool., vol.72, no.1, pp.195, 212, Nov. 5, 1935.

COPULATION IN THE WILD RABBIT, ORYCTOLAGUS CUNICULUS. Ian Rowley, B.C. Mollison. Behaviour, vol.8, no.1, pp. 81-84, 1955.

(HOLLAND'S RABBIT BREEDING.) Die Kaninchenzucht Hollands. F.C.Schaedtler. Verhandl.des I. Internat.Kaninchenzuechter-Kongresses, Leipzig, 1930, pp.127-132, 1931.

BREEDING AND HOME RANGE OF THE COTTONTAIL, SYLVILAGUS FLORIDANUS (ALLEN), IN CENTRAL MISSOURI. Charles W. Schwartz. AM thesis, Univ. Mo., 1940.

BREEDING SEASON OF THE COTTONTAIL IN CENTRAL MISSOURI. Charles W. Schwartz. Jour. Mamm., vol.23, no.1, pp. 1-16, Feb., 1942.

COTTONTAIL RABBIT PROPAGATION IN SMALL BREEDING PENS. Dale E. Scheffer. Jour. Wildl.Mgt., vol.21, no.1, p.90, Jan., 1957.

RABBIT PROPAGATION STUDY AT GWYNNBROOK STATE GAME FARM. Dale E.Scheffer. Md. Cons., vol.32, no.3, pp.23-24, illus., May, 1955.

SEXUAL AND AGGRESSIVE BEHAVIOR IN THE WILD RABBIT. H.N.Southern. Behaviour, vol.1, pp.173-194, 1948.

COTTONTAIL RABBIT PROPAGATION. James W. Stuber. Trans. 3rd N.Amer. Wildl.Conf., pp.651-658, 1938.

OHIO RABBIT PROPAGATION NOW IN VOGUE. James W. Stuber. Ohio Outdoor News, vol.2, no.6, pp.6, 8, Dec., 1936.

(ANORMAL GESTATION IN THE RABBIT.) Anormale Traechtigkeit bei Kaninchen. Sustmann. Der Deutsche Pelztierzuechter, Jahrg.1931, Munich, no.24, pp.664-665, figs., Dec. 15, 1931.

PRINCIPLES OF BREEDING RABBITS. Geo. S. Templeton. U.S.Dept.Agric., Wildlife Research and Management Leaflet, no.BS-101, pp.6, fig.1, Jan., 1938.

PSEUDOPREGNANCY IN DOMESTIC RABBITS. Geo.S. Templeton. U.S.Dept.Interior, Wildlife Circ.4, pp.1-11, fig.1, 1940.

HUMORAL EXCITATION OF THE NESTING INSTINCTS IN RABBITS. Esther Bogen Tietz. Science, n.s., vol.78, no.2023, p.316, Oct. 6, 1933.

REPRODUCTIVE FUNCTION IN THE COTTONTAIL RABBIT (SYLVILAGUS FLORIDANUS MEARNSII ALLEN) IN SOUTHERN MICHIGAN. R.E. Trippensee. Proc. N. Amer.Wildl.Conf., pp.344-350, 1936.

(RABBIT BREEDING IN SWITZERLAND.) Die Kaninchenzucht der Schweiz. A.Tschan. Verhandl.des I.Internat.Kaninchenzuechter-Kongresses, Leipzig, 1930, pp.170-173, 1931.

EFFECTS OF LOW ATMOSPHERIC PRESSURE ON THE FERTILITY OF MALE RABBITS. Arthur Walton, W.Uruski.Jour. Exp.Biol., London, vol.23, no.1, pp.71-76, Oct., 1946.

BREEDING SEASON OF THE WILD RABBIT IN NEW ZEALAND. J.S.Watson. Nature, London, vol.174, no.4430, p.608, Sep.25, 1954.

FERTILITY IN FLEMISH AND SMALLER BREEDS OF RABBIT. W.King Wilson. Nature, London, vol.146, no.3709, pp. 721-722, Nov. 30, 1941.

## Sex Cells

RATE AT WHICH SPERMATOGENESIS OCCURS IN THE RABBIT. S.A.Asdell, G. W. Salisbury. Anat.Record, Philadelphia, vol. 80, no.2, pp.145-151, pl.1, June 25, 1941.

DETECTION OF OVULATION IN THE INTACT RABBIT. H.S.Burr, R.T.Hill, Edgar Allen. Proc.Soc.Exp.Biol.and Med., New York, vol.33, no.1, pp.109-111, fig.1, Oct., 1935.

MORPHOLOGY OF THE LYMPHATICS OF THE RABBIT OVARY, AND THEIR POSSIBLE RELATION TO OVULATION. J.H.Burr, Jr., Joseph L.Davis. Anat. Record, Philadelphia, vol.105, no.3, p. 49, Nov., 1949. (Abstract.)

EFFECT OF DILUTION ON FERTILIZING CAPACITY OF RABBIT SPERMATOZOA. M.C. Chang. Science, Lancaster, vol.104, no.2703, pp.361-362, Oct. 18, 1946.

EFFECTS OF LOW TEMPERATURE ON FERTILIZED RABBIT OVA IN VITRO, AND THE NORMAL DEVELOPMENT OF OVA KEPT AT LOW TEMPERATURE FOR SEVERAL DAYS. M.C.Chang. Jour.Genetic Physiol., Baltimore, vol.31, no.5, pp.385-410, pls.8-10, May 20, 1948.

FERTILIZING CAPACITY OF SPERMATOZOA FOLLOWING COLD TREATMENT OF THE SCROTAL TESTES OF RABBITS. M.C. Chang. Jour.Exp.Biol., London, vol.22, nos.3-4, pp.95-100, May, 1946.

TRANSPLANTATION OF FERTILIZED RABBIT OVA: THE EFFECT ON VIABILITY OF AGE, IN VITRO STORAGE PERIOD, AND STORAGE TEMPERATURE. M.C.Chang. Nature, London, vol.161, no.4103, pp.978-979, June 19, 1948.

OBSERVATIONS ON THE MOTILITY OF RABBIT SPERMATOZOA IN DILUTE SUSPENSION. C.W.Emmons, G.I.M. Swyer. Jour.Gen.Physiol., Baltimore, vol. 32, no.1, pp.121-138, Sep. 20, 1948.

FERTILIZATION OF RABBIT OVA IN RELATION TO TIME. A METHOD OF CONTROLLING THE LITTER SIZE, THE DURATION OF PREGNANCY AND THE WEIGHT OF THE YOUNG AT BIRTH. John Hammond. Jour.Exp.Biol., vol.11, no.2, pp.140-161, Apr., 1934.

BREEDING OF SOME RABBITS PRODUCED BY RECIPIENTS OF ARTIFICIALLY ACTIVATED OVA. G.Pincus. Proc.Natl.Acad.

Sci., Washington, D.C., vol.25, no.11, pp.557-559, Nov., 1939.

SUPEROVULATION IN RABBITS. G.Pincus. Anat.Record, Philadelphia, vol.77, no.1, pp.1-8, May 25, 1940.

FERTILIZATION IN THE RABBIT. G.Pincus, E.V.Enzmann. Jour.Exp.Biol., vol.9, no.4, pp.403-408, figs.5, Oct., 1932.

OESTROUS CYCLE AND OVULATION IN THE RABBIT. Seigo Shibata. Jour.Coll. Agric.Imp.Univ.Tokyo, vol.11, no.3, pp. 309-340, pls.18-20, figs.4, Nov. 20, 1931.

(FERTILIZING CAPACITY OF RABBIT SPERMATOZOA PRESERVED IN A PHOSPHATE-BUFFERED DEXTROSE SOLUTION.) Ueber die Befruchtungsfaehigkeit der in der mit Phosphat gepufferten Dextroseloesung Konservierten Spermatozoen beim Kaninchen. J. Yamane, K.Kato. Biol. Zentralblatt, vol.48, pp.459-465, 1928.

South America

(THE WILD RABBIT.) El conejo silvestre. C.Camacho. Chile Min.Fomento Bol.Dept. Agric., vol.1, nos.10-12, pp.3-12, pl., figs.3, (1929) 1930.

MAMMALS OF NORTHERN COLOMBIA. PRELIMINARY REPORT NO. 6: RABBITS (LEPORIDAE), WITH NOTES ON THE CLASSIFICATION OF THE SOUTH AMERICAN FORMS. Philip Hershkovitz. Proc. U.S.Nat.Mus., Washington, vol.100, no. 3265, pp.327-375, illus., May 26, 1950.

REVIEW OF THE RABBITS OF THE ANDINUS GROUP AND THEIR DISTRIBUTION IN ECUADOR. Philip Hershkovitz. Occas. Papers Mus.Zool.Univ. Michigan, no.393, pp.1-15, map, Dec. 1, 1938.

NEW RABBIT FROM MARGARITE ISLAND, VENEZUELA. Gerrit S. Miller, Jr. Proc. Biol. Soc., Washington, vol.11, pp.97-98, Apr. 30, 1898.

NEW COTTONTAIL (SYLVILAGUS) FROM COLOMBIA. Oldfield Thomas. Ann. and Mag.Nat.Hist., ser.9, vol.8, pp.442-443, Oct., 1921.

TWO NEW SPECIES OF SYLVILAGUS FROM COLOMBIA. Oldfield Thomas. Ann. and Mag. Nat.Hist., ser.9, vol.5, pp.31-33, Jan., 1920.

Taxonomy

COMMENTS ON THE TAXONOMY AND GEOGRAPHIC DISTRIBUTION OF SOME NORTH AMERICAN RABBITS. E.Raymond Hall, Keith R. Kelson. Univ.Kansas Publ., Mus.Nat.Hist., Lawrence, vol.5, no.5, pp.49-58, Oct. 1, 1951.

ON SOME CHARACTERS OF TAXONOMIC VALUE APPERTAINING TO THE EGG AND THE OVARY OF RABBITS. Carl G. Hartman. Jour.Mamm., vol.6, no.2, pp.114-121, May, 1925.

RABBIT EGG AS A TAXONOMIC CHARACTER. Carl G. Hartman. Anat.Record, vol. 29, pp.113-114, Dec. 25, 1924.

COTTONTAIL RABBITS OF VIRGINIA. (Systematic and Distributional Study.) Leonard M. Llewellyn, C.O. Handley. Jour.Mamm., vol.26, no.4, pp.379-390, Nov., 1945.

TYPE OF THE GENUS PRONOLAGUS. Marcus W. Lyon, Jr. Proc.Biol.Soc. Washington, vol.19, p.95, June 4, 1906.

SPECIES IDENTIFICATION OF TWO MASSACHUSETTS COTTONTAIL RABBITS. James J. McDonough, Richard L. Hames. Mass.Div.Fisheries and Game, pp.4, illus., mimeo., 1954.

NEW SUBGENERIC NAME FOR THE WATER HARES (HYDROLAGUS GRAY.) Edgar A. Mearns. Science, New York, n.s., vol.5, no.114, p.393, Mar.5, 1897.

DESCRIPTIONS OF SIX NEW AMERICAN RABBITS. Gerrit S. Miller, Jr. Proc.Acad. Nat.Sci., Philadelphia, pp.380-390, 1899.

NOTE ON THE RELATIONSHIP OF ROMEROLAGUS NELSONI MERRIAM. E.W. Nelson. Soc.Cien."Antonio Alzate", Mexico, D.F., vol.16, no.3, pp.33-34, figs.6, Oct., 1901.

TAXONOMIC HISTORY OF THE NEOTROPICAL HARES OF THE GENUS SYLVILAGUS, SUBGENUS TAPETI. G. H. H. Tate. Amer. Mus. Novitates, no.661, pp. 10, Sep. 26, 1933.

RODENTIA

(THE DAEMONELIX PROBLEM.) Das Daemonelix-Problem. O. Abel. Palaeont. Zeitschr., vol.9, no.113, pp.179-180, 1927.

MUSKRAT--NUTRIA. Frank G. Ashbrook. La. Cons., 5 (6): 16-17, illus., Mar., 1953.

THE APPLE MOUSE. Vernon Bailey. Nature Mag., vol.4, pp.51-53, 63, 2 figs., July, 1924.

THE BIOLOGY OF RAT POPULATIONS. S. A. Barnett. Surgo, Glasgow, pp.111-115, illus., Candlemas, 1952.

THE CHISEL-TOOTH TRIBE. Wilfred S. Bronson. New York: Harcourt, Brace and Co., pp.6 plus 200, illus., pls.4, 1939.

RODENTS CARVE THEIR WAY TO SUCCESS. Maurice Burton. Illus. London News, vol.215, no.5765, p.592, illus., Oct.15, 1949.

THE MAMMALS OF JAVA. I. RODENTIA. K. W. Dammerman. Treubia, Buitenzorg, vol.13, nos.3-4, pp.429-470, figs.8, Dec., 1931.

RATS AND MICE. THEIR NATURAL HISTORY AND ECONOMIC IMPORTANCE. R. A. Davis. Discovery, London, 17 (3): 115-121, illus., Mar., 1956.

(CONTRIBUTIONS TO THE BIOLOGY OF THE DOMESTIC AND FIELD MOUSE, WITH SOME OBSERVATIONS OF OTHER RODENTS.) Beitraege zur Biologie der Haus- und der Ahrenmaus nebst einigen Beobachtungen an anderen Nagern. I. Eibl-Eibesfeldt. Zeits. fuer Tierpsychol., 7:558-587, 1950.

THE FAMILIES AND GENERA OF LIVING RODENTS. WITH A LIST OF NAMED FORMS (1758-1936) BY R. W. HAYMAN AND G. W. C. HOLT. J. R. Ellerman. Publ. Brit. Mus. (Nat. Hist), London, vol. 1 (Rodents other than Muridae), pp.xxvi, 689, figs.189, June 8, 1940; vol.2, (Family Muridae), pp.xii, 690, figs.50, Mar.21, 1941; vol.3, pt.1, pp.v, 210, Mar., 1949.

(Review by P. Rode of) THE FAMILIES AND GENERA OF LIVING RODENTS,. J. R. Ellerman. Mammalia, Paris, 9 (2): 61, June, 1945.

THE INFLUENCE OF AGRICULTURE ON THE NUMBERS OF MOUSE-LIKE RODENTS, AND THE BIOLOGICAL FOUNDATIONS OF RODENT CONTROL. B. K. Fenyuk. Rev. Microbiol., Epidemiol. et Parasitol (Rev. Microbiol.), Saratov, vol.16, nos.3-4, pp. 478-492, 1937. (In Russian).

(BIOMECHANICS OF THE RICOCHET JUMP OF RODENTS.) Biomekhanika rikoshetiruyuschego prizhka u grizunov. P. P. Gambaryan. Zool. Zhurnal, vol.34, no.3, pp.621-630, 1955.

INSIDE INFORMATION ON NATURE (X-RAYS OF BEAVER SKULL; MEADOW MICE REMAINS IN OWL PELLET). Percy Ghent. Carling Conserv. Digest, Toronto, vol.2, no.2, pp.5-6, illus., Second quarter, 1948.

MICE. Ross Hardy. Scribulus, Weber College, Ogden, pp.10-11, Winter, 1947.

JERBOAS, KANGAROO RATS AND JUMPING MICE. Robert T. Hatt. Nat. Hist., vol. 33, no.2, pp.199-208, Mar.-Apr., 1933.

BIOLOGICAL NOTES UPON FIBER, GEOMYS AND ERETHYZON. C. L. Herrick, C. Judson. Bull. Sci. Lab. Denison Univ., Granville, vol.6, pt.1, pp.15-25, May, 1891.

THE NOT SO TERRIBLE MOUSE. Walter H. Hodge. Nat. Hist., New York, vol.56, no.7, pp.310-311, illus., Sept., 1947.

(GARDEN MICE AND AQUATIC FIELD MICE.) La souris des jardins et les campagnols aquatiques. Albert Hugues. Bull. Soc. Nat. Acclimat, France, vol.80, no.1, pp.3-8, Jan., 1933.

IN QUEST OF APOLLO'S SACRED WHITE MICE. Clyde E. Keeler. Sci. Monthly, vol.34, no.1, pp.48-53, figs.3, Jan., 1932.

(NOTES ON RATS, MICE, AND ARVICOLES.) Notizen ueber Ratten, Maeuse und Wuehlmaeuse. Anton Krause. Archiv f. Naturg., Abt.A, Heft 4, pp.181-186, Apr., 1923.

RODENTS OF PAST AND PRESENT--ONE EVEN HAD HORNS! Paul O. McGrew. Field Mus. News, Chicago, vol.12, no.10, p.7, illus., Oct., 1941.

(THE ECOLOGY AND DISTRIBUTION OF SOME RODENTS IN THE LEVEL PART OF THE ZARAVSHAN VALLEY.) Zur Okologie und Verbreitung einiger Nagetiere im Ebene-Teil des Zerawschantales. R. N. Meklenburtzew. Acta Univ. Asiae Med., Taschkent, ser.8a, Zool., no.17, pp.3-30, figs.5, 1 table, 1935.

RATS' TALES. M. V. Morden. Game and Gun and Angler's Monthly, Lond., vol.18, no.194, pp.372-374, illus., Nov., 1941.

THE THIN-TOED GROUND-SQUIRREL, THE FAT DORMOUSE, THE MOLE-RAT, THE CHIPMUNK. S. P. Naumov, N. P. Lavrov, E. P. Spangenberg, N. M. Dukelskaya, I. M. Zaleskii, M. D. Zverev. All Union Cooperative Association Publ. House, Moscow and Leningrad, pp.36-70, figs.12-27, 1935.

THE FETAL MEMBRANES OF THE KANGAROO RAT, DIPODOMYS, WITH A CONSIDERATION OF THE PHYLOGENY OF THE GEOMYOIDEA. Paul E. Nielsen. Anat. Record, Phila., vol.77, pp.103-121, fig.1, pls.3, May 25, 1940.

EXPERIMENTS IN COMBINED REARING OF NUTRIA AND MUSKRATS IN THE KUBAN DELTA MARSHES. M. P. Pavloff. Translations of Russian Game Reports, Canadian Wildlife Service, 2: 131-143, 1957.

(SOME REMARKABLE RODENTS OF THE IMPERIAL ZOOLOGICAL MUSEUM (SPALACOMYS INDICUS, MUS TOMENTOSUS, AND MUS SQUAMIPES).) Ueber einige merkwuerdige Nagethiere (Spalacomys indicus, Mus tomentosus und Mus squamipes) des Koenigl. Wilhelm Peters. Abhandl., Koen., Akad., Wiss., Berlin, 1860, no.4, pp.139-156, pls.2, 1861.

(THE KING OF RATS.) Les rois de rats. G. Portevin. La Terre et la Vie, vol.8, no.1, pp.28-29, Jan.-Feb., 1938.

ABOUT SUBTERRANEAN MAMMALS. George H. Pournelle. Zoonooz, Zool. Soc. San Diego, 30 (10): 3-6, illus., Oct., 1957.

THERMAL CONDITIONS IN THE BURROWS OF SAND RODENTS, AND METHODS OF STUDYING THEM. Yu. M. Rall'. Zool. Zh., 18 (1): 110-119, 9 figs., 1939.

THE RODENTS OR GNAWING ANIMALS. Elwin R. Sanborn. Bull. New York Zool. Soc., vol.36, no.6, pp.143-175, Nov.-Dec., 1933.

ONE OF THE LARGEST OF LIVING RODENTS. R. W. Shufeldt. Nat. Humane Review, vol.5, no.3, p.45, Mar., 1917.

WOODCHUCKS AND PORCUPINES. R. W. Shufeldt. Amer. Forestry, vol.27, pp.147-154, 180, figs.1-15, Mar., 1921.

RODENT GIANTS. LIVING GNAWING ANIMALS FROM TINY MICE TO GIANT CAPYBARAS. George G. Simpson. Nat. Hist., vol.30, no.3, pp.305-313, May-June, 1930.

RODENTS: NATIVE AND FOREIGN. Ken Stott, Jr. Zoonooz, San Diego Zool. Soc., vol.13, no.1, pp.6-7, Jan., 1941.

RODENT MOUNTAINEERS. Walter P. Taylor. Jour. Mam., vol.2, no.1, pp.93-94, Nov., 1919.

MOUSE. Oldfield Thomas. Encycl. Brit., 9th ed., vol.17, 1884.

(CATALOGUE OF LIVING AND FOSSIL MAMMALS: RODENTS.) Catalogue des Mammiferes Vivants et Fossiles: Rongeurs. E. L. Trouessart. 1880-1881.

(COMPREHENSIVE REPORT ON THE EIGHT ANSWERS CONCERNING THE ESSAY COMPETITION ON THE REPRODUCTION BIOLOGY OF THE COYPU.) Zusammenfassender Bericht ueber die 8 Antworten zum Preisausschreiben ueber die Fortpflanzungsbiologie des Sumpfbibers. Ad. R. Walther-Hohenheim. Der Deutsch Pelztierzuechter, Jahrgang 1931, Muenchen, no.19, pp.519-520, Oct.1, 1931.

A NATURAL HISTORY OF THE MAMMALIA. VOL.II. RODENTIA, OR GNAWING MAMMALIA. G. R. Waterhouse. Paris, 480 pp., 21 pls., 1848.

ON THE GEOGRAPHICAL DISTRIBUTION OF THE RODENTIA. G. R. Waterhouse. Proc. Zool. Soc. Lond., pt.7, p.172, 1839.

GROUND SQUIRRELS 'N'GOPHERS. North Dakota Outdoors, Bismarck, vol.12, no.2, pp.4-5, 15, illus., Aug., 1949.

Africa

NEW AFRICAN RODENTS. Glover M. Allen. Bull. Mus. Comp. Zool. Harvard College, vol.54, no.14, pp.439-447, Apr., 1912.

SCIURIDAE, ANOMALURIDAE, AND IDIURIDAE COLLECTED BY THE AFRICAN MUSEUM CONGO EXPEDITION. J. A. Allen. Bull. Amer. Mus. Nat. Hist., vol. 47, 71, colored pl., Oct.27, 1922.

(ZOOLOGICAL COLLECTIONS MADE IN UGANDA BY DOLT. XVII. MAMMALS. PART III. RODENTIA.) Collezioni Zoologiche fatte nell' Uganda dal Dolt. XVIII. Mammiferi. Parte III. Rodentia. Oscar de Beaux. Ann. Mus. Cir. Stor. Nat. Genova, vol.51, pp.202-219, Apr.12, 1924.

KINDS AND DISTRIBUTION OF WILD RODENTS AND THEIR ECTOPARASITES IN EGYPT. M. S. Briscoe. Amer. Midland Nat., vol.55, no.2, pp.393-408, Apr., 1956.

REMARKS ON THE SKULLS OF SOME SOUTH AFRICAN MURIDAE. H. B. Fantham, K. M. M. Dall. South Afr. Jour. Sci., Pretoria, vol.23, pp.748-754, pls.10-12, Dec., 1926.

A NEW GENUS AND SOME NEW SPECIES AND SUBSPECIES OF ABYSSINIAN RODENTS. Childs Frick. Ann. Carnegie Mus., vol.9, nos.1-2, p.28, pls.1-15, June 6, 1914.

FOUR HITHERTO UNRECOGNIZED SUBSPECIES OF AFRICAN RODENTS. Robert T. Hatt. Amer. Mus. Nov., no.791, pp.1-4, Apr.11, 1935.

FOURTEEN HITHERTO UNRECOGNIZED AFRICAN RODENTS. Robert T. Hatt. Amer. Mus. Nov., no.708, pp.1-15, Fig.1, Apr. 4, 1934.

FIVE NEW RODENTS FROM BRITISH EAST AFRICA. Edmund Heller. Wash., Smithsonian Inst., vol.54, no.1924, 4 pp., 2 pls., 1910.

NEW RODENTS FROM BRITISH EAST AFRICA. Edmund Heller. Smiths. Misc. Coll., publ.2094, vol.59, no.16, pp.1-20, July 5, 1912.

TWO NEW RODENTS FROM BRITISH EAST AFRICA. Edmund Heller. Smiths. Misc. Coll., Wash., vol.LII (Quarterly issue, vol.V), pp.471-472, pl.LVI, 1910.

THE GEOGRAPHY OF AFRICAN RODENTS. John E. Hill. Trans. New York Acad. Sci., ser.2, vol.1, no.6, pp.95-99, Apr., 1939.

TEN NEW RODENTS FROM ANGOLA, AFRICA. John E. Hill, T. Donald Carter. Amer. Mus. Nov., no.913, pp.10, figs.5, Mar.8, 1937.

A NEW NAME FOR AN AFRICAN RAT. Ned Hollister. Proc. Biol. Soc. Wash., vol.31, p.97, June 29, 1918.

NEW RODENTS FROM BRITISH EAST AFRICA. Ned Hollister. Wash., Smiths. Inst., vol.68, no.10, 3 pp., 1918.

EIGHT NEW AFRICAN RODENTS. Wilfred H. Osgood. Ann. and Mag. Nat. Hist., London, ser.8, vol.5, pp.276-282, Mar., 1910.

A NEW GENUS OF AQUATIC RODENTS FROM ABYSSINIA. Wilfred H. Osgood. Field Mus. Nat. Hist., Publ.250, Zool. ser., vol.12, no.15, pp.185-189, illus., 1928.

(NOTES ON THE RODENTS OF THE WESTERN SAHARA.) Notes sur rongeurs du Sahara occidental. F. Petter. Mammalia, Paris, vol.15, no.3, pp.69-72, Sept., 1951.

(STUDY OF A COLLECTION OF RODENTS FROM THE NORTHWEST SAHARA.) Etude d'une collection de rongeurs du Sahara nord-occidental. F. Petter. Bull. Mus. Nat. Hist. Nat., Paris, vol.23, no. 5, pp.483-488, Oct., 1951.

(ECOLOGICAL DISTRIBUTION OF CERTAIN RODENTS OF CENTRAL AFRICA.) Distribution ecologique de certains rongeurs d'Afrique centrale. P. Pirlot. Rev. Zool. and Bot. Africaines, 47 (3-4): 348-389, Aug.8, 1953.

(RODENT ASSOCIATIONS IN THE HIGH REGIONS OF THE EASTERN BELGIAN CONGO AND RUANDA-URUNDI.) Associations de rongeurs dans les régions hautes de l'estdu Conge belge et du Ruanda-Urundi. P. L. Pirlot. Rev. Zool. Bot. Africain, vol.55, nos.3-4, pp.224-236, July 20, 1957.

(RODENTS HARMFUL TO THE AGRICULTURE ENVIRONS OF LAKE KIVU (BELGIAN CONGO). Rongeurs nuisibles aux cultures des environs du lac Kivu (Congo Belge). P. L. Pirlot. Bull. Agric. Congo Belge, vol.48, no.3, pp.703-730, illus., 1957.

THE RODENTS OF NIGERIA. D. R. Rosevear. Nigerian Field, vol.14, no.3, pp.93-101, pls.2, July, 1949.

A KEY TO THE FAMILIES AND GENERA OF AFRICAN RODENTS. J. St. Leger. Proc. Zool. Soc. Lond., pp.957-997, 10 col. pls., 1931.

TWO NEW SUBSPECIES OF MAMMALS FROM ANGOLA. J. St. Leger. Novitates Zoologicae, Lond., vol.39, no.3, pp.251-252, Aug., 1935.

(RODENTS FROM WEST AND CENTRAL AFRICA. RESULTS OF THE SECOND GERMAN CENTRAL AFRICA EXPEDITION.) Nagetiere aus West- und Zentral-Afrika. Ergebnisse der Zweiten Deutschen Zentral-Afrika-Exped. Ernst Schwarz. 1910-11, vol.1, Zoologie, pp.1063-1090, June, 1920.

DESCRIPTIVE LIST OF THE RODENTS OF SOUTH AFRICA. W. L. Sclater. Annals of the S. African Mus., vol.1, pt.2, p.181.

FOUR NEW MAMMALS FROM THE ANGLO-EGYPTIAN SUDAN. Henry W. Setzer. Jour. Wash. Acad. Sci., vol.43, no.10, pp.333-335, Oct.22, 1953.

DESCRIPTIONS OF TWO NEW RODENTS FROM THE VICTORIA NYANZA. Oldfield Thomas. Ann. and Mag. Nat. Hist. (6), vol.12, no.69, pp.267-269, Oct., 1893.

NEW AFRICAN EPIMYS AND JACULUS. Oldfield Thomas. Ann. and Mag. Nat. Hist. (8), vol.11, no.65, pp.482-485, May, 1913.

NOTES ON AFRICAN RODENTS. Oldfield Thomas. Ann. and Mag. Nat. Hist. (8), vol.6, no.32, pp.221-224, Aug., 1910.

ON A SMALL COLLECTION OF RODENTS FROM SOUTH-WESTERN AFRICA. Oldfield Thomas. Proc. Zool. Soc. Lond., pp.265-267, pl.14, Feb.21, 1882.

SOME RARITIES FROM ABYSSINIA, WITH THE DESCRIPTION OF A NEW MOLE-RAT (TACHYORYCTES), AND A NEW ARVICANTHIS. Oldfield Thomas. Ann. and Mag. Nat. Hist., ser.10, vol.1, pp.302-304, Feb., 1928.

THREE NEW AFRICAN RODENTS. Oldfield Thomas. Ann. and Mag. Nat. Hist. (8), vol.5, no.29, pp.419-422, May, 1910; vol. 7, no.42, pp.590-593, June, 1911.

(NOTE ON THE RODENTS OF TUNISIA COLLECTED BY MARIUS BLANE.) Note sur les Rongeurs de Tunisie Recueillis par Mr. Marius Blane. Oldfield Thomas, E. Trouessart. Bull. de la Societe zoologique de France, vol.28, pp.171-174, July 28, 1903.

(TREATING THE RODENT ACQUISITIONS. SCIENTIFIC RESULTS OF THE R. GRAUER EXPEDITION TO CENTRAL AFRICA, DEC., 1909 TO FEB., 1911.) Bearbeitung der Nagetierausbeute. Wissenschaftliche Ergebnisse der Expedition R. Grauer nach Zentral-afrika, Dezember 1909 bis Februar 1911. Otto Wettstein-Westerheim. Ann. Naturhist. Mus. Wien, vol.36, pp.15-24, Feb., 1923.

ON A COLLECTION OF RODENTS FROM ANGOLA. W. E. de Winton. Ann. and Mag. Nat. Hist., ser.6, vol.20, pp.320-324, Sept., 1897.

ON A NEW MOUSE FROM DAMARALAND. W. E. de Winton. Ann. and Mag. Nat. Hist., ser.6, vol.19, pp.349-350, Mar., 1897.

ON COLLECTIONS OF RODENTS MADE BY MR. J. FFOLIOTT DARLING IN MASHUNALAND AND MR. F. C. SELOUS IN MATABELELAND, WITH SHORT FIELD-NOTES BY THE COLLECTORS. W. E. de Winton. Proc. Zool. Soc. Lond., no.5, pp.798-808, pl.40, Nov.17, 1896.

Anatomy

(DEFECTIVE FORMATIONS OF THE DENTITION OF RODENTS.) Missbildungen des Gebisses bei Nagetieren. W. Banzhaf. Natur und Volk (Nat. u. Mus.), Frankfurt a.M., vol.64, no.8, pp.315-318, figs.4, Aug.1, 1934.

(SEX DIFFERENCES ON THE PELVIS OF MICE (MURINAE) AND ARVICOLAS (MICROTINAE).) Geschlechtsunterschiede am Becken von Maeusen (Murinae) und Wuehlmaeusen (Microtinae). Kurt Becker. Zool. Jahrbucher, vol.82, no.5, pp.453-462, May, 1954.

(COMPARATIVE INVESTIGATIONS ON THE HOMOLOGY OF THE INTESTINAL PARTS OF RODENTS WITH PARTIAL CONSIDERATION OF THE ARTERIAL BLOOD SUPPLY.) Vergleichende Untersuchungen ueber die Homologie der Darmteile bei Nagetieren unter teilweiser Beruecksichtigung der arteriellen Blut versorgung. A. Bonfert. Anat. Anzeiger, vol.65, pp.369-398, 13 figs., June 30, 1928.

(ON THE RELATIVE GYRENCEPHALY OF CERTAIN RODENTS.) Sur la gyrencéphalic relative de certains Rongeurs. S. Carette. Mammalia, Paris, vol.14, nos. 1-2, pp.20-25, figs.4, Mar.-June, 1950.

A COMPARATIVE STUDY OF THE CHROMOSOMES OF RODENTS. James Cecil Cross. Jour. Morphology, vol.52, no.2, pp.373-396, pls.1-3, Dec., 1931.

(CAUDAL AUTONOMY IN SOME MAMMALS OF THE RODENT GROUP.) L'autotomie caudlae chez quelques mammifères du groupe des rongeurs. L. Cuénot. Comp. Rend. Soc. Biol., 62: 174-6, 1907.

(SYSTEMATIC STUDY OF THE PENILE BONE OF MAMMALS (CONTINUATION).) Etude systématique de l'os pénien des mammifères (suite). Robert Didier. Mammalia, Paris, 20 (3): 238-247, Sept., 1956.

PHYSICAL NATURE OF MOUSE BRAIN. M. C. H. Dodson. Nature, London, vol. 162, no.4111, p.253, Aug.14, 1948.

SEX DIMORPHISM IN THE PELVIS OF RODENTS. William W. Dunmire. Jour. Mam., 36 (3): 356-361, illus., Aug., 1955.

CHROMOSOMES OF FIVE RODENT SPECIES. C. E. Ford, J. L. Hamerton. Nature, Lond., vol.177, no.4499, pp.140-141, Jan.21, 1956.

(DIFFERENTIAL CHARACTERISTICS OF THE FIRST MOLARS OF PORCUPINES OF THE NEW AND OLD WORLDS.) Caracteres differentiels des molaires vierges chez les procs-epics du nouveau et de l'ancien monde. Madeleine Friant. Bull. Soc. Zool. France, Paris, vol.60, pp.224-232, figs.10, 1935.

(THE PRIMITIVE TYPE OF UPPER MOLARS IN THE RODENTS.) Le type primitif des molaires supérieures chez les Rongeurs.

Madeleine Friant. Comptes Rendus Acad. Sci., Paris, vol.199, no.21, pp.1145-1147, fig.1, Nov., 1934.

(ETHMOTURBINAL STRUCTURE IN MICE AND VOLES.) Stroyeniye organov obonyaniya u mishyei i polyevok. L. V. Ganyeshina, N. N. Gurtovoi. Zool. Zhurnal, Moscow, vol.32, no.4, pp.722-729, 1953.

THE DEVELOPMENT OF ENAMEL AND DENTINE ON THE MOLARS OF THE MOUSE, WITH AN ACCOUNT OF THE ENAMEL-FREE AREAS. W. A. Gaunt. Acta Anatomica, Basel, 28 (1-2): 111-134, 1956.

(CONTRIBUTION TO THE STUDY OF THE MATERNAL PLACENTA OF RODENTS.) Contribution a l'étude du placenta maternel des rongeurs. Pol Gerard. Archives de Biologie, vol.37, pp.407-454, 3 pls., 14 figs., Sept.20, 1927.

(CONTRIBUTIONS TO THE OSTEOLOGY OF RODENTS.) Beitraege zur Osteologie der Nagethiere. C. G. Giebel. Abhandl. Naturwiss. Ver. Sachsen u. Thueringen in Halle, Berlin, vol.1, pt.2, pp.191-261, pls. 1-5, 1857.

(ON THE QUESTION OF CAUDAL AUTOTOMY IN RODENTS.) Zur Frage der Schwanzautotomie bei Nagern. H. Goegl. Zeitschr. Morph. u. Oekol. Tiere, vol.19, pp.135-143, 6 figs., Aug.14, 1930.

HEART-WEIGHT AND BODY-WEIGHT IN RODENTS. H. Gray. Jour. Mam., vol. 26, no.3, pp.285-299, figs.5, Aug., 1945.

DIFFERENTIAL GROWTH IN THE CRANIA OF MATURE MICE. C. V. Green. Jour. Mam., vol.14, no.2, pp.122-131, May, 1933.

ON THE NATURE OF SIZE FACTORS IN MICE. C. V. Green. Amer. Nat., vol. 65, no.700, pp.406-416, Sept.-Oct., 1931.

SOME CRANIAL ANOMALIES IN MICE. C. V. Green, Elizabeth Fekete. Anat. Record, vol.53, no.2, pp.187-190, pl.1, July 25, 1932.

THE VERTEBRAL COLUMNS OF RICOCHETAL RODENTS. Robert T. Hatt. Bull. Amer. Mus. Nat. Hist., vol.63, art. 6, pp.599-738, figs.27, pls.11-20, Nov.26, 1932.

STUDIES IN THE TOPOGRAPHY OF THE RODENT BRAIN; ERETHIZON DORSATUS AND GEOMYS BURSARIUS. C. Judson Herrick. Bull. Sci. Lab. Denison Univ., vol.6, pt.1, pp.26-46, pls.1-3, May, 1891.

THE CRANIAL FORAMINA IN RODENTS. John E. Hill. Jour. Mam., vol.16, no.2, pp.121-129, figs.3, May, 1935.

THE HOMOLOGY OF THE PRESEMIMEMBRANOSUS MUSCLE IN SOME RODENTS. John E. Hill. Anat. Rec., vol.59, no.3, pp.311-314, fig., June 25, 1934.

AN UNDESCRIBED STRUCTURE IN THE RODENT RHINARIUM. W. C. Osman Hill. Nature, London, vol.161, no.4086, pp.276-277, Feb.21, 1948.

THE OCCURRENCE AND SIGNIFICANCE OF EXTRA MOLAR TEETH IN RODENTS. David H. Johnson. Jour. Mam., vol.33, no.1, pp.70-72, illus., Feb., 1952.

(ATLAS OF MICROSCOPIC ANATOMY OF THE RAT.) Atlas de Anatomia Microscópica do Rato. Luiz Carlos Uchôa Junqueira, Euclydes Onofre Martins. Publ. Univ. São Paulo, pp.1-142, figs.132, 1947.

A MORPHOLOGICAL STUDY OF THE PANNICULUS CARNOSUS AND ITS GENETICAL RELATIONSHIP TO THE PECTORAL MUSCULATURE IN RODENTS. O. R. Langworthy. Amer. Jour. Anat., vol.35, pp.283-302, 18 figs., May 15, 1925.

INCISOR TIPS OF YOUNG RODENTS. Barbara Lawrence. Papers on Mammalogy, Field Mus. Nat. Hist., Zool. ser., vol.27, pp.313-317, figs.56-57, Dec.8, 1941.

A COMPARISON OF THE OSTEOLOGY OF THE JERBOAS AND JUMPING MICE. Marcus W. Lyon, Jr. Proc. U.S. Nat. Mus., vol.28, pp.659-668, pls.25-27, May 2, 1901.

CHROMOSOME NUMBERS OF SOME AMERICAN RODENTS. S. Makino. Science, vol. 118, no.3073, p.630, Nov.20, 1953; Misc. Repts. Yamashina's Inst. Ornithol. and Zool., Tokyo, no.3, p.4, Dec., 1953.

NOTES ON THE CHROMOSOMES OF THE PORCUPINE AND THE CHINCHILLA. S. Makino. Experientia, Sapporo, Japan, vol.9, no.6, pp.213-214, 1953.

(TAIL LOSS AND REGENERATION IN RODENTS.) Schwanzverlust und Schwanzregeneration bei Nagetieren. Erna Mohr. Zool. Anzeiger, Leipzig, vol.135, nos.3-4, pp.49-65, figs.14, Aug.1, 1941.

M. W. LYON'S COMPARISON OF THE OSTEOLOGY OF THE JERBOAS AND JUMPING MICE. Alfred Nehring. Sitz.-Ber. Gesell. Naturf. Freunde Berlin, Jahrg. 1901, no.5, pp.146-148, May 21, 1901.

ON THE PECULIARITIES OF THE SKELETON OF CAMPROMYS FOURNIERI DESM. AND DASYPROCTA ACOUCHY, F. CUV. R. Owen. Proc. Comm. Sci. and Corres. Zool. Soc. Lond., pt.2, pp.100-103, 1832.

THE CHROMOSOMES OF RODENTS. Theophilus S. Painter. Science, n.s., vol. 64, p.336, Oct.1, 1926.

THE EXTERNAL CHARACTERS OF SCARTURUS AND OTHER JERBOAS, COMPARED WITH THOSE OF ZAPUS AND PEDETES. R. I. Pocock. Proc. Zool. Soc. Lond., pp.659-682, Sept., 1922.

ON THE EXTERNAL CHARACTERS OF SOME HYSTRICOMORPH RODENTS. R. I. Pocock. Proc. Zool. Soc. Lond., pp.365-427, June, 1922.

ON THE EXTERNAL CHARACTERS OF THE BEAVER (CASTORIDAE) AND OF SOME SQUIRRELS (SCIURIDAE). R. I. Pocock. Proc. Zool. Soc. Lond., pt.4, pp.1071-1212, Feb., 1923.

(THE CHROMOSOME FORMULA IN SEVEN SPECIES OF NATIVE MUSCARDINIDAE AND MICROTINAE.) La formule chromosomiale chez sept espèces de Muscardinidae et de Microtinae indigènes. Pierre Renaud. Revue Suisse Zool., Ann. Soc. Zool. Suisse et Mus. Hist. Nat. Geneve, vol.45, no.7, pp.239-383, figs. 72, Mar., 1938.

GENERIC AND SPECIFIC DIFFERENCES OF THE AUTOPODIAL SKELETON IN RODENTS (SIMPLICIDENTATA). Anna Romankowowa. Zoologica Poloniae, vol. 8, nos.2-3, pp.271-282, 1957.

(ON THE MORPHOLOGY OF THE HAND OF THE MOUSE AS A GRASPING ORGAN.) Budowa anatomiczna reki myszy jako organiu chivytnego. Anna Romankowowa. Zool. Poloniae, Arch. Soc. Zool. Poloniae, Wroclaw, vol.6, fasc.2, pp.71-79, 1955.

(ADAPTIVE CHARACTERISTICS OF THE STRUCTURE OF THE NASAL CAVITY IN RODENTS.) Adaptiviniye osobyennosti stroyeniya nosovoi polosti grizunov. T. V. Sakharova. Zool. Zhurnal, Moscow, vol. 32, no.4, pp.714-721, 1953.

(INVESTIGATIONS OF THE BROWN ADIPOSE TISSUE, THE SO-CALLED HIBERNATION GLAND, OF THE EUROPEAN HAMSTER (CRICETUS CRICETUS L.) AND THE NORWEGIAN RAT (RATTUS NORVEGICUS ERXLEBEN).) Untersuchungen ueber das braune Fettgewebe, die sogenannte Winter schlafdruese, von europaeischen Hamster (Cricetus cricetus L.) und Wanderatte (Rattus norvegicus Erxleben). Hanna Schierer. Zool. Beitraege, Berlin, new ser. 2 (1): 63-126, 1956.

(THE TRITUBERCULY OF SIMPLICIDENT RODENTS.) Die Trigonodontie der simplicidentaten Nager. Hans G. Stehlin, Samuel Schaub. Schweizerischen Palaeontologischen Abhandlungen, vol.67, pp. 385, 1951.

COMPARATIVE STUDY OF AGE CHANGES DURING THE PERIOD OF GROWTH IN RODENTS. P. N. Stepanov. Zool. Jour. Moscou, vol.17, no.5, pp.787-794, figs.4, tables 2, 1938.

AUTOTOMY OF THE TAIL IN RODENTS. F. B. Sumner, H. H. Collins. Biol. Bull., vol.34, no.1, pp.1-6, figs.2, Jan., 1918.

MORPHOLOGICAL STUDY OF THE SPERM-HEAD IN SOME AMERICAN RODENTS. M. Takahashi. Misc. Repts. Yamashina's Inst. Ornithol. and Zool., Tokyo, no.6, pp.30-33, June, 1955.

ON REGENERATION OF THE TAILS OF MICE. Oldfield Thomas. Proc. Zool. Soc. Lond., vol.2, pp.491-494, Apr.5, 1906.

MATERIALS FOR THE SYSTEMATICS AND THE MORPHOLOGY OF RODENTS. IV. ON THE MECHANISM OF GNAWING AND MASTICATION IN SOME FOSSORIAL RODENTS. B. Vinogradov. Annuaire du Musee Zool. de l'Acad. Sci. Union Socialistic Soviet Republics, vol.27, 1926, pp.275-282, pls.18-20, 1927.

(ON THE REDUCED NUMBER OF MEIBOMIAN GLANDS IN THE EYELIDS OF CERTAIN RODENTS.) Sur le nombre réduit des glandes de Meibomius dans la paupière de certains rongeurs. V. Vrtis. Comptes Rendus Assoc. Anat., 23rd Reunion, (Prague, 2-4 Apr., 1928), pp.1-4, 1929.

ANTERIOR PROCESSES OF THE MALLEUS IN RODENTS. Kamal Wassif. Nature, Lond., vol.157, no.3993, p.630, May 11, 1946.

ON THE CRANIA OF THE RODENTS BELONGING TO THE FAMILIES CAVIIDAE AND CHINCHILLIDAE. G. R. Waterhouse. Proc. Zool. Soc. Lond., pt. 7, p.61., 1839.

DENTAL FORMULA IN THE MUROIDEA. Robert W. Wilson. Jour. Mam., 37 (2): 295-297, June 9, 1956.

THE HISTOCHEMISTRY OF THE RODENT'S PLACENTA. George B. Wislocki, Helen W. Deane, Edward W. Dempsey. Amer. Jour. Anat., Phila., vol.78, no.3, pp.281-345, pls.1-12, May, 1946.

(COMPARATIVE MEASUREMENT INVESTIGATIONS OF MURINES AND ARVICOLES.) Vergleichend-messende Untersuchungen an Muriden und Arvicoliden. Franz X. Zedwitz. Zool. Jahrbuecher (Anatomie), vol.51, pp.261-298, 3 figs., Nov.6, 1929.

## Asia

NOTES ON SOME RODENTS FROM YARKAND. John Anderson. Proc. Zool. Soc. Lond., pp.559-564, 1871.

THE RATS AND MICE OF FORMOSA, ILLUSTRATED. Bunichiro Aoki, Ryo Tanaka. Mem. Faculty Sci. and Agric., Taihoku Imperial Univ., Taiwan, vol.23, no.4, (Zool. no.13), pp.121-191, illus., May, 1941.

(MATERIALS ON THE RODENT FAUNA OF CENTRAL ASIA AND THE LIMITROPHE PARTS OF KAZAKHSTAN.) Matériaux pour la faune des rongeurs de l'Asie Centrale et des parties limitrophes du Kazachstan. A. I. Argyropulo. Trav. Inst. Zool. Acad. Sci. USSR, Leningrad, vol.4, no.2, pp.425-446, 1936.

(RODENTS OF KAZAKSTAN (MAMMALIA, RODENTIA).) Les rongeurs du Kazakstan (Mammalia, Rodentia). A. M. Beljaev. Trav. Inst. Zool. Acad. Sci. de l'URSS, Leningrad, vol.2, no.1, pp.37-40, 1934.

(TWO NEW RODENTS FROM THE USSURI REGION (SOUTHEAST SIBERIA).) Zwei neue Nagetiere aus dem Ussuri-Gebiet (Sudoest-Sibirien). N. M. Dukelski. Zool. Anzeiger, vol.77, pt.1-2, pp.39-45, May 15, 1928.

A KEY TO THE RODENTIA INHABITING INDIA, CEYLON, AND BURMA. PART II. J. R. Ellerman. Jour. Mam., vol.28, no. 4, pp.357-387, Nov.26, 1947.

KEY TO THE RODENTS OF SOUTH-WEST ASIA IN THE BRITISH MUSEUM COLLECTION. J. R. Ellerman. Proc. Zool. Soc. Lond., vol.118, pt.3, pp.765-816, Nov., 1948.

NOTES ON SOME ASIATIC RODENTS IN THE BRITISH MUSEUM. J. R. Ellerman. Proc. Zool. Soc. Lond., vol.117, pt.1, pp. 269-271, May, 1947.

FRESH RESEARCH ON THE RODENT FAUNA OF WESTERN TRANSBAIKALIA. A. S. Fetisov. Bull. Inst. Sci. Biol., Geogr., Irkutsk, 9: 121-144, 1942.

THE HABITAT DISTRIBUTION AND RELATIVE NUMBERS OF MOUSE-LIKE RODENTS IN THE FOREST-STEPPE AND FOREST ZONES OF THE SOUTHERN EXTREMITY OF WEST TRANSBAIKALIA. A. S. Fetisov. Bull. Inst. Sci (Irkutsk), 9 (1-2): 73-107, 1942.

PROPOSED CLASSIFICATION OF THE SMALLER INDIAN FIELD (OR JUNGLE) MICE. T. B. Fry. Jour. Bombay Nat. Hist. Soc., vol.34, no.4, pp.916-921, Mar.2, 1931.

NOTICE OF A COLLECTION OF MICE AND RATS, FORMED IN INDIA BY MR. ELLIOTT; OF TWO NEW SPECIES OF PARTRIDGE; OF SEVERAL UNDESCRIBED SHELLS; AND OF A CORAL INCRUSTING SHELLS. J. E. Gray. Proc. Zool. Soc. Lond., pt.3, p.108, 1835.

(MATERIAL ON THE HISTORY OF THE RODENTS OF THE LOWER URAL AND NORTHERN CASPIAN AREA.) Materiali poistorii fauni grizunov nizhnego Urala i severnogo Prikaspiya. I. M. Gromov. Trudi Zool. Inst. Akad. Nauk SSSR, 12: 192-245, 1947.

MALAYAN RODENTS. J. L. Harrison. Malayan Nature Jour., vol.4, no.1, pp. 32-36, Mar., 1949.

AN ACCOUNT OF THE RATS OF CALCUTTA. W. C. Hossack. Mem. Indian Mus., Calcutta, vol.1, no.1, pp.1-80, tables, Jul.7, 1907.

TWO NEW CHINESE RATS. A. Brazier Howell. Proc. Biol. Soc. Wash., vol.40, pp.43-46, Mar.5, 1927.

(BIOLOGICAL OBSERVATIONS ON SOME RODENTS IN THE SOUTH MANCHURIAN-MONGOLIAN BORDER REGION.) Biologische Beobachtungen uber einige Nagetiere im suedmandschurisch-mongolischen Grenzgebiet. H. M. Jettmar. Zeitschrift f, Saugetierkunde, vol.5, no.6, pp.344-361, pl.38, 1930.

RESULTS OF RODENT CENSUS WORK IN THE SOUTH-EAST OF THE U.S.S.R. IN 1939. (PRELIMINARY REPORT). G. A. Kaizer. In Symposium, "Rodents and rodent control," no.1, pp.225-233, From State Inst. Microbiol., (Saratov), 1941.

RODENTS OF WESTERN TIAN-SHAN COLLECTED IN THE SUMMER OF 1921 AND 1922. D. N. Kashkarov. Trans. Sci. Soc. Turkestan, Tashkent, vol.1, pp.175-220, pls.1-7, 1923.

ON TWO RODENTS NEW TO THE FAUNA OF THE MALAY PENINSULA, WITH THE DESCRIPTION OF A NEW SUBSPECIES, PITHECHEIRUS MELANURUS PARVUS. C. Boden Kloss. Jour. Fed. Malay States Mus., vol.6, pt.4, pp.249-252, Feb., 1916.

SEVEN NEW RATS COLLECTED BY DR. W. L. ABBOTT IN SIAM. Gerrit S. Miller, Jr. Proc. Biol. Soc., Wash., vol.8, pp. 137-150, pls.3-5, Apr.21, 1900.

(ON SOME RODENTS OF EASTERN SIBERIA.) Ueber einige Nagetiere Ostsibirens. S. J. Ogneff. Zool. Anzeiger, vol.84, pp.71-89, June 15, 1929.

ADDITIONS TO THE FAUNA OF CEYLON, NO.I. TWO NEW RODENTS FROM THE HILLS OF CENTRAL CEYLON. W. W. A. Phillips. Spolia Zeylanica, Ceylon Jour. Sci., vol.16, pt.3, pp.323-327, Mar.18, 1932.

GUIDE TO THE MAMMALS OF CEYLON. PART 8, RODENTIA. W. W. A. Phillips. Ceylon Jour. Sci., Sect.B, Zool. and Geol., Spolia Zeylonica, vol.14, no.2, pp.209-293, pls.2, 1928.

TWO NEW RODENTS FROM THE HIGHLANDS OF CEYLON. W. W. A. Phillips. Ceylon Jour. Sci., Sect.B, zool. and Geol., Spolia Zeylanica, vol.15, pt.2, pp.165-168, May, 20, 1929.

(SYSTEMATIC REVIEW OF THE FIELD MICE OF SIBERIA.) Sistematicheskii obzor Polevok Vodiashikhsia v Sibiri. Iv. S. Pollakov. Suppl. to Mem. Acad of Sci., St. Petersberg, vol.39, no.2, pp.92, figs. 18, 1881.

(MATERIALS ON THE RODENTS OF THE ALTAI HIGH MOUNTAIN REGION.) Materialien zur Kenntnis der Nagetiere des Hochgebirges von Altai. A. Rasorenova. Bull. Soc. Nat. Moscow, ser. biol., vol. 42, no.1, pp.78-84, fig.1, 1933.

(THE RODENTS FROM THE TEHERAN REGION.) Les rongeurs de la region de Tehran. R. Rousselot. Archives Inst. Hessarek, Fasc.5, pp.11, 1 pl., 1947.

(MATERIAL ON THE STUDY OF RODENTS OF NORTHERN SIBERIA.) Les matériaux sur l'étude des rongeurs de la Sibérie du Nord. V. N. Skalon. Les Travaux de la Defense de Plantes de la Sibérie, Nowosibirsk, no.1, (8), pp.183-208, figs.3, 1931.

A STUDY OF THE RODENTS OF EASTERN SIBERIA. V. N. Skalon. Bull. Plant Protection Eastern Siberia, Irkutsk and Moscow, Irkutsk (Govt) Stantsiia Zashchity rastenii ot vreditelyi. Vrednye saranchevye Vrediteli ogorodnichestva Gryzuny Priangar' ia Mokraia golvnia, Moscow, pp.146-186, 1944.

SIX NEW INDO-MALAYAN RATS. H. J. V. Sody. Natuurhist. Maanblad, Limburg, vol.21, no.12, pp.157-160, Dec.30, 1932.

DESCRIPTION OF A NEW RAT FROM CHINA. Oldfield Thomas. Ann. and Mag. Nat. Hist. (6), vol.20, no.115, pp.113-114, July, 1897.

DESCRIPTION OF A NEW SPECIES OF RAT FROM CHINA. Oldfield Thomas. Proc. Zool. Soc. Lond., pp.587-588, pl. 44, June 20, 1882.

NEW RODENTS FROM SZE-CHWAN COLLECTED BY CAPT. F. M. BAILEY. Oldfield Thomas. Ann. and Mag. Nat. Hist. (8), vol.8, no.48, pp.727-729, Dec., 1911.

ON TWO NEW CHINESE RODENTS. Oldfield Thomas. Ann. and Mag. Nat. Hist. (6), vol.13, no.76, pp.363-365, Apr., 1894.

ON TWO NEW RODENTS FROM VAN, KURDISTAN. Oldfield Thomas. Ann. and Mag. Nat. Hist. (6), vol.20, no.117, pp.308-310, Sept., 1897.

SCIENTIFIC RESULTS FROM THE MAMMAL SURVEY. XXV. (A) ON JUNGLE-MICE FROM ASSAM. (B) THE BRUSH-TAILED PORCUPINE OF ASSAM. Oldfield Thomas. Jour. Bombay Nat. Hist. Soc., vol.27, no.3, pp.596-599, 1921.

SCIENTIFIC RESULTS OF THE MAMMAL SURVEY. XXXV. TWO NEW RODENTS FROM THE MERGUI ARCHIPELAGO. Oldfield Thomas. Jour. Bombay, Nat. Hist. Soc., vol.2, no.4, pp.1067-1068, Dec.20, 1922.

SCIENTIFIC RESULTS FROM THE MAMMAL SURVEY. XL. A NEW MOUSE FROM MADURA, S. INDIA. Oldfield Thomas. Jour. Bombay Nat. Hist. Soc., vol.29, no. 1, p.87, Apr.20, 1923.

THREE NEW RODENTS FROM KAN-ZU. Oldfield Thomas. Ann. and Mag. Nat. Hist. (8), vol.8, no.48, pp.720-723, Dec., 1911.

(RODENTS OF THE KIRGHIZ REPUBLIC.) Gryzuny Kirgizll. A. Toktosunov. Frunze, Academy of Sciences Kirghiz SSR, illus., maps, tables, 1958.

(DIRECTIONS FOR THE DETERMINATION OF THE RODENTS OF CENTRAL ASIA.) Rukovodstvo k opredeleniiu gryzunov Srednei Azii. B. S. Vinogradov. Samarkand, 50 pp., 1930.

(OBSERVATIONS ON THE RODENTS OF EASTERN SIBERIA.) Observations sur les rongeurs de la Siberia occidentale. B. S. Vinogradov. Proc. Siberian Bureau of Entomology, no.3, pp.19-36, Feb., 1924.

(REMARK ON THE GEOGRAPHICAL DISTRIBUTION OF SOME RODENTS OF TRANSBAIKALIA AND OTHER REGIONS OF SOUTHERN SIBERIA.) Remarque sur la distribution geographique de quelques Rongeurs dans la Transbaicalie et autres regions de la Siberie meridionale. B. S. Vinogradov. Rendus de l'Academie des Sciences de L'URSS, pp.91-94, 1926.

(RODENTS OF TAJIKISTAN.) Gryzuny Tadzhikistana. B. S. Vinogradov. Stalinabad, Gosizdat pri CEK Tadzhikskoi SSR, 81 pp., 11 pls., 1945.

(MATERIALS ON THE RODENTS OF CENTRAL ASIA. I. BIOLOGICAL OBSERVATIONS ON THE JERBOAS (DIPODIDAE, MAMMALIA).) Materiaux pour servir a la connaissance des Rongeurs de l'Asie Centrale. l. Observations biologiques sur les Gerboises (Dipodidae, Mammalia). B. S. Vinogradov, A. Argyropulo. Ann. Mus. Zool. Acad. Sci. URSS, vol.32, no.2, pp. 135-156, figs.9, 1931.

RODENTS OF CENTRAL ASIATIC PART OF USSR. B. S. Vinogradov, A. I. Argyropulo, V. G. Heptner. Publ. Zool. Inst., Acad. Sci. USSR, Moscow and Leningrad, p.228, fig.46, 1936.

MATERIAL FOR RODENT FAUNA OF SOUTHERN PART OF ENISEISKOI, IRKUTSK GOVT., AND TRANSBAIKAL. B. S. Vinogradov, S. Obolensky. Citation missing. pp.15, 1925.

SOME RODENTS FROM TRANSBAICALIA, EAST SIBERIA. B. S. Vinogradov, S. Obolensky. Jour. Mam., vol.8, no.3, pp. 233-239, Aug., 1927.

ON A SMALL COLLECTION OF RODENTS FROM LOWER SIND. R. C. Wroughton. Jour. Bombay Nat. Hist. Soc., vol.20, no. 4, pp.1000-1001a, May 20, 1911.

SOME NEW INDIAN RODENTS. R. C. Wroughton. Jour. Bombay Nat. Hist. Soc., vol.21, no.2, pp.338-342, illus., Mar.31, 1912.

(THE GIANT, STRIPED, AND POINTED-NOSE SQUIRREL OF THE ORIENTAL REGION.) Die Reisen, Steifen, -und Spitznasenhoernchen der orientalischen Region. W. Zahn. Zeitschr. f. Saeugetierkunde, Berlin, vol.16, pp.1-182, 6 maps, 1942.

## Australia

DESCRIPTIONS OF FIVE NEW SPECIES OF MAMMALS. John Gould. Proc. Zool. Soc. Lond., pt.13, p.77, 1845.

NOTES ON CLASSIFICATION OF COMMON RODENTS WITH LIST OF AUSTRALIAN SPECIES. Heber A. Longman. Commonwealth of Australia Quarantine Serv., Serv. Publ. no.8, pp.1-27, figs.1-7, pls.1-8, 1916.

NOTICE OF CERTAIN AUSTRALIAN QUADRUPEDS, BELONGING TO THE ORDER RODENTIA. W. Ogilby. Trans. Linn. Soc. Lond., vol.18, pp.121-132, 1841.

RESULTS OF THE ARCHBOLD EXPEDITIONS. NO.65, THE RODENTS OF AUSTRALIA AND NEW GUINEA. G. H. H. Tate. Bull. Amer. Mus. Nat. Hist., New York, vol.97, art.4, pp.183-430, illus., Oct.30, 1951.

## Central America

FIVE NEW MAMMALS OF THE RODENT GENERA SCIURUS, ORTHOGEOMYS, HETEROMYS, AND RHEOMYS, FROM EL SALVADOR. Donald T. Dickey. Proc. Biol. Soc. Wash., vol.41, pp.7-14, Feb.1, 1928.

NEW RODENTS FROM MIDDLE AMERICA. E. A. Goldman. Jour. Wash. Acad. Sci., vol.27, no.10, pp.418-423, Oct.15, 1937.

FOUR NEW RODENTS FROM COSTA RICA. George G. Goodwin. Amer. Mus. Novitates, New York, no.1227, pp.4, Apr.22, 1943.

NOTE ON THE INDIGENOUS RODENT OF SANTO DOMINGO. Gerrit S. Miller, Jr. Proc. Biol. Soc., Wash., vol.29, p.47, Feb.24, 1916.

TWO NEW RODENTS FROM COSTA RICA. Wilfred H. Osgood. Field Mus. Nat. Hist., Publ. 295, Zool. ser., vol. 18, no. 5, pp. 143-145, pl. 4, Aug. 3, 1931.

THREE NEW SMALL MAMMALS FROM EASTERN PANAMA. Oliver P. Pearson. Notulae Naturae, Acad. Nat. Sci. Phila., no. 6, pp. 5, June 8, 1939.

ON A NEW RAT FROM GUATEMALA. Oldfield Thomas. Proc. Zool. Soc. Lond., pp. 669-670, Oct., 1909.

Diseases

SPONTANEOUS COCCIDIOIDAL GRANULOMA IN THE LUNGS OF WILD RODENTS. L. L. Ashburn, C. W. Emmons. Archives Path., 34 (5): 791-800, Nov., 1942.

TULAREMIA IN BEAVERS AND MUSKRATS, WATERTON LAKES NATIONAL PARK, ALBERTA, 1952-53. A. W. F. Banfield. Canadian Jour. Zool., vol. 32, no. 3, pp. 139-143, June, 1954.

(PLAGUE IN WILD RODENTS IN ARGENTINA.) Peste rural en La Argentina. José M. Barrera. Proc. 8th Amer. Sci. Congr., Wash., D.C., vol. 6, pp. 291-292, Aug. 3, 1942.

A FIELD STUDY OF LATENT TULAREMIA IN RODENTS WITH A LIST OF ALL KNOWN NATURALLY INFECTED VERTEBRATES. A. R. Burroughs, R. Holdenried, D. S. Longanecker, K. F. Meyer. Jour. Infectious Dis., 76 (2): 115-119, Mar.-Apr., 1945.

TWO EPIZOOTICS OF PLAGUE INFECTION IN WILD RODENTS IN THE WESTERN UNITED STATES IN 1938. L. B. Byington. Pub. Health Rep., 55 (33): 1496-1501, Aug. 16, 1940.

SYLVATIC PLAGUE. Albert M. Day. Tran. N. A. Wildl. Conf., 2: 555-560, 1937.

RECENT DEVELOPMENTS IN OUR KNOWLEDGE OF PLAGUE TRANSMISSION. C. R. Eskey. Pub. Health Rep. 53(2): 49-57, Jan. 14, 1938.

INFECTION IN RODENTS, EXPERIMENTAL TRANSMISSION BY FLEAS, AND INOCULATION TESTS FOR INFECTION. C. R. Eskey, V. H. Haas. Publ. Health Rep., vol. 54, no. 32, pp. 1467-1481, Aug. 11, 1939.

PLAGUE IN THE WESTERN PART OF THE UNITED STATES. C. R. Eskey, V. H. Haas. U. S. Pub. Health Serv., Bull. 254, 83 pp., 1940.

SURVEY OF ROCKY MOUNTAIN SPOTTED FEVER AND SYLVATIC PLAGUE IN WESTERN CANADA DURING 1938. R. J. Gibbons. Can. Jour. Pub. Health, 30 (4): 184-187, Apr., 1939.

PLAGUE INFECTION REPORTED IN THE UNITED STATES DURING 1944 AND SUMMARY OF HUMAN CASES, 1900-44. Brock C. Hampton. Pub. Health Rep., 60 (46): 1361-1365, Nov. 16, 1945.

AN OUTBREAK OF DERMATITIS AMONGST TROOPS IN NORTH WALES CAUSED BY RODENT MITES. M. A. Hill, R. M. Gordon. Ann. Trop. Med. Parasit., Liverpool, vol. 39, pp. 46-52, 1945.

SUSCEPTIBILITY OF NEW MEXICO RODENTS TO EXPERIMENTAL PLAGUE. R. Holdenried, S. F. Quan. Publ. Health Rep., U.S. Public Health Service, Wash., vol. 71, no. 10, pp. 979-984, Oct., 1956.

ATTEMPTED ADAPTATION OF THE VIRUS OF POLIOMYELITIS TO WILD RODENTS. Beatrice F. Howitt, William van Herick. Proc. Soc. Exper. Biol. and Med., Utica, vol. 46, no. 3, pp. 431-435, Mar., 1941.

RICKETTSIALPOX--A NEWLY RECOGNIZED RICKETTSIAL DISEASE. IV. ISOLATION OF RICKETTSIA APPARENTLY IDENTICAL WITH THE CAUSATIVE AGENT OF RICKETTSIALPOX FROM ALLODERMANYSSUS SANGUINEUS, A RODENT MITE. Robert J. Huebner, William L. Jellison, Charles Pomerantz. Public Health Reports, vol. 61, no. 47, pp. 1677-1682, Nov. 22, 1946.

TSUTSUGAMUSHI DISEASE; EPIDEMIOLOGY AND METHODS OF SURVEY AND CONTROL (RODENTS AS HOSTS). David H. Johnson, George W. Wharton. U. S. Naval Med. Bull., Wash., vol. 46, no. 3, pp. 459-472, illus., Mar., 1946.

RODENT PLAGUE IN CALIFORNIA. W. H. Kellogg. Jour. Amer. Med. Assoc., vol. 105, no. 11, pp. 856-859, Sept. 14, 1935.

RAT DISEASE AND MOUSE-FEVER CONNECTIONS BETWEEN DISTRIBUTION OF RODENTS AND TRANSMISSION OF DISEASES. I. Krumbiegel. Universum, 5: 733-737, 1950.

STUDIES ON SUSCEPTIBILITY OF NEOTROPICAL RODENTS TO DIFFERENT STRAINS OF YELLOW FEVER VIRUS. H. W. Laemmert, Jr. Amer. Jour. Trop. Med., Balto., vol. 28, no. 2, pp. 231-246, Mar., 1948.

AN OUTBREAK OF TULAREMIA IN BEAVER AND MUSKRAT IN WATERTON LAKES NATIONAL PARK, ALBERTA. E. V. Langford. Can. Jour. Compar. Med. and Vet. Sci., 18 (1): 28-30, Jan., 1954.

THE KNOWN AND UNKNOWN IN PLAGUE. K. F. Meyer. Amer. Jour. Trop. Med., 22 (1): 9-36, Jan., 1942.

REPORT OF THE SYLVATIC PLAGUE COMMITTEE. K. F. Meyer. Ann. Meeting W. Branch, Am. Pub. Health Assn., 7, 10 pp., 1936.

TWO HUMAN DISEASES WHICH MAY BE CONTRACTED FROM MONTANA RODENTS. Harlow B. Mills. Mont. State Bd. Ent., Misc. Pub., 1, 8 pp., 1941.

NATIVE RATS AND THE PLAGUE IN THE PACIFIC. Edward P. Mumford. Am. Sci., 30 (3): 212-217, July, 1942.

CONTAMINATION OF NATURAL WATERS AND MUD WITH PASTEURELLA TULARENSIS AND TULAREMIA IN BEAVERS AND MUSKRATS IN THE NORTHWESTERN UNITED STATES. R. R. Parker, Edward A. Steinhaus, Glen Kohls, William L. Jellison. Bull. Nat. Inst. Health, Wash., no. 193, pp. 61, illus., 1951.

PERIPHERAL INOCULATION OF LANSING POLIOMYELITIS VIRUS IN RODENTS: SUSCEPTIBILITY AND DEVELOPMENT OF IMMUNITY. Manuel R. Pinto. Amer. Jour. Hygiene, Lancaster, vol. 48, no. 3, pp. 361-380, Nov., 1948.

BIBLIOGRAPHY OF RUSSIAN LITERATURE ON THE ROLE OF RODENTS OF THE VOLGA BASIN AND WESTERN KAZAKSTAN IN THE EPIDEMIOLOGY OF PLAGUE AND TULAREMIA. G. Rall. Vestnik Mikrobiol., Epidemiol. i Parazitol. (Rev. Microbiol., Epidemiol. et Parasitol.), Saratov, vol. 12, no. 3, pp. 229-239, 1934.

THE FOCALITY OF RODENT PLAGUE IN THE LIGHT OF ECOLOGO-GEOGRAPHICAL IDEAS. Yu. M. Rall'. Zool. Zh., 23 (5): 258-266, 1944.

HYDATID DISEASE (ECHINOCOCCOSIS) IN ALASKA AND THE IMPORTANCE OF RODENT INTERMEDIATE HOSTS. Robert Rausch, Everett L. Schiller. Science, Lancaster, vol. 113, no. 2925, pp. 57-58, illus., Jan. 19, 1951.

(RODENTS SENSITIVE TO THE PLAGUE IN THE REGION OF NEFZAOUA.) Les rongeurs sensibles a la peste dans la region du Nefzaoua. A. Ristorcelli. Arch. Inst. Pasteur, Tunis, vol. 27, no. 3, pp. 298-304, map, Sept., 1938.

DEATH RIDES A RAT. BUBONIC PLAGUE'S EVER-MENACING INVASION KEEPS FORCES OF NATIONAL AND STATE PUBLIC HEALTH SERVICES ON THE ALERT. Jane Stafford. Science News Letter, vol. 34, no. 9, pp. 134-135, figs. 2, Aug. 27, 1938.

PRESENT KNOWLEDGE OF THE STATUS OF VECTORS OF SYLVATIC PLAGUE IN NORTH AMERICA. M. A. Stewart. Proc. Sixth Pac. Sci. Cong., 4: 433-437, 1940.

ON THE STREPTOCOCCAL EPIZOOTIC AMONG MICE IN THE NORTHERN CAUCASUS IN 1932-33. V. V. Suknev, V. A. Chizhova, E. L. Kazantzeva. Rev. Microbiol., 12: 175-182, 1933.

HEPATICOLEASIS: A FREQUENT AND SOMETIMES FATAL VERMINOUS INFESTATION OF THE LIVERS OF RATS AND OTHER RODENTS. Fred D. Weidman. Jour. Parasitology, vol. 12, pp. 19-25, pls. 3-4, Sept., 1925.

SUSCEPTIBILITY OF THE CANE RAT (ZYGODONTOMYS) AND OF THE BUSH RAT (PROECHIMYS) TO INFLUENZA VIRUSES. John M. Weir. Jour. Infec. Diseases, vol. 74, pp. 121-130, Mar.-Apr., 1944.

ISOLATION OF LCM VIRUS IN AN EFFORT TO ADAPT POLIOMYELITIS VIRUS TO RODENTS. H. A. Wenner. Jour. Infec. Diseases, Chicago, vol. 83, no. 2, pp. 155-163, Sept.-Oct., 1948.

OBSERVATIONS ON VECTORS OF CHAGAS' DISEASE IN THE UNITED STATES. I. CALIFORNIA. Sherwin F. Wood. Bull. S. Calif. Acad. Sci., 41 (2): 61-69, May-Aug., 1942.

THE BLACK DEATH IS HERE (BUBONIC PLAGUE IN WILD RODENTS OF WESTERN UNITED STATES). Time, the Weekly Newsmagazine, vol. 40, no. 8, pp. 52, 54, illus., Aug. 24, 1942.

PLAGUE INFECTION IN CALIFORNIA. Pub. Health Rep., 58 (4): 1528-1529, Oct. 8, 1943.

PLAGUE INFECTION IN CALIFORNIA, IDAHO, AND OREGON. Pub. Health Rep., 57(27): 1006-1007 to 57 (37): 1391, July 3, Sept. 11, 1942.

PLAGUE INFECTION REPORTED IN THE UNITED STATES DURING 1940. Pub. Health Rep. 56(9): 399-400, Feb. 28, 1941.

PLAGUE INFECTION REPORTED IN THE UNITED STATES DURING 1941. Pub. Health Rep., 57 (24): 903-905, June 12, 1942.

PLAGUE INFECTION REPORTED IN THE UNITED STATES DURING 1942. Pub. Health Rep., 58 (16): 640-645, Apr. 16, 1943.

PLAGUE INFECTION REPORTED IN THE UNITED STATES DURING 1943. Pub. Health Rep., 59 (28): 911-915, July 14, 1944.

PLAGUE INFECTION REPORTED IN THE UNITED STATES IN 1945. Pub. Health Rep., 62 (12): 431-433, Mar. 21, 1947.

PLAGUE INFECTION REPORTED IN THE UNITED STATES IN 1946. Pub. Health Rep., 62 (37): 1336-1340, Sept. 12, 1947.

PLAGUE INFECTION REPORTED IN THE UNITED STATES IN 1947. Pub. Health Rep., 63 (34): 1102-1105, Aug. 20, 1948.

RODENTS CARRY DISEASE. Rodent Mail, Rats and Mice, Lond., vol. 2, no. 5, pp. 55-57, July, 1946.

RODENTS CARRY DISEASE: V. SCRUB TYPHUS. Rodent Mail, Rats and Mice, Lond., vol. 3, no. 1, pp. 5-6, Mar., 1947.

AN UNIDENTIFIED DISEASE IN NEVADA BELIEVED TO BE TRANSMITTED BY RODENTS. Pub. Health Rep., 55 (22): 988, May 31, 1940.

Ecology

EFFECT OF BURNING AND GRAZING ON RODENT POPULATIONS. Rollin H. Baker. Jour. Mam., vol. 21, no. 2, p. 223, May 14, 1940.

RANGE RODENTS AND PLANT SUCCESSION. R. M. Bond. Trans. N. A. Wildl. Conf., 10: 229-234, 1945.

(RELATIONS BETWEEN CLIMATIC CONDITIONS AND THE ECOLOGY OF SOME COUNTRY RODENTS (CRICETIDAE).) Relaciones entre estados climaticos y la ecologia de algunos roedores de campo (Cricetidae). Jorge A. Crespo. Rev. Argentina Zoogeogr., Buenos Aires, vol. 4, no. 3, pp. 137-144, pls. 2, 1945.

CONTRIBUTIONS TO THE ECOLOGY AND BIOLOGY OF RODENTS OF THE TROITSK DISTRICT, FORM. URAL PROVINCE. 2. SOME OBSERVATIONS ON THE CHARACTER OF FOOD OF SOME RODENTS. N. P. Durymanova-Savik. Isvestiia biologicheskogo Nauchno-Issledovatel'skogo Instituta pri permskom gosudarstvennom Universitete, Perm (Bull. Inst. rech. biol. Perm), vol.10, no.3, pp.101-113, tables 7, 1936.

SUMMER POPULATIONS AND MOVEMENTS OF THE COTTON RAT AND OTHER RODENTS ON THE SAVANNAH RIVER REFUGE. Arnold B. Erickson. Jour. Mam., 30 (2): 133-140, May, 1949.

ACTIVITY OF RODENTS IN PASTURE LANDS AND MEADOWS. INFLUENCE OF THE SOCIAL FIELD-MOUSE AND SOME OTHER RODENTS UPON THE VEGETATION OF THE KISLIARSKI REGION OF DAGHESTAN. A. N. Formozov, I. B, Kiris. Uchenye Zapiski Moskovskogo Gosudarstvennogo Universiteta, zool., vol. 13, pp.59-70, figs.11-12, tables, 1937.

PRINCIPAL FEATURES OF THE ACTIVITY OF RODENTS ON PASTURES AND MEADOW LAND. A. N. Formozov, A. G. Voronov. Comptes Rendus (Doklady) Acad. Sci.URSS, Moscow, n.s., vol.3 (8), no.8 (68), pp.370-372, 1935.

RODENT POPULATIONS AND THEIR REACTION TO GRAZING INTENSITIES ON SAND SAGEBRUSH GRASSLANDS IN THE SOUTHERN GREAT PLAINS REGION. W. J. Frank. PhD thesis, Okla. A. and M. Coll., 1950.

THE INFLUENCE OF TWO BURROWING RODENTS, DIPODOMYS SPECTABILIS SPECTABILIS (KANGAROO RAT) AND NEOTOMA ALBIGULA ALBIGULA (PACK RAT), ON DESERT SOILS IN ARIZONA. II. PHYSICAL EFFECTS. Robert A. Green, Guy H. Murphy. Ecology, vol.13, no.4, pp. 359-363, Oct., 1932.

THE INFLUENCE OF TWO BURROWING RODENTS, DIPODOMYS SPECTABILIS SPECTABILIS (KANGAROO RAT) AND NEOTOMA ALBIGULA ALBIGULA (PACK RAT), ON DESERT SOILS IN ARIZONA. Robert A. Green, Charles Reynard. Ecology, vol.13, no.1, pp.73-80, Jan., 1932.

NATIVE CALIFORNIA RODENTS IN RELATION TO WATER SUPPLY. Joseph Grinnell. Jour. Mam., vol.14, no.4, pp. 293-298, Nov., 1933.

NUTRIA VERSUS MUSKRAT. James B. Hale. Wisconsin Conserv. Bull., Madison, vol.15, no.4, pp.15-16, Apr., 1950.

THE RELATION OF SMALL RODENTS TO FIELD BORDERS ON AGRICULTURAL LANDS IN CENTRAL MISSOURI. Van T. Harris. AM thesis, Univ. Mo., 1941.

SMALL RODENTS IN RELATION TO FIELD BORDERS. Van T. Harris. Proc. Missouri Acad. Sci., Columbia, vol.7, no. 4, whole no.24, p.96, Jan.25, 1942.

STUDIES ON RODENT POPULATIONS IN A FORESTED AREA. Donald M. Hatfield. Jour. Mam., vol.19, no.2 pp.207-211, figs. 2, May 14, 1938.

RELATION BETWEEN LOW TEMPERATURE AND AVAILABLE FOOD TO SURVIVAL OF SMALL RODENTS. Walter E. Howard. Jour. Mam., vol.32, no.3, pp.300-312, illus., Aug.23, 1951.

ON ECOLOGICAL CHARACTER OF CLOSELY RELATED SPECIES OF RODENTS. N. I. Kalabukhov. Zool. Zh., 17 (3): 521-532, 1938.

PECULIAR REACTIONS OF SEVERAL PLAINS RODENTS TO A LOWERING OF ATMOSPHERIC PRESSURE. N. I. Kalabukhov. Zoologicheskii Zhurnal, Moscow, vol.16, no.3, pp.483-495, 1937.

RESULTS OF INVESTIGATIONS ON THE ECOLOGY OF HARMFUL RODENTS IN THE USSR FOR TWENTY YEARS. N. I. Kalabukhov. Zool. Zhurnal, Moscow, vol. 16, no.5, pp.950-967, figs.10, tables 4, 1937.

SOME ECOLOGICAL PECULIARITIES OF CLOSELY RELATED SPECIES OF RODENTS. 3. PECULIARITIES OF THE REACTION OF WOOD-MICE AND YELLOW-NECKED FIELD-MICE (APODEMUS SYLVATICUS L. AND A. FLAVICOLLIS MELCH.) AND OF THE LITTLE GROUND SQUIRREL AND THE SPOTTED GROUND SQUIRREL (CITELLUS PYGMAEUS PALL. AND C. SUSLICA GUELD.) TO THE TEMPERATURE GRADIENT. N. I. Kalabukhov. Zool. Zh., 18 (5): 915-23, 2 figs., 1939.

SQUIRREL VS. PACK RAT. Chambers Kellar. Outdoor Life, New York, vol.102, no.5, pp.8, 11, Nov., 1948.

(THE DAILY RHYTHM OF ACTIVITY OF THE RODENTS CLETHRIONOMYS GLAREOLUS GLAREOLUS SCHREBER AND SYLVIMYS FLAVICOLLIS FLAVICOLLIS MELCHIOR, AND ITS DEPENDENCE ON LIGHTING CONDITIONS.) Rytmika dobowa aktywności gryzoni Clethrionomys glareolus glareolus Schreber i Sylvimus flavicollis flavicollis Melchior i jej zależność od warunków świetlnych. Kazimierz Kowalski. Rozprawy Wydzialu Matematyczno-Przy-rodniczego, Polska Akad. Umiejetnosci, Krakow, vol.74, sect. B (ser.3, vol.34), no.4, pp.12-37, 1950.

(VOYAGES IN SOUTH AMERICA FOR THE PURPOSE OF BIOLOGICAL STUDY. XV. ON THE ECOLOGY OF THE LARGE RODENTS OF THE GRAN CHACO AND ITS BORDERING REGIONS.) Biologische Reisestudien in Suedamerika. XV. Zur Oekologie der grossen Nager des Gran Chaco und seiner Grenzgebiete. Hans Krieg. Zeitschr. Wiss. Biol. Abt.A, Morphol. u. Oekol. Tiere, vol.15, no.4, pp.755-785, figs.14, 1929.

(OBSERVATIONS OF PYGMY MICE (MICROMY MINUTUS SORICINUS HERMANN, 1790) AND DORMICE (MUSCARDINUS A. AVELLANARIUS LINNÉ, 1758) LIVING TOGETHER.) Beobachtungen ueber das Zusammenleben von Zwergmaus, Micromy, minutus soricinus (Hermann, 1790), und Haselmaus, Muscardinus a. avellanarius (Linné, 1758). E. v. Lehmann. Saeugetierk. Mitteil., Stuttgart, vol.1, no.2, pp. 69-70, Apr., 1, 1953.

THE DISTRIBUTION OF RODENTS IN OVER-GRAZED AND NORMAL GRASSLANDS OF CENTRAL OKLAHOMA. Paul Phillips. Ecology, 17 (4): 673-679, Oct., 1936.

RODENT DISTRIBUTION IN OVERGRAZED AND NORMAL GRASSLAND. Paul Phillips. MS thesis, Univ. Okla., 1935.

THE RELATION BETWEEN RODENTS AND THE MOSAIC LANDSCAPE OF THE SANDY SEMI-DESERT. George M. Rall. Zool. Zhurnal, Moscow, vol.16, no.1, pp.149-164, figs.4, tables 11, 1937.

EFFECT OF SURROUNDING CONDITIONS ON THE BURROWS OF RODENTS. Z. Rodionov. Bull. Soc. Nat. Moscow, sect. biol., vol.45, no.4, pp.256-262, 1936.

DATA ON THE ECOLOGY OF THE WOOD-MOUSE (APODEMUS SYLVATICUS L.) AND THE PINE MOUSE (PITYMYS MAJORI THOS.) IN THE CAUCASUS. N. I. Ryabov. Misc. Sci. Works Severtzov Lab., pp.129-138, 1940.

CONTRIBUTIONS TO THE ECOLOGY AND BIOLOGY OF THE RODENTS OF THE TROITSK DISTRICT, FORM. URAL PROV. 4. INFLUENCE OF FARMING ON THE SPREAD OF RODENTS OF STEPPE STATIONS. F. V. Startseva, G. A. Glumov. Izvestiia Biologicheskogo Nauchno-Issledovatel'skogo Instituta pri Permakom Gosudarstvennom Universitete (Bull. Inst. recherches biol. Univ. Perm), vol.10, no. 3, pp.125-143, 1936.

EFFECTS OF CERTAIN ANIMALS THAT LIVE IN SOILS. James Thorp. Sci. Monthly, Lancaster, vol.68, no.3, pp.180-191, figs.8, Mar., 1949.

THE EFFECTS OF DROUTH ON RODENT POPULATION. L. D. Wooster. Turtox News, Chicago, vol.17, no.1, pp.26-27, Jan., 1939.

MEET THE CHAMP! (FIGHT BETWEEN PINE SQUIRREL AND PACK-RAT.) South Dakota Conserv. Digest, Madison, vol.15, no.8, p.16, Aug., 1948.

Economic Importance

CONSUMPTION OF PONDEROSA PINE SEED BY SMALL MAMMALS. Lowell Adams. USDA, N. Rocky Mt. Forest and Range Exp. Sta., Res. Note 80, 4 pp., Mar., 1950.

JACK PINE REGENERATION RETARDED BY RODENTS AND BIRDS. Shaler F. Aldous. Tech. Notes, Lake States Forest Expt. Sta., Univ. Farm, St. Paul, no.259, p. 1, July, 1946.

THE BACTERIOLOGICAL CONTROL OF RODENTS IN THE USSR UP TO 1930. A. I. Antonovskii. Zaschita Rastenii ot Vreditelei (Plant Protection), vol.7, nos. 4-6, pp.259-268, Dec.,1930, 1931.

RODENT CONTROL. Laurel L. Atkinson. 33rd Ann. Rep., Calif. Dept. Agr., pp.285-292, illus; Calif. Dept. Agr. Bull., 41 (4), Oct.-Dec., 1952.

NOTES ON SOME RATS DAMAGING CROPS IN SOUTH INDIA. P. N. K. Ayyar. Jour. Bombay Nat. Hist. Soc., vol.34, no. 4, pp.937-946, Mar.2, 1931.

THE WAR AGAINST RODENTS. Anthony Barnett. New Biology, Penguin Books, Lond., no.2, pp.9-29, pls.1-12, 1947.

RODENT CONTROL IN TOWNS. S. A. Barnett. Ann. Applied Biol., vol.34, no,2, pp.297-303, figs.2, May, 1947.

DEATH TO THE RODENTS. W. B. Bell. Yearbook U.S. Dept. Agric., 1920, sep. 855, pp.421-438, 1921.

NOTES ON SOME RATS DAMAGING CROPS IN KHANDESH AND THE DECCAN. P. N. Bhide. Agric. and Live-stock in India, Delhi, vol.4, pt.3, pp.275-286, figs.4, pl. 35, May, 1934.

FIELD MICE CONTROL IN PALESTINE. F. S. Bodenheimer, H. Z. Klein. Zionist Exec. Agric. Exp. Sta. and Colonisation Dept. Ext. Div. Circular 17, pp.1-12, Dec., 1928.

RODENTS AND SOIL CONSERVATION. R. M. Bond, A. E. Borell. Soil Cons., 4 (9): 220-223, Mar., 1939.

RODENTS AS A FACTOR IN DIRECT SEEDING ON SPOIL BANKS IN CENTRAL PENNSYLVANIA. William C. Bramble, Ward M. Sharp. Jour. Forestry, 47 (6): 477-478, June, 1949.

RODENT CONTROL AND GRAIN SANITATION. Noble E. Buell. Pest Control, 23 (8): 9-10, 21-24, illus., Aug., 1955.

NOTES ON RODENT PESTS. W. L. Burnett. Eleventh Ann. Rept. State Entomologist of Colorado, pp.47-62, 5 maps and figs., Aug., 1920.

CONTROL OF GROUND SQUIRRELS AND OTHER RODENTS IN NORTH DAKOTA. Fred D. Butcher. N. Dak. Agr. Coll., Ext. Cir., 142, 4 pp., Apr., 1936.

CONTROL OF RODENT PESTS IN MONTANA. E. C. Cates. Mont. State Coll., Ext. Serv., Bull.151, 32 pp., Feb., 1937.

RATS, MICE AND AGRICULTURE. Dennis Chitty. An. Applied Biol., 38 (3): 724-725, Sept., 1951.

CONTROL OF RATS AND MICE. Dennis Chitty, H. N. Southern. Oxford U. Press, 3 vols., 824 pp., illus., 1954.

PIVALYL, THE NEW INSECTICIDAL RODENTICIDE. D. Glen Crabtree, William H. Robinson. Pest Control, 21 (7): 22, 24, 58, July, 1953.

DAMAGE TO MANGOLDS BY RODENTS. W. Maldwyn Davies. Jour. Min. Agric. (Great Britain), vol.37, no.3, pp.269-276, figs.2, June, 1930.

THE EFFECT ON MOUSE POPULATIONS OF SPRINKLING INDUSTRIAL EFFLUENT IN AN OAK WOODS. David E. Davis, Robert Z. Brown, William B. Jackson. Trans. N. A. Wildl. Conf., 16: 283-288, 1951.

COMMON RODENT PESTS OF WYOMING. Albert M. Day. Wyoming Farm Bull., vol.11, no.4, 27 pp., 6 figs., July, 1923.

PROTECTIVE SEEDING WITH TETRAMINE-COATED DOUGLAS-FIR SEED. (RODENT CONTROL IN REFORESTATION.) James Dick, William H. Lawrence. Forestry Research Notes, Weyerhaeuser Timber Co., Centralia, Wash., pp.1-10 (mimeogr.), Aug., 1957.

RODENTS AND RECLAMATION IN THE IMPERIAL VALLEY. Joseph Dixon. Jour. Mam., vol.3, no.3, pp.136-146, Aug., 1922.

EXPERIMENT IN USING NEW MICRO-BIOLOGICAL CULTURE MEDIA FOR RODENT EXTERMINATION. N. A. Dmitrevskaya. Plant Prot., 7: 282-292, 1931.

WARFARIN (COMPOUND 42), A PROMISING NEW RODENTICIDE FOR CANE FIELDS. R. E. Doty. Hawaiian Planters' Record, first issue, pp.1-21, illus., 1951.

LATEST ON THE NEW SAFER ANTI-COAGULANT RODENTICIDES. Walter W. Dykstra. Pest Control, 21 (1): 18, 20, Jan., 1953.

NEW TECHNIQUES AND DEVELOPMENTS IN RODENT CONTROL. Walter W. Dykstra. Pest Control, 18 (12): 9-14, 39, Dec., 1950.

RODENT FILTH IN FOOD. Walter W. Dykstra. Pest Control, 22 (7): 9-10, 12, 14, illus., July, 1954.

UP-TO-DATE ON ANTICOAGULANT TYPE RODENTICIDES. Walter W. Dykstra. Pest Control, 20 (7): 12, 14, 46, 48, July, 1952.

AIRPLANE VS. MOUSE. Robert W. Eadie. Farm Res., 21 (4): 4, Oct., 1955.

(MICE NOTABLE FROM THE VIEWPOINT OF FORESTRY.) Etwas ueber forstlich beachtenswerte Maeuse. Karl Eckstein. Allg. Forst-u. Jagd-Zeitg., Frankfurt a.M., vol.112, no.1, pp.23-26, fig.1, Jan., 1936.

A FLEA AND RODENT CONTROL PROGRAM FOR PLAGUE PREVENTION IN THAILAND. Robert E. Elbel, Mali Thaineua. Amer. Jour. Tropical Med. and Hygiene, 6 (2): 280-293, Mar., 1957.

THE NATURAL CONTROL OF RODENT POPULATIONS. Charles Elton. Proc. Sixth Pac. Sci. Cong., 5: 109-114, 1940.

EXTERMINATION OF RATS AND MICE. Charles Elton, H. R. Hewer, A. D. Campbell, C. D. Hornby. Ministry of Food, Univ. College, Lond., pp.1-8, Aug., 1944.

NEW POISONS FOR THE CONTROL OF RODENTS. (PRELIMINARY NOTICE.) B. Yr. Fal'kenshtein. Plant Protection, Leningrad, no.18, p.183, 1939.

RODENT CONTROL BY WARFARIN ON OKINAWA. Frank G. Favorite. Medical Technicians Bull. U.S. Armed Forces, Wash., vol.3, no.3, pp.89-96, illus., May-June, 1952.

THE CONTROL OF ORGANISMS. Frederick L. Fitzpatrick. Teachers Coll., Columbia Univ., xi, 334 pp., 1940.

WARFARIN AND PERIMETER RODENT CONTROL. William D. Fitzwater, Jr. Food Tech., 6: 436-438, Nov., 1952.

MADAGASCAR: RATS. A MENACE TO COFFEE PLANTS. Edm Francois. Internat. Bull. Plant Protect., vol.4, no.1, pp.5-6, Jan., 1930.

CONTROLLING RODENTS AND OTHER SMALL ANIMAL PESTS IN OREGON. Ira N. Gabrielson. Oregon Extension Bull., Corvallis, no.629, pp.1-23, illus., 1944.

RODENT-CONTROL STUDIES DEVELOP SPECIFIC METHODS FOR THE DIFFERENT SPECIES. Ira N. Gabrielson. U.S. Dept. Agriculture, no.1342, p.4, 1932.

A NEW WAY OF PREPARING PHOSPHORUS PASTE FOR USE IN RODENT CONTROL. V. P. Gal'kov. Plant Prot., 6: 501-502, 1929.

THE PRESENT DAY POSITION OF THE BACTERIOLOGICAL METHOD OF RODENT CONTROL. O. Galler. Rev. Microbiol., 14: 441-447, 1935.

RODENT CONTROL INVESTIGATIONS IN CALIFORNIA. F. E. Garlough. Monthly Bull. Dept. Agri., California, Sacramento, vol.17, no.7, pp.406-412, July, 1928.

SOME OF THE LATEST DEVELOPMENTS IN THE CONTROL OF RATS AND MICE. F. E. Garlough. Pests and Their Control, Kansas City, vol.11, no.1, pp.6-7, 9, Jan., 1943.

CONTROL OF DESTRUCTIVE MICE. F. E. Garlough, Donald A. Spencer. USDI, Cons. Bull., 36, 37 pp., 1944.

(TESTING THE EFFICACY OF WARFARIN BAIT FOR THE DESTRUCTION OF RATS.) Essais d'efficacite d'Appats au Warfarine pour la destruction du surmulot. J. Giban. Phytiatrie-Phytopharmacie 1952, (1): 13-16, graphs, 1952.

RODENT CONTROL. J. Giban, P. Cuisance. Bull. Tech. Inform. Ingenieurs Serv. Agr., 49: 265-273, 1950.

STUDIES OF WARFARIN RAT POISON. Lorin R. Gillogly. Calif. Dept. Agr., Bull., 41 (3): 139-143, illus., July-Sept., 1952.

RODENT ERADICATION. Edward A. Goldman. The Medical Dept. of the U.S. Army in the World War 6 (Sanitation, Chap.14): 1071-1089, figs.137-148, Wash., Govt. Print. Office, 1927.

PRACTICAL BEAVER AND MUSKRAT FARMING. Wallace Grange. Sandhill Press, Babcock, Wis., 52 pp., 1947.

THE BURROWING RODENTS OF CALIFORNIA AS AGENTS IN SOIL FORMATION. Joseph Grinnell. Smithsonian Report, pp. 339-350, 3 pls., June, 1925.

USE OF WARFARIN-TREATED OATS AS A PLAGUE SUPPRESSIVE MEASURE IN HAWAII. Bertram Gross, Robert H. Baker, David D. Bonnet. Public Health Rep., 66 (52): 1727-1733, illus., Dec., 1951.

RODENT PESTS OF IOWA AND THEIR CONTROL. H. Gunderson, G. C. Decker. Iowa Agr. Exp. Sta., Bull., p43: 423-436, May, 1942.

DESTRUCTIVE RODENTS ELIMINATED BY CHEMICAL CONTROLS. W. J. Hamilton. Agric. Chemicals, Balto., vol. 2, no.12, pp.25-27, 69, illus., Dec., 1947.

AN INVESTIGATION OF INSECT AND RODENT CONTAMINATION OF WHEAT AND WHEAT FLOUR. Kenton L. Harris, others. Jour. Assn. Off. Agr. Chem., 35 (1): 115-158, illus., Feb., 1952.

MOUSE POPULATIONS IN ORCHARDS AND A NEW METHOD OF CONTROL. Don W. Hayne. Quart. Bull., 33 (2): 160-169, Nov., 1950.

ZINC PHOSPHIDE: ITS TOXICITY TO PHEASANTS AND EFFECT OF WEATHERING UPON ITS TOXICITY TO MICE. Don W. Hayne. Quart. Bull. Michigan Agric. Exper. Sta., East Lansing, vol.33, no.4, pp.412-425, May, 1951.

WHICH RODENTICIDE IS BEST? Ralph E. Heal. Pest Control, 22 (7): 26, 28, 30, 54, July, 1954.

(SUCCESSFUL AND QUICK EXTERMINATION OF MICE.) Erfolgreiche und schnelle Vertilgung von Maeusen. Heinze. Forstarchiv, vol.5, no.8, pp.163-164, 1929.

RATS AND MICE AS ENEMIES OF MANKIND. M. A. C. Hinton. 3rd ed. pp.70, pls.2, figs.6, British Mus. (Nat. Hist.), Econ. ser.8, 1931.

FURRED FOREST PLANTERS. J. V. Hoffman. Sci. Monthly, vol.16, pp.280-283, 1923.

REQUIREMENTS AND TECHNIQUES OF RODENT CONTROL. E. E. Horn. Trans. 8th N. Amer. Wildlife Conf., Wash., D.C., pp.417-423, 1943.

MOUSE CONTROL IN VIRGINIA ORCHARDS. Frank Horsfall, Jr. Va. Agr. Exp. Sta. Bull., 465, 1-26 pp., illus., Nov., 1953.

RODENT CONTROL ON CALIFORNIA RANGES. W. E. Howard. Jour. Range Management, vol.6, no.6, pp.423-434, Nov., 1953.

RANGE RODENT CONTROL BY PLANE. W. E. Howard, B. L. Kay, J. E. Street, C. F. Walker. California Agriculture, 10 (10): 8-9, 1956.

GUARD THOSE SPUDS. W. E. Howard, Kenneth A. Wagnon. Western Livestock Jour., Los Angeles, vol.29, no.7, pp.81-83, pl.1, Jan.15, 1951.

POISONING RODENTS--AND THEN? A. Brazier Howell. Science, n.s., vol.74, no.1929, p.632, Dec.18, 1931.

(FIELD VOLES AND MICE AND PROTECTION AGAINST THEM.) A mezei poczkok es egerek, valamint az ellenoek valo vedekezes. Jablonowski. pp.7-38, figs.1-7, 1898.

FILMS AND PUBLICATIONS ON RODENT CONTROL. John C. Jones. Pest Control, 23 (8): 16, 18, 59, Aug., 1955.

TIMELY FILMS AND PUBLICATIONS ON RODENT CONTROL. John C. Jones. Pest Control, 22 (7): 23-24, 52, July, 1954.

MANUAL FOR RODENT CONTROL. John C. Jones, J. Borches. U.S. Fish and Wildlife Service, Wash., 93 pp., illus., 1947.

BIOLOGICAL FOUNDATION OF CONTROLLING MOUSE-LIKE RODENTS IN A TULAREMIC AREA. N. Kalabukhov. Zool. Jour. USSR, Moscow, vol.23, no.6, pp.351-367, figs.2, tables 2, 1944.

THE CONTROL OF MOUSE-LIKE RODENTS TO PREVENT TULAREMIA. N. Kalabukhov. Voenno-Sanit, Delo no.10, "Problems connected with protection of the forces from epidemics.", pp.41-48, 1943.

A SYSTEM OF MEASURES FOR RODENT CONTROL IN FOCI OF TULAREMIA. N. Kalabukhov. Jour. Microbiol., Epidemiol. and Immunol., no.7-8, pp.59-66, 1943.

USE OF ZINC PHOSPHIDE IN RODENT CONTROL. N. Kalabukhov. Pharmacology and Toxicology, 9: 53-56, 1946.

"TEN-EIGHTY", A WAR-PRODUCED RODENTICIDE. E. R. Kalmbach. Science, Lancaster, n.s., vol.102, no.2644, pp. 232-233, Aug.31, 1945.

COLORED RODENT BAITS AND THEIR VALUE IN SAFEGUARDING BIRDS. E. R. Kalmbach, J. F. Welch. Jour. Wildlife Management, Menasha, vol.10, no.4, pp. 353-360, Oct., 1946.

STUDIES ON THE MECHANICAL CONTROL OF FIELD MICE. I. ON THE EFFECTS OF CONTROL OF FIELD MICE BY TRENCH. Eijiro Kinoshita, Yoshiharu Shibata. Rept. Hokkaido Branch, Govt. Forest Exper. Sta., Spec. Rept. no.2, pp.112-118, illus., Aug., 1954.

STUDIES ON THE MECHANICAL CONTROL OF FIELD MICE. II. ON THE EFFECTS OF CONTROL OF FIELD MICE BY TRENCH. Eijiro Kinoshita. Rept. Hokkaido Branch, Govt. Forest Exp. Sta., Spec. Rept.no.3, pp.65-70, Mar., 1955.

STUDIES ON THE MECHANICAL CONTROL OF FIELD MICE. IV. ON THE EFFECT OF CONTROL OF FIELD MICE BY TRENCH. Eijiro Kinoshita. Rept. Hokkaido Branch, Govt. Forest Exp. Sta., Spec. Rept. no.5, pp.50-62, Jan., 1956.

MATERIALS FOR THE STUDY OF THE SIGNIFICANCE OF SOME RODENTS FOR NEW RUBBER YIELDING CULTURES. I. I. Kolesnikov. Bull. Plant Protection, Leningrad, The Lenin Acad. Agric. Sci. USSR., ser.4, no.2, pp.9-22, figs.6, 1932.

CONTROL OF RODENTS IN DOUGLAS-FIR CUTOVER STANDS RELATIVELY MORE IMPORTANT THAN SEED SUPPLY. Hermann Krauch. USDA, Southwestern Forest and Range Exp. Sta., Res. Note 100, 2 pp., May, 1942.

INFLUENCE OF RODENTS ON NATURAL REGENERATION OF DOUGLAS FIR IN THE SOUTHWEST. Hermann Krauch. J. Forestry, 43 (8): 585-589, Aug., 1945.

COMPOUND 42, A NEW ANTI-COAGULANT AS A RODENTICIDE. Carl H. Kreiger. Pests and Their Control, Cleveland, vol. 17, no.5, pp.24-28, May, 1949.

NOTES ON SOME RATS DAMAGING CROPS IN SOUTH INDIA. P. N. Krishna Ayyar. Proc. Indian Sci. Congr., vol.17, p.60, 1930.

DESTROYING RODENT PESTS ON THE FARM. David E. Lantz. Yearbook, U.S. Dept. Agr., no.708, pp.1-23, fig.1, pls.1-5, 1917.

RODENT PESTS OF THE FARM. David E. Lantz. U.S. Dept. Agric., Farmers' Bull., no.932, pp.1-23, figs.1-15, July, 1918.

THE METHODS OF A QUANTITATIVE ACCOUNT (THE BIOACCOUNT) OF THE RODENTS AS INJURERS TO AGRICULTURE. M. K. Laptev. Trudy Turkmenskii sel' skokhoziaistvennyi institut Baku, vol.1, pp. 109-149, 1935.

CONCERNING BEAVER AND NUTRIA. Agnes Laut. Forest and Stream, vol.91, pp.57, 88, 89, Feb., 1921.

THE IMPORTANCE OF RODENT CONTROL IN GAME MANAGEMENT. George B. Lay. Ga. Sportsman, 1 (1), Nov., 1936.

PROGRESS REPORT: RODENT CONTROL IN SAN MATEO COUNTY. Max J. Leonard. California Dept. Agric. Bull., Sacramento, vol.35, no.3, pp.145-147, July-Sept., 1946.

THE BACTERIOLOGICAL CLASSIFICATION OF THE PRINCIPAL CULTURES USED IN RAT AND MOUSE CONTROL IN GREAT BRITAIN. P. H. Leslie. Jour. Hygiene, London, vol.42, no.5, pp.552-562, Oct., 1942.

FACTS CONCERNING THE USE OF THALLIUM IN CALIFORNIA TO POISON RODENTS--ITS DESTRUCTIVENESS TO GAME BIRDS, SONG BIRDS AND OTHER VALUABLE WILD LIFE. Jean M. Linsdale. Condor, vol.33, pp.92-106, fig.20, May, 1931.

SOME CONTRIBUTIONS OF THE LABORATORY RODENTS TO OUR UNDERSTANDING OF HUMAN BIOLOGY. C. C. Little. Amer. Nat., Lancaster, vol.73, no.745, pp.127-138, Mar.-Apr., 1939.

DEVELOPMENT OF A RODENT CONTROL PROGRAM ON A SOUTH PACIFIC MILITARY BASE. Jay Bass Long. MS thesis, Oregon State Coll., 1948.

RODENTS EAT BARK AND KILL SHRUBS. Jessop B. Low. Utah Fish and Game Bull., Salt Lake City, vol.4, no.8, pp.1-4, illus., Jan., 1948.

IMPROVE YOUR RANGE BY RODENT CONTROL. Sam C. McCampbell. Colo. State Coll., Ext. Serv., Cir.121-A, 8 pp., May, 1937.

(NOTES ON DAMAGE AND THE CAMPAIGN AGAINST THE BURROW RAT IN THE FLOWER DISTRICT OF AALSMEER.) Iets over de schade en de bestrijding van de woelrat in het bloemencentrum Aalsmeer. J. Marchal. Rat en Muis Plantenziektenkundige Dienst, Wageningen, Netherlands, 1956 (1): 12-17, illus., Mar., 1956.

(DESTRUCTION OF FIELD MICE.) Destruction des campagnols. Paul Marchal. Comptes Rendus Seances Acad. Agric. France, vol.8, pp.130-131, Feb., 1922.

AN ANALYSIS OF DATA RESULTING MAINLY FROM THE RATS AND MICE (DESTRUCTION) ACT, 1919. Colin Matheson. Naturalist, Londn, no.800, pp.61-70, figs.2, Mar., 1942.

RODENTS AS A FACTOR IN REDUCING AECIAL SPORULATION OF CRONARTIUM RIBICOLA. J. L. Meilke. Jour. Forestry, 33 (12): 994-1003, Dec., 1935.

HOW ANTICOAGULANT RODENTICIDES WERE DEVELOPED. Ernest M. Mills. Pest Control, 23 (9): 14-16, 19-21, Sept., 1955.

THE TREE RAT AS A PEST OF CACAO IN TRINIDAD. B. G. Montserin. Govt. Printing Office, Port-of-Spain, pp.1-12, figs.7, tables 7, 1937.

THE PHARMACOLOGY OF THALLIUM AND ITS USE IN RODENT CONTROL. James C. Munch, James Silver. Tech. Bull.238, U. S. Dept. Agric., pp.28, Apr., 1931.

RODENT CONTROL, U.S. NAVY, PACIFIC OCEAN AREAS, WORLD WAR II. Thomas B. Murray. U.S. Naval Med. Bull., Wash., D.C., vol.46, no.8, pp.1312-1341, figs.1-20, Aug., 1946.

"WARFARIN" AND ITS USE FOR CONTROL OF RODENTS. W. O. Nelson. Ariz. Cattlelog, 7: 39-41, Aug., 1952.

FIGHTING THE POCKET GOPHER, THE PRAIRIE DOG, AND OTHER RODENT PESTS. A. E. Oman. 24th Biennial Rept. Kansas State Board Agric., 1923-24, vol. 29, pp.46-60, 1925.

A STUDY OF THE TOXICITY OF ARSENIC PREPARATIONS FOR RODENTS. I. A. Parfent'ev. Plant Prot., 4: 484-507, 1927.

NOT ALWAYS VERMIN. Harry C. Parker. New England Nat., Boston, no.6, pp.1-6, illus., Mar., 1940.

FACTORS CAUSING RODENT DAMAGE TO TREE PLANTATIONS IN SOUTHEASTERN MINNESOTA. Lansing A. Parker. Jour. Wildlife Mgt., 5 (3): 297-303, July, 1941.

USE OF BARIUM CARBONATE AND BARIUM SELENITE IN RODENT CONTROL. A. A. Paseshnik. Trans. Cent. Disinfection Inst., Moscow, 1944 (2): 94-100, 1946.

NATURAL REPLACEMENT OF WEED HOSTS OF THE BEET LEAFHOPPER AS AFFECTED BY RODENTS. R. L. Piemeisel. U.S. Dept. Agric., Circ. no.739, pp. 48, figs.19, Dec., 1945.

SOME STUDIES OF PEROMYSCUS AND OTHER RODENTS IN THE SAN BERNARDINO MOUNTAINS OF CALIFORNIA 1937 TO 1940. S. E. Piper, Ethelbert Johnson. Calif. Dept. Agr. Bull., 29 (3): 131-145, 1940.

(RODENTS HARMFUL TO AGRICULTURE AROUND LAKE KIVU (BELGIAN CONGO).) Rongeurs nuisibles aux cultures des environs du lac Kivu (Congo belge). P. L. Pirlot. Bull. Agric. Congo Belge, 48 (3): 703-730, illus., 1957.

THE PRODUCTION METHOD FOR OBTAINING 'KRUISID-TZNIDI' (ALPHA-NAPHTHYL-THIOUREA). V. N. Polikarpov. Trans. Cent. Disinfection Inst. Moscow, 1944 (2): 81-84, 1946.

MENACE OF THE MUSK RAT AND THE NUTRIA. Vicomte Edmond de Poncins. Field, London, vol.160, no.4172, p.891, Dec.10, 1932.

INSECT AND RODENT CONTROL IN THE CORPS OF ENGINEERS. W. D. Reed. Jour. Econ. Ent. 37 (3): 333-335, June, 1944.

CONDITIONS INFLUENCING EROSION ON THE BOISE RIVER WATERSHED. F. G. Renner. U.S. Dept. Agric., Tech. Bull. 528, pp.22, figs.14, Oct., 1936.

WARFARIN, ITS PAST AND FUTURE. Ward Ross. Mod. Sanitation, 3: 24-27, 66, 1951.

(COMBATTING FIELD MICE.) Zur Bekampfung der Feldmaeuse. R. Schander, R. Meyer. Archiv. f. Naturgeschichte, Abteil.A, vol.89, Heft.9, pp.1-130, 4 figs., Dec., 1923.

FIELD TEST OF THE EFFICIENCY OF THE RODENTICIDE COMPOUND W.A.R.F. 42. Martin W. Schein. U.S. Public Health Repts., Wash., vol.65, no.11, pp. 368-372, Mar.17, 1950.

RODENTS AS INSECT CONTROL FACTORS IN ALLEGANY PARK, NEW YORK. Albert R. Shadle. Jour. Forestry, Wash., D.C., vol.40, no.3, p.269, Mar., 1942.

WINTER RODENT DAMAGE TO GAME COVER. Hilbert R. Siegler. Jour. Mam., 18 (1): 57-61, Feb., 1937.

MOUSE CONTROL IN FIELD AND ORCHARD. James Silver. U.S. Dept. Agr. Farmers' Bull.no.1397, pp.1-14, 13 figs., Mar., 1924.

RODENT ENEMIES OF FRUIT AND SHADE TREES. James Silver. Jour. Mam., vol. 5, no.3, pp. 165-173, Aug., 1924.

NATURAL REPELLENTS IN RODENT CONTROL. Charles V. Sparhawk. Pests, pp.20-22, Feb., 1945.

THE CONTROL OF SYLVATIC PLAGUE VECTORS. M. A. Stewart, D. B. Mackie. Amer. Jour. Hygiene 28 (3): 469-480, Nov., 1938.

ECOLOGICAL FACTORS INFLUENCING REFORESTATION IN NORTHERN WISCONSIN. J. H. Stoeckeler, Gustaf A. Limstrom. Ecol. Monog. 12 (2): 191-212, Apr., 1942.

TESTING REPELLENTS FOR RODENT CONTROL. Lawrence M. Stolurow. Sci. Monthly, Lancaster, vol.68, no.3, pp.210-212, figs.3, Mar., 1949.

CONTROL OF FIELD RODENTS IN CALIFORNIA. Tracy I. Storer. Circular California Agr. Extension Service, Univ. California, Berkeley, no.138, pp.50, illus., Revised, Nov., 1949.

CONTROL OF INJURIOUS RODENTS IN CALIFORNIA. Tracy I. Storer. California Agric. Extension Serv., Circ.79, Coll. Agric., Univ. California, Berkeley, pp. 66, figs.29, Nov., 1933.

CONTROL OF RATS AND MICE. Tracy I. Storer. Calif. Agr. Ext. Serv., Cir.142, 37 pp., Apr., 1948.

CONTROLLING RATS AND MICE. Tracy I. Storer. Calif. Agr. Exp. Sta., Ext. Serv., Cir.410, 35 pp., illus., 1952.

FIELD RODENT CONTROL BY DESTRUCTION OF BURROWS. Tracy I. Storer. Jour. Wildlife Mgt., 9 (2): 156-157, Apr., 1945.

BIBLIOGRAPHY OF RODENT CONTROL (FIRST SUPPLEMENT) AND BIBLIOGRAPHY OF ANTU. Tracy I. Storer, Margery P. Mann. U.S. Pub. Health Serv., Natl. Inst. Health, Rep.1, 76 pp., 1948.

BIBLIOGRAPHY OF RODENT CONTROL. Tracy I. Storer, Margery P. Mann. Natl. Res. Council, Insect Control Comm., Rep. 182, 324 pp., June, 1946.

A TEST OF SOME RODENTS AND BIRD INFLUENCES ON WESTERN YELLOW PINE REPRODUCTION AT FORT VALLEY, FLAGSTAFF, ARIZONA. W. P. Taylor, D. M. Gorsuch. Jour. Mam., vol.13, no. 3, pp.218-223, Aug., 1932.

RODENT DAMAGE ON ARIZONA RANGES. W. P. Taylor, J.V. G. Loftfield. Carnegie Institution of Washington, Yearbook no.24 (1925), pp.338-339, 1926.

DIRECT SEEDING--A REVIVAL. Selden L. Tinsley. Jour. Forestry 37 (11): 888-890, Nov., 1939.

(RATS AND HOW THE HAGUE COMBATS THEM.) Ratten! en hoe Den Haag ze bestrijdt. J. Toetenel. Rat en Muis, Plantenziektenkundige Dienst, Wageningen, 1957 (1): 8-10, illus., Mar., 1957.

THE SELECTIVE TOXIC EFFECT OF 'KRUISID-TZNIDI' (ALPHA-NAPHTHYL-THIOUREA) ON CERTAIN ANIMALS. V. X. Vashkov. Trans. Cent. Disinfection Inst. (Moscow), 1944 (2): 84-90, 1946.

INJURIOUS INSECTS AND OTHER ANIMALS IN U.S.S.R. IN THE YEARS 1921-1924. NO. 3. RODENTS. B. S. Vinogradov, S. J. Obolensky. State Inst. Exp. Agronomy, Bureau Applied Entomology, Works on Applied Entomol., vol. 13, pp.177-221, 1926.

RODENTS AND CONSERVATION. CONTROL PROJECTS PROVIDE EASY BUT DUBIOUS WAY TO SPEND MONEY. C. T. Vorhies. Nature Mag., vol.28, no.6, pp. 363-365, 379, illus., Dec., 1936.

A UNIQUE SOLUTION OF THE RANGE RODENT PROBLEM. C. T. Vorhies. Bull. Ecol. Soc. Amer., Tucson, vol.20, p.27, Dec., 1939.

CERTAIN NEW TECHNIQUES IN RODENT CONTROL. Justus C. Ward. Pests and Their Control, Kansas City, vol.15, no.2, pp.12-14, Mar., 1947.

RODENT REPELLENT STUDIES WITH "ARSAN"-TREATED SEED CORN. Jack F. Welch. Plant Dis. Rep. 36 (2): 57-59, illus. Feb., 1952.

RODENT CONTROL. Chas. L. Wilbar, Jr. Honolulu, 1943, 4 pp (Radio talk delivered Sept.26, 1943, Station KGU, Honolulu).

(RODENTS, ENEMIES OF THE COUNTRY.) Roedores, enemigos del campo. Jose Yepes. Buenos Aires, Editorial sudamericana, pp.9-216, illus., 1941.

RODENT CONTROL AIDED BY EMERGENCY CONSERVATION WORK. Stanley P. Young. Wildlife Research and Management Leaflet BS-54, U.S. Dept. Agric., Bur. Biol. Surv., pp.30, illus., Dec., 1936.

(Review by Donald M. Hatfield of) THE RODENT CONTROL AIDED BY EMERGENCY CONSERVATION WORK. Stanley P. Young. Jour. Mam., vol.18, no.2, pp.245-247, May 14, 1937.

BARK INJURY BY FEEDING RODENTS. Forest Res. Dig., 8-9, Jan.-Feb., 1936.

CHARACTERISTICS OF COMMON RODENTICIDES. U. S. Fish and Wildlife Service, U.S. F and W.S., Wildl. Leafl., 337, 1-4 pp., Jan., 1952.

EXTERMINATION OF RODENTS. Food Manufacture 27: 374, Sept., 1952.

FACTS ABOUT RODENT CONTROL. Division of Sanitary Engineering, Springfield, Illinois, 32 pp., illus., 1953.

HARVEST TIME IN THE MARSHES. Louisiana Conservationist, New Orleans, vol.1, no.3, pp.19-20, illus., Nov., 1948.

INSECTICIDES AND RODENTICIDES--1952 RECOMMENDATIONS FOR USE. U. S. Public Health Service, Public Health Rep., 67 (5): 455-458, May, 1952.

INVESTIGATION OF RODENT DAMAGE. Forest Res. Dig., Mar.,1935: 6, Mar., 1935.

THE LATEST ON MOUSE CONTROL. Pest Control 20 (8): 30, Aug., 1952.

MICE (TRAPS AND POISONS ON GOLF COURSES). Timely Turf Topics, 2 pp., Nov., 1941.

1953 COMMUNICABLE DISEASE CENTER RECOMMENDATIONS FOR THE USE OF INSECTICIDES AND RODENTICIDES. U. S. Public Health Service, Pest Control, 21 (4): 9-10, 12, 14, 16, 18, illus., Apr., 1953.

1954 REPORT FROM THE COMMUNICABLE DISEASE CENTER ON THE USE OF PESTICIDES. U.S. Public Health Service. Pest Control, 22 (3): 9-10, 12, 14, 16, 18, 20, illus., Mar., 1954.

USE OF WARFARIN FOR THE CONTROL OF RATS AND MICE. U.S. Fish and Wildlife Service. US F&WS, Wildl. Leafl., 361, 4 pp., Aug., 1950.

THE WORLD WAR AGAINST RODENTS. Rodent Mail, Rats and Mice, London, vol. 9, no.1, pp.6-7, illus., Nov., 1945.

Europe

(NOTES ON THE DISTRIBUTION AND SYSTEMATICS OF SOME RODENTS OF THE URALS.) Notizen ueber Verbreitung und Systematik einiger Nager des Ural. A. Argyropulo. Zool. Anzeiger, vol.87, pp.257-270, 10 figs., Mar.10, 1930.

(SHORT DESIGNATION TABLE OF THE RATS OF RUSSIA.) Kurze Bestimmungstabelle der Ratten Russlands. A. Argyropulo. Zeitschrift f. Saeugetierkunde, vol.2, pp.139-144, 1928.

ON A NEW SPECIES OF MOUSE AND OTHER RODENT REMAINS FROM CRETE. Dorothea M. A. Bate. Geol. Mag., vol.9, no.571, pp.4-6, Dec.5, 1912.

PECULIARITIES OF THE DISTRIBUTION OF MOUSE-LIKE RODENTS IN THE WESTERN PROVINCES OF UKRAINE AND IN SOUTHERN POLAND. K. N. Blagosklonov. Zool. Zh. 25: 87-94, 5 figs., 1946.

(THE RODENTS OF SPAIN.) Los roedores de Espana. Angel Cabrera. Asoc. Espanola para el Progreso de las Cienc., Seccion 3, Ciencias Nat., Madrid, pp.1-63, June, 1910.

(RESEARCH ON SMALL WOOD RODENTS IN SOLOGNE.) Recherches sur les petits rongeurs sylvicoles en Sologne. A. Chappellier. Epiphyties, Paris, vol.13, ent.4, pp.155-171, 1947.

(THE RODENTS OF FRANCE AND THE STRUGGLE AGAINST INJURIOUS ONES.) Les rongeurs de France et la lutte contre les rongeurs nuisibles. A. Chappellier. Archiv. d'Hist. Nat., Soc. Nat. d'Acclimat, France, Paris, 1-138, figs.49, pls.4, tables 3, 1932.

NOTES ON THE MICE OF ST. KILDE. W. Eagle Clark. Scottish Nat., Edinburgh, no.30, pp.124-128, illus., June, 1914.

(THE DISTRIBUTION OF SOME SPECIES OF FAMILY MUSCARDINIDAE IN THE USSR.) Ueber die Verbreitung einiger Arten der familie Muscardinidae in der U.d.S.S.R. A. P. Danilowitsch. Folia Zool. et Hydrobiol., Riga, vol.9, no.1, pp.61-62, May 23, 1936.

THE RED SQUIRREL AND THE DORMOUSE. G. Dent. Essex Nat., Stratford, vol.26, pt.5, p.281, Mar., 1940.

(THE MICROMAMMALS OF THE FRENCH FAUNA. II. RATS, MICE, FIELD MICE. ORDER OF RODENTS, FAMILY MURIDAE, SUBFAMILY MURINAE.) Les micromammiféres de la faune Francaise. II. Rats, souris, mulots. Ordre des rongeurs.--Famille des Muridés. Sous-famille des Murinés. Robert Didier, Paul Rode. Mammalia, Paris, vol.6, no.1, pp.36-45, figs. 5, Mar., 1942.

STUDIES OF A SMALL MAMMAL POPULATION IN BAGLEY WOOD, BERKSHIRE. F. C. Evans. Jour. Animal Ecol., 11 (2): 182-197, Nov., 1942.

THE MOUSELIKE RODENTS OF THE USSR IN THE YEAR 1932-33. B. Falkenstein. Sbornik VIZR'a Vsesoiuznii Institut Zashchity Rastenii, Leningrad, no.7, pp.77-82, maps 2, 1933.

(THE FIELD MICE AND SHREWS OF SWITZERLAND--SOME LITTLE KNOWN FORMS. VARIABLE IMPORTANCE OF CERTAIN CHARACTERS.) Campagnols et musaraignes Suisses quelques formes peu connues. Importance variable de certains caracteres. Victor Fatio. Archiv. Sci. Phys. et nat. Geneva, 110 année, 4th periode, vol.19, pp.188-202 (pp.15), Feb., 1905.

THE ZOO'S NEW RODENT HOUSE. James Fisher. The Listener, London, vol.22, no.554, pp.362-363, illus., Aug.24, 1939.

(RODENTS IN GERMANY AND ABROAD.) Nagetiere, bei uns und draussen. Kurt Floericke. Kosmos-Bandchen, Kosmos Gesell. Naturf. Franckschе Verlag., Stuttgart, pp.79, illus., 1932.

(NOTICES ON SOME RODENTS OF THE WESTERN CAUCASUS WITH DESCRIPTIONS OF TWO NEW FORMS.) Notizen ueber einige Nager des westlichen Kaukasus mit Beschreibungen zweier neuer Formen. A. N. Formozow. Folia Zoologica et Hydrobiologica, vol.3, no.1, pp.79-84, June 13, 1931.

(SOME OBSERVATIONS ON MOUSE FAUNA IN THE VICINITY OF THE ST. PETERSBURG.) Enige opmerkingen over de muizen-f una van de sint Pietersberg en omgeving. A. M. Husson. Natuurhistorisch Maandblad, 39, Jrg., no.4, pp.43-46, Apr.28, 1950.

KEY TO THE MAMMALS OF THE U.S.S.R. (RODENTIA). B. A. Kuznetzov. 1944.

RODENTS OF THE NORTH CAUCASIAN STEPPES. N. Y. Kuznetzov. (In Russian) pp.230, illus., 1935.

(KEY TO BURROWING RODENTS.) Kliuc za odrieivanie glodara. V. Martino. Glasnik Ministarstava Poloprivrede, Belgrade, no.29, pp.24, figs.36, 1930.

PRELIMINARY NOTE ON FOUR NEW RODENTS FROM KORAB MOUNTAINS. V. Martino, E. Martino. Ann. and Mag. Nat. Hist., London, ser.10, vol.19, no.113, pp. 514-518, May, 1937.

(THE RODENTS OF A LANDMARK IN THE BOBER-KATZBACH MOUNTAINS.) Die Nager einer Feldmark im Bober-Katzbachgebirge. F. W. Merkel. Zeitschr. f. Saeugetierkunde, Berlin, vol.8, nos.1-2, pp.127-128, pl.15, Apr.24, 1933.

MICE OF NORTHEASTERN UKRAINE. A. A. Migulin. Travaux de la Soc. de Naturalistes de Charkov, vol.50, pt.2, pp. 1-31, 1927.

(THE FREE-LIVING RODENTS OF GERMANY AND NEIGHBORING LANDS.) Die freilebenden Nagetiere Deutschlands und der Nachbarlaender. Erna Mohr. 2., ueberarbeitete Aufl. Jena, G. Fischer, 152 pp., illus., 1950.

(Review by P. Rode of) (THE FREE-LIVING RODENTS OF GERMANY.) Die freilebenden Nagetiere Deutschlands. Erna Mohr. Mammalia, Paris, 2 (4): 195, 1938.

THE RODENTS OF THE RIGHT COAST OF LOWER VOLGA. S. I. Obolensky. Materials Contr. Fauna Lower Volga Region, Saratow, vol.1, pp.1-26, 1927.

MAMMALIA OF THE TAURUS GOVERNMENT, ESPECIALLY THOSE OF THE CRIMEAN PENINSULA. PART I. RODENTS. S. I. Ognev. Bull. Soc. Nat. Criméе, Simferopol, vol.5, pp.1-63, pls.4, 1916.

NEW AND LESS KNOWN SPECIES OF RUSSIAN RODENTS. S. I. Ognev. Bull. Sec. Nat. Moscow, pp.67-98, figs.28, 1924.

(PECULIARITIES OF THE DISTRIBUTION OF MYOXIDAE AND EUTAMIAS.) Sur les particularites de la distribution des Myoxidae de l'Europe orientale et de l'Eutamias asiaticus ("Bouroundouk"). A. N. Formosof. Bull. Soc. Nat. de Moscow, Sect. Biol., n.s., vol.37, livr.3-4, pp. 205-249, maps 2, 1928.

RODENTIA OF THE NORTH CAUCASUS. S. I. Ognev. pp.1-61, Rostov-on-Don, 1924.

ON THE DISTRIBUTION AND POPULATION DENSITY OF MOUSE-LIKE RODENTS IN WESTERN PARTS OF RUSSIA. I. M. Oliger. Zool. Jour., Moscow, vol.25, fasc.4, pp.359-366, figs.3, Aug.5, 1946.

(THE STUDY OF EXTINCT AND RELICT RODENTS OF THE FOREST-STEPPE AND POLESIE.) Zum Studium ausgestorbener und Relikten-Nagetiere der Wald-steppe und Polesiens. I. G. Pidoplitshka. Vseukraienska Akad. Nauk, Trudy Prirodnichotedhnichnii Viddil, Kief, Livr.1-2, no.10, pp.153-166 (1930), 1931.

(THE DISPERSION AND PRE-HISTORY OF UNCOMMON DUTCH MICE.) Verspreiding en voorgeschiedenis der niet algemeene Nederlandsche muizen. A. Schreuder. Zool. Mededeel., Leiden, vol.25, pp.239-284, figs.11, 1945.

(STUDIES OF MICROMAMMALOGY. SUMMARY OF THE FIELD MICE, SHREWS AND RATS WITH A METHODICAL INDEX OF THE MAMMALS OF EUROPE.) Etudes de micromammalogie. Revue des musaraignes, des rats et des campagnols, suivie d'une index methodique des mammiferes d'Europe. Edmond de Selys-Longchamps. Paris, Librairie Encyclopedique de Roret, 2p, 1., 165 pp., 3 pls., 1839.

CLASSIFICATION AND ECOLOGY OF THE RODENTS OF THE SOUTHERN TRANS-URAL REGION. M. Serebrennikov. Ann. Mus. Zool., Acad. Sci. USSR., vol.30, no.2, pp.251-284, 3 pls., 1929.

(CONTRIBUTIONS TO THE CLASSIFICATION AND ECOLOGY OF THE RODENTS OF THE SAMARA GOVERNMENT.) Contributions a la classification et a l'oecologie des Rongeurs du Gouvernement de Samara. M. Serebrennikov.

Annuaire Mus. Zool., Leningrad, vol.27, no.4, pp.337-346, pls.24-25, 1927.

(THE QUESTION ABOUT THE SPECIES OF THE HOUSE- AND THE WOOD-MOUSE IN FINLAND.) Koti- ja metsaehiiremme lajikysymys. Lauri Siivonen. Eripainos Luonnon Tutkijasta, no.2, pp.37-43, illus., 1948.

A CRITICAL STUDY OF BRITISH RATS. F. J. Stubbs. Wild Life, p.13, illus., May, 1915.

A REVIEW OF FOREST MICE OF THE NORTHERN CAUCASUS. P. A. Sviridenko. Moscou Univ. Sbornik Nauchno issledovatel 'skogo inst. Zool. (Abstracts Works Zool. Inst. Moscow State Univ.), no.3, pp.96-107, figs.2, 1936.

RODENTS OF THE NORTHERN CAUCASUS AND OF THE CISCAUCASIAN STEPPES. P. A. Sviridenko. Moscou Univ. Sbornik Nauchno issledovatel'skogo inst. Zool. (Abstracts Works Zool. Inst. Moscou State Univ.), no.3, pp.86-89, 1936.

(CATALOGUE OF RODENTS IN THE COLLECTIONS OF THE ZOOLOGICAL MUSEUM IN COIMBRA.) Catalogue des Rongeurs existants dans les collections du Museum Zoologique de Coimbra. Antonio A. Themido. Mem. Mus. Zool. Univ. Coimbra, (1), no.20, pp.5-21, 1928.

OCCURRENCE OF VOLES, MICE AND RATS (MURIDAE) IN DENMARK. E. Ursin. Vidensk. Medd. Dansk. Naturh. Foren., vol.114, pp.217-244, 1952.

(SHORT LIST OF THE RODENTS OF THE USSR.) Kratkiĭ opredelitel'gryzunov fauny SSSR. B. Vinogradov. Moscow, Academy of Sciences USSR Press, 1956.

(FAUNA OF THE USSR. MAMMALS. ANALYTIC TABLES OF THE RODENTS.) Faune de l'URSS. Mammifères. Tableaux analytiques des rongeurs. B. S. Vinogradov, A. I. Argyropulo. Inst. Zool. Acad. Sci. URSS, Moscow and Leningrad, n.s., no. 29, pp.1-241, figs.109, 1941.

(RODENT FAUNA OF THE USSR.) Gryzuny fauny SSSR. B. S. Vinogradov, I. M. Gromov. Opryedyeliteli po Faunye SSSR, Zool. Inst. Akad. Nauk SSSR, Moscow, no.48, pp.1-296, 1952.

INJURIOUS INSECTS AND OTHER ANIMALS IN U.S.S.R. I. HABITS AND CLASSIFICATION; II. RODENT CONTROL IN U.S.S.R. IN 1925-1928. B. S. Vinogradov, S. I. Obolenskii. Lenin Acad. Agric., Sci. Works of Appl. Entomology, Leningrad, vol.13, no.5, pp.257-324, 1930.

ENGLAND INVADED. (INTRODUCED AMERICAN MUSKRAT AND GRAY SQUIRREL.) J. D. U. Ward. Fauna, Phila., vol.5, no.1, pp.26-27, illus., Mar., 1943.

(THE WILD MAMMALS OF CRETE. 4) RODENTIA OF CRETE. Die Wildsaeuger von Kreta. 4) Die Rodentia Kretas. Klaus Zimmerman. Zeitschr. Saeugetierk., vol.17, no.1, pp.21-51, pls.3-4, Feb.19, 1953.

Evolution

SAN FRANCISCO BAY AS A FACTOR INFLUENCING SPECIATION IN RODENTS. Emmet T. Hooper. Misc. Publ., Mus. Zool., Univ. Mich., Ann Arbor, no.59, pp.89, maps 18, pls.5, Jan.12, 1944.

SPECIATION IN RODENTS OF THE COLORADO RIVER DRAINAGE IN EASTERN UTAH. Keith R. Kelson. Biol. Ser. Univ. Utah, Salt Lake City, vol.11, no.3, pp.1-125, maps, 1951.

EVOLUTION OF THE EARLY TERTIARY RODENTS. Robert W. Wilson. Evolution, vol.5, no.3, pp.207-215, Sept., 1951.

Experimental Biology

INTERSPECIFIC TRANSFERS OF RODENT EGGS. H. Brionis, R. A. Beatty. Jour. Exper. Zool. Phila., vol.125, no.1, pp.98-118, Feb., 1954.

FIELD EXPERIMENTS ON THE ACTIVITY OF THE SMALL MAMMALS, APODEMUS, CLETHRIONOMYS AND MICROTUS. L. E. Brown. Proc. Zool. Soc. Lond., 126 (4): 549-564, July 31, 1956.

EXPERIMENTS WITH MICE AND FLEAS. P. A. Buxton. Parasitology, London, vol. 39, nos.1-2, pp.119-124, July, 1948.

WOOD RATS AND GROUND SQUIRRELS IN ACTIVITY WHEELS. Harold S. Colton. Jour. Mam., vol.14, no.4, pp.309-311, Nov., 1933.

THE INFLUENCE OF ROETGEN-RAY TREATMENTS OF THE HYPOPHYSIS ON REPRODUCTIVE SYSTEMS OF THE GROUND SQUIRREL AND RAT. Rollin Henry Denniston, II. Jour. Exper. Zool., Phila., vol.91, no.2, pp.237-263, figs.2, Nov.5, 1942.

PRELIMINARY EXPERIMENTAL STUDIES OF MICE OF MOUNT DESERT ISLAND, MAINE. Beatrice W. Johnson. Jour. Mam., vol.8, no.4, pp.276-284, Nov., 1927.

OVARIECTOMY AND CORPUS LUTEUM EXTRACT STUDIES ON RATS AND GROUND SQUIRRELS. George E. Johnson, Joanna Seiler Challans. Endocrinology, vol.16, no.3, pp.278-284, fig.1, May-June, 1932.

INDUCED ADENOCARCINOMA OF THE STOMACH IN MICE. P. R. Peacock, S. Beck. Nature, London, vol.162, no.4111, pp.252-253, Aug.14, 1948.

Fossils

A NEW FOSSIL RODENT FROM ECUADOR. H. E. Anthony. Amer. Mus. Novit., no. 35, pp.1-4, 2 figs., Mar.30, 1922.

NEW FOSSIL RODENTS FROM PORTO RICO, WITH ADDITIONAL NOTES ON ELASMODONTOMYS OBLIQUUS ANTHONY AND HETEROPSOMYS INSULANS ANTHONY. H. E. Anthony. Bull. Amer. Mus. Nat. Hist., vol.37, art.4, pp.183-189, Jan. 29, 1917.

SCIUROMORPHA AND DIPODIDAE (GLIRES, MAMMALIA) IN THE TERTIARY OF KAZAKHSTAN. A. I. Argyropulo. Comptes Rendus (Doklady) Acad. Sci. URSS, Moscou, n.s., vol.25, no.2, pp.171-175, figs.2, 1939.

(TWO NEW PALAEARCTIC ARVICOLAS.) Ueber zwei neue palaarktische wuehlmaeuse. Anatol J. Argyropulo. Zeitschrift f, Saeugetierkunde, vol.8, no.3, pp.180-183, Dec.20, 1933.

ON A NEW GENUS OF EXTINCT MUSCARDINE RODENT FROM THE BELEARIC ISLANDS. D. Bate. Proc. Zool. Soc. Lond., p.209, 1918.

A PRELIMINARY REPORT ON THE RODENTS FROM THE QUATERNARY DEPOSITS OF CRIMEA. A. A. Birula. Comptes Rendus Acad. Sci. URSS, ser.A, 1930, no. 23, pp.617-622, 1930.

VARIATION AND TOOTH-REPLACEMENT IN A MIOCENE MYLAGAULID RODENT. Craig C. Black, Albert E. Wood. Jour. Paleontol., 30 (3): 672-684, May, 1956.

THE FOSSIL RODENTS OF THE LIMESTONE CAVE AT TAUNGS. R. Broom. Ann. Transvaal Mus., Cambridge, vol.19, pt.3, pp.315-317, figs.2, May 24, 1939.

FOSSIL RODENTS FROM THE UINTA EOCENE SERIES. J. J. Burke. Annals Carnegie Mus., vol.25, pp.5-12, figs.4, Oct.21, 1935.

A NEW CYLINDRODONT RODENT FROM THE OLIGOCENE OF MONTANA. J. J. Burke. Ann. Carnegie Mus., vol.27, art. 16, pp.255-274, figs.4, pls.26-27, Oct.22, 1938.

NEW DUCHESNE RIVER RODENTS AND A PRELIMINARY SURVEY OF THE ADJIDAUMIDAE. J. J. Burke. Ann. Carnegie Mus., vol.23, pp.391-398, 5 figs., Nov.19, 1934.

A NEW SCIURAVUS FROM UTAH. J. J. Burke. Ann. Carnegie Mus., vol.27, pp. 1-9, fig.1, Dec.31, 1937.

PSEUDOCYLINDRODON, A NEW RODENT GENUS FROM THE PIPESTONE SPRINGS OLIGOCENE OF MONTANA. J. J. Burke. Annals Carnegie Mus., vol.25, pp.1-4, figs.2, Oct.21, 1935.

TWO NEW RODENTS FROM THE LOWER SIWALIK BEDS OF INDIA. Edwin H. Colbert. Amer. Mus. Novitates, no.633, pp.6, figs.2, June 10, 1933.

MESOGAULUS PRAECURSOR, A NEW RODENT FROM THE MIOCENE OF NEBRASKA. Harold J. Cook. Jour. Palaeont., Menasha, vol.15, no.5, pp.549-552, figs. 2, Sept., 1941.

MESOGAULUS PRAECURSOR, A NEW RODENT FROM THE MIOCENE OF NEBRASKA. Harold J. Cook, Joseph T. Gregory. Jour. Palaeont., Menasha, vol. 15, no.5, pp.549-552, figs.2, Sept., 1941.

(SOME DATA ON THE GENUS TRECHOMYS LARTET.) Quelques précisions sur le genre Trechomys Lartet. Colette Dechaseaux. Soc. Geol. France, Macon, vol.20, nos.1-2, pp.3-8, Oct., 1950.

NOTES ON THE MYLAGAULID RODENT DENTITION. John A. Dorr, Jr. Ann. Carnegie Mus., Pittsburgh, vol.32, art.8, pp.319-328, pl.23, 1952.

(CHARACTERISTIC RODENTS OF DIFFERENT STAGES OF THE QUATERNARY OF WESTERN EUROPE.) Rongeurs caracteristiques des differents etages du Quaternaire de l'Europe occidentale. Georges Dubois. Ann. Soc. Geol. Nord., vol.50, pp.115-118, 1925.

HYSTRICOMORPH RODENTS FROM THE LATE MIOCENE OF COLOMBIA, SOUTH AMERICA. Robert W. Fields. Univ. California Publ. Geol. Sci., 32 (5): 273-404, illus., Dec.11, 1957.

TO THE PROBLEM OF SOME STEPPE RODENT EXTINCTION IN LATE QUATERNARY AND HISTORIC TIME. A. N. Formosov. Zool. Jour., Moscou, vol.17, no.2, pp.260-272, tables 2, 1938.

(ON THE AFFINITIES OF ISSIODOROMYS, RODENT OF THE EUROPEAN OLIGOCENE.) Sur les affinités de l'Issiodoromys, Rongeur de l'Oligocène d'Europe. M. Friant. Comptes Rendus Acad. Sci. Paris, vol.197, no.19, pp.1059-1061, fig.1, 1933.

(ON THE VIRGIN MOLARS OF ISCHYROMYS.) Sur les molaires vierges de l'Ischyromys. M. Friant. Ann. and Mag. Nat. Hist., London, ser.10, vol.16, no.93, pp.392-394, figs.4, Sept., 1935.

(THE PRIMITIVE TYPE OF UPPER MOLARS IN RODENTS.) Le type primitif des molaires supérieures chez les Rongeurs. M. Friant. Comptes Rendus Acad. Sci. Paris, vol.199, no.21, pp.1145-1147, fig.1, Nov.19, 1934.

(A NEW RODENT FROM THE MIOCENE.) Sur un nouveau rongeur miocene. Cl. Gaillard. pp.2, Jan.22, 1900.

A NEW EOMYID RODENT FROM THE LOWER OLIGOCENE OF NORTHEASTERN COLORADO. Edwin C. Galbreath. Trans. Kansas Acad. Sci., vol.58, no.1, pp.75-78, illus., Mar.26, 1955.

A NEW HORNED RODENT FROM THE MIOCENE OF KANSAS. James W. Gidley. Proc. U.S. Nat. Museum, vol.32, no.1554, pp.627-636, pls.58-65, June 29, 1907.

(FOSSIL QUATERNARY RODENTS OF THE NORTHERN PARTS OF THE LOWER DON AND THE ADJACENT PART OF THE VOLGA DON WATERSHED.) Iskopaemie chetvertichnie grizyuni severnoi chasti nizhnego Dona i prilezhashchego uchastka volgodonskogo vodorazdela. I. M. Gromov. Trudi Zool. Inst. Akad. Nauk SSSR, 22: 246-317, 1957.

(SOME RESULTS AND PERSPECTIVES OF THE STUDY OF FOSSIL QUATERNARY RODENTS OF THE USSR.) Nekotorie itogi i perspektivi izucheniya iskopaemikh chetvertichikh grizunov SSSR. I. M. Gromov. Trudi Zool. Inst. Akad. Nauk SSSR, 22: 90-99, 1957.

(UPPER PLEISTOCENE RODENTS OF THE KAMAKUIYBISHEV VOLGA REGION.) Verknepleistotsenovi grizuni Kamsko-Kubishevskogo Povolzhya. I. M. Gromov. Trudi Zool. Inst. Akad. Nauk SSSR, 22: 151-191, 1957.

(UPPER QUATERNARY RODENTS OF THE SAMARA BEND AND THE CONDITIONS OF THE PRESERVATION AND ACCUMULATION OF THEIR REMAINS.) Verkhnechetvertichnie grizyuni Samarskoi luki i usloviya zakhoroneniya i nakopleniya ikh ostatkov. I. M. Gromov. Trudi Zool. Inst. Akad. Nauk SSSR, 22: 112-150, 1957.

THE OCCURRENCE OF EUCASTER AND EPIGAULUS IN THE LOWER PLIOCENE OF TREGO COUNTY, KANSAS. Claude W. Hibbard, Lester F. Phillis. Univ. Kansas Sci. Bull., Lawrence, vol.30, pt.2, no.16, pp.549-555, June 15, 1945.

A NEW RODENT FROM SUBSURFACE STRATUM IN BEE COUNTY, TEXAS. Claude M. Hibbard, John A. Wilson. Jour. of Paleontology, vol.24, no.5, pp.621-623, fig.1, Sept., 1950.

DIAGNOSES OF NEW GENERA AND SPECIES OF RODENTS FROM INDIAN TERTIARY DEPOSITS. Martin A. C. Hinton. Ann. and Mag. Nat. Hist., ser. 10, vol.12, pp.620-622, Dec., 1933.

A PALEOCENE RODENT, PARAMYS ATAVUS. Glenn L. Jepsen. Proc. Amer. Philos. Soc., Phila., vol.78, no.2, pp.291-301, pl.1, Dec.10, 1937.

PLEISTOCENE RODENTS OF CALIFORNIA. Louise Kellogg. Berkeley, Univ. California Press, Bull. Dept. Geology, vol.7, no.8, pp.151-168, illus., 1912.

RODENT FAUNA OF THE LATE TERTIARY BEDS AT VIRGIN VALLEY AND THOUSAND CREEK, NEVADA. Louise Kellogg. Univ. Calif. Publ., Berkeley, Bull. Dept. Geol., vol.5, no.29, pp.411-437, figs.20, July 13, 1910.

(BARANOMYS LOCZYI N.G. N.SP., A NEW RODENT FROM THE UPPER PLIOCENE IN HUNGARY.) Baranomys lóczyi n.g. n.sp., új Rágesáló a Magyarországi felsoe Pliocénboel. Theodor Kormos. Állatani Koezlemények, vol.30, nos.1-2, pp.45-54, figs.3, 1933.

(NEW PLIOCENE RODENTS FROM MOLDAVIA.) Neue pliozaene nagetiere aus der Moldau. Theodor Kormos. Palaeont. Zeitsch., Berlin, vol.14, no.3, pp.193-200, figs.1-2, 1932.

(RODENT FAUNA OF THE AUSTRALOPITHECAN CAVES.) La faune de rongeurs des Grottes a Australopithèques. R. Lavocat. Pal. Africana, 4: 69-75, illus., 1956.

A NEW SPECIES OF MYLAGAULID FROM CHALK CLIFFS LOCAL FAUNA. Malcolm C. McKenna. Jour. Wash. Acad. Sci., vol.45, no.4, pp.107-110, illus., Apr.25, 1955.

RODENTS FROM THE PLEISTOCENE OF THE WESTERN MEDITERRANEAN REGION. C. I. F. Major. Geol. Mag. Lond., n.s., decade 5, vol.2, pp.462-467, 501-506, illus., Oct.-Nov., 1905.

A HORNED RODENT FROM THE COLORADO MIOCENE. WITH A REVISION OF THE MYLAGAULI, BEAVERS, AND HARES OF THE AMERICAN TERTIARY. W. D. Matthew. Bull. Amer. Mus. Nat. Hist., New York, vol.16, art.22, pp.291-310, figs.17, Sept.25, 1902.

A NEW GENUS OF RODENTS FROM THE MIDDLE EOCENE. W. D. Matthew. Jour. Mam., vol.1, no.4, pp.168-169, Aug., 1920.

NEW BATHYERGIDAE FROM THE OLIGOCENE OF MONGOLIA. W. D. Matthew, Walter Granger. Amer. Mus. Novit., no. 101, pp.1-5, figs.1-4, Dec.28, 1923.

NINE NEW RODENTS FROM THE OLIGOCENE OF MONGOLIA. W. D. Matthew, Walter Granger. Amer. Mus. Novitates, New York, no.102, pp.10, figs.12, Dec.31, 1923.

REMAINS OF MAMMALS FROM CAVES IN THE REPUBLIC OF HAITI. Gerrit S. Miller, Jr. Smithsonian Misc. Coll., vol. 74, no.3, pp.1-8, Oct.16.

A NEW FOSSIL RODENT FROM THE OLIGOCENE OF SOUTH DAKOTA. Gerrit S. Miller, Jr., James W. Gidley. Jour. Mam., vol.1, no.2, pp.73-74, Feb., 1920.

A NEW RODENT FROM THE UPPER OLIGOCENE OF FRANCE. Gerrit S. Miller, Jr. Bull. Amer. Mus. Nat. Hist., vol.41, pp.596-601, figs.1-3, pl. 34, Dec.29, 1919.

(ABNORMAL TEETH IN AN EXTINCT RODENT OF THE DICOELOPHORUS GENUS.) Anomalia dentaria en un roedor extinguido del genero Dicoelophorus. Carlos Rusconi. Anales Soc. Cient. Argentina, Buenos Aires, no.3, pp.147-149, vol.114, figs.1-2, Sept., 1932.

(ON THE RODENTS PLATAEOMYS AND PSEUDOPLATAEOMYS.) Sobre los roedores Plataeomys y Pseudoplataeomys. Carlos Rusconi. Anales Soc. Cient. Argentina, Buenos Aires, entr.1, vol.125, pp.74-78, Jan., 1938.

PROTOPTYCHUS HATCHERI, A NEW RODENT FROM THE UINTA EOCENE. W. B. Scott. Proc. Acad. Nat. Sci. Phila., pp. 269-286, figs.6, 1896.

THE MAMMALIAN FAUNA OF THE WHITE RIVER OLIGOCENE. PT. 2. RODENTIA. W. B. Scott, Glenn L. Jepsen. Trans. Amer. Philos. Soc., Phila., n.s., vol.28, pt.2, pp.157-269, figs.8-70, pls.23-33, Sept., 1937.

A GIANT RODENT FROM THE OLIGOCENE. George G. Simpson. Science, Lancaster, n.s., vol.93, no.2420, pp.474-475, May 16, 1941; Amer. Mus. Novitates, New York, no.1149, 16 pp., 4 figs., Oct.20, 1941.

A NEW GENUS OF RODENT FROM THE SESPE EOCENE. Chester Stock. Bull. Geol. Soc. America, vol.46, pp.61-68, pl. 6, Jan.31, 1935.

ON SOME FOSSIL RODENTS FROM PLEISTOCENE DEPOSITS IN A SUBURB OF HARBIN, MANCHOUKUO. Mitosi Tokuda. Rept. 1st. Sci. Exped. Manchoukuo, Tokyo, Sect.2, pt.4, pp.1-19, figs.1-23, Mar., 1939.

OLIGOCENE RODENTS OF THE GENUS ISCHYROMYS. Edward L. Troxell. Amer. Jour. Sci., ser.5, vol.3, pp.123-130, 7 figs., Feb., 1922.

PAUROMYS PERDITUS, A SMALL RODENT. Edward L. Troxell. Amer. Jour. Sci., ser.5, vol.5, pp.155-156, Feb., 1923.

OLIGOCENE CYLINDRODONTS OF MONGOLIA AND KAZAKHSTAN (CYLINDRODONTIDAE, GLIRES, MAMMALIA). B. S. Vinogradov, P. P. Gambaryan. Proc. Paleo. Inst., Acad. Sci. U.S.S.R., vol. 41, pp.13-42, illus., 1952.

A NEW FOSSIL RODENT FROM PUERTO RICO. Ernest E. Williams, Karl F. Koopman. Amer. Mus. Novitates, New York, no.1515, pp.9, figs.2, June 4, 1951.

ADDITIONAL EOCENE RODENT MATERIAL FROM SOUTHERN CALIFORNIA. Robert W. Wilson. Carnegie Inst. Wash. Publ.584, pp.1-25, pls.2, June 22, 1949.

CALIFORNIA EOCENE RODENTS. Robert W. Wilson. Proc. Geol. Soc. America for 1937, p.298, June, 1938.

CALIFORNIAN PARAMYID RODENTS. Robert W. Wilson. Carnegie Inst. Wash., publ.514, pp.59-83, pls.2, June 27, 1940.

EARLY TERTIARY RODENTS OF NORTH AMERICA. Robert W. Wilson. Carnegie Inst. Wash. Publ.584, pp.67-164, figs.13, June 22, 1949.

ON SOME WHITE RIVER FOSSIL RODENTS. Robert W. Wilson. Carnegie Inst. Wash. Publ.584, pp.27-50, figs.2, pls.2, June, 1949.

PAREUMYS REMAINS FROM THE LATER EOCENE OF CALIFORNIA. Robert W. Wilson. Carnegie Inst. Wash. Publ.514, pp.97-108, pls.2, June 27, 1940.

PLEISTOCENE RODENT FAUNA FROM THE CARPINTERIA ASPHALT DEPOSITS. Robert W. Wilson. Bull. Geol. Soc. America, vol.44, no.1, pp.219-220, Feb. 28, 1933.

A PLIOCENE RODENT FAUNA FROM SMITHS VALLEY, NEVADA. Robert W. Wilson. Carnegie Inst. Wash (Contrib. Palaeont.), Publ.473, pp.15-34, pls.2, May 21, 1936.

PLIOCENE RODENTS OF WESTERN NORTH AMERICA. Robert W. Wilson. Carnegie Inst. Wash. Publ.487, pp.21-73, figs.2, July 23, 1937.

REVIEW OF SOME RODENT GENERA FROM THE BRIDGER EOCENE. PART I. Robert W. Wilson. Amer. Jour. Sci., New Haven, ser.5, vol.35, no.206, pp.123-137, figs.4, Feb., 1938.

REVIEW OF SOME RODENT GENERA FROM THE BRIDGER EOCENE. PT. 2. Robert W. Wilson. Amer. Jour. Sci., ser. 5, vol.35, no.207, pp.207-222, figs.12, Mar., 1938.

REVIEW OF SOME RODENT GENERA FROM THE BRIDGER EOCENE. PT. 3. Robert W. Wilson. Amer. Jour. Sci., ser.5, vol.35, no.208, pp.297-304, figs. 13-15, Apr., 1938.

RODENT FAUNA FROM LATER CENOZOIC BEDS OF SOUTHWESTERN IDAHO. Robert W. Wilson. Pan-Amer. Geol., vol.59, no. 5, p.377, June, 1933; Carnegie Inst. Wash. (Contrib. Palaeont.), Publ.440, pp.117-136, figs.8, pls.2, Dec., 1933.

RODENT FAUNA FROM SMITHS VALLEY, NEVADA. Robert W. Wilson. Pan-Amer. Geol., Des Moines, vol.64, no.1, pp.77-78, Aug., 1935.

RODENTS OF THE RINCON FAUNA, WESTERN CHIHUAHUA, MEXICO. Robert W. Wilson. Carnegie Inst. Wash. Publ. 584, pp.165-176, pls.2, June 22, 1949.

TWO NEW EOCENE RODENTS FROM CALIFORNIA. Robert W. Wilson. Carnegie Inst. Wash. Publ.514, pp.85-95, pls.2, June 27, 1940.

TWO NEW EOCENE RODENTS FROM THE GREEN RIVER BASIN, WYOMING. Robert W. Wilson. Amer. Jour. Sic., ser.5, vol. 34, no.204, pp.447-456, Dec., 1937.

FOSSIL RODENTS FROM THE SIWALIK BEDS OF INDIA. Albert E. Wood. Amer. Jour. Sci., ser.5, vol.34, no.199, pp.64-76, figs.14, July, 1937.

THE MAMMALIAN FAUNA OF THE WHITE RIVER OLIGOCENE. PT.2. RODENTIA. Albert E. Wood. Trans. Amer. Philos. Soc., n.s., vol.28, pt.2, pp.155-269, figs. 70, pls.23-33, Sept., 1937.

MIOCENE RODENTS FROM FLORIDA. Albert E. Wood. Bull. Mus. Comp. Zool., Cambridge, vol.99, no.3, pp.489-494, illus., 1947.

MYTONOMYS, A NEW GENUS OF PARAMYID RODENT FROM THE UPPER EOCENE. Albert E. Wood. Jour. Paleontol., 30 (3): 753-755, July, 1956.

A NEW OLIGOCENE RODENT GENUS FROM PATAGONIA. Albert E. Wood. Amer. Mus. Novitates, New York, no. 1435, pp.54, figs.8, Nov.18, 1949.

A NEW RODENT FROM THE PLIOCENE OF KANSAS. Albert E. Wood. Jour. Paleontology, vol.10, no.5, pp.392-394, figs.2, July, 1936.

RODENTS FROM THE LOWER OLIGOCENE YODER FORMATION OF WYOMING. Albert E. Wood. Jour. Paleontol., vol.29, no.3, pp.519-524, May, 1955.

TWO NEW RODENTS FROM THE JOHN DAY MIOCENE. Albert E. Wood. Amer. Jour. Sci., ser.5, vol.30, no.178, pp. 368-372, figs.3, Oct., 1935.

TWO NEW RODENTS FROM THE MIOCENE OF MONGOLIA. Albert E. Wood. Amer. Mus. Novitates no.865, pp.7, fig.1, June 26, 1936.

(FOSSIL RODENTS FROM NORTHERN CHINA.) Fossile Nagetiere aus Nord China. C. C. Young. Palaeontologia Sinica (C) vol. 5, pp.1-82, pls.3, 1927.

(THE STRATIGRAPHIC AND PALEONTOLOGICAL IMPORTANCE OF THE FOSSIL RODENTS OF CHINA.) Die Stratigraphische und palaeontologische Bedeutung der fossilen Nagetiere Chinas. C. C. Young. Bull. Geol. Soc. China, Peiping, vol.10, pp. 159-164, tables 1-3, 1931.

Habits, Behavior

MEAT-EATING PROPENSITIES OF SOME RODENTS OF MINNESOTA. Bernard Bailey. Jour. Mam., vol.4, no.2, p.129, May, 1923.

ON THE SUBJECT OF THE OBSERVATIONS MADE IN THE ZOOLOGICAL STATION OF THE "SAN FRANCISCO MOUNTAIN" ON BI-PEDAL RAT MOVEMENTS. P. Magne Del La Croix. Anales Soc. Cien. Argentina, vol.109, no.3, pp.144-146, Mar., 1930.

INGENUITY OF A MOUSE. G. Dent. Essex Nat., Stratford, vol.27, pt.1, pp.38-39, Apr.-Sept., 1940.

THE SONGS OF MICE. Lee R. Dice. Jour. Mam., vol.13, no.3, pp.187-196, Aug., 1932.

USE OF CALIFORNIA ANNUAL-PLANT FORAGE BY RANGE RODENTS. Henry S. Fitch, J. R. Bentley. Ecology, 30 (3): 306-321, July, 1949.

MAMMALIA IN THE STEPPE BIOCENOSE. A. N. Formosov. Ecology, Brooklyn, vol. 9, no.4, pp.449-460, Oct., 1928.

ACTIVITY OF RODENTS IN PASTURE LANDS AND MEADOWS. II. OBSERVA-TIONS OF RODENTS IN PASTURES AND MEADOWS OF THE SOUTH UKRAINE. A. N. Formosov, I. B, Kiris (Prosvirnina). Uchenye Zapiski Moskovskogo Gosudarst-vennogo Universiteta Zool., vol.13, pp.39-57, figs.9-10, tables, 1937.

COMPARATIVE WINTER FOOD HABITS OF THE MUSKRAT AND NUTRIA IN CAPTIVI-TY. Louis F. Gainey. MS thesis, La. State Univ., 1949.

ANIMAL CARTS. HOW MARMOTS, BADGERS AND BEAVERS SERVE AS SLEDS OR WAGONS. E. W. Gudger. Sci. Mo., vol.40, pp.153-157, Feb., 1935.

THE HEIGHT FROM WHICH RODENTS MAY FALL. William J. Hamilton, Jr. Jour. Mam., vol.9, no.1, pp.65-66, Feb., 1928.

RODENT ARCHITECTS. John E. Hill. Nat. Hist., New York, vol.56, no.1, p.23, Jan., 1947.

(OBSERVATIONS ON DOMESTIC RODENTS.) Beobachtungen an heimischen Nagetieren. Hermann Kahmann. Zeitschrift f. Saeugetierkunde, vol.6, no.3, pp.143-151, Dec.15, 1931.

(ON THE REACTIONS OF SMALL RODENTS (RODENTIA) INITIAL.) Ueber die initiative Reaktionen der Kleinnagetiere (Rodentia). Gabor von Kolosvary. Comptes Rendus, 12th Internat. Congr. Zool.1935, Lisboa, vol.2, pp.799-820, 12 figs., 1936-37.

RODENTS THAT OCCUR IN HUMAN DWELLINGS IN EASTERN MONGOLIA. V. V. Kucheruk. Zool. Zh. 25: 175-183, 1946.

(RODENT ABUNDANCE IN HAYCOCKS IN SOUTHERN MOSCOW PROVINCE.) Opredel-yayuschchie vidovoi sostav i chislennost grizunov v skirdakh, ometakh i stogakh yuzhnikh raionov moskovskoi oblasti. V. V. Kucheruk, M. A. Rubina. Zool. Zhurnal, Moscow, vol.32, no.3, pp.495-505, 1953.

HOW SQUIRRELS AND OTHER RODENTS CARRY THEIR YOUNG. Herbert Lang. Jour. Mam., vol.6, no.1, pp.18-24, pls.3, Feb.9, 1925.

WATER REQUIREMENTS OF CERTAIN RODENTS FROM XERIC AND MESIC HABITATS. Robert G. Lindeborg. PhD thesis, Univ. Mich., 1948; Contrib. Lab. Vert. Biol. Univ. Michigan, Ann Arbor, no. 58, pp.32, June, 1952.

WINTER RODENT POPULATIONS IN FIELD SHOCKED CORN. J. P. Linduska. Jour. Wildlife Mgt., 6 (4): 353-363, Oct., 1942.

(CONTRIBUTION TO KNOWLEDGE OF THE LIFE AND HABITS OF THE ARVICOLE IN APULIA.) Contributo alla conoscenza dells vita e dei costumi dells Arvicole in Puglia. Giovanni Martelli. Boll. Lab. Zool. Gen. et Agr. R. Scuola Super, d'Agric. in Portici, vol.13, pp.193-316, 1919.

ACTIVITY RHYTHMS IN THE WOOD MOUSE, APODEMUS SYLVATICUS AND THE BANK VOLE, CLETHRIONOMYS GLAREOLUS. Richard S. Miller. Proc. Zool. Soc. Lond., vol.125, pt.3-4, pp.505-519, illus., Nov.23, 1955.

FOOD HABITS OF THE WOOD-MOUSE, APODEMUS SYLVATICUS (LINNE, 1758), AND THE BANK VOLE, CLETHRIONOMYS GLAREOLUS (SCHREBER, 1780), IN WYTHAM WOODS, BERKSHIRE. Richard S. Miller, Saeugetierk. Mitteil., Stuttgart, vol.2, no.3, pp.109-114, July 1, 1954.

ON SOME PARTICULARITIES OF STA-TIONARY DISTRIBUTION OF MOUSE-LIKE RODENTS IN SOUTHERN UKRAINE. N. P. Naumov. Zool. Jour., Moscow, vol.15, no. 4, pp.674-696, 1936.

ON THE DISTRIBUTION OF MURIFORM RODENTS (MICROTUS ARVALIS PALL., MICROTUS SOCIALIS PALL., LAGURUS LAGURUS PALL., MUS MUSCULUS HORTULANUS NORDM.) AT DIFFERENT HABITATS. N. P. Naumov. Uchenye Zapiski Moskovskogo Gosudarstvennogo Universiteta, Zool., vol.13, pp.1-38, figs. 8, tables 9, 1937.

WATER CONSUMPTION OF CERTAIN MICE IN RELATION OF HABITAT SELEC-TION. Eugene P. Odum. Jour. Mam., vol.25, no.4, pp.404-405, Nov., 1944.

(NOTE ON THE ESTIVATION AND HIBER-NATION OBSERVED IN SEVERAL RODENT SPECIES.) Note sur l'estivation et l'hiber-nation observees chez plusieurs especes de rongeurs. F. Petter. Mammalia, Paris, vol.19, no.4, pp.444-446, Dec., 1955.

MATERIALS ON THE STUDY OF SUCCES-SION OF MOUSE-LIKE RODENTS OF SOUTHERN DISTRICTS OF THE FAR EASTERN REGION. K. Plyater-Plokhotsky. Bull. Far Eastern Branch Acad. Sci. USSR, Vladivostok, no.16, pp.175-177, 1936.

(OLFACTORY ANALYSIS AND FOOD GATHERING ACTIVITY IN RODENTS.) Obonyatelnii analizator i pishchedobivateln-aya royushchaya deyatelnost grizunov. A. G. Ponugaeva. Zool. Zhurnal, vol.33, no. 4, pp.869-875, July-Aug., 1954.

RODENT HABITAT PREFERENCES ON FOOTHILL PASTURES IN CALIFORNIA. Jay C. Quast. Jour. Mam., vol.35, no.4, pp.515-521, Nov.29, 1954.

THERMAL CONDITIONS IN THE BURROWS OF RODENTS LIVING ON SANDY SOILS AND THE METHOD OF THEIR INVESTIGA-TIONS. G. Rall. Zool. Zhurnal, Moscow, vol.18, no.1, pp.110-119, figs.8, tables 2, 1939.

PERIODICAL PHENOMENA IN BIOLOGY OF THE MOST IMPORTANT RODENTS OF SANDY SEMI-DESERT TERRITORIES (WEST KAZAKHSTAN). G. Rall, M. Demiashew, M. Sheikina. Vestnik Mikro-biol., Epidemiol. i Parazitorl (Rev. Microbiol., Epidemiol., et Parasitol.), Saratov, vol.15, nos.3-4, pp.380-406, figs.6, tables 15, 1936.

(CONTRIBUTION TO THE STUDY OF THE DIGGING OF SMALL RODENTS.) Contribu-tion a l'étude du fouissement chez les petits rongeurs. P. Rode. Bull. Soc. Zool. France, vol.54, no.6, pp.573-588, figs.2, Oct., 1929.

MICE EATING BUTTERFLIES. S. G. C. Russell. Entomologist's Record and Jour. Variation, London, vol.55, no.12, pp.122-123, Dec., 1943.

(TWO MICE KILLED WHILE CLIMBING IN BRANCHES--A REPLY.) Ueber zwei beim Klettern im Gezweige verunglueckte Maeuse --eine Entgegnung. Helmut Schaefer. Zeitschr. f. Saeugetierkunde, Berlin, vol. 9, nos.1-3, pp.384-386, fig.3, pl.17a, Dec.30, 1934.

A SOURCE OF MEAT FOR DIETS OF WILD RODENTS. Albert R. Shadle. Jour. Mam., Balto., vol.21, no.4, pp.460-461, Nov.14, 1940.

THE RODENTS AS PLUNDERERS OF SEEDS. P. A. Sviridenko. Zool. Jour. USSR, Moscow, vol.23, no.4, pp.170-180, figs.6, 1944.

(SEARCH BY RODENTS FOR FOOD IN SOIL AND CONDITIONED REFLEXES IN THEM BY AN OILY ODOR.) Raziskivanie grizunami korma v zemle i uslovinie re-fleksi u nikh nepishchevie zapakhi. P. A. Sviridenko. Zool. Zhurnal, vol.33, no.4, pp.876-888, July-Aug., 1954.

BEHAVIOR-RANGES AND POPULATIONS OF SOME RATS AND MICE. Ryo Tanaka. Seibutu, 4 (1): 16-20, 1949.

A FISH-EATING RODENT. Oldfield Thomas. Natural Science, vol.2, no.14, p.286, Apr., 1893.

LAWS GOVERNING THE SEASONAL MIGRA-TIONS OF MOUSE-LIKE RODENTS. S. N. Varshavskii. Zool. Zh., 16: 362-392, 1937.

THE RAT AND MOUSE POPULATIONS OF CORN RICKS. L. S. V. Venables, P. H. Leslie. Jour. Anim. Ecol., London, vol. 11, no.1, pp.44-68, illus., May, 1942.

(FEEDING ALLOWANCE OF CERTAIN RODENTS.) Osobennosti kormovogo ratsiona nekotorikh grizunov. A. G. Vornonov. Zool. Zhurnal, Moscow, vol. 3, no.1, pp.184-196, Jan.-Feb., 1954.

THE TOLERANCE OF RODENTS TO THE FEEDING OF CONE-NOSED BUGS (HEMI-PTERA, REDUVIIDAE). Sherwin F. Wood. Bull. Southern California Acad. Sci., Los Angeles, vol.46, pt.3, pp.144-153, Apr.20, 1948.

ANTLER EATING BY RODENTS. Angus M. Woodbury. Science, 92 (2380): 127-128, Aug.9, 1940.

INDIRECT EVIDENCE SUPPORTING OBSERVATIONS ON THE RANGE OF WILD RODENTS. C. Brooke Worth. Jour. Mam., vol.32, no.1, Feb., 1951.

Hematology

BLOOD RELATIONSHIP WITHIN THE ORDER RODENTIA. Robert A. Hicks. Science, n.s., vol.69, pp.190-191, Feb. 15, 1929.

CHANGES IN THE BLOOD OF ANIMALS ACCORDING TO AGE. 1. CHANGES IN THE BLOOD OF RODENTS (MUS MUSCU-LUS L. AND CITELLUS PYGMAEUS PALL.) AND BIRDS (PASSER MONTANUS L. AND LARUS RIDIBUNDUS L.) DURING THE PERIOD OF GROWTH. N. Kalabuchov, V. Rodionov. Moscou Univ. Sbornik Nauchno issledovatel's kogo inst. Zool. (Abstracts Works Zool. Inst. Moscou State Univ.), no. 3, pp.183-184, 1936.

SEROLOGICAL INVESTIGATION OF RO-DENT RELATIONSHIPS. Harry P. Levine, Paul A. Moody. Physiological Zoology, Chicago, vol.12, no.4, pp.400-411, Oct., 1939.

DELICACY OF DIFFERENTIATION BY THE SCHULTZ-DALE TEST AS REVEALED BY END-POINT DETERMINATIONS ON RO-DENT SERA. Paul A. Moody. Jour. Im-munology, Balto., vol.39, no.2, pp.113-123, figs.4, Aug., 1940.

Heredity

A LAMARCKIAN EXPERIMENT. Harold S. Cotton. Amer. Nat., vol.65, no.699, pp. 343-350, July-Aug., 1931.

COLOR INHERITANCE IN MICE. C. B. Davenport. Science, n.s., vol.19, no.472, pp.110-114, Jan.15, 1904.

UNIT CHARACTER VARIATION IN RO-DENTS. L. C. Dunn. Jour. Mam., vol.2, no.3, pp.125-140, Aug., 1921.

VERIFICATION IN MICE OF THE POS-SIBILITY OF MORE THAN FIFTY PER CENT RECOMBINATION. R. A. Fisher, K. Mather. Nature, London, vol.137, no. 3461, pp.362-363, Feb.29, 1936.

GENE RELATIONSHIPS IN TWO SPECIES OF MICE WITH REFERENCE TO THEIR POSSIBLE EVOLUTIONARY SIGNIFICANCE. C. V. Green. Amer. Nat., vol.69, no.720, pp.19-29, Jan.-Feb., 1935.

INHERITANCE OF YELLOW COLOR IN RODENTS. Arend L. Hagedoorn. Univ. California Publ. Physiol., Berkeley, vol.3, no.14, pp.95-99, Mar.30, 1909.

THE STRUCTURE OF THE SEX DETERMINING MECHANISM IN THE FIELD MOUSE. P. C. Koller. Jour. Genetics, London, vol.37, no.3, pp.2-3, May, 1939.

SELECTION AND CROSS-BREEDING IN RELATION TO THE INHERITANCE OF COAT-PIGMENT AND COAT-PATTERNS IN RATS AND GUINEA-PIGS. Hansford MacCurdy, W. E. Castle. Publ. Carnegie Inst. Wash., no.70, pp.1-50, pls.1-2, figs.1-5, May, 1907.

(NEW CONTRIBUTION TO STUDY OF HETEROCHROMOSOMES IN THE MAMMALS, IN PARTICULAR THE RODENTS.) Contribution nouvelle à l'étude des hétérochromosomes chez les mammifères, et singulièrement chez les rongeurs. Robert Matthey. Jour. Genetics, vol.36, no.1, pp.73-102, figs.6, pls.3-7, May, 1938.

(PRELIMINARY FINDINGS OF OBSERVATION OF THE TRANSMISSION OF ACQUIRED CHARACTERS.) Vorlaeufige Ergebnisse einer Beobachtung ueber die Vererbung erworbener Eigenschaften. G. P. Ssacharoff. Zeitschr. f. induktive Abstammungs-u. Vererbungslehre, vol.55, pp.145-154, 1930.

## Methods and Techniques

MANUAL FOR ANALYSIS OF RODENT POPULATION. David E. Davis. Lithoprinted by Edwards Brothers, Inc., Ann Arbor, Mich., pp.IV plus 82, 19 figs., Division of Vertebrate Ecology, The Johns Hopkins Univ., Balto. 5, Md., 1956.

NOTES ON EAR-TAGGING OF MICE. Gaines W. Eddy, C. R. Joyce. Jour. Mam., 25 (2): 199-200, May, 1944.

SIMULATED BURROW SYSTEMS FOR STUDIES WITH RODENT PESTS. Irvin Fuhr, Seymour D. Silver. Jour. Wildlife Management, Menasha, vol.11, no.2, pp. 150-153, Apr., 1947.

A METHOD FOR DETERMINING EXTENT OF RODENT DENS. R. Frank Hedges. Jour. Wildlife Management, Menasha, vol. 5, no.2, pp.129-130, Apr., 1941.

METHODS OF STUDYING SOME QUESTIONS ON THE ECOLOGY OF MOUSE LIKE RODENTS. N. I. Kalabukhov, V. V. Raevskii. Revue de Microbiol., Epidemiol. et Parasitol., Savatov, vol.12, no.1, pp. 47-62, 1933.

EXAMINATION OF PRACTICAL METHODS USED AT OBSERVATION POSTS FOR THE ESTIMATION OF RODENTS. M. A. Kotovshchikova. Itogi Nauchno-Issledovatel'skikh Rabot Vsesouiznogo Instituta Zashchity Rastenii za 1935 (Summary Sci. Research Work Inst. Plant Protection, Leningrad, 1935), pp.540-542, 1936.

OBTAINING BLOOD FROM MICE. L. R. Kuhn. Science, Lancaster, n.s., vol.93, no.2421, p.504, May 23, 1941.

DEVELOPMENT AND IMPROVEMENT OF ESTIMATION METHODS FOR MOUSELIKE RODENTS IN HOTBED STACKS AND PREMISES. N. B. Lomakina. Itogi Nauchno-Issledovatel'skikh Rabot Vsesoiuznogo Instituta Zashchity Rastenii za 1935 (Summary Sci. Research Work Inst. Plant Protection, Leningrad, 1935), pp.542-545, fig.1, 1936.

THE DYNAMIC DENSITY OF RODENTS AND SOME METHODS OF STUDYING IT. Yu. M. Rall'. Bull. Moscow Soc. Nat., 50: 62-64, 1945.

SOME METHODS OF ECOLOGICAL CENSUS FOR RODENTS. Yu. M. Rall'. Problems Ecol. and Biocenol., vol.3, pp. 140-157, fig.1, 1936.

THE ELECTRIC FENCE AS AN AID IN FIELD STUDIES OF RODENTS AND THEIR ECTOPARASITES. Raymond E. Ryckman, Karl C. Fischer, Charles T. Ames, Chester C. Lindt. California Fish and Game, vol. 39, no.4, pp.489-496, illus., Oct., 1953.

(THE METHODICS OF BIOMETRICAL MEASUREMENTS OF LABORATORY EXPERIMENTAL ANIMALS (THE FROG, LARGER RODENTS, AND DOMESTIC BIRDS).) Die Methodik biometricher Messungen an Laboratoriumsversuchstieren (Frosch, kleinere und groesser Nager und Hausvoegel). K. Saller. Handbuch der biologischen Arbeitsmethoden. Lieferung 265, Abt.VII, Methoden der vergleichenden morphologischen Forschung, Heft 4, Berlin, Urban and Schwarzenberg, pp.683-848, 44 figs., 1928.

EAR TAGS ON MICE. Thomas G. Scott. Jour. Mam., vol.23, no.3, p.339, Aug.14, 1942.

NUTS TO WILDLIFE. (HOW TO TELL WHAT ATE VARIOUS KINDS OF NUTS.) Ward M. Sharp, Jess W. Malcolm. Pa. Game News, 25 (11): 41-43, illus., Nov., 1954.

CONTRIBUTION TO THE STUDY OF RATS AND SOME METHODS OF THEIR INVESTIGATION. B. M. Shitkov. Zool. Jour. USSR, Moscow, vol.23, nos.2-3, pp.91-97, 1944.

AN ACCURATE METHOD FOR MEASURING NEW-BORN MICE. Arthur Svihla. Science, n.s., vol.77, no.1996, p.331, Mar.31, 1933.

SOME METHODS OF ESTIMATING THE POPULATION SIZE OF RATS OR VOLES LIVING IN A SPECIFIED AREA. Hideo Tanaka. Jour. Osaka City Med. Cent., 3 (1): 1-13, graphs, 1953.

METHODS OF DETERMINING RODENT PRESSURE ON THE RANGE. Walter P. Taylor. Ecology, vol.11, no.3, pp.523-524, 7 figs., July, 1930.

THE METHOD OF TAKING THE INCISIVE INDEX IN RODENTS. Oldfield Thomas. Ann. and Mag. Nat. Hist., ser.9, vol.4, pp.289-290, 1 fig., Oct., 1919.

AN EXPLORATORY STUDY OF QUANTITATIVE METHODS OF TRAPPING RODENTS. Dean Vest. Symposium on ecology of disease transmission in native animals, Univ. Utah, pp.16-19, 1955.

A SUGGESTED NOMENCLATURE FOR THE CUSPS OF THE CHEEK TEETH OF RODENTS. A. E. Wood, R. W. Wilson. Jour. Paleontol., vol.10, no.5, pp.388-391, figs. 2, July, 1936.

## Mexico

A NEW GENUS OF RODENTS FROM YUCATAN. H. E. Anthony. Amer. Mus. Nov., no.586, 3 pp., fig.1, Nov.16, 1932.

SIX NEW MAMMALS FROM THE STATE OF SAN LUIS POTOSI, MEXICO. Walter W. Dalquest. Jour. Wash. Acad. Sci., vol.41, no.11, pp.361-364, Nov.14, 1951.

DESCRIPTIONS OF FIVE NEW MAMMALS FROM MEXICO. E. A. Goldman. Proc. Biol. Soc. Wash., vol.17, pp.79-82, Mar. 21, 1904.

A NEW POCKET GOPHER (THOMOMYS) AND A NEW SPINY POCKET MOUSE (LIOMYS) FROM MICHOACAN, MEXICO. E. Raymond Hall, Bernardo Villa-R. Univ. Kansas Publ. Mus. Nat. Hist., vol.1, no. 14, pp.249-256, figs.6, July 26, 1948.

A DISCUSSION OF THE ZONAL STATUS OF THE SIERRA SAN PEDRO MARTIR, LOWER CALIFORNIA, MEXICO, WITH DESCRIPTIONS OF A NEW KANGAROO RAT AND A NEW WOOD-PECKER FROM THAT REGION. Laurence M. Huey. Trans. San Diego Soc. Nat. Hist., vol.5, no.1, pp.10, pl.1, Feb.20, 1927.

A NEW POCKET GOPHER AND A NEW ANTELOPE GROUND SQUIRREL FROM LOWER CALIFORNIA, MEXICO. Laurence M. Huey. Trans. San Diego Soc. Nat. Hist., vol.5, no.15, pp.241-244, Feb.27, 1929.

A NEW SILKY POCKET MOUSE AND A NEW POCKET GOPHER FROM LOWER CALIFORNIA, MEXICO. Laurence M. Huey. Trans. San Diego Soc. Nat. Hist., vol.5, no.8, pp.87-90, Jan.18, 1928.

RODENTS FROM BRITISH HONDURAS, MEXICO, TRINIDAD, HAITI AND JAMAICA COLLECTED BY MR. I. T. SANDERSON. Eleanor M. O. Laurie. Ann. Mag. Nat. Hist., ser.12, vol.6, no.65, pp.382-394, May, 1953.

PRELIMINARY DIAGNOSES OF NEW MAMMALS OF THE GENERA SCIURUS, CASTOR, NEOTOMA, AND SIGMODON, FROM THE MEXICAN BORDER OF THE UNITED STATES. Edgar A. Mearns. Proc. U.S. Nat. Mus., Wash.,D.C., vol. 20, no.1132, pp.501-505, Jan.19, 1898.

THREE NEW RODENTS FROM SOUTHERN MEXICO. E. W. Nelson, E. A. Goldman. Proc. Biol. Soc. Wash., vol.46, pp.195-198, Oct.26, 1933.

TWO NEW RODENTS FROM MEXICO. Wilfred H. Osgood. Jour. Mam., vol.26, no.3, pp.299-301, Aug., 1945.

(NOTE REGARDING SOME SPECIES OF RODENTS OF THE GENERA DIPODOMYS, PEROGNATHUS, AND PEROMYSCUS.) Nota acerca de algunas especies de roedores de los generos Dipodomys, Perognathus y Peromyscus. Bernardo Villa Ramirez. Anales Inst. Biol., Mexico City, vol.12, no.1, pp.355-399, 1941.

DESCRIPTION OF TWO NEW SPECIES OF RODENTS FROM MEXICO. Henry L. Ward. Amer. Nat., vol.25, no.290, pp. 158-161, Feb., 1891.

## North America

DESCRIPTION OF A NEW MOUSE FROM LAKE COUNTY, CALIFORNIA. J. A. Allen. Bull. Amer. Mus. Nat. Hist., vol. 5, pp.335-336, Dec.16, 1893.

DESCRIPTIONS OF FIVE NEW NORTH AMERICAN RODENTS. J. A. Allen. Bull. Amer. Mus. Nat. Hist., vol.12, pp. 11-17, Mar.4, 1899.

RODENTS IN NEBRASKA. Roald Amundson. Outdoor Nebraska, Lincoln, vol.21, no.1, pp.4-7, 20, Mar., 1943.

A SYNOPSIS OF THE RODENTS OF THE SOUTHERN PARTS OF THE PRAIRIE PROVINCES OF CANADA. R. M. Anderson, A. L. Rand. Nat. Mus. Canada, Ottawa, Special Contrib., 43-1, pp.1-25 (Mimeogr.), 1943.

THREE NEW RODENTS FROM LAVA BEDS OF SOUTHERN NEW MEXICO. Seth B. Benson. Univ. Calif. Publ. Zool., vol.38, pp.335-344, pls.3-4, Apr.14, 1932.

SIZE OF HOME RANGE AND NOTES ON THE LIFE HISTORY OF THE WOODLAND DEER-MOUSE AND EASTERN CHIPMUNK IN NORTHERN MICHIGAN. W. Frank Blair. Jour. Mam., 23 (1): 27-36, Feb., 1942.

FOUR NEW RODENTS FROM MONTEREY COUNTY, CALIFORNIA. Jack C. von Bloeker. Proc. Biol. Soc. Wash., vol.50, pp.153-158, Sept.10, 1937.

DESCRIPTION OF A NEW ROCK POCKET-MOUSE AND A NEW DESERT-MOUSE FROM SOUTHERN ARIZONA. Philip M. Blossom. Occas. Papers Mus. Zool., Univ. Michigan, no.265, pp.4, June 21, 1933.

ADDITIONAL NOTES FROM A COUNTRY HOME. (NOTES ON APLODONTIA RUFA RUFA AND PEROMYSCUS MANICULATUS AUSTERUS.) D. E. Brown. Murrelet, vol. 11, no.2, pp.18-19, May, 1930.

RODENT ACTIVITY IN A MIXED PRAIRIE NEAR HAYS, KANSAS. H. Leo Brown. Trans. Kansas Acad. Sci., 48 (4): 448-456, Mar., 1946.

MONOGRAPHS OF NORTH AMERICAN RODENTS. Elliott Coues, Joel Asaph Allen. U.S. Geol. Survey of the Territories, GPO, Wash., pp.1091, illus., 1877.

A STUDY OF WYOMING RODENTS FOR THE ELEMENTARY SCHOOLS. Albert M. Day, S. H. Dadisman. Univ. Wyoming,

College of Educ. Bull., vol.1, no.3, pp. 35, Jan., 1924.

DESCRIPTION OF TWO NEW POCKET MICE AND A NEW WOODRAT FROM NEW MEXICO. Lee R. Dice. Occas. Papers Mus. Zool. Univ. Michigan, no.203, pp.1-4, June, 1929.

STUDIES OF THE ECOLOGY AND GENETICS OF NORTH AMERICAN MAMMALS. Lee R. Dice. Carnegie Inst. Washington Year Book, no.35, 1935-36, pp.287-289, Dec.11, 1936.

(ON TRACES OF THE RODENTS FOUND ON THE WEST COAST OF GREENLAND.) A propos de traces de Rongeur relevées sur la cote ouest du Groenland. J. Dorst, P. Stahl. Mammalia, Paris, vol.16, no.2, pp.92-96, June, 1952.

VARIATIONS AND ADAPTATIONS OF THE RODENTS OF THE NORTH RIM OF THE GRAND CANYON, ARIZONA. Floyd E. Durham. Essays in the Natural Sciences in Honor of Captain Allen Hancock, Univ. Southern California, Los Angeles, pp.233-258, 2 maps, July 26, 1955.

PRELIMINARY DESCRIPTIONS OF NEW RODENTS FROM THE OLYMPIC MOUNTAINS. D. G. Elliot. Field Col. Mus. Pub.30, Zool. Ser., vol.1, no.11, pp.225-228, Feb.1, 1899.

DOUBLE CAPTURES OF SMALL RODENTS IN CALIFORNIA. F. C. Evans, R. Holdenried. Jour. Mam., vol.24, no.3, p. 401, Aug.17, 1943.

EXTENSIONS OF THE KNOWN RANGES OF THREE RODENTS IN ALAMEDA COUNTY, CALIFORNIA. F. C. Evans, R. Holdenried. Wasmann Collector, San Francisco, vol.4, no.3, pp.95-96, fig.1, Apr., 1941.

ON THE DWELLINGS OF THE MUSKRAT AND BEAVER OF NOVA SCOTIA. J. Bernard Gilpin. Nova Scotia Inst. Nat. Sci. Proc. and Trans., vol.6, pt.1, pp.275-282, 1882.

FIVE NEW RODENTS FROM ARIZONA AND NEW MEXICO. E. A. Goldman. Proc. Biol. Soc. Wash., vol.46, pp.71-78, Apr. 27, 1933.

FOUR NEW MAMMALS FROM UTAH. E. A. Goldman. Proc. Biol. Soc. Wash., vol. 50, pp.221-226, Dec.28, 1937.

THREE NEW RODENTS FROM ARIZONA AND NEW MEXICO. E. A. Goldman. Proc. Biol. Soc. Wash., vol.44, pp.133-136, Oct.17, 1931.

THREE NEW RODENTS FROM SOUTHERN UTAH. E. A. Goldman. Proc. Biol. Soc. Wash., vol.55, pp.75-78, June 25, 1942.

THREE NEW RODENTS FROM WESTERN ARIZONA. E. A. Goldman. Proc. Biol. Soc. Wash., vol.41, pp.203-206, Dec.18, 1928.

TWO NEW RODENTS FROM ARIZONA. E. A. Goldman. Proc. Biol. Soc. Wash., vol.45, pp.89-92, June 21, 1932.

TWO NEW RODENTS FROM OREGON AND NEVADA. E. A. Goldman. Jour. Mam., vol.2, no.4, pp.232-233, Nov., 1921.

RODENT POPULATIONS IN THE SAGEBRUSH DESERT OF THE YAKIMA VALLEY, WASHINGTON. John A. Gray, Jr. Jour. Mam., 24 (2): 191-193, May, 1943.

NOTES ON SOME SMALL CANADIAN RODENTS. Morris M. Green. Canadian Field-Nat., vol.44, no.3, p.69, Mar., 1930.

TWO NEW RODENTS (GENERA THOMOMYS AND MARMOTA) FROM THE EASTERN BORDER OF CALIFORNIA. Joseph Grinnell. Univ. California Pub. Zool., vol.21, pp. 239-244, 6 figs., Nov.7, 1921.

NEW HETEROMYID RODENTS FROM NEVADA. E. Raymond Hall. Proc. Biol. Soc. Wash., vol.54, pp.55-62, May 20, 1941.

TWO NEW RODENTS OF THE GENERA GLAUCOMYS AND ZAPUS FROM UTAH. E. Raymond Hall. Occas. Papers Mus. Zool., Univ. Michigan, no.296, pp.1-6, Nov.2, 1934.

NOTES ON ARIZONA RODENTS. E. Raymond Hall, William B. Davis. Proc. Biol. Soc. Wash., vol.47, pp.51-56, Feb. 9, 1934.

COMMENTS ON THE TAXONOMY AND GEOGRAPHIC DISTRIBUTION OF SOME NORTH AMERICAN RODENTS. E. Raymond Hall, Keith R. Kelson. Univ. Kansas Publ., Mus. Nat. Hist., Lawrence, vol.5, no.26, pp.343-371, Dec.15, 1952.

THREE NEW RODENTS FROM SOUTHERN UTAH. Ross Hardy. Proc. Biol. Soc. Wash., vol.55, pp.87-92, June 25, 1942.

FAUNAL RELATIONSHIPS OF RECENT NORTH AMERICAN RODENTS. Emmet T. Hooper. U. Mich. Mus. Zool., Misc. Publ. No.72, 1-28 pp., May, 1949.

A NEW RACE OF DIPODOMYS AND A NEW RACE OF THOMOMYS FROM ARIZONA. Laurence Markham Huey. Soc. Nat. Hist., San Diego, Calif., Trans., vol.12, no.6, pp.99-102, 1955.

MYSTERY MICE OF THE SAGEBRUSH. Elizabeth Ingles. Audubon Mag., New York, vol.57, no.5, pp.206-207, 238, illus., Oct., 1955.

A PRELIMINARY STUDY OF THE MICE OF MOUNT DESERT ISLAND. Beatrice W. Johnson. Anat. Record, vol.29, p.130, Dec.25, 1924.

ON TWO NEW SPECIES OF MAMMALS. J. K. Lord. Proc. Zool. Soc. Lond., pt. 31, pp.95-98, 1863.

SOME NEW RODENTS RECORDS FOR NORTHEASTERN CALIFORNIA. Joseph Mailliard. Jour. Mam., vol.6, no.1, pp. 57-58, Feb., 1925.

(SOME RODENTS WITH EXTERNAL CHEEK POUCHES FROM WESTERN NORTH AMERICA.) Ueber einige nager mit aeusseren backentaschen aus dem westlichen Nord-America. Prinzen zu Wied Maximilian. Breslau, Akad. eingegangen, pp.367-383, pl.34, 1839.

DESCRIPTION OF FIVE NEW RODENTS FROM THE COAST REGION OF ALASKA. C. Hart Merriam. Proc. Biol. Soc., Wash., vol.11, pp.221-223, July 15, 1897.

DESCRIPTIONS OF THREE NEW RODENTS FROM THE OLYMPIC MOUNTAINS, WASHINGTON. C. Hart Merriam. Proc. Acad. Nat. Sci. Phila., pt.2, pp.352-353, 1898.

FOUR NEW RODENTS FROM CALIFORNIA. C. Hart Merriam. Proc. Biol. Soc. Wash., vol.21, pp.145-148, June 9, 1908.

THREE NEW RODENTS FROM COLORADO. C. Hart Merriam. Proc. Biol. Soc. Wash., vol.21, pp.143-144, June 9, 1908.

TWO NEW RODENTS FROM NORTHWESTERN CALIFORNIA. C. Hart Merriam. Proc. Biol. Soc. Wash., vol.14, pp.125-126, July 19, 1901.

DESCRIPTION OF A NEW MOUSE FROM SOUTHERN CALIFORNIA. Gerrit S. Miller, Jr. American Naturalist 226, p.4, Mar., 1892.

DESCRIPTION OF A NEW MOUSE FROM SOUTHERN NEW MEXICO AND ARIZONA. Gerrit S. Miller, Jr. Amer. Mus. Nat. Hist., vol.5, art.18, pp.331-334, Dec.16, 1893.

LIFE HISTORY NOTES ON THE BANNER-TAILED KANGAROO RAT, MERRIAM'S KANGAROO RAT, AND THE WHITE-THROATED WOOD RAT IN ARIZONA AND NEW MEXICO. Gale Monson, Wayne Kessler. Jour. Wildlife Management, Menasha, vol.4, no.1, pp.37-43, Jan., 1940.

NOTES ON THREE ADDITIONS TO THE RODENT FAUNA OF ALBERTA. J. E. Moore. Canadian Field-Nat., vol.66, no. 5, pp.142-143, Sept.-Oct., 1952.

DESCRIPTIONS OF FOUR NEW RODENTS FROM CALIFORNIA. Samuel N. Rhoads. The American Naturalist, pp.831-836, Sept., 1893.

DESCRIPTIONS OF THREE NEW RODENTS FROM CALIFORNIA AND OREGON. Samuel N. Rhoads. Amer. Nat., pp.67-70, Jan.1, 1894.

STUDIES ON THE RODENTS OF MONTANA. Harry E. Sawyer. MA thesis, Mont. State Univ., 1935.

NOTES ON SOME IOWA RODENTS. Dayton Stoner. Proc. Iowa Acad. Sci., Des Moines, vol.24, pp.253-356, 1917.

THE RODENTS OF IOWA. Dayton Stoner. Iowa Geological Survey, Bull.no.5, Des Moines, 1918.

SOME RODENT POPULATIONS IN THE SIERRA NEVADA OF CALIFORNIA. Tracy I. Storer, Francis C. Evans, Fletcher G. Palmer. Ecological Monographs, Durham, no.14, pp.165-192, figs. 18, Apr., 1944.

TWO NEW RODENTS FROM NEVADA. Walter P. Taylor. Univ. Calif. Publ. Zool., vol.5, no.6, pp.283-302, pls.27-29, Feb.12, 1910.

KANGAROO RATS AND SCORPION MICE ON THE SANTA RITA RESERVE, ARIZONA. Walter P. Taylor, Charles T. Vorhies. Jour. Mam., vol.4, no.4, p.255, Nov., 1923.

MAMMALS OF WEST VIRGINIA. VI. OLD WORLD RATS AND MICE, BEAVER, PORCUPINE, AND JUMPING MICE. L. Wayne Wilson. West Virginia Conserv., Charleston, vol.10, no.3, pp.10, 22-23, July, 1946.

LIVE MOUSE FOUND ON AIRLINER FROM PUERTO RICO. Science News Letter, Wash., D.C., vol.41, no.21, p.335, May 23, 1942.

<u>Pacific Islands</u>

A STUDY OF RODENT POPULATION ON GUAM, MARIANA ISLANDS. Rollin H. Baker. Ecological Monographs, Durham, vol.16, no.4, pp.393-408, figs.11, Oct., 1946.

THE MAMMALS OF JAVA. 1. RODENTIA. K. W. Dammerman. Treubia, vol.13, nos. 3-4, pp.429-470, figs.8, Dec., 1931.

DISTRIBUTION OF FIELD MICE AND VOLES IN KYUSHU. Yoshi Kuni Hiraiwa, Mitoshi Tokuda, Teruaki Uchida, Hiroichi Yoshida. Sci. Bull. Faculty Agric. Kyushu Univ., 16 (1): 157-162, Mar., 1957.

TWO NEW PHILIPPINE RODENTS. Remington Kellogg. Proc. Biol. Soc. Wash., vol.58, pp.121-124, Sept.20, 1945.

THE RODENTS OF NEW CALEDONIA. Arnold J. Nicholson, Dwain W. Warner. Jour. Mam., vol.34, no.2, pp.168-179, illus., May 14, 1953.

A NEW RODENT FROM DUTCH NEW GUINEA. Wilfred H. Osgood. Fieldiana, Zool., Chicago Nat. Hist. Mus., vol.31, no.1, p.2, Sept.19, 1945.

ESTIMATION OF VOLE AND MOUSE POPULATIONS ON MT. ISHIZUCHI AND ON THE UPLANDS OF SOUTHERN SHIKOKU. Ryo Tanaka. Jour. Mam., vol.32, no.4, pp.450-458, illus., Nov.19, 1951.

FURTHER STUDY ON VOLE AND MOUSE POPULATIONS ON MT. ISHIZUCHI. Ryo Tanaka. Annot. Zool. Japonenses, vol.25, nos.1-2, pp.279-283, Jan., 1952.

REVISED DETERMINATIONS OF THREE OF THE NATUNA RODENTS. Oldfield Thomas. Novitates Zoologicae, vol.2, pp.26-28, Feb., 1895.

<u>Parasites</u>

LEPTOSPIRAL INFECTION AMONG RODENTS IN MICRONESIA. Joseph E. Alicata. Science, Lancaster, n.s., vol. 105, no.2722, p.236, fig.1, Feb.28, 1947.

A STUDY OF SUCKING LICE (ANOPLURA) ON RODENTS IN UTAH. Ian L. Bell. MS thesis, Univ. Utah, 1950.

A NEW GENUS AND SPECIES OF CHIGGER, CHATIA SETOSA (TROMBICULIDAE,

ACARINA) FROM NORTHWESTERN UNITED STATES. (SQUIRRELS, WHITE-FOOTED MICE, GROUND SQUIRRELS, WOODRATS, WOODCHUCKS.) James M. Brennan. Jour. Parasitology, Lancaster, vol.32, no.2, pp. 132-135, illus., Apr., 1946.

TWO NEW SPECIES OF TROMBICULA: T. MONTANENSIS AND T. APLODONTIAE (ACARINA, TROMBICULIDAE) FROM NORTHWESTERN UNITED STATES. James M. Brennan. Jour. Parasitol., Lancaster, vol.32, no.5, pp.441-444, Oct., 1946.

THE FLEA MALARAEUS TELCHICUM A VECTOR OF P. PESTIS. (FOUND ON RODENTS IN CALIFORNIA.) A. L. Burroughs. Proc. Soc. for Exp. Biol. and Med., 55 (1): 10-11, Jan., 1944.

TRICHURIS SPECIES FROM CALIFORNIA RODENTS. Asa C. Chandler. Jour. Parasitol., Lancaster, vol.31, no.4, pp. 284-286, Aug., 1945.

A STUDY OF RODENT ECTOPARASITES IN MOBILE, ALA. LaMont C. Cold, Jean A. Koepke. Pub. Health Rep. 61 (41): 1469-1487, Oct.11, 1946.

ORNITHODOROS PARKERI, A NEW SPECIES ON RODENTS. R. A. Cooley. Public Health Reports, U.S. Treas. Dept., vol.51, no.15, pp.431-433, pl.1, Apr.10, 1936.

A CONTRIBUTION TO THE KNOWLEDGE OF THE RODENT WARBLE FLIES. Herbert T. Dalmat. Jour. Parasitology, 29 (5): 311-318, Oct., 1943.

ORNITHODOROS PARKERI AND RELAPSING FEVER SPIROCHETES IN SOUTHERN IDAHO. Gordon E. Davis. Pub. Health Rep., 57 (40): 1501-1503, Oct.2, 1942.

A NOTE ON THE GENERA NAMATOSPIROIDES BAYLIS, 1926, AND SINCOSTA ROE, 1929 (NEMATODA, HELIGMOSOMIDAE), WITH DESCRIPTIONS OF TWO NEW SPECIES OF NEMATOSPIROIDES. (FROM RODENTS.) G. Dikmans. Proc. Helminth. Soc. Wash., 7 (2): 79-82, July, 1940.

A CATALOGUE OF THE PROTOZOA AND HELMINTHS OF NORTH AMERICAN RODENTS. I. PROTOZOA AND ACANTHOCEPHALA. David J. Doran. Am. Midl. Nat., 52 (1): 118-128, July, 1954.

A CATALOGUE OF THE PROTOZOA AND HELMINTHS OF NORTH AMERICAN RODENTS. II. CESTODA. David J. Doran. Am. Midl. Nat., 1954, 52 (2): 469-480, Oct., 1954.

A CATALOGUE OF THE PROTOZOA AND HELMINTHS OF NORTH AMERICAN RODENTS. III. NEMATODA. David J. Doran. Am. Midl. Nat., 53 (1): 162-175, Jan., 1955.

A CATALOGUE OF THE PROTOZOA AND HELMINTHS OF NORTH AMERICAN RODENTS. IV. TREMATODA. David J. Doran. Am. Midl. Nat., 53 (2): 446-454, Apr., 1955.

THE HEALTH AND PARASITES OF A WILD MOUSE POPULATION. C. Elton, E. B. Ford, J. R. Baker, A. D. Gardner. Proc. Zool. Soc. Lond., 1931: 657-721, 1931.

ISOLATION OF COCCIDIOIDES FROM SOIL AND RODENTS. C. W. Emmons. U.S. Public Health Service, Public Health Reports, vol.57, no.4, (reprint no.2349), pp.109-111, Jan.23, 1942.

PARASITES OF SOME MINNESOTA CRICETIDAE AND ZAPODIDAE, AND A HOST CATALOGUE OF HELMINTH PARASITES OF NATIVE AMERICAN MICE. Arnold B. Erickson. Amer. Midland Nat., Notre Dame, vol.20, no.3, pp.575-589, Nov., 1938.

PARASITES OF SOME MINNESOTA RODENTS. Arnold B. Erickson. Jour. Mam., 19 (2): 252-253, May, 1938.

OCCURRENCE OF THE ORIENTAL RAT FLEA IN THE INTERIOR OF THE UNITED STATES. H. E. Ewing, Irving Fox. Science, n.s., vol.88, no.2288, p.427, Nov.4, 1938.

ORNITHODOROS PUERTORICENSIS, A NEW TICK FROM RATS IN PUERTO RICO. Irving Fox. Jour. Parasitol., Balto., vol. 33, no.3, pp.253-259, June, 1947.

SIPHONAPTERA FROM WESTERN UNITED STATES. Irving Fox. Jour. Wash. Acad. Sci., 30 (6): 272-276, June, 1940.

NATURAL AMOEBIC INFECTIONS IN LABORATORY RODENTS. J. D. Fulton, L. P. Joyner. Nature, London, vol.161, no.4080, pp.66-68, figs.6, 1948.

STUDIES ON CESTODES OF RODENTS. Merle F. Hansen. PhD thesis, Univ. Nebr., 1948.

THE PARASITES OF SOME NORTH CAROLINA RODENTS. Reinard Harkema. PhD thesis, Duke Univ., 1935; Ecol. Monogr., vol.6, no.2, pp.153-232, Apr., 1936.

DESCRIPTIONS OF NEW ACARI, MAINLY PARASITIC ON RODENTS. Stanley Hirst. Proc. Zool. Soc. Lond., pt.1, pp.49-69, Apr., 1925.

NOTES ON SOME FLEAS FROM RODENTS NESTS IN NEW MEXICO. C. Clayton Hoff, Lelia A. Williams. Jour. Parasitology, Lancaster, vol.35, no.5, pp.545-546, Oct., 1949.

HOST DISTRIBUTION OF LICE ON NATIVE AMERICAN RODENTS NORTH OF MEXICO. William L. Jellison. Jour. Mam., 23 (3): 245-250, Aug., 1942.

OPISODASYS JORDAN 1933, A GENUS OF SIPHONAPTERA. (HOSTS ARE RODENTS.) William L. Jellison. Jour. Parasitology, 25 (5): 413-421, Oct., 1939.

THE PRESENCE OF A PULMONARY FUNGUS IN KOREAN RODENTS. William L. Jellison. Public Health Repts., U.S. Public Health Service, Wash., vol.69, no. 10, pp.996-997, Oct., 1954.

SIPHONAPTERA: THE GENUS OROPSYLLA IN NORTH AMERICA. (PRIMARY PARASITES OF RODENTS.) William L. Jellison. Jour. Parasitology, 31 (2): 83-97, Apr., 1945.

SIPHONAPTERA: NOTES ON TWO CALIFORNIA SPECIES. William L. Jellison. Public Health Reports, U.S. Pub. Health Serv., Washington, D.C., vol.55, no.12, pp.489-492, figs.2, Mar.22, 1940.

A NEW PARASITE OF THE LUNGS IN RODENTS. J. D. Kirschenblatt. Comptes Rendus (Doklady) Acad. Sci. URSS, Moscow, n.s., vol.23, no.4, pp.406-408, figs.2, tables 2, 1939.

A COMPARATIVE STUDY OF THE SUSCEPTIBILITY OF GUINEA PIGS AND HAMSTERS TO AN INFECTION WITH PIG ASCARIS. John E. Larsh, Jr., Margaret S. Gravatt. Jour. Elisha Mitchell Sci. Soc., Chapel Hill, vol.64, no.2, pp.192-195, Dec., 1948.

THE PHYSALOPTERA (NEMATODA) OF RODENTS. Banner Bill Morgan. The Wasmann Collector, San Francisco, vol. 5, no.3, pp.99-107, Apr., 1943.

TWO NEW NEMATODE WORMS FROM RODENTS. Emmett W. Price. Proc. U.S. Nat. Mus., vol.74, art.4, pp.1-5, pls.1-2, 1928.

PARASITIC MITES FROM SNAKES AND RODENTS (ACARINA: CHEYLETIDAE, LISTROPHORIDAE AND LAELAPTIDAE). Charles D. Radford. Proc. Zool. Soc. London, vol.117, pt.1, pp.228-240, figs.16, May 30, 1947.

A NEW NEMATODE, SINCOSTA ABERRANS, NEW GENUS, AND NEW SPECIES FROM A RODENT. Glenwood C. Roe. Proc. U.S. Nat. Mus., vol.75, art.17, pp.1-3, pl.1, 1929.

EPIDEMIOLOGICAL SIGNIFICANCE OF SEASONAL VARIATIONS IN RODENT-ECTOPARASITE DISTRIBUTION. A. S. Rumreich, Jean A. Koepke. Public Health Repts., Wash., vol.60, no.48, pp.1421-1428, illus., Nov.30, 1945.

A STUDY OF THE RODENT-ECTOPARASITE POPULATION OF JACKSONVILLE, FLA. A. S. Rumreich, R. S. Wynn. U.S. Publ. Health Repts., Wash., vol.60, no.31, pp.885-905, illus., Aug.3, 1945.

FOUR NEW SPECIES OF CESTODES OF RODENTS FROM THE HIGH PLAINS, CENTRAL AND SOUTHERN ROCKIES AND NOTES ON CATENOTAENIA DENDRITICA. Charles F. Smith. Jour. Parasit., 40 (3): 245-254, illus., June, 1954.

FATALITIES IN RODENTS CAUSED BY LARVAL ASCARIS IN THE CENTRAL NERVOUS SYSTEM. Jack D. Tiner. Jour. Mam., 34 (2): 153-167, May, 1953.

A PRELIMINARY STUDY OF THE SIPHONAPTEROUS ECTOPARASITES FOUND ON THE MAMMALS OF THE FAMILIES CRICETIDAE AND MURIDAE IN UTAH COUNTY. Vernon J. Tipton. MS thesis, Brigham Young Univ., 1949.

VARIATION IN SOME UNARMED HYMENOLEPIDIDAE (CESTODA) FROM RODENTS. Marietta Voge. U. Calif. Publ. Zool., vol. 57, no.1, 51 pp., illus., 1952.

A STUDY OF FLEAS OF RODENTS IN THE ALBUQUERQUE, NEW MEXICO AREA. Lelia Ann Williams. MS thesis, Univ. N. Mex., 1949.

FLEAS FROM THE UPPER SONORAN ZONE NEAR ALBUQUERQUE, N. MEX. Lelia A. Williams, C. Clayton Hoff. Smithsn. Inst., Proc. U.S. Natl. Mus., 101 (3278): 305-313, 1951.

Pelage, Coloration

CONCEALING COLORATION AMONG SOME DESERT RODENTS OF THE SOUTHWESTERN UNITED STATES. Seth B. Benson. Univ. Calif. Publ. Zool., Berkeley, vol.40, no.1, pp.1-70, figs.8, pls.2, June 13, 1933.

(Review by W. L. McAtee of) CONCEALING COLORATION AMONG SOME DESERT RODENTS OF THE SOUTHWESTERN UNITED STATES. Seth B. Benson. Privately printed, Washington, D.C., 4 pp., Oct., 1934.

RELATION BETWEEN COLOR OF DESERT RODENTS AND OF THE SOIL. Philip M. Blossom. Carnegie Inst. Wash., Yearbook, vol.30, p.266, 1931.

(THE FORMATION OF HAIR PIGMENT ACCORDING TO INVESTIGATIONS OF MICE.) Die Bildung des Haarpigments nach Untersuchungen an Maeusen. H. Henschel. Jena. Zeitschr. f. Naturwiss, vol.64, pp.551-596, 17 figs., 3 pls., May 22, 1930.

DICHROMATISM IN MICHIGAN RODENTS. Richard H. Manville. Jour. Mam., 36 (2): 293, May 26, 1955.

HYBRIDS IN NATURE: A SUPPOSED CROSS BETWEEN A RAT AND GUINEA PIG. R. I. Pocock. Field, London, vol. 153, p.832, May 24, 1929.

(MELANISM IN RODENTS.) Le Melanisme chez les rongeurs. Xavier Raspail. Bull. Mus. d'Histoire Nat., Paris, vol.18, no.5, pp.283-287, 1912.

DESERT AND LAVA-DWELLING MICE, AND THE PROBLEM OF PROTECTIVE COLORATION IN MAMMALS. Francis B. Sumner. Jour. Mam., vol.2, no.2, pp. 75-86, pl.6, May, 1921.

Physiology

MOISTURE-EXCHANGE IN THE SEXUAL CYCLE OF MUS MUSCULUS, MICROTUS ARVALIS AND MERIONES TRISTRAMI. V. E. Alikina. Proc. Lenin Acad. Agr., no.3, pp.44-48, 4 figs., 1949.

HEAT LOSS OF DIFFERENT SPECIES OF RODENTS IN RELATION TO THE CONDUCTION OF THEIR FUR AND THE SIZE OF THEIR BODY AND THEIR RESISTANCE AS REGARDS CLIMATIC FACTORS. V. Babenyscheff. Zool. Jour., Moscow, vol. 17, no.3, pp.540-548, tables 8, 1938.

ECOLOGICAL AND PHYSIOLOGICAL STUDIES ON SOME RODENTS. F. S. Bodenheimer. Physiologia Comparata et Oecologia 1 (3-4): 376-389, Oct., 1949.

THE VITAL LIMIT OF EXSICCATION OF CERTAIN ANIMALS. Frank Gregory Hall. Biol. Bull., vol.42, pp.31-51, Jan., 1922.

(MORPHOLOGY AND PHYSIOLOGY OF THE RODENT APPENDIX.) Zur Morphologie und Physiologie des Blinddarmes der Nagetiere Verhandl. Wilhelm Harder. Deutschen Zoologen in Mainz, 1949 (Zool. Anzeiger, 14 Supplementband), Leipzig, pp.95-109, 1950.

EFFECT OF TEMPERATURE AND WORK ON METABOLISM, BODY TEMPERATURE AND INSULATION: RESULTS WITH MICE. J. S. Hart. Canadian Jour. Zool., Ottawa, vol.30, no.1, pp.83-89, Feb., 1952.

RATE OF GAIN AND LOSS OF COLD RESISTANCE IN MICE. J. S. Hart. Canadian Jour. Zool., Ottawa, vol.31, no. 2, pp.112-116, Apr., 1953.

THE RELATION BETWEEN THERMAL HISTORY AND COLD RESISTANCE IN CERTAIN SPECIES OF RODENTS. J. S. Hart. Canadian Jour. Zool., Ottawa, vol. 31, no.2, pp.80-98, Apr., 1953.

USE OF DAILY METABOLIC PERIODICITIES AS A MEASURE OF THE ENERGY EXPENDED BY VOLUNTARY ACTIVITY OF MICE. J. S. Hart. Canadian Jour. Zool., Ottawa, vol.30, no.1, pp.49-54, Feb., 1952.

(THE THERMOTAXIC OPTIMUM IN RODENTS, A MENDELIAN SPECIES AND RACE CHARACTERISTIC.) Das thermotaktische Optimum bie Nagetieren, ein mendelndes Art- und Rassenmerkmal. K. Herter. Zeits. Vergl. Physiol., 23: 605-650, 1936.

WATER CONSERVATION IN PEROGNATHUS AND PEROMYSCUS. Robert G. Lindeborg. Ecology, Durham, vol.36, no.2, pp.338-339, Apr., 1955.

CERTAIN RODENTS FROM XERIC AND MESIC HABITATS. Robert G. Lindeborg. Contrib. Lab. Vert. Biol., no.58, 1-32 pp., graphs, June, 1952.

ON THE PROPERTIES OF THE GONADS AS CONTROLLERS OF SOMATIC AND PSYCHICAL CHARACTERISTICS. X. SPERMATOZOAN ACTIVITY AND THE TESTIS HORMONE. C. R. Moore. Jour. Exp. Zool., vol.50, no.3, pp.455-494.

A STUDY OF VASECTOMY ON RATS AND GUINEA PIGS. R. Oslund. Amer. Jour. Physiol., vol.67, pp.422-443, 1924.

(NOTE ON THE ESTIVATION AND HIBERNATION OBSERVED IN SEVERAL SPECIES OF RODENTS.) Note sur l'estivation et l'hibernation observees chez plusieurs especes de Rongeurs. F. Petter. Mammalia, Paris, vol.19, no.4, pp.444-446, Dec., 1955.

UREA EXCRETION IN WHITE RATS AND KANGAROO RATS AS INFLUENCED BY EXCITEMENT AND BY DIET. Bodil Schmidt-Nielsen. Amer. Jour. Physiol., Wash., vol.181, no.1, pp.131-139, Apr., 1955.

WATER CONSERVATION IN SMALL DESERT RODENTS. Bodil Schmidt-Nielsen. Biology of deserts, edited by J. L. Cloudsley-Thompson, Inst. of Biol., London, pp.173-181, 1954.

(THE WATER ECONOMY OF DESERT RODENTS.) Orkengnavernes vandusholdning. Bodil Schmidt-Nielsen. Naturens Verden, vol.34, no.1, pp.13-19, illus., 1950.

EVAPORATIVE WATER LOSS IN DESERT RODENTS IN THEIR NATURAL HABITAT. Bodil Schmidt-Nielsen, Knut Schmidt-Nielsen. Ecology, Lancaster, vol.31, no. 1, pp.75-85, illus., Jan., 1950.

PULMONARY WATER LOSS IN DESERT RODENTS. Bodil Schmidt-Nielsen, Knut Schmidt-Nielsen. Jour. Physiol., vol.162, no.1, pp.31-36, July, 1950.

UREA EXCRETION IN DESERT RODENTS EXPOSED TO HIGH PROTEIN DIETS. Bodil Schmidt-Nielsen, Knut Schmidt Nielsen, Adelaide Brokaw. Jour. Cellular and Comp. Physiol., vol.32, no.3, pp.361-379, Dec., 1948.

WATER CONSERVATION IN DESERT RODENTS. Bodil Schmidt-Nielsen, Knut Schmidt-Nielsen, Adelaide Brokaw, Howard Schneiderman. Jour. Cellular and Comp. Physiol., vol.32, no.3, pp.331-360, Dec., 1948.

PHYSIOLOGICAL BASIS OF THE OECOLOGY OF RODENTS. I. Strelnikov. Sbornik VIZR'a, Vsesoiuznii Institut Zashchity Rastenii (Magazin der WISR'a, Inst. f. Pflanzenschutz Lenin Akad. Landwirtschaftlichen Wiss.), Leningrad, no.7, pp.72, 1933.

### Population Dynamics

MOUSE PLAGUES. A MILLION MICE A YEAR FROM ONE PAIR PROVIDE AN EXPLANATION OF MOUSE PLAGUES. Vernon Bailey. Nature Magazine, Wash., D.C., vol.37, no.2, pp.77-79, illus., Feb., 1944.

MOUSE PLAGUES ARE CENTURIES OLD. Vernon Bailey. South Dakota Conserv. Digest, Pierre, vol.11, no.2, pp.2-3, Feb., 1944.

POPULATION DYNAMICS OF RODENTS AND OTHER SMALL MAMMALS. W. Frank Blair. Advances in Genetics, vol.5, pp.1-41, Acad. Press., 1953.

CAN HAWKS PREVENT MOUSE PLAGUES? Allan Brooks. Condor, vol.29, pp.249-250, Sept., 1927.

VOLES, MICE AND LEMMINGS. PROBLEMS IN POPULATION DYNAMICS. Charles Elton. Oxford Univ. Press, London, pp.496, figs.22, 1942.

(Review by W.C. Allee of) VOLES, MICE AND LEMMINGS. PROBLEMS IN POPULATION DYNAMICS. Charles Elton. Sci. Monthly, Lancaster, vol.56, no.6, pp.561-564, June, 1943.

(Review by W.H. Burt of) VOLES, MICE AND LEMMINGS. PROBLEMS IN POPULATION DYNAMICS. Charles Elton. Amer. Nat., Lancaster, vol.76, no.767, pp.611-614, Nov.-Dec., 1942.

(Review by F.C. Evans of ) VOLES, MICE AND LEMMINGS. PROBLEMS IN POPULATION DYNAMICS. Charles Elton. Jour. Wildl. Mgt., Menasha, vol.7, no.2, pp. 238-240, Apr., 1943.

(Review by W.L. Sclater of) VOLES, MICE AND LEMMINGS. PROBLEMS IN POPULATION DYNAMICS. Charles Elton. Geogr. Jour., London, vol.99, nos.5-6, pp.280-281, May-June, 1942.

THE MASS INCREASE OF MOUSE-LIKE RODENTS IN STALINGRAD REGION IN THE AUTUMN OF 1933. B. K. Fenyuk. Rev. Microbiol., Epidemiol. et Parasitol. (Rev. Microbiol.), Saratov, vol.13, no.3, pp.235-247, figs.3, 1934.

THE MASS INCREASE OF MOUSE-LIKE RODENTS IN THE SOUTH-EAST OF THE R.S.F.S.R. IN 1939. B. K. Fenyuk. In Symposium, "Rodents and rodent control," No.1, pp.209-223, from State Inst. Microbiol., 1941.

THE BARN OWL IN ITS RELATION TO THE RODENT POPULATION AT BERKELEY, CALIFORNIA. E. Raymond Hall. Condor, vol.29, pp.274-275, Nov., 1927.

MICE BY THE MILLION. A FARMER'S TRIBULATIONS IN THE WHEAT BELT. Ray Harris. Wild Life, Melbourne, vol. 7, no.1, pp.9-11, illus., Jan., 1945.

MICE AND MEN. Julian Huxley. Harper's Mag., pp.42-50, Dec., 1927.

ON THE CAUSES OF FLUCTUATIONS IN NUMBERS OF MOUSE-LIKE RODENTS. REVIEW OF THE LITERATURE. N. I. Kalabukhov. Zool. Zh., 14 (2): 209-242, 6 figs., 1935.

(PERIODICITY IN THE MASS MIGRATION OF ARCTIC-HIGH BOREAL SMALL RODENTS.) Zur Periodizitaet im Massenwechsel Arktisch-Hohboreales Kleinnager. Olavi Kalea. Soc. Zool. Bot. Fennicae "Vananco.", Helsinki, vol.3, pp.169-178, Nov.30, 1949.

ON THE PERIODICITY IN THE FLUCTUATION OF ARCTIC AND HIGH-BOREAL SMALL RODENTS. Olavi Kalela. Arch. Soc. Zool. "Vanamo" 3: 169-178, illus., 1948.

(SOME DATA ON THE MASS MULTIPLICATION OF RODENTS (FIELD MICE AND MICE) IN THE REGION OF MOSCOW IN 1934.) Quelques donnees sur la multiplication en masse des rongeurs (campagnoles et souris) dans la region de Moscou en 1934. W. A. Kutscheruk, A. Krotov, A. Rjumin, M. Sokolov. Bull. Soc. Nat. Moscow, sec. Biol., n.s., vol.44, nos.7-8, pp.414-427, figs.6, 1935.

NOTES UPON THE NUMBERICAL STATUS OF RODENT POPULATIONS IN PARTS OF CALIFORNIA. Joseph Mailliard. Jour. Mam., vol.6, no.2, pp.102-103, May, 1925.

MOUSE PLAGUES PAST AND FUTURE. Crosbie P. Morrison. Wildlife, Australian Nature Mag., Melbourne, vol.7, no.1, pp. 11-13, illus., Jan., 1945.

QUANTITATIVE STUDIES OF RODENTS IN THE USSR. S. I. Obolenskii. Bull. Plant Protection, vol.4, no.1, pp.85-93, 1931.

THE MOUSE INFESTATION OF BUENA VISTA LAKE BASIN, KERN COUNTY, CALIFORNIA, SEPTEMBER, 1926, TO FEBRUARY, 1927. Stanley E. Piper. Monthly Bull. Dept. Agric., State of California, vol.17, no.10, pp.538-560, illus., Oct., 1928.

THE NEVADA MOUSE PLAGUE OF 1907. Stanley E. Piper. U. S. Dept. Agric., Farmer's Bull., no.352, pp.23, figs.9, Mar.20, 1909.

STUDIES OF THE POPULATION DYNAMICS OF CERTAIN RODENTS OF THE GREAT SALT LAKE DESERT. M. Edwin Rosasco. Symposium on ecology of disease transmission in native animals, Univ. Utah, pp.23-28, 1955.

FACTORS LIMITING THE NUMBER OF MOUSE-LIKE RODENTS. P. A. Sviridenko. Moscou Univ. Sbornik Nauchno issledovatel' skogo inst. Zool. (Abstracts Work Zool. Inst. Moscow State Univ.), no.3, pp.94-96, 1936.

THE INCREASE AND DECREASE OF MOUSE-LIKE RODENTS. P. A. Sviridenko. Moscow Univ. Sbornik Nauchno issledovatel' skogo inst. Zool. (Abstracts Works Zool. Moscow State Univ.), no.3, pp.91-93, 1936.

INCREASE AND DECREASE OF POPULATION OF MOUSE-LIKE RODENTS. P. A. Sviridenko. Trudy po Zashite Rastenii (Bull. Plant Protection, ser.IV, Vertebrates, no.3), Leningrad, pp.5-59, figs.5, 1934.

ON THE ROLE OF HUMAN ACTIVITY UPON THE FLUCTUATION IN NUMBER OF FOREST MOUSE-LIKE RODENTS. P. A. Sviridenko. Zool. Jour. USSR, Moscow, vol.24, no.6, pp.347-360, figs.7, 1945.

STUDY OF THE LAWS GOVERNING MASS INCREASES OF MOUSE-LIKE RODENTS. P. A. Sviridenko. Summ. Res. Inst. Plant Prot., 1935, p.74, 1936.

RANDOM NOTES ON THE FLUCTUATION IN NUMBERS OF RODENTS AND GROUSE IN CANADA. P. A. Taverner. Canadian Field-Nat., vol.43, pp.162-164, Oct.1, 1929.

CONCERNING PECULIARITIES OF SEASONAL DYNAMICS OF MICROPOPULATIONS OF MICE AND VOLES IN THE PERIOD OF REDUCED NUMBERS. S. N. Varshavskii, K. T. Krylova, I. I. Luk'ianchenko. Akad. Nauk SSSR, Comptes Rendus, n.s., vol.61, no.5, pp.957-960, July-Aug., 1948.

MATERIALS FOR THE STUDY OF THE DYNAMICS OF THE FAUNA OF MURIFORM RODENTS IN USSR. (HISTORICAL REVIEW OF FLUCTUATIONS OF MICE IN USSR). B. S. Vinogradov. People's Commisariat Agriculture, Assoc. Pest and Disease Control in USSR Record Service, Leningrad, pp.63, 1934.

(ON THE POPULATION DYNAMICS OF SMALL RODENTS IN THE TROPICS AND ITS CAUSES.) Zur populationsdynamik der kleinnager in den tropen und ihre ursachen. Helmuth O. Wagner. Bonner Zool. Beitr., Heft 1-2, pp.1-12, 1953.

SIDE-LIGHTS ON THE "MOUSE INVASION." L. E. Wyman. Museum Graphic, Los

Angeles, vol.1, no.4, pp.140-142, Mar., 1927.

(SOME CONTRIBUTIONS TO THE MASS DEATH OF SMALL DILUVIAL AND RECENT RODENTS.) Einige Beitraege zum Massentode kleinerer diluvialer und rezenter Nagetiere. J. V. Zelizko. Palaeont. Zeitschr., vol.16, nos.3-4, pp.313-320, Dec.31, 1934.

MILLIONS AND MILLIONS OF MICE. Time, Chicago, vol.40, no.5, p.36, Aug.3, 1942.

Predators

FOOD OF THE BARN OWL AT SODA LAKE, NEVADA. J. R. Alcorn. Condor, Berkeley, vol.44, no.3, pp.128-129, May 15, 1942.

THE FOOD OF THE GREAT HORNED OWL. Allan Brooks. Canadian Field-Nat., vol. 44, no.2, p.50, Feb.1, 1930.

RELATIONSHIP OF PREDATORY MAMMALS AND BIRDS OF PREY TO RODENT LIFE. Leo K. Couch. Jour. Mam., vol. 9, no.1, pp.73-74, Feb., 1928.

FOOD PELLETS OF THE LONG-EARED OWL. C. Blair Coursen. Turtox News, Chicago, vol.6, no.3, p.18, Mar., 1928.

BIRDS OF PREY AND RODENTS. A. Formosov. Zool. Zhurn. (Zool. Jour. USSR), Moscow, vol.13, no.4, pp.664-700, 1934.

(ON THE QUESTION OF THE RELATIONSHIP BETWEEN BIRDS OF PREY AND RODENTS.) Uchenye Zapiski Moskovskogo Gosudarstvennogo Universiteta (Wiss. ber. Moskauer Staats univ.), Zool., vol.13, pp. 71-84, fig.13, tables 1-8, 1937.

MOUSE POPULATIONS IN RELATION TO PREDATION BY FOXES AND HAWKS. William Graf. Murrelet, Seattle, vol.28, no.2, pp.18-21, May-Aug,(Sept.12,), 1947.

THE BULL SNAKE AS A NATURAL ENEMY OF INJURIOUS RODENTS. Frederick L. Hisaw, Howard K. Gloyd. Jour. Mam., vol. 7, no.3, pp.200-205, Aug., 1926.

PLAGUE OF MICE AS FOOD FOR SHORT-EARED OWLS. John K. Terres, E. W. Jameson, Jr. Wilson Bull., Oberlin, vol. 55, no.2, p.131, June, 1943.

Raising in Captivity

AN EFFECTIVE SHIPPING CRATE FOR DESERT RODENTS. Lee W. Arnold. Jour. Wildlife Management, Menasha, vol.7, no.3, pp.345-346, July, 1943.

FEEDING AND BREEDING OF LABORATORY ANIMALS. A COMPLETE CUBED DIET FOR MICE AND RATS. H. M. Bruce, A. S. Parkes. Jour. Hyg., Cambridge, vol.47, no.2, pp.202-208, June, 1949.

RAISING LABORATORY MICE AND RATS. Orson N. Eaton, Charles A. Cabell. U.S. Dept. Agr., Wash., no.253, pp.10, illus., 1949.

DEVICE FOR HOLDING LIVE WILD RATS. John T. Emlen, Jr. Jour. Wildlife Management, Menasha, vol.8, no.3, pp.264-265, fig.1, July, 1944.

(RAISING IN A TERRARIUM SMALL RODENTS DESTINED FOR LABORATORY RESEARCH PROJECTS.) L'élevage, en terrarium, des petits rongeurs destinés aux recherches de laboratoire. P. Rode. Revue d'Histoire Naturelle, Pt.1, A, Mammifères, Paris, vol.11, no.7, pp.209-220, figs.3, July, 1930.

AN IMPROVED FEEDER FOR MICE. H. P. Rusch, V. R. Potter, J. A. Miller. Proc. Soc. Exper. Biol. and Med., Utica, vol.63, no.2, pp.431-432, fig.1, Nov., 1946.

AN INEXPENSIVE MOUSE CAGE. Duane G. Wenzel. Trans. Kansas Acad. Sci., vol. 58, no.3, pp.408-410, Sept.24, 1955.

Reproductive Biology

ON THE RATE OF PROPAGATION IN RODENTS. A. V. Afanassiev. Comptes Rendus (Doklady) Acad. Sci. URSS, Moscow, n.s., vol.35, no.8, pp.258-260, June 30, 1942.

SOME BREEDING NOTES ON RODENTS. Shaler E. Aldous. Jour. Mam., vol.16, no.2, pp.129-131, tables 2, May, 1935.

THE BREEDING-SEASON IN BRITISH WILD MICE. John R. Baker. Proc. Zool. Soc. Lond., no.1, pp.113-126, 1 pl., 9 figs., May 9, 1930.

DELAYED PREGNANCY IN MICE. E. V. Enzmann, N. R. Saphir, Gregory Pincus. Anat. Record, vol.54, no.3, pp.325-338, 1 pl., Nov.25, 1932.

UNUSUAL REPRODUCTIVE PHENOMENA IN RODENTS. Florence L. Evans. Science, 117 (3033): 159-160, Feb.13, 1953.

BREEDING RHYTHMS OF SELANGOR RODENTS. J. L. Harrison. Bull. Raffles Mus., Singapore, no.24, pp.109-131, Aug., 1952.

THE MOONLIGHT EFFECT ON RAT BREEDING. J. L. Harrison. Bull. Raffles Mus., Singapore, no.25, pp.166-170, Dec., 1954.

MASS INCREASE OF MICE IN THE YEAR 1933 IN THE KIEV REGION. P. Kryzhow. Akad. Sci. d'Ukraine, vol.4 (Trav. Mus. Zool. Kyiv, no.13), pp.25-40, figs.3, 1934.

(PERCENTAGE OF YOUNG AND PERIODS OF REPRODUCTION IN SOME RODENTS OF THE BELGIAN CONGO.) Pourcentages de jeunes et periodes de reproduction chez quelques rongeurs du Congo Belge. P. L. Pirlot. Ann. Mus. Royal Congo Belge, Tervuren, n.s., Sci. Zool., vol.1 (Miscellanea Zoologica H. Schouteden), pp.41-46, 1954.

CHARACTER OF THE PROPAGATION OF CERTAIN RODENTS AS A FACTOR OF THEIR NUMBER IN NATURE. G. M. Rall. Comptes Rendus (Doklady) Acad. Sci. URSS, Moscow, vol.4, (13), no.2 (106), pp.93-96, figs.4, 1936.

SPERM SURVIVAL IN RODENTS? Boris B. Rubenstein. Science, vol.118, no.3071, p. 564, Nov.6, 1953.

(NOTE ON THE FERTILITY OF MICROTUS ARVALIS AND APODEMUS SYLVATICUS.) Note sur la fécondité de Microtus arvalis et d'Apodemus sylvaticus. H. Saint-Girons, M. C. Saint-Girons. Mammalia, Paris, vol.16, no.2, pp.96-98, June, 1952.

(ON THE PROPAGATION CYCLE, NUMBER OF YOUNG, AND LONGEVITY OF SOME SMALL RODENTS.) Uber Fortpflanzungsszyklus, Wurfgroesse und Lebensdauer bei einigen kleinen Nagetieren. Georg H. W. Stein. Zeitschrift Schaedlingsbekaemfung, Staufen im Breisgau, Jahrg.42, Heft 5-6, 10 pp., May, 1950.

NOTES ON SUPERFETATION AND DEFERRED FERTILIZATION AMONG MICE. F. B. Sumner. Biol. Bull., vol.30, no.4, pp. 271-285, Apr., 1916.

(POSTPARTUM OESTRUS OF RODENTS.) Der Postpartum-Oestrus der Nagetiere. H. E. Voss. Biologia Generalis, vol.6, no.3, pp.433-456, figs.1-16, 1930.

South America

DESCRIPTIONS OF NEW RODENTS FROM SOUTHERN PATAGONIA, WITH A NOTE ON THE GENUS EUNEOMYS COUES, AND AN ADDENDUM TO ARTICLE (SUPRA, NO. 186) ON SIBERIAN MAMMALS. J. A. Allen. Bull. Amer. Mus. Nat. Hist., vol.19, no. pp.185-196, May 9, 1903.

NEW RODENTS FROM COLOMBIA AND VENEZUELA. J. A. Allen. Bull. Amer. Mus. Nat. Hist., vol.12, pp.195-218, Dec. 20, 1899.

TWO NEW GENERA OF RODENTS FROM SOUTH AMERICA. H. E. Anthony. Amer. Mus. Nov. no.383, pp.1-6, Nov.4, 1929.

WILD RATS AND MICE IN PARAMARIBO. A. B. Droogleever Fortuyn. Uitgave van den Dienst der Volksgezondheid, pp.13, 1945.

NEW RODENT RECORDS FOR CHILE AND FOR TWO CHILEAN PROVINCES. Carl B. Koford. Jour. Mam., 36 (3): 465-466, Aug. 30, 1955.

(PRELIMINARY NOTE ON NEW RODENT GENERA AND SPECIES OF ARGENTINIAN FAUNA.) Nota preliminar sobre nuevos géneros y especies de roedores de la Fauna argentina. Lucas Kraglievich. Rev. Soc. Argentina Cien. Nat., vol.8, pp.591-598, Nov.15, 1927.

(RODENTS OF BRAZIL.) Os roedores do Brasil. João Moojen. Instituto Nacional do Livro, Biblioteca cientifica brasileira, ser. A, 2, Rio de Janeiro, 214 pp., 35 pls., 1952.

A NEW OCTODONT RODENT FROM THE PARAGUAYAN CHACO. Wilfred H. Osgood. Natural History Museum, Chicago, Fieldiana, Zool. vol.31, no.6, Aug.30, 1946.

A NEW RODENT FROM THE GALAPAGOS ISLANDS. Wilfred H. Osgood. Field Mus. Nat. Hist., publ.261, zool. ser.vol.17, no. 2, pp.21-24, July 12, 1929.

NINE NEW SOUTH AMERICAN RODENTS. Wilfred H. Osgood. Zool. Ser. Field Mus. Nat. Hist., Chicago, vol.29, no.13, pp.191-204, July 12, 1944.

TWO NEW RODENTS FROM ARGENTINA. Wilfred H. Osgood. Field Mus. Nat. Hist. Chicago, vol.20, pp.11-14, Dec.11, 1933.

NOTES ON SEVERAL QUADRUPEDS IN MR. DARWIN'S COLLECTION. J. Reid. Proc. Zool. Soc. Lond., pt.5, p.4, 1837.

NOMENCLATURE OF SOUTH AMERICAN HYSTRICOID RODENTS. G. H. H. Tate. Jour. Mam., vol.17, no.2, p.174, May, 1936.

DESCRIPTIONS OF NEW RODENTS FROM THE ORINOCO AND ECUADOR. Oldfield Thomas. Ann. and Mag. Nat. Hist. (7), vol.4, no.23, pp.378-383, Nov., 1899.

DESCRIPTIONS OF NEW RODENTS FROM WESTERN SOUTH AMERICA. Oldfield Thomas. Ann. and Mag. Nat. Hist. (7), vol.6, no.33, pp.293-302, Sept., 1900; no. 34, pp.383-387, Oct., 1900.

DESCRIPTIONS OF TWO NEW ARGENTINE RODENTS. Oldfield Thomas. Ann. and Mag. Nat. Hist. (7), vol.1, no.4, pp.283-286, Apr., 1898.

FOUR NEW SOUTH AMERICAN RODENTS. Oldfield Thomas. Ann. and Mag. Nat. Hist. (8), vol.6, no.35, pp.503-506, Nov., 1910.

NEW HESPEROMYS AND GALEA FROM BOLIVIA. Oldfield Thomas. Ann. and Mag. Nat. Hist. (9), vol.8, no.48, pp.622-624, Dec., 1921.

NEW RODENTS FROM SOUTH AMERICA. Oldfield Thomas. Ann. and Mag. Nat. Hist. (8), vol.8, no.44, pp.250-256, Aug., 1911.

NEW SIGMODON ORYZOMYS, AND ECHIMYS FROM ECUADOR. Oldfield Thomas. Ann. and Mag. Nat. Hist., ser.9, vol.7, pp.448-450, May, 1921.

NEW SOUTH AMERICAN RODENTS. Oldfield Thomas. Ann. and Mag. Nat. Hist. (8), vol.14, no.81, pp.240-244, Sept., 1914.

NEW SPECIES OF OXYMYCTERUS, THRICHOMYS, AND CTENOMYS FROM SOUTH AMERICA. Oldfield Thomas. Ann. and Mag. Nat. Hist. (7), vol.11, no.62, pp. 226-229, Feb., 1903.

NEW SPECIES OF REITHRODON, ABROCOMA, AND SCAPTEROMYS FROM ARGENTINA. Oldfield Thomas. Ann. and Mag. Nat. Hist., ser.9, vol.5, pp.473-478, June, 1920.

NOTES ON SOUTH AMERICAN RODENTS. I. A NEW NAME FOR SCIURUS ROBERTI, THOS. II. ON THE ALLOCATION OF CERTAIN SPECIES HITHERTO REFERRED RESPECTIVELY TO ORYZOMYS, THOMASOMYS, AND RHIPIDOMYS. III. A NEW OECOMYS AND TWO NEW SPECIES OF HOLOCHILUS. Oldfield Thomas. Ann. and Mag. Nat. Hist. (7), vol.18, no.108, pp.442-448, Dec., 1906.

ON A COLLECTION OF RODENTS FROM NORTH PERU. Oldfield Thomas. Proc. Zool. Soc., Lond., pp.98-111, pl.4, Jan. 17, 1882.

ON SOME ARGENTINE MAMMALS. I. TWO NEW RODENTS FROM TUCUMAN PROVINCE. Oldfield Thomas. Ann. and tische Studies. Tycho Fredrik Hugo Tullberg. Druck der Akad. Buchdruckerei, Edv. Berling, Upsala, pp.514, pls.52, 1899.

ON THE STRUCTURE OF THE EXTERNAL GENITALIA IN DIPODIDAE AND ZAPODIDAE (RODENTIA) AS A CLASSIFICATORY CHARACTER. B. S. Vinogradov. Proc. Zool. Soc. Lond., pt.2, pp.577-585, pls.5, July, 1925.

COMMENTS ON THE CLASSIFICATION OF RODENTS. Albert E. Wood. Breviora Mus. Comp. Zool., Cambridge, no.41, pp. 1-9, Dec.17, 1954.

A REVISED CLASSIFICATION OF THE RODENTS. Albert E. Wood. Jour. Mam., vol.36, no.2, pp.165-187, May, 1955.

NEW SPECIES OF DENDROMUS AND TATERA. R. C. Wroughton. Ann. and Mag. Nat. Hist., ser.8, vol.3, pp.246-249, Mar., 1909.

Trapping

(TWO TRAPS FOR CAPTURING SMALL LIVING RODENTS.) Deux pièges pour la capture de petits rongeurs vivants. J. Aubry. Mammalia, Paris, vol.14, no.4, pp.174-177, illus., Dec., 1950.

AN IMPROVED TRAP FOR RODENTS. M. P. Demyashev. Rev. Microbiol., 12 (3): 211-212, 1933.

A MULTIPLE TYPE RAT AND MOUSE HOLDER. Arnold B. Erickson. Jour. Wildlife Management, Menasha, vol.11, no.4, p.351, Oct., 1947.

A NEW LIVE-CATCH RODENT TRAP AND COMPARISON WITH TWO OTHER TRAPS. Robert Holdenried. Jour. Mam., vol.35, no.2, pp.267-268, May 26, 1954.

REDUCTION OF MORTALITY IN LIVE-TRAPPING MICE. Leonard M. Llewellyn. Jour. Wildlife Management, Menasha, vol. 14, no.1, pp.84-85, Jan., 1950.

A MODIFIED RABBIT BOX TRAP FOR USE IN CATCHING LIVE WILD RATS FOR LABORATORY AND FIELD STUDIES. Curt P. Richter, John T. Emlen, Jr. U. S. Public Health Repts., Wash., vol.60, no. 44, pp.1303-1308, Nov.2, 1945.

West Indies

AN EXTINCT OCTODONT FROM THE ISLAND OF PORTO RICO, WEST INDIES. J. A. Allen. Ann. New York Acad. Sci., vol.27, pp.17-22, pls.1-5, Jan.25, 1916.

ON INDIGENOUS MURIDAE IN THE WEST INDIES; WITH THE DESCRIPTION OF A NEW MEXICAN ORYZOMYS. Oldfield Thomas. Ann. and Mag. Nat. Hist. (7), vol.1, no.2, pp.176-180, Feb., 1898.

Mag. Nat. Hist. (9), vol.15, no.89, pp. 582-584, May, 1925.

ON TWO NEW GENERA OF RODENTS FROM THE HIGHLANDS OF BOLIVIA. Oldfield Thomas. Proc. Zool. Soc. Lond., pp.114-117, pls.8-9, Feb.18, 1902.

TWO NEW RODENTS FROM TARTAGAL, SALTA, N. ARGENTINA. Oldfield Thomas. Ann. and Mag. Nat. Hist. (9), vol.4, no.21, pp.154-156, Sept., 1919.

DESCRIPTION OF A NEW RODENT, FROM CENTRAL CHILE. John A. Wolffsohn. Rev. Chile Hist. Nat., Ano 20, pp.6-7, 1916.

(SUMMARY OF THE SYSTEMATICS OF THE ARGENTINIAN RODENTS.) Epítome de la Sistemática de los roedores argentinos. José Yepes. Revista Instituto Bacteriologico, Buenos Aires, vol.7, no.2, pp.213-268, tables, pls.4-15, Nov., 1935.

Taxonomy

GENERIC AND FAMILY NAMES OF RODENTS. J. A. Allen. Amer. Nat., vol.33, pp.70-72, Jan., 1899.

THE GENERIC NAMES ECHIMYS AND LONCHERES. J. A. Allen. Bull. Amer. Mus. Nat. Hist., vol.12, pp.257-264, Dec. 26, 1899.

ON THE CLASSIFICATION OF THE ORDER GLIRES. Edward R. Alston. Proc. Zool. Soc. Lond., pp.61-98, Jan.18, 1876.

THE PHYLOGENETIC SIGNIFICANCE OF RODENT CHEEK POUCHES. Robert B. Chiasson. Jour. Mam., vol.35, no.3, pp. 425-427, Aug.20, 1954.

TAXONOMIC SIGNIFICANCE OF THE CECUM IN GNAWING MAMMALS. Edward D. Crabb, Margaret A. Kelsall. Jour. Colorado-Wyoming Acad. Sci., Denver, vol.3, no.1, pp.44-45, Apr., 1941.

THE USE OF SKULLS IN THE CLASSIFICATION OF COLORADO RODENTS. Elberta Louise Craig. Univ. Colorado Studies, vol.17, no.3, p.206, Dec., 1929.

(SYSTEMATIC STUDY OF THE PENIS BONE IN MAMMALS (CONTINUATION). RODENTS.) Etude systématique de l'os pénien des mammifères. (Suite). Rongeurs. Robert Didier. Mammalia, Paris, vol.16, no.1, pp.7-23, illus., Mar., 1952.

(MEMOIRE ON THE TYPE OF A NEW FAMILY OF THE ORDER OF RODENTS.) Memoire sur le type d'une Nouvelle famille de L'Ordre des rongeurs. Alphonse Milne Edwards. Mem. Nouv. Archiv. du Mus., Paris, vol.3, pp.81-118, pls.6-10, 1867.

ON THE PRIOR NAME FOR THE SIBERIAN LEMMING AND THE GENOTYPE OF GLIS ERXLEBEN. J. R. Ellerman. Ann. and Mag. Nat. Hist., Lond., ser.12, vol.2, no. 23, pp.893-894, Nov.11, 1949.

SIX NEW RODENTS FROM COAHUILA AND TEXAS AND NOTES ON THE STATUS OF SEVERAL DESCRIBED FORMS. E. A. Goldman. Proc. Biol. Soc. Wash., vol.51, pp.55-62, Mar.18, 1938.

(A DETERMINATION OF SOME MICE.) Eine Maeuse-Feststellung. Gerd Heinrich. Zeitschrift f, Saeugetierkunde, vol.8, no.6, p.274, Dec.20, 1933.

FOUR NEW NEOTROPICAL RODENTS. N. Hollister. Proc. Biol. Soc. Wash., vol. 27, pp.57-59, Mar.20, 1914.

THE INTERRELATIONSHIPS OF NEW AND OLD WORLD HYSTRICOMORPH RODENTS. Stuart O. Landry, Jr. Univ. California Publ. Zool., 56 (1): 1-118, pls.1-5, June 27, 1957.

(PARALLELISM IN RODENTS AND THE CLASSIFICATION OF PORCUPINES.) Le parallélisme chez les rongeurs et la classification des porcs-épics. R. Lavocat. Mammalia, Paris, vol.15, nos.1-2, pp.32-38, Mar.-June, 1951.

(REFLECTIONS ON THE CLASSIFICATION OF RODENTS.) Reflexions sur la classification des Rongeurs. R. Lavocat. Mammalia, Paris, vol.20, no.1, pp.49-56, Mar., 1956.'

(SYSTEMATIC SUMMARY OF THE RODENT MAMMALS, GLIRES. Systematisk oefversigt af de Gnagande Daggdjuren, Glires. Wilhelm Lilijeborg. Inbjudnings-Skrift till Morgondagens Philosophiae Doctors-Promotion, Den 31, pp.3-59, chart, May, 1866.

(TWO NEW SPECIES OF RODENTS.) Dos nuevas especies de roedores. Guillermo Mann F. Biológica, Santiago, fasc.1, pp. 95-113, figs.7, pls.12, Sept., 1944.

DESCRIPTIONS OF SIX NEW RODENTS OF THE GENERA APLODONTIA AND THOMOMYS. C. Hart Merriam. Proc. Biol. Soc. Wash., vol.13, pp.19-21, Jan.31, 1899.

SYNOPSIS OF THE SUPERGENERIC GROUPS OF RODENTS. Gerrit S. Miller, Jr., James W. Gidley. Jour. Wash. Acad. Sci., vol.8, pp.431-448, July 19, 1918.

A LIST OF THE GENERIC AND FAMILY NAMES OF RODENTS. T. S. Palmer. Proc. Biol. Soc. Wash., vol.11, pp.241-270, Dec.17, 1897.

(NOTE ON THE SYSTEMATICS OF SOME DESERT RODENTS.) Note sur la systematique de quelques rongeurs desertiques. F. Petter. Proc. International Symposium on Desert Research, Research Council of Israel, Jerusalem, pp.3, 1952.

(THE SYSTEMATICS OF SOME FORMS OF MICE ACCORDING TO E. AND H. SCHWARTZ.) La systematique des formes de la souris d'après E. et H. Schwarz. F. Petter. Mammalia, Paris, vol.18, no.1, pp.124-126, Mar., 1954.

REMARKS ON THE DISTRIBUTION AND CLASSIFICATION OF THE "HYSTRICOMORPHA." Samuel Schaub. Verh. Naturf. Ges. Basel, vol.64, no.2, pp.389-400, Dec.31, 1953.

NEW DATA ON THE SYSTEMATICS OF SOME RODENTS. S. U. Stroganov. Moscou Univ. Sbornik Nauchno-issledovatel' skogo inst. Zool. (Abstracts Works Zool. Inst. Moscow State Univ.), no.3, pp.110-114, 1936.

THE TAXONOMIC HISTORY OF THE SOUTH AND CENTRAL AMERICAN AKODONT RODENT GENERA: THALPOMYS, DELTAMYS, THAPTOMYS, HYPSIMYS, BOLOMYS, CHROEOMYS, ABROTHRIX, SCOTINOMYS, AKODON (CHALCOMYS AND AKODON), MICROXUS, PODOXYMYS, LENOXUS, OXYMYCTERUS, NOTIOMYS, AND BLARINOMYS. G. H. H. Tate. Amer. Mus. Novitates no.582, pp.32, Nov.14, 1932.

THE TAXONOMY OF THE GENERA OF NEOTROPICAL HYSTRICOID RODENTS. G. H. H. Tate. Bull. Amer. Mus. Nat. Hist., vol.68, art.5, pp.295-447, June 12, 1935.

(CATALOG OF RODENTS IN THE COLLECTIONS OF THE MUSEUM OF COIMBRA.) Catalogue des rongeurs existants dans les collections du Muséum de Coimbra. Antonio Armando Themido. Mem. e Est. do Museu Zoologico da Univ. de Coimbra, ser.1, no.20, pp.1-21, 1928.

NEW FORMS OF DENDROMUS, DIPODILLUS, AND GERBILLUS. Oldfield Thomas. Ann. and Mag. Nat. Hist. (9), vol.2, no.7, pp.59-64, July, 1918.

(Review by T.S. Palmer of) ON THE GENERA OF RODENTS: AN ATTEMPT TO BRING UP TO DATE THE CURRENT ARRANGEMENT OF THE ORDER. Oldfield Thomas. Science, Lancaster, n.s., vol.6, no.133, pp.103-197, July 16, 1897.

A SELECTION OF LECTOTYPES OF AMERICAN RODENTS IN THE COLLECTION OF THE BRITISH MUSEUM. Oldfield Thomas. Ann. and Mag. Nat. Hist. (9), vol.19, no.113, pp.545-554, May, 1927.

TYPES IN NATURAL HISTORY AND NOMENCLATURE OF RODENTS. Oldfield Thomas. Science, n.s., vol.6, no.143, pp.485-487, Sept.24, 1897.

(THE SYSTEM OF THE RODENTS. A PHYLOGENETIC STUDY.) Ueber das System der Nagethiere. Eine Phylogene-

Aplodontiidae

COLOR AND DENTAL ABNORMALTIES IN AN APLODONTIA. Sydney Anderson, Robert J. Russell. Trans. Kansas Acad. Sci., 60 (2): 181-182, illus., 1957.

HABITS OF APLODONTIA. H. E. Anthony. Bull. Amer. Mus. Nat. Hist., vol.35, art. 6, pp.53-63, Apr.1, 1916.

EXCAVATIONS OF BURROWS OF THE RODENT APLODONTIA, WITH OBSERVATIONS ON THE HABITS OF THE ANIMAL. Charles L. Camp. Univ. Calif. Publ. Zool., vol.17, no.18, pp.517-536, figs.6, June 22, 1918.

PARTURITION IN APLODONTIA. Howard M. Cramblet, Richard L. Ridenhour. Jour. Mam., 37 (1): 87-90, illus., Feb.28, 1956.

THE SYSTEMATIC STATUS OF THE RACES OF THE MOUNTAIN BEAVER (APLODONTIA RUFA) IN WASHINGTON. Walter W. Dalquest, Victor B. Scheffer. Murrelet, Seattle, vol.26, no.3, pp.35-37, 1 map, 1945.

NOTES ON A CAPTIVE MOUNTAIN BEAVER. Jared J. Davis. Murrelet, Seattle, vol.22, no.3, pp.60-61, Sept.-Dec., 1941.

GEOGRAPHIC VARIATION IN THE RODENT APLODONTIA RUFA. Robert B. Finley, Jr. Murrelet, Seattle, vol.22, no.3, pp.45-49, Sept.-Dec., 1941.

(APLODONTIA ASIATICA SSHL. OF THE PONTIEN OF MONGOLIA.) L'Aplodontia asiatica Sshl. du Pontien de Mongolie. M. Friant. Bull. Mus. Nat. d'Hist. Nat., Paris, ser.2, vol.8, no.1, p.115, Jan., 1936.

(THE CLAIMED GENUS PSEUDAPLODON OF GERRIT S. MILLER (APLODONTIA ASIATICA SCHLOSSER) OF THE PONTIEN OF MONGOLIA.) Le pretendu genre Pseudaplodon de Gerrit S. Miller (Aplodontia asiatica. Schlosser) du Pontien de Mongolie. M. Friant. Ann. and Mag. Nat. Hist., London, ser.10, vol.19, no.112, pp. 456-462, figs.11, Apr., 1937.

THE TYPE SPECIMEN OF APLODONTIA RUFA CALIFORNICA (PETERS). E. Raymond Hall. Murrelet, Seattle, vol.22, no.3, pp.50-51, Sept.-Dec., 1941.

MOUNTAIN BEAVER--BIOLOGICAL CURIOSITY. Emmett Herlocker. Audubon Mag., New York, vol.52, no.6, pp.387-390, illus., Nov.-Dec., 1950.

A NEW MITE, ICHORONYSSUS HUBBARDI, FROM THE MOUNTAIN BEAVER, APLODONTIA RUFA (RAFINESQUE). E. W. Jameson, Jr. Jour. Parasitology, Lancaster, vol.35, no.2, pp.109-115, Apr., 1949.

A NEW MITE, LAELAPS APLODONTIAE, FROM APLODONTIA. W. L. Jellison. Jour. Parasitology 31 (6): 373-374, Dec., 1945.

AN ALBINO MOUNTAIN BEAVER. Stanley G. Jewett. Murrelet, vol.16, no.1, p.18, Jan., 1935.

APLODONTIA CHRYSEOLA, A NEW MOUNTAIN BEAVER FROM THE TRINITY REGION OF NORTHERN CALIFORNIA. Louise Kellogg. Univ. California Publ. Zool., Berkeley, vol.12, no.5, pp.295-296, Apr.15, 1914.

THE MORPHOLOGY OF THE PECTORAL GIRDLE AND ANTERIOR LIMB IN APLODONTIA. Thomas H. Lewis. Jour. Morphol., Phila., vol.85, no.3, pp.533-558, pls.4, Nov., 1949.

OUR MOUNTAIN BEAVER OF THE WEST. J. Alden Loring. Nature Mag., Wash., vol.41, no.7, pp.355-357, 386, illus., Aug.-Sept., 1948.

THE SEWELLEL OR SHOW'TL. S. K. Lum. Amer. Nat., vol.12, no.1, pp.10-13, Jan., 1878.

THE APLODONTOIDEA. Paul O. McGrew. Geol. Ser., Field Mus. Nat. Hist., Chicago, vol.9, no.1, publ.510, pp.30, figs.13, Dec. 5, 1941.

DESCRIPTION OF A NEW SPECIES OF APLODONTIA (APLODONTIA MAJOR, SP. NOV.) FROM CALIFORNIA. C. Hart Merriam. Annals, N. Y. Acad. Sci., vol. 3, no.10, pp.312-328, pls.19-20, tables, May, 1886.

THE GENERA PSEUDAPLODON AND APLODONTIA. Gerrit S. Miller, Jr. Ann. Mag. Nat. Hist., London, ser.10, vol.20, no.120, p.635, Dec., 1937.

APLODONTIA ON SHEPHERD'S CREST. George Petrides, James Huss. Yosemite Nat. Notes, Stockton, vol.19, no.4, pp.31-32, Apr., 1940.

ANIMALS TRAPPED IN MOUNTAIN BEAVER (APLODONTIA RUFA) RUNWAYS, AND THE MOUNTAIN BEAVER IN CAPTIVITY. E. W. Pfeiffer. Jour. Mam., vol.34, no. 3, p.396, Aug.14, 1953.

HORMONALLY INDUCED "MAMMARY HAIRS" OF A PRIMITIVE RODENT APLODONTIA RUFA. E. W. Pfeiffer. Anat. Record, vol.122, no.2, pp.241-255, illus., June, 1955.

THE MALE REPRODUCTIVE TRACT OF A PRIMITIVE RODENT, APLODONTIA RUFA. E. W. Pfeiffer. Anat. Record, Phila., 124, (4): 629-635, Apr., 1956.

THE BOOMER--A WOODLAND TOJO. Arthur Priaulx. American Forests, Wash., D.C., vol.50, no.1, pp.22-23, photos 3, Jan., 1944.

TOJO OF THE TIMBERLANDS. Arthur Priaulx. Outdoorsman, Chicago, vol.86, no.2, whole no.507, pp.12-13, 30, illus., Mar.-Apr., 1944.

MOUNTAIN BEAVERS IN THE PACIFIC NORTHWEST: THEIR HABITS, ECONOMIC STATUS, AND CONTROL. Theo. H. Scheffer. Farmers' Bull.1598, U. S. Dept. Agric., pp.18, figs.13, Aug., 1929.

TREE FARM RAIDER. Jim Stevens. Forestry News, Washington, vol.1, no.4, p.5, Aug., 1946.

EXTENSION OF THE KNOWN RANGE OF THE OLYMPIC MOUNTAIN BEAVER. Arthur Svihla. The Murrelet, vol.11, no. 3, pp.75-76, 1930.

APLODONTIA HUMBOLDTIANA, A NEW MOUNTAIN BEAVER FROM THE HUMBOLDT BAY DISTRICT, CALIFORNIA. Walter P. Taylor. Proc. Biol. Soc. Wash., vol.29, pp.21-24, Feb.24, 1916.

A PREVIOUSLY UNDESCRIBED APLODONTIA FROM THE MIDDLE NORTH COAST OF CALIFORNIA. Walter P. Taylor. Univ. Calif. Publ. Zool., vol.12, no.6, pp.297-300, Apr.15, 1914.

REVISION OF THE RODENT GENUS APLODONTIA. Walter P. Taylor. Univ. Calif. Publ. Zool., vol.17, no.16, pp.435-504, figs.16, pls.25-29, May 29, 1918.

TWO NEW APLODONTIAS FROM WESTERN NORTH AMERICA. Walter P. Taylor. Univ. Calif. Publ. Zool., vol.12, no.16, pp.497-501, May 6, 1916.

## Sciuridae

THE AMERICAN CHIPMUNK. Charles C. Abbott. Pop. Sci. Monthly, vol.7, pp.433-436, figs.2, Aug., 1875.

NOTES ON THE COMMON WOODCHUCK. Jacob B. Abbott. Pennsylvania Game News, Harrisburg, vol.15, no.2, pp.6-7, 29, illus., May, 1944.

BIOGRAPHY OF A WHISTLEPIG--THE ANIMAL THAT IS SUPPOSED TO LOOK FOR HIS SHADOW ON GROUNDHOG DAY WAS A CURIOUS PET AND ONE THAT REQUIRED NO CARE WHILE HE HIBERNATED IN THE HOME. Roy L. Abbott. Natural History, New York, vol.43, no.2, pp.112-116, photo, Feb., 1939.

LIFE HISTORY NOTES ON THE PIUTE GROUND SQUIRREL. J. R. Alcorn. Jour. Mam., 21 (2): 160-170, May, 1940.

CHIPMUNK SECRETS. Elsa G. Allen. Animal Kingdom, New York Zool. Soc., vol.46, no.6, pp.133-140, illus., Nov.-Dec., 1943.

THE HABITS AND LIFE HISTORY OF THE EASTERN CHIPMUNK, TAMIAS STRIATUS LYSTERI. Elsa G. Allen. N. Y. State Mus., Bul.314, pp.122, Sept., 1938.

ON THE SQUIRRELS OF THE NEOTROPICAL REGION. Edward R. Alston. Proc. Zool. Soc. Lond., pp.656-670, pl.29, 1878.

SUPPLEMENTARY NOTE ON THE NEOTROPICAL SQUIRRELS. Edward R. Alston. Proc. Zool. Soc. Lond., p.954, 1878.

THE GRAY SQUIRREL. Rod Amundson. Wildlife in North Carolina, Raleigh, vol.13, no.3, pp.4-6, 16, 21, illus., Mar., 1949.

THE GROUNDHOG. Rod Amundson. Wildlife in North Carolina, Raleigh, vol. 14, no.2, pp.4-7, illus., Feb., 1950.

CHEERFUL CHIPMUNK. Elizabeth Bachmann. Cons. Volunteer, 10 (61): 18-21, Nov.-Dec., 1947; South Dakota Conserv. Digest, Pierre, vol.15, no.11, pp.2, 14, 16, Nov., 1948.

GLAMOROUS 'GOPHER.' (GROUND SQUIRREL.) Elizabeth Bachmann. Volunteer, St. Paul, vol.12, no.68, pp.10-13, Jan.-Feb., 1949.

WHISTLING WOODCHUCK. Elizabeth Bachmann. Conserv. Volunteer, St. Paul, vol.11, no.60, pp.31-35, illus., Jan.-Feb., 1948.

THE FLAG SQUIRREL. Vernon Bailey. Native Life (Bismarck, N.D.), vol.2, no.1, pp.7-8, Mar., 1922.

GRAY SQUIRRELS. Vernon Bailey. Frontiers, Phila., vol.5, no.1, pp.13-15, illus. , Oct., 1940.

THE HOARY MARMOT, OR GREAT GRAY WHISTLER. Vernon Bailey. National Parks Bull., no.53, pp.9-11, illus., July, 1927.

LITTLE FLYING SQUIRREL (GLAUCOMYS VOLANS VOLANS). N. R. Barger. Wisconsin Conserv. Bull., Madison, vol.12, no. 4, pp.28-29, illus., Apr., 1947.

NORTHERN GRAY SQUIRREL (SCIURUS CAROLINENSIS LEUCOTIS). N. R. Barger. Wisconsin Conserv. Bull., Madison, vol. 15, no.3, pp.38-39, illus., Mar., 1950.

RUFESCENT WOODCHUCK (MARMOTA MONAX RUFESCENS). N. R. Barger. Wisconsin Conserv. Bull., Madison, vol. 14, no.12, pp.26-27, illus., Dec., 1949.

THIRTEEN-LINED GROUND SQUIRREL (STRIPED GOPHER) CITELLUS T. TRIDECEMLINEATUS. N. R. Barger. Wisconsin Conserv. Bull., Madison, vol.14, no.2, pp.31-32, illus., Feb., 1949.

WESTERN FOX SQUIRREL (SCIURUS NIGER RUFIVENTER). N. R. Barger. Wisconsin Conserv. Bull., Madison, vol.15, no.9, pp. 33-34, illus., Sept., 1950.

THE GRAY SQUIRREL IN MELBOURNE. Charles Barrett. Victorian Nat., vol.51, no.4, pp.108-110, pl.21, Aug., 1934.

THE GREY SQUIRREL. James Bartholomew. Glasgow Nat., vol.11, pp.34-45, Apr., 1933.

A THREE-YEAR RECORD OF GROUND SQUIRREL TRAPPING. E. M. Becker. Calif. Dept. Agr. Bull., 29 (3): 153-156, 1940.

(THE GREY SQUIRREL.) L'ecureuil gris. Harry Bernard. Soc. Canadienne d'Hist. Nat., Bibliothèque des Jeunes Naturalistes, Montreal, tract 33, pp.4, fig.1, Apr.26, 1937.

INTERESTING FACTS ABOUT THE FLYING SQUIRREL. Jack H. Berryman. Utah Game and Fish Bull. Salt Lake City, vol.9, no.4, p.2, Sept., 1950.

INTERESTING FACTS ABOUT THE TOWNSEND GROUND SQUIRREL. Jack H. Berryman. Utah Fish and Game Bull., Salt Lake City, vol.7, no.12, p.6, Mar., 1950.

THE THIRTEEN-LINED GROUND SQUIRREL. Jack H. Berryman. Utah Fish and Game Bull., Salt Lake City, vol.8, no.1, p.8, Apr.-May, 1950.

AN EYE FOR SQUIRRELS. R. M. Blackman. Outdoorsman, Chicago, vol.86, no.5, whole no.510, pp.10-11, 35-36, Sept.-Oct., 1944.

(ON SPERMOPHILUS RUFESCENS KEYS. AND BLAS., THE ORENBURG GROUND SQUIRREL, PARTICULARLY ITS CHARACTERS, LIVING HABITS, BONE STRUCTURE, AND FOSSIL OCCURRENCE.) Ueber Spermophilus rufescens Keys. u. Blas., den Orenburger Ziesel, besonders dessen Eigenschaften, Lebensweise, Knochenbau und fossile Vorkommisse. Wilhelm Blasius. Ver. f. Naturw. z. Braunschweig, III, Jahresber, f. 1881/82 u. 1882/1883, pp.126-149.

GOPHERS. Paul N. Blide. Conserv. Volunteer, St. Paul, vol.7, no.41, p.47, July-Aug., 1944.

MY FRIEND, MR. CHIPMUNK. Gladys E. Blum. Audubon Mag., New York, vol.52, no.4, pp.234-237, 247, illus., July-Aug., 1950.

NOTES ON THE LIFE HISTORY OF THE FLYING SQUIRREL. Ernest S. Booth. Jour. Mam., vol.27, no.1, pp.28-30, Mar. 14, 1946.

(THE CRY OF THE MARMOT AS THE ACOUSTIC MARK OF A TERRITORY.) Der Schrei des Murmeltiers als akustische Territoriumsmarkierung. P. Bopp. Saeugetierk. Mitteil., Stuttgart, 3 (1): 28, Jan.1, 1955.

(WITH THE MARMOTS.) Bei den Murmeln. Aladàr von Boroviczény. Naturforscher, vol.10, no.4, pp.133-137, figs.4, July, 1933.

THE GAME SQUIRRELS--FOX, GRAY, AND BLACK. G. W. Bradt. Michigan Conserv., Lansing, vol.16, no.9, pp.4-5, illus., Oct., 1947.

THE LESSER SQUIRRELS. G. W. Bradt. Michigan Conserv., Lansing, vol.17, no.3, pp.4-5, illus., Mar., 1948.

THE WOODCHUCK--PROFESSIONAL EXCAVATOR. G. W. Bradt. Mich. Cons., 15 (5): 6-7, June, 1946.

LIFE HISTORY, BEHAVIOR, AND POPULATIONS OF THE WESTERN CHIPMUNK, EUTAMIAS AMOENUS AFFINIS (ALLEN). Harold E. Broadbooks. PhD thesis, Univ. Mich., 1950.

"PINTO" GROUND SQUIRRELS. C. Frank Brockman. Yosemite Nature Notes, vol.24, no.11, pp.111-112, Nov., 1945.

MARMOTS ARE DISAPPEARING. H. C. Bryant. Yosemite Nature Notes, vol.8, p. 94, Oct., 1929.

STUDYING PRAIRIEDOGS. Maurice Burton. Illus. London News, vol.137, no.3569, p. 490, illus., Sept.17, 1955.

(THE EMIGRATION OF YOUNG PIGMY SVSLIKS (CITELLUS PYGMAEUS) AS A CAUSE OF PEST EPIZOOTICS.) Die Auswanderung der jungen Zieselmaeusen (Citellus pygmaeus) Pallas. als Ursache der Pestepizootien. N. Calabuchow. Ber. Mikrobiol. Staats-Instituts. Rostow-am-Don, no.9, p.165, 1929.

FAMOUS GLIDERS. (FLYING SQUIRREL) Jewell Casey. Our Dumb Animals, Boston, vol.84, no.5, p.5, illus., May, 1951.

FOX SQUIRRELS AND GRAY SQUIRRELS. Floyd B. Chapman. Ohio Div. Cons., Bull. 127, 4 pp., July, 1936.

(NOTES ON THE SQUIRREL.) Notes sur l'ecureuil. Albert Chappellier. Bull. Soc. Nat. Acclimat. de France, Paris, vol.86, nos.3-4, pp.88-101, Apr., 1939.

(FOOD OF THE GROUND SQUIRREL (CITELLUS PYGMAEUS AND CITELLUS FULVUS) IN THE NATURAL CONDITIONS OF WESTERN KAZAKHSTAN.) Ernaehrung der Ziesel (Citellus pygmaeus und Citellus fulvus) in natuerlichen Bedingungen des Westlichen Kasakstan. I. Chudjakow, A. Fursajew, A. Kostina, E. Michajlowa. Revue de Mikrobiol., Épidem. et Parasitol. Saratov, vol.12, no.1, pp.63-74, 1933.

PRAIRIE DOGS. Kennedy N. Clapp. Natl. Park Serv., Region Three Quart., 3 (2): 21-25, Apr., 1941.

SOME NOTES ON HOARDING AND TERRITORIAL BEHAVIOR OF THE RED SQUIRREL, SCIURUS HUDSONICUS (ERXLEBEN). C. H. D. Clarke. Can. Field-Nat., 53 (3): 42-43, Mar., 1939.

CHICKAREE. H. F. Cofer. Yosemite Nat. Notes, Yosemite, vol.21, no.12, p. 103, Dec., 1942.

FLYING SQUIRREL. H. F. Cofer. Yosemite Nat. Notes, Yosemite, vol.21, no.11, p.91, Nov., 1942.

MEASURES OF PRODUCTIVITY IN THE FOX AND GRAY SQUIRREL AND A STUDY OF MOULTS IN FOX SQUIRRELS. Wayne F. Colin. MA thesis, Univ. Mo., 1949.

YOUR NEIGHBOR THE WOODCHUCK. David B. Cook. Audubon Mag., 47 (4): 201-206, July-Aug., 1945.

SQUIRRELS. Fannye A. Cook. Mississippi Game and Fish, Jackson, vol.10, no.4, pp.1,2, Oct., 1946.

NOTES ON THE PALLID YELLOW-BELLIED MARMOT. Leo King Couch. Murrelet, vol.11, no.2, pp.3-6, illus., May, 1930.

NOTES ON THE MEARNS FLYING SQUIRREL. A. F. Coventry. Canadian Field-Nat., vol.46, no.4, pp.75-78, figs.5, Apr., 1932.

THE RED SQUIRREL. William E. Cram. Jour. Mam., vol.5, no.1, pp.37-41, Feb., 1924.

THE TRUE MOUNTAINEER. (MARMOT) Lois Crisler. Nat. Hist., New York, vol. 59, no.9, pp.422-428, illus., Nov., 1950.

THE GRAY SQUIRREL. R. H. Cross. Va. Wildl., 7 (2): 14, 20, Aug., 1946.

NOTES ON THE GRAY EASTERN CHIPMUNK. David Damon. Jour. Mam., vol. 22, no.3, pp.326-327, Aug.14, 1941.

(CONTRIBUTION TO THE STUDY OF SCIURUS FEIGNOUXI POMEL.) Contribution à l'étude de Sciurus feignouxi Pomel. Colette Dechaseaux. Mammalia, Paris, vol.10, nos.3-4, pp.129-139, pl.1, Sept.-Dec., 1946 (issued in 1947).

THE WORLD OF A CHIPMUNK. Alan Devoe. Audubon Mag., New York, vol.44, no.4, pp.206-212, illus., July-Aug., 1942.

DWELLER OF THE ARID MOUNTAINS. Lee R. Dice. Nature Magazine, Wash., D.C., vol.32, no.10, pp.558-560, Dec., 1939.

THE FLYING SQUIRREL. Stuart C. Downing. Canadian Nature, Toronto, vol. 10, no.2, p.63, illus., Mar.-Apr., 1948.

THE MARMOT. Stuart Downing. Canadian Nature, Toronto, vol.8, no.4, pp.138-140, illus., Sept.-Oct., 1946.

HOW MUCH WOOD COULD A . . .? (WOODCHUCK) Eddy Dressen. Sports Afield, Minneapolis, vol.119, no.3, pp. 52-53, 112-113, Mar., 1948.

ANOTHER SQUIRREL FRIEND. A. D. DuBois. Nature Mag., vol.6, pp.281-282, 2 figs., Nov., 1925.

CHIPMUNK FRIENDS. Gertrude Emerson. Country Life, vol.36, no.5, pp.104-108, Sept., 1919.

SQUIRREL OF THE GOLDEN FOREST. Irene Finley. Nature Mag., Washington, D.C., vol.36, no.5, pp.263-264, illus., May, 1943.

THE FLYING SQUIRREL. W. L. Finley, Irene Finley. Outdoor America, Madison, vol.7, no.9, pp.4-5, Sept., 1942.

THE RED SQUIRREL: TERRITORIALISM, ACTIVITY, CENSUS METHODS. W. D. Fitzwater, Jr. MS thesis, Syracuse Univ., 1941.

(MARMOTS.) Murmeltiere. W. Flaig, E. Meerkamper, B. Schocher. Naturforscher, Jahrg.14, Heft 4, pp.110-115, 5 figs., 1 pl., July, 1937.

A BIBLIOGRAPHY OF THE TREE SQUIRRELS AND OTHER PERTINENT LITERATURE. Vagn F. Flyger. Pa. Coop. Wildl. Res. Unit, Quart. Rep., 13 (4): 19-38, Apr.-June, 1951.

GRAY AND RED SQUIRRELS. George W. Friedrich. Conservation Volunteer, St. Paul, vol.5, no.28, pp.9-10, Jan., 1943.

ANIMAL GLIDERS. (POPULAR ACCOUNT OF FLYING SQUIRREL.) Arthur B. Fuller. The Explorer, Cleveland, no.77, pp.6-7, Jan., 1944.

THE KAIBAB OR WHITE-TAILED SQUIRREL. E. A. Goldman. Jour. Mam., vol.9, no.2, pp.127-129, pl.16, May, 1928.

"NUTCRACKER SUITE." (SQUIRRELS.) Monroe H. Goode. Sports Afield, Minneapolis, vol.112, no.4, pp.30-31, 74-77-79, illus., Oct., 1944.

THE NATURAL HISTORY AND BEHAVIOR OF THE WESTERN CHIPMUNK AND THE MANTLED GROUND SQUIRREL. Kenneth Gordon. Oregon State Coll., Studies in Zool.5, pp.104, 1943.

A MERRY LITTLE FELLOW IS THAT CREATURE--THE LOVABLE CHIPMUNK. Henry H. Graham. Our Dumb Animals, Norwood, vol.80, no.8, p.7, Aug., 1947.

SLEEPY CALLIOPE. Burt Gresham. Canadian Nature, Toronto, vol.2, no.3, pp.22-23, illus., May-June, 1940.

THOSE PESKY PRAIRIE DOGS. Fred M. Griffin. New Mexico Mag., Santa Fe, vol. 18, no.10, pp.32-33, Oct., 1940.

LIFE HISTORY, ECOLOGY, AND MANAGEMENT OF THE SOUTHERN WOODCHUCK. Roy A. Grizzell, Jr. PhD thesis, Univ. Mich., 1951.

A STUDY OF THE SOUTHERN WOODCHUCK, MARMOTA MONAX MONAX. Roy A. Grizzell, Jr. Am. Midl. Nat., 53 (2): 257-293, illus., Apr., 1955.

CHIPMUNK. W. J. Hamilton, Jr. New York State Conservationist, Albany, vol. 4, no.1, p.14, illus., Aug.-Sept., 1949.

THE LIFE HISTORY OF THE RUFESCENT WOODCHUCK MARMOTA MONAX RUFESCENS. W. J. Hamilton, Jr. Ann. Carnegie Mus., 23:85-178, 1934.

THE WAYS OF CHIPMUNKS. Francis Harper. Bull. Boston Soc. Nat. Hist., no. 43, pp.3-9, Apr., 1927.

A NOTE ON THE GREY SQUIRREL. T. H. Harrisson. Field, London, vol.153, p.228, Feb.7, 1929.

LIFE HISTORY AND MANAGEMENT OF THE FOX SQUIRRELS, WITH PARTICULAR REFERENCE TO THE WESTERN RACE, SCIURUS NIGER RUFIVENTER (GEOFFROY). George P. Hartman. MS thesis, Univ. Mich., 1940.

NOTES ON THE GROUND-SQUIRREL, CALLOSPERMOPHILUS. Robert T. Hatt. Univ. Michigan, Occ. Papers Mus. Zool., no.185, 22 pp., 1 pl., 2 figs., June 29, 1927.

FOX AND GRAY SQUIRRELS. Ed Hibbard. N. Dak. Outdoors, 17 (1): 4-5, maps, July, 1954.

NOTES ON LAYARD'S FLYING SQUIRREL (PETINOMYS LAYARDI). W. C. Osman Hill. Loris, Ceylon, vol.2, no.2, pp.121-122, illus., June, 1940.

(ON THE SQUIRREL SHREW.) Ueber das Spitzhoernchen. H. Hofer. Natur und Volk, 85 (5): 145-155, May, 1957.

MAC--THE FLYING SQUIRREL. Elizabeth Ingles. Nature Mag., vol.30, no.4, p.229, illus., Oct., 1937.

THE PRAIRIE DOG, PICKET OF THE PLAINS. Hartley H. T. Jackson. Home Geogr. Monthly, vol.2, no.2, pp.19-24, figs.8, Aug., 1932.

THE RED SQUIRREL, CHATTERER OF THE SPRUCES. Hartley H. T. Jackson. Home Geogr. Monthly, vol.2, no.3, pp. 19-24, illus., Sept., 1932.

THE STRIPED GROUND SQUIRREL, CHIRPER OF THE PRAIRIES. Hartley H. T. Jackson. Home Geogr. Monthly, vol. 2, no.5, pp.19-24, figs.8, Nov., 1932.

SQUIRRELS. David H. Jenkins. Michigan Conservation, Lansing, vol.20, no.3, pp. 21-24, May-June, 1951.

NOTES ON A POPULATION OF EASTERN FLYING SQUIRRELS. James S. Jordan. Jour. Mam., 37 (2): 294-295, June 9, 1956.

THE BOMBING SQUIRREL. Phyllis Kelway. Game and Gun and the Angler's Monthly, London, vol.18, no.186, pp.102-104, illus., Mar., 1941.

THE GREY SQUIRREL. Phyllis Kelway. Game and Gun and the Angler's Monthly, 16 (162): 159-162, Mar., 1939.

"GRUNTS"--THE AMAZING STORY OF AN ALTOGETHER AMAZING SQUIRREL. Julie Closson Kenly. Nature Mag., vol.23, no.3, pp.111-114, 146, illus., Mar., 1934.

SQUIRREL RESEARCH. Joseph B. Kidd. La. Cons., 8 (2): 10-11, 21-22, illus., Nov., 1955.

MY ACQUAINTANCE WITH PICKET PINS. (BRIEF NOTES ON BELDING GROUND-SQUIRREL.) Ruth H. Kirkland. Yosemite Nature Notes, vol.6, p.68, illus., Sept., 1927.

MARMOTA. THE LITTLE SENTINEL OF THE HIGH COUNTRY. (NOTES ON THE NATURAL HISTORY OF MARMOTA OLYM-

PUS.) E. A. Kitchin. Privately printed, Port Angeles, Washington, pp.20, illus., Nov.1, 1942.

THE FLYING SQUIRREL. A. Brooker Klugh. Nature Mag., vol.3, pp.205-207, 5 figs., Apr., 1924.

WANTED--DATA ON THE RED SQUIRREL. A. Brooker Klugh. Jour. Mam., vol.3, no. 2, p.118, May, 1922.

(PRELIMINARY NOTE ON THE GENUS SCIUROIDES FORSYTH MAJOR.) Note préliminaire sur le genre Sciuroides Forsyth Major. R. Lavocat. Bull. Mus. Nat. Hist. Nat., Paris, ser.2, vol.18, no. 1, pp.130-131, Jan., 1946.

MAMMAL TRACKS. CHIPMUNK, GROUND SQUIRREL. Helen Lawson, Bill Lawson. Ohio Conserv. Bull., Columbus, vol.14, no.10, pp.15, 31-32, illus., Oct., 1950.

MAMMAL TRACKS. SQUIRRELS. Helen Lawson, Bill Lawson. Ohio Conserv. Bull., Columbus, vol.14, no.9, pp.8-9, illus., Sept., 1950.

BUSHY TAIL. (SQUIRREL.) E. Lee LeCompte. Maryland Conservationist, Baltimore, vol.19, no.4, pp.8-9, illus., Fall, 1942.

(OBSERVATIONS ON NORTH AMERICAN FLYING SQUIRRELS SCIUROPTERUS (GLAUCOMYS) VOLANS (THOMAS).) Beobachtungen an Nordamerikanischen Gleitflughoernchen Sciuropterus (Glaucomys) Volans (Thomas). Wolfgang Luther. Z. Tierpsych., 9 (2): 402-411, 1952.

THE ZUNI PRAIRIE DOG. S. C. McCampbell, W. L. Burnett. Colo. Agric. Coll. Cir.49, pp.3-15, Jan., 1926.

CALLING ON THE KAIBAB SQUIRREL. Eugene S. McCartney. Nature Mag., vol. 29, no.5, pp.271-272, illus., May, 1937.

NOTES ON THE WESTERN FOX SQUIRREL. H. Elliott McClure. Nature Notes, Peoria, Ill., vol.7, no.6, pp.159-161, figs.2, June, 1940.

A TALE OF A WOODCHUCK. C. H. McDonald. Amer. Forests and Forest Life, vol.34, pp.46-47, illus., Jan., 1928.

NOTE ON A RED SQUIRREL. Mark G. McElhinney. Canadian Field-Nat., vol.37, p.77, Apr., 1923.

A WOODCHUCK TALE. Tom McHugh. Explorer, Cleveland Mus. Bull., no.78, pp.4-5, Apr., 1944.

THE "PANDA BEAR" OF THE SQUIRREL WORLD. (FLYING SQUIRREL.) Robert N. McIntyre. Yosemite Nat. Notes, vol.29, no.4, pp.36-41, illus., Apr., 1950.

NOTES ON BERDMORE'S SQUIRREL (MENETES BERDMOREI). J. M. D. Mackenzie. Jour. Bombay Nat. Hist. Soc., vol.33, no.4, pp.980-981, Oct.15, 1929.

CHERBU OF ANIMAL KINGDOM: FLYING SQUIRRELS. Roberts Mann. Texas Game and Fish, Austin, vol.7, no.5, p.16, Apr.1.

FLYING SQUIRRELS. Roberts Mann. Iowa Conservationist, Des Moines, vol.8, no.2, pp.105-110, Feb.15, 1949.

THE STORY OF WOOLLY, A FLYING SQUIRREL. Karl H. Maslowski. Nature Mag., Washington, D.C., vol.32, no.8, pp.441-444, illus., Oct., 1939.

ON SOME MIOCENE SQUIRRELS, WITH REMARKS ON THE DENTITION AND CLASSIFICATION OF THE SCIURINAE. C. J. Forsyth Major. Proc. Zool. Soc. Lond., pp.179-215, 1893.

A PRELIMINARY STUDY OF THE BARROW GROUND SQUIRREL, CITELLUS PARRYI BARROWENSIS. William V. Mayer. Jour. Mam., 34 (3): 334-345, illus., Aug., 1953.

GOLDEN-MANTLED GROUND SQUIRREL--A LATE RISER. Enid Michael. Yosemite Nat. Notes, Yosemite, vol.19, no.7, p.50, July, 1940.

THE GREY SQUIRREL. A. D. Middleton. Bird Notes and News, Lond., vol.14, no.5, pp.114-115, 1931.

NOTES ON FLYING SQUIRREL (PETAURISTA SP.). F. C. Minett. Jour. Bombay Nat. Hist. Soc., vol.47, no.1, pp.52-56, figs.2, Aug., 1947.

THE SQUIRREL. C. H. Moffat. Irish Naturalists' Jour., vol.1, no.13, pp.250-252, 1 pl., Sept., 1927.

(GROUND SQUIRRELS OF THREE TYPES.) Ziesel von dreierlei Art. Erna Mohr. Mitteil. Zool. Garten, Leipzig, N.F., 1944/45, no.6, pp.14-18, figs.3, 1945.

(MY TWO SUSLIKS (CITELLUS CITELLUS L.).) Meine beiden Ziesel (Citellus Citellus L.). Erna Mohr. Zool. Garten, vol.1, pp.307-313, illus., 1929.

THE NATURAL HISTORY OF THE FOX SQUIRREL, SCIURUS NIGER SHERMANI. Joseph Curtis Moore. Bull. Amer. Mus. Nat. Hist., 113 (1): 1-71, pls.1-3, Aug.26, 1957.

WHAT IS THE RED SQUIRREL? H. W. Mossman. Trans. Wisconsin Acad. Sci. Arts and Letters, Madison, vol.32, pp.123-134, fig.1, pls.1-2, 1940.

CHIPMUNKS AND GEOGRAPHY. Philip N. Moulthrop. Explorer, Bull. Cleveland Mus. Nat. Hist., no.74, p.5, Spring, 1943.

GREY SQUIRRELS. Walter J. C. Murray. Canadian Nature, Toronto, vol.5, no.3, pp. 104-105, illus., May-June, 1944.

THE THIN-TOED GROUND SQUIRREL (SPERMOPHILOPSIS LEPTODACTYLUS LICHT.). (IN THE THIN-TOED GROUND SQUIRREL, THE FAT DORMOUSE, THE MOLE-RAT, AND THE CHIPMUNK.) S. P. Naumov, N. P. Lavrov, E. P. Spangenberg. All-Union Cooperative Assn. Publ. House, Moscow and Leningrad, pp.36-70, 1935.

IS THE GRAY SQUIRREL DISAPPEARING? Edwin A. Osborne. Nature Mag., vol.2, pp.122-123, 1 fig., Aug., 1923.

NATURE NOTELETS. (GRAY SQUIRREL, CHICKAREE.) H. C. Parker. Yosemite Nat. Notes, Yosemite, vol.26, no.6, p.80, June, 1947.

A WILDLIFE PAGEANT. (CHIPMUNKS.) Lloyd P. Parratt. Yosemite Nat. Notes, Yosemite, vol.21, no.8, p.72, Aug., 1942.

THE FLYING SQUIRREL. George H. Perkins. Amer. Nat., Boston, vol.7, no.3, pp.132-139, Mar., 1873.

GOLDEN-MANTLED MARMOT, WESTERN WOODCHUCK. Gayle Pickwell. Nature Mag., Washington, vol.41, no.6, pp.301-302, June-July, 1948.

OUR WILD NEIGHBORS: THE CHIPMUNK. Earl L. Poole. Pennsylvania Game News, vol.9, no.3, p.32, illus., June, 1938.

WOODCHUCK LEGACY. Bert Popowski. Field and Stream, New York, vol.51, no.3, pp.18-19, 95-96, illus., July, 1946.

(THE OCCURRENCE OF ASYMMETRIC ARRANGEMENT OF THE MAMMAE IN THE CALIFORNIA GROUND SQUIRREL (CITELLUS BEECHEYI RICHARDSON, 1829.) Das Vorkommen von asymetrischer Anordnung der Brustwarzen beim kalifornischen Erdhoernchen, Citellus beecheyi (Richardson, 1829). W. Prychodko. Saeugetierk. Mitteil., 5 (4): 168-169, Dec.1, 1957.

(NEW DATA ON THE MARMOT, MARMOTA M. MARMOTA LINNÉ, 1758.) Neues vom Murmeltier, Marmota m. marmota (Linné, 1758). Hans Psenner. Saeugetierk, Mitteil., 5 (1): 4-10, Jan.1, 1957.

ON THE BIOLOGY OF THE SQUIRREL. M. P. Raspopov, U. A. Issakov. The Biology of Hares and Squirrels: their diseases, Moscow, 140 pp., 1934 (in Russian).

PRAIRIE DOG TOWN. Margaret Thomsen Raymond, Carl O. Mohr. Dodd, Mead and Co., New York, pp.56, illus., 1942.

SQUIRREL SURVEY AND INVESTIGATION. Howard R. Redmond. Mississippi Game and Fish, Jackson, vol.14, no.3, pp.3-4, 13, Sept., 1950.

WOODCHUCKS AND CHIPMUNKS. Wirt Robinson. Jour. Mam., vol.4, no.4, pp. 256-257, Nov., 1923.

SATAN, THE FRIENDLY CHIPMUNK. William Rotmans. Nature Mag., vol.28, no.4, pp.223-225, illus., Nov., 1936.

STUDY OF A SMALL PRAIRIE-DOG TOWN. Theo. H. Scheffer. Trans. Kansas Acad. Sci., vol.40, pp.391-395, pl., 1938.

THE FOX SQUIRREL. Rex Gary Schmidt. Missouri Conserv., Jefferson City, vol.9, no.5, pp.8-9, illus., May, 1948.

THE WOODCHUCK. W. J. Schoonmaker. Nature Mag., Washington, vol.40, no.1, pp.29-32, illus., Jan., 1947.

THE WOODCHUCK: LORD OF THE CLOVER FIELD. W. J. Schoonmaker. Bull. New York Zool. Soc., vol.41, no.1, pp.3-12, illus., Jan.-Feb., 1938.

THE INSIDE ON THE OUTDOORS. (WOODCHUCK.) Clayt Seagears. New York State Conserv., Albany, vol.2, no.5, back cover opp. p.32, illus., Apr.-May, 1948.

THE RED SQUIRREL. Clayt Seagears. New York State Conservationist, Albany, vol.4, no.3, pp.40-44, illus., Dec., 1949-Jan., 1950.

WILDLIFE LANDLORD. (WOODCHUCK.) Clayt Seagears. New York State Conserv., Albany, vol.2, no.5, p.32, Apr.-May, 1948.

BANNERTAIL. THE STORY OF A GRAY-SQUIRREL. Ernest Thompson Seton. Charles Scribner's Sons, New York, 265 pp., 8 pls., 1922.

THE HOME LIFE OF THE COLUMBIAN GROUND SQUIRREL. William T. Shaw. Canadian Field-Nat., vol.38, nos.7-8, pp. 128-130, figs.6, Oct., 1924.

TRACKING THE COLUMBIAN GROUND SQUIRREL TO ITS BURROW. William T. Shaw. Nat. Geographic Mag., pp.587-596, pls.11, May, 1925.

(CONTRIBUTIONS TO THE GEOGRAPHICAL DISTRIBUTION OF SPERMOPHILOPSIS LEPTODACTYLUS (LICHT).) Contributions à la distribution géographique du Spermophilopsis leptodactylus (Licht). V. N. Shnitnikov. Annales Zool. Mus. Russian Acad. Sci., vol.22, pp.224-228, (1917) Mar., 1918. (In Russian.)

SQUIRRELS. Monica Shorten. Collins, xii plus 212 pp., illus., 1954.

THE CHIPMUNK. R. W. Shufeldt. Country Life, vol.35, no.6, pp.98, 102, Apr., 1919.

FOUR-FOOTED FORESTERS--THE SQUIRRELS. R. W. Shufeldt. Amer. Forestry, vol.26, pp.37-44, figs.1-10, Jan., 1920.

RICHARDSON'S GROUND SQUIRREL. J. Dewey Soper. Nat. Mag., vol.8, no.2, pp.105-106, illus., Aug., 1926.

THE MOUNTAIN "BOOMER." (RED SQUIRREL.) R. T. Speers. Virginia Wildlife, Richmond, vol.11, no.2, pp.16-17, 26, illus., Feb., 1950.

BIOLOGY OF SCIURUS VULGARIS VARIUS IN CAPTIVITY. V. G. Stakhrovskii. Zool. Zhurn., Moscow, vol.11, no.1, pp. 82-104, 14 figs., 1932.

FOX SQUIRREL SKETCHES. F. W. Stuewer. Michigan Conserv., Lansing, vol.24, no.5, pp.12-14, illus., Oct., 1955.

(THE GROUND SQUIRREL (CITELLUS SUSLICA GUELD.) IN THE REGION OF THE LUBLIN PROVINCE.) Der Ziesel (Citellus suslica Gueld.) im Gebiet der Wojewodschaft Lublin. Stanislaw Sturdacki. Ann. Univ. Mariae Curie-Sklodowska, Lublin, sec.C, 9 (7): 307-353, Mar.7, 1956, (In Polish, with German Summary).

A LIFE HISTORY STUDY OF THE GROUND SQUIRREL CITELLUS SPILOSOMA MAJOR (MERRIAM). Ferd Sumrell. MS thesis, Univ. N. Mex., 1949.

OUR PERT NEIGHBORS. AN INTRODUCTION TO GROUND SQUIRRELS. T. Surber. Conserv. Volunteer, St. Paul, vol.7, no.41, pp.42-45, illus., July-Aug., 1944.

OUR PERT NEIGHBORS: GRAY, RED, FOX, AND FLYING SQUIRRELS. T. Surber. Conserv. Volunteer, St. Paul, vol.7, no.40, pp.39-42, May-June, 1944.

CAPTIVE FOX SQUIRRELS. Ruth Dowell Svihla. Jour. Mam., vol.12, no.2, pp.152-156, May, 1931.

TUFT-EARED SQUIRRELS. Ross Thornburg, Florence Thornburg. Nature Mag., Washington, vol.39, no.10, pp.523-524, illus., Dec., 1946.

THE BIOLOGY OF THE REDDISH GROUND-SQUIRREL (CITELLUS RUFESCENS KEYS. ET BLAS.). V. I. Tikhvinsky. Raboty Volzhsko-Kamskoi Zonal'noi Okhotnich' epromyslonoi Biologischeskoi Stantsii, Kazan, no.2 (Uchen'ie Zapiski Kazanskogo Gosudarstvennogo Universiteta im V. I. Ul'ainova-Lenina, vol.92, nos.7-8), pp.46-89, figs.19, 1932.

WAYS OF THE WOODCHUCK. Richard F. Trump. Natural History, New York, vol. 52, no.5, pp.221-225, illus., Dec., 1943.

SQUIRRELS AS GUESTS. W. Bryant Tyrrell. Nature Mag., Washington, D.C., vol.36, no.5, pp.255-256, illus., May, 1943.

OUR NUMBER ONE TARGET. (GRAY SQUIRREL LIFE HISTORY.) Hans G. Uhlig. W. Va. Cons., 18 (7): 24-26 plus back cover, Sept., 1954.

PRAIRIE DOGS: JUST PESTS? J. V. K. Wagar. Colo. Cons., 2 (4): 6-8, illus., July-Aug., 1953.

"FLYING" SQUIRRELS, NATURE'S GLIDERS. Ernest P. Walker. Nat. Geog. Mag., Washington, vol.91, no.5, pp.662-674, illus., May, 1947.

GLIMPSES OF FLYING SQUIRRELS. Ernest P. Walker. Nature Mag., Washington, vol.44, no.2, pp.81-84, illus., Feb., 1951.

THEY GLIDE THROUGH THE AIR WITH THE GREATEST OF EASE. (FLYING SQUIRREL.) Ernest P. Walker. Fauna, Phila., vol.10, no.3, pp.82-84, illus., Sept., 1948.

MARMOTS IN THE HIGH COUNTRY. M. V. Walker. Yosemite Nat. Notes, Yosemite, vol.25, no.6, p.88, June, 1946.

(FROM THE HISTORY OF MARMOTS.) Aus der Geschichte der Murmeltiere. Hans Wehrli. Natur und Volk, Frankfurt, vol. 68, no.2, pp.76-87, figs.13, Feb., 1938.

(ON THE DISTRIBUTION AND HISTORY OF THE GROUND SQUIRRELS.) Zur Verbreitung und Geschichte des Ziesels. E. Werth. Arbeit. Biol. Reichsanstalt fuer Land-und Forstwirtschaft, Berlin, vol.21, no.2, pp. 255-267, fig.1, maps, 1934.

THE AUTOBIOGRAPH OF A GROUNDHOG. Dale E. Whitesell. Ohio Conserv. Bull., Columbus, vol.15, no.2, pp.15, 30-31, Feb., 1951.

MARMOTA MONAX. Charles R. Williams. Pennsylvania Game News, Harrisburg, vol. 13, no.5, p.7, illus., Aug., 1942.

THE LOW-DOWN ON "SCIURUS CAROLINENSIS." Robert Wingard. Pa. Game News, 22 (11): 9-13, illus., Feb., 1952.

SUNDOWN SQUIRREL. (FLYING SQUIRREL.) Kerry Wood. Fauna, Phila., vol.3, no.4, pp.107-112, illus., Dec., 1941.

THE COMMON STRIPED PALM SQUIRREL. R. C. Wroughton. Jour. Bombay Nat. Hist. Soc., vol.16, no.3, pp.406-413, pl., Aug.5, 1905.

(NOTES ON THE BIOLOGY OF MENZBIER'S MARMOT (MARMOTA MENZBIERI KASTCHK.).) Zametki po biologii surka menzbira (Marmota menzbieri Kastchk). P. A. Yanushko. Zool. Jurnal, Akad. Nauk SSSR, Moscow, vol.30, no.6, pp.629-635, 1951.

YOU CAN GROW BUSH-TAILS. (SQUIRRELS.) Lee E. Yeager. Field and Stream, New York, vol.52, no.2, pp.54-55, 105-107, illus., June, 1947.

GREY AND RED SQUIRRELS. John W. Young. Field, London, vol.156, no.4045, p.25, July 5, 1930.

THE CHIPMUNK (EUTAMIAS ASIATICUS). I. M. Zaleskii, M. D. Zverev. The thin-toed ground squirrel, the fat dormouse, the mole-rat, and the chipmunk. All-Union Coop. Assn. Publ. House, 1935.

FLYING SQUIRRELS ARE PLENTIFUL BUT--FEW PEOPLE HAVE SEEN THEM. Kentucky Happy Hunting Ground, Frankfort, vol.5, no.2, pp.33-34, illus., Mar., 1949.

THE GREY SQUIRREL. Bird Notes and News, vol.15, no.4, pp.85-86, 1932.

THE GRAY SQUIRREL. Louisiana Conservationist, New Orleans, vol.2, no. 1, pp.8-9, 26, illus., Sept., 1949.

HOARY MARMOT--OR MOUNTAIN WHISTLER. Nat. Nature News, Wash., D.C., vol.2, no.35, p.3, fig.1, Sept.1, 1938.

MORE ABOUT SQUIRRELS. Virginia Wildlife, Blacksburg, vol.3, no.3, p.4, Nov., 1939.

THE PRAIRIE DOG. Life, New York, vol.27, no.11, pp.156-158, illus., Sept.12, 1949.

SQUIRRELS OF THE GROUND. Canadian Nature, Toronto, vol.2, no.2, pp.36-37, Mar.-Apr., 1940.

Africa

NOTES ON THE STATUS OF THE AMERICAN GREY SQUIRREL (SCIURUS CAROLINENSIS GMELIN) IN THE SOUTH-WESTERN CAPE (SOUTH AFRICA). D. H. S. Davis. Proc. Zool. Soc. Lond., vol.120, pt.2, pp.265-268, Aug., 1950.

(NOTES ON MAMMALS. X. CONTRIBUTION TO THE CLASSIFICATION OF THE AFRICAN SQUIRRELS.) Notes sur les Mammiferes. X. Contribution a la classification des ecureuils africains. Serge Frechkop. Bull. Mus. Roy. Hist. Nat. Belgique, Brussels, vol.8, no.19, pp. 13, figs.3, July, 1932.

NOTICE OF A NEW SQUIRREL (SCIURUS ORNATUS) FROM NATAL. J. E. Gray. Proc. Zool. Soc. Lond., pp.13, pl.1, 1864.

SYNOPSIS OF THE AFRICAN SQUIRRELS (SCIURIDAE) IN THE COLLECTION OF THE BRITISH MUSEUM. J. E. Gray. Ann. and Mag. Nat. Hist. Lond., ser.3, vol.20, no.119, pp.323-334, Nov., 1867.

ZOOLOGICAL RESULTS OF THE SWEDISH EXPEDITION TO CENTRAL AFRICA 1921. VERTEBRATA. 4. A NEW SQUIRREL FROM THE BIRUNGA VOLCANOES, NORTH OF LAKE KIVU. Nils Gyldenstolpe. Arkiv. Zool., Uppsala, vol.19, no.6, pp.3, Dec. 14, 1927.

A NEW WEST AFRICAN SQUIRREL. R. W. Hayman. Ann. and Mag. Nat. Hist., London, ser.12, vol.7, no.73, p.16, Jan., 1954.

TWO NEW AFRICAN SQUIRRELS. R. W. Hayman. Ann. and Mag. Nat. Hist., Lond., ser.12, vol.3, no.27, pp.262-264, Mar., 1950.

THE SUBSPECIES OF PARAXERUS FLAVIVITTIS, PETERS. Martin A. C. Hinton. Ann. and Mag. Nat. Hist., ser.9, vol.5, pp.308-312, Mar., 1920.

A NEW NAME FOR THE WEST AFRICAN PYGMY SQUIRREL. N. Hollister. Proc. Biol. Soc. Wash., vol.34, p.135, June 30, 1921.

SOME NOTES ON THE AFRICAN SQUIRRELS OF THE GENUS HELIOSCIURUS. C. M. Ingoldby. Proc. Zool. Soc. Lond., pt.2, pp.471-487, 4 col. pls., July 12, 1927.

A MONOGRAPH OF THE AFRICAN SQUIRRELS, WITH AN ENUMERATION OF THE SPECIMENS IN THE LEYDEN MUSEUM. Fredericus Anna Jentink. Notes Leyden Mus., vol.4, no.1, pp.1-53, 1882.

(STUDIES OF ZOOGEOGRAPHY ON THE BARBARY COAST. THE RODENTS. I. SCIURIDAE.) Etudes de geographie zoologique sur las Berberie Les Rongeurs. I. Les Sciurides. L. Joleaud. Bull. Soc. Zool. France, vol.43, nos.5-7, pp.83-102, figs.1-2, 1918.

THE CORRECT NAME OF THE WEST AFRICAN PYGMY SQUIRREL. Herbert Lang. Jour. Mam., vol.3, no.2, pp.118-119, May, 1922.

(A NEW SQUIRREL FROM GERMAN EAST AFRICA (SC. PAULI).) Ein neues eichhornchen aus Deutsch-Ost Afrika (Sc. pauli). Paul Matschie. Sitz. Ber. Gesell. Naturf. Freunde Berlin, Jahrg., 1894, no. 10, pp.256-258, Dec.18, 1894.

(SCIURUS MUTABILIS AND SCIURUS UNDULATUS, WITH REMARKS ON THE SYSTEMATICS OF THE AFRICAN SCIURIDAE.) Sciurus mutabilis und Sciurus undulatus nebst Bemerkungen zur Systematik der afrikanischen Sciurinae. Ferdinand Mueller. Zool. Anzeiger, Leipzig, vol.37, nos.3-4, pp.75-83, figs.4, Jan.31, 1911.

(SYSTEMATIC POSITION AND OCCURRENCE OF SCIURUS MUTABILIS.) Die systematische Stellung und das Vorkommen von Sciurus mutabilis. Ferdinand Mueller. Sitz. Gesell. Naturf. Freunde Berlin, Jahrg. 1910, no.8, pp.316-319, 1910.

(SOME AFRICAN SQUIRRELS.) Einige afrikanische Eichhoernchen. Oscar Neumann. Sitz. Gesell. Naturf. Freunde Berlin, Jahrg.1902, nos.1-8, pp.175-181, Oct.21, 1902.

(TWO NEW RACES OF AETHOSCIURUS RUWENZORI SCHWANN FROM THE BELGIAN CONGO.) Deux nouvelles races d'Aethosciurus ruwenzori Schwann du Congo belge. A. Prigogine. Ann. Mus. Royal Congo Belge Tervuren, n.s., Sci. Zool., vol.1 (Miscellanea Zoologica H. Schouteden), pp.69-73, 1954.

RODENTS OF NIGERIA. PART II. SQUIRRELS. D. R. Rosevear. Nigerian Field, vol.15, no.1, pp.4-18, pls.7, Jan., 1950.

A NEW SQUIRREL FROM THE ANGLO-EGYPTIAN SUDAN. Henry W. Setzer. Proc. Biol. Soc. Washington, vol.67, pp. 87-88, Mar.22, 1954.

FOUR NEW AFRICAN SQUIRRELS. Oldfield Thomas. Ann. and Mag. Nat. Hist. (8), vol.4, no.23, pp.476-479, Nov., 1909.

THE GENERIC ARRANGEMENT OF THE AFRICAN SQUIRRELS. Oldfield Thomas. Ann. and Mag. Nat. Hist. (8), vol.3, no. 18, pp.467-475, June, 1909.

NEW SUBSPECIES OF PROTOXERUS STANGERI, THE GIANT SQUIRREL OF EQUATORIAL AFRICA. Oldfield Thomas.' Ann. and Mag. Nat. Hist., ser.9, vol.11, pp.527-529, Apr., 1923.

SOME NEW AFRICAN SQUIRRELS. Oldfield Thomas. Ann. and Mag. Nat. Hist., ser. 9, vol.11, pp.518-523, Apr., 1923.

THE WEST AFRICAN FORMS OF HELIOSCIURUS RUFOBRACHIUM. Oldfield Thomas. Ann. and Mag. Nat. Hist. (9), vol.11, no.64, pp.523-526, Apr., 1923.

THE OCHRE-FOOTED SCRUB-SQUIRRELS OF EAST AFRICA. W. E. de Winton. Ann. and Mag. of Nat. Hist., ser.6, vol.19, pp.573-575, May, 1897.

Aging

AGE CRITERIA IN MALE GRAY SQUIRRELS. Charles M. Kirkpatrick, Edward M. Barnett. Jour. Wildlife Management, 21 (3): 341-347, illus., July, 1957.

(METHOD AND TECHNIQUE FOR DETERMINING THE AGE OF A SQUIRREL AND ANALYZING SQUIRREL POPULATIONS ACCORDING TO AGE.) Méthode et technique pour la fixation de l'âge de l'écureuil et l'analysé des populations d'écureuils d'après l'âge. I. D. Kyris. Bull. Soc. Nat. Moscou, sect. biol., vol.46, no.1, pp.36-42, figs.11, 1937.

DETERMINING THE AGE OF THE LITTLE GROUND SQUIRREL (CITELIUS PYGMAEUS). N. Naumov. Plant Prot. 11: 131-134, 9 figs., 1936.

(DETERMINING THE AGE OF THE SQUIRREL.) N. Naumow. Wissensch. Berichte der Moskauer Staatsuniversitaet, vol.2, pp.275-291, 1934.

NOTES ON AGE DETERMINATION IN SQUIRRELS. George A. Petrides. Jour. Mam., vol.32, no.1, pp.111-112, pl.1, Feb.15, 1951.

AGING GRAY SQUIRRELS BY USE OF TAIL-PELAGE CHARACTERISTICS. Ward M. Sharp. Jour. Wildlife Management, 22 (1): 29-34, illus., Jan., 1958.

THE DETERMINATION OF AGE OF NESTLING AND SUB-ADULT GRAY SQUIRRELS IN WEST VIRGINIA. Hans G. Uhlig. Jour. Wildlife Management, vol.19, no.4, pp.479-483, Oct., 1955

Alaska

MARMOTA CALIGATA BROWERI, A NEW MARMOT FROM NORTHERN ALASKA. E. Raymond Hall, Raymond M. Gilmore. Canadian Field-Nat., vol.48, no.4, pp.57-59, figs.1-6, Apr., 1934.

DESCRIPTION OF A NEW RACE OF FLYING SQUIRREL FROM ALASKA. Arthur H. Howell. Jour. Mam., vol.15, no.1, p.64, Feb.15, 1934.

A NEW FLYING SQUIRREL FROM THE COAST OF ALASKA. Wilfred H. Osgood. Proc. Biol. Soc. Wash., vol.18, pp.133-134, Apr.18, 1905.

TWO NEW SPERMOPHILES FROM ALASKA. Wilfred H. Osgood. Proc. Biol. Soc. Wash., vol.16, pp.25-27, Mar.19, 1903.

THE RED SQUIRREL OF THE SITKAN DISTRICT, ALASKA. H. S. Swarth. Jour. Mam., vol.2, no.2, pp.92-94, May, 1921.

Anatomy

CHANGES IN THE REPRODUCTIVE ORGANS OF THE MALE GREY SQUIRREL (SCIURUS CAROLINENSIS). Marjorie Allanson. Philos. Trans. Roy. Soc. Lond., ser.B, vol.222, no.485, pp.79-96, pl.15, Apr.7, 1933.

THE EFFECT OF INJECTIONS OF ANTUITRIN-S ON THE SEXUALLY INACTIVE MALE GROUND SQUIRREL. Lowell Burton Baker, George Edwin Johnson. Endocrinology, Los Angeles, vol.20, no.2, pp. 219-233, Mar., 1936.

THE ORIGIN OF THE PENILE URETHRA AND BULBO-URETHRAL GLANDS WITH PARTICULAR REFERENCE TO THE RED SQUIRREL (TAMIASCIURUS HUDSONICUS). Norman J. Barnstein, H. W. Mossman. Anat. Record, Phila., vol.72, no.1, pp.67-86, table 1, pls.1-2, Sept.25, 1938.

THE DEVELOPMENT OF THE NOSE IN THE SPERMOPHILE, WITH PARTICULAR REFERENCE TO THE PART PLAYED BY THE PRIMITIVE CHOANAE IN THE FORMATION OF THE NASAL CAVITY IN MAMMALS. B. I. Burns. Anat. Record, vol.31, pp.27-42, 1 pl., Sept.25, 1925.

TWO UNUSUAL WOODCHUCK SKULLS. Alvin R. Cahn. Amer. Midland Nat., Notre Dame, vol.15, no.2, pp.197-198, illus., Mar., 1934.

NOTES ON VAGINAL SMEARS IN THE GROUND SQUIRREL CITELLUS TRIDECEMLINEATUS. R. M. Coco. Proc. Louisiana Acad. Sci., Baton Rouge, vol.6, pp.83-85, figs.6, Feb.15, 1942.

THE HYPOPHYSIS CEREBRI OF THE CALIFORNIA GROUND SQUIRREL, CITELLUS BEECHYI (RICHARDSON). Harold J. Cooper. Amer. Jour. Anat., vol.26, pp.185-207, Nov., 1919.

STUDIES ON FUNAMBULUS PALMARUM TRISTRIATUS WATERHOUSE (THE INDIAN PALM SQUIRREL): PART I. THE MUSCULATURE. F. M. Das. Jour. Zool. Soc. India, vol.7, no.1, pp.57-82, June, 1955.

THE GROSS ANATOMY OF THE VISCERA OF THE PRAIRIE DOG. Lyle C. Dearden. Jour. Mam., 34 (1): 15-27, illus., Feb., 1953.

(THE PENIS BONE OF THE SQUIRRELS OF SOUTH AMERICA.) L'os pénien de écureuils de l'Amérique du Sud. Robert Didier. Mammalia, Paris, vol.19, no.3, pp.416-426, illus., Sept., 1955.

VARIATION IN THE DOUGLAS GROUND SQUIRREL IN DIFFERENT PARTS OF ITS RANGE. Elton R. Edge. Amer. Nat., vol.69, no.725, pp.620-628, figs.2, Nov.-Dec., 1935.

OVERGROWTH OF TEETH IN RODENTS. (GRAY SQUIRREL.) Douglas England. Field, London, vol.167, no.4340, p.462, illus., Feb.29, 1936.

(NOTES ON THE MAMMALS. IX. THE FORM OF THE MOLARS OF SCIUROMORPHA.) Notes sur les Mammiferes. IX. De la forme des dents molaires des Rongeurs Sciuromorphes. Serge Frechkop. Bull. Mus. Roy. Hist. Nat. Belgique, Brussels, vol.8, no.12, pp.41, figs.12, June, 1932.

(THE CHEEK BONE DENTITION OF "PTEROMYS XANTHIPES".) La dentition jugale du "Pteromys xanthipes". Madeleine Friant. A. M. Edw. Comptes Rendus XII Congres Internat. Zool. Lisbonne 1935, Lisboa, vol.2, pp.685-695, 1 fig., pls.32-33, 1936-1937.

(THE HYPOPHYSIS OF THE MARMOTS DURING HIBERNATION AND IN THE SUMMER SEASON.) Su L'ipofisi belle Marmotte durante il letargo e nella stagione estiva. Agostino Gemelli. Archiv. Sci. Mediche, Torino, vol.30, no.17, pp. 1-9, Mar.8, 1906.

(NEW OBSERVATIONS ON THE HYPOPHYSIS OF THE MARMOTS DURING HIBERNATION AND IN THE SUMMER SEASON.) Nuove osservazioni su l'ipofisi delle marmotte durante il letargo e nella stagione estiva. Agostino Gemelli. Biologica, Torino, vol.1, no.9, pp.17, Mar.8, 1906.

GEOGRAPHIC VARIATION IN CITELLUS TERETICAUDUS. Joseph Grinnell. Proc. Biol. Soc. Wash., vol.31, pp.105-106, Nov. 29, 1918.

CHANGES DURING GROWTH IN THE SKULL OF THE RODENT OTOSPERMOPHILUS GRAMMURUS BEECHEYI. E. Raymond Hall. Univ. Calif. Publ. Zool., vol.21, no. 14, pp.355-404, figs.43, Mar.9, 1926.

A NEW DORSAL GLAND IN THE GROUND-SQUIRREL, CALLOSPERMOPHILUS, WITH A NOTE ON ITS ANAL GLAND. Robert Torrens Hatt. Jour. Morph. and Physiol., vol.42, pp.441-451, illus., Sept.5, 1926.

THE EXTRAHEPATIC BILIARY TRACT OF THE STRIPED GOPHER, WITH ESPECIAL REFERENCE TO THE GALL BLADDER DURING PREGNANCY. George M. Higgins. Ana. Rec., vol.37, pp.287-301, illus., Jan.25, 1928.

ON THE NEONATUS IN RATUFA AND FUNAMBULUS (MAMMALIA; SCIURIDAE). W. C. Osman Hill. Ceylon Jour. Sci. sect B, Zool. and Geol., vol.21, pt.2, pp. 189-191, Feb.10, 1939.

ON THE PENIS OF RATUFA MACROURA MELANOCHRA. W. C. Osman Hill. Ceylon Jour. Sci., sect.B, Zool. and Geol., Spolia Zeylanica, Colombo, vol.22, pt.1, pp.131-134, fig.1, June 12, 1940.

A HISTIOLOGICAL STUDY OF THE ACCESSORY SEX GLANDS OF THE MALE FOX AND GREY SQUIRRELS AS CRITERIA OF AGE AND SEXUAL ACTIVITY. Roger A. Hoffman. Master's thesis, Purdue Univ., 1952.

GEOGRAPHIC VARIATION IN THE EASTERN CHIPMUNK, TAMIAS STRIATUS, IN MICHIGAN. Emmet T. Hooper. Occas. Papers Mus. Zool. Univ. Michigan, Ann Arbor, no.461, pp.5, Sept.15, 1942.

ON THE ALIMENTARY TRACTS OF SQUIRRELS WITH DIVERSE FOOD HABITS. A. Brazier Howell. Jour. Wash. Acad. Sci., vol.15, no.7, pp.145-150, figs.1-2, Apr.4, 1925.

SPECIAL ANATOMICAL FEATURES OF THE CRANIAL NERVES OF THE FOX SQUIRREL, SCIURUS NIGER RUFIVENTER (GEOFFROY). Thomas William Jenkins. Anat. Record, 126 (2): 241-251, Oct., 1956.

THE EFFECT OF DAILY HETEROPITUITARY IMPLANTS INTO ADULT BUT SEXUALLY INACTIVE MALE GROUND SQUIRRELS. George E. Johnson, E. L. Gann, M. A. Foster, R. M. Coco. Endocrinology, vol.18, no.1, pp.86-96, figs.9, Jan.-Feb., 1934.

THE EAR MUSCLES OF THE WOODCHUCK. Gordon W. Jones. Jour. Mam., vol.18, no. 4, p.517, Nov., 1937.

THE TESTIS OF THE FOX SQUIRREL IN RELATION TO AGE AND SEASONS. Charles M. Kirkpatrick. Amer. Jour. Anat., vol.97, no.2, pp.229-256, illus., Sept., 1955.

CYTOLOGICAL STUDIES ON THE REPRODUCTIVE ORGANS. CHROMOSOME BEHAVIOUR IN THE MALE GREY SQUIRREL (SCIURUS CAROLINENSIS LEUCOTIS). P. C. Koller. Proc. Roy. Soc. Edinburgh, sess.1935-36, vol.56, pt.2, pp.196-208, figs.12, Sept.11, 1936.

(ON THE EYE OF THE MARMOT (MARMOTTA MARMOTTA).) Ueber das Auge des Murmeltiers (Marmotta marmotta). W. F. Kolmer. Zeitschr. f. Anat. u. Entwicklungs., vol.96, pp.806-812, figs.3, 1931.

VARIATION IN THE CHIPMUNKS OF WEST-CENTRAL WASHINGTON. Earl J. Larrison. Murrelet, Seattle, vol.29, no.3, pp.35-43, Mar.1, 1949.

VARIATION IN THE CHIPMUNKS OF WEST-CENTRAL WASHINGTON. PART II. Earl J. Larrison. Murrelet, Seattle, vol.30, no. 2, pp.27-34, illus., Oct.14, 1949.

THE OS CLITORIDIS OF SOME NORTH AMERICAN SCIURIDAE. James N. Layne. Jour. Mam., 35 (3): 357-366, illus., Aug., 1954.

THE OS GENITALE OF THE RED SQUIRREL, TAMIASCIURUS. James N. Layne. Jour. Mam., vol.33, no.4, pp.457-459, 1 fig., Nov.19, 1952.

MALOCCLUSION IN A WOODCHUCK SKULL. Alexander Lincoln, Jr. Jour. Mam., vol. 19, no.1, p.107, Feb.14, 1938.

(ON THE OCCURRENCE OF SINUS HAIRS IN THE UPPER LID OF THE SQUIRREL (SCIURUS VULGARIS).) Ueber das Vorkommen von Sinushaaren im Oberlid des Eichoernchen (Sciurus vulgaris.). Karl Otto Loewenstein. Zool. Anz., vol.87, nos.1-3, pp.35-41, figs.1-3, Aug.18, 1938.

VARIATION IN THE FOX SQUIRREL IN FLORIDA. Joseph Curtis Moore. Amer. Mid. Nat., Notre Dame, vol.55, no.1, pp. 41-65, illus., Jan., 1956.

THE ACCESSORY GENITAL GLANDS OF MALE GRAY AND FOX SQUIRRELS CORRELATED WITH AGE AND REPRODUCTIVE CYCLES. H. W. Mossman, Roger A. Hoffman, Charles M. Kirkpatrick. Amer. Jour. Anat., vol.97, no.2, pp.257-301, illus., Sept., 1955.

THE MALE REPRODUCTIVE TRACT OF THE SCIURIDAE. H. W. Mossman, John W. Lawlay, J. A. Bradley. Amer. Jour. Anat., vol.51, no.1, pp.89-155, figs.16, pls.7, Sept., 1932.

THE FETAL MEMBRANES OF A PRIMITIVE RODENT, THE THIRTEEN-STRIPED GROUND SQUIRREL. H. W. Mossman, L. A. Weisfeldt. Amer. Jour. Anat., Phila., vol.64, no.1, pp.59-110, pls.10, table 1, Jan.15, 1939.

(ON THE INFLUENCE OF FEEDING CONDITIONS ON THE STATE OF THE GONADS OF THE GROUND SQUIRREL (CITELLUS PIGMAEUS PALL.).) O vliyanii uslovii pitaniya na sostoyanie gonad malogo suslika (Citellus pigmaeus Pall.). A. F. Orlova. Dokladi Akad. Nauk SSSR, vol.42, no.1, pp.177-179, 1953.

ON THE OSTEOLOGY OF SCIUROPTERUS VOLUCELLA, GEOFF. (ABSTRACT). George H. Perkins. Proc. Amer. Assoc. Adv. Sci., Salam, vol.27, pp.289-296, Aug., 1878.

A STUDY OF THE MYOLOGY AND OSTEOLOGY OF TREE SCIURIDS WITH REGARD TO ADAPTATION TO ARBOREAL, GLISSANT AND FOSSORIAL HABITS. H. E. Peterka. Trans. Kansas Acad. Sci., vol. 39, pp.313-332, 1937.

THE FOLLICULAR CYCLE IN THE SEXUALLY MATURE THIRTEEN-LINED GROUND SQUIRREL (CITELLUS TRIDECEMLINEATUS MITCH.). Edward C. Pliske. Jour. Morph., Phila., vol.63, no. 2, pp.263-288, Sept., 1938.

THE MALE GENITAL TRACT OF TWO GENERA OF INDIAN SQUIRRELS. M. R. N. Prasad. Jour. Mam., vol.35, no.4, pp.471-485, illus., Nov.29, 1954.

ABERRANT CITELLUS BEECHEYI SPECIMENS FROM ORANGE COUNTY, CALIFORNIA. Raymond E. Ryckman, Chester C. Lindt. Jour. Mam., vol.34, no.2, p. 266, May 14, 1953.

A FREAK SKULL OF THE CALIFORNIA GROUND SQUIRREL. Theo. H. Scheffer. The Murrelet, vol.12, no.1, p.23, illus., Jan., 1931.

CHANGES IN THE INCISOR OF THE THIRTEEN-LINED GROUND SQUIRREL (CITELLUS TRIDECEMLINEATUS) FOLLOWING BILATERAL GONADECTOMY. I. Schour. Anat. Record, vol.65, no.2, pp. 177-194, May 25, 1936.

(THE VARIABILITY OF GROWTH AND THE PROCESS OF THE GROWTH OF THE CRANIUM OF THE SQUIRREL (SCIURUS VULGARIS L.).) La variabilite de croissance et le proces d'accroissement du crane de l'ecureuil (Sciurus vulgaris L.). M. Serebrennikov. Annuaire Mus. Zool. Acad. Sci. URSS, Leningrad, vol.31, nos.3-4, pp.399-418, figs.13, 1930.

THE EXTRUSIVE GROWTH AND ATTRITION OF THE INCISORS IN CYNOMYS L. LUDOVICIANUS (ORD.). Albert R. Shadle, Winifred Bolton, Barbara Garona, Darwin Farber. Anat. Record, Phila., vol.93, no.4, pp.349-353, Dec., 1945.

THE DEVELOPMENT OF THE PENILE URETHRA AND THE HOMOLOGY OF COWPER'S GLAND OF MALE SPERMOPHILE (CITELLUS TRIDECEMLINEATUS) WITH A NOTE ON THE PROSTATIC UTRICLE. M. A. H. Siddiqi. Jour. Anat. Lond., vol.72, pt.1, pp.107-115, figs.2, pl.1, Oct., 1937.

THE GENITO-URINARY SYSTEM OF THE INDIAN GROUND SQUIRREL (FUNAMBULUS PALMARUM). M. A. H. Siddiqi. Proc. Nat. Acad. Sci. India, vol.8, pt.1, pp.1-9, figs.14, Apr., 1938.

THE MORPHOLOGY OF THE VASCULAR SYSTEM OF THE RICHARDSON GROUND SQUIRREL, CITELLUS RICHARDSONI SABINE. George F. Sleggs. Anat. Record, vol.30, pp.165-184, 10 pls., June 25, 1925.

THE ADULT ANATOMY AND HISTOLOGY OF THE ANAL GLANDS OF THE RICHARDSON GROUND SQUIRREL, CITELLUS RICHARDSONII SABINE. George F. Sleggs. Anat. Record, vol.32, pp.1-44, 20 figs., Jan.25, 1926.

THE CHEEK POUCHES OF RICHARDSON'S GROUND-SQUIRREL, CITELLUS RICHARDSONII SABINE. George F. Sleggs. Jour. Morph. and Physiol., vol.41, pp.581-591, 2 pls., Mar.5, 1926.

(CHEWING MUSCULATURE OF MARMOTA MARMOTA L.) Die Kaumuskulatur von Marmota marmota L. Dietrich Starck, Hans Wehrli. Zeitschr. f. Saeugetierkunde, vol.10, no.1, pp.33-38, figs.5, Dec.31, 1935.

STUDIES ON THE FEMALE REPRODUCTIVE SYSTEM OF THE PRAIRIE DOG CYNOMYS LEUCURUS. I. GROSS MORPHOLOGY. Alfred H. Stockard. Papers Michigan Acad. Sci. Arts and Letters, Ann Arbor, vol.20, pp.725-735, pls.113-114, June 24, 1935.

STUDIES ON THE FEMALE REPRODUCTIVE SYSTEM OF THE PRAIRIE DOG, CYNOMYS LEUCURUS. II. NORMAL CYCLIC PHENOMENA OF THE OVARIAN FOLLICLES. Alfred H. Stockard. Papers Michigan Acad. Sci. Arts and Letters, vol.22, pp.671-689, pls.70-72, 1937.

AN UNUSUAL EXAMPLE OF INCISOR GROWTH IN THE WESTERN FOX SQUIRREL. Dayton Stoner. Iowa Acad. Science, vol.25, pp.105-106, pl.1, 1918.

THE SEASONAL CHANGES IN THE COMMON SQUIRREL. Oldfield Thomas. The Zoologish (3), vol.20, no.239, pp.401-407, Nov., 1896.

A REMARKABLE WOODCHUCK SKULL. Malcolm R. Thorpe. Jour. Mam., vol.11, no.1, pp.69-70, pl.5, Feb., 1930.

SILENT TEETH THAT TELL A TALE. (OVERGROWTH OF WOODCHUCK INCISORS.) Alvin L. Throne. Milwaukee Public Mus., Yearbook, vol.4, pp.147-149, illus., Oct.9, 1926.

(ANATOMICAL DESCRIPTION OF THE MARMOT EYE.) Anatomische Beschreibung des Murmelthier-Auges. Friedrick Tiedemann. Ann. Wetterau. Gesell., vol. 3, no.2, pp.345-348, pl.18, 1814.

WEIGHTS OF ADULT GRAY SQUIRRELS. Hans G. Uhlig. Jour. Mam., 36 (2): 293-296, May, 1955.

(ON THE POLYMORPHISM OF SCIURUS VULGARIS L. IN FINLAND.) Ueber die Polymorphie von Sciurus vulgaris L. in Finland. Paavo Voipio. Ann. Zool. Soc. Zool. Bot. Fennicae "Vanamo.", 18: (7): 1-24, 1957.

AN ODD MALIFORMATION IN A WOODCHUCK. George Wagner. Jour. Mam., vol.4, no.1, pl.4, p.21, Feb., 1923.

DWARF MARMOTS. Edward R. Warren. Jour. Mam., vol.7, no.4, pp.332-333, Nov., 1926.

ON THE DIFFERENCES OBSERVABLE IN THE SKULLS OF TWO SPECIES OF SQUIRREL, USUALLY CONFOUNDED UNDER THE NAME SCIURUS PALMARUM. G. R. Waterhouse. Proc. Zool. Soc. Lond., pt.7, p.118.

(ON THE OSTEOLOGY OF THE GENUS MARMOTA BLUMENB. (ARCTOMYS SCHREB.).) Zur Osteologie der Gattung Marmota Blumenb. (Arctomys Schreb.). Hans Wehrli. Zeitschr. f. Saeugetierkunde, vol.10, no.1, pp.1-32, figs.24, pl.1, Dec. 31, 1935.

SEASONAL SEXUAL RHYTHM AND ITS EXPERIMENTAL MODIFICATION IN THE MALE OF THE THIRTEEN-LINED GROUND SQUIRREL (CITELLUS TRIDECEMLINEATUS). L. J. Wells. Anat. Record, Phila., vol.62, no.4, pp.409-446, pl.1, July 25, 1935.

EFFECTS OF OESTRIN INJECTIONS ON ACCESSORY REPRODUTCIVE ORGANS OF THE MALE GROUND SQUIRREL (CITELLUS TRIDECEMLINEATUS.). L. J. Wells. Anat. Record, vol.64, no.4, pp.475-497, pls.3, Mar.25, 1936.

REPRODUCTIVE ORGANS OF TWO MAMMALIAN HERMAPHRODITES AND THEIR RESPONSE TO INJECTIONS OF PREGNANT MARE SERUM. L. J. Wells. Anat. Record, vol.67, no.2, pp.233-247, pls.2, Jan.25, 1937.

HORMONAL STIMULATION OF SPERMATOGENESIS IN THE TESTIS OF THE GROUND SQUIRREL. L. J. Wells, Carl R. Moore. Anat. Record, vol.66, no.2, pp.181-200, Sept.25, 1936.

EFFECTS OF ESTROGEN ON THE GENITAL TRACT AND URETHRA OF ANESTROUS FEMALE GROUND SQUIRRELS. L. J. Wells, M. D. Overholser. Anat. Record, Phila., vol.78, no.1, pp.43-57, 3 pls., Sept.25, 1940.

THE BACULUM IN THE CHIPMUNKS OF WESTERN NORTH AMERICA. John A. White. Univ. Kansas Publ., Mus. Nat. Hist., Lawrence, vol.5, no.35, pp.611-631, illus., Dec.1, 1953.

A CASE OF UNHINDERED GROWTH OF THE INCISOR TEETH OF THE WOODCHUCK. Stephen R. Williams. Ohio Jour. Sci., vol.22, pp.170-172, Apr., 1922.

ON THE ANATOMY OF THE LESSER AMERICAN FLYING SQUIRREL (PTEROMYS VOLUCELLA, CUV.). W. Yarrell. Proc. Comm. Sci. and Corres. Zool.Soc. London, pt.1, p.38, 1830-1831.

A STUDY OF THE SEASONAL CHANGES IN THE ADRENAL GLAND OF THE THIRTEEN-LINED GROUND SQUIRREL (CITELLUS TRIDECEMLINEATUS), WITH PARTICULAR REFERENCE TO ITS SEXUAL CYCLE. Moses Zalesky. Anat. Rec., vol. 60, no.3, pp.291-316, pls.2, Oct.25, 1934.

A STUDY OF THE SEASONAL CHANGES IN THE THYROID GLAND OF THE THIRTEEN-LINED GROUND SQUIRREL (CITELLUS TRIDECEMLINEATUS), WITH PARTICULAR REFERENCE TO ITS SEXUAL CYCLE. Moses Zalesky. Anat. Record, Phila., vol.62, no.2, pp.109-134, pl.1, figs. 3, May 25, 1935.

HYPOPHYSECTOMY AND ITS EFFECTS ON MALE REPRODUCTIVE ORGANS IN A WILD MAMMAL WITH ANNUAL RUT (CITELLUS). Moses Zalesky, E. T. Gomez. Anat. Record, vol.69, no.2, pp. 213-225, 1 fig., Sept.25, 1937.

EXPERIMENTAL STUDIES OF THE THYROID. I. EFFECTS OF THE THYROIDECTOMY ON REPRODUCTIVE ORGANS IN MALES OF AN ANNUAL-BREEDING GROUND SQUIRREL. Moses Zalesky, L. J. Wells. Anat. Record, vol.69, no.1, pp. 79-94, pl.1, Aug.25, 1937.

Aquatic Habits

RED SQUIRRELS SWIMMING A LAKE. Leon J. Cole. Jour. Mam., vol.3, no.1, pp.53-54, Feb., 1922.

ANOTHER SWIMMING WOODCHUCK. William E. Cram. Jour. Mam., vol.4, no.4, p.256, Nov., 1923.

GROUND SQUIRREL SWIMS RIVER. C. A. Harwell. Yosemite Nature Notes, vol.16, no.2, p.16, Feb., 1937.

AQUATIC HABITS OF THE WOODCHUCK. Charles E. Johnson. Jour. Mam., vol.4, no.2, pp.105-107, May, 1923.

A SWIMMING WOODCHUCK. John C. Phillips. Jour. Mam., vol.4, no.4, p.256, Nov., 1923.

SWIMMING RED SQUIRRELS. Alton S. Pope. Jour. Mam., vol.5, no.2, p.134 May, 1924.

(SWIMMING SQUIRREL.) Schwimmendes Eichhoernchen. Georg Steinbacher. Zool. Garten, Leipzig, n.F., vol.12, nos.4-6, p.335, Dec., 1940.

A SWIMMING WOODCHUCK. J. K. Twidale. Field, London, vol.168, no.4362, p.272, Aug.1, 1936.

Asia

SQUIRRELS COLLECTED BY THE AMERICAN MUSEUM ASIATIC EXPEDITIONS. Glover M. Allen. Amer. Mus. Novit., no. 163, pp.1-16, Apr.2, 1925.

A NEW FORM OF YELLOW SAND SUSLIK FROM THE MOUNTAIN RANGE KARA-TAU. V. M. Antipin. Comptes Rendus (Doklady) Acad. Sci. URSS, Moscou, n.s., vol.36, no.1, pp.29-31, 1942.

THE DISTRIBUTION OF THE GROUND-SQUIRREL (CITELLUS PYGMAEUS PALL.) WITHIN THE ORDJONIKDZE'S DISTRICT. V. P. Babenyshev, N. B. Birulya, B. D. Besedin, F. Z. Golosovskaya, A. N. Egorov, I. S. Ioff, P. A. Janushko. Zool. Jour., Moscou, vol.16, no.4, pp.736-739, map, 1937.

(DATA ON THE RED MARMOTS OF CENTRAL ASIA.) Zur Kenntnies der rothen Murmelthiere Central-Asiens. Eug.

Buchner. Melanges biologiques, vol.13, no.2, pp.309-324, 1892.

A NEW FLYING SQUIRREL OF THE GENUS PETAURISTA FROM NORTH-WESTERN SIAM. T. Donald Carter. Amer. Mus. Novitates, no.674, p.1, Nov.6, 1933.

A NOTE ON THE NOMENCLATURE OF TWO SCIURIDS FROM EASTERN SIBERIA. J. L. Chaworth-Musters. Ann. and Mag. Nat. Hist., Lond., ser.10, vol.13, pp. 335-557, May, 1934.

SHADRACH, THE SQUIRREL FROM KURDISTAN. Jocelyn Crane. Nature Mag., vol. 28, no.6, pp.332-334, 380, illus., Dec., 1936.

THE SQUIRREL OF SUNG-SHAN AND ITS VICINITY. T. S. Fu. Bull. Fan Mem. Inst. Biol., vol.6 (Zool.), no.6, pp.255-264, May 7, 1936.

SYNOPSIS OF THE ASIATIC SQUIRRELS (SCIURIDAE) IN THE COLLECTION OF THE BRITISH MUSEUM, DESCRIBING ONE NEW GENUS AND SOME NEW SPECIES. J. E. Gray. Ann. and Mag. Nat. Hist., Lond., ser.3, vol.20, no.118, pp.270-286, Oct., 1867.

A NEW SQUIRREL FROM CHINA. William P. Harris, Jr. Occas. Papers Mus. Zool., Univ. Michigan, no.228, pp.1-2, July 15, 1931.

GARDEN SQUIRRELS. J. L. Harrison. Malayan Nature Jour., Kuala Lumpur, vol. 4, no.2, pp.96-97, June, 1949.

A KEY TO THE SQUIRRELS OF MALAYA. J. L. Harrison. Malayan Nature Jour., vol.3, no.4, pp.201-209, pl.1, Dec., 1948.

FIVE NEW CHINESE SQUIRRELS. A. Brazier Howell. Jour. Washington Acad. Sci., vol.17, pp.80-84, Feb.19, 1927.

A NEW CHIPMUNK FROM KOREA. David H. Johnson, J. Knox Jones, Jr. Proc. Biol. Soc. Washington, vol.68, pp.175-176, Dec. 31, 1955.

THE YELLOW GROUND SQUIRREL OF TURKESTAN, CYNOMYS FULVUS OXIANUS THOMAS. D. Kashkarov, L. Lein. Ecology, Brooklyn, vol.8, no.1, pp.63-72, figs.3, table 1, Jan., 1927.

AN ECOLOGICAL SKETCH OF THE FIR-TREE WOODS OF NARYN-TAU (CENTRAL TIEN-SHAN) AND THE POSSIBILITY OF THE SQUIRREL'S ACCLIMATIZATION. S. V. Kirikov. Zool. Jour., Moscou, vol. 18, no.1, pp.120-129, 1939.

DIAGNOSES OF FOUR NEW SQUIRRELS FROM SIAM. C. Boden Kloss. Jour. Nat. Hist. Soc., Siam, vol.2, no.2, p.178, Dec., 1916.

A NEW GIANT SQUIRREL FROM PULO CONDORE. C. Boden Kloss. Jour. Nat. Hist. Soc. Siam, vol.4, pp.71-72, Mar., 1921.

A NEW SQUIRREL FROM TENGGOL ISLAND, EAST COAST OF THE MALAY PENINSULA. C. Boden Kloss. Jour. Roy. Asiatic Soc., Malayan Branch, vol.4, pt. 2, pp.259-261, Oct., 1926.

NOTES ON THE MALAYAN RACES OF RATUFA AFFINIS (RAFFLES). C. Boden Kloss. Bull. Raffles Mus., no.7, pp.1-2, Dec., 1932.

ON A NEW RACE OF FLYING SQUIRREL FROM SIAM. C. Boden Kloss. Jour. Nat. Hist. Soc., Siam, vol.2, pp.33-36, June, 1916.

ON THE CORRECT NAME FOR THE WHITE SQUIRREL OF SIAM. C. Boden Kloss. Jour. Nat. Hist. Soc., Siam, vol. 2, no.2, pp.179-182, Dec., 1916.

ON TWO NEW SQUIRRELS FROM THE INNER GULF OF SIAM. C. Boden Kloss. Jour. Nat. Hist. Soc., Siam, vol.1, no.3, pp.157-162, Mar., 1915.

SOME NOTES ON SCIURUS FINLAYSONI, AND OTHER SQUIRRELS OF SIAM. C. Boden Kloss. Jour. Nat. Hist. Soc., Siam, vol.1, no.4, pp.225-228, Dec., 1915.

A DESCRIPTION OF AN APPARENTLY NEW FORM OF CHIPMUNK FROM SOUTH KURILES, JAPAN. Nagamichi Kuroda. Jour. Mam., vol.13, no.1, pp.58-59, Feb., 1932.

(THE DISTRIBUTION AND BIOLOGY OF THE DESERT GROUND SQUIRREL IN TURKMENISTAN.) Die Verbreitung und Biologie des Wuestenziesels in Turkmenien USSR (Spermophilopsis leptodactylus Licht.). N. Lavrov, S. Naumov. Zoologitscheskij Jour. (vormals 'Revue Zool. Russe'), Moskau, vol.12, pt.2, pp. 80-116, 1933.

SCIENTIFIC RESULTS FROM THE MAMMAL SURVEY. NO.49. A NEW FLYING SQUIRREL FROM NEPAL. Helen M. Lindsay. Jour. Bombay Nat. Hist. Soc., vol.33, no.3, pp.565-569, May 31, 1929.

(OBSERVATIONS ON AN EAST ASIAN CHIPMUNK (EUTAMIAS ASIATICUS GM.) IN CAPTIVITY.) Beobachtungen an einem ostasiatischen Backenhoernchen (Eutamias asiaticus, Gm.) in Gefangenschaft. Wolfgang Luther. Zeitschr. Tierpsych., Berlin, vol.9, no.2, pp.411-415, 1952.

A NEW FLYING SQUIRREL FROM THE ISLAND OF TERATAU, WEST COAST OF MALAY PENINSULA. Marcus W. Lyon, Jr. Proc. Biol. Soc. Washington, vol.20, pp. 17-18, Feb.23, 1907.

DESCRIPTIONS OF TWO NEW SQUIRRELS FROM TRONG, LOWER SIAM. Gerrit S. Miller, Jr. Washington Acad. Sci., vol.2, pp.79-81, July 25, 1900.

THE GIANT SQUIRRELS OF BURMAH AND THE MALAY PENINSULA. Gerrit S. Miller, Jr. Proc. Wash. Acad. Sci., vol. 2, pp.69-77, July 25, 1900.

A NEW CHIPMUNK FROM NORTHEASTERN CHINA. Gerrit S. Miller, Jr. Proc. Acad. Nat. Sci., Phila., pp.348-350, Aug.1, 1898.

A NEW FLYING-SQUIRREL FROM EASTERN ASIA. Gerrit S. Miller, Jr. Proc. Biol. Soc., Washington, vol.31, pp.3-4, Feb.21, 1918.

A NEW SQUIRREL FROM LOWER SIAM. Gerrit S. Miller, Jr. Proc. Biol. Soc., Washington, vol.16, pp.147-148, Nov.12, 1903.

A NEW SQUIRREL FROM NORTHEASTERN CHINA. Gerrit S. Miller, Jr. Proc. Biol. Soc., Washington, vol.28, pp.115-116, May 27, 1915.

NEW STRIPED TREE SQUIRRELS FROM BURMA AND THAILAND. Joseph Curtis Moore. Amer. Mus. Novitates, 1879: 1-6, Feb.28, 1958.

NEW NAME FOR A KOREAN FLYING SQUIRREL. Tamezo Mori. Jour. Mam., vol.4, no.3, p.191, Aug., 1923.

MATERIALS ON THE GEOGRAPHICAL AND ECOLOGICAL DISTRIBUTION OF MARMOTS IN THE CENTRAL TIAN-SHAN. S. P. Naumov. Bull. Soc. Nat. Moscou, sect. biol., n.s., vol.50, nos.5-6, pp.33-44, 1945.

THE GIANT SQUIRREL (RATUFA) OF CEYLON. W. W. A. Phillips. Spolia Zeylanica, vol.16, pt.2, pp.209-216, Aug.8, 1931.

CONTRIBUTIONS TO THE STUDY OF THE BIOLOGY OF THE CHIPMUNK (EUTAMIAS ASIATICUS GM.) IN THE PACIFIC PROVINCE. K. A. Pijater-plokhozkij. Bull. Plant Protection, Lenin Acad. Agric. Sci., vol.4, no.2, pp.47-53, 1932.

A BIOLOGY OF THE CHIPMUNK (EUTAMIAS ASIATICUS) IN THE PACIFIC PROVINCE. K. A. Pliater-Plokohotskii. Bull. Plant Protection, Leningrad, The Lenin Acad. Agric. Sci. in USSR, ser.4, no.2, pp.47-53, 1932.

SUSLIKS, CITELLUS PYGMAEUS PALL. (MAMMALIA, GLIRES) IN THE VOLGA-URAL SANDS. G. Rall. Vestnik Mikrobiol., Epidemiol. i. Parazitol. (Rev. Microbiol., Epidemiol., et Parasitol.), Saratov, vol.15, nos.3-4, pp.363-379, figs.3, tables 2, 1936.

(DISTRIBUTION OF GROUND SQUIRRELS (CITELLUS PYGMAEUS PALL.) IN THE SAND STEPPE OF WESTERN KAZAKHSTAN.) Verbreitung der Zieseln Citellus pygmaeus Pall. in der Sand-steppe der Westlichen Kasakstans. G. Rall, I. Chudjakow. Vestnik Mikrobiol., Epidemiol. i Parazitol. (Rev. Microbiol., Epidemiol., et Parasitol.), Saratov, vol.12, no.3, pp. 189-198, fig.1, 1934.

THE LIFE OF THE GROUND SQUIRREL, CITELLUS RELICTUS KASHKAROV, ON THE BANKS OF THE LAKE ISSYK-KUL (CENTRAL TJAN-SHAN MOUNTAINS). Yu Rall. Zool. Jour. USSR, Moscow, vol.24, no.6, pp.361-372, tables 4, map 1, 1945.

NOTES ON THE BIOLOGY OF THE LITTLE GROUND SQUIRREL (CITELLUS PYGMAEUS PALL.) IN PLAGUE ENDEMIC AND PLAGUE-FREE AREAS OF WEST KAZAKHSTAN. Yu Rall. Rev. Microbiol., 12 (2): 139-150, 1929.

ON A NEW RACE OF CALLOSCIURUS VITTATUS (RAFFLES) FROM SINGAPORE ISLAND. H. C. Robinson. Jour. Fed. Malay States Mus., Kuala Lumpui, vol.7, pt.2, pp.73-74, Dec., 1916.

ON TWO NEW SUBSPECIES OF SQUIRREL FROM SOUTHERN INDIA. H. C. Robinson. Records Indian Mus., Calcutta, vol.13, pt.1, pp.41-42, Mar., 1917.

ON A NEW RACE OF CALLOSCIURUS ATRODORSALIS (GRAY) FROM NORTH SIAM. H. C. Robinson, R. C. Wroughton. Jour. Fed. Malay States Mus., Kuala Lumpui, vol.7, pt.2, p.91, Dec., 1916.

THE SQUIRREL SCIURUS VULGARIS EXALBIDUS PALL. IN THE FOREST-STEPPE OF TRANSURAL. V. S. Smirnov. Zool. Zhurnal, Moscow, 36 (6): 933-937, 1957.

THE CEYLON ROCK SQUIRREL. S. V. O. Somanader. Loris, Ceylon, vol.2, no.2, pp.118-120, illus., June, 1940.

NOTES ON THE EAST ASIATIC MEMBERS OF THE SPECIES SCIURUS VULGARIS, LINN., WITH DESCRIPTIONS OF TWO NEW SUBSPECIES. Arthur de C. Sowerby. Ann. and Mag. Nat. Hist., ser.9, vol.7, pp.249-254, Mar., 1921.

ON THE SCIURIDAE-FAUNA IN THE SOUTHERN PART OF YUNNAN-PROVINCE (CHINA). A. S. Stroganova. Zool. Zhurnal, Moscow, 36 (11): 1761-1769, 1957.

A NEW SQUIRREL FROM BURMA. George H. H. Tate. Amer. Mus. Novitates, New York, no.1676, pp.1-2, June 28, 1954.

DESCRIPTION OF A NEW CHINESE SQUIRREL. Oldfield Thomas. Ann. and Mag. Nat. Hist. (6), vol.16, no.93, p.242, Sept., 1895,

EUPETAURUS, A NEW FORM OF FLYING SQUIRREL FROM KASHMIR. Oldfield Thomas. Jour. Asiatic Soc. Bengal, vol. 57, pt.2, no.3, pp.256-260, pls.22-23, 1888.

EXHIBITION OF A SERIES OF SPECIMENS OF A SIAMESE SQUIRREL, SCIURUS FINLAYSONI. Oldfield Thomas. Proc. Zool. Soc., London, p.245-246, Apr.5, 1898.

A NEW MARMOT FROM CHITRAL. Oldfield Thomas. Jour. Bombay Nat. Hist. Soc., vol.24, no.2, pp.341-342, Jan.31, 1916.

ON A NEW MARMOT FROM NORTH SIBERIA. Oldfield Thomas. Ann. and Mag. Nat. Hist. (7), vol.9, no.54, pp.444-445, June, 1902.

ON A REMARKABLE NEW SQUIRREL FROM BURMA. Oldfield Thomas. Ann. and Mag. Nat. Hist. (7), vol.16, no.93, pp.314-315, Sept., 1905.

ON SOME SQUIRRELS FROM THE MERGUI ARCHIPELAGO. Oldfield Thomas. Jour. Bombay Nat. Hist. Soc., vol.29, pp.376-377, Aug.25, 1923.

A REMARKABLY COLOURED SQUIRREL FROM N. SIAM. Oldfield Thomas. Ann. and Mag. Nat. Hist. (10), vol.2, no.7, pp.100-101, July, 1928.

SCIENTIFIC RESULTS OF THE MAMMAL SURVEY. VIII. A NEW BURMESE SQUIRREL. Oldfield Thomas. Jour. Bombay Nat. Hist. Soc., vol.23, no.2, pp.203-204, Nov. 20, 1914.

SCIENTIFIC RESULTS OF THE MAMMAL SURVEY, VIII. ON UPPER BURMA SQUIRRELS REFERRABLE TO SCIURUS SLADENI AND HARINGTONI. Oldfield Thomas. Jour. Bombay Nat. Hist. Soc., vol.23, no.2, pp.197-199, Nov.20, 1914.

SCIENTIFIC RESULTS OF THE MAMMAL SURVEY. VIII. TWO NEW FLYING SQUIRRELS. Oldfield Thomas. Jour. Bombay Nat. Hist. Soc., vol.23, no.2, pp. 204-205, Nov.20, 1914.

SCIENTIFIC RESULTS FROM THE MAMMAL SURVEY. XI. B. THE GIANT SQUIRRELS OF CEYLON. Oldfield Thomas, R. C. Wroughton. Jour. Nat. Hist. Soc., vol.24, pp.34-36, Sept.30, 1915.

SCIENTIFIC RESULTS FROM THE MAMMAL SURVEY. XI. C. THE SINGHALESE SPECIES OF FUNAMBULUS. Oldfield Thomas, R. C. Wroughton. Jour. Bombay Nat. Hist. Soc., vol.24, pp.37-41, Sept. 30, 1915.

SCIENTIFIC RESULTS FROM THE MAMMAL SURVEY. XII. ON THE SQUIRRELS OBTAINED BY MESSRS. SHORTRIDGE AND MACMILLAN ON THE CHINDWIN RIVER, UPPER BURMA. Oldfield Thomas, R. C. Wroughton. Jour. Bombay Nat. Hist. Soc., vol.24, pp.224-239, pls.2, Jan.31, 1916.

SCIENTIFIC RESULTS FROM THE MAMMAL SURVEY. XIII. C. ON SQUIRRELS OF THE GENUS DREMOMYS. Oldfield Thomas. Jour. Bombay Nat. Hist. Soc., vol.24, no.3, pp.417-419, June 20, 1916.

SCIENTIFIC RESULTS FROM THE MAMMAL SURVEY. XIII. D. THE SQUIRRELS OF THE TOMEUTES LOKROIDES AND MEARSI GROUPS. Oldfield Thomas, R. C. Wroughton. Jour. Bombay Nat. Hist. Soc., vol.24, no.3, pp.419-422, June 20, 1916.

SCIENTIFIC RESULTS FROM THE MAMMAL SURVEY. XIII. E. A NEW FLYING SQUIRREL FROM TENASSERIM. Oldfield Thomas. Jour. Bombay Nat. Hist. Soc., vol.24, no.3, pp.419-422, June 20, 1916.

SCIENTIFIC RESULTS FROM THE MAMMAL SURVEY. XIII. F. A NEW FLYING SQUIRREL FROM THE CHIN HILLS. Oldfield Thomas, R. C. Wroughton. Jour. Bombay Hist. Soc., vol.24, no.3, pp.423-425, June 20, 1916.

SCIENTIFIC RESULTS FROM THE MAMMAL SURVEY. XIV. D. THE SQUIRRELS OF THE FUNAMBULUS PALMARUM-TRI TRIATUS GROUP IN THE PENINSULA. Oldfield Thomas, R. C. Wroughton. Jour. Bombay Nat. Hist. Soc., vol.24, no.4, pp. 644-646, Oct.25, 1916.

SCIENTIFIC RESULTS FROM THE MAMMAL SURVEY. XXXIX. ON THE LARGE SQUIRRELS OF THE RARUFA GIGANTEA GROUP. Oldfield Thomas. Jour. Bombay Nat. Hist. Soc., vol.29, no.1, pp.85-86, Apr.20, 1923.

SCIENTIFIC RESULTS OF THE MAMMAL SURVEY. XLV. TWO NEW FLYING SQUIRRELS FROM THE MERGUI ARCHIPELAGO. Oldfield Thomas. Jour. Bombay Nat. Hist. Soc., vol.31, no.1, p.22, May 15, 1926.

SOME NEW INSULAR SQUIRRELS OF THE CALLOSCIURUS CANICEPS-CONCOLOR GROUP FROM PENINSULAR SIAM. Oldfield Thomas, H. C. Robinson. Ann. and Mag.' Nat. Hist., ser.9, vol.7, pp.118-123, Jan., 1921.

BIOLOGY AND ECOLOGY OF THE MAMMALS OF THE BARSA-KELMES ISLAND IN THE ARAL SEA, TOGETHER WITH DATA ON THE ACCLIMATIZATION OF CITELLUS FULVUS ON THIS ISLAND. V. K. Timofeev. Zool. Zhurnal, Moscow, vol.13, no.4, pp.731-758, figs.77, 1934.

FLYING SQUIRRELS OF TENASSERIM. W. S. Wood. Jour. Bombay Nat. Hist. Soc., vol.32, p.373, Oct.20, 1927.

AN ASSAM REPRESENTATIVE OF THE C. CASTANEOVENTRIS GROUP OF SQUIRREL. R. C. Wroughton. Jour. Bombay Nat. Hist. Soc., vol.27, no.3, p.601, Mar.31, 1921.

A NEW SQUIRREL FROM BURMAH. R. C. Wroughton. Ann. Mag. Nat. Hist., ser.8, vol.2, p.491, Dec., 1908.

SCIENTIFIC RESULTS FROM THE MAMMAL SURVEY. XIII. G. NEW RODENTS FROM SIKKIM. I. A NEW CALLOSCIURUS OF THE ERYTHRAEUS GROUP. R. C. Wroughton. Jour. Bombay Nat. Hist. Soc., vol.24, no.3, pp.425-430, June 20, 1916.

SCIENTIFIC RESULTS FROM THE MAMMAL SURVEY. XX. C. TWO NEW FORMS OF THE FUNAMBULUS TRISTRIATUS GROUP. R. C. Wroughton, W. M. Davidson. Jour. Bombay Nat. Hist. Soc., vol. 26, no.3, pp.728-730, Oct.20, 1919.

SCIENTIFIC RESULTS FROM THE MAMMAL SURVEY. XXIV. THE MAINLAND REPRESENTATIVE OF RATUFA M. DANDOLENA. R. C. Wroughton. Jour. Bombay Nat. Hist. Soc., vol.27, no.2, pp.249-250, Dec.20, 1920.

SCIENTIFIC RESULTS FROM THE MAMMAL SURVEY. XXVII. ON THE ERYTHROEUS GROUP OF SQUIRRELS. R. C. Wroughton. Jour. Bombay Nat. Hist. Soc., vol.27, no.4, pp.773-777, July 31, 1921.

SOME NOTES ON THE GIANT SQUIRRELS OF INDIA, BURMA AND CEYLON. R. C. Wroughton. Jour. Bombay Nat. Hist. Soc., vol.19, no.4, pp.880-896, Feb.28, 1910.

NOTES ON INDO-MALAYAN SQUIRRELS. Jour. Fed. Malay States Mus., vol.4, no. 2, pp.166-168, Apr., 1911.

Biochemistry

STUDIES ON THE BIOCHEMISTRY OF THE ARCTIC GROUND SQUIRREL. Xavier J. Musacchia. Jour. Mam., 33 (3): 356-362, Aug., 1952.

BLEACHING EXPERIMENTS ON EYES OF LIVING GREY SQUIRRELS (SCIURUS CAROLINENSIS LEUCOTIS). R. A. Weale. Jour. Physiol., Lond., vol.127, no.3, pp. 587-591, Mar., 1955.

Canada

NOTES ON CHIPMUNKS OF THE GENUS EUTAMIAS IN CANADA. R. M. Anderson, A. L. Rand. Canadian Field-Nat., Sutton West, vol.57, nos.7, 8, pp.133-135, Oct.-Nov., 1943.

THE NORTHERN CHIPMUNK IN PARRY SOUND DISTRICT. James L. Baillie, Jr. Canadian Field-Naturalist, Ottawa, vol. 53, no.4, p.59, Apr.15, 1939.

(FAUNAL NOTE.) Note faunistique. (OCCURRENCE OF CITELLUS TRIDECEMLINEATUS IN THE PROVINCE OF QUEBEC.) Richard Bernard. Le Naturaliste Canadien, Quebec, vol.67 (ser.3, vol.11), nos.4-5, pp.155-156, Apr.-May, 1940.

THE RICHARDSON GROUND SQUIRREL, CITELLUS RICHARDSONII SABINE, IN SOUTHERN ALBERTA: ITS IMPORTANCE AND CONTROL. John H. Brown, G. Douglas Roy. Sci. Agr., 24 (4): 176-197, 1943.

THE BRITISH COLUMBIA WOODCHUCK MARMOTA MONAX PETRENSIS HOWELL. I. McTaggart Cowan. Canadian Field-Nat., vol.47, p.57, Mar., 1933.

THE DISTRIBUTION OF FLYING SQUIRRELS IN WESTERN BRITISH COLUMBIA WITH THE DESCRIPTION OF A NEW RACE. I. McTaggart Cowan. Proc. Biol. Soc. Washington, vol.50, pp.77-82, June 22, 1937.

NOTES ON THE DISTRIBUTION OF THE CHIPMUNKS (EUTAMIAS) IN SOUTHERN BRITISH COLUMBIA AND THE ROCKY MOUNTAIN REGION OF SOUTHERN ALBERTA WITH DESCRIPTIONS OF TWO NEW RACES. I. McTaggart Cowan. Proc. Biol. Soc. Washington, vol.59, pp.107-118, Oct.25, 1946.

THE VANCOUVER ISLAND MARMOT. G. Clifford Carl. Victoria Nat., vol.1, no.6, pp.77-78, 1944.

THE LITTLE NORTHERN CHIPMUNK IN SOUTHERN MANITOBA. Stuart Criddle. Can. Field-Nat., 57 (4-5): 81-86, Apr.-May, 1943.

THE THIRTEEN-STRIPED GROUND SQUIRREL IN MANITOBA. Stuart Criddle. Can. Field-Nat., 53 (1): 1-6, Jan., 1939.

THE FRANKLIN SPERMOPHILE IN ONTARIO. Morris M. Green. Jour. Mam., vol.13, no.3, pp.277-278, Aug., 1932.

RED NOSED RASCAL. (COLUMBIAN GROUND SQUIRREL.) Burt Gresham. Canadian Nature, Toronto, vol.3, no.3, p.91, illus., May-June, 1941.

OCCURRENCE OF GRAY SQUIRREL IN MANITOBA. V. W. Jackson. Canadian Field-Nat., Ottawa, vol.54, no.5, p.75, May, 1940.

CHANGES IN THE SQUIRREL POPULATION OF CHARLOTTEVILLE TOWNSHIP, NORFOLK COUNTY, ONTARIO, 1898-1940. Monroe Landon. Canadian Field-Nat., Ottawa, vol.55, no.7, pp.102-103, Oct., 1941.

WHAT IS WEE-NESKW OF THE LABRADOR INDIANS? Truman Michelson. Jour. Mam., vol.16, no.3, p.230, Aug., 1935.

GRAY SQUIRREL (SCIURUS CAROLINENSIS) IN SASKATCHEWAN. Robert W. Nero. Blue Jay, Saskatchewan Nat. Hist. Soc., 16 (1): 33-35, Mar., 1958.

AN INTRODUCED POPULATION OF THE GRAY SQUIRREL (SCUIRUS CAROLINENSIS GMELIN) IN BRITISH COLUMBIA. D. J. Robinson, I. McTaggart Cowan. Canadian Jour. Zool., vol.32, no.3, pp.261-282, June, 1954.

DISCOVERY, HABITAT AND DISTRIBUTION OF THE BLACK-TAILED PRAIRIE-DOG IN WESTERN CANADA. J. Dewey Soper. Jour. Mam., vol.19, no.3, pp.290-300, figs.2, Aug.18, 1938.

FURTHER DATA ON THE BLACK-TAILED PRAIRIE-DOG IN WESTERN CANADA. J. Dewey Soper. Jour. Mam., Balto., vol.25, no.1, pp.47-48, Feb., 1944.

NOTES ON GRAY SQUIRREL IN NEW BRUNSWICK. Susan K. Squires. Canadian Field-Nat., vol.38, pp.158-159, Oct (Nov.), 1924.

Care in Captivity

THE CHRONICLE OF OBADIAH. (ACCOUNT OF WOODCHUCK IN CAPTIVITY.) K. F. Bascom. Nat. Mag., vol.8, pp.201-204, illus., Oct., 1926.

EXPERIMENTAL FEEDING OF CAPTIVE FOX SQUIRRELS. Philip Baumgras. Jour. Wildlife Management, Menasha, vol.8, no. 4, pp.296-300, Oct., 1944.

PRAIRIE DOGS AS PETS. Don Dale. Oklahoma Game and Fish News, Oklahoma City, vol.2, no.12, pp.6-7, illus., Dec., 1946.

PRAIRIE DOGS AS PETS. H. F. Dale. Outdoor Nebraska, Lincoln, vol.24, no.4, p.22, 1947.

A SQUIRREL IN THE FAMILY. Olga F. DeGroff. Audubon Mag., New York, vol. 48, no.6, pp.269-372, illus., Nov.-Dec., 1946.

RASCAL, A FOUNDLING CHUCK. Charlotte B. Dowd. Audubon Mag., New York, vol.46, no.4, pp.217-220, illus., July-Aug., 1944.

(OBSERVATIONS ON RAISING SQUIRRELS (SCIURUS VULGARIS) IN CAPTIVITY.) Beobachtungen ueber die Aufzucht von Eichhoernchen (Sciurus vulgaris) in der Gefangenschaft. Wolfgang Gewalt. Zool. Garten, Leipzig, vol.19, no.1, pp.26-33, illus., 1952.

NIGERIAN PETS. V.--"WHISKERS" THE PALM SQUIRREL. F. D. Golding. Nigerian Field, London, vol.7, no.3, pp. 121-123, illus., July, 1938.

THE RED SQUIRREL FARM. Robert T. Hatt. Nat. Hist., vol.29, pp.319-326, illus., May, 1929.

GRAY SQUIRRELS BORN AND RAISED IN CAPTIVITY. Lawrence Kilham. Jour. Mam., vol.34, no.4, pp.509-510, Nov.13, 1953.

LIFE WITH A FLYING SQUIRREL INFANT. Eliza Robert. Nature Mag., Washington, vol.44, no.2, p.80, Feb., 1951.

CALIFORNIA SCIURIDAE IN CAPTIVITY. Roland Case Ross. Jour. Mam., vol.11, no.1, pp.76-78, Feb., 1930.

(THE MARMOT OF THE ALPS IN CAPTIVITY.) La marmotte des Alpes en captivite. P. Roux. La Terre et la Vie, 8e annee, no. 1, pp.3-12, illus., Jan.-Feb., 1938.

GOLDEN-MANTLED GROUND SQUIRRELS RAISED IN CAPTIVITY. Raymond M. Selle. Jour. Mam., vol.20, no.1, pp.106-107, Feb.14, 1939.

CUTIE, A PRAIRIE PET. (PRAIRIE-DOG.) Lorene Squire. Nature Mag., vol.6, pp. 135-139, 6 figs., 1 pl., Sept., 1925.

UNUSUAL PETS THAT ARE READILY TAMED: "FLYING" SQUIRRELS. Ernest P. Walker. Illus. London News, vol.218, no.5836, pp.302-303, illus., Feb.24, 1951.

FEEDING AND CARING FOR SQUIRRELS. USDA, Biol. Survey, Wildl. Leaflet 80, 2 pp., Jan., 1937.

SQUIRRELS AS PETS. All-Pets Mag., Fond du Lac, vol.16, no.13, p.54, June, 1945.

Central America

A NEW SQUIRREL FROM HONDURAS. E. A. Goldman. Jour. Washington Acad. Sci., vol.22, no.10, pp.274-275, May 19, 1932.

A NEW FLYING SQUIRREL FROM HONDURAS. George G. Goodwin. Amer. Mus. Novitates, no.898, pp.1-2, Dec.31, 1936.

A NEW SQUIRREL FROM GUATEMALA. George G. Goodwin. Amer. Mus. Novitates, no.574, pp.2, Oct.22, 1932.

TWO NEW SQUIRRELS FROM COSTA RICA. George G. Goodwin. Amer. Mus. Novitates, New York, no.1218, pp.2, Feb.11, 1943.

A NEW SQUIRREL FROM COSTA RICA. William P. Harris, Jr. Occas. Papers Mus. Zool. Univ. Michigan, no.219, pp.4, Oct.15, 1930.

A NEW SQUIRREL OF THE SCIURUS HOFFMANNI GROUP FROM COSTA RICA. William P. Harris, Jr. Occas. Papers Mus. Zool., Univ. Michigan, no.227, pp. 1-3, June 4, 1931.

REVISION OF SCIURUS VARIEGATOIDES, A SPECIES OF CENTRAL AMERICAN SQUIRREL. William P. Harris, Jr. Misc. Publ. no.38, Mus. Zool., Univ. Michigan, pp.39, figs.3, pls.2, folded map, Sept.4, 1937.

A NEW PIGMY SQUIRREL FROM CENTRAL AMERICA. E. W. Nelson. Proc. Biol. Soc. Washington, vol.16, pp.121-122, Sept.30, 1903.

Climbing Habits

TREE-CLIMBING WOODCHUCKS. B. S. Bowdish. Jour. Mam., vol.3, no.4, p.259, Nov., 1922.

TREE-CLIMBING CALLOSPERMOPHILUS. E. Raymond Hall. The Murrelet, vol.12, no.2, p.54, May, 1931.

WOODCHUCK CLIMBS TREES. Cleveland P. Hickman. Jour. Mam., vol.3, no.4, pp. 260-261, Nov., 1922.

OBSERVATIONS OF THE TREE-CLIMBING HABITS OF THE CALIFORNIA GROUND SQUIRREL. Lloyd G. Ingles. Jour. Mam., vol.26, no.4, p.438, Feb.12, 1946.

TREE-CLIMBING WOODCHUCKS AGAIN. Arthur M. Johnson. Jour. Mam., vol.7, no.2, pp.132-133, May, 1926.

THE TREE-CLIMBING HABITS OF WOODCHUCKS. Olvier P. Medsger. Jour. Mam., vol.3, no.4, pp.261-262, Nov., 1922.

CLIMBING ABILITY OF THE NORTHEASTERN CHIPMUNK. Norman A. Preble. Jour. Mam., vol.20, no.3, p.373, Aug.14, 1939.

ANOTHER TREE-CLIMBING WOODCHUCK. Wallace Havelock Robb. Jour. Mam., vol. 7, no.2, p.133, May, 1926.

TREE-CLIMBING WOODCHUCKS. C. Lee Shilliday. Jour. Mam., vol.6, no.2, pp. 127-128, May, 1925.

ANOTHER TREE-CLIMBING WOODCHUCK. Dayton Stoner. Jour. Mam., vol.3, no.4, p.260, Nov., 1922.

CALLOSPERMOPHILUS CLIMBING TREES. Arthur Svihla. The Murrelet, vol.12, no.3, p.80, Sept., 1931.

Development

RATE OF DEVELOPMENT OF YOUNG SPOTTED GROUND SQUIRRELS. W. Frank Blair. Jour. Mam., vol.23, no.3, pp.342-343, Aug.14, 1942.

SEASONAL ACTIVITY AND GROWTH IN THE DOUGLAS GROUND SQUIRREL. Elton R. Edge. Jour. Mam., vol.12, no.3, pp. 194-200, pls.2, 7-8, Aug., 1931.

(ON THE EARLY DEVELOPMENT OF THE SQUIRREL.) Ueber die Jugendentwicklung des Eichhoernchens. Harry Frank. Zeitschr. Tierpsych Berlin, vol.9, no.1, pp.12-22, 1952.

DEVELOPMENT OF CAPTIVE SQUIRRELS. Frank F. Gander. Jour. Mam., vol.11, no. 3, pp.315-317, Aug., 1930.

OBSERVATIONS ON YOUNG PRAIRIE-DOGS (CYNOMYS LUDOVICIANUS) BORN IN THE LABORATORY. George Edwin Johnson. Jour. Mam., vol.8, no.2, pp.110-115, pls. 3, 11-13, May, 1927.

PRELIMINARY GROWTH STUDIES OF THE BARROW GROUND SQUIRREL, CITELLUS PARRYI BARROWENSIS. William V. Mayer. Anatomical Record, Phila., vol.113, no.4, pp.585-586, Aug., 1952.

DEVELOPMENTAL PATTERNS IN THE BARROW GROUND SQUIRREL, SPERMOPHILUS UNDULATUS BARROWENSIS. William V. Mayer. Growth, vol.18, pp. 53-69, illus., 1954.

EARLY DEVELOPMENT IN SOME SCIURIDAE. J. P. Schooley. Jour. Morph., vol. 56, no.3, pp.477-506, 2 pls., 19 figs., Dec.5, 1934.

DEVELOPMENT OF YOUNG RED SQUIRRELS. Ruth Dowell Svihla. Jour. Mam., vol.11, no.1, pp.79-80, Feb., 1930.

(TABLE OF NORMS REGARDING THE DEVELOPMENTAL HISTORY OF THE GROUND SQUIRREL (SPERMOPHILUS CITILLUS).) Normentafel sur Entwicklungsgeschichte des Ziesels (Spermophilus citillus). Otomar Voelker. Norment. Entwickl. Wirbeltiere, Heft 13, pp.i-vi, 1-332, 3 pls., Jena., 1922.

ARE OHIO SQUIRRELS "SECOND BROODS?" Ohio Conserv. Bull., Columbus, vol.9, no. 9, p.27, illus., Sept., 1945.

Diseases and Parasites

ON A NEW NEMATODE PARASITE OF THE HIMALAYAN FLYING SQUIRREL (PTEROMYS INORNATUS GEOFFROY). M. Abdussalam. Proc. Indian Acad. Sci., Banglor City, vol.7, sect.B, no.6, pp.323-326, figs.3, June, 1938.

GREY SQUIRREL PARASITISM BY HEEL FLY LARVAE. Thomas Z. Atkeson, Lawrence Givens. Jour. Wildlife Mgt., 15 (1): 105-106, Jan., 1951.

THE FLEA GENUS THRASSIS AND SYLVATIC PLAGUE, WITH THE DESCRIPTION OF T. BRENNANI N. SP. (MARMOTS AND GROUND SQUIRRELS.) Gustaf F. Augustson. Jour. Parasitol., Lancaster, vol.30, no.4, pp.237-240, Aug., 1944.

A NOTE ON THE PROBABLE RELATIONSHIP OF FLEA INDEX TO EPIZOOTIC PLAGUE IN GROUND SQUIRRELS IN ALBERTA. John H. Brown. Jour. Ent. and Zool., 36 (3): 70-71, Sept., 1944.

SYLVATIC PLAGUE; A NOTE ON THE FINDING OF LARGE NUMBERS OF FLEAS ON GROUND SQUIRRELS (GOPHERS) IN ALBERTA. John H. Brown. Bull. Brklyn. Ent. Soc., 39 (3): 80-82, June, 1944.

HELMINTHS OF TREE SQUIRRELS IN SOUTHEAST TEXAS. Asa C. Chandler. Jour. Parasitology, 28 (2): 135-140, Apr., 1942.

NOTES ON MONILIFORMIS CLARKI IN NORTH AMERICAN SQUIRRELS. Asa C. Chandler. Jour. Parasitology, 33 (3): 278-281, June, 1947.

IXODES MARMOTAE. A NEW SPECIES OF TICK FROM MARMOTS (ACARINA: IXODIDAE). R. A. Cooley, Glen M. Kohls. Pub. Health Rep., 53 (49): 2174-2181, Dec., 1938.

THE ANIMAL PARASITES OF THE WOODCHUCK, MARMOTA MONAX LINN., WITH SPECIAL REFERENCE TO THE PROTOZOA. Hubert B. Crouch. PhD thesis, Iowa State Coll., 1936.

AMERICAN Q FEVER: EXPERIMENTAL TRANSMISSION BY THE ARGASID TICKS ORNITHODOROS MOUBATA AND O. HERMSI. Gordon E. Davis. Pub. Health Rep., 58 (26): 984-987, June, 1943.

SYLVATIC PLAGUE IN PARK COUNTY, COLORADO. (HEAVY MORTALITY AMONG PRAIRIE-DOGS AND GROUND SQUIRRELS.) Dean H. Ecke, Clifford W. Johnson. Trans. N.A. Wildl. Conf., 15: 191-196, 1950.

PLAGUE INFECTION DISCOVERED IN FLEAS AND LICE TAKEN FROM MARMOTS IN MONTANA AND IN A MARMOT FROM UTAH. C. R. Eskey. Pub. Health Rep., 51 (34): 1159-1160, Aug.21, 1936.

PLAGUE INFECTION IN FLEAS FROM MONTEREY COUNTY, AND THE LAKE TAHOE REGION, CALIFORNIA. (GROUND SQUIRRELS AND CHIPMUNKS.) C. R. Eskey, K. F. Meyer. Pub. Health Repts., U.S. Treasury Dept., vol.51, no. 44, p.1505, Oct.30, 1936.

FIELD STUDY OF GROUND SQUIRREL (CITELLUS BEECHEYI) IN RELATION TO SYLVATIC PLAGUE. F. C. Evans, R. Holdenried. Proc. Soc. for Exp. Biol. and Med., 47 (1): 63-64, May, 1941.

SYLVATIC PLAGUE STUDIES. III. AN EPIZOOTIC OF PLAGUE AMONG GROUND SQUIRRELS (CITELLUS BEECHEYI) IN KERN COUNTY, CALIFORNIA. F. C. Evans, C. M. Wheeler, J. R. Douglas. Jour. Infectious Dis., 72 (1): 68-76, Feb., 1943.

THE DISTRIBUTION OF ORCHOPEAS WICKHAMI (BAKER)(SIPHONAPTERA), IN RELATION TO ITS HOST, THE AMERICAN GREY SQUIRREL. R. B. Freeman. Entomol. Monthly Mag., London, vol.77, pp.82-89, 1941.

THE MORPHOLOGY AND TAXONOMY OF THE INTESTINAL PROTOZOA OF THE AMERICAN WOODCHUCK MARMOTA MONAX, LINNAEUS. James R. Gabel. Ph.D. thesis, U. Pa., 124 pp., 1953.

ANIMAL PARASITES OF THE FOX SQUIRREL, SCIURUS NIGER RUFIVENTER, IN SOUTHEASTERN KANSAS. Edward Graham, Jacob Uhrich. Jour. Parasitology, 29 (2): 159-160, Apr., 1943.

ON THE SUSCEPTIBILITY OF GROUND SQUIRRELS TO THE VIRUS OF EQUINE ENCEPHALOMYELITIS AND TICKS AS POSSIBLE VECTORS. Ronald Gwatkin. Can. Jour. Comp. Med., 3 (5): 131-133, May, 1939.

SKIN TUMORS ON SQUIRRELS. Carlton M. Herman, James R. Reilly. Jour. Wildlife Management, vol.19, no.3, pp.402-403, illus., July, 1955.

NOTES ON AFRICAN HAEMAPHYSALIS TICKS. II. THE GROUND-SQUIRREL PARASITES, H. CALCARATA NEUMANN, 1902, AND H. HOUYI NUTTALL AND WARBURTON, 1915 (IXODOIDEA, IXODIDAE). Harry Hoogstraal. Jour. Parasitol., 41 (4): 361-373, Aug., 1955.

A NEW THRASSIS (FLEA) FROM CALIFORNIA AND OREGON; AND FLEAS CARRIED BY SOME OF THE WEST'S

GROUND SQUIRRELS. C. Andersen Hubbard. Pac. Univ. Bull., 38 (6): 1-4, Aug., 1942.

A PICTORIAL REVIEW OF THE NORTH AMERICAN CHIPMUNK FLEAS. C. Andersen Hubbard. Ent. News, 60 (10): 253-261, Dec., 1949.

NOTES ON THE FLEAS OF PRAIRIE DOGS, WITH THE DESCRIPTION OF A NEW SUBSPECIES. William L. Jellison. Pub. Health Repts., Washington, D.C., vol.54, no.20, pp.840-844, illus., May 19, 1939.

SIPHONAPTERA: THE GENUS OROPSYLLA IN NORTH AMERICA. (CITELLUS, CALLOSPERMOPHILUS, CYNOMYS, AND MARMOTA PARASITIZED.) William L. Jellison. Jour. Parasitol., Lancaster, vol. 31, no.2, pp.83-97, illus., Apr., 1945.

SIPHONAPTERA: HOST DISTRIBUTION OF THE GENUS OPISOCROSTIS JORDAN. (PRAIRIE-DOGS AND GROUND SQUIRRELS.) William L. Jellison. Trans. Am. Micros. Soc., 66 (1): 64-69, Jan., 1947.

AN ANNOTATED BIBLIOGRAPHY OF REFERENCES CONCERNING PARASITES OF SQUIRRELS (FAMILY, SCIURIDAE). Julius S. Katz. Ohio Wildlife Res. Sta., Release 131, 21 pp., Dec., 1939.

A SURVEY OF THE PARASITES FOUND IN AND ON THE FOX SQUIRREL AND THE SOUTHERN GRAY SQUIRREL IN SOUTHERN OHIO. Julius S. Katz. MS thesis, Ohio State Univ., 1938.

RODENT PLAGUE IN CALIFORNIA. W. H. Kellogg. Jour. Amer. Med. Assoc., vol. 105, no.11, pp.856-859, Sept.14, 1935.

METASTASIZING VIRAL FIBROMAS OF GRAY SQUIRRELS: PATHOGENESIS AND MOSQUITO TRANSMISSION. Lawrence Kilham. Am. Jour. Hyg., 61 (1): 55-63, illus., Jan., 1955.

PLAGUE AMONG WILD RODENTS IN RIO ARRIBA COUNTY, NEW MEXICO. Vernon B. Link. Amer. Jour. Trop. Med., Balto., vol.29, no.4, pp.493-500, maps, 1949.

SYLVATIC PLAGUE STUDIES, IX. STUDIES OF THE MICROCLIMATE OF THE CALIFORNIA GROUND SQUIRREL BURROW AND ITS RELATION TO SEASONAL CHANGES IN THE FLEA POPULATION. D. S. Longanecker, A. L. Burroughs. Ecology, 33 (4): 488-499, illus., Oct., 1952.

THE TARBAGAN OR THE TRANSBAIKALIAN MARMOT AS A CARRIER OF PLAGUE. Anatoly S. Loukashkin. Comptes Rendus, 12th Internat. Congr. Zool. 1935, Lisboa, sect.10, pp.2097-2111, 1937.

A NEW TRICHOSTRONGYLID NEMATODE FROM THE STOMACHS OF AMERICAN SQUIRRELS. John T. Lucker. Jour. Wash. Acad. Sci., 33 (3): 75-79, Mar., 1943.

(INFECTIOUS DISEASES OF THE LITTLE GROUND SQUIRREL (CITELLUS PYGMAEUS PALL.) BY SEASON AND AGE.) Sezonnaya i vozrastnaya infektsionnaya chuvstvitelnost malogo suslika (Citellus pygmaeus Pall.) k tulgaremii. N. I. Makarov, E. P. Makarov, V. G. Bagaev. Zool. Zhurnal, vol.34, no.3, pp.652-657, 1955.

PERSISTENCE OF SYLVATIC PLAGUE. (IN CITELLUS BEECHEYI.) K. F. Meyer, B. Eddie. Proc. Soc. Exper. Biol. and Medicine, New York, vol.38, no.3, pp.333-334, Apr., 1938.

A PARASITOLOGICAL SURVEY OF THE GENUS CITELLUS IN MANITOBA. J. A. McLeod. Canadian Jour. Research, vol.9, no.2, pp.108-127, pl.1, figs.18, Aug., 1933.

ON THE PRESERVATION OF THE PLAGUE BACILLUS IN THE GROUND SQUIRREL'S CARCASS. E. I. Novikova, G. A. Lalazarov. Rev. Microbiol., 13: 53-54, 1934.

SUCKING LICE (ANOPLURA) ON MARMOTS. O. W. Olsen. Jour. Parasitology, vol.24, no.3, p.281, June, 1938.

TULAREMIA: SPONTANEOUS OCCURRENCE IN THE CHIPMUNK. R. R. Parker. Pub. Health Rep. 60 (1): 17, Jan.5, 1945.

THE RETURN OF THE CALIFORNIA GRAY SQUIRREL. Ernest A. Payne. Yosemite Nature Notes, 19 (1): 1-3, Jan., 1940.

A CASE OF PERITONEAL MONILIFORMIASIS IN A FOX SQUIRREL. Harold J. Perry. Trans. Am. Micros. Soc., 60 (3): 375-377, July, 1941.

SEASONAL CHANGE IN THE COMPOSITION OF FLEAS IN GROUND SQUIRREL BURROWS IN N.-CHIRSK DISTRICT. I. M. Polyak, V. M. Tumanskii. Rev. Microbiol., 11: 285-287, 1932.

PLAGUE--THE SURVIVAL OF THE INFECTION IN FLEAS OR HIBERNATING GROUND SQUIRRELS. F. M. Prince, N. E. Wayson. Pub. Health Rep., 62 (13): 463-467, Mar.28, 1947.

REPORT ON THE FLEAS OPISOCROSTIS BRUNERI (BAKER) AND THRASSIS BACCHI (ROTHS.) AS VECTORS OF PLAGUE. (THESE FLEAS, INFESTING 3 SPECIES OF CITELLUS, CAN TRANSMIT PLAGUE.) F. M. Prince. Pub. Health Rep., 58 (27): 1013-1016, July 2, 1943.

OBELISCOIDES CUNICULI FROM THE WOODCHUCK IN OHIO AND MICHIGAN. Robert Rausch, Jack D. Tiner. Jour. Mam., 27 (2): 177-178, May, 1946.

ANDRYA SCIURI N. SP., A CESTODE FROM THE NORTHERN FLYING SQUIRREL. Robert Rausch. Jour. Parasitology, Lancaster, vol.33, no.4, pp.316-318, Aug., 1947.

NEW RECORDS OF MACRACANTHORHYNCHUS HIRUDINACEUS IN SCIURIDAE. Robert Rausch. Jour. Parasitology, 32 (1): 94, Feb., 1946.

STUDIES ON THE PARASITIC HELMINTHS OF THE NORTH CENTRAL STATES. I. HELMINTHS OF SCIURIDAE. Robert Rausch, Jack D. Tiner. American Midland Nat., Notre Dame, vol.39, no.3, pp.728-747, fig.1, May, 1948.

SUSCEPTIBILITY OF THE INDIAN GARDEN SQUIRREL (SCIURUS PALMARUM) TO PLASMODIUM BERGHEI AND ITS ASEXUAL PERIODICITY. S. P. Remakrishman, Satya Prakash. Nature, London, vol.167, no.4248, p.533, Mar.31, 1951.

TWO EIMERIA FROM THE FLYING SQUIRREL, GLAUCOMYS VOLANS. Robert L. Roudabush. Jour. Parasitology, 23 (1): 107-108, Feb., 1937.

THREE NEW SPECIES OF NEOHAEMATOPINUS (ANOPLURA, HAEMATOPINIDAE). (GROUND SQUIRREL.) G. J. Rubin. Proc. Ent. Soc. Wash., 48 (5): 119-124, May, 1946.

CONTROL OF PLAGUE VECTORS ON THE CALIFORNIA GROUND SQUIRREL BY BURROW DUSTING WITH INSECTICIDES AND THE SEASONAL INCIDENCE OF FLEAS PRESENT. Raymond E. Ryckman, C. T. Ames, C. C. Lindt, R. D. Lee. Jour. Econ. Ent., 47 (4): 604-607, graphs, Aug., 1954.

SEASONAL INCIDENCE OF FLEAS ON THE CALIFORNIA GROUND SQUIRREL IN ORANGE COUNTY, CALIFORNIA. Raymond E. Ryckman, C. C. Lindt, Charles T. Ames, Robert D. Lee. Jour. Economic Entomol., vol.47, no.6, pp.1070-1074, Dec., 1954.

DOES THE CUTEREBRA EVER EMASCULATE ITS HOST? Ernest T. Seton. Jour. Mam., vol.1, no.2, pp.94-95, Nov., 1919.

A COMPARATIVE STUDY OF RODENT AND BURROW FLEA POPULATIONS. (CITELLUS BEECHEYI.) M. A. Stewart, F. C. Evans. Proc. Soc. for Exp. Biol. and Med., 47 (1): 140-142, May, 1941.

ON A MICROBE ISOLATED FROM GROUND SQUIRRELS IN CONDITIONS OF SPONTANEOUS EPIZOOTIC. P. N. Stupnitzkii, I. S. Tinker. Rev. Microbiol., 12 (3): 167-174, 1933.

SUSCEPTIBILITY OF THE "GOPHER" CITELLUS RICHARDSONII (SABINE), TO LEPTOSPIRA ICEROHEMORRHAGIAE. Jerome T. Syverton, William W. Stiles, George P. Berry. Proc. Soc. Exper. Biol. and Med., New York, vol.39, no.1, pp. 113-115, Oct., 1938.

THE TARBAGAN OR SIBERIAN MARMOT. RESEARCHES INTO THEIR RELATION WITH BUBONIC PLAGUE IN MAN. Wu Lien Teh. China Jour. Sci. and Arts, vol. 1, pp.39-50, 1 pl., Jan., 1923.

SYPHACIA EUTAMII N. SP. FROM THE LEAST CHIPMUNK, EUTAMIAS MINIMUS, WITH A KEY TO THE GENUS (NEMATODA: OXYURIDAE). Jack D. Tiner. Jour. Parasitol., Lancaster, vol.34, no.2, pp. 87-92, Apr., 1948.

SYPHACIA THOMPSONI (NEMATODA: OXYURIDAE) FROM THE RED SQUIRREL. Jack D. Tiner. Jour. Mam., Balto., vol. 30, no.2, pp.202-203, May 23, 1949.

ON THE BEGINNING OF SPONTANEOUS PLAGUE EPIZOOTICS IN GROUND SQUIRRELS (CITELLUS PYGMAEUS PALL.), AND THEIR COURSE. V. M. Tumanskii. Rev. Microbiol., 14: 419-424, 1935.

ON EPIZOOTOLOGY OF TULARAEMIA. I. THE ROLE OF ECTOPARASITES IN THE TULARAEMIC EPIZOOTIC OF GROUND-SQUIRRELS. A. Volferz, S. Kolpakova, A. Flegontova. Revue Microbiol., Epidemiol., et Parasitol., vol.13, no.2, pp.103-118, fig.1, tables 4, 1934.

THE STOMACH WORM, OBELISCOIDES CUNICULI, IN THE WOODCHUCK. F. G. Wallace. Jour. Wildl. Mgt., 6 (1): 92, Jan., 1942.

A CONTRIBUTION TO THE BIOLOGY OF ORNITHODOROS HERMSI WHEELER, HERMS AND MEYER. (SMALL MAMMALS, ESPECIALLY CHIPMUNKS.) C. M. Wheeler. Jour. Parasitol., 29 (1): 33-41, Feb., 1943.

ENTO- AND ECTO- PARASITES OF THE STEPPE GROUND SQUIRREL, CITELLUS PYGMAEUS PALL. D. Zasukhin, V. Tiflov. Rev. Microbiol., 11: 129-132, 1932.

RESEARCH ON THE EPIZOOTOLOGY OF PLAGUE AMONG GROUND SQUIRRELS (CITELLUS PYGMAEUS PALL.) IN AN ENDEMIC FOCUS. RESULTS OF THE WORK OF THE NORTHERN CAUCASUS ANTI-PLAGUE ORGANIZATION, 1926-33. Rev. Microbiol., 13: 219-222, 1934.

## Ecology

TALL GRASS DEFEATS PRAIRIE DOGS. Philip F. Allan, Ben Osborn. Soil Cons., 20 (5): 103-105, 113, illus., Dec., 1954.

AN ECOLOGICAL STUDY OF TREE SQUIRRELS IN EASTERN TEXAS. Rollin H. Baker. Jour. Mam., 25 (1): 8-24, Feb., 1944.

(ECOLOGIC LAWS OF THE STATIONARY DISTRIBUTION OF THE SMALL SPERMOPHILE (CITELLUS PYGMAEUS PALL.).) Les lois ecologiques de la distribution stationnaire du petit spermophile (Citellus pygmaeus Pall.). N. B. Birula. Moscou Univ. Sbornik Nauchno issledovatel'-skogo inst. Zool. (Abstracts Works Zool. Inst. Moscou State Univ.), no.3, pp.117-144, figs.5, 1936.

EUCALYPTUS TREE UTILIZED BY FOX SQUIRREL IN CALIFORNIA. Jean T. Boulware. Am. Midland Nat., 26 (3): 696-697, Nov., 1941.

WOODCHUCKS OBSERVED WHILE FIGHTING. Charles P. Brown. Jour. Mam., vol.29, no.1, p.70, Feb.13, 1948.

A NATURE DRAMA. (PRAIRIE DOGS.) E. C. Cates. Jour. Mam., vol.22, no.2, pp.198-199, May 14, 1941.

THE RED SQUIRREL AND THE BIRDS. Floyd B. Chapman. Cardinal, Sewickley, vol.6, no.1, p.6, Jan., 1943.

COOPERATION OF SQUIRREL AND GROUSE. H. H. Chapman. Jour. Wildlife Management, Menasha, vol.8, no.3, p.266, July, 1944.

DEFOLIATION ACTIVITIES OF GRAY SQUIRRELS IN AMERICAN ELM TREES. Carl G. Deuber. Sci. Monthly, vol.38, pp.60-63, illus., Jan., 1934.

A STUDY OF THE RELATION OF THE DOUGLAS GROUND SQUIRREL TO THE VEGETATION AND OTHER ECOLOGICAL FACTORS IN WESTERN OREGON. Elton R. Edge. American Midland Nat., vol.16, no.6, pp.949-959, figs.5, Nov., 1935.

ECOLOGY OF THE CALIFORNIA GROUND SQUIRREL ON GRAZING LANDS. Henry S. Fitch. Am. Midland Nat., 39 (3): 513-596, May, 1948.

(Review by E. Raymond Hall of) THE ECOLOGY OF THE CALIFORNIA GROUND SQUIRREL ON GRAZING LANDS. Henry S. Fitch. Ecology, Brooklyn, vol.30, no.1, p.112, Jan., 1949.

ON COMPETITION BETWEEN SPECIES. MUTUAL RELATIONS BETWEEN THE SQUIRREL (SCIURUS VULGARIS L.), THE CROSSBILL (LOXIA CURVIROSTRA L.), AND THE GREAT SPOTTED WOODPECKER (DRYOBATES MAJOR L.). A. Formozov. Comptes Rendus Acad. Sci. URSS, Leningrad, vol.3, no.3, pp.197-201, July 21, 1934.

(ON THE ECOLOGY OF CITELLUS PYGMAEUS PALL. IN THE PEST-ENDEMIC REGION OF WESTERN KAZAKHSTAN.) Ueber die Okologie von Citellus pygmaeus Pall, im pestendemischen Gebiete des westlichen Kasakstan. A. Furssajev. Zeitschr. f. Saeuget., vol.9, no.1-3, pp. 404-423, fig.1, Dec.12, 1934.

THE ECOLOGY OF THE MARMOT (BAIBAK OR BOBAC (MARMOTA BOBAC)) AND MARMOT TRAPPING. V. V. Gubar, N. M. Dukel'skaya, E. M. Korzinkina, V. P. Teplov. All-Union Sci. Res. Inst. Fur and Game Mgt., 89 pp., 1935.

A COMMENSAL RELATION OF THE CALIFORNIA QUAIL WITH THE CALIFORNIA GROUND SQUIRREL. E. Raymond Hall. Condor, vol.29, p.271, Nov., 1927.

MICROENVIRONMENTAL INFLUENCE OF PERIODICITY IN TOWNSEND GROUND SQUIRRELS. Richard M. Hansen. Jour. Mam., 37 (1): 124, Feb.28, 1956.

ENVIRONMENT OF THE NELSON ANTELOPE GROUND SQUIRREL. Albert C. Hawbecker. Jour. Mam., 34 (3): 324-334, maps, Aug., 1953.

ECOLOGICAL FACTORS AFFECTING THE ACTIVITY OF THE WESTERN FOX SQUIRREL, SCIURUS NIGER RUFIVENTER (GEOFFROY). Ellis A. Hicks. Iowa State Coll. Jour. Sci., 22 (1): 36-38, Oct., 1947; Ecol. Monog., 19 (4): 287-302, Oct., 1949.

SOME RELATIONSHIPS OF QUAIL AND GROUND SQUIRRELS IN CALIFORNIA. E. E. Horn. Jour. Wildl. Mgt., 2 (2): 58-60, Apr., 1938.

RED SQUIRRELS CHASED BY ROBINS. William Marcus Ingram. Jour. Mam., vol.21, no.2, pp.219-220, May 14, 1940.

(MATERIALS ON THE ECOLOGY OF THE TIEN-SHAN MARMOT (MARMOTA BOBAC CENTRALIS THOM.).) Materiali po ekologii tyanshanskogo surka (Marmota bobac centralis Thom.). M. I. Ismagilov. Zool. Zhurnal, Akad. Nauk SSSR, 35 (6): 908-915, 1956.

ECOLOGY OF MIDDLE OB RIVER TREE SQUIRREL. (SBORNIK "EKOLOGI BELKI," KEIZ, 1934.) I. D. Kiris. Moscou Univ. Sbornik Nauchno issledovatel'skogo inst. Zool. (Abstracts Works Zool. Inst. Moscou State Univ.), no.3, p.85, 1936.

ECOLOGY OF THE RED SQUIRREL. A. Brooker Klugh. Jour. Mam., vol.8, no.1, pp.1-32, pls.5, Feb., 1927; Ann. Rept. Board Regents Smithson. Inst. for 1928, pp.495-524, pls.5, Nov.18, 1929.

ON THE INFLUENCE OF THE MARMOT (MARMOTA BABAC MUELL.) ON THE SOIL WITH REFERENCE TO SOME FEATURES OF ITS ECOLOGY. I. A. Krupenikov, S. M. Stepanizkaya. Zool. Jour. USSR, Moscow, vol.22, no.6, pp.369-373, tables 2, 1943.

CONTRIBUTION TO THE ECOLOGY OF LONG-TAILED JACUT GROUND-SQUIRREL (CITELLUS EVERSMANNI JACUTENSIS BRANDT). P. D. Larionov. Zool. Jour. USSR, Moscow, vol.22, no.4, pp.234-246, figs.3, tables 5, 1943.

WOODCHUCKS SURVIVE BRUSH FIRE AND REMAIN IN THE AREA. Daniel L. Leedy. Jour. Mam., Balto., vol.30, no.1, p.73, 1949.

OBSERVATIONS ON THE ECOLOGY OF THE GUNNISON PRAIRIE DOG IN COLORADO. William M. Longhurst. Jour. Mam., 25 (1): 24-36, Feb., 1944.

SOME ASPECTS OF THE ECOLOGY OF THE BARROW GROUND SQUIRREL, CITELLUS PARRYI BARROWENSIS. William V. Mayer. Current Biological Research in the Alaskan Arctic, by I. L. Wiggins, editor, Stanford U. Publ., U. Ser., Biol. Sci., 11 (1): 48-55, 1953.

THE ECOLOGY OF THE AMERICAN GREY SQUIRREL (SCIURUS CAROLINENSIS GMELIN) IN THE BRITISH ISLES. A. D. Middleton. Proc. Zool. Soc. Lond., pt.3, pp.809-843, pls.1-6, figs.1-4, Oct., 1930.

SOME EFFECTS OF ALTITUDES AND LATITUDES ON THE COLUMBIAN GROUND SQUIRREL. A. W. Moore. Jour. Mam., vol.18, no.3, pp.368-369, table 1, Aug.14, 1937.

(CONTRIBUTIONS TO THE ECOLOGY OF MARMOTA M. MARMOTA L.) Beitraege zur Oekologie der Marmota m. marmota L. Detlev Mueller-Using. Zeitschr. Saeugetierk., Berlin, vol.19, no.3, pp.166-177, Dec.31, 1954.

PRAIRIE DOGS IN SHINNERY (OAK SCRUB) SAVANNAH. Ben Osborn. Ecology 23 (1): 110-115, Jan., 1942.

VEGETATION OF AN ABANDONED PRAIRIE-DOG TOWN IN TALL GRASS PRAIRIE. Ben Osborn, Philip F. Allan. Ecology, 30 (3): 322-332, July, 1949.

THE RELATION OF GRAY SQUIRREL POPULATIONS TO HABITAT CONDITIONS IN STONE COUNTY, MISSISSIPPI. Howard R. Redmond. MS thesis, La. State Univ., 1949.

ECOLOGICAL COMPARISONS OF THE PLAINS PRAIRIE-DOG AND THE ZUNI SPECIES. Theo. H. Scheffer. Trans. Kansas Acad. Sci., Lawrence, vol.49, no. 4, pp.401-406, illus., 1947.

MOISTURE AND ALTITUDE AS FACTORS IN DETERMINING THE SEASONAL ACTIVITIES OF THE TOWNSEND GROUND SQUIRREL IN WASHINGTON. William T. Shaw. Ecology, vol.2, pp.189-192, July, 1921.

NOTES ON THE ECOLOGY OF THE COLUMBIAN GROUND SQUIRREL, (CITELLUS COLUMBIANUS COLUMBIANUS) AT PULLMAN, WASHINGTON. William T. Shaw. Murrelet, vol.6, no.125, pp.46-54, Sept., 1925.

THE SEASONAL DIFFERENCES OF NORTH AND SOUTH SLOPES IN CONTROLLING THE ACTIVITIES OF THE COLUMBIAN GROUND SQUIRREL. William T. Shaw. Ecology, vol.6, pp.157-162, Apr. (May), 1925.

GRAY SQUIRREL UTILIZATION OF ELM. J. Kenneth Terres. Jour. Wildlife Management, Menasha, vol.3, no.4, pp.358-359, Oct., 1939.

INVASION OF A LOGGED AREA BY GOLDEN-MANTLED SQUIRRELS. Lloyd Tevis, Jr. Jour. Mam., 37 (2): 291-292, June 9, 1956.

RESULTS OF THE STATION STUDY OF ECOLOGY OF THE MARMOT IN VOLGA-KAMA REGION. V. I. Tikhvinsky. Raboty Volzhsko-Kamskoi Zonal'noi Okhotnich'epromyslonoi Biologischeskoi Stantsii, Kazan, no.3 (Uchen'ie Zapiski Kazanskogo Gosudarstvennogo Universiteta im V. I. Ul'ianova-Lenina, vol.94, no.8), pp.93-125, 1934.

WOODCHUCKS MAY AID THE RABBIT SUPPLY. Farley F. Tubbs. Mich. Cons., 5 (12): 4, May, 1936.

(SOME ASPECTS OF THE ECOLOGY OF C. (ITELLUS) ADOCETUS ARCELLIAE.) Algunos aspectos de la ecologia de C. (itellus) adocetus arcelliae, Villa R. Bernardo Villa R. Anal. Inst. Biol., Mexico, D.F., vol.14, no.1, pp.285-290, figs.A-B, 1943.

(ON THE ECOLOGY OF CITELLUS PYGMAEUS PALL. IN THE PEST ENDEMIC REGION OF WESTERN KAZAKHSTAN.) Ueber die Oekologie von Citellus pygmaeus Pall. im pestendemischen Gebiete des westlichen Kasakstan. J. Volcanezkij, A. Furssajev. Zeitschr. f. Saeugetierkunde, Berlin, vol.9, nos.1-3, pp.404-423, fig.1, Dec.30, 1934.

FOX SQUIRREL UTILIZATION OF OSAGE ORANGE IN KANSAS. H. L. Whitaker. Jour. Wildl. Mgt., 3 (2): 117, Apr., 1939.

POWERFUL GOOD SQUIRREL PASTURE. Lee E. Yeager. Field and Stream, New York, vol.52, no.6, pp.34-35, 127-128, illus., Oct., 1947.

GROWTH RATE OF TREES IN THE VICINITY OF WOODCHUCK BURROWS. Jour. Forestry, 45 (5): 372-373, May, 1947.

Economic Importance

PINE SQUIRRELS REDUCE FUTURE CROPS OF PONDEROSA PINE CONES. Lowell Adams. Jour. For., 53 (1): 35, illus., Jan., 1955.

"CONTROL NOT EXTERMINATION," OF CYNOMYS LUDOVICIANUS ARIZONENSIS. Annie M. Alexander. Jour. Mam., vol.13, no.2, p.302, Aug., 1932.

A NOTE ON SQUIRREL DAMAGE TO CONIFERS. R. E. Balch. Forestry Chron., 18 (1): 42, 1942.

CALIFORNIA GRAY SQUIRREL, AN ENEMY TO THE DOUGLAS FIR. J. Hooper Bowles. Amer. Forestry, vol.26, p.26, Jan., 1920.

WOODCHUCK DEFENSE. W. Z. Bradley. Pennsylvania Game News, Harrisburg, vol.15, pp.11, 28, no.12, Mar., 1945.

TREE DAMAGE BY SQUIRRELS: SILVICULTURALLY SIGNIFICANT? William S. Brenneman. Jour. For., 52 (8): 604, Aug., 1954.

THE RICHARDSON GROUND SQUIRREL, CITELLUS RICHARDSONII SABINE, IN SOUTHERN ALBERTA: ITS IMPORTANCE AND CONTROL. John H. Brown, G. Douglas Roy. Sci. Agric. Ottawa, vol.24, no.4, pp.176-197, maps, 1943.

PRAIRIE DOGS AND THEIR CONTROL. Noble E. Buell. US F&WS, Wildl. Leafl., 357, 4 pp., Aug., 1953.

THE ACTION OF STRYCHNINE ON THE WYOMING GROUND SQUIRREL (CITELLUS ELEGANS ELEGANS). W. L. Burnett. Bull.384, Colorado Agric. College, Ft. Collins, pp.19, Mar., 1932.

PRELIMINARY NOTES ON THE ACTION OF STRYCHNINE ON THE WYOMING GROUND SQUIRREL (CITELLUS ELEGANS ELEGANS). W. L. Burnett. Colorado Agric. Exper. Sta., Press Bull.72, pp.1-3, Apr., 1930.

THE GROUND-HOG MENACE AND PRACTICAL METHODS OF CONTROL. Carlyle Chap. Purdue Agriculturist, vol.19, p.2, Apr., 1925.

MR. WOODCHUCK, MASTER CONSERVATIONIST. Floyd B. Chapman. Ohio Conservation Bull., pp.26-27, June, 1938.

GREY SQUIRRELS. A PROBLEM FOR GAMEKEEPERS AND COUNTY COUNCILS. Cheviot. Field, London, vol.155, no.4040, p.797, May 31, 1930.

SUSCEPTIBILITY OF LARCH TO RED SQUIRREL DAMAGE. David B. Cook. Jour. For., 52 (7): 491-492, illus., July, 1954.

DESTRUCTION OF PAPER TREE TAGS BY SQUIRRELS. James D. Curtis. Jour. For., 50 (3): 220-221, Mar., 1952.

DISTRIBUTION OF GROUND SQUIRRELS AND THEIR IMPORTANCE IN AGRICULTURE IN USSR. B. Iu Falkenstein (Fal'kenshtein). Itogi Nauchno-Issledovatel'skikh Rabot Vsesoiuznogo Instituta Zashchity Rastenii za 1935 (Summary sci. research work Inst. Plant Protection, Leningrad, 1935), pp.40-43, map, 1936.

SQUIRREL DAMAGE TO YOUNG REDWOOD TREES. Emanuel Fritz. Jour. Mam., vol.13, no.1, p.76, Feb., 1932.

FLYING SQUIRRELS AS CITY NUISANCES. F. M. Fryxell. Jour. Mam., vol.7, no.2, p.133, May, 1926.

THE MENACE OF THE GRAY SQUIRREL. P. H. Grimshaw. Scottish Nat., Mar.-Apr., 1931, no.188, pp.33-35, 1931.

PROFIT IN PESTS. (SELLING PRAIRIE DOGS FOR PETS.) Ralph Hadley. All-Pets Mag., Fond du Lac, vol.19, no.9, p. 72, illus., Sept., 1948.

RED SQUIRREL DAMAGE TO PINE AND SPRUCE PLANTATIONS. Arthur C. Hart. Jour. For., 34 (7): 729-730, July, 1936.

OUR CHAMPION TREE PLANTER. (SQUIRREL.) Harriet S. Hawley. Our Dumb Animals, Norwood, vol.81, no.6, p.9, illus., June, 1948.

SQUIRRELS ARE PLANTERS. George Heinold. Forest and Outdoors, Montreal, vol.13, p.419, 1947.

ON THE DESTRUCTION OF THE GROUND SQUIRREL BY THE USE OF BI-SULPHID OF CARBON. E. W. Hilgard. Bull. Univ. Calif., vol.32, pp.339-344, Apr., 1878.

SQUIRRELS CAN BE PESTS. John C. Jones. Pest Control, 17 (11): 8-14, Nov., 1949.

THE CALIFORNIA GROUND SQUIRREL CONTROL PROGRAM. Eugene S. Kellogg. Special Publ.109, Dept. Agric. State Calif., Sacramento, pp.21, 1931.

EFFECTIVENESS OF HYDROGEN SULPHIDE IN VARIOUS HABITATS OF GROUND SQUIRREL IN CONNECTION WITH THE PERSISTENCY OF THIS GAS. K. T. Krylova. Itogi Nauchno Issledovatel'skikh Rabot Vsesoiuznogo Instituta Zashchity Rastenii za 1935 (Summary sci. Research work Inst. Plant Protection, Leningrad, 1935), pp.420-421, 1936.

TOO MANY RED SQUIRRELS. Dick Lederman. Outdoor Life, New York, vol. 102, no.6, p.9, Dec., 1948.

A SQUIRREL DESTRUCTOR. AN EFFICIENT ECONOMICAL METHOD OF DESTROYING GROUND SQUIRRELS. John D. Long. U.S. Publ. Health Serv., Wash., Govt. Print. Off., 1912.

THE TARBAGAN OR THE TRANSBAIKALIAN MARMOT AND ITS ECONOMIC VALUE. Anatoly S. Loukashkin. Comptes Rendus, 12th Internat. Congr. Zool. 1935, Lisboa, sect.10, pp.2233-2293, figs.5, pls.95-97, 1937.

BEFORE YOU CONTROL TREE SQUIRRELS AND CHIPMUNKS CHECK STATE AND LOCAL REGULATIONS. John Ludeman. Pest Control, 22 (9): 16, 18, 20, 22, 50, illus., Sept., 1954.

RED SQUIRRELS ATTACK JAPANESE LARCH. W. F. McCulloch. Jour. For., 35 (7): 692-693, July, 1937.

TABLE MOUNTAIN PINE--SQUIRREL FOOD OR TIMBER TREE? Wm. Mollenhauer, Jr. Jour. For., 37 (5): 420-421, May, 1939.

A FOE TO YOUNG TREES. (GREY SQUIRREL.) M. Portal. Country Life, Lond., vol.91, no.2371, p.1235, June 26, 1942.

EFFECT OF RED SQUIRRELS ON RED PINE SEED PRODUCTION IN OFF YEARS. Eugene I. Roe. Jour. For., 46 (7): 528-529, July, 1948.

RED SQUIRREL DAMAGE TO MATURE RED PINE. T. Schantz-Hansen. Jour. For., 43 (8): 604-605, Aug., 1945.

THE VALUE OF WOODCHUCKS. Walter J. Schoonmaker. Nature Mag., vol.27, no. 5, pp.302-303, illus., May, 1936.

PONDEROSA PINE CONE CUTTING BY SQUIRRELS. G. H. Schubert. Jour. For., 51 (3): 202, illus., Mar., 1953.

THE COST OF A SQUIRREL AND SQUIRREL CONTROL. William T. Shaw. State College of Washington, Agr. Exp. Sta., Pop. Bull. no.118, pp.1-19, 11 figs., Jan., 1920.

(Review by Walter P. Taylor of) THE COST OF A SQUIRREL AND SQUIRREL CONTROL. William T. Shaw. Jour. Mamm., vol.1, no.4, p.192, May, 1920.

WASHINGTON'S ANNUAL LOSSES FROM GROUND SQUIRRELS. William T. Shaw. Washington Agric. Exper. Station, bull.no. 118, pp.8, figs.4, Apr., 1921.

WOODCHUCK CONTROL IN THE EASTERN STATES. James Silver. U.S. Dept. Agric., Leafl. no.21, 6 pp., illus., Mar., 1928; Fur Jour., vol.2, no.5, pp.26, 48-50, May, 1928.

EFFECT OF SQUIRRELS ON THE SUPPLY OF PONDEROSA PINE SEED. A. E. Squillace. U. S. For. Serv., N. Rocky Mt. Exp. Sta., Res. Note No.131, pp.1-4, Dec., 1953.

SQUIRREL DAMAGE TO SAMPLE PLOT TAGS. Donald D. Stevenson. Jour. For., 36 (12): 1242-1243, Dec., 1938.

CARBON DISULPHIDE IN THE CONTROL OF SYLVATIC PLAGUE VECTORS. M. A. Stewart. Am. Jour. Hygiene, 36 (3): 243-246, Nov., 1942.

DAMAGE TO CONIFERS IN NORTHERN IDAHO BY THE RICHARDSON RED SQUIRREL. C. R. Stillinger. Jour. For., 42 (2): 143-145, Feb., 1944.

MENACE OF GRAY SQUIRRELS. SOME RESULTS OF THE FIRST YEAR'S CAMPAIGN. Laurance Swainson. Field, Lond., vol.159, no.4142, p.733, May 14, 1932.

THE PRAIRIE DOG AND ITS CONTROL. M. H. Swenk. Bull. Agri. Exper. Station, Nebraska, vol.28, art.2, pp.38, figs.3, tables 2, Aug.15, 1915.

DAMAGE TO RANGE GRASSES BY THE ZUNI PRAIRIE DOG. Walter P. Taylor, J. V. G. Loftfield. U. S. Dept. Agric., Dept. Bull. no.1227, pp.1-15, pls.1-6, Aug.10, 1924.

A COMPARISON OF THE VALUE OF GROUND SQUIRREL EXTERMINATION METHODS. I. I. Traut. Plant Protection, vol.4, no.1, pp.33-58, 1931.

THE PRESENT SITUATION AND THE FUTURE OF GROUND SQUIRREL CONTROL IN THE USSR. I. I. Traut. Bull. Plant Protection, vol.4, no.1, pp.3-31, 1931.

RESULTS OF A WOODCHUCK CONTROL EXPERIMENT. Antoon de Vos, Howard A. Merrill. Jour. Wildlife Management, 21 (4): 454-456, Oct., 1957.

FOX SQUIRREL SERIOUSLY DAMAGES ELM TREES. Lee E. Yeager. Jour. Mam., vol.17, no.4, pp.417-418, Nov., 1936.

CONTROL OF WOODCHUCKS. USDI, F&WS, Wildl. Leaflet 237, 4 pp., Apr., 1943.

DIRECTIONS FOR CONTROLLING TREE SQUIRRELS. USDI, F&WS, Wildl. Leaflet 197, 2 pp., Aug., 1941.

DIRECTIONS FOR POISONING THIRTEEN-STRIPED GROUND SQUIRRELS. USDI, F&WS, Wildl. Leaflet 195, 2 pp., July, 1941.

THE GREY SQUIRREL A WOODLAND PEST. Great Britain For. Comm., Leafl., no.31, 16 pp., illus., 1953.

SQUIRRELS TAKE 75 PERCENT OF THE 1951 PONDEROSA PINE SEED CROP. U.S. For. Serv., N. Rocky Mt. Exp. Sta., Res. Hi-Lites, Oct.17, 1952.

SQUIRRELS VS. BLACK SPRUCE. Forest Res. Dig., Winter 1939: 15-16, Winter 1939.

SQUIRRELS VS. JACK PINE. Forest Res. Dig., Sept.-Oct., 1936: 2-3, Sept.-Oct., 1936.

TIN SHIELD KEEPS SQUIRREL DAMAGE LOW IN ORCHARD. Texas Game and Fish, Austin, vol.3, no.6, p.15, illus., May, 1945.

Europe

(THE QUESTION OF THE MARMOT IN THE PYRENEES.) La question de la marmotte aux Pyrénées. Gaston Astre. Mammalia, Paris, vol.10, nos.3-4, pp.149-154, Sept.-Dec., 1946.

ON EUROPEAN SQUIRRELS. G. E. H. Barrett-Hamilton. Proc. Zool. Soc. Lond., pp.3-6, Jan.17, 1899.

SQUIRRELS IN UPPER WEARDALE. N. Beevers. Vasculum (Substitute), Newcastle upon Tyne, vol.31, no.1, p.4, Mar., 1946.

GREY SQUIRREL AT BAILDON. H. B. Booth. Naturalist, London, no.858, pp.206, July, 1928.

(THE SQUIRREL MISSING IN THE CAUCUSUS.) Ueber das Fehlen des Eichhoernchens im Kaukasus. Eug. Buechner. Mel. Biol. Bull. L'Acad. Imp. Sci., St. Petersburg, vol.13, pp.75-82, 1889.

GREY SQUIRREL IN BRITAIN. Maurice Burton. Illus. London News, vol.210, no. 5626, p.211, illus., Feb.15, 1947.

(A NEW SQUIRREL FROM GREECE.) Una nueva ardilla de Grecia. Angel Cabrera. Bol. Real. Soc. Espanola Hist. Nat., vol.24, pp.419-421, Nov.30, 1924.

(TAXONOMICAL, BIOLOGICAL AND BIOGEOGRAPHICAL INVESTIGATIONS OF THE GENUS CITELLUS OKEN IN RUMANIA.) Taxonomische, biologische und biogeographische Forschungen ueber die Gattung Citellus Oken in Rumaenien. R. J. Calinescu. Zeitschr. f. Saeugetierkunde, Berlin, vol.9, nos.1-3, pp.87-141, figs.15, pls.5-6, Dec.30, 1934.

THE HABITAT DISTRIBUTION OF THE GRAY SQUIRREL (SCIURUS CAROLINENSIS) IN SAVERNAKE FOREST. M. K. Colquhoun. Jour. Anim. Ecol., London, vol.11, no.1, pp.127-130, May, 1942.

GREY SQUIRREL AT WADWORTH. A. A. Dallman. Northwestern Nat., Arbroath, vol.11, no.1, p.45, Mar., 1936.

THE DISTRIBUTION OF THE GREY SQUIRREL IN THE LONDON AREA. R. S. R. Fitter. London Naturalist for 1938, pp.6-19, fig.1, 1939.

ADVANCE OF GREY SQUIRRELS (SCIURUS CAROLINENSIS) AND INCIDENCE OF MELANISM IN NORTH HERTFORDSHIRE. W. H. Fordham. Proc. Zool. Soc. Lond., vol.126, pt.1, pp.170-172, Jan.11, 1956.

GREY SQUIRREL AND PINK-FOOTED GEESE AT GOODMANHAM. R. Fortune. Naturalist, London, no.849, p.298, Oct., 1927.

A NOTE ON THE PRESENT STATUS OF THE RED SQUIRREL (SCIURUS VULGARIS) IN NORTHUMBERLAND. C. J. Gent. The Vasculum, North Country Quart. Sci. and Local Hist., vol.23, no.2, pp.55-56, May, 1937.

GREY SQUIRRELS. (DAMAGE WHEAT IN ENGLAND.) Arthur Hipgrave. Field, London, vol.156, no.4059, pp.517-518, Oct.11, 1930.

(THE GROUND SQUIRREL IN GERMANY: DISTRIBUTION AND HABITS.) Der Ziesel in Deutschland nach Verbreitung und Lebensweise. Arnold Jacobi. Archiv. fuer Naturgesch., vol.1, no.3, pp.199-238, figs.1-3, 1902.

THE DENSITY OF THE GROUND SQUIRREL (CITELLUS PYGMAEUS PALL.) POPULATION IN THE PLAGUE AREAS OF THE NORTHERN CAUCASUS AND THE POSSIBILITY OF ITS COMPLETE ERADICATION. N. I. Kalaburhov. Bull. Plant Protection, Leningrad, The Lenin Acad. Agric. Sci. in USSR, vol.4, no.2, pp.65-85, figs.4, 1932.

THE GREY SQUIRREL. (HABITS AND CHARACTERISTICS IN ENGLAND AND SCOTLAND COMPARED.) Phyllis Kelway. Game and Gun and Angler's Monthly, London, vol.16, no.162, pp.159-162, Mar., 1939.

THE DISTRIBUTION OF CITELLUS SUSLICUS SUSLICUS GUELD. IN THE PROVINCE OF RIAZAN. M. V. Kosulin. La Defence des Plantes, vol.5, nos.3-4, pp.374-376, 1928.

(ON THE OCCURRENCE OF THE MARMOT IN THE HIGH TATRA.) Zum Vorkommen des Murmeltieres in der Hohen Tatra. H. Kummerlowe. Zool. Garten, N.F., Leipzig, vol.8, nos.10-12, p.309, Sept., 1936.

(REMAINS OF A MARMOT IN THE "MALA PECI" CAVE IN THE ENVIRONS OF CIVIDALE.) Resti di marmotta della grotta "Mala Peci" nei dintorni di Cividale. Piero Leonardi. Atti Acad. Sci. Veneto-Trentino-Istriana, Padova, vol.24, pp.1-10, pl.1, 1933.

GREY SQUIRRELS. (HABITS IN ENGLAND.) A. D. C. Le Sueur. Field, London, vol.156, no.4062, p.621, Nov.1, 1930.

(THE OCCURRENCE OF SQUIRRELS IN BAS-LANGUEDOC AND THE BLACK MOUNTAINS AROUND 1917.) L'apparition des écureuils dans le Bas-Languedoc et la Montagne-Noire vers 1917. E. Maistre. Bull. Soc. Nat. Acclimat. France, vol.81, no.6, pp.266-280, June, 1934.

NEWS ABOUT COLLECTIONS. V. Martino. "Lovtsa" (Hunting?), pts.11-12, pp.2, illus., Nov.-Dec., 1937.

A NEW SOUSLIK FROM MACEDONIA. V. Martino, E. Martino. Jour. Mam., vol.10, no.1, pp.76-77, Feb., 1929.

NOTE ON THE YUGOSLAVIAN GROUND-SQUIRRELS (SOUSLIKS). V. Martino, E. Martino. Ann. and Mag. Nat. Hist., Lond., ser.11, vol.5, no.29, pp.465-471, May, 1940.

(IS THE CARPATHIAN MARMOT DIFFERENT FROM THE ALPINE MARMOT?) Ist das Karpathen-Murmeltier von dem Alpen-Murmeltier verschieden? Paul Matschie. Teckele, Beilage zur Deutchen Jaeger-Zeitung, Neudamm, vol.6, no.15, pp.113-115, 1910.

THE DISTRIBUTION OF THE GREY SQUIRREL (SCIURUS CAROLINENSIS) IN GREAT BRITAIN IN 1935. A. D. Middleton. Jour. Anim. Ecol., Lond., vol.4, no.2, pp.274-276, map, Nov., 1935.

THE GREY SQUIRREL. THE INTRODUCTION AND SPREAD OF THE AMERICAN GREY SQUIRREL IN THE BRITISH ISLES, ITS HABITS, FOOD AND RELATIONS WITH THE NATIVE FAUNA OF THE COUNTRY. A. D. Middleton. Sidgwick and Jackson, Ltd., London, pp.VIII plus 107, 8 pls., 1931.

THE GREY SQUIRREL IN THE BRITISH ISLES. A. D. Middleton. Jour. Ministry Agric., Great Britain, vol.37, no.11, pp. 1069-1078, Feb., 1931.

THE GREY SQUIRREL (SCIURUS CAROLINENSIS) IN THE BRITISH ISLES, 1930-1932. A. D. Middleton. Jour. Anim. Ecology, vol.1, no.2, pp.166-167, map, Nov., 1932.

THE SPERMOPHILES FOUND IN UKRAINE (TRANS. TITLE). A. A. Migulin. Travaux de la Soc. de Naturalistes de Charkov, vol.50, pt.2, pp.1-6 (of reprint), 1927. (In Russian.)

FOUR NEW EUROPEAN SQUIRRELS. Gerrit S. Miller, Jr. Ann. and Mag. Nat. Hist., ser.7, vol.20, pp.426-430, Nov., 1907.

(DESCRIPTION OF SOME NEW SPECIES OF SQUIRRELS FROM THE OLD CONTINENT.) Description de quelques espèces nouvelles d'écureuils de l'Ancien Continent. Alphonse Milne-Edwards. Nat. Hist., vol. 21, 1867.

(REMARKS ON THE PSEUDO-DISCOVERY OF SPERMOPHILUS CITELLUS IN SWITZERLAND.) Remarques sur la pseudo-decouverte du Spermophilus citellus en Suisse. Charles Mottaz. Bull. Soc. Zool. Geneve, vol.1, fasc.9, pp.209-212, Jan.15, 1909.

(A LITTLE-KNOWN MARMOT COLONY IN THE BAVARIAN ALPS.) Eine wenig bekannte Murmeltierkolonie in den bayerischen Alpen. D. Mueller-Using. Zeitschr. Saeugetierk. Berlin, 21 (3-4): 197, Feb.28, 1957.

(THE MARMOT IN SWITZERLAND, PARTICULARLY IN FRIBOURG CANTON.) La marmotte en Suisse et spécialement dans le canton de Fribourg. M. Musy. Comptes Rendus Assoc. Franc. Avanc. Sci., vol.49, pp.739-741, 1926.

THE PRESENT KNOWLEDGE OF GROUND SQUIRRELS IN THE USSR. S. I. Obolenskii. Bull. Plant Protection, vol.4, no.1, pp.65-72, 1931.

REVIEW OF THE CHIPMUNKS INHABITING USSR. S. I. Ognev. Wiss. Ber. Moskauer Staatsuniv., vol.4, pp.91-95, 1935.

REVIEW OF THE FLYING SQUIRRELS (PTEROMYS) LIVING IN USSR. S. I. Ognev. Bull. Soc. Nat. Moscou, sect. biol., vol.43, no.2, pp.303-315, 1934.

STRIPED SQUIRRELS OF THE USSR. (EUTAMIAS) S. I. Ognev. Moscow Univ. Sbornik Nauchno issledovatel'skogo inst. Zool. (Abstracts works Zool. Inst. Moscow State Univ.), no.3, pp.80-81, 1936.

A SYSTEMATICAL REVIEW OF THE SQUIRRELS IN USSR. S. I. Ognev. Abstracts works Zool. Inst. Moscou State Univ., no.2, pp.42-51, 1935.

DISTRIBUTION OF CITELLUS CITELLUS L. IN MOLDAVIAN SSSR AND CERTAIN DATA ON ITS BIONOMICS. V. I. Pakizh. Zool. Zhurnal, 37 (1): 105-119, Jan., 1958.

THE DISTRIBUTION OF THE GREY SQUIRREL (SCIURUS CAROLINENSIS) IN GREAT BRITAIN IN 1937. B. T. Parsons, A. D. Middleton. Jour. Animal Ecol., 6 (2): 286-290, Nov., 1937.

(THE MARMOT OF CA'NOVA IN THE VERONESE REGION.) La Marmotta di Ca'nova nel Veronese. Angelo Pasa. Natura, Milano, vol.30, no.3, pp.105-114, figs.2, 1939.

SPREAD OF AMERICAN GREY SQUIRREL IN SCOTLAND. James Ritchie. Scottish Nat., nos.137-138, pp.93-94, May-June, 1923.

SPREAD OF GROUND SQUIRRELS IN THE STEPPES OF CISCAUCASUS. V.K. Romanova Itogi Nauchno-Issledovatel'skikh Rabot Vsesoiuznogo Inst. Zashchity Rastnii za 1935 (Summary Sci. Research Work Inst. Plant Protection, Leningrad, 1935), pp.43-45, map, 1936.

(A FLYING SQUIRREL IN THE KIRGHIZ REGION.) Ein Flatterhoernchen aus dem Kirgisengebiet. M. Serebrennikov. Zeitschr. f. Saeugetierkunde, vol.4, no.3, pp.142-143, 1 pl., Sept.18, 1929.

SYNOPSIS OF RUSSIAN SQUIRRELS. M. Serebrennikov. Comptes Rendus Acad. Sci. Union Socialistic Soviet Republics, 1928, pp.421-426, 1928.

THE DISTRIBUTION OF THE GREY SQUIRREL AND THE BRITISH RED SQUIRREL IN LINCOLNSHIRE. Monica Shorten. Trans. Lincolnshire Nat. Union, pp.108-114, Nov., 1946.

GRAY SQUIRRELS IN BRITAIN. Monica Shorten. New Naturalist, vol.1, pp.42-46, 1948.

NOTES ON THE DISTRIBUTION OF THE GREY SQUIRREL (SCIURUS CAROLINENSIS) AND THE RED SQUIRREL (SCIURUS VULGARIS LEUCOURUS) IN ENGLAND AND WALES FROM 1945 TO 1952. Monica Shorten. Jour. Anim. Ecol., 22 (1): 134-140, maps, May, 1953.

SOME ASPECTS OF THE BIOLOGY OF THE GREY SQUIRREL (SCIURUS CAROLINENSIS) IN GREAT BRITAIN. Monica Shorten. Proc. Zool. Soc. Lond., vol.121, pt.2, pp. 427-459, pl.1, Aug., 1951.

A SURVEY OF THE DISTRIBUTION OF THE AMERICAN GREY SQUIRREL (SCIURUS CAROLINENSIS) AND THE BRITISH RED SQUIRREL (S. VULGARIS LEUCURUS) IN ENGLAND AND WALES, IN 1944-45. Monica Shorten. Jour. Animal Ecol., London, vol.15, no.1, pp. 82-92, May, 1946.

THE GREY SQUIRREL SPREADS TO WESTMEATH. A. W. Stelfox. Irish Naturalists' Jour., vol.1, no.14, p.275, Nov., 1927.

THE GROUND SQUIRREL OF GREATER CAUCASIA CITELLUS MUSICUS MENEF. AND ITS ORIGIN ON THE MOUNTAIN STEPPE. P. Sviridenko. Zooel. Jour. (Zooelogicheskii Zhurnal), Moscow, vol. 16, no.3, pp.448-482, 1937.

THE PAST AND PRESENT STATUS OF SQUIRRELS IN NORTHUMBERLAND AND DURHAM. George W. Temperley. Trans. Nat. Hist. Soc. Northumberland, Durham and Newcastle upon Tyne, vol.10, no.4, pp.153-164, July, 1953.

(ON THE SUBSPECIES OF THE EUROPEAN SQUIRREL (SCIURUS VULGARIS). Sur les Sous-Especes de l'Ecureuil d'Europe (Sciurus vulgaris). E. L. Trouessart. Bull. Mus. d'hist. Nat., Paris, no.6, pp. 360-366, Sept., 1906.

ON THE DISTRIBUTION OF THE GROUND SQUIRREL, CITELLUS CITELLUS (LINNE, 1766), IN SLOVAKIA. F. J. Turcek. Saeugetierk. Mitteil., Stuttgart, 3 (1): 19-21, Jan.1, 1955.

SOME REMARKS ON THE TAXONOMY OF FINISH SQUIRRELS. Paavo Voipio. Archivum Soc. Zool. Bot. Fennicae "Vanamo", vol.11, no.2, pp.97-107, 1956.

(ON SWISS SQUIRRELS.) Von den schweizerischen Eichhoernchen. G. von Burg. Der Weidmann (Buelach-Zuerich), Jahrg.1920, no.48, p.387, Dec.2, 1920.

OBSERVATIONS ON THE AMERICAN GREY SQUIRREL IN BRITAIN. Hugh Boyd Watt. School Nature Study, vol.21, no.82, pp.1-3 (of reprint), Jan., 1926.

ON THE AMERICAN GREY SQUIRREL (SCIURUS CAROLINENSIS) IN THE BRITISH ISLES. Hugh Boyd Watt. Essex Nat., vol. 20, pp.189-205, 1923.

(NOTES ON CITELLUS CITELLUS L. IN PODOLIA.) Notiz ueber Citellus citellus L. in Podolien. N. E. Werner. Acad. Sci. Ukraine, Mem. Cl. Sci. Phys. et Math., (Trav. Mus. Zool. No.7), vol.13, no.1, pp. 101-105, 1929.

(ON THE OCCURRENCE OF THE GROUND SQUIRREL, CITELLUS CITELLUS (L.) IN SAXONY AND SILESIA.) Zum Vorkommen des Ziesels, Citellus citellus (L.), in Sachsen und Schlesien. Rud Zimmermann. Zeitschr. f. Saeugetierkunde, Berlin, vol.8, nos.1-2, pp.108-112, Apr.24, 1933.

GRAY SQUIRREL IN ENGLAND. Nature Magazine, vol.16, no.3, p.190, Sept., 1930.

Evolution

PHYLOGENY OF NEARCTIC SCIURIDAE. Monroe D. Bryant. Amer. Midland Nat., Notre Dame, vol.33, no.2, pp.257-390, figs.48, pls.8, Mar., 1945.

DISTRIBUTION PATTERNS AND PHYLOGENY OF SOME WESTERN GROUND SQUIRRELS. Stephen D. Durrant, Richard M. Hansen. Systematic Zoology, Washington, vol.3, no.2, pp.82-85, illus., June, 1954.

INTERGRADATION VERSUS HYBRIDIZATION IN GROUND SQUIRRELS OF THE WESTERN UNITED STATES. E. Raymond Hall. Amer. Midland Nat., Notre Dame, vol.29, no.2, pp.375-378, fig.1, Mar., 1943.

(INTRASPECIFIC VARIABILITY AND DIFFUSION IN THE THIN TOED GROUND SQUIRREL.) Vnutrividovaya izmenchivost i rasprostranenne tonkopalogo suslika (Spermophilopsis leptodactylus Licht.; Mammalia, Glires). V. G. Heptner. Zool. Zhurnal, vol.33, no.4, pp.1157-1170, Sept.-Oct., 1954.

Food Habits

SIERRA CHICKAREE EATS YOUNG BLUE-FRONTED JAYS. Lowell Adams. Yosemite Nat. Notes, Stockton, vol.18, no.8, p.93, Aug., 1939.

FOOD HABITS OF CHIPMUNKS. Shaler E. Aldous. Jour. Mam., 22 (1): 18-24, Feb., 1941.

BONE CACHE OF A GRAY SQUIRREL. Philip F. Allan. Jour. Mam., vol.16, no. 4, p.326, Nov., 1935.

MAST PRODUCTION--A KEY TO SQUIRREL CROPS. John M. Allen. Outdoor Indiana, Indianapolis, vol.14, no.5, p.18, Aug., 1947.

SQUIRRELS AND BIRD WINDOW FEEDERS. Oakes I. Ames. Bull. Massachusetts Audubon Soc., Boston, vol.29, no.10, pp. 311-312, Jan., 1946.

ABERT SQUIRREL BURYING PINE CONES. Florence Merriam Bailey. Jour. Mam., vol.13, no.2, pp.165-166, May, 1932.

SQUIRRELS AS MUSHROOM EATERS. W. H. Ballou. Jour. Mam., vol.8, no.1, pp.57-58, Feb., 1927.

GRAY AND FOX SQUIRREL FOOD HABITS INVESTIGATIONS. Harold L. Barber. Presented at 8th Ann. Conf. S. E. Assn. Game and Fish Comm., New Orleans, La., pp.1-9, mimeo, Nov., 1954.

FOODS OF THE FOX SQUIRREL IN OHIO. Luther L. Baumgartner. Trans. 4th North Amer. Wildlife Conference, Washington, D.C., pp.579-584, 1939.

EXPERIMENTAL FEEDING OF CAPTIVE FOX SQUIRRELS. Philip Baumgras. Jour. Wildl. Mgt., 8 (4): 296-300, Oct., 1944.

CHIPMUNK FEEDING ON WHITE FIR APHIDS. Verlin G. Baysinger. Yosemite Nature Notes 19 (3): 19-20, Mar., 1940.

GROUND SQUIRREL SNARES ROBIN. M. E. Beatty. Yosemite Nature Notes, vol.12, no.8, p.81, Aug., 1933.

(HOW DOES THE SQUIRREL OPEN NUTS?) Wie oeffnet das Eichhoernchen die Nuesse? Gerhard Bechthold. Zeitschr. f. Saeugetierkunde, Berlin, vol.8, nos.3-6, pp.280-281, Dec.20, 1933.

CONE YEAR. (RED SQUIRREL.) John L. Blackford. Nature Magazine, Washington, vol.39, no.8, pp.409-412, 442, illus., Oct., 1946.

A FROG-EATING CHIPMUNK. Earle A. Brooks. Jour. Mam., vol.12, no.3, pp. 314-315, Aug., 1931.

NOTE ON A FEEDING HABIT OF THE GRAY SQUIRREL. Fred E. Brooks. Jour. Mam., vol.4, no.4, pp.257-258, Nov., 1923.

CHICKAREES EAT STEMS OF BLACK OAK LEAVES. Harold C. Bryant. Yosemite Nature Notes, vol.6, p.62, Aug., 1927.

SEASONAL FOOD CHOICES OF THE FOX SQUIRREL IN WESTERN KANSAS. Robert E. Bugbee, Andrew Riegel. Trans. Kansas Acad. Sci., Lawrence, vol.48, no.2, pp. 199-203, figs.4, Sept., 1945.

THE RED SQUIRREL OF NORTH AMERICA AS A MYCOPHAGIST. A. H. Reginald Buller. Trans. British Mycological Soc., vol.6, pt.4, pp.355-362, Sept.22, 1920.

SQUIRRELS AND THE FOOD CRISIS. Maurice Burton. Illus. London News, vol. 211, no.5671, p.726, illus., Dec.27, 1947.

A NEW DIET FOR THE RED SQUIRREL. Sidney S. Burton. Jour. Forestry, vol.28, no.2, p.233, Feb., 1930.

CARNIVOROUS GROUND SQUIRRELS ON ST. LAWRENCE ISLAND, ALASKA. Tom Cade. Jour. Mam., vol.32, no.3, pp.358-360, Aug.23, 1951.

CACHING AND RECOVERY OF FOOD BY THE WESTERN FOX SQUIRREL. Victor H. Cahalane. Jour. Wildl. Mgt., 6 (4): 338-352, Oct., 1942.

OUT-OF-SEASON CACHING BY FOX SQUIRREL. Victor H. Cahalane. Jour. Mam., vol.11, no.1, p.78, Feb., 1930.

CORN FED SQUIRRELS. C. M. Campbell. Pennsylvania Game News, Harrisburg, vol. 16, no.9, pp.3, 24-25, illus., Dec., 1945.

EATING OF BONE BY THE PREGNANT AND LACTATING GRAY SQUIRREL. A. J. Carlson. Science, N.S., vol.91, no.2372, p.573, June 14, 1940.

MODE OF DRINKING OF THE RED SQUIRREL. J. D. Caton. Amer. Naturalist, vol. 13, no.1, p.46, 1879.

WINTER FEEDING OF SQUIRRELS. Floyd B. Chapman. Ohio Cons. Bull., 3 (2): 6-7, Feb., 1939; Ohio Div. Cons., Bull.150, 8 pp., May, 1939.

TEXAS ROCK SQUIRRELS CATCH AND EAT YOUNG WILD TURKEYS. Arthur H. Cook, W. Herman Henry. Jour. Mam., vol.21, no.1, p.92, Feb.14, 1940.

THE CASE AGAINST THE TUFT-EARED SQUIRREL. Louis E. Coughlin. Rocky Mt. Region Bull., 21 (4): 10-12, Apr., 1938.

THE EATING OF BONE BY SQUIRRELS. A. F. Coventry. Science, 92 (2380): 128, Aug.9, 1940.

SQUIRREL OR PEACH-PIT--"WHO'S THE NUT?" L. Coville. Jour. Heredity, vol. 20, p.387, 1 fig., Aug., 1929.

A CHIPMUNK KILLS A SPARROW. Lee S. Crandall. Jour. Mam., vol.17, no.3, pp. 287-288, Aug., 1936.

(ON THE FEEDING OF THE SQUIRREL (SCIURUS VULGARIS FUSCOATER ALTUM, 1876.) Zur Ernaehrungsweise des Eichhoernchens, Sciurus vulgaris fuscoater Altum, 1876. Gerhard Creutz. Saeugetierk, Mitteil., Stuttgart, vol.1, no.1, p.31, Jan. 10, 1953.

THE WHEN, THE WHERE, THE WHAT OF SQUIRREL STORAGE. James D. Curtis. Frontiers, Phila., vol.10, no.1, pp.16-17, 21, illus., Oct., 1945.

GRAY SQUIRREL FEEDING ON CRATAEGUS. Charles A. Dambach. Jour. Mam., 23 (3): 337, Aug., 1942.

FOOD RESERVES OF FIR WOODS AND THEIR UTILIZATION BY THE SQUIRREL. D. N. Danilov. Narodnii Komissariat Zagotovok SSSR, Trudy Tsentralnoi Nauch-Issledovatelskoi Laboratorii Biologii, Oxotnichego Promysla i Tovarove deniia Zhivotnogo Syria, Moscou, no.6, pp. 99-123, 1944.

INSECTS AS THE FOOD OF SQUIRRELS. William T. Davis. Canadian Entomologist, vol.39, p.16, Jan., 1907.

OAK APPLE GALLS DESTROYED BY GRAY SQUIRRELS. William T. Davis. Bull. Brooklyn Entomological Soc., vol.19, pp.91-93, June, 1924.

REJECTION OF WORMY NUTS BY SQUIRRELS. Wayne Dennis. Jour. Mam., vol. 11, no.2, pp.195-201, May, 1930.

HOW DO SQUIRRELS FIND BURIED NUTS? L. R. Dice. Jour. Mam., vol.8, no.1, p. 55, Feb., 1927.

OUR SQUIRREL-FEEDING STATION. George A. Drew, Jr. Bull. Massachusetts Audubon Soc., North Abington, vol.32, no. 8, pp.301-303, illus., Dec., 1948.

GREY SQUIRRELS AND WALNUTS. R. Dymond. Field, London, vol.156, no. 4055, p.379, Sept.13, 1930.

EXPERIMENTAL EVIDENCE ON THE EATING OF BOB-WHITE EGGS BY SMALL SCIURIDAE. Paul L. Errington. Jour. Mam., vol.19, no.1, pp.107-108, Feb.14, 1938.

REPORT ON THE FOOD HABITS OF CITELLUS TRIDECEMLINEATUS TRIDECEMLINEATUS (MITCHILL). F. L. Fitzpatrick. Proc. Iowa Acad. Sci for 1926, vol.33, pp.291-293, 1927.

THE CROP OF CEDAR NUTS, INVASIONS INTO EUROPE OF THE SIBERIAN NUTCRACKER (NUCIFRAGA CARYOCATACTES MACRORHYNCHUS BREHM) AND FLUCTUATIONS OF THE SQUIRREL (SCIURUS VULGARIS L.). A. N. Formosof. Jour. Anim. Ecology, vol.2, no.1, pp.70-81, figs.1-3, May, 1933.

LITTLE NORTHERN CHIPMUNK EATS DOGWOOD BERRIES. Adrian C. Fox. Jour. Mam., vol.20, no.2, p.256, May, 1939.

RED SQUIRRELS EAT BASSWOOD AND BOXELDER SEEDS. Adrian C. Fox. Jour. Mam., vol.20, no.2, p.257, May, 1939.

SQUIRRELS AND DUMPLINGS. Lawrence S. Givens, Thomas Z. Atkeson. Alabama Conserv., Montgomery, vol.20, no.11, pp. 12, 22, Apr.-May, 1949.

CATEPILLARS AS FOOD OF THE GRAY SQUIRREL. W. J. Hamilton, Jr. Jour. Mam., vol.24, no.1, p.104, Feb.20, 1943.

RED SQUIRREL KILLING YOUNG COTTONTAIL AND YOUNG GRAY SQUIRREL. W. J. Hamilton, Jr. Jour. Mam., vol.15, no. 4, p.322, Nov., 1934.

SQUIRREL CACHE OF FUNGI. George A. Hardy. Canadian Field-Nat., Ottawa, vol. 63, no.2, pp.86-87, Mar.-Apr., 1949.

CHIPMUNK EATING A RED-BELLIED SNAKE. Samuel C. Harriot. Jour. Mam., vol.21, no.1, p.92, Feb.14, 1940.

FOOD AND MOISTURE REQUIREMENTS OF THE NELSON GROUND SQUIRREL. Albert C. Hawbecker. Jour. Mam., 28 (2): 115-125, May, 1947.

FEEDING HABITS OF THE RED SQUIRREL. C. Lynn Hayward. Jour. Mam., 21 (2): 220, May, 1940.

CHIPMUNK EATS FROG. Gene A. Hesterberg. Jour. Mam., vol.31, no.3, pp.350-351, Aug.21, 1950.

FOOD SELECTION OF GROUND SQUIRRELS, CITELLUS TRIDECEMILNEATUS. Frederick L. Hisaw, Frederick E. Emery. Jour. Mam., vol.8, no.1, pp.41-44, Feb., 1927.

(SQUIRRELS ARE FOND OF BIRCH JUICE.) Eichhoernchen nascht Birkensaft. Viktor Hornung. Zool. Garten, n.F., vol.19, no. 5, pp.258-259, 1952.

CHIPMUNKS AND BIRDS. D. Ralph Hostetter. Jour. Mam., vol.20, no.1, pp.107-108, Feb.14, 1939.

GUARD THOSE SPUDS--VORACIOUS SQUIRRELS SHOW APPETITE FOR CULL POTATOES. Walter E. Howard, Kenneth A. Wagnon. Western Livestock Jour., vol. 29, no.7, pp.81-83, Jan., 1951.

FOOD PREFERENCES OF ANTELOPE GROUND SQUIRRELS. A. Brazier Howell. Jour. Mam., vol.18, no.2, pp.243-244, May 14, 1937.

SOURCE OF FOOD FOR CHIPMUNKS. E. W. Jameson, Jr. Jour. Mam., vol.24, no.4, p.500, Nov.17, 1943.

CHERMES ABIETIS GALLS AND SQUIRRELS. Ad. S. Jensen. Det K. Danske Videnskabernes Selskab. Biologiske Meddelelser, Copenhagen, vol.20, no.13, pp.15, illus., 1948.

AN OBSERVATION ON THE CARNIVOROUS PROPENSITIES OF THE GRAY GOPHER. Arthur M. Johnson. Jour. Mam., vol.3, no.3, p.187, Aug., 1922.

A RED SQUIRREL'S CHRISTMAS DINNER. C. E. Johnson. Canadian Field-Naturalist, vol.38, p.137, Sept (Oct.16), 1924.

GRAY SQUIRRELS FEEDING UPON SAMARAS OF ELM. W. W. Judd. Jour. Mam., 36 (2): 296, May 26, 1955.

THE UTILIZATION OF THE 1939 CROP OF ACORNS AND HICKORY NUTS BY SQUIRRELS IN FRANKLIN COUNTY, OHIO. L. Kautz. MS thesis, Ohio State Univ., 1940.

FOOD HABITS OF PRAIRIE DOGS. Leon H. Kelso. USDA, Cir.529, 15 pp., June, 1939.

FOOD OF CITELLUS PYGMAEUS AND C. FULVUS UNDER NATURAL CONDITIONS IN WESTERN KAZAKSTAN. I. I. Khudiakov, A. D. Fursaev, A. I. Kosmina, E. P. Mikailova. Vestnik Mikrobiologii Epidemiologii i Parazitologii (Rev. Microbiol.,

Epidemiol. et Parasitol.), vol.12, no.1, pp. 63-74, 1933.

FOOD OF THE SQUIRREL AND ITS SIGNIFICANCE FOR NUMBER AND HUNTER. I. D. Kiriss. Narodnii Komissariat Zagotovok SSSR, Trudy Tsentralnoi Nauch-Issledovatelskoi Laboratorii Biologii, Oxotnichego Promysla i Tovarovedeniia Zhivotnogo Syria, Moscou, no.6, pp.45-98, 1944.

STORING OF FOOD ITEMS IN THE WINTER NEST OF THE ALASKAN GROUND SQUIRREL, CITELLUS UNDULATUS. John Krog. Jour. Mam., 35 (4): 586, Nov., 1954.

SEEDS OF THE EUCALYPTUS TREE A NEW FOOD FOR THE ANTHONY GRAY SQUIRREL. Luther Little. Jour. Mam., vol.15, no.2, pp.158-159, May, 1934.

CHIPMUNK VS. SNAKE. J. M. McArthur. Canadian Field-Nat., vol.47, no.4, p.76, Apr., 1933.

CHICKAREE HARVESTS GIANT SEQUOIA CONES. James W. McFarland. Yosemite Nat. Notes, Yosemite, vol.26, no.8, p.96, Aug., 1947.

AN APPARENTLY UNRECORDED FOOD OF THE RED SQUIRREL. Charles Macnamara. Canadian Field-Nat., 57 (6): 107, Sept., 1943.

REDWOOD CHICKAREE TESTING AND STORING HAZEL NUTS. Joseph Mailliard. Jour. Mam., vol.12, no.1, pp.68-70, Feb., 1931.

A PREDATORY SQUIRREL. Loye Miller. Jour. Mam., vol.16, no.4, pp.324-325, Nov., 1935.

GROUND SQUIRREL KILLS CHIPMUNK. Russell S. Miller. Yosemite Nat. Notes, Yosemite, vol.19, no.9, p.72, Sept., 1940.

FOOD HABITS OF SQUIRRELS. G. E. Moore. Missouri Conservationist, Jefferson City, vol.4, no.9, p.14, Dec., 1943.

THE CHIPMUNK AS A PREDATOR OF THE ADULT YELLOW SWALLOWTAIL BUTTERFLY. William A. Morris. Jour. Mam., vol.34, no.4, pp.510-511, Nov.13, 1953.

CARNIVOROUS HABITS OF THE NORTHEASTERN CHIPMUNK (TAMIAS STRIATUS LYSTERI). Edward W. Nelson. Jour. Mam., vol.16, no.1, pp.66-67, Feb., 1935.

NOTES ON THE FOOD HABITS OF THE GRAY SQUIRREL. John Treadwell Nichols. Jour. Mam., vol.8, no.1, pp.55-57, Feb., 1927.

FURTHER OBSERVATIONS ON SQUIRRELS EATING AMANITA MUSCARIA. W. S. Odell. Canadian Field-Nat., vol.40, p.184, Dec.24, 1926.

SQUIRRELS EATING AMANITA MUSCARIA. W. S. Odell. Canadian Field-Nat., vol.39, pp.180-181, Nov.30, 1925.

GROUND SQUIRRELS AND HORNED LARKS AS PREDATORS UPON GRUNION EGGS. Andrew C. Olson, Jr. California Fish and Game, San Francisco, vol.36, no. 3, pp.323-327, illus., July 10, 1950.

THE BARK-EATING PROPENSITIES OF THE FLYING SQUIRREL. A. E. Osmaston. Indian Forester, vol.57, no.9, pp.434-437, 2 pls., Sept., 1931.

A CHIPMUNK PURSUES A SNAKE. J. G. Palliser. Canadian Field-Nat., Ottawa, vol.55, no.9, p.138, Dec., 1941.

A GALL INSECT FOOD OF THE GRAY SQUIRREL. George A. Petrides. Jour. Mam., vol.25, no.4, p.410, Dec.12, 1944.

PREDACIOUS PINE SQUIRRELS. C. P. Russell. Yosemite Nature Notes, vol.8, p.68, June, 1929.

FURTHER OBSERVATIONS ON THE HUNGRY SQUIRRELS. Oscar A. Sedergren. Yosemite Nat. Notes, vol.28, no.3, p.20, Mar., 1949.

GRAY SQUIRRELS AND NUTS. Ernest Thompson Seton. Jour. Mam., vol.2, no.4, pp.238-239, Nov., 1921.

CARNIVOROUS HABITS OF THE BELDING GROUND SQUIRREL. Carl Sharsmith. Yosemite Nature Notes, vol.15, no.2, pp. 12-14, illus., Feb., 1936.

THE FOOD OF GROUND SQUIRRELS. William T. Shaw. Amer. Nat., vol.59, no.662, pp.250-265, May-June, 1925.

MOISTURE AND ITS RELATION TO THE CONE-STORING HABIT OF THE WESTERN PINE SQUIRREL. William T. Shaw. Jour. Mam., vol.17, no.4, pp.337-349, figs.6, Nov., 1936.

THE STORING HABIT OF THE COLUMBIAN GROUND SQUIRREL. William T. Shaw. Amer. Nat., vol.60, no.669, pp.367-373, 1926.

CHIPMUNKS KILL BIRDS IN BIRD TRAPS. Daniel Smiley, Jr. Jour. Mam., vol.23, no.1, pp.91-92, Feb.14, 1942.

SEED EATERS. (SPERMOPHILES.) George Smokey. South Dakota Conserv. Digest, Pierre, vol.11, no.8, p.11, Aug., 1944.

THE FRANKLIN GROUND SQUIRREL, CITELLUS FRANKLINII (SABINE), AND ITS RELATIONSHIP TO NESTING DUCKS. Lyle K. Sowls. Jour. Mam., 29 (2): 113-137, May, 1948.

THE FRANKLIN GROUND SQUIRREL, CITELLUS FRANKLINII (SABINE), AND ITS RELATIONSHIP TO NESTING DUCKS IN MANITOBA. Lyle K. Sowls. MS thesis, Univ. Wis., 1941.

DOUGLAS GROUND SQUIRREL AS A PREDATOR ON NESTS OF UPLAND GAME BIRDS IN OREGON. Frank W. Stanton. Jour. Wildl. Mgt., 8 (2): 153-161, Apr., 1944.

DOUGLAS'S GROUND SQUIRREL AS A PREDATOR UPON UPLAND GAME BIRD NESTS ON THE SOAP CREEK EXPERIMENTAL AREA IN OREGON. Frank W. Stanton. MS thesis, Oregon State Coll., 1941.

THE FLYING SQUIRREL AS A BIRD KILLER. H. L. Stoddard. Jour. Mam., vol.1, no.2, pp.95-96, Nov., 1919.

(MATERIAL ON THE FEEDING OF THE GRAY MARMOT (MARMOTA BAIBACINA KASTSCH.).) Materiali po pitaniya serogo surka (Marmota baibacina Kastsch.). I. I. Stolov. Zool. Zhurnal, Moscow, 35 (9): 1390-1394, 1956.

GRAY SQUIRREL UTILIZATION OF ELM. John K. Terres. Jour. Wildl. Mgt., 3 (4): 358-359, Oct., 1939.

AUTUMN FOODS OF CHIPMUNKS AND GOLDEN-MANTLED GROUND SQUIRRELS IN THE NORTHERN SIERRA NEVADA. Lloyd Tevis, Jr. Jour. Mam., 33 (2): 198-205, illus., May, 1952.

STOMACH CONTENTS OF CHIPMUNKS AND MANTLED SQUIRRELS IN NORTHEASTERN CALIFORNIA. Lloyd Tevis, Jr. Jour. Mam., 34 (3): 316-324, illus., Aug., 1953.

A CHIPMUNK CAPTURES A MOUSE. J. Kenneth Torres. Jour. Mam., vol.18, no. 1, p.100, Feb.14, 1937.

(THE WINTER FOOD OF THE SQUIRREL DURING CONE AND CONE FAILURE YEARS.) Oravan talvisesta ravinnosta kapy--ja kaepykatovuosina. Erkka Vartio. Suomen Riista, Suomen Riistanhoito-Saeaetioe, Riistantutkimuslaitos (Finnish Foundation for Game Preservation, Game Research Inst.), Helsinki, vol.1, pp.49-74, figs.10, 1946.

BELDING GROUND SQUIRREL AND CHIPMUNKS AT LUNCH. Allen W. Waldo. Yosemite Nat. Notes, vol.28, no.9, pp. 118-119, Sept., 1949.

NOTES ON THE FEEDING HABITS OF CITELLUS AND EUTAMIAS. Ernest P. Walker. Jour. Mam., vol.26, no.3, p.308, Aug., 1945.

A SOMEWHAT UNUSUAL KITCHEN MIDDEN OF FREMONT'S SQUIRREL (SCIURUS FREMONTI FREMONTI). Edward R. Warren. Jour. Mam., vol.13, no.3, p.278, Aug., 1932.

BUSHY TAILS LIKE BUTTERNUTS. R. L. Watts. Pennsylvania Game News, Harrisburg, vol.15, no.12, p.15, illus., Mar., 1945.

MID-SUMMER FOOD OF GRAY SQUIRRELS. Gordon T. Woods. Jour. Mam., vol.22, no.3, pp.321-322, Aug.14, 1941.

CONE-PILING BY MICHIGAN RED SQUIRRELS. Lee E. Yeager. Jour. Mam., 18 (2): 191-194, May, 1937.

THIRTEEN-LINED GROUND SQUIRREL FEEDS ON WHITE GRUBS. Lee E. Yeager. Jour. Mam., vol.18, no.2, p.243, May 14, 1937.

ARE SQUIRRELS BIRD-ENEMIES? Bird-Lore, vol.24, pp.206-207, Aug., 1922.

Fossils

THE OCCURRENCE OF CITELLUS RICHARDSONII (SABINE) IN THE PLEISTOCENE OF SHERIDAN COUNTY, KANSAS. Morton Green. Jour. Mam., vol.22, no.4, p.451, Nov.14, 1941.

(V. PALAEOZOOLOGY, VERTEBRATA. MARMOT REMAINS FROM THE YOUNGER LOESS OF NEBRA.) V. Palaeozoologie, Vertebrata. Murmeltierreste aus dem juengeren Loess von Nebra. Florian Heller. Leopoldina, vol.6, pp.581-586, 2 pls., 1930.

CYNOMYS LUDOVICANIUS LUDOVICIANUS FROM THE PLEISTOCENE OF KANSAS. Claude W. Hibbard. Jour. Mam., vol.18, no.4, pp.517-518, Nov., 1937.

A NEW FOSSIL GROUND SQUIRREL CITELLUS (PLIOCITELLUS) FRICKI FROM THE PLIOCENE OF CLARK COUNTY, KANSAS. Claude W. Hibbard. Trans. Kansas Acad. Sci., Topeka, vol.45, pp.253-257, pls.2, 1942.

A NEW SCIURID OF BLANCAN AGE FROM KANSAS AND NEBRASKA. Claude W. Hibbard, C. Bertrand Schultz. Bull. Univ. Nebraska State Mus., Lincoln, vol.3, no.3, pp.19-29, pls.3, Nov., 1948.

(THE FIRST FINDING OF MARMOTA MARMOTA PRIMIGENIA (KAUP 1839), THE ALP MARMOT IN THE LATE PLEISTOCENE OF THE NETHERLANDS.) De eerste vondst van Marmota marmota primigenia (Kaup 1839), de alpenmarmot, in het laatpleistoceen van Nederland. A. M. Husson, G. Kortenbout van der Slyus. Natuurhist. Maandblad, Leiden, vol.43, no.8, pp.51-56, no.9, pp.60-64, pl.1, Aug.31, Sept.30, 1954.

(REMAINS OF A MARMOT IN THE "MALA PECI" NEI DINTORNI DI CIVIDALE. Piero Leonardi. Atti. Acad. Sci. Veneto-Trentino-Istriana, Padova, vol.24, pp.1-10, pl. 1, May, 1933.

(ON DILUVIAL MARMOTS FROM THE SOUTHEAST ALPS.) Ueber diluviale Murmeltiere aus den Suedostalpen. Ivan Rakovec. Prirodoslovne Razprave, vol.2, no.5, pp.245-292, 3 pls., Aug.26, 1935.

(ARCTOMYS BOBAC IN THE QUATERNARY OF RUMANIA.) Arctomys bobac in cuaternarul din Romania. I. Simionescu. Acad. romana, Memoriile, Sectiunea stiintifica, Bukharest (3), vol.7, no.1, pp. 1-6, 1930.

A FOSSIL MARMOT FROM NEW MEXICO AND ITS CLIMATIC SIGNIFICANCE. Charles E. Stearns. Amer. Jour. Sci., New Haven, vol.240, no.12, pp.867-878, figs.3, Dec., 1942.

PLEISTOCENE PRAIRIE-DOG FROM FREDERICK, OKLAHOMA. Albert Elmer Wood. Jour. Mam., vol.14, no.2, p.160, May, 1933.

General Habits and Behavior

BEHAVIOR PATTERNS IN A LABORATORY COLONY OF PRAIRIE DOGS, CYNOMYS LUDOVICIANUS. Adam Anthony. Jour. Mam., 36 (1): 69-78, illus., Feb., 1955.

THE SONG OF THE FLAG SQUIRREL. Vernon Bailey. Nature Mag., vol.14, p.86, illus., Aug., 1929.

FURTHER OBSERVATIONS ON THE FAMILY LIFE OF THE FIVE STRIPED SQUIRREL, FUNAMBULUS PENNANTI WR. Aruna Banerji. Jour. Bombay Nat. Hist. Soc., 54 (2): 335-343, Apr., 1957.

NOTES ON THE BURROWING AND FOOD HABITS OF THE OLYMPIC MARMOT. Alex Beltz, Ernest S. Booth. Jour. Mam., vol.33, no.4, pp.495-496, Nov.19, 1952.

HOW OUR SQUIRRELS PASS THE WINTER. L. W. Brownell. Nature Mag., vol.2, pp. 289-291, 305, 8 figs., Nov., 1923.

NOTES ON THE HABITS OF THE MOHAVE GROUND SQUIRREL. William H. Burt. Jour. Mam., 17 (3): 221-224, Aug., 1936.

SOME OBSERVATIONS ON THE HABITS OF THE THIRTEEN-LINED GROUND SQUIRRELS, CITELLUS TRIDECEMLINEATUS TRIDECEMLINEATUS (MITCHILL) OF IOWA. Gow M. Bush. Proc. Iowa Acad. Sci., Des Moines, vol.46, pp.429-437, figs.4, June, 1940.

NOTES CONCERNING A CAPTIVE PRAIRIE-DOG. E. C. Cates. Jour. Mam., vol.8, no.1, pp.33-37, Feb., 1927.

AGILITY OF SQUIRRELS. R. Clapham. Field, London, vol.153, p.25, Jan.3, 1929.

SPEED OF GRAY SQUIRREL. Austin H. Clark. Jour. Mam., vol.12, no.1, p.70, Feb., 1931.

SOME NOTES ON HOARDING AND TERRITORIAL BEHAVIOR OF THE RED SQUIRREL SICURUS HUDSONICUS (ERXLEBEN). C. H. D. Clarke. Canadian Field-Nat., Ottawa, vol.53, no.3, pp.42-43, Mar., 1939.

HOW FAST CAN A FOX SQUIRREL RUN? Clarence Cottam. Jour. Mam., vol.22, no.3, p.323, Aug.14, 1941.

MUSCULAR POWER OF A SQUIRREL. J. M. Edson. Murrelet, vol.17, no.1, p. 18, Jan., 1936.

YELLOW-BELLIED MARMOT OUT OF BOUNDS. J. M. Edson. Jour. Mam., vol. 16, no.1, p.68, Feb., 1935.

MID-WINTER ACTIVITY IN A STRIPED SPERMOPHILE. William L. Engels. Jour. Mam., vol.13, no.2, pp.164-165, May, 1932.

NEST BUILDING AND FOOD STORAGE OF A CAPTIVE CHIPMUNK. William L. Engels. Jour. Mam., vol.28, no.3, pp. 296-297, Aug.19, 1947.

SQUIRREL SOCIOLOGY. Vagn F. Flyger. Md. Cons., 32 (3): 12-14, illus., May, 1955.

PROVISION OF PRAIRIE-DOG TO ESCAPE DROWNING WHEN TOWN IS SUBMERGED. B. E. Foster. Jour. Mam., vol.5, no.4, pp.266-268, Nov., 1924.

OBSERVATIONS ON RED SQUIRREL TRAVEL IN TREADWHEEL. Adrian C. Fox. Jour. Mam., vol.20, no.3, pp.373-374, Aug.14, 1939.

STRANGE BEHAVIOR OF AN EASTERN GRAY SQUIRREL. Bob Fussner. Murrelet, Seattle, vol.22, no.3, p.63, Sept.-Dec., 1941.

HABITS OF THE GROUND SQUIRREL CITELLUS LYRATUS ON ST. LAWRENCE ISLAND, ALASKA. Otto William Geist. Jour. Mam., vol.14, no.4, pp.306-308, Nov., 1933.

THE VALUE OF GROUNDHOG HOLES AS WINTER RETREATS FOR RABBITS. Richard Gerstell. Pennsylvania Game News, New Cumberland, vol.10, no.6, pp. 6-9, figs.6, tables 3, Sept., 1939.

TREE-CLIMBING AND INSECT-EATING WOODCHUCKS. Charles A. Gianini. Jour. Mam., vol.6, no.4, pp.281-282, Nov., 1925.

NOTES ON AN APPARENT DEFENSE ATTITUDE IN GROUND SQUIRRELS. Raymond M. Gilmore. Jour. Mam., vol.15, no.4, p. 322, Nov., 1934.

A FURIOUS WOODCHUCK. Fred A. Glover. Jour. Mam., vol.24, no.3, p.402, Aug.17, 1943.

OBSERVATIONS ON THE BEHAVIOR OF CALLOSPERMOPHILUS AND EUTAMIAS. Kenneth Gordon. Jour. Mam., vol.19, no. 1, pp.78-84, figs.2, table 1, Feb.14, 1938.

TERRITORIAL BEHAVIOR AND SOCIAL DOMINANCE AMONG SCIURIDAE. Kenneth Gordon. Jour. Mam., vol.17, no.2, pp. 171-172, May, 1936.

GROUNDHOG ACTIVE IN WINTER. E. R. S. Hall. Canadian Field-Nat., vol.44, no. 8, p.198, Nov., 1930.

SQUIRREL ICE-BOATS. William C. Hargrove. Popular Sci. News, Boston, vol. 31, no.11, p.256, Nov., 1897.

NOTES ON MINNESOTA SQUIRRELS. Donald M. Hatfield. Jour. Mam., vol.18, no.2, pp.242-243, May 14, 1937.

EXTRAORDINARY FEROCITY OF A GREY SQUIRREL. John C. Hartley. Field, London, vol.156, no.4061, p.590, Oct.25, 1930.

WINTERING WITH A GRAY SQUIRREL. Paul D. Harwood. Audubon Mag., New York, vol.45, no.6, pp.336-340, illus., Nov.-Dec., 1943.

THE ODYSSEY OF A GROUND SQUIRREL. Robert T. Hatt. Nat. Hist., vol.29, pp. 181-189, illus., Mar., 1929.

HAY STORAGE AND TUNNELING ACTIVITIES OF BELDING GROUND SQUIRRELS. Mary V. Hood. Yosemite Nat. Notes, vol.29, no.10, pp.98-99, Oct., 1950.

WHEN DOES A MARMOT GO TO BED? Mary V. Hood. Yosemite Nat. Notes, vol. 29, no.7, p.67, July, 1950.

OBSERVATIONS ON THE HOMING BEHAVIOR OF THE GRAY SQUIRREL (SCIURUS CAROLINENSIS). K. E. Hungerford, Norman Wilder. Jour. Wildl. Mgt., 5 (4): 458-460, Oct., 1941.

ON THE MOBILITY AND DIURNAL ACTIVITY RHYTHM OF THE MARMOTS (CITELLUS PYGMAEUS PALL.) IN WESTERN KAZAKHSTAN IN DIFFERENT PERIODS OF THEIR ACTIVITY. O. A. Ivanov. Zool. Zhurnal, Moscow, 38 (6): 922-932, 1957.

TERRITORIAL BEHAVIOR OF RED SQUIRREL. Lawrence Kilham. Jour. Mam., 35 (2): 252-253, May, 1954.

NOTES ON THE BEHAVIOR OF THE CHIPMUNK. A. Brooker Klugh. Canadian Field-Nat., vol.35, pp.18-19, Jan (June 8), 1921; Jour. Mam., vol.4, no.1, pp.29-32, pl.6, Feb., 1923.

DEPREDATIONS OF A GRAY SQUIRREL. Frederic J. Laughlin. Jour. Mam., vol.26, no.4, pp.440-441, Feb.12, 1946.

THE SQUIRRELS AND CHIPMUNKS--THEIR HABITS AND CONTROLS. John A. Ludeman. US F&WS, Wildl. Leafl., 355, 5 pp., July, 1953.

HOMING OF FLYING SQUIRRELS. R. A. McCabe. Jour. Mam., vol.28, no.4, p. 404, Nov.26, 1947.

THREE INSTANCES OF TANGLED SQUIRREL TAILS. Robert M. McClung. Animal Kingdom, New York Zool. Soc., vol.55, no.2, pp.46-47, Mar.-Apr., 1952.

SQUIRREL ANTICS. Donald Edward McHenry. Yosemite Nat. Notes, vol.28, no.3, pp.17-19, Mar., 1949.

SPECIFIC DIFFERENCES IN THE CALL NOTES OF CHIPMUNKS. Alden H. Miller. Jour. Mam., vol.25, no.1, pp.87-89, Feb., 1944.

FOX SQUIRREL RECEPTIONISTS. Joseph Curtis Moore. Everglades Nat. Hist., vol. 2, no.3, pp.153-160, illus., Sept., 1954.

THE ALASKA RED SQUIRREL PROVIDING FOR WINTER. Olaus J. Murie. Jour. Mam., vol.8, no.1, pp.37-40, pl.6, Feb., 1927.

CANNIBALISM AND OTHER OBSERVATIONS OF CAPTIVE GROUND SQUIRRELS. X. J. Musacchia. Jour. Mam., vol.35, no.3, pp. 445-447, Aug.20, 1954.

TROUBLES OF A CHICKAREE FAMILY. C. H. Oneal. Yosemite Nature Notes, vol. 7, p.68, Aug., 1928.

PRAIRIE DOG WAYS AND MEANS. Edalee Orcutt. San Diego Zoonooz, vol. 22, no.10, pp.6-8, illus., Oct., 1949.

APPARENT SEGREGATION OF SEXES IN FLYING SQUIRRELS. F. L. Osgood. Jour. Mam., vol.16, no.3, p.231, Aug., 1935.

NOTES ON THE DEFENSIVE BEHAVIOR OF GRAY AND FOX SQUIRRELS WHILE MOVING THEIR YOUNG. Robert L. Packard. Trans. Kansas Acad. Sci., vol.57, no.4, pp.471-472, 1954.

UNDERGROUND ACTIVITY BY RED SQUIRREL. F. J. Taylor Page. Proc. Zool. Soc. Lond., vol.126, pt.1, pp.164-165, Jan. 11, 1956.

HOW YOSEMITE SQUIRRELS SPEND THE WINTER. George A. Petrides. Yosemite Nat. Notes, Yosemite, vol.20, no.1, pp.1-3, Jan., 1941.

RED SQUIRRELS AND GRAY. F. W. Preston. Jour. Mam., vol.29, no.3, pp. 297-298, Aug.31, 1948.

NOTES ON THE BIOLOGY OF CITELLUS PYGMAEUS IN PLAGUE ENDEMIC AND PLAGUE FREE AREAS OF WESTERN KAZAKSTAN. Iu. M. Rall, A. A. Flegontova, M. V. Sheikina. Revue de Microbiol., Épidémiol. and Parasitol., vol.12, no.2, pp.139-150, 1933.

WINTER RAMBLING OF A WOODCHUCK. R. J. Rutter. Canadian Field-Nat., vol. 44, no.9, p.213, Dec., 1930.

(NOTES ON THE TERRITORY AND CYCLE OF ACTIVITY OF ALTANTOXERUS GETULUS L. IN THE MASSIVE OF THE TOUBKAL (HIGH ATLAS, MOROCCO).) Note sur le territoire et le cycle d'activité d'Atlantoxerus getulus L. dans le Massif du Toubkal (Haut Atlas marocain). M. C. Saint Girons. Mammalia, Paris, vol.17, no.2, pp.75-82, illus., June, 1953.

THE PRAIRIE DOGS (CYNOMYS LUDOVICIANUS) AT WASHINGTON ZOO. Ernest Thompson Seton. Jour. Mam., vol.7, no. 3, pp.229-230, Aug., 1926.

SEASONAL AND DAILY ACTIVITIES OF THE COLUMBIAN GROUND SQUIRREL AT PULLMAN, WASHINGTON. William T. Shaw. Ecology, Lancaster, vol.26, no.1, pp.74-84, illus., Jan., 1945.

PERIODICITY IN THE CALLING OF A CHIPMUNK. Althea R. Sherman. Jour. Mam., vol.7, no.4, pp.331-332, Nov., 1926.

SOME INTERESTING HABITS OF SQUIRRELS. George Smokey. South Dakota Conservation Digest, Pierre, vol.10, no.6, pl.6-7, July, 1943.

OBSERVATIONS ON THE SEASONAL ACTIVITIES OF THE WHITE-TAILED PRAIRIE-DOG, CYNOMYS LEUCURUS. Alfred H. Stockard. Papers Michigan Acad. Sci. arts, and Letters, vol.11, pp.471-479, (1929), 1930.

WINTER ACTIVITIES OF THE EASTERN CHIPMUNK. Frederick H. Test. Jour. Mam., vol.13, no.3, p.278, Aug., 1932.

SEASONAL VARIATIONS OF THE DAILY ACTIVITY CYCLES IN THE GREY GROUND SQUIRREL (CITELLUS PIGMAEUS PALL.). S. N. Varshavasky. Zool. Jour., Moscou, vol.17, no.5, pp.795-810, figs.8, tables 6, 1938.

A NOTE ON THE WINTER HABITS OF EUTAMIAS TOWNSENDII. Alex Walker. Jour. Mam., vol.4, no.4, p.257, Nov., 1923.

NOTES ON THE VOICE OF MARMOTS. Edward R. Warren. Jour. Mam., vol.16, no.2, pp.152-153, May, 1935.

NOTES ON PRAIRIE-DOGS. L. C. Whitehead. Jour. Mam., vol.8, no.1, p. 58, Feb., 1927.

GROUND SQUIRREL'S BACK SCRATCHER. Dorr C. Yeager. Yosemite Nature Notes, vol.6, p.64, Aug., 1927.

HOME RANGE, TERRITORIALITY, AND POPULATIONS OF THE CHIPMUNK IN CENTRAL NEW YORK. Ralph W. Yerger. Jour. Mam., vol.34, no.4, pp.448-458, Nov.13, 1953.

HABITS OF THE THIRTEEN-STRIPED GROUND SQUIRREL. Charles H. Young. Ohio Conserv. Bull. Columbus, vol.13, no.11, pp.27-28, illus., Nov., 1949.

SEVEN YEARS--WITHOUT WATER! UNKNOWN FACTS ABOUT LITTLE UNDERSTOOD PRAIRIE DOGS. THEY GO WITHOUT DRINKING A DROP OF WATER YEAR AFTER YEAR, YIP WITH DELIGHT WHEN PETTED, ARE AFFECTIONATE AND ANSWER TO THEIR NAMES. Stanley P. Young. Western Sportsman, Denver, vol. 6, no.1, pp.8-10, 26-27, Dec., 1940.

(ON THE CRY OF THE MARMOT AT THE APPROACH OF A HUMAN.) Zum Murmeltierschrei bei Annaeherung eines Menschen. K. Zimmerman. Saeugetierk. Mitteil., Stuttgart, 3 (3): 125, July 1, 1955.

THE HUMAN SIDE OF SQUIRRELS. Flower and Feather, Chattanooga, vol.2, no.4, pp.18-20, Oct., 1946.

Hibernation

HIBERNATING CHIPMUNKS. A. W. Anthony. Jour. Mam., vol.5, no.1, p.76, Feb., 1924.

EFFECTS OF HIBERNATION ON THE RATE OF OXYGEN CONSUMPTION IN THE THIRTEEN-LINED GROUND SQUIRREL. Francis M. Baldwin, Kenneth L. Johnson. Jour. Mam., vol.22, no.2, pp. 180-182, May 14, 1941.

HIBERNATION AND MARMOT PHYSIOLOGY. Francis G. Benedict, Robert C. Lee. Carnegie Institution, Washington, publ.497, pp.239, June 22, 1938.

THE WOODCHUCK WAKENS. Marion B. Carr. Jr. Nat. Hist. Mag., New York, vol.7, no.1, pp.11-13, illus., Mar., 1942.

HYBERNATION OF THE SPOTTED GOPHER. J. D. Caton. Amer. Naturalist, vol.17, no.9, p.983, 1883.

(CONTRIBUTIONS TO KNOWLEDGE OF INTERNALLY SECRETING ORGANS OF THE MARMOT (ARCTOMYS MARMOTA L.) AND THEIR CONNECTION TO THE PROBLEM OF HIBERNATION.) Beitraege zur Kenntnis innersekretorischer organe des Murmeltieres (Arctomys marmota L.) and ihrer Beziehungen zum Problem des Winterschlafes. Berta Coninx-Girardet. Acta Zoologica, vol.8, pt.2-3, pp.161-224, pls.1-5, 1927.

LATE RECORD OF THE YELLOW-BELLIED MARMOT. Leo K. Couch. Murrelet, vol.13, no.1, p.25, Jan., 1932.

ON THE FATTENING OF THE MARMOT (MARMOTA SIBIRICA RADDE) AND THEIR INFESTATION BY ASCARIDS BEFORE ENTERING THE HIBERNATION. V. B. Dubinin, L. I. Leshkovitch. Zool. Jour. USSR, Moscow, vol.24, no.6, pp.373-378, tables 5, 1945.

HIBERNATING GROUND SQUIRREL. A. Dawes DuBois. Natural History, New York, vol.39, no.3, pp.214-215, figs.2, Mar., 1937.

OBSERVATIONS OF THE BODY TEMPERATURE OF ARCTIC GROUND SQUIRRELS (CITELLUS PARRYI) DURING HIBERNATION. H. Erikson. Acta Physiologica Scandinavica, Stockholm, vol.36, fasc.1-2, pp.79-81, Mar., 1956.

HIBERNATING HABITS OF CHIPMUNKS. Arthur H. Howell. Jour. Mam., vol.4, no. 2, p.135, May, 1923.

ON HIBERNATION AS EXHIBITED IN THE STRIPED GOPHER. P. R. Hoy. Proc. Amer. Assoc. Adv. Sci., Detroit, pp.148-150, fig.1, Aug., 1875.

HIBERNATION OF THE THIRTEEN-LINED GROUND SQUIRREL, CITELLUS TRIDECEMLINEATUS (MITCHILL). I. A COMPARISON OF THE NORMAL AND HIBERNATING STATES. G. E. Johnson. Jour. Exper. Zool., vol.50, pp.15-30, 1928.

HIBERNATION OF THE THIRTEEN-LINED GROUND SQUIRREL, CITELLUS TRIDECEMLINEATUS (MITCHILL). II. THE GENERAL PROCESS OF WAKING FROM HIBERNATION. G. E. Johnson. Amer. Nat., vol. 63, pp.171-180, illus., Apr., 1929.

HIBERNATION OF THE THIRTEEN-LINED GROUND SQUIRREL, CITELLUS TRIDECEMLINEATUS (MITCHILL). III. THE RISE IN RESPIRATION, HEART BEAT AND TEMPERATURE IN WAKING FROM HIBERNATION. G. E. Johnson. Biol. Bull., vol.57, pp.107-129, 6 figs., Aug., 1929.

HIBERNATION OF THE THIRTEEN-LINED GROUND SQUIRREL, CITELLUS TRIDECEMLINEATUS (MITCHILL). IV. THE INFLUENCE OF THYROXIN, PITUITRIN, AND DESICATED THYMUS AND THYROID ON HIBERNATION. G. E. Johnson, Virginia B. Nanawalt. Amer. Nat., vol.64, no.692, pp.272-284, May-June, 1930.

HIBERNATION OF THE THIRTEEN-LINED GROUND SQUIRREL, CITELLUS TRIDECEMLINEATUS (MITCHILL). V. FOOD, LIGHT, CONFINED AIR, PRE-COOLING, CASTRATION, AND FATNESS IN RELATION TO PRODUCTION OF HIBERNATION. G. E. Johnson. Biol. Bull., vol.59, pp.114-127, 1930.

THE PROCESS OF AWAKENING FROM HIBERNATION IN THE 13-LINED GROUND SQUIRREL (CITELLUS TRIDECEMLINEATUS). G. E. Johnson. Anat. Record, vol. 29, pp.94-95, Dec.25, 1924.

HIBERNATION AND CORTICAL ELECTRICAL ACTIVITY IN THE WOODCHUCK (MARMOTA MONAX). Charles P. Lyman, Paul O. Chatfield. Science, 117 (3046): 533-534, May 15, 1953.

THE BLOOD SUGAR CONCENTRATION IN ACTIVE AND HIBERNATING GROUND SQUIRRELS. Rufus A. Lyman, Jr. Studies Zool. Lab. Univ. Nebraska, Lincoln, no.219, pp.467-474, 1943.

HIBERNATION IN THE GOLDEN-MANTLED GROUND SQUIRREL, CITELLUS LATERALIS BERNARDINUS. Don P. Mullally. Jour. Mam., 34 (1): 65-73, graph, Feb., 1953.

ELECTROCARDIOGRAM OF THE ARCTIC GROUND SQUIRREL DURING HIBERNATION AND HYPOTHERMIA. R. M. Nardone. Amer. Jour. Physiol., vol.182, no.2, pp. 364-368, Aug., 1955.

THE WINTER BURROWS OF CITELLUS PYGMAEUS PALL. AND UTILIZATION OF THEM FOR A SECOND HIBERNATION. Yu. M. Rall', M. P. Demyashev. Rev. Microbiol., 13 : 119-128, 1934.

THE CORPUSCLES, HEMOGLOBIN CONTENT AND SPECIFIC GRAVITY OF THE BLOOD DURING HIBERNATION IN THE WOODCHUCK (MARMOTA MONAX). Andrew Theodore Rasmussen. Amer. Jour. Physiol., vol.41, no.4, pp.464-482, Oct., 1916.

A FURTHER STUDY OF THE BLOOD GASES DURING HIBERNATION IN THE WOODCHUCK (MARMOTA MONAX). THE RESPIRATORY CAPACITY OF THE BLOOD. Andrew Theodore Rasmussen. Amer. Jour. Physiol., vol.41, no.2, pp.162-172, Aug., 1916.

THE HYPOPHYSIS CEREBRI OF THE WOODCHUCK (MARMOTA MONAX) WITH SPECIAL REFERENCE TO HIBERNATION AND INANITION. Andrew Theodore Rasmussen. Endocrinology, vol.5, pp.33-66, Jan., 1921.

THE OXYGEN AND CARBON DIOXIDE CONTENT OF THE BLOOD DURING HIBERNATION IN THE WOODCHUCK (MARMOTA MONAX). Andrew Theodore Rasmussen. Jour. Physiol., vol.39, no.1, pp.20-30, Nov., 1915.

THE VOLUME OF THE BLOOD DURING HIBERNATION AND OTHER PERIODS OF THE YEAR IN THE WOODCHUCK (MARMOTA MONAX). Andrew Theodore Rasmussen, Gertrude Rasmussen. Amer. Jour. Physiol., vol.44, no.2, pp.132-148, Sept., 1917.

AESTIVATION AND HIBERNATION PERIOD OF THE SMALLER GROUND SQUIRRELS IN THE PASCO-KENNEWICK COUNTRY, EASTERN WASHINGTON. Theo. H. Scheffer. Murrelet, vol.17, no.1, pp.17-18, Jan., 1936.

AGE OF THE ANIMAL AND SLOPE OF THE GROUND SURFACE, FACTORS MODIFYING THE STRUCTURE OF HIBERNATION DENS OF GROUND SQUIRRELS. William T. Shaw. Jour. Mam., vol.7, no. 2, pp.91-96, pl.12, May 1926.

DURATION OF THE AESTIVATION AND HIBERNATION OF THE COLUMBIAN GROUND SQUIRREL (CITELLUS COLUMBIANUS) AND SEX RELATION TO THE SAME. William T. Shaw. Ecology, vol. 6, no.1, pp.75-81, figs.2, Jan., 1925.

THE HIBERNATION OF THE COLUMBIAN GROUND SQUIRREL. William T. Shaw. Canadian Field-Nat., vol.39, pp.56-61, 79, 82, 11 figs., Mar.-Apr., 1925.

OBSERVATIONS ON THE HIBERNATION OF GROUND SQUIRRELS. William T. Shaw. Jour. Agric. Research, vol.31, no.8, pp. 761-769, figs.6, Oct.15, 1925.

NOTES ON THE HIBERNATION OF A WESTERN CHIPMUNK. Arthur Svihla. Jour. Mam., vol.17, no.3, pp.289-290, Aug., 1936.

STIMULI AND THEIR EFFECTS ON AWAKING OF DORMANT GROUND SQUIRRELS. Arthur Svihla, Howard Bowman, Ruth Ritenour. Amer. Jour. Physiol., Balto., vol.172, no.3, pp.681-683, Mar., 1953.

STUDIES ON THE ADRENAL AND THYROID GLANDS OF THE GROUND SQUIRREL DURING HIBERNATION. V. L. Vidovic, V. Popovic. Jour. Endocrinol., Lond., vol. 11, no.2, pp.125-133, Aug., 1954.

THE BEHAVIOR OF CERTAIN SPERMOPHILES WITH SPECIAL REFERENCE TO AESTIVATION AND HIBERNATION. Otis Wade. Jour. Mam., vol.11, no.2, pp. 160-188, pl.9, May, 1930.

RAPID FAT PRODUCTION BY GROUND SQUIRRELS PRECEDING HIBERNATION. Otis Wade. Nat. Hist. Miscellanea, Chicago, Acad. Sci., no.28, pp.1-3, Oct.12, 1948.

SOIL TEMPERATURES, WEATHER CONDITIONS, AND EMERGENCE OF GROUND SQUIRRELS FROM HIBERNATION. Otis Wade. Jour. Mam., 31 (2): 158-161, May, 1950.

PHYSIOLOGICAL STUDIES ON HIBERNATION IN THE CHIPMUNK. Alvalyn E. Woodward, John M. Condrin. Physiol. Zool., Chicago, vol.18, no.2, pp.162-167, Apr., 1945.

ADRENAL MEASUREMENTS FOLLOWING COLD EXPOSURE, STARVATION AND HIBERNATION IN THE GROUND SQUIRREL. M. L. Zimny. Anat. Record, Phila., 27 (2): 392, Feb., 1957.

CARBOHYDRATE METABOLISM DURING FASTING AND HIBERNATION IN THE GROUND SQUIRREL. M. L. Zimny, V. Tyrone. Amer. Jour. Physiol., Washington, 189 (2): 297-300, May, 1957.

Hunting and Trapping

AVERAGE SQUIRREL HUNTER BAGS ONLY ONE PER TRIP. John M. Allen. Outdoor Indiana, Indianapolis, vol.14, no.2, pp.2-3, illus., Apr., 1947.

MAST FRODUCTION--A KEY TO SQUIRREL CROPS. John M. Allen. Outdoor Ind., 14 (5): 18, Aug., 1947.

SQUIRRELITIS. (HABITS AND HUNTING SUCCESS OF GREY AND FOX SQUIRRELS IN INDIANA.) John M. Allen. Outdoor Indiana, Indianapolis, vol.15, no.8, pp.4-5, illus., Aug., 1948.

SHOTGUNS VERSUS RIFLES IN GRAY SQUIRREL HUNTING. Thomas Z. Atkeson. Jour. Wildlife Management, 22 (1): 99-100, Jan., 1958.

WHEELER SQUIRREL HUNT. Thomas Z. Atkeson, John L. Heflin. Alabama Conservation, Montgomery, vol.19, no.10, p.8, Apr., 1948.

CRIPPLING AS A FACTOR IN GRAY SQUIRREL HUNTING. Thomas Z. Atkeson, David C. Hulse. Jour. Wildlife Management, Ithaca, N.Y., vol.16, no.2, pp.230-232, Apr., 1952.

ARE HUNTING LAWS FAIR TO SQUIRRELS? Rollin H. Baker. Texas Game and Fish, Austin, vol.1, no.2, pp.5, 10, Jan., 1943.

AN EFFECTIVE GROUND SQUIRREL TRAP. E. M. Becker. Calif. Dept. Agr. Bull., 29 (3): 152, 1940.

FORCAST BETTER SQUIRREL HUNTING FOR 1942 SEASON. Louis G. Brown. Ill. Cons., 7 (2): 7-8, Summer, 1942.

CONTROLLED SQUIRREL HUNTING ON OHIO HUNTING PRESERVES, 1937. Floyd B. Chapman. Ohio Wildl. Res. Sta., Release 68, 8 pp., Jan., 1938.

CONTROLLED SQUIRREL HUNTING ON PUBLIC LANDS IN OHIO, 1938. Floyd B. Chapman. Ohio Wildl. Res. Sta., Release 101, 9 pp., Apr., 1939.

SQUIRRELS IN SEPTEMBER? R. H. Cross, Jr. Virginia Wildlife, Richmond, vol.10, no.9, pp.8-9, illus., Sept., 1949.

HUNTERS STALK WOODCHUCK. James J. Gilpin. Kentucky, Frankfort, vol.1, no.3, pp.27-28, May, 1946.

TRAPPING THE CALIFORNIA GROUND SQUIRREL. Everett E. Horn, Henry S. Fitch. Jour. Mam., vol.27, no.3, pp.220-224, figs.2, Aug.14, 1946.

ORGANIZATION OF THE SQUIRREL HUNTING IN FINLAND. Teppo Lampio. Suomen Riista, 8: 114-119, illus., 1953.

SQUIRREL HUNTING BASED ON THE ECOLOGY OF THE SPECIES. Teppo Lampio. Pap. Game Res., 8: 44-49, graph, 1952.

SQUIRRELS AND SQUIRREL HUNTING. W. O. Nagel. Missouri Conservationist, Jefferson City, vol.5, no.9, pp.1, 10-11, Sept., 1944.

A LIVE TRAP FOR GROUND SQUIRRELS. W. Prychodko. Jour. Mam., 33 (4): 497, illus., Nov., 1952.

SQUIRREL HUNTERS' SUCCESS. Howard R. Redmond. Miss. Game and Fish, 18 (3): 8-9, illus., Oct., 1954.

NOTES ON THE SAN BERNARDINO FLYING SQUIRREL. E. L. Sumner, Jr. Jour. Mam., vol.8, no.4, pp.314-316, Nov., 1927.

SOME RESULTS OF SQUIRREL HUNTING ON WEST VIRGINIA STATE LANDS. Hans G. Uhlig. Proc. 8th Ann. N.E. Wildl. Conf., Jackson's Mill, W. Va., Apr.1-4, 1952.

SQUIRRELS HOLD FIRST PLACE. (SQUIRREL HUNTING.) Hans G. Uhlig. West Virginia Conservation, Charleston, vol.12, no.11, p.9, Feb., 1949.

GRAY GHOSTS OF THE HARDWOODS. SQUIRREL HUNTING IN NEW ENGLAND. W. Dustin White. Field and Stream, no.5, pp.16-17, 67-68, Sept., 1929.

BUSHYTAILS--BEYOND THE LAW. Lee Yeager. Va. Wildl., 15 (9): 5-7, 12, 24, illus., Sept., 1954.

SQUIRREL HUNTING THE EASY WAY! Lee Yeager. Outdoorsman, Chicago, vol. 89, no.3, (whole no.526), pp.28, 63-66, illus., May-June, 1947.

Longevity

SUDDEN DEATH. (RED SQUIRRELS KILLED BY AUTOMOBILES.) Arthur Carthew. Yosemite Nat. Notes, vol.17, no.12, p.159, Dec., 1938.

A RECORD OF FOX SQUIRREL LONGEVITY. Howard C. Greene. Jour. Mam., vol.31, no.4, pp.454-455, Nov.21, 1950.

THE DURATION OF LIFE OF CITELLUS PYGMAEUS PALL. (RODENTIA) STUDIED BY MEANS OF THE BANDING METHOD. N. S. Kalaboukhov. Wissensch. Berichte der Moskauer Staats-Universitaet, pt.1, pp.29-34, 1933.

LONGEVITY AND OTHER DATA ON A MALE AND A FEMALE PRAIRIE DOG KEPT AS PETS. Stanley P. Young. Jour. Mam., Balto., vol.25, no.3, pp.317-319, Aug.,1944.

Lower California

A NEW LOUISIANA HERON AND A NEW ROUND-TAILED GROUND SQUIRREL FROM LOWER CALIFORNIA, MEXICO. Laurence M. Huey. Trans. San Diego Soc. Nat. Hist., vol.5, no.7, pp.83-86, Oct.10, 1927.

A NEW RACE OF CITELLUS TERETICAUDUS FROM LOWER CALIFORNIA. Laurence M. Huey. Proc. Biol. Soc. Washington, vol.39, pp.29-30, July 29, 1926.

TWO NEW GROUND SQUIRRELS FROM LOWER CALIFORNIA, MEXICO. Laurence M. Huey. Trans. San Diego Soc. Nat. Hist., vol.7, no.2, pp.17-20, Oct.6, 1931.

A NEW ANTELOPE SQUIRREL FROM LOWER CALIFORNIA. E. W. Nelson, E. A. Goldman. Jour. Wash. Acad. Sci., vol.19, no.13, pp.281-282, July 19, 1929.

DESCRIPTIONS OF A NEW EAGLE FROM ALASKA AND A NEW SQUIRREL FROM LOWER CALIFORNIA. C. H. Townsend. Proc. Biol. Soc. Wash., vol.11, pp.145-146, June 9, 1897.

Management

MICHIGAN FOX SQUIRREL MANAGEMENT. Durward L. Allen. Mich. Dept. Cons., Game Div., 404 pp., Oct., 1943.

GRAY AND FOX SQUIRREL MANAGEMENT IN INDIANA. John M. Allen. Ind. Dept. Cons., PR Bull. no.1, pp.1-112, illus., Mar., 1952.

WHAT ABOUT THE SQUIRREL SEASON? John M. Allen. Outdoor Ind., 17 (9): 14-15, 19, Sept., 1950.

KENTUCKY SQUIRREL STUDIES. BIOLOGISTS ARE FINDING OUT ABOUT HABITS OF BUSHYTAILS AND KNOWLEDGE WILL BE USED TO INCREASE POPULATIONS. Harold L. Barber. Ky. Happy Hunting Ground, 9 (2): 24-25, graph., Mar., 1953.

A SURVEY OF THE 1937 FOX SQUIRREL HARVEST IN 27 OHIO COUNTIES. Luther L. Baumgartner. Ohio Wildl. Res. Sta., Release 69, 8 pp., Dec., 1937.

A SURVEY OF THE 1939 SQUIRREL HARVEST IN OHIO. Luther L. Baumgartner. Ohio Wildl. Res. Sta., Release 128, 11 pp., Mar., 1940.

PROJECT DESIGNED TO OBTAIN DATA ON SQUIRREL HABITS AND HABITAT. E. Cooper Bertram. Ky. Happy Hunting Ground, 8 (1): 30-31, illus., Jan., 1952.

MORE SQUIRRELS IN PENN'S WOODS. Floyd B. Chapman. Pa. Game News, 13 (3): 5, 30, 32, June, 1942.

THE 1940 SQUIRREL HARVEST ON TEN PUBLIC HUNTING PRESERVES IN OHIO. Floyd B. Chapman. Ohio Wildl. Res. Sta., Release 162, 17 pp., June, 1941.

THE SQUIRREL HARVEST ON OHIO PUBLIC HUNTING PRESERVES, 1939. Floyd B. Chapman. Ohio Wildl. Res. Sta., Release 142, 8 pp., Aug., 1940.

ARE SQUIRRELS EXPENDABLE? Donald M. Christisen. Mo. Cons., 11 (8): 1-3, Aug., 1950.

TOO YOUNG TO DIE. Donald M. Christisen. Mo. Cons., 15 (5): 4-5, illus., May, 1954.

IMPLICATIONS OF SOCIAL BEHAVIOR IN GRAY SQUIRREL MANAGEMENT. Vagn F. Flyger. Trans. 20th N. A. Wildl. Conf., pp.381-389, 1 fig., 1955.

SQUIRREL MANAGEMENT IN EAST TEXAS. Phil D. Goodrum. Trans. N.A. Wildl. Conf., 3: 670-676, 1938.

WISE USE OF FORESTED LANDS NECESSARY FOR SQUIRREL CONSERVATION IN EAST TEXAS. Phil D. Goodrum. Texas Agr. Exp. Sta., Div. Wildl. Res., Prog. Rep.459, 4 pp., Aug., 1937.

TRANSPLANTATION OF THE DOUGLAS GROUND SQUIRREL. E. Raymond Hall. California Fish and Game, San Francisco, vol.26, no.1, p.77, Jan., 1940.

SQUIRREL BOX. Raymond Holtzapple. Pa. Game News, 10 (8): 30, Nov., 1939.

SQUIRREL ECONOMY IN FINLAND BASED ON NATURAL PREREQUISITES. Teppo Lampio. Suomen Riista, 2: 145-147, 1948.

GAME IN THE TREE TOPS. PROBLEMS AND PRINCIPLES OF SQUIRREL MANAGEMENT IN MISSOURI. W. O. Magel. Missouri Conservationist, Jefferson City, vol.7, no.7, pp.1-3, illus., July, 1946.

PERCENTAGE OF BREEDER SQUIRREL KILLED DURING THE 1949 SEASON AND ITS EFFECT UPON SETTING THE 1950-51 SEASON. Al Marsh. Jour. Tenn. Acad. Sci., 26 (1): 15-21, Jan., 1951.

SEPTEMBER BREEDER SQUIRREL KILL HIGH. Al Marsh. Tennessee Conservationist, Nashville, vol.15, no.4, pp.10-12, illus., July, 1950.

SQUIRREL MANAGEMENT IN SOUTHERN ILLINOIS. Richard J. Moran. Ill. Wildl., 8 (4): 5-6, illus., Sept., 1953.

SAVE THE WOODCHUCK. John M. Phillips. Pennsylvania Game News, New Cumberland, vol.10, no.2, p.12, May, 1939.

SOME FOREST SPRITES. VARIETIES OF WESTERN CHIPMUNKS MEAN MUCH TO THE OUTDOORS. Gayle Pickwell. Nature Magazine, vol.15, no.6, pp.359-362, figs. 9, June, 1930.

LATE OPEN SEASON MEANS LARGER SQUIRREL POPULATION. Ralph H. Quick. West Virginia Conservation, Charleston, vol.13, no.10, pp.11, 31, Oct., 1949.

MORE NOTES ON MOVING CHICKAREES. Ralph Teal. Yosemite Nature Notes, vol. 7, p.80, Sept., 1928.

BIOLOGIC BASES OF ORGANIZATION OF MARMOT TRADE-FARMING IN THE VOLGA-KAMA REGION. V. P. Teplov, V. I. Tikhvinsky. Raboty Volzhsko-Kamskoi Zonal'noi Okhotnich'epromyslonoi Biologischeskoi Stantsii, Kazan, no.2 (Uchen'ie Zapiski Kacanskogo Gosudarstvennogo Universiteta im V. I. Ul'ianova-Lenina, vol.92, nos.7-8), pp.3-45, figs. 12, 1932.

USING DEN BOXES TO BOOST SQUIRREL CROP. Harold V. Terrill, Bill T. Crawford. Mo. Cons., 7 (8): 4-5, Aug., 1946.

GOOD FORESTRY MEANS MORE SQUIRRELS IN WOODLOTS. Hans Uhlig. West Virginia Conserv., Charleston, vol. 12, no.6, pp.16-17, June, 1949.

MORE THAN 1,000,000 POUNDS IN STATE'S ANNUAL SQUIRREL CROP. Hans G. Uhlig, H. Lee Wilson. W. Va. Cons., 14 (4): 6, 29-30, July, 1950.

GRAY SQUIRREL HAS WITHSTOOD HUNTERS' FIRE, PREDATION, TO BE HAILED AS PLANTER OF FORESTS. Earl Wallace. Kentucky, Happy Hunting Ground, Frankfort, vol.2, no.2, pp.8-9, illus., Mar., 1947.

WE'RE PLANTING SQUIRRELS NOW. Mel Washburn. La. Cons., 2 (4): 4-5, 21-22, Dec., 1949.

SQUIRRELS NEED MANAGEMENT. F. R. Zimmerman. Wis. Cons. Bull., 4 (10): 40-43, Oct., 1939.

HIGH SQUIRREL POPULATION IN 1955 AND ITS RELATION TO LONGER SEASON. Ohio Div. Wildl., Game Surv. News, 2 (4): 4, maps and graph, Sept., 1955.

SEASON FOR SQUIRRELS. Outdoor Indiana, Indianapolis, vol.11, no.7, p.11, illus., Aug., 1944.

Methods, Techniques

TRAPPING, HANDLING, AND MARKING FOX SQUIRRELS. Luther L. Baumgartner. Jour. Wildlife Management, Menasha, vol. 4, no.4, pp.444-450, illus., Oct., 1940.

PLANT HISTOLOGY AS AN AID IN SQUIRREL FOOD-HABIT STUDIES. Luther L. Baumgartner, A. C. Martin. Jour. Wildlife Management, Menasha, vol.3, no. 3, pp.266-268, pls.14-17, July, 1939.

IMPROVED TOE-TAG FOR MARKING FOX SQUIRRELS. Marvin E. Cooley. Jour. Wildl. Mgt., 12 (2): 213, Apr., 1948.

METHODS FOR ESTIMATING CROPS OF THE SQUIRREL'S FOODS WHEN PREDICTING THE ANIMAL'S NUMBERS. D. N. Danilov. In Symposium, "Methods for predicting changes in the numbers of fur-bearing animals and renewing their natural supplies." Trans. Cent. Lab. Game Indus. no.5, pp.34-45, 1941.

COLOR MARKING OF MAMMALS, WITH SPECIAL REFERENCE TO SQUIRRELS. William D. Fitzwater, Jr. Jour. Wildl. Mgt., 7 (2): 190-192, Apr., 1943.

CRITERIA FOR ESTIMATING FALL FOX SQUIRREL POPULATIONS. Charles E. Friley, Jr. Jour. Wildlife Management, Ithaca, vol.19, no.1, pp.89-93, illus., Jan., 1955.

A COMPARISON OF INVENTORY METHODS APPLICABLE TO THE WESTERN FOX SQUIRRELS, SCIURUS NIGER RUFIVENTER (GEOFFROY). Ellis A. Hicks. MS thesis, Iowa State Coll., 1940.

SOME MAJOR FACTORS AFFECTING THE USE OF TWO INVENTORY METHODS APPLICABLE TO THE WESTERN FOX SQUIRREL, SCIURUS NIGER RUFIVENTER (GEOFFROY). Ellis A. Hicks. Iowa State Coll. Jour. Sci., 16 (2): 299-305, Jan., 1942.

SOME METHODS OF CENSUSING FOX SQUIRRELS, SCIURUS NIGER RUFIVENTER, GEOFFROY. George S. Hunt. MS thesis, Univ. Mich., 1950.

MARKING OF CITELLUS PYGMAEUS PALL. IN ORDER TO STUDY THEIR LENGTH OF LIFE IN NATURAL CONDITIONS. N. J. Kalabuchov. Rec. Trav. Sci. Univ. Moscow, 1:29-33, 1933. (In Russian.)

METHODS FOR FORCASTING CHANGES IN POPULATION OF THE COMMON SQUIRREL (SCIURUS VULGARIS L.). I. D. Kris. In Symposium, "Methods for forecasting changes in the numbers of fur-bearing animals and renewing their natural supplies." Trans. Cent. Lab. Game Indus., no.5, pp.17-34, 1941.

A NEW TECHNIQUE FOR MARKING FOX SQUIRRELS. J. P. Linduska. Jour. Wildl. Mgt., 6 (1): 93-94, Jan., 1942.

TRAPPING AND MARKING SQUIRRELS ON A REFUGE IN SOUTHERN ILLINOIS. Richard J. Moran. Trans. Illinois Acad. Sci., vol.46, pp.258-262, 1953.

ON METHODS OF STUDYING THE MICROCLIMATE OF THE GROUND SQUIRREL'S NEST. FIRST REPORT. Yu. M. Rall'. Rev. Microbiol., 11 (1): 43-52, 1932.

METHODS FOR TRAPPING AND TAGGING WOODCHUCKS. Richard F. Trump, George O. Hendrickson. Jour. Wildlife Management, Menasha, vol.7, no.4, pp. 420-421, Oct., 1943.

Mexico

TWO NEW FLYING SQUIRRELS FROM MEXICO. E. A. Goldman. Jour. Wash. Acad. Sci., vol.26, no.11, pp.462-464, Nov.15, 1936.

THE SUBSPECIES OF THE MEXICAN RED-BELLIED SQUIRREL, SCIURUS AUREOGASTER. Keith R. Kelson. Univ. Kansas Publ., Mus. Nat. Hist., Lawrence, vol.5, no.17, pp.243-250, Apr.10, 1952.

DESCRIPTION OF A NEW PRAIRIE DOG (CYNOMYS MEXICANUS) FROM MEXICO. C. Hart Merriam. Proc. Biol. Soc. Wash., vol.7, pp.157-158, July 27, 1892.

DESCRIPTIONS OF NEW SQUIRRELS FROM MEXICO. E. W. Nelson. Proc. Biol. Soc. Wash., vol.17, pp.147-150, Oct.6, 1904.

DESCRIPTIONS OF NEW SQUIRRELS FROM MEXICO AND CENTRAL AMERICA. E. W. Nelson. Proc. Biol. Soc. Wash., vol.12, pp.145-156, June 3, 1898.

DESCRIPTIONS OF TWO NEW SQUIRRELS FROM MEXICO. E. W. Nelson. Proc. Biol. Soc. Wash., vol.14, pp.131-132, Aug. 9, 1901.

REVISION OF THE SQUIRRELS OF MEXICO AND CENTRAL AMERICA. E. W. Nelson. Proc. Wash. Acad. Sci., vol.1, pp.15-106, pls.2, May 9, 1899.

ON THE MEXICAN REPRESENTATIVE SCIURUS ABERTI. Oldfield Thomas. Ann. and Mag. Nat. Hist. (6), vol.11, no.61, pp. 49-50, Jan., 1893.

CITELLUS VARIEGATUS RUPESTRIS ALLEN, OF IZUCAR DE MATAMOROS, PUEBLA. Bernardo Villa R. Anales Inst. Biol., Mexico, D.F., vol.13, no.2, pp. 555-569, figs.4, 1942. (In Spanish.)

Migrations

ON THE IMMIGRATION OF THE SQUIRREL INTO KAMTCHATKA. Sten Bergman. Arkiv. foer Zool., vol.23B, no.4, pp.1-4, Jan.12, 1932.

SQUIRRELS ON THE MARCH. George S. Fichter. Frontiers, Phila., vol.14, no.3, pp.73-74, Feb., 1950.

MIGRATIONS OF THE COMMON SQUIRREL (SCIURUS VULGARIS) IN USSR. A. Formozov. Trav. Inst. Zool. Acad. Sci. URSS, Moscou, vol.3, pp.97-164, figs.13, tables 3, 1936. (In Russian.)

MIGRATIONS OF THE RED SQUIRREL IN USSR. A. N. Formozov. Abstracts works Zool. Inst. Moscow Univ., no.2, pp.59-62, 1935. (In Russian.)

SQUIRRELS MIGRATE FROM WISCONSIN TO IOWA. F. M. Fryxell. Jour. Mam., vol.7, no.1, p.60, Feb., 1926.

THE GRAY SQUIRREL MIGRATION. George G. Goodwin. Nature Mag., vol. 23, no.5, pp.221-222, 255-256, illus., May, 1934.

MIGRATION OF GRAY SQUIRRELS. Earl F. Hoover. Science, n.s., vol.83, no.2151, pp.284-285, Mar.20, 1936.,

MIGRATION OF GRAY SQUIRRELS. Ralph C. Jackson. Science, vol.82, no.2136, pp.549-550, Dec.6, 1935.

A STUDY OF MIGRATIONS IN GROUND-SQUIRRELS (CITELLUS PYGMAEUS PALL.) IN STEPPE PART OF THE NORTHERN CAUCASUS BY MEANS OF BANDING METHOD. N. Kalabukhov, W. Raevsky. Problems of Ecology and Biocenology, Leningrad, pp.170-195, figs.5, tables 4, 1935.

SQUIRRELS JUST GOTTA GET FOOD. THAT TELLS THE STORY OF THEIR 1939 MASS MIGRATION FROM BANKHEAD FOREST. George C. Moore. Alabama Conservation, Montgomery, vol.14, no.5, pp.7, 15, Nov., 1942.

AN EMIGRATION OF SQUIRRELS IN WISCONSIN. A. W. Schorger. Jour. Mam., 28 (4): 401-403, Nov., 1947.

MIGRATIONS OF THE GRAY SQUIRREL (SCIURUS CAROLINENSIS). Ernest Thompson Seton. Jour. Mam,, vol.1, no. 2, pp.53-58, Feb., 1920.

THE INVASION OF THE GREY SQUIRREL. L. P. Shadbolt. Trans. Hertfordshire Nat. Hist. Soc. and Field Club, vol.19, pt. 3, pp.163-170, Jan., 1933.

MINUS COMPASS OR RADAR. (GRAY SQUIRREL MIGRATION.) Bill Wolf. Sports Afield, Minneapolis, vol.119, no.6, pp.50-51, 104-107, illus., June, 1948.

Nests and Burrows

RELATION OF WOODCHUCK DENS TO SOIL TYPES, TOPOGRAPHY AND OTHER ENVIRONMENTAL FACTORS IN WASHTENAW COUNTY, MICHIGAN. M. E. Anderson. MF thesis, Univ. Mich., 1949.

OUTSIDE NESTS OF FLYING SQUIRRELS. Jas. L. Baillie, Jr. Canadian Field-Nat., vol.44, no.4, p.94, Apr., 1930.

FOX SQUIRREL DENS. Luther L. Baumgartner. Jour. Mam., 20 (4): 456-465, Nov., 1939.

GIANT SEQUOIA HOUSES CHIPMUNK FAMILY. R. P. Beal. Yosemite Nature Notes, vol.12, no.8, pp.77, Aug., 1933.

WOODCHUCK--MASTER EXCAVATOR. G. W. Bradt. Ohio Conservation Bull., Columbus, vol.10, no.8, p.14, Aug., 1946.

EARLY NESTING OF THE RED SQUIRREL (SCIURUS VULGARIS, L.) IN DUMFRIESSHIRE. Bruce Campbell. Scottish Nat., no.217, p.7, Jan.-Feb., 1936.

(ON SQUIRRELS: THEIR HIDING PLACES.) Notes sur l'ecureuil. Les cachettes. A. Chappellier. Travaux de la Sta. Zool. de Wimereux, Paris, vol.13, pp.69-75, figs.5, 1938.

NESTING HABITS OF THE FLYING SQUIRREL GLAUCOMYS SABRINUS. Ian McTaggart Cowan. Jour. Mam., vol. 17, no.1, pp.58-60, Feb.14, 1936.

THE EFFECT OF DEN FLOODING ON WOODCHUCKS. W. W. Currier. Jour. Mam., 30:429-30, 1949.

SOME OBSERVATIONS ON DEN TREES IN THE MISSOURI OZARKS. (HEAVY CUTTING OF OAK FORESTS HAS MADE IT UNINHABITABLE FOR SQUIRRELS DURING BREEDING SEASON.) Paul D. Dalke. Jour. Wildl. Mgt., 12 (1): 107-109, Jan., 1948.

BURROWS AND BURROWING HABITS OF THE DOUGLAS GROUND SQUIRREL. Elton R. Edge. Jour. Mam., vol.15, no.3, pp.189-193, pl.7, Aug., 1934.

INVESTIGATIONS OF THE BURROWS OF THE AMERICAN MARMOT (ARCTOMYS MONAX). W. H. Fisher. Jour. Cincinnati Soc. Nat. Hist., pp.105-123, pls.6-10, July-Oct., 1893.

LEAF NESTS OF GRAY SQUIRREL IN CONNECTICUT. William D. Fitzwater, Jr., W. J. Frank. Jour. Mam., 25 (2): 160-170, May, 1944.

AIR RAID SHELTER. (HOARY MARMOT.) John Eric Hill. Nat. Hist., New York, vol. 50, no.3, p.158, illus., Oct., 1942.

AN OUTSIDE NEST OF A FLYING SQUIRREL. M. F. Landwer. Jour. Mam., vol. 16, no.1, p.67, Feb., 1935.

NOTES ON FLYING SQUIRRELS AND GRAY SQUIRRELS. D. Lange. Jour. Mam., vol.1, no.5, pp.243-244, Nov., 1920.

RED SQUIRREL NESTING ON THE GROUND. Harold Mayfield. Jour. Mam., vol.29, no. 2, p.186, May 15, 1948.

A NEST OF THE CALIFORNIA GRAY SQUIRREL (SCIURUS GRISEUS). C. Hart Merriam. Jour. Mam., vol.11, no.4, pp. 494, pl.25, Nov., 1930.

NESTS OF THE FLORIDA FLYING SQUIRREL. Joseph C. Moore. Amer. Midland Nat., Notre Dame, vol.38, no.1, pp.248-253, July, 1947.

THE WOODCHUCK AS A SOIL EXPERT. A. E. Moss. Jour. Wildl. Mgt., 4 (4): 441-443, Oct., 1940.

AN UNUSUAL CHIPMUNK NEST. Leslie W. Orr. Jour. Mam., vol.11, no.3, p.315, Aug., 1930.

THE BURROW OF TAMIAS STRIATUS. Joseph A. Panuska, Nelson J. Wade. Jour. Mam., 37 (1): 23-31, illus., Feb.28, 1956.

A GRAY SQUIRREL MOVES ITS HOME Ernest A. Payne. Yosemite Nat. Notes, Stockton, vol.18, no.9, pp.100-101, Sept., 1939.

SNOW BURROWS OF THE RED SQUIRREL (TAMIASCIURUS). George A. Petrides. Jour. Mam., vol.22, no.4, pp.393-394, Nov.14, 1941.

(ON THE STRUCTURE OF THE NEST OF THE SQUIRREL.) Ueber den Nestbau des

Eichhoernchens. Ludwig Schuster. Zool. Garten, Leipzig, n.F., vol.4, nos.8-9, pp.297-298, Oct., 1931.

THE COLUMBIAN GROUND SQUIRREL AS A HANDLER OF EARTH. William T. Shaw. Sci. Monthly, vol.20, pp.483-490, figs.8, May, 1925.

FOX SQUIRRELS' NESTS IN A BARN. Althea R. Sherman. Jour. Mam., vol.7, no.4, p.332, Nov., 1926.

CHIPMUNK NEST. Robert A. Smith. Nature Mag., Washington, D.C., vol.35, no.5, p.277, May, 1942.

AN OUTSIDE NEST OF A FLYING SQUIRREL. L. L. Snyder. Jour. Mam., vol.2, no.3, p.171, Aug., 1921.

NESTS OF THE WESTERN FOX SQUIRREL. H. L. Stoddard. Jour. Mam., vol.1, no.3, pp.122-123, pl.7, May, 1920.

A THEORY ON LEAF NESTS BUILT BY GRAY SQUIRRELS ON SENECA STATE FOREST, WEST VIRGINIA. Hans G. Uhlig. Jour. Wildlife Management, 20 (3): 263-266, July, 1956.

North America

THE HABITS AND LIFE HISTORY OF THE EASTERN CHIPMUNK, TAMIAS STRIATUS LYSTERI. Elsa G. Allen. Bull. New York State Museum, no.314, pp.122, illus., Sept., 1938.

THE NORTH AMERICAN ARBOREAL SQUIRRELS. J. A. Allen. Amer. Nat., vol.33, pp.635-642, Aug., 1899.

ON GEOGRAPHICAL VARIATION IN COLOR AMONG NORTH AMERICAN SQUIRRELS. WITH A LIST OF THE SPECIES AND VARIETIES OF THE AMERICAN SCIURIDAE OCCURRING NORTH OF MEXICO. J.A. Allen. Proc. Boston Soc. Nat. Hist., vol. 16, pp.276-294, Feb. 4, 1874.

A REVIEW OF SOME OF THE NORTH AMERICAN GROUND SQUIRRELS OF THE GENUS TAMIAS. J. A. Allen. Bull. Amer. Mus. Nat. Hist., vol.3, pp.45-116, June, 1890.

REVISION OF THE CHICKAREES, OR NORTH AMERICAN RED SQUIRRELS (SUBGENUS TAMIASCIURUS). J. A. Allen. Bull. Amer. Mus. Nat. Hist., vol.10, pp. 249-298, Aug.31, 1898.

SYNONYMATIC LIST OF THE AMERICAN SCIURI OR ARBOREAL SQUIRRELS. J. A. Allen. Bull. U.S. Geol. and Geogr. Surv. Terr., vol.4, no.4, pp.877-887, Dec., 1878.

THE EASTERN GRAY SQUIRREL. Ross Allen, Wilfred T. Neill. Florida Wildlife, Tallahassee, vol.9, no.5, pp.7, 49, illus., Oct., 1955.

NOTES ON THE DISTRIBUTION OF THE HOARY MARMOTS. R. M. Anderson. Canadian Field-Nat., vol.48, no.4, pp. 60-63, fig., Apr.2, 1934.

A REVIEW OF THE SQUIRRELS OF EASTERN NORTH AMERICA. Outram Bangs. Proc. Biol. Soc. Wash., vol.10, pp.145-167, figs.29-32, pls.8-10, Dec.28, 1896.

EXTENSION OF RANGE OF TAMIAS STRIATUS GRISEUS MEARNS. H. U. Green. Canadian Field-Nat., vol.51, no. 3, pp.39-40, Mar., 1937.

EXTENSION OF THE KNOWN GEOGRAPHIC RANGE OF THE STRIATED CHIPMUNK (TAMIAS STRIATUS). E. Raymond Hall. Amer. Midland Nat., Notre Dame, Indiana, vol.21, no.3, p.766, May, 1939.

DESCRIPTIONS OF SIX NEW NORTH AMERICAN GROUND SQUIRRELS. Arthur H. Howell. Proc. Biol. Soc. Wash., vol. 41, pp.211-214, Dec.18, 1928.

DESCRIPTIONS OF THREE NEW RED SQUIRRELS (TAMIASCIURUS) FROM NORTH AMERICA. Arthur H. Howell. Proc. Biol. Soc. Wash., vol.49, pp.133-136, Aug.22, 1936.

NOTES ON RANGE OF THE EASTERN CHIPMUNKS IN OHIO, INDIANA, AND QUEBEC. Arthur H. Howell. Jour. Mam., vol.13, no.2, pp.166-167, May, 1932.

PRELIMINARY DESCRIPTIONS OF FIVE NEW CHIPMUNKS FROM NORTH AMERICA. Arthur H. Howell. Jour. Mam., vol.6, no. 1, pp.51-54, Feb.9, 1925.

PRELIMINARY DESCRIPTIONS OF FOUR NEW NORTH AMERICAN GROUND SQUIRRELS. Arthur H. Howell. Jour. Mam., vol.12, no.2, pp.160-162, May 14, 1931.

REVISION OF THE AMERICAN CHIPMUNKS. (GENERA TAMIAS AND EUTAMIAS.) Arthur H. Howell. North Amer. Fauna no.52, Biol. Surv., U.S. Dept. Agric., pp.157, pls.10, maps 9, Nov.30, 1929.

REVISION OF THE AMERICAN FLYING SQUIRRELS. Arthur H. Howell. N. Amer. Fauna, no.44, pp.1-64, figs.1-4, pls.1-7, June 13, 1918.

REVISION OF THE NORTH AMERICAN GROUND SQUIRRELS, WITH A CLASSIFICATION OF THE NORTH AMERICAN SCIURIDAE. Arthur H. Howell. USDA, Biol. Survey, N. A. Fauna 56, pp.256, Apr., 1938.

TEN NEW MARMOTS FROM NORTH AMERICA. Arthur H. Howell. Proc. Biol. Soc. Wash., vol.27, pp.13-18, Feb.2, 1914.

THE GOLDEN MANTLED GROUND SQUIRREL. Ralph R. Huestis. Crater L. Nat. Notes, Spec. No., pp.1-22, illus., 1951.

(OBSERVATIONS OF NORTH AMERICAN FLYING SQUIRRELS SCIUROPTERUS (GLAUCOMYS) VOLANS THOMAS.) Beobachtungen an nordamerikanischen Gleitflughoernchen Sciuropterus (Glaucomys) volans (Thomas). Wolfgang Luther. Zeitschr. Tierpsych., Berlin, vol.9, no.2, pp.402-411, 1952.

NOTES ON THE EASTERN DISTRIBUTION OF EUTAMIAS MINIMUS. Randolph L. Peterson. Contrib. Royal Ontario Mus. Zool. and Palaeontol., Toronto, no.37, pp. 1-4, map, Dec.31, 1953.

A REVISION OF THE WEST AMERICAN FLYING SQUIRRELS. Samuel N. Rhoads. Proc. Acad. Nat. Sciences, Phila., pp.314-327, 1897.

TWO NEW SPECIES OF MARMOTS FROM NORTHWESTERN AMERICA. H. S. Swarth. Univ. Cal. Pub. Zool., vol.7, no. 6, pp.201-204, Feb.18, 1911.

NEW NAME FOR A NORTH AMERICAN SQUIRREL. Frederick W. True. Proc. Biol. Soc. Wash., vol.13, p.183, Nov.30, 1900.

Pacific Islands

RESULTS OF THE ARCHBOLD EXPEDITIONS. NO. I. A NEW GENUS AND SPECIES OF SQUIRREL FROM CELEBES. R. Archbold, G. H. H. Tate. Amer. Mus. Nov., New York, no.801, pp.6, figs.7, May 17, 1935.

THE FORMS OF PREVOST'S SQUIRREL FOUND IN SARAWAK. E. Banks. Proc. Zool. Soc. Lond., pt.4, pp.1335-1348, pl. 1, Dec., 1931.

A NEW FLYING-SQUIRREL FROM BORNEO. F. N. Chasen. Bull. Raffles Mus., Singapore, no.8, p.194, Dec., 1933.

A RARE BORNEAN SQUIRREL, GLYPHOTES SIMUS THOMAS. F. N. Chasen, C. Boden Kloss. Jour. Malayan Branch Royal Asiatic Soc., vol.5, pt.2, pp.349-350, Nov., 1927.

ON A NEW SPECIES OF SQUIRREL (SCIURUS MACROTIS) FROM BORNEO. John E. Gray. Proc. Zool. Soc. Lond., pt.24, p.341, pl.46, 1856.

SQUIRRELS FROM THE KELABIT UPLANDS. Tom Harrisson. Sarawak Mus. Jour., Kuching, vol.5, no.2, pp.297-299, Sept., 1950.

DESCRIPTION OF A NEW PHILIPPINE FLYING-SQUIRREL. Ned Hollister. Proc. Biol. Soc. Wash., vol.24, pp.185-186, June 23, 1911.

A NEW FLYING-SQUIRREL FROM BORNEO. Charles Hose. Ann. and Mag. Nat. Hist. London, ser.7, vol.5, pp.214-216, Feb., 1900.

ON A NEW FLYING SQUIRREL FROM DELI, SUMATRA. F. A. Jentink. Notes Leyden Mus., vol.12, no.21, pp.145-148, pl.7, Mar., 1890.

A NEW SQUIRREL FROM NORTH SARAWAK. C. Boden Kloss. Jour. Straits Branch, Royal Asiatic Soc., no.83, pp.151-152, Apr., 1921.

A NEW SQUIRREL FROM THE TENGGOL ISLAND, EAST COAST OF THE MALAY PENINSULA. C. Boden Kloss. Jour. Malayan Branch Royal Asiatic Soc., vol.4, pt.2, pp.259-261, Oct., 1926.

DESCRIPTION OF A NEW SQUIRREL OF THE SCIURUS PREVOSTII GROUP FROM PULO TEMAJU, WEST COAST OF BORNEO. Marcus W. Lyon, Jr. Smithsonian Misc. Coll., vol.48, pt.3, pp.275-276, no.1659, Feb.4, 1907.

LOCAL RACES OF BORNEAN SQUIRRELS. Marcus W. Lyon, Jr. Science, N.S., vol. 25, no.628, p.64, Jan.11, 1907.

A NEW SQUIRREL FROM DIRECTION ISLAND, SOUTH CHINA SEA. Marcus W. Lyon, Jr. Proc. U.S. Nat. Mus., vol.36, no.1686, pp.509-510, June 7, 1909.

REMARKS ON THE GIANT SQUIRRELS OF SUMATRA, WITH DESCRIPTIONS OF TWO NEW SPECIES. Marcus W. Lyon, Jr. Proc. U.S. Nat. Mus., vol.32, no.1534, pp.439-445, pl.33, May 23, 1907.

THE SQUIRRELS OF THE SCIURUS VITTATUS GROUP IN SUMATRA. Marcus W. Lyon, Jr. Smithsonian Misc. Coll., vol.48, pp.277-283, Feb.4, 1907.

DESCRIPTION OF A NEW SQUIRREL FROM THE PHILIPPINE ISLANDS. A. B. Meyer. Proc. Zool. Soc. Lond., pt.4, pp.599-601, Apr.1, 1891.

(ON TWO SQUIRREL SPECIES OF CELEBES.) Ueber Zwei Eichhoernchenaten von celebes. A. B. Meyer. Abhandl. Ber. K. Zool. Anthropol. Ethnogr. Mus. Dresden, vol.7, no.4, pp.1-3, Sept.7, 1898.

A NEW SQUIRREL FROM BORNEO. Gerrit S. Miller, Jr. Proc. Biol. Soc. Wash., vol.14, pp.33-34, Apr.5, 1901.

A NEW FLYING-SQUIRREL FROM THE PHILIPPINE ISLANDS. Wilfred H. Osgood. Proc. Biol. Soc. Wash., vol.31, pp.1-2, Feb.21, 1918.

SCIUROPTERUS MINDANENSIS SP. NOV., A NEW SPECIES OF FLYING SQUIRREL FROM MINDANAO. Dioscoro S. Rabor. Philippine Jour. Sci., Manila, vol.69, no. 4, pp.389-396, pls.4, Aug., 1939.

(CONTRIBUTION TO KNOWLEDGE OF THE SCIURUS SPECIES OF CELEBES.) Beitrag zur Kenntnis der Sciurus-Arten von Celebes. Jean Roux. Zool. Anzeiger, Leipzig, vol.35, no.17, pp.515-520, Mar.15, 1910.

A NEW FLYING SQUIRREL FROM SUMATRA. H. J. V. Sody. Natuurk. Tijdschr. Nederland.-Indie, vol.96, no.2, pp.146-147, 1936.

A NEW RACE OF CALLOSCIURUS NOTATUS FROM NORTH SUMATRA. H. J. V. Sody. Natuurk. Tijdschrift, vol.96, no.3, pp.217-218. 1936.

ON A COLLECTION OF SCIURIDAE FROM THE INDO-MALAYAN AND INDO-AUSTRALIAN REGIONS WITH DESCRIPTIONS OF 20 NEW SPECIES AND SUBSPECIES, AND WITH SOME REMARKS ON THE ESSENTIAL SIGNIFICANCE AND THE DENOMINATION OF SUBSPECIES. H. J. V. Sody. Treubia, Buitenzorg, vol.20, pt.1, pp.57-120, Apr., 1949.

DESCRIPTION OF A NEW SCIUROPTERUS FROM THE PHILIPPINES. Oldfield Thomas. Ann. and Mag. Nat. Hist. (6), vol.12, no. 67, pp.30-31, July, 1893.

DESCRIPTION OF A NEW SQUIRREL FROM BORNEO. Oldfield Thomas. Ann. and Mag. Nat. Hist. (6), vol.6, no.32, pp.171-172, Aug., 1890.

DESCRIPTION OF TWO NEW SQUIRRELS FROM NORTH BORNEO. Oldfield Thomas. Ann. and Mag. Nat. Hist. (5), vol.20, no. 116, pp.127-129, Aug., 1887.

DESCRIPTIONS OF TWO NEW BORNEAN SQUIRRELS. Oldfield Thomas. Ann. and Mag. Nat. Hist. (6), vol.10, no.57, pp.214-216, Sept., 1892.

DESCRIPTIONS OF TWO NEW SCIUROPTERI DISCOVERED BY CHARLES HOSE IN BORNEO. Oldfield Thomas. Ann. and Mag. Nat. Hist. (7), vol.5, no.27, pp.275-276, Mar., 1900.

A NEW FLYING SQUIRREL FROM FORMOSA. Oldfield Thomas. Ann. and Mag. Nat. Hist. (7), vol.20, no.120, pp.522-523, Dec., 1907.

ON A SPECIAL MOUNTAIN RACE OF THE PLANTAIN SQUIRREL FROM MOUNT DULIT, E. SARAWAK. Oldfield Thomas. Ann. and Mag. Nat. Hist. (6), vol.15, no. 90, pp.529-531, June, 1895.

THE RED FLYING SQUIRREL OF THE NATUNA ISLANDS. Oldfield Thomas. Novitates Zoologicae, vol.7, p.592, Dec., 1900.

THE SQUIRRELS DESCRIBED AS SCIURUS STEERII FROM BALABAC AND PALAWAN. Oldfield Thomas. Ann. and Mag Nat.Hist., ser.8, vol.2, no.12, p.498, Dec., 1908.

DESCRIPTION OF A NEW SPECIES OF SQUIRREL (SCIURUS PHILIPPINENSIS) FROM THE PHILIPPINE ISLANDS. G. R. Waterhouse. Proc. Zool. Soc. Lond., pt. 7, p.117, 1839.

A BRIEF ACCOUNT OF THE FORMOSAN FLYING SQUIRRELS. Dien Zuh-Ming. Quart. Jour. Taiwan Mus., Taipei, vol.8, no.3, pp.203-206, Sept., 1955.

Pelage, Coloration

COLOR VARIATION IN THE PIUTE GROUND SQUIRREL. J. R. Alcorn. Jour. Mam., Balto., vol.21, no.2, p.218, May 14, 1940.

ON SEASONAL VARIATIONS IN COLOR IN SCIURUS HUDSONICUS. J. A. Allen. Bull. Amer. Mus. Nat. Hist., vol.3, pp. 41-44, June, 1890.

A GRAY RED SQUIRREL. Jas. L. Baille, Jr. Canadian Field Nat., vol.45, no.8, p. 207, Nov., 1931.

PELAGE STUDIES OF FOX SQUIRRELS (SCIURUS NIGER RUFIVENTER). Luther L. Baumgartner. Amer. Midland Nat., Notre Dame, vol.29, no.3, pp.588-590, May, 1943.

COLOR VARIATION IN THE SPOTTED GROUND SQUIRRELS OF THE TULAROSA BASIN, NEW MEXICO. W. Frank Blair. Contrib. Lab. Vertebrate Genetics, Univ. Michigan, Ann Arbor, no.16, 6 pp., Nov., 1941.

AN UNUSUAL MELANISTIC SQUIRREL. W. J. Breckenridge. Jour. Mam., vol.28, no. 4, pp.403-404, Nov.26, 1947.

A PALE MUTATION IN THE GROUND SQUIRREL. ALBINOID COLORPHASE IN CITELLUS ELEGANS RESEMBLING THE RECESSIVE CREAM MUTATION IN THE RAT. Frank H. Clark, William L. Jellison. Jour. Heredity, Washington, D.C., vol.28, no.7, pp.259-260, illus., July, 1937.

AN ALBINO GROUND SQUIRREL. Ralph E. Dunbar. Nature Mag., vol.28, no.6, p. 338, illus., Dec., 1936.

A PALE VARIATION IN A GROUND SQUIRREL. NOTES ON A PALE INDIVIDUAL OF THE THIRTEEN-STRIPED GROUND SQUIRREL CITELLUS TRIDECEMLINEATUS (MITCHILL). Edson Fichter, Lloyd Don Davis. Jour. Heredity, Wash., D.C., vol.33, no.4, pp.153-155, fig.15, Apr., 1942.

MELANISTIC GREY SQUIRRELS AT ASHWELL. W. H. Fordham. Trans. Hertfordshire Nat. Hist. Soc. and Field Club, Hertford, vol.22, pt.4, pp.160-161, Aug., 1946.

MELANISM AMONG THE MARMOTS OF THE TETON RANGE, WYOMING. Fritiof M. Fryxell. Jour. Mam., vol.9, no.4, pp.336-337, Nov., 1928.

MOLT PATTERNS IN GROUND SQUIRRELS. Richard M. Hansen. Proc. Utah Acad. Sci., Arts, and Letters, vol.31, pp.57-60, 1954.

RETENTION OF THE "COLOR" PATTERN IN AN ALBINO THIRTEEN-LINED GROUND SQUIRREL (CITELLUS TRIDECEMLINEATUS). Donald F. Hoffmeister, M. Max Hensley. Amer. Midland Nat., Notre Dame, vol.42, no.2, pp.403-405, fig.1, Sept., 1949.

(ON PERIODIC COLOR CHANGE IN SCIURUS FINLAYSONI.) Ueber periodischen Farbenwechsel bei Sciurus finlaysoni. K. Kuiper. Zeitschr. f. Saeugetierkunde, vol.2, pp.174-176, 1 col. pl., Apr.29, 1929.

WHITE WOODCHUCKS. Henry Lambert. Nature Mag., Wash., D.C., vol.32, no.3, p.134, Mar., 1939.

HAIRLESS SQUIRRELS. Roger M. Latham. Jour. Mam., 36 (1): 136, Feb.25, 1955.

PELAGE STRUCTURE AND MOLTING OF SPERMOPHILOPSIS LEPTODACTYLUS LICHT. FROM THE KARA-KUM DESERT, CENTRAL ASIA. N. P. Lavrov, S. P. Naumov. Zool. Zhurnal, Moscow, vol.13, no.2, pp.311-331, figs.10, 1934.

(THE HAIR COVER OF SCIURUS VULGARIS L. AND THE DISTRIBUTION OF ITS COLOR VARIANTS IN GERMANY.) Das Haarkleid von Sciurus vulgaris L. und die Verteilung seiner Farb-Varianten in Deutschland. R. Luehring. Zeitschr. f. Morph. u. Oekologie der Tiere, vol.11, pp.667-762, 26 figs., 23 graphs, 2 pls., Sept.26, 1928.

COLOR VARIATIONS OF GROUND SQUIRRELS (CITELLUS MEXICANUS, SCIURIDAE) IN TEXAS. W. H. McCarley. Southwestern Naturalist, vol.1, no.1, pp. 30-34, June 4, 1956.

THE COAT COLOUR OF THE GREY SQUIRREL (SCIURUS CAROLINENSIS) WITH OTHER NOTES. T. C. S. Morrison-Scott, A. H. Bishop. Proc. Zool. Soc. Lond., vol.121, pt.4, pp.773-775, pls.1-3, Feb.8, 1952.

FADING OF COLOR ACCIDENTALLY INDUCED IN CAPTIVE CHIPMUNKS. H. W. Mossman. Jour. Mam., vol.12, no.2, pp. 167-168, May, 1931.

THE SPREAD OF THE BLACK SQUIRREL IN THE TORONTO REGION AND VICTORIA COUNTY, ONTARIO. J. A. Munro. Canadian Field-Nat., vol.43, p.108, May, 1929.

THE SPRING MOLT OF THE NORTHERN RED SQUIRREL IN MINNESOTA. Bernard A. Nelson. Jour. Mam., vol.26, no.4, pp. 397-400, Feb.12, 1946.

MELANIC GREY SQUIRRELS IN THE BERKHAMSTED DISTRICT. C. Oldham. Trans. Hertfordshire Nat. Hist. Soc., and Field Club, Hertford, vol.20, pt.3, p.152, Apr., 1937.

ABNORMALLY-COLOURED COMMON SQUIRRELS. R. I. Pocock. Proc. Zool. Soc. Lond., pp.516-517, Oct.8, 1907.

WHITE SQUIRREL TOWN. Harry Read. Nat. Hist., New York, vol.58, no.9, p. 403, illus., Nov., 1949.

ALBINO GRAY SQUIRRELS. O. M. Schantz. Nature Mag., vol.14, p.111, illus., Aug., 1929.

ON THE POLYCHROMATISM AND ALBINISM OF THE SIBERIAN SQUIRRELS. M. K. Serebrennikov. Proc. Zool. Soc. Lond., 1931, pt.2, pp.493-495, pls.1-3, June, 1931.

AN UNUSUAL MOULT RECORD FOR A YOUNG GREY SQUIRREL. Monica Shorten. Proc. Zool. Soc. Lond., vol.126, pt.1, pp.165-166, Jan.11, 1956.

WHITE PRAIRIE DOGS FOUND IN MONTANA. O. E. Stephl. Jour. Mam., vol.13, no.1, p.75, Feb., 1932.

AN ALBINO COLUMBIAN GROUND SQUIRREL TAKEN NEAR PULLMAN, WASHINGTON. Arthur Svihla. Murrelet, vol.13, no.2, p.55, May 19, 1932.

CHANGE IN COLOR PATTERN IN A CAPTIVE RED SQUIRREL. Arthur Svihla. Amer. Nat., vol.65, no.696, pp.92-95, fig.1, Jan.-Feb., 1931.

OCCURENCE OF A COLONY OF ALBINO GROUND SQUIRRELS NEAR PULLMAN WASHINGTON. Arthur Svihla. Murrelet, vol.14, no.3, p.78, Sept., 1933.

AN ABNORMALLY COLORED TOWNSEND CHIPMUNK. Arthur Svihla, Earl J. Larrison. Murrelet, Seattle, vol.31, no. 1, pp.9-11, illus., May 19, 1950.

ALBINO PRAIRIE-DOG. G. H. H. Tate. Jour. Mam., vol.28, no.1, p.62, Feb.15, 1947.

SOME RESULTS OF INVESTIGATIONS ON THE FUR QUALITY OF THE FINNISH SQUIRREL WITH NOTES ON PRACTICAL PROBLEMS INVOLVED. Paavo Voipio. Suomen Riista, 6: 128-135, 191-192, 1951 (1952).

CHANGE OF COAT IN THE COMMON PALM SQUIRREL--AN APPEAL. R. C. Wroughton. Jour. Bombay Nat. Hist. Soc., vol.26, pp.727-728, Oct.20, 1919.

ALBINO CHIPMUNKS IN RHODE ISLAND. Donald J. Zinn. Jour. Mam., vol.35, no. 4, pp.585-586, Nov.29, 1954.

ANOTHER ALBINO SQUIRREL BAGGED. (GRAY SQUIRREL.) Virginia Wildlife, Richmond, vol.11, no.2, p.25, illus., Feb., 1950.

Physiology

THE SPECTRAL SENSITIVITY OF THE PURE-CONE RETINA OF THE GREY SQUIRREL (SCIURUS CAROLINENSIS LEUCOTIS). G. B. Arden, K. Tansley. Jour. Physiol., Lond., vol.127, no.3, pp. 592-602, Mar., 1955.

THE SPECTRAL SENSITIVITY OF THE PURE-CONE RETINA OF THE SOUSLIK (CITELLUS CITELLUS). G. B. Arden, K. Tansley. Jour. Physiol., Cambridge, England, vol.130, no.1, pp.225-232, Oct., 1955.

THE BODY TEMPERATURE OF ARCTIC GROUND SQUIRRELS (CITELLUS PARRYI) AT VARYING ENVIRONMENTAL TEMPERATURE. H. Erikson. Acta Physiologica Scandinavica, Stockholm, vol.36, fasc.1-2, pp.75-76, Mar., 1956.

OBSERVATIONS ON THE METABOLISM OF ARCTIC GROUND SQUIRRELS (CITELLUS PARRYI) AT DIFFERENT ENVIRONMENTAL TEMPERATURES. H. Erikson. Acta Physiologica Scandinavica, Stockholm, vol. 36, fasc.1-2, pp.66-74, Mar., 1956.

SEASONAL CHANGES IN THE VISCOSITY OF THE BLOOD OF GROUND SQUIRRELS. Raymond J. Hock. Science in Alaska, pp. 137-138, 1952; Proc. 3rd. Alaskan Science Conference, Alaska Div. AAAS, Sept., 1954.

FLAGELLATES OF THE CAECUM OF GROUND SQUIRRELS. Harold Kirby, Bronislaw Honigberg. Univ. California Publ. Zool., Berkeley, vol.53, no.9, pp. 315-365, illus., Apr.29, 1949.

THE ACCLIMATIZATION OF THE FOX SQUIRREL AT PELEE ISLAND ONTARIO. Hoyes Lloyd. Canadian Field-Nat., vol. 39, no.6, p.138, Sept., 1925.

THE BLOOD SUGAR CONCENTRATION IN ACTIVE AND HIBERNATING GROUND SQUIRRELS. Rufus A. Lyman, Jr. Jour. Mam., vol.24, no.4, pp.467-474, Nov., 17, 1943.

ACCLIMATIZATION OF THE BARROW GROUND SQUIRREL, CITELLUS PARRYI BARROWENSIS. William V. Mayer. Anat. Rec., 117 (3): 607, Nov., 1953.

(THE ACCLIMITIZATION OF THE MARMOT IN THE ALPIAN NATURAL RESERVATION.) Die Einbuergerung des Murmeltieres im Alpennaturschutzparke. Hans Sammereyer. Naturforscher, Berlin, vol.7, no.2, pp.56-58, May, 1930.

CONDITIONED RESPONSE IN THE GOLDEN-MANTLED GROUND SQUIRREL. D. C. Smiley. Yosemite Nature Notes, U.S. Dept. Interior, vol.14, no.8, p.66, Aug., 1935.

FAT METABOLISM IN THE ARCTIC GROUND SQUIRREL. Charles G. Wilber. Anat. Record, Phila., vol.105, no.3, p.36, Nov., 1949.

FAT METABOLISM IN THE ARCTIC GROUND SQUIRREL. Charles G. Wilber, X. J. Musacchia. Jour. Mam., vol.31, no. 3, pp.304-309, illus., Aug.21, 1950.

ON THE LACK OF THE DISTANCE-SENSE IN PRAIRIE-DOGS. Burt G. Wilder. Ithaca Journal, 1 p., Oct.21, 1890.

ON THE LACK OF THE DISTANCE SENSE WITH THE PRAIRIE DOG (CYNOMYS LUDOVICIANUS). (ABSTRACTS.) Burt G. Wilder. Proc. Amer. Assoc. Adv. Sci., vol.39, p.340, 1890.

FLYING SQUIRRELS IN FLIGHT. Life, Chicago, vol.27, no.22, pp.16-18, illus., Nov.28, 1949.

THE GROUNDHOG AND HIS SHADOW. Virginia Wildlife, Richmond, vol.10, no.2, pp.8-9, illus., Feb., 1949.

Population Dynamics

POPULATION STUDIES OF THE FOX SQUIRREL IN OHIO. Luther L. Baumgartner. Trans. N. A. Wildl. Conf., 3: 685-689, 1938; Ohio Wildl. Res. Sta., Release 70, 6 pp., Feb., 1938.

A POPULATION STUDY OF THE BEECHEY GROUND SQUIRREL IN CENTRAL CALIFORNIA. F. C. Evans, R. Holdenried. Jour. Mam., 24 (2): 231-260, May, 1943.

A POPULATION STUDY OF THE GRAY SQUIRREL IN EASTERN TEXAS. Phil D. Goodrum. MS thesis, Texas A. and M. Coll., 1938; Texas Agr. Exp. Sta., Bull. 591, 34 pp., 1940.

DECLINE IN TOWNSEND GROUND SQUIRRELS IN UTAH. Richard M. Hansen. Jour. Mam., 37 (1): 123-124, Feb.28, 1956.

A POPULATION STUDY OF THE LONG-EARED CHIPMUNK (EUTAMIAS QUADRIMACULATUS) IN THE CENTRAL SIERRA NEVADA. R. Holdenreid. Jour. Mam., 21 (4): 405-411, Nov., 1940.

(FEATURES OF THE POPULATION OF THE GROUND SQUIRREL (CITELLUS FULVUS LICHT. ON BARSA-KELMES ISLAND.) Kharaktyeristika populyatsii suslika-peschanika (Citellus fulvus Licht.) na ostrove barsa-kelmes. M. I. Ismagilov. Zool. Zhurnal, Moscow, vol.31, no.6, pp. 932-939, 1952.

SOCIAL BEHAVIOR, SOCIAL ORGANIZATION, AND POPULATION DYNAMICS IN A BLACK-TAILED PRAIRIEDOG TOWN IN THE BLACK HILLS OF SOUTH DAKOTA. John A. King. Contrib. Laboratory Vertebrate Biology, Univ. of Michigan, Ann Arbor, no.67, pp.123, pls.4, Apr., 1955.

A STUDY OF A REFUGE POPULATION OF THE SOUTHERN GRAY SQUIRREL, SCIURUS CAROLINENSIS CAROLINENSIS GMELIN, AND WESTERN FOX SQUIRREL, SCIURUS NIGER RUFIVENTER (GEOFFROY), IN SOUTHERN ILLINOIS. Richard J. Moran. MS thesis, S. Ill. Univ., 76 pp., June, 1953.

GRAY SQUIRREL POPULATIONS IN EXTENSIVE FORESTED AREAS OF WEST VIRGINIA. Hans G. Uhlig. Jour. Wildlife Management, 21 (3): 335-341, July, 1957.

5 TO 10 PER CENT DECREASE IN GRAY-SQUIRREL POPULATION. Mississippi Game and Fish, Jackson, vol.10, no.2, p.3, Aug., 1946.

Predation

MOUNTAIN WEASEL CATCHES GOLDEN-MANTLED GROUND SQUIRREL. Verlin G. Baysinger. Yosemite Nature Notes, 19 (3): 22-23, Mar., 1940.

WEASEL VERSUS SQUIRREL IN SEQUOIA NATIONAL PARK. Richard H. Boyer. Jour. Mam., vol.24, no.1, pp.99-100, Feb. 20, 1943.

GOLDEN EAGLE CONTROLS GROUND SQUIRRELS IN YOSEMITE VALLEY. Otto Brown. Yosemite Nat. Notes, vol.17, no. 12, p.159, Dec., 1938.

BARRED OWL IN SEWICKLEY. (REFERENCE TO RED SQUIRRELS.) Bayard H. Christy. Cardinal, Sewickley, vol.5, no.8, pp.194-195, July, 1942.

RED SQUIRREL TAKEN BY EAGLE. Tom J. Dent. Audubon Soc. New Hampshire Bull., vol.18, no.1, pp.35-36, Spring, 1947.

THE INTERESTING FATE OF A FLYING SQUIRREL. James S. Findley. Jour. Mam., vol.26, no.4, p.437, Feb.12, 1946.

PREY OF WEASEL AND MINK. W. I. Follett. Jour. Mam., vol.18, no.3, p.365, Aug.14, 1937.

UNTIMELY END OF A GOLDEN-MANTLED GROUND SQUIRREL. (ATTACKED BY WEASEL.) William C. Godfrey. Yosemite Nature Notes, vol.7, p.93, Nov., 1928.

(DOMESTIC CAT AND BUZZARD--OCCASIONAL ENEMIES OF THE SQUIRREL.) Hauskatze und Maeusebussard gelegentliche Feinde des Eichhoernchens. Viktor Hornung. Zool. Garten, Leipzig, n.F., vol.12, nos.2-3, pp.197-198, July, 1940.

A GOLDEN MANTLED SQUIRREL'S RACE FOR LIFE. Merlin L. Killpack. Jour. Mam., vol.34, no.1, p.131, Feb.19, 1953.

AN UNWELCOME POACHER. (WEASEL CAPTURES A CHIPMUNK.) E. L. Lucas. Yosemite Nature Notes, vol.16, no.4, pp. 31-32, Apr., 1937.

GREAT HORNED OWL ATTACKING SQUIRREL NESTS. Robert L. Packard. Wilson Bull., 66 (4): 272, Dec., 1954.

BADGER ACTIVITIES IN PRAIRIE-DOG CONTROL. James Silver. Jour. Mam., vol.9, no.1, p.63, Feb., 1928.

GROUND SQUIRREL CAPTURED BY A GOPHER SNAKE. Clarence F. Smith. Jour. Mam., vol.20, no.1, p.106, Feb.14, 1939.

BATTLE BETWEEN PRAIRIE DOG AND RATTLESNAKE. O. E. Stephl. Jour. Mam., vol.13, no.1, pp.74-75, Feb., 1932.

(INFLUENCE OF FOREST MARTEN ON NUMBER OF SQUIRRELS IN NORTHERN TAIGA.) O vliyanii lesnoi kunitsi na chislennost belki v severnoi taige. P. B. Yurgenson. Zool. Zhurnal, Moscow, vol. 33, no.1, pp.166-173, Jan.-Feb., 1954. (In Russian.)

Psychology

THE WIT OF A RED SQUIRREL. William L. Finley, Irene Finley. Nature Mag., vol.5, pp.141-144, 3 figs., 1 pl., Mar., 1925.

(ON LEARNING UNNAMED QUANTITIES IN SQUIRRELS (SCIURUS VULGARIS). Vom Erlernen unbenannter Anzahlen bei Eichhoernchen (Sciurus vulgaris). M. Hassmann. Zeitschr. Tierpsych., Berlin, vol.9, no.2, pp.294-321, 1952.

INSTINCT AND MEMORY EXHIBITED BY THE FLYING SQUIRREL IN CONFINEMENT, WITH A THOUGHT ON THE ORIGIN OF WINGS IN BATS. F. H. King. Amer. Nat., vol.17, no.1, pp.36-42, Jan., 1883.

CAN THE FLYING SQUIRREL COUNT? Joseph Kittredge. Jour. Mam., vol.9, no. 3, pp.251-252, Aug., 1928.

Reproductive Biology

SEASONAL REPRODUCTIVE CYCLE IN THE NORMAL AND EXPERIMENTALLY TREATED MALE PRAIRIE DOG, CYNOMYS LUDOVICIANUS. Adam Anthony. Jour. Morphol. Phila., vol.93, no.2, pp. 331-370, Sept., 1953.

OBSERVATIONS ON THE SEASONAL AND REPRODUCTIVE ACTIVITIES OF THE EASTERN CHIPMUNK. John M. Condrin. Jour. Mam., vol.17, no.3, pp.231-234, fig. 1, table 1, Aug., 1936.

THE OESTROUS CYCLE OF THE GREY SQUIRREL (SCIURUS CAROLINENSIS). Ruth Deansely, A. S. Parkes. Philos. Trans. Roy. Soc. London, ser.B., vol. 222, no.485, pp.47-78, pls.9-14, Apr.7, 1933.

OBSERVATIONS ON BREEDING BIOLOGY AND DEVELOPMENT OF YOUNG SQUIRRELS. Irenaeus Eibl-Eibesfeldt. Z. Tierpsych., 8 (3): 370-400, illus., 1951.

(WINTER BROOD OF THE SQUIRREL.) Winterwurf des Eichhoernchens. Wolfgang Fischer. Zeitschr. Saeugetierk., 22 (1-2): 105-106, 1957.

A STUDY OF THE NEST BOX HABITS AND THE BREEDING SEASON OF THE GRAY SQUIRREL (SCIURUS CAROLINENSIS LEUCOTIS) IN MARYLAND AND PENNSYLVANIA. Vagn F. Flyger. MS thesis, Pa. State Coll., Jan., 1952.

THE REPRODUCTIVE CYCLE IN THE FEMALE GROUND SQUIRREL, CITELLUS TRIDECEMLINEATUS (MITCHILL). Mark A. Foster. Amer. Jour. Anat., vol.54, no.3, pp.487-506, pls.1-2, May 15, 1934.

(OBSERVATIONS OF THE BREEDING OF SQUIRRELS (SCIURUS VULGARIS) IN CAPTIVITY.) Beobachtungen ueber die Aufzucht von Eichhoernchen (Sciurus vulgaris) in der Gefangenschaft. Wolfgant Gewalt. Zool. Garten, Leipzig, vol.19, no.1, pp.26-33, illus., 1952.

REMARKS ON REPORTED HYBRID GROUND SQUIRRELS, CITELLUS. Richard M. Hansen. Jour. Mam., 37 (4): 550-552, Jan.9, 1957.

BREEDING SEASONS OF GRAY SQUIRREL AND FLYING SQUIRREL. Claude W. Hibbard. Jour. Mam., vol.16, no.4, pp. 325-326, Nov., 1935.

NOTE ON THE BREEDING OF THE MALABAR GIANT SQUIRREL (RATUFA INDICA MAXIMA) IN CAPTIVITY. W. C. Osman Hill. Jour. Bombay Nat. Hist. Soc., vol.43, no.3, pp.521-522, Dec., 1942.

ADDITIONAL NOTES ON THE GESTATION PERIOD OF THE WOODCHUCK. Sally F. Hoyt. Jour. Mamm., vol.33, no.3, pp.388-389, Aug. 19, 1952.

GESTATION PERIOD OF THE WOODCHUCK, MARMOTA MONAX. Southgate Y. Hoyt, Sally F. Hoyt. Jour. Mam., vol.31, no.4, p.454, Nov.21, 1950.

SEVEN FETUSES IN WESTERN FOX SQUIRREL (SCIURUS NIGER RUFIVENTER). Robert L. Hoover. Jour. Mam., 35 (3): 447-448, Aug., 1954.

(REPRODUCTION OF THE SQUIRREL.) La reproduction de l'écureuil (Sciurus vulgaris L.). Albert Hugues. Mammalia, Paris, vol.2, no.4, p.190, Dec., 1938.

RATE OF REPRODUCTION IN CITELLUS BEECHEYI. W. C. Jacobsen. Jour. Mam., vol.4, no.1, p.58, Feb., 1923.

A BREEDING RECORD OF CITELLUS MOLLIS. Stanley G. Jewett. Jour. Mam., vol.4, no.3, p.191, Aug., 1923.

THE SEXUAL CYCLE OF THE THIRTEEN-LINED GROUND SQUIRREL IN THE LABORATORY. George E. Johnson, Mark A. Foster, Russell M. Coca. Trans. Kansas Acad. Sci., vol.36, pp.250-269, figs.1-16, 1933.

LABORATORY REPRODUCTION STUDIES ON THE GROUND SQUIRREL, CITELLUS TRIDECEMLINEATUS PALLIDUS, ALLEN. George E. Johnson, Nelson J. Wade. Biological Bulletin, vol.61, no.1, pp.101-114, Aug., 1931.

THE BREEDING TIME OF THE FLYING SQUIRREL (GLAUCOMYS VOLANS VOLANS.). George Kelker. Jour. Mam., vol.12, no.2, pp.166-167, May, 1931.

BREEDING RED SQUIRRELS. Phyllis Kelway. Field, London, vol.174, no.4531, p.865, Oct.28, 1939.

(OBSERVATIONS ON THE REARING OF YOUNG SQUIRRELS.) Beobachtungen bei der Aufzucht junger Eichhoernchen. E. Libermann. Bericht Senckenbergische Naturforsch. Gesell., vol.60, no.3, pp. 130-133, figs.3, Mar., 1930.

(SQUIRREL BREEDING IN CAPTIVITY.) Eichhoernchenzucht in der Gefangenschaft. Detlef Meyer-Oehme. Zool. Garten, Leipzig, 21 (5-6): 386-387, 1956.

BREEDING POTENTIALITIES OF THE GRAY SQUIRREL AT BLACKSBURG, VIRGINIA. Charles H. Peery. MS thesis, Va. Polytechnic Inst., 1948.

ANALYSIS OF GRAY SQUIRREL BREEDING STUDIES AND THEIR RELATION TO HUNTING SEASON, GUNNING PRESSURE, AND HABITAT CONDITIONS. Howard R. Redmond. Trans. 18th N.A. Wildl. Conf., pp.378-389, graphs, 1953.

SQUIRREL BREEDING STUDIES AND THEIR RELATION TO HUNTING SEASON AND GUNNING PRESSURE, WITH NOTES ON HABITAT CONDITIONS. Howard R. Redmond. Presented at 5th Ann. Meeting S.E. Assn. Game and Fish Comm., pp.1-24, illus., Oct., 1951.

PRELIMINARY NOTE ON THE REPRODUCTIVE CYCLE OF THE RED SQUIRREL (SCIURUS VULGARIS). I. W. Rowlands. Proc. Zool. Soc. Lond., vol.108, ser.A, Gen. and Exper., pt.3, pp.441-443, tables 2, Sept., 1938.

"STREAK"--THE STORY OF A GROUND SQUIRREL AND HER BROOD. Marjorie Shanafelt. Nature Magazine, vol.16, no.3, pp.155-158, figs.8, Sept., 1930.

BREEDING AND DEVELOPMENT OF THE COLUMBIAN GROUND SQUIRREL. William T. Shaw. Jour. Mam., vol.6, no.2, pp. 106-113, pls.11-14, May, 1925.

A SHORT SEASON AND ITS EFFECT UPON THE PREPARATION FOR REPRODUCTION BY THE COLUMBIAN GROUND SQUIRREL. William T. Shaw. Ecology, vol.7, pp.136-139, pl.7, Apr., 1926.

ON THE REPRODUCTION CYCLE OF THE MALE COLUMBIAN GROUND SQUIRREL. P. S. Smith. MA thesis, Mont. State Univ., 1947.

NOTES ON THE BREEDING HABITS OF THE EASTERN FLYING SQUIRREL (GLAUCOMYS VOLANS VOLANS). Dwight E. Sollberger. Jour. Mam., 24 (2): 163-173, May, 1943.

OBSERVATIONS ON REPRODUCTION IN THE WHITE-TAILED PRAIRIE-DOG (CYNOMYS LEUCURUS). A. H. Stockard. Jour. Mam., vol.10, no.3, pp.209-212, Aug., 1929.

SUMMER AND AUTUMN BREEDING OF THE CALIFORNIA GROUND SQUIRREL. Tracy I. Storer. Jour. Mam., vol.11, no. 2, pp.235-237, May, 1930.

BREEDING HABITS OF TOWNSEND'S GROUND SQUIRREL. Arthur Svihla. Murrelet, 20 (1): 6-10, Jan.-Apr., 1939.

REPRODUCTION IN THE EASTERN FLYING SQUIRREL IN WEST VIRGINIA. Hans G. Uhlig. Jour. Mam., 37 (2): 295, 1 table, June 9, 1956.

USE OF THE BREEDING SEASON CURVE IN GRAY SQUIRREL INVESTIGATIONS. Hans G. Uhlig. Proc. N.E. Sect. Wildl. Soc. et al., 6 pp., graph, Mar., 1955.

FLUCTUATIONS IN THE FERTILITY OF THE LITTLE GROUND SQUIRREL (CITELLUS PYGMAEUS PALL.). S. N. Varshavskii. Plant Prot., 17: 3-13, 1938.

BREEDING HABITS AND EARLY LIFE OF THE THIRTEEN-STRIPED GROUND SQUIRREL, CITELLUS TRIDECEMLINEATUS (MITCHILL). Otis Wade. Jour. Mam., vol.8, no.4, pp.269-276, pl.23, Nov., 1927.

NOTES ON THE TIME OF BREEDING AND THE NUMBER OF YOUNG OF CYNOMYS LUDOVICIANUS. Otis Wade. Jour. Mam., vol.9, no.2, pp.149-151, May, 1928.

SEASONAL SEXUAL RHYTHM AND ITS EXPERIMENTAL MODIFICATION IN THE MALE OF THE THIRTEEN-LINED GROUND SQUIRREL (CITELLUS TRIDECEMLINEATUS). L. J. Wells. Anat. Record, 62:409-447, 1935.

SQUIRRELS WITH YOUNG LATE IN SEPTEMBER. North Carolina Wildlife Conservation, Raleigh, vol.5, no.11, p.7, Nov., 1941.

South America

NEW SOUTH AMERICAN SCIURIDAE. J. A. Allen. Bull. Amer. Mus. Nat. Hist., vol.33, pp.585-597, fig.1-2, Oct.8, 1914.

REVIEW OF THE SOUTH AMERICAN SCIURIDAE. J. A. Allen. Bull. Amer. Mus. Nat. Hist., vol.34, pp.147-309, pls. 1-14, 25, text figs., May 17, 1915.

NOTES ON SOUTH AMERICAN MAMMALS. NO. I. SCIURILLUS. H. E. Anthony, G. H. H. Tate. Amer. Mus. Novitates, no. 780, pp.11, figs.6, Feb.14, 1935.

ON SCIURUS VARIABILIS FROM THE SANTA MARTA REGION OF COLOMBIA. Outram Bangs. Proc. Biol. Soc. Wash., vol.12, pp.183-186, Nov.16, 1908.

DESCRIPTION OF A NEW SQUIRREL IN THE BRITISH MUSEUM, FROM NEW GRANADA. John E. Gray. Proc. Zool. Soc. Lond., pt.29, p.92, pl.16, 1861.

TWO NEW SQUIRRELS FROM ECUADOR. William P. Harris, Philip Hershkovitz. Occas. Papers Mus. Zool. Univ. Mich., no.391, pp.1-6, Nov.10, 1938.

MAMMALS OF NORTHERN COLOMBIA. PRELIMINARY REPORT NO. I: SQUIRRELS (SCIURIDAE). Philip Hershkovitz. Proc. U.S. Nat. Mus., Washington, vol.97, no. 3208, pp.1-46, fig.1, Aug.25, 1947.

DESCRIPTIONS OF THREE NEW SQUIRRELS FROM SOUTH AMERICA. E. W. Nelson. Bull. Amer. Mus. Nat. Hist., New York, vol.12, art.4, pp.77-80, fig.1, Apr.14, 1899.

ON A NEW SPECIES OF SQUIRREL (SCIURUS VARIEGATOIDES) FROM THE WEST COAST OF SOUTH AMERICA. William Ogilby. Proc. Zool. Soc. Lond., pt.7, p.117, 1839.

ON GIANT SQUIRRELS FROM THE AMAZONIAN REGION. Oldfield Thomas. Ann. and Mag. Nat. Hist. (7), vol.6, no. 31, pp.137-139, July, 1900.

Taxonomy

NOTE ON SCIURUS MOLLIPILOSUS AUDUBON AND BACHMAN. J. A. Allen. Proc. Biol. Soc. Wash., vol.16, p.126, Sept.30, 1903.

REVIEW OF THE GENUS MICROSCIURUS. J. A. Allen. Bull. Amer. Mus. Nat. Hist., vol.33, pp.145-165, Feb.26, 1914.

SCIURUS NIGER CINEREUS LINNE NEOTYPE DESIGNATION. Frederick S. Barkalow, Jr. Proc. Biol. Soc. Wash., 69: 13-21, illus., May 21, 1956.

THE STATUS OF THE NAMES SCIURUS NIGER CINEREUS LINNAEUS AND SCIURUS NIGER VULPINUS GMELIN. Frederick S. Barkalow, Jr. Jour. Elisha Mitchell Sci. Soc., vol.70, no.1, pp.19-26, June, 1954.

ON SCIURUS CANICEPS AND ALLIED SPECIES. J. L. Bonhote. Ann. and Mag. Nat. Hist., ser.7, vol.7, pp.270-275, Mar., 1901.

ON SCIURUS NOTATUS AND ALLIED SPECIES. J. L. Bonhote. Ann. and Mag. Nat. Hist., ser.7, vol.7, pp.444-455, May, 1901.

ON THE SQUIRRELS OF THE RATUFA (SCIURUS) BICOLOR GROUP. J. L. Bonhote. Ann. and Mag. Nat. Hist., ser.7, vol.5, pp.490-499, June, 1900.

ON THE SQUIRRELS OF THE SCIURUS ERYTHRAEUS GROUP. J. L. Bonhote. Ann. and Mag. Nat. Hist., ser.7, vol.7, pp.160-167, Feb., 1901.

ON SQUIRRELS OF THE SCIURUS MACCLELLANDI GROUP. J. L. Bonhote. Ann. and Mag. Nat. Hist., ser.7, vol.5, pp.50-54, Jan., 1900.

ON THE SQUIRRELS OF THE SCIURUS PREVOSTII GROUP. J. L. Bonhote. Ann. and Mag. Nat. Hist., ser.7, vol.7, pp.167-177, Feb., 1901.

REMARKS ON THE BLACK AND RED SQUIRRELS ALLIED TO SCIURUS PREVOSTI. F. N. Chasen, C. Boden Kloss. Jour. Malayan Branch Royal Asiatic Soc., vol.3, pt.1, pp.97-99, Apr., 1925.

THREE NEW RACES OF SCIURUS VITTATUS. F. N. Chasen, C. Boden Kloss. Jour. Malayan Branch Royal Asiatic Soc., vol.2, pt.1, pp.57-58, June, 1924.

A NOTE ON SCIUROPTERUS GORKHALI LINDSAY WITH REMARKS ON PETAURISTA CANICEPS AND ITS ALLIES. J. L. Chaworth-Musters. Jour. Bombay Nat. Hist. Soc., vol.37, no.2, pp.376-377, Aug.15, 1934.

A NOTE ON THE NOMENCLATURE OF TWO SCIURIDS FROM EASTERN SIBERIA. J. L. Chaworth-Musters. Ann. and Mag. Nat. Hist., Lond., ser.10, vol.13, no.77, pp.555-557, May, 1934.

ON THE NOMENCLATURE OF THE PALAEARCTIC CHIPMUNK. J. L. Chaworth-Musters. Ann. and Mag. Nat. Hist., Lond., vol.19, no.109, pp.158-159, Jan., 1937.

ON THE TYPE-LOCALITY OF THE CAUCASIAN SQUIRREL, SCIURUS ANOMALUS GULDENSTAEDT. J. L. Chaworth-Musters. Ann. and Mag. Nat. Hist., Lond., ser.10, vol.20, p.560, Nov., 1937.

ON THE USE OF THE NAME PTEROMYS RUSSICUS TIEDEMANN FOR THE EUROPEAN FLYING SQUIRREL. J. L. Chaworth-Musters. Ann. and Mag. Nat. Hist., Lond., ser.10, vol.20, no.117, pp.318-320, Sept., 1937.

(DESCRIPTION OF A TYPE OF ASIATIC SQUIRREL OF A. MILNE-EDWARDS: CALLOSCIURUS FINLAYSONI HARMANDI.) Description d'un type d'ecureuil asiatique dA. Milne-Edwards: Callosciurus Finlaysoni harmandi. Pierre L. Dekeyser. Bull. Mus. Nat. Hist. Nat., Paris, ser.2, vol. 15, no.5, pp.283-286, 1943.

(DESCRIPTION OF SOME NEW SPECIES OF SQUIRRELS OF THE OLD CONTINENT.) Description de Quelques especes nouvelles d'écureuils de l'ancien continent. Alphonse Milne-Edwards. Revue et Magasin de Zoologie, pp.1-12, pl.19, June, 1867.

THE TYPE LOCALITY OF SYNTHEOSCIURUS BROCHUS. Robert K. Enders. Jour. Mam., vol.34, no.4, p.509, Nov.13, 1953.

SYNOPSIS OF THE SPECIES OF AMERICAN SQUIRRELS IN THE COLLECTION OF THE BRITISH MUSEUM. J. E. Gray. Ann. and Mag. Nat. Hist. Lond., ser.3, vol.20, no. 120, pp.415-436, Dec., 1867.

DESCRIPTIONS OF THREE NEW SPECIES OF FLYING SQUIRRELS IN THE COLLECTION OF THE BRITISH MUSEUM. Albert Gunther. Proc. Zool. Soc. Lond., pp.413-414, pls.37-38, 1873.

ADDITIONS AND CORRECTIONS TO THE SECTION ON SCIURIDAE IN ELLERMAN'S FAMILIES AND GENERA OF LIVING RODENTS. William P. Harris, Jr. Occas. Papers Mus. Zool., Univ. Michigan, Ann Arbor, no.484, pp.21, Apr.17, 1944.

A SUBSTITUTE NAME FOR PETAURISTA PETAURISTA RUFIPES SODY. William P. Harris, Jr. Jour. Mam., vol.32, no.2, p.234, May 21, 1951.

SCIURUS VULGARIS SILANUS SUBSP. NOV. G. Hecht. Zeitschr. fuer Saeugetierkunde, Berlin, vol.6, no.6, pp.238-239, Dec.15, 1931.

THE MALE GENITAL TRACT AND THE SYSTEMATIC RELATIONS OF SPERMOPHILOPSIS LEPTODACTYLUS LICHT. (MAMMALIA, SCIURIDAE). V. G. Heptner. Zool. Zhurn., Moscow, 36 (8): 1233-1238, 1957.

(A NEW KIND OF THIN-TOED GROUND SQUIRREL.) Novaya forma tonkopalovo suslike (Spermophilopsis leptodactylus Licht.; Mammalia, Glires). V. G. Heptner, M. I. Ismagilov. Doklady Akad. Nauk SSSR, Moscow, vol.84, no.6, pp. 1255-1256, June 13, 1952.

TAXONOMIC AND ZOOGEOGRAPHICAL INTERRELATIONS OF SOME ASIATIC

AND NORTH AMERICAN GROUND-SQUIRRELS. V. G. Heptner. Zoogeographica, Jena, vol.4, no.1, pp.21-27, Mar., 1941.

THE PENIS AND ITS BONE IN CEYLONESE SQUIRRELS; WITH SPECIAL REFERENCE TO TAXONOMIC IMPORTANCE. W. C. Osman Hill. Ceylon Jour. Sci., sect.B, Zool. and Geol., Spolia Zeylanica, vol.20, pt.1, pp.99-113, figs.7, tables 5, Aug.5, 1936.

A NEW NAME FOR THE MARMOT OF THE CANADIAN ROCKIES. Ned Hollister. Science, Lancaster, n.s., vol.39, no.998, p.251, Feb.13, 1914.

A NEW NAME FOR THE WEST AFRICAN PYGMY SQUIRREL. Ned Hollister. Proc. Biol. Soc. Wash., vol.34, p.135, June 30, 1921.

A SYSTEMATIC ACCOUNT OF THE PRAIRIE-DOGS. Ned Hollister. North Amer. Fauna, no.4, pp.1-37, pls.1-7, June 20, 1916.

DESCRIPTIONS OF A NEW GENUS AND SEVEN NEW RACES OF FLYING SQUIRRELS. Arthur H. Howell. Proc. Biol. Soc. Wash., vol.28, pp.109-114, May 27, 1915.

DIAGNOSES OF SEVEN NEW CHIPMUNKS OF THE GENUS EUTAMIAS, WITH A LIST OF THE AMERICAN SPECIES. Arthur H. Howell. Jour. Mam., vol.3, no.3, pp. 178-185, Aug., 1922.

REVISION OF THE AMERICAN CHIPMUNKS (GENERA TAMIAS AND EUTAMIAS). Arthur H. Howell. North Amer. Fauna, no.52, pp.1-157, figs.1-8, pls.1-10, Nov., 1929.

ON A NEW SQUIRREL, SCIURUS SALAE. F. A. Jentink. Notes Leyden Mus., vol.3, pp.63-65, no.16, Jan., 1881.

OBSERVATIONS RELATING EUPETAURUS CINEREUS, OLDFIELD THOMAS. F. A. Jentink. Notes Leyden Mus., vol.12, no. 20, pp.143-144, pl.7, Mar., 1890.

ON THREE NEW SQUIRRELS. F. A. Jentink. Notes Leyden Mus., vol.1, no.13, pp.36-42, Dec., 1878.

TWO NEW RACES OF SCIURUS FINLAYSONI. C. Boden Kloss. Jour. Nat. Hist. Soc. Siam, vol.4, pp.103-104, Mar., 1921.

NEW NAME FOR SCIURUS MILLERI J.A. ALLEN. Barbara Lawrence. Jour. Mam., vol.14, no.4, pp.369-370, Nov., 1933.

NOTES ON SOME SQUIRRELS OF THE SCIURUS HIPPURUS GROUP, WITH DESCRIPTIONS OF TWO NEW SPECIES. Marcus W. Lyon, Jr. Smiths. Misc. Coll., vol.50, pt.1, no.1705, pp.24-29, Apr.8, 1907.

THE PIGMY SQUIRRELS OF THE NANNOSCIURUS MELANOTIS GROUP. Marcus W. Lyon, Jr. Proc. Biol. Soc. Wash., vol.19, pp.51-56, May 1, 1906.

SCIURUS POLIOPUS LYON CHANGED TO SCIURUS CONIPUS. Marcus W. Lyon, Jr. Proc. Biol. Soc. Wash., vol.24, p.97, May 15, 1911.

DESCRIPTION OF A NEW SUBSPECIES OF CHIPMUNK. (TAMIAS STRIATUS LYSTERI) C. Hart Merriam. Amer. Naturalist, vol. 20, no.2, pp.236-242, Feb., 1886.

DESCRIPTIONS OF EIGHT NEW GROUND SQUIRRELS OF THE GENERA SPERMOPHILUS AND TAMIAS FROM CALIFORNIA, TEXAS, AND MEXICO. C. Hart Merriam. Proc. Biol. Soc. Wash., vol. 8, pp.129-138, Dec.28, 1893.

DESCRIPTIONS OF FIVE NEW GROUND SQUIRRELS OF THE GENUS TAMIAS. C. Hart Merriam. North Amer. Fauna, no.4, U.S. Dept. Agric., pp.17-22, Oct., 1890.

DESCRIPTIONS OF THREE NEW GROUND SQUIRRELS OF THE SPERMOPHILUS SPILOSOMA GROUP. C. Hart Merriam. North American Fauna, no.4, pp.37-39, Oct., 1890.

DESCRIPTIONS OF THREE SPECIES OF THE TAMIAS LATERALIS GROUP. C. Hart Merriam. North Amer. Fauna, no.4, pp.17-22, Oct., 1890.

THE EARLIEST GENERIC NAME OF THE GROUND SQUIRRELS COMMONLY PLACED IN THE GENUS SPERMOPHILUS. C. Hart Merriam. Science, N.S., vol.1, no.1, pp. 18-19, Jan.4, 1895.

TWO NEW SQUIRRELS OF THE ABERTI GROUP. C. Hart Merriam. Proc. Biol. Soc. Wash., vol.17, pp.129-130, June 9, 1904.

ALTUM'S SQUIRREL NAMES. Gerrit S. Miller, Jr. Ann. and Mag. Nat. Hist., ser.8, vol.1, pp.127-128, Jan., 1908.

COMPARISON OF SCIURUS MELANOPS WITH COTYPES OF SCIURUS RAFFESI. Gerrit S. Miller, Jr. Proc. U.S. Nat. Mus., vol.34, no.1626, p.637, Sept.14, 1908.

THE GENERIC NAME OF THE COMMON FLYING SQUIRRELS. Gerrit S. Miller, Jr. Proc. Biol. Soc. Wash., vol.27, p. 216, Oct.31, 1914.

NOTE ON THE TYPE OF SCIURUS ALBICEPS DESMAREST. Gerrit S. Miller, Jr. Proc. U.S. Nat. Mus., vol.31, p.587, Dec.18, 1906.

NOTE ON THE TYPE OF SCIURUS ATRICAPILLUS SCHLEGEL. Gerrit S. Miller, Jr. Proc. U.S. Nat. Mus., vol.40, no.1809, p.80, Apr.25, 1911.

NOTE ON THE TYPE SPECIMEN OF PETAURISTA BATUANA. Gerrit S. Miller, Jr. Jour. Fed. Malay States Mus., vol.7, p.269, Dec., 1919.

NOTES ON ORIGINAL MATERIAL OF SCIURUS ATRICAPILLUS IN THE LEYDEN MUSEUM. Gerrit S. Miller, Jr. Proc. U.S. Nat. Mus., vol.40, no.1809, p.80, Apr.25, 1911.

NOTES ON THE COTYPES OF SCIURUS BORNEOENSIS. Gerrit S. Miller, Jr. Proc. U.S. Nat. Mus., vol.33, p.552, Dec.24, 1907.

NOTES ON TYPE OF RATUFA ALBICEPS. Gerrit S. Miller, Jr. Proc. U.S. Nat. Mus., vol.31, no.1498, p.587, Dec.18, 1906.

NOTES ON TYPE SPECIMENS OF SCIURUS RAFFLESI, SCIURUS PICEUS, AND MUS MULLERI. Gerrit S. Miller, Jr. Proc. U.S. Nat. Mus., vol.34, no.1626, pp.637-638, 646-647, Sept.14, 1908.

THE SUBGENUS RHINOSCIURUS OF TROUESSART. Gerrit S. Miller, Jr. Proc. Biol. Soc. Wash., vol.14, p.23, Apr.2, 1901.

A NEW SUBSPECIES OF AN ORIENTAL SQUIRREL, DREMOMYS LOKRIAH. Joseph Curtis Moore. Amer. Mus. Nov., New York, 1816: 1-2, Dec.28, 1956.

CHANGE OF NAME FOR SCIURUS ALBIPES QUERCINUS NELSON. E. W. Nelson. Science, Lancaster, n.s., vol.8, no.205, pp.783, Dec.2, 1898.

WHAT IS SCIURUS VARIEGATUS ERXLEBEN? E. W. Nelson. Science, Lancaster, n.s., vol.8, no.208, pp.897-898, Dec.23, 1898.

ON THE DISTRIBUTION AND SYSTEMATICAL PECULIARITIES OF THE SPOTTED GROUND-SQUIRREL (CITELLUS SUSLICA GUELD). (TRANSLATED TITLE.) S.'Obolensky. Proc. Lenin Sci. Research Inst. Agric. and Forest Econ., Branch Sta. War upon Pests, Minsk, vol.2, no.8, p.9, 1927. (In Russian.)

A PRELIMINARY REVIEW OF THE PALAEARCTIC SOUSLIKS (CITELLUS AND SPERMOPHILOPSIS). S.Obolensky. Comptes Rendus Acad. Sci. URSS., A, no.12, pp.188-193, 1927.

TABLES FOR DETERMINATION OF THE PALAEARCTIC SPERMOPHILES. S. Obolensky. Zaschita Rastenii ot Vreditelei (Plant Protection), Leningrad, vol.4 (?), pp. 1-8 (of separate), 1927. (In Russian.)

MATERIALS ON THE SYSTEMATICS OF THE PALEARCTIC SUSLIKS. S. I. Ognev. Published in book form by the Acad. Sci. USSR, Moscow, 1937, pp.317-337, 1937.

THE TYPE OF SCIURUS TEXIANUS BACHMAN. Wilfred H. Osgood. Jour. Mam., vol.26, no.4, pp.441-442, Feb.12, 1946.

THE CLASSIFICATION OF THE SCIURIDAE. R. I. Pocock. Proc. Zool. Soc. Lond., pt. 2, pp.209-246, July, 1923.

THE TECHNICAL NAMES OF THE NORTHEASTERN FOX SQUIRRELS. Earl L. Poole. Jour. Mam., vol.25, no.3, pp.315-317, Sept.8, 1944.

A NOTE ON CALLOSCIURUS FINLAYSON (HORSF.) AND ALLIED FORMS. Herbert C. Robinson. Jour. Fed. Malay States Mus., Kuala Lumpur, vol.7, pt.2, pp.35-36, Dec., 1916.

AEROMYS, A NEW GENUS OF FLYING SQUIRREL. Herbert C. Robinson, C. Boden Kloss. Jour. Fed. Malay States Mus., vol.6, pt.1, p.23, Apr., 1915.

A NOMINAL LIST OF THE SCIURIDAE OF THE ORIENTAL REGION WITH A LIST OF THE SPECIMENS IN THE COLLECTION OF THE ZOOLOGICAL SURVEY OF INDIA. Herbert C. Robinson, C. Boden Kloss. Records Indian Mus., Calcutta, vol.15, pt. 4, pp.171-254, Oct., 1918.

NOTES ON THE GENUS PETAURISTA, PALL., WITH DESCRIPTIONS OF TWO NEW RACES. Herbert C. Robinson, C. Boden Kloss. Jour. Fed. Malay States Mus., Singapore, vol.7, pt.4, pp.223-226, June, 1918.

ON FIVE NEW SUB-SPECIES OF ORIENTAL SQUIRRELS. Herbert C. Robinson, R. C. Wroughton. Jour. Fed. Malay States Mus., Kuala Lumpur, vol.4, nos.3-4, pp. 233-235, Nov., 1911.

(NOTES ON CALLOSCIURUS NOTATUS BODD., WITH A DESCRIPTION OF TWO NEW SUBSPECIES.) Over Callosciurus notatus Bodd. met beschrijving van 2 nieuwe subspecies. H. J. V. Sody. Natuurkundig Tijdschrift voor Nederlandsch-Indie, vol. 88, pp.325-332, 1928.

RESULTS OF THE ARCHBOLD EXPEDITIONS. NO. 9. A NEW RACE OF HYOSCIURUS. G. H. H. Tate, Richard Archbold. Amer. Mus. Novitates no.846, p.1, Apr.29, 1936.

FOUR NEW SQUIRRELS OF THE GENUS TAMIOPS. Oldfield Thomas. Ann. and Mag. Nat. Hist., ser.9, vol.5, pp.304-308, Mar., 1920.

THE GENERA AND SUBGENERA OF THE SCIUROPTERUS GROUP, WITH DESCRIPTIONS OF THREE NEW SPECIES. Oldfield Thomas. Ann. and Mag. Nat. Hist. (8), vol.1, no.1, pp.1-8, Jan., 1908.

THE GEOGRAPHICAL RACES OF CITELLUS FULVUS. Oldfield Thomas. Ann. and Mag. Nat. Hist. (8), vol.15, no.88, pp.421-424, Apr., 1915.

GEOGRAPHICAL RACES OF PETAURISTA ALBORUFUS. Oldfield Thomas. Ann. and Mag. Nat. Hist., ser.9, vol.12, pp.171-172, July, 1923.

A NEW GENUS FOR SCIURUS POENSIS AND ITS ALLIES. Oldfield Thomas. Ann. and Mag. Nat. Hist. (8), vol.17, no.99, pp.271-272, Mar., 1916.

NEW GROUND SQUIRRELS OF THE XERUS ERYTHROPUS GROUP. Oldfield Thomas. Ann. and Mag. Nat. Hist. (7), vol.15, no. 88, pp.387-390, Apr., 1905.

NOTE ON SCIURUS SPLENDIDUS, GRAY. Oldfield Thomas. Ann. and Mag. Nat. Hist., ser.10, vol.2, no.12, p.590, Dec., 1928.

NOTE ON THE SQUIRREL-GENUS "ZETIS." Oldfield Thomas. Ann. and Mag. Nat. Hist. (8), vol.2, no.7, pp.136, July, 1908.

ON THE ALLOCATION OF THE NAME SCIURUS FINLAYSONI HORSFIELD. Oldfield Thomas. Jour. Nat. Hist. Soc., Siam, Bankok, vol.2, no.343-346, Dec., 1917.

ON THE GENERIC POSITION OF THE GROUPS OF SQUIRRELS TYPIFIED BY "SCIURUS" BERDMOREI AND PERNYI

RESPECTIVELY, WITH DESCRIPTIONS OF SOME NEW ORIENTAL SPECIES. Oldfield Thomas. Jour. Bombay Nat. Hist. Soc., vol.18, no.2, pp.244-249, Apr.13, 1908.

ON THE LARGE FLYING-SQUIRRELS REFERRED TO PETAURISTA NITIDA, DESM. Oldfield Thomas. Ann. and Mag. Nat. Hist. (8), vol.1, no.3, pp. 250-252, Mar., 1908.

ON THE LARGE SQUIRRELS OF THE RATUFA GIGANTEA GROUP. Oldfield Thomas. Jour. Bombay Nat. Hist. Soc., vol.29, pp.85-86, Apr.20, 1923.

ON THE STRIPED SQUIRRELS HITHERTO REFERRED TO THE GENUS PARAXERUS. Oldfield Thomas. Ann. and Mag. Nat. Hist. (9), vol.1, no.1, pp.33-38, Jan., 1918.

ON TWO NEW SQUIRRELS OF THE FUNISCIURUS PYRRHOPUS GROUP. Oldfield Thomas. Ann. and Mag. Nat. Hist. (7), vol.11, no.61, pp.79-81, Jan., 1903.

THE PENIS-BONE, OR "BALCULUM," AS A GUIDE TO THE CLASSIFICATION OF CERTAIN SQUIRRELS. Oldfield Thomas. Ann. and Mag. Nat. Hist. (8), vol.15, no. 88, pp.383-387, Apr., 1915.

THE RACES OF DREMONYS PERNYI. Oldfield Thomas. Ann. and Mag. Nat. Hist. (8), vol.17, no.101, pp.391-394, May, 1916.

TWO NEW SUBSPECIES OF CALLOSCIURUS QUINQUESTRIATUS. Oldfield Thomas. Ann. and Mag. Nat. Hist., ser.9, vol.17, pp.639-641, June, 1926.

REVISION OF THE GENUS SCIURUS. (TRANSLATED, WITH NOTES, BY DR. ELLIOT COUES.) E. L. Trouessart. Bull. U.S. Geol. and Geogr. Survey, Dept. Interior, vol.6, no.2, pp.301-307, Sept.19, 1881.

THE TYPE LOCALITY OF SCIURUS APACHE ALLEN. A. J. Van Rossem. Jour. Mam., vol.17, no.4, pp.416-417, Nov., 1936.

THE BACULUM OF SOME SCIURIDAE AND ITS SIGNIFICANCE IN DETERMINING RELATIONSHIPS. Otis Wade, Paul T. Gilbert. Jour. Mam., vol.21, no.1, pp.52-63, figs. 3, Feb.14, 1940.

ON A NEW SPECIES OF SQUIRREL. G. R. Waterhouse. Proc. Zool. Soc. Lond., pt. 6, p.19, 1838.

ON A NEW SPECIES OF SQUIRREL (SCIURUS DIMIDIATUS). G. R. Waterhouse. Proc. Zool. Soc. Lond., pt.8, p.21, 1840.

GENERA AND SUBGENERA OF CHIPMUNKS. John A. White. Univ. Kansas Publ., Mus. Nat. Hist., Lawrence, vol.5, no.32, pp.543-561, illus., Dec.1, 1953.

TAXONOMY OF THE CHIPMUNKS, EUTAMIAS QUADRIVITATUS AND EUTAMIAS UMBRINUS. John A. White. Univ. Kansas Publ., Mus. Nat. Hist., Lawrence, vol.5, no.33, pp.563-582, illus., Dec.1, 1953.

THE MAINLAND REPRESENTATIVE OF RATUFA M. DANDOLENA. R. C. Wroughton. Jour. Bombay Nat. Hist. Soc., vol.27, pp.249-250, Dec.20, 1920.

ON THE ERYTHRAEUS GROUP OF SQUIRRELS. R. C. Wroughton. Jour. Bombay Nat. Hist. Soc., vol.27, pp.773-777, 1921.

ON THE FORMS OF SQUIRREL HITHERTO CLASSED UNDER SC. FINLAYSONI, HORSF. R. C. Wroughton. Ann. Mag. Nat. Hist., ser.8, vol.2, pp.393-401, Nov., 1908.

TWO NEW FORMS OF THE FUNAMBULUS TRISTRIATUS GROUP. R. C. Wroughton, Winifred M. Davidson. Jour. Bombay Nat. Hist. Soc., vol.26, pp.728-730, Oct.20, 1919.

United States, Eastern

POPULATIONS AND HABITS OF THE FOX SQUIRREL IN ALLEGAN COUNTY, MICHIGAN. Durward L. Allen. Amer. Midland Nat., Notre Dame, vol.27, no.2, pp.338-379, figs.19, Mar., 1942.

NORTH CAROLINA GRAY SQUIRREL INVESTIGATIONS, 1947-1950. Ray Allison. N. C. Wildl. Resources Comm., Final Rep. Proj. N.C. 26-R, vii plus 61 pp., 21 pls., appendix, illus., Sept., 1953.

PRELIMINARY REPORT ON GRAY SQUIRREL INVESTIGATION IN NORTH CAROLINA. Ray Allison. Jour. Elisha Mitchell Soc., Chapel Hill, vol.64, no.2, p.177, Dec., 1948.

A NEW FOX SQUIRREL FROM THE EASTERN SHORE OF MARYLAND. Harold H. Bailey. Bull. no.1, Bailey Mus. and Lib. Nat. Hist., Newport News, Va., 1 p., Aug. 1, 1920.

THE CAROLINA GRAY SQUIRREL. V. Bailey. Nature Mag., vol.5, pp.303-306, illus., May, 1925.

THE PRAIRIE GROUND SQUIRRELS OR SPERMOPHILES OF THE MISSISSIPPI VALLEY. V. Bailey. U.S. Dept. Agric., Div. Ornith., and Mamm., bull.no.4, pp. 5-69, pls.1-3, maps 2, 1893.

WISCONSIN WILDLIFE FOR BOYS AND GIRLS--ANIMALS. THE CHIPMUNK. N. R. Barger. Wisconsin Conserv. Bull., Madison, vol.12, no.11, pp.29-30, illus., Nov., 1947.

THE FOX SQUIRREL: ITS LIFE HISTORY, HABITS AND MANAGEMENT IN OHIO. Luther L. Baumgartner. PhD thesis, Ohio State Univ., 1940; Ohio Wildl. Res. Sta., Release 138, 7 pp., 1940.

FOX SQUIRRELS IN OHIO. Luther L. Baumgartner. Jour. Wildl. Mgt., 7 (2): 193-202, Apr., 1943.

KENTUCKY SQUIRRELS. E. Cooper Bertram, William L. Gault. Presented at 6th Ann. Conf., S.E. Assn. Game and Fish Comm., Savannah, Ga., pp.1-15, appendix, graphs, Oct.19-22, 1952.

FOX SQUIRRELS AND GRAY SQUIRRELS IN ILLINOIS. Louis C. Brown, Lee E. Yeager. Bull. Illinois Nat. Hist. Survey, Urbana, vol.23, no.5, pp.449-536, illus., Sept., 1945.

A SUMMARY OF THE GRAY SQUIRREL INVESTIGATION IN SOUTHEASTERN OHIO. Floyd B. Chapman. U.S. Bur. Biol. Surv., Wildlife Research and Management Leaflet BS-134, pp.9, tables 4, Apr., 1939.

SUMMARY OF THE OHIO GRAY SQUIRREL INVESTIGATION. Floyd B. Chapman. Trans. 3rd. North Amer. Wildlife Conf., pp.677-684, 1938; Ohio Wildl. Res. Sta., Release 71, 7 pp., Feb., 1938.

DISTRIBUTION OF CITELLUS TRIDECEMLINEATUS IN ILLINOIS. Robert B. Chiasson. Jour. Mam., vol.34, no.4, p. 510, Nov.13, 1953.

A STUDY OF THE HABITS AND MANAGEMENT OF THE GRAY SQUIRREL IN VIRGINIA. R. H. Cross. MS thesis, Va. Polytechnic Inst., 1942.

VIRGINIA ANIMALS EVERYONE SHOULD KNOW. THE GRAY SQUIRREL. R. H. Cross. Virginia Wildlife, Richmond, vol. 7, no.2, pp.14, 20, illus., Aug., 1946.

LOCAL NOTES ON THE GRAY SQUIRREL. William T. Davis. Proc. Staten Island Inst. Arts and Sci., vol.2, pp.126-134, 1924.

GLAUCOMYS SABRINUS IN PENNSYLVANIA. J. Kenneth Doutt. Jour. Mam., vol.11, no. 2, pp.239-240, May, 1930.

OBSERVATIONS ON THE BRYANT FOX SQUIRREL. Herbert L. Dozier, Harold E. Hall. Md. Cons., 21 (1): 2-7, Winter, 1944.

NOTES ON A POPULATION OF THE STRIPED GROUND SQUIRREL (CITELLUS TRIDECEMLINEATUS) IN AN ABANDONED FIELD IN SOUTHEASTERN MICHIGAN. F. C. Evans. Jour. Mam., 32 (4): 437-439, Nov., 1951.

FOX SQUIRREL STUDY INITIATED. V. F. Flyger. Maryland Tidewater News. Solomons, 13 (7): 3, May-June, 1957.

NEW RECORD FOR RED SQUIRREL IN MARYLAND. V. F. Flyger. Maryland Tidewater News, Solomons, 13 (6): 1, Mar.-Apr., 1957.

CAMPING WITH CHIPMUNKS. (ADIRONDACK MOUNTAINS, NEW YORK.) Lucy B. Fraleigh. Nature Mag., vol.10, pp.123-126, illus., Aug., 1927.

THE STRIPED SPERMOPHILE IN FAIRFIELD COUNTY, OHIO. Robert Goslin. Jour. Mam., vol.14, no.4, p.369, Nov., 1933.

OBSERVATIONS ON THE LIFE HISTORY OF THE RED SQUIRREL IN NEW YORK. W. J. Hamilton, Jr. Amer. Midland Nat., Notre Dame, vol.22, no.3, pp.732-745, figs.2, Nov., 1939.

MARYLAND NATURE LOG. THE SQUIRRELS OF MARYLAND. Irving E. Hampe. Maryland Conservationist, Balto., vol.21, no.3, p.11, Summer and Fall Issue, 1944.

A NEW FLYING SQUIRREL FROM THE SOUTHERN APPALACHIAN MOUNTAINS. Charles O. Handley, Jr. Proc. Biol. Soc. Wash., vol.68, pp.191-194, Dec.2, 1953.

GREY SQUIRREL IN THE ADIRONDACKS. George L. Harrison. Jour. Mam., vol.3, no.1, p.54, Feb., 1922.

THE RED SQUIRREL: ITS LIFE HISTORY AND HABITS, WITH SPECIAL REFERENCE TO THE ADIRONDACKS OF NEW YORK AND THE HARVARD FOREST. Robert T. Hatt. Bull. New York State College of Forestry, Roosevelt Wild Life Annals, vol. 2, no.1, pp.1-146, 52 text figs., 1929.

MIDWINTER RECORD OF THE WOODCHUCK IN WESTERN PENNSYLVANIA. Ernest G. Holt. Jour. Mam., vol.10, no.1, p.80, Feb., 1929.

WOODCHUCK IN ALABAMA. Ernest G. Holt. Jour. Mam., vol.5, no.1, pp.67-68, Feb., 1924.

GEOGRAPHIC VARIATION IN THE EASTERN CHIPMUNK, TAMIAS STRIATUS, IN MICHIGAN. Emmet T. Hooper. Occas. Papers Mus. Zool., Univ. Michigan, Ann Arbor, no.461, pp.5, Sept.15, 1942.

DESCRIPTION OF A NEW RED SQUIRREL FROM ISLE ROYALE, MICHIGAN. Arthur H. Howell. Occas. Papers Mus. Zool., Ann Arbor, no.338, pp.2, July 7, 1936.

DESCRIPTIONS OF A NEW RED SQUIRREL FROM NORTH CAROLINA. Arthur H. Howell. Jour. Mam., vol.10, no.1, pp.75-76, Feb.11, 1929.

NOTES ON THE FOX SQUIRRELS OF SOUTHEASTERN UNITED STATES, WITH DESCRIPTION OF A NEW FORM FROM FLORIDA. Arthur H. Howell. Jour. Mam., vol.1, no.1, pp.36-38, Nov.28, 1919.

THE STRIPED GOPHER, OR PRAIRIE GROUND SQUIRREL, OF WISCONSIN. Philo Romayne Hoy. U. S. Patent Office, Report, Agriculture, pp.68-70, 1853.

A MID-SUMMER STUDY OF THE EASTERN FLYING SQUIRREL. James S. Jordan. MS thesis, Univ. Mich., 1947.

A MIDSUMMER STUDY OF THE SOUTHERN FLYING SQUIRREL. James S. Jordan. Jour Mam., 29 (1): 44-48, Feb., 1948.

THE SUBSPECIES OF WOODCHUCK IN VERMONT. George L. Kirk. Jour. Mam., vol.3, no.4, pp.259-260, Nov., 1922.

THE OCCURRENCE OF TAMIAS STRIATUS IN GEORGIA. James C. Knepton, Jr. Jour. Mam., 36 (1): 136, Feb.25, 1955.

THE BIOLOGY OF THE RED SQUIRREL, TAMIASCIURUS HUDSONICUS LOQUAX (BANGS), IN CENTRAL NEW YORK. James N. Layne. Ecol. Monog., 24 (3): 227-267, illus., July, 1954.

THE LIFE HISTORY AND HABITAT OF THE NORTHERN GRAY SQUIRREL IN RELATION TO SOME PLANT COMMUNITIES IN CENTRE COUNTY, PENNSYLVANIA. MS Thesis, Pa. State Coll., 1951.

FRANKLIN'S GROUND SQUIRREL AND ITS DISTRIBUTION IN INDIANA. Marcus W. Lyon, Jr. Amer. Midland Nat., Notre Dame, vol.13, no.1, pp.16-20, pl.4, Jan., 1932.

DISTRIBUTION OF THE RED SQUIRREL IN INDIANA. Marcus W. Lyon, Jr.

Amer. Midland Nat., Notre Dame, vol.15, no.3, pp.375-376, 1934.

NOTES ON THE RED SQUIRREL IN PITTSBURGH. E. H. McClelland. Jour. Mam., 29 (4): 409-412, Nov., 1948.

COMMENTS ON THE FOX SQUIRRELS OF MARYLAND. Romeo Mansueti. Md. Nat., 22 (3-4): 30-41, illus., 1952.

MEET YOUR MARYLAND MAMMALS. SOUTHERN WOODCHUCK (MARMOTA MONAX MONAX). Romeo Mansueti. Maryland Conservationist, Balto., vol.26, no.1, p.23, Spring, 1949.

DESCRIPTION OF A NEW SUBSPECIES OF THE EASTERN CHIPMUNK, FROM THE UPPER MISSISSIPPI REGION, WEST OF THE GREAT LAKES. Edgar A. Mearns. Bull. Amer. Mus. Nat. Hist., New York, vol.3, no.2, pp.229-233, June 5, 1891.

A NEW FLYING SQUIRREL FROM WEST VIRGINIA. Gerrit S. Miller, Jr. Proc. Biol. Soc. Washington, vol.49, pp.143-144, Aug.22, 1936.

DISTRIBUTION OF GROUND SQUIRRELS IN ILLINOIS. Carl O. Mohr. Trans. Ill. State Acad. Sci., Springfield, vol.36, no. 2, pp.177-178, maps 2, May, 1943.

A REFUGE SQUIRREL POPULATION IN SOUTHERN ILLINOIS. Richard J. Moran. Presented at 14th Midwest Wildl. Conf., Des Moines, Iowa, pp.1-7, Dec.17-19, 1952.

THE FISHER CHIPMUNK IN MASSACHUSETTS. Norman A. Preble. Jour. Mam., vol.19, no.4, p.503, Nov.14, 1938.

NOTES ON NEW HAMPSHIRE CHIPMUNKS. Norman A. Preble. Jour. Mam., vol.17, no.3, pp.288-289, Aug., 1936.

SQUIRREL CONDITIONS IN MISSISSIPPI. Howard R. Redmond. Miss. Game and Fish, 14 (10): 4-7, 10-11, Apr., 1951.

THE BIOLOGY OF THE NORTHERN GRAY SQUIRREL (SCIURUS CAROLINENSIS LEUCOTIS GAPPER) IN CENTRAL NEW YORK. R. M. Roecker. PhD thesis, Cornell Univ., 1950.

SQUIRRELS IN EARLY WISCONSIN. A. W. Schorger. Trans. Wis. Acad. Sci., Arts and Letters, 39: 195-247, 1949.

A STUDY OF THE HABITS AND MANAGEMENT OF THE GRAY SQUIRREL IN SOUTHWEST VIRGINIA. D. D. Shipley. MS thesis, Va. Polytechnic Inst., 1941.

NOTES ON THE LIFE HISTORY OF THE SMALL EASTERN FLYING SQUIRREL. Dwight E. Sollberger. Jour. Mam., 21 (3): 282-293, Aug., 1940.

NOTES ON THE LIFE HISTORY OF THE SMALL EASTERN FLYING SQUIRREL, GLAUCOMYS VOLANS VOLANS (LINN.). Dwight E. Sollberger. PhD thesis, Cornell Univ., 1938.

THE GRAY SQUIRREL IN WEST VIRGINIA. Hans G. Uhlig. Bull. Div. Game Management, Conservation Comm. West Virginia, no.3, pp.1-83, illus., 1956.

THE GRAY SQUIRREL / ITS LIFE HISTORY, ECOLOGY, AND POPULATION CHARACTERISTICS IN WEST VIRGINIA. Hans G. Uhlig. Cons. Comm. W. Va., Final Rep. PR Proj. 31-R, pp.1-181, graphs, maps, July, 1955.

THE GRAY SQUIRREL IN WESTERN VILAS COUNTY. D. W. Waggoner. Wis. Cons. Bull., 11 (6): 3-5, June, 1946.

THE RED SQUIRREL EXTENDING ITS RANGE IN INDIANA. Ernest P. Walker. Jour. Mam., vol.4, no.2, pp.127-128, May, 1923.

MAMMALS OF WEST VIRGINIA. IV. THE SQUIRRELS. L. Wayne Wilson. West Virginia Conserv., Charleston, vol.10, no. 2, pp.6, 17, 18, May, 1946.

THE LIFE HISTORY AND HABITAT OF THE NORTHERN GRAY SQUIRREL IN RELATION TO SOME FOREST COMMUNITIES IN HUNTINGDON COUNTY, PENNSYLVANIA. Robert G. Wingard. MS thesis, Pa. State Coll., 1950.

THE BIOLOGY OF THE CHIPMUNK (TAMIAS STRIATUS LYSTERI) IN CENTRAL NEW YORK WITH SPECIAL REFERENCE TO HOME RANGE AND TERRITORIALITY. Ralph W. Yerger. PhD thesis, Cornell Univ., 1950.

HOME RANGE, TERRITORIALITY, AND POPULATIONS OF THE CHIPMUNK IN CENTRAL NEW YORK. Ralph W. Yerger. Jour. Mam., 34 (4): 448-458, Nov., 1953.

LIFE HISTORY NOTES ON THE EASTERN CHIPMUNK, TAMIAS STRIATUS LYSTERI (RICHARDSON), IN CENTRAL NEW YORK. Ralph W. Yerger. Amer. Midland Nat., Notre Dame, vol.53, no.2, pp.312-323, Apr., 1955.

DATA COLLECTED ON WEST VIRGINIA SQUIRRELS. West Virginia Conservation, Charleston, vol.7, no.7, pp.10, 19-20, Oct., 1943.

OHIO SQUIRRELS. Ohio Conserv. Bull., Columbus, vol.10, no.9, p.3, illus., Sept., 1946.

United States, Western

CALIFORNIA GRAY SQUIRRELS. M. E. Beatty. Yosemite Nature Notes, vol.11, no.11, pp.5-6, Nov., 1932.

MAMMALS OF UTAH: GENUS CITELLUS. Jack H. Berryman. Utah Fish and Game Bull., Salt Lake City, vol.7, no.11, p.2, Feb., 1950.

SOME INTERESTING FACTS ABOUT UTAH MAMMALS. CHICKAREES. Jack H. Berryman. Utah Fish and Game Bull., Salt Lake City, vol.8, no.3, p.3, July-Aug., 1950.

DESCRIPTION OF A RACE OF CHIPMUNK FROM SOUTH CENTRAL IDAHO. Phillip M. Blossom. Occas. Papers Mus. Zool. Univ. Michigan, no.366, pp.1-3, Dec.21, 1937.

A NEW CHIPMUNK FROM WASHINGTON STATE. Ernest S. Booth. Murrelet, Seattle, vol.28, no.1, pp.7-8, Apr.30, 1947.

HABITS AND DISTRIBUTION OF THE ROCK SQUIRREL IN SOUTHERN NEW MEXICO. Robert M. Bradley. Jour. Mam., vol.10, no.2, pp.168-169, May, 1929.

THE CHIPMUNKS OF THE YOSEMITE REGION. Martin R. Brittan. Yosemite Nature Notes 27 (7): 92-97, July, 1948.

THE COMMON GROUND SQUIRRELS OF CALIFORNIA. H. C. Bryant. Univ. Calif. Agric. Exp. Sta. Berkeley, cir. no. 82, pp.1-4, figs.2, Nov., 1912.

FLYING SQUIRRELS IN YOSEMITE CAMPS. H. C. Bryant. Yosemite Nature Notes, vol.6, p.87, Nov., 1927.

SIERRA MARMOT AT MERCED LAKE. H. C. Bryant. Yosemite Nature Notes, vol.7, p.54, July, 1928.

A CONTRIBUTION TO THE LIFE HISTORY OF THE WYOMING GROUND SQUIRREL (CITELLUS ELEGANS) IN COLORADO. PART I. W. L. Burnett. Circ. 30, Office of State Entomologist, Colorado Agr. Coll., pp.1-12, 2 figs., Sept., 1920.

THE GROUND SQUIRRELS OF COLORADO. W. L. Burnett. Colorado Agric. Coll. Fort Collins, Cir.44, pp.3-19, illus., Nov., 1924.

LIFE HISTORY STUDIES OF THE WYOMING GROUND SQUIRREL (CITELLUS ELEGANS ELEGANS) IN COLORADO. W. L. Burnett. Colorado Agric. College Bull. 373, pp.23, figs.7, 1931.

THE PRAIRIE-DOG SITUATION IN COLORADO. W. L. Burnett. Office of State Entomologist, Fort Collins, Cir.17, p.15, illus., Oct., 1915.

THE STRIPED GROUND SQUIRRELS OF COLORADO. W. L. Burnett. Office of State Entomologist, Fort Collins, Cir.14, p.19, fig.1, Oct., 1914.

THE WYOMING GROUND SQUIRREL IN COLORADO WITH SUGGESTIONS FOR CONTROL. W. L. Burnett. State Entomologist, Fort Collins, Colorado, Cir.20, pp.1-11, pls.1-2, col. illus., July, 1916.

THE ZUNI PRAIRIE DOG IN MONTEZUMA COUNTY COLORADO. W. L. Burnett, S. C. McCampbell. Colorado Agric. College, circ.49, 15 pp., Jan., 1926.

NOTES ON THE UTAH CHIPMUNK. William B. Davis. Murrelet, vol.15, no.1, pp.20-22, Jan., 1934.

THE TOWNSEND GROUND SQUIRRELS OF IDAHO. William B. Davis. Jour. Mam., 20 (2): 182-190, May, 1939.

A NEW SUBSPECIES OF THE ARIZONA GRAY SQUIRREL (SCIURUS ARIZONENSIS COUES). J. Kenneth Doutt. Ann. Carnegie Mus., vol.20, no.2, pp.271-273, June, 1931.

A NEW ABERT SQUIRREL FROM UTAH. Stephen D. Durrant. Proc. Biol. Soc. Wash., vol.60, pp.79-82, July 2, 1947.

A NEW ROCK SQUIRREL (CITELLUS VARIEGATUS) FROM THE GREAT BASIN WITH CRITICAL COMMENTS ON RELATED SUBSPECIES. Stephen D. Durrant, Richard M. Hansen. Proc. Biol. Soc. Wash., vol.67, pp.263-272, Nov.15, 1954.

TAXONOMY OF THE CHICKAREES (TAMIASCIURUS) OF UTAH. Stephen D. Durrant. Jour. Mam., 35 (1): 87-95, map, graph., Feb., 1954.

YELLOW-BELLIED MARMOT AT BELLINGHAM, WASHINGTON. J. M. Edson. Murrelet, vol.15, no.3, p.81, Sept., 1934.

SOME NOTES ON THE LIFE HISTORY OF THE MEXICAN GROUND SQUIRREL IN TEXAS. Robert L. Edwards. Jour. Mam., 27 (2): 105-115, May, 1946.

GAME SQUIRRELS OF TEXAS: THE GRAY SQUIRREL. Everett F. Evans. Tex. Game and Fish, 11 (3): 13-14, 27, Feb., 1953.

DIAGNOSIS OF A NEW SUBSPECIES OF MARMOT FROM COLORADO. J. D. Figgins. Proc. Biol. Soc. Wash., vol.28, pp.147-148, Sept.21, 1915.

EXOTIC SQUIRRELS IN THE SEATTLE AREA. Martha R. Flahaut. Murrelet, Seattle, vol.22, no.3, pp.63-64, Sept.-Dec., 1941.

THE BELDING GROUND SQUIRREL IN THE SIERRA NEVADA. F. E. Garlough. Jour. Mam., vol.5, no.1, p.68, Feb., 1924.

A NEW ANTELOPE SQUIRREL FROM ARIZONA. E. A. Goldman. Jour. Wash. Acad. Sci., vol.19, no.19, pp.435-436, Nov.19, 1929.

NOTES ON THE GRAY AND FOX SQUIRRELS OF EASTERN TEXAS. Phil Goodrum. Trans. Second North Amer. Wildlife Conference, Washington, D.C., pp.499-504, Mar., 1937.

EUTAMIAS SONOMAE, A NEW CHIPMUNK FROM THE INNER NORTHERN COAST BELT OF CALIFORNIA. Joseph Grinnell. Univ. Cal. Pub. Zool., vol.12, no.11, pp. 321-325, fig.1, Jan.20, 1915.

NATURAL HISTORY OF THE GROUND SQUIRRELS OF CALIFORNIA. Joseph Grinnell, Joseph Dixon. Monthly Bull. State Commiss. Horticulture, Sacramento, California, vol.7, nos.11-12, pp.597-708, figs.30, color pls.5, Jan.27, 1919.

(Review by Walter P. Taylor of) CALIFORNIA GROUND SQUIRRELS. BULLETIN DEALING WITH LIFE HISTORIES, HABITS AND CONTROL OF THE GROUND SQUIRRELS IN CALIFORNIA. Joseph Grinnell. Jour. Mamm., vol. 1, no.2, pp. 97-99, Feb., 1920.

A NEW RACE OF BELDING GROUND SQUIRREL FROM NEVADA. E. Raymond Hall. The Murrelet, Seattle, vol.21, no. 3, pp.59-61, Sept.-Dec., 1940.

A NEW RACE OF CHIPMUNK FROM THE GREAT BASIN OF WESTERN UNITED STATES. E. Raymond Hall, Donald M. Hatfield. Univ. Calif. Publ. in Zool., vol. 40, no.6, pp.321-326, fig.1, Feb.2, 1934.

A NEW CHIPMUNK OF THE EUTAMIAS AMOENUS GROUP FROM NEVADA. E. Raymond Hall, David H. Johnson. Proc. Biol. Soc. Wash., vol.53, pp.155-156, Dec. 19, 1940.

THE BELDING GROUND SQUIRREL, NORTH OF THE SNAKE RIVER IN IDAHO. Richard M. Hansen. Jour. Mam., vol.35, no.4, p. 587, Nov.29, 1954.

RICHARDSON GROUND SQUIRREL IN UTAH. Richard M. Hansen. Jour. Mam., vol.34, no.1, pp.131-132, Feb.19, 1953.

TWO NEW SUBSPECIES OF ANTELOPE GROUND SQUIRRELS FROM UTAH. Richard M. Hansen. Jour. Mam., 36 (2): 273-277, May 26, 1955.

EXTENSION OF RANGES OF THE PRAIRIE-DOG OF THE GENUS CYNOMYS IN UTAH. Ross Hardy. Proc. Utah Acad. Sci., Arts and Letters, vol.14, pp.197-198, Nov., 1937.

A NEW TREE SQUIRREL FROM CENTRAL UTAH. Ross Hardy. Proc. Biol. Soc. Wash., vol.63, pp.13-14, Apr.26, 1950.

THE TAXONOMIC STATUS OF SOME CHIPMUNKS OF THE GENUS EUTAMIAS IN SOUTHWESTERN UTAH. Ross Hardy. Proc. Biol. Soc. Wash., vol.58, pp.85-88, June 30, 1945.

THE PINE SQUIRREL IN COLORADO. Robert T. Hatt. Jour. Mam., 24 (3): 311-345, Aug., 1943.

RANGE AND SPREAD OF THE GRAY AND THE FOX SQUIRRELS IN NORTH DAKOTA. Edmund A. Hibbard. Jour. Mam., vol.37, no.4, pp.525-531, 1 fig., Nov., 1956.

STATUS OF THE FOX SQUIRREL IN NORTHEASTERN COLORADO. Robert L. Hoover, Lee E. Yeager. Jour. Mam., 34 (3): 359-365, map, Aug., 1953.

DESCRIPTION OF A NEW CHIPMUNK FROM GLACIER NATIONAL PARK, MONTANA. Arthur H. Howell. Proc. Biol. Soc. Wash., vol.33, pp.91-92, Dec.30, 1920.

DESCRIPTION OF A NEW SPECIES OF SAY'S GROUND SQUIRREL FROM WYOMING. Arthur H. Howell. Proc. Biol. Soc. Wash., vol.30, pp.105-106, May 23, 1917.

A NEW RED SQUIRREL FROM MINNESOTA. Arthur H. Howell. Proc. Biol. Soc. Wash., vol.56, pp.67-68, June 16, 1943.

A NEW RED SQUIRREL FROM NORTH DAKOTA. Arthur H. Howell. Proc. Biol. Soc. Wash., vol.55, pp.13-14, May 12, 1942.

ECOLOGY AND LIFE HISTORY OF THE CALIFORNIA GRAY SQUIRREL. Lloyd G. Ingles. California Fish and Game, vol.33, no.3, pp.139-158, July, 1947.

A PRELIMINARY STUDY OF THE SOUTHERN GRAY SQUIRREL, SCIURUS C. CAROLINENSIS GMELIN, IN MISSOURI. Lisle Jeffrey. AM thesis, Univ. Mo., 1937.

A RECORD OF EUTAMIAS AMOENUS FROM SNOW MOUNTAIN, CALIFORNIA. David H. Johnson. Jour. Mam., vol.28, no.1, pp.65-66, Feb.15, 1947.

SYSTEMATIC REVIEW AND ENVIRONMENTAL RELATIONS OF CALIFORNIAN CHIPMUNKS, GENUS EUTAMIAS. David H. Johnson. PhD thesis, Univ. Calif., 1940.

SYSTEMATIC REVIEW OF THE CHIPMUNKS (GENUS EUTAMIAS) OF CALIFORNIA. David H. Johnson. Univ. California Publ. Zool., Berkeley, vol.48, no.2, pp.63-148, pl.6, maps, Dec.24, 1943.

THE FOX AND GREY SQUIRRELS OF LOUISIANA. Joseph B. Kidd. La. Cons., 7 (1): 2-5, illus., Oct., 1954.

NOTES ON THE THIRTEEN-LINED GROUND SQUIRREL IN UTAH. Merlin L. Killpack. Jour. Mam., 36 (2): 296-297, May 26, 1955.

SOCIAL BEHAVIOR, SOCIAL ORGANIZATION, AND POPULATION DYNAMICS IN A BLACK-TAILED PRAIRIE-DOG TOWN IN THE BLACK HILLS OF SOUTH DAKOTA. John A. King. Ph. D. thesis, Univ. Mich., 1952; Contrib. Lab. Vert. Biol., Univ. Mich., Ann Arbor, no.67, pp.1-123, pls.1-4, Apr., 1955.

THE SUBSPECIFIC IDENTITY OF THE BLACK HILLS FLYING SQUIRRELS (GLAUCOMYS SABRINUS). John A. King. Jour. Mam., vol.32, no.4, pp.469-470, Nov.19, 1951.

WOODCHUCK REMAINS IN NORTHERN ARIZONA CAVES. Arthur L. Lange. Jour. Mam., 37 (2): 289-291, June 9, 1956.

NOTES ON THE CHIPMUNKS OF WEST-CENTRAL WASHINGTON. Earl J. Larrison. Murrelet, Seattle, vol.28, no.2, pp.23-30, May-Aug. (Sept.12), 1947.

SIERRA MARMOT. Russel L. Lewis. Yosemite Nat. Notes, Yosemite, vol.19, no.9, p.70, Sept., 1940.

THE CALIFORNIA GROUND SQUIRREL. A RECORD OF OBSERVATIONS MADE ON THE HASTINGS NATURAL HISTORY RESERVATION. Jean M. Linsdale. Univ. California Press, Berkeley, pp.475, figs. 140, map, frontisp., 1946.

(Review by William Henry Burt of) THE CALIFORNIA GROUND SQUIRREL. Jean M. Lindsdale. Science, Lancaster, vol.104, no.2705, p.430, Nov. 1, 1946.

(Review by Henry S. Fitch of) THE CALIFORNIA GROUND SQUIRREL. Jean M. Linsdale. Jour. Mam., vol.28, no.2, pp. 191-192, May 19, 1947.

(Review by E. Raymond Hall of) THE CALIFORNIA GROUND SQUIRREL. Jean M. Linsdale. Ecology, Lancaster, vol. 28, no.2, p.211, Apr., 1947.

(Review by P. Rode of) THE CALIFORNIA GROUND SQUIRREL. Jean M. Linsdale. Mammalia, Paris, vol.10, no.3, p.156, Sep.-Dec., 1946.

THE BIOLOGY OF CERTAIN MAMMALS IN COSTILLA COUNTY, COLORADO, WITH ESPECIAL REFERENCE TO THE PRAIRIE DOG. William Murray Longhurst. Abstracts of Theses, 1942, Cornell Univ., Ithaca, pp.302-305, 1943.

A REVISION OF THE FOX SQUIRRELS OF THE LOWER MISSISSIPPI VALLEY AND TEXAS. George H. Lowery, Jr., William B. Davis. Louisiana State Univ., Baton Rouge, Mus. Zool., Occas. Pap. no.9, pp. 153-172, Mar.4, 1942.

A NEW GROUND SQUIRREL FOR COLORADO. Sam C. McCampbell. Jour. Mam., vol.7, no.1, p.60, Feb., 1926.

DISTRIBUTION OF THE TASSEL-EARED SQUIRRELS. Edwin D. McKee. Plateau (continuing Museum Notes), Flagstaff, vol. 14, no.1, pp.12-20, illus., July, 1941.

AN UNUSUAL WINTER RECORD OF CITELLUS SPILOSOMA IN OKLAHOMA Frank B. McMurry. Jour. Mam., vol.28, no.3, p.292, Aug.19, 1947.

GROUND SQUIRRELS INVADING NEW TERRITORY IN THE SAN FRANCISCO BAY REGION. Joseph Mailliard. Jour. Mam., vol.13, no.1, pp.73-74, Feb., 1932.

OCCURRENCE OF GROUND SQUIRRELS ALONG HIGHWAYS. Robert F. Martin. Jour. Mam., vol.16, no.2, p.154, May, 1935.

VARIATION AND SYSTEMATIC POSITION OF THE FLYING SQUIRREL OF IDAHO. William V. Mayer. Murrelet, Seattle, vol. 22, no.2, pp.30-31, May-Aug., 1941.

DESCRIPTION OF A RARE SQUIRREL, NEW TO THE TERRITORY OF ARIZONA. Edgar A. Mearns. Extract, Bull. Amer. Mus. N. H., vol.1, no.7, pp.197-207, July, 1886.

THE CALIFORNIA GROUND SQUIRREL. C. Hart Merriam. U.S. Dept. Agric., Bur. Biol. Surv., Cir.no.76, pp.15, figs.4, Nov.25, 1910.

CALIFORNIA GROUND SQUIRRELS. C. Hart Merriam. U.S. Treasury Dept., Publ. Health and Marine-Hospital Serv., Wash., D.C., pp.8, 1909.

DESCRIPTION OF A NEW FLYING SQUIRREL FROM FT. KLAMATH, OREGON. C. Hart Merriam. Proc. Biol. Soc. Wash., vol.11, p.225, July 15, 1897.

DESCRIPTION OF A NEW MARMOT FROM THE BLACK HILLS OF DAKOTA. C. Hart Merriam. North American Fauna, no.2, U.S. Dept. Agric., pp.7-9, Oct., 1889.

DESCRIPTION OF A NEW PRAIRIE DOG FROM WYOMING. CYNOMYS LEUCURUS SP. NOV. C. Hart Merriam. North American Fauna, no.4, pp.33-35, Oct., 1890.

DESCRIPTION OF A NEW SPECIES OF CHIPMUNK FROM CALIFORNIA (TAMIAS MACRORHABDOTES SP. NOV.). C. Hart Merriam. Proc. Biol. Soc. Wash., vol.3, pp.25-28, illus., Jan.27, 1886.

DESCRIPTION OF A NEW SPECIES OF GROUND SQUIRREL FROM THE ARID LANDS OF THE SOUTHWEST. TAMIAS LEUCURUS SP. NO. C. Hart Merriam. North American Fauna, no.2, pp.19-21, Oct., 1899.

DESCRIPTION OF A NEW SPERMOPHILE FROM CALIFORNIA. SPERMOPHILUS BELDINGI, SP. NOV. C. Hart Merriam. Annals N. Y. Acad. Sci., vol.4, pp.317-320, figs.2, Dec.28, 1888.

DESCRIPTION OF A NEW SPERMOPHILE FROM NORTHWESTERN ARIZONA. SPERMOPHILUS NEGLECTUS SP. NOV. C. Hart Merriam. North American Fauna, no.2, p.17, Oct., 1899.

DESCRIPTION OF A NEW SPERMOPHILE FROM SOUTHERN CALIFORNIA. C. Hart Merriam. North American Fauna, no.2, U.S. Dept. Agric., pp.15-16, Oct., 1889.

DESCRIPTIONS OF SIX NEW GROUND SQUIRRELS FROM THE WESTERN UNITED STATES. C. Hart Merriam. Proc. Biol. Soc. Wash., vol.12, pp.69-71, Mar.24, 1898.

THE PRAIRIE DOG OF THE GREAT PLAINS. C. Hart Merriam. Yearbook U. S. Dept. Agric., 1901, pp.257-270, figs.24-25, pls.23-24, 1902.

PRELIMINARY DESCRIPTION OF A NEW SQUIRREL FROM MINNESOTA (SCIURUS CAROLINENSIS HYPOPHAEUS SP. NOV.). C. Hart Merriam. Science, vol.7, no.167, p.351, Apr.16, 1886.

SIX NEW GROUND SQUIRRELS OF THE CITELLUS MOLLIS GROUP FROM IDAHO, OREGON, AND NEVADA. C. Hart Merriam. Proc. Biol. Soc. Wash., vol. 26, pp.135-138, May 21, 1913.

TWO NEW CHIPMUNKS FROM COLORADO AND ARIZONA. C. Hart Merriam. Proc. Biol. Soc. Wash., vol.18, pp.163-166, June 29, 1905.

MY FRIEND THE MARIPOSA CHIPMUNK. Charles W. Michael. Yosemite Nat. Notes, Yosemite, vol.19, no.9, pp.71-72, Sept., 1940.

CALIFORNIA GRAY SQUIRRELS COMING BACK TO YOSEMITE. Enid Michael. Yosemite Nat. Notes, Yosemite, vol.19, no.5, pp.37-38, May, 1940.

SIERRA CHICKAREE (SCIURUS DOUGLASII ALBOLIMBATUS). Enid Michael. Yosemite Nat. Notes, vol.15, no.1, p.4, Jan., 1936.

NOTES ON THE SIERRA NEVADA FLYING SQUIRREL. Vincent Mowbray. Jour. Mam., vol.20, no.3, p.379, Aug.14, 1939.

THE TREE SQUIRRELS OF KANSAS: ECOLOGY AND ECONOMIC IMPORTANCE. Robert L. Packard. Mis. Publ. Univ. Kansas Mus. Nat. Hist., Lawrence, 11: 1-67, pls.2, Aug.20, 1956.

ECOLOGY AND ECONOMICS OF THE WESTERN FOX SQUIRREL, SCIURUS NIGER RUFIVENTER (GEOFFREY) IN PAYNE COUNTY, OKLAHOMA. Richard L. Parker. MS thesis, Okla. A. and M. Coll., May, 1952.

THE RETURN OF THE CALIFORNIA GRAY SQUIRREL. Ernest A. Payne. Yosemite Nat. Notes, Stockton, vol.19, no.1, pp.1-3, Jan., 1940.

A GOLDEN-MANTLED GROUND SQUIRREL MOVES IN. Harold E. Perry. Yosemite Nat. Notes, Stockton, vol.19, no.4, p.30, Apr., 1940.

A NOTE ON THE SQUIRRELS OF YOSEMITE. Fraser Poole. Yosemite Nat. Notes, 28 (4): 28-30, Apr., 1949.

BELDING GROUND SQUIRREL IN NORTHWESTERN UTAH. Richard D. Porter. Jour. Mam., vol.31, no.2, p.198, May 25, 1950.

AUTUMN RECORD FOR MARMOT IN WESTERN MONTANA. Webster H. Ransom. Murrelet, vol.13, no.2, p.56, Mar.2, 1932.

EARLY SPRING RECORDS FOR GROUND SQUIRRELS IN WASHINGTON. Webster H. Ransom. Murrelet, Seattle, vol.23, no.2, p.62, Aug.14, 1942.

THE SQUIRRELS, CHIPMUNKS AND GOPHERS OF COLORADO. HOW TO KNOW THEM AND WHAT TO KNOW ABOUT THEM. Robert B. Rockwell. Publ. Colorado Mountain Club, Denver, no.5, pp.20, illus., 1916.

GROUND SQUIRREL STUDIES IN THE FOUR-RIVERS COUNTRY, WASHINGTON. Theo. H. Scheffer. Jour. Mam., 22 (3): 270-279, Aug., 1941.

PRESENT DISTRIBUTION OF THE DOUGLAS GROUND SQUIRREL IN WASHINGTON. Victor B. Scheffer, Walter W. Dalquest. Murrelet, Seattle, vol.20, no.2, May-Aug., pp.44, Aug.10, 1939.

THE MARMOTS OF HANNEGAN PASS. William T. Shaw. Nat. Hist., vol.25, pp. 169-177, Mar.-Apr. (May), 1925.

THE MARMOT OF VIRGINIA CANYON. Lloyd M. Smith. Yosemite Nat. Notes, Yosemite, vol.19, no.5, pp.33-34, May, 1940.

THE PRAIRIE DOG IN MONTANA. O. E. Stephl. Montana Extension Service, Montana State College, no.83, pp.3-31, illus., Mar., 1927.

SOME SIERRAN CHIPMUNKS. WITH NOTES ON PHOTOGRAPHY OF SMALL MAMMALS BY JOSEPH DIXON. Harry S. Swarth. Sierra Club Bull., vol.10, pp.401-413, 3 pls., 1919.

DISTRIBUTION OF MARMOTA MONAX IN THE MISSOURI VALLEY REGION. Myron Swenk. Jour. Mam., vol.19, no.3, pp.348-353, fig.1, Aug., 1938.

ON A NEW SUBSPECIES OF FLYING SQUIRREL FROM NEBRASKA. Myron H. Swenk. Univ. Studies, Lincoln, Nebraska, vol.15, no.2, pp.151-154, 1 pl., Apr., 1915.

THE FLYING SQUIRREL COLLECTED IN GARFIELD COUNTY, UTAH. Vasco M. Tanner. Great Basin Nat., Provo, vol.1, nos.3-4, p.26, June 30, 1940.

A NEW SPERMOPHILE FROM THE SAN JOAQUIN VALLEY, CALIFORNIA, WITH NOTES ON AMMOSPERMOPHILUS NELSONI NELSONI MERRIAM. Walter P. Taylor. Univ. Calif. Publ. Zool., vol.17, no.4, pp.15-20, fig.1, Oct.3, 1916.

A PRELIMINARY STUDY OF THE WESTERN FOX SQUIRREL, SCIURUS NIGER RUFIVENTER (GEOFFROY) IN MISSOURI. Harold V. Terrill. AM thesis, Univ. Mo., 1941.

OBSERVATIONS ON CHIPMUNKS AND MANTLED SQUIRRELS IN NORTHEASTERN CALIFORNIA. Lloyd Tevis, Jr. Amer. Midland Nat., Notre Dame, vol.53, no.1, pp.71-78, Jan., 1955.

MOBILITY AND RANGE OF THE SOUTHERN WOODCHUCK, MARMOTA M. MONAX (L.), IN SOUTHEAST IOWA. R. F. Trump. MS thesis, Iowa State Coll., 1943.

NOTES ON THE SOUTHERN WOODCHUCK IN MISSOURI. A. R. Twichell. Jour. Mam., 20 (1): 71-74, Feb., 1939.

A PRELIMINARY STUDY OF THE SOUTHERN WOODCHUCK, MARMOTA M. MONAX (L.) IN MISSOURI. A. R. Twichell. AM thesis, Univ. Mo., 1938.

GRAY EASTERN CHIPMUNK IN NEBRASKA. Ralph Velich. Jour. Mam., vol.28, no.2, pp.185-186, May 19, 1947.

NOTES ON THE NORTHERN TUFT-EARED SQUIRREL, SCIURUS ABERTI FERREUS TRU, IN COLORADO. Otis Wade. Amer. Midland Nat., vol.16, no.2, pp.201-202, Mar., 1935.

THE MARMOTS OF COLORADO. Edward R. Warren. Jour. Mam., vol.17, no.4, pp.392-398, map, Nov., 1936.

A NEW CHIPMUNK FROM COLORADO. Edward R. Warren. Proc. Biol. Soc. Wash., vol.22, pp.105-106, June 25, 1909.

A NEW SUBSPECIES OF MARMOT FROM COLORADO. Edward R. Warren. Jour. Mam., vol.15, no.1, pp.62-63, Feb., 1934.

GEOGRAPHIC DISTRIBUTION AND TAXONOMY OF THE CHIPMUNKS OF WYOMING. John A. White. Univ. Kansas Publ., Mus. Nat. Hist., Lawrence, vol.5, no.34, pp. 583-610, illus., Dec.1, 1953.

A NEW CHIPMUNK (GENUS EUTAMIAS) FROM THE BLACK HILLS. John A. White. Univ. Kansas Publ., Mus. Nat. Hist., Lawrence, vol.5, no.19, pp.259-262, Apr. 10, 1952.

GOLDEN-MANTLED MARMOT IN NORTHWESTERN MONTANA. Philip L. Wright, Clinton H. Conaway. Murrelet, Seattle, vol.31, no.2, p.32, Aug.31, 1950.

COLORADO SQUIRRELS. Lee E. Yeager, Lyndle Dunn. Colorado Outdoors Mag., 5 (4): 16-17, July-Aug., 1956.

FOX SQUIRRELS IN ASOTIN COUNTY, WASHINGTON. Charles F. Yocom. Murrelet, Seattle, vol.31, no.2, p.34, Aug.31, 1950.

WESTERN MEMBER OF SQUIRREL FAMILY. National Nature News, Washington, D.C., vol.2, no.21, pp.3-4, illus., May 23, 1938.

Young, Observations and Paternal Care Of

OBSERVATIONS ON THE YOUNG OF EUTAMIAS. Ernest S. Booth. Murrelet, Seattle, vol.23, no.3, p.84, Feb.15, 1943.

PINE SQUIRREL CARRYING YOUNG. Wallace B. Grange. Jour. Mam., vol.9, no.2, pp.151-152, May, 1928.

A GRAY SQUIRREL CARRIES ITS YOUNG. Robert T. Hatt. Jour. Mam., vol.8, no.3, pp.244-245, Aug., 1927.

JENNIFER'S BABIES. (RED SQUIRREL.) Phyllis Kelway. Game and Gun and the Angler's Monthly, London, vol.17, no.176, pp.216-220, illus., May, 1940.

A FLYING SQUIRREL MOTHER. (MOVING THE YOUNG.) Percy A. Morris. Nature Mag., vol.22, no.4, p.177, illus., Oct., 1933.

BROOD NESTS AND YOUNG OF TWO WESTERN CHIPMUNKS IN THE OLYMPIC MOUNTAINS OF WASHINGTON. William T. Shaw. Jour. Mam., 25 (3): 274-284, Aug., 1944.

A METHOD EMPLOYED BY A BLACK SQUIRREL IN CARRYING ITS YOUNG. L. L. Snyder. Jour. Mam., vol.4, no.1, p.59, Feb., 1923.

THE YOUNG OF THE CALIFORNIA GRAY SQUIRREL. Tracy I. Storer. Jour. Mam., vol.3, no.3, pp.188-189, Aug., 1922.

HOW A CHIPMUNK CARRIED HER YOUNG. Arthur Svihla, Ruth Dowell Svihla. Jour. Mam., vol.11, no.3, pp.314-315, Aug., 1930.

A FAMILY OF FLYING SQUIRRELS. Ruth Dowell Svihla. Jour. Mam., vol.11, no.2, pp.211-213, pl.12, May, 1930.

YOUNG GRAY SQUIRRELS AT HUDSON, WISCONSIN. Essie W. Williams. Jour. Mam., vol.4, no.2, p.128, May, 1923.

Geomyidae

THE NATURAL HISTORY OF POCKET GOPHERS. Austin Burness Barrington, Jr. MS thesis, Univ. Fla., 1940.

ABSTRACT OF RESULTS OF A STUDY OF THE GENERA GEOMYS AND THOMOMYS: WITH ADDENDA ON THE OSTEOLOGY OF GEOMYIDAE, AND ON THE HABIT OF GEOMYS TUZA. Elliott Coues. Rept. Maj. J.W. Powell's Explor. Colorado River of the west and its tributaries, 1869, 1870, 1871 and 1872, under direction Sec. Smithson. Inst., chap.15, pp.215-291, 1875.

THE PRAIRIE POCKET GOPHER THOMOMYS TALPOIDES. S. Criddle. Jour. Mam., 11: 265-80, 1930.

REMARKS ON POCKET GOPHERS, WITH SPECIAL REFERENCE TO THOMOMYS TALPOIDES. E. A. Goldman. Jour. Mam., 20 (2): 231-244, May, 1939.

METHODS OF ESTIMATING POCKET GOPHER POPULATIONS. Lloyd G. Ingles, Ronald Clothier, Louis A. Crawford. Jour. Wildlife Management, Menasha, vol.13, no. 3, pp.311-312, July, 1949.

DIPLOSTOMA BULBIVORIUM AND ORYCTOMYS BOTTAE. Gerrit S. Miller, Jr. Bull. Amer. Mus. Nat. Hist., vol.57, Apr. 28, 1893.

A REMARKABLE RAT. (POCKET GOPHER). Robert W. Shufeldt. Nat. Humane Review, vol.5, no.1, p.6, illus., Albany, New York, Jan., 1917.

POCKET GOPHERS. George Smokey. South Dakota Conserv. Digest, Pierre, vol. 11, no.6, p.10, June, 1944.

THE BIOLOGY OF THE POCKET GOPHER, THOMOMYS TALPOIDES IN MONTANA. C. A. Tryon. PhD thesis, Cornell Univ., 1942; Montana State College Agric. Exper. Station, Bozeman, Technical Bull.448, pp. 1-30, figs.13, Dec., 1947.

Anatomy

THE CRANIAL AND DENTAL CHARACTERS OF GEOMYIDAE. Elliott Coues. Bull. U.S. Geol. and Geog. Surv. Terr., no.2, ser.2, pp.83-90, May 14, 1895.

STUDIES ON THE MALE REPRODUCTIVE SYSTEM OF THE CALIFORNIA POCKET GOPHER (THOMOMYS BOTTAE NAVUS MERRIAM). W. C. Gunther. Amer. Mid. Nat., Notre Dame, vol.55, no.1, pp.1-40, illus., Jan., 1956.

MORPHOLOGY OF THE POCKET GOPHER MAMMALIAN GENUS THOMOMYS. John Eric Hill. Univ. Calif. Publ. Zool., vol. 42, no.2, pp.81-172, figs.26, Aug.25, 1937.

THE RETRACTOR MUSCLE OF THE POUCH IN THE GEOMYIDAE. John Eric Hill. Science, n.s., vol.81, no.2093, p. 160, Feb.8, 1935.

THE ABSORPTION OF THE PUBIC SYMPHYSIS OF THE POCKET GOPHER, GEOMYS BURSARIUS (SHAW). Frederick L. Hisaw. Amer. Nat., vol.58, no.654, pp.93-96, Jan.-Feb., 1924.

THE INFLUENCE OF THE OVARY ON THE RESORPTION OF THE PUBIC BONES OF THE POCKET GOPHER, GEOMYS BURSARIUS (SHAW). Frederick L. Hisaw. Jour. Exper. Zool., vol.42, pp.411-433, 4 pls., 1925.

THE FETAL MEMBRANES OF THE POCKET GOPHER, ILLUSTRATING AN INTERMEDIATE TYPE OF RODENT MEMBRANE FORMATION. H. W. Mossman, F. L. Hisaw. Amer. Jour. Anat., Phila., vol.66, no.3, pp.367-391, figs.3, pls.5, May 15, 1940.

STUDIES ON THE MUSCLES OF THE HEAD, NECK, AND PECTORAL APPENDAGES OF GEOMYS BURSARIUS. Edward Eugene Orcutt. Jour. Mam., vol.21, no.1, pp.37-52, figs.18, Feb.14, 1940.

Canada

A REVISION OF THE POCKET GOPHER THOMOMYS TALPOIDES IN BRITISH COLUMBIA. Walter B. Johnstone. Can. Field-Nat., 68 (4): 155-164, illus., 2 pl., Oct.-Dec., 1954 (Sept., 1955).

THE PRAIRIE POCKET GOPHER IN MANITOBA. H. H. Pittman. Canadian Field-Nat., vol.40, pp.60-62, illus., Mar. 29, 1926.

THE MISSISSIPPI VALLEY POCKET GOPHER (GEOMYS BURSARIUS SHAW) IN MANITOBA. J. Dewey Soper. Canadian Field-Nat., Sutton West, vol.58, no.3, pp.71-72, May-June, 1944.

Captivity

HOUSING OF THE POCKET GOPHER IN CAPTIVITY. George H. Hanley. Jour. Mam., vol.25, no.4, pp.407-408, Dec.12, 1944.

NOTES ON A POCKET GOPHER IN CAPTIVITY. Charles Eugene Johnson. Jour. Mam., vol.7, no.1, pp.35-37, Feb., 1926.

Central America

DESCRIPTION OF A NEW SPECIES OF GEOMYS FROM COSTA RICA. J. A. Allen. Bull. Amer. Mus. Nat. Hist., vol.5, pp. 337-338, Dec.16, 1893.

A NEW POCKET GOPHER (HETEROGEOMYS) FROM BRITISH HONDURAS. William Henry Burt. Occas. Papers Mus. Zool. Univ. Michigan, no.365, pp.1-2, Dec.16, 1937.

A NEW POCKET GOPHER OF THE GENUS ORTHOGEOMYS FROM GUATEMALA. E. W. Nelson, E. A. Goldman. Proc. Biol. Soc. Washington, vol.44, pp.105-107, Oct. 17, 1931.

Control

DESTROYING POCKET GOPHERS. W. B. Bell. Bull. Green Section U.S. Golf Asso., vol.5, pp.36-38, Feb.16, 1925.

POCKET-GOPHER CONTROL. W. E. Crouch. U.S. Dept. Agric., Farmers' Bull. no.1709, pp.ii plus 1-21, figs.17, Sept., 1933; USDI, Cons. Bull.23, 20 pp., 1942.

A METHOD OF POISONING POCKET GOPHERS. Ralph De Ong. Univ. Calif. Publ., Agric. Exper. Sta., Bull.no.281, pp.14-15, fig.4, July, 1917.

CONTROL OF THE POCKET GOPHER IN CALIFORNIA. Joseph Dixon. Univ. Calif. Publ. Agric. Exper. Station, Bull.no.340, pp.337-350, figs.5, Feb., 1922.

POISONING POCKET GOPHERS. Clarence E. Mickel. Univ. Minnesota, Agric. Exten. Div., circ.14, pp.4, June, 1923.

ERADICATION OF POCKET GOPHERS. COMPARATIVE FIELD TESTS DEMONSTRATE BEST POISONS, BAITS, AND DOSAGES FOR PRACTICAL GOPHER CONTROL. Milton A. Miller. Calif. Agric. Calif. College Agric. Exper. Station, Berkeley, vol.4, no.12, Dec., 1950.

SIZE OF BAIT FOR POCKET GOPHER CONTROL. Milton A. Miller. Jour. Wildl. Mgt., 15 (1): 52-68, Jan., 1951.

CONTROLLING POCKET GOPHERS. H. L. Parten. Univ. Minn., Agr. Ext. Div., Ext. Folder 75, 6 pp., June, 1939.

BAITS VS. GAS FOR GOPHERS. H. H. Slawson. Pest Control, 22 (12): 16, Dec., 1954.

GAS CHAMBER FOR GOPHERS. Reclam. Era, 38 (2): 27, Feb., 1952.

(THE PLAGUE OF THE POCKET GOPHER AND WAYS TO COMBAT IT IN THE UNITED STATES OF MEXICO.) La plaga de las tuzas y manera de combatirlas Estados Unidos Mexicanos Secret. Agric. y Fomento Ofic. Fed. Defensa Agric. Bol. Divulg., vol.9, pp.1-16, figs.6, 1928.

POCKET GOPHER CONTROL. US F&WS, Wildl. Leafl.340, 1-6 pp., illus., May, 1952.

Ecology

INTERRELATIONSHIPS BETWEEN THE POCKET GOPHER AND LAND USE. Helmut K. Buechner. Jour. Mam., 23 (3): 346-348, Aug., 1942.

POCKET GOPHERS SPREAD CANADA THISTLE. J. B. Cook. Bull. Dept. Agric. Calif., Sacramento, vol.28, no.2, pp.142-143, figs.2, Feb., 1939.

RELATION OF SIZE OF POCKET GOPHERS TO SOIL AND ALTITUDE. W. B. Davis. Jour. Mam., 19: 338-42, 1938.

DISTRIBUTION OF POCKET GOPHERS (GEOMYS BREVICEPS) IN RELATION TO SOILS. W. B. Davis, R. R. Ramsey, J. M. Arendale, Jr. Jour. Mam., vol.19, no. 4, pp.412-418, figs.2, Nov.14, 1938.

THE POCKET GOPHER IN RELATION TO SOIL EROSION ON MOUNTAIN RANGE. Lincoln Ellison. Ecology, 27 (2): 101-114, Apr., 1946.

INFLUENCE OF POCKET GOPHERS ON VEGETATION OF SUBALPINE GRASSLAND IN CENTRAL UTAH. Lincoln Ellison, C. M. Aldous. Ecology, New York, vol. 33, no.2, pp.177-186, Apr., 1952.

OUTLINE FOR AN ECOLOGICAL LIFE HISTORY OF POCKET GOPHERS AND OTHER FOSSORIAL MAMMALS. Walter E. Howard, Lloyd G. Ingles. Ecology, vol.32, no.3, pp.537-544, July, 1951.

THE ECOLOGY OF THE MOUNTAIN POCKET GOPHER, THOMOMYS MONTICOLA. Lloyd G. Ingles. Ecology, Lancaster, vol.33, no.1, pp.87-95, Jan., 1952.

GROUND WATER AND SNOW AS FACTORS AFFECTING THE SEASONAL DISTRIBUTION OF POCKET GOPHERS, THOMOMYS MONTICOLA. Lloyd G. Ingles. Jour. Mam., 30 (4): 343-350, Nov., 1949.

THE CONTIGUITY OF THE RANGES OF TWO SUBSPECIES OF POCKET GOPHERS. Lloyd G. Ingles, Normand J. Biglione. Evolution, vol.6, no.2, pp.204-207, June, 1952.

POCKET GOPHER AND ECOLOGICAL SUCCESSION IN THE WENAS REGION OF WASHINGTON. Earl J. Larrison. Murrelet, 23 (2): 34-41, May-Aug., 1942.

AN ECOLOGICAL STUDY OF THE POCKET GOPHER (THOMOMYS TALPOIDES TENELLUS GOLDMAN) IN THE JACKSON HOLE REGION OF WYOMING. William H. Laycock. Wyo. Range Mgt., Issue no.64, 8 pp., mimeo., 1953; Abs. of this MS thesis, U. Wyo., 1953, in Jour. Range Mgt., 6 (6): 461-462, Nov., 1953.

THE WAY OF A SNAKE WITH A GOPHER. (BULL SNAKE CAPTURES POCKET GOPHER.) Albert P. Morse. Copeia, no. 164, pp.71-72, Sept., 1927.

AN ECOLOGICAL STUDY OF THE POCKET GOPHER IN A SANDY LOAM AREA IN ELLIS COUNTY, KANSAS. Benjamin D. Mosier. MS thesis, Ft. Hays Kansas State Coll., 1947.

POCKET GOPHERS AND SEEDLINGS OF RED FIR. Lloyd Tevis, Jr. Ecology, 37 (2): 379-381, Apr., 1956.

Economic Importance

THOMOMYS THE ENGINEER--FRIEND OR FOE? Lee R. Dice. Amer. Forests, 45 (10): 512, Oct., 1939.

THOMOMYS THE ENGINEER. (DAMAGE DONE TO FIELDS, ORCHARDS, AND MOUNTAIN MEADOWS.) Ira N. Gabrielson. Amer. Forests, 44 (10): 453-454, 478-479, Oct., 1938.

THE PESKY POCKET GOPHER. Walter E. Howard. Spreckels Sugar Beet Bull., 16 (3): 21-22, illus., May-June, 1952.

TESTS OF POCKET GOPHERS GNAWING ELECTRIC CABLES. Walter E. Howard. Jour. Wildlife Management, Ithaca, vol.17, no.3, pp.296-399, illus., July, 1953.

POCKET GOPHERS AS ENEMIES OF TREES. David E. Lantz. Yearbook U.S. Dept. Agric., 1909, pp.209-218, fig.1, pls.8-10, 1910.

THE POCKET GOPHER IN RELATION TO YELLOW PINE REPRODUCTION. A. W. Moore. Jour. Mam., 24 (2): 271-272, May, 1943.

THE DALLES POCKET GOPHER AND ITS INFLUENCE ON FORAGE PRODUCTION OF OREGON MOUNTAIN MEADOWS. A. W. Moore, Elbert H. Reid. USDA, Cir.884, 36 pp., Aug., 1951.

Evolution

GEOGRAPHY AND EVOLUTION IN THE POCKET GOPHER. J. Grinnell. Univ. California Chronicle, July, 1926, pp.247-262, 1 col. pl., 1926.

GEOGRAPHY AND EVOLUTION IN THE POCKET GOPHERS OF CALIFORNIA. Joseph Grinnell. Smithsonian Rep., 1926, publ.2894, pp.343-355, 1 pl., Sept., 1927.

PARALLEL RADIATION AMONG THE GEOMYOID RODENTS. Albert Elmer Wood. Jour. Mam., vol.18, no.2, pp.171-176, May 14, 1937.

Fossils

THE WHITE RIVER OLIGOCENE RODENT, DIPLOLOPHUS. Erwin Hinckley Barbour. Bull. Nebraska State Mus., Lincoln, vol.2, no.3, pp.29-36, figs.14, Sept., 1939.

THE POCKET GOPHER, GEOMYS QUINNI MCGREW, IN THE REXROAD FAUNA, BLANCAN AGE, OF SOUTHWESTERN KANSAS. Dorothea S. Franzen. Trans. Kansas Acad. Sci., vol.50, no.1, pp.55-59, 1947.

AN ADDITIONAL SPECIMEN OF THE RODENT DIKKOMYS FROM THE MIOCENE OF NEBRASKA. Edwin C. Galbreath. Trans. Kansas Acad. Sci., Topeka, vol.51, no.3, pp.316-317, fig.1, 1948.

THOMOMYS TALPOIDES (RICHARDSON) FROM A LATE PLEISTOCENE DEPOSIT IN KANSAS. Claude W. Hibbard. Jour. Mam., vol.32, no.2, pp.229-230, May 21, 1951.

A NEW RODENT FROM SUBSURFACE STRATUM IN BEE COUNTY, TEXAS. Claude W. Hibbard, John A. Wilson. Jour. Paleontol., Menasha, vol.24, no.5, pp.621-623, illus., Sept., 1950.

DIPLOLOPHUS, A NEW GENUS OF RODENTS. (MIDDLE OLIGOCENE, CHERRY CREEK, NEBRASKA. Edward Leffingwell Troxell. Jour. Sci., ser.5, vol.5, pp.157-159, 5 figs., Feb., 1923.

SECOND FIND OF THOMOMYS TALPOIDES FROM LATE PLEISTOCENE IN KANSAS. Joseph H. Waters. Jour. Mam., 37 (4): 540-542, Jan.9, 1957.

GEOMYID RODENTS FROM THE MIDDLE TERTIARY. Albert Elmer Wood. Amer. Mus. Novitates no.866, pp.31, figs.33, July 2, 1936.

Growth

GROWTH RATE OF NAILS ON ADULT POCKET GOPHERS. Walter E. Howard. Jour. Mam., vol.34, no.3, pp.394-396, 1 table, Aug.14, 1953.

RATE OF EXTRUSIVE GROWTH OF INCISORS OF POCKET GOPHERS. Walter E. Howard, Melvin E. Smith. Jour. Mam., vol.33, no.4, pp.485-487, 1 table, Nov.19, 1952.

FIELD OBSERVATIONS ON THE GROWTH OF YOUNG MOUNTAIN POCKET GOPHERS. Lloyd G. Ingles. Murrelet, vol.30, no.2, p.35, May-Aug., 1949.

THE ABNORMAL GROWTH OF THE MOLAR TEETH AND THE FRONT CLAWS OF AN ADULT POCKET GOPHER, GEOMYS BURSARIUS (SHAW). Otis Wade, Paul T. Gilbert. Amer. Midland Naturalist, vol. 16, no.6, pp.960-961, figs.4, 1935.

Habits and Behavior

THE FEEDING HABITS OF POCKET GOPHERS (THOMOMYS TALPOIDES MOOREI) IN THE HIGH MOUNTAIN RANGES OF CENTRAL UTAH. C. M. Aldous. Jour. Mam., 32 (1): 84-87, Feb., 1951.

POCKET GOPHER FOOD CACHES IN CENTRAL UTAH. C. M. Aldous. Jour. Wildlife Management, Menasha, vol.9, no. 4, pp.327-328, Oct., 1945.

THE ORIGIN OF MIMA MOUND (HOG-WALLOW) MICRORELIEF IN THE FAR WESTERN STATES. (POCKET GOPHERS.) Rodney J. Arkley, Herrick C. Brown. Proc. Soil Sci. Soc. Amer., vol.18, no.2, pp.195-199, Apr., 1954.

TUNNELERS EXTRAORDINARY. (POCKET GOPHER.) Bennie Bengtson. Fauna, Phila., vol.6, no.4, pp.110-111, Dec., 1944.

ACTIONS OF THE POCKET GOPHER (GEOMYS BURSARIUS). W. J. Breckenridge. Jour. Mam., vol.10, no.4, pp.336-339, Nov., 1929.

NOCTURNAL WANDERINGS OF THE CALIFORNIA POCKET GOPHER. Harold C. Bryant. Univ. Cal. Publ. Zool., vol.12, no.2, pp.25-29, fig.1, Nov.20, 1913.

THE ORIGIN OF THE MIMA MOUNDS OF WESTERN WASHINGTON. (FORMED BY BURROWING OF POCKET GOPHERS.) Walter W. Dalquest, Victor B. Scheffer. Jour. Geol., Chicago, vol.50, no.1, pp.68-84, figs.8, Jan.-Feb., 1942.

SOME HABITS OF THE POCKET GOPHER, GEOMYS BREVICEPS BREVICEPS. Pennoyer F. English. Jour. Mam., vol.13, no.2, pp.126-132, pls.9-10, May, 1932.

ON THE HABITS OF THE POUCHED RAT, OR SALAMANDER, (GEOMYS PINETI,) OF GEORGIA. William Gesner. Smithsonian Institution, Annual Report, 1860, pp.431-433, diagr., 1861.

FORAGE HABITS OF POCKET GOPHER. E. Raymond Hall. California Fish and Game, vol.12, p.152, July, 1926.

RODENT MINERS. John Eric Hill. Natural History, New York, vol.53, no.1, p.21, illus., Jan., 1944.

FLORIDA POCKET-GOPHER BURROWS AND THEIR ARTHROPOD INHABITANTS. T. H. Hubbell, C. C. Goff. Proc. Florida Acad. Sci., 1939, Gainesville, vol.4, pp.127-166, figs.2, Aug., 1940.

THE LITTLE PLOWMAN. (MOUNTAIN POCKET GOPHER.) Lloyd G. Ingles. Nat. Hist., 63 (3): 134-139, illus., Mar., 1954.

THOMOMYS AS BURROWERS IN THE SNOW. William H. Marshall. Jour. Mam., vol.22, no.2, pp.196-197, figs.2, May 14, 1941.

NATURAL MOUNDS OF NORTHEASTERN TEXAS, SOUTHERN ARKANSAS, AND NORTHERN LOUISIANA. Frank A. Melton. The Hopper, Oklahoma Geol. Survey, Norman, vol.14, no.7, pp.87-121 (Mimeogr), illus.

SEASONAL TRENDS IN BURROWING OF POCKET GOPHERS (THOMOMYS). Milton A. Miller. Jour. Mam., vol.29, no.1, pp. 38-44, figs.2, pl.1, Feb.13, 1948.

ABUNDANCE AND DIGGING RATE OF POCKET GOPHERS, GEOMYS BURSARIUS. Carl O. Mohr, William P. Mohr. Ecology, vol.17, no.2, pp.325-327, Apr., 1936.

ON THE HABITS OF THE GOPHER OF ILLINOIS (GEOMYS BURSARIUS). J. B. Parvin. Smithsonian Institution, Washington, Annual report, 1854, pp.293-294, 1855.

POCKET GOPHERS AS ARCHITECTS OF MIMA (PIMPLE) MOUNDS OF THE WESTERN UNITED STATES. W. Armstrong Price. Texas Jour. Sci., Huntsville, vol. 1, no.1, pp.1-17, illus., Mar., 1949.

A MULTIPLE CATCH OF CRATOGEOMYS. Robert J. Russell. Jour. Mam., vol.35, no.1, pp.121-122, Feb.10, 1954.

EXCAVATION OF A RUNWAY OF THE POCKET GOPHER (GEOMYS BURSARIUS). Theo. H. Scheffer. Trans. Kansas Acad. Sci., 43: 473-478, 1940.

HABITS AND ECONOMIC STATUS OF THE POCKET GOPHERS. Theo. H. Scheffer. Tech. Bull.224, U.S. Dept. Agric., pp.26, pls.8, Jan., 1931.

MOUND CONSTRUCTION OF THE POCKET GOPHER. Theo. H. Scheffer. Murrelet, Seattle, vol.29, no.1, pp.9-10, pls.1-2, Jan.-Apr., 1948.

IS MIMA MOUND MICRORELIEF CONFINED TO WESTERN NORTH AMERICA? Victor B. Scheffer. Invest. Zool. Chil., 2 (6): 89-94, illus., Oct., 1954.

THE MYSTERY OF THE MIMA MOUNDS. Victor B. Scheffer. Sci. Monthly, 65 (4): 283-294, Oct., 1947.

A POCKET GOPHER (GEOMYS LUTESCENS) TRAVELS BACKWARD. Ward M. Sharp. Jour. Mam., vol.24, no.1, p.99, Feb.20, 1943.

A BURROW OF THE POCKET GOPHER (GEOMYS BURSARIUS) IN EASTERN KANSAS. Charles F. Smith. Trans. Kansas Acad. Sci., vol.51, no.3, pp.313-315, 1948.

FORMATION OF DISCLIMAXES IN THE ALPINE TUNDRA BY THOMOMYS FOSSOR. John J. Sperry. Trans. Texas Acad. Sci., Houston, vol.26, p.55, 1943.

FOOD HABITS OF A POCKET GOPHER. Otis Wade. Jour. Mam., vol.8, no.4, pp. 310-311, Nov., 1927.

A GOPHER AT WORK. Edward R. Warren. Jour. Mam., vol.16, no.2, p.135, May, 1935.

NOTES ON POCKET GOPHERS. Edward R. Warren. Jour. Mam., vol.18, no.4, pp. 473-477, figs.3, Nov., 1937.

Mexico

THE POCKET GOPHERS (GENUS THOMOMYS) OF COAHUILA, MEXICO. Rollin H. Baker. Univ. Kansas Publ., Mus. Nat. Hist., Lawrence, vol.5, no.28, pp.499-514, June 1, 1953.

DESCRIPTIONS OF TWO SUBSPECIES OF POCKET GOPHER (THOMOMYS BOTTAE) FROM SONORA. Seth B. Benson, Daniel F. Tillotson. Proc. Biol. Soc. Wash., vol. 52, pp.151-153, Oct.11, 1939.

A NEW POCKET GOPHER FROM LOWER CALIFORNIA, MEXICO. (THOMOMYS BOTTAE LITORIS.) William Henry Burt. Occas. Papers Mus. Zool., Univ. Michigan, Ann Arbor, no.424, pp.3, Nov.29, 1940.

A NEW POCKET GOPHER (THOMOMYS) FROM SOUTHERN SONORA, MEXICO. William Henry Burt. Occas. Papers Mus. Zool., Univ. Michigan, no.344, pp.2, Jan.5, 1937.

A NEW POCKET GOPHER OF THE GENUS CRATOGEOMYS FROM MEXICO. E. A. Goldman. Proc. Washington Acad. Sci., vol.27, no.9, pp.402-404, Sept.15, 1937.

TWO NEW POCKET GOPHERS FROM LOWER CALIFORNIA. (THOMOMYS BOTTAE INCOMPTUS, T.B. IMITABILIS.) E. A. Goldman. Proc. Biol. Soc. Wash., vol.52, pp.29-32, Mar.11, 1939.

TWO NEW POCKET GOPHERS OF THE GENUS HETEROGEOMYS FROM MEXICO. E. A. Goldman. Jour. Washington Acad. Sci., vol.29, no.4, pp.175-177, Apr.15, 1939.

A NEW POCKET GOPHER OF THE GENUS HETEROGEOMYS FROM TAMAULIPAS. George G. Goodwin. Amer. Mus. Novitates, New York, no.1620, pp.3, May 4, 1953.

A NEW POCKET GOPHER FROM LOWER CALIFORNIA, MEXICO. (THOMOMYS BOTTAE LUCIDUS.) E. Raymond Hall. Proc. Biol. Soc. Washington, vol.45, pp.67-70, Apr.2, 1932.

A NEW POCKET GOPHER (THOMOMYS) AND A NEW SPINY POCKET MOUSE (LIOMYS) FROM MICHOACAN, MEXICO. E. Raymond Hall, Bernardo Villa R. Univ. Kansas Publ., Lawrence, vol.1, no. 14, pp.249-256, figs.6, July 26, 1948.

A NEW SUBSPECIES OF POCKET GOPHER FROM SONORA, MEXICO. (THOMOMYS BOTTAE VANROSSEMI.) Laurence M. Huey. Trans. San Diego Soc. Nat. Hist., vol.8, no.1, pp.1-2, Aug.10, 1934.

THE POCKET GOPHERS OF BAJA CALIFORNIA, MEXICO, WITH DESCRIPTIONS OF NINE NEW FORMS. Laurence M. Huey. Trans. San Diego Soc. Nat. Hist., vol.10, no.14, pp.245-268, 1 map, Aug.31, 1945.

THREE NEW RACES OF POCKET GOPHERS (THOMOMYS) FROM BAJA CALIFORNIA, MEXICO. Laurence M. Huey. Trans. San Diego Soc. Nat. Hist., vol.11, no.4, pp.53-56, Jan.31, 1949.

FOUR NEW POCKET GOPHERS OF THE GENUS HETEROGEOMYS FROM MEXICO. E. W. Nelson, E. A. Goldman. Proc. Biol. Soc. Washington, vol.42, pp.147-152, Mar.30, 1929.

POCKET GOPHERS OF THE GENUS THOMOMYS OF MEXICAN MAINLAND AND BORDERING TERRITORY. E. W. Nelson, E. A. Goldman. Jour. Mam., vol.15, no.2, pp.105-124, May, 1934.

FOUR NEW POCKET GOPHERS OF THE GENUS CRATOGEOMYS FROM JALISCO, MEXICO. Robert J. Russell. Univ. Kansas Publ., Mus. Nat. Hist., vol.5, no. 31, pp.535-542, Oct.15, 1953.

A NEW SPECIES OF POCKET GOPHER GENUS PAPPOGEOMYS FROM JALISCO, MEXICO. Robert J. Russell. Univ. Kansas Publ., Mus. Nat. Hist., 9 (11): 357-361, Jan.21, 1957.

GEOGRAPHIC VARIATION IN THE POCKET GOPHER, CRATOGEOMYS CASTANOPS, IN COAHUILA, MEXICO. Robert J. Russell, Rollin H. Baker. Univ. Kansas Publ., Mus. Nat. Hist., Lawrence, vol.7, no.12, pp. 591-608, Mar.15, 1955.

DIAGNOSIS OF A NEW MEXICAN GEOMYS. Oldfield Thomas. Ann. Mag. Nat. Hist. (6), vol.10, no.56, pp.196-197, Aug., 1892.

Parasites

A NEW SUBSPECIES OF FOXELLA IGNOTA (BAKER) FROM CALIFORNIA (SIPHONAPTERA: DELICHOPSYLLIDAE). (FROM THOMOMYS ALTIVALLIS.) G. F. Augustson. Bull. S. Calif. Acad. Sci., 41 (2): 69-71, May-Aug., 1942.

A STUDY OF THE HELMINTH PARASITES OF THE POCKET GOPHERS OF WOODS, ALFALFA, GRANT AND MARSHALL COUNTIES, OKLAHOMA. Gladys L. Burnham. MS thesis, Univ. Okla., 1952.

IXODES HOLDENRIEDI, A NEW SPECIES OF TICK FROM A POCKET GOPHER IN CALIFORNIA (ACARINA, IXODIDAE). R. A. Cooley. Pan-Pac. Ent., 22 (3): 103-104, July, 1946.

A NEW FLEA FROM THE POCKET GOPHER. R. B. Eads, G. C. Menzies. Jour. Parasitology, Lancaster, vol.35, no.2, pp.171-174, Apr., 1949.

CUTEREBRA THOMOMURIS SP. NOV., A WARBLE FROM THE POCKET GOPHER, THOMOMYS TALPOIDES (RODENTIA: GEOMYIDAE). William L. Jellison. Jour. Parasitol., Lancaster, vol.35, no.5, pp. 482-486, figs.3, Oct., 1949.

A NEW DILEPIDID CESTODE, CATENOTAENIA LINSDALEI, FROM A POCKET GOPHER IN CALIFORNIA. Allen McIntosh. Proc. Helminth. Soc. Wash., 8 (2): 60-62, July, 1941.

DESCRIPTIONS OF THREE NEW SPECIES OF DACTYLOPSYLLA JORDAN AND ONE NEW SUBSPECIES OF FOXELLA WAGNER, WITH RECORDS OF OTHER SPECIES IN THE GENERA (SIPHONAPTERA). ( NEW FORMS FROM POCKET GOPHERS.) F. M. Prince. Can. Ent., 77 (1): 15-20, Jan., 1945.

NOTE ON A NEW SPECIES OF COCCIDIA FROM THE POCKET GOPHER (GEOMYS BURSARIUS SHAW). L. V. Skidmore. Jour. Parasitology, vol.15, pp.183-184, 1 fig., Mar., 1929.

Pelage and Coloration

DICHROMATISM AND ALBINISM IN THOMOMYS TALPOIDES CLUSIUS. W. L. Burnett. Jour. Mam., vol.6, no.2, p.129, May, 1925.

PIGMENTAL VARIATIONS IN POPULATIONS OF POCKET GOPHERS. Lloyd G. Ingles. Evolution, Lancaster, vol.4, no.4, pp.353-357, fig.1, Dec., 1950.

COLOR MUTATIONSIN A SMALL, PARTIALLY ISOLATED POPULATION OF POCKET GOPHERS (GEOMYS BREVICEPS). W. H. McCarley. Jour. Mam., vol.32, no.3, pp.338-341, illus., Aug.23, 1951.

MOLT IN THE POCKET GOPHER, THOMOMYS BOTTAE. G. Victor Morejohn, Walter E. Howard. Jour. Mam., 37 (2): 201-213, illus., June 9, 1956.

COLOR ABERRATIONS IN THE POCKET GOPHER AND THEIR PROBABLE GENETIC EXPLANATION. Tracy Irwin Storer, Paul Wallace Gregory. Jour. Mam., vol. 15, no.4, pp.300-312, tables 2, Nov., 1934.

Reproductive Biology

NOTES ON THE YOUNG OF THE SOUTHERN POCKET GOPHER. A. W. Anthony. Jour. Mam., vol.4, no.2, pp.126-127, May, 1923.

DESCRIPTION OF BIRTH AND YOUNG OF THE POCKET GOPHER, GEOMYS FLORIDANUS. B. A. Barrington, Jr. Jour. Mam., vol.23, no.4, pp.428-430, fig.1, Nov.14, 1942.

THE BREEDING HABITS OF THOMOMYS BOTTAE IN ORANGE COUNTY, CALIFORNIA. R. M. Bond. Jour. Mam., Balto., vol.27, no.2, pp.172-174, fig.1, May 14, 1946.

ON THE BREEDING HABITS OF POCKET GOPHERS. William Henry Burt. Murrelet, vol.14, no.2, p.42, May, 1933.

THE BREEDING SEASON OF THE POCKET GOPHER IN CALIFORNIA. Joseph Dixon. Jour. Mam., vol.10, no.4, pp.327-328, pl. 25, Nov., 1929.

SOME DIETARY EFFECTS ON THE ESTROUS CYCLE OF THE FEMALE CALIFORNIA POCKET GOPHER, THOMOMYS BOTTAE NAVUS MERRIAM. W. C. Gunther. Proc. Indiana Acad. Sci., 66: 331-336, 1957.

EXTERNAL CHARACTERS OF NEWBORN POCKET GOPHERS. John Eric Hill. Jour. Mam., vol.15, no.3, pp.244-245, Aug.10, 1934.

SOME NOTES CONCERNING THE BREEDING HABITS OF THOMOMYS TOWNSENDI, OBSERVED NEAR VALE, MALHEUR COUNTY, OREGON, DURING THE SPRING OF 1921. Everett E. Horn. Jour. Mam., vol.4, no.1, pp.37-38, pl.7, Feb., 1923.

REPRODUCTIVE RATES AND CYCLES IN THE POCKET GOPHER. Milton A. Miller. Jour. Mam., 27 (4): 355-358, Nov., 1946.

THE THECAL GLAND AND ITS RELATION TO THE REPRODUCTIVE CYCLE. A STUDY OF THE CYCLIC CHANGES IN THE OVARY OF THE POCKET GOPHER, GEOMYS BURSARIUS (SHAW). H. W. Mossman. Amer. Jour. Anat., vol.61, no. 2, pp.289-319, figs.2, pls.4, July 15, 1937.

BREEDING HABITS AND ECONOMIC RELATIONS OF THE DALLES POCKET GOPHER. H. M. Wight. Jour. Mam., vol. 11, no.1, pp.40-48, Feb., 1930.

NOTES ON YOUNG POCKET GOPHERS. John E. Wood. Jour. Mam., 36 (1): 143-144, Feb.25, 1955.

REPRODUCTIVE PATTERN OF THE POCKET GOPHER. John E. Wood. MS thesis, A. and M. Coll. Texas, 1947; Jour. Mam., 30 (1): 36-44, Feb., 1949.

Size and Weight

SIZE CHARACTERISTICS OF THE SACRAMENTO VALLEY POCKET GOPHER (THOMOMYS BOTTAE NAVUS MERRIAM). Milton A. Miller. Jour. Mam., 33 (4): 442-456, graphs, Nov., 1952.

WEIGHTS OF POCKET GOPHERS. Clarence F. Smith. Jour. Mam., 21 (2): 220, May, 1940.

A STUDY OF LOCAL SIZE VARIATIONS IN THE PRAIRIE POCKET-GOPHER (GEOMYS BURSARIUS), WITH DESCRIPTION OF A NEW SUBSPECIES FROM NEBRASKA. Myron H. Swenk. Missouri Valley Fauna, Lincoln, Nebr., no.1, pp.1-8, Dec.5, 1939.

Taxonomy

DESCRIPTIONS OF FOUR NEW SPECIES OF THOMOMYS, WITH REMARKS ON OTHER SPECIES OF THE GENUS. J. A. Allen. Bull. Amer. Mus. Nat. Hist., vol.5, pp. 47-63, pl.1, Apr.28, 1893.

MONOGRAPHIC REVISION OF THE POCKET GOPHERS, FAMILY GEOMYIDAE (EXCLUSIVE OF THE GENUS THOMOMYS). J. A. Allen. Science, n.s., vol.1, pp.241-243, Mar.1, 1895.

NOTE ON MACROGEOMYS CHERRIEI (ALLEN). J. A. Allen. Bull. Amer. Mus. Nat. Hist., vol.8, pp.45-46, pl.1, Apr.15, 1896.

IDENTITY OF THOMOMYS UMBRINUS (RICHARDSON). Vernon Bailey. Proc. Biol. Soc. Wash., vol.19, pp.3-6, Jan.29, 1906.

REVISION OF THE POCKET GOPHERS OF THE GENUS THOMOMYS. Vernon Bailey. North American Fauna, no.39, pp.136, figs.10, pls.8, Nov.15, 1915.

TWO NEW POCKET GOPHERS OF THE GENUS THOMOMYS. Vernon Bailey. Proc. Biol. Soc. Wash., vol.23, pp.79-80, May 4, 1910.

THE TAXONOMIC STATUS OF GEOMYS BREVICEPS TEXENSIS MERRIAM AND GEOMYS BURSARIUS LLANENSIS BAILEY. Rollin H. Baker. Jour. Mam., vol.31, no. 3, pp.348-349, Aug.21, 1950.

THE TAXONOMIC STATUS OF THE POCKET GOPHERS, GEOMYS BURSARIUS AND GEOMYS BREVICEPS. Rollin H. Baker, Bryan P. Glass. Proc. Biol. Soc. Wash., vol.64, pp.55-58, Apr.13, 1951.

A SUBSTITUTE NAME FOR THOMOMYS BOTTAE OCCIPITALIS BENSON AND TILLOTSON. Seth B. Benson, Daniel F. Tillotson. Proc. Biol. Soc. Wash., vol.53, p.93, June 28, 1940.

SUBSTITUTE NAME FOR GEOMYS PERSONATUS MINOR DAVIS. W. B. Davis. Jour. Mam., vol.24, no.4, p.508, Nov.17, 1943.

VARIATIONS IN TOWNSEND POCKET GOPHERS. W. B. Davis. Jour. Mam., vol.18, no.2, pp.145-158, figs.5, May, 1937.

A NEW POCKET GOPHER OF THE GENUS ZYGOGEOMYS. E. A. Goldman. Proc. Biol. Soc. Wash., vol.51, pp.211-212, Dec. 23, 1938.

NEW POCKET GOPHERS OF THE GENUS THOMOMYS. E. A. Goldman. Jour. Wash. Acad. Sci., vol.26, no.3, pp.111-120, Mar. 15, 1936.

THE POCKET GOPHERS OF THE GENUS PAPPOGEOMYS. E. A. Goldman. Jour. Mam., vol.20, no.1, pp.93-98, Feb.14, 1939.

REMARKS ON POCKET GOPHERS, WITH SPECIAL REFERENCE TO THOMOMYS TALPOIDES. E. A. Goldman. Jour. Mam., vol.20, no.2, pp.231-244, May 14, 1939.

REVIEW OF THE POCKET GOPHERS OF THE GENUS PLATYGEOMYS. E. A. Goldman. Jour. Mam., vol.20, no.1, pp. 87-93, Feb.14, 1939.

STATUS OF THREE POCKET GOPHERS OF THE GENUS THOMOMYS. E. A. Goldman. Jour. Mam., vol.25, no.4, pp.414, Nov., 1944.

THE SYSTEMATIC STATUS OF CERTAIN POCKET GOPHERS, WITH SPECIAL REFERENCE TO THOMOMYS MONTICOLA. E. A. Goldman. Jour. Washington Acad. Sci., vol.33, no.5, pp.146-147, May 15, 1943.

TWO NEW POCKET GOPHERS OF THE GENUS THOMOMYS. E. A. Goldman. Proc. Biol. Soc. Wash., vol.48, pp.149-152, Oct.31, 1935.

TWO NEW POCKET GOPHERS OF THE THOMOMYS BOTTAE GROUP. E. A. Goldman. Proc. Biol. Soc. Wash., vol.50, pp.133-136, Sept.10, 1937.

ON THE CHARACTERS OF THE POCKET GOPHER THOMOMYS TALPOIDES COUCHI GOLDMAN. E. Raymond Hall, Walter W. Dalquest. Murrelet, Seattle, vol.20, pp. 38-39, Aug., 1939.

A LIST OF THE NAMED FORMS OF THE POCKET GOPHER GENUS CRATOGEOMYS. Emmet T. Hooper. Jour. Mam., vol.29, no.3, pp.301-302, Aug.31, 1948.

TWO GENERA OF POCKET GOPHERS SHOULD BE CONGENERIC. Emmet T. Hooper. Jour. Mam., vol.27, no.4, pp. 397-399, Nov.25, 1946.

TYPE LOCALITIES OF POCKET GOPHERS OF THE GENUS THOMOMYS. Emmet T. Hooper. Misc. Publ. Mus. Zool., Univ. Michigan, no.52, 26 pp., 1 map, July 21, 1941.

THE TYPE LOCALITY OF THOMOMYS BRIDGERI AND THOMOMYS OCIUS. Emmet T. Hooper. Jour. Mam., vol.24, no.4, p.503, Nov.17, 1943.

A NEW SPECIES AND A NEW SUBSPECIES OF POCKET GOPHER. Laurence M. Huey. Trans. San Diego Soc. Nat. Hist., vol.7, no.5, pp.43-46, Dec.19, 1931.

THE NAME SALAMANDER FOR THE POCKET GOPHER. John D. Kilby. Jour. Mam., vol.16, no.4, pp.326-327, Nov., 1935.

A NEW POCKET GOPHER OF THE GENUS ORTHOGEOMYS. Barbara Lawrence. Proc. New England Zool. Club., vol.13, pp.65-67, May 8, 1933.

THE EARLIEST SYSTEMATIC NAME FOR THE TUOZA OR GEORGIA POCKET GOPHER. Edgar A. Mearns. Proc. Biol. Soc. Wash., vol.27, p.102, May 11, 1914.

DESCRIPTIONS OF TWENTY-THREE NEW POCKET GOPHERS OF THE GENUS THOMOMYS. C. Hart Merriam. Proc. Biol. Soc. Wash., vol.14, pp.107-117, July 19, 1901.

MONOGRAPHIC REVISION OF THE POCKET GOPHERS FAMILY GEOMYIDAE (EXCLUSIVE OF THE SPECIES OF THOMOMYS). C. Hart Merriam. North American Fauna, no.8, U.S. Dept. Agric., pp.258, figs.71, pls.19, maps 4, Jan.31, 1895.

IDENTITY OF THOMOMYS UMBRINUS (RICHARDSON). Gerrit S. Miller, Jr. Proc. Biol. Soc., Wash., vol.19, pp.3-6, Jan.29, 1906.

NOTES ON THOMOMYS BULBIVORUS. Gerrit S. Miller, Jr. Proc. Biol. Soc. Wash., vol.8, pp.113-116, Aug.16, 1893.

THE POCKET GOPHERS OF THE GENUS ORTHOGEOMYS. E. W. Nelson, E. A. Goldman. Jour. Mam., vol.11, no.2, pp. 155-159, May, 1930.

REVISION OF THE POCKET GOPHERS OF THE GENUS CRATEOGEOMYS. E. W. Nelson, E. A. Goldman. Proc. Biol. Soc. Wash., vol.47, pp.135-154, June 13, 1934.

THE STATUS OF ORTHOGEOMYS CUNICULUS ELLIOT. E. W. Nelson, E. A. Goldman. Jour. Mam., vol.11, no.3, p.317, Aug.9, 1930.

THE TAXONOMIC STATUS OF GEOMYS BURSARIUS VINACEUS SWENK. Robert J. Russell, J. Knox Jones, Jr. Trans. Kansas Acad. Sci., vol.58, no.4, pp.512-513, Jan. 23, 1956.

ON SOME OF THE LARGER SPECIES OF GEOMYS. Oldfield Thomas. Ann. Mag. Nat. Hist. (6): vol.12, no.69, pp.269-273, Oct., 1893.

THE USE OF SKULL MEASUREMENTS AT THE SUBSPECIFIC LEVEL IN MAMMALIAN TAXONOMY, WITH SPECIAL REFERENCE TO THOMOMYS TALPOIDES. C. A. Tryon, Jr. Jour. Mam., vol.32, no.3, pp. 313-318, illus., Aug.23, 1951.

(A NEW RACE OF GOPHER OF THE GENUS ORTHOGEOMYS.) Una nueva raza de tuza del genero Orthogeomys. Bernardo Villa R. Anales Inst. Biol., Mexico, vol. 19 (1948), no.1, pp.267-271, illus., Apr.8, 1949.

Traps and Cages

A LIVE TRAP FOR POCKET GOPHERS. Walter E. Howard. Jour. Mam., 33 (1): 61-65, illus., Feb., 1952.

AN IMPROVED LIVE TRAP FOR POCKET GOPHERS. Lloyd G. Ingles. Murrelet, Seattle, vol.30, no.3, pp.55-56, illus., Feb.1, 1950.

A BOX TRAP FOR THE CAPTURE OF LIVE GEOMYS. H. B. Sherman. Jour. Mam., 22 (2): 182-184, May, 1941.

A POCKET-GOPHER CAGE. H. B. Sherman, B. A. Barrington. Jour. Mam., vol.22, no.1, pp.91-93, Feb.14, 1941.

United States

THE POCKET GOPHERS OF THE UNITED STATES. Vernon Bailey. U.S. Dept. Agric Div. Ornith. and Mam., bull.no.5, pp.47, figs.6, map, illus., 1895.

EXTENSION OF THE RANGES OF THREE POCKET GOPHERS IN SOUTHERN CALIFORNIA. Jack C. von Bloeker. Jour. Mam. vol.13, no.1, pp.76-77, Feb., 1932.

DESCRIPTION OF A NEW RACE OF POCKET GOPHER (GEOMYS LUTESCENS HYLAEUS) FROM NEBRASKA. Philip M. Blossom. Occas. Papers Mus. Zool. Univ. Michigan, no.368, pp.2, Apr.6, 1938.

A NEW POCKET GOPHER OF THE GENUS THOMOMYS FROM UTAH. W. H. Burt. Proc. Biol. Soc. Wash., vol.44, pp.37-40, May 8, 1931.

THE SYSTEMATIC STATUS AND GEOGRAPHIC RANGE OF THE SAN GABRIEL POCKET GOPHER (THOMOMYS NEGLECTUS BAILEY). William Henry Burt. Jour. Mam., vol.13, no.4, pp.369-370, Nov., 1932.

AN UNDESCRIBED GOPHER, GENUS THOMOMYS, FROM SOUTHEASTERN CALIFORNIA. W. H. Burt. Trans. San Diego Soc. Nat. Hist., vol.7, no.14, pp. 153-156, July 28, 1932.

THE DISTRIBUTION OF POCKET GOPHERS IN SOUTHEASTERN CALIFORNIA. John E. Chattin. Trans. San Diego Soc. Nat. Hist., vol.9, no.27, pp.265-284, fig.1, Apr.30, 1941.

A NEW POCKET GOPHER FROM SOUTHEASTERN WASHINGTON. Walter W. Dalquest. Murrelet, Seattle, vol.23, no.1, pp.3-4, May 14, 1942.

DISTRIBUTION AND VARIATION IN POCKET GOPHERS, THOMOMYS TALPOIDES, IN THE STATE OF WASHINGTON. Walter W. Dalquest, Victor B. Scheffer. Amer. Nat., Lancaster, vol.78, pp.308-333, 423-450, figs.8, July-Aug., Sept.-Oct., 1944.

THREE NEW POCKET GOPHERS (GENUS THOMOMYS) FROM WESTERN WASHINGTON. Walter W. Dalquest, Victor B. Scheffer. Proc. Biol. Soc. Wash., vol.55, pp.95-98, Aug.13, 1942.

CRITICAL NOTES ON POCKET GOPHERS FROM TEXAS. William B. Davis. Jour. Mam., vol.19, no.4, pp.488-490, Nov.14, 1938.

DISTRIBUTION AND VARIATION OF POCKET GOPHERS (GENUS GEOMYS) IN THE SOUTHWESTERN UNITED STATES. William B. Davis. Texas Agr. Exp. Sta., Bull.590, 38 pp., 1940.

A NEW THOMOMYS FROM TEXAS. William B. Davis. Jour. Mam., vol.21, no.2, pp.204-205, May 14, 1940.

POCKET GOPHERS (THOMOMYS) OF THE DAVIS MOUNTAINS, TEXAS. William B. Davis, Helmut K. Buechner. Jour. Mam., vol.27, no.3, pp.265-271, figs.2, Aug.14, 1946.

REVISION OF THE RANGES OF THE POCKET GOPHERS OF SOUTHEASTERN WASHINGTON AND NORTHEASTERN OREGON AND THE DESCRIPTION OF A NEW SUBSPECIES THOMOMYS TALPOIDES WHITMANI. Harold Drake, Ernest S. Booth. Walla Walla College Publ., Dept. Biol. Sci. and Biol. Sta., vol.1, no.3, pp.44-58, illus., Nov.25, 1952.

A NEW GOPHER FROM ANTELOPE ISLAND, GREAT SALT LAKE, UTAH. Stephen D. Durrant. Univ. Utah, Salt Lake City, vol. 27, no.2, pp.4, figs.2, Oct., 1936.

A NEW POCKET GOPHER FROM SOUTH-CENTRAL UTAH. Stephen D. Durrant. Proc. Biol. Soc. Wash., vol.68, pp.79-82, Aug.3, 1955.

A NEW POCKET GOPHER OF THE THOMOMYS QUADRATUS GROUP FROM THE NORTHERN GREAT BASIN REGION. Stephen D. Durrant. Bull. Univ. Utah, vol. 29, no.6, (biol. ser., vol.3, no.10), pp.6, Feb.28, 1939.

THE POCKET GOPHERS (GENUS THOMOMYS) OF UTAH. Stephen D. Durrant. Univ. Kansas Pub., Mus. Nat. Hist., 1 (1): 1-82, Aug., 1946.

TWO NEW GOPHERS FROM UTAH. Stephen D. Durrant. Bull. Univ. Utah, vol.28, no. 4, (biol. ser., vol.3, no.8), pp.1-6, Aug. 18, 1937.

TWO NEW GOPHERS (MAMMALIAN GENUS THOMOMYS) FROM WESTERN UTAH. Stephen D. Durrant. Proc. Biol. Soc. Wash., vol.52, pp.159-162, Oct.11, 1939.

NOTES ON THOMOMYS IN OREGON. Ira N. Gabrielson. Jour. Mam., vol.4, no.3, pp.189-190, Aug., 1923.

AN UNDESCRIBED WASHINGTON POCKET GOPHER. Marshall C. Gardner. Jour. Mam., vol.13, no.1, pp.92-93, Feb.21, 1950.

ECOLOGICAL FACTORS AFFECTING DISTRIBUTION AND SPECIATION OF POCKET GOPHERS IN OKLAHOMA. Bryan P. Glass. PhD thesis, Okla. A. and M. Coll., May, 1952.

NEW POCKET GOPHERS FROM ARIZONA AND UTAH. E. A. Goldman. Jour. Wash. Acad. Sci., vol.21, no.17, pp.416-426, Oct.19, 1931.

NEW POCKET GOPHERS OF THE GENUS THOMOMYS FROM ARIZONA AND UTAH. E. A. Goldman. Jour. Wash. Acad. Sci., vol.28, no.7, pp.333-343, July 15, 1938.

THE POCKET GOPHERS (GENUS THOMOMYS) OF ARIZONA. E. A. Goldman. U. S. Dept. Interior, Fish and Wildlife Serv., North American Fauna, no.59, pp.39, figs. 2, June 12, 1947.

POCKET GOPHERS OF THE THOMOMYS BOTTAE GROUP IN THE UNITED STATES. E. A. Goldman. Proc. Biol. Soc. Wash., vol.48, pp.153-158, Oct.31, 1935.

DIFFERENTIATION IN POCKET GOPHERS OF THE THOMOMYS BOTTAE GROUP IN NORTHERN CALIFORNIA AND SOUTHERN OREGON. Joseph Grinnell. Univ. Calif. Publ. in Zool., Berkeley, vol.40, no.11, pp.403-416, pls.3-4, Nov.14, 1935.

FOUR NEW POCKET GOPHERS FROM CALIFORNIA. Joseph Grinnell. Univ. Calif. Publ. Zool., vol.12, no.9, pp.311-316, Nov.21, 1914.

A NEW LAKE-SIDE POCKET GOPHER FROM SOUTH-CENTRAL CALIFORNIA. Joseph Grinnell. Univ. Calif. Publ. Zool., vol.38, no.10, pp.405-410, pl.7, Sept.20, 1932.

A NEW POCKET GOPHER FROM LASSEN COUNTY, CALIFORNIA. Joseph Grinnell. Proc. Biol. Soc. Wash., vol.47, pp.193-198, Oct.2, 1934.

A NEW POCKET GOPHER FROM SOUTHEASTERN CALIFORNIA. Joseph Grinnell. Univ. Calif. Publ. Zool., vol.38, no.1, pp.1-10, pls.1-2, Oct.17, 1931.

THE POCKET GOPHER OF HONEY LAKE VALLEY. Joseph Grinnell. Univ. Calif. Publ. Zool., vol.30, no.1, pp.1-6, pl.1, Aug.18, 1926.

THE POCKET GOPHER OF THE BOREAL ZONE ON SAN JACINTO PEAK. Joseph Grinnell, H. S. Swarth. Proc. Calif. Acad. Sci., vol.4, ser.4, pp.153-160, table, Dec. 30, 1914.

A SYSTEMATIC STUDY OF SOME POCKET GOPHERS FROM WESTERN NEVADA. Joseph Grinnell. Univ. Calif. Publ. Zool., vol.30, pp.177-188, pls.9-11, Dec.10, 1926.

THE TWO POCKET GOPHERS OF THE REGION CONTIGUOUS TO THE LOWER COLORADO RIVER, IN CALIFORNIA AND ARIZONA. Joseph Grinnell. Univ. Calif. Publ. Zool., vol.10, no.8, pp.171-178, pl. 5, tables, June 17, 1912.

A NEW POCKET GOPHER FROM KERN COUNTY, CALIFORNIA. Joseph Grinnell, John Eric Hill. Proc. Biol. Soc. Wash., vol.49, pp.103-104, Aug.22, 1936.

POCKET GOPHERS (THOMOMYS) OF THE LOWER COLORADO VALLEY. Joseph Grinnell, John Eric Hill. Jour. Mam., vol.17, no.1, pp.1-10, fig.1, Feb.14, 1936.

A NEW POCKET GOPHER FROM NEW MEXICO (THOMOMYS BOTTAE CONNECTENS). E. Raymond Hall. Jour. Wash. Acad. Sci., vol.26, no.7, pp.296-298, July 15, 1936.

A NEW POCKET GOPHER FROM NEW MEXICO (THOMOMYS BAILEYI TULAROSAE). E. Raymond Hall. Univ. Calif. Publ. Zool., vol.38, no.11, pp.411-412, Sept.20, 1932.

A NEW POCKET GOPHER (GENUS THOMOMYS) FROM EASTERN COLORADO. E. Raymond Hall. Univ. Kansas Publ., Mus. Nat. Hist., Lawrence, vol.5, no.8, pp.81-85, Oct.1, 1951.

A NEW POCKET GOPHER (GENUS THOMOMYS) FROM WYOMING AND COLORADO. E. Raymond Hall. Univ. Kansas Publ., Mus. Nat. Hist., Lawrence, vol.5, no.13, pp.219-222, Dec.15, 1951.

NEW POCKET GOPHERS FROM NEVADA. E. Raymond Hall. Univ. Calif. Publ. Zool., vol.33, no.4, pp.325-333, Feb.27, 1932.

THREE NEW POCKET GOPHERS FROM NEW MEXICO AND ARIZONA. E. Raymond Hall. Proc. Biol. Soc. Wash., vol.45, pp. 95-98, June 21, 1932.

THREE NEW POCKET GOPHERS FROM UTAH AND NEVADA. E. Raymond Hall. Univ. Calif. Publ. Zool., vol.32, no.6, pp.443-447, July 8, 1930.

THREE NEW POCKET GOPHERS (MAMMALIAN GENUS THOMOMYS) FROM WASHINGTON. E. Raymond Hall, Walter W. Dalquest. Murrelet, Seattle, vol.20, no.1, pp.3-5, Jan.-Apr., 1939.

GEOGRAPHIC DISTRIBUTION OF POCKET GOPHERS (GENUS THOMOMYS) IN NEVADA. E. Raymond Hall, William B. Davis. Univ. Calif. Publ. Zool., vol.40, no.10, pp.387-402, fig.1, Mar.13, 1935.

A NEW POCKET GOPHER FROM NEVADA E. Raymond Hall, Floyd E. Durham. Proc. Biol. Soc. Wash., vol.51, pp.15-16, Feb.18, 1938.

TWO POCKET GOPHERS FROM WYOMING AND COLORADO. E. Raymond Hall, H. Gordon Montague. Univ. Kansas Publ., Mus. Nat. Hist., vol.5, no.3, pp.25-32, Feb.28, 1951.

A NEW RACE OF POCKET GOPHER FOUND IN OREGON AND WASHINGTON. E. Raymond Hall, Robert T. Orr. Proc. Biol. Soc. Wash., vol.46, pp.41-43, Mar.24, 1933.

HISTORY AND NOMENCLATURE OF THE POCKET GOPHERS (GEOMYS) IN GEORGIA. Francis Harper. Proc. Biol. Soc. Wash., vol.65, pp.35-38, Jan.29, 1952.

DESCRIPTIONS OF POCKET GOPHERS (THOMOMYS BOTTAE) FROM NORTHEASTERN ARIZONA. Donald F. Hoffmeister. Jour. Wash. Acad. Sci., vol. 45, no.4, pp.126-128, Apr.25, 1955.

NEW POCKET GOPHERS FROM THE VICINITY OF MOUNT TAYLOR, NEW MEXICO. Emmet T. Hooper. Occas. Papers Mus. Zool. Univ. Michigan, Ann Arbor, no.422, 13 pp., map, Nov.14, 1940.

A NEW RACE OF POCKET GOPHER OF THE SPECIES GEOMYS LUTESCENS FROM COLORADO. Emmet T. Hooper. Occas. Papers Mus. Zool., Univ. Michigan, no. 420, pp.3, June 28, 1940.

A NEW FORM OF POCKET GOPHER FROM SOUTHERN MONO COUNTY, CALIFORNIA. Laurence M. Huey. Trans. San Diego Soc. Nat. Hist., vol.7, no.35, pp.373-374, May 31, 1934.

A NEW FORM OF POCKET GOPHER (THOMOMYS) FROM THE SANTA CRUZ MOUNTAINS, CALIFORNIA. Laurence M. Huey. Trans. San Diego Soc. Nat. Hist., vol.9, no.22, pp.219-226, July 31, 1940.

A NEW SPECIES OF POCKET GOPHER FROM SOUTHERN ARIZONA. Laurence M. Huey. Trans. San Diego Soc. Nat. Hist., vol.7, no.15, pp.157-160, July 28, 1932.

TWO NEW POCKET GOPHERS FROM THE DESERT SLOPE OF EASTERN SAN DIEGO COUNTY, CALIFORNIA. Laurence M. Huey. Trans. San Diego Soc. Nat. Hist., vol.9, no.15, pp.69-76, pls.4-5, Dec.8, 1939.

AN UNRECOGNIZED POCKET GOPHER FROM WISCONSIN. Hartley H. T. Jackson.

Proc. Biol. Soc. Wash., 70: 33-34, June 28, 1957.

THOMOMYS BOTTAE LATICEPS IN OREGON. Stanley G. Jewett. Jour. Mam., vol.10, no.1, pp.80-81, Feb., 1929.

A NEW POCKET GOPHER FROM SOUTH-EASTERN UTAH. Keith R. Kelson. Proc. Biol. Soc. Wash., vol.62, pp.143-146, Aug. 23, 1949.

TWO NEW SUBSPECIES OF THOMOMYS BOTTAE FROM NEW MEXICO AND COLORADO. Keith R. Kelson. Univ. Kansas Publ., Mus. Nat. Hist., vol.5, no.6, pp. 59-71, fig.1, Oct.1, 1951.

LOCAL DIFFERENTIATION IN THE POCKET GOPHER (GEOMYS PERSONATUS) IN SOUTHERN TEXAS. Thomas E. Kennerly, Jr. Texas Jour. Sci., vol.6, no. 3, pp.297-329, Sept., 1954.

A NEW POCKET GOPHER FROM ILLINOIS AND INDIANA. E. V. Komarek, Don A. Spencer. Jour. Mam., vol.12, no.4, pp. 404-408, pl.14, Nov., 1931.

REMARKS ON GEOMYS BURSARIUS ILLINOENSIS KOMAREK AND SPENCER. Marcus W. Lyon, Jr. Jour. Mam., vol.13, no.1, pp.77-78, Feb., 1932.

A NEW RACE OF THE POCKET GOPHER GEOMYS BURSARIUS FROM MISSOURI. Charles A. McLaughlin. Contrib. Sci. Los Angeles County Mus., 19: 1-4, Jan.29, 1958.

DESCRIPTION OF A NEW POCKET GOPHER OF THE GENUS GEOMYS, FROM WESTERN NEBRASKA. C. Hart Merriam. North American Fauna, no.4, p.51, Oct., 1890.

DESCRIPTIONS OF EIGHT NEW POCKET GOPHERS OF THE GENUS THOMOMYS, FROM OREGON, CALIFORNIA, AND NEVADA. C. Hart Merriam. Proc. Biol. Soc., Wash., vol.11, pp.213-216, July 15, 1897.

PRELIMINARY DESCRIPTION OF A NEW POCKET GOPHER FROM CALIFORNIA (THOMOMYS TALPOIDES PERPALLIDUS SUB-SP.NOV.). C. Hart Merriam. Science, vol.8, no.203, p.1, Dec.24, 1886.

A NEW COLORADO POCKET GOPHER OF THE GENUS THOMOMYS. Frederic W. Miller. Proc. Colorado Mus. Nat. Hist., vol.9, no.3, pp.41-43, fig.1, Dec.14, 1930.

DISTRIBUTION OF THE ILLINOIS POCKET GOPHER, GEOMYS BURSARIUS ILLINOENSIS. Carl O. Mohr. Jour. Mam., vol.16, no.2, pp.131-134, map, May, 1935.

EXTENSION OF RANGE OF TWO MEMBERS OF THOMOMYS DOUGLASII GROUP. A. W. Moore. Jour. Mam., vol.8, no.4, pp.308-310, Nov., 1927.

THOMOMYS IN MINNESOTA. Don Quimby. Jour. Mam., vol.23, no.2, pp.216-217, May 14, 1942.

A NEW SUBSPECIES OF GEOMYS FROM FLORIDA. H. B. Sherman. Proc. New England Zool. Club, Cambridge, vol.23, pp.37-40, Aug.30, 1944.

A STUDY OF SUBSPECIFIC VARIATION IN THE RICHARDSON POCKET-GOPHER (THOMOMYS TALPOIDES) IN NEBRASKA, WITH DESCRIPTIONS OF TWO NEW SUBSPECIES. Myron H. Swenk. Missouri Valley Fauna, Lincoln, no.4, pp.1-8, Mar.1, 1941.

A STUDY OF SUBSPECIFIC VARIATION IN THE YELLOW POCKET-GOPHER (GEOMYS LUTESCENS) IN NEBRASKA, AND OF THE GEOGRAPHICAL AND ECOLOGICAL DISTRIBUTION OF THE VARIANTS. Myron H. Swenk. Missouri Valley Fauna, Lincoln, no.2, pp.12, tables 2, Feb.1, 1940.

A NEW POCKET GOPHER FROM WESTERN WASHINGTON. Walter P. Taylor. Proc. Biol. Soc. Wash., vol.32, pp.169-171, Sept. 30, 1919.

THOMOMYS DOUGLASII SHAWI, A NEW SUBSPECIES OF POCKET GOPHER FROM MOUNT RAINIER, WASHINGTON. Walter P. Taylor. Proc. Biol. Soc. Wash., vol. 34, pp.121-122, June 30, 1921.

SUBSPECIATION IN POCKET GOPHERS OF KANSAS. Bernardo Villa-Ramirez. MA Thesis, Univ. Kansas, 1947.

SUBSPECIATION IN POCKET GOPHERS OF KANSAS. Bernardo Villa-Ramirez, E. Raymond Hall. Univ. Kansas Publ., Mus. Nat. Hist., 1 (11): 217-236, Nov., 1947.

THE POCKET GOPHER IN ALABAMA. Harlan H. York. Ala. Cons., 24 (6): 7, 25, illus., May-June, 1953.

GEOGRAPHIC VARIATION IN THE POCKET GOPHER, THOMOMYS BOTTAE, IN COLORADO. Phillip M. Youngman. Univ. Kansas Publ., Mus. Nat. Hist., 9 (12): 363-384, Feb.21, 1958.

## Heteromyidae

A METHOD FOR DETERMINING THE PRESENCE OR ABSENCE OF SPINES IN POCKET-MICE. Philip M. Blossom. Jour. Mam., vol.14, no.4, p.370, Nov., 1933.

PEROGNATHUS--THE POCKET MOUSE. G. M. Bradt. Nature Mag., Wash., D.C., vol.35, no.6, pp.298-329, illus., June-July, 1942.

THE SILKY POCKET MICE OF SOUTHERN CALIFORNIA AND NORTHERN LOWER CALIFORNIA, MEXICO, WITH THE DESCRIPTION OF A NEW RACE. Laurence M. Huey. Trans. San Diego Soc. Nat. Hist., vol.9, no.11, pp.47-54, map, table, Aug.31, 1939.

DIPO, THE LITTLE DESERT "KANGAROO." Walter E. Ketcham. Nat. Geographic Mag., vol.78, no.4, pp.537-548, illus., Oct., 1940.

BEAU BRUMMEL OF THE WILD. (KANGAROO RAT.) William M. Rush. Nat. Hist., New York, vol.54, no.1, pp.40-41, fig.1, Jan., 1945.

THE DESERT RAT. K. Schmidt-Nielsen, B. Schmidt-Nielsen. Scientific American, New York, vol.189, no.1, pp.73-79, July, 1953.

DIPO: SPRITE OF THE DESERT. (KANGAROO RAT.) Ernest T. Seton. Century Mag., vol.105, no.1, pp.106-115, 8 figs., Nov., 1922.

THE BANNER-TAIL AND OTHER BURROWERS. (KANGAROO RATS.) Walter P. Taylor. Amer. Forests, vol.42, no.2, pp. 68-70, 93, illus., Feb., 1936.

BANNERTAIL OF THE BAJADAS. (KANGAROO RAT.) Walter P. Taylor. Nature Mag., vol.4, no.3, pp.180-182, 188, Sept., 1924.

A NEW STUDY OF THE GENUS DIPODOMYS. Frederick W. True. Proc. U.S. Nat. Mus., vol.9, publ.580, pp.409-413, Feb.10, 1887.

ON THE RARE RODENT CRICETODIPUS PARVUS (BAIRD) COUES. Frederick W. True. Proc. U.S. Nat. Mus., vol.4, publ.256, pp.474-475, Aug.6, 1882.

(NOTES ON SOME RODENTS SPECIES OF THE GENERA DIPODOMYS, PEROGNATHUS, AND PEROMYSCUS.) Nota acerca de algunas especies de roedores de los generos Dipodomys, Perognathus y Peromyscus. Bernardo Villa. Anales Inst. Biol., Mexico City, vol.12, no.1, pp.355-399, figs.A-F, 1941.

"BRAINS." THE STORY OF SOME FIGHTING MEN, A "MOUSE," AND AN IDEA CALLED FREEDOM. (KANGAROO RAT IN ARIZONA.) Rouen J. Westcott. Nat. Hist., New York, vol.55, no.7, pp.331, 341-342, illus., Sept., 1946.

### Anatomy

A STUDY OF THE BACULUM IN THE GENERA PEROGNATHUS AND DIPODOMYS. William H. Burt. Jour. Mam., vol.17, no. 2, pp.145-156, figs.6, May 14, 1936.

A PRELIMINARY HISTOLOGICAL STUDY OF THE OVARY OF THE KANGAROO RAT, DIPODOMYS ORDII COLUMBIANUS. Kenneth L. Duke. Great Basin Nat., Provo, vol.1, no.2, pp.63-72, pl.1, Jan. 28, 1940.

SPECIALIZED CLAW IN LIOMYS. George B. Goodwin. Jour. Mam., vol.26, no.3, pp.308-309, Aug., 1945.

ABNORMAL HAIRY GROWTHS UPON THE TAILS OF THE HETEROMYIDAE. A. Brazier Howell. Jour. Mam., vol.4, no.1, pp.56-58, Feb.9, 1923.

THE SALTATORIAL RODENT DIPODOMYS: THE FUNCTIONAL AND COMPARATIVE ANATOMY OF ITS MUSCULAR AND OSSEOUS SYSTEMS. A. Brazier Howell. Proc. Amer. Acad. Arts and Sciences, vol.67, no.10, pp.377-536, figs.28, pl., Dec., 1932.

THE VISCERAL ANATOMY OF THE KANGAROO RAT. Edward E. Midgley. Jour. Mam., vol.19, no.3, pp.304-317, figs.15, Aug., 1938.

THE DORSAL HOLOCRINE SKIN GLAND OF THE KANGAROO RAT (DIPODOMYS). W. B. Quay. Anat. Record, Phila., vol. 119, no.2, pp.161-176, June, 1954.

AGE VARIATION IN ENAMEL PATTERNS IN THE SPINY POCKET MOUSE, LIOMYS PICTUS SONORANUS. William G. Reeder. Jour. Mam., vol.34, no.1, pp.59-64, illus., Feb.19, 1953.

### Canada

KANGAROO RAT. R. R. Carleton. Blue Jay, Saskatchewan Nat. Hist. Soc., 14 (3): 100, Sept., 1956.

THE KANGAROO RAT IN SASKATCHEWAN. R. W. Nero. Blue Jay, Saskatchewan Nat. Hist. Soc., 14 (1): 3-4, Mar., 1956.

THE POCKET MOUSE IN SASKATCHEWAN. R. W. Nero. Blue Jay, Saskatchewan Nat. Hist. Soc., 15 (4): 172-173, Dec., 1957.

KANGAROO RAT COLONIES FOUND. R. W. Nero, Richard W. Fyfe. Blue Jay, Saskatchewan Nat. Hist. Soc., 14 (4): 107-110, illus., Dec., 1956.

### Captivity

A SILKY POCKET MOUSE IN CAPTIVITY. Shaler E. Aldous. Jour. Mam., vol.11, no. 1, pp.80-81, Feb., 1930.

A POCKET MOUSE IN CONFINEMENT. J. A. Allen. Amer. Nat., vol.32, pp.583-584, Aug., 1898.

RAISING BANNERTAILS--AN UNRECORDED CHAPTER FROM THE HOME LIFE OF ONE OF OUR INTERESTING DESERT CREATURES. (DIPODOMYS.) Vernon Bailey. Natural History, New York, vol.45, no.4, pp.241-245, illus., Apr., 1940.

OBSERVATIONS ON THE KANGAROO RAT IN CAPTIVITY. Ernest S. Booth. Murrelet, Seattle, vol.24, no.1, pp.10-11, Apr.22, 1943.

REARING THE PALLID ORD KANGAROO RAT IN THE LABORATORY. William P. Jollie. Symposium on ecology of disease transmission in native animals, Univ. Utah, pp.54-56, 1955.

BEHAVIOUR OF A CAPTIVE POCKET MOUSE. R. W. Nero. Blue Jay, Saskatchewan Nat. Hist. Soc., 15 (4): 173-176, illus., Dec., 1957.

ON THE HABITS OF THE KANGAROO RATS IN CAPTIVITY. R. W. Shufeldt. Amer. Nat. Boston, vol.36, no.421, pp.47-51, figs.2, Jan., 1902.

### Central America

TWO NEW HARVEST MICE FROM COSTA RICA. George G. Goodwin. Amer. Mus. Novitates, New York, no.1231, p.2, June 2, 1943.

TWO NEW HARVEST MICE FROM HONDURAS. George G. Goodwin. Amer. Mus. Novitates, New York, no.921, p.2, May 3, 1937.

A DEFINITE LOCALITY RECORD FOR LIOMYS SALVINI NIGRESCENS (THOMAS). William P. Harris, Jr. Jour. Mam., vol. 12, no.4, p.431, Nov., 1931.

### Diseases and Parasites.

COCCIDIOSIS IN THE KANGAROO RATS OF CALIFORNIA. David J. Doran. Univ. Calif. Publ. Zool., vol.59, no.2, pp.31-60, illus., Apr.22, 1953.

SUSCEPTIBILITY OF KANGAROO RATS TO STRAINS OF HUMAN INFLUENZA VIRUS. Monroe D. Eaton, Walter P. Martin, John

C. Talbot. Proc. Soc. Exper. Biol. and Medicine, vol. 48, pp. 181-182, 1941.

THE ISOLATION OF HAPLOSPORANGIUM PARVUM N. SP. AND COCCIDIOIDES IMMITIS FROM WILD RODENTS. THEIR RELATIONSHIP TO COCCIDIOI-DOMYCOSIS. C. W. Emmons, L. L. Ashburn. Publ. Health Rep., 57 (46): 1715-1727, Nov. 13, 1942.

GIARDIA IN THE BLOOD OF A KANGAROO RAT. Carlton M. Herman. Jour. Parasitology, 29 (6): 423, Dec., 1943.

AMERICAN POCKET MOUSE FLEAS. (DISTRIBUTION AND HABITS OF POCKET MICE AND DISCUSSION OF FLEAS OF 2 GENERA AND 6 SPECIES.) C. A. Hubbard. Pac. Univ. Bull., 39 (9), 2 pp., June, 1943.

HERNIAS IN KANGAROO RATS. C. A. Hubbard. Jour. Mam., vol. 23, no. 2, pp. 219-220, May 14, 1942.

HELMINTH PARASITES IN KANGAROO RATS. Clark P. Read, Raymond E. Milleman. U. Calif. Publ. Zool., 59 (3): 61-80, illus., 1953.

RICTULARIA DIPODOMIS N. SP. (NEMATODA: THELAZIIDAE) FROM THE KANGAROO RAT DIPODOMYS SP. Jack D. Tiner. Jour. Parasitol., Lancaster, vol. 34, no. 4, pp. 332-335, Aug., 1948.

Ecology

THE KANGAROO RAT PREYED UPON BY THE SPARROW HAWK. Henry E. Childs, Jr. Jour. Mam., vol. 33, no. 4, pp. 493-494, Nov. 19, 1952.

VARIABILITY AND ENVIRONMENTAL RESPONSES OF THE KANGAROO RAT, DIPODOMYS HEERMANNI SAXATILIS. Frederick H. Dale. Amer. Midland Nat., Notre Dame, vol. 22, no. 3, pp. 703-731, fig. 1, Nov., 1939.

THE SYSTEMATICS AND ECOLOGY OF PEROGNATHUS HISPIDUS. Bryan P. Glass. MS thesis, A. and M. Coll. Texas, 1946; Jour. Mam., 28: 174, 1947.

SMALL MAMMAL RELATIONSHIPS IN AN EPHEDRA COMMUNITY. (HABITAT REQUIREMENTS AND LIMITATIONS OF 3 SPECIES OF DIPODOMYS.) Albert C. Hawbecker. Jour. Mam., 32 (1): 50-63, Feb., 1951.

Economic Importance

THE GIANT KANGAROO RAT AND SHEEP FORAGE. Albert C. Hawbecker. Jour. Wildl. Mgt., 8 (2): 161-165, Apr., 1944.

RELATION OF MERRIAM KANGAROO RATS TO RANGE VEGETATION IN SOUTHERN ARIZONA. Hudson G. Reynolds. Ecology, 31 (3): 456-463, July, 1950.

SOME INTERRELATIONS OF THE MERRIAM KANGAROO RAT TO VELVET MESQUITE. Hudson G. Reynolds. J. Range Mgt., 7 (4): 176-180, illus., July, 1954.

MERRIAM KANGAROO RAT A FACTOR IN MESQUITE PROPAGATION ON SOUTHERN ARIZONA RANGE LANDS. Hudson G. Reynolds, G. E. Glendening. J. Range Mgt., 2 (4): 193-197, Oct., 1949.

POCKET MICE OF WASHINGTON AND OREGON IN RELATION TO AGRICULTURE. (MAY DAMAGE SEED PLANTINGS AND RIPENING GRAIN.) Theo. H. Scheffer. USDA, Tech. Bull., 608, 15 pp., Mar., 1938.

DAMAGE BY KANGAROO RATS. Charles T. Vorhies, Walter P. Taylor. Jour. Mam., vol. 5, no. 2, p. 144, May, 1924.

Fossils

A NEW SPECIES OF HETEROMYID RODENT FROM THE MIDDLE OLIGOCENE OF NORTHEAST COLORADO WITH REMARKS ON THE SKULL. (HELISCOMYS TENUICEPS.) Edwin C. Galbreath. Univ. Kansas Publ. Mus. Nat. Hist., Lawrence, vol. 1, no. 18, pp. 285-300, pls. 2-3, Aug. 16, 1948.

HETEROMYIDS FROM THE MIOCENE AND LOWER OLIGOCENE. Paul O. McGrew. Geol. Ser., Field Mus. Nat. Hist., Chicago, vol. 8, no. 9, pp. 55-57, fig. 17, Oct. 31, 1941.

ADDITIONAL SPECIMENS OF THE HETEROMYID RODENT HELISCOMYS FROM THE OLIGOCENE OF NEBRASKA. Albert Elmer Wood. Amer. Jour. Sci., New Haven, vol. 237, no. 8, pp. 550-561, figs. 11, table 1, Aug., 1939.

EVOLUTION AND RELATIONSHIP OF THE HETEROMYID RODENTS WITH NEW FORMS FROM THE TERTIARY OF WESTERN NORTH AMERICA. Albert Elmer Wood. Annals Carnegie Mus., vol. 24, pp. 73-262, figs. 157, May 13, 1935.

FOSSIL HETEROMYID RODENTS IN THE COLLECTIONS OF THE UNIVERSITY OF CALIFORNIA. Albert Elmer Wood. Amer. Jour. Sci., ser. 5, vol. 32, no. 188, pp. 112-119, figs. 10, Aug., 1936.

A NEW HETEROMYID RODENT FROM THE OLIGOCENE OF MONTANA. Albert Elmer Wood. Jour. Mam., vol. 14, no. 2, pp. 134-141, May, 1933.

NEW HETEROMYID RODENTS FROM THE MIOCENE OF FLORIDA. Albert Elmer Wood. Bulletin 10, Florida State Geol. Surv., Tallahassee, pp. 45-51, figs. 24-29, 1932.

A NEW SUBFAMILY OF HETEROMYID RODENTS FROM THE MIOCENE OF THE WESTERN UNITED STATES. Albert Elmer Wood. Amer. Jour. Sci., ser. 5, vol. 31, no. 181, pp. 41-49, figs. 7, Jan. 1, 1936.

PHYLOGENY OF THE HETEROMYID RODENTS. Albert Elmer Wood. Amer. Mus. Nov. no. 501, pp. 19, 1 table, figs. 5, Oct. 16, 1931.

Geographic Distribution

GEOGRAPHIC DISTRIBUTION OF THE POCKET MOUSE, PEROGNATHUS FASCIATUS. J. Knox Jones, Jr. U. Kans. Publ., Mus. Nat. Hist., 5 (29): 515-526, illus., Aug., 1953.

A STUDY OF THE GEOGRAPHICAL AND ECOLOGICAL DISTRIBUTION OF THE BUFFY PLAINS POCKET MOUSE (PEROGNATHUS FLAVESCENS FLAVESCENS) WITH DESCRIPTION OF A NEW SUBSPECIES FROM NEBRASKA. Myron H. Swenk. Missouri Valley Fauna, Lincoln, Occas. Papers no. 3, pp. 1-8, June 5, 1940.

Habits, Behavior

NOTES ON DIPODOMYS ORDII RICHARDSONI. (HABITS AND FOOD AND WATER REQUIREMENTS.) Philip F. Allan. Jour. Mam., 27 (3): 271-273, Aug., 1946.

NOTES ON THE LIFE HISTORY OF THE SAND POCKET MOUSE. Lee W. Arnold. Jour. Mam., 23 (3): 339-341, Aug., 1942.

THE SOLITARY LIVES OF TWO LITTLE POCKET MICE. Vernon Bailey. Jour. Mam., vol. 20, no. 3, pp. 325-328, Aug. 14, 1939.

A PROTECTIVE HABIT OF DIPODOMYS DESERTI. Seth B. Benson. Jour. Mam., vol. 16, no. 1, pp. 67-68, Feb., 1935.

THE BURROWS AND FOOD OF THE PRAIRIE POCKET MOUSE. W. Frank Blair. Jour. Mam., 18 (2): 188-191, May, 1937.

NOTES ON THE LIFE HABITS OF THE SILKY POCKET MOUSE (PEROGNATHUS FLAVUS BAIRD). H. Garth Blakely. MS thesis, Univ. N. Mex., 1936.

KANGAROO RAT BURROWS IN EARTH STRUCTURES. Lawrence V. Compton, R. Frank Hedges. Jour. Wildl. Mgt., 7 (3): 306-316, July, 1943.

OBSERVATIONS ON THE NATURAL HISTORY OF THE FRESNO KANGAROO RAT. A. E. Culbertson. Jour. Mam., 27 (3): 189-203, Aug., 1946.

HABITAT RESTRICTION AND THE DIGGING ABILITY OF CERTAIN POCKET MICE. A. Arliss Denyes. Jour. Mam., vol. 35, no. 3, p. 453, Aug. 20, 1954.

HABITS AND ECONOMIC RELATIONSHIPS OF THE TULARE KANGAROO RAT. Henry S. Fitch. Jour. Mam., 29 (1): 5-35, Feb., 1948.

VOCAL SOUND PRODUCED BY THE KANGAROO RAT, DIPODOMYS SPECTABILIS. Robert H. Gibbs, Jr. Jour. Mam., 36 (3): 463, Aug. 30, 1955.

HABITAT RELATIONS OF THE GIANT KANGAROO RAT. Joseph Grinnell. Jour. Mam., vol. 13, no. 4, pp. 305-320, fig. 1, Nov., 1932.

NOTES ON THE LIFE HISTORY OF THE KANGAROO MOUSE (MICRODIPODOPS). E. Raymond Hall, Jean M. Linsdale. Jour. Mam., vol. 10, no. 4, pp. 298-305, pl. 22, Nov. 11, 1929.

THE BURROWING AND FEEDING HABITS OF DIPODOMYS VENUSTUS. Albert C. Hawbecker. Jour. Mam., 21 (4): 388-396, Nov., 1940.

THE GIANT KANGAROO RAT AND SHEEP REFUGE. Albert C. Hawbecker. Jour. Wildlife Management, Menasha, vol. 8, no. 2, pp. 161-165, pl. 8, Apr., 1944.

HARVEST HOME. (SEED STORING BY KANGAROO RATS.) John Eric Hill. Nat. Hist., New York, vol. 52, no. 3, p. 143, illus., Oct., 1943.

INSECTS IN THE DIET OF POCKET MICE, PEROGNATHUS PARVUS. E. W. Jameson, Jr. Jour. Mam., vol. 35, no. 4, pp. 592-593, Nov. 29, 1954.

RE-ASSIMILATION OF FOOD BY THE BANNER-TAIL KANGAROO RAT. F. W. Miller. Jour. Mam., vol. 20, no. 3, pp. 378-379, Aug. 14, 1939.

FOOD HABITS OF THE BANNER-TAILED KANGAROO RAT IN ARIZONA. Gale Monson. Jour. Wildlife Management, Menasha, vol. 7, no. 1, pp. 98-102, Jan., 1943.

THE HABITAT AND HOME LIFE OF THE KANGAROO RATS OF OUR WESTERN DESERT. Ernest T. Seton. Jour. Wash. Acad. Sci., vol. 10, pp. 306-307, May 19, 1920.

THE ABILITY OF THE GIANT KANGAROO RAT AS A HARVESTER AND STORER OF SEEDS. William T. Shaw. Jour. Mam., vol. 15, no. 4, pp. 275-286, pls. 9-10, Nov., 1934.

THE FALL FOOD OF BRUSHFIELD POCKET MICE. Clarence F. Smith. Jour. Mam., 23 (3): 337-339, Aug., 1942.

DESCRIPTION OF A NEW SPECIES OF DIPODOMYS, WITH SOME ACCOUNT OF ITS HABITS. F. Stephens. Amer. Nat., vol. 21, pp. 41-49, pl. 5, Jan., 1887.

NATURAL HISTORY OF THE TULARE KANGAROO RAT. Donald T. Tappe. Jour. Mam., vol. 22, no. 2, pp. 117-148, figs. 4, pls. 2, May 14, 1941.

LIFE HISTORY OF THE KANGAROO RAT, DIPODOMYS SPECTABILIS SPECTABILIS MERRIAM. Charles T. Vorhies, Walter P. Taylor. Washington: U.S. Dept. Agric Bull. no. 1091 (also Technical Bull. no. 1, Agric. Experiment Sta., University of Arizona), pp. 1-40, 9 half-tone pls., 3 figs, Sept. 13, 1922.

NOTES ON HOME RANGES AND POPULATION DENSITY OF TWO SPECIES OF HETEROMYID RODENTS IN SOUTHWESTERN TEXAS. (KANGAROO RATS AND POCKET MICE.) Christopher L. York. Texas Jour. Sci., 1 (3): 42-46, Sept., 1949.

Longevity

LONGEVITY OF CAPTIVE KANGAROO RATS, DIPODOMYS. Emmet T. Hooper. Jour. Mam., 37 (1): 124-125, Feb. 28, 1956.

LONGEVITY IN PEROGNATHUS LONGIMEMBRIS. Robert T. Orr. Jour. Mam., vol. 20, no. 4, p. 505, Nov. 14, 1939.

Lower California

THE DESCRIPTION OF A NEW SUBSPECIES OF PEROGNATHUS FROM LOWER CALIFORNIA WITH A SHORT DISCUSSION OF THE TAXONOMIC POSITION OF OTHER PENINSULAR MEMBERS OF THE GENUS. Laurence M. Huey. Proc. Biol. Soc. Wash., vol. 39, pp. 67-69, July 29, 1926.

THE KANGAROO RATS (DIPODOMYS) OF BAJA CALIFORNIA, MEXICO. Laurence M. Huey. Trans. San Diego Soc. Nat. Hist., vol. 11, no. 10, pp. 205-256, illus., Apr. 30, 1951.

A NEW FORM OF PEROGNATHUS FORMOSUS FROM BAJA CALIFORNIA, MEXICO.

Laurence M. Huey. Trans. San Diego Soc. Nat. Hist., vol.12, no.1, pp.1-2, Mar.1, 1954.

A NEW PEROGNATHUS ARENARIUS FROM NEAR THE U.S. MEXICAN BOUNDARY IN LOWER CALIFORNIA. Laurence M. Huey. Trans. San Diego Soc. Nat. Hist., vol.9, no.13, pp.57-58, Aug.31, 1939.

TWO NEW KANGAROO RATS OF THE GENUS DIPODOMYS FROM LOWER CALIFORNIA. Laurence M. Huey. Proc. Biol. Soc. Wash., vol.38, pp.83-84, May 26, 1925.

DESCRIPTION OF A NEW KANGAROO RAT FROM LOWER CALIFORNIA (DIPODOMYS MERRIAMI MELANURUS SUBSP. NOV.) COLLECTED BY WALTER E. BRYANT. C. Hart Merriam. Proc. California Acad. Sci., ser.2, vol.3, pp.345-346, June 3, 1893.

DESCRIPTIONS OF FOUR NEW POCKET MICE FROM LOWER CALIFORNIA COLLECTED BY WALTER E. BRYANT. C. Hart Merriam. Proc. California Acad. Sci., ser.2, vol.4, pp.457-462, figs.2, Sept.25, 1894.

A NEW POCKET MOUSE FROM SOUTHERN LOWER CALIFORNIA. E. W. Nelson, E. A. Goldman. Jour. Wash. Acad. Sci., vol.20, no.12, pp.223-224, June 19, 1930.

A NEW POCKET MOUSE FROM LOWER CALIFORNIA. E. W. Nelson, E. A. Goldman. Proc. Biol. Soc. Wash., vol. 36, pp.159-160, May 1, 1923.

Mexico

THE SILKY POCKET MOUSE (PEROGNATHUS FLAVUS) OF MEXICO. Rollin H. Baker. Univ. Kansas Publ., Mus. Nat. Hist., Lawrence, vol.7, no.3, pp.339-347, map, Feb.15, 1954.

A NEW KANGAROO RAT FROM SONORA. E. A. Goldman. Proc. Biol. Soc. Wash., vol.41, pp.141-142, Oct.15, 1928.

A NEW SILKY POCKET MOUSE FROM SONORA, MEXICO. Laurence M. Huey. Trans. San Diego Soc. Nat. Hist., vol.8, no.12, pp.73-74, Aug.24, 1935.

REDISCOVERY OF THE MEXICAN KANGAROO RAT (DIPODOMYS PHILLIPSI GRAY) FIELD NOTES BY E. W. NELSON. C. Hart Merriam. Proc. Biol. Soc. Wash., vol.8, pp.83-96, July 18, 1893.

TWENTY NEW POCKET MICE (HETEROMYS AND LIOMYS) FROM MEXICO. C. Hart Merriam. Proc. Biol. Soc. Wash., vol.15, pp.41-50, Mar.5, 1902.

Pelage, Coloration

SHADE OF PELAGE COLOR IN TWO POPULATIONS OF KANGAROO RATS AND REMARKS ON THE STATUS OF DIPODOMYS MERRIAMI AMBIGUUS MERRIAM. W. Frank Blair. Jour. Mam., vol.30, no.4, pp.388-390, Nov.17, 1949.

PELAGE COLOR CHANGES IN PEROGNATHUS LONGIMEMBRIS. C. Lynn Hayward. Jour. Mam., 37 (3): 451-452, Sept.11, 1956.

IN BLACK AND WHITE. IDENTICAL ANIMALS ON ADJACENT AREAS HAVE DEVELOPED EXTRAORDINARY NATURAL CAMOUFLAGE. John Eric Hill. Natural History, New York, vol.43, no.3, pp.172-173, photos, Mar., 1939.

AN ALBINO KANGAROO RAT. Jour. Mam., vol.11, no.2, p.237, May, 1930.

Physiology

TEMPERATURE REGULATION, HIBERNATION, AND AESTIVATION IN THE LITTLE POCKET MOUSE, PEROGNATHUS LONGIMEMBRIS. George A. Bartholomew, Jr., Tom J. Cade. Jour. Mam., vol.38, no.1, pp.60-72, Feb., 1957.

LOCOMOTION IN KANGAROO RATS AND ITS ADAPTIVE SIGNIFICANCE. George A. Bartholomew, Jr., Herbert H. Caswell, Jr. Jour. Mam., vol.32, no.2, pp.155-169, pls. 3, May 21, 1951.

LOCOMOTION IN POCKET MICE. George A. Bartholomew, Jr., Grant Reynolds Cary. Jour. Mam., vol.35, no.3, pp.386-392, illus., Aug.20, 1954.

CONSERVATION OF WATER BY THE RODENT DIPODOMYS. A. Brazier Howell, I. Gersh. Jour. Mam., vol.16, no.1, pp.1-9, Feb., 1935.

SEASONAL AND SEXUAL DIFFERENCES IN THE DORSAL SKIN GLAND OF THE KANGAROO RAT (DIPODOMYS). W. B. Quay. Jour. Mam., 34 (1): 1-14, graphs, Feb., 1953.

DO KANGAROO RATS THRIVE WHEN DRINKING SEA WATER? Bodil Schmidt-Nielsen, Knut Schmidt-Nielsen. Amer. Jour. Physiol., vol.160, no.2, pp.291-294, Feb., 1950.

EVAPORATIVE WATER LOSS IN DESERT RODENTS IN THEIR NATURAL HABITAT. Bodil Schmidt-Nielsen, Knut Schmidt-Nielsen. Ecology, 31 (1): 75-85, Jan., 1950.

THE WATER ECONOMY OF DESERT MAMMALS. Bodil Schmidt-Nielsen, Knut Schmidt-Nielsen. Sci. Monthly, 69 (3): 180-185, Sept., 1949.

THE ANIMAL THAT DOES NOT DRINK WATER. George Smokey. South Dakota Conserv. Digest, Pierre, vol.11, no.4, pp. 6, 14, Apr., 1944.

ELECTRICAL EXCITATION OF THE CEREBRUM OF THE KANGAROO RAT. William L. Straus. Jour. Mam., vol.17, no.4, pp. 374-382, figs.2, Nov., 1936.

Reproduction

THE BREEDING SEASON IN TWO SPECIES OF DIPODOMYS. Kenneth L. Duke. Jour. Mam., vol.25, no.2, pp.155-160, figs.2, May 25, 1944.

NOTES ON REPRODUCTION IN THE KANGAROO RAT, DIPODOMYS. E. W. Pfeiffer. Jour. Mam., 37 (3): 449-450, illus., Sept. 11, 1956.

Taxonomy

GEOGRAPHICAL VARIATION IN PEROGNATHUS MERRIAMI. Helmi S. Al-Uthman. MS thesis, U. Tex., 1952.

AN ANALYSIS OF SUBSPECIFIC VARIATIONS IN DIPODOMYS NITRATOIDES. Richard A. Boolootian. Jour. Mam., vol. 35, no.4, pp.570-577, Nov.29, 1954.

SYSTEMATIC STATUS OF DIPODOMYS MERRIAMI AMBIGUUS MERRIAM. W. B. Davis. Jour. Mam., vol.22, no.2, pp.192-194, May 14, 1941.

THE SYSTEMATIC STATUS OF FOUR KANGAROO RATS. W. B. Davis. Jour. Mam., vol.23, no.3, pp.328-333, Aug.14, 1942.

DESCRIPTION OF HETEROMYS DESMARESTIANUS CHIRIQUENSIS. Robert K. Enders. Proc. Acad. Nat. Sci., Phila., vol.90, pp.141-142, May 3, 1939.

GEOGRAPHIC VARIATION IN PEROGNATHUS HISPIDUS. Bryan P. Glass. Jour. Mam., vol.28, no.2, pp.174-179, figs.1, May 19, 1947.

REVISION OF THE SPINY POCKET MICE (GENERA HETEROMYS AND LIOMYS). E. A. Goldman. U.S. Dept. Agric., Bur. Biol. Surv., North American Fauna, no. 34, pp.70, figs.6, pls.3, Sept.7, 1911.

A SUBSTITUTE NAME FOR PEROGNATHUS PENICILLATUS SEORSUS. E. A. Goldman. Jour. Mam., vol.20, no.2, p.257, May, 1939.

THREE NEW KANGAROO RATS OF THE GENUS DIPODOMYS. E. A. Goldman. Proc. Biol. Soc. Wash., vol.36, pp.139-142, May 1, 1923.

A NEW MEMBER OF THE PEROGNATHUS PARVUS GROUP OF POCKET MICE. Joseph Grinnell. Proc. Biol. Soc. Wash., vol.25, pp.127-128, July 31, 1912.

REVISED LIST OF THE SPECIES IN THE GENUS DIPODOMYS. Joseph Grinnell. Jour. Mam., vol.2, no.2, pp.94-97, May, 1921.

REVISION OF THE RODENT GENUS MICRODIPODOPS. E. Raymond Hall. Papers on Mammalogy Published in Honor of Wilfred Hudson Osgood. Field Mus. Nat. Hist., pp.233-277, 1941.

GEOGRAPHIC RACES OF THE KANGAROO RAT, DIPODOMYS MICROPS. E. Raymond Hall, Fred H. Dale. Occ. Papers Mus. Zool., La. State Univ., 4, 63 pp., Nov., 1939.

(A NEW SUBSPECIES OF HETEROMYS ANOMALUS.) Una subspecie nueva de Heteromys anomalus (Mammalia: Rodentia). Jorge Hernandez-Camacho. Lozania, (Acta Zool. Colombiana), Inst. Cienc. Nat. Univ. Nac., Bogota, no.10, pp. 1-15, Apr.26, 1956.

A CHANGE IN THE DEFINITION OF THE GENERIC CHARACTERS OF THE GENUS DIPODOMYS GRAY. Claude W. Hibbard. Jour. Mam., vol.34, no.2, pp.264-265, May 14, 1953.

THE TAXONOMIC STATUS OF DIPODOMYS HEERMANNI BERKELEYANSIS GRINNELL. Emmet T. Hooper. Jour. Mam., vol.17, no.4, pp.418-419, Nov., 1936.

CHARACTER GRADIENTS IN THE SPINY POCKET MOUSE, LIOMYS IRROATUS. Emmet T. Hooper, Charles O. Handley, Jr. Occas. Papers Mus. Zool. Univ. Michigan, Ann Arbor, no.514, pp.1-34, Oct.29, 1948.

TWO NEW POCKET MICE OF THE SPINATUS GROUP AND ONE OF THE LONGIMEMBRIS GROUP. Laurence M. Huey. Trans. San Diego Soc. Nat. Hist., vol.6, no.17, pp.231-234, Dec.24, 1930.

COMPARISON BETWEEN FOSSIL AND RECENT SPECIES OF THE GENUS PEROGNATHUS. Thomas E. Kennerly, Jr. Texas Jour. Sci., Austin, vol.8, no.1, pp.74-86, illus., Mar., 1956.

NOTE ON DIPODOMYS MONTANUS BAIRD. Edgar A. Mearns. Proc. Biol. Soc. Wash., vol.13, p.167, Oct.31, 1900.

DESCRIPTIONS OF EIGHT NEW POCKET MICE. C. Hart Merriam. Proc. Acad. Nat. Sci., Phila., pp.262-268, figs.7, Sept.27, 1894.

DESCRIPTIONS OF TEN NEW KANGAROO RATS. C. Hart Merriam. Proc. Biol. Soc. Wash., vol.20, pp.75-80, July 22, 1907.

DESCRIPTIONS OF THREE NEW KANGAROO MICE OF THE GENUS MICRODIPODOPS. C. Hart Merriam. Proc. Biol. Soc. Wash., vol.14, pp.127-128, July 19, 1901.

DESCRIPTIONS OF THREE NEW KANGAROO RATS, WITH REMARKS ON THE IDENTITY OF DIPODOMYS ORDII OF WOODHOUSE. C. Hart Merriam. North American Fauna, no.4, U.S. Dept. Agric., pp.41-49, Oct., 1890.

NEW AND LITTLE KNOWN KANGAROO RATS OF THE GENUS PERODIPUS. C. Hart Merriam. Proc. Biol. Soc. Wash., vol.17, pp.139-146, July 14, 1904.

PRELIMINARY DESCRIPTIONS OF ELEVEN NEW KANGAROO RATS OF THE GENERA DIPODOMYS AND PERODIPUS. C. Hart Merriam. Proc. Biol. Soc. Wash., vol.9, pp.109-116, June 21, 1894.

PRELIMINARY REVISION OF THE NORTH AMERICAN POCKET MICE (GENERA PEROGNATHUS ET CRICETODIPUS AUCT.) WITH DESCRIPTIONS OF NEW SPECIES AND SUBSPECIES AND A KEY TO THE KNOWN FORMS. C. Hart Merriam. North American Fauna, no.1, pp.29, pls.4, Oct., 1889.

SIX NEW POCKET MICE FROM LOWER CALIFORNIA AND NOTES ON THE STATUS OF SEVERAL DESCRIBED SPECIES. E. W. Nelson, E. A. Goldman. Proc. Biol. Soc. Wash., vol.42, pp.103-112, Mar.25, 1929.

FOUR NEW POCKET MICE. Wilfred H. Osgood. Proc. Biol. Soc. Wash., vol.20, pp.19-21, Feb.23, 1907.

REVISION OF THE POCKET MICE OF THE GENUS PEROGNATHUS. Wilfred H. Osgood. North American Fauna, no.18, U.S. Dept. Agric., Wash., pp.1-65, pl.4, 1900.

THE STATUS OF PEROGNATHUS LONGIMEMBRIS (COUES). Wilfred H. Osgood. Proc. Biol. Soc. Wash., vol.31, pp.95-96, June 29, 1918.

TWO NEW POCKET MICE OF THE GENUS PEROGNATHUS. Wilfred H. Osgood. Proc. Biol. Soc. Wash., vol.17, pp.127-128, June 9, 1904.

DESCRIPTION OF A NEW PEROGNATHUS COLLECTED BY J. K. TOWNSEND IN 1834. PEROGNATHUS LATIROSTRIS, SP. NOV. Samuel N. Rhoads. Amer. Nat., pp.185-187, illus., Feb., 1894.

SUBSPECIATION IN THE KANGAROO RAT, DIPODOMYS ORDII. Henry W. Setzer. Univ. Kansas Publ., Mus. Nat. Hist., Lawrence, vol.1, no.23, pp.473-573, figs. 27, Dec.27, 1949.

DESCRIPTION OF TWO NEW "POCKET-MICE" OF THE GENUS HETEROMYS. Oldfield Thomas. Ann. and Mag. Nat. Hist. (6), vol.11, no.64, pp.329-332, Apr., 1893.

United States
DESCRIPTION OF A NEW SPECIES OF PEROGNATHUS FROM SOUTHEASTERN TEXAS. J. A. Allen. Bull. Amer. Mus. Nat. Hist., vol.4, pp.45-46, pl.3, Mar. 25, 1892.

AN ADDITION TO THE MAMMALIAN FAUNA OF MINNESOTA. Bernard Bailey. Feathers and Fur, no.27, p.8, Sept., 1921.

ORD KANGAROO RAT IN NORTH DAKOTA. Rollin H. Baker. Jour. Mam., vol.33, no. 4, p.493, Nov.19, 1952.

DESCRIPTION OF A RACE OF PEROGNATHUS PARVUS FROM ARIZONA. Seth B. Benson. Proc. Biol. Soc. Wash., vol.50, pp.181-182, Oct.28, 1937.

DESCRIPTIONS OF TWO RACES OF PEROGNATHUS AMPLUS FROM ARIZONA. Seth B. Benson. Proc. Biol. Soc. Wash., vol.46, pp.109-112, Apr.27, 1933.

TWO NEW POCKET MICE, GENUS PEROGNATHUS, FROM THE CALIFORNIAS. Seth B. Benson. Univ. Calif. Publ. Zool., vol.32, no.7, pp.449-454.

TWO NEW POCKET-MICE FROM WESTERN TEXAS. W. Frank Blair. Occas. Papers Mus. Zool. Univ. Michigan, no.381, pp.3, June 20, 1938.

NEW LOCALITY RECORDS FOR PEROGNATHUS BAILEYI FROM CALIFORNIA. Jack C. von Bloeker, Jr. Jour. Mam., vol.13, no.3, pp.279-280, Aug., 1932.

A NEW RACE OF PEROGNATHUS LONGIMEMBRIS FROM SOUTHERN CALIFORNIA. Jack C. von Bloeker, Jr. Proc. Biol. Soc. Wash., vol.45, pp.127-130, Sept.9, 1932.

PEROGNATHUS PACIFICUS FROM THE TYPE LOCALITY. Jack C. von Bloeker, Jr. Jour. Mam., vol.12, no.4, pp.369-372, Nov., 1931.

AN UNUSUAL ABUNDANCE OF BANGS' POCKET MICE IN LA PUERTA VALLEY, CALIFORNIA. Jack C. von Bloeker. Jour. Mam., vol.9, no.2, p.152, May, 1928.

UNUSUAL ABUNDANCE OF POCKET MICE AT SAN FELIPE NARROWS, CALIFORNIA. Jack C. von Bloeker, Jr. Jour. Mam., vol. 13, no.3, p.279, Aug., 1932.

WESTERN EXTENSION OF RANGE OF MICRODIPODOPS POLIONOTUS. EXTENSION OF RANGE OF PEROGNATHUS PACIFICUS. Jack C. von Bloeker, Jr. Jour. Mam., vol.12, no.4, pp.431-432, Nov., 1931.

A NEW POCKET MOUSE FROM EASTERN CALIFORNIA. (PEROGNATHUS LONGIMEMBRIS SALINENSIS.) B. P. Bole, Jr. Sci. Publs., Cleveland Mus. Nat. Hist., vol.5, no.2, pp.3-10, tables 4, Dec.4, 1937.

A NEW RACE OF KANGAROO RAT FROM SOUTHWESTERN UTAH. (DIPODOMYS MERRIAMI FRENATUS.) B. P. Bole, Jr. Sci. Publ., Cleveland Mus. Nat. Hist., vol.5, no.1, pp.1-2, Jan.17, 1936.

TWO NEW SUBSPECIES OF KANGAROO RATS (GENUS DIPODOMYS) FROM SOUTHERN CALIFORNIA. Jean T. Boulware. Univ. California Publ. Zool., Berkeley, vol.46, no.7, pp.391-396, figs.2, Sept.16, 1943.

A NEW KANGAROO RAT OF THE DIPODOMYS ORDII GROUP FROM THE BIG BEND REGION OF TEXAS. Monroe D. Bryant. Occas. Papers Mus. Zool., Louisiana State Univ., University, no.5, pp.65-66, Nov.10, 1939.

A NEW POCKET MOUSE (GENUS PEROGNATHUS) FROM KANSAS. E. Lendell Cockrum. Univ. Kansas Publ., Mus. Nat. Hist., Lawrence, vol.5, no.11, pp.203-206, Dec.15, 1951.

TWO NEW LONG-TAILED POCKET MICE (PEROGNATHUS FORMOSUS) FROM ARIZONA. E. Lendell Cockrum. Jour. Wash. Acad. Sci., 46 (4): 131-132, May 7, 1956.

REDISCOVERY OF DIPODOMYS NITRATOIDES EXILIS. A. E. Culbertson. Jour. Mam., vol.15, no.2, pp.161-162, May, 1934.

DIPODOMYS DESERTI IN UTAH. Stephen D. Durrant. Jour. Mam., vol.24, no.3, p.404, Aug.17, 1943.

(TWO NEW SUBSPECIES OF THE RODENT DIPODOMYS ORDII OF THE EASTERN U.S.A.) Deux sous-especes nouvelles du rongeur Dipodomys ordii de l'ouest des Etats-Unis d'Amerique. (Dipodomys ordii celeripes, D. o. fetosus.) Stephen D. Durrant, E. Raymond Hall. Mammalia, Paris, vol.3, no.1, pp.10-16, pl.1, Mar., 1939.

A NEW POCKET MOUSE FROM SOUTHEASTERN UTAH. (PEROGNATHUS PARVUS BULLATUS.) Stephen D. Durrant, M. Raymond Lee. Proc. Biol. Soc. Wash., 69: 183-186, Dec.31, 1956.

THE DISTRIBUTION AND TAXONOMY OF KANGAROO RATS (GENUS DIPODOMYS) OF UTAH. Stephen D. Durrant, Henry W. Setzer. Bull. Univ. Utah, 35 (26), 39 pp., June, 1945.

THE DUSKY POCKET MOUSE IN IOWA. Edson Fichter. Jour. Mam., vol.20, no.3, pp.377-378, fig.1, Aug.14, 1939.

A NEW KANGAROO MOUSE FROM CALIFORNIA. (MICRODIPODOPS MEGACEPHALUS DICKEYI.) E. A. Goldman. Proc. Biol. Soc. Wash., vol.40, pp.115-116, Sept.26, 1927.

A NEW KANGAROO MOUSE FROM NEVADA. (MICRODIPODOPS MEGACEPHALUS LUCIDUS.) E. A. Goldman. Proc. Biol. Soc. Wash., vol.39, pp.127-128, Dec.27, 1926.

A NEW KANGAROO RAT FROM SOUTHWESTERN ARIZONA. (DIPODOMYS MERRIAMI REGILLUS.) E. A. Goldman. Proc. Biol. Soc. Wash., vol.50, pp.75-76, June 22, 1937.

A NEW KANGAROO RAT OF THE GENUS DIPODOMYS FROM OREGON. (DIPODOMYS HEERMANNI GABRIELSONI.) E. A. Goldman. Proc. Biol. Soc. Wash., vol.38, pp.33-34, Mar.12, 1925.

A NEW POCKET MOUSE FROM COLORADO. (PEROGNATHUS APACHE RELICTUS.) E. A. Goldman. Jour. Mam., vol.19, no.4, pp.495-496, Nov.14, 1938.

A NEW POCKET MOUSE FROM IDAHO. (PEROGNATHUS PARVUS IDAHOENSIS.) E. A. Goldman. Proc. Biol. Soc. Wash., vol.35, pp.105-106, Oct.17, 1922.

A NEW POCKET MOUSE FROM SOUTHERN ARIZONA. (PEROGNATHUS AMPLUS TAYLORI.) E. A. Goldman. Jour. Wash. Acad. Sci., vol.22, nos.16-17, pp.488-489, Oct.19, 1932.

A NEW POCKET MOUSE OF THE GENUS PEROGNATHUS FROM NEVADA. (PEROGNATHUS PENICILLATUS SEORSUS.) E. A. Goldman. Proc. Biol. Soc. Wash., vol.52, pp.33-36, Mar.11, 1939.

TWO NEW KANGAROO RATS FROM ARIZONA. E. A. Goldman. Jour. Wash. Acad. Sci., vol.14, pp.372-373, Sept.19, 1924.

TWO NEW POCKET MICE FROM ARIZONA. E. A. Goldman. Jour. Wash. Acad. Sci., vol.22, no.13, pp.386-388, July 19, 1932.

TWO NEW POCKET MICE FROM WYOMING. E. A. Goldman. Proc. Biol. Soc. Wash., vol.30, pp.147-148, July 27, 1917.

FIVE NEW FIVE-TOED KANGAROO RATS FROM CALIFORNIA. Joseph Grinnell. Univ. Calif. Publ. Zool., vol.21, pp.43-47, Mar.29, 1919.

FOUR NEW KANGAROO RATS FROM WEST-CENTRAL CALIFORNIA. Joseph Grinnell. Proc. Biol. Soc. Wash., vol.32, pp.203-205, Dec.31, 1919.

A GEOGRAPHICAL STUDY OF THE KANGAROO RATS OF CALIFORNIA. Joseph Grinnell. Univ. Calif. Publ. Zool., vol. 24, no.1, 12 pp., figs., pls.6, June, 1922.

(Review by E. A. Goldman of) A GEOGRAPHICAL STUDY OF THE KANGAROO RATS OF CALIFORNIA. Joseph Grinnell. Jour. Mam., vol.3, no.4, pp. 264-267, Nov., 1922.

A NEW KANGAROO RAT FROM THE SAN JOAQUIN VALLEY, CALIFORNIA. Joseph Grinnell. Jour. Mam., vol.1, no.4, pp.178-179, Aug., 1920.

A SECOND SPECIES OF THE MAMMALIAN GENUS MICRODIPODOPS FROM CALIFORNIA. Joseph Grinnell. Univ. Calif. Publ. Zool., vol.12, no.7, pp.301-304, Apr.15, 1914.

A NEW KANGAROO RAT FROM THE UPPER SACRAMENTO VALLEY, CALIFORNIA. (DIPODOMYS HEERMANNI SAXATILIS.) Joseph Grinnell, Jean M. Linsdale. Univ. Calif. Publ. Zool., vol.30, no.17, pp.453-459, June 15, 1929.

NEW HETEROMYID RODENTS FROM NEVADA. E. Raymond Hall. Proc. Biol. Soc. Wash., vol.54, pp.55-62, May 20, 1941.

A NEW SUBSPECIES OF POCKET MOUSE FROM KANSAS. (PEROGNATHUS FLAVESCENS COCKRUMI.) E. Raymond Hall. Univ. Kansas Publ., Mus. Nat. Hist., vol. 7, no.11, pp.587-590, Nov.15, 1954.

A NEW KANGAROO MOUSE (MICRODIPODOPS) OF UTAH AND NEVADA. E. Raymond Hall, Stephen D. Durrant. Jour. Mam., vol.18, no.3, pp.357-359, Aug.14, 1937.

TWO NEW KANGAROO-MICE FROM UTAH. E. Raymond Hall, Stephen D. Durrant. Murrelet, Seattle, vol.22, no.1, pp.5-7, Jan.-Apr., 1941.

A NEW SOUTH DAKOTA LOCALITY FOR THE KANGAROO RAT, DIPODOMYS. Charles O. Handley, Jr. Jour. Mam., vol.34, no.2, p.264, May 14, 1953.

A NEW KANGAROO-RAT FROM SOUTH WESTERN UTAH. (DIPODOMYS ORDII CINDERENSIS.) Ross Hardy. Proc. Biol. Soc. Wash., vol.57, pp.53-56, Oct.31, 1944.

OCCURRENCE OF PEROGNATHUS FASCIATUS IN UTAH. C. Lynn Hayward, Merlin L. Killpack. Jour. Mam., 37 (3): 451, Sept.11, 1956.

A NEW RACE OF SILKY POCKET MOUSE (PEROGNATHUS) FROM THE SAN LUIS VALLEY, COLORADO. John Eric Hill. Amer. Mus. Novitates, New York, no.1212, p.1, Dec.7, 1942.

NEW SUBSPECIES OF KANGAROO RATS OF THE DIPODOMYS ORDII GROUP FROM MONTANA AND WYOMING. Donald F. Hoffmeister. Proc. Biol. Soc. Wash., vol. 55, pp.165-168, Dec.31, 1942.

THE SILKY POCKET MOUSE, PEROGNATHUS FLAVUS, IN ARIZONA, WITH A DESCRIPTION OF A NEW SUBSPECIES. Donald F. Hoffmeister. Proc. Biol. Soc. Wash., 69: 55-58, May 21, 1956.

POCKET MICE IN CRATER LAKE NATIONAL PARK. R. R. Huestis. Jour. Mam., vol.23, no.4, p.451, Nov.14, 1942.

A NEW FORM OF PEROGNATHUS FORMOSUS FROM THE MOHAVE DESERT REGION OF CALIFORNIA. (PEROGNATHUS FORMOSUS MOHAVENSIS.) Laurence M. Huey. Trans. San Diego Soc. Nat. Hist., vol.9, no.8, pp.35-36, Nov.21, 1938.

A NEW PEROGNATHUS FROM THE VICINITY OF MOUNT PINOS, KERN COUNTY,

CALIFORNIA. Laurence M. Huey. Proc. Biol. Soc. Wash., vol.39, pp.121-122, Dec. 27, 1926.

A NEW RACE OF KANGAROO RAT FROM THE ARGUS MOUNTAINS, CALIFORNIA. (DIPODOMYS MOHAVENSIS ARGUSENSIS.) Laurence M. Huey. Trans. San Diego Soc. Nat. Hist., vol.10, no.10, pp.131-132, Mar.9, 1945.

A NEW SILKY POCKET MOUSE FROM SOUTHWESTERN UTAH. (PEROGNATHUS LONGIMEMBRIS VIRGINIS.) Laurence M. Huey. Trans. San Diego Soc. Nat. Hist., vol.9, no.12, pp.55-56, Aug.31, 1939.

DESCRIPTIONS OF THREE NEW FORMS OF POCKET-MICE FROM THE MEXICAN BORDER OF THE UNITED STATES. Edgar A. Mearns. Bull. Amer. Mus. Nat. Hist., vol.10, art.15, pp.299-302, Aug. 31, 1898.

A NEW POCKET MOUSE FROM SOUTHERN CALIFORNIA. Edgar A. Mearns. Proc. Biol. Soc. Wash., vol.14, pp.135-136, Aug. 9, 1901.

DESCRIPTION OF A NEW GENUS AND SPECIES OF DWARF KANGAROO RAT FROM NEVADA (MICRODIPODOPS MEGACEPHALUS). C. Hart Merriam. North American Fauna, no.5, pp.115-117, July 30, 1891.

REVISION OF THE NORTH AMERICAN POCKET MICE. C. Hart Merriam. North American Fauna, no.1, U.S. Dept. Agric., pp.29, pls.4, Oct.25, 1889.

IDENTITY OF THE NORTHWEST COLORADO POCKET MOUSE. Frederick W. Miller. Jour. Mam., vol.9, no.4, p.337, Nov., 1928.

LIFE HISTORY NOTES ON PRICE AND BAILEY POCKET MICE OF SOUTHERN ARIZONA. Hudson G. Reynolds, Horace S. Haskell. Jour. Mam., 30 (2): 150-156, May, 1949.

DESCRIPTION OF A RACE OF PEROGNATHUS LONGIMEMBRIS FROM TULARE COUNTY, CALIFORNIA. William Bebb Richardson. Jour. Mam., vol.18, no.4, pp.510-511, Nov., 1937.

A NEW PEROGNATHUS FROM THE SAN JOAQUIN VALLEY, CALIFORNIA. Walter P. Taylor. Univ. Calif. Publ. Zool., vol. 10, no.6, pp.155-166, fig.1, May 21, 1912.

DESCRIPTION OF A NEW SPECIES OF PEROGNATHUS FROM COLORADO. Oldfield Thomas. Ann. and Mag. Nat. Hist. (6), vol.11, no.65, pp.405-406, May, 1893.

PEROGNATHUS NELSONI CANESCENS IN NEW MEXICO. Olin L. Webb. Jour. Mam., vol.35, no.3, p.453, Aug.20, 1954.

DIPODOMYS DESERTI SONORIENSIS IN ARIZONA. George Willett. Jour. Mam., vol.18, no.1, p.101, Feb.14, 1937.

A NEW KANGAROO RAT FROM NORTHEASTERN CALIFORNIA. George Willett. Jour. Mam., vol.16, no.1, pp.63-64, 1935.

Young COUNTS OF EMBRYOS IN NEVADAN KANGAROO RATS (GENUS DIPODOMYS). J. R. Alcorn. Jour. Mam., Balto., vol.22, no.1, pp.88-89, figs.2, Feb.14, 1941.

OBSERVATIONS ON THE YOUNG OF THE MERRIAM KANGAROO RAT. David J. Doran. Jour. Mam., vol.33, no.4, pp. 494-495, Nov.19, 1952.

Castoridae

THE STORY OF SPADEFOOT. Roy L. Abbott. Frontiers, Lancaster, vol.12, no. 2, pp.43-44, 64, illus., Dec., 1947.

THE BEAVER. Rod Amundson. Wildlife in North Carolina, Raleigh, vol.13, no.11, pp.4-6, illus., Nov., 1949.

BUSY BEAVER. Elizabeth Bachmann. Conserv. Volunteer, St. Paul, vol.11, no. 65, pp.41-46, July-Aug., 1948 (See also: Amer. Nat. Fur & Market Jour., Wausau, vol.27, no.3, pp.5, 22-23, Oct., 1948).

BEAVER. P. L. Beckie. Blue Jay Saskatchewan Nat. Hist. Soc., 14 (3): 100, Sept., 1956.

(THE BEAVER.) Der Biber (Castor fiber Linne.). Wilhelm Blasius. Raoul Rotter von Dombrowskis "Allgemeiner Encyklopadie der gesammten Forst-und Jagdwissenscraten, " Wien., pp.23, figs.3, 1886.

ENGINEER OF THE WILDS. G. W. Bradt. Michigan Conservation, Lansing, vol.15, no.3, pp.4-5, illus., Mar.-Apr., 1946.

THE RISE AND FALL OF THE BEAVER. J. G. Burr. Texas Game and Fish, Austin, vol.4, no.3, pp.4-5, 18-19, illus., Feb., 1946.

ANIMALS IN DECLINE: 4.BEAVERS. Maurice Burton. Illus. London News, vol. 218, no.5834, p.220, illus., Feb.10, 1951.

BUSY BROWN BEAVERS. Effie Butler. Our Dumb Animals, Norwood, vol.76, no. 5, p.97, May, 1943.

THE RETURN OF THE FUR BRIGADE. Arthur Hawthorne Carhart. Natural Hist., New York, vol.53, no.2, pp.68-71, illus., Feb., 1944.

BEAVER, BUILDER OF EMPIRE. William H. Carr. Nat. Hist., New York, vol.42, no.2, pp.100-106, Sept., 1938.

BEAVER. Lucie Chapman, Wendell Chapman. Natural Hist., New York, vol. 34, no.6, pp.554-566, illus., Oct., 1934.

THE WISE ONE. Frank Conibear, J. L. Blundell. William Sloane Associates, New York, pp.265, illus., 1949.

HISTORY OF A BEAVER COLONY. David B. Cook. Jour. Mam., 24 (1): 12-18, Feb., 1943.

THE HUT BUILDERS--BEAVER. Bonnycastle Dale, Jr. Rod and Gun in Canada, Montreal, vol.43, no.3, pp.10-11, 31-32, Aug., 1941.

(EXHIBIT OF BEAVER COLONIES.) Wykaz stanowisk bobra. (Castor fiber vistulanus.) August Dehnel. Fragmenta Faunistica Musei Zool., Polonici, Warsaw, vol.5, no. 13, pp.199-244, maps, 1948.

THE BUSY BEAVER. J. C. Dillon. Sylva, Toronto, vol.3, no.1, p.17, 1947.

EAGER BEAVER. Frank Dufresne. Sports Afield, Minneapolis, vol.120, no.6, pp.38-39, 118-121, illus., Dec., 1948.

THE ROMANCE OF THE BEAVER. Arthur Radclyffe Dugmore. London, pp. 255, illus., 1914.

FASTIDIOUS BEAVERS. Emil F. Ernst. Yosemite Nat. Notes, vol.28, no.3, p.24, Mar., 1949.

BEAVER, MUD SKIPPER AND PENGUIN ON STAMPS. I. R. Gaertner. Hobbies, the Magazine for collectors, Chicago, vol.43, no.5, pp.36-38, July, 1938.

SO! YOU BELIEVE IT, EH! Phil Goodrum. Texas Game and Fish, Austin, vol.1, no.12, pp.7, 17, illus., Nov., 1943.

THE AMERICAN BEAVER. George C. Goodwin. Nature Mag., vol.5, pp.217-219, 1 fig., 1 pl., Apr., 1925.

THE MAGNIFICENT RODENT. H. Raymond Gregg. Sci. Monthly, Lancaster, vol.67, no.2, pp.73-82, illus., Aug., 1948.

BEHOLD...THE BEAVER! Burt Gresham. Beaver, Winnipeg, outfit 270, no.3, pp.6-12, illus., Dec., 1939.

(SOME REMARKS ON CASTOR FIBER L.) Einige Bemerkungen ueber Castor fiber L. Adolph Gueinzius. Zeitschr. f. Saeugetierkunde, vol.11, no.2, pp.237-241, Dec.15, 1936.

"AH-MISK". (CASTOR CANADENSIS.) Pearl Guest. Canadian Nature, Toronto, vol.4, no.2, pp.52-56, illus., Mar.-Apr., 1942.

BEAVER. W. J. Hamilton, Jr. N. Y. Conservationist, vol.4 (4): 4-5, illus., Feb.-Mar., 1950.

THE EMBATTLED BEAVER. John D. Hart. Colorado Conservation, vol.3, no.4, pp.6-10, July, 1954.

THE BEAVER. Caroline A. Heppenstall. Pennsylvania Game News, Harrisburg, vol. 16, no.10, p.10, Jan., 1946.

(THE BIOLOGY OF THE BEAVER.) Zur Biologie des Bibers. Gustav Hinze. Der Biologe, vol.7, no.12, pp.404-406, Dec., 1938.

THE STORY OF THE BEAVER. William Davenport Hulbert. McClure's Mag., vol. 16, no.6, pp.483-496, Apr., 1901.

SOME MAINE BEAVER CARCASS STUDY RESULTS. John H. Hunt. Proc. 8th Ann. N.E. Wildl. Conf., Jackson's Mill, W. Va., Apr.1-4, pp.1-8, 1952.

THE UNNATURAL HISTORY OF THE BEAVER. Charles MacNamara. Canadian Field-Nat., vol.45, no.1, pp.1-7, Jan., 1931.

A NOTE ON THE BEAVER. Kenneth W. Martin. Wyoming Wild Life, Cheyenne, vol.11, no.9, pp.31-34, illus., Sept., 1947.

SUMMER IN BEAVER LAND. Enos A. Mills. Nature Mag., vol.2, pp.221-226, 8 figs., Oct., 1923.

OUR INDUSTRIOUS NEIGHBORS OF THE NAHA. Alda Orton. Alaska Sportsman, Ketchikan, vol.9, no.5, pp.14-16, illus., May, 1943.

A BACKYARD BEAVER. Clyde L. Patch. Canadian Field-Nat., Ottawa, vol.56, no. 3, p.46, Mar., 1942.

(BEAVERS, BUILDERS OF DAMS.) Bievres constructeurs de barrages. P. B. Richard. Mammalia, Paris, vol.19, no.2, pp.293-301, illus., June, 1955.

MRS. RICHARD'S BEAVERS. A. M. Richards. New York State Conservationist, Albany, vol.4, no.2, pp.18-19, illus., Oct.-Nov., 1949.

BEAVER--MAKER OF HISTORY. Beulah Rollins. Nature Mag., vol.22, no.5, pp. 210-212, illus., Nov., 1933.

MASTER BUILDERS OF THE ANIMAL WORLD. Wilbert Nathan Savage. Our Dumb Animals, Boston, vol.75, no.10, p. 185, Oct., 1942.

CONODONTES, TROGONTHERIUM AND THE OTHER CASTORIDAE. A. Schreuder. Palaeont. Zeitschr., vol.13, nos.1-2, pp. 148-176, figs.6, May 3, 1931.

THE AMERICAN BEAVER. Albert R. Shadle. Animal Kingdom, New York Zool. Soc., 59 (4): 98-104; (5): 152-156; (6) 181-185, July-Dec., 1956.

THE BEAVER RESCUE. Curtis Skinner. Yellowstone Nat. Notes, vol.10, nos.1-2, p.3, Jan.-Feb., 1933.

MY ACE-IN-THE-HOLE. Clayton H. Smith. Fur-Fish-Game, Harding's Mag., Columbus, vol.86, no.8, pp.34-35, illus., Aug., 1946.

OUR BEAVER. Dunc Storms. Nature Mag., vol.27, no.1, pp.48-49, Jan., 1936.

BEAVER SHOW. Edwin Way Teale. Nat. Hist., New York, vol.53, no.9, pp.390-395, illus., Nov., 1944.

THIS IS MY JOB. Reed Twitchell. Missouri Conservationist, Jefferson City, vol. 10, no.1, pp.4-7, Jan., 1949.

BEAVER NOTES. H. P. Ufford. Outing, pp.507-512, illus., Sept., 1887.

THE LIFE STORY OF THE BEAVER. Geoffrey M. Vevers. Transatlantic Arts, London and New York, pp.31, illus., 1946.

TWENTY YEARS IN A BEAVER POND. Edward R. Warren. American Forests, vol.38, no.8, pp.444-447, illus., Aug., 1932.

BEHIND THE DAM--WHILE THE WILDERNESS VANISHES FOR MAN, THIS PAIR OF YOUNG BEAVERS PIT TOOTH AND CLAW AND THEIR REMARKABLE ENGINEERING SKILL AGAINST THE MANIFOLD DANGERS WHICH NATURE, IN ALL HER VAST INDIFFERENCE, SETS IN THEIR PATH. A POIGNANT DRAMA OF THE WILD, SYMBOLIZING THE LIFE STORY OF ONE OF OUR MOST BELOVED ANIMALS. Kerry Wood. Natural History, New York, vol.43, no.5, pp.290-297, illus., May, 1939.

THE AMERICAN BEAVER CASTOR CANADENSIS. Wyoming Wild Life, Cheyenne, vol.4, no.4, p.14, Apr., 1939.

THE BEAVER BREAKS THE ICE: REMARKABLE LONDON "ZOO" PHOTOGRAPHS. Illus. London News, vol.210, no.5621, p.55, illus., Jan.11, 1947.

BEAVER CHIEF. Beaver, Winnipeg, outfit 275, p.44, Sept., 1944.

CASTOR CANADENSIS. (TEN PHOTOS OF BEAVERS.) Beaver, Winnipeg, outfit 277, pp.26-27, illus., Sept., 1946.

Alaska

GROWTH RATES AND AGE DETERMINATION IN ALASKAN BEAVER. John L. Buckley, W. L. Libby. Trans. 20th N. A. Wildl. Conf., pp.495-507, illus., 1955.

THE LIFE HISTORY AND GENERAL ECOLOGY OF THE BEAVER (CASTOR CANADENSIS KUHL) IN INTERIOR ALASKA. John B. Hakala. MS thesis, Univ. Alaska, pp.1-181, 1952.

PRODUCTIVITY AND GROWTH RATES OF BEAVER IN INTERIOR ALASKA. John B. Hakala. Science in Alaska 1951, Proc. 2nd. Alaskan Sci. Conf., Alaska Div. AAAS, pp. 327-330, 1953.

Anatomy

THE COMBING CLAWS OF THE BEAVER. Vernon Bailey. Jour. Mam., vol.4, no.2, pp.77-79, pl.9, May, 1923.

(OSTEOLOGICAL AND OSTEOMETRIC NOTES ON BEAVERS IN GENERAL AND THE RHONE BEAVER IN PARTICULAR.) Notes osteologiques et osteometriques sur les castors en general, sur le castor du Rhone en particulier. E. Bourdelle, M. Doublet. Bull. Mus. Hist. Nat., Marsielle, vol.7, no.1, p.31, 1947.

(CONTRIBUTIONS TO THE FUNCTIONAL ANATOMY OF THE BEAVER SKELETON.) Beitraege zur funktionellen Anatomie des Biber-skelettes. Hans-Albrecht Freye. Wissensch. Zeitsch. Martin-Luther-Universitaet Halle-Wittenberg, Jahrg. 3, Heft 5, pp.1101-1135, illus., Aug.30, 1954.

(REMARKS ON THE GENITAL SYSTEM OF THE MALE BEAVER, CASTOR FIBER L.) Bemerkungen zum Genital system des Mannlichen Bibers, Castor fiber L. Hans-Albrecht Freye. Wissensch. Z., Jahrg.2, Heft 11, pp.911-915, illus., 1953.

(RESEARCH ON THE OSTEOLOGICAL CHARACTERS OF BEAVERS (STENEOFIBER, CASTOR).) Recherches sur les caracteres osteologiques des castorides (Steneofiber, Castor). Madeleine Friant. Archiv. Mus. Nat. d'Hist. Nat., Paris, ser.6, vol.14, pp.105-123, figs.15, pls.8-9, Mar., 1937.

OSTEOLOGICAL RELATIONSHIPS OF THREE SPECIES OF BEAVERS. F. Harvey Holden. Univ. Calif. Publ. Zool., vol.17, no.8, pp. 75-114, figs.A-R, pls.5-12, Mar.3, 1917.

A PRELIMINARY REPORT ON AN ENDOURETHRAL CAST IN BEAVER. Gardiner F. Jones. Murrelet, Seattle, vol.31, no.1, p. 15, May 19, 1950.

ON A SUPERNUMBERARY MOLAR IN A BEAVER. C. I. Forsyth Major. Proc. Zool. Soc. Lond., p.630, Oct., 1908.

CRANIAL FORAMINA OF NORTH AMERICAN BEAVERS. Everett Claire Olson. Jour. Paleontology, Menasha, vol.14, no. 5, pp.495-501, figs.7, Sept., 1940.

ON THE ANATOMY OF THE BEAVER (CASTOR FIBER, L.). R. Owen. Proc. Comm. Sci. and Corres. Zool. Soc. Lond., pt.1, p.19, 1830-1831.

THE BEAVER'S REMARKABLE JAW. W. P. Pycraft. Illus. London News, vol.191, no.5131, p.302, figs.3, Aug.21, 1937.

NOTES ON BEAVER ANATOMY. W. M. Rush. Jour. Mam., vol.8, no.3, pp.245-246, Aug., 1927.

(CONTRIBUTIONS ON THE MORPHOLOGY OF BEAVER SPECIES.) Beitraege zur Morphologie der Biberarten. L. Wiesel. Zeitschr. f. Morphologie u. Oekologie der Tiere, vol.14, pp.421-512, 4 figs., Apr.23, 1929.

STUDIES OF OSTEOLOGY AND MYOLOGY OF THE BEAVER (CASTOR CANADENSIS). F. W. Young. Agric. Exper. Sta., Michigan State Coll., Mem.2, pp.1-84, pls.24, Apr., 1937.

Canada

TWO NEW BEAVERS FROM LABRADOR AND NEW BRUNSWICK. Vernon Bailey, J. Kenneth Doutt. Jour. Mam., vol.23, no.1, pp.86-88, Feb.14, 1942.

THE BEAVER IN CANADIAN ART. Marius Barbeau. Beaver, Winnipeg, outfit 272, pp.14-18, illus., Sept., 1941.

THE BEAVER: GOOD CANADIAN CITIZEN. Freda Davies. Canadian Nature, Toronto, vol.10, no.5, pp.158-160, illus., Nov.-Dec., 1948.

ON THE CONSTRUCTION OF A BEAVER DAM IN DIGBY COUNTY, NOVA SCOTIA, SEPT., 1871. J. Bernard Gilpin. Nova-Scotia Inst. Nat. Sci. Proc. and Trans., vol.3, pp.152-155, 1874.

ON THE BEAVER IN NOVA SCOTIA. Campbell Hardy. Proc. Nova Scotian Inst. Nat. Sci., vol.2, no.1, pp.17-25.

BEAVER ON THE NORTHERN BRITISH COLUMBIA ISLANDS. T. T. McCabe. Canadian Field-Nat., Ottawa, vol.62, no. 2, pp.72-74, Mar.-Apr., 1948.

CASTOROLOGIA OR THE HISTORY AND TRADITIONS OF THE CANADIAN BEAVER. Horace T. Martin. Montreal and London, pp.238, illus., 1892.

(THE CANADIAN BEAVER IN THE PRINCE ALBERT NATIONAL PARK IS IN A CONTINUOUS STATE OF INCREASE.) Il castoro canadese del Parco Nazionale Prince Albert è in continuo aumento. Edgardo Moltoni. Rivista Sci. Nat. "Natura," Milan, 46: 195-198, 1955.

ON THE NATURAL HISTORY AND HUNTING OF THE BEAVER, (CASTOR CANADENSIS KUHL) IN NEWFOUNDLAND; COMPARED WITH OBSERVATIONS MADE BY MESSRS. A. H. GREEN AND ROBERT BROWN, F.R.S.G., ON THE PACIFIC SLOPE OF THE ROCKY MOUNTAINS. Henry Reeks. The Zool., ser.2, vol.5, pp.1953-1972, Jan., 1870.

NOTES ON THE BEAVERS OF WOOD BUFFALO PARK, ALBERTA. J. Dewey Soper. Jour. Mam., 18 (1): 1-13, Feb., 1937.

BRINGING BACK THE BEAVER TO SASKATCHEWAN. Oryx, 1 (5): 244-245, 1952.

Captivity

RANCHING THE BEAVER, I-II-III-IV-V-VI. M. M. Atwater. Amer. Fur Breeder, vol.4, no.1, pp.17-18, July, 1931; vol.4, no. 2, pp.30-31, Aug., 1931; vol.4, no.3, pp. 20-22, Sept., 1931; vol.4, no.4, pp.20-22, Oct., 1931; vol.4, no.5, pp.29-30, Nov., 1931; vol.4, no.6, pp.32-34, Dec., 1931.

(METHODOLOGY OF BEAVER RAISING.) Methodik der Biberzucht. Gustav Hinze. Zool. Garten, Leipzig, 23 (1-3): 177-184, 1957.

BEAVER ARE EASY TO RAISE. Hamilton L. McNichol. Sports Afield, 128 (3): 113, illus., Sept., 1952.

RAISING BEAVER IN CAPTIVITY. Ward D. Walker. Parks and Recreation, vol.17, no. 4, pp.138-141, Dec., 1933.

RAISING BEAVER IN CAPTIVITY. M. L. Weaver. American Fur Breeder, Duluth, vol.19, no.10, pp.40-41, illus., Apr., 1947.

Diseases, Parasites

RANCHING THE BEAVER. III. BEAVER DISEASES. M. M. Atwater. American Fur Breeder, vol.5, no.1, pp.20-21, July, 1932.

RABIES IN BEAVER. George K. Brakhage, Frank W. Sampson. Jour. Wildlife Management, Ithaca, N.Y., vol.16, no.2, p. 226, Apr., 1952.

SCREWWORMS INFEST BEAVER IN TEXAS. Arthur H. Cook. Jour. Mam., vol.21, no. 1, p.93, Feb.14, 1940.

THE FUNGUS (HAPLOSPORANGIUM PARVUM) IN THE LUNGS OF THE BEAVER (CASTOR CANADENSIS). Arnold B. Erickson. Jour. Wildl. Mgt., 13 (4): 419-420, Oct., 1949.

PARASITES OF BEAVERS, WITH A NOTE ON PARAMPHISTOMUM CASTORI KOFOID AND PARK, 1937, A SYNONYM OF STICHORCHIS SUBTRIQUETRUS. Arnold B. Erickson. Am. Midland Nat., 31 (3): 625-630, May, 1944.

TULAREMIA IN A BEAVER. H. Hammersland, E. M. Joheschild. Jour. Amb. Vet. Med. Assn., 96 (754): 96-97, Jan., 1940.

(THE TREATMENT OF LIVER ROT IN THE SWAMP BEAVER.) Die Bekaempfung des Leberegels beim Sumpfbiber. E. Heidegger. Der Deutsche Pelztierzuechter, Muenchen, Jahrg.1932, no.17, pp.414-415, fig.1, Sept.1, 1932.

EPIZOOTIC TULAREMIA IN THE BEAVER, CASTOR CANADENSIS, AND THE CONTAMINATION OF STREAM WATER WITH PASTEURELLA TULARENSIS. William L. Jellison, Glen M. Kohls, W. J. Butler, James A. Weaver. Amer. Jour. Hygiene, Balto., vol.38, no.2, pp.168-182, Sept., 1942.

TRAUASSOSIUS RUFUS, GEN. ET SP. N: A NEMATODE (TRICHOSTRONGYLID PARASITE IN THE STOMACH OF THE NORWEGIAN BEAVER. M. Khalil. Ann. and Mag. Nat. Hist., ser.9, vol.10, pp.281-289, 7 figs., Sept., 1922.

A NEW TREMATODE, PARAMPHILSTOMUM CASTORI SP. NOV., FROM CASTOR CANADENSIS BAILEYI NELSON, FROM MARY'S RIVER, NEVADA. C. A. Kofoid, James T. Park. Univ. Calif. Publ. Zool., 41 (27): 419-422, 1937.

PARASITES AND DISEASES OF THE BEAVER (CASTOR CANADENSIS KUHL). AN ANNOTATED BIBLIOGRAPHY. William H. Lawrence, S. A. Graham. Mich. Wildl., no.2, pp.1-6, Nov., 1955.

REPORTS ON THE DISEASED APPEARANCES OF A BEAVER (CASTOR FIBER, L.). William Martin. Proc. Comm. Sci. and Corres. Zool. Soc. Lond., pt.1, pp.12-13, 1830-1831.

EXPERIMENTAL TREATMENT OF TRAVASSOSIOSIS IN RIVER BEAVERS. N. P. Romanova, V. S. Pokrovski. Trans. of Russian Game Reports, Canadian Wildlife Service, Ottawa, 1: 98-105, 1957.

NATURAL OCCURRENCE OF TULAREMIA IN BEAVER AND ITS TRANSMISSION TO MAN. John W. Scott. Science, 91 (2359): 263-264, Mar.15, 1940.

Ecology

BEAVERS VS. TROUT. Arthur K. Adams. Michigan Conserv., Lansing, vol.18, no.2, pp.15-16, illus., Apr., 1949.

SOME PHYSICO-CHEMICAL EFFECTS OF BEAVER DAMS UPON MICHIGAN TROUT STREAMS IN THE WATERSMEET AREA. Arthur K. Adams. PhD thesis, Univ. Mich., 332 pp., 1954.

SOME OBSERVATIONS ON ADAPTABILITY OF MICHIGAN BEAVERS RELEASED IN MISSOURI. Earl L. Atwood. Jour. Wildl. Mgt., 2 (3): 165-166, July, 1938.

EFFECTS OF BEAVERS ON FISH. R. Wayne Bailey, R. F. Stephens. W. Va. Cons., 15 (6): 11-16, 26, Sept., 1951.

BEAVER AND BIRDS. William H. Carr. Bird-Lore, 42 (2): 141-146, Mar.-Apr., 1940.

THE WISE ONE. (LIFE AND ECOLOGY OF THE BEAVER IN STORY FORM.) Frank Conibear, J. L. Blundell. Sloane, 265 pp., 1949.

BEAVER-TROUT RELATIONS. David B. Cook. Jour. Mam., 21 (4): 397-401, Nov., 1940.

BEAVER STUDY REVEALS DAMAGE TO TIMBER, CORN ONLY NEGLIGIBLE. Fannye A. Cook. Miss. Game and Fish, 4 (12): 4, Dec., 1940.

THE BEAVER--FRIEND OF THE FOREST. W. T. Cox. Amer. Forests, Washington, D.C., vol.46, no.10, pp.448-450, 476-477, illus., Oct., 1940.

BEAVER TRAPPED BY TREE. Robert S. Ellarson, Joseph J. Hickey. Jour. Mam., vol.33, no.4, pp.482-483, 1 pl., Nov.19, 1952.

THE BEAVER--CONSERVER OF SOIL AND WATER. William L. Finley. Trans. N.A. Wildl. Conf., 2: 295-297, 1937.

EXPERIMENTAL PLANTING OF WILLOWS IN BEAVER HABITAT IN THE TCHET-CHERSK DISTRICT. N. I. Fomicheva. Trans. of Russian Game Reports, Canadian Wildlife Service, Ottawa, 1: 106-109, 1957.

REFORESTATION OF ASPEN AFTER COMPLETE CUTTING BY BEAVERS. Edward C. Gese, Albert R. Shadle. Jour. Wildl. Mgt., 7 (2): 223-228, Apr., 1943.

BEAVER AND TROUT. James E. Grasse. Wyo. Wild Life, 13 (11): 4-13, 34, Dec., 1949.

BEAVER MANAGEMENT AND ECOLOGY. James E. Grasse, Euvern F. Putnam. Wyoming Wild Life, Cheyenne, vol.14, no. 2, pp.20-34, illus., Mar., 1950.

THE BEAVER OF THE RIDING MOUNTAIN, MANITOBA. AN ECOLOGICAL STUDY AND COMMENTARY. H. U. Green. Can. Field-Nat., 50: 1-8, 21-23, 36-50, 61-67, 85-92, Jan.-May, 1936.

BEAVER DAMS AND WILDLIFE. William C. Grimm. Pa. Game News, 13 (11): 10-11, 30, Feb., 1943.

SUMMARY OF THE DISSERTATION, "WILLOW AND ASPEN IN THE ECOLOGY OF BEAVER ON SAGEHEN CREEK, CALIFORNIA." Joseph G. Hall. Univ. California, 1 page, 1956.

FELLED TREE KILLS BEAVER. Harold B. Hitchock. Jour. Mam., 35 (3): 452, Aug., 1954.

USE OF OAKS BY BEAVERS IN NEW HAMPSHIRE. William J. Jahoda. Jour. Wildlife Management, Menasha, vol.10, no.4, pp. 366-367, Oct., 1946.

THE AMERICAN BEAVER SAVES THE LAND AND WATER. E. J. Keefe. Frontiers, Phila., vol.3, no.5, pp.154-155, 2 photos, June, 1939.

RIVER "DIES" WHEN BEAVER ARE REMOVED. W. F. Kellis. Texas Game and Fish, Austin, vol.2, no.6, pp.15, 18, May, 1944.

BEAVER AND WILDLIFE. Lawrence Kilham. Atlantic Naturalist, Washington, vol.6, no. 5, pp.210-213, May-Aug., 1951.

MICHIGAN BEAVER POPULATIONS AS INFLUENCED BY FIRE AND LOGGING. William H. Lawrence. PhD thesis, Univ. Mich., 232 pp., 1954.

BEAVER VS. TROUT--MORE TESTIMONY. James A. Lawrie. Fins, Feathers and Fur, no.27, p.5, Sept., 1921.

HOW MICHIGAN HANDLES THE BEAVER-TROUT PROBLEM. J. W. Leonard. Mich. Conservation, vol.7, no.8, p.11, illus., Apr., 1938.

AN INVESTIGATION OF SOME PROBLEMS OF ECOLOGY OF THE BEAVER IN NORTHERN MANITOBA. John Blake Nash. Dept. Mines and Natural Resources, Game and Fisheries Branch, Manitoba, pp.64, multilithed, Apr., 1951.

ECOLOGICAL EFFECTS OF BEAVER HABITAT ABANDONMENT IN THE COLORADO ROCKIES. Don J. Neff. Jour. Wildlife Management, 21 (1): 80-84, Jan., 1957.

BEAVER-TROUT RELATIONSHIPS. Donald Patterson. Wis. Cons. Bull., 15 (3): 9-11, Mar., 1950.

BEAVER-TROUT RELATIONSHIP IN THE ROCKY MOUNTAIN REGION. D. I. Rasmussen. Trans. N.A. Wildl. Conf., 5: 256-263, 1941.

EFFECTS OF BEAVER ON TROUT WATERS. Kenneth A. Reid. Md. Cons., 29 (4): 21-23, illus., Winter, 1952.

BEAVER-DAMS AS GEOLOGIC AGENTS. Rudolf Ruedemann, W. J. Schoonmaker. Science, 88 (2292): 523-525, Dec.2, 1938.

EFFECTS OF A SUMMER FLASH FLOOD UPON A BEAVER POPULATION. William H. Rutherford. Jour. Mam., vol.34, no.2, pp.261-266, May 14, 1953.

WILDLIFE AND ENVIRONMENTAL RELATIONSHIPS OF BEAVERS IN COLORADO FORESTS. Wm. H. Rutherford. Jour. For., 53 (11): 803-806, Nov., 1955.

EFFECT OF IMPOUNDMENTS ON WATER TEMPERATURES OF FULLER CREEK, MONTMORENCY COUNTY, MICHIGAN. David S. Shetter, Marvin J. Whalls. Jour. Wildl. Mgt., 19 (1): 47-54, map, Jan., 1955.

EFFECTS OF WATER RUN-OFF AND GRADIENT ON BEAVER IN MOUNTAIN STREAMS. Albert E. Smith. MF thesis, Univ. Mich., 1950.

THE EFFECT OF A BEAVER DAM ON THE INSECT FAUNA OF A TROUT STREAM. William M. Sprules. Trans. Amer. Fisheries Soc., Wash., vol.70, pp.236-248, 1940.

THE PRODUCTION OF ASPEN AND ITS UTILIZATION BY BEAVER ON THE HUNTINGTON FOREST. LeRoy C. Stegeman. Jour. Wildlife Management, Ithaca, vol.18, no.3, pp.348-358, July, 1954.

BEAVER ECOLOGY IN WESTERN MONTANA WITH SPECIAL REFERENCE TO MOVEMENTS. Joseph E. Twonsend. Jour. Mam., 34 (4): 459-479, map, graphs, Nov., 1953.

A STUDY IN BEAVER ECOLOGY IN WESTERN MONTANA WITH SPECIAL REFERENCE TO MOVEMENTS. Joseph E. Townsend. MS thesis, Mont. State Coll., 1952.

CHANGES IN COMPOSITION OF GROUND WATER, SOIL FERTILITY, AND FOREST GROWTH PRODUCED BY THE CONSTRUCTION AND REMOVAL OF BEAVER DAMS. S. A. Eilde, C. T. Youngberg, J. H. Hovind. Jour. Wildlife Management, Menasha, vol.14, no.2, pp.123-128, Apr., 1950.

Economic Importance

THE BEAVER IN MINNESOTA--A RESOURCE AND A RESPONSIBILITY. Shaler E. Aldous. Proc. Minn. Wildl. Cons. Short Course, 2: 14-17, 1940.

A TOOL FOR BEAVER DAM REMOVAL M. Clair Aldous. Jour. Wildl. Mgt., 19 (1): 153-154, illus., Jan., 1955.

BEAVER SANCTUARY. J. W. Anderson. The Beaver, Hudson's Bay Co., Winnipeg, Outfit 268, no.1, pp.8-11, illus., June, 1937.

7000 SQUARE MILES OF BEAVER SANCTUARY. J. W. Anderson. Beaver, Winnipeg, Outfit 265, no.1, pp.16-18, illus., June, 1934.

THE BEAVER AS A FACTOR IN THE DEVELOPMENT OF NEW ENGLAND. Harold L. Babcock. Bull. Boston Soc. Nat. Hist., no.37, pp.14, illus., Oct., 1925.

THE CASE AGAINST THE BEAVER. A. B. Beakbane. Forest and Stream, vol.92, no. 5, pp.203, 236, 239-240, May, 1922.

THE IMPORTANCE OF BEAVER IN WATERFOWL MANAGEMENT AT THE SENEY NATIONAL WILDLIFE REFUGE. Elizabeth B. Beard. Jour. Wildlife Management, Ithaca, vol.17, no.4, pp.398-436, illus., Oct., 1953.

THE BEAVER DEBATE. John H. Burris. Conserv. Volunteer, St. Paul, vol.7, no. 41, p.47, July-Aug., 1944.

COLORADO GARNERS HER BEAVER. Arthur H. Carhart. Amer. Forests, Wash., D.C., vol.46, no.2, pp.69-71, 89, 96, illus., Feb., 1940.

THE BEAVER--EMPIRE BUILDER AND CONSERVATIONIST. Edward P. Cliff. Utah Juniper, 7: 23-26, 1936.

BEAVER BECOMES AN IMPORTANT RESOURCE FOR SOUTH DAKOTA. J. W. Cluett. South Dakota Conserv. Digest, Pierre, pp.3, 11, June, 1940.

JAMES BAY BEAVER CONSERVATION. D. E. Denmark. Beaver, 279: 38-43, Sept., 1948.

VERMONT'S BEAVER PROBLEM. Leonard E. Foote. Vt. Fish and Game Serv., State Bull., Pittman-Robertson Ser.12, 21 pp., Feb., 1945.

BEAVERS AS WATER CONSERVATIONISTS. Adrian C. Fox. N. Dak. Outdoors, 2 (9): 5-6, Mar., 1940.

BEAVER PAY FOR LIFE WITH TAX-FREE DAMS. Wade M. Gustin. W. Farm Life, 42 (9): 9, May, 1940.

BEAVER PROBLEMS. Charles Hargrave. N. Dak. Outdoors, 15 (2): 4-5, Illus., Aug., 1952.

THE BEAVER CAN BE A NUISANCE. Lyn Harrington. Forest and Outdoors, Montreal, vol.13, pp.7-8, 1947.

THE HUNTERS' STAKE IN PENNSYLVANIA BEAVER. Hal H. Harrison. Pa. Game News, 19 (12): 6, 23, Mar., 1949.

THE EMBATTLED BEAVER. John D. Hart. Colo. Cons., 3 (4): 6-10, illus., July-Aug., 1954.

THE WARTIME STATUS OF BEAVER IN THE WESTERN UNITED STATES. A. B. Hatch. Trans. N.A. Wildl. Conf., 8: 302-307, 1943.

THE 1942 STATE BEAVER CATCH. RESULTS OF THE 15-DAY MARCH SEASON. Paul R. Highby. Conservation Volunteer, St. Paul, vol.4, no.24, pp.13-17, Sept., 1942.

NORTH WOODS BEAVER TROUBLE. John V. Hoene. Am. Forests, 52 (11): 538-539, 560, Nov., 1946.

BEAVER TROUBLE. James Hovind. Wisc. Conserv. Bull., Madison, vol.13, no.7, pp. 15-17, illus., July, 1948.

BEAVER SEASON. D. H. Jenkins. Michigan Conservation, Lansing, vol.23, no.2, pp.14-15, Mar., 1954.

OKLAHOMA'S PADDLE-TAIL. Glenn Jones. Okla. Game and Fish News, 3 (3): 4-5, 18, Mar., 1947.

OREGON'S BEAVER PROGRAM. Chester D. Kebbe. Proc. Ann. Conf. W. Assn. State Game and Fish Comm., 29: 201-204, 1949.

(BEAVER PROTECTION.) Der Biberschutz. A. Kruger. Zeitschr. fuer Saeugetierkunde, Berlin, vol.6, no.2, pp.52-56, Dec.15, 1931.

MILLION DOLLAR CONSERVATION TRIUMPH. Roger M. Latham. Pennsylvania Game News, Harrisburg, vol.21, no. 12, pp.35-40, illus., Mar., 1951.

UNNECESSARY DESTRUCTION OF BEAVER. Sidney M. Logan. The Big Horn (Missoula, Montana), vol.3, no.3, pp.3, 5, illus., Aug., 1926.

THE ODDS WERE AGAINST HIM. Leo A. Luttringer, Jr. Pennsylvania Game News, Harrisburg, vol.15, no.12, pp.12-13, 26, Mar., 1945.

BEAVER AS AN ECONOMIC ASSET. Lester McCann. Cons. Volunteer, 2 (12): 9-11, Sept., 1941.

BEAVER TO PAY THEIR OWN WAY. Gordon Mark. West Virginia Conservationist, Charleston, vol.11, no.1, pp.16, 20, May, 1947.

WHY WE SHOULD PROTECT THE BEAVER IN MASSACHUSETTS. John B. May. Bull. Massachusetts Audubon Soc., Boston, vol. 29, no.3, pp.93-95, Apr., 1945.

(PROTECTING THE BEAVER OF THE RHONE.) La protection du castor du Rhone. Galien Mingaud. Bull. Soc. d'Etude Sci. Nat. Nimes, no.1, 4 pp., 1896.

REPORT OF REMOVAL OF NUISANCE BEAVER. A. K. Momb. North Dakota Outdoors, Grand Forks, vol.8, no.4, p.9, Oct., 1945.

REPORT ON REMOVAL OF NUISANCE BEAVER JULY 1, 1947 TO JUNE 30, 1948. A. K. Momb. North Dakota Outdoors, Bismarck, vol.11, no.2, p.12, illus., Aug., 1948.

SALVATION OF OUR BEAVER. Albert Munday. Canadian Geographical Jour., Ottawa, vol.18, no.6, pp.341-345, illus., June, 1939.

THE FUTURE OF THE BEAVER. George Neale. California Fish and Game, vol.10, pp.114-115, July, 1924.

NUISANCE BEAVER. D. E. Ness. Sylva, Toronto, vol.4, no.3, pp.10-14, illus., 1948.

A PLEA FOR THE BEAVER. Grey Owl. Jour. Soc. Preservation of Fauna of Empire, Hertford, n.s., pt.26, pp.17-23, Sept., 1935.

BEAVER CRISIS IN THE NORTHEAST. Clay Perry. Am. Forests, 51 (2): 72-73, 94-95, Feb., 1945.

ARIZONA'S OPERATION BEAVER LIFT. Willis Peterson. Nat. Geogr. Mag., Wash., vol.107, no.5, pp.666-680, illus., May, 1955.

BEAVER LIFT. Willis Peterson. Arizona Highways, vol.29, no.5, pp.8-16, illus., May, 1953.

THE BEAVER. Chester F. Phelps. Va. Wildl., 8 (9): 5-6, 20, Sept., 1947.

BOATING FOR BEAVER. "Chub" Reid. Fur-Fish Game, Harding's Mag., Columbus, vol.79, no.4, pp.34-36, illus., Apr., 1945.

SOME OBSERVATIONS ON BEAVER CULTURE WITH REFERENCE ON THE NATIONAL FORESTS. Smith Riley. Jour. Mam., vol.2, no.4, pp.197-206, pl.15, Nov., 1921.

PRELIMINARY REPORT ON THE BEAVER-TROUT INVESTIGATION. J. Clark Salyer, II. Am. Game, 24 (1): 6, 13-15, Jan.-Feb., 1935.

IOWA'S 1949 BEAVER SEASON. Glen C. Sanderson. Iowa Conservationist, Des Moines, vol.9, no.3, pp.17, 23-24, illus., Mar.15, 1950.

BEAVER ON TRIAL. Paul M. Scheffer. Soil Cons., 7 (10): 239-241, Apr., 1942.

BRINGING BACK THE BEAVER. Theo. H. Scheffer. Amer. Forests and Forest Life, vol.33, pp.17-20, 58-59, illus., Jan., 1927.

(THE STRUGGLE AGAINST THE BEAVER: A CHAPTER FROM THE HISTORY OF THE CAMPAIGN AGAINST PESTS.) Im Kampf gegen die Bisamratte. Ein Kapitel aus der Geschichte der Schaedlingsbekaempfung. Ludwig Schuster. Naturforscher, Berlin, vol.6, no.12, pp.458-462, Mar., 1930.

IN PURSUIT OF BEAVERS. S. V. Sedlak. Pennsylvania Game News, Harrisburg, vol. 14, no.11, pp.12-13, 22, illus., Feb., 1944; no.12, pp.14-15, 29, illus., Mar., 1944.

BEAVER CONTROL. Francis W. Sherwood. N.Y. State Cons., 10 (1): 38, illus., Aug.-Sept., 1955.

CASTORS AND CASTOREUM. James R. Simon, Robert C. Brown. Wyo. Wild Life, 12 (6): 14-16, June, 1948.

BEAVER CONTROL IN WISCONSIN. Albert E. Smith, George J. Knudsen. Wis. Cons. Bull., 20 (7): 21-24, illus., July, 1955.

THE CONSERVATION OF BEAVER BY AN INDIAN. Harlan I. Smith. Science, n.s., vol.62, p.461, Nov.20, 1925.

BEAVER AND ITS POSSIBILITIES IN WATER REGULATION. Laurence H. Smith. Univ. Idaho Bull., 33 (22): 85-88, Dec., 1938.

NUISANCE BEAVERS. Bernard A. Stephansky. Mich. Cons., 19 (1): 15-19, Jan.-Feb., 1950.

THE WYOMING BEAVER PROJECT. Gail M. Thomas. Wyoming Wild Life, Cheyenne, vol.6, no.11, pp.3-5, illus., Nov., 1941.

OPEN SEASON ON STATE BEAVER NEXT YEAR IS RECOMMENDED. Ben F. Thompson. West Virginia Conservation, Charleston, vol.11, no.1, pp.15-17, 22-23, May, 1947.

THE BEAVER. PENNSYLVANIA'S MOST INTERESTING FUR-BEARER. George E. Trump. Pennsylvania Game News, New Cumberland, vol.9, no.12, pp.4-5, figs.5, Mar., 1939.

BRINGING BACK THE BEAVER. Howard Twining. Sierra Club Bull., San Francisco, vol.27, no.4, pp.116-118, Aug., 1942.

THE LAND RENEWED. THE STORY OF SOIL CONSERVATION. William R. Van Dersal, Edward H. Graham. Oxford, 109 pp., 1946.

BEAVER--TIMBER PROBLEM IN MINNESOTA'S 'BIG BOG'. David R. Vesall, R. H. Gensch, Ray Nyman. Cons. Volunteer, 10 (57): 45-50, Mar.-Apr., 1947.

THE RELATION OF BEAVER TO SWAMP TIMBER MANAGEMENT IN KOOCHICHING COUNTY, MINNESOTA. David Vesall, Ray Nyman, R. H. Gensch. Proc., Soc. Am. Foresters' Meeting, 1947: 195-200, 1948.

THE MODERN BEAVER HUNTERS. D. Wood. Hunter, Trader, Trapper, vol.64, no.3, pp.25-26, fig.3, Mar., 1932.

BEAVER CITY. WASKASOO CREEK IN RED DEER, ALBERTA, OFFERS A SANCTUARY FOR THE FAST DISAPPEARING BEAVER. Kerry Wood. Rod and Gun, Montreal, vol.41, no.4, pp.16-17, 33, illus., Sept., 1939.

LET'S ARGUE...ABOUT BEAVER! Lee E. Yeager. Hunting and Fishing, 31 (10): 22-25, 66-67, illus., Nov., 1954.

BEAVER LOCATION. Walter Zelinske. Wis. Cons. Bull., 6 (6): 42-44, June, 1941.

BEAVERS BENEFIT BY, AND AID IN, CONSERVATION. Missouri Conservationist, Jefferson City, vol.7, no.9, pp.8-9, illus., Sept., 1946.

BEAVERS, ENGINEERS OF ANIMAL WORLD, FIRST TO LURE NORTH AMERICA EXPLORERS. Iowa Conservationist, Des Moines, vol.2, no.12, pp.89, 91, 93, illus., Dec.15, 1943.

BEAVERS WATER HIS CATTLE. Capper's Farmer, 51 (4): 64, Apr., 1940.

HELP PROTECT OUR BEAVER. Arizona Game Protective Association, Arizona Wildlife and Sportsman, Tucson, vol.6, no.10, p.4, Aug., 1945.

MANY BEAVERS TAKEN. Pennsylvania Game News, Harrisburg, vol.11, no.2, p.17, May, 1940.

OUR FIRST BEAVER SEASON. Illinois Dept. of Cons., Outdoors in Ill., 18 (1): 12-13, illus., Spring, 1952.

THOSE PESKY BEAVERS. North Dakota Game and Fish Dept., N. Dak. Outdoors, 14 (7): 6-7, 15, illus., Jan., 1952.

WYOMING BEAVER PROBLEM. Wyoming Wild Life, Cheyenne, vol.5, no.5, pp.11-13, illus., May, 1940.

Europe

(FROM THE BEAVER SANCTUARIES IN THE ORIGINAL VALLEY OF THE ELBE RIVER.) Aus der Naturschutzgebieten des Bibers im Urstromtal der Elbe. Karl Baake. Wochenschrift fuer Aquarien - und Terrarienkunde, Braunschweig, Jahrg.34, pp. 597-599, figs.4, Oct.12, 1937.

(THE PROBABLE "MARKING" OF THE TERRITORY OF THE BEAVER OF THE RHONE.) Le "marquage" probable du territoire, chez le castor du Rhone. Maurice Blanchet. La Terre et la Vie, Paris, vol. 102, no.4, pp.329-335, illus., Dec., 1955.

(THE RHONE BEAVER.) Le castor du Rhone. (Castor fiber.) P. Cordier. La Terre et la Vie, Rev. d'Hist. Nat., vol.3, no.2, pp.80-91, illus., Feb., 1933.

(BEAVER IN WESTERN PRUSSIA.) Der Biber in Westpreussen. P. Dahms. Zool. Garten, vol.41, pp.85-95, 103-112, 214-215, figs., 1900.

(BEAVER OF THE MUSEUM OF SENS.) Le Castor du Musee de Sens. Ed Dechambre. Mammalia, Paris, 8 (2): 72-74, June, 1944.

(CONSTRUCTION OF HUTS AND EMBANKMENTS BY THE EUROPEAN BEAVER.) La construction de huttes et de digues par le castor d'Europe. Ed Dechambre. Terre et la Vie, Paris, vol.95, no.2, pp.90-97, Apr.-June, 1948.

(BRIEF CONTRIBUTIONS TO DENMARK'S PREHISTORICAL FAUNA.) Mindre Bidrag til Danmarks forhistoriske Dyreverden. 1. Et Fragment af Baever (Castor fiber L.) fra Bronzealderen. Magnus Degerbol. Videnskabeliga Meddelelser fra Dansk Naturhist, Forening, vol.86, pp.75-81, 1928.

(BEAVER COLONIES IN THE MIDDLE AND UPPER BASINS OF THE NEMAN RIVER AND THE UPPER REGIONS OF THE RIVER PRIPYAT IN 1937-1939.) Wukaz stanowisk bobra Castor fiber vistulanus. Matschie w dorzeczu górnego i środkowego Niemna oraz górnej Prypeci w latach 1937-39. August Dehnel. Relevé des colonies de Castor fiber vistulanus Matschie, dans le bassin superieur et moyen du Niemen et dans le cours superieur de la Prypec en 1937-1939. Warsaw, 1948, pp.199-224, maps, 1948.

(A VISIT TO THE ELBE BEAVER.) Ein Besuch beim Elbebiber. (Includes photographs of living beavers.) G. Eberle. Natur. und Museum (Frankfurt a. M.), vol.57, no.7, pp.335-346, 12 figs., July, 1927.

(BEAVERS IN SWEDEN AND NORWAY.) Baevern i sverige och Norge. Erik Geete. Skogen, vol.16, no.10, pp.296-301, 4 figs; no.11, pp.328-331, 7 figs, no.12, pp. 355-358, 2 figs; no.15, pp.417-418, 4 figs; no.16, pp.441-444, 1929.

(POPULATION OF THE ELBE BEAVER CASTOR FIBER ALBICUS MATSCHIE 1907.) Bestand des Elbe-Bibers, Castor fiber albicus Matschie, 1907. G. Hinze. Saeugetierk, Mitteil., Stuttgart, vol.1, no.4, p. 175, Oct.1, 1953.

(THE BEAVERS FROM THE RHONE AND THE INUNDATIONS.) Les Castors du Rhone et les Inondations. Albert Hugues. Mammalia, Paris, 1 (5): 217-218, pl.9, Sept., 1937.

(RHONE BEAVER.) Le castor du Rhone. Albert Hugues. Bull. Soc. Nat. Acclimat. France, vol.80, no.9, pp.341-350; no.10, pp.381-395, 1 fig; no.11, pp.425-439, Sept.-Oct.-Nov., 1933.

(GERMANY'S BEAVERS.) Tyskalnds Baevere. Hans Hvass. Naturens Verden, Copenhagen, vol.22, no.3, pp.97-111, figs. 14, Mar., 1938.

(DATA ON BAVARIAN FAUNA. THE BEAVER CASTOR FIBER LINN.) Materialien zur bayerischen Fauna. Der Biber Castor fiber Linn. Andreas Johannes Jackel. Korrespondenz-Blatt Zool.-mineral. ver. in Regensburg Jahrg.13, nos.1-8, pp.1-28, 1859.

DISTRIBUTION OF THE RIVER BEAVER IN THE UKRAINIAN SSR. Yu N. Kirilloff. Translations of Russian Game Reports, Canadian Wildlife Service, Ottawa, 1: 60-70, 1957.

(BEAVER COLONIES OF THE ZEGULANKA RIVER IN THE MOORLANDS OF WHITE RUSSIA.) Pruzkum bobřich osídlení-Castor fiber L.-v. provodi řeky Žegulanky v močálech rokytenských. K. Kostron. Sborník Klubu Přírodovědeckého, Brno, vol.26, pp.55-63, figs.4, 1946.

(THE OCCURRENCE OF BEAVER IN WIADOTUPIC PUSZTA.) Vyskyt bobra vislanskeho Castor fiber vistulnus Matschie v puste' wiadotupicke na severnim Polesi. K. Kostron. Acta Soc. Sci. Nat., Marov, vol.12, no.9, pp.1-16, figs.2, 1940.

(A COLONY OF CANADIAN BEAVERS IN THE USSR.) Koloniya kanadskikh bobrov (Castor canadensis Kuhl.) v SSSR. S. N. Marin. Zool. Zhurnal, Akad. Nauk SSSR, 35 (7): 1064-1071, 1956.

BEAVERS OF WESTERN RUSSIA AND EASTERN WHITE RUSSIA. V. A. Melander, V. V. Stanchinskii. Univ. Smolensk Wissenschaftl. Mitt., vol.6, no. 1, pp.119-132, figs.4, 1930. (In Russian.)

THE BEAVER ON KOLA PENINSULA. A. A. Nasimovich. Priroda no.7, pp.60-63, 1948.

(ON THE LIVING HABITS OF THE BEAVER IN SOUTHERN NORWAY.) Ueber die Lebensweise des Bibers in Sudnorwegen. Gunter Olberg. Natur und Volk, Frankfurt am Main, vol.80, no.3, pp.57-66, illus., Mar.15, 1950.

(OBSERVATIONS OF THE ELBE BEAVERS (CASTOR FIBER ALBICUS MATSCHIE) OF THE HALLE ZOOLOGICAL GARDEN.) Boebachtungen an den Elbe-Bibern (Castor fiber albicus Matschie) des halleschen Tiergartens. Hans Petzsch. Zool. Garten, Leipzig, N.F., vol.21, no.3, pp.156-160, illus., 1955.

RE-ACCLIMATIZATION OF THE RIVER BEAVER IN THE TATAR ASSR. A. V. Popoff. Translations of Russian Game Reports, Canadian Wildlife Service, Ottawa, 1: 93-97, 1957.

(BEAVER IN ALSACE AND FRANCE.) Bobr v Alsasku a ve Francii. Jan. Sv. Prochazka. Věda Přirodni Měs. pro Sír. a Pest. věd Přir, Prague, vol.10, nos.4-5, pp.143-145, 1929.

(BEAVER IN GERMANY.) Le castor en Allemagne. (Canadian beaver introduced in Mecklenburg.) Walther Schoenichen. La Terre et la Vie, Rev. d'Hist. Nat., vol.2, no.11, pp.653-661, figs.6, Nov., 1932.

THE RIVER BEAVER IN ARCHANGEL PROVINCE. B. T. Semyonoff. Trans. of Russian Game Reports, Canadian Wildlife Service, 1: 5-45, 1957.

(SWAMP BEAVERS IN THE WILD IN SCHLESWIG-HOLSTEIN.) Sumpfbiber in freier schleswig-holsteinischer Wildbahn. G. von Studnitz. Schriften Naturwiss. Vereins f. Schleswig-Holstein, Kiel u. Leipzig, vol.21, no.2, pp.287-290, 1935.

ACCLIMATIZATION OF THE BEAVER IN THE OB RIVER BASIN. A. P. Zhdanoff. Translations of Russian Game Reports, Canadian Wildlife Service, Ottawa, 1: 46-59, 1957.

(BEAVER IN CZECHOSLOVAK LANDS.) Bobr v. zemich Ceskoslovenskych. Cenek Zibrt. Le Castor en Tchecoslovaquie. V. Praze, Nakladem Ceskoslovenske Akademie zemedelske 1929, Vedecke spisy vydavane ceskoslovenskou akademii zemedelskou vol.2, pp.132, illus., 1929.

## Food Habits

BEAVER FOOD UTILIZATION STUDIES. Shaler E. Aldous. Jour. Wildl. Mgt., 2 (4): 213-222, Oct., 1938.

NOTES ON THE WINTER FOOD OF BEAVERS IN THE PALOUSE PRAIRIES, WASHINGTON. James Beer. Jour. Mam., 23 (4): 444-445, Nov., 1942.

NOTES ON THE SUMMER FOOD HABITS OF THE BEAVER. David B. Cook. Pa. Game News, 13 (4): 14, July, 1942.

UNDERWATER STORE. John Eric Hill. Natural History, New York, vol.52, no.5, p.233, illus., Dec., 1943.

OBSERVATIONS ON THE FORAGING HABITS OF BEAVERS. Laurence E. Hiner. Jour. Mam., 19 (3): 317-319, Aug., 1938.

(EATING OF FECES AND HAIR IN THE SWAMP BEAVER.) Kot- und Haarfressen beim Sumpfbiber. P. Kirner. Der Deutsche Pelztierzuechter, Jahrgang 1931, Muenchen, no.6, pp.153-154, fig., Mar.15, 1931.

(ON THE DIET OF THE BEAVER.) Zur Nahrung des Bibers. A. Mertens. Zeitschrift f. Saeugetierkunde, vol.5, no.6, p.364, 1930.

A QUALITATIVE AND QUANTITATIVE FOOD HABIT STUDY OF BEAVERS IN MAINE. Donald F. O'Brien. MS thesis, Univ. Maine, 1938.

HOW TWO CAPTIVE YOUNG BEAVERS CONSTRUCTED A FOOD PILE. Thomas S. Roberts. Proc. Minnesota Acad. Sci., vol.5, pp.24-27, 1937.

(SWAMP BEAVERS FEEDING ON LIVER MUSSELS.) Sumpfbiber als Flussmuschelfresser. Erich Schreiber. Der Deutsche Pelztierzuechter, Jahrgang 1931, Muenchen, no.24, pp.656-657, Dec.15, 1931.

(THE QUESTION OF THE FOOD OF THE RIVER BEAVER.) K voprosu o pitanii rechnogo bobra (Castor fiber L.). I. A. Shilov. Zool. Zhurnal, Moscow, vol.31, no.6, pp.924-931, 1952.

FOOD HABITS OF THE TEXAS BEAVER AS RELATED TO THE STATE RESTORATION PROGRAM. Garret H. Soulen. MS thesis, A. and M. Coll., Texas, 1942.

A BEAVER'S FOOD REQUIREMENTS. Edward R. Warren. Jour. Mam., vol.21, no.1, p.93, Feb.14, 1940.

## Fossils

REMAINS OF A BEAVER (AMBLYCASTOR CAUCASICUS SP. N.) FROM PLIOCENE OF THE CISCAUCASIA. A. I. Argyropulo. Comptes Rendus (Doklady) Acad. Sci. URSS, Moscou, n.s., vol.25, no.7, pp.636-639, illus., 1939.

A NEW RECORD OF CASTOROIDES OHIOENSIS FROM ILLINOIS. Frank Collins Baker. Science, vol.71, no.1841, p.389, Apr.11, 1930.

TWO NEW RECORDS OF THE PLEISTOCENE BEAVER, CASTOROIDES OHIOENSIS. William L. Engels. The American Midland Naturalist, Notre Dame, Indiana, vol. 12, no.12, pp.529-531, figs.3, Nov., 1931.

(ANATOMICAL RESEARCH ON CASTOR ANDERSSONI SCHL. AND CONSIDERATIONS ON THE DENTAL EVOLUTION OF CASTORIDAE.) Recherches anatomiques sur le Castor anderssoni Schl. et considerations sur l'évolution dentaire des Castoridés. M. Friant. Bull. Geol. Inst. Univ. Upsala, vol.26, pp.91-112, figs.27, 1937.

THE OCCURRENCE OF CASTOROIDES IN THE PLEISTOCENE OF KANSAS. Morton Green. Jour. Mam., vol.26, no.2, p.196, July 15, 1945.

ON THE GEOLOGICAL POSITION OF THE CASTOROIDES OHIOENSIS. James Hall. Boston Jour. Nat. Hist., vol.5, pp.3-19, 1846.

THE OCCURRENCE OF EUCASTOR TORTUS LEIDY IN PHILLIPS COUNTY, KANSAS. Claude W. Hibbard. Trans. Kansas Acad. Sci., Topeka, vol.45, pp.248-252, pl.1, 1942.

THE OCCURRENCE OF EUCASTOR AND EPIGAULUS IN THE LOWER PLIOCENE OF TREGO COUNTY, KANSAS. Claude W. Hibbard, Lester F. Phillis. Univ. Kansas Sci. Bull., Lawrence, vol.30, pt.2, no.16, pp.549-555, figs.3, June 15, 1945.

(ON DILUVIAL BEAVER FOSSILS OF THE MARK OF BRANDENBURG.) Ueber diluviale Biberreste aus der Mark Brandenburg. (Castor marchiae.) Max Hilzheimer. Zeitschr. fuer Saeugetierkunde, vol.7, no. 6, pp.241-251, pl.20, figs.1-7, Dec.15, 1932.

ON THE REMAINS OF FEN BEAVER IN THE SEDGWICK MUSEUM. Ivor Montagu. Proc. Zool. Soc. Lond., 1924, pt.4, pp. 1081-1086, 3 pls., 1925.

THE GIANT BEAVER (TROGONTHERIUM) FROM THE THAMES VALLEY. E. T. Newton. Geol. Mag. London, n.s., decade 4, vol.9, pp.385-388, fig.1, Sept., 1902.

TROGONTHERIUM FROM THE PLEISTOCENE OF COPFORD, ESSEX. E. T. Newton. Geol. Mag., Lond., decade 6, vol. 3, no.625, pp.322-323, illus., July, 1916.

THE GIANT BEAVER CASTOROIDES IN MINNESOTA. Louis H. Powell. Saint Paul Inst., St. Paul, Science Bull.2, 30 pp., illus., 1948.

A LARGE PALAEOCASTOR FROM THE LOWER MIOCENE. A. S. Romer, J. T. McCormack. Amer. Jour. Sci., vol.15, no.85, pp.58-60, fig.1, Jan., 1928.

(CASTOR PRAEFIBER DEPERET IN THE FAUNA OF ROUSSILLON.) Castor praefiber Deperet in der Fauna von Roussillon. A. Schreuder. Palaeont. Zeitschr., vol.9, no.4, pp.374-378, 1928.

CONODONTES (TROGONTHERIUM) AND CASTOR FROM THE TEGLIAN CLAY COMPARED WITH THE CASTORIDAE FROM OTHER LOCALITIES. A. Schreuder. Arch. Mus. Teyler, Haarlem, vol.6, no.3, pp.99-318, 16 pls., 12 figs., 1929.

THE THREE SPECIES OF TROGONOTHERIUM, WITH A REMARK ON ANCHITHERIOMYS. A. Schreuder. Archiv. Neerlandaises Zool., Leyden, vol.8, livr.4, pp.400-433, figs.5, pls.20-23, 1951.

REVIEW OF THE PLIOCENE BEAVER DIPOIDES. J. Arnold Shotwell. Jour. Paleontol., vol.29, no.1, pp.129-144, illus., Jan., 1955.

CASTORIDAE FROM THE TERTIARY OF NEVADA. R. A. Stirton. Bull. Geol. Soc. America, vol.43, no.1, p.288, Mar., 1932.

A NEW BEAVER FROM THE PLIOCENE OF ARIZONA WITH NOTES ON THE SPECIES OF DIPOIDES. R. A. Stirton. Jour. Mam., vol.17, no.3, pp.279-281, figs.2, Aug., 1936.

A NEW SPECIES OF AMBLYCASTOR FROM THE PLATYBELODON BEDS, TUNG GUR FORMATION, OF MONOGOLIA. R. A. Stirton. Amer. Mus. Novitates, no.694, pp.1-4, figs.6, Feb.21, 1934.

A REVIEW OF THE TERTIARY BEAVERS. R. A. Stirton. Univ. Calif. Publ. Bull. Dept. Geol. Sci., vol.23, no.13, pp.391-458, figs.142, 1 map, 2 charts, May 8, 1935.

A NEW SPECIES OF DIPOIDES FROM THE PLIOCENE OF EASTERN OREGON. Robert W. Wilson. Carnegie Inst. Washington, Publ.453, pp.19-29, fig.1, pl.1, Dec.20, 1934.

AN ADDITIONAL RECORD OF THE GIANT BEAVER. Albert Elmer Wood. Jour. Mam., vol.17, no.4, p.420, Nov., 1936.

LATE MIOCENE BEAVER FROM SOUTHEASTERN MONTANA. Horace Elmer Wood, 2nd. Amer. Mus. Novitates, New York, no.1299, pp.6, fig.1, Oct.17, 1945.

ON A NEW TROGONTHERIUM FROM HSIATSAOHWAN, SHIHHUNGHSIEN AND WITH NOTES ON THE MAMMALIAN REMAINS FROM CHI-TSU, WUHOHSIEN, ANHWEI. Chung-Chien Young. Acta Paleontol. Sinica, vol.3, no.1, pp.55-66, illus., 1955.

TROGONTHERIUM CUVIERI FISCHER FROM PREZLETICE (CENTRAL BOHEMIA) AND A COMPARISON WITH THE OTHER KNOWN LOCALITIES OF TROGONTHERIUM IN EUROPE. Vlastislav Zazvorka. Sbornik Narod. Mus. v Praze, Acta Mus. Nation, Pragae, vol.1 B, no.9, Geol. et Paleont. no.3, pp.125-138, fig.1, pl.1, 1938.

## Fur Farming

FUR BEARING ANIMALS OF THE UNITED STATES. THE BEAVER. Frank G. Ashbrook, Bridgewater M. Arnold. Fur Jour., vol.1, no.7, pp.28-30, illus., Nov., 1927.

BEAVER FARMING. Vernon Bailey. Jour. Heredity, vol.13, pp.315-318, July, 1922 (Apr., 1923).

A PEAK IN WISCONSIN'S BEAVER HARVEST. N. R. Barger. Wis. Cons. Bull., 12 (11): 11-15, Nov., 1947.

BEAVER FARMING. William Benesch. Nat. Fur News, Denver, vol.20, no.11, pp.20, 41, Dec., 1948.

THE BEAVER HARVEST. Dale Bonnycastle, Jr. Rod and Gun in Canada, Montreal, vol. 46, no.6, pp.8-9, illus., Nov., 1944.

THE BEAVER HARVEST. Dale Bonnycastle, Jr. Rod and Gun in Canada, Montreal, vol. 46, no.6, pp.8-9, illus., Nov., 1944.

(HOW TO SET UP THE RAISING OF THE SWAMP BEAVER.) Comment installer un élevage de castor des marais. Henry Duvernoy. Revue d'Histoire Naturelle, pt.1, A, Mammifères, Paris, vol.11, no.9, pp.288-298, Sept., 1930.

BEAVER FARMING PAYS. Earle W. Gage. The Game Breeder, vol.27, pp.101-102, July, 1925.

(THE FIRST BEAVER FARM AND BEAVER RAISING IN GERMANY.) La prèmiere ferme a castors et l'élevage du castor en Allemagne. Lutz Heck. La Terre et la vie, Paris, vol.5, 2 Sem., nos.2-3, pp.51-58, illus., Aug.-Sept., 1935.

BEAVER RANCHING. C. W. H. Heideman. Fur Farmer Mag., vol.2, no.5, pp.4, 10, May, 1921.

(THE SWAMP BEAVER--THE NEW FUR-FARMING ANIMAL.) Der Sumpfbiber--das neue Farmpelztier. (Myocastor.) Otto Maser. Die Umschau, Frankfurt a.M., Jahrg.37, no.10, pp.182-183, figs.4, Mar. 4, 1933.

RANCHING THE BEAVER. Mark L. Weaver. Nat. Fur News, Denver, vol.20, no.1, pp.20-21, 41, illus., Feb., 1948.

FARMING THE BEAVER. Kerry Wood. Fur-Fish-Game (Harding's Mag.), Columbus, vol.79, no.10, pp.30-31, 40, illus., Oct., 1945.

BEAVER PELTS BRING TRAPPERS BIG RETURNS. North Dakota Outdoors, Bismarck, vol.7, no.4, pp.4-5, illus., Oct., 1944.

FUR TRADE AND THE BEAVER. Wyoming Wild Life, Cheyenne, vol.10, no.8, pp.9-11, 36-38, Aug., 1946.

THE LAW AND THE BEAVER. FUR TRADE AND THE BEAVER. Wyo. Wild Life, 10 (8): 4-11, 36-38, Aug., 1946.

MISSISSIPPI BEAVER HARVEST. John H. Phares. Miss. Game and Fish, 16 (12): 3, graph, Aug., 1952.

N.Y. BEAVER HARVEST LARGEST IN HISTORY. Rally Sheet, League of Maryland Sportsmen, Balto., vol.4, no.7, p.5, Aug., 1946.

General Habits, Behavior

UNUSUAL HOME OF BEAVER. (IN A MINE TUNNEL.) Gordon D. Alcorn. Murrelet, vol.15, no.3, p.82, Sept., 1934.

THE "FLAPPER." (POPULAR ACCOUNT OF BEAVER HABITS.) Otto L. Anderson. Minnesota Conservationist, no.24, pp.8-9, 24-32, illus., May, 1935.

BEAVER HABITS AND EXPERIMENTS IN BEAVER CULTURE. Vernon Bailey. U.S. Dept. Agric. Tech. Bull.21, pp.1-40, figs. 107, pls.1-14, Oct., 1927.

BEAVER HABITS, BEAVER CONTROL AND POSSIBILITIES IN BEAVER FARMING. Vernon Bailey. U.S. Dept. Agric. Bull. 1078, pp.1-31, pls.1-7, Oct.18, 1922.

HOW BEAVERS BUILD THEIR HOUSES. Vernon Bailey. Smithsonian Rep., 1926, publ.2895, pp.357-360, 6 pls., Sept., 1927. (Reprinted from Jour. Mam., vol.7, pp.41-44, pls.5-9, 1926, with slight changes and addition of one plate.)

INTERESTING FACTS CONCERNING THE BEAVER. W. E. Barber. Wisconsin Conservationist, vol.1, no.4, pp.2, 3, Sept., 1919.

MOVEMENTS OF TAGGED BEAVER. James R. Beer. Jour. Wildlife Management, vol.19, no.4, pp.492-493, Oct., 1955.

(ON SUBMERSION DURATION IN THE BEAVER CASTOR FIBER L.) Ueber die Tauchdauer beim Biber, Castor fiber L. Rudolf Berndt. Zool. Garten, Leipzig, n.F., vol.12, nos.2-3, pp.195-196, July, 1940.

OBSERVATIONS ON A MONTANA BEAVER CANAL. S. Stillman Berry. Smithsonian Rept., 1922, pp.297-308, pls.6, 1924. (Reprinted with minor changes and additions from Jour. Mam., vol.4, no.2, May, 1923.)

ON THE HABITS OF THE BEAVER. Felix Reville Brunot. Smithsonian Inst. Annual Rept., Washington, pp.422-423, 1874.

QUIET! EAGER BEAVERS AT WORK. J. G. Burr. Texas Game and Fish, Austin, vol.8, no.4, pp.8-9, 22, illus., Mar., 1950.

BEAVER, BUILDER OF EMPIRE. William H. Carr. Nat. Hist., 42 (2): 100-106, Sept., 1938.

BEAVERS. INTIMATE GLIMPSES OF A COLONY IN THE WILDS. Wendell Chapman, Lucie Chapman. Nature Mag., vol.26, no. 2, pp.73-76, illus., Aug., 1935.

THE BEAVER'S LODGE. Frank Conibear. Beaver 282, pp.36-37, illus., Sept., 1951.

VITAL STATISTICS ON BEAVER. Art Cook. New York Conservationist, Albany, vol.5, no.3, p.33, Dec., 1950, Jan., 1951.

THOSE MIGHTY ENGINEERS. (BEAVERS.) F. Sheldon Dart. Yellowstone Nature Notes, vol.10, nos.1-2, p.8, Jan.-Feb., 1933.

MARVELS OF BEAVER WORK. A. Radclyffe Dugmore. Country Life, vol.36, no.2, pp.48-51, 11 figs., June, 1919.

THE TALE OF MICKEY THE BEAVER. Doris Forbes. Beaver, Winnipeg, outfit 272, pp.42-45, illus., Dec., 1941.

(HABITS OF BEAVERS.) Les moeurs des Castors. Victor Forbin. La Nature, Paris, vol.37, no.3013, pp.475-480, Nov. 15, 1937.

A BEAVER'S FEARLESSNESS. Wallace B. Grange. Jour. Mam., vol.9, no.1, pp.66-67, Feb., 1928.

AN UNUSUAL BEAVER HABITAT. Russell K. Grater. Jour. Mam., vol.17, no.1, p. 66, Feb., 1936.

BEAVERS AT WORK ON THEIR HOUSE. Tappan Gregory. Jour. Mam., vol.12, no. 3, pp.242-244, pl.10, Aug., 1931.

DID BEAVERS IMPOUND WATER FOR AMES PEAT BOG? Charles S. Gwynne. Proc. Iowa Acad. Sci., Des Moines, vol. 49, pp.351-357, figs.4, Sept., 1942.

MEANING IN PICTURES. SERIES PICTURES. (PHOTOS OF BEAVER WORK.) Norris W. Harkness. Nature Mag., Washington, D.C., vol.35, no.5, pp.226-227, illus., May, 1942.

BEAVERS RESUME EARLIER WORK. William M. Harlow. Jour. Mam., vol.9, no.3, p.252, Aug., 1928.

A STUDY OF BEAVER--COLONY COMPOSITION AND WOODY PLANT UTILIZATION ON TWO STREAMS IN PENOBSCOT COUNTY, MAINE. Frank T. Haseltine. MS thesis, Univ. Maine, 1950.

A LARGE BEAVER-FELLED TREE. Robert T. Hatt. Jour. Mam., 25 (3): 313, Aug., 1944.

BEAVER PONDS, DAMS, CANALS, AND ROADWAYS. Earl Hilfiker. Museum Serv., Rochester, vol.13, no.10, pp.196-199, figs., Dec., 1940.

BEAVER ENGINEERS. John Eric Hill. Nat. Hist., New York, vol.52, no.1, p.41, illus., June, 1943.

(THE BEAVER: BODY STRUCTURE AND LIVING HABITS, DISTRIBUTION AND HISTORY.) Der Biber. Koerperbau und Lebensweise, Verbreitung und Geschichte. Gustav Hinze. Akademie-Verlag, Berlin, pp.viii plus 216, pls.31, 1950.

A BEAVER HOUSE. J. Murray Hollister. Nat. Mag., 47 (4): 211, 220, illus., Apr., 1954.

HABITS OF THE BEAVER. B. Horsford. Amer. Nat., Lancaster, vol.17, no.11, pp. 1196-1198, Nov., 1883.

TOOTH MARKS. (BEAVER.) Raymond E. Janssen. Nature Notes, Peoria, vol.5, no. 8, pp.187-189, figs.4, Oct., 1938.

BEAVER "FORMS." Charles E. Johnson. Jour. Mam., vol.2, no.3, pp.171-172, Aug., 1921.

BOUGHS, BUTTS AND BEAVER DAMS. Charles E. Johnson. Science, n.s., vol. 75, no.1935, p.132, Jan.29, 1932.

THE HABITS OF THE BEAVER AND ITS FARMING. Paul Krueger. Suomen Riista, 3: 65-66, 1948. (Summary in English of article in Finnish.)

EVIDENCE OF THE AGE OF BEAVER PONDS. William H. Lawrence. Jour. Wildlife Management, Ithaca, N.Y., vol.16, no. 1, pp.69-79, illus., Jan., 1952.

DR. BEAVER, SPECIALIST. Daniel W. Lay. Texas Game and Fish: 2 (10): 4-5, 13, Sept., 1944.

SIX MONTHS IN A BEAVER DAM. W. A. Lee. Nat. Fur News, Denver, vol.22, no. 3, pp.10-11, 23, illus., Apr., 1950.

WINTERING WITH BEAVERS. William J. Long. Nature Mag., Washington, vol.44, no.2, pp.71-74, illus., Feb., 1951.

MICKEY THE BEAVER AN ANIMAL ENGINEER PERFORMS FOR THE CAMERA AS A STAR IN THE ACTIVITIES OF HIS SPECIES. James MacGillivary. Nat. Geog. Mag., vol.54, no.6, pp.741-756, illus., 1928.

BEAVERS AREN'T DUMB. Elwyn W. McIntosh . Fur-Fish-Game, Harding's Mag., Columbus, vol.86, no.8, pp.35-36, Aug., 1946.

BEAVERS RESUME EARLIER WORK. Charles Macnamara. Jour. Mam., vol.10, no.3, pp.255-256, Aug., 1929.

POSITION OF WOOD IN BEAVER DAMS. Charles Macnamara. Science, n.s., vol. 74, no.1929, p.630, Dec.18, 1931.

BEAVERS AT WORK IN NORTH DAKOTA. Wilford L. Miller, J. E. Campbell, Marion Piper. North Dakota Outdoors, Bismarck, vol.9, no.6, p.5, Dec., 1946.

(THE WORK OF THE BEAVER.) Die Arbeiten des Bibers. Clyde L. Patch. Natur und Volk (Nat. u. Mus.), Frankfurt, a.M., vol.64, no.8, pp.307-315, figs.6, Aug.1, 1934.

(STUDIES ON THE LIVING AREAS OF MICROTUS ARVALIS PALL.) Studie ueber die Standorte von Microtus arvalis Pall. Jaroslav Pelikan. Prace Brnevske Zakladny Ceskoslovenske Akad. Ved, vol.27, no.1, pp.1-32, 1955 (In Czech with German summary.)

(SOME NEW OBSERVATIONS ON THE DIVING ELBE BEAVERS, CASTOR FIBER ALBICUS MATSCHIE 1909, IN CAPTIVITY.) Einige neue Beobachtungen an tauchenden Elba-Bibern, Castor fiber albicus Matschie, 1909, in Gefangenschaft. H. Petzsch. Saeugetierk. Mitteil., Stuttgart, vol.2, no. 2, pp.79-80, Apr.1, 1954.

AN INDUSTRIOUS ANIMAL--THE BEAVER. O. L. Resner. Washington Outdoors, Tacoma, vol.1, no.3, pp.6-7, illus., June, 1946.

THE BEAVER--A TOOL IN THE WORKSHOP OF THE GODS. Paul B. Riis. Parks and Recreation, vol.9, pp.330-337, Feb., 1926.

BEAVER BEHAVIOR. W. M. Rush. Jour. Mam., vol.9, no.3, pp.252-253, Aug., 1928.

THE BEAVER AS AN UPSTREAM ENGINEER. Paul M. Scheffer. Soil Conservation, U.S. Dept. Agric. vol.3, no.7, pp.178-181, illus., Jan., 1938.

BEAVER--UPSTREAM ENGINEER. Paul M. Scheffer. Bull. Univ. Idaho, vol.33, no.22, (Bull. School Forestry, no.8), pp.78-79, Dec., 1938.

BEAVER BIOLOGY IN WINTER IN ARCHANGEL PROVINCE. B. T. Semyonoff. Trans. of Russian Game Reports, Canadian Wildlife Service, Ottawa, 1: 71-92, 1957.

COMPARISON OF TREE CUTTINGS OF SIX BEAVER COLONIES IN ALLEGANY STATE PARK, NEW YORK. Albert R. Shadle, Alma M. Nauth, Edward C. Gese, Thomas S. Austin. Jour. Mam., 24 (1): 32-39, Feb., 1943.

SIZES OF WOOD CUTTINGS HANDLED BY BEAVERS. Albert R. Shadle. Am. Midl. Nat., 52 (2): 510-512, Oct., 1954.

BEAVER FAMILY LIFE. Henry H. Sheldon. Frontiers, Phila., vol.15, no.1, p.5, illus., Oct., 1950.

VANDALS WRECK BEAVER COLONY. Harrison Shobe. West Virginia Conservation, Charleston, vol.10, no.4, p.18, Aug., 1946.

(FROM THE LIFE OF THE BEAVER.) Aus dem Leben des Bibers. G. Steinbacher. Natur und Volk, Frankfurt a.M., vol.69, no.3, pp.138-146, illus., Mar.1, 1939.

THE BEAVER AND HIS WORKS. G. Archie Stockwell. Pop. Science Monthly, vol.25, pp.14-22, figs.2, 1884.

AN INTERESTING BEAVER TRAIL. Arthur Svihla. Jour. Mam., vol.12, no.1, pp.70-71, Feb., 1931.

SUMMER BEHAVIOR OF A FAMILY OF BEAVERS IN NEW YORK STATE. Lloyd Tevis, Jr. Jour. Mam., 31 (1): 40-65, Feb., 1950.

THE ABANDONMENT AND REOCCUPATION OF POND SITES BY BEAVERS. Edward R. Warren. Jour. Mam., vol.13, no.4, pp.343-346, pl.16, Nov., 1932.

THE BEAVER: ITS WORK AND ITS WAYS. Edward R. Warren. Monographs of the American Society of Mammalogists, no.2, Balto., The Williams & Wilkins Company, 12 mo., 20 pls., 177 pp., 47 halftone plates, and 7 line drawings including one map, Apr., 1927.

CUTTING OF OAKS BY BEAVERS. Edward R. Warren. Jour. Mam., vol.9, no.3, pp.253-254, Aug., 1928.

THE MOST INTERESTING WILD ANIMAL IN AMERICA. (HABITS OF THE BEAVER.) Edward R. Warren. Sci. Monthly, vol.27, pp.33-41, illus., July, 1928.

POSITION OF WOOD IN BEAVER DAMS. Edward R. Warren. Science, n.s., vol. 75, no.1937, pp.194-195, Feb.12, 1932.

SOME INTERESTING BEAVER DAMS IN COLORADO. Edward R. Warren. Proc. Wash. Acad. Sci., vol.6, pp.429-437, pls. 25-34, Feb.26, 1905.

THE WORK OF BEAVERS. Edward R. Warren. Sci. Monthly, 47: 176-181, Aug., 1938.

A BEAVER DAM IN OHIO. C. E. Webb. Ohio Conservation Bull., Columbus, vol.10, no.12, p.25, illus., Dec., 1946.

AN UNUSUALLY FINE EXAMPLE OF BEAVER INDUSTRY. Ira A. Williams. Nat. Hist., vol.25, no.6, pp.593-601, Nov.-Dec., 1925 (Jan., 1926).

BEAVER TOOK OVER RANGER CABIN. Hunting & Fishing in Canada, vol.13, no.1, p.20, 1947.

BEAVERS, FLOOD CONTROL EXPERTS. Nat. Nature News, vol.1, no.32, pp.5,7, fig.1, Nov.1, 1937.

Introductions, Transplants

TRAPPING AND TRANSPLANTING LIVE BEAVERS. Leo K. Couch. U.S.D.I., Farmers' Bull. no.1768, pp.1-18, figs.15, Mar., 1937; U.S.D.I., Cons. Bull.30, 20 pp., 1942.

BEAVER PLANTING WITH PARACHUTE. Marshall Edson. Proc. Ann. Conf. W. Assn. State Game and Fish Comm.30:109-110, 1950.

BEAVER PROTECTION AND TRANSPLANTING BEAVER. Roy Fugate. Oregon Cattleman, vol.1, no.12, p.8, May 28, 1923.

BEAVER TRAPPING AND TRANSPLANTING. James E. Grasse. Proc. Ann. Conf. W. Assn. State Game and Fish Comm.29: 196-200, 1949; Wyo. Wild Life, 13 (9): 10-17, 34, Oct., 1949.

TRANSPLANTING BEAVERS BY AIRPLANE AND PARACHUTE. Elmo W. Heter. Jour. Wildl. Mgt., 14 (2): 143-147, Apr., 1950.

BEAVER INTRODUCED IN VERMONT. George L. Kirk. Jour. Mam., vol.4, no.1, pp.59-60, Feb., 1923.

EXPERIMENTAL BEAVER TRANSPLANTING IN UTAH. D. I. Rasmussen, Nolan West. Trans. N. A. Wildl. Conf., 8: 311-318, 1943.

UTAH BEAVER TRANSPLANTING MANUAL. Edwin V. Rawley. Utah State Dept. Fish and Game, Dept. Inf. Bull. No.12, pp.1-15, illus., May, 1954.

BEAVER PLANTINGS IN MICHIGAN. Harry D. Ruhl, Parish S. Lovejoy. Papers Michigan Acad. Sci. Arts and Let., vol.11, pp.465-469 (1929), 1930.

THE EXPERIMENT OF INTRODUCING THE BEAVER INTO ASTRAKHAN PROVINCE. N. N. Rukovskii. Priroda no.6, pp.65-66, 1948.

ILLICIT TRAFFICKING IN BEAVER. Calvin Rutstrum. Amer. Forests, vol.41, no.2, pp.61-63, 95, illus., Feb., 1935; no.3, pp.122-123, 149, illus., Mar., 1935; no.4, pp.174-175, 199-200, illus., Apr., 1935.

TAKING BEAVER FOR STOCKING PURPOSES. Theodore H. Scheffer. Oregon Sportsman, vol.2, no.5, pp.12-14, May, 1926.

LIVE-TRAPPING AND RESTOCKING BEAVERS. Rex Gary Schmidt. Missouri Conservationist, Jefferson City, vol.4, no. 7, pp.8-9, illus., Oct., 1943.

REHABILITATING THE BEAVER. James W. Spriggs. Wyo. Wild Life, 8 (2): 1-5, 15-17, Feb., 1943.

BEAVER PLANTED BY PARACHUTE. Texas Game and Fish, Austin, vol.7, no.1, p.26, Dec., 1948.

LIVE-TRAPPING AND TRANSPLANTING OF BEAVER. Montana Wildlife Bull., Helena, vol.1, no.4, p.5, illus., Aug., 1944.

Longevity

BEAVER DIE-OFF. George J. Knudsen. Wis. Cons. Bull., 18 (9): 20-23, map, Sept., 1953.

ADDITIONAL EVIDENCE PROVIDED ON BEAVER LONGEVITY. Edwin V. Rawley. Utah Fish and Game Bull., 10 (7): 2, 5, 6, illus., Jan.-Feb., 1954.

REPORT OF MINNESOTA BEAVER DIE-OFF, 1951-1952. Milton H. Stenlund. Jour. Wildl. Mgt., 17 (3): 376-377, July, 1953.

Management

BEAVER MANAGEMENT PAYS. G. W. Bradt. Mich. Cons., 10 (5): 4-5, Apr., 1941.

MICHIGAN BEAVER MANAGEMENT. G. W. Bradt. Mich. Dept. Cons., 56 pp., 1947.

PROBLEMS OF BEAVER MANAGEMENT IN A FISH AND GAME PROGRAM. Gardiner Bump. Trans. N.A. Wildl. Conf., 6: 300-306, 1941.

FEDERAL AID IN FUR-RESOURCES MANAGEMENT IN CANADA. Hugh R. Conn. Trans. N.A. Wildl. Conf., 16: 437-443, 1951.

A PROGRAM FOR ADMINISTRATION AND MANAGEMENT OF THE BEAVER IN COLORADO. Richard N. Denney. MS thesis, Colo. A. and M. Coll., 1951.

A SUMMARY OF NORTH AMERICAN BEAVER MANAGEMENT, 1946-1948. Richard N. Denney. Colo. Game and Fish Dept., Cur. Rep., 28, vii plus 58 pp., illus., Aug., 1952.

(AN EXAMPLE OF FAUNAL MANAGEMENT IN QUEBEC: THE BEAVER.) Une exemple d'amenagement faunique dans la province de Quebec: le castor. Jean Duquay. La Foret Quebecoise, vol.14, no.5, pp.315-323, May-June, 1949.

BEAVER MANAGEMENT IN THE NORTHERN BLACK HILLS OF SOUTH DAKOTA. Dave Harris, Shaler E. Aldous. Jour. Wildlife Management, Menasha, vol.10, no.4, pp. 348-353, pl.22, Oct., 1946.

A PROGRESS REPORT ON BEAVER MANAGEMENT IN CALIFORNIA. Arthur L. Hensley. California Fish and Game San Francisco, vol.32, no.2, pp.87-99, Apr., 1946.

EXPERIMENTS ON THE MANAGEMENT OF COLORADO RIVER BEAVER. Arthur L. Hensley, B. C. Fox. Calif. Fish and Game, 34 (3): 115-151, July, 1948.

BEAVER MANAGEMENT IN MAINE. Kenneth W. Hodgdon., John H. Hunt. Me. Dept. Inl. Fisheries and Game, Game Div. Bull., no.3, ix plus 102 pp., illus., June, 1953.

A BASIS FOR BEAVER MANAGEMENT IN ALASKA. Wilbur L. Libby. MS thesis, Univ. Alaska, xii plus 80 pp., illus., 1954.

BEAVER MANAGEMENT IN OREGON. A. V. Meyers. Oregon State Game Comm. Bull., Portland, vol.1, no.2, pp.1, 3-4, illus., May, 1946.

A PRELIMINARY REPORT ON INTENSIVE BEAVER MANAGEMENT. Earl F. Patric, William L. Webb. Trans. 18th N.A. Wildl. Conf., pp.533-537; Repr. in Jour. Forestry, 52 (1): 31-32, Jan., 1954.

PLANNING FOR WILDLIFE ON A MANAGED FOREST. Kenneth A. Reid. Jour. Forestry, 49 (6): 436-439, June, 1951.

A PROGRAM OF BEAVER MANAGEMENT. RECOMMENDED FOR THE MAINTENANCE OF BOTH BEAVER AND TROUT IN MICHIGAN. J. Clark Salyer, II. Am. Game, 24 (3): 39, 47-48, 24 (4): 55, 62-64, May-June, July-Aug., 1935.

MANAGEMENT STUDIES OF TRANSPLANTED BEAVERS IN THE PACIFIC NORTHWEST. Victor B. Scheffer. Trans. N. A. Wildl. Conf., 6: 320-325, 1941.

NATIONAL STATUS OF BEAVER AND BEAVER MANAGEMENT. Reed Twichell. Trans. 17th N. A. Wildl. Conf., pp.476-482, 1952.

ADMINISTRATION OF BEAVER IN THE WESTERN UNITED STATES. Frank B. Wire, A. B. Hatch. Jour. Wildl. Mgt., 7 (1): 81-92, Jan., 1943.

BEAVER MISMANAGEMENT. Lee E. Yeager. Colorado Conservation, vol.3, no.4, pp.11-15, July, 1954.

BEAVER MANAGEMENT PROBLEMS ON WESTERN PUBLIC LANDS. Lee E. Yeager, Ralph R. Hill. Trans. 19th N. A. Wildl. Conf., pp.462-478, illus., 1954.

IOWA BEAVER PRESENT EXAMPLE OF MODERN GAME MANAGEMENT. Iowa Conservationist, Des Moines, vol.3, no. 11, pp.83-84, illus., Nov.15, 1944.

VIRGINIA BEAVER MANAGEMENT. Virginia Wildlife, Richmond, vol.7, no.2, p.23, illus., Aug., 1946.

Methods, Techniques

A TOOL FOR BEAVER DAM REMOVAL. M. Clair Aldous. Jour. Wildlife Management, Ithaca, vol.19, no.1, pp.153-154, illus., Jan., 1955.

A METHOD OF MARKING BEAVERS. Shaler E. Aldous. Jour. Wildl. Mgt., 4 (2): 145-148, Apr., 1940.

SEX DETERMINATION OF BEAVER FETUSES. Arthur H. Cook, Edward R. Maunton. Jour. Mam., 30: 72-73, 1949.

A STUDY OF CRITERIA FOR ESTIMATING THE AGE OF BEAVERS. Arthur H. Cook, Edward R. Maunton. New York Fish and Game Jour., 1 (1): 27-46, Jan., 1954.

PROPER CARE OF BEAVER PELTS. W. B. Elley. South Dakota Conservation Digest, Pierre, vol.12, no.1, p.13, illus., Jan., 1945.

(SCENT MARKING OF THE LARGE ARVICOLA (ARVICOLA TERRESTRIS L.).) Das Duftmarkieren der Grossen Wuehlmaus, Arvicola terrestris (L.). Fritz Frank. Zeitschr. Saeugetierk., Berlin, 21 (3-4): 172-175, Feb.28, 1957.

USE OF THE BACULUM IN AGE DETERMINATION OF MICHIGAN BEAVER. Charles E. Friley, Jr. Jour. Mam., vol. 30, no.3, pp.261-267, pls.1, Aug.17, 1949.

HOW TO IDENTIFY BEAVER. J. E. Hautamaki, Alfred B. Hansen. Amer. Fur Breeder, vol.4, no.6, pp.12-14, Dec., 1931.

A PROGRESS REPORT ON A TECHNIQUE TO CONTROL WATER LEVELS IN BEAVER IMPOUNDMENTS. Roger S. Leighton, James A. Lee. Proc. 8th Ann. N. E. Wildl. Conf., Jackson's Mill, W. Va., Apr.1-4, 1952, pp.1-4.

A TECHNIQUE TO CONTROL WATER LEVELS IN BEAVER IMPOUNDMENTS. Roger S. Leighton, James A. Lee. N. H. Fish and Game Dept., 4 pp., mimeo, 1952.

PREPARE PELTS PROPERLY. A. K. Momb. North Dakota Outdoors, Grand Forks, vol. 8, no.6, p.13, illus., Dec., 1945.

TECHNIQUES OF SEXING BEAVER, CASTOR CANADENSIS. Dale J. Osborn. Jour. Mam., 36 (1): 141-142, Feb., 1955.

OSTEOGRAPHY AS A CRITERION OF AGE IN THE BEAVER (CASTOR CANADENSIS KUHL). Ralph A. Robertson. MS thesis, Univ. Buffalo, 1948.

OSTEOLOGIC CRITERIA OF AGE IN BEAVERS. Ralph A. Robertson, Albert R. Shadle. J. Mam., 35 (2): 197-203, graph, May, 1954.

PELTING THE BEAVER. James W. Spriggs. Wyoming Wild Life, Cheyenne, vol.9, no.3, pp.1-4, illus., Mar., 1944.

A METHOD FOR HANDLING LIVE BEAVER. C. J. Whitelaw, E. T. Pengelley. Jour. Wildlife Management, Ithaca, vol.18, no.4, pp.533-534, illus., Oct., 1954.

THE IDENTIFICATION OF THE SEX OF BEAVERS. Floyd W. Young. Agric. Exper. Station, Michigan State College, Special Bull.279, pp.8, figs.6, Nov., 1936.

Mexico

(PRESENT DISTRIBUTION OF BEAVER IN MEXICO.) Distribution actual de los castores en Mexico. Bernardo R. Villa. An.Inst.Biol., vol.25, pp.443-450, illus., 1954.

Pelage, Coloration

WHITE BEAVER ARE TRAPPED IN HILLS. E. R. Lamster. South Dakota Conserv. Digest Pierre, vol.14, no.1, p.11, illus., Jan., 1947.

(A WHITE CANADIAN BEAVER (CASTOR CANADENSIS KUHL).) Ein weisser Kanadabiber (Castor canadensis Kuhl). Robert Mertens. Bericht Senckenbergische Naturforsch. Ges. (Natur u. Mus.), vol. 59, no.8, p.423, fig.1, Aug., 1929.

(MICROSCOPICAL STUDY OF BEAVER FUR.) Etude microscopique des poils de castor. P. Rode. Bull. Soc. Nat. Acclimat. France, vol.81, no.7, pp.297-301, July, 1934.

WHITE BEAVERS. R. E. C. Stearns. Amer. Nat., Phila., vol.17, no.10, p.1079, Oct., 1883.

WHITE BEAVER--A NEW RACE. Friends Magazine, Detroit, pp.2-3, figs.7, Sept., 1948.

WHITE BEAVER FOUND IN SOUTH DAKOTA. Amer. Fur Breeder, Duluth, vol.21, no.2, p.62, Dec., 1948.

Photography

PHOTOGRAPHING BEAVERS. Tappan Gregory. Jour. Mam., vol.8, no.2, pp. 119-122, pls.2, May, 1927.

NOTES ON SET CAMERA WORK WITH BEAVERS IN NORTHERN MICHIGAN. William P. Harris, Jr., Harold Du Charme. Jour. Mam., vol.9, no.1, pls.7, pp.17-19, Feb., 1928.

CAMERA HUNTING ON THE CONTINENTAL DIVIDE. Eleanor B. Pack. Nature Mag., vol.11, pp.149-152, illus., Mar., 1928.

Physiology

(THE SWAMP BEAVER IN WINTER.) Der sumpfbiber im winter. M. Boeder. Deutsche Pelztierzuechter, Muenchen, vol. 14, no.6, pp.131-133, Mar.15, 1939.

THE RESPIRATION OF BEAVER. Laurence Irving. Jour. Cell. and Comp. Physiol., Phila., vol.9, no.3, pp.437-451, figs.9, Apr., 1937.

PRELIMINARY OBSERVATIONS ON THE DIGESTIVE ENZYME SYSTEM OF THE BEAVER, (CASTOR CANADENSIS). W. D. Kitts, R. J. Bose, A. J. Wood, I. McT. Cowan. Canadian Jour. Zool., Ottawa, 35 (3): 449-452, June, 1957.

A PHYSIOLOGICAL STUDY OF CEREBRAL MOTOR CORTEX AND DECEREBRATE RIGIDITY IN THE BEAVER. Orthello R. Langworthy, Curt P. Richter. Jour. Mam., vol.19, no.1, pp.70-77, figs.3, Feb.14, 1938.

GASTRIC SECRETION IN THE BEAVER (CASTOR CANADENSIS). E. S. Nasset. Jour. Mam., 34 (2): 204-209, illus., May, 1953.

Reproductive Biology

JOHNNY AND PADDY, TWO BABY BEAVERS. Vernon Bailey, Florence Merriam. Nature Mag., pp.3-7, 6 figs., Jan., 1923.

NOTES ON THE SEX RATIO AND BREEDING OF THE BEAVER IN MICHIGAN. Seth B. Benson. Occas. Papers Mus. Zool., no.335, pp.6, fig.1, June 2, 1936.

(ARE BEAVERS BORN BLIND?) Werden Biber blind geboren? Edmund Bickel. Pelztierzucht, vol.7, no.11, pp.207-208, Nov. 17, 1931.

BREEDING HABITS OF BEAVER. G. W. Bradt. Jour. Mam., 20 (4): 486-489, Nov., 1939.

NOTE ON BREEDING OF BEAVERS. G. W. Bradt. Jour. Mam., vol.21, no.2, pp.220-221, May 14, 1940.

(BEAVER COPULATION.) Ueber den Begattungsakt des Bibers. F. H. van den Brink. Zeitschr. f. Saeugetierkunde, bd.4, heft 4-6, p.252, Feb.10, 1930.

BEAVER CAGE MATES. William H. Carr. Fauna, Phila., vol.4, no.1, pp.25-26, illus., Mar., 1942.

BABY BEAVERS. T. J. Courtney. Jour. Mam., vol.28, no.3, pp.228-230, fig.1, Aug.19, 1947.

(AN INTERESTING OCCURRENCE IN SWAMP BEAVER BREEDING.) Ein interessenter Vorfall aus der Sumpfbiberzucht. F. Dahne. Der Deutsche Pelztierzuechter, Jahrg.1932, Muenchen, no.1, p.14, Jan.1, 1932.

(ON BEAVER COPULATION.) Ueber die Paarung des Bibers. Karl David. Der Naturforscher, vol.6, no.9, p.351, Dec., 1929.

BREEDING RECORD OF BEAVER. Earl Theron Engle. Jour. Mam., vol.5, no.3, p.202, Aug., 1924.

BEAVERS BORN IN CAPTIVITY. Roy Fugate. Murrelet, Seattle, vol.21, no.1, p.11, Jan.-Apr., 1940.

(OBSERVATIONS DURING BEAVER OESTRUS.) Beobachtungen waehrend der Biberranz. Ehrnegg Griffen. Der Deutsche Pelztierzuechter, Jahrgang 1931, Muenchen, no.10, pp.271-272, fig., May 15, 1931.

YOUNG BEAVERS. Stanley E. Guenther. Jour. Mam., vol.29, no.4, pp.419-420, Dec.31, 1948.

PRODUCTIVITY DATA FROM PLACENTAL SCARS IN BEAVER. Kenneth W. Hodgdon. Jour. Wildl. Mgt., 13 (4): 412-414, Oct., 1949.

(CONTRIBUTIONS TO THE COPULATION OF THE BEAVER.) Beitraege zum begattungsakt des Bibers. Ingo Krumbiegel. Zeitschrift F. Saeugetierkunde, vol.3, pp.62-63, June 11, 1928.

(LITERARY ADDENDUM ON BEAVER COPULATION.) Literarischer Nachtrag zum Begattungsakt des Bibers. Ingo Krumbiegel. Zeit. F. Saeugetierkunde, bd.4, heft 1, pp.33-35, July 6, 1929.

(ON BEAVER COPULATION.) Ueber den Begattungsakt des Bibers. A. Mertens. Zeitsch. f. Saeugetierkunde, vol.3, pp.60-61, illus., June 11, 1928.

EARLY BREEDING OF THE TEXAS BEAVER. F. W. Miller. Jour. Mam., vol.29, no.4, p.419, Dec.31, 1948.

AGE CLASSES, REPRODUCTION, AND SEX RATIOS OF WYOMING BEAVER. Dale J. Osborn. Jour. Mam., 34 (1): 27-44, illus., Feb., 1953.

A STUDY OF AGE CLASSES, REPRODUCTION AND SEX RATIOS OF BEAVER IN WYOMING. Dale J. Osborn. MS thesis, Univ. Wyo., 1949.

(ON BEAVER COPULATION.) Ueber den Paarungsakt des Bibers. Eberhard Riesenthal. Naturforscher, Berlin, vol.6, no.2, pp.66-67, May, 1929.

MATING OF BEAVERS. Adolph R. Roth. Jour. Mam., vol.19, no.1, p.108, Feb.14, 1938.

AN UNUSUAL CASE OF PARTURITION IN A BEAVER. Albert R. Shadle. Jour. Mam., vol.11, no.4, pp.483-485, Nov., 1930.

MONTANA RECORDS OF BEAVER EMBRYOS. Clarence Archer Tryon, Jr. Jour. Mam., vol.27, no.4, pp.396-397, Nov.25, 1946.

(ON BEAVER COPULATION.) Ueber den Begattungsakt des Bibers. F. H. Van den Brink. Zeitschr. fuer Saeugetierkunde, vol.4, nos.4-6, p.252, Feb.10, 1930.

TIME OF APPEARANCE OF YOUNG BEAVERS IN YELLOWSTONE NATIONAL PARK. Otis Wade. Jour. Mam., vol.16, no.2, p.155, May, 1935.

(YOUNG BEAVERS AT HIGH WATER LEVEL.) Jungbiber bei hochwasser. H. Winkler. Naturforscher, Berlin, vol.9, no.6, pp.222-224, pl.46, Sept., 1932.

Size and Weight

SOME MEASUREMENTS FROM A THREE AND ONE-HALF YEAR OLD BEAVER (CASTOR CANADENSIS). Arthur H. Cook. J. Mam., 35 (3): 452, Aug., 1954.

(THE WEIGHT OF YOUNG BEAVERS AND SOME MANIFESTATIONS OF THE INDUSTRY OF THE ADULTS.) Du poids des jeunes chez le castor, et de quelques manifestations de "l'industrie des adultes". Albert Hugues. Mammalia, Paris, vol.2, no.1, pp.49-51, Mar., 1938.

LARGE WISCONSIN BEAVER. A. W. Schorger. Jour. Mam., 34 (2): 260-261, May, 1953.

BUREAU OF MISSING BEAVER. (DATA ON WEIGHTS, GROWTH, AND MOVEMENTS.) William Webb. N. Y. State Cons., 8 (5): 12-13, illus., Apr.-May, 1954.

LARGE BEAVER. (WASHINGTON STATE GAME COMMISSION.) Wash. State Game Comm. Bull., 7 (3): 2, July, 1955.

LARGE BEAVER TRAPPED BY FRED WIEDRICK, FERN RIDGE, MONROE COUNTY. IT WEIGHED 68 POUNDS. Pennsylvania Game News, Harrisburg, p. 26, photo, May, 1941.

VERY LARGE BEAVER LIVE-TRAPPED IN COLORADO. Colorado Conserv. Comments, Denver, vol.10, no.8, p.17, Dec., 1948.

Surveys

SOUTH FORK (MONTANA) BEAVER SURVEY: 1939. M. M. Atwater. Jour. Wildl. Mgt., 4 (1): 100-103, Jan., 1940.

STATE-WIDE RESURVEY OF WEST VIRGINIA'S BEAVER POPULATION. R. Wayne Bailey. Cons. Comm. W. Va., Final Rep. PR Proj. W-30-R, pp.1-80, map, Oct., 1952.

BEAVER SURVEY. A. D. Coleman. Colorado Conservation Comments, Denver, vol.7, no.3, pp.15-16, Sept.15, 1944.

BEAVER SURVEY REVEALS MANY INTERESTING FACTS. Joe Davis. N. Dak. Outdoors, 5 (1): 3-9, July, 1942.

AERIAL SURVEYS FOR BEAVER IN THE MACKENZIE DISTRICT, NORTHWEST TERRITORIES. William A. Fuller. Trans. 18th N. A. Wildl. Conf., pp.329-335, 1953.

WYOMING BEAVER SURVEY. James E. Grasse. Wyoming Wildlife, Cheyenne, vol.12, no.9, pp.4-14, illus., Oct., 1948.

AERIAL SURVEY OF BEAVER, 1946-47. Brandt V. Hjelle. North Dakota Outdoors, Bismarck, vol.9, no.10, pp.10-11, Apr., 1947.

AERIAL BEAVER SURVEY. Arthur W. Holweg. N. Y. State Cons., 8 (5): 13, Apr.-May, 1954.

1952 BEAVER SURVEY, WEST VIRGINIA. Frank M. Johnson. W. Va. Cons., 16 (4): 36-37, July, 1952.

BEAVER SURVEY. Glenn E. Jones, Juanita Mahaffey. Okla. Game and Fish News, 8 (11): 8-10, illus., Nov., 1952.

CHECKING UP ON THE BEAVER. Ed. Maunton. N. Y. State Cons., 9 (3): 6-8, illus., Dec.-Jan., 1954-1955.

SURVEY OF 1936 / BOOK CLIFFS / SAN ISABEL NATIONAL FOREST. William M. Nemanic, H. S. Wallace, Lucas A. Dargan, James M. Coutts. Colo. Game and Fish Dept., Beaver Surv., vol.1, ii plus 33 pp., July, 1939.

SURVEY OF 1939 / BOOK CLIFFS / SAN ISABEL NATIONAL FOREST. William M. Nemanic, James M. Coutts, and Lucas M. Dargan. Colo. Game and Fish Dept., Beaver Surv., vol.2, ii plus 55 (mostly unnumbered) pp., Jan., 1940.

SURVEY OF 1940 / BOOK CLIFFS / WHITE RIVER / LOWER COLORADO. William M. Nemanic. Colo. Game and Fish Dept., Beaver Surv., vol.3, ii plus 50 pp., Jan., 1941.

SURVEY OF 1941 / WHITE RIVER WATER-SHED. William M. Nemanic, Wendell Bever, Nathan Lipmann, Donald Lauridson, Joe Nemanic. Colo. Game and Fish Dept., Beaver Surv., vol.4, 241 pp., Jan., 1942.

A BEAVER CENSUS IN ALGONQUIN PROVINCIAL PARK, 1939-1940. Donald L. Robb. Canadian Field-Nat., Ottawa, vol.56, no.6, pp.86-90, illus., Sept., 1942.

BEAVER CENSUSING BY AIRPLANE. Wendell G. Swank, Fred A. Glover. Jour. Wildl. Mgt., 12 (2): 214, Apr., 1948.

A BEAVER SURVEY ON THE POLE MOUNTAIN DIVISION OF THE MEDICINE BOW NATIONAL FOREST. William August Williges. MS thesis, Univ. Wyo., 1946.

BEAVER SURVEY FOR 1947. Wyoming Wild Life, Cheyenne, vol.11, pp.8-10, illus., Nov., 1947.

Taxonomy

(IS CASTOR CANADENSIS KUHL, THE AMERICAN BEAVER, A VALID SPECIES?) Ist Castor canadensis Kuhl, der amerikanische Biber, eine gute Art? Wilhelm Blasius. Ver. f. Naturw. z. Braunschweig IV, Jahresber. f. pp.73-83, 1883-1884, 1885-1886.

A STUDY OF THE VARIATION OF EUROPEAN BEAVERS. Einar Loennberg. Arkiv. Zool., Upsala, vol.5, no.6, pp.1-16, figs.1-5, 1909.

DESCRIPTION OF A NEW SUBSPECIES OF BEAVER. E. W. Nelson. Proc. Biol. Soc. Wash., vol.40, pp.125-126, Sept.26, 1927.

REVIEW OF THE BEAVERS OF THE PALEARCTIC REGION (CASTOR, RODENTIA). M. Serebrennikov. Comptes Rendus Acad. Sci. U.S.S.R., pp.271-276, illus., 1929.

Trapping

CONSTRUCTION AND OPERATION OF BIOLOGICAL SURVEY BEAVER TRAP. Vernon Bailey. U.S. Dept. Agric., miscl. circ. no.69, 4 pp., illus., June 29, 1926.

LITTLE RIVER BEAVER. AN ACCOUNT OF SOME SPRING BEAVER TRAPPING DURING 1944. E. J. Dailey. Fur-Fish-Game (Harding Mag.), Columbus, vol.79, no.2, pp.30-32, Feb., 1945.

TRAPPING SOUTH DAKOTA BEAVER. W. B. Elley. South Dakota Conservation Digest, Pierre, vol.10, no.2, p.11, Feb., 1943.

TRAPPING IS BIG BUSINESS. Arnold B. Erickson, Thomas A. Schrader. Cons. Volunteer, 7 (41): 1-6, July-Aug., 1944.

LIVE-TRAPPING AS A MEANS OF NUISANCE-BEAVER CONTROL. James E. Grasse. Proc. 31st Ann. conf. Western Assn. State Game and Fish Comm., pp.170-174, Apr.30-May 2, 1951.

HARVESTING BEAVERS BY PRIVATE TRAPPERS. Chester E. Kebbe. Proc. 34th Ann. Conf. Western Assn. State Game and Fish Comm., pp.216-218, May, 1954 (1955).

LIVE-TRAPPING BEAVER IN NORTH DAKOTA. A. K. Momb. North Dakota Outdoors, Grand Forks, vol.8, no.6, p. 13, illus., Dec., 1945.

LIVE TRAPPING OF BEAVERS TO BEGIN SOON. Charlie Pierle. Outdoor Georgia, Atlanta, vol.5, no.11, p.12, illus., June 15, 1944.

TRAPPING BEAVER IN THE ROCKY MOUNTAINS. O. D. Robertson. Outdoor Life, Denver, vol.23, no.4, pp.339-342, illus., Apr., 1909.

STEEL-TRAPPING THE BEAVER. James W. Spriggs. Wyoming Wild Life, Cheyenne, vol.9, no.1, pp.1-4, illus., Jan., 1944.

BEAVER TRAPPING SEASON. W. H. Trucotte. Miss. Game and Fish, 10 (5-10): 9, Apr., 1947.

BEAVER TRAPPING REPORT--1942-43. Wisconsin Conserv. Bull., Madison, vol.8, no.7, pp.27-28, July, 1943.

TRAPPERS DISCUSS THEIR PROBLEMS. (BEAVER TRAPPING QUOTAS.) Sylva, Toronto, vol.5, no.2, pp.36-41, illus., 1949.

BEAVER TRAPPING IN NORTH DAKOTA. N. Dak. Game and Fish Dept., PR Proj. 7R, pp.1-14, illus., Oct., 1952.

LIVE-TRAPPING BEAVERS. Texas Game and Fish, Austin, vol.2, no.1, pp.14-15, illus., Dec., 1943.

United States

THE FUTURE OF THE BEAVER IN UTAH. Mark Anderson. Utah State Agric. College, Logan, Utah, Misc. Publ.10, pp.30-32, May, 1933.

WESTERN MARYLAND BEAVER. Dale M. Arner. Maryland Conservationist, Balto., vol.26, no.2, pp.23-24, illus., Summer, 1949.

STATUS OF BEAVER IN WEST VIRGINIA. R. Wayne Bailey. Jour. Wildlife Management, Ithaca, vol.18, no.2, pp.184-190, illus., Apr., 1954.

THE GIANT BEAVER, CASTOROIDES, AND THE COMMON BEAVER, CASTOR, IN NEBRASKA. E. H. Barbour. Nebraska State Mus., vol.1, bull.20, pp.171-186, figs. 109-120, June, 1931.

INDUSTRIOUS BEAVER IS RETURNING TO THIS STATE. Frederick S. Barkalow, Jr. Alabama Game and Fish News, Montgomery, pp.5-7, fig.1, Sept., 1940.

PENNSYLVANIA BEAVER. Ted H. Beam. Fur-Fish-Game, Harding's Magazine, vol. 60, no.2, pp.12, 15, Aug., 1934.

THE INDIANS HAD A WORD FOR THEM--BEAVER PEOPLE. Bennie Bengtson. Frontiers, Lancaster, vol.6, no.4, pp.114-115, illus., Apr., 1942.

THE BEAVER MAKES A COMEBACK. William P. Blackwell. Va. Wildl., 10 (1): 19-20, Jan., 1949.

THE STATUS OF THE BEAVER IN VIRGINIA, 1947. William P. Blackwell. MS thesis, Va. Polytechnic Inst., 1948.

BEAVERS TWENTY MILES FROM B'WAY. Hiram Blauvelt. Nature Magazine, vol.19, no.1, p.42, figs.2, Jan., 1932.

A STUDY OF BEAVER COLONIES IN MICHIGAN. G. W. Bradt. PhD thesis, Univ. Mich., 1936; Jour. Mam., 19 (2): 139-162, May, 1938.

BUSY BEAVERS MAKE TRACKS. Allen Brohn. Mo. Cons., 14 (4): 1-3, 13, illus., Apr., 1953.

REAPPEARANCE OF BEAVERS IN WEST VIRGINIA. A. B. Brooks. Jour. Mam., vol.4, no.3, p.191, Aug., 1923.

NOTES ON ADIRONDACK BEAVER. Charles P. Brown. Jour. Mam., vol.27, no.4, pp.394-395, Nov.25, 1946.

A BREATHER FOR THE BEAVER. Gardiner Bump. N. Y. State Cons., 1 (5): 7, 9, Apr.-May, 1947.

BLACK GOLD--THE STORY OF THE BEAVER IN NEW YORK STATE. Gardiner Bump, Arthur H. Cook. N.Y. Cons. Dept. Mgt. Bull., no.2, 16 pp., 1941.

COLORADO GARNERS HER BEAVER. Arthur H. Carhart. Am. Forests, 46 (2): 69-71, 89, 96, Feb., 1940.

THE BEAVER IN OHIO. Floyd B. Chapman. Jour. Mam., 30 (2): 174-179, May, 1949.

BEAVER IN LOUISIANA. Bernard C. Dahlen. La. Cons. Rev., Summer, 1939: 15-17, Summer, 1939.

THE BEAVER IN MISSOURI. Paul D. Dalke. Mo. Cons., 8 (6): 1-3, June, 1947.

CRITICAL NOTES ON THE TEXAS BEAVER. William B. Davis. Jour. Mam., vol.21, no.1, pp.84-86, figs.2, Feb.14, 1940.

THREE NEW BEAVERS FROM UTAH. Stephen D. Durrant, Harold S. Crane. Univ. Kansas Publ. Mus. Nat. Hist., Lawrence, vol.1, no.20, pp.407-417, figs.7, Dec.24, 1948.

HISTORY OF THE BEAVER IN THE BLACK HILLS. W. B. Elley. South Dakota Conserv. Digest, Pierre, vol.12, no.12, p.5, Dec., 1945.

PRESENT STATUS OF THE BEAVER IN VIRGINIA. James W. Engle, Jr. Va. Wildl., 15 (4): 16-17, illus., Apr., 1954.

BEAVER POPULATIONS IN PINE COUNTY, MINNESOTA. Arnold B. Erickson. Jour. Mam., 20 (2): 195-201, May, 1939.

BEAVER IN ARIZONA. B. C. Fox. Arizona Wildlife and Sportsman, Safford, vol. 6, no.10, p.10, illus., Oct., 1944.

A NEW BEAVER FROM ARIZONA. E. A. Goldman. Jour. Mam., vol.13, no.3, pp. 266-267, Aug., 1932.

BEAVER ECOLOGY AND MANAGEMENT IN THE ROCKIES. James E. Grasse. Jour. Forestry, 49 (1): 3-6, Jan., 1951; Wyo. Wildl., 16 (6): 26-34, illus., June, 1952.

BEAVER MANAGEMENT AND ECOLOGY IN WYOMING. James E. Grasse, Euvern F. Putnam. Wyo. Game and Fish Comm., bull.6, 52 pp., 1950.

A STUDY OF BEAVER POPULATIONS OF SOME UTAH STREAMS. Phillips Haas. MS thesis, Utah State Agr. Coll., 1941.

BEAVER ON THE LOWER SOURIS REFUGE. Merrill C. Hammond. Jour. Wildl. Mgt., 7 (3): 316-321, July, 1943.

THE BEAVER IN NORTH DAKOTA. Charles W. Hargrave. North Dakota Outdoors, Bismarck, vol.13, no.3, pp.4-5, illus., Sept., 1950.

THE STORY OF MINNESOTA BEAVER. Paul R. Highby. Cons. Volunteer, 1 (2): 41-46, Nov., 1940.

A NEW RACE OF BEAVER FROM OREGON. Stanley G. Jewett, E. Raymond Hall. Jour. Mam., Balto., vol.21, no.1, pp.87-89, 1 fig., Feb.14, 1940.

THE BEAVER IN THE ADIRONDACKS: ITS ECONOMICS AND NATURAL HISTORY. Charles Eugene Johnson. Roosevelt Wild Life Bull., vol.4, no.4, pp.501-641, figs. 87-127, 3 maps, July, 1927.

AN INVESTIGATION OF THE BEAVER IN HERKIMER AND HAMILTON COUNTIES OF THE ADIRONDACKS. Charles Eugene Johnson. Roosevelt Wild Life Bull., vol.1, no.2, pp.117-186, figs.1-36, Aug., 1922.

THE BEAVER. George B. Johnson. Va. Wildl., 6 (1): 28-34, Fall-Winter, 1942.

WISCONSIN'S EAGER BEAVER. George J. Knudsen. Wis. Cons. Bull., 16 (2): 11-15, illus., Dec., 1951.

MILLION DOLLAR CONSERVATION TRIUMPH. Roger M. Latham. Pa. Game News, 21 (11): 4-8, 21 (12): 35-40, Feb.-Mar., 1951.

THE ODDS WERE AGAINST HIM. Leo A. Luttringer, Jr. Pa. Game News, 15 (12): 12-13, 26, Mar., 1945.

HOOSIER STATE HAS ITS OWN BEAVER VALLEY. M. L. McAbee. Outdoor Indiana, 20 (1): 20-21, illus., Jan., 1953.

BIG BEND BEAVER. Ellis McDougall. Fur-Fish-Game, Harding's Mag., Columbus, vol.79, no.7, pp.34-36, July, 1945.

MICKEY THE BEAVER. (NOTES ON BEAVER IN NORTHERN MICHIGAN.) James MacGillivray. Nat. Geog. Mag., vol.54, pp.741-756, illus., Dec., 1928.

A NEW PARK RESIDENT. Robert N. McIntyre. Yosemite Nature Notes, vol. 27, no.4, pp.69-74, illus., Apr., 1948.

THE FATE OF MORGAN'S BEAVER. Richard H. Manville. Sci. Monthly, 69 (3): 186-191, Sept., 1949.

WHERE'S THE BEAVER? Roland B. Miller. New York State Conservationist, Albany, vol.3, no.5, p.35, illus., Apr.-May, 1949.

BEAVER IN NEBRASKA. Levi Mohler. Outdoor Nebraska, Lincoln, vol.19, no.1, p.10, Winter, 1942.

ALABAMA'S BUSY BEAVER. George C. Moore. Ala. Cons., 15 (2): 8-9, 12, Aug., 1943.

STATUS OF BEAVER IN ALABAMA. George C. Moore, Ernest C. Martin. Ala. Dept. Cons. Game, Fish, and Seafoods Div., 30 pp., 1949.

FLOOD CONTROL ENGINEERS--THE BEAVER IS STAGING A COME-BACK. James O. Moynahan. Kentucky Happy Hunting Ground, Frankfort, vol.5, no.5, pp.5, 29, illus., Sept., 1949.

THE BEAVER--HISTORY MAKER--IS COMING BACK. W. O. Nagel. Mo. Cons., 7 (9): 6-7, 16, Sept., 1946.

DESCRIPTION OF A NEW SUBSPECIES OF BEAVER. E. W. Nelson. Proc. Biol. Soc. Wash., vol.40, pp.125-126, Sept.26, 1927.

A SURVEY OF THE BEAVER POPULATION OF ROCKY MOUNTAIN NATIONAL PARK, COLORADO. Fred M. Packard. Jour. Mam., 28 (3): 219-227, Aug., 1947.

THE RENAISSANCE OF THE BEAVER. (SUCCESS OF INTRODUCTIONS IN THE ADIRONDACKS.) Robert B. Peck. Forest and Stream, vol.91, pp.152-154, 182-187, Apr., 1921.

BEAVER COMEBACK IN NEW ENGLAND. Clay Perry. Beaver, 283, pp.32-35, illus., June, 1952.

BEAVER CRISIS IN THE NORTHEAST. Clay Perry. Amer. Forests, Wash., vol. 51, no.2, pp.72-73, 94-95, illus., Feb., 1945.

ARIZONA'S OPERATION BEAVER LIFT. Willis Peterson. Natl Geog. Mag., 107 (5): 666-680, illus., May, 1955.

A STUDY OF BEAVER IN AMITE COUNTY, MISSISSIPPI. John H. Phares. MS thesis, La. State Univ., 1950.

VIRGINIA ANIMALS EVERYONE SHOUD KNOW: THE BEAVER. Chester F. Phelps. Virginia Wildlife, Richmond, vol.8, no.9, pp.5-6, 20, illus., Sept., 1947.

BEAVERS MOVE IN. C. B. Pierle. W. Va. Cons., 5 (9): 4-5, 19, Dec., 1941.

THE BEAVER IN ILLINOIS. Lysle R. Pietsch. Trans. Illinois Acad. Sci., 49: 193-201, 1956.

BEAVER UPSWING IN MANY ILLINOIS AREAS. Lysle R. Pietsch. Outdoors in Ill., 18 (2): 12-13, 39, Spring, 1951.

AN INDUSTRIOUS ANIMAL--THE BEAVER. O. L. Resner. Wash. Outdoors, 1 (3): 6-7, June, 1946.

ITASCA PARK'S PIONEERING BEAVERS. Thomas S. Roberts. Conserv. Volunteer, St. Paul, vol.1, no.6, pp.37-40, illus., Mar., 1941.

WHAT ABOUT OUR BEAVERS? T. E. Rochester. Arizona Wildlife and Sportsman, Tucson, vol.6, no.13, p.6, Dec., 1945.

THE CAROLINA BEAVER: A VANISHING SPECIES? J. Clark Salyer, II. Jour. Mam., 27 (4): 331-335, Nov., 1946.

IOWA'S 1949 BEAVER SEASON. Glen C. Sanderson. Iowa Cons., 9 (3): 17, 23-24, Mar., 1950.

RECENT STATUS OF THE BEAVER IN IOWA. Glen C. Sanderson. Iowa Acad. Sci., 60: 746-753, map, 1953.

THE DISTRIBUTION OF BEAVER IN VERMONT. Roger Seamans. Vt. Fish and Game Serv., Bull.3-1, 5 pp., Jan., 1941; Vt. Fish and Game Serv., State Bull., PR Ser.No.7, pp.28-39, Feb., 1942.

TO THE NORTH WOODS IN SEARCH OF BEAVER. WITH A CANOE IN MINNESOTA. Helen Seth-Smith. Field, London, vol.164, no.4266, pp.732-733, illus., Sept.29, 1934.

FIFTEEN MONTHS OF BEAVER WORK AT ALLEGANY STATE PARK, N.Y. Albert R. Shadle, Thomas S. Austin. Jour. Mam., 20 (3): 299-303, Aug., 1939.

THE BEAVER IN MASSACHUSETTS, A RESEARCH AND MANAGEMENT STUDY. Samuel P. Shaw. Massachusetts Dept. Conserv., Div. Wildlife Research and Management, Boston, Research Bull.no.11, pp.45, illus., Sept., 1948.

BRAINY BUILDER BEAVER. Rowe Shawver. W. Sportsman, 5 (3): 6-10, 40, Aug., 1940.

A BEAVER COLONY OF YELLOWSTONE PARK. M. P. Skinner. Nat. Hist., New York vol.24, no.3, pp.347-349, illus., 1924.

BEAVER ECOLOGY AND MANAGEMENT IN WEST VIRGINIA. Wendell G. Swank. Bull. Div. Game Management, West Virginia Conservation Comm., Charleston, no.1, pp.65, illus., 1949.

THE STATUS OF BEAVERS IN CALIFORNIA. Donald T. Tappe. Game Bull. California Div. Fish and Game, San Francisco, no.3, pp.59, figs.26, 1942.

THE BEAVER OF WEST CENTRAL CALIFORNIA. Walter P. Taylor. Univ. Calif. Publ. Zool., vol.10, no.7, pp.167-169, May 21, 1912.

THE STATUS OF THE BEAVERS OF WESTERN NORTH AMERICA, WITH A CONSIDERATION OF THE FACTORS IN THEIR SPECIATION. Walter P. Taylor. Univ. Calif. Publ. Zool., vol.12, no.15, pp.413-495, figs., Mar.20, 1916.

A STUDY OF BEAVER IN LOUISIANA. Thomas D. Thigpen. MS thesis, La. State Univ., 1950.

THE BEAVER IN MISSISSIPPI. W. H. Turcotte. Miss. Game and Fish Comm., Surv. Bull.41 pp., Sept., 1941.

YOSEMITE BEAVERS AS OF TODAY. Orthello L. Wallis. Yosemite Nat. Notes, vol.30, no.1, pp.5-9, illus., Jan., 1951.

BEAVER IN THE PIKES PEAK REGION. Edward R. Warren. Trail and Timberline (Thd Colorado Mountain Club, Denver, Colorado), no.98, pp.4-6, Nov., 1926.

BEAVERS IN THE ELK MOUNTAIN REGION, COLORADO. Edward R. Warren. Jour. Mam., vol.9, no.4, pp.320-334, figs.3, Nov., 1928.

THE LIFE OF THE YELLOWSTONE BEAVER. Edward R. Warren. Roosevelt Wild Life Bull., vol.1, no.2, pp.187-221, 34 figs., map, Aug., 1922.

NOTES ON THE BEAVER COLONIES IN THE LONGS PEAK REGION OF ESTES PARK, COLORADO. Edward R. Warren. Roosevelt Wild Life Annals, New York State College of Forestry, vol.1, nos.1-2, pp. 192-234, figs.134-174, maps 13-15, Aug., 1927.

A STUDY OF THE BEAVER IN THE YANCEY REGION OF YELLOWSTONE NATIONAL PARK. Edward R. Warren. Roosevelt Wild Life Annals, New York' State College of Forestry, vol.1, nos.1-2, pp.1-191, figs.1-13B, maps 1-12, Aug., 1927.

A NEW SUBSPECIES OF BEAVER FROM COLORADO. Edward R. Warren, E. Raymond Hall. Jour. Mam., vol.20, no.3, pp.358-362, map, table, Aug.14, 1939.

UTAH BEAVER STUDY. Nolan West, D. I. Rasmussen. Utah Dept. Fish and Game Publ.no.1, 37 pp., Apr., 1947.

BEAVERS AND THE ADIRONDACKS. Charles H. Willoughby. Conservationist, vol.3, pp.67-70, May, 1920.

THE BEAVER IN NORTH CAROLINA. Kenneth A. Wilson. Wildl. in N.C., 19 (5): 6-8, 10, illus., May, 1955.

BEAVER COLONIES SPREADING. Virginia Wildlife, Blacksburg, vol.2, no.8, p.3, Apr., 1939.

THE BEAVER COMES BACK. Outdoor Ind., 11 (2): 3, 14, Mar., 1944.

BEAVER,ENGINEERS OF THE ANIMAL WORLD. Iowa Cons., 2 (12): 89, 91, 93, Dec., 1943.

BEAVER IN NORTH DAKOTA. North Dakota Outdoors, vol.1, no.6, pp.16-20, Dec., 1938.

BEAVER STAGING REMARKABLE COME-BACK IN INDIANA. Nature Notes, Peoria, ill., vol.6, no.11, pp.221-222, Nov., 1939.

BEAVER THRIVING IN NINE COUNTIES (VIRGINIA). Virginia Wildlife, Blacksburg, vol.1, no.3, pp.1, 7, Nov., 1937.

KNOWING OHIO WILDLIFE. BEAVER NOTES. Ohio Wildlife Research Unit. Ohio Conserv. Bull., Columbus, vol.14, no.5, pp.27-28, May, 1950.

PACIFIC BEAVER. The Murrelet, Seattle, vol.20, no.3, p.71, Sept-Dec., 1939.

STATE'S BEAVER POPULATION TRIPLED. Alabama Conserv., Montgomery, vol.22, nos.1-2, pp.15, 23, illus., July-Aug., 1950.

## Anomaluridae

ON ANOMALURUS, ITS STRUCTURE AND POSITION. Edward R. Alston. Proc. Zool. Soc. Lond., pp.88-97, figs.3, pl.31, 1875.

(ON LOCAL FORMS OF "ANOMALURUS FRASERI.") Las formas locales de "Anomalurus fraseri." Angel Cabrera. Bol. Real Soc. Espanola Hist. Nat., Madrid, vol.23, no.2, pp.68-69, Feb., 1923.

(FLYING SQUIRRELS.) A propos des ecureuils volants. (Anomaluridae) P. L. Dekeyser. Notes Africaines, no.6, pp.121-124, Oct., 1954.

(DESCRIPTION OF AN "ANOMALUROPS" OF THE BIGNONA REGION.) Description d'un "Anomalurops" de la région de Bignona. P. L. Dekeyser, A. Villiers. Conferência Internacional dos Africanistas Ocidentais, Lisbon, vol.3, pp.57-62, Aug., 1951.

SEASONAL CHANGES IN COLOUR OF ANOMALURUS JACKSONI. Guy Dollman. Proc. Linn. Soc. Lond., 144th Sess., pp. 68-71, June 6, 1932.

DESCRIPTION OF A NEW SPECIES OF ANOMALURUS, FROM FERNANDO PO. Louis Fraser. Proc. Zool. Soc. Lond., pt.20, pp.16-17, 1852.

SYSTEMATIC NOTES ON THE GENUS IDIURUS (ANOMALURIDAE). R. W. Hayman. Annals and Mag. Nat. Hist., London, ser.11, vol.13, pp.208-212, Mar., 1946.

(A NEW RODENT GENUS RELATED TO IDIURUS MTSCH.) Eine neue mit Idiurus Mtsch. verwandte gattung der Nagethiere. Paul Matschie. Sitz. Ber. Gesell. Berlin, Jahrg.1898, no.4, pp.23-30, Apr.19, 1898.

DESCRIPTION OF A NEW RODENT OF THE GENUS IDIURUS. Gerrit S. Miller, Jr. Proc. Biol. Soc. Wash., vol.12, pp.73-76, Mar.24, 1898.

(A NEW SPECIES OF THE RODENT GENUS ANOMALURUS OF ZANZIBAR.) Ueber eine neue Art der Nagergattung Anomalurus von Zanzibar. W. Peters. Monatsber. Akad. Wissensch. Berlin, pp.164-165, pl.1, Feb.12, 1880.

FLYING SQUIRRELS IN THE NORTH? (ANOMALURIDS) W. H. Ramsay. Nigerian Field, vol.15, no.2, pp.94-95, Apr., 1950.

(A FLYING SQUIRREL DIFFICULT TO CAPTURE.) Un Ecureuil volant difficile a obtenir. (Idiurus). H. Schouteden. Cercle Zool. Congo., vol.11, nos.1-2, p.44, Nov.-Dec., 1934.

(NOTE ON AN ANOMALURUS FRASERIE FOETUS.) Note sur un foetus d'Anomalurus fraserie. A. F. de Seabra. Bull. Soc. Portugaise Sci. Nat., Lisboa, vol.3, fasc.1, 1909, pp.6, figs.3, 1910.

(ON THE SYSTEMATIC CLASSIFICATION OF THE AFRICAN FLYING SQUIRREL (ANOMALURIDAE).) Ueber die systematische Einteilung der afrikanischen Dornschwanzhoernchen (Anomaluridae) H. Ruemmler. Sitz.-Ber. Gesell. Naturf. Freunde, Berlin, Jahrg.1933, nos.8-10, pp.389-391, 1934.

A NEW RODENT OF THE FAMILY ANOMALURIDAE FROM THE BENITO RIVER, FRENCH CONGO. W. E. de Winton. Abstracts, Zool. Soc. London, 2 pp., May 17, 1898.

ON A NEW GENUS AND SPECIES OF RODENTS OF THE FAMILY ANOMALURIDAE FROM WEST AFRICA. W. E. de Winton. Proc. Zool. Soc. Lond., pp.450-454, pls.34-35, May 17, 1898.

Pedetidae

ON A SECOND SPECIES OF LAGOTIS (LAG. PALLIPES). E. T. Bennett. Proc. Zool. Soc. Lond., pt.3, pp.67-68, 1835.

(BIRTH IN CAPTIVITY OF AN AFRICAN JUMPING HARE (PEDETES CAFFER).) Gefangenschaftsgeburt eines afrikanischen Springhasen, Pedetes caffer. H. Hediger. Zool. Garten, Leipzig, NF, vol.17, nos.1-5, pp.166-169, illus., 1950.

THE SPECIES OF PEDETES INHABITING ANGOLA. Martin A. C. Hinton. Ann. and Mag. Nat. Hist., ser.9, vol.6, pp.102-104, July, 1920.

ON THE REPRODUCTION OF THE SPRING-HARE, PEDETES CAFFER. C. J. van der Horst. South African Biol. Soc., Durban, pamphlet no.8, p.47, 1935.

THE EXTERNAL CHARACTERS OF A NEONATAL PEDETES. Frederic Wood Jones. Proc. Zool. Soc. Lond., vol.110, ser.B, pts.3-4, pp.199-206, figs.7, Mar., 1941.

A NEW PEDETES FROM TANGANYIKA TERRITORY (P. CAFER DENTATUS). Gerrit S. Miller, Jr. Proc. Biol. Soc. Washington, vol.40, pp.113-114, Sept.26, 1927.

THE SPRINGHAAS OR CAPE JUMPING HARE. R. I. Pocock. The Field, London, vol.147, p.388, Mar.4, 1926.

Cricetidae

THE MUSKRAT. Rod Amundson. Wildlife in North Carolina, Raleigh, vol.13, no.12, pp.4-7, illus., Dec., 1949.

THE MUSKRAT. H. B. Apel. Wisconsin Conserv. Bull., Madison, vol.8, no.1, pp.30-31, Jan., 1943.

THE WHITE-FOOTED MOUSE. Elizabeth Bachman. Conserv. Volunteer, St. Paul, vol.12, no.70, pp.19-21, May-June, 1949.

THE FURRY MUSKRAT. V. Bailey. Nature Mag., vol.6, pp.29-30, 4 figs., July, 1925.

LITTLE WARRIOR OF THE WEST. THE IMPORTANT GRASSHOPPER MOUSE OF THE PLAINS. V. Bailey. Nature Magazine, vol.18, no.4, pp.238-239, figs.3, Oct., 1931.

THE COTTON MOUSE, PEROMYSCUS GOSSYPINUS. Outram Bangs. Proc. Biol. Soc. Wash., vol.10, pp.119-125, Nov. 5, 1896.

COMMON MUSKRAT. N. R. Barger. Wisconsin Conserv. Bull., Madison, vol. 13, no.11, pp.25-26, illus., Nov., 1948.

NOTES ON THE LIFE HISTORY OF THE RED TREE MOUSE, PHENACOMYS LONGICAUDUS. Seth B. Benson, Adrey E. Borell. Jour. Mam., vol.12, no.3, pp.226-233, fig.1, Aug., 1931.

LE HAMSTER (CRICETUS CRICETUS L.). Robert Didier, P. Mathias. Mammalia, Paris, 1 (1): 15-23, illus., Sept., 1936.

A STATEMENT ON NEW INFORMATION OF THE SPECIES NICRETUS MIRHANROI-AI SCHAEFER. Gy Ehik. Sbornik Mus. Praze, Acia Mus. Nat., Prague, vol. 3, no.4, zool. no.2, pp.81-86, 1949.

WOOD RATS. H. Nelson Elliott. US F&WS, Wildl. Leafl.354, 2 pp., July, 1953.

THE DUSKY-FOOTED WOOD RAT (NEOTOMA FUSCIPES). Pennoyer F. English. Jour. Mam., vol.4, no.1, pp.1-9, pls.3, Feb., 1923.

THE MATHEMATICAL MUSKRAT. Paul L. Errington. Iowa Cons., 11 (6): 41, 47, illus., June, 1952.

THE MATHEMATICAL MUSKRAT. Paul L. Errington. Iowa Cons., 11 (7): 51, illus., July, 1952.

THE MUSKRAT. Paul L. Failor. Pennsylvania Game News, Harrisburg, vol.14, no. 8, pp.12, 32, illus., Nov., 1943.

(OBSERVATIONS ON THE LIFE OF THE WATER RAT.) Les observations de la vie du rat d'eau, Arvicola terrestris L. K. K. Flerov. Russischen Hydrobiologischen Zeits., Saratow, Russia, vol.4, nos.10-12, pp.194-201, 1925. (In Russian with French summary.)

NOTES ON THE STRIPED HAMSTER (CRICETULUS GRISEUS, THOMAS). A. B. Droogleever Fortuyn. China Med. Jour., Shanghai, vol.41, no.10, pp.859-863, fig.2, table 1, Oct., 1927.

(CONTRIBUTIONS TO THE BIOLOGY OF THE WOOD MOUSE (MICROTUS ARVAILS PALLAS).) Beitraege sur Biologie der Feldmaus, Microtus arvalis (Pallas). Fritz Frank. Zool. Jahrbuecher, vol.82, nos.3-4, pp.354-404, Jan.20, 1954; Zool. Jahr. Jena, vol.84, no.1, pp.32-74, Mar.12, 1956.

(THE BIOLOGY OF THE NORTHERN VOLE (MICROTUS OECONOMUS STIMMINGI NEHRING).) Zur Biologie der Nordischen Wuehlmaus (Microtus oeconomus stimmingi Nehring). Fritz Frank, Klaus Zimmermann. Zeitschr. Saeugetierk., 21 (1-2): 58-83, pl. 5, 1956.

EXPERIENCES WITH WOOD RATS, NEOTOMA FUSCIPES MACROTIS. Frank F. Gander. Jour. Mam., vol.10, no.1, pp.51-58, Feb., 1929.

CRICETUS CR. CRICETUS (LINNÉ, 1758). Dr. Hamster Gersdorf. Saeugetierk. Mitteil., Stuttgart, vol.1, no.2, p.81, Apr. 1, 1953.

NOTES ON THE UNALASKA COLLARED LEMMING (DICROSTONYX MALASCENSIS UNALASCENSIS MERRIAM). Raymond M. Gilmore. Jour. Mam., vol.14, no.3, pp. 257-258, Aug., 1933.

OBSERVATIONS ON MYODES HUDSONICUS AND THE OTHER SPECIES OF THE GENUS MYODES. J. E. Gray. Proc. Zool. Soc. Lond., pt.16, p.43, 1848.

A FEW WHITE-FOOTED MOUSE PICTURES. Tappan Gregory. Jour. Mam., vol.9, no.3, pp.205-208, pl.19, Aug., 1928.

MUSKRAT HINTS. J. Curtis Grigg. Outdoorsman, Chicago, vol.87, no.1 (whole no.512), pp.42, 44, illus., Jan.-Feb., 1945.

A MANUAL OF NEOTROPICAL SIGMODONT RODENTS. Nils Gyldenstolpe. Kungl. Svenska Vetensk. Handl., ser.3, vol.11, no.3, pp.1-164, pls.1-18, 1932.

FIELD MICE. W. J. Hamilton, Jr. Nature Mag., Washington, vol.43, no.2, pp.94-95, illus., Feb., 1950.

LIFE HISTORY NOTES ON THE NORTHERN PINE MOUSE. W. J. Hamilton, Jr. Jour. Mam., 19 (2): 163-170, May, 1938.

MUSKRAT, LIFE AND ECONOMY. W. J. Hamilton, Jr. New York Conservationist, vol.7, no.4, pp.12-13, illus., Feb.-Mar., 1953.

OBSERVATIONS ON THE LIFE HISTORY OF THE NORTHERN PINE MOUSE. Allen H. Benton. Jour. Mam., 36 (1): 52-62, Feb., 1955.

OBSERVATIONS ON THE LIFE HISTORY OF BAIOMYS TAYLORI SUBATER. W. Frank Blair. Jour. Mam., vol.22, no.4, pp.378-383, fig.1, Nov.14, 1941.

THE GOPHER MOUSE - PEROMYSCUS FLORIDANUS. W. Frank Blair, John D. Kilby. Jour. Mam., vol.17, no.4, pp.421-422, Nov., 1936.

(THE WATER RAT (ARVICOLA AMPHIBIUS VAR. TERRESTRIS).) Die Wasserratte (Arvicola amphibius var. terrestris). Wilhelm Blohm. Aus der Heimat, vol.42, no.10, pp.305-311, figs.2, 1929.

SOME FURTHER NOTES ON DOLOMYS MARAKOVICI BOLKAY. St. J. Bolkay. Glasnik Zemljskob Muzeja u Bosni i Hercegovini, I. Sveska (Za Prirodne Nauke), Sarajevo, vol.41, pp.79-81, figs.3, 1 pl., 1929.

(THREE STUDIES ON MUSKRATS (ONDATRA Z. ZIBETHICA L.).) Tre studier oever bisamrattan (Ondatra z. zibethica L.). T. Brander. Acta Soc. pro Fauna et Flora Fennica, vol.67, no.3, pp.1-54, 1951.

(REMARKS ON THE GENERA GERBILLUS, MERIONES, RHOMBOMYS, AND PSAMMOMYS.) Bemerkungen ueber die Gattungen Gerbillus, Meriones, Rhombomys und Psammomys. J. F. Brandt. Melanges Biologiques, Bull. Acad. Imp. Sci. St. Petersbourg., vol.2, pp.300-304, Dec., 1854.

HAYDEN'S VOLE, MICROTUS HAYDENI (BAIRD). W. L. Burnett. Occas. Papers Mus. Zool. and Ent., Colorado Agric. College, vol.1, no.2, pp.6-11, figs., Dec., 1930.

ADDITIONAL NOTES ON THE LIFE HISTORY OF THE GOSS LEMMING MOUSE. W. H. Burt. Jour. Mam., vol.9, no.3, pp.212-216, Aug., 1928.

THE COMMON AND THE GOLDEN HAMSTER. Maurice Burton. Illus. London News, vol.218, no.5837, p.340, illus., Mar.3, 1951.

(CONTRIBUTION TO STUDY OF THE GENUS ARVICOLA.) Contribution a l'étude du genre Arvicola (Lacepède). P. Cantuel. Mammalia, Paris, vol.7, no.3-4, pp.115-117, figs.3, Sept.-Dec., 1943.

COTTON RATS. Milton Caroline. US F&WS, Wildl. Leafl., 353, 2 pp., July, 1953.

JOHNNIE MUSKRAT. A. Dean Coleman. Colorado Conserv. Comments, Denver, vol.6, no.4, pp.19-20, Dec.15, 1943.

(ON THE BIOLOGY OF THE WATER RAT (ARVICOLA SCH. SCHERMAN SHAW).) Zur Biologie der Wasserratte, Arvicola sch. scherman (Shaw). Heinrich Dathe. Zeitschr. f. Saeugetierkunde, vol.10, no.2, pp.147-148, pl.4, Dec.31, 1935.

SOME OBSERVATIONS ON A COLONY OF WATER VOLES. Fred Dean. Naturalist, London, no.822, pp.105-107, July-Sept., 1947.

(RESEARCH ON THE GENERAL BIOLOGY OF THE FIELD MOUSE.) Recherches sur la biologie generale du campagnol des champs. (Microtus arvalis Pallas.) P. Delost. Bull. Soc. Zool. France, 45: 149-162, 1955.

WHITE-FOOT. (WHITE-FOOTED MOUSE.) Alan Devoe. Audubon Mag., New York, vol.46, no.1, illus., Jan.-Feb., 1944.

(THIS AND THAT ON THE SCREW-MOUSE.) Een en ander over de Huisspitsmuis. H. De Vries. De Levende Natuur, Nederlands Tijdschrift voor Veldbiologie, vol.57, no.5, pp.81-84, illus., May, 1954.

THE PRAIRIE DEER-MOUSE. Lee R. Dice. Bull 2, Cranbrook Inst. Sci. (Bloomfield Hills, Mich.), pp.8, pls.5, Nov., 1932.

MISCELLANEOUS NOTES ON THE WOOD-RAT. (NEOTOMA CINEREA OCCIDENTALIS.) Ford Dicks. Murrelet, vol.17, no.1, p.19, Jan., 1936.

WHAT IS HAPPENING TO THE MUSKRAT? Jerry D. Hardy, Jr. Maryland Conservationist, Balto., vol.27, no.3, pp.8-9, 27, illus., Fall, 1950.

A NATURAL HISTORY STUDY OF MICROTUS CALIFORNICUS. Donald M. Hatfield. Jour. Mam., vol.16, no.4, pp.261-271, fig. 1, Nov., 1935.

NOTES ON THE VOLES OF THE SPECIES MICROTUS OREGONI. Donald M. Hatfield, Emmet T. Hooper. Murrelet, vol.16, no. 2, pp.33-34, fig.1, May, 1935.

OCCURRENCE OF PEROMYSCUS. Albert C. Hawbecker. Jour. Mam., 36 (4): 569-571, 1 fig., Dec.14, 1955.

LEMMING, MEADOW, AND PINE MICE. Caroline A. Heppenstall. Pennsylvania Game News, Harrisburg, vol.17, no.5, pp.13, 23, Aug., 1946.

THE RED-BACKED MOUSE. Caroline A. Heppenstall. Pennsylvania Game News, Harrisburg, vol.17, no.4, p.18, July, 1946.

THE WHITE-FOOTED MOUSE. Caroline A. Heppenstall. Pennsylvania Game News, Harrisubrg, vol.17, no.2, p.8, illus., May, 1946.

NATURE'S SECOND-HAND MAN. (PACK RAT.) John Eric Hill. Nat. Hist., New York, vol.53, no.2, p.89, illus., Feb., 1944.

THE SNOW LEMMING. John Eric Hill. Nat. Hist., New York, vol.55, no.10, p. 487, Dec., 1946.

THE FIELD MOUSE: CHARACTERISTICS AND CONTROL. (MICROTUS PENNSYLVANICUS) Ruth Hine. Wisconsin Conservation Bull., Madison, vol.15, no.11, pp. 16-19, illus., Nov., 1950.

MONOGRAM OF VOLES AND LEMMINGS. Martin A. Hinton. British Museum, Lond., 1926.

NOTES ON MICE OF THE SPECIES (PEROMYSCUS BOYLEI AND P. PECTORALIS). Emmet T. Hooper. Jour. Mam., vol.33, no.3, pp.371-378, Aug.19, 1952.

VOLES OF THE GENUS PHENACOMYS. I. REVISION OF THE GENUS PHENACOMYS. II. LIFE HISTORY OF THE RED TREE MOUSE (PHENACOMYS LONGICAUDUS). A. Brazier Howell. North Amer. Fauna no.48, pp.IV plus 66, pls.1-7, Oct.12, 1926.

(NOTES ON THE HAMSTER.) Aantekeningen over de hamster. A. M. Husson. Natuurhist. Maandblad, vol.38, no.11, pp. 111-115, figs.3, Nov.30, 1949.

BIOLOGY AND LIFE HISTORY OF THE SAGEBRUSH VOLE. William B. James, Ernest S. Booth. Walla Walla Coll. Publ. Dept. Biol. Sci. and Biol. Sta., 1 (2): 23-43, July, 1952; Revised ed. Jan., 1954.

NATURAL HISTORY OF THE PRAIRIE VOLE (MAMMALIAN GENUS MICROTUS). E. W. Jameson, Jr. MA thesis, Univ. Kansas, 1946; Univ. Kansas Pub., Mus. Nat. Hist., 1 (7): 125-151, Oct.6, 1947.

(Review of) THE TALE OF THE WHITE-FOOT MOUSE. Henry B. Kane. Canadian Nature, Toronto, vol.10, no.3, pp.100-101, illus., May-June, 1948.

THE BANK VOLE. Phyllis Kelway. Game and Gun and the Angler's Monthly, London, vol.17, no.175, pp.169-171, Apr., 1940.

THE WATER VOLE. Phyllis Kelway. Game and Gun and Angler's Monthly, London, vol.18, no.191, pp.280-282, illus., Aug., 1941.

ON THE DISTRIBUTION OF THE BLACK HAMSTER (CRICETUS CRICETUS) AND THE NUMERICAL RELATION BETWEEN IT AND THE COMMON FORM. S. Kirikov. Zool. Zh., 13 :361-368, 1935.

THE BUSHY-TAILED WOODRAT. George Dunsford Klein. Nature Notes, Peoria, vol.8, no.5, pp.133-135, pl.1, May, 1941.

(THE MUSKRAT.) De Bisamrat. H. N. Kluyver. Tijdschr. Over Plantenziekten, vol.42, no.12, pp.311-341, figs.5, pls.22-25, Dec., 1936.

DOLOMYS AND ONDATRA. M. Kretzoi. Acta Geol., 3 (4): 347-355, 1955.

(PRELIMINARY INVESTIGATIONS OF THE GENUS ARVICOLA LACEPEDE.) Volaeufige Untersuchungen ueber die Gattung Arvicola Lacepede. Jerzy Kubik. Ann. Univ. Mariae Curie-Sklodowska, Lublin, sec.C, 10 (9): 245-268, Mar.9, 1957.

(OBSERVATIONS ON THE BIOLOGY OF HESPEROMYS MUSCULINUS THOMAS.) Beobachtungen ueber die Biologie von Hesperomys musculinus Thomas. Friedrich Kuehlhorn. Zeitschr. Saeugetierk., Berlin, vol.18, no.2, pp.116-124, Sept.28, 1952.

THE MUSKRAT. E. R. Lamster. South Dakota Conservation Digest, Pierre, vol. 12, no.1, p.12, Jan., 1945.

THE MUSKRAT. David E. Lantz. U. S. Dept. Agric. Farmer's Bull. no. 396, pp.1-48, figs.1-5, Apr.30, 1910.

TO THE BIOLOGY OF THE MUSK-RAT (MUSQUASH) FIBER ZIBETHICUS L. N. Lavrov. Zoologitscheskij Journal (vormals "Revue Zool. Russe"), Moskau, vol.12, pt. 1, pp.86-100, 1933. (In Russian, with German summary.)

MAMMAL TRACKS. MUSKRAT. Helen Lawson, Bill Lawson. Ohio Conserv. Bull., Columbus, vol.15, no.1, p.10, illus., Jan., 1951.

(OBSERVATIONS OF MUSKRATS.) Beobachtungen an Bisamratten. P. Leonhardt. Aus der Heimat, vol.43, no.6, p.189, 1930.

WHITE-FOOTED MICE AS CAMP COMPANIONS. Frederick C. Lincoln. Jour. Mam., vol.4, no.3, pp.185-186, Aug.19, 1923.

NOTES ON THE LIFE HISTORY OF SYNAPTOMYS. Jean Linsdale. Jour. Mam., vol. 8, no.1, pp.51-54, Feb., 1927.

THE DUSKY-FOOTED WOOD RAT. Jean M. Linsdale, Lloyd P. Tevis, Jr. Univ. Calif. Press, Berkeley, pp. x plus 664, illus., Aug.21, 1951.

(CONTRIBUTIONS TO THE BIOLOGY OF THE SYRIAN GOLDEN HAMSTER MESOCRICETUS AURATUS NEHRING.) Beitraege zur Biologie des syrischen Goldhamsters Mesocricetus auratus (Nehring). Antonie Lochbrunner. Zool. Jahrb., 66 (2-3): 389-428, May, 1956.

(MUSKRAT QUESTIONS.) Bisamrattfragen. E. Lonnberg. Fauna och Flora, Stockholm, pt.5, pp.219-227, 1931.

(Review by A. L. Rand of) PEROMYSCUS MANICULATUS MACRORHINUS AND THE PROBLEM OF INSULARITY. T. T. McCabe, Ian McTaggart Cowan. Canadian Field-Nat., Sutton West, vol.61, no.3, p. 118, June 30, 1947.

THREE SPECIES OF PEROMYSCUS. Thomas T. McCabe, Barbara D. Blanchard. Rood Associates, Publishers, Santa Barbara, Calif., 136 pp., 1950.

(Review by Francis C. Evans of) THE THREE SPECIES OF PEROMYSCUS. Thomas T. McCabe, Barbara D. Blanchard. Jour. Mam., vol.32, no.4, pp.475-477, Nov.19, 1951.

NOTE ON THE DESERT GERBILLE (CHELIONES HURRIANAE). C. McCann. Jour. Bombay Nat. Hist. Soc., vol.32, p. 213, Aug.1, 1927.

THE SYRIAN HAMSTER. Mavis McLellan. Nature Mag., Wash., D.C., vol.35, no.10, pp.541-542, illus., Dec., 1942.

PEROMYSCUS, MICROTUS NO.12--AND OTHERS. Shirley Anne MacMillan. Frontiers, Lancaster, vol.13, no.1, pp. 8-11, 28, illus., Oct., 1948.

(A FEW OBSERVATIONS ON THE MUSKRAT FIBER ZIBETHICUS L.) Kleine Beobachtungen an der Bisamratte, Fiber zibethicus L. Alfred Manner. Zool. Garten, Leipzig, n.F. vol.18, nos.3-4, pp.146-148, 1951.

DEVELOPMENTS IN MUSKRAT RESEARCH. Harold A. Mathiak. Amer. Nat. Fur and Market Jour., Wausau, vol.28, no.1, pp. 7-9, Aug., 1949.

(ZOOLOGICAL CONCEPTS: SYNAPTOMYS-THERIDOMYS.) Zoologische Begriffe: Synaptomys-Theridomys. Paul Matschie. Handworterbuch der Zoologie, Anthropologie und Ethnologie, Breslau, Bd.7, Lief.32, (Encyklopadie der Naturwissenschaften, Abt.1, Lief.71), pp.449-576, 1897.

CONTRIBUTION TO THE BIOLOGY OF THE WATER VOLE, ARVICOLA TERRESTRIS TERRESTRIS L. A. V. Mikheev. Arch. Mus. Zool. U. Moscow, 4: 3-26, 1937.

PRAIRIE MICE. J. M. Milligan. Amer. Nat., Lancaster, vol.9, no.9, pp.515-516, Sept., 1875.

(BIOLOGICAL OBSERVATIONS ON CAPTIVE FIELD MICE (MICROTUS ARVALIS PALL.).) Biologische Beobachtungen an gefangenen Feldmaeusen. (Microtus arvalis Pall.). Erna Mohr. Schriften Naturwissensch. Vereins. f. Schleswig-Holstein, vol.18, no.1, pp.40-48, 1927.

(DATA ON THE SNOW MOUSE, CHIONOMYS NIVALIS MART.) Zur Kenntnis der Schneemaus, Chinomys nivalis Mart. Erna Mohr. Zeitschrift f, Saeugetierkunde, vol.4, nos. 4-6, pp.194-204, Feb.10, 1930.

(A "RAT KING" OF FIELD MICE.) Ein "Rattenkoenig" von Waldmaeusen. Erna Mohr. Zeitschr. fuer Saeugetierkunde, vol.4, nos.4-6, p.252, Feb.10, 1930.

(THE SHORT TAILED FIELD MOUSE (PITYMYS SAVII DE SELYS-LONGCHAMPS).) Die kurzschwaenzige Erdmaus (Pitymys savii de Selys-Longchamps) in Holstein. Erna Mohr. Zool. Anzeiger, vol. 74, pp.141-144, Nov.5, 1927.

WEE TIM'ROUS WHITE-FOOT. William Byron Mowery. Nature Mag., Washington, vol.38, no.10, pp.516-519, illus., Dec., 1945.

THE BUSH-TAILED PACK RAT--FURRY TRADER. Norman C. Negus. Audubon Mag., New York, vol.53, no.1, pp.38-44, illus., Jan.-Feb., 1951.

(ON CRICETUS, CRICETULUS, AND MESOCRICETUS (N. SUBG.).) Ueber Cricetus, Cricetulus und Mesocricetus (n. subg.). A. Nehring. Zool. Anzeiger, Leipzig, vol.21, no.567, pp.493-495, Sept.5, 1898.

THE GRAY-BROWN MEADOW VOLE. W. W. Nicholas. Field, London, vol.85, no.4628, p.301, illus., Sept.6, 1941.

SOME BIOLOGICAL OBSERVATIONS ON HAMSTER. K. L, Novikoff. Abstr. works zool. inst. Moscow State Univ., pp.83-85, 1933. (In Russian.)

A STUDY OF THE CLETHRIONOMYS DAWSONI GROUP OF RED-BACKED MICE. Robert T. Orr. Jour. Mam., Balto., vol.26, no.1, pp.67-74, Feb.27, 1945.

LIFE HISTORY OF THE DEER MOUSE. A. L. Orr-Ewing. Forestry Chron., 26 (2): 115-126, June, 1950.

(THE ARVICOLE.) Le arvicole. Arturo Palombi. Rivista Fitosanitaria, Rome, vol.1, no.1, pp.25-32, illus., 1946.

THE BEAVER-RAT--NEITHER BEAVER NOR RAT. Elsie A. Parry. Nature Mag., Wash., D.C., vol.32, no.5, pp.256-258, photos 3, May, 1939.

(CONTRIBUTION TO STUDY OF THE GENUS PSAMMOMYS CRETZCHMAR (MURINE RODENTS).) Contribution a l'etude du genre Psammomys Cretzchmar (rongeurs murides). F. Petter. Mammalia, Paris, vol.15, nos.1-2, pp.39-46, Mar.-June, 1951.

(CONTRIBUTION TO STUDY OF MERIONES VINOGRADOVI HEPTNER 1931 (RODENTS, GERBILLIDAE).) Contribution a l'etude de Meriones vinogradovi Heptner 1931 (Rongeurs, Gerbillidae). F. Petter. Mammalia, Paris, vol.19, no.3, pp.391-398, illus., Sept., 1955.

MUSKRATS IN THE DUCK MARSH. Miles D. Pirnie. Trans. 6th N. Amer. Wildlife Conf., Wash., D.C., pp.308-313, illus., 1941.

GRASSHOPPER MICE. H. H. Pittman. Nature Mag., Wash., vol.42, no.6, pp. 266-292, illus., June-July, 1949.

THE LIFE HISTORY SKETCH OF THE ALLEGHENY WOODRAT. THE TECHNICAL NAME OF THE ALLEGHENY WOODRAT. Earl L. Poole. Jour. Mam., Balto., vol. 21, no.3, pp.249-270, 316-318, Aug.14, 1940.

WATER VOLES. M. Portal. Game and Gun, vol.4, pp.650-683, Dec., 1927.

ARCTIC MUSKRAT. Jay Ellis Ranson. Amer. Forests, Washington, vol.52, no.4, pp.164-165, 189-190, illus., Apr., 1946.

"MUSKIE," MY TAME MUSKRAT. Fred W. Riggs. Outdoorsman (Hunter-Trader-Trapper), vol.77, no.3, pp.51-52, illus., Sept., 1938.

(NOTE ON THE GENUS ARVICOLA LACEPEDE.) Note a propos du genre Arvicola Lacepede. P. Rode, R. Didier. Bull. Mus. Nation. Hist. Nat., Paris, vol.6, no.3, pp. 468-473, 1934.

WHITE-FOOTED MICE. R. J. Rutter. Nature Mag., Wash., 49 (4): 193-195, Apr., 1956.

THE MUSKRAT. Wilford E. Sanderson. School Nature League Bull., 13 (2), 4 pp., Oct., 1942.

MUSKY--THE TRUE STORY OF A FOOLISH AND LOVABLE LITTLE MUSKRAT. Mari Sandoz. Nature Nag., vol.22, no.5, pp.199-202, illus., Nov., 1933.

BUCK AND MINNIE, MARSH RESIDENTS. (MUSKRAT) Henry Sather. Outdoor Nebraska, Lincoln, vol.28, no.4, pp.26-29, illus., Fall, 1950.

PHENACOMYS UNGAVA. W. E. Saunders. Canadian Field-Nat., vol.40, p.18, Feb.5, 1926.

FIELD-MICE OF THE GROUP ARBUSTICOLA SCHIDL. M. V. Schidlovsky. Bull. Mus. Georgie, Tbilissi (Tiflis), vol. 9A, no.1, pp.80-100, figs.6, 1938. (In Russian, with resumes in Georgian and English.)

(OBSERVATIONS OF THE HAMSTER (CRICETUS CRICETUS L.).) Bemerkungen ueber den Hamster (Cricetus cricetus L.). W. Schreitmuller. Zeitschr. f. Saeugetierkunde, Berlin, vol.13, no.2, p.242, 1939.

ON MOUNTAIN-VOLES OF THE GENUS ALTICOLA BLANFORD: A TAXONOMIC AND GENETIC ANALYSIS. Ernst Schwarz. Proc. Zool. Soc. Lond., ser.B, vol.108, pt.4, pp.663-668, Jan.26, 1939.

THE MOLE-MOUSE, POTATO-MOUSE OR PINE-MOUSE. Ernest Thompson Seton. Jour. Mam., vol.1, no.4, p.185, Aug., 1920.

ALPINE LIFE OF THE HEATHER VOLE (PHENACOMYS OLYMPICUS). William T. Shaw. Jour. Mam., vol.5, no.1, pp.12-15, pls.3, Feb., 1924.

FIELD MOUSE. T. Sheppard. Naturalist, London, no.996 (no.769 of current ser.), p.30, Jan., 1940.

THE MUSKRAT. F. N. Shillaker. Rod and Gun and Canadian Silver Fox News, vol.34, no.2, p.42, July, 1932.

THE DEER MOUSE (PEROMYSCUS LEUCOPUS). Robert W. Shufeldt. Shooting and Fishing, vol.21, no.1, pp.6-7, fig.1, New York, Oct.22, 1896.

THE MUSQUASH. George Smokey. South Dakota Conserv. Digest, Pierre, vol.10, no.11, p.10, Nov., 1943.

KING OF THE FUR BEARERS. Kathryn Sollars. Fauna, 9 (1): 23-25, Mar., 1947.

FIELD NOTES ON THE PALLID MEADOW MOUSE, LAGURUS PALLIDUS (MERRIAM). J. Dewey Soper. Canadian Field Nat., vol. 45, no.9, pp.209-214, figs.3, Dec., 1931.

MICE UP A TREE. (WHITE-FOOTED MICE.) John H. Spicer. Our Dumb Animals, Norwood, vol.81, no.4, p.9, illus., Apr., 1948.

(DATA ON THE FIELD MOUSE MICROTUS ARVALIS P.) Materialien zur Kenntnis der Feldmaus Microtus arvalis P. Georg H. W. Stein. Zeitschr. Saeugetierk., 22 (3-4): 117-135, 1957.

(FAMILY FORMATION THE FIELD MOUSE, MICROTUS ARVALIS L.) Sippenbildung bei der Feldmaus, Microtus arvalis L. Georg H. W. Stein. Zeitschr. Saeugetierk, Berlin, 21 (3-4): 150-160, Feb. 28, 1957.

A COMPARATIVE LIFE HISTORY STUDY OF THE MICE OF THE GENUS PEROMYSCUS. Arthur Svihla. Univ. Mich. Mus. Zool., Misc. Publ. no.24, pp.5-39, July 8, 1932.

LIFE HISTORY NOTES ON SIGMODON HISPIDUS HISPIDUS. Arthur Svihla. Jour. Mam., vol.10 , no.4, pp.352-353, Nov., 1929.

NOTES ON THE DEER-MOUSE, PEROMYSCUS MANICULATUS OREAS (BANGS). Arthur Svihla. Murrelet, vol.14, no.1, pp. 13-14, Jan., 1933.

NOTES ON THE MEADOW MOUSE (MICROTUS OREGONI OREGONI). Arthur Svihla. Murrelet, vol.13, no.3, p.94-95, Sept., 1932.

NOTES ON THE LIFE HISTORY OF THE WOODRAT, NEOTOMA FLORIDANA RUBIDA BANGS. Arthur Svihla, Ruth Dowell Svihla. Jour. Mam., vol.14, no.1, pp.73-75, Feb., 1933.

NOTES ON DESERT AND DUSKY HARVEST MICE (REITHRO-DONTOMY MEGALOTIS MEGALOTIS AND R. M. NIGRESCENS.). Ruth Dowell Svihla. Jour. Mam., vol.12, no.4, pp.363-365, Nov., 1931.

NOTES ON THE GOLDEN HARVEST MOUSE. Ruth Dowell Svihla. Jour. Mam., vol.11, no.1, pp.53-54, pl.1, Feb., 1930.

ON OECOMYS PHELPSI TATE. G. H. H. Tate. Jour. Mam., vol.26, no.3, p.316, Aug., 1945.

THE FLORIDA MUSKRAT (NEOFIBER ALLENI, TRUE). Frederick True. U.S. Nat. Mus., Annual Report, 1884, pp.325-330, pl. III, 1885.

A MUSKRAT WITH A ROUND TAIL. Frederick W. True. Science, vol.4, no. 75, p.34, July 11, 1884.

THE WHISKERY WOOD-RAT. Ted Trueblood. Nature, Washington, D.C., vol.34, no.3, pp.151-152, illus., Mar., 1941.

TO THE BIOLOGY AND SPREADING OF PROMETHEOMYS SCHAPOSCHNIKOVI SATUNIN. S. Turov. Bull. Scientifique de l'Institut de l'Exploration Regional du Caucase du Nord, vol.1, pp.23-30, pl.1, 1926.

ON THE TRAIL OF THE WOOD RAT. Frederick A. Ulmer, Jr. Fauna, Phila., vol.6, no.4, pp.112-113, illus., Dec., 1944.

NOTES ON THE FOREST PHENACOMYS. Alex Walker. Jour. Mam., vol.11, no.2, pp.233-235, May, 1930.

NOTES ON THE TREE MOUSE, PHENACOMYS SILVICOLA. H. M. Wight. Jour. Mam., vol.6, no.4, pp.282-283, Nov., 1925.

(THE BIOLOGY AND FIGHT AGAINST THE WATER RAT IN THE NETHERLANDS.) Biologie en bestrijding van de woelrat, Arvicola terrestris terrestris (L.) in Nederland. A. van Wijngaarden. Doctoral Thesis Rijksuniv. Leiden, pp.147, illus., 1954.

(THE FIELDMOUSE AND EARTHMOUSE (MICROTUS ARVALIS PALLAS AND MICROTUS AGRESTIS LINNE).) De veldmuis en de aardmuis (Microtus arvalis Pallas en Microtus agrestis Linne). A. van Wijngaarden. De Levende Natur, vol.59, no.10, pp.217-221, Oct., 1956.

(SOME NOTES ON THE WOOD LEMMING, MYOPHUS SCHISTICOLOR.) Anteckningar om skogslaemmeln, Myopus schisticolor. Einar Wiren. Fauna och Flora, Upsala, Haeft.2, pp.97-106, figs. 2, 1936.

(OBSERVATIONS OF DOMESTIC VOLES.) Beobachtungen an heimischen Wuehlmaeusen. Karl Zalesky. Zeitschr. f. Saeugetierkunde, Berlin, vol.13, no.2, pp.240-242, 1939.

(THE BIOLOGY OF THE PYGMY HAMSTER (CRICETULUS MIGRATORIUS PALL.).) Zur Biologie des Zwerghamsters (Cricetulus migratorius Pall.). Klaus Zimmermann. Zeitschr. Saeugetierk., Berlin, vol.17, no. 3, pp.159-160, Feb.19, 1953.

(INFORMATION ON MICROTUS OECONOMUS (PALLAS).) Zur Kenntnis von Microtus oeconomus (Pallas). Klaus Zimmermann. Archiv f. Naturgesch., Leipzig, n.f., vol. 11, no.2, pp.174-197, figs.3, Sept.10, 1942.

(SHOULD LEMMINGS BE TRANSPLANTED TO WEST GREENLAND?) Bør man indføre Lemminger i Vestgrønland. F. W. Braestrup. Det Grønlandske Selskabs Aarsskrift, 1943, pp.99-104.

(COMMENTS ON THE MUSKRAT IN FINLAND.) Bisamråttan i Finland. Helena Hannelius. Svensk Jakt, Stockholm, vol.86, no.5, pp.128-129, illus., May 20, 1948.

(THE DIFFERENTIATION OF THE FIELD MICE MICROTUS ARVALIS AND MICROTUS AGRESTIS.) Die feldmammologische Unterscheidung von Feldmaus und Erdmaus (Microtus arvalis und Microtus agrestis). Fritz Frank. Bonner Zool. Beitraege, Heft 1-2, pp.13-16, 1953.

(LEMMING INVASIONS AND OTHER IRREGULAR ANIMAL MIGRATIONS.) Ueber Fjeldlemming-Invasionen und andere irregulaere Tierwanderungen. O. Kalela. Ann. Soc. Zool. Bot. Fennicae, Vanamo, vol.13, no.5, iv-90 pp., 1949.

(OBSERVATIONS ON LEMMINGS: LEMMUS LEMMUS (L.) AND MYOPUS SCHISTICOLOR (LILLJEBORG). Beobachtungen an Fjaell-und Waldlemmingen, Lemmus lemmus (L.) und Myopus schisticolor (Lilljeborg). Erna Mohr. Zool. Anzeiger, Leipzig, vol.145, nos.5-6, pp.126-137, Aug., 1950.

(ON THE VARIABILITY OF THE RED MOUSE CLETHRIONOMYS GLAREOLUS IN BAVARIA.) Zur Variabilitaet der Roetelmaus Clethrionomys glareolus in Bayern. William Prychodko. Zool. Jahrbuecher, Jena, vol.80, nos.5-6, pp.482-506, Dec., 1951.

(MICROTUS OECONOMUS STIMMINGI NEHRING 1899: A FIND FROM THE FOURTH CENTURY ON THE ISLAND OF FOEHR.) Ein Fund von Microtus oeconomus stimmingi Nehring, 1899 aus dem 4. Horts Requate. Jahrhundert auf der Insel Foehr. Saeugetierk. Mitteil., Stuttgart, 3 (3): 123-124, July 1, 1955.

THE BRANDENBURG RED MOUSE. ANALYSIS OF A POPULATION.) Die Maerkische Roetelmaus. Analyse einer Population. K. Zimmerman. Maerkische Tierwelt, 3:24-40, 1937.

THE BUSHY-TAILED WOOD RAT, NEOTOMA CINEREA. Wyoming Wild Life, Cheyenne, vol.8, no.12, pp.12-14, illus., Dec., 1943.

LONG-TAILED KLEPTOMANIAC. (NEOTOMA) Pest Control and Sanitation, Hollywood, vol.3, no.4, pp.16-17, illus., Apr., 1948.

MUSKRAT. Canadian Nature, Toronto, vol.2, no.1, p.30, Jan.-Feb., 1940.

THE MUSKRAT. Carling Conserv. Digest, Toronto, vol.1, no.4, p.13, Oct., 1947.

MUSKRATS. North Dakota Outdoors, Grand Forks, vol.12, no.4, p.17, Oct., 1949.

Africa

THE AFFINITIES OF THE SOUTH AFRICAN GERBILS OF THE GENUS TATERA. D. H. S. Davis. Proc. Zool. Soc. Lond., vol.118, pt.4, pp.1002-1018, figs.3, Feb., 1949.

NOTES ON THE AFRICAN CRESTED RAT (LOPHIOMYS IMHAUSI). G. H. Goldfinch. Proc. Zool. Soc. Lond., p.1091, Dec., 1923.

(MISSION TH. MONOD.-NEW RODENT GENUS (GERBILLINAE) OF MAURITANIE.) Mission Th. Monod.-Genre nouveau de rongeur (Gerbillinae) de Mauritanie. Henri Heim de Balsac. Bull. Mus. Nat. Hist. Nat., Paris, ser.2, vol.15, no.5, pp.287-288, 1943.

NOTE ON THE OCCURRENCE OF A VOLE IN NORTHERN AFRICA. Martin A. C. Hinton. Ann. and Mag. Nat. Hist., ser.9, vol.18, pp.304-306, Sept., 1926.

(DOES THE FIELDMOUSE EXIST IN ABYSSINIA? SOME CONSIDERATIONS ON A POINT OF NOMENCLATURE.) Le Campagnol des Champs (Microtus arvalis Pallas) existe-t-il en Abyssinie? ou, quelques considerations sur un point de nomenclature. P. Laurent. Bull. Soc. d'Hist. Nat. l'Afrique du Nord, Alger, vol.27, no. 8, pp.384-386, Nov., 1936.

EXTRACT OF A LETTER RELATING TO THE LOCALITY OF LOPHIOMYS IMHAUSII. William Peters. Proc. Zool. Soc. Lond., p.183, 1868.

(INTRA-GENERIC VARIABILITY IN AN AFRICAN RODENT (TATERA LATASTE).) Variabilité intra-générique chez un rongeur africain (Tatera Lataste). P. L. Pirlot. Ann. Mus. Roy. Congo Belge, Tervuren, vol.39, pp.66, illus., 1955.

A NEW GERBIL FROM KORDOFAN. (GERBILLUS ROSALINDA.) Jane St. Leger. Ann. and Mag. Nat. Hist., Ser.10, vol.4, pp.295-296, Sept., 1929.

A NEW JIRD FROM LIBYA. (MERIONES SHAWI AZIZI.) H. W. Setzer. Proc. Biol. Soc. Wash., 69: 205-206, Dec.31, 1956.

TWO NEW GERBILS FROM LIBYA. (GERBILLUS PYRAMIDUM AUREUS, G. P. FAVILLUS.) H. W. Setzer. Proc. Biol. Soc. Wash., 69: 179-182, Dec.31, 1956.

A NEW FAT-TAILED GERBIL (PACHYUROMYS) FROM WESTERN ALGERIA. Oldfield Thomas. Novitates Zoologicae, vol.27, pp.313-334, June, 1920.

ON SOME OF THE SPECIES OF PSAMMOMYS FOUND IN ALGERIA, TUNIS AND TRIPOLI. Oldfield Thomas. Ann. and Mag. Nat. Hist., ser.9, vol.16, pp.197-199, July, 1925.

THE PASAMMOMYS OF THE ALLUVIAL SOIL OF THE NILE DELTA. Oldfield Thomas. Ann. and Mag. Nat. Hist. (8), vol.2, no.7, pp.91-92, July, 1908.

STUDIES ON GERBILS OF THE SUBGENUS DIPODILLUS RECORDED FROM EGYPT. Kamal Wassif. A'in Shams Science Bull., Cairo, 1: 173-194, 1957.

(NEW GERBILLINAE FROM NORTHWESTERN AFRICA.) Neue Gerbillinae aus Nordostafrika. Otto von Wettstein. Anzeiger Kais. Akad. Wissench., Wien, vol.53, no.14, pp.151-154, 1916.

AFRICAN GERBILS OF THE GENERA TATERA AND TATERILLUS. R. C. Wroughton. Ann. Mag. Nat. Hist., ser.8, vol.6, pp.291-294, Sept., 1910.

Alaska

LIFE HISTORY AND ECOLOGIC OBSERVATIONS ON THE TUNDRA MOUSE (MICROTUS OECONOMUS) AND LEMMINGS (LEMMUS TRIMUCRONATUS AND DICROSTONYX GROENLANDICUS) AT BARTER ISLAND, ALASKA. Frederick S. Barkalow, Jr. Jour. Elisha Mitchell Sci. Soc., Chapel Hill, vol.68, no.2, pp.199-206, illus., Dec., 1952.

THE LEMMINGS OF POINT BARROW, ALASKA. Charles D. Brower. Zool. Soc. Bull., vol.26, no.1, p.9, Jan., 1923.

OCCURRENCE OF MICROTUS XANTHOGNATHUS IN ALASKA. Calvin J. Lensink. Jour. Mam., vol.35, no.2, pp.259, May 26, 1954.

A NEW ALASKAN MICROTUS. Olaus J. Murie. Jour. Mam., vol.11, no.1, pp.74-75, Feb., 1930.

DESCRIPTION OF A NEW LEMMING FROM ALASKA. (DICROSTONYX UNALASCENSIS STEVENSONI.) E. W. Nelson. Proc. Biol. Soc. Wash., vol.42, pp.143-146, pl.3, Mar.30, 1929.

DESCRIPTION OF A NEW SPECIES OF ARVICOLA, OF THE MYNOMES GROUP, FROM ALASKA. E. W. Nelson. Proc. Biol. Soc., Wash., vol.8, pp.139-142, Dec.28, 1893.

DESCRIPTION OF A NEW SPECIES OF LAGOMYS FROM ALASKA. E. W. Nelson. Proc. Biol. Soc., Wash., vol.8, pp.117-120, Dec.21, 1893.

A NEW VOLE OF THE SUBGENUS STENOCRANIUS FROM ALASKA. E. W. Nelson. Jour. Mam., Balto., vol.12, no.3, pp.310-312, Aug.24, 1931.

A NEW VOLE FROM MONTAGUE ISLAND, ALASKA. Wilfred H. Osgood. Proc. Biol. Soc. Wash., vol.19, pp.71-72, illus., May 1, 1906.

A NEW WHITE-FOOTED MOUSE FROM ALASKA. Wilfred H. Osgood. Proc. Biol. Soc. Wash., vol.21, pp.141-142, June 9, 1908.

NOTES ON MICROTINE RODENTS FROM THE BROOKS RANGE, ARCTIC ALASKA. Robert Rausch. Jour. Washington Acad. Sci., vol.40, no.4, pp.133-136, Apr.21, 1950.

A NEW SUBSPECIES OF MICROTUS OECONOMUS FROM ALASKA. (MICROTUS OECONOMUS GILMOREI.) Henry W. Setzer. Proc. Biol. Soc. Wash., vol.65, pp.75-76, Apr.25, 1952.

OBSERVATIONS ON LEMMINGS FROM BARTER ISLAND, ALASKA. Robert L. Strecker, Peter R. Morrison. Jour. Mam., vol.33, no.2, pp.180-184, illus., May 16, 1952.

THE LEMMING OF NUNIVAK ISLAND, ALASKA. Harry S. Swarth. Proc. Biol. Soc. Wash., vol.44, pp.101-104, Oct.17, 1931.

THE LONG-TAILED MEADOW-MOUSE OF SOUTHEASTERN ALASKA. Harry S. Swarth. Proc. Biol. Soc. Wash., vol.46, pp.207-212, Oct.26, 1933.

THE ECOLOGY AND POPULATION DYNAMICS OF THE BROWN LEMMING (LEMMUS TRIMUCRONATUS) AT POINT BARROW, ALASKA. Daniel Q. Thompson. Ph.D. thesis, U. Mo., 138 pp., illus., 1955.

THE ROLE OF LEMMINGS AT POINT BARROW, ALASKA. Neal A. Weber. Science, 111(2890): 552-553, May 19, 1950.

Anatomy

A CASE OF TRUE HERMAPHRODITISM IN THE FIELD MOUSE. S. A. Asdell, W. J. Hamilton, Jr., K. P. Hummel. Anat. Record, Phila., vol.80, no.1, suppl. no.1, pp.47-53, figs.3, May, 1941.

AN EXTREME CASE OF MALOCCLUSION IN THE MUSKRAT. Maurice M. Alexander, Herbert L. Dozier. Amer. Midland Nat., Notre Dame, vol.42, no.1, pp.252-254, fig.1, July, 1949.

(Review by George Wagner of) THE ANATOMY OF THE WOOD RAT. A. Brazier Howell. Jour. Mam., vol.8, no.2, p.166, May, 1927.

A COMPARATIVE STUDY OF THE BACULA OF WOOD RATS (SUBFAMILY NEOTOMINAE). William H. Burt, Frederick S. Barkalow, Jr. Jour. Mam., vol.23, no.2, pp.287-297, figs.3, Aug.14, 1942.

(THE FIELD MOUSE AND THE MOUSE (COMPARISON OF HEAD BONES).) Le mulot et la souris (comparaison des tetes osseuses). P. Cantuel. Mammalia, Paris, vol.6, no.1, pp.18-26, figs.9, Mar., 1942.

(REMARKS ON THE MORPHOLOGY OF THE UNDERGROUND FIELDMOUSE.) Remarques sur la morphologie du campagnol souterrain. C. J. Carpentier. Mammalia, Paris, vol.10, no.2, pp.92-93, 1946.

CORRELATION AND BODY PROPORTIONS IN MATURE MICE OF GENUS PEROMYSCUS. Frank H. Clark. Genetics, Princeton, vol.26, pp.283-300, May 10, 1941.

(ANATOMY AND HISTOLOGICAL STRUCTURE OF THE GENITAL APPARATUS OF THE ADULT FIELD MOUSE (MICROTUS ARVALIS PALLAS) IN SEXUAL ACTIVITY.) Anatomie et structure histologique de l'appareil genital du campagnol des champs (Microtus arvalis pallas) adulte en active sexuelle. P. Delost. Bull. Soc. Zool. France, 45: 207-222, 1955.

THE DEVELOPMENT OF THE HYPOPHYSEAL VASCULAR SYSTEM IN THE BANK-VOLE, CLETHRIONOMYS GLAREOLUS. A COMPARATIVE STUDY. A. Enemar. Acta Anatomica, 31 (1): 76-111, 1957.

(ON THE RELATIONSHIPS BETWEEN AGE AND MORPHOLOGICAL CHARACTERISTICS IN THE FIELD MOUSE.) Ueber die Beziehungen zwischen Lebensalter und morphologischen Merkmalen bei der Feldmaus. Fritz Frank, Klaus Zimmermann. Zool. Jahrb., Jena, 85 (3): 283-300, July, 1957.

(NOTES ON THE MAMMALS. XIX. THE HAMSTER SHOWING THE FUNDAMENTAL DIFFERENCE BETWEEN THE MOLARS OF RODENTS AND THOSE OF UNGULATES.) Notes sur les mammifères. XIX. Le hamster montrant la différence fondamentale entre les molaires des Rongeurs et celles des Ongulés. Serge Frechkop. Bull. Mus. Roy. Hist. Nat., Belgique, Bruxelles, vol.12, no.18, p.8, figs.4, June, 1936.

(THE OESOPHAGEAL DIVERTICULAE OF A RODENT, THE HAMSTER (MESOCRICETUS AURATUS WATERH.).) Les diverticules oesophagiens d'un rongeur, le hamster (Mesocricetus auratus Waterh.). Madeleine Friant. Comptes Rendus Acad. Sci. Paris, 245 (20): 1555-1557, Nov., 1956.

MEASUREMENTS AND WEIGHTS OF NORTHERN MUSKRATS. W. A. Fuller. Jour. Mam., vol.32, no.3, pp.360-362, illus., Aug.23, 1951.

TRIANGLES IN THE TEETH OF THE MAMMALIAN GENUS ONDATRA. Edwin C. Galbreath. Trans. Kansas Acad. Sci., vol.48, no.4, pp.457-458, Mar., 1946.

(VARIATION OF THE POSTERIOR EXTREMITY OF THE PALATIVE IN CLETHRIONOMYS GLAREOLUS.) Variation de la forme du bord posterieur du palatin chez Clethrionomys glareolus. M. Gatineau. Mammalia, Paris, vol.19, no.4, pp.482-490, Dec., 1955.

AN UNUSUALLY LONG-TAILED WHITE-FOOTED MOUSE. G. G. Goodwin. Jour. Mam., vol.10, no.4, p.352, Nov., 1929.

THE SKULL OF THE LOUISIANA MUSKRAT (ONDATRA ZIBETHICA RIVALICIA BANGS): I. THE SKULL IN ADVANCED AGE. Harley N. Gould, Florence B. Kreeger. Jour. Mam., vol.29, no.2, pp. 138-149, figs.2, pls.2, illus., May 14, 1948.

SOME UNUSUALLY LARGE SPECIMENS OF NORTH AMERICAN VOLES. Morris M. Green. Jour. Mam., vol.9, no.3, p.255, Aug., 1928.

SEXUAL DIMORPHISM IN THE PELVIC GIRDLE OF MICROTUS PENNSYLVANICUS. John E. Guilday. Jour. Mam., vol. 32, no.2, pp.216-217, May 21, 1951.

THE BUCCAL POUCH OF PEROMYSCUS. W. J. Hamilton, Jr. Jour. Mam., vol.23, no.4, pp.449-450, fig.1, Nov.14, 1942.

A STUDY OF THE BACULUM IN SOME NORTH AMERICAN MICROTINAE. W. J. Hamilton, Jr. Jour. Mam., vol.27, no.4, pp.378-387, figs.3, pl.1, Nov.25, 1946.

EXTRA INCISORS IN THE RODENT DICROSTONYX GROENLANDICUS. Richard M. Hansen. Jour. Mam., 37 (4): 549-550, pl.1, Jan.9, 1957.

DENTAL PATTERNS IN MICE OF THE GENUS PEROMYSCUS. Emmet T. Hooper. Misc. Publ. Mus. Zool. Univ. Michigan, no.99, pp.1-59, Mar.28, 1957.

EXTRA TEETH IN THE PYGMY MOUSE, BAIOMYS MUSCULUS. Emmet T. Hooper. Jour. Mam., 36 (2): 298-299, May 26, 1955.

ANATOMY OF THE WOOD RAT; COMPARATIVE ANATOMY OF THE SUBGENERA OF THE AMERICAN WOOD RAT (GENUS NEOTOMA). A. Brazier Howell. Balto., Williams and Wilkins Co., x, 225 pp., front., illus. pls., 1926.

AN INTERESTING ANOMALY IN PEROMYSCUS. R. R. Huestis. Jour. Mam., vol.10, no.3, p.256, Aug.10, 1929.

ON THE FORAMEN MAGNUM OCCIPITALE AND SOME OTHER SKULL-MEASUREMENTS OF CRICETUS CRICETUS CANESCENS NEHRING WITH RESPECT TO SEXUAL DIMORPHISM. I-II. A. M. Husson. Proc. Kon. Nederl. Akad. Wetensch., Amsterdam, ser.C, vol.56, no.5, pp.609-630, illus., 1953.

(A THREE-LEGGED LEMMING.) Eine dreibeinige Wanderratte. Friedrich Huter. Natur and Volk, Frankfurt am Main, vol.80, nos.9-10, pp.299-301, illus., Oct.15, 1950.

MEASUREMENTS OF THE SKULL AND OF SOME LONG BONES OF THE MUSKRAT (ONDATRA ZIBETHICA CINNAMOMINUS). Homer B. Latimer, Ray B. Riley. Jour. Morph., vol.56, no.1, pp.203-212, June 5, 1934.

A LESSON IN NATURE. (MUSKRAT WITH OVERGROWN INCISORS.) A. McKinlay. Amer. Fur Breeder, vol.1, no.6, p.20, illus., Dec., 1928.

(CONTRIBUTIONS TO THE ANATOMY AND DEVELOPMENTAL HISTORY OF THE MUSKRAT.) Beitraege zur Anatomie und Entwicklungsgeschichte der Bisamratte. Samuel Mehl. Arbeiten aus der Bayer. Landesanstalt fur Pflanzenbau und Pflanzenschutz, Muenchen, no.9, pp.60, figs. 32, pls.21, 1937.

(SEX DIFFERENCES ON THE PELVIS OF THE MUSKRAT ONDATRA ZIBETHICA LINNE 1766.) Geschlechtsunterschiede am Becken der Bisamratte, Ondatra zibethica Linne, 1766. G. Mueller. Saeugetierk, Mitteil., Stuttgart, 4 (4): 150-153, Oct.1, 1956.

(CONTRIBUTIONS TO THE ANATOMY, MORPHOLOGY, AND BIOLOGY OF THE "GREAT ARVICOLE" (ARVICOLA TERRESTRIS L., ARVICOLA TERRESTRIS SCHERMAN SHAW).) Beitraege zur Anatomie, Morphologie und Biologie der "Grossen Wuehlmaus" (Arvicola terrestris L., Arvicola terrestris scherman Shaw). H. Mueller-Boehme. Arbeit. aus der Biologischen Reichsanstalt fuer Land-und Forstwirtschaft, Berlin, vol.21, no.3, pp. 363-453, figs.18, May, 1935.

COMPARISON OF THE PALATINE SLITS OF PITMYS AND MICROTUS. D. G. Nichols. Jour. Mam., vol.18, no.1, p.103, Feb.14, 1937.

NOTES ON NEOTOMA PENNSYLVANICA WITH SPECIAL REFERENCE TO THE GENITAL ORGANIZATION. Robert C. Patterson. West Virginia Univ. Bull., ser. 33, no.15 (Proc. W. Virginia Acad. Sci., vol.6), pp.38-42, Mar., 1933.

FACIAL MUSCULATURE, NERVES AND BLOOD VESSELS OF THE HAMSTER IN RELATION TO THE CHEEK POUCH. Ralph B. Priddy, A. F. Brodie. Jour. Morphol., Phila., vol.83, no.2, pp.149-180, Sept., 1948.

THE ANATOMY OF THE DIASTEMAL PALATE IN MICROTINE RODENTS. Wilbur B. Quay. Misc. Publ. Mus. Zool., Univ. Mich., no.86, pp.41, Nov.12, 1954.

ANOMALIES OF THE CHEEKTEETH IN THE RED-BACKED VOLE, CLETHRIONOMYS GAPPERI (VIGORS, 1830). W. B. Quay. Saeugetierk. Mitteil., vol.1, no.3, pp.110-115, illus., July, 1953.

THE MEIBOMIAN GLANDS OF VOLES AND LEMMINGS (MICROTINAE). Wilbur B. Quay. Misc. Publ. Mus. Zool. Univ. Michigan, Ann Arbor, no.82, pp.17, pls.3, Mar.17, 1954.

THE SKIN GLANDS OF VOLES AND LEMMINGS (MICROTINAE). Wilbur B. Quay. PnD thesis, Univ. Mich., 153 pp., 1952.

MALARRANGEMENT OF TEETH IN CLETHRIONOMYS GAPPERI. E. M. Reilly, Jr. Jour. Mam., 37 (2): 298-299, illus., June 9, 1956.

THE COMPARATIVE MYOLOGY OF THE MAMMALIAN GENERA SIGMODON, ORYZOMYS, NEOTOMA, AND PEROMYSCUS (CRICETINAE), WITH REMARKS ON THEIR INTER-GENERIC RELATIONSHIPS. George C. Rinker. Misc. Publ. Mus. Zool. Univ. Michigan, Ann Arbor, no.83, pp.124, illus., June 4, 1954.

NOTES OF THE CRANIAL MUSCULATURE IN TWO SUBGENERA OF REITHRODONTOMYS (HARVEST MICE). George C. Rinker, Emmet T. Hooper. Occas. Papers Mus. Zool., Univ. Michigan, no. 528, pp.11, pl.1, Oct.21, 1950.

SKULL DIMENSIONS OF THE GREAT PLAINS MUSKRAT, ONDATRA ZIBETHICUS CINNAMOMINUS. J. Henry Sather. Jour. Mam., vol.37, no.4, pp.501-505, Nov., 1956.

THE DEVELOPMENT OF THE VERTEBRAL COLUMN IN THE DEER-MOUSE (PEROMYSCUS MANICULATUS RUFINUS). E. Carl Sensenig. (Abstract.) Anat. Record, Phila., vol.82, no.3, pp.445-446, Mar.25, 1942.

THE ORIGIN OF THE VERTEBRAL COLUMN IN THE DEER-MOUSE, PEROMYSCUS MANICULATUS RUFINUS. E. Carl Sensenig. Anatomical Record, vol.86, no. 2, pp.123-141, pls.2, figs.7, June, 1943.

OBSERVATIONS UPON THE DEVELOPMENT OF THE SKULL IN NEOTOMA FUSCIPES: A CONTRIBUTION TO THE MORPHOLOGY OF THE RODENTIA. R. W. Shufeldt. Proc. Acad. Nat. Sci. Phila., pp.14-28, pls.2, 1889.

ON THE GROWTH OF ROOTLESS MOLARS--PARTICULARLY IN THE FIELD-VOLE (MICROTUS AGRESTIS L.). Ivar Sperber. Arkiv for Zoologi, Stockholm, vol.40, no. 22, pp.1-12, 1948.

A PRELIMINARY STUDY OF THE BACULUM OF PEROMYSCUS LEUCOPUS AND P. MANICULATUS IN KANSAS. James M. Sprague. Trans. Kansas Acad. Sci., Topeka, vol.42, pp.495-497, figs.2-3, 1939.

A STUDY OF THE HYOID APPARATUS OF THE CRICETINAE. James M. Sprague. Jour. Mam., Balto., vol.22, no.3, pp.296-310, Aug.14, 1941.

(THE EPOOPHORON OF THE GOLDEN HAMSTER.) Das Epoophoron des Goldhamsters. Fritz Strauss, Fritz Bracher. Revue Suisse Zool., Neuchatel, vol.61, no.28, pp.494-503, illus., Mar., 1954.

(ON THE ANATOMY AND HISTOLOGY OF THE LIPS OF MICROTUS ARVALIS (PALLAS).) Zur Anatomie und Histologie der Lippen bei Microtus arvalis (Pallas). K. Sulc. Biologicke Spisy, Brno, vol.8, no.3, pp.1-14, figs.10, 1929.

NUMBER OF MAMMAE IN MUSKRATS. Arthur Svihla. Amer. Nat., vol.63, pp. 573-574, Nov.-Dec., 1929.

THE TONGUE AND GUSTATORY ORGANS OF FIBER ZIBETHICUS. Frederick Tuckerman. Jour. Anat. and Physiol., Edinburgh, vol.22, pp.135-141, pl.7, 1888.

DURATION OF MAINTENANCE OF PLACENTAL SPOTS IN LAGURUS LAGURUS. N. V. Tupikova. Zool. Zhurnal, 37 (2): 308-311, Feb., 1958. (In Russian, with English summary.)

ON THE CORRELATION BETWEEN THE MASTICATORY MUSCLES AND THE SKULL STRUCTURE IN THE MUSKRAT, ONDATRA ZIBETHICA (L.). I. N. H. van Vendeloo. Proc. Kon. Nederlandse Akad. Wetenschappen, vol.56, no.1, pp.116-127, 1953.

SOME EXTERNAL AND OSTEOLOGICAL CHARACTERS OF PROMETHEOMYS SCHAPOSCHNIKOVI SATUNIN. B. S. Vinogradov. Proc. Zool. Soc. London, 1926, pp.401-411, 4 pls., July, 1926.

CECAL VILLI IN DICROSTONYX TORQUATUS (RODENTIA: MICROTINAE). Marietta Voge, Howard A. Bern. Anat. Record, vol.123, no.1, pp.125-129, Sept., 1955.

THE STRUCTURE OF THE STOMACH AND THE RELATIVE DEVELOPMENT OF THE DIFFERENT SEGMENTS OF THE INTESTINE IN CRICETINAE (RODENTIA, MAMMALIA) FROM THE PALEARCTIC REGION AND THE NEW WORLD. N. N. Vorontsov. Doklady Akad. Nauk SSSR, 117 (3): 526-529, 1957. (In Russian, with English summary.)

THE ANAL GLANDS AND ANUS OF THE FIELD-VOLE (MICROTUS ARVALIS (PALL.). V. Vrtis. Biologické Spisy, Acad. Veterinariae, Brno, vol.8, no.11, pp.43, figs.5, 1929.

THE CUTANEOUS UMBILICAL GLANDULAR ORGAN OF THE HAMSTER CRICETUS CRICETUS (L.). V. Vrtis. Publ. Biol. l'École des Hautes Études Vétérinaires, Brno, vol.11, pt.13, no.B, 163 pp., pp.1-15, figs.5, 1932. (In Czechoslovakian, with resume in English.)

THE DEVELOPMENT OF THE SEBACEOUS ANAL GLANDS OF THE FIELD-VOLE (MICROTUS ARVALIS (PALL.)) AND THEIR CHANGES DURING BREEDING AND AGING. V. Vrtis. Biologické Spisy. Acad. Veterinariae, Brno, vol.8, no.12, pp.1-43, figs.9, 1929.

GLANDULAR ORGAN OF THE FLANKS OF THE WATER RAT, THEIR DEVELOPMENT AND CHANGES DURING BREEDING SEASON. V. Vrtis. Biologické Spisy. Acad. Veterinariae, Brno, vol.9, no.4, pp.1-51, 1930.

(ON THE GLANDULAR NAVEL POUCH OF THE HAMSTER.) Ueber den druesigen Nabelbeutel des Hamster. V. Vrtis. Archiv. Zool. Italiano, vol.16, pp.796-798, fig.1, 1931. See also, Atti dell' XI Congresso Internaz, Zool., Padova, 1930, pp.796-798, 1932.

(ON THE SO-CALLED LATERAL GLANDS OF THE WATER RAT (ARVICOLA) AND THE HAMSTER (CRICETUS).) Ueber s.g. Seitendruesen der Wasseratte (Arvicola) und des Hamsters (Cricetus). V. Vrtis. Archivo Zool. Ital 'XI Congresso Internaz, Zool., Padova, 1930, vol.16, pp.790-795, pl.XXV, 1931.

(INVESTIGATIONS OF THE MORPHOLOGY OF CLETHRIONOMYS GLAREOLUS GLAREOUS SCHREB.) Badania nad morfologia Clethrionomys glareolus glareolus Schreb. Waclaw Wasilewski. Ann. Univ. Mariae Curie-Sklodowska, Lublin, vol.7, no.3, pp.119-211, July 1, 1952. (In Polish, with German summary.)

THE DEVELOPMENT OF THE HAMSTER LOWER INCISOR AS OBSERVED BY ELECTRON MICROSCOPY. M. L. Watson, J. K. Avery. Amer. Jour. Anat., Phila., vol.95, no.1, pp.109-161, July, 1954.

LETTER RELATING TO THE NEARLY NAKED MARKS OBSERVED ON THE HIPS OF THE COMMON HAMSTER (CRICETUS VULGARIS). Dr. Weissenborn. Proc. Zool. Soc. Lond., pt.7, p.59, 1839.

ABNORMAL GROWTH OF INCISORS IN A MUSKRAT. Harry R. Woodward. Murrelet, Seattle, vol.23, no.3, pp.80-81, fig.1, Feb. 15, 1943.

ABNORMAL GROWTH OF INCISORS IN ONDATRA ZIBETHICA CINNAMOMINA. Harry R. Woodward. Bios, Mt. Vernon, vol.14, no.1, pp.42-43, fig.2, Mar., 1943.

## Aquatic Habits

A SWIMMING AND DIVING VOLE. (MICROTUS PENNSYLVANICUS PENNSYLVANICUS.) W. Frank Blair. Jour. Mam., vol.20, no.3, p.375, Aug.14, 1939.

SWIMMING OF THE MUSKRAT. Frank C. Kirkwood. Jour. Mam., vol.12, no.3, pp.317-318, Aug., 1931.

SWIMMING OF THE MUSKRAT. John D. Mizelle. Jour. Mam., vol.16, no.1, pp. 22-25, Feb., 1935.

AQUATIC HABITS OF PEROMYSCUS MANICULATUS. Robert T. Orr. Jour. Mam., vol.14, no.2, pp.160-161, May, 1933.

BACKWARD SWIMMING OF THE MUSKRAT. Arthur Ward Peterson. Jour. Mam., vol.31, no.4, p.453, Nov.21, 1950.

FURTHER OBSERVATIONS ON SWIMMING AND DIVING OF MEADOW VOLES. Randolph L. Peterson. Jour. Mam., vol. 28, no.3, pp.297-298, Aug.19, 1947.

SWIMMING ABILITY OF THE GRASSHOPPER MOUSE. Robert J. Russel, James S. Findley. Jour. Mam., vol.35, no.1, pp. 118-119, Feb.10, 1954.

MICROTINE AQUATICS. Thomas Smyth. Jour. Mam., vol.29, no.2, pp.185-186, May 14, 1948.

SWIMMING ABILITY OF A WOOD MOUSE. Robert Teeters. Jour. Mam., vol.26, no. 2, p.197, July 15, 1945.

Asia

HAMSTERS COLLECTED BY THE AMERICAN MUSEUM ASIATIC EXPEDITION. Glover M. Allen. Amer. Mus. Novit., no.179, pp.1-7, June 23, 1925.

MICROTINES COLLECTED BY THE ASIATIC EXPEDITIONS. Glover M. Allen. Amer. Mus. Novit., no.133, pp.1-13, Sept. 30, 1924.

A NEW CRICETINE GENUS FROM CHINA. Glover M. Allen. Jour. Mam., vol.9, no. 3, pp.244-246, Aug., 1928.

DESCRIPTION OF A NEW JAPANESE VOLE. Malcolm P. Anderson. Annals and Mag. Nat. Hist. (8), vol.4, 1909, pp.317-318.

(MATERIAL ADDING TO KNOWLEDGE OF THE RODENTS OF CENTRAL ASIA. III. A NEW SUBSPECIES OF HAMSTER (CRICETUS CRICETUS L.) OF THE SEMIRETSCHJE REGION.) Materiaux pour servir à la connaissance des Rongeurs de l'Asie Centrale. III. Une sousespèce nouvelle de l'Hamster (Cricetus cricetus L.) de la région de Semiretschje. A. I. Argyropulo. Trav. Inst. Zool. Acad. Sci. de l'URSS, Leningrad, vol.1, pp.235-237, (1932) 1933. (In Russian.)

ON THE MOUSE-LIKE RODENTS (FAMILY MURIDAE) OF THE COMMANDER ISLANDS. I. I. Barabash-Nikiforov. Zool. Zh., 22: 53-54, 1943.

(ON THE DISTRIBUTION AND ECOLOGY OF VINOGRADOV'S FIELD VOLE (PHAIOMYS VINOGRADOVI FETISSOV) IN EASTERN SIBERIA.) K rasprostraneniyu i ekologii polevki vinogradova (Phaiomys vinogradovi Fetissov) v vostochnoi sibiri. A. S. Fetisov. Doklady Akad. Nauk SSSR, vol.104, no.2, pp.326-328, 1955.

GERBILS FROM IRAQ, WITH DESCRIPTION OF A NEW GERBIL. David L. Harrison. Jour. Mam., 37 (3): 417-422, illus., Sept. 11, 1956.

A NEW SUBSPECIES OF VOLE FROM TURKESTAN. (MICROTUS (CHIONOMYS) NIVALIS DEMENTIEVI.) V. G. Heptner. Ann. Mag. Nat. Hist., London, ser.11, vol.4, no.20, pp.192-193, Aug., 1939.

(ON THE TAXONOMY AND DISTRIBUTION OF THE AFGHAN FIELD VOLE (MICROTUS AFGHANUS THOS.).) K Sistematike i rasprostraneniu afganskoi polebk (Microtus afghanus Thos.). V. H. Heptner, H. S. Shukurov. Doklady Akad. Nauk SSSR, Novaia Seriia Moscow, vol.74, no.1, pp. 149-152, 1950.

ON THE VOLES COLLECTED BY MR. G. FORREST IN YUNAN; WITH REMARKS UPON THE GENERA EOTHENOMYS AND NEODON AND UPON THEIR ALLIES. Martin A. C. Hinton. Ann. and Mag. Nat. Hist., Ser.9, vol.11, pp.145-162, Jan., 1923.

STUDY OF THE MAMMALS OF NANKING: A NEW SUBSPECIES OF CRICETIDAE FROM SHENSI. Hsi J. Ho. Contributions from Biol. Laboratory Sci. Soc. China, vol.X, nos.4-5, pp.245-287, figs.14, 1934.

TAXONOMIC STUDIES OF THE RED-BACKED VOLE FROM JAPAN. PART I. MAJOR DIVISIONS OF THE VOLE AND DESCRIPTIONS OF EOTHENOMYS WITH A NEW SPECIES. Yoshinori Imaizumi. Bull. National Sci. Mus., Tokyo, 3 (3): 195-216, pls.39-40, Mar., 1957.

COMMENTS ON TWO SPECIES OF RED-BACKED VOLES GENUS CLETHRIONOMYS, FROM KOREA AND MANCHURIA. J. Knox Jones, Jr., David H. Johnson. Nat. Hist. Misc., Chicago Acad. Sci., 157: 1-3, Oct. 30, 1956.

DESCRIPTION OF A NEW SPECIES OF ALACTAGA FROM MESOPOTAMIA. Oldfield Thomas. Ann. and Mag. Nat. Hist. (5), vol.8, no.43, pp.14-16, July, 1881.

DESCRIPTION OF A NEW SPECIES OF ARVICOLA FROM NORTHERN INDIA. Oldfield Thomas. Ann. and Mag. Nat. Hist., (5), vol.6, no.24, pp.322-323, Oct., 1880.

DESCRIPTION OF A NEW VOLE FROM CHINA. Oldfield Thomas. Ann. and Mag. Nat. Hist. (6), vol.8, no.44, pp. 117-119, Aug., 1891.

A NEW CRICETULUS FROM MONGOLIA. Oldfield Thomas. Ann. and Mag. Nat. Hist. (7), vol.15, no.87, pp.322-323, Mar., 1905.

A NEW VOLE FROM EASTERN ASIA. Oldfield Thomas. Ann. and Mag. Nat. Hist. (8), vol.7, no.40, pp.383-384, Apr., 1911.

A NEW VOLE FROM THE LOWER YANG-TSE-KIANG. Oldfield Thomas. Ann. and Mag. Nat. (7), vol.10, no.56, pp.166-169, Aug., 1902.

SCIENTIFIC RESULTS FROM THE MAMMAL SURVEY. XX. (A) NOTES ON THE GENUS CHELIONES. Oldfield Thomas. Jour. Bombay Nat. Hist. Soc., vol.26, pp. 726-727, Oct.20, 1919.

SCIENTIFIC RESULTS OF THE MAMMAL SURVEY. XXI. (B) TWO NEW SPECIES OF CALOMYSCUS. Oldfield Thomas. Jour. Bombay Nat. Hist. Soc., vol.26, no. 4, pp.938-940, Jan.31, 1920.

TWO NEW ASIATIC VOLES. Oldfield Thomas. Ann. and Mag. Nat. Hist. (8), vol.9, no.51, pp.348-350, Mar., 1912.

NEOASCHIZOMYS, A NEW GENUS OF MICROTINAE FROM SIKOTAN, A SOUTH KURILE ISLAND. Mitosi Tokua. Mem. College Sci., Kyoto Imperial Univ., ser.B, vol.10, no.3, pp.241-250, figs.6, pl.13, 1935.

MATERIALS FOR THE SYSTEMATICS AND THE MORPHOLOGY OF THE RODENTS. II. ON A NEW SPECIES OF MYOPUS FROM AMOUR-LAND. (M. MIDDENDORFFI SP. NOV.). B. S. Vinogradov. Yearbook Zool. Mus. Russian Acad. Sci., vol.23, pp.512-516, 1922.

NOTES ON THE MAMMALS OF YAKUTIA. I. ARVICOLES LEMMINGOIDES (GENUS ASCHIZOMYS). B. Vinogradov. Matériaux de la Commission pour l'Étude de la République Autonome Soviétique Socialiste Iakoute, livr.17, pp.19, illus., Pub. by Acad. Sci. Union Socialistic Soviet Republics, 1927. Text in Russian, with summary in English.)

NOTES ON SOME MAMMALS FROM YAKUTIA. 2. RED-BACKED VOLES (GENUS EVOTOMYS). B. S. Vinogradov. Matériaux de la Commission pour l'Étude de la République Autonome Soviétique Socialiste Iakoute, livr.18, pp.1-20, pls.3, 1927.

TWO NEW INTERESTING LEMMINGS FROM SIBERIA. B. S. Vinogradov. Ann. and Mag. Nat. Hist., ser.9, vol.14, pp.186-189, July, 1924.

THE INDIAN GERBILS OR ANTELOPE RATS. SCIENTIFIC RESULTS FROM THE MAMMAL SURVEY. NO. XV. R. C. Wroughton. Jour. Bombay Nat. Hist. Soc., vol.25, no. 1, pp.40-45, Mar.20, 1917.

Asia Minor

NOTE ON THE WATER-VOLES OF BOSNIA, ASIA MINOR, AND WESTERN PERSIA. G. E. H. Barrett-Hamilton. Ann. and Mag. Nat. Hist., ser.7, vol.3, pp.223-225, Mar., 1899.

(Review by P. Rode of) (FAUNA OF THE GERBILLIDAE (MAMMALIA, GLIRES) OF PERSIA AND THE ZOOGEOGRAPHICAL UNITS OF ASIA MINOR, IRAN, AND AFGHANISTAN.) Fauna der Gerbillidae (Mammalia, Glires) persiens und die tiergeographischen einheiten der Kleinasiatisch-Irano-Afganischen Laender. W. G. Heptner. Mammalia, Paris, 9 (3-4): 104 , Sept.-Dec., 1945.

A NEW REED VOLE, GENUS MICROTUS, FROM CENTRAL KOREA. (M. FORTIS ULIGINOSUS.) J. Knox Jones, Jr., David H. Johnson. Proc. Biol. Soc. Wash., vol. 68, pp.193-196, Dec.31, 1955.

(THE FIRST PROOF OF THE EXISTENCE OF THE GENUS MIMOMYS IN EASTERN ASIA.) Première preuve de l'existence du genre Mimomys en Asie Orientale. Th. Kormos. Trav. Lab. Géol. Fac. Sci. Lyons Univ., no.24, Mem.20, pp.1-8, fig. 1, 1934.

SOME REMARKS ON MOLE-RATS OF THE GENUS MYOS PALAX FROM CHINA. Einar Loennberg. Arkiv foer Zool. vol.18A, no.21, pp.1-11, illus., May 3, 1926.

THE GIANT RAT-HEADED HAMSTER, CRICETULUS TRITON NESTOR THOMAS, OF MANCHURIA. Anatole S. Loukashkin. Jour. Mam., vol.25, no.2, pp.170-177, figs.2, Pl.1, May 25, 1944.

DESCRIPTION OF A NEW GENUS AND SPECIES OF MICROTINE RODENT FROM SIBERIA. Gerrit S. Miller, Jr. Proc. Acad. Nat. Sci., Phila., pp.368-371, figs. 4, Oct.11, 1898.

DESCRIPTION OF A NEW VOLE FROM KASHMIR. Gerrit S. Miller, Jr. Proc. Biol. Soc., Wash., vol.11, p.141, May 13, 1897.

A NEW GERBILLE FROM EASTERN TURKESTAN. Gerrit S. Miller, Jr. Proc. Biol. Soc., Wash., vol.8, pp.163-164, Oct.31, 1900.

A NEW VOLE FROM EASTERN MONGOLIA. Gerrit S. Miller, Jr. Smithsonian Misc. Coll., vol.60, no.28, publ.2175, pp.2, 1 pl., Mar.31, 1913.

SOME VOLES FROM THE TIAN SHAN REGION. Gerrit S. Miller, Jr. Ann. and Mag. Nat. Hist., ser.7, vol.17, pp.371-375, Apr., 1906.

THE VOLES COLLECTED BY DR. W. L. ABBOTT IN CENTRAL ASIA. Gerrit S. Miller, Jr. Proc. Acad. Nat. Sci. Phila., vol.51, pp.281-298, pls.12-13, Aug.9, 1899.

A NEW SPECIES OF MICROTUS FROM KOREA. (MICROTUS KISHIDAI.) Tamezo Mori. Jour. Chosen Nat. Hist. Soc., no. 10, p.53, 1930.

ON THE OCCURRENCE OF CRICETULUS MIGRATORIUS PALL. IN THE TSCHUVASH REPUBLIC. A. N. Nikitin. Zaschita Rastenii ot Vrediteleí (Plant Protection), vol.7, nos.4-6, p.431, (1930) 1931. (In Russian.)

NOTES ON THE BIOLOGY OF ELLOBIUS TALPINUS PALL. IN CENTRAL KAZAKHSTAN. S. J. Obolenski. Bull. Soc. Nat. Moscow, sect. biol., n.s., vol.50, nos. 5-6, pp.65-71, 1945. (In Russian, with English summary.)

A LITTLE KNOWN VOLE FROM THE YAMAL PENINSULA. S. I. Ognev. Jour. Mam., Balto., vol.6, no.3, pp.192-195, figs.6, Aug.10, 1925.

NEW FORM OF WATER RAT FROM LAKE KUBAN. S. I. Ognev, K. L. Noviko. The Empire Medical Publication Moscow Leningrad, p.7, 1933.

(A FAMILY OF "GERBILS" IN THE RODENT FAUNA GEORGIA (RODENTIA, GERBILLIDAE).) Semeistvo peschanok v rodentofaune gruzzi (Rodentia, Gerbillidae). M. V. Shidlovski. Trudi Inst. Zool. Akad. Nauk Gruzinskoi SSR, vol.13, pp.63-69, 1954.

(CRICETULUS FURUNCULUS PALL. AND SICISTA MONTANA MEHELY IN WESTERN SIBERIA (NOVO-NIKOLAYEVSK GOVERNMENT DISTRICT).) Cricetulus furunculus Pall. und Sicista montana Mehely in Westsibirien (Regierungsbezirk Nowo-Nikolajewsk). W. N. Skalon. Zool. Anzeiger, Leipzig, vol.71, no.1-2, pp.14-18, Apr.20, 1927.

ON A FORM OF EOTHENOMYS MELANOGASTER (MILNE-EDWARDS) FROM TAIWAN, JAPAN. Ryo Tanaka. Trans. Nat. Hist. Soc. Formosa, vol.26, nos.155-156, pp.305-309, figs.3, Sept., 1936. (In Japanese with English summary.)

Canada

CANADIAN VOLES OF THE GENUS PHENACOMYS WITH DESCRIPTION OF TWO NEW CANADIAN SUBSPECIES. (PHENACOMYS UNGAVA SOPERI, P. INTERMEDIUS LAINGI.) R. Anderson. Canadian Field-Nat., Ottawa, vol.56, no. 4, pp.56-60, pl.1, June 8, 1942.

THE LONG-TAILED MEADOW MOUSE (MICROTUS LONGICAUDATUS) IN CANADA. R. M. Anderson, A. L. Rand. Canadian Field-Nat., Sutton West, vol.58, no.1, pp.19-21, Jan.-Feb., 1944.

A NEW LEMMING MOUSE (SYNAPTOMYS) FROM MANITOBA WITH NOTES ON SOME OTHER FORMS. R. M. Anderson, A. L. Rand. Canadian Field-Nat., Sutton West, vol.57, no.6, pp.101-103, Sept., 1943.

STATUS OF THE RICHARDSON VOLE (MICROTUS RICHARDSONI) IN CANADA. R. M. Anderson, A. L. Rand. Canadian Field-Nat., Sutton West, vol.57, no.6, pp. 106-107, Sept., 1943.

TOWNSEND VOLE (MICROTUS TOWNSENDI) IN CANADA. R. M. Anderson, A. L. Rand. Canadian Field-Nat., Sutton, West, vol.57, nos.3-4, pp.73-74, Apr.-May, 1943.

A NEW SPECIES OF EVOTOMYS FROM BRITISH COLUMBIA. Vernon Bailey. Proc. Biol. Soc. Wash., vol.12, pp.21-22, Jan.27, 1898.

RECORDS OF TWO MICROTINE RODENTS FROM THE QUEBEC TUNDRA. A. W. F. Banfield. Canadian Field-Nat., 70: 99, Apr.-June, 1950.

ADDITIONAL SPECIMENS OF PITYMYS PINETORUM SCALOPSOIDES FOR ELGIN COUNTY, ONTARIO. Ronald C. Brooman. Canadian Field-Nat., Ottawa, vol.63, no. 3, pp.114-115, May-June, 1949.

A NEW RACE OF PEROMYSCUS MANICULATUS FROM BRITISH COLUMBIA. Ian McTaggart Cowan. Proc. Biol. Soc. Wash., vol.50, pp.215-216, Dec.28, 1937.

THE PEROMYSCUS MANICULATUS BAIRDII COMPLEX IN MANITOBA. Stuart Criddle. Can. Field-Nat., 64 (5): 169-177, Sept.-Oct., 1950.

THE RED-BACKED VOLE (CLETHRIONOMYS GAPPERI LORINGI BAILEY) IN SOUTHERN MANITOBA. Stuart Criddle. Canadian Field-Nat., vol.46, no.8, pp.178-181, Nov., 1932.

SYNAPTOMYS BOREALIS FROM GODBOUT, QUEBEC. E. C. Cross. Jour. Mam., vol. 19, no.3, p.378, Aug., 1938.

FIRST ONTARIO RECORD OF THE SUBGENUS MICTOMYS. Stuart C. Downing. Canadian Field-Nat., Ottawa, vol.54, no. 7, pp.109-110, Oct., 1940.

THE PINE MOUSE IN ELGIN COUNTY, ONTARIO, WITH NOTES ON TWO OTHER SPECIES. Paul F. Elson. Canadian Field-Nat., vol.51, no.3, pp.36-37, Mar., 1937.

NATURAL HISTORY AND ECONOMIC IMPORTANCE OF THE MUSKRAT IN THE ATHABASCA-PEACE DELTA, WOOD BUFFALO PARK. W. A. Fuller. Can. Wildl. Serv., Wildl. Mgt. Bull., ser.1, no. 2, 82 pp., Mar., 1951.

NOTES ON SOME SASKATCHEWAN VOLES. Morris M. Green. Canadian Field-Nat., vol.40, pp.142-143, Oct.8, 1926.

UNDESCRIBED MAMMALS (PEROMYSCUS AND MICROTUS) FROM THE ISLANDS OF BRITISH COLUMBIA. C. J. Guiguet. Rept. Provincial Mus. Nat. Hist. and Anthropol., Victoria, British Columbia, 1954, pp.B64-B76, Aug.8, 1955.

A NEW MEADOW MOUSE FROM BOWEN ISLAND, BRITISH COLUMBIA. (MICROTUS TOWNSENDII CUMMINGI.) E. Raymond Hall. Murrelet, vol.17, no.1, pp.15-16, Jan. (Apr.), 1936.

A NEW RACE OF RED-BACKED VOLE (CLETHRIONOMYS) FROM THE BARREN GROUNDS OF CANADA. Harold C. Hanson. Jour. Mam., vol.33, no.4, pp. 500-501, 1 table, Nov.19, 1952.

OCCURRENCE OF THE ROCK VOLE IN NEW BRUNSWICK. F. C. Hirtle. Acadian Nat., Fredericton, vol.2, no.6, pp.112-113, Jan., 1946.

ON THE OCCURRENCE OF REITHRODONTOMYS IN BRITISH COLUMBIA. George P. Holland. Murrelet, Seattle, vol.23, no.2, p.60, Aug.14, 1942.

STUDIES ON THE BIOLOGY OF THE MUSKRAT IN MANITOBA. PART I. OESTROUS CYCLE AND BREEDING SEASON. J. A. McLeod, G. F. Bondar. Canadian Jour. Zool., Ottawa, vol.30, no. 4, pp.243-253, Aug., 1952.

A CORRECTION CONCERNING RECORD OF NEOTOMA C. DRUMMONDII FROM KITCHENER, B.C. Joseph Mailliard. Canadian Field-Nat., vol.46, no.6, p.145, Sept., 1932.

THE NORTHERN RED-BACKED MOUSE, CLETHRIONOMYS RUTILUS (PALLAS), IN CANADA. T. H. Manning. Nat. Mus. Canada Bull., Ottawa, 144: 1-67, pl.1, 1956.

THE VARYING LEMMING IN CAPTIVITY IN OTTAWA. T. H. Manning. Arctic Cir., 3 (2): 20-21, 1950.

RATTING IN THE DELTA. (MUSKRAT) D. B. Marsh. The Beaver, Winnipeg, Outfit no.278, pp.32-35, illus., Mar., 1948.

DESCRIPTION OF A NEW RED-BACKED MOUSE (EVOTOMYS DAWSONI) FROM THE HEADWATERS OF LIARD RIVER, NORTHWEST TERRITORY. C. Hart Merriam. Amer. Naturalist, pp.649-651, figs.2, July, 1888.

NOTES ON THE PALLID VOLE AND THE GRASSHOPPER MOUSE IN ALBERTA. J. E. Moore. Canadian Field-Nat., vol.67, no.4, pp.154-156, Oct.-Dec., 1953.

AN INSULAR FORM OF WHITE FOOTED MOUSE FROM ANTICOSTI ISLAND. Philip N. Moulthrop. Sci. Publ. Cleveland Mus. Nat. Hist., vol.5, no.3, pp.11-13, Dec.4, 1937.

A RECORD OF THE PACKRAT IN SASKATCHEWAN. R. W. Nero. Blue Jay, 14 (2): 43-44, illus., June, 1956.

DESCRIPTIONS OF NEW SPECIES OF SYNAPTOMYS AND PHENACOMYS FROM MACKENZIE, CANADA. Edward A. Preble. Proc. Biol. Soc. Wash., vol.15, pp.181-182, Aug.6, 1902.

SYNAPTOMYS BOREALIS FROM FORT SEVERN, HUDSON BAY, ONTARIO. Leslie A. Prince. Jour. Mam., vol.23, no.2, p.216, May 14, 1942.

WAS THE INTRODUCTION OF THE MUSKRAT TO GRAHAM ISLAND, QUEEN CHARLOTTE ISLANDS, UNWISE? A. L. Pritchard. Canadian Field-Nat., vol.48, no.6, p.103, Sept., 1934.

MICROTUS TETRAMERUS ON VANCOUVER ISLAND, B.C. Kenneth Racey. Canadian Field-Nat., vol.48, no.1, p.21, Jan., 1934.

CANADIAN FORMS OF THE MEADOW MOUSE. A. L. Rand. Canadian Field-Nat., Sutton West, vol.57, nos.7, 8, pp.115-123, Oct.-Nov., 1943.

SMALL-MAMMAL POPULATION OF A PRAIRIE GROVE. Glen C. Sanderson. Jour. Mam., 31 (1): 17-25, Feb., 1950.

NOVA SCOTIA RED-BACKED-MICE CLETHRIONOMYS GAPPERI OCHRACEUS. Carolyn Sheldon. Jour. Mam., vol.11, no. 3, pp.318-320, Aug., 1930.

A NEW GEOGRAPHIC RACE OF PEROMYSCUS LEUCOPUS FROM NOVA SCOTIA. Ronald W. Smith. Proc. Biol. Soc. Wash., vol.52, pp.157-158, Oct.11, 1939.

MICROTUS CHROTORRHINUS CHROTORRHINUS FROM LOWBUSH, LAKE ABITIBI, ONTARIO. L. L. Snyder. Jour. Mam., vol.8, no.4, p.311, Nov., 1927.

PEROMYSCUS MANICULATUS BAIRDII AT TORONTO. L. L. Snyder. Canadian Field-Nat., vol.39, p.25, Jan. (Feb.), 1925.

RECORDS FOR PHENACOMYS UNGAVA IN ONTARIO. L. L. Snyder. Jour. Mam., vol.10, no.1, pp.81-82, Feb., 1929.

THE NORTHWESTERN MUSKRAT OF THE MACKENZIE DELTA, NORTHWEST TERRITORIES, 1947-48. W. E. Stevens. Can. Wildl. Serv., Wildl. Mgt. Bull., ser. 1, no.8, pp.1-40, 7 pp. illus., Oct., 1953.

THE LIFE HISTORY AND ECOLOGY OF THE RED-BACKED MOUSE, CLETHRIONOMYS GAPPERI GAPPERI (VIGORS) IN THE WILDERNESS AREA, ALGONQUIN PARK, ONTARIO. Cameron Tanner. MA thesis, Univ. Toronto, 1950.

NOTES ON THE LIFE HISTORY OF THE MUSKRAT IN SOUTHERN ONTARIO. L. E. Wragg. Canadian Field-Nat., vol.67, no. 4, pp.174-177, Oct.-Dec., 1953.

Captivity

(DANGERS OF RAISING MUSKRATS (FIBER ZIBETHICUS LINNE).) Les dangers de l'elevage du rat musque (Fiber zibethicus Linne). A. Chappellier. Revue d'Histoire Naturelle, Pt.1, A. Mammiferes, Paris, vol.11, no.1, pp.1-25, figs.2, Jan., 1930

AN IMPROVED PEROMYSCUS RATION. Lee R. Dice. Jour. Mam., vol.15, no.2, pp.160-161, May, 1934.

A NEW LABORATORY CAGE FOR SMALL MAMMALS, WITH NOTES ON METHODS OF REARING PEROMYSCUS. Lee R. Dice. Jour. Mam., vol.10, no.2, pp.116-124, figs. 2, May, 1929.

HAMSTER RAISING. O. N. Eaton. Leaflet U.S. Dept. Agric., Wash., no.250, 6 pp., fig.1, Oct., 1948.

NOTES ON TWO SPECIES OF WOOD RATS IN CAPTIVITY. Horace W. Fellman. Jour. Mam., vol.16, no.4, pp.300-303, Nov., 1935.

RAISING CAPTIVE MEADOW VOLES (MICROTUS P. PENNSYLVANICUS). Chapman Grant. Jour. Mam., vol.30, no. 3, pp.317-318, illus., Aug.17, 1949.

NOTES ON SOME CAPTIVE DEER-MICE. Robert T. Hatt. Jour. Mam., vol.4, no.3, pp.186-187, Aug.10, 1923.

(SOME NOTES ON THE LIFE OF A CAPTIVE HAMSTER.) Einige Notizen ueber das Gefangenleben eines Hamsters. H. Hediger. Zool. Garten, Leipzig, n.F., vol.5, nos.1-3, pp.40-45, figs.6, June, 1932.

(KEEPING AND RAISING THE CHINESE PYGMY HAMSTER (CRICETULUS BARABENSIS GRISEUS A. MILNE-EDWARDS 1867).) Haltung und Aufzucht chinesischer Zwerg hamster (Cricetulus barabensis griseus A. Milne-Edwards 1867). Konrad Herter, Hans-Georg Rauch. Zeitschr Saeugetierk., Berlin, 21 (3-4): 161-171, pls. 9-10, Feb.28, 1957.

(OBSERVATIONS OF A CAPTIVE HAMSTER (CRICETUS CRICETUS L.).) Beobachtungen an einem gefangenen Hamster (Cricetus cricetus L.). Friedrich Kuehlhorn. Zool. Garten, Leipzig, (N.F.), vol.20, nos.2-3, pp.193-194, 1953.

RAISING "BLACK" MUSKRATS. N. P. Lavroff. Translations of Russian Game Reports, Canadian Wildlife Service, 2: 80-83, 1957.

REARING OF LEMMINGS AT FORT CHURCHILL, MANITOBA. J. S. Le Blanc. Jour. Mam., 37 (3): 447-448, Sept.11, 1956.

(THE RED MOUSE (EVOTOMYS GLAREOLUS SCHREB.) IN CAPTIVITY.) Roetelmaeuse (Evotomys glareolus Schreb.) in Gafangenschaft. Erna Mohr. Zeitschr. f. Saeugetierkunde, vol.4, pp.49-53, pl.2, 1929.

(THE HAMSTER AS HOUSE PET.) Der Hampster als Hausgenosse. Elisabeth Naundorff. Zeitsch. f. Saeugetierkunde, vol.3, pp.209-210, 1 pl., June 11, 1928.

(A CASE OF ACTUAL DOMESTICATION IN A HAMSTER (CRICETUS CRICETUS L.).) Ein Fall von wirklicher Zahmheit bei einem Hamster (Cricetus cricetus L.). Hans Petzsch. Zool. Garten, N.F., Leipzig, vol.8, nos.1-3, pp.25-26, Sept., 1935;

Zool. Garten, N.F., Leipzig, vol.8, nos. 7-9, p.228, June, 1936.

(COMPARATIVE BIOLOGICAL OBSERVATIONS OF CAPTIVE MESOCRICETUS AURATUS WATERHOUSE AND CRICETUS CRICETUS L.) Vergleichende biologische Beobachtungen an gefangenen Mesocricetus auratus Waterhouse und Cricetus cricetus L. Hans Petzsch. Zool. Anzeiger, Leipzig, vol.147, pp.237-246, Nov., 1951.

(SOME OBSERVATIONS OF CAPTIVE HAMSTERS (CRICETUS CRICETUS L.).) Einige Beobachtungen an gefangenen Hamstern (Cricetus cricetus L.). Hans Petzsch. Zeitschr. f. Saeugetierkunde, Berlin, vol.8, nos.3-6, pp.222-227, figs. 2, Dec.20, 1933.

THE REQUIREMENTS AND BIOLOGY OF THE COLLARED LEMMING, DICROSTONYX TORQUATUS PALLAS, 1778, IN CAPTIVITY. W. B. Quay, J. F. Quay. Saeugetierk, Mitteil., Stuttgart, 4 (4): 174-180, Oct.1, 1956.

(THE SHORT-EARED MOUSE (PITYMYS SUBTERRANEUS DE SELYS) IN CAPTIVITY.) Die Kurzohrmaus (Pitymys subterraneus DeSelys) in Gefangenschaft. Wilhelm Schreitmueller. Zeitschr. Saeugetierk., Berlin, vol.17, no.3, pp.166-169, Feb.19, 1953.

MICROTUS CALIFORNICUS IN CAPTIVITY. Raymond M. Selle. Jour. Mam., vol.9, no.2, pp.93-98, May, 1928.

ALBINO MICROTUS REARED IN THE LABORATORY. E. I. Sillman, A. A. Wellwood. Jour. Mam., 37 (2):298, June 9, 1956.

Central America

FIVE NEW MAMMALS OF THE GENUS PEROMYSCUS FROM EL SALVADOR. (P. BOYLII CORDILLERAE, P. B. SACARENSIS, P. MEXICANUS PHILOMBRIUS, P. M. SALVADORENSIS, AND P. STIRTONI.) Donald R. Dickey. Proc. Biol. Soc. Wash., vol.41, pp.1-6, Jan.25, 1928.

A NEW RODENT OF THE GENUS RHEOMYS FROM CHIRIQUI. (RHEOMYS HARTMANNI.) Robert K. Enders. Proc. Nat. Acad. Sci., Phila., vol.90, pp.295-296, Feb.3, 1939.

A NEW SUBSPECIES OF REITHRODONTOMYS MEXICANUS FROM PANAMA WITH REMARKS ON R. MEXICANUS CHERRII. (REITHRODONTOMYS MEXICANUS GARICHENSIS.) Robert K. Enders, Oliver P. Pearson. Notulae Naturae, Phila., no.60, pp.2, Oct.8, 1940.

THREE NEW RODENT SUBSPECIES OF SCOTINOMYS FROM CHIRIQUI, PANAMA. (SCOTINOMYS TEGUINA EPISCOPI, S. T. GARICHENSIS S. T. LERIDENSIS.) Robert K. Enders, Oliver P. Pearson. Notulae Naturae, Phila., no.34, pp.1-4, Nov.9, 1939.

FIVE NEW RICE RATS OF THE GENUS ORYZOMYS FROM MIDDLE AMERICA. E. A. Goldman. Proc. Biol. Soc. Wash., vol.28, pp.127-130, June 29, 1915.

A NEW CLIMBING MOUSE FROM PANAMA. (OECOMYS ENDERSI.) E. A. Goldman. Jour. Wash. Acad. Sci., vol.23, no.11, pp.525-526, Nov.15, 1933.

A NEW VESPER RAT FROM NICARAGUA. E. A. Goldman. Proc. Biol. Soc. Wash., vol.29, pp.155-156, Sept.6, 1916.

FOUR NEW RODENTS FROM COSTA RICA. (REITHRODONTOMYS MEXICANUS POTREROGRANDEI, R. HARRISI, ORYZOMYS FULVESCENS CREPER, O. F. REVENTAZONI.) George G. Goodwin. Amer. Mus. Novitates, New York, no.1293, p.3, July 20, 1945.

FOUR NEW SCOTINOMYS FROM COSTA RICA. (SCOTINOMYS TEGUINA CACABATUS, S. T. ESCAZUENSIS, S. LONGIPILOSUS, S. HARRISI.) George G. Goodwin. Amer. Mus. Novitates, New York, no.1279, pp.4, Feb.21, 1945.

A NEW PEROMYSCUS FROM WESTERN HONDURAS. (PEROMYSCUS HONDURENSIS.) George G. Goodwin. Amer. Mus. Novitates, New York, no.1121, p.1, June 9, 1941.

(THREE NEW REITHRODONTOMYS AND TWO NEW PEROMYSCUS FROM GUATEMALA. (REITHRODONTOMYS MEXICANUS HOWELLI, REITHRODONTOMYS PACIFICUS, REITHRODONTOMYS GRACILIS ANTHONYI, PEROMYSCUS GUATEMALENSIS TROPICALIS; P. GRANDIS.) George G. Goodwin. Amer. Mus. Nov., no.560, pp.1-5, Sept.16, 1932.

TWO NEW HARVEST MICE FROM COSTA RICA. (REITHRODONTOMYS BREVIROSTRIS, R. RODRIQUEZI.) George G. Goodwin. Amer. Mus. Novitates, New York, no.1231, pp.2, June 2, 1943.

TWO NEW HARVEST MICE FROM HONDURAS. (REITHRODONTOMYS MEXICANUS OCOTEPEQUENSIS, AND REITHRODONTOMYS DORSALIS UNDERWOODI.) George G. Goodwin. Amer. Mus. Nov., no.921, pp.2, May 3, 1937.

A NEW SUBSPECIES OF PEROMYSCUS FROM COSTA RICA. (PEROMYSCUS NUDIPES HESPERUS.) William P. Harris, Jr. Occas. Papers Mus. Zool. Univ. Michigan, Ann Arbor, no.423, 2 pp., Nov.29, 1940.

A NEW SUBSPECIES OF HARVEST MOUSE (REITHRODONTOMYS) FROM CENTRAL AMERICA. (REITHRODONTOMYS MEXICANUS ORINUS.) Emmet T. Hooper. Proc. Biol. Soc. Wash., vol.62, pp.169-172, Nov.16, 1949.

DESCRIPTIONS OF TWO NEW HARVEST MICE FROM HONDURAS. (REITHRODONTOMYS MEXICANUS LUCIFRONS; R. M. MINUSCULUS.) Arthur H. Howell. Proc. Biol. Soc. Wash., vol.45, pp.125-126, July 30, 1932.

A NEW ORYZOMYS FROM A PINE RIDGE IN BRITISH HONDURAS. (ORYZOMYS COUESI PINICOLA.) Adolph Murie. Occas. Papers Mus. Zool., Univ. Michigan, no. 245, pp.3, June 9, 1932.

DESCRIPTION OF A NEW SPECIES OF MOUSE (SITOMYS DECOLORUS) FROM CENTRAL AMERICA. Frederick W. True. Proc. U.S. Nat. Mus., vol.16, publ.963, pp.689-690, Feb.5, 1894.

Cytology

CYTOLOGICAL STUDY OF MALE REPRODUCTIVE CELLS OF THE GOLDEN HAMSTER (CRICETUS AURATUS WATERHOUSE). Virginia C. Carr, Thomas Edward Hennessy. Turtox News, Chicago, vol.28, no.11, pp.206-211, illus., Nov., 1950.

CHROMOSOMES OF THE GENUS PEROMYSCUS (DEER MOUSE). J. C. Cross. Cytologia, vol.8, nos.3-4, pp.408-419, figs.29, Feb., 1938.

NOTES ON THE CHROMOSOMES OF THE PEROMYSCI (RODENTIA-CRICETIDAE). S. Makino. Experientia, Sapporo, Japan, vol.9, no.6, p.214, 1953.

STUDIES ON MURINE CHROMOSOMES, VI. MORPHOLOGY OF THE SEX CHROMOSOMES IN TWO SPECIES OF MICROTUS. S. Makino. Annot. Zool. Japonenses, Tokyo, vol.23, no.2, pp.63-68, pl.6, Jan., 1950.

(THE CHROMOSOME FORMULA OF MICROTUS ORCADENSIS MILLAIS.) La formule chromosomique de Microtus orcadensis Millais. Robert Matthey. Rev. Suisse Zool., Geneva, vol.58, no.4, pp. 201-213, Jan., 1951.

(THE CYTOLOGY AND TAXONOMY OF THE GENUS MERIONES, ILLIGER (RODENTIA-MURIDAE-GERBILLINAE).) Cytologie et taxonomie du genre Meriones, Illiger (Rodentia-Muridae-Gerbillinae). Robert Matthey. Saeugetierk, Mitteil., 5 (4): 145-150, illus., Dec.1, 1957.

THE TROPHOBLASTIC GIANT CELLS AND ENDOVASCULAR CELLS ASSOCIATED WITH PREGNANCY IN THE HAMSTER, CRICETUS AURATUS. Margaret Ward Orsini. Amer. Jour. Anat., vol.94, no.2, pp.273-331, Mar., 1954.

MEIOSIS IN THE STRIPED HAMSTER (CRICETULUS GRISEUS MILNE-EDW.) AND THE PROBLEM OF HETEROCHROMATIN IN MAMMALIAN SEX-CHROMOSOMES. G. Pontecorvo. Proc. Roy. Soc. Edinburgh, sec.B, vol.62, pt.1, no.4, pp.32-42, figs. 3, 1943.

THE CHROMOSOMAL COMPLEMENT OF THE GERBIL, TATERA BRANTSI DRACO. P. V. Tobias. South African Jour. Sci., Johannesburg, vol.48, no.11, pp.366-373, illus., June, 1952.

CYTOLOGICAL CONTRIBUTIONS TO THE PHYLOGENY AND CLASSIFICATION OF THE RODENT GENUS GERBILLUS. J. Wahrman, A. Zahavi. Nature, London, vol.175, no.4457, pp.600-602, figs.2, Apr. 2, 1955.

Diseases

THE EXPERIMENTAL TRANSMISSION OF POLIOMYELITIS TO THE EASTERN COTTON RAT, SIGMODON HISPIDUS HISPIDUS. Charles Armstrong. Public Health Reports, Wash., D.C., vol.54, no.38, pp.1719-1721, Sept.22, 1939.

SPONTANEOUS TRANSMISSIBLE TUMOURS IN THE SYRIAN HAMSTER. R. Ashbel. Nature, London, vol.155, no.3942, p.607, May 19, 1945.

A RICKETTSIAL INFECTION IN CANADIAN VOLES. James A. Baker. Jour. Exper. Medicine, New York, vol.84, no.1, pp.37-50, pl.3, July 1, 1946.

THIS MYSTERIOUS MUSKRAT DISEASE. (HEMORRHAGIC DISEASE.) Karl Bednarik. Ohio Cons. Bull., 18 (7): 21, illus., July, 1954.

(STUDIES ON RODENTS. III. A SKIN DISEASE OF FIELD MICE (MICROTUS SP.) PROVOKED BY EUSCHONGASTIA COSTULATA WILL. (ACARINA TROMBICULIDAE).) Études sur les rongeurs. III. Une dermatose des campagnols (Microtus sp.) provoquée par Euschoengastia costulata Will. (Acarina-Tombiculidae). J. Bernard. Parasitica, vol.9, no.4, pp.132-138, 1 pl., 1953.

A STRAIN OF ENDEMIC TYPHUS FEVER ISOLATED FROM A FIELD MOUSE. George D. Brigham. Publ. Health Reports, vol.52, no.21, pp.659-660, May 21, 1937.

A RINGWORM DISEASE OF MUSKRATS TRANSFERABLE TO MAN. Vera K. Charles. Jour. Wash. Acad. Sci., 30 (8): 338-344, Aug., 1940.

TUBERCULOSIS AMONG WILD VOLES: WITH A DISCUSSION OF OTHER PATHOLOGICAL CONDITIONS AMONG CERTAIN MAMMALS AND BIRDS. Dennis Chitty. Ecology, Durham, vol.35, no.2, pp.227-237, illus., Apr., 1954.

TRYPANOSOMIASIS IN THE FLORIDA COTTON RAT, SIGMODON HISPIDUS LITTORALIS. James T. Culbertson. Jour. Parasitology, 27 (1): 45-52, Feb., 1941.

PARATYPHOID INFECTION IN THE NORTHERN WHITE-FOOTED MOUSE IN CENTRAL IOWA. Herbert T. Dalmat. Am. Midland Nat., 31 (1): 179-181, Jan., 1944.

OCCURRENCE OF RINGWORM DISEASE AND LUMPY JAW IN THE MUSKRAT IN MARYLAND. Herbert L. Dozier. Jour. Amer. Veterinary Med. Assoc., Chicago, vol.102, no.795, pp.451-455, illus., June, 1943.

(ON THE SUSCEPTIBILITY OF THE MUSKRAT (ANDATRA ZIBETHICA L.) TO TULAREMIA INFECTION.) O Vosprimiimchivosti Ondatra (Ondatra Zibethica L.) k Tularemiinoi Infektsii. T. N. Dunaeva, O. S. Emelanova. Zool. Zhurnal, Akad. Nauk SSSR, Moscow, vol.29, no.5, pp.459-465, 1950.

(ON THE SUSCEPTIBILITY TO AND ILLNESS FROM TULAREMIA ON THE PART OF FIELD VOLES (SUBFAMILY MICROTINAE).) O vospriimchivosti i infektsionnoi chuvstvitelnosti k tuliaremii nekotorikh vidov polevok (podsemeistvo Microtinae). T. N. Dunaeva, N. H. Olsufev. Zool. Jour.

Akad. Nauk SSSR, Moscow, vol.31, no.3, pp.457-466, 1952.

TULAREMIA FROM A WOOD RAT IN NEW MEXICO. Dean H. Ecke, Robert Holdenried. Public Health Report, 67 (6): 588-589, June, 1952.

AN EPIDEMIC AMONG VOLES (MICROTUS AGRESTIS) ON THE SCOTTISH BORDER IN THE SPRING OF 1934. Charles Elton, D. H. S. Davis, G. M. Findlay. Jour. Animal Ecol., 4 (2): 277-288, Nov., 1935.

ECOLOGY OF THE MUSKRAT. A CONTINUATION OF LOCAL FIELD STUDIES OF EPIZOOTIC DISEASE IN MUSKRATS, ESPECIALLY AT WALL LAKE, WRIGHT COUNTY, IOWA. Paul L. Errington. Iowa Coop. Wildlife Research Unit, Ames, Quart. Rept., pp.26-34, Jan.-Mar., 1949.

OBSERVATIONS ON A FUNGUS SKIN DISEASE OF IOWA MUSKRATS. Paul L. Errington. Amer. Jour. Veterinary Research, Chicago, vol.3, no.7, pp.195-201, Apr., 1942.

SPECIAL REPORT ON EPIZOOTIC DISEASE IN MUSKRATS AT WALL LAKE, WRIGHT COUNTY, IOWA. Paul L. Errington. Prog. Rept. Iowa Coop. Wildlife Research Unit, pp.32-40, July-Sept., 1948.

SPECIAL REPORT ON MUSKRAT DISEASE. Paul L. Errington. Iowa Coop. Wildl. Res. Unit, Quart. Rep., July-Sept., 1946: 34-51, July-Sept., 1946.

EPIDEMIC DISEASE AMONG VOLES (MICROTUS) WITH SPECIAL REFERENCE TO TOXOPLASMA. G. M. Findlay, A. D. Middleton. Jour. Anim. Ecol., vol.3, no. 2, pp.150-160, pl.7, Nov., 1934.

INFLUENZA VIRUS INFECTION IN THE HAMSTER. William F. Friedewald, E. W. Hook, Jr. Jour. Exper. Med., Balto., vol. 88, no.3, pp.343-354, Sept.1, 1948.

INFECTIONS BY LEISHMANIA DONOVANI IN THE COTTON RAT. J. D. Fulton, L. P. Joyner. Trop. Disease Bull., London, vol. 45, no.9, pp.775-776, Sept., 1948.

TESTICULAR HYPOPLASIA AND EPIDIDYMAL CYSTS IN THE SYRIAN HAMSTER. Humberto Grandos, Henrik Dam. Nature, London, vol.162, no.4112, p.297, Aug.21, 1948.

PREVENTION OF TRICHOBEZOAR IN THE COTTON RAT, SIGMODON HISPIDUS HISPIDUS. S. R. Howell, C. A. Schlack, C. M. McCay, B. L. Taylor. Science, Lancaster, vol.107, no.2782, pp.424-425, Apr.23, 1948.

TULAREMIA--MUSKRATS AS A SOURCE OF HUMAN INFECTION IN UTAH. William L. Jellison, Glen M. Kohls, Cornelius B. Philip. Rocky Mountain Med. Jour., Denver, vol.48, no.8, pp.594-597, Aug., 1951.

(MICROTUS AGRESTIS A RESERVOIR OF LEPTOSPIROSIS IN NATURE.) Microtus agrestis rezervoár leptospír v prírode. E. Kmety, E. Chylo, J. Kratochvil. Zool. a Entom. Listy, Praha, vol.4, no.4, pp. 291-294, 1955.

DISEASES AND PARASITES OF THE MUSKRAT (ONDATRA ZIBETHICA) IN BRITISH COLUMBIA. Iola Musfeldt Knight. Can. Jour. Zool., 29 (3): 188-214, June, 1951.

EXPERIMENTAL LEPTOSPIROSIS IN HAMSTERS (CRICETUS AURATUS). Carl L. Larson. U. S. Publ. Health Reports, Wash., vol.59, no.16, pp.522-527, Apr.21, 1944.

PATHOLOGY OF EXPERIMENTAL TULAREMIA IN THE GOLDEN HAMSTER (CRICETUS AURATUS). R. D. Lillie, Carl L. Larson. U. S. Publ. Health Reports, Wash., vol.60, no.42, pp.1243-1253, Oct. 19, 1945.

REPORT ON MUSKRAT DISEASE OUTBREAK. A. M. McDermid. Wis. Cons. Bull., 11 (8-9): 21-22, Aug.-Sept., 1946.

SUSCEPTIBILITY OF THE GOLDEN HAMSTER, MESOCRICETUS AURATUS, TO PLAGUE. Margaret C. McMahon. U. S. Public Health Reports, Wash., D.C., vol.59, no.7, pp.234-236, Feb.18, 1944.

SUSCEPTIBILITY OF SYRIAN HAMSTERS TO LEPTOSPIROSIS. Harry E. Morton. Proc. Soc. Exper. Biol. and Med., Utica, vol.49, no.4, pp.566-568, Apr., 1942.

SCHIZOTAENIASIS IN MUSKRAT. O. Wilford Olsen. Jour. Parasitology, 25 (3): 279, June, 1939.

SUSCEPTIBILITY AND RESISTANCE OF VARIOUS SPECIES OF PEROMYSCUS (AMERICAN DEER MICE) TO INFECTION WITH TRYPANOSOMA HIPPICUM, AND THE POSSIBILITY OF CERTAIN "WILD MICE" BEING RESERVOIR HOSTS TO PATHOGENIC TRYPANOSOMES. Ardzroony Packchanian. Amer. Jour. Trop. Med., vol.18, pp.587-593, Sept., 1938.

THE OCCURRENCE OF POROCEPHALIASIS IN THE LOUISIANA MUSKRAT. George H. Penn, Ernest C. Martin. Jour. Wildlife Mgt., 5 (1): 13-14, Jan., 1941.

(SKULL AND TOOTH LESIONS IN CAPTIVE HAMSTERS (CRICETUS CRICETUS L.) Schaedelknochen- und Zahnschaeden bei gefangenen Hamstern (Cricetus cricetus L.).) Hans Petzsch. Zool. Garten, N.F., Leipzig, vol.9, nos.3-4, pp.148-150, illus., May, 1937.

TRANSMISSION OF THE MURINE STRAIN OF POLIOMYELITIS TO THE SYRIAN HAMSTER. Harry Plotz, Reginald Reagan, Howard L. Hamilton. Proc. Soc. Exper. Biol. and Med., Utica, vol.51, no.1, pp. 124-126, Oct., 1942.

TULAREMIA FROM A MUSKRAT. Harold Schwartz. Jour. Amer. Med. Asso., vol. 92, pp.1180-1181, Apr.6, 1929.

COCCIDIOSIS IN MUSKRATS INFLUENCED BY WATER LEVELS. J. E. Shillinger. Jour. Wildl. Mgt., 2 (4): 233-234, Oct., 1938.

THE SUSCEPTIBILITY OF THE EASTERN COTTON RAT, SIGMODON HISPIDUS HISPIDUS, TO EUROPEAN TYPHUS. J. C. Snyder, C. R. Anderson. Science, Lancaster, n.s., vol.95, no.2453, p.23, Jan.2, 1942.

A REVIEW OF THE LITERATURE ON DISEASES AND PARASITES OF THE MUSKRAT. Michael J. Takos. Maine Coop. Wildl. Res. Unit., 14 pp., Dec., 1940.

A POPULATION OF THE JAPANESE FIELD VOLE INFESTED WITH TSUTSUGAMUSHI DISEASE. Ryo Tanaka, Seiyu Teramura. Jour. Mam., vol.34, no.3, pp.345-352, illus., Aug.14, 1953.

TULAREMIA IN MUSKRATS AND MEASURES TO BE TAKEN AGAINST IT. E. S. Tcherkasski. Translations of Russian Game Reports, Canadian Wildlife Service, 2: 40-73, 1957.

MERIONES MERIDANUS PALL., A RESERVOIR OF PLAGUE VIRUS IN SANDY REGIONS OF VOLGO-URAL STEPPES. M. Tikhomirova. Revue Microbiol., Epidemiol., et Parasitol., vol.13, no.2, pp.89-102, Tables 9, 1934. (In Russian with English summary.)

THE OCCURRENCE OF A DISEASE AMONG MUSKRATS (ONDATRA ZIBETHICA) IN GREAT BRITAIN DURING 1934. Tom Warwick. Jour. Animal Ecol., 6 (1): 112-114, May, 1937.

TUBERCULOSIS IN WILD VOLES. A. O. Wells. Lancet, 232 (5934): 1221, May 22, 1937.

THE SUSCEPTIBILITY OF VOLES TO HUMAN AND BOVINE STRAINS OF TUBERCLE BACILLI. A. Q. Wells. British Jour. Exper. Pathology, London, vol.19, pp.324-328, 1938.

THE RISE AND DISAPPEARANCE OF CONTINENTAL VOLE PLAGUE ZONES IN THE NETHERLANDS. A. van Wijngaarden. Verslagen Landbouwkundige Onderzoekingen, Plant Protection Service, Wageningen, no.63.15, pp.21, 1 map, 1957.

TULAREMIA. FIRST CASE TO BE REPORTED IN ALASKA. (INFECTION FROM MUSKRATS.) Ralph B. Williams. Public Health Reports, Wash., D.C., vol.61, no. 24, pp.873-876, June 14, 1946.

NOTES ON THE DISTRIBUTION AND HABITS OF REDUVIID VECTORS OF CHAGAS' DISEASE IN THE SOUTHWESTERN UNITED STATES. Sherwin F. Wood. Pan-Pac. Ent., 17 (2): 85-94, 17 (3): 115-118, Apr.-July, 1941.

OBSERVATIONS ON VECTORS OF CHAGAS' DISEASE IN THE UNITED STATES. II. ARIZONA. Sherwin F. Wood. Amer. Jour. Trop. Med., 23 (3): 315-320, May, 1943.

A GRANULOMA OF THE FORELEG OF A HAMSTER CRICETULUS GRISEUS ARTIFICIALLY INFECTED WITH CHINESE KALA-AZAR. Shutsu Young. Jour. Shanghai Sci. Inst., sect.4, vol.5, pp.125-132, pls.18-21, Apr., 1940.

## Distribution, Habitats, Range

A PRELIMINARY STUDY OF THE HOME RANGE AND TERRITORY OF THE COTTON RAT, SIGMODON HISPIDUS HISPIDUS (SAY AND ORD). Roland Abegg. MS thesis, La. State Univ., 1939.

VARIATIONS IN WINTER MUSKRAT HABITATS AND HARVESTS. Maurice M. Alexander. Amer. Midland Nat., Notre Dame, vol.53, no.1, pp.61-70, illus., Jan., 1955.

GEOGRAPHIC RANGE OF PEROMYSCUS MELANOPHRYS, WITH DESCRIPTION OF NEW SUBSPECIES. Rollin H. Baker. Univ. Kansas Publ., Mus. Nat. Hist., Lawrence, vol.5, no.17, pp.251-258, Apr.10, 1952.

NESTS AND HABITAT OF THE GOLDEN MOUSE IN EASTERN KENTUCKY. Roger W. Barbour. Jour. Mam., vol.23, no.1, pp.90-91, Feb.14, 1942.

(STUDIES OF RODENTS. II. NOTE ON THE ECOLOGIC DISTRIBUTION OF MICROTUS ARVALIS P. AND MICROTUS AGRESTIS L. IN ARDENNE, FAMENNE, AND IN THE MUDDY ZONE.) Études sur les rongeurs. II. Note sur la répartition écologique de Microtus arvalis P. et Microtus agrestis L. en Ardenne, en Famenne et dans la zone limoneuse. J. Bernard. Bull. Inst. Agronomique and Stations Recherches Gembloux, Brussels, vol.21, nos.1-2, pp.1-13 (reprint), 1953.

HOME RANGES AND POPULATIONS OF THE MEADOW VOLE IN SOUTHERN MICHIGAN. W. Frank Blair. Jour. Wildlife Management, Menasha, vol.4, no.2, pp.149-161, fig.1, Apr., 1940.

STRANGE HABITAT OF THE DESERT WOOD RAT. A. E. Borell. Jour. Mam., vol.16, no.4, p.327, Nov., 1935.

ABUNDANCE AND ACTIVITY OF THE WOOD MOUSE (PEROMYSCUS LEUCOPUS NOVEBORACENSIS) IN RELATION TO THE CHARACTER OF ITS HABITAT. Raymond H. Brand. PhD. thesis, Univ. Mich., 168 pp., 1955.

AN INVESTIGATION OF THE COTTON RAT HABITAT REQUIREMENTS. Charles I. Bunn. MS thesis, N.C. State Coll., 1941.

A STUDY OF MOVEMENTS AND HABITAT PREFERENCES OF MUSKRATS IN MAINE. Malcolm W. Coulter. Jour. Forestry, 47 (4): 291, Apr., 1949.

SYNAPTOMYS COOPERI IN FORESTED REGIONS. A. F. Coventry. Jour. Mam., vol.23, no.4, pp.450-451, Nov.14, 1942.

A DISTRIBUTIONAL STUDY OF THE PEROMYSCUS SITKENSIS GROUP OF WHITE-FOOTED MICE. Ian McTaggart Cowan. Univ. Calif. Publ. in Zool., Berkeley, vol. 40, no.13, pp.429-438, fig.1, Nov.14, 1935.

NOTES ON THE INSECT INHABITANTS OF WOOD RAT HOUSES IN CALIFORNIA. A. C. Davis. Bull. S. California Acad. Sci., vol.33, pt.1, pp.12-24, Jan.-Apr., 1934.

ECOLOGICAL DISTRIBUTION OF PEROMYSCUS AND NEOTOMA IN PARTS OF SOUTHERN NEW MEXICO. Lee R. Dice. Ecology, 23 (2): 199-208, Apr., 1942.

SOME FACTORS AFFECTING THE DISTRIBUTION OF THE PRAIRIE VOLE,

FOREST DEER MOUSE, AND PRAIRIE DEER MOUSE. Lee R. Dice. Ecology, vol.3, pp.29-47, Jan. (Mar.), 1922.

DISTANCE OF DISPERSAL BY PRAIRIE DEERMICE FROM BIRTHPLACES TO BREEDING SITES. Lee R. Dice, Walter E. Howard. Contrib. Lab. Vert. Biol., 50, 15 pp., Aug., 1951.

LATE FALL HOME RANGES OF THREE GOLDEN MICE, PEROMYSCUS NUTTALLI. Paul B. Dunaway. Jour. Mam., 36 (2): 297-298, May, 1955.

(A HAMSTER IN A KITCHEN GARDEN.) Hamster im Hausgarten. Wd. Eichler, Joh. Hertel. Zool. Garten, Leipzig, n.F., vol.18, nos.3-4, pp.153-154, 1951.

HABITAT REQUIREMENTS OF STREAM-DWELLING MUSKRATS. Paul L. Errington. Trans. N.A. Wildl. Conf., 2: 411-416, 1937.

HABITAT PREFERENCES OF FOUR SPECIES OF MICROTUS IN JACKSON HOLE, WYOMING. James S. Findley. Jour. Mam., 32 (1): 118-120, Feb., 1951.

ACTIVITY AND HOME RANGE OF THE FIELD MOUSE, MICROTUS PENNSYLVANICUS PENNSYLVANICUS (ORD.). W. J. Hamilton, Jr. Ecology, vol.18, no.2, pp.255-263, figs.2, Apr., 1937.

ON THE OCCURRENCE OF SYNAPTOMYS COOPERI IN FORESTED REGIONS. W. J. Hamilton, Jr. Jour. Mam., vol.22, no.2, p.195, May 14, 1941.

HABITAT OF THE GOLDEN MOUSE IN VIRGINIA. Charles O. Handley, Jr. Jour. Mam., vol.29, no.3, pp.298-299, Aug.31, 1948.

APPARENT HOME RANGE OF MICROTUS IN RELATION TO DISTANCE BETWEEN TRAPS. Don W. Hayne. Jour. Mam., vol.31, no.1, pp.26-39, figs.2, illus., Feb.21, 1950.

A HABITAT IN COASTAL CALIFORNIA UNFAVORABLE TO PEROMYSCUS MANICULATUS. Emmet T. Hooper. Jour. Mam., vol.20, no.2, pp.256-258, May, 1939.

ACTIVITY AND DISTRIBUTION OF CERTAIN WILD MICE IN RELATION TO BIOTIC COMMUNTIES. M. S. Johnson. Jour. Mam., vol.7, no.4, pp.245-277, Nov., 1926.

ON THE DISCONTINUED GEOGRAPHICAL DISTRIBUTION OF EVOTOMYS GLAREOLUS SCHREB. S. Kiriko. Bull. Soc. Nat. Moscou, sect. biol., n.s., vol.44, no.5, pp.250-252, 1935. (In Russian, with French résumé.)

(ON THE GEOGRAPHIC DISTRIBUTION OF THE BLACK HAMSTER AND ITS RELATIONS WITH THE NORMAL FORM OF CRICETUS CRICETUS.) S. Kirikov. Zoologicheskii Zhurnal (Zool. Jour. USSR), Moscou, vol.13, no.2, pp.361-368, fig.1, 1934. (In Russian, with French summary.)

DISTRIBUTION OF MICROTUS CHROTORRHINUS, WITH DESCRIPTION OF A NEW SUBSPECIES. E. V. Komarek. Jour. Mam., vol.13, no.2, pp.155-158, May, 1932.

NOTES ON THE HOME RANGE AND ECOLOGY OF THE ATWATER WOOD RAT. Daniel W. Lay, Rollin H. Baker. Jour. Mam., 19 (4): 418-423, Nov., 1938.

A FIVE-YEAR CHANGE IN AN ASSEMBLAGE OF WOOD RAT HOUSES. Jean M. Linsdale, Lloyd Tevis, Jr. Jour. Mam., 37 (3): 371-374, Sept.11, 1956.

THE ECOLOGICAL DISTRIBUTION OF THE PEROMYSCUS LEUCOPUS SPECIES GROUP IN EASTERN TEXAS. W. H. McCarley. Ecology, Durham, vol.35, no.3, pp.375-379, illus., July, 1954.

THE RANGE OF REITHRODONTOMYS ALBESCENS ALBESCENS. Frederic W. Miller. Jour. Mam., vol.9, no.4, p.338, Nov., 1928.

MUSKRAT HABITATIONS OF MARSH ISLAND, LOUISIANA. John D. Mizelle. American Midland Nat., vol.17, no.3, pp. 661-663, May, 1936.

(ON THE VARIATION OF THE DISTRIBUTION OF BURROWS OF THE LARGER SAND RAT IN SANDY RELIEF.) O zavisimosti razmeshcheniya nor bolshikh peschanok (Rhombomys opimus Licht.) of relefa peskov. N. P. Naumov, E. E. Siroechkovskii. Zool. Zhurnal, Moscow, 35 (11): 1713-1722, 1956.

HABITAT ADAPTABILITY OF PHENACOMYS IN WYOMING. N. C. Negus. Jour. Mam., vol.31, no.3, p.351, Aug.21, 1950.

RODENT HABITAT PREFERENCES ON FOOTHILL PASTURES IN CALIFORNIA. Jay C. Quast. Jour. Mam., 35 (4): 515-521, Nov., 1954.

THE PIGMY WOODRAT, NEOTOMA GOLDMANI, ITS DISTRIBUTION AND SYSTEMATIC POSITION. Dennis G. Rainey, Rollin H. Baker. Univ. Kansas Publ., Mus. Nat. Hist., Lawrence, vol.7, no.15, pp.619-624, June 10, 1955.

(GEOGRAPHICAL DISTRIBUTION OF FIELD MICE (ARVICOLA) IN EUROPE.) Distribution geographique des campagnols (Arvicola) en Europe. Edm. de Selys Longchamps. Revue Zool. Soc. Cuvierienne Paris, vol.10, pp.305-315, Oct., 1847.

THE MUSKRAT AS NATIVE AND ALIEN. Tracy I. Storer. Jour. Mam., 18 (4): 443-460, Nov., 1937.

THE MUSKRAT AS NATIVE AND ALIEN: A CHAPTER IN THE HISTORY OF ANIMAL ACCLIMATIZATION. Tracy I. Storer. Calif. Fish and Game, 24 (2): 159-175, Apr., 1938.

GENETIC AND DISTRIBUTIONAL STUDIES OF THREE SUB-SPECIES OF PEROMYSCUS. F. B. Sumner. Jour. Genetics, Cambridge, vol.23, no.2, pp.275-387, figs.27, pls.8-11, Nov., 1930.

GENETIC, DISTRIBUTIONAL, AND EVOLUTIONARY STUDIES OF THE SUBSPECIES OF DEER MICE (PEROMYSCUS). F. B. Sumner. Bibliographia Genetica, Tne Hague, vol.9, pp.1-106, figs.24, 1932.

THE ECOLOGICAL FACTORS RESPONSIBLE FOR THE GEOGRAPHICAL DISTRIBUTION AND EURYTOPY OF THE FIELD-MOUSE (APODEMUS AGARIUS). P. A. Sviridenko. Zool. Zh., 22: 280-298, 11 figs., 1943.

AN ECOLOGICAL STUDY OF A MUSKRAT HABITAT IN CENTRAL MAINE. Michael J. Takos. MS thesis, Univ. Maine, 1942.

PATTERN OF DISTRIBUTION OF THE WOOD-MOUSE IN A PART OF THE TEXAS PANHANDLE. W. A. Thornton, Hilmi S. Al-Uthman. Texas Jour. Sci., San Marcos, vol.4, no.1, pp.99-101, Mar.30, 1952.

(NEW DATA ON THE GEOGRAPHICAL DISTRIBUTION OF PROMETHEOMYS SCHAPOSCHNIKOVI SAT.) Neue Tatschen ueber die Geographische Verbreitung des Prometheomys schaposchnikovi Sat. S. Turov. Gorsky Paedagogischen Inst., vol.3, 1926.

BIOTIC RELATIONS OF THE WOOD RAT (NEOTOMA FUSCIPES) IN THE BERKELEY HILLS. Elden H. Vestal. Jour. Mam., 19 (1): 1-36, Feb., 1938.

(ON THE HABITAT OF A SPECIES OF THE GENUS PITYMYS MCMURTRIE IN SOUTHERN RUSSIA.) Sur l'habitat d'une espèce du genre Pitymys McMurtrie dans la Russie meridionale. B. S. Vinogradov. Bull. de la Station Régionale Protectrice des Plantes a Pétrograd, vol.3, pp.VII-X, 1922.

(THE PRESENT-DAY OCCURRENCE OF THE HAMSTER (CRICETUS CRICETUS L.) IN WUERTTEMBERG IN DEPENDENCE ON THE SOIL.) Das gegenwaertige Vorkomnen des Hamsters (Cricetus cricetus L.) in Wuerttemberg in seiner Abhangigkeit vom Boden. Richard Vogel. Jahreshefte Ver. f. vaterl. Naturk. in Wuerttemberg, pp.171-180, 1936.


Ecology


THE RELATIONSHIP OF MUSKRAT POPULATIONS TO VARIOUS MARSH AND AQUATIC PLANTS. Frank C. Bellrose. Jour. Wildl. Mgt., 14 (3): 299-315, July, 1950.

THE EFFECT OF FLUCTUATING WATER LEVELS ON THE MUSKRAT POPULATION OF THE ILLINOIS RIVER VALLEY. Frank C. Bellrose, Louis G. Brown. Jour. Wildl. Mgt., 5 (2): 206-212, Apr., 1941.

THE INFLUENCE OF FLOOD AND LOW WATER LEVELS ON THE SURVIVAL OF MUSKRATS. Frank C. Bellrose, Jessop B. Low. Jour. Mam., 24 (2): 173-188, May, 1943.

COMBAT BETWEEN HERON AND BLACK WATER-VOLE. John Berry. Scottish Nat., no.145, p.4, Jan.-Feb., 1924.

ACTIVITIES OF THE CHIHUAHUA DEER-MOUSE IN RELATION TO LIGHT INTENSITY. W. Frank Blair. Jour. Wildl. Mgt. Menasha, vol.7, no.1, pp.92-97, Jan., 1943.

POPULATION STRUCTURE, SOCIAL BEHAVIOR, AND ENVIRONMENTAL RELATIONS IN A NATURAL POPULATION OF THE BEACH MOUSE (PEROMYSCUS POLIONOTUS LEUCOCEPHALUS). W. Frank Blair. Contrib. Lab. Vert. Biol. Univ. Michigan, Ann Arbor, no.48, pp.47, illus., June, 1951.

POPULATIONS OF THE DEER-MOUSE AND ASSOCIATED SMALL MAMMALS IN THE MESQUITE ASSOCIATION OF SOUTHERN NEW MEXICO. W. Frank Blair. Contrib. Lab. Vert. Biol., no.21, Univ. Michigan, Ann Arbor, pp.1-40, figs.2, Mar.21, 1943.

CONTRIBUTIONS TO THE ECOLOGY AND BIOLOGY OF RODENTS OF THE TROITSK DISTRICT, FORM. URAL PROVINCE. 3. NOTES ON THE ANATOMY AND BIOLOGY OF CRICETULUS EVERSMANNI BR. E. S. Danini, N. A. Olschwang. Izvestiia biologicheskogo Nauchno-Issledovatel'skogo Instituta pri permskom gosudarstvennom Universitete, Perm (Bull. Inst. Rech. Biol. Perm), vol.10, no.3, pp.114-142, figs.9, tables 6, 1936. (In Russian, with English summary.)

SALINITY AS A FACTOR IN ATLANTIC COAST TIDEWATER MUSKRAT PRODUCTION. Herbert L. Dozier. Trans. N. A. Wildl. Conf., 12: 398-420, 1947.

RESPONSE OF MICROTUS TO VEGETATIVE COVER. W. Robert Eadie. Jour. Mam., vol.34, no.2, pp.263-264, 2 tables May 14, 1953.

(OBSERVATIONS OF A CAPTIVE PERSIAN GERBIL (MERIONES PERSICUS PERSICUS BLANFORD): A CONTRIBUTION TO THE COMPARATIVE ETHOLOGY OF THE RODENTS.) Gefangenschaftsbeobachtungen an den persischen Wuestenmaus (Meriones persicus persicus Blanford): Ein Beitrag zur vergleichenden Ethologie der Nager. I. Eibl-Eibesfeldt. Zeits. f. Tierpsychol., 8:400-23, 1951.

(ON THE ETHOLOGY OF THE HAMSTER (CRICETUS CRICETUS L.).) Zur ethologie des Hamsters (Cricetus cricetus L.). I. Eibl-Eibesfeldt. Zeitschr., Tierpsychol., 10 (2): 204-254, 1953. (With English summary.)

ECOLOGY OF THE MUSKRAT. Paul I. Errington. The Iowa Coop. Wildlife Research Unit, Quart. Rept., Ames, pp.10-16, Jan.-Mar., 1947; pp.25-35 (mimeog.), July-Sept., 1947; pp.52-94, Oct.-Dec., 1948; vol.15, no.4, pp.23-33, Apr.-June, 1950; vol.16, no.1, pp.17-30, July-Sept., 1950.

REACTIONS OF MUSKRAT POPULATIONS TO DROUGHT. Paul L. Errington. Ecology, 20 (2): 168-185, Apr., 1939.

(THE INFLUENCE OF THE WINTER OF 1939/40 ON THE FIELD MOUSE MICROTUS ARVALIS.) O vlivu zimy 1939/40 na hrabose polniho na Morave. O. Farsky, J. Mrkos. Ochrana Rostlin, vol.18, pp.42-49, 1942.

ECOLOGICAL OBSERVATIONS ON THE WOODRAT NEOTOMA FLORIDANA. Henry S. Fitch, Dennis G. Rainey. Univ. Kansas Publ. Mus. Nat. Hist., vol.8, no. 9, pp.499-533, June 12, 1956.

TIME MARCHES BACK.(COMBAT BETWEEN A DEER MOUSE AND A PRAYING MANTIS.) Mabel Gillespie. Nature Mag., Wash.,

D.C., vol.32, no.10, pp.561-563, Dec., 1939.

AN EFFECT ON THE PEROMYSCUS MANICULATUS RASSENKREIS OF LAND UTILIZATION IN MICHIGAN. Emmet T. Hooper. Jour. Mam., vol.23, no.2, pp. 193-196, fig.1, May 14, 1942.

THE WOOD RAT AS AN ECOLOGICAL FACTOR IN THE SOUTHERN CALIFORNIA WATERSHEDS. Jerome S. Horton, John T. Wright. Ecology, Lancaster, vol.25, no.3, pp.341-351, July, 1944.

THE TEMPERAMENTAL ECOLOGY OF DEER-MICE. G. Evelyn Hutchinson. Amer. Scientist, Burlington, vol.39, no. 4, pp.722-724, Oct., 1951.

POPULATIONS OF THE WOOD MOUSE (PEROMYSCUS LEUCOPUS) SUBJECTED TO THE APPLICATIONS OF DDT AND PARATHION. William B. Jackson. Ecological Monographs, vol.22, pp.259-281, Oct., 1952.

THE ECOLOGICAL LIFE HISTORY OF THE PACK RAT, NEOTOMA MICROPUS, IN THE BRUSHLANDS OF SOUTHWEST TEXAS. Clifford W. Johnson. MS thesis, Univ. Texas, 1952.

(ON THE INTERRELATIONSHIPS OF BIRDS OF PREY AND THE COMMON FIELD VOLE OF THE AZERBAIJAN STEPPE.) O vzaimootnoshenii khishchnikh pitits i obshchestvennoi polevki v stepnom Azerbaidzhane. N. P. Kadochnikov. Zool. Zhurnal, vol.32, no.6, pp.1222-1223, 1953.

ECOLOGY OF THE MUSKRAT OF SLAVE RIVER DELTA, N.W.T. Cecil Ernest Law. MA thesis, Univ. B.C., 1950.

(ON THE CHANGE IN NORTHERN GRANITE AREAS OF THE BLACKISH HAMSTER.) Ob izmenenii severnoi granitsi areala chernovatogo khomyaka (Mesocricetus raddei nigriculus Nehr., 1898. A. A. Lukyanchenko. Zool. Zhurnal, Moscow, vol.33, no.1, pp.218-220, Jan.-Feb., 1954.

ECOLOGY AND HELMINTHS OF THE OSAGE WOOD RAT, NEOTOMA FLORIDANA OSAGENSIS, INCLUDING THE DESCRIPTION OF LONGISTRIATA NEOTOMA N. SP. (TRICHOSTRONGYLIDAE). Melvin F. Murphy. Am. Midl. Nat., 48 (1): 204-218, illus., July, 1952.

(OUTLINES OF COMPARATIVE ECOLOGY OF MOUSE-LIKE RODENTS.) Ocherki sravnitel'noi ekologii myshevidnykh gryzunov. N. Naumov. Moskva, Akad. Nauk SSSR, 202 pp., 1948.

AN ECOLOGICAL STUDY OF THE ALLEGHENY CLIFF RAT (NEOTOMA PENNSYLVANICA STONE). C. L. Newcombe. Proc. West Virginia Acad. Sci., vol.3, pp.63-70, Aug., 1929 (West Virginia Univ. Bull., ser.30, no.1); Jour. Mam., Balto., vol.11, no.2, pp.204-211, pls.11-12, May 9, 1930.

ON THE ECOLOGY OF THE WOOD LEMMING (MYOPUS SCHISTICOLOR LILLJEB.) ON KOLA PENINSULA. G. A. Novikov. Zool. Zh., 20: 626-631, 1941.

(ECOLOGY OF THE SUBTERRANEAN FIELD VOLE (MICROTUS (PITYMYS) IN OAK-FOREST-STEPPE AREAS.) Ekologiya podzyemnoy polyevki (Microtus (Pitymys) subterraneus ukrainicus Vinogr.) v lyesostepnykh dubravakh. G. A. Novikov, O. V. Petrov. Zool. Zhurnal, Moscow, vol.32, no.1, pp.130-139, 1953.

SOME FACTS ABOUT COTTON RATS AND THEIR RELATION TO QUAIL. C. P. Patton. N. C. Wildl. Cons., 5 (11): 10-11, 15, Nov., 1941.

OBSERVATIONS CONCERNING THE LIFE HISTORY AND ECOLOGY OF THE WOOD-RAT, NEOTOMA FLORIDANA FLORIDANA (ORD). Paul G. Pearson. Jour. Mam., 33 (4): 459-463, graph., Nov., 1952.

COMMERCIAL PLANTING ON REDWOOD CUT-OVER LANDS. Hubert L. Person. USDA, Cir.434, 39 pp., July, 1937.

(PRELIMINARY NOTE ON THE ETHOLOGY AND ECOLOGY OF MERIONES LIBYCUS (RODENTS, GERBILS).) Note préliminaire sur l'éthologie et l'écologie de Meriones libycus (Rongeurs, Gerbillidés). Francis Petter. Mammalia, Paris, vol.17, no.4, pp.281-294, illus., Dec., 1953.

(PRELIMINARY NOTE ON THE ETHOLOGY AND ECOLOGY OF PSAMMOMYS OBESUS CRETZSCHMAR.) Note preliminaire sur l'ethologie et l'ecologie de Psammomys obesus Cretzschmar. F. Petter. Mammalia, Paris, vol.16, no.3, pp.137-147, illus., Sept., 1952.

EASTERN WOODRAT, NEOTOMA FLORIDANA: LIFE HISTORY AND ECOLOGY. Dennis G. Rainey. Univ. Kansas Publ., Mus. Nat. Hist., vol.8, no.10, pp.535-646, pls.12, Aug.15, 1956.

VOLES AS A FACTOR IN PLANT ECOLOGY. L. G. Romell. Svensk Bot. Tidskr., vol. 15, pp.43-45, 1921.

REACTIONS OF THE ROCKY MOUNTAIN MUSKRAT (ONDATRA ZIBETHICA OSOYOOSENSIS) TO DROUGHT CONDITIONS AT OGDEN BAY MIGRATORY WATERFOWL REFUGE, UTAH. Edward V. Saunders. MS thesis, Utah State Agr. Coll., 1951.

THE RELATIONSHIP OF NEST PROTECTION AND HUDDLING TO SURVIVAL OF PEROMYSCUS AT LOW TEMPERATURE. John A. Sealander, Jr. Ecology, Lancaster, vol.33, no.1, pp.63-71, illus., Jan., 1952.

FIELD STUDIES OF A PEROMYSCUS POPULATION IN AN AREA TREATED WITH DDT. Lucille F. Stickel. Jour. Wildl. Mgt., 10 (3): 216-218, July, 1946.

OBSERVATIONS ON THE EFFECT OF FLOOD ON ANIMALS. Lucille F. Stickel. Ecology, 29 (4): 505-507, Oct., 1948.

A SIGMODON AND BAIOMYS POPULATION IN UNGRAZED AND UNBURNED TEXAS PRAIRIE. Lucille F. Stickel, William H. Stickel. Jour. Mam., Balto., vol.30, no. 2, pp.141-150, illus., May 23, 1949.

WOOD MOUSE AND BOX TURTLE POPULATIONS IN AN AREA TREATED ANNUALLY WITH DDT FOR FIVE YEARS. Lucille F. Stickel. Jour. Wildl. Mgt., 15 (2): 161-164, Apr., 1951.

THE EFFECT OF VOLES (MICROTUS AGRESTIS) ON VEGETATION. V. S. Summerhayes. Jour. Ecol., 29 (1): 14-48, Feb., 1941.

CONTINUATION OF ECOLOGICAL AND GENETICAL STUDIES WITH PEROMYSCUS. F. B. Sumner. Carnegie Institution Wash., Yearbook no.27, 1927-1928, pp.335-339, Dec.13, 1928.

EFFECT OF A SLASH BURN ON FOREST MICE. Lloyd Tevis, Jr. Jour. Wildlife Management, 20 (4): 405-409, illus., Oct., 1956.

(ON THE ECOLOGY OF PROMETHEOMYS.) R. S. Uschatinskaja-Dekalenko. Priroda, Verlag Akad. Wiss. USSR., no.11, pp.71-72, 1933. (In Russian.)

LIFE HISTORY AND ECOLOGY OF THE WHITE-THROATED WOOD RAT, NEOTOMA ALBIGULA ALBIGULA HARTLEY, IN RELATION TO GRAZING IN ARIZONA. Charles T. Vorhies, Walter P. Taylor. Univ. Arizona, Coll. Agric., Agric., Exper. Station, Tech. bull.86, pp.453-529, figs.7, pls.8, June 1, 1940.

A CONTRIBUTION TO THE ECOLOGY OF THE MUSK-RAT (ONDATRA ZIBETHICA) IN THE BRITISH ISLES. Tom Warwick. Proc. Zool. Soc. London, ser.A, vol.110, pts.3-4, pp.165-201, figs.8, pl.1, Mar., 1941.

(NOTES ON THE CONNECTION BETWEEN THE EXPLOITATION OF MEADOWS AND FIELDMOUSE PLAGUES.) Over het verband tussen graslandexploitatie en veldmuisplagen. A. van Wijngaarden. Dreimaandelijks bericht betreffende Komgrondenbieden, vol.6, no.2, pp.112-120, 1956.

THE EFFECT OF D.D.T. AND OIL ON MUSKRATS. L. E. Wragg. Can. Field-Nat., 68 (1): 11-13, illus., Jan.-Mar., 1954.

HURRICANE FLOODS DAMAGE MUSKRAT POPULATION. Miss. Game and Fish, 11 (3): 13, Sept., 1947.

Economic Importance, Control, Management (Muskrats)

PENNSYLVANIA'S NUMBER ONE FUR BEARER--THE MUSKRAT. Jacob Bates Abbott. Pennsylvania Game News, Harrisburg, vol.20, no.10, pp.2-3, 27, illus., Jan., 1950.

A MUSKRAT TRAPPING ON SAND LAKE NATIONAL WILDLIFE REFUGE, SOUTH DAKOTA. Shaler E. Aldous. Jour. Wildl. Mgt., 11 (1): 77-90, Jan., 1947. Report of experiments to determine refuge trapping policy. Topics include relation of food types to muskrat numbers; factors in house freezing; sex ratios; size and growth; travels of marked animals; best times and ways to trap.

MARSH MANAGEMENT FOR FUR PRODUCTION. D. J. Allan. Trans. N. A. Wildl. Conf., 7: 263-269, 1942. Muskrats in the Canadian Northwest.

LEVEL DITCHING TO IMPROVE MUSKRAT MARSHES. Wallace L. Anderson. Jour. Wildl. Mgt., 12 (2): 172-176, Apr., 1948. Under certain Wisconsin conditions, level ditching greatly increased catch and profits.

HOW TO INCREASE MUSKRAT PRODUCTION. Atso Artimo. Suomen Riista, 7: 22-38, illus., 1952. Finnish, with English summary.

THE MUSKRAT IN WYOMING: PROPER MANAGEMENT OF A VALUABLE FUR RESOURCE DEMANDS LEGISLATIVE ACTION. Thomas A. Bell. Wyo. Wildl., 16 (12): 4-11, illus., Dec., 1952.

MUSKRATS IN RELATION TO FARM PONDS. Walter W. Beshears, Jr. Presented at 5th Ann. Meeting, S. E. Assn. Game and Fish Comm., pp.1-8, Oct., 1951.

MUSKRATS IN YOUR FARM POND. W. Walter Beshears, Jr. Ala. Cons., 25 (1): 4-5, 22, illus., July-Aug., 1953.

MUSKRATS IN RELATION TO FARM PONDS. W. Walter Beshears, Jr., Arnold O. Haugen. Jour. Wildl. Mgt., Ithaca, vol.17, no.4, pp.450-456, Oct., 1953.

(ON MUSKRAT FROM THE POINT OF VIEW OF GAME MANAGEMENT.) Om bisamrattan ur jaktvaerds-synpunkt. T. Brander. Suomen Riista, Helsinki, no.5, pp.84-142, illus., 1951. (Finnish, with English summary.)

THE ECONOMIC IMPORTANCE OF THE MUSKRAT IN VIRGINIA, WITH PARTICULAR EMPHASIS ON MONTGOMERY, A MOUNTAINOUS COUNTY. Mitchell A. Byrd. MS thesis, Va. Poly. Inst., 224 pp., illus., 1951.

MUSKRATS, DUCK PRODUCTION AND MARSH MANAGEMENT. B. W. Cartwright. Trans. 11th N. A. Wildl. Conf., Wash., pp. 454-457, 1946.

(THE BATTLE AGAINST THE MUSKRAT.) La lutte contre le Rat musqué (Fiber zibethicus). A. Chappellier. Institut des Recherches Agronomiques, Paris, pp.72, figs.25, pls.4, 1933.

THE MUSKRAT FUR INDUSTRY OF LOUISIANA. H. J. Chatterton. Jour. Geog., 43 (5): 185-195, May, 1944. Best use of coastal marshlands of Louisiana is for production of muskrats.

CONTROL OF MUSKRAT BURROW DAMAGE IN EARTHEN DIKES. Arthur H. Cook. New York Fish and Game Jour., 4 (2): 213-218, July, 1957.

FARM MARSH FOR MUSKRAT. Arthur H. Cook. N. Y. State Cons., 3 (3): 20, Dec.-Jan., 1948-1949.

THE RELATION OF MOSQUITO CONTROL TO THE MUSKRAT INDUSTRY ON THE SALT MARSHES. W. S. Corkran. Proc. Ann. Meeting N. J. Mosquito Extermin. Assn., 22: 137-141, 1935.

A COMPARISON OF SPRING AND AUTUMN MUSKRAT TRAPPING IN MAINE. Malcolm W. Coulter. Proc. 8th Ann. N. E. Wildl. Conf., Jackson's Mill, W. Va., pp.1-14, Apr.1-4, 1952.

MUSKRAT MEAT RECIPES. Herbert L. Dozier. Ohio Conserv. Bull., Columbus, vol.8, no.1, pp.4-5, Jan., 1944.

MUSKRAT PRODUCTION AND MANAGEMENT. Herbert L. Dozier. US F&WS, Cir.18, pp.1-42, illus., 1953.

RECIPES FOR COOKING MUSKRAT MEAT. Herbert L. Dozier. Maryland Conservationist, Balto., vol.20, no.1, pp.5, Winter, 1943.

WHAT HAS BECOME OF THE MUSKRAT? David Driscoll. Amer. Fur Breeder, vol. 4, no.8, p.29, Feb., 1932.

MUSKRAT ON THE MENU. Claire Dumond. Nature Mag., Washington, D.C., vol.37, no.2, pp.80-108, Feb., 1944.

DITCHING FOR MUSKRATS. Frank C. Edminster. League of Maryland Sportsmen, Rally Sheet, Balto., vol.3, no.2, p.5, Feb., 1945; Pa. Game News, 16 (1): 13, Apr., 1945.

MUSKRAT FARMING. James L. Edwards. Fur Farms Publishing Co., Utica, N. Y., 62 pp., illus., 1924.

ENVIRONMENTAL CONTROL FOR INCREASING MUSKRAT PRODUCTION. Paul L. Errington. Trans. N. A. Wildl. Conf., 13: 596-605, 1948.

FUR REFUGE EXPERIMENTS PAY OUT. Paul L. Errington. Iowa Cons., 4 (10): 175-176, Oct., 1945.

MUSKRATS IN THE CORN. Paul L. Errington. Farm Sci. Rep., 1 (4): 14-16, Oct., 1940.

NATURAL RESTOCKING OF MUSKRAT-VACANT HABITATS. Paul L. Errington. Jour. Wildl. Mgt., 4 (2): 173-185, Apr., 1940.

OBSERVATIONS ON MUSKRAT DAMAGE TO CORN AND OTHER CROPS IN CENTRAL IOWA. Paul L. Errington. Jour. Agric. Research, Wash., D.C., vol.57, no.6, pp. 415-421, Sept.15, 1939.

PIGMENTS AND PUBLIC; OR WHEN SHOULD THE MUSKRAT SEASON OPEN? Paul L. Errington. Iowa Conservationist, Des Moines, vol.2, no.12, pp.95-96, illus., Dec.15, 1943.

SPECIAL REPORT ON THE CASE HISTORY OF THE LITTLE WALL LAKE OBSERVATIONAL AREA. Paul L. Errington. Iowa Cooperative Wildl. Research Unit, Quart. Rept., pp.36-78 (mimeog.), July-Sept., 1947.

VERSATILITY IN FEEDING AND POPULATION MAINTENANCE OF THE MUSKRAT. Paul L. Errington. Jour. Wildl. Mgt., Menasha, vol.5, no.1, pp.68-89, Jan., 1941.

A SHIPMENT OF MUSKRATS TO KAMCHATKA. Walter J. Eyesdam. Jour. Mam., vol.13, no.3, pp.281-282, Aug., 1932.

MUSKRATS AND MUSKRAT FARMING. William H. Field. Wis. Cons. Bull., 13 (8): 9-13, Aug., 1948.

MONEY FROM MARSHES. C. W. Gee. Soil Cons., 11 (12): 270-271, 279, June-July, 1946.

MORE MUSKRATS ON THE FARM. Merrill C. Gilfillan. Ohio Cons. Bull., 10 (1): 12-13, 29, Jan., 1946.

OHIO MUSKRATS--VALUE, IMPORTANCE. Merrill C. Gilfillan. Ohio Conserv. Bull., Columbus, vol.7, no.8, pp.4-5, illus., Aug., 1943.

MUSKRAT FARMING. John Gillese. Hunter-Trader-Trapper, 78 (1): 49-50, Jan., 1939.

LOUISIANA MUSKRAT INDUSTRY AS A SOURCE OF HUMAN FOOD. James N. Gowanloch. Trans. N. A. Wildl. Conf., 8: 213-216, 1943.

THE 1949 AERIAL MUSKRAT SURVEY. Charles W. Hargrave. North Dakota Outdoors, Bismarck, vol.12, no.6, p.12, illus., Dec., 1949.

HOW MUSKRATS ARE BLENDED TO SIMULATE MINK. Bennett Harris. Amer. Fur Breeder, Duluth, vol.14, no.2, pp.20-21, Aug., 1941.

MUSKRAT CULTURE AND ITS ECONOMIC SIGNIFICANCE IN NEW JERSEY. Earl S. Harris. Proc. Ann. Meeting N. J. Mosquito Extermin. Assn., 24: 20-24, 1937.

THE MUSKRAT COMES BACK. Ernest C. Hartin. Alabama Conservation, Montgomery, vol.18, no.8, pp.9, 13, illus., Feb., 1947.

THE MUSKRAT IN THE PEN. Wilfred Head. Amer. Fur Breeder, vol.1, no.11, pp.14-15, May, 1929.

MANAGEMENT OF AN ARTIFICIAL MARSH IN SOUTHERN ONTARIO FOR DUCKS AND MUSKRATS. Oliver H. Hewitt. Trans. 7th N. Amer. Wildl. Conf., Wash., D.C., pp.277-283, 1942.

A MANAGEMENT PROGRAM FOR MINNESOTA MUSKRAT. Paul R. Highby. Proc. Minn. Acad. Sci., 9: 30-34, 1942.

MANAGING OUR MUSKRAT RESOURCE. Paul R. Highby. Cons. Volunteer, 2 (7): 17-20, Apr., 1941.

THE MUSKRAT MENACE. Martin A. C. Hinton. Nat. Hist. Mag., Lond., vol.3, no.22, pp.177-184, Apr., 1932.

TRAPPERS AND 'RATS. D. H. Jenkins. Michigan Conservation, Lansing, vol.22, no.1, pp.25-26, Jan., 1953.

(THE MUSKRAT. LEAFLETS FOR THE ADVANCEMENT OF CULTIVATION AND AGRICULTURAL PROTECTION.) Die Bisamratte. Flugblaetter zur Foerderung des Pflanzenbaues und Pflanzenschutzes, no.10, pp.1-8, 1 col. pl. Korff, A. Pustet. Landesanstalt f. Pflanzenbau und Pflanzenschutz, Muenchen, Mar., 1928.

MUSKRATS AND MUSKRAT FARMING. George S. La Bar. La Bar's Fur Farm, Austin, Minn., pp.21, illus., Feb., 1928.

THE MUSKRAT AS A FUR BEARER, WITH NOTES ON ITS USE AS FOOD. David E. Lantz. U. S. Dept. Agric., Farmers' Bull., no.869, pp.1-23, figs.1-13, Sept., 1917.

PRINCIPLES UNDERLYING AND METHODS FOR INTRODUCING THE MUSKRAT (FIBER ZIBETHICUS L.). N. P. Lavrov. Trans. Cent. Lab. Game Indus., no.5, pp.155-171, 1941.

SIGNIFICANCE OF BITTERNS (BOTAURUS STELLARIS, L.) IN MUSKRAT MANAGEMENT. N. P. Lavrov. Trans. Russian Game Reports, Canadian Wildl. Serv., 2: 74-79, 1957.

FURRY DIVIDENDS. Daniel W. Lay. Texas Game and Fish, 3 (10): 8-9, 20, Sept., 1945.

THE PROBLEM OF UNDERTRAPPING IN MUSKRAT MANAGEMENT. Daniel W. Lay. Trans. N. A. Wildl. Conf., 10: 75-78, 1945.

SURVEY INDICATES MUSKRAT CROP CAN BE INCREASED. Daniel W. Lay. Monthly Bull. Texas Game, Fish and Oyster Comm., 3 (1): 4-5, Dec., 1939.

THE MUSKRAT INDUSTRY OF MARYLAND. E. Lee Le'Compte. Int. Assoc. Game, Fish, and Cons. Comm., Nat. Conv., Denver, Colo., pp.24, figs.1-11, Aug.17-22, 1925.

THE VALUABLE MUSKRAT. Joseph Wharton Lippincott. Pennsylvania Game News, vol.9, no.9, pp.10-11, 26, Dec., 1938.

MUSKRAT HARVEST IN UTAH. Jessop B. Low. Utah Coop. Wildl. Res. Unit, 18 pp., 1949.

SPRING VERSUS FALL MUSKRAT SEASON. Jessop B. Low. Utah Fish and Game Bull., 10 (8): 3, 6, 8, Mar., 1954.

MANAGEMENT SIGNIFICANCE OF DAMAGE BY GEESE AND MUSKRATS TO GULF COAST MARSHES. John J. Lynch, Ted O'Neil, Daniel W. Lay. Jour. Wildl. Mgt., Menasha, vol.11, no.1, pp.50-76, pls.4-7, Jan., 1947.

RATTING IN THE DELTA. D. B. Marsh. Beaver, 278: 32-35, Mar., 1948.

EXPERIMENTAL LEVEL DITCHING FOR MUSKRAT MANAGEMENT. Harold A. Mathiak. Wis. Cons. Dept., Tech. Wildl. Bull. no.5, pp.1-35, illus., 1953.

WHY DECEMBER MUSKRAT TRAPPING? Lester J. McCann, Paul Highby. Conservation Volunteer, St. Paul, vol.3, no.17, pp. 11-14, Jan., 1942.

SOME ASPECTS OF MUSKRAT MANAGEMENT IN MANITOBA. J. A. McLeod. Conv. Internat. Assn. Game, Fish and Cons. Comm., 39: 64-71, 1949.

ROLE OF REFUGES IN MUSKRAT MANAGEMENT. Harold A. Mathiak, Arlyn F. Linde. Wis. Cons. Dept., Tech. Wildl. Bull. no.10, pp.1-16, map, 1954.

MUSKRATS IN GREAT BRITAIN. A NEW DANGER TO THE COUNTRY. A. D. Middleton. The Field, The Country Newspaper, London, vol.157, no.4105, p.319, illus., Aug.29, 1931.

MANITOBA'S MARSHES PRODUCE AGAIN. James Montagnes. Am. Forests, 51(4): 176-177, 191, Apr., 1945.

TRANSPLANTATION OF MUSKRATS INTO INLAND PONDS IN LOUISIANA. R. D. Moody. MS thesis, La. State, Univ., 1950.

NOTE ON MUSK-RATS AND OTHER ANIMALS KILLED SINCE THE INCEPTION OF THE CAMPAIGN AGAINST MUSK-RATS IN OCTOBER, 1932. T. Munro. Scottish Nat., no.211, pp.11-16, Jan.-Feb., 1935.

FUR--A WILD CROP OF GREAT VALUE. W. O. Nagel. Missouri Conservationist, Jefferson City, vol.6, no.12, pp.4-5, 10, illus., Dec., 1945. (Muskrat.)

CONTROLLING MUSKRAT DAMAGE IN PONDS. W. O. Nagel. Mo. Cons., 6 (4): 10-11, Apr., 1945.

(ATTEMPTS TO DESTROY MUSKRATS BY BACTERIOLOGICAL TECHNIQUES.) Essais de destruction des rats musques par des techniques bacteriologiques. P. Nelis, A. Lafontaine, S. Clemmpoel, W. E. van den Bruel, R. Moens. Parasitica, vol.8, no.2, pp.58-63, 1952.

LOCOMOTIVE SPRINGS IS SPORTSMEN'S PARADISE. RELATIONSHIP AND VALUE OF FURBEARERS (MUSKRAT). Marcu Nelson. Utah Fish and Game Bull., Salt Lake City, vol.2, no.5, pp.3-5, Apr., 1945.

MUSKRAT INDUSTRY IN SOUTHERN NEW JERSEY. John M. Pancoast. Trans. N. A. Wildl. Conf., 2: 527-530, 1937.

MUSKRATS IN THE DUCK MARSH. Miles D. Pirnie. Trans. N. A. Wildl. Conf., 6: 308-312, 1941.

HOW TO RECOGNIZE THE MUSKRAT. WHY IT IS A MENACE TO OUR COUNTRYSIDE. R. I. Pocock. Field, London, vol. 159, no.4141, p.688, figs.3, May 7, 1932.

WORSE THAN THE RABBIT PALGUE IN AUSTRALIA. THE MUSKRAT DANGER TO BRITAIN'S CANALS AND WATER SUPPLIES. R. I. Pocock. Field, London, vol.160, no.4171, p.846, illus., Dec.3, 1932.

(DEFENSE AND THE FIGHT AGAINST THE MUSKRAT.) Wering en bestrijding van de bisamrat. N. van Poeteren. Tijdschr. Plantenziekten, vol.36, no.10, pp.249-255, 1930.

THE PROVINCIAL MUSKRAT PROJECT AT THE PAS, MANITOBA, CANADA. Clifford C. Presnall. Pittman-Robertson Quart., 2 (2): 63-69, Apr., 1942.

(THE DANGER OF MUSKRATS FOR WATER-POWER PLANTS AND PROTECTIVE MEASURES.) Die Gefahr der Bisamratte fuer Wasserkraftanlagen und ihre Abwehr. A. Pustet. Die Wasserkraft, Zeitschr. fuer die gesamte Wasserwirtschaft und Wasser-Krafttechnik, 1925, Heft 8, pp.1-2, (of reprint), 1925.

(DEVELOPMENT AND RESULTS OF THE STRUGGLE AGAINST MUSKRATS IN BAVARIA IN THE YEARS 1926-27.) Ausbau und Ergebnisse der Bisamrattenbekaempfung in Bayern in den Jahren 1926 und

1927. A. Pustet. Arbeiten aus der Bayer, Landesanstalt fuer Pflanzenbau und Pflanzenschutz, Heft 6, pp.1-39, 1928.

(FIGHTING THE MUSKRAT.) Die Bekaempfung der Bisamratte. A. Pustet. Prakt. Blaetter Pflanzenbau und Pflanzensch., vol. 8, no.4, pp.80-98, July, 1930.

(FIGHTING THE MUSKRAT IN BAVARIA IN THE YEARS 1929-1931.) Die Bekaempfung der Bisamratte in Bayern in den Jahren 1929-1931. A. Pustet. Prakt. Blaetter. Pflanzenbau und Pflanzensch., Freising, n.s., Jahrg.10, nos.9-10, pp.222-242, map, 1933.

THE MUSKRAT/ A FARM CROP. Edwin Rawey, Jessop B. Low, David Sharp, Jr. Utah State Agr. Coll., Ext. Cir.168, pp.1-16, illus., 1952.

MENACE OF THE MUSKRAT. SERIOUS EXAMPLES FROM CANADA. R. S. Read. Field, London, vol.160, no.4173, p.931, Dec.17, 1932.

MICHIGAN'S "MILLION DOLLAR" MUSKRATS. H. D. Ruhl, Luther L. Baumgartner. Mich. Cons., 11 (8): 6-7, 11, Sept., 1942.

IS THE MUSK RAT STILL A MENACE? THE PRESENT POSITION REGARDING THIS ALIEN PEST. "Salopian." Field, London, vol.163, no.4237, p.485, illus., Mar.10, 1934.

THE ACCOMPLISHED MUSKRAT TRAPPER. A. E. Schmidt. Published by the Author, Chicago, 32 pp. (not numbered), 1922.

MUSKRAT MANAGEMENT AND WATER LEVEL CONTROL. Vic Schmidt. N. J. Outdoors, 3 (6): 18-21, illus., Dec., 1952.

MUSKRAT FARMS. Walter E. Scott. Wis. Cons. Bull., 12 (2): 16, Feb., 1947.

LAKE CHAMPLAIN FUR SURVEY. Roger Seamans. Vt. Fish and Game Serv., State Bull.3-4, 34 pp., 1941.

BONANZA FROM THE MARSHES. Joseph J. Shomon. Hunting and Fishing, 25 (3): 44-45, Mar., 1948.

A FAMILY TYPE LIVE TRAP, HANDLING CAGE, AND ASSOCIATED TECHNIQUES FOR MUSKRATS. I. Edwin Snead. Jour. Wildl. Mgt., Menasha, vol.14, no.1, pp. 67-79, Jan., 1950.

KING OF THE FUR BEARERS. Kathryn Sollars. Fauna, Phila., vol.9, no.1, pp.13-15, illus., Mar., 1947.

REPORT OF THE USE OF DDT AND PARIS GREEN ON MUSKRAT MARSHES. L. A. Stearns, Others. Proc. 34th Ann. Meeting New Jersey Extermination Assoc., New Brunswick, pp.82-95, illus., 1947.

MINNESOTA'S MUSKRAT RESOURCE. Sidel B. Swenson. Fins, Feathers, and Fur, nos.66-67, pp.259-264, Dec., 1928.

THE QUALIFICATIONS OF A GOOD MUSKRAT MARSH. Clyde B. Terrell. Amer. Fur Breeder, vol.1, no.1, pp.6-7, July, 1928.

THE MUSKRAT HARVEST ON HORICON MARSH. Wayne C. Truax. Wis. Cons. Bull.15 (7): 12-14, July, 1950.

MUSKRAT MANAGEMENT RESEARCH PROJECT. W. C. Truax. Wis. Wildl. Research Quart. Prog. Repts., Madison, vol.6, no.1, pp.41-54, Apr., 1947.

MUSKRAT MANAGEMENT RESEARCH. Wayne C. Truax. Wis. Cons. Bull.12 (10): 31-34, Oct., 1947.

INCREASE OF FOOD PRODUCTION AND IMPROVEMENT OF NESTING AND SHELTER CONDITIONS IN MUSKRAT HABITAT IN THE SELENGA DELTA (EAST BAIKAL DISTRICT). V. N. Vampiloff. Translations of Russian Game Reports, Canadian Wildl. Serv., 2: 5-23, 1957.

(THE FIGHT AGAINST THE MUSKRAT.) De bestrijding van de muskusrat, Ondatra zibethica L. in Nederland. A. van Wijngaarden. Vakblad voor Biologen, vol. 35, no.5, pp.68-74, May, 1955.

STUDY SHOWS IMPROVEMENT AT GRAY'S LAKE COULD TRIPLE PRESENT MUSKRAT POPULATION. Roger M. Williams. Idaho Wildl. Rev., 3 (2):12-14, Oct.-Nov., 1950.

MUSKRAT MANAGEMENT AND WATER LEVEL CONTROL. Kenneth A. Wilson. Wildl. in N. C., 14 (2): 8-10, 14-15, Feb., 1950.

MUSKRAT MANAGEMENT IN THE NORTHWEST RIVER MARSH. Kenneth A. Wilson. Wildl. in N.C., 13 (6): 14-16, June, 1949.

CAMPAIGN AGAINST MUSK-RATS IN ENGLAND. China Jour., vol.16, no.6, p.355, June, 1932.

EXPERIMENT AT STEEPROCK. Beaver, Winnipeg, outfit 270, no.1, pp.10-11, illus., June, 1939. (Restocking marsh with muskrats.)

LAWFUL TO ENGAGE IN MUSKRAT FARMING. North Dakota Outdoors, Bismarck, vol.2, no.1, p.11, July, 1939.

RAISING MUSKRATS. USDA, Biol. Survey, Wildl. Leaflet 35, 2 pp., Feb., 1936; Supersedes Biol. Survey, Wildl. Leaflet 35, Aug., 1941.

SMALL MARSH MANAGEMENT FOR FUR CROPS. N. Y. State Cons. Dept., Fish and Wildl. Inf. Bull.8, 11 pp., 1950.

Economic Importance, Control (Other Cricetids)

(THE RODENTS OF SAXONY, IMPORTANT AS REGARDS THE PROTECTION OF PLANTS, AND MEASURES IN COMBATTING THEM.) Die Pflanzenschutzlich wichtigen Nagetiere Sachsens und ihre Bekaempfung. (Arvicola arvalis Pall.). Baunacke. Die Kranke Pflanze, Dresden, Jahrg.5, heft3, pp.35-39, Mar., 1928.

COTTON-RAT CONTROL IN FLORIDA. Carlyle Carr. Univ. Fla., Agr. Ext. Cir. 41, 8 pp., Mar., 1936.

LIVE TRAPPING AND TRANSPORT OF VOLES IN GREAT BRITAIN. Dennis Chitty. Jour. Mam., 19 (1): 65-70, Feb, 1938.

THE PINE MOUSE IN YOUR ORCHARD. L. L. Davis. Proc. Tenn. State Hort. Soc., 38: 48-50, 1943.

WOOD RAT DAMAGE TO FRUIT TREES IN EASTERN OREGON. L. R. Dice. Jour. Mam., vol.6, no.4, p.282, Nov., 1925.

CONTRIBUTIONS TO THE KNOWLEDGE AND BIOLOGY OF THE HAMSTER (CRICETUS CRICETUS L.) AND THE METHODS OF ITS CONTROL. N. M. Dukelskaia, V. I. Stepanova. Bull. Plant Protection, Leningrad, The Lenin Acad. Agric. Sci. in U.S.S.R., vol.4, no.2, pp.55-63, fig.1, 1932. (Russian text with English summary.)

MACHINE-BAITING FOR CONTROL OF ORCHARD MICE. W. Robert Eadie. Farm Res., 16 (3): 9, July, 1950.

NEW TECHNIQUES IN CONTROL OF ORCHARD MICE. W. Robert Eadie. Cornell Univ. Agr. Exp. Sta., Bull.856, 16 pp., Aug., 1950.

EXPERIMENTAL USE OF BARIUM ARSENATE IN VOLE CONTROL. B. Yu Fal'kenshtein. Plant Protection, Leningrad, no.19, pp.29-36, 1939. (In Russian with English summary.)

FIELD MICE: FURROWERS AND BURROWERS. William D. Fitzwater. Pest Control, 20 (10): 30, 74, illus., Oct., 1952.

(ON THE DAMAGE DONE TO YOUNG FOREST PLANTINGS BY THE BLIND RATMOLE.) O povryezhdyenii slyepushonkoi molodix lyesnix nasazhdyenii. V. V. Gruzdyev. Zool. Zhurnal, Moscow, vol. 32, no.3, pp.376-379, 1953.

MOUSE POPULATIONS IN ORCHARDS AND A NEW METHOD OF CONTROL. Don W. Hayne. Quart. Bull. Michigan Agric. Exp. Stat., East Lansing, vol.33, no.2, pp.160-168, illus., Nov., 1950.

ZINC PHOSPHIDE: ITS TOXICITY TO PHEASANTS AND EFFECT OF WEATHERING UPON ITS TOXICITY TO MICE. Don W. Hayne. Michigan Agric. Exper. Station Quart. Bull., vol.33, no.4, pp.412-425, May, 1951.

RODENTICIDAL EFFECT ON PINE MICE OF ENDRIN USED AS A GROUND SPRAY. F. Horsfall, Jr. Science, Lancaster, vol.123, no.3185, p.61, Jan.13, 1956.

THE WOOD RAT AS AN ECOLOGICAL FACTOR IN SOUTHERN CALIFORNIA WATERSHEDS. J. S. Horton, J. T. Wright. Ecology, 25 (3): 341-351, July, 1944.

MICE AND CONIFERS. Robert Isaac. Am. Forests, 47 (1): 32-33, Jan., 1941.

(ON THE EXTERMINATION OF FIELD MICE.) Ueber die Vertilgung der Feldmaeuse. Andreas Johannes Jackel. Abdrunk Abhandl. Naturhist. Gesell. Nuernberg, no.2, pp.3-60, 1858.

THE COST AND EFFECTIVENESS OF CONTROLLING MICROTUS BY ZINC PHOSPHIDE. E. W. Jameson, Jr. Jour. Wildl. Mgt., 22 (1): 100-103, Jan., 1958.

STUDIES ON THE MECHANICAL CONTROL OF FIELD MICE. I. ON THE EFFECTS OF CONTROL OF FIELD MICE BY TRENCH. Eijiro Kinoshita, Yoshiharu Shibata. Rept. Govt. Forest Experiment Station Hokkaido Station Special Rept. no.2, Sapporo, Japan, pp.112-118, illus., Aug., 1954.

STUDIES ON THE MECHANICAL CONTROL OF FIELD MICE. II. ON THE EFFECTS OF CONTROL OF FIELD MICE BY TRENCH. Eijiro Kinoshita. Rept. Hokkaido Branch, Govt. Forest Exp. Sta., Spec. Rept. no.3, pp.65-70, Mar., 1955. (In Japanese with English summary.)

STUDIES ON THE MECHANICAL CONTROL OF FIELD MICE. IV. ON THE EFFECT OF CONTROL OF FIELD MICE BY TRENCH. Eijiro Kinoshita. Rept. Hokkaido Branch, Govt. Forest Exp. Sta., Spec. Rept. no.5, pp.50-62, Jan., 1956. (In Japanese with English summary.)

AN ECONOMIC STUDY OF FIELD MICE (GENUS MICROTUS). David E. Lantz. U. S. Dept. Agr. Biol. Sur. Bull. no.31, pp.1-64, fig.1, pls.8, Oct.28, 1907.

FIELD MICE AS FARM AND ORCHARD PESTS. David E. Lantz. U. S. Dept. Agric. Farmers' Bull. no.670, pp.1-10, figs.1-7, June 3, 1915.

FIELD MOUSE DAMAGE TO CONIFEROUS PLANTATIONS. E. W. Littlefield, W. J. Schoonmaker, David B. Cook. Jour. Forestry, 44 (10): 745-749, Oct., 1946.

(COMBATING FIELD MICE.) Die Bekaempfung der Feldmaeuse. Arthur Mahner. Nachrichten Schaedlingsbekaempfung. vol. 5, no.3, pp.152-153, fig.1, 1930.

(THE COMMON FIELD VOLE (MICROTUS SOCIALIS PALL.) IN TREE NURSERIES.) Polevka obshchestvennaya (Microtus socialis Pall.) v drevesnikh pitomnikakh. I. E. Morgilevskaya. Soobshcheniya Akad. Nauk Gruzinskoi SSR, vol.14, no.6, pp.351-355, 1953.

THE MEADOW MOUSE (MICROTUS CALIFORNICUS) PROBLEM IN SACRAMENTO COUNTY. A. E. Morrison. Calif. Dept. Agr., Bull.42 (2): 59-62, Apr.-June, 1953.

THE EFFICACY OF RODENT REPELLENTS ON THE MEADOW MOUSE, MICROTUS PENNSYLVANICUS. Tom Osmer. MS Thesis, Univ. Minn., 1938.

CONTROL OF MICE IN WATERMELON FIELDS. G. K. Parris. Fla. Agr. Exp. Sta., Cir. S-17, 4 pp., July, 1950.

(THE FIELD MOUSE (MICROTUS ARVALIS PALLAS) AND ITS DESTRUCTION.) Le campagnol des champs (Microtus arvalis Pallas) et sa destruction. R. Regnier, R. Pussard. Annales des Epiphyties, vol.12, nos.5-6, pp.385-522, pls.1-8, Nov.-Dec., 1926.

A BOX TRAP FOR COTTON RATS. J. Allen Scott. Science, Lancaster, n.s., vol.102, no.2657, p.567, Nov.30, 1945.

(ON THE BIOLOGY OF ALACTAGA JACULUS PALL. AS A PEST IN THE PLANTATIONS OF SCORZONERA TAUSAGHYZ LIPSH. ET BOSSE IN THE UKRAINE.) A. K. Schepe. Akad. Sci.

d'Ukraine, vol.4 (Trav. Mus. Zool. Kyiv, no.13), pp.166-167, 1934. (In Russian, with German summary.)

MOUSE CONTROL IN FIELD AND ORCHARD. James Silver. U. S. Dept. Agric., Farmers' Bull.1397, pp.14, figs. 13, Mar., 1924.

ORCHARD MOUSE CONTROL. James Silver. Mountaineer Grower, 7 (78): 3-6, Oct., 1936.

COMMERCIAL FERTILIZER FROM WOOD RAT NESTS. Clark P. Streator. Jour. Mam., vol.11, no.3, p.318, Aug., 1930.

(STRONG OCCURRENCE OF ARVICOLAS AND THE STRUGGLE AGAINST THEM.) Starkes Auftreten der Wudhlmaus und deren Bekaempfung. (Inspector) Westermeier. Pflanzenkrank. (Pflanzenpath.) u. Pflanzenschutz, Stuttgart, vol.44, no.11, pp.556-558, Nov., 1934.

INSECTICIDES OR BIOLOGICAL MEASURES IN THE CONTROL OF THE CONTINENTAL VOLE, MICROTUS ARVALIS (PALLAS), IN ORCHARDS. A. van Wijngaarden. Mededelingen Directeur van de Tuinbouw, 20: 369-374, 1957. (In Dutch, with English summary.)

CONTROL OF FIELD MICE IN APPLE ORCHARDS. A. M. Woodside, R. N. Jefferson, R. C. Moore, E. H. Glass. Va. Agr. Exp. Sta., Bull.344, 16 pp., 1942.

Embryology

DEVELOPMENT OF THE GOLDEN HAMSTER, CRICETUS AURATUS, WITH SPECIAL REFERENCE TO THE MAJOR CIRCULATORY CHANNELS. Charles C. Boyer. Jour. Morphol., Phila., vol.83, no.1, pp.1-38, July, 1948.

RESORPTION OF EMBRYOS IN THE MUSKRAT. Herbert L. Dozier. Jour. Mam., vol.28, no.4, p.398, pl.1, Nov.26, 1947.

A STUDY OF HORMONAL FACTORS IN THE EARLY SEX DEVELOPMENT OF THE GOLDEN HAMSTER. Faith Wilson LaVelle. Carnegie Inst. Wash., Publ.592, Contrib. to Embryology, vol.34, pp.19-53, Sept.5, 1951.

MONOZYGOTIC TWINING IN PEROMYSCUS MANICULATUS. T. T. Liu. Jour. Mam., vol.35, no.3, pp.449-450, Aug.20, 1956.

TRANSMIGRATION OF FERTILIZED EGGS IN PEROMYSCUS. T. T. Liu. Jour. Mam., vol.34, no.4, pp.507-508, Nov.13, 1953.

(THE RANGE OF IMPLANTATION IN THE HAMSTER UTERUS.) Die Implantationsvorbereitungen im Hamster-Uterus. Fritz Strauss. Verhandl. Anatomischen Gesellschaft 53, Versammlung, Stockholm, 1956, pp.92-98, 1957.

THE TIME AND PLACE OF FERTILIZATION OF THE GOLDEN HAMSTER EGG. Fritz Strauss. Jour. Embryol. and Exper. Morphol., Oxford, 4 (1): 42-56, illus., Mar., 1956.

PRE-IMPLANTATION STAGES IN THE GOLDEN HAMSTER (CRICETUS AURATUS). John H. Venable. Anat. Record, Phila., vol.94, no.1, pp.105-119, pls.2, Jan., 1946.

Europe

(NEW MICROTINAE OF CENTRAL SPAIN.) Un nuevo Microtinae del centro de España. E. Morales Agacino. Bol. Soc. Española, Hist. Nat., Madrid, vol.36, no.3, pp.151-154, figs.2.

(NEW FORM OF PITMYS IN CENTRAL SPAIN.) Une forme nouvelle de pitmys de l'Espagne Centrale. E. Morales Agacino. Mammalia, Paris, vol.2, no.1, pp.40-42, Mar., 1938.

MUSKRATS IN CENTRAL EUROPE. Theodor G. Ahrens. Jour. Mam., vol.2, no.4, pp.236-237, Nov., 1921.

CORRECT NAMING OF THE TRANSCAUCASIAN SPECIES OF SUBGENUS SUMERIOMYS A. ARG. (MICROTUS, GLIRES, MAMMALIA). A. I. Argyropulo. Zeits. des Aserbeidschaner Inst. f. Microbiol., vol.5, no.1, pp.229-230, 1935. (In Russian with German summary.)

DISTRIBUTION OF ARVICOLA TERRESTRIS L. IN CAUCASUS. A. I. Argyropulo. Trudy Tropicheskogo Instituta Narkomzdrava ASSR, Baku, vol.2, pp.287-289, map, 1935. (In Russian with German summary.)

(FINLAND A PROFITABLE MUSKRAT LAND.) Suomi tuottavana piisamimaana. A. Artimo. Suomen Riista, Helsinki, no.4, pp.7-61, illus., 1949. (Finnish, with English summary.)

DESCRIPTION OF A NEW SPECIES OF MICROTUS FROM THE IGMAN MOUNTAINS, NEAR SARAJEVO. (MICROTUS IGMANENSIS.) St. J. Bolkay. Novitates Musei Sarajevoensis, no.8, pp.1-3, Nov. 24, 1929.

(MUSKRATS IN EUROPE.) Bisamratten i Europa. Hj Broch. Naturen, Bergen, vol. 53, pp.1-8, Jan., 1929. (Account, with map of the spread of the muskrat in Europe from 1906 to 1921.)

(SOME MICROTINAE OF CATALONIA.) Sobre algunos Microtinae de Cataluna. Angel Cabrera. Trab. Mus. Cien. Nat. Barcelona, vol.7, no.3, pp.3-20, July, 1924.

(DISTRIBUTION AND OCCURRENCE OF CRICETUS CRICETUS NEHRINGI MTSCH. IN RUMANIA.) Ueber Verbreitung und Einfalle von Cricetus cricetus nehringi MTSCH. in Rumaenien. R. J. Calinescu. Zeitschrift f, Saugetierkunde, vol.6, no.6, pp.230-233, Dec.15, 1931.

(MICROTUS NIVALIS (MARTINS) OF CANTAL.) Le Microtus nivalis (Martins) du Cantal. P. Cantuel. Mammalia, Paris, 8 (2): 69-71, illus., June, 1944.

(THE MUSKRAT IN FRANCE.) Le rat musque en France, November, 1933. A. Chappellier. Bull. Soc. Nat. Acclimat. France, vol.81, no.4, pp.172-197, 2 maps, Apr., 1934.

THE HAMSTER (CRICETUS FRUMENTARIUS) IN MECKLENBURG-SCHWERIN. G. Clodius. Archiv. Ver. Freunde Naturgesch. Mecklenburg, Rostock, n.F., vol.5, pp. 56-58, (1930), 1931. (In German.)

(CONTRIBUTION TO KNOWLEDGE OF GENUS MICROTUS SCHRANK REPRESENTATIVES FROM POLESIE AND WILNO AREAS.) Przyczynek do znajomosci przedstawicieli rodzaju Microtus Schrank z Polesia i Wilenszczyzny. August Dehnel. Fragmenta faunistica Musei zoologici Polonici, Warsaw, vol.5, no.1, 24 pp., 1946.

(THE FIELD MICE.) Les campagnols. Robert Didier. Paris, Lechevalier, 46 pp., 1941.

(THE SMALL MAMMALS OF THE FRENCH FAUNA FIELD MICE.) Les micromammiferes de la Faune francaise. I. Campagnols. Robert Didier, Paul Rode. Mammalia, vol.3, no.1, pp.19-37, figs.11, pl.2, Mar., 1939; no.2, pp.59-75, figs. 10, pl.5, June, 1939; nos.3-4, pp.111-121, illus., Sept.-Dec., 1939.

(THE SMALL MAMMALS OF THE FRENCH FAUNA. I. FIELD MICE.) A correction. Les Micromammiferes de la faune francaise. I. Campagnols (Mammalia, vol.3, no.3-4, Sept.-Dec., 1939). Robert Didier, Paul Rode. Mammalia, Paris, vol.4, no.1, p. 34, Mar., 1940.

THE HUNGARIAN SPECIES OF THE GENUS PITYMYS. Julius Ehik. Ann. Musei Nat. Hungarici, vol.24, pp.54-80, pl.1, Nov.23, 1926. (In Hungarian and English.)

(A NEW ALP VOLE, MICROTUS (CHIONOMYS) RADNENSIS FROM SIEBENBUERGEN.) Eine neue Alpenwuehlmaus, Microtus (Chionomys) radnensis aus Siebenbuergen. Julius Ehik. Uj havasipocok, microtus (Chinomys) radnensis, Erdelyboel. pp.25-30. Ann. Hist.-Nat. Mus. Nat. Hungarici, Budapest, vol.35, pars Zool., pp.18-30, fig.1, pl.1, 1942.

A NEW PITYMYS FROM SLAVONIA. Julius Ehik. Allattani Koezlemenyek, vol. 32, nos.1-2, p.60, 1935.

THE OCCURRENCE OF THE ROOT-VOLE (MICROTUS OECONOMUS PALL.) AT THE KISBALATON. Julius Ehik. Ann. Hist. Nat. Mus. Nat. Hungarici, Budapest, ser. nov., vol.3, pp.251-256, pl.13, 1953.

PRELIMINARY DESCRIPTION OF A NEW MICROTUS AGRESTIS FROM HUNGARY. Julius Ehik. Ann. Mus. Nation, Hungarici, vol.21, pp.75-78, 1924.

(SUPPLEMENTARY DATA ON THE NORTHERN ARVICOLA MICROTUS RATTICEPS MEHELYI EHIK 1928 IN HUNGARY.) Ergaenzende Angaben zur Kenntnis der Nordischen Wuehlmaus, Microtus ratticeps mehelyi Ehik, 1928, in Ungarn. Julius Ehik. Saeugetierk. Mitteil., Stuttgart, vol.1, no.1, pp.28-29, Jan.10, 1953.

(TWO NEW FIELD MICE FROM HUNGARY.) Zwei neue erdmaeuse aus Ungarn. Julius Ehik. Ann. Hist. Nat. Mus. Nat. Hungarici, Budapest, vol.27, pp.252-258, 1930.

SHORT-TAILED VOLE ON HILBRE ISLAND, CHESHIRE. N. F. Ellison. Northwest Nat., Abroath, vol.20, pp.63-64, 1945.

(THE FIELD MICE OF THE LEMAN BASIN.) Les campagnols du bassin du Leman. Victor Fatio. Bale et Geneve, Georg; p.78, 6 pls., 1867.

NOTES ON THE FOREST VOLES OF THE NORTHERN PART, GORKY (NIJNI-NOVGOROD) DISTRICT. A. N. Formosov. Moscou Univ. Sbornik Nauchno issledovatel'skogo inst. Zool. (Abstracts Works Zool. Inst. Moscou State Univ.), no.3, pp. 116-117, 1936. (In Russian.)

(REMARK ON THE BELGIAN HAMSTER.) Remarque au sujet du hamster belge. Serge Frechkop. Ann. Soc. Roy. Zool. Belgique, vol.66, pp.123-126, 1935.

(DESCRIPTION OF A NEW SPECIES OF FIELD MOUSE OF FRANCE.) Description d'une espece nouvelle de campagnol de France. (Arvicola (Microtus) gerbei.) Z. Gerbe, A. de L'Isle. Bull. Soc. Zool. France, Paris, Annee 1880, vol.5, pp.49-60, pl.4, 1880.

DISTRIBUTION OF BLACK HAMSTER IN THE UKRAINIAN S.S.R. S. Gershenson. Compt. Rend. (Doklady), Acad. Sci., USSR, vol.47, pp.598-601, 1945.

(PRESENT EXTENSION OF THE MUSKRAT IN FRANCE.) Extension actuelle du Rat musque en France. J. Giban, J. Aubry. Mammalia, Paris, vol.20, no.1, pp.34-35, Mar., 1956.

DISTRIBUTION OF THE LONG-TAILED FIELD MOUSE, APODEMUS SYLVATICUS, ON SOUTH HAVEN PENINSULA, DORSET, IN 1937, WITH SOME OBSERVATIONS ON ITS WANDERING AND HOMING POWERS. H. P. Hacker, H. S. Pearson. Linnean Soc. 42 (283): 1-17, illus., May, 1951.

(THE ARVICOLAS OF THE MOSBACH SANDS.) Die Wuehlmaeuse der Mosbacher Sande. Florian Heller. Notizbl. Ver. Erdk. u. hess. geol. Landesanst. f. 1931-1932, Darmstadt, ser.5, vol.14, pp.108-116, pl.10, 1933.

A NEW BANK-VOLE FROM ESTHONIA. Martin A. C. Hinton. Ann. and Mag. Nat. Hist., ser.9, vol.8, pp.128-129, July, 1921.

(THE FIELD MOUSE OF LAVERNEDE IN CAMARGUE.) Le campagnol de Lavernede en Camargue. A. Hugues. Bull. Soc. Nat. d'Acclimat., pp.175-176, May-June, 1938.

(SUBTERRANEAN FIELD MOUSE PITYMYS SUBTERRANEUS SELYS IN NORMANDY.) Le campagnol souterrain Pitymys subterraneus Selys, en Normandie. A. Hugues. Rev. Franc. Mamm., vol.1, no.1, pp.40-41, Dec.7, 1927.

(NOTES ON THE OCCURRENCE OF THE HAMSTER CRICETUS CRICETUS L. IN HOLLAND.) Over het voorkomen van de hamster, Cricetus cricetus (L.), in Nederland. A. M. Husson. Publ, Natuurhist. Genootschap Limburg, vol.2, pp.12-54, 1949.

(OBSERVATIONS ON THE MOUSE FAUNA OF ST. PETERSBERG AND VICINITY.) Enige opmerkingen over de muizen-fauna van de sint pietersberg en omgeving. A. N. Husson. Overdruk uit het natuurhistorisch maandblad, Jrg.39, no.4, pp.43-46, Apr. 28, 1950.

THE MICROTUS OECONOMUS INHABITING THE NEIGHBOURHOOD OF LAKE NERO IN YAROSLAV REGION. E. V. Karaseva, E. V. Narskaya, A. D. Bernstein. Bull. Moskovskogo Obshchestva Ispytatelei Prirody, Biol., 62 (3): 5-18, May-June, 1957. (In Russian with English summary.)

(DISTRIBUTION AND BATTLE AGAINST THE MUSKRAT (ONDATRA ZIBETHICA L.) IN GERMANY 1946-1949.) Verbreitung und Bekampfung der Bismaratte (Ondatra zibethica L.) in Deutschland in den Jahren 1946-1949. M. Klemm. Deut. Pflanz. Nachr., 3 (11-12): 201-205, 1949.

(THOUGHTS ON THE PRE-GLACIAL ARVICOLAS OF HUNGARY.) Gedanken ueber die vorglazialen Wuehlmaeuse Ungarns. Th. Kormos. Folia Zool. et Hydrobiol., Riga, vol.8, no.1, pp.1-10, Aug.30, 1935.

MICROTUS NIVALIS (MARTENS, 1842) (RODENTIA) IN THE CARPATHIANS. Kazimierz Kowalski. Acta Theriologica, Inst. Zool. Polska Akad. Nauk, Warsaw, 1 (6): 159-182, Mar.9, 1957. (In English, with Polish and Russian summaries.)

(VOLES OF THE GENUS PITYMYS IN CSR.) Hrabosi rodu Pitymys Mc. Murtrie v Ceskoslovensku. Rozbor vnejsich telesnych znaku, bionomie mnozeni a chlorologie. J. Kratochvil. Prace Moravskoslezske Akad. Prirodnich (Acta Acad. Sci. Nat. Moravo-Silesiacae), Brno, vol.24, fasc.8, pp.155-194, 1952. (With English and Russian summaries.)

(REMARKS ON THE PENETRATION OF MICROTUS ARVALIS AS FAR AS THE TATRA NATIONAL PARK.) Poznámky o pronikaní hrabosè polniho do tatranskèho národního parku. J. Kratochvíl, J. Pelikán. Zool. a Entom. Listy, Praha, vol.4, no.4, pp.303-312, illus., 1955.

(THE SIBERIAN VOLE MICROTUS OECONOMUS, AN ICE AGE RELICT IN CZECHOSLOVAKIA.) Die sibirische Wuehlmaus Microtus oeconomus, ein Eiszeitrelikt in der CSR. J. Kratochvil, B. Rosicky. Prace Brnenske Zakladny Ceskoslovenske Akad. Ved, vol.27, no.1, pp.33-72, 1955. (In Czech with German summary.)

NOTES ON EUROPEAN SPECIES OF THE SUBGENUS PITYMYS (GENUS MICROTUS). C. I. Forsyth Major. Ann. and Mag. Nat. Hist., ser.7, vol.15, pp.508-516, May, 1905.

NOTE ON A NEW SNOW-VOLE FROM MONTENEGRO (MICROTUS (CHIONOMYS) BOGDANOVI, SP. N.). V. Martino, E. Martino. Ann. and Mag. Nat. Hist., ser. 9, vol.9, p.413, Apr., 1922.

EIGHTEEN NEW EUROPEAN VOLES. Gerrit S. Miller, Jr. Ann. and Mag. Nat. Hist., ser.8, vol.1, pp.194-206, Feb., 1908.

THE MUSKRAT, ONDATRA ZIBETHICA (LINNAEUS), IN EUROPE. Erna Mohr. Jour. Mam., vol.14, no.1, pp.58-63, Feb., 1933.

(THE SHORT-TAILED FIELD MOUSE (PITYMYS SAVII DE SELYS-LONGCHAMPS) IN HOLSTEIN.) Die kurzschwaenzige Erdmaus (Pitymys savii de Selys-Longchamps) in Holstein. Erna Mohr. Zool. Anzeiger, Leipzig, vol.74, nos.5-6, pp. 141-144, fig.1, Nov.5, 1927.

(NEW MICROTINAE OF CENTRAL SPAIN.) Un nuevo Microtinae del centro de Espana. (Microtus (Chionomys) nivalis abulensis.) E. Agacino Morales. Bol. Soc. Espanola, vol.36, no.3, pp.151-154, figs.2, 1936.

MUSQUASH IN SCOTLAND. T. M. Munro. Scottish Naturalist, vol.189, pp.65-70, May-June, 1931.

NOTES ON THE BIOLOGY OF THE SNOW MICE (CHIONOMYS NIVALIS NENJUKOVI FORMOS.) IN THE WESTERN CAUCASUS. A. A. Nasimovich. Bull. Soc. Nat. Moscou sec Biol., n.s., vol.44, nos.7-8, pp.386-390, 1935. (In Russian, with English summary.)

(MESOCRICETUS NEWTONI NHRG. FROM DOBRUJA.) Mesocricetus newtoni Nhrg. aus der Dobrudscha. Alfred Nehring. Sitz.-Ber. Gesell. Naturf. Freunde Berlin, Jahrg.1901, no.4, pp.129-133, figs.2, Apr. 16, 1901.

(MICROTUS RATTICEPS VAR. STIMMINGI NHRG. FROM THE SOLDIN KREISE, GOVERNMENT DISTRICT FRANKFURT-ON-THE-ODER.) Microtus ratticeps var. Stimmingi Nhrg. aus dem Kreise Soldin, Reg.-Bez. Frankfurt a. O. A. Nehring. Zool. Anzeiger, Leipzig, vol.22, no.595, pp.358-359, Aug.28, 1899.

ON CRICETUS NIGRICANS AS A EUROPEAN SPECIES. Alfred Newton. Proc. Zool. Soc. London, pp.331-332, pl.26, 1870.

(NEW SUBSPECIES OF THE FIELD MOUSE OF THE CAUCASUS.) Neue Unterart der Feldmaus aus dem Kaukasus. (Microtus arvalis gudauricus.) S. I. Ognev. Ber. Mikrobiol. Staats-Instituts, Rostow-am-Don, no.9, pp.163-164, 1929.

PROMETHEOMYS, A REMARKABLE RODENT FROM THE CAUCASUS. S. I. Ognev. Jour. Mam., Balto., vol.7, no.3, pp.215-220, pl.19, Aug.9, 1926.

A NEW FORM OF WATER-VOLE FROM DAGHESTAN (EAST CAUCASUS). (NEW SUBSPECIES: ARVICOLA AMPHIBIUS DJUKOVI.) S. I. Ognev, A. N. Formosov. Ann. and Mag. Nat. Hist., ser.9, vol.19, pp.138-141, Jan., 1927.

A NEW SUBSPECIES OF HAMSTER FROM DAGHESTAN (MESOCRICETUS RADDEI, NEHR.), AND SOME REMARKS ON THE RUSSIAN SPECIES OF MESOCRICETUS (WITH A KEY TO THEM). (M. R. AVARICUS) S. I. Ognev, W. G. Heptner. Ann. and Mag. Nat. Hist., ser.9, vol.19, pp.141-150, 1 table, Jan., 1927.

(THE MUSKRAT IN THE NETHERLANDS.) De muskusrat in Nederland. J. v.d. Peppel. Levende Natuur, vol.52, no.7, pp.129-133, illus., 1949.

NEW VOLE FROM SOUTH SERBIA. (SUMERIOMYS GUENTHERI MARTINOI.) B. Petrov. Prirodoslovne Razprave, Ljubljana, vol.3, no.16, pp.363-365, illus., table, Aug.13, 1939.

(THE MUSKRAT APPROACHES OUR BORDER.) De bisamrat nadert onze grens. N. van Poeteren. Tijdschr. Plantenziekten, vol.40, no.5, pp.130-135, map, 1 fig., 1934.

(THE SNOW MOUSE (CHIONOMYS) FOUND TO LIVE IN THE CARPATHIANS.) Die Schneemaus (Chionomys) in den Karpathen nachgewiesen. Hermann Pohle. Zeitschr. f. Saeugetierkunde, Berlin, vol.7, nos.1-6, p.259, Dec.15, 1932.

THE MUSK-RAT IN BRITAIN. James Ritchie. Nature, London, vol.131, no.3307, pp.385-387, figs.3, Mar.18, 1933.

ORKNEY GRASS MOUSE IN NEOLITHIC BURIAL. (MICROTUS ORCADENSIS.) James Ritchie. Scottish Nat., no.207, p. 70, May-June, 1934.

(THE HAMSTER OF ROTEN-BERG BEI SAALFELD.) Die Hamster vom Roten-Berg Bei Saalfeld. S. Schaub. Eclogae geologicae Helvetiae, Basel, vol.28, no.2, pp.580-590, figs.15, 1935.

(FURTHER CONTRIBUTIONS TO THE DISTRIBUTION OF THE SHORT-EARED EARTH MOUSE (MICROTUS SUBTERRANEUS, SELYS) IN SAXONY AND HESSE.) Weitere Beitraege zur Verbreitung der Kurzohrigen Erdmaus (Microtus subterraneous, Selys) in Sachsen und Hessen. W. Schreitmueller. Archiv. f. Nat., Abt. A, vol.89, Heft 8, pp.119-122, 1923.

(REFLECTIONS ON THE MUSKRAT (FIBER ZIBETHICUS CUV.).) Betrachtungen ueber die "Ondatra" oder Bisamratte (Fiber zibethicus Cuv.). W. Schreitmueller. Archiv. f. Nat., Abt. A, vol.89, Heft 7, pp.170-172, 1923.

MICROTINAE (ROD.) IN THE NETHERLANDS, EXTINCT AND RECENT. A. Schreuder. Verhandel. Kon. Akad. Wetensch. Amsterdam, Afd. Natuurk. (sect.2), vol.30, no.1, pp.37, figs.17, pl. 1933.

(NEW FIELD MOUSE APPEARANCE IN THE FAUNA OF THE U.S.S.R., MICROTUS MONTEBELLI.) Novii vid polevki v faune SSSR. V. E. Sokolov. Zool. Zhurnal, vol. 33, no.4, pp.947-950, July-Aug., 1954.

A NEW VOLE FROM SPAIN. Oldfield Thomas. Ann. and Mag. Nat. Hist. (7), vol.17, no.102, pp.576-577, June, 1906.

A SPECIAL PROODONT RACE OF WATER-VOLE, OCCURRING IN NORTHUMBRIA. Oldfield Thomas. Ann. and Mag. Nat. Hist., ser.10, vol.1, pp.316-318, Feb., 1928.

(THE MUSKRAT (FIBER ZIBETHICUS L.), WITH SPECIAL CONSIDERATION OF ITS OCCURRENCE IN AUSTRIA.) Die Bisamratte (Fiber zibethicus L.) mit besonderer Beruecksichtigung ihres Auftretens in Oesterreich. Karl Toldt, Jr. Verlag Heber: Leipzig, pp.98, maps 3, figs.14, 1929.

(CAPTURE OF A MUSKRAT, FIBER ZIBETHICUS, AT HONFLEUR (CALVADOS).) Capture d'un rat musqué, Fiber zibethicus L., à Honfleur (Calvados). L. Tolmer. Bull. Soc. Linn. Normandie, ser.8, vol.7, pp.71-73, (1934), 1935.

(THE SMALL MAMMALS OF FRANCE II. THE FIELD MICE. ARVICOLA.) Les petits mammiferes de la France. II. Les campagnols. Arvicola. E. L. Trouessart. Feuille des Jeunes Naturalistes, Paris, 1881. pp.77-91, 1881.

(THE MUSKRAT: LIVING HABITS, COURSE OF ITS SPREAD IN EUROPE, ECONOMIC IMPORTANCE, AND MEASURES TO COMBAT IT.) Die Bisamratte. Lebensweise, Gang ihrer Ausbreitung in Europa, wirtschaftliceh Bedeutung und Bekaempfung. Johannes Ulbrich. C. Heinrich, Dresden, pp.137, pls.46, 2 col. maps, 1930.

THE DISTRIBUTION OF THE MUSKRAT FIBER ZIBETHICUS IN THE BIRITSH ISLES. Tom Warwick. Jour. Anim. Ecol., vol.3, no.2, pp.250-267, pls.12-13, 6 maps, Nov., 1934.

(FIND OF THE NORTHERN VOLE MICROTUS RATTICEPS KEYS. AND BLAS.) Funde der nordischen Wuehlmaus Microtus ratticeps Keys. u. Blas. Ed Weber. Zeitschr. f. Saeugetierkunde, vol.10, no.1, pp.150-152, figs.2, pls.2, Dec.31, 1935.

(THE PRESENT STATUS OF THE HAMSTER QUESTION IN GERMANY.) Der gegenwaertige Stand der Hamsterfrage in Deutschland. E. Werth. Arbeiten aus der Biologischen Reichsanstalt fuer Land--und Forstwirtschaft, Berlin, vol.21, no.2, pp. 201-253, figs.4, maps, 1934.

(THE MOUSE RACE OF LOWER AUSTRIA.) Die mausrasse aus Oesterreich. (Evotomys glareolus ruttneri.) Otto Wettstein. Anzeiger kais. Akad. Wissenschaft., Wien, no.13, pp.2, June, 1926.

(A NEW MOUSE SPECIES FROM LOWER AUSTRIA.) Eine neue Mausart aus Niederoesterreich. (Pitymys kupelwieseri.) Otto Wettstein. Anzeiger kais. Akad. Wissenschaft., Wien, no.4, pp.3, Feb., 1925.

BIOLOGY AND CONTROL OF THE WATER VOLE, ARVICOLA TERRESTRIS TERRESTRIS (L.) IN THE NETHERLANDS. A. van Wijngaarden. Versl. Meded. Plantenziek. no.123, pp.1-147, illus., June, 1954. (Dutch with English summary.)

(TEMPORARY RESULTS OF THE INVESTIGATION OF THE FIELDMOUSE POPULATION OF THE BETUWE.) Voorlopige resultaten van het veldmuizenpopulatieonderzoek in de Betuwe. A. van Wijngaarden. Levende Natuur, vol.56, no.9, pp.171-179, 1953.

(COULD THE SYRIAN GOLD HAMSTER, MESOCRICETUS AURATUS, ESTABLISH ITSELF IN THE NETHERLANDS?) Zou de

Syrische goudhamster, Mesocricetus auratus Waterhouse, zich in Nederland kunnen vestigen? A. van Wijngaarden, H. de Vries. Verslag and Mededeel. Plantenziektenkundigen Dienst, Wagenigen, vol.127, pp.224-227, 1955.

THE EUROPEAN LEMMING. Calvin Dill Wilson. Popular Sci. News, Boston, vol. 31, no.11, p.247, illus., Nov., 1897.

(THE HAMSTER IN THE ROSTOV FOREST.) Nekotorie novie dannie po rasprostraneniu i ekologii predkavkazskogo khomyaka v rostovskoi oblasti. M. G. Yakovlev, I. M. Kolesnikov. Zool. Zhurnal, Moscow, vol. 33, no.3, pp.693-700, May-June, 1954.

(DATA FOR BIOLOGY AND INDUSTRY ON THE WATER-RAT IN THE TARTAR REPUBLIC. I. V. Zharkov, B. P. Teplov. Raboty Volzhsko-Kamskoi Krajevoi Promyslovoi Biologicheskoi Stantsii (Works of Volga-Kama Region Industrial Biological Station), Kazan, no.1, pp.127-152, 1931. (In Russian with Tartar summary.)

THE MUSKRAT IN EUROPE. Nature, London, vol.123, no.3107, p.775, May 18, 1929.

THE MUSKRAT IN GERMANY. Jour. Min. Agric. Great Britain, vol.39, no.8, pp.719-724, 1932.

MUSK-RATS IN SCOTLAND. Nature, London, vol.135, no.3409, p.336, Mar.2, 1935; Scottish Jour. Agric., Edinburgh, vol.18, no.2, pp.175-178, Apr., 1935.

Evolution, Phylogeny

ECOLOGICAL FACTORS IN SPECIATION OF PEROMYSCUS. W. Frank Blair. Evolution, vol.4, no.3, pp.253-275, Sept., 1950.

(THE QUESTION OF THE DERIVATION OF MESOCRICETUS NEWTONI NEHRING.) Zur Frage der Herkunft von Mesocricetus, newtoni Nehring. H. Boetticher. Zeitschr. f. Saeugetierkunde, vol.9, nos.1-3, pp.434-435, Dec.12, 1934.

INTERGRADATION BETWEEN TWO SUBSPECIES OF DEER-MOUSE (PEROMYSCUS MANICULATUS) ACROSS NORTH DAKOTA. Lee R. Dice. Contrib. Lab. Vert. Genetics, Univ. Mich., Ann Arbor, no.13, pp. 14, 1 map, May, 1940.

SPECIATION IN PEROMYSCUS. Lee R. Dice. Amer. Nat., Lancaster, vol.74, pp. 289-298, July-Aug., 1940.

SPECIATION IN AMERICAN MICROTINE RODENTS. E. Raymond Hall. Proc. XIV Internat. Congr. Zool., Copenhagen 1953, pp.160-162, 1956. (Summary.)

(EVOLUTION AND SPECIATION OF FIELD MICE OF THE GENUS ARVICOLA IN FRENCH TERRITORY.) Evolution et spéciation des campagnols du genre Arvicola en territoire francais. H. Heim de Balsac, Renée Guislain. Mammalia, Paris, vol.19, no.3, pp.367-390, illus., Sept., 1955.

NOTE ON THE EVOLUTION OF THE VOLES (MICROTINAE). M. A. C. Hinton. Nat. Hist. Mag., London, vol.1, no.3, pp. 69-71, July, 1927.

A TAXONOMIC AND EVOLUTIONARY STUDY OF THE PIÑON MOUSE, PEROMYSCUS TRUEI. Donald F. Hoffmeister. Ill. Biol. Monog., 21 (4): 1-104, 1951.

PHYLETIC RELATIONSHIPS AMONG SOME RODENTS WITH SPECIAL CONSIDERATION OF SIGMODON BASED ON EMBRYOLOGICAL DATA. Charles E. Keys. Trans. Kentucky Acad. Sci., vol.15, nos.1-2, pp. 1-11, July, 1954.

(EVOLUTION OF THE DESIGN ON THE SURFACE OF WEAR OF MOLARS OF GERBILLUS, MERIONES, PACHYUROMYS, AND SEKEETAMYS.) Evolution du dessin de la surface d'usure des molaires de Gerbillus, Meriones, Pachyuromys et Sekeetamys. F. Petter. Mammalia, Paris, (20) (4): 419-426, Dec., 1956.

(NATURAL SELECTION IN THE RED MOUSE CLETHRIONOMYS GL. GLAREOLUS SCHR.) Natuerliche Auslese bei der Roetelmaus Clethrionomys gl. glareolus Schr. Georg H. W. Stein. Zeitschr. Saeugetierk., 21 (1-2): 84-100, 1956.

THE ROLE OF ISOLATION IN THE FORMATION OF A NARROWLY LOCALIZED RACE OF DEER-MICE (PEROMYSCUS). F. B. Sumner. Amer. Nat., vol.51, pp. 173-185, fig.1, Mar., 1917.

SPECIATION AND DISPERSAL OF THE SOUTHERN BOG LEMMING, SYNAPTOMYS COOPERI (BAIRD). Ralph M. Wetzel. Jour. Mam., 36 (1): 1-20, map, graphs, Feb., 1955.

Experimental Biology

EXPERIMENTAL EVIDENCE OF SPECIES DISCRIMINATION IN THE SYMPATRIC SPECIES PEROMYSCUS TRUEI AND P. NASUTUS. W. Frank Blair. Amer. Nat., vol.87, no.833, pp.103-105, Mar.-Apr., 1953.

EXPERIMENTAL EVIDENCE OF SEXUAL ISOLATION BETWEEN THREE FORMS OF MICE OF THE CENOSPECIES PEROMYSCUS MANICULATUS. W. Frank Blair, Walter E. Howard. Contrib. Lab. Vert. Biol., Univ. Michigan, no.26, pp.1-19, Apr., 1944.

FIELD EXPERIMENTS ON THE ACTIVITY OF THE SMALL MAMMALS, APODEMUS, CLETHRIONOMYS AND MICROTUS. L. E. Brown. Proc. Zool. Soc. London, vol.126, pt.4, pp.549-564, July 31, 1956.

TESTOSTERONE-INDUCED MODIFICATIONS OF SEX DEVELOPMENT IN FEMALE HAMSTER. Joyce A. Bruner, Emil Witschi. Amer. Jour. Anat., Phila., vol.79, no.2, pp.293-320, figs.15, Sept., 1946.

HISTOLOGICAL EXPERIMENTS WITH THE BRAIN OF SOME RODENTS. Aemilius Bernardus Droegleever Fortuyn. Jour. Comp. Neurol., pp.349-391, illus., Feb. 15, 1927.

(ADOPTION EXPERIMENTS WITH FIELD MICE (MICROTUS ARVALIS PALL.).) Adoptionsversuche bei Feldmaeusen (Microtus arvalis Pall.). Fritz Frank. Zeitschr. Tierpsych., Berlin, vol.9, no.2, pp.415-423, 1952.

CHOLINE DEFICIENCY IN THE HAMSTER. Philip Handler, Frederick Bernheim. Proc. Soc. Exp. Biol. Med., Utica, vol.72, no.3, pp.569-571, Dec., 1949.

AN EXPERIMENTAL STUDY OF HABITAT SELECTION BY PRAIRIE AND FOREST RACES OF THE DEERMOUSE, PEROMYSCUS MANICULATUS. Van T. Harris. Contrib. Lab. Vert. Biol. Univ. Michigan, Ann Arbor, no.56, pp.53, illus., May, 1952.

TOXIC LEVELS OF MORPHINE FOR THE HAMSTER. O. Boyd Houchen. Proc. Soc. Exper. Biol. and Med., New York, vol.54, no.3, pp.339-340, Dec., 1943.

VAGINAL SMEARS AND MATING RESPONSES IN OVARIECTOMIZED HAMSTERS FOLLOWING ESTRONE AND PROGESTERONE INJECTIONS WITH SPECIAL REFERENCE TO THE VAGINAL SMEAR IN INDUCED MATING. Geo C. Kent, Jr., M. Jack Liberman. Jour. Exper. Zool., Phila., vol.106, no.3, pp.267-280, Dec., 1947.

DISTRIBUTION OF RADIOACTIVE ARSENIC FOLLOWING INTRAPERITONEAL INJECTION OF SODIUM ARSENITE INTO COTTON RATS INFECTED WITH LITOMOSOIDES CARINII. Alfred Lawton, A. T. Ness, Frederick, J. Brady, Dean B. Cowie. Science, Lancaster, n.s., vol.102, no. 2640, pp.120-122, Aug.3, 1945.

CARIOUS LESIONS IN COTTON RAT MOLARS. II. EFFECT OF REMOVAL PRINCIPAL SALIVARY GLANDS. James H. Shaw, David Weisberger. Proc. Soc. Exp. Biol. Med., Utica, vol.70, no.1, pp.103-105, Jan., 1949.

AN EXPERIMENT ON PEROMYSCUS HOMING. Lucille F. Stickel. Am. Midland Nat., 41 (3): 659-664, May, 1949.

EFFECTS OF HORMONES ON EMBRYONIC SEX DIFFERENTIATION IN THE GOLDEN HAMSTER. Marcia R. White. Jour. Exp. Zool., Phila., vol.110, no.2, pp.153-178, pls.1-2, Mar., 1949.

NUTRITION EXPERIMENT WITH WILD MICROTUS POPULATIONS. Leonard Wing. Jour. Wildl. Mgt., 6 (2): 182-183, Apr., 1942.

Food Habits

MILLIONS OF LITTLE TEETH. Durward L. Allen. Mich. Cons., 9 (11): 6-7, 10, Sept., 1940.

THE WOOD RAT AS A HARVESTER. A. W. Anthony. Jour. Mam., vol.2, no.3, pp.140-141, May, 1920.

ON THE FEEDING OF LAGURUS LAGURUS PALL. WHEN BREEDING IT IN CAPTIVITY. N. V. Bashenina. Zool. Zhurnal, Moscow, 36 (12): 1882-1895, 1957. (In Russian, with English summary.)

THE PLANT CONTENTS OF TWO MOUSE STOREHOUSES. Frieda Cobb Blanchard. Rhodora, Jour. New England Bot. Club, vol.37, no.437, pp.165-167, May, 1935.

A QUANTITATIVE STUDY OF MUSKRAT FOOD. L. Butler. Can. Field-Nat., 54 (3): 37-40, Mar., 1940.

FOOD HABITS OF DEER MICE OF THE GENUS PEROMYSCUS IN CAPTIVITY. Annetta Stow Cougshall. Jour. Mam., vol.9, no.3, pp.217-221, Aug., 1928.

STORING HABITS OF MICROTUS TOWNSENDII. Leo K. Couch. Jour. Mam., vol. 6, no.3, pp.200-201, Aug., 1925.

KILLING OF BEECH SEEDLINGS BY VOLES. Lord Cranbrook. Proc. Zool. Soc. Lond., vol.126, pt.1, p.164, Jan.11, 1956.

MICROTUS MINOR AND THE PRAIRIE LILY. Stuart Criddle. Canadian Field-Nat., Sutton West, vol.61, no.3, p.116, June 30, 1947.

A NOTE ON THE FOOD OF THE WATER VOLE. Fred Dean. Naturalist, London, no.819, p.153, Oct.-Dec., 1946.

FOOD OF THE MUSKRAT IN SUMMER. Robert K. Enders. Ohio Jour. Sci., vol. 32, no.1, pp.21-30, Jan., 1932.

EATING, DRINKING, AND ACTIVITY PATTERNS IN PEROMYSCUS MANICULATUS SONORIENSIS. Robert L. French. Jour. Mam., 37 (1): 74-79, 1 table, Feb.27, 1956.

(THE RED MOUSE'S FOOD (CLETHRIONOMYS GLAREOLUS SCHREBER 1780).) Frass der Roetelmaus, Clethrionomys glareolus (Schreber, 1780). Robert Gerber. Saeugetierk. Mitteil., Stuttgart, vol.1, no.2, p. 77, illus., Apr.1, 1953.

FOOD STORED BY THE BEAN MOUSE. Melvin R. Gilmore. Jour. Mam., vol.1, no.3, p.157, May, 1920.

THE GROUND BEAN AND ITS USES. (THE INDIANS AND MICROTUS PENNSYLVANICUS WAHEMA.) Melvin R. Gilmore. Indian Notes (Mus. American Indian, New York), vol.2, pp.178-186, July, 1925.

THE FOOD OF MICROTUS AGRESTIS HIRTUS (BELLAMY, 1839) IN WYTHAM, BERKSHIRE. Gillian K. Godfrey. Saeugetierk. Mitteil., Stuttgart, vol.1, no. 4, pp.148-151, Oct.1, 1953.

DIURNAL FEEDING ACTIVITY OF CALIFORNIA FIELD MOUSE (MICROTUS SP.). Audre Graff. Murrelet, vol.15, no.3, p. 82, Sept., 1934.

PHYTOBEZOARS (FOOD BALLS) IN PEROMYSCUS. Van T. Harris. Jour. Mam., Balto., vol.30, no.1, pp.77-78, Feb.14, 1949.

ACTIVITY AND FOOD CONSUMPTION IN MICROTUS AND PEROMYSCUS. Donald M. Hatfield. Jour. Mam., vol.21, no.1, pp.29-36, figs.3, Feb.14, 1940.

WHITE-FOOT'S HOARD. (WHITE-FOOTED MICE.) John Eric Hill. Nat. Hist., New York, vol.55, no.2, p.87, Feb., 1946.

TRICHOBEZOARS (HAIR BALLS) IN PEROMYSCUS. E. Elizabeth Horner. Jour. Mam., vol.31, no.1, pp.94-95, Feb.21, 1950.

THE FOOD AND HABITAT PREFERENCES OF PHENACOMYS ALBIPES. A. Brazier Howell. Jour. Mam., vol.9, no.2, pp.153-154, May, 1928.

FOOD HABITS OF THE GOLDEN HAMSTER. Don L. Jacobs. Jour. Mam., vol.26, no.2, p.199, July 15, 1945.

FOOD OF DEER MICE, PEROMYSCUS MANICULATUS AND P. BOYLEI, IN THE NORTHERN SIERRA NEVADA, CALIFORNIA. E. W. Jameson, Jr. Jour. Mam., 33 (1): 50-60, illus., Feb., 1952.

(FOOD OF RUSSIAN MUSKRATS.) O rastitelnikh kormakh russkikh vikhukholei. S. A. Krasovskaya. Zool. Zhurnal, Moscow, vol.32, no.3, pp.534-538, 1953.

(SOME FACTS ON THE FEEDING OF THE MUSKRAT (FIBER ZIBETHICUS L.).) N. Lawrow. Zoologitscheskij Journal (vormals "Revue Zool. Russe"), Moscow, vol.12, pt.2, pp.67-79, 1933. (In Russian, with German summary.).

RODENTS EAT BARK AND KILL SHRUBS. Jessop B. Low. Utah Fish and Game Bull., 4 (8): 1-4, Jan., 1948.

COMMENSAL FEEDING OF MUSKRAT AND RUSTY BLACKBIRD. R. W. Nero. Blue Jay, Saskatchewan Nat. Hist. Soc., 14 (1): 4, Mar., 1956.

STOMACH STONE IN A MUSKRAT. A. L. Rand, P. A. Orkin. Canadian Field-Nat., Ottawa, vol.62, no.1, p.41, Jan.-Feb., 1948.

FOOD CONSUMPTION IN PEROMYSCUS IN RELATION TO AIR TEMPERATURE AND PREVIOUS THERMAL EXPERIENCE. John A. Sealander. Jour. Mam., 33 (2): 206-218, illus., May, 1952.

CRESTED RATS AND THREE-INCH BUDS. (LOPHIOMYS IBEANUS.) D. Seth-Smith. Field, London, vol.161, no.4198, p.1339, illus., June 10, 1933.

FOOD HABITS OF THE WHITE-THROATED WOOD RAT IN ARIZONA. Donald A. Spencer, Alice L. Spencer. Jour. Mam., 22 (3): 280-284, Aug., 1941.

NOTES ON THE WINTER FEEDING OF THE MUSKRAT IN DELAWARE. L. A. Stearns, M. W. Goodwin. Jour. Wildl. Mgt., 5 (1): 1-12, Jan., 1941.

CANNIBALISM IN PEROMYSCUS. Kerry B. Sterling. Jour. Mam., vol.34, no.2, p. 262, May 14, 1953.

ACORNS STORED BY PEROMYSCUS CALIFORNICUS. Clark P. Streator. Jour. Mam., vol.12, no.3, pp.315-316, Aug., 1931.

A SEMI-QUANTITATIVE STUDY OF MUSKRAT FOOD HABITS. Michael J. Takos. Jour. Wildl. Mgt., 11 (4): 331-339, Oct., 1947.

WHITE-FOOTED MICE FED UPON GRASSHOPPER EGGS. H. S. Telford. North Dakota Outdoors, Bismarck, vol.6, no.11, p.14, May, 1944.

WHITE-FOOTED MICE FEEDING UPON GRASSHOPPER EGGS. H. S. Telford. Jour. Mam., 24 (3): 400-401, Aug., 1943.

SUMMER FOOD PREFERENCE OF THE BROWN AND COLLARED LEMMINGS. Daniel Q. Thompson. Science in Alaska, Proc. 2nd Alaskan Sci. Conf., Alaska Div. AAAS, p.347, 1953.

CANNIBALISM IN MICROTUS CALIFORNICUS. Marietta Voge. Jour. Mam., vol.31, no.1, p.96, Feb.21, 1950.

SOME FOOD PREFERENCES IN FIELD MICE. A. A. Wellwood. Jour. Mam., 37 (2): 297-298, June 9, 1956.

(SOME OBSERVATIONS OF THE ACTION OF THE FIELD MOUSE (MICROTUS SOCIALIS PALL.) LIVING IN SOCIETIES IN PASTURES SITUATED AT THE FOOT OF THE DAGHESTAN MOUNTAINS. 2. THE QUALITATIVE SIDE OF THE FOOD OF FIELD MICE LIVING IN SOCIETIES. A. Woronoff. Bull. Soc. Nat. Moscou, sec. Biol., n.s., vol.44, nos.7-8, pp.391-406, 1935. (In Russian, with French summary.)

Fossils

ON FOSSIL ARVICOLIDAE. Edward R. Alston, Humphrey Blackmore. Proc. Zool. Soc. Lond., pp.460-471, figs.3, 1874.

NEW CRICETIDAE (GLIRES, MAMMALIA) FROM THE OLIGOCENE OF MIDDLE ASIA. (EUMYSODON, E. SPURIUS, E. ORLOVI, ARALOMYS, A. GIGAS.) A. I. Argyropulo. Comptes Rendus (Doklady) Acad. Sci. URSS, Moscow, n.s., vol.23, no.1, pp.111-114, fig.1, 1939.

OCCURRENCE OF GENUS SCHAUBEUMYS WOOD (CRICETIDAE, MAMMALIA) IN THE UPPER OLIGOCENE OF MIDDLE ASIA. A. I. Argyropulo. Comptes Rendus (Doklady) Acad. Sci. URSS, Moscow, n.s., vol.23, no.2, pp.206-208, illus., 1939.

ON THE FAUNA OF TERTIARY CRICETIDAE OF THE USSR. A. I. Argyropulo. Comptes Rendus (Doklady) Acad. Sci. URSS, Moscow, n.s., vol.20, nos.2-3, pp. 223-226, 1938.

A FOSSIL VOLE FROM CYRENAICA. (MICROTUS CYRENAE.) Dorothea M. A. Bate. Ann. Mag. Nat. Hist., Lond., ser. 12, vol.3, no.35, pp.981-985, Nov., 1950.

PLEISTOCENE CRICETINAE FROM PALESTINE. Dorothea M.A. Bate. Ann. and Mag. Nat. Hist., Lond., ser.11, vol.10, no.72, pp.813-838, Dec., 1943.

FOSSIL VOLES. Lord Cranbrook. Trans. Suffolk Nat. Soc., vol.8, pt.3, pp.155-157, 1954.

(NEW SUBFOSSIL SPECIES OF HYPOGEOMYS, L'H. BOULEI G.G.) Une nouvelle espece subfossile d'Hypogeomys, l'H. Boulei G. G. G. Grandidier. Bull. Mus. hist. Nat., no.1, art.4, pp.2, pl.2, 1912.

ANOTHER RECORD OF THE FOSSIL VOLE MIMOMYS PRIMUS (WILSON) FROM CALIFORNIA. Curtis J. Hesse. Jour. Mam., vol.15, no.3, p.246, Aug.10, 1934.

MICROTUS PENNSYLVANICUS (ORD) FROM THE HAY SPRINGS LOCAL FAUNA OF NEBRASKA. Claude W. Hibbard. Jour. Paleontol., vol.30, no.5, pp.1263-1266, Oct.22, 1956.

A NEW PITYMYS FROM THE PLEISTOCENE OF KANSAS. Claude W. Hibbard. Jour. Mam., vol.18, no.2, p.235, fig.1, May, 1937.

A NEW SYNAPTOMYS, AN ADDITION TO THE BORCHERS INTERGLACIAL (YARMOUTH?) FAUNA. Claude W. Hibbard. Jour. Mam., vol.25, no.2, pp.249-252, illus., May 26, 1954.

A NEW SYNAPTOMYS FROM THE PLEISTOCENE. (SYNAPTOMYS BUNKERI.) Claude W. Hibbard. Bull. Univ. Kansas, Lawrence, vol.41, no.22 (sci. Bull., vol.26), pp.367-371, pl.40, Oct.1, 1939.

NOTES ON THE MICROTINE RODENTS FROM THE PORT KENNEDY CAVE DEPOSITS. Claude W. Hibbard. Proc. Acad. Nat. Sci., Phila., vol.57, pp.87-97, 2 figs., Nov.23, 1955.

TWO NEW CENOZOIC MICROTINE RODENTS. Claude W. Hibbard. Jour. Mam., vol.38, no.1, pp.39-44, Feb., 1957.

DIAGNOSES OF SPECIES OF PITYMYS AND MICROTUS OCCURRING IN THE UPPER FRESHWATER BED OF WEST RUNTON, NORFOLK. Martin A. C. Hinton. Ann. Mag. Nat. Hist., ser.9, vol.12, pp.541-542, Oct., 1923.

A FOSSIL RICE-RAT FROM THE PLEISTOCENE OF BARBUDA. Arthur T. Hopwood. Ann. and Mag. Nat. Hist., ser.9, vol.17, pp.328-330, Mar., 1926.

ON PLIOCENE VOLES. C. I. Forsyth Major. Proc. Zool. Soc. Lond., vol.2, pp.102-107, figs.13-15, June 1, 1902.

A LATE PLEISTOCENE VOLE FROM GUERNSEY. (MICROTUS ORCADENSIS.) T. C. S. Morrison-Scott. Rep't. Soc. Guernesiaise, Guernsey, C. I., vol.13, pp.24-25, 1937 (1938).

(ON DOLOMYS NOV. GEN. FOSS.) Ueber Dolomys nov. gen. foss. A. Nehring. Zool. Anzeiger, Leipzig, vol.21, no.549, pp.13-16, figs.3, Jan.10, 1898.

(ON MYODES LEMMUS CRASSIDENS, VAR. NOV. FOSS., OF PORTUGAL.) Ueber Myodes lemmus crassidens, var. nov. foss., aus Portugal. A. Nehring. Archiv. f. Naturg., Berlin, Jahrg., vol.1, pt.2, pp.175-182, figs.3, June, 1899.

MUSKRAT REMAINS FROM A PREHISTORIC INDIAN SITE IN JACKSON COUNTY, FLORIDA. Wilfred T. Neill, Ripley P. Bullen. Jour. Mam., 36 (1): 138, Feb.28, 1955.

HAMSTER REMAINS FROM THE NORFOLK FOREST BED. E. T. Newton. Geol. Mag. London, n.s., decade 5, vol.6, pp.110-113, illus., Mar., 1909.

(QUATERNARY AND EARLY TERTIARY HAMSTERS.) Quartaere und jungtertieare Hamster. S. Schaub. Abhandl. Schweizer, Palaeont., Gesellschaft, Basel, vol.49, pp. 1-50, figs.27, pls.2, 1930.

FOSSIL VOLES AND A LEMMUS OUT OF WELL-BORINGS IN THE NETHERLANDS. A. Schreuder. Kon. Akad. Wet., Verhand. (Tweede Sectie), vol.35, no.3, pp.1-24, figs.11, table 1, 1936.

MICROTINAE FROM THE MIDDLE GRAVELS OF SWANSCOMBE. A. Schreuder. Ann. and Mag. Nat. Hist., London, ser.12, vol.3, no.31, pp.629-635, July, 1950.

SHANSI MOLE-RAT, MYOSPHALAX FONTANUS THOMAS, FOUND IN THE LOESS OF SHANSI PROVINCE, CHINA. Fuyuji Takai. Japanese Jour. Geol. and Geogr. Trans. and Abstr., vol.17, nos.3-4, pp. 209-214, figs.4, pl.21, Oct., 1940.

PEROMYSCUS FROM THE LATE PLEISTOCENE OF TEXAS. J. R. Tamsitt. Texas Jour. Sci., 9 (3): 355-363, Sept., 1957.

SOME REMARKS ON FOSSIL LEMMINGS AND VOLES FROM SOUTHERN SIBERIA. B. S. Vinogradov. Yearbook Zool. Mus. Russian Acad. Sci., vol.23, pp.371-378, 1922.

COSOMYS, A NEW GENUS OF VOLE FROM THE PLIOCENE OF CALIFORNIA. Robert W. Wilson. Jour. Mam., vol.13, no.2, pp. 150-154, pl.12, 1932.

CRICETINE-LIKE RODENTS FROM THE SESPE EOCENE OF CALIFORNIA. Robert W. Wilson. Proc. Nat. Acad. Sci., vol.21, no.1, pp.26-32, pl.1, Jan., 1935.

A NEW PLEISTOCENE DEER-MOUSE FROM SANTA ROSA ISLAND, CALIFORNIA. Robert W. Wilson. Jour. Mam., vol.17, no.3, pp.408-410, fig.1, Nov., 1936.

THE CRICETID RODENTS DESCRIBED BY LEIDY AND COPE FROM THE TERTIARY OF NORTH AMERICA. Albert Elmer Wood. Amer. Mus. Novitates no.822, pp. 8, figs.5, Mar.9, 1936.

TWO NEW GENERA OF CRICETID RODENTS FROM THE MIOCENE OF WESTERN UNITED STATES. Albert Elmer Wood. Amer. Mus. Novitates no.789, pp. 1-3, figs.2, Apr.10, 1935.

General Habits, Behavior

THE MUSKRAT'S OFFENSIVE DEFENSIVE. Francis H. Allen. Jour. Mam., vol.12, no.3, p.318, Aug., 1931.

SIGNS OF MUSKRAT. Atso Artimo. Pap. Game Res., 8: 63-76, illus., 1952. (Swedish, with English summary.)

LIFE HISTORY AND HABITS OF GRASSHOPPER MICE, GENUS ONYCHOMYS. Vernon Bailey, Charles C. Sperry. Tech. Bull.145, pp.19, pls.4, Nov., 1929.

NOCTURNAL EXPLORATIONS OF THE FOREST DEER-MOUSE. W. H. Behney. Jour. Mam., vol.17, no.3, pp.225-230, figs.2, charts 2, Aug., 1936.

NEW TYPE DIME BANK. (NEOTOMA STORING DIMES.) John Bingaman. Yosemite Nature Notes, vol.16, no.7, p.55, illus., July, 1937.

SOME OBSERVATIONS ON THE BEHAVIOR OF THE GOLDEN HAMSTER (CRICETUS AURATUS). Jean Brust. Naturalist, no. 845, pp.61-65, Apr.-June, 1953.

DIEL ACTIVITY RHYTHMS OF THE RODENTS, MICROTUS OCHROGASTER AND SIGMODON HISPIDUS HISPIDUS. John B. Calhoun. Ecology, 26 (3): 251-273, July, 1945.

DESERT HOME-BUILDER. (WOODRAT) Wm. H. Carr. Nat. Hist., New York, vol. 57, no.1, pp.28-33, illus., Jan., 1948.

AGGRESSION, A COMPONENT OF POST-EPILEPTIC AUTOMATISM IN PEROMYSCUS. M. R. A. Chance. Nature, London, vol.161, no. 4081, pp.101-102, Jan.17, 1948.

ON THE HABITS OF THE ROUND-TAILED MUSKRAT (NEOFIBER ALLENI TRUE). Frank Michler Chapman. Amer. Mus. Nat. Hist., New York, Bull. New York, 1890, vol.11, pp.119-122, 1890.

BEHAVIOR OF MURINE RODENTS AFTER WITHHOLDING FOOD AND PROTECTING SEED IN THE FIELD FROM THEM. N. U. Chentsova. Povedenie mishevidnix grizunov pri otiskivanii pischi i zashchita ot nix semyan v posevax. (Microtus socialis, habits and food.) Zool. Jour. Akad. Nauk SSSR, Moscow, vol.31, no.3, pp.422-433, 1952.

GEOTROPIC BEHAVIOR ON A SLOPING PLANE OF ARBOREAL AND NON-ARBOREAL RACES OF MICE OF THE GENUS PEROMYSCUS. Frank H. Clark. Jour. Mam., vol.17, no.1, pp.44-47, Feb. 14, 1936.

THE AGGRESSIVE BEHAVIOUR OF THE VOLE. John R. Clarke. Behaviour, Leiden, vol.9, pt.1, pp.1-23, illus., 1956.

THE ACTIVITIES OF PACK RATS. Harold S. Colton. Arizona Wild Life, vol. 2, no.3, p.11, June, 1930.

THE HABITS OF MICROTUS MINOR IN MANITOBA. Stuart Criddle. Jour. Mam., vol.7, no.3, pp.193-200, Aug., 1926.

(BELGIAN FIELD MICE FROM THE ECOLOGICAL VIEWPOINT.) Les campagnols de Belgique au point de vue de l'ecologie. Paul Dalimier. Mammalia, Paris, vol.19, no.4, pp.498-506, Dec., 1955.

RHYTHMIC ACTIVITY IN THE SHORT-TAILED VOLE, MICROTUS. D. H. S. Davis. Jour. Animal Ecology, vol.2, no. 2, pp.232-238, Nov., 1933.

NOTES ON THE LIFE HISTORY AND BEHAVIOR OF NEOTOMA FUSCIPES. Fae Donat. Jour. Mam., vol.14, no.1, pp.19-26, Feb., 1933.

SPIRAL MOVEMENT IN MICE. (PEROMYSCUS MANICULATUS BAIRDI.) Inez Dunkelberger. Jour. Comp. Psych., vol. 6, no.5, pp.383-389, 1926.

(OBSERVATIONS ON THE RHYTHM OF THE ACTIVITY OF THE FIELD MOUSE (MICROTUS ARVALIS PALLAS).) Observations sur le rythme de l'activité du campagnol des champs (Microtus arvalis Pallas). Henri Durup. Mammalia, Paris, 20 (4): 390-404, Dec., 1956.

(INBORN AND ACQUIRED BEHAVIOR AS REGARDS NEST BUILDING IN THE LEMMING.) Angeborenes und Erworbenes im Nestbauverhalten der Wanderratte. Irenaeus Eibl-Eibesfeldt. Die Naturwissenschaften, Berlin, 42 (23): 633-634, 1955.

ADDITIONAL STUDIES ON TAGGED YOUNG MUSKRATS. Paul L. Errington. Jour. Wildlife Management, Menasha, vol.8, no. 4, pp.300-306, pl.16, Oct., 1944.

OBSERVATIONS ON YOUNG MUSKRATS IN IOWA. Paul L. Errington. Jour. Mam., 20 (4): 465-478, Nov., 1939.

(THE COLLECTING INSTINCT OF THE SYRIAN GOLDEN HAMSTER (MESOCRICETUS AURATUS WATERHOUSE 1839) IN THE LABORATORY.) Der Sammeltrieb des syrischen Goldhamsters, Mesocricetus auratus (Waterhouse, 1839), im Laboratorium. Albert Fellner. Saeugetierk. Mitteil, Stuttgart, 4 (4): 153-160, Oct.1, 1956.

UTILIZATION OF A BIRD'S NEST BY THE MEADOW VOLE. James S. Findley. Jour. Mam., 37 (1): 120, Feb.28, 1956.

OBSERVATIONS ON THE HABITS OF THE WATER RAT, ARVICOLA TERRESTRIS L. (TRANS. TITLE). Constantine C. Flerov. Russische Hydrobiol. Zeitschrift, vol.4, no.10-12, pp.194-201, 1925. (In Russian, Abstract in French.)

(ECOLOGY OF P. MAJORI IN THE CAUCASUS.) Kustarnikovaya polevka (Pitymys majori Thos.) v visokogorye zapadnoi chasti Glavnogo Kavkazskogo Khrebta. I. M. Gromov, B. L. Vorobev. Trudi. Zool. Inst. Akad. Nauk SSSR, 17: 135-159, 1955.

HABITS OF THE SWAMP RICE RAT, ORYZOMYS PALUSTRIS PALUSTRIS (HARLAN). W. J. Hamilton, Jr. Amer. Midland Nat., Notre Dame, vol.36, no.3, pp.730-736, figs.5, Nov., 1946.

LIFE AND HABITS OF FIELD MICE. W. J. Hamilton, Jr. Sci. Monthly, 50 (5): 425-434, May, 1940.

BURROWING HABITS OF PEROMYSCUS POLIONOTUS. Don W. Hayne. Jour. Mam., vol.17, no.4, pp.420-421, Nov., 1936.

NEST BUILDING. (NOTE ON NEST OF "BANK VOLE.") G. Hearn. Field, London, vol.151, p.437, illus., Mar.15, 1928.

UNUSUAL MUSKRAT HOUSE. William S. Heit. Jour. Wildlife Mgt., Menasha, vol. 10, no.3, p.276, pl.20, July, 1946.

CACTUS-PAVED RUNWAYS OF NEOTOMA ALBIGULA. John Eric Hill. Jour. Mam., vol.23, no.2, pp.213-214, May 14, 1942.

THE TALL TRUTH. ROAD-BUILDING RATS. John Eric Hill. Nat. Hist., New York, vol.43, no.5, p.308, May, 1939.

ARBOREAL ADAPTATIONS OF PEROMYSCUS, WITH SPECIAL REFERENCE TO USE OF THE TAIL. B. Elizabeth Horner. Contrib. Lab. Vert. Biol. Univ. Michigan, Ann Arbor, no.61, pp.1-77, pls.1-7, Feb., 1954.

MATERNAL BEHAVIOR IN THE DEER MOUSE. R. R. Huestis. Jour. Mam., vol.14, no.1, pp.47-49, pl.3, Feb., 1933.

NOTES ON THE PINE MOUSE. R. N. Jefferson. Va. Fruit, 31 (5): 10, 12, 14, May, 1943.

A NEST OF PHENACOMYS SILVICOLA IN OREGON. Stanley G. Jewett. Jour. Mam, vol.11, no.1, pp.81-83, Feb., 1930.

(LIVING HABITS OF THE SHORT-EARED MOUSE IN THE ALPS.) Lebensbild der Kurzohr-maus in den Alpen. Herman Kahmann. Natur und Volk, Frankfurt am Main, vol.80, no.3, pp.71-77, illus., Mar. 15, 1950.

(ON THE INITIATIVE REACTIONS OF SMALL RODENTS (RODENTIA).) Ueber die initiativen Reaktionen der Kleinnagetiere (Rodentia). G. v Kolosvary. Teil 2, Folia Zoologica et Hydrobiologica, Riga, vol.10, no.2, pp.381-382, Sept.5, 1940.

(DIURNAL ACTIVITY OF FIELD MICE AND STEPPE LEMMINGS IN NORTHERN KAZAKHSTAN.) O sutochnoi aktivnosti stadnoi polevki i stepnoi pestrushki v severnom kazakhstane. A. I. Kriltsov. Zool. Zhurnal, Moscow, vol.33, no.1, pp.197-206, Jan.-Feb., 1954.

(THE LIVING HABITS OF CLETHRIONOMYS GLAREOLUS (SCHREB).) Beitrag zur Lebensweise von Clethrionomys glareolus (Schreb). Herbert Lindner. Zeitschr. f. Saeugetierkunde, Berlin, vol. 9, nos.1-3, p.434, Dec.30, 1934.

MEADOW MICE USE WRENS' NESTS. Jessop B. Low. Jour. Mam., vol.25, no.3, p.308, Sept.8, 1944.

A VIEWPOINT ON THE DISAPPEARANCE OF RICE BEDS. (MUSKRAT SAID TO BE NECESSARY TO SURVIVAL OF WILD RICE BEDS.) C. E. Lucas. Fins, Feathers and Fur, no.36, pp.123-124, Dec., 1923.

THE MYSTERIOUS MOUSE. Adolph Murie. Audubon Mag., 50 (4): 202-210, July.-Aug., 1948.

HABITS OF NEOTOMA PENNSYLVANICA. Robert C. Patterson. West Virginia Univ. Bull., ser.34, no.15 (Proc. W. Virginia Acad. Sci., vol.7), pp.32-35, Mar., 1934.

ON THE TRAIL OF A DEER-MOUSE. (GENERAL ACCOUNT OF HABITS OF PEROMYSCUS, WITH PHOTOGRAPHS.) Edwin O. Perrin. Forest and Stream, vol. 90, pp.306-307, June, 1920.

(NOTABLE MOVEMENT STEREOTYPY IN A CAPTIVE FEMALE FIELD HAMSTER, CRICETUS CR. CRICETUS LINNÉ 1758.) Bemerkenswerte Bewegungsstereotypie bei einem gehaltenen Feldhamster, Cricetus cr. cricetus (Linné, 1758). Hans Petzsch. Saeugetierk. Mitteil., Stuttgart, 3 (1): 33-34, Jan.1, 1955.

SOME NOTES ON THE HABITS OF THE CEYLON GERBIL, TATERA CEYLONICA. W. W. A. Phillips. Jour. Bombay Nat. Hist. Soc., vol.29, pp.214-216, 1 fig., 1 pl., Apr.20, 1923.

THE HABITS OF SOME ARVICOLINAE. Edgar R. Quick, A. W. Butler. Amer. Nat., Phila., vol.19, no.2, pp.113-118, pl.2, Feb., 1885; Proc. Amer. Assoc. Adv. Sci., pp.539-542, 1885.

(WINTER BIOLOGY OF THE SAND MOUSE (GERBILLUS TAMARICINUS PALL.) AND OTHER RODENTS FROM THE ENVIRONS OF THE CITY OF URDA.) Iurii Rall. Rev. Microbiol., Épidémiol. et Parasitol., vol.10, no.2, pp.189-202, 1931. (In Russian, with German summary.)

(ON THE BEHAVIOR OF MERIONES TAMARISCINUS PALL. 1778.) Zum Verhalten von Meriones tamariscinus Pall. (1778). Hans-Georg Rauch. Zeitchr. Saeugetierk., 22 (3-4): 218-240, pls.9-11, 1957.

ON THE HABITS OF KEEN'S DEER MOUSE, PEROMYSCUS KEENII (RHOADS). Samuel N. Rhoads. Amer. Naturalist, p.753, Sept. 1, 1896.

THE RED-BACKED MOUSE AS A TREE INHABITER. William T. Shaw. Jour. Mam., vol.5, no.4, pp.268-269, Nov., 1924.

NOTES ON THE HABITS OF THE LONG-TAILED HARVEST MOUSE. Clarence F. Smith. Jour. Mam., vol.17, no.3, pp.274-278, illus., Aug., 1936.

THE DISTRIBUTION, ORIENTATION, AND ACTIVITIES OF THE VARYING LEMMING IN A GRADIENT OF TEMPERATURE. Donald A. Smith, Kenneth C. Fisher. Canadian Jour. Zool., 34 (4): 243-261, Aug., 1956.

THE TRANSFER OF A PEROMYSCUS FAMILY. Wendell P. Smith. Jour. Mam., vol.20, no.1, p.108, Feb.14, 1939.

TERRESTRIAL HABITS OF THE WATER VOLE (ARVICOLA AMPHIBIUS). H. N. Southern, W. P. Crowcroft. Proc. Zool. Soc. Lond., vol.126, pt.1, pp.166-167, Jan.11, 1956.

TEMPERATURE SELECTION IN DEER MICE. R. H. Stinson, Kenneth C. Fisher. Can. Jour. Zool., 31 (4): 404-416, illus., Aug., 1953.

NOTES ON THE BURROWING HABITS OF PEROMYSCUS POLIONOTUS. F. B. Sumner, J. J. Karol. Jour. Mam., vol.10, no.3, pp.213-215, pl.17, Aug., 1929.

DESCRIPTION OF A NEW SUBGENUS (ARBORIMUS) OF PHENACOMYS, WITH A CONTRIBUTION TO KNOWLEDGE OF THE HABITS AND DISTRIBUTION OF PHENACOMYS LONGICAUDUS TRUE. Walter P. Taylor. Proc. Calif. Acad. Sci., ser.4, vol.5, no.5, pp.111-161, pl.15, Dec.30, 1915.

A NOVEL NESTING PLACE OF THE RED-BACKED MOUSE. Walter P. Taylor. Jour. Mam., vol.1, no.2, p.92, Feb., 1920.

THE WOOD RAT AS A COLLECTOR. Walter P. Taylor. Jour. Mam., vol.1, no. 2, pp.91-92, Feb., 1920.

BEHAVIOR OF A POPULATION OF FOREST-MICE WHEN SUBJECTED TO POISON. Lloyd Tevis, Jr. Jour. Mam., 37 (3): 358-370, Sept.11, 1956.

THE WINTER HABITS OF THE NORTHERN WHITE-FOOTED MOUSE. Hans Peter Thomsen. Jour. Mam., 26 (2): 138-142, May, 1945.

(OBSERVATIONS ON THE ACTIVITY OF FIELDMICE (MICROTUS SOCIALIS PALL.) LIVING AS A SOCIETY ON PASTURES AT THE FOOT OF THE DAGHESTAN MOUNTAINS.) Quelques observations sur l'action du Campagnol vivanten société (Microtus socialis Pall.) sur les pâturages situés au pied des montagnes du Daghestan. A. G. Voronov. Bull. Soc. Nat. Moscow, sect. biol., n.s., vol.44, no.6, pp.314-323, figs.4, tables 5, 1935; nos.7-8, pp.391-406, 1935. (In Russian, with French summary.)

FAUNAL NEST STUDY OF THE WOODRAT, NEOTOMA FUSCIPES MONOCHROURA RHOADS. Roland D. Walters, Vincent D. Roth. Jour. Mam., vol.31, no.3, pp.290-292, Aug.21, 1950.

GRASSHOPPER MOUSE USES TOBACCO AS AN INSECTICIDE. Ernest P. Walker. Jour. Mam., vol.21, no.2, p.221, May 14, 1940.

A MUSKRAT MOVES ITS YOUNG. Edward R. Warren. Jour. Mam., vol.5, no.3, pp.202-203, Aug., 1924.

NOTES ON WOOD RAT WORK. Edward R. Warren. Jour. Mam., vol.1, no.5, pp.233-234, pls.10-11, Nov., 1920.

(HAMSTERS CLIMB ON SUNFLOWERS.) Hamster klettern auf Sonnenblumen. Bruno Weber. Saeugetierk., Mitteil., Stuttgart, 4 (3): 131, July 1, 1956.

LETTER RELATING TO THE HABITS OF THE HAMSTER (CRICETUS VULGARIS). Dr. Weissenborn. Proc. Zool. Soc. Lond., pt.5, p.50, 1837.

MOUSE KILLS SNAKE. F. C. Whitehouse. Canadian Field-Nat., Sutton West, vol.61, no.1, p.21, Mar.15, 1947.

TREE-CUTTING BY MUSKRATS? Thomas E. Winecoff. Jour. Mam., vol.14, no.1, p.75, Feb., 1933.

OBSERVATIONS ON THE BEHAVIOR AND BREEDING OF CAPTIVE RICE RATS AND WOODRATS. C. Brooke Worth. Jour. Mam., vol.31, no.4, pp.421-426, Nov.21, 1950.

HOUSE MOVERS IN "WOODRAT ROW." (NOTES ON WOOD-RAT HOUSE CONSTRUCTION.) George M. Wright. Yosemite Nature Notes, vol.7, pp.12-14, illus., Feb., 1928.

(THE BEHAVIOR OF SEPARATED FIELD MICE, MICROTUS ARVALIS PALL., WHEN AGAIN MEETING.) Das Verhalten verpaarter Feldmauesse, Microtus arvalis (Pall.), be Begegnung nach Trennung. Klaus Zimmermann. Tierpsych., Berlin, vol.9, no.1, pp.1-11, 1952.

LIFE HISTORY AND HABITS OF THE MUSKRAT. Maryland Conservationist, vol.11, no.4, pp.1-4, 21-26, fig.1, 1934.

Growth

THE DEVELOPMENT OF THE MUSKRAT ON THE MONTEZUMA NATIONAL WILDLIFE REFUGE. Maurice M. Alexander. PhD. thesis, Syracuse Univ., 1950.

GROWTH IN THE DEER-MOUSE, PEROMYSCUS MANICULATUS. Lee R. Dice, Robert M. Bradley. Jour. Mam., vol.23, no.4, pp.416-427, figs.5, Nov., 1942.

(CONTRIBUTION TO THE BIOLOGY, ESPECIALLY THE YOUNG DEVELOPMENT, OF THE SNOW MOUSE (CHIONOMYS NIVALIS MART.).) Beitrag zur Biologie insbesondere Jugendentwicklung der Schneemaus (Chionomys nivalis Mart.). Fritz Frank. Zeitschr. Tierpsychol., 11 (1): 1-9, 1954.

DEVELOPMENT OF THE GOLDEN HAMSTER, CRICETUS AURATUS WATERHOUSE, DURING THE FIRST NINE DAYS. Artis Paris Graves. Amer. Jour. Anat., Phila., vol.77, no.2, pp.219-251, pls.1-7, Sept., 1945.

GROWTH AND LIFE SPAN OF THE FIELD MOUSE. W. J. Hamilton, Jr. Amer. Nat., 71 (736): 500-507, Sept.-Oct., 1937.

DEVELOPMENT OF YOUNG VARYING LEMMINGS (DICROSTONYX). Richard M. Hansen. Arctic, Jour. Arctic Inst. North Amer., 10 (2): 105-117, 1957.

THE DEVELOPMENT OF A YOUNG HARVEST MOUSE, REITHRODONTOMYS. B. F. Holding, O. L. Royal. Jour. Mam., vol.33, no.3, p.388, Aug.19, 1952.

GROWTH AND THE DEVELOPMENT OF TEMPERATURE REGULATION IN THE TUNDRA REDBACK VOLE. Peter R. Morrison, Fred A. Ryser, Robert L. Strecker. Jour. Mam., vol.35, no.3, pp. 376-386, Aug.20, 1954.

DEVELOPMENT AND GROWTH OF DEER-MICE (PEROMYSCUS MANICULATUS ARTEMISIAE). Arthur Svihla. Jour. Mam., vol.15, no.2, figs.1-5, pp.100-104, May, 1934.

DEVELOPMENT AND GROWTH OF PEROMYSCUS MANICULATUS OREAS. Arthur Svihla. Jour. Mam., vol.17, no.2, pp.132-137, figs.2, table 1, May, 1936.

DEVELOPMENT AND GROWTH OF THE PRAIRIE DEERMOUSE, PEROMYSCUS MANICULATUS BAIRDII. Arthur Svihla. Jour. Mam., vol.16, no.2, pp.109-115, figs.3, May, 1935.

OBSERVATIONS ON THE GROWTH AND BEHAVIOR OF HARVEST MICE. Harold J. Leraas. Jour. Mam., vol.19, no.4, pp. 441-444, Nov.14, 1938.

Heredity

BOGGLER, AN INHERITED ABNORMALITY OF THE DEERMOUSE (PEROMYSCUS MANICULATUS), CHARACTERIZED BY A TREMOR AND A STAGGERING GAIT. Elizabeth Barto. Contrib. Lab. Vert. Biol. Univ. Michigan, Ann Arbor, no.71, pp.26, Aug., 1955.

INDEPENDENT INHERITANCE OF CERTAIN CHARACTERS IN THE DEER MOUSE, PEROMYSCUS MANICULATUS. Elizabeth Barto. Papers Michigan Acad. Sci., Arts and Letters, Ann Arbor, vol.27 (1941), pp. 195-213, Mar., 1942.

A SECOND OCCURRENCE OF THE CHARACTER PINK-EYE IN THE DEER MOUSE. Elizabeth Barto. Amer. Nat., Lancaster, vol.76, no.767, pp.634-636, Nov.-Dec., 1942.

SPINNER, AN INHERITED TYPE OF ABNORMAL BEHAVIOR IN THE BEACH MOUSE, PEROMYSCUS POLIONOTUS. Elizabeth Barto. Contrib. Lab. Vert. Biol., Univ. Michigan, Ann Arbor, no.66, pp.1-16, illus., Apr., 1954.

INHERITANCE OF A WHITE STAR IN THE DEER MOUSE. Elizabeth Barto, R. R. Huestis. Jour. Heredity, vol.24, no.6, pp.245-248, fig.10, June, 1933.

AN ANALYSIS OF CERTAIN GENETIC VARIATIONS IN PELAGE COLOR OF THE CHIHUAHUA DEER-MOUSE (PEROMYSCUS MANICULATUS BLANDUS). W. Frank Blair. Contrib. Lab. Vert. Biol. Univ. Michigan, Ann Arbor, no.35, pp.1-18, fig.1, May, 1947.

ESTIMATED FREQUENCIES OF THE BUFF AND GRAY GENES (G, Y) IN ADJACENT POPULATIONS OF DEER-MICE (PEROMYSCUS MANICULATUS BLANDUS)LIVING ON SOILS OF DIFFERENT COLORS. W. Frank Blair. Contrib. Lab. Vert. Biol., Univ. Michigan, Ann Arbor, no.36, pp.1-16, map, May, 1947.

FACTORS AFFECTING GENE EXCHANGE BETWEEN POPULATIONS IN THE PEROMYSCUS MANICULATUS GROUP. W. Frank Blair. Texas Jour. Sci., Austin, vol.5, no.1, pp.17-33, Mar., 1953.

COAT COLOR IN THE MEADOW-VOLE. INHERITANCE OF CREAM COAT-COLOR IN MICROTUS PENNSYLVANICUS, WITH DESCRIPTIONS OF SEVERAL OTHER COLOR VARIATIONS. Frank H. Clark. Jour. Heredity, vol.29, no.7, pp.265-266, fig.7, July, 1938.

INHERITANCE OF THE WHITE-CHEEK CHARACTER IN MICE OF THE GENUS PEROMYSCUS. W. Frank Blair. Contrib. Lab. Vert. Biol., Univ. Michigan, Ann Arbor, no.25, pp.1-7, Mar., 1944.

INHERITANCE AND LINKAGE RELATIONS OF MUTANT CHARACTERS IN THE DEER MOUSE, PEROMYSCUS MANICULATUS. Frank H. Clark. Contr. Lab. Vert. Genetics, Univ. Michigan, no.7, pp.1-11, tables 7, June, 1938.

LINKAGE OF PINK-EYE AND ALBINISM IN THE DEER-MOUSE. Frank H. Clark. Jour. Heredity, Washington, vol.27, no.7, pp.259-260, July, 1936.

SNOWBALL: A REPEATED MUTATION IN THE COTTON RAT. C. H. Danforth, Victor Schwentker. Jour. Heredity, Washington, vol.40, no.9, pp.252-256, illus., Sept., 1949.

THE INHERITANCE OF DICHROMATISM IN THE DEER-MOUSE, PEROMYSCUS MANICULATUS BLANDUS. Lee R. Dice. Amer. Nat., vol.67, no.713, pp.571-574, Nov.-Dec., 1933.

INTERGRADATION BETWEEN TWO SUBSPECIES OF DEER MOUSE (PEROMYSCUS MANICULATUS) ACROSS NORTH DAKOTA. Lee R. Dice. Contrib. Lab. Vert. Genetics, Univ. Michigan, Ann Arbor, no. 13, pp.1-14, May, 1940.

THE RELATION OF GENETICS TO GEOGRAPHICAL DISTRIBUTION AND SPECIATION. II. SPECIATION IN PEROMYSCUS. Lee R. Dice. Amer. Naturalist, Lancaster, vol.74, no.753, pp.289-298, July-Aug., 1940.

A STUDY OF RACIAL HYBRIDS IN THE DEER-MOUSE, PEROMYSCUS MANICULATUS. Lee R. Dice. Occas. Papers Mus. Zool., Univ. Michigan, no.312, pp.22, May 3, 1935.

COLOR MUTATIONS IN THE MUSKRAT (ONDATRA Z. MACRODON) AND THEIR INHERITANCE. Herbert L. Dozier. Jour. Mam., 29 (4): 393-405, Nov., 1948.

AN INSULAR POPULATION OF PEROMYSCUS MANICULATUS SUBSP. WITH MIXED RACIAL CHARACTERS. (BOWEN ISLAND, BRITISH COLUMBIA.) William L. Engels. Amer. Midland Nat., vol.17, no.4, pp.776-780, July, 1936.

PIEBALD CHARACTERS OF THE DEER MOUSE. Horace W. Feldman. Jour. Heredity, vol.27, no.8, pp.301-304, Aug., 1936.

SEGREGATION OF MUTANT CHARACTERS OF DEER MICE. Horace W. Feldman. Amer. Nat., vol.71, no.735, pp.426-429, July-Aug., 1937.

THE OCCURRENCE OF A "SILVER" TYPE MUSKRAT. J. Lane Fletcher. Jour. Heredity, Washington, vol.35, no.11, pp.351-352, Nov., 1944.

A MUTATION IN THE GOLDEN HAMSTER. Charles L. Foote. Jour. Heredity, Balto., vol.40, no.4, p.101, illus., Apr., 1949.

(COLORATION MUTATIONS OF THE FIELD MOUSE (MICROTUS ARVALIS PALL.).) Faerbungs-Mutationen der Feldmaus (Microtus arvalis (Pall.)). Fritz Frank, Klaus Zimmermann. Zeitschr. Saeugetierk, 22 (1-2): 87-100, pl.7, 1957.

INHERITANCE OF BLACK COAT COLOUR IN THE COMMON HAMSTER (CRICETUS CRICETUS L.). S. Gershenson, V. V. Polevoi. Comptes Rendus (Doklady) Acad. Sci. URSS, Moscow, n.s., vol.29, nos.8-9, pp.608-609, 1940. (In English.)

A DESCRIPTION OF MICROSCOPIC HAIR CHARACTERS AND OF THEIR INHERITANCE IN PEROMYSCUS. R. R. Huestis. Jour. Exper. Zool., vol.41, pp.429-470, Apr.5, 1925.

THE HEREDITY OF MICROSCOPIC HAIR CHARACTERS IN PEROMYSCUS. R. R.

Huestis. Proc. Nat. Acad. Sci., vol.9, pp.352-355, Oct., 1923.

IVORY, A FERAL MUTATION IN PEROMYSCUS. R. R. Huestis. Jour. Heredity, vol. 29, no.6, pp.235-237, June, 1938.

INHERITED JAUNDICE IN PEROMYSCUS. R. R. Huestis, Ruth Anderson. Science, vol.120, no.3126, pp.852-853, Nov.26, 1954.

BROWN AND SILVER DEER MICE. R. R. Huestis, Elizabeth Barto. Jour. Heredity, vol.25, no.6, pp.219-223, figs.3-4, June, 1934.

FLEXED-TAILED PEROMYSCUS. R. R. Huestis, Elizabeth Barto. Jour.Heredity, vol.27, no.2, pp.73-75, Feb., 1936.

LINKAGE RELATIONS OF FLEXED-TAIL IN PEROMYSCUS. R. R. Huestis, Greta Lindstedt. Amer. Nat., Lancaster, vol. 80, no.786, pp.85-91, Jan.1, 1946.

AN ABERRENT RATIO IN PEROMYSCUS. R. R. Huestis, Victor Piestrak. Jour. Heredity, Washington, D.C., vol.33, no. 8, pp.289-291, Aug., 1942.

HETEROCHROMIA IN PEROMYSCUS. R. R. Huestis, Ruth Willoughby. Jour. Heredity, Balto., vol.41, no.11, pp.287-290, Nov., 1950.

THE X-BIVALENT OF THE GOLDEN HAMSTER. Ladley Husted, J. T. Hopkins, Jr., M. B. Moore, Jr. Jour. Heredity, Washington, vol.36, no.3, pp.93-96, fig.9, Mar., 1943.

THE SEX BIVALENT OF THE CHINESE HAMSTER (CRICETULUS GRISEUS). Ladley Husted, Edward G. Pollock, Grover C. Smart, Jr. Virginia Jour. Sci., 8: 121-127, Apr., 1957.

LINKAGE IN PEROMYSCUS, AND SEQUENTIAL TESTS FOR INDEPENDENT ASSORTMENT. William B. McIntosh. Contrib. Lab. Vert. Biol., Ann Arbor, no.73, 27 pp., June, 1956.

WHITESIDE, A NEW MUTATION IN PEROMYSCUS. William B. McIntosh. Jour. Heredity, 47 (1): 28-32, Jan.-Feb., 1956.

YELLOW MUTATION IN THE CALIFORNIA MEADOW MOUSE, MICROTUS CALIFORNICUS (PEALE). Robert T. Orr. Wasmann Collector, San Francisco, vol.4, no.4, pp.129-130, Nov., 1941.

COLOR MUTANTS IN MICROTUS. L. L. Snyder. Jour. Mam., vol.11, no.1, p.83, Feb., 1930.

GENETIC STUDIES OF SEVERAL GEOGRAPHIC RACES OF CALIFORNIA DEER-MICE. F. B. Sumner. Amer. Nat., vol. 49, no.587, pp.688-701, map, Nov., 1915.

GEOGRAPHIC VARIATION AND MENDELIAN INHERITANCE. (EXPERIMENTS WITH DIFFERENT GEOGRAPHICAL RACES OF CALIFORNIA PEROMYSCUS.) F. B. Sumner. Jour. Exper. Zool., vol.30, pp. 369-402, figs.1-7, tab.1-4, Apr., 1920.

LINKAGE IN PEROMYSCUS. F. B. Sumner. Amer. Nat., vol.56, pp.412-417, Sept.-Oct., 1922.

OBSERVATIONS ON THE INHERITANCE OF A MULTIFACTOR COLOR VARIATION IN WHITE-FOOTED MICE (PEROMYSCUS). F. B. Sumner. Amer. Nat., vol.62, pp. 193-206, illus., June, 1928.

SEVERAL COLOR "MUTATIONS" IN MICE OF THE GENUS PEROMYSCUS. F. B. Sumner. Genetics 2, pp.291-300, May, 1917.

FURTHER STUDIES OF COLOR MUTATIONS IN MICE OF THE GENUS PEROMYSCUS. F.B.Sumner, H.H. Collins. Jour. Exper. Zool., vol.36, pp.289-321, 2 colored pls., Oct., 1922.

BILATERAL ASYMMETRY AND ITS RELATION TO CERTAIN PROBLEMS IN GENETICS. (STUDIES IN PEROMYSCUS.) F.B. Sumner, R. R. Huestis. Genetics, vol.6, pp.445-485, 5 figs., Sept., 1921.

STUDIES OF COAT-COLOR AND FOOT PIGMENTATION IN SUBSPECIFIC HYBRIDS OF PEROMYSCUS EREMICUS. F. B. Sumner, R. R. Huestis. Biol. Bull., vol. 48, pp.37-55, Jan., 1925.

OCCURRENCE OF A MUTANT MEADOW-MOUSE. Ruth Dowell Svihla, Arthur Svihla. Science, n.s., vol.67, p.531, May 25, 1928.

THE INHERITANCE OF EPILEPSY AND OF WALTZING IN PEROMYSCUS. Margaret Liebe Watson. Contrib. Lab. Vertebrate Gen., Univ. Michigan, Ann Arbor, no.11, pp.24, July, 1939.

Hybrids

A STUDY OF RACIAL HYBRIDS IN THE DEER-MOUSE, PEROMYSCUS MANICULATUS. Lee R. Dice. Occas. Papers Mus. Zool., Univ. Michigan, Ann Arbor, no.312, pp.1-22, May 3, 1935.

NATURAL HYBRIDIZATION IN THE PEROMYSCUS LEUCOPUS SPECIES GROUP OF MICE. W. H. McCarley. Evolution, Lancaster, vol.8, no.4, pp.314-323, illus., Dec., 1954.

RESUTLS OF EXPERIMENTS IN HYBRIDIZING SUBSPECIES OF PEROMYSCUS. F. B. Sumner. Jour. Exp. Zool., vol.38, pp.245-292, 7 figs., Oct., 1923.

STUDIES OF SUBSPECIFIC HYBRIDS IN PEROMYSCUS. F. B. Sumner. Proc. Nat. Acad. Sci., vol.9, no.2, pp.47-52, Feb., 1923.

STUDIES OF COAT-COLOR AND FOOT PIGMENTATION IN SUBSPECIFIC HYBRIDS OF PEROMYSCUS EREMICUS. F. B. Sumner, R. R. Huestis. Biol. Bull., vol. 48, no.1, pp.37-55, tables 3, Jan., 1925.

HYBRIDIZATION EXPERIMENTS BETWEEN PEROMYSCUS POLIONOTUS AND PEROMYSCUS MANICULATUS. Margaret Liebe Watson. Jour. Mam., vol.23, no.3, pp. 315-316, Aug.14, 1942.

Lower California

CRITICAL EXAMINATION OF THE MEADOW MICE OF LOWER CALIFORNIA. Joseph Grinnell. Jour. Mam., vol.7, no.3, pp.221-226, Aug., 1926.

A NEW SUBSPECIES OF PEROMYSCUS, FROM SAN JOSÉ ISLAND, LOWER CALIFORNIA, MEXICO. E. Raymond Hall. Proc. Biol. Soc. Wash., vol.44, pp.87-88, June 29, 1931.

A NEW MEADOW MOUSE FROM LOWER CALIFORNIA, MEXICO. Laurence M. Huey. Trans. San Diego Soc. Nat. Hist., vol.7, no.6, pp.47-49, Dec.19, 1931.

A NEW RACE OF WOOD RAT (NEOTOMA) FROM THE GULF SIDE OF CENTRAL BAJA CALIFORNIA, MEXICO. Laurence M. Huey. Trans. San Diego Soc. Nat. Hist., 12 (15): 287-288, Sept.25, 1957.

A NEW SUBSPECIES OF PEROMYSCUS FROM THE GULF COAST OF LOWER CALIFORNIA, MEXICO. Laurence M. Huey. Trans. San Diego Soc. Nat. Hist., vol.6, no.26, pp.389-390, Aug.28, 1931.

A NEW WOOD RAT, GENUS NEOTOMA, FROM THE VISCAINO DESERT REGION OF BAJA CALIFORNIA, MEXICO. Laurence M. Huey. Trans. San Diego Soc. Nat. Hist., vol.10, no.16, pp.307-310, Aug.31, 1945.

DESCRIPTION OF A NEW SPECIES OF WOOD-RAT FROM CERROS ISLAND, OFF LOWER CALIFORNIA (NEOTOMA BRYANTI SP. NOV.). C. Hart Merriam. Amer. Naturalist, vol.21, no.2, pp.191-193, Feb., 1887.

A NEW WHITE-FOOTED MOUSE FROM LOWER CALIFORNIA, MEXICO. E. W. Nelson, E. A. Goldman. Trans. San Diego Soc. Nat. Hist., vol.7, no.7, pp.51-52, Apr.15, 1932.

TWO NEW WOODRATS FROM LOWER CALIFORNIA. E. W. Nelson, E. A. Goldman. Proc. Biol. Soc. Wash., vol.44, pp.107-109, Oct.17, 1931.

TWO NEW WOODRATS FROM LOWER CALIFORNIA, MEXICO. Robert T. Orr. Proc. Biol. Soc. Wash., vol.47, pp.109-112, June 13, 1934.

Madagascar

(DESCRIPTION OF A NEW SPECIES OF NESOMYS.) Description d'une nouvelle espece de Nesomys. G. Grandidier. Bull. Acad. Malgache, vol.11, pp.95-99, pls.2, figs.8, (1928) 1929.

ON THE MALAGASY RODENT GENUS BRACHYUROMYS; AND ON THE MUTUAL RELATIONS OF SOME GROUPS OF THE MURIDAE (HESPEROMYINAE, MICROTINAE, MURINAE, AND "SPALACIDAE") WITH EACH OTHER AND WITH MALAGASY NESOMYINAE. C. I. Forsyth Major. Proc. Zool. Soc. Lond., pp.695-720, pls. 37-40, figs.4, Oct.1, 1897.

A NEW SPECIES OF THE MASCARENE GENUS ELIURUS. Oldfield Thomas. Ann. and Mag. Nat. Hist. (8), vol.2, no. 11, pp.453-454, Nov., 1908.

ON A NEW SPECIES OF ELIURUS. Oldfield Thomas. Ann. and Mag. Nat. Hist. (6), vol.16, no.92, pp.164-165, Aug., 1895.

Methods, Techniques

LIVE TRAPPING AND TAGGING MUSKRATS. Shaler E. Aldous. Jour. Wildlife Mgt., Menasha, vol.10, no.1, pp.42-44, pls.3-4, Jan., 1946.

THE AGING OF MUSKRATS ON THE MONTEZUMA NATIONAL WILDLIFE REFUGE. Maurice M. Alexander. Jour. Wildlife Mgt., 15 (2): 175-186, Apr., 1951.

(ON THE QUESTION OF DETERMINING THE AGE OF THE COMMON FIELD-VOLE.) K voprosu ob opryedyelyenii vozrasta obiknovyennoi polyevki (Microtus arvalis Pall.). N. V. Bashyenina. Zool. Zhurnal, vol.32, no.4, pp.730-743, 1953.

DETERMINATION OF SEX AND AGE IN MUSKRATS. Luther L. Baumgartner, Frank C. Bellrose. Jour. Wildlife Mgt., 7 (1): 77-81, Jan., 1943.

MUSKRATS "AGED" AT A GLANCE. James Beer. Wisconsin Conserv. Bull., Madison, vol.13, no.8, pp.13-14, illus., Aug., 1948.

TESTS FOR DISCRIMINATION BETWEEN FOUR SUBSPECIES OF DEER-MICE (PEROMYSCUS MANICULATUS). W. Frank Blair. Texas Jour. Sci., vol.6, no.2, pp.201-210, June, 1954.

INCISOR WIDTH AS AN AGE CRITERION IN MUSKRATS. Allen Brohn, Charles E. Shanks. Jour. Wildlife Mgt., 12 (4): 437-439, Oct., 1948.

THE STATISTICAL CONCEPT OF HOME RANGE AS APPLIED TO THE RECAPTURE RADIUS OF THE DEERMOUSE (PEROMYSCUS). Lee R. Dice. Contrib. Lab. Vert. Biol. no.62, pp.1-15, graphs, Feb., 1953.

AIR INFLATION AS AN AID IN PELTING MUSKRATS. Herbert L. Dozier. Jour. Wildlife Mgt., 15 (2): 199-205, Apr., 1951.

ESTIMATING MUSKRAT POPULATIONS BY HOUSE COUNTS. Herbert L. Dozier. Trans. N. A. Wildlife Conf., 13: 372-389, 1948.

ESTIMATING MUSKRAT POPULATIONS BY HOUSE COUNTS. Herbert L. Dozier. USDI, F&WS, Wildlife Leaflet 306, 17 pp., June, 1948.

IDENTIFICATION OF SEX IN LIVE MUSKRATS. Herbert L. Dozier. Jour. Wildlife Mgt., 6 (4): 292-293, Oct., 1942.

PELTING MUSKRATS BY AIR INFLATION. Herbert L. Dozier, Merton Radway. Jour. Wildlife Mgt., Menasha, vol.12, no.3, pp. 333-334, July, 1948.

AGING MEADOW MICE, MICROTUS CALIFORNICUS, BY OBSERVATION OF MOLT PROGRESSION. Dean H. Ecke, Alva R. Kinney. Jour. Mam., 37 (2):249-254, illus., June 9, 1956.

NOTES ON EAR-TAGGING OF MICE. Gaines W. Eidy, C. R. Joyce. Jour. Mam., vol.25, no.2, pp.199-200, May 25, 1944.

EXPERIMENTAL TAGGING OF YOUNG MUSKRATS FOR PURPOSES OF STUDY.

Paul L. Errington, Carolyn Storm Errington. Jour. Wildlife Mgt., 1 (3-4): 49-61, Oct., 1937.

A TECHNIQUE FOR FINDING MICROTUS NESTS. Gillian K. Godfrey. Jour. Mam., 34 (4): 503-505, Nov., 1953.

TRACING FIELD VOLES (MICROTUS AGRESTIS) WITH A GEIGER-MUELLER COUNTER. Gillian K. Godfrey. Ecology, vol. 35, no. 1, pp. 5-10, Jan., 1954.

A METHOD FOR DETERMINING THE RELATIVE ABUNDANCE OF MICROTUS PENNSYLVANICUS. R. J. Greffenius. Jour. Wildlife Mgt., 3 (3): 199-200, July, 1939.

PITUITARY REMOVAL IN MICROTUS WITH PRESERVATION OF SKULL. Jay Stuart Haft. Jour. Mam., 37 (3): 446-447, Sept. 11, 1956.

SUCCESSFUL MUSKRAT TRAPPING. John R. Hendley. Fur-Fish-Game, Harding's Mag., Columbus, vol. 79, no. 4, pp. 38-39, Apr., 1945.

USE OF NEST BOXES IN WOOD MOUSE POPULATION STUDIES. William B. Jackson. Jour. Mam., vol. 34, no. 4, pp. 505-507, Nov. 13, 1953.

(A METHOD OF DETERMINING THE AGE OF THE REDDISH FIELD VOLE AND RESULTS OF ITS APPLICATION.) Metod opredeleniya vozracta rizhikh polevol i opit ego primeneniya. (Microtine tooth development.) T. V. Koshkina. Zool. Zhurnal, vol. 34, no. 3, pp. 631-639, 1955.

THE MEASUREMENT OF FERTILITY AND ITS USE AS AN INDEX OF REPRODUCTIVE ISOLATION AMONG CERTAIN LABORATORY STOCKS OF PEROMYSCUS. T. T. Liu. Contrib. Lab. Vert. Biol. Univ. Michigan, Ann Arbor, no. 59, pp. 1-12, Feb., 1953.

REDUCTION OF MORTALITY IN LIVE-TRAPPED MICE. (USING CORN FOR BAIT OR BAIT SUPPLEMENT.) Leonard M. Llewellyn. Jour. Wildlife Mgt., 14 (1): 85-86, Jan., 1950.

THE APPLICABILITY OF COVARIANCE ANALYSIS FOR COMPARISON OF BODY AND SKELETAL MEASUREMENTS BETWEEN TWO RACES OF THE DEERMOUSE, PEROMYSCUS MANICULATUS. William B. McIntosh. Contrib. Lab. Vert. Biology, Univ. Michigan, Ann Arbor, no. 72, p. 55, Sept., 1955.

AN EVALUATION OF THE APPLICABILITY OF COVARIANCE ANALYSIS AS APPLIED TO THE COMPARISON OF BODY AND SKELETAL MEASUREMENTS BETWEEN TWO RACES OF THE DEER-MOUSE, PEROMYSCUS MANICULATUS. William B. McIntosh. PhD. thesis, Univ. Mich., 153 pp., 1954.

IDENTIFICATION OF MICE IN GENUS PEROMYSCUS BY A RED BLOOD CELL AGGLUTINATION TEST. Paul A. Moody. Jour. Mam., Balto., vol. 22, no. 1, pp. 40-47, fig. 1, Feb. 14, 1941.

FOREST TREE-SEED-EATERS AND METHODS USED TO MEASURE THEIR POPULATIONS IN THE PACIFIC NORTHWEST DOUGLAS FIR REGION. A. W. Moore. Univ. Wash. Forest Club Quart., 23 (1): 7-11, 25, 1949-1950.

BETTER WAYS OF TRAPPING MUSKRATS. A. K. Okolovitch. Translations of Russian Game Reports, Canadian Wildlife Serv., 2: 24-39, 1957.

THE DENTITION METHOD OF AGING MUSKRATS. J. Henry Sather. Chicago Acad. Sci., Nat. Hist. Misc. no. 130, pp. 1-3, illus., Mar., 1954.

ANALYSIS OF MUSKRAT AGE DETERMINATION METHODS AND THEIR APPLICATION IN MICHIGAN. Raymond D. Schofield. Jour. Wildlife Mgt., 19 (4): 463-466, 5 figs., Oct., 1955.

THE PELT-PRIMENESS METHOD OF AGING MUSKRATS. Charles E. Shanks. Amer. Midland Nat., 39 (1): 179-187, Jan., 1948.

EFFECT OF BAIT IN LIVE TRAPPING PEROMYSCUS. Lucille F. Stickel. Jour. Wildlife Mgt., 12 (2): 211-212, Apr., 1948.

EXPERIMENTAL ANALYSIS OF METHODS FOR MEASURING SMALL MAMMAL POPULATIONS. Lucille F. Stickel. Jour. Wildlife Mgt., 10 (2): 150-159, Apr., 1946.

THE TRAP LINE AS A MEASURE OF SMALL MAMMAL POPULATIONS. Lucille F. Stickel. Jour. Wildlife Mgt., 12 (2): 153-161, Apr., 1948.

TRAPPING AND BANDING MUSKRATS. Michael J. Takos. Jour. Wildlife Mgt., Menasha, vol. 7, no. 4, pp. 400-407, pls. 24-25, Oct., 1943.

(METHOD FOR DETERMINING THE AGE AND LONGEVITY OF THE MUSKRAT.) Metodika opredeleniya vozrasta i prodolzhitelnost zhizni ondatri (Fiber zibethicus). D. S. Tsigankov. Zool. Zhurnal, vol. 34, no. 3, pp. 640-651, 1955.

ON CERTAIN STATISTICAL METHODS USED IN BIOLOGY WITH SPECIAL REFERENCE TO HUSSON'S PAPER ON CRICETUS CRICETUS CANESCENS NEHRING. H. R. van der Vaart. Proc. Kon. Nederlandse Akad. Wetensch., Amsterdam, ser. C, vol. 56, no. 5, pp. 631-637, 1953.

METHODS OF DETECTING MUSKRATS. Tom Warwick. Annals Applied Biol., London, vol. 23, no. 1, pp. 165-174, figs. 2, Feb., 1936.

THE USE OF SCENT IN LIVE-TRAPPING MUSKRATS. Roger M. Williams. Jour. Wildlife Mgt., Menasha, vol. 15, no. 1, pp. 117-118, Jan., 1951.

Mexico

DESCRIPTIONS OF TWO SUPPOSED NEW SPECIES OF MICE FROM COSTA RICA AND MEXICO, WITH REMARKS ON HESPEROMYS MELANOPHRYS OF COUES. Joel Asaph Allen. U. S. Nat. Mus., Proc. Wash., 1892, vol. 14, pp. 193-196, July 24, 1891.

A NEW GENUS OF RODENTS FROM YUCATAN. (OTONYCTOMYS, O. HATTI.) H. E. Anthony. Amer. Mus. Novitates, no. 586, pp. 3, fig. 1, Nov. 16, 1932.

DESCRIPTIONS AND RECORDS OF HARVEST MICE (GENUS REITHRODONTOMYS) FROM MEXICO. Seth B. Benson. Proc. Biol. Soc. Wash., vol. 52, pp. 147-150, Oct. 11, 1939.

NEW SUBSPECIES OF THE CANYON MOUSE (PEROMYSCUS CRINITUS) FROM SONORA, MEXICO. Seth B. Benson. Proc. Biol. Soc. Wash., vol. 53, pp. 1-4, Feb. 16, 1940.

DESCRIPTION OF A RACE OF DESERT WOODRAT (NEOTOMA LEPIDA) FROM SONORA. Philip M. Blossom. Occas. Papers Mus. Zool. Univ. Michigan, no. 315, pp. 3, May 29, 1935.

A NEW RICE RAT (ORYZOMYS) FROM SONORA, MEXICO. William Henry Burt. Proc. Biol. Soc. Wash., vol. 47, pp. 107-108, June 13, 1934.

THE MEXICAN VOLCANO MOUSE, NEOTOMODON. William B. Davis, Lewis A. Follansbee. Jour. Mam., vol. 26, no. 4, pp. 401-411, illus., Feb. 12, 1946.

A NEW PINON MOUSE (PEROMYSCUS TRUEI) FROM DURANGO, MEXICO. Robert B. Finley, Jr. Univ. Kansas Publ., Mus. Nat. Hist., Lawrence, vol. 5, no. 20, pp. 263-267, May 23, 1952.

A NEW BROWN MOUSE OF THE GENUS SCOTINOMYS FROM MEXICO. (SCOTINOMYS TEGUINA SUBNUBILUS.) E. A. Goldman. Proc. Biol. Soc. Wash., vol. 48, pp. 141-142, Aug. 22, 1935.

A NEW HARVEST MOUSE OF THE GENUS REITHRODONTOMYS FROM TAMAULIPAS, MEXICO. George G. Goodwin. Amer. Mus. Novitates, New York, no. 1660, pp. 3, May 25, 1954.

A NEW WHITE-FOOTED MOUSE FROM MEXICO. E. A. Goldman. Proc. Biol. Soc. Wash., vol. 55, pp. 157-158, Oct. 17, 1942.

THREE NEW COTTON RATS FROM TEHAANTEPEC, MEXICO. George G. Goodwin. Amer. Mus. Novitates, New York, no. 1705, pp. 5, Feb. 4, 1955.

TWO WHITE-FOOTED MICE FROM OAXACA, MEXICO. George G. Goodwin. Amer. Mus. Novitates, New York, no. 1732, pp. 5, June 10, 1955.

A NEW SUBSPECIES OF COTTON RAT, SIGMODON HISPIDUS, FROM MICHOACAN, MEXICO. E. Raymond Hall. Proc. Biol. Soc. Wash., vol. 62, pp. 149-150, Aug. 23, 1949.

TWO NEW MEADOW MICE FROM MICHOACAN, MEXICO. E. Raymond Hall. Univ. Kansas Publ. Mus. Nat. Hist., Lawrence, vol. 1, no. 21, pp. 423-427, figs. 6, Dec. 24, 1948.

A NEW HARVEST MOUSE FROM MICHOACAN, MEXICO. E. Raymond Hall, Bernardo Villa R. Proc. Biol. Soc. Wash., vol. 62, pp. 163-164, Aug. 23, 1949.

DESCRIPTIONS OF TWO SUBSPECIES OF HARVEST MICE (GENUS REITHRODONTOMYS) FROM MEXICO. Emmet T. Hooper. Proc. Biol. Soc. Wash., vol. 63, pp. 167-170, Dec. 29, 1950.

A NEW SUBSPECIES OF HARVEST MOUSE (GENUS REITHRODONTOMYS) FROM CHIAPAS, MEXICO. Emmet T. Hooper. Jour. Wash. Acad. Sci., vol. 40, no. 12, pp. 418-419, Dec. 22, 1950.

A NEW SUBSPECIES OF PYGMY RICE RAT (ORYZOMYS FULVESCENS) FROM CHIAPAS, MEXICO. Emmet T. Hooper. Proc. Biol. Soc. Wash., vol. 65, pp. 23-26, Jan. 29, 1952.

EXPEDITION OF THE CALIFORNIA ACADEMY OF SCIENCES TO THE GULF OF CALIFORNIA IN 1921. XXXI. A NEW MOUSE (PEROMYSCUS SLEVINI) FROM THE GULF OF CALIFORNIA. Joseph Mailliard. Proc. Calif. Acad. Sci., ser. 4, vol. 12, no. 31, pp. 953-956, July 22, 1924.

DESCRIPTION OF A NEW GENUS AND SPECIES OF MURINE RAT (XENOMYS NELSONI) FROM THE STATE OF COLIMA, WESTERN MEXICO. C. Hart Merriam. Proc. Biol. Soc. Wash., vol. 7, pp. 159-163, Sept. 29, 1892.

DESCRIPTION OF A NEW HARVEST MOUSE (REITHRODONTOMYS) FROM MEXICO. C. Hart Merriam. Proc. Biol. Soc. Wash., vol. 13, p. 151, June 13, 1900.

DESCRIPTIONS OF TWENTY NEW SPECIES AND A NEW SUBGENUS OF PEROMYSCUS FROM MEXICO AND GUATEMALA. C. Hart Merriam. Proc. Biol. Soc. Wash., vol. 12, pp. 115-125, Apr. 30, 1898.

DESCRIPTION OF TWO NEW SUBGENERA AND THREE NEW SPECIES OF MICROTUS FROM MEXICO AND GUATEMALA. C. Hart Merriam. Proc. Biol. Soc. Wash., vol. 12, pp. 105-108, Apr. 30, 1898.

NELSONIA NEOTOMODON, A NEW GENUS AND SPECIES OF MURINE RODENT FROM MEXICO. C. Hart Merriam. Proc. Biol. Soc. Wash., vol. 11, pp. 277-279, Dec. 17, 1897.

A NEW GENUS (NEOTOMODON) AND THREE NEW SPECIES OF MURINE RODENTS FROM THE MOUNTAINS OF SOUTHERN MEXICO. C. Hart Merriam. Proc. Biol. Soc. Wash., vol. 12, pp. 127-129, Apr. 30, 1898.

TWO NEW WOOD RATS (GENUS NEOTOMA) FROM STATE OF COAHUILA, MEXICO. C. Hart Merriam. Proc. Biol. Soc. Wash., vol. 16, pp. 47-48, Mar. 19, 1903.

A NEW WOODRAT FROM MEXICO. Wilfred H. Osgood. Field Mus. Nat. Hist., Zool. ser., vol. 20, no. 35, pp. 475-476, Dec. 31, 1938.

THIRTY NEW MICE OF THE GENUS PEROMYSCUS FROM MEXICO AND GUATEMALA. Wilfred H. Osgood. Proc. Biol. Soc. Wash., vol. 17, pp. 55-77, Mar. 21, 1904.

A NEW COTTON RAT (GENUS SIGMODON) FROM MORELOS, MEXICO. Robert J. Russell. Biol. Soc. Wash., vol. 65, pp. 81-82, Apr. 25, 1952.

A NEW SUBSPECIES OF THE PYGMY MOUSE, BAIOMYS MUSCULUS, FROM MORELOS, MEXICO. Robert J. Russell. Proc. Biol. Soc. Wash., vol.65, pp.21-22, Jan.29, 1952.

NOTES ON SOME MEXICAN ORYZOMYS. Oldfield Thomas. Ann. and Mag. Nat. Hist. (6), vol.11, no.65, pp.402-405, May, 1893.

ON THREE NEW FORMS OF PEROMYSCUS OBTAINED BY DR. HANS GADOW, F.R.S., AND MRS. GADOW IN MEXICO. Oldfield Thomas. Ann. and Mag. Nat. Hist. (7), vol.11, no.65, pp.484-487, May, 1903.

North America

THE AMERICAN COLLARED LEMMINGS (DICROSTONYX). (COMPLETE REVISION; ONE NEW SPECIES, D. EXSUL, FROM ST. LAWRENCE ISLAND.) Glover M. Allen. Bull. Mus. Comp. Zool., vol.62, no.13, pp.509-540, text fig.1, pl.1, Feb., 1919.

THE RAMBLIN' 'RAT' COVERS THE CONTINENT. (MUSKRAT.) Elizabeth Bachman. South Dakota Conservation Digest, Pierre, vol.16, no.12, pp.1, 14, Dec., 1949.

NATIVE WILD MICE. John F. Breen. All-Pets Mag., Fond du Lac, vol.20, no.1, pp.71, 73, Jan., 1949.

THE RICE RATS OF NORTH AMERICA (GENUS ORYZOMYS). E. A. Goldman. U. S. Dept. Agric., Bur. Biol. Surv., N. Amer. Fauna, no.43, pp.100, figs.11, pls.6, Sept.23, 1918.

COMMENTS ON THE TAXONOMY AND DISTRIBUTION OF NORTH AMERICAN MICROTINES. E. Raymond Hall, E. Lendell Cockrum. Univ. Kansas Publ., Mus. Nat. Hist., Lawrence, vol.5, no.23, pp.293-312, Nov.17, 1952.

THREE NEW LEMMINGS (DICROSTONYX) FROM ARCTIC AMERICA. Charles O. Handley, Jr. Jour. Wash. Acad. Sci., vol.43, no.6, pp.197-200, June 24, 1953.

ABSTRACT OF GOLDMAN'S "THE RICE RATS OF NORTH AMERICA (GENUS ORYZOMYS)." Ned Hollister. Jour. Wash. Acad. Sci., vol.8, pp.659-660, Dec.4, 1918.

COMMENTS ON THE TAXONOMY AND GEOGRAPHIC DISTRIBUTION OF SOME NORTH AMERICAN WOODRATS (GENUS NEOTOMA). Keith R. Kelson. Univ. Kansas Publ., Mus. Nat. Hist., Lawrence, vol.5, no.16, pp.233-242, Apr.10, 1952.

DESCRIPTION OF THREE NEW SPECIES OF AMERICAN ARVICOLAE, WITH REMARKS UPON SOME OTHER AMERICAN RODENTS. John Le Conte. Proc. Acad. Nat. Sci. Phila., vol.6, pp.404-415, 1854.

(SKELETON REMAINS OF DICROSTONYX GROENLANDICUS TRAILL AS CONTENT OF HAIR BALLS OF BIRDS OF PREY GATHERED BY MEMBERS OF THE DANISH THREE-YEAR EXPEDITION TO NORTHEASTERN GREENLAND 1931-34.) Skelettreste von Dicrostonyx groenlandicus Traill als inhalt von Raubvogelgewoellen untersuchung von Raubvogelgewoellen, gesammelt von Mitgliedern des Daenischen Drei jahres-Expedition nach Nordostgroenland 1931-34. E. V. Mandach. Meddelelser om Gronland, Kommissionen for Videnskabelige undersogelser i Gronland, Copenhagen, vol.112, no.4, pp.54, figs.2, pls.1-22, 1938.

POSSIBLE ESTABLISHMENT OF THE HAMSTER IN THE UNITED STATES. Charles A. Reed. Amer. Midland Nat., Notre Dame, vol.35, no.3, pp.771-772, May, 1946.

DESCRIPTION OF A NEW GENUS AND SPECIES OF ARVICOLINE RODENT FROM THE UNITED STATES. Samuel N. Rhoads. Amer. Naturalist, pp.182-185, illus., Feb., 1894.

DESCRIPTIONS OF FOUR NEW SPECIES AND TWO SUBSPECIES OF WHITE-FOOTED MICE FROM THE UNITED STATES AND BRITISH COLUMBIA. Samuel N. Rhoads. Proc. Acad. Nat. Sci. Phila., pp.253-261, Sept.25 (pp.253-256), Octo. (pp.257-288). 1894.

THE LEMMING MOUSE IN NORTH AMERICA AND ITS OCCURRENCE IN THE STATE OF WASHINGTON. William T. Shaw. Murrelet, vol.11, no.2, pp.7-10, illus., May, 1930.

DIAGNOSIS OF A NEW SPECIES OF HESPEROMYS FROM NORTH AMERICA. Oldfield Thomas. Ann. and Mag. Nat. Hist. (5), vol.19, no.109, p.66, Jan., 1887.

Pacific Islands

A NEW VOLE FROM HALL ISLAND, BERING SEA. Gerrit S. Miller, Jr. Proc. Biol. Soc., Wash., vol.13, pp.13-14, Jan.31, 1899.

SIX NEW WHITE-FOOTED MICE (PEROMYSCUS MANICULATUS GROUP), FROM ISLANDS OFF THE PACIFIC COAST. E. W. Nelson, E. A. Goldman. Jour. Wash. Acad. Sci., vol.21, no.21, pp.530-535, Dec.19, 1931.

A NEW RODENT OF THE GENUS NESORYZOMYS FROM THE GALAPAGOS ISLANDS. Robert T. Orr. Proc. California Acad. Sci., ser.4, vol.23, no.21, pp.303-306, pl.25, Sept.1, 1938.

Palestine

(ANNOTATED LIST OF GERBIL SPECIES OF PALESTINE.) Liste commentee des especes de gerbillides de Palestine. Francis Petter. Mammalia, Paris, 21 (3): 241-257, Sept., 1957.

DESCRIPTION OF A NEW SPECIES OF MERIONES FROM PALESTINE. Oldfield Thomas. Ann. and Mag. Nat. Hist. (6), vol.9, no.50, pp.147-149, Feb., 1892.

A NEW JIRD (MERIONES) FROM SOUTHERN PALESTINE. Oldfield Thomas. Ann. and Mag. Nat. Hist., ser.9, vol.10, pp. 552-553, Nov., 1922.

A NEW VOLE FROM PALESTINE. Oldfield Thomas. Ann. and Mag. Nat. Hist. (8), vol.19, no.114, pp.450-451, June, 1917.

THE CYTOTAXONOMY, ECOLOGY AND EVOLUTION OF THE GERBILS AND JIRDS OF ISRAEL (RODENTIA: GERBILLINAE). A. Zahavi, J. Wahrman. Mammalia, Paris, 21 (4): 341-380, Dec., 1957.

Parasites

THE MUSKRAT, A NEW HOST FOR PARAGONIMUS. Donald J. Ameel. Science, n.s., vol.75, no.1945, p.382, Apr.8, 1932.

TWO LARVAL CESTODES FROM THE MUSKRAT. Donald J. Ameel. Trans. Am. Micros. Soc., 61 (3): 267-271, July, 1942.

A NEW FLEA FROM THE MOHAVE DESERT (CALIFORNIA). G. F. Augustson. Bull. Southern California Acad. Sci., Los Angeles, vol.40, no.3, pp.138-139, 3 figs., Sept.-Dec., 1941.

A NEW MOUSE FLEA, PLEOCHAETOIDES BULLISI, N. GEN. N. SP., FROM TEXAS. G. F. Augustson. Jour. Parasitology, 30 (6): 366-368, Dec., 1944.

A NEW SUBSPECIES OF ORCHOPEAS SEXDENTATUS (BAKER). G. F. Augustson. Bull. S. Calif. Acad. Sci., 42 (1): 49-51, Jan.-Apr., 1943.

HELMINTHS FROM THE AMERICAN COTTON-RAT (SIGMODON HISPIDUS). H. A. Baylis. Ann. and Mag. Nat. Hist., Ser.11, 12 (87): 189-195, Aug., 1945.

THE MORPHOLOGY AND LIFE HISTORY OF PSILOSTOMUM ONDATRAE PRICE, 1931, (TREMATODA: PSILOSTOMIDAE). Paul C. Beaver. Jour. Parasitology, 25 (5): 383-393, Oct., 1939.

SOME NOTES ON THE BIOLOGY OF THE PACK-RAT CUTEREBRID (CUTEREBRA BEAMERI HALL) IN KANSAS. R. H. Beamer, L. R. Penner, C. W. Hibbard. Jour. Kansas Entom. Soc., Lawrence, vol. 16, no.2, pp.47-50, Apr., 1943.

HIGH OCCURRENCE OF TAENIA TAENIAFORMIS IN THE MUSKRAT. Mitchell A. Byrd. Jour. Wildlife Mgt., Ithaca, vol.17, no.3, pp.384-385, illus., July, 1953.

TRICHOSTRONGYLUS CALCARATUS IN MUSKRAT. Asa C. Chandler. Jour. Parasitol., Lancaster, vol.36, no.1, p.87, Feb., 1950.

TRICHURIS PEROMYSCI N. SP. FROM PEROMYSCUS CALIFORNICUS AND FURTHER NOTES ON T. PEROGNATHI CHANDLER, 1945. Asa C. Chandler. Jour. Parasitol., Lancaster, vol.32, no.2, p.208, Apr., 1946.

THE LOUSE POPULATIONS OF SOME CRICETID RODENTS. Edwin F. Cook, James R. Beer. Parasitology, vol.45, nos. 3-4, pp.409-420, illus., Nov., 1955.

RICTULARIA ONYCHOMIS N. SP. (NEMATODA: THELAZIIDAE) FROM THE GRASSHOPPER MOUSE ONYCHOMYS LEUCOGASTER (WIED.). Ashton C. Cuckler. Jour. Parasitology, 25 (5): 431-435, Oct., 1939.

A NEW CUTEREBRA (DIPTERA; CUTEREBRIDAE) FROM IOWA WITH NOTES ON CERTAIN FACIAL STRUCTURES. Herbert T. Dalmat. Amer. Midland Nat., Notre Dame, vol.27, no.2, pp.418-421, illus., Mar., 1942.

TRIATOMA SANGUISUGA (LE CONTE) AND TRIATOMA AMBIGUA NEIVA AS NATURAL CARRIERS OF TRYPANOSOMA CRUZI IN TEXAS. Dorland J. Davis, Theodore McGregor, Thelma de Shazo. Pub. Health Rept., 58 (9): 353-354, Feb. 26, 1943.

(INFLUENCE OF FOOD STORES OF THE GREATER SAND RAT (RHOMBOMYS OPIMUS LICHT.) ON NUMBERS AND DISTRIBUTION OF FLEAS IN BURROWS.) Vliyanie kormovikh zapasov bolshoi peschanki (Rhombomys opimus Licht.) na chislennost i raspredeleniye blokh v norakh. A. I. Dyatlov. Zool. Zhurnal, 35 (9): 1406-1409, 1956.

A NEW SPECIES OF FLEA FROM THE FIELD MOUSE, BAIOMYS TAYLORI. R. B. Eads. Ann. Ent. Soc. Am., 39 (4): 545-548, Dec., 1946.

A NEW MITE FROM NESTS OF THE WOOD RAT, NEOTOMA MICROPUS. R. B. Eads, B. G. Hightower. Ent. News, 62 (8): 249-250, Oct., 1951.

INTERNAL PARASITES OF CENTRAL NEW YORK MUSKRATS (ONDATRA Z. ZIBETHICA L.). Robert L. Edwards. Jour. Parasitology, 35 (5): 547-548, Oct., 1949.

NEW RECORDS FOR ORYZOMYS PALUSTRIS (HARLAN) AND ASCARISCUS MASONI EWING. D. S. Farner. Proc. Biol. Soc. Wash., 60: 29-30, Apr., 1947. (Chiggers on rice rats in Maryland.)

NOTE ON RHADINOPSYLLA ISACANTHUS (ROETHS.) (SIPHONAPTERA). (PRINCIPAL HOST IS THE BANK VOLE CLETHRIONOMYS GLAREOLUS BRITTANICUS). R. B. Freeman. Entomologists' Monthly Mag., London, vol.78, pp.139-140, June 1942.

A SURVEY OF MUSKRAT HELMINTHS IN ILLINOIS. James H. Gilford. Jour. Parasit., 40 (6): 702-703, Dec., 1954.

DOG HEARTWORM IN THE MUSKRAT IN NEW YORK. Frans C. Goble. Jour. Mam., vol.23, no.3, p.346, Aug.14, 1942.

TWO PARASITES AFFECTING NORTH DAKOTA MUSKRATS. Alice I. Goldsby, J. W. Johnston. Bimonthly Bull., 14 (1): 22-24, Sept.-Oct., 1951.

STENISTOMERA (SIPHONPATERA): A REVALUATION OF THE GENUS, WITH THE DESCRIPTION OF A NEW SUBGENUS AND SPECIES. ( 2 WESTERN SPECIES FROM PEROMYSCUS AND WOODRAT.) Newell E. Good. Proc. Ent. Soc. Wash., 44 (7): 131-139, Oct., 1942.

RED-BACKED VOLE WITH A TICK ATTACHED NEAR EYEBALL. Harvey L. Gunderson. Jour. Mam., vol.33, no.4, p.495, Nov.19, 1952.

THREE ANOPLOCEPHALID CESTODES FROM THE PRAIRIE MEADOW VOLE, WITH DESCRIPTION OF ANDRYA MICROTI N. SP. Merle F. Hansen. Univ. Nebraska, Studies from Zool. Lab., Lincoln, no.228, pp.279-282, illus., 1947.

OBSERVATIONS ON THE HELMINTHS AND ECTOPARASITES OF THE COTTON RAT, SIGMODON HISPIDUS HISPIDUS, SAY AND ORD, IN GEORGIA AND NORTH CAROLINA. Reinard Harkema, Leo Kartman. Jour. Elisha Mitchell Scientific Soc., Chapel Hill, vol.64, no.2, pp.183-191, tbls.5, Dec., 1948.

OBSERVATIONS ON EGYPTIAN HYALOMMA TICKS (IXODOIDEA, IXODIDAE). 3. INFESTATION OF GREATER GERBILS, ESPECIALLY BY IMMATURE H. IMPELATATUM S. & S. Harry Hoogstraal, Makram N. Kaiser. Ann. Entomol. Soc. Amer., 51 (1): 17-19, Jan., 1958.

"WARBLES" ON NEOTOMA. Edmund C. Jaeger. Jour. Mam., vol.5, no.4, p.268, Nov., 1924.

EUBRACHYLAELAPS DEBILIS, A NEW LAELAPTID MITE (ACARINA: LAELAPTIDAE) PARASITIC ON THE DEER MOUSE, PEROMYSCUS MANICULATUS (MAMMALIA: CRICETIDAE). E. W. Jameson, Jr. Jour. Parasitol., Lancaster, vol.36, no.1, pp.62-64, Feb., 1950.

SIPHONAPTERA: A NEW SPECIES OF CONORHINOPSYLLA FROM KANSAS. (FROM NESTS OF WOODRATS.) Wm. L. Jellison. Jour. Kansas Ent. Soc., 18 (3): 109-111, July, 1945.

A REPORT ON MITES INFESTING THE MUSKRAT (ONDATRA ZIBETHICA OSOYOOSENSIS) IN BRITISH COLUMBIA. Iola W. Knight. Can. Ent., 53 (10): 279-280, Oct., 1951.

AN ECOLOGICAL STUDY OF HELMINTHS OF SOME WYOMING VOLES (MICROTUS SPP.) WITH A DESCRIPTION OF A NEW SPECIES OF NEMATOSPIROIDES (HELIGMOSOMIDAE: NEMATODA). Merle L. Kuns, Robert Rausch. Zoologica, 35 (15): 181-188, Nov., 1950.

A SURVEY OF THE PARASITES OF THE SOUTH FLORIDA COTTON RAT SIGMODON HISPIDUS. Grady E. Lanier. Masters' thesis, Univ. Miami, 1952.

INTERNAL AND EXTERNAL PARASITES OF MUSKRATS. N. P. Lavroff. Trans. of Russian Game Reports, Canadian Wildlife Serv., 2: 84-115, 9 tables, 1957.

A NEW DICROCOELIID TREMATODE, EURY-TREMA KOMAREKI N. SP., FROM WHITE FOOTED MOUSE. Allen McIntosh. Proc. Helminth. Soc. Wash., 6 (1): 18-19, Jan., 1939.

A SPECIES OF EIMERIA FROM THE MUSKRAT, ONDATRA ZIBETHICA. H. M. Martin. Archiv. f. Protistenkunde, vol.70, pp.273-278, 3 figs., May 1, 1930.

NEW HELMINTH RECORDS FROM THE COTTON RAT, SIGMODON HISPIDUS, INCLUDING A NEW SPECIES, STRONGYLOIDES SIGMODONTIS. Dorothy M. Melvin, Asa C. Chandler. Jour. Parasitol., Lancaster, vol.36, no.6, sec.1, pp.505-510, Dec., 1950.

PARASITES OF MUSKRATS IN MAINE. Marvin C. Meyer, James R. Reilly. Am. Midland Nat., 44 (2): 467-477, Sept., 1950.

THE ECOLOGY OF THE OSAGE WOOD RAT, NEOTOMA FLORIDANA OSAGENSIS BLAIR, WITH EMPHASIS ON THE HELMINTHS OF THE HOST. Melville Floyd Murphy. MS thesis, Okla. A. and M. Coll., 1950.

(FILARIAL PARASITES IN THE COUNTRY RATS.) Filaria parasita de las ratas de Compo, Micropleura sigmodoni Spec.Nov.) I. Ochoterena, E. Caballero. Ann. Inst. Biol., Univ. Mexico, Mexico, D.F., vol.3, no.2, pp.123-125, figs.2, 1932.

A NEW TREMATODE, ALLASOGONOPORUS MARGINALIS, FROM THE MUSKRAT. Louis Olivier. Jour. Parasitology, 24 (2): 155-160, Apr., 1938.

PARASITOLOGICAL SURVEY OF LOUISIANA MUSKRATS. George H. Penn. Jour. Parasitology, 28 (4): 348-349, Aug., 1942.

THE LIFE HISTORY OF POROCEPHALUS CROTALI, A PARASITE OF THE LOUISIANA MUSKRAT. George H. Penn. Jour. Parasitology, 28 (4): 277-283, Aug., 1942.

NOTE ON THE FIELD MOUSE, APODEMUS SPECIOSUS, AS A MITE HOST IN YAMAGATA-KEN. Cornelius B. Philip, Takeo Tamiya. Nippon Eiseigaku Zasshi (Japenese Jour. Health) vol.1, no.1, pp.15-16, Aug., 1946. (In Japanese with English Translation attached).

LIFE HISTORY OF SCHISTOSOMATIUM DOUTHITTI (CORT). ( IN MICHIGAN, MICROTUS PENNSYLVANICUS IS NATURAL HOST OF THIS TREMATODE PARASITE.) Helen Florence Price. Amer. Jour. Hygiene, vol.13, no.3, p.685-727, pls.4, May, 1931.

DISTRIBUTION AND SPECIFICITY OF HELMINTHS IN MICROTINE RODENTS: EVOLUTIONARY IMPLICATIONS. Robert Rausch. Evolution, vol.11, no.3, pp.361-368, Sept., 1957.

PARASITES OF OHIO MUSKRATS. Robert Rausch. Jour. Wildlife Mgt., Menasha, vol.10, no.1, p.70, Jan., 1946.

PARANOPLOCEPHALA TROESCHI, NEW SPECIES OF CESTODE FROM THE MEADOW VOLE, MICROTUS P. PENNSYLVANICUS ORD. Robert Rausch. Trans. Am. Micros. Soc., 65 (4): 354-356, Oct., 1946.

SOME OBSERVATIONS OF CESTODES OF THE GENUS PARANOPLOCEPHALA LUEHE, PARASITIC IN NORTH AMERICAN VOLES (MICROTUS SPP.). Robert Rausch, Everett L. Schiller. Proc. Helminth. Soc. Wash., 16 (1): 23-31, Jan., 1949.

STUDIES ON THE PARASITIC HELMINTHS OF THE NORTH CENTRAL STATES. II. HELMINTHS OF VOLES (MICROTUS SPP.) PRELIMINARY REPORT. Robert Rausch, Jack D. Tiner. Amer. Midland Nat., 41 (3): 665-694, May, 1949.

A STUDY OF THE METAZOAL PARASITES OF THE MAINE MUSKRAT (ONDATRA ZIBETHICA ZIBETHICA (LINNAEUS, 1758). James R. Reilly. MS thesis, Univ. Maine, 1948; Jour. Forestry, 47 (5): 391, May, 1949. (Abstract of thesis.)

BRACHYLAEMUS PEROMYSCI N. SP., TREMATODA, FROM THE DEER MOUSE. Bruce D. Reynolds. Jour. Parasitology, 24 (3): 245-248, June, 1938.

PRELIMINARY SURVEY OF THE HELMINTH PARASITES OF MUSKRATS IN NORTHWESTERN OREGON, WITH DESCRIPTION OF HYMENOLEPIS ONDATRAE N. SP. Carol Rider, Ralph W. Macy. Trans. Amer. Microscop. Soc., vol.66, no.2, pp.176-181, illus., Apr., 1947.

HELMINTH PARASITES OF MICE IN NORTHEASTERN QUEBEC AND THE COAST OF LABRADOR. G. A. Schad. Can. Jour. Zool., 32 (3): 215-224, illus., June, 1954.

HYMENOLEPIS JOHNSONI, N. SP., A CESTODE FROM THE VOLE MICROTUS PENNSYLVANICUS DRUMMONDII. Everett L. Schiller. Jour. Wash. Acad. Sci., 42 (2): 53-55, illus., Feb., 1952.

STUDIES ON THE TRANSMISSION OF THE FILARIAL WORMS OF THE COTTON RAT. J. A. Scott. Trop. Disease Bull., Lond., vol.45, no.9, pp.808-809, Sept., 1948.

WARBLES IN PEROMYSCUS LEUCOPUS NOVEBORACENSIS. Thomas G. Scott, Edwin Snead. Jour. Mam., 23 (1): 94-95, Feb., 1942.

ATRICHOLAELAPS SIGMODONI, A NEW SPECIES OF MITE PARASITIC ON THE COTTON RAT, AND NOTES ON THE GENERA ATRICHOLAELAPS AND ISCHNOLAELAPS (ACARINA: LAELAPTIDAE). R. W. Strandtmann. Jour. Parasitology, 32 (2): 164-169, Apr., 1946.

A NEW SPECIES OF MITE, ICHORONYSSUS DENTIPES (ACARINA: LIPONYSSINAE), FROM THE COTTON RAT. R. W. Strandtmann, R. B. Eads. Jour. Parasitol., 33 (1): 51-56, Feb., 1947.

ENDOPARASITES OF MUSKRATS IN THE VICINITY OF HAMILTON, ONTARIO. G. K. Sweatman. Jour. Mam., 33 (2): 248-250, May, 1952.

SERIAL PASSAGE OF THE HUMAN INFLUENZA VIRUS IN THE EUROPEAN HAMSTER (CRICETUS CRICETUS). R. M. Taylor, Milos Dreguss. Proc. Soc. Exper. Biol. and Medicine, vol.43, pp.100-101, 1940.

INCIDENCE OF DIPTERAN PARASITOSIS IN POPULATIONS OF SMALL MAMMALS. Frederick H. Test, Avery R. Test. Jour. Mam., 24 (4): 506-507, Nov., 1943.

THE FRACTION OF PEROMYSCUS LEUCOPUS FATALITIES CAUSED BY RACCOON ASCARID LARVAE. Jack D. Tiner. Jour. Mam., vol.35, no.4, pp.589-592, Nov.29, 1954.

THE OCCURRENCE OF ASCARIS LUMBRICOIDES L. 1758 IN THE MUSKRAT, ONDATRA ZIBETHICA L. Jack D. Tiner, Ta Hsiung Chin. Jour. Parasitol., Lancaster, vol.34, no.3, p.253, June, 1948.

NEMATODIRUS TORTUOSUS N. SP. (NEMATODA) FROM THE RAT, NEOTOMA. Hal Tucker. Jour. Parasitology, 28 (2): 159-163, Apr., 1942.

HAEMOBARTONELLA, N. G. (BARTONELLA OLIM PRO PARTE), H. MICROTI N. SP., OF FIELD VOLE MICROTUS PENNSYLVANICUS. Ernest Edward Tyzzer, David Weinman. Jour. Hygiene, Cambridge, vol. 30, no.3, pp.141-157, pl.1, Nov., 1939.

THE TRIATOMINAE OF NORTH AND CENTRAL AMERICA AND THE WEST INDIES AND THEIR PUBLIC HEALTH SIGNIFICANCE. (MOST FREQUENT HOSTS ARE WOODRATS.) Robert L. Usinger. U. S. Pub. Health Serv., Bull. 288, 83 pp., 1944.

A NEW ANOPLOCEPHALID CESTODE, ANDRYA NEOTOMAE, FROM THE WOOD RAT NEOTOMA FUSCIPES. Marietta Voge. Jour. Parasitology, 32 (1): 36-39, Feb., 1946.

A NEW LIVER FLUKE OF THE GENUS OPISTHORCHIS. (O. TONKAE FROM MINNESOTA MUSKRATS.) F. G. Wallace, L. R. Penner. Jour. Parasitology, 25 (5): 437-440, Oct., 1939.

THE PARASITES OF THE MUSKRAT (ONDATRA ZIBETHICA L.) IN THE BRITISH ISLES. Tom Warwick. Parasitology, 28 (3): 395-402, July, 1936.

STUDIES ON THE LIFE CYCLE OF LITOMOSOIDES CARINII, FILARIID PARASITE OF THE COTTON RAT, SIGMODON HISPIDUS LITORALIS. Roger W. Williams. Jour. Parasitol., Lancaster, vol.34, no.1, pp.24-43, pl.1, Feb., 1948.

PARASITES COLLECTED FROM WOOD MOUSE IN WEST VIRGINIA. L. Wayne Wilson. Jour. Mam., 26 (2): 200, May, 1945.

TRYPANOSOMA NEOTOMAE, SP. NOV., IN THE DUSKY-FOOTED WOOD RAT AND THE WOOD RAT FLEA. Donat Fae Wood. Univ. Calif. Publ. Zool., vol.41, no.11, pp.133-143, pls.9, Sept.29, 1936.

AN ADDITIONAL CALIFORNIA LOCALITY FOR TRYPANOSOMA CRUZI CHAGAS IN THE WESTERN CONE-NOSED BUG, TRIATOMA PROTRACTA (UHLER). ( MAMMALIAN HOST: NEOTOMA FUSCIPES MACROTIS.) Sherwin F. Wood. Jour. Parasitol., Lancaster, vol.30, no.3, p.199, June, 1944.

ENDO- AND ECTOPARASITES OF THE WATER-VOLE, ARVICOLA AMPHIBIUS L., 1758, REPORT 2. D. N. Zasukhin, V. E. Tiflov, R. E. Shul'tz. Rev. Microbiol., 13: 85-86, 1932.

## Pelage, Coloration

ON A VOLE, CLETHRIONOMYS RUFOCANUS BEDFORDIAE, WITH AN ABERRANT COAT COLOUR. Tamotsu Aizawa, Sajiro Makino. Trans. Sapporo Nat. Hist. Soc., vol.15, pt.3, pp.187-199, figs.4, table, July, 1938.

DICHROMATISM IN A LITTER OF RED-BACKED MICE. Glover M. Allen. Jour. Mam., vol.8, no.3, p.248, Aug., 1927.

COMPARATIVE STUDY OF THE PELAGE OF THREE FORMS OF PEROMYSCUS. Charles S. Apgar, Jr. Jour. Mamm., vol. 11, no.4, pp.485-493, pl.25, Nov., 1930.

OBSERVATIONS ON THE PRIMENESS OF A FALL COLLECTION OF MUSKRAT, ONDATRA Z. ZIBETHICA. Vernon C. Applegate. MS thesis, Univ. Mich., 1946.

AGE CLASSES AND PATTERNS OF PRIMENESS IN A FALL COLLECTION OF MUSKRAT PELTS. Vernon C. Applegate, Henry E. Predmore, Jr. Jour. Wildlife Mgt., 11 (4): 324-330, Oct., 1947.

PREVENTING WASTES OF FUR TRAPPING WHEN PELTS ARE NOT PRIME. Frank G. Ashbrook. Trans. N. A. Wildlife Conf., 3: 511-514, 1938.

ON SEASONAL VARIATIONS OF PELAGE COLORATION IN ZUNGARIAN HAMSTER CRICETULUS SONGARUS PALL. (RODENTIA) AS INFLUENCED BY TEMPERATURE AND ILLUMINATION. R. I. Athonskaja. Zool. Jour. USSR, Moscow, vol.22, no.2, pp.102-108, figs.3, table 1, 1943. (English summary.)

AN UNUSUAL CONCENTRATION OF ALBINO MUSKRATS. Allen H. Benton. Jour. Mam., vol.34, no.2, p.262, May 14, 1953.

THE OCCURRENCE OF BUFF AND GRAY PELAGE IN WIDELY SEPARATED GEOGRAPHIC RACES OF THE DEER-MOUSE (PEROMYSCUS MANICULATUS). W. Frank Blair. Contrib. Lab. Vertebrate Biol., Univ. Michigan, Ann Arbor, no.38, pp.1-13, May, 1947.

VARIATION IN SHADE OF PELAGE OF LOCAL POPULATIONS OF THE CACTUS-MOUSE (PEROMYSCUS EREMICUS) IN THE TULAROSA BASIN AND ADJACENT AREAS OF SOUTHERN NEW MEXICO. W. Frank Blair. Contrib. Lab. Vertebrate Biol., Univ. Michigan, Ann Arbor, no.37, pp.1-7, May, 1947.

TOTAL MELANISM IN MICROTUS FROM MICHIGAN. Phillip M. Blossom. Jour. Mam., vol.23, no.2, p.214, May 14, 1942.

SPOTTED RED-BACKED MOUSE. Ernest S. Booth. Murrelet, Seattle, vol.23, no.3, p.84, Feb.15, 1943.

(A CASE OF ALBINISM IN AKODON OLIVACEUS.) Un caso de albinismo en Akodon olivaceus (Partial albinism in a Chilean specimen). Dillman S. Bullock. Rev. Chilena Hist. Nat. Pura y Apl., Santiago, vol.35, pp.112-113, fig.1, (1931) 1932.

AN ALBINO WATER RAT. C. H. Calmedy-Hamlyn. Field, London, vol.153, p.1024, June 29, 1929.

POSTJUVENAL NUDE IN THE DEER-MOUSE. Frank H. Clark. Jour. Heredity, Washington, D. C., vol.30, no.5, pp.213-215, May, 1939.

ABERRATIONS IN THE COLOR OF THE PRAIRIE VOLE, MICROTUS OCHROGASTER. E. Lendell Cockrum. Trans. Kansas Acad. Sci., Topeka, vol.56, no.1, pp.86-88, illus., 1953.

STUDIES OF THE PELAGE PHASES AND OF THE NATURE OF COLOR VARIATIONS IN MICE OF THE GENUS PEROMYSCUS. H. H. Collins. Jour. Exper. Zool., vol. 38, pp.45-107, 7 pls., 15 figs., Aug.20, 1923.

A BLACK-EYED WHITE PEROMYSCUS. Lee R. Dice. Jour. Mam., vol.15, no.3, p.246, Aug., 1934.

WHITE MUSKRAT INTEREST WILDLIFE MEN. C. W. Dill. Sylva, Toronto, vol.4, no.5, pp.23-24, illus., 1948.

NOTE ON A WHITE ORKNEY VOLE MICROTUS ORCADENSIS VAR. ALBA. George Ellison. Proc. and Trans. Liverpool Biol. Soc., vol.33, p.67, pl.1, figs.3, 1919.

A WHITE MEADOW MOUSE. Harvey I. Fisher. Jour. Mam., vol.23, no.3, pp. 336, Aug.14, 1942.

THE OCCURRENCE OF A "SILVER" TYPE MUSKRAT. J. Lane Fletcher. Jour. Heredity, Washington, vol.35, no.11, pp. 351-352, Nov., 1944.

(COLORATION MUTATIONS OF THE FIELD MOUSE (MICROTUS ARVALIS (PALL.).) Faerbungs-Mutationen der Feldmaus (Microtus arvalis (Pall.)). Fritz Frank, Klaus Zimmermann. Zeitschr. Saeugetierk, vol.22, nos.1-2, pp.87-100, pl.7, 1957.

ALBINO COTTON RATS. Marshall C. Gardner. Jour. Mam., vol.29, no.2, p. 185, May 14, 1948.

LIGHT PELAGES IN PEROMYSCUS. R. R. Huestis. Jour. Mam., vol.16, no.3, pp.211-213, pl.6, Aug., 1935.

LOCAL DIFFERENCES IN PELAGE CHARACTERS OF PEROMYSCUS. R. R. Huestis. Jour. Mam., vol.13, no.3, pp. 210-218, Aug., 1932.

SEASONAL PELAGE DIFFERENCES IN PEROMYSCUS. R. R. Huestis. Jour. Mam., vol.12, no.4, pp.372-375, Nov., 1931.

A NEW YELLOW PEROMYSCUS. R. R. Huestis, Elizabeth Barto. Science, vol.76, no.1968, pp.255-256, Sept.16, 1932.

ON A CASE OF ABERRANT COAT COLOUR IN CLETHRIONOMYS GLAREOLUS (SCHREBER, 1780). A. M. Husson. Saeugetierk. Mitteil., Stuttgart, vol.1, no. 4, pp.175-176, Oct.1, 1953.

ALBINO MUSKRATS. V. W. Jackson. American Fur Breeder, vol.11, no.6, p.38, Dec., 1938.

(MELANISM IN CRICETUS CRICETUS.) Melanismus von Cricetus cricetus. A. Jacobi. Zeitschr. f. Saeugetierkunde, vol.2, p.199, Apr.29, 1929.

MUSKRAT PELTS: SECTIONAL AND SEASONAL EFFECTS ON GRADES. Charles E. Kellogg. Jour. Wildlife Mgt., vol.11, no.2, pp.153-161, Apr., 1947.

VARIATION IN PATTERN OF PRIMENESS OF MUSKRAT SKINS. Charles E. Kellogg. Jour. Wildlife Mgt., Menasha, vol.10, no. 1, pp.38-42, Jan., 1946; Fur of Canada, Winnipeg, vol.11, no.8, p.4, May, 1946; Nat. Fur News, Denver, vol.17, no.7, p. 14, illus., Aug., 1946; American Fur Breeder, Duluth, vol.20, no.3, pp.82-83, Sept., 1947.

MATERIAL ON THE MOULTING IN MURIDAE. I. MOULTING IN MASS SPECIES OF MICROTINAE IN NORTHERN KAZAKHSTAN. A. I. Kryltsov. Zool. Zhurnal, 37 (2): 271-286, Feb., 1958. (In Russian, with English summary.)

FUR STRUCTURE AND MOULT IN FIBER ZIBETHICUS L. N. P. Lavrov. Narodnii Komissariat Zagotovok SSSR, Trudy Tsentralnoi Naucho-Issledovatelskoi Laboratorii Biologii, Oxotnichego Promysla i Tovarovedeniia Zhivotnogo Syria, Moscou, no.6, pp.164-186, figs.16-19, 1944. (In Russian, with English summary.)

THE MUSKRAT AND HIS FUR. A. K. Momb. North Dakota Outdoors, Grand Forks, vol.13, no.5, pp.8-9, illus., Nov., 1950.

MELANISM IN AN ALASKAN VOLE. Olaus J. Murie. Jour. Mam., vol.15, no. 4, p.323, Nov., 1934.

EXHIBITION, THROUGH THE SECRETARY, OF A SPECIMEN OF A BLACK VARIETY OF THE WATER-VOLE (ARVICOLA AMPHIBIUS?), AND A RED-CRESTED DUCK (BRANTA RUFINA). J. W. Orde. Proc. Zool. Soc. Lond., pt.30, pp.163-164, 1862.

(OBSERVATIONS ON THE USE OF SOME CHEEK-GLANDS IN GROOMING THE FUR IN ARVICOLA AMPHIBIUS.) Beobachtung der Verwendung einer Wangendruese zum Eingetten des Felles bei Arvicola amphibius. Rolf Ortmann. Verhandl. Deutschen Zoologen in Mainz, 1949 (Zool. Anzeiger, 14 Supplementband), Leipzig, pp.336-341, 1950.

COLOR ABERRATIONS IN MICROTUS AND PITYMYS. R. D. Owen, R. M. Shackelford. Jour. Mam., vol.23, no.2, pp.306-314, pl. 1, Aug.14, 1942.

(NEW FINDINGS ON THE COLOR PATTERNS OF THE HAMSTER (CRICETUS CRICETUS).) Neue Fundnachweise von Farbspielen des Hamsters (Cricetus cricetus L.). Hans Petzsch. Zool. Anz., Leipzig, vol.125, no.9-10, pp.269-270, Mar.15, 1939.

A VARIETY OF THE WATER RAT. (AN ABNORMALLY COLORED WATER RAT.) R. I. Pocock. Field, London, vol.153, p. 832, May 24, 1929.

BLACK WATER VOLE IN ARGYLLSHIRE. James Ritchie. Scottish Nat., no.166, p. 100, July-Aug., 1927.

EXHIBITION ON BEHALF OF CAPT. J.W.P. ORDE, F.Z.S., OF A SPECIMEN OF A BLACK VARIETY OF THE WATER-VOLE (ARVICOLA AMPHIBIUS?), AND A RED-CRESTED DUCK (BRANTA RUFINA). Philip Lutley Sclater. Proc. Zool. Soc. Lond., pt.30, p.163, 1862.

ABERRANT COLOR PHASES OF THE COTTON RAT, SIGMODON. H. B. Sherman. Jour. Mam., vol.32, no.2, p. 217, May 21, 1951.

(THE HAIR COVER OF MICROTUS ARVALIS PALLAS.) Das Haarkleid von Microtus arvalis Pallas. K. Sulc. Biol. Spisy Acad. Veterinariae, Brno, vol.9, pts.10-11, no.B.136-137, pp.1-103, figs.27, 1930. (In Czechoslovakian, with resume in German.)

(A VARIATION OF COLORATION IN PROMETHEOMYS SCHAPOSCHNIKOVI (MAMMALIA, MURIDAE).) Une variation de coloration de Prometheomys schaposchnikovi (Mammalia, Muridae). S. S. Turov. Sbornik Trudov Gosudarstvennogo Zoologicheskogo Museia (Archiv. Mus. Zool. Univ. Moscou), no.1, pp.43-44, figs.2, 1934. (In Russian with French summary.)

AN ALBINO FIELD MOUSE. E. R. Warren. Jour. Mam., vol.10, no.1, p.82, Feb., 1929.

DICHROMATISM IN NEOTOMA MEXICANA FALLAX FROM COSTILLA COUNTY, COLORADO. E. R. Warren. Proc. Biol. Soc. Wash., vol.26, pp.35-38, pls.2, Feb.8, 1913.

BLACK WATER-VOLE IN KINROSS-SHIRE. Scottish Nat., vol.184, p.110, July-Aug., 1930.

HEAT CALLED CAUSE OF WAVY FUR IN MUSKRAT. Science News Letter, Wash., D.C., Vol.42, no.3, p.41, July 18, 1942.

Physiology

ACCLIMATIZATION OF MUSKRATS IN LENINGRAD PROVINCE (RELEASES AND NATURAL DISPERSAL.) M. P. Altshul. Trans. of Russian Game Reports, Canadian Wildlife Service, 2: 144-155, 1957.

ACCLIMATIZATION OF MUSKRATS IN THE VOLGA-KAMA REGION. D. I. Aspisoff. Trans. of Russian Game Repts., Canadian Wildlife Service, 2: 116-130, 1957.

ACCLIMATIZATION OF MUSKRATS IN THE VOLGA-KAMA REGION: MATERIAL ON MUSKRAT BIOLOGY. D. I. Aspisoff. Trans. of Russian Game Repts., Canadian Wildlife Serv., 2: 156-202, 1957.

ON HEAT EXCHANGE OF MICROTUS SOCIALIS IN CRIMEA. L. P. Astanin. Zool. Jour. USSR, Moscow, vol.23, nos. 2-3, pp.97-101, 1944. (English summary.)

SEASONAL CHANGES IN THE ENDOCRINE ORGANS AND BEHAVIOR PATTERNS OF THE MUSKRAT. James Beer, Roland K. Meyer. Jour. Mam., 32 (2): 173-191, May, 1951.

EFFECTS OF X-IRRADIATION ON A NATURAL POPULATION OF THE DEER-MOUSE (PEROMYSCUS MANICULATUS). W. Frank Blair. Ecology, 39 (1): 113-118, Jan., 1958.

(THE CYCLE OF THE GOLDEN HAMSTER EPOOPHORON.) Der Cyclus des Goldhamster-Epoophorons. Fritz Bracher. Zeitschr. Anat. Entwicklungsgesch., vol. 120, pp.201-210, 1957.

ENDOCRINE FACTORS IN THE WATER

METABOLISM OF THE DESERT MAMMAL G. GERBILLUS. T. W. Burns. Endocrinology, Springfield, vol.28, no.2, pp.243-254, Feb., 1956.

(FORMATION OF ANTIBODIES IN CRICETUS AURATUS, THE GOLDEN HAMSTER.) Formacion de anticuerpos en Cricetus auratus "golden hamster." S. Capurro, Luis Rosenmann, Mario Rosenmann. Investig. Zool. Chilenas, Univ. Chile, Santiago, 3: 111-113, June 25, 1957.

(ACCLIMATIZATIONS OF MUSKRATS IN EUROPE.) Acclimatations de rats musques en Europe. A. Chappellier. Bull. Soc. Nat. Acclimat., France, vol. 77, no.1, pp.7-8, Jan., 1930.

THE SKIN AND RESPIRATORY WATER LOSSES OF PEROMYSCUS MANICULATUS SONORIENSIS. Robert M. Chew. Ecology, Durham, vol.36, no.3, pp.463-467, July, 1955.

THE EFFECT OF FIGHTING ON THE ADRENALS, THYMUS AND SPLEEN OF THE VOLE (MICROTUS AGRESTIS). J. R. Clarke. Jour. Endocrinol. Lond., vol.9, no.1, pp.114-126, Jan., 1953.

VITAMIN C REQUIREMENTS OF THE SYRIAN HAMSTER. Donald F. Clausen, William G. Clark. Nature, London, vol. 152, no.3854, pp.300-301, Sept.11, 1943.

METABOLIC DIFFERENCES BETWEEN THREE STRAINS OF PEROMYSCUS MANICULATUS. S. F. Cook, J. P. Hannon. Jour. Mam., 35 (4): 553-560, Nov., 1954.

SEROLOGICAL DIFFERENCES IN THE GENUS PEROMYSCUS DEMONSTRABLE WITH NORMAL HUMAN SERA. C. W. Cotterman. Contrib. Lab. Vert. Biol., Univ. Michigan, Ann Arbor, no.29, pp.13, figs.2, July, 1944.

GROUND PERCEPTION IN A HARVEST MOUSE. Alonzo C. Davis. Jour. Mam., vol.8, no.2, pp.161-162, May, 1927.

BODY TEMPERATURE, THYROID AND ADRENAL CORTEX OF HAMSTERS DURING COLD EXPOSURE AND HIBERNATION, WITH COMPARISONS TO RATS. H. W. Deane, C. P. Lyman. Endocrinology, Springfield, Ill., vol.55, no.3, pp.300-315, Sept., 1954.

ABILITY OF MICE OF THE GENUS PEROMYSCUS TO HEAR ULTRASONIC SOUNDS. Lee R. Dice, Elizabeth Barto. Science, vol.116, no.3005, pp.110-111, Aug.1, 1952.

SOME STANDARD VALUES OF THE BLOOD AND SERUM OF THE COTTON RAT SIGMODON HISPIDUS TEXIANUS. Frank Dolyak, Charles A. Leone. Trans. Kansas Acad. Sci., vol.56, pp.242-245, 1953.

ACTIVITY OF THE GERMINAL EPITHELIUM IN THE OVARY OF A PREGNANT HARVEST MOUSE. Kenneth L. Duke. Anat. Record, Phila., vol.89, no.2, pp. 135-138, pl.1, June, 1944.

(OBSERVATIONS OF THE HIBERNATION OF THE HAMSTER, ESPECIALLY THE GOLDEN HAMSTER (MESOCRICETUS AURATUS WATERH.).) Beobachtungen ueber den Winterschlaf der Hamster, insbesondere des Goldhamsters (Mesocricetus auratus Waterh.) M. Eisentraut. Zool. Anzeiger, Leipzig, vol.149, nos.5-6, pp.115-124, Sept., 1952.

(ON THE NEST AND HIBERNATION OF THE HAMSTER (CRICETUS CRICETUS L.).) Ueber die Baue und den Winterschlaf des Hampsters (Cricetus cricetus L.). M. Eisentraut. Zeitsch. f. Saeugetierkunde, vol.3, pp.172-207, 2 pls., 14 figs., June 11, 1928.

THE EFFECT OF COLD STARVATION UPON CARBOHYDRATE RESERVES IN PEROMYSCUS MANICULATUS. Paul S. Eskridge, Robert H. Udall. Jour. Mam., 36 (1): 139-140, Feb.25, 1955.

(OBSERVATIONS OF HIBERNATING GOLDEN HAMSTERS (MESOCRICETUS AURATUS WATERHOUSE 1837).) Beobachtungen an winterschlafenden Goldhamstern, Mesocricetus auratus (Waterhouse, 1837). Albert Fellner. Saeugetierk. Mitteil., Stuttgart, 4 (3): 115-120, July 1, 1956.

OBSERVATIONS ON CORPORA LUTEA IN THE OVARIES OF MARYLAND MUSKRATS COLLECTED DURING THE WINTER MONTHS. Thomas R. Forbes, Robert K. Enders. Jour. Wildlife Mgt., Menasha, vol.4, no.2, pp.169-172, table 1, Apr., 1940.

OBSERVATIONS ON CORPORA LUTEA IN THE OVARIES OF MUSKRATS COLLECTED DURING THE WINTER. Thomas R. Forbes, Robert K. Enders. Maryland Conservationist, Balto., vol.17, no.3, pp.1-2, illus., 1940.

(SCENT IN LEMMINGS.) Ueber die Riechfaehigkeit bei Wanderratten. Werner Gruch. Zool. Jahrbuecher, Jena, 67 (1): 65-80, 1957.

ENERGY METABOLISM OF THE WHITE-FOOTED MOUSE, PEROMYSCUS LEUCOPUS NOVEBORACENSIS, AFTER ACCLIMATION AT VARIOUS ENVIRONMENTAL TEMPERATURES. J. Sanford Hart. Canadian Jour. Zool., Ottawa, vol.31, no. 2, pp.99-105, Apr., 1953.

THE INFLUENCE OF THERMAL ACCLIMATION ON LIMITATION OF RUNNING ACTIVITY BY COLD IN DEER MICE. J. Sanford Hart. Canadian Jour. Zool., Ottawa, vol.31, no.2, pp.117-120, Apr., 1953.

EFFECT OF LOW TEMPERATURE AND WORK ON BLOOD LACTIC ACID IN DEER MICE. J. Sanford Hart. Amer. Jour. Physiol., vol.176, no.3, pp.452-454, Mar., 1954.

RATE OF METABOLISM IN MICROTUS AND PEROMYSCUS. Donald M. Hatfield. Murrelet, Seattle, vol.20, no.3, Sept.-Dec., pp.54-56, Dec.16, 1939.

(HIBERNATION OF THE SYRIAN GOLDEN HAMSTER (MESOCRICETUS AURATUS WATERH.) IN NORTHERN GERMANY.) Die Ueberwinterung syrischer Goldhamster (Mesocricetus auratus Waterh.) in Norddeutschland. Zeitschr. Saeugetierk., Berlin, vol.20, nos.2-3, pp.37-54, illus., Aug.3, 1955.

VARIATIONS IN ADRENAL ASCORBIC ACID CONCENTRATION OF THE HAMSTER DURING THE PRE-HIBERNATORY PERIOD. W. N. Holmes. Endocrinology, vol.57, no.4, pp.409-413, Oct., 1955.

HOMING OF PEROMYSCUS MANICULATUR GRACILIS. S. Charles Kendeigh. Jour. Mam., vol.25, no.4, pp.405-407, map, Dec.12, 1944.

MATING AND THE ESTROUS SMEAR PICTURE IN THE GOLDEN HAMSTER. George C. Kent, Jr., Hal Weathersby. Anat. Record, Phila., vol.96, no.4, pp. 74-75, 1946.

EFFECT OF CASTRATION AND ANDROGENS ON BODY AND ORGAN WEIGHTS, AND THE ARGINASE AND PHOSPHATASES OF KIDNEY AND LIVER OF THE MALE SYRIAN HAMSTER. C. D. Kochakian, Mary N. Bartlett, Jose Gongora. Amer. Jour. Physiol., Balto., vol.153, no.2, pp. 210-214, May 1, 1948.

WEIGHT CHANGES OF LAGURUS LAGURUS PALL. WITH THEIR SEX AND AGE. A. I. Kryltsora. Zool. Zhurn., Moscow, 36 (8): 1239-1250, 1957. (In Russian, with English summary.)

A STUDY OF HORMONAL FACTORS IN THE EARLY SEX DEVELOPMENT OF THE GOLDEN HAMSTER. Faith Wilson LaVelle. Carnegie Inst. Wash., Publ.592, Contrib. to Embryology, vol.34, pp.19-53, Sept.5, 1951.

SPECIES DIFFERENCES IN RATES OF OSMOTIC HEMOLYSIS WITHIN THE GENUS PEROMYSCUS. Harry P. Levine. Bio. Bull., Woods Hole, vol.85, no.1, pp. 52-59, figs.2, Aug., 1943.

THE BLOOD PICTURE OF MUSKRATS UNDER PENTOBARBITAL SODIUM. G. H. Lord, A. C. Todd, C. Kabat. Amer. Jour. Vet. Res., 15 (54): 79-81, Jan., 1954.

THE OXYGEN CONSUMPTION AND TEMPERATURE REGULATION OF HIBERNATING HAMSTERS. Charles P. Lyman. Jour. Exper. Zool., Phila., vol.109, no.1, pp.55-78, Oct., 1948.

MECHANISMS OF AROUSAL IN THE HIBERNATING HAMSTER. Charles P. Lyman, Paul O. Chatfield. Jour. Exper. Zool., Phila., vol.114, no.3, pp.491-516, 1 pl., Aug., 1950.

CHANGES IN BLOOD SUGAR AND TISSUE GLYCOGEN IN THE HAMSTER DURING AROUSAL FROM HIBERNATION. Charles P. Lyman, E. H. Leduc. Jour. Cellular & Comp. Physiol., Phila., vol.41, no.3, pp. 471-492, June, 1953.

BRIGHTNESS VISION IN THE DEER-MOUSE, PEROMYSCUS MANICULATUS GRACILIS. Paul Amos Moody. Jour. Exper. Zool., vol.52, pp.367-405, illus., Feb., 1929.

CELLULAR ANTIGENS IN THREE STOCKS OF PEROMYSCUS MANICULATUS FROM THE COLUMBIA RIVER VALLEY. Paul A. Moody. Contrib. Lab. Vertebrate Biol., Univ. Michigan, Ann Arbor, no.39, pp.1-16, figs.2, Mar., 1948.

THE NORMAL SPERMATOGENETIC WAVE-CYCLE IN PEROMYSCUS. Ray Moree. Anat. Record, Phila., vol.99, no.2, pp. 163-175, 1947.

THE POSTNATAL DEVELOPMENT OF THE REPRODUCTIVE SYSTEM OF THE GOLDEN HAMSTER (CRICETUS AURATUS) AND ITS REACTIVITY TO HORMONES. Evelina Ortiz. Phys. Zool., Chicago, vol.20, no.1, pp.45-66, pl.1, Jan., 1947.

(THOUGHTS ON THE PROBLEM OF HIBERNATION, ESPECIALLY IN THE HAMSTER (CRICETUS CRICETUS L.).) Gedanken zum problem des Winterschlafes, insbesondere beim Hamster (Cricetus cricetus L.). Hans Petzsch. Festchrift fuer Dr. Berthold Klatt, Zool. Anzeiger, Leipzig, vol.145, pp.740-748, 1950.

(SOME CHANGES OF PHYSIOLOGICAL CHARACTERISTICS IN THE FIELD-VOLE IN THE PROCESS OF INDIVIDUAL DEVELOPMENT.) Nekotorie izmeneniya fiziologicheskikh osobennostei obiknovennoi i obshchestvennoi polevok v proshesse individualnogo razvitiya. I. Y. Polyakov, S. G. Pegelman. Zool. Zhurnal, Moscow, vol.32, no.6, pp.1259-1266, 1953.

(REMARKS ON THE HIBERNATION OF THE HAMSTER (CRICETUS CRICETUS L.).) Bemerkungen zur Ueberwinterung des Hamsters (Cricetus cricetus L.). Felix Portig. Festchrift fuer Dr. Berthold Klatt, Zool. Anzeiger, Leipzig, vol.145, pp.756-760, 1950.

(ORIENTATION EXPERIMENTS ON THE ABILITY TO RETURN HOME OF THE RED MOUSE (EVOTOMYS GLAREOLUS RUTTNERI).) Orientierende Versuche ueber die Heimkehrfaehigkeit der Roetelmaus (Evotomys glareolus ruttneri). W. M. Schleidt. Zeits. fuer Tierpsychol., 8: 132-7, 1951.

(OBSERVATIONS OF THE HIBERNATION OF GOLDEN HAMSTERS (MESOCRICETUS AURATUS WATERHOUSE 1839), AND OF THE DEPENDENCE ON WEATHER OF ITS HIBERNATION.) Beobachtungen ueber das Auftreten von Winterschlaf bei Goldhamstern, Mesocricetus auratus (Waterhouse, 1839), und ueber gewisse Wetterbhaengigkeit derselben. Leopold Schua, Beatrix Schnorrenberg. Saeugetierk. Mitteil., Stuttgart, vol.2, no.4, pp.163-166, illus., Oct.1, 1954.

BODY TEMPERATURES OF WHITE-FOOTED MICE IN RELATION TO ENVIRONMENTAL TEMPERATURE AND HEAT AND COLD STRESS. John A. Sealander, Jr. Biological Bull., Lancaster, vol.104, no.1, pp.87-99, Feb., 1953.

SURVIVAL OF PEROMYSCUS IN RELATION TO ENVIRONMENTAL TEMPERATURE AND ACCLIMATION AT HIGH AND LOW

TEMPERATURES. John A. Sealander, Jr. Amer. Midland Nat., Notre Dame, vol.46, no.2, pp.257-311, illus., Sept., 1951.

BLOOD VOLUMES IN THE GOLDEN HAMSTER. Arthur Svihla, Howard Bowman. Jour. Mam., 36 (1): 135-136, 1 table, Feb. 25, 1955.

(REMARKS ON THE HIBERNATION OF THE FIELD MOUSE (MICROTUS ARVALIS PALLAS 1779) ON BRISTLEGRASS MEADOWS.) Bemerkungen zur Ueberwinterung der Feldmaus, Microtus arvalis (Pallas, 1779), auf Borstgras-Wiesen. F. J. Turcek. Saeugetierk. Mitteil., 5 (4): 170, Dec.1, 1957.

OBSERVATIONS ON PSEUDOPREGNANCY AND ASSOCIATED BODY WEIGHT CHANGES IN THE GOLDEN HAMSTER. G. V. S. White. Jour. Tennessee Acad. Sci., vol. 24, no.3, pp.216-219, illus., 1949.

Population Dynamics

ON THE FLUCTUATION IN THE HARVEST OF THE MUSKRAT. Atso Artimo. Suomen Riista 8: 180-181, graphs, 1953. (Finnish with English summary.)

MOUSE PLAGUES. Vernon Bailey. Nature Mag., 37 (2): 77-79, Feb., 1944.

AN ESTIMATE OF THE TOTAL NUMBER OF BEACH-MICE OF THE SUBSPECIES PEROMYSCUS POLIONOTUS LEUCOCEPHALUS, OCCUPYING SANTA ROSA ISLAND, FLORIDA. W. Frank Blair. Amer. Nat., Lancaster, vol.80, pp.665-668, Nov.-Dec., 1946.

POPULATION STRUCTURE, SOCIAL BEHAVIOR, AND ENVIRONMENTAL RELATIONS IN A NATURAL POPULATION OF THE BEACH MOUSE (PEROMYSCUS POLIONOTUS LEUCOCEPHALUS). W. Frank Blair. Contrib. Lab. Vert. Biol., 48, 47 pp., June, 1951.

A STUDY OF PRAIRIE DEER-MOUSE POPULATIONS IN SOUTHERN MICHIGAN. W. Frank Blair. Amer. Midland Nat., Notre Dame, vol.24, no.2, pp.273-305, figs.4, Sept., 1940.

PROBLEMS OF VOLE POPULATIONS IN THE MIDDLE EAST: REPORT ON THE POPULATION DYNAMICS OF THE LEVANT VOLE (MICROTUS GUENTHERI D. ET A.). F. S. Bodenheimer. Research Council of Israel, Jerusalem, 77 pp., 1949.

A DYNAMIC MODEL FOR THE FLUCTUATION OF POPULATIONS OF THE LEVANT VOLE (MICROTUS GUENTHERI D.A.). F. S. Bodenheimer, A. Dvoretzky. Bull. Res. Council Israel, 1: 62-80, 1952.

THE PROLIFIC LEMMING. Paul Bulla. Nature Magazine, Washington, D.C., vol.36, no.8, pp.434-436, illus., Oct., 1943.

(GENERAL REFLECTIONS ON DENSITY FLUCTUATIONS IN THE FIELD MOUSE (MICROTUS AGRESTIS).) Allgemeine Gedankengaenge ueber die Dichteschwankungen bei der Erdmaus (Microtus agrestis). Dennis Chitty. Zeitschr. Saeugetierk., Berlin, vol.20, nos.2-3, pp.55-60, Aug.3, 1955.

MORTALITY AMONG VOLES (MICROTUS AGRESTIS) AT LAKE VYRNWY, MONTGOMERYSHIRE IN 1936-9. Dennis Chitty. Philos. Trans. Roy. Soc. Lond., ser. B, no.638, vol.236: 505-552, illus., July, 1952.

A STUDY OF MUSKRAT MORTALITY IN A TYPICAL BUTTONBUSH SWAMP. Henri D. Crawley. MS thesis, Univ. Mich., 1947.

AN ESTIMATE OF THE POPULATION OF DEER-MICE IN THE BLACK HILLS OF SOUTH DAKOTA AND WYOMING. Lee R. Dice. Contrib. Lab. Vert. Genetics, Univ. Michigan, Ann Arbor, no.10, pp.1-5, tables 2, Apr., 1939.

THE FIELD MOUSE CYCLE IN NEW YORK. W. Robert Eadie. Farm Res., 9 (4): 1, 15, Oct., 1943.

VOLES, MICE AND LEMMINGS. (VOLE AND MOUSE POPULATION FLUCTUATIONS AND PLAGUES IN MANY PARTS OF THE WORLD, ESPECIALLY NORTHERN LANDS.) Charles Elton. Oxford, 496 pp., June, 1942.

FLUCTUATIONS IN NUMBERS OF THE MUSKRAT (ONDATRA ZIBETHICA) IN CANADA. Charles Elton, Mary Nicholson. Jour. Animal Ecol., 11 (1): 96-126, May, 1942.

SUMMER POPULATIONS AND MOVEMENTS OF THE COTTON RAT AND OTHER RODENTS ON THE SAVANNAH RIVER REFUGE. Arnold B. Erickson. Jour. Mam., Balto., vol.30, no.2, pp.133-140, figs.3, pl.1, May 23, 1949.

THE SUICIDE RATS OF NORWAY. (BROWN LEMMING.) Eleanor Links Errett. Illus. London News, vol.215, no. 5758, p.318, illus., Aug. 27, 1949.

CONCERNING FLUCTUATIONS IN POPULATIONS OF THE PROLIFIC AND WIDELY DISTRIBUTED MUSKRAT. Paul L. Errington. Amer. Nat., 85 (824): 273-292, Sept.-Oct., 1951.

ON THE HAZARDS OF OVEREMPHASIZING NUMERICAL FLUCTUATIONS IN STUDIES OF "CYCLIC" PHENOMENA IN MUSKRAT POPULATIONS. Paul L. Errington. Jour. Wildlife Mgt., 18 (1): 66-90, graphs, Jan ., 1954.

A STUDY OF GERBILLE (MAMMALIA, GLIRES) MIGRATIONS BY THE RINGING METHOD. B. K. Fenyuk, M. P. Demyashev. Rev. Microbiol., 15 (1): 89-108, 8 figs., 1936.

A STUDY OF VOLE-MICROTUS ARVALIS PALL. (MAMMALIA)--MIGRATIONS BY THE RINGING METHOD. B. K. Fenyuk, M. V. Sheikina. Sci. Rep. Saratov Univ., 1 (14): Biol. Ser. no.2, pp.85-102, 2 figs., 1938.

LEMMINGS ARE ON THE MARCH TO THE SEA. Katherine Fields. Our Dumb Animals, Plymouth, vol.83, no.5, p.13, May, 1950.

THE CAUSALITY OF MICROTINE CYCLES IN GERMANY. Fritz Frank. Jour. Wildlife Mgt., 21 (2): 113-121, Apr., 1957.

THE CAUSALITY OF RODENT CYCLES IN THE LIGHT OF RECENT EXPERIMENTS ON THE POPULATION DYNAMICS OF GERMAN MICROTINES (AN INTERIM REPORT). Fritz Frank. Morph. U. Oekol. Tiere, 43: 321-356, 1954. (German.)

EXPERIMENTS ON THE CRASHES OF FIELDMOUSE POPULATIONS (MICROTUS ARVALIS, PALLAS). Fritz Frank. Zool. Jahrb. f. Syst., 82 (1/2): 95-136, 1953.

(ON THE ARISAL OF ABOVE-NORMAL POPULATION DENSITIES IN MASS CHANGE OF THE FIELD MOUSE MICROTUS ARVALIS (PALLAS).) Entstehung uebernormaler Populationsdichten im Massenwechsel der Feldmaus, Microtus arvalis (Pallas). Fritz Frank. Zool. Jahrbuecher, vol.81, nos.5-6, pp.610-624, Mar.20, 1953.

OBSERVATIONS ON THE NATURE OF THE DECLINE IN NUMBERS OF TWO MICROTUS POPULATIONS. Gillian K. Godfrey. Jour. Mam., 36 (2): 209-214, 2 tables, May 26, 1955.

THE LARCH SAWFLY AS AN INDICATOR OF MOUSE ABUNDANCE. Samuel A. Graham. Jour. Mam., vol.10, no.3, pp. 189-196, Aug., 1929.

THE BIOLOGY OF MICROTINE CYCLES. W. J. Hamilton, Jr. Jour. Agr. Res., 54 (10): 779-790, May 15, 1937.

ALLEGHENY WOODRAT POPULATIONS. William T. Heisler. MS thesis, Pa. State Coll., 1941.

(OBSERVATIONS ON THE INFLUENCE OF WEATHER ON THE MASS MIGRATION OF THE FIELD MOUSE.) Boebachtungen ueber den Witterungseinfluss auf den Massenwechsel der Feldmaus. W. Herold. Zeitschr. Saeugetierk., Berlin, vol.19, nos.1-2, pp.86-107, July 30, 1954.

LEMMING HORDE. John Eric Hill. League of Maryland Sportsmen, Balto., Rally Sheet, vol.3, no.6, pp.3, 7, June, 1945.

THE ROLE OF REPRODUCTION AND MORTALITY IN POPULATION FLUCTUATIONS OF VOLES (MICROTUS). Robert S. Hoffmann. Ecological Monographs, 28: 79-109, Jan., 1958.

A CONCENTRATION OF LEMMING MICE (SYNAPTOMYS COOPERI) IN CENTRAL ILLINOIS. Donald F. Hoffmeister. Trans. Illinois Acad. Sci., Springfield, vol.40, pp.190-193, fig.1, 1947.

(NOTES ON THE APPEARANCE, IN PAST YEARS, OF FIELDMOUSE PLAGUES IN THE NETHERLANDS.) Enige gegevens omtrent het optreden in vroegere jaren van veldmuizenplagen in Nederland. A. M. Husson. De Zwerver in Gods Vrije Natuur, Zeist, vol.16, no.2, pp.25-27, Feb., 1956.

SOME FACTORS AFFECTING FLUCTUATIONS OF MICROTUS AND PEROMYSCUS. E. W. Jameson, Jr. Jour. Mam., 36 (2): 206-209, May 26, 1955.

A POPULATION STUDY OF THE MEADOW MICE (MICROTUS) IN THREE SIERRA NEVADA MEADOWS. Hubert O. Jenkins. Proc. California Acad. Sci., San Francisco, ser.4, vol.26, no.3, pp.43-67, figs.11, tables 3, June 28, 1948.

(ON FIELD LEMMING INVASIONS AND OTHER IRREGULAR ANIMAL MIGRATIONS, WITH A SURVEY OF THE SMALL RODENT GRADATIONS IN FINNISH LAPLAND 1900-1948.) Ueber Fjeldlemming-Invasionen und anders irregulaere Tierwanderungen. Mit einer Ubersicht der Kleinnagergradationen in Finnisch-Lappland 1900-1948. Olavi Kalela. Ann. Zool. Soc. Zool.-Bot. Fennicae "Vanamo," Helsinki, vol.13, no. 5, pp.iv, 92, 1949.

FLUCTUATIONS AND FORECASTS OF MUSKRAT NUMBERS. N. P. Lavroff. Translations of Russian Game Reports, Canadian Wildlife Service, 2: 203-224, 1957.

CYCLES IN VIRGINIA VOLES. J. P. Linduska. Jour. Mam., vol.23, no.2, p. 210, May 14, 1942.

FLUCTUATIONS AND STRUCTURE OF PEROMYSCUS GOSSYPIMUS POPULATIONS IN EASTERN TEXAS. W. H. McCarley. Jour. Mam., vol.35, no.4, pp.526-532, Nov.29, 1954.

A POPULATION STUDY OF THE PRAIRIE VOLE (MICROTUS OCHROGASTER) IN NORTHEASTERN KANSAS. Edwin P. Martin. Univ. Kansas Publ., Mus. Nat. Hist., 8 (6): 361-416, Apr.2, 1956.

THE MUSKRAT COMES BACK. Ernest C. Martin. Ala. Cons., 18 (8): 9, 13, Feb., 1947.

FECUNDITY AND POPULATION DYNAMICS OF MICROTUS ARVALIS PALL. A. A. Maximov. Izvestia Akad. Naouk SSSR, 1948: 73-81, 1948. (In Russian.)

A FURTHER CONTRIBUTION TO THE STUDY OF CYCLES IN BRITISH VOLES (MICROTUS AGRESTIS). A. D. Middleton. Jour. Ecology, vol.19, no.1, pp.190-199, map, Feb., 1931.

FURTHER NOTES ON TRAVELS OF PEROMYSCUS. O. J. Murie, Adolph Murie. Jour. Mam., vol.13, no.1, pp.78-79, Feb., 1932.

TRAVELS OF PEROMYSCUS. O. J. Murie, Adolph Murie. Jour. Mam., vol.12, no.3, pp.200-209, Aug., 1931.

(DYNAMICS OF THE NUMBER OF FIELD VOLES AND METHODS OF PROGNOSIS IN THE CENTRAL ZONE OF THE USSR.) Dinamika chislyennosti obyknovyennoy polevki (Microtus arvalis Pall.) i myetody yeye prognozov v sryednyey polose SSSR. N. P. Naumov. Zool. Zhurnal, Moscow, vol.32, no.2, pp.300-311, 1953.

VOLE POPULATIONS. John Neess. Ecology, Lancaster, vol.31, no.3, pp.493-494, July, 1950.

FLUCTUATION IN THE POPULATION OF NEOTOMA CINERA (WOODRAT) IN JACKSON HOLE, WYOMING. N. C. Negus. Jour. Mam., vol.31, no.2, pp.196-197, May 25, 1950.

AN ELEVEN YEAR HISTORY OF A SIGMODON POPULATION. Eugene P. Odum. Jour. Mam., 36 (3): 368-378, illus., Aug. 30, 1955.

A FIELD STUDY OF PEROMYSCUS POPULATIONS IN GULF HAMMOCK, FLORIDA. Paul G. Pearson. Ecology, vol.34, no.1, pp.199-207, illus., Jan., 1953.

CYCLES IN DANISH VOLE POPULATIONS. Carsten Pederson. Danish Rev. Game Biol., 3 (2): 1-18, 1957.

SOME ASPECTS OF POPULATION STRUCTURE IN THE SHORT-TERM CYCLE OF THE BROWN LEMMING IN NORTHERN ALASKA. Frank A. Pitelka. Cold Spring Harbor Symposia on Quantitative Biology, 22: 237-251, 1957.

SOME CHARACTERISTICS OF MICROTINE CYCLES IN THE ARCTIC. Frank A. Pitelka. Arctic Biology, Biology Colloquium Proceedings, 18: 73-88, 1957.

THE LEMMING HORDES OF NORWAY. Frances Pitt. Field, London, vol.156, no. 4046, p.56, July 12, 1930.

A VOLE PLAGUE IN WALES. Frances Pitt. Field, London, vol.161, no.4192, p.915, illus., Apr.29, 1933.

A MASS INCREASE OF MICROTUS PELLICEUS IN THE SUTSHAN DISTRICT, RUSSIAN FAR EAST. K. A. Plater-Plochotzkij. Zashchita Rastenii ot Vreditelei (Plant Protection), Leningrad, vol. 6, nos.5-6, pp.817-818, 1930. (In Russian.)

DYNAMICS OF PEROMYSCUS POPULATIONS. Maurice W. Provost. MS thesis, Univ. N. H., 1940.

OBSERVATIONS ON A CYCLIC DECLINE OF LEMMINGS (LEMMUS) ON THE ARCTIC COAST OF ALASKA DURING THE SPRING OF 1949. Robert Rausch. Arctic Jour. Arctic Inst. North Amer., vol.3, no. 3, pp.166-177, Dec., 1950.

(THE CONSTITUTION OF THE RESERVE STORES OF FIELD MICE AND ITS IMPORTANCE RELATIVE TO THE MULTIPLICATION OF THIS RODENT.) La constitution des magasins de reserve du Microtus arvalis Pallas (campagnol des champs) et son importance pour la pullulation de ce rongeur. Robert Regnier, Roger Pussard. Comptes Rendus Acad. Sci., Paris, vol. 183, pp.92, 1926.

(ON THE DYNAMICS OF SEXUAL PROPORTION IN THE FIELD MOUSE, MICROTUS ARVALIS PALLAS.) Zur Dynamik der Sexualproportion bei der Feldmaus, Microtus arvalis (Pallas). H. Reichstein. Zeitschr. Saeugetierk., Berlin, 21 (3-4): 184-191, Feb.28, 1957.

MOVEMENTS AND POPULATION DYNAMICS OF FARM POND AND STREAM MUSKRATS IN MISSOURI. Charles E. Shanks, George C. Arthur. Mo. Cons. Comm. Fed. Aid to Wildl. Proj. Mo. 13-R & Ill. 30-R, pp.1-12, illus., Dec., 1951.

MUSKRAT MOVEMENTS AND POPULATION DYNAMICS IN MISSOURI FARM PONDS AND STREAMS. Charles E. Shanks, George C. Arthur. Jour. Wildlife Mgt., 16 (2): 138-147, illus., Apr., 1952.

THE ABUNDANCE OF THE COLLARED LEMMING (DICROSTONYX GROENLANDICUS (TR.) VAR. RICHARDSONI MER.) IN THE CHURCHILL AREA, 1929 TO 1940. V. E. Shelford. Ecology, 24 (4): 472-484, Oct., 1943.

A FIELD STUDY OF SPRING DISPERSAL AND ESTABLISHMENT OF BREEDING TERRITORIES IN CENTRAL IOWA MUSKRATS. George Sprugel. MS thesis, Iowa State Coll., 1947.

SPRING DISPERSAL AND SETTLING ACTIVITIES OF CENTRAL IOWA MUSKRATS. George Sprugel. Iowa State Coll. Jour. Sci., 26 (1): 71-84, illus., Oct., 1951.

(ON MASS INCREASE AND MASS BREAKDOWN IN THE FIELD MOUSE.) Ueber Massenvermehrung und Massenzusammenbruch bei der Feldmaus. George H. W. Stein. Zool. Jarbuecher, Jena, vol.81, nos. 1-2, pp.1-26, Mar.31, 1952.

THE SOURCE OF ANIMALS MOVING INTO A DEPOPULATED AREA. Lucille F. Stickel. Jour. Mam., 27 (4): 301-307, Nov., 1946.

A SIGMODON AND BAIOMYS POPULATION IN UNGRAZED AND UNBURNED TEXAS PRAIRIE. Lucille F. Stickel, William H. Stickel. Jour. Mam., 30 (2): 141-150, May, 1949.

SUMMER MOVEMENTS OF BANDED MUSKRATS. Michael J. Takos. Jour. Wildlife Mgt., 8 (4): 307-311, Oct., 1944.

FLUCTUATION IN VOLE POPULATIONS FOLLOWING THE WIDESPREAD SYNCHRONOUS FLOWERING OF BAMBOO-GRASSES ON MT. TURUGI. Ryo Tanaka. Bull. Kochi Women's Coll., Kochi City, vol.4, no.2, pp.61-68, illus., Mar., 1956.

HOME RANGES AND TERRITORIES IN A CLETHRIONOMYS-POPULATION ON A PEAT-BOG GRASSLAND IN HOKKAIDO. Ryo Tanaka. Bull. Kochi Women's Coll., Shikoku, Japan, vol.2, no.1, pp.10-20, illus., Dec., 1953.

YEARLY CHANGE IN SIZE AND STRUCTURE OF A CLETHRIONOMYS-POPULATION IN HOKKAIDO. Ryo Tanaka. Japanese Jour. Ecology, Tokyo, vol.4, no. 2, pp.51-55, illus., July, 1954.

THE 1953 LEMMING EMIGRATION AT POINT BARROW, ALASKA. Daniel Q. Thompson. Arctic, 8 (1): 37-45, illus., Winter, 1955.

THE ROLE OF FOOD AND COVER IN POPULATION FLUCTUATIONS OF THE BROWN LEMMING AT POINT BARROW, ALASKA. Daniel Q. Thompson. Trans. 20th N. A. Wildl. Conf., pp.166-176, 3 figs., 1955.

MIGRATING MUSKRATS. Chris Thomsen. Fins, Feathers and Fur, no.28, p.9, Dec., 1921.

CONCERNING PECULIARITIES OF SEASONAL DYNAMICS OF MICROPOPULATIONS OF MICE AND VOLES IN THE PERIOD OF REDUCED NUMBERS. S. N. Varshavskii, K. T. Krylova, I. I. Luk'ianchenko. 1948.

(MATERIALS ON THE DYNAMICS OF MURINE RODENTS (HISTORICAL SUMMARY OF MASS INCREASES).) Materialy po dinamike fauny myshevidnykh gryzunov SSSR (Istoricheskii obzor massovykh razmnozhenii). Boris Stefanovich Vinogradov. Leningrad, 61 pp., 1934.

PEAK POPULATIONS OF PEROMYSCUS MANICULATUS GRACILIS IN NORTHERN ONTARIO. A. de Vos. Jour. Mam., vol.32, no.4, p.462, Nov.19, 1951.

VOLE PLAGUE AT SMOKY FALLS, ONTARIO. R. V. Whelan. Canadian Field-Nat., 53 (4): 53-55, Apr., 1939.

(THE ECOLOGIC FACTORS WHICH MAKE THE DEVELOPMENT OF THE PLAGUES POSSIBLE.) De ecolgische factoren, die het ontstaan van een veldmuisplaag mogelijk maken. A. Wijngaarden. Tijdschrift over Plantenziekten, Amsterdam, vol.62, p.31, 1956.

(NOTES ON THE RELATIONSHIP BETWEEN THE EXPLOITATION OF MEADOWS AND FIELD MOUSE PLAGUES.) Over het verband tussen graslandexploitatie en veldmuisplagen. A. van Wijngaarden. Dreimaandelijks bericht betreffende Komgrondenbieden, 6 (2): 112-120, 1956.

(THE PERIODICITY OF THE MAXIMUM POPULATION OF THE FIELD MOUSE.) De periodiciteit in de populatiemaxima van de veldmuis, Microtus arvalis Pallas, in Nederland, 1806-1956. A. van Wijngaarden. Vakblad voor Biologen, 37 (4): 1-8 (reprint), April, 1957.

HOME RANGE OF PEROMYSCUS MANICULATUS RUFINUS IN A COLORADO PONDEROSA PINE COMMUNITY. Olwen Williams. Jour. Mam., 36 (1): 42-45, Feb.25, 1955.

INDIRECT EVIDENCE SUPPORTING OBSERVATIONS ON THE RANGE OF WILD RODENTS. C. Brooke Worth. Jour. Mam., 32 (1): 76-79, Feb., 1951.

(ANALYSIS OF THE SPRING POPULATION OF CLETHRYONOMYS GLAREOLUS.) Rozbor jarni populace nornika rudeho (Clethrionomys glareolus). J. Zejda. Zool. a Entom. Listy, Praha, vol.4, no.4, pp. 313-328, illus., 1955.

MASS DEVELOPMENT IN SIBERIA OF LAGURUS LAGURUS AND ARVICOLA AMPHIBIUS. M. Zverev. La Defence des Plantes, vol.5, no.1, pp.104-105, 1928. (In Russian.)

CLUE TO SUICIDE MARCHES. (LEMMINGS.) Science News Letter, Washington, vol.57, no.22, p.342, June 3, 1950.

POPULATION UNLIMITED. (MICE.) Ohio Conservation Bull., Columbus, vol.10, no.7, p.2 of cover, illus., July, 1946.

WHY DO LEMMINGS DO IT? (MASS MIGRATION.) Science Illus., Louisville, vol.2, no.3, pp.12-13, 102, illus., Mar., 1947.

Predation

(DISCUSSIONS OF MINK AND MUSKRAT.) Inlagg i diskussionen om mink och bisamratta. D. Anderson, E. Wibeck, S. Swahn, E. Busk. Svensk Jakt, Stockholm, vol.86, no.9, pp.232-236, Sept.17, 1948.

RED FOX PREYING ON MUSKRATS. Joe Brickner. Jour. Mam., vol.34, no.3, p. 389, Aug.14, 1953.

A MOUSE-CATCHING CROW. N. R. Brown. Candian Field-Nat., Sutton West, vol.61, no.2, p.68, Mar.-Apr., 1947.

WINTER NESTING AND WINTER FOOD OF THE BARN OWL IN SOUTH CAROLINA. Clarence Cottam, A. L. Nelson. Wilson Bull., vol.49, no.4, pp.283-285, Dec., 1937.

THE TUSSLE IN TIDE WATER CREEK. William Everett Cram. Jour. Mam., vol. 4, no.1, pp.22-26, figs.3, Feb., 1923.

EFFECTIVENESS OF SELECTION BY OWLS OF DEER-MICE (PEROMYSCUS MANICULATUS) WHICH CONTRAST IN COLOR WITH THEIR BACKGROUND. Lee R. Dice. Contrib. Lab. Vert. Biol. Univ. Michigan, Ann Arbor, no.34, pp.1-20, Apr., 1947.

THE SHORT-TAILED SHREW AND FIELD MOUSE PREDATION. W. Robert Eadie. Jour. Mam., 25 (4): 359-364, Nov., 1944.

SHREW-MOUSE PREDATION DURING LOW MOUSE ABUNDANCE. W. Robert Eadie. Jour. Mam., 29 (1): 35-37, Feb., 1948.,

SHREW PREDATION AND VOLE POPULATIONS ON A LOCALIZED AREA. W. Robert Eadie. Jour. Mam., 33 (2): 185-189, illus., May, 1952.

AN ANALYSIS OF MINK PREDATION UPON MUSKRATS IN NORTH-CENTRAL UNITED STATES. Paul L. Errington. Iowa Agr. Exp. Sta., Res. Bull.320: 797-924, June, 1943.

REDUCTION IN PRODUCTIVITY OF MUSKRAT PELTS ON AN IOWA MARSH THROUGH DEPREDATIONS OF RED FOXES. Paul L. Errington, Thomas G. Scott. Reprinted from Jour. Agricultural Research, vol.71, no.4, pp.137-148, Aug.15, 1945.

(DOMESTIC CATS HUNTING WATER RATS.) Hauskaetze auf der Jagd nach Wasserratten. Viktor Hornung. Zool. Garten, Leipzig, NF, vol.18, nos.1-2, p. 60, 1951.

THE FOOD OF THE SNOWY OWL (NYCTEA NYCTEA) DURING A MIGRATION TO THE GULF OF ST. LAWRENCE. R. A. Johnson. Canadian Field-Nat., vol.51, no. 9, pp.136-137, Dec., 1937.

A PILE OF MICROTUS. Marcus Ward Lyon, Jr. Jour. Mam., vol.11, no.3, p.320, Aug., 1930.

(SKELETAL REMAINS OF DICROSTONYX GROENLANDICUS TRAILL AS THE CONTENT OF THE HAIR BALLS OF BIRDS OF PREY.) Skelettreste von Dicrostonyx groelandicus Traill als Inhalt von Raubvogelgewoellen. Untersuchung von Raugvogelgewoellen, gesammelt von Mitgliedern der daenischen Dreijahres-Expedition nach Nordostgroenland 1931-34. E. V. Mandach. Meddelelser om Gronland, Kommissionen for Videnskabelige Undersogelser i Gronland, Kobenhavn, vol.112, no.4, pp.54, figs. 2, pls.1-22, 1938.

THE RED TREE-MOUSE PREYED UPON BY THE SPOTTED OWL. Alden H. Miller. Jour. Mam., Balto., vol.14, no.2, p.162, May 15, 1933.

HABITS OF THE WHITE-TAILED KITE. (MICROTUS CALIFORNICUS SANCTIDIEGI AS FOOD AND NEST MATERIAL.) Robert T. Moore, Arthur Barr. Auk, Lancaster, vol.58, no.4, pp.453-462, Oct., 1941.

MARSH HAWKS RESPONDING TO PEAK ABUNDANCE OF COTTON RATS. Eugene P. Odum. The Oriole, Atalnta, vol.12, no.4, pp.48-49, Oct., 1947.

PHENACOMYS EATEN BY SPECKLED TROUT. Randolph L. Peterson. Jour. Mam., 37 (1): 121, Feb.28, 1956.

ECOLOGICAL RELATIONS OF JAEGERS AND OWLS AS LEMMING PREDATORS NEAR BARROW, ALASKA. Frank A. Pitelka, Quentin Tomich, George W. Treichel. Ecol. Monographs, Durham, vol.25, no.1, pp.85-117, Jan., 1955.

ENTER HAWK--EXIT MOUSE. Richard H. Pough. Texas Game and Fish, Austin, vol.2, no.6, pp.5-7, 13-14, illus., May, 1944.

THE FORMATION OF PELLETS BY THE BARRED OWL. E. Carl Sensenig. Wilson Bull., Oberlin, vol.57, no.2, p.132, June, 1945.

THE RELATION OF SNOWY OWL MIGRATION TO THE ABUNDANCE OF THE COLLARED LEMMING. V. E. Shelford. Auk, Lancaster, vol.62, no.4, pp.592-596, Oct., 1945.

A PREDATOR-PREY RELATIONSHIP BETWEEN THE SHORT-EARED OWL AND THE MEADOW MOUSE. L. L. Snyder, C. E. Hope. Wilson Bull., vol.50, no.2, pp.110-112, June, 1938.

RACCOON PREDATION ON MUSKRATS NEAR CURRITUCK, NORTH CAROLINA. Kenneth A. Wilson. Jour. Wildlife Mgt., 17 (2): 113-119, illus., Apr., 1953.

THE ROLE OF MINK AND OTTER AS MUSKRAT PREDATORS IN NORTHEASTERN NORTH CAROLINA. Kenneth A. Wilson. Presented at 6th Ann. Conf. S. E. Assn. Game and Fish Comm., Oct.19-22, 1952, Savannah, Ga., pp.1-9, graphs; Wildlife Mgt., 18 (2): 199-207, Apr., 1954.

Reproductive Biology

BREEDING, FEEDING, AND OTHER LIFE HABITS OF MEADOW MICE (MICROTUS). Vernon Bailey. Jour. Agric. Res. vol.27, no.8, pp.523-536, pls.1-3, Feb.23, 1924.

FACTORS AFFECTING THE BREEDING OF THE FIELD MOUSE (MICROTUS AGRESTIS). PT. I. LIGHT. John R. Baker, R. M. Ranson. Proc. Roy. Soc. Lond., ser.B, vol.110, no.B 767, pp.313-322, Apr.1, 1932.

FACTORS AFFECTING THE BREEDING OF THE FIELD MOUSE (MICROTUS AGRESTIS). PT. 2. TEMPERATURE AND FOOD. John R. Baker, R. M. Ranson. Proc. Roy. Soc. Lond., ser.B, vol.112, no. B 774, pp.39-46, Nov.1, 1932.

FACTORS AFFECTING THE BREEDING OF THE FIELD MOUSE (MICROTUS AGRESTIS). PT. III. LOCALITY. John R. Baker, R. M. Ranson. Proc. Roy. Soc. Lond., ser. B, vol.113, no.B 784, pp. 486-495, figs.5, 1933.

THE REPRODUCTIVE CYCLE OF THE MUSKRAT IN WISCONSIN. James R. Beer. Jour. Wildlife Mgt., Menasha, vol.14, no. 2, pp.151-156, Apr., 1950.

STUDIES ON REPRODUCTION AND SURVIVAL IN WISCONSIN MUSKRATS. James Beer. PhD thesis, Univ. Wis., 1949.

OCTOBER BREEDING OF PEROMYSCUS IN NORTH CENTRAL COLORADO. Richard G. Beidleman. Jour. Mam., vol.35, no.1, p.118, Feb.10, 1954.

EXPERIMENTAL EVIDENCE OF SEXUAL ISOLATION BETWEEN THREE FORMS OF MICE OF THE CENOSPECIES PEROMYSCUS MANICULATUS. W. Frank Blair, Walter E. Howard. Contrib. Lab. Vert. Biol., Univ. Michigan, Ann Arbor, pp.26, pp.19, Apr., 1944.

THE ESTROUS CYCLE OF MICROTUS GUENTHERI D. AND A. AND ITS ECOLOGICAL IMPLICATIONS. F. S. Bodenheimer, F. Sulman. Ecology, Lancaster, vol.27, no.3, pp.255-256, July, 1946.

THE GOLDEN HAMSTER (CRICETUS AURATUS): CARE, BREEDING, AND GROWTH. Charlotte R. Bond. Physiological Zool., Chicago, vol.18, no.1, pp. 52-59, Jan., 1945.

REPRODUCTION OF THE FIELD VOLE, MICROTUS AGRESTIS HIRTUS BELLAMY. F. W. Rogers Brambell, Kathleen Hall. Proc. Zool. Soc. London, vol.109, ser.A, Gen and Exper., pts.2-3, pp.133-138, 1 table, July, 1939.

REPRODUCTION OF THE BANK VOLE (EVOTOMYS GLAREOLUS SCHREBER). 1. THE OESTROUS CYCLE OF THE FEMALE. F. W. Rogers Brambell, I. W. Rowlands. Philos. Trans. Roy. Soc., Lond., ser.B, no.531, vol. 226, pp.71-97, pls.10-11, Mar.18, 1936.

EVIDENCE OF WINTER BREEDING OF PEROMYSCUS. H. Lee Brown. Ecology, Lancaster, vol.26, no.3, pp.308-309, July, 1945.

THE GOLDEN HAMSTER, CRICETUS (MESOCRICETUS) AURATUS WATERHOUSE. NOTES ON ITS BREEDING AND GROWTH. H. M. Bruce, E. Hindle. Proc. Zool. Soc. Lond., pt.2, pp.361-366, fig.1, July, 1934.

GROWTH AND REPRODUCTION OF LABORATORY BRED HAMSTERS, CRICETULUS GRISEUS. Chang-Ying Chang, Hsien Wu. Chinese Jour. Physiol., Peking, vol.13, no.1, pp.109-118, figs.5, tables 3, Mar.15, 1938.

THE ESTROUS CYCLE IN THE WOODRAT, NEOTOMA FLORIDANA. Arthur O. Chapman. Univ. Kansas Sci. Bull., Lawrence, vol.34, pt.1, no.7, pp.267-299, illus., Oct.1, 1951.

THE OESTROUS CYCLE AND GESTATION PERIOD IN THE LACTATING FIELD VOLE, MICROTUS AGRESTIS. H. Chitty. Jour. Endocrinol., Lond., 15 (3): 279-283, July, 1957.

AGE OF SEXUAL MATURITY IN MICE OF THE GENUS PEROMYSCUS. Frank H. Clark. Jour. Mam., vol.19, no.2, pp.230-234, table 1, May 14, 1938.

THE ESTROUS CYCLE OF THE COTTON RAT, SIGMODON HISPIDUS. Frank H. Clark. Contrib. Lab. Vert. Genetics, no.2, pp.2, May, 1936.

THE ESTROUS CYCLE OF THE DEER-MOUSE, PEROMYSCUS MANICULATUS. Frank H. Clark. Contrib. Lab. Vert. Genetics, no.1, pp.8, pl.1, May, 1936.

INFLUENCE OF NUMBERS ON REPRODUCTION AND SURVIVAL IN TWO EXPERIMENTAL VOLE POPULATIONS. J. R. Clarke. Proc. Roy. Soc., Lond., ser. B, vol.144, no.914, pp.68-85, Aug., 1955.

THE REPRODUCTIVE CYCLE OF RICE RATS (ORYZOMYS PALUSTRIS PALUSTRIS) IN CAPTIVITY. Clinton H. Conaway. Jour. Mam., 35 (2): 263-266, May, 1954.

NOTES ON THE BREEDING OF SOME CRICETIDAE IN ONTARIO. A. F. Coventry. Jour. Mam., vol.18, no.4, pp. 489-496, figs.2, tables 2, Nov., 1937.

REPRODUCTION AND GROWTH IN THE CREEPING VOLE, MICROTUS OREGONI SERPENS MERRIAM. Ian McT. Cowan, Margaret G. Arsenault. Canadian Jour. Zool., vol.32, no.3, pp.198-208, June, 1954.

NOTES ON REPRODUCTION OF PEROMYSCUS EREMICUS IN A LABORATORY COLONY. David E. Davis, Dorland J. Davis. Jour. Mam., vol.28, no.2, pp.181-183, illus., May 19, 1947.

THE REPRODUCTIVE CYCLE OF THE GOLDEN HAMSTER (CRICETUS AURATUS). Ruth Deanesly. Abstract Proc. Zool. Soc. Lond., ser. C, vol.108, no.1, p.2, Jan.25, 1938; Proc. Zool. Soc. Lond., vol.108, ser. A, pt.1, pp.31-37, pls.1-4, Apr., 1938.

REMARKS ON THE BREEDING CONDITIONS AND MOULTING OF THE COLLARED LEMMING (DICROSTONYX). Magnus Degerbol, U. Mohl-Hansen. Meddelelser om Gronland, Copenhagen, vol.131, no.11, pp.1-40, figs.27, 1943.

(ON THE REPRODUCTION OF THE AMPHIBIOUS FIELD MOUSE IN CAPTIVITY.) De la reproduction du Campagnol amphibie en captivite. C. Desportes. Mammalia, Paris, vol.2, no.1, pp.35-39, Mar., 1938.

BREEDING OF PEROMYSCUS FLORIDANUS IN CAPTIVITY. Lee R. Dice. Jour. Mam., 35 (2): 260, May, 1954.

FERTILITY RELATIONS IN THE PEROMYSCUS LEUCOPUS GROUP OF MICE. Lee R. Dice. Contrib. Laboratory Vert. Genetics, Univ. Michigan, Ann Arbor, no.4, pp.3, Jan., 1937.

FERTILITY RELATIONSHIP BETWEEN SOME OF THE SPECIES AND SUBSPECIES OF MICE IN THE GENUS PEROMYSCUS. Lee R. Dice. Jour. Mam., vol.14, no.4, pp.298-305, Nov., 1933.

PARTIAL INFERTILITY BETWEEN TWO MEMBERS OF THE PEROMYSCUS TRUEI GROUP OF MICE. Lee R. Dice, Margaret Liebe. Contrib. Laboratory Vert. Genetics, Univ. Michigan, Ann Arbor, no.5, pp.4, Jan., 1937.

MUSKRAT GROWTH AND LITTER PRODUCTION. Robert S. Dorney, Alan J. Rusch. Wis. Cons. Dept., Tech. Wildl. Bull. no.8, pp.1-32, illus., 1953.

(REPRODUCTION OF THE HAMSTER IN BELGIUM.) La propagation du hamster en Belgique. Ch. Dupond. Bull. Mus. Roy. d'Hist. Nat., Belgique, Bruxelles, vol.8, no.26, pp.43, figs.9, Nov., 1932.

THE CORPUS LUTEUM AS AN INDICATOR OF THE BREEDING OF MUSKRATS. R. K. Enders. Trans. N. A. Wildl. Conf., 4:631-634, 1939.

MUSKRAT PROPAGATION IN OHIO. R. K. Enders. Bull. Ohio Dept. of Agric., Columbus, no.19, pp.5-17, Nov., 1931.

THE BREEDING SEASON OF THE MUSKRAT IN NORTHWEST IOWA. Paul L. Errington. Jour. Mam., 18 (3): 333-337, Aug., 1937.

ASPECTS OF REPRODUCTION AND DEVELOPMENT IN THE PRAIRIE VOLE (MICROTUS OCHROGASTER). Henry S. Fitch. Univ. Kansas Publ., Mus. Nat. Hist., 10 (4): 129-161, Dec.19, 1957.

THE PERIOD OF GONADAL ACTIVITY IN THE MARYLAND MUSKRAT. Thomas R. Forbes. Science, 95 (2467): 382-383, Apr.10, 1942.

(OESTRAL SCENT IN THE MALE FIELD MOUSE MICROTUS AGRESTIS L.) Brunstgeruch beim Erdmaus-Maennchen, Microtus agrestis (L.). Fritz Frank. Zeitschr. Saeugetierk., 22 (1-2): 104, 1957.

(THE PROPAGATION POTENTIAL OF THE FIELD MOUSE MICROTUS ARVALIS PALLAS--THE HIGHEST AMONG THE MAMMALS.) Das Fortpflanzungspotential der Feldmaus, Microtus arvalis (Pallas)--ein Spitzenleistung unter den Saeugetieren. Fritz Frank. Zeitschr. Saeugetierk., Berlin, 21 (3-4): 176-181, Feb.28, 1957.

A STUDY OF THE REPRODUCTIVE CAPACITY OF MAINE MUSKRATS. Jay S. Gashwiler. Jour. Mam., vol.31, no.2, pp. 180-185, May 25, 1950.

MATING SYSTEM IN A NATURAL POPULATION OF THE COMMON HAMSTER (CRICETUS CRICETUS L.). S. Gershenson, V. Polevoi. Comptes Rendus (Doklady) Acad. Sci. USSR, Moscou, n.s., vol.30, no.1, pp.64-65, 1941.

REPRODUCTION IN THE PINE VOLE, PITYMYS NEMORALIS. Bryan P. Glass. Jour. Mam., Balto., vol.30, no.1, pp.72-73, Feb.14, 1949.

MEADOW VOLE USES SAME NEST FOR TWO LITTERS. Woodrow Goodpaster, Karl Maslowski. Jour. Mam., Balto., vol.30, no.1, pp.73-74, Feb.14, 1949.

REPRODUCTION IN A COASTAL CALIFORNIA POPULATION OF THE FIELD MOUSE, MICROTUS CALIFORNICUS. Gilbert S. Greenwald. Univ. California Publ. Zool., 54 (7): 421-446, Apr.16, 1957.

THE REPRODUCTIVE CYCLE OF THE FIELD MOUSE, MICROTUS CALIFORNICUS. Gilbert S. Greenwald. Jour. Mam., 37 (2): 213-222, illus., June 9, 1956.

REPRODUCTION AND YOUNG OF THE FLORIDA WOOD RAT, NEOTOMA F. FLORIDANA (ORD). W. J. Hamilton, Jr. Jour. Mam., vol.34, no.2, pp.180-189, illus., May 14, 1953.

REPRODUCTION OF THE FIELD MOUSE, MICROTUS PENNSYLVANICUS (ORD). W. J. Hamilton, Jr. Cornell Univ. Agr. Exp. Sta., Mem.237, 23 pp., 1941.

EXPERIMENTAL EVIDENCE OF REPRODUCTIVE ISOLATION BETWEEN TWO SUBSPECIES OF PEROMYSCUS MANICULATUS. Van T. Harris. Contrib. Lab. Vert. Biol., Univ. Michigan, no.70, p.13, Oct., 1954.

DISPERSAL, AMOUNT OF INBREEDING, AND LONGEVITY IN A LOCAL POPULATION OF PRAIRIE DEERMICE ON THE GEORGE RESERVE, SOUTHERN MICHIGAN. Walter E. Howard. Contrib. Lab. Vert. Biol., Univ. Michigan, Ann Arbor, no.43, pp.50, figs.24, pls.2, Apr., 1949.

DISPERSAL AND AMOUNT OF INBREEDING IN A POPULATION OF PRAIRIE DEERMICE. Walter E. Howard. PhD thesis, Univ. Mich., 1948.

WINTER FECUNDITY OF CAGED MALE WHITE-FOOTED MICE IN MICHIGAN. Walter E. Howard. Jour. Mam., vol.31, no.3, pp.319-321, Aug.21, 1950.

REPRODUCTION OF DEER MICE (PEROMYSCUS MANICULATUS AND P. BOYLEI) IN THE SIERRA NEVADA, CALIFORNIA. E. W. Jameson, Jr. Jour. Mam., vol.34, no.1, pp.44-58, 6 tables, 4 figs., Feb.19, 1953.

A BREEDING RECORD OF PHENACOMYS LONGICAUDUS. Stanley G. Jewett. Jour. Mam., vol.4, no.2, p.125, May, 1923.

REGULATION OF REPRODUCTION RATE IN SUBARCTIC POPULATIONS OF THE VOLE CLETHRIONOMYS RUFOCANUS (SUND). Olavi Kalela. Suomalaisen Tied. Toim, Ann. Acad. Sci., Fennicae, ser.A, pt.4, no.34, pp.60, 1957.

BREEDING HARVEST MICE. Phyllis Kelway. Game and Gun and the Angler's Monthly, London, vol.18, no.185, pp.63-65, illus., Feb., 1941.

BREEDING OF ABNORMALLY COLORED MEADOW MICE. H. L. Kutz, Ralph H. Smith. Jour. Mam., vol.26, no.3, pp.307-308, Aug., 1945.

THE LONGEVITY AND FERTILITY OF THE ORKNEY VOLE, MICROTUS ORCADENSIS, AS OBSERVED IN THE LABORATORY. P. H. Leslie, J. S. Tener, Monica Vizoso, Helen Chitty. Proc. Zool. Soc. Lond., vol.125, p.1, pp.115-125, May 27, 1955.

THE MEASUREMENT OF FERTILITY AND ITS USE AS AN INDEX OF REPRODUCTIVE ISOLATION AMONG CERTAIN LABORATORY STOCKS OF PEROMYSCUS. T. T. Liu. Contrib. Lab. Vert. Biol., Univ. Michigan, no.59, pp.1-12, Feb., 1953.

PRENATAL MORTALITY IN THE DEER MOUSE, PEROMYSCUS, WITH SPECIAL REFERENCE TO ITS BEARING ON REDUCED FERTILITY IN SOME INTERSPECIFIC AND INTERSUBSPECIFIC CROSSES. T. T. Liu. PhD thesis, Univ. Mich., 64 pp., 1953; Contrib. Lab. Vert. Biol., Univ. Mich., Ann Arbor, no.60, pp.1-32, illus., Feb., 1953.

STUDIES ON THE BIOLOGY OF THE MUSKRAT IN MANITOBA. PART I. OESTROUS CYCLE AND BREEDING SEASON. J. A. McLeod, G. F. Bondar. Can. Jour. Zool., 30 (4): 243-253, graph, Aug., 1952.

PARTURITION OF A CAPTIVE MEADOW VOLE. David E. Manly. Jour. Mam., vol.34, no.1, pp.130-131, Feb.19, 1953.

REMARKS ON THE REPRODUCTION, SEX RATIO, AND LIFE EXPECTANCY OF THE VARYING LEMMING, DICROSTONYX GROENLANDICUS, IN NATURE AND CAPTIVITY. T. H. Manning. Arctic, Montreal, vol.7, no.1, pp.36-48, June, 1954.

A LATE BREEDING CYCLE IN PEROMYSCUS. Richard H. Manville. Jour. Mam., vol.33, no.3, p.389, Aug.19, 1952.

REPRODUCTION IN THE ORKNEY VOLE (MICROTUS ORCADENSIS) UNDER A SIX-HOUR DAY-LENGTH AND OTHER CONDITIONS. A. J. Marshall, O. Wilkinson. Proc. Zool. Soc. Lond., vol.2 pt.3, pp. 391-395, 1 pl., May 31, 1956.

GROWTH AND REPRODUCTION IN THE FEMALES OF TWO SPECIES OF GERBIL, TATERA BRANTSI (A. SMITH) AND TATERA AFRA (GRAY). Veronica Measroch. Proc. Zool. Soc. Lond., vol. 124, pt.3, pp.631-658, illus., Nov.15, 1954.

A STUDY OF GROWTH AND REPRODUCTION IN THE COTTON RAT, SIGMODON HISPIDUS HISPIDUS. Bert J. Meyer. PhD thesis, Univ. Wis., 1942.

GROWTH AND REPRODUCTION OF THE COTTON RAT, SIGMODON HISPIDUS HISPIDUS, UNDER LABORATORY CONDITIONS. Bert J. Meyer, Roland K. Meyer. Jour. Mam., 25 (2): 107-129, May, 1944.

EXTRA-UTERINE PREGNANCY IN PEROMYSCUS. A. W. Moore. Jour. Mam., vol.10, no.1, p.81, Feb., 1929.

MULTIPLICATION AND MORTALITY IN THE COMMON VOLE (MICROTUS ARVALIS PALL.). N. P. Naumov. Abstracts Works Zool. Inst. Moscou Univ., no.3, 1936, pp.144-170, figs.5, 1936. (In Russian with English summary.)

ON THE COMPARATIVE INTENSITY OF REPRODUCTION AND MORTALITY OF THE FIELD-VOLE AND STEPPE-LEMMING. N. P. Naumov. Zool. Zhurnal, vol.16, no.2, pp.336-361, figs.8, 1937. (In Russian with English summary.)

A STUDY OF MUSKRAT PRODUCTIVITY IN A BUTTONBUSH SWAMP. Knute J. Norstog. MS thesis, Univ. Mich., 1947.

ACTIONS OF SEX HORMONES ON OESTROUS CYCLE AND REPRODUCTION OF THE GOLDEN HAMSTER. O. Peczenik. Jour. Endocrinol., Lond., vol.3, no.2, pp.157-167, pl.1, Aug., 1942.

THE INDUCTION OF PREGNANCY IN THE GOLDEN HAMSTER DURING THE BREEDING PAUSE. O. Peczenik. Proc. Roy. Soc. Edinburgh, Sec.B, vol.61, pt.3 (no.26), pp. 368-374, Oct.2, 1942.

REPRODUCTION IN THE WATER-VOLE, ARVICOLA AMPHIBIUS LINN. J. S. Perry. Proc. Zool. Soc. Lond., vol.112, ser.A, pts.3-4, pp.118-130, figs.3, pl.1, Feb., 1943.

(CONTRIBUTIONS ON THE BIOLOGY, ESPECIALLY THE PROPAGATION BIOLOGY, OF THE HAMSTER (CRICETUS CRICETUS L.).) Beitraege zur Biologie, insbesondere Fortpflanzungs-biologie des Hamsters (Cricetus cricetus L.). Hans Petzsch. Zeitschr. f. Kleintierkunde u. Pelztierkunde "Kleintier und Pelztier," Jahrg. XII, no.1, Monogr. der Wildsaeugetiere, vol.1, Leipzig, pp.11-83, figs.7, Jan., 1936.'

(ON COHABITATION EXPERIMENTS WITH CRICETUS CRICETUS L., MESOCRICETUS AURATUS WATERHOUSE, AND ARVICOLA TERRESTRIS L., WITH THE OBSERVED FRUITLESS COPULATIONS.) Ueber Zusammengewoehnungsversuche zwischen Cricetus cricetus L., Mesocricetus auratus Waterhouse und Arvicola terrestris L., sowie dabei beobachtete ergebnislose Begattungen. Hans Petzsch. Zool. Anzeiger, vol.151, nos.7-8, pp.134-138, Oct., 1953.

REPRODUCTION AND EARLY POST-NATAL DEVELOPMENT OF THE COTTON MOUSE, PEROMYSCUS GOSSYPINUS GOSSYPINUS. G. H. Pournelle. PhD thesis, Univ. Fla., 1950.

REPRODUCTION AND EARLY POSTNATAL DEVELOPMENT OF THE COTTON MOUSE, PEROMYSCUS GOSSYPINUS. G. H. Pournelle. Jour. Mam., 33 (1): 1-20, illus., Feb., 1952.

(ON THE PROPOGATION OF EVOTOMYS GLAREOLUS IN SIBERIA.) Sur la propagation des Evotomys glareolus Schreb. en Siberie. A. P. Razorionova. Bull. Soc. Nat. Moscou, sect. biol. n.s., vol.47, no. 2, pp.174-176, 1938.

JANUARY BREEDING OF PEROMYSCUS IN NORTH CENTRAL COLORADO. Edward B. Reed. Jour. Mam., 36 (3): 462-463, Aug., 1955.

REPRODUCTION, SIZE, AND MORTALITY IN THE ROCKY MOUNTAIN MUSKRAT. Henry M. Reeves, Roger M. Williams. Jour. Mam., 37 (4): 494-500, Jan.9, 1957.

(THE CONSTITUTION OF RESERVE STORES OF MICROTUS ARVALIS PALLAS (FIELD MOUSE) AND ITS IMPORTANCE FOR THE REPRODUCTION OF THIS RODENT.) La constitution des magasins de reserve du Microtus arvalis Pallas (campagnol des champs) et son importance pour la pullulation de ce rongeur. Robert Regnier, Roger Pussard. Comptes Rendus Acad. Sci., Paris, vol.183, pp.92-94, 1926.

(FIELD MOUSE, MICROTUS ARVALIS, WITH 13 EMBRYOS.) Feldmaus, Microtus arvalis, mit 13 Embryonen. H. Reichstein. Saeugetierk. Mitteil., 5 (2): 77, Apr.1, 1957.

WOOD RATS (NEOTOMA ALBIGULA): THEIR GROWTH AND DEVELOPMENT. William B. Richardson. Jour. Mam., 24 (2): 130-143, May, 1943.

REPRODUCTION OF THE BANK VOLE (EVOTOMYS GLAREOLUS SCHREBER). II. SEASONAL CHANGES IN THE REPRODUCTIVE ORGANS OF THE MALE. I. W. Rowlands. Philos. Trans. Roy. Soc. Lond., ser.B, no.531, vol.226, pp.99-120, pls.12-15, Mar.18, 1936.

HAMSTER SEXUALLY MATURE AT TWENTY-EIGHT DAYS OF AGE. Raymond M. Selle. Science, Lancaster, n.s., vol. 102, no.2654, pp.485-486, Nov.9, 1945.

NOTES ON BREEDING HABITS OF CAPTIVE DEERMICE. Ernest Thompson Seton. Jour. Mam., vol.1, no.3, pp.134-138, May, 1920.

THE CARE, BREEDING HABITS, AND VAGINAL SMEAR CYCLE OF THE LABORATORY HAMSTER (CRICETUS AURATUS). John F. Sheehan, Joyce A. Bruner. Turtox News, Chicago, vol.23, no.4, pp.65-68, illus., Apr., 1945.

MATING OF MUSKRATS. Wendell P. Smith. Jour. Mam., vol.25, no.1, p.90, Feb., 1944.

A RECORDED INSTANCE OF SUPERFETATION IN THE GOLDEN HAMSTER. A. L. Soderwall, Alice L. Britenbaker. Jour. Mam., 36 (4): 573, Dec.14, 1955.

BREEDING HABITS AND YOUNG OF THE RED-BACKED MOUSE, EVOTOMYS. Arthur Svihla. Papers Michigan Acad. Sci. Arts and Letters, vol.11, pp.485-489, 1930.

BREEDING AND YOUNG OF THE GRASSHOPPER MOUSE (ONYCHOMYS LEUCOGASTER FUSCOGRISEUS). Ruth Dowell Svihla. Jour. Mam., vol.17, no.2, pp.172-173, May, 1936.

NOTES ON THE BREEDING OF WOOD RATS OF THE GENUS NEOTOMA. Edward R. Warren. Jour. Mam., vol.7, no.2, pp.97-101, May, 1926.

EFFECTS OF LIGHT ON THE REPRODUCTIVE CYCLE OF PEROMYSCUS LEUCOPUS NOVEBORACENSIS. Wayne L. Whitaker. Proc. Soc. Exper. Biol. and Med., vol.34, no.3, pp.329-330, 1 fig., Apr., 1936.

SOME EFFECTS OF ARTIFICIAL ILLUMINATION ON REPRODUCTION IN THE WHITE-FOOTED MOUSE, PEROMYSCUS LEUCOPUS NOVEBORACENSIS. Wayne L. Whitaker. Jour. Exper. Zool., Phila., vol.83, no.1, pp.33-60, figs.4, tables 5, Feb.5, 1940.

ON THE REPRODUCTION OF VOLES AND LEMMING IN NORWAY. Aage Wildhagen. Statens Viltundersokelser, 61 pp., 1953.

A COMPENDIUM OF THE PRINCIPAL DATA ON MUSKRAT REPRODUCTION. Kenneth A. Wilson. N. C. Wildl. Resour. Comm., Job Compl. Rep., Fed. Aid Proj. W-6-R, pp.1-11, processed, Sept., 1955.

NOTES ON THE BREEDING BEHAVIOR AND FERTILITY OF NEOTOMA FUSCIPES MACROTIS IN CAPTIVITY. Fae Donat Wood. Jour. Mam., vol.16, no.2, pp.105-109, May, 1935.

Sex and Age Ratios

SEX AND AGE RATIOS IN WISCONSIN MUSKRATS. James Beer, Wayne C. Truax. Jour. Wildlife Mgt., 14 (3): 323-331, July, 1950.

SEX RATIOS AND AGE CLASSES OF MAINE MUSKRATS. Jay S. Gashwiler. Jour. Wildlife Mgt., 14 (4): 384-389, Oct., 1950.

AGE AND SEX RATIOS OF MUSKRATS HARVESTED DURING 1951 SEASON. Charles Hargrave. N. Dak. Outdoors, 14 (10): 17, Apr., 1952.

NOTES ON SEX RATIO IN MINNESOTA MUSKRATS. Donald M. Hatfield. Jour. Mam., vol.20, no.2, p.258, May, 1939.

UNUSUAL SEX RATIO IN PEROMYSCUS. Richard H. Manville. Jour. Mam., 37 (1): 122, Feb.28, 1956.

MUSKRAT SEX RATIOS IN UTAH. William H. Marshall. Jour. Mam., 18 (4): 518-519, Nov., 1937.

A STUDY OF INFLUENCES WHICH MAY EFFECT THE SEX-RATIO OF THE DEER-MOUSE (PEROMYSCUS). Francis B. Sumner, Mary E. McDaniel, Ralph R. Huestis. Biol. Bull., vol.43, pp.123-165, 7 figs., Aug., 1922.

Sinai

TWO NEW GERBILS FROM SINAI. Oldfield Thomas. Ann. and Mag. Nat. Hist., ser.9, vol.3, pp.559-560, June, 1919.

THE BUSY-TAILED GERBIL, GERBILLUS CALURUS THOMAS, OF SOUTH SINAI. Kamal Wassif. Jour. Mam., 35 (2): 243-248, illus., May, 1954.

South America

NEW SOUTH AMERICAN MURIDAE. J. A. Allen. Bull. Amer. Mus. Nat. Hist., vol.32, pp.597-604, Dec.3, 1913.

A NEW SPECIES OF THOMASOMYS FROM VENEZUELA. (THOMASOMYS OTTLEYI.) H. E. Anthony. Amer. Mus. Novitates, no.548, pp.1-2, July 8, 1932.

TWO NEW GENERA OF RODENTS FROM SOUTH AMERICA. H. E. Anthony. Amer. Mus. Nov., no.383, pp.1-6, Nov.4, 1929.

TWO NEW RODENTS FROM BOLIVIA. (THOMASOMYS LADEWI AND T. OREAS.) H. E. Anthony. Amer. Mus. Novit., no. 239, 3 pp., Dec.4, 1926.

(TWO NEW RODENTS FROM CATAMARCA MOUNTAINS.) Dos roedores nuevos de las montanas de Catamarca. (Phyllotis oreigenus and Akodon leucolimnaeus.) Angel Cabrera. Rev. Chilena Hist. Nat., vol.30, pp.319-321, 1926.

THE CAPTURE OF THE BRAZILIAN MOUSE BLARINOMYS BREVICEPS. David E. Davis. Jour. Mam., vol.25, no.4, pp. 367-369, fig.1, Dec.12, 1944.

CYCLIC BEHAVIOR AND ECONOMIC IMPORTANCE OF THE RATA-MUCA (ORYZOMYS) IN PERU. Raymond M. Gilmore. Jour. Mam., 28 (3): 231-241, Aug., 1947.

A NEW SCAPTEROMYS FROM CHACO AUSTRAL, ARGENTINE. (SCAPTEROMYS CHACOEENSIS.) Nils Gyldenstolpe. Arkiv. foer Zoologi, vol.24 B, no.1, pp.1-2, Jan. 28, 1932.

FOUR NEW ORYZOMYINE RODENTS FROM ECUADOR. Philip Hershkovitz. Jour. Mam., vol.21, no.1, pp.78-84, Feb.14, 1940.

MAMMALS OF NORTHERN COLOMBIA. PRELIMINARY REPORT NO. 3: WATER RATS (GENUS NECTOMYS), WITH SUPPLEMENTAL NOTES ON RELATED FORMS. Philip Hershkovitz. Proc. U. S. Nat. Mus., Wash., vol.98, no.3221, pp. 49-56, June 30, 1948.

MAMMALS OF NORTHERN COLOMBIA, PRELIMINARY REPORT NO. 8: ARBOREAL RICE RATS, A SYSTEMATIC REVISION OF THE SUBGENUS OECOMYS, GENUS ORYZOMUS. Philip Hershkovitz. U. S. Nat. Mus. Proc., Wash., vol.110, no.3420, pp. 513-568, illus., pls., maps, tables, 1960.

A NEW SPINY MOUSE OF THE GENUS NEACOMYS FROM EASTERN ECUADOR. (NEACOMYS SPINOSUS CARCELENI.) Philip Hershkovitz. Occas. Papers Mus. Zool., Univ. Michigan, Ann Arbor, no.419, pp.4, June 27, 1940.

NOTES ON THE DISTRIBUTION OF THE AKODONT RODENT, AKODON MOLLIS, IN ECUADOR WITH A DESCRIPTION OF A NEW RACE. (AKODON MOLLIS FULVESCENS.) Philip Hershkovitz. Occas. Papers Mus. Zool., Univ. Michigan, Ann Arbor, no.418, pp.1-3, June 27, 1940.

THE SOUTH AMERICAN HARVEST MICE OF THE GENUS REITHRODONTOMYS. Philip Hershkovitz. Occas. Papers Mus. Zool. Univ. Michigan, Ann Arbor, no.441, 7 pp., July 18, 1941.

SOUTH AMERICAN MARSH RATS, GENUS HOLOCHILUS, WITH A SUMMARY OF SIGMODONT RODENTS. Philip Hershkovitz. Fieldiana: Zoology, Chicago Nat. Hist. Mus., vol.37, pp.639-688, illus., June 19, 1955.

NEACOMYS FROM NORTHWESTERN SOUTH AMERICA. Barbara Lawrence. Jour. Mam., vol.22, no.4, pp.418-427, figs.2, Nov.14, 1941.

AN APPARENTLY NEW FORM OF CRICETINE FROM BRITISH GUIANA. (HOLOCHILUS SCIUREUS BERBICENSIS.) T. C. S. Morrison-Scott. Ann. and Mag. Nat. Hist., London, ser.10, vol.20, no.119, pp.535-538, Nov., 1937.

THE LONG-CLAWED SOUTH AMERICAN RODENTS OF THE GENUS NOTIOMYS. Wilfred H. Osgood. Field Mus. Nat. Hist., publ.229, zool. ser., vol.12, no.9, pp.113-125, pl.10, Oct.26, 1925.

A NEW GENUS OF RODENTS FROM PERU. Wilfred H. Osgood. Jour. Mam., vol.24, no.3, pp.369-371, pl.1, Aug.17, 1943.

THE SOUTH AMERICAN MICE REFERRED TO MICRORYZOMYS AND THALLOMYSCUS. Wilfred H. Osgood. Zool. Ser. Field Mus. Nat. Hist., vol.20, pp.1-8, Dec.11, 1933.

TWO NEW RODENTS FROM ARGENTINA. (THOMASOMYS PICTICPES, HESPEROMYS BIMACULATUS BONARIENSIS.) Wilfred H. Osgood. Zool. Ser. Feild Mus. Nat. Hist., vol.20, pp.11-14, Dec.11, 1933.

(DESCRIPTIONS OF THE MURIDAE OF CHILE.) Descripciones De Los Muideos De Chile. Rudolph Amandus Philippi. Anales Del Museo Nacional De Chile - Publicados Por Orden Del Gobierno De Chile - Primera Seccion: Zoolojía - entrega 14a, pp.5-70, pls.25, Santiago, Chile, 1900.

A NEW OXYMYCTERUS FROM MISIONES, ARGENTINA. (OXYMYCTERUS MISIONALIS.) Colin Campbell Sanborn. Proc. Biol. Soc. Wash., vol.44, pp.1-2, Feb.21, 1931.

A NEW SPECIES OF RICE RAT (ORYZOMYS) FROM THE COAST OF PERU. (ORYZOMYS (MELANOMYS) ZUNIGAE.) Colin Campbell Sanborn. Publ. Mus. Hist. Nat. "Javier Prado," Univ. Nac. Mayor San Marcos, ser.A, zool., Ano.1, no.3, pp.1-4, Apr., 1949.

SMALL RODENTS FROM PERU AND BOLIVIA. Colin Campbell Sanborn. Publ. Mus. Hist. Nat. "Javier Prado," Lima, ser.A, Zool., no.5, pp.1-16, Aug., 1950.

THE SOUTH AMERICAN RODENTS OF THE GENUS NEOTOMYS. Colin Campbell Sanborn. Fieldiana, Zool., Chicago, vol. 31, no.7, pp.51-57, figs.5-6, Jan.20, 1947.

AKODON CHACOENSIS, A NEW CRICETINE RODENT FROM ARGENTINA. H. Harold Shamel. Jour. Wash. Acad. Sci., vol.21, no.17, pp.427-429, figs.2, Oct.19, 1931.

THE SOUTH AMERICAN CRICETIDAE DESCRIBED BY FELIX AZARA. G. H. H. Tate. Amer. Mus. Nov., no.557, 5 pp., Sept.12, 1932.

DESCRIPTION OF A NEW BRAZILIAN SPECIES OF HESPEROMYS. Oldfield Thomas. Ann. and Mag. Nat. Hist. (5), vol.17, no.99, pp.250-251, Mar., 1886.

THE GROUPING OF THE SOUTH-AMERICAN MURIDAE COMMONLY REFERRED TO AKODON. Oldfield Thomas. Ann. and Mag. Nat. Hist. (8), vol.18, no.106, pp.336-340, Oct., 1916.

A NEW AKODON FROM TIERRA DEL FUEGO. Oldfield Thomas. Ann. and Mag. Nat. Hist. (8), vol.2, no.12, pp.496-497, Dec., 1908.

A NEW AQUATIC GENUS OF MURIDAE DISCOVERED BY CONSUL L. SODERSTROM IN ECUADOR. Oldfield Thomas. Ann. and Mag. Nat. Hist. (7), vol.17, no.97, pp.86-88, Jan., 1906.

A NEW FISH-EATING RAT FROM ECUADOR. (ICHTHYOMYS CAURINUS.) Oldfield Thomas. Ann. and Mag. Nat. Hist., ser.9, vol.13, pp.541-542, May, 1924.

NEW SIGMODON, ORYZOMYS, AND ECHIMYS FROM ECUADOR. Oldfield Thomas. Ann. and Mag. Nat. Hist. (9), vol.7, no.41, pp.448-450, May, 1921.

A NEW SPECIES OF ELIGMODONTIA FROM CATAMARCA. Oldfield Thomas. Ann. and Mag. Nat. Hist. (9), vol.2, no.12, pp.482-484, Dec., 1918.

A NEW SPECIES OF EUNEOMYS FROM PATAGONIA. (E. DABBENEI SP. NOV. FROM SANTA CRUZ.) Oldfield Thomas. Ann. and Mag. Nat. Hist., ser.9, vol.4, pp.127-128, Sept., 1919.

NEW SPECIES OF REITHRODON, ABROCOMA, AND SCAPTEROMYS FROM ARGENTINA. Oldfield Thomas. Ann. and Mag. Nat. Hist. (9), vol.5, no.30, pp.473-478, June, 1920.

A NEW THOMASOMYS FROM RIO GRANDE DO SUL. (T. OENAX.) Oldfield Thomas. Ann. and Mag. Nat. Hist., ser.10, vol.1, pp.154-155, Jan., 1928.

NOTES ON ARGENTINE, PATAGONIAN, AND CAPE HORN MURIDAE. Oldfield Thomas. Ann. and Mag. Nat. Hist. (8), vol.16, no.98, pp.181-187, Feb., 1916.

NOTES ON SOME S. AMERICAN MURIDAE. I. ON THREE NEW SPECIES FROM THE LOWER AMAZON. Oldfield Thomas. Ann. and Mag. Nat. Hist. (6), vol.19, no.113, pp. 494-501, May, 1897.

ON A COLLECTION OF MURIDAE FROM CENTRAL PERU. Oldfield Thomas. Proc. Zool. Soc., Lond., pp.447-458, pls.42-44, June 17, 1884.

ON A NEW FISH-EATING RAT FROM BOGOTA. (ICHTHYOMYS NICEFORI.) Oldfield Thomas. Ann. and Mag. Nat. Hist., ser.9, vol.13, pp.164-165, Jan., 1924.

ON SOME ARGENTINE MAMMALS. II. A SPECIAL GENUS FOR EUNEOMYS FOSSOR. Oldfield Thomas. Ann. and Mag. Nat. Hist. (9), vol.15, no.89, pp.584-585, May, 1925.

ON SOME ARGENTINE MAMMALS. III. A SECOND SPECIES OF SPALACOPUS. Oldfield Thomas. Ann. and Mag. Nat. Hist. (9), vol.15, no.89, pp.585-586, May, 1925.

ON THE ARRANGEMENT OF THE SOUTH AMERICAN RATS ALLIED TO ORYZOMYS AND RHIPIDOMYS. Oldfield Thomas. Ann. and Mag. Nat. Hist. (8), vol.20, no.116, pp.192-198, 1917.

ON THE GROUPING OF THE SOUTH-AMERICAN MURIDAE THAT HAVE BEEN REFERRED TO PHYLLOTIS, EUNEOMYS, AND ELIGMODONTIA. Oldfield Thomas. Ann. and Mag. Nat. Hist. (8), vol.17, no. 97, pp.139-143, Jan., 1916.

TWO NEW ARGENTINE SPECIES OF AKODON. Oldfield Thomas. Ann. and Mag. Nat. Hist. (9), vol.3, no.14, pp.213-214, Feb., 1919.

TWO NEW MURIDAE DISCOVERED IN PARAGUAY BY THE MARQUIS DE WAVRIN. (ORYZOMYS WAVRINI AND AKODON TOBA.) Oldfield Thomas. Ann. and Mag. Nat. Hist. (9), vol.7, pp.177-179, Feb., 1921.

TWO NEW MURIDAE FROM SOUTH AMERICA. Oldfield Thomas. Ann. and Mag. Nat. Hist. (8), vol.18, no.108, pp.478-480, Dec., 1916.

TWO NEW SPECIES OF AKODON FROM ARGENTINA. Oldfield Thomas. Ann. and Mag. Nat. Hist. (8), vol.18, no.106, pp.334-336, Oct., 1916.

CHARACTERS OF NEW SPECIES OF THE GENUS MUS, FROM THE COLLECTION OF MR. DARWIN. G. R. Waterhouse. Proc. Zool. Soc. Lond., pt.5, pp.15-21, 27-29, 1837.

DESCRIPTION OF A NEW MAMMAL OF BOLIVIA (HESPEROMYS BOLIVIENSIS). G. R. Waterhouse. Proc. Zool. Soc. London, pt.14, p.8, 1846.

(SHORT MONOGRAPH ON THE FIELD RATS OF THE "PHYLLOTIS" DISTRIBUTED THRU ARGENTINA.) Breve monografia de los ratones de campo del genero "Phyllotis" distribuidos en la Argentina. Jose Yepes, Genaro Yepes. Physis, Buenos Aires, vol. 16, no.48, p.299, May, 1939.

Taxonomy

THE STATUS OF PEROMYSCUS AMMODYTES BANGS. Philip F. Allan. Jour. Mam., vol.20, no.1, pp.98-101, Feb.14, 1939.

ON THE SPECIES OF THE GENUS REITHODONTOMYS. J. A. Allen. Bull. Amer. Mus. Nat. Hist., vol.7, pp.107-143, May 21, 1895.

(Review by C. Hart Merriam of) ON THE (HARVEST MICE) SPECIES OF THE GENUS REITHRODONTOMYS. J. A. Allen. Science, New York, n.s., vol.1, no.26, pp. 720-721, June 28, 1895.

REVISION OF THE MELANOMYS GROUP OF AMERICAN MURIDAE. J. A. Allen. Bull. Am. Mus. Nat. Hist., vol.32 (1913), pp.533-555, pl.LXVIII.

A PRIOR NAME REVIVED FOR THE BEAN MOUSE. (MICROTUS PENNSYLVANICUS INSPERATUS (ALLEN 1894), ANTEDATES M. PENNSYLVANICUS WAHEMA BAILEY 1920.) R. M. Anderson. Canadian Field-Nat., Sutton West, vol.57, nos.3-4, p.92, Apr.-May, 1943.

SUBSPECIATION IN THE MEADOW MOUSE, MICROTUS MONTANUS, IN WYOMING AND COLORADO. Sydney Anderson. Univ. Kansas Publ., Mus. Nat. Hist., vol.7, no. 7, pp.489-506, July 23, 1954.

SUBSPECIATION IN THE MEADOW MOUSE, MICROTUS PENNSYLVANICUS, IN WYOMING, COLORADO, AND ADJACENT AREAS. Sydney Anderson. Univ. Kansas Publ., Mus. Nat. Hist., 9 (4): 85-104, May 10, 1956.

NEW SPECIES AND SUBSPECIES OF THOMASOMYS. H. E. Anthony. Amer. Mus. Novit., no.178, pp.1-4, June 22, 1925.

CONTRIBUTIONS TO THE SYSTEMATICS AND DISTRIBUTION OF THE FIELD MICE OF THE SOCIALIS GROUP. A. I. Argyropulo. Acad. Sci. USSR, Caucasian Br. Papers Zool. Soc., vol.1, pp.165-174, 1934. (In Russian with German summary.)

(THE GENERA AND SPECIES OF HAMSTER (CRICETINAE) OF THE PALEOARCTIC.) Die Gattungen und Arten der Hamster (Cricetinae) der Palaearktis. A. I. Argyropulo. Trav. Inst. Zool. Acad. Sci. de L'URSS, Leningrad, vol.1, pp.239-248, (1932) 1933. (In Russian with German summary.)

DESCRIPTIONS OF ELEVEN NEW SPECIES AND SUBSPECIES OF VOLES. Vernon Bailey. Proc. Biol. Soc. Wash., vol.12, pp.85-90, Apr.30, 1898.

IDENTITY OF THE BEAN MOUSE OF LEWIS AND CLARK. Vernon Bailey. Jour. Mam., vol.1, no.2, pp.70-72, Feb., 1920.

A NEW NAME FOR MICROTUS INSULARIS BAILEY. Vernon Bailey. Science, Lancaster, vol.8, no.205, pp.782-783, Dec.2, 1898.

REVISION OF AMERICAN VOLES OF THE GENUS MICROTUS. Vernon Bailey. North Amer. Fauna, no.17, U.S. Dept. Agric., pp.88, figs.17, pls.5, June 6, 1900.

REVISION OF THE AMERICAN VOLES OF THE GENUS EVOTOMYS. Vernon Bailey. Proc. Biol. Soc. Wash., vol.11, pp.113-138, pl.3, May 13, 1897.

SYNOPSIS OF THE NORTH AMERICAN SPECIES OF SIGMODON. Vernon Bailey. Proc. Biol. Soc. Wash., vol.15, pp.101-116, June 2, 1902.

NOTE ON THE HARVEST-MICE OF THE PALAEARCTIC REGION. G. E. H. Barrett-Hamilton. Ann. and Mag. Nat. Hist., ser.7, vol.3, pp.341-345, Apr., 1899.

THE STATUS OF REITHRODONTOMYS MONTANUS (BAIRD). Seth B. Benson. Jour. Mam., vol.16, no.2, pp.139-142, fig. 1, May 15, 1935.

SYSTEMATIC RELATIONSHIPS OF PEROMYSCUS AND SEVERAL RELATED GENERA AS SHOWN BY THE BACULUM. W. F. Blair. Jour. Mam., vol.23, no.2, pp.196-204, figs.2, May 14, 1942.

A NEW WOODRAT FROM SOUTHWESTERN ARIZONA AND A NEW ROCK POCKET-MOUSE FROM NORTHWESTERN SONORA. Philip M. Blossom. Occas. Papers Mus. Zool., Univ. Michigan, no.273, pp.5, Oct. 31, 1933.

(ON THE NOMENCLATURE OF TWO EUROPEAN MICROTUS SPECIES.) Zur Nomenklatur Zweier europaeischer Microtus-Formen. F. H. Van Den Brink. Zeitschr. fuer Saeugetierkunde, vol.4, nos. 4-6, p.251, Feb.10, 1930.

SUBGENERIC ALLOCATION OF THE WHITE-FOOTED MOUSE, PEROMYSCUS SLEVINI, FROM THE GULF OF CALIFORNIA, MEXICO. William Henry Burt. Jour. Mam., vol.15, no.2, pp.159-160, May, 1934.

A NOTE ON THE NOMENCLATURE OF PHODOPUS SUNGORUS (PALLAS) AND ITS GEOGRAPHICAL RACES. J. L. Chaworth-Musters. Ann. and Mag. Nat. Hist., Lond., ser.10, vol.13, no.78, pp.590-591, June, 1934.

A NOTE ON THE SYNONYMY OF CRICETULUS BARABENSIS PALLAS. J. L. Chaworth-Musters. Ann. and Mag. Nat. Hist., London, ser.10, vol.12, no.68, pp.221-223, Aug., 1933.

ON THE TYPE LOCALITY OF ELLOBIUS TALPINUS PALLAS. J. L. Chaworth-Musters. Ann. and Mag. Nat. Hist., London, vol.19, no.109, p.158, Jan., 1937.

ON THE TYPE-LOCALITY OF THE VOLE, PITYMYS DUODECIMCOSTATUS (DE SELYS-LONGCHAMPS). J. L. Chaworth-Musters. Ann. and Mag. Nat. Hist., London, ser.10, vol.20, no.119, pp.559-560, Nov., 1937.

A REVISION OF THE GENUS MERIONES. J. L. Chaworth-Musters, J. R. Ellerman. Proc. Zool. Soc., London, vol.117, pts.2-3, pp.478-504, Oct.30, 1947.

THE BACULUM IN THE TAXONOMY OF PEROMYSCUS BOYLEI AND P. PECTORALIS. William K. Clark. Jour. Mam., vol. 34, no.2, pp.189-192, illus., May 15, 1953.

REITHRODONTOMYS HUMULIS FROM THE TYPE LOCALITY. Robert H. Coleman. Jour. Mam., vol.10, no.3, p.257, Aug., 1929.

NOTE ON THE NOMENCLATURE OF HESPEROMYS AMERIDANUS COUES AND YARROW. E. Coues. Amer. Nat., vol. 13, p.784, Dec., 1879.

STATUS OF MICROTUS ENIXUS AND MICROTUS TERRAENOVAE. David E. Davis. Jour. Mam., vol.17, no.3, pp.290-291, Aug., 1936.

THE SYSTEMATIC STATUS OF THE LOUISIANA MUSKRAT. William B. Davis, George H. Lowery, Jr. Jour. Mam., Balto., vol.21, no.2, pp.212-213, May 14, 1940.

(MAMMALS. SYSTEMATIC STUDY BY SPECIES. MERIONES SHAWI (DUVERNOY).) Mammiferes. Étude systématique par espèces. Meriones shawi (Duvernoy). Robert Didier, Paul Rode. Paul Lechevalier, Paris, no.4, pp.11, figs.8, pls.2, 1937.

EXTERNAL CHARACTERS IN THE STRUCTURE OF THE FEET AND THEIR VALUE FOR THE CLASSIFICATION OF THE VOLES. N. M. Dukelski. Jour. Mam., vol.8, no.2, pp.133-140, figs.31, May, 1927.

AMMOMYS BP., AS A VALID SUBGENUS, WITH SOME REMARKS ABOUT ITS SYSTEMATICAL POSITION. J. Ehik. Ann. Mus. Nat. Hungarici, vol.22, pp.124-126, 1925.

IS SIGMODON AUSTERULUS A VALID SPECIES? Robert K. Enders. Jour. Mam., vol.34, no.4, pp.508-509, Nov.13, 1953.

A SYSTEMATIC STUDY OF THE RED-BACKED MICE, GENUS CLETHRIONOMYS, OF WYOMING. Kenneth L. Fitch. MS thesis, Univ. Kans., 1952.

MICROMYS MINUTUS SUBOBSCURUS SSP. NOV. Karl Fritsche. Zeitschr. f. Saeugetierkunde, vol.9, nos.1-3, p.431 Dec.30, 1934.

(DIFFERENTIATION OF MICROTUS RATTICEPS (KEYS. AND BLAS.) AND MICROTUS NIVALIS (MARTINS).) Zur Unterscheidung von Microtus ratticeps (Keys. und Blas.) und Microtus nivalis (Martins). Guenter Gaffrey. Zool. Anzeiger, Leipzig, vol.143, nos.7-8, pp.157-164, fig.1, Aug. 30, 1943.

TAXONOMIC REVIEW OF THE COTTON RATS (GENUS SIGMODON) OF THE EASTERN UNITED STATES. Marshall C. Gardner. MS thesis, Geo. Wash. Univ., 44 pp., 1950.

REVIEW OF MICROTUS VOLES OF THE SUBGENUS STENOCRANIUS (MAMMALIA: RODENTIA: MURIDAE), WITH SPECIES DISCUSSION OF THE BERING STRAIT REGION. Raymond Maurice Gilmore. Abstracts of Theses, 1942, Cornell Univ., Ithaca, pp.289-292, 1943.

A NEW RACE OF THE CANYON MOUSE. Olive B. Goein. Jour. Mam., vol.25, no. 2, pp.189-191, fig.1, May 25, 1944.

FIVE NEW WOODRATS OF THE GENUS NEOTOMA FROM MEXICO. E. A. Goldman. Proc. Biol. Soc. Wash., vol.22, pp.139-142, June 25, 1909.

A NEW WOODRAT OF THE GENUS HODOMYS. E. A. Goldman. Jour. Wash. Acad. Sci., vol.28, no.11, pp.498-499, Nov., 1938.

NOTES ON THE VOLES OF THE MICROTUS LONGICAUDUS GROUP. E. A. Goldman. Jour. Mam., vol.19, no.4, pp. 491-492, Nov.14, 1938.

REMARKS ON VOLES OF THE GENUS LEMMISCUS, WITH ONE DESCRIBED AS NEW. E. A. Goldman. Proc. Biol. Soc. Wash., vol.54, pp.69-72, July 31, 1941.

REVIEW OF WOOD RATS OF NEOTOMA LEPIDA GROUP. E. A. Goldman. Jour. Mam., vol.13, no.1, pp.59-67, Feb., 1932.

REVISION OF THE WOOD RATS OF THE GENUS NEOTOMA. E. A. Goldman. U. S. Dept. Agric. Bur. of Biol. Surv. N. Amer. Fauna, no.31, pp.124, figs.14, pls. 8, Oct.19, 1910.

STATUS OF PEROMYSCUS NUTTALLI AUREOLUS. E. A. Goldman. Jour. Mam., vol.25, no.4, p.414, Dec.12, 1944.

THREE NEW RACES OF MICROTUS MEXICANUS. (MICROTUS MEXICANUS HUALPAIENSIS; M. M. MADRENSIS; M. M. SUBSIMUS.) E. A. Goldman. Jour. Mam., vol. 19, no.4, pp.493-495, Nov.14, 1938.

TWELVE NEW WOOD RATS OF THE GENUS NEOTOMA. E. A. Goldman. Proc. Biol. Soc. Wash., vol.18, pp.27-34, Feb. 2, 1905.

TWO NEW COTTON RATS. E. A. Goldman, Marshall C. Gardner. Jour. Mam., vol. 28, no.1, pp.57-59, Feb.15, 1947.

NEW TREE-CLIMBING RATS FROM MEXICO AND COLOMBIA. (TYLOMYS NUDICAUDUS MICRODON T. MIRAE BOGOTENSIS.) George G. Goodwin. Amer. Mus. Novitates, New York, no.1738, p.5, June 10, 1955.

SYSTEMATIC REVIEW OF THE CALIFORNICUS GROUP OF THE RODENT GENUS PEROMYSCUS. Joseph Grinnell, Robert T. Orr. Jour. Mam., vol.15, no.3, pp.210-220, figs. 2, Aug., 1934.

A NEW RACE OF WOOD RAT (NEOTOMA LEPIDA). E. Raymond Hall. Univ. California Publ. Zool., Berkeley, vol.46, no.5, pp.369-370, July 3, 1942.

A SYNOPSIS OF THE NORTH AMERICAN MICROTINE RODENTS. E. Raymond Hall, E. Lendell Cockrum. Univ. Kansas Publ., Mus. Nat. Hist., Lawrence, vol.5, no.27, pp.373-498, illus., Jan.15, 1953.

ON A NEW SPECIES OF MERIONES (MER. MICROCEPHALUS). Dr. Harlan. Proc. Zool. Soc. London, pt.7, p.1, 1839.

DESCRIPTION OF A NEW RACE OF MICROTUS CALIFORNICUS. (MICROTUS CALIFORNICUS PALUDICOLA.) Donald M. Hatfield. Jour. Mam., vol.16, no.4, pp. 316-318, Nov., 1935.

IDENTITY OF HEOPEROMYS INDIANUS WIED. Robert T. Hatt. Jour. Mam., vol. 11, no.3, pp.317-318, Aug.9, 1930.

(FAUNA OF GERBIILIDAE (SIC) (MAMMALIA, GLIRES) OF PERSIA AND THE ZOOGEOGRAPHICAL CHARACTERISTICS OF THE ASIA MINOR COUNTRIES AND IRAN AND AFGHANISTAN.) Fauna der Gerbiilidae (sic) (Mammalia, Glires) Persiens und die tiergeographischen Eigenheiten der Kleinasiatisch-Irano-Afganischen Laender. V. G. Heptner. Nouv. Mem. Soc. Nat., Moscou, vol.20, pp.3-71, figs.1-69, maps 4, 1940. (With German summary.)

(NEW FORM OF FIELD MOUSE MICROTUS GREGALIS PALL. (MAMMALIA, MURIDAE).) Une nouvelle forme de campagnols Microtus gregalis Pall. (Mammalia, Muridae). (Microtus (Stenocranius) gregalis zachvatkini.) V. G. Heptner. Comptes Rendus (Doklady) Acad. Sci. URSS, Moscow, n.s., vol.49, no.5, pp.387-388, Nov.20, 1945.

(NOTES ON THE GERBILLINAE (MAMMALIA, MURIDAE) III. NEW GERBILLINAE OF TRANSCAUCASIA.) Notizen ueber die Gerbillinae (Mammalia, Muridae) III. Neue Gerbillinae aus Transkaukases. W. G. Heptner. Zool. Anzeiger, vol.94, nos.3-4, pp.119-122, 1931.

(NOTES ON THE GERBILLINAE (MAMMALIA, MURIDAE) IV. ON THE NAMING OF THE TRANSCAUCASIAN DESERT MICE OF THE MERIDIANUS ERYTHROURUS GROUP.) Notizen ueber die Gerbillinae (Mammalia, Muridae) IV. Ueber die Benannung der transkaukasische Wustenmaeuse der meridianus erythrourus gruppe. W. G. Heptner. Zool. Anzeiger, vol.94, nos.9-10, pp.273-276, 1931.

(NOTES ON THE GERBILLINAE. (MAMMALIA, MURIDAE). V. DIAGNOSES OF A NEW GENUS AND NINE NEW SUBSPECIES OF TURKESTAN.) Notizen ueber die Gerbillinae (Mammalia, Muridae). V. Diagnosen von einer neuen Gattung und neun neuen Unterarten aus Turkestan. W. G. Heptner. Zeitschr. f. Saeugetierkunde, vol.8, no.3, pp.150-155, figs.1-2, Dec.20, 1933.

(NOTES ON THE GERBILLIDAE (MAMMALIA, RODENTIA). VI. Notizen ueber die Gerbillidae (Mammalia, Rodentia). VI. Zool. Anzeiger, vol.102, nos.3-4, pp.107-112, Mar.10, 1933.

(NOTES ON THE GERBILLIDAE (MAMMALIA, RODENTIA). VII. ON THE FORMS AND GEOGRAPHICAL DISTRIBUTION OF THE GENUS BRACHIONES THOS.) Notizen ueber die Gerbillidae (Mammalia, Rodentia). VII. Ueber die Formen und geographische Verbreitung der Gattung Brachiones Thos. W. G. Heptner. Archiv. Mus. Zool. Univ. Moscow, vol.1, pp.3-11, 1934; Ann. Mus. Zool. Polonici, Warsaw, vol.11, no.2, pp.5-19, Jan.30, 1935.

(NOTES ON THE GERBILLIDAE (MAMMALIA, GLIRES). VIII. GERBILLIDAE OF THE CAUCASUS AND THE KALMUKEN STEPPE.) Notizen ueber die Gerbillidae (Mammalia, Glires). VIII. Gerbillidae der Kaukasuslaender und der Kalmuekensteppe. W. G. Heptner. Folia Zoologica et Hydrobiologica, Riga, vol.6, no.2, pp.179-268, fig.1, pls.7-11, Oct.10, 1934.

(NOTES ON THE GERBILS (MAMMALIA, GLIRES). X. NEW CONTRIBUTIONS TO THE GEOGRAPHICAL DISTRIBUTION AND SYSTEMATICS OF RHOMBOMYS OPIMUS LICHT.) Notes sur les gerbilles (Mammalia, Glires). X. Contributions nouvelles a la distribution geographique et a la systematique de Rhombomys opimus Licht. W. G. Heptner. Bull. Soc. Nat. Moscou, sect. biol., n.s., vol.48, no.4, pp.99-104, 1939.

(NOTES ON GERBILLIDAE (MAMMALIA, GLIRES). XI. ON THE RECIPROCAL RELATIONS OF CERTAIN GERBILS OF NORTHERN ARFICA AND ASIA.) Notes sur les Gerbillidae (Mammalia, Glires). XI. Sur les relations reciproques de certaines gerbilles de l'Afrique du Nord et de l'Asie. W. G. Heptner. Mammalia, Paris, vol.10, no.1, pp.4-12, fig.1, Mar., 1946.

NOTES ON GERBILLIDAE (MAMMALIA, GLIRES. REMARKS ON A NEW SPECIES OF MERIONES FROM TURKESTAN AND ON THE SYSTEMATIC POSITION OF THE GERBILS BELONGING TO THE MERIONES PERSICUS-GROUP. (MERIONES ZARUDNYI, PARAMERIONES.) W. G. Heptner. Bull. Soc. Nat. Moscou, sect. biol., n.s., vol.46, no.4, pp.189-193, 1937. (In Russian, with English summary.)

A SYSTEMATIC REVIEW OF THE NEOTROPICAL WATER RATS OF THE GENUS NECTOMYS (CRICETINAE). Philip Hershkovitz. Univ. Michigan Mus. Zool., Ann Arbor, Misc. Publ. no.58, pp.1-101, pls.1-4, map, Jan.4, 1944.

ERRONEOUS IDENTIFICATION, MICROTUS PENNSYLVANICUS PENNSYLVANICUS (ORD) - MICROTUS OCHROGASTER. Claude W. Hibbard. Jour. Mam., vol.19, no.3, pp.380-381, Aug., 1938.

THE STATUS OF THE GENERA ANAPTOGENIA AND SYCIUM COPE. Claude W. Hibbard. Jour. Mam., vol.38, no.1, p.67, Feb.15, 1947.

A NEW NAME FOR THE MEADOW MOUSE MICROTUS ROBERTI OCCIDENTALIS TUROV. Donald F. Hoffmeister. Jour. Wash. Acad. Sci., vol.39, no.6, pp.205-206, June 15, 1949.

DESCRIPTIONS OF TWO NEW MUSKRATS. Ned Hollister. Proc. Biol. Soc. Wash., vol.23, pp.1-2, Feb.2, 1910.

THE GENERIC NAME OF THE MUSKRAT. Ned Hollister. Proc. Biol. Soc. Wash., vol.24, pp.13-14, Jan.28, 1911.

A SYSTEMATIC ACCOUNT OF THE GRASSHOPPER MICE. Ned Hollister. Proc. U. S. Nat. Mus., vol.47, pp.427-489, pl.15, Oct.29, 1914.

A SYSTEMATIC SYNOPSIS OF THE MUSKRATS. Ned Hollister. U. S. Dept. Agric., Div. Biol. Surv., N. Amer. Fauna, no.32, pp.1-47, pls.1-6, Apr.29, 1911.

THREE NEW SUBSPECIES OF GRASSHOPPER MICE. Ned Hollister. Proc. Biol. Soc. Wash., vol.26, pp.215-216, Dec.20, 1913.

THE NAME NEOTOMA CINEREA CINNAMOMEA ALLEN APPLIED TO WOODRATS FROM SOUTHWESTERN WYOMING. Emmet T. Hooper. Jour. Mam., vol.25, no.4, pp.415, Nov., 1944.

A SYNOPSIS OF THE CRICETINE RODENT GENUS NELSONIA. Emmet T. Hooper. Occas. Pap. Mus. Zool. Univ. Michigan, Ann Arbor, no.558, p.12, Sept.17, 1954.

A SYSTEMATIC REVIEW OF THE HARVEST MICE (GENUS REITHRODONTOMYS) OF LATIN AMERICA. Emmet T. Hooper. Misc. Publ. Univ. Michigan Mus. Zool., Ann Arbor, no.77, pp.255, illus., Jan.16, 1952.

(Review by Keith R. Kelson of ) A SYSTEMATIC REVIEW OF THE HARVEST MICE (GENUS REITHRODONTOMYS) OF LATIN AMERICA. Emmet T. Hooper. Jour. Mamm., vol.34, no.3, pp.398-400, Aug. 14, 1953.

A NEW RACE OF MICROTUS PENNSILVANICUS. Reginald Heber Howe. Proc. Portland Soc. Nat. Hist., vol.2, pt.6, pp.201-202, pl.5, Dec.31, 1901.

DESCRIPTIONS OF TWO NEW RODENTS OF THE GENUS PHENACOMYS. (PHENACOMYS INTERMEDIUS LEVIS AND P. I. CELSUS.) A. Brazier Howell. Proc. Biol. Soc. Wash., vol.36, pp.157-158, May 1, 1923.

REVISION OF THE AMERICAN LEMMING MICE (GENUS SYNAPTOMYS). A. Brazier Howell. N. Amer. Fauna, no.50, pp.1-37, figs.1-11, pls.1-2, June 30, 1927.

DESCRIPTIONS OF A NEW SUBSPECIES OF THE GOLDEN MOUSE. Arthur H. Howell. Jour. Mam., vol.20, no.4, p.498, Nov.14, 1939.

REVISION OF THE AMERICAN HARVEST MICE (GENUS REITHRODONTOMYS). Arthur H. Howell. N. Amer. Fauna, no. 36, pp.1-97, pls.1-7, June 5, 1914.

REVISION OF THE AMERICAN MARMOTS. Arthur H. Howell. N. Amer. Fauna, no. 37, pp.1-80, figs.3, pls.1-15, Apr.7, 1915.

THE TYPE LOCALITY OF PITYMYS PARVULUS. Arthur H. Howell. Jour. Mam., vol.15, no.1, p.72, Feb., 1934.

CHANGE OF NAME. (MICROTUS CALIFORNICUS NEGLECTUS KELLOGG BECOMES M. C. SANCTIDIEGI.) Remington Kellogg. Proc. Biol. Soc. Wash., vol.35, p.78, Mar.20, 1922.

A REVISION OF THE MICROTUS CALIFORNICUS GROUP OF MEADOW MICE. Remington Kellogg. Univ. Calif. Publ. Zool., vol.21, no.1, 1918.

A STUDY OF THE CALIFORNIAN FORMS OF THE MICROTUS MONTANUS GROUP OF MEADOW MICE. Remington Kellogg. Univ. Calif. Publ. Zool., vol.21, no.7, pp.245-274, 25 figs., Apr.18, 1922.

A SYNOPSIS OF THE MICROTUS MORDAX GROUP OF MEADOW MICE IN CALIFORNIA. Remington Kellogg. Univ. Cali. Publ. Zool., vol.21, no.8, pp.275-302, pl.8, map, diagrs, 1922.

THE NOMENCLATURE OF EVOTOMYS AND A NEW LOCALITY. Nagamichi Kuroda. Dobutsugaku-Zasshi, Tokyo, vol. 43, no.517, pp.661-666, 1931. (In Japanese.)

(SYSTEMATIC REVIEW OF THE FIELD-MICE OF SIBERIA BY POLIAKOFF. ANALYSIS, WITH CRITICAL REMARKS.) Revue systematique des campagnols de Siberie par Poliakoff. Analyse avec annotations critiques. Fernand Lataste. Ann. Mus. Civ. Stor. Nat. di Genova, vol.20, pp.253-301, Mar.8-12, 1884. (Trans. of: Iv. S. Poliakov, 1881, Suppl. to mem. Acad. St. Petersbourg, vol.39, no.2, pp.92.)

THE AFFINITIES OF THE ORKNEY VOLE (MICROTUS ORCADENSIS, MILLAIS). C. I. Forsyth Major. Ann. and Mag. Nat. Hist., ser.7, vol.15, pp.323-324, Mar., 1905.

NEW NAMES FOR TWO SUBSPECIES OF PEROMYSCUS MANICULATUS (WAGNER). Edgar A. Mearns. Proc. Biol. Soc. Wash., vol.24, pp.101-102, May 15, 1911.

ABSTRACT OF THE STUDY OF THE AMERICAN WOOD RATS, WITH DESCRIPTIONS OF FOURTEEN NEW SPECIES AND SUBSPECIES OF THE GENUS NEOTOMA. C. Hart Merriam. Proc. Biol. Soc., Wash., vol.9, pp.117-128, July 2, 1894.

A CORRECTION: ARVICOLA (CHILOTUS) PALLIDUS. C. Hart Merriam. Amer. Nat., vol.23, no.265, p.60, figs.4, 1889.

DESCRIPTION OF A NEW GENUS (PHENOCOMYS) AND FOUR NEW SPECIES OF ARVICOLINAE. C. Hart Merriam. N. Amer. Fauna, no.2, pp.27-35, pls.1-8, figs.5-7, Oct., 1889.

DESCRIPTIONS OF 23 NEW HARVEST MICE (GENUS REITHRODONTOMYS). C. Hart Merriam. Proc. Wash. Acad. Sci., vol.3, pp.547-558, Nov.29, 1901.

DESCRIPTIONS OF NEW SPECIES AND SUBSPECIES. ONYCHOMYS LONGIPES SP. NOV. C. Hart Merriam. N. Amer. Fauna, no.2, pp.1-5, figs.2, Oct., 1889.

DESCRIPTIONS OF TWO NEW SPECIES AND ONE NEW SUBSPECIES OF GRASSHOPPER MOUSE. C. Hart Merriam. N. Amer. Fauna, no.2, U. S. Dept. Agric., pp.5, figs.2, tables, Oct., 1889.

FOUR NEW GRASSHOPPER MICE, GENUS ONYCHOMYS. C. Hart Merriam. Proc. Biol. Soc. Wash., vol.17, pp.123-126, June 9, 1904.

A NEW SUBFAMILY OF MURINE RODENTS-THE NEOTOMINAE--WITH DESCRIPTION OF A NEW GENUS AND SPECIES AND A SYNOPSIS OF THE KNOWN FORMS. C. Hart Merriam. Proc. Acad. Nat. Sci., Phila., pp.225-252, figs.5, pl.9, 1894.

REVISION OF THE LEMMINGS OF THE GENUS SYNAPTOMYS WITH DESCRIPTIONS OF NEW SPECIES. C. Hart Merriam. Proc. Biol. Soc., Wash., vol. 10, pp.55-64, figs.5, Mar.19, 1896.

SYNOPSIS OF THE RICE RATS (GENUS ORYZOMYS) OF THE UNITED STATES AND MEXICO. C. Hart Merriam. Proc. Wash. Acad. Sci., vol.3, pp.273-295, July 26, 1901.

THE VOLES OF THE SUBGENUS CHILOTUS, WITH DESCRIPTIONS OF NEW SPECIES. C. Hart Merriam. Proc. Biol. Soc., Wash., vol.11, pp.73-75, Apr.21, 1897.

BRIEF SYNOPSIS OF THE WATER-RATS OF EUROPE. Gerrit S. Miller, Jr. Proc. Biol. Soc., Wash., vol.23, pp.19-22, Mar. 23, 1910.

THE GENERA AND SUBGENERA OF VOLES AND LEMMINGS. Gerrit S. Miller, Jr. N. American Fauna, no.12, pp.76, figs.40, pls.3, July 23, 1896.

THE GENERIC NAME EVOTOMYS NOT INVALIDATED BY ANAPTOGONIA. Gerrit S. Miller, Jr. Proc. Biol. Soc., Wash., vol.8, p.154, June 13, 1900.

NEW NAMES FOR TWO EUROPEAN VOLES. Gerrit S. Miller, Jr. Proc. Biol. Soc., Wash., vol.24, p.39, Feb.24, 1911.

(THE NOMENCLATURE OF THE FIELD MICE.) Sur la nomenclature des Campagnols. Gerrit S. Miller, Jr. Actes Soc. Sci. di Chili, vol.4, Proc.-verb., p. clxxxviii, Jan.22, 1895.

NOTE ON THE TYPE OF FIBER OSOYOOSENSIS LORD. Gerrit S. Miller, Jr. N. Amer. Fauna, no.32, p.25, Apr.29, 1911.

NOTES ON THE ARCTIC RED-BACKED MICE. Gerrit S. Miller, Jr. Proc. Acad. Nat. Sci., Phila., pp.358-367, figs.2, Oct.11, 1898.

PRELIMINARY REVISION OF THE EUROPEAN REDBACKED MICE. Gerrit S. Miller, Jr. Proc. Wash. Acad. Sci., vol. 2, pp.83-109, July 26, 1900.

THE RECENT VOLES OF THE MICROTUS NIVALIS GROUP. Gerrit S. Miller, Jr. Ann. and Mag. Nat. Hist., ser.8, vol.1, pp.97-103, Jan., 1908.

THE STATUS OF THE GENUS ASCHIZOMYS MILLER. Gerrit S. Miller, Jr. Jour. Mam., vol.21, no.1, pp.94-95, Feb.14, 1940.

SYNOPSIS OF THE VOLES, OF THE GENUS PHENACOMYS. Gerrit S. Miller, Jr. Proc. Biol. Soc., Wash., vol.11, pp.77-87, Apr. 21, 1897.

THE TYPE OF THE GENUS ONDATRA LINK. Gerrit S. Miller, Jr. Smithsonian Inst. Publ.2169, pp.126-127, May 12, 1913.

(ON SOME GREEK RODENTS: MUS EPIMELAS N. SP., CRICETULUS ATTICUS N. SP., AND MYOXUS NITEDULA WINGEI N. SUBSP.) Ueber einige griechische Nager: Mus epimelas n. sp., Cricetulus atticus n. sp., und Myoxus nitedula Wingei n. subsp. A. Nehring. Sitz. Ber. Gesell. Naturf. Freunde, Berlin, no.1, pp.1-7, Jan.21, 1902.

THE NAME OF THE SAN MARTIN ISLAND MOUSE--A CORRECTION. E. W. Nelson, E. A. Goldman. Jour. Mam., Balto., vol. 13, no.4, Nov.13, 1932, pp.370-371.

SYSTEMATIC PECULIARITIES OF THE HAMSTER (CRICETUS CRICETUS L.). K. L. Novikov. Bull. Soc. Nat. Moscou, sect. Biol., n.s., vol.44, pt.6, pp.302-312, 1935. (In Russian, with English summary.)

CONTRIBUTIONS TO THE TAXONOMY OF MICROTUS RATTICEPS KEYSERL. ET BLAS. S. I. Ognev. Comptes Rendus (Doklady) Acad. Sci. URSS, Moscou, vol. 44, no.4, pp.165-168, Aug., 1944.

(MATERIALS ON THE SYSTEMATICS AND GEOGRAPHY OF THE RUSSIAN WATER RATS (ARVICOLA).) Materialien zur Systematik und Geographie der russischen Wasserratten (Arvicola). S. I. Ognev. Zeitschr. f. Saeugetierkunde, Berlin, vol. 8, nos.3-6, pp.156-179, figs.22, Dec.20, 1933.

A SYSTEMATIC REVIEW OF SPECIES OF GENUS MYOSPALAX. S. I. Ognev. Moscou Univ. Sbornik Nauchno-issledovatel 'skogo inst. Zool. (Abstracts Works Zool. Inst. Moscow State Univ.), no.3, pp.81-82, 1936.

A NEW FORM OF THE WATER RAT ARVICOLA TERRESTRIS (CUBANENSIS) SUBSP. NOVA. S. I. Ognev, K. L. Novikoff. Abstr. works zool. inst. Moscow State Univ., pp.63-64. (In Russian.)

AN ACCOUNT OF A NEW SPECIES OF THE GENUS ARVICOLA. George Ord. Jour. Phila. Acad. Sci., vol.4, pt.2, pp.305-306, 1825.

CRICETINE RODENTS ALLIED TO PHYLLOTIS. Wilfred H. Osgood. Jour. Mam., vol.28, no.2, pp.165-174, May 19, 1947.

THE GENERIC POSITION OF MUS PYRRHORHINUS WIED. Wilfred H. Osgood. Jour. Mam., Balto., vol.14, no.4, pp. 370-371, Nov.13, 1933.

HAPLOMYLOMYS, A NEW SUBGENUS OF PEROMYSCUS. Wilfred H. Osgood. Proc. Biol. Soc. Wash., vol.17, pp.53-54, fig.1, Mar.21, 1904.

THE IDENTITY OF MUS LONGIBARBUS PHILIPPI. Wilfred H. Osgood. Jour. Mam., vol.27, no.1, p.91, Mar.14, 1946.

A NEW NAME FOR THE PEROMYSCUS NEBRACENSIS OF CERTAIN AUTHORS. Wilfred H. Osgood. Proc. Biol. Soc. Wash., vol.18, p.77, Feb.21, 1905.

REVISION OF THE MICE OF THE AMERICAN GENUS PEROMYSCUS. Wilfred H. Osgood. N. Amer. Fauna, Wash., D.C., no.28, pp.285, pls.8, figs.12, Apr.17, 1909.

(Review by Edgar A. Mearns of) REVISION OF THE MICE OF THE AMERICAN GENUS PEROMYSCUS. Wilfred H. Osgood. Science, New York, n.s., vol.30, no.760, pp.119-121, July 23, 1909.

THE SUPPOSED GENERA AEPEOMYS AND INOMYS. Wilfred H. Osgood. Jour. Mam., Balto., vol.14, no.2, p.161, May 15, 1933.

AN EARLIER NAME FOR THE GENUS EVOTOMYS. T. S. Palmer. Proc. Biol. Soc. Wash., vol.41, p.87, Mar.16, 1928.

(COMPARATIVE CHARACTERS OF GERBILLUS ALLENBYI AND TWO OTHER SPECIES OF SUBGENUS GERBILLUS.) Caracteres compares de Gerbillus allenbyi et de deux autres especes du sous-genre Gerbillus. F. Petter. Mammalia, Paris, 20 (3): 231-237, pl.1, Sept., 1956.

(NOTE ON A TYPE OF F. CUVIER: GERBILLUS PYGARGUS, "THE GERBILLE OF SENEGAL." F. Petter. Mammalia, Paris, vol.16, no.1, pp.37-39, illus., Mar., 1952.

(MICROTUS AGRESTIS TRIDENTINUS DAL PIAZ IN TRE VENEZIE.) I. Microtus agrestis tridentinus Dal Piaz nelle Tre Venezie. Gian Battista Dal Piaz. Studi Trentini, ser.2, vol.7, pp.1-6 (of reprint), 1 pl., 1926.

(STUDY ON THE TRIDENTINE ARVICOLA.) Studio sulle Arvicole tridentine. Gian Battista Dal Piaz. Studi Trentini, vol.5, no.4, pp.1-17, 1924.

CORRECT NAME, AUTHORSHIP AND DATE OF BLYTH'S VOLE, PITYMYS (PHAIOMYS) LEUCURUS BLYTH, OCCURRING IN LADAK, KASHMIR. M. L. Roonwal. (Mammalia, Rodentia, family Muridae). Jour. Zool. Soc. India, Calcutta, vol.5, no.1, pp.41-43, June, 1953.

A COMPARATIVE STUDY OF DAILY WATER-INTAKE AMONG CERTAIN TAXONOMIC AND GEOGRAPHIC GROUPS WITHIN THE GENUS PEROMYSCUS. Llewellyn G. Ross. Biological Bulletin, vol.59, no.3, pp.326-338, Dec., 1930.

GEOGRAPHICAL RACES OF THE RODENT AKODON JELSKII THOMAS. Colin Campbell Sanborn. Fieldiana, Zool., Chicago, vol.31, no.17, pp.133-142, fig.21, May 14, 1947.

CRICETULUS SIMIONESCUI SP. NOV. S. Schaub. Bull. Acad. Roumaine, Bucarest, vol.14, nos.9-10, pp.243-244, figs. 2, 1931.

A SYSTEMATIC STUDY OF THE WATER RAT (NEOFIBER ALLENI). Albert Schwarz. Occas. Papers Mus. Zool. Univ. Michigan, Ann Arbor, no.547, p.28, pl.3, July 29, 1953.

DESCRIPTION OF HESPEROMYS TRUEI, A NEW SPECIES BELONGING TO THE SUBFAMILY MURINAE. Robert Wilson Shufeldt. U. S. Nat. Mus. Proc., Wash., vol.8, pp.403-408, pl.21, 1885.

A TAXONOMIC ANALYSIS OF THE PRAIRIE VOLES OF THE SUBGENUS PEDOMYS (GENUS PITYMYS). Tom A. Stombaugh. PhD thesis, Ind. Univ., 118 pp., 1953.

THE SOUTH AMERICAN CRICETIDAE DESCRIBED BY FELIX AZARA. G. H. H. Tate. Amer. Mus. Novitates no.557, p.5, Sept.12, 1932.

THE TAXONOMIC HISTORY OF CERTAIN SOUTH AND CENTRAL AMERICAN CRICETID RODENTIA: NEOTOMYS, WITH REMARKS UPON ITS RELATIONSHIPS; THE COTTON RATS (SIGNODON AND SIGMOMYS); AND THE "FISH-EATING" RATS (ICHTHYOMYS, ANOTOMYS, RHEOMYS, NEUSTICOMYS, AND DAPTOMYS. G. H. H. Tate. Amer. Mus. Nov., no.583, 10 pp., Nov. 14, 1932.

THE TAXONOMIC HISTORY OF THE GENUS REITHRODON WATERHOUSE (CRICETIDAE). G. H. H. Tate. Amer. Mus. Novit., no. 529, 4 pp., May 28, 1932.

THE TAXONOMIC HISTORY OF THE NEOTROPICAL CRICETID GENERA HOLOCHILUS, NECTOMYS, SCAPTEROMYS, MEGALOMYS, TYLOMYS AND OTOTYLOMYS. G. H. H. Tate. Amer. Mus. Novitates no.562, pp.19, Sept.17, 1932.

THE TAXONOMIC HISTORY OF THE SOUTH AMERICAN CRICETID GENERA EUNEOMYS (SUBGENERA EUNEOMYS AND GALEONOMYS), AULISCOMYS, CHELEMYSCUS, CHINCHILLULA, PHYLLOTIS, PARALOMYS, ELIGMODONTIA AND HESPER-

OMYS. G. H. H. Tate. Amer. Mus. Nov., no.541, 21 pp., June 16, 1932.

THE TAXONOMIC HISTORY OF THE SOUTH AND CENTRAL AMERICAN AKODENT GENERA: THALPOMYS, DELTAMYS, THAPTOMYS, HYPSIMYS, BOLOMYS, CHROEOMYS, ABROTHRIX, SCOTINOMYS, AKODON (CHALCOMYS AND AKODON), MICROXUS, PODOXYMYS, LENOXUS, OXYMYCTERUS, NOTIOMYS, AND BLARINOMYS. G. H. H. Tate. Amer. Mus. Nov., no.582, pp.32, Nov. 14, 1932.

THE TAXONOMIC HISTORY OF THE SOUTH AND CENTRAL AMERICAN CRICETID RODENTS OF THE GENUS OXYZOMYS. PART I: SUBGENUS ORYZOMYS. G. H. H. Tate. Amer. Mus. Nov., no.579, 18 pp., figs.1, Nov.14, 1932.

THE TAXONOMIC HISTORY OF THE SOUTH AND CENTRAL AMERICAN CRICETID RODENTS OF THE GENUS ORYZOMYS. PART II. SUBGENERA OLIGORYZOMYS, THALLOMYSCUS, AND MELANOMYS. G. H. H. Tate. Amer. Mus. Nov., no.580, 17 pp., Nov.14, 1932.

THE TAXONOMIC HISTORY OF THE SOUTH AND CENTRAL AMERICAN ORYZOMINE GENERA OF RODENTS (EXCLUDING ORYZOMYS): NESORYZOMYS, ZYGODONTOMYS, CHILOMYS, DELOMYS, PHAENOMYS, RHAGOMYS, RHIPIDOMYS, NYCTOMYS, OECOMYS, THOMASOMYS, INOMYS, AEPEOMYS, NEACOMYS AND SCOLOMYS. G. H. H. Tate. Amer. Mus. Nov., no.581, 28 pp., Nov.14, 1932.

DESCRIPTION OF A NEW SPECIES OF REITHRODON, WITH REMARKS ON OTHER SPECIES OF THE GENUS. Oldfield Thomas. Proc. Zool. Soc. Lond., pp.691-696, figs.4, Dec.14, 1880.

DESCRIPTIONS OF SOME NEW NEOTROPICAL MURIDAE. Oldfield Thomas. Ann. and Mag. Nat. Hist. (6), vol.14, no.83, pp.346-366, Nov., 1894.

DESCRIBTIONS OF THREE NEW GERBILLES IN THE BRITISH MUSEUM COLLECTION. Oldfield Thomas. Ann. and Mag. Nat. Hist. (6), vol.9, no.49, pp.76-79, Jan., 1892.

THE GENERIC POSITION OF GERBILLUS PRZEWALSKII BUCHNER. Oldfield Thomas. Ann. and Mag. Nat. Hist., vol.16, ser.9, p.548, Nov., 1925.

THE GEOGRAPHICAL RACES OF ORYZOMYS RATTICEPS. Oldfield Thomas. Ann. and Mag. Nat. Hist., ser.9, vol.14, pp.143-144, July, 1924.

NEW FORMS OF AKODON AND PHYLLOTIS AND A NEW GENUS FOR "AKODON" TEGUINA. Oldfield Thomas. Ann. and Mag. Nat. Hist. (8), vol.11, no.64, pp.404-409, Apr., 1913.

NEW SPECIES OF DIPODILLUS AND PSAMMOMYS. Oldfield Thomas. Ann. and Mag. Nat. Hist. (7), vol.9, no.3, pp. 362-365, May, 1902.

NEW SPECIES OF GERBILLUS AND TATERILLUS. Oldfield Thomas. Ann. and Mag. Nat. Hist. (9), vol.2, no.8, pp.146-151, Aug., 1918.

NOTE ON HESPEROMYS PYRRHORHINUS, PR. MAX. Oldfield Thomas. Ann. and Mag. Nat. Hist. (5), vol.18, no.108, pp. 421-423, Dec., 1886.

NOTES ON GERBILS REFERRED TO THE GENUS MERIONES, WITH DESCRIPTIONS OF NEW SPECIES AND SUBSPECIES. Oldfield Thomas. Ann. and Mag. Nat. Hist. (9), vol.3, no.15, pp.263-273, Mar., 1919.

ON THE SMALL HAMSTERS THAT HAVE BEEN REFERRED TO CRICETULUS PHAEUS AND CAMPBELLI. Oldfield Thomas. Ann. and Mag. Nat. Hist. (8), vol.19, no.114, pp.452-457, June, 1917.

ON TWO NEW MEMBERS OF THE GENUS HETEROMYS AND TWO OF NEOTOMA. Oldfield Thomas. Ann. and Mag. Nat. Hist. (6), vol.12, no.69, pp.233-235, Sept., 1893.

A THIRD GENUS OF THE ICHTHYOMYS GROUP. Oldfield Thomas. Ann. and Mag. Nat. Hist. (7), vol.17, no.100, pp.421-423, Apr., 1906.

REVISED DETERMINATIONS OF TWO FAR-EASTERN SPECIES OF MYOSPALAX. Oldfield Thomas. Ann. and Mag. Nat. Hist. (8), vol.9, no.49, pp.93-95, Jan., 1912.

TWO NEW SPECIES OF CALOMYSCUS. Oldfield Thomas. Jour. Bombay Nat. Hist. Soc., vol.26, pp.938-940, Jan., 1920.

DIAGNOSES OF SOME UNDESCRIBED WOOD RATS (GENUS NEOTOMA) IN THE NATIONAL MUSEUM. Frederick W. True. Proc. U. S. Nat. Mus., vol.17, publ.1006, pp.353-355, Advance sheets June 27, 1894, Regular edition, Nov.15, 1894.

ON THE RELATIONSHIPS OF TAYLOR'S MOUSE, SITOMYS TAYLORI. Frederick W. True. U.S. Nat. Mus., Proc., Wash., 1894, vol.16, p.757-758, 1893.

CONTRIBUTIONS TO THE SYSTEMATICS OF THE GENUS ELLOBIUS FISCHER. A. A. Ugarov. Acta Univ. Asiae Mediae, Taschkent, Zool., Fasc.4, pp.3-19, pl.1, figs.3, 1928. (Russian text; English summary.)

(A NEW FIELD RAT (TYLOMYS GYMNURUS SP. NOV.).) Una nueva rata de campo (Tylomys gymnurus sp. nov.). Bernardo Villa. Anales Inst. Biol., Mexico City, vol.12, no.2, pp.763-766, figs.4, 1941.

MATERIALS FOR THE SYSTEMATICS AND THE MORPHOLOGY OF THE RODENTS. 3. REMARKS ON THE CLASSIFICATION OF PALAEARCTIC LEMMINGS OF THE GENUS LEMMUS. B. Vinogradov. Ann. Mus. Zool. l'Acad. Sci. l'URSS., vol.26, pp.51-72, pls.3-4, (1925), 1926.

CHARACTERS OF TWO NEW GENERA OF RODENTIA (REITHRODON AND ABROCOMA), FROM MR. DARWIN'S COLLECTION. G. R. Waterhouse. Proc. Zool. Soc. London, pt.5, pp.29-32, 1837.

DESCRIPTION OF A NEW SPECIES OF HAMSTER (CRICETUS AURATUS). G. R. Waterhouse. Proc. Zool. Soc. London, pt.7, p.57, 1839.

WHAT IS CRICETUS BABYLONICUS NEHRING? Alice Wepner. Zeitschr. f. Saeugetierkunde, vol.9, nos.1-3, pp.437-438, Dec.12, 1934.

SPECIES STATUS OF THE BLOCK ISLAND FIELD MOUSE, MICROTUS PROVECTUS. Bernice Wheeler. Evolution, Lancaster, vol.6, no.1, pp.130-131, Mar., 1952.

(ON THE RIGHT OF ARVICOLA CAMPESTRIS BLASIUS TO BE CONSIDERED A DISTINCT SPECIES.) Sur le droit de l'Arvicola campestris Blasius d'etre considere comme une espece distincte. H. Winge. Videnskabelige Meddeleser Naturjistoriske Forening Kjobenhavn, Aarg. 27, p.10, 1875. (French resume.)

NOTES ON THE GENUS TATERA, WITH DESCRIPTION OF NEW SPECIES. R. C. Wroughton. Ann. Mag. Nat. Hist., ser.7, vol.17, pp.474-499, May, 1906.

THE VALIDITY OF THE PENOBSCOT FIELD MOUSE. Leland C. Wyman. Jour. Mam., vol.3, no.3, pp.163-166, Aug., 1922.

(CONSIDERATIONS ON THE GENUS ANDINOMYS (CRICETINAE) AND DESCRIPTION OF A NEW FORM.) Consideraciones sobre el genero "Andinomys" (Cricetinae) y descripcion de una forma nueva. Jose Yepes. Anal. Mus. Argentino Cienci. Nat., vol.38, pp.333-348, Dec.15, 1935.

(THE GENUS ARVICOLA LAC. IN THE SYSTEM OF MICROTINAE.) Die Gattung Arvicola Lac. im System der Microtinae. K. Zimmerman. Saeugetierk. Mitteil., Stuttgart, 3 (3): 110-112, July 1, 1955.

(ON THE RACIAL ANALYSIS OF THE CENTRAL EUROPEAN FIELD MICE.) Zur Rassenanalyse der mitteleuropaeischen Feldmaeuse. (Geographical distribution of Microtus arvalis according to color and tooth form.) K. Zimmerman. Zeitschr. Wiss. Zool. Abt.B, Leipzig, n.F., vol.4, no.2, pp.258-273, figs.3, June 25, 1935.

United States, Eastern

THE DISTRIBUTION AND PRODUCTION OF MUSKRATS ON THE MONTEZUMA NATIONAL WILDLIFE REFUGE. Maurice M. Alexander, Merton Radway. Jour. Wildlife Mgt., 15 (4): 360-367, Oct., 1951.

AN INSULAR RACE OF COTTON RAT FROM THE FLORIDA KEYS. Glover M. Allen. Jour. Mam., vol.1, no.5, pp.235-236, Nov., 1920.

SEX RATIO AND WEIGHTS OF SOUTHWESTERN LAKE ERIE MUSKRATS. John M. Anderson. Jour. Mam., 28 (4): 391-395, Nov., 1947.

THE MARYLAND MUSKRAT MARSHES. Vernon Bailey. Jour. Mam., 18 (3): 350-354, Aug., 1937.

NOTES ON THE DEER MICE (PEROMYSCUS) OF SOME OF THE ISLANDS OFF THE SOUTHERN NEW ENGLAND COAST. Outram Bangs. Proc. New Eng. Zool. Club, vol.4, pp.11-15, Feb.28, 1905.

SYNAPTOMYS COOPERII BAIRD IN EASTERN MASSACHUSETTS: WITH NOTES ON SYNAPTOMYS STONEI RHOADS, ESPECIALLY AS TO THE VALIDITY OF THIS SPECIES. Outram Bangs. Proc. Biol. Soc. Wash., vol.9, pp.99-104, Apr.14, 1894,

PRAIRIE VOLE, MICROTUS OCHROGASTER, IN EASTERN KENTUCKY. Roger W. Barbour. Jour. Mam., vol.33, no.3, pp. 398-399, Aug.19, 1952.

PEROMYSCUS MANICULATUS BAIRDI IN KENTUCKY. Roger W. Barbour, William L. Gault. Jour. Mam., vol.34, no.1, p. 130, Feb.19, 1953.

PITYMYS PINETORUM CARBONARIUS IN HARLAN COUNTY, KENTUCKY. Roger W. Barbour, Charles E. Smith, Jr. Jour. Mam., 37 (1): 121, Feb.28, 1956.

WISCONSIN WILDLIFE FOR BOYS AND GIRLS--ANIMALS: NORTHERN WHITE-FOOTED MOUSE OR DEER MOUSE (PEROMYSCUS LEUCOPUS NOVEBORACENSIS). N. R. Barger. Wisconsin Conserv. Bull., Madison, vol.12, no.10, p.46, Oct., 1947.

AN ECOLOGICAL AND FOOD HABITS STUDY OF THE MUSKRAT IN THE LAKE ERIE MARSHES. Karl Bednarik. MS thesis, Ohio State Univ., 123 pp., 1953.

A STUDY OF PRAIRIE DEER-MOUSE POPULATIONS IN SOUTHERN MICHIGAN. W. Frank Blair. Amer. Midland Nat., Notre Dame, vol.24, no.2, pp.273-305, figs.4, Sept., 1940.

THE PINE MOUSE OF SOUTHERN OHIO. B. P. Bole, Jr. Jour. Mam., vol.19, no.3, p.377, Aug., 1938.

MICHIGAN MICE. G. W. Bradt. Michigan Conserv., Lansing, vol.17, no.6, pp.4-5, illus., June, 1948.

CHARMS AND POWERS. CONCERNING THE RATS ON STACY MOUNTAIN AND OTHER MATTERS. George Washington Brown. Appalachia, pp.302-307, illus., June, 1945.

SEX RATIOS AND WEIGHTS OF MUSKRATS (ONDATRA ZIBETHICA ZIBETHICA) FROM WISCONSIN. Irven O. Buss. Jour. Mam., 22 (4): 403-406, Nov., 1941.

A STUDY OF PEROMYSCUS IN THE INNER BLUE GRASS REGION OF KENTUCKY. Deweese Y. Campbell. MS thesis, Univ. Ky., 1952.

THE FLORIDA WOOD RAT IN SOUTH CAROLINA. E. B. Chamberlain. Jour. Mam., vol.9, no.2, pp.152-153, May, 1928.

THE BLOCK ISLAND MEADOW MOUSE, MICROTUS PROVECTUS. J. L. Chamberlain. Jour. Mam., vol.35, no.4, pp.587-589, Nov.29, 1954.

DESCRIPTION OF A NEW SUBSPECIES OF ORYZOMYS FROM THE GULF STATES. Frank Michler Chapman. Amer. Mus.

Nat. Hist., New York, vol.5, pp.43-46, 1893.

DESCRIPTION OF A NEW SUBSPECIES OF THE GENUS SIGMODON FROM SOUTHERN FLORIDA. Frank Michler Chapman. Amer. Mus. Nat. Hist., New York, vol.2, p.118, 1890.

PRELIMINARY DESCRIPTIONS OF TWO APPARENTLY NEW SPECIES OF THE GENUS HESPEROMYS FROM FLORIDA. Frank Michler Chapman. Amer. Mus. Nat. Hist., New York, vol.11, p.117, 1890.

NEOTOMA FLORIDANA HAEMATOREIA (WOOD RAT) IN SOUTH CAROLINA. Robert H. Coleman. Jour. Mam., Balto., vol.30, no.2, p.200, May 23, 1949.

COOPER'S LEMMING IN NEW YORK. David B. Cook. Jour. Mam., vol.20, no.2, p.258, May, 1939.

PRELIMINARY OBSERVATIONS ON NORTHERN WHITE CEDAR IN MAINE. (RED-BACKED MOUSE.) James D. Curtis. Ecology, Lancaster, vol.27, no.1, pp.23-36, illus., Jan., 1946.

RELATIONSHIPS BETWEEN THE WOOD-MOUSE AND THE COTTON-MOUSE IN EASTERN VIRGINIA. Lee R. Dice. Jour. Mam., vol.21, no.1, pp.14-23, fig.1, Feb.14, 1940.

COLOR, SEX RATIOS, AND WEIGHTS OF MARYLAND MUSKRATS, II. Herbert L. Dozier. Jour. Wildlife Mgt., 8 (2): 165-169, Apr., 1944.

MUSKRAT INVESTIGATIONS AT THE BLACKWATER NATIONAL WILDLIFE REFUGE, MARYLAND. Herbert L. Dozier. Maryland Conserv., Balto., vol.21, no.1, pp.24-25, illus., Winter Issue, 1944.

MUSKRAT TRAPPING ON THE MONTEZUMA NATIONAL WILDLIFE REFUGE, NEW YORK, 1943-1948. Herbert L. Dozier. Jour. Wildlife Mgt., 14 (4): 403-412, Oct., 1950.

SEX RATIO AND WEIGHTS OF MUSKRATS FROM THE MONTEZUMA NATIONAL WILDLIFE REFUGE. Herbert L. Dozier. Jour. Wildlife Mgt., 9 (3): 232-237, July, 1945.

COLOR, SEX RATIOS, AND WEIGHTS OF MARYLAND MUSKRATS. Herbert L. Dozier Dozier. Jour. Wildlife Mgt., 6 (4): 294-300, Oct., 1942.

MUSKRAT INVESTIGATIONS ON THE BLACKWATER NATIONAL WILDLIFE REFUGE, MARYLAND, 1941-1945. Herbert L. Dozier. Jour. Wildlife Mgt., 12 (2): 177-190, Apr., 1948.

THE COOPER LEMMING MOUSE IN SOUTHERN NEW HAMPSHIRE. W. Robert Eadie. Jour. Mam., vol.18, no.1, pp.102-103, Feb.14, 1937.

THE PINE MOUSE RECORDED IN NEW HAMPSHIRE. W. Robert Eadie. Jour. Mam., vol.17, no.4, p.422, Nov., 1936.

CAPTURE OF THE PINE MOUSE AT SING SING, NEW YORK. A. K. Fisher. Amer. Nat. Extra, vol.19, p.896, Sept., 1885.

MUSKRATS IN MISSISSIPPI. R. M. Freeman. Miss. Game and Fish Comm., 48 pp., 1945.

A NEW COTTON RAT FROM VIRGINIA. (SIGMODON HISPIDUS VIRGINIANUS.) Marshall C. Gardner. Proc. Biol. Soc. Wash., vol.59, pp.137-148, Oct.25, 1946.

AN UNDESCRIBED EASTERN COTTON RAT. (SIGMODON HISPIDUS KOMAREKI.) Marshall C. Gardiner. Proc. Biol. Soc. Wash., vol.61, pp.97-98, June 16, 1948.

MAINE MUSKRAT INVESTIGATIONS. Jay S. Gashwiler. Bull. Maine Dept. Inland Fisheries and Game, 38 pp., Aug., 1948.

LIFE HISTORY OF THE GOLDEN MOUSE, PEROMYSCUS NUTTALLI, IN KENTUCKY. Woodrow W. Goodpaster, Donald F. Hoffmeister. Jour. Mam., 35 (1): 16-27, illus., Feb., 1954.

EVIDENCE OF THE OCCURRENCE OF THE RICE RAT IN PREHISTORIC INDIAN VILLAGE SITES IN OHIO. Robert M. Goslin. Bull. Ohio Indian Collectors Soc., Columbus, no.26, pp.19-22, (mimeog.), Jan., 1951.

THE HARVEST MOUSE IN CENTRAL OHIO. Robert Goslin. Jour. Mam., vol.20, no.2, p.257, May, 1939.

A LIFE HISTORY STUDY OF THE DEER MOUSE, PEROMYSCUS LEUCOPUS NOVEBORACENSIS (FISCHER) IN THE ITHACA, NEW YORK, REGION. Jack Louis Gottschang. PhD thesis, Cornell Univ., 1950.

ANALYSIS OF THE LATE FALL AND EARLY WINTER MUSKRAT POPULATION IN NORTHWESTERN PENNSYLVANIA. William C. Grimm. Pennsylvania Game News, Harrisburg, vol.15, no.10, pp.12-13, illus., Jan., 1945.

THE MUSKRAT IN NORTHWESTERN PENNSYLVANIA. William C. Grim. Pennsylvania Game News, 12 (2): 6-7, May, 1941.

AN OCCURRENCE OF THE RICE RAT (ORYZOMYS) IN WEST VIRGINIA. John E. Guilday, William J. Mayer-Oakes. Jour. Mam., vol.33, no.2, pp.253-254, May 16, 1952.

CENTRAL WISCONSIN MUSKRAT STUDY. F. N. Hamerstrom, Jr., James Blake. Amer. Midland Nat., 21 (2): 514-520, Mar., 1939.

THE PRAIRIE DEER MOUSE IN NEW YORK AND PENNSYLVANIA. W. J. Hamilton, Jr. Jour. Mam., vol.31, no.1, p.100, Feb.21, 1950.

TWO NEW RICE RATS (GENUS ORYZOMYS) FROM FLORIDA. (O. PALUSTRIS PLANIROSTRIS, O. P. SANIBELI.) William J. Hamilton, Jr. Proc. Biol. Soc. Wash., vol. 68, pp.83-86, Aug.3, 1955.

A NEW PINE MOUSE (PITYMYS PINETORUM CARBONARIUS) FROM THE SOUTHERN APPALACHIAN MOUNTAINS. Charles O. Handley, Jr. Jour. Wash. Acad. Sci., vol.42, no.5, pp.152-153, May 15, 1952.

A NEW HARVEST MOUSE FROM WISCONSIN. (REITHRODONTOMYS MEGALOTIS PECTORALIS.) Harold C. Hanson. Zool. Ser. Field Mus. Nat. Hist., Chicago, vol. 29, no.14, pp.205-209, fig.26, Oct. 26, 1944.

THE FLORIDA WATER-RAT (NEOFIBER ALLENI) IN OKEFINOKEE SWAMP, GEORGIA. Francis Harper. Jour. Mam., vol.1, no.2, pp.65-66, pl.3, Feb., 1920.

MUSKRATS ON TIDAL MARSHES OF DORCHESTER COUNTY. Van T. Harris. Md. Dept. Res. and Educ., Publ. no.91: 1-36, illus., 1952.

THE BIOLOGY OF THE VOLES OF NEW YORK. Robert T. Hatt. Bull. New York State Coll. Forestry, vol.3, no.2c, pp.505-623, pl.3, figs.161-190, Aug., 1930.

MUSKRAT WEIGHTS AND SEX RATIO IN THE RIVERBEND MARSHES OF WAYNE COUNTY, NEW YORK. William S. Heit. Jour. Mam., 30 (2): 122-124, May, 1949.

THE ALLEGHENY WOOD RAT IN INDIANA. P. F. Hickie, Thomas Harrison. Amer. Midland Nat., Notre Dame, Ind., vol.12, no.6, pp.169-174, fig., Nov., 1930.

THE HARVEST MOUSE (REITHRODONTOMYS MEGALOTIS) IN ILLINOIS AND ITS TAXONOMIC STATUS. Donald F. Hoffmeister, John E. Warnock. Trans. Illinois Acad. Sci., vol.47, pp.161-164, Apr., 1955.

DESCRIPTION OF A NEW PINE MOUSE FROM FLORIDA. Arthur H. Howell. Proc. Biol. Soc. Wash., vol.29, pp.83-84, Apr.4, 1916.

DESCRIPTION OF A NEW RACE OF THE FLORIDA WATER-RAT (NEOFIBER ALLENI). Arthur H. Howell. Jour. Mam., vol.1, no.2, pp.79-80, Mar.2, 1920.

DESCRIPTION OF A NEW SPECIES OF BEACH MOUSE FROM FLORIDA. Arthur H. Howell. Jour. Mam., vol.1, no.5, pp. 237-240, fig.1, Dec.4, 1920.

DESCRIPTION OF A NEW SUBSPECIES OF THE FLORIDA WOOD RAT. (NEOTOMA FLORIDANA HAEMATOREIA.) Arthur H. Howell. Proc. Acad. Nat. Sci. Phila., vol.86, pp.403-404, Oct.15, 1934.

THE FLORIDA WOOD RAT IN THE MOUNTAINS OF GEORGIA AND NORTH CAROLINA - WITH A CORRECTION. Arthur H. Howell. Jour. Mam., vol.14, no.4, pp. 371-372, Nov., 1933.

RANGE OF THE ALLEGHENY CLIFF RAT IN THE SOUTHERN APPALACHIANS. Arthur H. Howell. Jour. Mam., vol.12, no.2, pp.168-169, May 14, 1931.

THE RICE RAT IN MARYLAND. Arthur H. Howell. Jour. Mam., vol.8, no.4, p.312, Nov., 1927.

TWO NEW COTTON RATS FROM FLORIDA. (SIGMODON HISPIDUS FLORIDANUS, S. HISPIDUS INSULICOLA.) Arthur H. Howell. Proc. Biol. Soc. Wash., vol.56, pp.63-76, June 16, 1943.

LIFE HISTORY NOTES ON THREE MICE FROM THE FLORIDA EAST COAST. R. D. Ivey. Jour. Mam., 30 (2): 157-162, May, 1949.

A NEW SUBSPECIES OF PEROMYSCUS FROM THE NORTH SHORE OF THE GULF OF ST. LAWRENCE. (PEROMYSCUS MANICULATUS PLUMBEUS.) C. F. Jackson. Proc. Biol. Soc. Wash., vol.52, pp.101-104, June 5, 1939.

THE MUSKRAT IN NEW YORK: ITS NATURAL HISTORY AND ECONOMICS. Charles E. Johnson. Roosevelt Wild Life Bull., vol.3, no.2, pp.205-320, pl.5, maps 5-6, Mar., 1925.

A NEW PINE MOUSE, GENUS PITYMYS, FROM WISCONSIN. (PITYMYS PINETORUM SCHMIDTI.) Hartley H. T. Jackson. Proc. Biol. Soc. Wash., vol.54, pp.201-202, Dec.8, 1941.

PINE MOUSE IN ESSEX COUNTY, MASSACHUSETTS. Maynard S. Johnson. Jour. Mam., vol.16, no.1, pp.68-69, Feb., 1935.

A NEW RED-BACKED MOUSE FROM KENTUCKY AND VIRGINIA. (CLETHRIONOMYS GAPPERI MAURUS.) Remington Kellogg. Proc. Biol. Soc. Wash., vol.52, pp.37-40, Mar.11,1939.

DISTRIBUTION OF THE RICE RAT IN SOUTHERN ILLINOIS. Willard D. Klimstra, Thomas G. Scott. Nat. Hist. Misc., Chicago Acad. Sci., no.154, pp.1-3, Apr.30, 1956.

LITTLE KNOWN NEIGHBORS. (WHITE-FOOTED, MEADOW, AND PINE MICE.) C. Haven Kolb. Jour. Nat. Hist., Balto., vol.14, no.4, pp.93-96, Oct., 1944.

THE MUSKRAT IN FLORIDA. Barbara Lawrence. Proc. New England Zool. Club, Cambridge, vol.19, pp.17-20, Jan. 24, 1942.

ANNUAL REPORT OF SCIENTIFIC INVESTIGATION OF THE MUSKRAT INDUSTRY OF MARYLAND. E. Lee LeCompte, Frank R. Smith. Maryland Conservationist, vol.10, no.4, pp.13, 26-27, 1933.

COTTON RAT IN LOWER PIEDMONT VIRGINIA. John B. Lewis. Jour. Mam., vol.25, no.2, pp.195-196, May 25, 1944.

A CASE OF AN UNUSUALLY LOW JUVENILLE MORTALITY FOUND IN MUSKRATS IN NORTHERN NEW HAMPSHIRE. Robert A. McCullough. Proc. N.E. Sect. Wildl. Soc., 9th Ann. Conf., Bretton Woods, N. H., Sept.20-23, 1953. pp.1-3.

A NEW RECORD OF THE RICE RAT, ORYZOMYS PALUSTRIS PALUSTRIS, FROM SOUTHERN ILLINOIS. Charles A. McLaughlin, William B. Robertson. Nat. Hist. Misc., Chicago Acad. Sci., no.80, pp.2, Mar.30, 1951.

ON THE MAINLAND FORMS OF THE EASTERN DEERMOUSE, PEROMYSCUS LEUCOPUS (RAFINESQUE). Edgar A. Mearns. Proc. Biol. Soc. Wash., vol.14, pp.153-155, Aug.9, 1901.

ON THE RECURRENCE OF THE GENUS REITHRODONTOMYS IN VIRGINIA. Louis Zerega Mearns. Amer. Nat., p.161, Feb.1, 1897.

DESCRIPTION OF A NEW MUSKRAT FROM THE GREAT DISMAL SWAMP, VIRGINIA. C. Hart Merriam. Proc. Biol. Soc., Wash., vol.11, p.143, May 13, 1897.

DESCRIPTION OF A NEW SPECIES OF HESPEROMYS FROM SOUTHERN FLORIDA. C. Hart Merriam. North Amer. Fauna, no.4, U.S. Dept. Agric., pp.53-54, Oct., 1890.

THE OCCURRENCE OF COOPER'S LEMMING MOUSE (SYNAPTOMYS COOPERI) IN THE ATLANTIC STATES. C. Hart Merriam. Proc. Biol. Soc. Wash., vol.7, pp.175-177, Dec.22, 1892.

THE PINE MOUSE IN NORTHERN NEW YORK. C. Hart Merriam. Amer. Nat., vol.19, no.9, pp.895-896, Sept., 1885.

THE BEACH MOUSE OF MUSKEGET ISLAND. Gerrit S. Miller, Jr. Proc. Boston Soc. Nat. Hist., vol.27, pp.75-87, figs.2, pl.1, June, 1896.

DESCRIPTION OF A NEW WHITE-FOOTED MOUSE FROM THE EASTERN UNITED STATES. Gerrit S. Miller, Jr. Proc. Biol. Soc. Wash., vol.8, pp.55-70, June 20, 1893.

SOME ADDITIONAL RECORDS OF HARVEST MICE (GENUS REITHRODONTOMYS) IN THE MISSISSIPPI RIVER VALLEY. Lowell S. Miller, William B. Robertson. Nat. Hist. Misc., Chicago Acad. Sci., no.67, pp.1-4, Oct.11, 1950.

THE ALLEGHENY CAVE RAT AT NEWFOUNDLAND, N. J. W. DeW. Miller, James Chapin. Proc. Biol. Soc. Wash., vol.22, p.88, Apr.17, 1909.

A SURVEY OF THE MUSKRAT MARSHES IN THE MILLVILLE DISTRICT, CUMBERLAND CO., N. J. James E. Mills, Horace J. McMullen. Fur Jour., vol.2, no.8, pp.30-31, 37, Sept., 1928.

EASTERN EXTENSION OF THE RANGE OF PEROMYSCUS MANICULATUS BAIRDII. Alan L. Mitchell. Jour. Mam., vol.15, no. 1, p.71, Feb., 1934.

THE PRAIRIE WHITE-FOOTED MOUSE IN NEW YORK STATE. Philip N. Moulthrop. Jour. Mam., vol.19, no.4, p.503, Nov.14, 1938.

NOTES ON THE FLORIDA PINE MOUSE, PITYMYS PARVULUS HOWELL. Wilfred T. Neill, James M. Boyles. Jour. Mam., 36 (1): 138-139, Feb.25, 1955.

MICROTUS PENNSYLVANICUS IN COASTAL SOUTH CAROLINA. A. L. Nelson. Jour. Mam., vol.18, no.2, p.244, May 14, 1937.

THE HOME LIFE OF THE WOOD-MOUSE (PEROMYSCUS LEUCOPUS NOVEBORACENSIS) IN SOUTHERN MICHIGAN AS SHOWN BY THE USE OF NEST BOXES. Arnold Nicholson. PhD thesis, Univ. Mich., 1938.

THE HOMES AND SOCIAL HABITS OF THE WOOD-MOUSE (PEROMYSCUS LEUCOPUS NOVEBORACENSIS) IN SOUTHERN MICHIGAN. Arnold Nicholson. Amer. Midland Nat., 25 (1): 196-223, Jan., 1941.

MICROTUS FROM THE PIEDMONT OF GEORGIA. Eugene P. Odum. Jour. Mam., vol.29, no.1, p.74, Feb.13, 1948.

SYNAPTOMYS ON THE HIGHLANDS, NORTH CAROLINA, PLATEAU. Eugene P. Odum. Jour. Mam., vol.29, no.1, p.74, Feb.13, 1948.

NOTES ON LEMMING MICE AT CINCINNATI, OHIO. Charles Oehler. Jour. Mam., vol.23 (3): 341-342, Aug., 1942.

(Review by Paul L. Errington of) THE MUSKRAT IN THE LOUISIANA COASTAL MARSHES. Ted O'Neal. Jour. Mamm., vol.32, no.2, pp.127-128, Feb. 15, 1951.

FIRST VERMONT RECORD FOR THE ROCK VOLE. F. L. Osgood. Jour. Mam., vol.19, no.1, p.108, Feb.19, 1938.

PINE MICE IN VERMONT. F. L. Osgood. Jour. Mam., vol.17, no.3, pp.291-292, Aug., 1936.

A FIELD STUDY OF PEROMYSCUS POPULATIONS IN GULF HAMMOCK, FLORIDA. Paul G. Pearson. Ecol., 34 (1): 199-207, maps and graph., Jan., 1953.

GOLDEN MICE IN UPPER SOUTH CAROLINA. Andrew L. Pickens. Jour. Mam., vol.8, no.3, pp.246-248, Aug., 1927.

NEOTOMA IN PERKS COUNTY, PENNSYLVANIA. Earl L. Poole. Jour. Mam., vol. 4, no.2, p.125, May, 1923.

A NEW RACE OF THE RED-BACKED MOUSE (CLETHRIONOMYS) FROM PENNSYLVANIA. Earl L. Poole. Notulae Naturae, Acad. Nat. Sci. Phila., no.212, p.3, Jan.21, 1949.

SYNAPTOMYS COOPERI STONEI FROM THE EASTERN SHORE OF MARYLAND. Earl L. Poole. Jour. Mam., vol.24, no.1, p.103, Feb.20, 1943.

DESCRIPTION OF A NEW LEMMING MOUSE FROM THE WHITE MOUNTAINS, NEW HAMPSHIRE. Edward A. Preble. Proc. Biol. Soc. Wash., vol.13, pp.43-45, fig.3, May 29, 1899.

A CONTRIBUTION TO THE LIFE HISTORY OF THE ALLEGHENY CAVE RAT, NEOTOMA MAGISTER BAIRD. Samuel N. Rhoads. Proc. Acad. Nat. Sci. Phila., pp.213-221, 1894.

THE MARSH OR RICE-FIELD MICE OF THE EASTERN UNITED STATES. S. N. Rhoads. Amer. Nat., Boston, vol.36, no. 428, pp.661-663, Aug., 1902.

A NEW HARVEST MOUSE FROM FLORIDA. Samuel N. Rhoads. Amer. Nat., Phila., vol.29, no.342, pp.589-590, June 1, 1895.

A NEW SYNAPTOMYS FROM NEW JERSEY. Samuel N. Rhoads. Amer. Nat., pp.53-54, Jan., 1893.

THE SCARCITY OF MUSKRATS IN NORTHWESTERN PENNSYLVANIA. Neil D. Richmond. Pa. Game News, 18 (10): 11, 31, Jan., 1949.

THE WOOD RAT, NEOTOMA MAGISTER, IN VENANGO COUNTY, PENNSYLVANIA. Neil D. Richmond, Harry R. Roslund. Jour. Mam., vol.31, no.2, p.198, May 25, 1950.

A STUDY OF THE ALLEGHENY WOOD RAT IN CENTRAL PENNSYLVANIA. Daniel E. Sands. MS thesis, Pa. State Coll., 1951.

A NEW RACE OF THE ROUND-TAILED MUSKRAT, NEOFIBER ALLENI, FROM SOUTHERN FLORIDA. Albert Schwartz. Nat. Hist. Misc., Chicago Acad. Sci., no.101, pp.3, Feb.15, 1952.

OBSERVATIONS ON THE BIG PINE KEY COTTON RAT. Albert Schwartz. Jour. Mam., 35 (2): 260-263, May, 1954.

OLDFIELD MICE, PEROMYSCUS POLIONOTUS, OF SOUTH CAROLINA. Albert Schwartz. Jour. Mam., 35 (4): 561-569, map, Nov., 1954.

DESCRIPTION OF A NEW RACE OF WOODRAT FROM KEY LARGO, FLORIDA. H. B. Sherman. Jour. Mam., 36 (1): 113-120, illus., Feb.25, 1955.

MUSKRAT INVESTIGATIONS IN DORCHESTER COUNTY, MD., 1930-34. Frank R. Smith. USDA, Cir.474, 24 pp., May, 1938.

SYNAPTOMYS COOPERI IN SOUTHWESTERN VIRGINIA. Thomas Smyth. Jour. Mam., vol.27, no.3, p.277, Aug.14, 1946.

UPPER MISSISSIPPI MUSKRAT INVESTIGATION. I. Edwin Snead. Iowa Coop. Wildlife Research Unit, Ames, Quart. Rept., pp.17-21, Jan.-Mar., 1947; pp.29-31, Jan.-Mar., 1948.

SURVIVAL RATES, LONGEVITY, AND POPULATION FLUCTUATIONS IN THE WHITE-FOOTED MOUSE, PEROMYSCUS LEUCOPUS IN SOUTHEASTERN MICHIGAN. Dana P. Snyder. Misc. Publ. Mus. Zool. Univ. Michigan, no.95, pp.3, Jan.30, 1956.

PEROMYSCUS LEUCOPUS ON PEAK OF MT. WASHINGTON, COOS COUNTY, NEW HAMPSHIRE. A. Starrett, P. Starrett. Jour. Mam., vol.33, no.3, p.398, Aug.19, 1952.

EFFECTS OF DITCHING FOR MOSQUITO CONTROL ON THE MUSKRAT POPULATION OF A DELAWARE TIDAL MARSH. L. A. Stearns, Donald MacCreary, F. G. Daigh. Del. Agr. Exp. Sta., bull.225, 55 pp., Apr., 1940.

REPORT OF THE USE OF DDT AND PARIS GREEN ON MUSKRAT MARSHES. L. A. Stearns, others. Proc. Ann. Meeting N. J. Mosquito Extermin. Assn. 34: 82-95, 1947.

NOTES ON SYNAPTOMYS COOPERI COOPERI IN WASHTENAW COUNTY, MICHIGAN. Leroy C. Stegeman. Jour. Mam., vol.11, no.4, pp.460-466, Nov., 1930.

THE LEMMING MOUSE IN SHENANDOAH MOUNTAINS, VIRGINIA. Robert E. Stewart. Jour. Mam., vol.24, no.1, p.104, Feb.20, 1943.

OCCURRENCE AND IDENTIFICATION OF THE PRAIRIE DEER-MOUSE IN CENTRAL MARYLAND. William H. Stickel. Proc. Biol. Soc. Wash., vol.64, pp.25-32, Apr.13, 1951.

DESCRIPTION OF A NEW SPECIES OF NEOTOMA FROM PENNSYLVANIA. Witmer Stone. Proc. Acad. Nat. Sci. Phila., pp.16-18, Feb., 1893.

A NEW EVOTOMYS FROM SOUTHERN NEW JERSEY. Witmer Stone. Amer. Nat., vol.27, pp.54-56, Jan., 1893.

OCCURRENCE OF ORYZOMYS PALUSTRIS IN SOUTHERN NEW JERSEY. Witmer Stone. Proc. Acad. Nat. Sci. Phila., art.21, p.480, 1898.

THE LOUISIANA MUSKRAT. Arthur Svihla, Ruth Dowell Svihla. Jour. Mam., vol.12, no.1, pp.12-28, Feb., 1931.

ON A NEW MUSKRAT, NEOFIBER ALLENI FROM FLORIDA. Frederick W. True. Proc. U.S. Nat. Mus., vol.7, publ.419, pp.170-172, Sept.1, 1884.

FURTHER NOTES ON THE RICE RAT IN DELAWARE. Frederick A. Ulmer, Jr. Jour. Mam., vol.25, no.4, p.411, Dec.12, 1944.

NOTES ON THE RICE RAT IN NEW JERSEY AND PENNSYLVANIA. Frederick A. Ulmer, Jr. Jour. Mam., vol.32, no.1, pp.121-122, Feb.15, 1951.

THE WOOD RAT IN MARYLAND. Alexander Wetmore. Jour. Mam., vol.4, no.3, pp.187-188, Aug., 1923.

THE LEMMING VOLE, SYNAPTOMYS BOREALIS, IN NORTHERN MICHIGAN. Ralph M. Wetzel, Jarvey L. Gunderson. Jour. Mam., vol.30, no.4, p.437, Nov.17, 1949.

THE GENUS PEROMYSCUS IN WEST VIRGINIA. L. Wayne Wilson. Jour. Mam., vol.26, no.1, pp.95-96, Feb.23, 1945.

MAMMALS OF WEST VIRGINIA. V. NATIVE RATS AND MICE. L. Wayne Wilson. West Virginia Conserv., Charleston, vol. 10, no.3, pp.14-15, 21, June, 1946.

VIRGINIA ANIMALS EVERYONE SHOULD KNOW: THE MUSKRAT. Donald J. Woolley. Virginia Wildlife, Richmond, vol.8, no.11, pp.6-8, Nov., 1947.

MICROTUS CHROTORRHINUS IN MAINE. Leland C. Wyman. Jour. Mam., vol.4, no.2, pp.125-126, May, 1923.

United States, Western

MICROTUS OCHROGASTER IN MINNESOTA. Philip F. Allan. Jour. Mam., vol.17, no.3, p.291, Aug., 1936.

DESCRIPTION OF A NEW MOUSE FROM LAKE COUNTY, CALIFORNIA. Joel Asaph Allen. Amer. Mus. Nat. Hist., New York, vol.5, pp.335-336, 1893.

THE DISTRIBUTION AND GEOGRAPHIC VARIATION OF THE MONTANE MEADOW

MOUSE, MICROTUS MONTANUS IN WYOMING. Sydney Anderson. MS thesis, Univ. Kans., 1952.

A NEW WHITE-FOOTED MOUSE FROM TEXAS. Vernon Bailey. Proc. Biol. Soc. Wash., vol.19, pp.57-58, May 1, 1906.

DESCRIPTION OF A RACE OF THE MEXICAN VOLE, MICROTUS MEXICANUS, FROM SOUTHEASTERN UTAH. Seth B. Benson. Proc. Biol. Soc. Wash., vol.47, pp.49-50, Feb.9, 1934.

A NEW COTTON RAT (SIGMODON) FROM ARIZONA AND NEW MEXICO. Seth B. Benson. Proc. Biol. Soc. Wash., vol.53, pp.157-158, Dec.19, 1940.

GOLDEN HARVEST MOUSE IN ANDERSON COUNTY, KANSAS. J. D. Black. Jour. Mam., vol.16, no.3, pp.231-232, Aug., 1935.

BIOLOGICAL AND MORPHOLOGICAL DISTINCTNESS OF A PREVIOUSLY UNDESCRIBED SPECIES OF THE PEROMYSCUS TRUEI GROUP FROM TEXAS. W. Frank Blair. Contrib. Lab. Vert. Biol. Univ. Michigan, Ann Arbor, no.24, pp.8, fig.1, July, 1943.

CONTRIBUTIONS FROM THE LOS ANGELES MUSEUM CHANNEL ISLANDS BIOLOGICAL SURVEY. NO.22.-A NEW SUBSPECIES OF WHITE-FOOTED MOUSE FROM THE ANACAPA ISLANDS, CALIFORNIA. (PEROMYSCUS MANICULATUS ANACAPAE.) Jack C. von Bloeker. Bull. Southern California Acad. Sci., Los Angeles, vol.40, no.3, pp.161-162, Sept.-Dec., 1941.

A CORRECTION. (RANGE OF MICROTUS CALIFORNICUS HALOPHILUS.) Jack C. von Bloeker. Proc. Biol. Soc. Wash., vol. 50, pp.193-194, Oct.28, 1937.

A NEW RACE OF WHITE-FOOTED MOUSE, FROM SANTA ROSA ISLAND, CALIFORNIA. Jack C. von Bloeker. Bull. Southern Calif. Acad. Sci., Los Angeles, vol.39, pt.2, pp.172-174, May-Aug., 1940.

NORTHERN EXTENSION OF THE RANGE OF ONYCHOMYS TORRIDUS RAMONA RHOADS. Jack C. von Bloeker. Jour. Mam., vol.13, no.1, p.78, Feb., 1932.

A NEW RACE OF PYGMY MOUSE (BAIOMYS) FROM ARIZONA. Philip M. Blossom, William Henry Burt. Occas. Papers Mus. Zool., Univ. Michigan, Ann Arbor, no.465, pp.4, Oct.8, 1942.

A NEW RED-BACKED MOUSE FROM WASHINGTON STATE. (CLETHRIONOMYS GAPPERI CASCADENSIS.) Ernest S. Booth. Murrelet, Seattle, vol.26, no.2, pp.27-28, May-Aug (Aug.10), 1945.

A NEW RODENT FOR YOSEMITE VALLEY. (NEOTOMA CINEREA CINEREA.) A. E. Borell. Yosemite Nature Notes, vol.14, no.2, pp.1-20, fig.1, Feb., 1935.

A FAR SOUTHWESTERN OCCURRENCE OF PITYMYS IN TEXAS. Monroe D. Bryant. Jour. Mam., vol.22, no.2, p.202, May 14, 1941.

A NEW WOODRAT (NEOTOMA MEXICANA) FROM THE LAVA BEDS OF SOUTHERN NEW MEXICO. William Henry Burt. Occas. Papers Mus. Zool. Univ. Michigan, no.400, p.3, Mar.1, 1939.

THE LIFE HISTORY AND ECOLOGY OF THE RED-BACKED VOLE, CLETHRIONOMYS GAPPERI GAPPERI VIGORS, IN MINNESOTA. Robert S. Butsch. PhD. thesis, Univ. Mich., 161 pp., 1954.

A SPECIES OF NEOTOMA NEW FOR OKLAHOMA. H. D. Chase, B. D. Barclay. Proc. Oklahoma Acad. Sci., Norman, vol. 20, p.37, 1940.

THE DISTRIBUTION OF THE HISPID COTTON RAT IN KANSAS. E. Lendell Cockrum. Trans. Kansas Acad. Sci., Topeka, vol.51, no.3, pp.306-312, figs.3, 1948.

AN ISOLATED RACE OF MICROTUS MONTANUS FROM EASTERN WASHINGTON. Walter W. Dalquest. Proc. Biol. Soc. Wash., vol.54, pp.145-148, Sept.30, 1941.

NEW MEADOW MOUSE FROM THE SAN JUAN ISLANDS, WASHINGTON. (MICROTUS TOWNSENDII PUGETI.) Walter W. Dalquest. Murrelet, Seattle, vol.21, no.1, pp.7-8, Jan.-Apr., 1940.

THE RICE RAT, ORYZOMYS PALUSTRIS TEXENSIS, IN NORTHWESTERN ARKANSAS. Wayne H. Davis, William Z. Lidicker, Jr. Jour. Mam., 36 (2): 298, May 26, 1955.

A NEW PEROMYSCUS FROM TEXAS. William B. Davis. Occas. Papers Mus. Zool. Louisiana State Univ., no.2, 2 pp., Feb.1, 1939.

NEW SAGEBRUSH VOLE, GENUS LAGURUS, FROM UTAH. (LAGURUS CURTATUS ORBITUS.) Lyle C. Dearden, M. Raymond Lee. Jour. Mam., 36 (2): 270-273, May 26, 1955.

AN ESTIMATE OF THE POPULATION OF DEER-MICE IN THE BLACK HILLS OF SOUTH DAKOTA AND WYOMING. L. R. Dice. Contrib. Lab. Vert. Genetics, Univ. Michigan, Ann Arbor, no.10, p.5, Apr., 1939.

THE GRASSHOPPER MOUSE IN IOWA. L. R. Dice. Jour. Mam., vol.5, no.1, p.66, Feb., 1924.

AN EXTENSION OF THE RANGE OF THE MUSKRAT IN CALIFORNIA. Donald R. Dickey. Jour. Mam., vol.4, no.1, pp.55-56, Feb., 1923.

A NEW HARVEST MOUSE FROM PETALUMA, CALIFORNIA. Joseph Dixon. Univ. Calif. Publ. Zool., vol.5, no.4, pp.271-273, 1909.

NOTES ON THE NATURAL HISTORY OF THE BUSHY-TAILED WOOD RATS OF CALIFORNIA. (GENERAL ACCOUNT OF NEOTOMA CINERA CINERA AND N. C. OCCIDENTALIS.) Joseph Dixon. Univ. Calif. Publ. Zool., vol.21, pp.49-74, pls.1-3, Dec.10, 1919.

(Review by Walter P. Taylor of) SOME NOTES ON THE NATURAL HISTORY OF THE BUSHY-TAILED WOOD RAT OF CALIFORNIA. Joseph Dixon. Jour. Mam., vol.2, no.1, p.42, Feb., 1921.

NEW CLETHRIONOMYS FROM UTAH AND PENNSYLVANIA. (CLETHRIONOMYS GAPPERI UINTAENSIS, C.G. PALUDICOLA.) J. Kenneth Doutt. Proc. Biol. Soc. Wash., vol.54, pp.161-164, Dec.8, 1941.

A NEW WOOD RAT FROM SOUTHEASTERN UTAH. Stephen D. Durrant. Jour. Mam., vol.15, no.1, pp.65-67, Feb., 1934.

A NEW MOUSE OF THE PEROMYSCUS BOYLII GROUP FROM UTAH. Stephen D. Durrant. Proc. Biol. Soc. Wash., vol.59, pp.167-168, Dec.23, 1946.

IOWA MUSKRAT SITUATION IN THE FALL OF 1944. Paul L. Errington. Iowa Conserv., Des Moines, vol.3, no.10, p.80, Oct.15, 1944.

SPECIAL REPORT ON CERTAIN VITAL STATISTICS OF IOWA MUSKRATS. Paul L. Errington. Iowa Coop. Wildlife Research Unit, Quart. Rept., Ames, pp.21-23, Oct.-Dec., 1947.

THE GOSS LEMMING MOUSE, SYNAPTOMYS COOPERI GOSSII (COUES), IN NEBRASKA. Edson Fichter, Merle F. Hansen. Bull. Univ. Nebraska State Mus., vol.3, no.2, pp.1-8, figs.2, Sept., 1947.

A NEW SUBSPECIES OF WOOD RAT (NEOTOMA MEXICANA) FROM COLORADO. Robert B. Finley, Jr. Univ. Kansas Publ., Mus. Nat. Hist., vol.5, no.30, pp.527-534, Aug.15, 1953.

NOTES ON VOLES IN CENTRAL MISSOURI. Herbert J. Fisher. Jour. Mam., vol.26, no.4, pp.435-437, Feb.12, 1946.

A PRELIMINARY STUDY OF THE PRAIRIE VOLE, MICROTUS OCHROGASTER (WAGNER), IN CENTRAL MISSOURI. Herbert J. Fisher. AM thesis, Univ. Mo., 1944.

NEW LOCALITY RECORDS FOR THE DEER MOUSE, PEROMYSCUS M. PELLESCENS (ALLEN). Alvin Flury. Jour. Mam., Balto., vol.30, no.2, pp.199-200, May 23, 1949.

AN UNDESCRIBED COTTON RAT FROM NEW MEXICO. Marshall C. Gardner. Jour. Mam., vol.29, no.1, p.65, Feb.13, 1948.

FACTORS AFFECTING THE SURVIVAL OF THE PLAINS MUSKRAT, ONDATRA ZIBETHICA CINNAMOMINA, IN OKLAHOMA. Bryan P. Glass. Jour. Wildlife Mgt., Ithaca, vol.16, no.4, pp.484-491, Oct., 1952.

A NEW CANYON MOUSE OF THE GENUS PEROMYSCUS FROM ARIZONA. E. A. Goldman. Jour. Mam., vol.18, no.1, pp.92-93, Feb.14, 1937.

A NEW MUSKRAT FROM ARIZONA. (ONDATRA ZIBETHICA BERNARDI.) E. A. Goldman. Proc. Biol. Soc. Wash., vol.45, pp.93-94, June 21, 1932.

A NEW WESTERN SUBSPECIES OF GOLDEN MOUSE. (PEROMYSCUS NUTTALLI FLAMMEUS.) E. A. Goldman. Proc. Biol. Soc. Wash., vol.54, pp.189-192, Dec.8, 1941.

A NEW WOOD RAT FROM ARIZONA. E. A. Goldman. Proc. Biol. Soc. Wash., vol.40, pp.205-206, Dec.2, 1927.

A NEW RODENT RECORDED IN YOSEMITE. Ralph Goldman. Yosemite Nature Notes, vol.16, no.3, p.19, Mar., 1937.

SOME OREGON PHENACOMYS. Morris M. Green. Jour. Mam., vol.9, no.3, pp.254-255, Aug., 1928.

WYOMING'S BUSHY-TAILED KLEPTOMANIAC. (NEOTOMA.) Peter A. Gregg. Wyoming Wild Life, Cheyenne, vol.15, no. 2, pp.30-31, illus., Feb., 1951.

A NEW RACE OF MICROTUS MONTANUS FROM THE CENTRAL SIERRA NEVADA. Joseph Grinnell. Proc. Biol. Soc. Wash., vol.27, pp.207-208, Oct.31, 1914.

DISTRIBUTION OF MICROTINE RODENTS IN KANSAS. John M. Haines, H. T. Gier. Trans. Kansas Acad. Sci., 54 (1): 58-63, Mar., 1951.

NEVADAN RACES OF THE MICROTUS MONTANUS GROUP OF MEADOW MICE. E. Raymond Hall. Univ. Calif. Publ. in Zool., Berkeley, vol.40, no.12, pp.417-428, fig.1, Oct.25, 1935.

NOTES ON THE MEADOW MICE MICROTUS MONTANUS AND M. NANUS WITH DESCRIPTION OF A NEW SUBSPECIES FROM COLORADO. (MICROTUS MONTANUS FUSUS.) E. Raymond Hall. Proc. Biol. Soc. Wash., vol.51, pp.131-134, Aug.23, 1938.

THE PINYON MOUSE (PEROMYSCUS TRUEI) IN NEVADA, WITH DESCRIPTION OF A NEW SUBSPECIES. (PEROMYSCUS TRUEI NEVADENSIS.) E. Raymond Hall, Donald F. Hoffmeister. Univ. Calif. Publ. Zool., Berkeley, vol.42, no.8, pp.401-406, fig.1, Apr.30, 1940.

A NEW SUBSPECIES OF MICROTUS MONTANUS FROM MONTANA AND COMMENTS ON MICROTUS CANICAUDUS MILLER. (MICROTUS MONTANUS PRATINCOLUS.) E. Raymond Hall, Deith R. Kelson. Univ. Kansas Publ. Mus. Nat. Hist., Lawrence, vol.5, no.7, pp.73-79, Oct.1, 1951.

A MUSKRAT HOUSE ON THE LOWER COLORADO RIVER. Arthur F. Halloran. Jour. Mam., vol.27, no.1, pp.88-89, Mar.14, 1946.

PHENACOMYS IN MINNESOTA. Charles O. Handley, Jr. Jour. Mam., vol.35, no.2, p.260, May 26, 1954.

EXTENSION OF RANGE OF PEROGNATHUS FLAVUS FULIGINOSUS. Lyndon L. Hargrave. Jour. Mam., vol.18, no.1, p. 101, Feb.14, 1937.

DESCRIPTION OF A NEW SPECIES OF WOOD-RAT FROM ARIZONA. Flora

Hartley. Proc. Calif. Acad. Sci., San Francisco, ser. 2, vol. 4, pp. 157-160, pls. 12-13, May 9, 1894.

NORTHERN PINE MOUSE IN MINNESOTA. Donald M. Hatfield, Jour. Mam., vol. 20, no. 3, p. 376, Aug. 14, 1939.

SOME EARLY SUMMER OBSERVATIONS ON MUSKRATS IN A NORTHEASTERN CALIFORNIA MARSH. Arthur G. Hensley, Howard Twining. Calif. Fish and Game, San Francisco, vol. 32, no. 4, pp. 171-181, figs. 41-45, Oct., 1946.

DISTRIBUTION OF THE GENUS REITHRODONTOMYS IN KANSAS. Claude W. Hibbard. Bull. Univ. Kansas, Sci. Bull., vol. 25, no. 7, pp. 173-179, pl. 20, June 1, 1938.

PEROMYSCUS LEUCOPUS ARIDULUS IN KANSAS. Claude W. Hibbard. Jour. Mam., vol. 18, no. 1, pp. 101-102, Feb., 1937.

A NEW BOG-LEMMING (SYNAPTOMYS) FROM MEADE COUNTY, KANSAS. (SYNAPTOMYS COOPERI PALUDIS.) Claude W. Hibbard, George C. Rinker. Univ. Kansas Sci. Bull., Lawrence, vol. 28, no. 2, pp. 25-35, figs. 3, May 15, 1942.

A NEW MEADOW MOUSE (MICROTUS OCHROGASTER TAYLORI) FROM MEADE COUNTY, KANSAS. Claude W. Hibbard, George C. Rinker. Univ. Kansas Sci. Bull., Lawrence, vol. 29, pt. 2, no. 4, pp. 255-268, figs. 5, Oct. 15, 1943.

ECOLOGICAL DIFFERENTIATION BETWEEN TWO HARVEST MICE (REITHRODONTOMYS) IN WESTERN KANSAS. John Eric Hill, Claude W. Hibbard. Jour. Mam., vol. 24, no. 1, pp. 22-25, Feb. 20, 1943.

TWO NEW SUBSPECIES OF THE PINON MOUSE, PEROMYSCUS TRUEI, FROM CALIFORNIA. (PEROMYSCUS TRUEI SEQUOIENSIS, P. T. CHLORUS.) Donald F. Hoffmeister. Proc. Biol. Soc. Wash., vol. 54, pp. 129-132, Sept. 30, 1941.

A NEW MUSKRAT FROM THE GREAT PLAINS. Ned Hollister. Proc. Biol. Soc. Wash., vol. 23, pp. 125-126, Sept. 2, 1910.

THE NAME NEOTOMA CINEREA CINNAMOMEA ALLEN APPLIED TO WOOD-RATS FROM SOUTHWESTERN WYOMING. Emmet T. Hooper. Jour. Mam., vol. 25, no. 4, p. 415, Dec. 12, 1944.

DESCRIPTION OF A NEW MICROTINE RODENT FROM OREGON, WITH REMARKS ON SOME CONTIGUOUS FORMS. A. Brazier Howell. Jour. Mam., vol. 4, no. 1, pp. 33-37, Feb., 1923.

DESCRIPTION OF A NEW SPECIES OF PHENACOMYS FROM OREGON. A. Brazier Howell. Jour. Mam., vol. 2, no. 2, pp. 98-100, pl. 7, May 2, 1921.

THE HARVEST MICE OF THE SAN LUIS VALLEY, COLORADO. Arthur H. Howell. Jour. Mam., vol. 16, no. 2, pp. 143-144, May 15, 1935.

MICROTUS TOWNSENDI IN THE CASCADE MOUNTAINS OF OREGON. A. Brazier Howell. Jour. Mam., vol. 1, no. 3, pp. 141-142, May, 1920.

A NEW COTTON RAT FROM ARIZONA. (SIGMODON HISPIDUS CIENEGAE.) A. Brazier Howell. Proc. Biol. Soc. Wash., vol. 32, pp. 161-162, Sept. 30, 1919.

A SECOND RECORD OF PHENACOMYS ALBIPES IN CALIFORNIA, WITH A DISCUSSION OF THE SPECIES. A. Brazier Howell. Jour. Mam., vol. 1, no. 5, pp. 242-243, Dec. 4, 1920.

OCCURRENCE OF THE BUSHY-TAILED WOODRAT (NEOTOMA CINEREA) AT FRESNO, CALIFORNIA. Douglass H. Hubbard. Jour. Mam., vol. 20, no. 3, pp. 374-375, Aug. 14, 1939.

CRATER LAKE PEROMYSCUS. R. R. Huestis. Jour. Mam., vol. 20, no. 3, pp. 341-345, fig. 1, tables 2, Aug. 14, 1939.

MUSKRATS IN CRATER LAKE NATIONAL PARK. R. R. Huestis. Crater Lake Nat. Park Notes, vol. 11, no. 2, pp. 22-23, Aug., 1938.

A NEW MUSKRAT FROM UTAH. (ONDATRA ZIBETHICA GOLDMANI.) Laurence M. Huey. Trans. San Diego Soc. Nat. Hist., vol. 8, no. 32, pp. 409-410, Jan. 18, 1938.

LOCAL DISTRIBUTION OF WHITE-FOOTED MICE, PEROMYSCUS MANICULATUS AND P. BOYLEI, IN THE NORTHERN SIERRA NEVADA, CALIFORNIA. E. W. Jameson, Jr. Jour. Mam., 32 (2): 197-203, May, 1951.

A POPULATION STUDY OF THE MEADOW MICE (MICROTUS) IN THREE SIERRA NEVADA MEADOWS. Hubert O. Jenkins. PhD thesis, Stanford Univ., 1940; Proc. Calif. Acad. Sci., ser. 4, 26 (3): 43-67, June, 1948.

NOTES ON TWO SPECIES OF PHENACOMYS IN OREGON. Stanley G. Jewett. Jour. Mam., vol. 1, no. 4, pp. 165-168, Aug., 1920.

SYNAPTOMYS IN IDAHO AND NORTHEASTERN WASHINGTON. Murray L. Johnson, Phillip W. Cheney. Murrelet, Seattle, vol. 34, no. 1, p. 10, 1953.

THE SAGEBRUSH VOLE IN WASHINGTON STATE. Murray L. Johnson, C. Wesley Clanton, John Girard. Murrelet, 29 (3): 44-47, Sept.-Dec., 1948.

TWO NEW WOOD RATS FROM EASTERN UTAH. (NEOTOMA CINEREA MACRODON, N. LEPIDA SANRAFAELI.) Keith R. Kelson. Jour. Wash. Acad. Sci., vol. 39, no. 12, pp. 417-419, Dec. 15, 1949.

MUSKRAT INVESTIGATIONS IN TEXAS. Daniel W. Lay. Jour. Wildlife Mgt., Menasha, vol. 9, no. 1, pp. 56-76, figs. 5, Jan., 1945.

MUSKRATS ON THE TEXAS COAST. Daniel W. Lay, Ted O'Neil. Jour. Wildlife Mgt., Menasha, vol. 6, no. 4, pp. 301-311, figs. 2, pls. 27-28, Oct., 1942.

RANGE OF PEROMYSCUS EREMICUS EREMICUS IN NEVADA. Joshua A. Lee. Jour. Mam., vol. 35, no. 3, pp. 450, Aug. 20, 1956.

THE DUSKY-FOOTED WOOD RAT: A RECORD OF OBSERVATIONS MADE ON THE HASTINGS NATURAL HISTORY RESERVATION. Jean M. Linsdale, Lloyd Tevis, Jr. Univ. Calif. Press, 664 pp., 1951.

THE LIFE HISTORY AND ECOLOGY OF THE MUSKRAT IN UTAH. Jessop B. Low. Quart. Rept. Utah Coop. Wildlife Research Unit, Logan, vol. 14, no. 3, pp. 47-58, July-Sept., 1949.

NOTES ON GROWTH, SEX AND AGE RATIOS, AND SUGGESTED MANAGEMENT OF MINNESOTA MUSKRATS. Lester J. McCann. Jour. Mam., vol. 25, no. 1, pp. 59-63, Feb., 1944.

SOME STUDIES ON THE ECOLOGY AND MANAGEMENT OF THE MUSKRAT ON THE LOCOMOTIVE SPRINGS MIGRATORY WATERFOWL REFUGE, BOX ELDER COUNTY, UTAH. Robert A. McCullough. MS thesis, Utah State Agr. Coll., 1951.

THE CALIFORNIA RED-BACKED MOUSE IN THE OREGON COAST RANGE. James A. Macnab, Jane Claire Dirks. Jour. Mam., vol. 22, no. 2, pp. 174-180, May 14, 1941.

GLACIER POINT IN WINTER. OUR PACK RAT FRIENDS. Dorothy R. Mayer. Yosemite Nat. Notes, vol. 28, no. 7, pp. 96-98, July, 1949.

DESCRIPTION OF A NEW SPECIES OF COTTON RAT (SIGMODON MINIMUS) FROM NEW MEXICO. Edgar A. Mearns. Proc. U.S. Nat. Mus., vol. 27, no. 994, pp. 129-130, July 19, 1894.

DESCRIPTION OF A NEW EVOTOMYS FROM COLORADO. C. Hart Merriam. North Amer. Fauna, no. 4, U.S. Dept. Agric., pp. 23-24, fig., no. 3, Oct., 1890.

DESCRIPTION OF A NEW EVOTOMYS FROM THE BLACK HILLS OF SOUTH DAKOTA. C. Hart Merriam. North Amer. Fauna, no. 5, U.S. Dept. Agric., p. 119, July, 1891.

DESCRIPTION OF A NEW MOUSE FROM NEW MEXICO. C. Hart Merriam. Proc. Biol. Soc. Wash., vol. 4, p. 3, Apr. 15, 1887.

DESCRIPTION OF A NEW PRAIRIE MEADOW MOUSE (ARVICOLA AUSTERUS MINOR) FROM DAKOTA AND MINNESOTA. C. Hart Merriam. Amer. Naturalist, pp. 598-601, figs. 4, July, 1888.

DESCRIPTION OF A NEW SPECIES OF FIELD-MOUSE (ARVICOLA PALLIDUS) FROM DAKOTA. C. Hart Merriam. Amer. Nat., pp. 702-705, figs. 4, Aug., 1888.

DESCRIPTION OF A NEW SPECIES OF MEADOW MOUSE FROM THE BLACK HILLS OF DAKOTA. C. Hart Merriam. Amer. Nat., pp. 934-935, figs. 2, Oct., 1888.

DESCRIPTIONS OF TWO NEW RED BACKED MICE (EVOTOMYS) FROM OREGON. C. Hart Merriam. Proc. Biol. Soc. Wash., vol. 11, pp. 71-72, Apr. 21, 1897.

DESCRIPTIONS OF TWO NEW SPECIES OF EVOTOMYS FROM THE PACIFIC COAST REGION OF THE UNITED STATES. C. Hart Merriam. North Amer. Fauna, no. 4, U.S. Dept. Agric., pp. 25-26, Oct., 1890.

NOTES ON THE CHIPMUNKS OF THE GENUS EUTAMIAS OCCURRING WEST OF THE EAST BASE OF THE CASCADE-SIERRA SYSTEM. C. Hart Merriam. Proc. Biol. Soc. Wash., vol. 11, pp. 189-212, colored folded map, July 1, 1897.

OCCURRENCE OF THE SIBERIAN LEMNING-VOLE (LAGURUS) IN THE UNITED STATES. C. Hart Merriam. Amer. Nat., pp. 758-759, Aug. 1, 1895.

PHENACOMYS PREBLEI, A NEW VOLE FROM THE MOUNTAINS OF COLORADO. C. Hart Merriam. Proc. Biol. Soc. Wash., vol. 11, p. 45, Mar. 16, 1897.

TWO NEW WOOD RATS FROM THE PLATEAU REGION OF ARIZONA. (NEOTOMA PINETORUM AND N. ARIZONAE) C. Hart Merriam. Proc. Biol. Soc. Wash., vol. 8, pp. 108-112, July 31, 1893.

A NOTE ON THE PIGMY VOLE IN COLORADO. F. W. Miller. Jour. Mam., vol. 11, no. 1, pp. 83-84, Feb., 1930.

NOTES ON SOME COLORADO WOOD RATS. F. W. Miller. Jour. Mam., vol. 12, no. 4, p. 432, Nov., 1931.

A SIXTH COLORADO RECORD OF PHENACOMYS. F. W. Miller, R. L. Landberg. Jour. Mam., vol. 12, no. 2, pp. 165-166, May, 1931.

DESCRIPTION OF A NEW MOUSE FROM SOUTHERN NEW MEXICO AND ARIZONA. Gerrit Smith Miller, Jr. Amer. Mus. Nat. Hist., New York, vol. 5, pp. 331-334, 1893.

DESCRIPTION OF A NEW VOLE FROM OREGON. Gerrit S. Miller, Jr. Proc. Biol. Soc. Wash., vol. 11, pp. 67-68, Apr. 21, 1897,

NOTES ON THE SAGE MOUSE IN EASTERN OREGON. A. W. Moore. Jour. Mam., 24 (2): 188-191, May, 1943.

ATTWATER'S WOOD RAT IN MISSOURI. George E. Moore. Jour. Mam., vol. 19, no. 4, p. 503, Nov. 14, 1938.

A NEW RODENT FOR YOSEMITE NATIONAL PARK. (PEROMYSCUS TRUEI GILBERTI.) Vincent Mowbray. Yosemite Nat. Notes, Yosemite, vol. 19, no. 12, p. 93, Dec., 1940.

THE ECOLOGICAL RELATIONSHIP OF TWO SUBSPECIES OF PEROMYSCUS IN THE GLACIER PARK REGION, MONTANA. Adolph Murie. Occas. Papers Mus. Zool., Univ. Michigan, no. 270, pp. 17, July 1, 1933.

THE MUSKRAT IN THE LOUISIANA COASTAL MARSHES. Ted O'Neil. La. Dept. Wild Life and Fisheries, 152 pp., 1949.

OCCURRENCE OF THE SHORT-TAILED MEADOW MOUSE IN NORTHERN CALIFORNIA. Robert T. Orr. Jour. Mam., vol. 13, no. 2, p. 167, May, 1932.

A NEW WHITE FOOTED MOUSE FROM CALIFORNIA. Wilfred H. Osgood. Proc. Biol. Soc. Wash., vol.14, pp.193-194, Dec.12, 1901.

THE GENUS NEOTOMA IN THE SANTA CRUZ MOUNTAINS. Harold E. Parks. Jour. Mam., vol.3, no.4, pp.241-253, Nov., 1922.

THE HARVEST MOUSE IN IOWA. Frank C. Pellett. Proc. Iowa Acad. Sci., vol.19, p. 197, 1912.

LAGURUS IN SOUTHWESTERN UTAH. C. C. Presnall. Jour. Mam., vol.18, no. 3, p.369, Aug.14, 1937.

DESCRIPTION OF A NEW WOOD-RAT FROM THE COAST RANGE OF CENTRAL CALIFORNIA. W. W. Price. Proc. Calif. Acad. Sci., ser.2, vol.4, pp.154-156, pl. 11, May 9, 1894.

NOTES ON COLORADO PHENACOMYS AND PIKAS. William O. Pruitt, Jr. Jour. Mam., 35 (3): 450-452, Aug., 1954.

PHENACOMYS ALBIPES IN LINCOLN COUNTY, OREGON. W. B. Quay. Jour. Mam., vol.34, no.3, p.391, Aug.14, 1953.

OBSERVATIONS ON THE WHITE-FOOTED MOUSE IN EASTERN KANSAS. Dennis G. Rainey. Trans. Kansas Acad. Sci., vol.58, no.2, pp.225-228, 1955.

DESCRIPTIONS OF A NEW SUBGENUS AND NEW SPECIES OF ARVICOLINE RODENTS FROM BRITISH COLUMBIA AND WASHINGTON. Samuel N. Rhoads. Proc. Acad. Nat. Sci. Phila., pp.282-288, fig.1, Oct. 23, 1894.

A NEW GRASSHOPPER MOUSE FROM NEW MEXICO. Samuel N. Rhoads. Proc. Acad. Nat. Sci., Phila., pp.194-195, May 3, 1898.

AN EXTENSION OF THE RANGE OF THE TEXAS COTTON RAT IN KANSAS. George C. Rinker. Jour. Mam., Balto., vol.23, no.4, p.439, Nov., 1942.

A STUDY OF THE COTTON RAT IN NORTHWESTERN ARKANSAS. John A. Sealander, Jr., Barry O. Walker. Proc. Arkansas Acad. Sci., vol.8, pp.153-162, 1955.

RECENT EXTENSION OF THE RANGE OF MUSKRATS IN CALIFORNIA. George D. Seymour. Calif. Fish and Game, 40 (4): 374-384, illus., Oct., 1954.

POPULATIONS, PRODUCTIVITY, MOVEMENTS, AND FOOD HABITS OF MISSOURI MUSKRATS. Charles E. Shanks. AM thesis, Univ. Mo., 1947.

DESCRIPTION OF TRUE'S PINON MOUSE, A NEW SPECIES OF HESPEROMYS FROM NEW MEXICO. R. W. Shufeldt. Proc. U.S. Nat. Mus., vol.8, pp.403-408, 1885.

COMMON FIELD MICE OF SOUTH DAKOTA. George Smokey. South Dakota Conservation Digest, Pierre, vol.10, no.10, pp.6, 13, Oct., 1943.

MUSKRATS OF TULE LAKE REFUGE CALIFORNIA. Clarence A. Sooter. Jour. Wildlife Mgt., 10 (1): 68-70, Jan., 1946.

THE DISTRIBUTION OF THE GENUS PEROMYSCUS IN KANSAS. James M. Sprague. Trans. Kansas Acad. Sci., Topeka, vol.42, pp.487-493, figs.2, table 1, 1939.

NOTES ON THE TEXAS COTTON AND ATTWATER WOOD RATS IN TEXAS. John K. Strecker. Jour. Mam., vol.10, no.3, pp.216-220, Aug., 1929.

LIFE HISTORY OF THE TEXAS RICE RAT (ORYZOMYS PALUSTRIS TEXANSIS). Arthur Svihla. Jour. Mam., vol.12, no.3, pp.238-242, pl.9, 1931.

THE OLYMPIC RED-BACKED MOUSE. Arthur Svihla. Murrelet, vol.12, no.2, p.54, May, 1931.

OCCURRENCE OF THE GOLDEN-BREASTED CANYON MOUSE IN WYOMING AND UTAH. Arthur Svihla, Ruth Dowell Svihla. Jour. Mam., vol.12, no.3, p.315, Aug., 1931.

A CALIFORNIA RECORD OF MICROTUS GREGONI BAIRDI. Walter P. Taylor. Jour. Mam., vol.1, no.4, p.184, Aug., 1920.

A NEW MEADOW MOUSE FROM THE CASCADE MOUNTAINS OF WASHINGTON. Walter P. Taylor. Jour. Mam., vol.1, no. 4, pp.180-182, Aug.24, 1920.

THE FUR BEARING MAMMALS OF WYOMING. PT.14. (MUSKRAT.) Earl M. Thomas. Wyoming Wild Life, 17 (4): 4-9, 27, illus., Apr., 1953.

DESCRIPTION OF A NEW SPECIES OF MOUSE, PHENACOMYS LONGICAUDUS, FROM OREGON. Frederick W. True. U. S. Nat. Mus. Proc., Wash., vol.13, pp.303-304, Nov.15, 1890.

THE DISTRIBUTION OF MUSKRATS IN CALIFORNIA. Howard Twining, Arthur L. Hensley. Calif. Fish and Game, 29 (2): 64-78, Apr., 1943.

A STUDY OF THE COTTON RAT, SIGMODON HISPIDUS HISPIDUS, IN THE REGION OF NORTHWESTERN ARKANSAS. Barry Q. Walker. MS thesis, Univ. Ark., 1952.

OCCURRENCE OF THE TEXAS RICE RAT IN OKLAHOMA. H. L. Whitaker. Jour. Mam., vol.18, no.1, p.102, Feb.14, 1937.

NEW PHENACOMYS RECORDS FROM COLORADO. Olwen Williams. Jour. Mam., vol.33, no.3, p.399, Aug.19, 1952.

A PRELIMINARY INVESTIGATION OF THE MUSKRAT POPULATION OF GRAY'S LAKE, IDAHO. Roger M. Williams. MS thesis, Univ. Idaho, 1950.

SYNAPTOMYS BOREALIS FROM GLACIER NATIONAL PARK, MONTANA. Philip L. Wright. Jour. Mam., vol.31, no.4, p.460, Nov.21, 1950.

Use as Laboratory Animals

ORIGIN OF THE GOLDEN HAMSTER CRICETUS AURATUS AS A LABORATORY ANIMAL. S. Adler. Nature, London, vol.162, no.4111, pp.256-257, Aug.14, 1948.

THE DEER MOUSE, PEROMYSCUS, A VALUABLE LABORATORY MAMMAL. George T. McNair. Jour. Mam., vol.12, no.1, pp.48-52, Feb., 1931.

THE GOLDEN HAMSTER (CRICETUS AURATUS) AS A TEST ANIMAL FOR THE DIAGNOSIS OF LEPTOSPIROSIS. Raymond Randall, Harold K. Cooper. Science, Lancaster, n.s., vol.100, no.2589, pp.133-134, Aug.11, 1944.

THE FIELD VOLE (MICROTUS) AS A LABORATORY ANIMAL. R. M. Ranson. Jour. Animal Ecol., vol.3, no.1, pp.70-76, pl.4, May, 1934.

(NEW LABORATORY ANIMAL.) Novoe laboratornoe jivotnoe. I. V. Tupikova, S. M. Kulagin. Zool. Jour. Akad. Nauk, SSSR, Moscow, vol.31, no.3, pp.476-478, 1952.

THE GOLDEN HAMSTER AS A TEST ANIMAL FOR TUBERCULAR INFECTION. J. Ungar. Nature, London, vol.150, no.3806, p.432, Oct.10, 1942.

Variation

CRANIAL VARIATIONS IN NEOTOMA MICROPUS DUE TO GROWTH AND INDIVIDUAL DIFFERENTIATION. J.A. Allen. Bull. Amer. Mus. Nat. Hist., vol.6, pp. 233-246, pl.4, Aug.3, 1894.

(ON THE QUESTION OF INDIVIDUAL AND GEOGRAPHICAL CHANGE OF SEVERAL ASPECTS OF FIELD MICE (APODEMUS KAUP).) Kvoprocu ob individualnoi i geograficheskoi izmenchivosti u nokotorix vidov roda Apodemus Kaup (Mammalia). A. I. Argyropulo. Trudi Zool. Inst. Akad. Nauk SSSR, Moscow, vol.8, no.1, pp.195-200, 1946.

GEOGRAPHIC VARIATION IN NEOTOMA LEPIDA IN ARIZONA. Seth B. Benson. Occas. Papers Mus. Zool. Univ. Michigan, no.317, pp.9, fig.1, July 1, 1935.

VARIATION IN THE PYGMY MOUSE (BAIOMYS TAYLORI) FROM TEXAS AND ARIZONA. W. F. Blair, Philip M. Blossom. Contrib. Lab. Vertebrate Biol., Univ. Michigan, Ann Arbor, no.40, pp.1-7, Mar., 1948.

GEOGRAPHIC VARIATION IN NEOTOMA LEPIDA IN WEST-CENTRAL CALIFORNIA. Jack C. Von Bloeker, Jr. Proc. Biol. Soc. Wash., vol.51, pp.201-204, Dec.23, 1938.

DICE ON GEOGRAPHIC VARIATION IN PEROMYSCUS. W. E. Castle. Amer. Nat., vol.67, no.710, pp.276-278, May-June, 1933.

NON-GEOGRAPHIC VARIATION IN CRANIAL MEASUREMENTS OF WILD-TAKEN PEROMYSCUS LEUCOPUS NOVEBORACENSIS. E. Lendell Cockrum. Jour. Mam., vol.35, no.3, pp.367-376, Aug.20, 1954.

GEOGRAPHIC VARIATION IN RED-BACKED MICE (GENUS CLETHRIONOMYS) OF THE SOUTHERN ROCKY MOUNTAIN REGION. E. Lendell Cockrum, Kenneth L. Fitch. Univ. Kansas Publ., Mus. Nat. Hist., Lawrence, vol.5, no.22, pp.281-292, Nov.15, 1952.

GEOGRAPHIC VARIATION IN THE MEADOW MOUSE IN BRITISH COLUMBIA AND SOUTHEASTERN ALASKA. Frederick H. Dale. Jour. Mam., Balto., vol.21, no.3, pp.332-340, Aug.14, 1940.

GEOGRAPHIC VARIATION IN BROWN LEMMINGS (GENUS LEMMUS). William B. Davis. Murrelet, Seattle, vol.25, no.2, pp.19-25, Sept.19, 1944.

ADDITIONAL DATA ON VARIATION IN THE PRAIRIE DEER-MOUSE, PEROMYSCUS MANICULATUS BAIRDII. Lee R. Dice. Occas. Papers Mus. Zool., Univ. Michigan, Ann Arbor, no.351, pp.19, figs. 3, map 1, Apr.2, 1937.

ECOLOGICAL AND GENETIC VARIABILITY WITHIN SPECIES OF PEROMYSCUS. Lee R. Dice. Amer. Nat., Lancaster, vol.74, no.752, pp.212-221, May-June, 1940.

VARIATION IN A GEOGRAPHIC RACE OF THE DEER-MOUSE PEROMYSCUS MANICULATUS BAIRDII. Lee R. Dice. Occas. Papers Mus. Zool., Univ. Michigan, no. 239, pp.26, tables 12, Apr.8, 1932.

VARIATION IN BODY DIMENSIONS AND PELAGE COLOR OF CERTAIN LABORATORY-BRED STOCKS OF THE PEROMYSCUS TRUEI GROUP. Lee R. Dice. Contrib. Lab. Vert. Biol., Univ. Michigan, Ann Arbor, no.57, p.26, June, 1952.

VARIATION IN NINE STOCKS OF THE DEER-MOUSE, PEROMYSCUS MANICULATUS, FROM ARIZONA. Lee R. Dice. Occas. Papers, Mus. Zool., Univ. Michigan, Ann Arbor, no.375, pp.1-19, map 1, May 26, 1938.

VARIATION IN PEROMYSCUS MANICULATUS RUFINUS FROM COLORADO AND NEW MEXICO. Lee R. Dice. Occas. Papers Mus. Zool., Univ. Michigan, no. 271, p.32, tables 11, July 1, 1933.

VARIATION IN THE CACTUS-MOUSE, PEROMYSCUS EREMICUS. Lee R. Dice. Contrib. Lab. Vert. Genetics, Univ. Michigan, Ann Arbor, no.8, pp.1-27, map 1, Mar., 1939.

VARIATION IN THE DEER-MOUSE, PEROMYSCUS MANICULATUS, IN PARTS OF OREGON, CALIFORNIA, AND BAJA CALIFORNIA. Lee R. Dice. Contrib. Lab. Vert. Genetics, Univ. Michigan, Ann Arbor, no.18, 11 pp., 1 map, Dec., 1941.

VARIATION IN THE DEER-MOUSE (PEROMYSCUS MANICULATUS) IN THE COLUMBIA BASIN OF SOUTHEASTERN WASHINGTON AND ADJACENT IDAHO AND OREGON. Lee R. Dice. Contrib. Lab. Vertebrate Gen., Univ. Michigan, Ann Arbor, no.12, p.22, fig.1, Sept., 1939.

VARIATION IN THE DEER-MOUSE (PEROMYSCUS MANICULATUS) OF THE BAD LANDS AND BLACK HILLS OF SOUTH DAKOTA AND WYOMING. Lee R. Dice. Contrib. Lab. Vert. Genetics, Univ. Michigan, Ann Arbor, no.19, p.10, 1 map, May, 1942.

VARIATION IN THE WOOD-MOUSE, PEROMYSCUS LEUCOPUS, FROM SEVERAL LOCALITIES IN NEW ENGLAND AND NOVA SCOTIA. Lee R. Dice. Contrib. Lab. Vert. Genetics, Univ. Michigan, Ann Arbor, no.9, pp.1-16, 1 map, Mar., 1939.

VARIATION IN THE WOOD-MOUSE, PEROMYSCUS LEUCOPUS NOVEBORACENSIS, IN THE NORTHEASTERN UNITED STATES. Lee R. Dice. Occas. Papers Mus. Zool., Univ. Michigan, Ann Arbor, no.352, p.32, figs.2, map 1, Apr.17, 1937.

VARIATION OF PEROMYSCUS MANICULATUS IN PARTS OF WESTERN WASHINGTON AND ADJACENT OREGON. Lee R. Dice. Contrib. Lab. Vert. Biol. Univ. Michigan, Ann Arbor, no.44, p.34, illus., Oct., 1949.

VARIATION OF THE DEER-MOUSE (PEROMYSCUS MANICULATUS) IN PARTS OF IDAHO, MONTANA, UTAH, AND WYOMING. Lee R. Dice. Contrib. Lab. Vert. Biol., Univ. Michigan, Ann Arbor, no.28, p.13, map 1, Apr., 1944.

VARIATION OF THE DEER-MOUSE (PEROMYSCUS MANICULATUS) ON THE SAND HILLS OF NEBRASKA AND ADJACENT AREAS. Lee R. Dice. Contrib. Lab. Vert. Genetics, Univ. Michigan, Ann Arbor, no. 15, 19 pp., 1 map, July, 1941.

VARIATION IN THE SPONTANEOUS ACTIVITY OF PEROMYSCUS, AS SHOWN BY RECORDING WHEELS. Lee R. Dice, Sherman A. Hoslett. Contrib. Lab. Vert. Biol., Univ. Michigan, Ann Arbor, no.47, pp.18, Sept., 1950.

VARIATION IN THE DEER-MOUSE (PEROMYSCUS MANICULATUS) ALONG THE LOWER COLUMBIA RIVER. Wade Fox. Amer. Midland Nat., Notre Dame, vol.40, no.2, pp.420-452, figs.2, Sept., 1948.

GEOGRAPHIC VARIATION IN THE CANYON MOUSE, PEROMYSCUS CRINITUS. E. Raymond Hall, Donald F. Hoffmeister. Jour. Mam., vol.23, no.1, pp.51-65, fig.1, Feb.14, 1942.

RELIABILITY OF LABORATORY-BRED STOCKS AS SAMPLES OF WILD POPULATIONS, AS SHOWN IN A STUDY OF THE VARIATION OF PEROMYSCUS POLIONOTUS IN PARTS OF FLORIDA AND ALABAMA. Don W. Hayne. Contrib. Lab. Vert. Biol. Univ. Michigan, Ann Arbor, no.46, p.56, illus., May, 1950.

MORPHOLOGICAL VARIATION IN THE TEXAS RACES OF THE WOOD-MOUSE, PEROMYSCUS LEUCOPUS. Jack A. Herrmann. MS thesis, Univ. Texas, 1952.

GEOGRAPHIC VARIATION IN BUSHY-TAILED WOOD RATS. Emmet T. Hooper. Univ. Calif. Publ. Zool., Berkeley, vol.42, no.9, pp.407-424, May 17, 1940.

GEOGRAPHIC VARIATION IN HARVEST MICE OF THE SPECIES REITHRODONTOMYS HUMULIS. Emmet T. Hooper. Occas. Papers Mus. Zool., Univ. Michigan, Ann Arbor, no.477, pp.1-19, Nov.5, 1943.

GEOGRAPHICAL VARIATION IN WOOD RATS OF THE SPECIES NEOTOMA FUSCIPES. Emmett T. Hooper. Univ. Calif. Publ. Zool., vol.42, no.4, pp.213-246, pls.7-8, Mar.1, 1938.

INDIVIDUAL AND AGE VARIATION IN MICROTUS MONTANUS YOSEMITE. A. Brazier Howell. Jour. Agric. Research, vol.28, no.10, pp.977-1015, figs.1-25, pl. 1, Dec.4, 1924.

VARIATION IN PATTERN OF PRIMENESS OF MUSKRAT SKIN. Charles E. Kellogg. Jour. Wildlife Mgt., vol.10, no.1, pp.38-42, pl.3, Jan., 1946.

VARIATION IN PEROMYSCUS MANICULATUS OSGOODI FROM THE UINTA MOUNTAINS, UTAH. Harold J. Leraas. Contrib. Lab. Genetics Univ. Michigan, no.6, pp.1-13, figs.2, tables 3, Apr., 1938.

VOLUMETRIC AND CYTOLOGICAL VARIATION IN THE PINEAL BODY OF PEROMYSCUS LEUCOPUS (RODENTIA) WITH RESPECT TO SEX, CAPTIVITY AND DAY-LENGTH. W. B. Quay. Jour. Morphol., Phila., 98 (3): 471-496, May, 1956.

SKULL VARIATION IN THE MEADOW VOLE (MICROTUS P. PENNSYLVANICUS) IN PENNSYLVANIA. Dana P. Snyder. Ann. Carnegie Mus., Pittsburgh, vol.33, pp.201-234, Sept.21, 1954.

AN ANALYSIS OF GEOGRAPHIC VARIATION IN MICE OF THE PEROMYSCUS POLIONOTUS GROUP, FROM FLORIDA AND ALABAMA. Francis B. Sumner. Jour. Mam., vol.7, no.3, pp.149-184, pls. 15-18, Aug., 1926.

CONTINUOUS AND DISCONTINUOUS VARIATIONS AND THEIR INHERITANCE IN PEROMYSCUS. F. B. Sumner. Amer. Nat., vol.52, no.615, pp.177-208, vol.52, nos.618-619, pp.290-301, vol.52, nos.620-621, pp.439-454, figs.13, 1918.

VARIATION IN NUMBER OF ENAMEL LOOPS IN THE TWO ANTERIOR UPPER CHEEK-TEETH IN DANISH MICROTUS AGRESTIS (L). Erik Ursin. Vidensk. Medd. fra Dansk Naturh. Foren., Kobenhavn, vol.111, pp.257-261, figs.2, Nov.5, 1949.

(INVESTIGATIONS OF THE MORPHOLOGICAL VARIABILITY OF THE FIELD MOUSE (MICROTUS AGRESTIS LINNE).) Untersuchungen ueber die morphologische Veraenderlichkeit der Erdmaus (Microtus agrestis Linne). Waclaw Wasilewski. Ann. Univ. Mariae Curie-Sklodowska, Lublin, sec. C, 9 (6): 261-299, Mar.5, 1956.

(INVESTIGATION OF THE VARIABILITY OF MICROTUS OECONOMUS PALL. IN THE BIALOWIEZA NATIONAL PARK.) Untersuchungen ueber die Veraenderlichkeit des Microtus oeconomus Pall. in Bialowieza-Nationalpark. Waclaw Wasilewski. Ann. Univ. Mariae Curie-Sklodowska, Lublin, sec.C, 9 (8): 355-381, July 10, 1956.

West Indies

A NEW OECOMYS FROM TRINIDAD. (OECOMYS SPLENDENS.) R. W. Hayman. Ann. Mag. Nat. Hist., London, ser.11, vol.1, pp.381-383, table, Apr., 1938.

THE MUSKRAT OF THE ANTILLES (MUS PILORIDES) AS TYPE OF A VERY DISTINCT GENUS (MEGALOMYS, TRT.) UNDER THE NEW GENERIC NAME MOSCHOMYS. E. L. Trouessart. Ann. and Mag. Nat. Hist., ser.7, vol.11, pp.385-388, Apr., 1903.

Young

PRENATAL DEATH IN THE STRIPED HAMSTER. F. Droogleever. Archives de Biologie, vol.39, pp.583-606, 1 pl., 1929.

THE YOUNG OF NEOFIBER ALLENI. W. J. Hamilton, Jr. Jour. Mam., 37 (3): 448-449, illus., Sept. 11, 1956.

PATERNAL CARE OF YOUNG MICE OF THE GENUS PEROMYSCUS. B. Elizabeth Horner. Jour. Mam., vol.28, no.1, pp.31-36, Feb.15, 1947.

(TWO UNUSUAL CASES OF CARE OF YOUNG IN THE EUROPEAN HAMSTER (CRICETUS CRICETUS L.).) Zwei ungewoehnliche Faelle von Brutpflege beim europaeischen Hamster (Cricetus cricetus L.). Hans Petzsch. Zool. Garten, Leipzig, n.F. vol.19, no.5, pp.259-260, 1952.

NOTES ON THE YOUNG OF THE ALLEGHENY WOOD RAT. Earl L. Poole. Jour. Mam., vol.17, no.1, pp.22-26, illus., Feb., 1936.

PRE-NATAL AND INFANT MORTALITY IN A LABORATORY POPULATION OF VOLES (MICROTUS AGRESTIS). R. M. Ranson. Proc. Zool. Soc. London, vol.111, ser.A, pts.1-2, pp.45-57, fig.1, Sept., 1941.

NOTE ON THE DEATH OF A YOUNG DEER MOUSE. Richard Lee Weaver. Jour. Mam., vol.21, no.2, p.222, May 14, 1940.

Spalacidae

(ELEMENTS COMPRISING THE SURVIVING RELICS OF THE FAUNA OF THE GIGOULI HILLS.) Elements composant les reliques (survivants) de la faune des monts Gigouli. (Spalax.) I. Bachkiroff. Bull. Soc. Nat. Moscou, sect. biol., n.s., vol.44, no.5, pp.240-245, 1935.

(SPALAX OF HUNGARY.) Le spalax de Hongrie. (Spalax hungaricus Nehring.) Bodnar Bela. La Terre et la Vie, vol.4, no.6, pp.323-333, illus., June, 1934.

SHORT SKETCH OF THE ECOLOGY, DISTRIBUTION, ECONOMIC SIGNIFICANCE AND MEASURES OF COMBATING THE BLIND MOLE RAT (SPALAX) IN THE TERRITORY OF THE VILLAGE PRIMORSK-ACHTARSK, KUBAN DISTRICT. L. B. Boehme. Bull. Caucasus Plant Prot. Sta., nos.6-7, pp.227-238, 1930. (In Russian, with German summary.)

THE BOSNIAN- HERCEGOVINIAN RAT MOLES (SPALAX MONTICOLA MONTICOLA NHRG. AND SP. MONTICOLA HERCEGOVINENSIS MEH) L. St. J. Bolkay. L. Sveske Rada Fitopatoloskog Zavoda u Sarajevu, pp.1-24 (of separate), pls.1-2, (one colored), 1928.

BIOLOGY OF MOLE-RAT (SPALAX MICROPHTHALMUS FUELD.) AND EXPERIMENTS ON DIFFERENT METHODS OF ITS CONTROL. N. M. Dukelskaya. Bull. Plant Protection, Leningrad, The Lenin Acad. Agric. Sci. in USSR, ser.4, no.2, pp.23-45, figs.7, 1932. (Russian text with English summary.)

THE MOLE RAT (SPALAX) AND MOLE-RAT TRAPPING. N. M. Dukelskaya. in The thin-toed ground squirrel, the fat dormouse, the mole-rat, and the chipmunk. All-Union Coop. Assn. Publ. House, pp.71-79, figs.28-32, 1935.

THREE NEW SUBSPECIES OF SPALAX MONTICOLA. Martin A. C. Hinton. Ann. and Mag. Nat. Hist., ser.9, vol.5, pp.312-320, Mar., 1920.

(NEW CONTRIBUTIONS TO KNOWLEDGE OF THE GENUS PROSPALAX.) Neue Beitraege zur Kenntnis der Gattund Prospalax. Th. Kormos. Allattani Koezlemenyek, Budapest, vol.34, fasc.3-4, pp.130-142, figs.2, Dec.4, 1937.

(SPECIES GENERIS SPALAX. MOLE RAT SPECIES IN SYSTEMATIC AND PHYLOGENIC RELATIONSHIP.) Die Arten der Blindmaeuse in systematischer und phylogenetischer Beziehung. Ludwig Mehely. Math. u. Naturw. Berichte aus Ungarn, Leipzig, vol.28, pp.1-160, figs.1-7 (Incomplete; should include vol.28, pp.1-390, pls.33, vol.29, pp. i-xii, pls.36), 1913.

DESCRIPTION OF TWO NEW MOLE RATS. Gerrit S. Miller, Jr. Proc. Biol. Soc. Wash., vol.16, pp.161-164, Nov.30, 1903.

(ON THE LIVING HABITS OF SPALAX MONTICOLA NEHRING.) Zur Lebensweise von Spalax monticola Nehring. Erna Mohr. Zool. Garten, Leipzig, n.F., vol.4, nos. 8-9, pp.280-281, figs.2, Oct., 1931.

ON THE BURROW OF THE RODENT, SPALAX (MESOSPALAX). Ivor Montagu. Proc. Zool. Soc. Lond., 1924, pt.4, pp. 1153-1160, 2 pls., 1925.

(OCCURRENCE OF A SPALAX SPECIES IN CIRENAICA AS WELL AS SPALAX AEGYPTIACUS NHRG. AND SP. GIGANTEUS NHRG.) Das Vorkommen einer Spalax-Species in der Cyrenaica, sowie ueber Spalax aegyptiacus Nhrg. und Sp. giganteus Nhrg. A. Nehring. Sitz. Ber. Gesell., Naturf. Freunde, Berlin, Jahrg, 1900, no. 9, p.210, Nov.20, 1900.

(ON SPALAX GRAECUS N. SP.) Ueber Spalax graecus n. sp. A. Nehring. Zool. Anzeiger, Leipzig, vol.21, no.555, pp.228-230, figs.2, Mar.21, 1898.

(ON SPALAX HUNGARICUS N. SP.) Ueber Spalax hungaricus n. sp. A. Nehring. Zool. Anzeiger, Leipzig, vol.21, no.567, pp.479-481, figs.3, Sept.5, 1898.

(SOME AFTERTHOUGHTS ON THE SPECIES OF THE GENUS SPALAX.) Einige Nachtraege ueber die Species der Gattung Spalax. A. Nehring. Sitz. Ber. Gesell. Naturf. Freunde, Berlin, Jahrg., 1898, no. 1, pp.1-8, figs.4, Jan.18, 1898.

(SOME NEW SPALAX SPECIES.) Mehrere neue Spalax-Arten. A. Nehring. Sitz. Ber. Gesell. Naturf. Freunde Berlin, Jahrg. 1897, no.10, pp.163-183, figs.6, Dec.21, 1897.

(OBSERVATIONS OF AN ASIA MINOR MOLE RAT (SPALAX MONTICOLA LABAUMI MATSCHIE) IN CAPTIVITY.) Gefangenschaftsbeobachtungen an einem Kleinasiatischen Blindmoll (Spalax monticola labaumi Matschie). G. Niethammer, H. Kummerloewe. Der Zoologischer Garten, Leipzig, n.F., vol.7, nos.7-9, pp.179-182, figs.2, Nov., 1934.

(ON MUTUAL SYSTEMATIC RELATIONS AND THE PROBLEM OF RECIPROCAL PARENTHOOD AMONG DIFFERENT FORMS OF SPALAX.) Sur les rapports systematiques mutuels et sur le probleme de la parente reciproque entre differentes formes de Spalax. S. I. Ognev. Bull. Soc. Nat. Moscou, sect. biol., n.s., vol.49, no.2, pp.33-41, 1940. (In Russian, with French resume.)

(ON THE SYSTEMATICS AND GEOGRAPHICAL DISTRIBUTION OF THE SPALACIDAE OF THE UKRAINIAN SSR.) Zur Systematik und geographischen Verbreitung der Spalacidae der Ukrainischen SSR. E. G. Reshnetnik. Acad. Sci. Ukranian SSR (Inst. Zool. and Biol.), Kiev, Rpts. Zool. Mus., no.23, pp.3-21, figs.13, 1 table, 1939.

(RHIZOSPALAX POIRRIERI MILLER AND GIDLEY AND THE DENTAL FORMULA OF THE SPALACIDEN.) Rhizospalax poirrieri Miller et Gidley und die Gebissformel der Spalaciden. H. G. Stehlin. Verh. Naturf. Ges. Basel, vol.34, pp.233-263, 15 figs., 1923.

(THE FIRST PROOF OF A FOSSIL MOLE RAT (SPALAX HUNGARICUS NEHR.) IN AUSTRIA.) Der erste Nachweis einer fossilen Blindmaus (Spalax hungaricus Nehr.) in Oesterreich. Erich Thenius. Sitzungsber. Oesterreichische Acad. Wissensch., Vienna, Abt.1, vol.158, no.4, pp.287-298, fig.1, table 1, 1949.

THE SPALAX OF THE GRECIAN ARCHIPELAGO. Oldfield Thomas. Ann. and Mag. Nat. Hist. (8), vol.20, no.118, pp. 315-317, Oct., 1917.

MOLE RATS IN THE SOUTHERN SUDAN. Sudan Notes and Records, Khartoum, Egypt, vol.26, no.2, p.337, 1945.

## Rhizomyidae

ON THE SUBSPECIES OF RHIZOMYS SUMATRENSIS (RAFFLES) WITH SOME NOTES ON RELATED SPECIES. L. D. Brongersma. Zool. Mededeelingen, Leiden, vol.19, pp.137-164, figs.4, 1936.

ON RHIZOMYS SUMATRENSIS. F. A. Jentink. Notes Leyden Mus., vol.18, no. 27, pp.213-216, Read Dec., 1896.

(CONTRIBUTIONS TO KNOWLEDGE OF TACHYORCTES RUEPP.) Beitraege zur Kenntnis von Tachyorctes Ruepp. Oscar Neumann, Hans-Joachim Ruemmler. Zeitsch. f. Saeugetierkunde, vol.3, pp.295-306, 8 figs., June 11, 1928.

THE BAMBOO RAT'S NAME. (RHIZOMYS VESTITUS.) Arthur de C. Sowerby. China Jour., vol.20, no.2, p.109, Feb., 1934.

FURTHER NOTES ON ASIATIC BAMBOO-RATS. Oldfield Thomas. Ann. and Mag. Nat. Hist., (8), vol.16, no.94, pp.313-317, Oct., 1915.

A NEW BAMBOO-RAT FROM PERAK. Oldfield Thomas. Ann. and Mag. Nat. Hist. (8), vol.18, no.107, pp.445-446, Nov., 1916.

NOTES ON THE ASIATIC BAMBOO-RATS (RHIZOMYS, ETS.). Oldfield Thomas. Ann. and Mag. Nat. Hist. (8), vol.16, no. 91, pp.56-61, July, 1915.

## Muridae

BIOMETRICAL STUDIES ON RATTUS LOSEA (SWINHOE) 1. Bun'ichiro Aoki, Ryo Tanaka. Jour. Soc. Trop. Agric., Taiwan, vol.6, no.3, pp.475-494, figs.9, Nov., 1934. (In Japanese with English summary.)

(CONTRIBUTIONS TO KNOWLEDGE OF MURINAE BAIRD.) Beitraege zur Kenntnis der Murinae Baird. (Characters of male genitalia.) A. I. Argiropulo. Zeit. f. Saeugetierkunde, bd.4, heft 3, pp.144-156, 15 figs., Sept.18, 1929.

(CONTRIBUTIONS TO KNOWLEDGE OF MURINAE BAIRD. III. REMARKS ON MUS MUSCULUS L. MUS SPICILEGUS PET., AND MUS WAGNERI EV.) Beitraege zur Kenntnis der Murinae Baird. III. Bemerkungen ueber Mus musculus L., Mus spicilegus Pet. und Mus wagneri Ev. A. J. Argyropulo. Zeitschrift f. Saeugetierkunde, vol.5, nos.5-6, pp.304-313, pl.34, 1930.

CONTRIBUTIONS TO KNOWLEDGE OF THE GENUS RATTUS FITZINGER (1867). A. I. Argyropulo. Bull. Inst. Zool. Appl. et Phytopath., vol.4, pp.63-87, fig.1, pl.1, 1928. (In Russian.)

FURTHER NOTE ON THE HARVEST-MOUSE (MUS MINUTUS, PALLAS) AND ITS GEOGRAPHICAL VARIATIONS. G. E. H. Barrett-Hamilton. Ann. and Mag. Nat. Hist., ser.7, vol.5, pp.527-530, June, 1900.

(SOME OBSERVATIONS ON DORMICE.) Einige Beobachtungen an Haselmaeusen. Hans Bast. Zeitschrift f. Saeugetierkunde, vol.6, no.6, pp.239-240, Dec.15, 1931.

(DOMESTIC RATS.) Hausratten. G. von Burg. Der Weidmann, Jahrg., 1921, no.1, p.7, Jan.6, 1921.

PORTRAIT OF A HOUSE-MOUSE. Maurice Burton. Illus. London News, vol.138, no. 3587, p.100, illus., Jan.21, 1956.

NOTES ON THE LIFE HISTORY OF THE ALBINO MOUSE. C. L. Chang. China Jour., vol.10, pp.85-87, Feb., 1929.

PRELIMINARY OBSERVATIONS ON THE LIFE HISTORY OF THE ALBINO MOUSE, MUS DECUMANUS ALBINO. C. L. Chang. Contr. Biol. Lab. Science Soc. China, Zool. Ser., vol.6, no.7, pp.65-74, 1930.

THE RAT: DATA AND REFERENCE TABLES. Henry Herbert Donaldson. 2nd ed., revised. (American Anatomical Memoir No.6.) The Wistar Institute of Anatomy and Biology, Phila., vol.8, pp. XIV, 469, tables 212, charts 72, figs.13, 1924.

(Review by H.T. Hartley Jackson of) THE RAT: DATA AND REFERENCE TABLES. Henry Herbert Donaldson. Jour. Mamm., vol.6, no.2, p.132, May, 1925.

NOTES ON THE BIOLOGY OF THE FAEROE MOUSE (MUS MUSCULUS FAEROENSIS). F. C. Evans. Jour. Animal Ecology, London, vol.7, no.2, pp.290-297, pl.11, Nov., 1938.

ON MASTACOMYS FUSCUS (THOMAS). H. H. Finlayson. Trans. and Proc. Roy. Soc. South Australia, vol.57, pp.125-129, 2 pls., Dec.23, 1933.

SUPPLEMENTARY REMARKS ON B. M. ZHITKOV'S PAPER: 'NOTES ON RATS AND SOME CONDITIONS OF THEIR STUDY'. A. N. Formozov. Zool. Zh., 24: 126-132, 1945.

THE CHINESE HOUSE-MOUSE (MUS WAGNERI EVERSMANN) AND ITS TAME VARIETIES. A. B. Droogleever Fortuyn. Peking Soc. Nat. Hist. Bull., vol.3, no.4, pp.59-64, June, 1929.

(ON THE BIOLOGY OF THE DOMESTIC RAT, RATTUS RATTUS L.) Zur Biologie der Hausratte, Rattus rattus L. Guenter Gaffrey. Zeitschr. Saeugetierk., Berlin, vol.20, nos.2-3, p.183, Aug.3, 1955.

RATS ARE ROBBERS. Dorr D. Green. Reclamation Era, Wash., vol.34, no.8, pp.157-158, illus., Aug., 1948.

THE DISAPPEARING HARVEST-MOUSE. Eric Hardy. Field, London, vol.162, no.4201, p.45, July 1, 1933.

THE GREY FIELD MOUSE. (MASTOMYS COUCHA.) W. Victor Harris. East African Agric. Jour., Kenya, Tanganyika, Uganda, and Zanzibar, vol.2, no.4, pp. 315-318, figs.2, Jan., 1937.

(ON SYLVAEMUS SYLVATICUS L. AND FLAVICOLLIS MELCHIOR.) Ueber Sylvaemus sylvaticus L. und flavicollis Melchior. G. Heinrich. Zeitschr. f. Saeugetierkunde, vol.2, pp.186-194, 4 figs., Apr.29, 1929. (Characters and habits.)

(ON THE FORMS AND GEOGRAPHIC DISTRIBUTION OF THE GENUS CALOMYSCUS THOS. (MAMMALIA, MURIDAE).) Ueber die Formen und die geographische Verbreitung der Gattung Calomyscus Thos. (Mammalia, Muridae). W. G. Heptner. Archiv. Mus. Zool. Univ. Moscou, vol.1, pp.12-14, 1934. (In German, with Russian summary.)

(STUDIES OF ISLAND POPULATIONS OF THE WOOD MOUSE (APODEMUS SYLVATICUS L.).) Studien an Insel-Populationen der Waldmaus, Apodemus sylvaticus L. Werner Herold. Zeitschr. Humboldt-Univ. Berlin, Math.-Nat. Reihe, 5 (2): 143-149, 1956.

(BIOLOGICAL PARTICULARITIES OF RATTUS R. ROQUEI SODY AS COMPARED TO THOSE OF RATTUS R. JALORENSIS BONHOTE.) Biologische bijzonderheden van Rattus r. roquei Sody, vergeleken bij die van Rattus r. jalorensis Bonhote. W. C. Van Heurn. Zool. Mededeel., Leiden, vol.13, nos.3-4, pp.151-154, Dec.31, 1930.

THE BROWN RAT. T. Hyde-Parker. Naturalist, London, no.779, pp.143-146, June, 1940.

PITCHIR MELANURUS S. MUELLER. F. A. Jentink. Notes Leyden Mus., vol.14, no.21, pp.122-126, pls.3-4, Feb., 1892.

(OBSERVATIONS ON DOMESTIC RODENTS.) Beobachtungen an heimischen Nagetieren. Hermann Kahmann. Zeitschr. fuer Saeugetierkunde, Berlin, vol.6, no.4, pp. 143-151, Dec.15, 1931.

THE HARVEST MOUSE. (MICROMYS MINUTUS.) Phyllis Kelway. Game and Gun and Angler's Monthly, London, vol.16, no.167, pp.488-491, illus., Aug., 1939.

THE HOUSE MOUSE. Phyllis Kelway. Game and Gun and the Angler's Monthly, London, vol.17, no.182, pp.463-465, Nov., 1940.

THE WOOD MOUSE. Phyllis Kelway. Game and Gun and the Angler's Monthly, London, vol.18, no.188, pp.181-183, illus., May, 1941.

YELLOW-NECKED MOUSE. (APODEMUS FLAVICOLLIS WINTONI.) Phyllis Kelway. Game and Gun and Angler's Monthly, London, vol.16, no.165, pp.352-354, illus., June, 1939.

(GENUS MUS ARVALIS. COMMON FIELD MOUSE.) Realgattung Mus Arvalis. Gemeine Feldmaus. Otto Kleinschmidt. Berajah, Zoographia infinita, Halle a.S., p.2, 1920.

ON RATTUS BLYTHI KLOSS, (MUS CINNAMOMEUS BLYTH). C. B. Kloss. Jour. Nat. Hist. Soc. Siam, vol.4, no.2, pp.65-69, Mar., 1921.

(THE PYGMY MOUSE (MUS MINUTUS PALL.).) Die Zwergmaus (Mus minutus Pall.). Carl Koch. Blaetter fuer Aquarien- und Terrarienkunde, Jahrg.35, no.1, pp. 13-15, Jan., 1924.

MUS SPICELEGUS HEROLDI M. Anton Krausse. Zeitschr. fuer Forst-und Jagdw., Jahrg.54, Heft 6, pp.356-357, June, 1922.

(ON SOME FOREIGN DOMESTIC AND WOOD MICE.) Ueber einige auslaendische Haus-und Waldmaeuse. Anton Krausse. Archiv. f. Naturg., 1921, Abt.A, Heft 6, pp.40-42, May, 1921.

HOUSE RATS AND MICE. David E. Lantz. U.S. Dept. Agric., Farmers' Bull. no.896, pp.1-24, figs.1-10, Oct., 1917.

NOTES ON LEGGADA MUSCULOIDES (TEMMINCK). Barbara Lawrence. Proc. New England Zool. Club, Cambridge, vol. 23, pp.85-98, Aug.23, 1945.

NOTE UPON MUS TOMPSONI, RAMSAY. Allan R. McCulloch. Records Australian Mus., Sydney, vol.6, p.447, pt.4, Jan.23, 1907.

(MUS SERGII AS A SPECIES.) A. Migulin. Acad. Sci. RSS Ukraine, Travaux Mus. Zool., Kiev, vol.18, no.20, pp.116-120, 1937.

THE BLACK RAT. C. B. Moffat. Irish Naturalists' Jour., vol.2, no.3, pp.47-49, May, 1928.

THE BROWN RAT. C. B. Moffat. Irish Naturalists' Jour., vol.2, no.5, pp.87-89, Sept., 1928.

(A "RAT KING" OF WOOD MICE.) Ein "Rattenkoenig" von Waldmaeusen. Erna Mohr. Zeitschrift f, Saeugetierkunde, vol. 4, nos.4-6, p.252, Feb.10, 1930.

MOUSE OR SNAIL? (APODEMUS SYLVATICUS.) Claude Morley. Trans. Suffolk Nat. Soc., Norwich, vol.4, pt.4, pp.287-288, Dec., 1941.

REMARKS ON A RAT LATELY LIVING IN THE SOCIETY'S GARDENS. James Murie. Proc. Zool. Soc. Lond., pp.157-158, 1868.

VANDALS OF THE NIGHT. J. Laurens Nicholes. Publication Press, Pasadena, 118 p., 1948.

THE DISAPPEARING HARVEST MOUSE. A. H. Patterson. Field, London, vol.162, no.4216, p.979, Oct.14, 1933.

(DOMESTIC RAT AND ROVING RAT.) Hausratte und Wanderratte. Hermann Peters. Verhandl. Deutschen Zoologen in Mainz, 1949 (Zool. Anzeiger, 14 Supplementband), Leipzig, pp.330-336, 1950.

THE LONG-TAILED TREE MOUSE (VANDELEURIA OLERACEA?). W. W. A. Phillips. Spolia Zeylanica, Ceylon, vol.13, pt.3, pp.307-308, Mar.13, 1926.

BLACK AND BROWN RATS. R. I. Pocock. Field, London, vol.151, p.961, June 7, 1928.

(ON THE YELLOW-THROATED MOUSE, APODEMUS FLAVICOLLIS ALPICOLA HEINRICH 1951.) Zur Kenntnis der Gelbhalsmaus, Apodemus flavicollis alpicola Heinrich, 1951. Edwin Reinwaldt. Saeugetierk. Mitteil., Stuttgart, 3 (4): 151-154, Oct.1, 1955.

(ON A LARGE BLACK RAT (RATTUS NORVEGICUS BERK.) A. propos d'un Surmulot (Rattus norvegicus Berk.) Noir. P. Rode. Mammalia, Paris, 8 (2): 75-76, June, 1944.

(ON WATER RATS (HYDROMYINAE). ALSO, DESCRIPTION OF A NEW LEPTOMYS THOS., L. ERNSTMAYRI NEW SPECIES OF NEW GUINEA.) Ueber die Schwimmratten (Hydromyinae). Zugleich Beschreibung einer neuen Leptomys Thos., L. ernstmayri sp. n. aus Neu-Guinea. Hans Ruemmler. Aquarium, Berlin, pp. 131-135, photos 4, Aug., 1932.

(LOPHUROMYS RATS.) Les Rats Lophuromys. H. Schouteden. Rev. Zool. Bot. Afr., vol.26 (Suppl. Bull. Cercle Zool. Congo., vol.11, nos.1-2), p.8, Nov.-Dec., 1934.

NOTES ON COMMENSAL RATS. Ernst Schwarz. Am. Jour. Trop. Med., 22 (5): 577-579, Sept., 1942.

A FORGOTTEN MOUSE SPECIES. (MUS SERGII VALCH.) N. Sharleman. Priroda, Leningrad, no.4, pp.122-123, 1 fig., Apr., 1937. (In Russian.)

THE HOUSE RAT. James Silver. USDA, Cir.423, 18 pp., Jan., 1937; U.S. Dept. Interior, Fish and Wildlife Service, Wildlife Cir.6, pp.1-18, figs.15, 1941; U.S. Dept. Interior, Fish and Wildlife Serv., Wildlife Circ.6, pp.1-20, figs.15, Feb., 1942. (Revision of March 1941 edition.)

RATS. George Smokey. South Dakota Conserv. Digest, Pierre, vol.11, no.1, pp. 10, 16, Jan., 1944.

RATS. (NORWAY RAT.) L. L. Snyder. Canadian Nature, Toronto, vol.4, no.3, pp.80-81, illus., May-June, 1942.

THE MAMMAL FAUNA OF THE VALDAI HILLS. 1. THE TAXONOMIC POSITION OF RATTUS RATTUS L. AND ITS DISTRIBUTION IN THE USSR.) S. Stroganov. Zool. Zhurn. (Zool. Jour. USSR), Moscou, vol. 13, no.4, pp.714-730, 1934. (In Russian, with German summary.)

SOME STUDIES OF ENVIRONMENTAL INFLUENCE, HEREDITY, CORRELATION AND GROWTH, IN THE WHITE MOUSE. Francis B. Sumner. Jour. Exper. Zool., vol.18, no.3, pp.325-432, figs.17, tables, Apr., 1915.

THE HOPPING OR JERBOA MARSUPIAL-MICE. Ellis Troughton. Australian Mus. Mag., Sydney, vol.8, no.5, pp.159-160, pl.1, Sept.30, 1943.

RATTUS AND THETOMYS. Ellis Troughton. Rec. Australian Mus., Sidney, vol.20, no. 31, pp.279-281, Mar., 1939.

THE SHIP RAT. (RATTUS, R. RATTUS, RATTUS R. ALEXANDRINUS, RATTUS R. NORVEGICUS, AND MUS MUSCULUS; LIFE HISTORY DATA AND HABITS.) C. L. Williams. Pest Control and Sanitation, Hollywood, vol.3, no.4, pp.8-13, illus., Apr., 1948.

(THE ACTIVITY OF THE JAPANESE DANCING MOUSE AND ITS RHYTHMICAL DISTRIBUTION.) Die Aktivitaet der japanischen Tanzmaus und ihre rhythmische Verteilung. E. Wolf. Zeitschr. f. vergleich., Physiologie, vol.11, pp.321-344, 13 figs., Jan.18, 1930.

REMARKS ON RATS AND CERTAIN CONDITIONS TO BE OBSERVED IN STUDYING THEM. B. M. Zhitkov. Zool. Zh., 23: 91-97, 1944.

(INFORMATION ON MUS MUSCULUS L.) Zur Kenntnis von Mus musculus L. Klaus Zimmermann. Zeitschr. f. Saeugetierkunde, vol.10, no.1, pp.155-158, Dec.31, 1935.

DOOMED RATS. Science Illus., New York, vol.3, no.8, p.9, Aug., 1948.

THE HISTORY OF OUR TWO RAT SPECIES. (RATTUS NORVEGICUS, RATTUS RATTUS.) Rodent Mail, London, vol.3, no.3, pp.30-31, May, 1947.

OTHER RATS. 1. THE MIAROO. Rodent Mail, Rats and Mice, London, vol.2, no.2, pp.18-19, Apr., 1946.

RATS AND THE WAR. Nature, London, vol.150, no.3801, p.287, Sept.5, 1942.

ROUND THE MAP. (RATS.) Rodent Mail, Rats and Mice, London, vol.2, no.10, pp. 111-113, Dec., 1946.

SEEN IN EUROPE FOR THE FIRST TIME: A PALLID CLOUD RAT. (PHLOEOMYS) Illus. London News, vol.213, no.5714, p. 469, illus., Oct.23, 1948.

THE TRAIL OF THE RAT. Rodent Mail, Rats and Mice, London, vol.2, no.10, pp. 113-114, illus., Dec., 1946.

WHAT I KNOW AND THINK ABOUT RATS. Rodent Mail, Rats and Mice, London, vol. 9, no.1, p.5, Nov., 1945.

## Africa

(MURINAE OF MOROCCO.) Los Murinae de Marruecos. (New forms of Mus and Rattus.) Angel Cabrera. Roy. Soc. Esp. de Hist. Nat., Tomo del 50, aniv., pp.42-58, Mar.15, 1921.

(ON SOME NEW MOROCCAN RATS.) Sobre algunos ratones marroquies. (Two new subspecies of Musspicilegus.) Angel Cabrera. Bol. R. Soc. Esp. Hist. Nat., vol.23, pp.429-432, Dec., 1923.

A MOUSE NEW TO NIGERIA. (DENDROMUS MESSORIUS THOMS.) A. B. Cozens. Nigerian Field, vol.17, no.4, pp.159-160, Oct., 1952.

ON CRICETOMYS GAMBIANUS AND VARIOUS SPECIES OF BIRDS FROM WESTERN AFRICA. L. Fraser. Proc. Zool. Soc. Lond., pt.11, pp.51-55, 1843.

A NEW URANOMYS FROM NYASALAND. (URANOMYS RUDDI SHORTRIDGEI.) R. W. Hayman. Ann. Mag. Nat. Hist., ser. 12, vol.6, no.64, pp.317-318, Apr., 1953.

THREE NEW MURINE RODENTS FROM AFRICA. N. Hollister. Smithsonian Misc. Coll., vol.66, no.10, pp.1-3, Oct. 26, 1916.

(CONFIRMATION OF THE OCCURRENCE OF THE ALEXANDER RAT (RATTUS R. ALEXANDRINUS GEOFF.) AT BENI OUNIF (SUD-ORANAIS).) Confirmation de la presence du rat alexandrin (Rattus r. alexandrinus Geoff.) a Beni ounif (Sud-oranais). P. Laurent. Bull. Sanitaire Algerie, Alger, no.491, p.1706, 1938.

(A NEW FORM OF THE TRUE MOUSE MUS MUSCULUS L. IN EASTERN MOROCCO: MUS MUSCULUS CANDIDUS SUBSP. NOV.) Une forme nouvelle de la souris vraie Mus musculus L. au Maroc Oriental: Mus musculus candidus subsp. nov. P. Laurent. Bull. Soc. Sci. Nat. Maroc, vol. 17, no.1, pp.1-7, Mar.31, 1937.

(ON THE OCCURRENCE IN MOROCCO OF THE BLACK RAT (RATTUS RATTUS LINNE ATER MILLAIS) OR, AN ADDITION TO "LOS MAMIFEROS DE MARRUECOS" BY ANGEL CABRERA.) P. Laurent. Bull. Soc. Hist. Nat. Afrique du Nord, vol.27, no.5, pp.165-172, 1936.

(THE OCCURRENCE IN MOROCCO OF A RODENT BELONGING IN THE GENUS ACOMYS.) Presence, au Maroc, d'un rongeur appartenant au genre Acomys. J. de Lepiney. Bull. Soc. Sci. Nat. Maroc, vol.17, no.1, p.8, Mar.31, 1937.

REMARKS ON SOME SOUTH AFRICAN MURINAE. B. G. Lundholm. Ann. Transvaal Mus., 22 (3): 321-329, illus., Jan.24, 1955.

(ON APPARENTLY NEW AFRICAN MAMMALS (LEIMACOMYS N.G.).) Uber anscheinend neue afrikanische Saugethiere (Leimacomys n.g.). Paul Matschie. Sitz. Ber. Gesell. Naturf. Freunde Berlin, Jahrg. 1893, no.4, pp.107-114, Apr.18, 1893.

A NEW RODENT OF THE GENUS SACCOSTOMUS FROM BRITISH EAST AFRICA. Gerrit S. Miller, Jr. Smithsonian Miscel. Coll., vol.54, no.1925, pp.2, pl.1, Feb. 28, 1910.

A NEW GENUS OF AQUATIC RODENTS FROM ABYSSINIA. (NEW GEN. AND SP: NILOPEGAMYS PLUMBEUS.) Wilfred H. Osgood. Field Mus. Nat. Hist., publ.250, zool. ser. vol.12, no.15, pp.185-189, pl.15, Nov.21, 1928.

(ON DASYMYS, A NEW GENUS OF MURINE RODENTS FROM SOUTH AFRICA.) Ueber Dasymys, eine neue Gattung von murinen Nagethieren aus Suedafrika. W. Peters. Monats. Ber. Koen. Akad. Wiss. Berlin, pp.12-14, pls.2, Jan.7, 1875.

(BIOLOGICAL REMARKS ON THE SPRING RATS OF THE GENUS ACOMYS, DISTRIBUTION IN THE SAHARA.) Remarques biologiques sur des rats epineux du genre Acomys, repartition au Sahara. Francis Petter. Mammalia, Paris, vol.18, no.4, pp.389-396, illus., Dec., 1954.

DESCRIPTION OF A NEW MOUSE FROM BASUTOLAND. (DENDROMUS MELANOTIS BASUTICUS.) Austin Roberts. Records Albany Mus., vol.3, pt.5, p.484, July 31, 1927.

A NEW SPECIES OF MYOMYS FROM SOUTH-WEST AFRICA. (MYOMYS SHORTRIDGEI.) J. St. Leger. Proc. Zool. Soc. Lond., pt.2, p.411, June, 1933.

A NEW SUBSPECIES OF COLOMYS FROM KENYA. (COLOMYS GOSLINGI DENTI.) J. St. Leger. Ann. and Mag. Nat. Hist., ser.10, vol.6, no.34, pp.527-528, Oct., 1930.

A NEW SUBSPECIES OF GIANT RAT FROM BALOVALE, N. W. RHODESIA. (CRICETOMYS EMINI VAUGHAN-JONESI.) J. St. Leger. Ann. and Mag. Nat. Hist., Lond., ser.10, vol.20, no.115, pp.148-149, July, 1937.

A SHORT DESCRIPTION OF TWO NEW SPECIES OF DENDROMUS FROM S. W. AFRICA. (DENDROMUS MESOMELAS MAJOR (POEMYS) NIGRIFRONS SHORTRIDGEI.) J. St. Leger. Ann. and Mag.

Nat. Hist., ser.10, vol.6, no.35, p.622, Nov., 1930.

RODENTS (MURIDAE) FROM LUNDA DISTRICT, NORTHEASTERN ANGOLA. Colin Campbell Sanborn. Publicacoes Culturais da Companhia de Diamantes de Angola, Lisbon, no.14, pp.107-120, map, Aug.5, 1952.

(THE DOMESTIC RAT IN THE CONGO.) Le rat domestique au Congo. H. Schouteden. Rev. Zool. et Bot. Africaines, vol.22, (4 suppl.), pp.113-118, Mar.20, 1933.

THE ORIGIN OF AFRICAN HOUSE RATS. Ernst Schwarz. Proc. Zool. Soc. Lond., 1934, pt.4, pp.723-726, Jan., 1935.

DESCRIPTION OF A NEW ACOMYS FROM SOMALILAND. Oldfield Thomas. Ann. and Mag. Nat. Hist. (6), vol.18, no.105, pp.269-270, Sept., 1896.

DESCRIPTIONS OF THREE NEW AFRICAN MURIDAE. Oldfield Thomas. Ann. and Mag. Nat. Hist. (6), vol.10, no.56, pp.179-183, Aug., 1892.

A NEW GENUS OF AFRICAN MURIDAE ALLIED TO LEGGADA. Oldfield Thomas. Ann. and Mag. Nat. Hist. (9), vol.15, no. 90, pp.667-669, June, 1925.

A NEW RAT OF THE GENUS MYLOMYS FROM THE UPPER NILE. Oldfield Thomas. Ann. and Mag. Nat. Hist. (8), vol.20, no. 119, pp.362-363, Nov., 1917.

NOTE ON THE STEATOMYS OF ANGOLA. Oldfield Thomas. Ann. and Mag. Nat. Hist. (6), vol.10, no.57, pp.264-265, Sept., 1892.

ON NEW AFRICAN MURIDAE. Oldfield Thomas. Ann. and Mag. Nat. Hist. (8), vol.7, no.40, pp.378-383, Apr., 1911.

ON TWO NEW SPECIES OF MUS DISCOVERED BY MR. S. L. HINDE IN BRITISH EAST AFRICA. Oldfield Thomas. Ann. and Mag. Nat. Hist. (7), vol.9, no.51, pp.218-220, Mar., 1902.

THREE NEW AFRICAN MICE OF THE GENUS DENDROMUS. Oldfield Thomas. Ann. and Mag. Nat. Hist. (8), vol.18, no. 104, pp.241-243, Aug., 1916.

(ON SOME MURINES FROM THE CAMEROONS.) Ueber einige Muriden aus Kamerun. Tycho Tullberg. Konigl. Gesellschaft d. Wiss. zu Upsala, Stockholm, pp.1-66, pls. 4, June 27, 1893.

DESCRIPTIONS OF TWO NEW MURIDAE FROM CENTRAL AND WEST AFRICA. W. E. de Winton. Ann. and Mag. Nat. Hist., ser.6, vol.19, pp.463-466, Apr., 1897.

ON A NEW RODENT OF THE GENUS LOPHUROMYS FROM BRITISH EAST AFRICA. (LOPHUROMYS ANSORGEI.) W. E. de Winton. Proc. Zool. Soc. Lond., pp.607-608, pl.27, May 19, 1896.

EAST AFRICAN FORMS OF ARVICANTHIS ABYSSINICUS. R. C. Wroughton. Ann. and Mag. Nat. Hist., ser.8, vol.4, pp.536-539, Dec., 1909.

NEW MURIDAE FROM BRITISH EAST AFRICA. R. C. Wroughton. Ann. and Mag. Nat. Hist., ser.8, vol.4, pp.539-542, Dec., 1909.

THREE NEW AFRICAN SPECIES OF MUS. R. C. Wroughton. Ann. and Mag. Nat. Hist., ser.8, vol.1, pp.255-257, Mar., 1908.

Anatomy

STUDIES ON THE STRUCTURE AND DEVELOPMENT OF THE BURSA OVARICA AND THE TUBA UTERINA IN THE MOUSE. Erik Agduhr. Acta Zoologica, Stockholm, vol.8, pt.1, pp.1-133, 101 figs., 1927.

THE PERIOVARIAL SAC IN THE ALBINO RAT. Roland H. Alden. Anat. Record, Phila., vol.83, no.3, pp.421-435, 1 pl., fig.1, July 25, 1942.

AGE CHANGES IN THE SKIN OF WISTAR INSTITUTE RATS WITH PARTICULAR REFERENCE TO THE EPIDERMIS. Warren Andrew. Amer. Jour. Anat., Phila., vol. 89, no.2, pp.283-320, illus., Sept., 1951.

AN AGE INVOLUTION IN THE SMALL INTESTINE OF THE MOUSE, WITH A DESCRIPTION OF THE FUNDAMENTAL PROCESS OF LYMPHOEPITHELIAL METAMORPHOSIS IN INTESTINAL MUCOSA. Warren Andrew, Nancy V. Andrew. Jour. Gerontol., vol.12, no.2, pp.136-149, Apr., 1957.

ON THE POSTNATAL GROWTH OF THE KIDNEY, WITH SPECIAL REFERENCE TO THE NUMBER AND SIZE OF THE GLOMERULI (ALBINO RAT). M. Arataki. Amer. Jour. Anat., vol.36, pp.399-436, 9 charts, Jan.15, 1926.

(CONTRIBUTIONS TO KNOWLEDGE OF MURINAE BAIRD I, II. I. ON THE MALE GENITALS OF SOME PALEOARCTIC MURINAE. II. NOTES ON THE GENUS APODEMUS KAUP.) Beitraege zur Kenntnis der Murinae Baird I, II. I. Ueber die maennlichen Genitalien einiger palaearktischen Murinae. II. Notiz ueber die Gattung Apodemus Kaup. A. J. Argyropulo. Zeitschrift f, Saeugetierkunde, vol.4, no.3, pp.144-156, Sept.18, 1929.

CHANGES WITH AGE IN THE RETICULAR FIBERS OF THE MYOCARDIUM OF THE MOUSE. Robert L. Bacon. Amer. Jour. Anat., Phila., vol.82, no.3, pp.469-495, pls.1-3, May, 1948.

ON THE PRENATAL GROWTH OF THE MAMMARY GLAND RUDIMENT IN THE MOUSE. B. I. Balinsky. Jour. Anat., Lond., vol.84, pt.3, pp.227-235, illus., July, 1950.

THE CHANGES IN THE VASCULAR PATTERN OF THE OVARY OF THE ALBINO RAT DURING THE ESTROUS CYCLE. David L. Bassett. Amer. Jour. Anat., Phila., vol.73, no.2, pp.251-291, pls.1-5, Sept., 1943.

A MORPHOLOGICAL STUDY OF THE DEVELOPMENT OF THE PLACENTA OF THE RAT. Jane Bridgman. Jour. Morphol., Phila., vol.83, no.1, pp.61-80, pls.1-3, July, 1948; no.2, pp.195-223, pls.1-4, Sept., 1948.

DEVELOPMENT OF THE STERNUM IN SCREW TAIL MICE. Vernon Bryson. Anat. Record, Phila., vol.91, no.2, pp.119-138, figs.7, pls.2, Feb., 1945.

(THE LARGEST WOOD MOUSE.) Groesste Waldmaus. G. von Burg. "Pallasia" Zeitsch. Wirbeltierkunde, vol.2, no.1, pp.69-70, Apr.1, 1924.

THE DEVELOPMENT OF THE HEART IN THE RAT. Paul L. Burlingame, J. A. Long. Univ. Calif. Publ. Zool., Berkeley, vol.43, no.12, pp.249-320, pls.26-52, 1939.

A CASE OF SPONTANEOUS INTERSEXUALITY IN THE RAT. M. W. Burrill, R. R. Greene, A. C. Ivy. Anat. Record, Phila., vol.81, no.1, pp.99-117, 1 fig., 2 pls., Sept.25, 1941.

THE DEVELOPMENT OF POLYDACTYLISM IN A SPECIAL STRAIN OF MUS MUSCULUS. Tso-Kan Chang. Peking Nat. Hist. Bull., vol.14, pt.2, pp.119-133, tables 3, pl.1, Dec., 1939.

(ESSAY ON MEASUREMENTS OF MURIDAE (RODENT MAMMALS).) Essais de mensuration sur des Murides (Mammiferes rongeurs). A. Chappellier. Bull. Mus. Nat. Hist. Nat., Paris, no.5, pp.343-349, no.6, pp.480-485, 4 pls., 1927.

SEX DIFFERENCES IN THE STRUCTURE OF BOWMAN'S CAPSULE IN THE MOUSE. Charlotte Crabtree. Science, Lancaster, n.s., vol.91, no.2360, p.299, Mar.22, 1940.

(TAIL AUTOTOMY IN THE WOOD MOUSE (APODEMUS S. SYLVATICUS LINNE 1758.) Schwanz-Autotomie bei der Waldmaus, Apodemus s. sylvaticus (Linne, 1758). Gerhard Creutz. Saeugetierk. Mitteil., Stuttgart, vol.1, no.2, p.77, Apr. 1, 1953.

DEVELOPMENTAL ANOMALIES IN A SPECIAL STRAIN OF MICE. C. H. Danforth. Amer. Jour. Anat., vol.45, pp.275-288, 4 figs., Mar.15, 1930.

REGENERATION OF OVARIES IN MICE. C. B. Davenport. Jour. Exper. Zool., vol.42, pp.1-12, May 5, 1925.

POLYOVULY AND ANOVULAR FOLLICLES IN THE WILD NORWAY RAT. David E. Davis, Octavia Hall. Anat. Record, Phila., vol.107, no.2, pp.187-192, June, 1950.

THE AGE ORDER OF EPIPHYSEAL UNION IN THE LONG BONES OF THE ALBINO RAT. A. B. Dawson. Anat. Record, vol.31, pp. 1-10, 3 pls., Sept.25, 1925.

THE OSSICLE AT THE STERNAL END OF THE CLAVICLE IN THE ALBINO RAT; THE HOMOLOGUE OF THE STERNAL EPIPHYSIS OF THE CLAVICLE IN MAN. A. B. Dawson. Anat. Record, vol.30, pp.205-210, 2 figs., June 25, 1925.

THE FIBROUS TRANSFORMATION AND ARCHITECTURE OF THE COSTAL CARTILAGE OF THE ALBINO RAT. A. B. Dawson, Charles Spark. Amer. Jour. Anat., vol.42, pp.109-137, illus., Sept.15, 1928.

THE ULTRAVIOLET SPECTROGRAPHIC EXAMINATION OF THE FAT FRACTION OF MOUSE MILK AND MAMMARY GLANDS. K. B. DeOme, L. A. Strait, E. L. McCawley. Science, Lancaster, n.s., vol.96, no.2491, pp.301-302, Sept.25, 1942.

EYE DEFECTS IN A WHITE RAT. J. A. Detlefsen. Anat. Record, vol.29, p.142, Dec.25, 1924.

A COMPARISON OF THE EUROPEAN NORWAY AND ALBINO RATS (MUS NORVEGICUS AND MUS NORVEGICUS ALBINUS) WITH THOSE OF NORTH AMERICA IN RESPECT TO THE WEIGHT OF THE CENTRAL NERVOUS SYSTEM AND TO CRANIAL CAPACITY. H. H. Donaldson. Reprinted from the Jour. Comparative Neurology, vol.22, no.1, Feb., 1912.

NOTE ON THE CONTOUR OF THE FORAMEN MAGNUM IN DIFFERENT STRAINS OF THE NORWAY RAT. H. H. Donaldson. Anat. Record, vol.52, no.4, pp.313-320, fig.1, May 25, 1932.

ON CHANGES IN THE RELATIVE WEIGHTS OF THE VISCERA AND OTHER ORGANS FROM BIRTH TO MATURITY—ALBINO RAT. H. H. Donaldson. Amer. Jour. Physiol., vol.67, pp.1-21, 1923.

ON THE WEIGHT OF THE CRANIA OF NORWAY AND ALBINO RATS FROM THREE STATIONS IN WESTERN EUROPE AND ONE STATION IN THE UNITED STATES. H. H. Donaldson. Reprinted from Anatomical Record, vol.6, no.2, Feb., 1912.

THE INFLUENCE OF PREGNANCY AND LACTATION ON THE WEIGHT OF ADRENAL GLANDS IN THE ALBINO RAT. John C. Donaldson. Amer. Jour. Physiol., vol.68, pp.517-522, 1924.

A HISTOLOGICAL STUDY OF EYE ABNORMALITIES IN THE C57 BLACK STRAIN OF MICE. Patricia Douglass, W. L. Russell. Anat. Rec., Phila., vol.97, no.3, p.414, 1947.

OBSERVATIONS ON THE CHONDROCRANIUM OF RHABDOMYS PUMILIO. F. C. Eloff. Ann. Transvaal Mus., Pretoria, vol.21, pt.4, pp.369-379, illus., July 6, 1951.

DEGENERATION OF THE CORPORA LUTEA IN THE PREGNANT VITAMIN E-DEFICIENT RAT. Benjamin H. Ershoff. Anat. Record, Phila., vol.87, no.3, pp. 297-301, Nov., 1943.

THE MICROSCOPICALLY DEMONSTRABLE LIPIDS OF CYCLIC CORPORA LUTEA IN THE RAT. John W. Everett. Amer. Jour. Anat., Phila., vol.77, no.3, pp.293-323, pls.1-3, Nov., 1945.

A CASE OF LATERAL HERMAPHRODITISM IN MUS MUSCULUS. Elizabeth Fekete. Anat. Record, vol.69, no.2, pp.151-152, 1 fig., Sept.25, 1937.

THE ANATOMY OF THE TONGUE OF THE DOMESTIC NORWAY RAT. I. THE SKIN OF THE TONGUE; THE VARIOUS PAPILLAE; THEIR NUMBER AND DISTRIBUTION.

H. S. Fish, P. D. Malone, Curt Paul Richter. Anat. Record, Phila., vol.89, no.4, pp.429-440, figs.6, Aug., 1944.

COMPARATIVE NUMBERS OF FUNGIFORM AND FOLIATE PAPILLAE ON TONGUES OF DOMESTIC WILD NORWAY RATS. H. S. Fish, Curt Paul Richter. Proc. Soc. Exper. Biol. and Med., Utica, vol.63, no.2, pp. 352-355, fig.1, Nov., 1946.

MUS MUSCULUS AND MUS WAGNERI COMPARED. I. THE NUMBER OF TAIL-RINGS. II. THE BODY WEIGHT. A. B. Droogleever Fortuyn. Genetics, Brooklyn, vol.16, no.2, pp.160-174, fig.1, Mar., 1931.

ON A PECULIAR VARIETY OF MUS MUSCULUS. John S. Gaskoin. Proc. Zool. Soc. Lond., pt.24, pp.38-40, 1856.

(VARIABILITY OF THE NUMBER OF RADICULAR ALVEOLI OF THE UPPER JAW IN THE FIELD MOUSE (APODEMUS SYLVATICUS L.) AND THE WHITE MOUSE (MUS MUSCULUS L., ALBINOS).) Variabilite du nombre des alveoles radiculaires du maxillaire superieur chez le mulot (Apodemus sylvaticus L.) et chez la souris blanche (Mus musculus L., albinos). M. Gatineau. Mammalia, Paris, 20 (4): 427-438, Dec., 1956.

A CRANIOMETRIC STUDY OF THE NORWAY RAT. Joseph Gentile. Jour. Mam., 33 (2): 190-197, illus., May, 1952.

THE NATURE OF THE X-ZONE OF THE ADRENAL GLAND OF THE MOUSE. I. Gersh, Arthur Grollman. Anat. Record, Phila., vol.75, no.2, pp.131-153, 4 pls., Oct.25, 1939.

FUNCTIONAL AND MORPHOLOGICAL PROPERTIES IN THE THYROID GLAND, ULTIMOBRANCHIAL BODY, AND PERSISTING DUCTUS PHARYNGIOBRANCHIALIS IV OF AN ADULT MOUSE. Aubrey Gorbman. Anat. Record, Phila., vol.98, no.1, pp.93-101, figs.5, May, 1947.

HISTOLOGICAL OBSERVATIONS UPON THE PORPHYRIN-EXCRETING HARDERIAN GLAND OF THE ALBINO RAT. Allan L. Grafflin. Amer. Jour. Anat., Phila., vol. 71, no.1, pp.43-64, figs.8, July 15, 1942.

THE STORAGE AND DISTRIBUTION OF IRON-CONTAINING PIGMENT AND THE PROBLEM OF SEGMENTAL DIFFERENTIATION IN THE PROXIMAL TUBULE OF THE RAT NEPHRON. Allan L. Grafflin. Amer. Jour. Anat., Phila., vol.70, no.3, pp.399-425, 3 pls., May 15, 1942.

THE ASSOCIATION BETWEEN COLOR AND SIZE IN MICE. (MUS MUSCULUS AND M. BACTRIANUS.) C. V. Green. Amer. Nat., vol.69, no.725, pp.635-638, Nov., 1935.

A SKELETAL DIFFERENCE BETWEEN SUBLINES OF THE C3H STRAIN OF MICE. E. L. Green. Science, vol.117, no.3030, pp.81-82, Jan.23, 1953.

RELATIONSHIP OF SKELETAL TYPE AND BODY SIZE IN AN INBRED STRAIN OF MICE. E. L. Green, Margaret C. Green. Jour. Morphol., vol.78, no.1, pp.113-120, Jan., 1946.

A DIFFERENCE IN SKELETAL TYPE BETWEEN RECIPROCAL HYBRIDS OF TWO INBRED STRAINS OF MICE. E. L. Green, W. L. Russell. Genetics, Menasha, vol.36, no.6, pp.641-651, Nov., 1951.

ANATOMY OF THE RAT. Eunice C. Greene. Trans. Amer. Philos. Soc., vol. 27, pp.1-342, figs.338, partly in color, 1935.

TWO HERMAPHRODITIC RATS. Roy Orval Greep. Anat. Record, Phila., vol.83, no.1, pp.121-128, pls.2, May 25, 1932.

THE MODIFICATION OF THE TESTES OF THE MOUSE WITH AGE, WITH SPECIAL REFERENCE TO INTERSTITIAL TISSUE. J. R. Groome. Proc. Zool. Soc. Lond., pt.2, pp.235-240, figs.3, July, 1934.

THE ANATOMY OF THE MAMMARY GLAND IN MICE WITH REGARD TO THE DEGREE OF ITS DISPOSITION FOR CANCER. P. J. van Gulik, R. Kortweg. Proc. K. Nederlandsche Akad. Wetensch., Amsterdam, vol.43, no.7, pp.891-900, figs.1-10, Sept., 1940.

ANATOMICAL AND PHYSIOLOGICAL STUDIES ON THE THYROID GLAND OF THE ALBINO RAT. Ada R. Hall, Helen W. Kaan. Anat. Record, Phila., vol.84, no. 3, pp.221-239, figs.4, Nov.25, 1942.

COMPARISON OF THE PREPUTIAL GLANDS IN THE ALEXANDRINE, THE WILD, AND THE DOMESTIC NORWAY RAT. Charles E. Hall. Proc. Soc. Exper. Biol. and Med., Utica, vol.69, no.2, pp.233-237, figs.3, Nov., 1948.

THE STRUCTURE AND DEVELOPMENT OF THE URETHRAL SINUS IN THE MALE WHITE MOUSE, WITH NOTES ON ITS OCCURRENCE IN OTHER RODENTS. Kathleen Hall. Jour. Anat., Cambridge, vol.70, pt.3, pp.413-428, 1 pl., Apr., 1936.

ACCESSORY CORPOREA LUTEA IN THE WILD NORWAY RAT. Octavia Hall. Texas Repts. Biol. and Med., vol.10, no.1, pp. 32-38, Spring, 1952.

LONG-BONE LENGTH AND BODY SIZES. (ALBINO RAT.) Frederick S. Hammett. Science, N.S., vol.66, p.265, Sept.16, 1927.

SYSTEMIC AND SEX DETERMINANTS OF BONE GROWTH (MUS NORVEGICUS ALBINUS.) Frederick S. Hammett. Biol. Bull., vol.50, pp.61-71, 1 chart, Jan., 1926.

VARIATION IN SIZE AND WEIGHT IN FIVE SPECIES OF HOUSE RATS (RODENTIA: MURIDAE), IN RANGOON, BURMA. J. L. Harrison, H. C. Woodville. Records Indian Mus., Calcutta, vol.47, pt.1, pp. 65-71, Mar., 1949.

CHANGES IN THE COMPOSITION OF THE ENTIRE BODY OF THE ALBINO RAT DURING THE LIFE SPAN. Shinkishi Hatai. Amer. Jour. Anat., vol.21, no.1, pp.23-37, Jan., 1917.

ON THE WEIGHT OF SOME OF THE DUCTLESS GLANDS OF THE NORWAY AND OF THE ALBINO RAT ACCORDING TO SEX AND VARIETY. Shinkishi Hatai. Anat. Record, vol.8, no.12, pp.511-523, charts 5, Dec., 1914.

ON THE WEIGHT OF THE THYMUS GLAND OF THE ALBINO RAT (MUS NORVEGICUS ALBINUS) ACCORDING TO AGE. Shinkishi Hatai. Amer. Jour. Anat., vol.16, no.2, pp.251-257, chart 1, May, 1914.

ON THE WEIGHTS OF THE ABDOMINAL AND THE THORACIC VISCERA, THE SEX GLANDS, DUCTLESS GLANDS AND THE EYEBALLS OF THE ALBINO RAT (MUS NORVEGICUS ALBINUS) ACCORDING TO BODY WEIGHT. Shinkishi Hatai. Amer. Jour. Anat., vol.15, no.1, pp.87-119, charts 12, July, 1913.

STUDIES ON THE VARIATION AND CORRELATION OF SKULL MEASUREMENTS IN BOTH SEXES OF MATURE ALBINO RATS (MUS NORVEGICUS VAR. ALBUS). Shinkishi Hatai. Amer. Jour. Anat., vol. 7, no.4, pp.423-441, fig.1, tables 10, Feb.29, 1908.

QUANTITATIVE CHANGES IN MUSCLE PROTEIN FRACTIONS DURING RAT DEVELOPMENT. Heinz Hermann, J. S. Nicholas. Jour. Exper. Zool., Phila., vol.107, no.2, pp.165-176, pls.1-3, Mar., 1948.

(SIZE AND WEIGHT OF SOME YELLOW-THROATED MICE (APODEMUS FLAVICOLLIS MELCH.) OF USEDOM ISLANE.) Mass und Gewichte einiger Gelbhalsmaeuse (Apodemus flavicollis Melch.) von der Insel Usedom. Werner Herold. Zeit. f. Saeugetierkunde, vol.7, no.2, pp.55-57, Dec.15, 1932.

(TEETH FUSION IN A YELLOW-THROATED MOUSE (APODEMUS FLAVICOLLIS MELCH.).) Zahnverschmelzung bei einer Gelbhalsmaus (Apodemus flavicollis Melch.). Werner Herold. Zeitschr. Saeugetierk., Berlin, vol.20, nos.2-3, pp.184-186, Aug.3, 1955.

ON THE LYMPHATIC SYSTEM OF THE NEWBORN RAT (MUS NORVEGICUS ALBINUS). G. M. Higgins. Anat. Record, vol.30, pp.243-258, 4 figs., July 25, 1925.

DUPLICATION OF THE SEMINAL VESICLES IN MICE OF THE C STRAIN. Charles W. Hooker, Leonell C. Strong. Anat. Record, Phila., vol.81, no.3, pp. 333-349, 4 figs., Nov.25, 1941.

ACCESSORY PARATHYROIDS IN THE RAT. Margaret M. Hoskins, S. B. Chandler. Anat. Record, vol.30, pp.95-98, 1 fig., May 25, 1925.

SOME VARIATIONS IN THE SUPERFICIAL MUSCLES OF THE BACK OF THE ALBINO RAT (RATTUS NORVEGICUS). P. V. Hoyer, R. M. Lane. Jour. Mam., vol.31, no.3, pp.288-289, fig.1, Aug.21, 1950.

STUDIES ON THE PINEAL BODY. I. ON THE POSTNATAL GROWTH OF THE PINEAL BODY OF THE ALBINO RAT WITH OBSERVATIONS ON ITS HISTOLOGY. Yoshimate Izawa. Jour. Comp. Neur., vol.39, pp.1-18, 2 charts, 5 figs., Aug.15, 1925.

THE HISTOGENESIS OF THE CLAVICLE IN THE ALBINO RAT. Myra L. Johnson, Madeleine P. Grant. Anat. Record, vol. 54, no.3, pp.375-383, pls.2, Nov.25, 1932.

THE DEVELOPMENT OF THE GASTRO-INTESTINAL TRACT OF THE RAT. II. HOMOTRANSPLANTATION OF THE EMBRYONIC AND ADULT GASTRO-INTESTINAL TRACT MUCOSA OF THE RAT TO THE ANTERIOR CHAMBER OF THE EYE. Adrian Kammeraad. Jour. Exper. Zool., Phila., vol.91, no.1, pp.45-63, fig.1, pls.2, Oct.5, 1942.

A PRELIMINARY NOTE ON THE SHORT-TAIL IN LONG-EVANS RATS. K. Kano, A. Awa, A. Sato. Misc. Repts. Yamashina's Inst. Ornithol. and Zool., 10: 22-23, (408-409, June 1957. (In Japanese, with English summary.)

(THE MODIFICATIONS OF LENGTH OF TAIL IN COMPARISON WITH LENGTH OF BODY IN THE NORWEGIAN RAT.) Les modifications de la longueur de la queue en comparaison de la longueur du corps chez le rat Norvegien. C. E. Keeler. Bull. Soc. Zool. France, Paris, vol.72, no.1, pp.31-35, 1947.

THE DEVELOPMENT OF THE PERIOVARIAL SAC IN THE WHITE RAT. Margaret P. Kellogg. Anat. Record, Phila., vol.79, no.4, pp.465-473, Apr.25, 1941.

ANOMALIES IN THE SMALL INTESTINE AND CECUM OF INBRED STRAINS OF MICE. Margaret A. Kelsall. Anat. Record, Phila., vol.95, no.1, pp.1-5, pl.1, May, 1946.

A QUANTITATIVE STUDY OF THE HEMOPOIETIC ORGANS OF YOUNG ALBINO RATS. James E. Kindred. Amer. Jour. Anat., Phila., vol.67, no.1, pp.99-149, pls.2, July 15, 1940; vol.71, no.2, pp.207-243, Sept.15, 1942.

BIRTH WEIGHT IN THE GRAY NORWAY RAT AND THE FACTORS THAT INFLUENCE IT. H. D. King. Anat. Record, vol.63, no.4, pp.335-354, Nov.25, 1935.

LIFE PROCESSES AND SIZE OF THE BODY AND ORGANS OF THE GRAY NORWAY RAT DURING TEN GENERATIONS IN CAPTIVITY. H. D. King, H. H. Donaldson. Amer. Anat. Mem., vol.14, pp.1-106, 1929.

THE NUMBER AND DISTRIBUTION OF MACROPHAGES AND FIBROBLASTS IN KIDNEYS OF ALBINO RATS WITH EMPHASIS ON TWENTY-FIVE DAY MALES. Hadley Kirkman. Amer. Jour. Anat., Phila., vol.73, no.3, pp.451-482, figs.1-5, Nov., 1943.

(ON THE PRESENCE OF TASTE BUDS IN THE DUCTUS NASOPALATINUS OF THE RAT.) Ueber das Vorkommen von Geschmacksknospen im Ductus nasopalatinus der Ratte. W. Kolmer. Anat. Anzeiger, vol. 63, pp.248-251, 1 fig., July 23, 1927.

THE PRODUCTION OF DECIDUOMATA IN THE PREGNANT LACTATING RAT. Robert H. Krehbiel. Anat. Record, Phila., vol.81, no.1, pp.67-77, 4 figs., Sept.25, 1941.

THE OVARY OF THE ADULT RAT. Charles E. Lane. Anat. Record, Phila., vol.78, no.1, pp.31-41, Sept.25, 1940.

CHANGES IN THE FIBRILLAR TISSUE OF THE ANTERIOR PITUITARY OF THE RAT ASSOCIATED WITH ADVANCING AGE. Winifred Lansing, J. M. Wolfe. Anat. Record, Phila., vol.83, no.3, pp.355-365, pls.2, July 25, 1942.

(ON SEXUAL DIMORPHISM IN SOME MURINE SPECIES IN THE EIFEL MOUNTAIN REGION.) Uber deen Geschlechtsdimorphismus einiger Muridenarten in der Voreifel. Ernst von Lehmann. Saeugetierk, Mitteil., Stuttgart, 4 (1): 10-13, Jan.1, 1956.

ABNORMALITIES OF THE MAMMAE IN THE HOUSE MOUSE. C. C. Little, Helen McDonald. Jour. Heredity, Washington, vol.36, no.9, pp.285-288, fig.13, Sept., 1945.

THE MITOCHONDRIA AND COLLOID IN THE THYROID GLAND OF THE ADULT ALBINO RAT. W. C. Ma. Amer. Jour. Anat., vol.35, pp.199-216, 2 pls., May 15, 1925.

THE VASCULAR SYSTEM IN THE SPLEEN OF RAT AND MOUSE. W. C. Ma. Peking Nat. Hist. Bull., vol.12, pt.2, pp.71-77, pls.6, Dec., 1937.

THE RELATION OF PARITY, AGE AND BODY WEIGHT TO THE NUMBER OF CORPORA LUTEA IN MICE. E. C. MacDowell, Ezra Allen, C. G. MacDowell. Anat. Record, vol.41, pp.267-272, Feb.25, 1929.

THE NUMBER OF CORPORA LUTEA IN SUCCESSIVE MOUSE PREGNANCIES. E. C. MacDowell, E. M. Lord. Anat. Record, vol.31, pp.131-142, 4 figs., Oct., 25, 1925.

ON THE NUMBER OF CORPORA LUTEA PRODUCED AT SUCCESSIVE PREGNANCIES BY NORMAL AND HEAVILY ALCOHOLIZED MICE. E. C. MacDowell, E. M. Lord. Anat. Record, vol.29, p.141, Dec.25, 1924.

TWO TYPES OF EPITHELIUM OF THE FINEST BRONCHIOLES OF THE ALBINO MOUSE AS REVEALED BY SUPRAVITAL SILVERIZATION. Charles C. Macklin. Canadian Jour. Research, Ottawa, sect.D, vol.27, no.2, pp.50-58, figs.14, pls.2, Apr., 1949.

THE MOUSE ADRENAL. I. DEVELOPMENT, DEGENERATION AND REGENERATION OF THE X-ZONE. M. K. McPhail, H. C. Read. Anat. Record, Phila., vol. 84, no.1, pp.51-73, pls.3, Sept.25, 1942.

GENETIC AND HORMONAL DETERMINATION OF PROSTATE DEVELOPMENT IN THE FEMALE RAT. John Joseph Mahoney. Jour. Exper. Zool., Phila., vol.90, no.3, pp.413-439, figs.7, pl.1, Aug.5, 1942.

FOUR CASES OF POSTERIOR REDUPLICATION IN THE ALBINO NORWAY RAT. Phillip H. Mann. Jour. Tennessee Acad. Sci., vol.29, no.1, pp.9-11, Jan., 1954.

CORRELATION OF OVARIAN HISTOLOGY AND INTERSEXUALITY OF THE GENITAL APPARATUS, WITH SPECIAL REFERENCE TO APL-TREATED INFANTILE RATS. Lore Marx, J. T. Bradbury. Anat. Record, Phila., vol.78, no.1, pp.79-103, 2 pls., Sept.25, 1940.

WEIGHTS OF BROWN AND BLACK RATS. Colin Matheson. Naturalist, London, no. 980, pp.251-253, illus., Sept., 1938. (Maximum weight of brown rat male, 2 lbs.; average wgt. male, 9-10 oz.; maximum weight of black rat male, 1 lb. 8 oz.; average wgt. male, 6-7 oz.)

ON AN INTERSEXUAL WILD BROWN RAT, RATTUS NORVEGICUS (ERXLEBEN). L. Harrison Matthews. Proc. Zool. Soc. Lond., vol.117, pt.1, pp.44-48, figs.2, May, 1947.

THE TIME AND ORDER OF APPEARANCE OF OSSIFICATION CENTERS IN MUS MUSCULUS. T. H. Meng. Peking Nat. Hist. Bull., vol.9, pt.1, pp.7-14, Sept., 1934.

A MODEL OF THE NASAL CHAMBER OF A WHITE MOUSE AT BIRTH. Ida Merrill, E. Schoonover. Jour. Ent. and Zool. (Pomona Coll., Calif.,), vol.15, pp.1-2, illus., Mar., 1923.

(MORPHOLOGY OF THE SYMPATHICUS IN THE PELVIS OF THE MOUSE.) Morphologie des Sympathicus im Becken der Maus. J. Mestern. Zeitschr. f. Anat. u. Entwicklungs., vol.96, pp.92-97, figs. 2, 1931.

DEVELOPMENT OF THE MOUSE ADRENAL. E. Howard Miller. Science, n.s., vol.69, pp.406-407, Apr.12, 1929.

ON THE INTROITUS VAGINAE OF CERTAIN MURIDAE. Gerrit S. Miller, Jr. Proc. Boston Soc., Nat. Hist., vol.26, pp.459-468, pl.5, Feb., 1895.

THE HISTOLOGY OF THE PREPUTIAL GLAND OF THE RAT. William Montagna, Charles R. Noback. Anat. Record, Phila., vol.96, no.1, pp.41-54, figs.6, Sept., 1946.

RAT-PROSTATE CYTOLOGY AS A TESTIS-HORMONE INDICATOR AND THE PREVENTION OF CASTRATION CHANGES BY TESTIS-EXTRACT INJECTIONS. C. R. Moore, W. Hughes, T. F. Gallagher. Amer. Jour. Anat., vol.45, pp.71-108, 27 figs., 4 pls., Jan.15, 1930.

RAT SEMINAL-VESICLE CYTOLOGY AS A TESTIS-HORMONE INDICATOR AND THE PREVENTION OF CASTRATION CHANGES BY TESTIS-EXTRACT INJECTIONS. C. R. Moore, W. Hughes, T. F. Gallagher. Amer. Jour. Anat., vol.45, pp.109-136, 21 figs., 2 pls., Jan.15, 1930.

(MORPHOLOGICAL DESCRIPTION OF FOUR POPULATIONS OF FOREST MICE IN GEORGIA.) Morfologicheskoe opisanie chetirekh populyatsii lesnoi mishi v gruzii. (Silvimus.) I. E. Morgilevskaya. Trudi Inst. Zool. Akad. Nauk Gruzinskoi SSR, vol.13, pp.71-79, 1954.

COMPARATIVE HISTOLOGICAL STUDY OF THE ADRENAL CORTEX OF THE WILD AND DOMESTICATED NORWAY RAT. H. D. Mosier. Endocrinology, Springfield, 60 (4): 460-469, Apr., 1957.

POLYDACTYLISM IN MICE. Joseph M. Murray. Science, n.s., vol.75, no.1942, p.312, Mar.18, 1932.

THE WEIGHT OF RATS. A. E. Peck. Naturalist, London, no.977, p.181, June, 1938.

THE REACTIVITY OF THE PROSTATE GLAND OF THE FEMALE RAT IN RELATION TO AGE. Dorothy Price. Amer. Jour. Anat., Phila., vol.75, no.2, pp.207-231, fig.1, pl.1, Sept., 1944.

(DIRECT DEPENDENCE OF LENGTH OF TAIL ON TEMPERATURE IN THE RATS. MUS (EPIMYS) DECUMANUS PALL. AND M. (E.) RATTUS, L.) Direkte Temperaturabhaengigkeit der Schwanzlaenge bei Ratten, Mus (epimys) decumanus Pall. und M. (E.) rattus, L. H. Przibram. Arch. fuer Mikr. Anatomie und Entwicklungsmechanik, vol.104, pp.434-496, 6 figs., Mar.13, 1925.

(THE GROWTH OF RELATIVE TAIL LENGTH AND ITS TEMPERATURE QUOTIENT IN RATS.) Das Anwachsen der relativen Schwanzlaenge und dessen Temperaturquotient bei den Ratten. H. Przibram. Arch. fuer Mikr. Anatomie und Entwicklungsmechanik, vol.104, pp.611-648, 1 fig., Mar.13, 1925.

(TAIL LENGTH IN RATS AS FACULTATIVE SEX CHARACTER.) Die Schwanzlaenge bei Ratten, als fakultatives Geschlechtsmerkmal. H. Przibram. Arch. fuer Mikr. Anatomie und Entwicklungsmechanik, vol.104, pp.497-547, Mar.13, 1925.

(THE TAIL LENGTH OF SUCCESSIVE GENERATIONS OF RATS MODIFIED BY TEMPERATURE.) Die Schwanzlaenge der Nachkommen temperaturmodifizierter Ratten. H. Przibram. Arch. fuer Mikr. Anatomie und Entwicklungsmechanik, vol. 104, pp.548-610, 1 fig., Mar.13, 1925.

DEVELOPMENTAL ABNORMALITIES AND SPONTANEOUS DISEASES FOUND IN RATS OF THE MUTANT STRAIN, STUB. Herbert L. Ratcliffe, Helen Dean King. Anat. Record, Phila., vol.81, no.3, pp.283-305, 2 pls., Nov.25, 1941.

INCOMPLETE POSTERIOR DUPLICATION OF THE BODY (DIPYGUS) IN AN ALBINO RAT. Herbert L. Ratcliffe, Helen Dean King. Anat. Record, Phila., vol.77, no.1, pp.49-56, May 25, 1940.

THE MAMMARY GLAND DEVELOPMENT IN MALE MICE AT NINE WEEKS OF AGE. Flavia L. Richardson, Arthur M. Cloudman. Anat. Record, Phila., vol.97, no.2, pp.223-237, pls.2, Feb., 1947.

COMPARISON OF INTESTINAL LENGTHS AND PEYER'S PATCHES IN WILD AND DOMESTIC NORWAY AND WILD ALEXANDRINE RATS. Curt P. Richter, Charles E. Hall. Proc. Soc. Exper. Biol. and Med., Utica, vol.66, pp.561-566, figs.4, 1948.

ANATOMICAL COMPARISON BETWEEN THE ADRENAL GLANDS OF WILD NORWAY, WILD ALEXANDRINE AND DOMESTIC NORWAY RATS. Philip V. Rogers, Curt P. Richter. Endocrinology, Los Angeles, vol.42, no.1, pp.46-55, figs.3, Jan., 1948.

THE DEVELOPMENT OF THE PHARYNX AND THE PHARYNGEAL DERIVATIVES IN THE WHITE RAT (MUS NORVEGICUS ALBINUS). W. M. Rogers. Amer. Jour. Anat., vol.44, pp.283-317, 4 figs., 6 pls., 1929.

THE DEVELOPMENT AND MORPHOLOGY OF THE GONADS OF THE MOUSE. IV. THE POST-NATAL GROWTH OF THE TESTIS. I. W. Rowlands, F. W. Rogers Brambell. Proc. Roy. Soc. Lond., ser.B, vol.112, no.B776, pp.200-214, Jan.2, 1933.

THE SENESCENCE OF THE BROWN RAT (RATTUS NORVEGICUS BERK.) IN THE LIGHT OF CRANIOMETRY. Wlodzimierz Serafinski. Acta Theriologica, Inst. Zool. Polska Akad. Nauk, Warsaw, vol.1, no.1, pp.1-14, Jan.20, 1955. (In Polish, with Russian and English summaries.)

THE HISTOGENSIS OF THE ARGENTAFFIN CELLS IN THE STOMACH AND DUODENUM OF THE RAT. Wynne Sharples. Anat. Record, Phila., vol.91, no.2, pp.107-114, pls.2, Feb., 1945.

AGE CHANGES OF BONES AND JOINTS IN VARIOUS STRAINS OF MICE. Martin Silberberg, Ruth Silberberg. Amer. Jour. Anat., Phila., vol.68, no.1, pp.69-95, 3 pls., Jan.15, 1941.

THE INFLUENCE OF SEX AND BREEDING ON SKELETAL AGEING OF MICE. Martin Silberberg, Ruth Silberberg. Anat. Record, Phila., vol.91, no.2, pp.89-101, pls.2, Feb., 1945.

THE BLOOD OF NORMAL MICE. J. P. Simonds. Anat. Record, vol.30, pp.99-106, 1 fig., May 25, 1925.

MUSCLE FIBER OF THE RAT DIAPHRAGM. C. Sitaramayya, M. M. Bluhm. Nature, London, vol.166, no.4233, p.1030, Dec.16, 1950.

QUANTITATIVE ASPECTS OF GROWTH AND OOCYTE PRODUCTION IN THE EARLY PREPUBERTAL RAT OVARY. Daniel W. Slater, Ernst J. Dornfeld. Amer. Jour. Anat., Phila., vol.76, no.2, pp.253-275, figs.1-3, pls.1-2, Mar., 1945.

STUDIES ON THE THYMUS OF THE MAMMAL. I. THE DISTRIBUTION OF ARGYROPHIL FIBERS FROM BIRTH THROUGH OLD AGE IN THE THYMUS OF THE MOUSE. Christianna Smith, Louise M. Ireland. Anat. Record, Phila., vol.79, no.2, suppl. no.1, pp.133-153, pls.4, Feb., 1941.

MALFORMED HIND FOOT OF THE COMMON HOUSE MOUSE (MUS MUSCULUS). J. Dewey Soper. Jour. Mam., vol.2, no.4, p.237, Nov., 1921.

THE ORDER AND TIME OF APPEARANCE OF CENTERS OF OSSIFICATION IN THE FORE AND HIND LIMBS OF THE ALBINO RAT, WITH SPECIAL REFERENCE TO

THE POSSIBLE INFLUENCE OF THE SEX FACTOR. Charles Spark, Alden B. Dawson. Amer. Jour. Anat., vol.41, pp. 411-445, illus., July 15, 1928.

ORGAN: BODY WEIGHT, PROTEIN: ORGAN AND FAT: ORGAN RATIOS IN LARGE ALBINO RATS. Frederick Sperling. Growth, vol.17, no.1, pp.1-6, Mar., 1953.

THE DISCUSSION OF THE RAT. Edwin Chapin Starks, Richard D. Cutter. Stanford Univ., Calif., Stanford Univ. Press; London, H. Milford, Oxford Univ. Press, 45 pp., 1931.

SEX DIFFERENCES IN PIGMENT CONTENT OF HARDERIAN GLANDS OF MICE. Leonell C. Strong. Proc. Soc. Exper. Biol. and Med., Utica, vol.50, no.1, pp. 123-125, May, 1942.

THE ORDER, TIME, AND RATE OF OSSIFICATION OF THE ALBINO RAT (MUS NORVEGICUS ALBINUS) SKELETON. R. M. Strong. Amer. Jour. Anat., vol.36, pp.313-343, 1 fig., 5 pls., Nov.15, 1925.

A STATISTICAL STUDY ON FUNDAMENTAL SPECIFIC DIFFERENCES IN SKULL CHARACTERS BETWEEN THE ROOF RAT AND THE NORWAY RAT. Ryo Tanaka. Quarterly Jour. Taiwan Mus., Taipei, vol. 5, no.1, pp.57-70, Mar., 1952.

THE DEVELOPMENT OF THE URINOGENITAL SYSTEM OF THE ALBINO RAT. I. THE KIDNEY AND ITS DUCTS. Theodore W. Torrey. Amer. Jour. Anat., Phila., vol.72, no.1, pp.113-147, pls.3, Jan., 1943.

THE DEVELOPMENT OF THE URINOGENITAL SYSTEM OF THE ALBINO RAT. II. THE GONADS. Theodore W. Torrey. Amer. Jour. Anat., Phila., vol.76, no.3, pp.375-397, pls.2, May, 1945.

GROSS ANATOMY OF THE ORBITAL GLANDS IN THE ALBINO RAT. John H. Venable, Allan L. Grafflin. Jour. Mam., vol.21, no.1, pp.66-71, figs.4, Feb.14, 1940.

THE ADRENAL LIPIDS OF MICE WITH HIGH AND LOW MAMMARY GLAND TUMOR INDICES. Emilia M. Vicari. Anat. Record, Phila., vol.86, no.4, pp. 523-543, figs.2, Aug., 1943.

ON THE POSTNATAL GROWTH IN THE AREA OF THE OPTIC NERVE IN ALBINO AND IN GRAY NORWAY RATS. Chia Chi Wang. Jour. Comparative Neurology, vol.43, no.2, pp.201-220, tables 10, June, 1927.

CHANGES IN THE SKELETON DURING GESTATION AND LACTATION IN THE RAT. G. M. Warnock, J. Duckworth. Biochemical Jour., Cambridge, vol.38, no.3, pp.220-224, Oct., 1944.

A STUDY OF THE FAT ORGAN IN THE WHITE MOUSE. En-Lin Wei. Peking Nat. Hist. Bull., vol.7, pt.2, pp.93-97, pls.1-4, Dec., 1932.

VARIATIONS IN SIZE OF CORPORA LUTEA IN THE ALBINO RAT UNDER NORMAL AND EXPERIMENTAL CONDITIONS. Charles K. Weichert. Anat. Record, Phila., vol.83, no.3, pp.321-324, fig.1, July 25, 1942.

THE REGENERATION OF THE GUSTATORY APPARATUS IN THE RAT. Beatrice Whiteside. Jour. Comp. Neur., vol.40, pp.33-46, 5 figs., Feb.15, 1926.

NORMAL AND EXPERIMENTAL MAMMARY INVOLUTION IN THE MOUSE AS RELATED TO THE INCEPTION AND CESSATION OF LACTATION. W. Lane Williams. Amer. Jour. Anat., Phila., vol. 71, no.1, pp.1-41, pls.5, July 15, 1942.

CHANGES IN THE CONNECTIVE TISSUE OF THE UTERUS AND VAGINA OF THE RAT ASSOCIATED WITH ADVANCING AGE. J. M. Wolfe, Others. Science, Lancaster, n.s., vol.91, no.2372, pp.577-578, June 14, 1940.

THE EFFECTS OF ADVANCING AGE ON THE STRUCTURE OF THE ANTERIOR HYPOPHYSES AND OVARIES OF FEMALE RATS. J. M. Wolfe. Amer. Jour. Anat., Phila., vol.72, no.3, pp.361-383, figs.2, May, 1943.

Apparatus

DEVICE FOR HOLDING LIVE WILD RATS. John T. Emlen, Jr. Jour. Wildlife Mgt., Menasha, vol.8, no.3, pp.264-265, fig.1, July, 1944.

A MULTIPLE TYPE RAT AND MOUSE HOLDER. Arnold B. Erickson. Jour. Wildlife Mgt., 11 (4): 351, Oct., 1947.

DEVICE FOR MEASURING BLOOD PRESSURE IN THE UNANESTHETIZED RAT. Gordon L. Farrell, Evelyn Anderson. Proc. Soc. Exp. Biol. Med., Utica, vol.72, no.2, pp.461-464, Nov., 1949.

APPARATUS FOR RECORDING CYCLICAL ACTIVITY IN THE RAT. Edmond J. Farris. Anat. Record, Phila., vol.81, no. 3, pp.357-362, 1 pl., Nov.25, 1941.

(A NATIVE TRAP FOR RATS LIVING IN THE FIELDS OF THE MIINAHASA.) Een inlandsche val voor in het veld levende ratten in de Miinahasa. Jhr. W. C. van Heurn. Landbouw, Buitenzorg, vol.6, no. 2, pp.219-221, 1 fig., Aug., 1930.

TATTOO PUNCH FOR NUMBERING RATS. Clyde E. Keeler. Science, 92 (2383): 205-206, Aug.30, 1940.

A MODIFIED RABBIT BOX TRAP FOR USE IN CATCHING LIVE WILD RATS FOR LABORATORY AND FIELD STUDIES. Curt P. Richter, John T. Emlen, Jr. Public Health Repts., vol.60, no.44, pp.1303-1308, figs.3, Nov.2, 1945.

AN ULTRA-MODERN RAT TRAP. Robert L. Roudabush. Ward's Nat. Sci. Bull., Rochester, vol.16, no.3, pp.40-41, Dec., 1942.

AN APPARATUS FOR REMOVING TROPICAL RAT MITES FROM LARGE QUANTITIES OF BEDDING MATERIALS. J. Allen Scott. Jour. Parasitol., Lancaster, vol.34, no.2, pp.132-133, Apr., 1948.

EFFICIENT HANDLER FOR SMALL MAMMALS. Lyell J. Thomas. Science, 101 (2628): 496, May 11, 1945. A wire-mesh cone, stopper, and plunger that has proved satisfactory in handling rats.

Asia

(THE MURINES OF PALESTINE AND SYRIA.) Die Muriden von Palaestina und Syrien. Bathscheba Aharoni. Zeitschr. f. Saeugetierkunde, Berlin, vol.7, nos.1-6, pp.166-240, fig.1, pl.19, Dec.15, 1932.

MURID RODENTS FROM THE ASIATIC EXPEDITIONS. Glover M. Allen. Amer. Mus. Nov., no.270, pp.1-12, May 31, 1927.

RATS (GENUS RATTUS) FROM THE ASIATIC EXPEDITIONS. Glover M. Allen. Amer. Mus. Novit., no.217, pp.1-16, June 16, 1926.

A NEW SUBSPECIES OF MICROMYS MINUTUS PALL. FROM CENTRAL CHINA. (MICROMYS MINUTUS BEREZOWSKII.) A. I. Argiropulo. Comptes Rendus Acad. Sci. URSS., A., no.10, pp.253-255, figs.4, 1929.

ON THE MOUSE-LIKE RODENTS (FAMILY MURIDAE) OF THE COMMANDER ISLANDS. I. I. Barabash-Nikiforov. Zoologicheskii Zhurnal, 22: 53-54, 1943.

THE MAMMALIAN FAUNA OF CHINA. PART I. MURINAE. J. L. Bonhote. Proc. Zool. Soc. London, 1905, vol.2, pp.384-397, pp.2-15, Apr.5, 1906.

A NOTE ON MALAYSIAN GUNOMYS. F. N. Chasen. Bull. Raffles Mus., no.12, pp.135-136, May, 1936.

ON INSULAR RATTUS RATTUS FROM THE NORTH-WEST COAST OF THE MALAY PENINSULA. F. N. Chasen. Bull. Raffles Mus., Singapore, Straits Settlements, no.13, pp.81-93, Aug., 1937.

ON THE FORMS OF RATTUS RATTUS OCCURRING ON THE MAINLAND OF THE MALAY PENINSULA. F. N. Chasen. Bull. Raffles Mus., Singapore, Straits Settlements, no.8, pp.5-24, Dec., 1933.

ON "RATTUS" RATS OF THE COASTS AND ISLANDS OF MALACCA STRAITS. F. N. Chasen. Bull. Raffles Mus., Singapore, Straits Settlements, no.5, pp.76-79, Aug., 1931.

FIELD RATS IN THE DECCAN IN 1879. J. Davidson. Jour. Bombay Nat. Hist. Soc., vol.26, pp.1041-1042, Jan.31, 1920.

FURTHER NOTES ON TWO LITTLE-KNOWN INDIAN MURINE GENERA, AND PRELIMINARY DIAGNOSIS OF A NEW SPECIES OF RATTUS (SUBGENUS CREMNOMYS) FROM THE EASTERN GHATS. J. R. Ellerman. Ann. and Mag. Nat. Hist., Lond., ser.11, vol.13, no.99, pp.204-208, Mar., 1946 (Jan.8, 1947).

THE CHINESE HOUSE-MOUSE AND ITS TAME VARIETIES. A COMPARATIVE STUDY WITH MUS MUSCULUS. A. B. Droogleever Fortuyn. Peking Soc. Nat. Hist. Bull., vol.3, no.4, pp.59-64, June, 1929.

A RECORD OF RATTUS N. OTOMOI FROM MT. MYOKO IN HOKURIKU. E. Fujiwara. Trans. Mamm. Soc. Japan, no.8, pp.67-68, Feb., 1954. (In Japanese, with English summary.)

A NEW BANDICOOT FROM IRAN. (NESOKIA LEGENDREI.) George G. Goodwin. Amer. Mus. Novitates, New York, no.1048, p.1, Nov.22, 1939.

THE DOMESTIC RATS OF MALAYA. J. L. Harrison. Med. Jour. Malaya, vol.4, no. 2, pp.96-105, figs.1-4, Dec., 1949.

HABITAT OF SOME MALAYAN RATS. J. L. Harrison. Proc. Zool. Soc. Lond., 128 (1): 1-21, Feb.14, 1957.

A KEY TO THE RATS OF MALAYA. J. L. Harrison. Malayan Nature Jour., vol.3, no.3, pp.130-141, 1948.

RECORDS OF BANDICOOT RATS (BANDICOTA, RODENTIA, MURIDAE) NEW TO THE FAUNA OF MALAYA AND THAILAND. J. L. Harrison. Bull. Raffles Mus., 27: 27-31, Oct., 1956.

BIOLOGY OF THE VOLES (NESOKIA) OF TURKESTAN AND THEIR POSSIBLE UTILIZATION IN THE FUR TRADE. V. G. Heptner. Zool. Zhurn. Moscow, vol.11, no.2, pp.79-88, map, 1932. (In Russian.)

(A NEW VOLE (G. NESOKIA GRAY 1842) FROM RUSSIAN TURKESTAN.) Eine neue Wuehlratte (G. Nesokia Gray 1842; Mammalia, Muridae) aus russisch-Turkestan. W. G. Heptner. Zool. Anzeiger, vol.76, nos.11-12, pp.257-260, Jan.5, 1928.

(SOME INFORMATION CONCERNING THE TURKESTAN VOLES (NESOKIA GRAY 1842).) Einige Angaben ueber die Turkestanschen Wuehlratten (Nesokia Gray 1842. Mammalia, Muridae). W. G. Heptner. Archiv. f. Naturgesch., vol.92, heft 7, pp.112-134, 4 figs., 1928.

REPORT ON THE HOUSE RATS OF INDIA, BURMA, AND CEYLON. Martin A. C. Hinton. Jour. Bombay Nat. Hist. Soc., vol.26, pp.59-88, Dec.20, 1918; pp.384-416, May 20, 1919.

(Review by G. S. Miller, Jr. of) A REPORT ON THE HOUSE RATS OF INDIA. Martin A. C. Hinton. Jour. Mam., vol.1, no.3, pp.146-147, May, 1920.

THE HOUSE RATS OF NEPAL. Martin A. C. Hinton. Jour. Bombay Nat. Hist. Soc., vol.28, pp.1056-1066, Dec.20, 1922.

PRELIMINARY SURVEYS ON THE VERTICAL DISTRIBUTION OF MURINE MAMMALS IN MT. HIKO, FUKUOKA PREFECTURE. Yoshi Kuni Hiraiwa, Teruaki Uchida Satoru Minami, Seigo Sumikawa, Hiroichi Yoshida. Sci. Bull. Faculty Agric. Kyushu Univ., 16 (1): 165-170, Mar., 1957. (In Japanese, with English summary.)

TWO NEW CHINESE RATS. A. Brazier Howell. Proc. Biol. Soc. Wash., vol.40, pp.43-46, Mar.5, 1927.

THREE NEW RODENTS OF THE GENERA MICROMYS AND APODEMUS FROM KOREA. (MICROMYS MINUTUS HERTIGI, APODEMUS AGRARIUS PALLESCENS, A. A.

CHEJUENSIS.) David H. Johnson, J. Knox Jones, Jr. Proc. Biol. Soc. Wash., vol.68, pp.167-174, Dec.31, 1955.

A RECORD OF APODEMUS SPECIOSUS SPECIOSUS FROM MT. YARIGATAKE, JAPAN ALPS. T. Kimura. Trans. Mamm. Soc. Japan, no.8, p.67, Feb., 1954. (In Japanese, with English summary.)

NEW AND OTHER WHITE-TOOTHED RATS FROM SIAM. C. Boden Kloss. Jour. Nat. Hist. Soc. Siam, vol.3, no.2, pp.79-82, Feb.25, 1919.

A NEW SUB-SPECIES OF MALAYSIAN RAT. (RATTUS CANUS MALAISIA.) C. Boden Kloss. Bull. Raffles Mus., Singapore, Straits Settlements, no.5, pp.105-107, Aug., 1931.

ON A NEW MURINE GENUS AND SPECIES FROM SIAM. C. Boden Kloss. Jour. Nat. Hist. Soc. Siam, vol.2, pp.279-281, Dec., 1917. (See vol.III, no.II, 1918 for corrections.)

ON TWO NEW RATS FROM THE INNER GULF OF SIAM. C. Boden Kloss. Jour. Nat. Hist. Soc. Siam, vol.1, no.4, pp.221-224, Dec., 1915.

TWO NEW LEGGADA MICE FROM SIAM. (KEY TO INDOCHINESE GENERA OF MUS-LIKE RODENTS. NEW SPECIES AND SUB-SPECIES: LEGGADA PAHARI GAIRDNERI AND L. RAHENGIS, BOTH FROM ME TAW, WESTERN SIAM.) C. Boden Kloss. Jour. Nat. Hist. Soc. Siam, vol.4, pp.59-63, Mar., 1921.

DESCRIPTIONS OF THREE NEW FORMS OF RATTUS FROM HOKKAIDO AND SOUTH CHINA. Nagamichi Kuroda. Jour. Mam., Soc. Japan, vol.1,no.1, pp.1-4, 1952.

A NEW FORM OF MICROMYS FROM HONDE, JAPAN. Nagamichi Kuroda. Jour. Mam., vol.14, no.3, pp.243-244, Aug., 1933.

A NEW FORM OF MUS FROM HOKKAIDO. Nagamichi Kuroda. Jour. Mam., vol.9, no.2, p.147, May, 1928.

ON A SPECIMEN OF RARE RATTUS TANEZUMI OBTAINED IN AOMORI PREFECTURE. Nagamichi Kuroda. Annot. Zool. Japonenses, Tokyo, vol.24, no.4, pp.234-237, illus., Dec., 1951.

POSITIVE PRESENCE OF MICROMYS IN HONSHU. Nagamichi Kuroda. Amoeba, vol.3, no.3, pp.15-21, figs.1-6, pl.2, Dec.20, 1931.

TWO NEW MURINE RODENTS FROM KURILE ISLANDS, JAPAN. Nagamichi Kuroda. Jour. Mam., vol.5, no.2, pp.118-119, May, 1924.

RODENTS OF THE SEMIPALATINSK DISTRICT OF KAZAKSTAN. B. A. Kuznetsov. Bull. Soc. Nat. Moscou, Sect. Biol., vol.41, nos.1-2, pp.60-120, 1932. (In Russian.)

(A RECTIFICATION: THE BROWN RAT, RATTUS NORVEGICUS BERKENHAUT INCORRECTLY INDICATED FOR BENI OUNIF (SOUTHERN ORANAIS).) Une rectification: Le surmulot, Rattus norvegicus Berkenhaut a été signalé à tort à Beni Ounif (sud Oranais). P. Laurent. Bull. Soc. Zool. France, Paris, vol.62, pp.311-313, June, 1937.

TWO NEW MURINE RODENTS FROM BALTISTAN. Gerrit S. Miller, Jr. Proc. Biol. Soc. Wash., vol.26, pp.197-198, Oct.23, 1913.

TWO NEW MURINE RODENTS FROM EASTERN ASIA. Gerrit S. Miller, Jr. Proc. Biol. Soc. Wash., vol.27, pp.89-92, May 11, 1914.

TWO NEW MURINE RODENTS FROM TURKESTAN. Gerrit S. Miller, Jr. Proc. Biol. Soc. Wash., vol.25, pp.59-60, Apr.13, 1912.

(PRESENT GEOGRAPHICAL DISTRIBUTION OF RATTUS RATTUS LINN. 1758 AND RATTUS NORVEGICUS BERKENHOUT 1769 IN IRAN.) Repartition geographique actuelle de Rattus rattus Linne, 1758 et de Rattus norvegicus Berkenhout, 1769 en Iran. Xavier Misone. Bull. Inst. Roy. Sci. Nat. Belgique, 32 (49): 1-11, Sept., 1956.

THE IDENTITY OF ACOMYS MEGALOTIS (LICHTENSTEIN), DESCRIBED FROM ARABIA. T. C. S. Morrison-Scott. Ann. Mag. Nat. Hist. Lond., ser.11, vol.3, pp. 238-240, Feb., 1939.

(A NEW NESOKIA SPECIES FROM PALESTINE.) Eine neue Nesokia-Species aus Palaestina. Alfred Nehring. Sitz.-Ber. Gesell. Naturf. Freunde Berlin, Jahrg.1898, no.1, p.1, Jan.18, 1898.

(THE MURINES OF ASIA MINOR.) Die Muriden von Kleinasien. Gabriele Neuhaeuser. Zeitschr. f. Saeugetierkunde, vol.11, no.2, pp.161-236, Dec.15, 1936.

NOTE ON A COLLECTION OF MICE MADE BY CAPT. C. E. BEAVAN AT MAUBHOUM IN 1865. William Peters. Proc. Zool. Soc. Lond., pp.558-559, 1866.

THE INDIGENOUS RATS (GENUS RATTUS) OF CEYLON. W. W. A. Phillips. Spolia Zeylanica, Ceylon, vol.13, pt.3, pp.295-305, Mar.31, 1926.

CONTRIBUTIONS TO THE FAUNA OF MANIPUR STATE, ASSAM. PART III. MAMMALS, WITH SPECIAL REFERENCE TO THE FAMILY MURIDAE (ORDER RODENTIA). M. L. Roonwal. Records Indian Mus., Calcutta, vol.47, pt.1, pp.1-64, pls.1-9, Mar., 1949.

THREE NEW MURIDAE (MAMMALIA: RODENTIA) FROM ASSAM AND THE KABAW VALLEY, UPPER BURMA. M. L. Roonwal. Proc. Nat. Inst. Sci. India, Delhi, vol.14, no.9, pp.385-387, Nov.-Dec., 1948.

COMMUNITY ECOLOGY ON THE RAT PLAGUE IN THE COASTAL REGION OF UWAJIMA, SOUTH-WEST OF SHIKOKU. Ryo Tanaka. Bull. Kochi Women's Coll., Kochi City, vol.4, no.1, pp.23-32, illus., Dec., 1955.

DESCRIPTION OF A NEW SPECIES OF MUS FROM SOUTHERN INDIA. Oldfield Thomas. Ann. and Mag. Nat. Hist. (5), vol.7, no.37, p.24, Jan., 1881.

NEW ASIATIC MURIDAE. Oldfield Thomas. Ann. and Mag. Nat. Hist. (8), vol.7, no.38, pp.205-209, Feb., 1911.

A NEW BANDICOOT-RAT FROM WESTERN SIAM. (BANDICOTA SAVILEI CURTATA.) Oldfield Thomas. Ann. and Mag. Nat. Hist. ser.10, vol.3, p.205, Feb., 1929.

A NEW MOUSE FROM MADURA, S. INDIA. (LEGGADA PALNICA.) Oldfield Thomas. Jour. Bombay Nat. Hist. Soc., vol.29, p.87, Apr.20, 1923.

A NEW MURINE GENUS AND SPECIES FROM SIND, WITH DIAGNOSES OF THREE OTHER NEW GENERA BASED ON PREVIOUSLY KNOWN SPECIES OF "MUS". Oldfield Thomas. Jour. Bombay Nat. Hist. Soc., vol.20, no.4, pp.996-999a, May 20, 1911.

A NEW RAT FROM TENASSERIM. Oldfield Thomas. Ann. and Mag. Nat. Hist. (8), vol.17, no.102, p.425, June, 1916.

A NEW SPECIES OF NESOKIA FROM MESOPOTAMIA. Oldfield Thomas. Jour. Bombay Nat. Hist. Soc., vol.26, no.2, pp. 422-423, May 20, 1919.

ON JUNGLE-MICE FROM ASSAM. Oldfield Thomas. Jour. Bombay Nat. Hist. Soc., vol.27, pp.596-598, Mar.31, 1921. (Two new species of Leggada.)

ON THE INDIAN SPECIES OF THE GENUS MUS. Oldfield Thomas. Proc. Zool. Soc., Lond., pp.521-558, pls.50-51, May 3, 1881.

ON TWO NEW MURIDAE FROM SMYRNA. Oldfield Thomas. Ann. and Mag. Nat. Hist. (7), vol.12, no.67, pp.188-190, July, 1903.

SCIENTIFIC RESULTS FROM THE MAMMAL SURVEY. A NEW SPECIES OF LEGGADA FROM MYSORE. Oldfield Thomas, K. Ryley. Jour. Bombay Nat. Hist. Soc., Vol.22, no.2, p.242, Sept.30, 1913.

SCIENTIFIC RESULTS OF THE MAMMAL SURVEY. VIII. A NEW LEGGADILLA FROM KUMAON. Oldfield Thomas. Jour. Bombay Nat. Hist. Soc., vol.23, no.2, pp. 200, Nov.20, 1914.

SCIENTIFIC RESULTS FROM THE MAMMAL SURVEY. XI. G. A SECOND SPECIES OF COELOMYS FROM CEYLON. Oldfield Thomas. Jour. Bombay Nat. Hist. Soc., vol.24, pp.49-50, Sept.30, 1915.

SCIENTIFIC RESULTS FROM THE MAMMAL SURVEY. XI. I. ON SOME SPECIMENS OF VANDELEURIA FROM BENGAL, BIHAR AND ORISSA. Oldfield Thomas. Jour. Bombay Nat. Hist. Soc., vol.24, pp. 50-55, Sept.30, 1915.

SCIENTIFIC RESULTS FROM THE MAMMAL SURVEY. XIII. A. ON MURIDAE FROM DARJILING AND THE CHIN HILLS. I. A NEW GENUS OF GIANT RAT FROM SIKKIM. Oldfield Thomas. Jour. Bombay Nat. Hist. Soc., vol.24, pp.404-407, June 20, 1916.

SCIENTIFIC RESULTS FROM THE MAMMAL SURVEY. XIII. 2. A NEW RAT ALLIED TO EPIMYS SABANUS, FROM DARJILING. Oldfield Thomas. Jour. Bombay Nat. Hist. Soc., vol.24, no.3, pp.407-409, June 20, 1916.

SCIENTIFIC RESULTS FROM THE MAMMAL SURVEY. XIII. 3. ON THE LARGE RATS ALLIED TO EPIMYS BOWERSI. Oldfield Thomas. Jour. Bombay Nat. Hist. Soc., vol.24, no.3, pp.409-414, June 20, 1916.

SCIENTIFIC RESULTS FROM THE MAMMAL SURVEY. XIII. 4. THE RATS OF THE EPIMYS BERDMOREI GROUP. Oldfield Thomas. Jour. Bombay Nat. Hist. Soc., vol.24, pp.404-407, June 20, 1916.

SCIENTIFIC RESULTS FROM THE MAMMAL SURVEY. XIII. A NEW MOUSE FROM SIKKIM. Oldfield Thomas. Jour. Bombay Nat. Hist. Soc., vol.24, no.3, pp.415-416, June 20, 1916.

SCIENTIFIC RESULTS FROM THE MAMMAL SURVEY. XIV. (B). THE BANDICOOT OF MOUNT POPA, AND ITS ALLIES. Oldfield Thomas. Jour. Bombay Nat. Hist. Soc., vol.24, pp.640-643, Oct.25, 1916.

SCIENTIFIC RESULTS FROM THE MAMMAL SURVEY. XIV. (C). ON THE RAT KNOWN AS EPIMYS JERDONI FROM UPPER BURMA. Oldfield Thomas. Jour. Bombay Nat. Hist. Soc., vol.24, pp.643-644, Oct. 25, 1916.

SCIENTIFIC RESULTS FROM THE MAMMAL SURVEY. XVI. (C). A NEW GENUS OF MURIDAE. Oldfield Thomas. Jour. Bombay Nat. Hist. Soc., vol.25, pp.203-205, Sept.15, 1917.

SCIENTIFIC RESULTS FROM THE MAMMAL SURVEY. XVI. (D). THE SPINY MOUSE OF SIND. Oldfield Thomas. Jour. Bombay Nat. Hist. Soc., vol.25, pp.205-206, Sept.15, 1917.

SCIENTIFIC RESULTS FROM THE MAMMAL SURVEY. XIX. A SYNOPSIS OF THE GROUPS OF TRUE MICE FOUND WITHIN THE INDIAN EMPIRE. Oldfield Thomas. Jour. Bombay Nat. Hist. Soc., vol.26, no. 2, pp.417-421, May 20, 1919.

SCIENTIFIC RESULTS FROM THE MAMMAL SURVEY. XXXI. TWO NEW RATS FROM ASSAM. Oldfield Thomas. Bombay Nat. Hist. Soc., vol.28, no.1, pp.26-27, Dec.30, 1921.

SCIENTIFIC RESULTS FROM THE MAMMAL SURVEY. XLII. THE DISTRIBUTION AND GEOGRAPHICAL RACES OF THE GULANDI BUSH RATS (GOLUNDA ELLIOTI). Oldfield Thomas. Jour. Bombay Nat. Hist. Soc., vol.29, no.2, pp.373-376, Aug.25, 1923.

SCIENTIFIC RESULTS FROM THE MAMMAL SURVEY. XLIV. ON A NEW FIELD-MOUSE FROM NEPAL, WITH A NOTE ON THE CLASSIFICATION OF THE GENUS APODEMUS. Oldfield Thomas. Jour. Bombay Nat. Hist. Soc., vol.29, no.4, pp. 888-889, May 15, 1924.

A LIST OF SPECIMENS OF MURIDAE FROM NORTHERN JAPAN KEPT IN THE UNIVERSITY MUSEUM OF NATURAL HISTORY IN SAPPORO WITH A DESCRIPTION OF A NEW SUBSPECIES. Mitosi Tokuda. Trans. Sapporo Nat. Hist. Soc., vol.12, pt.4, pp.206-211, figs.1-2, 1932.

A REVISED MONOGRAPH OF THE JAPANESE AND MANCHOU-KOREAN MURIDAE. Mitosi Tokuda. Biogeographica (Trans. Biogeogr. Soc. Japan), Tokyo, vol.4, no.1, pp.1-155, figs.88, pls.9, Dec., 1941.

(Review by David H. Johnson of) A REVISED MONOGRAPH OF THE JAPANESE AND MANCHOU-KOREAN MURIDAE. Mitosi Tokuda. Jour. Mam., vol.28, no.2, pp.192-193, May 19, 1947.

(SMALL TABLE FOR DETERMINING MURIDAE OF JAPAN ACCORDING TO THE CHARACTER OF THE PENIS.) Kleine Best immungstabelle der Muridae Nippons nach dem Charakter des Penis. Mitosi Tokuda. Botany and Zoology, vol.2, no.12, pp.1995-2008, figs.16, 1934.

THE RICE RATS OF LOWER SIND AND THEIR CONTROL. P. V. Wagle. Jour. Bombay Nat. Hist. Soc., vol.32, pp.330-338, 3 pls., Oct.20, 1927.

A NEW SPECIES OF LEGGADA FROM BELLARY. R. C. Wroughton, Kathleen V. Ryley. Jour. Bombay Nat. Hist. Soc., vol. 22, no.1, pp.17-18, Apr.21, 1913.

A NEW SPECIES OF LEGGADA FROM KANARA. R. C. Wroughton, Kathleen V. Ryley. Jour. Bombay Nat. Hist. Soc., vol.22, no.1, pp.18-19, Apr.21, 1913.

ON SOME INDIAN FORMS OF THE GENUS MICROMYS. R. C. Wroughton. Jour. Bombay Nat. Hist. Soc., vol.18, no.2, pp. 280-283, Apr.13, 1908.

SCIENTIFIC RESULTS FROM THE MAMMAL SURVEY. XI. F. THE GENUS EPIMYS IN CEYLON. R. C. Wroughton. Jour. Bombay Nat. Hist. Soc., vol.24, pp. 46-49, Sept.30, 1915.

A POPULATION OF THE STRIPED FIELD MOUSE, APODEMUS AGRARIUS COREAE, IN CENTRAL KOREA. Philip M. Youngman. Jour. Mam., 37 (1): 1-10, illus., Feb.28, 1956.

Australia

MURIDAE RECORDED FROM VICTORIA. C. W. Brazenor. Mem. Nat. Mus. Melbourne, no.10, pp.62-85, pls.13-16, Nov., 1936.

A NEW SPECIES OF MOUSE, PSEUDOMYS (GYOMYS), AND A RECORD OF THE BROAD-TOOTHED RAT, MASTACOMYS, FROM VICTORIA. C. W. Brazenor. Mem. Nat. Mus. Melbourne, no.8, pp.158-161, pl.18, Sept., 1934.

TWO NEW RATS FROM CENTRAL AUSTRALIA. (RATTUS TUNNEYI DISPAR, NOTOMYS AMPLUS.) C. W. Brazenor. Mem. Nat. Mus. Melbourne, no.9, pp.5-8, pl.1, Nov., 1936.

A NEW MELOMYS FROM QUEENSLAND WITH NOTICE OF TWO OTHER QUEENSLAND RATS. H. H. Finlayson. Trans. Roy. Soc. S. Australia, Adelaide, vol.66, no.2, pp.243-247, pls.2, (1942) 1943.

ON CENTRAL AUSTRALIAN MAMMALS. PART I. THE MURIDAE. H. H. Finlayson. Trans. Roy. Soc. S. Australia, Adelaide, vol.64, pt.1, pp.125-136, fig.1, pls.2, July 26, 1940.

ON CENTRAL AUSTRALIAN MAMMALS. PART II. THE MURIDAE. H. H. Finlayson. Trans. Roy. Soc. South Australia, Adelaide, vol.65, no.2, pp.215-232, pls.10-13, Dec. 19, 1941.

RECORDS AND DESCRIPTIONS OF MURIDAE FROM OOLDEA, SOUTH AUSTRALIA. H. H. Finlayson. Trans. Roy. Soc. South Australia, Adelaide, vol.63, pt.2, pp.354-364, pls.12-13, Dec.22, 1939.

THE SHY AUSTRALIAN WATER RAT. David Fleay. Animal Kingdom, New York, vol.52, no.2, pp.54-58, illus., Mar.-Apr., 1949.

ON FOUR NEW SPECIES OF MUS AND ONE OF HAPALOTIS, FROM AUSTRALIA. John Gould. Proc. Zool. Soc. Lond., pt. 25, pp.241-243, 1857.

DESCRIPTION OF A NEW RAT FROM SOUTH AUSTRALIA. John E. Gray. Proc. Zool. Soc. Lond., pt.15, p.5, 1847.

NOTES ON THE VARIEGATED OR YELLOW-TAILED RATS OF AUSTRALIA. John E. Gray. Proc. Zool. Soc. Lond., pp.597-600, fig.1, 1867.

ON A NEW SUBSPECIES OF MESEMBRIOMYS HIRSUTUS FROM MELVILLE ISLAND. R. W. Hayman. Ann. and Mag. Nat. Hist., Lond., ser.10, vol.17, no.99, pp.366-368, Mar., 1936.

A REVISION OF THE SOUTH AUSTRALIAN JERBOA MICE, WITH THE DESCRIPTION OF A NEW SPECIES. Frederick Wood Jones. Rec. South Australian Mus., vol.3, no.1, pp.1-7, June 30, 1925.

A NEW AUSTRALIAN NAKED-TAILED RAT (MELOMYS). Remington Kellogg. Proc. Biol. Soc. Wash., vol.58, pp.69-72, May 7, 1945.

THE WATER RAT IN VICTORIA. (AUSTRALIAN WATER RAT.) F. Lewis. Victorian Nat., Melbourne, vol.58, no.2, pp.20-21, June, 1941.

LIST OF AUSTRALIAN AND AUSTRO-PACIFIC MURIDAE. Longman. Memoirs of Queensland Mus., vol.1916, p.23.

AN INVESTIGATION OF THE RAT PEST PROBLEM IN QUEENSLAND CANEFIELDS: 4. BREEDING AND LIFE HISTORIES. W. A. McDougall. Queensland Jour. Agric. Sci., Brisbane, vol.3, no.1, pp.1-43, Mar., 1946.

AN INVESTIGATION OF THE RAT PEST PROBLEM IN QUEENSLAND CANEFIELDS: 2. SPECIES AND GENERAL HABITS. W. A. McDougall. Queensland Jour. Agric. Sci., Brisbane, vol.1, no.2, pp.48-78, June, 1944.

AN INVESTIGATION OF THE RAT PEST PROBLEM IN QUEENSLAND CANEFIELDS: 5. POPULATIONS. W. A. McDougall. Queensland Jour. Agric. Sci., Brisbane, vol.3, no.4, pp.157-237, illus., Dec., 1946.

OBSERVATIONS UPON A SMALL AUSTRALIAN RODENT EXHIBITED BY MR. GOULD AND SUPPOSED TO BE IDENTICAL WITH THE DIPUS MITCHELLII. W. Ogilby. Proc. Zool. Soc. Lond., pt.8, p.151, 1840.

DESCRIPTION OF A NEW SPECIES OF MUS FROM SOUTH AUSTRALIA. Oldfield Thomas. Ann. and Mag. Nat. Hist. (6), vol.3, no.17, pp.433-435, May, 1889.

THE NATIVE RAT OF PEARSON'S ISLANDS, S. AUSTRALIA. (RATTUS MURRAYI, SP. N.) Oldfield Thomas. Ann. and Mag. Nat. Hist., ser.9, vol.11, pp.601-602, May, 1923.

A NEW AUSTRALIAN MOUSE OF THE GENUS PSEUDOMYS. Oldfield Thomas. Ann. and Mag. Nat. Hist., ser.9, vol.15, pp.669-671, June, 1925.

NEW AUSTRALIAN MURIDAE OF THE GENUS PSEUDOMYS. Oldfield Thomas. Ann. and Mag. Nat. Hist. (8), vol.6, no. 36, pp.607-610, Dec., 1910.

NEW GENERA OF AUSTRALASIAN MURIDAE. Oldfield Thomas. Ann. and Mag. Nat. Hist. (8), vol.6, no.35, pp.506-508, Nov., 1910.

A NEW SPECIES OF MASTACOMYS FROM A CAVE IN SOUTH AUSTRALIA. Oldfield Thomas. Ann. and Mag. Nat. Hist., ser. 9, vol.10, pp.550-551, Nov., 1922.

NOTES ON AUSTRALASIAN RATS, WITH A SELECTION OF LECTOTYPES OF AUSTRALASIAN MURIDAE. Oldfield Thomas. Ann. and Mag. Nat. Hist., ser. 9, vol.8, pp.425-433, Oct., 1921.

NOTES ON THE SPECIES OF NOTOMYS, THE AUSTRALIAN JERBOA-RATS. Oldfield Thomas. Ann. and Mag. Nat. Hist., ser. 9, vol.8, pp.536-541, Nov., 1921.

ON THE GENERIC ARRANGEMENT OF THE AUSTRALIAN RATS HITHERTO REFERRED TO CONILURUS, WITH REMARKS ON THE STRUCTURE AND EVOLUTION OF THEIR MOLAR CUSPS. Oldfield Thomas. Ann. and Mag. Nat. Hist. (7), vol.17, no.97, pp.81-85, Jan., 1906.

ON THE N. AUSTRALIAN RATS REFERRED TO THE GENUS MESEMBRIOMYS. Oldfield Thomas. Ann. and Mag. Nat. Hist. (8), vol.3, no.16, pp.372-374, Apr., 1909.

ON THREE NEW AUSTRALIAN RATS. Oldfield Thomas. Ann. and Mag. Nat. Hist. ser.9, vol.8, pp.618-622, Dec., 1921.

SOME NEW AUSTRALASIAN MURIDAE. Oldfield Thomas. Ann. and Mag. Nat. Hist. (9), vol.13, no.74, pp.296-299, Mar., 1924.

TWO NEW AUSTRALIAN MURIDAE. Oldfield Thomas. Ann. and Mag. Nat. Hist., ser.9, vol.18, pp.308-310, Sept., 1926.

TWO NEW JERBOA-RATS (NOTOMYS). Oldfield Thomas. Ann. and Mag. Nat. Hist., ser.9, vol.9, pp.315-317, Apr., 1922.

AUSTRALIAN WATER-RATS: THEIR ORIGIN AND HABITS. Ellis LeG. Troughton. Australian Mus. Mag., Sydney, vol.7, no.11, pp.377-381, illus., Dec.15, 1941.

DESCRIPTIONS OF NEW RATS AND MICE FROM QUEENSLAND. Ellis LeG. Troughton. Mem. Queensland Mus., vol. 11, pt.1, pp.14-22, Apr.17, 1936.

FIVE NEW RATS OF THE GENERA HYDROMYS AND MELOMYS FROM NORTHERN AUSTRALIA. Ellis LeG. Troughton. Records Australian Mus., vol.19, no.4, pp.251-258, figs.2, Sept.19, 1935.

QUEENSLAND RATS OF ECONOMIC IMPORTANCE, AND NEW FORMS OF RATTUS AND THETOMYS. Ellis LeG. Troughton. Records Australian Mus., Sydney, vol.20, no.4, pp.278-281, Mar. 31, 1939.

NEW FORMS OF MOSAIC-TAILED RATS (MELOMYS AND UROMYS) FROM HINCHINBROOK ISLAND, QUEENSLAND. Ellis LeG. Troughton. Australian Zool., vol.6, no.1, pp.96-99, Aug.13, 1929.

MURIDAE. Edgar R. Waite. Report Horn Exped. Central Australia, pt. II, Zool., pp.393-409, pls.25-26, Feb., 1896.

OBSERVATIONS ON MURIDAE FROM CENTRAL AUSTRALIA. Edgar R. Waite. Proc. Roy. Soc. Victoria, n.s., vol.10, pt.2, pp.114-128, pls.5-6, May, 1898.

Biochemistry

LYMPHOCYTES IN NORMAL EPIDERMIS OF YOUNG, OLDER MIDDLE-AGED, AND SENILE RATS. Warren Andrew, Nancy V. Andrew. Jour. Gerontology, vol.9, no.4, pp.412-420, illus., Oct., 1954.

LEUCOCYTES IN THE TRACHEAL EPITHELIUM OF THE MOUSE. Warren Andrew, Marjorie R. Burns. Jour. Morph., Phila., vol.81, no.3, pp.317-341, 5 pls., Nov., 1947.

FURTHER STUDIES ON LYSINE DEFICIENCY IN RATS. M. Gillespie, A. Neuberger, T. A. Webster. Biochemical Jour., Lond., vol.39, no.2, pp.203-208, 1945.

(ON BIOLOGICAL ALBUMIN DIFFERENTIATION IN MICE AND VARIOUS RAT SPECIES.) Ueber biologische Eiweissdifferenzierung bei Maeusen und verschidenen Rattenarten. Fr. Graetz. Zeitschr. fuer Immunitaetsforschung und experimentelle Therapie, Jena, vol.6, no.4, pp.627-643, tables 3, July 27, 1910.

THE MILK FACTOR IN BLOOD. (IN MICE.) Samuel Graff, Henry T. Randall, Gray E. Carpenter, Cushman D. Haagensen. Science, Lancaster, n.s., vol.104, no.2700, p.289, Sept.27, 1946.

BLOOD PRESSURE IN THE RAT. Walter Heymann, Milena Salehar. Proc. Soc. Exp.

Biol. Med., Utica, vol.72, no.1, pp.191-192, Oct., 1949.

TOTAL AND DIFFERENTIAL LEUCOCYTE VALUES OF BLOOD FROM ALBINO RATS OF THE WISTAR STRAIN. Annanell C. Jubb, Ruth Nitchals, Dena C. Cederquist, Margaret A. Ohlson. Quart. Bull. Michigan Agr. Exp. Sta., East Lansing, vol.31, no.1, pp.61-64, Aug., 1948.

HEMOGLOBIN CONTENT AND NUMBER OF ERYTHROCYTES IN THE BLOOD OF FOREST MICE OF THE PLAINS AND OF THE MOUNTAINS, BELONGING TO THE SAME SUBSPECIES (APODEMUS SYLVATICUS CISCAUCASICUS OGN.) AND THE ALTERATION OF THSES INDICATORS WHEN THE HABITAT CHANGES TO A DIFFERENT ALTITUDE. N. I. Kalabuchov, W. M. Rodionov. Bull. Soc. Nat. Moscou, n. s., vol.45, sect. biol., no.1, pp.22-35, figs.4, 1936. (In Russian, with English summary.)

CHANGES IN THE BLOOD LEUCOCYTE LEVEL OF ADRENALECTOMIZED AND NORMAL RATS FOLLOWING ADMINISTRATION OF TYPHOID VACCINE. Lena A. Lewis, I. H. Page. Amer. Jour. Physiol., Balto., vol.153, no.1, pp.148-152, Apr.1, 1948.

(CHOLESTEROLEMIA IN THE RAT.) La cholestérolémie chez le rat. Marcel Monnier, Ali Farchadi, Annie Maulbetsch. Compte Rendu Séances Soc. Phys. et Hist. Nat. Genève, vol.58, no.3, pp.244-248, Aug.-Dec., 1941.

PLASMA CHOLINESTERASE IN MALE AND FEMALE RATS. Dorothy B. Mundell. Nature, London, vol.153, no.3888, pp.557-558, May 6, 1944.

THE PARACRYSTALLINE STATE OF THE RAT RED CELL. Eric Ponder. Jour. General Physiol., Balto., vol.29, no.2, pp.89-102, Nov.20, 1945.

THE ZONE OF LOCALIZATION OF ANTI-MOUSE-KIDNEY SERUM AS DETERMINED BY RADIO-AUTOGRAPHS. D. Pressman, Ruth F. Hill, F. W. Foote. Science, Lancaster, vol.109, no.2821, pp.65-66, Jan.21, 1949.

ROLE OF PYRIODOXINE IN THE PRODUCTION OF LEUCOCYTES IN NORMAL AND LEUKEMIC MICE. David R. Weir, R. W. Heinle, Arnold D. Welch. Proc. Soc. Exp. Biol. Med., Utica, vol.72, no.2, pp.457-461, Nov., 1949.

Captive and Laboratory Animals

BEHAVIOUR OF WILD RATS IN THE LABORATORY. S. A. Barnett. Med. and Biol. Illus., London, 6 (2): 106-111, illus., Apr., 1956.

(MY DOMESTIC RAT.) Meine Hausratte. Hans von Berlepsch. Zool. Garten, Leipzig, n.F., vol.19, no.5, pp.220-222, 1952.

THE FEEDING AND BREEDING OF LABORATORY ANIMALS VI. THE BREEDING OF MICE. H. M. Bruce. Jour. Hygiene, Lond., vol.45, no.4, pp.420-430, Feb., 1948.

THE DOMESTICATION OF THE RAT. W. E. Castle. Proc. Nat. Acad. Sci., Easton, vol.33, no.5, pp.109-117, May, 1947.

(THE WOOD MOUSE (APODEMUS S. SYLVATICUS LINNE 1758) AS INHABITANT OF BREEDING CAGES.) Die Waldmaus, Apodemus s. sylvaticus (Linne, 1758), als Bewohnerin von Nistkaesten. Gerhard Creutz. Saeugetierk. Mitteil., Stuttgart, vol.1, no.1, pp.21-22, Jan.10, 1953.

BREEDING AND CARE OF THE ALBINO RAT FOR RESEARCH PURPOSES. Milton J. Greenman, F. Louise Duhring. Wistar Institute of Anatomy and Biology, Phila., 109 pp., 18 figs., 3 charts, Aug., 1923.

THE RAT IN LABORATORY INVESTIGATION. (MYOLOGY, TEETH, GROWTH, METABOLISM, BEHAVIOR, USE OF RATS IN BIOLOGIC ASSAY OF HORMONES, BLOOD GROUPS, AND OTHER TOPICS DISCUSSED BY 30 DIFFERENT AUTHORS.) John Q. Griffith, Edmond J. Farris. J. B. Lippincott Co., Phila., pp. xiv, 488, pl.1, figs.177, 1942.

(Review by Arthur Kirschbaum of) THE RAT IN LABORATORY INVESTIGATION, BY A STAFF OF 30 CONTRIBUTORS. John Q. Griffith, Jr., Edmond J. Farris. Anat. Record, Phila., vol.83, no.4, pp. 595-596, Aug.25, 1942.

(SOME OBSERVATIONS OF CAPTIVE FOREST MICE (APODEMUS SYLVATICUS LINNE 1758).) Einige Beobachtungen an gefangenen Waldmaeusen, Apodemus sylvaticus (Linne, 1758). Wilhelm Harder. Saeugetierk. Mitteil., Stuttgart, vol.2, no. 2, pp.72-74, Apr.1, 1954.

THE LABORATORY MOUSE. ITS ORIGIN, HEREDITY, AND CULTURE. Clyde E. Keeler. Harvard Univ. Press, pp.81, fig. 36, Cambridge, 1931.

A NEW DEAL FOR MICE. WHY MICE ARE USED IN RESEARCH ON HUMAN DISEASES. C. C. Little. Sci. American, vol. 152, no.1, pp.16-18, illus., Jan., 1935.

EPIMYS RATTUS IN CAPTIVITY. Erna W. Mohr. Jour. Mam., vol.9, no.2, pp.113-117, May, 1928.

(LIFE IN CAPTIVITY OF A DOMESTIC RAT.) Gefangenleben einer Hausratte. Erna Mohr. Der Zool. Garten, vol.1, pp. 99-105, 1928.

THE MORTALITY, FECUNDITY AND INTRINSIC RATE OF NATURAL INCREASE OF THE MULTIMAMMATE MOUSE, RATTUS (MASTOMYS) NATALENSIS (SMITH) IN THE LABORATORY. W. D. Oliff. Jour. Anim. Ecol., 22 (2): 217-226, graphs, Nov., 1953.

(OBSERVATIONS ON PYGMY MICE MICROMYS MINUTUS PALL. IN CAPTIVITY.) Beobachtungen an Zwergmaeusen, Micromys minutus, Pall., in Gefangenschaft. Rudolf Piechocki. Zool. Garten, Leipzig, vol.22, no.1, pp.11-29, illus., 1955.

THE USE OF MICE IN EXPERIMENTAL CHEMOTHERAPY OF TUBERCULOSIS. I., II., III. Gordon W. Raleigh, Guy P. Youmans. Jour. Infectious Diseases, Chicago, vol.82, no.3, pp.197-225, May-June, 1948.

DOMESTICATION OF THE NORWAY RAT AND ITS IMPLICATIONS FOR THE PROBLEM OF STRESS. Curt P. Richter. Proc. Assoc. Research Nervous and Mental Disease, Balto., vol.29, pp.19-47, illus., 1950.

(THAMNOMYS SURDASTER SURDASTER, LABORATORY ANIMAL.) Le Thamnomys surdaster surdaster, animal de Laboratoire. J. Rodhain. Ann. Mus. Roy. Congo Belge, Tervuren, n.s., Sci. Zool., vol.1 (Miscellanea Zoologica H. Schouteden), pp.74-76, illus., 1954.

IDENTIFICATION OF DOMESTIC RATS OF MEDICAL IMPORTANCE. Ernst Schwarz. Laboratory guide to protozoology and helminthology, U.S. Naval Medical School, Bethesda, Md., Appendix A, pp.169-178, figs.2, 4 maps, Mar.17, 1943.

BIOLOGY OF THE LABORATORY MOUSE. George D. Snell. Blakiston Company, Phila., pp.ix, 497, figs.172, 1941.

MOUSE BREEDING AS A HOBBY. P. M. Soderberg. All-Pets Mag., Fond du Lac, vol.19, no.2, pp.63-65, Feb., 1948.

THE ALBINO RAT. Olive Swezy. Science, n.s., vol.68, p.60, July 20, 1928.

Control

RAT CONTROL IN A PLAGUE OUTBREAK IN MALTA. S. A. Barnett. Jour. Hygiene, Lond., vol.46, no.1, pp.10-18, pls.1-2, Mar., 1948.

RAT POPULATIONS AND CONTROL IN TWO ENGLISH VILLAGES. S. A. Barnett, A. H. Bathard, Mary M. Spencer. Ann. Applied Biol., 38: 444-463, 1951.

(THE DOMESTIC MOUSE (MUS MUSCULUS L.) AND CONTROL MEASURES.) Die Hausmaus (Mus musculus L.) und ihre Behkaempfung, Mitteil. Dr. Baunacke. Ges. Vorratsschutz, vol.7, no.4, pp.43-47, July, 1931; vol.7, no.6, pp.71-72, fig.1, Nov., 1931.

RODDY THE RAT; A STORY OF THE SPREAD OF TYPHUS FEVER AND OF WAYS OF GETTING RID OF RATS. George S. Bote, Dorothy C. Stephens. Univ. Florida, Tampa, 68 pp., illus., 1946.

RATS: PUBLIC ENEMY NO. I. Maurice Burton. Illus. London News, vol.217, no. 5826, p.1006, illus., Dec.16, 1950.

RAT CONTROL. F. Gray Butcher. North Dakota Agric. College, Fargo, Special Circ.A31, 6 pp., illus., Nov., 1942.

(RESEARCH ON THE DAMAGE CAUSED BY THE BROWN RAT (MUS NORVEGICUS ERXLEBEN) IN GRAIN STOCKS.) Recherches sur les degats commis par le surmulot (Mus norvegicus Erxleben) dans les approvisionnements de graines. A. Chappellier. Annales des Epiphyties, 16 annee, nos.3-4, pp.219-231, May-Aug., 1930.

A PRACTICAL HANDBOOK ON RAT DESTRUCTION. C. Leopold Claremont. 180 pp., London: John Hart, 1926.

RAT CONTROL IN KRIAN, PERAK. A. E. Coleman-Doscas, W. d'Israeli Bird. Malayan Agric. Jour., Kuala Lumpur, vol.22, no.4, pp.170-176, Apr., 1934.

THE RAT AND THE POULTRYMAN. Leo K. Couch. Bi-monthly Bull. Western Washington Agric. Exper. Sta., vol.10, no. 2, pp.47-48, July, 1922.

THE RAT. A SANITARY MENACE AND ECONOMIC BURDEN. R. H. Creel. U.S. Public Health Repts., vol.28, no.27, pp. 1403-1408, July 4, 1913.

WHAT WE'RE DOING TO CONTROL FIELD RATS IN COTABATO, PHILIPPINE ISLANDS. Cornelio V. Crucillo, Faustino Q. Otanes, Jose L. Morales. Pest Control, 22 (11): 10, 12, 14, 16, illus., Nov., 1954.

A PERSPECTIVE ON RAT CONTROL. David E. Davis. Public Health Repts., Washington, vol.67, no.9, pp.888-893, Sept., 1952.

PRINCIPLES OF RAT MANAGEMENT. David E. Davis. Pests and Their Control, 16 (11): 9-12, Nov., 1948.

RELATION OF RAT CONTROL TO FARM GAME. David E. Davis. Proc. 8th Ann. N.E. Wildl. Conf., Jackson's Mill, W. Va., pp.1-14, Apr.1-4, 1952.

EXPERIMENTAL AREA-WIDE RAT CONTROL WITH PERMANENT FEEDER STATIONS. Robert B. Deen. Pest Control, 21 (7): 27-28, illus., July, 1953.

ON THE CONTROL OF THE RAT POPULATION. Henry H. Donaldson. Science, n. s., vol.61, pp.305-306, Mar.20, 1925.

NEW DATA ON THE CHEMICAL METHODS OF RAT CONTROL. N. M. Dukel'skaia. La Defence des Plantes, vol.5, nos.5-6, pp.579-585, 1928. (In Russian.)

EXTERMINATION OF RATS AND MICE. Charles Elton. Ministry of Food, London, 8 pp., Aug., 1944.

BALTIMORE'S COMMUNITY RAT CONTROL PROGRAM. John T. Emlen, Jr. Amer. Jour. Publ. Health, 37 (6): 721-727, June, 1947.

DECLARATION OF WAR ON RATS. John Fallowfield. Field, 174 (4531): 849, Oct. 28, 1939.

PERIMETER CONTROL OF RODENTS FOR THE PROTECTION OF FOOD PLANTS. William D. Fitzwater, Jr. Pest Control, 19 (10): 9-10, 28, Oct., 1951.

RATS AND RAT RIDDANCE. Edward Howe Forbush. 67th Annual Report Mass. State Board Agric., Boston, Econ. Biol. Bull. no. 1, pp.7-87, frontispiece, pls.1-11, illus., 1915.

SOME OF THE LATEST DEVELOPMENTS IN THE CONTROL OF RATS AND MICE. F. E. Garlough. Pests and Their Control, 11 (1): 6-7, 9, Jan., 1943.

OF THE RATS THAT ATTACK THE CAROUB TREES IN CYPRUS. P. Gennadius. Nicosia, pp.35-36, 1897. (Greek text attached.)

RAT CONTROL. Gaurchandra Ghosh. Sci. and Culture, Calcutta, vol.10, no.8, pp.344-346, fig.1, Feb., 1945.

CUTTING OUR $200,000,000 RAT BILL. Edward A. Goldman. Quartermaster Review, pp.27-34, figs., Jan.-Feb., 1922.

WHAT HEALTH OFFICERS CAN DO TO PROMOTE RAT EXTERMINATION. Edward A. Goldman. Amer. Jour. Public Health, 11 (7): 606-613, figs.3, July, 1921.

HOW MUCH DOES IT COST TO KILL A RAT. W. McAuley Gracie. Rodent Mail, Rats and Mice, London, vol.2, no.10, pp. 109-110, Dec., 1946.

RAT PROOFING ON LAND AND SEA. Samuel B. Grubbs. Jour. Pan-Pacific Res. Inst., Honolulu, vol.8, no.3, pp.11-13, pls.3, July-Sept., 1933.

HOW THE SIOUX CITY STOCKYARDS CONTROLLED ITS RAT POPULATION. Harold Gunderson. Pest Control, 20 (6): 12, 14, 48, illus., June, 1952.

RATS AND THEIR CONTROL. W. J. Hamilton, Jr. Cornell Extension Bull., Ithaca, no.353, pp.34, illus., Revised, Mar., 1947.

CONTROLLING RATS AND HOUSE MICE. D. W. Hayne, M. D. Pirnie, C. H. Jefferson. Michigan Agric. Exper. Sta., East Lansing, Circ. Bull.167, 40 pp., 25 figs., June, 1945.

(DAMAGE TO LEAD PIPES BY ANIMALS.) Zerstoerung von Bleiroehren durch Tiere. R. Hesse. Biologisches Zentralblatt, vol.45, pp.19-20, 2 figs., 1925.

(THE FIGHT AGAINST SAWAH RATS IN MOUNTAIN REGIONS.) Sawah-ratten-bestrijding in Bergterrein. W. C. van Heurn. Bull. Inst. Plantenz. van Algem. Proefstat. v. d. Landbouw (Dept. Landbouw Nijverheid en Handel), Batavia, vol.23, pp. 1-30, pls.9, 1931.

RATS AND HOW TO DESTROY THEM. I. Mark Hovell. John Bale Sons and Danielsson, London, pp.XLII, 465, illus., 1924.

INDIANAPOLIS IS SOLVING ITS RODENT CONTROL PROBLEMS. Jay W. Hundley. Pest Control, 19 (5): 9-11, 34, May, 1951.

HOUSE MICE AND THEIR CONTROL. Harlan B. Ives. Pests and Their Control, Cleveland, vol.16, no.10, pp.11-18, 54, illus., Oct., 1948.

WHAT RAT CONTROL MEANS TO BUSINESS. James W. Johnston, Jr. Trans. 11th North Amer. Wildlife Conf., Wash., pp.493-498, 1946.

THE HOUSE RAT: THE MOST DESTRUCTIVE ANIMAL IN THE WORLD. David E. Lantz. Yearbook, U.S. Dept. Agric., no. 725, pp.1-19, pls.1-4, 1918.

HOW TO DESTROY RATS. David E. Lantz. U.S. Dept. Agric., Farmers' Bull., no.369, pp.5-20, figs.1-5, 1909.

METHODS OF DESTROYING RATS. David E. Lantz. U.S. Dept. Agric., Farmer's Bull.297, pp.8, May 31, 1907.

RODENT CONTROL IN PROCESSING PLANTS. George B. Lay. Pests and Their Control, 16 (2): 28-32, Feb., 1948.

THE MILLION DOLLAR RAT. Francis X. Lueth. Illinois Conservation, Springfield, vol.8, no.3, pp.10-11, illus., Fall issue, 1943.

AN INVESTIGATION OF THE RAT PEST PROBLEM IN QUEENSLAND CANEFIELDS: I. ECONOMIC ASPECTS. W. A. McDougall. Queensland Jour. Agric. Sci., Brisbane, vol.1, no.2, pp.32-47, June, 1944.

EUROPEAN AND AMERICAN METHODS OF RAT CONTROL. E. M. Mills. USDA, Biol. Survey, Wildlife Leaflet 113, 6 pp., May, 1938.

TUNNEL RAT-TRAPS FOR STORES AND SHIPS. J. A. Mitchell. Ann. Trop. Med. and Parasit., Liverpool, vol.23, no.4, pp. 443-447, 2 pl., 1929.

(HOUSE AND ROOF RAT PROBLEMS.) Haus- und Dachratten-Fragen. Erna Mohr. Biologisches Zentralblatt, Leipzig, vol.67 (1948), no.7-8, pp.367-372, 1948.

(ON RATS AND CONTROLLING THEM.) Ueber Ratten und Rattenbekaempfung. Erna Mohr. Zool. Garten, n.F., vol.4, nos.1-2, pp.65-66, Feb., 1931.

THE TREE RAT AS A PEST OF CACAO IN TRINIDAD. B. G. Montserin. Government Printing Office, Port of Spain, pp.1-12, figs. 7, tables 7, 1937.

RODENT CONTROL IN THE AREA OF THE PORT OF LONDON HEALTH. M. T. Morgan, James Fisher, J. S. Watson. Messrs. Hodgetts, Ltd., London, pp.37-38, 45-46, July 31,-Aug.7, 1943.

WASHINGTON RAT RACE. (RAT CONTROL.) Edwin D. Neff. Nat. Hist., New York, vol. 55, no.6, pp.276-278, illus., June, 1946.

(Review by Margery P. Mann of) THE RODENT SPECIALIST. J. Laurens Nicholes. Jour. Mam., vol.29, no.3, pp.304-305, Aug.31, 1948.

COMBAT WITH RATS AND HOUSE MICE. S. I. Obolensky. All-Russian Village-economy and Forestry Industrial Exhibition, Leningrad, pp.16, 1923. (In Russian.)

RAT CONTROL ON PUBLIC DUMPS. G. C. Oderkirk, E. M. Mills, Milton Caroline. Pest Control, 23 (8): 24, 26, 28, illus., Aug., 1955.

INCREASE OF RAT INFESTATION ON VESSELS COMING TO NEW YORK. Robert Olesen. U.S. Publ. Health Repts., Wash., vol.60, no.44, pp.1295-1296, Nov.2, 1945.

INCREASE OF RAT INFESTATION ON OIL TANKERS. Robert Olesen, J. L. Stone. U.S. Publ. Health Repts., Wash., vol.60, no.44, pp.1296-1301, Nov.2, 1945.

OBSERVATIONS ON RAT DAMAGE TO COCONUTS ON TAVEUNI. R. W. Paine. Agric. Jour., Dept. Agric., Fiji, vol.7, no.1, pp.26-34, pl.1, 1934.

RAT CONTROL. T. H. Parks. Ohio State Univ., Columbus, Agric. Extension Serv. Bull., no.245, 4 pp., illus., Nov., 1943.

COST OF RATS TO INDUSTRY, ESPECIALLY SUGAR, AND METHODS OF CONTROL. C. E. Pemberton. Jour. Pan-Pacific Res. Inst., Honolulu, vol.8, no.3, pp.3-5, July-Sept., 1933.

THE FIELD RAT IN HAWAII AND ITS CONTROL. C. E. Pemberton. Bull. Exper. Sta. Hawaiian Sugar Planters' Assoc., Entomological Ser., no.17, pp. 46, figs.28, June, 1925.

RAT AND MOUSE CONTROL. Miles D. Pirnie. Michigan State Coll., Cooperative Extension Service, Extension Folder F-183, 6 pp., Feb., 1955.

THE USE OF CURTAIN WALLS IN RAT-PROOFING. Ralph Porges. U.S. Public Health Repts., Wash., D.C., vol.58, no. 52, pp.1881-1885, Dec.24, 1943.

ERADICATION OF RATS AT AN OVERSEAS NAVAL STATION. William C. Replogle, D. Ueno, Maynard S. Johnson. Medical Technicians Bull. (Suppl. U.S. Armed Forces Med. Jour.), 7 (4): 167-172, July-Aug., 1956.

INCIDENCE OF RAT BITES AND RAT BITE FEVER IN BALTIMORE. Curt P. Richter. Jour. Amer. Med. Assoc., Chicago, vol.128, pp.324-326, June 2, 1945.

(METHOD OF DESTRUCTION OF RATS WITH SCILLE POWDER.) Methode de destruction des rats par la poudre de Scille. P. Rode. Rev. Path. Veget. et Entom. Agric., vol.16, nos.9-10, pp.283-289, Nov.-Dec., 1929.

AN ANALYSIS OF RATBITES IN BALTIMORE, 1948-52. William Sallow. Publ. Health Rept., 68 (12): 1239-1242, Dec., 1953.

(ON RATS AND RAT CONTROL (WITH SPECIAL CONSIDERATION OF THE BROWN RAT MUS DECUMANUS PALL.) Uber Ratten und Rattenbekampfung (mit besonderer Berucksichtigung der Wanderratte Mus decumanus Pall.) R. Schander, Gotze. 1930.

(ON RATS AND THEIR CONTROL (WITH SPECIAL CONSIDERATION OF THE BROWN RAT MUS DECUMANUS PALL.) I. LIFE HABITS, OCCURRENCE, AND BIOLOGICAL CONTROL METHODS. II. THE USE OF BAIT AND CHEMICAL CONTROL. III. ASSESSMENT OF MEANS AND MECHANICAL CONTROL OF RATS.) Ueber Ratten und Rattenbekampfung (mit besonderer Beruecksichtigung der Wanderratte Mus decumanus Pall.) I. lebensgewohnheiten, Auftreten und biologische Bekaempfung. II. Koederanwendung und chemische Bekaempfung. III. Mittelbewertung und mechanishce Ratten-Bekaempfung. R. Schander, G. Goetze. Zentralbl. Bakt. II Abt., vol.81, no.8-14, pp.260-284, fig.3; pp.335-367, fig.1; pp.481-501, fig.8, 1930.

PREMISES FOR RAT CONTROL. Ernst Schwarz. Pests and Their Control, Kansas City, vol.12, no.9, p.7, Sept., 1944.

THE BENEFITS ACCRUING FROM THE RATPROOF CONSTRUCTION OF VESSELS. G. C. Sherrard. U.S. Publ. Health Repts., Wash., D.C., vol.58, no.52, pp.1888-1890, Dec.24, 1943.

A PLAN FOR RODENT CONTROL IN CITIES. G. C. Sherrard. Publ. Health Rept., 58 (22): 825-832, May 28, 1943.

RATS AS A SOURCE OF LOSS ON FUR FARMS. J. E. Shillinger. Amer. Fur Breeder, Duluth, vol.14, no.9, pp.12, 14-15, illus., Mar., 1942.

HOW TO GET RID OF RATS. James Silver. U.S. Dept. Agric. Farm Bull.1302, pp.1-14, 8 figs., Apr., 1923.

RAT CONTROL. James Silver. Bull. U.S. Dept. Agric., no.1533, pp.1-21, figs.10, June, 1927. (Revised 1930 and 1933.)

RED-SQUILL POWDER IN RAT CONTROL. James Silver. Leaflet 65, U.S. Dept. Agric., Wash., pp.1-8, figs.1-2, Jan., 1931.

RAT-PROOFING BUILDINGS AND PREMISES. James Silver, W. E. Crouch, M. C. Betts. U.S. Dept. Agric., Farmer's Bull. 1638, pp.25, figs.23, Dec., 1930; U.S. Dept. Interior, Conservation Bull.19, pp.1-26, 23 figs., 1942.

RAT CONTROL. James Silver, F. E. Garlough. U.S. Dept. Interior, Fish and Wildlife Serv., Conservation Bull. no.8, 27 pp., 10 figs., 1941.

RAT CONTROL AND WILDLIFE. Everett B. Speaker. Iowa Conservationist, Des Moines, vol.7, no.9, p.68, illus., Sept.15, 1948.

NOTICE OF THE PERFORATION OF LEADEN PIPES BY THE TEETH OF RATS. W. H. Sykes. Proc. Zool. Soc. London, pt.2, p.54, 1834.

THE RESISTANCE OF CONSTRUCTION MATERIALS TO PENETRATION BY RATS. C. M. Tarzwell, Others. Public Health Monog. no.11, 16 pp., illus., 1953.

FIFTH COLUMNISTS. (HOUSE RAT.) Frank Thone. Science News Letter, Wash., D.C., vol.42, no.2, p.30, July 11, 1942.

(DESTRUCTION OF HOUSE RATS.) Destruction des rats de case. Dominique Traore. Notes Africaines (Bull. Inst. Francaise d'Afrique Noire), Dakar, no.33, p.17, Jan., 1947.

CERTAIN NEW TECHNIQUES IN RODENT CONTROL. Justus C. Ward. Pests and Their Control, 15 (2): 12-14, Mar., 1947.

WARTIME IMPROVEMENTS IN RODENT CONTROL AGENTS. Justus C. Ward, Donald A. Spencer. Food Tech., 1: 51-55, 1947.

HOW WE RAN TORONTO'S RODENT CONTROL PROGRAM. Norton G. Whitaker. Pests and Their Control, 17 (6): 16-20, June, 1949.

ORGANIZED RAT CONTROL IN YUBA COUNTY. Arthur W. Worledge. California Dept. Agric., Bull., Sacramento, vol.35, no.3, pp.156-158, July-Sept., 1946.

THE RAT AND ITS RELATION TO THE PUBLIC HEALTH. W. Wyman, et al. 254 pp., 6 pls., 13 figs., Wash., 1910.

CONTROL OF HOUSE MICE. U.S. Fish and Wildlife Serv., Wildl. Leaflet 349, 1-4 pp., illus., 1953.

DIRECTIONS FOR DESTROYING HOUSE MICE. USDA, Biol. Survey, Wildl. Leaflet 78, 2 pp., Jan., 1937.

DIRECTIONS FOR DESTROYING HOUSE MICE. USDI, F&WS, Wildlife Leaflet 234, 3 pp., Feb., 1943.

(RAT CONTROL CAMPAIGN IN PORT OF CUXHAVEN, GERMANY.) Eeen havengebied van ratten gezuiverd. Rat en muis, Plantenziektenkundige Dienst, Wageningen, 1957, (1): 3-7, Mar., 1957.

RAT CONTROL METHODS. Fish and Wildlife Service in Coop. with U.S. Dept. Agric. Wash., 11 pp., illus., 1947.

RAT-CONTROL METHODS. U.S. Dept. Interior, Fish and Wildlife Service, Circ. 13, pp.16, illus., 1948.

RATS AND THEIR CONTROL. Honolulu Board of Health. Publ. rat and Mosquito Control Comm., Chamber of Commerce, Honolulu, 31 pp., illus., 1943.

RATS ARE COSTLY PESTS AND A DANGER TO HEALTH. Science News Letter, Wash., D.C., vol.41, no.24, p.374, June 13, 1942.

(REPORT ON THE GENERAL CAMPAIGN AGAINST THE BROWN RAT 1955.) Landelijke actie bruine rat 1955. Rat en Muis, Plantenziektenkundige Dienst, Wageningen, Netherlands, 1956, (2): 19-25, illus., Aug., 1956.

RODENT PROOFING. (RATS.) Rodent, Rats, and Mice Mail, Lond., vol.2, no.3, pp.30-32, illus., May, 1946.

Cytology

AGE CHANGES IN THE VASCULAR ARCHITECTURE AND CELL CONTENT IN THE SPLEENS OF 100 WISTAR INSTITUTE RATS, INCLUDING COMPARISONS WITH HUMAN MATERIAL. Warren Andrew. Amer. Jour. Anat., Phila., vol.79, no.1, pp.1-73, pls.1-9, July, 1946.

AN AGE DIFFERENCE IN PROPORTIONS OF CELL TYPES IN THE EPIDERMIS OF ABDOMINAL SKIN OF THE RAT. Warren Andrew, Nancy V. Andrew. Jour. Gerontol., vol.11, no.1, pp.18-27, illus., Jan., 1956.

THE ORIGIN OF BINUCLEATE AND LARGE MONONUCLEATE CELLS IN THE LIVER OF THE RAT. H. W. Beams, R. L. King. Anat. Record, Phila., vol.83, no.2, pp. 281-295, fig.1, pls.2, June 25, 1942.

ULTRACENTRIFUGATION OF RAT SPINAL GANGLION CELLS, WITH SPECIAL REFERENCE TO NEUROFIBRILLAE. H. W. Beams, H. W. Kirshenblit. Anat. Record, Phila., vol.76, no.1, pp.95-101, pl.1, Jan.25, 1940.

OBSERVATIONS ON THE RATE OF TRANSPORT OF SPERMATOZOA IN THE FEMALE GENITAL TRACT OF THE RAT. Richard J. Blandau, William L. Money. Anat. Record, Phila., vol.90, no.3, pp.255-260, Nov., 1944.

MITOTIC ACTIVITY IN THE ADULT FEMALE MOUSE, MUS MUSCULUS L. A STUDY OF ITS RELATION TO THE OESTROUS CYCLE IN NORMAL AND ABNORMAL CONDITIONS. W. S. Bullough. Philos. Trans. Roy. Soc. Lond., Ser.B, Biol. Sci., vol.231, no.585, pp.453-517, illus., May 21, 1946.

THE ORIGIN OF THE DEFINITIVE OVA IN THE WHITE RAT (MUS NORVEGICUS ALBINUS). Earl O. Butcher. Anat. Rec., vol.37, pp.13-29, illus., Nov.25, 1927.

MITOTIC RHYTHM IN THE EPIDERMIS OF THE MOUSE. Zola K. Cooper, H. Charles Franklin. Anat. Record, Phila., vol.78, no.1, pp.1-8, Sept.25, 1940.

OBSERVATIONS ON PRE- AND POST-PUBERTAL OOEGENESIS IN THE WHITE RAT, MUS NORVEGICUS ALBINUS. Marion H. Cowperthwaite. Amer. Jour. Anat., vol.36, pp.69-88, 1 pl., Sept.15, 1925.

THE STATE OF SPERM-AND FOLLICLE-CELLS OF THE RAT IN TISSUE CULTURES. N. Diomidova. Comptes Rendus (Doklady) Acad. Sci. USSR, Moscow, n.s., vol.32, no.1, pp.95-98, 1941.

OBSERVATIONAL AND EXPERIMENTAL EVIDENCES RELATING TO THE ORIGIN AND DIFFERENTIATION OF THE DEFINITIVE GERM CELLS IN MICE. N. B. Everett. Jour. Exper. Zool., Phila., vol. 92, no.1, pp.49-91, pls.6, Feb., 1943.

EFFECT OF HOMOLOGOUS AND HETEROLOGOUS TISSUE ON MITOSIS IN HETEROZYGOUS AND INBRED MICE. John C. Fardon, Sr., M. A. Winger, John E. Prince. Proc. Soc. Exp. Biol. Med., Utica, vol.72, no.3, pp.568-569, Dec., 1949.

DAY AND NIGHT PERIOD IN NUCLEAR DIVISIONS. C.E. Droogleever Fortuyn-van Leyden. Proc. Kon. Akad. van Wetenschappen te Amsterdam, vol.29, no.7, pp. 979-988, 1926.

MITOTIC ACTIVITY OF THE MOUSE PARATHYROID GLAND. C. L. Foster. Nature, London, vol.151, no.3827, p.211, fig.1, Mar.6, 1943.

THE SPERMS OF THE BRITISH MURIDAE. G. F. Friend. Quart. Jour. Microsc. Sci., vol.78, pt.3, pp.419-443, figs.30, Feb., 1936.

THE STRUCTURE AND FUNCTION OF THE PARENCHYMATOUS GLANDULAR CELLS IN THE NEUROHYPOPHYSIS OF THE RAT. I. Gersh. Amer. Jour. Anat., Phila., vol.64, no.3, pp.407-443, May 15, 1939.

A CYTOLOGICAL STUDY OF THE CENTRIFUGED OOCYTE OF THE MOUSE. R. A. R. Gresson. Quart. Jour. Microscop. Sci., London, n.s., no.324, vol.81, pt.4, pp.569-583, fig.1, pls.34-35, Jan., 1940.

THE ORIGIN AND DIFFERENTIATION OF THE ALPHA AND BETA CELLS IN THE PANCREATIC ISLETS OF THE RAT. Walter L. Hard. Amer. Jour. Anat., Phila., vol.75, no.3, pp.369-403, fig.1, pls.1-4, Nov., 1944.

THE FORMATION OF THE SEX GLANDS AND GERM CELLS OF MAMMALS. I. THE ORIGIN OF THE GERM CELLS OF THE ALBINO RAT. George T. Hargitt. Jour. Morph. and Physiol., vol.40, pp.517-558, 5 pls., Sept.5, 1925.

THE FORMATION OF THE SEX GLANDS AND GERM CELLS OF MAMMALS. II. THE HISTORY OF THE MALE GERM CELL IN THE ALBINO RAT. George T. Hargitt. Jour. Morph. and Physiol., vol. 42, pp.253-306, 5 pls., June 5, 1926.

THE FORMATION OF THE SEX GLANDS AND GERM CELLS OF MAMMALS. V. GERM CELLS IN THE OVARIES OF ADULT, PREGNANT, AND SENILE ALBINO RATS. George T. Hargitt. Jour. Morphol. and Physiol., vol.50, no.2, pp. 453-473, figs.1-17, Dec.5, 1930.

PRIMORDIAL SEX-CELLS OF THE ALBINO RAT. George T. Hargitt. Anat. Record, vol.29, p.167, Dec.25, 1924.

THE RELATION OF PREGNANCY CELLS IN THE PITUITARY OF THE RAT TO THE REPRODUCTIVE CYCLE. H. O. Haterius. Anat. Record, vol.54, no.3, pp.343-351, pl.1, Nov.25, 1932.

MITOTIC ACTIVITY IN THE ANTERIOR HYPOPHYSIS OF FEMALE RATS. Thomas E. Hunt. Anat. Record, Phila., vol.82, no. 3, pp.263-276, Mar.25, 1942.

MITOTIC ACTIVITY IN THE FEMALE MOUSE PITUITARY. T. Kerr. Jour. Exper. Biol., Lond., vol.20, no.1, pp.74-78, pl.3, Dec., 1943.

DIVERSITY OF CELL TYPES IN EPIDERMIS OF THE MOUSE UNDER NORMAL CONDITIONS AND FOLLOWING TOPICAL APPLICATION OF ESTROGEN. Charles E. McCreight, Warren Andrew. Anat. Rec., vol.125, no.4, pp.761-775, Aug., 1956.

EVIDENCE OF THE MACROPHAGAL ORIGIN OF ADIPOSE CELLS IN THE WHITE RAT AS SHOWN BY STUDIES ON STARVED ANIMALS. Albert William McCullough. Jour. Morphol., Phila., vol. 75, no.2, pp.193-201, Sept., 1944.

CYTOLOGICAL CHANGES IN UNFERTILIZED TUBAL EGGS OF THE RAT. Margaret C. Mann. Biol. Bull., vol.46, pp.316-327, June, 1924.

REPLACEMENT OF OVOCYTES IN THE OVARY OF NORMAL AND HORMONE-INJECTED YOUNG RATS. Lore Marx. Anat. Record, Phila., vol.79, no.1, pp.115-131, 2 pls., Jan.25, 1941.

(COMPARATIVE AND SYSTEMATIC CHROMOSOME CYTOLOGY OF MURIDAE.) Cytologie chromosomique comparée et systematique des Muridae. Robert Matthey. Mammalia, 20 (2): 93-123, June, 1956.

STUDIES ON REPRODUCTION IN THE ALBINO MOUSE. II. CONTRIBUTIONS ON THE MATURATION OF THE SPERM CELLS. (PHOTOGRAPHS OF LEUCOCYTES DEVOURING SPERMATOZOA.) Hugo Merton. Proc. Roy. Soc. Edinburgh, vol.59, pt.2, pp.145-152, figs.2, 1939.

STUDIES ON REPRODUCTION IN THE ALBINO MOUSE. III. THE DURATION OF LIFE OF SPERMATOZOA IN THE FEMALE REPRODUCTIVE TRACT. Hugo Merton. Proc. Roy. Soc. Edinburgh, vol.59, pt.2, pp.207-218, 1939.

CELL CHANGES IN THE PITUITARY AND OVARY OF THE WHITE RAT FOLLOWING EXPOSURE TO CONSTANT LIGHT OR DARKNESS. Gerard Roland Pomerat. Anat. Record, Phila., vol.82, no.4, pp. 531-542, Apr.25, 1942.

MITOTIC ACTIVITY IN THE PITUITARY OF THE WHITE RAT FOLLOWING CASTRATION. Gerard Roland Pomerat. Amer. Jour. Anat., Phila., vol.69, no.1, pp.89-121, figs.3, pls.2, July 15, 1941.

PIGMENT CELL MIGRATION IN MOUSE EPIDERMIS. Sheldon C. Reed, J. M. Henderson. Jour. Exper. Zool., Phila., vol.85, no.3, pp.409-418, Dec.5, 1940.

A CYTOLOGICAL STUDY OF THE CARTILAGE CELLS OF DEVELOPING LONG BONES OF THE RAT, WITH SPECIAL REFERENCE TO THE GOLGI APPARATUS, MITOCHONDRIA, NEUTRAL-RED BODIES AND LIPID INCLUSIONS. John F. Sheehan. Jour. Morphol., Phila., vol.82, no.2, pp. 151-199, pls.1-5, Mar., 1948.

ON THE ORIGIN AND MIGRATION OF THE SO-CALLED PRIMORDIAL GERM CELLS IN THE MOUSE AND THE RAT. C. S. Simpkins. Acta Zool., vol.4, pp.241-285, 6 pls., 1923.

A STUDY OF THE NUCLEUS IN THE NORMAL AND HYPERPLASTIC LIVER OF THE RAT. Norman Sulkin. Amer. Jour. Anat., Phila., vol.73, no.1, pp.107-125, figs.5, July, 1943.

SOME PROPERTIES OF LIVING THYROID CELLS AND FOLLICLES. (LABORATORY RATS AND MICE.) Roy G. Williams. Amer. Jour. Anat., Phila., vol.75, no.1, pp.95-119, fig.1, pl.1, July, 1944.

THE OCCURRENCE AND FORMATION OF BINUCLEATE AND MULTINUCLEATE CELLS AND POLYPLOID NUCLEI IN THE MOUSE LIVER. J. Walter Wilson, Elizabeth H. Leduc. Amer. Jour. Anat., Phila., vol.82, no.3, pp.353-392, pls.1-3, May, 1948.

SOME PHASES OF SPERMATOGENESIS IN THE MOUSE. Harry B. Yocom. Univ. Calif. Publ. Zool., Berkeley, vol.16, no. 19, pp.371-380, pl.30, Jan.22, 1917.

Dentition

HISTOCHEMICAL STUDIES OF PHOSPHATASE DISTRIBUTION IN DEVELOPING TEETH OF ALBINO RAT. Milton B. Engel, William Furuta. Proc. Soc. Exper. Biol. and Med., Utica, vol.50, no.1, pp.5-9, May, 1942.

THE DEVELOPMENT OF THE MOLAR PATTERN OF THE MOUSE (MUS MUSCULUS). W. A. Gaunt. Acta Anatomica, Basel, vol.24, nos.3-4, pp.249-267, 1955.

THE EFFECTS OF SIMULATED ALTITUDES UPON THE INCISOR OF THE RAT. I. Gersh, J. S. Restarski. Anat. Record, Phila., vol.90, no.3, pp.191-194, pl.1, Nov., 1944.

TWO CASES OF ABNORMAL INCISORS IN WHITE RATS. J. E. Guthrie. Proc. Iowa Acad. Sci., vol.37, pp.379-380, figs. 6, (1930) 1931.

(ON THE VARIABILITY OF THE MOLAR ROOTS OF THE UPPER JAW IN SOME APODEMUS SPECIES.) Ueber die Variabilitaet der Molaren-Wurzeln des Oberkiefers bei einigen Apodemus-Arten. Werner Herold. Wissensch. Zeitschr. Humboldt-Univ. Berlin, Math.-Nat. Reihe Jg.6, no.3, pp.237-243, illus., 1957.

THE DENTAL FORMULA OF THE MURIDAE WITH ESPECIAL REFERENCE TO THE "MP.4 THEORY." Martin A. C. Hinton. Ann. and Mag. Nat. Hist., ser.9, vol.11, pp.162-170, Jan., 1923.

QUANTITATIVE STUDIES IN THE DEVELOPMENT OF THE RAT MOLAR. I. THE GROWTH PATTERN OF THE PRIMARY AND SECONDARY DENTIN (FROM BIRTH TO 500 DAYS OF AGE). M. M. Hoffman, I. Schour. Anat. Record, Phila., vol.78, no.2, pp.233-251, figs.4, pl.1, Oct.25, 1940.

THE DISTRIBUTION OF CARIOUS CAVITIES IN THE LOWER MOLARS AND OF CARIES-SUSCEPTIBLE AND CARIES-RESISTANT ALBINO RATS (RATTUS NORVEGICUS). H. R. Hunt, C. A. Hoppert. Jour. Dental Research, St. Louis, vol.29, no.2, pp.157-164, Apr., 1950.

ON THE ATTRITION AND EXTRUSIVE GROWTH OF THE INCISORS IN A FORMOSAN WILD RAT, RATTUS LOSEA (SWINHOE). Kitao Huruhata. Jour. Soc. Trop. Agric., Formosa, vol.12, no.3, pp.171-182, Nov., 1940. (In Japanese, with English resumé.)

ENAMEL FORMATION IN THE RAT'S INCISOR TOOTH. J. T. Irving. Nature, London, vol.158, no.4014, p.486, illus., Oct.5, 1946.

ENAMEL ORGAN OF THE RAT'S INCISOR TOOTH IN VITAMIN E DEFICIENCY. J. T. Irving. Nature, London, vol.150, no.3795, pp.122-123, figs.A-E, July 25, 1942.

THE OCCURRENCE OF AN EYE AND OF A TOOTH ABNORMALITY IN A LINE OF ALBINO RATS. Elizabeth Jones. Anat. Record, vol.29, p.142, Dec.25, 1924.

ON THE DENTAL CHARACTERS OF CERTAIN AUSTRALIAN RATS. F. Wood Jones. Proc. Zool. Soc. Lond., pp.587-598, 12 figs., Sept., 1922.

MALOCCLUSION IN THE RAT. Richard H. Manville. Jour. Mam., vol.35, no.3, p. 427, Aug.20, 1954.

FRACTURING OF THE MOLAR TEETH IN CARIES-SUSCEPTIBLE AND CARIES-RESISTANT ALBINO RATS (RATTUS NORVEGICUS). E. C. Nakfoor, H. R. Hunt, C. A. Hoppert. Jour. Dental Research, St. Louis, vol.31, no.1, pp.143-150, illus., Feb., 1952.

THE GROWTH PATTERN AND DAILY RHYTHM OF THE INCISOR OF THE RAT. Isaac Schour, Sherwood R. Steadman. Anat. Record, vol.63, no.4, pp.325-332, figs.4, Nov.25, 1935.

ABNORMAL DENTAL GROWTH IN A RAT. R. L. Soni. Jour. Bombay Nat. Hist. Soc., vol.38, no.1, pp.181-183, illus., Aug.15, 1935.

(ON AN ABNORMAL RAT DENTITION.) Ueber ein abnormes Rattengebiss. R. Wiedersheim. Anatomischen Anzeiger, Jena, vol.22, no.25, pp.569-573, figs.4, 1903.

AN ANALYSIS OF THE RELATIVE GROWTH-RATES WITHIN THE INCISOR TOOTH OF THE RAT. J. L. Wierda. Anat. Record, Phila., vol.83, no.4, pp. 495-501, figs.2, Aug.25, 1942.

ALLEGED INCREASE IN DIAMETER OF ALBINO RAT MOLARS AFTER ERUPTION. Horace Elmer Wood. Jour. Mam., vol.9, no.1, pp.67-68, Feb., 1928.

DO RAT MOLARS GROW, DIAMETRICALLY, AFTER ERUPTION? Horace Elmer Wood. Jour. Dental Research, vol.15, no.1, pp.9-15, Feb., 1935.

REFUTATION OF THE ALLEGED DIAMETRIC GROWTH OF ERUPTED RAT MOLARS. Horace Elmer Wood, Florence Dowden Wood. Anat. Record, Phila., vol. 48, no.1, pp.169-183, Jan., 1931.

Diseases and Parasites

(CONTRIBUTION REGARDING INFECTION OF THE MOUSE WITH CARCOCYSTIS TENELLA.) Beitrag zur Infektion der Maus mit Sarcocystis tenella. Kei Arai. Archiv. Protistenkunde, vol.50, pp.213-218, 1 fig., 1 pl., Jan.24, 1925.

AN ANALYSIS OF ECTOPARASITES AND THEIR RAT HOSTS IN THE CITY OF DETROIT. William A. Ashe. Master's thesis, Univ. Detroit, 1952.

CARRIAGE OF PLAGUE BY THE COMMON BROWN RAT (RATTUS NORVEGICUS). S. A. Barnett. Nature, 157 (3978): 105, Jan.26, 1946.

ON A TRICHOSTRONGYLID NEMATODE FROM THE WOOD-MOUSE (APODEMUS SYLVATICUS). H. A. Baylis. Ann. and Mag. Nat. Hist., ser.9, vol.18, pp.455-464, illus., Nov., 1926.

A STRAIN OF TYPHUS RICKETTSIAE ISOLATED FROM THE BRAIN OF A WILD RAT IN CALIFORNIA. M. Dorthy Beck, Howard L. Bodily, Rosemary O'Donnell. Pub. Health Rep., 59 (22): 701-712, June 2, 1944.

(THE FINDING OF SCHIZOTRYPANUM CRUZI IN A RAT.) Hallazgo de Schizotrypanum cruzi en una rata (Rattus norvegicus) en la Ciudad de Mexico. E. Beltran, R. Perez. Rev. Inst. Salubridad y Enferm. Trop., vol.10, no.3, pp.235-238, illus., 1949.

A RAT PLAGUE IN TEA NURSERIES. Charles Bernard. De Thee, Batavia, vol. 7, no.1, pp.18-20, pl.3, 1926.

WEIL'S DISEASE, REPORT OF ELEVEN CASES. Lemann H. Bounds, Richard M. Kingery. U.S. Naval Med. Bull., Wash., vol.46, no.12, pp.1808-1812, Dec., 1946.

STUDIES WITH SHIGELLA DYSENTERIAE (SHIGA). I. INFECTION AND TOXIN ACTION IN MICE. S. E. Branham, S. A. Carlin. Jour. Infectious Diseases, Chicago, vol.83, no.1, pp.60-65, July-Aug., 1948.

STUDIES WITH SHIGELLA DYSENTERIAE (SHIGA). II. THE EFFECT OF SERUMS ON EXPERIMENTAL INFECTION AND INTOXICATION IN MICE. S. E. Branham, S. A. Carlin. Jour. Infectious Diseases, Chicago, vol.83, no.1, pp.66-77, July-Aug., 1948.

A STRAIN OF ENDEMIC TYPHUS FEVER ISOLATED FROM THE BRAIN OF A WILD RAT. George D. Brigham. Pub. Health Rept., 51 (13): 337-339, Mar., 1936.

ENDEMIC TYPHUS VIRUS IN MICE. George D. Brigham. Publ. Health Repts., vol.53, no.29, pp.1251-1256, July 22, 1938.

A STRAIN OF ENDEMIC TYPHUS FEVER VIRUS ISOLATED FROM HOUSE MICE (MUS MUSCULUS MUSCULUS). George D. Brigham, Edgar G. Pickens. Publ. Health Repts., 58 (4): 135-136, Jan.22, 1943.

AN UNSUSPECTED RELATIONSHIP BETWEEN THE VIRUSES OF VACCINIA AND INFECTIONS ECTROMELIA OF MICE. F. M. Burnet. Nature, London, vol.155, no.3940, p.543, May 5, 1945.

EXPERIMENTS WITH MICE AND FLEAS. I. THE BABY MOUSE. P. A. Buxton. Parasitology, Cambridge, vol.39, nos.1-2, pp.119-124, July, 1948.

HELMINTHS IN RATS FROM PANAMA CITY AND SUBURBS. Carlos Calero M., Pedro Ortiz O., Lionel de Souza. Jour. Parasitol., Lancaster, vol.36, no.5, p. 426, Oct., 1950.

INTESTINAL PROTOZOA AND CECAL MATERIAL IN RATS. David Causey. Science, n.s., vol.70, p.68, July 19, 1929.

EPIDEMIC DIARRHEAL DISEASE OF SUCKLING MICE. III. THE EFFECT OF STRAIN, LITTER, AND SEASON UPON THE INCIDENCE OF THE DISEASE. F. S. Cheever, J. H. Mueller. Jour. Exper. Med., Balto., vol.88, no.3, pp.309-316, Sept.1, 1948.

THE PHENOMENON OF INTRO HEMOLYSIS PRODUCED BY THE RICKETTSIAE OF TYPHUS FEVER, WITH A NOTE ON THE MECHANISM OF RICKETTSIAE TOXICITY IN MICE. D. H. Clarke, J. P. Fox. Jour. Exper. Med., Balto., vol.88, no.1, pp.25-41, July 1, 1948.

THE EFFECT OF TEMPERATURE ON THE SEX RATIO OF XENOPSYLLA CHEOPIS RECOVERED FROM LIVE RATS. La Mont C. Cole. U.S. Publ. Health Repts., Wash., vol.60, no.45, pp.1337-1342, Nov.9, 1945.

A NEW NEMATODE FROM THE RAT AND ITS LIFE HISTORY. Eloise B. Cram. Proc. U.S. Nat. Mus., vol.68, art.15, pp. 1-7, pls.1-2, Feb., 1926.

RAT PLAGUES IN WESTERN QUEENSLAND. A. C. Crombie. Nature, London, vol.154, no.3921, pp.803-804, Dec.23, 1944.

RATS AND THEIR FLEAS. Charles E. Crowe. Amer. Field, Chicago, vol.150, no.49, pp.726-727, illus., Dec.4, 1948.

NATURAL TRANSMISSION OF IMMUNITY AGAINST TRICHINELLA SPIRALIS FROM MOTHER RATS TO THEIR OFFSPRING. James T. Culbertson. Jour. Parasitol., Lancaster, vol.29, no.2, pp.114-116, Apr., 1943.

IMMUNIZATION OF MICE WITH UNMODIFIED MM MOUSE ENCEPHALOMYELITIS VIRUS AND ON PASSIVE PROTECTION FROM IMMUNE MOTHERS. F. J. Curley, J. E. Gordon. Amer. Jour. Hygiene, Lancaster, vol.48, no.1, pp.81-86, July, 1948.

THE CONTROL OF RAT FLEAS (XENOPSYLLA CHEOPSIS) BY DDT. David E. Davis. U.S. Publ. Health Repts., Wash., vol.60, no.18, pp.485-489, May 4, 1945.

OBSERVATIONS ON RAT ECTOPARASITES AND TYPHUS FEVER IN SAN ANTONIO, TEXAS. David E. Davis. Publ. Health Repts., 66 (52): 1717-1726, Dec., 1951.

OBSERVATIONS ON RATS AND TYPHUS FEVER IN SAN ANTONIO, TEXAS. David E. Davis. Publ. Health Repts., 63 (24): 783-790, June 11, 1948.

THE RELATION BETWEEN THE LEVEL OF POPULATION AND THE PREVALENCE OF LEPTOSPIRA, SALMONELLA, AND CAPILLARIA IN NORWAY RATS. David E. Davis. Ecology, Brookly, vol.32, no.3, pp.465-468, July, 1951.

THE USE OF DDT TO CONTROL MURINE TYPHUS FEVER IN SAN ANTONIO, TEXAS. David E. Davis. Publ. Health Repts., 62 (13): 449-463, Mar.28, 1947.

PRELIMINARY NOTE ON A RAT PLAGUE IN NORTH-WEST QUEENSLAND. G. M. Dunnet. C.S.I.R.O., Wildlife Res., Melbourne, 1 (2): 131-132, Dec., 1956.

HISTOPLASMOSIS IN WILD RATS. C. W. Emmons, L. L. Ashburn. Publ. Health Repts., 63 (44): 1416-1422, Oct.29, 1948.

NATURALLY OCCURRING HISTOPLASMOSIS IN MUS MUSCULUS AND RATTUS NORVEGICUS. C. W. Emmons, Joseph A. Bell, Byron J. Olson. U.S. Publ. Health

Repts., Wash., vol.62, no.46, pp.1642-1646, Nov.14, 1947.

(RESEARCH ON THE CHEMOTHERAPY OF RATS INFESTED WITH STRONGYLOIDES.) Recherches de chimiothérapie sur la strongyloidose des rats. Albert Erhardt, Karl Denecke. Annal. de Parasitologie Humaine et Comparée, Paris, vol.17, no.3, pp.199-205, May, 1939.

TSUTSUGAMUSHI DISEASE ON SAMAR, PHILIPPINE ISLANDS; RATS AS A RESERVOIR OF THE DISEASE. Allison F. Errington, Others. U.S. Naval Med. Bull., Wash., vol.46, no.11, pp.1669-1673, Nov., 1946.

MURINE TYPHUS FEVER CONTROL. C. R. Eskey. Publ. Health Repts., 58 (16): 631-638, Apr.16, 1943.

TRANSMISSION OF SALMONELLA ENTERITIDIS BY THE RAT FLEA XENOPSYLLA CHEOPIS AND NOSOPSYLLUS FASCIATUS. C. R. Eskey, Frank M. Prince, Frank B. Fuller. U.S. Publ. Health Repts., Wash., vol.64, no.30, pp.933-941, July 29, 1949.

ECTOPARASITES OF SOME POLYNESIAN AND MALAYSIAN RATS OF THE GENUS RATTUS. H. E. Ewing. Bernice P. Bishop Mus., bull.14, pp.8-11, 1924.

THE INFECTION OF RATS BY TRYPANOSOMES (T. RHODESIENSE) TAKEN FROM MAN EARLY IN THE DISEASE. H. Fairbairn. Ann. Trop. Med. and Parasitol., Liverpool, vol.41, no.2, pp.218-225, 1947.

ON THE CHARACTERISTICS OF THE HELMINTH FAUNA OF HILLOCK (HOUSE) MICE (MUS MUSCULUS HORTULANUS NORDM.) IN THE NORTHERN CAUCASUS REGION, AND THE CONNECTION BETWEEN INFECTION BY HELMINTHS AND INFECTION BY A STREPTOCOCCUS. T. V. Fedorova, V. A. Chizhova, A. A. Shmeleva. Rev. Microbiol., 12 (3): 183-188, 1933.

NUMBER OF LARVAE AND TIME REQUIRED TO PRODUCE ACTIVE IMMUNITY IN RATS AGAINST TRICHINELLA SPIRALIS. Jacob H. Fischthal. Jour. Parasitol., Lancaster, vol.29, no.2, pp.123-126, Apr., 1943.

SUSCEPTIBILITY TO TYPHUS OF RATS ON DEFICIENT DIETS. F. K. Fitzpatrick. Amer. Jour. Publ. Health, Albany, vol.38, no.5, pp.676-681, May, 1948; Trop. Disease Bull., Lond., vol.45, no.9, p.781, Sept., 1948.

HELMINTHS FROM THE NORWAY RAT IN NORTHEASTERN OHIO. William C. Forbes. Jour. Parasitology, 28 (5): 431, Oct., 1942.

A COMPARATIVE STUDY OF RAT-FLEA DATA FOR SEVERAL SEAPORTS OF THE UNITED STATES. Carroll Fox, E. C. Sullivan. U.S. Publ. Health Service, reprint no.1039 from Publ. Health Repts., Sept.11, 1925, pp.1909-1934, 28 pp., 16 charts, 1925.

ORNITHODOROS PUERTORICENSIS, A NEW TICK FROM RATS IN PUERTO RICO. Irving Fox. Jour. Parasitol., Balto., vol.33, no.3, pp.253-259, June, 1947.

RELATIVE AND SEASONAL ABUNDANCE OF THE COMMON RAT ECTOPARASITES OF SAN JUAN, PUERTO RICO. Irving Fox. Jour. Parasitol., Lancaster, vol.37, no.1, pp.85-95, Feb., 1951.

THREE NEW MITES FROM RATS IN PUERTO RICO. Irving Fox. Proc. Biol. Soc. Wash., vol.59, pp.173-176, figs.3, Dec.23, 1946.

TRANSMISSION OF TULARAEMIA BY THE MOUSE LOUSE, POLYPLAX SERRATUS (BURM). Edward Francis, G. C. Lake. U.S. Publ. Health Service, Hygienic Lab., bull.no.130, pp.38-43, Mar., 1922.

A STUDY ON THE INCIDENCE OF TRICHINOSIS IN WILD RATS IN THE MARITIME PROVINCES. J. F. Frank. Can. Jour. Compar. Med. and Vet. Sci., 15: 279-283, 1951.

STUDIES ON EXPERIMENTAL CHAGAS' DISEASE IN MICE IN RELATION TO CHEMOTHERAPEUTIC TESTING. Frans C. Goble. Jour. Parasitol., Lancaster, vol.37, no.4, pp.408-414, Aug., 1951.

MURINE TYPHUS FEVER IN LOUISVILLE, KENTUCKY. (RATTUS NORVEGICUS.) Newell E. Good, Emil Kotcher. U.S. Publ. Health Repts., Wash., vol.68, no.8, pp.229-237, Feb.25, 1949.

NEW PARASITIC MITES FROM NEW GUINEA (ACARINA: PARASITIDAE). Carl E. M. Gunther. Proc. Linnean Soc. New South Wales, Sydney, vol.67, pt.1-2, nos.299-300, pp.87-89, figs.14, May 15, 1942.

TWO NEW TROMBIDIID LARVAE FROM NEW GUINEA (ACARINA: TROMBIDIIDAE). Carl E. M. Gunther. Proc. Linnean Soc. New South Wales, Sydney, vol.66, nos.295-296, pts.3-4, pp.157-159, figs.5, 1941.

COMMON INFECTIONS AND DISEASE CONDITIONS OBSERVED IN WILD NORWAY RATS KEPT UNDER SIMULATED NATURAL CONDITIONS. R. T. Habermann, F. P. Williams, W.T.S. Thorp. Amer. Jour. Vet. Res., 15 (54): 152-156, illus., Jan., 1954.

PRELIMINARY STUDIES OF FLEAS ON RATS (RATTUS NORVEGICUS) IN NEW JERSEY. Elton J. Hansens, John Hadjinicolaou. Jour. N. Y. Ent. Soc., 60 (2): 91-95, June, 1952.

A PARASITOLOGICAL SURVEY OF WILD RATS IN THE NEW YORK ZOOLOGICAL PARK. Carlton M. Herman. Zoologica, 24 (3): 305-308, Nov., 1939.

A STUDY OF MURINE TYPHUS FEVER IN COFFEE COUNTY, ALABAMA. E. L. Hill, Samuel C. Ingraham II. Publ. Health Repts., 62 (24): 875-881, June 13, 1947.

EVALUATION OF COUNTY-WIDE DDT DUSTING OPERATIONS IN MURINE TYPHUS CONTROL. E. L. Hill, H. B. Morlan. Publ. Health Repts., 63 (51): 1635-1653, Dec.17, 1948.

THE BLACK RAT AS A NATIONAL MENACE. A ROOF CLIMBER THAY MAY BRING BACK THE PLAGUE. Martin A. C. Hinton. Field, London, vol.162, no.4223, p.1421, illus., Dec.2, 1933.

RICKETTSIAL POX—A NEWLY RECOGNIZED RICKETTSIAL DISEASE. Robert J. Huebner, William L. Jellison, Charles Pomerantz. U.S. Publ. Health Repts., Wash., vol.61, no.47, pp.1677-1682, Nov. 22, 1946; U.S. Publ. Health Repts., Wash., vol.62, no.22, pp.777-780, May 30, 1947.

A SURVEY OF THE HELMINTHS AND ECTOPARASITES OF ROOF AND COTTON RATS IN BRAZOS COUNTY, TEXAS. Ernest J. Hugghins. Amer. Midland Nat., 46 (1): 230-244, July, 1951.

ANTI-PLAGUE MEASURES IN TACOMA, WASHINGTON. James M. Hundley, Kaarlo W. Nasi. Publ. Health Repts., 59 (38): 1239-1255, Sept.22, 1944.

THE DISTRIBUTION OF ENDEMIC TYPHUS IN RATS IN LAVACA COUNTY, TEXAS. J. V. Irons, J. N. Murphy, Jr., David E. Davis. Publ. Health Repts., 63 (21): 692-694, May 21, 1948; Trop. Disease Bull., London, vol.45, no.9, p.780, Sept., 1948.

ROCKY MOUNTAIN SPOTTED FEVER. THE SUSCEPTIBILITY OF MICE. W. L. Jellison. U.S. Treas. Dept., Publ. Health Repts., Wash., vol.49, no.11, pp.363-367, Mar.16, 1934.

RAT-BITE FEVER IN MONTANA. W. L. Jellison, Paul L. Eneboe, R. R. Parker, Lyndahl E. Hughes. U.S. Publ. Health Repts., Wash., vol.64, no.52, pp.1661-1665, Dec.30, 1949.

COMPARATIVE SUSCEPTIBILITY OF DIFFERENT STRAINS OF MICE TO RABIES VIRUS. Harald N. Johnson, Charles N. Leach. Amer. Jour. Hygiene, vol.32, no. 2, sec.B, pp.38-45, Sept., 1940.

OBSERVATIONS ON RATS IN A ENZOOTIC PLAGUE REGION OF HAWAII. Leo Kartman, Richard P. Lonergan. Publ. Health Repts., U.S. Public Health Service, Wash., vol.70, no.6, pp.585-593, June, 1955.

EFFECTS OF THIAMIN DEFICIENCY ON WESTERN EQUINE ENCEPHALOMYELITIS IN MICE. E. B. Kearni, W. L. Pond, B.A. Plass, K. H. Maddy, C. A. Elvehjem, P. F. Clark. Jour. Infectious Diseases, Chicago, vol.82, no.2, pp.177-186, Mar.-Apr., 1948.

ECTOPARASITISM OF NORWAY RATS IN AN INLAND NEW ENGLAND VILLAGE AND IN A NEW ENGLAND SEAPORT. Herbert Knutson, Raymond T. Szymkowicz. Jour. Econ. Ent., 45 (2): 338-339, Apr., 1952.

HAEMAPHYSALIS RATTI, A NEW SPECIES OF TICK FROM RATS IN NEW GUINEA AND HAEMAPHYSALIS KRIJGSMANI, NEW NAME FOR HAEMAPHYSALIS NOVAE-GUINEAE KRIJGSMAN AND PONTO, 1932, PRE-OCCUPIED. Glen M. Kohls. Jour. Parasitol., Lancaster, vol.34, no.2, pp. 154-157, Apr., 1948.

TRICHINOSIS IN WILD RATS IN TORONTO. E. Kuitunen-Ekbaum, Dorothy Webster. Can. Jour. Publ. Health, 38 (2): 76-78, Feb., 1947.

THE RELATIONSHIP BETWEEN THE INTESTINAL SIZE OF YOUNG MICE AND THEIR SUSCEPTIBILITY TO INFECTION WITH THE CESTODE, HYMENOLEPIS NANA VAR. FRATERNA. John E. Larsh, Jr. Jour. Parasitol., Lancaster, vol.29, no.1, pp.61-64, Feb., 1943.

FURTHER STUDIES IN MICE ON THE EFFECT OF ALCOHOL ON ACQUIRED IMMUNITY TO TRICHINELLA SPIRALIS. John E. Larsh, Jr., Orlin K. Fletcher, Jr. Jour. Elisha Mitchell Sci. Soc., Chapel Hill, vol.64, no.2, pp.196-203, Dec., 1948.

IMMUNIZATION OF WHITE RATS AGAINST INFECTIONS WITH PASTEURELLA TULARENSIS. Carl L. Larson. U.S. Publ. Health Repts., Wash., vol.60, no.26, pp. 725-734, June 29, 1945.

LEPTOSPIROSIS IN RATS (R. NORVEGICUS) IN AND ABOUT WASHINGTON, D.C. Carl L. Larson. U.S. Publ. Health Repts., Wash., D.C., vol.58, no.25, pp.949-955, June 18, 1943.

THE PREVALENCE OF CARRIERS OF LEPTOSPIRA AND SALMONELLA IN NORWAY RATS OF BALTIMORE. Huan-Ying Li, David E. Davis. Amer. Jour. Hyg., 56 (1): 90-100, July, 1952.

(VERIFICATION OF MURINE LEPROSY IN THE CITY OF RIO DE JANEIRO. ITS GEOGRAPHIC DISTRIBUTION AND ENDEMIOLOGIC CONSIDERATIONS.) Verificacao da lepra murina na cidade do Rio de Janeiro. Sua distribuicao geografica e consideracoes endemiologicas. Herminio Linhares. Mem. Inst. Oswaldo Cruz, Rio de Janeiro, vol.37, no.3, pp.353-373, Sept., 1942.

THE INCIDENCE OF MAMMARY CANCER IN A CROSS BETWEEN TWO STRAINS OF MICE. C. C. Little, B. W. McPheters. Amer. Nat., vol.66, no.707, pp.568-571, Nov.-Dec., 1932.

THE CONTROL OF RAT ECTOPARASITES WITH DDT. Russell G. Ludwin, H. P. Nicholson. Publ. Health Repts., 62 (3): 77-84, Jan.17, 1947.

HELMINTH PARASITES OF CERTAIN RATS IN INDIA. P. A. Maplestone, N. V. Bhaduri. Records Indian Mus., Calcutta, vol.44, pt.2, pp.201-206, illus., Aug., 1942.

EXPECTED PLAGUE OF FIELD RATS IN 1920. W. S. Millard. Bombay Nat. Hist. Soc., vol.27, pp.165-168, July 1, 1920.

COMPARATIVE INFESTATIONS BY ECTOPARASITES OF TWO NATIVE RATS OF SANSAPOR, NEW GUINEA. Carl O. Mohr. Amer. Midland Nat., 55 (2): 382-392, illus., Apr., 1956.

ENTOMOLOGICAL BACKGROUND OF THE DISTRIBUTION OF MURINE TYPHUS AND MURINE PLAGUE IN THE UNITED STATES.

Carl O. Mohr. Amer. Jour. Trop. Med., Balto., vol.31, no.3, pp.355-372, illus., May, 1951.

ERADICATION OF MURINE TYPHUS FEVER IN A RURAL AREA. Carl O. Mohr, William W. Smith. Preliminary Report, Bull. World Health Organization, 16: 255-266, 1957.

(THE RELATION OF MURINE PETECHIAL FEVER TO CLASSIC PETECHIAL FEVER.) Die Beziehungen des murinen Fleckfiebers zum klassischen Fleckfieber. Hermann Mooser. Acta Tropica, Basel, suppl.4, pp.1-87, figs.2, 1945. (In German, with French and English summaries.)

ECTOPARASITES OF DOMESTIC RATS AND MICE AND THE DISEASES THEY TRANSMIT. Harvey B. Morlan. Pests and Their Control, Cleveland, vol.16, no. 12, pp.16-20, illus., Dec., 1948.

SEROLOGICAL SURVEY FOR MURINE TYPHUS INFECTION IN SOUTHWEST GEORGIA ANIMALS. Harvey B. Morlan, E. L. Hill, J. H. Schubert. Publ. Health Repts., Wash., vol.65, no.2, pp.57-63, Jan.13, 1950.

DOMESTIC RATS, RAT ECTOPARASITES, AND TYPHUS CONTROL. Harvey B. Morlan, B. C. Utterback, J. E. Dent, M. J. Wilcomb, Jr., M. E. Griffith, L. L. Ellis. Public Health Monog., no.5, 38 pp., 1952.

CHANGES IN THE GLUCOSE METABOLISM OF TRYPANOSOMA LEWISI DURING THE COURSE OF INFECTION IN THE RAT. J. W. Moulder. Jour. Infectious Diseases, Chicago, vol.83, no.1, pp.42-49, July-Aug., 1948.

ENTAMOEBA HISTOLYTICA IN WILD RATS CAUGHT IN LONDON. R. A. Neal. Jour. Hygiene, London, vol.46, no.1, pp. 90-93, pls.4, Mar., 1948.

ENTAMOEBA MURIS: A COMPLICATING FACTOR IN THE EXPERIMENTAL INFECTION OF RATS WITH E. HISTOLYTICA. R. A. Neal. Nature, London, vol.163, no. 4133, pp.99-100, Jan.15, 1949.

THE NASAL TRANSMISSION OF PLEURO-PNEUMONIA-LIKE ORGANISMS IN MICE AND RATS. John B. Nelson. Jour. Infectious Diseases, Chicago, vol.82, no.2, pp.169-176, Mar.-Apr., 1948.

SERUM TREATMENT OF WESTERN EQUINE ENCEPHALITIS IN MICE DETERMINED BY THE COURSE OF VIRAL INFECTION. P. K. Olitsky, A. C. Saenz. Proc. Soc. Exper. Biol. Med., Utica, vol. 68, no.1, pp.200-204, May, 1948.

EPIDEMIC DIARRHEAL DISEASE OF SUCKLING MICE. IV. CYTOPLASMIC INCLUSION BODIES IN INTESTINAL EPITHELIUM IN RELATION TO THE DISEASE. A. M. Pappenheimer, F. S. Cheever. Jour. Exper. Med., Balto., vol. 88, no.3, pp.317-324, Sept.1, 1948.

TOXOPLASMOSIS IN WILD RATS. Theodore L. Perrin, George D. Brigham, Edgar G. Pickens. Jour. Infectious Dis., 72 (1): 91-96, Feb., 1943.

NOTE ON THE FIELD MOUSE, APODEMUS SPECIOSUS, AS A MITE HOST IN YAMAGATA-KEN. Cornelius B. Philip, Takeo Tamiya. Nippon Eiseigaku Zasshi (Japenses Jour. Health), vol.1, no.1, pp.15-16, Aug., 1946.

MOUSE PLAGUES, THEIR CONTROL AND PREVENTION. Stanley E. Piper. Yearbook, U.S. Dept. Agric., Wash., D. C., 1908, pp.301-310, pls.21-25, 1909.

DISTRIBUTION OF SOME COMMON DOMESTIC RAT ECTOPARASITES IN THE UNITED STATES. Harry D. Pratt, Newell E. Good. Jour. Parasit., 40 (2): 113-129, graph, maps, Apr., 1954.

SPECIES OF FLEAS ON RATS COLLECTED IN STATES WEST OF THE 102D MERIDIAN AND THEIR RELATION TO THE DISSEMINATION OF PLAGUE. F. M. Prince. Publ. Health Repts., 58 (18): 700-708, Apr. 30, 1943.

HAPLOPLEURA OENOMYDIS FERRIS, A LOUSE FOUND ON DOMESTIC RATS IN THE UNITED STATES. A. Earl Pritchard. Jour. Parasitology, Lancaster, vol.33, no. 4, pp.374-375, Aug., 1947.

MITES FOUND UPON THE WHITE RAT. C. D. Radford. Northwestern Nat., Arbroath, vol.10, no.1, p.42, Mar., 1935.

(RATS AND THEIR FLEAS IN RELATION TO HUMAN PATHOLOGY AT SHANGHAI.) Les rats et les puces du rat dans leurs rapports avee la pathologie humaine a Chang-Hai. J. H. Raynal. Bull. Soc. Path. Exot., Paris, vol.40, nos.5-6, pp.212-238, 1947.

A STUDY OF THE GENUS HEMIMERUS (DERMAPTERA, HEMIMERINA, HEMIMERIDAE). (ECTOPARASITES ON MAMMALS, CHIEFLY CRICETOMYS.) James A. G. Rehn, John W. H. Rehn. Proc. Acad. Sci. Phila., vol.87, pp.457-508, Jan.14, 1936.

INVESTIGATIONS ON THE LIFE CYCLE OR OOCHORISTICA RATTI, A CESTODE FROM RATS AND MICE. R. C. Rendtorff. Jour. Parasitol., Lancaster, vol.34, no.3, pp.243-251, June, 1948.

INCIDENCE OF RAT BITES AND RAT BITE FEVER IN BALTIMORE. Curt P. Richter. Jour. Amer. Med. Assoc., Chicago, vol.128, pp.324-326, June 2, 1945.

FURTHER STUDIES OF THE EFFECT OF AGE OF MICE UPON ADULT TRICHINELLA SPIRALIS. Bernard B. Riedel. Jour. Parasitol., Lancaster, vol.36, no.1, pp. 27-28, Feb., 1950.

EPIDEMIOLOGICAL SIGNIFICANCE OF SEASONAL VARIATIONS IN RODENT-ECTOPARASITE DISTRIBUTION. A. S. Rumreich, Jean A. Koepke. Publ. Health Repts., 60 (48): 1421-1428, Nov.30, 1945.

A STUDY OF THE RODENT-ECTOPARASITE POPULATION OF JACKSONVILLE, FLA. A. S. Rumreich, R. S. Wynn. Publ. Health Rept., 60 (31): 885-905, Aug.3, 1945.

STUDIES ON THE HELMINTH FAUNA OF ALASKA V. NOTES ON ADAK RATS (RATTUS NORVEGICUS BERKENHOUT) WITH SPECIAL REFERENCE TO HELMINTH PARASITES. Everett L. Schiller. Jour. Mam., 33 (1): 38-49, illus., Feb., 1952.

COMMON ECTOPARASITES OF THE NORWAY RAT, RATTUS NORVEGICUS (ERXL.), IN NORTH CAROLINA AND THE EFFECTS OF 10 PER CENT DDT DUST TREATMENTS IN THEIR CONTROL AND UPON THE SEROLOGY OF THE RAT. N. F. Schoof. Jour. Elisha Mitchell Scientific Soc. Chapel Hill, vol.64, no.2, pp.208-215, Dec., 1948.

THE DEVELOPMENT OF THE TRICHOSTRONGYLE, NIPPOSTRONGYLUS MURIS, IN RATS FOLLOWING INGESTION OF LARVAE. Benjamin Schwartz, Joseph E. Alicata. Jour. Wash. Acad. Sci., vol.24, no.8, pp.334-338, Aug.15, 1934.

THE RELATIONSHIP OF BIOLOGICAL DEFENSE MECHANISMS TO THE ANTIBIOTIC ACTIVITY OF PENICILLIN. I. THE MODIFYING INFLUENCE OF PENICILLIN ON THE PATTERN OF PNEUMOCOCCIC INFECTION AND THE IMMUNE RESPONSE IN THE PROTEIN DEPLETED RAT. O. K. Skinsnes, R. L. Woolridge. Jour. Infectious Diseases, Chicago, vol.83, no.1, pp.77-86, July-Aug., 1948.

STUDIES ON HOST-PARASITE RELATIONS OF RATS AND MICE TO TRICHOSOMOIDES CRASSICAUDA. Vivian S. Smith. PhD thesis, Univ. Ill., 1944.

THE HOUSE MOUSE AND MURINE TYPHUS IN MISSISSIPPI. William W. Smith. Publ. Health Repts., U.S. Public Health Service, Wash., vol.69, no.6, pp.591-593, June, 1954.

SOME POINTS OF GENERAL INTEREST ON THE SUBJECT OF PLAGUE. C. E. Southon. Jour. East Africa and Uganda Nat. Hist. Soc., no.14, pp.361-381, July, 1919.

OBSERVATIONS ON HOST-PARASITE RELATIONS BETWEEN LABORATORY MICE AND NEMATOSPIROIDES DUBIUS BAYLIS. G. M. Spurlock. Jour. Parasitol., Lancaster, vol.29, no.5, pp.303-311, Oct., 1943.

THE PATHOLOGY OF AN EXPERIMENTAL AMOEBIC INFECTION IN THE RAT. G. T. Stewart, W. R. Jones. Ann. Trop. Med. Parasitol., Liverpool, vol.42, no.1, pp.33-45, pl.1, Apr., 1948.

A MINOR PLAGUE OF HOUSE MICE AT DAVIS, CALIFORNIA, IN 1926. Tracy I. Storer. Jour. Mam., vol.12, no.3, pp.316-317, Aug., 1931.

THE NATURE OF SUSCEPTIBILITY TO CANCER IN MICE. Leonell C. Strong. Jour. Heredity, vol.25, no.3, pp.119-121, Mar., 1934.

THE ENGLISH BLACK RAT AS DISSEMINATOR OF DISEASE. Mark R. Taylor. Trans. Suffolk Nat. Soc., vol.2, pt.3, pp.201-203, Dec., 1934.

NOTES ON THE TWO SPECIES OF SIPHUNCULATA OR SUCKING-LICE OCCURRING ON RATTUS SPP. IN THE MALAYAN AND PACIFIC REGIONS, WITH SPECIAL REFERENCE TO JAVA. Gordon B. Thompson. Zool. Mededeel., Leiden, vol.20, nos.3-4, pp.231-236, tables 3, 1938.

RAT PLAGUE IN YETOROFU ISLAND. Mitosi Tokuda. Dobutsugaku Zasshi (Zool. Soc. Japan), Tokyo, pp.441-442. (In Japanese.)

THE NORWAY RAT AND PLAGUE IN MONTANA (ABSTRACT). C. A. Tryon. Proc. Mont. Acad. Sci., 5, 6: 47, 1946.

HELMINTHS OF RATS TRAPPED WITHIN THE CITY LIMITS OF BUFFALO, NEW YORK. Edward Francis Van Jura. MS thesis, Univ. Buffalo, 1948.

HISTOLOGICAL OBSERVATIONS ON THE SKIN REACTION IN WHITE MOUSE TO THE BITES OF IXODES PERSULCATUS P. SCH. Z. V. Volodina. Zool. Jour. USSR, Moscow, vol.21, no.5, pp.179-186, figs.6, table 1, 1942. (English summary.)

A DISEASE IN WILD RATS WITH GROSS PATHOLOGY RESEMBLING PLAGUE. N. E. Wayson. U.S. Publ. Health Repts., vol.40, no.38, pp.1975-1979, 1925.

THE LABORATORY INFECTION OF TRIATOMA NEOTOMAE NEIVA WITH TRYPANOSOMA CRUZI CHAGAS AND SUBSEQUENT TRANSMISSION TO WHITE MICE. Paul P. Weinstein, Harry D. Pratt. Jour. Parasit., Lancaster, vol.34, no.3, pp.231-236, June, 1948.

THE ONE-HOST LIFE-CYCLE OF HYMENOLEPIS FRATERNA, STILES OF THE MOUSE. W.N.F. Woodland. Nature, vol. 112, p.436, Sept.22, 1923.

SEASONAL CHANGES IN ABUNDANCE OF FLEAS ON RATS AT BALTIMORE, MD. James Yeh, David E. Davis. U.S. Publ. Health Repts., Wash., vol.65, no.10, pp. 337-342, Mar.10, 1950.

(INHERITED BRAIN DISEASES OF THE DOMESTIC MOUSE.) Erbliche Gehirnerkrankungen der Hausmaus. K. Zimmermann. Der Erbarzt, Beilage zum Deutschen Aerzteblatt, 1935, no.8, pp.119-123, figs. 3, 1935.

PUBLIC HEALTH SERVICE FIGHTING PLAGUE IN RODENTS. CONCERN FELT OVER REPORTS OF LARGE NUMBERS OF NORWAY RATS IN PLAINS STATES, ALTHOUGH NO GERMS FOUND. Science News Letter, Wash., D.C., vol.42, no.6, p.86, Aug.8, 1942.

Ecology

A TREE MOUSE (VANDELURIA OLERACEA) IN THE NEST OF A SPIDER. H. G. Acharya. Jour. Bombay Nat. Hist. Soc., vol.40, no.4, pp.737-739, May, 1939.

APPROPRIATION OF WREN'S NESTS BY FIELD MICE. Edward A. Armstrong. Irish Nat. Jour., vol.10, no.3, p.73, July, 1950.

COMPETITION AMONG WILD RATS. S. A. Barnett. Nature, London, vol.175, no. 4446, pp.126-127, Jan.15, 1955.

EXODUS OF NORWAY RATS FROM FLOODED AREAS. Floyd B. Chapman. Jour. Mam., vol.19, no.3, pp.376-377, Aug., 1938.

THE ROLE OF INTRASPECIFIC COMPETITION IN GAME MANAGEMENT. David E. Davis. Trans. N.A. Wildl. Conf., 14: 225-231, 1939.

A BROWN RAT KILLS A RATTLER. Carl Hartman. Jour. Mam., vol.3, no.2, pp. 116-117, May, 1922.

AN ECOLOGICAL STUDY OF THE NORWAY RAT AND THE HOUSE MOUSE IN A CITY BLOCK IN LAWRENCE, KANSAS. Otis M. King. MA thesis, Univ. Kansas, 1950; Trans. Kansas Acad. Sci., 53 (4): 500-528, Dec., 1950.

(SOME ECOLOGIC-PHYSICAL CHARACTERISTICS OF THE ORDINARY AND KURGAN HOUSE-MOUSE (MUS MUSCULUS L.).) Nekotovie Ekologo-fiziologicheskie Osobennosti "Domovikh" i kurganchikovikh Domovikh Mishee (Mus musculus L.). M. S. Medvedeva. Zool. Zhurnal, Akad. Nauk SSSR, Moscow, vol.29, no.6, pp.556-558, 1950.

A REVIEW OF THE HISTORY, ECOLOGY AND ECONOMIC IMPORTANCE OF HOUSE MICE. Walter W. Dykstra. Pest Control, 18 (8): 9-14, Aug., 1950.

ON THE BIOLOGY AND ECOLOGY OF APODEMUS AGRARIUS MANTSCHURICUS THOM. AND DYNAMICS OF ITS REPRODUCTION. K. Plyater-Plokhotsky. Bull. Far Eastern Branch Acad. Sci. USSR, Vladivostok, no.19, pp.93-110, figs.10, 1936.

A PRELIMINARY ANALYSIS OF THE PHYSICAL ENVIRONMENT OF THE NORWAY RAT. Holmes Orgain, Martin W. Schein. Ecology, Durham, vol.34, no.4, pp.467-473, July, 1953.

THE INFLUENCE OF THE FLOOD ON SMALL MURIDAE-RODENTS IN THE VOLGA-DELTA. G. V. Romanov. Zool. Zhurnal, Moscow, 36 (12): 1874-1881, 1957. (In Russian, with English summary.)

RAT FOSTER MOTHER OF MICE. Albert R. Shadle. Jour. Mam., vol.26, no.2, pp. 193-194, July 15, 1945.

THE HOUSE-MOUSE (MUS MUSCULUS) IN CORN RICKS. (HABITS AND ECOLOGY IN GRAIN STACKS AND NEARBY FIELDS AND HEDGES IN GREAT BRITAIN.) H. N. Southern, E. M. O. Laurie. Jour. Animal Ecol., 15 (2): 134-149, Nov., 1946.

THE ECOLOGICAL FACTORS DETERMINING GEOGRAPHICAL DISTRIBUTION AND EURYTOPY OF THE FIELD MOUSE (APODEMUS AGRARIUS PALL.). P. A. Sviridenko. Zool. Jour. USSR, Moscow, vol.22, no.5, pp.280-298, figs.11, 1943. (English summary.)

Embryology

IMPLANTATION OF THE RAT EGG. Roland H. Alden. Amer. Jour. Anat., Phila., vol. 83, no.1, pp.143-179, pls.1-6, July, 1948.

THE OVIDUCT AND EGG TRANSPORT IN THE ALBINO RAT. Roland H. Alden. Anat. Record, Phila., vol.84, no.2, pp. 137-169, pls.4, Oct.26, 1942.

VARIATION IN MOUSE EMBRYOS OF 8 DAYS GESTATION. Ezra Allen, E. C. MacDowell. Anat. Record, Phila., vol.77, no.2, pp.165-173, pls.2, June 25, 1940.

THE DEVELOPMENT OF FETAL BEHAVIOR IN THE ALBINO RAT AND ITS CORRELATION WITH THE DEVELOPMENT OF THE NERVOUS SYSTEM. A. W. Angulo. (Summary). Proc. 8th Amer. Sci. Congr., Wash., D.C., vol.3, pp.19-20, Aug.3, 1942.

THE PRENATAL GROWTH OF THE ALBINO RAT. A. W. Angulo y Gonzalez. Anat. Record, vol.52, no.2, pp.117-138, Mar.25, 1932.

THE EFFECT OF DELAYED FERTILIZATION ON THE DEVELOPMENT OF THE RAT OVUM. Richard J. Blandau, Edwin S. Jordan. Amer. Jour. Anat., Phila., vol. 68, no.2, pp.275-291, 2 pls., Mar.15, 1941.

THE FATE OF THE UNFERTILIZED OVA IN THE ALBINO RAT. Richard J. Blandau. Anat. Record, Phila., vol.87, no.1, pp.17-27, pl.1, Sept., 1943.

CALCIFICATION AND OSSIFICATION; CALCIFICATION OF DEVELOPING BONES IN EMBRYONIC AND NEWBORN RATS. William Bloom, Margaret A. Bloom. Anat. Record, Phila., vol.78, no.4, and suppl., pp.497-523, pls.5, Dec.26, 1940.

THE EARLY DEVELOPMENT OF THE SKULL OF OTOMYS TROPICALIS. Frederik Christoffel Eloff. Ann. Transvaal Mus., Cambridge, vol.21, no.1, pp.103-152, figs.10, pl.1, Apr.6, 1948.

EXPERIMENTAL INTERSEXUALITY: THE EFFECTS OF COMBINED ESTROGENS AND ANDROGENS ON THE EMBRYONIC SEXUAL DEVELOPMENT OF THE RAT. R. R. Greene, M. W. Burrill, A. C. Ivy. Jour. Exper. Zool., Phila., vol.87, no.2, pp.211-232, July 5, 1941.

THE DEVELOPMENT OF SOME EXTERNAL FEATURES IN MOUSE EMBRYOS. Hans Gruneberg. Jour. Heredity, Wash., vol.34, no.3, pp.88-92, fig.3, Mar., 1943.

CORPORA LUTEA COUNTS AND THEIR RELATION TO THE NUMBERS OF EMBRYOS IN THE WILD NORWAY RAT. Octavia Hall, David E. Davis. Texas Repts. Biol. and Med., Galveston, vol.8, no.4, pp.564-582, pls.3, Winter, 1950.

THE RELATION OF THE NUMBERS OF CORPORA LUTEA AND OF EMBRYOS IN WILD RATS. Octavia Hall, David E. Davis. Anat. Record, Phila., vol.105, no. 3, pp.41-42, Nov., 1949. (Abstract.)

THE EFFECT OF ROENTGEN IRRADIATION OF SPERM UPON THE EMBRYONIC DEVELOPMENT OF THE ALBINO RAT (MUS NORVEGICUS ALBINUS). Margaret Henson. Jour. Exper. Zool., Phila., vol. 91, no.3, pp.405-433, pls.3, Dec.5, 1942.

IMPLANTATION IN NORMAL AND VITAMIN E DEFICIENT RATS. Hans Kaunitz, C. A. Slanetz. Jour. Nutrition, Phila., vol.36, no.3, pp.331-338, Sept.10, 1948.

THE DEVELOPMENT OF THE EXTERNAL FORM OF THE RAT, WITH OBSERVATIONS ON THE ORIGIN OF THE EXTRA-EMBRYONIC COELOM AND FOETAL MEMBRANES. J. A. Long, Paul L. Burlingame. Univ. Calif. Publ. Zool., vol.43, no.8, pp.143-184, pls.11-23, Apr. 14, 1938.

GROWTH IN VITRO OF OVARIAN GERMINAL EPITHELIUM. (MOUSE.) J. Herman Long. Carnegie Instn. Wash., publ.518, vol.28, no.172, pp.89-93, pls.2, Aug.15, 1940.

THE IMMUNOCHEMISTRY OF MOUSE TISSUE COMPONENTS. III. A COMPARISON OF THE ANTIGENIC COMPOSITION OF EMBRYONIC MOUSE ORGANS WITH THAT OF ADULT MOUSE ORGANS AND WITH MOUSE TUMORS. Esther S. Maculla. Yale Jour. Biol. Med., New Haven, vol.20, no.5, pp.465-472, May, 1948.

STUDIES ON EARLY STAGES OF DEVELOPMENT IN RATS AND MICE. THE LIVING EGGS OF RATS AND MICE WITH A DESCRIPTION OF APPARATUS FOR OBTAINING AND OBSERVING THEM. E. L. Mark, J. A. Long. Univ. Calif. Publ. Zool., vol.9, no.2, pp.105-136, pls.13-17, Feb.23, 1912.

STUDIES ON EARLY STAGES OF DEVELOPMENT IN RATS AND MICE. THE MATURATION OF THE MOUSE EGG. E. L. Mark, J. A. Long. Contrib. Zool. Lab. Mus. Comp. Zool. Harvard Coll., Cambridge, no.224 (from Verhandl. VIII, Internat. Zool. Kongr., Graz, 1910), pp.8, figs.2, Mar., 1912. (In German.)

SURGICAL INVESTIGATION OF THE FUNCTION OF THE INVERTED YOLK SAC PLACENTA IN THE RAT. H. Noer, H. W. Mossman, Anat. Record, Phila., vol.98, no.1, pp.31-37, fig.1, May, 1947.

(EMBRYOLOGICAL AND HISTOLOGICAL RESEARCH ON THE NORMAL SEXUAL DIFFERENTIATION OF THE MOUSE.) (Review by P. Rode, of) Recherches embryologiques et histologiques sur la differenciation sexuelle normale de la souris. A. Raynaud. Mammalia, Paris, 7 (2): 87, June, 1943.

ORIGIN OF PIGMENT CELLS FROM THE NEURAL CREST IN THE MOUSE EMBRYO. Mary E. Rawles. Physiological Zool., Chicago, vol.20, no.3, pp.248-266, pls.1-3, July, 1947.

THE NEOPLASTIC POTENTIALITIES OF MOUSE EMBRYO TISSUES. Wm. E. Smith, Peyton Rous. Jour. Exper. Med., Balto., vol.88, no.5, pp.529-554, pls.24-28, Nov.1, 1948.

A CASE OF PARALLEL EMBRYONIC DEVELOPMENT IN THE RAT AND ITS BEARING ON THE QUESTION OF SUPERFETATION. Charles K. Weichert. Anat. Record, Phila., vol.83, no.4, pp.511-519, pl.1, Aug.25, 1942.

Endocrinology

EFFECT OF TESTOSTERONE PROPIONATE ON THERMO-REGULATORY FUNCTION OF RAT SCROTUM. John O. Almquist, Frederick N. Andrews. Anat. Record, Phila., vol.89, no.2, pp.125-133, June, 1944.

A NOTE ON PITUITARY DWARFISM IN THE MOUSE. G. R. de Beer, Hans Grueneberg. Jour. Genetics, London, vol.39, no.2, pp. 297-300, Jan.30, 1940.

PRODUCTION OF NITROGEN RETENTION IN HYPOPHYSECTOMIZED RATS BY SMALL DOSES OF HYPOPHYSEAL GROWTH HORMONES. Leslie Bennett, Choh Hao Li, Barbara Laundrie. Proc. Soc. Exper. Biol. Med., Utica, vol.68, no.1, pp.94-95, May, 1948.

EFFECTS OF PITUITARY ADRENOCOTICOTROPIC HORMONE ON THE INTACT RAT, WITH SPECIAL REFERENCE TO CYTOCHEMICAL CHANGES IN THE ADRENAL CORTEX. G. E. Bergner, H. W. Deane, Endocrinology, Boston, vol.43, no.4, pp.240-260, pls.1-2, Oct., 1948.

THE EFFECT OF ENDOCRINE FEEDING UPON THE LEARNING OF WHITE RATS. W. E. Biatz, W. T. Heron. Jour. Exper. Psychol., vol.7, pp.291-311, 1924.

THE NATURE OF THE ANEMIA OF PREGNANCY IN THE RAT. Charles F. Bond. Endocrinology, Boston, vol.43, no. 3, pp.180-186, Sept., 1948.

ANDROGEN PRODUCTION DURING PREGNANCY AND LACTATION IN THE RAT. M. W. Burrill, R. R. Greene. Anat. Record, Phila., vol.83, no.2, pp.209-227, fig.1, pls.2, June 25, 1942.

VARIATIONS PRODUCED IN BONES OF GROWING RATS BY PARATHYROID EXTRACTS. Robert B. Burrows. Amer. Jour. Anat., vol.62, no.2, pp.237-290, illus., Jan.15, 1938.

ADRENAL AUTO-TRANSPLANTS IN THE HEPATIC PORTAL DRAINAGE IN THE RAT. Earl O. Butcher. Endocrinology, Boston, vol.43, no.1, pp.30-35, July, 1948.

THE EFFECTS OF OESTROGENS AND OF MILD CHRONIC STARVATION ON THE WHITE RAT. A. T. Cameron, Jean S. Guthrie, J. Carmichael. Canadian Jour. Research, Ottawa, vol.24, nos.3-4, sec. E (medical sciences), pp.105-118, Aug., 1946.

THE EFFECT OF SEX HORMONES ON THE NORMAL RESISTANCE OF RATS TO CYSTICERUS CRASSICOLLIS. Dan H. Campbell. Science, Lancaster, Pa., n.s., vol.89, no.2314, pp.415-416, table 1, May 5, 1939.

ADRENALECTOMY AND REPLACEMENT THERAPY IN LACTATING RATS. A. T. Cowie, S. J. Folley. Jour. Endrocinol., London, vol.5, no.6, pp.282-289, June, 1948.

HORMONAL FACTORS INVOLVED IN PARTURITION IN THE RAT. Fred E. D'Armour, Charlotte Dumont. Quart.

Jour. Exp. Physiol., London, vol.26, no. 3, pp.215-224, tables 5, Feb., 1937.

THE EFFECT OF REMOVING VARIOUS ENDOCRINE GLANDS ON THE HAIR CYCLES OF BLACK RATS. Sally H. Dieke. Endorcinology, Boston, vol.42, no.4, pp.315-319, fig.1, Apr., 1948.

THE EFFECT OF PROLACTIN ON THE ESTRUS CYCLE OF NON-PAROUS MICE. Irmgard Dresel. Science, n.s., vol.82, no.2121, p.173, Aug.23, 1935.

THE EFFECTS OF PITUITARY AND NON-PITUITARY GLAND FACTORS ON THE FORMATION OF INTRACELLULAR COLLOID DROPLETS IN THE THYROID EPITHELIUM OF HYPOPHYSECTOMIZED RATS. Samuel Dvoskin. Endocrinology, Boston, vol.43, no.1, pp.52-70, pls.2, July, 1948.

LOCAL MAINTENANCE OF SPERMATOGENESIS BY INTRATESTICULARLY IMPLANTED PELLETS OF TESTOSTERONE IN HYPOPHYSECTOMIZED RATS. Samuel Dvoskin. Amer. Jour. Anat., Phila., vol. 75, no.3, pp.289-327, pls.1-4, Nov., 1944.

SEBACEOUS GLANDS. I. THE EFFECT OF SEX HORMONES ON THE SEBACEOUS GLANDS OF THE FEMALE ALBINO RAT. F. J. Ebling. Jour. Endocrinol., Lond., vol.5, no.6, pp.297-302, pls.1-2, June, 1948.

EFFECTS OF LIGHT AND DARKNESS ON ACTIVITY OF THE PITUITARY OF THE RAT. Virginia M. Fiske. Proc. Soc. Exper. Biol. and Med., New York, vol.40, no.2, pp.189-191, tables 2, Feb., 1939.

THE INFLUENCE OF TESTOSTERONE PROPIONATE ON PIGMENTATION OF THE MAMMARY NIPPLES IN FEMALE MICE. J. Flaks. Jour. Endocrinol., Lond., vol. 5, no.6, pp.259-262, pls.2, June, 1948.

DEVELOPMENT OF ADRENAL CORTICAL ADENOMAS IN OVARIECTOMIZED MICE INJECTED WITH "PHYSIOLOGIC" DOSES OF SEX HORMONE. Mathella J. Frantz, Arthur Kirschbaum. Proc. Soc. Exper. Biol. Med., Utica, vol.72, no.2, pp.282-283, Nov., 1949.

EFFECTS OF THE IMPLANTATION OF THE MALE HUMAN ANTERIOR PITUITARY GLAND ON ENDOCRINE GLANDS OF THE FEMALE IMMATURE ALBINO RAT. John Gluckman. S. African Jour. Sci., Johannesburg, vol.37, pp.253-255, Feb., 1941.

THE EFFECTS OF POSTNATAL ANDROGENIC TREATMENT IN THE FEMALE RAT. R. R. Greene, M. W. Burrill, A. C. Ivy. Anat. Record, Phila., vol.83, no. 1, pp.19-29, pls.2, May 25, 1942.

EXPERIMENTAL INTERSEXUALITY. THE EFFECTS OF ESTROGENS ON THE ANTENATAL SEXUAL DEVELOPMENT OF THE RAT. R. R. Greene, M. W. Burrill, A. C. Ivy. Amer. Jour. Anat., Phila., vol. 67, no.2, pp.305-345, 5 pls., Sept.16, 1940.

THE PHYSIOLOGY OF PREGNANCY IN THE RAT: THE COMBINED ACTION OF MALE AND FEMALE HORMONES (TESTOSTERONE PROPIONATE AND AESTRONE). A. M. Hain. Quart. Jour. Exper. Physiol., Lond., vol.26, no.3, pp.293-298, tables 3, Feb., 1937.

THE PHYSIOLOGY OF PREGNANCY IN THE RAT: FURTHER DATA ON THE PASSAGE OF HORMONES VIA THE PLACENTA AND THE MOTHER'S MILK. A. M. Hain. Quart. Jour. Exper. Physiol., Lond., vol. 26, no.1, pp.29-43, tables 5, Apr., 1936.

ON THE MIGRATION OF OVA FROM ONE UTERINE HORN TO THE OTHER IN THE ALBINO RAT; AND SOME EVIDENCE INDICATING A NEW OVARIAN HORMONE. F. B. Hanson, C. Boone. Amer. Nat., vol.60, no.668, pp.257-265, 1926.

QUALITATIVE CHANGES IN THE GONADOTROPIC COMPLEX OF THE RAT PITUITARY FOLLOWING REMOVAL OF THE TESTES. Arthur A. Hellbaum, Roy O. Greep. Amer. Jour. Anat., Phila., vol. 67, no.2, pp.287-304, Sept.16, 1940.

HORMONAL AMBISEXUALITY OF OVARIAN GRAFTS IN FEMALE RATS. Thomas Hernandez. Amer. Jour. Anat., Phila., vol.73, no.2, pp.127-151, figs.1-3, pls.1-3, Sept., 1943.

THE PITUITARY-ADRENAL RELATIONSHIP IN THE INFANT RAT. Joseph W. Jailer. Proc. Soc. Exper. Biol. Med., Utica, vol.72, no.3, pp.638-639, Dec., 1949.

THE EFFECT OF ANTERIOR PITUITARY EXTRACT ON THE DEVELOPING ALBINO MOUSE. George Edwin Johnson, Robert Towner Hill. Endocrinology, vol.14, no.6, pp.400-410, Nov.-Dec., 1930.

THE DEVELOPMENT OF THE PITUITARY OF THE LABORATORY MOUSE. T. Kerr. Quart. Jour. Microscop. Sci., Oxford, n. s., vol.87, pt.1, pp.3-29, figs.1-6, pls.1-3, May, 1946.

HISTOCHEMICAL STUDY OF ALKALINE PHOSPHATASE OF THE KIDNEY OF THE CASTRATED MOUSE AFTER STIMULATION WITH VARIOUS ANDROGENS. Chas. D. Kochakian. Amer. Jour. Physiol., Balto., vol.152, no.2, pp.257-262, Feb.1, 1948.

EFFECT OF ADRENOCORTICOTROPIC HORMONE (ACTH) ON THE ANTERIOR PITUITARY OF THE ADRENALECTOMIZED YOUNG MALE RAT. Alexei A. Koneff. Anat. Record, Phila., vol.89, no. 2, pp.163-173, pl.1, June, 1944.

EFFECT OF HORMONES ON THE ARTIFICIAL PREMATURE CLIMACTERIC OF PURE GONADAL ORIGIN IN OVARIECTOMISED RATS. V. Korenchevsky, Vera E. Jones. Jour. Gerontology, St. Louis, vol. 3, no.1, pp.21-39, Jan., 1948.

EFFECT OF TESTOSTERONE PROPIONATE ON SPERMATOGENESIS IN HYPOPHYSECTOMIZED RATS FOLLOWING THE INJECTION OF GONADOTROPINS. James H. Leathem. Anat. Record, Phila., vol.83, no.4, pp.579-585, pl.1, Aug.25, 1942.

INFLUENCE OF TESTOSTERONE PROPIONATE ON THE ADRENALS AND TESTES OF HYPOPHYSECTOMIZED RATS. James H. Leathem. Anat. Record, Phila., vol. 89, no. 2, pp.155-161, June, 1944.

LACTOGENIC HORMONE PROLONGS THE TIME DURING WHICH DECIDUOMATA MAY BE INDUCED IN LACTATING RATS. Robert Lyon. Proc. Soc. Exper. Biol. and Med., Utica, vol.51, no.1, pp.156-157, Oct., 1942.

THE MOUSE ADRENAL. II. THE ACTION OF CERTAIN HORMONAL SUBSTANCES ON THE ADRENAL GLAND OF THE MOUSE WITH PARTICULAR REFERENCE TO THEIR ACTION ON THE X-ZONE. M. K. McPhail, H. C. Read. Anat. Record, Phila., vol.84, no.1, pp.75-89, pls.2, Sept.25, 1942.

THE EFFECT OF TESTOSTERONE PROPIONATE ON THE LIVER OF ADULT FEMALE RATS. G. L. M. Mannerfelt. Jour. Endocrinol., Lond., vol.5, no.6, pp.293-296, June, 1948.

PARTIAL MASCULINIZATION OF THE OVARY IN RATS TREATED WITH TESTOSTERONE PROPIONATE. Lore Marx. Jour. Exper. Zool., Phila., vol.91, no.3, pp.365-371, pl.1, Dec.5, 1942.

EFFECTS OF ADMINISTRATION OF TESTOSTERONE ON VITAMIN A-DEFICIENT RATS. Jean Mayer, Aldo P. Truant. Proc. Soc. Exp. Biol. Med., Utica, vol.72, no.2, pp.436-438, Nov., 1949.

(DEPRESSING METABOLIC ACTION OF THE HYPOPHYSIS ON FEMALE MICE TREATED WITH THYROIDS.) Acción metalbólico depresora de la hipófisis de ratas tratadas con tiroides. Juan Reforzo Membrives. Rev. Soc. Argentina Biol., Buenos Aires, vol.18, no.6, pp.556-565, figs.2, Dec., 1942.

THE RELATION OF THE ESTROGENIC HORMONE TO THE FORMATION AND MAINTENANCE OF CORPORA LUTEA IN MATURE AND IMMATURE RATS. Charles Merckel, Warren O. Nelson. Anat. Record, Phila., vol.76, no.4, pp. 391-409, Apr.25, 1940.

THE EFFECTS OF SEX HORMONES ON THE COPULATORY BEHAVIOR OF SENILE WHITE RATS. R. S. Minnick, C. J. Warden, S. Arieti. Science, Lancaster, vol.103, no.2687, pp.749-750, June 28, 1946.

THYROID SECRETION RATE OF ALBINO RATS DURING GROWTH, PREGNANCY AND LACTATION. R. A. Monroe, C. W. Turner. Research Bull. Missouri Agric. Sta., Columbia, no.403, pp.1-34, illus., 1946.

HORMONAL CONTROL OF MAMMOGENESIS AND LACTOGENESIS IN THE $C_3H/HE$ CRGL MOUSE. Satyabrata Nandi. Publ. Zool., Univ. Calif. Press, Berkeley, 127 pp., illus., tables, vol.65, no.1, 1959.

THE ROLE OF THE ADRENAL GLANDS IN PROTEIN CATABOLISM FOLLOWING TRAUMA IN THE RAT. R. L. Noble, C. Gwendoline Toby. Jour. Endocrinol., Lond., vol.5, no.6, pp.303-313, June, 1948.

GONAD RESPONSE OF MALE RATS TO EXPERIMENTAL HYPERADRENALISM. James C. Perry. Endocrinology, Boston, vol.29, no.4, pp.592-595, fig.1, Oct., 1941.

(INTERSEXUALITY OBTAINED EXPERIMENTALLY IN A FEMALE MOUSE BY HORMONE ACTION.) Intersexualité obtenue expérimentalement chez la souris femelle par action hormonale. Albert Raynaud. Bull. Biol. France et Belgique, Paris, vol.72, no.3, pp.297-354, figs.10, pls.8-10, 1938.

SALT TASTE THRESHOLDS OF NORMAL AND ADRENALECTOMIZED RATS. Curt P. Richter. Endocrinology: Bull. Asso. Study Internal Secretions, vol.24, no.3, pp.367-371, Mar., 1939.

CALCIUM APPETITE OF PARATHYROIDECTOMIZED RATS USED TO BIOSSAY SUBSTANCES WHICH AFFECT BLOOD CALCIUM. Curt P. Richter, John R. Birmingham. Endocrinology, Los Angeles, vol.29, no.5, pp.655-666, figs.5, Nov., 1941.

BEHAVIOR AND ANATOMICAL CHANGES PRODUCED IN RATS BY PANCREATECTOMY. Curt P. Richter, Edward C. H. Schmidt, Jr. Endocrinology, vol.25, no.5, pp.698-706, figs.3, Nov., 1939.

INCREASED FAT AND DECREASED CARBOHYDRATE APPETITE OF PANCREATECOTMIZED RATS. Curt P. Richter, Edward C. H. Schmidt, Jr. Endocrinology, Los Angeles, vol.28, no. 2, pp.179-192, figs.5, Feb., 1941.

EFFECT OF CHRONIC PROGESTERONE OVERDOSAGE ON THE FEMALE ACCESSORY SEX ORGANS OF NORMAL, OVARIECTOMIZED AND HYPOPHYSECTOMIZED RATS. Hans Selye. Anat. Record, Phila., vol.78, no.2, pp.253-271, pls.3, Oct.25, 1940.

THE EFFECT OF PROGESTERONE ON THE MOUSE OVARY AS INFLUENCED BY GESTATION. Hans Selye. Anat. Record, Phila., vol.75, no.1, pp.59-70, pls.1-2, Sept.25, 1939.

EFFECT OF TESTOSTERONE PROPIONATE ON MATING. H. A. Shapiro. Nature, London, vol.139, no.3518, pp.258-259, Apr.3, 1937.

STUDIES ON THE REPUTED ENDOCRINE FUNCTION OF THE THYMUS GLAND (ALBINO RAT). Matsuziro Takenouchi. Jour. Exper. Zool., vol.29, pp.311-342, Oct., 1919.

THE INFLUENCE OF TESTOSTERONE PROPIONATE UPON SEXUAL DIFFERENTIATION IN GENETIC FEMALE MICE: POSTNATAL ANDROGEN ALONE AND IN COMBINATION WITH PRENATAL TREATMENTS. C. Donnell Turner. Jour. Exper. Zool., Phila., vol.83, no.1, pp.1-31, figs.5, tables 3, pls.1-2, Feb.5, 1940.

THE MODIFICATION OF SEXUAL DIFFERENTIATION IN GENETIC FEMALE MICE BY THE PRENATAL ADMINISTRATION OF TESTOSTERONE PROPIONATE. C. Donnell Turner. Jour. Morph., Phila., vol.65, no.2, pp.353-378, pls.1-2, Sept.1, 1939.

THE EXPERIMENTAL CONTROL OF PROLONGED PREGNANCY IN THE LACTATING RAT BY MEANS OF ESTROGEN. Charles K. Weichert. Anat. Record, Phila., vol.83, no.1, pp.1-17, pls.2, May 25, 1942.

EFFECT OF GROWTH HORMONE ON THE NITROGEN EXCRETION AND BODY WEIGHT OF ADULT FEMALE RATS. J. E. Whitney, L. L. Bennett, Choh Hao Li, H. M. Evans. Endocrinology, Boston, vol. 43, no.4, pp.237-239, Oct., 1948.

THE VASCULAR ARCHITECTURE OF THE RAT UTERUS AS INFLUENCED BY ESTROGEN AND PROGESTERONE. Maude F. Williams. Amer. Jour. Anat., Phila., vol.83, no.2, pp.247-308, pls.7, Sept., 1948.

EFFECTS OF PROGESTERONE ON THE CELLS OF THE ANTERIOR HYPOPHYSIS OF THE RAT. J. M. Wolfe. Amer. Jour. Anat., Phila., vol.79, no.2, pp.199-239, Sept., 1946.

Europe

HABITAT DISTRIBUTION AND ECOLOGY OF THE BROWN RAT (RATTUS NORVEGICUS BERKENH.) IN THE NORTH-WEST OF THE EUROPEAN PART OF THE USSR. D. S. Aisenstadt. Zool. Jour. USSR, Moscow, vol.24, no.3, pp.182-189, figs.3, 1945. (English summary.)

A KEY TO THE RATS OF THE GENUS RATTUS FITZINGER OF THE USSR. A. I. Argyropulo. La Defence des Plantes, vol.5, nos.5-6, pp.663-666, figs.3, (1928) 1929. (In Russian.)

ON A COLLECTION OF THE MICE (MUS HIRTENSIS AND M MURALIS) FROM ST. KILDA. G.E.H. Barrett-Hamilton. Annals of Scottish Nat. Hist., no.57, pp. 1-4, Jan., 1906.

ON THE SPECIES OF THE GENUS MUS INHABITING ST. KILDA. G.E.H. Barrett-Hamilton. Proc. Zool. Soc. London, pp. 77-88, pl.9, Feb.7, 1899.

ON THE OCCURRENCE OF ACOMYS IN CYPRUS. Dorothy M.A. Bate. Ann. and Mag. Nat. Hist., ser.7, vol.11, pp.565-567, June, 1903.

(THE HOUSE RAT IN ESSEN.) Die Hausratte in Essen. Gerhard Bechthold. Zeischr. f. Saeugetierkunde, Berlin, vol. 7, nos.1-6, pp.262-263, Dec.15, 1932.

THE ST. KILDA FIELD MOUSE (APODEMUS SYLVATICUS HIRTENSIS BARRETT-HAMILTON), POPULATION IN THE VILLAGE AREA, HIRTA, MAY 1955. J. Morton Boyd. Oikos, 7 (1): 110-116, 1956.

(DOMESTIC MICE FROM THE UPPER TESSIN VALLEYS.) Hausmaeuse aus den oberen Tessintaelern. G. Von Burg. Der Weidmann, Jahrg., no.6, p.5, Feb.10, 1921.

(THE MURINE COLONY OF THE CAVE OF THE TIGNAHUSTES.) La colonie de murins de la grotte des Tignahustes. Norbert Castaret. Mammalia, Paris, vol.3, no.1, pp.1-9, map, Mar., 1939.

DISTRIBUTION OF THE YELLOW-NECKED MOUSE APODEMUS FLAVICOLLIS WINTONI BARRETT-HAMILTON IN WOODS AT GREAT GLEMHAM. N. Chandler, A. Heffer. Trans. Suffolk Nat. Soc., 9 (4): 313-315, 1956.

LONG TAILED FIELD MICE (APODEMUS SP.) FROM THE CHANNEL ISLANDS. Cranbrook. Proc. Zool. Soc. Lond., 128 (4): 597-600, July 24, 1957.

(THE DOMESTIC RAT, RATTUS RATTUS L., IN LEIPZIG.) Die Hausratte, Rattus rattus L. in Leipzig. Heinrich Dathe. Zeitschr. f. Naturwiss., Leipzig, vol.91, no.3, pp.172-174, 1937.

(A FOREST MOUSE FROM DALMATIA.) Eine Waldmaus aus Dalmatien. Heinrich Dathe. Zeitschr. f. Saeugetierkunde, vol. 10, no.2, pp.153-154, Dec.31, 1935.

OCCURRENCE OF THE BLACK RAT IN SEWERS IN BRITAIN. R. A. Davis. Nature, London, 175: 641, Apr.9, 1955.

ON MUS MUSCULUS SPICILEGUS PET. IN DENMARK. Magnus Degerbol. Vidensk., Meddel, Dansk naturhist, For. Kobenhavn, vol.99, pp.233-238, Feb.17, 1936.

(THE MICROMAMMALS OF THE FRENCH FAUNA. II. RATS, MICE, FIELD MICE. RATTUS RATTUS L. THE BLACK RAT OR GARRET RAT.) Les micromammifères de la faune Francaise. II. Rats, souris, mulots. Rattus rattus (L.). Le rat noir ou rat de greniers. Robert Didier, Paul Rode. Mammalia, Paris, vol.6, no.3-4, pp.120-125, figs.4, Sept.-Dec., 1942.

HOUSE MICE (MUS MUSCULUS) IN A COAL-MINE IN AYRSHIRE. Charles Elton. Ann. and Mag. Nat. Hist., London, ser.10, vol.17, no.101, pp.553-558, May, 1936.

NOTES ON THE BIOLOGY OF THE FAEROE MOUSE (MUS MUSCULUS FAEROENSIS). F. C. Evans, H. G. Vevers. Jour. Animal Ecol., London, vol.7, no.2, pp. 290-297, fig.1, pl.11, Nov., 1938.

(INVESTIGATIONS OF THE ECOLOGY AND MORPHOLOGY OF THE WOOD MOUSE (APODEMUS SYLVATICUS L.) AND THE YELLOW-THROATED MOUSE (APODEMUS FLAVICOLLIS MELCHIOR) IN THE RHINE-MAIN REGION.) Untersuchungen zur Oekologie und Morphologie der Waldmaus (Apodemus sylvaticus L.) und der Gelbhalsmaus (Apodemus flavicollis Melchior) im Rhein-Main-Gebiet. H. Felten. Bonner Zool. Beitraege, Jahrg.3, Heft 3-4, pp.187-206, Feb.20, 1953.

(LITTLE KNOWN MAMMALS OF OUR HOMELAND: THE PYGMY MOUSE.) Wenig bekannte Saeugtiere unserer Heimat: Die Zwergmaus. H. Felten. Natur and Volk, Frankfurt am Main, vol.80, nos.7-8, pp.248-251, illus., Aug.30, 1950.

THE YELLOW-NECKED FIELD MOUSE IN HERTFORDSHIRE. A. H. Foster. Trans. Hertfordshire Nat. Hist. Soc. and Field Club, Hertford, vol.22, pt.4, p.138, Aug., 1946.

APODEMUS SYLVATICUS SPADIX SSP. NOV. Karl Fritsche. Zeitschr. f. Saeugetierkunde, Berlin, vol.9, nos.1-3, pp.435-436, Dec.30, 1934.

MICROMYS MINUTUS SUBOBSCURUS SSP. NOV. Karl Fritsche. Zeitschr. f. Saeugetierkunde, Berlin, vol.9, nos.1-3, p.431, Dec.30, 1934.

DISTRIBUTION OF THE LONG-TAILED FIELD MOUSE, APODEMUS SYLVATICUS, ON SOUTH HAVEN PENINSULA, DORSET, IN 1937, WITH SOME OBSERVATIONS ON ITS WANDERING AND HOMING POWERS. H. P. Hacker, H. S. Pearson. Jour. Linnean Soc. London, vol.42, no.283, pp.1-17, illus., May 11, 1951.

A NEW CENTRAL MEDITERRANEAN SUBSPECIES OF FIELD MOUSE (APODEMUS SYLVATICUS LINN.), AND NOTES ON SURROUNDING FORMS. David L. Harrison. Proc. Zool. Soc. London, vol. 117, pt.4, pp.650-652, Feb.3, 1948.

OBSERVATIONS ON SPECIMENS OF MUS MUSCULUS AND APODEMUS SYLVATICUS RECENTLY COLLECTED IN SOUTH ITALY. David L. Harrison. Proc. Zool. Soc. Lond., vol.115, pt.1-2, pp.47-48, Oct., 1945.

ST. KILDA HOUSE MOUSE. T. H. Harrison, J. A. Moy-Thomas. Nature, London, vol.129, no.3247, p.131, Jan.23, 1932.

(ON THE RACES OF MUS MUSCULUS IN THE EASTERN CAUCASUS (CISCAUCASIA AND TRANSCAUCASIA).) Ueber die Rassen von Mus musculus im ostlichen Kaukasus (Zis- und Transkaukasien). W. G. Heptner. Zool. Anzeiger, vol.89, pp. 5-22, 2 figs., May 20, 1930.

THE FIELD MOUSE OF FOULA. (APODEMUS FRIDARIENSIS THULEO, SUBSP. NOV., FROM THE ISLAND OF FOULA, SCOTLAND.) Martin A. C. Hinton. Scottish Nat., pp.177-181, Nov.-Dec., 1919.

NOTES ON TWO COLLECTIONS OF MICE FROM LEWIS, OUTER HEBRIDES. Martin A. C. Hinton, G. Bathurst Hony. 1916.

(RATS ON AMELAND.) Ratten op Ameland. F.G.A. Huber. Rat en Muis, Plantenziektenkundige Dienst, Wageningen, 1957 (1): 11-12, Mar., 1957.

(THE DOMESTIC RAT, RATTUS RATTUS LINNE 1758, AGAIN IN CZECHOSLOVAKIA.) Die Hausratte, Rattus rattus (Linne, 1758), wieder in der Tschechoslowakei. Joseph Jirsik. Saeugetierk, Mitteil., Stuttgart, 3 (1): 21-28, Jan.1, 1955.

(AN INVESTIGATION OF RATTUS RATTUS LINNAEUS 1758 (MAM., ROD.) ON CORSICA.) Eine Untersuchung an Rattus rattus Linnaeus 1758 (Mamm., Rod.) auf der Insel Korsika. Herman Kahmann, Bernd Haedrich. Zool. Anzeiger, Leipzig, 158 (11-12): 233-257, June, 1957.

(RATTUS NORVEGICUS ERXLEBEN 1777 ON CORSICA.) Rattus norvegicus Erxleben 1777 auf der Insel Korsika. Herman Kahmann, Bernd Haedrich. Mammalia, Paris, 21 (1): 50-52, Mar., 1957.

(A NEW SPECIES OF MUS SYLVATICUS FROM NORTHERN THURINGIA.) Eine neue Form von Mus sylvaticus aus Nord-Thueringen. Anton Krause. Zeitschr. fuer Forst- und Jagdw., Jahrg.54, Heft 7, p. 430, July, 1922.

(ON A NEW SPECIES OF MUS SPICILEGUS (MUS SPICILEGUS HEROLDI M.) OF THE COAST OF THE BALTIC SEA.) Ueber eine neue Form von Mus spicilegus (Mus spicilegus Heroldi m.) von der Ostseekueste. Anton Krause. Archiv f. Naturg., Abt.A, Heft 4, pp.137-139, June, 1922.

(THE PYGMY MOUSE MICROMYS MINUTUS PALL. IN THE NATURAL PARK RESERVE OF BIALOWIEZA.) Micromys minutus Pall. w Bialowieskim Parku Narodowym. (Zwergmaus-Micromys minutus Pall. im Naturschutzpark von Bialowieza.) Jerzy Kubik. Ann. Univ. Mariae Curie-Sklodowska, Lublin, vol.7, no.7, pp.449-495, Oct.15, 1952. (In Polish, with German summary.)

THE BROWN AND THE BLACK RAT IN WALES. Colin Matheson. Publ. Nat. Mus. Wales and Press Board Univ. Wales, Cardiff, pp.vii, 46, pls.5, 1931.

A SURVEY OF THE STATUS OF RATTUS RATTUS AND ITS SUBSPECIES IN THE SEAPORTS OF GREAT BRITAIN AND IRELAND. Colin Matheson. Jour. Anim. Ecol., London, vol.8, no.1, pp.76-93, May, 1939.

(NEW CONTRIBUTIONS TO STUDY OF THE RATS OF RUMANIA.) Nouvelles contributions à l'étude des rats de Roumanie. N. Muntiu, George D. Vasiliu. Notationes Biologicae, Bucuretsi, vol.1, no.2, pp.78-83, figs.5, May 15, 1933.

NORWEGIAN MICE OF THE GENERA MUS AND APODEMUS. Eugene O'Mahony. Meddelelser fra det Zool. Mus., Oslo, no. 44, pp.137-139, Oct.31, 1934.

ON SOME FORMS OF THE HOUSE MOUSE, MUS MUSCULUS LINN., IN IRELAND. Eugene O'Mahony. Irish Nat. Jour., vol. 6, no.12, pp.288-290, Nov., 1937.

(THE OCCURRENCE OF EPIMYS NORVEGICUS (ERXL.) AND E. RATTUS (L.) IN SAXONY.) Zum Vorkommen von Epimys norvegicus (Erxl.) und E. rattus (L.) in Sachson. Felix Portig. Zool. Garten, N.F., Leipzig, vol.9, nos.1-2, pp.45-47, Feb., 1937.

(CONTRIBUTIONS ON THE MURINE FAUNA OF ESTONIA, WITH CONSIDERATION OF THE NEIGHBORING REGIONS.) Beitraege zur Muriden - Fauna Estlands mit Beruecksichtigung der Nachbargebiete. Edwin Reinwaldt. Acta et Commentationes Univ. Tartu. (Dorpat.), Tartu, vol.A-12, pp.65, figs.3, 1927.

(FIRST PROOF OF THE OCCURRENCE OF THE HOUSE RAT IN THE LEIPZIG AREA.) Erstmaliger nachweis des Vorkommens der Hausratte im Leipziger Gebiet. Richard Schlegel. Zeitschr. fuer Saeugetierkunde, Berlin, vol.6, no.6, pp.226-227, Dec.15, 1931.

THE ABUNDANCE AND DISTRIBUTION OF HARVEST MICE (MICROMYS MINUTUS) IN CORN RICKS NEAR OXFORD. Charles H. Southwick. Proc. Zool. Soc. Lond., vol.126, pt.3, pp.449-452, May 31, 1956.

(ON SOME MURINES OF LITHUANIA. CONTRIBUTIONS TO THE NATURAL AND CULTURAL HISTORY OF LITHUANIA AND THE BORDERING REGIONS.) Ueber einige Muriden aus Lithauen. Beitraege zur Natur- und Kultur geschichte Lithauens und angrenzender Gebiete. E. Stechow. Abhandl. math.-naturw. Abt. Bayer, Akad. Wiss., Muenchen, Suppl.Bd., 13, Abh., pp.508-510, 1929.

MAMMALS OF VALDAI, VOLGA REGION. I. THE TAXONOMIC POSITION OF RATTUS RATTUS AND ITS DISTRIBUTION IN USSR. S. Stroganov. Zoologischeskii Zhurnal, vol.13, no.4, pp.714-730, map, fig.1, 1934.

MUS MUSCULUS L. OF THE CAUCASUS AND ITS DISTRIBUTION THROUGH CLIMATIC ZONES. P. A. Sviridenko. Moscou Univ. Sbornik Nauchno issledovatel'skogo inst. Zool. (Abstracts Works Zool. Inst. Moscow State Univ.), no.3, pp.89-91, 1936; Uchenyie Zapiski Moskovorskogo Gosudarstvennogo Universiteta, vol.4, (Wiss Ber. Moskauer Staatsuniv.) pp.70-90, 1935. (In Russian with English summary.)

THE HARVEST MOUSE IN HUNGARY, I. J. Szunyoghy. Ann. Hist.-Nat. Mus. Nat. Hungarici, n.s., vol.3, pp.245-259, 1952.

ON A WILD LIVING MOUSE OF THE MUS MUSCULUS GROUP IN PORTUGAL. Oldfield Thomas. Zoologist (3), vol.20, pp.137-139, Apr., 1896.

GEOGRAPHICAL VARIATION IN APODEMUS SYLVATICUS AND A. FLAVICOLLIS RODENTIA MURIDAE, IN EUROPE, WITH SPECIAL REFERENCE TO DANISH AND LATVIAN POPULATIONS. Erik Ursin. Biol. Skrifter, Kong. Danske Vidensk. Selskab, 8 (4): 1-46, 1956.

A NEW SPECIES OF MOUSE. B. S. Valck. Travaux de la Soc. de Naturalistes de Charkov, vol.50, pt.2, 1927. (In Russian.)

THE BLACK OR SHIP RAT (EPIMYS RATTUS). Percy Wadham. Proc. Isle of Wight Nat. Hist. and Archaeol. Soc., Newport, vol.3, pt.5, pp.345-346, June, 1943.

RATTUS RATTUS ON LUNDY. J. D. Watson. Jour. Animal Ecol., London, vol.12, p.214, 1943.

(DATA ON THE EUROPEAN WOOD MOUSE SYLVAEMUS SYLVATICUS L. AND S. FLAVICOLLIS MELCH.) Zur Kenntnis der europaeischen Waldmause (Sylvaemus sylvaticus L. und S. flavicollis Melch.). K. Zimmermann. Archiv. Naturgesch, Zeitschr. Wiss. Zool. Leipzig, Abt.B., n.F., vol.5, pp.116-133, figs.2, Apr.20, 1936.

(THE DOMESTIC MOUSE OF HELGOLAND, MUS MUSCULUS HELGOLANDICUS SSPEC. NOV.) Die Hausmaus von Helgoland Mus musculus helgolandicus sspec. nov. K. Zimmermann. Zeitschr. Saeugetierk., vol.17, no.3, pp.163-166, Feb.19, 1953.

(ON RACE ANALYSIS OF CENTRAL EUROPEAN FIELD MICE.) Zur Rassenanalyse der mitteleuropaeischen Feldmaeuse. K. Zimmermann. Archiv. fuer Naturgeh., n.F., vol.4, no.2, pp.258-273, figs.3, tables 5, 1935.

Experimental Biology

FURTHER STUDY OF THE EFFECTS OF ADMINISTERING ANURAN ANTERIOR PITUITARIES TO IMMATURE FEMALE MICE. A. Elizabeth Adams, Barbara Granger. Amer. Jour. Anat., Phila., vol. 69, no.2, pp.229-264, illus., Sept.15, 1941.

(ACTION OF ATROPINE ON SOME ORGANS: HISTOLOGICAL MODIFICATIONS; A DECREASE IN RESISTANCE TO COLD.) Action de l'atropine sur quelques organes: modifications histologiques; diminution de la resistance au froid. (Experiments on white mice.) C. Agapi. Comptes Rendus des Seances de la Soc. de Biol., vol.97, pp.1120-1122, Oct.21, 1927.

THIRD REPORT ON A TEST OF MCDOUGALL'S LAMARCKIAN EXPERIMENT ON THE TRAINING OF RATS. W. E. Agar, F. H. Drummond, O. W. Tiegs. Jour. Exper. Biol., Lond., vol.25, no.2, pp.103-122, June, 1948.

A FIRST REPORT ON A TEST OF MCDOUGALL'S LAMARCKIAN EXPERIMENT ON THE TRAINING OF RATS. W. E. Agar, F. H. Drummond, O. W. Tiegs. Jour. Exper. Biol., London, vol.12, no.3, pp.191-211, July, 1935.

DIFFERENTIAL GROWTH IN THE OVARIES AND GENITAL TRACT NEAR THE TIME OF OVULATION IN RATS TREATED WITH COLCHICINE. Edgar Allen, Thurlo B. Thomas, James G. Wilson, Dorothy A. Hession. Amer. Jour. Anat., Phila., vol. 72, no.2, pp.291-337, figs.1-5, pls.1-5, Mar., 1943.

EXPERIMENTAL RESEARCHES ON THE COMPENSATORY ENLARGEMENT OF THE SURVIVING KIDNEY AFTER UNILATERAL NEPHRECTOMY (ALBINO RAT). M. Arataki. Amer. Jour. Anat., vol.36, pp. 437-450, Jan.15, 1926.

EXPERIMENTAL INQUIRY INTO THE TRANSMISSION OF RAT-BITE FEVER AMONG RATS, PART 2. SUCCESSFUL TRANSMISSION OF RAT-BITE FEVER BY FEEDING INFECTED ORGANS TO WHITE RATS. Shizuka Arima. Philippine Jour. Sci., vol.58, no.2, pp.179-181, Feb., 1934.

OVARIAN RESPONSE IN THE ALBINO RAT TO INJECTED COLLOIDAL SUBSTANCES. Ralph N. Baillif. Amer. Jour. Anat., Phila., vol.83, no.1, pp.109-135, pls.1-3, July, 1948.

EFFECT OF OXYGEN PRE-BREATHING ON ANOXEMIA IN ALBINO RATS. Francis March Baldwin, Harold D. Robinson. Proc. Soc. Exper. Biol. and Med., New York, vol.40, no.2, pp.255-256, table 1, Feb., 1939.

(THE ACTION OF CHOLESTEROL-FREE FOOD WITH VITAMIN E IN WHITE RATS.) Die Wirkungsweise cholesterolfreier Ernaehrung mit Vitamin E bei weissen Ratten. W. M. Baldwin. Anat. Anzeiger, vol.66, pp.348-353, 3 figs., Dec.20, 1928.

A LIMITED FEEDING REGIME FOR RATS. S. S. Barker. Proc. Soc. Exp. Biol. Med., Utica, vol.72, no.1, pp.198-200, Oct., 1949.

SOME EXPERIMENTS ON FEEDING RATS WITH SOYA BEANS AND OTHER MATERIALS. D. T. Barry, J. Freud. Sci. Proc. Roy. Dublin Soc., vol.18, n.s., no.46, pp. 513-519, Jan.9, 1928.

BISEXUAL MATING BEHAVIOR IN THE MALE RAT: EFFECTS OF CASTRATION AND HORMONE ADMINISTRATION. Frank A. Beach. Physiological Biol., Chicago, vol.18, no.4, pp.390-402, Oct., 1945.

MATING BEHAVIOR IN MALE RATS CASTRATED AT VARIOUS AGES AND INJECTED WITH ANDROGEN. Frank A. Beach, A. Marie Holz. Jour. Exper. Zool., Phila., vol.101, no.1, pp.91-142, Feb., 1946.

THE INFLUENCE OF THYROID AND THIOURACIL ON MICE EXPOSED TO ROENTGEN RADIATION. Henry C. Blount, Jr., Willie W. Smith. Science, Lancaster, vol.109, no.2822, pp.83-84, Jan.28, 1949.

(DOES ALCOHOLIZATION OF THE MALE WHITE MOUSE EFFECT AN INCREASE IN THE NUMBER OF MALES?) Bewirkt Alkoholisierung des Maennchens der weissen Maus eine Steigerung der Maennchenziffer? Agnes Bluhm. Biol. Zentralblatt, vol.46, pp.651-656, 1926.

(RESEARCH OF THE WOLFFIAN BODY AND THE ORIGIN OF THE UROGENITAL CONNECTIONS IN THE MOUSE.) Recherches sur le corps de Wolff et l'origine des connexions urogenitale chez la souris. J. Bovy. Archives de Biologie, vol.39, pp.139-174, 15 figs., 1929.

HYPERTENSION AFTER BILATERAL NEPHRECTOMY IN THE RAT. E. Braun-Menendez. Nature, London, vol. 160, no.4078, p.905, Dec.27, 1947.

A STUDY OF THE COMPLEMENT FIXATION AND WEIL-FELIX REACTIONS IN WILD RATS AS RELATED TO THE ISOLATION OF THE VIRUS OF ENDEMIC TYPHUS. George D. Brigham, Ida A. Bengtson. U.S. Publ. Health Repts., Wash., vol.60, no.2, pp.29-46, Jan.12, 1945.

THE EFFECT OF BILATERAL OPTIC ENUCLEATION ON THE VOLUNTARY MUSCULAR ACTIVITY OF THE ALBINO RAT. Ludvig G. Browman. Jour. Exper. Zool., Phila., vol.91, no.3, pp.331-344, Fig.1, Dec.5, 1942.

THE EFFECT OF OPTIC ENUCLEATION ON THE MALE ALBINO RAT. Ludvig G. Browman. Anat. Record, Phila., vol.78, no.1, pp.59-77, pls.2, Sept.25, 1940.

THE EFFECTS OF THYROXIN AND STILBESTROL ON HEALING OF FRACTURES IN THE RAT. Helen Viola Brush. Amer. Jour. Anat., Phila., vol.76, no.3, pp.339-373, figs.5, pls.3, May, 1945.

ERGOTOXINE HYPER- AND HYPOTHERMIA IN THE ALBINO RATS. A. R. Buchanan, J. E. Roberts, B. E. Robinson. Proc. Soc. Exper. Biol. Med., Utica, vol. 68, no.1, pp.143-150, May, 1948.

STANDARDIZATION OF PREPARATIONS OF OVARIAN FOLLICULAR HORMONE. (EXPERIMENTS ON RATS.) E. P. Bugbee, A. E. Simond. Endocrinology, vol.10, pp. 191-200, 1936.

EPIDERMAL THICKNESS FOLLOWING OESTRONE INJECTIONS IN THE MOUSE. Helena F. Bullough. Nature, London, vol. 159, no.4029, pp.101-102, Jan.18, 1947.

EFFECTS OF SODIUM FLOURIDE ON HAIR GROWTH IN THE RAT. Earl O. Butcher. Proc. Soc. Exper. Biol. and Med., Utica, vol.63, no.2, pp.474-476, fig.1, Nov., 1946.

GREYING OF HAIR. I. EFFECTS PRODUCED BY SINGLE DOSES OF X-RAYS ON MICE. Herman B. Chase. Jour. Morphol., Phila., vol.84, no.1, pp.57-80, pl.1, Jan., 1949.

INDUCED POLYCHTHAEMIA BY 1-ASCORBIC ACID IN ALBINO MICE. Jui-Ming Chen. Nature, London, vol.160, no.4072, p.681, Nov.15, 1947.

NEPHROTOXIC AND RENOTROPIC EFFECTS OF LEAD ON WHITE RATS AND ITS PREVENTION BY B.A.L. Hugo Chiodi, Rodolfo A. Sammartino. Nature, London, vol.160, no.4072, pp.680-681, Nov.15, 1947.

AN EXPERIMENTAL STUDY OF THALAMIC CONNECTIONS IN THE RAT. W. E. LeGros Clark. Philos. Trans. Roy. Soc. London, ser.B, vol.222, no.483, pp.1-28, pls.1-5, Nov.17, 1932.

(VAGINAL CYCLIC RESPONSE TO THE ADMINISTRATION OF ESTILBESTROL IN THE FEMALE MOUSE.) Respuesta vaginal ćiclica a la administración de estilbestrol en la rata. A. Coll, J. de Larrechea Muñoz. Rev. Soc. Argentina Biol., Buenos Aires, vol.18, no.3, pp.233-237, June, 1942.

INVASION BY SHIGELLA SONNEI OF TISSUES OF MICE FOLLOWING GAVAGE WITH VIABLE SHIGELLA. Merlin Cooper, Helen M. Keller. Proc. Soc. Exper. Biol. Med., Utica, vol.68, no.1, pp.87-90, May, 1948.

THE EFFECTS OF IRON, COPPER AND THYROZINE ON THE ANEMIA INDUCED BY HYPOPHYSECTOMY IN THE ADULT FEMALE RAT. Roger C. Crafts. Amer. Jour. Anat. Phila., vol.79, no.2, pp.267-291, figs.19, Sept., 1946.

BIOTIN DEFICIENCY AND OTHER CHANGES IN RATS GIVEN SULFANILYL-GUANIDINE OR SUCCINYL SULFATHIAZOLE IN PURIFIED DIETS. Floyd Daft, L. L. Ashburn, W. H. Sebrell. Science, Lancaster, n.s., vol.96, no.2492, pp.321-322, Oct.2, 1942.

PREVENTION BY CYSTINE OR METHIONINE OF HEMORRHAGE AND NECROSIS OF THE LIVER IN RATS. Floyd Daft, W. H. Sebrell, R. D. Lillie. Proc. Soc. Exper. Biol. Med., Utica, vol.50, no.1, pp.1-5, May, 1942.

BRAIN EXCITABILITY IN PYRIODOXINE DEFICIENT RATS. V. D. Davenport, H. W. Davenport. Jour. Nutrition, Phila., vol.36, no.2, pp.263-275, Aug.10, 1948.

EFFECTS OF OPERATIONS UPON THE THYROID GLANDS OF FEMALE MICE ON THE GROWTH OF THEIR OFFSPRING. C. B. Davenport, W. W. Swingle. Jour. Exper. Zool., vol.48, no.2, pp.395-440, 1927.

PIGMENTATION AND HAIR GROWTH IN BLACK RATS, AS MODIFIED BY THE CHRONIC ADMINISTRATION OF THIOUREA, PHENYL THIOUREA AND ALPHA-NAPTHYL THIOUREA. Sally H. Dieke. Endocrinology, Boston, vol.40, no.3, pp. 123-136, Mar., 1947.

(MORPHOLOGICAL AND GENETIC STUDY OF THE BRACHYURE DESCENDANTS OF MICE WHOSE TESTES WERE IRRADIATED.) Étude morphologique et génétique de la brachyourie chez les descendants de souris a testicules irradiés. N. Dobrovolskaia-Zavadskaia, N. Kobozieff, S. Veretennikoff. Archiv. de Zool. Exper. et Générale, vol.76, no.4, pp.249-358, figs.25, pls.8-11, Feb.15, 1934.

(EFFECT OF THYROID EXTRACTS ON THE SEXUAL BEHAVIOR OF OFFSPRING IN THE ALBINO RAT.) L'azione degli estratti tiroidei sul rapporto sessuale dei nati nel ratto albino. F. Dulzetts. Archives de Biologie, vol.38, pp.355-410, 1928.

THE EFFECT OF CASTRATION AND OF TESTOSTERONE UPON THE RESPIRATION OF RAT BRAIN. Eugene Eisenberg, Gilbert S. Gordan, Henry W. Elliott. Science, Lancaster, vol.109, no.2831, pp. 337-338, Apr.1, 1949.

FAILURE TO CURE OR PREVENT GRAYING OF RATS WITH P-AMINO BENZOIC ACID. Gladys A. Emerson. Proc. Soc. Exper. Biol. Med., New York, vol.47, no. 2, pp.448-449, June, 1941.

LESIONS IN RATS GIVEN SULFATHIAZOLE, SULFADIAZINE, SULFANILAMIDE, SULFAMERAZINE, SULFAPYRAZINE, OR ACETYSULFADIAZINE IN PURIFIED DIETS. K. M. Endicott, A. Kornberg, F. S. Daft. U.S. Public Health Repts., Wash.,D.C., vol.59, no.2, pp.49-54, Jan.14, 1944.

BENEFICIAL EFFECTS OF LIVER ON GROWTH AND SURVIVAL OF IMMATURE RATS FED LACTOSE-CONTAINING DIETS. Benjamin H. Ershoff. Proc. Soc. Exper. Biol. Med., Utica, vol.72, no.3, pp.648-651, Dec., 1949.

EFFECTS OF LIVER FEEDING ON GROWTH AND OVARIAN DEVELOPMENT IN THE HYPERTHYROID RAT. Benjamin H. Ershoff. Proc. Soc. Exper. Biol. Med., Utica, vol.64, no.4, pp.500-503, Apr., 1947.

THE EFFECT OF HEATED LINSEED OIL ON REPRODUCTION AND LACTATION IN THE RAT. Florence A. Farmer, E. W. Crampton, Margaret I. Sidall. Science, Lancaster, vol.113, no.2937, pp.408-410, illus., Apr., 1951.

REGENERATION OF VIRUS RECEPTORS IN MOUSE LUNGS AFTER ARTIFICIAL DESTRUCTION. S. Fazekas de St. Groth. Australian Jour. Exper. Biol. and Med. Sci., Adelaide, vol.26, no.4, pp.271-285, July, 1948.

(SKULL FORM AND INHERITANCE.) Schaedelform und Verebung. (Study of young rats deprived of vitamin A.) E. Fischer. Zeitschr. Indukt. Abstamm.-Vererbungsichre, vol.33, p.347, 1924.

EFFECT OF EXERCISE ON RATS FED A DIET DEFICIENT IN POTASSIUM. Richard H. Follis, Jr. Proc. Soc. Exper. Biol. Med., Utica, vol.51, no.1, pp.71-72, Oct., 1942.

ADRENALECTOMY AND REPLACEMENT THERAPY IN LACTATING RATS. S. J. Fouey, A. L. Greenbaum. Jour. Endocrinol., London, vol.5, no.5, pp.236-242, Jan., 1948.

THE EFFECT OF ORAL ADMINISTRATION OF VITAMIN A ON THE EXPRESSION OF THE RECESSIVE GENE "RHINO" IN THE MOUSE. F. Clarke Fraser. Anat. Rec., Phila., vol.97, no.3, p.415, 1947.

NICOTINE FACILITATION OF AUDIOGENIC SEIZURES IN LABORATORY MICE. Hubert Frings, Alan Kivert. Jour. Mam., vol.34, no.3, pp.391-393, Aug.14, 1953.

EFFECTS OF HYPOPHYSECTOMY AT MID-PREGNANCY IN THE MOUSE. W. U. Gardner, Edgar Allen. Anat. Record, Phila., vol.83, no.1, pp.75-97, charts 2, pls.3, May 25, 1942.

STUDIES ON PROTEINURIA IN THE RAT. Saul B. Gilson. Proc. Soc. Exper. Biol. Med., Utica, vol.72, no.3, pp.608-613, Dec., 1949.

(ON THE CHANGES IN THE PANCREAS OF THE WHITE MOUSE FOLLOWING THYROXINE INJECTIONS.) Ueber die Veranderungen im Pancreas der weissen Maus nach Thyroxininjektionen. M. Glaser. Archiv. fuer Entwicklungsmechanik, vol.107, pp.98-128, 12 figs., Jan.22, 1926.

THE EFFECTS OF THE INJECTION OF ANTUITRIN G UPON A STRAIN OF HARE-LIP MICE. L. C. Glass. Amer. Nat., Lancaster, vol.74, no.755, pp.566-568, Nov.-Dec., 1940.

ON THE VESTIBULAR LABYRINTH OF THE ALBINO RAT AFTER PROLONGED ROTATION. Harley N. Gould. Jour. Comp. Anat., vol.41, pp.223-252, illus., Aug.15, 1926.

EXPERIMENTAL INTERSEXUALITY. THE EFFECT OF ANTENATAL ANDROGENS ON SEXUAL DEVELOPMENT OF FEMALE RATS. R. R. Greene, M. W. Burrill, A. C. Ivy. Amer. Jour. Anatomy, Phila., vol.65, no.3, pp.415-469, 7 pls., Nov.15, 1939.

PROTECTIVE ACTION OF POTASSIUM IODIDE ON THIOUREA POISONING IN RATS. W. E. Griesbach, T. H. Kennedy, H. D. Purves. Nature, London, vol.154, no.3915, pp.610-611, Nov.11, 1944.

THE EFFECT UPON THE WHITE RAT OF CONTINUAL BODILY ROTATION. Coleman R. Griffith. Amer. Nat., vol.54, pp.524-534, Nov.-Dec. (Dec.6), 1920.

STUDIES OF BLOOD VOLUME IN ERGOTAMINE TARTRATE POISONING IN RATS. J. Q. Griffith, B. I. Comroe, C. J. Zinn. Proc. Soc. Exper. Biol. Med., New York, vol.40, no.2, pp.177-179, Feb., 1939.

AUDIOGENIC FITS PRODUCED BY MAGNESIUM DEFICIENCY IN TAME DOMESTIC NORWAY RATS AND IN WILD NORWAY AND ALEXANDRINE RATS. William J. Griffiths, Jr. Amer. Jour. Physiol., Balto., vol.149, no.1, pp.135-141, figs.3, Apr., 1947.

INFLUENCE OF SEX ON THE EVOLUTION OF A TRANSPLANTABLE MOUSE SARCOMA. Ludwik Gross. Proc. Soc. Exper. Biol. Med., New York, vol.47, no.2, pp. 273-276, June, 1941.

EFFECT OF STREPTOMYCIN AEROSOL ON FRIEDLANDER'S PNEUMONIA IN RATS. F. P. Hadley, A. M. Laurent, J. M. Onslow. Proc. Soc. Exper. Biol. Med., Utica, vol.68, no.1, pp.210-212, May, 1948.

CATARACTS DUE TO DEFICIENCIES OF PHENYLALANINE AND OF HISTIDINE IN THE RAT. A COMPARISON WITH OTHER TYPES OF CATARACTS. W. K. Hall, L. L. Bowles, V. P. Sydenstrickler, H. L. Schmidt, Jr. Jour. Nutrition, Phila., vol. 36, no.2, pp.277-291, pls.2, Aug.10, 1948.

STUDIES IN THYROID APPARATUS. XVI. THE GROWTH OF THE HUMERUS AND FEMUR OF MALE AND FEMALE ALBINO RATS THYRO-PARATHYROIDECTOMIZED AND PARATHYROIDECTOMIZED WHEN 100 DAYS OF AGE. Frederick S. Hammett. Jour. Exper. Zool., vol.39, pp.465-504, May 5, 1924.

STUDIES OF THE THYROID APPARATUS. XXIII. THE GROWTH OF THE GLANDS OF INTERNAL SECRETION IN THE ALBINO RAT AFTER THYROPARATHYROIDECTOMY AND PARATHYROIDECTOMY AT 75 DAYS OF AGE. Frederick S. Hammett. Amer. Jour. Anat., vol.35, pp. 133-152, Mar.15, 1925.

STUDIES OF THE THYROID APPARATUS. XXIV. THE GROWTH OF THE HEART, LUNGS, LIVER, KIDNEY, SPLEEN, SUBMAXILLARY GLANDS, AND EYEBALLS IN THE ALBINO RAT THYRO-PARATHYROIDECTOMIZED AND PARATHYROIDECTOMIZED AT 75 DAYS OF AGE. Frederick S. Hammett. Amer. Jour. Anat., vol.35, pp.223-238, May 15, 1925.

STUDIES OF THE THYROID APPARATUS. XXV. THE GROWTH OF THE HUMERUS AND FEMUR OF THE ALBINO RAT AFTER THYRO-PARATHYROIDECTOMY AND PARATHYROIDECTOMY AT 75 DAYS OF AGE. Frederick S. Hammett. Amer. Jour. Anat., vol.35, pp.421-454, July 15, 1925.

SPECIFICITY AND MODE OF ACTION OF CYTOTOXINS PRODUCED AGAINST ALIEN TRANSPLANTS IN RATS. Morgan Harris. Jour. Exper. Zool., Phila., vol.107, no.3, pp.439-449, pls.2, Apr., 1948.

SURVIVAL OF TRANSPLANTED OVARIES IN RATS. Morgan Harris, Richard M. Eakin. Jour. Exper. Zool., Phila., vol. 112, no.1, pp.131-156, Oct., 1949.

EFFECT OF BILATERAL OVARIECTOMY UPON THE DURATION OF PREGNANCY IN MICE. Reginald G. Harris. Anat. Rec., vol.37, pp.83-93, Nov.25, 1927.

THE EFFECT OF THE DURATION OF THE POST-OPERATIVE INTERVAL ON THE QUANTITATIVE CHANGES IN ADRENAL GLANDS OF OVARIECTOMIZED ALBINO RATS. E. I. Hashimoto. Anat. Record, Phila., vol.81, no.2, pp.205-213, fig.1, Oct.25, 1941.

THE EFFECT OF CASTRATION, SPAYING OR SEMI-SPAYING ON THE WEIGHT OF THE CENTRAL NERVOUS SYSTEM AND OF THE HYPOPHYSIS OF THE ALBINO RAT; ALSO THE EFFECT OF SEMI-SPAYING ON THE REMAINING OVARY. Shinkishi Hatai. Jour. Exper. Zool., vol. 15, no.3, pp.297-314, tables 3, Oct., 1913.

THE GROWTH OF ORGANS IN THE ALBINO RAT AS AFFECTED BY GONADECTOMY. Shinkishi Hatai. Jour. Exper. Zool., vol.18, no.1, pp.1-45, tables 1-20, Jan., 1915.

EFFECT OF PREGNANCY URINE EXTRACT ON LACTATION IN THE RAT. I. L. Hathaway, H . P. Davis, R. P. Reece, J. W. Bartlett. Proc. Soc. Exper. Biol. Med., New York, vol.40, no.2, pp. 214-218, table 1, Feb., 1939.

REPRODUCTION AND LACTATION OF RATS RECEIVING PORK DIETS. L. M. Henderson, B. S. Schweigert, A. K. Mozingo, C. A. Elvehjem. Jour. Nutrition, Phila., vol.36, no.4, pp.479-494, Oct.11, 1948.

THE RETENTION OF CALCIUM AND PHOSPHOROUS BY THE RAT FROM WHOLEMEAL BREAD, WITH AND WITHOUT ADDED CALCIUM AND FROM WHITE BREAD FORTIFIED WITH CALCIUM AND VITAMIN $B_1$. K. M. Henry, S. K. Kon. Biochemical Jour., London, vol.39, no.2, pp.117-122, 1945.

LIPEMIC NEPHROSIS IN RATS. Walter Heymann, Herbert Z. Lund. Science, Lancaster, vol.108, no.2808, pp.448-449, Oct.22, 1948.

SOME CYTOLOGICAL AND HORMONAL CHANGES IN THE POSTERIOR LOBE OF THE RAT'S PITUITARY AFTER WATER DEPRIVATION AND STALK SECTION. Robert C. Hickey, Kendrick Hare, Ruth S. Hare. Anat. Record, Phila., vol.81, no.3, pp.319-331, figs.6, pls.3, Nov.25, 1941.

EFFECTS OF "BENZEDRINE" SULFATE ON ESTROUS CYCLES OF RATS. J. E. Hill, P. L. Ewing, G. A. Emerson. Texas Repts. Biol., Austin, vol.6, no.2, pp.159-167, Summer, 1948.

GRAFTED MOUSE OVARIES AND THEIR ADRENAL CORTICAL FUNCTION. R. T. Hill. Endocrinology, Chicago, vol.42, no. 5, pp.339-351, May, 1948.

EFFECTS OF INJECTION OF LARGE MOLECULAR AND PARTICULATE SUBSTANCES ON BODY-TEMPERATURE OF RATS. Robert M. Hill, Enid K. Rutledge. Proc. Soc. Exper. Biol. Med., Utica, vol.72, no.2, pp.310-315, Nov., 1949.

STUDIES ON GRAFTS OF EMBRYONIC TISSUE OF THE RAT ON THE CHORIO-ALLANTOIC MEMBRANE OF THE CHICK. Y. K. Hiraiwa. Jour. Exper. Zool., vol. 49, no.2, pp.441-458, 1927.

THE INFLUENCE OF THYROXINE AND ADRENAL CORTICAL EXTRACT ON THE OXYGEN CONSUMPTION OF ADRENALECTOMIZED RATS. F. Hoffman, E. J. Hoffman, J. Talesnik. Jour. Physiol., London, vol.107, no.3, pp.251-264, June 25, 1948.

CHANGES IN THE INTESTINAL FLORA OF RATS ON A CALCIUM DEFICIENT DIET. R. E. Hoffstadt, S. J. Johnson. Amer. Jour. Hygiene, vol.5, no.6, pp. 709-723, illus., 1925.

EFFECT OF ADRENALECTOMY UPON THE TOLERANCE OF THE EVISCERATED RAT FOR INTRAVENOUSLY ADMINISTERED GLUCOSE. D. Ingle, J. E. Nezmis. Amer. Jour. Physiol., Balto., vol.152, no. 3, pp.598-602, Mar.1, 1948.

THE WORK PERFORMANCE OF ADRENALECTOMIZED RATS GIVEN CONTINUOUS INTRAVENOUS INFUSIONS OF GLUCOSE. D. Ingle, J. E. Nezamis. Endocrinology, Springfield, vol.43, no.4, pp.261-271, Oct., 1948.

EFFECT OF ADRENALECTOMY UPON THE URINARY EXCRETION OF GLUCOSE AND NON PROTEIN NITROGEN IN THE PARTIALLY DEPANCREATIZED, FORCE-FED RAT. D. Ingle, M. C. Prestrud. Amer. Jour. Physiol., Balto., vol.152, no. 3, pp.603-608, Mar.1, 1948.

EFFECT OF FOOD INTAKE UPON THE INCISOR TEETH OF RACHITIC RATS. J. T. Irving. Nature, London, vol.156, no.3970, pp.664-665, Dec.1, 1945.

RATE AND CHARACTER OF THE COMPENSATORY RENAL HYPERTROPHY AFTER UNILATERAL NEPHRECTOMY IN YOUNG ALBINO RATS. C. M. Jackson, N. M. Levine. Anat. Record, vol.41, pp.323-333, Feb.25, 1929.

THE EFFECTS OF INANITION IN THE YOUNG UPON ULTIMATE SIZE OF THE BODY AND OF THE VARIOUS ORGANS IN THE ALBINO RAT. C. M. Jackson, Chester A. Stewart. Jour. Exper. Zool., vol. 30, pp.97-128, Jan., 1920.

EFFECT OF PROTEIN DEPLETION UPON SUSCEPTIBILITY OF RATS TO TOTAL BODY IRRADIATION. F. Lamont Jennings. Proc. Soc. Exper. Biol. Med., Utica, vol. 72, no.2, pp.487-491, Nov., 1949.

STUDIES ON OXYURIASIS. XXVI. RESISTANCE OF WHITE RATS ON A VITAMIN A-DEFICIENT DIET TO EXPERIMENTAL INFECTION WITH ENTEROBIUS VERMICULARIS. Myrna F. Jones, M. O. Nolan. Proc. Helminthol. Soc. Wash., vol.9, no. 2, pp.63-65, July, 1942.

BLIND MICE. C. E. Keeler. Jour. Exper. Zool., vol.51, no.4, pp.495-508, 1928.

EXPERIMENTS ON THE HAIR SLOPE AND HAIR PATTERN IN RATS. Vilhelm Keil. Jour. Exper. Zool., Phila., vol.110, no.3, pp.397-439, Apr., 1949.

THE NASAL CAVITY OF THE RAT IN PHARMACOLOGICAL AND OTHER EXPERIMENTATION. George Kelemen. Science, Lancaster, vol.107, no.2776, pp.273-274, Mar.12, 1948.

THE PRODUCTION OF OSTEOMYELITIS IN RATS. J. Emerson Kempf, J. Arthur Herrick. Ohio Jour. Sci., Columbus, vol.46, no.1, pp.1-4, Jan., 1946.

ON THE EFFECTS OF COLCHICINE TREATMENT OF MOUSE EMBRYOS. T. Kerr. Proc. Zool. Soc. London, vol.116, pts.3-4, pp.551-564, pls.2, Feb.28, 1947.

EFFECTS OF INANITION AND REFEEDING UPON THE GROWTH OF THE KIDNEY OF THE ALBINO RAT. John A. Kittelson. Anat. Rec., vol.17, pp.281-295, Jan.20, (Feb.), 1920.

GRANULOCYTOPENIA AND ANEMIA IN RATS FED DIETS OF LOW CASEIN CONTENT. A. Kornberg, F. S. Daft, W. H. Sebrell. Science, Lancaster, n.s., vol. 103, no.2682, pp.646-648, May 24, 1946.

PRODUCTION OF VITAMIN K DEFICIENCY IN RATS BY VARIOUS SULFONAMIDES. A. Kornberg, F. S. Daft, W. H. Sebrell. U.S. Publ. Health Repts., Wash., D.C., vol.59, no.25, pp.832-844, June 30, 1944.

THE EFFECTS OF THEELIN ON DELAYED IMPLANTATION IN THE PREGNANT LACTATING RAT. Robert H. Krehbiel. Anat. Record, Phila., vol.81, no.3, pp.381-392, 2 figs., Nov.25, 1941.

CHEMISTRY OF THE LIVER CYTOPLASM OF NORMAL, FASTED AND CIRRHOTIC MICE. Norman Kretchmer, Cyrus P. Barnum. Proc. Soc. Exper. Biol. Med., Utica, vol.70, no.1, pp.153-155, Jan., 1949.

INFLUENCE OF COLD UPON THE METABOLISM AND BODY TEMPERATURE OF WILD RATS, ALBINO RATS AND ALBINO RATS CONDITIONED TO COLD. H. Krog, M. Monson, L. Irving. Jour. Applied Physiol., Wash., vol.7, no.4, pp.349-354, Jan., 1955.

(OBSERVATIONS AND EXPERIMENTS ON THE EPIDIDYMIS OF THE DOMESTIC MOUSE.) Beobachtungen und Versuche am Nebenhoden der Hausmaus. T. von Lanz. Zeitschr. Gesammte Anat., I. Abteil., vol.58, pp.761-815, 31 figs., Oct.31, 1924.

FORMATION OF HAEMOLYMPH NODES IN RATS TREATED WITH 1:2:5:6-DIBENZANTHRACENE. A. Lasnitzki, D. L. Woodhouse. Nature, London, vol.150, no. 3814, p.660, illus., Dec.5, 1942.

PENICILLIN AND STREPTOMYCIN IN LUNGS AND BLOOD SERUM OF RATS FOLLOWING INHALATION AND INTRAMUSCULAR ADMINISTRATION. A. M. Laurent, A. P. McIlroy, F. P. Hadley. Proc. Soc. Exper. Biol. Med., Utica, vol.68, no.1, pp.213-216, May, 1948.

DIFFERENCES IN RATS OF VARIOUS STRAINS SHOWN BY THEIR RATE OF RESPONSE TO CARCINOGENIC AGENTS. Margaret Reed Lewis, Helen Dean King. Anat. Record, Phila., vol.94, no.1, pp.25-34, Jan., 1946.

FACTORS INFLUENCING THE GROWTH OF A TRANSPLANTABLE TUMOR IN MICE. C. C. Little. Jour. Exper. Zool., vol.31, pp.307-326, Oct.5, 1920.

THE OCCURRENCE OF FOUR INHERITABLE MORPHOLOGICAL VARIATIONS IN MICE AND THEIR POSSIBLE RELATION TO TREATMENT WITH X-RAYS. C. C. Little, H. J. Bagg. Jour. Exper. Zool., vol.41, pp.45-92, 12 figs., Nov.5, 1924.

STRONG GENETIC STUDIES ON THE TRANSPLANTATION OF TWO ADENOCARCINOMATA. (WORK ON WHITE MICE.) C. C. Little, L. C. Strong. Jour. Exper. Zool., vol.41, pp.93-114, Nov.5, 1924.

THE EFFECTIVENESS OF OVARIAN AND HYPOPHYSIAL GRAFTS IN THE PRODUCTION OF MAMMARY CARCINOMA IN MICE. Leo Loeb, H. T. Blumenthal, Moskop Kirtz. Science, Lancaster, n.s., vol.99, no.2569, pp.230-232, Mar.24, 1944.

THE ANALYSIS OF THE ORGANISMAL DIFFERENTIALS OF GRAY NORWAY RATS AND OF TWO MUTANT RACES BY MEANS OF TRANSPLANTATION. Leo Loeb, Helen Dean King. Amer. Nat., vol. 69, no.720, pp.5-18, Jan.-Feb., 1935.

CHOLESTEROL STUDIES AND ADRENALS AND PLASMA IN PARTIALLY HEPATECTOMIZED AND PARTIALLY NEPHRECTOMIZED RATS AFTER INJECTION OF H N Z. S. Ludewig, Alfred Chanutin. Endocrinology, Chicago, vol.42, no.5, pp.352-355, May, 1948.

SURVIVAL OF DECIDUOMATA DURING LACTATION IN THE RAT. Robert A. Lyon. Proc. Soc. Exper. Biol. Med., New York, vol.40, no.2, pp.151-152, table 1, Feb., 1939.

ALCOHOLISM AND THE BEHAVIOR OF WHITE RATS. II. THE MAZE-BEHAVIOR OF TREATED RATS AND THEIR OFFSPRING. E. C. MacDowell. Jour. Exper. Zool., vol.37, pp.417-456, July 5, 1923.

REPRODUCTION IN ALCOHOLIC MICE. I. TREATED FEMALES. A STUDY OF THE INFLUENCE OF ALCOHOL ON OVARIAN ACTIVITY, PRENATAL MORTALITY, AND SEX RATIO. E. C. MacDowell, E. M. Lord. Archiv. Entwicklungsmechanik, vol.109, pp.549-583, 13 figs., 1927.

A PIGMENTED ADENOMA OF THE INTERMEDIATE LOBE IN A RAT CHRONICALLY TREATED WITH OESTRIN. C. S. McEuen, H. Selye, J. B. Collip. Proc. Soc. Exper. Biol. Med., New York, vol.40, no.2, pp. 241-244, figs.2, Feb., 1939.

MATERNAL BEHAVIOR IN MALE RATS. (INDUCED BY BOVINE ANTERIOR PITUITARY IMPLANTS AND BY THYROIDECTOMY.) Morvyth McQueen-Williams. Science, n.s., vol.82, no.2116, pp.67-68, July 19, 1935.

EFFECT OF OVARIECTOMY AND LUTEIN INJECTIONS ON THE BEHAVIOR OF RATS. (IN A CIRCULAR MAZE.) David I. Macht, Dorothy W. Seago. Jour. Comp. Psych., vol.4, pp.151-162, 1924.

A SEARCH FOR QUANTITATIVE DIFFERENCES IN THE NORMAL CONSTITUENTS OF THE URINE OF SHORT EAR AND NORMAL MICE. Caroline R. Madison. Jour. Exper. Zool., vol.120, no.3, pp.457-468, Aug., 1952.

STUDIES ON THE ELECTRICAL POTENTIALS OF LIVING ORGANISMS: I. BASE-LINES AND STRAIN DIFFERENCES IN MICE. Clyde Marshall, Ralph G. Meader. Yale Jour. Biol. and Med., New Haven, vol.10, no.1, pp.65-78, Oct., 1937.

A HISTOLOGICAL STUDY OF STERILITY IN THE ALBINO RAT DUE TO DIETARY DEFICIENCY. K. E. Mason. Nat. Acad. Sci. Proc., vol.11, no.7, pp.377-388, 1925.

TESTICULAR DEGENERATION IN ALBINO RATS FED A PURIFIED FOOD RATION. K. E. Mason. Jour. Exper. Zool., vol.45, pp.159-229, illus., May 5, 1926.

THE EFFECT OF GONADECTOMY ON THE STRUCTURE OF THE SUPRARENAL GLAND OF MICE, WITH REFERENCE TO FUNCTIONAL RELATION BETWEEN THIS GLAND AND THE SEX GLAND OF THE FEMALE. Kiyoshi Masui, Yasushige Tamura. Jour. College Agric., Imperial Univ. Tokyo, vol.7, no.4, pp.353-376, pls.25-28, May 25, 1926.

ACUTE ADAPTATION OF RATS TO VERY LOW OXYGEN PRESSURE. L. Van Middlesworth. Proc. Soc. Exper. Biol. Med., Utica, vol.72, no.2, pp.476-478, Nov., 1949.

ASCORBIC ACID CONCENTRATION AND CHOLESTEROL STORAGE IN THE CORPUS LUTEUM OF THE PREGNANT RAT UNDER EXPERIMENTAL CONDITIONS. D. C. Miller, J. W. Everett. Endocrinology, Chicago, vol.42, no.5, pp.421-423, May, 1948.

(THE EFFECTS OF "OVER-RENALIZED" FEEDING ON THE DEVELOPMENT OF

THE ORGANISM AND ITS SEXUAL FUNCTION.) Effets de l'alimentation surrenalisee sur le developpement de l'organisme et sur la fonction sexuelle. (Experiments upon mice.) Ferreira de Mira. Comptes Rendus des Seance de la Soc. de Biol., vol. 97, pp.709-711, Aug.26, 1927.

DIFFERENTIATION OF EMBRYONIC REPRODUCTIVE TISSUES OF THE RAT AFTER TRANSPLANTATION INTO POST NATAL HOSTS. C. R. Moore, Dorothy Price. Jour. Exper. Zool., Phila., vol.90, no.2, pp.229-265, 3 pls., July 6, 1942.

SEMINAL-VESICLE AND PROSTATE FUNCTION AS A TESTIS-HORMONE INDICATOR; THE ELECTRIC EJACULATION TEST. (ON RATS.) C. R. Moore, T. F. Gallagher. Amer. Jour. Anat., vol.45, pp.39-70, 2 figs., Jan.15, 1930.

COMPARATIVE TOXICITY OF THREE FORMS OF VITAMIN D FOR ALBINO RATS. Rudolph Mrazek, Clarence R. Novak, C. I. Reed. Proc. Soc. Exper. Biol. Med., Utica, vol.51, no.1, pp.49-50, fig.1, Oct., 1942.

STUDIES ON THE BIOLOGICAL EFFECTS OF ROENTGEN RAYS ON MICE. I. PRIMARY GENERAL EFFECTS. Joseph M. Murray. Michigan Acad. Sci., Arts, Letters, Papers, vol.8, pp.401-409, 3 figs., 1928.

FACTORS INVOLVED IN THE INCIDENCE OF SPONTANEOUS MAMMARY CANCER IN AN INBRED RACE OF MICE. W. S. Murray. Michigan Acad. Sci., Arts, Letters, Papers, vol.8, pp.411-420, 3 figs., 1928.

OVARIAN SECRETION AND TUMOR INCIDENCE. (WORK ON MICE.) W. S. Murray. Science, n.s., vol.66, pp.600-601, Dec.16, 1927.

INFLUENCE OF NEPHRECTOMY AND RENAL PEDICLE LIGATION ON THE ACTIVITY OF LIVER ARGINASE IN RATS. E. Mylon, P. Goldstein. Proc. Soc. Exper. Biol. Med., Utica, vol.68, no.1, pp.157-159, May, 1948.

RELATION OF VITAMIN DEFICIENCY TO MUSCLE FATIGUE IN RATS. V. E. Nelson, F. M. Baldwin, A. C. Riggs, M. C. Cunningham. (Abstract) Iowa Acad. Sci. Proc., vol.30, p.171, 1923.

EXPERIMENTAL APPROACHES TO PROBLEMS OF EARLY DEVELOPMENT IN THE RAT. J. S. Nicholas. Quart. Rev. Biol., Balto., vol.22, no.3, pp.179-195, Sept., 1947.

EXPERIMENTS ON DEVELOPING RATS. III. THE INDUCTION OF ARTIFICIAL PREGNANCY. J. S. Nicholas. Anat. Record, Phila., vol.83, no.3, pp.457-470, fig.1, July 25, 1942.

EXPERIMENTS ON DEVELOPING RATS. IV. THE GROWTH AND DIFFERENTIATION OF EGGS AND EGG-CYLINDERS WHEN TRANSPLANTED UNDER THE KIDNEY CAPSULE. J. S. Nicholas. Jour. Exper. Zool., Phila., vol.90, no.1, pp.41-64, fig.1, pls.3, June 5, 1942.

EXPERIMENTS ON DEVELOPING RATS. II. THE DEVELOPMENT OF ISOLATED BLASTOMERES AND FUSED EGGS. J. S. Nicholas. Jour. Exper. Zool., Phila., vol.90, no.3, pp.441-459, pl.1, Aug.5, 1942.

SOME UNUSUAL FINDINGS ON THE CARCINOGENIC ACTION OF URETHANE IN MICE. R. L. Noble, M. Jean Millar. Nature, London, vol.162, no.4111, pp.253-254, Aug.14, 1948.

EXPERIMENTAL STUDIES ON THE CARTILAGE PLATES IN THE LONG BONES OF THE RAT. Rudolph F. Nunnemacher. Amer. Jour. Anat., Phila., vol.65, no.2, pp.253-290, 5 pls., Sept.15, 1939.

EFFECT OF VITAMIN DEFICIENCIES ON BASAL METABOLISM AND RESPIRATORY QUOTIENT IN RATS. Demosthenes Orsini, H. A. Waisman, C. A. Elvehjem. Proc. Soc. Exper. Biol. Med., Utica, vol.51, no. 1, pp.99-102, Oct., 1942.

THE EFFECT OF CASTRATION UPON THE SIZE OF THE PARATHYROID GLANDS AND UPON THE SUSCEPTIBILITY TO TETANIA PARATHYROPRIVA IN THE ALBINO RAT. Milton D. Overholser. Anat. Record, vol. 41, pp.303-321, Feb.25, 1929.

X IRRADIATION OF THE HYPOPHYSECTOMIZED RAT. H. M. Patt, M. N. Swift, E. B. Tyree, R. L. Straube. Science, Lancaster, vol.108, no.2809, pp.475-476, Oct.29, 1948.

GONAD RESPONSE OF MALE RATS TO EXPERIMENTAL HYPERADRENALISM. James C. Perry. Endocrinology, Boston, vol.29, no.4, pp.592-595, fig.1, Oct., 1941.

INCREASED PROTEIN CATABOLISM IN THYROIDECTOMIZED RATS: ANATOMICAL CHANGES. Edward C. Persike. Endocrinology, Chicago, vol.42, no.5, pp.363-369, May, 1948.

INCREASED PROTEIN CATABOLISM IN THYROIDECTOMIZED RATS: RATES OF URINE UREA EXCRETION AND SERUM UREA CONCENTRATIONS. Edward C. Persike. Endocrinology, Chicago, vol.42, no.5, pp.356-362, May, 1948.

EARLY AND LATE EFFECTS OF DAILY TREATMENT WITH PREGNANT MARE SERUM UPON THE OVARY OF MICE OF THE A STRAIN. Carroll A. Pfeiffer, Charles W. Hooker. Anat. Record, Phila., vol.84, no.4, pp.311-329, pls.3, Dec.26, 1942.

EXPERIMENTS ON THE SOURCE OF OVARIAN ANDROGEN IN THE MOUSE. Carroll A. Pfeiffer, Charles W. Hooker. Anat. Record, Phila., vol.83, no.4, pp. 543-571, pls.2, Aug.25, 1942.

THE TRANSPLANTATION OF MOUSE OVARIES INTO THE RAT. Gregory Pincus. Anat. Record, vol.49, no.1, pp.97-101, Mar.25, 1931.

A PARTICULATE BODY ASSOCIATED WITH EPHITHELIAL CELLS CULTURED FROM MAMMARY CARCINOMAS OF MICE OF A MILK-FACTOR STRAIN. K. R. Porter, H. P. Thompson. Jour. Exper. Med., Balto., vol.88, no.1, pp.15-24, pls.5-7, July 1, 1948.

ANAPHYLAXIS IN THE PREGNANT RAT. Oscar D. Ratnoff. Proc. Soc. Exper. Biol. Med., New York, vol.40, no.2, pp. 248-251, table 1, Feb., 1939.

(EXPERIMENTAL MODIFICATION OF SEXUAL DIFFERENTIATION OF MICE EMBRYOS THROUGH THE ACTION OF ANDROGENOUS AND OESTROGENOUS HORMONES (STUDY OF RESULTING STATES OF INTERSEXUALITY).) (Review by P. Rode, of) Modification expérimentale de la différenciation sexuelle des embryons de souris par action des hormone hormones androgènes et oestrogènes (étude des états d'intersexualité qui en résultent). A. Raynaud. Mammalia, Paris, 7 (2): 86-87, June, 1943.

FEEDING CHLORINATED MILK TO THE ALBINO RAT. J. W. Read, Harrison Hale. Jour. Agric. Research, vol.30, pp.889-892, May (August), 1925.

THE RELATIVE THICKNESS OF MOUSE SKINS TREATED WITH SULFHYDRYL, DISULFOXIDE AND DIBENZANTHRACENE. Stanley P. Reimann, Nevart Chatalbash. Growth, Menasha, Wisc., vol.1, no.4, pp. 247-249, 1937.

EFFECT OF THE KIDNEY OF THE FASTING RAT ON BLOOD SUGAR AND HEMOGLOBIN CONCENTRATIONS BEFORE AND AFTER EVISCERATION OR PARTIAL HEPATECTOMY. R. M. Reinecke, G. G. Rudolph, M. J. Bryson, Leo T. Samuels. Amer. Jour. Physiol., Balto., vol.53, no. 1, pp.47-54, Apr.1, 1948.

DECREASED CARBOHYDRATE APPETITE OF ADRENALECTOMIZED RATS. Curt P. Richter. Proc. Soc. Exper. Biol. Med., New York, vol.48, pp.577-579, 1941.

A STUDY OF THE EFFECT AND MODERATE DOSES OF ALCOHOL ON THE GROWTH AND BEHAVIOR OF THE RAT. Curt P. Richter. Jour. Exper. Zool., vol. 44, pp.397-418, 11 figs., Apr.5, 1926.

PERSISTENCE OF THE 4 TO 5-DAY ACTIVITY CYCLES IN VITAMIN A DEFICIENT RATS WITH CONSTANT CORNIFICATION OF THE VAGINAL EPITHELIUM. Curt P. Richter, Bruno Barelare, Jr. Endocrinology, Los Angeles, vol.24, no.3, pp.364-366, fig.1, Mar., 1939.

TOXIC EFFECTS OF THE BITTER-TASTING PHENYLTHIOCARBAMIDE. Curt P. Richter, Kathryn H. Clisby. Arch. Pathol., Chicago, vol.33, pp.46-57, figs. 3, Jan., 1942.

MINERAL APPETITE OF PARATHYROIDECTOMIZED RATS. Curt P. Richter, John F. Eckert. Amer. Jour. Med. Sci., Phila., vol.198, no.1, pp.9-16, figs.3, July, 1939.

INCREASED SPONTANEOUS ACTIVITY AND FOOD INTAKE PRODUCED IN RATS BY REMOVAL OF THE FRONTAL POLES OF THE BRAIN. Curt P. Richter, C. D. Hawkes. Jour. Neurology, and Psychiatry, London, n.s., vol.2, no.3, pp.231-242, July, 1939.

BEHAVIOR AND ANATOMICAL CHANGES PRODUCED IN RATS BY PANCREATECTOMY. Curt P. Richter, Edward C. H. Schmidt, Jr. Endocrinology, Los Angeles, vol.25, no.5, pp.698-706, figs.3, Nov., 1939.

INCREASED FAT AND DECREASED CARBOHYDRATE APPETITE OF PANCREATECTOMIZED RATS. Curt P. Richter, Edward C. H. Schmidt, Jr. Endocrinology, Los Angeles, vol.28, no. 2, pp.179-192, figs.5, Feb., 1941.

COMPARISON OF THE EFFECTS OF GONADECTOMY ON SPONTANEOUS ACTIVITY OF WILD AND DOMESTICATED NORWAY RATS. Curt P. Richter, E. H. Uhlenhuth. Endocrinology, Springfield, Illinois, vol.54, no.3, pp.311-322, Mar., 1954.

OESTROUS REACTIONS, INCLUDING MATING PRODUCED BY TRIPHENYL ETHYLENE. (IN OVARIECTOMIZED MICE.) J. M. Robson, A. Schonberg. Nature, London, vol.140, no.3535, p.196, July 31, 1937.

EFFECT OF ELECTROCONVULSIVE SHOCKS ON NEST BUILDING IN THE MALE ALBINO RAT. H. Enger Rosvold, Alan M. Walker. Proc. Soc. Exp. Biol. Med., Utica, vol.72, no.1, pp.270-272, Oct., 1949.

PURE STRAIN MICE BORN TO HYBRID MOTHERS FOLLOWING OVARIAN TRANSPLANTATION. W. L. Russell, Jane Goodrich Hurst. Proc. Nat. Acad. Sci., Easton, vol.31, no.9, pp.267-273, figs.2, Sept., 1945.

SUCCESSFUL INTERCHANGE OF OVARIES BETWEEN ALBINO RATS AND MICE. James M. Sanders. Science, Lancaster, vol.104, no.2698, p.257, Sept.13, 1946.

A DEMONSTRATION OF NERVE FIBERS IN THE METAPLASTIC EPITHELIUM OF VITAMIN A DEFICIENT RATS. Mary Elmore Sauer. Anat. Record, Phila., vol. 74, pp.223-230, June 25, 1939.

EXPERIMENTAL SIMULATION OF GESTATIONAL CHANGES IN THE VAGINA OF THE MOUSE. R. Dean Schick. Jour. Morphol., Phila., vol.73, no.1, pp.143-175, illus., July, 1943.

THE EFFECT OF FLUORINE AS SODIUM FLUORIDE ON THE GROWTH AND REPRODUCTION OF ALBINO RATS. J. A. Schulz, A. R. Lamb. Science, vol.61, pp.93-94, Jan.23, 1925.

DISTRIBUTION OF RADIOACTIVE SULFUR IN THE RAT. H. O. Singher, L. Marinelli. Science, Lancaster, n.s., vol.101, no.2625, pp.414-415, Apr.20, 1945.

THE EFFECTS OF ACUTE AND CHRONIC INANITION UPON THE DEVELOPMENT AND STRUCTURE OF THE TESTIS IN THE ALBINO RAT. David M. Siperstein. Anat. Record, vol.20, pp.355-391, 14 figs., Mar.20, 1921.

THE EFFECT OF A STRICTLY VEGETABLE DIET ON THE SPONTANEOUS ACTIVITY, THE RATE OF GROWTH, AND THE LONGEVITY OF THE ALBINO RAT. James Rollin Slonaker. Leland Stanford Jr. Univ. Publ., Univ. Ser., pp.36, figs. 19, pl.1, 1912.

HYPOPHYSECTOMY AND A REPLACEMENT THERAPY IN THE RAT. P. E. Smith. Amer. Jour. Anat., vol.45, pp.205-274, 3 figs., 8 pls., Mar.15, 1930.

THE PRODUCTION OF STERILITY IN MALE MICE BY IRRADIATION WITH NEUTRONS. George D. Snell, Paul C. Aebersold. Proc. Nat. Acad. Sci. Wash., vol.23, no.7, pp.374-378, July, 1937.

THE EFFECT OF X-RAYS ON THE FERTILITY OF RATS. Laurence H. Snyder. Amer. Nat., vol.? no.660, pp.87-91, Jan.-Feb., 1925.

THE EFFECT OF X-RAYS ON RATS. Lawrence H. Snyder. Anat. Record, vol. 29, p.151, Dec.25, 1924.

AN EXPERIMENTAL STUDY OF THE MITOCHONDRIA IN THE HEPATIC CELLS OF THE WHITE RAT. Herman Walter Steffens. Anat. Record, Phila., vol.81, no.2, pp.243-263, fig.1, pls.2, Oct.25, 1941.

(THE EFFECT OF HIGHER OUTER TEMPERATURE ON THE GERM GLANDS OF THE DOMESTIC MOUSE.) Der einfluss hoeherer Aussentemperatur auf die Keimdruesen der Hausmaus. H. Stieve. Verhandl. Anat. Gesellsch., Anat. Anzeiger, Ergaenzungsheft zum, vol.57, pp.38-53, Dec., 1923.

DELAY IN THE AWAKENING OF COPULATORY ABILITY IN THE MALE ALBINO RAT INCURRED BY DEFECTIVE DIETS. II. QUALITATIVE DEFICIENCY. C. P. Stone. Jour. Comp. Psych., vol.5, pp.177-203, 1924.

THE RETENTION OF COPULATORY ABILITY IN MALE RATS FOLLOWING CASTRATION. C. P. Stone. Jour. Comp. Psych., vol.7, pp.369-387, illus., 1927.

THE EFFECTS OF THYROID AND VITAMIN B UPON THE ADRENAL GLANDS OF ALBINO RATS. Ruth Sumner. Jour. Colorado-Wyoming Acad. Sci., Denver, vol.3, no.1, pp.46-47, Apr., 1941.

ON THE OVARIAN GRAFTS IN THE SENILE MALE RATS WITH NOTE ON THE SENILE DEGENERATION OF THE SEX GLAND. Kiyoshi Takewaki. Jour. Faculty Sci. Imp. Univ. Tokyo, sec.4, Zool., vol.3, pt.3, pp.255-264, figs.9, pl.21, Dec.18, 1934.

THE DEVELOPMENT OF THE RAT EYE IN GRAFT. Katharine Tansley. Jour. Exper. Biol., London, vol.22, nos.3-4, pp.221-224, pls.8-9, May, 1946.

LOSS OF NERVE ENDINGS IN DEGENERATED SKELETAL MUSCLES OF YOUNG VITAMIN E DEFICIENT RATS. Ira R. Telford. Anat. Record, Phila., vol.81, no.2, pp.171-181, 2 pls., Oct.25, 1941.

THE DIRECTION OF HAIR AFTER ROTATION OF SKIN IN THE NEWBORN ALBINO RAT: A SECOND EXPERIMENT ON HAIR SLOPE. Mildred Trotter, Helen L. Dawson. Anat. Record, vol.53, no.1, pp. 19-29, pls.1-2, June 25, 1932.

COMPLEMENT FIXATION IN RAT'S BLOOD SERA. Gerardo Varela, Carlos Ortiz Mariotte, Roberto Silva. Science, Lancaster, vol.104, no.2700, p.303, Sept.27, 1946.

(EXPERIMENTAL INVESTIGATIONS OF THE EPIDIDYMIS OF THE MOUSE.) Experimentaluntersuchungen am Nebenhoden der Maus. F. Wagenseil. Zeitschr. Zelforschung, vol.7, pp.141-176, figs.11, Apr.27, 1928.

THE EFFECT OF REMOVAL OF THE ZYGOMATIC ARCH IN THE RAT. S. L. Washburn. Jour. Mam., vol.27, no.2, pp.169-172, pl.1, May 14, 1946.

(OVARIAN TRANSPLANTATION IN RATS.) Ovarial transplantation bei Ratten. Fr. Weber. Zeitschr. f. induktive Abstammungs- und Verebungslehre, vol.43, pp. 390-391, 1927.

THE EXPERIMENTAL SHORTENING OF DELAYED PREGNANCY IN THE ALBINO RAT. Charles K. Weichert. Anat. Record, Phila., vol.77, no.1, pp.31-47, 3 pls., May 25, 1940.

MEASUREMENTS AND OBSERVATIONS UPON THE INTESTINE OF RATS FED UNBALANCED AND SUPPLEMENTED DIETS. J. L. Wierda. Amer. Jour. Anat., Phila., vol.70, no.3, pp.433-451, 1 pl., May 15, 1942.

THE INFLUENCE OF GONADECTOMY ON THE RESPIRATORY METABOLISM OF THE CEREBRAL CORTEX IN ALBINO RATS. H. C. Wu. Contrib. Biol. Lab. Sci. Soc. China, Nanking, zool. ser., vol.12, no.2, pp.19-27, fig.1, 1936.

ADAPTATION OF THE TAIL PLETHYSMOGRAPH TO BLOOD PRESSURE MEASUREMENT IN THE MOUSE WITH SOME OBSERVATIONS ON THE EFFECTS OF TEMPERATURE. H. C. Wu, M. B. Visscher. Amer. Jour. Physiol., Balto., vol.153, no.2, pp. 330-335, May 1, 1948.

EVIDENCE OF ANOTHER FACTOR IN THE B COMPLEX FOR RATS. W. R. Wyatt. Proc. Soc. Exper. Biol. Med., New York, vol.40, no.2, pp.281-283, Feb., 1939.

### Food Habits

A FLY EATING MOUSE. Shaler E. Aldous. Jour. Mam., vol.12, no.3, p.316, Aug., 1931.

PREDATION BY THE COMMON RAT (RATTUS NORVEGICUS) IN THE CAPE COD COLONIES OF NESTING TERNS. Oliver L. Austin. Bird-Banding, 19 (2): 60-65, Apr., 1948.

FEEDING, SOCIAL BEHAVIOUR AND INTERSPECIFIC COMPETITION IN WILD RATS. S. A. Barnett, Mary M. Spencer. Behaviour, 3 (3): 229-242, 6 figs., 1951.

INFLUENCE OF TEXTURE OF FOOD ON ITS ACCEPTANCE BY RATS. A. J. Carlson, F. Hollzel. Science, Lancaster, vol.109, no.2821, pp.63-64, Jan.21, 1949.

BEHAVIOUR COMPONENTS IN THE FEEDING OF WILD AND LABORATORY RATS. S. A. Barnett. Behaviour, Leiden, 9 (1): 24-43, 1956.

EXPERIMENTS ON THE FOOD PREFERENCES OF WILD RATS (RATTUS NORVEGICUS BERKENHOUT). S. A. Barnett, Mary M. Spencer. Jour. Hyg., 51 (1): 16-34, illus., Mar., 1953.

A NOTE ON THE MOUSE, MUS MUSCULUS LINN. AS AN ENEMY TO LIZARDS. Charles E. Burt. Copeia, no.162, pp.15-16, Jan.-Mar. (Apr.), 1927.

(SOME OBSERVATIONS ON WOOD MICE IN CAPTIVITY.) Nogle Iagttragelser over Skovmus i Fangenskab. (Studies upon the feeding behavior of Apodemus sylvaticus.) Magnus Degerbol. Naturens Verden, vol.13, pp.163-180, illus., Apr., 1929.

THE CALIFORNIA CLAPPER RAIL, ITS NESTING HABITS, ENEMIES AND HABITAT. (NOTES ON NORWAY RAT AS ENEMY.) Dudley Sargent DeGroot. Condor, vol.29, pp.259-270, Nov., 1927.

THE RECURRENCE OF EATING IN RATS AFTER APPARENT SATIATION. G. C. Drew. Proc. Zool. Soc. Lond., vol.107, ser.A, Gen and Exper., pt.1, pp.95-106, Apr., 1937.

EFFECT OF RAIN ON THE FEEDING OF THE MALAYSIAN RICE-FIELD RAT. J. L. Harrison. Nature, Lond., vol.164, no. 4174, p.746, Oct.29, 1949.

NOTES ON THE FEEDING HABITS OF HOUSE-RATS IN RANGOON, BURMA. J. L. Harrison, H. C. Woodville. Ann. Applied Biol., Lond., vol.37, no.2, pp. 296-304, illus., June, 1950.

(CONTINUED INVESTIGATIONS OF CONE GNAWING IN THE WOOD MOUSE (MUS SYLVATICUS L.) WITH AN INTRODUCTORY SUMMARY OF THE DEVELOPMENT OF OUR KNOWLEDGE OF CONE GNAWING IN MICE.) Fortgesetzte Untersuchungen Ueber das Zapfennagen der Waldmaus (Mus sylvaticus L.) Mit einleitender Uebersicht ueber die Entwicklung unserer Kenntnis des Zapfennagens der Maeuse. Ad. S. Jensen. Vidensk. Medd. fra Dansk Naturh. Foren., Copenhagen, vol.82, pp.249-269, figs.6, 1926.

(RATS AND EGGS.) Ratten en eieren. D. W. Langeveld. De Levende Natuur, Nederlands Tijdschr. Veldebiol., vol.56, no.12, pp.221-224, illus., Dec., 1953.

INSECT FEEDING BY THE HOUSE MOUSE. J. P. Linduska. Jour. Mam., vol.23, no. 2, pp.212-213, May 14, 1942.

TRAGEDY IN BIRD LIFE. (RAT DEPREDATIONS.) George C. Munro. Elepaio, Jour. Honolulu Audubon Soc., vol.5, no.8, pp.48-51, Feb., 1945.

BURROWS AND FEEDING OF THE NORWAY RAT. Rocci G. Pisano, Tracy I. Storer. Jour. Mam., 29 (4): 374-383, Nov., 1948.

FOOD AND WATER ECONOMY OF THE YOUNG RAT DURING CHRONIC STARVATION AND RECOVERY. Freeman H. Quimby. Jour. Nutrition, Phila., vol.36, no.1, pp.177-186, July 10, 1948.

THE GRAZING OF WINTER CEREALS BY THE WOOD-MOUSE (APODEMUS SYLVATICUS). A. Roebuck, F. T. Baker, J. H. White. Jour. Anim. Ecol., Lond., vol.13, no.2, pp.105-109, pls.1-2, Nov., 1944.

THE HOUSE RAT AS AN ENEMY OF THE BANK SWALLOW. Dayton Stoner. Jour. Mam., vol.18, no.1, pp.87-89, Feb.14, 1937.

FOOD CONSUMPTION OF HOUSE MICE AT LOW TEMPERATURES. Robert L. Strecker. Jour. Mam., 36 (3): 460-462, graph, Aug., 1955.

(FOOD TRACES OF THE YELLOW-THROATED MOUSE (APODEMUS FLAVICOLLIS MELCHIOR 1834) AND THE WOOD MOUSE (APODEMUS SYLVATICUS LINNE 1758).) Frass-Spuren von Gelbhalsmaus, Apodemus flavicollis (Melchior, 1834) und Waldmaus, Apodemus sylvaticus (Linne, 1758). Kl. Zimmermann. Saeugetierk. Mitteil., Stuttgart, vol.2, no.1, p.34, illus., Jan.1, 1954.

### Fossils

NEW PLEISTOCENE MURINAE FROM CRETE. Dorothea M. A. Bate. Ann. and Mag. Nat. Hist., Lond., ser.11, vol.9, pp. 41-49, figs.2, Jan., 1942.

PLEISTOCENE MURINAE FROM PALESTINE. Dorothea M. A. Bate. Ann. and Mag. Nat. Hist., Lond., ser.11, vol.59, no.55, pp.465-486, figs.5, July, 1942.

THREE NEW GIANT PREHISTORIC RATS FROM FLORES, LESSER SUNDA ISLANDS. D. A. Hooijer. Zool. Meded., Leiden, vol.35, no.21, pp.299-314, Dec.23, 1957.

SIWALIK FOSSIL MASTOMYS. G. Edward Lewis. Bull. Geol. Soc. Amer. (Abstracts), vol.49, no.12, pt.2, p.1915, Dec.1, 1938; Amer. Jour. Sci., New Haven, vol.237, pp.341-344, pl.1, May, 1939.

(TERTIARY AND QUATERNARY MURINAE.) Tertiare und Quatare Murinae. Schaub. Abh. Schweiz. Pal. Ges., vol.61, pp.1-38, 1939.

### General Habits, Behavior

AN ANALYSIS OF SOCIAL BEHAVIOUR IN WILD RATS. S. A. Barnett. Proc. Zool. Soc. Lond., 130 (1): 107-152, pls.1-3, Jan. 23, 1958.

RESPONSES OF WILD RATS TO OFFENSIVE SMELLS AND TASTES. S. A. Barnett, Mary M. Spencer. Brit. Jour. Anim. Behaviour, 1 (1): 32-37, 8 figs., 1953.

HABIT FORMATION IN A STRAIN OF ALBINO RATS OF LESS THAN NORMAL BRAIN WEIGHT. Gardner Cheney Basset. Pub. Cambridge, Boston, Mass., New York, H. Holt & Co., 46 pp., illus., diagrs., 1914.

THE TAIL AS A BALANCING ORGAN IN MICE. C. W. Buck, N. Tolman, W.

Tolman. Jour. Mam., vol.6, no.3, pp. 267-271, Aug., 1925.

A MUSICAL MOUSE. Josiah Burnham. Jour. Mam., vol.8, no.2, pp.162-163, May, 1927.

A COMPARATIVE STUDY OF THE SOCIAL BEHAVIOR OF TWO INBRED STRAINS OF HOUSE MICE. John B. Calhoun. Ecol. Monogr., Durham, vol.26, no.1, pp.81-103, Jan., 1956.

(WHEN THE BROWN RAT "MIMICS" THE BLACK RAT.) Quande le surmulot "singe" le rat noir. P. Cantuel. Mammalia, Paris, vol.14, no.4, pp.179-181, illus., Dec., 1950.

A SINGING MOUSE. Sally Carrighar. Jour. Mam., vol.23, no.4, pp.445-446, Nov.14, 1942.

AQUATIC HABITS OF THE NORWAY RAT. Clarence Cottam. Jour. Mam., vol.29, no.2, pp.299, Aug.31, 1948.

(THE WOOD MOUSE (APODEMUS S. SYLVATICUS LINNE 1758) AS INHABITANT OF NESTING BOXES.) Die Waldmaus, Apodemus s. sylvaticus (Linne, 1758), als Bewohnerin von Nistkaesten. Gerhard Creutz. Saeugetierk. Mitteil., vol.1, no. 1, pp.21-22, Jan.10, 1953.

SOCIAL INTERACTION OF RATS AS INDICATED BY TRAPPING PROCEDURES. David E. Davis. Behaviour, Leiden, vol. 8, pt.4, pp.335-343, 1955.

DIFFERENTIAL TRAPABILITY OF RATS ACCORDING TO SIZE AND SEX. David E. Davis, John T. Emlen. Jour. Wildlife Mgt., 20 (3): 326-327, July, 1956.

(INBORN AND ACQUIRED TRAITS IN THE NEST-BUILDING BEHAVIOR OF THE BROWN RAT.) Angeborenes und Erworbenes im Nestbauverhalten der Wanderratte. Irenaeus Eibl-Eibesfeldt. Die Naturwissenschaften, Berlin, 42 (23): 633-634, 1955.

WINTERING OF FIELD-LIVING NORWAY RATS IN SOUTHCENTRAL WISCONSIN. Paul L. Errington. Ecology, vol.16, no.1, pp.122-123, Jan., 1935.

(BRIEF OBSERVATIONS ON THE PYGMY MOUSE (MICROMYS MINUTUS PALL.) WITH ECOLOGICAL INFERENCES.) Kleine Beobachtungen an der Zwergmaus (Micromys minutus Pall.) mit oekologischen Folgerungen. Fritz Frank. Bonner Zool. Beitraege, Jahrg.3, Heft 3-4, pp.207-209, Feb.20, 1953.

HOW RATS TRANSPORT EGGS. THE RAT-EGG-WAGON STORY TRACED BACK TO 1291 A.D. E. W. Gudger. Sci. Monthly, vol.40, pp.415-424, figs.4, May, 1935.

(ON THE ECOLOGY AND DISTRIBUTION OF THE FIELD MOUSE (APODEMUS AGRARIUS PALLAS).) Zur Oekologie und Verbreitung der Brandmaus (Apodemus agrarius Pallas). G. Heinrich. Bonner Zool. Beitraege, Jahrg. 5, Heft 1-2, pp.9-10, July 15, 1952.

SINGING MICE. John Eric Hill. Nat. Hist., New York, vol.53, no.10, p.436, Dec., 1944.

A SUPPOSED ADAPTATION AGAINST SUN STROKE IN AFRICAN DIURNAL RATS. John Eric Hill. Jour. Mam., vol.23, no. 2, p.210, May 14, 1942.

(THE SWIMMING ABILITY OF MICE (MURIDAE).) Die Schwimmfaehigkeit von Maeusen (Muridae). Eberhard Jany. Saeugetierk. Mitteil., Stuttgart, vol.2, no. 2, pp.75-78, illus., Apr.1, 1954.

RATS ARE GOOD SWIMMERS. F. N. Jarvis. Jour. Mam., vol.8, no.3, p.249, Aug., 1927.

(CONTINUED INVESTIGATIONS OF CONE GNAWING IN THE WOOD MOUSE (MUS SYLVATICUS L.), WITH A REVIEW OF THE DEVELOPMENT OF OUR KNOWLEDGE OF CONE GNAWING IN MICE.) Fortgesetzte Untersuchungen ueber das Zapfennagen der Waldmaus (Mus sylvaticus L.), mit einleiten der Uebersicht ueber die Entwicklung unserer Kenntnis des Zapfennagens der Maeuse. Ad. S. Jensen. Videnskalbelige Meddelelser fra Dansk Naturhist Forening, vol.82, pp.249-269, 1927.

ON THE NEST OF PITECHEIR MELANURUS. F. A. Jentink. Notes Leyden Mus., vol.17, no.26, pp.167-168, Nov., 1895.

A STUDY OF THE NEST-BUILDING ACTIVITY OF THE ALBINO RAT. Elaine Flitner Kinder. Jour. Exper. Zool., vol. 47, pp.117-161, illus., Apr.5, 1927.

A SUPPOSED WINTER NEST OF THE HARVEST MOUSE. Sydney H. Long. Trans. Norfolk and Norwich Nat. Soc., vol.12, pp.54-56, illus., 1926.

(HAS THE BROWN RAT OVERTAKEN THE BLACK RAT IN WESTERN EUROPE?) Heeft de bruine rat, de zwarte rat in West-Europa verdrongen? F. E. Loosjes. Rat en Muis, Plantenziektenkundige Dienst, Wageningen, Netherlands, 1956 (1): 1-7, illus., Mar., 1956.

HARBORAGE OF RATTUS RATTUS ALEXANDRINUS. B. K. Milmore. Pub. Health Rept., 58 (41): 1507-1509, Oct.8, 1943.

STRANGE ACTION OF A HOUSE MOUSE. Carl O. Mohr. Jour. Mam., vol.21, no.1, pp.93-94, fig.1, Feb.14, 1940.

THE RAT AS A MECHANIC. N. Morrison. Field, London, vol.153, p.152, Jan.24, 1929.

COMMUNAL NESTS OF THE HOUSE MOUSE (MUS MUSCULUS LINNAEUS). Robert T. Orr. Wasmann Collector, 6 (2): 35-37, Nov., 1944.

THE SINGING OF THE HOUSE MOUSE. Edwin B. Powers. Jour. Mam., vol.6, no. 3, p.201, Aug., 1925.

A BEHAVIORISTIC STUDY OF THE ACTIVITY OF THE RAT. Curt P. Richter. Dissert. Johns Hopkins Univ. Balto., p.55, figs.24, 1922.

THE NORMAL ACTIVITY OF THE WHITE RAT AT DIFFERENT AGES. James Rollin Slonaker. Jour. Compar. Neurol. and Psychol., vol.17, no.4, pp.342-359, figs.8, 1907.

THE ABUNDANCE AND DISTRIBUTION OF HARVEST MICE (MICROMYS MINUTUS) IN CORN RICKS NEAR OXFORD. Charles H. Southwick. Proc. Zool. Soc. Lond., 126, (3): 449-452, May 31, 1956.

COMMUNITY NESTS OF THE HOUSE MOUSE. Tracy I. Storer. Jour. Mam., vol.12, no.3, pp.316-337, Aug., 1931.

ON THE HABITS OF THE SYDNEY BUSH-RAT (MUS ARBORICOLA). Oldfield Thomas. Proc. Zool. Soc., Lond., pp. 857-860, Nov.16, 1897.

EXPERIMENTAL LIVE-TRAPPING OF RATS, WITH OBSERVATIONS ON THEIR BEHAVIOUR. H. V. Thompson. Brit. Jour. Anim. Behaviour, 1 (3): 96-111, 1 fig., 1953.

STUDIES OF THE BEHAVIOR OF THE COMMON BROWN RAT (RATTUS NORVEGICUS BERKENHOUT). H. V. Thompson. Bull. Animal Behavior, Lond., no.6, pp.26-40, 1948.

THE SOCIAL HIERARCHY IN ALBINO MICE. Jacob Uhrich. Trans. Kansas Acad. Sci., Topeka, vol.41, p.385, 1938.

UNUSUAL BEHAVIOR OF THE NORWAY RAT. Frederick A. Ulmer, Jr. Jour. Mam., vol.32, no.1, pp.117-118, Feb.15, 1951.

ON THE HABITS OF THE SYDNEY BUSH-RAT (MUS ARBORICOLA). Edgar R. Waite. Proc. Zool. Soc. Lond., pp.857-860, Nov.16, 1897.

FORMATION OF URINATING "POSTS" BY HOUSE MICE (MUS) HELD UNDER RESTRICTED CONDITION. Jack F. Welch. Jour. Mam., vol.34, no.4, pp.502-503, illus., Nov.13, 1953.

THE CANNIBALISM OF RATS. W. Mattieu Williams. Gentleman's Magazine, London, pp.99-100, July, 1886.

MODIFIABILITY OF BEHAVIOR IN ITS RELATIONS TO THE AGE AND SEX OF THE DANCING MOUSE. Robert M. Yerkes. Jour. Compar. Neurol., Phila., vol.19, no. 3, pp.237-271, figs.4, June, 1909.

HETEROGENEITY OF TRAP RESPONSE IN A POPULATION OF HOUSE MICE. Howard Young, John Neess, John T. Emlen, Jr. Jour. Wildlife Mgt., Ithaca, N. Y., vol.16, no.2, pp.169-180, illus., Apr., 1952.

LOCALIZATION OF ACTIVITY IN TWO INDOOR POPULATIONS OF HOUSE MICE, MUS MUSCULUS. Howard Young, Robert L. Strecker, John T. Emlen, Jr. Jour. Mam., vol.31, no.4, pp.403-410, figs.3, Nov.21, 1950.

Growth and Development

EFFECT OF DISCONTINUOUS EXPOSURE TO 25,000 FEET SIMULATED ALTITUDE ON GROWTH AND REPRODUCTION OF THE ALBINO RAT. Paul D. Altland. Jour. Exper. Zool., Phila., vol.110, no.1, pp.1-18, Feb., 1949.

2-AMINOFLOURENE AS GROWTH INHIBITOR FOR BACTERIA AND RATS. F. Bielschowsky, H. N. Green. Nature, London, vol.149, no.3784, pp.526-527, illus., May 9, 1942.

THE GROWTH OF CONFINED COLONIES OF THE WILD HOUSE-MOUSE (MUS MUSCULUS L.). Peter Crowcroft, F. P. Rowe. Proc. Zool. Soc. Lond., 129 (3): 359-370, Nov.11, 1957.

A PHENOTYPICAL DIFFERENCE IN GROWTH OF WILD RATS. David E. Davis. Growth, Menasha, vol.8, no.346, pp.1-6, fig.1, illus., 1949.

QUANTITATIVE STUDIES OF THE GROWTH OF THE SKELETON OF THE ALBINO RAT. Henry H. Donaldson. Amer. Jour. Anat., vol.26, pp.237-314, Nov., 1919.

THE BROWN VARIATION AND GROWTH OF THE HOUSE MOUSE. Horace W. Feldman. Amer. Nat., vol.69, no.723, pp.370-374, July-Aug., 1935.

LITTER SIZE, BIRTH WEIGHT, AND EARLY GROWTH RATE OF MICE (MUS MUSCULUS). W. H. Gates. Anat. Record, vol.29, pp.183-193, 4 charts, July 25, 1925.

GROWTH STUDIES WITH RATS KEPT UNDER CONDITIONS WHICH PREVENT COPROPHAGY. R. P. Geyer, B. R. Geyer, P. H. Derse, T. Zinkin, C. A. Elvehjem, E. B. Hart. Jour. Nutrition, 33: 129-142, 1947.

SIZE INHERITANCE AND GROWTH IN A MOUSE SPECIES CROSS (MUS MUSCULUS X MUS BACTRIANUS). 1. LITTER SIZE. 2. BIRTH WEIGHTS. C. V. Green. Jour. Exper. Zool., vol.58, pp.237-258, Jan.5, 1931.

DIFFERENTIAL GROWTH IN THE MOUSE. C. V. Green, Elizabeth Fekete. Jour. Exper. Zool., vol.66, no.3, pp.351-370, Nov.5, 1933.

THE GROWTH SURVIVAL, WANDERING AND VARIATION OF THE LONG-TAILED FIELD MOUSE, APODEMUS SYLVATICUS. I. GROWTH. H. P. Hacker, H. S. Pearson. Biometrika, Cambridge, England, vol.33, pt.2, pp.136-162, 11 figs., 3 folding charts, Aug.18, 1944.

ON THE INFLUENCE OF THE TEMPERATURE OF THE ENVIRONMENT UPON THE GROWTH OF MICE (MUS MUSCULUS L.). N. I. Kalabuchov. Bull. Soc. Nat. Moscou, n.s., vol.47, no.3, pp.218-222, fig.1, table 1, 1938. (In Russian, with French resume.)

(THE YOUNG DEVELOPMENT OF THE PYGMY MOUSE (MICROMYS MINUTUS SORICINUS).) Die Jugendentwicklung der Zwergmaus, Micromys minutus soricinus (Hermann, 1780). Werner Kaestle. Saeugetierk. Mitteil., Stuttgart, vol.1, no. 2, pp.49-59, illus., Apr.1, 1953.

ON THE WEIGHT OF THE ALBINO RAT AT BIRTH AND THE FACTORS THAT INFLUENCE IT. Helen Dean King. The Anatomical Record, vol.9, no.3, pp. 213-231, Mar., 1915.

STUDIES ON INBREEDING. IV. A FURTHER STUDY OF THE EFFECTS OF INBREEDING ON THE GROWTH AND VARIABILITY IN THE BODY WEIGHT OF THE ALBINO RAT. Helen Dean King. Jour. Exper. Zool., vol.29, pp.71-111, Aug., 1919.

THE DETERMINATION OF THE MEDIAN BODY-WEIGHT AT WHICH FEMALE RATS REACH MATURITY. P. H. Leslie, J. S. Perry, J. S. Watson. Proc. Zool. Soc. Lond., vol.115, pts.3-4, pp.473-488, fig. 1, Feb., 1946.

GROSS EFFICIENCY OF GROWTH OF THE RAT AS A SIMPLE MATHEMATICAL FUNCTION OF TIME. Jean Mayer. Yale Jour. Biol. Med., New Haven, vol.21, no.5, pp. 415-419, May, 1949.

INFLUENCE OF VITAMIN A DEFICIENCY ON THE GROSS EFFICIENCY OF GROWTH OF RATS. Jean Mayer. Yale Jour. Biol. Med., New Haven, vol.20, no.4, pp.403-405, Mar., 1948.

THE EFFECTS OF RATE OF GROWTH ON THE POST-NATAL DEVELOPMENT OF THE WHITE RAT. Gairdner Bostwick Moment. Jour. Exper. Zool., vol.65, no.3, pp.359-393, July 5, 1933.

(GROWTH AND SEXUAL MATURITY IN MASTOMYS COUCHA SMITH.) Croissance et maturite sexuelle chez Mastomys coucha Smith. P. L. Pirlot. Mammalia, Paris, 21 (4): 385-395, Dec., 1957.

SOUTHERN PEAS AND OTHER LEGUME SEEDS AS A SOURCE OF PROTEIN FOR THE GROWTH OF RATS. L. R. Richardson. Jour. Nutrition, Phila., vol.36, no.5, pp.451-462, Oct.11, 1948.

THE NORMAL ACTIVITY OF THE ALBINO RAT FROM BIRTH TO NATURAL DEATH, ITS RATE OF GROWTH AND THE DURATION OF LIFE. James Rollin Slonaker. Jour. Animal Behavior, vol.2, no.1, pp.20-42, figs.14, Jan.-Feb., 1912.

Heredity

RACIAL AND FAMILIAL CYCLIC INHERITANCE AND OTHER EVIDENCE FROM THE MOUSE CONCERNING THE CAUSE OF OESTROUS PHENOMENA. E. Allen. Amer. Jour. Anat., vol.32, pp.293-304, 1923.

HEREDITARY STRUCTURAL DEFECTS IN THE DESCENDANTS OF MICE EXPOSED TO X-RAY IRRADIATION. H. J. Bagg, C. C. Little. Amer. Jour. Anat., vol.33, pp.119-146, 3 pls., 1 chart, Mar.15, 1924.

SELECTION FOR TAIL SPOTTING IN THE HOUSE MOUSE. E. F. Barrows. Jour. Exper. Zool., Phila., vol.80, no.1, pp.107-111, Feb.5, 1939.

(ON A TYPE OF PHYSIOLOGICAL MUTATION OBSERVED IN THE MOUSE.) Sur une sorte de mutation physiologique observee chez la souris. Gabriel Bertrand, B. Benzon. Compt. Rend. Acad. Sci. Paris, vol.177, pp.297-299, 1923.

A RELATION BETWEEN CHROMOSOME SIZE AND B VITAMIN CONTENT OF RAT ORGANS. John J. Biesele. Amer. Nat., Lancaster, vol.78, no.777, pp.380-382, July-Aug., 1944.

THE AGE OF RATS AT SEXUAL MATURITY AS DETERMINED BY THEIR GENETIC CONSTITUTION. Cecil T. Blunn. Anat. Record, Phila., vol.74, pp.199-213, June 25, 1939.

ORDER OF GENES IN THE FIFTH LINKAGE OF THE HOUSE MOUSE. Robert Borger. Nature, London, vol.166, no.4225, p.697, Oct.21, 1950.

FACTORS INFLUENCING LUNG LOBATION IN THE MOUSE. I. GENETIC FACTORS: A PRELIMINARY REPORT. Sue Browder. Anat. Record, Phila., vol.83, no.1, pp.31-39, figs.9, May 25, 1942.

SPERMATOGENESIS AND FERTILITY IN MUS MUSCULUS AS AFFECTED BY FACTORS AT THE T LOCUS. Vernon Bryson. Jour. Morphol., Phila., vol.74, no.1, pp.131-187, illus., Jan., 1944.

A SEARCH FOR SOME EFFECTS OF THE "SHORT-EAR" GENE ON BEHAVIOR IN MICE. Roy Elton Bundy. Amer. Nat., Lancaster, vol.84, no.818, pp.393-399, Sept.-Oct., 1950.

HYPERGLUCAEMIA AS A MENDELIAN RECESSIVE CHARACTER IN MICE. P. J. Cammidge, H. A. H. Howard. Jour. Genetics, vol.16, pp.387-392, 1926.

A NEW MUTATION IN THE HOUSE MOUSE. F. G. Carnochan. Jour. Heredity, Wash., D.C., vol.28, no.10, pp.333-334, Oct., 1937.

POSITION OF 'LUXATE' IN THE THIRD LINKAGE GROUP OF THE HOUSE MOUSE. T. C. Carter. Nature, Lond., vol.164, no.4183, p.1138, Dec.31, 1949.

ICHTHYOSIS, NEW RECESSIVE MUTANT IN THE HOUSE MOUSE. T. C. Carter, Rita S. Phillips. Jour. Heredity, Balto., vol.41, no.11, pp.297-300, illus., Nov., 1950.

THE INHERITANCE OF A TAIL ABNORMALITY IN THE HOUSE MOUSE. Ernst Caspari, Paul R. David. Jour. Heredity, Wash., D.C., vol.31, no.10, pp.427-431, figs.2, Oct., 1940.

GREEN'S STUDIES OF LINKAGE IN SIZE INHERITANCE. (MUS MUSCULUS AND M. BACTRIANUS.) W. E. Castle. Amer. Nat., vol.66, no.702, pp.82-87, Jan.-Feb., 1932.

LINKAGE IN THE ALBINO CHROMOSOME OF THE RAT. W. E. Castle. Proc. Nat. Acad. Sci., Easton, vol.32, no.2, pp.33-36, Feb.15, 1946.

LINKAGE OF WALTZING IN THE RAT. W. E. Castle. Proc. Nat. Acad. Sci., Wash., vol.30, no.9, pp.226-230, Sept., 1944.

MUTATIONS OF WILD NORWAY RATS IN JAPAN. W. E. Castle. Jour. Heredity, Wash., vol.50, no.11, p.303, Nov., 1949.

SIZE GENES OF MICE. W. E. Castle. Proc. Nat. Acad. Sci., Wash., D.C., vol. 28, no.3, pp.69-72, Mar., 1942.

SIZE INHERITANCE IN MICE. W. E. Castle. Amer. Nat., vol.70, no.728, pp.209-217, May-June, 1936.

LINKAGE STUDIES OF THE RAT (RATTUS NORVEGICUS). III. W. E. Castle, Helen Dean King. Proc. Natl. Acad. Sci., Wash., D.C., vol.26, no.9, pp.578-580, Sept., 1940; IV. Proc. vol.27, no.6, pp. 250-254, June, 1941; V. vol.27, no.8, pp. 394-398, Aug., 1941; VI. vol.30, no.4, pp.79-82, Apr., 1944.

PIEBALD RATS AND SELECTION; AN EXPERIMENTAL TEST OF THE EFFECTIVENESS OF SELECTION AND OF THE THEORY OF GAMETIC PURITY IN MENDELIAN CROSSES. W. E. Castle, John C. Phillips. Carnegie Inst., Wash., D.C., 56 pp., tables 3 pls., Publ.195, 1914.

HOODED RATS AND SELECTION, A STUDY OF THE LIMITATIONS OF THE PURE-LINE THEORY. W. E. Castle, Gregory Pincus. Jour. Exper. Zool., vol.50, no.3, pp.409-439, 1928.

VARIATIONS OF LINKAGE IN RATS AND MICE. W. E. Castle, W. L. Wachter. Genetics, vol.9, pp.1-12, Jan., 1924.

INHERITANCE OF IMPERFORATE VAGINA IN THE MOUSE. Elizabeth Brown Chase. Jour. Heredity, Wash., vol.35, no.12, pp. 363-364, Dec., 1944.

DEVELOPMENT OF THE SHORT-TAILED MUTANT IN THE HOUSE MOUSE. Paul Chesley. Jour. Exper. Biol., vol.70, no. 3, pp.429-459, 2 pls., May 5, 1935.

LINKAGE RELATIONS OF HYDROCEPHALUS ($HY_1$) IN THE HOUSE MOUSE, MUS MUSCULUS. Frank H. Clark. Proc. Nat. Acad. Sci., Wash., vol.22, no.8, pp. 474-478, Aug., 1936.

THE VARITINT-WADDLER MOUSE. A DOMINANT MUTATION IN MUS MUSCULUS. Arthur M. Cloudman, Lester E. Bunker, Jr. Jour. Heredity, Wash., vol.36, no.9, pp. 258-263, fig.1, Sept., 1945.

HEREDITY OF WILDNESS AND SAVAGENESS IN MICE. Charles A. Coburn. Behavior Monographs, vol.4, no.5, ser.21, pp.iv, 71, 1922.

"HIGH BROW" ALBINO RATS. H. S. Colton. Jour. Heredity, vol.20, pp.225-227, 2 figs., May, 1929.

LINKAGE DATA ON THE REX CHARACTER IN THE HOUSE MOUSE. F.A.E. Crew, Charles Auerbach. Jour. Genetics, London, vol.39, no.2, pp.225-227, Jan.30, 1940.

"PIGTAIL," A HEREDITARY TAIL ABNORMALITY IN THE HOUSE MOUSE, MUS MUSCULUS. F.A.E. Crew, Ch. Auerbach. Jour. Genetics, London, vol.41, nos.2-3, pp.267-274, figs.2, pls.7-8, Jan.23, 1941.

TWO INDEPENDENT MUTATIONS OF THE HOODED OR PIEBALD GENE OF THE RAT, AND A STUDY OF THE PATTERN MODIFIERS. M. R. Curtis, W. F. Dunning. Jour. Heredity, vol.28, no.11, pp. 383-390, figs.3-5, Nov., 1937.

HEREDITARY ADIPOSITY IN MICE. C. H. Danforth. Jour. Heredity, vol.18, pp.153-162, illus., 1927.

HEREDITARY DOUBLING SUGGESTING ANOMALOUS CHROMATIN DISTRIBUTION IN THE MOUSE. C. H. Danforth. Soc. Exper. Biol. and Med. Proc., vol.23, pp. 145-147, 1925.

STUDIES OF MULTIPLE ALLELOMORPHIC SERIES IN THE HOUSE-MOUSE. III. A SPECTROPHOTOMETRIC STUDY OF MOUSE MELANIN. Janet Daniel. Jour. Genetics, vol.36, no.1, pp.138-143, fig.1, May, 1938.

A NEW RECESSIVE LETHAL MUTATION IN MICE. K. B. DeOme. Univ. Calif. Publ. Zool., Berkeley, vol.53, no.2, pp. 41-55, figs.3, pls.2, Aug.16, 1945.

ARE THE EFFECTS OF LONG-CONTINUED ROTATION IN RATS INHERITED? J. A. Detlefsen. Proc. Amer. Philos. Soc., vol. 62, pp.292-301, Nov.27, 1923.

THE LINKAGE OF DARK EYE AND COLOR IN MICE. J. A. Detlefsen. Genetics, vol.10, no.1, pp.17-32, Jan., 1925.

HEREDITARY OBESITY AND EFFICIENT FOOD UTILIZATION IN MICE. (AGOUTI) G. E. Dickerson. Science, Lancaster, vol.105, no.2732, pp.496-498, illus., 1947.

A UNIQUE "HIMALAYAN" MOUSE. Margaret M. Dickie. Jour. Heredity, Washington, vol.36, no.9, pp.264-265, figs.2-3, Sept., 1945.

FUZZY MICE. Margaret M. Dickie, George W. Woolley. Jour. Heredity, Balto., vol.41, no.7, pp.193-196, illus., July, 1950.

LINKAGE STUDIES WITH THE PIROUETTE GENE IN THE MOUSE. Margaret M. Dickie, George W. Woolley. Jour. Heredity, Wash., vol.37, no.11, pp.335-337, figs.6-7, Nov., 1946.

LOCATION OF THE PIROUETTE GENE IN MUS MUSCULUS. Margaret M. Dickie, George W. Woolley. Jour. Heredity, Balto., vol.39, no.10, p.288, Oct., 1948.

(ON A NEW MUTATION OF THE TAIL. "FILIFORM TAIL" IN THE MOUSE.) Sur une nouvelle mutation de la queue. "Queue filiforme" chez la souris. N. Dobrovolskaiea-Zavadskaiea, N. Kobosieff. Comptes Rendus des Seances de la Soc. de Biol., vol.97, pp.1140-1143, 2 figs., Oct.28, 1927.

(IRRADIATION OF THE TESTES AND HEREDITY IN THE MOUSE.) L'irradiation des testicules et l'hérédité chez la souris. N. Dobrovolskaia-Zavasdkaia. Archives de Biologie, vol.38, pp.457-501, 1928.

CHANGES IN THE DEGREE OF DOMINANCE OF FACTORS AFFECTING TAIL-LENGTH IN THE HOUSE MOUSE. L. C. Dunn. Amer. Nat., Lancaster, vol.76, no.767, pp.552-569, Nov.-Dec., 1942.

INDEPENDENT GENES IN MICE. L. C. Dunn. Genetics, vol.5, pp.344-361, May, 1920.

LINKAGE IN MICE AND RATS. L. C. Dunn. Genetics, vol.5, pp.325-343, May, 1920.

A NEW SERIES OF ALLELOMORPHS IN MICE. L. C. Dunn. Nature, London, vol.129, no.3247, p.130, Jan.23, 1932.

A NEW EYE COLOR MUTANT IN THE MOUSE WITH ASYMMETRICAL EXPRESSION. L. C. Dunn. Proc. Nat. Acad. Sci., Wash., vol.31, no.11, pp.343-346, Nov.15, 1945.

CLOSE LINKAGE BETWEEN MUTATIONS WITH SIMILAR EFFECTS. L. C. Dunn, Ernst Caspari. Proc. Nat. Acad. Sci., Wash., D.C., vol.28, no.5, pp.205-210, May, 1942.

STUDIES OF MULTIPLE ALLELOMORPHIC SERIES IN THE HOUSE-MOUSE. IV. QUANTITATIVE COMPARISONS OF MELANINS FROM MEMBERS OF THE ALBINO SERIES. L. C. Dunn, W. Einsele. Jour. Genetics, vol.36, no.1, pp.145-152, tables 2, May, 1938.

A DOMINANT SHORT-TAIL MUTATION IN THE HOUSE-MOUSE WITH RECESSIVE LETHAL EFFECT. L. C. Dunn, S. Gluecksohn-Schoenheimer. Genetics, vol. 23, pp.146-147, Jan., 1938.

A NEW COMPLEX OF HEREDITARY ABNORMALITIES IN THE HOUSE MOUSE. L. C. Dunn, S. Gluecksohn-Schoenheimer. Jour. Exper. Zool., Phila., vol.104, no.1, pp.25-51, figs.3, Feb., 1947.

STUB, A NEW MUTATION IN THE MOUSE, WITH MARKED EFFECTS ON THE SPINAL COLUMN. L. C. Dunn, S. Gluecksohn-Schoenheimer. Jour. Heredity, Wash., D.C., vol.33, no.6, pp.235-239, figs.13-15, June, 1942.

A NEW MUTATION IN THE MOUSE AFFECTING SPINAL COLUMN AND URO-GENITAL SYSTEM. L. C. Dunn, S. Gluecksohn-Schoenheimer, Vernon Bryson. Jour. Heredity, Wash., D.C., vol.31, no. 8, pp.343-348, figs.4, Aug., 1940.

HEREDITY AND ACCIDENT AS FACTORS IN THE PRODUCTION OF TAILLESSNESS IN THE RAT. L. C. Dunn, S. Gluecksohn-Schoenheimer, M. R. Curtis, W. F. Dunning. Jour. Heredity, Wash., D.C., vol.33, no.2, pp.65-67, figs.13, Feb., 1942.

A MUTABLE LOCUS IN WILD POPULATIONS OF HOUSE MICE. L. C. Dunn, W. C. Morgan, Jr. Amer. Nat., Lancaster, vol. 86, no.830, pp.321-323, Sept.-Oct., 1952.

CROSSES BETWEEN INBRED STRAINS OF MICE. Orson N. Eaton. Jour. Heredity, Wash., D.C., vol.32, no.11, pp.393-395, Nov., 1941.

THE "SNOW-BELLY" MOUSE. A DOMINANT ALLELE OF THE AGOUTI SERIES IN THE HOUSE MOUSE. Orson N. Eaton, E. Schwarz. Jour. Heredity, Wash., vol. 37, no.1, pp.31-32, Jan., 1946.

THE PATHOLOGY OF THE LUNGS IN A LETHAL MUTATION IN THE RAT (RATTUS NORVEGICUS). Stefan Engel, Hans Grueneberg. Jour. Genetics, Lond., vol. 39, no.2, pp.343-349, Jan., 1940.

SOME EFFECTS OF THE GENE $W^v$ (DOMINANT SPOTTING) IN MICE. Elizabeth Fekete, C. C. Little, A. M. Cloudman. Proc. Nat. Acad. Sci., Wash., D.C., vol. 27, no.2, pp.114-117, Feb., 1941.

A FIFTH ALLELOMORPH IN THE ALBINO SERIES OF THE HOUSE MOUSE. Horace W. Feldman. Jour. Mam., vol.16, no.3, pp.207-210, Aug., 1935.

LINKAGE OF ALBINO ALLELOMORPHS IN RATS AND MICE. Horace W. Feldman. Genetics, vol.9, no.5, pp.487-492, Sept., 1924.

ON THE INHERITANCE OF ALBINISM AND BROWN PIGMENTATION IN MICE. Horace W. Feldman, G. Pincus. Amer. Nat., vol. 60, no.667, pp.195-198, 1926.

A RECESSIVE BLACK VARIETY OF ROOF RAT. Horace W. Feldman. Science, n.s., vol.58, p.163, Aug.31, 1923.

A SYSTEM OF SCORING LINKAGE DATA, WITH SPECIAL REFERENCE TO THE PIED FACTORS IN MICE. R. A. Fisher. Amer. Nat., Lancaster, vol.80, no.794, pp.568-578, Sept.-Oct., 1946.

A REMARKABLE CROSS IN MUS MUSCULUS. A. B. D. Fortuyn. Genetica, vol. 16, nos.3-4, pp.321-359, 1934.

ABNORMALITIES IN THE SHAKER MOUSE. A.B.D. Fortuyn, T. H. Meng. Peking Nat. Hist. Bull., vol.12, pt.1, pp.9-12, Sept., 1937.

A CASE OF NON-DISJUNCTION IN THE MOUSE. W. H. Gates. Genetics, vol.12, pp.295-306, May, 1927.

THE JAPANESE WALTZING MOUSE, ITS ORIGIN AND GENETICS. W. H. Gates. Nat. Acad. Sci. Proc., vol.11, pp.651-653, 1925.

LINKAGE OF SHORT EAR AND DENSITY IN THE HOUSE MOUSE. W. H. Gates. Proc. Nat. Acad. Sci., vol.13, pp.575-578, Aug., 1927.

SYMBOLS FOR MUTATIONS IN MICE. W. H. Gates. Science, n.s., vol.64, p. 328, Oct.1, 1926.

THE EFFECTS OF A LETHAL MUTATION RESPONSIBLE FOR DUPLICATIONS AND TWINNING IN MOUSE EMBRYOS. S. Gluecksohn-Schoenheimer. Jour. Exper. Zool., Phila., vol.110, no.1, pp.47-76, Feb., 1949.

FURTHER PROGRESS WITH ARTIFICIAL SELECTION. (WHITE MARKINGS ON MICE.) H. D. Goodale. Amer. Nat., Lancaster, vol.76, no.766, pp.515-519, Sept-Oct., 1942.

A STUDY OF THE INHERITANCE OF BODY WEIGHT IN THE ALBINO MOUSE BY SELECTION. H. D. Goodale. Jour. Heredity, vol.29, no.3, pp.101-112, Mar., 1938.

ON THE PHYSICAL BASIS FOR GENETIC RESISTANCE TO MOUSE TYPHOID, SALMONELLA TYPHIMURIUM. John W. Gowen, M. Lois Calhoun. Proc. Nat. Acad. Sci., Wash., D.C., vol.29, no.5, pp.144-149, fig.1, May, 1943.

AN EVALUATION OF SIZE GENES. C. V. Green. Amer. Naturalist, vol.66, no.707, pp.566-568, Nov.-Dec., 1932.

A GENETIC CRANIOMETRIC STUDY OF TWO SPECIES OF MICE AND THEIR HYBRIDS. (MUS MUSCULUS AND M. BACTRIANUS.) C. V. Green. Jour. Exper. Zool., vol.63, no.2, pp.533-551, figs.1-7, Oct.5, 1932.

GROWTH. LINKAGE IN SIZE INHERITANCE. C. V. Green. Jour. Exper. Zool., vol.59, no.2, pp.213-263, Apr.5, 1931; Amer. Nat., vol.65, no.701, pp.502-511, Nov.-Dec., 1931.

INHERITANCE OF FOOT LENGTH IN A MOUSE SPECIES CROSS. C. V. Green. Jour. Heredity, vol.24, no.11, pp.440-442, figs.8, Nov., 1933.

MULTIPLE LETHAL GENES IN THE MOUSE. C. V. Green. Jour. Heredity, vol.27, no.5, pp.181-182, fig.1, May, 1936.

SIZE INHERITANCE AND GROWTH IN A MOUSE SPECIES CROSS (MUS MUSCULUS X MUS BACTRIANUS). INHERITANCE OF ADULT QUANTITATIVE CHARACTERS. C. V. Green.

THE GENETICS OF A DIFFERENCE IN SKELETAL TYPE BETWEEN TWO INBRED STRAINS OF MICE. Earl L. Green. Genetics, Menasha, vol.36, no.4, pp.391-409, July, 1951.

THE GENETICS OF A NEW HAIR DEFICIENCY, FURLESS, IN THE HOUSE MOUSE. Earl L. Green. Jour. Heredity, Wash., vol.45, no.3, pp.115-118, May-June, 1954.

EFFECT OF THE SHORT EAR GENE ON NUMBER OF RIBS AND PRESACRAL VERTEBRAE IN THE HOUSE MOUSE. Earl L. Green, Margaret C. Green. Amer. Nat., Lancaster, vol.80, no.795, pp.619-625, Nov.-Dec., 1946.

THE RELATIONSHIP OF SKELETAL TYPE AND BODY SIZE IN AN INBRED STRAIN OF MICE. Earl L. Green, Margaret C. Green. Jour. Morphol., Phila., vol.78, no.1, pp. 113-120, Jan., 1946.

BIFURCATED XIPHISTERNUM AND ITS RELATIONSHIP WITH SHORT EARS IN THE HOUSE MOUSE. E. L. Green, C. W. McNutt. Jour. Heredity, Balto., vol.32, no.3, pp.94-96, fig.1, Mar., 1941.

A DIFFERENCE IN SKELETAL TYPE BETWEEN RECIPROCAL HYBRIDS OF TWO INBRED STRAINS OF MICE. E. L. Green, W. L. Russell. Genetics, Menasha, vol.36, no.6, pp.641-651, Nov., 1951.

FURTHER MORPHOLOGICAL EFFECTS OF THE SHORT EAR GENE IN THE HOUSE MOUSE. Margaret C. Green. Jour. Morphol., Phila., vol.88, no.1, pp.1-17, pl.1, Jan., 1951.

MUTANT WHITE MICE. A NEW DOMINANT ACTOSOMAL MUTANT AFFECTING COAT COLOR IN MUS MUSCULUS. Arnold B. Grobman, Donald R. Charles. Jour. Heredity, Balto., vol.38, no.12, pp. 381-384, Dec., 1947.

THE GENETICS OF THE MOUSE. Hans Grueneberg. Univ. Press, Cambridge, pp. xii, 412, figs.43, pls.14, 1943.

GREY-LETHAL, A NEW MUTATION IN THE HOUSE MOUSE. Hans Grueneberg. Jour. Heredity, vol.27, no.3, pp.105-109, figs.5-10, Mar., 1936.

A NEW SUB-LETHAL COLOUR MUTATION IN THE HOUSE MOUSE. Hans Grueneberg. Proc. Roy. Soc., Lond., ser.B., vol.118, no.809, pp.321-342, pls.19-21, figs.12, Sept.2, 1935.

SOME OBSERVATIONS ON THE MICROPHTHALMIA GENE IN THE MOUSE. Hans Grueneberg. Jour. Genetics, London, vol. 49, no.1, pp.1-13, May, 1948.

THE ORIGIN OF JERKER, A NEW GENE MUTATION OF THE HOUSE MOUSE, AND LINKAGE STUDIES MADE WITH IT. Hans Grueneberg, Joshua B. Burnett, George D. Snell. Proc. Nat. Acad. Sci., Easton, vol.27, no.12, pp.562-565, Dec., 1941.

ORIGIN OF TWO NEW RETROGRESSIVE VARIETIES BY ONE MUTATION IN MICE. Arend L. Hagedoorn. Univ. Calif. Publ. Physiol., Berkeley, vol.3, no.12, pp.87-90, Sept.11, 1908.

GENETIC DIFFERENCES IN FATAL ANDIOGENIC SEIZURES BETWEEN 2 INBRED STRAINS OF HOUSE MICE. Calvin S. Hall. Jour. Heredity, Balto., vol.38, no.1, pp.3-6, illus., 1947.

ALTERING A MATURED GENETIC CHARACTER. (X-RAYS ON MICE.) Robert T. Hance. Jour. Heredity, vol. 18, pp.377-380, 2 figs., 1 pl., 1927.

MODIFICATIONS IN THE ALBINO RAT FOLLOWING TREATMENT WITH ALCOHOL FUMES AND X-RAYS; AND THE PROBLEM OF THEIR INHERITANCE. F. B. Hanson. Proc. Amer. Philos. Soc., vol.62, pp.301-311, 2 figs., Nov.27, 1923.

ALCOHOL AND EYE DEFECTS. IN THE ALBINO RAT (MUS NORVEGICUS ALBINUS). F. B. Hanson, F. Heys. Jour. Heredity, vol.18, pp.345-350, 1927.

DO ALBINO RATS HAVING TEN GENERATIONS OF ALCOHOLIC ANCESTRY INHERIT RESISTANCE TO ALCOHOL FUMES? F. B. Hanson, F. Heys. Amer. Nat., vol. 61, no.672, pp.43-53, 1927.

A WALTZING MOUSE. G. W. Harris. Nature, vol.112, p.939, Dec.29, 1923.

BENT-NOSE IN THE NORWAY RAT. Walter E. Heston. Jour. Heredity, Wash., D.C., vol.29, no.11, pp.437-448, Nov., 1938.

"RHINO," AN ALLELE OF HAIRLESS IN THE HOUSE MOUSE. Alma Howard. Jour. Heredity, Wash., D.C., vol.31, no.11, pp. 466-470, Nov., 1940.

CONGENITAL TAILLESSNESS IN THE RAT. F. B. Hutt, O. Mydland. Jour. Heredity, vol.23, no.9, pp.363-367, figs.13-14, Sept., 1932.

LINKAGE IN RATS. Heman L. Ibsen. Amer. Nat., Lancaster, vol.54, pp.61-67, tables 3, Jan.-Feb., 1920.

OBESE, A NEW MUTATION IN THE HOUSE MOUSE. Ann M. Ingalls, Margaret M. Dickie, G. D. Snell. Jour. Heredity, Balto., vol.41, no.12, pp.317-318, illus., Dec., 1950.

THE INHERITANCE OF RESISTANCE TO THE DANYSZ BACILLUS IN THE RAT. M. R. Irwin. Genetics, vol.14, pp.337-365, 4 figs., July, 1929.

THE INHERITANCE OF "WHITE-BELLY" IN THE HOUSE MOUSE. Nathan Kaliss. Jour. Heredity, Wash., D.C., vol.33, no. 1, pp.21-23, fig.16, Jan., 1942.

THE ASSOCIATION OF THE BLACK (NON-AGOUTI) GENE WITH BEHAVIOR IN THE NORWAY RAT. Clyde E. Keeler. Jour. Heredity, Wash., D.C., vol.33, no.11, pp. 371-384, figs.2-3, Nov., 1942.

THE INHERITANCE OF A RETINAL ABNORMALITY IN WHITE MICE. Clyde E. Keeler. Proc. Nat. Acad. Sci., Wash., D.C., vol.10, no.7, pp.329-333, fig.1-3, July, 1924.

INTERFRONTAL-A HERITABLE CRANIAL VARIATION OF THE HOUSE MOUSE. Clyde E. Keeler. Jour. Mam., vol.14, no. 1, pp.75-76, Feb., 1933.

A NEW MUTATION TO "DOMINANT SPOTTING" (W) IN THE HOUSE MOUSE. Clyde E. Keeler. Jour. Heredity, Wash., vol. 22, no.9, pp.273-276, figs.5-6, Sept., 1931.

MULTIPLE EFFECTS OF COAT COLOR GENES IN THE NORWAY RAT, WITH SPECIAL REFERENCE TO TEMPERAMENT AND DOMESTICATION. Clyde E. Keeler, Helen Dean King. Jour. Comp. Psychol., Balto., vol.34, no.4, pp.241-250, figs.3, Oct., 1942.

IS INBREEDING INJURIOUS? (WHITE RATS.) Helen Dean King. Williams and Wilkins Co., Balto., 1923.

A NEW OCCURRENCE OF THE BLACK-EYE YELLOW MUTATION IN RATS. Helen Dean King. Science, n.s., vol.58, pp.250-251, Sept.28, 1923.

A WALTZING MUTATION IN THE WHITE RAT. Helen Dean King. Jour. Mam., vol. 17,no.2, pp.157-163, 1 table, May, 1936.

LINKAGE STUDIES OF THE RAT (RATTUS NORVEGICUS). Helen Dean King, W. E. Castle. Proc. Nat. Acad. Sci., Wash., vol.21, no.6, pp.390-399, June, 1935; vol.23, no.2, pp.56-60, Feb., 1937.

A SECOND INDEPENDENT OCCURRENCE OF THE CURLY MUTATION IN THE RAT. Helen Dean King, Leon F. Whitney. Jour. Heredity, Wash., D.C., vol.30, no.5, pp. 211-212, May, 1939.

PYGMY, A DWARFING GENE IN THE HOUSE MOUSE. J.W.B. King. Jour. Heredity, Wash., vol.41, no.9, pp.249-252, illus., Sept., 1950.

THE GENETICAL AND MECHANICAL PROPERTIES OF THE SEX CHROMOSOMES. VII. APODEMUS SYLVATICUS AND A. HEBRIDENSIS. P. C. Koller. Jour. Genetics, London, vol.41, nos.2-3, pp.375-389, figs.9, Jan.23, 1941.

BIOCHEMISTRY AND TEMPERAMENT IN THE AGOUTI RAT. A. J. Lea. Jour. Heredity, Wash., D.C., vol.34, no.7, pp. 212-217, July, 1943.

(ATRICHIA AND ITS INHERITANCE IN ALBINOTIC DOMESTIC MICE.) Atrichosis und ihre Verebung bei der albinotischen Hausmaus. N. G. Lebedinsky, A. Dauwart. Biol. Zentralblatt, vol.47, pp.748-752, 7 figs., 1927.

THE INHERITANCE OF ABNORMAL APPENDAGES AMONG THE DESCENDANTS OF X-RAYED MICE. C. C. Little. Anat. Record, vol.29, p.151, Dec.25, 1924.

NOTES ON A SPECIES CROSS IN MICE AND ON AN HYPOTHESIS CONCERNING THE QUANTITATIVE POTENTIALITY OF GENES. C. C. Little. Science, n.s., vol.66, pp.542-543, Dec.2, 1927.

A REVERSE MUTATION TO A "REMOTE" ALLELE IN THE HOUSE MOUSE. C. C. Little, K. P. Hummel. Proc. Nat. Acad. Sci., Wash., D.C., vol.33, no.2, pp.42-43, 1947.

SHAKER, A NEW MUTATION OF THE HOUSE MOUSE (MUS MUSCULUS). Elizabeth M. Lord, William H. Gates. Amer. Nat., vol.63, pp.435-442, Sept., 1929.

GENETICS OF BODY SIZE AND RELATED CHARACTERS. I. SELECTING SMALL AND LARGE RACES OF THE LABORATORY MOUSE. John W. Macarthur. Amer. Nat. Lancaster, vol.78, no.775, pp.142-157, Mar.-Apr., 1944.

THE MANIFOLD EFFECTS OF THE SCREW TAIL MOUSE MUTATION. E. C. MacDowell, J. S. Potter, T. Laanes, E. N. Ward. Jour. Heredity, Wash., D.C., vol. 33, no.12, pp.439-449, figs.8-13, Dec., 1942.

HOUND-EARED MICE. B. W. McPheters, C. C. Little. Jour. Heredity, vol.24, pp. 157-158, illus., Apr., 1933.

A HAIRLESS MUTATION IN ASIATIC TAME MICE. S. Makino. Jour. Heredity, Balto., vol.16, no.10, pp.257-258, illus., Oct., 1950.

(MORE ON THE HETEROCHROMOSOMES OF APODEMUS.) Encore les heterochromosomes des Apodemus. Robert Matthey. Archiv. der Julius Klaus-Stiftung, vol.22, nos.1-2, pp.85-92, pls.2, 1947.

THE INTERNAL EAR OF THE SHAKER MUS MUSCULUS. T. H. Meng. Peking, Nat. Hist. Bull., vol.7, pt.4, pp.355-360, pls.1-2, June, 1933.

A NEW TAIL-SHORT MUTATION IN THE MOUSE. Walter C. Morgan. Jour. Heredity, Balto., vol.41, no.8, pp.208-215, illus., Aug., 1950.

"LEADEN," A RECENT COLOR MUTATION IN THE HOUSE MOUSE. J. M. Murray. Amer. Nat., vol.67, no.710, p.278-283, June, 1933.

INHERITANCE OF VENTRAL SPOTTING IN MICE. J. M. Murray, C. V. Green. Genetics, vol.18, no.6, pp.481-486, 1933.

BELTED, A NEW SIXTH CHROMOSOME MUTATION IN THE MOUSE. J. M. Murray, G. D. Snell. Jour. Heredity, Wash., vol.36, no.9, pp.266-268, fig.4, Sept., 1945.

THE CHROMOSOME CONSTITUTION OF THE LITTLE AND BAGG ABNORMAL EYED MICE. Theophilus S. Painter. Amer. Nat., vol.62, pp.284-286, May, 1928.

GENETIC DIFFERENCES IN THE BIOCHEMISTRY AND PHYSIOLOGY INFLUENCING FOOD UTILIZATION FOR GROWTH IN RATS. Leroy S. Palmer, Others. Tech. Bull., Minnesota Agric. Exper. Sta., St. Paul, no.176, pp.54, 1946.

(COLORATION MUTATION IN THE PYGMY MOUSE.) Faerbungs-Mutation der Zwergmaus. Rudolf Piechocki. Zeitschr. Saeugetierk., 22 (1-2): 106, 1957.

A COMPARATIVE STUDY OF THE CHROMOSOMES OF THE NORWAY RAT (RATTUS NORVEGICUS ERXL.) AND THE BLACK RAT (RATTUS RATTUS L.). G. Pincus. Jour. Morph. and Physiol., vol. 44, no.3, pp.515-532, 1927.

A SPONTANEOUS MUTATION IN THE HOUSE MOUSE. G. Pincus. Proc. Nat. Acad. Sci. U.S.A., vol.15, pp.85-88, Feb.15, 1929.

A NEW RECESSIVE SPOTTING GENE IN THE HOUSE MOUSE. Terry Pullig. Jour. Heredity, Balto., vol.40, no.8, pp.228-230, illus., Aug., 1949.

STUDIES ON INHERITANCE IN PHILIPPINE RATS (MUS NORVEGICUS ERXL.). Dioscoro S. Rabor. Univ. Philippines Nat. and Appl. Bull., vol.5, no.5, pp.373-384, Dec., 1936.

THE INHERITANCE AND EXPRESSIONS OF FUSED, A NEW MUTATION IN THE HOUSE MOUSE. S. C. Reed. Genetics, vol.22, no.1, pp.1-14, 1937.

INHERITANCE OF HYPOTRICHOSIS IN RATS. Elmer Roberts. Anat. Record, vol.29, p.141, Dec.25, 1924.

A CHROMOSOME MAP OF THE MOUSE. Staff of the Jackson B. Roscoe Memorial Laboratory. Jour. Heredity, Wash., vol. 36, no.9, pp.271-273, fig.5, Sept., 1945.

GENETIC ANALYSIS OF THE TEMPERAMENT OF RATS. M. P. Sadovnikova-Koltzova. Jour. Exper. Zool., vol.45, pp.301-318, illus., May 5, 1926.

(GENETIC ANALYSIS OF THE TEMPERAMENT OF RATS.) Genetische Analyse des Temperamentes der Ratten. M. P. Sadovnikova-Koltzova. II Teil., Zeitschr. f. Ind., Abstammungs- und Verebungslehre, vol.49, pp.131-145, 4 figs., 1929.

(ON THE PROBLEM OF CHROMOSOME NUMBER IN THE OVA OF WHITE MICE.) Zum Problem der Chromosomenzahl in den Eizellen weisser Maeuse. S. D. Schachow. Anat. Anz., vol.69, nos.13-17, pp.315-330, 12 figs., 1930.

ORIGIN OF THE JAPANESE WALTZING MOUSE. Ernst Schwarz. Science, Lancaster, n.s., vol.95, no.2454, p.46, Jan.9, 1942.

GENETIC DIFFERENCES IN THE SOCIAL BEHAVIOR OF INBRED STRAINS OF MICE. J. P. Scott. Jour. Heredity, Wash., D.C., vol.33, no.1, pp.11-15, fig.14, Jan., 1942.

HEREDITARY CATARACT. A NEW DOMINANT GENE IN THE RAT. Sedgwick E. Smith, B. F. Barrentine. Jour. Heredity, Wash., vol.34, no.1, pp.8-10, fig.5, Jan., 1943.

THE DETECTION OF MUTATIONS. RELATIVE EFFICIENCY OF VARIOUS SYSTEMS OF BROTHER-SISTER INBREEDING OF MICE. G. D. Snell. Jour. Heredity, Wash., vol.36, no.9, pp.275-278, figs.6-8, Sept., 1945.

LINKAGE OF JITTERY AND WALTZING IN THE MOUSE. G. D. Snell. Jour. Heredity, Wash., vol.36, no.9, pp.279-280, fig.9, Sept., 1945.

A LINKAGE BETWEEN SHAKER-2 AND WAVY-2 IN THE HOUSE MOUSE. G. D. Snell. Jour. Heredity, Wash., D.C., vol. 30, no.10, p.447, Oct., 1939.

A BALD MOUSE. L. L. Snyder. Jour. Mam., vol.11, no.2, pp.232-233, Feb., 1930.

THE "BALD MOUSE," A GENETICAL ANOMALY. L. L. Snyder. Jour. Mam., vol.12, no.1, p.71, Feb., 1931.

A CLASSIFIED BIBLIOGRAPHY OF INBRED STRAINS OF MICE. Joan A. Staats. Science, vol.119, no.3087, pp.295-296, illus., Feb.26, 1954.

MICE THAT WALTZ. H. E. Stebbins. Nature Magazine, vol.19, no.4, pp.237-238, figs.2, Apr., 1932.

THE PATHOLOGY OF THE LUNGS IN A LETHAL MUTATION IN THE RAT (RATTUS NORVEGICUS). Engel Stefan, Hans Grueneberg. Jour. Genetics, London, vol. 39, no.2, pp.343-349, 4 figs., Jan.30, 1940.

GENETIC STUDIES ON THE NATURE OF CANCER. (EXPERIMENTS ON MICE.) L. C. Strong. Amer. Nat., vol.60, pp. 201-226, 1926.

A GENETIC STUDY OF THE GROWTH OF A TRANSPLANTABLE TUMOR (ADENOCARCINOMA, dBrB). (EXPERIMENTS ON MICE.) L. C. Strong. Jour. Exper. Zool., vol.45, pp.231-253, illus., 1926.

HEREDITARY LOOP-TAIL IN THE HOUSE MOUSE. L. C. Strong, W. F. Hollander. Jour. Heredity, Balto., vol.40, no.12, pp. 329-334, illus., Dec., 1949.

HAIRLESS MICE. F. B.Sumner. Jour. Heredity, vol.15, no.12, 8 pp., illus., Dec., 1924.

THE CHROMOSOMES OF THE RAT. Olive Swezy. Science, n.s., vol.66, pp. 601-602, Dec.16, 1927.

ON THE EXISTENCE OF TWO CHROMOSOME NUMBERS IN A MIXED RAT STRAIN. Olive Swezy. Jour. Exper. Zool., vol.51, no.2, pp.135-162, 1928.

CHROMOSOMES OF THE WHITE-TAILED RAT (MYSTROMYS ALBICAUDATUS, WAGNER, 1841). L. S. Taitz. South African Jour. Sci., vol.51, no.5, pp.143-148, Dec., 1954.

INHERITED VISCERAL INVERSION IN MICE. J. A. Tihen, D. R. Charles, Theodore O. Sippel. Jour. Heredity, Balto., vol.39, no.1, pp.29-31, Jan., 1948.

THE CHARACTERIZATION OF THE SPERMATOGONIAN CHROMOSOMES OF THE ALBINO RAT (RATTUS NORVEGICUS ALBINUS). Phillip V. Tobias. South African Jour. Sci., Johannesburg, vol.43, pp.312-319, figs.13, July, 1947.

THE INHERITANCE OF MAZE-LEARNING ABILITY IN RATS. Edward Chase Tolman. Jour. Comp. Psych., vol.4, pp.1-18, 1924.

CONCERNING LINKAGE OF WALTZING IN RATS. Maurice Whittinghill. Proc. Nat. Acad. Sci., Wash., vol.30, no.9, pp.221-226, Sept., 1944.

MAMMARY TUMORS IN MICE. G. W. Woolley. Jour. Heredity, Balto., vol.41, no.4, p.96, Apr., 1950.

MISTY DILUTION IN THE MOUSE. G. W. Woolley. Jour. Heredity, Wash., vol.36, no.9, pp.269-270, Sept., 1945.

SPONTANEOUS TAIL AMPUTATION IN THE NORWAY RAT. G. W. Woolley, L. J. Cole. Jour. Heredity, Wash., D.C., vol. 29, no.4, pp.123-127, figs.4-6, Apr., 1938.

PIROUETTING MICE. G. W. Woolley, Margaret M. Dickie. Jour. Heredity, Wash., vol.36, no.9, pp.281-284, figs.10-12, Sept., 1945.

(A NEW MUTATION OF THE DOMESTIC MOUSE "HYDROCEPHALUS.") Eine neue Mutation der Hausmaus "Hydrocephalus". K. Zimmermann. Zeitschrift fuer induktive Abstammungs-und Verebungslehre, Berlin, vol.64, pp.176-180, figs.6, tables 2, 1932.

(HEREDITARY BRAIN DISEASES IN THE DOMESTIC MOUSE.) Erbliche Gehirnerkrankungen der Hausmaus. K. Zimmermann. Der Erbarzt, Berlin, Beilage zum "Deutschen Aerzteblatt", no.8, pp.119-125, 1935.

Longevity

PROLONGATION OF THE LIFE SPAN OF RATS BY BULK-FORMERS IN THE DIET. Anton J. Carlson, F. Houzel. Jour. Nutrition, Phila., vol.36, no.1, pp.27-40, July 10, 1948.

THE SURVIVAL OF WILD BROWN RATS ON A MARYLAND FARM. David E. Davis. Ecology, 29 (4): 437-448, Oct., 1948.

THE GROWTH, SURVIVAL, WANDERING AND VARIATION OF THE LONG-TAILED FIELD MOUSE, APODEMUS SYLVATICUS. II. SURVIVAL. H. P. Hacker, H. S. Pearson. Biometrika, Cambridge, England, vol.33, pt.4, pp.333-361, figs.5, June 28, 1946.

SURVIVAL RATES OF MALAYAN RATS. J. L. Harrison. Bull. Raffles Mus., 27: 5-26, Oct., 1956.

(GREAT AGE OF A WOOD MOUSE APODEMUS SYLVATIUS LINNE 1758.) Hohes Alter einer Waldmaus, Apodemus sylvatius (Linne, 1758). W. Neuhaus. Saeugetierk., Mitteil., 5 (4): 171-172, Dec.1, 1957.

(GREATEST LIFE SPAN OF THE YELLOW-THROATED MOUSE (APODEMUS FLAVICOLLIS MELCHIOR 1834).) Hoechstlebensalter der Gelbhalsmaus, Apodemus flavicollis Melchior, 1834. Gerth Rokitansky. Saeugetierk., Mitteil., Stuttgart, vol.1, no.1, pp.29-30, Jan.10, 1953.

ON THE AGED SPECIMEN OF THE FIELD MOUSE APODEMUS SYLVATICUS SYLVATICUS (L.). Tom Warwick. Scottish Naturalist, London, no.238, pp.99-100, July-Aug., 1939.

THE DURATION OF LIFE IN AN ALBINO RAT POPULATION. B. P. Wiesner, N. M. Sheard. Proc. Roy. Soc. Edinburgh, vol. 55, pt.1, pp.1-22, Feb.23, 1935.

Madagascar

(A NEW RODENT OF MADAGASCAR, MUS DECARYI.) Un rongeur nouveau de Madagascar: Mus decaryi. G. Grandidier. Bull. Mus. Nat.d'Hist. Nat., Paris, ser.2, vol.7, no.6, pp.478-481, figs.3, Nov., 1934.

(CONTRIBUTION TO STUDY OF RATS IMPORTED BY MAN TO MADAGASCAR.) Contribution à l'étude des Rats importés par l'Homme à Madagascar. G. Petit. Bull. Soc. Pathologie Exotique et de ses filiales de l'Ouest-African et de Madagascar, Paris, vol.27, no.3, pp.273-280, 1934.

Methods and Techniques

FURTHER OBSERVATIONS ON INDUCED OVULATION IN THE MOUSE AS A RAPID TEST FOR PREGNANCY. H. O. Burdick. Amer. Jour. Physiol., Memphis, vol.145, no.3, pp.387-390, figs.2, 1946.

A METHOD FOR SELF-CONTROL OF POPULATION GROWTH AMONG MAMMALS LIVING IN THE WILD. (EXPERIMENTS WITH A COLONY OF WILD NORWAY RATS.) John B. Calhoun. Science, 109 (2831): 333-335, Apr.1, 1949.

A RELATIVE CENSUS METHOD FOR BROWN RATS (RATTUS NORVEGICUS). (MEASURING THE FEEDING CAPACITY OF THE POPULATION.) Dennis Chitty. Nature, 150: 59, July 11, 1942.

TECHNIQUES FOR THE STUDY OF THE NORWAY RAT (RATTUS NORVEGICUS). (CENSUS BAITING, FOOD RECORDING MACHINE, DIRECT OBSERVATION OF ACTIVITIES, AND MARKING WITH DEPILATORY.) Dennis Chitty, Monica Shorten. Jour. Mam., 27 (1): 63-78, Feb., 1946.

THE PLACENTAL SCAR AS A MEASURE OF FERTILITY IN RATS. David E. Davis, John T. Emlen, Jr. Jour. Wildlife Mgt., 12 (2): 162-166, Apr., 1948.

MEASUREMENT OF URBAN RAT POPULATIONS. J. T. Emlen, Jr. Abs. in Biometrics Bull., 1 (1): 11, Feb., 1945.

METHODS FOR ESTIMATING POPULATIONS OF BROWN RATS IN URBAN HABITATS. John T. Emlen, Jr., Allen W. Stokes, David E. Davis. Ecology, 30 (4): 430-442, Oct., 1949.

A TECHNIQUE FOR THE PREPARATION OF SECTIONS OF EARLY MOUSE EMBRYOS. Elizabeth Fekete, Oliver Bartholomew, George D. Snell. Anat. Record, Phila., vol.76, no.4, pp.441-447, 1 pl., Apr.25, 1940.

A NEW METHOD OF ASSAYING THE POTENCY OF THE FEMALE SEX HORMONE BASED UPON ITS EFFECT ON THE SPONTANEOUS CONTRACTION OF THE UTERUS OF THE WHITE RAT. R. T. Frank, C. D. Bonham, R. G. Gustavson. Amer. Jour. Physiol., vol.74, pp.395-399, 1925.

RAT COLONY TESTING BY ZUCKER'S WEIGHT-AGE RELATION. H. Gray, T. Addis. Amer. Jour. Physiol., Balto., vol.153, no.1, pp.35-40, Apr.1, 1948.

(DETERMINATION OF AGE WITH SOME MURINE SPECIES.) Altersbestimmung an einigen Muriden-Arten. Brigitte Hagen. Zeitschr., Saeugetierk., 21 (1-2): 39-43, 1956.

DETECTION OF HETEROZYGOTES WITH X-RAYS. (EXPERIMENTS ON HOUSE MICE.) Robert T. Hance. Jour. Heredity, vol.19, pp.480-485, illus., Nov., 1928.

MUCIFICATION OF THE VAGINAL EPITHELIUM OF MICE AS A TEST FOR PREGNANCY-MAINTAINING POTENCY OF EXTRACT OF CORPORA LUTEA. Reginald G. Harris. Science, vol.76, no.1975, p. 408, Nov.4, 1932.

NOTE ON THE FORMULAS USED FOR CALCULATING THE WEIGHT OF THE BRAIN IN THE ALBINO RATS. Shinkishi Hatai. Jour. Compar. Neurol. Psychol., vol.19, no.2, pp.169-173, May, 1909.

A SIMPLE MEANS OF PRODUCING OBESITY IN THE RAT. Dwight J. Ingle. Proc. Soc. Exper. Biol. Med., Utica, vol. 72, no.3, pp.604-605, Dec., 1949.

SIMPLE TEST FOR PREGNANCY USING IMMATURE FEMALE ALBINO RATS. G. Lombard Kelly. Jour. Amer. Medical Assoc., vol.100, no.13, pp.1010-1013, figs. 2, Apr.1, 1933.

THE EFFECTS OF VARIOUS FIXATIVES ON THE BRAIN OF THE ALBINO RAT, WITH AN ACCOUNT OF A METHOD OF PREPARING THIS MATERIAL FOR A STUDY OF THE CELLS IN THE CORTEX. Helen Dean King. Anatomical Record, vol. 4, no.6, pp.213-244, figs.15, June, 1910.

LABYRINTHITIS IN THE RAT AND A METHOD FOR ITS CONTROL. Helen Dean King. Anat. Record, Phila., vol.74, pp. 215-222, June 25, 1939.

AN ATTEMPT TO DETERMINE THE ABSOLUTE NUMBER OF RATS ON A GIVEN AREA. P. H. Leslie, D.H.S. Davis. Jour. Animal Ecol., 8 (1): 94-113, May, 1939.

A RAPID METHOD FOR VALUMETRIC AND NUMERICAL ESTIMATION OF PANCREATIC ISLETS IN THE MOUSE. L. E. Mount. Jour. Endocrinol., Lond., vol.5, no.5, pp.243-246, Jan., 1948.

STUDIES IN ACTIVITY. I. CONSISTENCY OF THE REVOLVING DRUM METHOD OF MEASURING THE ACTIVITY OF THE RAT. Mary Shinley. Jour. Comp. Psych., vol.8, pp.23-38, 1928.

(THE VALUE OF FOOTPRINTS FOR THE DETERMINATION OF ASIATIC RATS.) De waarde van het voetzoolkenmerk voor de determinatie van Aziatische ratten. O.L.E. de Raadt. Zool. Mededeel. R. Mus. Nat. Hist , Leyden, vol.14, no.3, pp. 190-192, figs.2, Dec.31, 1931.

(QUANTITATIVE EVALUATION OF MAMMALS WITH THE RINGING METHOD.) (MUS MUSCULUS HORTULANUS.) V. V. Raevskii. Zool. Zhurn. (Zool. Jour. USSR), Moscow, vol.13, no.1, pp.90-96, 1934.

AN IDEAL PREPARATION FOR DISSECTION OF SPINAL, PERIPHERAL, AND AUTONOMIC NERVES OF THE RAT. Curt P. Richter. Science, Lancaster, vol.112, no. 2897, pp.20-21, July 7, 1950.

COLLECTION OF EGGS FROM THE FALLOPIAN TUBE OF THE RAT. I. W. Rowlands. Nature, London, vol.150, no. 3800, p.267, figs.2, Aug.29, 1942.

HEREDITARY OBESITY OF YELLOW MICE: A METHOD FOR THE STUDY OF OBESITY. David A. Rytand. Proc. Soc. Exper. Biol. Med., New York, vol.54, no. 3, pp.340-341, Dec., 1943.

A TECHNIQUE FOR CONTINUOUS RECORDING OF SUBEUTANEOUS TEMPERATURES OF WILD MICE. John A. Sealander. Jour. Mam., vol.32, no.1, pp.122-123, fig.1, Feb.15, 1951.

THE RELIABILITY AND VALIDITY OF MAZE-MEASURES FOR RATS. E. C. Tolman, D. B. Nyswander. Jour. Psych., vol.7, pp.425-460, illus., 1927.

(A METHOD OF MEASURING THE HEAD, TRUNK, AND TAIL LENGTH OF LIVING ALBINO MICE.) Eine methode sum Messen der Kopf-, Rumpf- und Schwanzlaenge bei lebenden Albino-Maeusen. Alexander N. Tsurikov. Saeugetierk., Mitteil., vol.5, no.2, pp.72-74, Apr.1, 1957.

A METHOD OF NUMBERING LABORATORY RATS. George Walker. Science, n.s., vol.82, no.2130, pp.397-398, figs.4, Oct. 25, 1935.

AN EXPERIMENTAL ANALYSIS OF THE OBSTRUCTION METHOD OF MEASURING ANIMAL DRIVES. (WHITE RATS.) C. J. Warden, H. W. Nissen. Jour. Comp. Psych., vol.8, pp.325-342, illus., 1928.

THE FLUORIMETRIC ESTIMATION OF 3:4-BENZPYRENE IN WHOLE MICE. H. Weil-Malherbe. Biochemical Jour., Cambridge Univ. Press, vol.38, no.2, pp.135-141, 1944.

Mortality

HIGH TEMPERATURE DEATHS AMONG EXPERIMENTAL RATS. Hazel C. Cameron. Science, n.s., vol.69, p.576, May 31, 1929.

MORTALITY IN AN INDUCED EPIDEMIC. David E. Davis, Wayne L. Jensen. Trans. 17th N.A. Wildlife Conf., pp.151-160, illus., 1952.

INTRA-UTERINE MORTALITY AND PLACENTAL FUSIONS IN THE MOUSE. W. F. Hollander, L. C. Strong. Jour. Exper. Zool., 115 (1): 131-150, illus., Oct., 1950.

Neurology

THE DEVELOPMENT OF THE NEURAL FOLDS AND CRANIAL GANGLIA OF THE RAT. Howard B. Adelmann. Jour. Comp. Neur., vol.39, pp.19-171, 6 figs., 24 pls., Aug.15, 1925.

(ON PIGMENT ACCUMULATION IN THE CENTRAL NERVOUS SYSTEM OF THE WHITE MOUSE AT VARIOUS AGE LEVELS.) Ueber die Farbstoffspeicherung im Zentralnervensystem der weissen Maus in verschiedenen Alterszustaenden. G. Behnsen. Zeitschr. f. Zellforschung u. Mikroskopische Anat., vol.4, pp.515-572, illus., Feb.19, 1927.

THE ORIGIN OF THE ANTERIOR COMMISSURE IN THE RAT. Alf Brodal. Jour. Comp. Neurol., Phila., vol.88, no.2, pp. 157-205, pls.1-2, Apr., 1948.

OBSERVATIONS ON DOUBLE MOTOR END PLATES IN THE RAT MUS NORVEGICUS). W. V. Cole. Turtox News, Chicago, vol. 27, no.4, pp.102-105, illus., Apr., 1949.

CHANGES IN VASCULARITY IN THE BRAIN STEM AND CEREBELLUM OF THE ALBINO RAT BETWEEN BIRTH AND MATURITY. E. H. Craigie. Jour. Comp. Neur., vol.38, pp.27-48, 9 figs., Dec.15, 1924.

POSTNATAL CHANGES IN VASCULARITY IN THE CEREBRAL CORTEX OF THE MALE ALBINO RAT. E. H. Craigie. Jour. Comp. Neur., vol.39, pp.301-324, 4 figs., Oct.15, 1925.

THE VESTIBULAR LABYRINTH OF THE ALBINO RAT; FORM AND DIMENSIONS, AND THE ORIENTATION OF THE SEMICIRCULAR CANALS, CRISTAE, AND MUCULAE. Harold Cummins. Jour. Comp. Neur., vol.38, pp.399-460, 7 pls., June 15, 1925.

A COMPARISON OF THE NORWAY RAT WITH THE ALBINO RAT IN RESPECT TO BODY LENGTH, BRAIN WEIGHT, SPINAL CORD WEIGHT AND THE PERCENTAGE OF WATER IN BOTH THE BRAIN AND THE SPINAL CORD. Henry H. Donaldson, Skinkishi Hatai. Jour. Comp. Neurol., vol.21, no.5, pp.417-458, figs.8, Oct., 1911.

(HOW THE NERVOUS FIBERS ARE DISTRIBUTED IN THE PARENCHYMA OF THE RAT.) Sur le mode de se distribuer des fibres nerveuses dans le parenchyme de la rate. Romeo Fusari. Archiv. Italiennes Biol., Turin, vol.19, no.2, pp.288-292, 1893.

NERVE TERMINALS ASSOCIATED WITH THE KNEE JOINT OF THE MOUSE. Ernest D. Gardner. Anat. Record, Phila., vol.83, no.3, pp.401-419, pls.3, July 25, 1942.

OLFACTORY CONNECTIONS IN THE ALBINO RAT, WITH SPECIAL REFERENCE TO THE STRIA MEDULLARIS AND THE ANTERIOR COMMISSURE. Elisha S. Gurdjiana. Jour. Comp. Neur., vol.38, pp.127-163, 18 figs., Feb.15, 1925.

STUDIES OF THE THYROID APPARATUS. XXXI. THE ROLE OF THE THYROID AND PARATHYROID GLANDS IN THE GROWTH OF THE CENTRAL NERVOUS SYSTEM. (WORK ON RATS.) Frederick S. Hammett. Jour. Comp. Neur., vol.41, pp.171-204, 6 charts, Aug.15, 1926.

STUDIES ON THE THYROID APPARATUS. XXXII. THE ROLE OF THE THYROID APPARATUS IN THE SOLIDS-WATER DIFFERENTIATION OF THE CENTRAL NERVOUS SYSTEM DURING GROWTH. Frederick S. Hammett. Jour. Comp. Neur., vol.41, pp.205-222, 3 charts, Aug.15, 1926.

A STUDY OF THE DIAMETERS OF THE CELLS AND NUCLEI IN THE SECOND CERVICAL SPINAL GANGLION OF THE ADULT ALBINO RAT. Shinkishi Hatai. Jour. Compar. Neurol. Psychol., vol.17, no.6, pp.469-491, figs.4, 1907.

THE MOTOR NUCLEI OF THE CRANIAL NERVES OF MUS NORVEGICUS ALBINUS AT BIRTH. I. D. Hogg. Jour. Comp. Neur., vol.44, pp.449-495, illus., 1927.

THE APPEARANCE OF NISSL SUBSTANCE IN NERVE CELLS FOLLOWING VARIATIONS IN FIXATION. (WORK ON WHITE RATS.) A. E. Hopkins. Anat. Record, vol.28, pp.157-164, July 25, 1924.

THE EFFECTS OF FORMALDEHYDE ON THE BRAIN OF THE ALBINO RAT. Helen Dean King. Jour. Comp. Neur., vol.23, no.3, pp.283-314, Aug., 1913.

CONTRIBUTIONS TO THE CHEMICAL DIFFERENTIATION OF THE CENTRAL NERVOUS SYSTEM. III. THE CHEMICAL DIFFERENTIATION OF THE BRAIN OF THE ALBINO RAT DURING GROWTH. W. Koch, M. L. Koch. Jour. Biol. Chem., vol.15, no.3, pp.423-448.

ADRENAL CORTICAL FUNCTION INDEPENDENT OF DIRECT NERVOUS ACTION . A NEUROLOGICAL STUDY OF NORMAL, DENERVATED, AND TRANSPLANTED ADRENAL GLANDS OF ALBINO RATS. W. E. MacFarland. Jour. Exper. Zool., Phila., vol.95, no.3, pp.345-359, illus., Apr., 1944.

NERVE REGENERATIONS FROM ONE INTO THE OTHER OF TWO RATS UNITED IN SIAMESE PAIRS. B. Morpurgo. Jour. Physiol., vol.58, pp.98-100, 1923.

THE DEVELOPMENT OF THE HYPOPHYSIS CEREBRI OF THE ALBINO RAT. Joseph L. Schwind. Amer. Jour. Anat., vol.41, pp.295-319, illus., May 15, 1928.

NERVE OVERLAP IN THE GUSTATORY APPARATUS OF THE RAT. Beatrice Whiteside. Jour. Comp. Neur., vol.44, pp.363-377, illus., 1927.

North America

THE HOUSE MOUSE IN GRAND CANYON NATIONAL PARK. John R. Arnold. Jour. Mam., vol.17, no.3, p.292, Aug., 1936.

THE ROOF RAT, RATTUS RATTUS ALEXANDRINUS (GEOFFROY), IN WEST VIRGINIA. Roger W. Barbour. Jour. Mam., vol.31, no.4, pp.461-462, Nov.21, 1950.

THE BROWN RAT, RATTUS NORVEGICUS, IN BRITISH COLUMBIA. Allan Brooks. Canadian Field Nat., Sutton West, vol.61, no.2, p.68, Mar.-Apr., 1947.

ALBERTA: THE ONLY RAT-FREE PROVINCE IN CANADA. John H. Brown. Can. Jour. Publ. Health, 39 (9): 367-374, Sept., 1948.

DISTRIBUTION OF THE HOUSE MOUSE IN ALBERTA. John H. Brown. Canadian Field-Nat., Ottawa, vol.62, no.5, p.161, Sept.-Oct., 1948.

RATS ON VANCOUVER ISLAND. G. Clifford Carl. Victoria Nat., vol.3, pp. 88-90, 1947.

NOTES ON COMMENSAL RATS IN LAVACA COUNTY, TEXAS. David E. Davis. Jour. Mam., 28 (3): 241-244, Aug., 1947.

THE DISTRIBUTION OF RATS IN BALTIMORE, MARYLAND. David E. Davis, W. T. Fales. Amer. Jour. Hygiene, 49 (3): 247-254, May, 1949.

THE BLACK RAT IN VERMONT. Morris M. Green. Jour. Mam., vol.17, no.2, p. 173, May, 1936.

THE BROWN HOUSE RAT IN N.D. Adolph S. Hamm. N. Dak. Outdoors, 10 (5): 6-7, Nov., 1947.

NOTES ON CERTAIN FORMS OF THE HOUSE MOUSE (MUS MUSCULUS) PARTICULARLY THOSE OF EASTERN NORTH AMERICA. Francis Harper. Jour. Mam., vol.11, no.1, pp.49-52, Feb.11, 1930.

THE BROWN RAT IN THE UNITED STATES. David E. Lantz. U. S. Dept. Agric., Biol. Surv. Bull., no.33, p.54, figs.1-2, pls.1-3, May 29, 1909.

FRUGIVOROUS RAT IN VIRGINIA. John B. Lewis. Jour. Mam., vol.26, no.3, p.309, Aug., 1945.

ON THE RECENT OCCURRENCE OF THE BLACK RAT IN BOSTON, MASSACHUSETTS. Edgar A. Mearns. Proc. Biol. Soc. Wash., vol.13, p.167, Oct.31, 1900.

FURTHER CONSIDERATION OF AMERICAN HOUSE MICE. David G. Nichols. Jour. Mam., vol.25, no.1, pp.82-84, Feb., 1944.

NOTE ON AMERICAN HOUSE MICE. David G. Nichols. Jour. Mam., vol.19, no.2, p.253, May 14, 1938.

NOTES ON THE HOUSE MICE OF CALIFORNIA. David G. Nichols. Jour. Mam., vol.20, no.3, pp.376-377, Aug.14, 1939.

BLACK RAT AND ROOF RAT TAKEN IN THE CENTRAL OREGON COAST STRIP. Richard A. Pimentel. Murrelet, Seattle, vol.30, no.3, p.52, Feb.1, 1950.

THE INTRODUCTION AND SPREAD OF HOUSE RATS IN THE UNITED STATES. James Silver. Jour. Mam., vol.8, no.1, pp.58-60, Feb., 1927.

FIELD AND LABORATORY OBSERVATIONS ON ROOF RATS, RATTUS RATTUS (LINNAEUS), IN FLORIDA. C. Brooke Worth. Jour. Mam., vol.31, no.3, pp.293-304, Aug., 1950.

Pacific Islands

ON THE AMAMI SPINOUS RAT (RATTUS JERDONI OSIMENSIS SUBSP. NOV.), WITH SPECIAL REMARKS UPON ITS SPINES. Y. Abe. Jour. Sci. Hiroshima Univ., ser.B, div.2, vol.3, pp.107-114, pl.1, Dec., 1934.

THE RATS AND MICE OF FORMOSA , ILLUSTRATED. Aoki, Tanaka. Mem. Fac. Sci. and Agric., Taihoku Imperial Univ., vol.23, no.4, May, 1941.

A NEW SUBSPECIES OF RATTUS BARTELSII (JENTINK) FROM CENTRAL JAVA. M. Bartels, Jr. Treubia, Buitenzorg, vol.16, no.3, pp.323-324, Aug., 1938.

ON TWO NEW MURIDAE FROM SUMATRA AND ANOTHER RAT NEW TO THE SUMATRAN FAUNA. (RATTUS BUKIT JACOBSONI, RATTUS CREMORIVENTER SUMATRAE.) M. Bartels. Natuurkundig Tijdschrift voor Nederlandsch-Indie, Batavia, vol.97, pp.121-124, June, 1937.

FOREST LORE OF THE MAORI. (NOTES ON THE KIORE OR NATIVE RAT, PP.416-460.) Elsdon Best. Dominion Mus. Bull., Wellington, no.14, pp.xi, 503, figs.31, 1942.

(TWO NEW FEMALE RATS FROM THE ISLE OF BORNEO.) Dos nuevas ratas de la isla de Borneo. (Rattus melinogaster, from Bongon, Northern Borneo; and R. trachynotus, from Kina Balu.) Angel Cabrera. Bol. Real Soc. Española Hist. Nat., vol.20, pp.211-213, July, 1920.

TWO NEW MAMMALS FROM NORTH SUMATRA. (RATTUS HOOGERWERFI, AND RATTUS BUKIT LIEFTINCKI.) F. N. Chasen. Treubia, Buitenzorg, vol. 17, no.3, pp.207-208, Aug., 1939.

MASTACOMYS FUSEUS! (MURIDAE) STILL EXTANT. H. H. Finlaysan. Nature, London, vol.132, no.3342, p.786, Nov.18, 1933.

(NOTES ON THE MAMMALS. XI. A LARGE RAT OF WAIGEU ISLAND (NEW GUINEA).) Notes sur les Mammifères. XI. Un grand rat de l'île Waigeu (Nouvelle Guinée). Serge Frechkop. Bull. Mus. Roy. Hist. Nat., Belgique, Bruxelles, vol.8, no.28, pp.11, figs.2, Nov., 1932.

THE RAT THAT DOES NOT GNAW. RARE HAWAIIAN RODENT LONG THOUGHT TO BE EXTINCT. (RATTUS HAWAIIENSIS.) Lorin Tarr Gill. Nature Magazine, vol.14, no.5, pp.278-280, figs.4, Nov., 1929.

CHARACTERS OF A NEW GENUS OF MAMMALIA, AND OF A NEW GENUS AND TWO NEW SPECIES OF LIZARDS, FROM NEW HOLLAND. J. E. Gray. Proc. Comm. Sci. and Corres. Zool. Soc. Lond., pt.2, p.39, 1832.

PRELIMINARY DIAGNOSES OF FIVE NEW MURINE RODENTS FROM NEW GUINEA. Martin A. C. Hinton. Ann. and Mag. Nat. Hist., London, ser.11, vol.10, no.68, pp. 552-557, Aug., 1943.

TWO NEW SPECIES OF EPIMYS FROM LUZON. Ned Hollister. Proc. Biol. Soc. Wash., vol.24, pp.89-90, May 15, 1911.

NOTE ON THE MAORI RAT. F. W. Hutton. Trans. New Zealand Inst., vol.9, pl.3 (missing), 1877.

ON A NEW MOUSE FROM JAVA. F. A. Jentink. Notes Leyden Mus., vol.33, no.2, p.69, May 1910.

ON A NEW SPECIES OF RAT FROM THE ISLAND OF FLORES. (MUS ARMANDVILLEI.) F. A. Jentink. Extract from Zool. Ergebnisse einer reise in Niederlandische Ost-Indien, vol.2, pp.78-83, pl.5, 1892.

ON VARIOUS SPECIES OF MUS, COLLECTED BY S.C.I.W. VAN MUSSCHENBROEK ESQ. IN CELEBES. F. A. Jentink. Notes Leyden Mus., vol.1, no.2, pp.7-13, Dec., 1878.

A NEW PHILIPPINE RAT ALLIED TO "BULLIMUS" BAGOBUS MEARNS. (RATTUS BAGOBUS BARKERI.) David H. Johnson. Jour. Wash. Acad. Sci., Menasha, vol.36, no.9, pp.317-320, figs. 2, Sept.15, 1946.

THE RAT POPULATION OF A NEWLY ESTABLISHED MILITARY BASE IN THE SOLOMON ISLANDS. David H. Johnson. U.S. Naval Medical Bull., Wash., vol.46, no.10, pp.1628-1632, Oct., 1946.

THE SPINY RATS OF THE RIU KIU ISLANDS. David H. Johnson. Proc. Biol. Soc. Wash., vol.59, pp.169-172, Dec.23, 1946.

TWO NEW PHILIPPINE RODENTS. (RATTUS RATTUS UMBRIVENTER, CHROTOMYS WHITEHEADI MINDORENSIS.) Remington Kellogg. Proc. Biol. Soc. Wash., vol.58, pp.121-124, Sept.20, 1945.

TWO RATS FROM MOROTAI ISLAND. (RATTUS CONCOLOR SOLATUS, RATTUS MOROTAIENSIS.) Remington Kellogg. Proc. Biol. Soc. Wash., vol.58, pp.65-68, May 7, 1945.

A NEW RAT FROM THE MOUNTAINS OF EAST JAVA. C. Boden Kloss, H. C. Robinson. Jour. Fed. Malay States Mus., vol.13, pt.4, 1 p., Aug., 1927.

SOME RATS AND MICE OF THE MALAY ARCHIPELAGO. (NEW FORMS OF GUNOMYS, MUS, AND RATTUS.) C. Boden Kloss. Treubia, vol.2, livr.1, pp.115-124, pls.2, 1921.

(THE ECOLOGY OF JAVANESE RATS AND THEIR IMPORTANCE AS REGARDS THE EPIDEMIOLOGY OF THE PEST.) Die Oekologie der Javanischen Ratten und ihre Bedeutung fuer die Epidemiologie der pest. Felix Kopstein. Zeitschr. fuer Morphol. und Oekologie der Tiere, vol.22, pp.774-807, 1931.

DESCRIPTION OF A NEW SPECIES OF THE GENUS MUS FROM FORMOSA. Nagamichi Kuroda. Dobutsugaku Zasshi, vol.37, no.435, p.16, Jan.15, 1925.

THE OCCURRENCE OF THE SPINOUS RAT IN OKINAWA ISLAND IN THE CENTRAL RIU KIU ISLANDS. Nagamichi Kuroda. Bull. Biogeogr. Soc. Japan, Tokyo, vol.13, no.9, pp.50-64, pl.2, Apr., 1943. (In Japanese, with English summary.)

ON TWO RARE SPECIES OF MURIDAE FROM THE CENTRAL MOUNTAINS OF FORMOSA. Nagamichi Kuroda. Dobutsugaku Zasshi, vol.32, pp.36-43, figs.1-2, 1920.

A RECORD OF RATTUS R. ALEXANDRINUS FROM THE MARCUS ISLAND. Nagamichi Kuroda. Trans. Mam., Soc. Japan, no.8, pp.65-66, Feb., 1954. (In Japanese, with English summary.)

RATTUS EXULANS IN WESTERN SAMOA. R. R. Marples. Pacific Science, vol.9, no.2, pp.171-176, Apr., 1955.

ATOLLS VISITED DURING THE FIRST YEAR OF THE PACIFIC ISLANDS RAT ECOLOGY PROJECT. J. T. Marshall, Jr. Atoll Research Bull., Pacific Science Board, no.56, pp.1-11, Sept.15, 1957.

RATS OF ARNO ATOLL, MARSHALL ISLANDS. J. T. Marshall, Jr. Jour. Mam., 36 (2): 259-263, May 26, 1955.

(THE PHILIPPINO BARKRAT, PHLOEOMYS CUMINGI WATERH., LIVING IN THE DRESDEN ZOOLOGICAL GARDEN.) Die borkenratte der Philippinen, Phloeomys Cumingi Waterh., lebend im Dresdner zoologischen garten. A. B. Meyer. Zool. Garten, Jahrg., 31, no.7, pp.195-200, 1890.

THE CHARACTERS AND PROBABLE HISTORY OF THE HAWAIIAN RAT. Gerrit S. Miller, Jr. Bernice P. Bishop Museum Bull.14, pp.3-6, Oct., 1924.

DESCRIPTIONS OF SIXTEEN NEW MURINE RODENTS FROM CELEBES. Gerrit S. Miller, Jr., N. Hollister. Proc. Biol. Soc. Wash., vol.34, pp.67-76, Mar.31, 1921.

NOTES ON CHIGGERS, RATS AND HABITATS ON NEW GUINEA AND LUZON. Carl O. Mohr. Ecology, Lancaster, vol. 28, no.2, pp.194-199, illus., Apr., 1947.

ON THE WILD RAT AND ITS EXTERMINATION IN OKINAWA PREFECTURE. A. Moritzugu. II. Formosan Agric. Rev., no. 273, pp.655-668, Sept., 1929. (In Japanese.)'

NATIVE RATS AND THE PLAGUE IN THE PACIFIC. Edward P. Mumford. Amer. Scientist, New Haven, vol.30, no.3, pp. 212-217, July, 1942.

THE RODENTS OF NEW CALEDONIA. Arnold J. Nicholson. Jour. Mam., 34 (2): 168-179, illus., May, 1953.

A NEW RODENT FROM DUTCH NEW GUINEA. (PARALEPTOMYS RUFILATUS.) Wilfred H. Osgood. Fieldiana, Zool., Chicago Nat. Hist. Mus., vol.31, no.1, pp. 2, Sept.19, 1945.

(NOTES ON INDONESIAN RATS.) Aanteekeningen over Indische ratten. O.L.E. de Raadt. Zool. Mededeel., Leiden, vol. 14, no.1-2, pp.43-51, 1931.

ON TWO LITTLE-KNOWN RATS FROM WESTERN JAVA. H. C. Robinson. Jour. Fed. Malay States Mus., Singapore, vol. 7, pt.3, pp.93-99, Sept., 1917.

TWO NEW INDO-MALAYAN RATS. (RATTUS BANDAHARA, FROM KINA BALU, BORNEO; AND R. PANGLIMA, FROM PALAWAN, P.I.) H. C. Robinson. Ann. and Mag. Nat. Hist., ser.9, vol.7, pp. 234-236, Mar., 1921.

A NEW RAT FROM THE MOUNTAINS OF EAST JAVA. (RATTUS CONCOLOR EQUILE.) H. C. Robinson, C. Boden Kloss. Jour. Federated Malay States Mus., vol.13, pt.4, p.209, Aug., 1927.

(A NEW RAT, HYOMYS STROBILURUS SP. N., OF SATTELBERG, GERMAN NEW GUINEA.) Ueber eine neue Ratte, Hyomys strobilurus sp. n., vom Sattelberg, Deutsch-Neuguinea. Hans Ruemmler. Zeitschrift f. Saeugetierkunde, vol.8, no.2, pp.96-99, Apr.24, 1933.

(A NEW MURINE GENUS FROM THE HIGH MOUNTAINS OF NEW GUINEA.) Eine neue Muridengattung aus dem Hochgebirge Neuguineas. Hans Ruemmler. Zeitschr. f. Saeugetierkunde, vol.9, nos. 1-3, pp.47-48, Dec.12, 1934.

(NEW MURINES FROM NEW GUINEA.) Neue Muriden aus Neuguinea. Hans Ruemmler. Zeitschr. f. Saeugetierkunde, vol.10, no.1, pp.105-118, Dec.31, 1935.

(THE SYSTEMATICS AND DISTRIBUTION OF THE MURINES OF NEW GUINEA.) Die Systematik und Verbreitung der Muriden Neuguineas. Hans Ruemmler. Mitteilungen aus dem Zoologischen Museum, Berlin, band 23, Heft 1, pp.1-297, Table 1-9, Ausgegeben am 24, Mar., 1938.

(A NEW MURIDE OF TIMOR.) Ein neuer Muride von Timor. S. Schaub. Verhandl. Naturforsch. Ges. Basel, vol.48, pp.1-6, figs.2, 1937.

NEW RATS FROM JAVA AND NEW GUINEA. H.J.V. Sody. Natuurk. Tijdschr. Nederl.-Indiee, Batavia, vol.94, no.2, pp.170-177, 1934.

(NOTES ON RATTUS ROQUEI SODY, WITH A DESCRIPTION OF A NEW RACE OF RATTUS RATTUS OF SOEMBA.) Over Rattus rattus roquei Sody met beschrijving van een nieuw ras van Rattus rattus van Soemba. H.J.V. Sody. Zool. Mededeel., Leiden, vol.13, nos.1-2, pp.94-99, Aug.15, 1930.

ON A COLLECTION OF RATS FROM THE INDO-MALAYAN AND INDO-AUSTRALIAN REGIONS. H.J.V. Sody. Treubia, Buiteborg, vol.18, pt.2, pp.255-325, Dec., 1941.

(SURVEY OF THE RATS OF JAVA, WITH A DESCRIPTION OF A NEW SUBSPECIES.) Overzicht van de Ratten van Java, met beschrijving van een nieuwe subspecies. H.J.V. Sody. Zool. Mededeel. Leiden, vol.13, no.1-2, pp.100-140, 1930.

SIX NEW INDO-MALAYAN RATS. (RATTUS MAXI, RATTUS THYSANURUS, RATTUS TAERAE, RATTUS TONDANUS, RATTUS RATTUS SANTALUM, RATTUS RATTUS SAMATI.) H.J.V. Sody. Natuurhistorisch Maandblad, Jahrg.21, no.12, pp.157-160, Dec.30, 1932.

TWO NEW RACES OF RATTUS LEPTURUS FROM JAVA. (RATTUS LEPTURUS FREDERICAE; R.L. BESUKI.) H.J.V. Sody. Natuurkundig Tijdschr. Nederlandsch Indiee, vol.91, no.2, pp.212-215, 1931.

MOVEMENTS AND SURVIVAL OF RATS IN HAWAII. H. J. Spencer, David E. Davis. Jour. Mam., vol.31, no.2, pp.154-157, pl.1, May 25, 1950.

NOTES ON THE HAWAIIAN RAT. John F. G. Stokes. Occas. Papers Bernice Pauahi Bishop Mus., Polynesian Ethology Nat. Hist., vol.3, no.4, pp.261-271, pls.7-15, 1917.

THE HAWAIIAN RAT. Witmer Stone. Occas. Paper Bernice Pauahi Bishop Mus., Polynesian Ethnology Nat. Hist., vol.3, no.4, pp.253-260, pls.8-15, 1917.

THE HAWAIIAN RAT. (RATTUS HAWAIIENSIS.) Arthur Svihla. Mid-Pacific Mag., vol.48, no.4, pp.344-346, fig.1, Oct. Dec., 1935; Murrelet, vol.17, no.1, pp.3-14, illus., Jan., 1936.

ON A NEW RAT FROM FORMOSA. Robert Swinhoe. Proc. Zool. Soc. Lond., pp.185-187, 1864.

(Review by William B. McCintosh of) A COMPARATIVE STUDY ON FORMOSAN COMMON RATS AND MICE OF FOUR SPECIES BELONGING TO THE GENERA RATTUS APODEMUS AND MUS FROM THE STANDPOINT OF VARIATION STATISTICS. Tyo Tanaka. Jour. Mam., vol.32, no.4, pp.477-478, Nov.19, 1951.

THE MURIDAE OF THE COCOS-KEELING ISLANDS. G.H.H. Tate. Bull. Raffles Mus., Singapore, no.22, pp.271-277, Apr., 1950.

RODENTS OF THE GENERA RATTUS AND MUS FROM THE PACIFIC ISLANDS, COLLECTED BY THE WHITNEY SOUTH SEA EXPEDITION, WITH A DISCUSSION OF THE ORIGIN AND RACES OF THE PACIFIC ISLAND RAT. G.H.H. Tate. Bull. Amer. Mus. Nat. Hist., vol.68, art.3, pp.145-178, Feb.11, 1935.

RESULTS OF THE ARCHBOLD EXPEDITIONS, NO.2. TWELVE APPARENTLY NEW FORMS OF RATTUS FROM THE

INDO-AUSTRALIAN REGION. G.H.H. Tate, Richard Archbold. American Mus. Nov., no.802, pp.10, May 18, 1935.

RESULTS OF THE ARCHBOLD EXPEDITIONS, NO.3. TWELVE APPARENTLY NEW FORMS OF MURIDAE (OTHER THAN RATTUS) FROM THE INDO-AUSTRALIAN REGION. G.H.H. Tate, Richard Archbold. Amer. Mus. Nov., no.803, pp.9, May 18, 1935.

RESULTS OF THE ARCHBOLD EXPEDITIONS NO. 61. A NEW SPECIES OF RATTUS FROM THE SNOW MOUNTAINS OF NETHERLANDS NEW GUINEA. (RATTUS RICHARDSONI). G.H.H. Tate. Amer. Mus. Nov., no.1421, pp.1-3, July 29, 1949.

A SECOND SPECIMEN OF THE PAPUAN EARLESS WATER RAT, CROSSOMYS MONCKTONI. G.H.H. Tate. Amer. Mus. Nov., New York, no.1523, pp.1-4, Illus., June 19, 1951.

SOME MURIDAE OF THE INDO-AUSTRALIAN REGION. G.H.H. Tate. Bull. Amer. Mus. Nat. Hist., vol.72, art.6, pp.501-728, figs.32, tables, Dec. 31, 1936.

TWO NEW MURIDAE FROM THE WESTERN DIVISION OF PAPUA.(CONILURUS RANDI; LEPTOMYS SIGNATUS.) G.H.H. Tate, Richard Archbold. (Results of the Archbold Expeditions. No.18.) Amer. Mus. Nov., no.982, pp.1-2, May 12, 1938.

DESCRIPTION OF A NEW GENUS AND SPECIES OF RAT FROM NEW GUINEA. Oldfield Thomas. Proc. Zool. Soc., Lond., pp.237-250, figs.2, Feb.21, 1888.

DESCRIPTION OF A NEW RAT FROM NORTH BORNEO. Oldfield Thomas. Ann. and Mag. Nat. Hist., (5), vol.20, no.118, pp.269-270, Oct., 1887.

DESCRIPTION OF A NEW SPECIES OF MUS FROM THE FIJI ISLANDS. Oldfield Thomas. Proc. Zool. Soc. Lond., pp.11-13, fig.1, Jan 6, 1880 (June, 1880).

DESCRIPTION OF A NEW UROMYS FROM THE SOLOMON ISLANDS. Oldfield Thomas. Ann. and Mag. Nat. Hist., (7), vol.9, no. 54, pp.446-447.

DESCRIPTIONS OF TWO GIANT RATS FROM NEW GUINEA, PRESENTED TO THE BRITISH MUSEUM BY THE HON. WALTER ROTHSCHILD, F.R.S. Oldfield Thomas. Novitates Zoologicae, Tring, vol.19, pp.91-92, Apr., 1912.

A NEW UROMYS FROM THE KEI ISLANDS. (NEW SPECIES: UROMYS SIEBERSI.) Oldfield Thomas. Treubia, vol.3, pp.3-4, 1923.

ON A SECOND SPECIES OF LENOTHRIX FROM THE LIU KIU ISLANDS. Oldfield Thomas. Ann. and Mag. Nat. Hist., (7), vol.17, no.97, pp.88-89, Jan., 1906.

ON TWO NEW MURIDAE FROM TASMANIA. Oldfield Thomas. Ann. and Mag. Nat. Hist., (5), vol.9, no.54, pp.413-416, June, 1882.

A PRELIMINARY REVISION OF THE BORNEAN SPECIES OF THE GENUS MUS. Oldfield Thomas. Ann. and Mag. Nat. Hist., (6), vol.14, no.84, pp.449-460, Dec., 1894.

ON SOME RATS AND MICE FROM THE SOUTH SEA ISLANDS (PART I, RATTUS CONCOLOR GROUP). Mitosi Tokuda. Annotationes Zoologicae Japonenses, vol. 14, no.1, pp.79-86, fig.1, pl.5, June 10, 1933.

DESCRIPTIONS OF SOME NEW GUINEA MAMMALS. Ellis LeG. Troughton. Records Australian Mus., Sydney, vol.20, no.2, pp.115-127, Aug.27, 1937.

DIAGNOSES OF NEW RATS FROM THE NEW GUINEA AREA. (RATTUS RINGENS DOBODURAE, R. GESTRI BUNAE, R. PURDIENSIS, R. SANSAPOR, R. BIAKENSIS.) Ellis LeG. Troughton. Records Australian Mus., Sydney, vol.21, no.7, pp. 406-410, June 24, 1946.

A NEW GENUS AND SPECIES OF GIANT RAT FROM THE SOLOMONS. (UNICOMYS, U. PANCELETI.) Ellis LeG. Troughton. Records Australian Mus., vol.19, no.4, pp.259-262, pl.19, Sept.19, 1935.

DESCRIPTIONS OF TWO NEW SPECIES OF THE GENUS MUS. G. R. Waterhouse. Proc. Zool. Soc. Lond., pt.10, pp.145-146, 1842.

ON A NEW GENUS OF RODENTS FROM THE PHILIPPINE ISLANDS (PHLOEOMYS CUMINGI). G. R. Waterhouse. Proc. Zool. Soc. Lond., pt.7, p.107, 1839.

THE PRESENT DISTRIBUTION OF RATTUS EXULANS (PEALE) IN NEW ZEALAND. J. S. Watson. New Zealand Jour. Sci., Tech., vol.37, no.5, pp.560-570, Mar., 1956.

RATS ON MIDWAY. Rodent Mail, Rats and Mice, London, vol.2, no.8, pp.91-92, illus., Oct., 1946.

## Pelage, Coloration

(ON THE OCCURRENCE OF BLACK NORWAY RATS (RATTUS NORVEGICUS (ERXL.).) Ueber das Vorkommen schwarzer Wanderratten (Rattus norvegicus (Erxl.). K. Becker. Zool. Garten, Leipzig, n.F., vol.19, no.5, pp.223-233, 1952

HAIRLESS MICE. H. C. Brooke. Jour. Heredity, vol.17, pp.173-174, illus., May, 1926.

THE HAIR CYCLES IN THE ALBINO RAT. Earl O. Butcher. Anat. Record, vol.61, no.1, pp.5-14, pls.1-2, Dec.25, 1934.

THE EFFECT OF LOCATION ON THE QUALITY OF THE HAIR AND SKIN IN THE WHITE RAT. Karl O. Butcher. Anat. Record, Phila., vol.83, no.4, pp.503-509, pl.1, Aug.25, 1942.

APPEARANCE OF A RUSTY-RED PIGMENTATION IN THE COATS OF ALBINO RATS IN THE TROPICS. (RATS IMPORTED INTO TRINIDAD FROM LONDON.) Alfred Clark. Nature, London, vol.130, no.3278, p.311, Aug.27, 1932.

TYPES OF WHITE SPOTTING IN MICE. L. C. Dunn. Amer. Nat., vol.54, pp. 465-495, Nov.-Dec. (Dec.6), 1920.

THE ISOLATION OF A PATTERN VARIETY IN PIEBALD HOUSE MICE. L. C. Dunn, G. B. Durham. Amer. Nat., vol.59, no. 660, pp.36-49, Jan.-Feb., 1925.

WHITE-BELLIED HOUSE MICE ON SOME NORTH CAROLINA COASTAL ISLANDS. Wm. L. Engels. Jour. Heredity, Balto., vol.39, no.3, pp.94-96, Mar., 1948.

THE DEVELOPMENT OF THE SKIN OF THE BACK OF THE ALBINO RAT UNTIL THE ERUPTION OF THE FIRST HAIRS. Doris A. Fraser. Anat. Rec., vol.38, pp.203-223, illus., Apr.25, 1928.

A SECOND OCCURRENCE OF HEADDOT SPOTTING IN THE HOUSE MOUSE. Hubert D. Goodale. Jour. Mam., vol.17, no.3, pp.263-265, table 1, fig.1, Aug., 1936.

DIETARY DEPIGMENTATION OF YOUNG RATS. F. J. Gorter. Nature, Lond., vol. 134, no.3384, p.382, Sept.8, 1934.

ARTIFICIAL PRODUCTION OF COAT COLOUR IN THE ALBINO RAT, ITS RELATION TO PATTERN IN THE GROWTH OF HAIR. Alexander Haddow, L. A. Elsen, Edna M.F. Roe, K.M. Rudall, G. M. Timmis. Nature, Lond., vol.155, no.3935, pp.379-381, illus., Mar. 31, 1945.

ARTIFICIAL COAT COLORATION AND THE GROWTH OF HAIR. (WHITE RATS.) Alexander Haddow, K. M. Rudall. Endeavor, Lond., vol.4, no.16, pp.141-147, diagrams 1-2, figs.1-15, (colored), Oct., 1945.

THE OCCURRENCE OF ALBINO AND MELANIC RATS. J. L. Harrison. Jour. Bombay Nat. Hist. Soc., vol.49, no.3, pp.548-549, Dec., 1950.

ON THE APPEARANCE OF ALBINO MUTANTS IN LITTERS OF THE COMMON NORWAY RAT, MUS NORVEGICUS. S. Hatai. Science, n.s., vol.35, no.909, pp.875-876, May 31, 1912.

PIGMENTATION IN BLACK-HAIRED RATS. Mykola H. Haydak. Science, n.s., vol.82, no.2118, pp.107-108, Aug.2, 1935.

ON A MELANISTIC SPECIMEN OF THE LONG-TAILED FIELD MOUSE, APODEMUS SYLVATICUS SYLVATICUS (L.). A. M. Husson. Mammalia, Paris, vol.18, no.3, pp.329-330, Sept., 1954.

HEADDOT: AN INCOMPLETELY RECESSIVE WHITE SPOTTING CHARACTER OF THE HOUSE MOUSE. Clyde E. Keeler. Proc. Nat. Acad. Sci., Wash., vol.21, no.6, pp.379-383, figs.5, June, 1935.

NOTE ON COAT COLOR AND PHYSIOGNOMY IN NORWAY RATS. Clyde E. Keeler. Jour. Tennessee Acad. Sci., vol. 28, no.1, pp.49-52, Jan., 1953.

A SECOND OCCURRENCE OF HEADDOT SPOTTING IN THE HOUSE MOUSE. Clyde E. Keeler, Hubert D. Goodale. Jour. Mam., vol.17, no.3, pp.263-265, table 1, fig.1, Aug., 1936.

(SEMI ALBINISM IN THE BLACK RAT.) Semi-albinisme chez le rat noir. P. Laurent. Bull. sanitaire Algerie, Alger, no.482, pp.1494-1496, 1938.

THE "DILUTE" FORMS OF YELLOW MICE. C. C. Little. Science, Lancaster, n.s., vol.33, no.858, pp.896-897, June 9, 1911.

OCCURRENCE OF PIEBALD SPOTTING IN A WILD HOUSE MOUSE. Robert A. Littleford. Amer. Nat., Lancaster, vol. 80, no.790, pp.283-288, Mar.1, 1946.

"LIGHT"--A NEW MOUSE COLOR. E. C. MacDowell. Jour. Heredity, Wash., vol. 41, no.2, pp.35-36, illus., Feb., 1950.

THE TACTILE HAIR FOLLICLES IN THE MOUSE. H. P. Melargno, W. Montagna. Anat. Record, Phila., vol.115, no.2, pp. 129-150, Feb., 1953.

(ACROMELANISM IN MUS MUSCULUS L.) Akromelanismus bei Mus musculus L. Erna Mohr. Zool. Anz., Leipzig, vol.126, nos.1-2, pp.45-46, Apr.15, 1939.

EFFECT OF CHANGE OF COAT ON THE GROWTH OF EPIDERMAL WARTS IN MICE. J. C. Mottram. Nature, London, vol.155, no.3946, pp.729-730, June 16, 1945.

A NEW VARIETY OF THE ROOF RAT. (A CINNAMON VARIATION AMONG SPECIMENS OF RATTUS ALEXANDRINUS IN TEXAS.) J. T. Patterson. Science, n.s., vol.52, pp.249-250, Sept.10, 1920.

A MODIFIER OF PIEBALD SPOTTING IN MICE. G. Pincus. Amer. Nat., vol.65, no.698, pp.283-286, May-June, 1931.

A MOSAIC (BLACK-BROWN) COAT PATTERN IN THE MOUSE. G. Pincus. Jour. Exper. Zool., vol.52, no.3, pp.439-442, 1929.

A DARK RACE OF THE COMMON HOUSE-MOUSE (MUS MUSCULUS) IN THE NORTH-WEST OF ENGLAND. Fred W. Smalley. Scottish Nat., no.197, pp.125-127, Sept.-Oct., 1932.

MELANIC RACE OF HOUSE MOUSE. Fred W. Smalley. Northwestern Naturalist, Scotland, vol.7, no.4, pp.311-312, Dec., 1932.

(MELANOTIC PIGMENT OF THE SKIN IN THE GREY DOMESTIC MOUSE (MUS MUSCULUS L.).) Das melanotische Pigment der Haut bei der grauen Hausmaus (Mus musculus, L.). Aida Steiner-Wourlisch. Zeitschr. fuer Zellforschung und mikro. Anatomie, vol.2, pp.453-479, 8 figs., Aug.3, 1925.

HAIRLESS MICE. F. B. Sumner. Jour. Heredity, vol.15, pp.475-481, Dec., 1924.

THE OCCURRENCE OF ALBINO AND SPOTTED RATS UNDER FERAL CONDITIONS. Arthur Svihla. Amer. Nat., vol. 70, no.729, pp.403-404, July-Aug., 1936.

SEASONAL VARIATIONS IN THE PELAGE CHARACTERS OF A FORMOSAN WILD RAT, RATTUS LOSEA (SWINHOE). Ryo Tanaka. Mem. Faculty Sci. and Agric., Taihoku Imp. Univ., Formosa, vol.23, no. 2, Zool. no.11, pp.75-93, figs.4, tables 6, Nov., 1939.

THYROXIN AND COAT COLOR IN DILUTE RACES OF MICE AND RATS. Harry Beal Torrey. Science, n.s., vol.66, pp.380-381, Oct.21, 1927.

THE MELANIC FORM OF RATTUS NORVEGICUS IN LONDON. J. S. Watson. Nature, vol.154, pp.334, Sept.9, 1944.

"MISTY" A NEW COAT COLOR DILUTION IN THE MOUSE, MUS MUSCULUS. George W. Woolley. Amer. Nat., Lancaster, vol.75, no.760, pp.507-508, Sept.-Oct., 1941.

Physiology

TOLERANCE TO COLD AND ANOXIA IN INFANT RATS. E. F. Adolph. Amer. Jour. Physiol., 155: 266-277, 1948.

ON CATARACT AND CERTAIN OTHER MANIFESTATIONS OF TRYPTOPHANE DEFICIENCY IN RATS. Anthony A. Albanese, Wilhelm Buschke. Science, Lancaster, n.s., vol.95, no.2475, pp. 584-586, June 5, 1942.

ASPECTS OF THE EGG-OVARY-OVIDUCT RELATIONSHIP IN THE ALBINO RAT. Roland H. Alden. Jour. Exper. Zool., Phila., vol.90, no.2, pp.159-181, pls.3, July 6, 1942.

EFFECTS OF VISIBLE RADIATIONS UPON ALBINO RATS. John Allardyce, John Aldous, William Cooper, Jean Pratt, Ernest Sutherland. Amer. Jour. Physiol., Balto., vol.137, no.4, pp.761-768, fig.1, Nov., 1942.

INFLUENCE OF NUTRITIONAL FACTORS ON SKELETAL ATROPHY FROM DISUSE AND ON NORMAL BONES OF MATURE RATS. W. D. Armstrong. Jour. Nutrition, Phila., vol.35, no.5, pp.597-609, May 10, 1948.

ABSORPTION FROM THE VAGINA OF THE ALBINO RAT AT VARIOUS PERIODS OF THE OESTROUS CYCLE. Dan D. Baker. Anat. Rec., vol.39, pp.339-341, Aug.25, 1928.

ENDOTHERMY AND ECTOTHERMY IN MICE AT $-3^{\circ}$ C. S. A. Barnett. Jour. Exper. Biol., 33 (1): 124-133, Mar., 1956.

VITAMIN E DEFICIENCY IN THE RAT. V. UTERINE CHANGES IN CHRONIC DEFICIENCY. Barrie, M.M.O. Sweeten. Biochemical Jour., Cambridge, England, vol.37, no.5, pp.523-525, 1943.

SOME EFFECTS OF THIAMIN ON THE WINNING OF SOCIAL CONTACTS IN MICE. Elizabeth A. Beeman, W. C. Allee. Physiological Zool., Chicago, vol.18, no.2, pp.195-221, Apr., 1945.

THE MILK-INFLUENCE OF BREAST TUMORS IN MICE. John J. Bittner. Science, Lancaster, n.s., vol.95, no. 2470, pp.462-463, May 1, 1942.

THE LENGTH OF HEAT IN THE ALBINO RAT AS DETERMINED BY THE COPULATORY RESPONSE. Richard J. Blandau, John L. Boling, William C. Young. Anat. Record, Phila., vol.79, no.4, pp.453-463, 1 fig., Apr.25, 1941.

(ON THE CYCLICAL CHANGES IN THE GANGLION CERVICALE UTERI OF THE MOUSE.) Zu den zyklischen Veraenderungen im Ganglion cervicale uteri der Maus. W. Blotevogel. Anat. Anzeiger, vol.63, pp.169-170, June 11, 1927.

A STUDY OF THE PLACENTAL PERMEABILITY OF THE WHITE RAT, AS DETERMINED BY ITS REACTION TO HERMOLYSINS. C. M. Boucek. Amer. Jour. Anat., vol.41, pp.1-24, Mar.15, 1928.

(PHYSIOLOGICAL RESEARCH ON THE SENESCENCE OF MAMMALS. III. ANATOMICAL INVOLUTION DURING THE SENESCENCE OF THE RAT.) Recherches physiologiques sur la senescence des Mammiferes. III. L'involution anatomique au cours de la senescence chez le rat. F. Bourliere. Bull. Soc. Zool. France, Paris, vol.71, nos.4-5, pp.204-207, 1946.

THE EFFECT OF CONTROLLED TEMPERATURES UPON THE SPONTANEOUS ACTIVITY RHYTHMS OF THE ALBINO RAT. Ludvig G. Browman. Jour. Exper. Zool., Phila., vol.94, no.3, pp.477-489, Dec., 1943.

SOLAR AND LUNAR RHYTHMICITY IN THE RAT IN 'CONSTANT CONDITIONS' AND THE MECHANISM OF PHYSIOLOGICAL TIME MEASUREMENT. F. A. Brown, Jr., J. Shriner, C. L. Ralph. Amer. Jour. Physiol., 184 (3): 491-496, Mar., 1956.

ISOLATION OF A NEW "CAROTENOID" FROM RAT LIVER. Christopher Carruthers, Frank Urban. Science, Lancaster, n.s., vol.96, no.2490, pp.279-280, Sept. 18, 1942.

MEASUREMENT OF RENAL FUNCTIONS IN RATS. A. C. Corcoran, Georges Masson, Ruth Renting, Irvine H. Page. Amer. Jour. Physiol., Balto., vol.154, no. 1, pp.170-173, July 1, 1948.

A MICROSCOPIC STUDY OF PANCREATIC SECRETION IN THE LIVING ANIMAL. (EXPERIMENTS ON MICE.) W. P. Covell. Anat. Rec., vol.40, pp.213-233, illus., Oct.25, 1928.

STEREOTROPISM IN RATS AND MICE. (RATTUS NORVEGICUS AND MUS MUSCULUS.) W. J. Crozier, G. Pinctus. Jour. Gen. Physiol., vol.10, pp.195-203, illus., Sept.20, 1926.'

THE FUNCTIONAL INTERRELATION OF THE OVARIES AS INDICATED BY THE DISTRIBUTION OF FOETUSES IN MOUSE UTERI. C. H. Danforth, S. B. DeAberle. Amer. Jour. Anat., vol.41, pp.65-74, Mar.15, 1928.

THE RELATION BETWEEN STARVATION, METABOLIC ACIDOSIS AND CONVULSIVE SEIZURES IN RATS. V. D. Davenport, H. W. Davenport. Jour. Nutrition, Phila., vol.36, no.1, pp.139-151, July 10, 1948.

SOME FACTORS WHICH INFLUENCE THE NATURE OF AFTER-NYSTAGMUS IN THE WHITE RAT. J. A. Detlefsen. Anat. Record, vol.29, p.87, Dec.25, 1924.

THE ADRENAL GLANDS IN PREGNANCY: CORTICO-MEDULLARY RELATIONS IN ALBINO RAT. John C. Donaldson. Anat. Record, vol.38, pp.239-240, Apr.25, 1928.

(TRYPAN BLUE ACCUMULATION DURING THE CYCLIC CHANGES IN THE FEMALE SEX APPARATUS OF THE WHITE MOUSE.) Ueber die Trypanblauspeicherung waehrend der cyclischen Wandlungen im weiblichen Geschlechtsapparat der weissen Maus. Bela Eisler. Zeitschr. fuer Zellforschung und Mikroscopische Anat., vol.3, pp.383-416, 9 figs., Apr.8, 1926.

INHERITED DIFFERENCES IN THE CHOLINE REQUIREMENTS OF RATS. R. W. Engel. Proc. Soc. Exper. Biol. Med., Utica, vol.52, no.4, pp.281-282, Apr., 1943.

EFFECT OF PROTEIN INTAKE ON THE BONES OF MATURE RATS. H. R. Estremera, W. Armstrong. Jour. Nutrition, Phila., vol.35, no.5, pp.611-618, May 10, 1948.

CERTAIN FUNCTIONAL INTERRELATIONSHIPS BETWEEN SPONTANEOUS PERSISTENT ESTRUS, "LIGHT ESTRUS" AND SHORT-DAY ANESTRUS IN THE ALBINO RAT. John W. Everett. (Abstract.) Anat. Record, Phila., vol.82, no.3, p.409, Mar. 25, 1942.

EFFECTS OF COLD ON INFANT RATS: BODY TEMPERATURES, OXYGEN CONSUMPTION ELECTROCARDIOGRAMS. J. Fairfield. Amer. Jour. Physiol., 155: 355-365, 1948.

FERTILITY OF THE RAT, MUS NORVEGICUS. Horace W. Feldman. Proc. Nat. Acad. Sci., vol.11, no.12, pp.718-721, Dec., 1925.

LATENT PERIODS OF AUDIOGENIC SEIZURES IN MICE. Hubert Frings, Mable Frings. Jour. Mam., vol.33, no.4, pp. 487-491, 1 table, Nov.19, 1952.

BEHAVIOR PATTERNS OF THE LABORATORY MOUSE UNDER AUDITORY STRESS. Hubert Frings, Mable Frings, Alan Kivert. Jour. Mam., vol.32, no.1, pp.60-75, pls. 2, Feb.15, 1951.

THE RELATION OF EXERCISE TO RICKETS IN WHITE RATS. Agnes W. Frost. Science, n.s., vol.61, pp.447-448, Apr. 24, 1925.

EFFECT OF MAGNESIUM DEFICIENCY ON DENTIN APPOSITION AND ERUPTION IN INCISOR OF RAT. J. Gagnon, I. Schour, M. C. Patras. Proc. Soc. Exper. Biol. Med., Utica, vol.49, no.4, pp.662-666, figs.2, Apr., 1942.

THE NUTRITION OF THE MOUSE. III. RELATION OF DIET TO THE SYNTHETIC ACTIVITY OF THE PREDOMINATING FLORA ISOLATED FROM THE SMALL INTESTINE AND CECUM. Lorraine S. Gall, Barbara A. Illingworth, George R. Cowgill, Paul F. Fenton. Jour. Nutrition, Phila., vol.35, no.1, pp.27-38, 1948.

THE INFLUENCE OF SEX ON NUTRITIONAL ACHROMOTRICHIA IN MICE. B. Gerstl, B. Lustig, A. R. Goldfarb. Science, Lancaster, n.s., vol.96, no.2498, pp.447-448, Nov.13, 1942.

EFFECT OF UTERINE ENVIRONMENT ON THE SKELETON OF THE MOUSE. Earl L. Green, Margaret C. Green. Jour. Morphol., vol.78, no.1, pp.105-112, Jan., 1946.

(ON THE EFFECT OF LOW TEMPERATURE ON THE TESTES OF WHITE RATS.) Ueber die Wirkung der niedrigen Temperatur auf die Hoden der weissen Ratten bei deren Lokalanwendung. N. Gronsky. Anat. Anz., vol.69, nos.7-12, pp.228-238, 6 figs., Mar.20, 1930.

CONGENITAL HYPERGLYCAEMIA IN MICE. Hans Grueneberg, J.B.S. Haldane. Nature, London, vol.145, no.3679, pp.704-705, May 4, 1940.

THYROID ADRENAL ASSOCIATION. (WORK ON RATS.) F. S. Hammett. Anat. Record, vol.29, pp.99-100, Dec.25, 1924.

RATE OF GAIN AND LOSS OF COLD RESISTANCE IN MICE. J. Sanford Hart. Can. Jour. Zool., 31 (2): 112-116, graphs, Apr., 1953.

STUDIES ON THE POTASSIUM METABOLISM OF THE RAT DURING PREGNANCY, LACTATION, AND GROWTH. Leon A. Heppel, Carl L.A. Schmidt. Univ. Calif. Publ. Physiol., Berkeley, vol.8, no.14, pp. 189-206, figs.9, Dec.28, 1938.

ENZYMATIC LIBERATION OF INORGANIC PHOSPHATE FROM ADENOSINETRIPHOSPHATE IN DEVELOPING RAT MUSCLE. Heinz Herrmann, J. S. Nicholas. Jour. Exper. Zool., Phila., vol.107, no.2, pp. 177-181, Mar., 1948.

ELEMENTARY EFFECT OF ARGINASE IN THE WEIGHT PHYSIOLOGY OF THE MOUSE. W. G. Irons, O. B. Wiswell. Science, Lancaster, vol.106, no.2756, pp. 393-394, figs.2, 1947.

PANTOTHENIC ACID AND CARBOHYDRATE METABOLISM IN THE RAT. Leslie Irwin, Elaine P. Ralli. Amer. Jour. Physiol., Balto., vol.153, no.3, pp.606-610, June 1, 1948.

RELATIVE SIGNIFICANCE OF GROWTH AND METABOLIC RATE UPON THE UTILIZATION OF VITAMIN A BY THE RAT. R. M. Johnson, C. A. Baumann. Jour. Nutrition, Phila., vol.35, no.6, pp. 703-715, June 10, 1948.

THE OESTROUS CYCLE OF FEMALE RATTUS (MASTOMYS) NATALENSIS (SMITH) AS OBSERVED IN THE LABORATORY. Helen L. Johnston, W. D. Oliff. Proc. Zool. Soc. Lond., vol.124, pt.3, pp.605-613, Nov.15, 1954.

THE PHYSIOLOGICAL PECULIARITIES OF THE MOUNTAIN AND PLAIN SUB SPECIES OF THE FOREST MOUSE (APODEMUS SYLVATICUS CISCAUCASICUS OGN. AND A. S. MOSQUENSIS OGN., RODENTIA). N. J. Kalabuchov. Doklady Akad. Nauk SSSR (Comptes Rendus Acad. Sci. URSS), Leningrad, vol.2, no.1, pp.82-88, Apr.1, 1935.

SOME PHYSIOLOGICAL ADAPTATIONS OF THE MOUNTAIN AND PLAIN FORMS OF

THE WOOD-MOUSE (APODEMUS SYLVATICUS) AND OTHER SPECIES OF MOUSE-LIKE RODENTS. N. J. Kalabuchov. Jour. Animal Ecol., 6:254-272, 1937.

GASTRIC ABSORPTION OF ETHYL ALCOHOL IN THE RAT. L. Karel, J.H. Fleisher. Amer. Jour. Physiol., Balto., vol.153, no.2, pp.268-276, May 1, 1948.

RENAL FILTRATION SURFACE IN THE ALBINO RAT. Hadley Kirkman, R. E. Stowell. Anat. Record, Phila., vol.82, no. 3, pp.373-389, pl.1, Mar.25, 1942.

THE EFFECTS OF LACTATION ON THE IMPLANTATION OF OVA OF A CONCURRENT PREGNANCY IN THE RAT. Robert H. Krehbiel. Anat. Record, Phila., vol. 81, no.1, pp.43-65, 1 pl., Sept.25, 1941.

ROLE OF GENOTYPICAL AND HUMORAL FACTORS IN THE DEVELOPMENT AND BEHAVIOUR OF RATS. L. V. Krushinsky. Comptes Rendus (Doklady) Acad. Sci. URSS, Moscow, vol.52, no.6, pp.541-544, figs.2, May 30, 1946.

THE INNERVATION OF THE SENSORY CELLS OF THE MACULA ACUSTICA IN THE RAT. H. H. Lane. Kansas Univ. Sci. Bull., vol.15, no.4, pp.257-261, Dec., 1924 (1925).

TWO FRACTIONS OF SPECIFIC CHOLINESTERASE PRESENT IN HOMOGENIZED NORMAL MOUSE BRAIN. J. M. Little. Amer. Jour. Physiol., Balto., vol.153, no. 3, pp.436-443, June 1, 1948.

INFLUENCES OF ENVIRONMENTAL LIGHTING CONDITIONS ON THE ESTROUS CYCLE OF THE RAT. Rowland E. Logan. Ph. D. thesis, Northwestern Univ., 162 pp., 1954.

THE THRESHOLD OF FERTILITY IN RATS AND ITS RELATION TO DIET EFFICIENCY. Daniel Macomber. Amer. Nat., vol.57, pp.519-531, Dec., 1923.

POST-PARTUM OESTRUS IN RAT. L. Harrison Matthews. Nature, London, vol. 143, no.3624, p.643, Apr.15, 1939.

EGG WHITES VS. CASEIN AS SOURCE OF PROTEIN IN THE DIET OF RATS. Helen S. Mitchell. Amer. Jour. Physiol., vol. 74, pp.359-362, 1925.

DETERMINATION OF OXYGEN CONSUMPTION IN THE ALBINO RAT. Louis E. Moses. Proc. Soc. Exper. Biol. Med., Utica, vol.64, no.1, pp.54-57, figs.2, Jan., 1947.

THE INNERVATION OF THE PYLORIC SPHINCTER OF THE RAT. M. Nakanishi. Jour. Physiol., vol.58, pp.482-484, May, 1924.

(THE INFLUENCE OF THE OVARIUM CAPSULA ON THE FECUNDITY OF THE WHITE RAT.) L'influence de la capsule ovarienne sur la fecondite de la rate blanche. Casmir Neugebauer. Roczniki Prac Naukowych Zrzezenia Asystentow Uniwersyte tu Jozefa Pilsudskiego W. Warszawie, vol.1, no.8, pp.167-183, 2 figs., 1936.

FERTILITY IN MICE. A. S. Parkes. British Jour. Exper. Biol., vol.2, no.1, pp.21-31, Oct., 1924.

HIGH LEVELS OF DIETARY POTASSIUM AND MAGNESIUM AND GROWTH OF RATS. P. B. Pearson. Amer. Jour. Physiol., Balto., vol.153, no.3, pp.432-435, June 1, 1948.

THE LOSS OF RESISTANCE TO MURINE TYPHUS INFECTION RESULTING FROM RIBOFLAVIN DEFICIENCY IN RATS. Henry Pinkerton, Otto A. Bessey. Science, Lancaster, Pa., n.s., vol.89, no.2312, pp.368-370, Apr.21, 1939.

INCREASED DEXTROSE APPETITE OF NORMAL RATS TREATED WITH INSULIN. Curt P. Richter. Amer. Jour. Physiol., Balto., vol.135, no.3, pp.781-787, fig.1, Feb., 1942.

NUTRITIVE VALUE OF FRUCTOSE FOR RATS AND EFFECTS PRODUCED ON ITS UTILIZATION BY THIAMINE. Curt P. Richter. Amer. Jour. Physiol., Balto., vol.154, no.3, pp.499-505, figs.4, Sept., 1948.

FURTHER OBSERVATIONS ON THE CARBOHYDRATE, FAT, AND PROTEIN APPETITE OF VITAMIN B DEFICIENT RATS. Curt P. Richter, Bruno Barelare, Jr. Amer. Jour. Physiology, vol.127, no. 1, pp.199-210, Aug., 1939.

THE DEPENDENCE OF THE CARBOHYDRATE, FAT AND PROTEIN APPETITE OF RATS ON THE VARIOUS COMPONENTS OF THE VITAMIN B COMPLEX. Curt P. Richter, Clarence D. Hawkes. Amer. Jour. Physiol., Memphis, vol.131, no.3, pp.639-649, figs.3, Jan., 1941.

MAXIMUM SODIUM CHLORIDE INTAKE AND THIRST IN DOMESTICATED AND WILD NORWAY RATS. Curt P. Richter, H. D. Mosier, Jr. Amer. Jour. Physiol., vol.176, no.2, pp.213-222, Feb., 1954.

THE RELATION BETWEEN URINARY EXCRETION AND TISSUE CONCENTRATIONS OF THIAMINE IN RATS. Juan Salcedo, Jr., V. A. Najjar, L. E. Holt, Jr., E. W. Hutzler. Jour. Nutrition, Phila., vol.36, no.2, pp.307-313, Aug.10, 1948.

THE EFFECT OF MINERAL SUPPLEMENTS ON REPRODUCTION OF THE ALBINO RAT. W. D. Salmon. Science, vol.62, pp.420-421, Nov.6, 1925.

THE RELATION OF ASCORBIC ACID METABOLISM IN THE RAT TO DIETS HIGH IN PROTEIN, CARBOHYDRATE OR FAT. Leo T. Samuels. Jour. Nutrition, Phila., vol.36, no.2, pp.205-213, Aug.10, 1948.

THYROID-FED RATS AND HIGH ROOM TEMPERATURES. Raymond M. Selle. Science, n.s., vol.68, pp.573-574, Dec. 7, 1928.

STUDIES IN ACTIVITY. II. ACTIVITY RHYTHMS; AGE AND ACTIVITY; ACTIVITY AFTER REST. (WHITE RATS.) Mary Shinley. Jour. Comp. Psych., vol.8, pp. 159-186, illus., 1928.

THE EFFECT OF PUBESCENCE, OESTRUATION AND MENOPAUSE ON THE VOLUNTARY ACTIVITY IN THE ALBINO RAT. J. R. Slonaker. Amer. Jour. Physiol., vol. 68, pp.294-315, 1924.

THE RELATION OF MATING, OVULATION AND THE ESTROUS SMEAR IN THE HOUSE MOUSE TO TIME OF DAY. G. D. Snell, Elizabeth Fekete, Katharine P. Hummel, L. W. Law. Anat. Record, Phila., vol.76, no.1, pp.39-54, Jan.25, 1940.

EXPERIMENTAL RAT CARIES. R. F. Sognnaes. Jour. Nutrition, Phila., vol.36, no.1, pp.1-13, July 10, 1948.

p-BROMOPHENOL AS THE INTERMEDIATE IN SYNTHESIS OF p-BROMOPHENYLMERCAPTURIC ACID FROM BROMOBENZENE IN THE RAT. Jacob A. Stekol, Harriman H. Dash. Proc. Soc. Exper. Biol. Med., New York, vol.40, no.2, pp.261-263, table 1, Feb., 1939.

THE AWAKENING OF COPULATORY ABILITY IN THE MALE ALBINO RAT. C. P. Stone. Amer. Jour. Physiol., vol. 68, pp.407-424, 1924.

SOME EFFECTS OF EXTERNAL CONDITIONS UPON THE WHITE MOUSE. Francis B. Sumner. Jour. Exper. Zool., vol.7, no. 1, pp.97-155, figs.14, Aug., 1909.

PHYSIOLOGICAL FACTORS IN HYPOPHYSIAL-GONADAL INTERACTION. I. LIGHT AND THE FOLLICULAR MECHANISM OF THE RAT. B. Lionel Truscott. Jour. Exper. Zool., Phila., vol.95, no.3, pp.291-305, illus., Apr., 1944.

A SEXUAL ACTIVITY RHYTHM IN THE FEMALE RAT. G. H. Wang. Amer. Nat., vol.58, no.654, pp.36-42, 3 figs., Jan.-Feb., 1924.

TRICHOMONAD FLAGELLATES IN THE COECUM OF RATS AND MICE. D. H. Wenrich. Anat. Record, vol.29, p.118, Dec.25, 1924.

THE EFFECTS OF ACUTE STRESS AND OF ACTH UPON ASCORBIC ACID AND LIPID CONTENT OF THE ADRENAL GLANDS OF WILD RATS. J. W. Woods. Jour. Physiol., Cambridge, England, 135 (2): 390-399, Feb., 1957.

THE EFFECTS OF LONG-TERM EXPOSURE TO COLD UPON ADRENAL WEIGHT AND ASCORBIC ACID CONTENT IN WILD AND DOMESTICATED NORWAY RATS. J. W. Woods. Jour. Physiol., Cambridge, England, 135 (2): 384-389, Feb., 1957.

Population Dynamics

THE BIOLOGY OF RAT POPULATIONS. S. A. Barnett. Surgo, pp.111-115, illus., Candlemas, 1952.

POPULATION DYNAMICS OF SEWER RATS. S. A. Barnett, A. H. Bathard. Jour. Hyg., 51: 483-491, Dec., 1953.

SOCIAL BEHAVIOR, REPRODUCTION, AND POPULATION CHANGES IN THE HOUSE MOUSE (MUS MUSCULUS L.). Robert Z. Brown. Ecol. Monogr., Durham, vol.23, no.3, pp.217-240, July, 1953.

THE RAT POPULATION OF BALTIMORE, 1952. Robert Z. Brown, William Sallow, David E. Davis, William G. Cochran. Amer. Jour. Hyg., 61 (1): 89-102, maps, Jan., 1955.

MORTALITY AND MOVEMENT OF BROWN RATS (RATTUS NORVEGICUS) IN ARTIFICIALLY SUPERSATURATED POPULATIONS. John B. Calhoun. Jour. Wildlife Mgt., 12 (2): 167-172, Apr., 1948.

THE RELATIONSHIP BETWEEN ADRENAL WEIGHT AND POPULATION STATUS OF URBAN NORWAY RATS. John J. Christian, David E. Davis. Research Report Naval Medical Research Institute, Bethesda, 14: 173-184, Feb.23, 1956.

THE CHARACTERISTICS OF GLOBAL RAT POPULATIONS. David E. Davis. Amer. Jour. Publ. Health, 41 (2): 158-163, Feb., 1951.

THE CHARACTERISTICS OF RAT POPULATIONS. David E. Davis. Quart. Rev. Biol., 28 (4): 373-401, illus., Dec., 1953.

THE MECHANICS OF RAT POPULATIONS. David E. Davis. Trans. N.A. Wildlife Conf., 15: 461-465, 1950.

THE RAT POPULATION OF NEW YORK, 1949. David E. Davis. Amer. Jour. Hygiene, 52 (2): 147-152, Sept., 1950.

THE RELATION BETWEEN LEVEL OF POPULATION AND PREGNANCY OF NORWAY RATS. David E. Davis. Ecology, Brooklyn, vol.32, no.3, pp.459-461, July, 1951.

THE RELATION BETWEEN THE LEVEL OF POPULATION AND THE PREVALENCE OF LEPTOSPIRA, SALMONELLA, AND CAPILLARIA IN NORWAY RATS. David E. Davis. Ecology, Brooklyn, vol.32, no.3, pp.465-468, July, 1951.

THE RELATION BETWEEN LEVEL OF POPULATION AND SIZE AND SEX OF NORWAY RATS. David E. Davis. Ecology, Brooklyn, vol.32, no.3, pp.462-464, July, 1951.

CHANGES IN NORWAY RAT POPULATIONS INDUCED BY INTRODUCTION OF RATS. David E. Davis, John J. Christian. Jour. Wildlife Mgt., 20 (4): 378-383, Oct., 1956.

THE RAT POPULATION OF BALTIMORE, 1949. David E. Davis, W. T. Fales. Amer. Jour. Hygiene, 52 (2): 143-146, Sept., 1950.

ANALYSIS OF POPULATIONS OF THE ROOF RAT IN SOUTHWEST GEORGIA. Dean H. Ecke. Publ. Health Monog., U.S. Publ. Health Service, no.27, pp.1-20, illus., 1955.

AN INVASION OF NORWAY RATS IN SOUTHWEST GEORGIA. Dean H. Ecke. Jour. Mam., vol.35, no.4, pp.521-525, Nov.29, 1954.

THE RATE OF RECOVERY OF DECIMATED POPULATIONS OF BROWN RATS IN NATURE. John T. Emlen, Jr., Allen W. Stokes, Charles P. Winsor. Ecology, 29 (2): 133-145, Apr., 1948.

ABUNDANCE OF HOUSE MICE AT DAVIS, CALIFORNIA, IN 1941-42. F. C. Evans, T. I. Storer. Jour. Mam., vol.25, no.1, pp.89-90, Feb., 1944.

A POPULATION STUDY OF HOUSE MICE (MUS MUSCULUS) FOLLOWING A PERIOD OF LOCAL ABUNDANCE. F. C. Evans. Jour. Mam., 30 (4): 351-363, Nov., 1949.

ON MAMMALS FROM THE LAKE EYRE BASIN. PART V. GENERAL REMARKS ON THE INCREASE OF MURIDS AND THEIR POPULATION MOVEMENTS IN THE LAKE EYRE BASIN DURING THE YEARS 1930-1936. H. H. Finlayson. Trans. Roy. Soc. S. Australia, Adelaide, vol.63, no.2, pp. 348-355, Dec.22, 1939.

NOTES ON A HEAVY NORWAY RAT POPULATION. H. Gunderson. Jour. Mam., 25 (3): 307-308, Aug., 1944.

THE GROWTH-SURVIVAL, WANDERING AND VARIATION OF THE LONG-TAILED FIELD MOUSE, APODEMUS SYLVATICUS. III. WANDERING POWER AND DISTRIBUTION. H. P. Hacker, H. S. Pearson. Biometrika, vol.39, pts.3-4, pp.389-413, Dec.4, 1952.

AN OUTBREAK OF HOUSE MICE IN KERN COUNTY, CALIFORNIA. E. Raymond Hall. Univ. Calif. Publ. Zool., vol.30, no.7, pp. 189-203, Feb.21, 1927.

MICE BY THE MILLION. A FARMER'S TRIBULATIONS IN THE WHEAT BELT. Ray Harris. Wildlife, Australian Nature Mag., Melbourne, vol.7, no.1, pp.9-11, illus., Jan., 1945.

THE MICE OF ST. KILDA, WITH ESPECIAL REFERENCE TO THEIR PROSPECTS OF EXTINCTION AND PRESENT STATUS. T. H. Harrison, J. A. Moy-Thomas. Jour. Anim. Ecology, vol.2, no.1, pp.109-115, pl.4, May, 1933.

A NOTE ON THE ABUNDANCE OF HARVEST MICE (MICROMYS MINUTUS) IN NORTH HAMPSHIRE IN 1955. David Jenkins. Proc. Zool. Soc. Lond., 128 (4): 604, July 24, 1957.

(POPULATION DENSITY OF THE WOOD MOUSE APODEMUS S. SYLVATICUS IN AN EXPERIMENTAL DISTRICT OF THE EIFEL REGION.) Die Bestandsdichte der Waldmaus, Apodemus s. sylvaticus, in einem Versuchsrevier der Voreifel. E. v. Lehmann. Saeugetierk., Mitteil., 5 (2): 70-72, Apr.1, 1957.

MIGRATION OF RATS. (RATTUS RATTUS JALORENSIS.) Arieant Manjikul. Jour. Siam Soc., Nat. Hist. Suppl., vol.9, no.1, pp.149-150, June, 1933.

THE POPULATION DYNAMICS OF CONFINED HOUSE MICE SUPPLIED WITH UNLIMITED FOOD. Charles H. Southwick. Ecology, Durham, vol.36, no.2, pp.212-225, illus., Apr., 1955.

REGULATORY MECHANISMS OF HOUSE MOUSE POPULATIONS: SOCIAL BEHAVIOR AFFECTING LITTER SURVIVAL. Charles H. Southwick. Ecol., 36 (4): 627-634, graphs, Oct., 1955.

REGULATORY MECHANISMS IN HOUSE-MOUSE POPULATIONS: THE EFFECT OF LIMITED FOOD SUPPLY ON A CONFINED POPULATION. Robert L. Strecker, John T. Emlen, Jr. Ecology, Lancaster, vol.34, no.2, pp.375-335, illus., Apr., 1953.

REGULATORY MECHANISMS IN HOUSE-MOUSE POPULATIONS: THE EFFECT OF LIMITED FOOD SUPPLY ON AN UNCONFINED POPULATION. Robert L. Strecker. Ecology, Durham, vol.35, no.2, pp.249-253, illus., Apr., 1954.

STUDY OF LAWS CONCERNING THE MASS OUTBREAKS OF MURINE RODENTS. P. A. Sviridenko. Itogi Nauchno-Issledovatel'skikh Rabot Vsesoiuznogo Instituta Zashchity Rastenii za 1935 (Summary Sci. Research Work Inst. Plant Protection, Leningrad, 1935), p.74, 1936. (In Russian.)

MOVEMENT AND POPULATION OF THE BROWN RAT IN KOCHI CITY. Ryo Tanaka, Fumio Kawashima. Annot. Zool. Japonenses, Tokyo, vol.24, no.4, pp.225-233, illus., Dec., 1951.

AN OUTBREAK OF COMMENSAL RATS IN THE ISLAND OF UGURU. Ryo Tanaka, Fumio Kawashima. Publ. Health Dept. Kochi Pref., 1-15 pp., 1946. (Japanese with English summary.)

THE RAT AND MOUSE POPULATIONS OF CORN RICKS. L.S.V. Venables, P.H. Leslie. Jour. Animal Ecol., 11 (1): 44-68, May, 1942.

Psychology

THE INFLUENCE OF MANUAL GUIDANCE UPON MAZE LEARNING. (EXPERIMENTS ON WHITE RATS.) Agustin S. Alonzo. Jour. Comp. Psych., vol.6, no.2, pp.143-157, 1926.

THE EFFECT OF QUANTITATIVE AND QUALITATIVE STUNTING UPON MAZE LEARNING IN THE WHITE RAT. John E. Anderson, Arthur H. Smith. Jour. Comp. Psych., vol.6, no.5, pp.337-359, 1926.

A STUDY OF DIRECTION TRENDS IN MAZE LEARNING OF WHITE RATS. John C. Bagwell. Jour. Elisha Mitchell Sci. Soc., vol.43, nos.1-2, pp.105-107, Nov. (Dec.), 1927.

(EXPERIMENTAL INVESTIGATIONS OF THE LEARNING PROCESS.) Experimentelle Untersuchungen ueber den Lernprozess. W. M. Borovski. Nr.5, Biol., Zentralblatt, vol.50, pp.566-572, 1930.

THE INFLUENCE OF THE LIGATION OF THE TWO COMMON CAROTID ARTERIES ON MAZE PERFORMANCE BY THE WHITE RAT. H. C. Chang, S. Y. Liu. Jour. Comp. Psych., vol.8, pp.71-74, 1928.

THE EFFECT OF TIME ON DISTANCE DISCRIMINATION IN THE ALBINO RAT. F. E. Clements. Jour. Comp. Psych., vol.8, pp.317-324, illus., 1928.

THE LEARNING BY WHITE RATS OF AN INCLINED PLANE MAZE. J. F. Dashiell, H. A. Helms. Jour. Comp. Psych., vol.5, pp.397-405, 1925.

FORM DISCRIMINATION IN THE WHITE RAT. P. E. Fields. Jour. Comp. Psych., vol.8, pp.143-158, illus., 1928.

THE WHITE RAT'S USE OF VISUAL STIMULI IN THE DISCRIMINATION OF GEOMETRICAL FIGURES. P. E. Fields. Jour. Comp. Psych., vol.9, pp.107-122, Feb., 1929.

THE DISCRIMINATION OF RELATIVE AND ABSOLUTE STIMULI BY ALBINO RATS. A. H. Gayton. Jour. Comp. Psych., vol.7, pp.93-105, 1 fig., 1927.

THE EFFECT OF ROTATING THE MAZE ON THE PERFORMANCE OF THE HOODED RAT. J. A. Gengerelli. Jour. Comp. Psych., vol.8, pp.377-384, 3 figs., Dec., 1928.

DISTURBANCE AND "INSIGHT" IN RATS. Charles M. Harsh. Univ. Calif. Publ. Physchol., vol.6, no.11, pp.163-168, fig.1, table 1, 1937.

VISUAL DISCRIMINATION OF MOVEMENT BY WHITE RATS. James H. Hawley, Norman L. Munn. Jour. Comp. Psych., vol.16, no.1, pp.137-141, Aug., 1933.

TRANSFER AND DEGREE OF INTEGRATION. (ALBINO RATS.) Y. H. Ho. Jour. Comp. Psych., vol.8, pp.87-99, 1928.

MAZE LEARNING IN RATS IN THE ABSENCE OF SPECIFIC INTRA-AND EXTRA-MAZE STIMULI. C. H. Honzik. Univ. Calif. Publ., Psych., vol.6, no.8, pp.99-144, figs.1-9, Oct.30, 1933.

EXPERIMENTS ON COLOR VISION IN MICE IN RELATION TO THE DUPLICITY THEORY. A. E. Hopkins. Zeitschr. f. Vergleich. Physiol., vol.6, pp.299-344, 15 figs., Oct.26, 1927.

VISION IN MICE WITH "RODLESS" RETINAE. A. E. Hopkins. Zeitschr. f. Vergleich. Physiol., vol.6, pp.345-360, 9 figs., Oct.26, 1927.

DISTANCE PERCEPTION IN MUS MUSCULUS. Milton Hopkins, Jr. Jour. Mam., vol.34, no.3, p.393, Aug.14, 1953.

NORMAL AND "RODLESS" RETINAE OF THE HOUSE MOUSE WITH RESPECT TO THE ELECTROMOTIVE FORCE GENERATED THROUGH STIMULATION BY LIGHT. Clyde E. Keeler, Evelyn Chaffee, E. L. Chaffee. Proc. Nat. Acad. Sci., vol.14, no.6, pp.477-484, pls.1-2, June, 1928.

STUDIES OF CEREBRAL FUNCTION IN LEARNING. VII. THE RELATION BETWEEN CEREBRAL MASS, LEARNING AND RETENTION. (WORK ON RATS.) K. S. Lashley. Jour. Comp. Neur., vol. 41, pp.1-58, illus., Aug.15, 1926.

SPINAL CONDUCTION AND KINESTHETIC SENSITIVITY IN THE MAZE HABIT. (WHITE RATS.) K. S. Lashley, J. Ball. Jour. Comp. Psych., vol.9, pp.71-105, 1 fig., 2 pls., Feb., 1929.

THE SURVIVAL OF THE MAZE AFTER CEREBELLAR INJURIES. (EXPERIMENTS ON WHITE RATS.) K.S. Lashley, Dorothea A. McCarthy. Jour. Comp. Psych., vol.6, no.6, pp.423-432, 1926.

NOTE ON ORIENTATION IN THE WHITE RAT. J. H. Leuba, V. Fain. Jour. Comp. Psych., vol.9, pp.239-244, 1 fig., June, 1929.

THE RELATION OF AGE TO THE LEARNING ABILITY OF THE WHITE RAT. S. Y. Liu. Jour. Comp. Psych., vol.8, pp.75-85, illus., 1928.

STUDIES OF ABNORMAL BEHAVIOR IN THE RAT. XIV. WATER SPRAY AS A MEANS OF INDUCING SEIZURES. N.R.F. Maier, R.S. Feldman. Jour. Comp. Psychol., Balto., vol.39, no.5, pp.275-286, 1946.

(CAN A DWARF MOUSE THINK?) Kan Dvaergmus (Mus minutus) taenke? Leo Novrup. Naturens, Verden, Bergen, Aarg. 24, no.2, pp.77-80, 1940.

"FREEZING" BEHAVIOR IN RATS AND ITS SOCIAL CAUSATION. Bernard F. Riess. Jour. Soc. Psychol., Worcester, vol.24, no.2, pp.249-251, 1946.

PRELIMINARY STUDY OF THE ABILITY OF THE ALBINO RAT TO DISCRIMINATE INCLINED PLANES. T. C. Ruch. Jour. Comp. Psych., vol.7, pp.405-423, illus., 1927.

CENTRAL INHIBITION IN THE ALBINO RAT. L. T. Spencer. Jour. Comp. Psych., vol.3, pp.389-408, 2 figs., 1923.

(ATTRACTING RATS WITH PIPE WHISTLES.) Ueber das Anlocken von Ratten durch Pfeiftoene. F. Steiniger. Zeitschr. Tierpsychol., 11 (1): 141-143, 1954. (English summary.)

THE CONGENITAL SEXUAL BEHAVIOR OF THE YOUNG MALE ALBINO RAT. Calvin P. Stone. Jour. Comp. Psychol., vol.2, pp.95-153, Apr. (May), 1922.

EFFECTS OF ELECTROCONVULSIVE SHOCK ON INNATE AND LEARNED BEHAVIOR IN ALBINO RATS. Calvin P. Stone. Science, Lancaster, vol.107, no. 2784, pp.459-460, May 7, 1948.

FURTHER STUDY OF SENSORY FUNCTIONS IN THE ACTIVATION OF SEXUAL BEHAVIOR IN THE YOUNG MALE ALBINO RAT. Calvin P. Stone. Jour. Comp. Psychol., vol.3, pp.469-473, 2 figs., 1923.

THE INITIAL COPULATORY RESPONSE OF FEMALE RATS REARED IN ISOLATION FROM THE AGE OF TWENTY DAYS TO THE AGE OF PUBERTY. Calvin P. Stone. Jour. Comp. Psychol., vol.6, no.1, pp.73-83, 1926.

A NOTE ON "FEMININE" BEHAVIOR IN ADULT MALE RATS. Calvin P. Stone. Amer. Jour. Physiol., vol.68, pp.39-41, 1924.

MATERNAL BEHAVIOR IN THE ALBINO RAT. M. Sturman-Hulbe, C. P. Stone.

Jour. Comp. Psych., vol.9, pp.203-327, 8 figs., June, 1929.

A NOTE ON THE CORRELATIONS BETWEEN TWO MAZES. (EXPERIMENTS ON WHITE RATS.) Edward C. Tolman, Frank C. Davis. Jour. Comp. Psychol., vol.4, pp.125-135, 1924.

THE RELATIVE STRENGTH OF SEX AND HUNGER MOTIVES IN THE ALBINO RAT. Chiao Tsai. Jour. Comp. Psychol., vol.5, pp.407-415, 1925.

VISUAL PERCEPTION IN THE WHITE RAT. W. L. Valentine. Jour. Comp. Psychol., vol.8, pp.369-375, fig., Dec., 1928.

THE RELATIVE VALUE OF REWARD AND PUNISHMENT IN THE FORMATION OF A VISUAL DISCRIMINATION HABIT IN THE WHITE RAT. C. J. Warden, M. Aylesworth. Jour. Comp. Psychol., vol.7, pp. 117-127, illus., 1927.

THE EFFECT OF SHORT INTERVALS OF DELAY IN FEEDING UPON SPEED OF MAZE LEARNING. (WHITE RATS.) C. J. Warden, E. L. Haas. Jour. Comp. Psych., vol.7, pp.107-116, illus., 1927.

A STUDY OF HUNGER BEHAVIOR IN THE WHITE RAT BY MEANS OF THE OBSTRUCTION METHOD. A COMPARISON OF SEX AND HUNGER BEHAVIOR. L. H. Warner. Jour. Comp. Psych., vol.8, pp.273-299, illus., 1928.

HUNGER AND SPEED OF RUNNING AS FACTORS IN MAZE LEARNING IN MICE. Margaret Floy Washburn. Jour. Comp. Psychol., vol.6, no.2, pp.181-187, 1926.

KINAESTHETIC AND ORGANIC SENSATIONS: THEIR ROLE IN THE REACTIONS OF THE WHITE RAT TO THE MAZE. John B. Watson. Psychol. Review, Monogr. Suppl., Lancaster, vol.8, no.2, pp.100, May, 1907.

THE ROLE OF VISION IN THE MENTAL LIFE OF THE MOUSE. Karl T. Waugh. Jour. Neurol. Psychol., vol.20, no.6, pp. 549-599, Dec., 1910.

A NOTE ON THE ELIMINATION OF SHORT AND LONG BLIND ALLEYS. (STUDY OF LEARNING PROCESS IN RATS.) Alfred E. White, Edward C. Tolman. Jour. Comp. Psychol., vol.3, pp.327-331, 1 fig., 1923.

A NOTE ON A RIGHT OR LEFT GOING POSITION HABIT WITH RATS. J. G. Yoshioka. Jour. Comp. Psychol., vol.8, pp.429-433, 1 fig., Dec., 1928.

(USE OF A TOOL BY A PYGMY MOUSE.) Werkzeug-Benutzung durch eine Zwergmaus. Klaus Zimmermann. Zeitschr. Tierpsychol. Berlin, vol.9, no.1, p.12, 1952.

STUDIES IN SOMESTHESIS. I. ROLE OF THE SOMESTHETIC CORTEX IN ROUGHNESS DISCRIMINATION IN THE RAT. John P. Zubek. Jour. Comp. Phys., Psychol., Balto., vol.44, no.4, pp.339-353, illus., Aug., 1951.

## Reproductive Biology

NUMBER OF YOUNG OF LONG-TAILED TREE-MOUSE VANDELURIA OLERACEA. H. G. Acharya. Jour. Bombay Nat. Hist. Soc., vol.40, no.4, p.739, May, 1939.

THE OESTROUS CYCLE IN THE MOUSE. Edgar Allen. Amer. Jour. Anatomy, vol. 30, no.3, pp.297-348, pls.1-11, May, 1922.

AUTOCESAREAN SECTION IN A MOUSE. J. F. Baldwin. Jour. Amer. Med. Ass., vol.80, p.128, Jan.13, 1923.

REPRODUCTION AND GROWTH OF MICE OF THREE STRAINS, AFTER TRANSFER TO $-3^{o}$C. S. A. Barnett, Brenda M. Manly. Jour. Exper. Biol., 33 (2): 325-329, June, 1956.

DIURNAL VARIATIONS IN THE MATING BEHAVIOR OF MALE RATS. Frank A. Beach, Gilbert Levinson. Proc. Soc. Exper. Biol. Med., Utica, vol.72, no.1, pp.78-80, 1949.

PREGNANCY RATES IN TWO DIFFERENT SAMPLES OF BROWN RATS. Kurt Becker. Jour. Mam., 35 (1): 119-121, Feb., 1954.

THE ATTAINMENT OF SEXUAL MATURITY IN THE FEMALE RAT. Richard J. Blandau. (Abstract.) Anat. Record, Phila., vol.82, no.3, p.401, Mar.25, 1942.

THE ATTAINMENT OF SEXUAL MATURITY IN THE FEMALE ALBINO RATS AS DETERMINED BY THE COPULATORY RESPONSE. Richard J. Blandau, William L. Money. Anat. Record, Phila., vol.86, no.2, pp.197-215, fig.1, June, 1943.

ON THE FACTORS INVOLVED IN SPERM TRANSPORT THROUGH THE CERVIX UTERI OF THE ALBINO RAT. Richard J. Blandau. Amer. Jour. Anat., Phila., vol.77, no.2, pp.253-272, fig.1, Sept., 1945.

FACTORS UNDERLYING THE FAILURE OF CYCLIC MATING BEHAVIOR IN THE ALBINO RAT. John L. Boling, Richard J. Blandau, Brewster Rundlett, William C. Young. Anat. Record, Phila., vol.80, no. 2, pp.155-170, pl.1, June 25, 1941.

GROWTH OF THE GRAAFIAN FOLLICLE AND THE TIME OF OVULATION IN THE ALBINO RAT. John Boling, Richard J. Blandau, Arnold L. Soderwall, William C. Young. Anat. Record, Phila., vol.79, no. 3, pp.313-331, 2 pls., Mar.25, 1941.

ABSTRACT OF A TALK ON YOUNG OF THE SPINY MOUSE. J. Lewis Bonhote. Proc. Zool. Soc. Lond., pp.5-6, 1911.

(ON THE REPRODUCTION AND GROWTH OF CRICETOMYS GAMBIANUS.) Sur le reproduction et la croissance de Cricetomys gambianus. F. Bourliere. Terre et Vie, 1948: 65-68, pl.4, 1948.

REPRODUCTION OF THE MULTIMAMMATE MOUSE (MASTOMYS ERYTHROLECUS TEMM.) OF SIERRA LEONE. F. W. Brambell, D.H.S. Davis. Proc. Zool. Soc. Lond., vol.111, ser.B, pts.1-2, pp.1-11, figs.2, pls.2, Oct., 1941.

BREEDING RATES OF DOMESTIC RATS TRAPPED IN LAGOS, NIGERIA, AND CERTAIN OTHER COUNTRIES. P. A. Buxton. Jour. Anim. Ecol., vol.5, no.1, pp.53-66, May, 1936.

THE MAMMARY GLAND OF THE MOUSE, DURING THE OESTROUS CYCLE, PREGNANCY AND LACTATION. H. A. Cole. Proc. Roy. Soc. Lond., ser.B., vol.114, no.B 787, pp.136-161, figs.28, pls.9-14, Dec.1, 1933.

MATING DURING PREGNANCY IN THE MOUSE. F.A.E. Crew, L. Miskala. Nature, London, vol.125, no.3154, p.564, Apr.12, 1930.

A COMPARISON OF REPRODUCTIVE POTENTIAL OF TWO RAT POPULATIONS. David E. Davis. Ecology, Brooklyn, vol. 32, no.3, pp.469-475, July, 1951.

THE WEIGHT OF WILD BROWN RATS AT SEXUAL MATURITY. David E. Davis. Jour. Mam., Balto., vol.30, no.2, pp.125-130, fig.1, illus., May 23, 1949.

THE SEASONAL REPRODUCTIVE CONDITION OF MALE BROWN RATS IN BALTIMORE, MARYLAND. David E. Davis, Octavia Hall. Physiol. Zool., Chicago, vol.21, no.3, pp.272-282, July, 1948.

THE SEASONAL REPRODUCTIVE CONDITION OF FEMALE NORWAY (BROWN) RATS IN BALTIMORE, MARYLAND. David E. Davis, Octavia Hall. Physiol. Zool., Chicago, vol.24, no.1, pp.9-20, illus., Jan., 1951.

REPRODUCTION RATE IN WILD RATS. Paul Eaton, C. S. Stirrett. Science, n.s., vol.67, pp.555-556, June 1, 1928.

DETERMINATION OF REPRODUCTIVE RATES IN RAT POPULATIONS BY EXAMINATION OF CARCASSES. J. T. Emlen, Jr., David E. Davis. Physiol. Zool., Chicago, vol.21, no.1, pp.59-65, Jan., 1948.

THE AGE OF THE ALBINO MOUSE AT NORMAL SEXUAL MATURITY. Earl T. Engle, John Rosasco. Anat. Record, vol. 36, pp.383-388, Oct.25, 1927.

A STUDY OF THE EFFECT OF HETEROZYGOSIS ON LITTER SIZE IN THE MOUSE MUS MUSCULUS. Paulinus F. Forsthoefel. Ohio Jour. Sci., vol.54, no.2, pp.135-141, Mar., 1954.

(THE BREEDING AND CAPTIVITY BIOLOGY OF THE PYGMY MOUSE (MICROMYS MINUTUS SUBOBSCURUS FRITSCHE).) Zucht und Gefangenschafts-Biologie der Zwergmaus (Micromys minutus subobscurus Fritsche). Fritz Frank. Zeitschr. Saeugetierk., 22 (1-2): 1-44, pl.1, 1957.

BREEDING HABITS IN CAPTIVITY OF MUS BACTRIANUS BLYTH. C. V. Green. Jour. Mam., vol.13, no.1, pp.45-47, Feb., 1932.

MOONLIGHT AND THE PREGNANCY OF MALAYAN FOREST RATS. J. L. Harrison. Nature, 170 (4315): 73-74, July 12, 1952.

THE MOONLIGHT EFFECT ON RAT BREEDING. J. L. Harrison. Bull. Raffles Mus. No.25, pp.166-170, Dec., 1954.

REPRODUCTION IN RATS OF THE SUBGENUS RATTUS. J. L. Harrison. Proc. Zool. Soc. Lond., 121 (3): 673-694, graphs, Nov., 1951.

OBSERVATIONS ON THE SEXUAL CYCLE OF THE WHITE RAT. O. Ishii. Anat. Record, vol.23, pp.311-314, May, 1922.

SOME ANOMALIES IN THE GESTATION OF THE ALBINO RAT (MUS NORVEGICUS ALBINUS). Helen Dean King. Biol. Bull., vol.24, no.6, pp.377-391, May, 1913.

THE REPRODUCTION OF THE HOUSE-MOUSE (MUS MUSCULUS) LIVING IN DIFFERENT ENVIRONMENTS. E. M. O. Laurie. Proc. Roy. Soc. Ser.B, Biol. Sci., 133 (872): 248-281, Aug., 1946.

THE FERTILITY AND POPULATION STRUCTURE OF THE BROWN RAT (RATTUS NORVEGICUS) IN CORN-RICKS AND SOME OTHER HABITATS. P. H. Leslie, Ursula M. Venables, L.S.V. Venables. Proc. Zool. Soc. Lond., 122 (1): 187-238, May, 1952.

NOTES ON THE NESTING AND BREEDING HABITS OF THE HOUSE BUILDING RAT (CONILURUS CONDITOR) AND BANFIELD RAT (UROMYS BANFIELDI). A. S. Le Souef. Australian Zoologist, vol.3, pp.15-16, 2 pls.

PRELIMINARY REPORT ON A SPECIES CROSS IN RODENTS MUS MUSCULUS X MUS WAGNERI. Clarence Cook Little. Michigan Acad. Sci. Arts, Letters, Papers, vol.8, pp.393-399, 1928.

BREEDING EXPERIMENTS OF WHITE RATS AND MICE, V. FURTHER DATA ON BREEDING RATS WITH DESCRIPTIONS OF SIXTEEN RAT STRAINS. S. Makino, K. Kano, M. Takahashi. Misc. Repts. Yamashina's Inst. Ornithol. and Zool., Tokyo, no.6, pp.22-29, June, 1955. (In Japanese, with English summary.)

A STRAIN OF WISTAR ALBINOS PRODUCING A LARGE LITTER. S. Makino, K. Kano, Masaaki Takahashi. Misc. Repts. Yamashina's Inst. Ornithol. and Zool., Tokyo, no.3, pp.47-50, Dec., 1953. (In Japanese, with English summary.)

STUDIES ON REPRODUCTION IN THE ALBINO MOUSE. Hugo Merton. Proc. Roy. Soc. Edinburgh, vol.58, pt.1, pp. 80-96, 1937-1938.

BREEDING EXPERIMENTS WITH RATS. T. H. Morgan. Amer. Nat., vol.18, pp. 182-185, Mar., 1909.

THE REPRODUCTION OF THE WILD BROWN RAT (RATTUS NORVEGICUS ERXLEBEN). J. S. Perry. Proc. Zool. Soc. Lond., vol.115, pts.1, 2, pp.19-46, figs.7, Oct., 1945.

BREEDING OF THE HARVEST MOUSE IN CAPTIVITY. Frances Pitt. Nature, Lond., vol.155, no.3945, p.700, June 9, 1945.

(RESEARCH ON SEASONAL VARIATIONS IN THE GENITAL ACTIVITY OF FIELD MICE (APODEMUS SYLVATICUS L.) OF THE DEPARTMENT OF FARN.) Recherches sur les variations saisonnières de l'activité génitale des mulots (Apodemus sylvaticus L.) du Département du Farn.

Albert Raynaud. Bull. Soc. Hist. Nat. Toulouse, vol.86, pp.133-150, 1951.

THE REPRODUCTIVE POTENTIAL OF RATS. James Silver. Jour. Mam., vol. 5, no.1, pp.66-67, Feb., 1924.

LACTATION VS. IMPROVED GROWTH IN STOCK ALBINO RATS. Arthur H. Smith, William E. Anderson. Science, n.s., vol. 70, pp.98-99, July 26, 1929.

REPRODUCTION IN THE HOUSE MOUSE, MUS MUSCULUS L., IN MISSISSIPPI. William W. Smith. Jour. Mam., vol.35, no.4, pp.509-515, Nov.29, 1954.

GROWTH AND REPRODUCTION OF RATS FED ARMY COMBAT RATIONS. Eugene Sporn, C. A. Elvehjem. Jour. Nutrition, Phila., vol.35, no.5, pp.549-558, May 10, 1948.

MATERIAL ON THE REPRODUCTIVE BIOLOGY OF RATS AND MICE AT BATUMI. I. V. Stepanov. Bull. Moscow Soc. Nat., 51 (6): 29-35, 4 figs., 1946.

STUDIES ON RAT REPRODUCTION IN SAN FRANCISCO. Tracy I. Storer, David E. Davis. Jour. Mam., vol.34, no.3, pp.365-373, 6 tables, Aug.14, 1954.

A CASE OF PROBABLE SUPERFETATION IN A MOUSE. R. E. Stowell. Anat. Record, Phila., vol.81, no.2, pp.215-220, Oct.25, 1941.

DIETARY REQUIREMENTS FOR REPRODUCTION. XII. THE INEFFICIENCY OF THE LACTATING MOTHER (MUS NORWEGICUS ALBINUS) TO SECRETE VITAMIN B IN THE MILK AND THE RELATION OF SUCH PHENOMENON TO INFANT MORTALITY. Barnett Sure. Science, n.s., vol.66, pp.265-266, Sept.16, 1927.

AN EIGHTEENTH CENTURY JAPANESE GUIDE-BOOK ON MOUSE BREEDING. Mitosi Tokuda. Jour. Heredity, Wash., vol.26, no.12, pp.481-484, fig.1, frontispiece, Dec., 1935.

SOME OBSERVATIONS ON THE REPRODUCTION OF RATTUS RATTUS L. J. S. Watson. Proc. Zool. Soc. Lond., 120 (1): 1-12, May, 1950.

FREQUENCY DISTRIBUTION OF LITTER SIZE IN MICE. Lucy J. Watt. Jour. Mam., vol.15, no.3, pp.185-189, Aug., 1934.

BREEDING EXPERIMENTS OF WHITE RATS AND MICE, IV. T. H. Yosida, S. Makino. Misc. Repts. Yamashina's Inst. Ornithol. and Zool., Tokyo, no.5, pp.7-15 (185-193), Dec., 1954. (In Japanese.)

(CAN THE YELLOW-THROATED MOUSE AND THE WOOD MOUSE INTERBREED?) Sind Gelbhalsmaus und Waldmaus miteinander kreuzbar? K. Zimmermann. Zeitschr. Saeugetierk., 22 (3-4): 214-217, 1957.

THYMUS GLAND AND SEXUAL MATURITY IN RATS. Science, Lancaster, n.s., vol. 79, no.2054, p.8, May 11, 1934.

Rodenticides

RELATIONSHIP BETWEEN CHEMICAL STRUCTURE AND RAT REPELLENCY. E. Bellack, J. B. DeWitt, R. Treichler. Natl. Res. Council, Chem.-Biol. Coordination Cent. Rev. No.5, pt.2, pp.48-156, 1953.

SUSCEPTIBILITY OF RATTUS HAWAIIENSIS STONE TO WARFARIN. David D. Bonnet, Bertram Gross. Science, 118 (3054): 44-45, July 10, 1953.

CAGE TESTS WITH WARFARIN ON THE HAWAIIAN RAT, RATTUS HAWAIIENSIS STONE, AND THE HOUSE MOUSE, MUS MUSCULUS LINN., IN HAWAII. David D. Bonnet, Edward S.C. Mau, Bertram Gross. Public Health Rep., 66 (52): 1734-1737, illus., Dec., 1951.

EVALUATION RAT BAITS BY FIELD ACCEPTANCE TRIALS ON GUAM. Wilfred D. Crabb, Leon Otis Emik. Jour. Wildlife Mgt., Menasha, vol.10, no.2, pp.162-171, pl.13, Apr., 1946.

THE FORTIFICATION OF RED SQUILL (URGINEA MARITIMA) BY MEANS OF AN EXTRACT OF RED SQUILL. D. Glen Crabtree, Justus C. Ward, F. E. Garlough. Jour. Amer. Pharm. Assn., Sci. Ed., 31 (5): 142-144, May, 1942.

EFFECTS OF DDT DUSTING ON DOMESTIC RATS UNDER COLONY AND FIELD CONDITIONS. Jack E. Dent, Harvey B. Morlan, Elmer L. Hill. U.S. Public Health Repts., Wash., vol.64, no.21, pp. 666-671, May 27,1949.

RELATIONSHIP BETWEEN CHEMICAL STRUCTURE AND TOXIC ACTION ON RATS. J. B. DeWitt, E. Bellack, C. W. Klingensmith, J. C. Ward, R. Treichler. Nat. Res. Council, Chem-Biol. Coordination Cent. Rev. No.5, pt.1, pp.1-47, 1953.

COMPARATIVE ASSAYS OF RODENTICIDES ON WILD NORWAY RATS. II. ACCEPTANCE. Sally H. Dieke. Proc. Soc. Exper. Biol. Med., Utica, vol.69, no.593-597, 1948.

THE ACUTE TOXICITY OF THIOUREAS AND RELATED COMPOUNDS TO WILD AND DOMESTIC NORWAY RATS. Sally H. Dieke, George S. Allen, Curt P. Richter. Jour. Pharmacol. Exper. Therapeutics, vol.90, no.3, pp.260-270, July, 1947.

COMPARATIVE ASSAYS OF RODENTICIDES ON WILD NORWAY RATS. Sally H. Dieke, Curt P. Richter. Pub. Health Rep., 61 (19): 672-679, May 10, 1946.

EFFECTIVENESS OF VARIOUS RODENTICIDES ON POPULATIONS OF BROWN RATS IN BALTIMORE, MARYLAND. John T. Emlen, Jr. Allen W. Stokes. Amer. Jour. Hygiene, 45 (2): 254-257, Mar., 1947.

THE ABILITY OF RATS TO DISCRIMINATE BETWEEN DIETS OF VARYING DEGREES OF TOXICITY. Kurt W. Franke, Van R. Potter. Science, n.s., vol.83, no.2153, pp.330-332, fig.1, Apr.3, 1936.

BAIT SHYNESS TO ANTU IN WILD NORWAY RATS. T. B. Gaines, W. J. Hayes. Publ. Health Rep., 67 (3): 306-311, Mar., 1952.

EFFECT OF SODIUM FLUORACETATE (1080) IN POISONED RATS ON PLAGUE DIAGNOSIS PROCEDURES. I. Gratch, P. L. Purlia, M. L. Martin. U.S. Publ. Health Repts., Wash., vol.64, no.11, pp. 399-342, Mar.18, 1949.

RED SQUILL AS A RATICIDE. Dorr D. Green. Soap and Sanitary Chem., 20 (11): 101-102, 133, Nov., 1944.

CONTROL OF NORWAY RATS WITH RESIDUAL RODENTICIDE WARFARIN. Wayland J. Hayes, Jr., Thomas B. Gaines. U.S. Publ. Health Repts., Wash., vol.65, no.47, pp.1537-1555, Nov.24, 1950.

"TEN-EIGHTY", A WAR-PRODUCED RODENTICIDE. E. R. Kalmbach. Science, 102 (2644): 232-233, Aug.31, 1945.

COMPOUND 42, A NEW ANTICOAGULANT AS A RODENTICIDE. Carl H. Kreiger. Pests and Their Control, 17 (5): 24-28, May, 1949.

ACCIDENTAL CANINE THALLOTOXICOSIS AND DANGERS OF THALLIUM USED AS A RODENTICIDAL AGENT. Charles P. Larson, William N. Keller, J. D. Manges. Jour. Amer. Vet. Med. Assn., 95 (751): 486-489, Oct., 1939.

THE BACTERIOLOGICAL CLASSIFICATION OF THE PRINCIPAL CULTURES USED IN RAT AND MOUSE CONTROL IN GREAT BRITAIN. P. H. Leslie. Jour. Hygiene, 42 (5): 552-562, Oct., 1942.

AN INVESTIGATION OF THE RAT PEST PROBLEM IN QUEENSLAND CANEFIELDS: 3. LABORATORY EXPERIMENTS ON FOOD INTAKE AND TOXICITY. (RATTUS CONATUS.) W. A. McDougall. Queensland Jour. Agric. Sci., Brisbane, vol.1, no. 3, pp.1-32, fig.1, Sept., 1944.

NOTES ON RAT BAITS, RAT POISONS, AND RAT POPULATION. W. A. McDougall. Cane Growers' Quart. Bull., 6 (2): 36-38, Oct., 1938.

RATS AND POISON. N. Morrison. Field, London, vol.153, p.152, Jan.24, 1929.

RED-SQUILL POWDERS AS RATICIDES. J. C. Munch, James Silver, E. E. Horn. Tech. Bull.134, U.S. Dept. Agric., pp.1-36, pl.1, Nov., 1929; Jour. Amer. Pharmaceut. Assoc., vol.19, no.8, pp.837-840, pl.1, Aug., 1930.

(EXPERIENCES IN THE DESTRUCTION OF RATS BY THE USE OF SOME POISONS.) Experiences de destruction des rats au moyen de quelques poisons. S. I. Obolensky, N. Sokolov. Bull. Station Regionale Protectrice des Plantes a Leningrad, vol. 6, pt.3, pp.573-577, 1929. (In Russian.)

TESTING OF VARIOUS POISONS FOR THE EXTERMINATION OF RATS. S. I. Obolenskii, N. M. Sokolov. Zashchita Rastenii ot Vreditelei (Plant Protection), vol.7, nos. 4-6, pp.377-381, (1930) 1931. (In Russian.)

(THE REFUSAL OF BAIT CONTAINING SCILLA BY BROWN RATS AFTER REPEATED PRESENTATION.) Het weigeren van lokaas met scilla door bruine ratten bij herhaald aanbieden. A. J. Ophof, H. de Vries. Verslag and Mededeel, Plantenziektenk, Dienst, Wageningen, 127: 211-215, 1955.

USE OF 'KRUISID-TzNIDI' FOR POISONING BROWN RATS. A. A. Paseshnik. Trans. Cent. Disinfection Inst. (Moscow), 1944 (2): 90-94, 1946.

BIOLOGICAL FACTORS INVOLVED IN POISONING RATS WITH ALPHANAPHTHYL THIOUREA (ANTU). Curt P. Richter. Proc. Soc. Exper. Biol. Med., Utica, vol. 63, no.2, pp.364-372, fig.1, Nov., 1946.

THE DEVELOPMENT AND USE OF ALPHA-NAPHTHYL THIOUREA (ANTU) AS A RAT POISON. Curt P. Richter. Jour. Amer. Med. Assn., 129 (14): 927-931, Dec.1, 1945.

INSTRUCTIONS FOR USING ANTU AS A POISON FOR THE COMMON NORWAY RAT. Curt P. Richter, John T. Emlen, Jr. U.S. Publ. Health Repts., Wash., vol.61, no.17, pp.602-607, Apr.26, 1946.

BAIT SHYNESS, A STUDY IN RAT BEHAVIOUR. Julian Rzoska. Brit. Jour. Anim. Behaviour, 1 (4): 128-135, 1953.

THE DEVELOPMENT OF BAITS FOR RATTUS NORVEGICUS, WITH SPECIAL REFERENCE TO INITIAL ACCEPTABILITY. Harlan R. Shuyler. Ph.D. thesis, Purdue Univ., 594 pp., 1954.

RED-SQUILL POWDER IN RAT CONTROL. James Silver, J. C. Munch. U.S. Dept. Agric. Leaflet no.65, pp.8, figs.2, Jan., 1931.

EMETIC AGENT IN TOXIC RAT BAIT, A SAFEGUARD. H. J. Spencer. USDI, F&WS, Wildlife Leaflet 264, 5 pp., Dec., 1944.

(THE EXECUTION OF SO-CALLED "UP-AND DOWN" OR "LADDER" TESTS IN THE INVESTIGATION OF ANTI-RAT POISONS.) Het uitvoreren van zg. "op-en-neer-proeven" of "ladderproeven" bij onderzoek van vergiften tegen ratten. P.M.L. Tammes, H. de Vries. Verslag and Mededeel. Plantenziektenk, Dienst, Wageningen, 127: 216-223, 1955.

THE TOXICITY OF METHALLYL CHLORIDE AND METHYL BROMIDE TOWARDS WHITE RATS. N. Vantiel. Jour. Hygiene, London, vol.46, no.2, pp.217-221, July, 1948.

RODENTICIDES--PRESENT AND FUTURE. Justus C. Ward. Soap and Sanitary Chem., 21 (9): 117, 119, 127, Sept., 1945.

FACTS ABOUT ANTU. USDI, F&WS, Wildlife, Leaflet, 288, 2 pp., May, 1946.

FACTS ABOUT 1080. USDI, F&WS, Wildlife Leaflet 287, 2 pp., May, 1946.

RATS. DEADLY NEW POISONS JOIN THE FIGHT ON MANKIND'S MOST PERSISTENT PEST. Sci. Illus., New York, vol.1, no.1, pp.100-104, illus., Apr., 1946.

Sex and Age Ratios

THE STRUCTURE OF BOWMAN'S CAPSULE AS AN INDEX OF AGE AND SEX VARIATIONS IN NORMAL MICE. Charlotte Crabtree. Anat. Record, Phila., vol.79, no.3, pp.395-413, Mar.25, 1941.

AN ATTEMPT TO DISTURB THE SEX RATIO IN THE MOUSE BY THE CONTINUED ADMINISTRATION OF ALCOHOL TO THE MALE PARENT. F.A.E. Crew. Proc. Roy. Phys. Soc., Edinburgh, vol.21, pt.2, pp.89-96, Dec., 1926.

ALCOHOL AND THE SEX RATIO IN MICE. C. H. Danforth. Soc. Exper. Biol. Med. Proc., vol.23, pp.305-308, 1926.

DATA ON THE PRIMARY SEX RATIO IN THE MOUSE. E. C. MacDowell, E. M. Lord. Anat. Record, vol.31, pp.143-148, Oct.25, 1925.

THE RELATION OF SEX RATIO TO PHYSIOLOGICAL AGE IN THE WILD BROWN RAT. Martin W. Schein. Amer. Naturalist, Lancaster, vol.84, no.819, pp.489-496, Nov.-Dec., 1950.

MALE INFLUENCE ON SEX RATIO OF OFFSPRING IN HIGH AND LOW BLOOD-pH LINES OF MICE. J. A. Weir. Jour. Heredity, vol.46, no.6, pp.277-283, Dec., 1955.

Taxonomy

BIOSTATISTICAL RESEARCH ON RATTUS LOSEA (SWINHOE, 1870), A FORMOSAN WILD RAT, WITH SPECIAL REFERENCE TO ITS DIAGNOSTIC CHARACTERS FOR TAXONOMY. Bunichiro Aoki, Ryo Tanaka. Mem. Fac. Sci. and Agric., Taihoku Imp. Univ. Formosa, vol.23, no.1, pp.1-74, figs.14, tables 13, July, 1938.

(CONTRIBUTIONS TO THE SYSTEMATICS AND DISTRIBUTION OF WOOD MICE OF THE "SOCIALIS" GROUP.) A. M. Argiropulo. Acad. Sci. USSR, Caucasian Br. Papers Zool. Sci., vol.1, pp.165-174, 1934. (In Russian with German summary.)

REMARKS ON THE SYSTEMATICS OF THE DOMESTIC MOUSE. (MUS MUSCULUS L.) (MAMMALIA.) A. I. Argiropulo. Trav. Inst. zool. Acad. Sci. de URSS, Leningrad, vol.1, pp.223-228 (1932), 1933. (In Russian, with German diagnoses.)

SYSTEMATIC POSITION OF THE TURKESTAN RAT. (RATTUS TURKESTANICUS SAT.) A. I. Argiropulo. Comptes Rendus Acad. Sci. URSS., A., no.22, pp.465-466, 1928.

ON THE MUS ORTHODON OF HENSEL. G.E.H. Barrett-Hamilton. Ann. and Mag. Nat. Hist., ser.7, vol.16, pp.452-453, Oct., 1905.

AN EXTENDED DESCRIPTION OF PSEUDOMYS NOVAE-HOLLANDIAE, WITH REMARKS ON ITS AFFINITY TO P. HERMANNSBURGENSIS. C. W. Brazenor. Mem. Nat. Mus. Melbourne, no.9, pp.9-13, pl.2, Nov., 1936.

A REVISION OF THE AUSTRALIAN JERBOA MICE. C. W. Brazenor. Mem. Nat. Mus. Melbourne, no.8, pp.74-89, figs.3, Sept., 1934.

(THE IMPORTANCE OF ANATOMICAL INVESTIGATION FOR SYSTEMATICS.) Het belang van antomisch onderzoek voor de systematiek. L. D. Brongersma. E. J. Brill, Leiden, pp.1-11, 1938.

(NOMENCLATURE RECTIFICATION.) Rectification de nomenclatura. (Rattus rattus sueirensis, new name for R. r. chionogaster Cabrera, 1921, not of Loennberg, 1916.) Angel Cabrera. Bol. R, Soc. Española Hist. Nat., vol.21, p. 159, July 25, 1921.

ON SOME FORMS OF MUS MUSCULUS LINN., WITH DESCRIPTION OF A NEW SUBSPECIES FROM THE FAROE ISLANDS. William Eagle Clarke. Proc. Roy. Phys. Soc. Edinburgh, Sess.1903-1904, vol.15, pt.2, pp.160-167, 1904.

ON THE MURIDAE OF THE NORTHERN BOUNDARY SURVEY, WITH A CRITICAL REVISION OF THE NORTH AMERICAN GENERA AND SPECIES. Elliott Coues. Proc. Acad. Nat. Sci. Phila., vol.18, pt.3, pp.3-28, Feb., 1875.

AMMOMYS BP., AS A VALID SUBGENUS WITH SOME REMARKS ABOUT ITS SYSTEMATICAL POSITION. J. Ehik. Ann. Musei Nat. Hungarici, vol.22, pp. 124-126, Oct., 1925.

(ON THE MORPHOLOGY OF THE MOLARS AND THE SYSTEMATIC POSITION OF RODENTS OF THE OTOMYINAE GROUP.) Sur la morphologie des molaires et la position systematique des rongeurs du groupe des Otomyinae. Madeleine Friant. Ann. Soc. Roy. Zool. Belgique, vol.83, fasc.2, pp.195-199, 1952.

APODEMUS SYLVATICUS SPADIX SSP. NOV. Karl Fritsche. Zeitschr. f. Saeugetierkunde, vol.9, nos.1-3, pp.435-436, Dec.30, 1934.

MUS MUSCULUS SUBCAERULEUS SSP. N. K. Fritsche. Zeitschrift f. Saeugetierkunde, vol.3, pp.307-308, June 11, 1928.

ON THE SPECIFIC DISTINCTION OF MUS GIGANTEUS, HARDW., AND MUS SETIFER, HORSF. J. E. Gray. Proc. Comm. Sci. and Corres. Zool. Soc., Lond., pt.2, pp.40-41, 1832.

SYNOPSIS OF THE SPECIES OF SACCOMYINAE, OR POUCHED MICE, IN THE COLLECTION OF THE BRITISH MUSEUM. J. E. Gray. Proc. Zool. Soc. Lond., pp.199-206, 1868.

SYSTEMATIC CHARACTERS OF MUS MUSCULUS HORTULANUS NORDM. G. I. Gulij. Bull. North Caucas. Plant Prot. Station, vol.5, pp.105-128, 1930. ( In Russian, with German summary.)

ON THE ZOOLOGICAL POSITION OF THE ALBINO RAT. Shinkishi Hatai. Biol. Bull., Phila., vol.12, no.4, pp.266-273, figs.3, Mar., 1907.

TAXONOMIC NOTES CONCERNING ARVICANTHINE RODENTS. Robert T. Hatt. Amer. Mus. Novitates no.790, pp.4, Apr.10, 1935.

(ON THE NOMENCLATURE OF WOOD MICE.) Zur Nomenclatur der Waldmaeuse. Zeitschr. Saeugetierk., vol.17, no.3, pp. 160-161, Feb.19, 1953.

(ON THE SYSTEMATIC PLACE OF APODEMUS AGRARIUS PALLAS.) Zur Systematischen Stellung von Apodemus agrarius Pallas. W. Herold. Mitt. Zool. Mus. Berlin, 32 (1): 105-196, 1956.

NOTES ON THE GENUS CRICETOMYS, WITH DESCRIPTIONS OF FOUR NEW FORMS. Martin A. C. Hinton. Ann. and Mag. Nat. Hist., ser.9, vol.4, pp. 282-289, Oct., 1919.

THE GENERIC NAMES OF EPIMYS AND RATTUS. N. Hollister. Proc. Biol. Soc. Wash., vol.29, p.126, June 6, 1916.

THE TYPE SPECIES OF RATTUS. N. Hollister. Proc. Biol. Soc. Wash., vol. 29, pp.206-207, Sept.22, 1916.

COMMENTS ON THE TAXONOMIC STATUS OF APODEMUS PENINSULAE, WITH DESCRIPTION OF A NEW SUBSPECIES FROM NORTH CHINA. (NEW: A. P. SOWERBYI.) J. Knox Jones, Jr. Univ. Kansas Publ., Mus. Nat. Hist., 9 (9): 337-346, Aug.15, 1956.

A NECESSARY AMENDMENT TO THE DESCRIPTION OF TAUTATUS. C. Boden Kloss. Jour. Nat. Hist. Soc. Siam, vol.3, no.2, p.71, Feb.25, 1919.

A NEW NAME FOR MUS MICRODON, KLOSS. G. Boden Kloss. Jour. Fed. Malay States Mus., vol.5, no.4, p.223, Mar., 1915.

NOTES ON THE TYPE SPECIMENS OF SOME BURMESE AND HIMALAYAN RATS. C. Boden Kloss. Indian Mus., vol.13, pt.1, no.2, pp.5-10, Mar., 1917.

ON RATTUS BLYTHI KLOSS (MUS CINNAMOMEUS BLYTH). C. Boden Kloss. With remarks on allied forms. Jour. Nat. Hist. Soc. Siam, vol.4, pp.65-69, Mar., 1921.

NOTE ON THE TYPE SPECIMEN OF THE MAORI RAT. R. R. Marples. Trans. Royal Soc. New Zealand, vol.82, pt.3, pp.703-704, Nov., 1954.

(COMPARATIVE AND SYSTEMATIC CHROMOSOME CYTOLOGY OF THE MURIDAE.) Cytologie chromosomique comparée et systématique des Muridae. Robert Matthey. Mammalia, Paris, vol. 20, no.2, pp.93-123, illus., June, 1956.

(A NEW PHLOEOMYS SPECIES.) Eine neue Phloeomys-art. A. B. Meyer. Abhandl. Ber. K. Zool. Anthropol. Ethno. Mus. Dresden, no.6, pp.1-2, 1894.

COMPARISON OF A SPECIMEN WITH THE TYPE OF EPIMYS LEPIDUS. Gerrit S. Miller, Jr. Jour. Nat. Hist. Soc., Siam, vol.3, p.61, Feb.25, 1919.

THE GENERIC NAME OF THE HOUSE-RATS. Gerrit S. Miller, Jr. Proc. Biol. Soc., Wash., vol.23, pp.57-60, Apr.19, 1910.

A NEW NAME FOR MUS ATRATUS MILLER. Gerrit S. Miller, Jr. Proc. Biol. Soc., Wash., vol.16, p.50, Mar.19, 1903.

A NEW NAME FOR MUS OBSCURUS MILLER. Gerrit S. Miller, Jr. Proc. Biol. Soc., Wash., vol.14, p.178, Sept.25, 1901.

NOTE ON THE MUS COMMISSARIUS OF MEARNS. Gerrit S. Miller, Jr. Proc. Biol. Soc., Wash., vol.24, p.38, Feb.24, 1911.

NOTES ON TYPE OF MUS MULLERI. Gerrit S. Miller, Jr. Proc. U.S. Nat. Mus., vol.34, no.1626, pp.646-647, Sept.14, 1908.

TWO NEW GENERA OF MURINE RODENTS. Gerrit S. Miller, Jr. Smithsonian Misc. Coll., vol.52, pp.497-498, Jan.12, 1910.

(ON THE FORMENKREIS OF MUS MUSCULUS L.) Vom "Formenkreis" des Mus musculus L. Erna Mohr, George Duncker. Zoologische Jahrbuecher, vol.59, pp.65-72, 1930.

THE IDENTITY OF ACOMYS MEGALOTIS (LICHTENSTEIN), DESCRIBED FROM ARABIA. (A SYNONYM OF ACOMYS DIMIDIATUS (CRETZ).) T.C.S. Morrison-Scott. Ann. Mag. Nat. Hist., Lond., ser. 11, vol.3, no.14, pp.238-240, Feb., 1939.

(ON NESOKIA BACHERI N. SP.) Ueber Nesokia Bacheri n. sp. A. Nehring. Zool. Anzeiger, Leipzig, vol.20, no.547, pp. 503-505, Dec.13, 1897.

(A NESOKIA SPECIES FROM THE MERW OASIS AND ONE FROM THE NOAB COUNTRY.) Eine Nesokia-art aus der Oase Merw und eine solche aus dem Lande Moab. A. Nehring. Sitz. Ber. Gesell. Naturf. Freunde, Berlin, Jahrg.1899, no.7, pp.107-111, figs.2, July 18, 1899.

A NEW SUBSPECIES OF THE BLACK RAT (RATTUS RATTUS L.). RATTUS RATTUS RUTHENUS.) S. I. Ognev, S. U. Stroganov. Moscou Univ. Sbornik Nauchno-issledovatel'skogo inst. Zool. (Abstracts Works Zool. Inst. Moscou State Univ.), no.3, pp.82-84, 1936.

(A CRITICAL REVIEW OF THE PRESENT NOMENCLATURE OF INDONESIAN RATS.) Een critische beschouwing over de huidige nomenclatuur der Indische ratten. O.L.E. de Raadt. Zool. Mededeel. R. Mus. Nat. Hist., Leyden, vol.14, no.3, pp.184-189, Dec.31, 1931.

(THE IDENTITY OF RATTUS BUKIT BONHOTE.) De identiteit van Rattus bukit Bonhote. O.L.E. de Raadt. Zool. Mededeel., Leiden, vol.16, nos.1-2, p.30, Sept.1, 1933.

(THE NAMES OF RATS OCCURRING IN THE NETHERLANDS INDIES.) De namen der in Nederlandsch-Indiee voorkomende ratten. O.L.E. de Raadt. Zool. Mededeel., Leiden, vol.16, nos.1-2, pp. 31-32, Sept.1, 1933.

A NEW FOSSIL MASTACOMYS (MURIDAE) AND A REVISION OF THE GENUS. W.D.L. Ride. Proc. Zool. Soc. Lond., 127 (3): 431-439, Nov.29, 1956.

ON A COLLECTION OF RATS FROM THE INDO-MALAYAN AND INDO-AUSTRALIAN

REGIONS. H.J.V. Sody. Treubia, Buitenzorg, vol.18, pt.2, pp.255-325, Dec., 1941.

A BIOSTATISTICAL ANALYSIS OF APODEMUS AGRARIUS (PALLAS) FROM FORMOSA WITH SPECIAL REFERENCE TO ITS SYSTEMATIC CHARACTERS. Ryô Tanaka. Mem. Faculty Sci. Taihoku Imperial Univ., Taihoku, Formosa, vol.23, no.6, pp.211-285, figs.27, Sept., 1942.

COMPARATIVE ANALYSIS OF TWO SPECIES OF MUS FROM FORMOSA FROM THE STANDPOINT OF VARIATION-STATISTICS. Ryô Tanaka. Mem. Faculty Sci. Taihoku Imperial Univ., Taihoku, Formosa, ser.2, vol.1, no.1, pp.64, figs. 21, Apr., 1944.

A COMPARATIVE STUDY ON FORMOSAN RATS AND MICE OF FOUR SPECIES BELONGING TO THE GENERA, RATTUS, APODEMUS AND MUS FROM THE STANDPOINT OF VARIATION-STATISTICS. Ryô Tanaka. Mem. Faculty Sci. Taihoku Imperial Univ., Taihoku, Formosa, ser. 2, vol.1, no.2, pp.65-118, figs.6, July, 1944. (In Japanese with English summary.)

THE DISTRIBUTION AND GEOGRAPHICAL RACES OF THE GULANDI BUSH RATS. (GOLUNDA ELLIOTI.) Oldfield Thomas. Jour. Bombay Nat. Hist. Soc., vol.29, pp. 373-376, Aug.25, 1923.

DESCRIPTION OF A NEW GENUS OF MURIDAE ALLIED TO HYDROMYS. Oldfield Thomas. Proc. Zool. Soc. Lond., pp.247-250, pl.29 (May 7, 1889), 1890.

DESCRIPTION OF A NEW SPECIES OF ACOMYS. Oldfield Thomas. Ann. and Mag. Nat. Hist. (6), vol.10, no.55, p.22, July, 1892.

THE GENERIC ARRANGEMENT OF THE AUSTRALIAN MURINES HITHERTO REFERRED TO "MUS." Oldfield Thomas. Ann. and Mag. Nat. Hist. (8), vol.6, no. 36, pp.603-607, Dec., 1910.

THE GENERIC POSITION OF CERTAIN AFRICAN MURIDAE, HITHERTO REFERRED TO AETHOMYS AND PRAOMYS. Oldfield Thomas. Ann. and Mag. Nat. Hist., ser.9, vol.17, pp.174-179, Jan., 1926.

THE GENERIC POSITIONS OF "MUS" NIGRICAUDA, THOS., AND WOOSNAMI, SCHWANN. Oldfield Thomas. Ann. and Mag. Nat. Hist., ser.9, vol.5, pp.140-142, Jan., 1920.

A NEW POGONOMYS PRESENTED TO THE BRITISH MUSEUM BY SIR WILLIAM INGRAM. Oldfield Thomas. Ann. and Mag. Nat. Hist. (8), vol.2, no.12, pp. 495-496, Dec., 1908.

NOTE ON LIMNOMYS. Oldfield Thomas. Proc. Biol. Soc. Wash., vol.19, p.199, Dec.31, 1906.

NOTE ON MUS BURTONI, THOS. Oldfield Thomas. Ann. and Mag. Nat. Hist. (6), vol.13, no.74, pp.204-205, Feb., 1894.

NOTES ON SOME SPINY MICE (ACOMYS). (NEW FORMS FROM ADEN DISTRICT AND SOMALILAND.) Oldfield Thomas. Ann. and Mag. Nat. Hist., ser.9, vol.12, pp. 173-174, July, 1923.

NOTES ON THE GENUS LEGGADA. Oldfield Thomas. Jour. Bombay Nat. Hist. Soc., vol.22, no.4, p.682, Mar.31, 1914.

ON A NEW AND INTERESTING ANNECTENT GENUS OF MURIDAE, WITH REMARKS ON THE RELATION OF THE OLD- AND NEW-WORLD MEMBERS OF THE FAMILY. Oldfield Thomas. Proc. Zool. Soc., Lond., 1888, pp.130-135, pl.5, Feb. 21, 1888.

ON RATTUS AS A GENERIC NAME, WITH A NOTE ON THE NOMENCLATURE OF ECHIMYS AND LONCHERES. Oldfield Thomas. Ann. and Mag. Nat. Hist. (8), vol.18, no.103, pp.70-72, July, 1916.

ON SOME NEW FORMS OF OTOMYS. Oldfield Thomas. Ann. and Mag. Nat. Hist. (7), vol.10, no.58, pp.311-314, Oct., 1902.

ON THE GENERIC NAMES RATTUS AND PHYLLOMYS. Oldfield Thomas. Ann. and Mag. Nat. Hist. (8), vol.18, no.104, p.240, Aug., 1916.

ON THE RATS USUALLY INCLUDED IN THE GENUS ARVICANTHIS. Oldfield Thomas. Ann. and Mag. Nat. Hist. (8), vol.18, no.103, pp.67-70, July, 1916.

A REVISED CLASSIFICATION OF THE OTOMYINAE, WITH DESCRIPTION OF NEW GENERA AND SPECIES. Oldfield Thomas. Ann. and Mag. Nat. Hist. (9), vol.2, no.9, pp.203-211, Sept., 1918.

SCIENTIFIC RESULTS FROM THE MAMMAL SURVEY. XII. NOTES ON THE GENUS CREMNOMYS. Oldfield Thomas. Jour. Bombay Nat. Hist. Soc., vol.24, no. 2, pp.230-243, Jan.31, 1916.

SCIENTIFIC RESULTS OF THE MAMMAL SURVEY. VIII. NOTES ON VANDELEURIA. Oldfield Thomas. Jour. Bombay Nat. Hist. Soc., vol.23, no.2, pp.200-203, Nov.20, 1914.

SCIENTIFIC RESULTS FROM THE MAMMAL SURVEY. XVI. B. NOTES ON MILLARDIA AND ITS ALLIES. Oldfield Thomas. Jour. Bombay Nat. Hist. Soc., vol.25, pp.201-203, Sept.15, 1917.

SOME NEW SPECIES OF UROMYS. Oldfield Thomas. Ann. and Mag. Nat. Hist., (8), vol.12, no.68, pp.212-217, Aug., 1913.

A SUBDIVISION OF THE GENUS UROMYS. (NEW GENUS, MELOMYS, FOR UROMYS RUFESCENS AND ALLIED FORMS.) Oldfield Thomas. Ann. and Mag. Nat. Hist., ser.9, vol.9, pp.260-261, Mar., 1922.

A SUBDIVISION OF THE OLD GENUS NESOKIA, WITH DESCRIPTIONS OF THREE NEW MEMBERS OF THE GROUP AND OF A MUS FROM THE ANDAMANS. Oldfield Thomas. Ann. and Mag. Nat. Hist. (7), vol.20, no.117, pp.202-207, Sept., 1907.

TWO NEW FORMS OF LEGGADA. Oldfield Thomas. Ann. and Mag. Nat. Hist. (9), vol.2, no.12, pp.484-486, Dec., 1918.

TWO NEW JERBOA-RATS (NOTOMYS). Oldfield Thomas. Ann. and Mag. Nat. Hist. (9), vol.9, no.52, pp.315-317, Apr., 1922.

TWO NEW RATS OF THE RATTUS CONFUCIANUS GROUP. Oldfield Thomas. Ann. and Mag. Nat. Hist. (8), vol.20, pp. 198-200, Aug., 1917.

ON FIVE NEW RATS OF THE GENUS PSEUDOMYS. (PSEUDOMYS (PSEUDOMYS) MINNIE, P. (P.) RAWLINNAE, P. (LEGGADINA) WAITEI, P. HERMANNSBURGENSIS BOLAMI, P. (GYOMYS) DESERTOR.) Ellis LeG. Troughton. Records Australian Mus., vol.18, no.6, pp.287-294, Apr.20, 1932.

ON NEW FORMS OF THE EASTERN SWAMP RAT AND THE RELATIONSHIP OF MASTACOMYS. (NEW: RATTUS LUTREOLUS CAMBRICUS, R. L. IMBIL.) Ellis LeG. Troughton. Australian Zool. Sydney, vol.8, pt.4, pp.281-286, Mar.12, 1937.

A REDESCRIPTION OF SOLOMYS ("MUS") SALAMONIS RAMSAY. Ellis LeG. Troughton. Proc. Linnean Soc. New South Wales, vol.61, pts.3-4, pp.128-130, Sept.15, 1936.

A REVISION OF THE RATS OF THE GENUS LEPORILLUS AND THE STATUS OF HAPALOTIS PERSONATA KREFFT. Ellis LeG. Troughton. Records Australian Mus., vol.14, no.1, pp.23-41, pls.5-6, 1923.

THE STATUS OF "MUS" NOVAEHOLLANDIAE WATERHOUSE, AND ALLIED FORMS. Ellis LeG. Troughton. Records Australian Mus., Sydney, vol.20, no.2, pp.183-190, Aug.27, 1937.

AN ECCENTRIC RAT. (UROMYS BANFIELD MELOMYS CERVINIPES MELICUS, THOMAS.) de Vis. Annals of the Queensland Mus., no.7, pp.8-9.

AN EXTENDED DESCRIPTION OF MUS FUSCIPES, WATERHOUSE. E. R. Waite. Records Australian Mus., vol.3, no.7, pp.190-193, figs.4, June 15, 1900.

ON A NEW GENUS OF THE FAMILY MURIDAE AND ORDER RODENTIA. G. R. Waterhouse. Proc. Zool. Soc. Lond., pt. 8, p.1, 1840.

(NUMBER OF TAIL RINGS AS SPECIES CHARACTERISTIC IN APODEMUS SYLVATICUS L. AND FLAVICOLLIS MELCHIOR.) Zahl der Schwanzringe bei Apodemus sylvaticus L. und flavicollis Melchior als Artmerkmal. K. O. Wedemeyer. Zool. Anz., vol.113, nos.7-8, pp. 205-207, Feb.15, 1936.

NOTES ON SOME RATS OF THE MUS METTADA GROUP. R. C. Wroughton. Jour. Bombay Nat. Hist. Soc., vol.17, no. 4, pp.997-1000, June 29, 1907.

NOTES ON THE GENUS OTOMYS. R. C. Wroughton. Ann. Mag. Nat. Hist., ser.7, vol.18, pp.264-278, Oct., 1906.

NOTES ON THE VARIOUS FORMS OF ARVICANTHIS PUMILIO, SPARRM. R. C. Wroughton. Ann. Mag. Nat. Hist., ser.7, vol.16, pp.629-639, Dec., 1905.

THE GENERA LEGGADA AND MUS. R. C. Wroughton, Kathleen V. Ryley. Jour. Bombay Nat. Hist. Soc., vol.22, no.1, pp. 16-17, Apr.21, 1913.

GENERIC CLASSIFICATION OF THE INDIAN MURINAE. R. C. Wroughton, Kathleen V. Ryley. Jour. Bombay Nat. Hist. Soc., vol.22, no.1, pp.19-21, Apr.21, 1913.

Territoriality and Home Range

TERRITORIALITY IN WILD HOUSE MICE, MUS MUSCULUS L. Peter Crowcroft. Jour. Mam., 36 (2): 299-301, diagram, May, 1955.

STUDIES ON HOME RANGE IN THE BROWN RAT. David E. Davis, John T. Emlen, Jr., Allen W. Stokes. Jour. Mam., 29 (3): 207-225, Aug., 1948.

HOW FAR WILL A MOUSE TRAVEL TO A POISONED BAIT? John T. Emlen, Jr. Pest Control, 18 (8): 16-20, Aug., 1950.

(ON THE ABILITY TO RETURN HOME OF WOOD MICE MUS SYLVATICUS L.) Ueber die Heimkehrtaehigkeit von Waldmaeusen (Mus sylvaticus L.). Bastian Schmid. Zeitschr. f. Vergleich. Physiol., Berlin, vol.23, no.4, pp.592-604, figs.2, Sept.10, 1936.

MOVEMENT AND POPULATION OF THE BROWN RAT IN KOCHI CITY. Ryo Tanaka, Fumio Kawashima. Annot. Zool. Japon., 24 (4): 225-233, illus., Dec., 1951.

West Indies

RATS IN THE WEST INDIES. H. A. Ballou. Agricultural News, Barbados, vol.18, pp. 406-407, Dec.27, 1919.

(Review by G. S. Miller of) RATS IN THE WEST INDIES. H. A. Ballou. Jour. Mam., vol.1, no.4, pp.192-193, May, 1920.

DESCRIPTION OF A NEW HOUSE MOUSE FROM CUBA. (MUS MUSCULUS PERCNONOTUS.) Philip N. Moulthrop. Sci. Publ. Cleveland Mus. Nat. Hist., vol.5, no.5, pp.79-82, June 1, 1942.

Gliridae

(GEOGRAPHIC DISTRIBUTION OF ELIOMYS LUSITANICUS.) La distribucion geografica del Eliomys lusitanicus (reuv.). E. Morales Agacino. Bol. Soc. Española Hist. Nat., Madrid, vol.34, no.7, pp.389-392, fig.1, Nov.5, 1934.

A NEW GENUS AND A NEW SUBSPECIES OF AFRICAN DORMOUSE. (AETHOGLIS, A. HUETI ARGENTEUS.) Glover M. Allen. Jour. Mam., vol.17, no.3, pp.292-293, Aug., 1936.

THE DORMOUSE AT HOME. Grant Allen. Eng. Ill. Mag., pp.22-28, Oct., 1883.

(ON THE DORMOUSE (DRYOMYS NITEDULA OBOLENSKII OGN.) IN SOUTHERN RUSSIA.) Vom Baumschlaefer (Dryomys nitedula obolenskii Ogn.) in Suedrussland. Konrad Banz. Zeitschr. Saeugetierk., Berlin, vol.17, no.3, pp.153-155, Feb.19, 1953.

NOTE ON THE ELIOMYS OF SARDINIA. G.E.H. Barrett-Hamilton. Ann. and Mag. Nat. Hist., ser.7, vol.7, pp.340-341, Apr., 1901.

NOTE ON THE EUROPEAN DORMICE OF THE GENERA MUSCARDINUS AND GLIS. G.E.H. Barrett-Hamilton. Ann. and Mag. Nat. Hist., ser.7, vol.2, pp.423-426, Nov., 1898.

NOTE ON THE SICILIAN DORMICE OF THE GENERA ELIOMYS AND GLIS. G.E.H. Barrett-Hamilton. Ann. and Mag. Nat. Hist., ser.7, vol.3, pp.226-228, Mar., 1899.

ON THE GENUS MUSCARDINUS. G.E.H. Barrett-Hamilton. Proc. Zool. Soc. Lond., pp.85-87, Feb.6, 1900.

(SOME OBSERVATIONS ON DORMICE.) Einige Beobachtungen an Haselmaeusen. Hans Bast. Zeitschr. Fuer Saeugetierkunde, Berlin, vol.6, no.6, pp.239-240, fig.1, Dec.15, 1931.

(REMARKS ON THE DORMOUSE.) Bemerkungen ueber die Haselmaus. Oscar De Beaux. Zool. Garten, Leipzig, n.F., vol. 2, nos.10-12, pp.285-289, figs.4, Mar., 1930.

THE EDIBLE DORMOUSE: UNDESIRABLE ALIEN? Maurice Burton. Illus. London News, vol.218, no.5838, p.376, illus., Mar.10, 1951.

ON MUSCARDINIDAE FROM THE IBERIAN PENINSULA. Angel Cabrera. Ann. and Mag. Nat. Hist., ser.8, vol.1, pp.188-194, Feb., 1908.

(THE SPANISH SPECIES OF THE GENUS "ELIOMYS".) Las especies españolas del genero "Eliomys". Angel Cabrera. Bol. Real Soc. Española Hist. Nat., Madrid, vol.4, no.4, pp.180-188, illus., Apr., 1904.

(OBSERVATIONS ON DORMICE IN FRANCE.) Observations de muscardins en France. Doctor Duckert. Mammalia, Paris, vol.14, no.4, p.183, Dec., 1950.

(OBSERVATIONS ON THE HIBERNATION OF THE DORMOUSE (MUSCARDINUS AVELLANARIUS L.).) Beobachtungen ueber den Winterschlaf der Haselmaus (Muscardinus avellanarius L.). M. Eisentraut. Zeitschr. Saeugetierkunde, vol.4, nos.4-6, pp.213-239, 1 fig., Feb.10, 1930.

(THE DISTRIBUTION OF THE DORMOUSE (GLIRIDAE) IN MECKLENBURG.) Die Verbreitung der Bilche oder Schlaefer (Gliridae) in Mecklenburg. Albert Erhardt. Archiv. Ver. Freunde Naturgeschichte Mecklenburg, n.F., vol.9, 1934, pp.98-106, map, 1935.

(ON DORMICE, ELIOMYS QUERCINUS L., AND WEASELS, PUTORIUS NIVALIS L., IN MECKLENBURG.) Ueber Gartenschlaefer (Eliomys quercinus (L.) und Mauswiesel (Putorius nivalis (L.) in Mecklenburg. Albert Erhardt. Archiv Ver. Freunde Naturgeschichte Meckburg, n.F., vol.10, 1935, pp.97-99, 1936.

ON THE OCCURRENCE OF ELIOMYS QUERCINUS L. IN THE GOVERNMENT OF VLADIMIR. L. K. Esterberg. Zashchita Rastenii ot Vreditelei (Plant Protection), Leningrad, vol.6, nos.1-2, p.231, 1929. (In Russian.)

(MYOXUS DRYAS INTERMEDIUS NEHRING IN SWITZERLAND.) Le Myoxus Dryas, intermedius Nehring, en Suisse. Victor Fatio. Archiv. Sci. Phy. et Nat. Geneva, 110 annee, 4th période, vol.20, pp.586-598, (pp.7), Mélanges zoologiques Nov., 1905.

(MYOXUS INTERMEDIUS NEHRING IN THE ITALIAN ALPS.) Il Myoxus intermedius Nehring, nelle Alpi italiane. E. Festa. Boll. Mus. Zool. ed. anat. comp. R. Univ. Torine, vol.23, no.585, pp.3, May 23, 1908.

(OBSERVATIONS ON THE LIFE OF DORMICE (RODENTIA, MYOXIDAE) IN THE GOVERNMENT OF NIZHNIY NOVGOROD.) Observations sur la vie des loires (Rodentia Myoxidae) dans le gouvernement de Nijini Novgorod. A. Formozov. Ann. Mus. Zool. Acad. Sci., Union Socialistic Soviet Republics, pp.1-8, illus., 1926.

ON THE BIOLOGY OF THE COMMON DORMOUSE (MUSCARDINUS AVELLANARIUS L.) IN THE GOVERNMENT OF NIZHNIY NOVGOROD. A. Formozov. Mem. Mus. d'etat de la region industrielle centrale, Moscow, no.2, pp.14, illus., 1925. (In Russian, with English summary.)

(THE SYSTEMATIC POSITION OF THE LARGE EXTINCT RODENT OF THE ISLE OF MALTA, LEITHIA MELITENSIS LEITH-ADAMS.) Sur la position systematique du grand rongeur eteint de l'ile de Malte, Leithia melitensis Leith-Adams. Madeleine Friant. Proc. Zool. Soc. Lond., vol.121, pt.3, pp.695-701, figs.2, Nov.19, 1951.

(THE MYOXINES OF TICINO.) I Myoxidi ticinesi. Angelo Ghidini. Boll. Soc. ticinese Sci. Nat., Locarno, Anno 2, no. 3, pp.50-56, Aug., 1905.

A RECORD OF JAPANESE DORMOUSE (GLIRULUS JAPONICUS) FROM MT. JONEN, JAPAN. A. A. Hosono. Alps Trans. Mamm. Soc. Japan, no.8, p.68, Feb., 1954. (In Japanese, with English summary.)

THE DORMOUSE. Phyllis Kelway. Game and Gun and Angler's Monthly, London, vol.16, no.160, pp.33-36, illus., Jan., 1939.

(OBSERVATIONS ON HIBERNATING DORMICE.) Beobachtungen an winterschlafenden Haselmausen. Von Carl Klaas. Natur. und Volk, Frankfurt, a.M., vol.77, nos.10-12, pp.147-153, illus., Nov., 1947.

(ON THE EYE OF THE MYOXINES AND THE IMPORTANCE OF THE EYE AS A SPECIFIC CHARACTER.) Ueber das Auge der Myoxiden und die Bedeutung des Auges als spezifisches Merkmal. W. Kolmer. Anat. Anzeiger, vol.67, pp.156-158, 1 fig., Apr.20, 1929.

(OBSERVATIONS ON THE DORMOUSE (ELIOMYS QUERCINUS L.).) Beobachtungen am Gartenschlaefer (Eliomys quercinus L.). Hans Krieg. Zeitschr. fuer Saeugetierkunde, Berlin, vol.6, no.4, pp.137-142, figs.3, pl.8, Dec.15, 1931.

(REPRODUCTION AND NUMBER OF YOUNG IN THE TREE DORMOUSE.) Razmnozhenie i chislennost oreshnikovoi soni. G. N. Likhachev. Zool. Zhurnal, vol.33, no.4, pp.1171-1182, Sept.-Oct., 1954.

(DROP IN DORMOUSE POPULATION (GLIS GLIS GLIS LINNE 1758) IN 1954.) Vermehrungsausfall beim Siebenschlaefer, Glis glis glis (Linne, 1758), im jahr 1954. H. Loehrl. Saeugetierk. Mitteil., Stuttgart, 3 (4): 177, Oct.1, 1955.

ON AFFINITIES OF "SO-CALLED" EXTINCT GIANT DORMOUSE OF MALTA. Lydekker. Proc. Zool. Soc. Lond., pt.4, pp.860-863, 1898.

(THE DORMOUSE (GLIS GLIS (L.)) AND THE GARDEN DORMOUSE (ELIOMYS QUERCINUS (L.).) Sur le loir (Glis glis (L.)) et le lerot (Eliomys quercinus (L.)). M. P. Mathias. Bull. Mus. Nat. Hist. Nat., Paris, ser.2, vol.3, no.7, pp.602-605, Nov., 1931.

A NEW DORMOUSE FROM ITALY. Gerrit S. Miller, Jr. Proc. Biol. Soc., Wash., vol.14, pp.39-40, Apr.25, 1901.

(THE DORMOUSE (ELIOMYS QUERCINUS L.) IN CAPTIVITY.) Der Gartenschlaefer (Eliomys quercinus L.) in Gefangenshcaft. Erna Mohr. Zeitschr. f. Saeugetierkunde, vol.2, pp.144-148, illus., Apr.29, 1929.

(THE GERMAN DORMICE.) Die deutschen Schlafmaeuse. Erna Mohr. Der Naturforscher, Berlin, vol.16, nos.7-8, pp.224-229, Oct.-Nov., 1939.

(THE TAIL OF THE DORMICE.) Der Schwanz der Haselmaeuse. Erna Mohr. Zool. Anzeiger, Leipzig, 158 (11-12): 285-288, June, 1957.

(DISTRIBUTION OF ELIOMYS LUSITANICUS (REUV.).) La distribución del Eliomys lusitanicus (Reuv.). Agacino E. Morales. Bol. Soc. Española Hist. Nat., vol.34, no.7, pp.389-392, fig.1, Nov.5, 1934.

(THE DORMOUSE AS PET.) Die Siebenschlaefer als Hausgenosse. Elisabeth Naundorff. Zeitschr. f. Saeugetierkunde, Bd.4, heft 1, pp.54-56, 2 figs., July 6, 1929.

(CHARACTERISTICS OF THE MUSCULAR STRUCTURE OF THE LIMBS OF THE DESERT DORMOUSE.) Ob osobyennostyakh stroyeniya muskulatury konyechnostey pustynnoy soni Selevinia betpakdalensis Vasch. et Belosl. V. N. Nikolskaya. Zool. Zhurnal. Moscow, vol. 31, no.6, pp.940-943, 1952.

A NEW FORM OF DORMICE (ELIOMYS QUERCINUS). S. I. Ognev, S. U. Stroganov. Moscow Univ. Sbornik Nauchnoissledovatel'skogo inst. Zool. (Abstracts Works Zool. Moscow State Univ.), no.3, pp.84-85, 1936.

A REMARKABLE SMALL MAMMAL. S. I. Ognev. Nature and Sport in Ukraine (Kharkov), nos.1-2, pp.1-2 (of reprint), 1924. (In Russian.)

REVIEW OF THE DORMICE OF THE GENUS DYROMYS OF RUSSIAN FAUNA. S. I. Ognev, S. S. Turov. Wiss. Ber. Moskauer Staatsuniv., vol.4, pp.96-105, 1935. (In Russian.)

SYNOPSIS OF DORMICE OF GENUS DYROMYS OF OUR FAUNA. S. I. Ognev, S. S. Turov. Moscow Univ. Sbornik Nauchno issledovatel'skogo inst. Zool. (Abstracts Works Zool. Inst. Moscow State Univ.), no.3, pp.79-80, 1936. (In Russian.)

THE FAMILY NAME OF THE DORMICE. T. S. Palmer. Science, Lancaster, n.s., vol.10, no.247, pp.412-413, Sept.22, 1899.

(NATURAL IMMUNITY OF THE COMMON GARDEN DORMOUSE (ELIOMYS NITELA SCHREB.) TO BEE VENOM.) Immunite naturelle du lerot commun (Eliomys nitela Schreb.) vis-a-vis du venin d'abeilles. M. Phsalix. Bull. Soc. Zool. France, Paris, vol.60, pp.235-238, 1935.

(DRYOMIS NITEDULA INTERMEDIUS NEHRING IN TRENTINO.) Il dyromys nitedula intermedius Nehring nel Trentino. G. B. Dal Piaz. Studi Trentini, ann.5, no. 1, p.3, 1924.

SPRING'S AWAKENING. MARCH WINDS STIR CHILLY SLEEPERS TO LIFE AND ACTIVITY. (HIBERNATION OF DORMOUSE.) Frances Pitt. Field, London, vol.167, no.4343, p.643, illus., Mar.21, 1936.

(A PURPOSEFUL CAGE FOR DORMICE.) Ein zwecimaessiger Kaefig fuer Schlafmaeuse. Adolf Priesner. Zool. Garten N.F., Leipzig, vol.7, nos.4-6, pp.134-136, Aug., 1934.

(THE FIRST PROOF OF THE TYROLEAN DORMOUSE (DRYOMYS NITEDULA INTERMEDIUS NEHRING 1902) IN THE NORTHERN TYROL.) Die ersten Nachweise des Tiroler Baumschlaefers, Dryomys nitedula intermedius (Nehring, 1902), fuer Nordtirol. Saeugetierk., Mitteil., 5 (4): 172, Dec.1, 1957.

(THE MYOXIDAE OR DORMICE: A CONTRIBUTION TO THE OSTOLOGY AND SYSTEMATICS OF MAMMALS.) Die Myoxidae oder Schlaefer ein beitrag zur Osteologie und Systematik der Nagethiere. C. L. Reuvens. Leiden, pp.80, pls.4, 1890.

(THE DORMOUSE (DRYOMYS NITEDULA PALL.) IN CAPTIVITY.) Der Baumschlaefer (Dryomys nitedula Pall.) in Gefangenschaft. Wilhelm Schreitmueller. Zeitschr. Saeugetierk., Berlin, vol.17, no.3, pp.155-157, Feb.19, 1953.

(TAXONOMY AND DISTRIBUTION OF THE DORMOUSE GLIS GLIS L. IN GEORGIA.) K sistematike i raspro-straneniyu polchka Glis glis L. v gruzii. M. V. Shidlovski. Trudi Inst. Zool. Akad. Nauk Gruzinoskoi SSR, vol.13, pp.47-61, 1954.

(THE WILD MAMMALS OF CRETE. 5. THE CRETAN DORMOUSE.) Die Wildsaeuger von Kreta. 5. Der Siebenschlaefer Kretas. Horst Siewert. Zeitschr.

Saeugetierk., Berlin, vol.17, no.1, pp.52-57, pl.8, Feb.19, 1953.

THE FAT DORMOUSE (GLIS GLIS L.). E. P. Spangenberg. The thin-toed ground-squirrel, the fat dormouse, the mole-rat, and the chipmunk, pp.36-70, map, illus., All Union Coop. Assn. Publ. House, 1935.

THE GARDEN DORMOUSE (ELIOMYS) OF FORMENTERA, BALEARIC ISLANDS. Oldfield Thomas. Ann. and Mag. Nat. Hist., ser.9, vol.16, pp.389-390, Oct., 1925.

ON A NEW DORMOUSE FROM ASIA MINOR WITH REMARKS ON THE SUB-GENUS "DRYOMYS." Oldfield Thomas. Ann. and Mag. Nat. Hist. (7), vol.20, no. 119, pp.406-407, Nov., 1907.

ON A NEW DORMOUSE FROM MASHUNA-LAND. Oldfield Thomas. Ann. and Mag. Nat. Hist. (6), vol.19, no.112, pp.388-389, Apr., 1897.

ON THE OCCURRENCE OF THE EDIBLE DORMOUSE (GENUS GLIS) IN SARDINIA. Oldfield Thomas. Ann. and Mag. Nat. Hist. (7), vol.19, no.113, pp.444-445, May, 1907.

ON THE MYOXUS ELEGANS OF TEM-MINCK. Oldfield Thomas. Proc. Zool. Soc. Lond., pp.40-41, Feb.3, 1880.

TWO NEW DORMICE OF THE GENUS ELIOMYS. Oldfield Thomas. Ann. and Mag. Nat. Hist. (7), vol.11, no.65, pp.494-496, May, 1903.

THE EDIBLE DORMOUSE (GLIS GLIS L.) IN ENGLAND, 1902-1951. Harry V. Thompson. Proc. Zool. Soc. Lond., vol.122, pt. 4, pp.1017-1024, pls.2, Feb., 1953.

SOME DATA ON THE THERMOREGULATIONS IN MUSCARDINUS AVELLANARIUS. CHANGE OF THE RESPIRATION CHARACTER AND BODY TEMPERATURE DURING DORMANCY AND ACTIVITY. A. G. Tomilin. Zool. Zhurnal, 37 (1): 120-139, Jan., 1958. (In Russian, with English summary.)

(THE TYROLEAN TREE DORMOUSE IN THE SALZBURG REGION.) Der Tiroler Baumschlaefer, Dryomys nitedula intermedius (Nehring, 1902), im Lande Salzburg. Eduard Paul Tratz. Saeugetierk, Mitteil., Stuttgart, 3 (3): 125, July 1, 1955.

NOTES ON ELIOMYS MELANURUS AND ON SOME OTHER RODENTS OF PALESTINE. H. B. Tristram. Proc. Zool. Soc. Lond., pt.1, pp.40-42, pl.6, 1877.

WELCOME OR UNWELCOME GUEST? A NEW ADDITION TO THE BRITISH FAUNA. (GLIS GLIS). Brian Vesey-Fitzgerald. Field, London, vol.168, no.4375, p.1075, illus., Oct.31, 1936.

(ARE DORMICE YOUNG (GLIS GLIS) BORN IN JUNE?) Gibt es im Juni geworfene Siebenschlaefer (Glis glis)? A. Frh. v. Vietinghoff-Riesch. Saeugetierk., Mitteil., 5 (2): 74, Apr.1, 1957.

(CONTRIBUTIONS TO THE BIOLOGY OF THE DORMOUSE (GLIS GLIS L.).) Beitraege zur Biologie des Siebenschlaefers (Glis glis L.). A. Frhr. V. Vietinghoff-Riesch. Bonner Zool. Beitraege, Jahrg.3, Heft 3-4, pp.167-186, Feb.20, 1953.

(CONTRIBUTIONS TO THE ECOLOGY AND BIOLOGY OF THE DORMOUSE (MUS CARDINUS AVELLANARIUS) IN THE ALPEN FORELAND.) Beitraege zur Oekologie und Biologie der Haselmaus (Mus cardinus avellanarius) im Alpenvorland. Wolfgang Wachtendorf. Zool. Jahrbuecher, Jena, vol.80, nos.3-4, pp.189-204, Nov., 1951.

(ON THE DISTRUBITION OF THE TREE DORMOUSE, DRYOMYS NITEDULA PALL.) Zur Verbreitung des Baumschlaefers, Dryomys nitedula Pall. Rud Zimmermann. Zeitschr. f. Saeugetierkunde, Berlin, vol. 7, nos.1-6, p.261, Dec.15, 1932.

(ON THE OCCURRENCE OF THE HAZEL MOUSE (MUSCARDINUS AVELLANARIUS L.) IN SAXONY.) Zum Vorkommen der Haselmaus (Muscardinus avellanarius L.) in Sachsen. Rud Zimmermann. Zool. Garten, Leipzig, n.F., vol.5, nos.7-9, pp.226-227, Oct., 1932.

(OUR KNOWLEDGE OF THE DISTRIBUTION AND HABITS OF THE DORMICE OF SAXONY.) Unsere Kenntnisse ueber die Verbreitung und Lebensweise der Schlafmaeuse in Sachsen. Rud Zimmermann. Archiv fur Naturgesch., Jahrg.87, abt.A, heft 10, pp.199-200, Dec., 1921.

(ETHOLOGICAL OBSERVATIONS OF HAZELMICE (MUSCARDINUS A. AVELLANARIUS L.).) Ethologische Beobachtungen an Haselmaeusen (Muscardinus a. avellanarius L.). H. M. Zippelius, F. Goethe. Zeits. f. Tierpsychol., 8:348-367, 1951.

THE DORMOUSE. Nature Mag., Wash., vol.38, no.7, p.365, illus., Aug.-Sept., 1945.

## Platacanthomyidae

EXHIBITION OF A SPECIMEN OF A NEW FORM OF DORMOUSE, PLATACANTHOMYS LASIURUS. Philip Lutley Sclater. Proc. Zool. Soc. London, pt.28, pp.260-269, figs.4, 1860.

## Seleviniidae

A REMARKABLE FAMILY OF RODENTS FROM KASAKHSTAN, U.S.S.R. B. S. Bashanov, B. A. Belosludov. Jour. Mam., vol.22, no.3, pp.311-315, pl.1, Aug.14, 1941.

A NEW GENUS AND SPECIES OF RODENT FROM THE CENTRAL KAZAKHSTAN (U.S.S.R.). (SELEVINIA, S. BETPAKDALAENSIS.) B. A. Belosludov, V. S. Bashanav. Uchenyie Zapiski Kazakhskogo Gosudarstvennogo Universiteta, Alma-Ata, vol.1, Biol., pp.81-86, 2 figs., Feb.5, 1939.

(ON THE BIOLOGY OF THE DESERT DORMOUSE.) Zur Biologie des Wuestenschlaefers. M. D. Zwerew. Zeitschr. Saeugetierk., Berlin, vol.17, no.3, pp.158-159, Feb.19, 1953.

## Zapodidae

(SOME NOTES ON BUSH-MICE, SICISTA, WHICH HAVE BEEN KEPT ALIVE IN THE RIKSMUSEET MUSEUM.) Nagra antechningar om buskmoess, Sicista, som hallits levande i Riksmuseet. Einar Loennberg. Fauna och Flora, vol.4, pp.149-152, 1930.

(KNOWLEDGE OF SICISTA SUBTILIS (PALLAS).) Till kaennedomen om buskmusen, Sicista subtilis (Pallas). Ivar Arwidsson. Fauna och Flora, no.4, pp. 145-148, pl.1, 1930.

MEADOW JUMPING MOUSE (ZAPUS HUDSONIUS HUDSONIUS). N. R. Barger. Wisconsin Conserv. Bull., Madison, vol. 15, no.12, p.28, illus., Dec., 1950.

NOTES ON TWO CAPTIVE MEADOW JUMPING MICE (ZAPUS HUDSONIUS). R. York Edwards. Canadian Field-Nat., Sutton West, vol.59, no.2, pp.49-50, Mar.-Apr., 1945.

SOME NOTES ON A NORTHWEST JUMPING MOUSE (ZAPUS TRINOTATUS TRINOTATUS). Marion P. Harthill. Murrelet, vol.16, no.1, pp.18-19, Jan., 1935.

JUMPING MICE. Caroline A. Heppenstall. Pennsylvania Game News, Harrisburg, vol. 17, no.6, p.12, Sept., 1946.

A JUMPING MOUSE (ZAPUS INSIGNIS MILLER). Gerrit S. Miller, Jr. Proc. Biol. Soc., Wash., vol.8, pp.1-8, Apr.22, 1893.

WAUH PEH SOUS (ZAPUS, NAPAEOZAPUS). Carolyne Sheldon Murdock. Canadian Nature, Toronto, vol.2, no.5, pp.26-27, illus., Nov.-Dec., 1940.

NOTES ON THE LIFE HISTORY OF NAPAEOZAPUS. Norman A. Preble. Jour. Mam., 37 (2): 196-200, June 9, 1956.

THE LIFE HISTORY AND ECOLOGY OF THE JUMPING MOUSE (ZAPUS HUDSONIUS). Don C. Quimby. PhD thesis, Univ. Minn., 1949; Ecol. Mong., 21 (1): 61-95, Jan., 1951.

THE WOODLAND JUMPER. Lloyd Scherer, Jr. Nature Mag., Wash., vol.41, no.2, pp.77-78, illus., Feb., 1948.

SOME DETAILS ON THE LIFE HISTORY AND BEHAVIOR OF NAPAEOZAPUS INSIGNIS ABIETORUM (PREBLE). L. L. Snyder. Jour. Mam., vol.5, no.4, pp.233-237, Nov., 1924.

THE RARE NAPAEOZAPUS INSIGNIS. J. Dewey Soper. Jour. Mam., vol.4, no.2, p.127, May, 1923.

NOTES ON THE JUMPING MOUSE ZAPUS TRINOTATUS TRINOTATUS RHOADS. Arthur Svihla, Ruth D. Svihla. Jour. Mam., vol.14, no.2, pp.131-134, May, 1933.

### Anatomy

WHITE TIPS ON NAPAEOZAPUS TAILS. C.H.D. Clarke. Canadian Field-Nat., vol.49, no.8, p.139, Nov., 1935.

ON TAIL COLOR IN NAPAEOZAPUS. G. Arthur Foster. Jour. Mam., vol.28, no. 1, p.62, Feb.15, 1947.

SUPERNUMERARY MOLARS IN THE JUMPING MOUSE (ZAPUS PRINCEP). Philip H. Krutzsch. Jour. Mam., vol.34, no.2, p. 265, May 14, 1953.

SEXUAL DIMORPHISM IN NAPAEOZAPUS. Norman A. Preble. Jour. Mam., vol.19, no.2, p.254, May 14, 1938.

### Diseases

TULAREMIA IN THE JUMPING MOUSE. Mitsuru Nakamura. Jour. Mam., vol.31, no.2, p.194, May 25, 1950.

### Europe

(THE STRIPED MOUSE (SICISTA SUBTILUS TRIGONA PETENYI) IN AUSTRIA.) Die Streifenmaus (Sicista subtilus trigona Petenyi) in Oesterreich. Kurt Bauer. Zool. Anzeiger, Leipzig, vol.152, nos.9-10, pp. 206-213, May, 1954.

SICISTA SUBTILIS, FOUND IN NORWAY IN 1907 AND 1908. R. Collett. Zool. Anz., vol.34, nos.11-12, pp.379-381, June 1, 1909.

(NEW REMARKS ON THE DISTRIBUTION OF SICISTA BETULINA IN BERGSLAGEN.) Nyare uppgifter om bjoerkmusens (Sicista betulina) utbredning i Bergslagen. Bertil Hanstroem. Fauna och Flora, pts.4-5, pp.129-138, 1955. (In Swedish, with English summary.)

(BIOLOGICAL AND MORPHOLOGICAL INVESTIGATIONS OF THE BIRCH MOUSE IN THE NATURAL PARK RESERVE OF BIALOWIEZA.) Biologische und morphologische Untersuchungen ueber die Birkenmaus im Naturschutzpark von Bialowieza. (Sicista betulina). Jerzy Kubik. Ann. Univ. Mariae Curie-Sklodowska, vol.7, no.1, pp.1-63, June 25, 1952.

(THE STRIPED MOUSE (SICISTINAE) OF EUROPE.) Die Streifenmaeuse (Sicistinae) Europas. L. v. Mehely. Ann. Mus. Nat. Hungarici, vol.11, pp.220-256, pls.12-14, 1913.

SICISTA BETULINA PALL., A RARE REPRESENTATIVE OF POLISH FAUNA. Zdzislaw Pucek. Przeglad Zoologiczny, 2 (3): 168-182, 2 photos, 1958. (In Polish, with English summary.)

(SICISTA FIND IN UPPER SILESIA.) Sicista-Fund aus Oberschlesien. Martin Schlott. Zeitschr. f. Saeugetierkunde, Berlin, vol.8, nos.3-6, p.274, Dec.20, 1933.

### Fossils

A NEW JUMPING MOUSE FROM THE UPPER PLIOCENE OF KANSAS. Claude W. Hibbard. Jour. Mam., vol.32, no.3, pp. 351-352, illus., Aug.23, 1951.

(FOSSIL SICISTINAE.) Fossile Sicistinae. S. Schaub. Ecologae Geologicae Helvetiae, vol.23, no.2, pp.616-637, figs.17, Dec., 1930.

### Habits and Behavior

HOME RANGES AND POPULATIONS OF THE JUMPING MOUSE. W. Frank Blair. Amer. Midland Nat., 23 (1): 244-250, Jan., 1940.

NOTES ON NESTS OF THE MEADOW JUMPING MOUSE, ZAPUS HUDSONIUS. Ralph W. Dexter. Jour. Mam., vol.35, no.1, p.121, Feb.10, 1954.

HABITS OF JUMPING MICE. W. J. Hamilton, Jr. Amer. Midland Nat., vol. 16, no.2, pp.187-200, figs.2, pl.6, Mar., 1935.

ANOTHER RECORD OF A SWIMMING JUMPING MOUSE. J. Knox Jones, Jr. Jour. Mam., vol.31, no.4, pp.453-454, Nov.21, 1950.

A SWIMMING JUMPING MOUSE. Norman A. Preble. Jour. Mam., vol.25, no.2, pp.200-201, May 25, 1944.

JUMPING MOUSE, UNDERWATER SWIMMER. Ralph B. Priddy. Jour. Mam., Balto., vol.30, no.1, p.74, Feb.14, 1949.
(OBSERVATIONS OF A CAPTIVE STRIPED MOUSE (SICISTA SUBTILIS PALLAS).) Gefangenschaftsbeobachtungen an der Streifenmaus (Sicista subtilis Pallas). Gerth Rokitansky. Bonner Zool. Beitraege, Jahrg.3, Heft 1-2, pp.1-9, July 15, 1952.

AQUATIC BEHAVIOUR OF A JUMPING MOUSE. L. L. Snyder. Canadian Field-Nat., Ottawa, vol.61, no.6, pp.198-199, Feb.13, 1948.

AQUATIC TENDENCIES IN THE JUMPING MOUSE. R. W. Sutton. Jour. Mam., 37 (2): 299, June 9, 1956.

Hibernation

THE BEGINNING OF HIBERNATION OF JUMPING MICE ON MOUNT DESERT ISLAND. Manlif Lelyn Branin. Bull. New England Mus. Nat. Hist., Boston, no.80, pp.5-6, July, 1936.

HIBERNATION SITE OF THE MEADOW JUMPING MOUSE. William C. Dilger. Jour. Mam., vol.29, no.3, pp.299-300, Aug.31, 1948.

HIBERNATING MEADOW JUMPING MOUSE. W. Robert Eadie. Jour. Mam., vol.30, no.3, pp.307-308, Aug.17, 1949.

HIBERNATION OF THE NORTHWEST JUMPING MOUSE. J. M. Edson. Murrelet, vol.13, no.2, pp.55-56, Apr.26, 1932.

UNUSUAL LOCATION OF HIBERNATING JUMPING MICE. (ZAPUS IN BASEMENT OF HOUSE.) Martha Reekie Flahaut. Murrelet, Seattle, vol.20, no.1, pp.17-18, illus., Jan.-Apr., 1939.

HIBERNATING JUMPING MICE IN WOODCHUCK DENS. Roy A. Grizzell, Jr. Jour. Mam., Balto., vol.30, no.1, pp.74-75, Feb.14, 1949.

HIBERNATION OF MEADOW JUMPING MOUSE. Richard H. Manville. Jour. Mam., 37 (1): 122, Feb.28, 1956.

A HIBERNATING JUMPING MOUSE. Arnold J. Nicholson. Jour. Mam., vol.18, no.1, p.103, Feb.14, 1937.

A NEW RECORD OF ZAPUS HUDSONIUS IN MISSOURI AND NOTES ON ITS HIBERNATION. Charles W. Schwartz. Jour. Mam., 32 (2): 227-228, May, 1951.

India

DESCRIPTION OF A NEW SPECIES OF SMINTHUS FROM KASHMIR. Oldfield Thomas. Ann. and Mag. Nat. Hist. (6), vol. 11, no.62, pp.184-186, Feb., 1893.

ON RODENTS OF THE GENUS SMINTHUS IN KASHMIR. Frederick W. True. Proc. U.S. Nat. Mus., vol.17, publ.1004, pp.341-343, Nov.15, 1894.

North America

THE NORTH AMERICAN JUMPING MICE. J. A. Allen. Amer. Nat., vol.34, pp.199-202, Mar., 1900.

WOODLAND JUMPING MOUSE (NAPAEOZAPUS) IN GEORGIA. H. V. Autrey, Eugene P. Odum. Jour. Mam., Balto., vol.30, no. 2, p.200, May 23, 1949.

NAPAEOZAPUS INSIGNIS INSIGNIS IN OHIO. B. P. Bole, Jr. Jour. Mam., vol.16, no.2, pp.153-154, May, 1935.

NAPAEOZAPUS ON MOUNT DESERT ISLAND. M. Lelyn Branin. Jour. Mam., vol.17, no.2, p.175, May, 1936.

WOODLAND JUMPING MOUSE NEAR TUXEDO, NEW YORK. James P. Chapin. Jour. Mam., vol.3, no.2, p.117, May, 1922.

A NEW JUMPING MOUSE (GENUS ZAPUS) FROM KANSAS (ZAPUS HUDSONIUS PALLIDUS). E. Lendell Cockrum, Rollin H. Baker. Proc. Biol. Soc. Wash., vol.63, pp.1-4, Apr.26, 1950.

NAPAEOZAPUS INSIGNIS ROANENSIS IN SOUTH CAROLINA. Robert H. Coleman. Jour. Mam., vol.21, no.1, p.95, Feb.14, 1940.

A STUDY OF THE IDAHO JUMPING MICE OF THE GENUS ZAPUS, WITH REMARKS ON A FEW SPECIMENS FROM BRITISH COLUMBIA. William B. Davis. Jour. Mam., vol.15, no.3, pp.221-227, fig.1, Aug., 1934.

DISTRIBUTION OF THE MEADOW JUMPING MOUSE ZAPUS HUDSONIUS IN OHIO. Ralph W. Dexter. Jour. Mam., 35 (2): 233-239, map, May, 1954.

THE MEADOW JUMPING MOUSE IN SOUTHERN ILLINOIS. Willard Gersbacher, Julius R. Swayne. Jour. Mam., vol.32, no. 1, p.122, Feb.15, 1951.

NAPAEOZAPUS INSIGNIS IN VIRGINIA. Ray Greenfield. Jour. Mam., vol.19, no.2, p.254, May 14, 1938.

UTAH JUMPING MOUSE RECORDED FROM IDAHO. E. Raymond Hall. Murrelet, Seattle, vol.20, no.3, Sept-Dec., p.71, Dec.16, 1939.

A STUDY OF THE CALIFORNIA JUMPING MICE OF THE GENUS ZAPUS. A. Brazier Howell. Univ. Calif. Publ. Zool., vol.21, pp.225-238, 1 fig., May 20, 1920.

THE WISCONSIN NAPAEOZAPUS. Hartley H. T. Jackson. Proc. Biol. Soc. Wash., vol.32, pp.9-10, Feb.14, 1919.

ADDITIONAL RECORDS OF THE JUMPING MOUSE, ZAPUS HUDSONIUS, FROM GEORGIA. James H. Jenkins, David W. Johnston. Jour. Mam., vol.31, no.4, p. 461, Nov.21, 1950.

NORTH AMERICAN JUMPING MICE (GENUS ZAPUS). Philip H. Krutzsch. Univ. Kansas Publ., Mus. Nat. Hist., vol.7, no.4, pp.349-472, illus., Apr.21, 1954.

THREE NEW JUMPING MICE (ZAPUS) FROM THE NORTHWEST. C. Hart Merriam. Proc. Biol. Soc., Wash., vol. 11, pp.103-104, Apr.26, 1897.

DESCRIPTION OF A NEW JUMPING MOUSE FROM NOVA SCOTIA AND NEW BRUNSWICK. (ZAPUS INSIGNIS.) Gerrit S. Miller, Jr. American Naturalist, pp.742-743, Aug., 1891.

A NEW JUMPING MOUSE FROM NEW MEXICO. Gerrit S. Miller, Jr. Proc. Biol. Soc., Wash., vol.24, pp.253-254, Dec.23, 1911.

ZAPUS PRINCEPS PRINCEPS IN UTAH. A. W. Moore. Jour. Mam., vol.9, no. 2, pp.154-155, May , 1928.

THE JUMPING MOUSE IN GEORGIA. George A. Petrides. Jour. Mam., vol.29, no.1, pp.75-76, Feb.13, 1948.

A NEW RACE OF NAPAEOZAPUS INSIGNIS FROM ONTARIO. Leslie A. Prince. Occas. Papers Roy. Ontario Mus. Zool., Toronto, no.7, pp.3, Dec.12, 1941.

A NEW JUMPING MOUSE FROM THE PACIFIC SLOPE. Samuel N. Rhoads. Proc. Acad. Nat. Sci. Phila., pp.421-422, Jan.15, 1895.

STUDIES ON THE LIFE HISTORIES OF ZAPUS AND NAPAEOZAPUS IN NOVA SCOTIA. Carolyn Sheldon. Jour. Mam., vol.15, no.4, pp.290-300, Nov., 1934.

VERMONT JUMPING MICE OF THE GENUS NAPAEOZAPUS. Carolyn Sheldon. Jour. Mam., vol.19, no.4, pp.444-453, pls.1-2, Nov.14, 1938.

VERMONT JUMPING MICE OF THE GENUS ZAPUS. Carolyn Sheldon. Jour. Mam., vol.19, no.3, pp.324-332, figs.8, Aug.18, 1938.

ADDITIONAL NOTE ON NAPAEOZAPUS IN EASTERN MANITOBA. J. Dewey Soper. Jour. Mam., vol.19, no.1, pp.108-109, Feb.14, 1938.

NAPAEOZAPUS IN EASTERN MANITOBA. J. Dewey Soper. Jour. Mam., vol.18, no. 3, p.369, Aug.14, 1937.

ZAPUS HUDSONIUS REPORTED FROM LEE COUNTY, ALABAMA. Edward G. Sullivan. Jour. Mam., vol.35, no.4, p.592, Nov.29, 1954.

THE OCCURRENCE OF THE WOODLAND JUMPING MOUSE IN MINNESOTA. Thaddeus Surber. Fins, Feathers and Fur, no.35, p.106, Sept., 1923.

A NEW LOCALITY RECORD FOR THE BLUE MOUNTAIN JUMPING MOUSE. Edward D. Wagner. Murrelet, Seattle, vol.23, no.2, p.60, Aug.14, 1942.

NOTES ON THE CAROLINIAN JUMPING MOUSE IN CONNECTICUT. Sydney S. Walton, Jr. Jour. Mam., 36 (1): 140-141, Feb.25, 1955.

UTAH RECORD FOR ZAPUS PRINCEPS PRINCEPS. L. R. Wolfe. Jour. Mam., vol.9, no.2, p.154, May, 1928.

Taxonomy

A NEW SPECIES OF THE GENUS SICISTA. J. L. Chaworth-Musters. Ann. and Mag. Nat. Hist., ser.9, vol.19, pp.542-543, May, 1927.

A NOTE ON THE NOMENCLATURE OF THE SPECIES OF THE "SUBTILIS" GROUP OF THE GENUS SICISTA. J. L. Chaworth-Musters. Ann. and Mag. Nat. Hist., London, ser.10, vol.14, no.83, pp.554-556, Nov., 1934.

A SYSTEMATICAL REVIEW OF THE RUSSIAN SPECIES OF THE GENUS SICISTA. S. I. Ognev. Abstracts works Zool. Inst. Moscou State Univ., no.2, pp.51-58, 1935.

REVISION OF THE JUMPING MICE OF THE GENUS ZAPUS. Edward A. Preble. North American Fauna, no.15, Wash., pp.1-42, illus., Aug.8, 1899.

Young

NOTES ON THE REARING OF CAPTIVE YOUNG MEADOW JUMPING MICE. H. Roy Ivor. Canadian Field-Nat., vol.48, no.1, pp.8-10, Jan., 1934.

THE YOUNG OF THE WOODLAND JUMPING MOUSE, NAPAEOZAPUS INSIGNIS INSIGNIS (MILLER). James N. Layne, W. J. Hamilton, Jr. Amer. Midland Nat., vol.52, no. 1, pp.242-247, July, 1954.

Dipodidae

MATING BEHAVIOR OF DIPODOMYS ORDII RICHARDSONI. Philip F. Allan. Jour. Mam., vol.25, no.4, pp.403-404, Dec.12, 1944.

JERBOAS FROM MONGOLIA. Glover M. Allen. Amer. Mus. Novit., no.161, pp. 1-6, Mar.31, 1925.

(ECOLOGY OF JERBOAS IN S. RUSSIA.) I. V. Andvienski, L. N. Eliseev. Bull. Soc. Nat., Moscow, 57 (6): 19-24, 3 figs. (In Russian.)

DISTRIBUTION OF THE JERBOA ON THE WEST SIDE OF THE DNIEPER IN THE UKRAINE. B. Bielskij. Acad. Sci. Ukraine, Mem. Cl. Sci. Phys., et Math., (Trav. Mus. Zool. no.7), vol.13, no.1, pp.145-178, maps 2, 1929. (In Russian, with German summary.)

ON THE NOMENCLATURE OF CERTAIN SPECIES OF THE GENERA ALLACTAGA AND ALACTAGULUS. J. L. Chaworth-Musters. Ann. and Mag. Nat. Hist., London, ser.10, vol.14, no.83, pp.556-560, Nov., 1934.

ON THE NOMENCLATURE OF THE FIVE-TOED JERBOA OF EASTERN SIBERIA. J. L. Chaworth-Musters. Ann. and Mag. Nat. Hist., London, ser.10, vol.20, no. 115, p.96, July, 1937.

THE ECOLOGY OF DIPUS SAGITTA. B. K. Feniuk, J. M. Kazantzeva. Jour. Mam., 18: 409-426, 1937.

(A NEW SUBSPECIES OF JERBOA, ALACTABULUS ACONTION LICHT., OF TURKESTAN.) Une nouvelle sous-espece de gerboise Alactagulus acontion Licht. de Turkestan. W. G. Heptner, A. W. Samorodow. Mammalia, Paris, vol.3, nos.3-4, pp.109-110, Dec., 1939.

LETTER ON THE JERBOAS WHICH HAVE PRODUCED YOUNG IN HIS COLLECTION.

Robert Heron. Proc. Zool. Soc. Lond., pt.12, p.123, 1844.

(ON THE ECOLOGY OF THE JERBOA, DIPUS SAGITTA PALL. (MAMMALIA).) Zur Oekologie des Erdhasen Dipus sagitta Pall. (Mammalia). J. M. Kazantzewa, B. K. Feniuk. Uchenye zapiski Saratovskogo gosudarstvennogo universiteta imeni N. G. Chernyshevskogo (Abhandl. Tschernyschewsky-Staatsuniversitaet Saratow), Saratov, vol.1, biol. ser., no. 14, pp.134-166, figs.27, 1937. (In Russian, with German summary.)

NOTES ON THE ECOLOGY OF SMALL DIPODIDAE (MAMMALIA) OF THE KALMUCK STEPPES. N. J. Larina. Abhandl. Tschernyschewsky-Staatsuniversitaet Saratov, vol.1, (XIV) biol. ser., no.2, pp.101-120, figs.9, tables 3, 1939.

(EXPLAINING COAPTATIONS.) Zur Erklaerung der Koaptationen. (Jaculus hirtipes.) L. v. Mehely. Jenaische Zeitschr. fuer Naturw., Jena, vol.67, pp. 158-162, figs.1, Aug.16, 1932.

THE AFRICAN JERBOA. Ida Mellen. Nature Magazine, vol.18, no.1, pp.42-44, figs.2, July, 1931.

THE EGYPTIAN JERBOA. Ida M. Mellen. Scottish Zoo and Wild Life, Edinburgh, vol. 1, pt.2, pp.62-64, illus., July, 1948.

(ALACTAGA WILLIAMSI THOMAS OF THE TALYSCH MOUNTAINS AND THE GREAT ARARAT.) Alactaga williamsi Thomas vom Talysch-Gebirge und vom Gr. Ararat. A. Nehring. Sitz.-Ber. Gesell. Naturf. Freunde Berlin, Jahrg.1901, no.5, pp.145-146, May 21, 1901.

(ADDENDUM TO ALACTAGA ANNULATA MILNE EDW. OF THE KENTEI SHAN.) Nachtrag zu Alactaga annulata Milne Edw. aus dem Kentei-Gebirge. A. Nehring. Zool. Anzeiger, Leipzig, vol.23, no.614, pp.263-264, fig.1, May 7, 1900.

(ON ALACTAGA SUSCHKINI SAT. AND ALACTAGA ANNULATA MILNE EDW.) Ueber Alactaga Suschkini Sat. und Alactaga annulata Milne Edw. A. Nehring. Zool. Anzeiger, Leipzig, vol.23, no.612, pp.201-205, figs.2, Apr.9, 1900.

(ON DENTITION AND SKULL DIFFERENCES BETWEEN ALACTAGA ELATER LICHT. AND A. ACONTION PALL.) Gebiss- und Schadelunterschiede von Alactaga elater Licht. und A. acontion Pall. A. Nehring. Sitz.- Ber. Gesell. Naturf. Freunde Berlin, Jahrg.1897, no.9, pp.151-155, figs. 2, Nov.16, 1897.

DIPUS (ALACTAGA) AULACOTIS WAGNER. A. Nehring. Zool. Anzeiger, Leipzig, vol. 25, no.662, pp.89-91, Jan.27, 1902.

(DIPUS SCHLUTERI N. SP. AND SOME OTHER RODENTS FROM PALESTINE.) Dipus Schlueteri n. sp. und einige andere nager aus Palastina. A. Nehring. Sitz. Ber. Gesell. Naturf. Freunde Berlin, Jahrg.1901, no.8, pp.163-176, Oct.15, 1901.

(GEOGRAPHICAL DISTRIBUTION OF ALACTAGULUS ACONTION (PALL.) AND ALACTAGA ELATER (LICHT.).) Die geographische Verbreitung von Alactagulus acontion (Pall.) und Alactaga elater (Licht.). A. Nehring. Sitz.-Ber. Gesell. Naturf. Freunde Berlin, Jahrg.1900, no.2, pp.61-70, figs.2, Feb.20, 1900.

(ON SKULL, DENTITION, AND TAIL FORMATION IN PLATYCERCOMYS PLATYURUS LICHT.) Ueber Schaedel-, Gebiss- und Schwanzbildung von Platycercomys platyurus Licht. A. Nehring. Zool. Anzeiger, Leipzig, vol.23, no.619, pp.361-366, figs.2, July 9, 1900.

REVIEW OF CERTAIN DIPODIDAE OF THE RUSSIAN FAUNA. S. I. Ognev. Comptes Rendus (Doklady) Acad. Sci. URSS, Moscow, vol.52, no.5, pp.461-463, May 20, 1946.

(ON THE BIOLOGY OF ALACTAGA JACULUS PALL. AS A PEST ATTACKING PLANTATIONS OF SCORZONERA TAU-SAGHYZ LIPSH. ET BOSSE IN THE UKRAINE.) Zur Biologie von Alactaga jaculus Pall. als Schaedling auf den Pflanzungen von Scorzonera tau-saghyz Lipsh. et Bosse in der Ukraine. A. K. Schepe. Zbirnik Prats' Zoologichnogo Muzeiu Vseukrains'ka Akademiia Nauk Institut Zoologii tai Biologii (Trav. Mus. Zool. Acad. Sci. Urkaine, Inst. Zool. et Biol.), no.13, pp.166-167, 1934. (In Ukranian with German summary.)

THE JERBOAS OF EGYPT. Henry W. Setzer. Jour. Egyptian Public Health Assoc., Cairo, 32 (6): 265-271, Oct.23, 1957.

TWO NEW JERBOAS FROM EGYPT. Henry W. Setzer. Proc. Biol. Soc., Wash., vol.68, pp.183-184, Dec.31, 1955.

A NEW THREE-TOED JERBOA FROM CHINA. Arthur de Carle Sowerby. Ann. and Mag. Nat. Hist., ser.9, vol.5, pp.279-281, Mar., 1920.

ON THE OCCURRENCE OF THE JERBOA JACULUS TURCMENICUS VINOGR. ET BONDAR IN THE NORTHERN KARA-KUM AND ON SOME OF ITS ECOLOGICAL AND MORPHOLOGICAL PECULIARITIES. V.A. Stalmakova. Zool. Zhurnal, Moscow, 36 (2): 275-279, 1957. (In Russian, with English summary.)

THE FORMS OF JACULUS JACULUS IN EGYPT AND SYRIA. Oldfield Thomas. Ann. and Mag. Nat. Hist., ser.9, vol.9, pp.295-297, Apr., 1922.

THE JERBOA OF MUSCAT. Oldfield Thomas. Ann. and Mag. Nat. Hist., ser.9, vol.8, pp.440-441, Oct., 1921.

A NEW JERBOA FROM CHINA. Oldfield Thomas. Ann. and Mag. Nat. Hist. (8), vol.2, no.9, pp.307-308, Sept., 1908.

SCIENTIFIC RESULTS FROM THE MAMMAL SURVEY NO.47. ON THE GENERIC POSITION OF THE AFGHAN JERBOA (ALACTAGA INDICA). Oldfield Thomas. Jour. Bombay Nat. Hist. Soc., vol.32, p. 133, Aug.1, 1927.

FAUNA OF USSR. MAMMALS. B. S. Vinogradov. Publ. Acad. Sci. USSR, Moscow and Leningrad, vol.3, no.4, (Fam. Dipodidae), pp.viii, 197, figs.69, 1937. (In Russian.)

ON A NEW PECULIAR GENUS AND SPECIES OF JUMPING MICE FROM KHARA-KHOTO, MONGOLIA (SALPINGOTUS KOZLOVI GEN. ET SPEC. NOV.). B. S. Vinogradov. Kozlov, Mongolia and Amdo, pp.540-545, 2 pls., St. Petersburg, 1922.

(ON A NEW SPECIES OF GERBOA (SCIRTOPODA CTENODACTYLA SP. N., FAM. DIPODIDAE, RODENTIA) OF REPETEK, TURKMENIA.) B. S. Vinogradov. Comptes Rendus Acad. Sci. URSS., A., no.10, pp. 248-252, figs.4, 1929.

ON THE CLASSIFICATION OF DIPODIDAE (RODENTIA). I. CRANIAL AND DENTAL CHARACTERS. PT. I. B. S. Vinogradov. Bull. Acad. Sci. USSR, no.4, pp.331-350, pls.6, 1930. (In Russian.)

ON THE CLASSIFICATION OF DIPODIDAE (RODENTIA). I. CRANIAL AND DENTAL CHARACTERS. PT. II. B. S. Vinogradov. Bull. Acad. Sci. USSR, no.5, pp.453-466, pls.7-10, 1930. (In Russian.)

NOTES ON SOME GERBOAS FROM MONGOLIA. B. S. Vinogradov. Comptes Rendus de l'Acad. Sci. Union Socialistic Soviet Republics, 1926, pp.232-234, 1927. (In Russian.)

A SECOND INTERESTING SPECIES OF MONGOLIAN GERBOA OF THE GENUS SALPINGOTUS VINOGR. (SALPINGOTUS CRASSICAUDA SP. N.). B. S. Vinogradov. Zool. Anzeiger, vol.61, pp.150-152, 5 figs., Oct.20, 1924.

A THIRD SPECIES OF DWARF JERBOA, SALPINGOTUS THOMASI, SP. N. B. S. Vinogradov. Ann. and Mag. Nat. Hist., ser.10, vol.1, pp.372-374, Mar., 1928.

(OBSERVATIONS TO KNOWLEDGE OF CENTRAL ASIAN RODENTS. I. BIOLOGIC OBSERVATIONS OF GERBOAS (DIPODIDAE, MAMMALIA).) Materiaux pour servir a la connaissance des Rongeurs de l'Asie Centrale. I. Observations biologiques sur les Gerboises (Dipodidae, Mammalia). B. S. Vinogradov, A. Argyropulo. Annuaire Mus. Zool. Acad. Sci. URSS, Leningrad, vol.32, no.2, pp.135-156, figs.9, 1931.

(CONTRIBUTIONS TO KNOWLEDGE OF CENTRAL ASIAN RODENTS. I. BIOLOGIC OBSERVATIONS OF GERBOAS. (DIPODIDAE, MAMMALIA.) Materiaux pour servir a la connaissance des Rongeurs de l'Asie Centrale. I. Observations biologiques sur les Gerboises (Dipodidae, Mammalia). B. S. Vinogradov, A. Argyropulo. Annuaire Mus. Zool. Acad. Sci. URSS, Leningrad, vol.32, no.2, pp.135-156, figs.9, 1931.

(ON THE BIOLOGY OF THE TURKESTAN DIPODIDAE.) Zur Biologie der turkestanischen Springmaeuse (Dipodidae). B. S. Vinogradov, A. I. Argyropulo. Zeitschr. fuer Saeugetierkunde, Berlin, vol.6, no.4, pp.164-176, pls.9-14, Dec.15, 1931.

TREE CLIMBING JERBOAS. B. S. Vinogradov, V. Smal'makova. Priroda, Leningrad, no.12, pp.98-100, figs.3, 1937. (In Russian.)

## Hystricidae

BONE CARRYING BY PORCUPINE. Anne J. Alexander. South African Jour. Sci., 52 (11): 257-258, June, 1956.

PORCUPINES FROM CHINA. Glover M. Allen. Amer. Mus. Novitates, no.290, 4 pp., Oct.24, 1927.

ERYTHRISM IN THE CEYLON PORCUPINE ACANTHION LEUCURUS. P.E.P. Deraniyagala. Spolia Zeylanica, Bull. Nat. Mus. Ceylon, vol.27, pt.2, p.287, May 25, 1955.

A NEW SPECIMEN OF THE COMMON PORCUPINE. Guy Dollman. Nat. Hist. Mag., London, vol.2, no.13, pp.145-146, fig.1, Jan., 1930.

(MONOGRAPH OF THE ITALIAN PORCUPINE.) Monographie du porc-epic d'Italie. Guy De Germiny. Revue d'Histoire Naturelle, Pt.1. A, Mammiferes, Paris, vol.10, no.11, pp.386-391, figs.2, Nov., 1929.

ON THE PORCUPINES OF THE OLDER OR EASTERN CONTINENT, WITH DESCRIPTIONS OF SOME NEW SPECIES. John E. Gray. Proc. Zool. Soc. London, pt.15, pp.97-104, 128, 1847.

ON THE SPECIES OF PORCUPINES IN THE GARDENS OF THE SOCIETY AND IN THE BRITISH MUSEUM. John E. Gray. Proc. Zool. Soc. London, pp.306-311, 1866.

(ON THE TAXONOMY OF PORCUPINES LIVING IN THE USSR (HYSTRIX L., MAMMALIA, GLIRES).) K sistematike dikobrazov (Hystrix L.; Mammalia, Glires), obitayutsix v SSSR. V. H. Heptner. Doklady Akad. Nauk SSSR, Moscow, vol.84, no.5, pp.1081-1085, 1952.

SOME REMARKS ON RECENT, PREHISTORIC AND FOSSIL PORCUPINES FROM THE MALAY ARCHIPELAGO. D. A. Hooijer. Zool Mededeelingen, vol.26, pp. 251-267, figs.20, 1946.

ON TRICHYS FASCICULATA (SHAW). F. A. Jentink. Notes Leyden Mus., vol. 16, no.21, pp.205-209, Dec., 1894.

DO PORCUPINES SHOOT THEIR QUILLS? Kim. Jour. Bombay Nat. Hist. Soc., vol.39, no.1, pp.162-163, Dec.1, 1936.

(THE HAIRS, BRISTLES, AND THORNS OF THE PORCUPINE (HYSTRIX HIRSUTIROSTRIS).) Die Haare, Borsten und Stacheln des Stachelschweines (Hystrix hirsutirostris). Th. Lochte. Zool. Garten, Leipzig, 23 (1-3): 145-162, 1957.

ON A NEW FOSSIL PORCUPINE FROM HONAN WITH SOME REMARKS ABOUT THE DEVELOPMENT OF THE HYSTRICIDAE. Einar Loennberg. Palaeontologia Sinica, series C, vol.1, fasc.3, 15 pp., 1 pl., 1924.

ON THE CHINESE PORCUPINE, HYSTRIX SUBCRISTATA SWINHOE, WITH REMARKS ON OTHER MEMBERS OF THE GENUS. Einar Loennberg. Arkiv foer Zoologi, vol. 15, no.18, pp.1-10, Feb.15, 1923.

HUNTING PORCUPINES WITH A WITCH DOCTOR. Arthur Loveridge. Nat. Hist., New York, vol.56, no.9, pp.404-407, illus., Nov., 1947.

NOTES ON THE PORCUPINES OF THE MALAY PENINSULA AND ARCHIPELAGO. Marcus W. Lyon, Jr. Proc. U.S. Nat. Mus., vol.32, no.1552, pp.575-594, pls. 54-57, June 29, 1907.

TYPE OF THE GENUS ATHERURUS, BRUSH-TAILED PORCUPINES. Marcus W. Lyon, Jr. Proc. Biol. Soc. Wash., vol. 19, pp.199-200, Dec.31, 1906.

HABITS OF THE PORCUPINE (HYSTRIX LEUCURA). C. McCann. Jour. Bombay Nat. Hist. Soc., vol.32, p.214, Aug.1, 1927.

HABITS OF THE PORCUPINE. R. C. Morris. Jour. Bombay Nat. Hist. Soc., vol.32, pp.791-792, May 31, 1928.

PORCUPINE'S METHOD OF ATTACK. R. C. Morris. Jour. Bombay Nat. Hist. Soc., vol.26, p.1040, Jan.31, 1920.

SOUNDS MADE BY PORCUPINES. R. C. Morris. Jour. Bombay Nat. Hist. Soc., vol.34, no.3, pp.799-800, Nov.15, 1930.

(CONTRIBUTIONS TO KNOWLEDGE OF THE PORCUPINES OF ASIA, ESPECIALLY OF PALESTINE.) Beitraege zur Kenntnis der Stachelschweine Asiens, insbesondere Palaestinas. I. Ferdinand Mueller. Sitz.-Ber. Gesell. Naturf. Freunde, Berlin, no.2, pp.110-130, figs.2, 1911.

(DESCRIPTION OF SOME HYSTRIX SKULLS FROM GERMAN EAST AFRICA.) Besprechung einiger Hystrix-Schaedel aus Deutsch-Ost-Afrika. Ferdinand Mueller. Sitz.-Ber. Gesell. Naturf. Freunde, Berlin, Jahrg.1910, vol., no.8, pp.309-315, figs.4, 1910.

(A NEW HYSTRIX SPECIES OF NORTH-WEST GERMAN EAST AFRICA.) Eine neue Hystrix-Art aus dem Nord-westen Deutsch-Ostafrikas. Ferdinand Mueller. Archiv. f. Naturg. Berlin, vol.1, no.2, pp. 181-188, figs.6, 1910.

NOTES ON PORCUPINES. C.R.S. Pitman. Jour. Bombay Nat. Hist. Soc., vol.29, pp. 831-834, Dec.31, 1923.

PORCUPINE'S METHOD OF ATTACK. C.R.S. Pitman. Jour. Bombay Nat. Hist. Soc., vol.26, pp.1039-1040, Jan. 31, 1920.

ON THE "RATTLE" OF THE PORCUPINE. R. I. Pocock. Proc. Zool. Soc. Lond., 1906, pp.903-904, Apr.11, 1907.

DESCRIPTION OF A NEW SPECIES OF BRUSH-TAILED PORCUPINE WITH NOTES ON CHAEROMYS, FROM KAKAMEGA FOREST, KENYA (ATHERURA TURNERI). J. St. Leger. Ann. and Mag. Nat. Hist., ser.10, vol.10, no.57, pp.231-233, Sept., 1932.

DESCRIPTION OF A NEW SPECIES OF INDIAN PORCUPINE. Philip Lutley Sclater. Proc. Zool. Soc. Lond., pp.352-356, figs. 2, pl. 16, 1865.

THE FRETFUL PORCUPINE. Arthur de C Sowerby. China Jour., vol.11, no.5, pp. 249-252, pl.1, Nov., 1929.

THE BRUSH-TAILED PORCUPINE OF ASSAM. Oldfield Thomas. Jour. Bombay Nat. Hist. Soc., vol.27, pp.598-599, Mar.31, 1921.

DESCRIPTION OF A NEW PORCUPINE FROM EAST AFRICA. Oldfield Thomas. Ann. and Mag. Nat. Hist. (6), vol.11, no. 63, pp.229-231, Mar., 1893.

ON A NEW SPECIES OF ATHERURA DISCOVERED BY CAPT. GUY BURROWSON THE CONGO. Oldfield Thomas. Ann. and Mag. Nat. Hist. (7), vol.9, no.52, pp.270-271, Apr., 1901.

ON THE BRUSH-TAILED PORCUPINE OF CENTRAL AFRICA. Oldfield Thomas. Ann. and Mag. Nat. Hist. (6), vol.15, no. 85, pp.88-89, Jan., 1895.

THE PORCUPINE OF ASSAM. Oldfield Thomas. Jour. Bombay Nat. Hist. Soc., vol.28, pp.431-432, Mar.25, 1922.

THE PORCUPINE OF TENASSERIM AND SOUTHERN SIAM. Oldfield Thomas. Ann. and Mag. Nat. Hist. (8), vol.17, no.97, pp.136-139, Jan., 1916.

DO PORCUPINES CARRY WATER FOR THEIR YOUNG? A. C. Tutein-Nolthenius. Jour. Soc. Preservation Fauna of the Empire, Hartford, n.s., pt.37, pp.56-58, illus., Aug., 1939.

## Erethizontidae

PORKY-OAF OF THE WOODS. Roy L. Abbott. Fauna, Phila., vol.8, no.4, pp. 118-119, illus., Dec., 1946.

PERNICIOUS 'PORKY' SQUIRE OF THE PINE COUNTRY. Elizabeth Bachmann. Conserv. Volunteer, St. Paul, vol.10, no. 60, pp.42-45, Sept.-Oct., 1947.

POINTS ABOUT PORCUPINES. Ernest Harold Bayner. Nature Mag., vol.5, pp. 25-29, 7 figs., Jan., 1925.

THE PORCUPINE—WOODLAND FOOL. G. W. Bradt. Michigan Conserv., Lansing, vol.16, no.11, pp.4-5, illus., Dec., 1947.

HEART'S RUE AND SELF-DEFENSE, WITH AN EPILOGUE ON THE FOIBLES OF FATIMA AS RECORDED IN WORD AND PICTURE. (PORCUPINE.) Wilfrid S. Bronson. Nature Mag., Wash., D.C., vol. 36, no.10, pp.513-518, 548, illus., Dec., 1943.

ADVENTURE WITH PORCUPINE. Sam Campbell. Amer. Forests, Washington, D.C., vol.49, no.9, pp.426-427, 463, Sept., 1943.

PORKY LORE. Bonnycastle Dale, Jr. Rod and Gun in Can., 39 (6): 15-16, 33-34, Nov., 1937.

(RESEARCH ON THE DENTAL MORPHOLOGY AND AFFINITIES OF FOSSIL AND LIVING RODENTS OF THE COENDINAE GROUP (STEIROMYS-ERETHIZON-COENDU).) Recherches sur la morphologie dentaire et les affinites des Rongeurs fossiles et actuels du groupe des Coendines (Steiromys-Erethizon-Coendu). M. Friant. Proc. Zool. Soc. Lond., pt.3, pp.725-732, pls.4, Sept., 1936.

A PORCUPINE OUT-PATIENT. Lawrence Kilham. Bull. Massachusetts Audubon Soc., North Abington, vol.33, no.6, pp. 244-245, Oct., 1949.

PORCUPINES. Dan McDonald. Beaver, Winnipeg, outfit no.282, pp.16-17, illus., Dec., 1951.

SEROLOGICAL LIGHT ON PORCUPINE RELATIONSHIPS. Paul A. Moody, David E. Doniger. Evolution, 10 (1): 47-55, Mar. 31, 1956.

SOFTER SIDE OF A PORCUPINE. Neil W. Owen. Our Dumb Animals, Norwood, vol. 79, no.1, p.7, illus., Jan., 1946.

NOTES ON A LARGE PORCUPINE. George A. Petrides. Yosemite Nat. Notes, Yosemite, vol.20, no.3, pp.20-21, Mar., 1941.

SURVIVAL OF THE FITTEST. (PORCUPINE.) Bob W. Prudhomme. Yosemite Nat. Notes, Yosemite, vol.21, no.9, p.76, Sept., 1942.

THE NORTHERN PORCUPINES. A CHAPTER IN DEGENERACY. Samuel Rhoads. Forest and Stream, New York, vol.52, no. 15, pp.284-285, illus., Apr.15, 1899.

THE WELL-ARMED PORCUPINE. Albert R. Shadle. Anim. Kingdom, 57 (5): 130-137, illus., Oct., 1954.

PORCUPINES, RAMBLING PINCUSHIONS. Donald A. Spencer. Natl. Geog. Mag., 98 (2): 247-264, Aug., 1950.

DIAGNOSIS OF A NEW CENTRAL-AMERICAN PORCUPINE. Oldfield Thomas. Ann. and Mag. Nat. Hist. (7), vol.10, no.56, p. 169, Aug., 1902.

(ECHINOPROCTA RUFESCENS (HYSTRICIDAE), DESCRIBED BY GRAY IN 1865, FOUND IN COLOMBIA, NEAR BOGOTA.) L'Echinoprocta rufescens (Hystricidae), decrit par Gray en 1865, retrouve en Colombie, pres de Bogota. E. L. Trouessart. Bull. Mus. d'Hist. Nat., pp.448-453, 3 figs., 1920.

YELLOW HAIRED PORCUPINE. Murrelet, Seattle, vol.20, no.3, p.71, Sept.-Dec., 1939.

### Anatomy

STUDY TO DETERMINE CRANIAL AND DENTAL CORRELATIONS WITH AGE AND SEX IN THE CANADIAN PORCUPINE, ERETHIZON DORSATUM DORSATUM (LINNAEUS). Robert C. Kochersberger. MS thesis, Univ. Buffalo, 1950.

A PORCUPINE SKULL WITH A PAIR OF SUPERNUMERARY WELL DEVELOPED INCISORS IN THE UPPER JAW. Marcus W. Lyon, Jr. Anat. Record, vol.10, no.6, pp. 459-462, fig.1, Apr., 1916.

NOTE ON THE FEMALE ORGANS OF ERETHIZON DORSATUS. Alexander Meek. Studies from the Museum of Zoology, Univ. College, Dundee, vol.1, no.12, p.9, pl.1, Aug., 1890.

GROSS ANATOMY OF THE MALE REPRODUCTIVE SYSTEM OF THE PORCUPINE. Edwin Mirand, Albert R. Shadle. Jour. Mam., vol.34, no.2, pp.210-220, illus., May 14, 1953.

ACCESSORY CORPORA LUTEA, LUTEIN CELLS, ORIGIN, AND THE OVARIAN CYCLE IN THE CANADIAN PORCUPINE. H. W. Mossman, Ilse Judas. Amer. Jour. Anat., Phila., vol.85, no.1, pp.1-39, illus., 1949.

A RETENTION OF PLACENTA IN PORCUPINE. Albert R. Shadle, William R. Ploss. North Amer. Veterinarian, Chicago, vol.26, pp.611-612, Oct., 1945.

THE EXTRUSIVE GROWTH AND ATTRITION OF THE INCISOR TEETH OF ERETHIZON DORSATUM. Albert R. Shadle, William R. Ploss, Eugene M. Marks. Anat. Record, Phila., vol.90, no.4, pp.337-341, Dec., 1944.

THE PRENATAL DEVELOPMENT OF THE PANCREATIC AND EXTRA-HEPATIC DUCTS IN THE CANADIAN PORCUPINE ERETHIZON DORSATUM. P. H. Struthers. Anat. Record, Phila., vol.81, no. 2, pp.145-161, 6 figs., 1 pl., Oct.25, 1941.

THE PRENATAL SKULL OF THE CANADIAN PORCUPINE (ERETHIZON DORSATUS). P. H. Struthers. Jour. Morph. and Physiol., vol.44, no.2, pp. 127-216, 1927.

OSTEOLOGY OF THE COMMON PORCUPINE ERETHIZON DORSATUM. Richard Swena, Laurence M. Ashley. Publ. Dept. Biol. Sci. and Biol. Sta., Walla Walla College, no.18, pp.1-26, Dec.15, 1956.

### Captivity

DINTY, A PET PORCUPINE. William L. Finley, Irene Finley. Nature Mag., vol.3, pp.133-137, 170, 11 figs., Mar., 1924.

THE TRUE STORY OF A PET PORCUPINE. Alfred Kay. Canadian Field-Nat., vol.46, no.1, p.6, Jan., 1932.

FEEDING, CARE, AND HANDLING OF CAPTIVE PORCUPINES (ERETHIZON). Albert R. Shadle. Jour. Mam., vol.31, no.4, pp.411-416, Nov.21, 1950.

### Economic Importance

WHY SLAUGHTER PORCUPINES? Morley Cooper. Our Dumb Animals, Norwood, vol.73, no.12, p.188, Dec., 1940.

APPRAISAL OF PORCUPINE DAMAGE. James D. Curtis. Jour. Wildlife Mgt., 8 (1): 88-91, Jan., 1944.

THE SILVICULTURAL SIGNIFICANCE OF THE PORCUPINE. James D. Curtis. Jour. Forestry, 39 (7): 583-594, July, 1941.

WHAT THEY SAY ABOUT PORKY. James D. Curtis. Amer. Forests, Washington, vol.52, no.10, pp.474-475, illus., Oct., 1946.

PORCUPINE FEEDING ON PONDEROSA PINE IN CENTRAL IDAHO. James D. Curtis, Alvin K. Wilson. Jour. For., 51 (5): 339-341, graphs, May, 1953.

THE PORCUPINE—FRIEND OR FOE. K. D. Flock. Amer. Forests, vol.40, no.7, pp.308-310, 330, July, 1934.

PORCUPINE CONTROL IN THE WESTERN STATES. Ira N. Gabrielson, E. E. Horn. Leaflet 60, pp.8, figs.6, May, 1930.

PORCUPINE CONTROL ON FORESTS OF CALIFORNIA. Joseph Keyes. California Fish and Game, vol.20, no.2, pp.148-150, Apr., 1934.

PORCUPINE CONTROL: A PROBLEM ANALYSIS. William H. Lawrence, Forestry Research Notes, Weyerhaeuser Timber Co., Centralia, Wash., pp.1-43 (mimeogr.), July, 1957.

HERE'S ONE EXPERT'S OPINION ON PORCUPINE CONTROL. John Ludeman. Pest Control, 22 (4): 26, 28, 30, 44, illus., Apr., 1954.

PORCUPINE PERIL. Margaret Williams Osborn. New Mexico Mag., Albuquerque, vol.27, no.11, pp.25, 46-47, illus., Nov., 1949.

PORCUPINE'S PREFERENCES IN PINE PLANTATIONS. P. O. Rudolf. Jour. Forestry, 47 (3): 207-209, Mar., 1949.

AN ELECTRIC FENCE FOR USE IN CHECKING PORCUPINE AND OTHER MAMMALIAN CROP DEPREDATIONS. Donald A. Spencer. Jour. Wildlife Mgt., 12 (1): 110-111, Jan., 1948.

A FOREST MAMMAL MOVES TO THE FARM--THE PORCUPINE. Donald A. Spencer. Trans. N.A. Wildlife Conf., 11: 195-199, 1946.

THE PORCUPINE: ITS ECONOMIC STATUS AND CONTROL. Donald A. Spencer. USDI, F&WS, Wildlife Leaflet 328, 7 pp., May, 1950.

PORCUPINE DAMAGE TO TREES SERIOUS IN NORTHWEST. J. Herbert Stone. Jour. Forestry, 50 (11): 891, Nov., 1952.

PORCUPINES DESTROY BEAN CROP. Colorado Conserv. Comments, Denver, vol.9, no.3, p.16, Sept.15, 1946.

Fossils

A FOSSIL PORCUPINE FROM ARIZONA. J. A. Allen. Bull. Amer. Mus. Nat. Hist., vol.20, pp.383-384, Oct.15, 1904.

(RESEARCH ON THE DENTAL MORPHOLOGY AND THE AFFINITIES OF FOSSIL AND LIVING RODENTS OF THE COENDINE GROUP (STEIROMYS-ERETHIZON-COENDU).) Recherches sur la morphologie dentaire et les affinites des Rongeurs fossiles et actuels du groupe des Coendines (Steiromys-Erethizon-Coendu). M. Friant. Proc. Zool. Soc., Lond., pt.3, pp.725-732, pl.4, Sept., 1936.

A NEW SPECIES OF PORCUPINE FROM THE LATER CENOZOIC OF IDAHO. Robert W. Wilson. Jour. Mam., vol.16, no.3, pp.220-222, fig.1, Aug., 1935.

Habits, Behavior

BONE CARRYING BY A PORCUPINE. Anne J. Alexander. South African Jour. Sci., vol.52, no.11, pp.257-258, June, 1956.

THE VOICE OF THE PORCUPINE. Charles Foster Batchelder. Jour. Mam., vol.11, no.2, pp.237-239, May, 1930.

A PORCUPINE MISCALCULATES. C. Frank Brockman. Yosemite Nat. Notes, Yosemite, vol.21, no.6, pp.49-50, June, 1942.

PORCUPINE SWIMS FOR FOOD. Howard J. Dean. Jour. Mam., vol.31, no.1, p.94, Feb.21, 1950.

NOTES ON THE HABITS AND BEHAVIOR OF THE PORCUPINE IN OREGON. Ira N. Gabrielson. Jour. Mam., vol.9, no.1, pp. 33-38, pl.8, Feb., 1928.

PORCUPINE SUBWAY. Lon Garrison. Yosemite Nat. Notes, Stockton, Calif., vol.18, no.3, p.23, Mar., 1939.

A PORCUPINE INCIDENT. O. J. Gromme. Milwaukee Public Mus. Yearbook, vol.6 (1926), pp.188-189, illus., Sept.1, 1927.

AN INQUISITIVE PORCUPINE. Hartley H. T. Jackson. Jour. Mam., vol.2, no.4, p. 238, Nov.29, 1921.

TROUT ENCOUNTERS PORCUPINE. E. R. Kalmbach. Jour. Mam., vol.34, no.4, p. 511, Nov.13, 1953.

NOTES ON THE HABITS OF THE PORCUPINE. Alfred Kay. Canadian Field-Nat., vol.46, no.8, p.187, Nov., 1932.

PORCUPINES GNAW BOTTLES. F. W. Preston. Jour. Mam., vol.29, no.1, pp. 72-73, pl.1, Feb.13, 1948.

PORCUPINE DAMAGE TO BIGHORN SHEEP. Albert Van S. Pulling. Jour. Wildlife Mgt., 9 (4): 329, Oct., 1945.

KETTLE EATEN BY PORCUPINES. W. E. Scott. Wisconsin Conserv. Bull., Madison, vol.6, no.2, p.38, illus., Feb., 1941; Jour. Mam., vol.22, no.3, pp.325-326, Aug.14, 1941.

THE SONG OF THE PORCUPINE (ERETHIZON EPIXANTHUM). Ernest Thompson Seton. Jour. Mam., vol.13, no.2, pp. 168-169, May, 1932.

THE PLAY OF AMERICAN PORCUPINES (ERETHIZON D. DORSATUM AND E. EPIXANTHUM). Albert R. Shadle. Jour. Comp. Psychol., Balto., vol.37, no.3, pp.145-150, June, 1944.

AN INTERESTING CAESAREAN OPERATION. Donald A. Spencer. Jour. Mam., vol.11, no.1, pp.84-86, Feb., 1930.

"PORCUPINE TREE." Charles B. Todd. Yosemite Nat. Notes, Yosemite, vol.20, no.12, p.112, Dec., 1941.

THE VOICE OF THE PORCUPINE. Otis Wade. Jour. Mam., vol.12, no.1, p.71, Feb., 1931.

A HUNGRY PORCUPINE. Leland C. Wyman. Jour. Mam., vol.4, no.3, p.190, Aug., 1923.

North America

VARIATION IN THE PORCUPINE (GENUS ERETHIZON) IN CANADA. R. M. Anderson, A. L. Rand. Can. Jour. Res., Sec.D, 21 (9): 292-309, Sept., 1943.

NOTES ON THE CANADA PORCUPINE. Charles Foster Batchelder. Jour. Mam., 29 (3): 260-268, Aug., 1948.

A RECORD OF THE PORCUPINE (ERETHIZON DORSATUM) FROM SONORA, MEXICO. Seth B. Benson. Jour. Mam., vol.34, no.4, pp.511-512, Nov.13, 1953.

NOTES ON PORCUPINES OF THE GRAND CANYON REGION. Charles M. Bogert. Grand Canyon Nat. Notes, vol.8, no.1, p.137-140, Apr., 1933.

OCCURRENCE OF A YELLOW-HAIRED SPECIMEN OF THE EASTERN PORCUPINE (ERETHIZON DORSATUM DORSATUM L.) IN ONTARIO. N. R. Brown. Canadian Field-Nat., Ottawa, vol.62, no.1, pp.38-39, illus., Jan.-Feb., 1948.

THE PORCUPINE IN THE BLACK HILLS. G. W. Coats. South Dakota Conserv. Digest, Pierre, vol.12, no.7, p.7, July, 1945.

PORCUPINES IN FRANKLIN COUNTY, WASHINGTON. Leo K. Couch. Murrelet, vol.13, no.2, p.55, May 23, 1932.

OBSERVATIONS ON THE EASTERN PORCUPINE. James D. Curtis, Edward L. Kozicky. Jour. Mam., 25 (2): 137-146, May, 1944.

A CANADA PORCUPINE FROM LAKE COUNTY, ILLINOIS. D. Dwight Davis. Jour. Mam., vol.14, no.1, pp.76-77, Feb., 1933.

OCCURRENCE OF PORCUPINES IN WESTERN WASHINGTON. Ford Dicks. Murrelet, vol.19, nos.1-2, p.19, Jan.-May, 1938.

PORCUPINES IN SOUTHWESTERN ARIZONA. O. E. Frye, Jr. Jour. Mam., vol.29, no. 2, p.182, May 14, 1948.

THE OCCURRENCE OF THE CANADA PORCUPINE IN WEST VIRGINIA. George Brown Goode. U.S. Nat. Mus. Proc., Wash., vol.1, pp.264-265, 1879.

NOTICE OF AN APPARENTLY UNDESCRIBED SPECIES OF AMERICAN PORCUPINE. John E. Gray. Proc. Zool. Soc. London, pp.321-322, pl.11, 1865.

FIRST RECORDS OF PORCUPINE ON THE MOHAVE DESERT OF CALIFORNIA. Edmund C. Jaeger. Jour. Mam., Balto., vol.50, no.2, pp.200-201, May 23, 1949.

PORCUPINE IN VIRGINIA. John B. Lewis. Jour. Mam., vol.22, no.4, p.452, Nov.14, 1941.

PORCUPINE RECORDS IN OKLAHOMA. Frank B. McMurry. Jour. Mam., vol.25, no.4, p.413, Dec.12, 1944.

THE OCCURRENCE OF THE CANADA PORCUPINE IN MARYLAND. Otto Lugger. Proc. U. S. Nat. Mus. Wash., 1882, vol.4, pp.161-162, Aug.11, 1881.

PORCUPINE IN MARIN COUNTY, CALIFORNIA. Joseph Mailliard. Jour. Mam., vol.12, no.2, p.169, May, 1931.

COUES PORCUPINE IN COLORADO. Frederick W. Miller. Jour. Mam., vol. 5, no.2, p.134, May, 1924.

PORCUPINES IN SOUTHWESTERN ARIZONA. Gale Monson. Jour. Mam., vol.29, no.2, p.182, May 14, 1948.

THE PORCUPINE IN NORTHERN ALASKA. Olaus J. Murie. Jour. Mam., vol.7, no.2, pp.109-113, May, 1926.

SOME PORCUPINE RECORDS FOR THE COLORADO RIVER, NEVADA. Warren Pulich. Jour. Mam., vol.34, no.2, pp. 259-260, 1953.

NOTES ON THE CANADA PORCUPINE IN THE MARITIME PROVINCES. W. A. Reeks. Forestry Chron., 18 (4): 182-187, Dec., 1942.

THE NORTH AMERICAN PORCUPINE UP-TO-DATE. Albert R. Shadle. Ward's Nat. Sci. Bull., Rochester, vol.24, no.1, pp.5, 6, 11, illus., Sept., 1950.

ECOLOGICAL AND LIFE HISTORY NOTES ON THE PORCUPINE IN THE ADIRONDACKS. Jacob Shapiro. Jour. Mam., vol. 30, no.3, pp.247-257, illus., Aug.17, 1949.

LIFE HISTORY AND ECOLOGY OF THE PORCUPINE, ERETHIZON D. DORSATUM L., ON THE HUNTINGTON WILDLIFE FOREST EXPERIMENT STATION, NEWCOMB, NEW YORK. Jacob Shapiro. MS thesis, Syracuse Univ., 1947.

ON A NEW SUBSPECIES OF PORCUPINE FROM NEBRASKA. Myron Harmon Swenk. Univ. Studies, Lincoln, Nebraska, vol.16, no.1-2, pp.115-125, pls.3, Nov.21, 1916.

ECOLOGY AND LIFE HISTORY OF THE PORCUPINE (ERETHIZON EPIXANTHUM) AS RELATED TO THE FORESTS OF ARIZONA AND THE SOUTH-WESTERN UNITED STATES. Walter P. Taylor. Bull. Univ. Arizona Biol. Sci., no.3, vol. 6, no.5, pp.1-177, July 1, 1935.

(Review by A. Brazier Howell of ) THE ECOLOGY AND LIFE HISTORY OF THE PORCUPINE (ERETHIZON EPIZANTHUM) AS RELATED TO THE FORESTS OF ARIZONA AND SOUTH-WESTERN UNITED STATES. Walter P. Taylor. Jour. Mam., vol.17, no.1, p.69, Feb., 1936.

(Review by Aldo Leopold of) THE ECOLOGY AND LIFE HISTORY OF THE PORCUPINE (ERETHIZON EPIXANTHUM) AS RELATED TO THE FORESTS OF ARIZONA AND THE SOUTHWESTERN UNITED STATES. Walter P. Taylor. Jour. Forestry, vol.34, no.6, pp.632-633, June, 1936.

TWO PORCUPINES KILLED IN OKLAHOMA IN JULY. Oklahoma Game and Fish News, Oklahoma City, vol.1, no.8, p.7, Aug., 1945.

Parasites

THE GENUS SCHIZOTAENIA IN PORCUPINES. Asa C. Chandler. Jour. Parasitology, 22 (5): 513, Oct., 1936.

NOTES ON THE MORPHOLOGY AND LIFE CYCLE OF THE GENUS MONECOCESTUS BEDDARD, 1914, FROM THE PORCUPINE. Reino S. Freeman. Jour. Parasitol., Lancaster, vol.35, no.6, pp.605-612, Dec., 1949.

DIPETALONEMA ARBUTA N. SP. (NEMATODA) FROM THE PORCUPINE, ERETHIZON DORSATUM (L.). Paul R. Highby. Jour. Parasitology, 29 (4): 239-242, Aug., 1943.

MOSQUITO VECTORS AND LARVAL DEVELOPMENT OF DIPETALONEMA ARBUTA HIGHBY (NEMATODA) FROM THE PORCUPINE ERETHIZON DORSATUM. Paul R. Highby. Jour. Parasitology, 29 (4): 243-252, Aug., 1943.

A NEW PROLIFERATING LARVAL TAPEWORM FROM A PORCUPINE. Benjamin Swartz. Proc. U.S. Nat. Mus., vol.66, art.24, pp.4, pl.1, Dec., 1924.

Pelage (Quills) and Coloration

AN ALBINO PORCUPINE (ERETHIZON DORSATUM). Harry Bernard. Canadian Field-Nat., Ottawa, vol.55, no.1, p.14, fig., Jan., 1941.

PORCUPINE EXTRACTS QUILL. Austin W. Cameron. Canadian Field-Nat., Ottawa, vol.63, no.1, p.43, Jan.-Feb., 1949.

QUILLS. Helen V. Merritts. Pennsylvania Game News, Harrisburg, vol.14, no.10, p. 25, illus., Jan., 1944.

PELAGE OF THE PORCUPINE, ERETHIZON DORSATUM DORSATUM. Donald S. Po-Chedley, Albert R. Shadle. Jour. Mam., vol.36, no.1, pp.84-95, 1 fig., 2 tables, Feb.25, 1955.

OCCURRENCE OF PORCUPINE QUILLS IN CARNIVOROUS MAMMALS. Horace F. Quick. Jour. Mam., 34 (2): 256-259, May, 1953.

EFFECTS OF PORCUPINE QUILLS IN HUMANS. Albert R. Shadle. Amer. Nat., 89 (844): 47-49, Jan.-Feb., 1955.

PORCUPINE SPINE PENETRATION. Albert R. Shadle. Jour. Mam., vol.28, no. 2, pp.180-181, May 19, 1947.

REMOVAL OF FOREIGN QUILLS BY PORCUPINES. Albert R. Shadle. Jour. Mam., 36 (3): 463-465, Aug.30, 1955.

RATE OF PENETRATION OF A PORCUPINE SPINE. Albert R. Shadle, Donald Po-Chedley. Jour. Mam., Balto., vol.30, no. 2, pp.172-173, fig.1, May 23, 1949.

BARBLESS QUILLS OF PORCUPINE. Leon F. Whitney. Jour. Mam., vol.12, no.4, p.433, Nov., 1931.

(THE PELAGE OF A PORCUPINE.) Les poils du porc-epic. Edmond Yourans. Naturaliste Canadien, vol.57, no.10, p.205, 1930.

HOW TO REMOVE PORCUPINE QUILLS. Blue Jay, Saskatchewan Nat. Hist. Soc., 14 (3): 101, Sept., 1956.

Predation and Mortality

PORCUPINE QUILLS IN A FOX SKULL. Charles E. Johnson. Jour. Mam., vol.15, no.4, p.319, Nov., 1934.

PORCUPINE KILLED AND EATEN BY A COYOTE. L. Floyd Keller. Jour. Mam., vol.16, no.3, p.232, Aug., 1935.

ACCIDENTAL DEATH OF A PORCUPINE. William H. Marshall. Jour. Mam., vol. 32, no.2, p.221, May 21, 1951.

THE CANADA PORCUPINE AS A HIGHWAY CASUALTY. Dayton Stoner. Jour. Mam., vol.21, no.3, pp.360-361, Aug.14, 1940.

THE CANADIAN PORCUPINE AGAIN A HIGHWAY MORTALITY VICTIM. Lillian C. Stoner. Jour. Mam., vol.28, no.4, p.398, Nov.26, 1947.

BOBCAT PREYING ON PORCUPINE? A. de Vos. Jour. Mam., vol.34, no.1, pp.129-130, Feb.19, 1953.

ATTACKS ON PORCUPINE BY GRAY FOX AND WILD CATS. Richard Lee Weaver. Jour. Mam., vol.20, no.3, p.379, Aug.14, 1939.

Reproductive Biology

MATING BEHAVIOUR OF THE PORCUPINE ERETHIZON DORSATUM. R. W. Hawkins. Candian Field-Nat., Sutton West, vol.60, no.5, p.109, Sept-Oct., 1946 (published in 1947).

A PREGNANT PORCUPINE. Lawrence Kilham. Jour. Mam., vol.12, no.3, pp. 318-319, Aug., 1930.

A BABY PORCUPINE. Charles Macnamara. Canadian Field Nat., vol.35, pp.70-72, Apr., 1921.

THE NEW-BORN OF THE BRAZILIAN TREE-PORCUPINE (COENDOU PREHENSILIS LINN.) AND OF THE HAIRY TREE-PORCUPINE (SPHINGURUS VILLOSUS F. CUV.). Alipio de Miranda-Ribeiro. Proc. Zool. Soc. Lond., 1936, pt.4, pp.971-974, pl.1, Jan., 1937.

COPULATION IN THE PORCUPINE. Albert R. Shadle. Jour. Wildlife Mgt., 10 (2): 159-162, Apr., 1946.

GESTATION PERIOD IN THE PORCUPINE, ERETHIZON DORSATUM DORSATUM. Albert R. Shadle. Jour. Mam., vol.29, no.2, pp.162-164, May 14, 1948.

LABORATORY COPULATIONS AND GESTATIONS OF PORCUPINE, ERETHIZON DORSATUM. Albert R. Shadle. Jour. Mam., vol.32, no.2, pp.219-221, May 21, 1951.

NATURAL PARTURITION OF A PORCUPINE AND FIRST REACTIONS OF THE PORCUPETTE. Albert R. Shadle. Ohio Jour. Sci., 54 (1): 42-44, Jan., 1954.

SEXUAL MATURITY AND FIRST RECORDED COPULATION OF A 16-MONTH MALE PORCUPINE, ERETHIZON DORSATUM DORSATUM. Albert R. Shadle. Jour. Mam., vol.33, no.2, pp.239-241, May 16, 1952.

AN UNUSUAL PORCUPINE PARTURITION AND DEVELOPMENT OF THE YOUNG. Albert R. Shadle, William R. Ploss. Jour. Mam., vol.24, no.4, pp.492-496, fig.1, Nov.17, 1943.

THE SEX REACTIONS OF PORCUPINES (ERETHIZON D. DORSATUM) BEFORE AND AFTER COPULATION. Albert R. Shadle, Marilyn Smelzer, Margery Metz. Jour. Mam., vol.27, no.2, pp.116-121, May 14, 1946.

UNUSUAL SEX BEHAVIOR OF A MALE PORCUPINE, ERETHIZON DORSATUM EPIXANTHUM. Jeff Richard Spalsbury. Jour. Mam., 37 (3): 452-453, Sept.11, 1956.

A YELLOW-HAIRED PORCUPINE BORN IN CAPTIVITY. James M. Sprague. Jour. Mam., Balto., vol.18, no.4, p.519, Nov., 1937.

BREEDING HABITS OF THE CANADIAN PORCUPINE (ERETHIZON DORSATUM). Parke H. Struthers. Jour. Mam., vol.9, no.4, pp.300-308, pls.22-23, 1928.

BEHAVIOR AND POST-NATAL DEVELOPMENT OF A PORCUPINE. Clarence Archer Tryon, Jr. Jour. Wildlife Mgt., Menasha, vol.11, no.3, pp.282-283, July, 1947.

BIRTH OF PORCUPINE IS RARE BLESSED EVENT. Science News Letter, Wash., D. C., vol.41, no.22, p.345, May 30, 1942.

Caviidae

(THE NEW SUBGENUS "PARADOLICHOTIS" KRAGL.) A proposito del nuevo subgenero "Paradolichotis" Kragl. L. Kraglievich. Buenos Aires, pp.1-2, Dec.12, 1927.

NOTE ON THE CAVIES OF THE GENUS DOLICHOTIS AND ON LIVING SPECIMENS OF D. SALINICOLA. Edmund Loder. Proc. Zool. Soc. Lond., vol.1, pp.96-97, pl.4, June 7, 1906.

(ON THE ORIGIN OF THE GUINEA PIG, CAVIA COBAYA MARCGR.) Ueber die Herkunft des Meerschweinchens (Cavia cobaya Marcgr.). Alfred Nehring. Sitz.-Ber. Gesell. Naturf. Freunde, Berlin, no.1, pp.1-4, figs.3, Jan.15, 1889.

GUINEA-PIGS. W. P. Pycraft. Illus. London News, vol.194, no.5222, p.876, figs.4, May 20, 1939.

GIFTS OF THE AMERICAS. THE GUINEA PIG. Jane W. Roller. Agriculture in the Americas, U.S. Dept. Agric., Office of Foreign Agric. Relations, Wash., vol.5, no.6, p.119, June, 1945.

Anatomy

DISTRIBUTION OF THE FIBERS ORIGINATING FROM THE DIFFERENT BASAL CEREBELLAR NUCLEI. (WORK ON GUINEA PIG.) William F. Allen. Jour. Comp. Neur., vol.36, pp.399-440, 10 figs., Apr. 15, 1924.

THE STRUCTURE, FUNCTION, AND REGENERATION OF THE SEMINAL VESICLES OF THE GUINEA PIG. Reo B. Armitstead. Jour. Exper. Zool., vol.41, pp.215-233, Jan.5, 1925.

THE FIBRILLAR STRUCTURE OF THE DENTAL ENAMEL MATRIX OF THE GUINEA PIG. T. D. Beckwith, Adrienne Williams. Science, n.s., vol.65, pp.165-166, Feb.11, 1927.

POST-NATAL GROWTH IN WEIGHT OF THE BODY AND OF THE VARIOUS ORGANS IN THE GUINEA-PIG. A. N. Bessesen, Jr., H. A. Carlson. Amer. Jour. Anat., vol.31, pp.483-523, 25 charts, May, 1923.

NORMAL BLOOD PICTURE OF THE GUINEA PIG. D.L.J. Bilbey, T. Nicol. Nature, London, vol.176, no.4495, p.1218, Dec.24, 1955.

(APPEARANCE OF THE KURLOFF BODY DURING THE COURSE OF THE GRAVID INVOLUTION OF THE THYMUS GLAND IN THE GUINEA PIG.) Apparition de corps de Kurloff au cours de l'involution gravidique du thymus chez le cobaye. C. Bimes. Bull. Soc. Hist. Nat. Toulouse, vol.78, fasc.3, pp.191-198, figs.5, Oct.10, 1943.

(THE DENTAL FOLLICLES OF THE GUINEA-PIG. MORPHOLOGY, HISTOLOGY, AND NOTES ON THE VASCULARIZATION OF THE ENAMEL ORGAN.) Les follicules dentaires du cobaye. Morphologie, histologie et considerations sur la vascularisation de l'organe de l'email. Pierre Bourgeois. Rev. Suisse Zool., Geneva, vol.53, fasc.2 (nos.6-8), pp.227-328, figs. 65, May, 1946.

THE ORIGIN OF DUST-CELLS IN THE LUNG. (WORK ON GUINEA PIGS.) H. M. Carleton. Quart. Jour. Micro. Sci., vol. 71, pp.223-237, 1 pl., Aug., 1927.

A STUDY OF HAIR GROWTH IN THE GUINEA-PIG (CAVIA COBAYA). Helen L. Dawson. Amer. Jour. Anat., vol.45, no. 3, pp.461-484, 8 figs., 1930.

A COMPARATIVE ANALYSIS OF THE MEASUREMENTS OF THE LIMB BONES OF INBRED FAMILIES OF GUINEA PIGS AND THEIR HYBRIDS AS AFFECTED BY FAMILY, SEX, AND AGE. O. N. Eaton. Amer. Jour. Anat., Phila., vol.64, no.3, pp.485-499, May 15, 1939.

MIDDLE-PIECE BEADS IN THE CAVIA SPERMATOZOON. J. Brontie Gatenby, L. Collery. Nature, London, vol.151, no.3826, pp.253-254, figs.3, Feb.27, 1943.

A HISTOLOGICAL DESCRIPTION OF PIGMENT DISTRIBUTION IN THE EYES OF GUINEA-PIGS OF VARIOUS GENETIC TYPES. P. W. Gregory. Jour. Morphol. and Physiol., vol.47, pp.227-249, 5 pls., 1929.

THE WIDTH OF THE BASILAR MEMBRANE. Stacy R. Guild. Science, n.s., vol.65, pp. 67-69, Jan.21, 1927.

A HISTOCHEMICAL AND QUANTITATIVE STUDY OF PHOSPHATASE IN THE PLACENTA AND FETAL MEMBRANES OF THE GUINEA PIG. Walter L. Hard. Amer. Jour. Anat., Phila., vol.78, no.1, pp.47-77, figs.1-2, pls.1-5, Jan., 1946.

THE DEVELOPMENT OF THE EXTERNAL FORM OF THE GUINEA-PIG (CAVIA COBAYA) BETWEEN THE AGES OF 21 DAYS AND 35 DAYS OF GESTATION. Mary

T. Harman, Marjorie Prickett Dobrovolny. Jour. Morph., vol.54, no.3, pp.493-515, pls.2, June, 1933.

SOME OBSERVATIONS ON THE DEVELOPMENT OF THE TEETH OF CAVIA COBAYA. Mary T. Harman, Arlene Smith. Anat. Rec., vol.66, no.1, pp.97-106, pls. 1-2, Aug.25, 1936.

THE DEVELOPMENT OF THE PHARYNX OF THE GUINEA PIG WITH SPECIAL EMPHASIS ON THE FATE OF THE ULTIMOBRANCHIAL BODY. Clarence E. Klapper. Amer. Jour. Anat., Phila., vol.79, no.3, pp.361-397, figs.29, Nov., 1946.

THE DEVELOPMENT OF THE PHARYNX OF THE GUINEA PIG WITH SPECIAL EMPHASIS ON THE MORPHOGENESIS OF THE THYMUS. Clarence E. Klapper. Amer. Jour. Anat., Phila., vol.78, no.2, pp.139-179, pls.1-5, Mar., 1946.

CORRELATED CHEMICAL AND HISTOLOGICAL STUDIES OF THE ADRENAL LIPIDS. I. THE EFFECT OF EXTREME MUSCULAR ACTIVITY ON THE ADRENAL LIPIDS OF THE GUINEA PIG. R. A. Knouff, J. B. Brown, B. M. Schneider. Anat. Record, Phila., vol.79, no.1, pp.17-38, Jan.25, 1941.

(CRANIO-DENTAL CHARACTERISTICS OF THE LIVING RODENT MONTICAVIA (NANOCAVIA) SHIPTONI THOM.) Caracteres craneodentarios del roedor vivente Monticavia (Nanocavia) shiptoni Thom. Lucas Kraglievich. Anales Soc. Cient. Argentina, vol.112, no.6, pp.337-342, figs.3, 1931.

(OSTEOLOGIC DENTITION DIAGNOSIS OF THE LIVING GENERA OF SUB-FAMILY CAVIINAE.) Diagnosis osteologico-dentaria de los generos vivientes de la subfamilia Caviinae. Lucas Kraglievich. Anal. Mus. Nac. Hist. Nat. Bernardino Rivadavia, Buenos Aires, vol.36, pp.59-96, figs.5, pls.11, Feb.11, 1930.

PARTICULATE GLYCOGEN: A SUBMICROSCOPIC COMPONENT OF THE GUINEA PIG LIVER CELL; ITS SIGNIFICANCE IN GLYCOGEN STORAGE AND THE REGULATION OF BLOOD SUGAR. Arnold Lazarow. Anat. Record, Phila., vol.84, no.1, pp.31-50, Sept.25, 1942.

THE CYCLIC CHANGES IN THE OVARY OF THE GUINEA PIG. Leo Loeb. Jour. Morph., vol.22, no.1, pp.37-70, Mar.20, 1911.

(DATA ON THE SEMINAL VESICLES OF THE GUINEA PIG.) Zur Kenntniss der Samenblasen beim Meerschweinchen. Charles Sedgwick Minot. Archiv. f. Mikroskop. Anat., Bonn, vol.24, pp.211-215, pl.12, 1885.

VISUAL CELLS OF THE GUINEA PIG. Kevin O'Day. Nature, London, vol.160, no.4071, p.648, Nov.8, 1947.

(THE SKELETAL DEVELOPMENT OF THE GUINEA PIG.) Die Skelettentwicklung beim Meerschwein. Charles Petri. Vierteljahrschrift d. Narturf. Ges. Zurich, vol.80, pts.1-2, pp.157-240, figs.54, June 30, 1935.

(THE DEVELOPMENT OF THE FORM OF THE TONGUE AND OF THE ENTRANCE TO THE LARYNX OF THE GUINEA PIG.) Die Entwicklung der Form der Zunge und des Kehlkopfeinganges beim Meerschweinchen. Hans Rabl. Zeitschr. f. Anat. u. Entwicklungsgesch., vol.83, pp.1-44, 48 figs., July 11, 1927.

PROLIFERATION AND OVOGENESIS IN THE GERMINAL EPITHELIUM OF THE NORMAL MATURE GUINEA PIG OVARY, AS SHOWN BY THE COLCHICINE TECHNIQUE. Ida G. Schmidt, Franklin G. Hoffman. Amer. Jour. Anat., Phila., vol.68, no.2, pp.263-273, 1 pl., Mar.15, 1941.

THE EXTRUSIVE GROWTH AND ATTRITION OF THE INCISOR TEETH OF CAVIA COBAYA. Albert R. Shadle, Nicholas Ignatius Valvo, Kenneth Harry Eckhert. Anat. Rec., vol.71, no.4, pp.497-502, Aug.25, 1938.

THE EFFECT OF AGING IN THE FEMALE GENITAL TRACT ON THE FERTILIZING CAPACITY OF GUINEA PIG SPERMATOZOA. Arnold L. Soderwall, William C. Young. Anat. Record, Phila., vol.78, no.1, pp.19-29, Sept.25, 1940.

(ON THE DEGENERATIVE CHANGES OF THE CEREBELLAR CORTEX IN THE COURSE OF THE INDIVIDUAL CYCLE OF CAVIA COBAYA MARCGR.) Ueber die degenerativen Veraenderungen in der Kleinthirnrinde im Verlauf des Individualzyklus von Cavia cobaya Marcgr. A. Spiegel. Zool. Anzeiger, vol.79, pp.173-182, figs.2, Nov.15, 1928.

THE THECAL GLAND IN THE GUINEA PIG OVARY. W. T. Stafford, R. F. Collins, H. W. Mossman. Anat. Record, Phila., vol.83, no.2, pp.193-207, pls.2, June 25, 1942.

(HAIRLESS GUINEA PIG (CAVIA PORCELLUS LINNE 1758).) Haarlose Meerschweinchen, Cavia porcellus (Linne, 1758). G. Steinbacher. Saeugetierk., Mitteil., Stuttgart, vol.1, no.2, p.77, illus., Apr.1, 1953.

THE HISTOLOGICAL CHARACTERS OF LEISHMANIAL GRANULOMA OF THE GUINEA PIG. C. M. Torres, J. Muniz, Rita A. de A. Cardoso, Eitel Duarte. Trop. Disease Bull., London, vol.45, no.9, p.776, Sept., 1948.

THE INTRACELLULAR LIPIN, MUCOID, GLYCOGEN OF THE VAGINAL EPITHELIUM OF THE GUINEA PIG. C. L. Tribby. Anat. Record, Phila., vol.86, no.3, pp. 425-551, pls.2, July, 1943.

A CONTRIBUTION TO THE EARLY DEVELOPMENT OF THE HEART IN MAMMALIA, WITH SPECIAL REFERENCE TO THE GUINEA-PIG. Tanzo Yoshinaga. Anat. Record, vol.21, pp.239-308, June, 1921.

AGE ORDER OF EPIPHYSEAL UNION IN THE GUINEA PIG. Theodore T. Zuck. Anat. Rec., vol.70, no.4, pp.389-399, 1 fig., Mar.25, 1938.

Behavior

(ON "URINE SQUIRTING" AND SIMILAR BEHAVIOR IN THE GUINEA PIG CAVIA PORCELLUS LINNE 1758.) Ueber das "Harnspritzen" und aehnliche Verhaltens - weisen beim Meerschweinschen, Cavia porcellus Linne, 1758. Adelheid Fruehling. Saeugetierk. Mitteil., Stuttgart, 3 (4): 168-171, Oct.1, 1955.

A STUDY OF THE SPONTANEOUS ACTIVITY OF THE GUINEA PIG. Edith E. Nicholls. Jour. Comp. Psychol., vol.2, pp.303-330, Aug. (Oct.), 1922.

(CANNIBALISM IN GUINEA PIGS.) Kannibalismus bei Meerschweinchen. Hans Petzsch. Zool. Garten, Leipzig, n.F., vol.4, nos.10-12, p.375, Dec.16, 1931.

Captivity

GUINEA PIGS; A PRACTICAL TREATISE ON THEIR BREEDING, FEEDING AND MANAGEMENT. Walter E. Clarke. Chatham, N.Y., and New York City, Dunlap-Clarke Co., pp.7-47, illus., 1913.

RAISING GUINEA PIGS. David E. Lantz. U.S. Dept. Agric., Farmers' Bull. no.525, pp.1-12, figs.1-5, Mar.22, 1913.

Diseases and Parasites

ASCARIS LUMBRICOIDES INFECTION IN GUINEA PIGS WITH SPECIAL REFERENCE TO EOSINOPHILIA AND RESISTANCE. A. Murray Fallis. Canadian Jour. Research, Ottawa, sect.D., vol.26, no.5, pp.307-327, figs.20, pls.3, Oct., 1948.

(ON CHANGES IN THE BLOOD IN THE GUINEA PIG AFTER SINGULAR AND REPEATED ASCARID INFECTION.) Ueber die Blutveraenderung beim Meerschweinchen nach einmalige und wiederholter Ascarideninfektion. G. G. Smirnow, M. Theo. Glasunow. Zeitschr. f. Parasitenkunde, vol.1, pp.174-197, 18 figs., Apr.17, 1928.

THE EFFECT OF VACCINATION OF GUINEA-PIGS WITH THE VOLE ACID-FAST BACILLUS ON SUBSEQUENT TUBERCULOUS INFECTION. A. Q. Wells. British Jour. Exper. Pathology, London, vol.21, pp.104-110, 1940.

Embryology

HAIR DIRECTION IN MAMMALS; EMBRYOGENESIS OF HAIR FOLLICLES IN THE GUINEA PIG. Edward C. Colin. Jour. Morphol., Phila., vol.72, no.2, pp.191-224, illus., Mar., 1943.

PRENATAL GROWTH IN GUINEA-PIGS WITH SPECIAL REFERENCE TO ENVIRONMENTAL FACTORS AFFECTING WEIGHT AT BIRTH. H. L. Ibsen. Jour. Exper. Zool., vol.51, no.1, pp.51-91, 1928.

(ABOUT THE FORMATION OF THE MESODERM AND THE SIGNIFICATION OF THE LIEBERKUHN DUCT IN THE GUINEA-PIG.) Sur la formation du mesoblaate et la signification du canal de Lieberkuhn chez Reunion. Charles Julin. Comptes Rendus Assoc. Anat., 18th Reunion, pp.1-9, 1923.

THE PARTHENOGENETIC DEVELOPMENT OF EGGS IN THE OVARY OF THE GUINEA PIG. Leo Loeb. Science, n.s., vol.58, pp. 35-36, July 13, 1923.

THE EARLY DEVELOPMENT OF CAVIA: NOTE ON ASSOCIATED REMAINS OF PREVIOUS PLACENTATION. N.H.W. Maclaren. Proc. Roy. Soc. Lond., ser.B, vol.99, pp.230-231, 1 pl., 1926.

NOTES ON IRREGULARITIES OF OVOGENESIS AND ABNORMAL DEVELOPMENT OF EMBRYO IN CAVIA. Thomas Nicol. Jour. Anat., Cambridge, vol.68, pt.1, pp. 75-84, pls.1-3, Oct., 1933.

THE EMBRYOLOGY OF THE GUINEA PIG. I. A TABLE OF NORMAL DEVELOPMENT. J. P. Scott. Amer. Jour. Anat., vol.60, no.3, pp.397-432, Mar.15, 1937.

THE EMBRYOLOGY OF THE GUINEA PIG. II. THE POLYDACTYLOUS MONSTER. A NEW TERAS PRODUCED BY THE GENES PX PX. J. P. Scott. Jour. Morphol., Phila., vol.62, no.2, pp.299-321, fig.1, pls.3, Mar.1, 1938.

Experimental Biology

THE PRINCIPAL FEATURES OF THE REACTION OF THE ANTERIOR PITUITARY OF THE GUINEA PIG TO PARTIAL ULTRAVIOLET IRRADIATION OF THE HEAD. Leo Abolins. Arkiv. Zool., Stockholm, vol.41A, pt.4, no.17, pp.1-24, figs.9, pl. 1, Mar.23, 1949.

INDUCTION OF HEAT IN SPAYED FEMALE GUINEA PIGS BY SUBCUTANEOUS HORMONAL IMPLANTS. P. Bacsich, G. M. Wyburn. Nature, London, vol.155, no. 3936, p.430, Apr.7, 1945.

(OVARIAN GRAFT IN THE MALE GUINEA-PIG. FORMATION OF THE CORPUS LUTEUM. CONDITION OF RECOVERY.) La greffe d'ovaire chez le Cobaye male. Formation de Corps jaunes. Conditions de reprise. W. Bartschi, Kitty Ponse. 1934.

VITAMIN P DEFICIENCY IN GUINEA PIGS. Geoffrey H. Bourne. Nature, London, vol. 152, no.3866, pp.659-660, Dec.4, 1943.

THE EFFECT OF INANITION ON THE ANTERIOR PITUITARY-ADRENO-CORTICAL INTERRELATIONSHIP IN THE GUINEA PIG. Savino A. D'Angelo, A. S. Gordon, H. A. Charipper. Endocrinology, Chicago, vol.42, no.5, pp.399-411, May, 1948.

CHANGES IN OVARIES AND UTERI IN GUINEA PIGS WITH HYPOTHALAMIC LESIONS. F. L. Dey. Amer. Jour. Anat., Phila., vol.69, no.1, pp.61-87, figs.11, July 15, 1941.

A STUDY OF THE EFFECTS OF TESTICULAR EXTRACT UPON THE PREGNANT GUINEA-PIG AND THE FETUS. Frederick E. Emery. Trans. Amer. Micro. Soc., vol.45, pp.44-52, pl.4, Jan., 1926.

THE DURATION OF PREGNANCY IN GUINEA-PIGS AFTER REMOVAL AND ALSO AFTER TRANSPLANTATION OF THE OVARIES. Earl H. Herrick. Anat. Record, vol.39, pp.193-200, July 25, 1928.

THE HISTOLOGICAL TRANSFORMATION IN THE VAGINAL EPITHELIUM OF THE GUINEA-PIG. G. Lombard Kelly. Amer. Jour. Anat., vol.43, pp.247-288, 7 pls., 1929.

SIMPLIFIED RATIONS FOR GUINEA PIGS SUITABLE FOR ASSAY OF THE GRASS JUICE FACTOR. G. O. Kohler, S. B. Randle, C. A. Elvehjem, E. B. Hart. Proc. Soc. Exper. Biol. and Med., vol.40, no.2, pp.154-157, chart 1, Feb., 1939.

EXPERIMENTAL HERMAPHRODATION ON QUANTITATIVE LINES. (EXPERIMENTS ON GUINEA PIGS.) (INTRATESTICULAR OVARIAN TRANSPLANTATION BY THE METHOD OF SAND.) A. Lipschuetz, W. Krause, H.E.V. Voss. Jour. Physiol., vol.58, pp.461-465, May 23, 1924.

TRANSPLANTATION OF TISSUES IN HYBRIDS OF INBRED FAMILIES OF GUINEA PIGS AND THE INDIVIDUALITY DIFFERENTIAL. Leo Loeb, Hugh G. McPhee. Amer. Nat., vol.65, no.700, pp.385-405, Sept.-Oct., 1931.

(AN ELECTROCARDIOGRAM OF THE NORMAL GUINEA PIG.) O electrocardiograma do cobaio normal. Bernardo F. Magalhaes, Adir Rocha. Rev. Brasileira Biol., Rio de Janeiro, vol.2, no.1, pp.47-52, fig.1, Mar., 1942.

BILE ACIDS AND THEIR CHLORINE SALTS APPLIED TO THE INNER SURFACE OF THE ISOLATED COLON AND ILEUM OF THE GUINEA PIG. A. E. Meyer, J. P. McEwen. Amer. Jour. Physiol., Balto., vol.153, no.2, pp.386-392, May 1, 1948.

THE RELATION OF THE SCROTUM TO GERM CELL DIFFERENTIATION IN GONAD GRAFTS IN THE GUINEA PIG. C. R. Moore. Amer. Nat., vol.60, no.69, pp. 324-333, 1926.

THE UTERUS OF CAVIA AFTER INTRAVITAM STAINING WITH TRYPAN BLUE. T. Nicol. Jour. Anat., vol.66, pp.181-188, figs.6, 1932.

(ACTION OF PLACENTAL LIPOIDS ON THE PERCENTAGE OF WATER OF BLOOD MUSCULAR TISSUE, AND SOME ORGANS.) Action des lipoides placentaires sur la teneur en eau du sang, du tissu musculaire et de quelques organes. C. I. Parhon, M. Cahane, V. Marza. Comptes Rendus des Seances de la Soc. de Biol., vol.97, pp. 1112-1114, Oct.21, 1927.

ENDOMETRIAL HYPERPLASIA AS OBSERVED IN EXPERIMENTAL GUINEA PIGS. Olga Saffry, Mary T. Harman, Martha M. Kramer. Trans. Kansas Acad. Sci., vol.40, pp.389-390, 1937.

THE EFFECTS OF CASTRATION UPON THE REPRODUCTIVE ORGANS OF THE ADULT MALE GUINEA PIG. E. Duane Sayles. Jour. Exper. Zool. Phila., vol. 90, no.2, pp.183-197, July 6, 1942.

MITOTIC PROLIFERATION IN THE OVARY OF THE NORMAL MATURE GUINEA PIG TREATED WITH COLCHICINE. Ida G. Schmidt. Amer. Jour. Anat., Phila., vol. 71, no.2, pp.245-270, figs.3, Sept.15, 1942.

A STUDY OF RETROBULBAR TISSUES IN EXPERIMENTAL EXOPHTHALMOS IN GUINEA PIGS WITH REFERENCE TO PRIMARY AND SECONDARY MODIFICATIONS. George K. Smelser. Amer. Jour. Anat., Phila., vol.72, no. 2, pp.149-169, pls.1-2, Mar., 1943.

BILATERAL HYPERTHELIA IN A GUINEA PIG. Harold Speert. Anat. Record, Phila., vol.83, no.2, pp.317-320, fig.1, June 25, 1942.

EFFECTS OF CASTRATION ON IMMATURE GUINEA PIGS. Manuel D. Sumulong. Philippine Jour. Sci., vol.27, pp.325-347, 4 figs., July, 1925.

(NEW RESULTS OF THE STUDY IN VITRO OF THE SMOOTH MUSCULATURE OF THE GENITALS OF THE MALE GUINEA PIG. THE INFLUENCE OF ESTILBOESTROL.) Novos resultados do estudo invitro da musculatura lisa genital masculina do cobaio. Influencia do estilboestrol. Jose R. Valle, Ananias Porto. Mem. Inst. Butantan, Sao Paulo, vol.15, pp.1-7, figs. 5, 1941. (In Portuguese, with German summary.)

THE INHERITANCE, HISTOLOGY, AND PHYSIOLOGY OF A NEW TYPE OF STERILITY, SEXUAL HYPOGENESIS, IN THE GUINEA-PIG. Eldyn Everett Van Lone. Jour. Exper. Zool., vol.64, no.1, pp.1-29, pl.1, Nov., 1932.

THE INFLUENCE OF HIGH TEMPERATURE ON THE GUINEA-PIG TESTIS. W. C. Young. Jour. Exper. Zool., vol.49, no.2, pp.459-499, 1927.

THE HORMONAL INDUCTION OF HOMOSEXUAL BEHAVIOR IN THE SPAYED FEMALE GUINEA PIG. W. C. Young, Brewster Rundlett. Psychosomatic Medicine, Wash., D.C., vol.1, no.4, pp. 449-460, figs.3, tables 5, Oct., 1939.

Heredity

REVERSION IN GUINEA-PIGS AND ITS EXPLANATION. EXPERIMENTAL STUDIES OF THE INHERITANCE OF COLOR IN MICE. W. E. Castle, C. C. Little. Carnegie Inst., Wash., D.C., pp.102, pls. 5, 1913. Publ. no.179.

SILVERING IN A STRAIN OF GUINEA PIGS. Orson N. Eaton. Jour. Heredity, Wash., D.C., vol.34, no.4, pp.105-107, fig.3, Apr., 1943.

SOME NEW GENETIC TYPES OF EYES IN THE GUINEA-PIG. P. W. Gregory. Jour. Exper. Zool., vol.52, no.1, pp.159-182, 1928.

(AN APPARANT MENDELIAN ANOMALY IN THE GUINEA PIG: RECESSIVES YIELDING DOMINANTS.) Une apparente anomalie mendélienne chez le cobaye: récessifs donnant des dominants. E. Guyénot, A. Pictet. Compt. Rend. Soc. Biol. Paris, vol.89, pp.1086-1088, 1923.

THE INFLUENCE OF CERTAIN GENETIC FACTORS UPON EYE COLOR IN THE GUINEA PIG. Mary T. Harman, Annette Alsop Case. Trans. Kansas Acad. Sci., Lawrence, vol.45, pp.344-357, figs.A-N, 1942.

NEW DATA SHOWING ABERRANT RATIOS IN THE E ALLELOMORPHIC SERIES IN GUINEA-PIGS. H. L. Ibsen. Anat. Rec., vol.29, pp.140-141, Dec.25, 1924.

TRICOLOR INHERITANCE. IV. THE TRIPLE ALLELOMORPHIC SERIES IN GUINEA PIGS. H. L. Ibsen. Genetics, vol.4, pp.597-606, Nov., 1919 (Feb., 1920).

THE SALMON-EYED GENE IN GUINEA-PIGS. H. L. Ibsen, P. W. Gregory. Anat. Record, vol.29, p.140, Dec.25, 1924.

(COMPARITIVE STUDY OF MITOSES IN THE GUINEA PIG.) Étude comparative des Mitoses chez le Cobaye. G. Mols. Archives de Biologie, vol.38, pp.31-86, 2 pls., 1928.

(RESEARCH ON THE GENETIC CONSTITUTION OF THE ROSETTE GUINEA PIG.) Recherches sur la constitution génêtique du Cobaye à rosette. Arnold Pictet, M. A. Ferrero. Zeitschr. f. Ind. Abstmmungs- und Verebungslehre, vol.52, pp.236-286, 5 pls., 1929.

A QUANTITATIVE STUDY OF GENIC EFFECTS ON GUINEA-PIG COAT COLORS. Elizabeth S. Russell. Genetics, vol.24, pp.332-355, figs.5, May, 1939.

SKELETAL VARIATIONS IN GUINEA PIGS AND THEIR INHERITANCE. Herluf H. Strandskov. Jour. Mam., vol.23, no.1, pp.65-75, fig.1, Feb.14, 1942.

GENETIC STUDIES ON A CAVY SPECIES CROSS. CAVIA RUFESCENS (LUND) AND CAVIA PORCELLUS (LINNE). G. v. Ubisch, R. F. Mello. Jour. Heredity, Wash., D.C., vol.31, no.9, pp.389-398, fig.8-12, Sept., 1940.

THE EFFECTS OF INBREEDING AND CROSSBREEDING ON GUINEA PIGS. III. CROSSES BETWEEN HIGHLY INBRED FAMILIES. Sewall Wright. U.S. Dept. Agric., Bull.1121, pp.61, figs.27, Dec., 1922.

TWO NEW COLOR FACTORS OF THE GUINEA PIG. Sewall Wright. Amer. Nat., vol.57, pp.42-51, Feb., 1923.

FACTORS IN THE RESISTANCE OF GUINEA PIGS TO TUBERCULOSIS, WITH ESPECIAL REGARD TO INBREEDING AND HEREDITY. Sewall Wright, Paul A. Lewis. Amer. Nat., vol.55, pp.20-50, Feb., 1921.

Physiology

OBSERVATIONS ON THE OESTROUS CYCLE OF THE GUINEA-PIG. P. Bacsich, G. M. Wyburn. Proc. Roy. Soc. Edinburgh, vol.60, pt.1, pp.33-39, figs.3, 1940.

CARBOHYDRATE, FAT, AND MOISTURE RELATIONSHIPS IN THE PREGNANT, FETAL, AND NEWBORN GUINEA PIG. Walter L. Hard, Orr E. Reynolds, Martin Winbury. Jour. Exper. Zool., Phila., vol. 96, no.3, pp.189-199, Aug., 1944.

STUDIES ON THE PHYSIOLOGY OF THE ACCESSORY GLANDS OF REPRODUCTION OF THE MALE GUINEA-PIG. John Wesley Lawlah. Anat. Record, vol.45, no.2, pp. 163-175, figs.7, Mar., 1930.

STUDIES ON THE REPRODUCTIVE SYSTEM IN THE GUINEA-PIG: VARIATIONS IN THE OESTROUS CYCLE IN THE VIRGIN ANIMAL, AFTER PARTURITION, AND DURING PREGNANCY. Thomas Nicol. Proc. Roy. Soc. Edinburgh, vol.53, pt.3, pp.220-238, Aug.4, 1933.

(COMPARATIVE STUDY OF THE REMOVAL OF IRON BY THE KIDNEY AND SALIVARY GLANDS IN THE GUINEA PIG.) Etude comparée del l'élimination du fer par le rein et les glandes salivaires chez le cobaye. Jaques Odier. Compte Rendu Séances Soc. Phys. et Hist. Nat. Genève, vol.58, no.3, pp.256-259, Aug.-Dec., 1941.

THE GUINEA PIG IN RESEARCH: BIOLOGY, NUTRITION, PHYSIOLOGY. Mary Elizabeth Reid. Publ. No.557, Human Factors Research Bureau, Nat. Press Bldg., Wash., D.C., pp.1-87, 1958.

URINARY EXCRETION OF ASCORBIC ACID BY GUINEA PIGS AT DIFFERENT AGES. Mary E. Reid. Jour. Nutrition, Phila., vol.35, no.5, pp.619-627, May 10, 1948.

Psychology

MODIFICATION OF THE PATTERN OF THE GUINEA PIG'S REFLEX RESPONSE TO NOISE. Raymond Dodge, C. M. Louttit. Jour. Comp. Psych., vol.6, no.3, pp.267-285, 1926.

PLASTICITY AND MECHANIZATION OF THE PROBLEM BOX HABIT IN GUINEA PIGS. K. F. Muenzinger. Jour. Comp. Psych., vol.8, pp.45-69, illus., 1928.

Reproductive Biology

NOTES ON REPRODUCTION IN GUINEA PIGS. George T. Avery. Jour. Comp. Psychol., vol.5, pp.373-396, 1925.

A STATISTICAL STUDY OF THE RELATION BETWEEN VARIOUS EXPRESSIONS OF FERTILITY AND VIGOR IN THE GUINEA PIG. G. Haines. Jour. Agric. Resources, vol.xlii, pp.123-164, London, 1931.

FURTHER OBSERVATIONS ON REPRODUCTION IN GUINEA PIGS FED VITAMIN C AT DIFFERENT LEVELS. Mary T. Harman, Isabelle Gillum. Trans. Kansas Acad. Sci., vol.40, pp.369-376, illus., 1937.

REPRODUCTIVE BEHAVIOR OF THE GUINEA PIG. I. THE NORMAL MATING BEHAVIOR. C. M. Louttit. Jour. Comp. Psych., vol.7, pp.247-263, 1927.

REPRODUCTIVE BEHAVIOR OF THE GUINEA PIG. II. THE ONTOGENESIS OF THE REPRODUCTIVE BEHAVIOR PATTERN. C. M. Louttit. Jour. Comp. Psych., vol.9, pp.293-304, 1 fig., Aug., 1929.

(HYBRIDS OF TAME AND WILD CAVIES (CAVIA COBAYA AND CAVIA APEREA).) Kreuzungen von zahmen und wilden Meerschweinchen, Cavia cobaya und Cavia aperea. A. Nehring. Zool. Garten, Frankfurt, Jahrg.35, no.1, pp.1-6; no.2, pp.39-43; no.3, pp.74-78, 1894.

OBSERVATIONS ON THE SUCKLING PERIOD IN THE GUINEA PIG. Marion J. Read. Univ. California Publ. Zool., Berkeley, vol.9, no.7, pp.341-351, figs.3, Sept.14, 1912.

POST-PARTUM BREEDING IN THE GUINEA-PIG. I. W. Rowlands. Jour. Hyg., Cambridge, vol.47, no.3, pp.281-287, Sept., 1949.

South America

(THE ARGENTINIAN RODENTS OF FAMILY "CAVIIDAE".) Los roedores argentinos de la familia "Caviidae". A. Cabrera. Publ. Escuela Vet., Facultad de Agron. y Vet. Univ. Buenos Aires, no.6, pp.93, June, 1954.

(A NEW AND INTERESTING RODENT OF THE TERTIARY FAUNA OF ENTRE RIOS CAVIODON (LELONGIA) PARANENSIS N. SUBGEN. N. SP.) Un nuevo e interesante roedor de la fauna terciaria de Entre Rios, caviodon (Lelongia) paranensis n. subgen. n. sp. Lucas Kraglievich. Anales Soc. Cient. Argentina, vol.110, no.3, pp.178-184, fig.1, 1930.

CAVIES OF SOUTHERN PERU. Colin Campbell Sanborn. Proc. Biol. Soc. Wash., vol.62, pp.133-134, Aug.23, 1949.

A NEW GENUS OF CAVY FROM CATAMARCA, NANOCAVIA SHIPTONI. Oldfield Thomas. Ann. and Mag. Nat. Hist., ser. 9, vol.15, pp.418-420, Mar., 1925.

Taxonomy

(THE NEW SUBGENUS "PARADOLICHOTIS.") A proposito del nuevo subgenero "Paradolichotis" Kragl. Lucas Kraglievich. Physis. (Rev. Soc. Argentina Ciencias Nat.), vol. 8, no.31, pp.591-598, Nov.15, 1927.

NOTES ON THE SPECIES OF THE GENUS CAVIA. Oldfield Thomas. Ann. and Mag. Nat. Hist. (8), vol.19, no.109, pp.152-160, Jan., 1917.

ON THE CAVIES OF THE GENUS CAVIELLA. Oldfield Thomas. Ann. and Mag. Nat. Hist., ser.9, vol.7, pp.445-448, May, 1921.

ON THE CLASSIFICATION OF THE CAVIES. Oldfield Thomas. Ann. and Mag. Nat. Hist. (8), vol.18, no.105, pp.301-303, Sept., 1916.

## Hydrochoeridae

THE QUEEREST RODENT: THE CAPYBARA. Maurice Burton. Illus. London News, vol. 219, no.5856, p.61, illus., July 14, 1951.

(THE BRAIN OF A RODENT FOETUS (HYDROCHOERUS CAPYBARA ERXL., CABIAI).) Le cerveau d'un foetus de rongeur (Hydrochoerus capybara Erxl., Cabiai). Madelein Friant. Comptes Rendus Acad. Sci., Paris, vol.237, no.23, pp.1550-1552, Dec.9, 1953.

ON THE CAECUM COLI OF THE CAPYBARA (HYDROCHOERUS CAPYBARA). Alfred Henry Garrod. Proc. Zool. Soc. Lond., pp.20-23, figs.2, 1876.

"PIGSKIN" AND CAPYBARA SKIN. Edmund G. Loder. Proc. Zool. Soc. Lond., pt.2, pp.286-287, 1915.

(MAMMALS OF VENEZUELA: THE CAPYBARA.) Mamiferos de Venezuela: El Chigueire. Edgardo Mondolfi. El Farol, Caracas, 18 (168): 38-40, enero/ feb., 1957, illus., port.

ON THE ANATOMY OF THE CAPYBARA (HYDROCHOERUS CAPYBARA, ERXL.). R. Owen. Proc. Zool. Soc. Lond., pt.2, p.9, 1834.

ON THE TEETH OF THE CAPYBARA (HYDROCHAERUS CAPYBARA, ERXL.). R. Owen. Proc. Comm. Sci. and Corres. Zool. Soc. Lond., pt.2, p.187, 1832.

HYPERTROPHY OF SEBACEOUS GLANDS ON THE SNOUT AS A SECONDARY MALE SEXUAL CHARACTER IN THE CAPYBARA, HYDROCHOERUS HYDROCHOERIS. R. E. Rewell. Proc. Zool. Soc. Lond., vol.119, pt.4, pp.817-819, pl.1, Feb.1, 1950.

RIMA, THE CAPOOA. (A PET CAPYBARA.) Ivan T. Sanderson. Nature Mag., Wash., D.C., vol.36, no.9, pp.456-460, 500, illus., Nov., 1943.

(ON THE FINER STRUCTURE OF HEPATIC VEINS IN HYDROCHOERUS CAPYBARA.) Ueber den feineren Bau der Lebervenen von Hydrochoerus capybara. Dietrich Starck. Anat. Anz., vol.78, nos.11-14, pp.240-246, figs.1-5, July 25, 1934.

THE ISTHMIAN CAPYBARA IN THE CANAL ZONE. Harold Trapido. Jour. Mam., vol. 28, no.4, pp.408-409, Nov.26, 1947.

THE ISTHMIAN CAPYBARA IN THE TODUMEN SAVANNAS, PANAMA. J. Dan Webster. Jour. Mam., vol.30, no.1, pp. 80-81, Feb.14, 1949.

(COMPANY FOR A CAPYBARA.) Gezelschap voor een Capibara. Artis, Amsterdam, vol.1, no.3, pp.60-61, illus., Oct., 1955.

## Dinomyidae

RUKUPI, RARE RODENT. (DINOMYS BRANICKII.) W. E. Eigsti. Nature, Mag., Wash., D.C., vol.36, no.2, pp.100-101, illus., Feb., 1943.

THE TYPE SPECIES OF CUNICULUS BRISSON. N. Hollister. Proc. Biol. Soc. Wash., vol.26, p.79, Mar.22, 1913.

(THE PACARANA (DINOMYS BRANICKII PETERS).) Vom Pacarana (Dinomys branickii Peters). Erna Mohr. Zool. Garten, Leipzig, n.s., vol.9, no.5, pp. 204-209, figs.10, Oct., 1937.

(BIOLOGICAL NOTES ON THE PACARANA (DINOMYS BRANICKII PETERS).) Notas biologicas sôbre a pacarana "Dinomys branickii Peters". A. Olalla. Fauna, São Paulo, Brazil, vol.14, no.3, pp.32-49, illus., Mar., 1955.

(ON DINOMYS, A REMARKABLE NEW PORCUPINE RODENT GENUS OF THE HIGH MOUNTAINS OF PERU.) Ueber Dinomys, eine merkwueridge neue Gattung der stachelschweinartigen Nagethiere aus den Hochgebirgen von Peru. W. Peters. Auszug Monatsber Kon. Akad. Wiss. Berlin, pp.551-552, July 10, 1873.

(ON DINOMYS, A REMARKABLE NEW RODENT GENUS OF PERU.) Ueber Dinomys, eine merkwueridge neue Gattung von Nagethieren aus Peru. W. Peters. Festschr. z. Feier 100th-Jaehrigen Gesell. naturforsch. Freunde zu Berlin, pp.227-234, pls.4, 1873; Zeischr-Gesammt Naturwiss., vol.9, pp.3-10, pls.1-4, 1874.

THE EXTERNAL CHARACTERS OF A YOUNG FEMALE DINOMYS BRANICKII EXHIBITED IN THE SOCIETY'S GARDENS. R. I. Pocock. Proc. Zool. Soc. London, pp.212-230, illus., Apr.29, 1926.

NOTES ON DINOMYS. C. C. Sanborn. Field Mus. Nat. Hist., Publ.296, Zool. Ser., vol.18, no.6, pp.149-155, pl.5, Aug.31, 1931.

SOME NOTES ON PACAS. Oldfield Thomas. Ann. and Mag. Nat. Hist. (9), vol.13, no. 74, pp.237-239, Feb., 1924.

RARE PACARANA NOW LIVES AT PHILADELPHIA ZOO. Science News Letter, Wash., vol.51, no.4, p.55, Jan. 25, 1947.

ZOOLOGICAL JACKPOT, PACARANA. Fauna, Philadelphia, vol.9, no.1, p.31, illus., Mar., 1947.

## Heptaxodontidae

(DESCRIPTION OF AN INTERESTING RODENT DISCOVERED IN URUGUAY: GYRIABRUS TEISSEIREI N. SP.) Descripcion de un interesante roedor eumegámido descubierto en el Uruguay: Gyriabrus teisseirei n. sp. Lucas Kraglievich. Revista Soc. "Amigos de la Arqveologia," Montevideo, vol.4, pp.219-224, (1930) 1931.

SKULL REMAINS OF AMBLYRHIZA FROM ST. MARTIN. A. Schreuder. Tijdschrift Ned. Dierkundige Vereeniging, Leiden, ser. 3, vol.3, no.4, pp.242-266, figs.6, 1933.

## Dasyproctidae

HAIR AND SCALES OF THE PACA. G. M. Allen. Jour. Mam., Balto., vol.21, no.4, pp.438-441, fig.1, Nov.14, 1940.

A NEW AGOUTI FROM GUADELOUPE ISLAND, WEST INDIES. G. M. Allen. Proc. New England Zooel. Club, vol.5, pp.69-71, Oct.7, 1914.

TWO YOUNG AGOUTIS. Lee S. Crandall. Animal Kingdom, New York, vol.47, no.5, p.125, Sept.-Oct., 1944.

PARTURITION IN THE AGOUTI, WITH NOTES ON SEVERAL PREGNANT UTERI. Robert K. Enders. Jour. Mam., vol.12, no.4, pp.390-396, Nov., 1931.

A NEW AGOUTI FROM COSTA RICA, DASYPROCTA PUNCIATA UNDERWOODI. E. A. Goldman. Jour. Wash. Acad. Sci., vol.21, no.19, p.481, Nov.19, 1931.

ON THE CHEEK POUCHES OF THE TROPICAL AMERICAN PACA, AGOUTI PACA (LINNAEUS,1766). Philip Hershkovitz. Saeugetierk. Mitteil., Stuttgart, vol.3, no.2, pp.67-70, illus., 1955.

NOTES ON THE DISSECTION OF AN AGOUTI (DASYPROCTA AGUTI, ILL.). R. Jones. Proc. Zool. Soc. London, pt.2, p.82, 1834.

ON THE VISCERAL ANATOMY OF THE SPOTTED CAVY (COELOGENYS SUBNIGER, CUV.). W. Martin. Proc. Zool. Soc. Lond., pt.6, pp.52-55, 1838.

ON THE ANATOMY OF THE CRESTED AGOUTI (DASYPROCTA CRISTATA, DESM.). St. George J. Mivart. Proc. Zool. Soc. Lond., p.383, 1866.

ON THE ANATOMY OF THE CRESTED AGOUTI (DASYPROCTA CRISTATA, DESM.). James Murie. Proc. Zool. Soc. Lond., pp.383-417, figs.5, 1866.

THE NAME OF AZARA'S AGOUARACHAY. Wilfred H. Osgood. Proc. Biol. Soc. Wash., vol.28, pp.142-143, June 29, 1915.

(NOTES ON THE ONTOGENETIC EVOLUTION OF THE MOLARS OF THE GENUS AGOUTI (RODENTIA).) Apuntes sobre la Evolucion Ontogenetica de los Molares del Genero Agouti (Rodentia). Carlos Rusconi. Revista Odontologica, pp.1-10, figs.11, Apr., 1934.

A NEW AGOUTI FROM THE MOON MOUNTAINS, SOUTHERN BRITISH GUIANA, WITH NOTES ON OTHER SPECIES. Oldfield Thomas. Ann. and Mag. Nat. Hist. (8), vol.20, no.117, pp.259-261, Sept., 1917.

NOTES ON AGOUTIS WITH DESCRIPTIONS OF NEW FORMS. Oldfield Thomas. Ann. and Mag. Nat. Hist. (9), vol.20, no.118, pp. 310-313, Oct., 1917.

SOME NOTES ON PACAS. Oldfield Thomas. Ann. and Mag. Nat. Hist., ser.9, vol.13, pp.237-239, Feb., 1924.

SOUTH AMERICAN "PACA". Pennsylvania Game News, Allentown, vol.11, no.10, p.19, photo, Jan., 1940.

## Chinchillidae

Chinchillas

GIFTS OF THE AMERICAS. THE CHINCHILLA. F. G. Ashbrook. Agriculture in the Americas, U.S. Dept. Agric., Wash., D.C., vol.3, no.9, p.179, Sept., 1942.

(ON CHINCHILLA BREEDING.) Ueber Chinchilla-Zucht. Edmund Bickel. Zool. Garten, Leipzig, n.F., vol.4, nos.1-2, pp.63-65, figs.1-3, Feb., 1931.

NOTES ON THE GENUS CHINCHILLA. Theodore C. Bidlingmaier. Jour. Mam., vol.18, no.2, pp.159-163, May 14, 1937.

EVOLUTION OF CHINCHILLA HOUSING. Chester C. Bilderback. Amer. Fur Breeder, Duluth, vol.16, no.11, pp.6, 8, 10, illus., June, 1944.

OUT OF THE CLOUDS A CHINCHILLA INDUSTRY IS BEING BORN. Chester C. Bilderback. Amer. Fur Breeder, Duluth, vol.16, no.9, pp.16, 18, Mar., 1944.

NATURALIZING THE CHINCHILLA. John L. von Blon. Scientific American, vol.133, no.6, pp.394-395, Dec., 1925.

CROSS-BREEDING OF CHINCHILLAS. George M. Brun. Amer. Fur Breeder, Duluth, vol.15, no.5, pp.20, 22, 26, illus., Nov., 1942.

LITTLE FUR KING. (CHINCHILLA.) Hebe Bulley. Frontiers, Lancaster, vol.

9, no.3, pp.67-69, 97, illus., Feb., 1945, Frontiers, Phila., vol.13, no.5, pp.151-154, illus., June, 1949.

FIT FOR A QUEEN--WORTH A KING'S RANSOM. (CHINCHILLAS.) James M. Cain. McCall's Mag., New York, vol.64, no.6, pp.16, 67, 75, illus., Mar., 1937.

DO CHINCHILLAS NEED HEATED QUARTERS? J.D.W. Clarke. Amer. Fur Breeder, Duluth, vol.23, no.3, pp.12-13, Sept., 1950.

CHINCHILLAS, PRODUCERS OF RAREST LUXURY FUR, THRIVE IN CAPTIVITY. Gertrude M. Cox. Virginia Wildlife, Blacksburg, vol.3, no.1, pp.2-3, Sept., 1939.

A FRANK DISCUSSION OF CHINCHILLA TYPES. A. H. Crow. National Fur News, Denver, vol.15, no.11, pp.7, 29-30, Dec., 1943.

(CONTRIBUTIONS TO KNOWLEDGE OF THE CHINCHILLA.) Beitraege zur Kenntnis der Chinchilla. G. Dennler. Deutsche Pelztierzuechter, Muenchen, vol. 14, nos.17-18, pp.388-390, Sept., 1939.

(TRUE CHINCHILLA AND "WOOL MOUSE".) Echte Chinchilla und Wollmaus. G. Dennler. Der Deutsche Pelztierzuechter, Jahrgang 1931, Muenchen, no.22, pp.594-596, figs., Nov.15, 1931.

(EXPLANATION IN THE SYSTEMATICS OF THE CHINCHILLAS AND THEIR BIBLIOGRAPHY WITH COMMENTS.) Aclaraciones en la sistemática de las "chinchillas" y su bibliografiá comentada (Resumen). J. G. Dennler, Jose Yepes. Physis, Buenos Aires, vol.16, no.48, p.303, May, 1939.

THE EYE OF THE CHINCHILLA (C. LANIGERA). S. R. Detwiler. Jour. Morphol., Phila., vol.84, no.1, pp.123-144, Jan., 1949.

CHINCHILLA TYPES. S. De Wanger. Amer. Fur Breeder, Duluth, vol.13, no. 4, p.10, Oct., 1940.

FUR EATING IN CHINCHILLAS. Lynn Erickson. Nat. Fur News, Denver, vol. 16, no.12, pp.12, 17, 37, Jan., 1945.

(MEMORIES OF CHINCHILLAS.) Chinchilla-Erinnerungen. Richard Gloeck. Der Deutsche Pelztierzuechter, Munich, Jahrg.9, no.1, pp.12-15, illus., Jan.1, 1934.

A NEW PROGRAM FOR THE CHINCHILLA INDUSTRY. Richard F. Gorman. Amer. Fur Breeder, Duluth, vol.21, no.1, pp.48-54, July, 1948.

WHAT YOU SHOULD KNOW ABOUT BUYING CHINCHILLAS. Rudolf A. Graef. Black Fox Mag., New York, vol.32, no.2, pp.17, 33, June, 1948.

TOXOPLASMA IN THE CHINCHILLA. Hilan F. Keagy. Jour. Amer. Vet. Med. Assoc., Chicago, vol.114, no.862, p.15, illus., 1949.

(CHINCHILLAS AND CHINCHILLA FUR.) Chinchillas und Chinchillafelle. Otto Lindekam. Der Deutsche Pelztierzuechter, Muenchen, 8 Jahrgang, 1933, no.8, pp.169-175, fig.5, Apr.15, 1933.

CHINCHILLAS. Irving Lorwin. Science Illus., Louisville, vol.2, no.7, pp.33-35, 62, illus., July, 1947.

NOTES ON THE OSTEOLOGY OF CHINCHILLA LANIGERA. G. E. Manigault. Proc. Elliott Soc. Nat. Hist., Charleston, vol.2, pp.237-239, 2 figs., 1890.

(BREEDING THE CHINCHILLA IN CAPTIVITY.) L'élevage du chinchilla en captivité. B. Métayer. La Terre et la Vie, Rev. d'Hist. Nat., vol.3, no.9, pp.516-522, Sept., 1933.

THE TECHNICAL NAME OF THE CHINCHILLA. Wilfred H. Osgood. Jour. Mam., vol.22, no.4, pp.407-411, Nov.14, 1941.

(THE CHINCHILLA SPECIES.) Chinchilla-Arten. H. Prell. Kleintier und Pelztier, Leipzig, Jahrg.10, nos.22-24, pp.309-314, Dec.1, 1934.

(ON MUS LANIGER MOLINA (DATA ON THE CHINCHILLA I).) Ueber Mus laniger Molina (Beitraege zur Kenntnis der Chinchilla I). H. Prell. Zool. Garten, Leipzig, n.F., vol.7, nos.7-9, pp.207-209, Nov., 1934.

(THE PRESENTLY KNOWN SPECIES OF THE GENUS CHINCHILLA BENNETT.) Die gegenwaertig bekannten Arten der Gattung Chinchilla Bennett. H. Prell. Zool. Anz., Leipzig, vol.108, nos.5-6, pp.97-104, Nov., 1934.

DENTAL DEFORMITIES OF CHINCHILLAS. E. R. Quortrup. Nat. Fur News, Denver, vol.19, no.12, pp.24-25, illus., Jan., 1948; The Black Fox Mag., New York, vol.31, no.11, pp.13, 25-26, illus., Mar., 1948.

SOME OBSERVATIONS ON THE GROSS ANATOMY OF THE GENITAL SYSTEM AND TWO ENDOCRINE ORGANS AND BODY WEIGHTS IN THE CHINCHILLA. T. B. Roos, R. M. S. Shackelford. Anat. Rec., Phila., vol.123, no.3, pp.301-312, Nov., 1955.

STUDIES OF "FUR-EATING HABIT" OF THE CHINCHILLA. George S. Templeton. Nat. Fur News, Denver, vol.19, no.5, pp. 14, 34, June, 1947; Fur of Canada, Winnipeg, vol.12, no.9, pp.14, 16, June, 1947; Amer. Fur Breeder, Duluth, vol.20, no.2, pp.38, 44, Aug., 1947.

CHINCHILLA BREEDING FOR QUALITY. Lewis Van Meter. Nat. Fur News, Denver, vol.22, no.1, pp.18, 34, illus., Feb., 1950.

FUR CHEWING IN CHINCHILLAS. Lewis Van Meter. Nat. Fur News, Denver, vol. 22, no.8, pp.15, 32-33, Sept., 1950.

NOTES ON CHINCHILLA LIBERATIONS IN CALIFORNIA. John C. Voris, James D. Yoakum, Charles F. Yocom. Jour. Mam., 36 (2): 302, May, 1955.

THE CHINCHILLA IN CAPTIVITY. Senta de Wanger. Amer. Fur Breeder, Duluth, vol.14, no.4, pp.38-39, Oct., 1941.

FACTS FOR CHINCHILLA BREEDERS—HUMIDITY. Senta De Wanger. Amer. Fur Breeder, Duluth, vol.13, no.8, pp. 10-11, fig.1, Feb., 1941.

HOME-GROWN CHINCHILLA. (HABITS IN CAPTIVITY.) Alberta Williams. Collier's, New York, vol.104, no.22, pp.11, 73-75, illus., Nov.25, 1939.

(THE REPRODUCTION OF CHINCHILLAS.) Die Fortpflanzung der Chinchillas. S. M. Winter. Der Deutsche Palztierzuechter, Munich, Jahrg.9, no.24, pp.473-475, illus., Dec.15, 1934.

ON THE ANATOMY OF THE CHINCHILLA (CHINCHILLA LANIGERA). W. Yarrell. Proc. Comm. Sci. and Corres. Zool. Soc. Lond., pt.1, p.31, 1830-1831.

BREEDING HABITS OF CHINCHILLAS. Marjorie Zetty. Black Fox Mag. and Modern Mink Breeder, New York, vol.33, no.6, pp.14, 22-23, 32-33, Oct., 1949.

CHINCHILLAS SHOULD BE INSPECTED DAILY. Marjorie Zetty. Black Fox Mag. and Modern Mink Breeder, New York, vol. 32, no.11, pp.17, 34, illus., Mar., 1949.

FUR CHEWING IN CHINCHILLAS. Marjorie Zetty. Nat. Fur News, Denver, vol.22, no. 11, pp.26, 38-39, Dec., 1950.

HEALTHY CHINCHILLAS DEPEND ON DAILY INSPECTION. Marjorie Zetty. Black Fox Mag. and Modern Mink Breeder, New York, vol.32, no.12, pp.13, 25, illus., Apr., 1949.

HOW I CARE FOR CHINCHILLA MOTHERS. Marjorie Zetty. Black Fox Mag. and Modern Mink Breeder, New York, vol.33, no.12, pp.8, 15-16, illus., Apr., 1950.

HOW I FEED MY CHINCHILLAS. Marjorie Zetty. Black Fox Mag. and Modern Mink Breeder, New York, vol.33, no.4, pp.13, 20-21, illus., Aug., 1949.

HOW TO CARE FOR CHINCHILLA BABIES. Marjorie Zetty. Black Fox Mag. and Modern Mink Breeder, New York vol.34, no.2, pp.11, 26-27, illus., June, 1950.

HOW TO HANDLE CHINCHILLAS. Marjorie Zetty. Black Fox Mag. and Modern Mink Breeder, New York, vol.33, no.1, pp.13-23-25, illus., May, 1949.

HOW TO MAKE SUCCESSFUL CHINCHILLA MATINGS. Marjorie Zetty. Black Fox Mag. and Modern Mink Breeder, New York, vol.33, no.7, pp.15, 32-37, illus., Nov., 1949.

HOW TO START A CHINCHILLA RANCH. Marjorie Zetty. Black Fox Mag., New York, vol.32, no.8, pp.18, 33-35, Dec., 1948.

IMPORTANT TIPS ON THE CARE OF CHINCHILLA BABIES. Marjorie Zetty. Black Fox Mag. and Modern Mink Breeder, New York, vol.34, no.3, pp.12, 23-24, July, 1950.

AN INFORMAL DISCUSSION OF CHINCHILLA FEEDING. Marjorie Zetty. Black Fox Mag. and Modern Mink Breeder, New York, vol.33, no.3, pp.13, 23, July, 1949.

BRITONS START CHINCHILLA FARM. Life, New York, vol.6, no.3, p.38, illus., Jan.16, 1939.

RAISING CHINCHILLAS. American Fur Breeder, Duluth, vol.20, no.1, pp.78, 80, July, 1947.

RAISING CHINCHILLAS IN CAPTIVITY. U.S. Dept. Agric., Bur. Biol. Surv. (Bi-1190, 3-32), pp.2, Mar.28, 1932.

WANT TO GET RICH? Western Outdoors, Oswego, vol.6, no.4, pp.8-9, illus., Apr., 1949. (Chinchillas.)

Viscachas

A FURTHER NOTE ON THE NAME OF THE ARGENTINE VISCACHA. J. A. Allen. Proc. Biol. Soc. Wash., vol.15, p.196, Oct.10, 1902.

THE PROPER GENERIC NAMES OF THE VISCACHA, CHINCHILLAS AND THEIR ALLIES. J. A. Allen. Proc. Biol. Soc. Wash., vol.14, pp.181-182, Dec.12, 1901.

THE PROPER NAME OF THE VISCACHA. J. A. Allen. Proc. Biol. Soc. Wash., vol. 13, p.183, Nov.30, 1900.

ON THE FAMILY OF CHINCHILLIDOE, AND ON A NEW GENUS REFERRIBLE TO IT. E. T. Bennett. Proc. Zool. Soc. Lond., pt.1, pp.57-58, 1833.

ON THE HABITS OF THE VISCACHA (LAGOSTOMUS TRICHODACTYLUS). William H. Hudson. Proc. Zool. Soc. Lond., pp.822-833, 1872.

(ECOLOGY OF THE VISCACHA ("LAGOSTOMUS MAXIMUS MAXIMUS" BLAINV.) IN THE NORTHEAST OF ENTRE RIOS PROVINCE.) Ecologia de la vizcacha "Lagostomus maximus maximus" Blainv.) en el nordeste de la Provincia de Entre Rios. Augusto C. Llanos, Jorge A. Crespo. Rev. Investig. Agricolas, Instituto Sanidad Vegetal, Buenos Aires, vol.6, nos.3-4, pp. 289-378, pls.1-9, 1952.

THE SCIENTIFIC NAME OF THE VISCACHA. T. S. Palmer. Science, Lancaster, n.s., vol.6, no.131, pp.21-22, July 2, 1897.

LIFE HISTORY OF MOUNTAIN VISCACHAS IN PERU. O. P. Pearson. Jour. Mam., 29: 345-373.

REPRODUCTION OF A SOUTH AMERICAN RODENT, THE MOUNTAIN VISCACHA. O. P. Pearson. Amer. Jour. Anat., Phila., vol.84, no.1, pp.143-174, figs.3, pls.3, Jan., 1949.

THE NAME OF THE VISCACHA. Oldfield Thomas. Proc. Biol. Soc. Wash., vol.14, p.25, Apr.2, 1901.

A NEW MOUNTAIN VIZCACHA (LAGIDIUM) FROM N. W. PATAGONIA. Oldfield Thomas. Ann. and Mag. Nat. Hist., ser. 9, vol.7, pp.179-181, Feb., 1921.

ON A NEW SPECIES OF LAGIDIUM FROM THE EASTERN COAST OF PATAGONIA. Oldfield Thomas. Ann. and Mag. Nat. Hist. (6), vol.19, no.112, pp.466-467, Apr., 1897.

ON A REMARKABLE MOUNTAIN VISCACHA FROM SOUTHERN PATAGONIA, WITH

DIAGNOSES OF OTHER MEMBERS OF THE GROUP. Oldfield Thomas. Ann. and Mag. Nat. Hist. (7), vol.19, no.113, pp. 439-444, May, 1907.

Capromyidae

Anatomy and Physiology (Nutria)

(THE QUESTION OF NUTRIA ESTRUS AND ITS RETURN.) Fur Frage der Nutriaranz und ihrer Wiederkehr. Hans Frick. Der Deutsche Pelztierzuechter, Jahrgang 1391, Muenchen, no.19, pp.520-521, fig., Oct.1, 1931.

(CONTRIBUTIONS TO THE ANATOMY OF THE COYPU (MYOCASTOR COYPUS MOL.) 4. THE SKELETON OF THE UPPER AND LOWER SHANK.) Beitraege zur Anatomie des Sumpfbibers (Myocastor coypus Mol.) 4. Das Skelett des Ober- und Unterschenkels. G. Hoffman, L. Schroeder. Zool. Anzeiger, Leipzig, 158 (3-4): 44-49, Feb., 1957.

(DATA ON THE POSITION OF THE TESTES AND INTESTINAL INVAGINATION IN THE COYPU.) Einiges ueber die Lage der Hoden imd doe Darminvagination beim Sumpfbiber. P. Korner. Der Deutsche Pelztierzuechter, Jahrgang 1931, Muenchen, no.8, pp.216-217, Apr.15, 1931.

(ON THE STRUCTURE OF THE HAIR COVER OF FUR ANIMALS, PARTICULARLY IN THE NUTRIA (MYOCASTOR COYPUS MOL).) Ueber den Aufbau des Haarkleides bei Pelztieren, insbesondere beim Sumpfbiber--Nutria--(Myocaster coypus Mol). Ludwig Licht. Zeitschr. f. Saeugetierkunde, Berlin, vol.9, nos.1-3, pp.49-75, figs.2, Dec.30, 1934.

VISCERAL AND OSTEOLOGICAL ANATOMY OF THE COYPUS (MYOPOTAMUS COYPUS, COMM.). W. Martin. Proc. Zool. Soc. Lond., pt.3, pp.173-182, 1835.

(MECHANISM OF GLANDULAR PROLIFERATION IN THE ENDOMETRIUM OF THE NUTRIA.) Mecanismo de la proliferacion glandular en el endometrio de la nutria. J. B. Molina-Ahumada, O. Orias. Rev. Soc. Argentina Biol., Buenos Aires, vol. 18, no.4, pp.321-325, figs.12, July, 1942.

EXTRACT OF A LETTER FROM, RELATING TO THE LIGAMENTUM TERES IN THE COYPOU. Mr. Otley. Proc. Zool. Soc. Lond., pt.6, p.118, 1838.

NUTRIA. C. R. Partik. Amer. Fur Breeder, vol.5, no.1, p.22, July, 1932.

(AN ANOMALOUS INCISOR OF THE NUTRIA.) Sobre un incisivo anomalo de nutria. Carlos Rusconi. Physis, Buenos Aires, vol.10, no.35, pp.162-166, 4 figs., July 12, 1930.

(CRANIO-DENTAL EVOLUTION OF THE NUTRIA (MYOCASTOR COYPUS BONARIENSIS) THROUGH ITS POST EMBRYONIC DEVELOPMENT.) Evolucion craneodental de la nutria (Myocastor coypus bonariensis) a traves de su desarrollo postembrionario. Carlos Rusconi. Anales Soc. Cient. Argentina, Buenos Aires, vol.110, pp.3-29, figs.49, 1930.

(ON THE QUESTION OF THE APPEARANCE AND REGULAR RETURN OF OESTRAL PHENOMENA IN THE COYPU.) Zur Frage des Auftrentens und der regelmaessigen Wiederkehr der Brunsterscheinungen beim Sumpfbiber (Nutria). G. Vogel. Der Deutsche Pelztierzuechter, Jahrgang 1931, Muenchen, no.19, pp.515-518, figs., Oct. 1, 1931.

Economic Importance (Nutria)

NUTRIA: FOR BETTER OR FOR WORSE. William H. Adams. Alabama Conservation, 29 (1): 24-26, June-July, 1957.

(EXPERIENCE IN USING THE NUTRIA TO COMBAT UNDESIRABLE AQUATIC PLANT GROWTH.) Opit primeneniia nutrii dlya borbi s vrednoi vodnoi rastitelnosti. I. I. Barabash-Nikiforov, S. V. Morozova. Zool. Jour. Akad. Nauk SSSR, Moscow, vol.31, no.3, pp.443-456, 1952.

NUTRIA. J. H. Bleistein. Amer. Fur Breeder, Duluth, vol.14, no.4, pp.32, 34, 35, Oct., 1941.

LET'S PLANT NUTRIAS. Talbott Denmead. Maryland Conserv., Balto., vol.27, no.2, pp.15, 27, Summer, 1950.

A PRACTICAL DRYING FRAME FOR NUTRIA PELTS. Herbert L. Dozier, Frank G. Ashbrook. Louisiana Conserv., New Orleans, vol.3, no.2, pp.16-18, illus., Oct., 1950.

THE ECONOMIC STATUS OF NUTRIA IN LOUISIANA. Allan B. Ensminger. Pres. 9th Ann. Meeting, S.E. Assn. Game and Fish Comm., 10 pp., processed, Oct., 1955.

NUTRIA FARMING. Matthew N. Federspiel. Amer. Fur Breeder, Duluth, vol. 13, no.8, pp.12-13, Feb., 1941; no.9, p. 26, Mar., 1941; no.10, pp.16-17, Apr., 1941; no.11, pp.18-20, May, 1941.

WINTER CARE FOR NUTRIA. Matthew Federspiel. Amer. Fur Breeder, Duluth, vol.15, no.6, pp.18, 20, figs.3, Dec., 1942.

FOUR-LEGGED WEED CUTTER. Jefferson C. Fuller. S. C. Wildlife, 2(2): 5, 23, illus., Spring, 1955.

NUTRIA FARMING IN ARGENTINA. M. H. Gibson. Field, London, vol.156, no.4057, p.447, Sept.27, 1930.

THE NUTRIA AND ITS POSSIBILITIES. W. W. Harder. Amer. Fur Breeder, Duluth, vol.12, no.5, pp.41-42, Nov., 1939.

(PRINCIPLES OF FEEDING FOR COYPU BREEDERS.) Grundlagen der Fuetterungslehre fuer Sumpfbiberzuechter. W. Koch. Der Deutsche Pelztierzuechter, Muechen, 8 Jahrgang, 1933, no.3, pp.51-55, fig.3, Feb., 1933.

(THE EVALUATION OF THE COYPU FROM FUR ANIMAL SHOWS.) Die Bewertung des Sumpfbibers aus Pelztierschauen. Ernst Kraetge, G. V. Hein, Dr. Walther. Deutsche Pelztierzuechter, Munich, vol.14, no.10, pp.217-225, May 15, 1939.

(EXPERIENCES WITH DIFFERENT BREEDING EXPERIMENTS WITH THE NUTRIA.) Erfahrungen mit verschiedenen Zuchtverfahren beim Sumpfbiber. Werner Lange-Seedeck. Deutsche Pelztierzuechter, Muenchen, vol.14, no.4, pp.73-76, Feb. 15, 1939.

A NUTRIA FARM. Ernest T. Lloyd. Field, London, vol.151, p.164, illus., Feb.2, 1928.

(PROBLEMS OF PRACTICAL NUTRIA BREEDING.) Fragen der praktischen Nutriazucht. Otto Maser. Der Deutsche Pelztierzuechter, Jahrg.1932, Muenchen, no.13, pp.303-306, July 1, 1932.

NUTRIA. A PROFITABLE FUR DISCOVERY. K. E. Kurt Matthias. Amer. Fur Breeder, Duluth, vol.14, no.1, pp.18, 20, fig.1, July, 1941.

A PLEA FOR THE NUTRIA. E. A. Relton. Field, London, vol.160, no.4174, p.966, Dec.24, 1932.

NUTRIA FARMING. Kathleen M. Thompson. Amer. Fur Breeder, Duluth, vol.28, no.9, pp.18, 58-60, Sept., 1955.

HOW TO BUILD NUTRIA PENS. Walter G. Thwaites. Nat. Fur News, Denver, vol.21, no.1, pp.16-17, 28-29, illus., Feb., 1949.

IN DEFENSE OF RANCH-RAISED NUTRIA. Walter G. Thwaites. Nat. Fur News, Denver, vol.20, no.10, p.8, Nov., 1948.

NUTRIA PELTS AND PELTING. Walter G. Thwaites. Nat. Fur News, Denver, vol.20, no.7, pp.18-19, 28-31, illus., Aug., 1948.

NUTRIA RAISING. Walter G. Thwaites. Nat. Fur News, Denver, vol.19, no.5, pp. 10-11, 25, no.6, pp.18, 36-38, illus., June, July, 1947.

(ON BREEDING PRESERVES AND THE QUESTION OF PROFITABILITY IN NUTRIA RAISING.) Gehege-und Rentabilitaetsfrage in der Nutriazucht. Lehrer Zanker. Peltztierzucht verb. mit Kleintierzucht, vol.8, no.4, pp.66-68, figs.2, Apr.20, 1932.

FIRST NUTRIA FUR COAT. Louisiana Conserv., New Orleans, vol.1, no.4, pp. 14-15, 26, illus., Dec., 1948.

WILD NUTRIA IN U.S. INCREASING IN ECONOMIC IMPORTANCE. Amer. Fur Breeder, Duluth, vol.22, no.10, p.10, Apr., 1950.

Europe (Nutria)

(ACCLIMATIZATION AND IMPLANTATION IN FRANCE OF THE NUTRIA.) L'acclimatation et l'implantation en France du myopotame ou ragondin. E. Bourdelle. La Terre et La Vie, 8 Annee, no.3, pp.67-69, illus., May-June, 1938.

(GEOGRAPHIC RACES AND LOCAL VARIETIES OF NUTRIA.) Geographische Rassen und Standortsvarietaeten der Nutria. G. Dennler. Pelztierzucht, vol. 7, no.11, pp.206-207, Nov.17, 1931.

RAISING NUTRIA IN GERMANY. J. O. Derkson. Nat. Fur. News, Denver, vol. 21, no.4, p.18, May, 1949.

CARING FOR AND ACCLIMATIZING NUTRIAS IN A FREE STATE IN ASCANIA-NOVA. A. P. Gunall, I. M. Danil'chenko, O. V. Perovskaia. Trudy Instituta Sel'skokhoziaistevennoi Gibridizatsii i Akklimatizatsii Zhivotnykh v Askanii-Nova (Bull. Inst. Agric. Hybridization and Acclimatization of Animals), Moscow, vol. 1, pp.206-224, figs.5, 1933. (In Russian, with English summary.)

(NUTRIA IN GRAU-DU-ROI (GARD).) Un ragondin au Grau-du-Roi (Gard) (Myocastor). Albert Hugues. Bull. Soc. Nat. Acclimat. France, vol.79, no.10, p.486, Oct., 1932.

(CZECHOSLOVAKIA RAISING MYOCASTOR COYPUS MOL. (MYOPOTAMUS COYPU).) Tchecoslovaquie L'elevage du myocastor coypus mol. (Myopotamus coypu.) Georges Kincl. 15th Congres Internat. D'Agric., vol.5, sect.b, pp.1482-1494, illus., 1931.

THE COYPU (MYOCASTOR COYPUS) IN GREAT BRITAIN. E.M.O. Laurie. Jour. Animal Ecol., 15 (1): 22-34, May, 1946.

NUTRIA BREEDING IN BRISTOL. G. P. MacClellan. Field, London, vol.158, p. 403, figs.2, Sept.12, 1931.

(NUTRIA ACCLIMATIZED IN SOLOGNE.) Le ragondin acclimate en Sologne. A. Maurice. Bull. Soc. Nat. Acclimat. France, nos.7-8, pp.311-316, July-Aug., 1938.

(CAPTURING NUTRIA IN EURE.) Capture de ragondins dans l'Eure. (Myopotamus coypus.) Robert Regnier. Bull. Soc. Amis Sci. Nat. Rouen, ser. 7, 8, Années 70-71, pp.6-7, 1934-35, 1936.

(NEW FACTOR ON THE ACCLIMATIZATION OF MYOCASTOR COYPUS BONARIENSIS REN. IN THE USSR.) L. V. Schapochnikov. Bull. Soc. Nat. Moscow, sect. biol., n.s., vol.48, no.1, pp.65-73, figs.2, 1939. (In Russian, with French résumé.)

COYPUS AT LARGE. (ESCAPES FROM NUTRIA FARMS IN ENGLAND.) C. Turner. Field, London, vol.167, no.4347, p.903, illus., Apr.18, 1936.

ESTABLISHMENT OF THE NUTRIA (MYOCASTOR COYPUS MOL.) IN WEST GEORGIA. N. K. Vereshchagin. Trav. Inst. Zool. Acad. Sci. Rssg, 4: 3-42, 1941.

SOME ESCAPES OF COYPUS (MYOPOTAMUS COYPU) FROM NUTRIA FARMS IN GREAT BRITAIN. Tom Warwick. Jour. Anim. Ecol., London, vol.4, no.1, pp. 141-147, May, 1935.

RE-APPEARANCE OF COYPUS IN HAMPSHIRE. Field, London, vol.179, no.4668, p.636, June 13, 1942.

Fossils (Nutria)

(REVIEW OF THE ARGENTINE FOSSIL SPECIES OF MYOCASTOR, WITH DESCRIPTIONS OF NEW SPECIES.) Revisión de las especies fósiles argentinae del género Myocastor, con descripción de nuevas especies. Carlos Rusconi. Anales Soc. Argentina Estudios Geog. "Gaea", Buenos Aires, vol.3, no.2, pp.505-518, Oct., 1929.

Habits, Behavior (Nutria)

(ZOOLOGICAL AND BIOLOGICAL CONSIDERATIONS OF THE NUTRIA.) Considerations zoologiques et biologiques sur le myopotame ou ragondin. E. Bourdelle. Bull. Soc. Nat. d'Acclimat. de France, Paris, 81 annee, no.12, pp.468-478, Dec., 1934.

(IS THE NUTRIA CARNIVOROUS?) Le ragondin est-il carnivore? A. Chappellier. Bull. Soc. Nat. d'Acclimat. de France, Paris, 82 année, no.4, pp.108-120, Apr., 1935.

THE NUTRIA, SOUTH AMERICAN BEAVER. V. M. Couch. All-Pets Mag., Fond du Lac, vol.19, no.8, pp.63-64, Aug., 1947.

"MIGRATING" NUTRIA. Armand P. Daspit. Louisiana Conserv., New Orleans, vol.2, no.5, pp.7-8, illus., Jan., 1950.

THE COYPU. R. A. Davis. Discovery, London, 16 (6): 237-239, illus., June, 1955; Agriculture, 63: 127-129, illus., 1956.

NUTRIA PROSPECTS. (HABITS IN CAPTIVITY OF MYOPOTAMUS COYPU.) Brothers Edwardson. Amer. Fur Breeder, Duluth, vol.12, no.8, p.30, illus., Feb., 1940.

(SOME OBSERVATIONS OF A FEMALE COYPU (MYOCASTOR COYPUS) KEPT IN THE OPEN.) Einige Beobachtungen an einer in Freiheit gehaltenen weiblichen Biberratte (Myocastor coypus). Irenaeus Eibl-Eibesfeldt. Zool. Garten, Leipzig, n.F., vol.19, no.6, pp.277-283, illus., 1952.

COYPUS EATING MARSH PLANTS. E. A. Ellis. Trans. Norfolk and Norw. Nat. Soc., vol.16, pp.328-329, 1948.

(NOTES AND GUIDE ON THE FOOD OF THE NUTRIA AT THE BREEDING PLACE.) Guia y apuntes sobre la alimentacion de nutria en criadero. Juan Carlos Gody. Misc. Pub. Ministerio de Agricultura y Ganderia, Buenos Aires, no.337, pp.23, illus., 1950.

NUTRIA--THE AMPHIBIAN. W. W. Harder. Amer. Fur Breeder, Duluth, vol.12, no.9, pp.14-15, illus., Mar., 1940.

(NUTRIA BREEDING IN WINTER.) Nutriaauszucht im Winter. Frau M. Heller. Der Deutsche Pelztierzuechter, Munich, Jahrg.9, no.2, pp.35-36, Jan.15, 1934.

ADDITIONAL NOTE ON FERAL COYPUS. Martin W. Holdom. Murrelet, Seattle, vol.25, no.2, p.30, May-Aug. (Sept.19), 1944.

(WHICH CAUSES CAN EFFECT A SLIGHT INCREASE OF COYPUS?) Welche Ursachen koennen eine geringe Vermehrung beim Sumpfbiber bewirken. Julius Kaufmann. Deutsche Pelztierzuechter, Muenchen, vol. 14, no.3, pp.51-52, Feb.1, 1939.

NUTRIA GOOD DIVER. Clarence A. Sooter. Jour. Mam., vol.24, no.4, pp. 503-504, Nov.17, 1943.

(MORE ON PENIS AMPUTATION IN THE COYPU.) Weiteres ueber Penisabschnuerung beim Sumpfbiber. Fr. Westermann. Der Deutsche Pelztierzuechter, Jahrg.1932, Muenchen, no.11, p.266, June 1, 1932.

ROVING RODENT. Florida Game and Fresh Water Fish Commission. Fla. Wildlife, 8 (9): 10-11, 41, illus., Feb., 1955.

North America (Nutria)

THE NUTRIA IN COASTAL LOUISIANA. William H. Adams, Jr. Proc. Louisiana Acad. Sci., 19: 28-41, Nov., 1956.

NUTRIAS GROW IN UNITED STATES. Frank G. Ashbrook. Jour. Wildlife Mgt., Menasha, vol.12, no.1, pp.87-95, pl.2, Jan., 1948; Nat. Fur News, Denver, vol. 20, no.8, pp.17, 22-23, illus., Sept., 1948; Fur of Canada, Winnipeg, vol.13, no.7, pp. 3-4, 6, Apr., 1948.

LIFE HISTORY STUDIES OF NUTRIA OR COYPU, IN COASTAL LOUISIANA. Earl L. Atwood. Jour. Wildlife Mgt., 14 (3): 249-265, July, 1950.

DEVELOPMENT OF NUTRIA IN FEW YEARS SINCE ITS INTRODUCTION IN LOUISIANA HAS BEEN VIRTUALLY PHENOMENAL. Armand P. Daspit. Louisiana Game, Fur and Fish, 6 (1): 4, Dec., 1947.

THE PRESENT STATUS AND FUTURE OF NUTRIA IN THE SOUTHEASTERN STATES. Herbert L. Dozier. 5th Ann. Meeting, S.E. Assn. Game and Fish Comm., pp.1-10, Oct., 1951.

THE STATUS OF THE NUTRIA IN FLORIDA. James V. Griffo, Jr. Quart. Jour. Florida Acad. Sci., 20 (3): 209-215, Sept., 1957.

NUTRIA. Stanley E. Guenther. Game Bull., 2 (1): 5, Jan., 1950.

NUTRIA, MYOCASTER COYPUS, IN MINNESOTA. Harvey L. Gunderson. Jour. Mam., 36 (3): 465, Aug., 1955.

THE NUTRIA, A SOUTH AMERICAN RODENT, IN KANSAS. Donald F. Hoffmeister, Charles D. Kennedy. Trans. Kansas Acad. Sci., Topeka, vol.49, no.4, pp.445-446, fig.1, 1947.

COYPU AT CRESCENT, B.C. M. W. Holdum. Candian Field-Nat., Sutton-West, vol.58, no.1, p.22, Jan.-Feb., 1944.

NUTRIA (MYOCASTOR COYPUS) IN CALIFORNIA. Walter E. Howard. Jour. Mam., 34 (4): 512-513, Nov., 1953.

NUTRIA. Alden Kimsey. Okla. Game and Fish News, 9 (3): 10-11, illus., Mar., 1953.

FERAL COYPUS IN THE PACIFIC NORTHWEST. Earl J. Larrison. Murrelet, 24 (1): 3-9, Jan.-Apr., 1943.

NUTRIA INTRODUCED IN UTAH MARSHLANDS NEAR SALT LAKE. Jessop B. Low. Utah Fish and Game Bull., Salt Lake City, vol.3, no.4, pp.4-5, June-July, 1946.

MEET MR. AND MRS. NUTRIA. Francis X. Lueth. Ala. Cons., 20 (12): 4, 22, June, 1949.

NUTRIA. C. R. Partik. Amer. Fur Breeder, vol.4, no.8, p.26, Feb., 1932.

THE NUTRIA COMES TO TEXAS. George A. Petrides. Texas Game and Fish, 8 (6): 4-5, 27, May, 1950.

THE NUTRIA IN OHIO. George A. Petrides, Daniel L. Leedy. Jour. Mam., vol.29, no. 2, pp.182-183, May 14, 1948.

ESTABLISHMENT AND FOOD HABITS OF THE NUTRIA IN TEXAS. Wendell G. Swank, George A. Petrides. Ecology, Durham, vol.35, no.2, pp.172-176, illus., Apr., 1954.

NUTRIA IN CALIFORNIA. California Vector News, State Dept. Public Health, 4 (5): 30, May, 1957.

TWO IOWA TRAPPERS ASTOUND CITY WITH CURIOUS FUR BEARING CATCH. (COYPU.) South Dakota Conserv. Digest, Pierre, vol.10, no.1, p.10, illus., Jan., 1943.

Parasites (Nutria)

LONGISTRIATA MALDONADOI N. SP. (NEMATODA) TRICHOSTRONGILIDAE PARASITE OF MYOCASTER COYPUS. Paulo Artigas, Genesio Pacheco. Rev. Biol. e Hyg., vol.4, no.2, pp.68-71, figs.7, Aug., 1933.

A NEW SPECIES OF FILARIA FROM MYOCASTOR COIPUS. DIPETALONEMA TRAVASSOSI N. SP. (NEMATODA: FILARIOIDEA). Paulo T. Artigas, Genesio Pacheco. Rev. Biol. e Hyg., vol.4, no.1, pp.23-27, figs.4, Apr., 1933.

(Other Capromyids)

AN EXTINCT CUBAN CAPROMYS. Glover M. Allen. Proc. New England Zool. Club, vol.6, pp.53-56, Mar.28, 1917.

GEOCAPROMYS REMAINS FROM EXUMA ISLAND. Glover M. Allen. Jour. Mam., vol.18, no.3, pp.369-370, Aug.14, 1937.

DESCRIPTION OF A NEW SPECIES OF CAPROMYS, FROM THE PLANA KEYS, BAHAMAS. J. A. Allen. Bull. Amer. Mus. Nat. Hist., vol.3, pp.329-336, Aug.31, 1891.

A MULTILOCULAR COENURUS OF MULTICEPS SP. IN CAPROMYS PILORIDES (SAY, 1822) DESMAREST, 1822. Juan J. Angulo, Agustin L. Roque. Jour. Parasitol., Lancaster, vol.34, no.2, pp.96-100, Apr., 1948.

NOTES ON LIFE-HISTORY OF CAPROMYS. G. C. Bucher. Mem. Soc. Cubana Hist. Nat., vol.11, no.2, pp.93-107, pls.8-13, May, 1937.

NENA. (CAPTIVE JUTIA, CAPROMYS PILORIDES.) Kathleen Hill Bucher. Nature Mag., vol.23, no.6, pp.278-280, illus., June, 1934.

A REVISION OF THE GENUS CAPROMYS. Frank M. Chapman. Bull. Amer. Mus. Nat. Hist., vol.14, art.21, pp.313-323.

(SKULL AND BRAIN OF THE CAPROMYIDAE.) Schaedel und Gehirn der Capromyidae. J. Draeseke. Zeitschr. f. Saeugetierkunde, Berlin, vol.16, pp.238-244, figs.14, pls.2-3, 1942.

A REDISCOVERED HAITIAN RODENT, PLAGIODONTIA AEDIUM, WITH A SYNOPSIS OF RELATED SPECIES. David H. Johnson. Proc. Biol. Soc. Wash., vol.61, pp.69-76, June 16, 1948.

NEW GEOCAPROMYS FROM THE BAHAMAS. Barbara Lawrence. Occas. Papers Boston Soc. Nat. Hist., vol.8, pp. 189-196, Nov.7, 1934.

THE CHARACTERS OF THE GENUS GEOCAPROMYS CHAPMAN. Gerrit S. Miller, Jr. Smithson. Misc. Coll., vol. 82, no.4, publ.3029, pp.1-3, pl.1, Dec.9, 1929.

REMAINS OF TWO SPECIES OF CAPROMYS FROM ANCIENT BURIAL SITES IN JAMAICA. Gerrit S. Miller, Jr. Proc. Biol. Soc., Wash., vol.29, p.48, Feb.24, 1916.

THE RODENTS OF THE GENUS PLAGIODONTIA. Gerrit S. Miller, Jr. Proc. U.S. Nat. Mus., vol.72, art.16, pp.5, pl.1, Sept.30, 1927.

(THE TREE AND PIG RAT GENERA CAPROMYS DESMAREST (SENS. AMPL.) AND PLAGIODONTIA CUVIER.) Die Baum-und Ferkelratten-Gattungen Capromys Desmarest (sens. ampl.) und Plagiodontia Cuvier. Erna Mohr. Mitteil. Hamburgischen Mus. und Inst., Hamburg, vol.48, pp.48-118, figs.53, May, 1939.

DESCRIPTION OF CAPROMYS NANA ALLEN, A SUPPOSEDLY EXTINCT CUBAN HUTIA. T.C.S. Morrison-Scott. Ann. Mag. Nat. Hist. London, ser.11, vol.3, pp.214-216, pls.5, Feb., 1939.

ON THE ANATOMY OF CAPROMYS FOURNIERI, DESM. R. Owen. Proc. Comm. Sci. and Corres. Zool. Soc. Lond., pt.2, p.68, 1832.

A CUBAN TREE DWELLER. (HUTIAS.) Elsie A. Parry. Fauna, Phila., vol.6, no.2, pp.53-54, illus., June, 1944.

THE EXTERNAL CHARACTERS OF AN ADULT FEMALE OF THE RARE CUBAN HUTIA (CAPROMYS NANA). R. I. Pocock. Proc. Zool. Soc. Lond., ser.B, vol.113, 1943, pt.4, pp.198-200, figs.2, Feb., 1944.

THE EXTERNAL CHARACTERS OF THE JAMAICAN HUTIA (CAPROMYS BROWNII). R. I. Pocock. Proc. Zool. Soc. Lond., pt.2, pp.413-418, figs.13-15, July 15, 1926.

LETTER RELATING TO TWO SPECIMENS OF CAPROMYS FOURNIERI, PRESENTED BY HIM TO THE SOCIETY. P. Poey. Proc. Zool. Soc. Lond., pt.6, p.167, 1838.

NOTES ON THE HAITIAN HUTIA, PLAGIODONTIA, AND EXTINCT RELATED GENERA. G.H.H. Tate. Jour. Mam., vol.29, no.2, pp.176-178, May 14, 1948.

## Octodontidae

CHARACTERS OF A NEW GENUS OF RODENT MAMMALIA, FROM CHILI, PRESENTED BY MR. CUMING. E. T. Bennett. Proc. Comm. Sci. and Corres. Zool. Soc. Lond., pt.2, p.46, 1832.

(CONTRIBUTION TO THE ANATOMY OF THE OCTODONTS.) Contribucion a la anatomia de los octodontidos. Guillermo Mann Fischer. Bol. Mus. Nac. Hist. Nat. Santiago de Chile, vol.18, pp.103-124, figs. 29, 1940.

NOTES ON SEVERAL RODENTS COLLECTED DURING A SURVEY OF THE STRAITS OF MAGALHAENS. P. P. King. Proc. Zool. Soc. London, pt.3, p.189, 1835.

A NEW SPECIES OF OCTOMYS FROM ARGENTINA. Barbara Lawrence. Proc. New England Zool. Club, Cambridge, vol. 18, pp.43-46, fig.1, Jan.28, 1941.

THE GENOTYPE OF DICOELOPHORUS AMEGHINO. Gerrit S. Miller, Jr. Jour. Mam., Balto., vol.14, no.3, pp.259-260, Aug.17, 1933.

A NEW OCTODONT RODENT FROM THE PARAGUAYAN CHACO. Wilfred H. Osgood. Fieldiana, Zoology, Chicago Nat. Hist. Mus., vol.31, no.6, pp.47-49, fig.4, Aug. 30, 1946.

A NEW SPECIES OF ACONAEMYS FROM SOUTHERN CHILI. Oldfield Thomas. Ann. and Mag. Nat. Hist. (8), vol.19, no. 111, pp.281-282, Mar., 1917.

THE OCTODON OF THE HIGHLANDS OF SANTIAGO. Oldfield Thomas. Ann. and Mag. Nat. Hist., ser.9, vol.19, pp.556-557, May, 1927.

ON A NEW GENUS OF RODENTS ALLIED TO THE GENERA POEPHAGOMYS, CTENOMYS. G. R. Waterhouse. Proc. Zool. Soc. Lond., pt.9, pp.89-92, 1841.

(OBSERVATIONS ON THE OCTODONTIDS OF CHILE.) Observaciones sobre los Octodóntidos de Chile. John A. Wolfsohn. Rev. Chilena Hist. Nat. Pura y Aplicada, Santiago, vol.31, pp.176-181, (1927) 1928.

(THE OCTODON OF THE HIGHLANDS NEAR SANTIAGO.) Los octodon de las alturas cerca de Santiago. John A. Wolfsohn. Rev. Chilena Hist. Nat. Pura y Aplicada, Santiago, vol.31, pp.118-120, (1927) 1928.

## Ctenomyidae

ON A NEW SPECIES OF CTENOMYS, BLAINV., AND ON OTHER RODENTS COLLECTED NEAR THE STRAITS OF MAGELLAN BY CAPT. P. P. KING, R. N. E. T. Bennett. Proc. Zool. Soc. London, pt.3, p.189, 1835.

(ECOLOGICAL FACTS ABOUT THE "TUCO-TUCO".) Notas ecologicas acerca del "tuco-tuco". Victoria Maria Escariz de Peverelli. Ministerio de Agricultura y Ganaderia, Republica Argentina, Buenos Aires, año 8, no.53, pp.1-15, illus., 1952.

(THE GENUS CTENOMYS.) A propósito del género "Ctenomys." Joaquín Frenguelli. Physis, Buenos Aires, vol.11, no.38, pp.143-144, Dec.31, 1932.

(THE SKULL OF CTENOMYS MINUTUS NHRG., CT. TORQUATUS LICHT., AND CT. PUNDTI NHRG.) Die Schaedel von Ctenomys minutus Nhrg., Ct. torquatus Licht., und Ct. pundti Nhrg. Alfred Nehring. Sitz.-Ber. Gesell. Naturf. Freunde Berlin, Jahrg.1900, no.9, pp.201-210, figs.7, Nov.20, 1900.

A NEW OCTODONT RODENT FROM THE PARAGUAYAN CHACO. Wilfred H. Osgood. Fieldiana-Zoology, Chicago Nat. Hist. Mus., vol.31, no.6, pp.47-49, fig.4, Aug. 30, 1946.

(CONCERNING CTENOMYS LATIDENS AND DICOELOPHORUS LATIDENS.) A proposito de "Ctenomys latidens" y "Dicoelophorus latidens". Carlos Rusconi. Anales Soc. Cient. Argentina, Buenos Aires, vol.114, pp.198-200, Oct., 1932.

(FOSSIL SPECIES OF THE GENUS CTENOMYS, WITH DESCRIPTION OF NEW SPECIES.) Las especies fosiles del genero "Ctenomys", con descripcion de Nuevas especies. Carlos Rusconi. Anales Soc. Cient. Argentina, Buenos Aires, vol.112, pp.129-142, figs.11, Oct., 1931.

(GEOGRAPHICAL DISPERSION OF LIVING TUCO-TUCOS IN THE NEOTROPICAL REGION.) Dispersión geográfica de los Tuco-tucos vivientes (Ctenomys) en la región neotropical. Carlos Rusconi. Anales soc. Argentina de Estudios Geográficos "GAEA," Buenos Aires, vol.3, no.1, pp.235-250, with map, 1928.

(A NEW LIVING SUBSPECIES OF TUCO-TUCO.) Una Nueva subespecie de tuco-tuco viviente. Carlos Rusconi. Rev. Chilena Hist. Nat. Año 38, pp.108-110, 1934.

(A NEW RODENT SPECIES OF THE SUBGENUS PARACTENOMYS.) Una nueva especie de roedor del subgenero "Paractenomys." Carlos Rusconi. Anales Soc. Cient. Argentina, vol.110, pp.153-158, figs.3.

THE TUCO-TUCOS OF PERU (GENUS CTENOMYS). Colin C. Sanborn, Oliver P. Pearson. Proc. Biol. Soc. Wash., vol.60, pp.135-138, Dec.31, 1947.

A NEW TUCO-TUCO FROM BOLIVIA. (CTENOMYS GOODFELLOWI, SP. NOV.) Oldfield Thomas. Ann. and Mag. Nat. Hist. ser.9, vol.7, pp.136-137, Jan., 1921.

A NEW TUCO-TUCO FROM TUCUMAN. (CTENOMYS OCCULTUS.) Oldfield Thomas. Ann. and Mag. Nat. Hist., ser. 9, vol.6, pp.243-244, Aug., 1920.

THE TUCO-TUCO OF SAN JUAN, ARGENTINA. Oldfield Thomas. Ann. and Mag. Nat. Hist., ser.9, vol.7, pp.523-524, June, 1921.

TWO NEW ARGENTINE RODENTS, WITH A NEW SUBGENUS OF CTENOMYS. Oldfield Thomas. Ann. and Mag. Nat. Hist. (8), vol.18, no.105, pp.304-306, Sept., 1916.

TWO NEW TUCO-TUCOS FROM ARGENTINA. Oldfield Thomas. Ann. and Mag. Nat. Hist. (9), vol.1, no.1, pp.38-40, Jan., 1918.

## Echimyidae

THE GENOTYPES OF ECHIMYS AND LONCHERES. J. A. Allen. Proc. Biol. Soc. Wash., vol.29, pp.205-206, Sept. 22, 1916.

THE ADAPTATION OF A CANE RAT (ZYGODONTOMYS) TO THE LABORATORY AND ITS SUSCEPTIBILITY TO THE VIRUS OF YELLOW FEVER. Marston Bates, John M. Weir. Amer. Jour. Trop. Med., Balto., vol.24, no.1, pp.35-37, Jan., 1944.

THE PANNICULUS CARNOSUS IN AN OCTODONT RODENT. Robert K. Enders. Anat. Rec., vol.59, no.2, pp.153-156, figs. 3, May 25, 1934.

THE GENERIC NAMES CERCOMYS AND PROECHIMYS. E. A. Goldman. Proc. Biol. Soc. Wash., vol.25, pp.93-96, May 4, 1912.

MAMMALS OF NORTHERN COLOMBIA. PRELIMINARY REPORT NO.2: SPINY RATS. (ECHIMYIDAE), WITH SUPPLEMENTAL NOTES ON RELATED FORMS. Philip Hershkovitz. Proc. U.S. Nat. Mus., Wash., vol.97, no.3214, pp.125-140, Jan. 6, 1948.

THE GENOTYPES OF ECHIMYS AND LONCHERES. Ned Hollister. Proc. Biol. Soc. Wash., vol.29, pp.205-208, Sept.22, 1916.

ON DACTYLOMYS DACTYLINUS AND KANNABATEOMYS AMBLONYX. F. A. Jentink. Notes Leyden Mus., vol.13, pp. 105-110, pl.7, Mar., 1891.

THE GENERIC NAMES CERCOMYS AND PROECHIMYS. Gerrit S. Miller, Jr. Proc. Biol. Soc. Wash., vol.25, pp.115-117, June 29, 1912.

SPECIATION IN THE BRAZILIAN SPINY RATS (GENUS PROECHIMYS, FAMILY ECHIMYIDAE). Joao Moojen. Univ. Kansas Publ. Mus. Nat. Hist., Lawrence, vol.1, no.19, pp.301-406, figs.140, Dec.10, 1948.

DESCRIPTION OF ECHIMYS HISPIDUS GEOFFROY. F. J. Pictet. Mem. Soc. Phys., Geneve, vol.9, pp.156-159, pl.5, 1841. (In French.)

(DESCRIPTION OF THE SKELETON OF ECHIMYS CAYENNENSIS GEOFFROY.) Description du squelette de l'Echimys cayennensis Geoffroy. F. J. Pictet. Mem. Soc. Phys., Geneve, vol.9, pp.154-156, pl.4, 1841.

(FIRST NOTICE ON NEW OR LITTLE KNOWN ANIMALS OF THE GENEVA MUSEUM. OBSERVATIONS ON SOME SPINY RODENTS OF BRAZIL.) Première notice sur les animaux nouv au ou peu connus du Musee de Genève. Observations sur quelques rongeurs epineux du Bresil. F. J. Pictet. Mem. Soc. Phys., Genève, vol.9, pp.143-153, pls.1-3, 1841.

DESCRIPTION OF A NEW ECHIMYS FROM THE NEIGHBORHOOD OF BOGOTA. Oldfield Thomas. Ann. and Mag. Nat. Hist. (7), vol.1, no.3, pp.243-245, Mar., 1898.

THE GENERIC NAMES CERCOMYS AND PROECHIMYS. Oldfield Thomas. Proc. Biol. Soc. Wash., vol.25, pp.115-116, June 29, 1912.

A NEW ECHIMYS FROM EASTERN ECUADOR. Oldfield Thomas. Ann. and Mag. Nat. Hist. (10), vol.2, no.11, pp.409-410, Nov., 1928.

A NEW GENUS OF ECHIMYINAE. (LONCHOTHRIX EMILIAE GEN. ET SPEC. NOV., FROM RIO TAPAJOZ, BRAZIL.) Oldfield Thomas. Ann. and Mag. Nat. Hist., ser.9, vol.6, pp.113-115, July, 1920.

A NEW SPINY RAT FROM LA GUAIRA, VENEZUELA. Oldfield Thomas. Proc. Biol. Soc. Wash., vol.14, pp.27-28, Apr. 2, 1901.

ON A NEW SPECIES OF LONCHERES FROM BRITISH GUIANA. Oldfield Thomas. Ann. and Mag. Nat. Hist. (6), vol.2, no. 10, p.326, Oct., 1888.

SOME NOTES ON THE ECHIMYINAE. Oldfield Thomas. Ann. and Mag. Nat. Hist. (8), vol.18, no.105, pp.294-301, Sept., 1916.

ON SPINY RATS OF THE PROECHIMYS GROUP FROM SOUTH-EASTERN BRAZIL. Oldfield Thomas. Ann. and Mag. Nat. Hist., ser.9, vol.8, pp.140-143, July, 1921.

ON THE OCCURRENCE OF ECHINOMYS SEMISPINOSUS, TOMES IN NICARAGUA. Frederick W. True. Proc. U.S. Nat. Mus., Wash., vol.11, pp.467-468, Sept.3, 1889.

ON THE OCCURRENCE OF LONCHERES ARMATUS (GEOFF.) WAGNER, IN THE ISLAND OF MARTINIQUE, WEST INDIES. Frederick W. True. Proc. U.S. Nat. Mus., vol.7, publ.468, pp.550-551, Mar. 28, 1885.

SUSCEPTIBILITY OF THE CANE RAT (ZYGODONTOMYS) AND OF THE BUSH RAT (PROECHIMYS) TO INFLUENZA VIRUSES. John M. Weir. Jour. Infectious Diseases, Menasha, vol.74, pp. 121-130, Mar.-Apr., 1944.

A NEW FOSSIL RODENT FROM PUERTO RICO. (PROECHIMUS COROZALUS.) Ernest E. Williams, Karl F. Koopman. Amer. Mus. Novitates, New York, no. 1515, pp.9, figs.2, June 4, 1951.

## Thryonomyidae

ON THE VISCERAL ANATOMY OF THE GROUND-RAT (AULACODUS SWINDERNIANUS). Alfred Henry Garrod. Proc. Zool. Soc. Lond., pp.786-789, figs.1, 1873.

AN EXTINCT CANE-RAT (THRYONOMYS LOGANI, SP. N.) FROM THE CENTRAL SAHARA. Alfred S. Romer, Paul H. Nesbitt. Ann. and Mag. Nat. Hist., ser. 10, vol.6, no.36, pp.687-690, fig. 1, Dec., 1930.

DESCRIPTION OF A NEW SPECIES OF REED-RAT (AULACODUS) FROM EAST AFRICA, WITH REMARKS ON THE MILK-DENTITION OF THE GENUS. Oldfield Thomas. Ann. and Mag. Nat. Hist. (6), vol.13, no.74, pp.202-204, Feb., 1894.

ON THE ANIMALS KNOWN AS "GROUND-HOGS" OR "CANE-RATS" IN AFRICA.

Oldfield Thomas. Ann. and Mag. Nat. Hist., ser.9, vol.9, pp.389-392, Apr., 1922.

Bathyergidae

THE GIANT RODENT MOLE, GYPSORHYCHUS. R. Broom. Ann. Transvaal Mus., Cambridge, vol.21, pt.1, pp.47-49, illus., Apr.6, 1948.

THE NAKED MOLE RAT OF EAST AFRICA. Maurice Burton. Illus. London News, vol.218, no.5840, p.464, illus., Mar.24, 1951.

THE GROSS MORPHOLOGY AND ARTERIAL SUPPLY OF THE BRAIN OF THE GREY RODENT-MOLE (CRYPTOMYS). L.G.R. van Dongen. South African Jour. Sci., Johannesburg, vol.39, pp.164-175, figs.5, Jan., 1943.

NOTES ON THE SPECIES OF SAND-MOLES (GEORYCHUS). John E. Gray. Proc. Zool. Soc. Lond., pp.123-125, figs.7, 1864.

HETEROCEPHALUS, THE REMARKABLE AFRICAN BURROWING RODENT. W. J. Hamilton, Jr. Brooklyn Mus. Sci. Bull., vol.3, no.5, pp.173-184, pls.1-4, Oct.25, 1928.

A NEW RODENT OF THE GENUS GEORYCHUS. Edmund Heller. Smith. Misc. Coll., Wash., vol. lii (Quarterly issue, vol.v), Publ.1879, pp.469-470, pl.lv, 1910.

FIELD AND LABORATORY STUDIES ON THE NAKED MOLE RAT, HETEROCEPHALUS GLABER. W. C. Osman Hill, Annie Porter, R. T. Bloom, J. Seago, Margaret D. Southwick. Proc. Zool. Soc. Lond. 128, (4): 455-514, pls.1-8, July 24, 1957.

(A NEW VARIETY OF GEORYCHUS FROM TOGO, GERMAN WEST AFRICA.) Eine neue abart von Georhychus aus Togo, Deutsch-West-Afrika. Paul Matschie. Sitz.-Ber. Gesell. Naturf. Freunde Berlin, Jahrg.1900, no.4, pp.145-146, Apr.17, 1900.

NEW BATHYERGIDAE FROM THE OLIGOCENE OF MONGOLIA. W. D. Matthew, Walter Granger. Amer. Mus. Nov., New York, no.101, p.5, fig.4, Dec.28, 1923.

MORPHOLOGY AND AFFINITIES OF ENTOZOA AND ENDOPHYTA OF THE NAKED MOLE RAT HETEROCEPHALUS GLABER. Annie Porter. Proc. Zool. Soc. Lond., 128 (4): 515-527, pls.1-2, July 24, 1957.

THE NAKED SAND RAT OR "FARUMFER": A STUDY IN UGLINESS (HETEROCEPHALUS). W. P. Pycraft. Illus. London News, vol.182, no.4910, p.762, illus., May 27, 1933.

(OBSERVATIONS OF HETEROCEPHALUS GLABER RUEPPELL 1842 (RODENTIA, BATHYERGIDAE IN HARAR PROVINCE).) Beobachtungen an Heterocephalus glaber Rueppell 1842 (Rodentia, Bathyergiade in der Provinz Harar). Dietrich Starck. Zeitschr. Saeugetierk., 22 (1-2): 50-56, pls.2-4, 1957.

A NEW HELIOPHOBIUS FROM NORTH-EASTERN RHODESIA. Oldfield Thomas. Ann. and Mag. Nat. Hist. (8), vol.20, no. 118, pp.314-315, Oct., 1917.

NOTES ON GEORYCHUS AND ITS ALLIES. Oldfield Thomas. Ann. and Mag. Nat. Hist. (8), vol.20, no.120, pp. 441-444, Dec., 1917.

NOTES ON THE RODENT GENUS HETEROCEPHALUS. Oldfield Thomas. Proc. Zool. Soc., Lond., pp.845-849, pl.54, Nov.17, 1885.

ON AFRICAN MOLE-RATS OF THE GENERA GEORYCHUS AND MYOSCALOPS. Oldfield Thomas. Ann. and Mag. Nat. Hist. (6), vol.16, no.93, pp.238-241, Sept., 1895.

ON SPECIMENS OF NAKED RODENTS FROM EAST AFRICA. Oldfield Thomas. Proc. Zool. Soc. Lond., pt.2, pp.336-337, Apr.1, 1904 (Dec.1, 1903).

REMARKS ON A BURROWING RODENT, HETEROCEPHALUS PHILLIPSI, N. SP. Oldfield Thomas. Proc. Zool. Soc., Lond., pp.611-612, July 30, 1885.

Ctenodactylidae

ON THE IDENTITY OF THE CTENODACTYLUS MASSONII, GRAY, WITH THE MUS GUNDI, ROTHM. J. E. Gray. Proc. Comm. Sci. and Corres. Zool. Soc. Lond., pt.1, p.50, 1830-1831.

EARLY DEVELOPMENTAL STAGES OF CTENODACTYLUS. D. de Lange. Bio-Morphosis, Leipzig, vol.1, nos.3-4, pp.320-321, 1938.

(ON A NEW RODENT FROM THE ALGERIAN SAHARA (CTENODACTYLUS MZABI N. SP.).) Sur un rongeur nouveau du Sahara Algerien (Ctenodactylus mzabi n. sp.). Fernand Lataste. Bull. Soc. Zool. de France, Paris, Annee 1881, vol. 6, pp.214-225, figs.8, 1881.

ON THE IDENTITY OF THE CTENODACTYLUS MASSONII, GRAY, WITH THE GUNDI MARMOT (MUS GUNDI, ROTHM.). W. Ogilby. Proc. Comm. Sci. and Corres. Zool. Soc. Lond., pt.1, p.50, 1830-1831.

(OBSERVATIONS OF THE GUNDI, CTENODACTYLUS GUNDI ROTHMANN 1776.) Beobachtungen am Gundi, Ctenodactylus gundi (Rothmann, 1776). Helli Roth. Saeugetierk. Mitteil., Stuttgart, 4 (3): 120-123, July 1, 1956.

A NOTE ON THE TYPE-LOCALITY AND GEOGRAPHICAL RACES OF THE GUNDI (CTENODACTYLUS GUNDI ROTHM). Oldfield Thomas. Novitates Zoologicae, vol.27, pp.506-507, Nov., 1920.

(ZOOGEOGRAPHICAL STUDIES ON THE BARBARY. THE RODENTS. III. THE CTENODACTYLINES.) Etudes de geographie zoologique sur la Berberie. Les rongeurs- III, Les ctenodactylines. L. Voleaud. Bull. Soc. Hist. Nat. de l'Afrique du Nord., vol.15, pp.59-67, Feb., 1924.

ON THE ANATOMY ETC., OF THE CTENODACTYLUS MASSONII GRAY (MUS GUNDI, ROTHM.). W. Yarrell. Proc. Comm. Sci. and Corres. Zool. Soc. Lond., pt.1, p.48, 1830-1831.

CETACEA

A WHALE IS KILLED. George Anderson. Beaver, Winnipeg, outfit 277, pp.18-21, illus., Mar., 1947.

WHALER'S EYE. Christopher Ash. Macmillan Company, New York, 241 pp., illus., 1962.

A YEAR AMONGST WHALES AND PENGUINS. Thomas W. Bagshawe. Jour. Soc. Preservation Fauna of Empire, Hertford, n.s., pt.36, pp.30-36, 4 photos, May, 1939.

SOME TOOTHY TRICKS OF NATURE. (WHALES.) John Y. Beaty. Nature Mag., Wash., vol.38, no.1, pp.34-35, illus., Jan., 1945.

A BOOK OF WHALES. F. E. Beddard. London, 1900.

(DISSERTATION AS AN ANSWER TO THE QUESTION --- A NATURAL HISTORY AND NATURAL DESCRIPTION OF WHALES.) Verhandeling ter Beantwoording der Vraag --- eene naturlijke historie en naturkundige beschrijving der walvisschen. Jan Arnold Bennet. 1808.

SOME SMALLER WHALES. H. Boschma. Endeavour, London, vol.10, no.39, pp.131-135, figs.4, July, 1951.

SOME WHALE FACTS. Harry B. Bradford. Nature Mag., Wash., vol.38, no.2, pp.99-100, illus., Feb., 1945.

GILCHRIST'S WHALE. Joseph P. Brewer. Texas Game & Fish, Austin, vol.9, no.7, pp.24-25, illus., June, 1951.

(BIOLOGY OF WHALES.) Zur Biologie der Wale. A. Bueckmann. Zool. Garten, n.F., vol.3, nos.4-8, pp.221-222, Aug.11, 1930.

(BIOLOGY OF WHALES.) Zur Biologie der Wale. (Reviews recent literature.) A. Bueckmann. Zool. Garten, Leipzig, n.F., vol.6, nos.1-3, pp.59-60, May, 1933.

BELMULLET WHALING STATION.-- REPORT OF THE COMMITTEE, CONSISTING OF DR. A.E. SHIPLEY (CHAIRMAN), PROFESSOR J. STANLEY GARDINER (SECRETARY), PROFESSOR W.A. HERDMAN, REV. W. SPOTSWOOD GREEN, MR. E.S. GOODRICH, DR. H.W. MARETT TIM TIMS, AND MR. R.M. BARRINGTON, APPOINTED TO INVESTIGATE THE BIOLOGICAL PROBLEMS INCIDENTAL TO BELMULLET WHALING STATION. S. T. Burfield. Reports State Sci. Brit. Assoc., Sect.D, Dundee, pp.1-42, figs.5, tables 19, 1912.

FROM THE WHALE'S MOUTH. Pauline Chastain Burkher. Alaska Sportsman, Ketchikan, vol.10, no.2, pp.14-15, 24, illus., Feb., 1944.

THE WHALE'S SECRETS. Maurice Burton. Illus. London News, vol.221, no.5910, p. 142, illus., July 26, 1952.

RIGHT WHALES AND WRONG WHALES. Ralph E. Butler. Alaska Sportsman, Ketchikan, vol.11, no.5, pp.12-13, 25-31, illus., May, 1945.

SOME NOTES ON THE NATURAL HISTORY OF WHALES. Leslie Comrie. Trans and Proc. Perthshire Soc. Nat. Sci., Perth, vol.9, pt.6, pp.182-189, pls.36, 1937.

WHALES AND DOLPHINS. A FEW NOTES ABOUT THE GIANT OF THE SEA AND HIS CLOWNING KIN, THE PORPOISE. Anita E. Daugherty. Outdoor California, 18 (10): 3, 7, illus., 1957.

BIOLOGICAL INTERESTS AT A WHALING STATION. W. H. Dawbin. Tuatara, Wellington, New Zealand, vol.1, no.3, pp. 14-20, illus., Sept., 1948.

NOTES ON THE BIOLOGY OF THE WHALE. H. J. Deason. Biology Briefs, Denoyer-Geppert Co., Chicago, vol.5, no.2, pp.14-15, Apr., 1942.

WHALES 1-52 AND WHALES-2. Talbott Denmead, Esther E. Dodd. USDI, Bur. Fisheries, pp.10, 30, 1940. (2 leaflets.)

SHARK'S TEETH AND CETACEAN BONES. C. R. Eastman. Bull. Mus. Comp. Zool., Harvard College, vol.50, no.4, pp.75-98, figs.A-G, pls.3, Nov., 1906.

(DEVELOPMENT OF THE QUESTIONNAIRE RELATIVE TO THE CETACEANS.) Développement du questionnaire relatif aux Cétacés. D. F. Eschricht. Actes Soc. Linneenne de Bordeaux, vol.22, pp.427-431, Aug.12, 1859.

(INVESTIGATIONS OF NORTHERN WHALES.) Om Undersoegelsen af de nordiske Hvaler. D. F. Eschricht. Skandinaviske Narur. Forsamling i Stockholm, p.23, July, 1842.

(INVESTIGATIONS OF WHALES.) Undersoegelser over Hvaldyrene. D. F. Eschricht. Om Naebhavalen, pp.1-58, pls. 4, Copenhagen, 1845.

(INVESTIGATIONS OF WHALES.) Undersogelser over Hvaldyrene. No.5, Finhvalernes osteologie og Artsadskillelse. D. F. Eschricht. K. Danske Videnskabs-Selski; Afhandl.12, pp.227-396, pl.9-16, 1846.

(ZOOLOGICAL, ANATOMICAL, AND PHYSIOLOGICAL INVESTIGATIONS OF NORTHERN CETACEA.) Zoologisch-anatomisch-physiologische untersuchungen uber die Nordischen Walthiere. D. F. Eschricht. Leipzig, 1849.

RECENT RESEARCHES ON WHALES. R. F. Ewer. New Biology, Penguin Books, London, no.9, pp.113-118, Oct., 1950.

WHALES. R. F. Ewer. New Biology, Penguin Books, London, no.2, pp.53-73, illus., 1947.

ON WHALES, PAST AND PRESENT, AND THEIR PROBABLE ORIGIN. A DISCOURSE. William Henry Flower. Proc. Roy. Inst. Great Brit., Lond., vol.10, pp.360-376, 1883.

WHALES, AND BRITISH AND COLONIAL WHALE FISHERIES. William Henry Flower. Jour. Roy. Colonial Inst., Lond., no.3, sess.1894-1895, vol.26, pt.3, pp. 153-177, figs.5, 1895.

WHALE SHIPS AND WHALING SCENES AS PORTRAYED BY BENJAMIN RUSSELL. Allan Forbes. Second Bank-State Street Trust Company, Boston, pp.78, illus., 1955.

FISH OR FLESH? (WHALES.) F. C. Fraser. Illus. London News, vol.210, no.5623, p.121, illus., Jan.25, 1947.

CETACEA. Ludwig Freund. In G. Grimpe and E. Wagler: Die Tierwelt der Nordund Ostsee, Leipzig, Leif.22, vol.12, pt.12, kl, pp.1-64, figs.57, 1932.

CETACEA. Raymond M. Gilmore. Collier's Encyclopedia, New York, vol.4, pp.652-655, illus., 1949.

THE WHALES AND PORPOISES. C. Brown Goode. The Fishery Industry of the United States, pp.7-32, pls.277, 1884.

NOTES ON THE WHALEBONE-WHALES; WITH A SYNOPSIS OF THE SPECIES. J. E. Gray. Ann. and Mag. Nat. Hist., vol.14, pp.345-353, 1864.

OBSERVATIONS ON WHALES DESCRIBED IN THE 'OSTEOGRAPHIC DES CETACES' OF MM. VAN BENEDEN AND GERVAIS. J. E. Gray. Annals and Mag. Nat. Hist., 4th ser., no.33, pp.193-204, Sept., 1870.

ON THE CETACEOUS ANIMALS. J. E. Gray. 1846.

ATTRIBUTES OF WHALES. R. W. Gray. Naturalist, London, no.976, pp.145-153, May, 1938.

(CETOLOGICAL NOTES.) Cetologiske notiser. James A. Grieg. Bergen Mus., Aarsberetning, no.4, pp.1-23, tables, 1889.

(ZOOLOGICAL AND PALEONTOLOGICAL STUDIES ON THE FAMILY OF CETACEANS.) Etudes Zoologiques et Paleontologiques sur la famille des Cétacés. Raoul Guerin. Paris, pp.145, 3 pls., 1874.

(ON THE LIFE, DISTRIBUTION, AND HUNTING OF WHALES.) Om hvaldyrenes levevis, udbredning og fangst. G. A. Guldberg. Naturen, Bergen, pp.257-270, figs.3, Sept., 1907.

TWO SHORT NOTES ON CETACEA. 1. COITUS STENO ROSTRATUS. 2. FUNCTION OF THE FLIPPERS AND TAIL. BALOENOPTERA AND ORCINUS. J. E. Hamilton. Proc. Zool. Soc. Lond., vol. 114, pt.4, pp.549-550, Mar., 1945.

WHALING PRINTS. Charles E. Harris. Avocations, New York, vol.3, no.4, pp. 213-217, 4 prints, Jan., 1939.

WHALES AND WHALING. HVALRADETS SKRIFTER. Johan Hjort. Scientific results of marine biological research, Oslo, no.7, pp.7-29, figs.23, May, 1933.

CONSIDER THE WHALE. A. Brazier Howell. Frontiers, Phila., vol.4, no.2, pp.39-43, figs.5, Dec., 1939.

(CONTRIBUTIONS TO THE NATURAL HISTORY OF WHALE SPECIES.) Beytrage zur naturgeschichte der Wallfischarten. Johann Hunter. Leipzig, pp.258, 1795.

MAMMALS AND BIRDS. V. CETACEANS. Jacquinot and Pucheran. Zool. Voyage of the Asteolabo and Zélée, vol.3, pp.37-46, 1853.

THE NATURAL HISTORY OF THE ORDINARY CETACEA OR WHALES. William Jardine. The Naturalist's Library, vol.4, pp.33-264, illus., 1837.

THE STORY OF A WHALE. Charles Johnson. People's Jour., pp.3-7, Jan.19, 1884.

THE BOOMING WHALE. David Starr Jordan. Nature Mag., vol.14, pp.80-82, illus., Aug., 1929.

THE HISTORY OF WHALES—THEIR ADAPTATION TO LIFE IN THE WATER. Remington Kellogg. Quart. Rev. Biol., vol.3, pp.29-76, illus; pp.174-208, illus., Mar., June, 1928.

WHALES, GIANTS OF THE SEA. Remington Kellogg. Natl. Geog. Mag., 77 (1): 35-90, Jan., 1940.

PROGRESS OF THE DISCOVERY INVESTIGATIONS. (NOTES ON WHALES AND WHALE MARKING.) Stanley Kemp. Nature, London, vol.124, no.3126, pp.483-486, figs. 3, Sept.28, 1929.

ON THE BALAENIDAE OR WHALES WITH BALEEN. WITH NOTES ON THE CETACEA, IN THE COLONIAL MUSEUM, WELLINGTON, BY DR. HECTOR, F.R.S. F. J. Knox. Trans. New Zealand Instit., vol.2, pp.21-28, pl.2b, 1869.

CONTRIBUTIONS TO THE ANATOMY AND NATURAL HISTORY OF THE CETACEA. R. Knox. Jour. Linn. Proc. Zoology, vol. 3, pp.63-76, 1859.

SOME NOTES ON CETACEA. Nagamichi Kuroda. Botany and Zool., Tokyo, vol.3, no.12, pp.2173-2176, Dec., 1935.

(NATURAL HISTORY OF THE CETACEANS.) Histoire Naturelle des Cétacées. B.G.E. Lacepede. vol.1, (octavo), 1803-1804.

NATURAL HISTORY OF THE LARGER WHALES. R. M. Laws. Zoo Life, Lond., vol.10, no.2, pp.41-46, illus., Summer, 1955.

SYSTEMA NATURRAE. Linnaeus. 10th Ed., vol.1, pp.75-77, 1758.

CETOLOGICAL NOTES. Einar Loennberg. Arkiv. f. Zool., vol.15, no.24, pp.1-18, 6 figs., 1923.

SCIENTIFIC ZOOLOGICAL PUBLICATIONS OF THE AMERICAN MUSEUM. SUMMARY OF WORK ON WHALES. (REVIEWS OF PAPERS ON KOGIA AND ZIPHIUA.) Frank E. Lutz. Nat. Hist., vol.20, pp.107-109, Jan.-Feb., 1920.

THE NATURAL HISTORY OF WHALEBONE WHALES. N. A. Mackintosh. Smithsonian Rept., pp.235-264, (Appeared also in Biol. Reviews, vol.21, no.2), 1946.

WHALES AND WHALING. N. A. Mackintosh. International Conference, Nature, London, vol.142, no.3585, pp.101-102, July 16, 1938.

(INFORMATION ON WHALES IN GENERAL, AND BALAENOPTERA CAROLINAE IN PARTICULAR.) Einiges von den Walfischen im Allgemeinen und Balaenoptera carolinae im Besonderen. A. W. Maim. Berlin, published by the author, pp.14, 1866.

(ICONOGRAPHICAL DOCUMENTS ON THE CETACEANS OF THE ARGENTINIAN COASTS.) Documentos iconograficos sobre cetaceos de las costas Argentinas. Carlos A. Marelli. Anales Mus. Naheul Huapi, Buenos Aires, vol.3, pp.133-143, illus., 1953.

WHALES. L. Harrison Matthews. Proc. Royal Philos. Soc. Glasgow, 147 sess., 1948-1949, vol.73, pt.1, pp.1-13, illus., 1948.

WHALES AND WHALING. L. Harrison Matthews. Endeavor, London, vol.5, no. 19, pp.116-122, figs.6, July, 1946.

BIOLOGICAL INVESTIGATION ON THE WHALES CAUGHT BY THE JAPANESE ANTARCTIC WHALING FLEETS SEASON 1949-50. Kazuhiro Mizue, Tadashi Murata. Sci. Repts. Whales Research Inst., Tokyo, no.6, pp.73-131, illus., Dec., 1951.

(GEOGRAPHICAL DISTRIBUTION AND LIVING HABITS OF WHALES OF VALUE TO MAN.) Die geographische Verbreitung und Lebensweise der nutzbaren Walfische. K. Moebius. Verhandl. Gesell. Erdkunde Berlin, vol.21, no.6, pp.324-327, 1894.

GIANT FISHES, WHALES AND DOLPHINS. J. R. Norman, F. C. Fraser. Putnam, London, pp.xiii, 361, figs.94, pls.8, Sept., 1937.

(Review by E. Bourdelle of) THE GIANT FISHES, WHALES, AND DOLPHINS. J. R. Norman, F. C. Fraser. Bibliothèque scientifique, Payot, Paris, vol.1, pp.426, figs.97, 1938, Mammalia, Paris, vol.3, no. 2, p.81, June, 1939.

(Review by Richard S. Croker of) THE GIANT FISHES, WHALES AND DOLPHINS. J. R. Norman, F. C. Fraser. W. W. Norton Co., 1938, 361 pp., 8 color pls., figs. 97, illus.; Calif. Fish and Game, vol.24, no.3, p.298, July, 1938.

(Review by A.H. Laurie of) GIANT FISHES, WHALES AND DOLPHINS. J. R. Norman, F. C. Fraser. London and New York: Putnam and Co., Ltd., 1937, pp. xxviii, 366, pls.8; Nature, Lond., vol.140, no.3552, pp.911-912, Nov.27, 1937.

BIOLOGICAL INVESTIGATION ON THE WHALES CAUGHT BY THE JAPANESE ANTARCTIC WHALING FLEETS, SEASON 1950-1951. Mizuho Ohino, Kazuo Fujino. Sci. Repts. Whales Research Inst., Tokyo, no.7, pp.125-188, illus., July, 1952.

LEAPING WHALES AND FALLING GLACIERS. Arthur Newton Pack. Nature Mag., vol.19, no.4, pp.213-216, figs.8, Apr., 1932.

TALES OF ANCIENT WHALES. Katherine V. W. Palmer. Nature Mag., Wash., D.C., vol.35, no.4, pp.213-214, 221, illus., Apr., 1942.

(OBSERVATIONS ON SOME CETACEANS AT THE HALLES DE PARIS.) Observations sur quelques cétacés aux Halles de Paris. Maurice Prudhomme. Mammalia, Paris, vol.8, no.1, pp.16-18, fig.1, Mar., 1944.

(THE CETACEANS REPRESENTED ZOOLOGICALLY AND ANATOMICALLY.) Die Cetaceen zoologisch-anatomisch dargestellt. Wilhelm Rapp. Stuttgart, pp.182, 8 pls., 1837.

(THE CETACEANS.) Die Cetaceen oder Walthiere. Heinrich G. Ludwig Reichenbach. Dresden and Leipzig, pp.172, pls. 24, 1846.

(CETOLOGICAL NOTES.) Notes cetologiques. Alípio de Miranda Ribeiro. Bull. Soc. Portugaise Sci. Nat., Lisbonne, vol. 11, no.11, pp.145-153, figs.4, Dec., 1931.

WHALES AND WHALE FOETUSES. STATISTICS OF CATCH AND MEASUREMENTS COLLECTED FROM THE NORWEGIAN WHALERS ASSOCIATION 1922-25. Sigurd Risting. Rapports et Procès-Verbaux des Réunions, Conseil Permanent International pour l'Exploration de la Mer Copenhagen, vol.50, pp.122, Dec., 1928.

OF WHALES AND MEN. Robert B. Robertson. Knopf., xii, 300 pp., illus., 1954.

(Review by W. Robert Eadie of) OF WHALES AND MEN. Robert B. Robertson. Jour. Mamm., vol.35, no.4, p.604, Nov.29, 1954.

(BOOKS ON SALT WATER FISH, IN WHICH TRUE PICTURES OF FISH ARE SHOWN.) Libri de Piscibus Marinis, in quibus verae Piscium effigies expressae sunt. Gulielmi Rondeletii. pp.442-487, 1554.

(FEATURES OF THE BIOLOGY OF WHALES.) Trekk av hvalenes biologi. Johan T. Rund. Naturen, Bergen, Arg.54, no.9, pp.261-282, figs.9, Sept., 1930.

BIOLOGICAL INVESTIGATION OF THE NORTHERN PACIFIC BALEEN WHALES CAUGHT BY THE JAPANESE WHALING FLEET IN 1952. Haruyuki Sakiura, Katsunari Ozaki, Kazuo Fujino. Fisheries Agency Japanese Govt., Tokyo, pp.64, May, 1953.

(IDENTIFICATION OF ANTARCTIC CETACEANS.) L'identification des Cétacés antarctiques a la mer. J. Sapin-Jaloustre. Mammalia, Paris, vol.17, no.4, pp.221-259, illsu., pl. 10, Dec., 1953.

(NEW DATA ON THE BIOLOGY OF WHALES.) Neues zur Biologie der Wale. Ernst Schermer. Wochenschrift f. Aquarien u. Terraienkunde, Jahrg.33, pp. 426, July 7, 1936.

IN INLAND CHICAGO—THE WHALES OF ALL THE WORLD'S SEAS AND OCEANS. (QUESTIONS AND ANSWERS.) Karl P. Schmidt. Chicago Nat. Hist. Mus. Bull., vol.16, nos.7-8, pp.1-3, figs.4, July-Aug., 1945.

(THE CETACEANS. COMPARATIVE ANATOMY AND SYSTEMATICS. A CONTRIBUTION TO THE COMPARATIVE ANATOMY OF THE BLOOD-VESSEL, NERVE, AND MUSCLE SYSTEM, AS WELL AS OF THE TRUNK SKELETON, OF THE MAMMALS, WITH STUDIES ON THE THEORY OF EXTINCTION AND FERTALIZATION.) Die Cetaceen. Vergleichend-Anatomisch und Systematisch. Ein Beitrag zur vergleichenden Anatomie des Blutegefaess-Nerven-und Muskelsystems sowie des Rumpfskelettes der Saeugetiere, mit Studien ueber die Theorie des Aussterbens und der Foetalisation. E. J. Slijper. Capita Zoologica, vol.6-7, pp.1-589, figs.256, tables, 1936.

WHALES. E. J. Slijper. Publ. by A. J. Pomerans, Basic Books, Inc., New York, 1962.

NOTES ON THE NATURAL HISTORY, INCLUDING DESCRIPTIONS OF NEW CETACEANS. Leonhard Hess Stejneger. U.S. Nat. Mus., Proc., Wash., vol.6, pp. 58-59, 1883.

(NOTES ON CETACEA.) Note sui cetacei. Giuseppe Tamino. Italiana Sci. Nat., Mus. Civ. Stor. Nat., Milan, vol.43, nos.3-4, pp.489-537, Dec., 1954.

RIMMER SWALLOWS WHALE STORY. Woolsey Teller. Truth Seeker, New York, vol.67, no.11, pp.169-171, Nov., 1940.

THE DISTRIBUTION OF CERTAIN WHALES AS SHOWN BY LOGBOOK RECORDS OF AMERICAN WHALESHIPS. Charles Haskins Townsend. Zoologica (Sci. Contrib. New York Zool. Soc.), vol.19, no.1, pp.50, figs.2, pls.4, Apr.3, 1935.

(ARTICLES PREPARED ON THE FOLLOWING SUBJECTS) MAMMALS, GRAMPUS, KILLER, NARWHAL, PORPOISE RORQUAL, SPERMACETI, WHALE, WHALEBONE, WHALING. Frederick W. True. Encyclopedia Americana, 1904.

MILITARY CETOLOGY. Frederick W. True. Science, vol.5, no.100, pp.2-3, Jan.2, 1885.

OBSERVATIONS ON LIVING WHITE WHALES (DELPHINAPTERUS LEUCAS); WITH A NOTE ON THE DENTITION OF DELPHINAPTERUS AND STENODELPHIS. Frederick W. True. Smithsonian Misc. Coll., vol.52, pt.3, publ.1864, pp.325-330, pl.23, Apr.28, 1909.

THE WHALEBONE WHALES OF THE WESTERN NORTH ATLANTIC COMPARED WITH THOSE OCCURRING IN EUROPEAN WATERS WITH SOME OBSERVATIONS ON THE SPECIES OF THE NORTH PACIFIC. Frederick W. True. Smithsonian Contrib. to Knowledge, vol.33, pp.332, pls.50, Aug.29, 1904.

(Review by F. A. Lucas of) THE WHALEBONE WHALES OF THE WESTERN NORTH ATLANTIC, COMPARED WITH THOSE OCCURRING IN EUROPEAN WATERS, WITH SOME OBSERVATIONS ON THE SPECIES OF THE NORTH PACIFIC. Frederick W. True. Science, n.s., vol. 21, no.543, pp.814-816, May 26, 1905.

THE SOUTHERN WHALING INDUSTRY AND THE PROBLEM OF AGE IN WHALES. J.F.G. Wheeler. Trans. Roy. Soc. Arts and Sci. Nauritius, Port-Louis, ser.C, no.12, 1943-44, pp.26-36, figs.2, 1944.

THE SIGN OF THE PROPHET JONAH AND ITS MODERN CONFIRMATIONS. Ambrose John Wilson. Princeton Theological Review, vol.25, pp.630-642, Oct., 1927.

(AIRPLANES AGAINST WHALES.) Les avions contre les baleines. La Nature, Paris, no.3122, p.319, Oct.15, 1946.

THE BREEDING, GROWTH AND MIGRATIONS OF WHALES. Fisheries Newsletter, Ministry Post War Reconstruction, Cronulla, vol.5, no.1, pp.4-5, fig.1, Feb., 1946.

"DISCOVERY II" AND THE EXPLORATION OF THE WHALE'S HABITAT. Current Science, Bangalore, vol.4, no.1, p.52, July, 1935.

THE LARGEST BEAST IN THE WORLD. GIANT OF ALL CREATURES IS THE WHALE—THE AMAZING ANIMAL THAT MAKES ITS HOME IN THE OCEAN, THOUGH IT IS A TRUE MAMMAL. Junior Nat. Hist. Mag., New York, vol.2, no.3, pp.4-8, figs.5, May, 1937.

THE LARGEST MAMMALS AND THE LARGEST FISH. Nature League News, vol. 3, no.9, pl.1, fig.1, Sept., 1937.

WHALES ON SHOW. Norsk Hvalfangst-Tidende (Norwegian Whaling Gazette), Sandefjord, vol.43, no.8, pp.457-459, Aug., 1954. (In Norwegian and English.)

Africa and Madagascar

(SCIENTIFIC REPORT ON THE WHALE EXPEDITIONS AROUND MADAGASCAR.) Rapport scientifique sur les expéditions baleinieres autour de Madagascar. M. Angot. Mem. Inst. Sci. Madagascar, ser. A., vol.6, no.2, pp.439-486, 1951.

A GUIDE BOOK TO SOUTH AFRICAN WHALES AND DOLPHINS. K.H. Barnard. Guide South African Mus., no.4, pp.3, 1954.

(A FLUVIATIC CETACEAN OF AFRICA.) Un cétacé fluviatile d'Afrique. P. J. van Beneden. Bull. Acad. Roy. Sci., Belgique, ser.3, vol.23, no.4, pp.350-355, illus., 1892.

(SOME CONSIDERATIONS ON THE WHALING CAMPAIGN OF 1951 AT CAPE LOPEZ (GABON).) Quelques considérations sur la campagne baleinière 1951 au Cap Lopez (Gabon). Paul Budker. Mammalia, Paris, vol.16, no.1, pp.1-6, illus., Mar., 1952.

NOTES ON THE WHALES OF THE CAPE; BY E.L. LAYARD, OF CAPE TOWN, CORR. MEMB. WITH DESCRIPTIONS OF TWO NEW SPECIES. John E. Gray. Proc. Zool. Soc. Lond., pp.357-359, figs.5, 1865.

MODERN WHALING IN SOUTH AFRICA. Lawrence G. Green. Field, Lond., vol. 152, p.157, illus., July 25, 1928.

(CETACEANS OF MOROCCO.) Cétacés du Maroc. L. Joleaud. La Nature, Paris, no. 2927, pp.360-363, figs.2, Apr.15, 1934.

NOTES ON THE WHALES OF THE CAPE. Edgar Leopold Layard. Proc. Zool. Soc. Lond., pp.357-359, figs.5, 1865.

(WHALES AND WHALING IN SOUTH AFRICA.) Hvaler og hvalfangst i Sydafrika. Orjan Olsen. Bergens Mus. Aarbok, 1914-1915, no.5, pp.56, figs.21, 1914.

THE SUEZ "SEA-MONSTER." (WHALE.) Illus. London News, vol.216, no.5779, p. 101, illus., Jan.21, 1950.

Anatomy

(THE MORPHOLOGY OF THE HIP BONE RUDIMENTS OF CETACEANS.) Die Morphologie der Hueftbeinrudimente der Cetaceen. O. Abel. Denkschr. math-naturw. kl. kais. Akad. Wiss. Wien, vol. 81, pp.139-195, figs.55, 1907.

AN ACCOUNT OF A WHALE SKELETON. E. A. Andrews, R. P. Cowles. Maryland Conservation, Balto., vol.18, no.3, pp.43-44, Summer, 1948.

(ANATOMICAL INVESTIGATIONS OF THE MALE GENITO-URINAL ORGANS OF MESOPLODON AND OF CETACEANS IN GENERAL.) Recherches anatomiques sur l'appareil génito-urinaire mâle du Mesoplodon et des cétacés en general. R. Anthony. Mem. Inst. Español de Oceanogr., vol.3, pp.35-112, pls.1-5, text figs.1-64, 1922.

(THE ASYMMETRY OF THE CRANIUM OF CETACEANS.) L'asimmetria del cranio dei Cetacei. C. Borri. Archiv. Zool. ital., vol.16, fasc.1-2, pp.751-759, figs.4, 1931.

OBSERVATIONS ON ENDOCRANIAL CASTS OF RECENT AND FOSSIL CETACEANS. A. S. Breathnach. Jour. Anat., Cambridge, England, vol.89, pt.4, pp.532-546, Oct., 1955.

HANDBOOK OF CETACEAN DISSECTIONS. R. H. Burne. British Mus. Nat. Hist. Lond., pp.70, illus., Aug.29, 1952.

EXHIBIT SHOWS THE VESTIGIAL HIND LIMBS OF WHALES. (MOUNTED SKELETON OF EUBALAENA, 45 FT. LONG.) D. Dwight Davis. Field Mus. News, vol.7, no.11, p.3, Nov., 1936.

(THE SKELETON OF THE WHALE OF HERMAN KESSEL DEC. 1928.) Het geraamte van de walvis van Herman Kessels, Dec. 1928 Rotterdam. A. B. Van Deinse. Rotterdams Jaarboekje, pp.1-8, pls.2, 1950.

(THE TAIL OF THE CETACEA AND SEVERAL CASES OF TAPE SHAPED TAILS IN PHOCAENA PHOCOENA L.) De staart der Cetacea en eenige gevallen van lintvormige staarten bij Phocaena phocoena (L.). A. B. Van Deinse. Zool. Mededeel., Leiden, vol.25, pp.23-35, 1945.

NOTES ON THE SKELETONS OF WHALES IN THE PRINCIPAL MUSEUMS OF HOLLAND AND BELGIUM, WITH DESCRIPTIONS OF TWO SPECIES APPARENTLY NEW TO SCIENCE. W. H. Flower. Proc. Zool. Soc. Lond., pp.384-420, figs.17, 1864.

ON THE BONES OF A WHALE FOUND AT PENTUAN, NOW IN THE MUSEUM OF THE ROYAL GEOLOGICAL SOCIETY OF CORNWALL. W. H. Flower. Trans. Roy. Geol. Soc., Cornwall, vol.9, pp.114-121 (8), 1872.

HANDBOOK OF R.H. BURNE'S CETACEAN DISSECTIONS. F. C. Fraser. British Mus. (Nat. Hist.), London, pp.70, illus., May 20, 1952.

(NOTES ON THE MAMMALS. XXVIII. BIOLOGICAL INTERPRETATION OF THE STRUCTURE OF THE CETACEANS.) Notes sur les mammifères. XXVIII. Essai d'interprétation biologique de la structure des Cétacés. Serge Frechkop. Bull. Mus. Roy. Hist. Nat. Belgique, Bruxelles, vol.20, no.13, pp.1-28, figs.15, June, 1944.

THE HYPOPHYSIS CEREBRI OF THE FINBACK (BALAENOPTERA PHYSALUS) AND SPERM (PHYSETER MEGALOCEPHALUS) WHALE. E.M.K. Geiling. Bull. Johns Hopkins Hospital, Balto., vol.57, no.3, pp. 123-142, pls.1-2, Sept., 1935.

THE PITUITARY GLAND OF WHALES. E.M.K. Geiling. Science, vol.85, no.2192, pp.22-23, Jan.1, 1937.

THE POSTERIOR LOBE OF THE PITUITARY GLAND OF THE WHALE; AND PITUITRIN AND ITS FRACTIONS, PITRESSIN AND PITOCIN. E.M.K. Geiling, L. L. Robbins. Proc. Assoc. Res. Nerv. Mental Dis., vol. 17, pp.437-462, figs.90-104, Dec., 1936.

ON THE STRUCTURE AND USE OF THE MONOTREMATIC GLANDS, AND PARTICULARLY ON THOSE GLANDS IN THE CETACEA. M. Geoffroy St. Hilaire. Proc. Zool. Soc. Lond., pt.2, pp.26-27, 1834.

OBSERVATIONS UPON THE STRUCTURE OF THE THYROID GLAND IN WHALES. Allan L. Grafflin. Anat. Record, Phila., vol.83, no.3, pp.367-379, fig.1, pls.3, July 25, 1942.

EXTRACT FROM A LETTER FROM PROF. W. LILLJEBORG, FOR. MEMB., ON THE SKELETONS OF WHALES IN THE JARDIN DES PLANTES. John E. Gray. Proc. Zool. Soc. Lond., pp.730-732, 1865.

(ON THE CENTRAL NERVOUS SYSTEM OF WHALEBONE WHALES.) Ueber das Centralnervensystem der Bartenwale. G. A. Guldberg. Christiania Videnskabs-Selskabs Forhl., no.4, pp.154, pls.1-4, 1885.

(ON THE SIZE AND WEIGHT RATIO OF THE BRAIN OF BONE WHALES AND THEIR COMPARISON WITH THE BRAINS OF THE REST OF THE CETACEA AND OTHER MAMMALS.) Ueber die Groessen- und Gewichtsverhaeltnisse des Gehirns bei den Bartenwalen und ihren. Vergleich mit dem Gehirn der uebrigen Cetaceen und anderen Saeugethiere. G. A. Guldberg. Meddelelser Naturhist. Forening i Kristiania, pp.53-66, 1885.

ADAPTATION OF STRUCTURE IN WHALES. Remington Kellogg. In:—Cooeperation in research by staff members and research associates of the Carnegie Institution of Washington. Publ.501, Carnegie Inst. Wash., pp.649-682, Dec.9, 1938.

(ANATOMICAL NOTES ON THE CETACEANS (LARYNX-AMYGDALES).) Notes anatomiques sur les cétacés (Larynx-amygdales). Max Kollman. Annales Faculté Sci. Marseille, ser.2, vol.9, no. 1, pp.3-19, figs.1-11, 1936.

NOTES ON THE SKELETON OF A RARE WHALE, PROBABLY IDENTICAL WITH DIOPLODON SECHELLENSIS. Gerard Krefft. Proc. Zool. Soc. Lond., pp.426-427, 1870.

(ON THE CETACEAN HAND (PART 1-3).) Ueber die Hand der Cetaceen. Willy Kuekenthal. Anat. Anz., vol.3, no.22, pp.638-646, figs.1-4, 1888; no.3, pp.912-916, figs.1-2, 1888; vol.5, no.2, pp.44-52, figs.1-8, 1890.

PRELIMINARY REPORT ON THE STUDY OF THE MAMMARY GLANDS OF WHALES. E. W. van Lennep, W. L. van Utrecht. Norsk Hvalfangst-Tidende (Norwegian Whaling Gazette), Sandefjord, vol.5, no.42, pp.249-258, May, 1953.

NOTES ON THE SKELETON OF EPIODON NOVAE ZEALANDIAE. Julius von Haast. Trans. New Zealand Inst., vol.9, art.54, pp.429-442, pls.24-26, 1876.

GLIA/NERVE CELL INDEX FOR CORTEX OF THE WHALE. A. Hawkins, J. Olszewski. Science, 125 (3263): 76-77, July, 1957.

ON THE HISTOLOGICAL STRUCTURE OF CETACEAN LUNGS. F. Haynes, Alec H. Laurie. Discovery Reports, vol.17, pp. 1-6, pl.1, July, 1937.

OBSERVATIONS ON THE STRUCTURE OF THE DIFFERENT CAVITIES, WHICH CONSTITUTE THE STOMACH OF THE WHALE, COMPARED WITH THOSE OF RUMINATING ANIMALS, WITH A VIEW TO ASCERTAIN THE SITUATION OF THE DIGESTIVE ORGAN. Everard Home. Philos. Trans., vol.77, pp.93-102, pls.3-4, 1807.

ON THE CETACEAN LARYNX, WITH SPECIAL REMARKS ON THE LARYNGEAL SACK OF THE SEI WHALE AND THE ARYTENO-EPIGLOTTIDEAL TUBE OF THE SPERM WHALE. Hiroshi Hosokawa. Sci. Reports Whales Research Inst., Tokyo, no.3, pp.23-62, figs.19, Feb., 1950.

ON THE EXTRINSIC EYE MUSCULES OF THE WHALE, WITH SPECIAL REMARKS UPON THE INNERVATION AND FUNCTION OF THE MUSCULUS RETRACTOR BULBI. Hiroshi Hosokawa. Sci. Repts., Whales Research Inst., Tokyo, no.6, pp.1-33, illus., Dec., 1951.

OBSERVATIONS ON THE STRUCTURE AND OECONOMY OF WHALES. John Hunter. Philos. Trans., vol.77, pp.333-392, 1787.

DESCRIPTION OF SOME PLATES OF BALEEN IN THE OTAGO MUSEUM. F. W. Hutton. Trans. New Zealand Inst., vol.7, p.266, 1875.

(SOME REMARKS ON CHANGES OF THE TEETH OF MAMMALS IN THE COURSE OF THEIR DEVELOPMENT, SPECIFICALLY IN THE NARWHAL (MONODON MONOCEROS) AND CACHALOT (PHYSETER MACROCEPHALUS).) Bemerkungen ueber die Veraenderung der Zaehne von Saeugethieren im Laufe ihrer Entwickelung, namentlich bei dem Narwhal (Monodon monoceros) und dem Cachalot (Physeter macrocephalus). G. von Jaeger. Bull. Soc. Nat. Moscou, vol.30, pt.2, pp.571-580, 1857.

ON THE WHALE BRAIN. Jan Jansen. Norwegian Whaling Gazette, 41 (9): 480-486, 1952.

(THE STOMACH OF CETACEANS.) Der Magen der Cetaceen. Friedrich Junglaus. Thesis, Univ. Jena, pp.1-97, figs.1-2, 1897.

ON CERTAIN SKELETONS OF WHALES IN THE JARDIN DES PLANTES. W. Lilljeborg. Extract from a letter addressed to Dr. J. E. Gray. Proc. Zool. Soc. Lond., pp.730-732, 1865.

THE PELVIC BONES OF SOME CETACEA. Einar Loennberg. Arkiv. Zool., Upsala, vol.7, no.10, pp.1-15, figs.1-12, Dec.16, 1910.

(STUDIES OF THE VERTEBRAL COLUMN OF WHALES.) Studien an der Wirbelsaeule von Walen. Johannes Luettschwager. Festschrift fuer Dr. Berthold Klatt, Zool. Anzeiger, Leipzig, vol.145, pp.543-560, 1950.

THE TELESCOPING OF THE CETACEAN SKULL. Gerrit S. Miller, Jr. Smithsonian Misc. Coll., vol.76, no.5, pp.1-70, 8 pls., Aug.31, 1923.

OBSERVATIONS ON THE ORBITAL REGIONS OF THE SKULL OF THE MYSTACOCETI. Johanna Muller. Zool. Mededel. Rijksmus. Nat. Hist. Leiden, vol.32, no. 23, pp.279-290, illus., Feb.22, 1954.

HISTOLOGICAL STUDIES ON THE RESPIRATORY PORTIONS OF THE LUNGS OF CETACEA. Tadashi Murata. Sci. Repts. Whales Research Inst., Tokyo, no.6, pp. 33-47, illus., Dec., 1951.

(COMPARATIVE RESEARCH ON THE DENTITION OF CETODONTS. STUDY OF MORPHOLOGY AND ETHOLOGY.) Recherches comparatives sur la dentition des Cétodontes. Étude de morphologie et d'éthologie. H. Neuville. Annales Sci. Nat. Zool., ser.10, vol.15, pp.186-361, pls.1-16, figs.1-62, 1932.

ON THE MUSCULATURE OF THE SINUS VENOSUS AND ITS CONTINUATION WITH THE SO-CALLED CONDUCTING SYSTEM OF THE WHALE'S HEART. Teizo Ogawa. Sci. Repts. Whales Research Inst., Tokyo, no.9, pp.11-31, illus., June, 1954.

THE ANATOMICAL BASIS OF SWIMMING IN WHALES. D. A. Parry. Proc. Zool. Soc. Lond., vol.119, pt.1, pp.49-60, figs. 5, May 16, 1949.

SOME MORPHOLOGICAL ADAPTATIONS OF CETACEANS (WHALES AND PORPOISES) FOR LIFE IN THE WATER. H. C. Raven. Trans. New York Acad. Sci., ser.2, vol.5, no.2, pp.23-29, Dec., 1942.

THE SPERMACETI ORGAN AND NASAL PASSAGES OF THE SPERM WHALE (PHYSETER CATODON) AND OTHER ODONTOCETES. H. C. Raven, William K. Gregory. Amer. Mus. Novitates, New York, no.677, pp.1-18, figs.9, Dec.2, 1933.

(ON THE FORM AND FUNCTION OF THE CERVICAL VETEBRAE OF WHALES.) Ueber form und Funktion der Halswirbelsaeule der Wale. Otto Reche. Inaugural-Dissertation, Univ. Breslau, p.42, 1904.

A STUDY OF THE SURFACE STRUCTURE OF THE BRAIN OF THE WHALE (BALAENOPTERA PHYSALUS AND PHYSETER CATODON). Fred August Ries, Orthello Richardson Langworthy. Jour. Comp. Neur., vol.68, pp.1-36, figs.2, pls.5, Dec.15, 1937.

(THE STRUCTURE OF THE RETINA, DESCRIBED IN ACCORDANCE WITH INVESTIGATIONS OF THE WHALE EYE.) Die structur der Retina dargestellt nach Untersuchungen uber das Walfischauge. Carl Ritter. Wilhelm Engelmann, Leipzig, pp.72, pls.2, 1864.

(THE COLLECTION OF CETACEANS OF THE OCEANOGRAPHIC MUSEUM OF MONACO.) La collection de Cetaces du Musee Oceanographique de Monaco. P. Rode. Notes osteometriques. Bull. Inst. Oceanographique, Monaco, no.780, pp.1-20, Sept.30, 1939.

ON THE DEVELOPMENT OF THE MAMMARY GLANDS AND GENITALIA OF THE CETACEA. John A. Ryder. Bull. U.S. Fish Comm., Wash., D.C., vol.5, pp.135-142, illus., 1885.

ON THE GENESIS OF THE EXTRA TERMINAL PHALANGES IN THE CETACEA. John A. Ryder. Amer. Nat., Phila., vol. 19, no.10, pp.1013-1015, Oct., 1885.

A WHALE'S EAR-BONE. T. Sheppard. Naturalist, London, no.990, p.178, fig.1, July, 1939.

(COMPARATIVE MICROSCOPIC-ANATOMIC INVESTIGATIONS OF THE CORPUS CAVERNOSUM PENIS IN THE CETACEANS.) Vergleichend mikroskopisch-anatomische Untersuchungen ueber das Corpus cavernosum Penis der Cetaceen. E. J. Slijper. Archiv. Nederlandaises Zool., vol.3, supplement, pp.205-218, figs.5, tables, May, 1938.

(ON CAUSE OF THE ASYMMETRY OF WHALES.) Ueber die Ursache der Asymmetrie der Wale. G. Steinmann-Bonn. Anat. Anzeiger, Jena, vol.41, nos. 2-3, pp.45-54, figs.5, 1912.

(OSTEOLOGICAL DESCRIPTION OF THE WHALE.) Osteologische Beschreibung des Walls. Fried. Wilhelm Ludwig Suckow. Mannheim, pp.vi, 7-16, pls.5, 1837.

(THE INTESTINE OF THE CETACEANS.) Der Darm der Cetaceen. Siegmund Suessbach. Thesis: Koenigl. Universitaet Breslau, Jena, 48 pp., 1901.

ON THE CETACEAN LARYNX. D'Arcy W. Thompson. Studies from the Mus. of Zool. Univ. College, Dundee, vol.1, no.11, pp. 1-8, text figs.14, Aug., 1890.

ADDITIONAL OBSERVATIONS ON THE STOMACH IN THE ZIPHIOID AND DELPHINOID WHALES. William Turner. Jour. Anat. Physiol., Edinburg, vol.23, pp.465-492, figs.5, Apr., 1889.

OBSERVATIONS ON THE AUDITORY ORGAN IN THE CETACEA. William Turner. Proc. Roy. Soc. Edinburg, Sess. 1913-1914, vol.34, pt.1, no.2, pp.10-22, figs.4, Dec.31, 1913.

THE SKELETON OF A SOWERBY'S WHALE, MESOPLODON BIDENS, STRANDED AT ST. ANDREWS, AND THE MORPHOLOGY OF THE MANUS IN MESOPLODON, HYPEROODON AND THE DELPHINIDAE. William Turner. Proc. Roy. Soc., Edinburgh, Sess.1908-1909, vol.29, pt.7, no.41, pp. 687-720, figs.11, Oct.14, 1909.

UPON THE THYROID GLANDS IN THE CETACEA, WITH OBSERVATIONS ON THE RELATIONS OF THE THYMUS TO THE THYROID IN THESE AND CERTAIN OTHER MAMMALS. William Turner. Trans. Roy. Soc., Edinburgh, vol.22, pp.319-325, figs.2, 1862.

(ON THE DENTITION OF THE CETACEANS.) De la dentition des Cetaces. M. Vrolik. Extrait des Memoires de l'Academie imperiale de Dijon, p.3, Sept.26, 1856.

(ANATOMICAL DATA ON CETACEANS.) Anatomisches ueber Cetaceen. Max Weber. Morphol. Jahrbuch, vol.13, pp.616-653, figs.2, pls.27-28, 1888.

THE LUNGS OF THE LARGER CETACEA COMPARED TO THOSE OF SMALLER SPECIES. George B. Wislocki, Leonard F. Belanger. Biol. Bull. Lancaster, vol.78, no.2, pp.289-297, pls.1-2, Apr., 1940.

THE ANATOMY OF THE HYPOPHYSIS OF WHALES. George B. Wislocki, E.M.K. Geiling. Anatomical Record, vol.66, no. 1, pp.17-36, figs.4, table 1, pls.3, Aug., 1936.

CONTRIBUTION TO THE ANATOMY OF THE ORGAN OF HEARING OF WHALES. Munesato Yamada. Sci. Repts. Whales Research Inst., no.8, pp.1-78, illus., 1953.

### Arctic Ocean and Northern Seas

JAN MAYEN ISLAND. A SUMMER VISIT IN 1934. (Cetacean skulls and bones strewn on beach are valueless because of poor state of preservation.) E. G. Bird. Geogr. Jour., Lond., vol.85, no.6, pp.553-557, pls.2, June, 1935.

PURSUING THE WHALE. A QUARTER-CENTURY OF WHALING IN THE ARCTIC.

John A. Cook. Riverside Press, Cambridge, pp.x, 344, illus., 1926.

(INVESTIGATIONS OF THE DISTRIBUTION OF CETACEANS IN THE NORTHERN SEAS.) Recherches sur la distribution des Cétacés dans les mers Boréales. Daniel F. Eschricht. Ann. Sci. Nat. Zool., vol.1, pp.301-224, 1864.

CETACEA. Ludwig Freund. Die Tierwelt der Nord- und Ostsee, Leipzig, Lieferung 22, Teil 12, kl, pp.1-64, figs.1-57, Oct., 1932.

THE ZOOLOGY OF THE VOYAGE OF H.M.S. EREBUS AND TERROR, UNDER COMMAND OF CAPT. SIR JAMES CLARK ROSS, R.N., DURING YEARS 1839 TO 1848. John E. Gray. Vol.1, Mammalia, pt.3, on the Cetaceous animals (by John E. Gray), pp. 13-53, pls.30, 1846.

THE COLOR OF THE GREENLAND SEA AND THE MIGRATIONS OF THE GREENLAND WHALE AND NARWHAL. R. W. Gray. Geographical Jour., vol.78, no.3, pp.284-290, Sept., 1931.

GREENLAND WHALES AND THE ESKIMOS OF N.E. GREENLAND. R. W. Gray. Scottish Nat., no.213, pp.75-77, May-June, 1935.

THE ARCTIC WHALEMAN; OR WINTER IN THE ARCTIC OCEAN. Lewis Holmes. Boston: Wentworth & Co., pp.296, illus., 1857.

WHALING ACTIVITY IN ICELAND. Bjorgulv Iversen. Norsk Hvalfangst-Tidende (Norwegian Whaling Gazette), vol.44, no.10, pp.598-606, illus., Oct., 1955.

(NOTABLE WHALING TRIP ON THE "ELISABETH" TOWARD GREENLAND (7 APRIL 1769).) Merkwurdige Reise, welcher mit dem Schiffe die Frau Elisabeth den 7 ten April nach Groenland auf den Wallfischfang...1769. Jacob Janssens. Hamburg, 27 pp., illus., 1770.

(CLASSIFICATION OF WHALES OBSERVED UP TO NOW IN THE BALTIC SEA.) Zusammenstellung der in der Ostsee bisher Beobachteten Wale. Arnold Japha. Schrift. Physik.-okonom. Gesell. Konigsbert, i, Pr., vol.49, pp.119-189, 1908.

(WHALES OBSERVED IN THE BALTIC SEA.) Die in der Ostsee beobachteten Wale. A. Japha. Schrift. Physik.-Okonom. Gesell. Koenigsberg. i. Pr., vol.48, pp.81-87, 1907.

JOURNAL OF A VOYAGE TO THE NORTHERN WHALE-FISHERY; INCLUDING RESEARCHES AND DISCOVERIES ON THE EASTERN COAST OF WEST GREENLAND, MADE IN THE SUMMER OF 1822, IN THE SHIP BAFFIN OF LIVERPOOL. William Scoresby, Jr. Archibald Constable and Co., Edinburgh, pp.472, maps, 1823.

BIOLOGY AND WHALING IN THE SEAS OF THE FAR EAST. M.M. Sleptsov. Food Industry Publ. House, Moscow, pp.64, illus., 1955. (In Russian.)

CETACEANS OF THE SEAS OF THE FAR EAST. M. M. Sleptsov. Pacific Research Inst. Fisheries and Oceanogr., Ministry Fisheries USSR, Vladivostok, pp.162, illus., 1955. (In Russian.)

NOTES ON THE ARCTIC WHALE-FISHERY FROM YARMOUTH AND LYNN. Thomas Southwell. Trans. Norfolk and Norwich Nat. Soc., vol.8, pp.202-215, illus., 1906.

NOTES ON THE ARCTIC WHALING VOYAGE OF 1905. Thomas Southwell. Zoologist, London, ser.4, vol.10, no.776, pp.41-48, Feb., 1906.

NOTES ON THE ARCTIC WHALING VOYAGE OF 1906. Thomas Southwell. Zoologist, London, ser.4, vol.11, vol.65, no.788, pp.66-68, Feb., 1907.

OBSERVATIONS ON FAR-EASTERN WHALES. A. G. Tomilin. Doklady Acad. Sci. USSR, Moscow, n.s., vol.14, no.6, pp.399-402, 1937. (In English.)

THE WHALES OF THE FAR EAST. A. G. Tomilin. Uchenye Zapiski Moskovskogo Gosudarstvennogo Universiteta, zool., vol. 13, pp.119-167, figs.38-45, tables 1-9, 1937. (In Russian, with English summary.)

COMMERCIAL WHALING IN THE ARCTIC OCEAN. James W. Vanstone. Pacific Northwest Quart., 49 (1): 1-10, Jan., 1958.

SOME DATA ON WHALES OF THE FAR EAST. B. Zenkovich. Doklady Akademii Nauk SSSR, vol.2, no.6, pp.388-392, May 21, 1934. (In Russian and in English.)

SOME OBSERVATIONS ON THE WHALES OF THE FAR EAST WHALE INDUSTRY IN THE KAMTCHATKA AND BERING SEAS. B. Zenkovich. Pacific Sci. Inst. Fishery Economy and Oceanography, Moscow, nos. 1-2, pp.111-118, 1934. (In Russian.)

WHALING OFF KAMCHATKA. Asia, vol. 38, no.4, pp.237-240, illus., Apr., 1938.

Asia

SOME ODONTOCETI FROM CEYLON. P.E.P. Deraniyagala. Spolia Zeylanica, Colombo, vol.24, pt.2, pp.113-120, figs. 4, pls.14-16, Dec.22, 1945.

LETTER OF PROF. OWEN RELATING TO A PREVIOUS PAPER BY PROF. OWEN ON INDIAN CETACEA. Sir Walter Elliot. Proc. Zool. Soc. Lond., p.474, 1867.

THE WHALES, PORPOISES AND DOLPHINS KNOWN IN MALAYAN WATERS. C. A. Gibson-Hill. Malayan Nature Jour., Kuala Lumpur, vol.4, no.2, pp.44-61, illus., June, 1949.

ON THE POSTWAR WHALING IN THE ADJACENT WATERS OF JAPAN. Hiroshi Kasahara. Repts. Research Lab. Nippon Suisan Co., pp.1-8 (separately paged 25-32 and 313-320, 1952. (In Japanese with English summary.)

(NOTES ON THE CETACEANS OF THE SEAS ADJACENT TO JAPAN.) Note sur des cetacees des Mers Voisines du Japon. Le Cte. Lacepede. Mem.Mus. Hist. Nat., Paris, vol.4, pp.467-475, 1818.

ON TWO CETACEANS FROM TRAVANCORE, BY H.S. FERGUSON, WITH A NOTE ON THE SAME, BY R. LYDEKKER. R. Lydekker. Jour. Bombay Nat. Hist. Soc., vol.15, pp.38-41, 1903.

SURVEY OF WHALING OPERATIONS FROM LAND STATIONS IN WATERS ADJACENT TO JAPAN IN 1953. Ichiro Miyazaki. Norsk Hvalfangst-Tidende (Norwegian Whaling Gazette), Sandefjord, vol.43, no.4, pp.181-192, illus., Apr., 1954. (In Norwegian and English.)

WHALES IN BARODA, WITH NOTES ON THE ANATOMY OF THE FIN-WHALE (BALAENOPTERA INDICA) STRANDED AT MULVEL IN MARCH 1939. S. T. Moses. Jour. Bombay Nat. Hist. Soc., vol.41, no. 4, pp.895-897, Aug., 1940.

LIST OF THE ODONTOCETI IN JAPAN. Teizo Ogawa. Ann. Report work Saito Hō-on Kai, Sendai, no.12, pp.63-65, June, 1937.

(STUDIES OF THE TOOTHED WHALES IN JAPAN.) Studien ueber die Zahnwale in Japan. Teizo Ogawa. Botany and Zool., Tokyo, vol.4, no.7, July 1936, pp.1159-1171, figs.1-5; no.8, Aug., 1936, pp.1337-1344, figs.6-11; no.9, Sept.1936, pp.1495-1504, figs.12-16; no.10, Oct., 1936, pp. 1685-1694, figs.17-25; no.11, Nov., 1936, pp.1837-1844, figs.26-29; no.12, Dec., 1936, pp.2017-2024, figs.30-38; vol.5, no. 1, Jan., 1937, pp.25-34, figs.39-49; no.2, Feb., 1937, pp.409-416, figs.49-53; no.3, pp.591-598, figs.54-58, Mar., 1937. (In Japanese.)

(STUDIES ON THE TOOTHED WHALE IN JAPAN, PARTICULARLY ON THE FOUR PREVIOUSLY UNKNOWN GENERA TURSIOPS STENO, PSEUDORCA, AND MESOPLODON.) Studien ueber die Zahnwale in Japan, insbesondere ueber die vier bei uns bisher unbekannten Gattung Tursiops, Steno, Pseudorca, und Mesoplodon. Teizo Ogawa. Arbeiten aus dem Anatomischen Institut der Kaiserlich-Japanischen Universitaet zu Sendai, Heft 21, pp.173-218, pls.14, May 30, 1938.

VON SIEBOLD AND JAPANESE WHALES. Teizo Ogawa. Siebold Kenkyû, p.32, fig.16, 1938. (In Japanese.)

WHALES IN THE ADJACENT WATERS OF JAPAN. Hideo Omura. Sci. Repts. Whales Research Inst., Tokyo, no.4, pp.27-113, Aug., 1950.

WHALING IN THE ADJACENT WATERS OF JAPAN. Hideo Omura, Keijiro Maeda, Ichiro Miyazaki. Norsk Hvalfangst-Tidende (Norwegian Whaling Gazette), Sandefjord, vol.42, no.4, pp.199-212, illus., Apr., 1953.

DESCRIPTIONS OF NEW SPECIES OF INDIAN CETACEANS OBSERVED AND COLLECTED BY WALTER ELLIOT. Richard Owen. Proc. Zool. Soc. Lond., p.511, 1865.

ON SOME INDIAN CETACEA COLLECTED BY WALTER ELLIOT. Richard Owen. vol.6, pt.1, pp.17-47, pls.3-14, 1865.

WHALING IN NORTHEASTERN JAPANESE WATERS. Miles L. Peelle. Science, n.s., vol.75, no.1956, pp.666-667, June 24, 1932.

LIST OF CETACEANS TAKEN IN TRAVANCORE FROM 1902 TO 1925. R. Shunkara Narayan Pillay. Jour. Bombay Nat. Hist. Soc., vol.31, pp.815-817, Nov.1, 1926.

(RECORD OF WHALING BY UKITSU GROUP IN MUROTO, TOSA PROVINCE.) Tosa Muroto Ukitsu-gumi hogei jitsuroku. Yoshioka Takakichi. Attic Museum ser. no.35, Tokyo; Maruzen, publ.), p.75, fig. 6, pl.20, 1938.

(WHALING AT TAIJII. Munesato Yamada. Shizen, vol.7, no.3, pp.64-70, illus., 1952. (In Japanese.)

WHALES IN THE SEAS ADJACENT TO CHINA. China Jour., vol.16, no.6, pp. 354-355, June, 1932.

Atlantic Ocean

(ON THE MOST IMPORTANT WHALES OF THE ATLANTIC OCEAN AND THEIR DISTRIBUTION THEREIN.) Ueber die wichtigsten Wale des Atlantischen Ozeans und ihre Verbreitung in demselben. Heinrich Bolau. Segelhandbuchs Atlantischen Ozeans, vol.14, zool. Anz., vol. 8, p.520, illus., 1884.

OPEN BOAT WHALING IN THE AZORES. THE HISTORY AND PRESENT METHODS OF A RELIC INDUSTRY. Robert Clarke. Discovery Reports, Cambridge, vol.26, pp.281-354, pls.13-18, Feb., 1954.

WHALING AND FISHING IN THE NORTH ATLANTIC. Johan Hjort, Johan T. Ruud. Conseil Permanent Internat. Explor. Mer, Rapp. et Proc. Verb. Reunions, Copenhagen, vol.56, pp.1-123, 24 maps, 35 figs., May, 1929.

WHALES CAUGHT IN THE NORTH ATLANTIC AND OTHER SEAS. Andr Ingebrigtsen. Conseil Permanent Internat. Explor. Mer, Rapp. et Proc. Verb. Reunions, Copenhague, vol.56, pp.1-26, May, 1929.

OBSERVATIONS ON WHALES IN THE SOUTH ATLANTIC OCEAN IN 1943. J.F.G. Wheeler. Proc. Zool. Soc. Lond., vol.116, pt.2, pp.221-224, fig.1, Nov., 1946.

Bibliographies

BIBLIOGRAPHY OF WHALING. James T. Jenkins. Jour. Soc. Biblio. Nat. Hist., London, vol.2, pt.4, pp.71-166, Nov.3, 1948.

A BIBLIOGRAPHY OF WHALES AND WHALING. Torbjorn Pedersen, Johan T. Ruud. Selected Papers from the Norwegian Research work 1860-1945. Hvalradets Skrifter, Sci. Results Marine Biol. Res., Oslo, no.30, p.31, 1946.

Biochemistry

STUDIES ON DIGESTIVE ENZYME IN WHALE. Schiro Akiya. Sci. Repts. Whales Research Inst., Tokyo, no.1, pp. 3-7, illus., June, 1948.

ISOLATION OF HISTIDINE FROM WHALE BLOOD USING 3, 4-DICHLOROBENZENE SULFONIC ACID. Shichiro Akiya, Otomatsu Hoshino. Sci. Reports Whales

Research Inst., Tokyo, no.5, pp.41-47, June, 1951.

VITAMINS IN WHALE LIVER. Olaf R. Braekkan. Hvalradets Skrifter, Sci. Results Marine Biol. Research, Oslo, no. 32, pp.1-25, figs.4, 1948.

EFFECT ON VITAMIN-A WHEN WATER SOLUBLE EFFECTIVE INGREDIENTS ARE EXTRACTED FROM WHALE LIVER. Hisashi Fujii, Kosaku Suzuki. Repts. Research Lab. Nippon Suisan Co., pp.27-31 (separately paged 19-23), 1952. (In Japanese with English summary.)

ON THE SEROLOGICAL CONSTITUTION OF THE SPERM AND BAIRD BEAKED WHALES. I. BLOOD GROUPS OF THE SPERM AND BAIRD BEAKED WHALES. Kazuo Fujino. Sci. Repts. Whales Research Inst., Tokyo, no.9, pp.105-120, June, 1954.

THE INSULIN CONTENT OF WHALE PANCREAS. J. Erik Jorpes. Hvalradets Skrifter, Sci. Res. Marine Biol. Res., Oslo, no.35, p.15, 1950.

ELECTROPHORETIC PROPERTIES AND ANALYSIS OF WHALE MYOGLOBIN. K. Schmid. Nature, London, vol.163, no. 4143, pp.481-482, Mar.26, 1949.

ON THE COMPOSITION OF THE FAT FROM A SAMPLE OF WHALE MILK. S. Schmidt-Nielsen, F. Frog. K. norske Vidensk. Selsk. Trondheim, vol.6, no.33, pp.127-129, June 26, 1933.

ON THE RESPIRATORY PIGMENTS OF WHALE (STUDIES ON WHALE BLOOD. II). Tadashi Tawara. Sci. Reports Whales Research Inst., Tokyo, no.3, pp.96-101, Feb., 1950.

STUDIES ON WHALE BLOOD. I. Tadashi Tawara. Sci. Repts. Whales Research Inst. Tokyo, no.1, pp.38-40, June, 1948.

RESEARCH ON METHIONINE IN WHALE. Masami Yoshida. Sci. Reports Whales Research Inst., Tokyo, no.3, pp.102-105, Feb., 1950.

MILK OF LARGE-SIZED CETACEANS. B. A. Zenkovich. Doklady Acad. Sci. USSR, Moscow, n.s., vol.20, nos.2-3, pp.203-205, 1938.

Captivity

WHALES IN AQUARIUM. Åge Jonsgård. Norsk-Hvalfangst-Tidende (Norwegian Whaling Gazette), Sandefjord, vol.42, no.6, pp.309-321, June, 1953.

Determination of Age

AGE CHARACTERISTICS IN BALEEN PLATES. Masaharu Nishiwaki. Sci. Repts. Whales Research Inst., Tokyo, no.4, pp.162-183, illus., Aug., 1950.

ON THE PERIODIC MARK ON THE BALEEN PLATES AS THE SIGN OF ANNUAL GROWTH. Masaharu Nishiwaki. Sci. Repts. Whales Research Inst., Tokyo, no. 6, pp.133-152, illus., Dec., 1951.

FURTHER STUDIES ON THE STRUCTURE OF THE BALEEN PLATES AND THEIR APPLICATION TO AGE DETERMINATION. Johan T. Ruud. Hvalradets Skrifter, Scientific Results of Marine Biological Research, Oslo, no.29, pp.69, figs. 28, 1945.

THE SURFACE STRUCTURE OF THE BALEEN PLATES AS A POSSIBLE CLUE TO AGE IN WHALES. Johan T. Ruud. Hvalradets Skrifter, Sci. Res. Marine Biol. Res., Oslo, no.23, pp.1-24, figs.11, 1940.

THE AGE OF WHALES AS DETERMINED FROM THEIR BALEEN APPARATUS. A.G. Tomilin. Doklady Acad. Sci.USSR, Moscow, n.s., vol.49, no.6, pp.460-463, figs. 2, Nov.30, 1945.

Development, Early

DEVELOPMENT OF THE OSTEOCRANIUM OF ODONTOCETI DURING ONTOGENESIS AND PHYLOGENESIS. M. M. Sleptsov. Doklady Acad. Sci., USSR, Moscow, n.s., vol.28, no.4, pp.363-366, fig.1, 1940.

SOME PECULIARITIES IN THE DEVELOPMENT OF THE EARLY EMBRYONIC STAGES OF CETACEANS. M. M. Sleptsov. Trans. Inst. Oceanology, Acad. Sci. USSR, Moscow, 18: 48-59, 1955.

THE FOETAL GROWTH RATE OF WHALES. H.W. Symons. Norsk Hvalfangst-Tidende (Norwegian Whaling Gazette), vol.44, no.9, pp.519-528, illus., Sept., 1955.

Diseases and Parasites

ON ODONTOBIUS CETI, ROUSSEL DE VAUZEME, A NEMATODE LIVING ON THE BALEEN OF WHALES. H.A. Baylis. Ann. and Mag. Nat. Hist., ser.9, vol.12, pp.617-623, Nov., 1923.

PARASITES OF WHALES. H.A. Baylis. Nat. Hist. Mag., London, vol.1, no.2, pp.55-57, Apr., 1927.

WHALES AND CAISSON DISEASE. J. Argyll Campbell. Nature, Lond., vol.134, no.3390, p.629, Oct.20, 1934.

ON THE DIATOMS OF THE SKIN FILM OF WHALES AND THEIR POSSIBLE BEARING ON PROBLEMS OF WHALE MOVEMENTS. T. John Hart. Discovery Reports, Gov. Depend. Falkland Is., vol.10, pp.247-282, figs.8, pl.1, June, 1935.

THE PROTECTION OF WHALES FROM THE DANGER OF CAISSON DISEASE. Laurence Irving. Science, n.s., vol.81, no.2110, pp.560-561, June 7, 1935.

(TWO NEW CESTODES FROM WHALEBONE WHALES.) Zwei neue Cestoden aus Bartenwalen. O. Nybelin. Zool. Anzeiger, vol. 78, pp.309-314, 6 figs., Oct.1, 1928.

(REGARDING THE WHALE LOUSE (CYAMUS OVALIS E C-ERRATICUS ROUSSEL DE VAUZEME 1834).) Sobre o "piolho da Baleia" (Cyamus ovalis e C. erraticus Roussel de Vauzème 1834). Paulo Sawaya. Bol. Fac. Phil., Sci., Letr. Univ. S. Paulo, IV, Zoologia, no.2, pp.197-268, pls.30-38, 1938.

(ON INJURIES AND DISEASES OF THE VERTEBRAE AND RIBS OF CETACEANS.) Ueber Verletzungen und Erkrankungen der Wirbelsaeule und Rippen bei den Cetaceen. E. J. Slyper. Anat. Anz., vol.71, nos.7-9, pp.156-185, figs.17, Jan.24, 1931.

SOME INFLAMMATIONS IN WHALES. (PARTS 1-2.) A. Stolk. Proc. Kon. Nederlandse Akad. Wetensch., Amsterdam, ser.C, vol.56, no.3, pp.364-368, illus., 1953; vol.57, no.3, pp.254-257, figs.5-6, 1954.

SOME TUMOURS IN WHALES. A. Stolk. Proc. Kon. Nederlandse Akad. Wetensch., Amsterdam, ser.C, vol.55, no.3, pp.275-278; vol.56, no.3, pp.369-374, illus., 1952-1953.

TUMOURS IN WHALES. A. Stolk. Amsterdam Naturalist, vol.1, no.1, pp.28-33, figs. 6, Apr.14, 1950.

Diving

THE DEPTH TO WHICH WHALES DESCEND. R.W. Gray. Nature, no.3016, vol.120, p.263, Aug.20, 1927.

DO WHALES DESCEND TO GREAT DEPTHS? R. W. Gray et al. Nature London, vol.135, no.3401, pp.34-35, Jan. 5, 1935; no.3411, pp. 429-430, Mar. 16, 1935; no.3417, pp.656-657, Apr. 27, 1935.

WHALES ENTANGLED IN DEEP SEA CABLES. Bruce C. Heezen. Deep-Sea Research, London, vol.4, pp.105-115, 1957.

Europe

(SOME NOTES ON THE CETACEA OF THE IRISH ATLANTIC COAST.) Richard J. Anderson. Comptes rendus, 6 Congrés international Zoologie, Sess. Berne, pp. 703-711, pls.1-4, May 25, 1904.

(INVESTIGATIONS ON THE LITTORAL FAUNA OF BELGIUM; CETACEANS.) Recherches sur la faune littorale de Belgique; Cetaces. P.J. van Beneden. Mem. l'Acad. royale Belgique, vol.32, pp.1-58, pl.1, 1860.

(NATURAL HISTORY OF THE CETACEANS OF THE SEAS OF EUROPE.) Histoire naturelle des cetaces des mers d'Europe. P.J. van Beneden. Bruxelles: F. Hayez, 664 pp., 1889.

KEY TO THE MAMMALS OF THE U.S.S.R. V. CETACEA. N.A. Bobrinskii, B. A. Kuznetsov, A.P. Kuzyakin. State Publ. House "Sovetzkaya Nauka", Moscow, 1944.

(CONTRIBUTIONS TO KNOWLEDGE OF THE CETACEANS OBSERVED ON THE COASTS OF FRANCE.) Contributions à la Connaissance des Cétacés Observés sur les Côtes de France. L. Brasil. Soc. Linn, de Normandie, Caen., pp.1-26, 1912.

(THE GREAT CETACEANS OF THE STRAITS OF GIBRALTAR.) Los grandes cetaceos del Estrecho de Gibraltar, su pesca y explotacion. Angel Cabrera. Trabajos de Museo Nat. Ciencias Nat. (Madrid), ser. Zool., no.52, pp.1-51, pls. 1-12, Nov.2, 1925.

(NOTES ON THE CETACEANS OF THE FRENCH COASTS.) Note sur les cétacés des côtes Francaises. Carpentier. Bull. Soc. Linnéene du Nord de la France, Chauny, année 1933, no.426, pp.10-12, fig. 1, 1934.

WHALES AS AN ECONOMIC FACTOR IN PREHISTORIC EUROPE. Grahame Clark. Antiquity, Gloucester, no.82, pp.84-104, figs.10, pls.2, June, 1947.

ROYAL FISH. (CETACEANS OF SUFFOLK COAST.) Lord Cranbrook. Trans. Suffolk Nat. Soc., vol.8, pt.3, pp.112-115, 1954.

(THE DETERMINATION OF DUTCH CETACEA.) Het determineeren van de Nederlandsche Cetacea. A.B. van Deinse. Natuurhistorisch Museum te Rotterdam, no.1, pp.11-22, figs., 1932.

(THE RECENT CETACEA OF THE NETHERLANDS FROM 1931 UNTIL 1944.) De recente Cetacea van Nederland van 1931 tot en met 1944. A.B. van Deinse. Zool. Mededeel., Leiden, vol.26, pp.139-210, figs.4, 1946.

(INVESTIGATIONS OF THE SCANDINAVIAN WHALES.) Om undersoegelsen af de nordiske Hvaler. D.F. Eschricht. Forhandlinger ved de skandinavishe Naturforskeres Moede i Kjoebenhavn, pp. 3-28, 1841.

(CETACEANS OF THE SOUTHWEST OF FRANCE.) Cetaces du Sud-Ouest de la France. P. Fischer. Extrait des Actes de la Societe Linneenne de Bordeaux, vol. 35, pp.1-220, illus., 1881.

EXHIBITION OF A DRAWING OF A CETACEAN TAKEN OFF THE COAST OF CORNWALL. William Henry Flower. Proc. Zool. Soc. Lond., p.128, 1870.

(CETACEANS OF THE FRENCH MEDITERRANEAN COASTS.) Cétacés des côtes Francaises de la Méditerranée. Paul Gervais. Comptes rendus séances de l'Acad. Sci., Inst. Impérial de France, vol.59, pp.1-5, Nov.28, 1864.

(MARINE MAMMALS IN THE SOUTH OF FRANCE, AND A NEW SPECIES OF DOLPHIN OF THE MEDITERRANEAN.) Mammifères marins qui fréquentent la midi de la France, et plus particulièrement sur une nouvelle espèce de Dauphins propre a la Méditerranée. Paul Gervais. Bull. Soc. Agric. l'Herault, Montpelier, pp.16, pl.1, Apr., May, June, 1853.

ADDITIONAL OBSERVATIONS ON THE CETACEA OF THE BRITISH ISLANDS. John E. Gray. Proc. Zool. Soc. Lond., pt.15, pp.117-118, 1847.

ON THE CETACEA WHICH HAVE BEEN OBSERVED IN THE SEAS SURROUNDING THE BRITISH ISLANDS. John E. Gray. Proc. Zool. Soc. Lond., pp.195-248, figs. 24, 1864.

SPITSBERGEN WHALE FISHERY OF THE SEVENTEENTH CENTURY. Robert W. Gray. Nature, London, vol.126, no.3171, p.204, Aug.9, 1930.

(THE CETACEANS OF THE KOENIGSSPIEGEL.) Die Waltiere des Koenigsspiegels. Gustav Guldberg. Zoologische Annalen, Wurzburg, vol.1, pp.29-40, 1894.

NOTES ON WHALING IN SHETLAND, 1904. R.C. Haldane. Ann. Scottish Nat. Hist., Edinburgh, no.54, pp.65-72, pl.3, illus., Apr., 1905.

WHALING IN SCOTLAND. R.C. Haldane. Ann. Scottish Nat. Hist., no.59, pp.130-137, pl.4, July, 1906; no.61, pp.10-15, pl. 1, Jan., 1907.

CETACEA OF THE FALKLAND ISLANDS. J.E. Hamilton. Comunic. Zool. Mus. Hist. Nat. Montevideo, vol.4, no.66, pp.1-6, 1952.

RECORDS OF LANCASHIRE CETACEA. Eric Hardy. Nature, London, vol.150, no. 3808, p.492, Oct.24, 1942.

ON THE DISTINGUISHING CHARACTERS OF THE BRITISH CETACEA. J.E. Harting. Zoologist, London, pp.1-13, Jan., 1878.

(MORE ABOUT EAST PRUSSIAN WHALE-BONE FINDS.) Weiteres ueber ostpreussische Walknochenfunde. Arnold Japha. Schrift. Physik.-oekomom. Gesell. Koenigsberg. i. Pr., vol.48, pp.250-251, 1907.

(ON SUBFOSSIL AND RECENT WHALE-BONE FINDS FROM EAST AND WEST PRUSSIA.) Ueber subfossile und recente Walknochenfunde aus Ost- und West-preussen. Arnold Japha. Schrift. Physik. oekonom. Gesell. Koenigsberg i. Pr., vol. 48, pp.237-243, 1907.

THE WHALE FISHERY IN THE SOVIET UNION. S.E. Kleynenberg, T.U. Makarovo, editors. Ministry of Fisheries Industry USSR, Moscow, pp.118, 1955. (In Russian.)

THE HISTORY OF BASQUE ISLAND AND THE TWO RAZADES. Claire Leclerc, George A. Leclerc. Bird sanctuaries of the Provancher Society of Natural History of Canada. Ann. Rept. Provancher Soc. 1947, pp.46-98, illus., 1949. (Basque whaling, pp.59-63.)

(WHALE BONES FOUND IN THE EARTH IN GRAESOEN IN ROSLAGEN (SWEDEN).) Om hvalben funna i jorden pa Graesoen i Roslagen i sverige. W. Lilljeborg. Pp. 599-616, 1860.

THE CETACEA OF THE SUFFOLK CRAG. Richard Lydekker. Quart. Jour. Geol. Soc., vol.43, pp.7-18, pl.2, 1887.

WORK OF THE MARINE STATION AT GRYTVIKEN. (NOTES ON WHALES.) N.A. Mackintosh. Nature, vol.118, pp.629-630, 1926.

(RECENT CAPTURES OF GREAT CETACEANS IN ITALIAN SEAS.) Catture Recenti di Grandi Cetacei nei mari Italiani. Corrado Parona. Atti Soc. Lingustica Sci. Nat. and Geog., Genova, vol.19, nos.3-4, pp.173-205, 1908.

(INFORMATION IN TABULAR FORM ON NORWEGIAN WHALING SOCIETIES.) Tabellariske oplysninger om norske hvalfangstselskaper. Sigurd Risting. Norsk Hvalfangst-Tidende (The Norwegian Whaling Gazette), Sandfjord, Aarg.19, no. 1, pp.16-19, Jan., 1930.

(A STRANGE CETACEAN ON THE VALENCIA COAST, ZIPHIUS CAVIROSTRIS CUVIER.) Un extraño cetaceo en las costas de Valencia Ziphius cavirostris Cuvier. Ignacio Sala de Castellarnau. Anales Asoc. Española Progreso Cien., Rev. Trimestral, Madrid, ano 10, no.3, pp.576-583, illus., 1945.

(COMMUNICATION ON THE CETACEANS OF PORTUGAL.) Note sur les Cétacés du Portugal. A.F. de Seabra. Extrait du Bulletin de la Société Portugaise de Sciences Naturelles, vol.1, fasc.2, pp.10-11, 1917.

(COMMUNICATION ON THE CETACEANS OF PORTUGAL. ON A NEW SPECIES OF PORTUGUESE FAUNA.) Note sur les Cétacés du Portugal. A propos d'une nouvelle espèce pour la faune portugaise. A.F. de Seabra. Bull. Soc. Portugaise Sci. Nat., Lisbonne, vol.1, fasc.2, pp.46-47, 1907.

(AN APPEAL TO DUTCH FISHERMEN FOR ASSISTANCE IN SPOTTING WHALES.) Verzoek om Medewerking aan Nederlandse Zeevarenden voor het Waarnemen van Walvissen. E.J. Slijper. Netherlands Whale Research Group T.N.O., Zooelogisch Laboratorium Univ. Amsterdam, pp. 1-22, figs.17, 1954.

(THE COLLECTION OF RECENT CETACEA OF THE ROYAL MUSEUM OF NATURAL HISTORY OF BELGIUM.) Die Sammlung Rezenter Cetacea des Musee Royal d'Histoire Naturelle de Belgique. E.J. Slijper. Bull. Mus. Roy. Hist. Nat. Belgique, Bruxelles, vol.14, no.10, pp.1-33, figs.4, Mar., 1938.

ANCIENT RECORDS OF THE OCCURRENCE OF CERTAIN CETACEANS ON THE NORFOLK COAST. Thomas Southwell. Trans. Norfolk and Norwich Nat. Soc., vol.7, pp.303-312, illus., 1901.

MAMMALS OF USSR AND ADJACENT REGIONS. VOL. IX. CETACEANS. A. G. Tomilin. Akad. Nauk SSSR, Moscow, pp.756, pls.11, 1957. (Continuation of "Mammals of Eastern Europe and Northern Asia" by S. I. Ognev. In Russian.)

### Exhibtions and Collections

AMERICAN MUSEUM WHALE COLLECTION. Roy C. Andrews. Amer. Mus. Jour., New York, vol.14, no.8, pp.275-294, illus., Dec., 1914.

DO WHAT YOU CAN NOW WITH WHAT YOU HAVE.( MOUNTING A WHALE SKELETON.) H.H. Brimley. Museum News, vol.8, no.10, pp.8-12, illus., Nov. 15, 1930.

(HISTORY OF THE CETACEAN COLLECTION OF THE PARIS MUSEUM.)Historie des collections cetologiques du museum de Paris, H. Filhol. Mem. Soc. Zool., France, Paris, vol.9, pp.45-69, 1896.

LIST OF THE SPECIMENS OF CETACEA IN THE ZOOLOGICAL DEPARTMENT OF THE BRITISH MUSEUM. William Henry Flower. Privately printed, p.36, 1885.

CATALOGUE OF THE SPECIMENS OF MAMMALIA IN THE COLLECTION OF THE BRITISH MUSEUM. John E. Gray. Pt.1, Cetacea. Publ. Brit. Mus., Lond., pp.153, 1850.

SYNOPSIS OF THE SPECIES OF WHALES AND DOLPHINS IN THE COLLECTION OF THE BRITISH MUSEUM. John E. Gray. Bernard Quaritch, London, pp.1-10, pls.1-37, 1868.

INSTRUCTIONS FOR COLLECTORS. NO. I. MAMMALS, PART 2. SKELETONS, WITH SPECIAL NOTES ON THE COLLECTION OF SPECIMENS OF CETACEA. S.F. Harmer. British Mus. Nat. Hist., Lond., pp.1-8, figs.1-4, 1917.

GUIDE TO THE WHALES, PORPOISES, AND DOLPHINS (ORDER CETACEA) EXHIBITED IN THE DEPARTMENT OF ZOOLOGY, BRITISH MUSEUM (NATURAL HISTORY), CROMWELL ROAD, LONDON, S.W. R. Lydekker. Brit. Mus., Lond., p.47, figs.1-33; pp.1-48, figs.1-32, 1922. (Revised 1922 by Sidney Harmer.)

(WHALES IN THE MUSEUMS OF SWEDEN.) Hvaldjur I Sveriges Museer, År 1869. Kongl. Svenska Vetensk.-Akad. Handlinger, Bd.9, no.2, pls.1-6, 1871.

(OBSERVATIONS ON SOME CETACEANS AT THE HALLES DE PARIS.) Observations sur quelques Cétacés aux Halles de Paris. Maurice Prudhomme. Mammalia, Paris, 8 (1): 16-18, illus., Mar., 1944.

THE EXHIBITION OF CETACEANS BY PAPIER MACHÉ CASTS. Frederick W. True. Science, n.s., vol.8, no.186, pp. 108-109, July 22, 1898.

SUGGESTIONS TO THE KEEPERS OF THE U.S. LIFESAVING STATIONS, LIGHT-HOUSES, AND LIGHT-SHIPS; AND TO OTHER OBSERVERS, RELATIVE TO THE BEST MEANS OF COLLECTING AND PRESERVING SPECIMENS OF WHALES AND PORPOISES. Frederick W. True. Extracted from Annual Report Commissioner of Fish and Fisheries for 1883, pp.1-26, pls. 11, figs.5, 1884.

REPORT ON THE BONES OF CETACEA COLLECTED DURING THE VOYAGE OF H.M.S. CHALLENGER IN THE YEARS 1873-1876. William Turner. Report on the Scientific Results of the Voyage of H.M.S. Challenger, Zool., vol.1, pt.4, Report on the Bones of Cetacea, pp.45, pls.3, 1880.

(DESCRIPTION OF THE GREAT WHALE FROM THE KATTEGAT, PLACED ON EXHIBITION IN BERLIN AT THE ORANIENBURG GATE.) Beschreibung des in Berlin am Oranienburger Thor ausgestellen grossen Walfisches aus dem Kattegat. Berlin, pp.3, 1889.

(THE WHALE SKELETON IN THE BERLIN AQUARIUM.) Das Walfisch - Skelet im Berliner Aquarium. pp.3, 1883.

### Food Habits

FOOD OF THE WHALEBONE WHALES IN THE KURILE ISLANDS REGION. E. I. Betesheva. Trans. Inst. Oceanology, Acad. Sci. USSR, Moscow, 18: 78-85, 1955.

PLANKTON OF THE OFFSHORE WATERS OF THE GULF OF MAINE. (INFORMATION CONCERNING THE FOOD OF WHALES.) Henry B. Bigelow. Bull. U.S. Bur. Fisheries, vol.40, pt.2, doc. no.968, 509 pp., 134 figs., 1926.

PRO-VITAMIN A IN THE FOOD OF WHALES. J.C. Drummond, R.J. Macwalter. Jour. Exper. Biol., London, vol. 12, no.2, pp.105-107, Apr., 1935.

EUPHAUSIA SUPERBA AND THE ANTARCTIC SURFACE CURRENTS; AN ADVANCE NOTE ON THE DISTRIBUTION OF WHALE FOOD. J.W.S. Marr. Norsk Hvalfangstid, 1956: 127-134, 1956.

LOBSTER-KRILL. ANOMURAN CRUSTACEA THAT ARE THE FOOD OF WHALES. L. Harrison Mathews. Discovery Reports, Cambridge, England, vol.5, pp.467-484, fig.1, pl.4, Nov., 1932.

FOOD OF WHALES (IN THE ADJACENT WATERS OF JAPAN). Kazuhiro Mizue. Scientific Reports Whales Research Inst., Tokyo, no.5, pp.81-90, June, 1951.

ON THE BIOLOGY OF SOUTHERN EUPHAUSIIDAE. (CONTAINS ACCOUNT OF PLANKTON CONDITIONS ON THE SOUTHERN WHALING GROUNDS.) Johan T. Ruud. Hvalradets Skrifter. Scientific results of Marine biological research, Oslo, no.2, pp.105, figs.37, 1932.

ANALYSIS OF STOMACH CONTENTS OF WHALES TAKEN DURING THE YEARS 1937 AND 1938 FROM THE NORTH PACIFIC. Robert J. Thompson. MS thesis, Univ. Wash., 1941.

THE FOOD OF THE FAR-EASTERN WHALES. B.A. Zenkovic. Doklady Acad. Sci., USSR, n.s., vol.16, no.4, pp.231-234, 1937. (In English.)

### Fossils

FOSSIL CETACEANS FROM THE FLORIDA PHOSPHATE BEDS. G. M. Allen. Jour. Mam., vol.2, no.3, pp.144-157, pls.9-12, Aug., 1921.

A FOSSIL RIVER DOLPHIN FROM FLORIDA. (NEW: GONIODELPHIS, G. HUDSONI.) G. M. Allen. Bull. Mus. Comp. Zool., Harvard Coll., Cambridge, vol.89, no.1, pp.8, pls.3, Oct., 1941.

A NEW FOSSIL CETACEAN. (ARCHAEODELPHIS PATRIUS, GEN. ET SP. NOV.) G. M. Allen. Bull. Mus. Comp. Zool., vol.65, no.1, pp.1-14, 1 pl., Aug., 1921.

THE TYPE-SPECIMEN OF SAUROCETUS GIBBESII AGASSIZ. G. M. Allen. Jour. Mam., vol.5,no.2, pp.120-121, pl.16, May, 1924.

JAW OF FOSSIL WHALEBONE WHALE: SIPHONOCETUS PRISCUS. Arthur R. Barwick. Proc. Biol. Soc. Wash., vol.51, pp.121-122, May 19, 1938.

SKULL OF FOSSIL CETOTHEREAN WHALE, SIPHONOCETUS PRISCUS, FROM

THE MIOCENE OF THE CHESAPEAKE BAY REGION. Arthur R. Barwick. Amer. Midland Nat., Notre Dame, vol.23, no.3, pp.746-750, pl.1, May, 1940.

FOSSIL CETACEA OF NEW ZEALAND. V. MAUICETUS, A GENERIC NAME SUBSTITUTED FOR LOPHOCEPHALUS BENHAM. W. B. Benham. Trans. Roy. Soc. New Zealand, Wellington, vol.71, pt.4, pp.260-270, pls.44-47, Mar., 1942.

MAUICETUS: A FOSSIL WHALE. W. B. Benham. Nature, London, vol.143, no. 3627, p.765, May 6, 1939.

NOTES ON SOME OF THE BONES OF KEKENODON ONAMATA HECTOR. W. B. Benham. Trans. and Proc. Roy Soc. New Zealand, vol.67, pt.1, pp.15-20, pl.8, June, 1937.

ON LOPHOCEPHALUS, A NEW GENUS OF ZEUGLODONT CETACEA. W. B. Benham. Trans. Proc. Roy. Soc. New Zealand, vol. 67, pt.1, pp.1-7, pls.3, June, 1937.

THE SKULL AND OTHER PARTS OF THE SKELETON OF PROSQUALODON HAMILTONI N. SP. W. B. Benham. Trans. Proc. Roy. Soc. New Zealand, vol.67, pt.1, pp. 8-14, pls.4-7, June, 1937.

THE TEETH OF AN EXTINCT WHALE, MICROCETUS HECTORI N. SP. W. B. Benham. Trans. Roy. Soc. New Zealand, vol.65, pp.239-243, pls.28-29, Dec., 1935.

THE PLEISTOCENE FAUNA OF WAILES BLUFF AND LANGLEYS BLUFF, MARYLAND. (CETACEANS.) S. F. Blake. Smithsonian Misc. Coll., Wash., vol.121, no.12, pp.1-32, pl.1, Aug.11, 1953.

COMPARISON OF THE MICROSCOPIC STRUCTURE OF THE ENAMEL IN THE TEETH OF ZEUGLODON OSIRIS DAMES, AND OF PROSQUALODON DAVIDI FLYNN. J. Thornton Carter. Trans. Zool. Soc. Lond., vol.26, no.2, pp.192-193, pls.5-6, 1948.

A SPECIMEN OF A LONG-NOSED DOLPHIN FROM THE BONE VALLEY GRAVELS OF POLK COUNTY, FLORIDA. E. C. Case. Contrib. Mus. Paleont., Univ. Michigan, vol.4, no.6, pp.105-113, pls.2, Jan.15, 1934.

A NEW FOSSIL WHALE FROM THE MIOCENE OF PERU. Edwin H. Colbert. Bull. Amer. Mus. Nat. Hist., New York, vol.83, art.3, pp.195-216, figs.1-3, pls. 11-14, July 29, 1944.

THE BRAIN OF ZEUGLODONTIDAE (CETACEA); WITH A NOTE ON THE SKULLS FROM WHICH THE ENDOCRANIAL CASTS WERE TAKEN, BY C.W. ANDREWS. Raymond A. Dart. Proc. Zool. Soc. London, pt.3, pp.615-654, Oct., 1923.

(THE FOSSIL CETACEA OF LIMBURG.) De fossiele Cetacea van Limburg. A. G. van Deinse. Gedenkboek Dr. Ir. P. Tesch, Verhandelingen van het Geologisch-Mijnbouwkundig Genootschap voor Nederland en Kolonien, 's-Gravenhage, Geol. Ser., vol.14, pp.147-156, figs.10, 1945.

TYPES OF FOSSIL CETACEANS IN THE MUSEUM OF COMPARATIVE ZOOLOGY. C. R. Eastman. Bull. Mus. Comp. Zool. Harvard Coll., vol.51, no.3, pp.79-94, figs.A-B, pls.4, June, 1907.

(NOTE ON THE FOSSIL CETACEA OF THE AQUITAINE.) Note sur les Cétacés fossiles de l'Aquitaine. Leon Flot. Bull. Soc. Geol. France, Paris, ser.3, vol.24, pp.270-282, 1896.

DESCRIPTION OF PROSQUALODON DAVIDI FLYNN, A FOSSIL CETACEAN FROM TASMANIA. WITH A NOTE ON THE MICROSCOPIC TOOTH STRUCTURE, BY J. THORNTON CARTER. T. Thomson Flynn. Trans. Zool. Soc. Lond., vol.26, pt.2, pp. 153-196, figs.11, pls.6, 1948.

A NEW SPECIES OF FOSSIL CETACEAN FROM TASMANIA. T. Thomson Flynn. Geol. Mag., vol.69, no.817, pp.327-329, July, 1932.

(ABOUT THE SQUALODON.) Sur les squalodon. Paul Gervais. Bull. Acad. Roy. de Belgique, Bruxelles, 2 me ser., vol.13, no.5, pp.8, pls.1, 1862.

ON THE FOSSIL BASILOSAURUS, HARLAN (ZEUGLODON, OWEN,) WITH A NOTICE OF SPECIMENS FROM THE EOCENE GREEN SAND OF SOUTH CAROLINA. Robert W. Gibbes. Jour. Acad. Nat. Sci., Phila., n.s., vol.1, pt.1, pp.15, pls.6, 1847.

PRELIMINARY REPORT ON FOSSIL WHALE MANDIBLE. (TWO MANDIBLES FOUND AT GOVERNOR'S RUN, CALVERT CLIFFS, MARYLAND, IN 1932.) O.L. Helm. Bull. Nat. Hist. Soc. Balto., Md., vol.9, no.12, pp.107-110, figs.3, Aug., 1939.

ON A FOSSIL BIRD AND A FOSSIL CETACEAN FROM NEW ZEALAND. Huxley. Ann. Mag. Nat. Hist., ser.3, pp.509-510, 1859.

(NOTES ON SO-CALLED GRASS-EATING FOSSIL WHALES.) Notitzen ueber die fossilen sogenannten Gras-fressenden Wale. J. J. Kaup. Leonhard u. Bronn. N. Jahrb., pp.673-679, 1840.

ANCIENT RELATIVES OF LIVING WHALES. Remington Kellogg. Explorations and field-work of the Smithsonian Inst., 1930, Publ.3111, pp.83-90, figs.76-80, Mar.26, 1931.

DESCRIPTION OF A NEW GENUS AND SPECIES OF WHALEBONE WHALE FROM THE CALVERT CLIFFS, MARYLAND. Remington Kellogg. Proc. U.S. Nat. Mus., Wash., vol.63, art.15, pp.14, pls.6, February 5, 1924.

DESCRIPTION OF AN APPARENTLY NEW TOOTHED CETACEAN FROM SOUTH CAROLINA. Remington Kellogg. Smithsonian Misc. Coll., vol.76, no.7, pp.1-7, 2 pls., July 25, 1923.

DESCRIPTION OF TWO SQUALODONTS RECENTLY DISCOVERED IN THE CALVERT CLIFFS, MARYLAND; AND NOTES ON THE SHARK-TOOTHED CETACEANS. Remington Kellogg. Proc. U.S. Nat. Mus., vol.62, art.16, pp.1-69, 20 pls., Apr.24, 1923.

FOSSIL CETACEANS FROM THE FLORIDA TERTIARY. Remington Kellogg. Bull. Mus. Comp. Zool. Harvard College, Cambridge, vol.94, no.9, pp.433-471, figs.10, pls.1-6, Nov., 1944.

A MIOCENE LONG-BEAKED PORPOISE FROM CALIFORNIA. Remington Kellogg. Smithsonian Misc. Coll., vol.87, no.2, pp.1-11, pls.4, Jan.22, 1932.

A NEW CETOTHERE FROM SOUTHERN CALIFORNIA (NANNOCETUS EREMUS). Remington Kellogg. Univ. Calif. Publ. Bull. Dept. Geol. Sci., Berkeley, vol.18, no.15, pp.449-457, figs.2, Dec.19, 1929.

A NEW CETOTHERE FROM THE MODELO FORMATION AT LOS ANGELES, CALIFORNIA. Remington Kellogg. Contrib. Palaeont. Carnegie Inst. Wash., Publ.447, pp.83-104, figs.3, pl.1, Jan.10, 1934.

A NEW FOSSIL TOOTHED WHALE FROM FLORIDA. Remington Kellogg. Amer.Mus. Nov., no.389, pp.1-10, figs.1-3, Dec. 5, 1929.

ON THE CETOTHERES FIGURED BY VANDELLI. Remington Kellogg. Boletim do Museu e Laboratorio Mineralogico e Geologico da Universidade de Lisboa, ser. 3a, nos.7-8, pp.13-22, pls.3, 1941.

ON THE OCCURRENCE OF REMAINS OF FOSSIL PORPOISES OF THE GENUS EURHINODELPHIS IN NORTH AMERICA. Remington Kellogg. Proc. U.S.Nat. Mus., vol.66, no.2563, pp.1-40, May 25, 1925.

THE PATAGONIAN FOSSIL WHALEBONE WHALE, CETOTHERIUM MORENI (LYDEKKER). Remington Kellogg. Contrib. Palaeont. Carnegie Inst. Wash., Publ.447, pp.63-81, figs.2, pls.4, Jan. 10, 1934.

A REVIEW OF THE ARCHAEOCETI. Remington Kellogg. Publ.482, Carnegie Inst., Wash., pp.xv+366, figs.88, pls. 37, Dec. 14, 1936.

(Review by G.G. Simpson of) A REVIEW OF THE ARCHAEOCETI. Remington Kellogg. Jour. Mamm., vol.19, no.1, pp. 113-114, 1938.

ON TWO SUBFOSSIL WHALES DISCOVERED IN SWEDEN. Wilhelm Lilljeborg. Nova acta of the Roy. Soc. Sci., Upsala, ser.3, vol.6, p.48, pl.11, 1867.

ON ZEUGLODONT AND OTHER CETACEAN REMAINS FROM THE TERTIARY OF THE CAUCASUS. R. Lydekker. Proc. Zool. Soc., Lond., pp.558-564, pls.36-38, Nov. 1, 1892.

CETOTHERES (CETACEA) FROM THE OLIGOCENE OF NEW ZEALAND. B. J. Marples. Proc. Zool. Soc. Lond., 126 (4): 565-580, pl.1, July 31, 1956.

TWO ENDOCRANIAL CASTS OF CETACEANS FROM THE OLIGOCENE OF NEW ZEALAND. B. J. Marples. Amer. Jour. Sci., New Haven, vol.247, pp.462-471, fig. 3, July, 1949.

ON SOME FOSSIL CETACEANS OF JAPAN. H. Matsumoto. Sci. Reps. Tohoku Imp. Univ., ser.2 (Geology), vol.10, no.1, pp. 17-27, pl.8, 1926.

NOTE ON THE OCCURRENCE OF THE REMAINS OF A CETACEAN IN THE ALLUVIAL TIN DEPOSITS OF THE ISLAND OF BILLITON. G.A de Neve. Chron. Nat., Batavia, vol.105, no.4, pp.118-120, figs.2, Apr., 1949.

A CONTRIBUTION TO THE HISTORY OF THE CETACEA OF THE NORFOLK "FOREST-BED." E. T. Newton. Quart. Jour. Geol. Soc., Lond., vol.42, pt.3, no. 167, pp.316-324, pl.11, Aug., 1886.

FOSSIL BALEEN FROM THE PLIOCENE OF CAPE BLANCO, OREGON. Earl L. Packard. Oregon State Monographs, Studies in Geol., Corvallis, no.5, pp.1-8, pl.1, Dec., 1947.

A NEW CETOTHERE FROM THE MIOCENE ASTORIA FORMATION OF NEWPORT, OREGON. Earl L. Packard, Remington Kellogg. Contrib. Palaeont. Carnegie Inst. Wash., Publ.447, pp.1-62, figs.24, pls.3, Jan.10, 1934.

BASILOSAURUS IN ARKANSAS. Katherine V.W. Palmer. Bull. Amer. Assoc. Petroleum Geol., Tulsa, vol.23, no.8, pp. 1228-1229, Aug., 1939.

(THE EAR SKELETON OF ZEUGLODON.) Das Ohrskelett von Zeuglodon. J. F. Pompeckj. Senckenbergiana, vol.4, pp. 43-100, pl.2, Oct.20, 1922.

(THE ASYMMETRY OF THE FACE IN CETODONTS.) De L'Asymétrie de la face chez Les Cétodontes. M. G. Pouchet. Libraire de l'Académie de Médecine, Paris, pp.1-16, 1886.

ON THE DISCOVERY OF A FOSSIL WHALE IN THE OLDER TERTIARIES OF TORQUAY, VICTORIA (MAMMALODON, M. COLLIVERI). B. G. Pritchard. Victorian Nat., Melbourne, vol.55, no.9, pp.151-159, figs.1-5, Jan., 1939.

FOSSIL WHALES OF THE NORTH CAROLINA MIOCENE. W.F. Prouty. Jour. Elisha Mitchell Sci. Soc., Chapel Hill, vol.50, nos.1-2, p.52, Dec., 1934.

ON A CETACEAN, SQUALODON (MICROZEUGLODON?) WINGEI NOV. SP., FROM THE OLIGOCENE OF JUTLAND. J.P.J. Ravn. Medelelser fra Dansk Geol. Forening, vol.7, pp.45-54, pl.1, 1926.

A MOUNTED SKELETON OF CETOTHERIUM MAYERI JUN BRANDT. A. N. Riabinin. Annuaire de la Société paléontologique de Russie, Moscou, vol.11, pp.139-141, pl.17, 1937.

NEW CONTRIBUTIONS TO THE OSTEOLOGY OF CETOTHERIUM MAYERI BRANDT, FROM THE UPPER SARMATIAN OF THE NORTH CAUCASUS. A. N. Riabinin. Trans. United Geol. and Prospecting Serv., USSR, fasc.350, pp.19, figs.5, pls. 4, 1934.

FOSSIL WHALE FOUND IN NAGANO PREFECTURE. S. Tokunaga. Jour. Geol. Soc. Japan, Tokyo, vol.46, no.547, pp.199-200, fig.1, Apr.20, 1939.

THE FOSSIL CETACEAN DORUDON SERRATUS GIBBES. Frederick W. True. Bull. Mus. Comp. Zool. Harvard College, vol. 52, no.4, pp.65-78, pls.1-3, Sept., 1908.

A FOSSIL TOOTHED CETACEAN FROM CALIFORNIA, REPRESENTING A NEW GENUS AND SPECIES. Frederick W. True. Smithsonian Misc. Coll., vol.60, no.11, publ.2151, no.11, pp.1-7, pls.1-2, Nov.1, 1912.

A NEW GENUS OF FOSSIL CETACEANS FROM SANTA CRUZ TERRITORY, PATAGONIA; AND DESCRIPTION OF A MANDIBLE AND VERTEBRAE OF PROSQUALODON. Frederick W. True. Smithsonian Misc. Coll., vol.5, pp.441-456, pls.XLIII-XLV, illus., 1910.

ON THE CORRELATION OF NORTH AMERICA AND EUROPEAN GENERA OF FOSSIL CETACEANS. Frederick W. True. Proc. VII Intern.Zool. Cong., Cambridge, Mass., pp.779-781, 1912.

ON THE OCCURRENCE OF REMAINS OF FOSSIL CETACEANS OF THE GENUS SCHIZODELPHIS IN THE UNITED STATES AND ON PRISCODELPHINUS (?) CRASSANGULUM CASE. Frederick W. True. Smithsonian Misc. Coll., vol.50, pt.4, publ.1782, pp.449-460, pls.39-40, Jan.27, 1908.

REMARKS ON THE FOSSIL CETACEAN RHABDOSTEUS LATIRADIX COPE. Frederick W. True. Proc. Acad. Nat. Sci. Phila., vol.60, pt.1, pp.24-29, pl.6, fig.3, Apr.22, 1908.

REMARKS ON THE TYPE OF THE FOSSIL CETACEAN AGOROPHIUS PYGMAEUS (MUELLER). Frederick W. True. Special Publ. Smithsonian Inst., no.1694, p.8, pl.1, 1907.

(ON SQUALODON BARIENSIS OF LOWER BAVARIA.) Ueber Squalodon Bariensis aus Niederbayern. Karl Alfred Zittel. Palaeontographica, n.f., vol.4, no.6, (24) pp.233-246, pl.35, 1876-1877.

A FOSSIL WHALE FROM AUSTRALIA. Nature, London, vol.143, no.3621, p.525, Mar.25, 1939.

MASS OF WHALE FOSSILS NEAR VIENNA EXPLORED. Science New Letter, p.139, Aug.27, 1938.

General Habits, Behavior

NOTES RELATING TO THE HABITS OF THE SPERMACETI WHALE, AND TO A LARGE SPECIES OF GRAMPUS, CALLED THE KILLER. G. Bennett. Proc. Zool. Soc. Lond., pt.4, p.53, 1836.

OBSERVATIONS OF CAPTIVE AND WILD CETACEANS. David H. Brown, Kenneth S. Norris. Jour. Mam., 37 (3): 311-326, illus., Sept.11, 1956.

LAMPREY MARKS ON WHALES. Gordon C. Pike. Jour. Fisheries Research Board Canada, vol.8, no.4, pp.275-280, illus., 1951.

TRUTH STRANGER THAN FICTION. (GRAY WHALES ATTACKED BY KILLER WHALES.) John E. Pond. Proc. U.S. Naval Inst., Menasha, vol.65, no.439, pp.1309-1310, 1330-1332, photos, Sept., 1939.

BIVALVES AND ANEMONES ON WHALE'S SKULL. A. C. Stephen. Scottish Nat., no.163, p.24, Jan.-Feb., 1927.

AN UNUSUAL RECORD OF THREE SPECIES OF WHALE BEING RESTRICTED TO POOLS IN ANTARCTIC SEA-ICE. R.J.F. Taylor. Proc. Zool. Soc. Lond., 129 (3): 325-331, pls.1-7, Nov.11, 1957.

JUMPS AND THE "INSTINCT OF PURSUIT" IN THE CETACEA. A. G. Tomilin. Priroda, Leningrad, no.1, pp.102-105, Jan., 1937. (In Russian.)

MATERNAL INSTINCT AND SEXUAL ATTACHMENT IN WHALES. A. G. Tomilin. Bull. Soc. Nat. Moscow, sec. Biol., n.s., vol.44, nos.7-8, pp.351-361, 1935. (In Russian, with English summary.)

ON BEHAVIOR AND SONIC SIGNALING IN CETACEANS. A.G. Tomilin. Trans. Inst. Oceanology, Acad. Sci. USSR, Moscow, 18: 28-47, 1955.

WHALES FOUND LOQUACIOUS. Science News Letter, Washington, vol.55, no.8, p.119, Feb.19, 1949.

WOUNDED WHALE ATTACKS CATCHING BOAT. Norsk Hvalfangst-Tidende (Norwegian Whaling Gazette), vol.44, no.3, pp. 133-134, Mar., 1955. (In Norwegian and English.)

Growth

GROWTH AND LONGEVITY OF WHALES. Robert W. Gray. Nature, London, vol.123, no.3111, pp.910-911, June 15, 1929.

STUDY ON MATURITY AND BODY LENGTH OF WHALES CAUGHT IN THE WATERS ADJACENT TO JAPAN. Ichiro Miyazaki. Fisheries Agency Japanese Govt., Tokyo, Publ. Japan Whaling Assoc., pp.27, figs. 29, May, 1952.

STUDY ON MATURITY AND BLUBBER THICKNESS OF THE WHALES CAUGHT IN THE ADJACENT WATERS OF JAPAN. Haruyuki Sakiura, Yasutake Nozawa, Katsunari Ozaki. Fisheries agency Japanese Govt., Tokyo, p.25, May, 1953.

Indian Ocean

(THE MOST IMPORTANT WHALES OF THE INDIAN OCEAN AND THEIR DISTRIBUTION THEREIN.) Heinrich Bolau. Die wichtigstem Wale des Indischen Ozeans und ihre Verbreitung in Demselben. Segelhandbuch Indischen Ozean, Hamburg, 8 pp., pl.35, illus., 1899.

Marking

WHALE MARKS RECOVERED DURING THE ANTARCTIC WHALING SEASON 1956/1957. S. G. Brown. Norsk Hvalfangst-Tidende (Norwegian Whaling Gazette), 46 (10): 555-559, Oct., 1957.

(THE MARKING OF WHALES.) Le marquage des baleines. Paul Budker. Mammalia, Paris, vol.19, no.4, pp.464-469, Dec., 1955.

A REVIEW OF WHALE MARKING AND SOME TRIALS OF A MODIFIED WHALE MARK. R. G. Chittleborough, K. Godfrey. Norsk Hvalfangst-Tidende (Norwegian Whaling Gazette), 46 (5): 238-248, May, 1957.

MARKING WHALES FROM A HELICOPTER. Robert Clarke. Norsk Hvalfangst-Tidende (Norwegian Whaling Gazette), 45 (6): 311-318, illus., June, 1956. (In English and Norwegian.) Proc. Zool. Soc. Lond., 126 (4): 646, July 31, 1956.

INTERNATIONAL CO-OPERATION IN ANTARCTIC WHALE MARKING FROM 1945 TO 1957. Robert Clarke, S. G. Brown. Norsk Hvalfangst-Tidende (Norwegian Whaling Gazette), 46 (9): 513-517, Sept., 1957.

INTERNATIONAL CO-OPERATION IN WHALE MARKING: THE VOYAGE OF THE "ENERN" TO THE ANTARCTIC 1953. Robert Clarke, Johan T. Ruud. Norsk Hvalfangst-Tidende (Norwegian Whaling Gazette), Sandefjord, vol.43, no.3, pp. 128-145, illus., Mar., 1954.

WHALE MARKING IN SOUTH PACIFIC WATERS. W.H. Dawbin. Norsk Hvalfangst-Tidende (Norwegian Whaling Gazette) 45 (9): 485-508, illus., Sept., 1956.

(ON A NEW METHOD OF STUDY OF CETACEANS.) Sur une nouvelle Méthode de l'Étude des cétacés. Daniel Fredrik Eschricht. Institut Impérial de France, Académie des Sciences. Extrait des Comptes rendus des séances de l'Académie des Sciences, vol.47, séance du 12, juillet 1858, pp.1-11, 1858.

WHALE MARKING IN THE SOUTHERN OCEAN. A.C. Hardy. Geogr. Jour., London, vol.96, no.5, pp.345-350, figs. 2, Nov., 1940.

WHALE MARKING IN THE ANTARCTIC. H.F.P. Herdman. The Trident, vol.16, no.177, pp.21-23, Jan., 1954.

THE BONIN ISLANDS AREAS. Takehiko Kawakami, Ken Otsuro, Setsuo Watase, Ken-ichi Iguchi. Report on Whale Marking in Japan, Japanese Fisheries Agency Tokyo, no.4, pp.1-10, figs.1-4, Apr., 1953.

ON THE LOCATING OF WHALE HERDS S. K. Klumov. Trudy Inst. Okeanol., Akad. Nauk SSSR, Moscow, 18: 7-27, 1955.

THE MARKING OF WHALES. N. A. Mackintosh. Nature, 169 (4298): 435-437, Mar.15, 1952; Norsk Hvalfangst-Tidende (Norwegian Whaling Gazette), Sandefjord, vol.45, no.5, pp.236-240, May, 1952.

A WHALE-MARKING EXPEDITION. N.A. Mackintosh. Nature, London, vol.172, p. 933, Nov.21, 1953.

RESULTS OF CAPTURE OF MARKED WHALES. Ichiro Miyazaki. Rep. Whale Marking in Japan no.4, pp.18-20, Apr., 1953.

THE SANRIKU-HOKKAIDO AND SOUTH KURILE ISLANDS AREAS. Ichiro Miyazaki, Ken Otsuro, Setsuo Watase. Report on Whale Marking in Japan, Japanese Fisheries Agency, Tokyo, no.4, pp.10-18, figs.5-10, Apr., 1953.

REPORT ON WHALE MARKING IN THE NORTH PACIFIC, 1950. NO. 2. THE NORTH PACIFIC AREA, 1950. Setsuo Nishimoto. Committee for Improvement of Equipment of Whaling Vessels, Fisheries Agency Japanese Govt., Tokyo, pp.1-245, charts 3, June, 1951.

JAPANESE WHALE MARKING IN THE NORTH PACIFIC. Hideo Omura, Takehiko Kawakami. Norsk Hvalfangst-Tidende (Norwegian Whaling Gazette), 45 (10): 555-563, Oct., 1956.

REPORT ON THE WHALE MARKING VOYAGE OF THE "ENERN" TO THE ANTARCTIC 1954. R. Ravninger. Norsk Hvalfangst-Tidende (Norwegian Whaling Gazette), vol.44, no.6, pp.310-315, June, 1955.

PRELIMINARY RESULTS OF THE MARKING OF WHALES BY THE DISCOVERY COMMITTEE. George W. Rayner. Nature, London, vol.144, no.3659, pp.999-1002, charts 7, Dec.16, 1939.

WHALE MARKING PROGRESS AND RESULTS TO DECEMBER 1939. George W. Rayner. Discovery Reports, Cambridge, vol.19, pp.245-285, pls.43-68, July, 1940.

WHALE MARKING TRIALS AT STEINSHAMN, NORWAY. Johan T. Ruud, Robert Clarke, Age Jonsgard. Norsk Hvalfangst-Tidende, (Norwegian Whaling Gazette), Sandefjord, vol.42, no.8, pp.429-441, Aug., 1953.

THE ROYAL RESEARCH SHIP WILLIAM SCORESBY. Illus. London News, vol.216, no.5777, p.35, illus., Jan.7, 1950.

WHALE MARKING. Nature, London, vol. 147, no.3724, p.324, Mar.15, 1941.

North America

THE WHALEBONE WHALES OF NEW ENGLAND. Glover M. Allen. Memoirs of the Boston Society of Nat. Hist., vol.8, no.2, pp.108-322, illus., Sept., 1916.

WHALES AND WHALING IN NEW ENGLAND. Glover M. Allen. Sci. Monthly, vol.27, pp.340-343, Oct., 1928.

WHALING OFF HUMBOLDT BAY. Whitney Allyn. Western Outdoors, Oswego, vol.5, no.5, pp.7-8, illus., May, 1948.

(TANUMSVALEN—A WHALE FROM GREENLAND.) "Tanumsvalen"—en groenlandsval. Harry Berquist. Fauna och Flora, pts.4-5, pp.139-144, 1955. (In Swedish, with German summary.)

THE WHALES OF CALIFORNIA. Paul Bonnot. Calif. Fish and Game, vol.15, pp. 203-215, 10 figs., July, 1929.

CETACEANS OF NEWFOUNDLAND. Richard Bonnycastle. Newfoundland in 1842, vol.1, pp.239-255, 1842.

KOGIA BREVICEPS AND MESOPLODON MIRUS IN THE NEIGHBORHOOD OF THE OREGON INLET, NORTH CAROLINA. H. H. Brimley. Jour. Mam., vol.26, no.4, p.434, Feb.12, 1946.

WHALE FISHING IN NORTH CAROLINA. H. H. Brimley. Bull. N.C. Dept. Agric. vol.14, no.7, pp.4-8, illus., Apr., 1894.

NOTES ON THE HISTORY AND GEOGRAPHICAL RELATIONS OF THE CETACEA FREQUENTING DAVIS STRAIT AND BAFFIN'S BAY. Robert Brown. Proc. Zool. Soc. Lond., pp.533-556, 1868.

WHALING IN FLORIDA WATERS. August Burghard. Florida Conservator, Tallahassee, vol.1, no.10, pp.4-5, 12, illus., Apr.-May, 1935.

CAPE COD WHALES TODAY. Eugene S. Clark, Jr. Your Weekly Guide to Cape Cod, Plymouth, vol.4, no.8, pp.20-21, Aug.6, 1949.

COLLECTING AT CACHALOT WHALING STATION. (VANCOUVER ISLAND.) Ira E. Cornwall. Canadian Field-Nat., vol.42, pp.9-12, Feb.20, 1928.

VISIT TO A CALIFORNIA WHALING STATION. A. Brazier Howell. Explorations and Field-Work Smithsonian Inst., 1926, Smithsonian Misc. Coll., vol.78, no.7, pp.71-79, illus., 1927.

WHALE-HO! (SHORE STATION AT EUREKA, CALIFORNIA.) Robert M. Hyatt. Westways, Los Angeles, vol.35, no.11, pp.20-21, illus., Nov., 1943.

VIRGINIA ANIMALS EVERYONE SHOUD KNOW: THE WHALES. George B. Johnson. Virginia Wildlife, Richmond, vol.8, no.10, pp.6-8, illus., Oct., 1947.

WHALING STATISTICS FOR THE PACIFIC COAST OF NORTH AMERICA. Remington Kellogg. Jour. Mam., vol.12, no.1, pp.73-77, Feb., 1931.

THE ALASKAN WHALE CULT AND ITS AFFINITIES. Margaret Lantis. Amer. Anthrop., n.s., vol.40, no.4, pp.438-464, July-Sept., 1938.

ESKIMO WHALING AT POINT BARROW. George E. Lindsay. Zoonooz, Zool. Soc. San Diego, 30 (12): 3-6, illus., Dec., 1957.

THE NEWFOUNDLAND WHALE FISHERIES. F.A. Lucas. Science, n.s., vol.21, no. 540, p.713, May 5, 1905.

CETACEAN RECORDS FROM THE PACIFIC COAST OF NORTH AMERICA. Robert T. Orr. Wasmann Jour. Biol., San Francisco, vol.9, no.2, pp.147-148, Summer, 1951.

ON A SKELETON OF A WHALE IN THE PROVINCIAL MUSEUM, HALIFAX, NOVA SCOTIA; WITH NOTES ON THE FOSSIL CETACEA OF NORTH AMERICA. George H. Perkins. Proc. Trans. Nova Scotian Inst. Sci., Halifax, vol.12, pt.2, pp.139-163, pls.8, Sept.28, 1908.

GUIDE TO THE WHALES, PORPOISES AND DOLPHINS OF THE NORTHEAST PACIFIC AND ARCTIC WATERS OF CANADA AND ALASKA. Gordon C. Pike. Fisheries Res. Board Can., Pac. Biol. Sta., Cir.No.32, pp.1-6, illus, May, 1954.

WHALING ON THE COAST OF BRITISH COLUMBIA. Gordon C. Pike. Norsk Hvalfangst-Tidende (Norwegian Whaling Gazette), Sandefjord, vol.43, no.3, pp. 117-127, illus., Mar., 1954.

THE WHALE HUNTERS OF TIGARA. Froelich G. Rainey. Anthropol. Papers Amer. Mus. Nat. Hist., New York, vol. 41, no. pt.2, pp.231-283, 1947.

WHALING OF THE OLYMPIC PENINSULA INDIANS OF WASHINGTON. Albert B. Reagen. Nat. Hist., vol.25, pp.24-32, Feb., 1925.

SHORE WHALER. Berton Roueché. New Yorker, pp.37-49, Sep. 24, 1949.

ORGANISMS COLLECTED FROM WHALES IN THE ALEUTIAN ISLANDS. Victor B. Scheffer. Murrelet, Seattle, vol.20, no.3, Sep.-Dec., pp.66-69, Dec. 16, 1939.

THE WHALES AND DOLPHINS OF WASHINGTON STATE WITH A KEY TO THE CETACEANS OF THE WEST COAST OF NORTH AMERICA. Victor B. Sheffer, John W. Slipp. Amer. Midland Nat., Notre Dame, vol.39, no.2, pp.257-337, illus., Mar., 1948.

WHALING IN NEWFOUNDLAND AND LABRADOR WATERS. David E. Sergeant. Norsk Hvalfangst-Tidende (Norwegian Whaling Gazette), Sandefjord, vol.42, no. 12, pp.687-695, Dec., 1953.

WHALING IN MANITOBA. Phil Shackleton. Forest and Outdoors, Montreal, vol.13, p. 406, 1947.

THE BERMUDA ISLANDS (CETACEA). A. E. Verrill. Trans. Connecticut Acad., vol.11, pp.673-688, June, 1902; pp.277-308, July, 1902.

THE NANTUCKET WHALING MUSEUM. Norsk Hvalfangst-Tidende (Norwegian Whaling Gazette), 47 (1): 6-17, illus., Jan., 1958.

AN ACT FOR THE ENCOURAGEMENT OF THE WHALE FISHERY IN THE GULPH AND RIVER OF SAINT LAWRENCE, AND ON THE COASTS OF HIS MAJESTY'S COLONIES IN AMERICA. Whale Fishery. Twelfth Parliament of Great Britain. Anno quarto Georgii III, Regis, pp.431-432, London, 1764.

## Pacific and Antarctic Oceans

ANTARCTIC WHALING AND EXPLORATIONS. B. Aagaard. Scottish Geogr. Mag. Edinburgh, vol.45, no.1, pp.23-34, 65-81, illus., Jan.-Mar., 1929.

INTERNATIONAL WHALING STATISTICS ANTARCTIC 1938-1939. A. Barriol. Jour. Soc. Statistique Paris, Année 81, no.5, pp. 106-109, Dec., 1940.

WHALING IN THE ANTARCTIC. A. G. Bennett. Edinburgh and London, Wm. Blackwood and Sons, Ltd., pp. x, 222, illus., May 12, 1931.

PELAGIC WHALING IN THE ANTARCTIC. VIII. THE SEASON 1937-1938. Birger Bergersen, J. Lie, Johan T. Rudd. Det. Norske Videnskaps-Akademi i Oslo, Hvalradets Skrifter, Scientific results of marine biological research, Oslo, no.20, pp.5-42, figs.6, tables 7, pls.2, 1939.

(THE GEOGRAPHICAL DISTRIBUTION OF THE MOST IMPORTANT WHALES OF THE PACIFIC.) Die geographische Verbreitung der wichtigsten Wale des stillen Ozeans. Heinrich Bolau. Abhandl. Gebiete Natur. heraus. Naturwiss. Verr., Hamburg, vol. 13, no., pp.3-22, 1895.

MODERN WHALING IN THE ANTARCTIC. S. G. Brown. Zoo Life, London, vol.10, no.2, pp.35-40, illus., Summer, 1955.

(THREE TRIPS TO THE ANTARCTIC SEAS. BRIEF BIOLOGICAL AND ECONOMIC OBSERVATIONS ON THE CETACEANS.) Tres viajes a los mares antarticos. Breves observaciones biologicas y economicas sobre cetaceos. Alberto Carcelles. Physis, Buenos Aires, vol.11, no.38, pp. 48-81, figs.9, Dec.31, 1932.

SCIENTIFIC EXPEDITION TO THE ANTARCTIC WHALING GROUNDS, 1946-1947. R.A.M. Case. Nature, London, vol.159, no., p.88, Jan.18, 1947.

MAORI WHALING. W.H. Dawbin. Norsk Havalfangst-Tidende (Norwegian Whaling Gazette), Sandefjord, vol.43, no.8, pp. 433-445, illus., Aug., 1954.

WHALES AND WHALING IN THE SOUTHERN OCEAN. W. H. Dawbin. The Antarctic Today: A Mid-Century Survey by the New Zealand Antarctic Society, by Frank Simpson, editor, Reed., pp.151-194, illus., 1952.

"THAR SHE BLOWS:" WHALING IN ANTARCTIC SEAS. H.O. Fletcher. Australian Mus. Mag., Sydney, vol.9, no.12, pp.393-397, illus., Sept.30, 1949.

WHALEBONE WHALES IN THE ANTARCTIC. F. C. Fraser. A review of: the southern stocks of whalebone whale, by Dr. N.A. Mackintosh, Cambridge at the University Press, 1942, Nature, London, vol.153, no.3889, pp.569-570, May 13, 1944.

JAPANESE ANTARCTIC WHALING EXPEDITION, 1950-51. STATISTICAL SUMMARY. Benajamin Goldberg, Leland M. Lucas. Nat. Res. Sect., Gen Hdqrs. Supreme Commander Allied Powers, Tokyo, Preliminary Study no.62, pp.1-48, figs.4, July, 1951.

NOTES ON DR. HECTOR'S PAPER ON THE WHALES AND DOLPHINS OF THE NEW ZEALAND SEAS. J. E. Gray. Trans. New Zealand Inst., vol.6, pp.93-97, 1874.

RARE WHALES IN SOUTH AUSTRALIA. BERARDIUS ARNOUXII, MESOPLODON LAYARDII, HYPEROOEDON PLANIFRONS, KOGIA BREVICEPS. Herbert M. Hale. South Australian Naturalist, Adelaide, vol.19, no.4, pp.5-8, figs.3, June 1, 1939.

SOUTHERN WHALING. Sidney F. Harmer. Proc. Linn. Soc. London, Session 142, pp. 85-163, 1931.

(Review of) SOUTHERN WHALING. Sidney Harmer. Nature, London, vol. 128, no.3225, pp.292-294, Aug.22, 1931.

SUBANTARCTIC WHALES AND WHALING. Sidney F. Harmer. Abstract, Weekly Evening Meeting (May 16, 1919), Roy. Inst. Great Britain, pp.1-5, 1919.

NOTES ON THE NEW ZEALAND CETACEA. James Hector. Trans. New Zealand Inst., vol.9, pp.477-486, pls.11-13, 1877.

NOTES ON NEW ZEALAND CETACEA, RECENT AND FOSSIL. James Hector. Trans. New Zealand Inst., vol.13, pp.434-436, pl.18, 1880.

NOTES ON NEW ZEALAND WHALES. James Hector. Trans. New Zealand Inst., vol.7, pp.251-265, pls.16-18, 1875.

NOTES ON THE WHALES OF THE NEW ZEALAND SEAS. James Hector. Trans. New Zealand Inst., vol.10, pp.331-343, pls.16-17, 1878.

ON THE WHALES AND DOLPHINS OF THE NEW ZEALAND SEAS. James Hector. Trans. New Zealand Inst., Wilmington, vol.5, pp.153-170, pls.1-6, 1873.

NORWEGIAN PELAGIC WHALING IN THE ANTARCTIC. I. WHALING GROUNDS IN 1929-1930 AND 1930-1931. Johan Hjort, J. Lie, Johan T. Ruud. Hvalradets Skrifter, Scientific Results of Marine Biological Research, Oslo, no.3, p.37, charts 6, 1932; (Article II), no.7, pp.128-152, figs.75-80, pls.6, May, 1933; III. The season 1932-1933, no.8, pp.1-36, figs.9, pls.2, 1933; IV. The season 1933-1934, with a note on: Limits of the pack ice in the Antarctic in the area between 40° W. and 110° E., by H.E. Hanson, Oslo, no.9, pp. 1-59, figs.10, pls.7, 1934, V. The season 1934-1935, no.12, pp.1-52, figs.7, pls.2, 1935; VI. The season 1935-1936, no.14, p. 45, fig.7, pl.2, 1937.

WHALING; THE GREAT ANTARCTIC INDUSTRY'S FUTURE. J. E. Hodgson. Field, London, vol.155, no.4020, p.44, Jan.11, 1930.

REVIEW OF ANDREW'S "MONOGRAPHS OF THE PACIFIC CETACEA. N. Hollister. Naturwissenschaften, vol.2, p.720, July 17, 1914.

MODERN NORWEGIAN WHALING IN THE ANTARCTIC. Gunnar Isachsen. Geogr. Rev., New York, vol.19, no.3, pp.387-403, 1 map, pls.3, figs.21, July, 1929.

ANTARCTIC WHALES. D. Dilwyn John. Jour. Soc. Preservation Fauna Empire, Hertford, n.s., pt.31, pp.15-23, 1937.

ON THE DISTRIBUTION AND MOVEMENTS OF WHALES ON THE SOUTH GEORGIA AND SOUTH SHETLAND WHALING GROUNDS. Stanley Kemp, A.G. Bennett. Discovery Reports, vol.6, pp.167-190, pls. 7, 42, 1932.

CETACEAE (OF THE BRITISH ANTARCTIC "TERRA NOVA" EXPEDITION). D. G. Lillie. London, 40 pp., 8 pls., 14 figs., 1915.

THE ANTARCTIC WHALING SEASONS OF 1948-49, 1949-50 AND 1950-51. N. A. Mackintosh. Polar Rec., 6 (43): 403-404, Jan., 1952.

WHALING IN NEW ZEALAND WATERS. Ronald McIntosh. Railways Mag., Wellington, vol.12, no.12, pp.12,13, 15, illus., Mar.1, 1938.

FACTORY SHIP WHALING AROUND BONIN ISLANDS IN 1948. Kazuhiro Mizue. Sci.

Reports Whales Research Inst., Tokyo, no.3, pp.106-118, Feb., 1950.

BIOLOGICAL INVESTIGATION ON THE WHALES CAUGHT BY THE JAPANESE ANTARCTIC WHALING FLEETS SEASON 1949-50. Kazuhiro Mizue, Tadashi Murata. Sci. Rep. Whales Res. Inst. (Tokyo), no.6, pp.73-131, illus., Dec., 1951.

SUBANTARCTIC WHALING. Robert C. Murphy. Sea Power, Wash., D.C., vol. 3, no.3, pp.44-47, Sept., 1917.

A REVIEW OF THE CETACEA OF THE NEW ZEALAND SEAS. I. W.B.R. Ogilby. Proc. Zool. Soc. Lond., 1922.

BIOLOGICAL INVESTIGATION ON THE WHALES CAUGHT BY THE JAPANESE ANTARCTIC WHALING FLEETS, SEASON 1950-1951. Mizuho Ohino, Kazuo Fujino. Sci. Rep. Whales Res. Inst. (Tokyo), no. 7, pp.125-188, illus., July, 1952.

A REVIEW OF THE CETACEA OF NEW ZEALAND SEAS.—I. W.R.B. Oliver. Proc. Zool. Soc. Lond., pp.557-583, 4 pls., Sept., 1922.

THE WHALES AND DOLPHINS OF NEW ZEALAND. W.R.B. Oliver. New Zealand Jour. Sci. and Technol., Wellington, vol.5, no.3, pp.129-141, figs.22, July, 1922.

WHALING IN THE ANTARCTIC. Y. Oma. Nat. Sci. and Mus., Tokyo Sci. Mus., vol. 7, no.7, pp.12-15, July, 1936.

WHALING IN THE DOMINION OF NEW ZEALAND. F.D. Ommanney. Discovery Reports, Cambridge, England, vol.7, pp. 239-252, fig.1, pls.11-13, 1933.

WHALES IN THE NORTHERN PART OF THE NORTH PACIFIC. Hideo Omura. Norsk Hvalfangst-Tidende (Norwegian Whaling Gazette), vol.44, no.6, pp.323-342, no.7, pp.395-405, illus., June, July, 1955.

THE DISTRIBUTION OF THE MORE IMPORTANT MARINE MAMMALS OF THE PACIFIC OCEAN, AS IT AFFECTS THEIR CONSERVATION. Robert T. Orr. Proc. Sixth Pac. Sci. Cong., 3: 217-222, 1940.

THE R. R. S. WILLIAM SCORESBY, 1934-35. (700-800 whales—blue, finback, humpback, and sperm—tagged in Antarctic seas.) G. W. Rayner. Nature, London, vol.136, no.3442, pp.630-631, Oct.19, 1935.

(THE ANTARCTIC SEASON 1929-30.) Sydhavssaesongen 1929-30. Sigurd Risting. Norsk Hvalfangst-Tidende (The Norwegian Whaling Gazette), Sandefjord, Aarg.19, no. 1, pp.1-2, Jan., 1930.

MODERN WHALING IN THE ANTARCTIC. Harold Keith Salvesen. Jour. Roy. Soc. Arts, vol.81, no.4191, pp.408-423, Mar.17, 1933.

(THE IDENTIFICATION OF ANTARCTIC CETACEANS.) L'identification des Cétacés antarctiques a la mer. J. Sapin-Jaloustre. Mammalia, Paris, vol.17, no. 4, pp.221-259, illus., pl.10, Dec., 1953.

STUDIES OF TASMANIAN CETACEA. PART II. H.H. Scott, Clive E. Lord. Roy. Soc. Tasmania, Pap. and Proc., pp.23-32, 1 pl., July 24, 1919.

JAPANESE WHALING IN THE BONIN ISLAND AREA (A PRELIMINARY REPORT). B. M. Shimada. U.S. Fish and Wildlife Service Fishery Leaflet, no.248, pp.16, illus. (mimeogr.), June, 1947.

GIANTS AND PIGMIES OF THE DEEP. A STORY OF AUSTRALIAN SEA DENIZENS. David G. Stead. Shakespeare Head Press, Sydney, pp.108, illus., 1933.

THE GREAT WHALES OF AUSTRALIA AND ANTARCTICA. David G. Stead. Australian Mus. Mag., vol.4, no.4, pp. 123-132, figs.5, Oct.16, 1930.

JAPANESE ANTARCTIC WHALING EXPEDITION, 1947-1948. William M. Terry. Supreme Commander for the Allied Powers, Nat. Resources Sec., Prelim. Study no.29, pp.31, illus., 1948.

JAPANESE ANTARCTIC WHALING EXPEDITION, 1948-49. STATISTICAL SUMMARY. William M. Terry. Supreme Commander for Allied Powers, Tokyo, Nat. Resources Sec. Prelim. Study no.34, pp.35, 1949.

WHALING IN THE FROZEN SOUTH. BEING THE STORY OF THE 1923-24 NORWEGIAN WHALING EXPEDITION TO THE ANTARCTIC. Alan John Villiers. Bobb-Merrill Co., Indianapolis, pp.292, illus., 1925.

NOTES ON THREE NOTABLE NEW ZEALAND WHALES. E. R. Waite Rec. Cant. Mus., vol.1, no.4, pp.323-328, pls.59-63, Dec.28, 1912.

(THE CETACEA OF THE SIBOGA EXPEDITION.) Die Cetaceen deer Siboga-Expedition. Max Weber. Siboga-Exped., Monogr. 58, pp.1-38, 3 pls., Leiden, Dec., 1923.

ON THE STOCK OF WHALES AT SOUTH GEORGIA. J.F.G. Wheeler. Discovery Reports, Cambridge, vol.9, pp.351-372, figs.3, Dec., 1934.

THE ANTARCTIC SEASON 1946/47. (WHALING STATISTICS.) Norsk Hvalfangst-Tidende (Norwegian Whaling Gazette), Sandefjord, Arg.36, no.2, p.41, Feb., 1947; no.3, pp.81-83, Mar., 1947.

ANTARCTIC WHALING. Arctic, Montreal, vol.1, no.2, p.143, Autumn, 1948.

ANTARCTIC WHALING. BRITISH SHIPS HUNT HUGE ANIMALS FOR EDIBLE OIL. Life, New York, vol.21, no.14, pp.123-126, illus., Sept.30, 1946.

BRIEF HISTORY OF MODERN WHALING IN WESTERN AUSTRALIA. Fisheries Newsletter, Ministry Post War Reconstruction, Cronulla, vol.5, no.2, p.15, illus., Apr., 1946.

WHALE FISHING IN ANTARCTIC OCEAN. Jour. Geog., Tokyo, vol.50, no.590, Apr., 1938. (In Japanese.)

WHALING IN AUSTRALIA IN 1956. Norsk Hvalfangst-Tidende (Norwegian Whaling Gazette), 46 (5): 254-258, May, 1957.

WHALING IN ANTARCTIC. The Nautical Magazine, Glasgow, vol.131, pp.518-524, figs.5, June, 1934.

THE WHALING INDUSTRY. WESTERN AUSTRALIAN WATERS. Fisheries Newsletter, Ministry Post War Reconstruction, Cronulla, vol.5, no.2, p.14, illus., Apr., 1946.

### Pelage, Blubber, Coloration

THE INTEGUMENTS OF WHALES. Robert W. Gray. Nature, London, vol.125, no.3159, p.744, May 17, 1930.

(ON THE TEXTURE AND FORMATION OF WHALE HAIRS. ANATOMICAL-PHYSIOLOGICAL INAUGURATION DISSERTAION. WITH THE GRACIOUS APPROVAL AND AUTHORITY OF THE HEAD OF THE SCHOOL OF MEDICINE OF THE UNIVERSITY OF PALESTINE, BRANCH OF LETTERS, FOR MAXIMUM HONORS IN MEDICINE.) De Tectura Et Formatione Barbae Balaenae. Dissertatio Inauguralis Anatomico-Physiologica Quam Consenu Et Auctoritate Gratiosi Medicorum Ordinis Universitate Litterarum Caesarea Dorpatensi Ad Summos In Medicina Honores Rite Capessendos. Martinus Hehn. Dorpati Livonorum, pp.1-54, tables 2, 1849.

(FURTHER CONTRIBUTIONS TO KNOWLEDGE OF WHALESKIN.) Weitere Beitraege zur Kenntnis der Walhaut. Arnold Japha. Zool. Jahrb., Jena, Supp.12, no.3, pp.711-718, pl.21, 1910.

(THE HAIR OF CETACEANS.) Die Haare der Waltiere. Arnold Japha. Zool. Jahrb., vol.32, no.1, pp.42, pls.1-3, 1911.

(ON THE STRUCTURE OF THE SKIN COVERING OF THE CETACEANS.) Ueber die structur der Hautbedeckungen der Cetacheen. J. C. Mayer. Akad. Eingegangen den 24 Dec., 1854, vol.25, pt.1, pp.451-475, pls.3, figs.17, Dec.24, 1854.

THE STRUCTURE OF WHALE BLUBBER, AND A DISCUSSION OF ITS THERMAL PROPERTIES. D. A. Parry. Quart. Jour. Micr. Sci., vol.90. pt.1, pp.13-25, figs.3, pl.1, Mar., 1949.

ON THE IMPORTANCE OF MEASURING THE THICKNESS OF THE LAYER OF BLUBBER IN WHALES. E. J. Slijper. Norsk Hvalfangst-Tidende (Norwegian Whaling Gazette), Sandefjord, vol.43, no. 9, pp.510-516, illus., Sept., 1954.

### Physiology

ADRENOCORTICOTROPIC HORMONE IN THE WHALE. Finn Boe, Hugo Holtermann, Sigbjorn Salvesen, Karl Fr. Stoa, Arne Sverdrup. Nature, London, vol.167, no. 4242, p.280, Feb.17, 1951.

HOW DO WHALES SWIM? Edwin T. Brewster. Guide to Nature, vol.18, p. 161, Apr., 1926.

HEARING IN CETACEA. Robert Clarke. Nature, London, vol.161, no.4103, pp.979-980, June 19, 1948.

PHYSIOLOGY OF DEEP DIVING IN THE WHALE. G.C.C. Damant. Nature, London, vol.133, no.3371, p.874, June 9, 1934.

HEARING AND SMELL IN CETACEAN HISTORY. Tilly Edinger. Monatschr. Psychiat. and Neurol., Basle, vol.129, nos. 1-3, pp.37-58, illus., 1955.

THE "BLOW" OF WHALES. F. C. Fraser, P. E. Purves. Nature, London, vol.176, no.4495, pp.1221-1222, Dec.24, 1955.

HEARING IN CETACEANS. F. C. Fraser, P. E. Purves. Bull. British Mus. Nat. Hist. London, Zool., vol.2, no.5, pp.103-113, illus., 1954.

ASPECTS OF THE LOCOMOTION OF WHALES. R.W.L. Gawn. Nature, Lond., vol.161, no.4080, pp.44-46, figs.1-4, Jan. 10, 1948.

(ON THE BODY TEMPERATURE OF THE CETACEANS.) Ueber die Eoerpertemperatur der Cetaceen. Gustav Guldberg. Nyt. Mag. Naturv., vol.38, no.1, pp.65-70, 1900.

A REVIEW OF CERTAIN ASPECTS OF CETACEAN PHYSIOLOGY. Lela M. Jeffrey. Tex. Jour. Sci., 3 (4): 542-553, illus., Dec., 1951.

THERMAL REGULATION IN WHALES. J. Kanwisher, H. Leivestad. Norwegian Whaling Gazette, 46 (1): 1-5, 1957.

PECULIARITIES OF THE RESPIRATION OF CETACEANS. S. E. Kleynenberg. Progress of Contemporary Biology, USSR, Acad. Sci., Moscow, 41 (3): 366-380, 1956. (In Russian.)

EVIDENCE FOR ECHOLOCATION BY CETACEANS. Arthur F. McBride. Deep-Sea Research, London, vol.3, no.2, pp. 153-154, Feb., 1956.

(THE EYES AND VISION OF WHALES.) Ojo y Visión de las Ballenas. Guillermo Mann. Biologica, Santiago, pp.81, figs. 31, pls.9, July, 1946.

(WHY DO SOME DEAD WHALES FLOAT WHILE OTHERS SINK?) Warum treiben einige tote Wale, waehrend andere untersinken? E. Mohr. Der Zoologische Garten, Leipzig n.f., vol.2, nos.1-3, pp. 47-48, 1929.

THE COLLECTION OF FOETAL WHALE THYMUS GLANDS ON F.F. "BALAENA" FOR MEDICAL RESEARCH. P. T. Nowell. Norsk Hvalfangst-Tidende (Norwegian Whaling Gazette), 45 (4): 165-171, illus., Apr., 1956.

ON THE ACOUSTIC SYSTEM IN CETACEAN BRAINS. Teizo Ogawa, Shozo Arifuku. Sci. Repts. Whales Research Inst., Tokyo, no.2, pp.1-20, figs.14, Dec., 1948.

THE SWIMMING OF WHALES AND A DISCUSSION OF GRAY'S PARADOX. D. A. Pairy. Jour. Exper. Biol., London, vol. 26, no.1, pp.24-34, illus., 1949.

(COMPARATIVE PHYSIOLOGICAL RESEARCH DONE ON BOARD THE "PRINCESS ALICE." THE TEMPERATURE OF CETACEANS.) Recherches de Physiologie comparée faites à bord de la Princesse Alice. Température des cétacés. Paul Portier. Resultats Campagnes Sci. accomplies sur son yacht par Albert I

Prince souverain de Monaco, fasc. 98, pp.72-73, table, 1938; Mechanism of "blowing" in whales, pp.79-81, 1938.

(ON THE PHYSIOLOGY OF GIANT ANIMALS.) Zur Physiologie der Riesentiere. (Notes on large whales.) Aug. Puetter. Zool. Jahrb., Abt. fuer Allg. Zool. und Physiologie, Bd. 40, pp.217-240, 1923.

EVIDENCE FOR ECHOLOCATION BY CETACEANS. William E. Schevill. Deep Sea Research, vol.3, pp.153, Pergamon Press Ltd., London, 1956.

COUNTER-CURRENT VASCULAR HEAT EXCHANGE IN THE FINS OF WHALES. P. F. Scholander, W. E. Schevill. Jour. Applied Physiol., vol.8, no.3, pp.279-282, Nov., 1955.

RETIA MIRABILIA OF CETACEANS. W. L. Strays. Science, 124:167, 1956.

ON THE EXPLOSIONS OF WHALES. A.G. Tomilin. Priroda, Leningrad, no.1, p.105, Jan., 1937. (In Russian.)

(SOME PROBLEMS IN REGARD TO THE ECOLOGY OF THE CETACEANS (ADAPTATIONS TO THE TEMPERATURE OF SURROUNDINGS).) A. G. Tomilin. Bull. Soc. Nat. Moscow, Sect. Biol., n.s., vol.49, nos.5-6, pp.43-46, 1940. (In Russian, with French résumé.)

THERMOREGULATION AND THE GEOGRAPHICAL RACES OF CETACEANS. A.G. Tomilin. Comptes Rendus (Doklady) Acad. Sci. USSR, Moscow, n.s., vol.54, no.5, pp.465-468, Nov.20, 1946.

AUDITORY ORGAN OF THE WHALEBONE WHALES. Munesato Yamada. Sci. Repts. Whales Research Inst., Tokyo, no.2, pp. 21-30, figs.7, Dec., 1948.

THE TEMPERATURE OF WHALES. B. A. Zencovich. Doklady Acad. Sci. USSR, vol. 18, no.9, pp.685-687, 1937.

ZOOPHYSIOLOGICAL EXPEDITION TO BARRO COLORADO, PANAMA. Norwegian Whaling Gazette, 44 (11): 638-640, 1955.

WHALES' BRAINS ARE ADAPTED TO THE WHALE WAY OF LIFE. Science News Letter, vol.32, no.871, p.389, Dec.18, 1937.

Populations and Migrations

(ON THE WANDERINGS OF VARIOUS BEARDED WHALES.) Ueber die Wanderungen verschiedener Bartenwale. Gustav Guldberg. Biologischen Centralblatt, Leipzig, vol.23, no.24, pp.803-816, Dec. 15, 1903; vol.24, nos.11-12, pp.371-396, June 15, 1904.

EFFECT OF PRESENT-DAY WHALING ON THE STOCK OF WHALES. J. E. Hamilton. Nature, 161 (4102): 913-914, June 12, 1948.

WHALE STOCKS AND WHALING. J. E. Hamilton. Nature, London, vol.157, no. 3987, p.412, Mar.30, 1946.

WHAT IS KNOWN OF THE MIGRATIONS OF SOME OF THE WHALEBONE WHALES. Remington Kellogg. Ann. Rept. Board Regents Smithson. Inst., 1928, publ.2981, pp.467-494, pls.3, figs.6, Nov.18, 1929.

ON THE LOCAL STOCK OF WHALES. S. K. Klumov. Trans. Inst. Oceanology, Acad. Sci. USSR, Moscow, 18: 7-27, 1955.

CHARTING OF WHALE STOCKS IN THE ANTARCTIC ON THE BASIS OF IODINE VALUES. Jakob Lund. Norsk Hvalfangst-Tidende (Norwegian Whaling Gazette), Sandefjord, arg.39, no.2, pp.53-60, Feb., 1950. (In Norwegian and English.)

THE STOCK OF WHALES. N.A. Mackintosh. Nature, London, vol.162, no.4108, p.148, July 24, 1948.

PRELIMINARY ESTIMATES OF THE SOUTHERN POPULATIONS OF THE LARGER BALEEN WHALES. N. A. Mackintosh, S. G. Brown. Norsk Hvalfangst-Tidende (Norwegian Whaling Gazette), 45 (9): 469-480, Sept., 1956.

A SUMMARY OF GENERAL OBSERVATIONS ON THE SPOUTING AND MOVEMENTS OF WHALES. Emile G. Racovitza. Ann. Rept., 1903, Smithsonian Inst., Wash., pp. 627-645, 1904.

(TRAVEL ROUTES OF THE WHALE.) Wanderwege der Wale. K. Schubert. Die Umschau, Frankfurt a.M., Jahrg.49, no.5, pp.138-140, figs.4, Mar.1, 1949.

(THE WHALE POPULATION OF THE ANTARCTIC OCEAN.) Walbestand im Suedlichen eismeer. K. Schubert. Fischwirtschaft, 5 (6): 146-147, 1953.

THE STOCKS OF WHALES IN THE ANTARCTIC. K. Schubert. Norsk Hvalfangst-Tidende (Norwegian Whaling Gazette), Sandefjord, vol.42, no.7, pp.391-394, July, 1953.

ON THE MIGRATION OF WHALES IN THE NORTHERN PARTS OF THE PACIFIC OCEAN. B. A. Zencovich. Bull. Pacific Sci. Inst. Fisheries and Oceanography, Vladivostok, vol.10, pp.3-18, 1937. (In Russian with English summary.)

Reproductive Biology

(WHAT THE GREENLANDERS WANT TO KNOW ABOUT THE BIRTH OF WHALES.) Hvad Gronlaenderne ville vide om Hvaldyrenes Fodsel. Chr. Luetken. Vidensk. Meddel. Naturh. Foren., 1887, Kjoebenhavn, pp.397-401, 1888.

(WHAT GREENLANDERS WANT TO KNOW ABOUT WHALE BIRTHS.) Was die Groenlander von der Geburt der Wale wissen wollen. Chr. Luetken. Zool. Jahrb., vol.3, pp.802-804, 1890.

STATISTIC STUDY OF FOETUSES OF WHALES. Kazuhiro Mizue, Hisako Jimbo. Sci. Rep. Whales Res. Inst. (Tokyo), no. 3, pp.119-131, illus., 1950.

ON SOME PHENOMENA CONCERNING PREGNANCY AND PARTURITION OF THE CETACEA. E. J. Slkjper. Bijdragen tot de Dierkunde, Leiden, vol.28, pp.416-448, pls.21-25, 1949.

Scrimshaw

SCRIMSHAW: ART OF THE WHALE HUNTERS. Cedric Larson. Think, International Business Machines Corp., New York, vol. 21, no.11, pp.14-15, illus., Nov., 1955.

SCRIMSHAW:—WHALING MEN'S WORK IN WHALE TEETH. Norsk Hvalfangst-Tidende (Norwegian Whaling Gazette), vol.45, no.2, pp.61-65, illus., Feb., 1956.

South America

(CETACEANS IN ARGENTINE WATERS.) Cétaceos en las aguas argentinas. Alberto Carcelles. Argentina Austral, Buenos Aires, año 20, no.208, pp.10, illus., Oct., 1948.

(THE WHALES AND THEIR EXPLOTATION IN PERU.) Las ballenas y su aprovechamiento en el Peru. León Kostritsky. Pesca y Caza, Ministerio de Agricultura, Lima, no.4, pp.33-48b, illus., 1952.

(NOTICE REGARDING SOME FOSSIL AND LIVING CETACEANS OF THE REPUBLIC OF ARGENTINA CONSERVED IN THE LA PLATA MUSEUM.) Noticias sobre algunos cetáceos fósiles y actuales de la República Argentina conservados en el Museo de La Plata. Francisco P. Moreno. Rev. Mus. La Plata, vol.3, pp.381-400, pls.8-9, 1892.

WET LANDS AND DRY SEAS. (WHALES, BLACKFISH, ETC., OFF COAST OF COLOMBIA.) Robert Cushman Murphy. Nat. Hist., New York, vol.53, no.8, pp. 350-356, illus., Oct., 1944.

WHALING ACTIVITY ON THE CHILEAN COAST. Norsk Hvalfangst-Tidende (Norwegian Whaling Gazette), Sandefjord, vol. 43, no.5, pp.267-272, illus., May, 1954.

Stranded Cetaceans

STONE WHALES FROM SANTA BARBARA'S BEACH. John L. von Blon. Westways, Los Angeles, vol.28, no.10, pp.26-27, illus., Oct., 1936.

(TETSAM OF CETACEA IN THE NETHERLANDS IN 1931 AND 1932.) Aanspoelingen van Cetacea in Nederland in de Jaren 1931 en 1932. A. B. van Deinse. Natuurhistorisch Museum te Rotterdam, no.2, pp.7-20, 1933.

(NOTE ON A CETACEAN STRANDED ON NOV. 27, 1826 ON THE DEPENDENT COAST OF THE ST. CYPRIEN COMMUNE.) Memoire sur un cetace echoue, le 27 Novembre 1828, sur la cote dependente de la commune de Saint-Cyprien. Bull. Sci. Nat. Paris, sect.2, vol.19, pp.349-350, 1829.

CETACEA STRANDED ON THE BRITISH COAST DURING 1944. F. C. Fraser. Ann. Mag. Nat. Hist., London, ser.11, vol.12, pp.347-350, May, 1945.

REPORT ON CETACEA STRANDED ON THE BRITISH COASTS FROM 1927 TO 1932. F. C. Fraser. No.11, Brit. Mus. Nat. Hist., London, pp.41, figs.8, maps 6, Aug.18, 1934.

REPORT ON CETACEA STRANDED ON THE BRITISH COASTS FROM 1933 TO 1937. F. C. Fraser. Publ. Brit. Mus. Nat. Hist., London, no.12, pp.56, figs.11, maps 7, Sept.1, 1946.

REPORT ON CETACEA STRANDED ON THE BRITISH COASTS FROM 1938 TO 1947. F. C. Fraser. Brit. Mus. Nat. Hist., no. 13, pp.1-48, illus., 9 maps, Sept.1, 1953.

GUIDE FOR THE IDENTIFICATION AND REPORTING OF STRANDED WHALES, DOLPHINS, PORPOISES AND TURTLES ON THE BRITISH COASTS. F. C. Fraser, H. W. Parker. Publ. Brit. Mus. Nat. Hist., London, pp.viii, 42, figs.41, 1949; 2nd ed., 1953.

WHALES AGROUND IN CORTES' SEA. Raymond M. Gilmore. Pacific Discovery, 10 (1): 22-27, Jan.-Feb., 1957.

A STRANDED SCHOOL OF WHALES. Herbert M. Hale. Public Service Review, Adelaide, vol.51, no.10, pp.12-14, illus., 1944.

REPORT ON CETACEA STRANDED ON THE BRITISH COASTS DURING 1913. Sidney F. Harmer. Brit. Mus. Nat. Hist., London, pp.12, pls.3, Feb., 1914.

NOTES ON CETACEA STRANDED ON THE BRITISH COASTS DURING 1913-1917. Sidney F. Harmer. Proc. Zool. Soc. Lond., pp. 147-161, Aug., 1918.

REPORT ON CETACEA STRANDED ON THE BRITISH COASTS FROM 1913-1926. Sidney F. Harmer. Brit. Mus. Nat. Hist., London, no.10, pp.91, illus., 7 maps, Feb.26, 1927.

REPORT ON CETACEA STRANDED ON THE BRITISH COASTS DURING 1914. Sidney F. Harmer. Brit. Mus. Nat. Hist., London, no.2, pp.16, 3 maps, Feb.27, 1915.

REPORT ON CETACEA STRANDED ON THE BRITISH COASTS DURING 1915. Sidney F. Harmer. Brit. Mus. Nat. Hist., no.3, pp.12, map, Feb.26, 1916.

REPORT OF CETACEA STRANDED ON THE BRITISH COASTS DURING 1916. Sidney F. Harmer. Brit. Mus. Nat. Hist., no.4, pp.13, illus., 1 map, Feb. 24, 1917.

REPORT ON CETACEA STRANDED ON THE BRITISH COASTS DURING 1917. Sidney F. Harmer. Brit. Mus. Nat. Hist., no.5, pp.21, illus., 1 map, Mar.23, 1918.

REPORT ON CETACEA STRANDED ON THE BRITISH COASTS DURING 1918. Sidney F. Harmer. Brit. Mus. Nat. Hist., no.6, pp.24, illus., 1 map, Mar.22, 1919.

REPORT ON CETACEA STRANDED ON THE BRITISH COASTS DURING 1919 AND 1920. Sidney F. Harmer. Brit. Mus. Nat. Hist., London, no.7, pp.18, map, Feb.26, 1921.

REPORT ON CETACEA STRANDED ON THE BRITISH COASTS DURING 1921 AND 1922. Sidney F. Harmer. Brit. Mus. Nat. Hist., London, no.8, pp.17, illus., 1 map, Feb.24, 1923.

REPORT ON CETACEA STRANDED ON THE BEITISH COASTS DURING 1923 AND 1924. Sidney F. Harmer. Brit. Mus. Nat. Hist., London, no.9, pp.24, illus., 1 map, Feb.28, 1925.

(NOTES ON SOME LARGE CETACEANS WASHED ASHORE IN EUROPE DURING THE LAST TEN YEARS.) Notes sur quelques grands cétacés échoués sur les côtes d'europe pendant les dix dernieres années. Henri Jouan. Rev. Italiana Sci. Nat., Siena, vol.11, no.12, pp.227-238, illus., 1879.

WHY DO STRANDED WHALES DIE? W. A. Osborne. Nature, London, vol.140, no. 3554, p.1017, Dec.11, 1937.

WHALE-BONE WHALE STRANDED ON THE TRAVANCORE COAST. R. V. Poduval. Jour. Bombay Nat. Hist. Soc., vol.39, no.3, p.620, Sept.25, 1937.

(THREE COMMUNICATIONS ON CETACEANS. TWO STRANDINGS OF LARGE CETACEANS IN THE 7TH AND 9TH CENTURIES.) Trois communications sur les Cetaces. Deux échougages de grands cétacés au VII et au IX siècles. Georges Pouchet. Comptes Rendus Seances et. Mem. Soc. Biol., Paris, vol.42 (ser.9, vol.2), no.36, pp.686-688, Dec.12, 1890.

(NEW LIST OF LARGE CETACEANS STRANDED ON THE FRENCH COAST.) Nouvelle liste d'échouements de grands Cétacés sur la côte francaise. Georges Pouchet, Beauregard, Henri. Comp. Rend. Acad. Sci., vol.113, pp.810-813, Paris, 1891.

A STRANDED WHALE. E. A. Preble. Nature Mag., vol.4, no.4, pp.208, 212, Oct., 1924.

CETACEA RECENTLY STRANDED IN SCOTLAND. A. C. Stephen. Scottish Nat., no.201, p.86, May-June, 1933.

NOTES ON SOME WHALES RECENTLY STRANDED ON THE SCOTTISH COAST. A. C. Stephen. Scottish Nat., no.198, pp.163-167, Nov.-Dec., 1932.

RECORDS OF CETACEANS STRANDED ON THE SCOTTISH COAST. A. C. Stephen. Scottish Naturalist, no.189, pp.85-86, May-June, 1931.

(SOME PARTICULARITIES OF WHALE HABITS. THEIR APPROACHING OF COASTS AND "DRYING.") A. G. Tomilin. Bull. Soc. Nat. Moscou, sect. biol., n.s., vol.46, no.4, pp.194-203, 1937. (In Russian with French summary.)

Systematics

(THE PHYLOGENIC DEVELOPMENT OF CETACEAN DENTITION AND THE SYSTEMATIC POSITION OF THE PHYSETERINES.) Die phylogenetische Entwicklung des Cetaceengebisses und die systematische Stelleng der Physeteriden. O. Abel. Verhandl. d. Deutsch. Zool. Gesellschaft, p. 84-96, 1905.

THE RELATIVE POSITION OF THE CETACEA AMONG THE ORDERS OF MAMMALIA AS INDICATED BY PRECIPITIN TESTS. Alan Boyden, Douglas Gemeroy. Anat. Record, Phila., vol.105, no.3, p.50, Nov., 1949; Zoologica, New York, vol.35, pt.2, pp.145-151, Aug.1, 1950.

ON THE GENETIC RELATIONS OF THE CETACEANS AND THE METHODS INVOLVED IN DISCOVERY. Theodore Gill. Amer. Nat., vol.7, pp.11, Jan., 1873.

SYNOPSIS OF THE PRIMARY SUBDIVISIONS OF THE CETACEANS. Theodore Gill. Proc. and Communications, Essex Inst., vol.6, pp.121-126, Mar., 1871.

ON THE ARRANGEMENT OF THE CETACEANS. John E. Gray. Proc. Zool Soc. London, pt.31, pp.197-202, 1863.

ON THE NATURAL ARRANGEMENT OF VERTEBROSE ANIMALS. John E. Gray. London Med. Repository, vol.15, no.88, pp.296-310, Apr.1, 1821.

(ANSWER TO A.M. BUREAU ON THE NEW CLASSIFICATION OF CETACEANS.) Reponse adressee A.M. Bureau sur La Nouvelle Classification des Cetaces. M. E. Guitton. Extrait Revue et Mag. Zool., no. 6, pp.7, 1855.

(INVESTIGATIONS ON THE CETACEA. XXVI. FURTHER INVESTIGATION ON THE RELATIONSHIPS BETWEEN THE VARIOUS WHALE SPECIES.) Untersuchungen ueber Cetacea. XXVI. Weitere untersuchung ueber die Verwandtschaftsverhaeltnisse zwischen den verschiedenen Walarten. Kyo Hayasi. Japanese Jour. Med. Sci. Trans.II., Biochem., vol.1, no.2, pp.127-129, 1927.

THE PHYLOGENY OF THE TOOTHED WHALES. F. A. Lucas. Science, vol. 14, no.355, pp.618-619, Oct.18, 1901.

(REMARKS ON STENO GASTALDII BRANDT AND ON THE EVOLUTION OF THE DENTITION OF CETODONTS.) Remarques sur le Steno gastaldii Brandt et sur l'evolution de la dentition des Cetodontes. H. Neuville. Bull. Mus. Nat. Hist., Paris, vol.34, no.2, pp.135-138, 1928.

WHALE IDENTIFICATION. Gordon C. Pike. Progress Rept. Pacific Coast Sta., Fisheries Res. Board of Canada, no.81, pp.84-86, Dec., 1949.

THE SHADY PAST OF GRANDPA WHALE. Morton Stark. Science Illus., Albany, vol. 4, no.7, pp.22-25, illus., July, 1949.

(ECOLOGICAL CLASSIFICATION OF CETACEA.) Prisposobitelnie tipi otryada kitoobraznikh (k voprosu ob ekologicheskoi klassifikatsii Cetacea). A. G. Tomilin. Zool. Zhurnal, Moscow, vol.33, no.3, pp. 677-692, May-June, 1954. (In Russian.)

ON THE CLASSIFICATION OF THE CETACEA. Frederick W. True. Proc. Amer. Philos. Soc. Phila., vol.47, no.189, pp.385-391, Nov.4, 1908.

ON THE NOMENCLATURE OF THE WHALEBONE WHALES OF THE TENTH EDITION OF LINNAEUS'S SYSTEMA NATURAE. Frederick W. True. Proc. U.S. Nat. Mus., vol.21, publ.1163, pp.617-635, Nov.4, 1898.

(STUDIES ON MAMMALS. A CONTRIBUTION ON THE QUESTION OF THE ORIGIN OF THE CETACEA.) Studien ueber Saeugethiere. Ein beitrage sur frage nach dem Ursprung der Cetaceen. Max Weber. Privately printed, pp.252, pls.9, 1886.

(A NEW VIEW ON THE RELATIONSHIPS AMONG THE WHALES.) Udsigt over Hvalernes indbyrdes Slaegtskab. Herluf Winge. Publikationer fra Universitetets Zoologiske Museum, Kobenhavn, no.3, 1918. (In Danish.)

A REVIEW OF THE INTERRELATIONSHIPS OF THE CETACEA. Herluf Winge. Smithsonian Misc. Coll., vol.72, no.8, 97 pp., 1921.

THE INTERNATIONAL WHALING CONFERENCE 1946. ANNEX NOMENCLATURE OF WHALES. Norsk Hvalfangst-Tidende (Norwegian Whaling Gazette), Sandefjord, Arg.36, no.6, pp.56-58, Feb., 1947.

Weights and Volumes

(WHALE WEIGHTS.) Hvalens vekt. (Formulae for calculating weight of whales.) C. E. Ash. Norsk. Hval.-Tid., 41 (7): 364-370, 373-374, 1952.

SOME WEIGHT MEASUREMENTS OF WHALES. Ingi Bjarnason, Per Lingaas. Norsk Hvalfangst-Tidende (Norwegian Whaling Gazette), Sandefjord, vol.43, no. 1, pp.8-11, illus., Jan., 1954.

(ON THE METHOD OF COMPUTING THE VOLUME AND WEIGHT OF THE GREAT CETACEANS.) Ueber das Verfahren bei Berechnung des Rauminhaltes und Gewichtes der grossen Waltiere. Gustav Guldberg. Vid.-Selsk. Forh., Christiania, no.3, pp. 12, Feb.19, 1907.

ON THE WEIGHT AND CHEMICAL COMPOSITION OF WHALES. J. Kharkof. Trans. Inst. Marine Fisheries and Oceanogr., USSR, Moscow, vol.15, pp.3-50, illus., 1940. (English summary.)

ON THE BODY WEIGHT OF WHALES. Masaharu Nishiwaki. Sci.Repts. Whales Research Inst., Tokyo, no.4, pp.184-209, Aug., 1950.

ON THE BODY WEIGHT OF SPERM AND SEI WHALES LOCATED IN THE ADJACENT WATERS OF JAPAN. Hideo Omura. Sci. Repts. Whales Research Inst., Tokyo, no. 4, pp.1-13, Aug., 1950.

WEIGHT DATA ON FIVE WHALES. (3 Humpback, 1 sperm, 1 finback.) Daniel P. Quiring. Jour. Mam., 24 (1): 39-45, Feb., 1943.

WEIGHING OF WHALES. B. A. Zenkovic. Doklady Acad. Sci. USSR, n.s., vol.16, no.3, pp.177-182, 1937.

Whale Meat, Oils, and Oil Derivatives

ATTEMPT TO PRESERVE FRESHNESS OF WHALE MEAT WITH GERMICIDES. II. Shichiro Akiya, Otomatsu Hoshino, Nobuo Motohasi. Sci. Repts. Whales Research Inst., Tokyo, no.9, pp.1-10, illus., June, 1954.

ON AN ATTEMPT TO PRESERVE WHALE MEAT FRESHNESS WITH 5-NITROFURFURIDEN AMINOGUANIDINE FROM DECAY. Shichiro Akiya, Otomatsu Hoshino, Nobuo Motohashi. Sci. Repts. Whales Research Inst., Tokyo, no.7, pp.23-26, July, 1952.

DETERMINATION OF TRYPTOPHANE IN WHALE MEAT. Schichiro Akiya, Keiichi Takahashi. Sci. Repts. Whales Research Inst., Tokyo, no.2, pp.51-54, Dec., 1948.

STUDIES ON THE UTILIZATION OF WHALE MEAT BY THE USE OF PANCREATIC TRYPTASE OF WHALES. Shichiro Akiya, Setsuzo Tejima, Yasutaro Ishikawa. Sci. Repts. Whales Research Inst., Tokyo, no. 1, pp.11-14, illus., June, 1948.

BACTERIOLOGICAL STUDIES ON FRESHNESS OF WHALE MEAT. Tomoichiro Akiba, Takeshi Tsuchiya, Makoto Umehara, Yoskiharu Natsume. Sci. Repts. Whales Research Inst., Tokyo, no.3, pp.63-70, Feb., 1950; no.5, pp.1-4, folding table, June, 1951.

WHALE MEAT IN NUTRITION. Yoro Arai, Shigeru Sakai. Sci. Repts. Whales Research Inst., Tokyo, no.7, pp.51-67, July, 1952.

COMPARING THE FATNESS OF WHALES. C. E. Ash. Norsk Hvalfangst-Tidende (Norwegian Whaling Gazette), Sandefjord, vol.44, no.1, pp.20-24, Jan., 1955.

WHALEMEAT. E. C. Bate-Smith, J. G. Sharp. Food Manufacture, London, vol.21, no.9, pp.371-377, illus., Sept.1, 1946.

WHALE OILS. M. P. Belopolsky, O. B. Maksimov. Pacific Sci. Inst. Fishery Economics and Oceanography, Moscow, nos.1-2, pp.119-125, 1934. (In Russian.)

WHALE OIL. AN ECONOMIC ANALYSIS. Karl Brandt. Food Res. Inst., Stanford Univ., xii, 264 pp., 1940.

WHALING AND WHALE OIL DURING AND AFTER WORLD WAR II. Karl Brandt. War-Peace Pamphlets, Food Research Inst., Stanford Univ., Stanford, no.11, pp.1-48, charts 3, Jan., 1948.

NORWEGIAN WHALEMEAT PRODUCTION. M. Ingram. DSIR Food Investigation Memoir, London, no.555, pp.8, illus.

THERMAL DECOMPOSITION OF KITOL. Seiichi Ishikawa, Yoshimori Omote, Masao Kijima, Hiroshi Okuda. Sci. Repts. Whales Research Inst., Tokyo, no.5, pp. 61-69, June, 1951.

SUBSTANCES RELATED TO VITAMIN A IN THE WHALE LIVER OIL. Seiichi Ishikawa, Yoshimori Omote, Hiroshi Okuda. Sci. Reports Whales Research Inst., Tokyo, no.5, pp.53-59, figs.5, June, 1951.

ANALYTICAL DISTILLATION OF VITAMIN A IN THE WHALE LIVER OIL. Seiichi Ishikawa, Yoshimori Omote, Yoshitaka Soma. Sci. Repts. Whales Research Inst., Tokyo, no.2, pp.35-41, figs.5, Dec., 1948.

CONTRIBUTIONS TO THE STUDY OF THE OILS OF MARINE CRUSTACEA. I. THE OILS OF MEGANYCTIPHANES NORVEGICA M. SARS AND CALANUS FINMARCHICUS GUNN. (Discussion of possible influence of crustacea oil on the composition of whale oil.) Alf Klem. Hvalradets Skrifter, Sci. Results of Marine Biological Research, Oslo, no.6, pp.24, figs.9, 1932.

CONTRIBUTIONS TO THE STUDY OF WHALE OILS. STUDIES IN THE BIOCHEMISTRY OF WHALE OILS. Alf Klem. Hvalradets Skrifter, Sci. Res. Marine Biol. Res., Oslo, no.11, pp.49-108, 1935.

WHALE MEAT. A POTENTIAL PROTEIN FOOD RESOURCE. Mogens Kondrup. Fisheries Bull. Food and Agric. Organization United Nations, Rome, vol.5, no.5, pp. 165-183, Sept.-Oct., 1952.

CHEMICAL STUDIES ON THE FRESHNESS OF WHALE MEAT. I, II, III. Tadashi Nakai. Sci. Rept. Whales Research Inst., Tokyo, no.1, pp.17-26, 27-30; no.2, pp.31-34, illus., June, Dec., 1948.

CHEMICAL STUDIES ON FRESHNESS OF WHALE MEAT. IV. SOME INFORMATION OF ACHROMOBACTER UBIQUITUM ISOLATED FROM WHALE CARCASS. Tadashi Nakai. Sci. Repts. Whales Research Inst., Tokyo, no.6, pp.167-176, illus., Dec., 1951.

STUDIES ON THE QUALITY OF WHALE OIL. Shinichi Okura, et al. Repts. Research Lab. Nippon Suisan Co., pp.19-27, 32-49, 1952. (Ten separate articles by Shunichi Okura, Shigehide Yamada, Mituo Nagata, and Mikio Mori; in Japanese with English summaries.)

A RAPID METHOD FOR THE SEPARATE DETERMINATION OF VITAMIN A AND KITOL IN THE WHALE-LIVER OIL. Yoshimori Omoto. Sci. Repts. Whales Research Inst., Tokyo, no.7, pp.47-50, July, 1952.

STUDIES IN WHALE OILS. ON THE CONTENT OF SATURATED FATTY ACIDS IN WHALE OILS WITH A NOTE ON THE CONTENT OF POSITIONAL ISOMERIC HEXADECENOIC AND OCTADECONOIC ACIDS IN PARTIALLY HARDENED ANTARCTIC WHALE OIL. Torbjorn Pedersen. Hvalradets Skrifter, Sci. Res. Marine Biol. Res., Oslo, no.34, pp.64, 1950.

A SHORT SURVEY OF SPERM OIL AND ITS APPLICATIONS. Johan T. Ruud. Norsk Hvalfangst-Tidende (Norwegian Whaling Gazette), Sandefjord, vol.37, no.11, pp.451-456, Nov., 1948.

(THE OILS AND FLUIDS OF SOME BEARDED WHALES. THE ANALYSIS CONSTANTS OF THE FATS OF SOME MARINE ANIMALS.) Die Oele und Traene einiger Bartenwale. Die Analysenkonstante der Fette einiger marinen Tiere. S. Schmidt-Nielsen, Arne Flood. K. Norske Vidensk. Selsk. Trondheim, vol.6, no.30, pp.115-118, June 26, 1933.

STUDIES ON KITOL. I. PREPARATION OF KITOL FROM WHALE LIVER OIL. Tadashi Tawara, Ryusuke Fukazawa. Sci. Repts. Whales Research Inst., Tokyo, no.3, pp. 85-88, figs.4, Feb., 1950.

STUDIES ON KITOL. II. INFLUENCE OF KITOL FRACTION ON THE DETERMINATION OF THE INTERNATIONAL UNIT OF VITAMIN A. Tadashi Tawara, Ryusuke Fukazawa. Sci. Reports Whales Research Inst., Tokyo, no.3, pp.89-91, Feb., 1950.

STUDIES ON KITOL. III. THE EFFECT OF SUNLIGHT, AIR AND HEAT ON THE VITAMIN A AND KITOL FRACTIONS. Tadashi Tawara, Ryusuke Fukazawa. Sci. Reports Whales Research Inst., Tokyo, no. 3, pp.92-95, Feb., 1950.

STUDIES ON KITOL IV. PURIFICATION OF KITOL BY CHROMATOGRAPHIE. Tadashi Tawara, Ryusuke Fukazawa. Sci. Repts. Research Inst., Tokyo, no.5, pp.49-51, fig.1, June, 1951.

EXPERIMENT ON DIGESTION OF WHALE MEAT BY KOJI-MOULD. Saburo Tsukamoto. Sci. Repts. Whales Research Inst., Tokyo, no.2, pp.61-66, Dec., 1948.

CONTRIBUTIONS TO THE STUDY OF WHALE OILS. CHEMICAL ANALYSIS OF SAMPLES OF BLUE WHALE OILS. I. Tveraaen. Hvalradets Skrifter, Sci. Res. Marine Biol. Res., Oslo, no.11, pp.5-48, 1935.

CHROMATOGRAPHIC FRACTIONATION OF WHALE-LIVER OIL. Harry Willstaedt, Hans Behrnts Jensen. Nature, London, vol. 143, no.3630, p.474, Mar.18, 1939.

EXPERIMENT (OR TEST) ON MILD CURED WHALE MEAT USING ANTISEPTICS. Haruo Yamada, et al. Repts. Research Lab. Nippon Suisan Co., pp.9-18, 1952. (Three articles by Haruo Yamada, Elizaburo Akitsu, Shyoji Takagi, and Yoshihiko Taguti; in Japanese with English summaries.)

STUDIES ON THE MOLECULAR DISTILLATION OF WHALE LIVER OILS. Takeshige Yamakawa, et al. Repts. Research Lab. Nippon Suisan Co., pp.51-68, (separately paged 1-18), 1952. (In Japanese with English summary.)

WHALE LIVER OIL NEW SOURCE OF VITAMIN A. Amer. Fur Breeder, Duluth, vol.15, no.7, p.19, Jan., 1943.

Whalebone

WHALEBONE AND ITS USES. Henry Granville. Home Magazine, New York, pp.407-409, May, 1898.

THE MYSTERY OF WHALEBONE. S. H. Pycraft. Illus. London News, vol.190,no. 5106, p.338, figs.3, Feb.27, 1937.

Whaling, Commercial

SUMMARY OF THE LOG OF THE BARK "ACTIVE" - NEW BEDFORD, O.G. ROBINSON MASTER FROM THE FIRST ENTRY NOV. 8, 1865 UNTIL ABOUT JAN. 1, 1869 - S.M. BLACKMER NAMED MASTER FROM JUNE 30, 1870. "Active" (Summary of the log of) 1865-1870.

LOG OF THE 1ST AND 2ND VOYAGES OF THE SCHOONER "ADELIA CHASE" OF NEW BEDFORD - B.A. HIGGINS, MASTER. "Adelia Chase" - (Logbook of). 1880.

FISHERY STATISTICS OF THE UNITED STATES 1942. A. W. Anderson, E. A. Power. U.S. Dept. Interior, Fish and Wildlife Serv., Statistical Digest no.11, pp.248, illus., 1946.

SHORE-WHALING: A WORLD INDUSTRY. Roy Chapman Andrews. Nat. Geog. Mag., vol.22, no.5, pp.411-442, illus., May, 1911.

WHALE HUNTING WITH GUN AND CAMERA. Roy Chapman Andrews. D. Appleton and Co., N.Y. and London, pp. 331, illus., 1931.

THE YANKEE WHALER. WITH AN INTRODUCTION BY ROBERT CUSHMAN MURPHY AND A PREFACE TO THE PICTURES BY ZEPHANIAH W. PEASE. Clifford W. Ashley. Houghton Mifflin Co., Boston, pp.viii-xxviii, 156, illus., 1938.

AMERICAN CONTRIBUTIONS TO GEOGRAPHICAL KNOWLEDGE OF THE CENTRAL PACIFIC. S. Whittemore Boggs. Geographical Review, vol.28, no.2, pp. 177-192, maps, Apr., 1938.

ETCHINGS OF A WHALING CRUISE, WITH NOTES OF A SOJOURN ON THE ISLAND OF ZANZIBAR. TO WHICH IS APPENDED A BRIEF HISTORY OF THE WHALE FISHERY, ITS PAST AND PRESENT CONDITION. J. Ross Browne. Harper & Bros., pp.580, illus., 1846.

WHALING IN FRENCH OVERSEA TERRITORIES. Paul Budker. Norsk Hvalfangst-Tidende (Norwegian Whaling Gazette), Sandefjord, vol.43, no.6, pp.320-326, June, 1954.

WHALERS AND WHALING. THE STORY OF WHALING SHIPS UP TO THE PRESENT DAY. E. Keble Chatterton. J.B. Lippincott Co., Phila., pp.248, illus., 1926.

ELECTRIC WHALING. Robert Clarke. Nature, 169 (4308): 859-860, May 24, 1952.

OPEN BOAT WHALING IN THE AZORES, THE HISTORY AND PRESENT METHODS OF A RELIC INDUSTRY. Robert Clarke. Cambridge Univ. Press, Discovery Rep., vol.26, pp.74, 6 pls., 1954.

THE CALIFORNIA WHALING ROCKET AND PATENT BOMB LANCE. John E. Cushing, Jr. Pacific Discovery, California Acad. Sci., 8 (5): 12-15, Sept.-Oct., 1955.

WHALEMEN ADVENTURERS. THE STORY OF WHALING IN AUSTRALIAN WATERS AND OTHER SOUTHERN SEAS RELATED THERETO, FROM THE DAYS OF SAILS TO MODERN TIMES. William John Dakin. Sydney, Australia: Angus and Robertson, Ltd., pp.xx, 263, pls.40, 1934.

WHALE SHIPS AND WHALING. A PICTORIAL HISTORY OF WHALING DURING THREE CENTURIES, WITH AN ACCOUNT OF THE WHALE FISHERY IN COLONIAL NEW ENGLAND. George Francis Dow. Salem: Marine Research Soc., pp.xi, 446, illus., 1925.

WHERE WHALES ARE CAUGHT IN NETS. D.W.O. Fagan. Wide World Mag., vol.26, no.54, pp.423-432, illus., Mar., 1911.

HARPOONER: A FOUR-YEAR VOYAGE ON THE BARQUE KATHLEEN. 1880-1884. Robert Ferguson. Univ. Pennsylvania Press, Phila., pp.vii-xv, 1-316, illus., 1936.

EARLY JAPANESE WHALING. F. C. Fraser. Proc. Linnean Soc. Lond., 150th Sess., pt.1, pp.19-20, pl.2, Dec.31, 1937.

THE WHALING INDUSTRY. WHALES, DOLPHINS, AND PORPOISES. Raymond M. Gilmore. Marine Products of Commerce, by Donald K. Tressler and James McW. Lemon, Reinhold Publ. Co., New York, ed.2, pp.680-715, illus., 1951.

A WRITER GOES WHALING. W. J. Granberg. Frontiers, Phila., vol.14, no.5, pp.143-150, illus., June, 1950.

GREASY LUCK. A WHALING SKETCH BOOK. Gordon Grant. Stratford Press, Inc., New York, pp.xiv, 126, illus., 1932.

HARPOONS AND THE CAPTURE OF WHALES. R.W. Gray. Naturalist, Lond., no.992 (no.765 current ser.), pp.245-249, Sept., 1939.

PETERHEAD SEALERS AND WHALERS. A CONTRIBUTION TO THE HISTORY OF THE WHALING INDUSTRY. R. W. Gray. Scottish Nat., no.197, pp.129-133; Sept.-Oct., 1932; no.198, pp.157-162, Nov.-Dec., 1932; no.199, pp.1-10, Jan.-Feb., 1933; no. 200, pp.33-38, Mar.-Apr., 1933; no.202, pp.97-104, July-Aug., 1933; no.203, pp. 129-138, Sept.-Oct., 1933; no.204, pp.161-170, Nov.-Dec., 1933.

STATISTICS OF PETERHEAD WHALING FLEET. R. W. Gray. Naturalist, Lond., no.987 (no.760 current Ser.), pp.101-104, Apr., 1939.

(A SHORT HISTORICAL SUMMARY OF WHALING IN THE OLDER TIMES.) En kort historisk Udsigt over Hvalfangsten i aeldre Tider. Gustav A. Guldberg. Folkevennen, Christiania, n.s., vol.13, pp.17-64, 1889.

A VANISHING RACE? (WHALING INDUSTRY) David Gunston. Mag. of the Future, Lond., vol.4, no.6, pp.52-57, illus., Jan., 1950.

THE HISTORY OF WHALING. Sidney F. Harmer. Proc. Linn. Soc. Lond., 140 Session, pp.51-95, 1928.

THE DEVELOPMENT OF WHALING IMPLEMENTS. P. Leroy Harwood. Publ. Marine Hist. Assoc., Inc., Mystic, Conn., vol.1, no.9, pp.157-167, illus., Mar.8, 1935.

WHALING. Charles B. Hawes. William Heinemann, Ltd., London, pp.viii, 358, illus., 1924.

ACONITE POISON WHALING IN ASIA AND AMERICA: AN ALEUTION TRANSFER TO THE NEW WORLD. Robert F. Heizer. Bur. Amer. Ethnology, Wash., D.C., Bull.153, Anthrop. Papers no.24, pp.415-468, pls.18-23A, 1943.

CATCHING WHALES WITH PATHOGENIC BACILLI. (WHALES SHOT BY EARLY NORWEGIANS WITH CROSSBOW DARTS COVERED WITH SEPTICEMIC BACILLI.) Robert F. Heizer. Ciba Symposia, Ciba Pharmaceutical Products, Inc., Summit, New Jersey, vol.5, nos.1-2, pp.1486-1488, illus., Apr.-May, 1943.

A PACIFIC ESKIMO INVENTION IN WHALE HUNTING IN HISTORIC TIMES. Robert F. Heizer. Amer. Anthropol., Menasha, n.s., vol.45, no.1, pp.120-122, pl.1, Jan.-Mar., 1943.

THE STORY OF WHALING. A PARABLE OF SOCIOLOGY. Johan Hjort. Sci. Monthly, vol.45, no.1, pp.19-34, figs.15, July, 1937.

THE OPTIMUM CATCH. ( DISCUSSION OF WHALING OPERATIONS AND THE POSSIBLE EFFECT ON WHALE POPULATIONS.) Johan Hjort, Gunnar Jahn, Per Ottestad. Scientific results of marine biological research, Oslo, no.7, pp.92-127, figs.59-74, May, 1933.

INTERNATIONAL WHALING STATISTICS. Edited by the Committee for Whaling Statistics appointed by the Norwegian Government, Oslo. I, pp.23, 1930; II, pp. 68, 1931; III, pp.31, 1932; IV, pp.48, 1933; V, pp.36, 1934; VI, pp.38, 1935; VII, pp. 54, 1936; VIII, pp.54, 1937; IX, pp.22, 1937; X, pp.56, 1937; XI, pp.36, 1938; XII, pp. 73, 1939; XIII, pp.27, 1938; XIV, pp.70, 1940; XV, pp.21, 1941; XVI, pp.139, 1942; XVII, pp.97, 1947; XVIII, pp.75, 1948; XIX, pp.43, 1948; XX, pp.63, 1949; XXI, pp.56, 1949, XXII, pp.74, 1949.(Nos. I-IV prepared by Johan Hjort, Gunnar Jahn, and Sigurd Risting; nos.V-VI by Gunnar Jahn, Johan Hjort, and Sigurd Risting; no.VII by Gunnar Jahn and Johan Hjort; nos.VIII-XII by Gunnar Jahn, Johan Hjort, and Harald B. Paulsen; nos.XIII-XXII by gunnar Jahn, B Birger Bergersen, and Harald B. Paulsen); XXIV, 71 pp., 1950; XXV, pp.71, 1951; XXVI by Jahn, Gunnar, Birger Bergerwen, Harald B. Paulsen, pp.82, 1951; XXVII by Gunnar Jahn, Birger Bergersen, Einar Vangstein, pp.75, 1952; XXIX Gunnar Jahn, Birger Bergersen, Einar Vangstein, pp.80, 1953; XXX Gunnar Jahn, Birger Bergersen, Einar Vangstein, pp.92, 1953.

COD AND WHALE FISHERIES. Thomas Jefferson. Report made to the House of Representative, Feb.1, 1791, Also report of Lorenzo Sabine Esq., on the principal fisheries of the American seas, being part of House Executive Document no.23, of the second session, Thirty-second Congress. Reprint, H.R. Misc. Doc., no.32, 42nd Congr., 2nd Sess., pp.1-272, 1876.

A HISTORY OF WHALE FISHERIES. J.T. Jenkins. H.F.& G. Witherby, London, 336 pp., illus., 1921.

(Review by F. A. Lucas of) A HISTORY OF THE WHALE FISHERIES, FROM THE BASQUE FISHERIES OF THE TENTH CENTURY TO THE HUNTING OF THE FINNER WHALE AT THE PRESENT DATE. J. T. Jenkins. Science, n.s., vol.56, pp. 109-111, July 28, 1922.

(NEW DESCRIPTION OF WHALE AND HERRING FISHING.) Nieuwe beschryving der walvisvangst en haringvisschery... Dirk de Jong. Met XXI. fraaye kaarten en plaaten vercierd, door D. de Jong, H. Kobel en M. Salieth... Amsteldam, J. Roos, etc., 1791.

DEVELOPMENT OF THE MODERN NORWEGIAN SMALL WHALE INDUSTRY. Age Jonsgard. Norsk Hvalfangst-Tidende (Norwegian Whaling Gazette), vol.44, no. 12, pp.697-718, illus., Dec., 1955.

THE INTERNATIONAL WHALING COMMISSION. Remington Kellogg. Pap. Pres. Int. Tech. Conf. Cons. Living Resources of the Sea, U.N., A/CONF. 10/7, pp.256-261, 1956.

REMARKS ON THE PROVISIONS OF THE WASHINGTON CONFERENCE RESPECTING UTILIZATION OF CAPTURED WHALES. H. Th. Knudtzon. Norsk Hvalfangst-Tidende (Norwegian Whaling Gazette), Sandefjord, vol.36, no.3, pp.90-96, Mar., 1947.

FOUR MONTHS ON A JAP WHALER. David R. McCracken. McBride, New York, 228 pp., illus., 1948.

THE WHALING INDUSTRY: ECONOMIC ASPECTS. W. C. MacKenzie. Canadian Geog. Jour., Ottawa, vol.38, no.3, pp.140-143, Mar., 1949.

ELECTRICAL METHOD OF KILLING WHALES. Robert Marsden. World Fishing, 1 (3): 97-100, 1 (4): 127-133, illus., 1952.

WHALING. Gavin Maxwell. Progress, Unilever Ltd., London, vol.43, no.238, pp.70-80, illus., Spring, 1953.

(ON THE CATCHING AND USE OF WHALES IN JAPAN.) Ueber den Fang und die Verwerthung der Walfische in Japan. K. Mobius. Sitz.-Ber. k. Preuss. Akad. Wiss., Berlin, vol.52, pp.1053-1072 (1-20 of separate), figs.9, 1893.

WHALING. NORTH AND SOUTH. Frank V. Morley, J. S. Hodgson. The Century Co., N.Y., pp.235, illus., 1926.

(A WHALE HUNTING TRIP THROUGH THE TROPICS TO THE ANTARCTIC OCEAN.) En Hvalfangerfaerd gennem Troperne til Sydishavet. Aage Krarup Nielsen. Copenhagen: H. Aschehoug & Co., 160 pp., 1921.

THE NORWEGIAN SMALL WHALE HUNTING. Harald Ostby. Norsk Hvalfangst-Tidende (Norwegian Whaling Gazette), Sandefjord, vol.42, no.12, pp.698-712, Dec., 1953.

AN ACCOUNT OF PRESENT-DAY OFF-SHORE WHALING. C. R. Patterson. Metropolitan Mag., New York, vol., no., pp.439-451, illus., July, 1907.

CALL ALL HANDS. (WHALING.) Theodore Pedersen. Alaska Sportsman, Ketchikan, vol.10, no.4, pp.12-13, 26-30, illus., Apr., 1944.

(GERMANY AGAIN HUNTING WHALE.) Deutschland wieder auf Walfang. Nicolaus Peters. Natur und volk, Frankfurt, vol.67, no.2, pp.546-554, figs.12, Nov.1, 1937.

THE WHALE FISHERIES OF WORLD. Charles Rabot. Ann. Rept. Smithsonian Inst., Wash., D.C., 1913, pp.481-489, pls.3, figs.3, 1914.

THE WHALING INDUSTRY. Lewis Radcliffe. Industrial and Engineering Chemistry, vol.25, no.7, pp.764-767, figs.2, July, 1933.

WHALING ADVENTURE. THE STORY OF THE EXCITING CAPTURE OF A GIANT OF THE SEA, WHOSE SKELETON MAY NOW BE SEEN AT THE AMERICAN MUSEUM. Jeanette Edwards Rattray. Junior Nat. Hist. Mag., vol.3, no.7, pp.13-14, 16, illus., Sept., 1938.

(THE HISTORY OF WHALING.) Av Hvalfangstens Historie. Sigurd Risttig. J.W. Cappelens Forlag, Kristiania, pp. 625, illus., 1922.

THE PURSUIT OF WHALES. James Ritchie. The Scottish Naturalist, no.176, pp.33-63, Mar.-Apr., 1929.

WHALING AND OLD SALEM: A CHRONICLE OF THE SEA, WITH AN ACCOUNT OF THE SEAL FISHERIES, EXCERPTS FROM WHALING LOGS AND WHALING STATISTICS. Frances Diane Robotti. Newcomb & Gauss Co., Salem, Mass., 192 pp., 1950.

MODERN WHALING AND ITS PROSPECTS. Johan T. Ruud. Fisheries Bull. Food & Agric. Organization United Nations, Rome, vol.5, no.5, pp.165-183, Sept.-Oct., 1952. (Reprinted in : Norsk Hvalfangst Tidende (Norwegian Whaling Gazette): Sandfjord, vol.41, no.12, pp.649-662, Dec., 1952.)

"THAR SHE BLOWS!" WHALING AGES, GOLDEN AND OTHERWISE. Ivan T. Sanderson. Nature Mag., Wash., vol.40, no.1, pp.8-13, 50, illus., Jan., 1947.

(WHALE CATCH AND POPULATION.) Walfang und Walbestand. K. Schubert. Fette Seifen Anstrichmittel, Hamburg, vol.56, no.7, pp.568-573, illus., 1954.

(THE JOURNAL OF WILLIAM SCORESBY THE YOUNGER CONCERNING A WHALING TRIP.) William Scoresby's des Juengern Tagebuch einer Reise auf den Wallfischfang... 1822. William Scoresby. Hamburg, pp.xvi, 414, xvii-xviii, 9 pls., 1 map, 1825.

THE OLD DUTCH WHALERS. Thomas Sheppard. Hull Museum Publ., Hull, England, no.202, pp.1-20, figs.25, 1939.

ON THE WHALE FISHERY FROM SCOTLAND, WITH SOME ACCOUNT OF THE CHANGES IN THAT INDUSTRY AND OF THE SPECIES HUNTED. Thomas Southwell. Ann. Scot. Nat. Hist., Edinburgh, pp.77-89, pl.4, Apr., 1904.

THE SEA HUNTERS: THE NEW ENGLAND WHALEMEN DURING TWO CENTURIES, 1635-1835. Edouard A. Stackpole. Lippincott, 510 pp., illus., 1953.

JAPANESE WHALING INDUSTRY PRIOR TO 1946. William M. Terry. Fishery Leaflet U.S. Fish and Wildlife Service, no.371, pp.47, illus., 1950.

LOG OF THE BARK "THOMAS POPE" - NEW BEDFORD, ROBERT P. REYNARD, MASTER. "Thomas Pope" (logbook of). 1856-1859.

ON WHALES LANDED AT THE SCOTTISH WHALING STATIONS DURING THE YEARS 1908-1914 AND 1920-1927. D'Arcy W. Thompson. Scotland Fish. Board, Sci. Invest., no.3, pp.3-39, figs.18, 1928.

A HISTORY OF THE AMERICAN WHALE FISHERY. Walter S. Tower. Publ. Univ. Pennsylvania; ser. Pol. Econ. Pub. Law, no.20, 1907.

A WHALING TRIP. R. W. Towerre. Wisconsin Conservationist, vol.4, no.1, pp.8, 10, Mar. (May 11), 1922.

TWENTIETH CENTURY WHALING. C. H. Townsend. Bull. New York Zool. Soc., vol.33, no.1, Jan.-Feb., 1930, pp.3-31, illus., 1930.

THE WHALING SITUATION. C. H. Townsend. Science, vol.72, no.1878, pp.652-653, Dec.26, 1930.

WHERE THE NINETEENTH CENTURY WHALER MADE HIS CATCH. C. H. Townsend. Bull. New York Zool. Soc., vol.34, no.6, pp.173-179, illus., map, Nov.-Dec., 1931.

"THERE GOES FLUKES." THE STORY OF NEW BEDFORD'S LAST WHALER BEING THE NARRATIVE OF THE VOYAGE OF SCHOONER JOHN R. MANTA ON HATTERAS GROUNDS 1925, AND WHALEMEN'S TRUE YARNS OF ADVENTURES IN OLD DEEP-SEA WHALING DAYS. William H. Tripp. Published by Reynolds Printing Co., New Bedford, Mass., pp.1-262, illus., 1938.

STUDIES OF THE RELATION BETWEEN THE WHALING GROUNDS AND THE HYDROGRAPHICAL CONDITIONS. (I). Michitaka Uda. Sci. Repts. Whales Research Inst., Tokyo, no.9, pp.179-187, June, 1954.

FOUR YEARS ABOARD THE WHALESHIP. EMBRACING CRUISES IN THE PACIFIC, ATLANTIC, INDIAN, AND ANTARCTIC OCEANS, IN THE YEARS 1855, '6, '7, '8, '9. William B. Whitecar, Jr. J. B. Lippincott & Co., Phila., pp.xii, 413, 1860.

THE LAST OF THE WHALERS. John J. Wright. Home Mag., pp.404-407, May, 1898.

ABRIDGEMENT OF SERIES OF ARTICLES ON WHALING INDUSTRY PUBLISHED IN COURRIER MARITIME DE FRANCE. Bol. Pescas Inst. Español. Oceanogr., vol. 14, no.152, pp.113-123, 1929.

CAPTAIN AHAB IN MODERN DRESS. THE 1932 WHALER COMMANDS 20,000-TON FACTORY SHIPS, BOMBS HIS WHALES, DEPLORES THE PASSING OF CORSETS, AND REJOICES IN THE POPULARITY OF MARGARINE. Fortune, Chicago, vol.6, no.4, pp.52-59, 106-107, figs. (8 in color), Oct., 1932.

ELECTROCUTION OF WHALES. Fishing News No.2040, pp.10-11, illus., 1952.

GERMAN WHALING. Whaling Committee of the Chambers of Industry and Commerce, (pp.9, Sections in German and in English), 1947.

THE HISTORY OF THE WHALE, GIVING GRAPHIC ACCOUNTS OF ITS PURSUIT, ESCAPE, RECOVERY, AND SUBSEQUENT ADVENTURES. Dundee, 15 pp., illus., Dundee, 1884.

INTERNATIONAL CO-OPERATION IN WHALING. Fisheries Newsletter, Ministry Post War Reconstruction, Cronulla, vol.5, no.1, pp.10-13, illus., Feb., 1946.

THE INTERNATIONAL WHALING CONVENTION OF 1946. Norsk Hvalfangst-Tidende (Norwegian Whaling Gazette), Sandefjord, vol.41, no.9, pp.469-479, illus., Sept., 1952.

JAPANESE WHALING. Foreign Office, Japanese Government, Tokyo, pp.1-17, Jan., 1949.

THE JAPANESE WHALING INDUSTRY. Norsk Hvalfangst-Tidende (Norwegian Whaling Gazette), Sandefjord, vol.43, no.11, pp.625-631, illus., Nov., 1954. (In Norwegian and English.)

JAPAN'S WHALING INDUSTRY. Science News Letter, Washington, vol.50, no.8, p.119, Aug.24, 1946.

LEVIATHAN HUNTED BY MODERN METHODS; WHALES KILLED AND IMMEDIATELY PROCESSED. Illus. London News, vol.210, no.5639, pp.512-513, illus., May 17, 1947.

MODERN WHALING. Life, Chicago, vol. 32, no.12, pp.56-61, illus., Mar.24, 1952.

NOTE ON METHODS OF KILLING WHALES. Naturalist, London, no.792, p.156, July, 1941.

A PICTORIAL STORY ON WHALING. Canadian Fisherman, Montreal, vol.34, no.8, p.26, 1947.

SOME MATERIALS SHOWING THE STATUS OF WHALING OF JAPAN (II). Fisheries Agency Japanese Govt., Tokyo, Publ. Japan Whaling Assoc., pp.19, illus., 1952.

THE WAR AND WHALING. Jour. Soc. Preservation Fauna of Empire, Hertford, n.s., pt.38, pp.27-28, Dec., 1939.

WHALE FISHERY - REVIEW OF THE WHALE FISHERY, 1876-1886. Published by I.H. Bartlett & Sons, New Bedford, Mass., pp. 3 (each).

WHALING MASTERS VOYAGES, 1731-1925. Reynolds Printing, Mass., pp.314, illus., 1938.

Whaling, Regulation of

THE THREATENED WHALE. James Blake. Jour. Soc. Preservation Fauna Empire, Hertford, n.s., pt.33, pp.65-70, Mar., 1938.

INTERNATIONAL AGREEMENT FOR THE REGULATION OF WHALING. J. O. Borley. Nature, London, vol.140, no.3535, pp.180-181, July 31, 1937.

(THE WHALING INDUSTRY AND THE PROTECTION OF CETACEANS.) L'industrie baleinière et la protection des cétacés. Paul Budker. Pro Natura, Bâle, Switzerland, vol.1, no.1, pp.2-10, illus., Aug., 1948.

CONSERVATION OF WHALES--A WORLD-WIDE PROJECT. H. J. Deason. Trans. N.A. Wildl. Conf., 11: 260-273, 1946.

(ON THE NECESSITY OF PROTECTING THE GREAT CETACEANS OF THE PACIFIC.) De la nécessité de protéger les grands Cétaces dans le Pacifique. A. Gruvel. Third Pan-Pacific Sci. Congress, Tokyo, vol.1, pp.1074-1078, (1926) 1928.

A CALL FOR THE PROTECTION OF THE WHALE. Kyo Hayasi. Proc. Third Pan-Pacific Sci. Congress, Tokyo, vol.1, pp. 1079-1085, figs.3 (1926), 1928.

MINUTES OF THE MEETINGS OF THE WHALING CONFERENCE HELD AT THE NORWEGIAN MINISTRY OF COMMERCE, OSLO, ON THE 4TH AND 5TH OCTOBER, 1935, TO DISCUSS THE CONTROL OF PELAGIC WHALING IN THE ANTARCTIC DURING THE SEASON 1936-37. Johan Hjort (Chairman). Hvalradets Skrifter, Sci. Res. Marine Biol. Research, Oslo, no. 12, pp. i-xvi, 1935.

THE COUNCIL FOR THE CONSERVATION OF WHALES. A. Brazier Howell. Jour. Mam., vol.11, no.1, pp.100-103, Feb., 1930; no.2, p.263, May, 1930.

COMMENTS ON THE WHALING TREATY ACT (S.3413). A. Brazier Howell. Jour. Mam., vol.17, no.3, p.314, Aug., 1936.

THE LAST PHASE IN THE HISTORY OF WHALING. HEARING BEFORE A SPECIAL COMMITTEE ON WILD LIFE RESOURCES. Remington Kellogg. United States Senate, Seventy-Second Congress, first session. On the Conservation of whales and other marine mammals. Washington, D.C., pp. 20-29, Mar.20, 1931.

THE PASSING OF THE WHALE. F. A. Lucas. Supp. Zool. Soc. Bull., no.3, pp. 445-448, July, 1908.

LO, THE POOR WHALE! Robert Cushman Murphy. Science, 91 (2364): 373-376, Apr. 19, 1940.

HEARING BEFORE A SPECIAL COMMITTEE ON WILD LIFE RESOURCES, U.S. SENATE 72nd CONG., 1st SESS. ON THE CONSERVATION OF WHALES AND OTHER MARINE MAMMALS, MARCH 20, 1931. T. S. Palmer. 1931.

THE DOOM OF THE GREAT WHALES. W. P. Pycraft. Illus. London News, vol. 186, no.5004, p.436, figs.3, Mar.16, 1935.

ECONOMICS OF THE WHALING INDUSTRY WITH RELATIONSHIP TO THE CONVENTION FOR THE REGULATION OF WHALING. Lewis Radcliffe. Special Committee on the Conservation of Wild Life Resources, United States Senate, 73d Congress, 2d Session, pp.79, July 27, 1933.

STATUS OF INTERNATIONAL CONVENTION FOR PROTECTION OF WHALES. Lewis Radcliffe. Jour. Mam., vol.13, no.3, pp. 251-255, Aug., 1932.

OBSERVATIONS ON THE USE OF SIZE LIMITS IN THE REGULATION OF WHALING. Johan T. Ruud. Norsk Hvalfangst-Tidende (Norwegian Whaling Gazette) Sandefjord, vol.43, no.4, pp.192-198, Apr., 1954. (In Norwegian and English.)

(SUGGESTIONS ON MEASURES TO BE TAKEN IN THE CONSERVATION OF WHALES.) Vorschlaege zu Schonmassnahmen fuer Wale. W. Schnakenbeck. Der Zoologische Garten, Leipzig (N.F.), vol.2, pts.4-6, pp.135-137, 1929.

(THE SIGNIFICANCE OF BIOLOGICAL INVESTIGATION FOR THE PRESERVATION OF THE WHALE.) De betekenis van het biologisch onderzoek voor het behoud van de walvissenstand. E. J. Slijper. Nederlandsche Commissie voor Internationale Natuurbescherming, Amsterdam, Mededelingen no.15, pp.1-8, figs.2, Jan., 1955.

A TEMPORARY RESPITE FOR THE WHALE. C. H. Townsend. Science, n.s., vol.75, no.1941, p.288, Mar.11, 1932.

CONTROL OF THE WHALING INDUSTRY. Nature, London, vol.134, no.3379, pp.174-175, Aug.4, 1934.

CONVENTION AND PROTOCOLS DEALING WITH THE REGULATIONS OF WHALING. Rept. to Accompany Executives L, K, and P, 80th Cong., 1st Sess., Exec. Rept. no. 6, 3 pp., 1947.

THE INTERNATIONAL WHALING CONFERENCE, WASHINGTON, D.C. NOVEMBER 20-DECEMBER 2, 1946. Norsk Hvalfangst-Tidende (Norwegian Whaling Gazette), Sandefjord, Arg.36, no.1, pp.5-23, illus., Jan., 1947.

INTERNATIONAL WHALING CONFERENCE. DRAFT PROTOCOL ON WHALING CONTROL. Fisheries Newsletter, Ministry Post War Reconstruction, Cronulla, vol.5, no.1, p.8, figs.3, Feb., 1946.

PROTECTION OF WHALES (FREDNING OF HVAL. TRANSLATED BY HERMAN JACOBSON). Bull. U.S. Fish Comm., vol.1, pp. 17-19, Apr.13, 1881.

WHALING. CONVENTION BETWEEN THE UNITED STATES OF AMERICA AND OTHER GOVERNMENTS. U.S. Govt., Dept. of State, Publ.3383, pp.17, 1949.

Platanistidae

ON THE GANGETIC DOLPHIN. D. F. Eschricht. Ann. and Mag. Nat. Hist. Lond., ser.2, vol.9, pp.161-292, pls. 5-7, Mar., 1852.

(ON THE GANGETIC DOLPHIN.) Om Gangesdelphinen - Tillaegs--Afhandling til Sammes Undersoegelser over Hvaldyrene. D. F. Eschricht. Videnskabernes Selskabs Skrifter, Nat. og mathematisk, vol.2, pp.3-43, pls.3, Kjoebenhavn, 1851.

BOTO OF THE AMAZON. Arthur H. Fisher. Nature Mag., Wash., D.C., vol. 34, no.9, pp.510-512, Nov., 1941.

DESCRIPTION OF THE SKELETON OF INIA GEOFFRENSIS AND OF THE SKULL OF PONTOPORIA BLAINVILLII, WITH REMARKS ON THE SYSTEMATIC POSITION OF THESE ANIMALS IN THE ORDER CETACEA. William H. Flower. Trans. Zool. Soc. Lond., vol.6, pt.3, pp.87-116, pls.25-28, 1866.

MEMOIR ON INIA AND PONTOPORIA. William H. Flower. Proc. Zool. Soc. Lond., p.426, 1866.

SOME INTERESTING POINTS IN THE ANATOMY OF THE FRESHWATER DOLPHIN LIPOTES AND ITS ALLIES. M.A.C. Hinton. Proc. Linn. Soc. Lond., 148th sess., 1935-36, pt.3, pp.183-185, Aug.26, 1936.

PRELIMINARY NOTE ON THE AFFINITIES OF THE GENUS LIPOTES. M.A.C. Hinton, W. P. Pycraft. Ann. and Mag. Nat. Hist., ser.9, vol.10, pp.232-234, Aug., 1922.

A DESCRIPTION OF THE TEETH OF THE DELPHINUS GANGETICUS. Everard Home. Philos. Trans., pp.417-419, pl.20, 4 figs., London, 1818.

THE "WHITE-FLAG" DOLPHIN OF THE TUNG TING LAKE. Charles M. Hoy. China Jour. Sci. and Arts, vol.1, pp.154-157, 1 pl., Mar., 1922.

SUPPLEMENTARY OBSERVATIONS ON THE SKULL OF THE FOSSIL PORPOISE ZARHACHIS FLAGELLATOR COPE. Remington Kellogg. Proc. U.S. Nat. Mus., vol.67, art.28, pp.1-18, pls.1-5, Feb.24, 1926.

(ON A HAND SKELETON WITH SIX FINGERS IN THE AMAZONE-DELPHIN (INIA AMAZONICA MARTIUS).) Ueber ein Handskelett mit sechs Fingern bei dem Amazonas-Delphin (Inia amazonica Martius). W. Leisewitz. Sitzungsber. Gesell. Morph. Physiol., Munich, pp.1-7, figs.1-3, 1921.

SOME REMARKS ON A SKELETON OF INIA GEOFFRENSIS BLAINV. Einar Loennberg. Arkiv foer Zool., vol.20A, no.11, pp.1-3, pl.1, Dec.19, 1928.

A NEW RIVER-DOLPHIN FROM CHINA (WITH 13 PLATES). Gerrit S. Miller, Jr. Smiths. Misc. Coll., publ.2486, vol.68, no.9, 1918.

INIA GEOFFRENSIS (BLAINVILLE). Alipio de Miranda-Ribeiro. Arquivos do Museu Nacional, Rio de Janeiro, vol.37, pp.23-58, figs.25, 1943.

(REMARKS ON A NEW CETACEAN GENUS OF THE RIVERS OF CENTRAL SOUTH AMERICA.) Notice sur un nouveau genre de Cetace, des rivieres du centre de l'amerique meridionale. A. Orbigny. Paris, Mus. Hist. Nat. Nouv. Ann. III, pp.28-36, pl.3, 1834.

(ASYMMETRY IN PLATANISTA GANGETICA.) O asymetryi czaszki wielorybow. Stefan Sterling. Sprawozdan z Posiedzen Towarzystiva Nauk., Warszawskiego, vol. 3, Zesz.5, pp.231-235, figs.1-2, 1910.

THE MORPHOLOGY OF THE MANUS IN PLATANISTA GANGETICA, THE DOLPHIN OF THE GANGES. William Turner. Proc. Roy. Soc., Edinburgh, Sess. 1909-1910, vol. 30, pt. 6, no. 35, pp. 508-514, pls. 1-4, Aug. 1, 1910.

Ziphiidae

(NOTE ON THE APPEARANCE AND STRANDING OF A HYPEROODON ROSTRATUS AT SAINTE-ANNE-DO-LA-POCATIERE.) Note sur l'apparition et l'echouage d'un Hyperoodon rostratus a Sainte-Anne-de-la-Pocatiere. Commandant Beauge. Ann. Report Provancher Soc. Nat. Hist. Canada, Quebec, 1941, pp. 23-30, figs. 10, 1942.

(ACCOUNT OF THE CETACEANS OF THE GENUS ZIPHIUS CUVIER.) Memoire sur les Cetaces du genre Ziphius, Cuvier. P. Fischer. Nouvelles Archives du Museum, vol. 3, pp. 41-78, pls. 4.

A FURTHER CONTRIBUTION TO THE KNOWLEDGE OF THE EXISTING ZIPHIOID WHALES. GENUS MESOPLODON. William H. Flower. Trans. Zool. Soc. London, vol. 10, pt. 9, no. 2, pp. 415-437, figs. 4, pls. 3, Aug. 1, 1878.

NOTICE OF A MEMOIR ON THE EXISTING ZIPHIOID WHALES, OF THE GENUS MESOPLODON. William H. Flower. Proc. Zool. Soc. Lond., pt. 4, p. 684, 1877.

NOTICE OF A MEMOIR ON THE ZIPHIOID WHALES, AND ON THE SKELETON OF BERARDIUS ARNOUXI. William H. Flower. Proc. Zool. Soc. Lond., p. 631, 1871.

ON THE RECENT ZIPHIOID WHALES, WITH A DESCRIPTION OF THE SKELETON OF BERARDIUS ARNOUXI. William H. Flower. Trans. Zool. Soc. Lond., vol. 8, pt. 3, pp. 203-234, pls. 27, 28, 29, 1871.

ON THE WHALES OF THE GENUS HYPEROODON. William H. Flower. Proc. Zool. Soc. Lond., pp. 722-726, Dec. 19, 1882.

REMARKS UPON DR. VON HAAST'S COMMUNICATION ON MESOPLODON FLOWERI. William H. Flower. Proc. Zool. Soc. Lond., pp. 485-486, 1876.

REMARKS UPON DR. VON HAAST'S COMMUNICATION OF ZIPHIUS NOVAE-ZEALANDIAE. William H. Flower. Proc. Zool. Soc. Lond., pp. 477-478, 1876.

ON A SPECIMEN OF THE SOUTHERN BOTTLE-NOSED WHALE, HYPEROODON PLANIFRONS. F. C. Fraser. Discovery Reports, Cambridge, vol. 23, pp. 19-36, figs. 11, Mar., 1945.

(NOTES ON AN ORCA, WHICH WAS FOUND ON THE COAST OF BOHUSLAN IN DECEMBER 1871.) Anteckningar angaende en Orca som antraeffats vid Bohuslaenska kusten i December 1871. Otto von Friesen. Kongl. Vetenskaps-Akademiens Foerhandlingar, no. 10, Stockholm, pp. 3-16, pls. 12-15, 1872.

NOTES ON THE CHARACTERS AND HABITS OF THE BOTTLENOSE WHALE (HYPEROODON ROSTRATUS). David Gray. Proc. Zool. Soc. Lond., pp. 726-731, figs. 9, Dec. 19, 1882.

THE BOTTLENOSE WHALE. R. W. Gray. Naturalist, London, no. 791, pp. 129-132, June, 1941.

(CONTRIBUTIONS TO KNOWLEDGE OF MESOPLODON BIDENS SOW.) Bidrag til kjendskaben om Mesoplodon bidens, Sow. James A. Grieg. Bergens Mus. Aarbog 1904, no. 3, pp. 1-39, figs. 14, 1904.

MESOPLODON BIDENS, SOW. James A. Grieg. Bergens Mus. Aarbog, 1897, no. 5, pp. 3-31, figs. 6, pl. 1, 1897.

(SOME NOTES ON A KILLER WHALE HUNT AT BILDØSTRØMMEN IN JANUARY 1904.) Nogle notiser fra et spaekhuggerstaeng ved Bildøstrømmen i januar 1904. James A. Grieg. Bergens Mus. Aarbog 1906, no. 2, pp. 3-28, figs. 8, tables, 1906.

(THE WHALE-HUNT AT BILDOEN, APRIL 15, 1889.) Hvalstaenget ved Bildoen den 15de April, 1889. James A. Grieg. Bergens mus., Aarsberetning 1889, no. 3, p. 17, figs., tables, 1889.

(RUDIMENTARY REAR LEGS OF A FETAL WHALE.) Rudimentaere baglemmer hos hvaldyrene i fosterlivet. G. Guldberg. Chirstiania Videnskaba-Selskabs Forhl., no. 6, 7 pp., 1894.

NOTES ON MESOPLODON FLOWERI. Julius von Haast. Trans. New Zealand Inst., vol. 9, art. 55, pp. 442-450, pls. 25-26, 1876; Proc. Zool. Soc. Lond., pp. 478-486, pls. XLV, XLVI, 1876.

NOTES ON ZIPHIUS (EPIODON) NOVAE-ZEALANDISE, VON HAAST- GOOSE-BACKED WHALE. Julius von Haast. Trans. New Zealand Inst., vol. 12, art. 21, pp. 241-246, pl. 8, 1879.

ON MESOPLODON AND OTHER BEAKED WHALES. Sidney F. Harmer. Proc. Zool. Soc. Lond., pp. 541-587, 4 pls., 3 figs., July, 1924.

(SOTALIA TEEUSZII N. SP., A PLANT-EATING (?) DOLPHIN OF THE CAMERONS.) Sotalia teeuszii n. sp., ein pflanzenfressender (?) Dolphin aus Kamerun. Willy Kuekenthal. Zool. Jahrb. Jena, vol. 6, pp. 442-446, pl. 21, 1892.

(A SUMMARY OF MAMMALS BELONGING TO THE WHALE FAMILY (CETACEA) WHICH HAVE BEEN FOUND IN SWEDEN AND NORWAY.) Ofversigt af de inom Skandinavien (Sverige och Norrige) antraeffade Hvalartade daggdjur (Cetacea). Wilhelm Lilljeborg. Upsala Univ. Arsskrift, 1862, Math. and Naturvetenskap., pt. 1, pp. 1-80, 1862.

(THE ORIGIN OF THE WHALES.) Om hvalarnes haerstamning. Einar Loennberg. K. Svenska Vetenskapsakad. Arsbok, Uppsala, 1910, pp. 219-259, figs. 1-8, 1910.

A RARE BEAKED WHALE. R. A. Lydekker. Proc. Zool. Soc. London, 1911.

(COMMENTS ON A WHALE STRANDED AT BOHUSLAN.) Om den i Bohuslaen strandade hvalen. A. W. Malm. Kongl. Vetenskaps-Akademiens Foerhandlingar, Stockholm, 1866, no. 3, pp. 29-32, 1866.

(ON SOWERBY'S WHALE.) Om Sowerby's Hval. A. H. Malm. Kongl. Vetenskaps-Akademiens Foerhandlingar, Stockholm, no. 5, pp. 121-154, pl. 9, 1885.

(SKELETON PARTS OF A WHALE COLLECTED DURING THE VEGA-EXPEDITION 1878-1880.) Skelettdelar af Hval insamlade under Expeditionen med Vega 1878-1880. A. W. Malm. Konal. Svenska vet.-Akad. Handlingar, Stockholm, vol. 8, no. 4, pp. 1-114, figs. 50, 1883.

(SOME NOTES ON WHALES IN GENERAL AND BALAENOPTERA CAROLONAE IN PARTICULAR.) Naegra blad om hvaldjur i allmanhet och Balaenoptera carolonae i synnerhet. A. W. Malm. Goteborg, 20 pp., 1866.

(NOTE ON MESOPLODON MIRUS.) Note sur le Mesoplodon mirus. G. Mousset, R. Duperier. Bull. Centre Etudes Recherches Sci., Biarritz, 1 (1): 33-39, 1956.

(THE GREENLAND WHALE OF GULDHEDEN AND THE SWEDENBORG WHALE OF LANDERIGATAN.) Groenlandsvalen fran Guldheden och Swedenborgsvalen fran Landerigatan. Orvar Nybelin. Goeteborgs Mus. Arstryck, pp. 103-115, figs. 7, 1946.

SOME REMARKS ON THE BOTTLENOSE WHALE (HYPEROODON). Axel Ohlin. Kongl. Fysiogr. Saelisk. I Lund Handlingar vol. 4, Lunds. Univ. Arskr. 1893, vol. 29, pp. 1-13, pl., 1893.

A RARE WHALE IN TROPICAL SEAS (MESOPLODON EUROPAEUS). Jessie J. Rankin. Everglades Nat. Hist., Coral Gables, vol. 3, no. 1, pp. 25-31, illus., Mar., 1955.

NOTES ON THE TAXONOMY AND OSTEOLOGY OF TWO SPECIES OF MESOPLODON (M. EUROPAEUS GERVAIS, M. MIRUS TRUE). H. C. Raven. Amer. Mus. Novitates, no. 905, pp. 30, figs. 15, Jan. 14, 1937.

(MESOPLODON BIDENS, A NEW ADDITION TO THE DANISH SEA-FAUNA.) Mesoplodon bidens, en Tilvaext til den danske Havfauna. J. Reinhardt. K. Danske Vidensk. Selsk. Forhandl., pp. 63-72, pl. 2, July 10, 1880.

(NINE PICTURES ILLUSTRATING THE STRUCTURE OF THE WHALES, IN CONNECTION WITH PUBLISHED SPEECHES BY THE LATE DR. D. F. ESCHRICHT, MINISTER.) Ni Tavler til Oplysning af Hvaldyrenes Bygning, udforte til utrykte Foredrag af afdode Etatsraad Dr. D. F. Eschricht. (Med tilhorende Forklaring.) J. Reinhardt. Vidensk. Selsk. Skr. 5, Raekke, naturvidenskabelig og mathematisk, ser. 9, vol. 1, pp. 3-14, pls. 9, Kjobenhavn, 1869.

(COMPARATIVE ANATOMY AND SYSTEMATICS AS REGARDS THE CETACEANS. A CONTRIBUTION TO THE COMPARATIVE ANATOMY OF THE BLOOD VESSELS, NERVES, AND MUSCULAR SYSTEM, AS WELL AS BODY SKELETON, OF MAMMALS, WITH STUDIES OF THE THEORY OF EXTINCTION AND FETAL DEVELOPMENT.) Die Cetaceen vergleichend-anatomisch und systematisch. Ein Beitrag zur vergleichenden Anatomie des Blutgefaess-Nerven-und Muskelsystems, sowie des Rumpfskelettes der Saeugetiere, mit Studien ueber die Theorie des Aussterbens und der Foetalisation. E. J. Slijper. Capita Zoologica, Hague, vols. 6-7, pp. xv, 590, figs. 256, July-Dec., 1936.

ON THE BEAKED OR BOTTLE-NOSE WHALE (HYPEROODON ROSTRATUS). Thomas Southwell. Trans. Norfolk and Norwich Nat. Soc., Norwich, vol. 3, pp. 476-481, 1883.

(THE HYPEROODON (HYPEROODON ROSTRATUS PONTOP.) AND THE SMALL BALAENOPTERIDAE OF THE FAR EAST.) A. G. Tomilin. Bull. Soc. Nat. Moscou, sect. biol., n. s., vol. 47, no. 3, pp. 210-217, 1 table, 1938. (In Russian with French résumé.)

(THE KAMCHATKA SPERM WHALE.) A. G. Tomilin. Zool. Zhurnal, vol. 15, no. 3, pp. 483-519, figs. 2, Nov. 13, 1936. (In Russian, with German summary.)

AN ACCOUNT OF THE BEAKED WHALES OF THE FAMILY ZIPHIDAE IN THE COLLECTION OF THE UNITED STATES NATIONAL MUSEUM, WITH REMARKS ON SOME SPECIMENS IN OTHER AMERICAN MUSEUMS. Frederick W. True. Smithson. Inst., U.S. Nat. Mus., Bull. 73, vol. 89, p. 89, pl. 42, 1910.

ON MESOPLODON LAYARDI. C. W. de Vis. Proc. Roy. Soc. Queensland, vol. 1, pt. 19, 2 p., illus., 1885.

(ZOOLOGICAL NOTES ON A BEAKED WHALE.) Notice Zoologique sur Un Hyperodon. C. Wesmael. Brux. Acad. Sci. Mem., vol. 13, pp. 1-13, pls. 2, 1841.

(A MASS DEATH OF PHOCAENA COMMUNIS.) Massdoed av tumlare Phocaena communis. Fauna och Flora, Stockholm, Haeft 6, pp. 284-285, 1940.

(SOME PERSONAL CONTRIBUTIONS TO THE LITERATURE ON WHALES FOUND ALONG THE COAST.) Nog eene Bijdrage tot de Berigten over de Walvischaardige Dieren op onze Kusten. Algemeene Konst-- en Letter-Bode, no. 38, pp. 119-120, 1836.

The Americas

SOWERBY'S WHALE ON THE AMERICAN COAST. Glover M. Allen. Amer. Nat., vol. 30, no. 473, pp. 357-370, figs. 4, 1906.

TRUE'S BEAKED WHALE IN NOVA SCOTIA. Glover M. Allen. Jour. Mam., vol. 20, no. 2, pp. 259-260, May, 1939.

NOTICE OF A RARE ZIPHIOID WHALE, MESOPLODON DENSIROSTRIS, ON THE NEW JERSEY COAST. Roy Chapman Andrews. Proc. Acad. Nat. Sci. Phila., pp. 437-440, pls. 16-18, May, 1914.

(NOTICE ON THE APPEARANCE AND STRANDING OF A HYPERODON ROSTRATUS AT SAINT-ANNE-DE-LA-POCATIERE.)

Note sur l'apparition et l'echouage d'un Hyperodon rostratus a Sainte-Anne-de-la-Pocatiere. Cmdt. Beauge. Ann. Report Soc. Provancher Hist. Nat. Canada, Quebec, 1941, pp.23-30, illus., July 14, 1942.

A SECOND SPECIMEN OF TRUE'S BEAKED WHALE, MESOPLODON MIRUS TRUE, FROM NORTH CAROLINA. H. H. Brimley. Jour. Mam., Balto., vol.24, no.2, pp.199-203, pls.2, May, 1943.

A BEAKED WHALE STRANDED ON THE COAST OF BRITISH COLUMBIA. I. McT. Cowan. Jour. Mam., vol.25, no.1, pp. 93-94, pl.1, Feb.23, 1945.

BAIRD'S BEAKED WHALE AT SANTA CRUZ, CALIFORNIA. M. E. McLellian Davidson. Jour. Mam., vol.10, no.4, pp. 356-358, Nov., 1929.

A SKULL OF MESOPLODON GERVAISI (DESLONGCHAMPS) FROM TRINIDAD, WEST INDIES. F. C. Fraser. Ann. and Mag. Nat. Hist., ser.12, vol.8, no.92, pp. 624-630, Aug., 1955.

BLAINVILLE'S BEAKED WHALE, MESOPLODON DENSIROSTRIS, ON THE TEXAS COAST. Gordon Gunter. Jour. Mam., 36 (4): 573-574, Dec.14, 1955.

FIRST RECORDS OF TWO BEAKED WHALES, MESOPLODON BOWIOINI AND ZIPHIUS CAVIROSTRIS, FROM THE PACIFIC COAST OF THE UNITED STATES. Carl L. Hubbs. Jour. Mam., vol.27, no.3, pp.242-255, pls.4, Aug.14, 1946.

PROBABLE RECORD OF THE BEAKED WHALE, ZIPHIUS CAVIROSTRIS, IN BAJA CALIFORNIA. Carl L. Hubbs. Jour. Mam., vol.32, no.3, pp.365-366, Aug.23, 1951.

A BEAKED WHALE, MESOPLODON SP., FROM THE PRIBILOFS. William L. Jellison. Jour. Mam., vol.34, no.2, pp. 249-251, illus., May 14, 1953.

SOME MARINE RECORDS FROM NOVA SCOTIAN FISHING WATERS. R. A. McKenzie. Proc. Nova Scotian Inst. Sci., Halifax, vol.20, pt.2, pp.42-46, Oct.17, 1940.

BEAKED WHALE (MESOPLODON) FROM CALIFORNIA, WITH COMMENTS ON TAXONOMY. Robert T. Orr. Jour. Mam., 34 (2): 239-249, illus., May, 1953.

RARITY OF THE DEEP (MESOPLODON STRANDED ON CALIFORNIA COAST). Robert T. Orr. Pacific Discovery, Berkeley, vol.3, no.6, pp.13-51, illus., Nov.-Dec., 1950.

A SECOND RECORD FOR CUVIER'S WHALE FROM THE PACIFIC COAST OF UNITED STATES. Robert T. Orr. Jour. Mam., vol.29, no.4, pp.420-421, Dec.31, 1948.

TWO RECORDS OF BERARDIUS BAIRDI FROM THE COAST OF BRITISH COLUMBIA. Gordon C. Pike. Jour. Mam., vol.34, no. 1, pp.98-104, illus., Feb.19, 1953.

BEAKED WHALES. H. C. Raven. Nat. Hist., New York, vol.34, no.5, p.501, Sept., 1934.

CUVIER'S BEAKED WHALE (ZIPHIUS CAVIROSTRIS) FROM OREGON. A. I. Roest, R. M. Storm, P. C. Dumas. Jour. Mam., vol.34, no.2, pp.251-252, 1 table, May 14, 1953.

NOTES ON THREE BEAKED WHALES FROM THE ALEUTIAN ISLANDS. Victor B. Scheffer. Pacific Science, Honolulu, vol.3, no.4, p.353, illus., Oct., 1949.

THE BEAKED WHALE BERARDIUS ON THE WASHINGTON COAST. J. W. Slipp, Ford Wilke. Jour. Mam., vol.34, no.1, pp.105-113, illus., Feb.19, 1953.

THE BOTTLE-NOSE WHALE FISHERY IN THE NORTH ATLANTIC OCEAN. Thomas Southwell. Report W. S. Comm. Fish and Fisheries for 1882, pp.221-227, 1884.

DESCRIPTION OF MESOPLODON MIRUM, A BEAKED WHALE RECENTLY DISCOVERED ON THE COAST OF NORTH CAROLINA. Frederick W. True. Proc. U.S. Nat. Mus., vol.45, publ.2007, pp. 651-657, pls.52-57, Nov.29, 1913.

OCCURRENCE OF THREE SPECIES OF BEAKED WHALES OF THE GENUS MESOPLODON ON THE ATLANTIC COAST OF THE UNITED STATES. Frederick W. True. Science, n.s., vol.26, no. 675, p.796, Dec.6, 1907.

ZIPHIUS ON THE NEW JERSEY COAST. Frederick W. True. Science, vol.2, no. 37, p.540, Oct.19, 1883.

RECORD OF A BEAKED WHALE FROM BALANDRA. T. F. Twist, D. M. Twist. Jour. Trinidad Field Nat. Club, 1956: 26-27, 1956.

MESOPLODON MIRUS IN NEW JERSEY, WITH ADDITIONAL NOTES ON THE NEW JERSEY M. DENSIROSTRIS, AND A LIST AND KEY TO THE ZIPHOID WHALES OF THE ATLANTIC COAST OF NORTH AMERICA. Frederick A. Ulmer, Jr. Proc. Acad. Nat. Sci., Phila., vol.93, pp.107-122, fig.1, pls.20-21, Sept.11, 1941.

A SECOND FLORIDA RECORD OF MESOPLODON EUROPAEUS. Frederick A. Ulmer, Jr. Jour. Mam., vol.28, no.2, pp. 184-185, May 19, 1947.

THE MYSTERY WHALE OF VILANO BEACH (ZIPHIUS). F. G. Wood, Jr., Joseph Curtis Moore. Everglades Nat. Hist., vol.2, no.3, pp.136-142, illus., Sept., 1954.

Anatomy

MAXILLARY TEETH IN SPECIMENS OF HYPEROODON ROSTRATUS (MUELLER) AND MESOPLODON GRAYI VON HAAST STRANDED ON THE DUTCH COASTS. H. Boschma. Proc. Kon. Nederl. Akad. Wetenschappen, Amsterdam, vol.53, no.6, pp.775-786, pls.3-4, 1950.

ROWS OF SMALL TEETH IN ZIPHOID WHALES. H. Boschma. Zool. Mededelingen, Leiden, vol.31, no.14, pp.139-148, Dec.28, 1951.

ON THE ORANIUM OF A NEW SPECIES OF HYPERODON FROM THE AUSTRALIAN SEAS. William H. Flower. Proc. Zool. Soc. Lond., pp.392-396, figs.2, May 2, 1882.

OBSERVATIONS ON THE DEVELOPMENT OF THE ROSTRUM IN THE CETACEAN GENUS MESOPLODON, WITH REMARKS ON SOME OF THE SPECIES. Henry C. Forbes. Proc. Zool. Soc. Lond., pp.216-236, figs.2, pls.12-15, Feb.28, 1893.

THE MESOROSTRAL OSSIFICATION OF ZIPHIUS CAVIROSTRIS. F. C. Fraser. Proc. Zool. Soc. Lond., vol.112, ser.B, pts.1-2, pp.21-30, pls.1-3, Oct., 1942.

NOTE ON THE SKULL OF HECTOR'S BEAKED WHALE MESOPLODON HECTORI (GRAY) FROM THE FALKLAND ISLANDS. F. C. Fraser. Proc. Linnean Soc. London, Session 162, 1949-50, pt.1, pp.50-52, pls.3-4, Oct.31, 1950.

VESTIGIAL TEETH IN SPECIMENS OF CUVIER'S WHALE (ZIPHIUS CAVIROSTRIS) STRANDED ON THE SCOTTISH COAST. F. C. Fraser. Scottish Nat., no.222, pp.153-157, figs.3, Nov.-Dec., 1936.

(OBSERVATIONS ON A CETACEAN OF THE GENUS ZIPHIUS DEAD OFF ALGIERS.) Observations sur un Cetace du genre Ziphius mort en large d'Alger. Henri Gauthiere. Bull. Travaus Station Aquiculture and Peche Castiglione, Algiers, fasc.1, pp.181-204, 1936.

(THE SKELETON OF THE BOTTLE-NOSE WHALE, HYPERODON ROSTRATUS (PONT.) A CONTRIBUTION TO THE OSTEOLOGY OF THE CETACEANS AND TO THE COMPARATIVE MORPHOLOGY OF THE VERTEBRAL COLUMN.) Das skelet des Doeglings Hyperoodon Rostratus (Pont.) Ein Beitrag zur Osteologie der Cetaceen und zur vergleichenden Morphologie der Wirbelsaeule. A. Gerstaecker. C. F. Winter'sche Verlagshandlung, Leipzig, pp.1-175, pls.2, 1887.

NOTES ON THE SKELETON OF ZIPHIUS NOVAE-ZEALANDIAE. Julius von Haast. Proc. Zool. Soc. Lond., pp.466-476, pls.xlv, xlvi, 1876.

THE SKULL OF ZIPHIUS CAVIROSTRIS. John D. Kernan. Bull. Amer. Mus. Nat. Hist., vol.38, art.11, pp.349-394, pls.20-32, Aug.1, 1918.

ON THE NUMBER OF TEETH AND ITS VARIABILITY IN BERARDIUS BAIRDI, A GENUS OF THE BEAKED WHALE. Tadao Kirino. Okajimas Folia Anat. Japonica, 28 (1-6): 429-434, Sept., 1956.

ON THE STRUCTURE OF THE TOOTH IN ZIPHIUS SOVERBIENSIS (MICROPTERON SOWERBIENSIS, ESCHRICHT), AND ON SOME FOSSIL CETACEAN TEETH. E. Ray Lankester. Trans. Roy. Micro. Soc., vol.15, pp.55-64, pls.5-6, 1867.

DIFFERENCES BETWEEN THE BEAKED WHALES MESOPLODON MIRUS AND MESOPLODON GERVAISI. Joseph C. Moore, F. G. Wood, Jr. Amer. Mus. Novitates, 1831: 1-25, June 21, 1957.

ON THE CARDIAC NERVES OF SOME CETACEA, WITH SPECIAL REFERENCE TO THOSE OF BERARDIUS BAIRDII STEJNEGER. Teizo Ogawa. Sci. Repts. Whales Research Inst., Tokyo, no.7, pp. 1-22, illus., July, 1952.

(ON THE DENTAL DEVELOPMENT OF HYPEROODON.) Om tandutvecklingen hos Hyperoodon. Axel Ohlin. K. Svenska Vet-Akad. Handlingar, Stockholm, vol.22, pt. 4, no.4, pp.1-31, pls.2, Sept.9, 1896.

ON THE STRUCTURE OF MESOPLODON DENSIROSTRIS, A RARE BEAKED WHALE. Henry C. Raven. Bull. Amer. Mus. Nat. Hist., New York, vol.80, art.2, pp.23-50, figs.1-26, Sept.1, 1942.

ACCOUNT OF RUDIMENTARY FINGER MUSCLES FOUND IN A TOOTHED WHALE (HYPEROODON BIDENS). John Struthers. Jour. Anat. and Physiol., vol.8, pp.114-119, 1873.

NOTES ON THE OSTEOLOGY OF A BEAKED WHALE. Malcolm Rutherford Thorpe. Jour. Mam., vol.19, no.3, pp.354-362, figs.4, tables, Aug., 1938.

THE ANATOMY OF A SECOND SPECIMEN OF SOWERBY'S WHALE (MESOPLODON BIDENS) FROM SHETLAND. William Turner. Jour. Anat. and Physiol., pp.144-188, pl.4, figs., Oct., 1885.

THE FORM AND STRUCTURE OF THE TEETH OF MESOPLODON LAYARDII AND MESOPLODON SOWERBYII. William Turner. Jour. Anat. and Physiol., vol.13, pp.465-480, 1879.

NOTES ON THE SKULL OF AN AGED MALE HYPEROODON ROSTRATUS FROM SHETLAND. William Turner. Proc. Roy. Phys. Soc. Edinburgh, 1888-89, vol.10, pp.19-23, 1889.

Eurasia

BERARDIUS BAIRDII IN JAPAN. Roy C. Andrews. Science, Lancaster, n.s., vol. 36, no.939, pp.902-903, Dec.27, 1912.

(THREE ZIPHIUS STRANDED ON THE COASTS OF MOORS AND OF BASSES-PYRENEES.) Sur trois Ziphius échoués sur les cotes des landes et des Basses-Pyrénées. Paul Arné. Archiv. Mus. Nat. d'Hist. Nat. Paris, ser.6, vol.14, pp.125-131, figs.5, pls.10-13, Mar., 1937.

(THE ZIPHIOIDES OF THE SEAS OF EUROPE.) Les Ziphioiedes des mers d'Europe. P. J. van Beneden. Mém. cour. Ac. Roy. Belg., 41, 1888.

(TWO EXAMPLES OF ZIPHIUS FROM THE MEDITERRANEAN COAST OF SPAIN.) Dos ejemplares de "Ziphius" de las costas mediterraneas de España. Angel Cabrera. Bol. Real Soc. española Hist. Nat., vol.19, pp.468-470, Dec., 1919.

(MEMOIR ON THE FAMILY OF CETACEANS, ZIPHIOIDES, AND PARTICULARLY ON ZIPHIUS CAVIROSTRIS OF THE MEDITERRANEAN.) Memoire sur la famille des cetaces Ziphioides, et plus particulierement sur le Ziphius cavirostris de la Mediterranee. Paul Gervais. Ann. Sci. Nat. Paris, vol.14, no.1, pp.4-17, 1850.

BOTTLE-NOSE WHALES (HYPEROODON ROSTRATUS) IN THE RIVER TAY. Frank Greenshields. Scottish Naturalist, no.226, p.102, July-Aug., 1937.

ON SPECIMENS OF CUVIER'S WHALE (ZIPHIUS CAVIROSTRIS) FROM THE IRISH COAST. Sidney F. Harmer. Proc. Zool. Soc. Lond., pp.559-566, Dec., 1915.

STRANDINGS OF SOWERBY'S WHALE (MESOPLODON BIDENS) ON THE WEST COAST OF NORWAY. Age Jonsgard, Peder Hoidal. Norsk Hvalfangst-Tidende (Norwegian Whaling Gazette) 46 (9): 507-512, illus., Sept., 1957.

BOTTLE-NOSED WHALE. J. D. Mercer. Field, London, vol.168, no.4375, p.1087, illus., Oct.31, 1936.

WHALES WASHED ASHORE. F. O'Kane. Field, London, vol.162, no.4201, p.44, figs., July 1, 1933.

ON A SPECIMEN OF ZIPHIUS RECENTLY OBTAINED NEAR DUNEDIN. John H. Scott, Parker T. Jeffery. Trans. Zool. Soc. Lond., vol.12, pt.8, no.1, pp.241-248, pls.3, Feb., 1889.

OCCURRENCE OF SOWERBY'S WHALE (MESOPLODON BIDENS) ON THE NORFOLK COAST. Thomas Southwell. Zoologist, London, vol.17, no.194, pp.41-42, Feb., 1893.

ON THE OCCURRENCE OF SOWERBY'S WHALE (MESOPLODON BIDENS) ON THE YORKSHIRE COAST. Thomas Southwell, William E. Clarke. Ann. Mag. Nat. Hist., Lond., vol.17, ser.5, no.97, pp.53-59, Jan., 1886.

NOTES ON A SPECIMEN OF SOWERBY'S WHALE (MESOPLODON BIDENS), STRANDED ON THE NORFOLK COAST. Thomas Southwell, Sidney F. Harmer. Ann. and Mag. Nat. Hist., Lond., ser.6, vol.11, pp.275-284, pl.15, Apr., 1893.

BOTTLE-NOSED WHALE IN THE FORTH. A. C. Stephen. Scottish Nat., no.227, p.152, Sept.-Oct., 1937.

CUVIER'S WHALE STRANDED IN ARGYLL. A. C. Stephen. Scottish Nat., no.207, p. 86, May-June, 1934.

SOWERBY'S WHALE (MESOPLODON BIDENS) AT IVERNESS. A. C. Stephen. Scottish Nat., no.197, p.133, Sept.-Oct., 1932.

TRUE'S BEAKED WHALE (MESOPLODON MIRUS) NEW TO THE SCOTTISH FAUNA. A. C. Stephen. Scottish Naturalist, vol. 188, pp.37-39, figs.2, Mar.-Apr., 1931.

WHALES STRANDED ON THE SCOTTISH COAST (ZIPHIUS CAVIROSTRIS AND MESOPLODON BIDENS). A. C. Stephen. Scottish Nat., no.204, p.183, Nov.-Dec., 1933.

(NOTES ON ITALIAN CETACEA; FINDING OF A ZIPHIUS CAVIROSTRIS NEAR THE BEACH OF FREGENE (ROME) ON MARCH 9, 1957.) Note sui cetacei italiani; rinvenimento di uno Ziphius cavirostris Cuv. presso il Lido di Fregene (Roma) il giorno 9-III-1957. Giuseppe Tamino. Atti. Soc. Italiana Sci. Nat. Mus. Civ. Stor. Nat. Milano, 46 (3-4): 203-210, Dec., 1957.

(THE ODONTOCETE CETACEAN ZIPHIUS CAVIROSTRIS IN THE GULF OF GENOA.) Il cetaceo odontocete Ziphius cavirostris G. Cuv. nel Golfo di Genova. Enrico Tortonese. Doriana, Suppl. Ann. Mus. Civ. Storia Nat. Genova, 2 (71): 1-7, illus., Mar.6, 1957.

ON A SPECIMEN OF SOWERBY'S WHALE (MESOPLODON BIDENS) CAPTURED IN SHETLAND. William Turner. Proc. Roy. Soc. Edinburg, Sess.1881-82, pp.443-456, 1882.

ON THE OCCURRENCE OF SOWERBY'S WHALE (MICROPTERON BIDENS) IN THE FIRTH OF FORTH. William Turner. Proc. Roy. Physical Soc., Edinburgh, 1888-89, vol.10, pp.5-13, illus., 1889.

ON THE OCCURRENCE OF THE BOTTLE-NOSED OR BEAKED WHALE (HYPEROODON ROSTRATUS) IN THE SCOTTISH SEAS, WITH OBSERVATIONS ON ITS EXTERNAL CHARACTERS. William Turner. Proc. Roy. Physical Soc., Edinburgh, vol.9, pp. 25-47, figs.4, 1885-86.

ON THE OCCURRENCE OF ZIPHIUS CAVIROSTRIS IN THE SHETLAND SEAS, AND A COMPARISON OF ITS SKULL WITH THAT OF SOWERBY'S WHALE, (MESOPLODON SOWERBYI.). William Turner. Trans. Roy. Soc. Edinburgh, vol.26, pp.759-778, pls.29-30, 1872.

A SPECIMEN OF SOWERBY'S WHALE (MESOPLODON BIDENS) CAPTURED IN SHETLAND. William Turner. Jour. Anat. and Physiol., vol.16, pp.458-470, Apr., 1882.

Food Habits

(BASIC FOOD ITEM OF THE BOTTLE-NOSE WHALE (HYPEROODON ROSTRATUS MUELLER).) Osnovnoi obekt pitaniya butilkonosa (Hyperoodon rostratus Mueller). I. I. Akimushkin. Doklady Akad. Nauk SSSR, n.s., vol.45, no.2, pp.419-420, 1954.

ON THE GENUS HYPEROODON: THE TWO BRITISH KINDS AND THEIR FOOD. John E. Gray. Proc. Zool. Soc. Lond., pt.28, pp.422-426, 1860.

FOOD OF A BEAKED WHALE. A. J. Nicholson. Jour. Mam., vol.35, no.1, p. 124, Feb.10, 1954.

Fossils

A FOSSIL BEAKED WHALE FROM LAKES ENTRANCE, VICTORIA. M. F. Glaessner. Proc. Roy. Soc. Victoria, n.s., vol.58, pts.1-2, pp.25-34, fig.1, pl.1, June 25, 1947.

ON THE CETACEAN FOSSILS TERMED "ZIPHIUS" BY CUVIER WITH A NOTICE OF A NEW SPECIES (BELEMNOZIPHIUS COMPRESSUS) FROM THE RED CRAG. Thomas H. Huxley. Proc. Geol. Soc., vol.20, pp.387-396, pl.19, May 25, 1864.

MONOGRAPH ON THE BRITISH FOSSIL CETACEA FROM THE RED CRAG. David D. Owen. Palaeont. Soc., no.1, pp.1-40, pls.5, 1870.

DESCRIPTION OF A SKULL AND SOME VERTEBRAE OF THE FOSSIL CETACEAN DIOCHOTICHUS VENBENEDENI FROM SANTA CRUZ, PATAGONIA. Frederick W. True. Bull. Amer. Mus. Nat. Hist., N.Y., vol.28, art.4, pp.19-32, pls.1-5, Mar.22, 1910.

OBSERVATIONS ON THE TYPE SPECIMEN OF THE FOSSIL CETACEAN ANOPLONASSA FORCIPATA COPE. Frederick W. True. Bull. Mus. Comp. Zool., Harvard Coll., vol.51, no.4, pp.97-106, pls.1-3, July, 1907.

Indonesian and Australian Regions

FIRST RECORD OF A BEAKED WHALE (MESOPLODON GREYI) FROM VICTORIA. C. W. Brazenor. Proc. Roy. Soc. Victoria, vol.45, pt.1, pp.23-24, pl.1, Feb.28, 1933.

ZIPHIUS CAVIROSTRIS IN THE INDO-AUSTRALIAN ARCHIPELAGO. K. W. Dammerman. Treubia, vol.8, nos.3-4, pp.336-339, pls.3, 1926.

REMARKS ON A RARE AUSTRALIAN WHALE OF THE GENUS ZIPHIUS. William H. Flower. Proc. Zool. Soc. Lond., p.631, 1871.

THE GENUS MESOPLODON IN WESTERN AUSTRALIAN SEAS. L. Glauert. Australian Zoologist, Sydney, vol.11, no. 2, pp.73-75, figs.3, June 20, 1947.

BEAKED WHALES--HYPEROODON PLANIFRONS AND MESOPLODON LAYARDII--FROM SOUTH AUSTRALIA. Herbert M. Hale. Records S. Australian Mus., vol.4, no.3, pp.291-311, figs.27, June 30, 1931.

THE GOOSE-BEAKED WHALE (ZIPHIUS CAVIROSTRIS) IN NEW IRELAND. Herbert M. Hale. Records S. Australian Mus., vol.4, no.3, pp.312-313, figs.2, June 30, 1931.

THE NEW ZEALAND SCAMPERDOWN WHALE (MESOPLODON GRAYI) IN SOUTH AUSTRALIAN WATERS. Herbert M. Hale. Records S. Australian Mus., vol.4, no.4, pp.489-496, figs.10, July 30, 1932.

LETTER FROM, CONTAINING NOTICES OF RARE AUSTRALIAN WHALES OF THE GENERA DIOPLODON AND ZIPHIUS. Gerard Krefft. Proc. Zool. Soc. Lond., pp.630-631, 1871.

NEW RECORDS OF CETACEA, WITH A LIST OF QUEENSLAND SPECIES. Heber A. Longman. Mem. Queensland Mus., vol.8, pt.3, pp.266-278, 1 pl., Mar.31, 1926.

ZIPHIUS CAVIROSTRIS ON THE QUEENSLAND COAST. Heber A. Longman. Proc. Roy. Soc. Queensland, vol.31, pp.90-93, pls.3-4, Aug.8, 1919.

STUDIES OF TASMANIAN CETACEA (ZIPHIUS CAVIROSTRIS). PART II. H. H. Scott, Clive Lord. Roy. Soc. Tasmania: Papers and Proc., Hobart, pp.23-32, pl.10, July 24, 1919.

STUDIES IN TASMANIAN CETACEA (ZIPHIUS CAVIROSTRIS). H. H. Scott, Clive Lord. Part VI. Papers and Proc. Roy. Soc. Tasmania, 1927, pp.156-157, Feb.29, 1928.

A SUPPOSED OCCURRENCE OF THE BOTTLE-NOSED WHALE (HYPEROODON) IN NEW ZEALAND. E. R. Waite. Rec. Cant. Mus., vol.2, pp.23-26, pls.7-8, pt.2, Dec.23, 1913.

TWO ZIPHIOID WHALES NOT PREVIOUSLY RECORDED FROM SOUTH AUSTRALIA. E. R. Waite. Rec. South Australian Mus., vol.2, pp.209-214, 2 pls., Apr.3, 1922.

Pacific Ocean

CUVIER'S BEAKED WHALE FROM HAWAII. Lawrence P. Richards. Jour. Mam., vol. 33, no.2, p.255, May 16, 1952.

NOTE ON THREE VERY LARGE BEAKED WHALES FROM THE NORTH PACIFIC. Frederick W. True. Science, n.s., vol. 20, no.521, pp.888-889, Dec.23, 1904.

Taxonomy

AN ADDITION TO THE KNOWLEDGE OF THE GENETIC ORIGIN OF THE SPECIES HYPERCODON ROSTRATUS--A MUELLER (TRANS. TITLE). Milutin Gligic. Novitates Musei Sarojevoensis, no.2, 30 pp., July 1, 1925.

FURTHER NOTES ON OULODON, A NEW GENUS OF ZIPHIOID WHALES FROM THE NEW ZEALAND SEAS. J. von Haast. Proc. Zool. Soc. Lond., pp.457-458, 1876.

ON A NEW ZIPHIOID WHALE. J. von Haast. Proc. Zool. Soc. London, 1876.

ON OULODON: A NEW GENUS OF ZIPHOID WHALES. J. von Haast. Trans. New Zealand Inst., vol.9, pp.450-457, 1876.

TASMACETUS SHEPHERDI: A NEW GENUS AND SPECIES OF BEAKED WHALE FROM NEW ZEALAND. W.R.B. Oliver. Proc. Zool. Soc., Lond., ser.B, vol.107, pt.3, pp.371-381, pls.1-5, Sept., 1937.

DESCRIPTION OF A NEW SPECIES OF MESOPLODON, M. STEJNEGERI, OBTAINED BY DR. LEONHARD STEJNEGER, IN BERING ISLAND. Frederick W. True. Proc. U.S. Nat. Mus., Wash., 1885, vol. 8, pp.584-585, pl.25, 1886.

DIAGNOSIS OF A NEW BEAKED WHALE OF THE GENUS MESOPLODON FROM THE COAST OF NORTH CAROLINA. Frederick W. True. Smithsonian Misc. Coll., vol.60, publ.2172, no.25, pp.1-2, Mar.14, 1913.

A NOTE UPON THE HYPEROODON SEMIJUNCTUS OF COPE. Frederick W. True. Proc. U.S. Nat. Mus., vol.8, publ.541, pp.585-586, Nov.21, 1885.

## Physeteridae

NOTES ON COGIA BREVICEPS, THE LESSER SPERM-WHALE. W. B. Benham. Trans. New Zealand Inst., vol.34, pp.155-168, 1901.

ON THE NATURAL HISTORY OF THE SPERMACETI WHALE (PHYSETER MACROCEPHALUS). F. DeBell Bennett. Proc. Zool. Soc. Lond., pt.5, pp.37-39, 1837.

(REMARKS ON CETACEANS WITH TEETH AND IN PARTICULAR ON THE CACHALOT.) Remarques sur les cetaces a dents, et en particulier sur le cachalot. H. Boschma. Bull. Inst. Oceanographique, Monaco, no.991, pp.1-28, figs.11, pl.1, Apr.30, 1951.

(THE SPERM WHALE.) A propos de cachalot. J. Cadenat. Notes Africaines, 71: 82-92, July, 1956.

NOTES ON A STRANDED PIGMY SPERM WHALE (KOGIA BREVICEPS). Robert K. Enders. Notulae Naturae, Phila., no.111, pp.6, figs.4, Nov.12, 1942.

THE SPERM WHALES, GIANT AND PYGMY. Theodore Gill. Amer. Nat., Lancaster, vol.4, pp.21, figs.164-176, Feb., 1871.

APPENDIX TO J.F.G. WHEELER, NOTES ON A YOUNG SPERM-WHALE FROM THE BERMUDA ISLANDS. S. F. Harmer. Proc. Zool. Soc. London, pt.2, pp.409-410, June 30, 1933.

ON THE PIGMY SPERM-WHALE, KOGIA BREVICEPS (BLAINVILLE). Kyosuke Hirasaka. Mem. Faculty Sci. and Agric., Taihoku Imp. Univ., Formosa, vol.14, no. 4, (Zoology no.7) pp.117-142, tables 6, map 1, pls.5, Oct., 1937.

A PIGMY SPERM-WHALE. Kyosuke Hirasaka. Zool. Mag. (Japan), Tokyo, vol.48, no.2, pp.72-74, fig.1, Feb., 1936.

THE SPERM WHALE, PHYSETER CATODON. L. Harrison Matthews. Discovery Reports, Cambridge, vol.17, pp.93-168, figs.67, tables 16, pls.3-11, Mar., 1938.

ON THE SEXUAL MATURITY OF THE SPERM WHALE (PHYSETER CATODON) FOUND IN THE ADJACENT WATERS OF JAPAN (PART I). Masaharu Nishiwaki. Sci. Repts. Whales Research Inst., Tokyo, no.6, pp.153-165, illus., Dec., 1951; (Part 2), no.7, pp.121-124, illus., July, 1952.

A SCHOOL OF WHALES, KOGIA? Ralph S. Palmer. Jour. Mam., vol.29, no.4, p.421, Dec.31, 1948.

(ON AN EXHIBITION OF THE SPERM WHALE (PHYSETER MACROCEPHALUS L.).) Ueber eine Darstellung des Pottwales. (Physeter macrocephalus L.). Nichlaus Peters. Zool. Anzeiger, vol.87, nos.11-12, pp.312-314, fig.1, 1930.

THE OCCURRENCE OF THE SPERM WHALE OR CACHALOT IN THE SHETLAND SEAS, WITH NOTES ON THE TYMPANO-PETROUS BONES OF PHYSETER, KOGIA, AND OTHER ODONTOCETI. Sir William Turner. Proc. Roy. Soc., Edinburg, Sess.1902-1903, vol.24, pt.5, pp.423-436, illus., June 5, 1903.

HISTORY AND DESCRIPTION OF THE SKELETON OF THE NEW SPERM WHALE, LATELY SET UP IN THE AUSTRALIAN MUSEUM, SYDNEY TOGETHER WITH SOME ACCOUNT OF A NEW GENUS OF SPERM WHALES CALLED EUPHYSETES. William S. Wall. Memoirs no.1, Australian Museum, pp.1-66, pls.2, 1887.

NOTES ON A YOUNG SPERM-WHALE FROM THE BERMUDA ISLANDS. J.F.G. Wheeler. Proc. Zool. Soc. Lond., pp. 407-410, pl.1, June 30, 1933.

UNDERWATER SOUNDS HEARD FROM SPERM WHALES. L.V. Worthington, William E. Schevill. Nature, London, 180: 291, Aug.10, 1957.

SOME REMARKS ON THE PYGMY SPERM WHALE, KOGIA. Munesato Yamada. Sci. Repts. Whales Research Inst., Tokyo, no. 9, pp.37-58, illus., 1 pl., 1954.

A WHALE OF A STORY (SPERM WHALE). Nat. Nature News, vol.1, no.32, pp.3, 7, fig.1, Nov.1, 1937.

Africa and Asia

(THE STRANDING OF A SPERM WHALE ON THE COAST OF SENEGAL.) Echouage d'un cachalot sur les cotes du Senegal. J. Cadenat. Notes Africaines, no.64, pp. 119-121, Oct., 1954.

A REMARKABLE WHALE FROM JAPAN. Kyosuke Hirasaka. Nature, London, vol. 137, no.3459, p.267, fig.1, Feb.15, 1936.

(ON THE STRANDING OF A KOGIA BREVICEPS GRAY NEAR THE OCEANOGRAPHIC INSTITUTE OF NHATRANG (ANNAM).) Sur un echouage de Kogia breviceps Gray a proximite de l'Institut Oceanographique de Nhatrang (Annam). Rauol Serene. Bull. Mus. Nat. Hist. Nat., Paris, ser.2, vol.6, no.4, pp.398-399, June, 1934.

DISCOVERY OF UKI-KUJIRA, KOGIA. Munesato Yamada. Shizen, vol.7, no.9, p.65, 1952. (In Japanese.)

Ambergris

A GREAT HAUL OF AMBERGRIS. Robert Clarke. Nature, London, vol. 174, no.4421, pp.155-156, illus., July 24, 1954. (Reprinted in Norsk Hvalfansgt-Tidende (Norwegian Whaling Gazette), vol. 43, no.8, pp.450-453, Aug., 1954.)

CURIOSITIES FOR THE SEASHORE--AMBERGRIS. F. C. Fraser. Illus. London News, vol.211, no.5651, p.160, illus., Aug.9, 1947.

BEACHCOMBER'S BONANZA. (AMBERGRIS.) Samuel Hudson. Nature Mag., Wash., D.C., vol.36, no.2, pp.70-72, 108, illus., Feb., 1943.

FLOATING GOLD. THE ROMANCE OF AMBERGRIS. R. C. Murphy. Natural History, New York, vol.33, no.2, pp.117-130, figs., Mar.-Apr., 1933; no.3, pp. 303-310, figs., May-June, 1933.

THE MYSTERY OF AMBERGRIS. N. W. Gregory Walker. Discovery, vol.18, no. 206, pp.52-53, figs.2, Feb., 1937.

AMBERGRIS FROM A BRITISH COLUMBIA SPERM WHALE. Norsk Hvalfangst-Tidende (Norwegian Whaling Gazette), Sandefjord, vol.43, no.12, pp.707-708, Dec., 1954.

Anatomy

ON SOME POINTS IN THE STRUCTURE OF THE VENOUS SYSTEM AND THE BLOOD-GLANDS OF THE NECK IN THE CACHALOT (PHYSETER MACROCEPHALUS). Frank E. Beddard. Ann. and Mag. Nat. Hist., ser. 9, vol.13, pp.274-282, Mar., 1924.

ON THE BLOW-HOLES AND NASAL PASSAGES OF THE CACHALOT (PHYSETER MACROCEPHALUS). Frank E. Beddard. Ann. and Mag. Nat. Hist., ser.9, vol.11, pp.641-655, June, 1923.

SOME OBSERVATIONS UPON THE DEVELOPMENT OF THE TEETH OF PHYSETER MACROCEPHALUS. Frank E. Beddard. Quart. Jour. Microscopical Sci., vol.67, pp.1-32, Apr., 1923.

ABSORPTION OF TOOTH TISSUE IN THE SPERM WHALE. H. Boschma. Proc. Kon. Nederl. Akad. Wetenschappen, Amsterdam, vol.53, no.3, pp.289-293, illus., 1950.

DOUBLE TEETH IN THE SPERM WHALE (PHYSETER MACROCEPHALUS L.). H. Boschma. Zool. Mededeel., Leiden, vol. 20, nos.3-4, pp.211-221, figs.8, 1938.

ON THE TEETH AND SOME OTHER PARTICULARS OF THE SPERM WHALE (PHYSETER MACROCEPHALUS L.). H. Boschma. Temminckia, Leiden, vol.3, pp.151-278, pls.10-13, figs.1-19, 1938.

THE PELVIC BONES OF PHYSETER MACROCEPHALUS L. A. B. van Deinse. Zool. Med. Rijksmus. Nat. Hist. Leiden, vol.33, no.4, pp.25-32, June 9, 1954.

MEMOIR ON THE OSTEOLOGY OF THE SPERM-WHALE. PART I. William H. Flower. Proc. Zool. Soc. Lond., p.81, 1866.

NOTICE OF A MEMOIR ON THE OSTEOLOGY OF THE SPERM-WHALE (PHYSETER MACROCEPHALUS). William H. Flower. Proc. Zool. Soc. Lond., p. 823, 1867.

ON THE OSTEOLOGY OF THE CACHALOT OR SPERM-WHALE (PHYSETER MACROCEPHALUS). William H. Flower. Trans. Zool. Soc., vol.6, pp.309-369, pls.55-60, figs.1-13, 1867.

CHARACTERISTICS OF BODY PROPORTIONS IN SPERM WHALES (PHYSETER CATODON). E. I. Ivanova. Trans. Inst. Oceanography, Acad. Sci. USSR, Moscow, 18: 100-112, 1955.

ON THE BRAIN OF THE SPERM WHALE (PHYSETER CATODON L.). Tokuzo Kojima. Sci. Repts. Whales Research Inst., Tokyo, no.6, pp.49-72, illus., Dec., 1951.

ON DEFORMITY OF THE LOWER JAW IN THE CACHALOT (PHYSETER MACROCEPHALUS, LINN.). James Murie. Proc. Zool. Soc. Lond., pp.389-396, figs.2, 1865.

(REMARKS ON THE DENTAL DEVELOPMENT OF THE SPERM-WHALE.) Remarques a propos du developpement des dents du cachalot (Physeter macrocephalus L.). Henri Neuville. Ann. Sci. Nat., Paris, ser.10, Zool., vol.18, pp.171-195, 1935.

(THE EXTERIOR FORMS OF THE SPERM WHALE.) Des formes exterieures du cachalot. G. Pouchet, F. A. Chaves. Jour. Anat. et Physiol., Paris, vol.26, pp.260-272, figs.3, pl.9, 1890.

(RESEARCH ON THE CACHALOT. PART ONE: ANATOMY.) Recherches sur le Cachalot. Premiere Partie: Anatomie. G. Pouchet, H. Beauregarde. Nouv. Archiv. du Mus., 3 me Serie, Memoires, vol.1, pp.1-92, pls.1-8, 1889.

(THE STOMACH OF THE SPERMWHALE.) Sur L'estomac du Cachalot. G. Pouchet, H. Beauregard. Soc. Biol., Paris, Mem., vol.41, n.s., vol.1, pp.92-94, 1889.

(ON THE VARIATION OF THE PELVIS IN THE SPERM WHALE.) De la variation du bassin chez le Cachalot. G. Pouchet, H. Beauregard. Comp. Rend. Acad. Sci., pp.162-164, Paris, 1891.

AUTOPSY OF A MALE PIGMY SPERM WHALE (KOGIA BREVICEPS). Herbert L. Ratcliffe. Notulae Naturae, Phila., no.112, pp.4, Nov.12, 1942.

(A PECULIAR ASYMMETRY OF THE PHYSETERIDAE (HEMAPOPHYSEAL ASYMMETRY) AND ITS RELATIONS TO THE CRANIAL ASYMMETRY.) Di una peculiare asimmetria dei fiseteridi (asimmetria emapofisaria) e delle sue relazioni con l'asimmetria cranica. C. Richard. Rendiconti della R. Accad. Nazionale dei Lincei, Cl. Sci. fis. matem. e nat., Roma (6), vol.12, fasc.3-4, pp. 165-172, 1930.

ON THE OCCURRENCE OF FUNCTIONAL TEETH IN THE UPPER JAW OF THE SPERM WHALE. James Ritchie, A.J.H. Edwards. Proc. Roy. Soc. Edinburgh, vol.33, pt.2, no.15, pp.166-168, figs.3, Apr.22, 1913.

THE EXTERNAL CHARACTERS, SKELETAL MUSCLES AND PERIPHERAL NERVES OF KOGIA BREVICEPS (BLAINVILLE). H. von W. Schulte, M. de Forest Smith. 1918.

LETTER RELATING TO THE OCCASIONAL DEFORMITY OF THE LOWER JAW OF THE SPERM-WHALE. J. H. Thomson. Proc. Zool. Soc. Lond., pp.246-247, figs. 5, 1867.

ON THE STERNUM OF THE SPERM WHALE (PHYSETER MACROCEPHALUS). William Turner. Jour. Anat. and Physiol., vol.6, pp.377-380, illus., 1872.

Atlantic Ocean and Islands

PYGMY SPERM WHALE IN THE ATLANTIC. Glover M. Allen. Papers on Mammalogy, Zool. Ser., Field Mus. Nat. Hist., Chicago, vol.27, pp.17-34, figs.4, Dec.8, 1941.

THE BIOLOGY OF SPERM WHALES CAPTURED IN THE AZORES. Robert Clarke. Norsk Hvalfangst Tidende (Norwegian Whaling Gazette), 45 (8): 439-444, Aug., 1956.

(ON A SPERM WHALE OF THE AZORES.) Sur un Cachalot des Acores. Prince Albert de Monaco. Comptes rendus Seances l'Acad. Sci., Paris, 4 pp., figs. 2, 1888.

Australia and Pacific Islands

RECORDS OF KOGIA BREVICEPS FROM THE HAWAIIAN ISLANDS. C. H. Edmondson. Jour. Mam., vol.29, no.1, pp.76-77, illus., Feb.13, 1948.

NOTICE OF A NEW SPECIES OF AUSTRALIAN SPERM-WHALE (CATODON KREFFTII) IN THE SYDNEY MUSEUM. John E. Gray. Proc. Zool. Soc. Lond., pp.439-442, figs.4, 1865.

ON THE OCCURRENCE OF A NEW SPECIES OF EUPHYSETES (EUPHYSETES POTTSII), A REMARKABLY SMALL CATODONT WHALE, ON THE COAST OF NEW ZEALAND. Julius Haast. Proc. Zool. Soc. Lond., pp.260-264, 1874; Trans. New Zealand Inst., vol.6, pp.97-102, pl.15, 1874.

THE PIGMY SPERM WHALE (KOGIA BREVICEPS BLAINVILLE) ON SOUTH AUSTRALIAN COASTS. Herbert M. Hale. Records South Australian Museum, Adelaide, vol.8, no.4, pp.531-546, pls. 14-18, Dec.10, 1947.

Biochemistry

PROTEIN DIGESTIVE POWER OF SPERM WHALE PANCREATIC ENZYME. II. Yasutaro Ishikawa. Sci. Reports Whales Research Inst., Tokyo, no.3, pp.71-78, Feb., 1950.

PROTEIN DIGESTIVE POWER OF SPERM WHALE PANCREATIC ENZYME. Yasutaro Ishikawa, Setsuzo Tejima. Sci. Repts. Whales Research Inst., Tokyo, no.2, pp. 55-60, illus., Dec., 1948.

PROPERTIES OF FATS AND OILS CONTAINED IN VARIOUS PARTS OF A SPERM WHALE BODY. Takajiro Mori, Masamichi Saiki. Sci. Reports Whales Research Inst., Tokyo, no.3, pp.79-84, Feb., 1950.

Economic Importance

SAILS AND WHALES: WITH AN INTRODUCTION BY HENRY BEETLE HOUGH. Harry A. Chippendale. Melrose, 192 pp., illus., 1953. Autobiography.

SPERM WHALING FROM OPEN BOATS IN THE AZORES. Robert Clarke. Norsk Hvalfangst-Tidende (Norwegian Whaling Gazette), Sandefjord, vol.42, no.7, pp. 373-385, July, 1953; Zoo Life, London, vol.10, no.2, pp.47-55, illus., Summer, 1955.

MOLECULAR DISTILLATION OF SPERM WHALE BLUBBER OIL. Seiichi Ishikawa, Yoshimori Omote, Hideo Kanno. Sci. Repts. Whales Research Inst., Tokyo, no. 2, pp.42-45, figs.2, Dec., 1948.

(THE SPERM WHALE, ITS HUNTING AND USE IN PERU.) El cachalote, su caza y aprovechamiento en el Peru. Leon Kostritsky B., Alvary Piazza L. Pesca y Caza, Minist. Agric., Lima, Peru, no.5, pp.31-52, illus., 1952.

THE MILK FAT OF SPERM WHALE (PHYSETER CATODON). Torbjorn Pedersen. Norsk Hvalfangst Tidende (Norwegian Whaling Gazette), Sandefjord, vol.41, no.6, p.300, June, 1952.

OIL FROM THE MEAT OF SPERM WHALE (PHYSETER CATODON). Torbjorn Pedersen. Norsk Hvalfangst Tidende (Norwegian Whaling Gazette), Sandefjord, vol.41, no.6, pp.296-299, June, 1952.

(CONTRIBUTION TO THE HISTORY OF SPERMACETI.) Contribution a l'histoire du spermaceti. G. Pouchet. Bergens Mus. Aarbog, no.1, pp.1-25, 1894.

(NOTE ON THE "SPERMACETI ORGAN.") Note sur "l'organe des spermaceti." G. Pouchet, Henry Beauregard. Mem. Soc. Biol., Paris, vol.37, pp.342-344, 1885.

(ON SPERMACETI.) Sur la boite a spermaceti. G. Pouchet, Henry Beauregard. Comp. Rend. Acad. Sci., Paris, pp.1-3, 1884.

STUDIES ON UTILIZATION OF HIGHER FATTY ALCOHOL FROM SPERM WHALE OIL. Shinichi Tomiyama, Masayasu Takao. Sci. Repts. Whales Research Inst., Tokyo, no.7, pp.37-46, July, 1952.

SPERM OIL AND SPERMACETI WAX. COPY OF PRESIDENTIAL PROCLAMATION - "DECREASING RATES OF DUTY ON SPERM OIL, CRUDE, AND SPERMACETI WAX." (In) Report of the U.S. Tariff Commission to the President of the United States, pp.31-35, 1930.

Europe

(CONCERNING THE RECENT CAPTURE OF SOME SPECIMENS OF SPERM-WHALE (PHYSETERMACROCEPHALUS).) A proposite della recente cattura di alcuni esemplari di Capodoglio (Physeter macrocephalus L.) Monaco (1949). Arturo Bolognari. Bull. Institut Oceanographique, no.949, p.1, illus., maps, tables, 1949.

SPERM WHALE AT BRIDLINGTON. W. J. Clarke. Naturalist, London, no.966, pp. 157-158, July, 1937.

(ON THE STRANDING OF A CACHALOT ON THE ISLAND OF RÉ.) Sur un echouement de Cachalot a l'ile de Ré. G. Pouchet, Henry Beauregard. Comp. Rendus. Acad. Sci., vol.110, pp.1-3, Paris, 1890.

THE BRIDLINGTON SPERM-WHALE. S.H. Pycraft. Illus. London News, vol.190, no. 5113, p.676, figs.3, Apr.17, 1937.

SPERM WHALE IN FIRTH OF FORTH IN PREHISTORIC TIMES. James Ritchie. Scottish Nat., no.159, p.96, 1926.

A SPERM WHALE IN THE MORAY FIRTH. William Taylor. Scottish Nat., Edinburgh, no.26, pp.28-30, Feb., 1914.

THE FIRST OF THEIR KIND WASHED ASHORE ON THE DUTCH COAST FOR 175 YEARS: TWO CACHALOTS (SPERM-WHALES) BROUGHT TO ROTTERDAM. Illus. London News, vol.190, no.5108, p.438, illus., Mar.13, 1937.

SPERM WHALE STRANDED AT LISLARY, CO. SLIGO, 1936. Report Nat. Mus. Ireland, Dublin, p.13, pl.1935-36.

SPERM WHALE AT THE NATURAL HISTORY MUSEUM. Nature, London, vol.139, no.3512, p.318, Feb.20, 1937.

WHALE WASHED UP AT BRIDLINGTON (SPERM WHALE). Hull Mus. Publ., no. 196, pp.4, illus., 1938.

Food Habits

FOOD OF THE SPERM WHALE (PHYSETER CATODON) IN THE KURILE ISLANDS REGION. E. I. Betesheva, I. I. Akimushkin. Trans. Inst. Oceanology, Acad. Sci. USSR, Moscow, 18: 86-94, 1955.

A GIANT SQUID SWALLOWED BY A SPERM WHALE. Robert Clarke. Norsk. Hvalfangst-Tidende (Norwegian Whaling Gazette), vol.44, no.10, pp.589-593, illus., Oct., 1955; Proc. Zool. Soc. Lond., 126 (4): 645, July 31, 1956.

SEALS AS SPERM WHALE FOOD. Robert C. Murphy. Jour. Mam., vol.5, no.2, p.132, May, 1924.

THE STOMACH CONTENTS OF SPERM WHALES CAUGHT OFF THE WEST COAST OF BRITISH COLUMBIA. Lewis L. Robbins, Francis K. Oldham, E.M.K. Geiling. Report British Columbia Mus., 1937, pp.19-20, figs.3, 1938.

SPERM WHALE AND SQUID. N.W. Gregory Walker. Discovery, London, vol. 18, no.214, pp.308-312, figs.5, Oct., 1937.

Fossils

(FOSSIL SPERM WHALE, SCALDICETUS CARETTI, OF MIDDEN-LIMBURG.) De fossiele potvisch Scaldicetus caretti in Midden-Limburg aangetoond. A. B. Van Deinse. Natuurhist. Maandblad, Maastricht 28 Jaargang, no.10, pp.97-98, fig.1, Oct. 27, 1939.

A FOSSIL PHYSETEROID CETACEAN FROM SANTA BARBARA COUNTY, CALIFORNIA. Remington Kellogg. Proc. U.S. Nat. Mus., Wash., 1926, vol.66, art. 27, pp.8, pls.2, Feb.28, 1925.

A NEW FOSSIL TOOTHED WHALE FROM FLORIDA (KOGIOPSIS FLORIDANA). Remington Kellogg. Amer. Mus. Novitates, no.389, pp.10, figs.3, Dec.5, 1929.

STUDY OF THE SKULL OF A FOSSIL SPERM-WHALE FROM THE TREMBLOR MIOCENE OF SOUTHERN CALIFORNIA. Remington Kellogg. Carnegie Inst. Wash., publ.346, pp.1-23, 9 pls., Nov.3, 1927.

Geographic Distribution

EASTERN PACIFIC RECORDS AND GENERAL DISTRIBUTION OF THE PYGMY SPERM WHALE. Carl L. Hubbs. Jour. Mam., vol.32, no.4, pp.403-410, pls.3, Nov.19, 1951.

ON PRESENT DISTRIBUTION OF THE CACHALOT IN THE WORLD OCEAN ACCORDING TO WHALING DATA. A. A. Kirpichnikov. Bull. Moscow Soc. Nat., New Ser., Biol. Sect., 55 (5): 11-25, 1950. (Russian.)

North America

RECORDS OF KOGIA BREVICEPS FROM TEXAS, WITH REMARKS ON MOVEMENTS AND DISTRIBUTION. Gordon Gunter, Carl L. Hubbs, M. Allan Beal. Jour. Mam., 36 (2): 263-270, illus., May, 1955.

SPERM WHALES AT ST. GEORGE ISLAND, BERING SEA. G. Dallas Hanna. Jour. Mam., vol.5, no.1, p.64, Feb., 1924.

(ON A SPERM WHALE CAUGHT NEAR NEWFOUNDLAND (PHYSETER MACROCEPHALUS L.).) Ueber einen bei Neufundland gefangenen Pottwal (Physeter macrocephalus L.). Ernst Hentschel. Zoologischen Anzeiger, vol.36, no.25, pp.417-425, figs. 1-4, Dec.6, 1910.

YOUNG SPERM WHALE BEACHED AT MONTEREY. J. B. Phillips. California Fish and Game, San Francisco, vol.29, no.3, pp.150-151, July, 1943.

A PIGMY SPERM WHALE FROM THE SAVANNAH RIVER ENTRANCE. Ivan R. Tomkins. Jour. Mam., vol.15, no.3, pp. 250-251, Aug., 1934.

NOTICE OF THE CAPTURE OF A MALE PYGMY SPERM WHALE KOGIA BREVICEPS, AT KITTY HAWK, NORTH CAROLINA. Frederick W. True. Bull. U.S. Fish Comm., vol.5, pp.132-133, 1885.

KOGIA BREVICEPS IN SOUTH CAROLINA AND NEW JERSEY. Frederick A. Ulmer, Jr. Jour. Mam., vol.22, no.4, pp.450-451, Nov.14, 1941.

Parasites

AN ASCARID FROM THE SPERM-WHALE. H. A. Baylis. Ann. and Mag. Nat. Hist., ser.9, vol.11, pp.211-217, 4 figs., Feb., 1923.

NOTE ON THE OCCURRENCE OF "CYSTICERCUS TAENIAE GRIMALDII" IN A NEW HOST. H. A. Baylis. Ann. and Mag. Nat. Hist., ser.9, vol.18, pp.665-667, Dec., 1926.

INTERNAL PARASITES OF THE PIGMY SPERM WHALE. T. Harvey Johnston, Patricia M. Mawson. Rec. South Australian Mus., Adelaide, vol.6, no.3, pp.263-274, figs.14, Dec.16, 1939.

Taxonomy

NOTICE OF A NEW SPECIES OF SPERM-WHALE BELONGING TO THE GENUS EUPHYSETES OF MACLEAY. Gerard Krefft. Proc. Zool. Soc. Lond., pp.708-713, figs.6, 1865.

(PRELIMINARY NOTE ON A NEW SPECIES OF CACHALOT OF THE RIO DE LA PLATA (PHOCAENA DIOPTRICA).) Nota preliminar sobre una nueva especie de marsopa del rio de la Plata (Phocaena dioptrica). Fernando Lahille. Ann. Mus. Nacional Hist. Nat., Buenos Aires, vol. 23, pp.271-278, pls.6-8, 1912.

Monodontidae

(Elphinapterus)

ON THE MIGRATIONS OF THE BELUGA IN THE SAKHALIN REGION. V. A. Arsenyev. Bull. Pacific Sci. Inst. of Fisheries and Oceanography, Vladivostok, vol.10, pp.19-26, 1937. (In Russian with English summary.)

SOME DATA ON THE DIET OF THE BELUGA. V. A. Arsenyev. Bull. Pacific Sci. Inst. of Fisheries and Oceanography, Vladivostok, vol.10, pp.27-34, 1937. (In Russian with English summary.)

TAXONOMIC OBSERVATIONS ON WHITE WHALES. I. I. Barabash. Jour. Mam., vol.18, no.4, pp.507-509, Nov., 1937.

THE PACIFIC OCEAN FORM OF WHITE WHALE. I. I. Barabash, S. Klumov. Biulleten' rybnogo Khoziaistvo SSSR (Sea Fishery Economics in USSR), Moscow, no.11, p.24, 1935. (In Russian.)

ACCOUNT OF A BELUGA OR WHITE WHALE, KILLED IN THE FIRTH OF FORTH. John Barclay, P. Neill. Wern. Mam., vol.3, pp.371-396, pls.17-18, 1816.

WHITE WHALES. Eva Beckett. Canadian Nature, Toronto, vol.7, no.2, p.44, illus., Mar.-Apr., 1945.

(STUDY OF AQUATIC MAMMALS. I. SKIN OF THE WHITE WHALE OR BELUGA.) Etude sur les mammiferes aquatiques. I. La peau du marsouin blanc ou beluga (Delphinapterus leucas). W. Bonin, V. D. Vladykov. Le Naturaliste Canadien, Quebec, vol.67, nos.10-11, pp.253-287, figs.18, Oct.-Nov., 1940.

KILLING WHITE WHALES WITH NOISE. N. Milton Browne. Forest and Outdoors, vol.28, no.10, pp.369-370, illus., Oct., 1932.

MIGRATIONS AND HUNTING OF WHITE WHALE IN THE NORTHERN PART OF OB BAY. K. K. Chapsky. Trans. Arctic Inst., Leningrad, vol.71, Biol., pp.60, figs.7, 1937. (In Russian with English summary.)

(BIOLOGICAL OBSERVATIONS AND MEASUREMENTS OF THE WHITE WHALE AND ITS FETUS.) Biologiske iagttagelser over og maalinger in hvidhvalen (Delphinapterus leucas (Pall.) ) og dens fostre. Magnus Degerbol, N. L. Nielsen. Meddelelser om Gronland, Kobenhavn, vol. 77, pp.119-144, figs.5, 1930. (In Danish, with English summary.)

(MATERIALS ON THE GEOGRAPHICAL DISTRIBUTION AND BIOLOGY OF DELPHINAPTERUS IN THE WHITE SEA.) Materialien zur Kenntnis der geographischen Verbreitung und Biologie von Delphinapterus im Weissen Meere. A. W. Dmochowsky. Bull. Soc. Nat. Moscow, ser. biol., vol. 42, no.1, pp.85-90, 1933. (In Russian.)

BELUGA OF THE CHURCHILL REGION OF HUDSON BAY. K. H. Doan, C. W. Douglas. Bull. Fisheries Research Board Canada, Ottawa, no.98, pp.27, illus., 1953.

A RECORD OF THE WHITE WHALE IN THE BAY OF FUNDY. H. D. Fisher, D. E. Sargeant. Canadian Field Nat., vol.68, no.3, pp.138-139, July-Sept., 1954.

ON THE SKULL OF A BELUGA OR WHITE WHALE. William H. Flower. Proc. Zool. Soc., Lond., pp.667-669, figs.2, Nov.18, 1879.

(DATA ON THE GEOGRAPHICAL DISTRIBUTION AND BIOLOGY OF THE WHITE WHALE (DELPHINAPTERUS).) Materiale zur Kenntnis der geographischen Verbreitung und Biologie des Weisswales (Delphinapterus). W. G. Heptner. Proc. Sci. Invest. Inst. Zool., Moscow, vol.4, no.2, pp.7-100, figs.8, 1930. (In Russian.)

OBSERVATIONS ON THE WHITE WHALE. A. Brazier Howell. Jour. Mam., vol.16, no.2, pp.155-156, May, 1935.

THE ELECTROCARDIOGRAM OF A BELUGA WHALE. Robert L. King, James L. Jenks, Jr., Paul D. White. Circulation, vol.8, no.3, pp.387-393, illus., Sept., 1953.

A NEW FORM OF BELUKHA. S. K. Klumov. Bull. Acad. Sci. USSR, cl. sci. math. et nat., ser. biol., Moscow, no.1, pp.199-209, figs.7, 1937.

A NEW FORM OF WHITE WHALE (DELPHINAPTERUS FREIMANI). S. Klumov. Biulleten' rybnogo Khoziaistvo SSSR (Sea Fishery Economics in USSR), Moscow, no.7, pp.26-28, figs.2, 1935. (In Russian.)

THE WHITE WHALE OF THE SOVIET FAR NORTH; STOCKS AND FISHERY. S. K. Klumov. Trans. Inst. Marine Fisheries and Oceanography USSR, vol.12, pp.1-79, 1939. (In Russian, with English summary.)

MIGRATIONS AND HUNTING OF THE BELUGA IN THE GULFS OF THE YENISEI AND PIASINA. K. Kovalev. Trans. Arctic Inst. Chief Administration Northern Sea Route, Leningrad, vol.123, pp.71-111, figs. 5, tables 7, 1938. (In Russian.)

WHITE WHALE DRIVE. Enna-Kwee. The Beaver, Winnipeg, Outfit 270, no.4, pp.23-25, illus., Mar., 1940.

REMARKS ON THE DENTITION OF DELPHINAPTERUS LEUCAS. Einar Loennberg. Arkiv. Zool., Upsala, vol.7, no.2, pp.1-18, figs.1-7, July 5, 1910.

(CAPTURE OF DELPHINAPTERUS LEUCAS PALLAS IN THE LOIRE-INFERIEURE.) Capture de Delphinapterus leucas Pallas (Cetace odontocete) dans la Loire-Inferieure. P. L. Niort. Bull. Soc. Zool. France, Paris, vol.74, nos.4-5, pp.244-246, 1949.

THE WHITE GRAMPUS DELPHINAPTERUS LEUCAS PAL. AND TRADING WITH IT IN THE GULF OF ENISSEI, SIBERIA. N. Ostrounov. Rept. Siberian Sci. Sta. Fisher, Krasnoiarsk, Siberia, USSR, vol. 4, no.1, pp.3-37, 9 pls., 1929.

THE BLOOD CELLS OF CETACEA WITH PARTICULAR REFERENCE TO THE BELUGA DELPHINAPTERUS LEUCAS PALLAS, 1776. W. B. Quay. Saeugetierk. Mitteil., Stuttgart, vol.2, no.2, pp.49-54, illus., Apr.1, 1954.

(SMALL WHALE HUNT IN CANADA.) Kleine Waljagd in Kanada. Ernst Scharrer. Natur und Volk, Frankfurt a.M., vol.68, no.3, pp.130-140, figs.16, Mar.1, 1938.

UNDERWATER LISTENING TO THE WHITE PORPOISE (DELPHINAPTERUS LEUCAS). William E. Schevill, Barbara Lawrence. Science, Lancaster, vol.109, no.2824, pp.143-144, Feb.11, 1949.

RECORDS OF PELAGIC ANIMALS IN SCOTTISH WATERS. (DELPHINAPTERUS LEUCAS.) A. C. Stephen. Nature, Lond., vol.130, no.3293, p.889, Dec.10, 1932.

ON THE EXTERNAL CHARACTERS AND SOME PARTS OF THE ANATOMY OF A BELUGA (DELPHINAPTERUS LEUCAS). John Struthers. Jour. Anat. and Physiol., Edinburgh, vol.30, pp.124-156, pl.4, Oct., 1895.

THE WHITE WHALE IN IPSWICH, MASSACHUSETTS. Charles W. Townsend. Jour. Mam., vol.10, no.2, p.171, May, 1929.

(ON THE WHITE WHALE (DELPHINAPTERUS LEUCAS PALL.) AND ITS CATCHING IN TSCHESCHA-INDIGA-BAI (BARENTS SEA).) A. Tschirkowa, S. Folitarek. Trudy Nauchno-Issledovatel'skogo Instituta Zoologii (Works Sci. Invest. Inst. Zool.), Moscow, vol.4, no.2, pp.101-127, fig.1, 1930. (In Russian.)

A MODIFICATION OF THE PECTORAL FINS IN THE BELUGA FROM THE ST. LAWRENCE RIVER. Vadim D. Vladykov. Naturaliste Canadien, Quebec, vol.70 (ser. 3, vol.14), nos.1-2, pp.23-40, figs.7, Jan.-Feb., 1943.

(STUDY OF AQUATIC MAMMALS. III. HUNTING, BIOLOGY, AND ECONOMIC VALUE OF THE WHITE WHALE OR BELUGA OF THE ST. LAWRENCE GULF AND RIVER.) Etudes sur les mammiferes aquatiques. III.--Chasse, biologie et valeur economique du marsouin blanc ou beluga (Delphinapterus leucas) du fleuve et du golfe Saint-Laurent. Vadim D. Vladykov. Dept. Pecheries, Prov. Quebec, pp.194, figs.57, 1944.

THE ANATOMY OF THE NORTHERN BELUGA (BELUGA CATODON, GRAY; DELPHINAPTERUS LEUCAS, PALLAS) COMPARED WITH THAT OF OTHER WHALES. Morrison Watson, Alfred H. Young. Trans. Roy. Soc., Edinburgh, vol.29, pp.393-435, pls.2, 1879.

DESCRIPTION OF A "WHITE FISH" OR "WHITE WHALE" BELUGA BOREALIS, LESSON. Jeffries Wyman. Boston Jour. Nat. Hist., vol.7, pp.603-612, pls.13, 1863.

HUNTING THE WHITE WHALE. Hunting and Fishing, Phila., vol.27, no.1, p.16, Jan., 1950.

(Monodon)

HISTORIC NARWHAL TUSKS. Dudley W. Collings. Trans. Suffolk Naturalists' Soc., vol.2, no.1, pp.52-54, pl.1, 1932.

THE MANUS OF THE NARWHAL, MONODON MONOCEROS L. N. B. Eales. Proc. Zool. Soc. Lond., vol.124, pt.2, pp.201-211, illus., Aug.20, 1954.

THE SKULL OF THE FOETAL NARWHAL, MONODON MONOCEROS L. N. B. Eales. Philos. Trans. Roy. Soc. Lond., ser.B, Biol. Sci., vol.235, no.621, pp.33, illus., 1950.

DESCRIPTION OF A SMALL-HEADED NARWAL; CAST ASHORE IN ZETLAND. John Fleming. Mem. Wernerian Soc., vol.1, pp.131-148, pl.6, 1811.

A NARWHAL IN THE THAMES ESTUARY. F. C. Fraser. Nature, London, vol.163, no.4145, p.575, Apr.9, 1949.

SKULL OF THE FOETAL NARWHAL. F. C. Fraser. Nature, London, vol.167, no. 4254, p.765, May 12, 1951.

VESTIGIAL TEETH IN THE NARWHAL. F. C. Fraser. Proc. Linn. Soc. Lond., 150th Sess., pt.3, pp.155-162, figs.6, pl. 3, 1938.

ON THE TUSKS OF THE NARWHALE. Everard Home. Philos. Trans., pp.126-130, pl.7, Lond., Feb., 1813.

MYOLOGY OF THE NARWHAL (MONODON MONOCEROS). Alfred Brazier Howell. Amer. Jour. Anat., vol.46, no. 2, pp.185-215, figs.8, Sept.15, 1930.

AN ALASKAN RECORD OF THE NARWHAL. Laurence M. Huey. Jour. Mam., vol.33, no.4, p.496, Nov.19, 1952.

NOTE ON THE GEOGRAPHICAL DISTRIBUTION OF THE NARWHAL (MONODON MONOCEROS). W. Lilljeborge. Proc. Zool. Soc. Lond., pp.559-560, 1866.

NARWHALS, SMALL WHALES ARMED WITH SPEARS, ARE SHOWN IN NEW EXHIBIT. Wilfred H. Osgood. Field Mus. News, vol.9, no.11, p.1, illus., Nov., 1938.

(THE NARWHAL. THREE YEARS OF INVESTIGATION TRIPS ON THE EASTERN COAST OF GREENLAND.) Der Scoresbysund. Drei Jahre Forschungsreisen an der Ostkueste Groenlands. Alwin Pedersen. Berlin: August Scherl, p.157, figs.56, map 1, 1930. (Contains interesting photographs of narwhal.)

NORWHAL TUSKS. R. I. Pocock. Field, London, vol.151, p.961, June 7, 1928.

SCATTERED OBSERVATIONS ON NARWHALS. Morten P. Porsild. Jour. Mam., vol.3, no.1, Balto., pp.8-13, pl.1, Feb.8, 1922.

NORTHWARD FOR NARWHAL. H. C. Raven. Nat. Hist., vol.27, no.1, pp. 33-44, illus., Feb., 1927.

(SOME REMARKS ON THE NARWHAL TUSK.) Nogle Bemaerkninger om Narhvalens Stoedtand. J. Reinhardt. Vidensk. Meddel. Naturhist. Foren., Kjhnenhavn, 1862, pp.326-335, 1863.

NARWHAL TUSKS. T. Sheppard. Naturalist, London, no.782, pp.223-225, Sept., 1940.

NARWHALS WITH TWO TUSKS. T. Sheppard. Naturalist, London, no.960, pp.7-9, fig.1, Jan., 1937; Hull Mus. Publ. no.196, pp.7-9, illus., 1938.

(SOME REMARKS ON THE NARWHAL TUSK.) Nogle bemaerkninger om narhvalens stodtand, specielt med hensyn til spiralsnoningen. R. Spaerck. Vidensk. Medd. Dansk. Naturh. Foren., Publ. Univ. Zool. Mus., Kobenhavn, no.12, vol. 71, pp.165-168, 1919.

THE "HORN" OF THE NARWHAL. D'Arcy Wentworth Thompson. Vsesoiuznyi nauchno-issledovatel'skii institut morskogo rybnogo khoziaistva i okeanografii SSSR, Volume in honour of sci. activity of N.M. Knipovich, Inst. Marine Fisheries and Oceanography USSR (VNIRO), Peoples Commissariat for Food Industry USSR, Moscow and Leningrad, pp.347-352, 1939. (In English, with Russian résumé.)

SOME OBSERVATIONS ON THE DENTITION OF THE NARWHAL (MONODON MONOCEROS). William Turner. Jour. Anat. and Physiol., vol.7, pp.75-79, 1873.

ON THE STOMACH OF A NARWHAL (MONODON MONOCEROS). G. Sims Woodhead. Proc. Roy. Soc. Edinburgh, Sess.1888-1889, pp.792-808, pls.4, 1889.

## Delphinidae

THE BLACK FINLESS PORPOISE, MEOMERIS. Glover M. Allen. Bull. Mus. Comp. Zool., vol.65, pp.233-256, pls.3, Jan., 1923.

BURMEISTER'S PORPOISE (PHOCAENA SPINIPINNIS). Glover M. Allen. Bull. Mus. Comp. Zool., Harvard Coll., Cambridge, vol.67, no.5, pp.251-261, pls.4, July, 1925.

OCEANS DOLPHINS. Glover M. Allen. Bull. Boston Soc. Nat. Hist., no.61, pp. 3-7, Oct., 1931.

DOLPHINS. J. L. Baughman. Texas Game and Fish, Austin, vol.4, no.6, pp.11, 20, illus., May, 1946.

FURTHER NOTES ON THE DALL PORPOISE. Seth B. Benson. Jour. Mam., vol.27, no.4, pp.368-374, Nov.25, 1946.

NOTES ON THE DALL PORPOISE (PHOCOENOIDES DALLI). Seth B. Benson, Thomas C. Groody. Jour. Mam., vol.23, no.1, pp.41-51, pl.1, Feb.14, 1942.

REMARKS UPON THE SPECIES OF THE GENUS LAGENORHYNCHUS. I AND II. W. H. Bierman, E. J. Slijper. Proc. Kon. Nederl. Akad. van Wetenschappen, Amsterdam, vol.50, no.10, pp.1353-1364, figs.3, 1947; vol.51, no.1, pp.127-133, fig.4, 1948.

NOTES ON A SPECIMEN OF PHOCOENA VOMERINA (GILL), THE HARBOUR PORPOISE. Richard A. Boolootian. Zool. Garten, Leipzig, 23 (1-3): 227-229, illus., 1957.

(ON DOLPHINS (DELPHINUS ORCA L.).) Om Spaekhuggeren (Delphinus Orca, L.). D. F. Eschricht. Kgl. Danske Videnskabernes Selskabs Forhandlinger, pp.27, 1862.

THE DANDY DOLPHIN. Kip Farrington. Field and Stream, New York, vol.49, no.9, pp.74-75, illus., Jan., 1945.

NOTICE OF A MEMOIR ON RISSO'S DOLPHIN (DELPHINUS RISSOANUS). William H. Flower. Proc. Zool. Soc. London, p.506, 1871.

ON THE CHARACTERS AND DIVISIONS OF THE FAMILY DELPHINIDAE. William H. Flower. Proc. Zool. Soc. Lond., pp. 465-513, 1883.

ON THE COMMON DOLPHIN, DELPHINUS DELPHIS, LINN. William H. Flower. Proc. Zool. Soc. Lond., pp.382-384, Apr.1, 1879.

ON RISSO'S DOLPHIN, GRAMPUS GRISEUS. William H. Flower. Trans. Zool. Soc. Lond., vol.8, pt.1, pp.1-21, pls.1-2, 1872.

THE DOLPHIN FAMILY. F. C. Fraser. Zoo Life, London, vol.10, no.3, pp.74-78, illus., Autumn, 1955.

EXHIBITION OF FILM OF KILLER WHALES. F. C. Fraser. Proc. Zool. Soc. Lond., 126 (3): 489, May 31, 1956.

PORPOISES AND DOLPHINS. F. C. Fraser. Illus. London News, vol.211, no. 5669, p.668, illus., Dec.13, 1947.

THE FINLESS BLACK PORPOISE (NEOMERIS PHOCAENOIDES). F. C. Fraser. Nat. Hist. Mag., British Mus., vol.5, no.34, pp.90-91, illus., Apr., 1935.

THE SOUTHERN RIGHT WHALE DOLPHIN, LISSODELPHIS PERONI (LACEPEDE). F. C. Fraser. Bull. British Mus. (Nat. Hist.), London, vol.2, no.11, pp.339-346, pl.12, Jan., 1955.

(THREE SPECIES OF DOLPHIN.) Trois especes de dauphins. P. Gervais. pp.89-94, 1 pl., 1855.

DOLPHINS AND PORPOISES. Raymond M. Gilmore. Collier's Encyclopedia, New York, vol.5, pp.526-528, illus., 1950.

NOTE ON THE BOTTLE-NOSE WHALES (TURSIO). John E. Gray. Proc. Zool. Soc. Lond., pp.560-562, figs.2, 1868.

(CONTRIBUTIONS TO KNOWLEDGE OF DELPHINUS ALBIROSTRIS, GRAY.) Bidrag t il kundskab om Delphinus albirostris, J.E. Gray. Gustav A. Guldberg. Christiania Videnskabsselskabs Forhl., no.3, pp.7, 1882.

THE FALSE KILLER DOLPHIN. Sidney F. Harmer. Nature, London, vol.127, no. 3193, p.60, Jan.10, 1931.

ON COMMERSON'S DOLPHIN AND OTHER SPECIES OF CEPHALORHYNCHUS. Sidney F. Harmer. Proc. Zool. Soc. Lond., pp. 627-638, 3 pls., Sept., 1922.

(KILLER WHALE.) Spaekhuggeren. O. Helms. Naturens Verden, vol.21, no.5, pp.223-235, figs.9, May, 1937.

(NOTE ON ONE DOLPHIN.) Nota sobre und Delfin (Tursiops gephyreus Lah.). Fernando Lahille. Ann. Mus. Nac., Buenos Aires, vol.16, ser.3, vol.9, pp. 347-365, pls.3-4, figs.4, 1908.

(SOME REMARKS ON PSEUDORCA CRASSIDENS OWEN.) Nagra ord om halvspaeckhuggaren, Pseudorca crassidens Owen. Einar Lonnberg. Fauna och Flora, Upsala, Haeft 2, pp.87-92, fig.1, 1936.

(CRITICAL STUDIES OF SOME TOOTHED WHALES OF THE GENERA TURSIOPS, ORCA, AND LAGENORHYNCHUS.) Kritiske Studier over nogle Tandhvaler af Slaegterne Tursiops, Orca og Lagenorhynchus. Chr. Fr. Lutken. Vidensk, Selsk. Skr., 6 Raekke, naturvidenskabelig og mathematisk Afd. IV, Bd.6, pp.337-397, pls.2, illus., 1887.

MEET MISTER PORPOISE (TURSIOPS TRUNCATUS). Arthur F. McBride. Natural History, New York, vol.45, no. 1, pp.16-29, illus., Jan., 1940.

(ON LAGENORHYNCHUS ALBIROSTRIS GRAY.) Ueber Lagenorhynchus albirostris Gray. Julius Muenter. Ruegen Greifswald, Jahrg.8, pp.1-38, 1 pl., 1876.

ON RISSO'S GRAMPUS (GRAMPUS RISSOANUS, DESM.). James Murie. Jour. Anat. and Physiol., Cambridge, vol.5, pp.118-138, figs.2, pl.5, Nov., 1870.

(INVESTIGATIONS OF GENUS STENO AND REMARKS ON SOME OTHER CETACEANS.) Recherches sur le genre "Steno" et remarques sur quelques autres Cétacés. H. Neuville. Archives du Museum d'Hist. Nat. Paris (6), vol.3, pp.69-241, figs.61, pls.1-16, 1928.

(OBSERVATIONS ON GENUS STENO GRAY 1844 (GLYPHIDELPHIS P. GERV. 1859).) Observations sur le genre Steno Gray, 1844 (Glyphidelphis P. Gerv. 1859). H. Neuville. Compte rendu Association Franc. Adv. Sci. Congres de Constantine, pp.1-5, figs.2, 1927.

ADDITIONAL DATA ON THE OCCURRENCE OF DALL'S PORPOISE. J. T. Nichols. Jour. Mam., vol.31, no.1, p.99, Feb.21, 1950.

"ORCA GLADIATOR" THE PIEBALD TERROR OF THE LONELY SEAS. Charles R. Patterson. Yachting, Concord, vol.67, no.6, pp.45, 85-86, June, 1940.

(AGE DETERMINATION OF DELPHINUS DELPHIS L.) M. M. Sleptzov. Bull. Soc. Nat. Moscow, sect. biol., n.s., vol.49, no.2, pp.43-51, figs.3, 1940. (In Russian, with French resume.)

NOTES ON THE WHITE-BEAKED DOLPHIN (LAGENORHYNCHUS ALBIROSTRIS). Thomas Southwell. Trans. Norfolk and Norwich. Nat. Soc., Norwich, vol.4, pp. 120-124, 1885.

CONTRIBUTIONS TO THE NATURAL HISTORY OF THE CETACEANS. A REVIEW OF THE FAMILY DELPHINIDAE. Frederick W. True. Bull. U.S. Nat. Mus., no.36, pp.191, 1889.

OBSERVATIONS ON THE LIFE HISTORY OF THE BOTTLENOSE PORPOISE. Frederick W. True. Proc. U.S. Nat. Mus., vol.13, publ.812, pp.197-203, fig.1, Sept.9, 1890.

ON TURSIOPS CATALANIA AND OTHER EXISTING SPECIES OF BOTTLENOSE PORPOISES OF THAT GENUS. Frederick W. True. Annals Durban Mus., vol.1, pt. 1, pp.10-24, June 1, 1914.

A RARE DOLPHIN (PRODELPHINUS). Frederick W. True. Science, vol.6, no. 128, p.44, July 17, 1885.

SOME POINTS ABOUT PORPOISES. Frederick W. True. (Interview) News and Courier, Charlestown, S.C., Thursday April 2, 1885.

NOTES ON THE WHITE-BEAKED DOLPHIN (DELPHINUS LAGENORHYNCHUS ALBIROSTRIS). William Turner. Proc. Roy. Phys. Soc. Edinburgh, vol.10, pp.14-19, illus., 1889.

TWO RECORDS OF DALL'S PORPOISE (PHOCOENOIDES DALLI). Frederick A. Ulmer, Jr. Jour. Mam., vol.24, no.3, p.394, Aug.17, 1943.

NOTES ON THE CAAING WHALE. Kenneth Williamson. Scottish Naturalist, Edinburgh, vol.61, no.2, pp.68-72, pls. 4-5, Summer, 1949.

MEET MISTER PORPOISE. Natural History Mag., vol.XLV, no.1, Jan., 1940.

### Africa

COMMON OR HARBOUR PORPOISES FROM FRENCH WEST AFRICA. F. C. Fraser. Bull. Inst. Francais Afrique Nord, ser.A, 20 (1): 276-285, 1958.

DESCRIPTION OF A DOLPHIN STENELLA FRONTALIS (CUVIER) FROM THE COAST OF FRENCH EQUATORIAL AFRICA. F.C. Fraser. Atlantide Report no.1, Sci. Results Danish Exped. to Coasts of tropical West Africa 1945-1946, Copenhagen, pp.61-84, pls.6-9, 1950.

A SPECIMEN OF SOTALIA TEUSZII KUKENTHAL FROM THE COAST OF SENEGAL. F. C. Fraser. Jour. Mam., vol.30, no.3, pp.274-276, pls.1-2, Aug. 17, 1949.

TWO SKULLS OF GLOBICEPHALA MACRORHYNCHA (GRAY) FROM DAKAR. F. C. Fraser. Atlantide Report no.1, Sci. Results Danish Exped. to Coasts of tropical West Africa 1945-1946, Copenhagen, pp.49-60, pls.1-5, 1950.

NOTICE OF CLYMENE SIMILIS, A NEW DOLPHIN SENT FROM THE CAPE BY MR. LAYARD. John E. Gray. Proc. Zool. Soc. Lond., pp.146-149, figs.2, 1868.

NOTICES OF A NEW GENUS OF DELPHINOID WHALES FROM THE CAPE OF GOOD HOPE, AND OF OTHER CETACEANS FROM THE SAME SEAS. John E. Gray. Proc. Zool. Soc. Lond., pp.522-529, figs.2, 1865.

(TURSIOPS TRUNCATUS MONTAGU IN THE

GULF OF TUNIS.) Tursiops truncatus Montagu dans le Golfe de Tunis. J. H. Heldt. Bull. Soc. Sci. Nat. Tunis, vol.6, pp.61-62, 1953.

PSEUDORCA CRASSIDENS OWEN FROM MEDITERRANEAN SHORES OF EGYPT. Kamal Wassif. Jour. Mam., 37 (3): 456, Sept.11, 1957.

THE PLAYFUL DOLPHIN: A SHIP'S LEADING ESCORT IN AFRICAN WATERS. Illus. London News, vol.216, no.5791, p.589, illus., Apr.15, 1950.

Anatomy

(STRUCTURE OF THE LUNG OF DELPHINAPTERUS LEUCAS.) Sur la structure du poumon de Delphinapterus leucas. Wilbrod Bonin, Leonard F. Belanger. Trans. Roy. Soc. Canada, Ottawa, ser.3, vol.33, sec.5, pp.19-22, May, 1939.

THE OLFACTORY TUBERCLE, PREPYRIFORM CORTEX AND PRECOMMISURAL REGION OF THE PORPOISE (PHOCAENA PHOCAENA). A. S. Breathnach. Jour. Anat., Cambridge, England, vol.87, pt.2, pp.96-113, Apr., 1953.

THE AMYGDALOID NUCLEI, HIPPOCAMPUS AND OTHER PARTS OF THE RHINENCEPHALON IN THE PORPOISE (PHOCAENA PHOCAENA). A. S. Breathnach, F. Goldby. Jour. Anat., London, vol.88, pt. 3, pp.267-291, July, 1954.

DENTO-ALVEOLAR ABSCESS IN A GRAMPUS (ORCA GLADIATOR BONN.). J. F. Colyer. Scottish Naturalist, Edinburgh and London, no.230, pp.53-55, fig. 1, Mar.-Apr., 1938.

THE FEMALE REPRODUCTIVE SYSTEM AND CORPORA LUTEA OF THE FALSE KILLER WHALE, PSEUDORCA CRASSIDENS OWEN. L. C. Comrie, Ann B. Adam. Trans. Roy. Soc. Edinburgh, vol. 59, pt.2, sess.1937-38, pp.521-531, figs. 4, tables 3, pl.1, Sept.30, 1938.

THE SKULL OF THE FALSE KILLER DOLPHIN, PSEUDORCA CRASSIDENS (OWEN). Lionel F. Cowley. Proc. Zool. Soc. Lond., vol.114, pt.3, pp.382-387, pls.2, Dec., 1944.

DESCRIPTION OF THE SKELETON OF THE CHINESE WHITE DOLPHIN (DELPHINUS SINENSIS, OSBECK). William H. Flower. Trans. Zool. Soc., vol.7, pt.2, pp.151-160, pls.17-18, Jan., 1870.

ON THE EXTERNAL CHARACTERS OF TWO SPECIES OF BRITISH DOLPHINS (DELPHINUS DELPHIS, LINN., AND DELPHINUS TURSIO, FABR.). William H. Flower. Trans. Zool. Soc., Lond., vol. 11, pt.1, pp.1-5, pl.1, 1880.

TWO SKELETONS OF THE CETACEAN PSEUDORCA CRASSIDENS FROM THRONEY FEN. J. R. Garrood. Proc. Zool. Soc. Lond., pp.177-193, 3 pls., 1924.

ON THE CRANIUM OF THE ROUND-HEADED GRAMPUS (DELPHINUS GLOBICEPS, CUV.). R. E. Grant. Proc. Zool. Soc. Lond., pt.1, pp.65-66, 1833.

NOTES ON THE SKULLS OF DOLPHINS, OR BOTTLENOSE WHALES, IN THE BRITISH MUSEUM. John E. Gray. Proc. Zool. Soc. Lond., pp.211-216, p.24, 1866.

NOTES ON THE SKULLS OF THE GENUS ORCA IN THE BRITISH MUSEUM, AND NOTICE OF A SPECIMEN OF THE GENUS FROM SEYCHELLES. John E. Gray. Proc. Zool. Soc., Lond., pp.70-77, figs.4, Jan.27, 1870.

ON THE DEVELOPMENT AND STRUCTURE OF THE WHALE. PART I. ON THE DEVELOPMENT OF THE DOLPHIN. Gustav Guldberg, Fridtjof Nansen. Bergens Mus., pp.70, pls.7, 1894.

OBSERVATIONS ON THE FEMALE REPRODUCTIVE ORGANS OF THE CAAING WHALE GLOBIOCEPHALA MELAENA TRAILL. R. J. Harrison. Jour. Anat., Cambridge, vol.83, pt.3, pp.238-253, figs.2, pls.4, July, 1949.

(COMMUNICATION ON A MATURE PLACENTA OF PHOCAENA PHOCAENA (LINNAEUS).) Mitteilung ueber eine reife Plazenta von Phocaena phocaena (Linnaeus). N. J. Ten Cate Hoedemaker. Archiv. Neerlandaises de Zool., vol.1, no.3, pp.330-338, figs.11, 1935.

CONTRIBUTION TO THE ANATOMY OF THE CHINESE FINLESS PORPOISE NEOMERIS PHOCAENOIDES. A. Brazier Howell. Proc. U.S. Nat. Mus., vol.70, art.13, pp.1-43, pl.1, Mar.11, 1927.

SOME FEATURES IN THE ANATOMY AND LATER DEVELOPMENT OF THE HEAD OF DELPHINUS DELPHINUS LINNE. H. Leighton Kesteven. Records Australian Mus., Sydney, vol.21, no.1, pp.59-80, figs.1-29, July 4, 1941.

(THE EGGSHELLS OF PHOCAENA COMMUNIS CUV.) Die Eihullen von Phocaena communis Cuv. Hermann Klastsoh. Inaugural-Dissertation, Friedrich Wilhelms, Univ., Berlin, pp.1-52, pls.1-2, 1885.

THE THALAMUS OF THE PORPOISE. Lawrence Kruger. Anat. Record, Phila., 127 (2): 319-320, Feb., 1957.

(STRUCTURE OF THE PULMONARY ARTERIES OF THE DOLPHIN (DELPHINUS DELPHIS).) Structure des arteres pulmonaires du dauphin (Delphinus delphis). A. Lacoste, A. Baudrimont. Comptes Rendus Seances Soc. Biol., Paris, vol.94, pp.1148-1149, 1926.

CENTRAL NERVOUS SYSTEM OF THE PORPOISE TURSIOPS TRUNCATUS. Orthello R. Langworthy. Jour. Mam., vol.12, no.4, pp.381-389, Nov., 1931.

A DESCRIPTION OF THE CENTRAL NERVOUS SYSTEM OF THE PORPOISE (TURSIOPS TRUNCATUS). O. R. Langworthy. Jour. Comp. Neurol., vol.54, pp.437-500, 8 figs., 7 pls., 1932.

FACTORS DETERMINING THE DIFFERENTIATION OF THE CEREBRAL CORTEX IN SEA-LIVING MAMMALS (THE CETACEA). A STUDY OF THE BRAIN OF THE PORPOISE, TURSIOPS TRUNCATUS. O. R. Langworthy. Brain, vol.54, pt.2, pp.225-236, figs.3, pls.5-6, 1931.

THE FUNCTIONAL ANATOMY OF THE DELPHINID NOSE. Barbara Lawrence, William E. Schevill. Bull. Mus. Comp. Zool., Cambridge, vol.114, no.4, pp.103-151, figs.30, Feb., 1956.

NOTES ON THE SKELETON OF PRODELPHINUS GRAFFMANI LOENNB. Einar Lonnberg. Arkiv Zool., Stockholm, vol. 30A, no.20, pp.1-21, fig.7, 1938.

ON SOME POINTS IN THE ANATOMY OF GLOBIOCEPHALUS SVINEVAL (GRAY). Alexander Macalister. Proc. Zool. Soc. Lond., pp.477-482, fig.1, 1867.

AUTOPSY OF A BLACK FISH (GLOBICEPHALUS MELAS). G. A. MacCallum. Science, n.s., vol.52, p.387, Oct.22, 1920.

THE ARTERIES OF THE HEAD AND NECK AND THE RETE MIRABILE OF THE PORPOISE (PHOCOENA COMMUNIS). John Y. Mackay. Glasgow Phil. Soc. Proc., vol.17, no.6, pp.61-71, pl.7, 1886.

THE MALE UROGENITAL TRACT IN STENELLA FRONTALIS (G. CUVIER). L. Harrison Matthews. Atlantide Report No.1, Sci. Res. Danish Exped. to Coasts of Tropical West Africa 1945-1946, Copenhagen, pp.223-247, figs.13, 1950.

OBSERVATIONS ON THE REPRODUCTIVE ORGANS, AND ON THE FOETUS OF THE DELPHINUS NESARNAK. Charles D. Meigs. Jour. Acad. Nat. Sci., Phila., n. s., 49, vol.1, pp.267-273, pls.2, 1849.

THE GUMS OF THE PORPOISE PHOCOENOIDES DALLI TRUE. Gerrit S. Miller, Jr. Proc. U.S. Nat. Mus., vol.74, art. 26, pp.1-4, 4 pls., Jan.26, 1929.

A NOTE ON THE SKELETONS OF TWO ALASKAN PORPOISES (PHOCAENA PHOCAENA AND PHOCAENOIDES DALLI.). Gerrit S. Miller, Jr. Smithsonian Misc. Coll., vol.82, publ.3107, pp.1-2, pl.1, Dec.23, 1930.

NOTICE OF A MEMOIR ON THE ANATOMY OF THE PILOT WHALE (GLOBIOCEPHALUS MELAS). James Murie. Proc. Zool. Soc. Lond., p.686, 1867.

ON THE ORGANIZATION OF THE CAAING WHALE, GLOBIOCEPHALUS MELAS. James Murie. Trans. Zool. Soc. Lond., vol.8, pt.4, pp.235-301, pls.30-38, 1873.

THE MORPHOLOGY OF MUSCLES IN THE CAUDAL REGION OF DELPHINUS DELPHIS AND TURSIOPS TURSIO. A. S. Narkhov. Zool. Jour., Moscow, vol.16, no.4, pp.713-722, figs.4, 1937. (In Russian, with English summary.)

(ON THE DENTITION OF THE CETACEANS OF GENUS STENO.) Sur la Dentition des Cetaces du Genre Steno. H. Neuville. Bull. Mus. Nat. Hist., Paris, vol.34, no.1, pp.57-62, figs.3, 1928.

HERMAPHRODITISM IN A DOLPHIN (PRODELPHINUS CAERULEO-ALBUS). Masaharu Nishiwaki. Sci. Repts. Whales Research Inst., Tokyo, no.8, pp.147-150, illus., 1953.

ON THE AGE AND THE GROWTH OF TEETH IN A DOLPHIN (PRODELPHINUS CAERULEO-ALBUS). (I). Masaharu Nishiwaki, Teiji Yagi. Sci. Repts. Whales Research Inst., Tokyo, no.8, pp.133-146, illus., 1953.

(THE SKULLS OF CHILEAN DOLPHINS.) Los Craneos De Los Delfines Chilenos. Rudolph A. Philippi. Anales Del Museo Nacional De Chile, Publicados Por Orden Del Gobierno De Chile, Primera Seccion: Zoolojia - entrega 12a, pp.5-18, pls.6, Santiago, Chile, 1896.

ON SOME PARTS OF THE VISCERAL ANATOMY OF THE PORPOISE, NEOMERIS PHOCOENOIDES. Chi Ping. Anat. Record, Phila., vol.33, no.1, pp.13-28, figs.10, May 25, 1926.

ON THE TESTIS AND ITS ACCESSORY STRUCTURES IN THE PORPOISE. Chi Ping. Anat. Record, Phila., vol.32, no. 2, pp.113-117, figs.2, Feb.25, 1926.

ON THE GENITAL ORGANS OF A FEMALE COMMON DOLPHIN (DELPHINUS DELPHIS). W. P. Pycraft. Proc. Zool. Soc. Lond., pt. 3, pp.807-811, Sept., 1932.

(THE ANATOMY OF THE LARYNX AND SNOUT OF PHOCAENA COMMUNIS CUV.) Die Anatomie des Kehlkopfes und der Nase von Phocaena communis Cuv. Bernhard Rawitz. Internat. Monatssch. Anat. Physiol., Leipzig, vol.17, nos.6-7, pp.245-354, pls.7-10, 1900.

(CONTRIBUTIONS TO THE MICROSCOPIC ANATOMY OF THE CETACEANS. I. THE SUPRARENAL CAPSULE OF PHOCAENA COMMUNIS CUV.) Beitraege zur mikroskopischen Anatomie der Cetaceen. I. Die Nebeniere von Phocaena communis Cuv. Bernard Rawitz. Internat. Monatssch. Anat. Physiol., Leipzig, vol.20, nos.7-9. pp.267-273, figs.2, 1903.

(CONTRIBUTIONS TO THE MICROSCOPIC ANATOMY OF THE CETACEANS. II. ON THE TONGUE OF DELPHINUS DELPHIS L.) Beitraege zur mikroskopischen Anatomie der Cetaceen. II. Ueber die Zunge von Delphinus delphis L. Bernhard Rawitz. Internat. Monatssch. Anat. Physiol., Leipzig, vol.20, nos.10-12, pp.429-435, figs. 4, 1903.

DENSITY OF THE BLACKFISH PETROSAL. L. R. Richardson. Nature, London, vol. 162, no.4108, p.150, July 24, 1948.

THE SKULL OF CHINESE FINLESS PORPOISE (NEOMERIS PHOCAENOIDES). Tsen-Hwang Shaw. Bull. Fan. Mem. Inst. Biol., Zool. Ser., vol.8, no.5, pp.373-386, figs.7, tables, Nov.10, 1938.

ON THE BLOW-HOLE OF THE PORPOISE. Francis Sibson. Philos. Trans. Lond., vol.138, pp.117-123, pl.1, 1848.

(ON THE DEVELOPMENT OF THE CAUDAL LOBES OF DELPHINUS DELPHIS L.) M. M. Sleptzov. Bull. Soc. Nat. Moscow, Sect. Biol., n.s., vol.49, nos.5-6, pp.105-111, fig.1, 1940. (In Russian, with French resume.)

(PSEUDORCA CRASSIDENS (OWEN), A CONTRIBUTION TO THE COMPARATIVE ANATOMY OF THE CETACEANS.) Pseudorca crassidens (Owen), ein beitrag zur vergleichen den anatomie der Cetaceen. E. J. Slijper. Zool. Mededeelingen Leiden, pp.241-366, figs.43, tables 3, 1939.

(SOME NOTES ON THE MYOLOGY OF THE DOLPHINS.) Einige Daten zur Myologie der Delphine. B. N. Smirnowsky. Anat. Anzeiger, vol.66, pp.193-199, 4 figs., Nov. 3, 1928.

ON THE DIGESTIVE ORGANS OF THE WHITE DOLPHIN (SOTALIA SINENSIS). D. S. Tang, F. T. Huang. Lingnan Sci. Jour., Lingnan Univ., Canton, vol.19, no. 1, pp.39-48, figs.10, Jan.22, 1940.

(VARIABILITY OF THE SKULL OF THE DOLPHIN OF THE BLACK SEA ACCORDING TO AGE, SEX, AND INDIVIDUALITY.) J. F. Truber. Bull. Soc. Nat. Moscow, sect. biol., n.s., vol.46, no.1, pp.17-24, figs.2, 1937. (In Russian, with French summary.)

NOTES ON SOME SKELETONS AND SKULLS OF PORPOISES OF THE GENUS PRODELPHINUS, COLLECTED BY DR. W. L. ABBOTT IN THE INDIAN OCEAN. Frederick W. True. Proc. U.S. Nat. Mus., vol.17, publ.982, pp.33-37, July 19, 1894.

NOTES ON SOME OF THE VISCERA OF RISSE'S DOLPHIN (GRAMPUS GRISEUS). William Turner. Jour. Anatomy and Physiol., Edinburgh, vol.16, pp.258-270, figs.3, 1892.

THE LUNGS OF THE CETACEA, WITH SPECIAL REFERENCE TO THE HARBOR PORPOISE (PHOCAENA PHOCOENA LINNAEUS). George B. Wislocki. Anat. Record, Phila., vol.84, no.2, pp.117-123, figs.2, pl.1, Oct.26, 1942.

ON THE PLACENTATION OF THE HARBOR PORPOISE (PHOCAENA PHOCOENA (LINNAEUS)). George B. Wislocki. Biol. Bull., vol.65, no.1, pp.80-98, pls.5, Aug., 1933.

ON THE STRUCTURE OF THE LUNGS OF THE PORPOISE (TURSIOPS TRUNCATUS). George B. Wislocki. Amer. Jour. Anat., vol.44, pp.47-78, 3 pls., 1929.

THE PLACENTATION OF THE BOTTLE-NOSED PORPOISE (TURSIOPS TRUNCATUS). George B. Wislocki, Robert K. Enders. Amer. Jour. Anat., Phila., vol.68, no.1, pp.97-125, figs.3, pls.6, Jan.15, 1941.

AN ANALYSIS IN MASS OSTEOLOGY OF THE FALSE KILLER WHALE PSEUDORCA CRASSIDENS (OWEN). PART I. Munesato Yamada. Okajimas Folia Anat. Japonica, 28 (1-6): 451-463, Sept., 1956.

ON THE SEROLOGICAL CONSTITUTION OF STRIPED DOLPHIN (PRODELPHINUS CAERULEO-ALBUS (MEYEN)). K. Yamaguchi, K. Fujino. Sci. Repts. Whales Research Inst., Tokyo, no.7, pp.69-77, July, 1952; Proc. Japan Acad., vol.29, no. 2, pp.61-67, Feb., 1953.

Arctic Ocean and Northern Seas

ON THE SPECIES OF THE GENUS ORCA INHABITING THE NORTHERN SEAS. D.F. Eschricht. In Recent memoirs on the Cetacea, by Eschricht et al., London, Ray Soc., publ.40, 312 pp., 6 pls., 1866.

COMMON DOLPHINS IN THE NORTH SEA. F. C. Fraser. Scottish Naturalist, no. 226, pp.103-105, fig.1, July-Aug., 1937.

(ON TWO STRIPED DOLPHINS (GRAMPUS GRISEUS CUV.) FROM THE NORTH SEA AND ON THE CETACEANS OBSERVED IN THE BAY OF KIEL.) Ueber zwei gestreifte Delphine (Grampus griseus Cuv.) aus der Nordsee und ueber die in der Kieler Bucht beobachteten Cetaceen. K. Moebius. Schriften Naturwiss. Vereins Schlewig-Holstein, Kiel, vol.1, no.2, pp.196-201, 1874.

ON THE CAPTURE OF DELPHINUS ORCA IN SOUTH GREENLAND. Proc. Zool. Soc. Lond., pt.21, p.103, 1853.

WHITE-SIDED DOLPHIN IN NORTH SEA. James Ritchie. Scottish Nat., no.180, p.168, 1929.

ON A NEW SPECIES OF DOLPHIN FROM THE FAR-EASTERN SEAS (LAGENORHYNCHUS OGNEVI.). M. M. Selpsov. Trans. Inst. Oceanology, Acad. Sci. USSR, Moscow, 18: 60-68, 1955.

WAR AGAINST KILLER WHALES NEAR ICELAND. Norsk Hvalfangst-Tidende (Norwegian Whaling Gazette), 45 (10): 570-573, Oct., 1956.

Asia

A VISIT TO THE LACCADIVE ISLANDS. (CAPTURE OF A SCHOOL OF RISSO'S PORPOISES AND A BOTTLENOSE PORPOISE.) R. W. Burton. Jour. Bombay Nat. Hist. Soc., vol.41, no.3, pp.489-513, pls. 4, Apr., 1940.

NOTICE OF A MEMOIR ON THE WHITE DOLPHIN (DELPHINUS SINENSIS). William H. Flower. Proc. Zool. Soc. London, p. 430, 1869.

ON AN INDIAN DOLPHIN AND PORPOISE. R. Lydekker. Proc. Zool. Soc. London, pp.802-808, Apr., 1909.

A STUDY OF JAPANESE DELPHINIDAE (I). (PRODELPHINUS CAERULEO-ALBUS.) Yaichiro Okada. Sci. Reports Tokyo Univ. Lit. and Sci., sec.B, vol.3, no.44, pp.1-16, figs.8, pls.5, June 30, 1936.

A STUDY OF JAPANESE DELPHINIDAE (II). (DELPHINUS DELPHIS LINNAEUS. "MAIRUKA.") Yaichiro Okada, Toshimasa Hanaoka. Science Reports Tokyo Bunrika Daigaku, sect.B, vol.3, nos.57-59, pp. 243-267, figs.3, tables 16, pls.21-25, Sept.10, 1938.

A STUDY OF JAPANESE DELPHINIDAE (III). LAGENORHYNCHUS OBLIQUIDENS GILL. "KAMA-IRUKA." Yaichiro Okada, Toshimasa Hanaoka. Sci. Reports Tokyo Bunrika Daigaku, sect.B, vol.4, no. 72, pp.139-157, figs.5, pls.12-14, Sept.25, 1939.

A STUDY OF JAPANESE DELPHINIDAE (IV). TURSIO BOREALIS (PEALE). "SEMI-IRUKA." Yaichiro Okada, Toshimasa Hanaoka. Sci. Reports Tokyo Bunrika Daigaku, sect.B, vol.4, no.77, pp.285-306, figs.26, Apr.30, 1940.

STUDIES ON THE DELPHINIDAE OF JAPAN (IV). NOTES ON THE MIGRATION AND FOETUS OF PHOCAENOIDES DALLI (TRUE) IN JAPAN. Yaichiro Okada, Ryoji Hayashi. Rept. Faculty Fisheries Prefectural Univ. Mie, vol.1, no.1, pp.4-6, pl.1, Sept.30, 1951.

AN ACCOUNT OF A NEW SPECIES OF DELPHINUS, AND INHABITANT OF THE GANGES. William Roxburgh. Asiat. Researches, vol.7, pp.170-174, pl.5, 1801.

ON TWO SPECIMENS OF PORPOISE CAPTURED ON THE COAST OF OZERNAYA, KAMCHATKA. Jiro Seno. Bull. Japanese Soc. Sci. Fisheries, Tokyo, vol. 8, no.6, pp.357-364, figs.12 (1 map), Mar., 1940. (In Japanese with English synopsis. Phocaenoides dalli True.)

THE INDIAN BOTTLE-NOSED DOLPHIN. Arthur de Carle Sowerby. China Jour., Shanghai, vol.26, no.1, pp.42-43, illus., Jan., 1937.

PHOCOENOIDES AND LAGENORHYNCHUS IN JAPAN, WITH NOTES ON HUNTING. Ford Wilke, Takenshi Taniwaki, Nagahisa Kuroda. Jour. Mam., 34 (4): 488-497, illus., Nov., 1953.

AN ACCOUNT OF A RARE PORPOISE, FERESA GRAY FROM JAPAN. Munesato Yamada. Sci. Repts. Whales Research Inst., Tokyo, no.9, pp.59-88, illus., 1954.

Atlantic Ocean and Islands

RECORD OF A PORPOISE NEW TO THE ATLANTIC. George G. Goodwin. Jour. Mam., vol.26, no.2, p.195, pl.1, July 15, 1945.

("GLOBICEPHALUS MELAS" IN THE SEAS OF THE MADEIRA ARCHIPELAGO.) O "Globicephalus melas" nos mares do Arquipelago da Maderia. Augusto Nobre. Anais Fac. Cien., Porto, vol.22, no.4, pp.234-240, pls.3, 1938.

A NOTE ON THE COMMON BOTTLENOSED PORPOISE OF THE NORTH ATLANTIC, TURSIOPS TRUNCATUS (MONTAGU). Frederick W. True. Proc. Acad. Nat. Sci. Phila., vol.55, pp.313-314, July 3, 1903.

Auditory Response and Sound Emission

PRODUCTION OF UNDERWATER SOUND BY THE WHITE WHALE OR BELUGA, DELPHINAPTERUS LEUCAS (PALLAS). Marie P. Fish, W. H. Mowbray. Jour. Marine Research, vol.20, no.2, pp.149-162, July 15, 1962.

SOUND EMITTED BY DOLPHINS. F. C. Fraser. Nature, vol.160, p.759, Nov.29, 1947.

REACTIONS OF THE PORPOISE TO ULTRASONIC FREQUENCIES. W. N. Kellogg, Robert Kohler. Science, Lancaster, vol. 116, no.3010, pp.250-252, Sept.5, 1952.

PORPOISE SOUNDS AS SONAR SIGNALS. W. N. Kellogg, Robert Kohler, H. N. Morris. Science, Lancaster, vol.117, no.3036, pp.239-243, illus., Mar.6, 1953.

SOUND EMITTED BY DOLPHINS. B. Kullenberg. Nature, London, vol.160, no.4071, p.648, Nov.8, 1947.

AUDITORY RESPONSE OF A BOTTLE-NOSED PORPOISE, TURSIOPS TRUNCATUS, TO FREQUENCIES ABOVE 100 KC. W. E. Schevill, B. Lawrence. Jour. Exper. Zool. Phila., vol.124, no.1, pp.147-166, illus., Oct., 1953.

HIGH-FREQUENCY AUDITORY RESPONSE OF A BOTTLENOSED PORPOISE, TURSIOPS TRUNCATUS (MONTAGU). W. E. Schevill, B. Lawrence. Jour. Acoustical Soc. Amer., vol.25, no.5, pp.1016-1017, Sept., 1953.

UNDERWATER LISTENING TO THE WHITE PORPOISE. W. E. Schevill, B. Lawrence. Science, 109: 143-144, 1949.

UNDERWATER SOUND PRODUCTION AND CONCURRENT BEHAVIOR OF CAPTIVE PORPOISES, TURSIOPS TRUNCATUS AND STENELLA PLAGIODON. F. G. Wood, Jr. Bull. Marine Sci. Gulf and Caribbean, vol. 3, no.2, pp.120-133, Sept., 1953.

Black Sea

ON THE DISTRIBUTION OF THE COMMON DOLPHIN (D. DELPHIS L.) IN THE BLACK SEA. V. I. Calkin. Comptes Rendus (Doklady) Acad. Sci. USSR, 1937, vol.16, nos.2-7, pp.127-128. (In English.)

(ON THE ORIGIN OF THE BLACK SEA DOLPHIN.) O proiskhozdyenii chyernomorskogo dyelfina Phocaena phocaena relicta Abel. A. A. Kirpichnikov. Zool. Zhurnal, Moscow, vol.31, no.5, pp.722-726, 1952.

ON THE METHODS OF ESTIMATING THE STOCKS OF THE BLACK SEA DOLPHIN (DOLPHINUS DELPHIS PONTICUS BARABASCH). S. E. Kleinberg. Comptes Rendus (Doklady) Acad. Sci. USSR, Moscow, n.s., vol.23, no.5, pp.495-498, tables 3, 1939.

(DOLPHINS OF THE BLACK SEA.) Del'finy chernogo morya. E. N. Malm. Leningrad, Academy of Sciences USSR Press, 23 pp., illus., 1932.

SOME OBSERVATIONS OF THE BIOLOGY OF THE AZOV AND BLACK SEA DOLPHINS. V. I. Zalkin. Bull. Soc. Nat. Moscow, sec. biol., n.s., vol.49, no.1, pp.68-70, 1940.

Coloration

WHITE KILLER WHALE. G. Clifford Carl. Prog. Rept. Pacific Biol. Station, Nanaimo, no.71, pp.36-40, 1947.

(PSEUDO-ALBINISM IN PHOCAENA PHOCAENA.) Pseudo-albinisme bij Phocaena phocaena. A. B. van Deinse. De Levende Natuur, Jahrg., pp.113-117, figs.7, 1935.

A COMMON DOLPHIN--UNCOMMONLY MARKED. Frank S. Essapian. Everglades Nat. Hist., vol.2, no.4, p.1, pl., Dec., 1954.

ON SOME MARKINGS ON THE SKIN OF A DOLPHIN (DELPHINUS DELPHIS). Sidney F. Harmer. Trans. Norfolk and Norwich Nat. Soc., vol.7, pp.185-187, pl.1, 1901.

ON SOME MISINTERPRETED MARKINGS IN THE SKIN OF THE CAAING WHALE. (THE FJELSTRUP "PORE FIGURES.") Ad. S. Jensen. Vidensk. Meddel. f. Dansk Naturh. Foren., Copenhagen, vol.67, pp. 1-8, figs.9, 1915.

ADDENDUM TO PAPER: ON SOME MISINTERPRETED MARKINGS IN THE SKIN OF THE CAAING WHALE. A. S. Jensen. Vidensk. Meddel. f. Dansk Naturh. Foren., Copenhagen, vol.67, pp.221-222, 1916.

A PIED VARIETY OF THE COASTAL PORPOISE (CEPHALORHYNCHUS HECTORI BICOLOR). W.R.B. Oliver. Dominion Mus. Records Zool., Wellington, vol.1, no.1, pp.1-4, figs.3, Apr., 1946.

Economic Importance

(INDUSTRIAL BIOLOGY OF THE DELPHINIDAE.) Biologia industriale dei Delfinidi. Gustavo Brunelli. Boll. Pesca, Piscicol. e Idrobiol., Roma, vol.8, no.3, pp.343-359, figs.10, May-June, 1932.

ON A LARGE CATCH OF THE FINLESS BLACK PORPOISE NEOMERIS PHOCAENOIDES (CUVIER). Egbert Dawson. Jour. Marine Biol. Assoc., India, 1: 259-260, 1959.

(DOLPHIN HUNTING.) A Delfinek Vadaszata. Nandor Hommonnay. A Tenger, Tudomanyos es Tengereszeti Ismeretterjesztoe Folyoirat, Budapest, vol.27, nos.10-12, pp.133-136, illus., Oct.-Dec., 1937.

THE TWILIGHT OF THE INDIAN PORPOISE HUNTERS. Alexander H. Leighton. Natural History, New York, vol.40, no.1, pp.410-416, illus., June, 1937.

(DELPHINUS DELPHIS AND ITS USE IN FISHING IN THE GULF OF NAPLES.) Il Delphinus delphis e la sua utilizzazione nella pesca nel Golfo di Napoli. Gesualdo Police. Boll. Pesca, Piscicol. Idrobiol., Roma, vol.8, no.3, pp.360-379, May-June, 1932.

(Interview) DOLPHINE FOR DINNER. A ROYAL DISH OF THE OLDEN TIME TO BE REVIVED. Frederick W. True. The Evening Star, Washington, D.C., Mar.21, 1885.

THE PORPOISE FISHERY AT HATTERAS, N.C. Frederick W. True. Bull. U.S. Fish Comm., vol.5, pp.3-6, 1885.

THE PORPOISE FISHERY OF CAPE HATTERAS. Frederick W. True. Forest and Stream, vol.24, pp.412-413, June 18, 1885. (Abstracted in Science, vol.5, no. 120, p.424, May 22, 1885.

PORPOISE FISHING. Frederick W. True. The American Angler, N. Y., vol.6, no. 18, p.1, Nov.1, 1884.

PORPOISE FISHING AT CAPE MAY, NEW JERSEY. Frederick W. True. Bull. U.S. Fish Comm., vol.4, pp.431-432, 1884.

PORPOISE STEAK. Frederick W. True. Forest and Stream, N. Y., vol.24, pp. 411-412, June 18, 1885.

Europe

RISSO'S GRAMPUS IN HANTS. Henry Andrews. Trans. Suffolk Nat. Soc., Norwich, vol.4, pt.4, p.289, Dec., 1941.

PORPOISE (PHOCAENA COMMUNIS) AT NORTH BERWICK. K. H. Balmain. Scottish Nat., no.212, p.54, Mar.-Apr., 1935.

(CAPTURE OF A BELUGA (LAGENORHYNCHUS ALBIROSTRIS) AT CROIX-DE-VIE (VENDEE).) Capture d'un Beluga (Lagenorhynchus albirostris) a Croix-de-Vie (Vendee). Marcel Baudouin. Bull. Soc. Sci. Nat. Ouest, 5th ser., vol.1, pp.27-29, 1931.

(STRANDING OF A DOLPHIN (DELPHINORHYNCHUS ROSTRATUS) ON THE BEACH OF PEGE IN SAINT-HILAIRE-DE-RIEZ (VENDEE).) Echouement d'un Delphinorhynque (Delphinorhynchus rostratus) sur la plage de la Pege, en Saint-Hilaire-de-Riez (Vendee). Marcel Baudouin. Bull. Soc. Sci. Nat. Ouest France, Nantes, ser.4, vol.9, nos.1-4, pp.25-28, Mar.31, 1930.

THE BOTTLE-NOSED DOLPHIN IN MANX WATERS. AND A GENERAL NOTE ON CAPTURED CETACEANS. J. R. Bruce. Jour. Manx Mus., Douglas, vol.4, no.62, pp.183-184, pl.178, June, 1940.

WHALES OFF DEVON (ORCA GLADIATOR). A. D. Budd. Field, London, vol.172, no. 4479, p.1030, illus., Oct.29, 1938.

(ON THE OCCURRENCE OF TURSIOPS TRUNCATUS AT MENORCA.) Sobre la presencia de Tursiops truncatus (Montagu) en Menorca. E. Castanos. Butl. Inst. Catalana Hist. Nat., Barcelona, vol.34, nos.6-7, pp.196-197, 1934.

KILLER WHALE (ORCINUS ORCA) AT SCARBOROUGH. W. J. Clarke. Naturalist London, no.852, pp.15-16, 1 fig., Jan., 1928.

WHITE BEAKED DOLPHINS NEAR SCARBOROUGH. W. J. Clarke. Naturalist, London, no.994, p.288, Nov., 1939.

(GRAMPUSES (GRAMPUS GRISEUS CUV.) STRANDED IN DENMARK.) Halvgrindehvalen (Grampus griseus Cuv.) strandet i Danmark. Magnus Degerbol. Naturens Verden, Copenhagen, pp.226-232, figs.4, 1939.

(LAGENORHYNCHUS ACUTUS GRAY IN DANISH WATERS.) Hvidsiden eller Hvidskaevingen, (Lagenorhynchus acutus Gray) i danske Farvande. Magnus Degerbol. Naturens Verden, Copenhagen, pp.164-174, figs.8, 1943.

(A FINDING OF THE WHITE DOLPHIN, DELPHINAPTERUS LEUCAS PALL., IN THE NETHERLANDS.) Een vondst van den witten dolfijn, Delphinapterus leucas (Pall.) in Nederland. A. B. van Deinse, G. C. A. Junge. Zool. Mededeel., Leiden, vol.25, pp.1-4, figs.2, 1945.

(THE "SWORDFISH" OF TERSCHELLING.) De zwaardvisch van Terschelling (Orcinus orca L., 20 Juli 1931). J. W. van Dieren. De Levende Natuur, Amsterdam, Jaargang 36, no.8, pp.225-238, figs.8, Dec. 1, 1931.

DELPHINAPTERUS LEUCAS IN THE OB BAY. M. M. Douhovny. Abstr. works zool. inst. Moscow State Univ., pp.79-82, 1933. (In Russian.)

(PROOF OF THE GREAT TURSIO (TURSIOPS TURSIO BONNATTERRE) AT MECKLENBURG.) Nachweis des Grossen Tummlers (Tursiops tursio (Bonnatterre)) fuer Mecklenburg. Albert Erhardt. Arch. Ver. Freunde Naturg. Mecklenburg, Rostock, n.F., vol.12, pp. 59-60, 1937.

RISSO'S DOLPHINS ON THE COAST OF ORKNEY. F. C. Fraser. Scottish Nat., no.231, p.82, May-June, 1938.

THREE ANOMALOUS DOLPHINS FROM BLACKSOD BAY, IRELAND (GRAMPUS AND TURSIOPS). F. C. Fraser. Proc. Roy. Irish Acad., Dublin, vol.45, sect.B, no.17, pp.413-455, figs.14, pls.32-37, Mar., 1940.

(NOTE ON AN ORC FOUND NEAR TREPORT.) Note sur un Orque Epaulard peche aux environs du Treport. Henri Gadeau de Kerville. Bull. Soc. Amis Sci. Nat. Rouen, annee 1884, 1st semester, pp.105-109, 1884.

NOTICE OF A NEW SPECIES OF PILOT WHALE (GLOBIOCEPHALUS) FROM THE COAST OF DORESTSHIRE. John E. Gray. Proc. Zool. Soc. Lond., pt.29, pp.309-313, figs.4, 1861.

NOTICE OF A NEW SPECIES OF PORPOISE (PHOCAENA TUBERCULIFERA) INHABITING THE MOUTH OF THE THAMES. John E. Gray. Proc. Zool. Soc. Lond., pp. 318-321, 1865.

A BOTTLE-NOSED DOLPHIN IN KINTYRE. E.M.M. Hall. Scottish Nat., no.212, p. 46, Mar.-Apr., 1935.

(THE DOLPHIN AND GRAMPUS IN DANISH WATERS.) Delfinen, Springeren (Delphinus delphis L.) i de danske Farvande. O. Helm. Naturens Verden, Bergen, vol. 23, no.9, pp.385-391, illus., 1939.

(THE OCCURRENCE OF LAGENORHYNCHUS ALBUS (SIC) GRAY IN DENMARK.) Hvidnaesedelfinens (Lagenorhynchus albus (sic) Gray) Forekomst i Danmark. O. Helm. Naturens Verden, Copenhagen, 23 Argang, no.5, pp.232-238, illus., 1939.

PILOT WHALES ON THE NORTH WALES COAST (GLOBICEPHALA MELAENA). L. H. Jackson. Trans. Anglesey Antiq. Soc. and Field Club 1945, pp.67-72, 1946.

CONCERNING A CATCH OF WHITE-SIDED DOLPHINS (LAGENORHYNCHUS ACUTUS) ON THE WEST COAST OF NORWAY, WINTER 1952. Age Jonsgard, Ottar Nordli. Norsk Hvalfangst-Tidende (Norwegian Whaling Gazette), Sandefjord, vol.45, no.5, pp.229-232, illus., May, 1952.

ON THE CAPTURE OF A SPECIMEN OF RISSO'S GRAMPUS AT SIDLESHAM, NEAR CHICHESTER. Henry Lee. Proc. Zool. Soc. Lond., pt.4, pp.808-809, 1877.

ON TWO DOLPHINS FROM MADRAS. R. Lydekker. Jour. Bombay Nat. Hist. Soc., vol.15, pp.408-414, pls.C-D, 1903.

THE BLACK WHALE CAPTURED IN CHARLESTON HARBOR JANUARY 1880. G. E. Manigault. Proc. Elliot Soc. Nat. Hist. Charleston, vol.2, pp.98-104, figs. 3, 1885.

(DELPHINUS DELPHIS ON THE COAST OF HOLLAND.) Delphinus delphis an der niederlaendischen Kueste. E. Mohr. Zool. Garten, Leipzig, n.F., vol.5, nos. 1-3, p.59, June, 1932.

(A LARGE SCHOOL OF GLOBICEPHALA MELAENA IN THE HARBOR OF LERWICK.) Grosse Schule von Globicephala melaena im Hafen von Lerwick. E. Mohr. Der Zoologische Garten, Leipzig (N.F.), vol. 2, pts.4-6, p.135, 1929.

(NOTES ON "PSEUDORCA CRASSIDENS," A NEW CETACEAN FOR THE IBERIAN FAUNA.) Nota sobre el "Pseudorca crassidens, " cetaceo nuevo para la fauna Iberica. E. Morales. Bol. Soc. Espanola Hist. Nat., Madrid, vol.32, pp.155-157, fig.2, 1932.

(GLOBICEPHALA SPECIMEN FOUND DEAD IN THE SEA NEAR LADISPOLI (ROME).) Di un Globicefalo trovato morto nel mare presso Ladispoli (Roma). Antonio Neviana. Mem. Pont. Accad. Sci. Nouvi Lincei, Roma, ser.2, vol.16, pp.273-308, figs.3, 1932.

RISSO'S DOLPHIN OFF THE COAST OF CAERNARVONSHIRE. Charles Oldham. North Western Naturalist, vol.9, no.1, pp.50-51, Mar., 1934.

WHITE-SIDED DOLPHIN (LAGENORHYNCHUS ACUTUS) IN SCOTTISH WATERS. Charles Oldham. Scottish Nat., no.179, pp.133-135, 1929.

THE BLACKFISH SHOT IN SALEM HARBOR IN OCTOBER, 1873, KNOWN UNDER THE NAME OF GLOBIOCEPHALUS INTERMEDIUS. F. W. Putnam. Bull. Essex Inst., Salem, vol.6, no.2, pp.22-24, Feb., 1874.

(PSEUDORCA CRASSIDENS, A WHALE NEW FOR DANISH FAUNA.) Pseudorca crassidens, et for den Danske Fauna hyt Hvaldyr. J. Reinhardt. Saerskilt Aftryk af Oversigten over d.K.D. vid Selsk. Forhandl, pp.103-152, figs.2, Nov. 1, 1862.

DOLPHINS OFF THE BANFFSHIRE COAST. Jeffrey Rintoul, Evelyn V. Baxter. Scottish Naturalist, Edinburgh, no.216, p. 160, Nov.-Dec., 1935.

A REMARKABLE WHALE INVASION. James Ritchie. Scottish Nat., no.168, pp. 161-163, Nov.-Dec., 1927.

SCOTTISH WHALE RECORDS. James Ritchie. Scottish Nat., no.169, p.15, Jan.-Feb., 1928.

COMMON PORPOISE IN THE FIRTH OF FORTH. A. C. Stephen. Scottish Nat., no.170, p.50, Mar.-Apr., 1928.

KILLER WHALE (ORCINUS ORCA) AT FAIR ISLE. A. C. Stephen. Scottish Nat., no.202, p.125, July-Aug., 1933.

KILLER WHALE (ORCINUS ORCA) LANDED AT ALLOA. A. C. Stephen. Scottish Nat., no.195, no.90, May-June, 1932.

NOTICE OF THE CAPTURE OF DELPHINUS DELPHIS IN THE FIRTH OF FORTH. William Turner. Proc. Roy. Physical Soc., Edinburgh, 1886-1887, vol.9, pp.346-348, 1887.

OCCURRENCE OF RISSO'S DOLPHIN (GRAMPUS GRISEUS) IN THE SHETLAND SEAS. William Turner. Proc. Roy. Physical Soc., Edinburgh, 1891-92, vol.11, pp.6, 1892.

Experimental Biology

WATER AND ELECTROLYTE CONTENT OF DOLPHIN KIDNEY AND EXTRACTION OF PRESSOR SUBSTANCE (RENIN). Lillian Eichelberger, Louis Leiter, E.M. K. Geiling. Proc. Soc. Exper. Biol. and Medicine, Utica, vol.44, no.2, pp.356-359, figs.2, June, 1940.

EXPERIMENTS ON THE OSMOTIC REGULATION OF DOLPHINS. E. S. Fetcher, Jr., Gertrude W. Fetcher. Jour. Cell. and Comp. Physiol., Phila., vol.19, no.1, pp.123-130, Feb.20, 1942.

(NEW EXPERIMENTS ON THE RUDIMENTS OF REAR FINS AND THE MILK GLANDS IN YOUNG DOLPHIN EMBRYOS.) Neue Untersuchunge n ueber die Rudimente von Hinterflossen und die Milchdruesenanlage bei jungen Delphinembryonen. Gustav Guldberg. Internat. Monatsschrift f. Anat. u. Physiol., vol.16, nos.11-12, 20 pp., figs.9, pl.20, 1899.

TURSIOPS AS AN EXPERIMENTAL SUBJECT. Barbara Lawrence, William E. Schevill. Jour. Mam., 35 (2): 225-232, May, 1954.

Food Habits

CONTRIBUTIONS TO THE NATURAL HISTORY OF THE BOTTLE-NOSE DOLPHIN, TURSIOPS TRUNCATUS (MONTAGUE), ON THE TEXAS COAST, WITH PARTICULAR REFERENCE TO FOOD HABITS. G. Gunter. Jour. Mam., 23 (3): 267-276, Aug., 1942.

CONSUMPTION OF SHRIMP BY THE BOTTLE-NOSED DOLPHIN. G. Gunter. Jour. Mam., vol.32, no.4, pp.465-466, Nov.19, 1951.

PORPOISE FEEDING (ST. AUGUSTINE BAY, FLORIDA). J. Carver Harris. Life, vol.5, no.12, p.67, illus., Sept.19, 1938.

(FEEDING AND DYNAMICS OF THE CORPULANCE OF DELPHINUS DELPHIS PONTICUS BARABASCH.) S. E. Kleinenberg. Soc. Nat. Moscow, 135th anniversary, pp.1-39, 1940. (In Russian, with French summary.)

SOME DATA ON THE FOOD OF TURSIOPS TURSIO FABR. IN THE BLACK SEA. S. E. Kleinenberg. Bull. Soc. Nat. Moscow, sect. Biol., n.s., vol.47, nos.5-6, pp.406-413, 1938.

ON THE FOOD OF THE DOLPHINS OF THE BLACK SEA. S. E. Kleinenberg. Bull. Soc. Nat. Moscow, sect. Biol., n.s., vol. 45, no.5, pp.338-347, figs.3, 1936. (In Russian with French summary.)

AN INSTANCE OF KILLER WHALES FEEDING ON DUCKS. Gordon C. Odlum. Canadian Field-Nat., Ottawa, vol.62, no.1, p.42, Jan.-Feb., 1948.

A PORPOISE CHOKES ON A SHARK (PHOCAENA PHOCENA). Robert T. Orr. Jour. Mam., vol.18, no.3, p.370, Aug.14, 1937.

FOOD-FINDING BY A CAPTIVE PORPOISE (TURSIOPS TRUNCATUS). William E. Schevill, Barbara Lawrence. Breviora Mus. Comp. Zool., no.53, pp.1-15, Apr. 6, 1956.

Fossils

A FOSSIL RIVER DOLPHIN FROM FLORIDA. Glover M. Allen. Bull. Mus. Comp. Zool., Harvard Coll., Cambridge, vol.89, no.1, 8 pp., 3 pls., Oct., 1941.

MIOCENE PORPOISE (DELPHINODON DIVIDUM) FROM SOUTHERN MARYLAND. Arthur R. Barwick. Amer. Midland Nat., Notre Dame, vol.22, no.1, pp.154-159, illus., July, 1939.

SKULL OF FOSSIL PORPOISE, DELPHINODON DIVIDUM, FROM BANKS OF POTOMAC RIVER, AT WAKEFIELD, VIRGINIA. Arthur R. Barwick. Proc. Biol. Soc. Wash., vol.53, pp.91-92, June 28, 1940.

A FOSSIL PORPOISE FROM CALIFORNIA. William K. Gregory, Remington Kellogg. Amer. Mus. Novitates, no.269, pp.7, figs.3, May 20, 1927.

PHOCAENA OCCIDUUS. Gilbert, Jordan. Leland Stanford Junior Univ. Publ., Univ. Series, Fossil Fishes of Southern California, 1919, II, pp.59, 60, pl.9, fig.2, pl.28, figs.1, 3, 1919.

A FOSSIL PORPOISE FROM THE CALVERT FORMATION OF MARYLAND. Remington Kellogg. Proc. U.S. Nat. Mus., Wash., vol.63, art.14, 39 pp., 18 pls., Mar.26, 1924.

KENTRIODON PERNIX, A MIOCENE PORPOISE FROM MARYLAND. Remington Kellogg. Proc. U.S. Nat. Mus., Wash., vol.69, art.19, 55 pp., illus., 14 pls., Feb.5, 1927.

ON THE IDENTITY OF THE PORPOISE SAGMATIAS AMBLODON. PAPERS ON MAMMALOGY. Remington Kellogg. Zool. Ser., Field Mus. Nat. Hist., Chicago, vol.27, pp.293-311, pls.6-12, Dec.8, 1941.

THREE MIOCENE PORPOISES FROM THE CALVERT CLIFFS, MARYLAND. Remington Kellogg. Proc. U.S. Nat. Mus., vol.105, no.3354, pp.101-154, pls.21, Dec. 14, 1955.

TWO ADDITIONAL MIOCENE PORPOISES FROM THE CALVERT CLIFFS OF MARYLAND. Remington Kellogg. Proc. U.S. Nat. Mus., 107 (3387): 279-337, pls.1-30, Dec.9, 1957.

(ON THE DOLPHIN FROM A DEPOSIT OF THE APSHERON LAYER.) O Delfina iz otlozheniia Apsheronskogo Iarusa. A. A. Kirpichnikov. Doklady Akad. Nauk SSSR, Novaia Seriia, Moscow, vol.79, no.6, pp. 1021-1024, 1951.

TWO NEW GENERA OF DOLPHINS FROM THE SARMATION OF THE USSR. A. A. Kirpichnikov. Proc. Paleo. Int., Acad. Sci. USSR, vol.47, pp.181-190, illus., 1954.

SINANODELPHIS IZUMIDAENSIS, A NEW MIOCENE DOLPHIN OF JAPAN. Jiro Makiyama. Mem. College Sci. Kyoto Imp. Univ., ser.B, vol.11, no.2, art.3, pp.115-134, figs.2, pls.3, 1936.

A NEW SPECIES OF ORCA FROM THE BASAL CALABRIAN AT NAGANUMA, MINATO TOWN, PROVINCE OF KUZUSA, JAPAN. Hikoshichiro Matsumoto. Zool. Mag. (Japan), vol.49, no.5, pp.191-193, figs.2, May, 1937. (In Japanese with English summary.)

DISCOVERY OF A FOSSIL DELPHINOID CETACEAN, WITH TUBERCULATE TEETH. Frederick W. True. Proc. Biol. Soc. Wash., vol.24, pp.37-38, Feb.24, 1911.

DESCRIPTION OF A NEW FOSSIL PORPOISE OF THE GENUS DELPHINODON FROM THE MIOCENE FORMATION OF MARYLAND. Frederick W. True. Jour. Acad. Nat. Sci. Phila., ser.2, vol. 15, pp.165-194, pls.17-26, 1912.

General Habits, Behavior

DOLPHIN PLAY. Maurice Burton. Illus. London News, 228 (6096): 260-263, illus., Apr.7, 1956.

EVIDENCE OF HOME RANGE OF AN ATLANTIC BOTTLENOSE DOLPHIN. David K. Caldwell. Jour. Mam., 36 (2): 304-305, May, 1955.

(DOLPHINS HELP SICK COMRADES.) Delphine helfen kranken Artgenossen. Bernhard Grzimek. Saeugetierk. Mitteil., 5 (4): 160-162, Dec.1, 1957.

DOLPHIN PROTECTING DEAD YOUNG. Carl L. Hubbs. Jour. Mam., vol.34, no.4, p.498, Nov.13, 1953.

ON THE CYCLE OF INCREASE OF THE BLACK "BELOBOCHKI" DOLPHIN (DELPHINUS DELPHIS PONTICUS BARAB.). S. K. Klumov. Trudy Inst. Okeanol., Akad. Nauk SSSR, Moscow, 7: 206-219, 1954.

DOLPHINS AND WEATHER. Charles J. Marten. Trans. Suffolk Nat. Soc., Norwich, vol.4, pt.4, p.289, Dec., 1941.

BOTTLE-NOSED DOLPHINS SUPPORT REMAINS OF YOUNG. Joseph C. Moore. Jour. Mam., 36 (3): 466-467, Aug.30, 1955.

COOPERATION AMONG ADULT DOLPHINS. J. B. Siebenaler, David K. Caldwell. Jour. Mam., 37 (1): 126-128, illus., Feb. 28, 1956.

OBSERVATIONS ON YOUNG BLACKFISH, GLOBICEPHALA. Andrew Starrett, Priscilla Starrett. Jour. Mam., vol.36, no.3, pp.424-429, illus., Aug., 1955.

NOTE ON A DOLPHIN SHOWING TRACES OF AN ENCOUNTER WITH A CUTTLE-FISH. D'Arcy W. Thompson. Ann. Mag. Nat. Hist., London, ser.9, vol.7, pp.503-505, illus., June, 1901.

THE SWORDFISH AND THRESHER SHARK DELUSION. C. H. Townsend. Zool. Soc. Bull., vol.26, pp.76-80, 5 figs., July, 1923.

ATHLETE OF THE SEA (PORPOISE). Edward B. Tracy. Nature Mag., Wash., D.C., vol.36, no.7, pp.355-356, 388, illus., Aug., 1943.

CLOWNS OF THE SEA (DOLPHINS). Dorothy Whittington. Fauna, Phila., vol.4, no.3, pp.76-78, illus., Sept., 1943.

Locomotion

SPEED-INDUCED SKIN FOLDS IN THE BOTTLE-NOSED PORPOISE, TURSIOPS TRUNCATUS. Frank S. Essapian. Breviora Mus. Comp. Zool. Cambridge, no.43, pp.1-4, pls.9, Apr.7, 1955.

STUDIES IN ANIMAL LOCOMOTION. VI. THE PROPULSIVE POWERS OF THE DOLPHIN . J. Gray. Jour. Exper. Biol., vol.13, no.2, pp.192-199, Apr., 1936.

THE SWIMMING OF DOLPHINS. L. Harrison Matthews. Nature, London, vol.161, no.4097, p.731, May 8, 1948.

THE SWIMMING OF DOLPHINS. Alfred H. Woodcock. Nature, London, vol.161, no. 4094, p.602, Apr.17, 1948.

North America

THE BRIDLED DOLPHIN (PRODELPHINUS FROENATUS) ON THE FLORIDA COAST. Glover M. Allen. Jour. Mam., vol.6, no. 1, p.59, Feb., 1925.

THE FALSE KILLER WHALE ON THE NORTH CAROLINA COAST. H. H. Brimley. Jour. Mam., vol.18, no.1, pp. 71-73, illus., Feb.14, 1937.

TWO OCCURRENCES OF FALSE KILLER WHALES, AND A SUMMARY OF AMERICAN RECORDS. Harvey R. Bullis, Jr., Joseph C. Moore. Amer. Mus. Nov., New York, no.1756, pp.5, Mar.8, 1956.

NOTES ON A KILLER WHALE (ORCINUS ORCA) FROM THE NORTHEASTERN GULF OF MEXICO. David K. Caldwell, James N. Layne, J. B. Siebenaler. Quart. Jour. Florida Acad. Sci., vol.19, no.4, pp.189-196, Dec., 1956.

A RIGHT WHALE DOLPHIN COLLECTED IN WASHINGTON (LISSODELPHIS BOREALIS). Wilbert M. Chapman. Murrelet, Seattle, vol.21, no.1, p.10, Jan.-Apr., 1940.

ON TWO SPECIES OF DELPHINIDAE, FROM CALIFORNIA IN THE SMITHSONIAN INST. Theodore Gill. Proc. Acad. Nat. Sci., Phila., pp.177-178, 1865.

A RECORD OF BAIRD'S DOLPHIN (DELPHINUS BAIRDII DALL) IN BRITISH

COLUMBIA. C. J. Guiguet. Canadian Field Nat., vol.68, no.3, p.136, July-Sept., 1954.

A RECORD OF THE LONG-SNOUTED DOLPHIN, STENELLA PLAGIODON (COPE), FROM THE TEXAS COAST. Gordon Gunter. Jour. Mam., vol.22, no.4, pp.447-448, Nov.14, 1941.

TEXAS PORPOISES. Gordon Gunter. Texas Game and Fish, 2 (12): 11, 20-21, Nov., 1944.

OCCURRENCE OF THE HARBOR PORPOISE AT POINT BARROW, ALASKA. E. Raymond Hall, James W. Bee. Jour. Mam., vol.35, no.1, 1954.

DESCRIPTION OF A NEW SPECIES OF GRAMPUS, (DELPHINUS, CUV.) INHABITING THE COAST OF NEW ENGLAND. Richard Harlan. Jour. Acad. Nat. Sci., Phila., vol.6, pp.51-53, 1829.

DESCRIPTION OF THE DELPHINUS INTERMEDIUS--A NEW SPECIES OF GRAMPUS, INHABITING THE COAST OF NEW ENGLAND. Richard Harlan. Med. and Phys. Researches, Phila., pp.71-73, figs.3, 1835.

OCCURRENCE OF STENELLA EUPHROSYNE OFF THE OREGON COAST. Remington Kellogg, Victor B. Scheffer. Murrelet, vol.28, no.1, pp.9-10, 1 pl., Jan.-Apr., 1947.

A BOTTLENOSE DOLPHIN FROM THE CALIFORNIA COAST. Karl W. Kenyon. Jour. Mam., vol.33, no.3, pp.385-387, Aug.19, 1952.

A LONG-SNOUTED DOLPHIN FROM THE WASHINGTON COAST. Karl W. Kenyon, Victor B. Scheffer. Jour. Mam., vol.30, no.3, pp.267-268, pl.1, Aug.17, 1949.

SIGHT RECORDS OF DALL PORPOISES OFF THE CHANNEL ISLANDS, CALIFORNIA. B. L. Lustig. Jour. Mam., vol.29, no.2, p.183, May 14, 1948.

(BLACK DOLPHINS IN TROIS-PISTOLES.) Dauphins noirs aux Trois-Pistoles. Georges Maheux. Naturaliste Canadien, vol.57, no.10, pp.205-206, 1930.

BLACKFISH IN THE GULF OF ST. LAWRENCE. S. J. Mathewson. Jour. Mam., vol.16, no.3, p.234, Aug., 1935.

AMERICAN RECORDS OF WHALES OF THE GENUS PSEUDORCA. Gerrit S. Miller, Jr. Proc. U.S. Nat. Mus., vol. 57, pp.205-207, pls.27-31, June, 1920.

BIOLOGICAL FIELD-WORK IN FLORIDA. (NOTE ON PORPOISES.) Gerrit S. Miller, Jr. Explorations and Field-Work Smithsonian Inst., 1926, Smithsonian Misc. Coll., vol.78, no.7, pp.67-71, illus., 1927.

KILLER WHALES AT GREEN ISLAND LIGHTHOUSE. J. Moran. Canadian Field-Nat., vol.38, pp.84-85, May, 1924.

CETACEAN RECORDS FROM THE PACIFIC COAST OF NORTH AMERICA. Robert T. Orr. Wasmann Jour. Biol., vol.9, no.2, pp.147-148, Summer, 1951.

(NOTES ON GLOBICEPHALA MELAENA (TRAILL).) Notes sur Globicephala melaena (Traill). Georges Prefontaine. Rapport Annuel Societe Provancher, Quebec, 1930, pp.49-66, figs.7, pls.2, 1931.

THE DALL PORPOISE, PHOCOENOIDES DALLI, IN ALASKA. Victor B. Scheffer. Jour. Mam., 30 (2): 116-121, May, 1949.

THE STRIPED DOLPHIN, LAGENORHYNCHUS OBLIQUIDENS GILL 1865, ON THE COAST OF NORTH AMERICA. Victor B. Scheffer. Amer. Midland Nat., Notre Dame, vol.44, no.3, pp.750-758, illus., Nov., 1950.

KILLER WHALE IN SLOUGH AT PORTLAND, OREGON. George S. Shepherd. Jour. Mam., vol.13, no.2, pp.171-172, May, 1932.

CONTRIBUTIONS FROM LOS ANGELES COUNTY MUSEUM-CHANNEL ISLANDS BIOLOGICAL SURVEY. NO.35. OCCURRENCE OF THE FALSE KILLER WHALE PSEUDORCA ON THE CALIFORNIA COAST. Kenneth E. Stager, William G. Reeder. Bull. Southern California Acad. Sci., Los Angeles, vol.50, pt.1, pp.14-20, illus., Jan.-Apr., 1951.

NEW YORK STATE RECORDS FOR THE COMMON DOLPHIN, DELPHINUS DELPHIS. Dayton Stoner. New York State Mus., circ. 21, pp.16, figs.12, May, 1938.

THE BOTTLE-NOSE DOLPHIN, TURSIOPS TURSIO, AS SEEN AT CAPE MAY, NEW JERSEY. Frederick W. True. Science, vol.5, no.116, pp.338-339, Apr.24, 1885.

NOTES ON A KILLER WHALE (GENUS ORCINUS) FROM THE COAST OF MAINE. Frederick W. True. Proc. U.S. Nat. Mus., vol.27, publ.1357, pp.227-230, pls. 7-8, Jan.27, 1904.

OCCURRENCE OF THE KILLER WHALE (ORCINUS ORCA) ON THE NEW JERSEY COAST. Frederick W. True. Science, n.s., vol.29, no.750, p.790, May 14, 1909.

ON A NEW SPECIES OF PORPOISE, PHOCAENA DALLI, FROM ALASKA. Frederick W. True. Proc. U.S. Nat. Mus., vol.8, publ.495, pp.95-98, pls.2-5, June 19, 1885.

NOTES ON A KILLER WHALE (GRAMPUS ORCA) FROM THE COAST OF NEW JERSEY. Frederick A. Ulmer, Jr. Notulae Naturae, Phila., no.83, 5 pp., illus., Aug.11, 1941.

NOTES ON THE DALL PORPOISE OFF CALIFORNIA. Charles F. Yocom. Jour. Mam., vol.27, no.4, pp.364-368, Nov.25, 1946.

AN ALASKAN "SEA MONSTER." (KILLER WHALE.) Illus. London News, vol.216, no.5789, p.513, illus., Apr.1, 1950.

PILOT OR POTHEAD WHALES OUTSIDE NEWFOUNDLAND. Norsk Hvalfangst-Tidende (Norwegian Whaling Gazette), vol.44, no.2, pp.81-83, Feb., 1955. (In Norwegian and English.)

Pacific Ocean and Islands

THE DALL PORPOISE, PHOCOENOIDES DALLI (TRUE), OF THE NORTHERN PACIFIC OCEAN. Ian McT. Cowan. Jour. Mam., vol.25, no.3, pp.295-306, figs.4, pl.1, Sept.8, 1944.

ON GLOBICEPHALA AND SOME OTHER DELPHINIDAE FROM THE INDO-AUSTRALIAN ARCHIPELAGO. K. W. Dammerman. Treubia, vol.5, pp.340-352, pls.6-9, 1924.

THE BLACKS OF MORETON BAY AND THE PORPOISES. J.K.E. Fairhoime. Proc. Zool. Soc. Lond., pt.24, pp.353-354, 1856.

ON A NEW SPECIES OF GRAMPUS (ORCA MERIDIONALIS) FROM TASMANIA. W.H. Flower. Proc. Zool. Soc. Lond., pp.420-426, figs.2, Nov.8, 1864.

A NEW SARAWAK DOLPHIN (LAGENODELPHIS, L. HOSEI.). F. C. Fraser. Sarawak Mus. Jour., Kuching, 7 (8): 478-503, pls.22-26, Dec., 1956.

NOTICE OF A NEW SPECIES OF DOLPHIN (DELPHINUS CATALANIA) DISCOVERED IN NORTH AUSTRALIA BY MR. W. H. PEASE. John E. Gray. Proc. Zool. Soc. Lond., pt.30, pp.143-145, 1862.

PELOROUS JACK. Sidney F. Harmer. Proc. Linnean Soc. Lond., no.141, pp.48-50, (1928-29), 1930.

DESCRIPTION OF THE "COW-FISH" OR "BOTTLE-NOSED DOLPHIN" (TURSIO METIS) OF THE SOUNDS, ON THE WEST COAST OF OTAGO. F. W. Hutton. Trans. New Zealand Inst., Wellington, vol.8, p., Oct., 1875.

NOTICE OF AN APPARENTLY NEW ESTUARINE DOLPHIN FROM BORNEO. Richard Lydekker. Proc. Zool. Soc. Lond., vol.1, pp.88-92, figs.11-12, pls.8, 1901.

NOTES ON TWO PORPOISES CAPTURED ON A VOYAGE INTO THE PACIFIC OCEAN. John T. Nichols. Bull. Amer. Mus. Nat. Hist., New York, vol.24, art.14, pp.217-219, figs.3, pls.14, Feb.26, 1908.

DOLPHINS--LITTLE KNOWN MAMMALS OF THE PACIFIC. Victor B. Scheffer. Pac. Discovery, 2 (4): 18-22, July-Aug., 1949.

MEASUREMENTS AND STOMACH CONTENTS OF ELEVEN DELPHINIDS FROM THE NORTHEAST PACIFIC. Victor B. Scheffer. Murrelet, Seattle, vol.34, no. 2, pp.27-30, illus., 1953.

PORPOISES ASSEMBLING IN THE NORTH PACIFIC OCEAN. Victor B. Scheffer. Murrelet, Seattle, vol.31, no.1, p.16, May 19, 1950.

STUDIES OF TASMANIAN CETACEA. PART I. (ORCA GLADIATOR, PSEUDORCA CRASSIDENS, GLOBICEPHALUS MELAS.) H. H. Scott, Clive E. Lord. Roy. Soc. Tasmania: Papers and Proc., Hobart, pp.1-17, pls.9, May 10, 1919

STUDIES OF TASMANIAN CETACEA. PART III. TURSIOPS TURSIO. SOUTHERN FORM. H. H. Scott, Clive E. Lord. Roy. Soc. Tasmania: Papers and Proc., Hobart, pp.96-109, pls.23-25, Nov.24, 1919.

STUDIES OF TASMANIAN CETACEA. PART IV. DELPHINUS DELPHIS (THE COMMON DOLPHIN). H. H. Scott, Clive E. Lord. Roy. Soc. Tasmania: Papers and Proc., pp.1-10, pls.1-5, May 29, 1920.

THE OCCURRENCE OF A MALE AND FEMALE GRAMPUS GRISEUS (DELPHINIDAE) AT SYDNEY, NEW SOUTH WALES. Ellis Le. G. Troughton. Proc. Zool. Soc. Lond., pt.2, pp.565-569, pl.1, June, 1931.

NOTES ON A PORPOISE OF THE GENUS PRODELPHINUS FROM THE HAWAIIAN ISLANDS. Frederick W. True. U. S. Fish Commission Bulletin, pp.41-45, pls. 1-2, 1903.

Parasites

HEAVY PARASITIC INFECTION IN WHALES (PSEUDORCA CRASSIDENS). H. A. Baylis. Nat. Hist. Mag., London, vol.1, no.7, pp.242-244, photo, July, 1928.

A REMARKABLE CYSTICERCUS FROM A RARE DOLPHIN (CYSTICERCUS TAENIAE GRIMALDII, MONIEZ, 1889). H. A. Baylis. Ann. and Mag. Nat. Hist., ser.9, vol.3, pp.417-424, Apr., 1919.

NOTES ON THE LUNGWORMS OF PORPOISES AND THEIR OCCURRENCE ON THE CALIFORNIA COAST. Ellsworth C. Dougherty. Proc. Helminthol. Soc. Wash., vol.10, no.1, pp.16-22, Jan., 1943.

(ON COLI BACILLUS IN MARINE MAMMALS.) Sur le Bacille coli chez les Mammiferes marins (Phocaena). G. Fleury. Comptes Rendus Acad. Sci., Paris, vol.196, no.20, pp.1547-1549, May 15, 1933.

ON HALOCERCUS PINGI N. SP. A LUNGWORM FROM THE PORPOISE, MEOMERIS PHOCOENOIDES. H. W. Wu. Jour. Parasitology, vol.15, pp.276-279, 7 figs., June, 1929.

Physiology

STUDIES ON THE INTERMEDIATE CARBOHYDRATE METABOLISM OF AQUATIC ANIMALS. I. THE DISTRIBUTION OF ACID-SOLUBLE PHOSPHORUS AND CERTAIN ENZYMES IN DOLPHIN TISSUES. Kenneth P. Dubois, et al. 1948.

ON THE RESPIRATORY FUNCTION OF THE BLOOD OF THE PORPOISE. Arda A. Green, Alfred C. Redfield. Biol. Bull., vol.64, no.1, pp.44-52, Feb., 1933.

THE RESPIRATION OF THE PORPOISE, TURSIOPS TRUNCATUS. Laurence Irving, P. F. Scholander, S. W. Grinnell. Jour. Cell. and Comp. Physiol., Phila., vol.17, no.2, pp.145-168, Apr.21, 1941.

KINEMATICS OF THE DOLPHIN. V. Sulejkin. Bull. Acad. Sci. USSR, ser.7, no.4, pp.651-671, figs.14, 1935. (In Russian, with English summary.)

Reproductive Biology

SCIENTISTS LEARN GESTATION PERIOD OF PORPOISE. Fred Booth. Morning Journal, Daytona Beach, Florida, Feb.13, 1940.

(DOLPHIN FETUSES.) Sur des foetus de Dauphin. P. A. Dizerbo Desbrusses, R. Legendre. Bull. Soc. Zool. France, vol. 71, no.3, pp.158-160, 1947.

THE BIRTH AND GROWTH OF A PORPOISE. AN INSIGHT INTO THE PROCESSES AND BEHAVIOR OF AN AIR-BREATHING ANIMAL THAT GIVES BIRTH AND SUCKLES ITS YOUNG UNDER WATER. Frank S. Essapian. Nat. Hist. Mag., 11 figs., Nov., 1953.

(ON THE GESTATION OF PHOCAENA COMMUNIS LESS.) Ueber die Tragzeit der Phocaena communis Less. James A. Grieg. Jena Zeitschr., n.f.18, vol.25, pp.544-552, 1891.

NOTE ON EMBRYO PORPOISE (LAGENORHYNCHUS OBLIQUIDENS). John E. Guberlet. Murrelet, Seattle, Wash., vol. 17, nos.1-2, p.56, Nov.14, 1936.

BIRTH OF A PORPOISE AT THE BRIGHTON AQUARIUM. Lewis H. James. Proc. Zool. Soc. Lond., pp.1061-1062, Dec., 1914.

OBSERVATIONS ON PREGNANCY, PARTURITION, AND POSTNATAL BEHAVIOR IN THE BOTTLENOSE DOLPHIN. Arthur F. McBride. Jour. Mam., 32 (3): 251-266, Aug., 1951.

INVESTIGATIONS ON REPRODUCTION AND GROWTH OF THE PORPOISE (PHOCAENA PHOCAENA (L.)) FROM THE BALTIC. U. Mohl-Hansen. Vidensk. Meddelelser Dansk Naturhist. Forening, Copenhagen, 116 (for 1954): 369-398, pls.2-3, Feb.23, 1955.

THE BEHAVIOR OF THE BOTTLENOSED DOLPHIN (TURSIOPS TRUNCATUS): MATING, PREGNANCY, PARTURITION AND MOTHER-INFANT BEHAVIOR. C. Margaret Tavolga, Frank S. Essapian. Zoologica, New York Zool. Soc., 42 (1): 11-31, pls.1-3, May 20, 1957.

South America and Mexico

A NEW DOLPHIN FROM THE PACIFIC COAST OF MEXICO (PRODELPHINUS GRAFFMANI). Einar Loennberg. Arkiv. foer Zoologi, vol.26A, no.19, pp.1-11, fig. 1, pl.1, 1934.

(THE DOLPHINS OF THE SOUTHERN TIP OF SOUTH AMERICA.) Die Delphine An Der Sudspitze Sudamerikas. R. A. Philippi. Anales Del Museo Nacional De Chile, pp.1-16, pls.5, F. A. Brockhaus, Leipzig, 1893.

(FURTHER OBSERVATIONS ON CHILEAN DOLPHINS (DELPHINIDAE). Observaciones ulteriores sobre los delfines Chilenos. R. A. Philippi. Anales Univ. Chile, Santiago, vol.88, pp.101-106, vol.90, pp. 281-285, 1894, 1895.

ON SPECIES OF SOUTH AMERICAN DELPHINIDAE DESCRIBED BY DR. R. A. PHILIPPI IN 1893 AND 1896. Frederick W. True. Proc. Biol. Soc. Wash., vol.16, pp.133-143, Nov.12, 1903.

A RIVER DOLPHIN FROM KARTABO, BARTICA DISTRICT, BRITISH GUIANA (SOTALIA GUIANENSIS). Samuel H. Williams. Zoologica (publ. by New York Zool. Soc.), vol.7, no.4, pp.105-128, illus., Dec.13, 1928.

Strandings

TWO HUNDRED FALSE KILLERS HURL THEMSELVES ASHORE; A MYSTERIOUS STRANDING NEAR THE CAPE, WHICH IS PARALLELED BY CASES OF FALSE KILLERS RECENTLY STRANDED ON THE EAST COAST OF ENGLAND. Carel Birkby. Illus. London News, vol.187, no.5044, pp.1124-1125, illus., Dec.21, 1935.

GRAMPUS AT SCARBOROUGH (YOUNG ORCINUS ORCA, WASHED ASHORE). W. J. Clarke. Field, London, vol.151, p.763, illus., May 3, 1928.

A SCHOOL OF KILLER WHALES STRANDED AT ESTEVAN POINT, VANCOUVER ISLAND. G. Clifford Carl. Rept. Prov. Mus. Nat. Hist. and Anthrop., 1945, Victoria, pp.B21-B28, figs.9, 1946.

WHALE INVASION AT ZANZIBAR (LESSER KILLER WHALES). Hugh Copley. Field, London, vol.163, no.4231, p.180, Jan.27, 1934.

RECENT STRANDING OF THE FALSE KILLER WHALE, PSEUDORCA CRASSIDENS, WITH SPECIAL REFERENCE TO THOSE FOUND AT DONNA NOOK, LINCOLNSHIRE. F. C. Fraser. Scottish Nat., no.220, pp.105-114, July-Aug., 1936.

NOTES ON A CETACEOUS ANIMAL STRANDED ON THE NORTHEAST COAST OF IRELAND. George Gulliver. Proc. Zool. Soc. Lond., pt.21, pp.63-67, 1853.

THE PILOT WHALE STRANDING ON THE ORKNEY ISLAND OF WESTRAY, 1955. L. L. de Kock. Scottish Nat., 68 (2): 63-70, 1956.

THE PILOT WHALE AT MARINELAND. Henry Kritzler. Nat. Hist., New York, vol.58, no.7, pp.302-308, illus., Sept., 1949.

(THE BLACK DOLPHINS OF TROIS-PISTOLES.) Dauphins noirs aux Trois-Pistoles . (School of Globicephala melas stranded.) George Maheux. Naturaliste Canadien, vol.57, no.10, pp.205-206, Oct., 1930.

PSEUDORCA CRASSIDENS (OWEN) ON THE GLAMORGAN COAST. Colin Matheson, Lionel F. Cowley. Nature, London, vol. 133, no.3371, p.870, fig.1, June 9, 1934.

BLACK FISH (GLOBIOCEPHALUS) STRANDED ON THE SOUTH COAST OF PRINCE EDWARD ISLAND. A.W.H. Needler. Canadian Field-Nat., vol.45, no.7, pp.157-158, illus., Oct., 1931.

THE FALSE KILLER WHALES STRANDED IN THE TAY ESTUARY. (PSEUDORCA CRASSIDENS.) A. D. Peacock. Scottish Nat., no.220, pp.93-104, illus., July-Aug., 1936.

THE FALSE KILLER DOLPHIN. (SCHOOL OF PSEUDORCA CRASSIDENS STRANDED ON CEYLON.) J. Pearson. Nature, Lond., vol.127, no.3201, p.340, Mar.7, 1931.

A NOTE ON PSEUDORCA CRASSIDENS, THE FALSE KILLER WHALE. (SCHOOL OF FALSE KILLER WHALES STRANDED ON ISLAND OF VELANAI, CEYLON.) J. Pearson. Spoilia Zeylanica, vol.16, pt. 2, pp.199-203, pls.3, Aug.8, 1931.

(ON A DELPHINUS ESCHRICHTII STRANDED AT FLESSINGUE.) Sur un Delphinus Eschrichtii, echoue a Flessingue. M. Poelman. Bull. Acad. Roy. Belgique, Brussels, vol.17, ser.2, pp.604-608, pl. 1, 1864.

LESSER RORQUAL STRANDED IN LEWIS. James Ritchie. Scottish Nat., no.171, p.76, May-June, 1928.

OBSERVATIONS ON A PILOT WHALE STRANDED IN THE FIRTH OF FORTH. James Ritchie. Scottish Nat., no.146, pp.37-43, 2 figs., Mar.-Apr., 1924.

RISSO'S DOLPHIN STRANDED IN CAITHNESS. James Ritchie. Scottish Nat., no.164, p.60, Mar.-Apr., 1927.

STRANDED WHALE AT WHITSTABLE. (GLOBICEPHALA MELAENA.) H. W. Robinson. Field, London, vol.163, no. 4234, p.343, illus., Feb.17, 1934.

BOTTLE-NOSED DOLPHIN (TURSIOPS TRUNCATUS) ASHORE ON THE WIGTOWNSHIRE COAST. A. C. Stephen. Scottish Nat., no.176, p.38, Mar.-Apr., 1929.

PILOT WHALE (GLOBICEPHALA MELAENA) STRANDED IN NORTH UIST. A. C. Stephen. Scottish Nat., no.204, p.183, Nov.-Dec., 1933.

PILOT WHALE STRANDED IN THE FIRTH OF FORTH. A. C. Stephen. Scottish Nat., no.170, p.50, Mar.-Apr., 1928.

RISSO'S DOLPHIN STRANDED IN BANFFSHIRE. A. C. Stephen. Scottish Nat., Edinburgh, no.216, p.175, Nov.-Dec., 1935.

RISSO'S DOLPHIN STRANDED IN ORKNEY (GRAMPUS GRISEUS). A. C. Stephen. Scottish Nat., no.207, p.86, May-June, 1934.

WHITE-BEAKED DOLPHIN (LAGENORHYNCHUS ALBIROSTRIS) STRANDED IN ABERDEENSHIRE. A. C. Stephen. Scottish Nat., no.210, p.164, Nov.-Dec., 1934.

NOTE ON A RARE DOLPHIN (DEPHINUS ACUTUS) RECENTLY STRANDED ON THE COAST OF SUTHERLAND. William Turner. Proc. Roy. Soc. Edinburgh, Sess.1905-06, vol.26, pt.4, pp.310-319, figs.4, Aug.29, 1906.

WERE THEY CAUGHT BY THE TIDE? (PSEUDORCA CRASSIDENS AT ZANZIBAR.) H. Waterland. Field, London, vol.163, no. 4229, p.78, illus., Jan.13, 1934.

FALSE-KILLER WHALE IN SCOTLAND. Nature, London, vol.138, no.3488, p.408, Sept.5, 1936.

"FOLLOW MY LEADER"--EVEN TO DEATH: THE STRANDING OF 97 WHALES...STRONSAY. (GLOBICEPHALUS MELAS, ORKNEY ISLANDS.) Illus. London News, vol.216, no.5794, p.693, illus., May 6, 1950.

THE MASS "SUICIDE" OF FORTY-FOUR WHALES WHICH BEACHED THEMSELVES ON THE FLORIDA COAST: THREE OF THE VICTIMS STRANDED IN SHALLOW WATER. Illus. London News, vol.213, no.5714, p.452, illus., Oct.23, 1948.

147 WHALES STRANDED NEAR DUNBAR, SCOTLAND. Illus. London News, vol. 216, no.5796, p.789, illus., May 20, 1950.

WHALES' LAST ROUNDUP. (STRANDED PILOT WHALES.) Life, Chicago, vol.28, no.10, p.24, illus., Mar.6, 1950.

Taxonomy

THE DELPHINUS OCCIDUUS OF LEIDY. Glover M. Allen. Jour. Mam., vol.5, no. 3, pp.194-195, Aug., 1924.

DELPHINUS DELPHIS PONTICUS SUBSP. N. I. I. Barabash. Bull. Soc. Nat., Moscow, vol.44, n.s., no.5, pp.346-349, 1935.

ON THE METHODS OF TAXONOMIC INVESTIGATION OF THE DELPHINIDAE. I. I. Barabash. Zool. Jour., Moscow, vol. 17, no.6, pp.1091-1104, figs.8, table 1, 1938. (In Russian, with English summary.)

NOTE ON PSEUDORCA MERIDIONALIS. William H. Flower. Proc. Zool. Soc. Lond., pp.470-471, 1865.

NOTE ON THE NAMES OF TWO GENERA OF DELPHINIDAE. William H. Flower. Proc. Zool. Soc. Lond., pp.417-418, June 17, 1884.

ON THE CHARACTERS AND DIVISIONS OF THE FAMILY DELPHINIDAE. William H. Flower. Proc. Zool. Soc. Lond., pp.466-513, figs.9, Nov.20, 1883.

THE SPECIFIC NAME OF THE NORTHERN PILOT WHALE OR BLACKFISH. F. C. Fraser. Annals and Mag. Nat. Hist., ser. 12, vol.4, p.942, Sept., 1951.

DESCRIPTIONS OF THREE NEW SPECIES OF DELPHINIDAE. John E. Gray. Proc. Zool. Soc. Lond., pt.17, pp.1-2, 1849.

DESCRIPTIONS OF THREE SPECIES OF DOLPHINS IN THE FREE MUSEUM OF LIVERPOOL. John E. Gray. Proc. Zool. Soc. Lond., pp.735-739, figs.3, 1865.

NOTES ON THE ARRANGEMENT OF THE GENERA OF DELPHINOID WHALES. John E. Gray. Proc. Zool. Soc. Lond., pp.772-773, 1870.

THE CORRECT GENERIC NAMES FOR THE GRAMPUS OR KILLER WHALE AND THE SO-CALLED GRAMPUS OR RISSO'S DOLPHIN. Tom Iredale, E. Le G. Troughton. Records Australian Mus., vol.19, no.1, pp.28-36, pl.10, Aug.2, 1933.

FERESA INTERMEDIA (GRAY) PREOCCUPIED. J. Knox Jones, Jr., Robert L.

Packard. Proc. Biol. Soc. Wash., 69: 167, Dec.31, 1956.

ON THE AFFINITY OF DALL'S AND TRUE'S PORPOISES. Nagahisa Kuroda. Misc. Repts. Yamashina's Inst. Ornithol. and Zool., Tokyo, no.5, pp.44-46 (222-224), illus., Dec., 1954. (In Japanese, with English summary.)

TURSIOPS GILLII, THE BOTTLENOSED DOLPHIN, A NEW RECORD FROM THE GULF OF CALIFORNIA, WITH REMARKS ON TURSIOPS NUUANU. William V. Mayer. Amer. Midland Nat., Notre Dame, vol.43, no.1, pp.183-185, Jan., 1950.

THE GENERIC POSITION OF THE PORPOISE DESCRIBED BY PHILIPPI AS TURSIO? PANOPE. Gerrit S. Miller, Jr. Proc. Biol. Soc. Wash., vol.41, p.171, Oct.15, 1928.

THE STATUS OF DELPHINUS BAIRDII DALL. Gerrit S. Miller, Jr. Proc. Biol. Soc. Wash., vol.49, pp.145-146, Aug.22, 1936.

ON THE CLASSIFICATION OF DELPHINIDAE IN JAPAN. Teizo Ogawa. Saito Ho-on Kai Jiho, Sendai, Japan, nos.69-70, pp. 57, figs.20, 1932. (In Japanese.)

NOTES ON THREE GENERA OF DOLPHINS. T. S. Palmer. Proc. Biol. Soc. Wash., vol.13, pp.23-24, Jan.31, 1899.

GLOBICEPHALA LEUCOSAGMAPHORA, A NEW SPECIES OF THE GENUS GLOBICEPHALA. George W. Rayner. Ann. and Mag. Nat. Hist., Lond., ser.11, vol.4, no. 23, pp.543-544, Nov., 1939.

THE GENERIC NAME DELPHAX IN MAMMALOGY. Oldfield Thomas. Ann. and Mag. Nat. Hist., ser.10, vol.1, p.623, May, 1928.

THE GENERIC NAME OF THE FINLESS-BACKED PORPOISE. Oldfield Thomas. Ann. and Mag. Nat. Hist., ser.9, vol. 16, p.655, Dec., 1925.

THE GENERIC NAME OF THE FINLESS-BACKED PORPOISE, FORMERLY KNOWN AS NEOMERIS PHOCAENOIDES. Oldfield Thomas. Ann. and Mag. Nat. Hist., ser. 9, vol.9, pp.676-677, June, 1922.

ON A SPOTTED DOLPHIN APPARENTLY IDENTICAL WITH THE PRODELPHINUS DORIS OF GRAY. Frederick W. True. Annual Report Board Regents Smithsonian Institution, 1884, pt.2, Rep. U.S. Nat. Mus., pp.317-324, pls.1-6, 1885.

ON A NEW SPECIES OF THE GENUS DELPHINUS. G. R. Waterhouse. Proc. Zool. Soc. Lond., pt.6, p.23, 1838.

TAXONOMY AND ORIGIN OF THE PORPOISES OF THE AZOPH AND BLACK SEAS. V. I. Zalkin. Zool. Jour., Moscow, vol.17, no.4, pp.706-733, figs.10, tables 9, 1938. (In Russian, with English summary.)

## Trained and Captive Specimens

OBSERVATIONS AT THE MARINE STUDIOS. C. M. Breder, Jr. Bull. New York Zool. Soc., vol.41, no.4, pp.123-129, illus., July-Aug., 1938.

(TRAINING ATTEMPTS WITH DOLPHINS.) Dressurversuche mit Delphinen. H. Hediger. Zeitschr. Tierpsych., Berlin, vol.9, no.2, pp.321-328, 1952.

WHALES IN AQUARIUM (TURSIOPS). Age Jonsgard. Norwegian Whaling Gazette, 42 (6): 309-321, 1953.

OBSERVATIONS ON THE PILOT WHALE IN CAPTIVITY. Henry Kritzler. Jour. Mam., vol.33, no.3, pp.321-334, 1952.

BEHAVIOR OF THE CAPTIVE BOTTLE-NOSE DOLPHIN, TURSIOPS TRUNCATUS. Arthur F. McBride, D. O. Hebb. Jour. Comp. and Physiol. Psychology, vol.41, no.2, pp.111-123, Apr., 1948.

THE PORPOISE IN CAPTIVITY. C. H. Townsend. Bull. Zool. Soc., New York, vol.16, no.60, p.1041, illus., Nov., 1913.

THE ACCOMPLISHED DOLPHIN OF A U.S. AQUARIUM:...DISPLAYING HIS REPERTOIRE OF TRICKS (TURSIOPS TRUNCATUS). Illus. London News, vol.220, no.5905, p. 1059, illus., June 21, 1952.

AT THE "MARINELAND" AQUARIUM, FLA., A NEW DOLPHIN WHICH OUTLEAPS THE REST. Illus. London News, vol.221, no. 5910, p.145, illus., July 25, 1952.

"FLIPPY," THE DOCILE DOLPHIN: A STRANGE TRIUMPH OF ANIMAL TRAINING. Illus. London News, vol.218, no. 5837, p.341, illus., Mar.3, 1951.

## Eschrichtidae

MONOGRAPHS OF THE PACIFIC CETACEA. I. THE CALIFORNIA GRAY WHALE (RHACHINANECTES GLAUCUS COPE). Roy C. Andrews. Mem. Amer. Mus. Nat. Hist., n.s., vol.1, pt.5, pp.231-248, pls.20-27, figs.22, Mar., 1914.

THE CALIFORNIA GRAY WHALE ON THE COAST OF SOUTHERN CALIFORNIA. A. W. Anthony. Jour. Mam., vol.2, no.3, p.174, Aug., 1921.

(THE GRAY WHALE IN THE WATERS OF LOWER CALIFORNIA.) La ballena gris, Rhachianectes glaucus, en aguas de Baja California, Mexico. Julio Berdegue. Rev. Soc. Mex. Hist. Nat., Tomo XVII, 1956.

RECENT AND OLDER FINDS OF THE CALIFORNIA GRAY WHALE IN THE ATLANTIC. A. B. Van Deinse, G. C. A. Junge. Temminckia, vol.2, pp.161-188, 1937.

ON A SUBFOSSIL WHALE (ESCHRICHTIUS ROBUSTUS). William H. Flower. Ann. and Mag. Nat. Hist., pp.440-442, June, 1872.

THE CALIFORNIA GRAY WHALE. Raymond M. Gilmore. Zoonooz, vol.29, no.2, pp.3-6, Feb., 1956.

CALVING OF THE CALIFORNIA GRAYS. Raymond M. Gilmore, Gifford Ewing. Pacific Discovery, California Acad. Sci., vol.7, no.3, pp.13-16, illus., May-June, 1954.

THE RETURN OF THE GRAY WHALE. Raymond M. Gilmore. Scientific American, New York, vol.192, no.1, pp.62-67, illus., Jan., 1955.

NOTICE OF A NEW WHALEBONE-WHALE FROM THE COAST OF DEVONSHIRE, PROPOSED TO BE CALLED ESCHRICHTIUS ROBUSTUS. John E. Gray. Proc. Zool. Soc. Lond., pp.40-43, illus., 1865.

FOOD OF THE GRAY AND OTHER WHALES. A. Brazier Howell, Laurence M. Huey. Jour. Mam., vol.11, no.3, pp.321-322, Aug., 1930.

NOTES ON THE CALIFORNIA GRAY WHALE. Laurence M. Huey. Jour. Mam., vol.9, no.1, pp.71-73, Feb., 1928.

OBSERVATIONS ON THE GRAY WHALE J. I. Manzer. Jour. Mam., vol.35, no.3, pp.444-445, Aug.20, 1954.

GREY WHALES IN THE EAST SEA AREA OF KOREA. Kazuhiro Mizue. Sci. Repts. Whales Research Inst., Tokyo, no.5, pp. 71-79, illus., June, 1951.

ON THE NOMENCLATURE OF THE PACIFIC GRAY WHALE. William E. Schevill. Breviora Mus. Comp. Zool., Cambridge, no.7, pp.3, Sept.29, 1952.

NURSERY OF THE GRAY WHALES. Lewis Wayne Walker. Nat. Hist., New York, vol.58, no.6, pp.248-256, illus., June, 1949.

OBSERVATIONS ON THE MOVEMENTS OF THE PACIFIC GRAY WHALE ESCHRICHTIUS GLAUCUS (COPE). Ralph F. Wyrick. Jour. Mam., vol.35, no.4, pp.596-598, 1 fig., Nov.29, 1954.

FURTHER STUDIES ON THE GREY OR CALIFORNIA WHALE (RACHIANECTES GLAUCUS COPE, 1864). B. A. Zenkovic. Bull. Far Eastern Branch Acad. Sci., USSR, no.23, pp.91-103, 1937.

## Balaenopteridae

MONOGRAPHS OF THE PACIFIC CETACEA: II. THE SEI WHALE (BALAENOPTERA BOREALIS LESSON). Roy Chapman Andrews. Memoirs Amer. Mus. Nat. Hist., n.s., vol.1, pt.6, pp.291-502, figs. 9, pls.29-57, 1916.

(ON THE ETYMOLOGY OF THE WORD "RORQUAL".) Sur l'etymologie du mot "Rorqual". Paul Budker. Mammalia, Paris, vol.18, no.3, pp.257-261, Sept., 1954.

THE BLUE COW (SIBBALDUS MUSCULUS). Ralph E. Butler. Alaska Sportsman, Ketchikan, vol.11, no.4, pp.8-9, 33-41, illus., Apr., 1945.

AERIAL OBSERVATIONS ON THE HUMPBACK WHALE, MEGAPTERA NODOSO (BONNATERRE), WITH NOTES ON OTHER SPECIES. R. G. Chittleborough. Australian Jour. Marine and Freshwater Research, Melbourne, vol.4, no.2, pp.219-226, pl.2, Nov., 1953.

(A STRANDED WHALE.) Een walvisch gestrand. (Sibbaldus musculus.) H. G. Delsman. De Tropische Natuur, Jaarg.21, no.3, p.49, illus., Mar., 1932.

ON PHYSALUS SIBBALDII, GRAY. William H. Flower. Proc. Zool. Soc. Lond., pp. 472-474, 1865.

THE HABITS OF FIN WHALES. E. R. Gunther. Discovery Repts., Cambridge Univ., Lond., vol.25, pp.113-142, pl.33, July, 1949.

NOTES ON BALAENOPTERA ROSTRATA, FABRICIUS, (B. HUTTONI, GRAY). Julius von Haast. Trans. New Zealand Inst., art.18, vol.13, pp.169-175, pl.3, 1880.

THE SULPHUR BOTTOM WHALE (SIBBALDUS MUSCULUS). Irving E. Hampe. Maryland Nat., Balto., vol.18, no.3, p. 44, Summer, 1948.

THE LARGEST ANIMAL (BLUE WHALE). John E. Hill. Nat. Hist., New York, vol.49, no.5, p.285, illus., May, 1942.

STUDIES ON THE LITTLE PIKED WHALE OR MINKE WHALE. Age Jonsgard. Norsk Hvalfangst-Tidende (Norwegian Whaling Gazette), Sandefjord, vol.40, no.5, pp.209-232, figs.11, illus., May, 1951.

SOUTHERN BLUE AND FIN WHALES. WITH APPENDICES BY A.J. CLOWES. N. A. Mackintosh, J.F.G. Wheeler. Discovery Reports, Cambridge, England, vol.1, pp.257-540, pls.25-44, figs.157, Nov., 1929.

(Review by Remington Kellogg of) THE SOUTHERN BLUE AND FIN WHALES. N. A. Mackintosh, J.F.G. Wheeler. Jour. Mam., vol.11, no.2, pp.242-245, May, 1930.

NOTE ON A MINKE WHALE KEPT ALIVE IN AQUARIUM. Seiji Kimura, Takahisa Nemoto. Norsk Hvalfangst-Tidende (Norwegian Whaling Gazette), 45 (12): 666-674, illus., Dec., 1956.

THE HUMPBACK WHALE, MEGAPTERA NODOSA. L. Harrison Matthews. Discovery Reports, Cambridge, vol.17, pp.7-92, figs.84, pl.2, Dec., 1937.

THE SEI WHALE, BALAENOPTERA BOREALIS. L. Harrison Matthews. Discovery Reports, Cambridge, England, vol.17, pp.183-290, pls.18-19, June, 1938.

SOME HITHERTO UNPUBLISHED PHOTOGRAPHS AND MEASUREMENTS OF THE BULE WHALE. Gerrit S. Miller, Jr. Proc. U.S. Nat. Mus., vol.66, art.7, pp. 1-4, pls.1-9, Nov.3, 1924.

(ON MEGAPTERA BOOPS FABR., WITH REMARKS ON THE BIOLOGY OF THE NORWEGIAN MYSTACOCETES.) Ueber Megaptera boops Fabr., nebst Bemerkungen zur Biologie der norwegischen Mystacoceten. Bernhard Rawitz. Arch. Naturgesch., Berlin, Jahrg.66, vol.1, pp.71-114, pl.5, 1900.

THE BLUE WHALE. Johan T. Ruud. Scientific American, 195 (6): 46-50, Dec., 1956.

NOTES ON THE LITTLE PIKED WHALE (WITH BIBLIOGRAPHY). Leslie W. Scattergood. Murrelet, Seattle, vol.30, no.1, pp.3-16, Jan.-Apr., 1949.

NOTES RELATING TO A FEMALE RORQUAL WHALE (BALAENOPTERA BOOPS OF AUTHORS). R. H. Sweeting. Proc. Zool. Soc. Lond., pt.8, p.11, 1840.

(SOME DATA ON THE BLUE WHALE.) Quelques donnees sur la baleine bleue. A. G. Tomilin. Bull. Soc. Nat. Moscou, sect. biol., n.s., vol.47, no.2, pp.177-181, 1938.

THE LESSER RORQUAL (BALAENOPTERA ROSTRATA) IN THE SCOTTISH SEAS, WITH OBSERVATIONS ON ITS ANATOMY. William Turner. Proc. Roy. Soc., Edingurgh, vol.11, pp.36-75, figs.4, pl.3, Feb.15, 1892.

A YOUNG BLUE WHALE. Edgar R. Waite. Rec. S. Australian Mus., vol.3, pp.135-144, illus., 1926.

THE LARGEST WHALE EVER WEIGHED. Waldon C. Winston. Nat. Hist., New York, vol.59, no.9, pp.393-399, illus., Nov., 1950.

THE HUMPBACK WHALE. B. A. Zencovich. Bull. Far Eastern Branch Acad. Sci. USSR, Vladivostok, no.27, pp.37-62, fig.1, 1937.

LARGEST ANIMAL IN THE WORLD (BLUE WHALE). Illus. London News, vol.218, no. 5831, pp.102, 103, illus., Jan.20, 1951.

Africa

(ON A RUDOLPHI RORQUAL OR "SEI-WHALE" CAPTURED AT CAPE LOPEZ (GABON).) Sur un rorqual du Rudolphi, ou sei-whale (Balaenoptera borealis, Lesson) capture au Cap Lopez (Gabon). P. Budker. Mammalia, Paris, vol.14, no.4, pp.154-158, fig.1, pl.1, Dec., 1950.

(THE WHALE CAMPAIGNS OF 1949-1952 AT GABON (FIRST NOTE).) Les campagnes baleinieres 1949-1952 au Gabon (Note preliminaire). P. Budker. Mammalia, Paris, vol.17, no.3, pp.129-148, Sept., 1953.

ON THE EXTERNAL CHARACTERS AND BIOLOGY OF BRYDE'S WHALE (BALAENOPTERA BRYDEI), A NEW RORQUAL FROM THE COAST OF SOUTH AFRICA. Orjan Olsen. Proc. Zool. Soc. Lond., pt. 4, pp.1073-1090, pl.109-113, Dec., 1913.

CATCHES OF BRYDE-WHALE OFF FRENCH EQUATORIAL AFRICA. Johan T. Ruud. Norsk Hvalfangst-Tidende (Norwegian Whaling Gazette), Sandefjord, vol. 41, no.12, pp.662-663, Dec., 1952.

Age Studies

THE EAR PLUG OF THE MYSTICETI AS AN INDICATION OF AGE WITH SPECIAL REFERENCE TO THE NORTH ATLANTIC FIN WHALE. R. M. Laws, P. E. Purves. Norsk Hvalfanst-Tidende (Norwegian Whaling Gazette), 45 (8): 413-425, illus., Aug., 1956.

AGE CHARACTERISTICS IN BALEEN PLATES. Masaharu Nishiwaki. Sci. Reports Whales Research Inst., Tokyo, no.4, pp.162-165, figs.19, Aug., 1950.

DETERMINATION OF THE AGE OF ANTARCTIC BLUE AND FIN WHALES BY THE COLOUR CHANGES IN CRYSTALLINE LENS. Masaharu Nishiwaki. Sci. Repts. Whales Research Inst., Tokyo, no. 4, pp.115-161, Aug., 1950.

ON THE AGE-DETERMINATION OF MYSTACOCETI, CHIEFLY BLUE AND FIN WHALES. Masaharu Nishiwaki. Sci. Repts. Whales Research Inst., Tokyo, no. 7, pp.87-119, illus., July, 1952.

EAR PLUG LAMINATIONS IN RELATION TO THE AGE COMPOSITION OF A POPULATION OF FIN WHALES (BALAENOPTERA PHYSALUS). P. E. Purves, M. D. Mountford. Bull. Zool., British Mus. Nat. Hist., Lond., vol.5, no.6, pp.123-161, pls., diagrs., tables, 1959.

AGE STUDIES ON BLUE WHALES. Johan T. Ruud. Hvalradets Skrifter, Oslo, no.33, pp.72, 1950.

THE AGE OF FIN WHALES AT PHYSICAL MATURITY WITH A NOTE ON MULTIPLE OVULATIONS. J.F.G. Wheeler. Discovery Reports, Colonial Office, London, vol.2, pp.403-434, pl.5, figs.5, 1930.

The Americas and Adjacent Islands

CALIFORNIA RECORD OF A SHARP-HEADED FINNER WHALE. Clinton G. Abbott. Jour. Mam., vol.11, no.2, pp. 240-241, May, 1930.

SOME OBSERVATIONS ON RORQUALS OFF SOUTHERN NEWFOUNDLAND. Glover M. Allen. Amer. Nat., vol.38, no.453, pp. 613-623, figs.6, Sept., 1904.

THE FINBACK WHALE IN VIRGINIA WATERS. John Wendell Bailey. Jour. Mam., vol.29, no.2, pp.183-184, May 14, 1948.

ON THE OCCURRENCE OF A RORQUAL WHALE ON THE TEXAS COAST. J. L. Baughman. Jour. Mam., vol.27, no.4, pp.392-393, Nov.25, 1946.

SHARP-HEADED FINNER WHALE STRANDED AT SIDNEY, VANCOUVER ISLAND, BRITISH COLUMBIA. Clifford G. Carl. Murrelet, Seattle, vol.27, no.3, pp.47-49, illus., Sept.-Dec. (Dec.27), 1946.

RARE WHALE TAKEN AT SAN PEDRO (BALAENOPTERA DAVIDSONI). D. H. Fry, Jr. Calif. Fish and Game, vol.19, no.2, p.158, Apr., 1933.

SHARP-HEADED FINNER WHALE TAKEN AT LOS ANGELES HARBOR. D.H. Fry, Jr. Jour. Mam., vol.16, no.3, pp.205-207, figs.2, Aug., 1935.

BALAENOPTERA ACUTOROSTRATA OFF MONTAUK POINT, NEW YORK. William T. Helmuth, 3rd. Jour. Mam., vol.12, no.1, pp.72-73, Feb., 1931.

A WHALE FOR THE LOS ANGELES MUSEUM (FINBACK WHALE). Howard R. Hill. Museum Graphic Los Angeles Mus., vol.1, no.2, pp.64-66, illus., Nov., 1926.

A POLLACK WHALE FROM FLORIDA PRESENTED TO THE NATIONAL MUSEUM BY THE MIAMI AQUARIUM ASSOCIATION. Gerrit S. Miller, Jr. Proc. U.S. Nat. Mus., vol.66, art.9, pp.1-15, pls.1-22, Dec.11, 1924.

THE POLLACK WHALE IN THE GULF OF CAMPECHE. Gerrit S. Miller. Proc. Biol. Soc. Wash., vol.41, p.171, Oct.15, 1928.

A POLLACK WHALE ON THE COAST OF VIRGINIA. Gerrit S. Miller, Jr. Proc. Biol. Soc. Wash., vol.40, pp.111-112, Sept. 26, 1927.

A RECORD OF THE PIKED WHALE, BALAENOPTERA ACUTOROSTRATA, OFF THE LOUISIANA COAST. Norman Negus, Robert K. Chipman. Proc. Louisiana Acad. Sci., 19: 41-42, 1956.

ON SOME PHOTOGRAPHS OF LIVING FINBACK WHALES FROM NEWFOUNDLAND. Frederick W. True. Smithsonian Misc. Coll., Wash., publ.1423, vol.XLV (Quarterly issue, vol.1), pp.91-94, pl.24-26, 1903.

ON A HUMPBACK WHALE TAKEN AT BERMUDA. J.F.G. Wheeler. Proc. Zool. Soc. Lond., vol.111, ser.B, pts.1-2, pp. 37-38. Oct., 1941.

ON A HUMPBACK WHALE TAKEN AT BERMUDA IN 1942. J.F.G. Wheeler. Proc. Zool. Soc. Lond., 1943, ser.A, vol.113, pts.3-4, pp.121-125, fig.1, Feb., 1944.

Anatomy

A REMARKABLE CASE OF EXTERNAL HIND LIMBS IN A HUMPBACK WHALE. Roy Chapman Adrews. Rept. Provincial Mus. (British Columbia) 1921, pp.9-11, pls.1-11, 1922.

WEIGHTS OF ANTARCTIC HUMPBACK WHALES. C. E. Ash. Norsk Hvalfangst-Tidende (Norwegian Whaling Gazette), Sandefjord, vol.42, no.7, pp.387-391, July, 1953.

THE SURFACE FEATURES OF THE BRAIN OF THE HUMPBACK WHALE (MEGAPTERA NOVAEANGLIAE). A. S. Breathnach. Jour. Anat., Cambridge, England, vol.89, pt.3, pp.343-354, July, 1954.

ON THE ANATOMY OF BALAENOPTERA ROSTRATA. Alexander Carte, Alexander Macalister. 1868.

ON A WHALE SKELETON IN THE COLLECTIONS OF THE CALIFORNIA ACADEMY OF SCIENCES. M. E. Davidson. Science, n.s., vol.80, no.2066, p.118, Aug.3, 1934.

THE STRUCTURE OF THE OVARY OF THE HUMPBACK WHALE (MEGAPTERA NODOSA). E. W. Dempsey, G. B. Wislocki. Anat. Record, Phila., vol.80, no.2, pp.243-256, fig.1, pls.3, June 25, 1941.

DEVELOPMENT OF THE TEETH IN FETAL BALAENOPTERA PHYSALUS (L) (CETACEA, MYSTACOCETI). I, II. M. C. van Dissel-Scherft, W. Vervoort. Proc. Kon. Nederlandse Akad. Weten., vol.57, no.2, pp.196-210, Mar.-Apr., 1954.

(THE RORQUAL BRAIN (BALAENOPTERA SP.).) Le cerveau du baleinoptere (Balaenoptera sp.). M. Friant. Acta Anatomica, Basel, vol.23, no.3, pp.243-250, 1955.

ON THE BODY PORPORTIONS OF THE FIN WHALES (BALAENOPTERA PHYSALUS (L.)) CAUGHT IN THE NORTHERN PACIFIC OCEAN (I). Kazuo Fujino. Sci. Repts. Whales Research Inst., Tokyo, no.9, pp. 121-163, illus., June, 1954.

SHORT ACCOUNT OF PART OF A SKELETON OF A FINNER WHALE, SENT BY MR. SWINHOE FROM THE COAST OF FORMOSA. John E. Gray. Proc. Zool. Soc. Lond., pp.725-728, figs.6, 1865.

CERVICAL VERTEBRAE OF A GIGANTIC BLUE WHALE FROM PANAMA. Sidney F. Harmer. Proc. Zool. Soc. Lond., pp. 1083-1089, fig.1, Dec., 1923.

ON THE PELVIC CARTILAGES OF THE BALAENOPTERA FOETUSES, WITH REMARKS ON THE SPECIFICAL AND SEXUAL DIFFERENCE. H. Hosokawa. Sci. Repts. Whales Research Inst., Tokyo, no. 5, pp.5-15, figs.9, June, 1951.

ON THE WHALE BRAIN WITH SPECIAL REFERENCE TO THE WEIGHT OF THE BRAIN OF THE FIN WHALE (BALAENOPTERA PHYSALUS). Jan Jansen. Norsk Hvalfangst-Tidende (Norwegian Whaling Gazette), Sandefjord, vol.41, no.9, pp. 480-486, illus., Sept., 1952.

STUDIES ON THE CETACEAN BRAIN. THE GROSS ANATOMY OF THE RHOMBENCEPHALON OF THE FIN WHALE (BALAENOPTERA PHYSALUS (L.)). Jan Jansen. Hvalradets Skrifter, Sci. Results Marine Biol. Research, Oslo, no.37, pp. 35, figs.13, 1953.

A NOTE ON THE AMYGDALOID COMPLEX IN THE FIN WHALE (BALAENOPTERA PHYSALUS (L.)). Jan Jansen, Jr., Jan Jansen. Hvalradets Skrifter, Sci. Results Marine Biol. Research, Oslo, no.39, pp. 14, illus., 1953.

(RESEARCH ON THE OSSIFICATION OF THE LOWER JAW AND ON THE CONSTITUTION OF THE DENTAL SYSTEM IN THE FETUS OF BALAENOPTERA ROSTRATA.) Recherches sur l'ossification du maxillaire inferieur et sur la constitution du systeme dentaire chez le foetus de la Balaenoptera rostrata. Charles Julin. Arch. Biol., vol.1, pp.75-136, pls.2-3, 1880.

ACCOUNT OF THE RORQUAL, THE SKELETON OF WHICH IS NOW EXHIBITED IN THE GREAT ROOMS OF THE ROYAL INSTITUTION, PRINCES STREET. Frederick J. Knox. Edinburgh, pp.1-15, 1835.

(NOTES ON A WHALE 10 METERS LONG (BALAENOPTERA ACUTO-ROSTRATA LAC.).) Notas sobre un Ballenato de 10 metros de largo (Balaenoptera acuto-rostrata Lac.). F. Lahille. Ann. Mus.

Nac., Buenos Aires, vol.XVI, ser.3, vol. IX, pp.375-401, figs.8, pl.V, 1908.

(OSTEOLOGY OF THE RORQUAL OF MIRAMAR.) Osteologie du Baleinoptere de miramar. F. Lahille. Revista Mus. La Plata, vol.9, pp.40, pls.9, 1898.

THE BRAIN OF THE WHALEBONE WHALE, BALAENOPTERA PHYSALUS. Orthello R. Langworthy. Johns Hopkins Hospital, Balto., vol.57, no.3, pp.143-147, fig.1, Sept., 1935.

GIANT OVARIES OF A BLUE WHALE. R. M. Laws. Nature, London, vol.173, p.1003, May 22, 1954.

CETOLOGICAL NOTES. I. THE RIGHT WHALES ARE PENTADACTYLNUS. II. SKELETAL DIFFERENCES BETWEEN EUBALAENA GLACIALIS BONNATERRE AND E. AUSTRALIS DESMOULIN. Einar Loennberg. Arkiv Zool., Upsala, vol.15, no.24, pp.1-18, figs.6, Nov.23, 1923.

THE SKELETON OF BALAENOPTERA BRYDEI O. OLSEN. Einar Loennberg. Arkiv. foer Zoologi, Stockholm, vol.23A, no.1, pp.23, pls.6, 1931.

ON THE SKELETON OF AN ADULT FEMALE SMALL FINNER OR PIKED WHALE (BALAENOPTERA ACUTOROSTRATA, LACEPEDE). William C. M'Intosh. Jour. Zool. Research, Lond., vol.2, no.2, pp. 37-73, pls.5, 1917.

(ON A SKELETON OF BALAENOPTERA MUSCULUS COMPANYO FROM FINNMARK IN THE NATIONAL ZOOLOGICAL MUSEUM.) Om ett i Zoologiska Riksmuseum befintligt skelett af Balaenoptera musculus Companyo fran Finmarken. A. W. Malm. Kongl. Vetenskaps-Akademiens Forhandlingar, Stockholm, no.2, pp.95-104, 1868.

CYCLIC CHANGES IN THE UTERINE MUCOSA OF BALAENOPTERID WHALES. L. Harrison Matthews. Jour. Anat., Cambridge, vol.82, no., pt.3, pp.207-232, figs.4, pls.4, Oct., 1948.

(ON THE PHYSICAL-OPTICAL STRUCTURE OF THE EYES OF THE HUMPBACKED WHALE (MEGAPTERA BOOPS, FABR.) AND THE FIN-WHALE (BALAENOPTERA MUSCULUS COMP.).) Ueber den physidalisch-optischen Bau der Augen vom Knoelwal (Megaptera boops, Fabr.) und Finwal (Balaenoptera musculus Comp.). Ludwig Matthiessen. Zeitsch. Vergleich. Augenheilkunde, Wiesbaden, vol.7, pp.77-101, pls.2, 1893.

(SKELETON OF THE WIDE-HEADED FINWHALE. (PTEROBALAENA LATICEPS).) Scelet des breitkoepfigen finnwals Pterobalaena laticeps. A. Menge. Schriften naturfors. Gesell., Danzig, vol. 3, no.4, pp.3-32, 1875.

ON THE ANATOMY OF A FIN-WHALE (PHYSALUS ANTIQUORUM, GRAY) CAPTURED NEAR GRAVESEND. James Murie. Proc. Zool. Soc., Lond., pp.206-227, figs.4, 1865.

ICONOGRAPHY ON THE ABDOMINAL CAVITY AND VISCERA OF THE BALAENOPTERA, WITH SPECIAL REMARKS UPON THE PERITONEAL COVERINGS. Tadahiro Ohe. Sci. Repts. Whales Research Inst., Tokyo, no.5, pp.17-39, illus., June, 1951.

THE URINO-GENITAL SYSTEM OF THE FIN WHALE (BALAENOPTERA PHYSALUS), WITH APPENDIX: THE DIMENSIONS AND GROWTH OF THE KIDNEY OF BLUE AND FIN WHALES. F. D. Ommanney. Discovery Repts., Cambridge, vol.5, pp. 363-466, figs.39, pls.2-3, 1932.

THE VASCULAR NETWORKS (RETIA MIRABILIA) OF THE FIN WHALE (BALAENOPTERA PHYSALUS). F. D. Ommanney. Discovery Repts., Cambridge, vol.5, pp.327-362, figs.10, 1932.

ON THE BODY WEIGHT OF SPERM AND SEI WHALES LOCATED IN THE ADJACENT WATERS OF JAPAN. Hideo Omura. Sci. Repts. Whales Research Inst., Tokyo, no.4, pp.1-113, figs.71, Aug., 1950.

NOTES ON THE SKELETON AND BALEEN OF A FIN-WHALE (BALAENOPTERA MUSCULUS?) RECENTLY ACQUIRED BY THE OTAGO UNIVERSITY MUSEUM. T. Jeffery Parker. Trans. New Zealand Inst., Wellington, vol.17, pp.13, pl.6, 1884.

NOTES ON THE ANATOMY OF BALAENOPTERA ROSTRATA. J. B. Perrin. Proc. Zool. Soc. Lond., pp.805-817, 1870.

(THE CENTRAL NERVOUS SYSTEM OF THE CETACEANS. III. THE FISSURES AND CONVOLUTIONS OF THE CEREBRUM IN BALAENOPTERA ROSTRATA FABR.) Das Zentralnervensystem der Cetaceen. III. Die Furchen und Windungen des Grosshirns von Balaenoptera rostrata Fabr. Bernhard Rawitz. Arch. Mikroskopische Anatomie Entwicklungsgesch., Bonn, vol. 75, pp.225-239, figs.a-b, pls.6-7, 1910.

(INDIVIDUAL VARIATIONS OF BALAENOPTERA MUSCULUS.) Sulle variazioni individuali della Balaenoptera Musculus. S. Richiardi. Atti. Soc. Toscana Sci. Nat., Pisa, vol.1, fasc.3, pp.14, pl.3-4, 1874.

OBSERVATIONS ON THE SKULL IN FOETAL SPECIMENS OF WHALES OF THE GENERA MEGAPTERA AND BALAENOPTERA. W. G. Ridewood. Phil. Trans. Roy. Soc. Lond., ser.B, vol.211, pp.209-272, 16 figs., May 8, 1922.

(ON THE FOREBRAIN OF THE WHALE FETUS (MEGAPTERA BOOPS).) Ueber das Vorderhirn des Walfoetus (Megaptera Boops). Walther Riese. Anat. Anz., vol. 65, pp.255-260, 4 text figs., 1928.

OVULATION AND PREGNANCY CORPORA LUTEA IN THE OVARIES OF THE HUMPBACK WHALE. J. P. Robins. Nature, 173 (4396): 201-203, illus., Jan.30, 1954.

(NOTES ON THE HEAD OF A FETUS OF BALAENOPTERA SIBBALDII (GRAY).) Notes sur la tete d'un foetus de Balaenoptera sibbaldii (Gray). Gerard Smets. Annales Soc. Sci., Bruxelles, vol.9, pt.2, pp.187-204, figs.5, 1885.

(OBSERVATIONS ON AN ABNORMAL SKELETON OF A RORQUAL OF THE INSTITUTE OF COMPARATIVE ZOOLOGY AND ANATOMY OF PISA.) Osservazioni su uno scheletro anormale di balenottera dell'Instituto di Zoologia e Anatomia comparata di Pisa. G. G. Storlazzi. Atti. Soc. Nat. Pisa, Mem., vol.45, pp. 192-224, figs.12, 1935.

NOTE ON THE SPINAL CORD OF THE FINBACK WHALE (BALAENOPTERA PHYSALUS). William L. Straus, Jr. Bull. Johns Hopkins Hospital, vol.57, no.6, pp. 317-329, Dec., 1935.

MEMOIR ON THE ANATOMY OF THE HUMPBACK WHALE. John Struthers. Jour. Anat. and Physiol., 1887-1889, pp.188, pls.6, 1889.

ON FINGER MUSCLES IN MEGAPTERA LONGIMANA AND IN OTHER WHALES. John Struthers. Amer. Nat., vol.2, pp. 126-127, Feb., 1885.

ON SOME POINTS IN THE ANATOMY OF A GREAT FIN-WHALE (BALAENOPTERA MUSCULUS). John Struthers. Jour. Anat. and Physiol., vol.6, pp.107-125, pls.16-17, Nov., 1871.

ON THE CERVICAL VERTEBRAE AND THEIR ARTICULATIONS IN FIN-WHALES. John Struthers. Jour. Anat. and Physiol., vol.7, pp.1-55, pls.2, Nov., 1872.

ON THE RUDIMENTARY HIND-LIMB OF A GREAT FIN-WHALE (BALAENOPTERA MUSCULUS) IN COMPARISON WITH THOSE OF THE HUMPBACK WHALE AND THE GREENLAND RIGHT-WHALE. John Struthers. Jour. Anat. and Physiol., vol. 27, (N.S. vol.VII), pp.291-335, pls.17-20, Apr., 1893.

ON THE RUDIMENTARY HIND LIMB OF MEGAPTERA LONGIMANA. John Struthers. Amer. Nat., pp.124-125, Feb., 1885.

SOME OBSERVATIONS ON THE EAR OF BLUE AND FIN WHALES. H. W. Symons. Norsk Hvalfangst-Tidende (Norwegian Whaling Gazette), vol.45, no.1, pp.37-45, illus., Jan., 1956. (In Norwegian and English.)

MANUSCRIPT NOTES: EXTERNAL CHARACTERS OF B. PHYSALUS OR COMMON FINBACK; EXTERNAL CHARACTERS OF BALAENOPTERA BOREALIS-LESSON - RUDOLPHI'S RORQUAL; EXTERNAL CHARACTERS OF B. MUSCULUS L. (BLUE WHALE); AND EXTERNAL CHARACTERS OF MEGAPTERA NODOSA (PROVISIONAL). F. W. True.

(STRUCTURE AND DEVELOPMENT OF THE BEARD OF BALAENOPTERA SIBBSLDII.) Bau und Entwicklung der Barten Bei Balaenoptera sibbaldii. Tycho Tullberg. Konigl. Gessellschaft d. Wiss. zu Upsala, May 31, 1882, pp.1-36, pls.3, Upsala, 1883.

AN ACCOUNT OF THE GREAT FINNER WHALE (BALAENOPTERA SIBBALDII), STRANDED AT LONGNIDDRY. PART I. THE SOFT PARTS. William Turner. Trans. Roy. Soc. Edinburgh, vol.26, pp.197-251, pls.5-8, 1870.

(NOTE ON THE ANATOMY OF A BALEIN STRANDED IN SEPTEMBER 1835 ON THE DUTCH COAST NEAR WIJK AAN ZEE VILLAGE.) Note sur l'anatomie d'une Baleinoptère à bec (Balaenoptera rostrata) échouée au mois de Septembre de l'année 1835 sur les côtes de la Hollande, pres du village de Wijk aan Zee. W. Vrolik. Ann. Sci. Nat., pp.1-13, Feb., 1838.

SOME OBSERVATIONS ON THE VASCULAR SYSTEM OF A FEMALE FETAL FINBACK. Robert Walmsley. Carnegie Inst. Wash., publ.496 (Contrib. Embryol. no.164), pp. 107-178, figs.27, pls.1-5, tables, May 31, 1938.

THE ANATOMY OF THE BRAIN OF THE WHALE (BALAENOPTERA SULFUREA). Richard B. Wilson. Jour. Comp. Neurol., vol.58, no.2, pp.419-480, figs.35, Oct., 1933.

Antarctic

STUDIES ON FEMALE FIN AND BLUE WHALES. REPORT ON INVESTIGATIONS CARRIED OUT IN THE ANTARCTIC DURING THE SEASON 1939-1940. August Brinkmann, Jr. Hvalradets Skrifter, Sci. Results Marine Biol. Research, Oslo, no. 31, pp.1-38, figs.13, 1948.

THE STOCK OF ANTARCTIC BLUE WHALES. Alec H. Laurie. Nature, London, vol.138, no.3479, p.33, July 4, 1936.

BIOLOGICAL SURVEY OF FIN AND BLUE WHALES TAKEN IN THE ANTARCTIC SEASON 1947-48 BY THE JAPANESE FLEET. Masaharu Nishiwaki, Kazuo Hayashi. Sci. Reports Whales Research Inst., Tokyo, no. 3, pp.132-190, figs.50, Feb., 1950.

BIOLOGICAL INVESTIGATION ON BLUE WHALES (BALAENOPTERA MUSCULUS) AND FIN WHALES (BALAENOPTERA PHYSALUS) CAUGHT BY THE JAPANESE ANTARCTIC WHALING FLEETS. Masaharu Nishiwaki, Tadahiro Oye. Sci. Reports Whales Research Inst., Tokyo, no. 5, pp.91-167, June, 1951.

STUDIES ON THE HUMPBACK WHALE (MEGAPTERA NODOSA) IN THE BELLINGSHAUSEN SEA. H. W. Symons, R. D. Weston. Norsk Hvalfangst-Tidende (Norwegian Whaling Gazette), 47 (2): 53-81, Feb., 1958.

BLUE WHALE STOCKS IN THE ANTARCTIC. Norsk Hvalfangst Tidende (Norwegian Whaling Gazette), Sandefjord, vol. 39, no.3, pp.106-115, Mar., 1950.

Biochemistry

STUDIES ON TRYPTASE FROM A WHALE (BALAENOPTERA BOREALIS L.). Schiro Akiya, Yasutaro Ishikawa, Setsuzo Tejima, Toyohiko Tanzawa. Sci. Repts. Whales Research Inst., Tokyo, no.1, pp.8-10, June, 1948.

MOLECULAR DISTILLATION OF FIN WHALE LIVER OIL. Akji Kaneko. Sci. Repts. Whales Research Inst., Tokyo, no. 2, pp.46-50, Dec., 1948.

DISTRIBUTION OF THE RED MARROW IN BONES OF THE FIN WHALE. Tadahiro Ohe. Sci. Reports Whales Research Inst., Tokyo, no.3, pp.17-22, fig.1, Feb., 1950.

ON THE SIMULTANEOUS EXTRACTION OF VITAMIN A-D AND VITAMIN $B_2$ COMPLEX FROM THE LIVER OF A FIN WHALE (NAGASU-KUJIRA, BALAENOPTERA PHYSALUS L). Tadashi Tawara. Sci. Repts. Whales Research Inst., Tokyo, no. 1, pp.31-37, June, 1948.

Commercial Products

THE OIL YIELD OF FIN WHALES. C. E. Ash. Norsk Hvalfangst-Tidende (Norwegian Whaling Gazette), 46 (10): 559-569, Oct., 1957.

PRODUCTION OF OIL AND MEAT FROM NORTH ATLANTIC FIN WHALES. Age Jonsgard. Norsk Hvalfangst-Tidende (Norwegian Whaling Gazette), 45 (10): 541-550, Oct., 1956.

A NOTE ON HUMPBACK OIL AND ON THE MILK AND MILK FAT FROM THIS SPECIES (MEGAPTERA NODOSA). Torbjorn Pedersen. Norsk Hvalfangst-Tidende (Norwegian Wnaling Gazette), Sandefjord, vol.41, no.7, pp.375-378, July, 1952.

Diseases and Parasites

SOME TETRABOTHRIID CESTODES FROM WHALES OF THE GENUS BALAENOPTERA. H. A. Baylis. Jour. Linn. Soc. London, Zoology, vol.36, pp.161-172, illus., Feb.9, 1926.

DIATOM INFECTION ON BLUE AND FIN WHALES IN THE ANTARCTIC WHALING AREA V (THE ROSS SEA AREA). Hideo Omura. Sci. Repts. Whales Research Inst., Tokyo, no.4, pp.14-26, Aug., 1950.

HEPATIC CIRRHOSIS IN THE BLUE WHALE, BALAENOPTERA MUSCULUS. A. Stolk. Proc. Kon. Nederlandse Akad. Wetensch., Amsterdam, ser.C, vol.56, no.3, pp.375-378, illus., 1953.

A NEW CASE OF HEPATIC CIRRHOSIS IN THE BLUE WHALE BALAENOPTERA MUSCULUS (L.). A. Stolk. Proc. Kon. Nederlandse Akad. Wetensch., Amsterdam, ser.C, vol.57, no.3, pp.258-260, figs.5-8, 1954.

ON PENNELLA BALAENOPTERAE: A CRUSTACEAN, PARASITIC ON A FINNER WHALE, BALAENOPTERA MUSCULUS. William Turner. Trans. Roy. Soc., Edinburgh, vol.41, pt.2 (no.18), pp.409-434, pls.4, 1905.

Eurasia

SOME NOTES ON THE NORWEGIAN FIN-WHALES. J. L. Chaworth-Musters. Det Kgl. Norske Videnskabers Selskabs Skrifter 1931, Trondheim, no.4, pp.1-10, 1931.

A STRANDED BLUE WHALE. P.E.P. Deraniyagala. Ceylon Jour. Sci., Sect.B, Zool. and Geol. (Spolia Zeylanica), vol.17, no.1, pp.55-58, pl.1, Oct.11, 1932.

ON THE OCCURRENCE OF THE COMMON RORQUAL (BALAENOPTERA PHYSALUS (L)) IN THE FIRTH OF FORTH. William Evans. Ann. Scottish Nat. Hist., no.50, pp.71-74, pls.2-3, Apr., 1904.

ADDITIONAL NOTE ON A SPECIMEN OF THE COMMON FIN-WHALE (PHYSALUS ANTIQUORUM, GRAY, BALAENOPTERA MUSCULUS, AUCT.). William H. Flower. Proc. Zool. Soc. Lond., pp.330-331, 1870.

NOTES ON FOUR SPECIMENS OF THE COMMON FIN-WHALE (PHYSALUS ANTIQUORUM, GRAY, BALAENOPTERA MUSCULUS, AUCT.) STRANDED ON THE SOUTH COAST OF ENGLAND. William H. Flower. Proc. Zool. Soc., pp.604-610, pl.47, 1869.

OBSERVATIONS UPON A FIN-WHALE (PHYSALUS ANTIQUORUM, GRAY) RECENTLY STRANDED IN PEVENSEY BAY. William H. Flower. Proc. Zool. Soc. Lond., pp.699-705, illus., 1865.

ON A LESSER FIN-WHALE (BALAENOPTERA ROSTRATA, FABR.) RECENTLY STRANDED ON THE NORFOLK COAST. William H. Flower. Proc. Zool. Soc. Lond., pp.252-258, 1864.

ON A SPECIMEN OF RUDOLPHI'S RORQUAL (BALAENOPTERA BOREALIS, LESSON), LATELY TAKEN ON THE ESSEX COAST. William H. Flower. Proc. Zool. Soc. Lond., pp.513-517, illus., Nov.20, 1883.

THE BLUE WHALE SKELETON IN THE WHALE HALL. F. C. Fraser. Nat. Hist. Mag. (Brit. Mus.), vol.4, no.30, pp.228-230, Apr., 1934.

(ON A NEW SPECIES OF GENUS MEGAPTERA FROM THE BAY OF BASORA (PERSIAN GULF).) Sur une nouvelle espece du Genre Megaptere, Provenant de la Baie de Basora (Golfe Persique). H. P. Gervais. Comptes Rendus Seances Acad. Sci. Paris, pp.4, Dec.31, 1883.

ON A WHALE OF THE GENUS PHYSALUS, GRAY, CAPTURED IN ORKNEY. Robert Heddle. Proc. Zool. Soc. Lond., pt.24, pp.187-198, fig.2, pls.44-45, 1856.

(A CETACEUM (BALAENOPTERA LACEP?) FROM THE RED SEA.) Ueber ein Cetaceum (Balaenoptera Lacep?), aus dem rothen Meere. Heuglin. Sitzber. Math. naturw. Cl., 1851, pp.449-452, pl.21, Oct.16, 1851.

(THE WHALE OF MORSALINES (BALAENOPTERA BOREALIS FISCHER?).) La baleine de Morsalines (Balaenoptera borealis Fischer?). Henri Jouan. Cherbourg Soc. Nat. Mem., vol.29, pp.37-52, 1892-1893.

ON A SPECIMEN OF THE RARE FIN WHALE, BALAENOPTERA EDENI ANDERSON, STRANDED ON PULU SUGI NEAR SINGAPORE. G.C.A. Junge. Verhandel. Rijksmus. Nat. Hist. Leiden, no.9, pp. 1-26, pls.9, June 10, 1950.

(CETOLOGICAL NOTES. CONCERNING A BALAENOPTERA ACUTOROSTRATA LACEPEDE OBSERVED AT CONCARNEAU.) Notes cetologiques. A propos d'une Balaenoptera acutorostrata Lacepede observee a Concarneau, Monaco, (1943). Rene Legendre. Bull. de l'Institut Oceanographique, no.856, p.6, Dec.23, 1943.

LETTERS ANNOUNCING THE STRANDING IN SUFFOLK OF AN ENORMOUS WHALE (BALAENA PHYSALUS, LINN.). R. N. Manby. Proc. Zool. Soc. Lond., pt.3, p. 119, 1835.

SOME ACCOUNT OF A FIN-WHALE STRANDED NEAR ALLOA. Patrick Neill. Mem. Wermerian Nat. Hist. Soc., Edinburgh, vol.1, pp.201-214, 1811.

SEI WHALES IN THE ADJACENT WATER OF JAPAN. II. FURTHER STUDIES ON THE EXTERNAL CHARACTERS. Hideo Omura, Kazuo Fujino. Sci. Repts. Whales Research Inst., Tokyo, no.9, pp.89-103, illus., June, 1954.

SEI WHALES (BALAENOPTERA BOREALIS) IN THE ADJACENT WATERS OF JAPAN. Hideo Omura, Setsuo Nishimoto, Kazuo Fujino. Fisheries Agency Japanese Govt., Tokyo, Publ. Japan Whaling Assoc., pp. 79, pls.5, May, 1952.

STUDIES ON THE LITTLE PIKED WHALE FROM THE COAST OF JAPAN. Hideo Omura, Haruyuki Sakiura. Sci. Repts. Whales Research Inst., Tokyo, 11: 1-37, illus., June, 1956.

(THE GIANTS OF OUR SEAS. CAPTURE OF FOUR RORQUALS IN LIGURIA.) I colossi dei nostri mari, Cattura di quattro Balenottere in Liguria. Corrado Parona. Illustrazione Italiana, Milan, no. 48, pp.8, illus., 1896.

(BALAENOPTERA PHYSALUS (L.) STRANDED ON BEACH OF ST. GIOVANNI AT TEDUCCIO.) La Balaenoptera physalus (L.) arenatasi sulla spiaggia di S. Giovanni a Teduccio. U. Pierantoni. Boll. Soc. Nat. Napoli, vol.41, pp.152-155, fig.1 (1929), May 10, 1930.

AN ACCOUNT OF A FINBACK-WHALE (BALAENOPTERA SPEC.) WHICH WAS WASHED ASHORE ON THE SOUTH COAST OF THE PREANGER REGENCIES IN DECEMBER, 1916. W. Reuter. Treubus, vol.1, pt.3, pp.101-138, pls.1-20, fig.1, Dec., 1918.

LESSER RORQUAL (BALAENOPTERA ACUTOROSTRATA) AT BUDDON-NESS. A. C. Stephen. Scottish Nat., no.159, pp. 94-95, 1926.

LESSER RORQUAL IN ABERDEENSHIRE. A. C. Stephen. Scottish Naturalist, Edinburgh, no.216, p.175, Nov.-Dec., 1935.

LESSER RORQUAL (BALAENOPTERA ACUTOROSTRATA) IN KINCARDINESHIRE. A. C. Stephen. Scottish Nat., no. 204, p.183, Nov.-Dec., 1933.

THE LESSER RORQUAL IN BRITISH WATERS. W. Stephenson. Rep. Dove Marine Lab., 12: 7-48 (1949), 1951.

ON A SPECIMEN OF BALAENOPTERA BOREALIS OR LATICEPS CAPTURED IN THE FIRTH OF FORTH. William Turner. Proc. Roy. Soc. Edinburgh, vol.11, no.3, pp.515-528, Feb., 1882.

A SPECIMEN OF RUDOLPHI'S WHALE (BALAENOPTERA BOREALIS OR LATICEPS) CAPTURED IN THE FIRTH OF FORTH. William Turner. Jour. Anat. and Physiol., vol.16, pp.471-484, Apr., 1882.

LESSER RORQUAL (BALAENOPTERA ACUTOROSTRATA) ASHORE IN FIFE. D. Wotherspoon. Scottish Nat., no.197, p.133, Sept.-Oct., 1932.

(DESCRIPTION OF A BLUE WHALE, BALAENOPTERA MUSCULUS CAMP.) Beschreibung eines Finnwales, Balaenoptera musculus Camp. G. Zaddach. Archiv. Naturg., vol.41, pp.338-386, pl.10, 1875.

Food Habits

EUPHAUSIA SUPERBA DANA FROM A HUMPBACK WHALE, MEGAPTERA NODOSA (BONNATERRE), CAUGHT OFF SOUTHERN QUEENSLAND. (WITH A COMMENT BY AGE JONSGARD.) W. Dall, D. Dunstan. Norsk Hvalfangst-Tidende (Norwegian Whaling Gazette), 46, (1): 6-12, Jan., 1957.

THE PISCIVOROUS HABITS OF THE RORQUAL OR FIN WHALE, (BALAENOPTERA SP.). P. K. Jacob, M. D. Menon. Jour. Bombay Nat. Hist. Soc., vol.47, no.1, pp. 156-158, Aug., 1947.

FOOD OF SEI WHALES (BALAENOPTERA BOREALIS) CAUGHT IN THE BONIN ISLAND WATERS. Setsuo Nishimoto, Masaaki Tozawa, Takehiko Kawakami. Sci. Repts. Whales Research Inst., Tokyo, no.7, pp.79-85, July, 1952.

(ON THE FOOD OF SOUTHERN BLUE WHALES.) Uber die Ernaehrung der suedlichen Bartenwale. Nicolaus Peters. Natur und Volk, Frankfurt a.M., vol.68, no.3, pp.124-130, figs.8, Mar.1, 1938.

Fossils

(A FOSSIL RORQUAL SPECIES.) Sur une espece de rorqual fossile. Paul Gervais. Ann. Sci. Nat., Paris, 4th ser., vol.3, cahier no.6, pp.4, 1855.

A NEW SPECIES OF WHALE FROM THE TYPE LOCALITY OF THE MONTEREY GROUP. (BALAENOPTERA RYANI.) G. Dallas Hanna, Mary E. McLellan. Proc. Calif. Acad. Sci., ser.4, vol.13, pp.237-241, pls.5-9, June 14, 1924.

DESCRIPTION OF THE SKULL OF MEGAPTERA MIOCAENA, A FOSSIL HUMPBACK WHALE FROM THE MIOCENE DIATOMACEOUS EARTH OF LOMPOC, CALIFORNIA. Remington Kellogg. U.S. Nat. Mus., Proc., Wash., vol.61, art.14, pp. 18, illus., pl.4, July 3, 1922.

THE GENERA OF FOSSIL WHALEBONE WHALES ALLIED TO BALAENOPTERA. Frederick W. True. Smithsonian Misc. Coll., vol.59, no.6, publ.2081, no.6, pp. 1-8, Apr.3, 1912.

Growth and Maturity

PUBERTY, PHYSICAL MATURITY, AND RELATIVE GROWTH OF THE FEMALE HUMPBACK WHALE, MEGAPTERA NODOSA (BONNATERRE), ON THE

WESTERN AUSTRALIAN COAST. R. G. Chittleborough. Australian Jour. Marine and Freshwater Research, Melbourne, vol. 6, no.3, pp.315-327, Oct., 1955.

ON THE SEXUAL MATURITY OF THE SEI WHALE OF THE BONIN WATERS. Masaharu Nishiwaki, Takashi Hibiya, Seiji Kimura. Sci. Repts. Whales Research Inst., Tokyo, no.9, pp.165-177, illus., June, 1954.

(ON SIZE, GROWTH, AND AGE OF THE BLUE WHALE (BALAENOPTERA MUSCULUS L.) AND THE FINBACK (BALAENOPTERA PHYSALUS L.) Ueber Groesse, Wachstum und Alter des Blauwales (Balaenoptera musculus (L.) ) und Finnwales (Balaenoptera physalus (L.) ). Nicolaus Peters. Zool. Anz., Leipzig, vol.127, nos.7-8, pp.193-204, figs.3, Sept.1, 1939.

Hair, Skin, Blubber

VARIATION IN BLUBBER THICKNESS WITH LENGTH IN FIN WHALES. C. E. Ash. Norsk Hvalfangst-Tidende (Norwegian Whaling Gazette), 45 (10): 550-554, Oct., 1956.

ON THE STRUCTURE OF THE HAIR OF THE SEI WHALE (BALAENOPTERA BOREALIS). Leon Augustus Hausman. Amer. Nat., vol.68, no.714, pp.84-88, figs.6, Jan.-Feb., 1934.

STRUCTURE OF THE HAIR OF THE SEI WHALE (BALAENOPTERA BOREALIS). Leon Augustus Hausman. Anat. Rec., vol. 54, no.3, suppl., pp.107-108, Nov.25, 1932.

(ON THE STRUCTURE OF THE SKIN OF THE SEI WHALE (BALAENOPTERA BOREALIS LESSON).) Ueber den Bau der Haut des Seihwales (Balaenoptera borealis Lesson). Arnold Japha. Zool. Anzeiger, vol.29, no.14, pp.442-445, 1905.

SINUS-HAIRS OF THE SEIWHALE (BALAENOPTERA BOREALIS). Junnosuke Nakai, Toshitomo Shida. Sci. Rept. Whales Research Inst., Tokyo, no.1, pp. 41-47, June, 1948.

ON THE SENSORY TUBERCLES OF LIPS AND OF ORAL CAVITY IN THE SEI AND FIN WHALE. Teizo Ogawa, Toshitomo Shida. Sci. Reports Whales Research Inst., Tokyo, no.3, pp.1-16, figs.9, Feb., 1950.

Locomotion

LIVING FIN WHALES AND INFERENCES FROM THEIR SWIMMING MOVEMENTS. E. R. Gunther. Proc. Linn. Soc. Lond., 150th Sess., pt.3, pp.136-137, 1938.

THE PROPULSIVE POWERS OF BLUE AND FIN WHALES. K. A. Kermack. Jour. Exper. Biol., Lond., vol.25, no.3, pp. 237-240, Sept., 1948.

Migration, Movements

DISPERSAL IN BLUE AND FIN WHALES. S. G. Brown. Discovery Repts., Cambridge, vol.26, pp.355-384, illus., Jan., 1954.

THE MOVEMENTS OF FIN AND BLUE WHALES IN ANTARCTIC WATERS. S. G. Brown. Norsk Hvalfangst-Tidende (Norwegian Whaling Gazette), Sandefjord, vol. 43, no.6, pp.301-309, June, 1954. (In Norwegian and English.)

THE MIGRATIONS OF HUMPBACK WHALES WHICH PASS THE NEW ZEALAND COAST. W. H. Dawson. Trans. Roy. Soc. New Zealand, 84 (1): 147-196, Oct., 1956.

WHALE MARKING II. DISTRIBUTION OF BLUE, FIN AND HUMPBACK WHALES MARKED FROM 1932 TO 1938. George W. Rayner. Discovery Reports, Cambridge, vol.25, pp.31-38, pls.5-22, May, 1948.

THE MIGRATION OF THE RIGHT WHALE (BALAENA MYSTICETUS). T. Southwell. Nat. Sci., Edinburgh, vol.12, no.76, pp. 397-414, pl.12, June, 1898.

DO BRYDE WHALES MIGRATE TO THE ANTARCTIC? H. W. Symons. Norsk Hvalfangst-Tidende (Norwegian Whaling Gazette), Sandefjord, vol.44, no.2, pp. 84-87, illus., Feb., 1955. (In Norwegian and English.)

Northern Waters

(ON THE BIOLOGY OF THE NORTH ATLANTIC FIN WHALE SPECIES.) Zur biologie der Nordatlantischen Finwalarten. G. A. Guldberg. Zoologischen Jahrbuechern Jena, vol.11, pp.127-174, tables, 1886.

(ON THE EXISTENCE OF A FOURTH SPECIES OF THE GENUS BALAENOPTERA IN THE NORTHERN SEAS OF EUROPE.) Sur l'existence d'une quatrieme espece du genre Balaenoptera dans les mers septentrionales de l'Europe. G. A. Guldberg. Bull. Bruxelles Acad., vol.7, pp.360-374, 1884.

THE STOCKS OF BLUE WHALES (BALAENOPTERA MUSCULUS) IN THE NORTHERN ATLANTIC OCEAN AND ADJACENT ARCTIC WATERS. Age Jonsgard. Norsk Hvalfangst-Tidende (Norwegian Whaling Gazette), vol.44, no. 9, pp.505-519, Sept., 1955.

MORE PIKED WHALES FROM SOUTHERN NORTH ATLANTIC. Joseph C. Moore, Ralph S. Palmer. Jour. Mam., 36 (3): 429-433, 2 pls., Aug.30, 1955.

FIRST RECORD OF THE POLLACK WHALE (BALAENOPTERA BOREALIS) IN THE WESTERN NORTH ATLANTIC. Frederick W. True. Science, n.s., vol. 17, no.421, p.150, Jan.23, 1903.

Pacific Ocean and Islands

OBSERVATIONS ON THE HABITS OF THE FINBACK AND HUMPBACK WHALES OF THE EASTERN NORTH PACIFIC. Roy C. Andrews. Bull. Amer. Mus. Nat. Hist., vol.26, art.14, pp.213-226, Apr.17, 1909.

THE SHARP-HEADED FINNER WHALE OF THE EASTERN PACIFIC. Ian McT. Cowan. Jour. Mam., vol.20, no.2, pp.215-225, figs.3, pls.3, May 14, 1939.

HUMPBACK WHALES OFF WEST AUSTRALIA. W. G. Dakin. Nature, London, vol. 145, no.3681, pp.783-784, May 18, 1940.

A PHILIPPINE RORQUAL. Albert W. Herre. Science, n.s., vol.61, p.541, May 22, 1925.

Physiology

NOTE ON PINEAL GLAND OF THE HUMPBACK WHALE. I. Gersh. Jour. Mam., vol.19, no.4, pp.477-480, figs.1-5, Nov.14, 1938.

ENDOCRINE ORGANS OF THE BLUE WHALE. Alf. P. Jacobsen. Nature, London, vol.136, no.3452, p.1029, Dec. 28, 1935.

ENDOCRINOLOGICAL STUDIES IN THE BLUE WHALE (BALAENOPTERA MUSCULUS L.). Alf. P. Jacobsen. Hvalradets Skrifter, Oslo, no.24, pp.84, pls.8, 1941.

PHYSIOLOGY OF THE BLUE WHALE. August Krogh. Nature, London, vol.133, no.3365, pp.635-637, Apr.28, 1934.

SOME ASPECTS OF RESPIRATION IN BLUE AND FIN WHALES. Alec H. Laurie. Discovery Reports, Cambridge, England, vol.7, pp.363-406, figs.4, pl.15, 1933.

INVESTIGATIONS ON THE ANTERIOR LOBE OF THE HYPOPHYSIS OF THE FINBACK WHALE (B. PHYSALUS L.). Arne Sverdrup, Kristen Arnesen. Hvalradets Skrifter, Sci. Res. Marine Biol. Res., Oslo, no.36, pp.15, illus., 1952.

Reproductive Biology

ASPECTS OF REPRODUCTION IN THE MALE HUMPBACK WHALE, MEGAPTERA NODOSA (BONNATERRE). R. G. Chittleborough. Australian Jour. Marine and Freshwater Research, vol.6, no.1, pp.1-29, Feb., 1955.

CAUDAL PRESENTATION AT BIRTH OF A HUMPBACK WHALE, MEGAPTERA NODOSA (BONNATERRE). D. J. Dunstan. Norsk Hvalfangst-Tidende (Norwegian Whaling Gazette), 46 (10): 553-555, Oct., 1957.

NOTES ON THE SEXUAL CYCLE OF THE PACIFIC CETACEA OF THE GENERA MEGAPTERA AND BALAENOPTERA. Earl Theron Engle. Jour. Mam., vol.8, no.1, pp.48-51, Feb., 1927.

FIN WHALE (BALAENOPTERA PHYSALUS) WITH SIX FOETUSES. Age Jonsgard. Norsk Hvalfangst Tidende (Norwegian Whaling Gazette), Sandefjord, vol.42, no. 12, pp.685-686, Dec., 1953. (In Norwegian and English.)

ON THE BREEDING HABITS OF SEI WHALE (BALAENOPTERA BOREALIS LESSON). Yoshio Matsuura. Syokubutu oyobi Dobutu (Botany and Zoology), Tokyo, vol.3, no.5, pp.1007-1010, May, 1935.

FOETUS MEASUREMENTS AND OCCURRENCES OF TWINS AND MULTIPLE FOETUSES. Harald B. Paulsen. Norsk Hvalfangst-Tidende, Sandefjord, no.12, pp.464-471, figs.2, Dec., 1939.

Taxonomy

ON THE PROBABLE IDENTITY OF THE FIN-WHALE DESCRIBED AS BALAENOPTERA CAROLINA, MALM, AND PHYSALUS SIBBALDII GRAY. William Henry Flower. Proc. Zool. Soc. Lond., pp.187-189, Mar. 12, 1868.

EXTRACT FROM A LETTER ADDRESSED TO HIM BY DR. H. BURMEISTER OF BUENOS AYRES, ON A NEW SPECIES OF WHALE, PROPOSED TO BE CALLED BALAENOPTERA PATACHONICA. John E. Gray. Proc. Zool. Soc. Lond., pp.190-195, figs.11, 1865.

ON THE FINNER WHALES, WITH THE DESCRIPTION OF A NEW SPECIES. John E. Gray. Proc. Zool. Soc. Lond., pt.15, p.88, 1847.

Whaling

ON THE SIZE OF THE STOCK OF ANTARCTIC FIN WHALES RELATIVE TO THE SIZE OF THE CATCH. C. E. Ash. Norsk Hvalfangst-Tidende (Norwegian Whaling Gazette), 45 (8): 432, 435, Aug., 1956.

FIN WHALE FISHERY IN NORTH LAPLAND. H. Balfour. Midland Nat., vol.12, p.1-14, 1889.

(SOME CONSIDERATIONS ON THE WHALING CAMPAIGN OF 1951 AT CAPE LOPEZ (GABON).) Quelques considerations sur la campagne baleiniere 1951 au Cap Lopez (Gabon). Paul Budker. Mammalia, Paris, vol.16, no.1, pp.1-6, Mar., 1952.

(THE WHALING CAMPAIGNS OF 1949-1952 AT GABON (PRELIMINARY NOTE).) Les campagnes Baleinieres 1949-1952 au Gabon (note preliminaire). Paul Budker. Mammalia, Paris, vol.17, no.3, pp.129-148, Sept., 1953.

AN ANALYSIS OF RECENT CATCHES OF HUMPBACK WHALES FROM THE STOCKS IN GROUPS IV AND V. R. G. Chittleborough. Norsk Hvalfangst-Tidende (Norwegian Whaling Gazette), 47 (3): 109-137, Mar., 1958.

SOME REMARKS ON THE APPLICATION OF THE MINIMUM SIZE REGULATION TO FIN WHALES IN THE ANTARCTIC. Aksel Froili. Norsk Hvalfangst-Tidende (Norwegian Whaling Gazette), Sandefjord, vol. 43, no.6, pp.330-336, 338, June, 1954. (In Norwegian and English.)

IS IT DESIRABLE AND JUSTIFIED TO EXTEND THE OPEN SEASON FOR HUMPBACK WHALING IN THE ANTARCTIC? Age Jonsgard, Johan T. Ruud, Per Oynes. Norsk Hvalfangst-Tidende (Norwegian Whaling Gazette), 46 (4): 160-177, Apr., 1957.

THE AGE OF FEMALE BLUE WHALES AND THE EFFECT OF WHALING ON THE STOCK. Alec H. Laurie. Discovery Reports, Cambridge, vol.15, pp.223-284, figs.14, charts, May, 1937.

FIN WHALES AND WHALING OPERATIONS IN THE EAST CHINA SEA. Ichiro Miyazaki. Norsk Hvalfangst-Tidende (Norwegian Whaling Gazette), 47 (1): 21-26, Jan., 1958.

ON THE SIZE OF THE STOCK OF ANTARCTIC FIN WHALES RELATIVE TO THE SIZE OF THE CATCH. Per Ottestad. Norsk Hvalfangst-Tidende (Norwegian Whaling Gazette), 45 (6): 298-308, June, 1956. (In English and Norwegian.)

NEWFOUNDLAND FIN WHALE FISHING IN 1905. Thomas Southwell. Ann. Scot. Nat. Hist., Edinburgh, pp.193-195, Oct., 1906.

SOME RESULTS OF THE NORTH-ATLANTIC FIN-WHALE FISHERY. Thomas Southwell. Ann. and Mag. Nat. Hist. Lond., vol.16, ser.7, pp.403-421, Oct., 1905.

AN UNDERFISHED HUMPBACK POPULATION? M. A. Symons, R. D. Weston. Norsk Hvalfangst-Tidende (Norwegian Whaling Gazette), 46 (5): 231-238, May, 1957.

FARMER WHALERS. Canadian Geogr. Jour., Ottawa, vol.38, pp.144-147, illus., Mar., 1949.

Balaenidae

THE NORTH ATLANTIC RIGHT WHALE AND ITS NEAR ALLIES. J. A. Allen. Bull. Amer. Mus. Nat. Hist., vol.24, pp. 277-329, pls.24-29, figs.1, Apr. 8, 1908.

HUNTING THE BOWHEAD. C. L. Andrews. Field and Stream, vol.34, no.1, pp.38-39, 110-111, illus., May, 1929.

FURTHER NOTES ON EUBALAENA GLACIALIS (BONN.). Roy C. Andrews. Bull. Amer. Mus. Nat. Hist., vol.26, pp. 273-275, figs.46-50, May 15, 1909.

NOTES UPON THE EXTERNAL AND INTERNAL ANATOMY OF BALAENA GLACIALIS BONN. Roy C. Andrews. Bull. Amer. Mus. Nat. Hist., vol.24, art.10, pp.171-182, figs.1-6, Feb.20, 1908.

GREENLAND RIGHT WHALE RECORDED IN GASPE COUNTY, QUEBEC. Austin W. Cameron. Bull. Nat. Mus. Canada, no. 123, pp.116-119, illus., 1951.

RIGHT WHALE (BALAENA GLACIALIS) ENTERS CAPE COD CANAL, MASSACHUSETTS, U.S.A. Eugene S. Clark, Jr. Norsk Hvalfangst-Tidende (Norwegian Whaling Gazette), 47 (3): 138-143, Mar., 1958.

A FEW NOTES ON THE WHALE BALAENA GLACIALIS AND ITS CAPTURE IN RECENT YEARS IN THE NORTH ATLANTIC BY NORWEGIAN WHALERS. R. Collett. Proc. Zool. Soc. Lond., pp. 91-98, fig.5, pls.25-27, June, 1909.

A NOTE ON THE PYGMY RIGHT WHALE, CAPEREA MARGINATA GRAY. J. L. Davies, E. R. Guiler. Proc. Zool. Soc. Lond., 129 (4): 579-589, 2 pls., Dec.17, 1957.

(ON THE NORTHERN WHALE.) Om Nordhvalen (Baleana mysticetus L.). D. F. Eschricht, J. Reinhardt. Vidensk. Selsk. Shr., 5 Raekke, naturvidensk. og mathem. Afd. 5 Bd. 1861: 435-593, 6 pls., 1861.

ON THE GREENLAND RIGHT-WHALE (BALAENA MYSTICETUS, LINN.). WITH ESPECIAL REFERENCE TO ITS GEOGRAPHICAL DISTRIBUTION AND MIGRATIONS IN TIMES PAST AND PRESENT, AND TO ITS EXTERNAL AND INTERNAL CHARACTERISTICS. D. F. Eschricht, J. Reinhardt. London, 1866.

(THE BISCAY WHALE (BALAENA BISCAYENSIS).) Sur la Baleine des Basques (Balaena Biscayensis). P. Fischer. Comptes Rendus l'Acad. Sci., Paris, vol.72, pp.298-300, 1871.

WHALE! (CAPTURE OF BOWHEAD WHALE.) Elizabeth C. Forrest. The Atlantic Monthly, vol.157, no.3, pp.326-330, Mar., 1936.

RARE RIGHT WHALE VISITS CALIFORNIA. Raymond M. Gilmore. Pacific Discovery, 9 (4): 20-25, July-Aug., 1956.

NOTES FROM PERSONAL OBSERVATIONS ON THE HABITS OF THE GREENLAND WHALEBONE WHALE. David Gray. 7th Ann. Report Fishery Board, Scotland for 1888, pt.3, pp.365-366, 1889.

NOTE ON THE BONNET OF THE RIGHT WHALE. John E. Gray. Proc. Zool. Soc. Lond., pp.170-171, illus., 1864.

NOTICE OF THE ATLAS AND CERVICAL VERTEBRAE OF A RIGHT WHALE IN THE MUSEUM OF SYDNEY, NEW SOUTH WALES. John E. Gray. Proc. Zool. Soc. Lond., pp.587-594, figs.5, 1864.

NOTICE OF THE SKELETON OF THE NEW ZEALAND RIGHT WHALE (MACLEAYIUS AUSTRALIENSIS). John E. Gray. Trans. New Zealand Inst., vol.6, pp.90-92, pls. 16-17, 1874.

NOTICE OF THE SKELETON OF THE NEW ZEALAND RIGHT WHALE (MACLEAYIUS AUSTRALIENSIS) AND OTHER WHALES, AND OTHER NEW ZEALAND MARINE MAMMALIA. John E. Gray. Proc. Zool. Soc. Lond., pp.129-144, figs.5b, Jan.21, 1873.

THE ATLANTIC OR BISCAY WHALE, BALAENA GLACIALIS AND THE SPITSBERGEN WHALE FISHERY OF THE SEVENTEENTH CENTURY. R. W. Gray. Naturalist, London, no.966, pp.153-156, July, 1937.

BALAENA MYSTICETUS--THE GREENLAND, ARCTIC OR BOW-HEAD WHALE. R. W. Gray. Naturalist, London, no.781, pp.193-199, figs.2, Aug., 1940; no.795, pp. 229-232, Oct., 1941.

BREEDING HABITS OF THE GREENLAND WHALE. R. W. Gray. Nature, London, vol.123, no.3102, pp.564-565, Apr.13, 1929.

(CONTRIBUTIONS TO PRECISE KNOWLEDGE OF THE ATLANTIC WHALE EVBALAENA BISCAYENSIS, ESCHRICHT.) Bidrag til noiere kindskab om Atlanterhavets rethval, (Evbalaena biscayensis, Eschricht). Gustav Guldberg. Christiania Videnskabs-Selskabs Forhl., no.8, pp.1-14, 1891.

(ON THE OCCURRENCE IN ANCIENT AND MODERN TIMES OF THE BISCAY WHALE ON THE NORWEGIAN COASTS.) Sur la presence aux temps anciens et modernes, de la Baleine de Biscaye (ou Nordcaper) sur les cotes de Norwege. G. A. Guldberg. Bruxelles Acad. Bull., vol.7, pp.374-402, 1884.

THE PIGMY RIGHT WHALE (NEOBALAENA MARGINATA) IN SOUTH AUSTRALIAN WATERS. Herbert M. Hale. Records S. Australian Mus., vol.4, no.3, pp.314-319, figs.4, June 30, 1931.

THE ATLANTIC RIGHT WHALES. J. B. Holder. Bull. Amer. Mus. Nat. Hist., vol.1, no.4, pp.99-137, pls.10-13, May 1, 1883.

AN ACCOUNT OF SOME PECULIARITIES IN THE STRUCTURE OF THE ORGAN OF HEARING IN THE BALAENA MYSTICETUS OF LINNEAES (WHALE-BONE WHALE). Everard Home. Philos. Trans., pp.83-90, pls.2, Lond., 1812.

NOTES ON THE SOUTHERN RIGHT WHALE, EUBALAENA AUSTRALIS. L. Harrison Matthews. Discovery Reports, vol.17, pp. 169-182, pls.12-17, Apr., 1938.

(SKELETON OF THE BROAD-HEADED WHALE PTEROBALAENA LATICEPS.) Scelet des breitkoepfigen Finnwals Pterobalaena laticeps. A. Menge. Schrift. Natuurf. Gesell. Danzig, vol.3, no.4, pp. 1-29, pls.4, figs.2, 1875.

REPORT ON TWO RIGHT WHALES CAUGHT OFF JAPAN FOR SCIENTIFIC PURPOSES UNDER ARTICLE VIII, OF THE INTERNATIONAL CONVENTION FOR THE REGULATION OF WHALING. Hideo Omura. Norsk Hvalfangst-Tidende (Norwegian Whaling Gazette), 46 (7): 374-390, illus., July, 1957.

(TWO PHOTOGRAPHS OF FRENCH BALEEN WHALES.) A propos deu deux photographies de balienes Franches (Balaena Biscayensis). Georges Pouchet. Comptes Rendus Seances et Mem. Soc. Biol., Paris, vol.42 (ser.9, vol.2), no.37, pp.705-708, Dec.19, 1890.

ESKIMO METHOD OF CAPTURING BOWHEAD WHALES. Froelich Rainey. Jour. Mam., Balto., vol.21, no.3, p.362, Aug. 14, 1940.

(ON THE BEARD OF THE RIGHT WHALE (BALAENA ROSTRATA).) Ueber die Barten des Schnabel Walfisches (Balaena rostrata). Friedrich Christian Rosenthal. Abhandl. Akad. der Wiss., pp.127-132, pls.3, Berlin, 1829.

BALAENA LONGIMANA. Carl A. Rudolphi. Abhandl. Akad. der Wiss., pp.133-144, pls. 5, Berlin, 1829.

ACCOUNT OF THE BALAENA MYSTICETUS OR GREAT NORTHERN OR GREENLAND WHALE. William Scoresby. Mem. Wern. Soc., Edinburgh, vol.1, pp.578-586, pl.12, 1808-1810.

AN EMBALMED WHALE IN SHANGHAI (EUBALAENA GLACIALIS). Arthur de C. Sowerby. China Jour., vol.19, no.4, pp. 210-211, figs., Oct., 1933.

THE TYPE LOCALITY OF BALAENA CISARCTICA COPE. Witmer Stone. Jour. Mam., vol.13, no.1, pp.81-82, Feb., 1939.

ACCOUNT OF RUDIMENTARY FINGER MUSCLES FOUND IN THE GREENLAND RIGHT-WHALE (BALAENA MYSTICETUS). John Struthers. Jour. Anat. and Physiol., vol.12, pp.1-8, Jan., 1878.

ON THE BONES, ARTICULATIONS, AND MUSCLES OF THE RUDIMENTARY HIND-LIMB OF THE GREENLAND RIGHT-WHALE. John Struthers. Jour. Anat. and Physiol., vol.15, pp.58, pls.14-17, Jan., 1881.

ON THE CARPUS OF THE GREENLAND RIGHT-WHALE, AND OF FIN-WHALES. John Struthers. Jour. Anat. and Physiol., vol.29, pp.145-187, pls.2-4, Jan., 1895.

ON THE FORM OF THE STERNUM IN THE GREENLAND RIGHT-WHALE (BALAENA MYSTICETUS). John Struthers. Jour. Anat. and Physiol., vol.29, pp.593-612, pl.14, July, 1895.

THE ATLANTIC RIGHT WHALES. Frederick W. True. Scientific and Literary Gossip, Boston, vol.1, no.8, pp.72-73, June 15, 1883.

REPORT OF A TRIP TO LONG ISLAND IN SEARCH OF SKELETONS OF THE RIGHT WHALE, BALAENA CISARCTICA. Frederick W. True. Bull. U.S. Fish Comm., vol.5, pp.131-132, 1885.

THE RIGHT WHALE OF THE NORTH ATLANTIC, BALAENA BISCAYENSIS: ITS SKELETON DESCRIBED AND COMPARED WITH THAT OF THE GREENLAND RIGHT WHALE, BALAENA MYSTICETUS. William Turner. Trans. Roy. Soc., Edinburgh, vol.48, pt.4, no.33, pp.889-922, figs.25, pls.3, 1913.

CARNIVORA

MISHI THE MAN-EATER, AND OTHER TALES OF BIG GAME. E.C.S. Baker. H.F.& G. Witherby, London, pp.1-222, pls.4, 1929.

ROCK SABLES AND BALTIC LIONS. Bennie Bengtson. Fauna, Phila., vol.5, no.4, pp.108-109, Dec., 1943.

MEAT FOR CARNIVORA. C. L. Brock. Parks and Recreation, vol.9, no.2, pp.190-191, Nov.-Dec., 1925.

THE WILD HUNTERS; THE WOLVES, THE BEARS, AND THE BIG CATS. Gene Caesar. Putnam, New York, pp.252, illus., 1957.

ANIMALS THAT HUNT. Henri Coupin. Smithson. Report publ.1521, pp.567-571, 1904.

MALAY BELIEFS AND LEGENDS ABOUT TIGERS AND WILD DOGS. Alexander Cross. Jour. Bombay Nat. Hist. Soc., vol.34, no.1, pp.235-236, Mar.1, 1930.

(BEASTS OF PREY AND THE MANAGEMENT OF HUNTING GROUNDS.) Rovviltet i vor jagthusholdning. Knut Dahl. Norsk Jaeger og Fisker Forening Tideskrifts, heft 6, pp. 1-9 (of reprint), 1 chart, 1927.

THE SMALLER CARNIVORES. Raymond L. Ditmars. Bull. New York Zool. Soc., vol.36, no.5, pp.119-140, figs., Sept.-Oct., 1933.

(NOTES ON MAMMALS. XLIV. THE DIFFERENTIATION OF AILUROID CARNIVORES.) Notes sur les mammiferes.

XLIV. De la differenciation des carnivores aeluroides. Serge Frechkop. Bull. Inst. Roy. Sci. Nat. Beligique, vol.32, no. 36, pp.1-11, July, 1956.

SPOTTED SKUNKS AND BOB-CAT. William H. Gates. Jour. Mam., vol.18, no.2, p.240, May 14, 1937.

COUGAR AND COYOTE. Charles A. Gianini. Jour. Mam., vol.16, no.3, p. 229, Aug., 1935.

THE CARNIVORES--PART II--RACCOONS AND THEIR ALLIES. George G. Goodwin. Audubon Nature Bull., 18 (3): pp.4, Nov., 1947.

GENERAL AND PARTICULAR DESCRIPTIONS OF THE VERTEBRATED ANIMALS. ORDER CARNIVORA. Edward Griffith. 1821.

CONTRIBUTIONS TO THE BIOLOGY AND MORPHOLOGY OF THE BADGER, MELES TAXUS, AND SOME OTHER CARNIVORA. Einar Loennberg. Arkiv for Zool., vol. 19A, no.26, pp.11, pls.2, Jan.21, 1928.

A HAND-BOOK TO THE CARNIVORA. PART I. CATS, CIVETS, AND MUNGOOSES. Richard Lydekker. Lloyd's Nat. Hist., p.312, pls.32, 1896.

CATS AND DOGS. Phil H. Moore. Field and Stream, New York, vol.52, no.7, pp. 30-31, 119-120, illus., Nov., 1947; Caza Tiro y Pesca, Mexico, vol.18, nos.184-187, pp.20-24, illus., Aug., 1948. (In Spanish.)

NIGHT ANIMALS UNDER THE FLASH-LIGHT. (FOX, RACCOON, SKUNK, AND RING-TAILED CAT.) Gayle Pickwell. Nat. Hist., New York, vol.45, no.3, pp. 162-167, photos, Mar., 1940.

(CARNIVORES EXISTING IN THE EDUCATIONAL MUSEUM OF MENDOZA UP TO 25 MAY 1916.) Los mamiferos carnivoros existentes en el Museo Educacional de Mendoza hasta el 25 de Mayo de 1916. Carlos S. Reed. Mus. Educac. Mendoza, pp.21, 1916.

MASTICATORY APPARATUS IN THE GIANT PANDA AND THE BEARS. Harry Sicher. Zool. Ser., Field Mus. Nat. Hist., Chicago, vol.29, no.4, pp.61-73, figs.13-17, Jan.28, 1944.

THE PANDAS OR CAT BEARS AND THE TRUE BEARS. Arthur de C. Sowerby. China Jour., vol.19, no.5, pp.257-259, Nov., 1933.

SMALL CARNIVORES IN THE ZOO. Ken Stott, Jr. San Diego Zoonooz, vol.15, no.5, pp.3-4, illus., June, 1942.

OBSERVATIONS ON THE CANIS JUBATUS AND SOME SKINS OF THE FELIS PARDINA. Lieut. Col. Sykes. Proc. Zool. Soc. Lond., pt.6, pp.111-113, 1838.

(CATALOGUE OF CARNIVORES IN THE COLLECTIONS OF THE ZOOLOGICAL MUSEUM OF COIMBRA.) Catalogue des Carnivores existants dans les collections du Museum Zoologique de Coimbra. Antonio Armando Themido. Mem. e Estud. Museu Zoologico Univ. Coimbra (1), no.30, pp.5-25, 1928.

JACKALS (?) AND A CAPTIVE PANTHER. Noel J.S. Thompson. Jour. Bombay Nat. Hist. Soc., vol.40, no.2, pp.321-322, Sept., 1938.

(CATALOG OF MAMMALS LIVING AND FOSSIL (CARNIVORES).) Catalogue des Mammiferes. Vivants et Fossiles (Carnivores). E. L. Trouessart. Bull. Soc. d'Etudes Sci. Angers. Suppl. a l 'Annee, pp.1-108, 1884.

OBSERVATIONS ON SOME OF THE FORAMINA AT THE BASE OF THE SKULL IN MAMMALIA, AND ON THE CLASSIFICATION OF ORDER CARNIVORA. H. N. Turner. Proc. Zool. Soc. Lond., pt.16, p.63, 1848.

BOBCATS AND BLACK BEARS. West Virginia Conservation, Charleston, vol. 7, no.6, p.8, Sept., 1943.

(DETERMINATION OF THE DOG SPECIES KROKUTE AND THE BEAR SPECIES SARIBUR.) Bestimmung der Hundsart Krokute und der Baerenart Saribur. Prague, 1788.

LITTLE THINGS. (OCELOT, FOXES, PANDAS.) Zoonooz, San Diego, vol.13, no.6, pp.3-4, illus., June, 1941.

Africa

CARNIVORA COLLECTED BY THE AMERICAN MUSEUM CONGO EXPEDITION. J.A. Allen. Bull. Amer. Mus. Nat. Hist., vol. 47, no.3, pp.73-281, Apr.11, 1924.

(Review by N. Hollister of) CARNIVORA COLLECTED BY THE AMERICAN MUSEUM CONGO EXPEDITION. J.A. Allen. Jour. Mam., vol.5, no.3, p.209, Aug.11, 1924.

DESCRIPTION OF A NEW FOX (VULPES DORSALIS) FROM SENEGAL, AND EXHIBITION OF A VERY YOUNG SPECIMEN OF THE GENETTA SENEGALENSIS, GEOFF. J. E. Gray. Proc. Zool. Soc. Lond., pt. 5, p.132, 1837.

A NEW CARNIVORE FROM BRITISH EAST AFRICA. Gerrit S. Miller, Jr. Smithson. Misc. Coll., vol.52, pp.485-487, pls.2, Dec.18, 1909.

THE FLESH-EATING MAMMALS OF NIGERIA. D. R. Rosevear. Nigerian Field, Lond., vol.4, no.2, pp.64-69, pls.2, Apr., 1935.

FOUR NEW AFRICAN CARNIVORES. Oldfield Thomas. Ann. and Mag. Nat. Hist. (8), vol.8, no.48, pp.724-726, Dec., 1911.

Anatomy

(STUDY OF THE NASAL CAVITIES OF CARNIVORES.) Etude sur les cavites nasales des carnassiers. R.L.F. Anthony, G. M. Iliesco. Proc. Zool. Soc. Lond., pt.4, pp.989-1015, illus., Dec., 1926.

(THE LATERAL STRAND OF THE DORSAL MUSCULATURE IN CARNIVORES.) Der laterale Strang der Dorsalmuskulatur bei den fleischfressenden Tieren. B. W. Bogorodsky. Anat. Anzeiger, vol.69, pp. 82-121, figs.10, Feb.26, 1930.

(SEXUAL DIMORPHISM OF THE CRANIUM IN CARNIVORES.) Le dimorphisme sexuel cranien chez les carnivores. Jean Bouchud. Bull. Mus. Nat. Hist. Nat., Paris, vol.22, no.4, pp.438-442, June, 1950.

THE MECHANICAL ORIGIN OF THE SECTORIAL TEETH OF THE CARNIVORA. Edward D. Cope. Proc. Amer. Assoc. Adv. Sci., vol.36, pp.254-257, 1888.

THE ORIGIN OF THE SPECIALIZED TEETH OF THE CARNIVORA. Edward D. Cope. Amer. Nat., vol.13, pp.171-173, Feb., 1879.

REPORT ON RECENTLY DISCOVERED BONES OF THE WILD CAT, FELIS SILVESTRIS SCHREB., FROM THE STONE AGE IN SWEDEN, WITH SOME NOTES ON THE MORPHOLOGICAL STRUCTURE OF THE TARSUS IN DIVERSE FAMILIES AMONG THE CARNIVORA. E. Dahr. Arkiv. for Zoologi, Stockholm, vol.28A, no.12, pp.1-7, figs.3, 1935.

THE ARTERIES OF THE FOREARM IN CARNIVORES. D. Dwight Davis. Papers on Mammalogy, Zool. Ser., Field Mus. Nat. Hist., Chicago, vol.27, pp.137-227, figs.11-44, Dec.8, 1941.

THE SHOULDER ARCHITECTURE OF BEARS AND OTHER CARNIVORES. D. Dwight Davis. Fieldiana-Zoology, Chicago Nat. Hist. Mus., vol.31, no.34, pp.285-305, figs.70-77, Sept.16, 1949.

(THE DEVELOPMENT AND STRUCTURE OF THE PLACENTA IN CARNIVORES.) Entwickelung und Structur der Placenta bei Raubthieren. Fleischmann. Sitz.-Ber. k. Preuss. Akad. Wiss. Berlin, no.35, pp. 661-670 (pp.10), July 9, 1891.

(NOTES ON MAMMALS. XLIV. DIFFERENTIATION OF AILUROID CARNIVORES.) Notes sur les mammifères. XLIC. De la differenciation des carnivores aeluroiedes. Serge Frechkop. Bull. Inst. Roy. Sci. Nat. Belgique, 32 (36): 1-11, July, 1956.

(A CHARACTER OF THE ADAPTATION OF THE ANTERIOR EXTREMITY TO PREDATORY FUNCTIONS IN FELIDAE AND URSIDAE.) Un caractère de l'adaptation de l'extrémité antérieure aux fonctions prédatrices chez les felidés et les ursidés. M. Friant. Bull. Soc. Zool. France, vol. 61, no.4, pp.260-265, figs.6, July 5, 1936.

CHARACTERS OF SOME NEW SPECIES OF MAMMALIA IN THE SOCIETY'S COLLECTION, WITH REMARKS UPON THE DENTITION OF THE CARNIVORA, AND UPON THE VALUE OF THE CHARACTERS USED BY M. CUVIER TO SEPARATE THE PLANTIGRADE FROM THE DIGITIGRADE. John E. Gray. Proc. Zool. Soc. Lond., pt. 4, p.87, 1836.

THE AUDITORY REGION IN SOME MEMBERS OF THE PROCYONIDAE, CANIDAE, AND URSIDAE. ITS SIGNIFICANCE IN THE PHYLOGENY OF THE CARNIVORA. Jean Ringier Hough. Bull. Amer. Mus. Nat. Hist., New York, vol.92, pp.67-118, figs.11, pls.9-15, Nov.1, 1948.

THE AUDITORY REGION IN SOME MIOCENE CARNIVORES. Margaret Jean Hough. Jour. Paleontol., Menasha, vol. 18, no.5, pp.470-479, figs.3, Sept., 1944.

THE PANNICULUS CARNOSUS IN CAT AND DOG AND ITS GENETICAL RELATION TO THE PECTORAL MUSCULATURE. Orthello R. Langworthy. Jour. Mam., vol.5, no. 1, pp.49-63, Feb., 1924.

(MODIFICATIONS IN CONNECTION WITH FUNCTION AND JOINT SURFACE FORMATION ON THE CARPAL SEGMENT OF ARCTOID CARNIVORES.) Modifikationen im Zusammenhang von Funktion und Gelenkflachenausbildung am Carpalsegment arctoider Carnivoren. Rudolf Lips. Zeitschrift f, Saeugetierkunde, vol.5, nos. 3-4, pp.206-240, pls.15-19, Nov.10, 1930.

(THE PENILE BONES OF TWO RARE CARNIVORES.) Der Penisknochen zweier seltener Carnivoren. Einar Loennberg. Anat. Anzeig., Jena, vol.38, pp.230-232, 1911.

(CRANIAL OSTEOLOGY OF CARNIVOROUS MAMMALS.) Ostéologie cranienne des mammifères carnivores. Viger Plamondon. Ann. Rept. Provancher Soc., Quebec, 1945, pp.59-76, figs.11, 1946.

THE ALISPHENOID CANAL IN CIVETS AND HYAENAS. R. I. Pocock. Proc. Zool. Soc. Lond., pt.2, pp.442-445, figs.2, June 20, 1916.

ON THE FEET AND OTHER EXTERNAL FEATURES OF THE CANIDAE AND URSIDAE. R. I. Pocock. Proc. Zool. Soc. Lond., pt.3, pp.913-941, figs.13, Sept.7, 1914.

THE STRUCTURE OF THE AUDITORY BULLA IN THE PROCYONIDAE AND THE URSIDAE, WITH A NOTE ON THE BULLA OF HYAENA. R. I. Pocock. Proc. Zool. Soc. Lond., 1928, pt.4, pp.963-974, figs. 1-8, Jan.31, 1929.

STUDIES ON THE DIENCEPHALON OF CARNIVORA. PT.I. THE NUCLEAR CONFIGURATION OF THE THALAMUS, EPITHALAMUS, AND HYPOTHALAMUS OF THE DOG AND CAT. David Mackenzie Rioch. Jour. Comp. Neurol., vol.49, no. 1, pp.1-120, 24 figs., 1929.

STUDIES ON THE DIENCEPHALON OF CARNIVORA. PT.II. CERTAIN NUCLEAR CONFIGURATIONS AND FIBER CONNECTIONS OF THE SUBTHALAMUS AND MIDBRAIN OF THE DOG AND CAT. David McKenzie Rioch. Jour. Comp. Neurol., vol.49, no.1, pp.121-154, figs.9, 1929.

THE AUDITORY REGION OF THE ARCTOID CARNIVORES. Walter Segall. Zool. Ser. Field Mus. Nat. Hist., Chicago, vol. 29, no.3, pp.33-59, figs.9-12, Dec.31, 1943.

MASTICATORY APPARATUS IN THE GIANT PANDA AND THE BEARS. Harry Sicher. Zool. Ser. Field Mus. Nat. Hist., Chicago, vol.29, no.4, pp.61-73, figs.13-17, Jan.28, 1944.

THE FUNCTION OF SABER-LIKE CANINES IN CARNIVOROUS MAMMALS. George Gaylord Simpson. Amer. Mus. Novitates, New York, no.1130, pp.1-12, figs.4, Aug.4, 1941.

THE COMPARATIVE ANATOMY OF THE TONGUES OF THE MAMMALIA. VIII. CARNIVORA. Charles F. Sonntag. Proc. Zool. Soc. Lond., pt.1, pp.129-153, Apr., 1923.

ON SOME ABNORMALITIES IN THE CARNIVORA. Charles F. Sonntag. Proc. Zool. Soc. Lond., pt.3, pp.587-590, Sept., 1921.

ON THE VAGUS AND SYMPATHETIC NERVES OF THE TERRESTRIAL CARNIVORA. Charles F. Sonntag. Proc. Zool. Soc. Lond., pt.1, pp.65-83, Apr., 1923.

ON THE SKULLS AND DENTITION OF THE CARNIVORA. G. R. Waterhouse. Proc. Zool. Soc. Lond., pt.7, p.135, 1839.

Biochemistry

(CONTRIBUTION TO STUDY OF NORMAL CALCEMIA IN THE DOG.) Contribution à l'étude de la calcemie normale du chien. Joaquim Monteiro Bastos. Comptes Rendus, 12th Internat. Congr. Zool. 1935, Lisboa, vol.2, pp.742-747, 1936-1937.

BLOOD GLUCOSE, PLASMA INORGANIC PHOSPHORUS, PLASMA CALCIUM, HEMATOCRIT, AND BONE ASH VALUES OF NORMAL MINKS (MUSTELA VISON) AND FOXES (VULPES FULVA). Sedgwick E. Smith. Cornell Veterinarian, Ithaca, vol. 31, no.1, pp.56-62, Jan., 1941.

THE VITAMIN A REQUIREMENT FOR GROWTH OF FOXES AND MINKS AS INFLUENCED BY ASCORBIC ACID AND POTATOES. C.F. Bassett, J.K. Loosli, Ford Wilke. Jour. Nutrition, Phila., vol. 35, no.6, pp.629-638, June 10, 1948; Fur of Canada, Winnipeg, vol.13, no.12, pp. 14, 16, 18, Sept., 1948; Nat. Fur News, Denver, vol.21, no.2, pp.18, 28-31, Mar., 1949.

Cytology

A NUCLEAR RING IN THE DEVELOPING MALE GERM CELLS OF THE DOG AND CAT. J. Brontee Gatenby. Nature, London, vol.152, no.3846, p.79, July 17, 1943.

OBSERVATIONS ON THE BLOOD-CORPUSCLES OF THE ORDER FERAE. G. Gulliver. Proc. Zool. Soc. Lond., pt.9, p.42, 1841.

CYTOLOGY OF THE BLOOD OF NORMAL MINK AND RACCOON. I. MORPHOLOGY OF MINK'S BLOOD. Arnold H. Kennedy. Candian Jour. Research, vol.12, no.4, pp.479-483, pl.1, Apr., 1935.

CYTOLOGY OF THE BLOOD OF NORMAL MINK AND RACCOON. II. THE NUMBERS OF THE BLOOD ELEMENTS IN NORMAL MINK. Arnold H. Kennedy. Canadian Jour. Research., vol.12, no.4, pp.484-494, Apr., 1935.

CYTOLOGY OF THE BLOOD OF NORMAL MINK AND RACCOON. III. MORPHOLOGY AND NUMBERS OF THE BLOOD ELEMENTS IN RACCOON. Arnold H. Kennedy. Canadian Jour. Research, vol.12, no.4, pp.495-507, pl.1, Apr., 1935.

COMPARATIVE SEROLOGY OF CARNIVORES. Charles A. Leone, Alvin L. Wiens. Jour. Mam., 37 (1): 11-23, Feb.28, 1957.

SEROLOGICAL RELATIONSHIPS AMONG MEMBERS OF THE ORDER CARNIVORA. Ludwig K. Pauly, Harold R. Wolfe. Zoologica, New York Zool. Soc., 42 (4): 159-166, Dec.31, 1957.

A NUCLEAR RING IN THE DEVELOPING MALE GERM CELLS OF DOG AND CAT. I. Zlotnik. Nature, London, vol.151, no. 3841, p.670, illus., June 12, 1943.

Diseases and Parasites

(PARASITE HELMINTHS OF DOGS AND CATS IN EGYPT.) Helminthes parasites des chiens et des chats en Egypte. Azim M. Abdel. Annales de Parasitologie Humaine et Comparée, Paris, vol.17, no.1, pp.32-36, Jan., 1939.

THE OCCURRENCE OF THE GUINEA WORM, DRACUNCULUS MEDINENSIS, IN A DOG AND IN A MINK, WITH A REVIEW OF THIS PARASITISM. E.A. Benbrook. Jour. Amer. Vet. Med. Assn., 96 (755): 260-263, Feb., 1940.

ON THE OCCURRENCE OF THE NORTH AMERICAN GUINEA WORM IN MINK, OTTER, RACCOON, AND SKUNK, IN NEW YORK STATE. E. L. Cheatum, Arthur H. Cook. Cornell Veterinarian, Ithaca, vol.38, no.4, pp.421-423, illus., Oct., 1948.

"CHASTEK PARALYSIS" IN MINK AND FOXES. H. C. Collins. Fur of Canada, Winnipeg, vol.13, no.7, pp.16-17, Apr., 1948; vol.14, no.1, pp.8, 10, Oct., 1948.

WILD CARNIVORES AS HOSTS OF THE TREMATODE PREVIOUSLY FOUND IN DOGS AS THE RESULT OF SALMON POISONING. E. B. Cram. North Amer. Veterinarian, vol.7, no.7, pp.42-43, July, 1926.

RABIES IN THE WILD. H. G. Gier. Jour. Wildlife Mgt., 12 (2): 142-153, Apr., 1948.

DISEASE MAY BE PREVENTED BY CLEANLINESS. J. R. Gorham. Amer. Nat. Fur and Market Jour., Wausau, vol.27, no.12, pp.16, 18-19, July, 1949.

MINK, FOX SUSCEPTIBLE TO TULAREMIA. J. R. Gorham. Amer. Nat. Fur and Market Jour., Wausau, vol.28, no.3, p.21, Oct., 1949.

PARASITES OF DOGS AND CATS OF OKLAHOMA. John E. Guberlet. Proc. Oklahoma Acad. Sci., vol.3, pp.71-78, n.s., no.271, Oct.1, 1923.

THE ADULT TAENIOID CESTODES OF DOGS AND CATS, AND RELATED CARNIVORES IN NORTH AMERICA. Maurice C. Hall. Proc. U.S. Nat. Mus., vol.55, pp. 1-94, Apr.11, 1919.

(Review by Hartley H. T. Jackson of) THE ADULT TAENIOID CESTODES OF DOGS AND CATS, AND RELATED CARNIVORES IN NORTH AMERICA. Maurice C. Hall. Jour. Mam., vol.1, no.1, p.44, Nov. 28, 1919.

DISTEMPER COMPLEX IN WILD CARNIVORES SIMULATING RABIES. C. F. Helmboldt, E. L. Jungherr. Amer. Jour. Vet. Res., 16 (60): 463-469, illus., July, 1955.

(ANCANTHOCEPHALANS OF THE DOMESTIC CAT AND DOG.) Acanthocephalen des Hauskatze und des Haushunds. N. Kostilew. Zool. Anzeiger, vol.68, pp.263-269, illus., Oct.5, 1926.

CHASTEK PARALYSIS PRODUCED IN OREGON MINK AND FOXES BY FEEDING FRESH FROZEN SMELT. J. B. Long, J. N. Shaw. Amer. Fur Breeder, Duluth, vol.15, no.11, pp.12, 14, figs.2, May, 1943.

ON THE CESTODE GENUS DIPYLIDIUM FROM CATS AND DOGS. Theresa Marie Millzner. Univ. California Publ. Zool., vol.28, no.17, pp.317-356, pls.33-39, Feb., 1926.

THE PHYSALOPTERA (NEMATODA) OF CARNIVORES. B. B. Morgan. Trans. Wis. Acad. Sci., Arts and Letters, 36: 375-388, 1944.

A REDESCRIPTION OF HETEROBILHARZIA AMERICANA PRICE (TREMATODA: SCHISTOSOMATIDAE). Emmett W. Price. Proc. Helminth. Soc. Wash., 10 (2): 85-86, July, 1943.

SUSCEPTIBILITY OF FURBEARING ANIMALS TO THE TOXINS OF CLOSTRIDIUM BOTULLINUM TYPES A, B, C, AND E. E.R. Quortrup, J.R. Gorham. Amer. Jour. Vet. Res., 10 (36): 268-271, July, 1949.

HOOKWORMS OF THE GENUS UNCINARIA OF THE DOG, FOX AND BADGER. B. H. Ransom. Proc. U.S. Nat. Mus., vol.65, art.20, pp.1-5, pl.1, July, 1924.

TRICHINOSIS IN ARCTIC ANIMALS. Hans Roth. Nature, 163 (4151): 805-806, May 21, 1949.

(INVESTIGATIONS OF PSEUDORACHITIS IN YOUNG CARNIVORES.) Untersuchungen ueber die Pseudorachitis (Sterngucker-krankbeit) der jungen Raubtiere. S. Scheidegger, W. Wendnagel. Zool. Garten, N.F., Leipzig, vol.10, nos.3-4, pp.122-131, illus., Sept., 1938.

DESCRIPTION OF ANCYLOSTOMA PLURIDENTATUM, A HOOKWORM OF CARNIVORES, AND A REVIEW OF THE GENUS ANCYLOSTOMA. Benjamin Schwartz. Proc. U.S. Nat. Mus., vol.72, art.1, pp. 9, illus., Oct.27, 1927.

STRAINS OF THE DOG HOOKWORM, ANCYLOSTOMA CANINUM, SPECIFIC TO THE DOG AND TO THE CAT. J. Allen Scott. Science, vol.69, p.526, May 17, 1929.

RABIES PROBLEMS AND CONTROL, A NATION-WIDE PRGRAM. James H. Steele, Ernest S. Tierkel. Pub. Health Rep., 64 (25): 785-796, June 24, 1949.

DISSEMINATION OF THE BROAD TAPEWORM BY WILD CARNIVORA. Teunis Vergeer. Candian Med. Assoc. Jour., vol.19, pp.692-694, 1928.

DOGS AND CATS CONCERNED IN THE CAUSATION OF CREEPING ERUPTION. G. F. White, W. E. Dove. Reprint from Official Record, U.S. Dept. Agric., vol. 5, no.43, pp.2, Oct.27, 1926.

RABIES IN THE WILD. Stanley P. Young. Amer. Forests, 56 (8): 26, 30, 42, Aug., 1950.

Ecology

NOTES ON THE ANIMAL ECOLOGY OF BEAR ISLAND. G.C.L. Bertram, David Lack. Jour. Animal Ecol., Cambridge, vol.7, no.1, pp.27-52, fig.1, pls.3-4, May, 1938.

BADGER-COYOTE "PARTNERSHIPS". Victor H. Cahalane. Jour. Mam., vol.31, no.3, pp.354-355, Aug.21, 1950.

GRIZZLY FIGHT. (GRIZZLIES AND WOLVES.) Frank Dufresne. Field and Stream, New York, vol.48, no.6, pp.22-23, 64, illus., Oct., 1943.

FOXES AND BADGERS SHARING AN EARTH. G. G. Parker-Hutchinson. Field, London, vol. 56, no.4050, p.207, Aug., 1930.

OCCURRENCE OF PORCUPINE QUILLS IN CARNIVOROUS MAMMALS. Horace F. Quick. Jour. Mam., vol.34, no.2, pp.256-258, 1 table, May 14, 1953.

CAT-FOX ASSOCIATION. F. H. Schultz. Canadian Field-Nat., Ottawa, vol.65, no. 4, p.154, July-Aug., 1950.

THE EFFECT OF CLIMATE ON THE ABUNDANCE OF FOXES, RACCOONS, AND OPOSSUMS. Dwight A. Shanks. Thesis, Univ. Ill., 1946.

THE ROLE OF THE PREDATOR. P. A. Taverner. Canadian Field-Nat., Ottawa, vol.53, no.6, pp.88-90, Sept., 1939.

AN ATTEMPT AT AN ECOLOGICAL EVALUATION OF PREDATORS ON A MIXED PRAIRIE AREA IN WESTERN KANSAS. L. D. Wooster. Trans. Kansas Acad. Sci., Topeka, vol.41, pp. 387-394, fig.1, tables 2, 1938.

Economic Value

THE CONSERVATION OF PREDATORY MAMMALS. Charles C. Adams. Jour. Mam., vol.6, no.2, pp.83-96, May, 1925.

SHALL WE SAVE THE LARGER CARNIVORES? Victor H. Cahalane. Living Wilderness, vol., no.17, pp.17-22, illus., June, 1946.

USEFULNESS OF PREDATORY ANIMALS. Henry R. Carey. Jour. Mam., vol.11, no. 2, pp.229, May, 1930.

MARKET TYPES OF FOX AND MINK. Michael E. Dederer. Nat. Fur News, Denver, vol.18, no.8, pp.14, 34, 47, Sept., 1946.

THE SCIENTIFIC VALUE OF PREDATORY MAMMALS. Lee R. Dice. Jour. Mam., vol.6, no.1, pp.25-27, Feb., 1925.

THE VALUE OF PREDATORY MAMMALS. W. J. Hamilton, Jr. Bull. N. Y. Zool. Soc., 40 (2): 39-45, Mar.-Apr., 1937.

PRODUCTION STUDY OF FOXES AND MINK IN THE UNITED STATES. Roy Harmon, William P. Bender. Fur of Canada, Winnipeg, vol.14, no.1, pp.24-25, Oct., 1948.

ECONOMIC VALUE OF PREDATORY ANIMALS. L. W. Walker. Zool. Soc. San Diego, pp.15, illus., 1930.

Eurasia

CARNIVORA FROM THE ASIATIC EXPEDITIONS. Glover M. Allen. Amer. Mus. Novitates, no.360, pp.1-14, July 17, 1929.

KEY TO THE MAMMALS OF THE U.S.S.R. N. A. Bobrinskii, others. State Publ. House "Sovetzkaya Nauka", Moscow, 1944. (English translation)

ON THE REMAINS OF CARNIVORA FROM CAVE DEPOSITS IN JAVA AND SUMATRA, WITH NOTES ON RECENT SPECIMENS. I. L. D. Brongersma. Zool. Mededeelingen, Leiden, vol.23, nos.1-2, pp.114-148, fig.1, pl.4, Nov., 1941.

(PRESENT DISTRIBUTION AND DENSITY OF CARNIVORES IN THE DEPARTMENT OF DEUX-SEVRES AND NEIGHBORING AREAS.) Répartition et densité actuelle des carnivores dans le Département des Deux-Sèvres et les régions voisines. A. Brosset. Mammalia, Paris, vol.18, no.2, pp.216-218, June, 1954.

(DATA CONCERNING THE MAMMAL FAUNA OF TRANSYLVANIA. 1. THE MINK'S (MUSTELA LUTREOLA L.) OCCURRENCE IN TRANSYLVANIA. 2. THE LYNX (LYNX LYNX L.) IN MAROS-TORDA COUNTY.) Adatok erdély Emloesfaunájahoz. 1. A nyérc (Mustela lutreola L.) erdélyi eloefordulása. 2. A hiúz (Lynx lynx L.) Maros-Torda megyében. J. Ehik. Allattani Koezlemények, vol.31, nos.1-2, pp.91-95, 1934. (In Hungarian, with German summary.)

WAR STATUS OF PREDATORS IN NORWAY. Aldo Leopold, Hans Peter Thomsen. Jour. Mam., vol.26, no.1, pp.88-89, Feb.23, 1945.

A NEW CARNIVORE FROM CHINA. Gerrit S. Miller, Jr. Proc. U.S. Nat. Mus., vol.38, pp.385-386, pl.17, 1911.

TWO NEW CARNIVORES FROM THE MALAY PENINSULA. Gerrit S. Miller, Jr. Proc. Biol. Soc., Wash., vol.19, pp. 25-28, Feb.26, 1906.

(PREDATORY MAMMALS IN THE USSR.) Khishchniye mlekopitayushchiye fauni SSSR. G. A. Novikov. Opredeliteli profaunye SSSR, Izdavayemiye Zool. Inst. Akad. Nauk SSSR., no.62, pp.293, illus., 1956.

A GUIDE TO THE MAMMALS OF CEYLON. PART II. CARNIVORA. W.W.A. Phillips. Spolia Zeylanica (Ceylon), vol.13, pt.2, pp. 143-184, July 31, 1925.

NOTE ON A BEAR AND A PANTHER OBTAINED BY COL. F.M. BAILEY FROM TIBET AND A PANTHER FROM ASIA MINOR OBTAINED BY MR. J.E. WHITTALL. (PANTHERA PARDUS BEDFORDI, URSUS ARCTOS PRUINOSUS.) R. I. Pocock. Jour. Bombay Nat. Hist. Soc., vol.37, no. 4, pp.947-948, Apr.15, 1935.

(SMALL CARNIVORES OF EUROPE.) Les petits carnivores d'Europe. René Thévenin. Paris, Payot, pp.203, illus., 1952.

THE MAMMALS AND BIRDS OF KASHMIR AND THE ADJACENT HILL PROVINCES. PART 8. ARCTOIDEA. A. E. Ward. Jour. Bombay Nat. Hist. Soc., vol.33, no. 1, pp.65-72, pl.1, Sept.30, 1928.

(THE WILD MAMMALS OF CRETE. 6) CRETAN CARNIVORES.) Die Wildsaeuger von Kreta. 6) Die Carnivora von Kreta. Klaus Zimmermann. Zeitschr. Saeugetierk, vol.17, no.1, pp.58-65, pl.9, Feb.19, 1953.

THE WILD ANIMALS OF THE INDIAN EMPIRE AND THE PROBLEM OF THEIR PRESERVATION. PART 4. CARNIVORA (CONT.). Jour. Bombay Nat. Hist. Soc., vol.38, no.2 (suppl.), pp.189-219, pls.53-67, Dec.1, 1935.

Experimental Biology

REPORTS ON CERTAIN EXPERIMENTS ON THE FEEDING OF CARNIVOROUS MAMMALIA. Devereux Fuller. Proc. Comm. Sci. and Corres. Zool. Soc. Lond., pt.2, pp.49-50, 1832.

EXPERIMENTAL DEGENERATION OF THE EXTRINSIC NERVES OF THE SMALL INTESTINE IN RELATION TO THE STRUCTURE OF THE MYENTERIC PLEXUS. (WORK ON DOG AND CAT.) Sydney E. Johnson. Jour. Comp. Neur., vol.38, pp. 299-314, figs.9, Apr.15, 1925.

(COMPARATIVE INVESTIGATIONS OF CANIDES AND PROCYONIDS.) Vergleichende Untersuchungen an Caniden und Procyoniden. Berthold Klatt. Zool. Jahrbuecher (Allgemeines), vol.45, pp. 217-292, 8 figs., 1928.

Fossils

PRELIMINARY NOTE ON THE QUATERNARY CARNIVORA OF THE CRIMEA. A. A. Birula. Comptes Rendus Acad. Sci. USSR, ser.A, no.6, pp.139-144, 1930. (In Russian.)

A PRELIMINARY ACCOUNT OF THE PLEISTOCENE CARNIVORES OF THE TRANSVAAL CAVES. R. Broom. Ann. Transvaal Mus., Cambridge, vol.19, pt. 3, pp.331-338, figs.5, May 24, 1939.

CAMPYLOCYNODON PERSONI, A NEW OLIGOCENE CARNIVORE FROM THE BEAVER DIVIDE, WYOMING. Robert G. Chaffee. Jour. Palaeontol., vol.28, no.1, pp.43-46, illus., Jan., 1954.

MIACIS GRACILIS, A NEW CARNIVORE FROM THE UINTA EOCENE. John Clark. Ann. Carnegie Mus., Pittsburgh, vol.27, pp.349-370, figs.2, pls.34-37, Nov.6, 1939.

CARNIVORA OF THE TUNG GUR FORMATION OF MONGOLIA. Edwin H. Colbert. Bull. Amer. Mus. Nat. Hist., vol.76, art. 2, pp.47-81, figs.19, tables, Apr.27, 1939.

A MIOCENE CREODONT FROM JACKSON HOLE, WYOMING. Edwin H. Colbert. Jour. Paleontol., Menasha, vol.17, no.3, pp.298-304, figs.3, May, 1943.

CARNIVORA FROM THE DERA BUGTI DEPOSITS OF BALUCHISTAN. C. Forster Cooper. Ann. and Mag. Nat. Hist., ser.9, vol.12, pp.259-263, 4 figs., Aug., 1923.

ON THE NIMRAVIDAE AND CANIDAE OF THE MIOCENE PERIOD. Edward Drinker Cope. U.S. Geological and Geographical Survey of the Territories, Bull., Wash. Govt. Print. Off., vol.6, no.1, art.7, pp. 165-181, 1882.

THE BROAD-SKULLED PSEUDOCREODI. Robert Howland Denison. Ann. New York Acad. Sci., vol.37, art.3, pp.163-256, figs.32, May 14, 1938.

(CONTRIBUTION TO KNOWLEDGE OF THE BEAN ORE FORMATION IN SWABIA. 3. CARNIVORA FROM THE BEAN ORE SEDIMENT IN THE ALPS AROUND ULM AND EICHSTATT.) Beitrag zur Kenntnis der Bohnerzformation in Schwaben. 3. Raubtiere aus den Bohnerzablagerungen der Ulmer und der Eichstaetter Alb. W. O. Dietrich. Neuen Jahrbuch f. Mineral., bd. 63, Abt.B, pp.451-474, pls.27-29, 1930.

(NOTE ON THE GENUS URSAVUS AND ON STEINHEIM CARNIVORES.) Bemerkung zur Gattung Ursavus und zu Steinheimer Raubtieren. W. O. Dietrich. Centralblatt Min., B, vol.8, pp.332-334, 1927.

SOME FOSSIL CARNIVORES FROM THE MAKAPANSGAT VALLEY. R. F. Ewer. Palaeontol. Afr., 4: 57-67, illus., 1956.

FOSSIL CARNIVORA FROM HOPEFIELD. R. F. Ewer, R. Singer. Ann. South African Mus., vol.42, pt.4, pp.335-349, Mar., 1956.

THE HEMICYONINAE AND AN AMERICAN TERTIARY BEAR. Childs Frick. Bull. Amer. Mus. Nat. Hist., vol.56, art.1, pp. 1-119, illus., Apr.8, 1926.

MACHAEROIDES EOTHEN MATTHEW, THE SABERTOOTH CREODONT OF THE BRIDGER EOCENE. C. Lewis Gazin. Proc. U.S. Nat. Mus., Washington, vol. 96, no.3202, pp.335-347, pls.45-46, Dec. 16, 1946.

A SKULL OF THE BRIDGER MIDDLE EOCENE CREODONT, PATRIOFELIS ULTA LEIDY. C. Lewis Gazin. Smithson. Misc. Coll., Wash., 134 (8): 1-20, illus., Apr.30, 1957.

NEW SPECIES OF CLAENODONTS FROM FORT UNION (BASAL EOCENE) OF MONTANA. James W. Gidley. Bull. Amer. Mus. Nat. Hist., vol.41, art.14, pp.541-555, figs.10, pl.28, Dec.8, 1919.

A GIANT OXYAENID FROM THE UPPER EOCENE OF MONGOLIA. Walter Granger. Amer. Mus. Novitates no.969, pp.5, figs. 5, Apr.21, 1938.

BASSARISCUS IN MIOCENE FAUNAS AND "POTAMOTHERIUM LYCOPOTAMICUM COPE." Joseph T. Gregory, Theodore Downs. Postilla, Yale Peabody Mus. Nat. Hist., New Haven, no.8, pp.10, May 10, 1951.

ON PRIMITIVE CARNIVORES FROM THE PALEOGENE OF MONGOLIA AND KAZAKHSTAN. Vera Gromova. Proc. Paleo. Inst., Acad. Sci. U.S.S.R., vol.41, pp. 51-77, illus., 1952.

A BASSARISK AND A NEW MUSTELID FROM THE LATER TERTIARY OF CALIFORNIA. E. Raymond Hall. Jour. Mam., vol.11, no. 1, pp.23-25, fig.1, Feb.11, 1930.

DESCRIPTION OF A NEW MUSTELID FROM THE LATER TERTIARY OF OREGON, WITH ASSIGNMENT OF PARICITS PRIMAEVUS TO THE CANIDAE. E. Raymond Hall. Jour. Mam., vol.12, no.2, pp.156-158, pl.5, May, 1931.

(ON THE CARNIVORE FAUNA OF MIOCENE HABITATS OF SOUTHERN GERMANY.) Zur Carnivorenfauna sueddeutscher Miocaenfundorte. H. Helbing. Actes Soc. Helvétique Sci. Nat., no.109, pt.2, pp.221-222, 1928.

(THE GEOLOGIC AGE OF BEAR AND GLUTTON REMAINS.) Das geologische Alter der Baeren-und Vielfrassreste. Max Hilzheimer. Zeitschrift f. Saeugetierkunde, vol.11, pp.317-319, Mar.13, 1936.

DYSPTERNA WOODI, GEN. ET SP. N., A CARNIVORE FROM THE OLIGOCENE ISLE OF WIGHT. A. Tindel Hopwood. Ann. and Mag. Nat. Hist., ser.9, vol.20, pp. 174-176, July, 1927.

(EXTINCT BAVARIAN CARNIVORES.) Ausgestorbene bayerische Raubtiere. Gustav Kuestardt. Zeitschr. f. Saeugetierkunde Berlin, vol.12, no.3, pp.241-244, pls.14-16, July 15, 1938.

(NOTES ON THE AFFINITIES OF SOME CARNIVORES OF OLIGOCENE EUROPE, NOTABLY OF THE GENERA PLESICTIS POMEL AND PROAILURUS FILHOL.) Sur les affinités de quelques carnassiers de l'Oligocene d'Europe, notamment du genre Plesictis Pomel et du genre Porailurus Filhol. R. Lavocat. Mammalia, Paris, vol.16, no.2, pp.62-72, illus., June, 1952.

THE SMALL CARNIVORES OF THE MIOCENE. F. B. Loomis. Amer. Jour. Sci., ser.5, vol.26, no.155, pp.316-329, figs. 10, Nov., 1933.

TWO NEW CARNIVORES FROM THE PLIOCENE OF KANSAS. Handel T. Martin. Jour. Mam., vol.9, no.3, pp.233-236, pls.2, Aug., 1928.

A REVISION OF THE LOWER EOCENE WASATCH AND WIND RIVER FAUNAS. PART I. ORDER FERAE (CARNIVORA), SUBORDER CREODONTA. W. D. Matthew. Bull. Amer. Mus. Nat. Hist., New York, vol.34, art.1, pp.1-103, figs. 87, Mar.3, 1915.

NEW CARNIVORA FROM THE TERTIARY OF MONGOLIA. W. D. Matthew, Walter Granger. Amer. Mus. Novit., no.104, pp. 1-9, figs.1-7, Jan.15, 1924.

RECENT DISCOVERIES OF CARNIVORA IN THE PLEISTOCENE OF RANCHO LA BREA. John C. Merriam. Univ. Calif. Publ., Bull. Dept. Geol., vol.7, no.3, pp. 39-46, figs.10, Sept.12, 1912.

ANDREWSARCHUS, GIANT MESONYCHID OF MONGOLIA. Henry Fairfield Osborn. Amer. Mus. Nov., New York, no.146, pp. 5, figs.3, Nov.11, 1924.

NEW CARNIVOROUS MAMMALS FROM THE FAYUM OLIGOCENE, EGYPT. Henry Fairfield Osborn. Bull. Amer. Mus. Nat. Hist., New York, vol.36, art. 281, pp.415-424, figs.9, Sept.9, 1909.

OXYAENA AND PATRIOFELIS RESTUDIED AS TERRESTRIAL CREODONTS. Henry Fairfield Osborn. Bull. Amer. Mus. Nat. Hist., New York, vol.13, art.20, pp.269-279, figs.8, pl.18, Dec.21, 1900.

ON THE CARNIVORA FROM LOCALITY 1 OF CHOUKOUTIEN. Wen-Chung Pei. Palaeontologia Sinica, Peiping, ser.C, vol. 8, fasc.1, pp.216, figs.47, pls.24, May, 1934.

NEW MESONYCHIDS FROM THE UINTA. O. A. Peterson. Ann. Carnegie Mus., vol.20, nos.3-4, pp.333-339, pls.2, figs. 4, 1931.

(ON A CARNIVORE SKULL FROM THE "MEERESMOLASSE" BEDS OF WILDENSBUCH, ZURICH CANTON.) Ueber einen Schaedelrest eines Carnivoren aus der Meeresmolasse von Wildensbuch, Kt. Zuerich. B. Peyer. Eclogae geol. Helvetiae, Basel, vol.31, no.2, pp.311-316, figs.4, Dec., 1938.

CATALOGUE OF THE PONTIAN CARNIVORA OF EUROPE IN THE DEPARTMENT OF GEOLOGY. Guy E. Pilgrim. Publ. Brit. Mus. Nat. Hist., London, pp.vi, 174, figs.30, pls.2, Oct.24, 1931.

THE FOSSIL CARNIVORA OF INDIA. Guy E. Pilgrim. Mem. Geol. Surv. India, Palaeontologia Indica, Calcutta (n.s.), vol. 18, pp.iii, 232, figs.2, pls.10, 1932.

PRELIMINARY DESCRIPTION OF TWO LOWER MIOCENE CARNIVORES. Elmer S. Riggs. Geol. Ser. Field Mus. Nat. Hist., publ.520, vol.8, no.10, pp.59-62, June 25, 1942.

SOME EARLY MIOCENE CARNIVORES. E. S. Riggs. Field Mus. Nat. Hist., Geol. Ser., Chicago, vol.9, no.3, publ. 573, pp.69-114, figs.23-45, Oct.4, 1945.

A NEW ARCTOID CARNIVORE FROM THE LOWER MIOCENE. A. S. Romer, A. H. Sutton. Amer. Jour. Sci., vol.14, no.84, pp.459-464, 1927.

SKULL OF HEMIPSALODON GRANDIS COPE. Loris S. Russell. Proc. Geol. Soc. America, 1937, p.288, June, 1938.

THE SKULL OF HEMIPSALODON GRANDIS, A GIANT OLIGOCENE CREODONT. Loris S. Russell. Trans. Roy. Soc. Canada, Ottawa, ser.3, sect.4, vol.32, pp.61-66, pls.1-5, 1938.

TWO NEW MIDDLE PLIOCENE CARNIVORES FROM OKLAHOMA WITH NOTES ON THE OPTIMA FAUNA (VULPES STENOGNATHUS, FELIS PROTEROLYNCIS). Donald E. Savage. Amer. Midland Nat., Notre Dame, vol.25, no.3, pp.692-710, pls.4, May, 1941.

A NOTE ON THE CARNIVORA OF THE TEGELEN CLAY, WITH SOME REMARKS ON THE GRISONINAE. A. Schreuder. Archiv. Néerlandaises de Zool., vol.2, no. 1, pp.73-94, pl.1, figs.3, 1935.

A REMARKABLE SABRETOOTH-LIKE CREODONT FROM THE EOCENE OF UTAH. W. M. Scott. Science, n.s., vol.85, no.2210, pp.454-455, May 7, 1937.

A MOUNTED SKELETON OF PALAEONICTIS. William J. Sinclair, Glenn L. Jepsen. Proc. Amer. Philos. Soc., vol. 68, no.3, pp.163-173, figs.5, 1929.

CARNIVORA FROM THE SESPE OF THE LAS POSAS HILLS, CALIFORNIA. Chester Stock. Contrib. to Paleont., Carnegie Inst. Wash., Publ.440, pp.29-41, pls.3, Nov.15, 1933.

CARNIVORA NEW TO THE MASCALL MIOCENE FAUNA OF EASTERN OREGON. Chester Stock. Contrib. to Palaeontology, Carnegie Inst. Wash., Publ.404, pp.43-48, figs.2, pl.1, Aug., 1930.

CARNIVORA OF THE SESPE UPPER EOCENE, SIMI VALLEY REGION, CALIFORNIA. Chester Stock. Bull. Geol. Soc. America, vol.44, no.1, p.199, Feb. 28, 1933.

HYAENODONTIDAE OF THE UPPER EOCENE OF CALIFORNIA. Chester Stock. Proc. Nat. Acad. Sci., vol.19, no.4, pp.434-440, 1933.

A MIACID FROM THE SESPE UPPER EOCENE, CALIFORNIA. Chester Stock. Proc. Nat. Acad. Sci., vol.19, pp.481-486, pl.1, 1933.

NEW CREODONTA FROM THE SESPE UPPER EOCENE, CALIFORNIA. Chester Stock. Proc. Nat. Acad. Sci., vol.20, no.7, pp.423-427, pl.1, July, 1934.

A PECULIAR NEW CARNIVORE FROM THE CUYAMA MIOCENE, CALIFORNIA. Chester Stock. Bull. Southern California Acad. Sci., Los Angeles, vol.46, no.2, pp.84-89, pl.1, Feb.5, 1948.

PLESIOMIACIS, A NEW CREODONT FROM THE SESPE UPPER EOCENE, CALIFORNIA. Chester Stock. Proc. Nat. Acad. Sci., vol. 21, no.2, pp.119-122, fig.1, Feb., 1935.

(NEW AND LITTLE KNOWN CARNIVORES FROM THE DINOTHERIUM SANDS, LOWER PLIOCENE, OF RHEINHESSE.) Neue und wenig bekannte Carnivoren aus den unterpliozaenen Dinotheriensanden Rheinhessens. H. Tobein. Notizbl. Hess. L.-Amt. Bodenforsch., 83: 7-31, illus., Sept.13, 1955.

(CONTRIBUTION TO STUDY OF MIOCENE CARNIVORES OF THE GRIVE-SAINT-ALBAN (ISERE).) Contribution à l'étude des Carnassiers Miocènes de la Grive-Saint-Alban (Isère). J. Viret. Trav. Lab. Géol. Fac. Sci. Lyon, no.21, Mém.18, pp. 1-30, figs.8, pls.1-2, 1933.

OSTEOLOGY OF PATRIOFELIS, A MIDDLE EOCENE CREODONT. J. L. Wortman. Bull. Amer. Mus. Nat. Hist., vol.6, art.5, pp.129-164, figs.5, pl.1, May, 1894.

RESTORATION OF OXYAENA LUPINA COPE, WITH DESCRIPTIONS OF CERTAIN NEW SPECIES OF EOCENE CREODONTS. J. L. Wortman. Bull. Amer. Mus. Nat. Hist., New York, vol.12, art.7, pp.139-148, figs.3, pl.7, 1899.

(EARLY TERTIARY CARNIVORES OF CHINA.) Jungtertiaere carnivoren Chinas. Otto Zdansky. Palaeontologia Sinica, ser. C, vol.2, fasc.1, pp.149, pls.33, figs.21, Peking, 1924.

(FURTHER REMARKS ON FOSSIL CARNIVORES FROM CHINA.) Weitere Bemerkungen ueber fossile Carnivoren aus China. Otto Zdansky. Palaeontologia Sinica (C), vol.4, fasc.4, pp.1-30, pls.1-2, figs.6, 1927.

### Feeding

SUBSTITUTES IN THE FOX AND MINK RATION. Charles F. Bassett. Nat. Fur News, Denver, vol.15, no.12, pp.11, 24, Jan., 1944.

NOTES ON FEEDING FOXES AND MINK. R. J. Kirk. Fur of Canada, Winnipeg, vol.13, no.5, p.3, Feb., 1948.

(ORIENTATION AND TRAINING OF SMALL MAMMALS. Elis Naundorff. Carnivore Studies, vol.2, Small and Fur Animals, Leipzig, Jahrg.12, no.8, pp.103-106, Dec., 1936.

CARBOHYDRATES IN MINK AND FOX FEEDING. W. L. Roberts. Amer. Fur Breeder, Duluth, vol.21, no.12, pp.46-48, 50, June, 1949; Amer. Nat. Fur and Market Jour., Wausau, vol.27, no.10, pp.11, 21-22, May, 1949; Nat. Fur News, Denver, vol.21, no.4, pp.16, 24; no.5, pp.22-23, May-June, 1949.

FATS IN MINK AND FOX FEEDING. W.L. Roberts. Nat. Fur News, Denver, vol.21, no.5, pp.12, 24-25, June, 1949.

NUTRITION AND ECONOMY IN MINK AND FOX FEEDING. W.L. Roberts. Nat. Fur News, Denver, vol.21, no.2, pp.14-15, 33-34, Mar., 1949; Amer. Fur Breeder, Duluth, vol.21, no.10, pp.14, 16, 18, 20, 22, Apr., 1949.

STUDY OF THE NUTRITIONAL REQUIREMENTS OF FOX AND MINK BY THE USE OF PURIFIED RATIONS. A.E. Schaefer, C. K. Whitehair, C. A. Elvehjem. Nat. Fur News, Denver, vol.19, no.7, pp.20, 32-33, 35, Sept., 1947; Amer. Fur Breeder, Duluth, vol.20, no.5, pp.54, 56, 58, 60, illus., Nov., 1947.

### Food Habits

DO FUR BEARERS AFFECT UPLAND GAME BIRDS IN WINTER? Watson E. Beed. Trans. N. A. Wildl. Conf., 3: 508-510, 1938.

THE PALATABILITY OF THE EGGS OF BIRDS: ILLUSTRATED BY EXPERIMENTS ON THE FOOD PREFERENCES OF THE FERRET (PUTORIUS FURO) AND CAT (FELIX CATUS); WITH NOTES ON OTHER EGG-EATING CARNIVORA. Hugh B. Cott. Proc. Zool. Soc. London, vol.123, pt.1, pp.123-141, June 10, 1953.

FOODS OF SOME PREDATORY FUR-BEARING ANIMALS IN MICHIGAN. Ned Dearborn. Univ. Michigan Sch. Forestry and Conservation Bull. no.1, pp.52, figs.8, charts 22, maps, 1932; American Fur Breeder, vol.5, no.12, pp.4-5, 7, figs.2, June, 1933.

THE SUMMER FOOD OF MINKS AND RACCOONS ON THE MONTEZUMA MARSH, NEW YORK. W. J. Hamilton, Jr. Jour. Wildlife Management, Menasha, vol.4, no. 1, pp.80-84, tables 2, Jan., 1940.

THE FOOD OF PREDACEOUS ANIMALS IN NORTHEASTERN UNITED STATES. Roger M. Latham. Final Rept., Pittman-Robertson Project 36-R, Report I, Pennsylvania Game Comm., Harrisburg, pp.68, illus., 1950.

FOOD HABITS OF PREDATORY MAMMALS. W. L. McAtee. Jour. Mam., vol.15, no.3, pp.243-244, Aug., 1934.

FOODS OF TRAPPED NORTH DAKOTA PREDATORY ANIMALS. William T. McKean. Bimonthly Bull., 10 (3): 105-112, Jan.-Feb., 1948.

WINTER FOODS OF NORTH DAKOTA PREDATORY ANIMALS. William T. McKean. North Dakota Outdoors, 10 (8): 5-6, Feb., 1948.

FOOD HABITS OF YOSEMITE MAMMALS AS INDICATED BY THEIR TEETH. PT.2. FLESH EATING MAMMALS (CARNIVORA). Richard G. Miller. Yosemite Nature Notes, vol.24, no.3, pp.46-48, illus., Mar., 1945.

VALUE OF PREY-INDIVIDUAL ANALYSIS OF STOMACH CONTENTS OF PREDATORY MAMMALS. Carl O. Mohr. Jour. Mam., 16 (4): 323-324, Nov., 1935.

A PREDATOR ELIMINATES A SICK ANIMAL. Adolph Murie. Jour. Mam., vol. 17, no.4, p.418, Nov., 1936.

DO THE CARNIVORA HUNT BY SCENT? R. I. Pocock. Field, London, vol.152, p. 291, Aug.16, 1928.

THE KILLER. N. B. Scofield. Calif. Fish and Game, vol.11, no.2, pp.86-87, Apr., 1925.

### Genetics

GENETIC PROBLEMS IN BREEDING FOXES AND MINK. Alma Erekson. Nat. Fur News, Denver, vol.19, no.1, pp.11-13, 33-35, illus., Feb., 1947.

SOME COLOR MUTATIONS IN FOXES AND MINK. E. M. Gildow. Nat. Fur News, Denver, vol.16, no.10, pp.8-9, 14, 19, 23, 29, Nov., 1944.

GENETIC RESEARCH IN MINK AND FOXES. Richard M. Shackelford. Nat. Fur News, Denver, vol.19, no.7, pp.10-11, 20-21, 38, illus., Aug., 1947.

### Methods, Techniques

TAKING A CENSUS OF THE FOODS OF THE FOX AND ERMINE (SMALL RODENTS

AND INSECTIVORES). N. V. Bashenina, N. P. Lavrov. In Symposium, "Methods for forecasting changes in the numbers of fur-bearing animals and renewing their natural supplies." Trans. Cent. Lab. Game Indus., no.5, pp.100-104, 1941.

THE PROPER PELTING OF SILVER FOX AND MINK. Michael Dederer. Amer. Fur Breeder, Duluth, vol.13, no.5, pp. 10-11, 12, illus., Nov., 1940.

THE LOSS OF EAR TAGS IN THE GRAY FOX AND RACCOON. Rexford D. Lord, Jr. Jour. Mam., 37 (4): 548, Jan.9, 1958.

THE TRACKING TECHNIQUE IN THE STUDY OF THE LARGER PREDATORY MAMMALS. A. M. Stebler. Trans. N. A. Wildl. Conf., 4: 203-208, 1939.

North America

GEOGRAPHIC DISTRIBUTION OF COLOR PHASES OF THE RED FOX AND BLACK BEAR IN THE PACIFIC NORTHWEST. Ian McTaggart Cowan. Jour. Mam., vol.19, no.2, pp.202-206, map, May 14, 1938.

NOTES ON NEW ENGLAND CARNIVORES. William Everett Cram. Jour. Mam., vol. 6, no.3, p.199, Aug., 1925.

A NEW KINKAJOU FROM MEXICO AND A NEW HOODED SKUNK FROM CENTRAL AMERICA. George G. Goodwin. Amer. Mus. Novitates, New York, 1830: 1-4, May 3, 1957.

THE CARNIVORES OF THE SAN ANDRES MOUNTAINS, NEW MEXICO. Arthur F. Halloran. Jour. Mam., 27 (2): 154-161, May, 1946.

CARNIVORES OF YUMA COUNTY, ARIZONA. Arthur F. Halloran, Willard E. Blanchard. Amer. Midland Nat., vol.51, no.2, pp.481-487, Apr., 1954.

SOME AMERICAN BIG GAME (COUGAR, GRAY WOLF, COYOTE). Edmund Heller. Parks and Recreation, vol.12, pp.193-195, Apr., 1929.

FIELD NOTES REGARDING THE STATUS OF SEVERAL NORTH DAKOTA FUR BEARERS (WEASEL, RED FOX). Brandt V. Hjelle. North Dakota Outdoors, Grand Forks, vol.10, no.6, p.6, Dec., 1947.

DESCRIPTION OF A NEW SPECIES OF WEASEL, AND A NEW SUBSPECIES OF THE GRAY FOX, FROM ARIZONA. Edgar A. Mearns. Bull. Amer. Mus. Nat. Hist., vol.3, no.2, pp.234-238, June 5, 1891.

PRELIMINARY DIAGNOSES OF NEW MAMMALS OF THE GENERA LYNX, UROCYON, SPILOGALE, AND MEPHITIS, FROM THE MEXICAN BOUNDARY LINE. Edgar A. Mearns. Washington, D.C., pp.1-4, Jan. 12, 1897 (advance sheet); Reprinted in Proc. U.S. Nat. Mus., vol.20, no.1126, pp.457-461, Dec.24, 1897.

A CENSUS OF RED FOXES AND STRIPED SKUNKS IN CLAY AND BOONE COUNTIES, IOWA. Thomas G. Scott, Lyle F. Selko. Jour. Wildl. Mgt., 3 (2): 92-98, Apr., 1939.

SOME OBSERVATIONS ON WILD ANIMALS (PUMA, BEAR, AND WOLF IN PENNSYLVANIA). Henry W. Shoemaker. Publ. Altoona Tribune Press, Altoona, Pa., pp.5, Apr., 1923.

INDIAN RECORDS OF CALIFORNIA CARNIVORES. William Duncan Strong. Jour. Mam., vol.7, no.1, pp.59-60, Feb., 1926.

OUR WILD DOGS AND CATS. THE WOLVES, FOXES AND LYNXES. T. Surber. Conservation Volunteer, St. Paul, vol.4, no.24, pp.44-47, Sept., 1942.

THE PREDATORS OF MINNESOTA. Harold B. Swanson. Minnesota Conserv., St. Paul, no.69, pp.11-12, June, 1939.

THE FUR-BEARING MAMMALS OF WYOMING (COUGAR AND WOLF). PT. 17. Earl M. Thomas. Wyo. Wild Life, 17 (7): 24-28, illus., July, 1953.

BLACKWATER REFUGE (MARYLAND) RECORDS FIRST GRAY FOX AND SKUNK. Rally Sheet, League of Maryland Sportsmen, vol.2, no.1, p.8, Jan., 1944.

FUR ANIMALS OF TEXAS (BLACK BEAR, RACCOON). Texas Game and Fish, Austin, vol.1, no.12, pp.13, 15, Nov., 1943.

MAMMALS OF PREY OF OREGON. Oregon State Game Comm., Information Education Division, Information leaflet no.12, p.4, illus., 1960.

Pelage and Coloration

BLACK CROSS MINK AND ARCTIC BLUE AND WHITE FOXES. Lewis Palmer. Amer. Fur Breeder, Duluth, vol.17, no.2, pp.22, 24, illus., Aug., 1944.

WHAT WE CAN EXPECT IN SILVER FOX AND MINK COLOR PHASES. Richard M. Shackelford. Pt. I, American Nat. Fur and Market Jour., Wausau, vol.26, no.3, pp. 5-6, 17-18, Oct., 1947; Pt.II, no.4, pp.11-12, 22-23, 24-26, illus., Nov., 1947; Pt. III, no.5, pp.9-10, Dec., 1947.

Physiology

THE URINARY NITROGEN DISTRIBUTION OF REPRESENTATIVE MEMBERS OF THE CARNIVORA. Richard W. Jackson, Thomas J. Dring, Charles R. Schroeder. Zoologica New York, vol.24, pt.3, pp.345-354, figs. 5, Nov.2, 1939.

EFFECTIVE OSMOTIC PRESSURE OF PLASMA PROTEINS AND OTHER QUANTITIES ASSOCIATED WITH CAPILLARY CIRCULATION IN HIND-LIMBS OF CATS AND DOGS. J. R. Pappenheimer, A. Soto-Rivera. Amer. Jour. Physiol., Balto., vol. 152, no.3, pp.471-491, Mar., 1948.

SUSCEPTIBILITY OF CATS AND DOGS TO PROGRESSIVE ANOXIA. Ralph W. Stacy, W. V. Whitehorn, Fred A. Hitchcock. Amer. Jour. Physiol., Balto., vol.153, no. 1, pp.87-92, Apr.1, 1948.

Predation and Control

PREDATORY MAMMAL CONTROL WORK OF THE U.S. BIOLOGICAL SURVEY. Charles C. Adams. Jour. Mam., vol.10, no.3, p.275, Aug., 1929.

THE PREDATORY MAMMAL PROBLEM. Charles C. Adams. Roosevelt Wild Life Bull., Syracuse, vol.4, no.2, pp.283-284, June, 1927.

RATIONAL PREDATORY ANIMAL CONTROL. Charles C. Adams. Jour. Mam., vol.11, no.3, pp.353-358, Aug., 1930.

(Comments by A. E. Fisher on) THE RATIONAL PREDATORY ANIMAL CONTROL. C. C. Adams. Jour. Mam., vol. 11, no.3, pp.358-359, Aug., 1930.

(Comments by E. A. Goldman on) THE RATIONAL PREDATORY ANIMAL CONTROL. C. C. Adams. Jour. Mam., vol. 11, no.3, pp.360-361, Aug., 1930.

(Comments by W. C. Henderson on) THE RATIONAL PREDATORY ANIMAL CONTROL. C. C. Adams. Jour. Mam., vol. 11, no.3, p.361, Aug., 1930.

OPERATION DRAINPIPE (BOUNTY SYSTEM). Durward L. Allen. Field and Stream, New York, vol.54, no.2, pp.60, 126-128, June, 1949.

THE CONTROL OF PREDATORY MAMMALS. H. E. Anthony. Science, vol. 74, no.1916, pp.288-290, Sept.18, 1931.

WHY PICK ON THE PREDATORS? Sherman Baker. Conservation, Wash., D.C., vol.7, no.6, pp.10-13, Nov.-Dec., 1941.

PREDATORS A MAJOR PROBLEM. Elliott S. Barker. New Mexico Mag., Albuquerque, vol.22, no.12, pp.21, 23, Dec., 1944.

PREDATOR CONTROL--FACTS AND FANCIES. Robert O. Beatty. Outdoor America, Madison, vol.12, no.11, pp. 6-8, illus., Dec., 1947.

HUNTING DOWN STOCK KILLERS (ACCOUNT OF PREDATORY ANIMAL WORK OF THE BIOLOGICAL SURVEY). W. B. Bell. Yearbook U.S. Dept. Agric., 1920, separate 845, pp.289-300, 1921.

DO PREDATORS ERADICATE DISEASE? Allan Brooks. Rod and Gun in Canada, Montreal, vol.45, no.8, pp.13, 29, illus., Jan., 1944.

DISPUTING THE SWAY OF THE PREDATOR. J. G. Burr. Texas Game and Fish, Austin, vol.2, no.8, pp.7-8, 19, illus., July, 1944.

STALKING THE DESTROYER (MOUNTAIN LION, COYOTE). J. G. Burr. Texas Game and Fish, Austin, vol.4, no.7, pp. 4-5, 26-28, illus., June, 1946.

THE EVOLUTION OF PREDATOR CONTROL POLICY IN THE NATIONAL PARKS. Victor H. Cahalane. Jour. Wildlife Management, Menasha, vol.3, no.3, pp.229-237, July, 1939.

PREDATORS AND PEOPLE. Victor H. Cahalane. Natl. Parks Mag., 22 (95): 5-12, Oct-Dec., 1948.

BOUNTIES AND PREDATOR CONTROL. J. L. Carey. Rally Sheet, League of Maryland Sportsmen, Balto., vol.4, no. 7, p.6, Aug., 1946.

LET'S TALK ABOUT PREDATOR CONTROL. Floyd B. Chapman. Ohio Conservation Bull., Columbus, vol.14, no.12, pp. 6-7, 28-29, illus., Dec., 1950.

ARE BOUNTIES BLUNDERS? Robert Chiasson. Outdoors in Illinois, Springfield, vol.16, no.3, p.16, Autumn Issue, 1950.

CONCERNING PREDATORS. Dave Cook. Audubon Mag., New York, vol.48, no.3, pp.130-136, illus., May-June, 1946; South Dakota Conservation Digest, Pierre, vol. 13, no.8, pp.6-7, Aug., 1946.

A STUDY OF PREDATOR CONTROL ON VALCOUR ISLAND. Walter F. Crissey, Robert W. Darrow. Research Ser. Div. Fish and Game, New York State Conserv. Dept., no.1, pp.28, illus., 1949.

MUTINY ON THE BOUNTY--SYSTEM. T. H. Cunningham. Hunting and Fishing, 25 (1): 8, 32, Jan., 1948.

HANDBOOK FOR HUNTERS OF PREDATORY ANIMALS. Albert M. Day. U.S. Dept. Agric., Bureau Biological Survey, pp.52, figs.17, Sept., 1932.

BOUNTIES DON'T WORK OUT AS THEY ARE SUPPOSED TO. Donald W. Douglass, A. M. Stebler. Mich. Cons., 15 (2): 6-7, 10, Feb., 1946.

WHAT OF THE PREDATOR? J. R. Dymond. Proc. 5th Pacific Sci. Congress, Canada, 1933, Univ. Toronto Press, vol.5, pp.4079-4080, 1934.

PREDATOR CONTROL IN THE LIGHT OF RECENT WILDLIFE MANAGEMENT CONCEPTS. William H. Elder, Charles M. Kirkpatrick. Wilson Bull., Lawrence, vol. 64, no.2, pp.126-128, June, 1952.

CONTROL OF PREDATORY ANIMALS CARRIED ON BY TRAPPER-WARDENS OF THE GAME AND FISH DEPARTMENT. W. B. Elley. South Dakota Conservation Digest, Pierre, vol.10, no.1, pp.3, 16, illus., Jan., 1943.

PREDATIONS AND VERTEBRATE POPULATIONS. Paul L. Errington. Quart. Rev. Biol., Balto., vol.21, no.2, pp.144-177; no.3, pp.221-245, June, Sept., 1946.

RECENT PREDATOR STUDIES. Paul L. Errington. Pennsylvania Game News, vol. 7, no.12, pp.14, 30, Mar., 1937.

WHAT IS THE MEANING OF PREDATION? Paul L. Errington. Iowa Agric. Exper. Sta., Jour. Paper J 374. (Reprinted in Ann. Smithsonian Inst., 1936, publ.3425, pp.243-252, 1937.)

WHAT ABOUT THOSE PREDATORS. Thomas R. Evans. Conserv. Volunteer, St. Paul, vol.11, no.64, pp.16-21, May-June, 1948; South Dakota Conserv. Digest, Pierre, vol.15, no. 9, pp.2, 9, 12, Sept., 1948.

THE ADVISABILITY OF PAYING BOUNTIES FOR THE KILLING OF PREDATORS. Richard Gerstell. Trans. 6th N. Amer. Wildlife Conf., Wash., D.C., pp.278-282, 1941.

PREDATORS--A MENACE. KILLERS THAT HUNT 365 DAYS EACH YEAR, NOT TO MENTION NIGHTS. C.E. Gillham.

Field and Stream, New York, vol.36, no.8, pp.28-29, 64-65, illus., Dec., 1931.

THE PREDATORY MAMMAL PROBLEM AND THE BALANCE OF NATURE. E. A. Goldman. Jour. Mam., vol.6, no.1, pp. 28-33, Feb., 1925.

SYMPOSIUM ON PREDATORY ANIMAL CONTROL. E. A. Goldman, Charles C. Adams, E. Raymond Hall, Joseph S. Dixon, A. Brazier Howell. Jour. Mam., vol.11, no.3, pp.325-389, figs.2, Aug., 1930.

CONTROLLING PREDATORY ANIMALS. Dorr D. Green. Amer. Wildlife, 29 (1): 35-40, Jan.-Feb., 1940.

NEW METHOD OF PREDATORY MAMMAL CONTROL. E. Raymond Hall. California Fish and Game, vol.12, p.154, July, 1926.

PREDATORY MAMMAL DESTRUCTION. E. Raymond Hall. Jour. Mam., vol.11, no.3, pp.362-369, Aug.9, 1930.

(Comments by E. A. Goldman on) THE PREDATORY MAMMAL DESTRUCTION. E. R. Hall. Jour. Mam., vol.11, no.3, p.372, Aug., 1930.

(Comments by W. C. Henderson on) THE PREDATORY MAMMAL DESTRUCTION. E. R. Hall. Jour. Mam., vol.11, no.3, pp.369-370, 371, Aug., 1930.

NATURE'S WISE LAW OF SURVIVAL. W.E.D. Halliday. Forest and Outdoors, 36 (10): 317-318, 324, 326, 329, Oct., 1940.

THE BOUNTY SYSTEM. W. J. Hamilton, Jr. New York State Cons., 2 (1): 4-5, Aug.-Sept., 1947.

THE BOUNTY SYSTEM DOESN'T WORK. W. J. Hamilton, Jr., David B. Cook. Animal Kingdom, New York, vol.49, no. 4, pp.130-138, illus., July-Aug., 1946.

ARIZONA UNITED PREDATOR CONTROL. Dan Hankin. Arizona Wildlife and Sportsman, Tucson, vol.6, no.6, p.14, Apr., 1945.

IS THE BOUNTY SYSTEM A NATIONAL FARCE? David Hellyer. Virginia Wildlife, Richmond, vol.10, no.1, pp.16-18, 21, illus., Jan., 1949; North Dakota Outdoors, Bismarck, vol.11, no.9, pp.9, 12, Mar., 1949; Louisiana Conservationist, New Orleans, vol.2, no.5, pp.18-19, Jan., 1950.

CONCERNING OUR PREDATORS. Walter E. Howard. California Farmer, San Francisco, vol.196, no.4, pp.184-185, Feb.23, 1952.

(Comments by A. Brazier Howell on) THE PREDATORY ANIMALS, ACTIVITIES OF W.P.A. Jour. Mam., vol.17, no.4, p.438, Nov., 1936.

THE BOUNTY SYSTEM AND PREDATOR CONTROL. W. C. Jacobsen. California, Fish and Game, San Francisco, vol.31 no.2, pp.53-63, Apr., 1945.

(BOUNTY STATISTICS FOR PREDATORY MAMMALS AND BIRDS IN NORWAY.) Rovdyr- og rovfuglstatistikken i Norge. Sigurd Johnsen. Bergens Mus. Aarbok, 1929, vol.1, no.2, pp.1-140, figs.21, pls. 4, 1929.

DESIRABILITY FOR CONTROL OF PREDATORS IN WILDLIFE MANAGEMENT AS EXPERIENCED IN ARIZONA. K. C. Kartchner. Trans. 6th N. Amer. Wildlife Conf., Wash., D.C., pp.273-277, 1941.

PREDATOR CONTROL IS WASTE OF TIME. Claude D. Kelley. Alabama Conservation, Montgomery, vol.20, no.11, p.4, Apr.-May, 1949.

ON THE SIGNIFICANCE OF PREDATORS IN THE CONTROL AND DISPERSAL OF THE DISEASES OF GAME. Teppo Lampio. Papers on Game Res., 6: 3-20, 1951.

PREDATION IN RELATION TO GAME DISEASES. Tony Lascelles. Rod and Gun in Canada, Montreal, vol.46, no.4, p.16, Sept., 1944.

DOES PREDATOR CONTROL PAY? Roger M. Latham. Field and Stream, New York, vol.52, no.9, pp.40, 94-95, Jan., 1948.

IS PREDATOR CONTROL EFFECTIVE? Benjamin Leavitt. Florida Wildlife, Tallahassee, vol.2, no.6, pp.6-7, illus., Nov., 1948.

THE PREDATOR IN WILDLIFE MANAGEMENT. A. Starker Leopold. Sierra Club Bull., vol.39, no.6, pp.34-38, June, 1954.

PREDATORS HELP SAVE GAME. Hayes Lloyd. Michigan Conservation, vol.7, no. 5, pp.6-7, illus., Jan., 1938.

DOES PREDATOR CONTROL PAY? C. E. Logue. Pennsylvania Game News, vol.8, no.8, pp.11-31, Nov., 1937.

REPORT OF PREDATOR CONTROL PROGRAM IN BURLINGTON COUNTY, N.J. H. E. Longsdorf. Amer. Field, Chicago, vol.143, no.26, p.507, June 30, 1945.

PREDATORY ANIMAL STUDIES. Donald D. McLean. California Fish and Game, vol. 20, no.1, pp.30-36, Jan., 1934.

PREDATORS. E. G. Marsh, Jr. Texas Game and Fish, Austin, vol.1, no.4, pp. 1, 15, Mar., 1943.

THE REAL MEANING OF PREDATION. W. O. Nagel. Wyoming Wild Life, Cheyenne, vol.11, nos.1-2, pp.4-7, 37, illus., Jan.-Feb., 1947.

HISTORY OF PREDATOR CONTROL IN THE STATE OF WASHINGTON. Walter Neubrech. Washington Outdoors, Tacoma, vol.1, nos.5-6, pp.5, 15, Aug.-Sept., 1946.

PREDATOR CONTROL POLICY OF THE WASHINGTON STATE DEPARTMENT OF GAME. Walter Neubrech. Murrelet, Seattle, vol.30, no.2, pp.37-39, Oct.14, 1949.

THE WAR AGAINST THE PREDATORS. Michael Norman. Outdoor Life, New York, vol.103, no.3, pp.37-39, 125-127, illus., Mar., 1949.

SOME FACTS ABOUT PREDATORY ANIMAL CONTROL. Charles G. Poole. California Fish and Game, vol.19, no.1, pp.1-9, figs.1-2, Jan., 1933.

PREDATORS ON A GAME REFUGE. Earl L. Poole. Pennsylvania Game News, Harrisburg, vol.14, no.10, pp.10-13, illus., Jan., 1944.

THE PREDATION QUESTION--FACTS VERSUS FANCIES. Clifford C. Presnall. Trans. 15th North Amer. Wildlife Conf., Wash., pp.197-208, 1950.

POLICY OF THE U.S. BIOLOGICAL SURVEY IN REGARD TO PREDATORY MAMMAL CONTROL. Paul G. Redington. Jour. Mam., vol.10, no.3, pp.276-279, Aug., 1929.

PREDATOR CONTROL. Albert M. Reese. Proc. W. Virginia Acad. Sci., Morgantown, vol.14 (W. Virginia Univ. Bull. ser.41, no. 4-11), pp.21-26, Oct., 1940.

CONTROL OF THE PREDATOR. Lynn B. Rosenkrans. Pennsylvania Game News, Harrisburg, vol.19, no.10, pp.12, 25, 27, illus., Jan., 1949.

WAYS AND MEANS IN WOLF-COYOTE-BOBCAT CONTROL. Frank W. Sampson, Rudolf Bennitt. Mo. Cons., 8 (12): 4-6, 9 (1): 4-5, Dec., 1947, Jan., 1948.

MISSOURI'S PROGRAM OF EXTENSION PREDATOR CONTROL. Frank W. Sampson, Allen Brohn. Jour. Wildlife Management, Ithaca, vol.19, no.2, pp.272-280, Apr., 1955.

PREDATOR CONTROL IN SOUTHEASTERN QUAIL MANAGEMENT. Herbert L. Stoddard, Ed. V. Komarek. Trans. 6th N. Amer. Wildlife Conf., Wash., D.C., pp. 288-293, 1941.

PREDATOR CONTROL. D. F. Switzenberg. Michigan Conserv., Lansing, vol.17, no.8, pp.6-7, 14, illus., Aug., 1948; Minnesota Sportsmen's Digest, vol.9, no.4, pp.10-11, Nov.-Dec., 1948.

PREDATORS AREN'T ALL BAD. D. F. Switzenberg. Michigan Conservation, Lansing, vol.16, no.9, pp.7, 14, Oct., 1947.

A REPORT OF PREDATORY ANIMAL CONTROL ACTIVITIES FOR THE YEAR ENDING JUNE 30, 1939. Gordon H. True, Jr. California Fish and Game, San Francisco, vol.26, no.2, pp.167-173, figs.73-75, Apr., 1940.

(Comments by C.T. Vorhies on) RATIONAL PREDATORY ANIMAL CONTROL. C. C. Adams. Jour. Mamm., vol.11, no.3, pp. 359-360, Aug., 1930.

PREDATORS. Earl Wallace. South Dakota Conserv. Digest, Pierre, vol.14, no.1, p. 3, Jan., 1947.

MUTINY ON THE BOUNTIES. Bill Wolf. Louisiana Conservationist, New Orleans, vol.1, no.8, pp.14-15, 23-24, illus., Apr., 1949.

THE 10 WORST PREDATORS. (HOUSE CAT, RED FOX, WEASEL.) Frank Woolner. Sports Afield, Mt. Morris, vol.117, no.3, pp.24-25, 115-118, illus., Mar., 1947.

THE BOUNTY SYSTEM. Stanley P. Young. Atlantic Naturalist, Wash., vol.8, no.1, pp.10-17, illus., Sept.-Oct., 1952.

OUR FEDERAL PREDATOR CONTROL WORK. Stanley P. Young. Trans. 20th Amer. Game Conference, 1934, Amer. Game Assoc., New York, pp.172-176, 1934.

MUTINY ON THE BOUNTY. Audubon Mag., New York, vol.47, no.3, pp.183-184, May-June, 1945.

PENNSYLVANIA GAME NEWS: BOUNTY SUCCESSFULLY CONTROLS PREDATORS IN PENNSYLVANIA. Outdoor Life, vol.67, no.2, p.40, Feb., 1931.

PREDATOR CONTROL ON THE WATERFOWL REFUGE. Game Breeder and Sportsman, New York, vol.44, no.5, pp. 57-62, May, 1944.

RESOLUTIONS BY NEW YORK ZOOLOGICAL SOCIETY, AND BY BOONE AND CROCKETT. (PREDATORY ANIMALS.) Jour. Mam., vol.10, no.1, pp.95-96, Feb., 1929.

SUMMARY STATEMENT OF BOUNTIES PAID ON PREDATORS DURING FISCAL YEAR, JUNE 1, 1947 TO MAY 31, 1948. Pennsylvania Game News, Harrisburg, vol.19, no.5, p.13, Aug., 1948.

VALUES OF BOUNTY SYSTEM. Mississippi Game and Fish, Jackson, vol.12, no.9, pp.13-14, Mar., 1949.

Reproductive Biology

(STUDIES OF NEWBORN MAMMALS (EXTERNAL FORM). CARNIVORA FISSIPEDIA.) Studien ueber neugeborene Saeugetiere (aeussere Form). Carnivora fissipedia. Oscar De Beaux. Kapitel X u. XI, Zool. Jahrbuecher, Abteil. fuer Systematik, etc., vol.47, pp.331-378, figs. 24, pl.3, June 25, 1924.

(HYBRIDS.) Bastarde. (Polar and brown bear cross, tiger and lion cross, German fox and dog cross.) H. Heck. Kosmos, Stuttgart, vol.29, no.12, pp.406-409, figs. 3, Dec., 1932.

(ON THE GESTATION OF ARCTOID CARNIVORES.) Ueber die Tragzeitverhaeltnisse der arctoiden Raubtiere. H. Prell. Zeitschr. fuer Saeugetierkunde, Berlin, vol.6, no.2, pp.57-65, Dec.15, 1931.

EARLY BREEDING OF CERTAIN CARNIVORES. Thomas E. Winecoff. Jour. Mam., vol.16, no.1, p.66, Feb., 1935.

South America

(NOTES ON SOUTH AMERICAN CARNIVORES.) Notas sobre carnivoros sudamericanos. Angel Cabrera. Inst. Mus. Univ. Nac. La Plata, Notas del Museo de La Plata, Buenos Aires, vol.5, Zool., no. 29, pp.22, Mar.25, 1940.

(MAMMALS OF SOUTHERN BRAZIL. FIRST CONTRIBUTION: CARNIVORA.) Os mammiferos co Brazil meriodinal. I. contribuicao: Carnivora. Hermann von Ihering. Rev. Mus. Paulista, vol.8, pp. 147-272, 1911.

WINGE ON BRAZILIAN CARNIVORA. Gerrit S. Miller, Jr. Science, vol.3, no.64, pp.6, Mar.20, 1896.

(CARNIVORES OF SAO PAULO STATE.) Carnivoros do estado de Sao Paulo. C. Vieira. Arquivos de Zool., Sao Paulo, Brasil, vol.5, no.3, pp.137-175, illus., Dec.28, 1946.

Taxonomy

THE EVOLUTION OF CARNASSIAL DENTITIONS IN THE MAMMALIA. P. M. Butler. Proc. Zool. Soc. Lond., vol.116, pt.2, pp. 198-220, figs.13, Nov., 1946.

(SOME CHANGES OF NAMES OF CARNIVORA.) Algunos nomina mutanda en los carnívores. Angel Cabrera. Bol. Real Soc. Española Hist. Nat., Madrid, vol.17, no.8, pp.487-488, Oct., 1917.

ON THE GENERA OF FELIDAE AND CANIDAE. E. D. Cope. Proc. Acad. Nat. Sci. Phila., vol.13, pp.1-27, July 8, 1879.

ON THE VALUE OF THE CHARACTERS OF THE BASE OF THE CRANIUM IN THE CLASSIFICATION OF THE ORDER CARNIVORA, AND ON THE SYSTEMATIC POSITION OF BASSARIS AND OTHER DISPUTED FORMS. William H. Flower. Proc. Zool. Soc. Lond., pp.4-37, figs.15, Jan.14, 1869.

(A NEW CARNIVORE FROM STEINHEM-ON-THE-ALBUCH.) Ein neuer Carnivor von Steinhem am Albuch. H. Helbing. Verhandl. Schweizer, Naturforsch, Ges., vol. 110, p.192, 1929.

(CRYPTOPROCTA AND THE MONOPHYLETIC ORIGIN OF THE CARNIVORES.) Cryptoprocta und die monophyletische Entstehung der Carnivoren. M. Kretzoi. Zeitschr. Saeugetierk., 22 (1-2): 45-49, 1957.

(MATERIAL ON THE PHYLOGENIC CLASSIFICATION OF AILUROIDS.) Materialien zur phylogenetischen Klassifikation der Aeluroideen. Nickolaus Kretzoi. X Congès International de Zoologie tenu à Budapest (Sept.4-10, 1927), pt.2, pp.1293-1355, 1929.

(ON THE QUESTION OF THE PHYLOGENIC IMPORTANCE OF THE DECIDUOUS DENTITION OF MAMMALS. II. VIVERRIDAE, HYAENIDAE, FELIDAE, MUSTELIDAE, CREODONTA.) Zur Frage nach der Stammesgeschichtlichen Bedeutung des Milchgebisses bei den Saeugetieren. II. Viverridae, Hyaenidae, Felidae, Mustelidae, Creodonta. W. Leche. Zool. Jahrb., Jena, vol.38, no.5, pp.275-370, figs.1-126, 1915.

EVIDENCE OF TOOTH STRUCTURE ON THE RELATIONSHIPS OF THE EARLY GROUPS OF CARNIVORA. Loris S. Russell. Evolution, Lancaster, vol.8, no.2, pp.166-171, illus., June, 1954.

SOME NEW FERAE FROM ASIA AND AFRICA. Oldfield Thomas. Ann. and Mag. Nat. Hist. (8), vol.12, no.67, pp. 88-92, July, 1913.

THE ANCESTRY OF CERTAIN MEMBERS OF THE CANIDAE, THE VIVERRIDAE, AND PROCYCONIDAE. J. L. Wortman, W. D. Matthew. Bull. Amer. Mus. Nat. Hist., vol.12, pp.109-138, figs.9, pl.6, 1899.

Trapping

TRAPPING IN NORTHEASTERN TEXAS. (MINK, RACCOON.) David J. Arnold. Fur-Fish-Game, Columbus, vol.87, no.9, pp.46-47, Sept., 1946.

TRAPPING OUT THE MENACE. James Brown. Louisana Conservationist, New Orleans, vol.1, nos.9-10, pp.14-15, 20, illus., May-June, 1949.

PREDATOR TRAPPING. (HABITS AND FOOD OF COYOTES, BOBCATS, AND FOXES.) E. J. Goza. New Mexico Mag., Albuquerque, vol.16, no.11, pp.27, 37, Nov., 1938.

COYOTE AND WILDCAT TRAPPING. James F. Mast. L.R. Morris: Ontario, California, pp.78, illus., 1932.

TRAPPING THE RACCOON AND THE MINK. B. G. Roberts. Amer. Nat. Fur and Market Jour., Wausau, vol.28, no.8, pp. 17, 22, Mar., 1950.

THE "HUMANE COYOTE-GETTER" VS. THE STEEL TRAP IN CONTROL OF PREDATORY ANIMALS. Weldon B. Robinson. Jour. Wildlife Management, Menasha, vol. 7, no.2, pp.179-189, Apr., 1943.

Canidae

General (Canids)

(COMMENTS ON THE GREYHOUND AND THE BADGER.) Grahund och graevling. Jan Akerman. Svensk Jakt, Stockholm, vol. 87, no.10, pp.288-289, 292, illus., Oct., 1949.

(NEW EXPERIMENTS IN THE FIELD OF TRACKING PRECISION AND IDENTIFICATION IN TRACKING.) Neue Versuche auf dem Gebiet der Faehrtenreinheit und des Identifizierens auf der Faehrte. (Dogs.) R. Belleville. Zeitschr. f. Hundeforschung, Leipzig, n.F., vol.13, pp.17-28, 1938.

(A DOG WHISTLE IMPERCEPTIBLE TO HUMANS.) Eine vom Menschen nicht wahrnehmbare Hundepfeife. Caesar R. Boettger. Sitz. Ber. Ges. naturforsch. Freunde, Berlin, 1 p., Mar.15, 1938.

THE GROWING KIT. E. Rendle Bowness. Nat. Fur. News, Denver, vol.17, no.6, pp.10, 19, 22, 24-26, July, 1945.

WOLF AND COYOTE--WILD DOGS OF FORESTS AND PLAINS. G. W. Bradt. Michigan Conserv., Lansing, vol.17, no. 1, pp.4-5, illus., Jan., 1948.

IT'S THE "FEARSOME WARRACABA TIGER". (ICTICYON VENATICUS.) William Bridges. Animal Kingdom, New York Zool. Soc., vol.57, no.1, pp.25-28, illus., Feb., 1954.

(CANID STUDIES.) Canidenstudien. August Brinkmann. Vidensk. Meddel. fra Dansk naturhist. Foren Kjobenhavn, vol. 72, pp.1-43, pls.1-3, figs.1-6, 1921.

(ON A TWO-LEGGED DOG.) Uber einen zweibeinigen Hund. G. H. Brueckner. Zeitschr. f. Hundeforschung, Leipzig, n.F., vol.13, pp.1-16, figs.4, 1938.

THE MANED WOLF AND OTHER "DOGS." Maurice Burton. Illus. London News, vol. 137, no.3562, p.194, illus., July 30, 1955.

ERA OF LOBO. Vern Craig. Montana Wildlife, pp.20-25, July, 1961.

(A ZOOLOGICAL ENIGMA. THE DOG (CANIS FAMILIARIS LINNE).) Une enigme zoologique: Le chien (Canis familiaris Linne). Ed Dechambre. Mammalia, Paris, vol.5, no.3-4, pp.86-93, Sept.-Dec., 1941.

YELLOW-DOG, DINGO. Georgia Dittoe. San Diego Zoonooz, vol.19, no.4, pp.3-4, Apr., 1946.

BROTHER TO THE WOLF. C. H. Easton. Hunting and Fishing, Phila., vol.25, no.1, pp.52-53, 61, illus., Jan., 1948.

(WHAT IS UNDERSTOOD BY THE "ROHRWOLF"?) Was versteht man unter dem "Rohrwolf"? Julius Ehk. Zool. Garten, Leipzig, n.F., vol.11, no.6, pp.232-238, figs.4, Dec., 1939.

WILD DOGS. J. C. Faunthopre. Jour. Bombay Nat. Hist. Soc., vol.32, p.590, Jan.15, 1928.

(THE CANIDAE.) Les Canides. G. Fertois. La Nature, Paris, no.3248, pp. 465-471, illus., Dec., 1955.

(OBSERVATIONS OF CAPTIVE RACCOON DOGS (NYCTEREUTES PROCYONOIDES GRAY).) Gefangenschaftsbeobachtungen am Marderhund (Nyctereutes procyonoides Gray). Otto Franz. Zool. Garten, Leipzig, NF, vol.17, nos.1-5, pp.226-234, illus., 1950.

NATURE'S WILD DOG SHOW. William K. Gregory. Bull. New York Zool. Soc., vol.36, no.4, pp.83-96, figs., July-Aug., 1933.

(WOLVES AND WILD DOGS.) Woelfe und wildhunde. Aga Graefin Hagen. Naturforscher, Berlin, vol.13, no.1, pp.19-24, figs.1-7, Apr., 1936.

(WHERE IS THE DIFFERENCE BETWEEN WOLF AND DOG?) Wodurch unterscheidet sich der Wolf vom Hund? E. Hauck. Wiener Tieraerztl., Monatsschr., vol.17, no.16, pp.600-611, Aug.15, 1930.

(A BRIEF SURVEY OF WILD DOGS.) Eine kurze Uebersicht ueber die Wildhunde. Max Hilzheimer. Kleintier und Pelztier, Leipzig, Jahrg.11, no.3, pp.83-95, figs.11, May, 1935.

DOGS AND SAVAGES. Bernhard August Langkavel. Ann. Report, Smithsonian Inst., Wash, 1898, pp.651-675, 1899.

ON JACKALS (CANIS INDICUS). E. S. Lewis. Jour. Bombay Nat. Hist. Soc., vol.41, no.4, pp.891-892, Aug., 1940.

(COMMENTS ON TRACKING-DOG TRAINED TO HUNT FOXES, AND HOW TO TRAIN THEM.) Om grythundar for rav och deras ovning. Lindorm Liljefors. Svensk Jakt, Stockholm, vol.88, no.3, pp.60-63, illus., Mar.15, 1950.

NOTES ON THE DINGO, THE INDIAN WILD DOG, AND A PAPUAN DOG. H. A. Longmann. Mem. Queens. Mus., vol.9, no.2, pp.151-157, 1928.

WILD DOGS (CUON). T. C. Masters. Malayan Nature Jour., Kuala Lumpur, vol. 8, no.4, p.165, pl.31, Mar., 1954.

DINGOES "DOWN UNDER". Max Meredith. Our Dumb Animals, Norwood, vol.77, no. 3, p.48, Mar., 1944.

(THE DOG OF THE SENCHENBERG MOOR, A COMPANION OF THE AUROCHS.) Der Hund aus dem Senckenberg-Moor, ein Begleiter des Ur's. Rob Mertens. Natur und Volk, Frankfurt a.M., vol.66, no.10, pp.506-510, figs.4, Oct.1, 1936.

THE COYOTE AND THE BLACK-BACKED JACKAL. A COMPARISON OF CERTAIN SIMILAR CHARACTERISTICS. N. J. van der Merwe. Fauna and Flora no.3, pp.45-51, illus., 1953.

THE JACKAL. N. J. van der Merwe. Fauna and Flora no.4, pp.2-77, illus., 1953.

A MONOGRAPH OF THE CANIDAE: DOGS, JACKALS, WOLVES, AND FOXES. St. George Mivart. 1890.

WILD DOGS. Randolph C. Morris. Jour. Bombay Nat. Hist. Soc., vol.36, no.2, pp.491-492, Apr.15, 1933.

("DOG-HEDGEHOG," "SWINE-HEDGEHOG," AND "STONE DOG.") "Hundsigel", "Schweinsigel" und "Steinhund". Using D. Muller. Zeitschr. f. Saeugetierkunde, Berlin, vol.13, no.2, pp.238-239, 1939.

(WOLF AND DOG.) Wolf und Hund. A. Nehring. Naturwissenschaftliche Wochenschrift, vol.2, no.1, pp.1-2, Berlin, Apr. 1, 1888.

(STUDIES OF PREHISTORIC DOGS.) Studien an fruehgeschichtlichen Hunden. Guenter Nobis. Festschrift fuer Dr. Berthold Klatt, Zool. Anzeiger, Leipzig, vol. 145, pp.672-696, 1950.

REMARKS UPON CANIS HIMALAICUS, OGILB. W. Ogilby. Proc. Zool. Soc. Lond., pt.4, p.103, 1836.

(THE KARAKATCHAN DOG.) Der Karakatschan-Hund. H. B. Peters. Zeitschr. f. Hundeforschung, Leipzig, n.F., vol.13, pp.55-62, figs.4, 1938.

LIFE-HISTORY OF THE JACKAL (THOS MESOMELAS). Austin Roberts. Jour. Dept. Agric., Union of South Africa, Pretoria, vol.5, pp.234-244, fig.1, Sept., 1922.

(POLYGAMOUS MALES AND POLYGAMOUS BREEDING METHODS IN SILVER FOX RAISING.) Polygame Rueden und polygame Zuchtmethoden in der Silberfuchszucht. Fritz Schmidt. Deutsche Pelztierzuechter, Muenchen, vol.14, no.2, pp.25-30, Jan. 15, 1939.

(THE EARLY DEVELOPMENT OF CAPTIVE WILD CANIDS IN RELATION TO WEIGHT, ALONG WITH A TEMPORAL DETERMINATION OF THEIR REPRODUCTION.) Zur gewichtsmaessigen Jugendentwicklung gefangen gehaltener Wildcaniden nebst einigen zeitlichen Bestimmungen ueber ihre Fortpflanzung. Karl Max Schneider. Verhandl. Deutschen Zoologen in Mainz, 1949 (Zool. Anzeiger, 14 Supplementband), Leipzig, pp.373-387, 1950.

(ON THE "GUARDING" OF DOGS.) Vom "Wachen" der Hunde. Linde Schuller. Saeugetierk. Mitteil., 5 (3): 106-111, Aug. 1, 1957.

(THE NORMAL DENTITION OF THE GERMAN SHEPHERD DOG IN THE VARIOUS AGE LEVELS.) Das Normalgebiss des Deutschen Schaeferhundes in den verschiedenen Altersstufen. Eugene Seiferle, Leo Meyer. Vierteljahrsschr. Naturforsch, Gesell, Zuerich, Jahrg.87, nos.3-4, pp. 205-252, abb.39, Dec., 1942.

RACCOON-LIKE DOGS. (NYCTEREUTES.) David Seth-Smith. Field, London, vol.166, no.4323, p.1030, illus., Nov.2, 1935.

(THE HUNTING DOG AND THE PRESERVATION OF HUNTING.) Drevhunden och jaktvarden. Eric Soderstrom. Svensk Jakt, Stockholm, vol.88, no.3, pp.56-59, illus., Mar.15, 1950.

(THE WILD DOG (CUON JAVANICUS DESMAREST).) De Adjag (Cuon javanicus, Desmarest). H.J.V. Sody. Natuur. Tijdschrift voor Nederlandsch-Indiee, vol. 89, no.2, pp.210-290, 1929.

(MORE ON THE WILD DOG.) Nogmaals: De Adjag. H.J.V. Sody. Natuurkundig Tijdschrift voor Nederlandsch-Indiee, vol. 91, no.1, pp.50-56, 1931.

(THE HAIRLESS DOGS OF MEXICO.) Die Nackthunde Mexicos. Helm. Otto Wagner. Zool. Garten, Leipzig, vol.11, no.3, pp. 98-102, illus., Sept., 1939.

IDENTIFICATION OF WOLF, COYOTE, DOG SIMPLIFIED. S. C. Whitlock. Michigan Conserv., Lansing, vol.17, no. 10, pp.6-7, 15, illus., Oct., 1948.

(HOUNDS.) Die Bracken. Jungklaus Willmshaide. Zeitschr. fuer Hundeforschung, n.F., vol.2, Kleintier und Pelztier, Leipzig, Jahrg.12, no.7, pp.95, figs.56, Nov., 1936.

THE GENETIC AND PHYLOGENETIC SIGNIFICANCE OF THE PRESENCE OF A THIRD UPPER MOLAR IN A MODERN DOG. Albert Elmer Wood, Horace Elmer Wood, II. Amer. Midland Nat., Notre Dame, vol.14, no.1, pp.36-48, figs.3, Nov.-Dec., 1933.

OBSERVATIONS ON THE WILD DOG. (CUON DUKHUNENSIS.) H. S. Wood. Jour. Darjeeling Nat. Hist. Soc., vol.4, no.1, pp.7-14, June, 1929.

WHAT WAS THE EARLY INDIAN DOG? WOLF OR HOUND--OR A LITTLE OF EACH? NEW LIGHT ON AN AGE-OLD RIDDLE. Stanley P. Young. Amer. Forests, Washington, D.C., vol.49, no. 12, pp.571-573, 594, 603, illus., Dec., 1943; vol.50, no.1, pp.26-28, 32, 45, Jan., 1944.

A DOG WHICH KICKS LIKE A HORSE AND MOVES LIKE A RAT: A RECENT ARRIVAL AT THE LONDON ZOO. (GUIANA BUSH DOG, ICTICYON.) Illus. London News, vol.215, no.5758, p.319, illus., Aug.27, 1949.

General (Coyotes)

COYOTES. David A. Arnold. Michigan Conserv., Lansing, vol.23, no.6, pp.28-30, Nov., 1954.

COYOTE (CANIS LATRANS LATRANS). N. R. Barger. Wisconsin Conserv. Bull., Madison, vol.15, no.4, p.32, Apr., 1950.

THE LIFE HISTORY OF THE COYOTE. Samuel William Bowman, Jr. MS thesis, Univ. N. Mexico, 1940.

COYOTES. (FOR CHILDREN.) Wilfrid S. Bronson. Harcourt, Brace and Co., New York, pp.58, illus., 1946.

FANGED FURY. (COYOTE.) J. G. Burr. Texas Game and Fish, Austin, vol.6, no. 6, pp.4, 18, illus., May, 1948.

TRICKY DON COYOTE. Jim Chapman. Outdoorsman, Chicago, vol.88, no.6 (whole no. 523), pp.23, 34-36, Nov.-Dec., 1946.

MOJAVE JOE. (COYOTE.) Verne Chute. Sports Afield, Minneapolis, vol.116, no.4, pp.43, 124-127, illus., Oct., 1946.

FACTS ABOUT, AND EXPERIENCE WITH COYOTES. Frank C. Clarke. National Wool Grower, Salt Lake City, vol.30, no. 5, pp.19-22, May, 1940.

COYOTES FROM THE AIR. Ellwood Colahan. Field and Stream, New York, vol.50, no.9, pp.42-43, illus., Jan., 1946.

COYOTE...IN CIVILIZED PERSPECTIVE. J. Frank Dobie. Living Wilderness, Wash., vol.14, no.28, pp.4-9, illus., Mar., 1949.

THE SMART COYOTE. J. Frank Dobie. Nat. Hist., New York, vol.49, no.2, pp. 71-75, illus., Feb., 1942.

THE VOICE OF THE COYOTE. J. Frank Dobie. Little, Brown and Co., Boston, pp. 386, illus., Apr., 1949.

(Review by A. A. Hightower of) THE VOICE OF THE COYOTE. J. Frank Dobie. Calif. Fish and Game, San Francisco, vol.36, no. 2, p.168, Apr., 1950.

THE SPREAD OF THE COYOTE. Hal G. Evarts. Sat. Even. Post, vol.196, no.24, p.44, Dec.15, 1923.

WATCHING COYOTES. Edson Fichter. Jour. Mam., 31 (1): 66-73, Feb., 1950.

COYOTE, THE PRAIRIE WOLF. William L. Finley, Irene Finley. Nature Mag., vol.5, pp.233-237, illus., Apr., 1925.

THE COYOTE. William C. Godfrey. Yosemite Nature Notes, vol.8, pp.33-34, Mar., 1929.

A GLIMPSE OF THE MOUNTAIN COYOTE. E. D. Godwin. Yosemite Nature Notes, vol.15, no.2, pp.11-12, Feb., 1936.

IS IT COYOTE OR DOG? James B. Hale. Wisconsin Conserv. Bull., Madison, vol. 17, no.7, pp.16-17, July, 1950.

THE STORY OF "SKEEZIX," AN ALBINO COYOTE. F. S. Hall. Murrelet, vol.11, no.2, p.16, May, 1930.

WOLF OR COYOTE? James R. Harlan. Iowa Conservationist, Des Moines, vol. 9, no.2, p.11, Feb.15, 1950.

COYOTES--FROM THE AIR. Bud Jackson. Fur-Fish-Game, Harding's Mag., Columbus vol.86, no.8, pp.12, 31-32, illus., Aug., 1946.

AN OUTCAST IN GREY. (COYOTE.) Jim Keefe. Mo. Cons., 14 (2): 6-7, 14-15, illus., Feb., 1953.

THE CUNNING COYOTE. Herbert F. Lystrup. Yellowsonte Nat. Notes, Yellowstone Park, vol.18, nos.9-10, pp. 49-50, Sept.-Oct., 1941.

SPEAKING OF COYOTES. Ed Maunton. New York State Cons., 6 (3): 8-9, illus., Dec.-Jan., 1951-52.

COOPERATION AND COYOTES. Ryland A. Miller. Missouri Conservationist, Jefferson City, vol.8, no.11, p.13, illus., Nov., 1947.

MARCO AND SHEBA. (COYOTE.) Joanne Murie. Nature Mag., Wash., D.C., vol. 36, no.10, pp.542-543, illus., Dec., 1943.

WONDER DOG. (COYOTE.) Olaus J. Murie. Audubon Mag., New York, vol.50, no.5, pp.268-275, illus., Sept.-Oct., 1948.

THE COYOTE--DESERT RACKETEER. Jack O'Connor. Mag. Sigma Chi, 56th year, no.1, pp.24-31, illus., Feb., 1937.

LITTLE GRAY WOLF. (COYOTE.) Andy Russell. Field and Stream, New York, vol. 52, no.5, pp.26, 129-131, illus., Sept., 1947.

THE COYOTE. Rex Gary Schmidt. Missouri Conservationist, Jefferson City, vol.8, no.6, pp.8-9, illus., June, 1947.

COYOTES. Otis H. Smokey. South Dakota Conserv. Digest, Pierre, vol.10, no.12, pp.11, 13, Dec., 1943.

THE STORY OF THE COYOTE THAT LEARNED HOW. Ernest Thompson Seton. Scribner's Mag., New York, vol.28, no. 2, pp.131-145, illus., Aug., 1900.

THAT CANNY COYOTE. Kerry Wood. Fauna, Phila., vol.9, no.1, pp.2-5, illus., Mar., 1947.

HOW SHOULD WE PRONOUNCE C-O-Y-O-T-E? Harry R. Woodward. Yellowstone Nat. Notes, vol.10, nos.1-2, p.7, Jan.-Feb., 1933.

THE COYOTE MARCHES ON. Stanley P. Young. Amer. Forests, 45 (11): 538-540,' 574-576, Nov., 1939.

THE CLEVER COYOTE. PART I. ITS HISTORY, LIFE HABITS, ECONOMIC STATUS AND CONTROL, BY STANLEY P. YOUNG. PART II. CLASSIFICATION OF THE RACES OF THE COYOTE, BY HARTLEY H.T. JACKSON. Stanley P. Young, Hartley H.T. Jackson. Stackpole Co, Harrisburg, and Wildlife Management Inst., Wash., pp.411, illus., col. frontisp., Dec., 1951.

(Review by Tracy I. Storer of) THE CLEVER COYOTE. Stanley P. Young, H.H.T.Jackson. Jour. Wildl. Mgt., Ithaca, vol.16, no. 3, pp.384-385, July, 1952.

THE COYOTE. South Dakota Conservation Digest, Pierre, vol.11, no.12, p.6, Dec., 1944.

COYOTE CANIS LATRANS. Wyoming Wild Life, Cheyenne, vol.5, no.4, pp. 6, 18, Apr., 1940.

General (Foxes)

I KNEW A FOX--THE STORY OF RUSTY, A "PHANTOM" TWO-TOED FOX, WILY INVADER OF HENHOUSES, CUNNING HUNTER, AND FEARLESS SPIRIT OF THE WILD. Roy L. Abbott. Natural History, New York, vol.45, no.3, pp.168-171, Mar., 1940.

MEMOIR OF A FOX. Roy L. Abbott. Faune, Phila., vol.7, no.3, pp.72-74, Sept., 1945.

THE FOXES. Rod Amundson. Wildlife in North Carolina, Raleigh, vol.13, no.6, pp. 4-7, illus., June, 1949.

(TRAITS OF VULPES VULGARIS AND VULPES LAGOPUS.) Les traits de Vulpes vulgaris et de Vulpes lagopus. Jean Bouchud. Mammalia, Paris, vol.15, no.3, pp.92-102, illus., Sept., 1951.

RED FOX--WISE GUY OF THE WILD. G. W. Bradt. Michigan Cons., 16 (2): 4, Feb., 1947.

(COMMENTS ON FLUCTUATIONS IN THE NUMBER OF FOXES AND OTHER ANIMALS IN THE ARCTIC AND THE RESULTS THEREOF.) Om Svingninger i Antallet af Raeve og andre Dyri Arktisderes Aarsagen og Virkninger. F. W. Bradstrup. Det Gronlandske Selskabs Aarsskrift, Kobenhavn, 1942, pp.129-151, 1942.

THE KIT FOX. C. D. Bunker. Science, 92 (2376): 35-36, July 12, 1940.

(GOOD DAYS FOR HUNTING FOX.) Raevvaedersdagar. Edor Burman. Svensk Jakt, Stockholm, vol.88, no.3, pp.66-67, Mar.15, 1950.

A FOX SEES RED. Maurice Burton. Illus. London News, vol.137, no.3576, p.792, Nov.5, 1955.

FOXES BY DAY AND NIGHT. Maurice Burton. Illus. London News, vol.137, no. 3570, p.532, illus., Sept.24, 1955.

FOXES' TRYST. Maurice Burton. Illus. London News, vol.138, no.3588, p.146, Jan.28, 1956.

GRAY FOX ADVENTURES. William H. Carr. Nat. Hist., New York, vol.54, no. 1, pp.4-9, illus., Jan., 1945.

CONSIDER THE FOX. Alan Devoe. Audubon Mag., New York, vol.46, no.4, pp.205-210, illus., July-Aug., 1944.

RED FOX. S. C. Downing. Canadian Nature, Toronto, vol.10, no.1, p.9, illus., Jan., 1948.

FOX STUDIES. W. Newbold Ely. Pennsylvania Game News, New Cumberland, vol.9, no.12, pp.28-29, Mar., 1939.

OUR LITTLE WILD DOGS--THE FOXES. Paul L. Errington. Audubon Mag., 57 (1): 14-17, 27, illus., Jan.-Feb., 1955.

(FACE OF THE FOX.) Das Gesicht des Fuchses. Werner Fischel. Aus der Natur (Der Naturforscher), Berlin, Jahrg. 15, no.6, pp.183-187, figs.4 , Sept., 1938.

THE FENNEC. Arthur H. Fisher. Nature Mag., Wash., D.C., vol.33, no. 10, p.576, Dec., 1940.

VULPES, THE RED FOX. John L. George, Jean George. Dutton, pp.184, 1948.

FOXES IN CAPTIVITY. George Bird Grinnell. Jour. Mam., vol.4, no.3, p.184, Aug., 1923.

FOX FACTS. Frank D. Haller. Outdoor Ind., 18 (9): 2, 19, Sept., 1951.

ROWDY, A FOX THAT LIVED IN TWO WORLDS. Norman D. Harris. Nat. Hist., New York, vol.50, no.4, pp.220-221, illus., Nov., 1942.

THE RED FOX. Jack Hogue. Colorado Outdoors Mag., 7 (1): 12-14, illus., Jan., 1958.

(THE BARN-FOX.) Ladraeven. Sign Hubertus. Svensk Jakt, Stockholm, vol.88, no.2, pp.30-33, Feb.15, 1950.

(CHANGES IN CAPTIVE FOXES.) Gefangenschaftsveraenderungen bei Fuechsen. B. Klatt. Jenaische Zeitschr. fuer Naturw., Jena, vol.67, pp.452-468, figs.5, Aug.16, 1932.

THE REDS AND THE GRAYS. Joseph W. Lippincott. Fauna, Phila., vol.10, no.1, pp.20-22, illus., Mar., 1948.

THE RED FOX. Clifton Lisle. Frontiers, Phila., vol.3, no.1, pp.7-10, figs.2, Oct., 1938; vol.14, no.4, pp.126-128, illus., Apr., 1950.

(THE STOCK OF ARCTIC FOX IN SWEDEN, 1926.) Fjaellraevstammen i Sverige 1926. Einar Loennberg. K. Svenska Vetensk. Skrifter i Naturskyddsaerenden no.7, pp.1-23, 1926.

(OUR WILD ANIMAL: THE FOX.) Vart villebrad. Raeven. Gustaf Lundburg. II. Skogen, vol.19, no.7, pp.167-171, figs. 3, Apr.1, 1932.

THE FOX. C. H. Moffat. Irish Naturalists' Jour., vol.1, no.12, pp.231-233, July, 1927.

WISEST IN THE WILDS: BEING THE LIFE STORY OF THE FOX. B. Melville Nicholas. MacDonald and Co., London, pp.96, 1948.

HELLO, MR. REYNARD! Cyril Plattes. Minn. Cons., 65: 11, 32, 34, Jan., 1939.

THE RED FOX. E. L. Poole. South Dakota Conservation Digest, Pierre, vol. 10, no.1, inside back cover, illus., Jan., 1943.

(OBSERVATIONS OF A FENNEC, MEGALOTIS ZERDA ZIMM.) Beobachtungen an einem Fenek, Megalotis zerda Zimm. B. Rensch. Zool. Garten, Leipzig, NF, vol. 17, nos.1-5, pp.30-40, illus., 1950.

(NEW OBSERVATIONS ON THE GERMAN FOX.) Neue Beobachtungen an unserem Fuchs. Bastian Schmid. Naturforscher, Berlin, vol.12, no.6, pp.192-196, illus., Sept., 1935.

ECOLOGY AND MANAGEMENT OF THE RED FOX. Thomas G. Scott. Iowa Cooperative Wildlife Research Unit, Quart. Rept., pp.86-87 (Mimeog.), July-Sept., 1947; Iowa Coop. Wildlife Research Unit, Ames, Quart. Rept., pp.24-27, Jan.-Mar., 1947.

THE BIOGRAPHY OF AN ARCTIC FOX. Ernest Thompson Seton. New York, 1937.

THE MANE ON THE TAIL OF THE GRAY-FOX. Ernest Thompson Seton. Jour. Mam., vol.4, no.3, pp.180-182, Aug., 1923.

RED FOX: MASTER MIND OF THE FOREST. Don Cameron Shafer. Amer. Forests and Forest Life, vol.35, pp.135-137, 174, illus., Mar., 1929.

FOXES--AND WHAT WE KNOW OF THEM. Clarence R. Shoemaker. Amer. Forestry, vol.26, pp.673-681, figs.1-10, Nov., 1920.

THE GRAY FOX IN CAPTIVITY. Walter P. Taylor. Texas Game and Fish, Austin, vol.1, no.10, pp.12-13, 19, illus., Sept., 1943.

THE FRIENDLY FOX. George H. Williams. Sylva, Toronto, vol.3, no.3, p.37, 1947.

THE FOX. Carling Conserv. Digest, Toronto, vol.1, no.2, pp.10, 13, illus., Apr., 1947.

THE FOXES. (HABITAT GROUP OF RED FOXES.) Living Museum, Springfield, vol.4, no.2, pp.9-10, illus., June, 1942.

LIMELIGHT ON FOXES. Audubon Mag., New York, vol.46, no.3, pp.182-183, May-June, 1944.

LONG-TAILED RED FOX VULPES MACROURA. Wyoming Wildlife, Cheyenne, vol.5, no.5, pp.6, 14, May, 1940.

RED FOX. Canadian Nat., Toronto, vol. 10, no.1, p.9, Jan.-Feb., 1948.

WHO'S WHO IN THE ZOO--MEPHISTOPHELES, THE LONG-EARED FOX. Fauna, Phila., vol.5, no.1, p.30, illus., Mar., 1943.

General (Wolves)

ABOUT WOLVES. David A. Arnold. Michigan Conserv., Lansing, vol.21, no.1, pp.23-25, illus., Jan., 1952.

THE HOME LIFE OF THE BIG WOLVES. Vernon Bailey. Natural History, New York, vol.46, no.2, pp.120-122, fig., Sept., 1940.

A FRIENDLY ENCOUNTER WITH WOLVES. W. J. Banks. Our Dumb Animals, Norwood, vol.76, no.6, p.109, June, 1943.

THE TRUTH ABOUT WOLVES. W. J. Banks. Our Dumb Animals, Norwood, vol. 73, no.12, p.180, Dec., 1940.

AN EXPERIENCE WITH WOLVES. C. P. Barager. Rod and Gun in Canada, Montreal, vol.46, no.7, pp.6-7, illus., Jan., 1945.

GRAY WOLF--TIMBER WOLF. N. R. Barger. Wisconsin Conserv. Bull., Madison, vol.13, no.10, p.26, illus., Oct., 1948.

THE LADY AND THE WOLVES. J. L. Baughman. Texas Game and Fish, Austin, vol.5, no.10, pp.4-5, 28-29, illus., Sept., 1947.

TIMBER WOLVES--WILD AND TAME. Ernest H. Baynes. Nature Mag., vol.2, pp.333-338, 356, 10 figs., Dec., 1923.

NEARING EXTINCTION IS THE GRAY WOLF. J. G. Burr. Texas Game and Fish, Austin, vol.6, no.5, pp.6, 13-14, Apr., 1948.

WOLF! E. C. Cross. Rod and Gun in Canada, 38 (8): 18-19, 32-33, Jan., 1937.

BLOOD ON THE SNOW. (WOLF.) Frank Dufresne. Sports Afield, Minneapolis, vol.117, no.2, pp.28-29, 84-85, illus., Feb., 1947.

GHOSTS THAT KILL GAME. (WOLF.) Frank Dufresne. Outdoor Life, New York, vol.101, no.4, pp.36-37, illus., Apr., 1948.

GREEK WOLF-LORE. Richard Preston Eckels. A dissertation in Greek presented to the faculty of the graduate school of the University of Pennsylvania in partial fulfillment of the requirements for the degree of Doctor of Philosophy, Phila., pp.88, 1937.

THE GREAT GRAY WOLF. Laurie York Erskine. Frontiers, Phila., vol.15, no.2, pp.41-44, 65, illus., Dec., 1950.

THE WOLVES UNDERSTOOD HIM. L. H. Fowler. Alaska Sportsman, Ketchikan, vol.13, no.11, pp.8-9, 34-36, illus., Nov., 1947.

WOLVES LOVE A KILLERS' MOON. John Patrick Gillese. Rod and Gun in Canada, Gardenvale, vol.52, no.8, pp.8-9, 31-33, illus., Jan., 1951.

WOLF AT THE CROSSING. Hamilton M. Laing. Field and Stream, New York, vol. 48, no.11, pp.28-29, 73, illus., Mar., 1944.

WOLVES ARE QUEER DEVILS. Bob Lane. Alaska Sportsman, Ketchikan, vol.7, no.1, pp.10-11, 32-34, Jan., 1941.

LEARNING FROM THE WOLVES. William J. Long. Sports Afield, New York, vol.122, no.6, pp.28-29, 69-73, illus., Dec., 1949.

THE BIG WOLF OF THE TIMBERLANDS. William MacMillan. Nature Mag., vol.5, pp.285-286, illus., May, 1925.

THE GREY WOLF. Colin Matheson. Jour. Soc. Preservation Fauna Empire, Hertford, pt.L, pp.31-42, Dec., 1944.

WOLF! Olaus J. Murie. The Living Wilderness, Wash., vol.13, no.25, pp.5-6, Summer, 1948.

I MATCH WITS WITH WOLVES. Albert Schueneman. Alaska Sportsman, Ketchikan, vol.7, no.4, pp.18-20, Apr., 1941.

SNOWY TRAIL LEADS TO WOLF, HIS LAIR, AND LOOT. A. M. Stebler. Michigan Conserv., vol.8, no.4, pp.6-7, 11, Dec., 1938.

WOLVES CAN BE TOUGH. C. V. Tench. Rod and Gun in Canada, Montreal, vol.50, no.12, pp.11, 48, May, 1949.

Africa and Madagascar

(A NEW SUBSPECIES OF "VULPES RUEPPELLI" IN LIBYA.) Una nuova sottospecie di Vulpes rueppelli in Libia. (Vulpes rueppelli cufrana.) Oscar de Beaux. Ann. Mus. Libico Storia Nat., Tripoli, vol.1, pp.393-396, pl.18, 1939.

THE AFRICAN WILD DOG. R. M. Bere. Oryx, London, 3 (4): 180-182, May, 1956.

WOLVES IN EGYPT. J. Nield Cameron. Field, London, vol.167, no.4356, p.1510, June 30, 1936.

(ADDITIONAL NOTES ON THE WILD DOGS OF CENTRAL AFRICA.) Notes additionelles sur les chiens sauvages de l'Afrique centrale. J. M. Derscheid. Rev. Zool. Africaine, vol.14, no.2, pp.3-8, illus., 1926.

(BEASTS OF PREY ON MADAGASCAR.) Madagascar rovdjur. B. Ljungquist. Fauna och Flora, Uppsala, pp.255-262, 1930.

KIP, AN INTERESTING AND UNUSUAL PET OF EAST AFRICA. (GREAT-EARED FOX.) Arthur Loveridge. Nat. Hist., New York, vol.55, no.10, pp.472-473, 490, Dec., 1946.

(A PRAIRIE FOX FROM CAMEROON, CANIS (CYNALOPEX) PALLIDUS OERTZENI.) Ein Steppenfuchs aus Kamerun, Canis (Cynalopex) pallidus Oertzeni. Paul Matschie. Sitz. Ber. Gesell, Natur. f. Freunde, Berlin, Jahrg.1910, no.8, pp. 370-371, June 7, 1910.

(ON THE OCCURRENCE OF LYCAON PICTUS (TEMM.) IN THE SAHARA.) Sur la presence au Sahara du Lycaon pictus (Temm.). Th. Monod. Bull. Soc. Zool., France, vol.53, no.4, pp.262-264, Apr., 1928.

(CONTRIBUTION TO KNOWLEDGE OF THE SOUTH AFRICAN HOUSE DOG.) Beitrag zur Kenntnis der suedafrikanischen Haushunde. V. Petters. Zeitschr. f. Saeugetierkunde, Berlin, vol.9, nos.1-3, pp.142-163, pls.8-10, Dec.30, 1934.

(ON THE OCCURRENCE OF SO-CALLED WOLVES IN NORTHEAST AFRICA.) Ueber das Vorkommen sogennanter Woelfe in Nordostafrica. C. Reinberger. Zeitschr. f. Saeugetierkunde, Berlin, vol.13, no.2, pp.243-245, 1939.

THE FOXES AND JACKALS OF NIGERIA. D. R. Rosevear. Nigerian Field, vol.5, no.2, pp.57-59, figs.3, Apr., 1936.

SOME NOTES ON THE SMALL SAND-FOXES OF NORTH AFRICA. Oldfield

Thomas. Ann. and Mag. Nat. Hist., (9), vol.1, no.3, pp.242-245, Mar., 1918.

LETTER FROM, ADDRESSED TO THE SECRETARY, CONTAINING REMARKS ON CANIS CHAMA, SMITH. Roland Trimen. Proc. Zool. Soc. Lond., p.2, 1876.

THE AFRICAN WILD DOG. Nature, London, 178 (4526): 191, July 28, 1956.

Alaska

WOLF TROUBLE IN ALASKA. Russell Annabel. Field and Stream, New York, vol.51, no.10, pp.19-21, 73-76, illus., Feb., 1947.

POLARIS. THE STORY OF AN ESKIMO DOG. Ernest Harold Baynes. Macmillan Co., New York, pp.i-xv, 1-137, illus., Oct., 1922.

A COYOTE FROM MOUNT MCKINLEY, ALASKA. Joseph Dixon. Jour. Mam., vol.9, no.1, p.64, Feb., 1928.

SEA BIRD CITIES OF THE ALEUTIANS. (BLUE FOX AND ARCTIC FOX.) Ben East. Nat. Hist., New York, vol.51, no.2, pp. 64-71, illus., Feb., 1943.

ALASKA WOLF HAWKS. (WOLVES.) Charles E. Gillham. Sports Afield, Minneapolis, vol.121, no.1, pp.30-31, 82-83, illus., Jan., 1949.

THE HUSKY IS MUCH THE LARGER BREED. E. L. Keithahn. Alaska Sportsman, Ketchikan, vol.9, no.11, pp.18-20, 23-24, illus., Nov., 1943.

THE WOLVES OF MOUNT MCKINLEY. Adolph Murie. USDI, Natl. Park Serv., Fauna Ser.5, xix, pp.238, 1944; Living Wilderness, Wash., vol.10, no.12, pp. 9-25, illus., Feb., 1945.

WOLVES OF THE NAHA. Alda Orton. Alaska Sportsman, Ketchikan, vol.8, no. 1, pp.8-9, 28-30, illus., Jan., 1942.

Anatomy

DENTAL ANOMALY IN AN ESKIMO DOG. Glover M. Allen. Jour. Mam., vol.20, no.3, pp.372, illus., Aug.14, 1939.

DOG SKULLS FROM UYAK BAY, KODIAK ISLAND. Glover M. Allen. Jour. Mam., vol.20, no.3, pp.336-340, Aug.14, 1939.

IDENTIFICATION OF THE CELLS AND FIBERS CONCERNED IN THE INNERVATION OF THE TEETH. (WORK ON DOG.) William F. Allen. Jour. Comp. Neur., vol.39, pp.325-343, figs.5, Dec.15, 1925.

COMPARISON OF THE WEIGHTS OF SUPRARENALS OF DOGS IN OESTRUS, PREGNANCY AND LACTATION. Dan D. Baker. Jour. Morphol., Phila., vol.62, no.1, pp.3-15, figs.2, tables 5, Jan.1, 1938.

THE MAXILLARY SINUS OF THE DOG, WITH SPECIAL REFERENCE TO CERTAIN NEW STRUCTURES, PROBABLY SENSORY IN NATURE. T. H. Bast. Amer. Jour. Anat., vol.33, pp.449-484, figs.2, pls.5, July 15, 1924.

(ON J.M. JOSIFOFF'S ARTICLE "THE DEEP LYMPHATIC VESSELS OF THE EXTREMITIES OF THE DOG.") Zu dem Artikel von J.M. Josifoff: "Die tiefen Lymphgefaesse der Extremitaeten des Hundes." H. Baum. Anat. Anzeiger, vol. 65, pp.421-428, July 18, 1928.

(THE POSTEMBRYONIC GROWTH OF THE SKULL OF THE GERMAN SHEEP-DOG.) Das postembryonale wachstum des deutschen Schaeferhundschaedels. Alfred Becker. Archiv. f. Naturgeschichte, Abteil. A., vol.89, Heft 9, pp.131-197, figs.18, Dec.7, 1923.

(ON SOME PECULIARITIES OF THE TEMPORAL REGION OF THE DOG.) Sur quelques particularités de la région du temporal chez le chien. Philippe Belloco. Comptes Rendus soc. Biol., vol.96, pp.991-994, illus., 1927.

EXPERIMENTAL STUDIES ON THE MOVEMENTS OF THE MAMMALIAN TONGUE. I. MOVEMENTS OF THE SPLIT TONGUE (DOG). G. A. Bennett, A. J. Ramsay. Anat. Record, Phila., vol.79, no.1, pp. 39-51, pls.2, Jan.25, 1941.

RECORDS OF LARGE FOXES. Harry B. Booth. Scottish Nat., no.164, p.60, Mar.-Apr., 1927.

TOPOGRAPHICAL ANATOMY OF THE DOG. O. Charnock Bradley. Revised by Tom Graham, Macmillan Co., New York, 4th ed., xii, 316 pp., illus., 1944; 5th ed., revised by Tom Graham, Macmillan, New York, pp.xii, 319, illus., 1949.

LARGE VASCULAR SINUSES IN THE MYOCARDIUM OF A DOG. Howard B. Burchell. Anat. Record, Phila., vol.74, pp.195-197, June 25, 1939.

INTRAMUSCULAR NERVE ENDINGS OF SENSORY TYPE IN THE SMALL INTESTINE, WITH A CONSIDERATION OF THEIR PROBABLE FUNCTION. (WORK ON DOG.) F. W. Carpenter. Jour. Comp. Neur., vol.37, pp.439-454, figs.4, Oct.15, 1924.

THE DENTITION OF ADULT DOGS. F. Gordon Cawston. S. African Dental Jour., Port Elizabeth, vol.16, no.5, pp.167-168, illus., May, 1942.

MEASUREMENTS OF A LARGE INDIAN WOLF (CANIS PALLIPES.). R. Y. Chavan. Jour. Bombay Nat. Hist. Soc., vol.34, no. 4, p.1055, Mar.2, 1931.

THE ANATOMY OF AN OTOCEPHALIC DOG. F. E. Chidester. Anat. Record, vol.28, pp.1-4, figs.2, June 25, 1924.

THE WEIGHT OF FOXES. R. Clapham. Field, London, vol.168, p.861, Nov.11, 1926.

WEIGHTS AND MEASUREMENTS OF FOXES. BIG HILL RANGERS OF THE GRAMPIANS AND THE FELLS. Richard Clapham. Field, London, vol.163, no.4244, p.959, illus., Apr.28, 1934.

A CASE OF THE INFERIOR VENA CAVA UNITING WITH THE AZYGOS CAVA IN THE DOG. A. R. Cooper. Anat. Rec., vol.17, pp.299-306, figs.2, Jan.30 (Feb.), 1920.

THE GROSS WEIGHT OF WOODHOUSE'S WOLF. E. D. Crabb. Jour. Mam., vol. 5, no.3, pp.199-200, Aug.1924.

THE WEIGHT OF AN ADULT "COYOTE." E. D. Crabb. Univ. Oklahoma Bull., Norman, n.s., no.322 (Univ. Studies, no. 21), p.43, Dec.1, 1925.

(ON THE VARIATION OF THE CRANIUM IN WILD AND TAME CANINES. A CONTRIBUTION TO THE GENEALOGY OF DOMESTIC DOGS.) Ueber die Variation der Hirnschale bei wilden und zahmen Caniden. Ein Beitrag zur Genealogie der Haushunde. E. Dahr. Arkiv f. Zool., Stockholm, vol.33 A, no.16, pp.56, figs. 3, 1942.

(THE NERVES OF THE ESOPHAGUS IN THE DOG.) Die Nerven der Speiseroehre beim Hund. N. D. Dowgiallo. Zeitschr. f. Anat. u. Entwicklungsgesch., vol.83, pp.591-597, fig.1, July 23, 1927.

(THE PENIS BONE OF THE WOLF (CANIS LUPUS L.).) A Farkas (Canis lupus L.) peniscsontjáról. J. Ehik. Allattani Koezlemények, vol.31, nos.1-2, pp.88-91, 1934. (In Hungarian, with German summary.)

THE AFFERENT AND PARASYMPATHETIC INNERVATION OF THE LUNGS AND TRACHEA OF THE DOG. Alice Gooding Elftman. Amer. Jour. Anat., Phila., vol. 72, no.1, pp.1-27, pls.4, Jan., 1943.

LYMPHATIC PATHWAYS FROM THE INTESTINE IN THE DOG. L. Willard Freeman. Anat. Record, Phila., vol.82, no.4, pp. 543-550, Apr.25, 1942.

NOTE ON THE CAECUM OF CANIS CANCRIVORUS. Alfred Henry Garrod. Proc. Zool. Soc. Lond., pp.748-750, figs. 3, 1873.

NOTES ON THE VISCERAL ANATOMY OF LYCAON PICTUS, AND OF NYCTEREUTES PROCYONIDES. Alfred Henry Garrod. Proc. Zool. Soc. Lond., pp.373-377, fig.1, 1878.

STUDIES IN SKULL GROWTH. CORONAL SUTURE FIXATION. (DOG SKULLS.) N. Giblin, A. Alley. Anat. Record, Phila., vol.88, no.2, pp.143-153, figs.7, Feb., 1944.

THE MAMMALIAN THYMUS. IV. THE DEVELOPMENT IN THE DOG. Melvin Crawford Godwin. Amer. Jour. Anat., Phila., vol.64, no.1, pp.165-192, Jan.15, 1939.

NOTES ON THE SKULLS OF THE SPECIES OF DOGS, WOLVES, AND FOXES (CANIDAE) IN THE COLLECTION OF THE BRITISH MUSEUM. John E. Gray. Proc. Zool. Soc. Lond., pp.492-523, figs.7, 1868.

ON THE SKULL OF THE CHINESE PUG-NOSED SPANIEL OR LAP-DOG. John E. Gray. Proc. Zool. Soc. Lond., pp.40-43, figs.2, 1867.

AN OSTEOMETRIC ANALYSIS OF SOME ABORIGINAL DOGS. William G. Haag. Univ. Kentucky Reports Anthropol., Lexington, vol.7, no.3, pp.105-264, figs. 16, Dec., 1948.

CRANIAN CHARACTERS OF A DOG-COYOTE HYBRID. E. Raymond Hall. Amer. Midland Nat., Notre Dame, vol.29, no.2, pp.371-374, figs.2, Mar., 1943.

(ON THE SKULL AND LOWER JAW OF JAPANESE DOG RACES OF THE STONE AGE.) Ueber die Schaedel und Unterkiefer von den steinzeitlich-japanischen Hundrassen. Kotondo Hasebe. Arb. aus den Anat. Inst. der Kais-Japan, Univ. zu Sendai, pt. 10, pp.1-33, pls.1-7, Aug.30, 1924.

AN ANALYSIS OF BODY PROPORTIONS IN THE CANIDAE. Milton Hildebrand. Amer. Jour. Anat., vol.90, no.2, pp.217-256, illus., Mar., 1952.

COMPARATIVE MORPHOLOGY OF THE BODY SKELETON IN RECENT CANIDAE. Milton Hildebrand. Univ. Calif. Publ. Zool., vol.52, no.5, pp.399-470, illus., Apr.14, 1954.

THE INTEGUMENT IN CANIDAE. Milton Hildebrand. Jour. Mam., 33 (4): 419-428, illus., Nov., 1952.

A MEANS TO DISTINGUISH SKULLS OF COYOTES AND DOMESTIC DOGS. Walter E. Howard. Jour. Mam., 30 (2): 169-171, May, 1949.

(ON THE MUSCULAR REGION OF THE NERVUS FACILIA IN THE DOG, WITH GENERAL OBSERVATIONS ON THE FACIAL MUSCULATURE.) Ueber das Muskelgebiet des Nervus facialis beim Hund, nebst allgemeinen Betrachtungen ueber die Facialis-Muskulatur. Ernst Huber. Morphologisches Jahrbuch, vol.52, 1st part: pp.1-110, 1922; 2nd part: pp.354-414, 1923.

ON THE CRANIAL AND DENTAL CHARACTERS OF THE CANIDAE. T. H. Huxley. Proc. Zool. Soc. Lond., pp.238-288, illus., Apr.6, 1880.

THE CRANIAL CHARACTERS OF THE HAWAIIAN DOG. Frederic Wood Jones. Jour. Mam., vol.12, no.1, pp.39-41, Feb., 1931.

THE CRANIAL CHARACTERS OF THE PAPUAN DOG. Frederic Wood Jones. Jour. Mam., vol.10, no.4, pp.329-333, Nov., 1929.

(THE DEEP LYMPH NODES OF THE EXTREMETIES OF DOGS.) Die tiefen Lymphgefaesse der Extremitaeten des Hundes. J. M. Josifoff. Anat. Anzeiger, vol.65, pp.65-76, figs.3, Mar.12, 1928.

(REPLIES DIRECTED TO MR. BAUM REGARDING HIS "ON J.M. JOSIFOFF'S 'THE LYMPHATIC VESSELS OF THE EXTREMITIES OF THE DOG.') Erwiderungen an Herrn Baum auf: Zu dem Artikel von J.M. Josifoff: Die Lymphgefaesse der Extremitaeten des Hundes. J. M. Josifoff. Anat. Anzeiger, vol.67, pp.507-511, Aug. 16, 1929.

(THE M. OBLIQUUS ABDOMINIS EXTERNUS PROFUNDUS IN THE DOG.) Der M. obliquus abdominis externus profundus beim Hunde. W. Kassianenko. Anat. Anzeiger, vol.64, pp.298-303, fig.1, Dec.1, 1927.

NOTE ON THE OCCURRENCE OF A SUPERNUMERARY TOOTH IN A DOG. Lawrence M. Lambe. Ottawa Nat., vol.21, pp.25-26, May 7, 1907.

(TWO DOGS WITH ANORMAL DENTITION.) Ceux chiens a dentition anormale. C. Lamberton. Mammalia, vol.4, no.1, pp. 30-33, pl.2, Mar., 1940.

THE WEIGHT OF THE BRAIN, OF ITS PARTS, AND OF THE SPINAL CORD OF THE FROG, TURTLE, AND DOG. Homer B. Latimer. Jour. Comp. Neur., vol.38, pp.49-72, Dec.15, 1924.

WILD COYOTE WITH AN UNDERSHOT JAW. Barbara Lawrence. Jour. Mam., vol.15, no.4, pp.319-320, Nov., 1934.

(ON THE THEORY OF THE INNERVATION OF THE LYMPHATIC SYSTEM. COMMUNICATION I: ON THE NERVES OF THE DUCTUS THORACICUS IN THE DOG.) Zur Lehre von der Innervation des Lymphsystems. I. Mitteilung: Ueber die Nerven des Ductus thoracicus beim Hunde. A. P. Lawrentjew. Anat. Anzeiger, vol.60, pp. 475-481, illus., Feb.1, 1926.

(NOTE ON THE END NERVE (ACCORDING TO A STUDY ON THE DOG).) Note sur le nerf terminal (d'apres une etude sur le chien). G. Lazorthes. Bull. Soc. Hist. Nat., Toulouse, vol.78, fasc.2, pp.102-106, fig.1, June 30, 1943.

A REMARKABLE OCCURRENCE OF THE FIRST HIND TOE IN THE COMMON FOX (VULPES VULPES). Einar Loennberg. Arkiv Zool., Upsala, vol.10, no.21, pp.1-5, figs.1-2, July 27, 1916.

EVOLUTIONARY ALLOMETRY IN THE SKELETON OF THE DOMESTICATED DOG. Hyman Lumer. Amer. Nat., Lancaster, vol.74, no.754, pp.439-467, figs.9, Sept.-Oct., 1940.

PIGMENTED AREAS IN THE UTERUS OF THE ARCTIC FOX ALOPEX LAGOPUS INNUITUS MERRIAM. Eoin H. McEwen, Alexander Scott. Proc. Zool. Soc. Lond., 128 (3): 347-348, pl.1, June 6, 1957.

CRYPTORCHIDISM IN A COYOTE. Frank B. McMurry. Jour. Mam., vol.23, no.2, p.220, May 14, 1942.

OBSERVATIONS UPON A NEW FOX FROM MR. DARWIN'S COLLECTION (VULPES FULVIPES). W. Martin. Proc. Zool. Soc., Lond., pt.5, p.11, 1837.

GUIDE TO THE DISSECTION OF THE DOG. Malcolm E. Miller. Third ed. Edwards Brothers, Ann Arbor, pp. xi, 369, illus., 1952.

(REVIEW BY GEORGE C. RINKER, OF) GUIDE TO THE DISSECTION OF THE DOG. Malcolm E. Miller. Jour. Mam., vol.34, no.2, pp.271-272, May 14, 1953.

QUANTITATIVE STUDIES ON THE BONE MARROW OF THE DOG. R. M. Mulligan. Anat. Record, Phila., vol.79, no.1, pp.101-108, Jan.25, 1941.

DOG SKULLS FROM IPIUTAK. Olaus J. Murie. Anthropol. Papers Amer. Mus. Nat. Hist., New York, vol.42, pp.255-259, illus., 1948.

(THE SECOND GERMAN NORTH POLE EXPEDITION IN 1869 AND 1870 UNDER THE DIRECTION OF CAPT. KARL KOLDEWEY. II) ZOOLOGY. PART 3: NOTES ON THE SKULLS OF ESKIMO DOGS.) Die Zweite Deutsche Nordpolarfahrt in den Jahren 1869 und 1870 unter Fuehrung der Kapitaen Karl Koldewey. II. Zoologie. Pt. 3: Bemerkungen ueber die Schaedel der Eskimohunde. Hermann von Nathusius. E. A. Brockhaus, Leipzig, vol.2, pp.175-177, 1874.

(ON THE SKULL AND SKELETON OF THE INCA DOGS FROM THE TOMBS OF ANCON, WITH NOTES ON THE ORIGIN OF THESE DOGS.) Ueber Schaedel und Skelet der Inca-Hunde aus den Graebern von Ancon, nebst Bemerkungen ueber die Abstammung derselben. Alfred Nehring. Tageblatt der--Versammlung Deutscher Naturforscher und Aerzte, Berlin, pp.169-173, 1884.

(SKULL FORM AND THE DENTITION OF CANIS JUBATUS DESM.) Die Schaedelform und das Gebiss des Canis jubatus Desm. Alfred Nehring. Sitz. Ber. Gesell. Naturf. Freunde Berlin, no.5, pp.109-122, figs.2, May 19, 1885.

A CASE OF ABNORMAL DENTITION IN A DHOLE, OR INDIAN RED DOG (CUON DUKHUNENSIS). R. I. Pocock. Ann. and Mag. Nat. Hist., ser.8, London, vol.11, pp.196-198, figs.1, Aug., 1908.

THE EXTERNAL CHARACTERS OF A BUSH-DOG (SPEOTHOS VENATICUS) AND OF A MANED WOLF (CHRYSOCYON BRACHYURUS), EXHIBITED IN THE SOCIETY'S GARDENS. R. I. Pocock. Proc. Zool. Soc. Lond., pt.2, pp.307-321, illus., July 12, 1927.

ON THE FEET OF DOMESTIC DOGS. R.I. Pocock. Proc. Zool. Soc. Lond., pp.478-484, figs.1-3, June 16, 1914.

(THE OS PENIS AS A POINT OF DIFFERENTIATION BETWEEN CANIS LUPUS L. AND CANIS FAMILIARIS L.) Das Os penis als Unterscheidungs-Merkmal von Canis lupus L. und Canis familiaris L. L. Pohl. Anat. Anzeiger, vol.64, pp.437-440, fig.1, Jan. 30, 1928.

(SOME REMARKS ON THE QUESTION OF THE CANINE TOOTH.) Einige Bemerkungen zur Eckzahnfrage. A. Remane. Anthropol. Anzeiger, Stuttgart, Jahrg., vol. 1, no.1, pp.35-40, figs.6, 1924.

SOME RECORDS OF LARGE FOXES. H. W. Robinson. Socttish Nat., no.163, pp.15-16, Feb., 1927.

(THE THORACIC CANAL OF THE DOG.) Le canal thoracique du chien. Alvaro Rodrigues. Comptes Rendus, 12th Internat. Congr. Zool.1935, Lisboa, vol.2, pp.702-712, pls.35-36, 1936-37.

THE TIME OF CLOSURE OF THE LOWER FEMORAL EPIPHYSES AND UPPER TIBIAL EPIPHYSES IN THE DOG AS DETERMINED BY ROENTGENOGRAM. Carl F. Schlotthauer, Joseph M. Janes. Amer. Jour. Vet. Res., 13 (46): 90, Jan., 1952.

EXHIBITION OF, AND REMARKS UPON, A TYPICAL SPECIMEN OF A NEW FOX (VULPES CANA). Philip L. Sclater. Proc. Zool. Soc. Lond., p.392, 1878.

THE OSTEOLOGY OF VULPES MACROTIS. R. W. Shufeldt. Jour. Acad. Nat. Sci. Phila., vol.11, pt.3, pp.395-418, pls.2, Aug., 1900.

WEIGHT OF FOXES. George W. Templer. Field, London, vol.149, p.153, Jan.27, 1927.

(ON THE INNERVATION OF THE TRACHEA AND BRONCHI IN THE DOG.) Ueber die Innervation der Trachea und der Bronchen beim Hunde. M. N. Tscheliustken. Zeitschr. f. Anat. u. Entwicklungsgesch., vol.83, pp.605-614, figs.13, July 23, 1927.

HISTOLOGICAL OBSERVATIONS ON THE EPIPHYSIS CEREBRI AND ON THE CHORIOID PLEXUS OF THE THIRD VENTRICLE OF THE DOG. W. G. Venzke, J. W. Gilmore. Proc. Iowa Acad. Sci., Des Moines, vol.47, pp.409-413, 1940.

(RECENT DOG RACES: AN OSTEOLOGICAL INVESTIGATION.) Rezente Hunderassen. Eine Osteologische Untersuchung. K. Wagner. Det Norske Videnskaps-Akademi, math.-naturv. Kl., Oslo, 1929, no.9, pp. 157, figs.36, pls.12, 1930.

INTRANUCLEAR CRYSTALS IN THE HEPATIC CELLS OF CANIDAE--WOLVES, FOXES, JACKALS, AND NON-DOMESTIC DOGS. Harold L. Weatherford. Anat. Record, Phila., vol.73, no.1, pp.29-36, Jan.25, 1939.

ON THE DEFICIENCY OF TEETH IN THE HAIRLESS EGYPTIAN VARIETY OF THE DOG. W. Yarrell. Proc. Zool. Soc. Lond., pt.1, p.113, 1833.

GEOGRAPHICAL VARIABILITY IN THE SKULL STRUCTURE OF THE EURASIAN POLAR FOX. V. I. Zalkin. Zool. Jour. USSR, Moscow, vol.23, no.4, pp.156-169, figs.13, 1944. (English summary.)

Arctic Regions

THE BIOLOGY OF THE ARTIC FOXES OF THE COMMANDER ISLANDS. I. I. Barabash-Nikiforov. Trans. Arctic Inst. USSR, Leningrad, vol.65, Biol., pp.145-167, fig.1, tables 3, 1937.

A STUDY ON THE ARCTIC FOX IN GREENLAND. IMMIGRATIONS, FLUCTUATIONS IN NUMBERS BASED MAINLY ON TRADING STATISTICS. F. W. Braestrup. Meddelelser om Gronland, Kobenhavn, vol.131, pp. 101, figs.6, pl.1, 1941.

THE ESKIMO DOGS OF THE EASTERN ARCTIC. S. Hadwen. Beaver, Winnipeg, outfit 266, no.1, pp.33-36, 66, illus., June, 1935.

FOUR NEW ARCTIC FOXES. C. Hart Merriam. Proc. Biol. Soc. Wash., vol.15, pp.167-172, Aug.6, 1902.

DOGS OF THE ARCTIC FRONTIER. O. J. Murie. Nature Mag., vol.6, pp.75-78, figs.8, Aug., 1925.

NOTICE OF THE CAPTURE OF AN ARCTIC FOX (CANIS LAGOPUS, L.) ON AN ICEBERG. W. Smith. Proc. Comm. Sci. and Corres. Zool. Soc. Lond., pt.2, p.189, 1832.

ESKIMO DOGS OF THE CANADIAN ARCTIC. J. Dewey Soper. Canadian Geogr. Jour., Ottawa, vol.20, no.2, pp.97-108, illus., Feb., 1940.

(CONTINUED INVESTIGATIONS OF GREENLAND'S FOX POPULATIONS.) Fortsatte undersogeler over Gronlands Raevebestand. Christian Vibe. Atuagagdliutit-Gronlandsposten, 93 (14): 230-233, illus., table, 1953.

DOGS OF THE ARCTIC. Beaver, Winnipeg, outfit 273, pp.4-7, illus., Dec., 1942.

Asia

ON THE COREAN AND JAPANESE WOLVES. Abe Yoshio. Jour. Sci. Hiroshima Univ., Japan, ser.B, div.1, vol.1, art.2, pp.33-37, pls.1-5, table, Dec., 1930.

NOTE ON THE FOX OF JAPAN. Arthur Adams. Proc. Zool. Soc. Lond., pt.28, p.195, 1860.

(DATA ON MALAYAN BONE DISEASES (CONDITIONS IN THE DOG, GOAT, FOX, LION).) Zur Kenntnis der malazischen Knochenerkrankungen. (Befunde an Hund, Ziege, Fuchs, Loewe). Hans Joachim Arndt. Zeitschr. f. Saeugetierkunde, Berlin, vol.9, nos.1-3, pp.377-383, pl.17, Dec.30, 1934.

THE WOLF (CANIS LUPUS LINN.) IN BALUCHISTAN. R.K.M. Battye. Jour. Bombay Nat. Hist. Soc., vol.43, no.2, pp.252-253, Aug., 1942.

(NOTES ON THE OCCURRENCE OF THE ARCTIC FOX IN TURKESTAN.) Notiz ueber das Vorkommen des Eisfuchses in Turkestan. Eug. Buchner. Ann. Mus. Zool. Acad. Imp. Sci., St. Petersbourg, pp.1-3 (393-395), 1897.

THE INDIAN WILD DOG. R. W. Burton. Jour. Bombay Nat. Hist. Soc., vol.41, no. 4, pp.691-715, figs.4, Aug., 1940; vol.42, no.2, pp.436-437, Apr., 1941.

THE INDIAN WILD DOG. (A CORRECTION.) R. W. Burton. Jour. Bombay Nat. Hist. Soc., vol.43, no.1, p.99, Apr., 1942.

WOLVES IN PALESTINE. (CANIS PALLIPES.) Douglas Carruthers. Field, London, vol.167, no.4342, p.587, illus., Mar.14, 1936.

NOTICE OF THE CHANCO, OR GOLDEN WOLF (CANIS CHANCO), FROM CHINESE TARTARY. John E. Gray. Proc. Zool. Soc. Lond., pt.31, p.94, 1863.

THE SOUTH-CHINA FOX, VULPES VULPES HOOLE SWINHOE. G.A.C. Herklots. Hong Kong Nat., vol.5, no.1, pp.71-73, pls.3, Mar., 1934.

WOLVES IN PALESTINE? C. S. Jarvis. Field, London, vol.167, no.4340, p.460, illus., Feb.29, 1936.

THE DOG OF THE TENGGER. F. A. Jentink. Notes Leyden Mus., vol.18, no. 25, pp.217-220, pls.4-5, Jan., 1897.

THE HABITAT OF THE RACCOON DOG ON MUKO-ZIMA, A SMALL ISLAND IN THE

INLAND SEA ALONG THE COAST OF YAMAGUTI PREFECTURE. Tokio Kaburaki. Report on the survey of the natural monuments, Sect.Zool.no.4, Dept. Interior, Tokyo, pp.4, pl.1, Jan., 1938. (In Japanese.)

(ON THE BIOLOGY OF THE BLUE FOX OF THE SOUTHWEST LITTORAL OF TAIMYR.) A. A. Kirpitchnikoff. Bull. Soc. Nat. Moscow, sect. biol., n.s., vol.46, no.1, pp.52-58, 1937. (In Russian, with French summary.)

WOLVES IN PALESTINE AND EGYPT. (CANIS LUPASTER.) Philip Manson-Bahr. Field, London, vol.167, no.4355, pp.1448, June 13, 1936.

WILD DOGS IN BURMA. C. E. Milner. Jour. Bombay Nat. Hist. Soc., vol.28, pp.266-267, Dec.30, 1921.

ON THE INDIAN WILD DOG. James Murie. Proc. Zool. Soc. Lond., pp.715-721, figs. 4, 1872.

NOTES ON WILD DOGS IN INDIA AND BURMA. O. C. Ollenbach. Jour. Darjeeling Nat. Hist. Soc., vol.4, no.4, pp.83-86, Apr., 1930.

A NOTE ON THE MALAYAN WILD DOG (CUON RUTILANS). E. H. Peacock. Jour. Bombay Nat. Hist. Soc., vol.33, no.1, p. 200, pl.1, Sept.30, 1928.

WILD DOGS IN MYSORE. E. G. Phythian-Adams. Jour. Bombay Nat. Hist. Soc., vol.31, pp.1028-1029, Feb.20, 1927.

IN THE HAUNTS OF THE RED INDIAN WILD DOG (CUON DUKHUNENSIS). C.R. S. Pitman. Jour. Bombay Nat. Hist. Soc., vol.29, pp.1046-1048, May 15, 1924.

THE ALLEGED WILD DOG OF MT. POPA, BURMA. R. I. Pocock. Jour. Bombay Nat. Hist. Soc., vol.39, no.4, pp.851-852, Dec. 15, 1937.

THE ASIATIC WILD DOG OR DHOLE (CUON JAVANICUS). R. I. Pocock. Proc. Zool. Soc. Lond., pt.1, pp.33-55, fig.1, Apr.16, 1936.

THE FOXES OF BRITISH INDIA. R. I. Pocock. Jour. Bombay Nat. Hist. Soc., vol.39, no.1, pp.36-57, figs.3, Dec.1, 1936.

WOLVES IN PALESTINE. R. I. Pocock. Field, London, vol.167, no.4344, p.711, Mar.28, 1936.

ON THE BLACK WOLF OF THIBET. P. L. Sclater. Proc. Zool. Soc. Lond., pp.654-655, pl.78, Nov.17, 1874.

AN INCIDENT WITH WILD DOG IN NIMAR. R. M. Simmons. Jour. Bombay Nat. Hist. Soc., vol.35, no.2, pp.442-444, Oct.15, 1931.

THE WOLF SCOURGE IN CHINA. Arthur de C. Sowerby. China Jour., vol.21, no.2, pp.88-89, Aug., 1934.

WOLVES IN CHINKIANG. Arthur de C. Sowerby. China Jour., vol.18, no.4, pp. 213-214, fig.1, Apr., 1933.

ACCOUNT OF A WILD DOG FROM THE MAHABLISHWAR HILLS. W. A. Wooler. Proc. Zool. Soc. Lond., pt.1, p.113, 1833.

SCIENTIFIC RESULTS FROM THE MAMMAL SURVEY. XIV. (E). THE INDIAN JACKALS. R. C. Wroughton. Jour. Bombay Nat. Hist. Soc., vol.24, pp.649-653, Oct.25, 1916.

THE WOLF IN CHINA. China Jour., vol. 26, no.4, pp.213-214, illus., Apr., 1937.

Biochemistry

URINARY CALCULI ASSOCIATED WITH VITAMIN A DEFICIENCY IN THE FOX. Charles F. Bassett, Lorin E. Harris, Sedgwick E. Smith, Elden D. Yeoman. Fur of Canada, Winnipeg, vol.11, no.8, pp.6, 9, May, 1946.

A COMPARISON OF CAROTENE AND VITAMIN A UTILIZATION BY THE FOX. Charles F. Bassett, Lorin E. Harris, C. Ford Wilke. Fur of Canada, Winnipeg, vol.11, no.8, pp.22-24, May, 1946; Nat. Fur News, Denver, vol.17, no.7, pp.9, 18, 28-29, Aug., 1946.

THE INACTIVATION OF VITAMIN $B_1$ IN DIETS CONTAINING WHOLE FISH. R. G. Green, W. E. Carlson, C. A. Evans. Amer. Fur Breeder, Duluth, vol.16, no.3, pp.18, 20, 22, 24, Sept., 1943.

THE CALCIUM REQUIREMENT OF GROWING FOXES. Lorin E. Harris, C. F. Bassett, S. E. Smith, E. D. Yeoman. Fur of Canada, Winnipeg, vol.10, no.1, pp.3-5, Apr., 1945; Nat. Fur News, Denver, vol. 17, no.5, pp.4-5, 12, 18-19, 21, June, 1945.

THIAMINE REQUIREMENT OF MATURE SILVER FOXES. Lorin E. Harris, John K. Loosli. Nat. Fur News, Denver, vol.22, no.4, pp.11, 19, May, 1950.

THIAMIN DEFICIENCY AND CHASTEK PARALYSIS IN FOXES. Adrian Z. Hobson, Sedgwick E. Smith. Fur of Canada, Winnipeg, vol.11, no.1, pp.3, 10, Oct., 1945.

A STUDY OF VITAMIN A IN THE NUTRITION OF FOXES. Arthur D. Holmes, Francis Tripp, Frank G. Ashbrook, Charles E. Kellogg. U.S. Dept. Interior, Fish and Wildlife Service, Wildlife Research Bull.3, pp.1-15, tab.8, 1941.

THE DETERMINATION OF THE MINIMUM NITROGEN REQUIREMENT OF THE ADULT DOG FOR MAINTENANCE OF NITROGEN BALANCE. C. F. Kade, Jr., J. H. Phillips, William A. Phillips. Jour. Nutrition, Phila., vol.36, no.1, pp.109-121, July 10, 1948.

VITAMIN A DEFICIENCY IN SILVER FOXES. Sedgwick E. Smith. Amer. Fur Breeder, Duluth, vol.14, no.3, pp.10, 12, Sept., 1941.

Bounties

THE FOX BOUNTY - CONTROL OR COINCIDENCE? David A. Arnold. Mich. Cons., 21 (4): 28-31, July-Aug., 1952.

COYOTES AND THE LUXURY TAX. Elliott S. Barker. New Mexico Mag., Santa Fe, vol.23, no.4, pp.21-22, May, 1945.

THE COYOTE BOUNTY SYSTEM IN MISSOURI, 1936-1947. Rudolf Bennitt. Trans. N.A. Wildl. Conf., 13: 314-321, 1948.

THE FOX BOUNTY QUESTION AGAIN. G. W. Bradt. Mich. Cons., 12 (3): 4-5, Apr., 1943.

WOLF! WOLF! HAS ONTARIO JUST WASTED MONEY IN PAYING WOLF BOUNTY? YES, SAYS THIS BIOLOGIST. HERE IS FOOD FOR THOUGHT FOR EVERY CONSERVATIONIST--AND FOR ACTION! Ewart C. Cross. Rod and Gun in Canada, Montreal, vol.38, no.8, pp. 18-19, 32-33, maps 3, Jan., 1937.

REVIVAL OF THE BOUNTY QUESTION. Charles A. Dambach. Wilson Bull., Ann Arbor, vol.57, no.2, p.136, June, 1945.

NECESSITY FOR UNIFORM BOUNTIES ON PREDATORS. Kenneth F. MacDonald. Calif. Fish and Game, 23 (1): 66-67, Jan., 1937.

THE BOUNTY SYSTEM IN ONTARIO. D.N. Omand. MA thesis, Univ. Toronto, 1946; Jour. Wildl. Mgt., 14 (4): 425-434, Oct., 1950.

RED FOXES AND THE BOUNTY. S. V. Sedlak. Pennsylvania Game News, Harrisburg, vol.15, no.2, pp.9, 30, illus., May, 1944.

EXAMINATION OF A STATE FOX BOUNTY. D. F. Switzenberg. Jour. Wildl. Mgt., 15 (3): 288-299, July, 1951.

A LOOK AT THE FOX BOUNTY. D. F. Switzenberg. Mich. Cons., 19 (1): 3-6, Jan.-Feb., 1950.

THE VALUE OF THE TIMBER WOLF BOUNTY SYSTEMS TO NORTHERN ONTARIO. A. de Vos. Sylva, 5 (1): 15-23, Jan.-Feb., 1949.

COMMISSION PLACES $3 BOUNTY ON GRAY FOXES. West Virginia Conservation, Charleston, vol.9, no.11, pp.4, 15-16, Feb., 1946.

COYOTE BOUNTIES. New York Conservation Dept., N.Y. State Cons., 6 (4): 34, Feb.-Mar., 1952.

THE FOX AND THE BOUNTY QUESTION. Iowa Conservationist, Des Moines, vol.5, no.3, pp.17, 20, illus., Mar.15, 1946.

Canada

THE NEWFOUNDLAND WOLF. Glover M. Allen, Thomas Barbour. Jour. Mam., vol. 18, no.2, pp.229-234, illus., May 14, 1937.

SUMMARY OF THE LARGE WOLVES OF CANADA, WITH DESCRIPTION OF THREE NEW ARCTIC RACES. Rudolph Martin Anderson. Jour. Mam., vol.24, no.3, pp. 386-393, Aug.17, 1943.

POPULATION CYCLES AND COLOR PHASE GENETICS OF THE COLORED FOX IN QUEBEC. L. Butler. Canadian Jour. Zool., Ottawa, vol.29, no.1, pp.24-41, Feb., 1951.

ARCTIC FOX ON CAPE BRETON ISLAND. Austin W. Cameron. Canadian Field-Nat., Ottawa, vol.65, no.4, p.154, July-Aug., 1950.

THE TIMBER WOLF IN THE ROCKY MOUNTAIN NATIONAL PARKS OF CANADA. I. McT. Cowan. Can. Jour. Res., Sec.D, 25 (5): 139-174, Oct., 1947.

THE COYOTE IN MANITOBA. N. Criddle, E. Criddle. Canadian Field Nat., vol.37, pp.41-45, Mar., 1923.

ARCTIC FOX SHOT IN CAPE BRETON. J. L. DeVany. Canadian Field Nat., vol. 37, p.118, Sept., 1923.

THE HISTORY OF THE GRAY FOX IN ONTARIO. S. C. Downing. Can. Field Nat., 60 (2): 45-46, Mar.-Apr., 1946.

REPORT ON WOLVES FOLLOWED DURING FEBRUARY AND MARCH, 1939. (TIMBER WOLVES.) A. L. Dunne. Canadian Field Nat., Ottawa, vol.53, no.8, pp.117-118, Nov., 1939.

ARCTIC FOX (ALOPEX LAGOPUS) AT CHURCHILL, MANITOBA. Bristol Foster. Ontario Field Biologist, Toronto, no.9, pp. 17-19, illus., May, 1955.

THE WOLVES OF BANFF NATIONAL PARK. H. U. Green. Can. Dept. Resources and Development, Natl. Park Branch, p.47, July, 1951.

THE STRANGE "DOG" OF FORT SELKIRK. (WOLF.) John Gregg. Beaver, Winnipeg, outfit 273, p.31, illus., Mar., 1943.

A WOLF RECORD FROM THE WINNIPEG AREA. Burt Gresham. Canadian Field Nat., vol.52, no.2, p.29, Feb., 1938.

THE INFLUX OF THE RED FOX AND ITS COLOUR PHASES INTO THE BARREN LANDS. Donald B. Marsh. Canadian Field Nat., vol.52, no.4, pp.60-61, Apr., 1938.

THE GRAY FOX IN ALBERTA. J. E. Moore. Jour. Mam., vol.33, no.2, p.253, May 16, 1952.

EARLY RECORDS OF THE RED AND THE GRAY FOX IN ONTARIO. R. L. Peterson, R. O. Standfield, E. H. McEwen, A. C. Brooks. Jour. Mam., vol.34, 1, pp.126-127, Feb.19, 1953.

(RED FOX VULPES FULVA FULVA (DESMAREST) AND ITS ECOLOGIC AND ECONOMIC INFLUENCE DURING FALL IN ONE PART OF MONTREAL ISLAND.) Le renard roux Vulpes fulva fulva (Desmarest) et son influence econogique et economique durant la Saison Hivernale sur une partie de L'Ile de Montreal. Lionel Philippe. Le Naturaliste Canadien, 77 (1-2): 5-43, Jan.-Feb., 1950.

THREE YEARS IN THE WOLVES' WILDERNESS. (CANADA.) John F. Stanwell-Fletcher. Nat. Hist., New York, vol.49, no.3, pp.136-147, illus., Mar., 1942.

WHERE IS THE KIT FOX? R. D. Symons. Blue Jay, Saskatchewan Nat. Hist. Soc., 14 (2): 63-65, June, 1956.

TIMBER WOLF MOVEMENTS ON SIBLEY PENINSULA, ONTARIO. A. de Vos. Jour. Mam., vol.31, no.2, pp.169-175, fig.1, May 25, 1950.

ARCHAEOLOGICAL EVIDENCE CONCERNING THE PRESENCE OF THE GRAY FOX

(UROCYON SP.) IN ONTARIO. W. J. Wintemberg. Canadian Field Nat., vol.35, pp.19-20, Jan. (June 8), 1921.

VICIOUS BLACK WOLVES ON PROWL IN MANITOBA. Rod and Gun in Canada, Montreal, vol.48, no.9, p.5, 1947.

Control

DIRECTIONS FOR THE DESTRUCTION OF WOLVES AND COYOTES. Vernon Bailey. U.S. Dept. Agric., Biol. Survey Cir.no. 55, pp.1-6, Mar.13, 1907.

HUNTING DOWN STOCK KILLERS. W. B. Bell. Yearbook, U.S. Dept. Agric., 1920, Separate no.845, pp.289-300, illus., 1921.

WOLF AND COYOTE CONTROL. W. B. Bell. The Producer (Denver), vol.7, no.9, pp.3-4; no.10, pp.6-8, Feb.-Mar., 1926.

CONTROLLING PREDATORS. (FOX.) Henry P. Bridges. Pennsylvania Game News, Harrisburg, vol.17, no.5, pp.8-9, 28, Aug., 1946.

COMPARISON OF COYOTE TRAPPING METHODS. William Casto, Clifford C. Presnall. Jour. Wildlife Mgt., Menasha, vol.8, no.1, pp.65-70, Jan., 1944.

NEW YORK'S COYOTE CONTROL PROBLEM. Greenleaf Chase. New York State Cons., 4 (3): 14-15, Dec.-Jan., 1949-50.

(HUNTING THE WOLF IN PERU.) Le caza de lobos en el Peru. Roberto E. Coker. Bol. Compania Admin. Guano, Lima, Peru, vol.9, no.8, pp.223-245, figs.4, Aug., 1933.

THE CONTROL OF WOLVES AND COYOTES. I. McT. Cowan. Conv. Internat. Assn. Game, Fish and Cons. Comm., 39: 49-57, 1949.

CONTROL OF THE COYOTE IN CALIFORNIA. Joseph Dixon. Univ. Calif. Exper. Station Bull.no.320, pp.379-397, Apr., 1920.

COYOTE PUP HUNTING. W. B. Elley. South Dakota Conservation Digest, Pierre, vol.12, no.5, pp.13, 16, May, 1945.

MANAGEMENT OF THE RED FOX IN IOWA. Paul L. Errington. Amer. Wildl. 26 (2): 24, 30-31, Mar.-Apr., 1937; Pennsylvania Game News, vol.9, no.7, pp. 12, 31, illus., Oct., 1938.

WOLF CONTROL OPERATIONS, WOOD BUFFALO NATIONAL PARK, 1951-52. W. A. Fuller, N. S. Novakowski. Can. Wildl. Serv., Wildl. Mgt. Bull. Ser.1, no.11, pp.ii, 23, illus., 1955.

HUNTING WOLVES WITH AN AIRPLANE. Lew L. Gourley. Fur-Fish-Game (Harding's Mag.), Columbus, vol.79, no.11, pp. 12-13, illus., Nov., 1945.

COYOTE CONTROL. R. M. Graham. Jour. For., 52 (6): 451, June, 1954.

SUGGESTIONS ON TRAPPING COYOTES AND WOLVES IN ALASKA. Harlan H. Gubser. U.S. Dept. Agric., Biol. Surv., Wildlife Research and Mgt. Leaflet Bs-62, pp.6, Aug., 1936.

METHODS OF COYOTE CONTROL IN KANSAS. William F. Gusey. Master's thesis, Kans. State Coll., 1952.

THE COYOTE AND HIS CONTROL. E. Raymond Hall. California Fish and Game, Sacramento, vol.17, no.3, pp.1-8, figs.88-89, July, 1931; Outdoor Life, vol.73, no.4, Apr., pp.30-32, Mar., 1934.

THE CONTROL OF THE COYOTE. W. C. Henderson. Jour. Mam., vol.11, no.3, pp. 336-350, Aug., 1930.

(Comments by A.K. Fisher on) THE CONTROL OF THE COYOTE. W.C. Henderson. Jour. Mamm., vol.11, no.3, p.352, Aug., 1930.

(Comments by E. A. Goldman on) THE CONTROL OF THE COYOTE. W.C. Henderson. Jour. Mamm., vol.11, no.3, p.351, Aug., 1930.

(Comments by A.R. Shadle on) THE CONTROL OF THE COYOTE. W.C. Henderson. Jour. Mamm., vol.11, no.3, p.352, Aug., 1930.

(Comments by T.I. Storer on) THE CONTROL OF THE COYOTE. W.C.Henderson. Jour. Mamm., vol.11, no.3, p.352, Aug., 1930.

EL VALLE DE LA TRINIDAD, THE COYOTE POISONER'S PROVING GROUND. Lawrence M. Huey. Jour. Mam., vol.18, no.1, pp.74-76, Feb.14, 1937.

COYOTE CONTROL METHODS. C. A. Hurd. Colo. Cons. Comments, 8 (3): 9-10, Sept., 1945.

WOLF TRAPPER. J. H. Kimberly. Sylva, Toronto, vol.4, no.3, p.23, illus., 1948.

COYOTE HUNT AT GETTYSBURG. E.R. Lamster. South Dakota Conservation Digest, Pierre, vol.12, no.1, pp.11, 15, illus., Jan., 1945.

COURSING THE PRAIRIE WOLF. J. A. McGuire. Outdoor Life, Denver, vol.23, no.4, pp.314-323, illus., Apr., 1909.

PURSUIT OF THE PRAIRIE WOLF. Louis T. McKim. Forest and Outdoors, Montreal, vol.13, p.17, 1947.

COYOTE ROUND-UP. Juanita Mahaffey. Okla. Game and Fish News, 1 (2): 4-6, 17, Jan., 1946.

HOW TO CONTROL THE FOX POPULATION. Tauno V. Maeki. Suomen Riista 6: 136-148, 192, illus., 1951 (1952).

BIG GAME HUNTING IN THE WILD WEST. IV. WOLVES. Randolph B. Marcy. Outing, Albany, vol.11, no.4, pp.291-299, illus., Jan., 1888.

COYOTES ARE SPORT TO THEM. William Noland. Missouri Conserv., Jefferson City, vol.9, no.1, p.12, illus., May, 1948.

TRY COYOTES. Clyde Ormond. Field and Stream, New York, vol.49, no.10, pp.24-25, 94-95, illus., Feb., 1945.

THE TRICKS OF TRAPPING WOLVES. B. G. Roberts. Forest and Outdoors, 35 (11): 340-341, Nov., 1939.

DEN HUNTING AS A MEANS OF FOX CONTROL. Milton O. Robinson. N. Dak. Agr. Coll., Ext. Serv., Spec. Cir. A-72, p.6, Apr., 1944.

COYOTE CONTROL WITH COMPOUND 1080 STATIONS IN NATIONAL FORESTS. Weldon B. Robinson. Jour. For., 51 (12): 880-885, Dec., 1953.

THE "HUMANE COYOTE-GETTER" VS. THE STEEL TRAP IN CONTROL OF PREDATORY ANIMALS. Weldon B. Robinson. Jour. Wildl. Mgt., 7 (2): 179-189, Apr., 1943.

THALLIUM AND COMPOUND 1080 IMPREGNATED STATIONS IN COYOTE CONTROL. Weldon B. Robinson. Jour. Wildlife Mgt., Menasha, vol.12, no.3, pp. 279-295, July, 1948.

ANOTHER VIEW OF COYOTE CONTROL. William M. Rush. Natl. Wool Grower, 29 (11): 13-14, 30-31, Nov., 1939.

CONTROLLING COYOTE AND FOX DAMAGE ON THE FARM. Frank W. Sampson, W. O. Nagel. Mo. Cons. Comm., Bull.18, pp.22, 1949.

HUNT THEM IN SEPTEMBER. (WOLVES.) C. R. Snow. Alaska Sportsman, Ketchikan, vol.13, no.9, pp.28-29, 38-41, illus., Sept., 1947.

NORTH FLORIDA'S WAR ON FOXES. Bill Snyder. Florida Wildlife, Tallahassee, vol.2, no.1, pp.8-9, illus., June, 1948.

A FOOT IN A TRAP--A HEAD IN A SNARE. (WOLF.) Otis H. Speer. Alaska Sportsman, Ketchikan, vol.10, no.1, pp.12-13, 28-29, illus., Jan., 1944.

RAIDING THE SOUTH AFRICAN JACKAL. W. L. Speight. Field, London, vol.153, p.724, illus., May 2, 1929.

FOX AND COYOTE TRAPPING SIMPLIFIED. A. M. Stebler. Michigan Dept. Conservation, Lansing, pp.15, 1944.

CONTROL OF THE COYOTE IN CALIFORNIA. Walter P. Taylor. Joseph Dixon. Jour. Mam., vol.2, no.3, pp.176-177, Aug., 1921.

WESTERN SPOT TRAPPING. (COYOTES.) Raymond Thompson. Outdoorsman, Chicago, vol.86, no.1, whole no.506, pp. 16-17, 33, illus., Jan.-Feb., 1944.

TIMBER WOLF. (METHODS OF TRAPPING.) A. F. Wallace. Wisconsin Conservationist, vol.3, no.6, p.11, Jan. (March), 1922.

COYOTES VIA AIRPLANE AND ROUND-UP. NOVEL METHODS OF HUNTING THE MARAUDER OF THE PLAINS. Waldo Willhoft. Forest and Stream, vol.98, pp. 338-339, 370-372, illus., June, 1928.

HINTS ON WOLF AND COYOTE TRAPPING. Stanley P. Young. Leaflet no.59, U.S. Dept. Agric., pp.8, figs.3, July, 1930; USDI, F and WS, Cir.2, p.8, 1941.

THE STEEL WOLF TRAP IN NORTH AMERICA. Stanley P. Young. W. Sportsman, 6 (3): 10-11, 30-31, Feb., 1941.

THE WAR ON THE WOLF. Stanley P. Young. Amer. Forests, 48 (11): 552-555, 572-574, Dec., 1942.

COYOTE CONTROL BY MEANS OF DEN HUNTING. Stanley P. Young, Harold W. Dobyns. U.S. Dept. Interior, Fish and Wildlife Serv., Wash., Circ.no.7, pp.8, illus., 1945.

DEN HUNTING AS A MEANS OF COYOTE CONTROL. Stanley P. Young, Harold W. Dobyns. U.S. Dept. Agric. leaflet 132, pp.1-8, figs.2, Oct., 1937.

AMERICA'S LONGEST WAR: THE BATTLE WITH THE WOLVES. Fred R. Zepp. Outdoor Life, New York, vol.101, no.5, pp.38-41, 118-120, illus., May, 1948.

CYANIDE GUN USED TO CONTROL COYOTES IN OTHER STATES. N. Dak. Outdoors, 6 (6): 4-6, Dec., 1943.

DOGS REPLACE GUNS AS WEAPON IN COYOTE HUNTING. Nebraska Game, Forestation, and Parks Comm., Outdoor Nebr., 30 (2): 12-13, illus., Spring, 1952.

HUNTING COYOTES FROM AEROPLANES A THRILLING SPORT! South Dakota Conservation Digest, Pierre, vol.9, no.3, p.9, illus., Mar., 1942.

PRACTICAL PREDATOR CONTROL, FEATURING COYOTE TRAPPING. N. Mex. Dept. Game and Fish, pp.16, 1936.

A STUDY OF FOX CONTROL AS A MEANS OF INCREASING PHEASANT ABUNDANCE. New York Conservation Dept., New York Cons. Dept., Res. Ser. no.3, pp.1-22, maps, 1951.

Cytology

GERM CELL STUDIES IN THE MALE FOX (VULPES FULVA). David W. Bishop. Anat. Record, Phila., vol.84, no.2, pp. 99-115, pls.4, Oct.26, 1942.

OXYGEN CONSUMPTION OF FOX SPERM. David W. Bishop. Biol. Bull., Lancaster, vol.83, no.3, pp.353-362, figs.4, Dec., 1942.

INDIVIDUAL SPECIFICITY OF DOG SERUM AND PLASMA. Norman E. Freeman, A. E. Schecter. Science, Lancaster, n.s., vol. 96, no.2480, p.39, July 10, 1942.

ON THE BLOOD GROUP SUBSTANCE OF A RACCOON-DOG. Tanemoto Furuhata, Kokugi Ro. Proc. Japan Acad., vol.23, no. 11, pp.153-156, Dec.12, 1947.

A CYTOLOGICAL STUDY OF THE ANTERIOR HYPOPHYSIS OF THE DOG WITH PARTICULAR REFERENCE TO THE PRESENCE OF A FOURTH CELL TYPE. J. Francis Hartmann, W. R. Fain, J. M. Wolfe. Anat. Record, Phila., vol.95, no. 1, pp.11-27, pl.1, May, 1946.

A GRAPHICAL STUDY OF THE BLOOD OF NORMAL FOXES. Arnold H. Kennedy. Canadian Jour. Research, vol.12, no.6, pp. 796-802, June, 1935.

THE BLOOD PICTURE OF MATURE NORMAL DOGS. J. Walter Landsberg. Anat. Record, Phila., vol.84, no.4, pp. 415-421, Dec.26, 1942.

QUANTITATIVE STUDIES ON THE BLOOD AND BONE MARROW OF NEWBORN MONGREL PUPPIES. R.M. Mulligan. Anat. Record, Phila., vol.91, no.2, pp.161-167, Feb., 1945.

(CONTRIBUTION TO THE DETERMINATION OF THE NUMBER OF OVA IN VARIOUS AGE PERIODS OF THE BITCH.) Beitrag zur Feststellung der Eianzahl in verschiedenen Altersperioden der Huendin. A. Schotterer. Anat. Anzeiger, vol.65, pp.177-192, Apr.30, 1928.

CHROMOSOMES OF THE RED FOX. Louise Wipf, Richard M. Shackelford. Proc. Nat. Acad. Sci., Wash., D.C., vol.28, no.7, pp.265-268, figs.5, July 15, 1942.

Diseases (Except Rabies)

INCIDENCE OF LEPTOSPIROSUS AMONG DOGS IN HONOLULU AS DETERMINED BY SEROLOGICAL AGGLUTINATION TESTS. Joseph E. Alicata, Virginia Breaks. Jour. Wash. Acad. Sci., vol.32, no.10, pp.305-308, Oct.15, 1942.

HISTOLOGIC ADAPTATION OF THE VIRUS OF FOX ENCEPHALITIS. J.C. Barton, R.G. Green. Amer. Jour. Hygiene, 37 (1): 21-36, Jan., 1943.

ENCEPHALITIS (?) IN RED FOX IN SOUTHWESTERN OHIO. Hubert Bezdek. Jour. Mam., vol.23, no.1, p.98, Feb.14, 1942.

(DIAPHRAGMATIC HERNIA IN THE DOG.) Hernia diaphragmatica beim Hunde. A.P. Bystrow. Anat. Anz., vol.70, nos.8-10, pp.192-212, figs.7, 1930.

CONTROL OF DISEASES OF FOXES. C.L. Campbell. Nat. Fur News, Denver, vol.17, no.2, pp.7, 14-15, 22-23, Mar., 1945.

ARTHRITIS AMONG WOLVES. E. C. Cross. Canadian Field Nat., Ottawa, vol. 54, no.1, pp.2-4, Jan., 1940.

SO-CALLED SALMON POISONING OF DOGS. C. R. Donham. Science, vol.61, p.341, Mar.27, 1925.

EPIDEMICS AMONG SLEDGE DOGS IN THE CANADIAN ARCTIC AND THEIR RELATION TO DISEASE IN THE ARCTIC FOX. Charles Elton. Canadian Jour. Res., Nat. Res. Council Canada, vol.5, no.6, pp.673-692, map, 1931.

CHASTEK PARALYSIS. R.G. Green. Amer. Fur Breeder, vol.11, no.1, pp.4, 5, 6, photo, table, July, 1938.

CHASTEK PARALYSIS IN NURSING FOX PUPS. R.G. Green. Amer. Fur Breeder, vol.11, no.3, pp.6, 8, illus., Sept., 1938.

CONTROL OF DISTEMPER IN FOXES. Robert G. Green. Fur of Canada, Winnipeg, vol.10, no.8, pp.10, 18-19, May, 1945; Nat. Fur News, Denver, vol.17, no.7, pp. 6, 20-21, July, 1945.

EPIZOOTIC ENCEPHALITIS OF FOXES. II. GENERAL CONSIDERATION OF FUR-RANGE EPIZOOTICS. R.G. Green. Amer. Jour. Hygiene, vol.13, no.1, pp.201-223, Jan., 1931.

THE ETIOLOGY OF CANINE DISTEMPER. R.G. Green. Science, vol.62, pp.133-134, Aug.7, 1925.

FOX ENCEPHALITIS. R.G. Green. Veterinary Medicine, Chicago, vol.31, no.12, pp.1-5, figs.8, Dec., 1936.

A DEFICIENCY DISEASE OF FOXES PRODUCED BY FEEDING FISH. R.G. Green, W. E. Carlson, C.A. Evans. Amer. Fur Breeder, Duluth, vol.14, no.6, pp.28, 30, 31; no.7, pp.24, 26; no.8, pp.22-23, Dec., 1941; Jan., Feb., 1942.

A COMPARATIVE STUDY OF DISTEMPER INCLUSIONS. R.G. Green, C.A. Evans. Amer. Jour. Hygiene, 29 (2): 73-87, Mar., 1939.

A DEFICIENCY DISEASE OF FOXES. R.G. Green, C.A. Evans. Science, 92 (2381): 154-155, Aug.16, 1940.

RAPID DIAGNOSIS OF CANINE DISTEMPER. R.G. Green, C.A. Evans. Amer. Fur Breeder, Duluth, vol.11, no.10, pp.10, 12-14, figs.2, photo, Apr., 1939; Cornell Vet., 29 (1): 35-40, Jan., 1939.

EPIZOOTIC FOX ENCEPHALITIS. I. GENERAL DESCRIPTION. R.G. Green, N.R. Ziegler, B.B. Green, E.T. Dewey. Amer. Jour. Hygiene, vol.12, no.1, pp. 109-129, figs.13, July, 1930.

EPIZOOTIC FOX ENCEPHALITIS. IV. THE INTRANUCLEAR INCLUSIONS. R.G. Green, M.S. Katter, J.E. Shillinger, K.B. Hanson. Amer. Jour. Hygiene, vol.18, no. 2, pp.462-481, figs.13, Sept., 1933.

EPIZOOTIC FOX ENCEPHALITIS. V. GENERAL AND PATHOGENIC PROPERTIES OF THE VIRUS. R.G. Green, W.E. Ziegler, W.E. Carlson, J.E. Shillinger, S.H. Tyler, E.T. Dewey. Amer. Jour. Hygiene, vol.19, no.2, pp.343-361, Mar., 1934.

EPIZOOTIC FOX ENCEPHALITIS. VI. A DESCRIPTION OF THE EXPERIMENTAL INFECTION IN DOGS. R.G. Green, J.E. Shillinger. Amer. Jour. Hygiene, vol.19, no.2, pp.362-391, figs.1-10, Mar., 1934.

EPIZOOTIC FOX ENCEPHALITIS. VII. NATURE OF THE IMMUNITY. R.G. Green, N.R. Zeigler, B.B. Green, J.E. Shillinger, E.T. Dewey, W.E. Carlson. Amer. Jour. Hygiene, Balto., Md., vol.21, no.2, pp.366-388, Mar., 1935.

EPIZOOTIC FOX ENCEPHALITIS. VIII. THE OCCURRENCE OF THE VIRUS IN THE UPPER RESPIRATORY TRACT IN NATURAL AND EXPERIMENTAL INFECTIONS. R.G. Green, B.B. Green, W.E. Carlson, J.E. Shillinger. Amer. Jour. Hygiene, Balto., vol.24, no.1, pp.57-70, figs.3, July, 1936.

SUSCEPTIBILITY OF THE GRAY FOX TO FOX ENCEPHALITIS. R.G. Green, C.S. Stulberg. Proc. Soc. Exper. Biol. and Med., Utica, vol.64, no.4, pp.450-452, Apr., 1947.

CONTROL OF EARMITE DISEASE. (FOXES.) C.K. Gunn. Fur of Canada, Winnipeg, vol. 9, no.8, p.18, May, 1944.

PRELIMINARY NOTE ON THE TREATMENT OF ANEMIA IN MUTANT FOX PUPS. C.K. Gunn. Fur of Canada, Winnipeg, vol.10, no.5, pp.14-15, illus., Feb., 1945.

TREATMENT OF ANAEMIA IN MUTANT FOX PUPS. C.K. Gunn. Nat. Fur News, Denver, vol.17, no.3, pp.8, 15, 26, Apr., 1945.

CRITICAL TESTS OF TETRACHLORETHYLENE AS AN ANTHELMINTHIC FOR FOXES. Karl B. Hanson. Jour. Agric. Research, vol.34, pp.129-136, Jan.15, 1927.

EAR MANGE IN FOXES. Karl B. Hanson. Amer. Fur Breeder, vol.11, no.3, p.13, Sept., 1929.

ON THE BASE FOR THE DEVELOPMENT OF DIABETES AND THE CHIEF TYPES OF THIS DISEASE (WITH A FEW REMARKS AS TO CERTAIN CHANGES OF THE PANCREAS IN DOGS). K.A. Heiberg. Nord. Med. Ariv., Stockholm, Avd.2, (Arkiv foer inre medicin), vol.50, pt.6, no.14, pp.663-670, 1918.

THE TREATMENT OF ASCARIASIS IN DOGS WITH 1-DIETHYLCARBAMYL-4-METHYLPIPERAZINE HYDROCHLORIDE. Redginal Hewitt, Wyeth White, E. White, Y. Subbarow. Jour. Parasitol., Lancaster, vol. 34, no.3, pp.237-239, June, 1948.

RENAL HYPERLIPEMIA IN DOGS. Walter Heymann. Science, Lancaster, n.s., vol. 96, no.2485, pp.163-164, figs.2, Aug.14, 1942.

ON THE PERIODIC IMMUNITY OF FOXES TO ENCEPHALITIS. Yu A. Isakov. Bull. de la Societe des Naturalistes de Moscou, Sect. Biol., vol.50, no.3-4, pp.72-79, 1945.

A STUDY OF CANINE ENCEPHALITIS. G.A. Jervis, T.R. James, R.L. Burknart, G.C. Poppensiek. Amer. Jour. Hyg., Balto., vol.51, no.1, pp.63-75, Jan., 1950.

COCCIDIA AND THE FOX. H.B. Kellogg, Jr. Wis. Sportsman, 2 (8): 2, May, 1938.

THE DIFFERENTIAL BLOOD CHANGES IN ASCARIASIS IN FOXES. Arnold H. Kennedy, Ronald G. Law. Canadian Jour. Research, vol.12, no.3, pp.277-285, Mar., 1935.

TRICHINOSIS IN DOGS OF THE CANADIAN NORTH. E. Kuitunen-Ekbaum, Zoe W. Fleming. Canadian Jour. Pub. Health, Toronto, vol.40, no.12, pp.514-515, Dec., 1949.

REPORT OF CASE OF TULARAEMIA CONTRACTED FROM A COYOTE (CANIS LESTES) IN NEW MEXICO. G.M. Kunkel. Public Health Reports, vol.45, no.9, pp. 439-440, Feb.28, 1930.

SARCOPTIC MANGE IN A WILD RED FOX. E.K. Ledune. Amer. Fur Breeder, vol.11, no.1, p.38, July, 1938.

ENZOOTIC JAUNDICE (YELLOWS) IN DOGS. C.C. Okell, T. Dalling, L.P. Pugh. Veterinary Record, London, vol.4, no.48, p.1002, Nov.29, 1924.

LEPTOSPIRAL JAUNDICE IN DOGS (YELLOWS). C.C. Okell, T. Dalling, L.P. Pugh. Veterinary Jour., vol.81, no.1, pp. 1-35, figs.2, 1925.

SARCOPTIC MANGE IN THE RED FOX IN OHIO. John R. Olive, Charles V. Riley. Jour. Mam., 29 (1): 73-74, Feb., 1948.

TREATMENT OF FOX DISTEMPER. George L. Ott, Jr. Jour. Amer. Vet. Med. Assn., 47 (5): 522-525, May, 1939.

DISTEMPER AT WHELPING TIME. George L. Ott, A.M. McDermid. Amer. Fur Breeder, Duluth, vol.19, no.5, pp.14, 18, Nov., 1946.

BOTULISM IN FOXES. Norman J. Pyle, Richard M. Brown. Jour. Amer. Vet. Med. Assn., 94 (4): 436-439, Apr., 1939.

SARCOPTIC MANGE IN WILD FOXES IN PENNSYLVANIA. Lorenzo B. Pryor. Jour. Mam., 37 (1): 90-93, table 1, figs.2, Feb. 28, 1956.

FIELD INVESTIGATIONS OF PROPHYLAXIS AGAINST EPIZOOTIC DISTEMPER IN ARCTIC SLED DOGS. K.R. Reinhard, R.L. Rausch, R.L. Gray. Proceedings Book, 92nd Ann. Meeting Amer. Vet. Med. Assoc., pp.223-226, 1955.

CARCINOMA OF THE TONSIL IN A COMMON WOLF (CANIS LUPUS). H. Harold Scott. Proc. Zool. Soc. Lond., pt.1, pp. 43-47, pls.1-3, Apr., 1928.

ULCERS IN STOMACHS OF RANCH FOXES. J. E. Shillinger. Jour. Amer. Veterinary Med. Assoc., vol.27, no.6, pp. 536-537, May, 1929.

A NERVOUS DISEASE AMONG FOXES. (IN ENGLAND.) George Tickner. Jour. Animal Ecology, vol.1, no.1, pp.83-84, May, 1932.

HEMOLYTIC DISEASE IN NEWBORN DOGS FOLLOWING ISOIMMUNIZATION OF THE DAM BY TRANSFUSION. Lawrence E. Young, et al. Science, Lancaster, vol.109, no.2843, pp.630-631, June 24, 1949.

A DEFICIENCY DISEASE IN FOXES. Jour. Amer. Med. Assoc., Chicago, vol.116, no. 3, pp.234-235, Jan.18, 1941.

FOX ENCEPHALITIS AND CANINE DISTEMPER ARE NOT ALIKE. Amer. Fur Breeder, vol.2, no.8, p.14, Feb., 1930.

Domesticated Canids

DOGS AND THEIR BREEDS. Jack Baird. Ohio Conserv. Bull., Columbus, vol.11, no.9, pp.4-5, illus., Sept., 1947.

A FOX AS A HOUSE GUEST. Ernest H. Baynes. Nature Mag., vol.1, no.4, pp.10-13, Apr., 1923.

(THE DOMESTIC DOG IN THE PALAEARCTIC.) Haushunde des Palaearctis. A. Brauner. Mem. Soc. Nat. d'Odessa, vol. 44, pp.321-340, tables 4, 1928.

A WILD DOG TAMED. (DINGO.) Maurice Burton. Illus. London News, vol. 214, no.5735, p.380, illus., Mar.19, 1949.

BREEDING, TRAINING, MANAGEMENT, DISEASES, AND CARE OF DOGS: TOGETHER WITH AN EASY AND AGREEABLE

METHOD OF INSTRUCTING ALL BREEDS OF DOGS IN A GREAT VARIETY OF AMUSING AND USEFUL PERFORMANCES. INCLUDING THIRTY-ONE ILLUSTRATIONS OF THE DIFFERENT BREEDS OF DOGS, POETICALLY DESCRIBED. Francis Butler. 5th ed. , rev. and enl., with an appendix, Brooklyn, D.S. Holmes, pp.406, pl.6, illus., 1877.

A DAY WITH PURE-BRED OTTER-HOUNDS. Robert Colville. Field, London, vol.174, no.4522, pp.500-501, illus., Aug.26, 1939.

THE DOG AS A DETECTIVE. W. Craig. Sci. Monthly, vol.18, pp.38-47, 1924.

STAREEK: THE STORY OF A SLEDGE DOG. Frank Debenham. Polar Record, Cambridge, vol.4, no.25, pp.19-24, Jan., 1943.

TOY DOGS; THEIR ORIGIN, DIFFERENT BREEDS, HOW TO SELECT, BREED AND MANAGE THEM, TOGETHER WITH THEIR DISEASES AND SYMPTOMS, WITH REMEDIES FOR THE SAME BY HOMOEOPATHIC AND ALLOPATHIC TREATMENTS. John E. Diehl. Phila, Pa., The Associated Fanciers, pp.5-76, illus., 1899.

A STALWART PARIAH DOG. J. A. Duke. Jour. Bombay Nat. Hist. Soc., vol.33, no. 2, pp.428-430, Feb.15, 1929.

A TAME RED FOX CUB. James S. Findley. Jour. Mam., vol.32, no.1, p.117, Feb.15, 1951.

(DOMESTIC DOGS.) Haushunde. Werner Fischel. Handbuch der Zoologie, Berlin, vol.8, pt.10, no.16, pp.1-16, 1956.

(RACES OF THE TAME DOG.) Die Racen des zahmen Hundes. L. J. Fitzinger. Sitz.-Ber. math.-naturw. cl. Akad. Wiss., Wien, vol.56, pt.1, pp.377-507, 1867.

RETRIEVER DOGS: THE GOLDEN. C.H. Hammes. South Dakota Conserv. Digest, Pierre, vol.15, no.4, p.3, Apr., 1948.

RETRIEVER DOGS: THE SPORTSMAN'S PAL. (LABRADOR AND CHESAPEAKE RETRIEVERS.) C.H. Hammes. South Dakota Conserv. Digest, Pierre, vol.15, no.3, pp.1, 11, illus., Mar., 1948.

THE DOG. Henry William Herbert. Dinks (pseud.), Mayhew and Hutchinson, Comp., abridged, ed., and illus. by Frank Forester, complete and rev. ed., New York, W. A. Townsend, pp.663, illus., pls., 1866.

DOGS. Max Hilzheimer. Antiquity, vol.6, no.24, pp.411-419, pls.1-12, Dec., 1932.

MY DOG AND I; BEING A CONCISE TREATISE OF THE VARIOUS BREEDS OF DOGS, THEIR ORIGIN AND USES. WRITTEN EXPRESSLY FOR THE NOVICE, CONTAINING A COMPREHENSIVE MODE OF TREATMENT BOTH IN HEALTH AND SICKNESS, TOGETHER WITH THE NAMES OF SOME PROMINENT BREEDERS. Harry Woodworth Huntington. Illustrated with half-tones of typical dogs, original marginal illus. by Neville Cain, New York Pub. by Caxton Press, pp.141, illus., 1897.

TERRIER DOGS: SHOWING THE BEST METHODS OF BREEDING, REARING, FEEDING, CROPPING, PHYSICING, CURE OF DISEASES, ETC. ...ALSO, RATS AND RAT KILLING ... TOGETHER WITH THE ART OF LEARNING DOGS TRICKS. AND TRAINING FOR FIELD SPORTS. Ed. James. Illus. with 40 original engravings. New York, E. James, pp.72, front., pls., 1873.

A HARE INDIAN DOG. D. Jenness. Canadian Field Nat., vol.51, no.4, pp.47-50, figs.5, Apr., 1937.

GUN DOG BOOKS. Herbert Kendrick. Pa. Game News, 25 (5): 59-60, May, 1954.

FLEECE-BEARING DOGS. Douglas Leechman. Nature Mag., vol.14, no.3, pp.177-178, figs.3, Sept., 1929.

MAN'S OLDEST ALLY, THE DOG. SINCE CAVE-DWELLER DAYS THIS FAITHFUL FRIEND HAS SHARED THE WORK, EXPLORATION, AND SPORT OF HUMANKIND. Freeman Lloyd. Nat. Geogr. Mag., vol.69, no.2, pp.247-274, illus., Feb., 1936.

NON-SPORTING DOGS. Freeman Lloyd. Nat. Geogr. Mag., Wash., D.C., vol. 84, no.5, pp.569-588, col. pls.8, illus., Nov., 1943.

WORKING DOGS OF THE WORLD. Freeman Lloyd. Nat. Geogr. Mag., Wash., vol.80, no.6, pp.775-806, illus., 20 paintings from life by Edward Herbert Miner, Dec., 1941.

MAN MEETS DOG. Konrad Z. Lorenz. (A loving study of the canine personality, a valuable work on animal behavior.) Boston, pp.221, illus., 1955.

THE ENGLISH SETTER. J. H. Lytle. Nature Mag., vol.5, pp.145-147, Mar., 1925.

THE POINTER. J. H. Lytle. Nature Mag., vol.5, pp.374-376, illus., June, 1925.

THE DEERHOUND IN AMERICA. George Macdougall. California Mag., vol.4, pp. 701-709, Nov., 1893.

A LETTER RELATING TO A KIND OF DOG USED BY THE WANDERING TRIBES IN PERSIA TO GUARD THEIR FLOCKS. Sir John McNeill. Proc. Zool. Soc. Lond., pt. 7, p.111, 1839.

THE DOMESTICATION OF THE DOG. N.J. Marr. Trudy Lab. Genet., Akad. Nauk, Leningrad, USSR, vol.1, pp.63-78, 1933.

(THE DOMESTIC DOG AND ITS ORIGIN.) Le Chien domestique et son origine. Robert Matthey. Bull. Soc. Vaudoise Sci. Nat., Lausanne, vol.63, no.267, pp.251-268, 1946.

ALL ABOUT AIREDALES; A BOOK OF GENERAL INFORMATION VALUABLE TO DOG LOVERS AND OWNERS, BREEDERS AND FANCIERS, ILLUSTRATED FROM SELECTED PHOTOGRAPHS OF NOTED DOGS AND RARE SCENES. THE AIREDALE TERRIER REVIEWED. Robert Manning Palmer. 3d. ed., rev. and enl. Seattle, Wash., The A-A-A publ. Co., pp. 144, illus., 1913.

PLAYING WITH A DOG. E. S. Russell. Quart. Rev. Biol., vol.11, no.1, pp.1-15, Mar., 1936.

THE ILLUSTRATED BOOK OF THE DOG. Vero Shaw. London: Cassell, Petter, Galpin and Co., pp.viii, 664, illus., 1881.

BREEDS OF DOGS. S. R. Speelman, J.O. Williams. U.S. Dept. Agric. Farmers' Bull. no.1491, pp.46, illus., May, 1926.

ONE HUNDRED ARISTOCRATS OF THE DOG WORLD. Morgan Stinemetz. Nat. Hist., New York, vol.43, no.2, pp.96-101, figs.100, Feb., 1939.

THE AIREDALE TERRIER. A. P. Terhune. Nature Mag., vol.6, pp.201-203, figs.5, pl.1, Oct., 1925.

THE COLLIE. A.P. Terhune. Nat. Mag., vol.5, pp.79-81, figs.6, Feb., 1925.

THE GERMAN SHEPHERD-DOG OF ANCIENT LINEAGE. A.P. Terhune. Nature Mag., vol.6, pp.329-331, figs.4, Dec., 1925.

THE BOOK OF THE DOG. Brian Vesey-Fitzgerald. Borden Publ. Co., Los Angeles, pp.1039, illus., 1948.

DOGS OF DUTY AND DEVOTION. Frederick G. Vosburgh. Natl. Geogr. Mag., Wash., vol.80, no.6, pp.769-774, illus., Dec., 1941.

SLED-DOGS. Arthur T. Walden. Appalachia, Battleboro, n.s., vol.8, no.12, pp.192-198, illus., Dec., 1942.

OTHER WORKING DOGS AND THE WILD SPECIES. Stanley P. Young. Nat. Geogr. Mag., Wash., vol.86, no.3, pp.363-384, pls.8, illus., Sept., 1944.

FAMOUS SEEING EYE DOG IS DEAD. Nat. Nature News, Wash., D.C., vol.2, no.22, p.6, May 30, 1938.

HOUSE AND PET DOGS; THEIR SELECTION, CARE AND TRAINING. WITH PORTRAITS OF PRIZE WINNING SPECIMENS OF ALL PRINCIPAL BREEDS. New York, Forest and Stream Publ. Co., pp.115, illus., 1890.

Economic Importance

NORTHERN PREDATOR NO. 1. THE RAVAGES OF THE COYOTE IN ALASKA. Russell Annabel. Field and Stream, New York, vol.46, no.1, pp.30-31, 115, May, 1941.

AN ALL IMPORTANT WILDLIFE CONSERVATION PROBLEM. R. B. Armfield. N.C. Wildl. Cons., 5 (6): 10-13, June, 1941.

FUR BEARING ANIMALS OF THE UNITED STATES. THE GRAY FOX. Frank G. Ashbrook, Bridgewater M. Arnold. Fur Jour., vol.2, no.2, pp.30-35, illus., Feb., 1928.

FUR BEARING ANIMALS OF THE UNITED STATES. THE WOLF. Frank G. Ashbrook, J. Ellison Mills. Fur Jour., vol.2, no.5, pp.22, 58-61, illus., May, 1928.

THE COYOTE REAPPRAISED. James W. Atz. Animal Kingdom, New York Zool. Soc., vol.54, no.5, pp.154, 159, illus., Sept.-Oct., 1951.

THE RED FOX VERSUS THE FARMER IN NORTH DAKOTA. Roy N. Bach. North Dakota Outdoors, Bismarck, vol.8, no.11, pp.3-4, May, 1946.

WOLVES IN RELATION TO STOCK, GAME, AND THE NATIONAL FOREST RESERVES. Vernon Bailey. U.S. Dept. Agric. Forest Serv. Bull.72, pp.2-31, pls.1-3, Jan.19, 1907.

DON COYOTE, SABOTEUR. Elliott S. Barker. New Mexico Mag., Albuquerque, vol.22, no.3, pp.23, 25, Mar., 1944.

IS THE TIMBER WOLF DANGEROUS? SOME EXPERIENCES OF WOLF TRAGEDIES. H. Mortimer Batten. Field, Lond., vol.156, no.4047, p.92, July 19, 1930.

COYOTE DAMAGE IN THE STATE OF KANSAS. Robert J. Boles. MS thesis, Kansas State Coll., 1949.

THE FREE-RUNNING DOG MENACE. Robert R. Bowers. Va. Wildl., 14 (10): 5-7, illus., Oct., 1953.

A KIND WORD FOR THE COYOTE. J.G. Burr. Texas Game and Fish, Austin, vol. 6, no.7, pp.9, 14, June, 1948.

SHALL WE SAVE THE LARGER CARNIVORES? Victor H. Cahalane. Living Wilderness, 11 (17): 17-22, June, 1946.

A DILEMMA IN NATURE / COYOTES OR RODENTS. E. C. Cates. S. Dak. Cons. Digest, 22 (7): 5-6, 10, July, 1955.

RED FOX--RESOURCEFUL RESOURCE. Paul Churcher. Nature Mag., Wash., vol. 39, no.6, pp.296-297, 330, illus., June-July, 1946; Conserv. Volunteer, St. Paul, vol.9, no.54, pp.8-12, Sept.-Oct., 1946.

THE CASE AGAINST THE COYOTE. Albert M. Day. Outdoor Life, vol.75, no. 5, pp.26-27, 90, illus., May, 1935.

THE COYOTE--AN ANOMALY. L. H. Douglas. Amer. Cattle Producer, pp.14, 16, Apr., 1954.

THE RED FOX--FRIEND OR FOE? Donald W. Douglass, G.W. Bradt. Michigan Conservation, Lansing, vol.14, no.5, pp.7-8, illus., May, 1945.

THE COYOTE AND HIS BAD NAME. George L. Egbert. Mich. Cons., 8 (7): 5, Mar., 1939.

THAT THIEVING FOX. George Eicher, Jr. Alaska Sportsman, Ketchikan, vol.10, no.1, pp.14-15, 23-24, illus., Jan., 1944.

WHAT MAKES A BAD COYOTE BAD. W. B. Elley. South Dakota Conservation Digest, Pierre, vol.12, no.3, p.16, Mar., 1945.

ARCH VILLAINS OF THE WILDERNESS. (TIMBER WOLF.) Chick Ferguson. Field and Stream, New York, vol.51, no.3, pp. 38, 97-99, July, 1946.

THE COYOTE--ARCHPREDATOR. E. A. Goldman. Jour. Mam., vol.11, no.3, pp. 325-335, Aug., 1930.

(Comments by A.B. Howell on) THE COYOTE--ARCHPREDATOR. E. A. Goldman. Jour. Mamm., vol.11, no.3, p.335, Aug., 1930.

NATURE OF DOG BITES. John G. Hanna. Jour. Amer. Med. Assoc., vol.107, no.15, p.1239, Oct.10, 1936.

CRIES OF "WOLF, WOLF!" ARE FALSE. Hal H. Harrison. Pennsylvania Game News, Harrisburg, vol.19, no.9, p.11, Dec., 1948.

A WORD FOR THE DINGO. Leo Hodge, W. Tree. Victorian Naturalist, Melbourne, vol.70, no.11, p.207, Mar., 1954.

THAT DARNED OLD COYOTE PROBLEM. L. G. Hubbs. Arizona Wildlife and Sportsman, Tucson, vol.6, no.10, p.4, Aug., 1945.

THE CASE FOR THE TIMBER WOLF. John M. Keener. Wis. Cons. Bull., 20 (11): 22-24, illus., Nov., 1955.

COYOTES IN THEIR ECONOMIC RELATIONS. D. E. Lantz. U.S. Dept. Agric., Biol. Surv. Bull., no.20, pp.1-28, 1905.

SOME PRACTICAL ASPECTS OF SELECTING AND MAINTAINING DOGS FOR MEDICAL RESEARCH. Mark L. Morris. Trans. New York Acad. Sci., ser.2, vol.8, no.8, pp.267-271, June, 1946.

THE WOLVES ALMOST GOT ME. Barney Mulvany. Alaska Sportsman, Ketchikan, vol.9, no.5, pp.12-13, 16, 19, illus., May, 1943.

A RECORD OF A TIMBER WOLF ATTACKING A MAN. Randolph L. Peterson. Jour. Mam., vol.28, no.3, pp.294-295, Aug.19, 1947.

THE DOG PROBLEM: DOGS AND CONSERVATION. Michael Petruska. New York State Cons., 4 (1): 2, Aug.-Sept., 1949.

(THE WOLF AND ITS DAMAGE.) El lobo y sus danos. Joaquin de Prada. Montes, Madrid, vol.3, no.17, pp.458-462, figs.4, maps 2, Sept.-Oct., 1947.

COYOTES CAN'T WIN AGAINST RODENTS. Clifford C. Presnall. Natl. Wool Grower, 43 (6): 22-23, illus., June, 1953.

THE COYOTE PROBLEM IN MISSOURI. Frank W. Sampson. Mo. Cons., 6 (7): 4-5, 14-15, July, 1945.

LET'S STOP THE SELF-HUNTING DOG. George X. Sand. Pa. Game News, 22 (11): 4-8, illus., Feb., 1952.

AN EVALUATION OF THE RED FOX. Thomas G. Scott. Ill. Nat. Hist. Surv., Biol. Notes no.35, pp.1-16, illus., July, 1955.

COYOTES PROTECTED. E. C. Shindorf. Audubon Mag., 55 (5): 205, illus., Sept.-Oct., 1953.

WOLVES JUST WON'T LIVE UP TO THEIR REPUTATIONS. George Smokey. South Dakota Conserv. Digest, Pierre, vol.11, no.5, pp.10, 15, May, 1944.

RAW RACCOON SKINS EXPORT. Arthur de C. Sowerby. China Jour., vol.20, no. 6, p.362, June, 1934.

SIR REYNARD--SAINT OR SINNER? Thaddeus Surber. Cons. Volunteer, 6 (33): 13-16, June, 1943.

MICHIGAN'S FOXES CAN FURNISH SPORT AND PROFIT. D. F. Switzenberg. Mich. Cons., 16 (1): 6-7, Jan., 1947.

THE FOX SITUATION. W. H. Turcotte. Mississippi Game and Fish, Jackson, vol. 11, no.8, pp.3-5, 7, Feb., 1948.

FOX: NOT AS BLACK AS PAINTED. W.H. DeC. Wright. Ralley Sheet, League of Maryland Sportsmen, Baltimore, vol.4, no.1, pp.6, 8, Jan., 1946.

COYOTE, WOLF, WILD DOG, OR JUST VARMINT? Kentucky Happy Hunting Ground, Frankfort, vol.6, no.3, p.26, illus., May, 1950.

COYOTES PROTECTED. Okla. Game and Fish News, 9 (7-8): 9, July-Aug., 1953.

HALF-BREED COYOTES ON RAMPAGE. Kentucky Happy Hunting Ground, Frankfort, vol.5, no.2, p.31, illus., Mar., 1949.

IMPARTIAL ANALYSIS. (RED AND GRAY FOXES.) Pennsylvania Game News, Harrisburg, vol.15, no.1, pp.6-7, illus., Apr., 1944.

A PLEA FOR THE WOLVES. Canadian Nature, Toronto, vol.5, no.1, p.39, illus., Jan.-Feb., 1943.

SKINNING A COYOTE. South Dakota Conservation Digest, Pierre, vol.11, no.12, p.14, Dec., 1944.

YOUR RED FOX IS WAITING. Iowa Conserv. Des Moines, vol.6, no.11, pp.179-180, illus., Nov.15, 1947.

Europe

(ON SOME WILD DOGS OF SCHOENBRUNN.) Ueber einige Schoenbrunner Wildhunde. Otto Antonius. Zool. Garten (NF), vol.13, nos.3-4, pp.211-224, illus., 1941.

(MOUNTAIN FOX, ALOPEX LAGOPUS L., CAUGHT AT SUNDOM NEAR VASA.) Fjaellraev, Alopex lagopus L., in angad i Sundom utanfoer Vasa. Ragnar Baeck. Memoranda Soc. pro Fauna et Flora Fennica, Helsingfors, no.27, p.62, 1952.

INTRODUCTION OF ARCTIC FOX. L. V. Boitsov. Trans. Arctic Inst. USSR, Leningrad, vol.65, Biol., pp.7-144, figs.19, tables 40, 1937.

(WOLVES IN FRANCE.) Les loups en France. Paul Buffault. Rev. Gen. Sci. Pures et Appl., vol.43, no.23, pp.676-681, map 1, Dec.15, 1932.

(THE SPANISH WOLVES.) Los lobos de Espana. Angel Cabrera. Bol. Real Soc. Espanola Hist. Nat., Madrid, vol.7, no.5, pp.193-197, pl.3, May, 1907.

(JACKALS IN RUMANIA.) Schakale in Rumaenien. Raul J. Calinescu. Zeitschr. Saeugetierkunde, vol.5, nos.5-6, pp.373-375, map 1, Dec.22, 1930.

THE WOLF IN BRITAIN. Patrick Chalmers. Field, London, vol.156, no.4057, p.439, fig.1, Sept.27, 1930.

(SOME MEMOIRS ON THE SUBJECT OF WOLVES.) Vieux souvenirs au sujet des loups. F. De Chapel. Bull. Soc. Nat. Acclimat. France, vol.77, no.2, pp.27-28, Feb., 1930.

(ON PREHISTORIC DANISH DOGS.) Ueber praehistorische daenische Hunde. Magnus Degerbol. Vidensk. Medd. Dansk naturh. Foren., vol.84, pp.17-71, pls.1-4, 1927.

JACKAL OR REED-WOLF FROM HUNGARY. Julius Ehik. Annal. Mus. Nat. Hungarici 1937-38, Budapest, vol.31, zool., pp.11-15, 1938. (In Hungarian and English.)

(HABITATS OF SOME RARE CARNIVORES IN THE WESTERN CARPATHIANS AND POSSIBILITIES FOR AN INCREASE IN THEIR POPULATION.) Wohngebiete und Vermehrungsmoeglichkeiten einiger seltener Raubtiere in den Westkarpaten. Z. Feriancova, J. Komarek. Saeugetierk. Mitteil., Stuttgart, 3 (2): 71-76, Apr.1, 1955.

THE LAST IRISH WOLF. Nora Fisher. Irish Nat. Jour., vol.5, no.2, p.41, Mar., 1934.

(FOX HUNT.) Och en ravjakt. Sign Geha. Svensk Jakt., Stockholm, vol.89, no.6, p. 181, June 14, 1951.

MEASUREMENTS OF FOXES FROM SCOTLAND AND ENGLAND. Ivan Hattingh. Proc. Zool. Soc. Lond., 127 (2): 191-199, Oct.29, 1956.

(A FORGOTTEN MAMMAL OF FRANCHE-COMTE: THE WOLF.) Un mammifere Franc-Comtois oublie: Le loup. A. Jullien, R. Moreau. Etude de Faunistique, Ann. Sci. Univ. Besancon, ser.2, no.3, pp.41-51, 1955.

ON THE BIOLOGY OF THE KORSAK FOX AND THE FOX OF THE STEPPES. A. M. Kolosov. Bull. Soc. Natur. Moscow, ser. Biol., 44: 165-77, 1935. (In Russian.)

(MATERIALS ON THE STUDY OF THE BIOLOGY OF A RACCOON-LIKE DOG IN GORKY OBLAST.) Materialy k izucheniyu biologii enotovidnoi sobaki (Nyctereutes procyonoides Gray) v gorkovskoi oblasti. V. I. Kozlov. Zool. Zhurnal, Moscow, vol.31, no.5, pp.761-768, 1952.

(THE DALMATIAN JACKALS.) Die Dalmatinischen Schakale. Wolfgang Kuhn. Zeitschr. f. Saeugetierkunde, vol.10, no. 1, pp.144-146, Dec.31, 1935.

(HISTORY OF THE WOLF IN SWEDEN.) Bidrag till vargens historia i Sverige. Einar Loennberg. K. Svenska Vetenskapsakademiens Skrifter i naturskyddaerenden, no. 26, pp.1-33, figs.2, table, 1934.

(ONE FOX PER HOUR.) En rav i timmen. Hjalmar Mansson. Svensk Jakt, Stockholm, vol.87, no.2, pp.35-36, Feb.20, 1949.

A LARGE SCOTTISH FOX. L. Harrison Matthews. Proc. Zool. Soc. Lond., vol. 120, pt.4, pp.679-681, Feb., 1951.

(THE "LAST" WOLVES OF LOWER SAXONY.) Die "letzten" Wolfe von Niedersachsen. Erna Mohr. Saeugetierk. Mitteil., vol.1, no.1, pp.22-26, illus., Jan.10, 1953.

(PYRENEAN DOG.) Der Pyrenaenhund. Erna Mohr. Rundschau fuer Jagd und Hundesport, Plauen, pp.94-96, figs.4, Sept., 1940.

(THE COMMON WOLF CANIS LUPUS LINNE. SOME OF ITS MISDEEDS, ITS ALMOST COMPLETE DISAPPEARANCE FROM FRANCE.) Le Loup Commun Canis lupus Linne. Quelques-uns de ses mefaits sa disparition presque complete de France. Raymond Rollinat. Revue d'Histoire Naturelle, pt.1, A, Mammiferes, Paris, vol.10, no.4, pp.105-129, pl, Apr., 1929; no.7, pp.209-238, July, 1929; no.9, pp. 289-308, Sept., 1929.

RACCOON DOG, NYCTEREUTES PROCYONOIDES GRAY, THE NEWEST GAME SPECIES OF FINLAND. Lauri Siivonen. Suomen Riista, 8: 177-179, map, illus., 1953. (Finnish with English summary.)

THE RACCOON DOG, NYCTEREUTES PROCYONOIDES GRAY (CANIDAE) FOUND IN FINLAND. Esko Suomalainen. Archiv. Soc. Zool. Bot. Fennicae "Vanamo", Helsinki, vol.5, no.1, pp.20-22, Sept., 1950.

ON THE SCOTTISH FOX. H. Tetley. Proc. Zool. Soc. Lond., vol.111, ser.B, pts.1-2, pp.25-35, fig.1, Oct., 1941.

CHERISHED NUISANCES. Frank Thone. Science News Letter, Wash., D.C., vol. 41, no.11, p.175, illus., Mar.14, 1942. (Fox hunting in England.)

CANIS SPECIES, SCANDINAVIAN INHABITANTS. C. P. Thunberg. Quas venia exp. facult. med. Upsaliae, Botanico die xv Junii MDCCCXXIV, pp.8, pl.1, 1824.

(ESKIMO DOGS OF GREENLAND AND THEIR ACCLIMATIZATION IN FRANCE.) Les Chiens Eskimo du Groeland et leur acclimatation en France. Paul-Emile Victor. La Terre et la vie, Paris, annee 9, no.1, pp.3-9, illus., Jan.-Feb., 1939.

THE EUROPEAN WOLF. Nature, London, vol.132, no.3345, p.906, Dec.9, 1933.

Experimental Biology

(RESULTS OF PARTIAL OVARIECTOMY ON A BITCH.) Resultado de ovariectomias parciales en la perra. N. Arenas, R. Sammartino. Rev. Soc. Argentina Biol., Buenos Aires, vol.18, no.3, pp.257-260, June, 1942.

(INFLUENCE OF PILOCARPINE ON THE CARDIAC EFFECTS OF THE WAVE EXCITATION IN THE DOG.) Influence de la pilocarpine sur les effets cardiaques de l'excitation du vague chez le chien. M. Athias, J. Fontes. Comptes Rendus des Seances de la Soc. de Biol., vol.97, pp. 715-717, Aug.26, 1927.

NOTES ON THE VASO-REACTION IN DOGS PRODUCED BY INJECTIONS OF EXTRACTS

OF THE TUBERCLE BACILLUS. J. P. Atkinson, Charles B. Fitzpatrick. 1910.

ISOLATION OF DIFFERENT PARTS OF THE DIGESTIVE TRACT AS A METHOD OF STUDYING ITS MOVEMENTS. (EXPERIMENTS ON A DOG.) B. P. Babkin, E. I. Sinelnikov. Jour. Physiol., vol.58, pp.15-17, Oct., 1923.

BLOOD STUDIES IN DOGS FOLLOWING THE INJECTION OF PENICILLIN. W. O. Brinker. North American Veterinarian, vol.25, pp.31-33, 1947.

CIRRHOSIS AND OTHER HEPATIC LESIONS PRODUCED IN DOGS BY THYROIDECTOMY AND BY COMBINED HYPOPHYSECTOMY AND THYROIDECTOMY. I.L. Chaikoff, T. Gillman, E. Entenman, J.F. Rinehart, F.L. Reichert. Jour. Exper. Med., Baltimore, vol.88, no.1, pp.1-14, pls.4, July 1, 1948.

PHOSPHOLIPID METABOLISM IN DIABETES: TURNOVER RATE OF PLASMA PHOSPHOLIPIDS IN COMPLETELY DEPANCREATIZED DOGS. I.L. Chaikoff, D.B. Zilversmit, C. Entenman. Proc. Soc. Exper. Biol. Med., Utica, vol.68, no.1, pp.6-9, May, 1948.

RELEASE OF POTASSIUM BY THE BRAIN OF THE DOG DURING ELECTRICAL STIMULATION. V.H. Cicardo, A. Torino. Science, n.s., Lancaster, vol.95, no. 2477, p.625, June 19, 1942.

EFFECT OF RESECTION OF MESENTERIC LYMPH NODES ON INTESTINAL FAT ABSORPTION IN THE DOG. B.G. Clarke, A. C. Ivy, D. Goodman. Amer. Jour. Physiol., Baltimore, vol.153, no.2, pp.264-267, May 1, 1948.

PERMANENT DEVOCALIZATION OF DOGS BY REMOVAL OF BOTH THE TRUE AND THE FALSE VOCAL CORDS. G.L. Donnelly. Proc. Soc. Exper. Biol. and Med., Utica, vol.50, no.1, pp.79-80, May, 1942.

FAT AND NITROGEN ABSORPTION AFTER FOLIC ACID ADMINISTRATION IN DOGS DEPRIVED OF EXTERNAL PANCREATIC SECRETION. G.F. Douglas, Jr., T.D. Pratt. Proc. Soc. Exper. Biol. Med., Utica, vol.68, no.1, pp.171-174, May, 1948.

EFFECT OF SODIUM SALICYLATE UPON THE URIC ACID CLEARANCE OF THE DALMATIAN DOG. Meyer Friedman, Sanford O. Byers. Amer. Jour. Physiol., Baltimore, vol.154, no.1, pp.167-168, July 1, 1948.

CHANGES IN TOTAL GASEOUS METABOLISM OF UNANESTHETIZED DOGS AFTER INTRAVENOUS INJECTION OF POSTERIOR PITUITARY EXTRACTS. E.M.K. Geiling, A.M. DeLawder. Bull. Johns Hopkins Hospital, vol.51, no.6, pp.335-345, Dec., 1932.

CHANGES IN ARTERIAL INFLOW IN THE DOG'S LEG FOLLOWING VENOUS OCCLUSION: EVALUATION OF RESULTS OBTAINED WITH DIFFERENT TYPES OF FLOW RECORDERS. D.E. Gregg, W.H. Pritchard, R.E. Shipley. Amer. Jour. Physiol., Baltimore, vol.153, no.1, pp.153-158, Apr.1, 1948.

INHIBITION BY HISTAMINE OF GASTRIC SECRETION IN DOGS. M.I. Grossman, C.R. Robertson. Amer. Jour. Physiol., Baltimore, vol.153, no.3, pp.447-453, June 1, 1948.

ACUTE HYPERTENSION IN DOGS WITH CEREBRAL ISCHEMIA. A.C. Guyton. Amer. Jour. Physiol., Baltimore, vol.154, no.1, pp.45-54, July 1, 1948.

EXPERIMENTAL HYPOTHERMIA AND REWARMING IN THE DOG RECOVERY AFTER SEVERE REDUCTION IN BODY TEMPERATURE. Hans O. Hatterius, George L. Maison. Amer. Jour. Physiol., Baltimore, vol.152, no.2, pp.225-232, Feb.1, 1948.

(ANAPHYLACTIC REACTIONS OF THE SEVERED HEAD OF A DOG.) Les reactions anaphylactiques de la tete "isolee" du chien. C. Heymans, Jean Dalsace. Comptes Rendus des Seances de la Soc. de Biol., vol.97, pp.741-743, Aug.26, 1927.

COMPARISON OF THE ELECTROCARDIOGRAPHIC CHANGES PRODUCED BY HEATING AND COOLING EPICARDIAL AND ENDOCARDIAL SURFACES OF THE DOG VENTRICAL. H.E. Hoff, L.H. Nahum. Amer. Jour. Physiol., Baltimore, vol.153, no.1, pp.176-182, Apr.1, 1948.

RENAL HYPEREMIA AFTER THE INTRAVENEOUS INFUSION OF ADENYLIC ACID, ADENOSIVE, OR ADENOSINETRIPHOSPHATE IN THE DOG. C.R. Houck, R.J. Bing, F.N. Craig, F.E. Visscher. Amer. Jour. Physiol. Baltimore, vol.153, no.1, pp. 159-168, Apr.1, 1948.

FACTORS CONTROLLING THE ARTERIAL SUPPLY OF THE TESTIS UNDER EXPERIMENTAL CONDITIONS. (EXPERIMENTS ON DOGS.) Y. Joranson, V.E. Emmel, H. J. Pilka. Anat. Rec., vol.41, pp.157-176, illus., Jan.25, 1929.

AN ELECTROCHEMICAL STUDY OF THE SYNOVIALIS IN DOGS. N.R. Joseph, C.I. Reed, I.E. Steck, Frank Folk, Ervin Kaplan. Amer. Jour. Physiol., Baltimore, vol.153, no.2, pp.364-380, May 1, 1948.

DETERMINATION OF THE HEAT PRODUCTION IN DOGS BY THE GASOMETER METHOD. Hubert D. Kitchen. Amer. Jour. Physiol., vol.67, pp.487-497, 1924.

OBSERVATIONS ON THE URINE, BLOOD AND ARTERIAL PRESSURE OF DOGS BEFORE AND AFTER THE PRODUCTION OF RENAL ISCHAEMIA. H. Konzett, E.B. Verney. Jour. Physiol., Lond., vol.107, no.3, pp.336-345, June 25, 1948.

BLOOD PRESSURE CHANGES IN RESPONSE TO ELECTRICAL AND CHEMICAL STIMULATION OF THE CEREBRAL CORTEX IN DOGS. Willem F. Kremer. Amer. Jour. Physiol., Baltimore, vol.152, no.2, pp.314-323, Feb.1, 1948.

EXPERIMENTAL DEGENERATION IN THE TESTIS OF THE DOG. Albert Kuntz. Anat. Rec., vol.17, pp.221-234, figs.4, Dec.20, 1919 (Jan., 1920).

THE INERVATION OF THE GONADS IN THE DOG. Albert Kuntz. Anat. Rec., vol.17, pp.203-219, figs.4, Dec.20, 1919 (Jan., 1920).

AN ATTEMPT AT EXPERIMENTAL HOMOPLASTIC TRANSPLANTATION OF TEETH IN THE DOG. A.G. Lapchinsky, A.A. Malinovsky. Doklady Acad. Sci., Moscow, n.s., vol.28, no.8, pp.750-753, 1940. (In English.)

(BATTLING AGING PHENOMENA THROUGH PARTIAL DESTRUCTION AND CRUSHING OF TESTICULAR TISSUE.) Bekaempfung der Alterserscheinungen durch teilweises Zerreissen und Zerdruecken des Hodengewebes. (Deals with dogs.) N. G. Lebedinsky. Biol. Zentralblatt, vol.50, pp.392-422, figs.12, 1930.

EFFECT OF AGE ON HISTAMINE INDUCED ULCER IN DOGS. C.W. Lillehei, O.H. Wangensteen. Proc. Soc. Exper. Biol., Med. Utica, vol.68, no.1, pp.129-131, May, 1948.

THE REGULATION OF RESPIRATION. PART I. (EXPERIMENTS ON DOGS.) Thomas Lumsden. Jour. Physiol., vol.58, pp.81-91, 1923.

PRODUCTION OF ALLOXAN DIABETES IN THE DOG. L.J. Manhoff, A.W. DeLoach. Proc. Soc. Exper. Biol. Med., Utica, vol. 68, no.1, pp.120-122, May, 1948.

ON THE OVARIAN FACTOR CONCERNED IN THE OCCURRENCE OF OESTRUS. (EXPERIMENTS ON DOGS.) F.H.A. Marshall, W.A. Wood. Jour. Physiol., vol.58, pp.74-80, 1923.

CHEMICAL CHANGES IN THE BLOOD DURING FASTING AND SUBSEQUENT REFEEDING. EXPERIMENTS ON DOGS. I. Sergius Morgulis, A.C. Edwards. Amer. Jour. Physiol., vol.68, pp.477-498, 1924.

INFLUENCE OF DIURESIS ON UREA PRODUCTION IN THE FASTING DOG. Eric Ogden, Eleanore Tripp. Amer. Jour. Physiol., Balto., vol.153, no.1, pp.190-196, Apr.1, 1948.

THE PRODUCTION OF FATTY ACIDS IN THE ALIMENTARY TRACT OF THE DOG. A.T. Phillipson. Jour. Exper. Biol., Lond., vol.23, nos.3-4, pp.346-349, Apr., 1947.

RENAL GLUCOGENESIS IN THE EVISCERATED DOG. R.M. Reinecke, P.J. Hauser. Amer. Jour. Physiol., Balto., vol.153, no.2, pp.205-209, May 1, 1948.

PRODUCTION OF EXPERIMENTAL HEART FAILURE IN DOGS WITH INTACT CIRCULATION. Albert Roos, J.R. Smith. Amer. Jour. Physiol., Balto., vol.153, no.3, pp. 558-566, June 1, 1948.

RESPONSE OF DOGS TO LIVER EXTRACTS CONTAINING THE PERNICIOUS ANEMIA FACTOR. W.R. Ruegamer, W.L. Brickson, N.J. Torbet, C.A. Elvehjem. Jour. Nutrition, Phila., vol.36, no.4, pp.425-435, Oct.11, 1948.

EFFECT OF D-AMPHETAMINE ON GASTRIC HUNGER CONTRACTIONS AND FOOD INTAKE IN THE DOG. W. Sangster, M.I. Grossman, A.C. Ivy. Amer. Jour. Physiol., Balto., vol.153, no.2, pp.259-263, May 1, 1948.

TRAUMATIC SHOCK XVI: AMINO ACID METABOLISM IN HEMORRHAGIC SHOCK IN THE DOG. A.M. Seligman, B. Alexander, H.A. Frank, Jacob Fine. Amer. Jour. Physiol., Balto., vol.152, no.3, pp. 531-544, Mar.1, 1948.

CHOLIN IN THE BLOOD AFTER PARATHYROIDECTOMY. (EXPERIMENTS ON DOGS.) W.F. Shanks. Jour. Physiol., vol.58, pp.466-469, May, 1924.

NOTES ON TEMPERATURE AFTER SPINAL TRANSECTION, WITH SOME OBSERVATIONS ON SHIVERING. (EXPERIMENTS ON DOGS.) C.S. Sherrington. Jour. Physiol., vol.58, pp.405-423, May, 1924.

PRESSOR SUBSTANCES IN DOG PLASMA INCUBATED WITH RENIN. E. Tripp, Eric Ogden. Amer. Jour. Physiol., Balto., vol.153, no.2, pp.336-340, May 1, 1948.

UTILIZATION BY DOGS OF THE NITROGEN OF HEATED CASEIN. E.O. Weast, Mary Groody, Agnes Fay Morgan. Amer. Jour. Physiol., Balto., vol.152, no.2, pp.286-301, Feb.1, 1948.

EXCRETION OF SODIUM AND WATER DURING OSMOTIC DIURESIS IN THE DOG. L. G. Wesson, W.P. Anslow, Jr. Amer. Jour. Physiol., Balto., vol.153, no.3, pp.465-474, June 1, 1948.

Food Habits (Canis)

SOURCE OF SMALL BIRDS EATEN BY THE COYOTE. William Bebe. Jour. Mam., vol. 15, no.4, pp.320-321, Nov., 1934.

COYOTE FOOD HABITS ON THE LAVA BEDS NATIONAL MONUMENT. R.M. Bond. Jour. Wildl. Mgt., 3 (3): 180-198, July, 1939.

WOLF PREDATION IN THE NORTH COUNTRY. I.P. Callison. I.P. Callison, Seattle, pp.89, July, 1948.

MOTHER WOLF CARRIES FOOD TWELVE MILES TO HER YOUNG. Joseph S. Dixon. Jour. Mam., vol.15, no.2, p.158, May, 1934.

FOOD HABITS OF THE COYOTE IN CALIFORNIA. Carol M. Ferrel, Howard R. Leach, Daniel F. Tillotson. California Fish and Game, vol.39, no.3, pp.301-341, July, 1953.

SOME FEEDING PATTERNS OF COYOTES IN NEBRASKA. Edson Fichter, George Schildman, J. Henry Sather. Ecological Monographs, Durham, vol.25, no.1, pp.1-37, Jan., 1955.

A STUDY OF COYOTE RELATIONSHIPS ON CATTLE RANGE. Henry S. Fitch. Jour. Wildl. Mgt., 12 (1): 73-78, Jan., 1948.

AN OBSERVATION ON THE HUNTING METHODS OF THE TIMBER WOLF. F.M. Fryxell. Jour. Mam., vol.7, no.3, pp.226-227, Aug., 1926.

COYOTE APPETITES. Lon Garrison. Yosemite Nature Notes, vol.16, no.3, p.19, March, 1937.

COYOTE FOODS NEAR BOULDER DAM. Russell K. Grater. Jour. Wildl. Mgt., 7 (4): 422-423, Oct., 1943.

TROUT AND CRAYFISH EATEN BY COYOTES. Rudolf L. Grimm. Jour. Mam., 21 (4): 458-459, Nov., 1940.

A PRELIMINARY PREDATOR-PREY STUDY WITH RESPECT TO THE COYOTE CANIS LATRANS IN JASPER NATIONAL PARK. James Hatter. pp.41, illus.

(PREFERENCE OF THE DOG FOR RAW FRUITS.) Vorliebe des Hundes fuer rohe Fruechte. Viktor Hornung. Zool. Garten, vol.14, nos.1-2, pp.103-104, 1942.

COYOTE AND BULL SNAKE. Jerry Johnson. Jour. Mam., vol.17, no.2, pp.169-170, May, 1936.

VILLAGE DOGS HUNTING. W.P. Keelan. Jour. Bombay Nat. Hist. Soc., Bombay, vol.42, no.2, pp.437-438, Apr., 1941.

HAPPY HUNTING GROUNDS FOR COYOTE IN A YOSEMITE MEADOW. Ruth Kales Knowles. Yosemite Nat. Notes, Stockton, vol.18, no.7, pp.84-85, July, 1939.

FOOD HABITS OF THE COYOTE IN MISSOURI. Leroy J. Korschgen. Jour. Wildl. Mgt., 21 (4): 424-435, Oct., 1937.

DON COYOTE, ARCH ENEMY OF NESTING BOBWHITES. V. W. Lehmann, W. G. Fuller. Texas Game and Fish, Austin, vol. 1, no.9, pp.9, 15, Aug., 1943.

CANIS LATRANS LESTES MERRIAN FEEDING ON TADPOLES AND FROGS. Robert D. Moore. Jour. Mam., Balto., vol.10, no.3, p.255, Aug.10, 1929.

COYOTE FOOD HABITS ON A SOUTHWESTERN CATTLE RANGE. Adolph Murie. Jour. Mam., 32 (3): 291-295, Aug., 1951.

FOOD HABITS OF THE COYOTE IN JACKSON HOLE, WYOMING. Olaus J. Murie. Circular no.362, U.S. Dept. Agric., pp. 24, Oct., 1935.

NOTES ON COYOTE FOOD HABITS IN MONTANA AND BRITISH COLUMBIA. Olaus J. Murie. Jour. Mam., 26 (1): 33-40, Feb., 1945.

A STUDY IN PREDATORY RELATIONSHIP WITH PARTICULAR REFERENCE TO THE WOLF. Sigurd F. Olson. Sci. Monthly, 46: 323-336, Apr., 1938.

APPLIED ECOLOGY OF PREDATION ON LIVESTOCK RANGES. Clifford C. Presnall. Jour. Mam., 29 (2): 155-161, May, 1948.

COYOTE PREDATION ON SAGE GROUSE. Clifford C. Presnall, Alvin Wood. Jour. Mam., vol.34, no.1, p.127, Feb.19, 1953.

SOME OBSERVATIONS ON COYOTE PREDATION IN YELLOWSTONE NATIONAL PARK. Weldon B. Robinson. Jour. Mam., vol.33, no.4, pp.470-476, Nov.19, 1952.

LOSSES OF SHEEP FROM PREDATORY ANIMALS ON SUMMER RANGES IN IRON COUNTY, UTAH. Leo Rosko. Utah Coop. Wildl. Res. Unit, pp.16, Feb.1, 1948.

DOGS DISLIKE FOX FLESH BUT RELISH THAT OF WILD-CATS. Roland Case Ross. Jour. Mam., vol.9, no.3, p.250, Aug., 1928.

HABITS OF COYOTES IN DESTROYING NESTS AND EGGS OF WATERFOWL. Clarence A. Sooter. Jour. Wildl. Mgt., 10 (1): 33-38, Jan., 1946.

FOOD HABITS OF THE COYOTE. Garrett H. Soulen. Minn. Cons., 58: 20, 27-30, 32, June, 1938.

AUTUMN FOOD HABITS OF COYOTES, A REPORT OF PROGRESS, 1932. Charles C. Sperry. Jour. Mam., vol.14, no.3, pp.216-220, Aug., 1933.

FOOD HABITS OF PEG-LEG COYOTES. Charles C. Sperry. Jour. Mam., 20 (2): 190-194, May, 1939.

FOOD HABITS OF THE COYOTE. Charles C. Sperry. USDI, F&WS, Wildl. Res. Bull. 4, pp.70, 1941.

WINTER FOOD HABITS OF COYOTES: A REPORT OF PROGRESS, 1933. Charles C. Sperry. Jour. Mam., vol.15, no.4, pp.286-290, Nov., 1934.

THE HUNT OF THE COYOTE. Lorene Squire. Nature Mag., vol.22, no.4, pp. 151-154, illus., Oct., 1933.

TEAMWORK BY COYOTES. William Stevenson. Yosemite Nat. Notes, Yosemite, vol.23, no.4, pp.42-43, Apr., 1944.

WINTER FOODS OF KANSAS COYOTES. Otto W. Tiemeier. Kans. Fish and Game, 12 (3): 14-15, graphs, Jan., 1955; Trans. Kansas Acad. Sci., vol.58, no.2, pp.196-207, June 21, 1955.

STUDIES OF PELAGE CHANGES, FOOD HABITS, AND BREEDING HABITS OF CAPTIVE COYOTES, CANIS L. LATRANS. Eldon E. Whiteman. MS thesis, Mich. State Coll., 1940.

OUTSMARTED. (WOLF-KILLING SHEEP.) Louisiana Conservationist, New Orleans, vol.1, no.1, pp.2-3, illus., Sept., 1948.

Food Habits (Cuon)

HOW DO WILD DOGS KILL THEIR PREY? Salim A. Ali. Jour. Bombay Nat. Hist. Soc., vol.31, p.813, Nov.1, 1926.

HOW WILD DOGS KILL THEIR PREY. A.A. Dunbar Brander. Jour. Bombay Nat. Hist. Soc., vol.32, pp.591-592, Jan.15, 1928.

WILD DOGS KILLING BY NIGHT. T.H. Carlisle. Jour. Bombay Nat. Hist. Soc., vol.36, no.1, pp.239-240, Nov.15, 1932.

WILD DOGS HUNTING AND KILLING BY NIGHT. V. S. La Personne. Jour. Bombay Nat. Hist. Soc., vol.36, no.1, pp.240-241, Nov.15, 1932.

DO WILD DOGS HUNT AND KILL BY NIGHT. Ramanuj of Surguja. Jour. Bombay Nat. Hist. Soc., vol.35, no.3, p.673, Feb.15, 1932.

HOW WILD DOGS KILL THEIR PREY. L. A.J. Rijk. Jour. Bombay Nat. Hist. Soc., vol.33, no.3, pp.704-705, May 31, 1929.

Food Habits (Foxes)

THE RELATIONSHIP BETWEEN RING-NECKED PHEASANT AND RED FOX POPULATION TRENDS. David A. Arnold. Pap. Mich. Acad. Sci., Arts and Letters, 37: 121-127, map and graphs, 1951 (1952).

(MATERIALS FOR THE STUDY OF THE QUESTION OF THE FOOD OF THE TRANSCAUCASIAN FOX.) Materiali k izucheniu voprosa o pitanii zakavkazskoi stepnoi lisitsi (Vulpes vulpes alpherakyi Sat.) R.S. Avaliani. Soobshcheniya Akad. Nauk Gruzinskoi SSR, vol.14, no.5, pp.309-312, 1953.

FOOD HABITS OF THE FOX (VULPES VULPES L.). T.N. Baranovskaya, A.M. Kolosov. Zool. Jour. USSR, Moscow, vol. 14, no.3, pp.523-550, 1935. (In Russian, with German summary.)

FOOD HABITS OF THE GREY FOX IN PENNSYLVANIA. Logan J. Bennett, P.F. English. Pa. Game News, 12 (12): 10-22, Mar., 1942.

FROGS AS FOOD OF FOXES. H. B. Booth. Naturalist, London, no.856, pp.157-158, May, 1928.

FOOD OF FOXES. Maurice Burton. Illus. London News, vol.138, no.3585, p.11, illus., Jan.7, 1956.

PHEASANTS, FOX, AND QUAIL. Irven O. Buss. Wis. Cons. Bull., 11 (4): 8-15, Apr., 1946.

REPORT ON GREY AND RED FOX STOMACH EXAMINATIONS. T.T. Chaddock. Wis. Cons. Bull., 4 (9): 53-54, Sept., 1939.

THE ECOLOGICAL RELATIONSHIPS OF RED FOX FOOD IN EASTERN NEW YORK. David B. Cook, W.J. Hamilton, Jr. Ecology, 25 (1): 91-104, Jan., 1944.

NOTES ON THE FOOD OF THE RED FOX. Julius Crosman. Bull. Boston Soc. Nat. Hist., no.42, pp.8-9, Jan., 1927.

FOX FOOD HABITS. Robert W. Darrow. Western New York Conservationist, Buffalo, vol.5, no.5, pp.10, 11, May, 1945.

RELATION OF BUFFER SPECIES ABUNDANCE TO FOX PREDATION ON GROUSE NESTS. Robert W. Darrow. Trans. 10th N. Amer. Wildlife Conf., Wash., pp.270-273, 1945.

A CYCLE IN NORTHERN SHRIKE EMIGRATIONS. David E. Davis. Auk, vol.54, no. 1, pp.43-49, Jan., 1937.

FOOD OF A CRIPPLED RED FOX. Ralph W. Dexter. Jour. Mam., vol.32, no.4, p.464, Nov.19, 1951.

FOOD HABITS OF THE NEWFOUNDLAND RED FOX. Donald G. Dodds. Jour. Mam., 36 (2): 291, May, 1955.

FOXES AND PHEASANTS. J.B. Drought. Field, London, vol.162, no.4201, p.47, figs., July 1, 1933.

FOOD OF THE RED FOX IN SOUTHERN NEW HAMPSHIRE. W. Robert Eadie. Jour. Wildlife Mgt., Menasha, vol.7, no. 1, pp.74-77, Jan., 1943.

THE FOOD OF THE RED FOX (VULPES FULVA FULVA). John Edmonds. Canadian Field-Nat., vol.42, p.94, Apr., 1928.

RED FOX FOOD HABITS STUDY IN PENNSYLVANIA. P. J. English, Logan J. Bennett. Pennsylvania Game News, Harrisburg, vol.12, no.11, pp.6-7, 22-23, Feb., 1942.

BOBWHITE WINTER SURVIVAL IN AN AREA HEAVILY POPULATED WITH GREY FOXES. Paul L. Errington. Iowa State Coll. Jour. Sci., vol.8, no.1, pp.127-130, Oct., 1933.

FOOD HABITS OF IOWA RED FOXES DURING A DROUGHT SUMMER. Paul L. Errington. Ecology, vol.18, no.1, pp.53-61, Jan., 1937.

FOOD HABITS OF MID-WEST FOXES. Paul L. Errington. Jour. Mam., 16 (3): 192-200, Aug., 1935.

FOOD HABITS OF THE RED FOX IN IOWA. Paul L. Errington. Amer. Wildlife, vol. 26, no.1, pp.5, 6, 13, illus., Jan.-Feb., 1937.

FACTS ABOUT FOX FOODS. Larry Gale. Kentucky Happy Hunting Ground, Frankfort, vol.4, no.2, pp.14, 34, illus., Mar.-Apr., 1948.

FOX FOODS ON WEST VIRGINIA WILD TURKEY RANGE. Fred A. Glover. Jour. Mam., 30 (1): 78-79, Feb., 1949.

NOTES ON FOOD OF RED FOXES IN NEW YORK AND NEW ENGLAND. W.J. Hamilton, Jr. Jour. Mam., 16 (1): 16-21, Feb., 1935.

LATE SUMMER AND EARLY FALL FOODS OF THE RED FOX IN CENTRAL MASSACHUSETTS. W.J. Hamilton, Jr., N.W. Hosley, A.E. MacGregor. Jour. Mam., 18 (3): 366-367, Aug., 1937.

LATE SUMMER AND EARLY FALL FOODS OF THE RED FOX IN CENTRAL MASSACHUSETTS. W.J. Hamilton, Jr., N.W. Hosley, A.E. MacGregor. Jour. Mam., vol.18, no.3, pp.366-367, Aug.14, 1937.

THE FOX-QUAIL PROBLEM IN NORTH CAROLINA. Dennis Hart. Wildl. in N.C., 10 (3): 13, 18, Oct., 1946.

WINTER FOOD HABITS OF FOXES IN MINNESOTA. Donald M. Hatfield. Jour. Mam., vol.20, no.2, pp.202-206, tables 2, May, 1939.

FOOD OF THE SAN JOAQUIN KIT FOX. Albert C. Hawbecker. Jour. Mam., 24 (4): 499, Nov., 1943.

FOOD HABITS OF RED FOXES OF THE MARYLAND MARSHES. William S. Heit. Jour. Mam., 25 (1): 55-58, Feb., 1944.

FOOD HABITS OF FOXES IN ALABAMA. Joseph E. Herbert. MS thesis, Ala. Polytechnic Inst., 1941.

MATERIALS ON FOOD OF THE FOX (VULPES VULPES L.) IN THE TARTAR

REPUBLIC. I.V. Jarkov, V.P. Teplov, V.I. Tikhvinsky. Raboty Volzhsko-Kamskoi Zonal'noi Okhotnich'epromyslonoi Biologischeskoi Stantsii, Kazan, no.2, (Uchen'ie Zapiski Kazanskogo Gosudarstvennogo Universiteta im V.I. Ul'ainova-Lenina, vol.92, nos.7-8), pp.90-109, 1932. (In Russian, with English summary.)

FOXES MUST EAT TOO. John C. Kase. Outdoor Ind., 13 (4): 14-15, June, 1946.

FOOD HABITS OF FOXES IN WILD TURKEY TERRITORY. Edward L. Kozicky. Pa. Game News, 14 (4): 8-9, 28, July, 1943.

ON THE FOOD OF THE FOX. Teppo Lampio. Suomen Riista, 8: 156-164, illus., 1953. (Finnish with English summary.)

TWO RECORDS OF FOXES EATING LARVAL HOVER FLIES AND DOR BEETLES. R.A. Lever. Proc. Zool. Soc. Lond., 128 (4): 596-597, July 24, 1957.

LATE FALL AND WINTER FOOD OF FOXES IN CENTRAL MASSACHUSETTS. Arthur E. MacGregor. Jour. Wildlife Mgt., Menasha, vol.6, no.3, pp.221-224, July, 1942.

FOXES, DENS, AND FARMERS. William T. McKean. N. Dak. Outdoors, 10 (2): 22, Aug., 1947.

A NEW WILDLIFE STUDY IN NORTH DAKOTA. William T. McKean. North Dak. Outdoors, 9 (11): 13-14, May, 1947.

MARSH DISCUSSES QUAIL-FOX RELATIONSHIP. A. Marsh. Tennessee Conservationist, Nashville, vol.13, nos.5-6, pp.4-5, May-June, 1948.

QUAIL-FOX RELATIONSHIP. A. Marsh. Tennessee Conservationist, Nashville, vol. 14, no.3, pp.1012, May-June, 1949.

RED FOX FOOD HABITS IN THE VICINITY OF A VULNERABLE CAPTIVE GOOSE FLOCK. Frank R. Martin. Jour. Wildl. Mgt., vol.19, no.4, pp.496-497, Oct., 1955.

NATURAL PREDATION AND QUAIL. Ted R. Mitchell. Wildlife in North Carolina, Raleigh, vol.12, no.1, pp.4-6, illus., Jan., 1948.

(FOX (VULPES VULPES CRUCIGERA BECHSTEIN 1789) PICKING RASPBERRIES.) Fuchs, Vulpes vulpes crucigera (Bechstein, 1789), beim Himbeerpfluecken. D. Mueller-Using. Saeugetierk. Mitteil., Stuttgart, vol.1, no.2, p.79, Apr.1, 1953.

FOLLOWING FOX TRAILS. Adolph Murie. Mus. Zool., Univ. Mich., Misc. Publ.32, pp.45, Aug., 1936.

(Review by A. L. Nelson of) FOLLOWING FOX TRAILS. Adolph Murie. Jour. Mam., vol.18, no.1, pp.107-108, Feb.14, 1937.

A PRELIMINARY REPORT ON THE WINTER FOOD OF VIRGINIA FOXES. A. L. Nelson. Jour. Mam., vol.14, no. 1, pp.40-43, Feb., 1933.

BEHAVIOR OF GRAY FOXES IN RAIDING QUAIL NESTS. A.L. Nelson, C.O. Handley. Jour. Wildl. Mgt., 2 (3): 73-78, July, 1938.

(FOOD OF THE FOX IN PLAINS ABOVE THE SEA OF AZOV THAT ARE POPULATED WITH NUTRIAS.) Pitaniye listisi (Vulpes vulpes L.) v priazovskikh plavnyakh kubani zasyelnnikh nutriyei (Myocastor coypus Mol.). M. P. Pavlov, I. B. Kiris. Zool. Zhurnal, Akad. Nauk SSSR, 35 (6): 897-907, 1956.

THE WINTER DIET OF THE ARCTIC FOX IN YAMAL AREA. S. D. Pereleshin. Zool. Zh., 22: 299-313, 1943.

(THE FAMISHED FOX.) Le renard famelique. Francis Petter. Terre et Vie, pp. 190-193, illus., 1952.

FOX - PHEASANT RELATIONS. Stacey B. Robeson. N.Y. Cons. Dept., Final Rep., PR Proj., 27-R, pp.20, June, 1950.

A CORRELATION OF FOX FOOD HABITS WITH FOODS AVAILABLE ON THE HUNTINGTON FOREST. Robert Schueler. MS thesis, Syracuse Univ., 1948.

RED FOX FOOD HABITS IN A WILDERNESS AREA. Robert Schueler. Jour. Mam., 32 (4): 462-464, Nov., 1951.

COMPARATIVE ANALYSIS OF RED FOX FEEDING TRENDS ON TWO CENTRAL IOWA AREAS. Thomas G. Scott. Iowa Agr. Exp. Sta., Res. Bull., 353: 425-487, Aug., 1947.

DIETARY PATTERNS OF RED AND GRAY FOXES. Thomas G. Scott. Ecology, Durham, vol.36, no.2, pp.366-367, Apr., 1955.

FOOD REMAINS IN STOMACHS AND INTESTINES OF IOWA RED FOXES. Thomas G. Scott. Jour. Wildl. Mgt., 14 (4): 478-480, Oct., 1950.

AN INVESTIGATION OF THE FOOD COACTIONS OF THE NORTHERN PLAINS RED FOX. Thomas G. Scott. PhD thesis, Iowa State Coll., 1942; Iowa State Coll. J. Sci., 17 (1): 117-119, Oct., 1942.

SOME FOOD COACTIONS OF THE NORTHERN PLAINS RED FOX. Thomas G. Scott. Ecol. Monog., 13 (4): 427-479, Oct., 1943.

RED FOXES AND A DECLINING PREY POPULATION. Thomas G. Scott, Willard D. Klimstra. Monograph Ser. Southern Illinois Univ., Carbondale, no.1, pp.123, 1955.

FOOD OF THE RED FOX. Ernest Thompson Seton. Jour. Mam., vol.1, no.3, p. 140, May, 1920.

RED FOX'S METHOD OF HUNTING FIELD MICE. Wendell P. Smith. Jour. Mam., vol.25, no.1, pp.90-91, Feb., 1944.

SUMMER FOOD OF THE RED FOX (VULPES VULPES) IN GREAT BRITAIN: A PRELIMINARY REPORT. H.N. Southern, J.S. Watson. Jour. Anim. Ecol., Cambridge, England, vol.10, no.1, pp.1-11, May, 1941.

SUMMER FOOD HABITS OF THE GRAY FOX IN ALABAMA. Reynolds White Thrasher. MS thesis, Ala. Polytechnic Inst., 1949.

ANALYSES SHOW FOXES PREFER FRUITS, INSECTS. W.H. Turcotte. S. Outdoors, 7 (12-13): 3, Jan., 1947.

WHAT DOES A FOX EAT? W.H. Turcott. Miss. Game and Fish, 18 (8): 3, graph, Mar., 1955.

FOXES KILL RABBITS. Upshur Vincent. Texas Game and Fish, Austin, vol.6, no. 6, p.16, May, 1948.

THE FOX-PHEASANT PROBLEM. Max J. Wilcomb. Oregon State Game Comm. Bull., Portland, vol.3, no.11, pp.1, 6-7, illus., Nov., 1948.

FOX POPULATIONS AND FOOD HABITS IN RELATION TO GAME BIRDS IN THE WILLAMETTE VALLEY, OREGON. M.J. Wilcomb. MS thesis, Oregon State Coll., 1948.

FOXES AS SNAKE-KILLERS. Victorian Nat., Melbourne, vol.63, no.7, p.159, Nov., 1946.

Fossils

STRATIGRAPHY OF THE BOROPHAGUS LITTORALIS LOCALITY, CALIFORNIA. W.F. Barbat, A. Allen Weymouth. Univ. Calif. Publ., Dept. Geol. Sci., vol.21, no.3, pp. 25-36, figs.2, pls.4-5, Nov.5, 1931.

A NEW MIOCENE DOG, MESOCYON GERINGENSIS, SP. NOV. Erwin Hinckley Barbour, C. Bertrand Schultz. Nebraska State Mus., vol.1, bull.43, pp.407-418, figs.192-197, May, 1935.

A MIOCENE DOG FROM MARYLAND. Charles T. Berry. Proc. U.S. Nat. Mus., vol.85, no.3035, pp.159-161, fig.1, Aug.10, 1938.

(DOGS OF THE STONE AGE IN THE AMOUR BASIN.) Les chiens de l'age de pierre du bassin de l'Amour. A. Brauner. Mem. du Comite Geol., Petrograd, livr. 160, pp.1-24, pls.1-2, 1923.

(ON THE CRANIUM OF CANIS LUPIS L. OF THE BRONZE AGE FOUND AT RIVAROLO MANTOVANO, (MANTOVA).) Su un cranio di Canis lupus L. dell'eta del Bronzo rinvenuto a rivarolo mantovano (Mantova). Gian Carlo Cadeo. Atti Soc. Italiana Sci. Nat. Mus. Civ. Stor. Nat., Milan, vol.43, nos.3-4, pp.432-436, Dec., 1954.

ON SOME TRIASSIC CYNODONTS FROM TANGANYIKA. A. W. Crompton. Proc. Zool. Soc. Lond., vol.125, pts.3-4, pp. 617-669, illus., Nov.23, 1955.

THE FOSSIL CARNIVORES OF THE TRANSVAAL CAVES: CANIDAE. R.F. Ewer. Proc. Zool. Soc. Lond., vol.126, pt.1, pp. 97-119, pls.2, Jan.11, 1956.

(ON THE OCCURRENCE OF CANIDAE IN THE CHAPALMALENSE OF MIRAMAR.) Sobre la presencia de Canidae en el chapalmalense de Miramar. Joaquin Frenguelli. Anales Soc. Cientifica Argentina, vol.115, no.6, pp.331-334, fig. 1, June, 1933.

A NEW SPECIES OF DOG FROM THE LOWER PLIOCENE OF CALIFORNIA. (TOMARCTUS ROBUSTUS.) Morton Green. Univ. California Publ., Bull. Dept. Geol. Sci., Berkeley, vol.28, no.4, pp.81-90, figs.5, Aug.31, 1948.

A SKULL OF NOTHOCYON FROM THE JOHN DAY OLIGOCENE. E. Raymond Hall, Handel T. Martin. Univ. Kansas Sci. Bull., vol.19, no.13, pp.283-287, pl.29, July, 1930.

(ON THE DECIDUOUS DENTITION OF AMPHICYON LEMANENSIS POMEL.) Zur Milchbezahnung von Amphicyon lemanensis Pomel. H. Helbing. Ecologae geologicae Helvetiae, vol.18, pp.295-300, figs.2, Basel, 1923.

A SYSTEMATIC REVISION OF DAPHOENUS AND SOME ALLIED GENERA. Jean Ringier Hough. Jour. Paleontol., Menasha, vol.22, no.5, pp.573-600, figs.3, pls.84-87, Sept., 1948.

PRELIMINARY REPORT ON THE VERTEBRATE TYPE LOCALITY OF CITA CANYON, AND THE DESCRIPTION OF AN ANCESTRAL COYOTE. C. Stuart Johnston. Amer. Jour. Sci., ser.5, vol.35, no.209, pp.383-390, pls.3, May, 1938.

A SKULL OF OSTEOBORUS VALIDUS FROM THE EARLY MIDDLE PLIOCENE OF TEXAS. C. Stuart Johnston. Jour. Paleont., Chicago, vol.13, no.5, pp.526-530, figs.8, Sept., 1939.

PLIOCYON WALKERAE, A NEW PLIOCENE CANID FROM TEXAS. C. Stuart Johnston, Wayne G. Christian. Jour. Palaeontology, Menasha, vol.15, no.1, pp.56-60, figs.5, Jan., 1941.

(THE FOXES OF THE NEW PLIOCENE IN HUNGARY.) Die fuechse des ungarischen Oberpliozaens. Theodor Kormos. Folia Zool. and Hydrobiol., Univ. Lettlands, Riga, vol.4, no.2, pp.167-188, pl.5, Dec. 31, 1932.

(THE WOLVES OF THE HUNGARIAN UPPER PLIOCENE.) Die Wolfe des ungarischen Oberpliozaens. Theodor Kormos. Folia Zool. and Hydrobiol., Univ. Lettlands, Riga, vol.5, no.1, pp.13-35, pl.1, July 19, 1933.

(CONTRIBUTION TO KNOWLEDGE OF THE GREAT CANIDS EXTINCT IN SOUTH AMERICA.) Contribución al conocimiento de los grandes cánidos extinguidos de Sud America. Lucas Kraglievich. Anales Soc. Cient. Argentina, vol.106, pts.1-3, pp.25-66, pls.1-9, July-Sept., 1928.

EVIDENCE OF THE DOG AND THE WOLF IN THE ESTONIAN MESOLITHIC. Johannes Lepiksaar. Apophoreta Tartuensia, Stockholm, pp.434-439, 1949.

A NEW OLIGOCENE DOG. (BRACHICYON B. INTERMEDIUS.) F. B. Loomis. Amer. Jour. Sci., vol.22, no.128, pp.100-102, figs.4, Aug., 1931.

THREE NEW MIOCENE DOGS AND THEIR PHYLOGENY. (MAMMACYON, M. OBTUSIDENS, DAPHAENODON NIOBRARENSIS, AND TEMNOCYON TYPICUS.) F.B.

Loomis. Jour. Paleont., vol.10, no.1, pp. 44-52, figs.6, Jan., 1936.

THE AELURODON SAEVUS GROUP. Paul O. McGrew. Geol. Ser. Field Mus. Nat. Hist., Chicago, vol.8, no.13, pp.79-84, fig.26, Aug.14, 1944.

A NEW AMPHICYON FROM THE DEEP RIVER MIOCENE. (AMPHICYON RIGGSI.) Paul O. McGrew. Field Mus. Nat. Hist., Geol. Ser., vol.6, no.23, pp.341-350, figs. 95-99, Mar.24, 1939.

A NEW CYNODESMUS FROM THE LOWER PLIOCENE OF NEBRASKA WITH NOTES ON THE PHYLOGENY OF THE DOGS. (CYNODESMUS EUTHOS.) Paul O. McGrew. Univ. Calif. Publ. Bull. Dept. Geol. Sci., vol.23, no.10, pp.305-312, figs.4, Mar.15, 1935.

AN OSTEOBORUS FROM HONDURAS. (OSTEOBORUS CYNOIDES.) Paul O. McGrew. Geol. Ser. Field Mus. Nat. Hist., Chicago, vol.8, no.12, pp.75-77, fig.25, Aug.14, 1944.

THE GRIM WOLF OF THE TAR PITS. W.D. Matthew. Amer. Mus. Jour., vol. 16, no.1, pp.45-47, illus., Jan., 1916.

NEW CANIDAE FROM THE MIOCENE OF COLORADO. W.D. Matthew. Bull. Amer. Mus. Nat. Hist., New York, vol.16, art. 21, pp.281-290, figs.4, Sept.18, 1902.

A SKULL OF DINOCYON FROM THE MIOCENE OF TEXAS. W.D. Matthew. Bull. Amer. Mus. Nat. Hist., New York, vol. 16, art.11, pp.129-136, figs.4, Apr.7, 1902.

OSTEOLOGY AND AFFINITIES OF BOROPHAGUS. W.D. Matthew, R.A. Stirton. Univ. Calif. Publ. Bull. Dept. Geol. Sci., vol.19, no.7, pp.171-216, pls.21-34, May 9, 1930.

ALLOCYON, A NEW CANID GENUS FROM THE JOHN DAY BEDS OF OREGON. Charles W. Merriam. Univ. Calif. Publ. Bull. Dept. Geol. Sci., vol.19, no.9, pp. 229-244, pls.35-36, figs.5, May 10, 1930.

THE FAUNA OF RANCHO LA BREA. PART 2. CANIDAE. John C. Merriam. Mem. Univ. Calif., vol.1, no.2, pp.217-272, figs.43, pls.5, 1912.

NOTES ON THE CANID GENUS TEPHROCYON. John C. Merriam. Univ. Calif. Publ. Bull. Dept. Geol., vol.7, no.18, pp. 359-372, Sept.23, 1913.

A SUGGESTION OF RICKETS IN THE PLEISTOCENE. Roy L. Moodie. Amer. Jour. Surgery, New York (n.s.), vol.10, no.1, pp.162-163, fig.1, Oct., 1930.

THE CANIDAE OF THE THOMAS FARM MIOCENE. S. J. Olsen. Breviora Mus. Comp. Zool., 66: 1-12, illus., Nov.27, 1956.

A NEW SPECIES OF OSTEOBORUS FROM THE BONE VALLEY FORMATION OF FLORIDA. S.J. Olsen. Special Publ. Florida Geol. Surv., 2: 1-5, illus., June, 1956.

UPPER MOLARS OF CANIS ARMBRUSTERI GIDLEY FROM CUMBERLAND CAVE, MARYLAND. Bryan Patterson. Amer. Jour. Sci., ser.5, vol.23, no.136, pp.334-336, fig.1, Apr., 1932.

OSTEOBORUS DIABLOENSIS, A NEW DOG FROM THE BLACK HAWK RANCH FAUNA, MOUNT DIABLO, CALIFORNIA. K.A. Richey. Univ. Calif. Publ., Bull. Dept. Geol. Sci., vol.24, no.10, pp.303-308, fig. 1, Apr.23, 1938.

A RADIAL EXOSTOSIS IN THE FOSSIL CANID DAPHOENUS. Alfred Sherwood Romer. Amer. Jour. Sci., ser.5, vol.8, no.45, pp.235-240, fig.1, Sept., 1924.

OSTEOBORUS, A NEW GENUS OF DOGS, AND ITS RELATIONS TO BOROPHAGUS COPE. R.A. Stirton, V.L. Vanderhoff. Univ. Calif. Publ. Bull. Dept. Geol. Sci., vol.23, no.4, pp.175-182, figs.3, July 19, 1933.

A COYOTE-LIKE WOLF JAW FROM THE RANCHO LA BREA PLEISTOCENE. Chester Stock. Bull. S. California Acad. Sci., vol.37, pt.2, pp.49-51, pl.10 (May-Aug., 1938), Oct.10, 1938.

HYAENOGNATHUS FROM THE LATE PLIOCENE OF THE COSO MOUNTAINS, CALIFORNIA. Chester Stock. Jour. Mam., vol.13, no.3, pp.263-266, Aug., 1932; Bull. Geol. Soc. America, vol.44, no.1, p.218, Feb.28, 1933. (Abstract.)

THE RELATIVE LENGTHS OF LIMB ELEMENTS IN CANIS DIRUS. Chester Stock, John F. Lance. Bull. S. Calif. Acad. Sci., Los Angeles, vol.47, pt.3, pp.79-84, pls. 14-16, Feb.5, 1949.

A NEWLY MOUNTED SKELETON OF THE EXTINCT DIRE WOLF FROM THE PLEISTOCENE OF RANCHO LA BREA. Chester Stock, John F. Lance, John O. Nigra. Bull. S. Calif. Acad. Sci., Los Angeles, vol.45, pt.2, pp.108-110, pls.8-9, May-Aug., 1946.

BOROPHAGUS LITTORALIS FROM THE MARINE TERTIARY OF CALIFORNIA. V.L. Vanderhoof. Univ. Calif. Publ., Bull. Dept. Geol. Sci., vol.21, no.2, pp. 15-24, pls.1-3, Nov.5, 1931.

NOTES ON THE TYPE OF BOROPHAGUS DIVERSIDENS COPE. V.L. Vanderhoof. Jour. Mam., vol.17, no.4, pp.415-416, illus., Nov., 1936.

A REVIEW OF THE GENUS AELURODON. V.L. Vanderhoof, Joseph T. Gregory. Univ. Calif. Publ., Bull. Dept. Geol. Sci., Berkeley, vol.25, no.3, pp.143-164, figs. 8, May 9, 1940.

A NEW SPECIES OF DOG FROM THE MIOCENE OF COLORADO. John A. Wilson. Contrib. Mus. Paleont., Univ. Michigan, Ann Arbor, vol.5, no.12, pp.315-318, figs. 2, July 1, 1939.

Fur Farming

FOX RANCHING IN CANADA. J.A. Allen, J. Ennis Smith. Dom. Canada Dept. Agric., Bull.no.12, new ser., 41 pp., illus., 1925.

SILVER-FOX FARMING. Frank G. Ashbrook. U.S. Dept. Agric. Bull.1151, pp.60, figs.46, June 20, 1923.

A COMPARISON OF FEED COSTS WITH PELT VALUES OF SILVER FOXES. Frank G. Ashbrook, Karl B. Hanson. Fur Jour., vol.2, no.11, pp.24-25, Dec., 1928.

FUR BEARING ANIMALS OF THE UNITED STATES. THE COYOTE. Frank G. Ashbrook, Horace J. McMullen. Fur Jour., vol.2, no.9, pp.18, 59-60, illus., Oct., 1928.

BLUE FOX FARMING IN ALASKA. Frank G. Ashbrook, Ernest P. Walker. U.S. Dept. Agric., Dept. bull. no.1350, pp.1-33, Oct., 1925.

BREEDING FOR QUALITY IN THE SILVER MUTATION FOX. Bert Avery. Fur Breeder, Duluth, vol.21, no.12, pp.18, 20, 22, June, 1949.

MODERN FOX MUTATIONS. PLATINUMS AND WHITE FACE SILVERS. Bert Avery. Amer. Fur Breeder, Duluth, vol.13, no.12, pp.16, 20, fig.1, June, 1941.

YEARLY FOX FEEDING SCHEDULE. Bert Avery. Nat. Fur News, Denver, vol.19, no.1, p.14, Feb., 1947.

THE RAISING OF BLUE FOXES. Jack K.L. Aylwin. Nat. Fur News, Denver, vol.17, no.7, pp.6, 30-31, 37, Aug., 1945.

AN EFFICIENT TRAP FOR THE FOX RANCH. Charles F. Bassett. USDA, Biol. Survey, Wildl. Leaflet 127, p.2, Mar., 1939.

A FEEDER FOR FOXES. Charles F. Bassett. USDA, Biol. Survey, Wildl. Leaflet 128, p.2, Mar., 1939.

LOW MEAT DIET FOR BREEDING FOXES. Charles F. Bassett. Fur of Canada, Winnipeg, vol.14, no.2, pp.6, 8, Nov., 1948; Nat. Fur News, Denver, vol.20, no.11, pp. 22, 41, Dec., 1948.

SEASONAL FOX RATIONS AND QUANTITIES TO FEED. Charles F. Bassett. U.S. Bur. Biol. Surv., Wildlife Research and Mgt. Leaflet BS-130, pp.3, tables 2, Apr., 1939.

HOW TO MEET THE CALCIUM NEEDS OF GROWING FOXES. Charles F. Bassett, Lorin E. Harris. Fur of Canada, Winnipeg, vol.13, no.6, pp.3-4, 6, Mar., 1948; Nat. Fur News, Denver, vol.20, no.3, pp. 10, 26-27, 30-31, Apr., 1948; Black Fox Mag., New York, vol.31, no.12, pp.10-11, 33-35, Apr., 1948.

TIMING FOX MATINGS FOR MAXIMUM PRODUCTION. Charles F. Bassett, Leonard M. Llewellyn. Amer. Fur Breeder, Duluth, vol.19, no.6, pp.46, 48, 50, 52, Dec., 1946.

MATING FOX VIXENS FOR MAXIMUM PRODUCTIVITY. Charles F. Bassett, Oliver P. Pearson, Edward Martin. Fur of Canada, Winnipeg, vol.10, no.5, pp.22-23, Feb., 1945; Nat. Fur News, Denver, vol.17, no.2, pp.6, 20, Mar., 1945.

THE EFFECT OF MATING TIME ON PRODUCTIVITY OF FOXES. Charles F. Bassett, Ford Wilke. Amer. Fur Breeder, Duluth, vol.16, no.6, pp.22, 24, 26, Dec., 1943.

EFFECTS OF LOW MEAT DIETS ON BREEDING FOXES. Charles F. Bassett, Ford Wilke. Amer. Nat. Fur and Market Jour., Wausau, vol.27, no.5, pp.15, 33-34, Dec., 1948.

EFFECT OF MATING TIME ON PRODUCTIVITY IN FOXES. Charles F. Bassett, Ford Wilke, Oliver Pearson, Edward Martin. Nat. Fur News, Denver, vol.15, no.12, pp.10, 26, Jan., 1944.

THE GREENLAND ARCTIC BLUE FOX. R.H. Beatty. Amer. Fur Breeder, Duluth, vol.17, no.5, pp.24, 26, Nov., 1944.

UNSUCCESSFUL ATTEMPTS AT COLLECTING SEMEN FROM CAPTIVE FOXES. Frances H. Bezdek. Amer. Fur Breeder, Duluth, vol.19, no.6, pp.54, 56, Dec., 1946.

RAISING OF ARCTIC FOXES. L.V. Boitsov. Trans. Arctic Inst. Biol., Leningrad, vol.65, pp.7-144, figs.19, 1937.

THE PEARL PLATINUM FOX. E. Rendle Bowness. Fur of Canada, Winnipeg, vol. 9, no.9, pp.6-7, 14, June, 1944; Amer. Fur Breeder, Duluth, vol.17, no.5, pp.38, 40, 42, 44, Nov., 1944; no.7, pp.34-36, Jan., 1945.

WEANING KITS EARLY MAY PREVENT NURSING SICKNESS. E. Rendle Bowness. Black Fox Mag., New York, vol.33, no.2, pp.8, 22, June, 1949.

IS THE BLUE FOX WORTHWHILE? Frank M. Chastek. Amer. Fur Breeder, vol.4, no.8, p.18, Feb., 1932.

CARE OF VIXEN AND PUPPIES. Jack Chastek. Amer. Fur Breeder, vol.1, no. 12, p.4, June, 1929.

BREEDING GLACIER BLUE AND PEARLATINA FOXES. Leon J. Cole. Nat. Fur News, Denver, vol.17, no.1, p.10, Feb., 1945; Amer. Fur Breeder, Duluth, vol.17, no.8, p.24, Feb., 1945; Amer. Nat. Fur and Market Jour., Wausau, vol.23, no.7, pp.9-10, Feb., 1945; Fur of Canada, Winnipeg, vol.10, no.1, p.17, Apr., 1945.

WHAT YOU SHOULD KNOW ABOUT FOX HYBRIDS. Leon J. Cole, Richard M. Shackelford. Black Fox Mag., New York, vol.31, no.11, pp.11, 33-35, 37-38; no.12, pp.14, 24; vol.32, no.1, pp.14, 20-21, illus., Mar., Apr., May, 1948.

(THE BLUE FOX.) Der Blaufuchs. A.M. Comsia. Pelztierzucht verb. mit Kleintierzucht, vol.8, no.4, pp.61-65, fig.1, Apr.20, 1932.

THE CULTURE OF BLACK AND SILVER FOXES; A WORK OF PRACTICAL INFORMATION. R. B. Croft. Woodstock, Rod and Gun Press, pp.83, illus., 1913.

BLUE FOX RANCHING. A.E. Crooks. Amer. Fur Breeder, Duluth, vol.19, no. 12, pp.6, 8, June, 1947.

COMMENTS ON THE SILVER FOX SITUATION. A.H. Crow. Nat. Fur News, Denver, vol.20, no.2, p.14, Mar., 1948.

OBSERVED AT THE GRADING TABLE. (FOX.) A.H. Crow. Nat. Fur News, Denver, vol.15, no.12, p.9, Jan., 1944.

THE DOMESTICATED SILVER FOX. Ned Dearborn. Farmers' Bull.795, U.S. Dept. Agric., pp.32, figs.22, Mar., 1917.

SILVER FOX FARMING IN EASTERN NORTH AMERICA. Ned Dearborn. U.S. Dept. Agric., Bull.no.301, pp.35, figs.21, Oct.29, 1915.

HOW THE FIRST NORWEGIAN PLATINA FOXES CAME TO THIS COUNTRY. T.M. Dix. Amer. Fur Breeder, Duluth, vol.14, no.3, pp.14, 16, Sept., 1941.

MATING PROBLEMS ON THE FOX RANCH. William Donat. Nat. Fur News, Denver, vol.17, no.4, pp.4, 14-15, 18, May, 1945.

WHELPING TIME ON THE FOX RANCH. William Donat. Nat. Fur News, Denver, vol.17, no.4, pp.8, 16, May, 1946.

TRAINING THE POLYGAMOUS MALE. Robert K. Enders. Fur of Canada, Winnipeg, vol.10, no.10, pp.7, 22, July, 1945; Nat. Fur News, Denver, vol.17, no.8, pp. 12, 46, Sept., 1945.

ACTIVITY IN CANADIAN FOX FARMING. Wesley Frost. Daily Consular and Trade Reports, 16th year, no.9, pp.177-189, Jan. 11, 1913.

MONEY IN FOX FARMING. Stephen A. Gillis. Jersey City, N.J., International Letter Club, pp.32, illus., 1915.

HISTORY OF THE AMERICAN PLATINUM ON THE BUFFALO BILL FUR FARM AT CODY, WYOMING. W.A. Granquist. Amer. Fur Breeder, Duluth, vol.13, no.12, pp.10, 12-13, figs.3, June, 1941.

BREEDING OF NEW TYPE FOXES. C.K. Gunn. Fur of Canada, Winnipeg, vol.9, no.2, pp.12-13, Nov., 1943.

CHOOSING FOX BREEDING STOCK. C.K. Gunn. Nat. Fur News, Denver, vol.17, no. 10, pp.12, 38, Nov., 1945.

CONSTRUCTION OF FOX SHEDS. C.K. Gunn. Fur of Canada, Winnipeg, vol.10, no.9, pp.20, 22, June, 1945; Nat. Fur News, Denver, vol.17, no.8, pp.14, 46, Sept., 1945.

CUTTING OF FOX TENDONS. C.K. Gunn. Fur of Canada, Winnipeg, vol.10, no.8, p. 23, May, 1945.

FOX RATIONS DURING THE GESTATION PERIOD. C.K. Gunn. Nat. Fur News, Denver, vol.16, no.2, p.5, Mar., 1944.

FOX RATIONS IN THE BREEDING SEASON. C.K. Gunn. Nat. Fur News, Denver, vol. 16, no.12, p.7, Jan., 1945.

A PROGRAM OF IMPROVED METHODS OF SELECTION AND BREEDING IS URGENTLY NEEDED IN THE CANADIAN FOX RANCHING INDUSTRY. C.K. Gunn. Fur of Canada, Winnipeg, vol.13, no.10, pp.24-25, July, 1948.

RATIONS FOR GROWING FOX PUPS. C.K. Gunn. Fur of Canada, Winnipeg, vol.11, no.8, p.11, May, 1946.

THE REDUCTION OF LOSSES AT WHELPING TIME. (FOXES.) C.K. Gunn. Nat. Fur News, Denver, vol.16, no.5, pp.6, 19, June, 1944.

SUMMARY OF WORK AT EXPERIMENTAL FOX RANCH, SUMMERSIDE, P.E.I., FOR 1947. C.K. Gunn. Amer. Fur Breeder, Duluth, vol.20, no.9, p.26, Mar., 1948.

TEN-YEAR REPORT OF WORK AT THE DOMINION EXPERIMENTAL FOX RANCH, SUMMERSIDE, P.E.I. C.K. Gunn. Fur of Canada, Winnipeg, vol.13, no.6, pp.8, 10, 12-13; vol.13, no.7, pp.8, 10-13; no.8, pp.6-8, illus., Mar., Apr., May, 1948.

HYGIENE IN FOX FARMING. Karl B. Hanson. Leaflet no.47, U.S. Dept. Agric., pp.6, figs.4, Oct., 1929; Amer. Fur Breeder, vol.2, no.9, pp.4-6, Mar., 1930.

ANTHELMINTIC EFFICIENCY OF CARBON TETRACHLORID IN THE TREATMENT OF FOXES. Karl B. Hanson, H.L. Van Volkenberg. Jour. Agric. Research, vol.28, no.4, pp.331-337, 1924.

FOX CARCASSES AS A POSSIBLE SOURCE OF PROTEIN. Lorin E. Harris, John K. Loosli. Nat. Fur News, Denver, vol.15, no.11, pp.10, 22, Dec., 1943.

BLUE FOX. Benjamin H. Herzig. Amer. Fur Breeder, vol.11, no.6, pp.18, 22, Dec., 1938.

HOW WE FEED BLUE FOXES IN THE FALL MONTHS. L.C. Hobson. Amer. Fur Breeder, vol.3, no.4, p.33, Oct., 1930.

INCREASING FOX PUP PRODUCTION. S.T. Johnson. Nat. Fur News, Denver, vol.18, no.8, pp.11, 38-39, Sept., 1946.

ON A SILVER FOX FARM. THE BREEDING SEASON. C.J. Johnstone. Field, London, vol.155, no.4039, p.778, May 24, 1930.

SILVER FOX BREEDING. C.J. Johnstone. Field, London, vol.154, no.4011, p.704, Nov.9, 1929.

CLASSIFICATION AND PRICE TRENDS OF SILVER FOX SKINS. Charles E. Kellogg. U.S. Dept. Agric., Bur. Biol. Surv., Wildlife Research and Mgt. Leaflet, pp.1-12, figs.1-4, June, 1936.

SILVER FOX PELT PRICES AS AFFECTED BY TIME OF PELTING, SEX, AND AGE. Charles E. Kellogg. U.S. Dept. Agric., Circ.460, pp.1-28, figs.7, pls.1-2, tables 4, Dec., 1937.

SILVER FOX PUP VALUES IN RELATION TO DATE OF BIRTH, AGE OF VIXENS AND OTHER FACTORS. Charles E. Kellogg. U.S. Dept. Interior, Fish and Wildlife Service, Wildlife Cir.8, pp.15, figs.2, 1941.

(A PRACTICAL CONTRIBUTION ON THE TOPIC OF FOX CROSSING.) Ein praktischer Beitrag zum Kapitel Fuchskreuzungen. P. Kirner. Der Deutsche Pelztierzuechter, Jahrg.1932, Muenchen, no.1, pp.10-12, Jan.1, 1932.

(INFLUENCING THE REPRODUCTION OF FOXES WITH THE HELP OF HORMONES.) Beeinflussung der Fortpflanzung der Fuechse mit Hilfe von Hormonen. W. Koch. Deutsche Pelztierzuechter, Muenchen, vol.14, no.1, pp.2-6, Jan.1, 1939.

THE MUSKEGON FOX SHOW. Harry Jay LaDue. Fins, Feathers and Fur, no.30, pp.10-11, June, 1922.

BREEDING METHODS IN CANADA. (FOXES.) George McLeod. Fur of Canada, Winnipeg, vol.13, no.12, pp. 28-30, Sept., 1948.

STATUS OF CANADIAN FOX INDUSTRY. Livingston T. Mays. U.S. Commerce Reports, U.S. Dept. Commerce, Wash., D.C., pp.198-199, Jan., 1915.

(ON PLATINUM FOXES.) Om - og omkring-platinarevene. Otto L. Mohr. Naturen, Bergen, Argang 64, no.2, pp.38-49, figs. 4, Feb., 1940.

THE NORWEGIAN PLATINUM FOX. A COAT COLOR MUTATION HAVING GREAT ECONOMIC VALUE. Otto L. Mohr, Per Tuff. Jour. Heredity, Wash., D.C., vol. 30, no.6, pp.227-234, June, 1939.

RAISING BLUE FOX PUPPIES. C.A. Oliver. Amer. Fur Breeder, vol.1, no.12, p.18, June, 1929.

SILVER FOX FARMING. Wilfred H. Osgood. U.S. Dept. Agric., Farmers Bull., Wash., D.C., no.328, pp.1-22, figs.10, Aug.8, 1908; Rept. Amer. Breeders Assoc., vol.5, pp.320-325, fig. 1, 1909.

RAISING ARCTIC FOXES. Lewis Palmer. Amer. Fur Breeder, Duluth, vol.14, no.3, p.18, Sept., 1941.

LET'S GO AHEAD AND BREED BETTER FOXES. W. T. Perry. Fur of Canada, Winnipeg, vol.11, no.1, p.12, Oct., 1945.

BALANCE IN FOX BREEDING. L. Merle Pierce. Nat. Fur News, Denver, vol.18, no.8, pp.20, 44, Sept., 1946.

BREEDING EXPERIMENTS NEEDED TO REVIVE THE RANCH FOX. L. Merle Pierce. Amer. Fur Breeder, Duluth, vol.21, no.7, pp.34, 36, 38, Jan., 1949.

SILVER FOX, PRINCE OF FUR-BEARERS. E. A. Preble. Nature Mag., vol.7, pp.73-75, figs.5, Feb., 1926.

LET'S GET BACK TO BREEDING QUALITY FOXES. Arthur C. Prentice. Nat. Fur Breeder, Denver, vol.17, no.3, p.4, Apr., 1945.

THE SECOND MILE. (FOXES.) Paul L. Reinhardt. Amer. Fur Breeder, Duluth, vol.20, no.8, pp.8, 10, illus., Feb., 1948.

BREEDING FOXES. G. Ennis Smith. Amer. Fur Breeder, vol.4, no.8, pp.4-6, Feb., 1932.

SEASONAL NUTRITIONAL REQUIREMENTS OF SILVER FOXES. G. Ennis Smith. Amer. Fur Breeder, vol.4, no.3, pp.4-7, Sept., 1931; vol.4, no.4, p.31, Oct., 1931.

THE NEW PLATINUM BLUE FOX. C.W. Stacey. Amer. Fur Breeder, Duluth, vol. 20, no.2, pp.20, 22, 24, 26, illus., Aug., 1947.

NEW PLATINUM BLUE FOXES. C.W. Stacey. Nat. Fur News, Denver, vol.19, no.7, pp.13, 33, 38, Aug., 1947.

SOME IMPORTANT PHASES OF SILVER FOX RANCH PRACTICE. Ronald G. Stephenson. Nat. Fur News, Denver, vol. 19, no.7, pp.15, 38, Aug., 1947.

REDUCING MORTALITY IN MUTANT FOXES. Wilfrid T. Todd. Nat. Fur News, Denver, vol.15, no.11, pp.9, 32, Dec., 1943; Nat. Fur News, Denver, vol.16, no.1, pp.5, 26, Feb., 1944.

FOX RANCHING IN SOUTHERN CALIFORNIA. Edward L. Vail. California Fish and Game, San Francisco, vol.28, no.2, pp.87-88, Apr., 1942.

VETERINARY AID IN THE FOX RANCH. F.S. Wadsworth. Amer. Fur Breeder, vol.11, no.4, pp.25-26, Oct., 1929.

HORSEMEAT SUBSTITUTES FOR GROWING FOXES. Ford Wilke, Charles F. Bassett. Fur of Canada, Winnipeg, vol.14, no.8, pp.6, 8, May, 1949; Nat. Fur News, Denver, vol.21, no.6, pp.24-25, July, 1949.

THE SILVER FOX INDUSTRY. E. Witte. Field, London, vol.152, pp.424-425, Sept.13, 1928.

CLAY FUR FARMS. RED AND CROSS FOXES. Amer. Fur Breeder, vol.4, no. 5, p.15, Nov., 1931.

THE PROBLEMS OF THE FOX FARMER. Amer. Fur Breeder, vol.4, no.8, p.27, Feb., 1932.

THE STORY OF THE SILVER FOX. Ivy Press, Seattle, pp.32, illus., 1909.

General Habits, Behavior, Ecology

ON THE DECOYING OF COYOTES. J. R. Alcorn. Jour. Mam., 27 (2): 122-126, May, 1946.

(UTTERANCES OF THE SILVER FOX.) Silberfuchsplauderei. Edgar Bahr. Der Pelztierzuechter, Munich, Jahrg.9, no.2, pp.29-32, illus., Jan.15, 1934.

POPULATIONS AND MOVEMENTS OF THE SASKATCHEWAN TIMBER WOLF (CANIS LUPUS KNIGHTII) IN PRINCE ALBERT NATIONAL PARK, SASKATCHEWAN, 1947 TO 1951. A.W.F. Banfield. Can. Wildl. Serv., Wildl. Mgt. Bull. Ser.1, no.4, pp. 1-21, illus., 1951.

THE RANGE OF INDIVIDUAL TIMBER WOLVES (CANIS LUPUS). A.W.F. Banfield. Jour. Mam., vol.34, no.3, pp.389-390, Aug.14, 1953.

BLACK VULTURE AND RED FOX FOUND IN UNUSUAL ASSOCIATION. Frederick S. Barkalow, Jr. Wilson Bull., Sioux City, vol.52, no.4, pp.278-279, Dec., 1940.

THE COYOTE AND THE AUTOMOBILE. William Bebb. Jour. Mam., vol.16, no. 4, p.323, Nov., 1935.

THE COYOTE NOT AFRAID OF WATER. Harold C. Bryant. Jour. Mam., vol.1, no. 2, pp.87-88, Nov., 1919.

WILD DOGS ATTACKING A TIGER. R.W. Burton. Jour. Bombay Nat. Hist. Soc., vol.45, no.2, p.232, Apr., 1945.

CIRCUMSTANTIAL ACCOUNT OF A PANTHER ATTACKED BY WILD DOGS. J.McC. Clive. Jour. Bombay Nat. Hist. Soc., vol.32, p.590, Jan.15, 1928.

FOX CAUSING ROAD SUBSIDENCE. F.A. Coleridge. Field, London, vol.151, p. 164, Feb.2, 1928.

PECULIAR BEHAVIOR OF A RED FOX. William P. Comstock, Jr. Jour. Mam., vol.28, no.4, p.405, Nov.26, 1947.

A COYOTE FRIENDSHIP. F. Fraser Darling. Animal Kingdom, New York Zool. Soc., vol.55, no.1, pp.19-21, illus., Jan.-Feb., 1952.

RED FOX ATTACKED BY A GOLDEN EAGLE. Joseph S. Dixon. Jour. Mam., vol.14, no.3, p.257, Aug., 1933.

RED FOX TRANSPORTS PLAY OR TRAINING ITEMS TO NEW DEN. W. Robert Eadie. Jour. Mam., vol.30, no.3, p.308, Aug.17, 1949.

INTRODUCTION OF FOXES INTO AN ISOLATED, CARNIVORE-FREE POPULATION: A CASE HISTORY. William L. Engels. Jour. Mam., vol.22, no.3, pp. 320-321, Aug.14, 1941.

TAGGING STUDIES OF RED FOXES. Paul L. Errington, R.M. Berry. Jour. Mam., 18 (2): 203-205, May, 1937.

WATCHING COYOTES. Edson Fichter. Jour. Mam., vol.31, no.1, pp.66-73, Feb.21, 1950.

A STUDY OF COYOTE RELATIONSHIPS ON CATTLE RANGE. Henry S. Fitch. Jour. Wildlife Mgt., Menasha, vol.12, no.1, pp. 73-78, Jan., 1948.

JACKALS IN RESIDENTAL COMPOUNDS. Rodney Foster. Jour. Bombay Nat. Hist. Soc., vol.32, p.211, Aug.1, 1927.

SWIFT FOX DEN FOUND. Roy Fugate. Murrelet, Seattle, vol.20, no.2, May-Aug., p.44, Aug.10, 1939.

THE FOX AS A VOCALIST. Douglas Gordon. Field, London, vol.156, no.4055, p.375, Sept.13, 1930.

THE DESERT KIT FOX MOVES HIS FAMILY. Russell K. Grater. Nature Notes, Peoria, Ill., vol.6, no.4, pp.77-81, photos 3, Apr., 1939.

SOME COYOTE-WILDLIFE RELATIONSHIPS. E.E. Horn. Trans. N.A. Wildl. Conf., 6: 283-286, 1941.

A COYOTE SURVIVING UNDER DIFFICULTIES. A. Brazier Howell. Jour. Mam., vol.9, no.1, pp.63-64, Feb., 1928.

JACKALS ATTACKING A SPANIEL IN THE COMPOUND. Charles M. Inglis. Jour. Bombay Nat. Hist. Soc., vol.28, pp.1122-1123, Dec.20, 1922.

NOTE ON JACKALS (CANIS INDICUS INDICUS) ETC., IN A COMPOUND. Charles M. Inglis. Jour. Nat. Hist. Soc., vol.28, p.1122, Dec.20, 1922.

THE COYOTE AS A SEED DISTRIBUTOR. Edmund C. Jaeger. Jour. Mam., 31 (4): 452-453, Nov., 1950.

A NOTE ON THE HABITS OF THE TIMBER WOLF. Charles Eugene Johnson. Jour. Mam., vol.2, no.1, pp.11-15, Feb., 1921.

AUDITION AND HABIT FORMATION IN THE DOG. Harry Miles Johnson. Publ. Cambridge, Boston, Mass., New York, H. Holt and Co., pp.78, illus., 1913.

CLOSED SOCIAL GROUPS AMONG DOMESTIC DOGS. John A. King. Proc. Amer. Philos. Soc., Phila., vol.98, no.5, pp.327-336, Oct.15, 1954.

A STORY OF A GREY FOX. Hermann Lea. Field, London, vol.152, p.1040, Dec.27, 1928.

BEHAVIOUR OF THE WILD DOG (CUON DUKHUNENSIS SYKES). T.R. Livesey. Jour. Bombay Nat. Hist. Soc., vol.38, no. 2, pp.388-390, Dec.1, 1935.

CROSS FOX SWIMMING. Raymond W. McIntyre. Jour. Mam., vol.22, no.4, p. 447, Nov.14, 1941.

WILD DOGS DRIVING A PANTHER FROM ITS 'KILL.' R.C. Morris. Jour. Bombay Nat. Hist. Soc., vol.36, no.3, pp.744-745, Aug.15, 1933.

ECOLOGY OF THE COYOTE IN THE YELLOWSTONE. Adolph Murie. USDI, Natl. Park Serv., Fauna Ser.4, pp.206, 1940.

COYOTE CUNNING. Lewis Nordyke. Nature Mag., Wash., vol.37, no.3, pp. 120-124, illus., Mar., 1944.

ORGANIZATION AND RANGE OF THE PACK. Sigurd F. Olson. Ecology, 19 (1): 168-170, Jan., 1938.

AQUATIC ACTIVITY OF A DESERT KIT FOX. William G. Reeder. Jour. Mam., Balto., vol.30, no.2, p.196, May 23, 1949.

MOVEMENTS OF COYOTES FROM AND TO YELLOWSTONE NATIONAL PARK. Weldon B. Robinson, Maynard W. Cummings. US F&WS, Spec. Sci. Rep., Wildl. no.11, pp.1-17, illus., Dec., 1951.

NOTES ON BEHAVIOR OF COYOTES. Weldon B. Robinson, Maynard W. Cummings. Jour. Mam., 28 (1): 63-65, Feb., 1947.

WINTER HABITS AND NUMBERS OF TIMBER WOLVES. William Rowan. Jour. Mam., 31 (2): 167-169, May, 1950.

(FOXES BUILDING.) Fuchse am Bau. M. Schroot. Deutsche Jagd, Berlin, nos. 31-32, pp.295-297, illus., Nov.8, 1940.

A FOX ASSOCIATING WITH MOUNTAIN SHEEP ON THE KENAI PENINSULA, ALASKA. Charles Sheldon. Jour. Mam., vol.2, no.4, p.234, Nov., 1921.

DENNING HABITS AND HOME RANGE OF RED FOXES IN NEW YORK STATE. William G. Sheldon. Jour. Wildl. Mgt., 14 (1): 33-42, Jan., 1950.

RETURNS ON BANDED RED AND GRAY FOXES IN NEW YORK STATE. William G. Sheldon. Jour. Mam., vol.34, no.1, p.125, table 1, Feb.9, 1953.

THE ECOLOGY OF MICHIGAN COYOTES AND WOLVES. Adolph Marvin Stebler. Ann Arbor, Univ. Microfilms, publ.no. 2657, microfilm copy of typescript, 1951.

BREEDING, DENNING AND RANGE OF ACTIVITY OF FOXES IN ALABAMA. Edward G. Sullivan. MS thesis, Ala. Poly. Inst., Dec., 1953.

EFFECTS OF THE RED FOX ON OTHER GAME. Nelson F. Swink, Jr. Va. Wildl. 13 (10): 20-22, illus., Oct., 1952.

THE EFFECTS OF RED FOX POPULATIONS ON OTHER GAME SPECIES. F. Nelson Swink, Jr. MS thesis, Va. Poly. Inst., 1952.

KILLER OF THE NORTHWOODS. (HABITS OF TIMBER WOLVES.) C. Roy Teller. Minnesota Conservationist, St. Paul, no. 51, pp.9, 19-21, illus., Nov., 1937.

(THE BEHAVIOR OF THE RED FOX. Das Verhalten des Rotfuchses. Guenter Tembrock. Handbuch der Zoologie, Berlin, Bd.8, Teil 10, no.15 (Lief.9), pp. 1-20, illus., Apr., 1957.

(IMPOSING BEHAVIOR IN THE RED FOX IN COMPARISON WITH OTHER MAMMALS.) Imponiergehaben beim Rotfuchs im Vergleich zu anderen Saeugetieren. Guenter Tembrock. Saeugetieren. Zool. Garten, Leipzig, n.F., vol.19, no.6, pp. 283-288, 1952.

(RED FOX AND WOLF: COMPARISON OF BEHAVIOR.) Rotfuchs und Wolf, ein Verhaltensvergleich. Guenter Tembrock. Zeitschr. Saeugetierk., Berlin, vol.19, no. 3, pp.152-159, illus., Dec.31, 1954.

TREE-CLIMBING TECHNIQUE OF A GRAY FOX. J. Kenneth Terres. Jour. Mam., vol.20, no.2, p.256, May, 1939.

CRAFTY COYOTES. Raymond Thompson. Outdoorsman, Chicago, vol.87, no.1, (whole no.512), pp.18-19, 24-25, illus., Jan.-Feb., 1945.

TIMBER WOLF MOVEMENTS ON SIBLEY PENINSULA, ONTARIO. A. de Vos. Jour. Mam., 31 (2): 169-175, May, 1950.

THE GRAY FOX ATTRACTED BY A CROW CALL. Alexander Wetmore. Jour. Mam., vol.33, no.2, pp.244-245, May 16, 1952.

WILD DOG (CUON DUKHUNENSIS) KILLED BY DOMESTIC DOGS. J. Williams. Jour. Bombay Nat. Hist. Soc., vol.37, no.4, pp. 949-950, Apr.15, 1935.

THE DISTRIBUTION OF FOX POPULATIONS IN RELATION TO VEGETATION IN SOUTHERN GEORGIA. John E. Wood, David E. Davis, E.V. Komarek. Ecology, 39 (1): 160-162, Jan., 1958.

TREE-CLIMBING BY A GRAY FOX. Lee E. Yeager. Jour. Mam., vol.19, no.3, p.376, Aug., 1938.

THE COYOTE AND EXAMPLES OF ITS PERSISTENCY. Stanley P. Young. Outdoor Life, vol.57, no.1, p.17, Jan., 1926. (Published Dec., 1925.)

THE COYOTE MARCHES ON. CUNNING, CRAFTY AND ADAPTABLE HE IS HOLDING HIS OWN AND EXTENDING HIS RANGE DESPITE ETERNAL WARFARE AGAINST HIM. (IN ALASKA BEYOND ARCTIC CIRCLE.) Stanley P. Young. Amer. Forests, Wash., D.C., vol.45, no.11, pp. 538-540, 574-576, fig.7, Nov., 1939.

DOG RUNS WITH COYOTES. Nat. Nature News, Wash., D.C., vol.2, no.22, p.6, May 30, 1938.

AN EAGLE HUNTS DOWN A WOLF. Life, Chicago, vol.32, no.16, pp.119-120, illus., Apr.21, 1952.

## Heredity

DOGS OF THE AMERICAN ABORIGINES. (HISTORY, ORIGIN, DESCRIPTIONS OF BREEDS OF AMERICAN ABORIGINAL DOGS; WITH REMARKS ON ORIGIN OF DOMESTIC DOG, ITS SPECIFIC STATUS AND CROSSING OF DOGS WITH WILD SPECIES OF CANIDAE.) Glover M. Allen. Bull. Mus. Comp. Zool., vol.63, pp.431-517, pls.1-12, Mar., 1920.

DOGS - THEIR HISTORY AND DEVELOPMENT. Eward C. Ash. Vols. I, II.

COAT COLOR INHERITANCE IN BULL TERRIERS. L. Cabot Briggs, Nathan Kaliss. Jour. Heredity, Wash., D.C., vol.33, no.6, pp.223-228, fig.5, June, 1942.

THE GENETICS OF THE DOG. Marca Burns. Commonwealth Agric. Bur., pp. 122, illus., 1952.

THE GENETICS OF THE COLOUR PHASES OF THE RED FOX IN THE MACKENZIE RIVER LOCALITY. L. Butler. Canadian Jour. Research, Ottawa, vol.25, D, pp. 190-215, 1947.

WILD DOGS AND TAME--PAST AND PRESENT--A PANORAMA OF THE ORIGIN, GENEALOGY AND "SOCIAL" BACKGROUND OF THE TRACTABLE WOLF THAT EMERGED FROM THE WILDERNESS TO BECOME MAN'S BEST FRIEND. Edwin Colbert. Nat. Hist., New York, vol.43, no.2, pp.90-95, illus., Feb., 1939.

(A ZOOLOGICAL ENIGMA: THE DOG (CANIS FAMILIARIS LINNE).) Une enigme zoologique: le Chien (Canis familiaris Linne). Ed Dechambre. Mammalia, Paris, 5 (3-4): 86-93, Sept.-Dec., 1941.

GENETICS OF SOME NEW TYPE FOXES. C.K. Gunn. Fur of Canada, Winnipeg, vol.10, no.6, pp.8-14, Mar., 1945; Nat. Fur News, Denver, vol.17, no.4, pp.7, 13, 16, May; no.5, pp.10, 13, June; no.6, pp.12, 18, July, 1945.

A CURIOUS MUTATION IN A COYOTE FROM KERN COUNTY, CALIFORNIA. E. Raymond Hall. California Fish and Game, San Francisco, vol.26, no.4, pp. 393-395, fig.138, Oct., 1940.

SEX-LINKED HEMOPHILIA IN DOGS. F.B. Hutt, C.G. Rickard, R.A. Field. Jour. Heredity, Balto., vol.39, no.1, pp. 3-9, Jan., 1948.

THE INHERITANCE OF THE COLOUR IN FOXES. E.D. Iljina. Zool. Zhurn. (Zool. Jour. USSR), Moscow, vol.13, no.4, pp. 701-713, 1934. (In Russian, with English summary.)

(THE ANCESTORS OF OUR DOG RACES.) Die Stammvaeter unserer Hunde-Rassen. L.H. Jeitteles. Wien, pp.1-68, figs.10, 1877.

INHERITANCE OF DEGREE OF SILVERING IN FOXES. Charles E. Kellogg. U.S. Dept. Interior, Fish and Wildlife Ser., Wildlife Leaflet 178, pp.1-8, Mar., 1941.

(SHORT-TAILED AND TAILLESS VARIANTS IN DOGS.) Kurzschwaenzige und Schwanzlose varianten bei Hunden. I. Klodnitzky, G. Spett. Zeitschrift fuer induktive Abstammungs- und Verebungslebre, vol.38, pp.72-74, 1925.

GENETICS PROVE FALLACY OF NORWEGIAN PLATINA FOX CLAIMS. Harry J. Ladue. Amer. Fur Breeder, Duluth, vol. 14, no.12, pp.14, 16, 17, 25, figs.2, June, 1942.

THE DOG LLEWELLIN PLANNED. (HISTORY OF ENGLISH SETTER AND ITS STRAIN THE LLEWELLIN.) L.T. Lazell. Field and Stream, New York, vol.53, no. 5, pp.128, 130-133, illus., Sept., 1948.

GENETICS OF COCKER SPANIELS. C.C. Little. Jour. Heredity, Balto., vol.39, no. 6, pp.181-185, June, 1948.

A PECULIAR EYE-COLOR AMONG MALAMUTE DOGS. J.P. Lotsy. Genetica, vol. 5, pp.77-78, Jan., 1923.

THE PHYLOGENY OF DOGS. W.D. Matthew. Jour. Mam., Balto., vol.11, no.2, pp.117-138, figs.3, May 9, 1930.

(ON RACE FORMATION IN THE CASE OF THE INCA DOGS OF THE CAVES OF ANCON.) Ueber Rassebildung bei den Inca-Hunden aus den Graebern von Ancon. Alfred Nehring. Kosmos, Stuttgart, vol.2, pp.94-111, figs.3, 1884.

GENETICS OF THE DARK PHASES OF THE RED FOX IN EXPERIMENT AND IN NATURE. Tarvo Oksala. Pap. Game Res. 11, pp.1-16, illus., 1954.

ON THE SAMSON CHARACTER OF THE RED FOX. Tarvo Oksala. Pap. Game Res.11, pp.17-23, illus., 1954.

ORIGIN OF THE AMERICAN VARIETIES OF THE DOG. A.S. Packard. Amer. Nat., vol.19, no.9, pp.896-901, Sept., 1885.

(THE GALLO-ROMAIN DOGS OF CHASSENON, THEIR SELECTION.) Les chiens Gallo-Romains de Chassenon (Charente), leur selection. Etienne Patte. Mammalia, Paris, vol.2, no.3, pp.120-124, figs.1-2b, Sept., 1938.

(A STUDY ON THE DESCENT OF DOG BREEDS.) Eine Studie ueber die Abstammung der Hunderassen. August Von Pelzein. Zool. Jahrb., Jena, bd.1, pp.225-240, 1886.

"PIG JAW" IN COCKER SPANIELS. RETROGNATHIA OF THE MANDIBLE IN THE COCKER SPANIEL AND ITS RELATIONSHIP TO OTHER DEFORMITIES OF THE JAW. James McIlvaine Phillips. Jour. Heredity, Wash., vol.36, no.6, pp.177-181, figs.8-9, June, 1945.

(ON THE TRANSMISSION OF HAIR COLOR IN THE DOG.) Ueber die Verebung der Haarfarben beim Hund. A.L.v. Steiger. Zeitschr. f. Hundeforschung, Leipzig, n. F., vol.13, pp.79-82, 1938.

(ON THE ORIGIN OF THE RED WOLF (GENUS CUON HODGSON).) Zur Abstammung der Rotwoelfe (Gattung Cuon Hodgson). E. Thenius. Oesterreichische Zool. Zeit., vol.5, no.3, pp.377-387, 1954.

(THE WOLF OF INDIA (CANIS PALLIPES SYKES) ANCESTRAL STEM OF THE DOMESTIC DOG.) Le Loup de l'Inde (Canis pallipes Sykes), souche ancestrale du Chien domestique. E.L Trouessart. Comptes-Rendus Acad. Sci., Paris, vol. 152, pp.909-912, 1911.

TRANSMISSION OF THE PLATINA-TRAITS IN SILVER FOXES. Per Tuff, Otto Louis Mohr. Amer. Fur Breeder, vol.11, no.1, pp.12, 13, 14, 16, 18, illus., tables, July, 1938.

COLOR INHERITANCE IN POODLES. David D. Whitney. Jour. Canine Genetics, Independence, pp.3-8, Apr., 1955.

THE INHERITANCE OF A TICKING FACTOR IN HOUNDS. Leon F. Whitney. Jour. Heredity, vol.19, pp.498-502, illus., Nov., 1928.

Hunting (Foxes)

HOW TO CATCH A FOX. Henry P. Bridges. Field and Stream, New York, vol.51, no.5, pp.38-39, 84, illus., Sept., 1946.

"SPORT OF KINGS" AVAILABLE TO SOUTH DAKOTA SPORTSMEN. Ury Dahling. South Dakota Conservation Digest, Pierre, vol.9, no.3, p.8, Mar., 1942.

(THE FOX: MONOGRAPHICAL CONTRIBUTION TO HUNTING ZOOLOGY.) Der Fuchs: Monographischer Beitrag zur Jadg--Zoologie. Raoul von Dombrowski. 1883.

FOXY FOX HUNTING. Lenn Donaldson. Pennsylvania Game News, Harrisburg, vol.14, no.12, p.3, Mar., 1944.

FOX HUNTING NOTES. W. Newbold Ely. Pennsylvania Game News, New Cumberland, vol.9, no.12, pp.28-29, Mar., 1939.

CAPTURING FOXES. F.E. Garlough. Circ. no.8, Fish and Wildlife Serv., U.S. Dept. Interior, Wash., pp.1-11, figs.5, 1945; Maryland Conservationist, Balto., vol.23, no.2, pp.1-5, illus., Spring, 1946.

FOX TRAPPING THE HILL RIMS. J.R. Harlan. Iowa Conservationist, Des Moines, vol.8, no.1, pp.97, 104, illus., Jan.15, 1949.

FOX HUNTING IS BIG BUSINESS. Fred Jones. Florida Wildlife, Tallahassee, vol. 3, no.3, pp.6-7, 21, illus., Aug., 1949.

FOX TRAPPING ON THE FARM. Earl F. Kennamer. Ala. Poly. Inst., Cir.373 (revised), pp.1-8, illus., Apr., 1954.

A NEBRASKA "WOLF" HUNT. J.W. Kimball. Outdoor Nebraska, Lincoln, vol.23, no.4, pp.15-17, Spring, 1946.

TRAPPING THE ARCTIC FOX. (ESKIMO METHOD.) D.B. Marsh. Beaver, Winnipeg, outfit 273, pp.14-15, illus., Mar., 1943.

FOX HUNTING FOR SPORT AND PREDATOR CONTROL. C.C. Moore. Game Breeder and Sportsman, New York, vol.51, no.1, pp.3, 8-9, Jan., 1946.

THE FOXHUNTERS' FRATERNITY. Andrew Potter. Texas Game and Fish, Austin, vol.2, no.5, p.4, Apr., 1944.

LET'S HUNT 'EM FOR SPORT. (FOX.) Thomas G. Scott. Outdoors in Illinois, Springfield, vol.16, no.3, pp.14-15, Autumn Issue, 1950.

LET'S GO HUNTING FOR FOXES. J.H. Stephenson. Michigan Conserv., Lansing, vol.18, no.1, pp.14-16, Feb., 1949.

NO CLOSED SEASON ON FOX. J.H. Stephenson. Michigan Conserv., Lansing, vol.12, no.10, pp.3, 11, Dec., 1943.

FOX TRAPPING IN MARYLAND. William M. Stine. Fur-Fish-Game, Harding's Mag., Columbus, vol.86, no.8, p.38, illus., Aug., 1946.

SKYLINE FOX HUNT. Fred S. Streeter. Field and Stream, New York, vol.62, no. 11, pp.48-49, 140, Mar., 1948.

FOX FUSS FOAMS AGAIN; HUNTERS HOUND HATERS. Outdoor Georgia, Atlanta, vol.6, no.4, p.6, Aug.15, 1945.

HOW TO SHOOT FOXES. Victorian Nat., Melbourne, vol.58, no.11, p.171, Mar., 1942.

UNIFORM PLAN FOR SPECIAL FOX HUNTING SEASONS ADOPTED. Pennsylvania Game News, Harrisburg, vol.15, no.5, pp. 19, 22, Aug., 1944.

Methods, Techniques

ON THE DECOYING OF COYOTES. J.R. Alcorn. Jour. Mam., vol.27, no.2, pp. 122-126, fig.1, May 14, 1946.

METHODS FOR FORECASTING POPULATION CHANGES IN THE COMMON FOX (VULPES VULPES L.). In Symposium, "Methods for forecasting changes in the numbers of fur-bearing animals and renewing their natural supplies." A.F. Chirkova. Trans. Cent. Lab. Game Indus. no.5, pp.78-99, 1941.

A METHOD FOR TREATING EAR MITES IN FOXES. John R. Gorham. Amer. Fur Breeders, Duluth, vol.21, no.7, p.42, Jan., 1949.

PROPER METHODS OF PELTING FOXES AND PREPARING PELTS FOR THE RAW FUR MARKET. Art Gudim. Amer. Fur Breeder, vol.3, no.4, pp.14-18, Oct., 1930.

TREATMENT OF EARMITE DISEASES IN FOXES. C.K. Gunn. Amer. Fur Breeder, Duluth, vol.20, no.11, p.44, May, 1948.

HOW I DO MY PELTING. Hugh Montgomery. Black Fox Mag., New York, vol.32, no.7, p.21, Nov., 1948.

EVALUATING DUPLICATIONS IN ANALYSES OF COYOTE SCATS. Olaus J. Murie. Jour. Wildl. Mgt., 10 (3): 275-276, July, 1946.

RELIABLE METHODS OF GROWING TAPEWORMS IN FOXES. William A. Riley, Reed O. Christenson. Amer. Fur Breeder, vol.1, no.6, pp.10-11, illus., Dec., 1928.

A METHOD FOR ESTIMATING THE RED FOX POPULATION. Thomas G. Scott. Iowa State Coll. Jour. Sci., 15 (2): 155-159, Jan., 1941.

METHODS AND COMPUTATION IN FECAL ANALYSIS WITH REFERENCE TO THE RED FOX. Thomas G. Scott. Iowa State Coll. Jour. Sci., 15 (3): 279-285, Apr., 1941.

A TRAPPING AND TAGGING TECHNIQUE FOR WILD FOXES. William G. Sheldon. Jour. Wildl. Mgt., 13 (3): 309-311, July, 1949.

INSTRUCTION FOR THE COLLECTION OF MATERIALS ON STUDY AND HUNTING OF THE ARCTIC FOX (ALOPEX LAGOPUS L.). K. E. Vorobyeva. Vsesoiuzyni arkticheskii institute, PRI TSIK SSSR, Leningrad, no.2, pp.12, 1932. (Arctic Institute of USSR.)

Mexico and Central America

NOTES ON KIT FOXES (VULPES MACROTIS) FROM MEXICO. Seth B. Benson. Proc. Biol. Soc. Wash., vol.51, pp.17-24, Feb.18, 1938.

LIST OF THE GRAY FOXES OF MEXICO. E.A. Goldman. Jour. Wash. Acad. Sci., vol.28, no.11, pp.494-498, Nov.15, 1938.

A NEW COYOTE FROM HONDURAS. (CANIS HONDURENSIS.) E.A. Goldman. Jour. Wash. Acad. Sci., vol.26, no.1, pp. 32-34, Jan.15, 1936.

A NEW FOX FROM THE CAPE REGION OF LOWER CALIFORNIA, MEXICO. (UROCYON CINEREOARGENTEUS PENINSULARIS.) Laurence M. Huey. Trans. San Diego Soc. Nat. Hist., vol.5, pp.203-210, pls.25-26, Sept.1, 1928.

A NEW COYOTE FROM SOUTHERN MEXICO. C. Hart Merriam. Proc. Biol. Soc. Wash., vol.17, pp.157-158, Oct.6, 1904.

REMARKS ON COYOTES WITH DESCRIPTION OF A NEW SUBSPECIES FROM SALVADOR. (CANIS LATRANS DICKEYI.) E.W. Nelson. Proc. Biol. Soc. Wash., vol.45, pp.223-226, Nov.26, 1932.

A NEW WOLF FROM MEXICO. E.W. Nelson, E.A. Goldman. Jour. Mam., vol.10, no.2, pp.165-166, May, 1929.

North America

THREE NEW WOLVES FROM NORTH AMERICA. (CANIS LUPUS ALCES, C.L. COLUMBIANUS, C. L. HUDSONICUS.) E.A. Goldman. Proc. Biol. Soc. Wash., vol.54, pp.109-114, Sept.30, 1941.

THE WOLVES OF NORTH AMERICA. E.A. Goldman. Jour. Mam., vol.18, no.1, pp. 37-45, Feb.14, 1937.

(Review by Paul H. Oehser of) THE WOLVES OF NORTH AMERICA. Stanley P. Young, E. A. Goldman. Scientific Monthly, Lancaster, vol.59, no.6, pp.478-479, Dec., 1944.

ON THE GIANT WOLF OF NORTH AMERICA-LUPUS GIGAS. John K. Townsend. Nat. Hist., vol.70; Jour. Acad. Nat. Sci., (2) vol.2, pp.75-79, 1850-1854.

ON THE NORTH AMERICAN JACKAL CANIS FRUSTROR. S.W. Woodhouse. Jour. Acad. Nat. Sci., (2) vol.2, pp.87-88, 1850-1854.

THE WOLF IN NORTH AMERICAN HISTORY. Stanley P. Young. Caxton Printers, Caldwell, Idaho, pp.149, illus., 1946.

THE WOLVES OF NORTH AMERICA. Stanley P. Young, E.A. Goldman. Amer. Wildl. Inst., xx, 636 pp., 1944.

(Review By H. E. Anthony of) THE WOLVES OF NORTH AMERICA. Stanley P. Young, E.A. Goldman. Nat. Hist., New York, vol.54, no.3, p.101, Mar., 1945.

(Review by Paul L. Errington of) THE WOLVES OF NORTH AMERICA. Stanley P. Young, E. A. Goldman. Ecology, Lancaster, vol.26, no.1, p.108, Jan., 1945.

Pacific Islands and Australia

THE WARRIGAL, OR "DINGO", INTRODUCED OR INDIGENOUS? R. Etheridge. Mem. Geol. Sur., N.S. Wales, Ethnol. ser., no.2, pp.43-54, pls.10-12, 1916.

(THE DOG IN POLYNESIA.) Le chien en Polynesie. Rey Lescure. Bull. Soc. Etudes Oceaniennes, Papeete, no.77, (vol. 7, no.5), pp.266-272, Dec., 1946.

THE FOX MENACE AND ITS EFFECT ON OUR NATIVE ANIMALS. (INTRODUCED FOX IN AUSTRALIA.) A.S. Le Souef. Zool. Soc. Bull., vol.27, pp.69, 71, May, 1924.

BLUE FOXES ON THE PRIBYLOF ISLANDS. Leonhard Stejneger. Science, Lancaster, n.s., vol.16, no.399, pp.310-311, Aug.22, 1902.

A NEW NATIVE DOG FROM THE PAPUAN HIGHLANDS. (CANIS HALLSTROMI.) Ellis Troughton. Proc. Roy. Zool. Soc., New South Wales, 1955-56: 93-94, May 8, 1957.

Parasites

PARASITES OF THE COYOTE IN KANSAS. Donald J. Ameel. Trans. Kansas Acad. Sci., vol.58, no.2, pp.208-210, June 21, 1955.

ON THE OCCURRENCE OF THE BAT FLUKE, PROSTHODENDRIUM OVIMAGNOSUM (BHALERAO, 1926) IN A DOG. G.D. Bhalerao. Records Indian Mus., Calcutta, vol.43, pt.4, pp.415-416, Dec., 1941.

HELMINTH PARASITES OF THE GRAY FOX. Helmut K. Buechner. Jour. Mam., 25 (2): 185-188, May, 1944.

THE INTESTINAL HELMINTHS OF THE COYOTE CANIS LATRANS SAY, IN UTAH. Joseph M. Butler, Albert W. Grundmann. Jour. Parasit., 40 (4): 440-443, Aug., 1954.

A NEW SPECIES OF MESOCESTOIDES, M. KIRBYI, FROM CANIS LATRANS. Asa C. Chandler. Jour. Parasit., 30 (4): 273, Aug., 1944.

MESOCESTOIDES JONESI, N. SP., FROM THE GRAY FOX, WITH DESCRIPTIONS OF THE CHROMOSOME COMPLEMENT AND A DICEPHALIC SPECIMEN. H. Ciordia. Rep. Reelfoot L. Biol. Sta., 19: 57-63, illus., Jan., 1955.

ECTOPARASITES FROM A SERIES OF TEXAS COYOTES. R.B. Eads. Jour. Mam., 29 (3): 268-271, Aug., 1948.

FOX ECTOPARASITES COLLECTED INCIDENT TO A RABIES CONTROL PROGRAM. R.B. Eads, George C. Menzies. Jour. Mam., vol.31, no.1, pp.78-80, illus., Feb.21, 1950.

THE SEASONAL HISTORY AND HOSTS OF THE AMERICAN DOG TICK, DERMACENTOR VARIABILIS, IN IOWA. Gaines W. Eddy, C.R. Joyce. Iowa State Coll. Jour. Sci., Ames, vol.18, no.3, pp.313-324, Apr., 1944.

HELMINTHS OF MINNESOTA CANIDAE IN RELATION TO FOOD HABITS AND A HOST LIST AND KEY TO THE SPECIES REPORTED FROM NORTH AMERICA. Arnold B. Erickson. Amer. Midland Nat., 32 (2): 358-372, Sept., 1944.

PARASITISM AND ITS EFFECTS ON FOXES. F.X. Gassner. Fur of Canada, Winnipeg, vol.16, no.4, pp.10-11, Apr., 1944; Nat. Fur News Denver, vol.16, no.3, pp.3, 17-18, Apr., 1944; no.4, pp.3, 13-14, 16-17, 19, May, 1944.

PARASITISM OF FOXES BY MAGGOTS IN THE ROCKY MOUNTAIN REGION. F.X. Gassner, Maurice T. James. Nat. Fur News, Denver, vol.17, no.3, pp.7, 29-30, Apr., 1946.

SOME LUNGWORM RECORDS FROM FOXES IN NEW YORK. Frans C. Goble, Arthur H. Cook. Jour. Mam., 22 (4): 456, Nov., 1941.

THE CONTROL OF FOX PARASITES. C.K. Gunn. Amer. Fur Breeder, Duluth, vol.15, no.11, pp.18, 20-21, May, 1943; Nat. Fur News, Denver, vol.17, no.7, pp. 10, 15, 22-25, 27, 32, 36, Aug., 1946.

PARASITES CAUSING DEATHS IN PRINCE EDWARD ISLAND FOXES. C.K. Gunn. Amer. Fur Breeder, Duluth, vol.19, no.3, pp.56, 58, Sept., 1946.

PARASITES AND PARASITIC DISEASES OF DOGS. Maurice C. Hall. U.S. Dept. Agric., Dept. Circ.338, pp.28, figs.32, May, 1925.

LUNGWORM TROUBLE IN FOXES—ITS TREATMENT AND CONTROL. Karl B. Hanson. Amer. Fur Breeder, vol.1, no. 6, pp.16-17, Dec., 1928; Rod and Gun and Canadian Silver Fox News, vol.31, no.1, pp.78-80, June, 1929.

LUNGWORMS IN FOXES AND THEIR TREATMENT. Karl B. Hanson. Fox Breeders Gazette, vol.1, pp.11-12, Mar., 1925.

PARASITES OF RANCH FOXES AND THEIR TREATMENT. K.B. Hanson. Black Fox Mag., vol.16, no.4, pp.10, 12, 16, 32-33, 35, May, 1932.

NEWER ASPECTS OF THE LUNGWORM (CRENOSOMA) IN FOXES. M. Hobmaier. Amer. Jour. Vet. Res., 2 (4): 352-354, July, 1941.

REPORT ON A CONDITION AFFECTING FOXES CAUSED BY SHIGELLA ORGANISMS. A.H. Kennedy. Canadian Jour. Comp. Med. and Vet. Sci., vol.14, no.2, pp.49-53, 1950.

(A FOX, VULPES V. CRUCIGERA BECHSTEIN 1798, WITH SERIOUS ECHINOCOCCUS INFESTATION.) Ein Fuchs, Vulpes v. crucigera (Bechstein, 1798), mit Massenbefall von Echinococcus. Hans Mendheim. Saeugetierk. Mitteil., Stuttgart, 3 (1): 10-12, Jan.1, 1955.

STUDIES ON THE LIFE HISTORY OF TRICHOCEPHALUS VULPIS, THE WHIPWORM OF DOGS. M.J. Miller. Candian Jour. Research, Ottawa, sect.D, vol.25, no.1, pp.1-11, figs.21, pls.3, Apr.5, 1947.

ON A NEW HOOKWORM, ANCYLOSTOMA MARTINAGLIAI FROM A JACKAL. H.O. Monnig. Jour. S. African Vet. Med. Assoc., vol.2, no.2, pp.3, 1931.

INFESTATION OF A RED FOX BY AMBLYOMMA AMERICANUM. Roland W. Portman, Paul D. Dalke. Jour. Econ. Ent., 38 (3): 397, June, 1945.

(A CONTRIBUTION TO THE STUDY OF THE HELMINTH FAUNA OF DOGS IN THE USSR (SOUTHERN UKRAINE).) Ein Beitrag zum Studium der Helminthenfauna der Hunde in der UdSSR. (Sudliche Ukraine). A.R. Prendel. Zool. Anzeiger, vol.89, pp.323-326, fig.1, July 1, 1930.

WORM PROBLEMS IN BLUE FOXES. Joseph Rowell. Amer. Fur Breeder, vol. 4, no.6, p.18, Dec., 1931.

INTERNAL PARASITES OF THE RED FOX IN IOWA. Lawrence F. Smith. Jour. Wildl. Mgt., Menasha, vol.7, no.2, pp.174-178, April, 1943.

(NEW DICROCOELIIDAE PARASITE OF CARNIVORES: PSEUDATHESMIA PARADOXA N.G., N.SP., WITH A NOTE ON THE GENUS "ATHESMIA" LOOSS, 1899.) Novo Dicrocoeliidae parasito de carnivoros: "Pseudathesmia paradoxa" n.g., n.sp., com uma nota sobre o genero "Athesmia" Looss, 1899. Lauro Travassos. Rev. Brasileira Biol., Rio de Janeiro, vol.2, no. 3, pp.349-351, fig.1, Sept., 1942.

TWO NEW INTESTINAL TREMATODES FROM THE DOG IN CHINA. Marcos A. Tubangui. Proc. U.S. Nat. Mus., vol. 60, art.20, pp.1-12, 4 pls., May, 1922.

THE INFLUENCE OF DIPHYLLOBOTHRIUM LATUM INFESTATION UPON DOGS. Robert Arnold Wardle, Mary Jane Gotschall, Lillian Jean Horder. Trans. Roy. Soc. Canada, Ottawa, ser.3, vol.31, sec.5, pp.59-69, May, 1937.

Pelage, Coloration

(COMPLETE ALBINISM IN A FOX OF THE EASTERN PYRENEES.) Albinisme complet d'un Renard des Pyrenees-Orientales. G. Astre. Mammalia, Paris, vol.12, no.4, pp.158-160, Dec., 1948.

COYOTE FUR. Vernon Bailey. Pennsylvania Game News, New Cumberland, vol. 10, no.3, pp.12, 32, June, 1939.

EFFECT OF INCREASED OR DECREASED LENGTH OF DAYLIGHT ON PELT PRIMENESS OF GROWING FOXES. Charles F. Bassett, Leonard M. Llewellyn. Fur of Canada, Winnipeg, vol.12, no.11, pp.21-26, Aug., 1947; Nat. Fur News, Denver, vol. 19, no.9, pp.24-25, 34-35, illus., Oct., 1947; Amer. Fur Breeder, Duluth, vol.20, no.9, pp.22, 24, 26, 28, illus., Feb., 1948.

THE MOLTING AND FUR GROWTH PATTERN IN THE ADULT SILVER FOX. Charles F. Bassett, Leonard M. Llewellyn. Amer. Midland Nat., Notre Dame, vol.39, pp.597-601, pl.1, illus., May, 1948; Amer. Nat. Fur and Market Jour., Wausau, vol. 27, no.11, pp.20-21, June, 1949; Nat. Fur News, Denver, vol.21, no.7, pp.12, 24, Aug., 1949.

THE EFFECT OF ARTIFICIALLY-INCREASED LENGTH OF DAY ON MOLT, GROWTH, AND PRIMING OF SILVER FOX PELTS. Charles F. Bassett, Oliver P. Pearson, Ford Wilke. Jour. Exper. Zool., Phila., vol.96, no.1, pp.77-83, June, 1944; Fur of Canada, Winnipeg, vol.9, no.10, pp. 5-6, 22-23, July, 1944; Amer. Fur Breeder, Duluth, vol.17, no.3, pp.32, 34, 36, 38, figs.2, Sept., 1944.

WHITE SPOTTING IN THE FOX. Leon J. Cole, Richard M. Shackelford. Amer. Nat., Lancaster, vol.77, no.771, pp.289-321, figs.11, July-Aug., 1943; Amer. Fur Breeder, Duluth, vol.16, no.8, pp.22, 24, figs.4-5, Feb., 1944; no.9, pp.24-26, Mar., 1944; vol.16, no.11, pp.24, 26, 28-29, June, 1944; National Fur News, Denver, vol.16, no.1, pp.11, 16, 19, 22, Feb., 1944; no.3, pp. 8, 22, Apr., 1944; no.4, p.4, May, 1944.

COAT COLOUR IN GREYHOUNDS. Adair Dighton. Proc. Zool. Soc. Lond., 1923, pt.1, pp.1-9, Apr., 1923.

COLOR PHASE FOXES. William B. Erekson. Amer. Fur Breeder, Duluth, vol.15, no.4, pp.22, 24, 26, 28, illus., Oct., 1942.

EFFECT OF THE CLIMATIC AMELIORATION OF THE PAST DECADE ON THE AUTUMN CHANGE OF COAT OF THE ARCTIC FOX IN GREENLAND. K. Faester. Meddelelser om Gronland, Copenhagen, vol.142, no.2, pp.1-18, pls.1-2, 1945.

GEOGRAPHIC VARIATION IN THE INCIDENCE OF OCCURRENCE OF THE BLUE PHASE OF THE ARCTIC FOX IN CANADA. K. Fetherston. Canadian Field-Nat., Sutton West, vol.61, no.1, pp.15-18, map, Mar. 15, 1947.

ALBINO COYOTES ARE RARE. D. D. Green. Jour. Mam., vol.28, no.1, p.63, Feb.15, 1947.

SPONTANEOUS SUPERCONTRACTION OF ANIMAL HAIR. (WHITE AND RED FOXES.) R. O. Hall. Nature, London, vol.136, no. 3427, p.29, July 6, 1935.

THE COLORATION OF THE AFRICAN HUNTING DOG (LYCAON PICTUS). J. Stevenson Hamilton. Proc. Zool. Soc. Lond., pp.403-406, June, 1914.

SEASONAL DIMORPHISM IN THE COLOR OF THE ARCTIC FOX. N.A. Il'in. Trans. Lab. Exper. Biol. Zool. Park Moscow, vol.2, pp.239-250, illus., 1926. (In Russian, with German resume.)

(THE CAUSES OF THE GREY SNOUT OF SILVER FOXES.) Die Ursachen der Grauschnaeuzigkeit bei Silberfuechsen. E. Jacob. Freude am Leben, Berlin, vol. 17, nos.4-5, p.74, July-Aug., 1940.

A VARIATION OF COLOUR IN THE COMMON WOLF AND ITS HYBRIDS WITH DOMESTIC DOGS. Alexander Kohts. Proc. Zool. Soc. Lond., vol.117, no.4, pp.784-790, pls.3, 1948.

THE EFFECT OF INCREASED AND (OR) DECREASED LENGTH OF DAYLIGHT ON PELT PRIMENESS IN ADULT SILVER FOXES. Leonard M. Llewellyn, Charles F. Bassett. Fur of Canada, Winnipeg, vol. 12, no.11, pp.6, 8, 10, illus., Aug., 1947; Natl. Fur News, Denver, vol.19, no.7, pp. 19, 24-25, 29, Sept., 1947; Amer. Fur Breeder, Duluth, vol.20, no.4, pp.74, 76-78, Oct., 1947.

SEASONAL FUR PRIMENESS OF THE COYOTE IN THE WESTERN UNITED STATES. Merle H. Markley. Jour. Wildl. Mgt., Menasha, vol.9, no.3, pp.227-231, July, 1945.

(THE PROBLEM OF THE COLORATION OF LYCAON PICTUS TEMMINCK 1820.) Zum Problem der Faerbung von Lycaon pictus (Temminck, 1820). Hans Petzsch. Saeugetierk. Mitteil., Stuttgart, 3 (2): 82-83, Apr.1, 1955.

BETTER COLOR IN FOXES. L. Merle Pierce. Fur of Canada, Winnipeg, vol.11, no.7, p.27, Apr., 1946.

ON THE MOULTING OF AN ARCTIC FOX (VULPES LAGOPUS) IN THE SOCIETY'S GARDENS. R.I. Pocock. Proc. Zool. Soc. Lond., 1912, pt.1, pp.55-60, figs.6-13, Mar.13, 1912.

EXHIBITION OF A SKIN OF A VARIETY OF THE COMMON FOX (CANIS VULPES, LINN.), FROM SMYRNA, AND A SPECIMEN OF THE ARGONAUTA, BROUGHT TO MR. STRICKLAND WITH THE ANIMAL ALIVE. H.E. Strickland. Proc. Zool. Soc. Lond., pt.4, p.102, 1836.

AN ALBINO COYOTE. G.N. Stroman. Jour. Heredity, vol.16, pp.342-343, Sept., 1925.

INDENTIFICATION OF THE ORIGINAL COLORS OF BLACK-NOSED WHITE DOGS. David D. Whitney. Jour. Canine Genetics, Soc. Advancement Canine Genetics, Independence, Missouri, pp.1-6, Sept., 1956.

BLACK WOLVES. Carl Wurm, Jr. Field and Stream, no.4, pp.22-23, 105, Aug., 1929.

### Photography

FOX CUBS AND THE CAMERA. H. Mortimer Batten. Field, London, vol.154, no.4015, p.861, Dec.7, 1929.

FOXES IN THE SEA CLIFFS. STALKING WITH A CAMERA. H. Mortimer Batten. Field, London, vol.154, p.178, illus., Aug.3, 1929.

THE BLACK WOLF OF THE TENSAS. WOLFING WITH THE CAMERA. Tappan Gregory. Program of Activities, Chicago Acad. Sci., vol.6, no.3, pp.35-68, illus., July, 1935.

KIT FOX AND CAMERA. Laurence M. Huey. Nature Mag., Wash., D.C., vol.31, no.10, pp.587-588, Dec., 1938.

PHOTOGRAPHS OF RED FOX. Myrton S. Reed. Nat. Hist., New York, vol.52, no. 1, p.4, illus., June, 1943.

I PHOTOGRAPHED A FOX. (GRAY FOX.) Richard F. Trump. Photography, Boston, vol.43, no.6, pp.350-351, illus., June, 1949.

FOXING THE FOX BY FLASHLIGHT. CAMERA ADVENTURES ON SANTA CATALINA ISLAND. William V. Ward. Nature Mag., vol.18, no.5, pp.291-294, figs.5, Nov., 1931.

### Physiology

THE PHYSIOLOGICAL AND BIOCHEMICAL STANDARDIZATION OF THE DOG. James B. Allison. Trans. New York Acad. Sci., ser.2, vol.8, no.8, pp.260-266, June, 1946.

THE METABOLISM OF THE SALIVARY GLANDS. V. THE PROCESS OF RECONSTRUCTION OF THE SUBMAXILLARY GLAND. (EXPERIMENTS ON A DOG.) G.V. Anrep, H.N. Khan. Jour. Physiol., vol.58, pp.302-309, Mar., 1924.

SOME FACTORS INVOLVED IN FOOD AND WATER INGESTION IN THE DOG. J.W. Archdeacon, R.S. Allen. Amer. Jour. Physiol., Balto., vol.153, no.1, pp.27-30, Apr.1, 1948.

THE INFLUENCE OF THE BLOOD SUPPLY ON PANCREATIC SECRETION. (EXPERIMENTS ON DOGS.) B.P. Babkin. Jour. Physiol., vol.59, pp.153-163, Oct., 1924.

HEAT REGULATION AND WATER EXCHANGE. I. THE EFFECTS OF HOT AND COLD BATHS UPON BLOOD CONCENTRATION AND BRAIN VOLUME IN DOGS. Henry G. Barbour. Amer. Jour. Physiol., vol.67, pp.366-398, 1923.

(SENSE OF SMELL IN THE DOG.) L'odorat du chien. E.J.J. Buytendijk. Archives neerl. Physiol., pp.434-457, 1920.

NONEXCRETION OF JAUNDICE-SERUM ALKALINE PHOSPHATASE IN BILE OF NORMAL DOGS. A. Cantarow, L.L. Miller. Amer. Jour. Physiol., Balto., vol.153, no.3, pp.444-446, June 1, 1948.

SPEED ENDURANCE OF THE COYOTE. Clarence Cottam. Jour. Mam., 26 (1): 94, Feb., 1945.

SPEED OF THE GRAY FOX. Clarence Cottam. Jour. Mam., vol.18, no.2, pp. 240-241, May 14, 1937.

AN INTRODUCTION TO THE STUDY OF THE OESTROUS CYCLE IN THE DOG. Herbert McLean Evans, Harold H. Cole. Mem. Univ. California, vol.9, no.2, pp. 65-103, pls.12-18, Dec.19, 1931.

STATISTICAL ANALYSIS OF FILTRATION RATE AND EFFECTIVE RENAL PLASMA FLOW RELATED TO WEIGHT AND SURFACE AREA IN DOGS. C.R. Houck. Amer. Jour. Physiol., Balto., vol.153, no.1, pp. 169-175, Apr.1, 1948.

DISSECTION OF THE DOG AS A BASIS FOR THE STUDY OF PHYSIOLOGY. William Henry Howell. New York, H. Holt Co., pp.100, illus., pls.2, 1888.

PROPERTIES OF FOX BLOOD FOR RESPIRATORY TRANSPORT. Laurence Irving, V. Safford, W.J. Scott. Jour. Cell. and Comp. Physiol., Phila., vol.13, no.3, pp.297-302, fig.1, June, 1939.

SOME ECOLOGICO-PHYSIOLOGICAL PECULIARITIES OF THE ARCTIC AND DESERT SPECIES OF FOXES: THE ARCTIC FOX (ALOPEX LAGOPUS L.), AND CORSAC FOX (VULPES CORSAC L.). N. I. Kalabukhov, O.B. Poluzadova. C. R. Acad. Sci. USSR, 54 (4): 373-376, 1946.

SEX DIFFERENCES IN BLOOD PRESSURE OF DOGS. Edward J. Van Liere, J. Clifford Stickney, David F. Marsh. Science, Lancaster, vol.109, no.2837, p.489, May, 1949.

(INVESTIGATIONS ON THE PHYSIOLOGICAL OLFACTORY CAPABILITY OF POLICE DOGS.) Untersuchungen ueber die geruschphysiologische Leistungsfaehigkeit von Polizeihunden. L. Loehner. Pfluegers Archiv., 212: 84-94, 1926.

(ACCLIMITIZATION OF THE USSURI RACCOON AS AN EXAMPLE OF SUCCESSFUL TRANSFORMATION OF EUROPEAN FUR ANIMALS.) Akklimatizatsiya ussuriiskogo yenota (Nyctereutes procyonoides Gray) kak primer uspyeshnogo pryeobrazovaniya fauni pushnix svyeryei yevropeiskoi territorii SSSR. B.F. Morozov. Zool. Zhurnal, Moscow, vol.32, no.3, pp.524-533, 1953.

THE DIRECT INFLUENCE OF GRADUAL VARIATIONS OF TEMPERATURE UPON THE RATE OF BEAT OF THE DOG'S HEART. H. Newell. Amer. Nat., Lancaster, vol.17, no.6, p.680, June, 1883.

OVULATION, MATURATION AND FERTILIZATION IN THE FOX. Oliver P. Pearson, Robert K. Enders. Anat. Record, Phila., vol.85, no.1, pp.69-83, pls.4, Jan., 1943.

(ATTEMPT AT ACCLIMATIZATION OF USSURI RACCOONS IN ROSTOV OBLAST.) Opyt akklimatizatsii ussuriiskix yenotov v rostovskoi oblasti. (Nyctereutes) U. M. Rall, T. I. Kritskaya. Zool. Zhurnal, Moscow, vol.32, no.3, pp.513-523, 1953.

INTERRELATION BETWEEN THE LENGTH OF SYSTOLE, STROKE VOLUMES AND LEFT VENTRICULAE WORK IN THE DOG. J.W. Remington, W.F. Hamilton, R.P. Ahlquist. Amer. Jour. Physiol., Balto., vol.154, no.1, pp.6-15, July 1, 1948.

REACTIONS OF THE DOG TO HOT ATMOSPHERES. Kathleen Robinson, Douglas H.K. Lee. Proc. Roy. Soc. Queensland, Brisbane, vol.53, no.11, pp. 171-188, figs.7, Feb.23, 1942.

ABSORPTION OF BLOOD FROM THE PERITONEAL CAVITY OF THE DOG. G.S. Samuelsen, G.E. Griffin, E. Muntwyler, Sam Seifter. Amer. Jour. Physiol., Balto., vol.153, no.2, pp.277-286, May 1, 1948.

THE WORK OUTPUT OF SLEDGE DOGS. R.J.F. Taylor. Jour. Physiol., London, vol.137, no.2, pp.210-217, July, 1957.

A COYOTE'S SPEED AND ENDURANCE. R. Scott Zimmerman. Jour. Mam., vol. 24, no.3, p.400, Aug.17, 1943.

EYE COLOR, STRUCTURE AND EFFICIENCY. (DOGS.) Jour. Canine Genetics, Independence, pp.1-2, Feb., 1956.

### Population Dynamics and Migrations

POPULATION CYCLES AND GENE FREQUENCY FLUCTUATIONS IN FOXES OF THE GENUS VULPES, IN CANADA. John B. Calhoun. Canadian Jour. Research, Ottawa, vol.28, pp.45-57, Apr., 1950.

FLUCTUATIONS OF SOME ILLINOIS FOX POPULATIONS. Robert B. Chiasson. Ecol., 34 (3): 617-619, graphs, July, 1953.

LONGEVITY AND MORTALITY OF IRISH WOLFHOUNDS. A. Comfort. Proc. Zool. Soc. Lond., 127 (1): 27-34, Sept.28, 1956.

PERIODIC FLUCTUATIONS IN NUMBERS OF THE RED FOX IN ONTARIO. E.C. Cross. Jour. Mam., 21 (3): 294-306, Aug., 1940.

MOVEMENTS OF ARCTIC FOX POPULATIONS IN THE REGION OF BAFFIN BAY AND SMITH SOUND. Charles Elton. Polar Record, 5 (37, 38): 296-305, Jan.-July, 1949.

CURIOUS COYOTE CASUALTIES. Niska Elwell. Fur-Fish-Game (Harding's Mag.), Columbus, vol.83, no.5, pp.14-15, May, 1946.

A STUDY OF FLUCTUATIONS IN COYOTE NUMBERS AND POSSIBLE CAUSES.

Sherwin B. Griswold. MS thesis, Ft. Hays Kansas State Coll., 1942.

CAUSES OF DEATH AMONG YOUNG FOX PUPS. C.K. Gunn. Amer. Nat. Fur and Market Jour., Wausau, vol.21, no.10, pp. 9-10, May, 1943; Nat. Fur News, Denver, vol.18, no.12, p.11, Jan., 1947.

A SENILE GRAY FOX. John Eric Hill. Jour. Mam., vol.21, no.2, pp.217-218, May 14, 1940.

A PRELIMINARY SURVEY OF THE TIMBER WOLF CANIS LUPUS POPULATIONS IN THE NORTHWEST MOUNTAIN REGION. W. Winston Mair. MA thesis, Univ. B.C., 1949.

MIGRATIONS OF THE ARCTIC FOX IN THE NORTH OF THE EUROPEAN PART OF THE USSR. A.A. Maksimov. Bull. Moscow Soc. Nat., 50 (5-6): 45-61, figs. 3, 1945.

LONGEVITY OF THE COYOTE. Richard H. Manville. Jour. Mam., vol.34, no.3, p. 390, Aug.14, 1953.

FLUCTUATIONS IN GRAY FOX POPULATION IN PENNSYLVANIA AND THEIR RELATIONSHIP TO PRECIPITATION. Neil D. Richmond. Jour. Wildl. Mgt., 16(2): 198-206, illus., Apr., 1952.

ANALYSIS OF FOX POPULATIONS AFTER HARDY'S FORMULA. D.D. Romashov, E.D. Ilyina. Doklady Acad. Sci. USSR, Moscow, vol.37, nos.5-6, pp.193-196, Nov. 30, 1942.

GREY FOXES KILLED. F.H. Snudling. South Dakota Conserv. Digest, Pierre, vol. 15, no.2, p.13, Feb., 1948.

TIMBER WOLVES (CANIS LUPUS LYCAON) KILLED BY CARS ON ONTARIO HIGHWAYS. A. de Vos. Jour. Mam., Balto., vol.30, no.2, p.197, May 23, 1949.

SOME MORE FOXY BUSINESS. Douglas E. Wade. Pa. Game News, 11 (6): 6-7, 29, Sept., 1940.

Psychology

A FACTOR ANALYSIS OF THE PERFORMANCE OF DOGS ON CERTAIN LEARNING TESTS. Anne Anastasi, J.L. Fuller, J.P. Scott, J.R. Schmitt. Zoologica, New York Zool. Soc., vol.40, pt.1, pp.33-46, May 14, 1955.

(INQUIRY: IS FEAR OF THUNDER AND LIGHTNING IN DOGS A DEGENERATION PHENOMENON?) Umfrage: Ist Gewitterangst bei Hunden eine Degenerationserscheinung? Konrad Andreas. Saeugetierk. Mitteil., Stuttgart, vol.1, no.4, p. 180, Oct.1, 1953.

HOW BRIGHT IS THE DOG? D.R. Barton. Natural History, New York, vol.43, no.2, pp.117-123, illus., Feb., 1939.

PRELIMINARY REPORT ON MASTURBATION OF RANCH RAISED FOXES. Andre Belzile. Fur of Canada, Winnipeg, vol.13, no.4, pp.26-27, Jan., 1948; Amer. Fur Breeder, Duluth, vol.20, no.6, pp.36, 40-42, Dec., 1947.

(LUMPI, THE "CLEVER DOG" OF WEIMAR.) Lumpi, der "kluge Hund" von Weimar. H. Graupner. Zool. Garten, n. F., vol.5, nos.4-6, p.150, Aug., 1932.

EXTRAORDINARY INSTANCE OF WANT OF SAGACITY IN A DOG. R. Heron. Proc. Zool. Soc. Lond., pt.3, p.188, 1835.

(ON THE INTELLIGENT WEIMAR DOG.) Ueber den klugen Weimarer Hund. Gustav Kramer. Zool. Anzeiger, vol.96, nos.11-12, pp.317-320, Nov.15, 1931.

EXHIBITION OF TWO POINTER DOGS, IN ILLUSTRATION OF HIS OBSERVATIONS ON THE INTELLIGENCE OF THESE ANIMALS. M. Leonard. Proc. Zool. Soc. Lond., pt.9, p.47, 1841.

(CRETINISM IN SILVER FOXES?) Kretinismus bei Silberfuechsen? H. Oboussier. Zool. Anzeiger, Leipzig, vol. 146, pp.1-20, Jan., 1951.

(OBSERVATIONS ON "LUMPI", THE INTELLIGENT DOG OF WEIMAR.) Beobachtungen an Lumpi, dem klugen Hund von Weimar. L. Plate, A.N. Sewertzoff. Zool. Anzeiger, vol.95, pp.250-254, July 20, 1931.

(EXPRESSION STUDIES CONDUCTED ON WOLVES: CAPTIVITY OBSERVATIONS.) Ausdrucks-Studien an Woelfen; Gefangenschafts-beobachtungen. R. Schenkel. Behaviour, 1 (2): 81-129, figs.57, 1947.

(PSYCHOLOGY OF THE CANIDS. WOLF, DOG, FOX.) Zur Psychologie der Caniden. Wolf--Hund--Fuchs. Bastian Schmid. Carnivoren Studien, vol.1, Kleintier und Pelztier, Leipzig, Jahrg.12, no.6, pp.77, pls.11, Oct., 1936.

(THE PSYCHOLOGY OF THE DINGO.) Zur Psychologie des Dingo (Canis dingo Blch.) Bastian Schmid. Natur u. Volk, Frankfurt, vol.68, no.5, pp.205-215, figs.17, May 1, 1938.

(INVESTIGATIONS OF INBORN BEHAVIOR TRAITS IN CANIDS.) Untersuchungen ueber angeborene Verhaltensweisen bei Caniden. A. Seitz. Zeits. f. Tierpsychol., 7: 1-46, 1950.

THE CHARACTER OF DOGS. Robert Louis Stevenson. English Illus. Mag., London, vol.1, pp.300-305, 1883.

THE SENSORY CAPACITIES AND INTELLIGENCE OF DOGS, WITH A REPORT ON THE ABILITY OF THE NOTED DOG "FELLOW" TO RESPOND TO VERBAL STIMULI. C.J. Warden, L.H. Warner. Quart. Rev. Biol., vol.3, no.1, pp.1-28, frontis, Mar., 1928.

EXPERIMENTS WITH FORM PERCEPTION AND LEARNING IN DOGS. Joseph A. Williams. Comp. Psych. Monographs, vol.4, ser.no.18, pp.1-70, 1926.

Rabies

RABIES AND FOX CONTROL. Ben O. Bradley. N.Y. State Cons., 3 (2): 14-15, Oct.-Nov., 1948.

RABID FOXES. J.G. Burr. Texas Game and Fish, 5 (10): 6-7, 24, Sept., 1947.

COYOTE RUNS AMUCK. E.C. Cates. Jour. Mam., vol.22, no.2, pp.203-204, May 14, 1941.

RABIES IN WILD FOXES. Lyle S. Compton. Cornell Vet., 35 (1): 68-72, Jan., 1945.

RABIES AS A POSSIBLE POPULATION CONTROL OF ARCTIC CANIDAE. I. McT. Cowan. Jour. Mam., 30 (4): 396-398, Nov., 1949.

RABID FOXES REPORTED IN GEORGIA. Albert W. Gill. Alabama Conservation, Montgomery, vol.14, no.5, p.6, Nov., 1942.

RABIES PREVALENT. H.M. Guilford. Wis. Cons. Bull., 3 (11): 30-31, Nov., 1938.

WIDESPREAD RABIES AMONG WILD DOGS ON THE BILLIGIRIRANGAN HILLS (S. INDIA). R. C. Morris. Jour. Bombay Nat. Hist. Soc., vol.43, no.1, p.100, Apr., 1942.

FOX POPULATION DENSITIES IN RELATION TO RABIES. Richard L. Parker, James W. Kelly, E.L. Cheatum, Donald J. Dean. New York Fish and Game Jour., 4 (2): 219-228, July, 1957.

THE MAD WOLF AT FORT CHURCHILL. (Mrs.) George R. Ray. Beaver, Winnipeg, outfit 271, no.2, p.30, illus., Sept., 1940.

RABIES IN FOXES. J.H. Rietz. Jour. Amer. Vet. Med. Assoc., Chicago, vol. 111, no.845, pp.138-139, Aug., 1947; Nat. Fur News, Denver, vol.19, no.10, pp.38-39, Nov., 1947.

SYMPTOMS OF RABIES IN FOXES. J.H. Rietz. Black Fox Mag., 31 (10): 16, 25-26, Feb., 1948.

RABIES IN A WILD FOX. F.J. Tice, W.M. Evans. Cornell Vet., 32 (1): 98-99, Jan., 1942.

INVESTIGATION OF FOX POPULATIONS AND SYLVATIC RABIES IN THE SOUTHEAST. John E. Wood. Trans. 19th N.A. Wildl. Conf., pp.131-139, 1954.

LAD KILLS RABID FOX ATTACKING BROTHER. West Virginia Conservation, Charleston, vol.10, no.7, p.29, Nov., 1946.

MAD FOXES. Alabama Conservation, Montgomery, vol.15, no.8, p.14, Feb., 1944.

Reproductive Biology

STUDIES ON REPRODUCTION IN THE FOX. Shirley H. Barker. PhD Thesis, Univ. Wis., 1943.

THE EFFECT OF DURATION AND INTERRUPTION OF COUPLING ON THE PRODUCTION OF YOUNG BY THE SILVER FOX VIXEN. Charles F. Bassett, L.M. Llewellyn. Fur of Canada, Winnipeg, vol. 12, no.4, p.22, Jan., 1947. (Reprinted in Nat. Fur News, Denver, vol.19, no.1, pp. 15, 28-29, Feb., 1947; Amer. Fur Breeder, Duluth, vol.19, no.8, pp.38-40, Feb., 1947.)

RESPONSE OF MALE DOGS TO URINE FROM FEMALES IN HEAT. Frank A. Beach, Robert W. Gilmore. 1949.

AN INSTANCE OF COYOTE-DOG HYBRIDIZATION. James Bee, E. Raymond Hall. Trans. Kansas Acad. Sci., Topeka, vol. 54, no.1, pp.73-77, 1951.

A RED-GREY FOX HYBRID. Hubert Bezdek. Jour. Mam., vol.25, no.1, p.90, Feb., 1944.

THE NUMBER OF PUPS IN A WILD DOG'S LITTER. R.W. Burton. Jour. Bombay Nat. Hist. Soc., vol.35, no.2, p.442, Oct.15, 1931.

FOX HYBRIDS. Leon J. Cole, Richard M. Shackelford. Trans. Wisconsin Acad. Sci., Arts, and Letters, Madison, vol.38, pp.315-332, 1946 (Dec.30, 1927).

TIMBER WOLF DEN AND PUPS. Stuart Criddle. Canadian Field-Nat., Sutton West., vol.61, no.3, p.115, June 30, 1947.

A FAMILY OF DOG-COYOTE HYBRIDS. Lee R. Dice. Jour. Mam., vol.23, no.2, pp.186-192, pls.1, May 14, 1942.

FOX GIVES BIRTH TO THREE LIVE PUPS AFTER CESARIAN OPERATION. Robert Dixon. Amer. Fur Breeder, vol.4, no.6, p.19, Dec., 1931.

MONOZYGOTIC TWINS IN THE DOG. Kenneth L. Duke. Anat. Record, Phila., vol.94, no.1, pp.35-41, fig.1, pl.1, Jan., 1946.

FALSE HEAT IN THE YEARLING COYOTE, CANIS LATRANS. Robert K. Enders. Jour. Mam., 36 (1): 133, Feb.25, 1955.

NO SEASONAL BREEDING CYCLE IN DOGS. Earl T. Engle. Jour. Mam., vol. 25, no.1, pp.79-81, Mar.14, 1946.

(PROPAGATION BIOLOGY OF DOGS.) Zur Fortpflanzungsbiologie bei Hunden. G. Gaffrey. Zool. Garten, Leipzig, 23 (1-3): 251-252, 1957.

(THE YELLOW BODY OF THE GRAVID BITCH.) Le corps jaune de la chienne gravide. N. Goormaghtigh. Archives de Biologie, vol.37, pp.46-120, pls.4, Mar.1, 1927.

EFFECT OF MATING TIME UPON REPRODUCTION IN FOXES. C.K. Gunn. Nat. Fur News, Denver, vol.19, no.11, pp.16-17, 42, 49, Dec., 1947.

REPRODUCTIVE CYCLE OF THE COYOTE. G.W.D. Hamlett. Trans. N.A. Wildl. Conf., 3 : 524-526, 1938; U.S. Dept. Agric. Tech. Bull. no.616, pp.1-12, figs.2, pls.1-2, table 1, July, 1938.

(Review by Charles E. Kellogg of) THE REPRODUCTIVE CYCLE OF THE COYOTE. G.W.D. Hamlett. Trans. 3rd. North Amer. Wildl. Conf., pp.524-526, 1938.

RED FOX WEIGHTS AND REPRODUCTION IN TIPPECANOE COUNTY, INDIANA. Roger A. Hoffman, Charles M. Kirkpatrick. Jour. Mam., 35 (4): 504-509, Nov., 1954.

JACKAL HYBRIDS. G.S. Hurst. Field, London, vol.162, no.4206, p.381, figs., Aug.5, 1933.

POLYGAMOUS MATING OF FOXES. Charles E. Kellogg. Wildlife Research and

Management Leaflet BS-66, Bur. Biol. Sur., U.S. Dept. Agric., pp.4, Oct., 1936.

POLYGAMOUS MATING OF FOXES. Wayne C. Liddell. Nat. Fur News, Denver, vol. 16, no.9, pp.21, 41, Oct., 1944; Fur-Fish-Game, Columbus, vol.87, no.9, pp.38-39, Sept., 1946.

(BIRTH PROCESS IN FEMALE SILVER FOXES.) Geburtsvorgang bei Silberfuchsfaehen. Franz Lober. Der Deutsche Pelztierzuechter, Jahrgang 1931, Muenchen, no.14, pp.383-386, figs., July 15, 1931.

(A CROSS BETWEEN THE ARCTIC FOX AND THE COMMON FOX?) En bastard mellan fjellraef och vanlig raef? Einar Loennberg. Svenska Jaegarfoerbundets Nya Tidskrift, Stockholm, Arg.34, pt.3, pp.154-164, pl.1, 1896.

RED FOX BREEDING IN SALT MARSH. A.L. Nelson, Clarence Cottam, W.S. Bourn. Jour. Mam., vol.26, no.1, pp.91-92, Feb.23, 1945.

(BLUE FOX BREEDING ON ISLANDS.) Blaufuchszucht auf Inseln. Lars G. Olsson. Deutsche Pelztierzuechter, Munich, vol.14, no.6, pp.127-130, Mar.15, 1939.

REFERENCE TO HUNTER'S OPINION RESPECTING THE PRODUCTIVE POWER OF HYBRIDS. R. Owen. Proc. Zool. Soc. Lond., pt.4, p.85, 1836.

ASPECTS OF REPRODUCTION IN SILVER FOXES. Oliver P. Pearson, Charles F. Bassett. Nat. Fur News, Denver, vol.18, no.12, pp.18, 46-48, 50-52, Jan., 1947.

CERTAIN ASPECTS OF REPRODUCTION IN A HERD OF SILVER FOXES. Oliver P. Pearson, Charles F. Bassett. Amer. Nat., Lancaster, vol.80, no.786, pp.45-67, Jan. 1, 1946.

SIZE OF THE VULVA AND ITS RELATION TO FERTILITY IN FOXES. Oliver P. Pearson, Charles F. Bassett. Amer. Fur Breeder, Duluth, vol.17, no.5, pp.12, 14, Nov., 1944.

TIME OF OVULATION AND FERTILIZATION IN THE FOX. Oliver P. Pearson, Robert K. Enders. Amer. Fur Breeder, Denver, vol.16, no.7, pp.32-34, figs.1, Jan., 1944.

(REPRODUCTION OF THE FENNEC.) La reproduction du fennec. Francis Petter. Mammalia, Paris, 21 (3): 307-309, Sept., 1957.

(ON DOG CROSSES.) Ueber Hundekreuzungen. L. Plate. Zool. Anzeiger, Supplement band, vol.1, pp.89-91, fig.1, 1925.

LORD AUCKLAND'S GIFT TO THE ZOOLOGICAL GARDENS. (HYBRID WOLF-DOG AND PLAINS WOLF.) R.I. Pocock. Field, London, vol.1, 152, p.775, illus., Nov.15, 1928.

(ARE THERE CROSSES BETWEEN FOX AND DOG?) Gibt es Kreuzungen zwischen Fuchs und Hund? A. Priesner. Der Deutsche Pelztierzuechter, Muenchen, 8 Jahrgang, 1933, no.6, pp.131-134, figs.2, Mar.15, 1933.

(STORY OF A CROSS BETWEEN A DOG AND WOLF.) Histoire d'un metis de chien et de loup precedee d'un hommage a G. Herve. Joseph Recamier. Revue anthropologique, Paris, annee 43, nos.1-3, pp.125-130, Jan.-Mar., 1933.

(DOG-WOLF HYBRIDS IN THE WILD.) Bastarde von hund und wolf in freier natur. Landgerichtsdirektor Reinberger. Zeitschrift f. Saeugetierkunde, vol.5, no. 6, pp.367-369, 1930.

THE REPRODUCTIVE PROCESSES OF CERTAIN MAMMALS. 8. REPRODUCTION IN FOXES (VULPES SPP.). I.W. Rowlands, A.S. Parkes. Proc. Zool. Soc. Lond., 1935, pt.4, pp.823-841, pls.6, figs.2, Jan., 1936.

(BREEDING THE RACCOON DOG.) Ueber die Zucht des Marderhundes. F. Schmidt. Deutsche Pelztierzuechter, Berlin, 12, Jahrg., nos.11-12, pp.235-237, fig.1, June 1-15, 1937.

(ON THE BIRTH PROCESS IN THE SILVER FOX.) Ueber den Geburtsvorgang beim Silberfuchs. F. Schmidt. Der Deutsche Pelztierzuechter, Munich, Jahrg.9, no.5, pp.85-91, illus., Mar.1, 1934.

(POLYGAMOUS SILVER FOX BREEDING IN PRACTICE.) Die polygame Silberfuchszucht in der Praxis. F. Schmidt. Der Deutsche Pelztierzuechter, Munich, Jahrg.9, no.1, pp.2-9, illus., Jan.1, 1934.

(THE YOUNG DEVELOPMENT (EMPHASIZING WEIGHT) OF CAPTIVE WILD CANIDS, WITH SOME TEMPORAL DETERMINATIONS REGARDING THEIR REPRODUCTION.) Zur gewichtsmaessigen Jugendentwicklung gefangen gehaltener Wildcaniden nebst einigen zeitlichen Bestimmungen ueber ihre Fortpflanzung. Karl Max Schneider. Festschrift fuer Dr. Berthold Klatt, Zool. Anzeiger, Leipzig, vol.145, pp.867-910, 1950.

A CASE OF HYBRIDIZATION BETWEEN THE WILD-DOG AND THE JACKAL. S.Z. Shah. Jour. Bombay Nat. Hist. Soc., vol. 35, no.1, pp.198-199, June 15, 1931.

REPRODUCTIVE BEHAVIOR OF FOXES IN NEW YORK STATE. William G. Sheldon. Jour. Mam., 30 (3): 236-246, Aug., 1949.

(AT REYNARD'S DEN HOLE.) An Reinekes Kinderstube. Fritz Siedel. Natur u. Volk, Frankfurt, vol.68, no.5, pp.201-205, figs. 3, May 1, 1938.

(WEIGHTS AT BIRTH AND DURING GROWTH OF PURE-BRED DOGS.) Geburts-und Aufzuchtgewichte von Rassehunden. U. Sierts-Roth. Zeitschrift fur Hundeforschung, vol. 20, Dr. Paul Schops, Frankfurt Main, Germany, pp.122, 1953.

(Review by A. de Vos of) GEBURTS-UND AUFZUCHTGEWICHTE VON RASSEHUNDEN. U. Sierts-Roth. Jour. Mam., vol.35, no.2, p.272, May 25, 1954.

BREEDING PRODUCTIVITY IN MICHIGAN RED FOXES. D.F. Switzenberg. Jour. Mam., vol.31, no.2, pp.194-195, May 25, 1950.

(ON THE ETHOLOGY OF THE RED FOX (VULPES VULPES L.) WITH SPECIAL CONSIDERATION OF PROPAGATION.) Zur Ethologie des Rotfuchses (Vulpes vulpes L.), unter besonderer Beruecksichtigung der Fortpflanzung. Guenter Tembrock. Zool. Garten, Leipzig, 23 (4-6): 289-532, illus., 1957.

(THE QUESTION OF MONOGAMOUS OR POLYGAMOUS RELATIONS BETWEEN MALE AND FEMALE IN THE SILVER AND RED FOX.) Zur Frage des monogamen oder polygamen Verhaeltnisses zwischen Ruede und Faehe beim Silberfuchs und Rotfuchs. A. Usinger. Der Deutsche Palztierzuechter, Munich, Jahrg.9, no.23, pp.454-456, illus., Dec.1, 1934.

THE BREEDING OF THE ARCTIC FOX. Henry Varigny. Ann. Report Smithsonian Inst., Wash., pp.527-533, 1901.

(REPRODUCTION OF THE FENNEC.) A propos de la reproduction du fennec. Jiri Volf. Mammalia, Paris, 21 (4): 454-455, Dec., 1957.

FOX GESTATION CALENDAR. Amer. Fur Breeder, vol.4, no.7, p.36, Jan., 1932.

South America

THE PAMPA FOX OF THE BOGOTA SAVANNA. (CERDOCYON THOUS GERMANUS.) Glover M. Allen. Proc. Biol. Soc. Wash., vol.36, pp.55-58, Mar.28, 1923.

(THE DOMESTIC DOGS OF THE ABORIGINES OF ARGENTINA.) Los perros domesticos de los indigenas del Territorio Argentino. Angel Cabrera. Actas XXV Congreso Internacional de Americanistas, Univ. Nac. de La Plata, vol.1, pp.81-93, figs.5, (Canis familiaris), 1932.

ON SOME SOUTH AMERICAN CANINE GENERA. Angel Cabrera. Jour. Mam., vol.12, no.1, pp.54-67, Feb., 1931.

(SYNOPSIS OF THE ARGENTINE CANIDS.) Sinopsis de los canidos Argentinos. Angel Cabrera. Rev. Centro Ing. Agronomos y Centro E. Agronomia, no.145, pp.489-501, Apr., 1932.

(WILD DOG OF THE ARGENTINE PAMPAS.) El perro cimarron de la pampa Argentina. (Canis familiaris.) Angel Cabrera. Publ. Mus. Antrop. y Etnograf. Facultad de Filos y Let., Buenos Aires, ser.A, vol.2, pp.7-29, pls.6, 1932.

SOUTH AMERICAN CANIDAE. T.D.A. Cockrell. Jour. Mam., vol.15, no.3, p. 243, Aug., 1934.

A SYNOPSIS OF THE WILD DOGS OF COLOMBIA. Philip Hershkovitz. Novedades Colombianas, Mus. Nat. Hist. Univ. del Cauca, 3: 157-161, Dec.1, 1957.

(THE PREHISPANIC AMERICAN DOGS.) Sobre los perros americanos prehispanicos. Robert Hoffstetter. Bol. Inf. Cient. Nacionales, Quito, Ecuador, vol.5, no.40, pp. 102-136, June-July, 1952.

(CHILEAN FOX OR AMERICAN JACKALS.) Las zorras de Chile o chacales americanos. Rafael Housse. Rev. Universitaria, Anales Acad. Chilena Ciencias Nat., Santiago, ano 34, no.1, pp.33-56, 1949.

(IN THE LAND OF THE MANED WOLF.) Im Lande des Maehnenwolfes. Hans Kreig. Zool. Garten, (NF), vol.13, nos.5-6, pp. 333-335, illus., Dec., 1941.

(INDIAN DOGS IN THE GRAN CHACO.) Indianerhunde im Gran Chaco. Hans Krieg. Der Naturforscher, Jahrg.11, no.11, pp.387-390, figs.3, Feb., 1935; Physis, Buenos Aires, vol.16, no.48, pp.153-158, figs.3, May, 1939.

(JOURNEYS IN SOUTH AMERICA FOR THE PURPOSE OF BIOLOGICAL STUDY. VII. NOTES ON A DOG-PAMPAS FOX HYBRID (PSEUDALOPEX (CANIS) AZARAE), WITH REMARKS ON THE SYSTEMATICS OF ARGENTINIAN AND CHILEAN FOXES.) Biologische Reisestudien in Suedamerika. VII. Notiz ueber einen Bastard zwischen Hund und Pampafuchs (Pseudalopex (Canis) azarae), nebst Bemerkungen ueber die Systematik der argentinisch-chilenischen Fuechse. Hans Krieg. Zeitschr. f. Morph. u. Oekologie der Tiere, vol.4, pp.702-710, figs.3, Oct.29, 1925.

(THE "ANDES WOLF," DASYCYON HAGENBECKI (KRUMBIEGEL, 1949).) Der "Andenwolf," Dasycyon hagenbecki (Krumbiegel, 1949). Ingo Krumbiegel. Saeugetierk. Mitteil., vol.1, no.3, pp.97-104, July 1, 1953.

REMARKS ON SOME SOUTH AMERICAN CANIDAE. (AFFINITIES OF PSEUDALOPEX LYCOIDES PHILIPPI AND DOG OF YAGHAN INDIANS, TIERRA DEL FUEGO.) Einar Loennberg. Arkiv foer Zoologi, vol. 12, no.13, pp.1-18, figs.1-4, 1919.

(Review by G. S. Miller of) REMARKS ON SOME SOUTH AMERICAN CANIDAE. Einar Loennberg. Jour. Mam., vol.1, no. 3, pp.149-150, 1920.

(OLD PERUVIAN DOG-MUMMIES: ON RACIAL TYPES IN THE SO-CALLED INCA DOGS.) Altperuanische Hundemumien und ueber Rassebildung bei den sogenannten Inca-Hunden. Alfred Nehring. Verhandl. Berliner f. Anthrop., Gesell, Ethnol. and Uregesch., Jahrg.1885, pp.518-521, Nov.21, 1885.

(NEW CHILEAN SPECIES OF FOXES.) Nueva especie Chilena de Zorras. Rudolph A. Philippi. Anales. Univ. Santiago de Chile, pp.3-6, pl.1, 1901.

ON THE SOUTH AMERICAN WILD DOG. R.I. Pocock. Proc. Zool. Soc. Lond., pp. 64-65, fig.15, July 3, 1908.

(HAIRLESS DOGS OF MENDOZA.) Acerca de los perros pelados de Mendoza. Carlos Rusconi. El Campo, suelo Argentino, Buenos Aires, Ano 32, no.375, pp.4, Jan., 1948.

(SOUTH AMERICAN CANIDS OF THE NATURAL HISTORY MUSEUM IN BERNE.) Ueber suedamerikanische Caniden des Naturhistorischen Museums in Bern. Theophil Studer. Mitteil. Naturforsch. Gesell. Bern 1905, pp.35, pls.5, 1905.

NEW FOXES OF THE GENERA CERDOCYON AND PSEUDALOPEX FROM NORTHERN ARGENTINA. (CERDOCYON TECUMANUS, C. THOUS JUCUNDUS, AND PSEUDALOPEX ZORRULA.) Oldfield Thomas. Ann. and Mag. Nat. Hist., ser.9, vol.7, pp.381-385, Apr., 1921.

A NEW WILD DOG FROM THE BOGOTA CORDILLERA. Oldfield Thomas. Ann. and Mag. Nat. Hist. (9), vol.1, no.6, pp. 370-371, May, 1918.

Taxonomy

CONTRIBUTION TO THE SYSTEMATICS AND DISTRIBUTION OF THE RED WOLF. A. Afanasjev, N. Zolotarev. Izvestiia Akademii Nauk USSR, Otdelenie Matematicheskikh i Estestvennykh Nauk, no.3, pp. 425-429, 1935. (In Russian, with English summary.)

THE GENERIC NAMES SPEOTHOS AND ICTICYON. J.A. Allen. Proc. Biol. Soc. Wash., vol.27, p.147, July 10, 1914.

(SYNOPSIS OF THE ARGENTINE CANIDS.) Sinopsis de los canidos Argentinos. Angel Cabrera. Revista del Centro de Ing. Agronomos v Centro E. de Agronomia, no. 145, pp.489-501, Apr., 1932.

THE WOLF STRAIN IN ALSATIANS. P.H. Duncan, A. deC. Sowerby. China Jour., vol.6, pp.211-214, Apr., 1927.

THE TYPE LOCALITY OF VULPES MACROTIS NEOMEXICANUS. Arthur F. Halloran. Jour. Mam., vol.26, no.1, pp.92-93, Feb. 23, 1945.

THE NAME OF THE FLORIDA WOLF. Francis Harper. Jour. Mam., vol.23, no. 3, p.339, Aug.14, 1942.

A NEW SPECIES OF RACCOON DOG. William T. Hornaday. 8th Ann. Rep., New York Zool. Soc., pp.1-5, illus., 1904.

THE STATUS OF THE DINGO. F. Wood Jones. Trans. Roy. Soc. South Australia, vol.14, pp.254-263, 1921.

(CRANIOMETRY AND CLASSIFICATION OF THE SOUTH AMERICAN CANIDAE, IN PARTICULAR LIVING AND FOSSIL ARGENTINE CANIDAE.) Craneometria y clasificacion de los canidos sudamericanos especialmente los argentinos actuales y fosiles. Lucas Kraglievich. Physis, Revista Soc. Argentina Cien. Nat., Buenos Aires, vol.10, no.35, pp.35-73, figs.12, pls.7, July 12, 1930.

(CONTRIBUTION TO THE SYSTEMATICS OF THE SOUTH AMERICAN CANIDS.) Beitrag zur Systematik der suedamerikanischen Caniden. Friedrich Kuhlhorn. Archiv. f. Naturgesch., Leipzig, n.F., vol.7, no.1, pp.29-45, figs.5, 1938.

MATERIAL ON THE SYSTEMATIC OF THE JUGOSLAVIAN FOX. V. Martino. Lovtsa, nos.1-2, pp.1-3, figs.2, 1936. (In Russian.)

ON THE SYSTEMATIC OF GAME (ANIMALS). V. Martino. Lovtsa, nos. 5-6, pp.1-5, illus., tables, May-June, 1938. (Bulgarian.)

(CHROMOSOMES AND SYSTEMATICS OF SOME CANIDS.) Chromosomes et systematique des Canides. Robert Matthey. Mammalia, Paris, vol.18, no.3, pp.225-230, illus., Sept., 1954.

PRELIMINARY REVISION OF THE NORTH AMERICAN RED FOXES. C. Hart Merriam. Proc. Wash. Acad. Sci., vol. 2, pp.661-676, pls.36-37, Dec.28, 1900.

REVISION OF THE COYOTES OR PRAIRIE WOLVES, WITH DESCRIPTIONS OF NEW FORMS. C. Hart Merriam. Proc. Biol. Soc., Wash., vol.11, pp.19-33, Mar.15, 1897.

THREE NEW FOXES OF THE KIT AND DESERT FOX GROUPS. C. Hart Merriam. Proc. Biol. Soc. Wash., vol.15, pp.73-74, Mar.22, 1902.

DESCRIPTIONS OF TWO NEW GRAY FOXES. Gerrit S. Miller, Jr. Proc. Acad. Nat. Sci., Phila., pp.276-280, Aug.1, 1899.

THE NAMES OF THE LARGE WOLVES OF NORTHERN AND WESTERN NORTH AMERICA. Gerrit S. Miller, Jr. Smithsonian Miscl. Coll., vol.59, no.15, publ.2093, pp.5, June 8, 1912.

THE NAMES OF TWO NORTH AMERICAN WOLVES. Gerrit S. Miller, Jr. Proc. Biol. Soc., Wash., vol.25, p.95, May 4, 1912.

A SYSTEMATIC REVIEW OF THE MAMMALS OF RUSSIA. ON FOXES LIVING IN RUSSIA. S. I. Ognev. Annal. Musei. Nat. Hungarici, vol.23, pp.202-240, pls.5-10, Dec.29, 1926.

THE GENERA AND SUBGENERA OF SOUTH AMERICAN CANIDS. Wilfred H. Osgood. Jour. Mam., Balto., vol.15, no. 1, pp.45-50, Feb.15, 1934.

THE AFFINITIES OF THE ANTARTIC WOLF (CANIS ANTARTICUS). R.I. Pocock. Proc. Zool. Soc. Lond., pt.3, pp.382-393, figs.70-74, Sept.1, 1913.

THE JACKALS OF S.W. ASIA AND S.E. EUROPE. R.I. Pocock. Proc. Zool. Soc. Lond., vol.108, ser.B, syst. and morph., pp.37-39, Apr., 1938.

THE RACES OF CANIS LUPUS. R.I. Pocock. Proc. Zool. Soc. Lond., pt.3, pp.647-686, pls.2, Sept.12, 1935.

(ON TYPE SPECIMENS OF JACKALS.) Ueber Typenexamplare von Schakalen. Ernst Schwarz. Senckenbergiana, vol.8, pp.39-47, 1926.

THE TYPE-SPECIES OF THE SOUTH AMERICAN CANINE GENERA CERDOCYON, CERCODOCON, LYCALOPEX, AND PSEUDALOPEX. C.W. Stiles, O. Baker. Jour. Mam., vol.11, no.2, pp. 226-227, May, 1930.

A NEW PEKINGESE DOG, "VERITY MINNI-ATUA." Queenie Verity-Steele. Nat. Hist. Mag., Lond., vol.2, no.12, pp.129-133, figs.5, Oct., 1929.

United States

GRAY FOXES--ALL AMERICANS. Vernon Bailey. Nature Mag., 34 (9): 493-495, 528, Nov., 1941.

THE RED FOX IN AMERICA. Vernon Bailey. Nature Mag., vol.28, no.5, pp. 269-272, 317, illus., Nov., 1936.

THE GREY FOX OF THE UNITED STATES. John L. Given. Field, London, vol.161, no. 4198, p.1345, illus., June 10, 1933.

TWO NEW COYOTES FROM THE UNITED STATES. (CANIS LATRANS THAMNOS, C. L. UMPQUENSIS.) Hartley H.T. Jackson. Proc. Biol. Soc. Wash., vol.62, pp.31-32, Mar.17, 1949.

United States, Eastern

COYOTES IN MAINE. Clarence M. Aldous. Jour. Mam., vol.20, no.1, pp.104-107, Feb. 14, 1939.

WOLVES AND FOXES PLENTIFUL. H.T. Ames. Wisconsin Conservationist, vol.3, no.1, pp.15-16, Mar., 1921.

SUMMER FOXES. David A. Arnold. Michigan Conservation, Lansing, vol.20, no.4, pp.13-14, 30, July-Aug., 1951.

ADIRONDACK COYOTES. A.W. Bromley. New York State Conservationist, Albany, vol.10, no.4, pp.8-9, illus., Mar., 1956.

THE LATEST ON COYOTES. Greenleaf Chase, Earl Westervelt. New York State Conservationist, Albany, vol.5, no.3, pp. 12-13, illus., Dec., 1950, Jan., 1951.

KENTUCKY FOXES NOT DIFFERENT! Larry Gale. Ky. Happy Hunting Ground, 5 (2): 13, 28, Mar., 1949.

OCCURRENCE OF THE COYOTE IN KENTUCKY. Larry R. Gale, Robert A. Pierce. Jour. Mam., vol.35, no.2, pp. 256-258, May 26, 1956.

OLD CRIP' OF ROCKY RIDGE. (RED FOX.) Richard Gerstell. Pennsylvania Game News, Harrisburg, vol.18, no.6, pp.4-5, 30-31, illus., Sept., 1947.

WOLF ON ISLE ROYALE! D. Robert Hakala. Nature Mag., Wash., vol.47, no. 1, pp.35-37, illus., Jan., 1954.

OCCURRENCE OF SCOTT'S GRAY FOX IN PROBABLY RECENT CAVE DEPOSITS IN KENTUCKY. Oliver P. Hay. Proc. Biol. Soc. Wash., vol.35, pp.53-54, Mar.20, 1922.

THE STATUS OF THE RED FOX IN EASTERN OHIO. E.V. Hendon. MS thesis, Ohio State Univ., 1940.

THE WOLVES AND COYOTES OF ILLINOIS. Donald F. Hoffmeister, Sadako Hayase. Illinois Wildlife, Champaign, vol.4, no.2, pp.4-5, illus., Mar., 1949.

THE SPREAD OF THE COYOTE. R.P. Holland. Outers' Recreation, vol.62, p. 453, June, 1920.

WOLF, FOX, OR DOG? R.P. Holland. Outers' Recreation, vol.63, p.99, Aug., 1920.

A COYOTE IN MARYLAND. Hartley H.T. Jackson. Jour. Mam., vol.3, no.3, pp. 186-187, Aug., 1922.

THE PRIVATE LIFE OF A VIRGINIA FOX. George B. Johnson. Virginia Wild Life, vol.2, no.2, pp.2-3, Oct., 1938.

OHIO'S FOXES. Bill Lawson, Helen Lawson. Ohio Conserv. Bull., Columbus, vol.15, no.2, pp.6-7, illus., Feb., 1951.

RED FOX IS POPULAR ILLINOIS FURBEARER. Francis X. Lueth. Ill. Cons., 7 (2): 13-14, Summer, 1942.

THE STATUS OF THE RED FOX IN WEST-CENTRAL OHIO. Kenneth A. Mitchell. MS thesis, Ohio State Univ., 1940; Ohio Wildl. Res. Sta., Release 163, pp.29, Aug., 1941.

VIRGINIA ANIMALS EVERYONE SHOULD KNOW. THE FOXES OF VIRGINIA--A CONTROVERSIAL SUBJECT. Henry S. Mosby. Virginia Wildlife, Richmond, vol. 9, no.5, pp.8-10, illus., May, 1948.

A COYOTE, CANIS LATRANS, FROM PREBLE COUNTY, OHIO. N.C. Negus. Jour. Mam., vol.29, no.3, p.295, Aug.31, 1948.

GRAY FOX IN THE NORTHEAST. Ralph S. Palmer. Maine Field Nat., 12 (3): 62-70, Aug.28, 1956.

BEAR DOGS ARE LONG SHOTS. John H. Phipps. Florida Wildlife, Tallahassee, vol. 2, no.7, pp.8-9, illus., Dec., 1948.

FOX RESEARCH. Stephen H. Richards. Wisconsin Wildlife Research, Wis. Conserv. Dept., Madison, Quart. Prog. Repts., vol. 7, no.1, pp.42-48, Apr., 1948.

FOX RESEARCH PROJECT. Stephen H. Richards. Wisconsin Wildlife Research Quart. Prog. Repts., Madison, vol.6, no. 1, pp.36-40, Apr., 1947.

WISCONSIN FOX POPULATIONS. Stephen H. Richards, Ruth L. Hine. Wis. Cons. Dept., Tech. Wildl. Bull.no.6, pp.1-78, illus., 1953.

RED FOXES IN THE CHICAGO AREA--CASE FOR THE DEFENSE. Colin Campbell Sanborn. Chicago Nat. Hist. Mus. Bull., vol.19, no.9, pp.3-4, illus., Sept., 1948.

STATUS OF THE COYOTE AND RELATED FORMS IN TENNESSEE. Vincent Schultz. Jour. Tennessee Acad. Sci., vol.30, no.1, pp.44-46, Jan., 1955; Rep. Reelfoot L. Biol. Sta., 19: 44-46, Jan., 1955.

THE COYOTE--UNBIDDEN GUEST. Clayton B. Seagers. New York State Conservationist, Albany, vol.3, no.5, pp. 40-41, illus., Apr.-May, 1949.

THE FOX IN NEW YORK. Clayton B. Seagers. New York State Cons. Dept., Educ. Bull., pp.83, 1944; Western New York Conserv., Buffalo, vol.5, no.2, pp. 5-6, Feb., 1945; no.3, pp.5-6, Mar., 1945; no.5, pp.5, 7, 10, May, 1945; vol.5, nos. 6-7, pp.5, 11, June-July; no.8, pp.5, 11, Aug; no.9, pp.5, 11, Oct., 1945; vol.5, no. 10, p.5, Nov., 1945; vol.6, no.3, p.5; no. 4, p.5, Apr., May, 1946.

A CONTRIBUTION TO THE BIOLOGY OF FOXES IN NEW YORK STATE. William G. Sheldon. PhD thesis, Cornell Univ., 1948.

WOLF DAYS IN PENNSYLVANIA. Henry W. Shoemaker. Tribune Press, pp.85, illus., 1914.

THE RED FOX IN INDIANA. Paul R. Squires. Outdoor Indiana, Indianapolis, vol.13, no.2, pp.8-9, 15, illus., Mar.-Apr., 1946.

THE STATUS OF THE WOLF IN MICHIGAN. A.M. Stebler. Jour. Mam., 25 (1): 37-43, Feb., 1944.

MYSTERY ANIMAL. (COYOTE CAPTURED IN NEW YORK.) Fred Streever. Nat. Hist., vol.38, no.2, pp.156-165, illus., Sept., 1936.

GRAY FOX REPRODUCTION, DENNING, RANGE, AND WEIGHTS IN ALABAMA. Edward G. Sullivan. Jour. Mam., 37 (3): 346-351, Sept.11, 1956.

PRELIMINARY STUDY OF WISCONSIN TIMBER WOLVES. Daniel Q. Thompson. MS thesis, Univ. Wis., 1950.

TRAVEL, RANGE, AND FOOD HABITS OF TIMBER WOLVES IN WISCONSIN. Daniel Q. Thompson. Jour. Mam., 33 (4): 429-442, graph, Nov., 1952.

SOME LATE RECORDS OF THE TIMBER WOLF IN PENNSYLVANIA. Ivan R. Tomkins. Jour. Mam., vol.12, no.2, p. 165, May, 1931.

RECENT RECORDS OF COYOTES IN PENNSYLVANIA AND NEW JERSEY. Frederick A. Ulmer, Jr. Jour. Mam., vol.30, no.4, pp.435-436, Nov.17, 1949.

A COYOTE IN HAMPSHIRE COUNTY, MASSACHUSETTS. H.E. Warfel. Jour. Mam., vol.18, no.2, p.241, May 14, 1937.

THE DISTRIBUTION OF FOXES IN PENNSYLVANIA. Samuel H. Williams. Jour. Mam., vol.11, no.3, pp.313-314, Aug., 1930.

A STUDY OF THE FOX IN RHODE ISLAND. Thomas Wright. R.I. Dept. Agr. and Cons., Div. Fish and Game, Pamphlet 3, pp.21, Oct., 1949; (revised), pp.1-19, illus., Oct., 1952.

THE FOX IN NEW HAMPSHIRE. N.H. Fish and Game Dept., Tech. Cir.1, pp.9, No date.

WOLF KILLED NEAR STAUNTON, VIRGINIA. Wildlife, Richmond, vol.11, no.2, pp.24-25, Feb., 1950.

United States, Western

YELLOWSTONE WOLVES. Marguerite L. Arnold. Nature Mag., vol.30, no.2, pp. 111-112, figs.3, Aug., 1937.

COOPERATIVE FOX STUDY CONTINUING. Roy N. Bach. North Dakota Outdoors, Grand Forks, vol.8, no.6, p.15, Dec., 1945.

GRAY WOLF KILLED IN NORTH DAKOTA. Roy N. Bach. North Dakota Outdoors, Bismarck, vol.5, no.11, p.12, illus., May, 1943.

PRELIMINARY STUDY ON NORTH DAKOTA RED FOX COMPLETED. Roy N. Bach. North Dakota Outdoors, Bismarck, vol.7, no.3, pp.18-19, Sept., 1944.

A NOTE CONCERNING WOLVES IN GLACIER NATIONAL PARK, MONTANA. Martin R. Brittan. Jour. Mam., vol.34, no.1, pp.127-129, Feb.19, 1953.

THE RED FOX OF NORTH DAKOTA (VULPES FULVA REGALIS). J. E. Campbell. North Dakota Outdoors, Grand Forks, vol.8, no.1, pp.6-7, illus., July, 1945.

A NORTHERN COAST FORM OF THE CALIFORNIA GRAY FOX. Joseph Dixon. Univ. Calif. Publ. Zool., Berkeley, Univ. Press, vol.5, no.7, pp.303-305, 1910.

THE TIMBER WOLF IN CALIFORNIA. Joseph Dixon. California Fish and Game, San Francisco, vol.2, no.3, pp.125-128, figs.43-45, July, 1916.

PRELIMINARY STUDIES OF THE KIT FOX IN UTAH. Harold J. Egoscue. Jour. Mam., 37 (3): 351-357, fig.1, Sept.11, 1956.

SLASH RANCH HOUNDS. (PUMA, GRIZZLY, BLACK BEAR, AND BOBCATS.) Dub (G.W.) Evans. Univ. New Mexico Press, Albuquerque, pp.256, 1951.

NOTES ON THE RED FOX (VULPES FULVA) IN MISSOURI. Harvey I. Fisher. Jour. Mam., vol.32, no.3, pp.296-299, illus., Aug.23, 1951.

THE COYOTE ON A NATURAL AREA IN NORTHEASTERN KANSAS. Henry S. Fitch, Robert L. Packard. Trans. Kans. Acad. Sci., vol.58, no.2, pp.211-221, 1955.

COYOTES IN KANSAS. H.T. Gier. Bull. Kansas State College Agric. Exper. Sta., Manhattan, 3: 1-96, illus., Aug., 1957.

TWO NEW DESERT FOXES. (VULPES MACROTIS ARIZONENSIS; V. M. NEVADENSIS.) E.A. Goldman. Jour. Wash. Acad. Sci., vol.21, no.11, pp.249-251, June 4, 1931.

TWO NEW FOXES FROM THE SOUTHERN CALIFORNIAN ISLANDS. (UROCYON LITTORALIS SANTAROSAE; UROCYON LITTORALIS DICKEYI.) J. Grinnell, J.M. Linsdale. Proc. Biol. Soc. Wash., vol.43, pp.153-156, Sept.26, 1930.

THE WESTERN RED FOX IN SOUTHERN NEW MEXICO. Arthur F. Halloran. Jour. Mam., vol.23, no.2, p.223, May 14, 1942.

CAPTURES RARE SPECIMEN OF COYOTE. Leo D. Harris. North Dakota Outdoors, Grand Forks, vol.8, no.6, pp.5-6, illus., Dec., 1945.

THE RED FOX IN NORTH DAKOTA. Brandt V. Hjelle, Roy N. Bach, William T. McKean. N. Dak. Game and Fish Dept., pp.31, May, 1949.

CANIS GIGAS IN THE BLUE MOUNTAINS OF OREGON. Stanley G. Jewett. Jour. Mam., vol.4, no.1, p.54, Feb., 1923.

A "WILD" BLUE FOX TRAPPED IN OREGON. Stanley G. Jewett. Murrelet, Seattle, vol.27, no.1, p.13, Apr.30, 1946.

THE WILD DOGS. Burt Kempers. Colorado Outdoors Mag., 7 (1): 16-17, illus., Jan., 1958.

THE GRAY WOLVES' LAST STAND. Lans Leneve. Oregon Sportsman, vol.1, no.1, p.17, fig.1, Sept., 1924.

NOTES ON THE WESTERN RED FOX. Robert Livezey, Fred G. Evenden, Jr. Jour. Mam., 24 (4): 500-501, Nov., 1943.

A NEW WILDLIFE STUDY IN NORTH DAKOTA. William T. McKean. North Dakota Outdoors, Bismarck, vol.9, no.11, pp.13-14, May, 1947.

SWIFT FOX AGAIN APPEARS ON WESTERN KANSAS PRAIRIE. Edwin P. Martin, George F. Sternberg. Kans. Fish and Game, 13 (1): 5, illus., July, 1955.

A SWIFT FOX, VULPES VELOX VELOX (SAY), FROM WESTERN KANSAS. Edwin P. Martin, George F. Sternberg. Trans. Kansas Acad. Sci., vol.58, no.3, pp.345-346, Sept.24, 1955.

DESCRIPTION OF A NEW FOX FROM SOUTHERN CALIFORNIA. VULPES MACROTIS, SP. NOV. LONG-EARED FOX. C. Hart Merriam. Proc. Biol. Soc., Wash., vol.4, pp.5-8, Feb.18, 1888.

THE OJAI EXPEDITION. Phil C. Orr. Santa Barbara Mus. Nat. Hist., Mus. Leaflet, vol.17, no.7, pp.79-82, Oct., 1942.

WOLVES IN IOWA. William J. Petersen. Iowa Jour. History and Politics, Iowa City, vol.38, no.1, pp.50-93, Jan., 1940.

COYOTES NUMEROUS. Orville Randall. South Dakota Conserv. Digest, Pierre, vol. 15, no.2, p.13, Feb., 1948.

THE GRAY WOLF IN NORTH DAKOTA. Russell Reid. North Dakota Outdoors, Grand Forks, vol.9, no.3, pp.11-13, illus., Sept., 1948.

GRAY FOX IN YOSEMITE VALLEY. Robert J. Rodin. Yosemite Nature Notes, Yosemite, vol.25, no.10, p.124, Oct., 1946.

THE RECEDING RANGE OF THE TIMBER WOLF IN WESTERN OREGON. Robert A. Rowe. Murrelet, Seattle, vol.22, no.3, pp.52-54, Sept.-Dec., 1941.

A RECENT RECORD OF THE TIMBER WOLF IN WESTERN OREGON. Robert A. Rowe. Murrelet, Seattle, vol.24, no.1, p.11, Apr.22, 1943.

COYOTES AT GLACIER POINT. Ralph Teall. Yosemite Nature Notes, vol.8, p. 89, Sept., 1929.

THE FUR-BEARING MAMMALS OF WYOMING. (GRAY FOX.) Earl M. Thomas. Wyo. Wild Life, 17 (2): 28-31, illus., Feb., 1953; (Red and kit foxes.) (3): 10-15, illus., Mar., 1953; (Coyote.) (8): 22-29, 38, illus., Aug., 1953.

BR'ER FOX IN TEXAS. Eugene A. Walker. Tex. Game and Fish, 10 (8): 19-21, illus., July, 1952.

"IT'S RED," BUT TRULY AMERICAN. (CANIS RUFUS.) Stanley P. Young. Western Sportsman, Denver, vol.5, no.6, pp.10-12, 26, illus., Nov., 1940.

WANDERLUST FROM THE PLAINS. (COYOTE.) Stanley P. Young. Western Sportsman, Denver, vol.7, no.2, pp.9-12, illus., July, 1941.

BUFFALO WOLF KILLED NEAR BEACH, N. D. North Dakota Outdoors, Bismarck, vol.7, no.6, p.10, illus., Dec., 1944.

THE GRAY WOLF IN NORTH DAKOTA. Mus. Review, State Hist. Soc. North Dakota, Bismarck, vol.2, no.2, pp.6, (not numbered), illus., Feb., 1947.

OKLAHOMA WOLVES. Oklahoma Game and Fish News, Oklahoma City, vol.3, no. 9, p. back cover, Sept., 1947.

THE RED FOX IN NORTH DAKOTA. North Dakota Outdoors, Bismarck, vol.1, no.7, pp.11-12, Jan., 1939.

Ursidae

BLACK ROWDY OF THE WOODS. (BLACK BEAR.) Jacob B. Abbott. Pennsylvania Game News, Harrisburg, vol.21, no.1, pp. 4-5, 25, illus., Apr., 1950.

THE BLACK BEAR. Rod Amundson. Wildlife in North Carolina, Raleigh, vol.13, no. 7, pp.4-7, illus., July, 1949.

A BEAR STORY. Belle J. Benchley. Zoonooz, San Diego, vol.13, no.12, pp.6-7, Dec., 1941.

KODIAKS AND OTHER BROWN BEARS. Maurice Burton. Illus. London News, vol.216, no.5783, p.260, illus., Feb.18, 1950.

A TALE OF TWO BEARS. Maurice Burton. Illus. London News, vol.216, no.5789, pp. 510-511, illus., Apr.1, 1950.

ARE BEARS PHOTOGENIC? I.P. Callison. Field and Stream, New York, vol.52, no.9, pp.19-21, 100-103, Jan., 1948.

BEARS WILL BE BOYS. Wendell Chapman. Nature Mag., vol.24, no.3, pp.103-107, illus., Sept., 1934.

BEAR FACTS. Greenleaf Chase. N.Y. State Cons., 8 (3): 10, 31, illus., Dec.-Jan., 1953-54; 9 (2): 2, Oct.-Nov., 1954.

THE GRIZZLY BEAR. Robert F. Cooney. Out Endangered Wildlife, Nat. Wildlife Federation, pp.3-4, illus., Jan., 1956.

(THE BROWN BEAR URSUS ARCTOS L.
PART I: NATURAL HISTORY
PART II: ETHOLOGY
PART III: HUNTING.)
L'ours brun Ursus arctos L. Partie I. Histoire naturelle. Partie II. Ethologie Partie III. Chasse. Marcel A. J. Couturier. Published by the author, Grenoble, France, pp.903, illus., 1954.

(REVIEW BY W. ROBERT EADIE, OF) (THE BROWN BEAR, URSUS ARCTOS L.) L'ours brun, Ursus arctos L. Marcel A. J. Couturier. Jour. Mam., 36 (1): 149-151, Feb.25, 1955.

THE DEATH OF TWO GRIZZLY BEARS. Edward C. Crabtree. Yosemite Nat. Notes, vol.28, no.9, pp.119-121, Sept., 1949.

(MAN AND THE CAVE BEAR.) Mensch und Hoehlenbaer. Helmuth Cramer. Naturforscher, Berlin, vol.11, no.11, pp. 282-287, illus., Feb., 1935.

MORE ROOM FOR THE BEARS. (POPULAR ACCOUNT OF SEVERAL SPECIES OF BEARS.) Raymond L. Ditmars. Bull. New York Zool. Soc., vol.39, no.2, pp.77-81, illus., Mar.-Apr., 1936.

THE BLACK BEAR. Stuart C. Downing. Canadian Nat., Toronto, vol.9, no.5, pp.168-169, illus., Nov.-Dec., 1947.

GRIZZLY AND BLACK BEARS. Stuart C. Downing. Canadian Nature, Toronto, vol. 10, no.5, pp.168-169, illus., Nov.-Dec., 1948.

THE GRIZZLY BEAR. Stuart C. Downing. Canadian Nature, Toronto, vol.18, no.1, p.8, illus., Feb., 1956.

THE POLAR BEAR. Stuart C. Downing. Canadian Nature, Toronto, vol.11, no.1, pp.8-9, pl.1, Jan.-Feb., 1949.

NOTES ON BEARS. (NAT. HIST.) Nick Drahos. New York State Cons., 7 (2): 14-18, illus., Oct.-Nov., 1952.

LOOK OUT FOR THE GRIZZILY! Frank Dufresne. Sunday Star (mag. sect.), Wash., pp.4-5, 28, May 11, 1947.

WHITE BEAR. Frank Dufresne. Field and Stream, New York, vol.49, no.10, pp.16-17, 64-66, illus., Feb., 1945.

KING OF THE BEARS. (GIANT BROWN BEAR.) Ben East. Nat. Hist., New York, vol.54, no.8, pp.377-379, illus., Oct., 1945.

WHO ARE THE BAD ACTORS? (KODIAK BEAR.) Ben East. Field and Stream, New York, vol.50, no.12, pp.26-27, 100-102, 105-106, illus., Apr., 1946.

(URSUS DENINGERI V. REICH. AND URSUS SPELAEUS ROSENM.) Ursus Deningeri v. Reich. und Ursus speraeus Rosenm. Kurt Ehrenberg. Sitz. der Math.-naturw. Kl., Akad. Wiss. Wien, Akad. Anz., no.10, pp.4, Aprl.26, 1928.

(BEAR HUNTING IN FOG.) Bjornjakt i dimma. Mauritz Eriksson. Svensk Jakt, Stockholm, vol.89, no.3, pp.66-69, illus., Mar.16, 1951.

NON-SKID FEET. (POLAR BEAR.) Arthur H. Fisher. Nature Mag., Wash., D.C., vol.33, no.2, p.104, Feb., 1940.

A DAY WITH A BEAR. Erwin Freeburn. Yosemite Nature Notes, vol.14, no.10, pp. 77-79, illus., Oct., 1935.

INOPINATUS--THE UNEXPECTED. (BARREN GROUND BEAR.) George G. Goodwin. Nat. Hist., New York, vol.55, no.9, pp. 404-406, illus., Nov., 1946.

MONARCH OF THE ARCTIC WASTES. (POLAR BEAR.) George G. Goodwin. Anim. Kingdom, 55 (6): 182-187, illus., Nov.-Dec., 1952.

THE BLACK BEAR. William L. Hamnett. Wildlife in North Carolina, Raleigh, vol. 1, no.3, pp.9, 17, Jan., 1947.

KODIAK OR GIANT ALASKAN BEARS. Edmund Heller. Bull. Wash. Park Zool. Soc., Milwaukee, vol.3, nos.2-3, p.11, Sept., 1932.

(KNOWLEDGE OF THE POLAR BEAR IN THE MIDDLE AGES.) Die Kenntnis des Eisbaeren im Mittelalter. R. Hennig. Zool. Garten, Leipzig, n.F., vol.3, nos. 1-3, pp.64-67, May, 1930.

SOME BEAR FACTS. Carra E. Horsfall. Nature Mag., vol.12, pp.145-146, col. illus., Sept., 1928.

(WHERE THE POLAR BEAR ROAMS.) Hvor isbjornen ferdes. Thor Iversen. Nature, Bergen, argang 65, no.2, pp.36-50, figs.5, Feb., 1941.

THE POLAR BEAR, NOMAD OF THE ICE FIELDS. Hartley H.T. Jackson. Home Geographic Monthly, vol.2, no.1, pp.19-24, figs.8, July, 1932.

HOT HONEY. (BLACK BEAR.) Duane D. Jacobs. Yosemite Nat. Notes, vol.29, no. 2, p.20, Feb., 1930.

THE WAYS OF A BEAR. Paul B. Kinney. Nature Mag., Washington, D.C., vol.33, no.10, pp.573-576, figs.5, Dec., 1940.

(THE BEAR CULT IN THE LIGHT OF ETHNOLOGICAL AND PREHISTORIC STUDIES.) Der Baerenkult in ethnologischer und praehistorischer Beleuchtung. Wilh Koppers. Palaeobiologica, vol.5, pp.47-64, 1933.

BEAR FACTS, PRO AND CON. Dad Lammon. Minnesota Div. of Izaak Walton League, Minneapolis, Bull., p.12 (unpaged), Fall, 1943.

TWO BEARS CAME TO TOWN. (BLACK BEAR.) Lee M. Larson. Nature Mag., Wash., vol.39, no.9, p.480, illus., Nov., 1946.

THE POLAR BEAR. Herbert Patrick Lee. Outdoor Life, vol.68, no.2, pp.30, 58-59, figs.3, Aug., 1931.

JUST BEAR FACTS. Claude W. Leister. Fauna, Phila., vol.6, no.4, pp.102-109, illus., Dec., 1944.

BARE FACTS ABOUT BEARS. (STOCK-KILLING BEARS.) Bill Lindau. Wildl. in N.C., 16 (12): 8-9, 20, illus., Dec., 1952.

(REPORTS ON THE BEAR PROBLEM, 1935.) Handlingar Bjoernfragan 1935. (Reports relating to bear industry.) Einar Loennberg. Uppsala, pp.3-66, 1935.

THE BLACK BEAR. Dan McCowan. Nature Mag., vol.2, pp.359-360, figs.3, Dec., 1923.

OUTGROWN BEAR. (GRIZZLY.) Dan McCowan. Beaver, Winnipeg, outfit 275, pp.8-10, illus., Mar., 1945.

THE BEAST THAT WALKS LIKE MAN. THE STORY OF THE GRIZZLY BEAR. Harold McCracken. Hanover House, Garden City, New York, pp.319, pls., 1955.

BEARS AND THEIR CURIOUS WAYS. Donald Marcy. Animal Kingdom, New York, vol.46, no.4, pp.74-82, illus., Aug.6, 1943.

NANOOK THE HUNTER. (POLAR BEARS.) E. B. Maurice. Beaver, Winnipeg, outfit 271, pp.42-45, illus., Dec., 1940.

THE BEAR. C. Hart Merriam. (In) North American Big Game. A book of the Boone and Crockett Club, compiled by the Committee on Records of North American Big Game. Charles Scribners Sons, New York, pp.371-378, 1939.

THE GRIZZLY, OUR GREATEST WILD ANIMAL. Enos A. Mills. pp.289, pls.10, Houghton Mifflin Co., Boston, N.Y., the Riverside Press, Cambridge, Sept., 1919.

THE HAPPY-GO-LUCKY BLACK BEAR. Enos A. Mills. Country Life, vol.39, no. 2, pp.61-62, Dec., 1920.

THE GREAT BROWN BEAR. Olaus J. Murie. Frontiers, Phila., vol.15, no.4, pp.114-116, Apr., 1951.

THE GRIZZLY BEAR AND THE WILDERNESS. Olaus J. Murie. Animal Kingdom, New York Zool. Soc., 60 (3): 68-73, illus., June, 1957.

THE LARGEST CARNIVORE. (URSUS MIDDENDORFI AND U. GYAS.) Olaus J. Murie. Frontiers, Phila., vol.3, no.3, pp.85-88, Feb., 1939.

POLAR BEARS IN THE MIDDLE AGES. T.J. Oleson. Can. Hist. Rev., 31 (1): 47-55, 1950.

THE STORY OF THE BEAR IN THE FIRST PRINTING OF DARWIN'S "ORIGIN OF SPECIES." Henry Fairfield Osborn. Science, Lancaster, n.s., vol.65, no.1695, p.616, June 24, 1927.

OBSERVATIONS ON THE GRIZZLY. James S. Paton. Forest and Stream, vol. 91, pp.155-188, Apr., 1921.

SIDELIGHTS ON THE BEAR. Archie Pendergraft. Wyoming Wildlife, Cheyenne, vol.10, no.6, pp.36-37, illus., June, 1946.

THE BEAR. J. W. Rees. Indian Wild Life, Agra, vol.4, no.1, pp.40-45, Jan.-Mar., 1939.

SULTANA, POLAR BEAR QUEEN. Oliver E. Remey. Nature Mag., Wash., vol.40, no.8, pp.429-430, 442, illus., Oct., 1947.

TOO CLOSE TO BEARS. Robert H. Rockwell. Nat. Hist., New York, vol.47, no.3, pp.136-138, Mar., 1941.

TINY BUT TOUGH. (SUN BEAR.) Jane Fergus Ross. San Diego Zoonooz, vol.21, no.5, pp.3-4, illus., May, 1948.

BANDITS BY NATURE. (BEARS.) William Rowan. Fauna, Phila., vol.6, no.4, pp. 99-101, illus., Dec., 1944.

OUR NOTEBOOK. (BEAR.) R.C. Rowe. Rod and Gun in Canada, Montreal, vol. 51, no.2, p.19, July, 1949.

BEAR FACTS. (HIMALAYAN BEAR.) Jacqueline Schermerhorn. San Diego Zoonooz, vol.18, no.11, pp.6-7, illus., Nov., 1945.

BEARS I CAN'T FORGET. Wallace G. Schwass. Living Wilderness, Wash., vol. 16, no.37, pp.10-11, illus., Summer, 1951.

THE BIOGRAPHY OF A GRIZZLY AND 75 DRAWINGS. Ernest Thompson Seton. New York, Century Co., pp.167, illus. pls., 1900.

URSUS LEUCONYX, NOB. N. Severtzow. Nachr. Gesel. Moscou, vol.8, p.79, 1873.

THE BLACK BEAR. Martin L. Shaffer. Pennsylvania Game News, Harrisburg, vol. 13, no.12, pp.7, 30, illus., Mar., 1943.

THE POLAR BEAR. T. M. Shortt. Canadian Nature, Toronto, vol.3, no.2, pp. 46-47, illus., Mar.-Apr., 1941; vol.9, no. 1, p.28, illus., Jan.-Feb., 1947.

BEAR FACTS. Bertrand E. Smith. Jour. Mam., vol.27, no.1, pp.31-37, Mar.14, 1946.

BEARS. L. L. Snyder. Canadian Nature, Toronto, vol.7, no.1, pp.20-25, Jan.-Feb., 1945.

BEAR ARE FUNNY FELLOWS. W. M. (Bill) Steele. Oregon Outdoors, Oswego, vol.4, no.1, pp.10-11, 17-18, illus., Jan., 1947.

(Review by Aldo Leopold of) MEET MR. GRIZZLY. Montague Stevens. Jour. Forestry, Washington, vol.42, no.3, p. 222, Mar., 1944.

A WORD ABOUT BEARS. Ken Stott, Jr. Educational Ser. Zool. Soc. San Diego, pp. E1-E15, illus., 1946.

ABOUT BEARS! F. W. Stuewer. Michigan Conserv., Lansing, vol.19, no.6, pp.21-25, illus., Nov., 1950.

THE BEAR OF OUR NORTHWOODS. CAMP ROBBER AND WOODS CLOWN. T. Surber. Conservation Volunteer, St. Paul, vol.3, no.13, pp.21-24, Oct., 1941.

FROM A WARM CLIMATE. (POLAR BEARS.) Frank Thone. Science News Letter, Wash., D.C., vol.42, no.6, pp.94-95, Aug.8, 1942.

(POPULATION OF ALPEN BEARS (URSUS ARCTOS LINNE 1758).) Bestand des Alpenbaeren, Ursus arctos Linne, 1758. E. P. Tratz. Saeugetierk. Mitteil., Stuttgart, vol.1, no.4, pp.174-175, Oct.1, 1953.

SOME BEAR FACTS. Hans G. Uhlig. W. Va. Cons., 15 (12): 34-35, Mar., 1952.

KNOW YOUR BIG GAME. COMMON BLACK BEAR (EUARCTOS AMERICANUS). Walter J. Wilwerding. Sports Afield, Minneapolis, vol.121, no.6, p.38, June, 1949.

KNOW YOUR BIG GAME. (GRIZZLY BEAR.) Walter J. Wilwerding. Sports Afield, Minneapolis, vol.122, no.4, pp.46-47, illus., Oct., 1949.

KNOW YOUR BIG GAME: KENAI GIANT BROWN BEAR (URSUS KENAIENSIS). Walter J. Wilwerding. Sports Afield, Minneapolis, vol.123, no.1, pp.44-45, illus., Jan., 1950.

SOME OBSERVATIONS ON THE BLACK BEAR. Leslie H. Wood. Pennsylvania Game News, Harrisburg, vol.15, no.6, pp.8, 30, Sept., 1944.

THE BLACK BEAR. William H. Wright. Charles Scribner's Sons, New York, pp. 127, illus., 1910.

THE GRIZZLY BEAR. THE NARRATIVE OF A HUNTER-NATURALIST. William H. Wright. Charles Scribner's Sons, New York, pp. x, 274, illus., 1909.

(BEAR HUNT IN DENMARK.) Bruinvisvangst in Denemarken. Artis, 3e Jaargang no.6, Maart-Apr., 1958, pp.200-215, illus., 1958.

BLACK BEAR. Canadian Nature, Toronto, vol.1, no.2, p.28, Nov.-Dec., 1939.

BLACK BEAR EUARCTOS AMERICANUS. Wyoming Wild Life, Cheyenne, vol.4, no. 11, pp.6, 13, Nov., 1939.

GRIZZLY BEAR URSUS HORRIBILIS. Wyoming Wild Life, Cheyenne, vol.4, no. 12, pp.6, 18, Dec., 1939.

PHOTOGRAPH OF SPECTACLED BEAR. San Diego Zoonooz, vol.16, no.1, p.1, Jan., 1943.

THE POLAR BEAR. Nat. Mus. Canada, Guide to Mammalian Habitat Exhibits, Leaflet 4, pp.4, 1951.

Africa

THE STORY OF THE NANDI BEAR. R. I. Pocock. Nat. Hist. Mag., London, vol.2, no.13, pp.162-169, figs.2, Jan., 1930.

NANDI BEAR AGAIN. Jour. East Africa and Uganda Nat. Hist. Soc., Nairobi, vol. 16, nos.2, 3 (71, 72), p.136, Feb., 1942.

Alaska

ALASKA'S MAMMOTH BROWN BEARS. William H. Chase. Kansas City, Mo., Burton, pp.129, 1947.

BROWN BEAR ON THE BEACH. Lora B. Cody. Alaska Sportsman, Ketchikan, vol. 11, no.4, pp.10-11, 29-33, illus., Apr., 1945.

BEARS PROWL KODIAK ISLAND. Carl E. Davidson. Sports Afield, Minneapolis, vol.112, no.4, pp.38-40, 59-65, illus., Oct., 1944.

BROWN BEAR SEEN ON ST. LAWRENCE ISLAND. Otto William Geist. Jour. Mam., vol.15, no.4, pp.316-317, Nov., 1934.

THE GRIZZLY AND BROWN BEARS OF ALASKA AT HOME. John M. Holzworth. Series of radio talks given in Aug., 1930, over station WEAF, under auspices of Amer. Soc. of Mammalogists, 1930.

"MR. HOOTS" OF ADMIRALTY ISLAND. (GRIZZLY AND BROWN BEARS.) John M. Holzworth. Outdoor Life, vol.68, no.1, pp.12-13, 72-73, figs.4, July, 1931; no.2, pp.26-27, 70, figs.3, Aug., 1931; no.3, pp. 30-31, figs.5, Sept., 1931.

THE WILD GRIZZLIES OF ALASKA. John M. Holzworth. G. P. Putnam's Sons, New York, London, pp.417, illus., 1930.

BROWN BEAR KILLED ON ST. LAWRENCE ISLAND. Arthur H. Howell. Jour. Mam., vol.21, no.2, p.216, May 14, 1940.

THE GREAT ALASKAN BROWN BEAR. H. McCracken. Nature Mag., vol.6, pp.212-216, figs.4, pl.1, Oct., 1925.

NEW ALASKAN BEAR LANDS. H. McCracken. Field and Stream, no.4, pp.11-13, 69, 97, Aug., 1929.

TWO NEW BEARS FROM THE ALASKA PENINSULA. C. Hart Merriam. Proc. Biol. Soc. Wash., vol.15, pp.77-79, Mar. 22, 1902.

URSUS HOLZWORTHI, A NEW GRIZZLY FROM THE TALKEETNA MOUNTAINS, ALASKA. C. Hart Merriam. Proc. Biol. Soc. Wash., vol.42, pp.173-174, June 15, 1929.

URSUS SHELDONI, A NEW BEAR FROM MONTAGUE ISLAND, ALASKA. C. Hart Merriam. Proc. Biol. Soc. Wash., vol. 23, pp.127-130, Sept.2, 1910.

A PECULIAR BEAR FROM ALASKA. Wilfred H. Osgood. Field Mus. Nat. Hist., Chicago, Zool. ser., vol.10, no.1, pp.1-3, pl.1, Nov., 1909.

ADMIRALTY'S BEARS. Arthur Newton Pack. Nature Mag., vol.26, no.2, pp.111-112, illus., Aug., 1935.

THE BEARS OF ADMIRALTY. Arthur Newton Pack. Nature Mag., vol.23, no.1, pp.23-30, figs.22, Jan., 1934.

BEARS OF ADMIRALTY. WITH THE BIG BROWNIES AND GRIZZLIES OF SOUTH-EAST ALASKA. Arthur Newton Pack. Nature Mag., vol.19, no.2, pp.79-86, figs.24, Feb., 1932.

THE BROWN BEARS OF CHICAGOF ISLAND, ALASKA. Stanton Warburton. Murrelet, vol.12, no.3, p.79, Sept., 1931.

THE TRUTH ABOUT THE ALASKA GRIZZLY AND BROWN BEARS. Stewart Edward White. Amer. Field, vol.118, no. 36, pp.220-222, figs.4, Sept.3, 1932.

Anatomy

(OSTEOMETRIC NOTES ON THE HEAD OF A BEAR OF THE PYRENEES.) Notes ostéométriques sur la tête de l'ours des Pyrénées. Ed Bourdelle, Mme M. Deziliere. Mammalia, Paris, vol.13, no.4, pp.125-128, Dec., 1949.

MASTICATORY APPARATUS IN THE SPECTACLED BEAR (TREMARCTOS ORNATUS). D. Dwight Davis. Fieldiana: Zoology, Chicago Nat. Hist. Mus., vol.37, pp.25-46, illus., June 19, 1955.

(ANALYSIS OF THE DENTITION OF THE POLAR BEAR URSUS (THALARCTOS) MARITIMUS PHIPPS, 1774.) Zur Analyse des Gebisses des Eisbaeren, Ursus (Thalarctos) maritimus Phipps, 1774. Thenius Erich. Saeugetierk. Mitteil., vol. 1, no.1, pp.14-20, illus., Jan.10, 1953.

(THE PENIS BONE OF THE BROWN BEAR.) Sur l'os pénien de l'ours brun. Maurice Gourdon. Bull. Soc. Sci. Nat. l'Ouest France, Nantes, annee 43, nos.3-4, pp. 159-163, Sept.30, 1934.

NOTE ON THE SPERMATOZOA OF THE POLAR BEAR (URSUS MARITIMUS). George Gulliver. Proc. Zool. Soc. Lond., pt.14, p.11, 1846.

RECORDS OF SUPERNUMERARY TEETH IN BEARS. E. Raymond Hall. Univ. Calif. Publ. Zool., vol.30, no.11, pp.243-250, pls.14-15, fig.1, Mar.2, 1928.

A RECORD BLACK BEAR. Hartley H. T. Jackson. Jour. Mam., vol.20, pp.252-253, May, 1939.

SKULL OF A CALIFORNIA GRIZZLY. Barbara Lawrence. California Fish and Game, San Francisco, vol.30, no.2, p.98, fig.43, Apr., 1944.

DEFORMED JAW IN AN ALASKAN BROWN BEAR (URSUS). Calvin J. Lensink. Jour. Mam., vol.35, no.3, pp.438-439, Aug.20, 1954.

ON THE ANATOMY OF THE THIBET BEAR (URSUS THIBETANUS, F. CUV.). R. Owen. Proc. Comm. Sci. and Corres. Zool. Soc. London, pt.1, p.76, 1830-1831.

FURTHER NOTES ON SOME EXTERNAL CHARACTERS OF THE BEARS (URSIDAE). R. I. Pocock. Ann. and Mag. Nat. Hist., Lond., ser.9, vol.1, pp.375-384, figs.2, May, 1918.

ON THE FEET AND RHINARIUM OF THE POLAR BEAR. R. I. Pocock. Proc. Zool. Soc. Lond., pt.1, pp.159-160, Apr., 1923.

(THE OVARY OF A BEAR FOUR YEARS OLD.) L'ovaire d'une ourse ("Ursus arctos") de quatre ans. Note preliminaire. Nicolas Popoff. Comptes Rendus Assoc. Anatom., (29 Reunion, Bruxelles, 25-28 Mars 1934), pp.471-484, figs.9, 1934.

THE MYOLOGY OF THE INFERIOR EXTREMITY OF THE MALAY BEAR, URSUS MALAYANUS. L. J. Ray. Proc. Zool. Soc. Lond., vol.119, pt.1, pp.121-132, figs.6, May 16, 1949.

(INVESTIGATIONS OF THE DENTITION OF BEARS.) Untersuchungen ueber das Gebiss der Baeren. Karl Rode. Monographien Geol. u. Palaeont., Leipzig, ser. 11, no.7, pp.1-162, figs.25, pls.8, tables 59, 1935.

(ON THE FIRST LOWER MOLARS OF BEARS.) Ueber den ersten Unterkiefermolaren der Baeren. K. Rode. Centralbl. F. Mineral, Geol. u. Palaeont. (2), Abt.B, Jahrg.1930, pp.83-90, 1930.

SHORT NOTE ON THE MYOLOGY OF THE AMERICAN BLACK BEAR (URSUS AMERICANUS). Francis J. Shepherd. Jour. Anat. and Physiol., Cambridge, vol.18, pp.103-117, 1884.

CEREBRAL HEMISPHERES OF THE AMERICAN BLACK BEAR (URSUS AMERICANUS). Wilbur K. Smith. Morphologic and Phylogenetic characteristics. Wilbur K. Smith. Archiv. Neur. and Psych., vol.30, pp.1-13, figs.8, July, 1933.

(CHEWING MUSCULATURE AND MAXILLARY JOINTS OF URSIDAE.) Kaumuskulatur und Kiefergelenk der Ursiden. Dietrich Starck. Morpholog. Jahrb., vol.76, pp. 104-147, figs.19, 1935.

BLOOD PICTURE OF THE AMERICAN BLACK BEAR, URSUS AMERICANUS. Arthur Svihla, Howard Bowman, Roger Pearson. Jour. Mam., 36 (1): 134-135, Feb., 1955.

(ANALYSIS OF THE DENTITION OF POLAR BEARS (URSUS THALARCTOS MARITIMUS PHIPPS 1774).) Zur Analyse des Gebisses des Eisbaeren, Ursus (Thalarctos) maritimus Phipps, 1774. Erich Thenius. Saeugetierk. Mitteil., Stuttgart, vol.1, no.1, pp.14-20, illus., Jan.10, 1953.

Bear Meat as Food

TOXICITY OF POLAR BEAR LIVER. J. Kenneth Doutt. Jour. Mam., Balto., vol.21, no.3, pp.356-357, Aug.14, 1940.

BEAR MEAT CAN BE DANGEROUS. Norman A. Meinkoth. Wyoming Wild Life, Cheyenne, vol.14, no.9, pp.19-20, illus., Oct., 1950.

TOXICITY OF POLAR BEAR LIVER. Kare Rodahl. Nature, London, vol.164, no. 4169, pp.530-531, Sept.24, 1949.

TRICHINOSIS FROM POLAR BEAR MEAT. Arctic, Montreal, vol.1, no.2, p.144, Autumn, 1948.

Canada

THE BLACK BEAR OF LABRADOR. J. A. Allen. Bull. Amer. Mus. Nat. Hist., vol. 28, pp.1-6, Jan.5, 1910.

THE WHITE BEAR OF SOUTHWESTERN BRITISH COLUMBIA. J. A. Allen. Bull. Amer. Mus. Nat. Hist., vol.26, pp.233-238, figs.1-4, Apr.17, 1909.

POLAR BEARS IN THE GULF OF ST. LAWRENCE. J. Kenneth Doutt. Jour. Mam., vol.21, no.1, pp.90-92, Feb.14, 1940.

FURTHER EVIDENCE ABOUT THE BARREN-GROUND GRIZZLY BEAR IN NORTHEAST LABRADOR AND QUEBEC. C. S. Elton. Jour. Mam., 35 (3): 345-357, map, Aug., 1954.

A NEW RACE OF BLACK BEAR FROM VANCOUVER ISLAND, BRITISH COLUMBIA, WITH REMARKS ON OTHER NORTHWEST COAST FORMS OF EUARCTOS. (URSUS AMERICANUS VANCOUWERI.) E. Raymond Hall. Univ. Calif. Publ. Zool., vol.30, no.10, pp.231-242, pls.12-13, Mar.2, 1928.

A NEW WHITE BEAR, FROM BRITISH COLUMBIA. William T. Hornaway. 9th Ann. Rep. New York Zool. Soc., pp.5-10, Jan.10, 1905.

POLAR BEAR IN LAKE ST. JOHN DISTRICT, QUEBEC. (THALARCTOS MARITIMUS UNGAVENSIS.) Hartley H. T. Jackson. Jour. Mam., vol.20, no.2, p.253, May, 1939.

THRILLS IN THE WILD. SOME EXPERIENCES WITH BLACK BEARS AND GRIZZLIES IN WESTERN CANADA. G. B. Mitchell. Nature Mag., Wash., D.C., vol. 31, no.5, pp.273-276, May, 1938.

MANITOBA'S THREE BEARS. L.T.S. Norris-Elye. Manitoba Calling, Winnipeg, vol.11, no.1, pp.6-7, Jan., 1947.

BRITISH COLUMBIA'S BEEF-EATING BEARS. C.V. Tench. Rod and Gun in Canada, Montreal, vol.46, no.7, pp.8-9, illus., Jan., 1945.

THE BEAR INVASION OF 1953. G. C. Toner. Fed. Ont. Nat., Bull. no.64, pp.3, 27, illus., Spring, 1954.

(THE MYSTERIOUS PLANTIGRADE OF THE CANADIAN ARCTIC.) Le mysterieux plantigrade de l'Arctic canadien. La Nature, Paris, no.3133, p.118, Apr.1, 1947.

Captivity

FURTHER NOTES ON THE BREEDING OF THE AMERICAN BLACK BEAR IN CAPTIVITY. A. B. Baker. Smithsonian Misc. Coll., vol.59, no.10, publ.2086, pp.4, May 17, 1912.

A NOTABLE SUCCESS IN THE BREEDING OF BLACK BEARS. A. B. Baker. Smithsonian Misc. Coll., vol.XLV (Quarterly issue, vol.1), pp.175-179, illus., pl.LI-LII, publ.1434, 1903.

REARING POLAR BEARS. Ed. H. Bean. Parks and Recreation, vol.10, pp.154-155, Dec., 1926.

THE BEAR GROUPS IN THE NEW BARLESS BEAR DENS. Edmund Heller. Bull. Wash. Park Zool. Soc., Milwaukee, vol.3, nos.2-3, pp.7-10, photo, Sept., 1932.

POLAR BEARS REARED IN MILWAUKEE. Edmund Heller. Bull. Wash. Park Zool. Soc., Milwaukee, vol.1, no.2, pp.1-5, Mar.-Apr., 1930.

(ENCLOSURE FOR BROWN BEARS IN THE IMPERIAL ZOOLOGICAL GARDEN OF SOFIA.) Das neue Freigehege fur Braunbaeren im Koeniglichen Zoologischen Garten zu Sofia. H. B. Peters. Zool. Garten, N.F., Leipzig, vol.7, nos.7-9, pp.202-205, Nov., 1934.

(REARING POLAR BEARS IN THE NUERNBERG ZOOLOGICAL GARDEN.) Eisbaerenzucht im Nuernberger Tiergarten. Alfred Seitz. Zool. Garten, n.F., vol.19, no.5, pp.180-189, 1952.

(ARTIFICIAL RAISING OF A POLAR BEAR (THALARCTOS MARITIMUS PHIPPS).) Ueber kuenstliche Aufzucht eines Eisbaeren Thalarctos maritimus Phipps. Jan Vlasak. Zool. Garten, Leipzig, N.F., vol.16, no.5, pp.159-179, illus., 1950.

"SNOW WHITE" OF THE PRAGUE ZOO: THE POLAR BEAR CUB WHICH GREW UP IN A CITY FLAT. Jan Vlasak. Illus. London News, vol.211, no.5656, pp.302-305, illus., Sept.13, 1947.

BUDDY, THE POLAR BEAR. FROM MOUNTIE FOOT-WARMER TO PLAYBOY AT BANFF. Beaver, Winnipeg, outfit 264, no.4, pp.30-31, illus., Mar., 1934.

LONDON'S CHIEF ATTRACTION—BRUMAS, THE FOUR-MONTH OLD POLAR BEAR CUB. Illus. London News, vol.216, no.5790, pp.540-541, illus., Apr.8, 1950.

MAKING HER DEBUT: THE FIRST POLAR BEAR CUB TO BE REARED IN THIS COUNTRY. Illus. London News, vol.216, no.5784, p.305, illus., Feb.25, 1950.

A ROLY-POLY POLAR BEAR NAMED BRUMAS BECOMES THE MOST POPULAR BABY IN LONDON. Life, New York, vol.28, no.18, pp.18-20, illus., May 1, 1950.

Central and South America

ON THE POSSIBLE OCCURRENCE OF THE SPECTACLED BEAR, TREMARCTOS ORNATUS (F. CUVIER, 1825), IN PANAMA. Philip Hershkovitz. Saeugetierk. Mitteil., 5 (3): 122-123, illus., Aug.1, 1957.

(A SPECIMEN OF TREMARCTOS ORNATUS FROM VENEZUELA.) Ein exemplar von Tremarctos ornatus aus Venezuela. Einar Loennberg. Zool. Anzeig., Leipzig, vol.36, nos.2-3, pp.49-50, Aug.9, 1910.

ON THE BEAR OF ECUADOR. Oldfield Thomas. Ann. Mag. Nat. Hist. (7), vol.9, no.51, pp.215-217, Mar., 1902.

Diseases and Parasites

DESCRIPTION AND RELATIONSHIPS OF DIROFILARIA URSI YAMAGUTI, 1941, AND A REVIEW OF THE GENUS DIROFILARIA RAILLIET AND HENRY, 1911. (NEMATODES FROM BLACK BEARS.) Roy C. Anderson. Trans. Roy. Can. Inst., 29 (2): 35-65, illus., 1952.

A NOTE ON TRICHINOSIS IN ANIMALS OF THE CANADIAN NORTHWEST TERRITORIES. (FOUND IN POLAR BEARS.) Malcolm Brown, others. Can. Jour. Publ. Health, 40 (1): 20-21, Jan., 1949.

(URINARY CALCULUS OF A CAVE BEAR.) Harnsteine eines Hoehlenbaeren. Tilly Edinger. Palaeont. Zeitschr., Berlin, vol.15, no.4, pp.349-355, figs.5, Dec.31, 1933.

(ON THE HEALED SHOT-WOUND IN THE LEFT MANDIBLE OF A SPECTACLED BEAR (TREMARCTOS ORNATUS). Ueber eine verheilte Schussverletzung am linken Unterkiefer eines Brilleabaren (Ursus Tremarctos ornatus). K. Ehrenberg. Zeitschr. fuer Stomatologie, 23 Jahrg., Heft 7, pp.581-588, figs.5, July, 1925.

DENTAL CARIES IN WILD BEARS. E. Raymond Hall. Trans. Kansas Acad. Sci., 48 (1): 79-85, June, 1945.

A SURVEY OF PARASITES OF THE BLACK BEARS IN SOUTHWESTERN COLORADO. Billy Neal Horstman. MS thesis, Colo. A. & M. Coll., 1949.

STUDIES ON THE HELMINTH FAUNA OF ALASKA. XXI. TAXONOMY, MORPHOLOGICAL VARIATION, AND ECOLOGY OF DIPHYLLOBOTHRIUM URSI N. SP. PROVIS. ON KODIAK ISLAND. Robert Rausch. Jour. Parasit., 40 (5): 540-563, illus., Oct., 1954.

DIPHYLLOBOTHRIUM LATUM IN BEAR. W. M. Rush. Jour. Mam., vol.13, no.3, pp.274-275, Aug., 1932.

(SOME INTERESTING CASES OF DISEASE IN BEARS.) Einige interessante Krankheitsfaelle bei Baeren. Wilhelm Schulze. Zool. Garten, Leipzig, (N.F.), vol.20, nos.2-3, pp.101-108, illus., 1953.

SUSCEPTIBILITY OF THE BEAR TO FOX ENCEPHALITIS. C. S. Stulberg, R. G. Green. Proc. Soc. Expt. Biol. Med., New York, vol.64, no.1, pp.88-89, 1947.

Economic Importance, Control, Protection

NEEDED: A NEW DEAL FOR ALASKA'S BEARS. Russell Annabel. Sports Afield, 127 (6): 40-41, 93-98, illus., June, 1952.

BEAR FOR THE FUTURE? Lester Bagley. Wyo. Wild Life, 19 (2): 2, Feb., 1955.

ARE WE LOSING THE BLACK BEAR IN WEST VIRGINIA? R. Wayne Bailey. W. Va. Cons., 17 (11): 4-9, 28-29, illus., Jan., 1954.

DON'T FEED THE BEARS. Victor H. Cahalane. Sat. Evening Post, 211 (4): 23, 62-63, 65, July 23, 1938.

NATIONAL PARK SERVICE BEAR PROBLEM. Victor H. Cahalane. Planning and Civic Comment, 4 (1): 32, Jan.-Mar., 1938.

BEAR DAMAGE TO YOUNG DOUGLAS-FIR. Thomas W. Childs, Norman P. Worthington. U.S. For. Serv., Pac. N. W. Exp. Sta., Res. Note no.113, pp.1-4, illus., Apr., 1955.

AGRICULTURAL DEPREDATION BY THE BLACK BEAR IN VIRGINIA. Leslie B. Davenport. Jour. Wildlife Mgt., Ithaca, vol.17, no.3, pp.331-340, illus., July, 1953.

THE ECONOMIC IMPORTANCE OF THE BLACK BEAR IN VIRGINIA. Leslie B. Davenport, Jr. MS thesis, Va. Poly. Inst., 1951.

ALASKA BROWN BEAR PROTECTION. Morgan Davis. Forest and Stream, vol.90, pp.361, 362, 414, 415, July, 1920.

TO FEED OR NOT TO FEED--THAT IS THE BEAR QUESTION IN YELLOWSTONE NATIONAL PARK. William L. Finley, Irene Finley. Amer. Forests, 46 (8): 344-347, 369, 383-384, Aug., 1940.

THE BLACK BEAR, SAINT OR SINNER? O. Earl Frye. Florida Wildlife, Tallahassee, vol.5, no.6, pp.6-7, 28, illus., Nov., 1950.

CONTROL OF BEAR PREDATION IN COLORADO. Paul F. Gilbert. Proc. Ann. Conf. W. Assn. State Game and Fish Comm., 29: 98-101, 1949.

BLACK BEAR DAMAGE TO REDWOOD REPRODUCTION. Fred A. Glover. Jour. Wildlife Mgt., vol.19, no.4, pp.437-443, illus., Oct., 1955.

THE CASE OF THE BROWN BEAR. IS THE GREAT KODIAK, LARGEST CARNIVOROUS ANIMAL IN THE WORLD, A MENACE TO THE SOCIAL AND INDUSTRIAL DEVELOPMENT OF ALASKA? George F. Hatch. Amer. Forests, vol.36, no.3, pp.131-134, Mar., 1930.

RESOLUTION RECOMMENDING ADMIRALTY ISLAND AS A BEAR SANCTUARY. R. T. Hatt. Jour. Mam., vol.13, no.3, p.287, Aug., 1932.

ALASKA BROWN BEAR CONSERVATION. B. F. Heintzleman. Jour. Forestry, 37 (6): 510-511, June, 1939.

MANAGING THE ALASKA BROWN BEAR. B. F. Heintzleman. Louisiana Conserv. Rev., New Orleans, vol.3, no.1, pp.5-8, 46-47, illus., Jan., 1933.

A PLAN FOR THE MANAGEMENT OF BROWN BEAR IN RELATION TO OTHER RESOURCES ON ADMIRALITY ISLAND, ALASKA. B. F. Heintzleman, H. W. Terhune. U.S. Dept. Agric., Misc. Pub. 195, pp.20, 1934.

THE BLACK BEAR AS A DESTROYER OF GAME. A. Brazier Howell. Jour. Mam., vol.2, no.1, p.36, Feb.10, 1921.

THE SOUTH OLYMPIC TREE FARM. Oscar R. Levin. Jour. For., 52 (4): 243-249, illus., Apr., 1954.

(REPORTS RELATING TO THE BEAR INDUSTRY.) Handlingar I Bjoernfraegan 1935. Einar Loennberg. Stockholm, pp. 3-66, 1935.

THE TRUTH ABOUT THE BLACK BEAR. (NATIONWIDE CENSUS INDICATES BLACK BEAR WILL DISAPPEAR UNLESS PROTECTED.) Leo A. Luttringer, Jr. Nature Mag., vol.25, no.8, pp.323-325, illus., June, 1935.

DAMAGE TO TREES BY BLACK BEARS IN ALASKA. H. J. Lutz. Jour. Forestry, 49 (7): 522-523, July, 1951.

THE STATUS OF THE BEAR. Harry McGuire. Outdoor Life, vol.67, no.3, pp.16-17, 56-58, Mar., 1931.

THE BLACK BEAR: A GOOD CITIZEN. J.R. Matson. Bull. to the Schools, New York, vol.36, no.7, pp.190-194, illus., Mar., 1950.

BEARS HAMPER TREE GROWING IN CALIFORNIA. Alfred H. Merrill. Jour. For., 51 (12): 928-929, Dec., 1953.

DAMAGE TO CONIFERS BY BEAR. O. L. Resner. Proc. 33rd Ann. Conf. Western Assn. State Game and Fish Comm., June 1-3, 1953, pp.109-111, 1954.

VIRGINIA'S BLACK BEAR--GOOD OR BAD? E. V. Richards. Va. Wildl., 14 (2): 16-17, 21, 23, illus., Feb., 1953.

YOU CAN'T BLAME BRUIN FOR BITING THE HANDS THAT FEED HIM. Grace V. Sharritt. Amer. Forests, Wash., vol.51, no.6, pp.269-271, 306, June, 1945.

PROTECTION OF MOUNTAIN APIARIES FROM BEARS BY USE OF ELECTRIC FENCE. Tracy I. Storer, George H. Vansell, Ben D. Moses. Jour. Wildlife Mgt., Menasha, vol.2, no.4, pp.172-178, fig.1, Oct., 1938.

CONSERVING ALASKA'S BROWN BEARS. H. W. Terhune. U.S. Daily, vol.7, no.84, p.8, June 10, 1932.

TRAMP BEARS. Farley F. Tubbs. Mich. Cons., 11 (9): 6-7, Oct., 1942.

OUR GREAT BEARS. REFUGES MUST BE ESTABLISHED IF THE SPORT OF HUNTING THE WORLD'S LARGEST CARNIVORE IS TO BE PERPETUATED. Stewart Edward White. Field and Stream, vol.39, no.10, pp.36-38, 83, illus., Feb., 1935.

SANCTUARY FOR THE ALASKA BEAR. Stewart Edward White. Sierra Club Bulletin, vol.17, no.1, pp.59-66, figs., Feb., 1932.

BEAR DEPREDATION. Rep. Subcom. Publ. Lands, Grazing and For. Practices of Calif. Assembly Interim Com. on Agr. Assembly Interim Com. Rep.1953-1955, 17 (1): 1-58, illus., Mar., 1954.

BLACK BEAR NEEDS MORE PROTECTION. Colorado Conservation Comments, Denver, vol.7, no.3, pp.3-5, Sept.15, 1944.

OUR BEARS NEED A BREAK. Mich. Out-of-Doors, 2 (9): 14-17, illus., Feb., 1952.

Eurasia

(INFORMATION ON THE KAMCHATKA BEAR.) Zur Kenntnis des Kamtschatka-Baeren. Sten Bergman. Zool. Garten, vol.14, nos.1-2, pp.26-35, illus., 1942.

OBSERVATIONS ON THE KAMCHATKAN BEAR. Sten Bergman. Jour. Mam., vol. 17, no.2, pp.115-120, May, 1936.

(THE BEAR IN FRANCE: PRESENT STATE AND PROTECTION.) A propos de l'ours en France. Etat actuel et protection. E. Bourdelle. Mammalia, Paris, vol.1, no.4, pp.178-181, June, 1937.

(SOME DATA ON THE PRESENT DISTRIBUTION OF THE BEAR IN THE FRENCH PYRENEES.) Quelques precisions sur la repartition actuelle de l'ours dans les Pyrenees Francaises. E. Bourdelle. Bull. Nat. Soc. Acclimat., Paris, nos.11-12, pp. 1-8, map, 1937.

A LARGE BEAR (U. LABIATUS) SHOT NEAR GUNA. Stewart Capper. Jour. Bombay Nat. Hist. Soc., vol.27, p.937, July 31, 1921.

THE JUNGLE IN SUNLIGHT AND SHADOW. PART 2. ABOUT BHALOO THE BEAR: AND SOME NEW VIEWS ON PROTECTIVE COLOURING. F. W. Champion. Field, London, vol.162, no.4206, pp.358-359, figs., Aug.5, 1933.

THE TERMITE-HUNTER: A REMARKABLE NATURE STUDY FROM INDIA. F. W. Champion. Illus. London News, vol.181, no.4874, p.419, illus., Sept.17, 1932.

(THE BROWN BEAR IN THE FRENCH ALPS. ITS PRESENT DISTRIBUTION. THE LAST BEAR KILLED (MAURIENNE, SAVOY). THE LAST BEAR SEEN (VERCORS, DROME). L1ours brun dans les Alpes francaises. Sa chorologie actuelle. Le dernier ours tue (Maurienne, Savoie). Le dernier ours vu (Vercors, Drome). Marcel A. J. Couturier. Mammalia, Paris, vol.6, no.2, pp.65-73, maps. 2, June, 1942.

THE SUN BEAR OF CEYLON. P.E.P. Deraniyagala. Spolia Zeylanica, Bull. Nat. Mus. Ceylon, vol.27, pt.2, pp.289-290, May 25, 1955.

A REVIEW OF FOSSIL AND RECENT BEARS OF THE OLD WORLD WITH REMARKS ON THEIR PHYLOGENY BASED UPON THEIR DENTITION. Dirk Pieter Erdbrink. Drukkerij Jan de Lange, Deventer, pp.xii, 597, illus, pls.22, maps, tables 11, 1953.

(Review by D. A. Hooijer of) A REVIEW OF FOSSIL AND RECENT BEARS OF THE OLD WORLD, WITH REMARKS ON THEIR PHYLOGENY, BASED UPON THEIR DENTITION. D. P. Erdbrink. Mammalia, Paris, vol.17, no.4, p.362, Dec., 1953.

SOME NOTES ON MALAYAN BEARS. A. H. Fetherstonhaugh. Malayan Nature, Jour., Kuala Lumpur, Selangor, vol.1, no.1, pp. 15-22, pls.4, Aug., 1940.

(ESSAY ON THE LIFE OF THE BROWN BEAR IN THE NORTHERN URALS.) K. K. Flerov. Ann. Mus. Zool. Acad. URSS, vol.30, pp.351-358, 1929. (In Russian.) Review d'Histoire Naturelle, Pt. 1, A, Mammiferes, Paris, vol.11, no.7, pp.237-240, July, 1930. (In French.)

THE MALAY BEAR. J. C. Higgins. Jour. Bombay Nat. Hist. Soc., vol.35, no. 3, p.673, Feb.15, 1932.

(HEAD OF AN URUS FOUND IN CHARENTE IN YEAR 1884.) Etude d'une tete d'urus trouvee dans la Charente, en 1884. Edelestan Jardin. Bull. Soc. Geog. Rochefort, Annee, pp.1-4, 1884-1885.

WHAT ABOUT THE JAVAN BEAR? A. F. Jentink. Notes Leyden Mus., vol.20, no. 19, pp.109-112, June, 1898.

(THE MOST ANCIENT BEAR OF HUNGARY.) Ungarns aeltester Baer. Theodor Kormos. Folia Sabariensia, vol.1, no.1, pp.1-7, 1933. (In German, with introduction in Hungarian.)

(ON THE RACE QUESTION AND THE REPRODUCTION BIOLOGY OF THE CARPATHIAN BROWN BEAR URSUS ARCTOS ARCTOS LINNE 1758.) Zur Rassenfrage und Fortpflanzungsbiologie des Karpatischen Braunbaeren, Ursus arctos arctos Linne, 1758. Waldemar Lindemann. Saeugetierk. Mitt., 2 (1): 1-8, Jan., 1954.

(THE BEAR IN SWEDEN.) Bjoernen I Sverige 1856-1928. Einar Loennberg. Uppsala, pp.1-31, 1929.

REMARKS ON SOME PALEARCTIC BEARS. Einar Loennberg. Proc. Zool. Soc. Lond., pt.1, pp.85-95, pls.2, Apr., 1923.

THE ABOMINABLE SNOW-MAN. (TRACK OF HIMALAYAN BEAR.) M. S. Mani. Turtox News, Chicago, 35 (8): 172-173, Aug., 1957.

"DEMENT" AS CONFIRMED. (URSUS ARCTOS FROM S. SERBIA.) V. Martino. Lovtsa, nos.11-12, pp.2, figs.2, Nov.-Dec., 1936.

(THE BEAR CAVE OF MONTRICHER.) La grotte aux ours de Montricher. (Ursus arctos.) A. Mathey-Dupraz. Bull. du Centenaire, Neuchatel, pt.2, vol.57, pp. 201-202, (1932) 1933.

(A BEAR CAVE AT KLAUSEN PASS.) Ueber eine Baerenhoehle am Klausenpass. P. F. Muheim. Eclogae Geologicae Helvetiae, Basel, vol.28, no.2, pp.591-592, (1935) Jan.8, 1936.

THE BEARS OCCURRING IN RUSSIA. S. I. Ognev. Nature and Sport in Ukraine (Kharkov), 1924, nos.1-2, pp.1-8 (of reprint), 1924. (In Russian.)

NOTE ON THE MALAY BEAR (URSUS MALAYANUS). E. G. Phythian-Adams. Jour. Bombay Nat. Hist. Soc., vol.34, no. 3, pp.798-799, Nov.15, 1930.

THE BLACK AND BROWN BEARS OF EUROPE AND ASIA. PARTS I AND II. R.I. Pocock. Jour. Bombay Nat. Hist. Soc., vol.35, no.4, pp.771-823, July 15, 1932; vol.36, no.1, pp.101-138, Nov.15, 1932.

WANTED BEARS. R. I. Pocock. Jour. Bombay Nat. Hist. Soc., vol.34, no.4, p. 1052, Mar.2, 1931.

NOTE ON THE JAPANESE BEAR. Philip Lutley Sclater. Proc. Zool. Soc. Lond., pt.30, p.261, pl.32, 1862.

THE ASIATIC GRIZZLY BEARS. Arthur deC. Sowerby. China Jour., vol.20, no. 2, p.109, illus., Feb., 1934.

THE MANCHURIAN BLACK BEAR. Arthur deC. Sowerby. China Jour., vol.20, no.1, p.53, illus., Jan., 1934.

NOTES ON HEUDE'S BEARS IN THE SIKAWEI MUSEUM, AND ON THE BEARS OF PALAEARCTIC EASTERN ASIA. Arthur deC. Sowerby. Jour. Mam., vol.1, no.5, pp.213-232, Nov., 1920.

ABOMINABLE SNOWMAN. (HIMALAYAN RED BEAR.) William L. Straus. Science, 123 (3206): 1024-1025, June 8, 1956.

ON THE BIOLOGY OF THE WHITE BEAR OF THE FRANZ-JOSEPH ARCHIPELAGO. V. Zalkin. Bull. Soc. Nat. Moscou, sect. Biol., n.s., vol.45, no.5, pp.355-363, 1936.

THE "ABOMINABLE SNOWMAN" UNMASKED! AN URSINE "MAN FRIDAY." (URSUS ARCTOS ISABELLINUS.) Illus. London News, vol.191, no.5145, p.941, illus., Nov.27, 1937.

"GOOD CHEER" IN MANCHUKUO: BEAR'S PAWS. Illus. London News, vol.181, no. 4888, p.1027, photo, Dec.24, 1932.

THE MANCHURIAN GRIZZLY. (SPELAEUS CAVIFRONS.) China Jour., vol.16, no.2, pp.102-103, illus., Feb., 1932.

SHOOTING "THE SHAITAN." A HUNT FOR BLACK BEAR IN KASHMIR WHICH PROVIDED PLENTY OF EXCITEMENT. Field, London, vol.168, no.4382, pp.1596-1597, illus., Dec.26, 1936.

Food Habits

FALL FOOD OF THE BLACK BEAR IN PENNSYLVANIA. Dale M. Arner. Pennsylvania Game News, Harrisburg, vol.19, no.9, p.13, Dec., 1948.

BEARS EAT CASCARA BERRIES. Vernon Bailey. Jour. Mam., vol.4, no.1, pp.53-54, Feb., 1923.

THE FOOD HABITS OF THE BLACK BEAR IN PENNSYLVANIA. Logan J. Bennett, P.F. English, R.L. Watts. Jour. Mam., 24 (1): 25-31, Feb., 1943.

THE BLACK BEAR IN RELATION TO STOCK. Jay Bruce. California Fish and Game, vol. 9, pp.16-18, Jan., 1923.

BEARS LIKE HONEY--BUT THINK TWICE BEFORE YOU TRY TO FILM THEM EATING IT. Lynwood Chace. Nat. Hist., New York, vol.55, no.8, pp.376-380, illus., Oct., 1946.

LADYBIRD BEETLES AND ARMY CUTWORM ADULTS AS FOOD FOR GRIZZLY BEARS IN MONTANA. John A. Chapman, John I. Romer, John Stark. Ecology, Durham, vol.36, no.1, pp.156-158, Jan., 1955.

NOTES ON EARLY WINTER FOOD HABITS OF THE BLACK BEAR IN GEORGE WASHINGTON NATIONAL FOREST. Clarence Cottam, Arnold L. Nelson, Talbott E. Clarke. Jour. Mam., 20 (3): 310-314, Aug., 1939.

A CLEVER HUNTER AT WORK IN THE ARCTIC. THE POLAR BEAR AND HIS INGENIOUS METHODS. David Haig-Thomas. Field, London, vol.175, no.4555, pp.575-576, figs.5, Apr.13, 1940.

BEARS FEEDING ON HONEYDEW. C. A. Harwell. Yosemite Nature Notes, vol.16, no.11, p.87, Nov., 1937.

IS THE BLACK BEAR A GAME KILLER? William J. Long. Sports Afield, Mt. Morris, vol.119, no.1, pp.52-53, 83-85, illus., Jan., 1948.

A SHEEP-KILLING BEAR. L.N. Lorenzen. California Fish and Game, vol.9, pp.151-152, Oct., 1923.

A CARNIVOROUS BEAR. (FOOD HABITS OF SELENARCTOS THIBETANUS.) Kutch of Madansinh. Jour. Bombay Nat. Hist. Soc., vol.36, no.1, pp.238-239, Nov.15, 1932.

CATTLE ON GRIZZLY BEAR RANGE. Adolph Murie. Jour. Wildl. Mgt., 12 (1): 57-72, Jan., 1948.

SOME FOOD HABITS OF THE BLACK BEAR. Adolph Murie. Jour. Mam., 18 (2): 238-240, May, 1937.

PROGRESS REPORT ON THE YELLOWSTONE BEAR STUDY. (FOOD HABITS OF GRIZZLIES AND BLACKS.) Olaus J. Murie. USDI, Nat. Park Serv., pp.13, 1944.

WHEN GIANT BEARS GO FISHING. (ALASKAN BROWN BEARS.) Cecil E. Rhode. Nat. Geogr. Mag., Wash., vol. 106, no.2, pp.195-205, illus., Aug., 1954.

BEARS AND BIRDS' EGGS. William Rowan. Condor, vol.30, p.246, July, 1928.

BLACK BEAR FEEDS ON "HONEYDEW" AND MAGNOLIA LEAVES. Albert R. Shadle. Jour. Mam., vol.22, no.3, p.321, Aug.14, 1941.

BEAR DEPREDATIONS ON RED SALMON SPAWNING POPULATIONS IN THE KARLUK RIVER SYSTEM, 1947. Richard F. Shuman. Jour. Wildl. Mgt., 14 (1): 1-9, Jan., 1950.

SLOTH BEAR (MELURSUS URSINUS SHAW) ATTACKING A LIVE BAIT. Maharaja of Surguja. Jour. Bombay Nat. Hist. Soc., vol.38, no.2, pp.391-392, Dec.1, 1935.

BLACK BEAR KILLS FAWN. George L. Unnewehr. Yosemite Nature Notes, vol. 8, p.83, Aug., 1929.

BILLY, THE BEAR, SETS A RECORD. (BLACK BEAR EATS 72 FLAPJACKS.) P.J. White. Yosemite Nature Notes, vol. 8, pp.96-97, Oct., 1929.

FOOD HABITS OF THE BLACK BEAR. Pennsylvania Game News, Harrisburg, vol.14, no.12, pp.8-9, 30, illus., Mar., 1944.

Fossils

(ON A PRIMITIVE SKULL OF THE CAVE BEAR FROM THE BASAL DEPOSITIONS OF THE DRAGON CAVE OF MIXNITZ IN STEIERMARK.) Ueber einen primitiven Schaedel des Hoehlenbaeren aus den basalen Ablagerungen der Drachenhohle von Mixnitz in Steiermark by O. Ontonius. O. Abel. Sitz. Akad. Wiss. Wien, math.-naturw. kl., Akad. Anz., Jahrg.60, no.10, pp.2 (65-66), Apr., 1923.

NOTE ON A BEAR (URSUS SAVINI, SP. N.) FROM THE CROMER FOREST-BED. C.W. Andrews. Ann. Mag. Nat. Hist., ser.9, vol.9, pp.204-207, Feb., 1922.

(FOSSIL BEARS OF NORTHERN AFRICA.) Les Ours fossiles de l'Afrique du Nord. C. Arambourg. Compte Rendu Somm. Seances Soc. Biogeogr. no.74, annee 9, pp. 29-32, May, 1932.

(ON THE VARIATION OF THE FACIAL REGION OF THE CAVE BEAR SKULL.) Sur une variation du crane facial de l'ours des cavernes. Gaston Astre. Bull. Soc. Hist. Nat. Toulouse, vol.54, pp.371-376, illus., 1926.

ABNORMAL TOOTH ARRANGEMENT IN THE JAWS OF URSUS DENINGERI FROM MOSBACH.) Abnorme Zahnstellung bei Kiefern von Ursus deningeri aus Mosbach. Adolf Bachofen-Echt. Palaeobiologica, Wien and Leipzig, Jahrg.4, vol.4, nos.6-7, pp.345-351, pls.31-32, 1931.

(REMAINS OF A YOUNG CAVE BEAR (URSUS SPELAEUS ROS.) FROM THE CAVE OF POPOVACI.) Ernoe Balogh. Erdélyi Múzeum (egyesuelet kőzlőnye), vol.43, no. 2, pp.168-170, figs.3, 1938. (In Hungarian with German summary.)

(URSUS SPELAEUS BLUMEBACH IN THE CAVERNS (IN PARTICULAR THE ONE AT HERM, NEAR FOIX).) L'Ursus spelaeus Blumebach dans les Cavernes. (En particulier dans celle de l'Herm, près Foix.) G. Baquié-Rambaud. Bull. Soc. Études Sci. Aude, Carcassonne, vol.32, pp.325-334, 1928.

(NOTE ON THE METACARPALS AND METATARSI OF THE CAVE BEAR (URSUS SPELAEUS ROSENM.).) Note sur les metacarpiens et metatarsiens de l'ours des cavernes (Ursus spelaeus Rosenm.). A. Birula. Comptes Rendus Acad. Sci. URSS, no.24, pp.655-658, fig.1, 1930. (In Russian.)

URSUS SPELAEUS ROSSICUS NOV. N. A.A. Borisiak. Comptes Rendus Acad. Sci. URSS, ser.A, vol.5, pp.102-104, 1930.

(ON THE OCCURRENCE OF SO-CALLED WEDGE-SHAPED DEFECTS ON THE TEETH OF URSUS SPELAEUS AND THEIR IMPORTANCE FOR PALEOBIOLOGY.) Ueber das Vorkommen sogenannter keilfoermiger Defekte an den Zaehnen von Ursus spelaeus und deren Bedeutung fuer die Palaeobiologie. Richard Breuer. Palaeobiologica, vol.5, pp.103-113, pls.6-10, 1933.

(THE GRUBENLOCH NEAR OBERKLAUSEN. A LATE DILUVIAL FAUNA WITH URSUS ARCTOS L. AND GULO GULO L.) Das Grubenloch bei Oberklausen. Eine spaetdiluviale Fauna mit Ursus arctos L. und Gulo gulo L. Georg Brunner. Zeitschr. f. Saeugetierkunde, vol.11, pp.257-276, figs.24, pls.8, Mar.13, 1936.

(ON THE QUESTION OF THE SKULL ATTITUDE OF CAVE BEARS.) Zur Frage der Schaedelhaltung des Hoehlenbaeren. Hans Buergl. Palaeobiologica, Wien u. Leipzig, vol.5, pp.65-80, figs.2, pls.2-3, 1933.

(FOSSIL REMAINS OF A CAVE BEAR FROM THE NATURE MUSEUM OF SERBIA.) Fosilini ostatsi pecinskog medveda (ursus spelaeus Rosenmueller) i prirodyachkom mizeii srpske zemle. A. Ciric. Glasnik Prerodyachkog Museia Srpske Zemle, Belgrade, ser.A, vol.5, pp.277-292, 1952. (In Serbian with French summary.)

THE ANCESTRAL URSID, HEMICYON, IN NEBRASKA. Edwin H. Colbert. Bull. Univ. Nebraska State Mus., Lincoln, vol. 2, no.5, pp.49-57, figs.20-22, Jan., 1941.

(THE HYOID APPARATUS OF THE CAVE BEAR.) L'appareil hyoidien de l'ours des cavernes (Ursus spelaeus Rosen). Robert Didier. Mammalia, Paris, vol.2, no.4, pp.177-181, Dec., 1938.

(PENILE BONE IN URSUS SPELAEUS ROSEN.) L'os Penien chez "Ursus spelaeus" Rosen. R. Didier. Mammalia, Paris, vol. 1, no.3, pp.106-110, pl.7, Mar., 1937.

(THE CAVE BEAR.) Der Hoehlenbaer. Kurt Ehrenberg. Aus der Heimat, Naturwiss, Monatsschrift, Stuttgart, 44 Jahrg., no.3, pp.65-80, figs.14, Mar., 1931.

(ON A REMARKABLE BEAR SKULL FROM THE BEAR CAVE NEAR WINDEN IN BURGENLAND.) Ueber einen bemerkenswerten Baerenschaedel aus der Baerenkoehle bei Winden im Burgenland. K. Ehrenberg. Anzeiger Akad. Wiss. Wien., math.-naturw. Kl., vol.65, no.26, pp.1-2, 1928.

(ON THE QUESTION OF THE SYSTEMATIC AND PHYLOGENETIC POSITION OF THE BEAR REMAINS OF HUNDSHEIM AND DEUTSCH-ALTENBURG IN LOWER AUSTRIA.) Zur Frage der Systematischen und Phylogenetischen Stellung der Baerenreste von Hundsheim und Deutsch-Altenburg in Niederoesterreich. K. Ehrenberg. Palaeobiologica, vol.2, nos.4-5, pp.213-221, pls.19-20, 1929.

(THE ONTOGENETIC DEVELOPMENT OF THE CAVE BEAR SKELETON.) Die ontogenetische Entwicklung des Hoehlenbaerenskelettes. K. Ehrenberg. Palaeonbilogischen Zeitschr., band 7, heft 1, pp. 48-53, 1925.

(THE PLEISTOCENE BEARS OF BELGIUM. I. PRELIMINARY COMMUNICATION: THE BEAR OF HASTIERE.) Die Plistozaenen Baeren Belgiens. 1. Vorlaeufige Mitteilung: Der Baer von Hastiere. K. Ehrenberg. Bull. Mus. Roy. d'Hist. Nat. de Belgique, vol.7, no.3, pp.1-7, Feb., 1931.

(THOUGHTS ON THE PHYLOGENIC DEVELOPMENT OF BEARS IN THE PLEISTOCENE.) Gedanken zur Stammesentwicklung der Baeren im Plistozaen. K. Ehrenberg. Palaeont. Zeitschr., Berlin, vol.11, no.1, pp.68-76, 1929.

URSUS DENINGERI V. REICH AND URSUS SPELAEUS ROSENM. K. Ehrenberg. Anzeiger Akad. Wiss. Wien., math.-naturw. Kl., vol.65, nos.1-27, pp.96-98, 1928; Sitz. der Math.-naturw. Kl., Akad. Wiss. Wien, Akad. Anz. no.10, pp.4, Apr.26, 1928. (In German.)

(THE VARIABILITY OF THE MOLARS OF THE CAVE BEAR.) Die variabilitaet der Molaren des Hoehlenbaeren. K. Ehrenberg. Palaeont. Zeitschr., vol.9, pp.240-250, 1927.

(ON THE SKULL OF URSUS PRISCUS OF THE PASTORE OR LIVREA CAVE IN LIGURIA.) Sopra un cranio d'Ursus priscus della Caverna del Pastore o Livrea in Liguria. Ramiro Fabiani. pp.16, figs.3, pl.1, 1921.

(SOME CHARACTERS OF THE EVOLUTION OF THE CAVE BEAR (URSUS SPELAEUS ROSENM.).) Quelques caracteres d'evolution de l'ours des cavernes (Ursus spelaeus Rosenm.). Madeleine Friant. Ann. Soc. Roy. Zool. Belgique, vol.83, fasc.2, pp. 189-194, 1952.

A NEW SPECIES OF BEAR FROM THE PLEISTOCENE OF FLORIDA. (ARCTODUS FLORIDANUS.) James W. Gidley. Jour. Wash. Acad. Sci., vol.18, no.15, pp.430-433, Sept.19, 1928.

OBSERVATIONS ON THE MIOCENE SPECIES URSUS PRIMAEVUS GAILLARD. James W. Gidley. Jour. Mam., vol.4, no. 4, pp.240-243, pl.27, Nov., 1923.

DISCOVERY OF FOSSIL BEARS NEAR KRASNODAR, CAUCASUS. G. G. Grigor. Trudy Geologicheskogo Muzeia Akademii Nauk SSSR, vol.6, pp.31-36, fig.1, 1930. (In Russian.)

URSUS ANGLICUS, A NEW SPECIES OF BRITISH BEAR. Robert T. Gunther. Ann. Mag. Nat. Hist., ser.9, vol.11, pp.490-496, pls.2, Apr., 1923.

(REMARKS ON THE GENUS INDARCTOS.) Bemerkungen zum Genus Indarctos. H. Helbing. Ecologae geologicae Helvetiae, vol.24, no.2, p.1, 1931.

(THE BEAR OF THE GRUBENLOCH.) Der Baer aus dem Grubenloch (Ursus arctos nemoralis Degerboel). Max Hilzheimer. Zeitschrift f. Saeugetierkunde, vol.11, pp. 279-307, tables, pls.9-14, Mar.13, 1936.

(A SKELETON OF THE BROWN BEAR OF THE ITALIAN PLEISTOCENE.) Un squelette d'ours brun du pleistocene italien. F. Ed Koby. Verhandl. Naturforsch., Gesell. Basel, vol.56, pt.1, pp.58-85, figs. 1-5, 1945.

SEX DIMORPHISM AND SIZE TRENDS IN THE CAVE BEAR, URSUS SPELAEUS ROSENMUELLER AND HEINROTH. Bjoern Kurten. Acta Zool. Fennica.90, pp.1-48, illus., 1955.

URSUS SPELAEUS ROSSICUS BORISSJAK AND URSUS SPELAEUS MINOR V. NORDMANN. Wladimir Lehmann. Bull. Comm. geol. Finlande, Helsingfors, no.101, pp. 14-22, figs.2, Apr., 1933.

NOTES ON A NEW SUBFOSSIL BEAR FROM SWEDEN. (URSUS ARCTOS NUCIFRAGUS.) Einar Loennberg. Ann. and Mag. Nat. Hist., ser.9, vol.11, pp.502-506, pl., Apr.1923.

RELATIONSHIPS AND STRUCTURE OF THE SHORT-FACED BEAR, ARCTOTHERIUM, FROM THE PLEISTOCENE OF CALIFORNIA. John C. Merriam, Chester Stock. Carnegie Inst. Wash., Contrib. to Palaeontol., Publ. 347, pp.1-35, pls.10, figs.5, Oct.8, 1925.

AN AMERICAN PLIOCENE BEAR. John C. Merriam, Chester Stock, Clarence L. Moody. Univ. Calif. Publ., Bull. Dept. Geol., vol.10, no.7, pp.87-109, figs.23, Nov.1, 1916.

A NEW FOSSIL BEAR FROM OHIO. Gerrit S. Miller, Jr. Proc. Biol. Soc., Wash., vol.13, pp.53-56, May 29, 1899.

(ON THE MORPHOLOGY OF THE CRANIUM OF A CAVE BEAR OF IGRIC CAVE.) Zur morphologie der Hoehlenbaerenschaedel aus der Igric-Hoehle. M. Mottl. Ann. Inst. Regii hungar. geol., Budapest, vol.29, no. 4, pp.187-246, figs.35, 1933.

ON THE REMAINS OF URSUS ETRUSCUS (U. ARVERNENSIS) FROM THE PLIOCENE DEPOSITS OF TEGELEN SUR MEUSE. E.T. Newton. Verhandel, Geol. Mijnbouwk. Genootsch. Nederland Kol., Granenhage, Geol. ser., vol.1, pp.249-254, illus., June, 1913.

(A FOSSIL JAW FROM URSUS MARITIMUS L. IN DENMARK.) En fossil Kaebe af Isbjorn (Ursus maritimus L.) fra Danmark. V. Nordmann, Magnus Degerbol. Vidensk. Meddel. Dansk. Naturhist. Foren. Kjobenhavn, vol.88, pp.273-286, maps 2, pl.1, (1929) 1930.

A BONE DIGGER'S HOLIDAY. (BEAR SKELETON.) P. C. Orr. Santa Barbara

Mus. Nat. Hist., Museum Leaflet, vol.17, no.4, pp.43-45, Apr., 1942.

(THE EXISTENCE OF PREMOLARS IN URSUS SPELAEUS.) L'existence des premolaires chez l'Ursus spelaeus. L. Pales. Rev. Anthrop., vol.36, pp.477-481, illus., 1926.

TREMARCTOTHERIUM FROM THE PLEISTOCENE OF MEADE COUNTY, KANSAS. George C. Rinker. Contrib. Mus. Paleontol. Univ. Michigan, Ann Arbor, vol.7, no.6, pp.107-112, pl.1, Apr. 7, 1949.

(ON A NOTEWORTHY DENTITION ANOMALY IN THE LOWER JAW OF A FOSSIL BEAR.) Ueber eine merkwuerdige Gebissanomalie am Unterkiefer eines fossilen Baeren. K. Rode. Morph. Jahrb., vol.65, nos.1-2, pp.164-177, 1930.

(ON THE BEAR REMAINS OF STEINHEIM-ON-THE-MURR.) Ueber die Baerenreste von Steinheim an der Murr. K. Rode. Zeitschr. f. Saeugetierkunde, Berlin, vol. 8, nos.1-2, pp.73-86, pl.12, Apr.24, 1933.

A NEW ARCTOID CARNIVORE FROM THE LOWER MIOCENE. (ALETOCYON MULTICUSPIS.) Alfred S. Romer, A.H. Sutton. Amer. Jour. Sci., ser.5, vol.14, pp.459-464, Dec., 1927.

(SOME BEAR REMAINS OF ENSENADA FAUNA.) Sobre varios restos de osos de la fauna Ensenadense. Carlos Rusconi. Anales Soc. Cient. Argentina, Buenos Aires, ser.3, vol.126, pp.227-237, figs.4, tables, Sept., 1938.

FOSSIL BEAR FROM KOHURA CITY. T. Shikama. Jour. Geol. Soc. Japan, Tokyo, vol.43, no.515, pp.647-659, figs.2, pl.36, Aug.20, 1936. (In Japanese.)

(THE GROTTOS OF CAVE BEARS (URSUS PELAEUS) OF TANAYSUR VOUVRY (VALAIS).) Les grottes a ours des cavernes (Ursus spelaeus) de Tanay sur Vouvry (Valais). Jean C. Spahni. Bull. Soc. Vandoise Sci. Nat. (Lausanne), vol. 65, pp.127-145, Nov., 1951.

BEARS FROM THE PLEISTOCENE CAVE OF SAN JOSECITO, NUEVO LEON, MEXICO. Chester Stock. Jour. Wash. Acad. Sci., vol.40, no.10, pp.317-321, fig.1, Oct. 23, 1950.

NOTE ON A HYAENARCTID BEAR FROM THE MIDDLE PLIOCENE OF CHIHUAHUA, MEXICO. Chester Stock. Bull. S. Calif. Acad. Sci., Los Angeles, vol.49, pt.1, pp. 1-2, pl.1, Jan.-Apr., 1950.

A RECENT GRIZZLY BEAR SKULL FOUND FOSSIL IN OKLAHOMA. J. Willis Stovall. Amer. Midland Nat., vol.17, no.4, pp.781-783, July, 1936.

TWO FOSSIL GRIZZLY BEARS FROM THE PLEISTOCENE OF OKLAHOMA. J. Willis Stovall, C. Stuart Johnston. Jour. Geol., Chicago, vol.43, no.2, pp.208-213, figs.4, Feb.-Mar., 1935.

(FOSSIL BROWN BEARS (URSIDAE, MAMMAL.).) Zur Kenntnis der fossilen Braunbaeren (Ursidae, Mammal.). Erich Thenius. Sitzungsber. Oesterreichische Akad. Wiss., 165 (2-3): 153-172, 1956.

EXTINCT BEAR "ARCTOTHERIUM BRASILIENSIS" FROM LAGOA FUNDA CAVE, MINAS GERAES. H.V. Walter. Contrib. Brazilian Paleont., Rio de Janeiro, pp.37, pl.8, Oct., 1940.

## General Habits, Behavior

AN INSTANCE OF UNPROVOKED ATTACK BY A BROWN BEAR. A.C. Bonebrake. Jour. Mam., vol.3, no.3, pp.185-186, Aug., 1922.

THE BLACK BEAR--BUFFOON OF THE NORTH WOODS. G.W. Bradt. Mich. Cons., 15 (11): 5, Dec., 1946.

HOW LONG WILL A BEAR STAY UP A TREE? Harold C. Bryant. Yosemite Nature Notes, vol.6, p.86, Nov., 1927.

BEARS--BROWN, BLACK, AND GRIZZLY: WHAT THEY DO AND HOW THEY LIVE. Ralph C. Conway. Nat. Humane Review, Albany, vol.38, no.4, pp.14-16, 32, illus., Apr., 1950.

BLACK BEAR TRIES TO GNAW INTO A WOODPECKER'S NEST. Joseph Dixon. Condor, vol.29, pp.271-272, Nov., 1927.

THE GRIZZLY BEAR AS A TREE-CLIMBER. Arthur H. Fisher. Jour. Mam., vol.3, no. 1, p.53, Feb., 1922.

BEARS' VOCABULARY. Lon Garrison. Yosemite Nature Notes, vol.16, no.10, pp. 78-79, Oct., 1937.

A TIMID BEAR TAKES A DIP. Elizabeth H. Godfrey. Yosemite Nat. Notes, Yosemite, vol.20, no.11, pp.100-101, Nov., 1941.

THE CARNIVORES. PART I. BEARS. (Summary of distribution, characteristics, and habits.) George G. Goodwin. School Nature League Bull.17 (5), pp.4, Jan., 1947.

A CLIMBING GRIZZLY. Rudolf Grimm. Yellowstone Nature Notes, vol.15, nos.11-12, pp.58-59, Nov.-Dec., 1938.

THE "UNPROVOKED" ATTACK BY A BEAR. Geo. Bird Grinnell. Jour. Mam., vol.4, no. 1, pp.52-53, Feb., 1923.

POLAR AND BLACK BEARS PLAYING TAG IN A TREE. Edmund Heller. Bull. Wash. Park Zool. Soc., Milwaukee, vol.2, no.1, pp.2-3, photo, Dec., 1931.

THE GRIZZLY BEAR. WILL HE ATTACK UNPROVOKED? R. Leckie-Ewing. Field, London, vol.153, p.543, Apr.4, 1929.

THE BLACK BEAR AS A PREDATOR OF MAN. L.T.S. Norris-Elye. Jour. Mam., vol.32, no.2, pp.222-223, May 21, 1951.

HOW FAST DOES A BLACK BEAR CLIMB? W. M. Rush. Jour. Mam., vol.9, no.4, pp.335-336, Nov., 1928.

THE "UNPROVOKED" ATTACK BY A "BROWN" BEAR. Charles Sheldon. Jour. Mam., vol.4, no.1, pp.51-52, Feb., 1923.

RANCHER KILLED BY GRIZZLY BEAR IN MONTANA. M. P. Skinner. Jour. Mam., vol.4, no.1, p.53, Feb., 1923.

BLACK BEAR DENNING IN TREE. D. F. Switzenberg. Jour. Mam., 36 (3): 459, Aug.30, 1955.

BEARS AND HAWKS. P. A. Taverner. Condor, vol.30, p.157, Mar., 1928.

THE BLACK BEAR. (LIFE HISTORY, HABITS, RANGE IN VIRGINIA, AND HUNTING.) J. E. Thornton. Va. Wildl., 8 (3): 6-7, 9, 20, Mar., 1947.

THE FEROCITY OF BEARS. Stewart Edward White. Outdoor Life, vol.67, no. 5, pp.22-23, 63-64, figs.3, May, 1931.

THE BLACK BEAR AS A PREDATOR OF MAN. S.C. Whitlock. Jour. Mam., vol. 31, no.2, pp.135-138, pl.1, May 25, 1950.

POLAR BEARS KEEPING COOL. Amer. Motorist, Gettysburg, vol.22, no.8, p.1, illus., Aug., 1949.

## Growth, Maturity

HOW MUCH DOES A BEAR CUB WEIGH? James E. Cole, Jr. Yosemite Nature Notes, vol.15, no.4, p.32, Apr., 1936.

THE GROWTH AND SIZE OF PENNSYLVANIA BLACK BEARS. Richard Gerstell. Pennsylvania Game News, New Cumberland, vol.10, no.8, pp.4-7, illus., Nov., 1939.

(POLAR BEARS AND THEIR GROWTH.) Eisbaeren und ihr Wachstum. E. J. Kostjan. Zool. Garten, Leipzig, n.F., vol.7, nos.7-9, pp.157-164, figs.4, Nov., 1934.

THE GROWTH OF THE CRANIA OF YEZO BROWN BEAR. Kozo Mukasa. Trans. Sapporo Nat. Hist. Soc., vol.15, pt.2, pp. 96-111, figs.10, pls.2-4, Dec., 1937.

(ON THE BIRTH AND YOUNG DEVELOPMENT OF A POLAR BEAR.) Ueber Geburt und Jugendentwicklung eine Eisbaeren. C.W. Ouwehand. Zoologische Garten, Leipzig, n.F., vol.11, no.3, pp.102-107, illus., Sept., 1939.

(ON THE DEVELOPMENT OF THE YOUNG BLACK BEAR.) Zur Kenntniss der Jugendentwicklung des Baribals (Euarctos americanus Pall.). M. Schlott. Zool. Garten, Leipzig, NF, vol.17, nos.1-5, pp. 40-44, illus., 1950.

(THE DEVELOPMENT OF A YOUNG POLAR BEAR. II. BEHAVIOR: POSITION, MOVEMENTS, SUCKLING, UTTERANCES.) Zur Jugendentwicklung eines Eisbaeren. II. Aus dem Verhalten: Lage, Bewegung, Saugen, Stimmliche Aeusserung. Karl Max Schneider. Zool. Garten, Leipzig, N.F., vol.6, nos.10-12, pp.224-237, figs.5, Dec., 1933.

(ON THE DEVELOPMENT OF A YOUNG POLAR BEAR.) Zur Jungendentwicklung eines Eisbaeren. Karl Max Schneider. Zool. Garten, Leipzig, n.F., vol.6, nos. 7-9, pp.156-165, figs.3, Oct., 1933.

(ON THE DEGREE OF MATURITY OF NEWBORN URSIDAE IN COMPARISON WITH OTHER CARNIVORA.) Ueber den Reifegrad neugeborener Ursiden im Vergleich mit anderen Carnivoren. Dietrich Starck. Saeugetierk., Mitteil., Stuttgart, 4 (1): 21-27, Jan.1, 1956.

## Hibernation

A HIBERNATING BLACK BEAR WITH CUBS. Shaler E. Aldous. Jour. Mam., vol.18, no. 4, pp.466-468, Nov., 1937.

HIBERNATING BEARS. C. A. Harwell. Yosemite Nature Notes, vol.11, no.4, pp.1-3, Apr., 1932.

OUR CHANGING BEARS. (PHOTO OF BEAR IN HIBERNATING DEN.) C. A. Harwell. Yosemite Nature Notes, vol.16, no.4, pp. 28-30, illus., Apr., 1937.

RECTAL TEMPERATURES OF THE BLACK BEAR DURING ITS "HIBERNATION." Raymond J. Hock. Science in Alaska, 1951, Proc. 2nd Alaskan Sci. Conf., Alaska Div. AAAS, pp.310-312, 1953.

NOTES ON THE HIBERNATION OF A CAPTIVE BLACK BEAR. William Johnston Howard. Jour. Mam., vol.16, no.4, p.321, Nov., 1935.

OBSERVATIONS ON THE HIBERNATION LAIR OF THE YEZO BROWN BEAR. T. Inukai. Trans. Sapporo Nat. Hist. Soc., vol.12, pts.2-3, pp.175-179, figs.5, 1932.

VISITING BRUIN IN MIDWINTER. "SHOOTING" A BEAR IN THE NORTH WOODS. Thelma Kautto. Conservation Vol., St. Paul, vol.4, no.21, pp.69-70, illus., June, 1942.

NOTES ON DORMANCY IN THE BLACK BEAR. J.R. Matson. Jour. Mam., 27 (3): 203-212, Aug., 1946.

OBSERVATIONS ON THE DORMANT PHASE OF A FEMALE BLACK BEAR. J.R. Matson. Jour. Mam., 35 (1): 28-35, illus., Feb., 1954.

HIBERNATION AND BREEDING OF THE BLACK BEAR. Marius A. Morse. Jour. Mam., vol.18, no.4, pp.460-465, Nov., 1937.

NOTES ON THE HOKKAIDO BEAR URSUS ARCTOS YESOENSIS LYDEKKER LEAVING HIBERNATION AS REPORTED IN ETOROFU ISLAND OF THE KURILE GROUP. M. L. Peelie. Trans. Sapporo Nat. Hist. Soc., vol.12, pt.1, pp.49-53, fig.1, 1931.

HIBERNATION IN THE AMERICAN BLACK BEAR. Arthur Svihla, Howard S. Bowman. Amer. Midland Nat., vol.52, no.1, pp.248-252, July, 1954.

BEDTIME FOR BEARS. Frank Thone. Science News Letter, Wash., vol.50, no. 11, p.174, Sept.14, 1946.

DO BEARS HIBERNATE? Frederick A. Ulmer, Jr. Frontiers, Lancaster, vol. 12, no.5, pp.131-134, illus., June, 1948.

## Hunting, Trapping

TRAILING THE KODIAK BEAR. John Q. Adams. Alaskan Sportsman, vol.3, no.2, pp.6, 7, 18, 20, 22, 23, illus., Feb., 1937.

THE FISH-HOLE BEAR. Eaves Allison. Field and Stream, New York, vol.50, no. 8, pp.52-54, 95, Dec., 1945.

BEARS DO ALL RIGHT. Russell Annabel. Sports Afield, Minneapolis, vol.118, no.4, pp.44-45, 70, 73-74, 76-80, Oct., 1947.

BLACK GRIZZLY--HE MAKETH ME FOR SCARE. Frederick M. Baker. Rod and Gun in Canada, Montreal, vol.49, no.2, pp.13-14, 44, 47, illus., July, 1947.

A BEAR HUNT ON THE CLEARWATER. Arthur H. Bannon. Forest and Stream, vol.90, pp.103-106, 144, 146, Mar., 1920.

A SPRING BEAR HUNT IN CASSIAR. Arthur H. Bannon. Forest and Stream, vol. 89, pp.151-155, 184-186, Apr., 1919.

BEAR HUNT IN MEXICO--STORY OF MUSEUM'S GRIZZLY GROUP. C. M. Barber. Chicago Nat. Hist. Mus. Bull., vol.18, no.10, pp.1-2, illus., Oct., 1947.

HUNTING THE POLAR BEAR. Robert Bartlett. North Amer. Big Game. A book of the Boone and Crockett Club, compiled by the Committee on Records of N. Amer. Big Game. Charles Scribners Sons, New York, pp.400-405, 1939.

NINE POLAR BEARS. Waldo Bodfish. Alaska Sportsman, Ketchikan, vol.13, no. 9, pp.22-23, 41-42, illus., Sept., 1947.

A TEXAS GRIZZLY HUNT. J.G. Burr. Texas Game and Fish, Austin, vol.6, no. 9, pp.4-5, 16-18, illus., Aug., 1948.

THE BEAR'S NEST. Bonnycastle Dale, Jr. Rod and Gun in Canada, Montreal, vol.47, no.8, pp.10-11, 38, Jan., 1946.

THREE BEARS AND A CATHOUND. Bonnycastle Dale, Jr. Rod and Gun, Montreal, vol.47, no.10, pp.8-9, Mar., 1946.

GRIZZLY HATER. J. Frank Dobie. New Mexico Mag., Albuquerque, vol.21, no.10, pp.14, 29-31, Oct., 1943.

KILLER BEAR. Frank Dufresne. Field and Stream, New York, vol.52, no.7, pp. 50-52, 111-112, illus., Nov., 1947.

YOU CAN'T TELL ABOUT BEARS. (BLACK BEAR.) Ben East. Field and Stream, New York, vol.53, no.1, pp.48-49, 162-163, illus., May, 1948.

THE BEAR WENT OVER THE MOUNTAIN. (GRIZZLY BEAR.) Helene Fischer. Field and Stream, New York, vol.53, no. 11, pp.61-63, Mar., 1949.

HUNTING THE GRIZZLY BEAR. Ned W. Frost. North American Big Game. A book of the Boone and Crockett Club, compiled by the Committee on Records of N. Amer. Big Game. Charles Scribners Sons, New York, pp.385-394, 1939.

OLD GROANER. F. W. Gabler. Alaska Sportsman, vol.2, no.2, pp.16-19, 28, illus., Feb., 1936.

POLAR BEARS ARE BAD MEDICINE. Philip H. Godsell. Outdoorsman, Chicago, vol.86, no.5, whole no.510, pp.16-17, 59, Sept.-Oct., 1944.

THE BLACK BEAR AS A GAME ANIMAL IN PENNSYLVANIA. Seth E. Gordon. Amer. Game Protective Assoc., 8th Nat'l Game Conf., New York, pp.11, illus., Dec.12-13, 1921.

A DOUBLE ON GRIZZLIES. Bradshaw Harrison. Field and Stream, New York, vol.50, no.3, pp.22-23, 56-58, illus., July, 1945.

KING OF THE ARCTIC. HUNTING THE POLAR BEAR WITH GUN AND CAMERA. John Hegness. Field and Stream, vol.39, no.9, pp.26-27, 62-63, illus., Jan., 1935.

GHOST-TOWN GRIZZLY. Frank C. Hibben. Outdoor Life, New York vol.103, no.2, pp.42-49, illus., Feb., 1949.

BEARS ON THE CARIBOO RANGE. C. L. Hilliard. Outdoor Life, vol.68, no.6, pp. 16-17, 51, figs.5, Dec., 1931.

AN ADVENTUROUS DAY IN THE ARCTIC AND THE CAPTURE OF TWO POLAR BEARS. F. G. Jackson. Field, London, vol.165, no.4301, p.1356, illus., June 1, 1935.

HIGH-LIVING REDBONES. (BLACK BEAR.) Milt E. Jacob. Field and Stream, New York, vol.51, no.12, pp.38-39, 128, illus., Apr., 1947.

A YEN FOR A GRIZZLY. Flloyd D. Johnson. Alaska Sportsman, Ketchikan, vol.14, no.10, pp.10-13, 34-36, illus., Oct., 1948.

GAMBLE IN GRIZZLIES. Robert L. Kellogg. Outdoor Life, New York vol.101, no.5, pp.34-35, illus., May, 1948.

GRIZZLIES ON THE PROD. Cariboo King. Rod and Gun in Canada, Montreal, vol.45, no.6, pp.10-11, 28, illus., Nov., 1943.

THE GRIZZLY AND THE SET-GUN. T. T. McCabe. Canadian Field Nat., Sutton West, vol.60, no.2, pp.23-25, Mar.-Apr., 1946.

GOODBYE, OLD GRIZZLY. Harry McGuire. Outdoor Life, Denver, vol.72, no.4, pp.2, Oct., 1933.

UN-GUESSING A GRIZZLY. (HUNTING GRIZZLY BEARS IN BRITISH COLUMBIA.) Clyde Ormond. Outdoor Life, New York, vol.101, no.4, pp.26-27, 123-125, illus., Apr., 1948.

HUNTING THE SPECTACLED BEAR OF THE ANDES. Wilfred H. Osgood. Bull. Pan-Amer. Union, Wash., D.C., vol.39, no.6, pp.900-903, illus., Dec., 1914.

AN ALASKAN GRIZZLY'S CHARGE. Robert Patterson. Sportsman, vol.17, no. 6, pp.40, 66, June, 1935.

AN ENCOUNTER WITH A GRIZZLY BEAR. Charles B. Penrose. Hunting and Conservation, the book of the Boone and Crockett Club, New Haven, Yale Press, pp.66-73, 1925.

A NOVEL METHOD OF SHOOTING BLACK BEAR IN THE "GALIS." C.R.S. Pitman. Jour. Bombay Nat. Hist. Soc., vol.29, pp. 1049-1050, May 15, 1924.

AFTER BEAR WITH BOW AND ARROW. Saxton Pope. Forest and Stream, vol.89, pp.330-331, 382, July, 1919.

BEAR HUNTING WITH BOWS AND ARROWS. Saxton Pope. California Fish and Game, vol.5, no.2, pp.69, 70, Apr., 1919.

HUNTING GRIZZLY WITH THE BOW. Saxton Pope. Forest and Stream, vol.90, pp.533-536, 565-568, Oct., 1920.

HUNTING THE BLACK BEAR. F. H. Riggall. North American Big Game. A book of the Boone and Crockett Club, compiled by the Committee on Records of North American Big Game. Charles Scribners Sons, New York, pp.394-400, 1939.

TRAILING THE KADIAK. Harold Rondthaler. Outers' Recreation, vol.63, pp.276, 277, 323-326, Oct., 1920.

FIRST SHOT AT GRIZZLY. Andy Russell. Field and Stream, New York, vol.51, no. 10, pp.46-47, 78-81, illus., Feb., 1947.

THE LAND OF THE GRUMBLING BEARS. Robert H. Savery. Rod and Gun in Canada, Ottawa, vol.50, no.5, pp.7-8, 23, 26, illus., Oct., 1948.

BEAR TRACKS AND HOUND MUSIC. Warren W. Shapton. Michigan Conserv., Lansing, vol.19, no.1, pp.7-10, Jan.-Feb., 1950.

SILVERTIP SEARCH. (GRIZZLY BEAR.) Mitchell G. Sheldon. Colorado Outdoors Mag., vol.5, no.1, pp.28-29, illus., Jan., 1956.

HUNTING THE GRIZZLY BEAR. G. O. Shields. Harper's New Monthly Mag., pp. 368-372, illus., Aug., 1887.

HUNTING THE ALASKA BROWN BEAR. Andy Simons. North American Big Game, A book of the Boone and Crockett Club, compiled by the Committee on Records of N. Amer. Big Game. Charles Scribners Sons, New York, pp.378-384, 1939.

BIG BEARS ARE BOLD. Otis H. Speer. Alaska Sportsman, Ketchikan, vol.9, no. 12, pp.20-22, 25-26, illus., Dec., 1943.

PAUL BUNYAN WAS A SISSY. OKEFENOKEE SWAMPER KILLED 350-LB. BEAR BAREHANDED. Paul Stearns. Outdoor Georgia, Atlanta, vol.12, no.8, pp.10-11, illus., Mar., 1944.

STORY OF HUNT IN ALASKA FOR WORLD'S LARGEST BEAR. Janice Street. Bull. Chicago Nat. Hist. Mus., vol.20, no. 4, pp.3-4, illus., Apr., 1949.

HUNTING DOWN BEEF-EATING BEARS. C. V. Tench. Forest and Outdoors, 35 (11): 331-332, Nov., 1939.

WAS THIS THE BIGGEST GRIZZLY EVER SHOT? Jack Van Clute. Outdoor Life, Denver, vol.103, no.5, pp.44-45, 92-94, May, 1949.

BEAR CRIMINALS. Clee Woods. Outdoorsman, Chicago, vol.88, no.2, pp. 20-21, 54-55, Mar., 1946.

1951 BEAR BOUNTIES. Me. Dept. Inl. Fisheries and Game, p.1, map, 1952.

BOUNTY ON BEARS. Maryland Tidewater News, Solomons, vol.3, no.5, p.4, Oct., 1946.

WORLD RECORD BROWNIE KILLED IN 1948. (BROWN BEAR.) South Dakota Cons. Digest, Pierre, vol.16, no.11, p.14, Nov., 1949.

Hybrids

NOTE ON SOME YOUNG HYBRID BEARS BRED IN THE GARDENS OF THE SOCIETY. A. D. Bartlett. Proc. Zool. Soc. Lond., pt.28, pp.130-131, 1860.

HYBRIDS OF THE POLAR AND KADIAK BEAR. Malcolm Davis. Jour. Mam., vol. 31, no.4, pp.449-450, Nov.21, 1950.

"GENE"--THE HYBRID BEAR. Jour. Heredity, Wash., vol.41, no.2, p.34, Feb., 1950.

Neurology

(HISTOGENESIS OF THE OPERCULIZATION OF THE BRAIN OF THE NEWLY BORN BEAR.) L'Histogenese de l'operculisation du cerveau de l'ours nouveau-ne. Walter Riese. Bull. Mus. Nat. Hist. Paris, ser. 2, vol.10, no.6, pp.567-568, illus., Nov., 1938.

STRUCTURE AND FUNCTION OF THE BRAIN OF THE NEW-BORN BEAR (URSUS ARCTOS L.). Walther Riese. Rev. Canadienne Biol., Montreal, vol.1, no.2, pp.157-170, figs.2, Feb., 1942; Comptes Rendus Seances Acad. Sci. Paris, vol.206, no.24, pp.1834-1837, June 13, 1938. (In French.)

CEREBRAL HEMISPHERES OF THE AMERICAN BLACK BEAR (URSUS AMERICANUS). MORPHOLOGIC AND PHYLOGENETIC CHARACTERISTICS. Wilbur K. Smith. Archives Neurol. and Psych., Chicago, vol.30, no.1, pp.1-13, figs.8, July, 1933.

MOTOR CORTEX OF THE BEAR (URSUS AMERICANUS). A PHYSIOLOGIC AND HISTOLOGIC STUDY. Wilbur K. Smith. Archiv. Neur. and Psych., vol.30, pp.14-39, figs.10, July, 1933.

North America

NORTH AMERICAN BEARS. THEY ARE CALLED "THE NOBLEST OF OUR CARNIVORES." Claude W. Leister. New York Zool. Soc., Popular Ser. no.3, pp.7, 1944.

THE BEARS OF NORTH AMERICA. J. Alden Loring. Outdoor Life, Denver, vol. 19, no.5, pp.433-438, illus., 1907.

DESCRIPTIONS OF THIRTY APPARENTLY NEW GRIZZLY AND BROWN BEARS FROM NORTH AMERICA. C. Hart Merriam. Proc. Biol. Soc. Wash., vol.27, pp.173-196, Aug.13, 1914.

FOUR NEW BEARS FROM NORTH AMERICA. C. Hart Merriam. Proc. Biol. Soc. Wash., vol.17, pp.153-156, Oct.6, 1904.

NINETEEN APPARENTLY NEW GRIZZLY AND BROWN BEARS FROM WESTERN AMERICA. C. Hart Merriam. Proc. Biol. Soc. Wash., vol.29, pp.133-154, Sept.6, 1916.

REMARKS ON AMERICAN BLACK BEARS. Axel Reventlow. Zool. Garten, Leipzig, N.F., vol.20, nos.2-3, pp.185-187, 1953.

AMERICAN BEARS. R.W. Shufeldt. Amer. Forestry, vol.27, pp.22-31, figs. 1-12, Jan., 1921.

Pelage, Coloration

THE GLACIER OR BLUE BEAR. H. A. Bryden. Field, London, vol.147, p.388, Mar.4, 1926.

A BROWN VARIETY OF THE SLOTH BEAR (MELURSUS URSINUS). J. A. Duke. Jour. Bombay Nat. Hist. Soc., vol.33, no.3, p.702, May 31,1929.

A BROWN FORM OF THE HIMALAYAN BLACK BEAR (SELENARCTOS THIBETANUS). Botha Van Ingen. Jour. Bombay Nat. Hist. Soc., Bombay, vol.42, no.2, p. 436, Apr., 1941.

YOUNG YEZO BROWN BEAR WITH A WHITE COLLAR. Nagamichi Kuroda. Syokukutu oyobi Dobutu (Botany and Zool.), vol.6, no.5, pp.119-120, fig.1, May 1, 1938. (Japanese only.)

(THE HAIR OF BROWN BEARS, GRIZZLY BEARS, AND MIXTURES.) Das Haar des Braunbaeren, Grizzlybaeren und ihres Mischlings. Th. Lochte. Zool. Garten, Leipzig, N.F., vol.21, no.3, pp.163-167, illus., 1955.

THE GLACIER BEAR. C. Hart Merriam. Field, London, vol.147, no.3825, p.658, Apr.15, 1926.

COLOR CHANGE IN THE BLACK BEAR, URSUS AMERICANUS. Loye Miller. Jour. Mam., 36 (3): 460, Aug.30, 1955.

DESCRIPTION OF A BLUE BEAR (URSUS ARCTOS PRUINOSUS BLYTH) FROM TIBET. S. H. Prater. Jour. Bombay Nat. Hist. Soc., vol.38, no.3, p.610, Apr.15, 1936.

ALBINISM IN THE BLACK BEAR. Paul C. Standley. Science, n.s., vol.54, p.74, July 22, 1921.

Predation Upon

MOUNTAIN COYOTES KILL YEARLING BLACK BEAR IN SEQUOIA NATIONAL PARK. Richard H. Boyer. Jour. Mam., Balto., vol.30, no.1, p.75, Feb.14, 1949.

HYAENA CARRYING OFF A BEAR CUB. H.E. Shortt. Jour. Bombay Nat. Hist. Soc., vol.41, no.4, p.891, Aug., 1940.

Reproductive Biology

(THE BIRTH OF A MALAYAN BEAR IN THE AARHUS ZOO.) Eine Malayenbaerengeburt im Zoo Aarhus. Hubert B. Hutzelsider. Zool. Garten, N.F., vol.12, nos.2-3, pp.157-161, illus., July, 1940.

(NEW DATA ON REPRODUCTION IN THE WHITE BEAR.) Novie dannie po razmnozheniyu belikh medvedei. E.J. Kastyan. Zool. Zhurnal, Moscow, vol.33, no.1, pp. 207-215, Jan.-Feb., 1954.

LITTER SIZE IN THE BLACK BEAR. J.R. Matson. Jour. Mam., 33 (2): 246-247, May, 1952.

(ON DOUBLE OESTRUS AND EXTENDED GESTATION IN THE EUROPEAN FORMS OF THE GENUS URSUS LINNE'.) Ueber doppelte Brunstzeit und verlaengerte Tragzeit bei den europaeischen Arten der Gattung Ursus Linne. H. Prell. Biol. Zentralblatt, vol.50, pp.257-271, 1930.

(ON THE PROPAGATION BIOLOGY OF EUROPEAN BEARS.) Ueber die Fortpflanzungsbiologie der europaeische Baeren. H. Prell. Zool. Garten, Leipzig, n.F., vol.3, nos.3-8, pp.168-172, Aug.11, 1930.

A CASE OF SIX CUBS IN THE COMMON BLACK BEAR. William Rowan. Jour. Mam., vol.28, no.4, pp.404-405, Nov.26, 1947.

NUMBERS OF YOUNG IN THE COMMON BLACK AND GRIZZLY BEARS IN WESTERN CANADA. William Rowan. Jour. Mam., vol.26, no.2, pp.197-199, pls.2, July 15, 1945.

(THE GESTATION OF POLAR BEARS (THALASSARCTUS MARITIMUS ERXL.).) Ueber die Tragzeit des Eisbaeren (Thalassarctus maritimus Erxl.). Karl Max Schneider. Zool. Anzeiger, vol.151, nos. 7-8, pp.210-225, Oct., 1953.

NOTES ON REPRODUCTION OF THE PENINSULA BEAR. Arthur Svihla. Murrelet, Seattle, vol.30, no.3, pp.53-54, Feb. 1, 1950.

Taxonomy

BROWN BEARS OF THE CAUCASUS (A SYSTEMATIC STUDY). G. Adlerberg. Bull. Acad. Sci. USSR, Leningrad, ser. 7, no.1, pp.73-100, 1935. (In Russian, with English summary.)

SUMMARY OF CANADIAN BLACK BEARS WITH DESCRIPTION OF TWO NEW NORTHWESTERN SPECIES. (EUARCTOS RANDI, E. HUNTERI.) Rudolph Martin Anderson. Ann. Rept., Provancher Soc. Nat. Hist., Canada, Quebec, pp.17-33, 1944.

(ON THE QUESTION OF THE GEOGRAPHICAL FORMS OF THE POLAR BEAR (THALASSARCTOS MARITIMUS PHIPPS.) CONTRIBUTIONS TO THE SYSTEMATICS AND GEOGRAPHICAL DISTRIBUTION OF MAMMALS.) A. Birula. Trudy Zool. Inst. Akad. Nauk SSSR, vol.1, no.1, pp. 99-134, pls.3, 1932. (In Russian, with German summary.)

A REVISION OF THE GENERA AND SPECIES OF URSINE ANIMALS (URSIDAE), FOUNDED ON THE COLLECTION IN THE BRITISH MUSEUM. J. E. Gray. Proc. Zool. Soc. Lond., pp.677-709, illus., Dec.13, 1864.

ADDITION TO SYSTEMATIC OF THE YUGOSLAVIAN BROWN BEAR. V. Martino. Lovtsa, nos.7-10, pp.1-7, figs. 8, July-Oct., 1936. (In Bulgarian, with English summary.)

PRELIMINARY SYNOPSIS OF THE AMERICAN BEARS. C. Hart Merriam. Proc. Biol. Soc., Wash., vol.10, pp.65-83, figs. 17, pls.4-6, Apr.13, 1896.

REVIEW OF THE GRIZZLY AND BIG BROWN BEARS OF NORTH AMERICA, (GENUS URSUS) WITH DESCRIPTIONS OF A NEW GENUS, VETULARCTOS. C. Hart Merriam. U.S. Dept. Agric., Div. Biol. Surv. North Amer. Fauna no.41, pp.133, pls.26, Feb.9, 1918.

NOTE ON THE RELATIONSHIP OF THE EUROPEAN CAVE BEARS TO THE AMERICAN GRIZZLY AND BROWN BEARS. Gerrit S. Miller, Jr. Jour. Mam., vol.1, p.229, Dec.4, 1920.

A NEW GENUS OF URSIDAE. R, I. Pocock. Ann. and Mag. Nat. Hist., ser.8, vol.20, pp.128-130, July, 1917.

THE PROPER NAME OF THE POLAR BEAR. Leonhard Stejneger. Science, Lancaster, n.s., vol.10, no.246, pp.377-378, Sept.15, 1899.

ON A NEW FORM OF BEAR. Oldfield Thomas. Proc. Zool. Soc., Lond., vol. 1, pp.231-232, figs.58-59, Aug.23, 1906.

INSTRUCTION FOR THE COLLECTION OF MATERIALS ON BIOLOGY, HUNTING AND CLASSIFICATION OF THE POLAR BEAR (THALASSARCTOS MARITIMUS PHIPPS). K. E. Vorobyeva. Vsesoiuzyi arkticheskii institute, PRI TSIK SSSR, Leningrad, no.1, pp.14, 1932. (Arctic Institute of USSR.)

(ON THE INDEPENDENCE OF THE SPECIES OF URSUS FEROX DESM. BY PRINCE MAX VON WIED, WITH ANATOMICAL REMARKS BY DR. C. MAYER.) Ueber die selbststaendigkeit der species des Ursus ferox Desm. von Prinz Max von Wied, mit anatomischen bemerkungen von Dr. C. Mayer. Prinz Max von Wied, C. Mayer. Verhandl. Kais. Leop.-Carol. Akad. Naturf. vol.26, pt.1, pp.35-87, pls.3-5, 1857.

United States

BEARS IN SAN DIEGO COUNTY, CALIFORNIA. Clinton G. Abbott. Jour. Mam., vol.16, no.2, pp.149-151, May, 1935.

THE BLACK BEAR RETURNS. Harold E. Alexander. Kentucky Happy Hunting Ground, Frankfort, vol.5, no.5, p.36, illus., Sept., 1947.

EARLY MASSACHUSETTS RECORDS OF THE BLACK BEAR. Harold L. Babcock. Bull. Boston Soc. Nat. Hist., no.45, pp.3-5, Oct., 1927.

STATUS AND DISTRIBUTION OF THE GRIZZLY BEAR (URSUS HORRIBILIS) IN THE UNITED STATES. George F. Baggley. Proc. N.A. Wildl. Conf., pp.646-650, 1936.

BEARS OF YOSEMITE. M. E. Beatty. Yosemite Nat. Notes, Yosemite, vol.22, no.1, pp.1-16, Jan., 1943.

YOSEMITE'S BEAR BANQUET. M. E. Beatty. Yosemite Nat. Notes, vol.12, no. 6, pp.59-60, June, 1933.

A "SPECIMEN" OF GRIZZLY BEAR FROM ALAMEDA COUNTY, CALIFORNIA. Seth B. Benson. California Fish and Game, San Francisco, vol.30, no.2, pp.98-100, Apr., 1944.

FACTS OF INTEREST ABOUT UTAH MAMMALS. (BLACK AND GRIZZLY BEARS.) Jack H. Berryman. Utah Fish and Game Bull., Salt Lake City, vol.6, no.3, pp.3-5, Oct., 1948.

BEAR MOUNTAIN BEARS. William E. Carr. Nat. Hist., New York, vol.53, no.7, pp. 296-302, illus., Sept., 1944.

1939 BEAR POPULATION OF THE GLACIER POINT AREA. Arthur Carthew. Yosemite Nat. Notes, Yosemite, vol.21, no.8, pp. 68-71, Aug., 1942.

OHIO'S BLACK BEARS. Floyd B. Chapman. Ohio Cons. Bull., 10 (3): 12-13, Mar., 1946.

BARABOO BEAR TALES. Harry Ellsworth Cole. Baraboo, Wis., Baraboo News Publ. Co., pp.110, 1915.

THARS BAR IN THEM THAR HILLS. Bob Cooney. Mont. Wildl., 3 (3): 15-18, illus., Fall, 1953.

THE ST. ELIAS BEAR. William Dall. Science, N.S., vol.2, no.30, p.87, July 26, 1895.

IDENTITY OF THE CENTRAL TEXAS BEAR. William B. Davis. Jour. Mam., vol.26, no.4, p.434, Feb.12, 1946.

TO FEED OR NOT TO FEED--THAT IS THE BEAR QUESTION IN YELLOWSTONE NATIONAL PARK. William L. Finley, Irene Finley. Amer. Forests, Wash., D. C., vol.46, no.8, pp.344-347, 368, 383, 384, illus., Aug., 1940.

AN ANALYSIS OF PENNSYLVANIA BLACK BEAR KILLS 1939-1941. Richard Gerstell. Pennsylvania Game News, Harrisburg, vol. 17, no.11, pp.8-9, 27, 32, illus., Feb., 1948.

ECONOMICS AND RELATED BIOLOGY OF THE BLACK BEAR IN COLORADO. Douglas L. Gilbert. MS thesis, Colo. A. & M. Coll., 1951.

ECONOMICS, ECOLOGY, AND BIOLOGY OF THE BLACK BEAR IN COLORADO. Douglas L. Gilbert. Quart. Rept. Colorado Coop. Wildlife Research Unit, Fort Collins, vol.3, no.3, pp.28-55, Jan.-Mar., 1950.

BEAR STUDIES IN COLORADO. Paul Gilbert. Colorado Conservation Comments, Denver, vol.9, no.3, p.18, Sept.15, 1946.

COLORADO BLACK BEAR STUDIES. Paul Gilbert. Colorado Conserv. Comments, Denver, vol.10, no.1, pp.27-28, Mar., 1947.

BEAR DENS IN CASTLE ROCKS. E. D. Godwin. Yosemite Nature Notes, vol.15, no.1, p.5, Jan., 1936.

THE 1937 BEAR SEASON. (HABITS OF BLACK BEAR IN WISCONSIN.) W. F. Grimmer. Wisconsin Conserv. Bull., vol.2, no.10, pp.4-6, Oct., 1937.

CALIFORNIA'S GRIZZLY BEARS. Joseph Grinnell. Sierra Club Bull., 23 (2): 70-81, Apr., 1938.

THE TWO RACES OF BLACK BEAR IN CALIFORNIA. Joseph Grinnell. Univ. California Publ. Zool., vol.32, pp.395-408, pls.5-7, July 19, 1929.

THE GRIZZLY BEAR OF CALIFORNIA. E. Raymond Hall. California Fish and Game, San Francisco, vol.25, no.3, pp. 237-244, figs.90-92, July, 1939.

THE BLACK BEAR ON MOUNT KATAHDIN. Francis Harper. Bull. Boston Soc. Nat. Hist., no.49, pp.8-12, illus., Oct., 1928.

DEATH GULCH, A NATURAL BEAR-TRAP. T. A. Jaggar. Appleton's Popular Sci. Monthly, pp.1-7, illus., Feb., 1899.

A SECOND SPECIMEN OF INDIANA BEAR SKULL. Marcus W. Lyon, Jr. American Midland Nat., Notre Dame, vol.23, no.3, p.751, May, 1940.

ADDITIONAL INFORMATION ON THE RANGE OF URSUS PLANICEPS, A COLORADO GRIZZLY. C. Hart Merriam. Proc. Biol. Soc. Wash., vol.42, pp.171-172, June 15, 1929.

THE YELLOW BEAR OF LOUISIANA, URSUS LUTEOLUS GRIFFITH. C. Hart Merriam. Proc. Biol. Soc., Wash., vol. 8, pp.147-152, Dec.29, 1893.

MOLLIE OF THE MISSISSIPPI. (BLACK BEAR.) Lee Miles. Nature Mag., Wash., vol.37, no.4, pp.210-212, illus., Apr., 1944.

ECHO MOUNTAIN GRIZZLY. (STORY OF COLORADO GRIZZLY BEAR.) Enos A. Mills. Sat. Even. Post, vol.192, no.13, pp.56, 59, Sept.27 (24), 1919.

ADDITIONAL RECORDS OF URSUS CALIFORNICUS. Robert T. Orr. Jour. Mam., vol.31, no.3, pp.362-363, Aug.21, 1950.

GRIZZLY BEAR KILLED IN WASHINGTON. Victor B. Scheffer. Murrelet, Seattle, vol.31, no.1, p.15, May 19, 1950.

NOTES ON THE BLACK BEAR IN NEW YORK STATE. W. J. Schoonmaker. Jour. Mam., 19 (4): 501-502, Nov., 1938.

THE BLACK BEAR IN EARLY WISCONSIN. A. W. Schorger. Trans. Wis. Acad. Sci., Arts and Letters, 39: 151-194, 1949.

STATUS OF THE BLACK BEAR IN TENNESSEE. Vincent Schultz. Rep. Reelfoot L. Biol. Sta., 19: 40-43, Jan., 1955; Jour. Tenn. Acad. Sci., vol.30, no.1, pp.40-43, Jan., 1955.

THE BLACK BEAR IN WISCONSIN. Walter E. Scott. Wis. Cons. Bull., 12 (11): 3-10, Nov., 1947.

THE BLACK BEAR OF PENNSYLVANIA (URSUS AMERICANUS). Henry W. Shoemaker. Times Tribune Co., Altoona, Pa., pp.92, illus., 1921.

BEARS IN THE YELLOWSTONE. M. P. Skinner. Chicago, A. C. McClurg & Co., pp.158, illus., 1925.

(Review by Hartley H. T. Jackson of) BEARS IN THE YELLOWSTONE. M. P. Skinner. Jour. Mam., vol.6, no.4, p.284, Nov.14, 1925.

THE BLACK BEAR AND ITS STATUS IN MAINE. Howard E. Spencer, Jr. Me. Dept. Inl. Fisheries and Game, Game Div. Bull. No.4, pp.1-55, illus., Jan., 1955.

GRIZZLY BEARS IN OREGON. Paul Stenzel. Western Outdoors, Oswego, vol. 5, no.4, pp.6-8, 20-21, illus., Apr., 1948.

THE BLACK BEAR IN NEW HAMPSHIRE. Clark L. Stevens. Granite State Forester, 5: 37-66, 1943.

URSUS, OR THE PAST OF THE CALIFORNIA BEARS. Chester Stock. Westways, Beverly Hills, vol.28, no.11, p.30, Nov., 1936.

CALIFORNIA GRIZZLY. Tracy I. Storer, Lloyd P. Tevis, Jr. Univ. Calif. Press, pp.xii, 335, 36, figs., pls.2, 1955.

(Review by W. Robert Eadie of) THE CALIFORNIA GRIZZLY. Tracy I. Storer, Lloyd P. Tevis, Jr. Jour. Mam., 37 (2): 301, June 9, 1956.

ON A CINNAMON BEAR FROM PENNSYLVANIA. Frederick W. True. Proc. U.S. Nat. Mus., Wash., vol.5, pp.653-656, May 23, 1883.

NOTES ON THE FORMER PRESENCE OF GRIZZLY AND BLACK BEARS IN MARIN COUNTY, CALIFORNIA. C. E. Van Atta. California Fish and Game, San Francisco, vol.32, no.1, pp.27-29, Jan.2, 1946.

THE GRIZZLY BEARS OF COLORADO. Edward R. Warren. Proc. Colorado Mus. Nat. Hist., vol.11, no.3, pp.19-24, map, Dec.22, 1932.

BEARS IN ESTES PARK, COLORADO. Dorothy Welch. Jour. Mam., vol.15, no. 3, p.242, Aug., 1934.

THE BLACK BEAR IN PENNSYLVANIA. Pennsylvania Game Commision, Pa. Game News, 23 (4): 11-18, illus., July, 1952.

GRIZZLY BEAR IN MONTANA. Montana Wildlife Bull., Helena, vol.1, no.3, pp.6-7, May, 1944.

Young

A YOUNG SLOTH-BEAR. J.G. Dollman. Nat. Hist. Mag., London, vol.2, no.9, pp.38-41, illus., Jan., 1929.

CRANE FLAT TRIPLETS. (BLACK BEAR.) Eugene A. Drown. Yosemite Nat. Notes, vol.26, no.8, p.96, Aug., 1947.

BLACK BEAR CUBS AT LAST. Sam Dunton. Animal Kingdom, New York Zool. Soc., vol.58, no.3, cover, pp.80-81, June, 1955.

BEAR QUADRUPLETS. Harry R. During. Yosemite Nat. Notes, Stockton, vol.18, no. 10, p.107, Oct., 1939.

QUADS ON PARADE. (BLACK BEAR.) Paul B. Kinney. Nat. Hist., New York, vol.48, no.3, pp.150-154, illus., Oct., 1941.

ORPHAN BEAR CUBS. Felix Klet. Cons. Volunteer, St. Paul, vol.4, no.21, p.38, June, 1942.

BIG BERTHA. (BLACK BEAR AND 4 CUBS.) Leo A. Luttringer, Jr. Pennsylvania Game News, Harrisburg, vol.20, no.12, pp.2-3, 29, Mar., 1950.

GRIZZLY MOTHERS IN THE ALASKA RANGE. Adolph Murie. Living Wilderness, Wash., vol.17, no.42, pp.15-21, illus., Autumn, 1952.

THE KODIAK BEAR CUB, "URSULA." Axel Reventlow. Zool. Garten, Leipzig, N.F., vol.20, nos.4-5, pp.279-282, illus., 1954.

AVALANCHE LILY AND HER CUBS. (BLACK BEAR AND CUBS.) F. W. Schmoe. Nature Mag., vol.5, pp.347-350, illus., June, 1925.

BLACK BEARS AS MOTHERS. B. A. Thaxter. Yosemite Nature Notes, vol.12, no.9, pp.84-86, Sept., 1933.

GRIZZLY FAMILY. Harry V. Truman. Yellowstone Nat. Notes, Yellowstone Park, vol.18, nos.9-10, p.58, Sept.-Oct., 1941.

SYRIAN BROWN BEARS, 3 1/2 MONTHS TWINS. Illus. London News, vol.216, no. 5795, p.751, illus., May 13, 1950.

## Procyonidae

(Procyonidae) Anatomy

DENTAL MORPHOLOGY OF THE PROCYONIDAE WITH A DESCRIPTION OF CYNARCTOIDES, GEN. NOV. Paul O. McGrew. Geol. Ser. Field Mus. Nat. Hist., vol.6, no.22, pp.323-338, figs.85-94, Oct.31, 1938.

A WORK ON THE COMPARATIVE OSTEOLOGY OF THE PROCYONIDAE. R. W. Shufeldt. Jour. Mam., vol.1, no.4, pp. 196-197, Aug., 1920.

THE CAROTID ARTERIES IN THE PROCYONIDAE. H. Elizabeth Story. Fieldiana, Zoology, Chicago Nat. Hist. Mus., vol.32, no.8, pp.477-557, illus., 1951.

(Procyonidae) Fossils

ON THE SYSTEMATIC POSITION OF PHLAOCYON LEUCOSTEUS MATTHEW AND SOME RELATED FORMS. Elias Dahr. Arkiv. Zool., Stockholm, vol. 41A, pt.4, no.11, pp.1-15, figs.3, Mar.28, 1949.

REMARKS ON CYNARCTOIDES ARCIDENS FROM THE MIOCENE OF NORTHEASTERN COLORADO. Edwin C. Galbreath. Trans. Kansas Acad. Sci., 59 (3): 373-378, illus., Oct.31, 1956.

A FOSSIL RACCOON FROM A CALIFORNIA PLEISTOCENE CAVE DEPOSIT. (PROCYON SIMUS.) James W. Gidley. Proc. U.S. Nat. Mus., vol.29, no.1435, pp.553-554, pl.12, 1906.

A CYNARCTINE FROM THE UPPER OLIGOCENE OF SOUTH DAKOTA. (OXETOCYON, O. CUSPIDATUS.) Morton A. Green. Trans. Kans. Acad. Sci., vol. 57, no.2, pp.218-220, illus., Aug.2, 1954.

A NEW BASSARISCUS FROM THE LOWER PLIOCENE OF NEBRASKA. Claude W. Hibbard. Bull. Univ. Kansas, vol.34, no. 5, (Univ. Kansas Sci. Bull., vol.21, no.7), pp.273-278, pl.26, Mar.15, 1933.

A NEW BASSARISCUS FROM THE UPPER PLIOCENE OF KANSAS. Claude W. Hibbard. Jour. Mam., vol.33, no.3, pp.379-381, Aug.19, 1952.

THE GENUS CYNARCTUS. Paul O. McGrew. Jour. Paleont., vol.11, no.5, pp.444-449, figs.2, July, 1937.

A NEW PROCYONID FROM THE MIOCENE OF NEBRASKA. (PHLAOCYON MARSLANDENSIS.) Paul O. McGrew. Geol. Series Field Mus. Nat. Hist., Chicago, vol.8, no. 5, pp.33-36, figs.12-13, Sept.20, 1941.

PHLAOCYON--A CORRECTION. Paul O. McGrew. Jour. Palaeontology, Chicago, vol.13, no.3, p.365, May, 1939.

(Procyonidae) Taxonomy

THE GENERA AND SUBGENERA OF RACCOONS AND THEIR ALLIES. N. Hollister. Proc. U.S. Nat. Mus., vol.49, pp.143-150, pls.38-39, Aug.13, 1915.

THE EXTERNAL CHARACTERS AND CLASSIFICATION OF THE PROCYONIDAE. R. I. Pocock. Proc. Zool. Soc. Lond., pp. 389-422, figs.13, June, 1921.

ON THE TAXONOMY OF THE PROCYONIDAE. R. W. Shufeldt. Science, Lancaster, n.s., vol.41, no.1062, pp.691-692, May 7, 1915.

(Ailurus and Ailuropoda)

ON THE SYSTEMATIC POSITION OF AELUROPUS MELANOLEUCUS. K. S. Bardenfleth. Mindeskrift f.J. Steenstrup, vol.17, pp.1-15, 1913.

PANDORA IN HER NEW HOME. THE BABY GIANT PANDA HAS QUICKLY SETTLED INTO A ROUTINE THAT INCLUDES PLENTY OF TIME FOR SLEEP. W. Reid Blair. Bull. New York Zool. Soc., vol.41, no.4, pp.115-122, figs.4, July-Aug., 1938.

(ON AILURUS FULGENS.) Ueber Ailurus fulgens. (Anatomical) Albertina Carlsson. Acta Zoologica, vol.6, pp.269-305, pls.3, 1925.

THE GIANT PANDA. T. Donald Carter. Bull. New York Zool. Soc., vol.40, no.1, pp.6-14, illus., Jan.-Feb., 1937.

THE PANDA: A STUDY IN EMIGRATION--SEEMINGLY A RARE CHINESE BEAR, ASIA'S MOST PUBLICIZED MAMMAL OF RECENT YEARS HAS BEEN TRACED BACK TO A PURE AMERICAN ANCESTRY AND TURNS OUT TO BE A COUSIN OF OUR FAMILIAR RACCOON. Edwin H. Colbert. Nat. Hist., New York, vol.42, no.1, pp. 33-39, illus., June, 1938.

LESSER PANDAS. Georgie Dittoe. San Diego Zoonooz, vol.17, no.12, pp.4-5, illus., Dec., 1944.

THE HAUNTS OF THE GIANT PANDA. J. H. Edgar. Jour. West China Border Res. Soc., vol.3, p.29 (1926-29), 1930.

ON THE ANATOMY OF AELURUS FULGENS, FR. CUVIER. William H. Flower. Proc. Zool. Soc. Lond., pp.752-769, figs. 10, Nov.15, 1870.

ACUTE HEMORRHAGIC GASTRO--ENTERITIS IN A GIANT PANDA. Leonard J. Goss. Zoologica, Sci. Contrib. New York Zool. Soc., vol.25, pt.2, pp.261-262, July 3, 1940.

HOW ARE THE GIANT PANDAS? Leonard J. Goss. Animal Kingdom, New York, vol. 45, no.5, pp.120-122, illus., Sept.-Oct., 1942.

HOW THE BABY PANDAS WERE CAPTURED. David Crockett Graham. Animal Kingdom,

New York, vol. 45, no. 1, pp. 19-23, illus., Jan.-Feb., 1942.

ON THE PHYLOGENETIC RELATIONSHIPS OF THE GIANT PANDA (AILUROPODA) TO OTHER ARCTOID CARNIVORA. William K. Gregory. Amer. Mus. Novitates, no. 878, pp. 29, figs. 22, Aug. 8, 1936.

(FROM THE PUBLIC EXHIBITION: THE TIBETAN BEAR.) Aus der Schausammlung. Der tibetanische Baer. (Ailuropus melanoleucus.) F. Haas. 42 Bericht Senckenbergischen Naturforsch. Gesell., Frankfurt a.M., Heft 4, pp. 259-261, pl., 1911.

SU-LIN, RECREATED BY THE TAXIDERMIST'S ART, JOINS MUSEUM EXHIBIT. (GIANT PANDA.) H. B. Harte. Field Mus. News, vol. 9, no. 7, p. 1, July, 1938.

SEVENTY YEARS AGO THE GIANT PANDA WAS DISCOVERED BY THE WANDERING ABBE. Edward G. Huey. Frontiers, Phila., vol. 3, no. 2, pp. 40-44, Dec., 1938.

THE FOREARM AND MANUS OF THE GIANT PANDA AILUROPODA MELANOLEUCA M. EDW. WITH AN ACCOUNT OF THE MECHANISM OF ITS GRASP. Frederic Wood Jones. Proc. Zool. Soc. Lond., vol. 109, ser. B, pt. I, pp. 113-129, figs. 15, 1939.

THE "THUMB" OF THE GIANT PANDA. Frederic Wood Jones. Nature, London, vol. 143, no. 3613, p. 157, Jan. 28, 1939; no. 3615, p. 246, Feb. 11, 1939.

THE GIANT PANDA. "SUPER-CLOWN OF THE ANIMAL WORLD." Calude W. Leister. Popular Ser. no. 5, Dept. Education New York Zool. Soc., pp. 8 (not numbered), illus., 1944.

FIVE GIANT PANDAS. Rosa Loseby. Field, London, vol. 172, no. 4487, p. 1532, illus., Dec. 24, 1938.

BAMBOO AS PANDA FOOD. F. A. McClure. Jour. Mam., Balto., vol. 24, no. 2, pp. 267-268, May, 1943.

A NEW NEMATODE, ASCARIS SCHROEDERI, FROM A GIANT PANDA, AILUROPODA MELANOLEUCA. Allen McIntosh. Zoologica, New York, vol. 24, pt. 3, pp. 355-357, figs. 2, Nov. 2, 1939.

THE GIANT PANDA. FINDING THE SOLUTION TO A ZOOLOGICAL PUZZLE. T.C.S. Morrison-Scott. Field, London, vol. 173, no. 4494, p. 283, illus., Feb. 11, 1939.

SOME NOTES ON THE GIANT PANDA. Hung-Shou Pen. Bull. Fan Mem. Inst. Biol., 1 (1): 64-70, 1943.

THE PREHENSILE PAW OF THE GIANT PANDA. R. I. Pocock. Nature, London, vol. 143, no. 3614, p. 206, Feb. 4, 1939; no. 3618, p. 681, Mar. 4, 1939. (Reply to Wood Jones, Feb. 4, 1939.)

SOME EXTERNAL CHARACTERS OF THE GIANT PANDA (AILUROPODA MELANOLEUCA). R. I. Pocock. Proc. Zool. Soc. Lond., 1928, pt. 4, pp. 975-981, figs. 1-3, Jan. 31, 1929.

(CARIES IN THE BAMBOO BEAR.) Karies beim Bambusbaeren. (Ailuropus melanoleucus M. Edw.) Hermann Pohle. Zeitschr. f. Saeugetierkunde, Berlin, vol. 9, nos. 1-3, pp. 436-437, figs. 2, Dec. 30, 1934.

(THE GIANT PANDA.) Le grand panda. G. Portevin. La Terre et la Vie, vol. 7, no. 3, pp. 93-94, Mai-Juin, 1937.

THE GIANT PANDA. W. P. Pycraft. Illus. London News, vol. 191, no. 5142, p. 796, figs. 3, Nov. 6, 1937.

NOTES ON THE ANATOMY OF THE VISCERA OF THE GIANT PANDA (AILUROPODA MELANOLEUCA). H. C. Raven. Amer. Mus. Novitates no. 877, pp. 23, figs., Aug. 8, 1936.

AELUROPUS MELANOLEUCUS. Kermit Roosevelt. Hunting Trails on Three Continents, New York, Chap. 3, pp. 60-91, pl., 1933.

THE SEARCH FOR THE GIANT PANDA. THE STORY OF THE FIRST EXPEDITION EVER TO COLLECT THE STRANGE RACCOON BEAR NEAR THE BORDER OF TIBET--HOW THE FIELD MUSEUM EXPEDITION OBTAINED THE FIRST SPECIMEN OF THE RARE BEISHUNG, AN ANIMAL NEVER BEFORE SEEN BY WHITE MEN. Kermit Roosevelt. Nat. Hist., New York, vol. 30, no. 1, pp. 1-16, illus., Jan.-Feb., 1930.

HOW "PANDORA" CAME TO THE ZOOLOGICAL PARK. THE BABY GIANT PANDA IS THE FIRST OF MANY SPECIMENS THAT MAY COME THROUGH WEST CHINA UNION UNIVERSITY. Dean Sage, Jr. Bull. New York Zool. Soc., vol. 41, no. 4, pp. 115-118, illus., July-Aug., 1938.

HUNTING THE GIANT PANDA. Dean Sage, Jr. China Jour., vol. 22, no. 1, pp. 35-40, illus., Jan., 1935.

IN QUEST OF THE GIANT PANDA. Dean Sage, Jr. Nat. Hist., New York, vol. 35, no. 4, pp. 309-320, Apr., 1935.

IN THE LAND OF THE GIANT PANDA. Dean Sage, Jr. Field, London, vol. 166, no. 4308, pp. 138-139, illus., July 20, 1935.

(THE GIANT PANDA (AILUROPUS MELANOLEUCUS A. M. EDW.) Der Bambusbaer (Ailuropus melanoleucus A. M-Edw.) Ernst Schaefer. Zool. Garten, n.f., Leipzig, vol. 10, nos. 1-2, pp. 21-31, illus., May, 1938.

(DATA ON THE LARGE AND SMALL PANDA.) Einiges vom Grossen und Kleinen Panda. Karl Max Schneider. Der Zoologische Garten, Leipzig, n. F., vol. 12, no. 1, pp. 38-48, illus., Mar., 1940.

NOTES ON THE GIANT PANDA. W. G. Sheldon. Jour. Mam., vol. 18, no. 1, pp. 13-19, Feb. 14, 1937.

NOTE ON AILURUS FULGENS. B. Simpson. Proc. Zool. Soc. Lond., p. 507, pl. XLI, 1869.

A BABY PANDA COMES TO TOWN. Arthur deC. Sowerby. China Jour., vol. 25, no. 6, pp. 335-339, illus., Dec., 1936.

THE GIANT PANDA'S DIET. Arthur deC. Sowerby. China Jour., vol. 26, no. 4, pp. 209-210, Apr., 1937.

HUNTING THE GIANT PANDA. Arthur deC. Sowerby. China Jour., vol. 21, no. 1, pp. 30-32, illus., July, 1934.

THE PANDAS OR CAT-BEARS. Arthur deC. Sowerby. China Jour., vol. 17, no. 6, pp. 296-299, figs. 3, Dec., 1932.

BAMBOO EATERS. (LESSER PANDA.) Ken Stott, Jr. Zoonooz, San Diego, vol. 12, no. 11, p. 5, Nov., 1940.

TWO PANDAS--CHINA'S GIFT TO AMERICA. John Tee-Van. Animal Kingdom, New York, vol. 45, no. 1, pp. 2-18, illus., Jan.-Feb., 1942.

ON THE PANDA OF SZE-CHUEN. Oldfield Thomas. Ann. and Mag. Nat. Hist. (7), vol. 10, no. 57, pp. 251-252, Sept., 1902.

ANOTHER GIANT PANDA CUB CAPTURED--BUT A DISAPPOINTMENT! DIANA. Illus. London News, vol. 192, no. 5155, p. 223, illus., Feb. 5, 1938.

CARRYING ON AT THE ZOO. Zoonooz, San Diego, vol. 12, no. 12, pp. 5-6, Dec., 1940.

THE FAMOUS GIANT PANDA CUB FILMED: A UNIQUE CAPTIVE ANIMAL. Illus. London News, vol. 190, no. 5099, p. 45, Jan. 9, 1937.

THE GIANT PANDA. Nature, London, vol. 160, no. 4071, p. 635, Nov. 8, 1947.

THE LONDON ZOO'S GIANT PANDA, TAKEN SERIOUSLY ILL... EATING BAMBOO SHOOTS. Illus. London News, vol. 216, no. 5777, p. 25, illus., Jan. 7, 1950.

NURSE BEAN BRINGS UP BABY MEI-MEI: THE LITTLE GIANT PANDA IN CHICAGO'S ZOO. Illus. London News, vol. 192, no. 5166, p. 699, illus., Apr. 23, 1938.

THE PANDA. Field Mus. News, vol. 9, no. 6, pp. 2, June, 1938.

PANDA UP A TREE. (GIANT PANDA IN NEW YORK ZOOLOGICAL PARK.) Animal Kingdom, New York, vol. 45, no. 3, p. 79, illus., May-June, 1942.

PANDORA ENJOYS HER BREAKFAST: A GIANT PANDA'S DIET IN CAPTIVITY. Illus. London News, vol. 194, no. 5203, p. 29, photos 5, Jan. 7, 1939.

A POPULAR INVALID: THE ZOO'S GIANT PANDA SITTING UP AND TAKING NOURISHMENT. Illus. London News, vol. 216, no. 5779, p. 103, illus., Jan. 21, 1950.

WE RECEIVE A GIANT PANDA. New York Zool. Park School News, vol. 3, no. 5, pp. 1-2, illus., June-July, 1938.

(Bassariscus)

ON THE SPECIES OF THE GENUS BASSARIS. J. A. Allen. Bull. U.S. Geol. and Geogr. Surv. Terr., vol. 5, no. 3, pp. 331-340, Nov. 30, 1879.

OUR FRIEND, THE RING-TAIL. (BASSARISCUS.) Agnes Akin Atkinson. Nature Mag., vol. 24, no. 3, pp. 110-112, illus., Sept., 1934.

CACOMIXL IN ALABAMA. Peter A. Brannon. Jour. Mam., vol. 4, no. 1, p. 54, Feb., 1923.

THE RINGTAIL. Byron Dalrymple. Sports Afield, Minneapolis, vol. 123, no. 4, p. 80, Apr., 1950.

OBSERVATIONS ON THE RING-TAILED CAT. Robert L. Edwards. Jour. Mam., 36 (2): 292-293, May, 1955.

A NOTE ON BASSARISCUS. Edna M. Fisher. Jour. Mam., vol. 14, no. 3, p. 257, Aug., 1933.

THE CALIFORNIA RING-TAILED CAT. Walter Fry. California Fish and Game, vol. 12, pp. 77-78, Apr., 1926.

A NEW CACOMISTLE FROM ARIZONA. (BASSARISCUS ASTUTUS ARIZONENSIS.) E. A. Goldman. Proc. Biol. Soc. Wash., vol. 45, pp. 87-88, June 21, 1932.

A NEW CACOMISTLE FROM GUERRERO. (BASSARISCUS ASTUTUS BOLEI.) E. A. Goldman. Proc. Biol. Soc. Wash., vol. 58, pp. 105-106, July 18, 1945.

SPECIES OF THE MAMMALIAN SUBFAMILY BASSARISCINAE. E. Raymond Hall. Univ. California Publ., Bull. Dept. Geol. Sci., vol. 16, no. 11, pp. 435-448, pl. 64, Mar. 17, 1927.

SYSTEMATIC NOTES ON THE SUBSPECIES OF BASSARISCUS ASTUTUS WITH DESCRIPTION OF ONE NEW FORM FROM CALIFORNIA. E. Raymond Hall. Univ. California Publ. Zool., vol. 30, no. 3, pp. 39-50, pls. 2-3, Sept. 8, 1926.

RING-TAILED CATS AT GLACIER POINT. J. B. Herschler. Yosemite Nature Notes, vol. 8, pp. 5-6, Jan., 1929.

THE CACOMIXL CAT OF THE RIO GRANDE VALLEY. Edgar A. Mearns. Proc. U.S. Nat. Mus., Wash., D.C., vol. 24, no. 1251, pp. 207-210, Oct. 4, 1901.

DESCRIPTION OF A NEW BASSARISCUS FROM LOWER CALIFORNIA WITH REMARKS ON BASSARIS RAPTOR BAIRD. C. Hart Merriam. Proc. Biol. Soc., Wash., vol. 11, pp. 185-187, July 1, 1897.

ADVENTURES WITH A PAIR OF RING-TAILED CATS. (BASSARISCUS ASTUTUS RAPTOR.) Enid Michael. Yosemite Nature Notes, U.S. Dept. Interior, vol. 14, no. 8, pp. 61-63, illus., Aug., 1935.

A NEW CACOMISTLE FROM NEVADA. Gerrit S. Miller, Jr. Proc. Biol. Soc., Wash., vol. 26, pp. 1259-1260, June 30, 1913.

UNUSUAL OCCURRENCE OF THE RING-TAILED CAT. A. E. Naylor, G. W. Wilson. California Fish and Game, 42 (3): 231, July, 1956.

TWO NEW CACOMISTLES FROM MEXICO, WITH REMARKS ON THE GENUS JENTINKIA. (JENTINKIA SUMICHRASTI CAMPECHENSIS, BASSARISCUS ASTUTUS CONSITUS.) E. W. Nelson. Jour. Wash. Acad. Sci., vol. 22, nos. 15-16, pp. 484-488, Oct. 19, 1932.

GEOGRAPHIC VARIATION IN BASSARISCUS ASTUTUS, WITH DESCRIPTION OF A NEW SUBSPECIES. Samuel N. Rhoads. Proc. Acad. Nat. Sciences, Phila., pp.413-418, Nov., 1893.

RING-TAILED CATS (BASSARISCUS ASTUTUS): THEIR GROWTH AND DEVELOPMENT. William B. Richardson. Jour. Mam., 23 (1): 17-26, Feb., 1942.

A NATIVE MOUSER. (NOTES ON BASSARISCUS.) C. P. Russell. Yosemite Nature Notes, vol.7, pp.6-7, Jan., 1928.

A RECORD OF THE RINGTAIL (BASSARISCUS ASTUTUS) IN COLORADO. William H. Rutherford. Jour. Mam., vol.35, no.3, pp.442-443, Aug.20, 1954.

A NEW CACOMISTLE FROM SOUTHEASTERN CALIFORNIA. (BASSARISCUS ASTUTUS WILLETTI.) Kenneth E. Stager. Proc. Biol. Soc. Wash., vol.63, pp.203-204, Dec.29, 1950.

FOOD HABITS AND NOTES ON LIFE HISTORY OF THE RING-TAILED CAT IN TEXAS. Walter P. Taylor. Jour. Mam., 35 (1): 55-63, Feb., 1954.

NOTES ON THE HABITS OF THE BASSARIS ASTUTA. T. S. Thomson. Proc. Zool. Soc. Lond., pt.10, p.10, 1842.

FAMOUS RINGTAIL CAT. (An unusual photograph.) Arizona Wildlife and Sportsman, Tucson, vol.6, no.9, p.5, July, 1945.

FUR ANIMALS OF TEXAS. (RING-TAILED CAT.) Texas Game and Fish, Austin, vol. 2, no.1, p.13, illus., Dec., 1943.

(Nasua)

ON THE COATIS (GENUS NASUA STORR). J. A. Allen. Bull. U.S. Geol. and Geogr. Surv. Terr., vol.5, no.2, pp.153-174, Sept., 1879.

(A NEW FORM OF THE GENUS NASUA.) Una nueva forma del genero Nasua. Angel Cabrera. Neotropica, Notas Zool. Sudamericanas, vol.2, no.7, pp.2-4, Apr.1, 1956.

JOSE. TWO MONTHS FROM THE LIFE OF A BARRO COLORADO COATI. Frank M. Chapman. Natural History, New York, vol. 35, no.4, pp.299-308, Apr., 1935.

JOSE--1936. (HISTORY OF A COATI AT BARRO COLORADO, CONTINUED.) Frank M. Chapman. Nat. Hist., vol.38, no.2, pp.126-134, illus., Sept., 1936.

JOSE--1937--THE THIRD AND FINAL CHAPTER IN THE LIFE OF A BARRO COLORADO COATI WHO SOUGHT MAN'S CARE AND PROTECTION BETWEEN HIS PERIODIC FORAYS INTO THE JUNGLE IN SEARCH OF A MATE. Frank M. Chapman. Nat. Hist., New York, vol.40, no.2, pp. 524-526, 538, figs.3, Sept., 1937.

A FOURTH RECORD OF THE COATI IN TEXAS. W. B. Davis. Jour. Mam., vol. 24, no.4, pp.501-502, Nov.17, 1943.

A NEW COATI FROM NICARAGUA. (NASUA NARICA RICHMONDI.) E. A. Goldman. Jour. Wash. Acad. Sci., vol. 22, no.11, pp.312-313, June 4, 1932.

NOTES ON THE COATIS OF THE MEXICAN MAINLAND. E. A. Goldman. Proc. Biol. Soc. Wash., vol.55, pp.79-82, June 25, 1942.

CAPTURE OF A COATI (NASUA NARICA) IN SAN DIEGO COUNTY, CALIFORNIA. E. Raymond Hall. California Fish and Game, San Francisco, vol.26, no.4, p. 395, Oct., 1940.

A STRAY COATI IN INDIANA. M. W. Lyon. Jour. Mam., vol.4, no.3, pp.184-185, Aug., 1923.

ON THE OCCURRENCE OF ANEURISM OF THE AORTA IN THE BROWN COATI (NASUA FUSCA, F. CUV.). W. Martin. Proc. Zool. Soc. Lond., pt.2, p.9, 1834.

(TUBERCULOSIS IN THE COATI DETERMINED BY BOVINE-TYPE BACILLUS.) Tuberculose em coati (Nasua narica) determinada pelo bacilo do tipo bovino. P. Nobrega, J. Reis. Arquivos Inst. Biol., Sao Paulo, vol.12, art.21, pp.303-305, Nov., 1941.

BREEDING RECORD OF THE COATI MUNDI IN THE UNITED STATES. William G. Reeder. Jour. Mam., vol.32, no.3, pp. 362-363, Aug.23, 1951.

LAUGHING GAS. (COATIMUNDI.) Jacqueline Schermerhorn. San Diego Zoonooz, vol.18, no.10, pp.5-6, illus., Oct., 1945.

RANGE OF THE COATI IN THE UNITED STATES. F. Wallace Taber. Jour. Mam., vol.21, no.1, pp.11-14, fig.1, Feb.14, 1940.

COATI ADDED TO THE LIST OF UNITED STATES MAMMALS. Walter P. Taylor. Jour. Mam., vol.15, no.4, pp.317-318, Nov., 1934.

TWO NEW SPECIES OF NASUA. Oldfield Thomas. Ann. and Mag. Nat. Hist. (8), vol.10, no.56, pp.228-230, Aug., 1912.

STATUS OF THE COATI IN ARIZONA. O. C. Wallmo, Steve Gallizioli. Jour. Mam., vol.35, no.1, pp.48-54, Feb.10, 1954.

PHOTOGRAPH OF COATIMUNDI, SOUTH AMERICAN RACCOON SHOT IN CUMBERLAND--YORK COUNTY HILLS, PA.--AN ESCAPED PET. Penn. Game News, New Cumberland, Pa., p.27, fig., Feb., 1939.

(Potos and Bassaricyon)

ADDITIONAL NOTE ON BASSARICYON GABBI. J. A. Allen. Proc. Acad. Nat. Sci. Phila., pp.267-268, pl.2, 1877.

DESCRIPTION OF A NEW GENERIC TYPE (BASSARICYON) OF PROCYONIDAE FROM COSTA RICA. J. A. Allen. Proc. Acad. Nat. Sci. Phila., pp.20-23, pl.1, Apr.18, 1876.

"KINKY," (CAPTIVE KINKAJOU.) D. Irma Cooke. Santa Barbara Mus. Leaflet, vol. 17, no.9, pp.99-103, Dec., 1942.

BASSARICYON PAULI, A NEW SPECIES FROM PANAMA. Robert K. Enders. Proc. Acad. Nat. Sci. Phila., vol.88, 1936, pp.365-366, Feb., 1937.

NOTE ON THE HABITS OF THE KINKAJOU (CERCOLEPTES CAUDIVOLVULUS). John E. Gray. Proc. Zool. Soc. Lond., p. 680, 1865.

THE KINKAJOU WITH NOTES ON THE FIRST RECORD OF BREEDING AND REARING IN CAPTIVITY. Edmund Heller. Bull. Wash. Park Zool. Soc. Milwaukee, vol.3, nos.2-3, pp.4-7, fig.1, Sept., 1932.

KINKAJOU. Marie-Anne Jordan. Nature Mag., vol.28, no.2, pp.80-82, illus., Aug., 1936.

THIS "KINKAJOU" WAS REALLY THE VERY RARE OLINGO. (BASSARICYON AND POTOS.) Richard H. Manville. Animal Kingdom, New York Zool. Soc., 59 (4): 109-111, illus., Aug., 1956.

DESCRIPTION OF TWO SPECIES OF THE GENUS CERCOLEPTES. W. Martin. Proc. Zool. Soc. Lond., pt.4, p.82, 1836.

A NEW KINKAJOU FROM MEXICO. (POTOS FLAVUS CAMPECHENSIS.) E. W. Nelson, E. A. Goldman. Jour. Wash. Acad. Sci., vol.21, no.19, pp.482-483, Nov.19, 1931.

NOTES ON THE ANATOMY OF THE KINKAJOU (CERCOLEPTES CAUDIVOLVULUS, Ill). R. Owen. Proc. Zool. Soc. Lond., pt.3, p.119, 1835.

ON THE MYOLOGY OF THE LIMBS OF THE KINKAJOU (CERCOLEPTES CAUDIVOLVULUS). J. Beswick Perrin. Proc. Zool. Soc. Lond., pp.547-559, 1871.

A NEW SPECIES OF BASSARICYON. R. I. Pocock. Ann. and Mag. Nat. Hist., ser. 9, vol.7, pp.229-234, figs.2, Mar., 1921.

A NEW SUBSPECIES OF BASSARICYON FROM COLOMBIA. (BASSARICYON MEDIUS SICCATUS.) Oldfield Thomas. Ann. and Mag. Nat. Hist., ser.9, vol.20, p.80, July, 1927.

ON THE GEOGRAPHICAL RACES OF THE KINKAJOU. Oldfield Thomas. Ann. and Mag. Nat. Hist. (7), vol.9, no.52, pp. 266-270, Apr., 1902.

ALBERT LEADS THE LIFE OF RILEY. (KINKAJOU.) Nat. Mag., Wash., vol.40, no.9, pp.77-78, illus., Nov., 1947.

(Procyon) General

THE WAY OF A COON. Roy L. Abbott. Nat. Hist., New York, vol.53, no.7, pp. 310-311, 336, illus., Sept., 1944.

THE RACCOON. Rod Amundson. Wildlife in North Carolina, Raleigh, vol.13, no.5, pp.4-6, 20, illus., May, 1949.

BASIC STUDY OF THE RACCOON. Edward V. Berard. Cons. Comm. W. Va., pp.iii, 53, maps, graph, 1951 (Jan.1952).

ADVENTURE WITH RACCOON. Sam Campbell. Amer. Forests, Wash., D.C., vol.50, no.7, pp.348-350, 362, illus., July, 1944.

RACCOONS WE HAVE KNOWN. William H. Carr. Nat. Hist., New York, vol.54, no. 4, pp.152-157, illus., Apr., 1945.

THE RACCOON, PERT, WHIMSICAL AND "NEXT-TO-GODLY" THIEF. James Nelson Gowanloch. Louisiana Conservationist, New Orleans, vol.3, no.2, pp.12-13, illus., Oct., 1950.

THE MASKED BANDIT OF THE WOODS. (RACCOON.) Lyn Harrington. Canadian Nature, Toronto, vol.6, no.5, pp.154-155, illus., Nov.-Dec., 1944.

BRUIN'S LITTLE BROTHER. (RACCOON.) Howard Taylor Middleton. Nature Mag., vol.10, pp.230-232, illus., Oct., 1927.

RINGTAIL, THE RACCOON. Florence Nelson. Our Dumb Animals, Norwood, vol.80, no.5, p.5, illus., May, 1947.

SNIFFY--A ROGUISH RACCOON. J. T. Sackett. Fauna, Phila., vol.3, no.3, pp.98-100, Sept., 1941.

MISTER MONKEY MITTS. (RACCOON.) Clayt Seagears. New York State Cons., Albany, vol.5, no.4, p.40, illus., Feb.-Mar., 1951.

RING-TAILED RASCAL. (RACCOON.) F. W. Stuewer. Michigan Conserv., Lansing, vol.23, no.5, pp.12-14, Sept., 1954.

THE RACCOON. Leon F. Whitney, Acil B. Underwood. Practical Sci. Publ. Co., Orange, Conn., pp.155, illus., 1952.

(Review by W. J. Hamilton, Jr. of) THE RACCOON. Leon F. Whitney, Acil B. Underwood. Jour. Mam., vol.34, no.1, pp.141-142, Feb.19, 1955.

INTRODUCING BOBBY COON. Canadian Nature, Toronto, vol.2, no.1, p.5, Jan.-Feb., 1940.

(Procyon) The Americas

THE RACCOON IN NORTH DAKOTA. J.E. Campbell. North Dakota Outdoors, Bismarck, vol.7, no.8, p.4, Feb., 1945.

WILD LIFE IN BARABOO HILLS. (RACCOON FARM AND RACCOON HABITS.) H. E. Cole. Wisconsin Conservationist, vol.3, no.6, p.9, Jan. (Mar.), 1922.

RACCOONS IN YELLOWSTONE NATIONAL PARK. David Condon. Yellowstone Nat. Notes, Yellowstone Park, vol.18, nos.3-4, pp.18-19, Mar.-Apr., 1941.

BREEDING SEASON, PRODUCTIVITY, AND POPULATION TRENDS OF RACCOONS IN MISSOURI. George P. Dellinger. MA thesis, U. Mo., pp.v, 86, graphs, 1954.

A NEW EASTERN MARSH-INHABITING RACE OF RACCOON. Herbert L. Dozier. Jour. Mam., 29 (3): 286-290, Aug., 1948.

RACCOONS OF NORTH AND MIDDLE AMERICA. E. A. Goldman. USDI, F&WS, N. A. Fauna 60, pp.153, 1950.

THE RACCOON IN THE SALT MARSHES OF NORTHEASTERN FLORIDA. R. D. Ivey. Jour. Mam., 29 (3): 290-291, Aug., 1948.

LIFE HISTORY AND MANAGEMENT STUDIES OF RACCOON IN MAINE. Robert H. Johnson. MS thesis, Univ. Maine, 1939.

THE RACCOON IN OKLAHOMA. Glenn Jones. Okla. Game and Fish News, 2(12): 4-5, 7, Dec., 1946.

KNEE DEEP IN COONS. Jim Keefe. Mo. Cons., 14 (11): 10-11, Nov., 1953.

THE RACCOON IN SOUTHWESTERN VIRGINIA. William C. Kellner. Va. Wildl., 15 (1): 16-17, 21, illus., Jan., 1954.

CALIFORNIA COONS IN YOSEMITE. R. N. McIntyre. Yosemite Nat. Notes, Yosemite, vol.22, no.5, pp.47-48, May, 1943.

COON VISITS SOUTH ENTRANCE. (YOSEMITE NATIONAL PARK.) R. N. McIntyre. Yosemite Nat. Notes, Yosemite, vol.23, no.3, pp.35-36, Mar., 1944.

RACCOONS IN SASKATCHEWAN. S. A. Mann, Joyce Gunn. Blue Jay, Saskatchewan Nat. Hist. Soc., 14 (1): 27, Mar., 1956.

DESCRIPTIONS OF THREE NEW RACCOONS FROM THE MEXICAN BOUNDARY REGION. Edgar A. Mearns. Proc. Biol. Soc. Wash., vol.27, pp.63-67, Mar.30, 1914.

VIRGINIA ANIMALS EVERYONE SHOULD KNOW: THE RACCOON. Henry S. Mosby. Virginia Wildlife, Richmond, vol.8, no.2, pp.8-9, 20, Feb., 1947.

FOUR NEW RACCOONS FROM THE KEYS OF SOUTHERN FLORIDA. (PROCYON LOTOR MARINUS; PROCYON L. INESPERATUS; PROCYON L. AUSPICATUS; PROCYON L. INCAUTUS.) E. W. Nelson. Smithson. Misc. Coll., vol.82, no.8, pp. 1-12, pls.5, July 10, 1930.

A NEW RACCOON FROM LOWER CALIFORNIA. (PROCYON LOTOR GRINNELLI.) E. W. Nelson, E. A. Goldman. Jour. Wash. Acad. Sci., vol.20, no.5, pp.82-83, Mar.4, 1930.

A NEW RACCOON FROM SOUTH CAROLINA. E. W. Nelson, E. A. Goldman. Jour. Mam., Balto., vol.12, no.3, pp.308-309, Aug.24, 1931.

THREE NEW RACCOONS FROM MEXICO AND SALVADOR. (PROCYON LOTOR SHUFELDTI; PROCYON LOTOR DICKEYI; PROCYON INSULARIS VICINUS.) E. W. Nelson, E. A. Goldman. Proc. Biol. Soc. Wash., vol.44, pp.17-22, Feb.21, 1931.

A PRELIMINARY STUDY OF THE EASTERN RACCOON, PROCYON L. LOTOR L., IN MISSOURI: POPULATION, DENNING, AND FOOD HABITS. Carl R. Noren. AM thesis, Univ. Mo., 1941.

THE CLOWNING COONS OF ASH MOUNTAIN CALIFORNIA. Gayle Pickwell. Nature Mag., Wash., vol.37, no.3, pp. 137-139, illus., Mar., 1944.

HISTORY OF THE RACCOON (PROCYON LOTOR L.) IN NOVA SCOTIA. A. L. Rand. Canadian Field Nat., Sutton West, vol.57, nos.3-4, p.95, Apr.-May, 1943.

IN THE ROOFGARDEN OF PENNSYLVANIA. (RACCOON) Robert D. Reed. Pennsylvania Game News, Harrisburg, vol.19, no.8, pp. 7, 31, illus., Nov., 1948.

BREEDING HABITS AND A HISTORY OF THE MISSOURI RACCOON POPULATION FROM 1941 TO 1948. Glen C. Sanderson. Trans. N. A. Wildl. Conf., 16: 445-460, 1951.

RACCOON STUDIES IN IOWA. Glen C. Sanderson. Iowa Cons., 11 (3): 1, 23, illus., Mar., 1952.

SEX AND AGE DETERMINATION, BREEDING HABITS, AND POPULATION CHARACTERISTICS OF MISSOURI RACCOONS. Glen C. Sanderson. MA thesis, Univ. Mo., 1949.

THE STATUS OF THE RACCOON IN IOWA FOR THE PAST TWENTY YEARS AS REVEALED BY FUR REPORTS. Glen C. Sanderson. Proc. Iowa Acad. Sci., Des Moines, vol.58, pp.527-531, 1951.

A STUDY OF RACCOON (PROCYON LOTOR HIRTUS NELSON AND GOLDMAN) IN NORTH-CENTRAL MINNESOTA. Lyle J. Schoonover. MS thesis, Univ. Minn., 1950.

A STUDY OF RACCOONS IN PRINCESS ANNE COUNTY, VIRGINIA. C. H. Shaffer. MS thesis, Va. Poly. Inst., 1948.

RACCOONS OF THE BAHAMA ISLANDS. H. B. Sherman. Jour. Mam., 35 (1): 126, Feb., 1954.

THE RACCOONS OF NORTH AMERICA. R. W. Shufeldt. Amer. Forestry, vol.25, pp.1531-1536, figs.5, Dec., 1919.

NOTES ON THE RACCOON (PROCYON LOTOR HIRTUS) IN MANITOBA. Lyle K. Sowls. Jour. Mam., vol.30, no.3, pp.313-314, Aug.17, 1949.

THE RACCOON IN KANSAS. NATURAL HISTORY, MANAGEMENT, AND ECONOMIC IMPORTANCE. Howard J. Stains. Misc. Publ. Univ. Kansas Mus. Nat. Hist., Lawrence, 10: 1-76, pls.1-4, July 6, 1956.

LIFE HISTORY AND MANAGEMENT STUDIES OF THE RACCOON (PROCYON LOTOR) IN MICHIGAN. Frederick W. Stuewer. PhD thesis, Mich. State Coll., 1941.

RACCOONS: THEIR HABITS AND MANAGEMENT IN MICHIGAN. Frederick W. Stuewer. Ecol. Monog., 13 (2): 203-257, Apr., 1943.

FUR YIELD AND AUTUMN FOODS OF THE RACCOON IN ILLINOIS RIVER BOTTOM LANDS. Lee E. Yeager, R. G. Rennels. Jour. Wildl. Mgt., 7 (1): 45-60, Jan., 1943.

WISCONSIN RACCOON. Wisconsin Conserv. Bull., Madison, vol.4, no.10, p.56, Oct., 1939.

(Procyon) Anatomy

THE MUSCLES OF THE LIMBS OF THE RACCOON (PROCYON LOTOR). Harrison Allen. Proc. Acad. Nat. Sci., Phila., pp. 115-144, May, 1882.

(A MULTIPLE TAIL OF PROCYON.) Une queque multiple de Procyon. M. R. Anthony. Bull. Mus. Nat. Hist. Nat., Paris, ser.2, vol.3, no.7, pp.562-565, figs.2, Nov., 1931.

SUMMER WEIGHTS OF RACCOONS IN NORTHERN MINNESOTA. William H. Marshall. Jour. Mam., 37 (3): 445, Sept.11, 1956.

HOW BIG IS A 'COON? W. O. Nagel. Mo. Cons., 4 (7): 6-7, Oct., 1943.

OS CLITORIDIS FROM THE RACCOON. George C. Rinker. Jour. Mam., vol.25, no.1, pp.91-92, fig.1, Feb., 1944.

(A MULTIPLE TAIL OF PROCYON.) Une queue multiple de Procyon. J. Vellard, J. Penteado. Bull. Soc. Zool., France, vol.56, pp.355-360, fig.1, 1931.

(Procyon) Breeding

FUR BEARING ANIMALS OF THE UNITED STATES. THE RACCOON. Frank G. Ashbrook, Horace J. McMullen. Fur Jour., vol.2, no.3, pp.30-31, 59-61, illus., Mar., 1928.

THE BLACK RACCOON OFFERS FUR AND FOOD. Hugo Belz. Amer. Fur Breeder, vol.4, no.4, pp.26-27, Oct., 1931.

ANSWERING SOME ARGUMENTS AGAINST THE WHITE RACCOON. W. J. Boston. Amer. Fur Breeder, vol.4, no.3, p.29, Sept., 1931.

RACCOON RANCH STATUS. Larry R. Gale. Ky. Happy Hunting Ground, 8 (1): 12-13, illus., Jan., 1952.

PROPAGATION OF OHIO RACCOONS IN PENS. E. D. Martin. Ohio Div. Wildl., Game Mgt. Leafl. No.16, p.4, Feb., 1950.

BREEDING THE BLACK RACCOON. L. S. Russell. Amer. Fur Breeder, vol.1, no.1, pp.18-19, July, 1928.

TIMELY SUGGESTIONS FOR BREEDING BLACK RACCOON. L. S. Russell. Amer. Fur Breeder, vol.1, no.11, pp.12-13, May, 1929.

THE WHITE RACCOON. W. J. Schoonmaker. National Humane Review, Albany, vol.32, no.12, pp.16-17, illus., Dec., 1944.

THE RACCOON STORY. Jack Stephens. Amer. Nat. Fur. and Market Jour., Wausau, vol.27, no.8, pp.9, 12, 24, 26, 28, Mar., 1949.

PROPAGATION IS BIG BUSINESS. (RACCOON.) Outdoor Indiana, Indianapolis, vol. 12, no.7, pp.6-7, illus., Sept.-Oct., 1945.

RAISING RACCOONS. USDA, Biol. Survey, Wildl. Leaflet 34, pp.2, Jan., 1936.

RAISING RACCOONS. U.S. Fish and Wildlife Serv., Wildlife Leaflet no.251, pp.2, Mar., 1944.

WISCONSIN RACCOON RAISING, POYNETTE STATE EXPERIMENTAL GAME AND FUR FARM (1941). Wisconsin Conserv. Dept., Madison, Publ. no.313, pp.6 (mimeogr.), illus., 1941.

(Procyon) Captivity

OLD ZIP COON--A GIANT OF HIS KIND, HE FOLLOWED HIS MASTER ON HUNTING TRIPS AND COULD LICK HIS WEIGHT IN DOGS, BUT HE PROVED ONE OF THE MOST RAMBUNCTIOUS PETS THAT EVER HAD THE RUN OF A NATURALIST'S HOUSE. Roy L. Abbott. Natural History, New York, vol.43, no.5, pp.262-265, May, 1939.

ARTISTIC AND PRACTICAL RACCOON ENCLOSURE AT TULSA. M. E. Erwin. Parks and Recreation, vol.12, pp.98-100, illus., Dec., 1928.

IVAN AND ABDULLA. (TAME ALBINO RACCOONS.) Clifford H. Pope. Nat. Hist., New York, vol.51, no.3, pp.116-119, 154, illus., Mar., 1943.

(Procyon) Diseases and Parasites

TUBERCULOSIS IN THE CANADA RACCOON (PROCYON LOTOR). M. H. Brown. Trans. Roy. Soc. Canada, Sec.5, Biol. Sci., vol.25, pp.159-162, 1931.

THE GUINEA WORM, DRACUNCULUS INSIGNIS (LEIDY 1858), A COMMON PARASITE OF RACCOONS IN EAST TEXAS. Asa C. Chandler. Amer. Jour. Trop. Med., 22 (2): 153-157, Mar., 1942.

THE HELMINTHS OF RACCOONS IN EAST TEXAS. Asa C. Chandler. Jour. Parasitology, 28 (4): 255-268, Aug., 1942.

THE MORPHOLOGY AND LIFE CYCLE OF A NEW STRIGEID, FIBRICOLA TEXENSIS, PARASITIC IN RACCOONS. Asa C. Chandler. Trans. Amer. Micros. Soc., 61 (2): 156-167, Apr., 1942.

EURYTREMA PROCYONIS N. SP. (TREMATODA: DICROCOELIIDAE), FROM THE RACCOON, PROCYON LOTOR. J. Fred Denton. Proc. Helminth. Soc. Wash., 9 (1): 29-30, Jan., 1942.

LISTERIOSIS IN CONNECTICUT WITH PARTICULAR REFERENCE TO A SEPTICEMIC CASE IN A WILD RACCOON. Rebecca Gifford, Erwin Jungherr. Cornell Vet., 37 (1): 39-48, Jan., 1947.

PHARYNGOSTOMOIDES PROCYONIS N. G., N. SP. (STRIGEIDA), A TREMATODE FROM THE RACCOON IN NORTH CAROLINA AND TEXAS. Reinard Harkema. Jour. Parasitology, 28 (2): 117-122, Apr., 1942.

THE HELMINTH FAUNA OF A RACCOON. William M. Ingram. Jour. Parasitology, 27 (6): 539-540, Dec., 1941.

ISOLATION OF AN AGENT CAUSING BILIRUBINEMIA AND JAUNDICE IN RACCOONS. Lawrence Kilham, Carlton M. Herman. Proc. Soc. Exp. Biol. and Med., 85 (2): 272-275, Feb., 1954.

SEVERE INFESTATION OF BLOW FLIES IN A RACCOON. Lawrence Kilham, Carlton M. Herman. Jour. Wildl. Mgt., 19 (4): 499, Oct., 1955.

INFECTIOUS GASTRO-ENTERITIS IN RACCOON. A. M. McDermid. Wis. Cons. Bull., 4 (3): 21-22, Mar., 1939.

PARASITES OF RACCOONS IN SOUTHWEST WASHINGTON. Charles W. McNeil, Joanna T. Krogsdale. Jour. Mam., vol.34, no.1, pp.123-124, Feb.19, 1953.

STUDIES ON THE LIFE HISTORY AND DEVELOPMENT OF MACRACANTHORHYNCHUS INGENS MEYER 1933, WITH A REDESCRIPTION OF THE ADULT WORM. (ACANTHOCEPHALAN FROM RACCOONS.) Donald V. Moore. Jour. Parasitology, 32 (4): 387-399, Aug., 1946.

SEVERE PARASITISM IN A RACCOON (PROCYON LOTOR LOTOR, LINNAEUS). B. B. Morgan, E. F. Waller. Trans. Amer. Micros. Soc., 59 (4): 523-527, Oct., 1940.

A NOTE ON MACRACANTHORHYNCHUS INGENS IN A CONNECTICUT RACCOON. Lawrence R. Penner. Jour. Mam., 35 (3): 459, Aug., 1954.

DIPETALONEMA PROCYONIS N. SP. FROM PROCYON LOTOR LOTOR (LINNAEUS). Donald L. Price. Proc. Helminth Soc. Wash., 22 (1): 38-41, illus., Jan., 1955.

THE RACCOON, A NEW HOST FOR MICROPHALLUS SP., WITH ADDITIONAL NOTES ON M. OVATUS FROM TURTLES. Robert Rausch. Jour. Parasitology, 32 (2): 208-209, Apr., 1946.

THE RACCOON AS A WILDLIFE RESERVOIR OF LEPTOSPIRA CANICOLA. James R. Reilly. New York Fish and Game Jour., 1 (2): 220, July, 1954.

A NEW SPECIES OF HOOKWORM FROM THE NORTH AMERICAN RACCOON. Benjamin Schwartz. Proc. U.S. Nat. Mus., vol.67, art.26, pp.1-4, 1925.

GUINEA WORM INFESTATION OF RACCOONS IN NEW HAMPSHIRE. Hilbert R. Siegler. Jour. Mam., 27 (2): 179, May, 1946.

INFECTIOUS GASTROENTERITIS IN RACCOONS (PROCYON LOTOR). E. F. Waller. Jour. Amer. Vet. Med. Assn., 96 (755): 266-268, Feb., 1940.

## (Procyon) Embryology

GROWTH RATE OF THE RACCOON FETUS. Leonard M. Llewellyn. Jour. Wildlife Mgt., Ithaca, vol.17, no.3, pp.320-321, illus., July, 1953.

OVULATION IN THE RACCOON. Leonard M. Llewellyn, Robert K. Enders. Jour. Mam., 35 (3): 440, Aug., 1954.

TRANS-UTERINE MIGRATION IN THE RACCOON. Leonard M. Llewellyn, Robert K. Enders. Jour. Mam., 35 (3): 439, Aug., 1954.

## (Procyon) Experimental Biology

MODIFICATION OF MAMMALIAN SEXUAL CYCLES. VII. FERTILE MATINGS OF RACCOONS IN DECEMBER INSTEAD OF FEBRUARY INDUCED BY INCREASING DAILY PERIODS OF LIGHT. Thomas Hume Bissonnette, Albert G. Csech. Proc. Roy. Soc. Lond., ser.B, no.827, vol.122, pp.246-254, Apr., 1937.

SEXUAL PHOTO-PERIODICITY OF RACCONS ON LOW PROTEIN DIET AND SECOND LITTERS IN THE SAME BREEDING SEASON. Thomas Hume Bissonnette, Albert G. Csech. Jour. Mam., 19 (3): 342-348, Aug., 1938.

A THIRD YEAR OF MODIFIED BREEDING BEHAVIOR WITH RACCOONS. Thomas Hume Bissonnette, Albert George Csech. Ecology, Brooklyn, vol.20, no.2, pp.156-162, tables 7, Apr., 1939.

## (Procyon) Food Habits

FOOD HABITS OF THE RACCOON IN EASTERN TEXAS. Rollin H. Baker, Coleman C. Newman, Ford Wilke. Jour. Wildl. Mgt., 9 (1): 45-48, Jan., 1945.

A NEW KILLER. (RACCOONS KILLING SHEEP.) J. D. Bankston, Hart Stilwell. Outdoor Life, 112 (6): 48-49, 140, illus., Dec., 1953.

NOTES ON THE RACCOON, PROCYON LOTOR MEGALODOUS LOWERY. (HABITAT AND FOODS ON MISSISSIPPI DELTA.) Fred R. Cagle. Jour. Mam., 30 (1): 45-47, Feb., 1949.

FOOD PREFERENCES OF THE RACCOON IN WASHTENAW COUNTY, MICHIGAN. Thomas G. Clark. MS thesis, Univ. Mich., 1947.

FOOD HABITS OF THE RACCOON, PROCYON LOTOR HIRTUS N. AND G., IN CENTRAL IOWA. Robert R. Costa. MS thesis, Iowa State Coll., 1951.

THE RACCOON AS A PREDATOR OF TURTLES. Arnold B. Erickson, Harvey I. Scudder. Jour. Mam., vol.28, no.4, pp. 406-407, Nov.26, 1947.

FALL FOOD HABITS OF THE RACCOON IN CENTRAL IOWA. LeRoy W. Giles. Jour. Mam., 20 (1): 68-70, Feb., 1939.

FOOD HABITS OF THE EASTERN RACCOON, PROCYON L. LOTOR L., IN EASTERN IOWA. LeRoy W. Giles. MS thesis, Iowa State Coll., 1939.

FOOD HABITS OF THE RACCOON IN EASTERN IOWA. LeRoy W. Giles. Jour. Wildlife Mgt., Menasha, vol.4, no.4, pp. 375-382, Oct., 1940.

WARM WEATHER FOODS OF THE RACCOON IN NEW YORK STATE. W. J. Hamilton, Jr. Jour. Mam., vol.32, no.3, pp.341-344, illus., Aug.23, 1951.

FOOD HABITS OF THE RACCOON. George O. Hendrickson. Iowa Cons., 2 (12): 95, Dec., 1943.

(CONTRIBUTION TO THE NUTRITION AND DIGESTION OF THE RACCOONS.) Beitrag zur Ernaehrung und Verdauung des Waschbaeren. Raimund Neseni. Zeitschr. f. Saeugetierkunde, vol.13, no.1, pp.77-113, tables 8, pl.37, Aug.1, 1938.

(FEEDING HABITS OF THE RACCOON.) Materiali po pitaniyu e nota (Procyon lotor L.). N. N. Rusovski. Zool. Zhurnal, Moscow, 36 (2): 280-288, 1957. In Russian, with English summary.)

FOOD HABITS OF THE RACCOON (PROCYON LOTOR HIRTUS) IN NORTH-CENTRAL MINNESOTA. Lyle J. Schoonover, William H. Marshall. Jour. Mam., 32 (4): 422-428, Nov., 1951.

FOOD HABIT STUDY OF MARYLAND RACCOONS. MATERIAL FURNISHED BY THE WICOMICO COON HUNTERS CLUB AND OTHER HUNTERS ON THE EASTERN SHORE. Lucille F. Stickel, Robert T. Mitchell. Maryland Conserv., Balto., vol. 21, no.1, pp.26-28, 1944.

FALL FOOD HABITS OF THE RACCOON IN THE SOUTH PLATTE VALLEY OF NORTHEASTERN COLORADO. John R. Tester. Jour. Mam., vol.34, no.4, pp.500-502, Nov.13, 1953.

SUMMER FOOD HABITS OF THE RACCOON IN SOUTHWEST WASHINGTON. Edwin L. Tyson. Jour. Mam., vol.31, no.4, pp.448-449, Nov.21, 1950.

FOOD HABIT STUDY OF MARYLAND RACCOONS. Ernest A. Vaughn. Maryland Conserv., Balto., vol.21, no.1, pp.26-28, Winter Issue, 1944.

PRE- AND POST-HUNTING SEASON FOODS OF RACCOONS ON AN ILLINOIS GOOSE REFUGE. Lee E. Yeager, William H. Elder. Jour. Wildl. Mgt., 9 (1): 48-56, Jan., 1945.

## (Procyon) General Habits, Ecology, Behavior

NOTE ON THE DEN SITE OF A RACCOON FAMILY. Rollin H. Baker, Coleman C. Newman. Jour. Mam., vol.23, no.2, pp. 214-215, May 14, 1942.

UNUSUAL NESTING OF A RACCOON. W. H. Bergtold. Jour. Mam., vol.6, no.4, pp.280-281, Nov., 1925.

(ON THE SO-CALLED "WASHING" OF RACCOONS (PROCYON LOTOR), WITH SOME REMARKS ON THE FORMS AND SIGNIFICANCE OF ANIMAL PLAY.) Ueber das sogenannte "Waschen" des Waschbaeren (Procyon lotor), nebst einigen Bemerkungen ueber die Formen und die Bedeutung der tierischen Spiele. J. A. Bierens de Haan. Biol. Zentralbl., vol.52, no.6, pp.329-343, 1932.

THE RACCOON--MASKED CLOWN OF THE WOOD-LOTS. G. W. Bradt. Mich. Cons., 15 (8): 6-7, Sept., 1946.

POPULATIONS, HUNTING PRESSURE, AND MOVEMENT OF OHIO RACCOONS. Robert T. Butterfield. Trans. 9th N. Amer. Wildlife Conference, Wash., pp.337-344, 1944.

RESTING HABITS OF THE RACCOON, PROCYON LOTOR HIRTUS N. AND G., IN CENTRAL IOWA. James L. Cabalka. MS thesis, Iowa State Coll., pp.35, 1952.

ECOLOGY OF THE RACCOON IN CENTRAL IOWA. James L. Cabalka, R. R. Costa, G. O. Hendrickson. Proc. Iowa Acad. Sci., 60: 616-620, 1953.

ECOLOGY OF MARSH RACCOONS. Robert S. Dorney. Jour. Wildlife Mgt., Ithaca, vol.18, no.2, pp.217-225, illus., Apr., 1954.

BEHAVIOR AND FOOD OF PENNED RACCOONS. Homer E. Fairchild, George O. Hendrickson. Iowa Conservationist, Des Moines, vol.4, no.2, p.112, illus., Feb. 15, 1945.

(ON THE "WASHING" OF PROCYON LOTOR L.) Ueber das "Waschen" von Procyon lotor L. Wolfgang Gewalt. Zeitschr. Saeugetierk., Berlin, 21 (3-4): 149-155, pl.8, Feb.28, 1957.

EVIDENCES OF RACCOON MOBILITY OBTAINED BY TAGGING. LeRoy W. Giles. Jour. Wildl. Mgt., 7 (2): 235, Apr., 1943.

UTILIZATION OF ROCK EXPOSURES FOR DENS AND ESCAPE COVER BY RACCOONS. LeRoy W. Giles. Amer. Midland Nat., 27 (1): 171-176, Jan., 1942.

(ON THE "WASHING" OF RACCOONS.) Ueber das "Waschen" der Waschbaeren. Siegfried Haubold. Der Deutsche Pelztierzuechter, Muenchen, Jahrg. 1932, no. 18, pp.442-443, Sept.15, 1932.

RACCOONS SNAP THEIR OWN PICTURES. R. D. Maar. Field and Stream, New York, vol.52, no.6, pp.112-113, illus., Oct., 1947.

RACCOON PARADE. Joseph C. Moore. Everglades Nat. Hist., 1 (3): 119-126, illus., Sept., 1953.

THE RACCOON. (APPEARANCE, DISTRIBUTION, HABITS, FOOD, VALUE, AND MANAGEMENT.) Henry S. Mosby. Va. Wildl., 8 (2): 8-9, 20, Feb., 1947.

NOCTURNAL MOVEMENTS AND BEHAVIOR OF WILD RACCOONS AT A WINTER FEEDING STATION. Ward M. Sharp, Louise H. Sharp. Jour. Mam., 37 (2): 170-177, pl.1, June 9, 1956.

RACCOONS AND GEESE. Ernest E. Shepard. Hunting and Fishing in Canada, Montreal, vol.13, no.7, p.46, 1947.

A RACCOON EXPLORES NEW COUNTRY. HOW ONE OF THESE PIONEERS VISITED A CAMP ON THE SOUTH SHORE OF LAKE SUPERIOR, AND WAS ENCOURAGED TO REMAIN. George Shiras 3rd. Forest and Stream, vol.90, pp.10, 11, 44, Jan., 1920.

SUMMER ACTIVITY OF CALIFORNIA RACCOONS. Lloyd Tevis, Jr. Jour. Mam., 28 (4): 323-332, Nov., 1947.

WINTER DENS FOR RACCOONS. R. F. Zeches. Amer. Fur Breeder, vol.1, no. 6, p.9, Dec., 1928.

## (Procyon) Hunting and Trapping

COON HUNTING IN OHIO. Robert W. Barr. Fur-Fish-Game, Harding's Mag., Columbus, vol.86, no.9, p.40, Aug., 1946.

DEATH OF A MASKED RAIDER. (RACCOON.) Stuart Bruce. Outdoor Life, New York, vol.102, no.3, pp.50-56, illus., Sept., 1948.

THIS RACCOON RACKET. John W. Currie. Kentucky Happy Hunting Ground, Frankfort, vol.5, no.2, pp.5, 19, Mar., 1949.

COON ON THE CRICK. Eddy Dressen. Sports Afield, Minneapolis, vol.118, no. 6, pp.30-31, 86-87, illus., Dec., 1947.

BAD COON. Ben East. Field and Stream, New York, vol.48, no.8, pp.16-17, 68, 71, Dec., 1943.

RACCOON TRAPPING. Clayton G. Gates. Fur-Fish-Game (Harding's Mag.), Columbus, vol.79, no.1, pp.33-35, Jan., 1946.

OUR FIRST COON. Floyd Gose. Fur-Fish-Game, Harding's Mag., Columbus, vol.86, no.8, pp.22-23, illus., Aug., 1946.

TRAPPING THE RACCOON. C. A. McMahon. Texas Game and Fish, Austin, vol.4, no.12, p.30, Nov., 1946.

ONE HUNDRED RACCOONS FROM ONE HUNDRED AND TWO ACRES. A. R. Twichell, Herbert H. Dill. Jour. Mam., 30 (2): 130-133, May, 1949.

COON AND "COONIN." Oliver J. Valley. Wisconsin Conservation, Madison, vol.13, no.9, pp.15-18, illus., Sept., 1948.

THE RACCOON AND ITS HUNTING. Leon F. Whitney. Jour. Mam., vol.12, no.1, pp.29-38, Feb., 1931.

THE COON HUNTER'S HANDBOOK. Leon F. Whitney. Holt, pp.210, illus., 1952.

RACCOON HUNTING AND THE TRAPPER. Kenneth A. Wilson. Wildl. in N.C., 15 (11): 8-9, 22, illus., Nov., 1952.

(Procyon) Industrial Products

A TEST OF RACCOON SKINS FOR SUEDE LEATHER. Ira D. Clarke, Frank G. Ashbrook. Jour. Amer. Leather Chemists Assoc., vol.48, no.5, pp.294-299, May, 1953.

(DOES THE RACCOON PROVIDE US WITH A NEW GERMAN INDUSTRIAL MATERIAL?) Bringt uns der Waschbaer einen neuen deutschen Werkstoff? Anton Eberle, Elfriede Reichert. Deutsche Pelztierzuechter, Munich, vol.14, no.8, pp.174-176, Apr.15, 1939.

USE OF THE OS PHALLUS OF THE RACCOON AS RIPPING TOOL. Edmund C. Jaeger. Jour. Mam., vol.28, no.3, p.297, Aug.19, 1947.

(Procyon) Longevity

LONGEVITY OF THE RACCOON IN THE WILD. Orland L. Haugen. Jour. Mam., 35 (3): 439, Aug., 1954.

RACCOON (PROCYON LOTOR) MORTALITY IN SOUTHERN IOWA. Robert E. Mangold. Jour. Mam., vol.32, no.2, pp.218-219, May 21, 1951.

(Procyon) Management

THE BUYING OF DEN TREES FOR RACCOON MANAGEMENT. Robert T. Butterfield. Jour. Wildlife Mgt., Menasha, vol.14, no.2, pp.244-246, Apr., 1950.

RACCOON MANAGEMENT. Robert T. Butterfield. Ohio Conserv. Bull., Columbus, vol.8, no.3, pp.20-21, illus., Mar., 1944.

FACTORS INFLUENCING THE RACCOON AND ITS MANAGEMENT IN SOUTHWESTERN VIRGINIA. William C. Kellner. MS thesis, Va. Poly. Inst., 1953.

FACTORS INFLUENCING THE RACCOON AND ITS MANAGEMENT IN SOUTHWESTERN VIRGINIA. John H. McLaughlin. MS thesis, Va. Poly. Inst., pp.33, 1953.

THE RACCOON RESPONDS TO GOOD MANAGEMENT. Werner O. Nagel. Missouri Conserv., Jefferson City, vol. 5, no.5, pp.2-3, 11, illus., May, 1944.

THE PLACE OF STOCKING IN GAME MANAGEMENT. Frank P. Nelson. S.C. Wildl., 2 (1): 2-3, illus., Winter, 1955.

RACCOON MANAGEMENT IN CENTRAL OHIO. Norman A. Preble. Ohio Wildl. Res. Sta., Release 161, pp.9, Apr., 1941.

THE STATUS AND MANAGEMENT OF RACCOON IN CENTRAL OHIO. Norman A. Preble. MS thesis, Ohio State Univ., 1940.

RACCOONS TRANSPLANTED IN ALASKA. Victor B. Scheffer. Jour. Wildl. Mgt., 11 (4): 350-351, Oct., 1947.

ARTIFICIAL DENS FOR RACCOONS. Frederick W. Stuewer. Jour. Wildl. Mgt., 12 (3): 296-301, July, 1948.

'COON STOCKING NOT FOR MICHIGAN. Frederick W. Stuewer. Mich. Cons., 10 (8): 3, 11, July, 1941.

MARSH RACCOON CONTROL. Norman Wilder, Henry Cofer, Robert Beck. Del. Bd. Game and Fish Comm., pp.2, June, 1951.

CLOSED SEASONS FAIL TO INCREASE 'COONS. Mich. Cons., 8 (1): 3, Sept., 1938.

(Procyon) Methods, Techniques

TAGGED RACCOONS--1943-44. Robert T. Butterfield. Ohio Conserv. Bull., Columbus, vol.8, no.7, p.11, July, 1944.

TRAPS, LIVE-TRAPPING, AND MARKING OF RACCOONS. Robert T. Butterfield. Jour. Mam., vol.35, no.3, pp.440-442, illus., Aug.20, 1954.

METHODS OF MEASURING PRODUCTIVITY IN RACCOONS. Glen C. Sanderson. Jour. Wildl. Mgt., 14 (4): 389-402, Oct., 1950.

(Procyon) Pelage, Coloration

ALBINISTIC SIBLING RACCOONS FROM FLORIDA. E. Ross Allen, Wilfred T. Neill. Jour. Mam., 37 (1): 120, Feb.28, 1956.

FUR CHARACTERISTICS OF TWO EASTERN RACCOONS. Herbert L. Dozier, Thora M. Plitt Hardy, Merle H. Markley. Jour. Mam., vol.29, no.4, pp.383-393, pls.2, tbls.2, Dec.31, 1948.

TWO ERYTHRISTIC RACCOONS FROM FLORIDA. Wilfred T. Neill. Jour. Mam., vol.34, no.4, p.500, Nov.13, 1953.

STUDIES OF MOLTING AND PRIMING OF THE FUR OF THE EASTERN RACCOON. Frederick W. Stuewer. Jour. Mam., 23 (4): 399-404, Nov., 1942.

(Procyon) Physiology

(DOES THE RACCOON (PROCYON LOTOR L.) REALLY HIBERNATE?) Haelt der Waschbaer (Procyon lotor L.) wirklich Winterschlaf? M. Eisentraut. Zool. Anzeiger, vol.151, nos.5-6, pp.98-101, Sept., 1953.

(HIBERNATION OF RACCOONS. CONTRIBUTION TO THE METABOLISM OF RACCOONS IN WINTER.) Winterruhe oder Winterschlaf des Waschbaeren. Ein Beitrag zum Stoffwechsel des Waschbaeren zur Winterszeit. Raimund Neseni. Zeitschr. Saeugetierk., Berlin, vol.18, no.2, pp.81-109, Sept.28, 1952.

(HIBERNATION OF RACCOONS.) Der Winterschlaf des Waschbaeren. Hans Dietrich Rohrs. Der Deutsche Pelztierzuechter, Muenchen, Jahrg.1932, no.22, pp.529-533, fig., Nov.15, 1932.

ELECTROCARDIOGRAM OF THE RACCOON. Charles G. Wilber. Jour. Mam., 36 (2): 283-284, tables 2, May 26, 1955.

(Procyon) Psychology

DELAYED ALTERNATION IN RACCOONS. J. H. Elder, H. W. Nissen. Jour. Comp. Psych., vol.16, no.1, pp.117-135, Aug., 1933.

THE RACCOON--SOME MENTAL ATTRIBUTES. Leon F. Whitney. Jour. Mam., vol.14, no.2, pp.108-114, May, 1933.

(Procyon) Reproductive Biology and Young

EVIDENCE OF A LATE BIRTH FOR THE RACCOON. Edward V. Berardm. Jour. Mam., vol.33, no.2, pp.247-248, May 16, 1952.

(RACCOON BREEDING.) Waschbaerenzucht. Hermann Bode. Der Deutsche Pelztierzuechter, Munich, Jahrg.9, no.20, pp.387-391, illus., Oct.15, 1934.

SOME UNUSUAL JUVENILE RACCOON WEIGHTS. Robert S. Dorney. Jour. Mam., 34 (1): 122-123, Feb., 1953.

MARCH LITTERS OF RACCOONS (PROCYON LOTOR) IN MICHIGAN. John L. George, Merle Stitt. Jour. Mam., vol.32, no.2, p.218, May 21, 1951.

THE FOOD AND BREEDING HABITS OF THE RACCOON. W. J. Hamilton, Jr. Ohio Jour. Sci., 36 (3): 131-140, May, 1936.

GEOGRAPHIC VARIATION IN RACCOON LITTER SIZE. Leonard M. Llewellyn Proc. 8th Ann. N.E. Wildl. Conf., Jackson's Mill, W.Va., pp.1-7, Apr.1-4, 1952.

RACCOON EXPERIMENT. (2 LITTERS PER SEASON LEFT FEMALES IN AS GOOD CONDITION AS THOSE THAT HAD ONLY 1 LITTER.) Clarence Millard. Wis. Cons. Bull., 4 (3): 28-29, Mar., 1939.

ATTAINMENT OF SEXUAL MATURITY IN RACCOONS. Clifford H. Pope. Jour. Mam., vol.25, no.1, p.91, Feb., 1944.

(ESTRUS IN THE RACCOON.) Die Waschbaerenranz. Hans Dietrich Roehrs. Der Deutsche Pelztierzuechter, Munich, Jahrg.9, no.2, pp.34-35, illus., Jan.15, 1934.

REPRODUCTION OF RACCOONS IN MICHIGAN. Frederick W. Stuewer. Jour. Wildlife Mgt., Menasha, vol.7, no.1, pp.60-73, pl.3, Jan., 1943.

NOTES ON REPRODUCTION AND RATE OF INCREASE OF RACCOONS IN THE POST OAK REGION OF TEXAS. John E. Wood. Jour. Wildlife Mgt., vol.18, no.3, pp.409-410, July, 1955.

(Procyon) Taxonomy

THE SYSTEMATIC NAME OF THE BRAZILIAN CRAB-EATING RACCOON. N. Hollister. Proc. Biol. Soc. Wash., vol.27, p. 215, Oct.31, 1914.

DESCRIPTIONS OF TWO NEW RACCOONS. Gerrit S. Miller, Jr. Proc. Biol. Soc. Wash., vol.24, pp.3-6, Jan.28, 1911.

SIX NEW RACCOONS OF THE PROCYON LOTOR GROUP. E. W. Nelson, E. A. Goldman. Jour. Mam., vol.11, no.4, pp. 453-459, Nov., 1930.

THE TYPE LOCALITY OF URSUS LOTOR LINNE. E. W. Nelson, E. A. Goldman. Jour. Mam., vol.13, no.4, p.367, Nov., 1932.

## Mustelidae

(Mustelidae) General

NEW DISCOVERY AND A NEW HOME OF THE DWARF WEASEL, MUSTELA MINUTA POMEL, IN SWEDEN.) Ett nytt fynd och en ny lokal for dvargvessla, Mustela minuta Pomel i Sverige. Lars Bark, A. Lundstrom. Fauna och Flora, Stockholm, vol.3, pp.81-86, 1952.

WOLVERINE, MARTEN, FISHER. G.W. Bradt. Mich. Cons., vol.16, no.7, p.4, Aug., 1947.

(TUSSLE WITH A GLUTTON.) Nappatag med Jarv. Edor Burman. Svensk Jakt., Stockholm, vol.87, no.4, pp.92-94, illus., Apr. 20, 1949.

SUPPLEMENTARY NOTES ON THE MUSTELIDAE. John Edward Gray. Proc. Zool. Soc. London, p.680, figs.2, 1865.

MUSTELID MAMMALS FROM THE PLEISTOCENE OF NORTH AMERICA WITH SYSTEMATIC NOTES ON SOME RECENT MEMBERS OF THE GENERA MUSTELA, TAXIDEA AND MEPHITIS. E. R. Hall. Carnegie Inst. Washington (Contrib. Palaeont.), publ.no.473, pp.41-119, figs. 6, pls.5, Nov. 20, 1936.

(WOLVERINE FROM THE GRUBENLOCH.) Der Vielfrass (Gulo gulo L.) aus dem Grubenloch. Max Hilzheimer. Zeitschr. f. Saeugetierk., vol.11, pp.308-315, pls.14-16, Mar. 13, 1936.

(MAMMALS OF THE SOUTH AMERICAN EXPEDITIONS OF PROF. DR. KRIEG. 17. TAYRAS AND GRISONS.) Die Saeugetiere der Suedamerika-Expeditionen Prof. Dr. Kriegs. 17. Hyrare und Grisons (Tayra und Grison). Ingo Krumbiegel. Zool. Anzeiger, Leipzig, vol.139, nos 5-6 pp. 81-108, figs.9, Aug. 15, 1942.

(HUNTING MARTEN AND OTTER.) Ringa mard och vaka utter. K.H. Lundin. Svensk Jakt, Stockholm, vol.89, no.1, pp.9-11, illus., Jan. 20, 1951.

LUTRA BRASILIENSIS, LUTRA PARANENSIS, GALICTIS CRASSIDENS AND GALERA MACRODON. Alfred Nehring. Sitz.Ber. Gesell. Naturf. Freunde Berlin, no.10, pp. 144-152, figs.2, Dec. 21, 1886. (In German.)

WARNING COLORATION IN THE MUSTELINE CARNIVORA. R.I. Pocock. Proc. Zool. Soc. London, 1908, pp.944-959, Apr., 1909.

(HOW MANY FEMALES CAN A MALE MINK SERVICE?) Zu wieviel Faehen kann ein Nerzruede Verwendung finden? Kurt Preimel. Der Deutsche Pelztierzuechter, Muenchen, no.2, p.38, Jan. 15, 1931.

(ON THE QUESTION: MOUSE WEASEL OR DWARF WEASEL.)Zur Frage:Mauswiesel-Zwergwiesel. Hans Psenner. Saeugetierk. Mitteil., vol.5, no.4, p.172, Dec. 1, 1957.

BADGER AND ITS ALLIES. W.P. Pycraft. Illus. London News, vol.193, no.5179, p. 150, figs.3, July 23, 1938.

WOLVERINE, FISHER, AND MARTEN STUDIES IN A WILDERNESS REGION. Horace F. Quick. Trans. 18th N.Amer. Wildl. Conf., pp.513-532, 1953.

(ON THE SPECIES CHARACTERS OF PINE AND STONE MARTENS.) Ueber die Artmerkmale von Baum- und Steinmarder. G. Reinberger. Zeitschr. f. Saeugetierk., Berlin, vol.8, nos.3-6, pp.275-277, Dec. 20, 1933.

PINE MARTEN AND POLECAT. Mrs. Oliver Ruck. Jour. Soc. Preservation Fauna Empire, Hertford, n.s., pt.45, pp.14-17, Aug., 1942.

(ON THE REPRODUCTION BIOLOGY OF THE SIBERIAN SABLE (MARTES ZIBELLINA L.) AND THE EUROPEAN PINE MARTEN (MARTES MARTES L.).) Ueber die Fortpflanzungsbiologie vom sibirischen Zobel (Martes zibellina L.) und europaeischem Baumarder (Martes martes L.). Fritz Schmidt. Zeitschr. f. Saeugetierk., Berlin, vol.9, nos.1-3, pp.392-403, figs. 3, pl.18, Dec. 30, 1934.

(EVERMANN'S FITCHET (PUTORIUS EVERSMANNI LESS.) IN THE WERMUT STEPPES OF NORTHERN KAZAKHSTAN.) Eversmanns Iltis (Putorius eversmanni Less.) in den Wermut-Steppen des noerdlichen Kasakstan. M.K. Serebrennikov. Zeitschr. f. Saeugetierk., vol.4, nos.4-6, pp.205-212, pls.2, Feb. 10, 1930.

BADGERS AND WOLVERENES. (Popular Account of American Forms.) R.W. Schufeldt. Amer. Forestry, vol.28, pp. 105-112, figs.8, Feb., 1922.

(PROBLEM OF THE SPECIES CHARACTERISTICS AND HYBRIDIZATION OF PINE AND STONE MARTENS.) Zur Frage der Artmerkmale und der Bastardierung von Baum- und Steinmarder. Alfred Streuli. Zeitschr. f. Saeugetierk., Berlin, vol.7, nos.1-6, pp.58-72, figs.12, pls.1-5, Dec. 15, 1932.

(Mustelidae) Africa

WEASELS AND OTTERS OF NIGERIA. D.R. Rosevear. Nigerian Field, vol.5, no.3, pp.111-113, figs.3, July, 1936.

ON A NEW AFRICAN GENUS OF MUSTELIDAE. Oldfield Thomas. Ann. and Mag. Nat. Hist., ser.6, vol.13, no.78, pp.522-524, June, 1894.

(Mustelidae) Anatomy

MUSCULAR ANATOMY OF THREE MUSTELID MAMMALS, MEPHITIS, SPILOGALE, AND MARTES. E. Raymond Hall. Univ. Calif. Publ. Zool., vol.30, no.2, pp.7-38, illus., Sep. 14, 1926.

(THE LARYNX OF MUSTELIDAE.) Sur le larynx des mustelidés. P. Morel, G. Thiery. Mammalia, Paris, vol.17, no.3, pp.187-188, illus., Sep., 1953.

AUDITORY BULLA AND OTHER CRANIAL CHARACTERS IN THE MUSTELIDAE. R.I. Pocock. Proc. Zool. Soc. London, pt.3, pp. 473-486, Sep., 1921.

BACULUM OR OS PENIS OF SOME GENERA OF MUSTELIDAE. R.I. Pocock. Ann. and Mag. Nat. Hist., London, ser.9, vol.1, pp. 307-312, fig.1, Apr., 1918.

EXTERNAL CHARACTERS OF AN AMERICAN BADGER (TAXIDAE TAXUS) AND AN AMERICAN MINK (MUSTELA VISON), RECENTLY EXHIBITED IN THE SOCIETY'S GARDENS. R.I. Pocock. Proc. Zool. Soc. London, pt.1, pp.17-25, Apr., 1925.

(Mustelidae) Economic Importance

CLOSED SEASON NEEDED FOR FISHER, MARTEN AND WOLVERINE IN CALIFORNIA. Joseph Dixon. California Fish and Game, vol.11, pp.23-25, fig.1, Jan., 1925.

NOTES ON FUR-BEARERS. (Mustelids--their values, numbers in western national forests, causes of depletion, and restoration.) William H. Marshall. Univ. Idaho Bull., vol.33, no.22, pp.82-83, Dec., 1938.

STUDY OF THE FUR TRADE, WITH EMPHASIS ON THE NORTH AMERICAN MUSTELIDAE FURBEARERS. Joseph J. Shomon. MS thesis, Univ. Mich., 1947.

FISHER AND OTTER TAKE, FALL AND WINTER 1953-54. New York Conservation Dept., N.Y. State Cons., vol.8, no.5, p. 32, Apr.-May, 1954.

(Mustelidae) Eurasia

MUSTELIDS FROM THE ASIATIC EXPEDITIONS. Glover M. Allen. Amer. Mus. Nov., no.358, pp.1-12, July 10, 1929.

NOTE ON THE BEECH-MARTEN AND BADGER OF CRETE. G.E.H. Barrett-Hamilton. Ann. and Mag. Nat. Hist., ser. 7, vol.4, pp.383-384, Nov., 1899.

MATERIALS ON THE BIOLOGY AND AGRICULTURAL SIGNIFICANCE IN SIBERIA OF THE POLECAT AND OTHER SMALL PREDATORS OF THE FAMILY MUSTELIDAE. M.D. Zverev. Trudy po Zashchite Rastenii Sibiri (Bull. Plant Protection Siberia), Novosibirsk, vol.1, no.8, pp.5-46, tbls., 1931. (In Russian.)

(Mustelidae) Fossils

NOTE ON THE HABITS OF ENHYDRICTIS GALICTOIDES, WITH DESCRIPTION OF SOME LIMB-BONES OF THE MUSTELID FROM THE PLEISTOCENE OF SARDINIA. Dorothea M.A. Bate. Proc. Zool. Soc. London, pt.2, pp.241-245, figs.2, July 4, 1935.

NEW MUSTELID FROM THE LOWER SIWALIK BEDS OF NORTHERN INDIA. (Mustela lydekkeri.) Edwin H. Colbert. Amer. Mus. Novitates, no.605, pp.3, fig.1, Mar. 30, 1933.

HYPSOPARIA BOZEMANENSIS; A NEW GENUS AND SPECIES OF LEPTARCTINE MUSTELID FROM THE LATE MIOCENE MADISON VALLEY FORMATION OF MONTANA. John A. Dorr, Jr. Ann. Carnegie Mus., vol.33, ar.9, pp.179-184, illus., June 1, 1954.

LOWER JAW OF MARTINOGALE ALVEODENS HALL. David Hosbrook Dunkle. Bull. Univ. Kansas, Sci. Bull., vol.25, no.8, pp.181-185, pl.21, June 1, 1938; vol. 25, no.8, pp.181-184, pl.21, July 10, 1939.

(THE CEREBRAL PALLIUM OF ARCTOID CARNIVORES AND FOSSIL POTAMOTHERIUM, IN PARTICULAR.) A propos du pallium cerebral des carnivores arctoides et du Potamotherium fossile, en particulier. Madeleine Friant. Comptes Rendus Acad. Sci., Paris, vol.239, no.1, pp.104-105, July 5, 1954.

SKULL AND SKELETON OF A MUSTELID, BRACHYPSALIS, FROM THE MIOCENE OF NORTHEASTERN COLORADO. Edwin Galbreath. Univ. Kansas Paleont. Contrib., Vertebrata, art.5, pp.1-15, illus., June 1, 1955.

NEW MUSTELID CARNIVORE FROM THE NEOCENE BEDS OF NORTHWESTERN NEBRASKA. C. Lewis Gazin. Jour. Wash. Acad. Sci., vol.26, no.5, pp.199-207, figs.3, May 15, 1936. (Craterogale, C. simus.)

NOTES ON FOSSIL MUSTELIDS FROM THE UPPER PLIOCENE OF IDAHO AND TEXAS. C. Lewis Gazin. Jour. Mamm., vol.18, no.3, pp.363-364, Aug. 14, 1937.

UPPER PLIOCENE MUSTELIDS FROM THE SNAKE RIVER BASIN OF IDAHO. C. Lewis Gazin. Jour. Mamm., vol.15, no.2, pp.137-149, figs.5, May, 1934.

NEW MUSTELID GENUS FROM THE PLIOCENE OF CALIFORNIA. E. Raymond Hall. Jour. Mamm., vol.16, no.2, pp.137-138, figs.3, May, 1935.

MUSTELID MAMMALS FROM THE PLEISTOCENE OF NORTH AMERICA. WITH SYSTEMATIC NOTES ON SOME RECENT MEMBERS OF THE GENERA MUSTELA, TAXIDEA AND MEPHITIS. E. Raymond Hall. Carnegie Inst. Wash., Publ. no.473, pp.41-119, figs.6, pls.5, Nov. 20, 1936.

THREE NEW GENERA OF MUSTELIDAE FROM THE LATER TERTIARY OF NORTH AMERICA. E. Raymond Hall. Jour. Mamm., vol.11, no.2, pp.146-154, pls.7-8, May 9, 1930.

(CYRNAONYX ANTIQUA, A LUTRINE FROM THE EUROPEAN PLEISTOCENE.) Carnaonyx antiqua, eine Lutrine aus dem europaeischen Pleistocaen. H. Helbing. Ver. Schweiz. Nat. Ges., vols.116-117, p.337, 1935-36.

(KNOWLEDGE OF THE MIOCENE "MUSTELA" IBETHOIDES BLAINVILLE.) Zur Kenntnis der miocaenen "Mustela" zibethoides Blainville. H. Helbing. Eclogae geologicae Helvetiae, Basel, vol.23, no.2, pp.637-644.

(ON THE DEFINITION OF THE GENUS TROCHICTIS.) Zur Definition des Genus Trochictis. H. Helbing. Eclogae Geologicae Helvetiae, vol.20, no.2, pp.302-307, figs. 3, 1927.

PANNONICTIS PLIOCAENICA N.G., N.SP., A NEW GIANT MUSTELID FROM THE LATE PLIOCENE OF HUNGARY. Theodor Kormos. Annales Inst. Regii Hungarici Geologici, Budapest, vol.29, no.3, pp. 167-177, pl.3, Apr. 30, 1931.

(TIGER POLECAT, THE POLECAT AND THE MINK IN THE HUNGARIAN PLEISTOCENE.) Tigrisgoreny, Gorény és Nyérc a Magyar Pleisztocénben. M. Kretzoi. Foldtani Kozlony, vol.72, pp.237-255, figs.3; pp.323-344, figs.3, pl.23, 1942.

NOTICE OF THE DISCOVERY OF PLESIOGULO BRACHYGNATHUS IN THE SIWALIK MEASURES OF INDIA. G. Edward Lewis. Amer. Jour. Sci., vol.26, July, 1933.

ON THE SKULL OF BUNAELURUS, A MUSTELINE FROM THE WHITE RIVER OLIGOCENS. W.D. Matthew. Bull. Amer. Mus. Nat. Hist., New York, vol.16, art. 12, pp.137-140, figs.3, Apr. 7, 1902.

LEPTARCTINES FROM THE FLORIDA MIOCENE (CARNIVORA, MUSTELIDAE). Stanley J. Olsen. Amer. Mus. Novitates, New York, vol.1861, pp.1-7, illus., Dec. 6, 1957.

SMALL MUSTELID FROM THE THOMAS FARM MIOCENE. Stanley J. Olsen. Breviora, no.51, pp.5, Jan. 27, 1956.

ON THE STRUCTURE OF EXTREMITIES OF PARATAXIDEA CRASSA ZDANSKY. J.A. Orlov. Doklady Akad. Nauk SSSR, Moscow, n.s., vol.22, no.8, pp.527-529, Mar. 15, 1939.

(PERUNIINAE A NEW SUBFAMILY OF MARTENS FROM THE NEOCENE ERA.) Peruniiae, novoe podsemeistoo kunitz iz neogena evrazii. J.A. Orlov. Trudi Paleon. Inst., Akad. Nauk SSSR, Moscow, vol.10, no.3, pp.56, 1947.

TERTIARY CARNIVORA OF WEST SIBERIA. II. MELINAE. TERTIARY MAMMALIA AND THE LOCALITIES OF THEIR REMAINS. J.A. Orlov. Trav. Inst. Paleont., Moscow and Leningrad, vol.8, no.3, pp.5-29, figs.17, 1931. (In Russian with English summary.)

TERTIARY CARNIVORA OF THE WEST SIBERIA. III. MUSTELINAE. TERTIARY MAMMALIA AND THE LOCALITIES OF THEIR REMAINS. J.A. Orlov. Trav. Inst. Paleont., Moscow and Leningrad, vol.8, no.3, pp.30-39, figs.8, 1931. (In Russian with English summary.)

GENERA TROCHICTIS, ENHYDRICTIS, AND TROCHARION, WITH REMARKS ON THE TAXONOMY OF THE MUSTELIDAE. Guy E. Pilgrim. Proc. Zool. Soc. London, pt.4, pp.845-867, fig.1, pls.2, Jan. 6, 1933.

(A MUSTELID OF GENUS GALICTIS OF THE EOQUATERNARY BUENOS AIRES

PROVINCE.) Un mustelido del genero Galictis del eocuatario de la provincia de Buenos Aires. Osvaldo A. Reig. Ameghiniana, vol.1, nos.1-2, pp.33-47, illus., 1957.

(PRELIMINARY NOTE ON A NEW GENUS OF FOSSIL MUSTELIDS OF THE PLEISTOCENE IN THE REPUBLIC OF ARGENTINA.) Note préliminaire sur un nouveau genre de mustelides fossiles du Pleistocene de la Republique Argentine. (Stipanicicia, S. pettorutii.) Osvaldo A. Reig. Mammalia, Paris, vol.20, no.3, pp.223-230, Sep., 1956.

ANATOMY OF POTAMOTHERIUM, AN OLIGOCENE LUTRINE. R.J.G. Savage. Proc. Zool. Soc. London, vol.129, no.2, pp.153-244, pls.1-3, Oct. 15, 1957.

PALAEOGALE AND ALLIED EARLY MUSTELIDS. George Gaylord Simpson. Amer. Mus. Novitates, New York, no. 1320, pp.14, figs.2, May 28, 1946.

ASIATIC GENUS EOMELLIVORA IN THE PLIOCENE OF CALIFORNIA. Chester Stock, E. Raymond Hall. Jour. Mamm., vol.14, no.1, pp.63-65, pl.4, Feb., 1933.

ON THE AFFINITIES OF LEPTARCTUS PRIMUS LEIDY. J.L. Wortman. Bull. Amer. Mus. Nat. Hist., vol.6, art.8, pp. 229-231, 1894.

(Mustelidae) Methods, Techniques

CONTROL BY LIGHT OF REPRODUCTION IN FERRETS AND MINK. John Hammond, Jr. Nature, London, vol.167, no.4239, pp.150-151, Jan. 27, 1951.

(METHODOLOGY OF EVALUATING A HUNTING DISTRICT FOR FUR ANIMALS OF FAMILY MUSTELIDAE.) P. Jurgenson. Zool. Zhurn. (Zool.Jour.USSR), Moscow, vol.13, no.1, pp.117-127, 1934. (In Russian with German summary.)

NEW AGE INDEX IN MUSTELIDAE. V.A. Popov. Doklady Akad. Nauk SSSR, Moscow, vol.38, no.8, pp.258-260, illus., Mar. 20, 1943.

(Mustelidae) North America

THREE MAMMALS OF THE WEASEL FAMILY (MUSTELIDAE) ADDED TO THE QUEBEC LIST WITH DESCRIPTIONS OF TWO NEW FORMS. (Mustela vison lowii, Lutra canadensis chima.) Rudolph Martin Anderson. Ann. Rept., Provancher Soc.Nat.Hist.Canada, Quebec, pp.56-61, 1944.

FACTS OF INTEREST ABOUT UTAH MAMMALS. VI. ORDER CARNIVORA FAMILY MUSTELIDAE. (Mink, Otter.) Jack H. Berryman. Utah Fish and Game Bull., Salt Lake City, vol.7, no.1, pp.6-8, illus., Jan.-Feb., 1949.

FACTS OF INTEREST ABOUT UTAH MAMMALS. VII. FAMILY MUSTELIDAE. Jack H. Berryman. Utah Fish and Game Bull., Salt Lake City, vol.7, no.2, pp.3-4, illus., Mar., 1949.

FUR-BEARING ANIMALS: A MONOGRAPH OF NORTH AMERICAN MUSTELIDAE. Elliot Coues. Dept. Interior, Misc.Publ., no.8, 1877.

NEW AMERICAN MUSTELIDS OF THE GENERA MARTES, GULO, AND LUTRA. E.A. Goldman. Proc. Biol. Soc. Wash., vol.48, pp.175-186, Nov. 15, 1935.

MUSTELIDAE--WYOMING'S WEASEL FAMILY. James E. Grasse. Wyoming Wild Life, Cheyenne, vol.13, no.1, pp. 12-14, illus., Jan., 1949.

WEASELS AND SKUNKS OF ILLINOIS. Donald F. Hoffmeister. Illinois Wildlife, Champaign, vol.5, no.2, p.10, illus., Mar., 1950.

NOTES ON THE OTTER (LUTRA CANADENSIS) AND SKUNKS (GENERA SPILOGALE AND MEPHITIS) OF ARIZONA. Edgar A. Mearns. Bull. Amer. Mus. Nat. Hist., New York, vol.3, no.2, pp.252-262, June 5, 1891.

WYOMING MUSTELIDAE. Charles Ritter. Wyoming Wild Life, Cheyenne, vol.7, no. 4, pp.5-6, 15-18, illus., Apr., 1942.

NOTES ON WOLVERINE AND FISHER IN THE STATE OF WASHINGTON. Victor B. Scheffer. Murrelet, vol.19, nos.1-2, pp. 8-10, Jan.-May, 1938.

HOW SKUNKS DEFEND THEMSELVES. (Popular Account of North American Mustelidae.) R.W. Shufeldt. Amer.Forestry, vol.28, pp.26-29, 41, figs.10, Jan., 1922.

(Mustelidae) Parasites

INCIDENCE OF WORM PARASITES IN MINNESOTA MUSTELIDAE AND HOST LISTS AND KEYS TO NORTH AMERICAN SPECIES. Arnold B. Erickson. Amer. Midland Nat., vol.36, no.2, pp.494-509, Sep., 1946.

NEW HOST RECORDS OF NEMATODES FROM MUSTELIDAE (CARNIVORA). Banner Bill Morgan. Jour.Parasitol., Lancaster, vol. 29, no.2, pp.158-159, Apr., 1943.

PARASITIC WORMS OF MUSTELIDAE OF THE MOSCOW ZOOLOGICAL GARDENS. A.M. Petrov. Proc. Moscow Zool. Park, vol.1, pp.202-231, 1940. (In Russian with English summary.)

ALARIA TAXIDEAE N. SP. FROM THE BADGER AND OTHER MUSTELIDS. Gustav Swanson, Arnold B. Erickson. Jour.Parasitol., vol.33, no.1, pp.17-19, Feb., 1946.

(Mustelidae) Physiology

(SENSORY PHYSIOLOGICAL AND PSYCHOLOGICAL INVESTIGATIONS OF MUSTELIDS.) Sinnesphysiologische und psychologische Untersuchungen an Musteliden. Detlev Mueller. Zeitschr. f. vergleichende Physiologie, Berlin, vol.12, pt.2, pp.293-328, July 30, 1930.

REACTIONS OF SOME MUSTELIDAE TO THE TEMPERATURE GRADIENT. A.L. Ponomarev. Zool. Jour. USSR, Moscow, vol.23, no.1, pp.51-55, figs.3, tbls.2, 1944. (With English summary.)

CHARACTERISTICS FOR THE TRANSPORT OF OXYGEN BY THE BLOOD OF MINK AND MARTEN. Walter J. Scott et al. Jour. Cell. and Comp. Physiol., Philadelphia, vol.14, no.3, pp.281-286, figs.2, Dec. 20, 1939.

(Mustelidae) Reproductive Biology

DURATION OF PREGNANCY IN CERTAIN MUSTELIDS. Oliver P. Pearson. Jour. Exp. Biol., vol.95, no.1, pp.21-35, Feb., 1944.

DURATION OF PREGNANCY IN MARTEN, MINK, AND RELATED SPECIES. Oliver P. Pearson, Robert K. Enders. Fur of Canada, Winnipeg, vol.9, no.8, pp.3-6, May, 1944; Amer. Fur Breeder, Duluth, vol. 17, no.1, pp.24, 26, 28, fig.1, July, 1944; no.2, pp.26, 28, 30, 42, Aug., 1944; Nat. Fur News, Denver, vol.16, no.7, pp.10, 14-16, Aug., 1944.

DELAYED IMPLANTATION IN THE LONG-TAILED WEASEL (MUSTELA FRENATA), THE SHORT-TAILED WEASEL (MUSTELA CICOGNANI), AND THE MARTEN (MARTES AMERICANA). Philip L. Wright. Anat. Rec., Philadelphia, vol.83, no.3, pp.341-353, pls. 2, July 25, 1942.

(Mustelidae) Taxonomy

NOTES AND DESCRIPTIONS OF SOME NEW SPECIES AND SUBSPECIES OF MUSTELIDAE. G.E.H. Barrett-Hamilton. Ann. and Mag. Nat. Hist., ser.7, vol.13, pp.388-395, May, 1904.

(SYSTEMATIC STUDY OF THE PENILE BONE OF MAMMALS (CONTINUATION). CARNIVORES. FAMILY MUSTELIDAE.) Etude systematique de l'os pénien des Mammifères (suite). Carnivores. Famille des Mustelides. Robert Didier. Mammalia, Paris, vol.11, nos.1-2, pp.30-43, figs.8, Mar.-June, 1947.

REVISION OF THE GENERA AND SPECIES OF MUSTELIDAE CONTAINED IN THE BRITISH MUSEUM. John Edward Gray. Proc. Zool. Soc. London, pp.100-154, figs.3, pl.7, 1865.

TECHNICAL NAMES OF THE AFRICAN MUISHOND (GENUS ZORILLA) AND THE COLOMBIAN HOG-NOSED SKUNK (GENUS CONEPATUS). Philip Hershkovitz. Proc. Biol. Soc. Wash., vol.62, pp.13-16, Mar. 17, 1949.

ZORILLA. I. GEOFFROY AND SPILOGALE GRAY, GENERIC NAMES FOR AFRICAN AND AMERICAN POLECATS, RESPECTIVELY. Philip Hershkovitz. Jour. Mamm., vol. 34, no.3, pp.378-382, Aug. 14, 1953.

TECHNICAL NAMES OF THE COMMON SKUNK AND MINK OF THE EASTERN STATES. N. Hollister. Proc. Biol. Soc. Wash., vol.27, p.215, Oct. 31, 1914.

ON THE EXTERNAL CHARACTERS AND CLASSIFICATION OF THE MUSTELIDAE. R.I. Pocock. Proc. Zool. Soc. London, for 1921, pt.4, pp.803-837, Jan., 1922.

(Mink) General

THE MINK. Rod Amundson. Wildlife in North Carolina, Raleigh, vol.14, no.1, pp. 4-6, illus., Jan., 1950.

MIGHTY MINK. Elizabeth Bachmann. Conserv.Volunteer, St. Paul, vol.12, no.71, pp. 17-19, July-Aug., 1949.

PUTOR, THE MINK'S LAST FIGHT. C.T. Barnes. Nature Mag., vol.1, no.4, pp.17-20, Apr., 1923.

MISCELLANEOUS NOTES. (Mink Stomachs Distended by Kidney Worms.) Ned Dearborn. Jour. Mamm., vol.27, no.2, p.178, May, 1946.

VISON, THE MINK. (Fictional Biography of Mink and Associates.) John L. George, Jean George. Dutton, p.184, 1949.

FURY IN A FUR COAT. (Mink Decline in Ohio.) Merill C. Gilfillan. Ohio Cons.Bull., vol.17, no.8 (sic), pp.2-3, 32, illus., Sep., 1953.

(DANGER OF MINK WITH RESPECT TO ITS SPREAD IN SWEDEN.) Minkfaran i belysning av minkens utbredning i Sverige. H. Hamilton. Svensk Jakt, Stockholm, vol. 86, no.3, pp.58-63, illus., Mar. 20, 1948.

THE MINK. Francis X. Lueth. Illinois Conserv., Springfield, vol.9, no.2, pp.20-21, Summer Issue, 1944.

LABRADOR MINK. L.D.McClintock. Fur of Canada, Winnipeg, vol.12, no.12, p.17, Aug., 1947.

(POSTWAR SAMLAND MINK FIND.) Ein Nachkriegsfund des Nerzes aus dem Samland. Using D. Muller. Zeitschr. f. Saeugetierk., Berlin, vol.12, no.3, pp. 327-328, July 15, 1938.

THE MINK (MUSTELA VISON). Charles Ritter. Wyoming Wild Life, Cheyenne, vol. 7, no.6, pp.5-6, illus., June, 1942.

MINKS. S.V. Sedlak. Pennsylvania Game News, Harrisburg, vol.15, no.5, pp.14-15, illus., Aug., 1944.

LITTLE WARRIER OF THE WILDS. (Account of Mink.) Sidel B. Swenson. Fins, Feathers and Fur, no.69, pp.7, 15-16, illus., Jan., 1929.

(Mink) Age Criteria

BACULUM AS AN AGE CRITERION IN MINK. William H. Elder. Jour. Mamm., vol.32, no.1, pp.43-50, Feb., 1951.

AGE CRITERIA IN MINK, MUSTELA VISON. R.R. Lechleitner. Jour.Mamm., vol.35, no.4, pp.496-503, illus., Nov., 1954.

(Mink) Anatomy

HISTOCHEMICAL STUDY OF THE REPRODUCTIVE TRACT OF THE FEMALE MINK (MUSTELA VISON). Allen C. Enders. PhD thesis, Harvard Univ., pp.136, photomicrographs 97, 1954.

HISTOLOGICAL OBSERVATIONS ON THE CHORIOALLANTOIC PLACENTA OF THE MINK. Allen C. Enders. Anat. Record, Philadelphia, vol.127, no.2, pp.231-246, Feb., 1957.

SEX RATIO AND SIZE VARIATION IN SOUTH DAKOTA MINK. Paul L. Errington. Jour. Mamm., vol.17, no.3, p.287, Aug., 1936.

GROSS ANATOMY OF THE DIGESTIVE SYSTEM OF THE MINK. I. HEADGUT AND FOREGUT. II. MIDGUT AND THE HINDGUT. Robert A. Kainer. Amer. Jour.Vet. Res., vol.15, no.54, pp.82-97, illus., Jan., 1954.

CHROMOSOMES OF THE MINK. Richard M. Shackelford, Louise Wipf. Nat. Fur News, Denver, vol.19, no.6, p.12, July, 1947; Fur of Canada, Winnipeg, vol.12, no.10, pp.28-29, July, 1947; Amer. Fur Breeder, Duluth, vol.20, no.1, pp.26, 28, July, 1947.

(Mink) Commercial Breeding

MINK BREEDING SEASON. Jesse Ames. Amer. Fur Breeder, vol.4, no.8, p.14, Feb., 1932.

RELATIVE PRODUCTIVITY UNDER DIFFERENT SYSTEMS OF MINK MATINGS. Charles F. Bassett. Fur of Canada, Winnipeg, vol.9, no.12, pp.14-15, Sep., 1944.

RELATIVE PRODUCTIVITY UNDER DIFFERENT SYSTEMS OF MINK MATINGS. Charles F. Bassett, et al. Nat. Fur News, Denver, vol.16, no.3, pp.5, 20-21, Apr., 1944; Amer. Fur Breeder, Duluth, vol.16, no.11, pp.16, 18, 20, 22, illus., June, 1944.

MINK BREEDING. C.H. Booth. Amer. Fur Breeder, vol.1, no.1, pp.4-5; no.2, pp.6-7, 1928.

FACTORS AFFECTING REPRODUCTION IN MINK. E. Rendle Bowness. Nat. Fur News, Denver, vol.22, no.2, pp.11, 26-27, 30-31, Mar., 1950.

FALL FACTS FOR MINK BREEDERS. E. Randle Bowness. Amer. Fur Breeder, Duluth, vol.14, no.4, pp.28-31, Oct., 1941.

HANDLING OF MINK BREEDERS. E. Rendle Bowness. Amer. Fur Breeder, Duluth, vol.20, no.9, pp.6, 8, 10, 12, 14, illus., Mar., 1948.

MINK MATING PROBLEMS. E. Rendle Bowness. Fur of Canada, Winnipeg, vol. 9, no.9, pp.18-22, June, 1944; Nat. Fur News, Denver, vol.16, no.7, pp.8, 18-20, Aug., 1944; Amer. Fur Breeder, Duluth, vol.17, no.7, pp.40-44, Jan., 1945; Fur-Fish-Game, Harding's Mag., Columbus, vol.79, no.7, pp.28-30, July, 1945.

SOME TIMELY SUGGESTIONS FOR MINK MATING. E. Rendle Bowness. Amer. Nat. Fur and Market Jour., Wausau, vol.23, no. 7, pp.5-6, Feb., 1945.

MINK BREEDING--ELEMENTARY PRINCIPLES. Robert K. Enders. U.S.Dept. Int., Fish and Wildl. Serv., Leaflet no.169, pp. 4,fig.1, Aug., 1940; Amer. Fur Breeder, Duluth, vol.13, no.5, pp.6, 8, Nov., 1940.

MINK BREEDING THROUGH THE MICROSCOPE. Robert K. Enders. Amer. Fur Breeder, Duluth, vol.11, no.7, pp.6, 8, figs.4, Jan., 1939.

MULTIPLE OVULATION IN MINK BREEDING. Robert K. Enders. Amer. Fur Breeder, Duluth, vol.21, no.10, pp.6, 8, Apr., 1949; Amer. Nat. Fur and Market Jour., Wausau, vol.27, no.9, pp.5-6, Apr., 1949; Black Fox Mag. and Modern Mink Breeder, New York, vol.32, no.12, pp.10, 22, Apr., 1949; Fur of Canada, Winnipeg, vol.14, no.7, pp. 6, 9, Apr., 1949; Nat. Fur News, Denver, vol.21, no.4, pp.20, 29, May, 1949.

PRIMER FOR MINK BREEDERS. Robert K. Enders. Amer. Fur Breeder, Duluth, vol.12, no.9, pp.6, 8, Mar., 1940.

THEORY AND PRACTICE IN MINK BREEDING. Robert K. Enders. Amer. Fur Breeder, Duluth, vol.13, no.11, pp.6-7, figs.3, May, 1941.

BREEDING MINK. G.J. Estinson. Amer. Fur Breeder, vol.1, no.4, pp.16-18, illus., Oct., 1928.

JULY SUGGESTIONS FOR MINK BREEDERS. James Freer. Amer. Fur Breeder, vol.2, no. 1, pp.6-8, July, 1929.

TIMELY SUGGESTIONS FOR THE CONSIDERATION OF THE MINK BREEDER. James Freer. Amer. Fur Breeder, vol.1, no.9, p.8, Mar., 1929.

MINK BREEDING PROBLEMS. Mrs. James Freer. Amer. Fur Breeder, vol.11, no.3, pp.23-24, Sep., 1929.

HANDLING MINK DURING THE MATING AND WHELPING SEASON. Frank C. Gothier. Amer. Fur Breeder, vol.1, no.10, pp.17-19, Apr., 1929.

MATING MINK. Theo. P. Grahl. Amer. Fur Breeder, St. Peter, Minn., vol.7, no.8, pp.12-13, Feb., 1935.

HOW TO MATE MINK SUCCESSFULLY. Clarence S. Grubbs. Nat. Fur News, Denver, vol.17, no.2, pp.5, 12-13, 18-19, Mar., 1945.

LITTER LOSSES IN MINK. Clarence S. Grubbs. Nat. Fur News, Denver, vol. 17, no. 5, pp. 7, 14, 16, 19, 21, June, 1945.

BREEDING MINK FOR THEIR FUR. George F. Norton. New York Swenarton Stationery Co., pp. 22, illus., pl., 1913.

HOW TO BREED QUALITY IN SILVERBLU MINK. F. LeGrand Noyes. Amer. Fur Breeder, Duluth, vol. 16, no. 9, pp. 20-22, Mar., 1944.

MINK BREEDING-- TRIAL AND ERROR. Lauri O. Pernu, Esther A. Pernu. Amer. Fur Breeder, Duluth, vol. 21, no. 9, pp. 16, 18, 20, Mar., 1949.

MINK BREEDING. H.B. Plumer. Amer. Fur Breeder, vol.11, no.2, pp.17-18, Aug., 1929.

(ARTIFICIAL FERTILIZATION IN MINK BREEDING.) Die kuenstliche Befruchtung in der Nerzzucht. Paul H. Seck. Der Deutsche Pelztierzuechter, Munich, Jahrg.9, no.5, pp.95-96, Mar. 1, 1934.

SUPERFETATION IN THE RANCH MINK. Richard M. Shackleford. Amer. Nat., Lancaster, vol.86, no.830, pp.311-319, illus., Sep.-Oct., 1952.

SOME POINTS ABOUT MINK BREEDING. Hans Viola. Fur of Canada, Winnipeg, vol. 10, no.5, p.18, Feb., 1945.

"ACIDOSIS-STERILITY" IN MALE MINK. Lawrence Wakefield. Amer. Fur Breeder, Duluth, vol.15, no.2, p.16, Aug., 1942.

ARTIFICIAL INSEMINATION IN MINK. E.E. Wegner. Fur of Canada, Winnipeg, vol.14, no.8, p.14, May 1949; Black Fox Mag., New York, vol.33, no.2, pp.5, 19-20, June, 1949; Nat. Fur News, Denver, vol.21, no.5, pp.15, 29, June, 1949.

HOW TO MATE MINK. L.E. Whiting. Amer. Fur Breeder, vol.1, no.9, pp.16-17, Mar., 1929.

(MINK BREEDER IN WINTER.) Die Nerzzucht im Winter. F. Zigan. Der Deutsche Pelztierzuechter, Munich, Jahrg.9, no.2, pp.32-33, illus., Jan. 15, 1934.

(Mink) Commercial Feeding

FEEDING AND CARE OF MINK. Paul M. Allyn. Fur-Fish-Game (Harding's Mag.), Columbus, vol.79, no.1, pp.28-29, Jan., 1946.

MEATLESS MEALS FOR MINK. Fred W. Ashley, Jack L. Houghton. Amer. Fur Breeder, Duluth, vol.19, no.11, pp.43-44, May, 1947.

PRACTICAL ECONOMIES IN FEEDING MINK KITS. Chas. F. Bassett. Fur of Canada, Winnipeg, vol.14, no.10, pp. 4, 6, July 1949; Nat. Fur News, Denver, vol.21, no.6, pp.16-17, 29, 31, July, 1949; Amer. Nat. Fur and Market Jour. Wausau, vol.28, no.10, pp.15, 21-22, May, 1950.

PROTEIN REQUIREMENT OF GROWING MINKS. Charles F. Bassett. Amer. Nat. Fur and Market Jour., Wausau, vol.27, no.3, pp.7-8, Oct., 1948; Nat. Fur News, Denver, vol.20, no.11, pp.19, 45-46, Dec., 1948; Amer. Fur Breeder, Duluth, vol.21, no.6, pp.52, 54, Dec., 1948.

RESULTS OF 13 YEARS EXPERIMENT IN FEEDING MINK. Charles F. Bassett. Black Fox Mag., New York, vol.32, no.3, pp.10-11, 20, July 1948.

SOME COMMON FALLACIES IN OUR PRESENT MINK FEEDING PRACTICES. Charles F. Bassett. Fur of Canada, Winnipeg, vol.13, no.10, pp.3-4, 6, July, 1948; Nat. Fur News, Denver, vol.20, no.7, pp.14, 34-38, Aug., 1948.

USING FISH MEAL AS A PARTIAL SUBSTITUTE FOR RAW MEAT IN THE YEAR AROUND MINK RATION. Charles F. Bassett. Amer. Fur Breeder, Duluth, vol.15, no.3, pp.12, 14, 16-17, 22, Sep., 1942.

COMPARATIVE VALUE OF POULTRY WASTE AND HORSE MEAT FOR FEEDING MINK. Charles F. Bassett, Ford Wilke. Amer. Fur Breeder, Duluth, vol.21, no.5, pp.40, 42, 44, Nov., 1948.

POULTRY WASTE AS MINK FEED. Charles F. Bassett, Ford Wilke. Nat. Fur News, Denver, vol.20, no.8, pp.14, 34, Sep., 1948.

VALUE OF POULTRY WASTE FOR FEEDING MINK. Charles F. Bassett, Ford Wilke. Amer. Nat. Fur and Market Jour., Wausau, vol.27, no.4, pp.5-6, Nov., 1948.

CRITICAL FACTORS AFFECTING MINK FEEDING AND HOUSING. E. Rendle Bowness. Black Fox Mag. and Modern Mink Breeder, New York, vol.34, no.4, pp.9-10, 23-24, Aug., 1950.

MINK FEEDING PROBLEM. Clarence S. Grubbs. Nat. Fur News, Denver, vol.17, no.1, pp.9, 23, Feb., 1945.

OUR PRESENT FEEDING PROBLEMS. G.R. Hartsough. Nat. Fur News, Denver, vol.17, no.7, pp.7, 26, Aug., 1946.

FRESH, CLEAN WATER IS A MINK NECESSITY. L.F. Jonas. Black Fox Mag., New York, vol.32, no.1, pp.15, 29-30, May, 1948.

MINK AND WATER. L.F. Jonas. Nat. Fur News, Denver, vol.20, no.5, pp.15, 26, June, 1948.

SALMON CANNERY WASTE FOR MINK FEED. James R. Leekley et al. U.S. Fish and Wildl. Serv., Fishery Leafl. no. 405, pp.1-31, illus., Nov., 1952.

MINK RATIONS AND THEIR MANAGEMENT. S.J. McCorkle. Nat. Fur News, Denver, vol. 23, no.2, pp.11, 21, 27, 30-31, Mar., 1951.

DISCUSSION ON "FORCE FEEDING THE SICK MINK." George L. Ott. Amer. Nat. Fur and Market Jour. Wausau, vol.27, no.7, p. 19, Feb., 1949.

FORCE-FEEDING THE SICK MINK. George L. Ott. Fur of Canada, Winnipeg, vol.14, no.4, p.21, Jan., 1949.

HOW TO FEED SICK MINK. George L. Ott. Black Fox Mag., New York, vol.32, no.10, p.14, Feb., 1949.

SOME NUTRITIONAL STUDIES WITH MINK. S.E. Smith, J.K. Loosli. Nat. Fur News, vol.12, no.4, pp.3, 14, May, 1940.

MEAT REQUIREMENTS OF FEMALE MINK DURING REPRODUCTIVE CYCLE. C. Ford Wilke, Chas. F. Bassett. Amer. Fur Breeder, Duluth, vol.20, no.7, pp.42, 43, Jan., 1948; Amer. Fur and Market Jour., Wausau, vol. 26, no.8, pp.5-6, 26, Mar., 1948; Fur of Canada, Winnipeg, vol.13, no.4, pp.20, 22-23, Jan., 1948; vol.13, no.5, p.6, Feb., 1948; Nat. Fur News, Denver, vol.20, no.1, pp. 16, 34-35, Feb., 1948.

VALUE OF FAT IN THE DIET OF GROWING MINK. Ford Wilke, Chas. F. Bassett. Amer. Nat. Fur and Market Jour., Wausau, vol.27, no.2, p.11, Sep., 1948?

FUNCTIONS OF VITAMINS IN MINK FEEDS. A.L. Wright. Fur of Canada, Winnipeg, vol. 14, no.8, pp.3-4, May, 1949.

(Mink) Diseases and Parasites

MORPHOLOGY AND LIFE CYCLE OF EURYHELINIS MONORCHIS N. SP. (TREMATODA) FROM THE MINK. Donald J. Ameel. Jour. Parasitology, vol.24, no. 3, pp.219-224, June, 1938.

STUDIES ON THE LIFE HISTORY OF EUPARYPHIUM MELIS (TREMATODA: ECHINOSTOMIDAE). Paul C. Beaver. Jour. Parasitology, vol.27, no.1, pp.35-44, Feb., 1941.

ACARIASIS OF MINK. Frances R. Bushnell, O.J. Hummon. Fur of Canada, Winnipeg, vol.9, no.7, p.7, Apr., 1944.

DISEASES OF MINK. T.T. Chaddock. Amer. Fur Breeder, Duluth, vol.12, no.11, pp.6-7, May, 1940; vol.13, no.1, pp.8-9, July, 1940.

FACTS CONCERNING DISTEMPER IN MINK AND OTHER PRESENT DAY PROBLEMS. T.T. Chaddock. Amer. Fur Breeder, Duluth, vol.15, no.8, pp.18-22, photo, Feb., 1943.

NEWER KNOWLEDGE CONCERNING MINK DISTEMPER. T.T. Chaddock. Nat. Fur News, Denver, vol.16, no.3, pp.4, 18, 20, 23, 24, illus., Apr., 1944; Amer. Fur Breeder, Duluth, vol.16, no.11, pp.30, 32, 34-35, June, 1944.

CONTROL OF BOILS IN MINK. T.T. Chaddock. Fur of Canada, Winnipeg, vol.11, no.7, p.18, Apr., 1946.

FATTY DEGENERATION OF THE LIVER IN MINK. T.T. Chaddock. Fur of Canada, Winnipeg, vol.13, no.8, pp.3-4, May, 1948; Black Fox Mag., New York, vol.32, no.1, pp.13, 28; no.2, pp.14, 26, May, June, 1948; Nat. Fur News, Denver, vol. 20, no.5, pp.10, 29, 31, 34, June, 1948; Amer. Fur Breeder, Duluth, vol.21, no.1, pp.6, 8, 10, July, 1948.

GRUBS OR SCREW FLY IN MINK. T.T. Chaddock. Fur of Canada, Winnipeg, vol. 14, no.10, p.3, July, 1949; Nat. Fur News, Denver, vol.21, no.6, pp.14, 28, July, 1949.

PNEUMONIA AS IT OCCURS IN MINK. T. T. Chaddock. Fur of Canada, Winnipeg, vol.13, no.5, p.15, Feb., 1948.

MONORCHIDISM IN MINK. Merwyn Chapman. Amer. Fur Breeder, Duluth, vol.20, no.2, p.44, Aug., 1947.

COCCIDIOSIS IN MINK. H.C. Collins. Fur of Canada, Winnipeg, vol.14, no.5, p.12, Feb., 1949.

BOTULISM IN MINK IN SWEDEN. Z. von Dinter, K.E. Kull. Nord. Vet., vol.2, pp.286-301, 1950.

TREATMENT OF BOILS IN MINK. Howard R. Foreman. Amer. Fur Breeder, Duluth, vol.21, no.2, p.30, July, 1948.

BOTULISM IN MINK. John R. Gorham. Fur of Canada, Winnipeg, vol.15, no.9, pp.9-10, illus., June, 1950.

CAUSE AND PREVENTION OF BOTULISM IN MINK. John R. Gorham. Black Fox Mag. and Modern Mink Breeder, New York, vol. 34, no.2, pp.10, 22-23, June, 1950.

HERNIA IN MINK. John R. Gorham. Black Fox Mag., New York, vol.32, no.8, p.21, illus., Dec., 1948.

HYDROCEPHALUS IN MINK. John R. Gorham. Nat. Fur News, Denver, vol.19, no.3, p.10, Apr., 1947; Amer. Fur Breeder, Duluth, vol.19, no.12, p.20, illus., June, 1947; Fur of Canada, Winnipeg, vol.15, no.6, p. 11, Mar., 1950.

SCROTAL HERNIA IN MINK. John R. Gorham. Fur of Canada, Winnipeg, vol.14, no. 3, p.8, Dec., 1948.

SCROTAL HERNIA SELDOM APPEARS IN RANCH MINK. John R. Gorham. Amer. Nat. Fur and Market Jour., Wausau, vol.27, no.6, p.15, Jan., 1949.

SUPPURATIVE NEPHRITIS IN MINK. John R. Gorham. Fur of Canada, Winnipeg, vol. 14, no.2, p.33, Nov., 1948.

TULAREMIA KILLS MINK TOO. John R. Gorham. Amer. Fur Breeder, Duluth, vol. 23, no.1, p.15, July, 1950.

DISEASES AND PARASITES OF MINKS. John R. Gorham. U.S. Dept. Agric., Farmer's Bull., no.2050, pp.1-41, illus., Nov., 1952.

CARCINOMA (CANCER) OF THE SKIN IN MINK. John R. Gorham, E.R. Quortrup. Fur of Canada, Winnipeg, vol.14, no.1, p. 33, Oct., 1948; Nat. Fur News, Denver, vol.20, no.10, p.6, Nov., 1948; Amer. Fur Breeder, Duluth, vol.21, no.5, p.52, illus., Nov., 1948.

DISTEMPER AND ITS CONTROL IN MINK. Robert G. Green. Fur of Canada, Winnipeg, vol.10, no.12, p.3, Sep., 1945; Nat. Fur News, Denver, vol.17, no.10, pp.8, 52-53, Nov., 1945.

BOILS AND CALCULI IN MINK. Clarence S. Grubbs. Nat. Fur News, Denver, vol. 17, no.6, pp.9, 16, July, 1945.

SCREW FLY LARVAE AND CURRENT MINK PROBLEMS. Clarens S. Grubbs. Nat. Fur News, Denver, vol.17, no.4, pp.6, 20-21, 25, May, 1945.

OUTBREAK OF BOTULISM IN CAPTIVE MINK ON A FUR FARM IN COLORADO. I.C. Hall, G.W. Stiles. Jour. Bact., vol. 36, no.3, p.282, Mar., 1938.

STEATITIS (YELLOW FAT) IN MINK. G.R. Hartsough, John R. Gorham. Fur of Canada, Winnipeg, vol.14, no.10, pp.10-11, July, 1949; Nat. Fur News, Denver, vol.21, no.7, pp.13, 22, Aug., 1949.

ANTHRAX IN FARM-RAISED MINK IN OREGON. C.R. Howarth, L. Seghetti. Jour. Amer. Vet. Med. Assn., vol.94, no.4, pp.433-434, Apr., 1939.

NUTRITIONAL ANEMIA IN MINKS. Arnold H. Kennedy. Fur of Canada, Winnipeg, vol.11, no.8, p.3, May, 1946.

VETERINARIAN'S APPROACH TO DISEASE PROBLEMS IN THE MINK. Arnold H. Kennedy. Cornell Vet., Ithaca, vol.39, no.1, pp.64-68, 1949.

NUTRITIONAL ANAEMIA IN MINK. Ronald G. Law, Arnold H. Kennedy. Canadian Field Nat., vol.48, no.3, pp.47-49, Mar., 1934.

EIMERIA AND ISOSPORA OF THE MINK (MUSTELA VISON). Norman D. Levine. Jour. Parasitology, Lancaster, vol.34, no. 6, pp.486-492, Dec., 1948.

"YELLOW FAT" AS OBSERVED IN MINK. A.M. McDermid. Amer. Fur Breeder, Duluth, vol.19, no.11, p.32, May, 1947.

ON THE LIFE CYCLE AND TAXONOMIC RELATIONS OF CEPHALOPHALLUS OBSCURUS N.G., N.SP., AN INTESTINAL TREMATODE (LECITHODENDRIIDAE) OF MINK. Ralph W. Macy, Donald J. Moore. Jour. Parasitology, vol.40, no.3, pp.328-335, illus., June, 1954.

MY EXPERIENCES WITH MINK BOILS. Rudolph W. Menzel. Amer. Fur Breeder, vol.4, no.2, p.36, Aug., 1931.

KLEBSIELLA OZAENAE INFECTION IN RANCH RAISED MINKS. J. Anthony Morris, E.R. Quortrup. Amer. Nat. Fur and Market Jour., Wausau, vol.26, no.12, pp.20, 24, July, 1948.

KLEBSIELLA OZAENAE INFECTION OF MINK. J. Anthony Morris, E.R. Quortrup. Fur in Canada, Winnipeg, vol.13, no.2, pp.22-23, Nov., 1947; Nat. Fur News, Denver, vol.19, no.10, pp.40-41, 44, Nov., 1947; Amer. Fur Breeder, Duluth, vol.20, no.6, pp.54, 56, Dec., 1947.

REPORT OF FLESH FLIES IN MINK IN ALBERTA. J.G. O'Donoghue. Fur of Canada, Winnipeg, vol.14, no.2, p.8, Nov., 1948.

IDENTIFICATION OF CYSTINE CALCULI IN MINK. J.E. Oldfield et al. Proc. Soc. Exper. Biol. and Med., Utica, vol.91, no. 4, pp.560-561, Apr., 1956.

FOOD-BORNE INFECTIONS. (Mink) George L. Ott. Nat. Fur News, Denver, vol.20, no. 2, pp.10, 32, Mar., 1948; Amer. Fur Breeder, Duluth, vol.20, no.9, pp.22, 24, Mar., 1948; Fur of Canada, Winnipeg, vol.13, no. 7, p.14, Apr., 1948.

WHAT CAUSES BLADDER STONES? (Mink) George L. Ott. Amer. Fur Breeder, Duluth, vol.20, no.9, p.28, Mar., 1948.

SOME COMMON MINK DISEASES. Katherine E. Penn. Nat. Fur News, Denver, vol. 21, no.12, p.31, Jan., 1950.

STREPTOCOCCI INFECTIONS CAUSE MUCH TROUBLE ON MINK RANCHES. Katherine E. Penn. Amer. Nat. Fur and Market Jour., Wausau, vol.25, no.11, pp.12-24, June, 1947.

SALMONELLA INFECTIONS IN MINK. Katherine E. Penn. Amer. Fur Breeder, Duluth, vol.19, no.7, p.38, Jan., 1947; vol.20, no. 2, pp.58, 60, Aug., 1947; Nat. Fur News, Denver, vol.19, no.4, pp.11, 18, May, 1947.

IMMUNOLOGICAL AND HISTOLOGICAL STUDIES ON MINK DISTEMPER. Henry Pinkerton. Jour. Amer. Vet. Med. Assn., vol.96, no.756, pp.347-355, Mar., 1940.

BOTULISM; A MESSAGE TO THE MINK FARMER. E.R. Quortrup. Fur of Canada, Winnipeg, vol.9, no.10, pp.9, 11, July, 1944; Amer. Fur Breeder, Duluth, vol.17, no.3, pp.28, 30, Sep., 1944; Nat. Fur News, Denver, vol.16, no.8, pp.10, 34, Sep., 1944.

PROBLEM OF MINK DISTEMPER. C.E. van Rooyen. Canadian Jour. Comp. Med., Quebec, vol.13, no.12, pp.320-321, 1949.

NOTES ON SOME PARASITES OF THE MINKS IN SOUTHERN MICHIGAN. John A. Sealander. Jour. Parasitol., Lancaster, vol.29, no.5, pp.361-362, Oct., 1943.

DISTEMPER IN MINKS. Richard N. Shaw. Vet. Med., vol.27, no.12, pp.511-515, Dec., 1932.

GRUBS IN MINKS. J.E. Shillinger. U.S. Dpet. Int., Fish and Wildl. Serv., Leaflet 167, pp.2, Sep., 1940.

ANTHRAX IN MINKS. G.W. Stiles, C.L. Davis. Jour. Amer. Vet. Med. Assn., vol. 96, no.756, pp.407-409, Mar., 1940.

MINK AND STAPHYLOCOCCUS. Amy E. Wild. Amer. Fur Breeder, Duluth, vol.22, no.8, pp.40, 42, Feb., 1950.

PREVENTION OF BOTULISM IN MINK. Daniel T. Woolfe. Amer. Fur Breeder, Duluth, vol.22, no.2, p.20, Aug., 1949.

OBSERVATIONS ON GNATHOSTOMA SPINIGERUM OWEN 1836, CAUSE OF ESOPHAGEAL TUMOR IN THE JAPANESE MINK (LUTREOLA ITATSI ITATSI (TEMMINCK 1844)), WITH ESPECIAL REFERENCE TO ITS HISTORY. Sadao Yoshida. Japanese Jour. Zool., vol.6, no.1, pp.113-122, figs.10, Sep. 30, 1934.

(Mink) Eurasia

(THE MINK OF LANDES.) Le vison des Landes. G. Astre. Mammalia, Paris, vol. 14, nos.1-2, pp.40-42, Mar.-June, 1950.

(EXPERIMENT AT ACCLIMATIZATION OF THE AMERICAN MINK IN THE KVAREL RAYON.) Opit akklimatizatsii Amerikanskoi norki (Lutreola vison Gray) y Kvarelskom raione. Z.S. Ekvtimishvili, N.H. Gamarashvili. Soobshcheniya Akad. Nauk Gruzinskoi SSR, Tbilisi, vol.12, no. 2, pp.117-121, 1951.

(NOTICE ON THE LIFE OF THE EUROPEAN MINK LUTREOLA LUTREOLA L. (CARNIVORA, MUSTELIDAE).) K. K. Flerov. Ann. Mus. Zool. Acad. Sci. l'Urss. 1926, pp.73-75, fig.1, pl.4, 1926. (In Russian.)

NEW MINK-LIKE MUSTELA FROM JAVA. H.C. Robinson, O. Thomas. Ann. and Mag. Nat. Hist., ser.8, vol.20, no.117, pp.261-262, Sep., 1917.

MINK SITUATION IN SWEDEN. Eric Soderstrom. Amer. Fur Breeder, vol.4, no.1, p. 29, July, 1931.

(WILD MINK CAUGHT IN THE NETHERLANDS.) Nertsen in Nederland in het wild gevangen. A. van Wijngaarden, H. de Vries. De Levende Natuur, vol.60, pp. 303-304, 1957.

PRESENT DISTRIBUTION OF NORTH AMERICAN MINK IN NORWAY. Aage Wildhagen. Jour. Mamm., vol.37, no.1, pp.116-118, Feb. 28, 1956.

(Mink) Farming

MINK RAISING. Frank G. Ashbrook. U.S. Dept. Agric., Bur. Biol. Surv., Leaflet 8, pp.6, figs.5, Oct., 1927.

AUTOMATIC DRINKING FOUNTAIN FOR MINKS. Charles F. Bassett. U.S. Dept. Agric., Biol. Surv., Wildl. Leaflet 40, p.3, Mar., 1936.

MUTATION MINK AND THEIR USE IN COATS. Herman Bock. Amer. Fur Breeder, Duluth, vol.15, no.4, pp.14, 16, illus., Oct., 1942.

CRITICAL FACTORS IN SHED CONSTRUCTION. (Mink) E. Rendle Bowness. Fur of Canada, Winnipeg, vol.13, no.10, pp.15-20, July, 1948; Nat. Fur News, Denver, vol. 20, no.7, pp.15, 32; no.8, pp.21, 35-41, Aug., Sep., 1948.

RISING STAR OF WILD MINK. R. Rendle Bowness. Nat. Fur News, Denver, vol.17, no.3, pp.5, 18-19, Apr., 1945.

HEMOPHILIA LIKE, OR "BREEDERS" IN ALEUTIAN MINK. T.T. Chaddock. Amer. Fur Breeder, Duluth, vol.22, no.4, pp.26, 28, Oct., 1949.

KEEPING YOUR HERD ALIVE. T.T.Chaddock. Nat. Fur News, Denver, vol.20, no. 8, pp.12, 32, Sep., 1948; Amer. Fur Breeder, Duluth, vol.21, no.5, pp.30, 34, 36, 38, Nov., 1948.

SOME PRACTICAL SUGGESTIONS FOR MINK RANCHERS. T.T. Chaddock.Amer. Nat. Fur and Market Jour. Wausau, vol.27, no.6, pp.5-6, 29-34, Jan., 1949.

WIN, LOSE OR DRAW. T.T. Chaddock. Fur of Canada, Winnipeg, vol.14, no.4, p.3, Jan., 1949; Nat. Fur News, Denver, vol.21, no.1, pp.27, 30-33, Feb., 1949.

HOT WEATHER CARE OF MINK.Chester Chastek. Fur of Canada, Winnipeg, vol.11, no.11, p.6, Aug., 1946; Nat. Fur News, Denver, vol.17, no.7, pp.11, 38, Aug., 1946.

MINK RANCHING AND ITS POSSIBILITIES. Alfred L. Colby. Fur-Fish-Game, Harding's Mag., Columbus, vol.79, pp.30-31, illus., Apr., 1945.

POOR MAN'S MINK. Fern M. Crehan. Nat. Fur News, Denver, vol.17, no.8, pp.15, 45, Sep., 1945.

MINK PRODUCTION FOR 1943.A.B.DeHaan. Nat. Fur News, Denver, vol.15, no.9, pp. 9, 25, Oct., 1943.

MINK PRODUCTION IN RELATION TO STILBESTROL. Robert K. Enders. W.L. Merritts. Fur of Canada, Winnipeg, vol. 15, no.11, p.11, Aug., 1950.

SUMMER ON THE MINK RANCH. G.J. Estinson. Amer. Fur Breeder, vol.2, no. 1, p.13, July, 1929.

MAY SUGGESTIONS FOR THE MINK RANCHER. James Freer. Amer. Fur Breeder, vol.1, no.11, pp.10-11, May, 1929.

JUNE SUGGESTIONS FOR MINK BREEDERS. James Freer. Amer. Fur Breeder, vol.1, no. 12, pp.6-9, June, 1929.

BEWARE! RED LEAD POISONING WILL KILL YOUR ANIMALS. John R. Gorham. Black Fox Mag., New York, vol.32, no. 10, p.15, Feb., 1949.

RED LEAD POISONING IN MINK. John R. Gorham. Amer. Fur Breeder, Duluth, vol. 21, no.12, p.56, illus., June 1949; Fur of Canada, Winnipeg, vol.14, no.5, p.13, Feb., 1949; Nat. Fur News, Denver, vol. 21, no.2, p.8, Mar., 1949.

TRACHEA RINGS MAY ENCIRCLE MINK'S TONGUE. J.R. Gorham. Amer. Nat. Fur and Market Jour., Wausau, vol.27, no.10, p.14, May, 1949.

MINK RANCHING BY MODERN METHODS. Josie Greenberg. Amer. Fur Breeder, Duluth, vol.23, no.2, pp.11-12, 33, illus., Aug., 1950.

GROWING BETTER MINK. Otto H. Grosse. Nat. Fur News, Denver, vol.21, no.2, p. 24, Mar., 1949.

ART OF GROWING LARGER MINK. Clarence S. Grubbs. Nat. Fur News, Denver, vol.18, no.7, pp.8, 37, Aug., 1945.

CARE OF MINK IN APRIL. Clarence S. Grubbs. Nat. Fur News, Denver, vol.17, no.3, pp.7, 20, 26, Apr., 1945.

DETAILS ON MINK RAISING. C. K.Gunn. Fur of Canada, Winnipeg, vol.12, no.1, pp. 3-4, 49-50, 52, Oct., 1946.

MINK FARMING NO "GET RICH QUICK" PROFESSION. W.J. Hamilton, Jr. Farm Research, vol.13, no.3, July, 1947. (New York State Agricultural Experiment Station, Geneva, N.Y.)

HINTS FOR THE CARE OF MINK KITS. L.F. Jonas. Amer. Nat. Fur and Market Jour., Wausau, vol.27, no.10, pp.7-8, 18, May, 1949; Black Fox Mag. and Modern Mink Breeder, New York, vol.33, no.1, pp. 15, 25-27, May, 1949; Fur of Canada, Winnipeg, vol. 14, no.7, p.4, Apr., 1949; Nat. Fur News, Denver, vol.21, no.3, pp.16, 30-31, Apr., 1949.

MINK FARMING IN 1913. J. Walter Jones. Fur of Canada, Winnipeg, vol.11, no.8, pp. 14-15, 18, May, 1946.

LOCATING A MINK RANCH. W.E. Kane. Outdoorsman, Columbus, vol.84, no.1, p. 41, Jan., 1942.

WAR TIME PENS. W.E. Kane. Outdoorsman, Chicago, vol.86, no.2, whole no. 507, pp.44-45, illus., Mar.-Apr., 1944.

MINK RAISING. Charles E. Kellogg, Charles F. Bassett. Bur. Animal Industry, U.S.Dept. Agric., pp.42, 1949.

DDT AND MINKS. A.A. Kingscote. Fur of Canada, Winnipeg, vol.11, no.11, pp.27-28, Aug., 1946.

MINK NURSERY. Mollie L. McClintock. Amer. Fur Breeder, vol.4, no.1, pp.21-22, July, 1931.

MINK RANCH EQUIPMENT. B.R.McCrory, Al Leonard. Amer. Fur Breeder, Duluth, vol.19, no.2, pp.28, 30, 32, illus., Aug., 1946.

DDT POISONING IN MINK. A.M. McDermid. Amer. Fur Breeder, Duluth, vol.19, no.11, pp.40-41, May, 1947.

FUNDAMENTALS OF SUCCESSFUL MINK RANCHING. Wm. L. Michaelis. Amer.Fur Breeder, Duluth, vol.21, no.3, pp.56, 58, 60, 62-63, Sep., 1948.

ADVISES USE OF SPERM CHECK AS RANCHER AID. George L. Ott. Amer. Nat. Fur and Market Jour. Wausau, vol. 27, no.8, p.20, Mar., 1949.

"YELLOW FAT" AS IT AFFECTS RANCH MINK. George L. Ott. Amer. Nat.Fur and Market Jour. Wausau, vol.27, no.11, pp.27, 65, June, 1949.

FINDING SPERM. George L. Ott. Fur of Canada, Winnipeg, vol.14, no.5, p.18, Feb., 1949; Amer. Fur Breeder, Duluth, vol.21, no.9, p.36, Mar., 1949.

CARE OF THE FEMALE MINK AND YOUNG. H.B. Plumer. Amer. Fur Breeder, vol.1, no. 12, pp.12-13, June, 1929.

MINK FADING AND CAUSES. Jack Retzel. Amer. Fur Breeder, Duluth, vol.12, no.3, pp.8, 10, illus., Sep., 1939.

RELATIVE IMPORTANCE OF THE MINK RANCHING INDUSTRY IN THE VARIOUS STATES OF THE UNITED STATES. Willard B. Sheldon. Amer. Fur Breeder, Duluth, vol.21, no.4, pp.58, 60, Oct., 1948.

MINK RANCHER'S CYCLE. Ed.F.Sommers. Fur of Canada, Winnipeg, vol.11, no.7, pp. 22-23, Apr., 1946; Fur-Fish-Game, Harding's Mag., Columbus, vol.86, no.8, pp. 24-27, illus., Aug., 1946.

SUCCEEDS IN RAISING MINK ON GULF COAST. Rebecca L. Tumlinson. Amer. Nat. Fur and Market Jour., Wausau, vol. 27, no.10, p.9, May, 1949.

WHAT CAUSES PRODUCTION FAILURES? Lawrence Wakefield. Amer. Fur Breeder, Duluth, vol.21, no.5, pp.8, 10, 12, 14, Nov., 1948.

MINK FARMING, HOW TO START, BUILDINGS, CARE AND FEED, AND ITS POSSIBILITIES. A.S. White. Pine River Sentinel, Pine River, Minn., pp.15, illus., 1913.

CENSUS SHOWS 2,836 MINK FARMS IN UNITED STATES. Amer. Fur Breeder, Duluth, vol.14, no.9, p.22, Mar., 1942.

MINK RAISING. Poynette State Experimental Game and Fur Farm. Wisconsin Conserv. Dept., Madison, pp.14, mimeog., 1943.

MINK RAISING. U.S. Dept. Agric., Wildl. Research and Mgt. Leaflet, no.BS-82, pp. 8, Jan., 1937.

MINK RAISING. U.S. Dept. Interior, Fish and Wildl. Serv., Wildl. Leaflet, no.191, pp.10, May, 1941.

<u>(Mink) Food Habits</u>

KILLER OF THE SWAMPS. (Mink, Cottontail, Muskrat.) Ben East. Field and Stream, New York, vol.52, no.10, pp.50-51, 74, 108-110, illus., Feb., 1948.

BIRD PROTECTION IN ICELAND. Finnur Gudmundsson. Bull. Internat. Com. Bird Prot., no.6, pp.153-160. (Predation by Introduced Mustela Vison.)

WINTER FOOD OF PENNSYLVANIA MINK. John E. Guilday. Pennsylvania Game News, Harrisburg, vol.20, no.9, pp.12, 32, Dec., 1949.

FOOD HABITS OF THE MINK IN NEW YORK. W.J. Hamilton, Jr. Jour.Mamm., vol.17, no. 2, p.169, May, 1936.

WHAT DO MINK EAT IN THE WILD? Harry J. LaDue. Amer. Fur Breeder, vol.3, no.3, p.20, Sep., 1930.

WINTER FOOD HABITS OF MINK IN SOUTHERN MICHIGAN. John A. Sealander. Jour. Wildl. Mgt., Menasha, vol.7, no.4, pp.411-417, Oct., 1943.

MINK FEEDING ON CLAMS. Arthur Svihla, Ruth Dowell Svihla. Murrelet, vol.12, no.1, p.22, Jan., 1931.

STORING OF MUSKRATS AND OTHER FOODS BY MINKS. Lee E. Yeager. Jour. Mamm., vol.24, no.1, pp.100-101, Feb., 1943.

ICELAND'S MINK ARE MENACE TO WILDLIFE. Mod. Game Breeding and Hunting Club News 23, vol.8, p.13, Aug., 1953.

<u>(Mink) Fossils</u>

NEW MINK FROM THE SHELL HEAPS OF MAINE. F.B. Loomis. Amer. Jour. Sci., ser.4, vol.31, pp.227-229, 1911.

MYSTERY MINK. (Extinct Sea Mink, Mustela macrodon.) Romeo Mansueti.Nat. Mag., vol.47, no.4, pp.185-186, 218, illus., Apr., 1954.

DESCRIPTION OF AN EXTINCT MINK FROM THE SHELL-HEAPS OF THE MAINE COAST. Daniel Webster Prentiss. Proc. U.S. Nat. Mus., Wash., D.C., vol.26, no.1336, pp.887-888, fig.1, July 6, 1903.

SEA MINK, MUSTELA MACRODON (PRENTISS). Ernest Thompson Seton. Jour. Mamm., vol.2, no.3, p.168, Aug., 1921.

<u>(Mink) General Habits</u>

MINK--JACK OF ALL TRADES. (Habits, Life History, Economic Importance.) G. W. Bradt. Mich. Cons., vol.16, no.4, p. 4, May, 1947.

TAIL CHEWERS IN MINK. T.T.Chaddock. Nat. Fur News, Denver, vol.19, no.7, p. 17, Aug., 1947; Fur of Canada, Winnipeg, vol.13, no.1, p.18, Oct., 1947.

DECLINE OF A MINK POPULATION.Paul L. Errington. Jour. Mamm., vol.19, no. 2, pp.250-251, May 14, 1938.

SPECIAL RESPONSIVENESS OF MINKS TO EPIZOOTICS IN MUSKRAT POPULATIONS. Paul L. Errington. Ecol. Monog., vol.24, no.4, pp.377-393, Oct., 1954.

INTELLIGENCE IN MINK. C.T. Gadsden. Amer. Fur Breeder, vol.4, no.8, p.16, Feb., 1932.

UNUSUAL HABIT OF THE MINK.Charles A. Gianini. Jour. Mamm., vol.8, no.3, p.244, Aug., 1927.

CALIFORNIA MINK IN MARINE HABITAT. E. Raymond Hall. Jour. Mamm., vol.10, no.4, pp.351-352, Nov. 11, 1929.

A MINK FIGHT. John B. Lewis. Jour. Mamm., vol.8, no.4, p.308, Nov., 1927.

MINK DISPLAYS SLIDING HABITS. William H. Marshall. Jour. Mamm., vol.16, no.3, pp.228-229, Aug., 1935.

STUDY OF THE WINTER ACTIVITIES OF THE MINK. William H. Marshall. Jour. Mamm., vol.17, no.4, pp.382-392, Nov., 1936.

MINK GNAWS IRON WIRE. Fred Mather. Amer. Nat., Lancaster, vol.21, no.12, pp.1124-1125, Dec., 1887.

HABITS OF THE LOUISIANA MINK (MUSTELA VISON VULGIVAGUS). Arthur Svihla. Jour. Mamm., vol.12, no.4, pp.366-368, Nov., 1931.

(MOTHER LOVE OF MINKS.) Die Mutterliebe der Nerze. Der Deutsche Pelztierzuechter, Jahrg.1931, Muenchen, no.11, p.312, June 1, 1931.

(Mink) Growth

WEIGHING YOUNG MINK TO ASCERTAIN RATE OF GROWTH. J.E. Ames. Amer. Fur Breeder, vol.3, no.4, p.24, Oct., 1930.

GROWING KIT IN FALL. E. Rendle Bowness. Nat. Fur News, Denver, vol.17, no.10, pp.14, 24-28, Nov., 1945; Fur of Canada, Winnipeg, vol.11, no.1, pp.22-24, Oct., 1945; vol.11, no.3, p.23, Dec., 1945.

GROWING MINK KIT. PART 1. E. Rendle Bowness. Fur-Fish-Game (Harding's Mag.), Columbus, vol.79, no. 11, pp.28-30, illus., Nov., 1945.

MINK GROWING SEASON. E.R. Bowness. Nat. Fur News, Denver, vol.20, no.4, pp. 13, 34; no.5, pp.12, 24, May, June, 1948.

SEASONS GROWING. (Mink.) E.F.Sommers. Amer. Fur Breeder, Duluth, vol.19, no.12, pp.10-16, June, 1947.

(Mink) Heredity

PLATINUM MINK GENETICS AND BREEDING PROCEDURE. Herman Bock. Amer. Fur Breeder, Duluth, vol.14, no.12, pp.8, 10, 12, figs.5, June, 1942.

SOME OBSERVATIONS ON INHERITANCE IN MUTANT MINK. E. Rendle Bowness. Amer. Fur Breeder, Duluth, vol.19, no.7, pp.46, 48, 50, 52, 54, Jan., 1947.

COLOR INHERITANCE IN MINK. W.E. Castle. Amer. Fur Breeder, Duluth, vol. 19, no.5, pp.8, 12, Nov., 1946.

GENETIC UTILITY OF BLUFROST MINK. Alma Erekson. Nat. Fur News, Denver, vol.19, no.7, pp.12, 37, Aug., 1947.

GENETIC SURVEY BEING MADE OF STEWART MINK. David W. Henderson. Black Fox Mag., New York, vol.32, no.2, p.20, June, 1948.

STUDIES OF COTTON MINKS WITH REFERENCE TO HEREDITY AND BLOOD ELEMENTS. O.J. Hummon, F. R. Bushnell. Amer. Fur Breeder, Duluth, vol.16, no.5, pp.30, 32, 34, Nov., 1943; Nat.Fur News, Denver, vol.15, no.12, pp.13, 22, Jan., 1944.

INHERITANCE OF THREE COAT COLOR MUTATIONS IN RANCH-RAISED MINKS. Sedgwick E. Smith et al. Jour. Heredity, Washington, D.C., vol.32, no.5, pp.173-176, figs.2, May, 1941.

(Mink) Methods, Techniques

HOW TO GRADE MINK. Frank C. Gothier. Nat. Fur News, Denver, vol.15, no.11, pp. 8, 27, illus., Dec., 1943.

GRADING AND PELTING MINK. Clarence S. Grubbs. Nat. Fur News, Denver, vol.17, no.10, pp.10-11, Nov., 1945.

DEVICE FOR THE RESTRAINT OF MINK DURING CERTAIN EXPERIMENTAL PROCEDURE. O.J. Hummon. Jour.Amer. Vet. Med. Assn., vol.106, no.815, pp. 104-105, Feb., 1945.

HOW NOT TO HANDLE MINK PELTS. Dave Loffman. Amer. Fur Breeder, Duluth, vol. 20, no.4, pp.8, 10, 12, 14, 16, 18, 20, 22, illus., Oct., 1947.

HOW TO SKIN AND PREPARE MINK PELTS. Arthur MacArthur. Amer. Fur Breeder, Duluth, vol.19, no.4, pp.52, 54, 58, Oct., 1946; Fur of Canada, Winnipeg, vol.12, no. 2, pp.49-50, illus., Nov., 1946.

METHOD OF RESTRAINING MINK FOR TREATMENT. George Ott, Kenneth L. Mills. Amer. Fur Breeder, Duluth, vol.20, no.3, p.66, Sep., 1947.

HERE'S A PRACTICAL WAY TO IDENTIFY YOUR MINK. (Tattooing Foot Pads With India Ink.) E.R. Quortrup. Black Fox Mag., vol.31, no.2, pp.19, 34, June 1947.

PRACTICAL MARKING SYSTEM FOR MINK. E.R. Quortrup. Fur of Canada, Winnipeg, vol.12, no.7, pp.18-19, illus., Apr., 1947; Nat. Fur News, Denver, vol.19, no.4, p. 13, May, 1947; Amer. Fur Breeder, Duluth, vol.19, no.11, p.30, May, 1947.

CRITICISM OF MARSHALL'S METHOD FOR CENSUSING MINK. (Tracks of Sexes Not Always Clearly Separable.) John A. Sealander. Jour. Mamm., vol.25, no.1, pp.84-86, Feb., 1944.

(Mink) Mutations

HISTORY OF PLATINUM MINK. Herman Bock. Amer. Fur Breeder, Duluth, vol.14, no.11, pp.8, 10, illus., May, 1942.

DR. OSBORN'S EXPERIMENTS WITH MINK MUTATIONS. W.E. Castle. Amer. Fur Breeder, Duluth, vol.17, no.9, p.18, Mar., 1945.

MUTATIONS OF MINK UNDER DOMESTICATION. W.E. Castle, Larry Moore, Jour. Heredity, Washington, vol.37, no.5, pp. 137-145, figs.3-6, May, 1946.

BREEDING PROBLEMS ENCOUNTERED IN NEWER MUTATION MINK. T.T.Chaddock. Fur of Canada, Winnipeg, vol.14, no.8, pp.7-8, May, 1949, Nat. Fur News, Denver, vol.21, no.5, pp.13, 29-30, June, 1949.

WHAT MAKES A MUTATION MINK DESIRABLE. Michael Dederer. Black Fox Mag., New York, vol.32, no.4, pp.11, 29, Aug., 1948.

CROSS-BREEDING MUTATION MINK. August H. Genetti. Fur of Canada, Winnipeg, vol.9, no.11, p.8, Aug., 1944; Nat. Fur News, Denver, vol.16, no.7, p.9, Aug., 1944.

HOW I DEVELOPED A NEW STRAIN OF MINK. Frank C. Gothier. Amer. Fur Breeder, Duluth, vol.21, no.1, pp.18-28, July, 1948; vol.21, no.3, pp.24, 26, Sep., 1948.

PLATINUM MINK. Guy S. Ingham. Amer. Fur Breeder, Duluth, vol.13, no.12, p.8, fig.1, June, 1941.

ALEUTIAN BLUE MINK. A.W. King. Fur-Fish-Game, Columbus, vol.87, no.9, p. 38, Sep., 1946.

BREEDS AND STRAINS IN MINK. A.W. King. Amer. Fur Breeder, Duluth, vol.15, no.4, p.20, illus., Oct., 1942.

MUTATION MINK TRADE NAMES. A.W. King. Amer. Fur Breeder, Duluth, vol.20, no.3, pp.56, 58, 60, Sep., 1947; Fur of Canada, Winnipeg, vol.13, no.1, pp.22-23, 26, Oct., 1947.

NEW MINK MUTATIONS OFFER GREAT POSSIBILITIES. Harry J. LaDue. Amer. Fur Breeder, Duluth, vol.15, no.11, pp.8, 10, illus., May, 1943.

STEWART PLATINUM MINK. Harry J. LaDue. Amer. Fur Breeder, Duluth, vol. 20, no.8, pp.12, 14, illus., Feb., 1948.

BREEDING THE MINK MUTATIONS. Harry I. Landon. Amer. Fur Breeder, Duluth, vol.15, no.12, pp.14, 18, June, 1943.

MUTATION MINK--FEAST AND FAMINE! A.L. Langenfeldt. Nat. Fur News, Denver, vol.20, no.10, pp.48, 110, Nov., 1948.

ALEUTIAN BLUE MAGIC IN MINK. Edwin P. Langenfeld. Amer. Fur Breeder, Duluth, vol.19, no.9, pp.8, 10, 12, 14, Mar., 1947.

BREEDING A DARK MINK WITH ESKIMO BAY WILD MINK QUALITY. Arthur MacArthur. Nat. Fur News, Denver, vol.17, no. 10, p.13, illus., Nov., 1945.

MY SILVER TAUPE MINK. R.G.MacDuffie. Amer. Fur Breeder, Duluth, vol.16, no.6, p.41, Dec., 1943.

HOW TO PRODUCE THE DOUBLE RECESSIVE MINK. Floyd R. Marsh. Amer.Fur Breeder, Duluth, vol.20, no.2, pp.6, 8, 10, 12, Aug., 1947.

MUTATION MINK PRODUCED IN PACIFIC NORTHWEST. Floyd R. Marsh. Nat. Fur News, Denver, vol.19, no.4, pp.10, 18-19, 22-23, May, 1947.

MUTATION MINK COMES OF AGE. Herbert P. Mezger. Nat. Fur News, Denver, vol.18, no.8, pp.13, 40-41, 45, Sep., 1946.

NEW TYPES OF MINK. Larry Moore. Amer. Fur Breeder, Duluth, vol.15, no.4, pp.8, 10, 13, illus., Oct., 1942.

HOW I PRODUCED MY MINK MUTATIONS. Percy V. Noble. Amer. Fur Breeder, Duluth, vol.11, no.10, pp.30-31, illus., Apr., 1939.

BREEDING OF MUTATION MINK. Seth S. Osborn. Amer. Fur Breeder, Duluth, vol. 18, no.9, pp.30-32, illus., Mar., 1946; Nat. Fur News, Denver, vol.17, no.3, pp.8, 19, Apr., 1946.

HOW TO PRODUCE THE VARIOUS TYPES OF SAPPHIRE MINK. Seth S. Osborn. Amer. Fur Breeder, Duluth, vol.21, no.12, pp.38-40, June, 1949.

MUTATION MINK TYPES. Seth S. Osborn. Nat. Fur News, Denver, vol.17, no.1, pp. 7, 26, Feb., 1945.

MY EXPERIMENTAL WORK WITH MINK MUTATIONS. Seth S. Osborn. Amer.Fur Breeder, Duluth, vol.17, no.7, pp.30-32, illus., Jan., 1945.

ALBINO FEMALE MINK AS A GOVERNOR IN THE PRODUCTION OF COLOR PHASE MINK. Morley B. Pirt. Amer. Fur Breeder, Duluth, vol.17, no.1, pp.10, 12, 14, fig., July, 1944.

ARCTIC SNOW MINK. (History of the Development of Albino Strain of Mink.) M.B. Pirt. Amer. Fur Breeder, Duluth, vol.16, no.2, pp.22, 24, Aug., 1943.

HOW THE ALBINO FEMALE CAN BE USED TO CONTROL THE PRODUCTION OF MUTANT MINKS. M.B. Pirt. Fur of Canada, Winnipeg, vol.9, no.9, p.12, June, 1944.

IMPORTANCE OF THE ALBINO FEMALE IN THE DEVELOPMENT OF COLOR PHASE MINK. M.B. Pirt. Amer. Nat. Fur and Market Jour., Wausau, vol.23, no.2, pp.11-12, 32, illus., Sep., 1944.

RETZEL ORCHID MINK. Joseph F. Retzel. Amer. Fur Breeder, Duluth, vol.20, no.3, pp.36-38, Sep., 1947.

COTTON MINK PARADOX. Curtis K.Saxton. Fur-Fish-Game (Harding's Mag.), Columbus, vol.79, no.11, pp.31-33, Nov., 1945.

MUTATIONS IN MINKS. Richard M.Shackelford. Trans. Wisc. Acad. Sci., Arts and Letters, Madison, vol.34, p.45, 1942.

BREEDING MUTATION MINK. Richard M. Shackelford. Fur of Canada, Winnipeg, vol. 12, no.1, pp.6, 8, 10, Oct., 1946; Amer. Fur Breeder, Duluth, vol.19, no.2, pp.8-14, no.3, pp.10-26; no.5, pp.30-32, illus., Aug., Sep., Nov., 1946.

DISCUSSION ON MINK MUTATION MATINGS. Richard M. Shackelford. Amer. Nat. Fur and Market Jour., Wausau, vol.26, no.12, p.5, July, 1948.

SIX MUTATIONS AFFECTING COAT COLOR IN RANCH-BRED MINK. Richard M.Shackelford. Amer. Nat., Lancaster, vol.83, no. 809, pp.49-67, Mar.-Apr., 1949.

"SCREW NECK" IN THE PASTEL COLOR PHASE OF RANCH-BRED MINK. Richard M. Shackelford, Leon J. Cole. Nat. Fur News, Denver, vol.20, no.1, pp.23, 26-27, 29, illus., Feb., 1948; vol.20, no.2, pp. 19, 30-31, 35, illus., Mar., 1948.

BREEDING MINK TO OBTAIN SIZE. Nels Spencer. Nat. Fur News, Denver, vol.20, no.7, pp.26-27, Aug., 1948.

HOW TO GET THE BEST RESULTS IN BREEDING THE STEWART PLATINUM

MINK. Joe Stuekerjuergen. Amer. Fur Breeder, Duluth, vol.21, no.12, pp.28-30, June, 1949.

BREEDING DOMINANT WHITE MINK. Lawrence Wakefield. Amer. Fur Breeder, Duluth, vol.20, no.1, pp.30, 32, 34, July, 1947; Fur of Canada, Winnipeg, vol.12, no.10, pp.26-27, July, 1947.

(Mink) North America

NOTES ON THE ABUNDANCE OF THE EVERGLADES MINK. E. Ross Allen, Wilfred T. Neill. Jour. Mamm., vol.33, no.1, pp.113-114, Feb., 1952.

FUR BEARING ANIMALS OF THE UNITED STATES. THE MINK. Frank G. Ashbrook, Bridgewater M. Arnold. Fur Jour., vol.1, no.4, pp.34-35, illus., Aug., 1927.

NOTES ON THE SYNONYMY OF THE NORTH AMERICAN MINK WITH DESCRIPTION OF A NEW SUBSPECIES. Outram Bangs. Proc. Boston Soc. Nat. Hist., vol.27, pp.1-6, pls. 1-2, Mar., 1896.

MISSISSIPPI VALLEY MINK. N.R. Barger. Wisconsin Conserv. Bull., Madison, vol.13, no.12, p.28, illus., Dec., 1948.

CALIFORNIA LOWLAND MINK A DISTINCT RACE. Joseph Grinnell. Proc. Biol. Soc. Wash., vol.29, pp.213-214, Sep. 22, 1916.

NEW MINK FROM THE FLORIDA EVERGLADES. (Mustela vison evergladensis.) Wm. J. Hamilton, Jr. Proc. Biol. Soc. Washington, vol.61, pp.139-140, Sep. 3, 1948.

MINK IN NORTH DAKOTA. Brandt V. Hjelle. N.Dakota Outdoors, Grand Forks, vol.10, no.9, pp.12-14, illus., Mar., 1948.

SYNOPSIS OF THE AMERICAN MINKS. N. Hollister. Proc. U.S. Nat. Mus., vol.44, pp.471-480, Apr., 1913.

MINK OBSERVATIONS AT PACKWOOD LAKE, WASHINGTON. Frank B. McMurry. Murrelet, Seattle, vol.21, no.2, p.47, May-Aug., 1940.

STUDIES ON TRAPPED MINK, MUSTELA VISON MINK, IN MICHIGAN. John A. Sealander. MS thesis, Mich. State Coll., 1942.

OCCURRENCE OF THE MINK, WEST OF THE HUNDREDTH MERIDIAN, IN KANSAS. Howard J. Stains, Robert L. Packard. Trans. Kans. Acad. Sci., vol.58, no.2, pp.222-224, map, 1955.

EXTENSION OF RANGE OF THE MINK IN TEXAS. Walter P. Taylor. Jour. Mamm., vol.25, no.4, pp.411-412, Dec. 12, 1944.

FUR-BEARING MAMMALS OF WYOMING. (Mink.) Earl M. Thomas. Wyo. Wild Life, part 7, vol.16, no.9, pp.30-34, illus., Sep., 1952.

AMERICAN MINK. South Dakota Conservation Digest, Pierre, vol.12, no.3, p.13, Mar., 1945.

(Mink) Pelage

MOLTING AND FUR GROWTH PATTERN IN THE ADULT MINK. Charles F. Bassett, Leonard M. Llewellyn. Amer. Midl. Nat., vol.42, no.3, pp.751-756, Nov., 1949; Amer. Fur Breeder, Duluth, vol.22, no.9, pp.8-13, illus., Mar., 1950.

REPORT OF EXPERIMENT TO DETERMINE VARIATION IN MINK FUR TEXTURE. R.H. Burns. Amer. Fur Breeder, vol.11, no.12, pp. 12-16, June, 1930.

COLMIRA COLOR PHASE IN THE MINK. Richard M. Shackelford. Nat. Fur News, Denver, vol.21, no.7, p.11, Aug., 1949.

MINK WHITER THAN ALBINO. Science News Letter, Washington, vol.50, no.10, p.156, illus., Sep. 7, 1946.

(Mink) Physiology

SHORTENING DAYLIGHT PERIODS BETWEEN MAY 15 AND SEPTEMBER 12, AND THE PELT CYCLE OF THE MINK. Thomas Hume Bissonette, Everett Wilson. Science, Lancaster, Pa., n.s., vol.89, no.2314, pp. 418-419, May 5, 1939.

HEAT EXHAUSTION IN MINK. John R. Gorham. Fur of Canada, Winnipeg, vol.15, no.7, p.11, illus., Apr., 1950.

DIGESTIBILITY OF ANIMAL PRODUCTS AND CEREALS BY MINKS. J.K. Loosli. U.S. Dept. Int., Fish and Wildl. Serv., Leaflet 168, pp.5, tbls.3, Sep., 1940.

MINK FEEDING EXPERIMENTS: REPORT I. H. F. Travis et al. Bull. Michigan Agric. Exp. Sta., East Lansing, vol.32, no.1, pp.64-69, Aug., 1949.

(Mink) Reproductive Biology

(INFORMATION ON ESTRUS IN THE MINK.) Etwas ueber die Ranz des Nerzes. Hans Beckenbach. Der Deutsche Pelztierzuechter, Jahrg.1931, Muenchen, no.9, pp.243-244, fig., May 1, 1931.

FAILURE OF PLACENTAL SCARS TO REVEAL BREEDING HISTORY IN MINK. William H. Elder. Jour. Wildl. Mgt., vol. 16, no.1, p.110, Jan., 1952.

PHYSIOLOGY OF REPRODUCTION IN THE MINK. Robert K. Enders. Amer. Fur Breeder, Duluth, vol.11, no.10, pp.6, 8, photo, Apr., 1939.

REPRODUCTION IN THE MINK. (Mustela vision). Robert K. Enders. Proc. Amer. Philos. Soc., Philadelphia, vol.96, no.6, pp.691-755, illus., Dec., 1952.

(AUTUMN OESTRUS IN THE MINK.) Herbstranz bei Nerzen. Emil Engelhart. Der Deutsche Pelztierzuechter, Jahrg.1931, Muenchen, no.22, p.601, Nov. 15, 1931.

GONADOTROPHIN-INDUCED OVULATION IN MINK. John Hammond, Jr. Jour. Mamm., vol.33, no.2, pp.218-233, illus., May 16, 1952.

PHYSIOLOGY OF REPRODUCTION IN MINK (MUSTELA VISON, SCHREB.) WITH SPECIAL REFERENCE TO DELAYED IMPLANTATION. Artur Hansson. Acta Zoologica, Stockholm, vol.28, no.1, pp.1-136, figs.77, 1947.

MOTHER MINK. Rutherford Montgomery. Pennsylvania Game News, Harrisburg, vol. 20, no.5, pp.18-20, illus., Aug., 1949.

REPRODUCTIVE HABITS OF EASTERN MINK. Harry R. Saxton. Amer. Fur Breeder, vol.4, no.4, p.12, Oct., 1931.

MOTHER MINK AND YOUNG. George A. Winter. Amer. Fur Breeder, vol.1, no.10, p.14, Apr., 1929.

(Mink) Trapping

NOTES ON LIVE-TRAPPING MINK. Robert A. McCabe. Jour. Mamm., vol.30, no.4, pp.416-423, Nov., 1949.

LIVE TRAPPING MINK IN BRITISH COLUMBIA. R.W. Ritcey, R.Y. Edwards. Jour. Mamm., vol.37, no.1, pp.114-116, Feb. 28, 1956.

(Mustela) General

TALA-ELAN. (PUTORIUS FOETIDUS GRAY (MUSTELA PUTORIUS LINNE.) Israel Aharoni. Mada'e ha-yahaduth, Jerusalem, pp. 1-6, 1926. (Text mostly in Hebrew.)

LEAST WEASEL A CIRCUMBOREAL SPECIES. Glover M. Allen. Jour. Mamm., vol. 14, no.4, pp.316-319, Nov., 1933.

THE WEASELS. Rod Admundson. Wildl. in N. Carolina, Raleigh, vol.14, no.9, pp.4-6, illus., Sep., 1950.

WILY WEASEL--VERSATILE VILLAIN. Elizabeth Bachmann. Conserv. Volunteer, St. Paul, vol.13, no.75, pp.9-11, Mar.-Apr., 1950.

BONAPARTE'S WEASEL (MUSTELA ERMINEA BANGSI.) N.R. Barger. Wisconsin Conserv. Bull., Madison, vol.15, no.10, pp.39-40, Oct., 1950.

WEASEL--NEMESIS OF NATURE'S LITTLE PEOPLE. G.W. Bradt. Mich. Cons., vol.16, no.5, p.4, June, 1947.

NOTE ON MUSTELA LUTREOLINA ROB AND THOS. L.D. Brongersma. Temminckia, Leiden, vol.5, pp.257-263, figs.2, 1940.

DISAPPEARING POLECAT. H.A. Bryden. Field, London, vol.160, no.4158, p.342, illus., Sep. 3, 1932.

TRUE WEASEL STORIES. G.W. Coats. S.Dakota Conserv. Digest, Pierre, vol.12, no.8, p.10, Aug., 1945.

VISITATION OF WEASELS. J.M. Edson. Murrelet, vol.14, no.3, pp.76-77, Sep., 1933.

(ON THE BIOLOGY OF THE POLECAT (PUTORIUS PUTORIOUS L.).) Zur Biologie des Iltis (Putorius putorius L.). Irenhaeus Eibl-Eibesfeldt. Zool. Anz., Verh.Deutschen Zool. Gesell., suppl.19, pp.304-314, 1956.

(CONTRIBUTIONS TO THE BIOLOGY OF THE POLECAT.) Beitraege zur Biologie des Iltis. F. Goethe. Zeitschr. f. Saeugetierkunde, Berlin, vol.15, no.1, pp.180-223, figs.22, pls.10-14, 1940.

(ON THE LIFE OF THE WEASEL (MUSTELA N. NIVALIS L.).) Vom Leben des Mauswiesels (Mustela n. nivalis L.). F. Goethe. Zool. Garten, Leipzig, n.F., vol.17, nos. 1-5, pp.193-204, illus., 1950.

DISAPPEARANCE OF POLECATS. J.M. Howell. Field, London, vol.162, no.4202, p.115, July 8, 1933.

(ERMINE AND WEASEL.) Hermelin and Wiesel. Konrad Klemmer. Natur und Volk, Hamburg, vol.84, no.2, pp.62-65, illus., Feb. 1, 1954.

THE WEASEL: BEHAVIOR IN CAPTIVITY AND COLOR CHANGE.) Gefangenhaltung und Farbwechsel der Wiesel. Ingo Krumbiegel. Zool. Garten, Leipzig, n.F., vol. 8, nos.1-3, pp.8-15, figs.2, Sep., 1935.

(BIOLOGY OF THE COMMON POLECAT (PUTORIUS PUTORIUS L.).) N.P. Lavrov. Bull. Soc. Nat. Moscow, sect.biol., n.s., vol.44, nos.7-8, pp.362-373, tbls.10, 1935. (In Russian with French summary.)

CONTRIBUTION TO THE BIOLOGY OF THE KOLONOCK (KOLONOCUS SIBIRICUS L.). N.P. Lavrov. Zool. Jour., Moscow, vol.16, no.4, pp.740-754, figs.3, tbsl.4, 1937. (In Russian with English summary.)

MAMMAL TRACKS. THE WEASEL. Helen Lawson, Bill Lawson. Ohio Conserv.Bull., Columbus, vol.14, no.11, p.12, illus., Nov., 1950.

PACK OF STOATS. R.E. Longfield. Irish Naturalists' Jour., vol.2, no.4, p.73, July, 1928.

ORIGIN OF THE FERRET. Gerrit S. Miller, Jr. Scottish Naturalist, no.203, pp. 153-154, Sep.-Oct., 1933.

(NOTE ON A VARIETY OF WEASEL.) Note sur une variete de Belette. P. Narbel. Rév.Suisse Zool., Geneve, vol.13, fasc. 1, pp.411-414, 1905.

FRIENDLESS HUNTER. (Mountain Weasel.) John F. Nolan. Yosemite Nature Notes, vol. 29, no.2, pp.14-15, Feb., 1950.

THE WEASEL: VANDAL OR VAMPIRE. Neil Payne. Virginia Wildl., Richmond, vol.11, no.1, pp.20-21, illus., Jan., 1950.

BLACK-FOOTED FERRETS USED AS CEREMONIAL OBJECTS BY MONTANA INDIANS. Liven A. Peterson, Elihu D. Berg. Jour. Mamm., vol.35, no.4, pp. 593-594, Nov. 29, 1954.

WEASEL-WISE. (Account of Weasels.) Gayle Pickwell. Nature Mag., vol.13, pp. 32-34, illus., Jan., 1929.

LONG-TAILED WEASEL. H.H. Pittman. Nature Mag., Washington, D.C., vol.37, no.6, pp.299-301, illus., June-July, 1944.

FERRETS AND POLECATS. R.I. Pocock. Scottish Naturalist, no.196, pp.97-108, fig., July-Aug., 1932.

IS THE FERRET A DOMESTICATED POLECAT? R.I. Pocock. Field, London, vol.159, no.4134, p.410, fig.1, Mar. 19, 1932.

WEASEL VISITS PARASITOLOGY LABORATORY--AND LIVES. Charles A. Reed, Ralph W. Macy. Murrelet, Seattle, vol.26, no.2, pp.30-31, (May-Aug.) Aug. 10, 1945.

THE KILLER FAMILY. (Stoat.) Hugh Ross. Forest and Bird, Wellington, vol.85, pp.3-4, Aug., 1947.

WEASEL AND HIS FAMILY. Benjamin Scott. English Illust. Mag., London, vol. 6, no.70, pp.619-626, illus., July, 1889.

WEASELS. George Smokey. S.Dakota Conserv. Digest, Pierre, vol.11, no.2, pp.7, 11, Feb., 1944.

(ON PUTORIUS ERMINEUS MINIMUS CAVAZZA, A PYGMY FORM OF ERMINE, PUTORIUS ERMINEUS L.) Ueber Putorius ermineus minimus Cavazza. Eine Zwergform des Hermelins, Putorius ermineus (L.). Th. Studer. Mitteil. Naturforsch. Gesell. Bern, pp.13, figs.8, 1913.

BLACK-FOOTED FERRET. Walker van Riper, Robert J. Niedrach. Nat. Hist., New York, vol.55, no.10, pp.466-467, illus., Dec., 1946.

NEW TYPE OF MUSEUM EXHIBIT.(Mustela noveboracensis group.) Bradford Washburn. New England Naturalist, Boston, no.4, pp. 20, illus., Sep., 1939.

(CONTRIBUTION TO KNOWLEDGE OF THE BIOLOGY OF MUSTELA ERMINEA.) Bidrag till kannedomen om lekattens (Mustela erminea) biologi. Johan Wiklund. Fauna och Flora, nos.1-2, pp.16-24, 1953.

THE FIVE O'CLOCK KILLER. (Weasel.) Kerry Wood. Fauna, Philadelphia, vol.8, no.2, pp.44-46, illus., June, 1946.

(Mustela) Africa

NOTE ON AN UNDESCRIBED WEASEL FROM THE ATLAS MOUNTAINS, AND ON THE OCCURRENCE OF A WEASEL IN THE AZORES. G.E.G.Barrett-Hamilton. Ann. and Mag. Nat. Hist., ser.7, vol.13, pp.323-325, Apr., 1904.

(THE FATHERLAND OF "PUTORIUS FURO".) (Atlas Mountains, Spanish Morocco.) A. Cabrera. Boletin Real Soc. Espanola Hist. Nat., vol.30, pp.477-480, 1930.

ON THE REPRESENTATIVES OF PUTORIUS ERMINEUS IN ALGERIA AND FERGHANA. Oldfield Thomas. Ann.and Mag. Nat. Hist., ser.6, vol.15, no.89, pp.451-454, May, 1895.

(Mustela) Anatomy

SOME CHARACTERS OF THE SKULLS OF THE EUROPEAN POLECAT, THE ASIATIC POLECAT AND THE DOMESTIC FERRET. (ADDENDUM.) E.H. Ashton. Proc. Zool. Soc. London, vol.125, pts.3-4, pp.807-809, illus., Nov. 23, 1955.

SOME CHARACTERS OF THE SKULLS AND SKINS OF THE EUROPEAN POLECAT, THE ASIATIC POLECAT AND THE DOMESTIC FERRET. E.H. Ashton, A.P.D. Thomson. Proc. Zool. Soc.London, vol.125, pt.2, pp.317-333, Aug.31, 1955.

ON THE VARIATION OF MESTELA (LUTREOLA) NUDIPES DESM. L. D. Brongersma, G.C.A. Junge. Zool.Mededeel., Leiden, vol.23, nos.3-4, pp. 149-170, fig.1, pls.5-8, 1942.

DIAGNOSTIC CHARACTERS OF YOUNG PUTORIUS PUTORIUS L. AND LUTREOLA LUTREOLA L. Constantine C. Flerov. Comptes Rendus Acad. Sci. de l'Union des Républiques Sovietiques Socialistes, A, pp.164-166, Sep., 1926.

WEIGHTS AND MEASUREMENTS OF STOATS AND WEASELS. R.J. Flintoff. Northwestern Nat., Arbroath, vol.10, no.1, pp.29-34, Mar., 1935.

(ON THE VARIABILITY OF THE ERMINE SKULL (MUSTELA ERMINEA L.).) P. Jurgenson. Zoologitscheskij Journal, Moscow, vol.12, pt.1, pp.60-68, 1933. (In Russian with German summary.)

(ON THE SEXUAL DIMORPHISM OF THE SKULL OF THE ERMINE (MUSTELA ERMINEA L.).) O polovom dimorfizme cherepa gornostaya (Mustela erminea L.). O.V. Petrov. Vestnik Leningradskogo Univ., vol.15, no.3, pp.41-56, 1956.

CURIOUS PALATAL OBSTRUCTION IN MUSTELA LONGICAUDA. J. Dewey Soper. Jour. Mamm., vol.2, no.1, pp.37-38, Feb., 1921.

DEVELOPMENT OF THE BACULUM OF THE LONG-TAILED WEASEL. Philip L. Wright. Proc. Soc. Exper. Biol. and Med., New York, vol.75, pp.820-822, 1950.

DEVELOPMENT OF THE BACULUM OR OS PENIS IN THE LONG-TAILED WEASEL. Philip L. Wright. Anat. Record, Philadelphia, vol.105, no.3, p.79, Nov., 1949. (Abstract.)

(Mustela) Captivity

NOTES ON A BLACK-FOOTED FERRET RAISED IN CAPTIVITY. Shaler E.Aldous. Jour. Mamm., vol.21, no.1, pp.23-26, Feb. 14, 1940.

A TAME POLECAT. J.C. Bristow-Noble. Field, London, vol.152, p.74, July 12, 1928.

DOMESTIC STOAT. Charles Bunbury. Trans. Suffolk Nat. Soc., Norwich, vol.5, pt.4, p.201, Dec., 1945.

WEASELS IN CAPTIVITY. F.W. Frohawk. Field, London, vol.151, p.390, Mar. 8, 1928.

(ERMINE AS PET.) Hermelin als Hausgenosse. Kaethe Hecht. Naturforscher, Berlin, vol.12, no.7, pp.236-238, illus., Oct., 1935.

TAMING A FERRET. Desmond MacManus. Field, London, vol.168, no.4358, p.37, illus., July 4. 1936.

CAPTIVE NEW YORK WEASEL. John Pearce. Jour. Mamm., vol.18, no.4, pp.483-488, Nov., 1937.

(LITTLE WEASEL IN CAPTIVITY.) Das kleine Wiesel in der Gefangenschaft. Anton Pinsker. Zeitschr. f. Saeugetierk., Berlin, vol.6, no.6, pp.237-238, Dec. 15, 1931.

(OBSERVATIONS ON A LARGE CAPTIVE WEASEL (MUSTELA ERMINEA L.).) Beobachtungen an einem gefangenen grossen Wiesel (Mustela erminea L.). Hans Psenner. Zool. Garten, Leipzig, n.F., vol.12, nos. 4-6, pp.315-322, figs.2, Dec., 1940.

HABITS OF NEW YORK WEASEL IN CAPTIVITY. Arthur Svihla. Jour. Mamm., vol. 12, no.1, pp.67-68, Feb., 1931.

(OBSERVATIONS ON THE STEPPE POLECAT (PUTORIUS EVERSMANNI LESS.) IN CAPTIVITY.) Gefangenschaftsbeobachtungen am Steppeniltis (Putorius eversmanni Less.). I. Volsčanezkij. Zool.Garten, Leipzig, n.F., vol.7, nos.10-12, pp. 262-273, figs.7, Feb., 1935.

FERRETS AND FERRETING. CONTAINING INSTRUCTIONS FOR THE BREEDING, MANAGEMENT, AND WORKING OF FERRETS. 2nd ed., rev. and enl., London, L.U. Gill, pp.39, illus., pl., 1888.

(Mustela) Diseases and Parasites

BIOLOGICAL RELATIONSHIPS BETWEEN AMERICAN WEASEL (GENUS MUSTELA) AND NEMATODES OF THE GENUS SKRJABINGYLUS PETROV, 1927 (NEMATODA: METASTRONGYLIDAE), THE CAUSATIVE ORGANISMS OF CERTAIN LESIONS IN WEASEL SKULLS. Ellsworth C. Dougherty, E. Raymond Hall. Rev.Ibérica Parasitol., Granada, tomo extraordinario, pp.531-576, illus., Mar., 1955.

GUINEA-WORM IN A BONAPARTE WEASEL. Frans C. Goble. Jour. Mamm., vol. 23, no.2, p.221, May 14, 1942.

SKRJABINGYLUS CHITWOODORUM FROM THE FRONTAL SINUSES OF MEPHITIS NIGRA IN NEW YORK. Frans C. Goble. Jour. Mamm., vol.23, no.1, pp.95-97, Feb. 14, 1942.

SYNERGISM OF HUMAN INFLUENZA AND CANINE DISTEMPER VIRUSES IN FERRETS. Frank L. Horsfall, Edwin H. Lennette. Jour. Exper. Med., vol.72, no.3, pp.247-259, Sep.1, 1940.

ROLE OF HELMINTHIC INVASIONS AND INFECTIOUS DISEASES IN NUMBER DYNAMICS OF MUSTELA ERMINEA L. N.P. Lavrov. Narodnii Komissariat Zagotovok SSSR, Trudy Tsentralnoi Nauch-Issledovatelskoi Laboratorii Biologii, Oxotnichego Promysla i Tovarovedeniia Zhivotnogo Syria, Moscow, no.6, pp.151-163, 1944. (In Russian with English summary.)

SOME OBSERVATIONS ON FILAROIDES MUSTELARUM, A LITTLE-KNOWN NEMATODE, OCCURRING IN STOATS AND WEASELS. H.B. de Montmorency. Scottish Nat., no.214, pp.99-101, July-Aug., 1935.

(Mustela) Economic Importance

WEASELS ARE PROFITABLE. L.J.Kopp. Pennsylvania Game News, Harrisburg, vol. 21, no.10, pp.45-47, illus., Jan., 1951.

(IMPORTANCE OF BLACK WEASEL SKIN IN THE SHOE INDUSTRY.) Importancia de la piel de comadreja negra en la industria peletera. Carlos A. Marelli. La Chacra, vol.1, no.10, pp.54-55, 60, illus., Aug., 1931.

LIGHT FERRET (PUTORIUS EVERSMANNI) AND ITS ECONOMIC IMPORTANCE. P.A. Sviridenko. Trudy po Zaschite Rastenii. IV. seriia: Pozvonochyne (Bull. Plant. Protection, IV. ser: Vertebrates), Leningrad and Moscow, no.4, pp.1-62, figs.14, 1935. (In Russian with English summary.)

A TALK ON FITCH. K. Vanderbilt. Amer. Fur Breeder, vol.4, no.2, p.33, Aug., 1931.

GOLDEN WEASEL. China Jour., vol.12, no.5, p.302, May, 1930.

WEASEL AND THEIR CONTROL. U.S. Fish and Wildl. Serv., Wildl. Leaflet 360, p.1, July, 1954.

(Mustela) Embryology

EARLY STAGES IN THE DEVELOPMENT OF THE FERRET: THE FORMATION OF THE MESOBLAST AND NOTOCHORD. William J. Hamilton, Jr. Trans. Roy.Soc. Edinburgh, vol.59, pt.1, Session 1936-37, pp.165-195, figs.12, pls.7, June 18, 1937.

EARLY DEVELOPMENT OF FORRET: THE PRONUCLEI. Donald Mainland. Jour. Anat. vol.64, pp.262-287, 1930.

MEASUREMENT OF FERRET PRONUCLEI. Donald Mainland. Trans. Roy. Soc. Canada, ser.3, vol.25, sect.5, pp.33-42, May, 1931.

SIZES OF FERRET PRONUCLEI. Donald Mainland. Anat. Record, vol.49, no.2, pp.103-120, Apr., 1931.

PREIMPLANTATION STAGES IN THE LONG-TAILED WEASEL (MUSTELA FRENATA). Philip L. Wright. Anat. Record, vol.100, no.4, pp.593-608, Apr., 1948.

(Mustela) Eurasia

RECORD STOAT FROM NEAR GLASGOW. R. Gregory Absalom. Scottish Nat., no. 232, p.117, July-Aug., 1938.

STOATS, PUTORIUS ERMINEUS (LINNAEUS), OF JURA AND ISLAY. G.E.H. Barrett-Hamilton. Ann. Scot. Hist., no. 52, pp.203-206, Oct., 1904.

ON A NEW WEASEL FROM NORTHERN TONKIN. (Mustela tonkinensis) Bertil Björkegren. Arkiv f. Zool., Uppsala, vol. 33B, no.15, pp.1-4, figs.2, July 12, 1941.

(ERMINE OF THE UPPER ENGADIN.) Hermeline aus dem oberen Engadin. G. von Burg. Der Weidemann, no.51, p.409, Dec. 23, 1920.

(SWISS WEASELS AND ERMINES.) Schweizerische Wiesel und Hermeline. G. von Burg. Der Weidemann, no.48, pp.387-388, Dec. 2, 1920.

(WEASEL SPECIES OF THE SWISS ALPS.) Die Wieselarten der schweizerischen Alpen. G. von Burg. Der Weidemann, Wochenschrift f. Jagd, Fischfang, Hundezucht und Naturfreunde, Bulach, Switzerland, p. 388, Dec. 20, 1920.

(THE STEPPE POLECAT AND ITS GEOGRAPHIC DISTRIBUTION IN RUMANIA.) Dihorul de stepă şi distribuţia sa geografică in România. R.I. Călinescu. Bul. Soc. Regale Române Geogr., Bucureşti, vol.51, pp.107-114, map, pl.1, 1932. (With French summary.)

OCCURRENCE OF THE ERMINE IN THE PUNJAB. C.H. Donald. Jour. Bombay Nat. Hist. Soc., vol.27, pp.624-625, Mar. 31, 1921.

MOTTLED POLECAT (PUTORIUS SARMATICUS). EXTENSION OF KNOWN RANGE. J.O.S. Donald. Jour. Bombay Nat. Hist. Soc., vol.41, no.2, p.416, Dec., 1939. (Kohat District N.W. Frontier Prov., India.)

(THE FIELD POLECAT (MUSTELA EVERSMANNI LESS.) IN OUR COUNTRY.) A mezei görény (Mustela eversmanni Less.) hazánkban. Julius Éhik. Ann. Mus. Nat. Hungarici, vol.25, pp.1-38, illus., 1928. (Also translated in German.)

BIOLOGY OF THE SIBERIAN WEASEL. A.S. Fetisoff. Jour. Mamm., vol.17, no.1, pp.36-38, tbl.1, Feb., 1936.

GREAT STOATS. R.J. Flintoff. Northestern Nat., Arbroath, vol.11, no.3, pp. 266-267, Sep., 1936.

STOATS AND WEASELS--BROWN AND WHITE. R.J. Flintoff. Northwestern Nat., Arbroath, Scotland, vol.8, no.1, pp.36-45, Mar., 1933.

STOATS, BROWN AND WHITE: A NEW RECORD. R.J. Flintoff. Northwestern Nat., Arbroath, Scotland, vol.11, no.1, pp.43-45, Mar., 1936.

STOAT IN WINTER DRESS IN HERTFORDSHIRE. A.H. Foster. Trans. Hertfordshire Nat. Hist. Soc. and Field Club, Hertford, vol.22, pt.4, p.160, Aug., 1946.

OCCURRENCE OF THE STRIPE-BACKED WEASEL (MUSTELA STRIGIDORSA) IN THE NAGA HILLS. J.H. Hutton. Jour. Bombay Nat. Hist. Soc., vol.28, pp.795-796, June 30, 1922.

EXTENSION OF RANGE OF THE MARBLED POLE CAT (VORMELA PEREGUSNA GÜLD). R.S. Johnson. Jour. Bombay Nat. Hist. Soc., vol.43, no.2, pp.253-254, Aug., 1942.

CHANGES IN THE DISTRIBUTION OF THE POLECAT IN FINLAND. Olavi Kalela. Suomen Riista, Helsinki, vol.2, pp.77-96, figs.4, maps 3, 1948. (In Finnish with English summary.)

(OCCURRENCE OF THE TIGER POLECAT (PUTORIUS SARMATICUS) NEAR MARBURG.) Ueber das Vorkommen des Tigeriltis (Putorius sarmaticus) bei Marburg (S.H.S.) Otto Koller. Zool. Anzeiger, vol.83, p.70, 1929.

POLECAT OF EVERSMANN, A NEW MAMMAL FROM THE PLAINS OF CZECHOSLOVAKIA. Karel Kostron. Acta Acad.Sci. Moravo-Silesiacae (Práce Moravskoslezské Akad. ved Prirodnich), Brno, vol.20, no.3, pp.1-96, figs.18, 1948.

NEW FORM OF KOLONOCK OR MINK FROM NORTH MANCHURIA. (Mustela (Kolonocus) sibirica charbinensis.) A. S. Loukashkin. China Jour., vol.20, no.1, pp.47-52, illus., Jan., 1934.

(NEW LOOK AT THE CENTRAL ASIATIC WEASEL.) Novii podvid laski iz srednei Azii. L.G. Morozova-Turova. Zool.Zhurnal, Moscow, vol.32, no.6, pp.1267-1269, 1953.

BIOLOGY OF THE WEASEL IN KOLA PENINSULA IN CONNECTION WITH ITS COMPETITIVE RELATIONS WITH THE ERMINE. A.A. Nasimovich. Zool.Zhurnal, vol.28, pp.177-182, 1949.

(ON THE OCCURRENCE OF FOETORIUS BOCCAMELA IN RUMANIA.) Ueber das Vorkommen von Foetorius boccamela in Rumaenien. Alfred Nehring. Sitz. Ber. Gesell. Naturf. Freunde Berlin, no.8, p. 177, Oct. 15, 1901.

WHERE THE FOUMART HOLDS ITS OWN. WELSH VALLEYS WHERE POLECATS ARE STILL NUMEROUS. Frances Pitt. Field, London, vol.156, no.4057, p.444, figs.2, Sep. 27, 1930.

CHINESE MINK OR GOLDEN WEASEL. Arthur de C. Sowerby. China Jour., vol. 20, no.1, pp.44-47, Jan., 1934.

INCREASE IN STOATS AND WEASELS. A.H. Stewart. The Scottish Naturalist, no.176, p.38, Mar.-Apr., 1929.

ON THE VARIABILITY OF THE POLECAT (PUTORIUS PUTORIUS L.), ESPECIALLY ON A PECULIAR SPECIMEN FOUND IN LATVIA. Embrik Strand. Acta Univ. Latviensis, Riga, vol.20, pp.71-76, figs. 2, 1929.

NOTES ON BRITISH POLECATS AND FERRETS. H. Tetley. Proc. Zool. Soc. London, vol.115, pts.1-2, pp.212-217, fig.1, Oct., 1945.

ON THE BRITISH POLECATS. H.Tetley. Proc. Zool. Soc. London, vol.109, ser.B, pt.1, pp.37-39, pl.1, May 5, 1939.

ASSOGUE (PUTORIUS HIBERNICUS): A PECULIAR BRITISH MAMMAL. Oldfield Thomas. Nat. Science, vol.6, no.40, pp.377-378, pl.4, June, 1895.

ON THE LONG-LOST PUTORIUS AFRICANUS, DESM., AND ITS OCCURRENCE IN MALTA. Oldfield Thomas. Proc. Zool. Soc. London, pp.128-131, Feb. 5, 1895.

(MUSTELA HUNGARICA NOV. SPEC., A NEW WEASEL SPECIES OF HUNGARIAN MAMMAL FAUNA.) Mustela hungarica nov.spec., eine neue Wieselart der ungarischen Saeugetierfauna. Stephan Vasarhelyi. Zool. Anzeiger, Leipzig, vol.137, nos.11-12, pp.221-226, figs.3, Apr.1, 1942.

(TIGER POLECAT IN BULGARIA.) Der Tigeriltis (Vormela peregusna Gueldenstaedt) in Bulgarien. Heinrich Wolf. Zool. Garten, n.F., vol.12, nos.4-6, pp.322-325, illus., Dec., 1940.

ON THE SPECIFIC IDENTITY OF THE WEASEL FOUND IN MALTA. Charles A. Wright. Proc. Zool. Soc. London, pp.312-313, 1875.

AN INDIAN STOAT. R.C. Wroughton. Jour. Bombay Nat. Hist. Soc., vol.18, no.4, pp.882-883, Nov. 15, 1908.

(Mustela) Habits, Behavior

WINTER FOOD HABITS OF THE SHORT-TAILED WEASEL IN NORTHERN MINNESOTA. Shaler E. Aldous, J. Manweiler. Jour. Mamm., vol.23, no.3, pp.250-255, Aug. 14, 1942.

NOTES ON THE KILLING TECHNIQUE OF THE NEW YORK WEASEL. Durward L. Allen. Jour. Mamm., vol.19, no.2, pp.225-229, May 14, 1938.

A STOAT'S STRANGE CONDUCT. ATTACKING A HORSE AND A DONKEY. H. Mortimer Batten. Field, London, vol. 153, p.73, Jan. 10, 1929.

WEASELS AND STOATS. DO THEY MESMERIZE THEIR PREY? H. Mortimer Batten. Field, London, vol.168, no.4366, p.504, Aug. 29, 1936.

(WEASEL HUNTING A GREEN LIZARD.) Wieseljagd auf eine Smaragdeidechse. O. de Beaux. Zeitschr. f. Saeugetierk., vol. 2, no.3, pp.199-200, 1929.

ACCOUNT OF A WEASEL IN A TREE. Ernest S. Booth. Jour. Mamm., vol.26, no.4, p.439, Feb. 12, 1946.

HABITS OF THE MOUNTAIN WEASEL (MUSTELA ARIZONENSI MEARNS), M.D. Bryant. Yosemite Nat. Notes, Yosemite, vol.19, no.5, p.36, May, 1940.

WEASEL LEARNS BY EXPERIENCE. A.R. Cahn. Jour. Mamm., vol.17, no.3, p.286, Aug., 1936.

STOAT FEEDING YOUNG ON ROCK PIPITS. E.F. Clowes. Irish Naturalists' Jour., vol.4, no.11, pp.217-218, Sep., 1933.

NEST OF THE LEAST WEASEL. Stuart Criddle. Canadian Field-Nat., Sutton West, vol.61, no.2, p.69, Mar.-Apr., 1947.

WEASEL NOT ALWAYS WICKED. J.M. Edson. Murrelet, vol.11, no.2, pp.16-17, May, 1930.

(INBORN AND ACQUIRED IN THE TECHNIQUE OF KILLING PREY (EXPERIMENTS WITH THE POLECAT PUTORIUS PUTORIUS L.).) Angeborenes und Erworbenes in der Technik des Beutetoetens (Versuche am Iltis, Putorius putorius L.). Irenäus Eibl-Eibesfeldt. Zeitschr. f. Saeugetierk., Berlin, vol.21, nos.3-4, pp.135-137, Feb. 28, 1957.

WEASEL CAUGHT IN MOLE'S RUN (MUSTELA NIVALIS). N.F. Ellison. Northwest Nat., Seattle, vol.21, pp.246-247, 1946.

FOOD HABITS OF A WEASEL FAMILY. Paul L. Errington. Jour. Mamm., vol.17, no.4, pp.406-407, Nov., 1936.

EGG STEALING BY STOATS. Theodore Fisher. Field, London, vol.167, no.4355, p.1444, June 13, 1936.

WEASEL IN POCKET GOPHER BURROW. Clifford Florine. Jour. Mamm., vol.23, no.2, p.213, May 14, 1942.

EGG-STEALING STOATS. J.H.B. Forster. Field, London, vol.168, no.4358, p.35, July 4, 1936.

SPEED OF THE WEASEL. F.W. Frohawk. Field, London, vol.158, no.4112, p.585, Oct. 17, 1931.

KILLING TECHNIQUES OF THE NEW YORK WEASEL. Fred A. Glover. Pa.Game News, vol.13, no.10, pp.11, 23, Jan., 1943.

POPULATION STUDY OF WEASEL IN PENNSYLVANIA. Fred A. Glover. MS thesis, Pa. State Coll., 1942.

STUDY OF THE ACTIVITIES OF THE NEW YORK WEASEL. Fred A. Glover. Pa.Game News, Harrisburg, vol. 14, no.6, pp.8-9, illus., Sep., 1943.

WEASEL FIRES THE FLASH. Tappan Gregory. Jour. Mamm., vol.10, no.3, pp.221-224, pls.18-19, Aug., 1929.

PERSISTENT WEASEL. Mary S. Grosjean. Jour. Mamm., vol.23, no.4, p.443, Nov. 14, 1942.

NOTES ON BEHAVIOR OF LONG-TAILED WEASEL IN UTAH. Richard M. Hansen. Jour. Mamm., vol.33, no.4, p.492, Nov. 19, 1952.

OBSERVATIONS ON A NEST OF THE LONG-TAILED WEASEL. Lloyd G. Ingles. Jour. Mamm., vol.20, no.2, pp.253-254, May, 1939.

OBSERVATIONS ON THE SHORT-TAILED WEASEL IN CALIFORNIA. Lloyd G. Ingles. Jour. Mamm., vol.23, no.4, pp.446-448, pl.1, Nov. 14, 1942.

PECULIARITIES OF THE ACTIVITY RHYTHM AND TEMPERATURE PREFERENCE IN COMMON AND STEPPE POLECATS (PUTORIUS PUTORIUS L. AND P. EVERSMANNI LESS.). N. Kalabukhov. Zool. Jour. USSR, Moscow, vol.22, no.3, pp.178-192, figs.6, tbls.6, 1943. (With English summary.)

KILLING TECHNIQUE OF THE WEASEL. Aldo Leopold. Jour. Mamm., vol.18, no.1, pp.98-99, Feb. 14, 1937.

I TRAP NO MORE WEASELS. Joseph W. Lippincott. Pa.Game News, vol.10, no.12, pp.6, 25, Mar., 1940.

NOTES ON THE BEHAVIOUR OF THE WEASEL. Bertram Lloyd. Trans.Hertforshire Nat. Hist. Soc., and Field Club, vol.21, pt.2, pp.164-166, Feb., 1940.

OBSERVATIONS ON THE POLECAT (PUTORIUS PUTORIUS LINN.) IN NEW ZEALAND. Charles McCann. Rec. Dom. Mus., vol.2, pt.3, pp.151-165, Jan., 1956.

AN INQUISITIVE WEASEL. D.A. Miller. Yosemite Nat. Notes, vol.24, no.10, pp.103-104, Oct., 1945.

FEEDING HABIT OF THE LONG-TAILED WEASEL. Frederic W. Miller. Jour. Mamm., vol.12, no.2, p.164, May, 1931.

NOTES ON MUSTELA FRENATA FRENATA. Stanley Mulaik. Jour. Mamm., vol.19, no. 1, pp.104-105, Feb. 14, 1938.

WEASEL GOES HUNGRY. Adolph Murie. Jour. Mamm., vol.16, no.4, pp.321-322, Nov., 1935.

WEASEL FORAGING PATTERNS IN THE ROBINSON LAKE AREA, IDAHO. Bill F.

Musgrove. Murrelet, vol.32, no.1, pp.8-11, Jan.-Apr., 1951.

WEASEL ASLEEP. Richard Oakley. Field, London, vol.149, p.677, Apr. 21, 1927.

NOTES ON THE TEMPERAMENT OF THE NEW YORK WEASEL. Charles Oehler. Jour. Mamm., vol.25, no.2, p.198, May 25, 1945.

MOUNTAIN WEASEL MAKES A KILL. Herbert O'Neal. Yosemite Nature Notes, vol.12, no. 11, p.101, Nov., 1933.

EARTHWORMS AS A SUPPLEMENTARY FOOD OF WEASELS. F.L. Osgood. Jour. Mamm., vol.17, no.1, p.64, Feb., 1936.

INVETERATE POACHER. (Stoat.) Arthur J. Parr. Field, London, vol.162, no.4201, p.45, figs., July 1, 1933.

(GROUP BEHAVIOR OF A LARGER NUMBER OF FITCHETS (PUTORIUS PUTORIUS L.) AND FERRETS (PUTORIUS FURO L.) OF VARIOUS AGE LEVELS.) Gesellschaftshaltung einer groesseren Anzahl von Iltissen (Putorius putorius L.) und Frettchen (Putorius furo L.) verschiedener Altersstufen. Hans Petzsch. Zool. Garten, Leipzig, n.F., vol.21, no.3, pp.188-190, illus., 1955.

HABITS OF THE LEAST WEASEL (MUSTELA RIXOSA) IN NORTHEASTERN IOWA. Emmett B. Polderboer. Jour. Mamm., vol. 23, no.2, pp.145-147, May, 1942.

WINTER AND SPRING HABITS OF WEASEL IN CENTRAL IOWA. Emmet B. Polderboer et al. Jour. Wildl. Mgt., vol.5, no.1, pp. 115-119, Jan., 1941.

NOTES ON THE ECOLOGY OF WEASELS IN GUNNISON COUNTY, COLORADO. H.F. Quick. Jour. Mamm., vol.32, no.3, pp.281-290, Aug., 1951.

TREE CLIMBING WEASEL. R.J. Rutter. Canadian Field-Nat., vol.44, pp.20-21, Jan. 2, 1930.

WEASELS AND SNAKES IN GOPHER BURROWS. Theo. H. Scheffer. Murrelet, vol. 13, no.2, pp.54-55, May 30, 1932.

(OBSERVATIONS DURING THE RAISING OF ERMINES (MUSTELA ERMINEA AESTIVA KERR 1792).) Beobachtungen bei der Aufzucht von Hermelinen, Mustela erminea aestiva Kerr, 1892. Fritz Schmidt. Saeugetierk. Mitteil., Stuttgart, vol.2, no. 4, pp.166-174, illus., Oct. 1, 1954.

NEST OF THE WASHINGTON WEASEL (MUSTELA WASHINGTONI). William T. Shaw. Jour. Mamm., vol.2, no.3, pp. 167-168, Aug., 1921.

WEASELS AND THEIR HABITS. R. W. Shuffeldt. Amer. Forestry, vol.26, pp. 163-169, figs.1-10, Mar., 1920.

(BRIEF OBSERVATIONS ON THE ERMINE MUSTELA ERMINEA L.) Kleine Beboachtungen am Hermelin, Mustela erminea L. G. Steinbacher. Zool. Garten, Leipzig, n.F., vol.18, nos.1-2, p.61, 1951.

WEASEL PREYS ON LARVAL SALAMANDER. Franklin W. Sturges. Jour. Mamm., vol. 26, no.4, pp.567-568, Dec. 14, 1955.

ACTIVITIES OF A WEASEL AT A WOODRAT COLONY. Elden H. Vestal. Jour. Mamm., vol.18, no.3, p.364, Aug., 1937.

BEHAVIOUR OF STOATS. M.V. Wenner. Field, London, vol.148, p.205, July 29, 1926.

WEASEL ATTACKS A MAN. H.M. Wight. Jour. Mamm., vol.13, no.2, pp.163-164, May, 1932.

(Mustela) Mexico, Central and South America

NEOTROPICAL WEASELS. J.A. Allen. Bull. Amer. Mus. Nat. Hist., vol.35, pp.89-111, Apr. 28, 1916.

(THE FIRST AUTHENTIC EXAMPLE OF A GENUINE WEASEL OF BRAZIL.) O primeiro exemplar authentico de uma genuina doninha do Brazil. E.A. Goeldi. Bol. Mus. Paraense, vol.3, pp.195-203, 1901.

NEW WEASEL FROM COSTA RICA. E.A. Goldman. Proc. Biol. Soc. Washington, vol.25, pp.9-10, Jan. 23, 1912.

DESCRIPTION OF A NEW MUSTELA FROM QUITO. John Edward Gray. Proc. Zool. Soc. London, p.55, 1864.

NEW WEASEL FROM BOLIVIA AND PERU. (Mustela frenata boliviensis.) E. Raymond Hall. Proc. Biol. Soc. Washington, vol.51, pp.67-68, Mar. 18, 1938.

NEW WEASEL FROM PANAMA. (Mustela frenata panamensis.) E. Raymond Hall. Proc. Biol. Soc. Washington, vol.45, pp.139-140, Sep.9, 1932.

NEW WEASEL FROM PERU. (Mustela frenata helleri.) E. Raymond Hall. Proc. Biol. Soc. Washington, vol.48, pp.143-146, Aug. 22, 1935.

REMARKS ON THE PRIMITIVE STRUCTURE OF "MUSTELA STOLZMANNI. "WITH A LIST OF SOUTH AMERICAN SPECIES AND SUBSPECIES OF THE GENUS "MUSTELA." E. Raymond Hall. Physis, Buenos Aires, vol.16, no.48, pp.159-178, pl.1, maps 2, May, 1939.

(DESCRIPTION OF A NEW SPECIES OF MUSTELA FROM CENTRAL PERU.) Description d'une nouvell Espèce de Mustela du Pérou Central. L. Taczanowski. Proc. Zool. Soc. London, pp.311-312, pl., 1874.

(Mustela) North America

RICHARDSON'S ERMINE ADDED TO THE LIST OF QUEBEC MAMMALS WITH A SURVEY OF THE WEASELS FOUND IN THE PROVINCE. Rudolph Martin Anderson. Rapport Annuel 1945 Seciéte Provancher, Québec, pp.20-32, 1946.

BLACK-FOOTED FERRET IN OKLAHOMA. M. Dale Arvey, Bryan P. Glass. Jour. Mamm., vol.31, no.4, p.460, Nov. 21, 1950.

OCCURRENCE OF MUSTELA FRENATA ARHURI IN TEXAS. Rollin H. Baker. Jour. Mamm., vol.25, no.3, p.319, Sep. 8, 1944.

REVIEW OF THE WEASELS OF EASTERN NORTH AMERICA. Outram Bangs. Proc. Biol. Soc. Washington, vol.10, pp.1-24, pls.1-3, Feb. 25, 1896.

(Review by C. Hart Merriam of) REVIEW OF THE WEASELS OF EASTERN NORTH AMERICA. Outram Bangs. Science, n.s., vol.3, no.67, p.525, Apr. 10, 1896.

LEAST WEASEL (MUSTELA RIXOSA) IN WASHINGTON. James R. Beer. Jour. Mamm., vol.29, no.3, pp.296-297, Aug. 31, 1948.

LEAST WEASEL IN WISCONSIN. James R. Beer. Jour. Mamm., vol.31, no.2, pp.146-149, fig.1, May 25, 1950.

NOTES ON THE SHORT-TAILED WEASEL IN UTAH. William H. Behle, Richard M. Hansen. Jour. Mamm., vol.32, no.2, pp. 226-227, May 21, 1951.

NOTE ON THE NEST AND YOUNG OF THE SMALL BROWN WEASEL. Sherman C. Bishop. Jour. Mamm., vol.4, no.1, pl.5, pp.26-27, Feb., 1923.

FIRST NEW BRUNSWICK SPECIMEN OF THE NORTHEASTERN LONG-TAILED ERMINE (MUSTELA FRENATA OCCISOR (BANGS)). N.R. Brown. Canadian Field-Nat., Ottawa, vol.62, no.1, pp.43-44, Jan.-Feb., 1948.

STATUS OF THE BLACK-FOOTED FERRET. Victor H. Cahalane. Jour. Mamm., vol.35, no.3, pp.418-424, map, Aug.20, 1954.

LONG-TALIED WEASEL NEAR QUEBEC CITY. Austin W. Cameron. Jour. Mamm., vol.33, no.2, p.253, May 16, 1952.

WEASELS OF NORTH DAKOTA. J.E. Campbell. N.Dakota Outdoors, Bismarck, vol.7, no.9, pp.13-14, illus., Mar., 1945.

MUSTELA ALLEGHENIENSIS IN NORTH CAROLINA. L. Church. Jour. Mamm., vol.6, no.4, p.281, Nov., 1925.

LEAST WEASEL IN NEW YORK. Arthur H. Cook. Jour. Mamm., vol.32, no.2, p.225, May 21, 1951.

BLACK-FOOTED FERRET IN MONTANA. Wilfred D. Crabb, Gordon W. Watson. Jour. Mamm., vol.31, no.1, p.99, Feb. 21, 1950.

WEASELS OF SOUTHERN MANITOBA. Norman Criddle, Stuart Criddle. Canadian Field-Nat., vol.39, pp.142-148, Sep. 30, 1925.

OCCURRENCE OF THE LEAST WEASEL IN MICHIGAN. Ned Dearborn. Jour. Mamm., vol.13, no.3, p.277, Aug., 1932.

LEAST WEASEL IN INDIANA. L.C. Dice. Jour. Mamm., vol.9, no.1, p.63, Feb., 1928.

LEAST WEASEL IN SASKATCHEWAN. F. A. Dunk. Jour. Mamm., vol.27, no.4, p. 392, Nov. 25, 1946.

OCCURRENCE OF THE BLACK-FOOTED FERRET IN NEBRASKA. Edson Fichter, J. Knox Jones, Jr. Jour. Mamm., vol. 34, no.3, pp.385-388, fig.1, Aug. 14, 1953.

BLACK-FOOTED FERRET IN SOUTH DAKOTA. W.E. Garst. Jour. Mamm., vol. 35, no.4, p.594, Nov. 29, 1954.

OBSERVATIONS ON THE NEW YORK WEASEL, WITH REMARKS ON ITS WINTER DICHROMATISM. C.V. Green. Jour. Mamm., vol.17, no.3, pp.247-249, Aug., 1936.

FOUR NEW ERMINES FROM THE ISLANDS OF SOUTHEASTERN ALASKA. E. Raymond Hall. Proc. Biol. Soc. Washington, vol.57, pp.35-42, June 28, 1944.

FOUR NEW ERMINES FROM THE PACIFIC NORTHWEST. E. Raymond Hall. Jour. Mamm., vol.26, no.1, pp.75-78, Feb.27, 1945.

MUSTELA CICOGNANII, THE SHORT TAILED WEASEL, INCORRECTLY ASCRIBED TO OHIO. E. Raymond Hall. Amer. Midland Nat., vol.18, no.2, p. 304, Mar., 1937.

NEW WEASEL FROM LOUISIANA. E. Raymond Hall. Proc. Biol. Soc. Washington, vol.40, pp.193-194, Dec. 2, 1927.

WEASELS OF NEW YORK. THEIR NATURAL HISTORY AND ECONOMIC STATUS. W.J. Hamilton, Jr. Amer. Midland Nat., vol.14, no.4, pp.289-344, figs.3, pls. 6-9, July, 1933.

MICHIGAN RECORDS OF THE LEAST WEASEL. Robert T. Hatt. Jour. Mamm., vol.17, no.4, pp.414-415, Nov., 1936.

SMALLEST CARNIVORE. Robert T. Hatt. Cranbrook Inst. Sci., Bloomfield Hills, Mich., News-Letter, vol.5, no.5, p.2, Apr., 1936. (Mustela rixosa allegheniensis.)

SHORT-TAILED WEASEL IN UTAH AND COLORADO. C. Lynn Hayward. Jour. Mamm., vol.30, no.4, pp.436-437, Nov. 17, 1950.

SOUTHERN LIMITS OF THE LEAST WEASEL (MUSTELA RIXOSA) IN CENTRAL UNITED STATES. Donald F. Hoffmeister. Trans. Illinois Acad. Sci., vol.48, pp.195-196, 1956.

DESCRIPTION OF A NEW WEASEL FROM ALABAMA. Arthur H. Howell. Proc. Biol. Soc. Washington, vol.26, pp.139-140, May 21, 1913.

TWO NEW WEASELS FROM THE UNITED STATES. Harltey H.T. Jackson. Proc. Biol. Soc. Washington, vol.26, pp.123-124, May 21, 1913.

LEAST WEASEL IN GLACIER NATIONAL PARK. R.R. Lechleitner. Jour. Mamm., vol.35, no.4, p.594, Nov. 29, 1954.

NOTES ON THE ALLEGHENIAN LEAST WEASEL IN VIRGINIA. Leonard M. Llewellyn. Jour. Mamm., vol.23, no.4, pp.439-440, Nov. 14, 1942.

LEAST WEASEL IN ST. JOSEPH COUNTY (INDIANA). Marcus Ward Lyon, Jr. Amer. Midland Nat., Notre Dame, vol.22, no. 1, p.216, July, 1939.

MORE LEAST WEASELS IN INDIANA. Marcus Ward Lyon, Jr. Amer. Midland Nat., Notre Dame, vol.23, no.1, p.253, Jan., 1940.

TWO NEW RECORDS OF THE LEAST WEASEL IN INDIANA. Marcus Ward

Lyon, Jr. Amer. Midland Nat., vol.14, no.4, pp.345-349, figs.2, July, 1933.

THE NEW YORK WEASEL. Frank McCamey. New England Nat., Boston, vol.2, no.13, p.22, illus., Dec., 1941.

SYNOPSIS OF THE WEASELS OF NORTH AMERICA. C. Hart Merriam. N.American Fauna, no.11, pp.33, figs.16, pls.5, June 30, 1896.

CONCERNING A RECENT RECORD OF MUSTELA RIXOSA IN COLORADO. F.W. Miller. Jour. Mamm., vol.14, no.4, p. 368, Nov., 1933.

LIFE HISTORY NOTES ON THE FLORIDA WEASEL. Joseph C. Moore. Proc. Florida Acad. Sci., Gainesville, vol.7, no.4, pp. 247-263, 1944 (1945).

ALLEGHENIAN LEAST WEASEL IN PENNSYLVANIA. Robert D. Moore. Jour. Mamm., vol.10, no.3, pp.252-254, Aug. 1929.

LEAST WEASEL IN IOWA. Thomas J. Morrissey. Jour. Mamm., vol.22, no.3, p.326, Aug. 14, 1941.

NOTES ON THE NEW YORK WEASEL (MUSTELA NOVEBORACENSIS). D.G. Nichols, J.T. Nichols. Jour. Mamm., vol. 16, no.4, pp.297-299, Nov., 1935.

DESCRIPTION OF A NEW WEASEL FROM THE QUEEN CHARLOTTE ISLANDS, B.C. Edward Preble. Proc. Biol. Soc. Washington, vol.12, pp.169-170, Aug. 10, 1898.

NORTHERN LONG-TAILED WEASEL IN NEW HAMPSHIRE. Norman A. Preble. Jour. Mamm., vol.18, no.4, p.515, Nov., 1937.

HABITS AND ECONOMICS OF THE NEW YORK WEASEL IN MICHIGAN. H.F.Quick. Jour. Wildl.Mgt., vol.8, no.1, pp.71-78, Jan., 1944.

AN INVESTIGATION OF THE HABITS AND ECONOMICS OF THE NEW YORK WEASEL IN WASHINGTON COUNTY MICHIGAN. H.F. Quick. MS thesis, Univ. Mich., 1940.

NEW WEASEL FROM WESTERN PENNSYLVANIA. Samuel N. Rhoads. Proc. Acad. Nat. Sci., Philadelphia, pp.751-754, Feb. 7, 1901.

LEAST WEASEL (MUSTELA RIXOSA) IN PENNSYLVANIA. Neil D. Richmond, Robert D. McDowell. Jour. Mamm., vol. 33, no.2, pp.251-253, illus., May 16, 1952.

LEAST WEASEL MUSTELA RIXUSA (sic ) (BANGS) IN ONTARIO. W.E. Saunders. Canadian Field-Nat., vol.46, no.6, p. 146, Sep., 1932.

OCCURRENCE OF THE LEAST WEASEL NEAR DENVER. Ernest Thompson Seton. Jour. Mamm., vol.14, no.1, p.70, Feb., 1933.

WEASEL OBSERVED AT SWINGING BRIDGE. Lloyd Mason Smith. Yosemite Nat.Notes, vol.26, no.10, pp.110-111, illus., Oct., 1947.

ANOTHER LEAST WEASEL SPECIMEN FROM ONTARIO. (MUSTELA RIXOSA RIXOSA.) L.L. Snyder. Canadian Field-Nat., vol.49, no.6, p.109, Sep., 1935.

NEW ARCTIC WEASEL FROM SOUTHAMPTON ISLAND, HUDSON BAY. (Mustela arctica semplei.) Geo.Miksch Sutton, Wm. J. Hamilton, Jr. Ann.Carnegie Mus., vol. 21, no.2, pp.79-81, Apr., 1932.

LEAST WEASEL IN THE STATE OF WASHINGTON. Arthur Svihla. Murrelet, vol.13, no.1, p.24, Jan., 1932.

LEAST WEASEL IN MINNESOTA AND ITS FLUCTUATION IN NUMBERS. Gustav Swanson, P.O. Fryklund. Amer.Midland Nat., Notre Dame, vol.16, no.1, pp.120-126, figs. 1-6, Jan., 1935.

RECORDS OF THE NEW-MEXICAN BRIDLED WEASEL IN KANSAS. Marvin D. Swilling. Jour. Mamm., vol.36, no.2, p.292, May 26, 1955.

FUR-BEARING MAMMALS OF WYOMING. Earl M. Thomas. Wyo. Wild Life, pt.6, vol.16, no.8, pp.20-26, illus., Aug., 1952. (Weasels.)

THE AMERICAN FERRET. Frederick W. True. Science, vol.6, no.150, pp.549-550, Dec. 18, 1885.

NEW SOUTHERN RECORD FOR MUSTELA ERMINEA CICORGNANII. Alberto Wanous Vázquez. Jour. Mamm., vol.37, no.1, pp. 113-114, Feb. 28, 1956.

LEAST WEASEL IN NORTH DAKOTA. Alex. Walker. Jour. Mamm., vol.8, no. 2, p.158, May, 1927.

(Footnote by Hartley H.T. Jackson to)LEAST WEASEL IN NORTH DAKOTA. Alex.Walker. Jour. Mamm., vol.8, no.2, p.158, May 11, 1927.

WEASEL NEW TO WISCONSIN'S FAUNA. Henry L. Ward. Bull. Wisc.Nat.Hist.Soc., vol.5, no.1, pp.63-64, Jan., 1907.

LEAST WEASEL IN PENNSYLVANIA. Thos. E. Winecoff. Jour. Mamm., vol.11, no.3, pp.312-313, Aug., 1930.

OUR SMALLEST CARNIVORE. Albert A. Wright. Ohio Naturalist, vol.5, no.3, pp. 251-254, fig.1, 1905.

BLACK-FOOTED FERRET (MUSTELA NIGRIPES) IN SOUTH DAKOTA. Stanley P. Young. Jour. Mamm., vol.35, no.3, p.443, Aug. 20, 1954.

ARIZONA SPECIMENS OF THE BLACK-FOOTED FERRET. Stanley P. Young, Arthur F. Halloran. Jour. Mamm., vol.33, no.2, p.251, May 16, 1952.

LEAST WEASEL TRAPPED IN WESTERN NORTH DAKOTA. FIRST OF SPECIES CAUGHT IN STATE IN RECENT YEARS. N. Dakota Outdoors, Bismarck, vol.6, no.9, p.3, Mar., 1944.

(Mustela) Pelage, Coloration

ANOMALOUS SEASONAL COAT-COLOR-CHANGES IN A SMALL MALE BONAPARTE'S WEASEL (MUSTELA CICOGNANII CICOGNANII BONAPARTE). Thomas Hume Bissonette. Amer. Midland Nat., Notre Dame, vol.28, no.2, pp.327-333, illus., Sep., 1942.

EXPERIMENTAL MODIFICATION AND CONTROL OF MOLTS AND CHANGES OF COAT-COLOR IN WEASELS BY CONTROLLED LIGHTING. Thomas Hume Bissonette, Earl Elmore Bailey. Ann. New York Acad. Sci., vol.45, art.6, pp. 221-260, fig.1, pls.7, Apr.7, 1944.

(Review by N.W. Hosley of) EXPERIMENTAL MODIFICATION AND CONTROL OF MOLTS AND CHANGES OF COAT-COLOR IN WEASELS BY CONTROLLED LIGHTING. Thomas Hume Bissonette, Earl Elmore Bailey. Jour. Mamm., vol.28, no.3, pp.303-304, Aug. 19, 1947.

WHITE WEASEL FROM THE LOWER WHITE RIVER, WASHINGTON. Philip W. Chenney. Murrelet, Seattle, vol.29, no.2, p.29, Dec. 1, 1948.

A WHITE STOAT. R.J. Flintoff. Northwestern Nat., Arbroath, vol.11, no.3, p. 267, pl.11, Sep., 1936.

SEASONAL COLOUR CHANGES OF STOAT. A.S. Frank. North Western Nat., Scotland, vol.8, no.3, pp.242-243, Sep., 1933.

COLOUR CHANGE IN THE STOAT. F. W. Frohawk. Field, London, vol.149, p.201, Feb. 3, 1927.

SPRING COLOR CHANGE OF THE NEW YORK WEASEL. Fred A. Glover. Pa. Game News, Harrisburg, vol.13, no.7, pp.18, 32, 1942.

ON A PECULIARLY COLORED STOAT IN THE COLLECTIONS OF THE LEYDEN MUSEUM. A.F. Jentink. Notes Leyden Mus., vol.22, no.2, pp.25-26, Nov., 1899.

STOAT'S WINTER COAT. Herbert Maxwell. Scottish Nat., no.212, p.50, Mar.-Apr., 1935.

(RED-YELLOW VARIETY OF POLECAT (PUTORIUS PUTORIUS LINN.) IN THE GOVERNMENT OF SMOLENSK.) W. A. Melander. Wissensch. Mitteil. Univ. Smolensk., vol.3, pp.135-143, 1926. (In Russian with German summary.)

FALL MOULT OF MUSTELA LONGICAUDA. Frederic W. Miller. Jour. Mamm., vol.12, no.2, pp.150-152, May, 1931.

THE SPRING MOULT OF MUSTELA LONGICAUDA. Frederic W. Miller. Jour. Mamm., vol.11, no.4, pp.471-473, Nov., 1930.

OBSERVATIONS ON THE SEASONAL HAIR MOULT IN A NEW YORK STATE WEASEL (MUSTELA NOVEBORACENSIS). Charles V. Noback. Bull. New York Zool. Soc., vol. 38, no.1, pp.25-27, pls.6, Jan.-Feb., 1935.

(COLOR CHANGE IN THE ERMINE.) Der Farbenwechsel beim Hermelin. Hans Psenner. Zool. Garten, vol.14, no.3, pp.149-153, illus., 1942.

CHANGE OF PELAGE IN THE STOAT MUSTELA ERMINEA L. Miriam Rothschild. Nature, London, vol.149, no.3768, p.78, Jan. 17, 1942.

PELAGE CHANGE OF THE STOAT, MUSTELA ERMINEA L. Miriam Rothschild. Nature, London, vol.154, no.3901, pp.180-181, Aug. 5, 1944.

NOTE ON CHANGE OF PELAGE IN THE STOAT (MUSTELA ERMINEA L.). Meriam Rothschild, Charles Lane. Proc. Zool.Soc. London, vol.128, no.4, p.602, July 24, 1957.

(HOW DOES THE SPOTTY YELLOW COLORATION OF THE ERMINE (MUSTELA ERMINEA L.) COME ABOUT?) Wie kommt die stellenweise Gelbfaerbung des winterweissen Wiesels (Mustela erinea L.) zustande? S. Schumacher. Zeitschr. f. Morph. u.Ökologie der Tiere, vol.11, pp.229-234, fig.1, July 3, 1928.

ALBINO WEASEL IN LANCASHIRE. Fredk. J. Stubbs. Naturalist, London, no.850, p. 336, Nov., 1927.

(ON THE VARIATIONS IN THE COAT OF PUTORIUS AURIVENTER HODGSON OF SOUTHERN CHINA.) Sur les variations de pelage du Putorius auriventer (Hodgson) du Sud de la Chine. E. Trouessart. Bull. Mus. d'hist. nat., Paris, no.6, pp.1-2, July, 1895.

(Mustela) Physiology, Experimental Biology

INDUCTION OF FERTILITY AND PREGNANCY IN THE ANOESTROUS FERRET. M. Allanson et al. Proc. Roy. Soc. London, ser.B., vol.115, no.B 795, pp.410-421, pls.17-18, Aug. 1, 1934.

INFLUENCE OF LIGHT ON THE HYPOPHYSIS, EFFECTS OF LONG-CONTINUED "NIGHT LIGHTING" ON HYPOPHYSECTOMIZED FEMALE FERRETS AND THOSE WITH OPTIC NERVES CUT. Thomas Hume Bissonnette. Endocrinology, Bull.Assoc. Study Internal Secretions, vol.22, no.1, pp. 92-103, tbls.3, Jan., 1938.

LIGHT AND SEXUAL CYCLES IN STARLINGS AND FERRETS. Thomas Hume Bissonnette. Quart. Review Biol., vol.8, no.2, pp.201-208, June, 1933.

MODIFICATION OF MAMMALIAN SEXUAL CYCLES; REACTIONS OF FERRETS (PUTORIUS VULGARIS) OF BOTH SEXES TO ELECTRIC LIGHT ADDED AFTER DARK IN NOVEMBER AND DECEMBER. Thomas Hume Bissonnette. Proc. Roy. Soc. London, ser.B, vol.110, no.B 767, pp.322-336, pl.13, Apr. 1, 1932.

MODIFICATION OF MAMMALIAN SEXUAL CYCLES. II. EFFECTS UPON YOUNG MALE FERRETS (PUTORIUS VULGARIS) OF CONSTANT EIGHT AND ONE-HALF HOUR DAYS AND OF SIX HOURS OF ILLUMINATION AFTER DARK, BETWEEN NOVEMBER AND JUNE. Thomas Hume Bissonnette. Biol. Bull., vol.68, no.2, pp. 300-313, pl.1, Apr., 1935.

MODIFICATION OF MAMMALIAN SEXUAL CYCLES. III. REVERSAL OF THE CYCLE IN MALE FERRETS (PUTORIUS VULGARIS) BY INCREASING PERIODS OF EXPOSURE TO LIGHT BETWEEN OCTOBER SECOND AND MARCH THIRTIETH. Thomas Hume Bissonnette. Jour. Exper. Zool., Philadelphia, vol.71, no.2, pp.341-368, pls.3, Aug. 5, 1935.

MODIFICATION OF MAMMALIAN SEXUAL CYCLES. IV. DELAY OF OESTRUS AND INDUCTION OF ANOESTRUS IN FEMALE FERRETS BY REDUCTION OF ITENSITY AND DURATION OF DAILY LIGHT PERIODS IN THE NORMAL OESTROUS SEASON. Thomas Hume Bissonnette. Jour. Exper. Biol., vol.12, no.4, pp.315-320, Oct., 1935.

RELATIONS OF HAIR CYCLES IN FERRETS TO CHANGES IN THE ANTERIOR HYPOPHYSIS AND TO LIGHT CYCLES. Thomas Hume Bissonnette. Anat. Rec., vol.63, no. 2, pp.159-168, Sep. 25, 1935.

SOME RECENT STUDIES ON PHOTO-PERIODICITY IN ANIMALS. Thomas Hume Bissonnette. Trans. New York Acad. Sci., ser.2, vol.5, no.3, pp.43-51, Jan., 1943. (Experiments with molting of weasels.)

LITTERS FROM FERRETS IN JANUARY INDUCED BY INCREASED EXPOSURES TO LIGHT AFTER NIGHTFALL. Thomas Hume Bissonnette, Earl E. Bailey. Amer. Nat., Lancaster, vol.70, no.730, pp.454-458, Sep.-Oct., 1936.

DELAYED IMPLANTATION IN THE STOAT (MUSTELA MUSTELA). Ruth Deanesly. Nature, London, vol.151, no.3830, pp.365-366, Mar. 27, 1943.

THE EFFECT OF PITUITARY STALK SECTION ON LIGHT-INDUCED OESTRUS IN THE FERRET. B.T. Donovan, G.W.Harris. Jour. Physiol., London, vol.131, no.1, pp. 102-114, Jan., 1956.

CERVICAL SYMPATHETIC SYSTEM AND LIGHT-INDUCED OESTRUS IN THE FERRET. B.T. Donovan, J.J. van der Werff ten Bosch. Jour. Physiol., London, vol.132, no.1, pp.123-129, Apr., 1956.

NOTES ON OVULATION AND FERTILIZATION IN THE FERRET. J. Hammond, A. Walton. Jour. Exper. Biol., vol.11, no.3, pp.307-319, July, 1934.

PREGNANCY DURING THE ANOESTROUS SEASON IN THE FERRET. J. Hammond, A. Walton. Jour. Exper. Biol., vol.11, no. 3, pp.320-325, July, 1934.

PHOTOPERIODICITY IN THE FEMALE FERRET. D.S. Hart. Jour. Exper.Biol., London, vol.28, no.1, pp.1-12, Mar., 1951.

EFFECT OF ABSENCE OF LIGHT ON THE BREEDING SEASON OF THE FERRET. M. Hill, A.S. Parkes. Proc. Roy. Soc., London, ser.B, vol.115, no.B 791, pp.14-17, pl.1, Mar. 29, 1934.

ON THE RELATION BETWEEN THE ANTERIOR PITUITARY BODY AND THE GONADS. PART II. INDUCTION OF OVULATION IN THE ANOESTROUS FERRET. M. Hill, A.S. Parkes. Proc. Roy. Soc. London, ser.B, vol.107, no.B 748, pp.30-49, pls.2-4, Sep. 3, 1930.

CARDIAC OUTPUT AND CIRCULATION TIME OF FERRETS. J. Emerson Kempf, H.T. Chang. Proc. Soc. Exp. Biol.Med., Utica, vol.72, no.3, pp.711-714, Dec., 1949.

EFFECT OF IRRADIATION WITH DIFFERENT WAVE-LENGTHS ON THE OESTROUS CYCLE OF THE FERRET, WITH REMARKS ON THE FACTORS CONTROLLING SEXUAL PERIODICITY. F.H.A. Marshall, F.P. Bowden. Jour. Exper. Biol., Edinburgh, vol. 11, no.4, pp.409-422, Oct., 1934.

ONSET OF OESTRUS IN NORMAL AND BLINDED FERRETS. A.P.D. Thomson. Proc. Roy. Soc. London, ser.B, vol.142, no.906, pp.126-135, Feb., 1954.

EFFECT OF PITUITARY-STALK SECTION ON LIGHT-INDUCED OESTRUS IN FERRETS. A.P.D.Thomson, S. Zuckerman. Proc. Royal Soc., Cambridge, England, ser.B, vol.142, no.909, pp.437-452, Sep., 1954.

CORRELATION BETWEEN THE SPRING MOLT AND SPRING CHANGES IN THE SEXUAL CYCLE IN THE WEASEL. Philip L. Wright. Jour. Exper. Zool., Philadelphia, vol.91, no.1, pp.103-110, figs.2, Oct. 5, 1942.

(Mustela) Predation Upon

DOMESTIC CAT CATCHES AN ERMINE (MUSTELA ERMINEA L.).) Hauskatze erbeutet Hermelin, Mustela erminea L. Heinrich Dathe. Zool.Garten, n.F., Leipzig, vol.16, nos.1-2, p.49, 1944.

DOMESTIC CAT PREDATION ON SHORT-TAILED WEASEL. George R.L. Gaughran. Jour. Mamm., vol.31, no.3, p.356, Aug. 21, 1950.

LEAST WEASEL, PREY OF BARN OWL. Charles O. Handley, Jr. Jour.Mamm., vol.30, no.4, p.431, Nov.17, 1949.

FOX AS A FACTOR IN THE CONTROL OF WEASEL POPULATIONS. Roger M. Latham. Jour. Wildl. Mgt., Ithaca, vol.16, no.4, pp.516-517, illus., Oct., 1952.

WEASEL BADLY INJURED BY KING SNAKE. W.C. Russell. Jour. Mamm., vol.11, no.4, pp.504-505, Nov., 1930.

(Mustela) Reproductive Biology

REPRODUCTIVE PROCESSES OF CERTAIN MAMMALS. III. THE REPRODUCTIVE CYCLE OF THE MALE FERRET. Marjorie Allanson. Proc. Roy. Soc. London, ser.B, vol.110, no.B767, pp.295-312, figs.7, pls. 10-12, Apr. 1, 1932.

NUMBER OF YOUNG IN STOAT'S FAMILY. James Bartholomew. Scottish Nat., p.181, Nov.-Dec., 1919.

BREEDING OF THE MOTTLED POLE-CAT (PUTORIUS SARMATICUS). A.F.P. Christison. Jour. Bombay Nat. Hist. Soc., vol.41, no.2, p.413, illus., Dec., 1939.

REPRODUCTIVE CYCLE OF THE FEMALE WEASEL (MUSTELA NIVALIS). Ruth Deanesly. Proc. Zool. Soc. London, vol.114, pt.3, pp.339-349, fig.1, pls.3, Dec., 1944.

REPRODUCTIVE PROCESSES OF CERTAIN MAMMALS. PART IX. GROWTH AND REPRODUCTION IN THE STOAT (MUSTELA ERMINEA). Ruth Deanesly. Philos. Trans. Roy. Soc., London, ser.B, vol.225, no.528, pp.459-492, pls.28-31, Dec. 24, 1935.

ON THE REPRODUCTION OF THE STOAT (MUSTELA ERMINEA). N.D. Grigoriev. Zool. Jour., Moscow, vol.17, no.5, pp.811-814, 1938. (In Russian with English summary.)

GESTATION PERIOD IN THE LONG-TAILED WEASEL. E. Raymond Hall. Jour. Mamm., vol.19, no.2, pp.249-250, May 14, 1938.

REPRODUCTIVE CYCLE OF THE MALE WEASEL (MUSTELA NIVALIS). Margaret Hill. Proc. Zool. Soc. London, vol.109, ser.B, pts.3-4, pp.481-512, figs.16, pls. 3, Dec., 1939.

BIOLOGY OF ERMINE REPRODUCTION (MUSTELA ERMINEA L.). N.P.Lavrov. Narodnii Komissariat Zagotovok SSSR, Trudy Tsentralnoi Nauch-Issledovatelskoi Laboratorii Biologii, Oxotnichego Promysla i Tovarovedeniia Zhivotnogo Syria, Moscow, no.6, pp.124-150, figs.10-15, 1944. (In Russian with English summary.)

(OBSERVATION OF THE GESTATION OF THE ERMINE (PUTORIUS ERMINEUS L.).) Beobachtung ueber die Tragzeit des Hermelins (Putorius ermineus L.). Juerg Mathis, Hans Psenner. Anat. Anz., Jena, vol.85, nos.12-18, pp.292-299, Jan. 2, 1938.

(ON THE REPRODUCTION BIOLOGY OF THE ERMINE MUSTELA ERMINEA L.) Zur Fortpflanzungsbiologie des Hermelins (Mustela erminea L.). Heinrich Mueller. Rev. Suisse Zool., vol.61, no.3, pp.451-453, Sep., 1954.

(A CASE OF ANAL RUTTING IN THE FERRET (PUTORIUS FURO L.).) Ein Fall von Afterbrunst beim Frettchen (Putorius furo L.). Erich Murr. Der Deutsche Pelztierzuechter, Jahrg.1932, Munich, no.13, p. 314, July 1, 1932.

(REPRODUCTION BIOLOGY OF THE FERRET (PUTORIUS FURO L.).) Aus der Fortpflanzungsbiologie des Frettchens (Putorius furo L.). Erich Murr. Zeitschr. f. Saeugetierk., Berlin, vol.8, nos.1-2, pp.26-32, Apr. 24, 1933.

(OBSERVATIONS ON FERRET COPULATION.) Beobachtungen ueber die Paarung des Frettchens. Erich Murr. Zool. Garten, Leipzig, n.F., vol.4, nos.8-9, pp.289-291, Oct., 1931.

(THE REPRODUCTION OF THE FERRET (PUTORIUS FURO L.). A SUMMARY OF OUR KNOWLEDGE ON THE BASIS OF OUR OWN AND FOREIGN INVESTIGATIONS, BEING ALSO AN INTRODUCTION TO THE REPRODUCTIVE BIOLOGY OF THE MAMMALS.) Die Fortpflanzung des Frettchens (Putorius furo L.). Eine Zusammenfassung unserer Kenntnisse auf Grund eigener und fremder Untersuchungen, zugleich eine Einfuehrung in die Fortpflanzungskunde der Saeugetiere. Erich Murr. Zeitschr. f.Zuechtung, Reihe B, Tierzuechtung u. Zuechtungsbiologie einschliesslich Tierernaehrung, Berlin, vol.32, no.3, pp.385-408, figs.29, June, 1935.

LATE FALL SEXUAL ACTIVITY IN AN IOWA LEAST WEASEL. Emmet B. Polderboer. Jour. Mamm., vol.29, no.3, p.296, Aug. 31, 1948.

(OBSERVATIONS OF OESTRUS, COPULATION, GESTATION, BIRTH, AND CROSSES IN MEMBERS OF SUBGENUS PUTORIUS.) Beobachtungen ueber Brunst, Paarung, Tragzeit, Geburt und Kreuzungen bei Mitgliedern der Untergattung Putorius. Udo Rempe. Saeugetierk. Mitteil., vol.5, no.3, pp.111-113, Aug. 1, 1957.

(STEPPE POLECAT (PUTORIUS EVERSMANNI LESS.). A CONTRIBUTION TO ITS REPRODUCTIVE BIOLOGY.) Der Steppeniltis (Putorius eversmanni Less.). Ein Beitrag zu seiner Forpflanzungsbiologie. Fritz Schmidt. Der Deutsche Pelztierzuechter, Munich, no.19, pp.453-458, Oct. 1, 1932.

STOATS MATING IN AUTUMN. V.I. Tichwinsky, N.D. Grigorieff. Jour.Mamm., vol.18, no.4, p.515, Nov., 1937.

WHEN DO WEASELS MATE? Edward R. Warren. Jour. Mamm., vol.13, no.1, pp. 71-72, Feb., 1932.

BREEDING HABITS OF CAPTIVE LONG-TAILED WEASELS (MUSTELA FRENATA). Philip L. Wright. Amer.Midland Nat., Notre Dame, vol.39, no.2, pp.338-344, Mar., 1948.

SEXUAL CYCLE OF THE MALE LONG-TAILED WEASEL (MUSTELA FRENATA). Philip L. Wright. Jour. Mamm., vol.28, no.4, pp.343-352, Nov., 1947.

(Mustela) Taxonomy

CHANGE OF NAME FOR MUSTELA MINOR DOUGLASS. Earl Douglass. Jour. Mamm., vol.10, no.2, p.168, May, 1929.

AMERICAN WEASELS. E. Raymond Hall. Univ. Kansas Publ., Mus.Nat.Hist., Lawrence, vol.4, pp.1-466, pls.1-41, Dec.27, 1951.

CLASSIFICATION OF THE ERMINES OF EASTERN SIBERIA. E. Raymond Hall. Proc. Calif. Acad. Sci., San Francisco, ser.4, vol.23, no.37, pp.555-560, fig.1, Aug. 22, 1944.

REVISED CLASSIFICATION OF THE AMERICAN ERMINES WITH DESCRIPTION OF A NEW SUBSPECIES FROM THE WESTERN GREAT LAKES REGION. E. Raymond Hall. Jour. Mamm., vol.26, no.2, pp.175-182, May, 1945.

SPECIATION IN AMERICAN WEASELS (GENUS MUSTELA). E. Raymond Hall. 13th Congress Internat. Zool. Paris du 21 au 27 Juillet 1948, 5e sect.B, communications, pp.404-405, 1949.

ON THE STATUS OF MUSTELA ALLEGHENIENSIS. W.F. Henninger. Jour. Mamm., vol.4, no.2, p.121, May, 1923.

TWO NEW POLECATS RELATED TO MUSTELA LARVATA. Ned Hollister. Proc. Biol. Soc. Washington, vol.26, pp.1-3, Jan. 18, 1913.

ADDITION TO THE SYSTEMATIC OF THE WEASEL. (Vormela and Putorius.) Vladimir Martino. Lovtsa, nos.9-10, pp.1-5, figs.4, Sep.-Oct., 1937. (In Bulgarian.)

POLECATS OF THE GENERA PUTORIUS AND VORMELA IN THE BRITISH MUSEUM.

R.I. Pocock. Proc. Zool. Soc. London, pt.3, pp.691-723, figs.2, pls.2, Sep., 1936.

NOTES ON MUSTELA CAMPESTRIS JACKSON, AND THE AMERICAN FORMS OF LEAST WEASELS. Myron H. Swenk. Jour. Mamm., vol.7, no.4, pp.313-330, fig.1, Nov., 1926.

IRISH STOAT DISTINCT FROM BRITISH SPECIES. O. Thomas, G.E.H. Barrett-Hamilton. Zoologist, ser.3, vol.19, pp. 124-129, Apr., 1895; Ann. and Mag. Nat. Hist., ser.6, vol.15, no.88, p.374, Apr., 1895.

ON THE PROPER SPECIFIC NAME OF THE WEASEL. Oldfield Thomas. Zoologist, ser. 3, vol.19, pp.177-178, May, 1895.

(Mustela) Techniques, Methods

DETERMINATION OF WEASEL SEX RATIOS BY PELT EXAMINATION. William H. Elder. Jour. Wildl. Mgt., Menasha, vol. 15, no.1, pp.114-116, Jan., 1951.

TRAPPING WEASEL. Clayton G. Gates. Fur-Fish-Game, Harding's Mag., Columbus, vol.79, no.7, pp.38-39, July, 1945.

SIMPLE METHOD IDENTIFICATION OF LEAST WEASEL. Roger M. Latham. Jour. Mamm., vol.34, no.3, p.385, Aug. 14, 1953.

METHODS FOR FORECASTING POPULATION CHANGES IN THE ERMINE (MUSTELA ERMINEA L.). N.P. Lavrov. (In) Symposium, "Methods for forecasting changes in the numbers of fur-bearing animals and renewing their natural supplies." Trans. Cent. Lab. Game Indus., no.5, pp.60-77, 1941.

THE FERRET AS AN AID TO WINTER RABBIT STUDIES. J.P. Linduska. Jour. Wildl. Mgt., vol.11, no.3, pp.252-255, July, 1947. (Use of Ferret to Drive Cottontails from Winter Burrows.)

(Martes) General

FUR-BEARING DYNAMITE--THE FISHER. Jacob B. Abbott. Pa. Game News, vol.16, no.2, pp.4-5, 22, May, 1945.

FISHER FACTS. A.K. Cameron. Amer. Fur Breeder, vol.4, no.2, pp.26-27, Aug., 1931.

THE FISHER. Arthur H. Cook. New York State Conservationist, Albany, vol.4, no.3, p.24, illus., Dec., 1949-Jan., 1950.

(PINE MARTEN (MARTES MARTES).) Der Edel- oder Baummarder (Martes martes). H. Felten. Natur und Volk, Frankfurt am Main, vol.81, no.10, pp.265-267, Oct. 1, 1951.

TRUE MARTEN FROM THE MADISON VALLEY(MIOCENE) OF MONTANA. James W. Gidley. Jour. Mamm., vol.8, no.3, pp. 239-242, Aug., 1927.

NEW MARTEN FROM THE PLEISTOCENE CAVE DEPOSITS OF CALIFORNIA. E. Raymond Hall. Jour. Mamm., vol.7, no.2, pp.127-130, pl.14, May, 1926.

LORDS OF THE TREETOPS. (Marten.) Robert J. Higgins. Fauna, Philadelphia, vol.10, no.2, pp.43-45, June, 1948.

FISHER. QUESTIONS AND ANSWERS. C.S. James. Amer. Fur Breeder, Duluth, vol.13, no.8, pp.14-15, Feb., 1941.

MUSIC HAS ITS CHARMS. (Pine Marten.) John Jay. Yellowstone Nature Notes, vol. 9, nos.10-11, p.46, Oct., Nov., 1932.

(PHOTOGRAPH OF THE SABLE (MARTES ZIBELLINA L.).) Ein Photo vom Zobel (Martes zibellina L.). M. Klemm. Zeitschr. f. Saeugetierk., vol.5, no.6, p.367, pl.37, Dec. 12, 1930.

PECULIAR MUTATION OF THE PINE MARTEN. Marcus W. Lyon, Jr. Science, n.s., vol.24, no.611, p.341, Sep. 14, 1906.

THE FISHER. J. Macartney. Sylva, Ottawa, vol.3, no.6, pp.10-12, illus., 1947.

AN AGE DETERMINATION METHOD FOR THE PINE MARTEN. William H. Marshall. Jour. Wildl. Mgt., vol.15, no.3, pp.276-283, July, 1951.

MARTEN IN THE WOODPILE. Dorothy R. Mayer. Yosemite Nat. Notes, vol.29, no.2, pp.17-18, illus., Feb., 1950.

FISHER EXPERIENCES. Carl M. Mitchell. Amer. Fur Breeder, vol.8, no.3, p.8, Sep., 1935.

THE PINE MARTEN. C.H. Moffat. Irish Naturalists' Jour., vol.1, no.9, pp.170-171, Jan., 1927.

MARTES PENNANTI (FISHER). C.R. Partik. Amer. Fur Breeder, vol.4, no.6, pp.22-24, Dec., 1931; vol.4, no.7, p.33, Jan., 1932.

MORE FISHER FACTS. C.R. Partik. Amer. Fur Breeder, vol.5, no.1, pp.4, 6-7, July, 1932.

ON PINE AND BEECH MARTENS. R. I. Pocock. Proc. Zool. Soc. London, pt.4, pp.1062-1068, figs.4, Dec. 18, 1914.

(NATURAL HISTORY OF THE PINE AND STONE MARTEN.) Naturgeschichte des Baum- und Steinmarders. F. Schmidt. Leipzig, Monographie der Wildsaeugetiere, no. 10, pp.258, pls.32, 1943.

AN AIR-MINDED MARTEN. DeLyle Stevens. Yellowstone Nat. Notes, Yellowstone Park, vol.18, nos.3-4, pp.19-20, Mar.-Apr., 1941.

MARTES GAMLITZENSIS H. V. MEYER. Erich Thenius. Sitz. Ber. Österr. Akad. Wiss., Vienna, Math.-Naturw. Kl., vol. 158, pp.793-797, 1949.

SIBERIAN SABLE AND HIS RELATIONS. Geo. van der Bellen. Amer. Fur Breeder, vol.11, no.7, pp.16-20, Jan., 1930.

FISHER FACTS. Amer. Fur Breeder, Duluth, vol.19, no.9, p.34, Mar., 1947.

(Martes) Anatomy

CYCLIC CHANGES IN THE VULVA OF THE MARTEN (MARTES AMERICANA). R.K. Enders, James R. Leekley. Anat. Record, Philadelphia, vol.79, no.1, pp. 1-11, pls.2, Jan. 25, 1941.

BLASTOCYST OF THE FISHER. R.K. Enders, O.P. Pearson. Anat. Record, Philadelphia, vol.85, pp.285-287, Mar., 1943.

ABDOMINAL SKIN GLAND OF MARTES. E. Raymond Hall. Jour. Mamm., vol.7, no.3, pp.227-228, Aug., 1926.

BLASTOCYST OF THE MARTEN(MARTES). William H. Marshal, R.K. Enders. Anat. Record, Philadelphia, vol.84, no.3, pp. 307-310, figs.2, Nov. 25, 1942.

NOTES OF DISSECTION OF A PEKAN, OR FISHER MARTEN (MUSTELA CANADENSIS, SCHREB.). W. Martin. Proc. Zool. Soc. London, pt.1, p.97, 1833.

ON THE SKIN, ITS GLANDS AND THE SOLE SKIN GLANDULAR ORGANS OF THE SABLE (MARTES ZIBELLINA L.). B.S. Matveiev. Zool. Jour. USSR, Moscow, vol.21, no.5, pp. 207-214, figs.7, 1942. (With English summary.)

ON THE VARIABILITY AND INHERITANCE OF COLOUR AND PATTERN IN THE SABLE (MARTES ZIBELLINA L.). A.L. Ponomarev. Zool. Jour. Moscow, vol.17, no.3, pp.482-504, figs.7, tbls.10, 1938. (In Russian with English summary.)

DERMATOGLYPHICS IN YELLOW THROATED MARTIN, CHARRONIA FLAVIGULA BOREALIS (RADDE). Tsen-Hwang Shaw. Bull. Fan Mem. Inst. Biol., Peiping, (Zool.), vol.6, no.3, pp.145-149, figs.4, Mar., 1935.

(Martes) Breeding

BREEDING MARTENS IN CAPTIVITY. Frank G. Ashbrook, Karl B. Hanson. Jour. Heredity, vol.18, pp.498-503, illus., Nov., 1927.

FUR BEARING ANIMALS OF THE UNITED STATES. THE FISHER. Frank G. Ashbrook, Bridgewater M. Arnold. Fur Jour., vol.1, no.6, pp.24-25, illus., map, Oct., 1927.

FUR BEARING ANIMALS OF THE UNITED STATES. THE MARTEN. Frank G. Ashbrook, Bridgewater M. Arnold. Fur Jour., vol.1, no.8, pp.26-27, illus., Dec., 1927.

PROGRESS REPORT OF MARTEN BREEDING EXPERIMENTS. Frank G. Ashbrook, Karl B. Hanson. Northern Fur Trade, vol. 3, no.9, pp.14-16, Nov., 1928.

AMERICAN MARTEN. Joseph M. Bossak. Amer. Fur Breeder, vol.11, no.6, p.18, Dec., 1938.

MARTEN BREEDING. H.E. Bowles. Amer. Fur Breeder, vol.1, no.12, p.10, June, 1929.

AT LONG LAST. (Breeding of Marten in Captivity.) Kenneth P. Button. Amer. Fur Breeder, vol.11, no.11, p.12, illus., May, 1939.

FISHER FARMING. W.O. Douglas. Nat. Fur News, Denver, vol.20, no.10, pp.38, 109, illus., Nov., 1948.

FISHER FARMING HAS ARRIVED. W.O. Douglas. Amer. Fur Breeder, Duluth, vol. 16, no.2, pp.18, 20, illus., Aug., 1943.

HOW TO PRODUCE A PROLIFIC STRAIN OF MARTEN. Lloyd Drury. Amer. Fur Breeder, Duluth, vol.18, no.3, pp.42, 44, Sep., 1945.

FIRST AUTHENTIC REPORT OF FISHER BRED IN CAPTIVITY. Lester D. Lowe. Amer. Fur Breeder, vol.11, no.12, pp.34-36, June, 1939.

(BREEDING RESULTS WITH THE STONE MARTEN.) Zuchterfolg beim Steinmarder. H. Reinhardt. Die Pelztierzucht, vol.5, no.10, pp.195-197, figs.4, Oct. 4, 1929.

RANCHING OF MARTEN. J.W. Ritchie. Amer. Fur Breeder, Duluth, vol.21, no.1, pp.36-42, July, 1948; vol.21, no.3, pp.18, 20, 22, Sep., 1948; Fur of Canada, Winnipeg, vol.13, no.12, pp.20, 22, 24, Sep., 1948; vol.14, no.1, pp.30-32, Oct., 1948.

TIPS ON MARTEN RAISING. J.W. Ritchie. Amer. Fur Breeder, Duluth, vol.13, no.12, pp.22-23, fig.1, June, 1941; vol.14, no.1, pp.16-17, July, 1941.

AMERICAN SABLE. William M. Rush. Fauna, Philadelphia, vol.7, no.2, pp.57-58, June, 1945.

SABLE PRESERVE ON THE SHORE OF LAKE BAIKAL. Olga Serova. Amer. Fur Breeder, Duluth, vol.19, no.3, p.60, Sep., 1946.

ON THE BARGUZINSK SABLE RESERVATION. S. Turov. Mem. East Siberian Branch Russ. Geogr. Soc., Irkutsk, vol.41, no.2, pp.1-20, 1923.

(Martes) Diseases and Parasites

STUDIES ON THE NEMATODE SOBOLIPHYME BATURINI PETROW, 1930. Hubert Bezdek. Trans. Amer. Micros. Soc., vol. 61, no.4, pp.398-403, Oct., 1942.

AN INSTANCE OF SCABIES IN THE MARTEN (MARTES AMERICANA). I. McT. Cowan. Jour. Wildl. Mgt., vol.19, no.4, p.499, Oct., 1955.

(Martes) Eurasia

NOTES ON THE BEECH-MARTENS OF THE PALOEARCTIC REGION. G.E.H. Barrett-Hamilton. Ann. and Mag. Nat. Hist., ser.7, vol.1, pp.441-443, June, 1898.

ON THE BIOLOGY OF THE SABLE AND THE SABLE FARMING ON THE ISLAND OF GREAT SHANTER. G.D. Dulkeit. Bull. Pacific Sci. Fishery Research Sta., Vladivostok, vol.3, pt.3, pp.120, 1929.

SABLE (MARTES ZIBELLINA (L.)) IN THE YAMAL NATIONAL DISTRICT. A. N. Dybrouskii. Priroda, Leningrad, no.9, pp. 88-90, 1937. (In Russian.)

KAMCHATKA SABLE NEARING EXTINCTION. Walter J. Eyerdam. Jour. Mamm., vol.13, no.3, pp.276-277, Aug., 1932.

PINE MARTEN IN NORTHERN SCOTLAND. E.J. Fergusson. Jour. Soc. Preservation Fauna of Empire, Hertford, n.s., pt.36, pp.27-30, May, 1939.

PINE MARTEN VISITOR. R.G. Gethin. Irish Nat. Jour., vol.6, no.6, pp.145-146, Nov., 1936.

(ON THE PECULIARITIES OF THE RANGES OF THE MARTEN (GENUS MARTES) IN EASTERN EUROPE.) P. Jurgenson. Bull.

Soc. Nat. Moscow, ser. biol., vol.42, no. 1, pp.62-77, 1933. (In Russian.)

(ON THE DISTRIBUTION OF MARTES BUNITES BATE.) Zur Verbreitung von Martes bunites Bate. Otto Koller. Zool. Anzeiger, vol.75, nos.5-6, p.114, Feb. 1, 1928.

LIFE OF MARTES ZIBELLINA IN THE SAIAN MOUNTAINS AND ITS GEOGRAPHICAL DISTRIBUTION. I. Kožhančhikov. Comptes Rendus Acad. Sci. USSR, ser.A, no.12, pp.299-304, 1930. (In Russian.)

SABLE IN SAIAN AND ITS GEOGRAPHIC DISTRIBUTION IN THE PALAEARCTIC REGION. I. Kožhančhikov. Priroda, Leningrad, no.6, pp.672-674, 1930.

ON THE BIOLOGY OF THE SABLE AND THE SABLE FARMING ON THE ISLAND OF GREAT SHANTER. G.D. Kulkeit. Bull. Pacific Sci. Fish. Research Sta., vol.3, pt.3, pp.1-120, 1929. (In Russian with English summary.)

AN ABNORMAL EXAMPLE OF LONG-HAIRED YELLOW MARTEN FROM MT. OSORE, AOMORI PREF., N. JAPAN. Nagamichi Kuroda, Tatsurokuro Ishiwata. Jour. Mamm. Soc. Japan, vol.1, no.4, pp. 49-50, pl.1, June, 1957.

ON THE SEX RATIO, SEX DIFFERENTIATION, AND REGIONAL VARIATION IN THE MARTEN IN FINLAND. Teppo Lampio. Papers on Game Research, Helsinki, no.7, pp.20, illus., 1951.

PINE MARTEN IN IRELAND. Dermot McCalmont. Field, London, vol.153, p. 73, Jan. 10, 1929.

OCCURRENCE OF THE PINE MARTEN NEAR BRISTOL. L. Harrison Matthews, W.E. Mayer. Proc. Bristol Nat. Soc., vol.27, pt.2, pp.121-122, July 1, 1946.

PINE MARTENS IN MORAY AND WIGTOWNSHIRE. Herbert Maxwell. The Scottish Naturalist, no.179, p.136, Sep.-Oct., 1929.

PINE MARTEN IN IRELAND. A.T. Mitchell. Field, London, vol.153, p.228, Feb. 7, 1929.

PINE MARTEN NEAR SHEFFIELD. Charles Mosley. Naturalist, London, no.841, p.38, Feb., 1927.

MARTENS IN NORTH WALES. G.Owen. Field, London, vol.156, no.4051, p.243, Aug. 16, 1930.

IS THE PINE MARTEN DOOMED? GROWING SCARCITY OF OUR RAREST BEAST OF PREY. Frances Pitt. Field, London, vol.163, no.4239, p.629, illus., Mar.24, 1934.

JAVAN RACE OF THE ORIENTAL YELLOW-THROATED MARTEN, LAMPROGALE FLAVIGULA. R.I. Pocock. Ann. and Mag. Nat. Hist., ser.10, vol.17, no.99, pp.403-404, Mar., 1936.

ORIENTAL YELLOW-THROATED MARTEN (LAMPROGALE). R.I. Pocock. Proc. Zool. Soc. London, pt.2, pp.531-553, figs.2, July 20, 1936.

PINE MARTEN IN YORKSHIRE. R. I. Pocock. Field, London, vol.148, p.594, Sep. 30, 1926.

PINE MARTEN IN WIGTOWNSHIRE. Maurice Portal. Scottish Naturalist, no.182, p.49, Mar.-Apr., 1930.

(INDONESIAN TREE MARTEN.) De Indische Boommarter, Lamprogale flavigula robinsoni. H.J.V. Sody. De Tropische Natuur, Jrg.29, afl.11-12, pp.173-177, 1940.

(DISTRIBUTION AND FREQUENCY OF MARTES MARTES IN DENMARK.) Bidrag til dansk zoogeografi og faunistik III. Om skovmaarens udbredelse og hyppighed i Danmark. R. Spärck. Vidensk. Meddel. Dansk naturhist. For. Kobenhavn, vol.92, pp.301-304, 1930.

PINE MARTEN IN CO. LONDONDERRY. J.A. Sidney Stendall. Irish Nat. Jour., Belfast, vol.7, no.11, p.314, Mar., 1941.

ON THE TSU-SHIMA REPRESENTATIVE OF THE JAPANESE SABLE. Oldfield Thomas. Ann. and Mag. Nat. Hist., ser. 6, vol.19, no.110, pp.161-162, Feb., 1897.

SABLE IN THE YENESEI DISTRICT. THE PRESENT CONDITION AND THE MEANING OF THE SABLE TRADE. A.Y. Tugarinov. G.U.Z. and Z. Yenesei Emigrant District, Krasnoyarsk, pp.1-20, pls.5, map, 1913.

(SOME CONTROVERSIAL QUESTIONS ON THE NATURAL HISTORY AND BREEDING OF THE GERMAN PINE MARTEN.) Einige Streitfragen aus der Naturgeschichte und Zucht unserer heimischen Marder. A. Usinger. Der Deutsche Pelztierzuechter, Munich, Jahrg.9, no.22, pp.429-431, illus., Nov. 15, 1934.

PINE MARTEN IN ARGYLLSHIRE. Edward Valpy. Scottish Nat., no.151, p.4, Jan.-Feb., 1925.

(Martes) Habits, Behavior, Ecology

FISHER IS A QUILL-JOY! Nancy Bode. San Diego Zoonooz, vol.23, no.12, p.5, illus., Dec., 1950.

FOOD HABITS OF THE MARTEN (MARTES AMERICANA) IN THE ROCKY MOUNTAIN REGION OF CANADA. I.McT. Cowan, R. H. Mackay. Canadian Field-Nat., Ottawa, vol.64, no.3, pp.100-104, May-June, 1950.

ACTIVITY OF THE SIERRA PINE MARTEN. Albert C. Hawbecker. Jour. Mamm., vol. 26, no.4, p.435, Feb. 12, 1946.

(ON THE RAISING AND BEHAVIOR OF TWO PINE MARTENS (MARTES MARTES L.).) Ueber die Aufzucht und das Verhalten zweier Baummarder (Martes martes L.). Konrad Herter et al. Zeitschr. Tierpsychol., vol. 11, no.1, pp.113-137, 1954.

(ECOLOGICAL AND GEOGRAPHICAL ASPECTS OF THE FOOD OF FOREST MARTENS AND THE GEOGRAPHICAL VARIATION IN ECOLOGICAL AND MORPHOLOGICAL ADAPTATIONS OF THEIR CHEWING APPARATUS.) Ekologo-Geograficheskie Aspektia v Pitanii Lesnoi Kunitsia i Geograficheskia Ismenchivost Ekologo-Morfologicheskikh Adaptatsii ee Zhevatelnogo Apparata. P.B. Jurgenson. Zool.Zh., vol.30, no.2, pp.172-185, 1951.

(CONTRIBUTION TO KNOWLEDGE OF THE ECOLOGY, BIOLOGY, AND GEOGRAPHY OF THE SABLE (MARTES ZIBELLINA L.).) Ein Beitrag zur Kenntniss der Ökologie, Biologie und Geographie des Zobels (Martes zibellina L.). I. Kozhantschikov. Zeitschr. Morph. u. Ökol. Tiere, vol.19, pp.291-320, figs.2, Oct. 9, 1930.

FOOD HABITS OF MARTEN IN INTERIOR ALASKA AND THEIR SIGNIFICANCE. C.J. Lensink et al. Jour. Wildl. Mgt., vol. 19, no.3, pp.364-368, July, 1955.

HABITS OF CAPTIVE MARTEN. Merle H. Markley, Charles F. Bassett. Amer. Midland Nat., Notre Dame, vol.28, no.3, pp.604-616, Nov., 1942; Amer. Fur Breeder, Duluth, vol.16, no.3, pp.26, 28, 30, fig., Sep., 1943; vol.16, no.4, pp.22, 24, Oct., 1943; vol.16, no.5, pp.42-46, Nov., 1943.

WINTER FOOD HABITS OF THE PINE MARTEN IN MONTANA. William H. Marshall. Jour. Mamm., vol.27, no.1, pp.83-84, Feb., 1946.

EFFECTS OF EXPLOITATION ON A MARTEN POPULATION. Horace F. Quick. Jour. Wildl. Mgt., vol.20, no.3, pp.267-274, July, 1956.

FOOD HABITS OF MARTEN (MARTES AMERICANA) IN NORTHERN BRITISH COLUMBIA. Horace F. Quick. Canadian Field-Nat., vol.69, no.4, pp.144-147, Oct.-Dec., 1955.

ON THE FOOD COMPOSITION OF THE SABLE (MARTES ZIBELLINA L.) OF THE NORTH URAL MOUNTAINS. V. V. Raevsky. Zool. Jour. Moscow, vol.17, no.2, pp.337-341, tbls.2, 1938. (In Russian with English summary.)

FOOD HABITS, GROWTH AND BEHAVIOR OF TWO CAPTIVE PINE MARTENS. Jack D. Remington. Jour. Mamm., vol.33, no. 1, pp.66-70, Feb., 1952.

OVERFLOW AND DISPERSAL OF MARTEN AND FISHER FROM WILDLIFE REFUGES. A. de Vos. Jour. Wildl. Mgt., vol.15, no. 2, pp.164-175, Apr., 1951.

RECENT FINDINGS IN FISHER AND MARTEN ECOLOGY AND MANAGEMENT. A. de Vos. Trans. N. Amer. Wildl.Conf., vol.16, pp.498-505, 1951.

PRELIMINARY LIVE-TRAPPING STUDIES OF MARTEN. A. de Vos, Stanley E. Guenther. Jour. Wildl. Mgt., Ithaca, N.Y., vol.16, no.2, pp.207-214, illus., Apr., 1952.

(Martes) Management

(PROTECTION OF THE MARTEN.) Mårdens fridlysning. Albert Eklundh. Svensk Jakt., Stockholm, vol.78, no.2, pp.73-74, Feb. 12, 1940.

MARTEN ARE BACK! (Planted on Island.) Harold C. Jordahl, Jr. Wis. Cons. Bull., vol.19, no.2, pp.26-28, illus., Feb., 1954.

PINE MARTEN AS A FOREST PRODUCT. William H. Marshall. Jour. Forest., vol.49, no.12, pp.899-905, illus., Dec., 1951.

BRINGING BACK THE MARTEN. (Reintroduction in Northern New Hampshire.) Robert S. Monahan. Dartmouth Alumni Mag., Hanover, vol.46, no.2, p.88, Nov., 1953.

NOTE ON MARTEN MANAGEMENT. Jack Parsell. N. Region News, June, 1938.

MARTEN PROBLEM. Clayt Seagears. N.Y. State Cons., vol.6, no.4, p.40, illus., Feb.-Mar., 1952.

IMPLICATIONS OF SOME HARVEST AND HABITAT FACTORS ON PINE MARTEN MANAGEMENT. Lee E. Yeager. Trans. 15th N. Amer. Wildl. Conf., Washington, pp.319-334, 1950.

(Martes) North America

FISHER RETURNS TO WISCONSIN. B.J. Bradle. Wisc.Conservation Bull., vol.22, no.11, pp.9-11, Nov., 1957.

DESCRIPTION OF AN APPARENTLY NEW SUBSPECIES OF MARTEN FROM THE KENAI PENINSULA, ALASKA. (Mustela americana kenaiensis.) D.G. Elliot. Field Col. Mus., Publ.72, Zool. Ser., vol.3, no.9, pp.151-152, pl.32, Feb., 1903.

TWO NEW RACES OF THE PINE MARTEN FROM THE PACIFIC COAST OF NORTH AMERICA. (Martes caurina humboldtensis and M.c. vancouverensis.) Joseph Grinnel, Joseph Dixon. Univ. Calif. Publ. Zool., vol.21, no.16, pp.411-417, illus., Mar.17, 1926.

ARCHEOLOGICAL EVIDENCE OF THE FISHER IN WEST VIRGINIA. John E. Guilday. Jour. Mamm., vol.37, no.2, p. 287, June 9, 1956.

DISTRIBUTION OF MARTEN AND FISHER IN NORTH AMERICA. Edwin M. Hagmeier. Canadian Field-Nat., vol.70, no.4, pp. 149-168, 1956.

RESURGENCE OF THE FISHER IN NEW HAMPSHIRE. George T. Hamilton. Appalachia, Appalachian Mountain Club, n.s., vol.23, no.12, pp.485-490, pl., Dec., 1957.

BIOLOGY AND MANAGEMENT OF THE FISHER IN NEW YORK. W.J.Hamilton, Jr., Arthur H. Cook. New York Fish and Game Jour., vol.2, no.1, pp.13-35, map, Jan., 1955.

LOW ALTITUDINAL RECORD OF THE SIERRA NEVADA PINE MARTEN. Fred L. Jones. Jour. Mamm., vol.36, no.4, pp. 568-569, Dec. 14, 1955.

INVESTIGATION OF THE MARTEN IN INTERIOR ALASKA. Calvin J. Lensink. MS thesis, Univ. Alaska, pp.xi+89, illus., 1953.

BIOLOGY AND MANAGEMENT OF THE PINE MARTEN IN IDAHO. William H. Marshall. PhD thesis, Univ. Mich., 1942.

DESCRIPTION OF A NEW MARTEN (MUSTELA CAURINA) FROM THE NORTHWEST COAST REGION OF THE UNITED STATES. C. Hart Merriam. N.Amer.Fauna, no.4, U.S.Dept.Agric., pp.27-29, Oct., 1890.

GOLDEN SABLE OF MYSTERY BASIN. (Marten.) Bill Nelson. Fur-Fish-Game, Harding's Mag., Columbus, vol.86, no. 8, pp.14-15, 40, illus., Aug., 1946.

MARTEN IN MONTANA. Fletcher E. Newby. Mont. Wildl., vol.2, no.3, pp.14-15, illus., Autumn, 1952.

NORTH AMERICAN MARTEN. Edward A. Preble. Nature Mag., Washington, vol.38, no.1, p.32, illus., Jan., 1945.

STATUS OF THE FISHER, MARTES PENNANTI (ERXLEBEN), IN CANADA. A.L. Rand. Can. Field-Nat., vol.58, no.5, pp. 77-81, May-June, 1944.

ECOLOGY AND ECONOMICS OF THE ROCKY MOUNTAIN MARTEN. Jack D. Remington. Quart. Rept. Colorado Coop. Wildl. Research Unit, Fort Collins, vol. 3, no.3, pp.21-27, Jan.-Mar., 1950.

VANISHING ANIMALS. (Fisher.) E.J. Sawyer. Western Sportsman, Denver, vol. 7, no.5, pp.28-29, Oct., 1941.

RECENT RECORD OF THE MARTEN IN MINNESOTA. Milton H. Stenlund. Jour. Mamm., vol.36, no.1, p.133, Feb. 25, 1955.

FUR-BEARING MAMMALS OF WYOMING. (Marten and Fisher.) Earl M. Thomas. Wyo. Wildl., vol.16, no.6, pp.12-17, illus., June, 1952; vol.16, no.7, pp.23-27, illus., July, 1952.

STUDY OF MARTEN IN MONTANA. W.K. Thompson. Proc. Ann. Conf. W. Assn. State Game and Fish Comm., vol.29, pp. 181-188, 1949?

STATUS OF PINE MARTENS IN CALIFORNIA. Howard Twining, Arthur Hensley. Calif. Fish and Game, San Francisco, vol. 33, no.3, pp.133-137, July, 1947.

ECOLOGY AND MANAGEMENT OF FISHER AND MARTEN IN ONTARIO. Antoon de Vos. Tech. Bull. Ontario Dept. Lands and Forests, pp.89, illus., 1952.

PACIFIC FISHER. Georgie Ware. Yosemite Nat. Notes, Yosemite, vol.22, no.9, p.80, Sep., 1943.

MARTEN IN COLORADO. Curtis M. Williams. Colo.Cons.Comments, vol.10, no. 2, pp.12-13, June, 1947.

PEKANS OF THE ADIRONDACKS. Richard K. Wood. Outdoorsman, Columbus, vol. 84, no.1, pp.18-19, 36-37, 39-40, illus., Jan., 1942.

SIGHT OBSERVATIONS OF COLORADO MARTENS, 1950-1955. Lee E. Yeager, Jack D. Remington. Jour. Mamm., vol. 37, no.4, pp.521-524, Jan. 9, 1957.

ROCKY MOUNTAIN MARTEN MARTES CAURINA ORIGENES. Wyo. Wildl., Cheyenne, vol.5, no.6, pp.6, 16, June, 1940.

(Martes) Reproductive Biology

NORMAL BREEDING SEASON AND GESTATION PERIOD OF MARTENS. Frank G. Ashbrook, Karl B. Hanson. Circular 107, U.S. Dept. Agric., pp.6, Feb., 1930; Amer. Fur Breeder, vol.2, no.10, pp.4-6, Apr., 1930.

OBSERVATIONS ON BREEDING AND DEVELOPMENT OF MARTEN, MARTES A. AMERICANA (KERR). J.A. Brassard, Richard Bernard. Canadian Field-Nat., Ottawa, vol.53, no.2, pp.15-21, figs.4, Feb., 1939.

PROPAGATION OF MARTENS. Mrs.M.J. Dikeman. Amer. Fur Breeder, vol.11, no. 4, pp.14-15, Oct., 1929.

REPRODUCTION IN THE FISHER IN NEW YORK. W.Robert Eadie, W.J.Hamilton, Jr. New York Fish and Game Jour., vol.5, no. 1, pp.77-83, Jan., 1958.

SHORTENING GESTATION BY INDUCING EARLY IMPLANTATION WITH INCREASED LIGHT IN THE MARTEN. Robert K. Enders, Oliver P. Pearson. Amer. Fur Breeder, Duluth, vol.15, no.7, p.18, illus., Jan., 1943.

GESTATION PERIOD IN THE FISHER WITH RECOMMENDATIONS FOR THE ANIMAL'S PROTECTION IN CALIFORNIA. E. Raymond Hall. Calif. Fish and Game, San Francisco, vol.28, no.3, pp.143-147, July, 1942.

(REPRODUCTION IN CAPTIVITY OF MARTEN.) Reproduction en captivité des fouines et des Martres. M. Jouan. Revue d'Hist. Nat., pt.1, A. Mammifères, Paris, vol.11, no.11, pp.364-366, Nov., 1930.

(SEASONS OF RUT AND PARTURITION OF MARTENS.) Les saisons du rut et de la parturition des Martes. F. Lataste. Rev. Française Mammal., ser.1, no.2, pp.49-51, Dec. 7, 1928.

DETERMINATION OF HEAT IN THE MARTEN. James R. Leekley. Amer. Fur Breeder, Duluth, vol.13, no.12, pp.26-28, figs.2, June, 1941.

(GESTATION CYCLE IN MARTENS AND SABLES.) Der Gestationswechsel bei Mardern und Zobeln. Felix Mallner. Der Deutsche Pelztierzuechter, Munich, Jahrg. 9, no.8, pp.145-150, Apr. 15, 1934; no.9, pp.165-170, illus., May 1, 1934.

BREEDING HABITS OF MARTEN. Merle H. Merkley. Amer. Fur Breeder, Duluth, vol.14, no.11, pp.14-15, illus., May, 1942.

(PROLONGED GESTATION OF DOMESTIC MARTES SPECIES.) Die verlaengerte Tragzeit der einheimischen Martes-Arten. H. Prell. Zool. Anzeiger, vol.87, p.273, Mar. 20, 1930; vol.88, pp.17-31, Apr.1, 1930.

(PROPAGATION BIOLOGY OF THE AMERICAN PINE MARTEN (MARTES AMERICANA TURT.).) Die Fortpflanzungsbiologie des amerikanischen Fichtenmarders (Martes americana Turt.). H. Prell. Die Pelztierzucht, Leipzig, vol.4, no.4, pp.67-70, 1928; Arbeiten und Reichszentr. f. Pelztier.-u. Rauchw.-Forsch., no.11, Leipzig, 1928.

(ON THE PROBLEM OF THE SPECIES CHARACTERISTICS AND CROSS BREEDING OF PINE AND STONE MARTENS.) Zur Frage der Artmerkmale und der Bastardierung von Baum- und Steinmarder. Alfred Streuli. Zeitschr. f. Saeugetierk., vol.7, no.2, pp. 58-72, Dec. 15, 1932.

EVIDENCE ON THE GESTATION PERIOD OF MARTENS. Ernest P. Walker. Jour. Mamm., vol.10, no.3, pp.206-209, pl.16, Aug., 1929.

(CONTRIBUTIONS TO THE PROBLEM OF THE DURATION OF GESTATION IN THE STONE MARTEN.) Beitrag zur Frage der Traechtigkeitsdauer des Edelmarders. Adolf Wendnagel. Zool. Garten, vol.2, nos.4-6, pp.117-120, 1929.

(Martes) Taxonomy

ON THE MARTENS OF THE MUSTELA FLAVIGULA GROUP. J.L. Bonhote. Ann. and Mag. Nat. Hist., ser.7, vol.7, pp. 342-349, Apr., 1901.

SYSTEMATICAL REVIEW OF THE RUSSIAN SABLES. S.I. Ognev. Jour.Mamm., Baltimore, vol.6, no.4, pp.276-280, pl. 26, Nov. 14, 1925.

(ON THE SPECIES CHARACTERISTICS OF PINE AND STONE MARTENS.) Ueber die Artmerkmale von Baum- und Steinmarder. G. Reinberger. Zeitschr. f. Saeugetierk., vol.8, no.6, pp.276-277, Dec. 20, 1933.

INTERGRADATION BETWEEN MARTES AMERICANA AND MARTES CAURINA IN WESTERN MONTANA. Philip L. Wright. Jour. Mamm., vol.34, no.1, pp.74-86, illus., Feb., 1953.

SYNOPSIS OF THE AMERICAN MARTENS. Samuel N. Rhoads. Proc. Acad. Nat.Sci., Philadelphia, pp.443-460, Sep. 30, 1902.

(Martes) Trapping

LIVE-TRAPPING MARTEN IN BRITISH COLUMBIA. R.G. Miller, R.W.Ritcey, R.Y. Edwards. Murrelet, vol.36, no.1, pp.1-8, map, Jan.-Apr. (Sep.), 1955.

PROGRESS ON A MARTEN LIVE-TRAPPING STUDY. Fletcher E. Newby, Vernon D. Hawley. Trans.19th N.Amer. Wildl. Conf., pp.452-460, illus., 1954.

TRAPPING THE MARTEN. Leonard C. Parker, James W. Spriggs. Wyo. Wildl., Cheyenne, vol.11, no.6, pp.16-19, June, 1947.

LIVE-TRAPPING OF MARTEN. P.W. Swanson. Sylva, Toronto, vol.5, no.6, pp.10-14, illus., Nov.-Dec., 1949.

(Grison)

BEHAVIOR OF YOUNG GRISONS IN CAPTIVITY. Walter W. Dalquest, J. Harvey Roberts. Amer.Midland Nat., Notre Dame, vol.46, no.2, pp.359-366, illus., Sep., 1951.

NEW SOUTH AMERICAN TRICHODECTID. (Host: Grison furax furax.) Stefan Kéler. Ann. Mus. Zool. Polonoci, vol.10, no.18, pp.333-337, pls.55-57, July 30, 1934.

NOTES OF THE DISSECTION OF A GRISON. (Galictis vittata, Bell.) W. Martin. Proc. Zool. Soc. London, pt.1, p.140, 1833.

(CONTRIBUTIONS TO KNOWLEDGE OF THE GALICTIS SPECIES.) Beitraege zur Kenntniss der Galictis-Arten. A.Nehring. Zool. Jahrbuch, Jena, vol.1, pp.177-212, figs.3, 1886.

(ON CLASSIFYING, AS REGARDS SPECIES, THE LARGE GRISON (GALICTIS CRASSIDENS NEHRING RESP. G. ALLAMANDI BELL) ALONGSIDE THE SMALL GRISON (G. VITTATA BELL).) Ueber die Artberechtigung des grossen Grison (Galictis crassidens Nehring resp. G. allamandi Bell) neben dem kleinen Grison (G. vittata Bell). A. Nehring. Sitz.Ber.Gesell. Naturf.Freunde Berlin, no.4, pp.43-55, figs.2, Apr. 20, 1886.

(ON A NEW GRISON SPECIES, GALICTIS (GRISONIAL) CRASSIDENS N.SP., FROM TROPICAL SOUTH AMERICA.) Ueber eine neue Grison-Art, Galictis (Grisonia) crassidens n.sp., aus dem tropischen Suedamerika. A. Nehring. Sitz.Ber.Gesell. Naturf.Freunde Berlin, no.9, pp.167-175, Nov. 17, 1885.

NEW SPECIES OF GALICTIS FROM MEXICO. E.W. Nelson. Proc. Biol. Soc. Washington, vol.14, pp.129-130, Aug. 9, 1901.

THE "HURON" OF THE ARGENTINE. (Grisonella huronax.) Oldfield Thomas. Ann. and Mag. Nat. Hist., ser.9, vol. 8, pp.212-213, Aug., 1921.

(Gulo)

ATOMIC POWER IN FUR. (Description, Distribution, and Habits of Wolverine.) Jacob B. Abbott. Penna. Game News, vol. 16, no.10, pp.3, 20-21, Jan., 1946.

MYTH OF THE INJUN DEVIL. (Wolverine.) Russell Annabel. Sports Afield, New York, vol.123, no.5, pp.42-43, 139-145, illus., May, 1950.

FUR BEARING ANIMALS OF THE UNITED STATES. Frank G. Ashbrook, Horace J. McMullen. Fur Jour., vol.2, no.6, pp.18, 62, illus., July, 1928. (The Wolverene.)

WOLVERINES AND MEN. William Beebe. Bull. New York Zool. Soc., vol.43, no.2, pp.54-59, Mar.-Apr., 1940.

(RAISING WOLVERINES.) Aufzucht von Vielfrassen. Ulf Behm. Zool. Garten, Leipzig, n.F., vol.20, nos.2-3, pp.77-81, illus., 1953.

(GEOLOGIC AGE OF GLUTTON REMAINS.) Das geologische Alter der Vielfrassreste. Walter Biese. Zeitschr. f. Saeugetierk., vol.11, pp.319-320, pls.16, Mar. 13, 1936.

TRAP ROBBER. (Wolverine.) Bud Branham. Alaska Sportsman, Ketchikan, vol.16, no.2, pp.14-15, 24, illus., Feb., 1950.

WOLVERINE DISPUTES TRAIL. Norman Clyde. Calif. Fish and Game, vol.11, no.4, p.189, Oct., 1925.

THE SO-CALLED WOLVERINE, A MISNOMER AND A MYTH IN MICHIGAN. Richard E. Follett. Michigan Zool. Soc. Bull., Detroit, pp.3, illus., Mar., 1939.

ARE THERE WOLVERINES IN MINNESOTA? Edward M. Franey. Cons. Volunteer, vol. 16, no.91, pp.18-20, Jan.-Feb., 1953.

THE WOLVERINE. Walter Fry. Calif.Fish and Game, vol.9, pp.129-134, Oct., 1923.

AS TO THE WOLVERINE. George Bird Grinnell. Jour. Mamm., vol.1, no.4, pp. 182-184, Aug., 1920.

SOME HABITS OF THE WOLVERINE. George Bird Grinnell. Jour. Mamm., vol.7, no.1, pp.30-34, Feb., 1926.

TREE-CLIMBING WOLVERINE. George Bird Grinnell. Jour. Mamm., vol.2, no.1, p.37, Feb., 1921.

AN ACCOUNT OF WOLVERINE ATTACKING MOUNTAIN GOAT. C.J. Guiguet. Canadian Field-Nat., vol.65, no.5, p.187, Sep.-Oct., 1951.

WOLVERINE FUR FROSTING. Thora M. Plitt Hardy. Jour. Wildl. Mgt., Menasha, vol.12, no.3, pp.331-334, July, 1948.

(DID THE GLUTTON LIVE IN NORTHERN GERMANY IN A WILD STATE DURING MODERN TIMES?) Hat der Vielfrass noch in der Neuzeit in Norddeutschland wild gelebt? Max Hilzheimer. Zeitschr. f. Saeugetierk., Berlin, vol.8, nos.3-6, pp.219-221, Dec. 20, 1933. (Gulo luscus L.)

WOLVERINE (GULO LUSCUS) SPECIMENS FROM WISCONSIN. Hartley H.T. Jackson. Jour. Mamm., vol.35, no.2, p.254, May 26, 1954.

WOLVERENE IN ITASCA COUNTY, MINNESOTA. Hartley H.T. Jackson. Jour. Mamm., vol.3, no.1, p.53, Feb., 1922.

RECENT REPORT OF THE WOLVERENE IN MINNESOTA. Charles Eugene Johnson. Jour. Mamm., vol.4, no.1, pp.54-55, Feb., 1923.

RECENT RECORDS OF THE WOLVERINE (GULO LUSCUS LUTEUS) IN CALIFORNIA. Fred L. Jones. Calif. Fish and Game, San Francisco, vol.36, no.3, pp.320-322, illus., July 10, 1950.

RECORDS OF SOUTHERN WOLVERINE, GULO LUSCUS LUTEUS, IN CALIFORNIA. Fred L. Jones. Jour. Mamm., vol.36, no.4, p.569, Dec. 14, 1955.

(PRESENTDAY OCCURRENCE OF THE WOLVERINE (GULO GULO L.) IN EUROPE.) Das heutige Vorkommen des Vielfrasses (Gulo gulo L.) in Europa. Peter Krott. Zeitschr. f. Saeugetierk., vol.22, nos.3-4, pp.208-213, 1957.

(RECOVERY OF A WOLVERINE THAT HAD ESCAPED DURING TRANSPORT.) Das Wiederfinden eines auf einem Transport entsprungenen Vielfrasses. Peter Krott. Zeitschr. Tierpsychol., vol.10, no.2, pp.254-268, 1953. (With English summary.)

(A GLUTTON, GULO GULO L., HIDING IN UPPLAND.) En järv, Gulo gulo L., skjuten i Uppland. E. Lönnberg. Fauna och Flora, Stockholm, pt.6, pp.269-272, illus., 1931.

THE WOLVERINE, SOMETIMES CALLED THE GLUTTON. William MacMillan. Nature Mag., vol.5, pp.41, 64, fig.1, Jan., 1925.

THE WOLVERINE IN MICHIGAN. Richard H. Manville. Jack Pine Warbler, vol.28, no.4, pp.127-129, Dec., 1950.

THE WOLVERINE OR GLUTTON. Ida M. Mellen. San Diego Zoonooz; vol.19, no.12, p.3, illus., Dec., 1946.

(GLUTTON (GULO GULO L.).) Vom Jaerv (Gulo gulo L.). Erna Mohr. Zool. Garten, Leipzig, n.F., vol.10, nos.1-2, pp.14-21, illus., May, 1938.

WOLVERINE TRAILS AT DENALI. Adolph Murie. Living Wilderness, vol.16, no.39, pp.13-20, illus., Winter, 1951-52.

MONTANA'S WILDERNESS WANDERERS. (Status of Wolverine.) Fletcher E. Newby. Mont. Wildl., vol.3, no.1, pp.14-15, illus., Winter (Mar.), 1953.

DISTRIBUTION AND STATUS OF THE WOLVERINE IN MONTANA. Fletcher E. Newby, Philip L. Wright. Jour. Mamm., vol.36, no.2, pp.248-253, map, May, 1955.

RECENT RECORDS OF WOLVERINE IN IDAHO. W. Leslie Pengelly. Jour. Mamm., vol.32, no.2, pp.224-225, May 21, 1951.

WOLVERENE (CARCAJOU OR GLUTTON), VEEL-VRAAT, GLUTTON, LOUP-CERVIER; URSUS-LUSCUS, GULO-LUCUS. PARTS I AND II. J. Watts de Peyster. Tivoli, New York, Frank O. Green, pp.30+xx, illus., 1901.

(ON GESTATION IN THE GLUTTON GULO LINNÉ.) Ueber die Tragzeitverhaeltnisse beim Vielfrass (Gulo Linné). H. Prell. Zool. Anzeiger, vol.97, nos.5-6, pp.113-123, Jan. 1, 1932.

SOME CHARACTERISTICS OF WOLVERINE FUR. Horace F. Quick. Jour. Mamm., vol. 33, no.4, pp.492-493, Nov., 1952.

COMMON WOLVERINE GULO LUSCUS. Charles Ritter. Wyo. Wildl., Cheyenne, vol.7, no.9, pp.5-6, 16, Sep., 1942.

WOLVERINE SEEN IN SQUAW VALLEY, CALIFORNIA. Ferdinand S. Ruth. Jour. Mamm., vol.35, no.4, pp.594-595, Nov. 29, 1954.

WOLVERINE CAPTURED IN OKANOGAN COUNTY, WASHINGTON. Victor B. Scheffer. Murrelet, Seattle, vol.22, no.2, p.37, May-Aug., 1941.

SKULL OF THE WOLVERENE (GULO LUSCUS). R.W. Schufeldt. Jour. Mamm., vol.5, no.3, pp.189-193, pls.21-22, Aug., 1924.

WOLVERINE. John J. Spahn. Colorado Conservation, vol.3, no.2, pp.1-3, Mar.-Apr., 1954.

(GLUTTON, A LITTLE KNOWN NORTHERN WILD CARNIVORE.) Der Vielfrass, ein wenig bekanntes nordisches Raubwild. Geo. Steinbacher. Aus der Natur (Der Naturforscher), Berlin, Jahrg.15, no.6, pp.190-191, Sep., 1938.

FUR-BEARING MAMMALS OF WYOMING. Earl M. Thomas. Wyo. Wildl., pt.8, vol. 16, no.10, pp.24-27, illus., Oct., 1952. (Wolverine.)

PLACENTA OF THE WOLVERINE (GULO GULO LUSCUS (LINNAEUS)). George B. Wislocki, Emmanuel C. Amoroso. Bull. Mus. Comp. Zool., Harvard, vol.114, no. 3, pp.91-100, illus., Feb., 1956.

WOLVERINE IN A TREE. N.A. Wood. Jour. Mamm., vol.2, no.4, p.234, Nov., 1921.

LONGEVITY OF CAPTIVE WOLVERINES. Gordon T. Woods. Amer. Midland Nat., Notre Dame, vol.31, no.2, p.505, fig.1, Mar., 1944.

THE WOLVERINE. Gordon T. Woods. Nature Mag., vol.39, no.8, pp.426-428, 444, Oct., 1946.

REPRODUCTION IN THE WOLVERINE, GULO GULO. Philip L. Wright, Robert Rausch. Jour. Mamm., vol.36, no.3, pp. 346-355, illus., Aug., 1955.

WOLVERINE IN OHIO? YES, AND NOW IT'S A MUSEUM PIECE. Ohio Conserv. Bull., Columbus, vol.8, no.6, p.10, illus., June, 1944.

(Ictonyx)
NOTES ON A CAPTIVE ICTICYON. Marston Bates. Jour. Mamm., vol.25, no.2, pp. 152-154, pl.1, May 25, 1944.

ICTONYX KAUP, 1835, THE CORRECT GENERIC NAME, AND ICTONYX STRIATUS (PERRY), 1810, THE CORRECT SPECIFIC NAME FOR THE AFRICAN STINKMUISHOND. J.R. Ellerman, T.C.S. Morrison-Scott. Jour. Mamm., vol.35, no. 1, pp.130-131, Feb. 10, 1956.

TECHNICAL NAME OF THE AFRICAN MUISHOND (GENUS ICTONYX). J. R. Ellerman, T.C.S. Morrison-Scott. Jour. Mamm., vol.34, no.1, pp.114-116, pl. 1, Feb. 19, 1952.

NOTICE OF A NEW SPECIES OF ZORILLA. John Edward Gray. Proc. Zool. Soc. London, pp.69-70, pl.10, 1864.

STATUS OF THE GENERIC NAME ZORILLA (MAMMALIA): NOMENCLATURE BY RULE OR BY CAPRICE. Philip Hershkovitz. Proc. Biol. Soc. Washington, vol.68, pp. 185-192, Dec. 31, 1955.

THE SPECIFIC NAME OF THE STRIPED MUISHOND OF SOUTH AFRICA. N. Hollister. Proc. Biol. Soc. Washington, vol. 28, p.184, Nov. 29, 1915.

GENERIC NAME ZORILLA. Arthur H. Howell. Proc. Biol. Soc. Washington, vol. 19, p.46, Feb. 26, 1906.

THE PROPER NAME FOR THE STRIPED MUISHOND OF SOUTH AFRICA. (Ictonyx capensis (A.Smith).) Arthur H. Howell. Proc. Biol. Soc. Washington, vol.19, p.46, Feb. 26, 1906.

(NORTHERN AFRICA MAMMALOGICAL NOTES. THE ZORILLA.) Notes de mammalogie Nord-Africaine. Le zorille. Louis Lavauden. Bull. Soc. Zool. France, vol. 49, nos.8-10, pp.630-634, fig.1, 1924.

(Lyncodon)
LYNCODON PATAGONICUS, WITH A DESCRIPTION OF A NEW SUBSPECIES. )Sobre Lyncodon patagonicus con descripcion de una neuva sub-especie. Angel Cabrera. Rev. Chilena de Hist. Nat., year 32, pp. 259-263, Oct. 2, 1928.

LYNCODON PATAGONICUM (BLAINV.). Paul Matschie. Sitz. Ber. Gesell. Naturf. Freunde Berlin, no.9, pp.171-177, Nov. 19, 1895.

EXTERNAL CHARACTERS OF THE PATAGONIAN WEASEL (LYNCODON PATAGONICUS.) R.I. Pocock. Proc. Zool. Soc. London, pt.4, pp.1085-1094, illus., Dec., 1926.

(Mellivora)
RATELS AND CORPSES. A.A. Dunbar Brander. Jour. Bombay Nat. Hist. Soc., vol.37, no.3, pp.719-722, Dec. 15, 1934; vol.39, no.1, pp.161-162, Dec. 1, 1936.

RATELS AND CORPSES. F.W. Champion. Jour. Bombay Nat. Hist. Soc., vol.37, no. 4, pp.952-953, Apr. 15, 1935; vol.39, no. 1, pp.159-161, Dec. 1, 1936.

EARLIEST NAME FOR THE CAPE RATEL. Ned Hollister. Proc. Biol. Soc. Washington, vol.25, p.96, May 4, 1912.

TWO NEW AFRICAN RATELS. Ned Hollister. Smiths. Misc. Coll., vol.56, no. 13, publ.1988, pp.3, Oct. 10, 1910.

TYPE LOCALITY OF MELLIVORA OBYSSINICA. Ned Hollister. Proc. Biol. Soc. Washington, vol.24, p.37, Feb. 24, 1911.

(THE RATEL OF KILIMANJARO.) Der honigdachs vom Kilimandscharo. Einar Lönnberg. Zool. Anzeiger, vol.37, nos. 3-4, pp.74-75, Jan. 31, 1911.

NOTICE OF A NEW SPECIES OF RATEL (MELLIVORA LEUCONOTA). Philip Lutley Sclater. Proc. Zool. Soc. London, p.98, pl.8, 1867.

STRANGE PARTNERSHIP. HOW MAYIMBA, A BIRD, AND KAMBOLE, A HONEYBADGER, COMBINE THEIR EFFORTS TO MUTUAL ADVANTAGE. Don H. Selchow. Nat. Hist., New York, vol.36, no.5, pp.431-437, illus., Dec., 1935.

NEW RATEL FROM BRITISH EAST AFRICA. (Mellivora maxwelli.) Oldfield Thomas. Ann. and Mag. Nat. Hist., ser.9, vol.12, p.340, Sep., 1923.

RATELS AND CORPSES. C.G. Toogood. Jour. Bombay Nat. Hist. Soc., vol.38, no. 3, pp.612-613, Apr. 15, 1936.

NEW SPECIES OF MELLIVORA FROM SOMALILAND. (Mellivora brockmani.) R.C. Wroughton, R.E. Cheesman. Ann. and Mag. Nat. Hist., ser.9, vol.5, p. 197, Feb., 1920.

(Tayra)
GEOGRAPHICAL RACES OF THE TAYRA (GALICTIS BARBARA), WITH NOTES ON ABNORMALLY COLOURED INDIVIDUALS. Oldfield Thomas. Ann. and Mag. Nat. Hist., ser.7, vol.5, no.25, pp.145-148, Jan., 1900.

(Poecilictis, Poecilogale)
EXTERNAL CHARACTERS OF THE SOUTH AFRICAN STRIPED WEASEL (POECILOGALE ALBINUCHA). R.I. Pocock. Proc. Zool. Soc. London, pt.1, pp.125-133, illus., Apr. 6, 1927.

ON MUSTELA ALBINUCHA, GRAY. Oldfield Thomas. Ann. and Mag. Nat. Hist., ser.5, vol.11, no.65, pp.370-371, figs., May, 1883.

(Badgers) General

CAGEY BADGER. Elizabeth Bachmann. Conserv. Volunteer, St. Paul, vol.11, no.64, pp.10-12, May-June, 1948.

BADGER--LIVING STEAM SHOVEL. G.W. Bradt. Mich. Cons., vol.16, no.6, p.4, July, 1947.

TRACKS IN DESERT DUNES. (Badger.) Raymond B. Cowles. Nat. Hist., New York, vol.58, no.5, pp.206-212, illus., May, 1949.

BILLY, THE BADGER. William L. Finley, Irene Finley. Nat. Mag., vol.4, pp.284-288, illus., Nov., 1924.

IN PURSUIT OF BADGERS. Tappan Gregory. Jour. Mamm., vol.13, no.4, pp.329-330, pl.15, Nov., 1932.

THE BADGER. Eric Hardy. Discovery, London, vol.5, no.10, pp.314-315, illus., Oct., 1944.

THE BADGER, MASTER EXCAVATOR. Donald F. Hoffmeister. Living Museum, Springfield, vol.15, no.6, pp.421-422, illus., Oct., 1953.

BADGER. Jack E. Hogue. Colo.Cons., vol. 4, no.2, pp.28-29, illus., Mar.-Apr., 1955.

FRIEND BADGER. A. Brazier Howell. Nature Mag., vol.20, no.5, pp.227-228, illus., Nov., 1932.

THE BADGER. T. Hyde-Parker. Naturalist, London, no.791, pp.141-145, June, 1941.

ARCTONYX COLLARIS HOEVENI HUBRECHT. Edward Jacobson. Tropische Natuur, Buitenzorg, vol.21, no.3, pp.41-43, fig.1, Mar., 1932.

(CONTRIBUTION TO THE BIOLOGY OF THE BADGER.) Ett bidrag till grävlingens biologi. Kurt Knaak. Svenska Jägareförbundets Tidskrift, Stockholm, vol.78, no.7, pp.322-325, July 11, 1940.

BADGERS' YEAR. F. Howard Lancum. Crosby Lockwood, pp.72, illus., 1954?

VETERANS OF THE BLACKOUT. (European Badger.) L.J. Langford. Nature Mag., Washington, D.C., vol.35, no.8, pp.407, 409, illus., Oct., 1942.

(THE BADGER.) Der Dachs. Dieter Melhardt. Verlag Naturkundliche Korrespondenz, Berlin, pp.79, 1949.

THE BADGER. Ernest Neal. New Naturalist Monograph Series, London, and Glasgow, Wm.Collins, Sons and Co., pp.158, 1948.

(INVESTIGATIONS ON THE BIOLOGY OF THE BADGER (MELES MELES). Biologiska undersokningar over gravlingen (Meles meles). Gösta Notini. Svenska Jagareforbundets Meddelande, Uppsala, no.13, pp. 256, illus., 1948.

(ON THE BADGER AND THE GAMEKEEPER.) Grävling och viltvården. Gösta Notini. Svensk Jakt, Stockholm, vol.86, no. 6, pp.137-143, illus., June 15, 1948.

(YOU'LL MEET HIM--AND WHY!) Honom man möter-och varför! Gösta Notini. Svensk Jakt, Stockholm, vol.89, no.5, pp.141-142, illus., May 21, 1951. (Badger.)

BADGERS WE HAVE KNOWN. 1. THE LAWN-KEEPER. Philip Pilditch. Countryman, Idbury, Kingham, Oxfordshire, vol. 17, no.1, pp.173-174, Apr.-June, 1938.

THE MYSTERIOUS BADGER. Frances Pitt. Field, London, vol.162, no.4205, p.291, illus., July 29, 1933.

THE BADGER. W.P. Pycraft. Illus. London News, vol.181, no.4874, p.416, illus., Sep. 17, 1932.

(Badgers) Anatomy

MUSCULAR ANATOMY OF THE AMERICAN BADGER (TAXIDEA TAXUS). Raymond Hall. Univ. Calif. Publ. Zool., vol.30, no.8, pp. 205-219, figs.2, July 28, 1927.

ON THE SKULL OF THE BADGER, MELES MELES LINN. Ellen Hazelwood, Alfred Hazelwood. Naturalist, London, no.793, pp.175-176, figs.2, Aug., 1941.

(ON THE SKULL OF THE BADGER (MELES MELES L.) IN SEXUAL VARIATION.) Der Schaedel des Dachses (Meles meles L.) in seiner geschlechtlichen Verschiedenheit. A. Jacobi. Mitteil. Zool. Mus., Berlin, vol. 20, no.2, pp.321-333, figs.3, 1935.

(THE LARYNGEAL CARTILAGE OF THE BADGER.) Les cartilages laryngés du blaireau. P. Morel. Mammalia, Paris, vol. 15, nos.1-2, pp.47-49, illus., Mar.-June, 1951.

REMARKABLE CHANGES IN THE SKULL OF THE AMERICAN BADGER (TAXIDEA TAXUS) DUE TO ADVANCED AGE. R.W. Shufeldt. Jour. Mamm., vol.3, no.3, pp. 173-175, pl.10, Aug., 1922.

ON THE SKULL AND DENTITION OF THE AMERICAN BADGER (MELES LABRADORIA). G.R. Waterhouse. Proc. Zool. Soc. London, pt.6, p.153, 1938.

OSSICULA AUDITUS OF THE COMMON BADGER, MELES TAXUS. H.C. Wilkie. Proc. Zool. Soc. London, pt.3, pp.815-823, illus., 1926.

SOME NOTES UPON THE ANATOMY OF THE FERRET-BADGER, HELICTIS PERCONATA. Proc. Zool. Soc. London, pp.21-29, 1905.

(Badgers) Breeding, Raising in Captivity

FUR BEARING ANIMALS OF THE UNITED STATES. THE BADGER. Frank Ashbrook, Horace J. McMullen. Fur Jour., vol.2, no. 7, pp.30-31, 51, illus., Aug., 1928.

BREEDING BADGER IN CAPTIVITY. Frank Kruse. Amer. Fur Breeder, vol.2, no.2, pp.14-16, Aug., 1929.

SOME BADGER BREEDING PROBLEMS. W.J. McIntyre. Amer. Fur Breeder, vol. 11, no.6, pp.24-26, Dec., 1929.

(ADVICE FOR SILVER BADGER BREEDERS.) Ratschlaege fuer Silberdachszuechter. P. Muller. Der Deutsche Pelztierzuechter, Munich, no.8, pp.209-213, figs., Apr. 15, 1931.

(THE BADGER AS A PET.) Der Dachs als Hausgenosse. Elizabeth Naundorff. Zeitschr. f. Saeugetierk., vol.4, no.2, pp. 122-124, fig.1, Aug. 6, 1929.

(BIOLOGICAL AND PSYCHOLOGICAL OBSERVATIONS ON A CAPTIVE FEMALE BADGER (MELES MELES L.).) Biologische und psychologische Beobachtungen an einem in Gefangenschaft gehaltenen weiblichen Dachs (Meles meles L.). Bastian Schmid. Zeitschr. f. Saeugetierk., Berlin, vol.7, nos.1-6, pp.156-165, figs.5, pl.18, Dec. 15, 1932.

RAISING BADGERS IN CAPTIVITY. U.S. Dept. Agric., Biol.Survey, Wildl. Leaflet 32, pp.2, Jan., 1936.

(Badgers) Ecology, Habits, Behavior

FOOD OF THE DANISH BADGER (MELES MELES DANICUS DEGERBØL) WITH SPECIAL REFERENCE TO THE SUMMER MONTHS. Johannes Anderson. Danish Rev. Game Biol., vol.3, no.1, pp.1-75, illus., 1954. (In English.)

BADGER AFIELD AND UNDERGROUND. (Account of European Badger, with Occasional Notes on American Badger.) H. Mortimer Batten. London, H.F. and G. Witherby, pp.159, pls.12, 1923.

BADGER'S COLD STORAGE PLANT. Joyce Dew. Blue Jay, Saskatchewan Nat. Hist. Soc., vol.15, no.4, p.177, Dec., 1957.

BADGER PREYING UPON CARP. Guy E. Drake, Clifford C. Presnall. Jour. Mamm., vol.31, no.3, pp.355-356, Aug. 21, 1950.

JOURNEY OF A UTAH BADGER. (Badger Swimming.) J. Curtis Earl. Utah Fish and Game Bull., Salt Lake City, vol.6, no.2, p.8, Oct., 1948.

(ON THE EARLY DEVELOPMENT OF THE BEHAVIOR OF A MALE BADGER (MELES MELES L.), WITH SPECIAL CONSIDERATION OF ITS PLAY.) Ueber die Jugendentwicklung des Verhaltens eines maennlichen Dachses (Meles meles L.) unter besonderer Beruecksichtigung des Spieles. I. Eibl-Eibesfeldt. Zeitschr. f. Tierpsychol., vol. 7, pp.327-355, 1950.

(DOES OUR BADGER (MELES MELES L.) HIBERNATE?) Haelt unser Dachs (Meles meles L.) Winterschlaf? M. Eisenstraut. Zeitschr. f. Saeugetierk., Berlin, vol.6, no.4, pp.152-159, Dec. 15, 1931.

SUMMER FOOD HABITS OF THE BADGER IN NORTHWESTERN IOWA. Paul L. Errington. Jour. Mamm., vol.18, no.2, pp. 213-216, May, 1937.

BADGERS AND EGGS. Arthur Heinemann. Field, London, vol.153, p.798, May 16, 1929.

(BADGER SEEKING SNAILS.) Der Dachs auf der Schneckensuche. Viktor Hornung. Zool. Garten, Leipzig, n.F., vol.12, no. 1, pp.61-62, Mar., 1940.

BADGER AND RATTLESNAKES. A.M. Jackley. Colorado Conserv.Comments, Denver, vol.7, no.1, p.11, Mar. 15, 1944.

BADGER, RATTLESNAKE ENEMY, SAYS EXPERT. A.M. Jackley. S.Dakota Conserv. Digest, Pierre, vol.11, no.1, pp.2-3, 16, illus., Jan., 1944.

BADGERS FEED ON RATTLESNAKES. A.M. Jackley. Jour. Mamm., vol.19, no. 3, pp.374-375, Aug., 1938.

MATERIALS ON THE FOOD OF THE BADGER (MELES MELES L.) IN THE TARTAR REPUBLIC. I.V. Jarkov, V.P. Teplov. Raboty Volzhsko-Kamskoi Zonal'noi Okhotnich'epromyslonoi Biologischeskoi Stantsii, Kazan, no.2, (Unchen'ie Zapiski Kazanskogo Gosudarstvennogo Universiteta im V. I. Ul'ianova-Lenina, vol.92, nos.7-8), pp.110-124, 1932. (In Russian with English summary.)

THE NIGHT LIFE OF THE BADGER. REVEALED BY FLASHLIGHT PHOTOGRAPHY. L.J. Langford. Field, London, vol.166, no.4321, p.915, illus., Oct. 19, 1935.

BADGERS AND HUNTING. (Badger Kills Fox Cubs.) Jocelyn Lucas. Field, London, vol.156, no.4060, p.559, Oct. 18, 1930.

FOOD OF A BADGER (MELES MELES). A.D. Middleton. Jour. Anim.Ecol., London, vol.4, no.2, p.291, Nov., 1935.

CONCERNING BADGERS. (Notes on Gestation Period, Condition of Young, Weight, and Feeding and Other Habits.) Vivian Nickalls. Field, London, vol.152, p.291, Aug. 16, 1928.

NOTES ON A CAPTIVE BADGER. Mary Louise Perry. Murrelet, Seattle, vol.20, no.3, Sep.-Dec., pp.49-53, Dec. 16, 1939.

BADGER DIGS FOR BANK SWALLOWS. Laurence B. Potter. Condor, vol.26, p. 191, Sep., 1924.

CALIFORNIA BADGER AT WORK. Helen K. Sharsmith. Yosemite Nature Notes, Yosemite, vol.21, no.12, pp.103-104, Dec., 1942.

FOOD HABITS OF THE COMMON BADGER, TAXIDEA T. TAXUS (SCHREBER), IN IOWA. Edwin Snead. MS thesis, Iowa State Coll., 1941.

FOOD HABITS OF THE BADGER IN IOWA. Edwin Snead, Geo. O. Hendrickson. Jour. Mamm., vol.23, no.4, pp.380-391, Nov., 1942.

BADGER AS A SWIMMER. N.A. Wood. Jour. Mamm., vol.2, no.3, p.170, Aug., 1921.

(Badgers) Economic Importance

ALLIES OF THE FARMER. (American Badger.) Vernon Bailey. Nature Mag., Wash., D.C., vol.35, no.8, pp.406, 408, illus., Oct., 1942.

BADGER CONTROL. O.E. Bremner. Calif. Dept. Agr. Bull., vol.35, no.3, pp.151-153, July-Sep., 1946.

GOOD WORD FOR THE BADGER. C.Curle. Irish Naturalists' Jour., vol.4, no.6, p.120, Nov., 1932.

IN DEFENCE OF THE BADGER. Alfred Pease. Field, London, vol.158, no.4121, p.927, illus., Dec. 19, 1931.

THE BADGER. (Shaving Brushes Manufactured from Hair of Meles leptorhynchus; Pelts also Used for Rugs and Clothing.) China Jour., vol.12, no.5, p.302, May, 1930.

BROCK IN THE DOCK:THE CASE FOR THE OMNIVOROUS BADGER. (Meles) Illus. London News, vol.218, no.5844, p.627, illus., Apr. 21, 1951.

IN DEFENSE OF THE BADGER. Colorado Conserv. Comments, Denver, vol.7, no.1, p.1, Mar. 15, 1944.

(Badgers) Embryology

OBSERVATIONS ON THE EMBRYOLOGY OF THE BADGER. G. W. D. Hamlett. Anat. Record, vol.53, no.3, pp.283-303, pl.1, Aug., 1932.

(Badgers) Eurasia

BADGER'S MURDER AT CAPEL. George Bird. Trans. Suffolk Nat. Soc., Norwich, vol.4, pt.4, pp.288-289, illus., Dec., 1941.

SUFFOLK BADGERS. Lord Cranbrook. Trans. Suffolk Nat. Soc., vol.8, pt.3, pp.109-110, 1954.

DISTRIBUTION OF THE BADGER (MELES MELES) AROUND DENBIGH WITH NOTES ON ITS FOOD AND HABITS. Gwion Davies. Jour. Anim. Ecol., vol.5, no.1, pp.97-104, map 1, May, 1936.

BADGERS IN SUSSEX. R. Fortune. London, Naturalist, no.848, p.265, Sep., 1927.

BADGER IN CUMBERLAND. R.Graham. Trans. Carlisle Nat. Hist. Soc., vol.7, pp.88-99, 1946.

NOTICE OF A BADGER FROM CHINA (MELES CHINENSIS), SENT BY MR. SWINHOE, H. M. COUNSUL AT AMOY, AND BY DR. HARTLAND, FROM HONGKONG. John Edward Gray. Proc.Zool.Soc. London, pp.206-209, figs.2, 1868.

BADGER AT ROMFORD. Percy W. Horn. Essex Nat., Stratford, vol.27, pt.1, pp. 37-38, Apr.-Sep., 1940.

NOTE ON BORNEAN BADGERS (MYDAUS). C. Boden Kloss. Jour. Malayan Branch Royal Asiatic Soc., vol.5, pt.2, pp.348-349, Nov., 1927.

BADGER NOTES. G. Thelwall Maurice. Jour Soc. Preservation Fauna Empire, Hertford, pt.L, pp.45-47, Dec., 1944.

THE BADGER. (In England.) H.G.Maurice. Jour. Soc. Preservation Fauna Empire, Hertford, n.s., pt.47, pp.26-27, Aug., 1943.

(TELEDU OF THE PHILIPPINES (MYDAUS MARCHEI MUET).) Der Stinkdachs der Philippinen (Mydaus marchei Muet). A.B. Meyer. Abhandl. and Ber. K. Zool. Anthropol. Ethno. Mus., Dresden, no.13, pp. 1-4, 1894-1895.

OCCURRENCE OF THE MALAYAN BADGER OR TELEDU IN BORNEO. J.C. Moulton. Jour. Straits Branch, Royal Asiatic Soc., no.83, pp.142-146, Apr., 1921.

(JAPANESE MAMMALS, IN PARTICULAR THE JAPANESE BADGER AND ITS RELATIONSHIP TO MELES TAXUS.) Ueber japanische Saeugethiere, insbesondere ueber den japanischen Dachs und sein Verhaeltniss zu Meles taxus. A. Nehring. Sitz. Ber.Gesell. Naturf. Freunde Berlin, no.2, pp.18-26, figs.2, Feb. 16, 1886.

(THE JAPANESE BADGER (MELES ANAKUMA TEMM.).) Ueber den japanischen Dachs (Meles anakuma Temm.). A.Nehring. Zool. Garten, Frankfurt, Jahrg.26, no.8, illus., Aug., 1885.

INCREASE OF THE BADGER (MELES MELES) IN GREAT BRITAIN DURING THE PERIOD 190-1934; WITH ESPECIAL REFERENCE TO AN AREA IN SOUTH SHROPSHIRE KNOWN AS THE WHEATLAND COUNTRY. Frances Pitt. Jour. Anim.Ecol., London, vol.4, no.1, pp.1-6, pl.1, maps 2, May, 1935.

HOG-BADGERS (ARCTONYS) OF BRITISH INDIA. R.I. Pocock. Jour. Bombay Nat. Hist. Soc., vol.41, no.3, pp.461-469, figs. 3, Apr., 1940.

BADGER IN FOX EARTH. Charles Russell. Field, London, vol. 152, p.157, July 26, 1928.

BADGERS AT HOME IN COUNTY DOWN. J.A. Sidney Stendall. Irish Naturalists' Jour., vol.4, no.11, pp.218-219, Sep., 1933.

ARCTONYX OF ANNAM. Oldfield Thomas. Ann. and Mag. Nat. Hist., ser.9, vol.7, p.524, June, 1921.

DESCRIPTION OF A NEW SPECIES OF HILICTIS FROM BORNEO. Oldfield Thomas. Ann. and Mag. Nat. Hist., ser.6, vol.15, no.88, pp.331-332, Apr., 1895.

ON BORNEAN SPECIMENS OF THE TELEDU (MYDAUS). Oldfield Thomas. Ann. and Mag. Nat. Hist., ser.9, vol.20, p.288, Sep., 1927.

ON THE SPECIES OF MYDAUS FOUND IN BORNEO AND THE NATUNA ISLANDS. Oldfield Thomas. Ann. and Mag. Nat. Hist., ser.7, vol.9, no.54, pp.442-444, June, 1902.

SCIENTIFIC RESULTS OF THE MAMMAL SURVEY. NO. XXXII (C). A NEW FERRET BADGER (HELICTIS) FROM THE NAGA HILLS. Oldfield Thomas. Jour. Bombay Nat. Hist. Soc., vol.28, no.2, p.432, Mar. 25, 1922.

(Badgers) Fossils

NEW PLIOCENE BADGER FROM MEXICO. (Taxidea mexicana.) Arthur B. Drescher. Bull. S. Calif. Acad. Sci., Los Angeles, vol.38, pp.57-62, pls.13, Sep. 30, 1939.

NEW PLIOCENE BADGER FROM NEW MEXICO. (Taxidea mexicana.) Arthur B. Drescher. Bull. S. Calif. Acad. Sci., Los Angeles, vol.38, pt.2, pp.57-62, pl.13, May-Aug., 1939.

(Badgers) Mortality

ADDITIONAL RECORDS OF BADGERS KILLED ON HIGHWAYS. W.B. Davis. Jour. Mamm., vol.26, no.1, p.89, Feb. 23, 1945.

FURTHER NOTES ON BADGERS. W.B. Davis. Jour. Mamm., vol.27, no.2, p.175, May 14, 1946.

ANOTHER RECORD OF THE BADGER AS A HIGHWAY CASUALTY. Ralph W. Dexter. Jour. Mamm., vol.26, no.1, p. 89, Feb. 23, 1945.

(Badgers) North America

RARE VISITOR, A BADGER. R.M.Barnes. Oologist, Albion, vol.58, no.6, whole no. 649, pp.64-65, June, 1941. (Lacon, Ill.)

BADGERS IN NORTHEASTERN MISSOURI AND SOUTHEASTERN IOWA. Rudolf Bennitt. Jour. Mamm., vol.20, no.3, p. 373, Aug. 14, 1939.

FACTS OF INTEREST ABOUT UTAH MAMMALS. VIII. TAXIDEA TAXUS-BADGER. Jack H. Berryman. Utah Fish and Game Bull., Salt Lake City, vol.7, no.3, p.3, Apr., 194?

DESCRIPTION OF A NEW SUBSPECIFIC FORM OF TAXIDEA TAXUS FROM COLORADO. J.D. Figgins. Proc. Colo. Mus. Nat. Hist., Denver, vol.2, no.2, p.1, Apr. 10, 1918.

CALIFORNIA BADGER. Walter Fry.Sequoia Nat'l. Park Service, Bull.22, p.3, Jan. 8, 1926, (Mimeog.); Calif. Fish and Game, vol. 14, no.3, pp.204-208, July, 1928.

NEW BADGER FROM SONORA.(Taxidea taxus sonoriensis.) E.A. Goldman. Jour. Washington Acad. Sci., vol.29, no.7, pp. 300-301, July 15, 1939.

BADGER TAXIDEA TAXUS (SCHREBER) IN INDIANA. Marcus Ward Lyon, Jr. Amer. Midland Nat., vol.13, no.3, pp.124-129, illus., May, 1932.

OBSERVATIONS ON THE NORTH AMERICAN BADGERS, WITH ESPECIAL REFERENCE TO THE FORMS FOUND IN ARIZONA, WITH DESCRIPTION OF A NEW SUBSPECIES FROM NORTHERN CALIFORNIA. Edgar A. Mearns. Bull. Amer. Mus. Nat. Hist., New York, vol. 3, no.2, pp.239-251, June 5, 1891.

STATUS OF THE BADGER IN NORTH DAKOTA. W.L. Miller. N. Dakota Outdoors, Grand Forks, vol.8, no.5, p.6, Nov., 1945.

INCREASE OF BADGERS IN NORTHWESTERN OHIO. E.L. Moseley. Jour. Mamm., vol.15, no.2, pp.156-158, May, 1934.

NEW BADGER FROM SOUTH DAKOTA. (Taxidea taxus dacotensis.) Viola S. Schantz. Proc. Biol. Soc. Washington, vol.59, pp.81-82, June 19, 1946.

NEW BADGER FROM MEXICO-UNITED STATES BOUNDARY. (Taxidae taxus apache.) Viola S. Schantz. Proc. Biol.Soc. Washington, vol.61, pp.175-176, Nov. 12, 1948.

NEW RACE OF BADGER (TAXIDEA) FROM KANSAS. (Taxidea taxus merriami.) Viola S. Schantz. Jour. Washington Acad. Sci., vol.40, no.3, pp.92-93, Mar. 15, 1950.

BADGER SPECIMEN FROM PORT DOVER, NORFOLK COUNTY, ONTARIO. L.L. Snyder. Canadian Field-Nat., vol.49, no. 8, pp.136-137, Nov., 1935.

FUR-BEARING MAMMALS OF WYOMING. Earl M. Thomas. Wyo. Wild Life, pt.11, vol.17, no.1, pp.28-32, illus., Jan., 1953.

EXHIBITION OF A BADGER FROM LOWER CALIFORNIA. Oldfield Thomas. Proc. Zool. Soc. London, p.899, Nov. 30, 1897.

BADGER IN OHIO. Ohio Conserv. Bull., Columbus, vol.9, no.7, p.27, July, 1945.

(Badgers) Pelage and Coloration

A RED BADGER. H.E. Forrest. Northwestern Nat., Arbroath, vol.10, no.2, p. 132, June, 1935.

A GOLDEN BADGER. Hope Hewett. Northwestern Nat., Arboath, vol.11, no.2, p. 154, June, 1936.

ALBINO BADGERS. P.C. Puckle. Field, London, vol.148, p.763, Oct. 28, 1926.

WARNING MARKINGS OF THE STINK BADGER. (Mydaus).China Jour., vol.13, no.4, p.232, Oct., 1930.

(Badgers) Reproductive Biology

OVULATION DURING DELAYED IMPLANTATION AND OTHER REPRODUCTIVE PHENOMENA IN THE BADGER (MELES MELES L.). R.J. Harrison, E.G. Neal. Nature, London, vol.177, no.4517, pp.977-979, illus., May 26, 1956.

REPRODUCTIVE CYCLE IN THE BADGER AND ASSOCIATED BEHAVIOUR. Ernest G. Neal. Proc. Zool. Soc. London, vol.128, no.1, pp.147-148, Feb. 14, 1957. (Summary.)

BREEDING OF BADGERS. Vivian Nickalls. Field, London, vol.151, p.829, May 17, 1928.

(BADGER OESTRUS.) Zur Rollzeit des Dachses. Ludwig Schuster. Zool. Garten, Leipzig, n.F., vol.4, nos.8-9, p.299, 1931.

(Badgers) Taxonomy

NEW GENUS OF AMERICAN PLIOCENE BADGER, WITH REMARKS ON THE RELATIONSHIPS OF BADGERS OF THE NORTHERN HEMISPHERE. (Pliotaxidea.) E. Raymond Hall. Contrib. Paleontol., Carnegie Inst. Washington, Publ.no.551, pp.9-23, figs.2, pls.2, July 18, 1944.

NOTES ON ARCTONYX. Einar Lönnberg. Ann. and Mag. Nat. Hist., ser.9, vol.11, pp.322-326, figs.4, Mar., 1923.

SOME NOTES ON FERRET-BADGERS. (New Forms of Melogale and Helictis.) Oldfield Thomas. Ann. and Mag. Nat. Hist., ser.9, vol.9, pp.193-196, Feb., 1922.

(Skunks) General

THE STRIPED SKUNK. Ross Allen, W.T. Neill. Florida Wildl., Tallahassee, vol.9, no.4, pp.6, 42, illus., Sep., 1955.

STRIPED AND SPOTTED SKUNKS. Rod Amundson. Wildl. in N. Carolina, Raleigh, vol.14, no.6, pp.4-7, illus., June, 1950.

MEET MISTER MEPHITIS. Elizabeth Bachmann. Conserv. Volunteer, St.Paul, vol.11, no.63, pp.29-32, Mar.-Apr., 1948.

THE SKUNK. Thorton W. Burgess. Bull. Massachusetts Audubon Soc., Boston, vol. 28, no.9, p.279, Jan., 1945.

BROAD-STRIPED SKUNK (MEPHITIS HUDSONICUS RICH.). Norman Griddle, Stuart Griddle. The Ottawa Naturalist, vol.27, pp.64-69, Aug.-Sep., 1913.

THE STRIPED SKUNK. Ned Dearborn. Virginia Wildl., Blacksburg, vol.3, no.7, p.6, Mar., 1940.

ERRONEOUS IDEAS CONCERNING SKUNKS. Lee R. Dice. Jour. Mamm., vol.2, no.1, p.38, Feb., 1921.

A STUDY IN BLACK AND WHITE.(Skunks) Paul Easterbook. Yosemite Nature Notes, vol.23, no.10, p.92, Oct., 1944.

ON MEPHITIS OLIDA BOITARD. D. G. Elliot. Proc. Biol. Soc. Washington, vol. 19, p.95, 1906.

LITTLE SACHET. (Skunk.) Ellsworth Jaeger. Canadian Nature, Toronto, vol.6, no.1, pp.27-29, illus., Jan.-Feb., 1944.

OUR STRIPED FRIEND. (Notes on a striped skunk.) C.H. Oneal. Yosemite Nature Notes, vol.7, p.94, Nov., 1928.

FOSSIL SKUNK FROM SAMOS. Guy E. Pilgrim. Amer. Mus. Novitates, no.663, pp.1-15, figs.6, Sep. 27, 1933.

THE SO-CALLED CIVET CAT. E.J. Sawyer. Western Sportsman, Denver, vol.7, no.5, pp.4, 29-30, Oct., 1941.

HAIL TO HIS MAJESTY. (Skunk.)Jacqueline Schermerhorn. San Diego Zoonooz, vol.20, no.8, pp.3-4, illus., Aug., 1947.

THE SKUNK LINE. S.V. Sedlak. Penna. Game News, Harrisburg, vol.11, no.1, pp. 19, 29, 32, Apr., 1940.

THE WAYS OF SPILOGALE. William E. Sherwood. Nature Mag., vol.17, no.4, p.224, fig.2, Apr., 1931.

THE SKUNK. George Smokey. S.Dakota Conservation Digest, Pierre, vol.10, no. 6, pp.10, 12, June, 1943.

POLECAT OR JIMMIE SKUNK. W. A. Swallow. Our Dumb Animals, Norwood, vol.78, no.7, p.125, illus., July, 1945.

"HYDROPHOBIA" SKUNK. (Spilogale) Lewis W. Walker. Nature Mag., vol.19, no.4, p.253, figs.3, Apr., 1932.

SKUNK SENSE. Tom Wallace. Nature Mag., Washington, vol.39, no.1, p.47, illus., Jan., 1946.

GREASE FOR THE AXIS. (Skunk) Penna. Game News, Harrisburg, vol.13, no.9, p.13, Dec., 1942.

HOODED SKUNK. Nature Mag., Washington, D.C., vol.32, no.5, p.272, photos 3, May, 1939.

MAKE SKUNKS BEHAVE. Texas Game and Fish, Austin, vol.1, no.9, p.13, Aug., 1943.

THE SKUNK. Canadian Nature, Toronto, vol.2, no.1, p.31, Jan.-Feb., 1940.

(Skunks) Anatomy

(THE PERIANAL GLAND OF MEPHITIS MACROURA MACROURA LICHTENSTEIN AND CONEPATUS MESOLEUCUS MESOLEUCUS (LICHTENSTEIN).) La glandula perianal de Mephitis macroura macroura Lichtenstein y conepatus mesoleucus mesoleucus (Lichtenstein). Amelia S.Bishop. An. Inst. Biol., vol.25, pp.463-472, illus., 1954.

WEIGHTS AND LINEAR DIMENSIONS OF THE SKULL AND SOME OF THE LONG BONES OF THE SKUNK (MEPHITIS MESOMELAS AVIA). Homer B. Latimer. Jour. Morph., vol.60, no.2, pp.379-391, fig.1, Mar. 5, 1937.

TONGUE AND GUSTATORY ORGANS OF MEPHITIS MEPHITICA. Frederick Tuckerman. Quart. Jour. Micros. Soc., n.s., vol. 28, 1887, pp.149-168, pl.11, 1888.

(Skunks) Coloration

AN ALBINO FLORIDA STRIPED SKUNK. J.M. Hollister. Nat. Hist., New York, vol.51, no.4, p.162, illus., Apr., 1943.

(COLOR CHANGE IN PREGNANT SKUNKS.) Verfaerbung traechtiger Iltisfaehen. Hans Dietrich Rohrs. Der Deutsche Pelztierzuechter, Munich, no.13, p.362, fig., July 1, 1931.

(Skunks) Diseases and Parasites

ALLOTYPE OF AMPHIPSYLLA NEOTOMAE I. FOX, 1940. (SIPHONAPTERA: DOLICHOPSYLLIDAE.) (From Spilogale gracilis arizonae.) G.F. Augustson. Bull. Southern Calif. Acad. Sci., Los Angeles, vol.41, no.1, pp.39-41, illus., Jan.-Apr., 1942.

LISTERIOSIS OF A SKUNK. F.M. Bolin et al. Bimonthly Bull., N.Dakota Agr. Exp. Sta., vol.18, no.2, pp.49-50, illus., Nov.-Dec., 1955.

TWO NEW SPECIES OF OOCHORISTICA FROM MINNESOTA SKUNKS. Asa C. Chandler. Amer. Midl. Nat., vol.48, no. 1, pp.69-73, illus., July, 1952.

PULMONARY ASPERGILLOSIS IN A SKUNK. A.J. Durant, E.R. Doll. Jour. Amer. Vet. Med. Assn., vol.95, no.752, pp.645-646, Nov., 1939.

CRENOSOMA ZEDERI N. SP. (NEMATODA: METASTRONGYLOIDEA), A NEW LUNGWORM FROM THE SKUNK (MEPHITIS NIGRA). Frans C. Goble. Jour.Parasitology, vol.28, no.5, pp.381-384, Oct., 1942.

THE NEMATODE SKRAJABINGYLUS CHITWOODORUM N. SP. FROM THE SKUNK. William C. Hill. Jour.Parasitology, vol.25, no.6, pp.475-478, Dec., 1939.

DESCRIPTION AND EXTRAMAMMALIAN LIFE OF CRENOSOMA MEPHITIDIS N. SP. (NEMATODA) IN SKUNKS. M. Hobmaier. Jour. Parasitology, vol.27, no.3, pp.229-232, June, 1941.

PLEURITIS IN WILD SKUNK. Fred L. Junod. Jour. Mamm., vol.26, no.3, pp. 309-310, Aug., 1945.

MICROFILARIA IN BRAIN TISSUE OF A SKUNK. F.T. Lynd, Geo. E. Short. Jour. Amer. Vet. Med. Assn., vol.120, no. 902, p.297, May, 1952.

SKUNKS AND HYDROPHOBIA. C. Hart Merriam. Forest and Stream, vol.16, no.24, p.473, July 14, 1881.

NEW UNARMED TAPEWORM FROM THE SPOTTED SKUNK. Harold J. Peery. Jour. Parasitology, vol.25, no.6, pp.487-490, Dec., 1939.

SOME PARASITES AND PATHOLOGICAL CONDITIONS OF THE SKUNK (MEPHITIS MEPHITIS NIGRA) IN CENTRAL NEW YORK. LeRoy C. Stegeman. Jour.Mamm., vol.20, no.4, pp.493-496, Nov., 1939.

SOME HELMINTH PARASITES OF SKUNKS IN TEXAS. Jack D. Tiner. Jour. Mamm., vol.27, no.1, pp.82-83, Feb., 1946.

CRENOSOMA MICROBURSA N. SP. FROM THE SKUNK. F.G. Wallace. Proc. Helminth. Soc. Wash., vol.8, no.2, pp.58-60, July, 1941.

ON THE OCCURRENCE OF FILAROIDES MUSTELARUM VAN BEN. IN AMERICAN SKUNKS. W.McM. Woodworth. Amer. Naturalist, vol.31, no.363, pp.234-235, Mar., 1897.

(Skunks) Ecology, General Habits, Behavior

AN ECOLOGICAL STUDY OF WINTER DENS, WITH SPECIAL REFERENCE TO THE EASTERN SKUNK. Durward L. Allen, Warren Shapter. Ecology, vol.23, no.1, pp.60-68, Jan., 1942.

RELATION OF THE SKUNK TO GAME AND BURROW-USING ANIMALS IN VIRGINIA. Nathaniel R. Bowman. MS thesis, Va.Poly. Inst., pp.41, 1953.

SKUNK--MASTER OF DEFENSE. G.W. Bradt. Mich. Cons., vol.15, no.7, pp. 6-7, Aug., 1946.

A SWIMMING SKUNK. H.E. Cole. Wisconsin Conservationist, vol.3, no.4, p.6, Sep. (Oct.), 1921.

OBSERVATIONS ON THE HABITS OF THE STRIPED SKUNK (MEPHITIS MESOMALAS VARIANS). W. Kenneth Guyler. Jour. Mamm., vol.5, no.3, pp.180-189, Aug., 1924.

GENTLE WOOD-PUSSY. (Habits of Skunk.) William L. Finley, Irene Finley. Nat. Mag., vol.4, pp.141-142, 186, illus., Sep., 1924.

UNSEASONABLE ACTIVITY OF SKUNK. Joyce Gunn. Blue Jay, Saskatchewan Nat. Hist. Soc., vol.14, no.1, p.27, Mar., 1956.

SKUNK RAKING HAY. C.T. Helstrom. Blue Jay, Saskatchewan Nat. Hist. Soc., vol.14, no.3, p.100, Sep., 1956.

FLORIDA SPOTTED SKUNK AS AN ACROBAT. Arthur H. Howell. Jour. Mamm., vol. 1, no.2, p.88, Nov., 1919.

THE "HAND-STAND" HABIT OF THE SPOTTED SKUNK. Charles Eugene Johnson. Jour. Mamm., vol.2, no.2, pp.87-89, May, 1921.

USE OF CACTUS AS PROTECTION BY HOODED SKUNK. C.A. Reed, W.H.Carr. Jour. Mamm., vol.30, pp.79-80, 1949; Nat. Hist., vol.57, pp.28-33, 1948.

CROSS-FIRES FROM A SKUNK'S BATTERY. Samuel N. Rhoads. Forest and Stream, New York, vol.52, no.2, pp.25-26, illus., Jan. 14, 1899.

THE SKUNK. Wilford E. Sanderson. School Nature League Bull., vol.14, no.7, p.4, Mar., 1944.

NOTES ON THE DEN ECOLOGY OF THE STRIPED SKUNK IN IOWA. Lyle F.Selko. Amer. Midl. Nat., vol.20, no.2, pp. 455-463, figs.5, tbls.3, Sep., 1938.

ACROBATIC SKUNKS. Ernest Thompson Seton. Jour. Mamm., vol.1, no.3, p. 140, May, 1920.

MORE ACROBATIC SKUNKS. Ernest Thompson Seton. Jour. Mamm., vol.3, no.1, p.53, Feb., 1922.

SKUNK ENTRAPPED BY NATURE. Althea R. Sherman. Jour. Mamm., vol.7, no.4, p.331, Nov., 1926.

AN OUTLINE OF THE HABITS OF THE STRIPED SKUNK AND LITTLE SPOTTED SKUNK WITH SOME DIRECTIONS FOR TRAPPING. E.L. Summer, Jr. Calif.Fish and Game, vol.18, no.1, pp.34-43, Jan., 1932.

NOTES ON THE WINTER ACTIVITY OF A CAPTIVE SKUNK. J. Kenneth Terres. Jour. Mamm., vol.21, no.2, pp.216-217, May 14, 1940.

THE "HAND STAND" AND SOME OTHER HABITS OF THE OREGON SPOTTED SKUNK. Alex Walker. Jour. Mamm., vol.11, no.2, pp.227-229, May, 1930.

MR. SKUNK HAS A VERY POTENT WEAPON. Kentucky Happy Hunting Ground, Frankfort, vol.6, no.3, p.3, May, 1950.

(Skunks) Economic Importance

FUR BEARER OR FOR WORSE. Durward L. Allen. Field and Stream, vol.56, no.12, pp. 42-43, 134-137, illus., Apr., 1952.

THE SKUNK: A BOON OR PEST? Durward L. Allen. Michigan Conservation, vol.7, no.4, pp.3, 9-10, Dec., 1937.

ALASKA SABLE, IN THE ORIGINAL.(Skunk) Bennie Bengton. Fauna, Philadelphia, vol. 4, no.3, pp.91-92, illus., Sep., 1942.

CONTROL OF SKUNKS. Dorr D. Green, E. M. Mills. U.S. Dept. Interior, Fish and Wildl. Service, Wildl. Leaflet 181, pp.4, Mar., 1941; Ohio Conservation Bull., Columbus, vol.5, no.9, pp.18-19, Sep., 1941.

SKUNKS AND HOW TO CONTROL THEM. John C. Jones. Pests and Their Control, vol.17, no.2, pp.9-11, Feb., 1949.

SKUNK CONTROL IS YOUR BUSINESS. Wesley R. Jones. Pest Control, vol.23, no.2, pp.23-24, 36, illus., Feb., 1954.

ECONOMIC VALUE OF NORTH AMERICAN SKUNKS. D.E. Lantz. U.S.Dept. Agric., Farmers' Bull., no.587, pp.1-22, figs.1-10, June 4, 1914; no.587, pp.24, figs.10, July, 1917.

FUR FARMING FOR PROFIT; WITH ESPECIAL REFERENCE TO SKUNK RAISING. Hermon Basil Laymon. Spencer, Inc., The Laymon Fur Farm Co., pp.78, illus., 1913.

THE SKUNK. A DISCUSSION ABOUT A MUCH CUSSED ANIMAL. Francis X. Lueth. Illinois Conservation, Springfield, vol.8, no.4, pp.14-15, illus., Winter Issue, 1943.

MONROE COUNTY SKUNK FARM. M.L. Michael. Recreation, vol.15, no.5, pp.361-362, Nov., 1901.

TRAPPING SKUNK IS PROFITABLE BUSINESS. A.K. Momb. N.Dakota Outdoors, Bismarck, vol.7, no.4, pp.6-7, Oct., 1944.

ON SKUNKS AND HOW TO REMOVE THEM. R.F. Morris. Acadian Nat., Fredericton, vol.2, no.5, pp.34-39, pl.2, May, 1945.

A PLEA FOR THE SKUNK. S.V. Sedlak. Penna. Game News, New Cumberland, vol. 10, no.3, p.8, June, 1939.

ALMOST AM OUTCAST. (Skunk) R.V. Whelan. Sylva, Toronto, vol.3, no.5, pp. 44-46, 1947.

CONTROL OF SKUNKS. U.S. Fish and Wildl. Service, Wildl. Leaflet, no.181, pp.2, revised 1952.

SKUNKS ARE A NUISANCE--SOMETIMES. Va. Wildl., Richmond, vol.6, no.1, pp. 38-39, Fall-Winter, 1942.

(Skunks) Embryology

TRANS-UTERINE MIGRATION OF BLASTOCYSTS IN THE EASTERN SKUNK. L.M. Llewellyn, R.K. Enders. Jour. Mamm., vol.36, no.3, p.459, Aug. 30, 1955.

(Skunks) Food Habits

THE SKUNK: A BOON OR PEST? (Food Habits.) Durward L. Allen. Mich. Cons., vol.7, no.4, pp.3, 9-10, Dec., 1937.

INSECT FOOD OF THE DUSKY SKUNK. K.F. Chamberlain. New York State Mus. Handbook, no.4, pp.93-103, 1928.

AN INTERESTING FEEDING HABIT OF SKUNKS. Floyd B. Chapman. Jour.Mamm., vol.27, no.4, p.397, Nov., 1946.

CIVETS ARE RAT KILLERS. (Spotted Skunks) Wilfred D. Crabb. Farm Sci.Rep., pp.12-13, Jan., 1941.

FOOD HABITS OF THE PRAIRIE SPOTTED SKUNK, SPILOGALE INTERRUPTA (RAFINESQUE), IN SOUTHEASTERN IOWA. Wilfred D. Crabb. MS thesis, Iowa State Coll., 1940;Jour.Mamm., vol.22, no.4, pp.349-364, figs.3, pls.2, Nov.14, 1941.

SEASONAL FOOD OF SKUNKS IN NEW YORK. W.J. Hamilton, Jr. Jour.Mamm., vol.17, no.3, pp.240-246, tbls., Aug., 1936.

WINTER FOOD OF THE EASTERN SKUNK. W.J. Hamilton, Jr. Amer.Fur Breeder, vol. 11, no.1, p.4, July, 1929.

INSECT FOOD OF SKUNKS. George H. Kelker. Jour. Mamm., vol.18 no.2, pp. 164-170, May, 1937.

FOOD HABITS OF THE SKUNK. Frank C. Pellett. Proc. Iowa Acad. Sci., pp.307-309, 1913.

THE BEE-EATING PROCLIVITY OF THE SKUNK. O.E. Plath. Amer. Nat., vol.57, pp.570-574, Dec., 1923.

FOOD HABITS OF IOWA SKUNKS IN THE FALL OF 1936. Lyle F. Selko. Jour. Wildl. Mgt., vol.1, nos.3-4, pp.70-76, tbl.1, Oct., 1937.

FEEDING BEHAVIOR OF A SKUNK. A.M. Stebler. Jour. Mamm., vol.19, no.3, p. 374, Aug., 1938.

BEE-EATING PROCLIVITIES OF THE STRIPED SKUNK. Tracy I. Storer, Geo. H. Vansell. Jour. Mamm., vol.16, no.2, pp.118-121, May, 1935.

EGG-OPENING TECHNIQUE OF A SPOTTED SKUNK. Richard G. Van Gelder. Jour. Mamm., vol.34, no.2, pp.255-256, May, 1953.

FOOD TAKEN BY THE EASTERN SKUNK (MEPHITIS M. NIGRA) WITH PARTICULAR REFERENCE TO BIRDS AND EGGS. H.M. Wight. Penna.Game News, vol.9, no.2, pp.12-13, 30, June, 1938.

(Skunks) Growth, Mortality

GROWTH, DEVELOPMENT AND SEASONAL WEIGHT OF SPOTTED SKUNKS. Wilfred D. Crabb. Jour.Mamm., vol.25, no.3, pp. 213-221, Aug., 1944.

SKUNK MORTALITY ON THE HIGHWAY. J.T. Nichols, H.C. Raven. Jour.Mamm., vol.18, no.3, pp.365-366, Aug. 14, 1937.

SKUNK MORTALITY ON THE HIGHWAY. B.H. Wilford, J.F. Wilford. Science, n.s., vol.84, no.2184, p.421, Nov. 6, 1936.

(Skunks) In Captivity, As Pets

BLACK SKUNK MAKES AN ENGAGING HOUSE PET. Roy L. Abbott. Nat.Hist., New York, vol.43, no.3, pp.144-149, photo, Mar., 1939.

MY PET SKUNKS. F.S. Crawford. Our Dumb Animals, Boston, vol.76, no.10, p.189, Oct., 1943.

OLIVE'S STRANGE PETS. (Striped Skunk) Grace F. Malkin. Canadian Nature, Toronto, vol.8, no.5, pp.173-175, illus., Nov.-Dec., 1946.

SPRING AND SUMMER ACTIVITIES OF THE DUSKY SKUNK IN CAPTIVITY. WITH A CHAPTER ON THE INSECT FOOD OF THE DUSKY SKUNK. William T. Shaw, K.F. Chamberlain. New York State Mus.Handbook 4, pp.103, figs.40, 1928. (Mephitis mephitis nigra.)

NOTES ON YOUNG SKUNKS IN CAPTIVITY. LeRoy C. Stegeman. Jour. Mamm., vol. 18, no.2, pp.194-202, figs.4, May 14, 1937.

(Skunks) Methods and Techniques

DEODORIZING SKUNKS. Vernon Bailey. Jour. Mamm., vol.18, no.4, pp.481-482, Nov., 1937.

TECHNIQUE FOR TRAPPING AND TAGGING SPOTTED SKUNKS. Wilfred D. Crabb. Jour. Wildl. Mgt., Menasha, vol. 5, no.4, pp.371-374, Oct., 1941.

ABLATION OF THE SCENT GLANDS OF SKUNKS. Robert K. Enders, Eleanor M. Paxson. Jour. Amer. Vet. Med. Assn., vol.108, no.827, pp.84-86, Feb., 1946.

MAIN CONSIDERATIONS IN AND METHODS FOR INTRODUCING THE SKUNK (MEPHITIS MEPHITIS SCHREB.) INTO THE U.S.S.R. L.V.Shaposhnikov. Trans. Cent. Lab. Game Indus., no.5, pp.207-211, 1941.

ON THE OPERATION FOR PREPARING A SKUNK (MEPHITIS) FOR A ZOOLOGICAL GARDEN. R.W. Shufeldt. Jour. Compar.Med. and Surg., Philadelphia, vol.10, pp.89-91, 1889.

(Skunks) Mexico, Central and South America

A NEW SPOTTED SKUNK (SPILOGALE) FROM YUCATAN. William Henry Burt. Occas. Papers Mus. Zool. Univ. Mich., no.383, pp.1-3, Aug. 27, 1938.

NEW SKUNK OF THE GENUS CONEPATUS FROM MEXICO. (Conepatus tropicalis yucatanicus.) E.A. Goldman. Proc. Biol. Soc. Washington, vol.56, pp.89-90, Oct. 1, 1943.

NOTES ON THE SPOTTED SKUNKS (GENUS SPILOGALE), WITH ACCOUNTS OF NEW SUBSPECIES FROM MEXICO AND COSTA RICA. E. Raymond Hall. Ann.and Mag. Nat. Hist., London, ser.11, vol.1, pp.510-515, May, 1938.

A NEW SKUNK FROM PERU. Oldfield Thomas. Ann. and Mag. Nat. Hist., ser.7, vol.5, no.30, pp.499-500, June, 1900.

TWO NEW ARGENTINE FORMS OF SKUNK. (Conepatus suffocans pampanus and C.s. mendosus.) Oldfield Thomas. Ann. and Mag. Nat. Hist., ser.9, vol.8, pp.221-222, Aug., 1921.

(Skunks) North America

SKUNKS WON'T STAY DOWN. Durward L. Allen. Mich. Cons., vol.15, no.2, pp. 3-4, Feb., 1946; Rally Sheet, League of Maryland Sportsmen, Baltimore, vol.4, no. 7, p.7, Aug., 1946.

WINTER HABITS OF MICHIGAN SKUNKS. Durward L. Allen. Jour. Wildl. Mgt., Menasha, vol.3, no.3, pp.212-228, pls. 7-10, July, 1939.

NOTES ON NORTH AMERICAN MAMMALS. THE SYNONYMY OF THE EASTERN SKUNK, MEPHITIS MEPHITICA (SHAW), WITH THE DESCRIPTION OF A NEW SUBSPECIES FROM FLORIDA. Outram Bangs. Proc. Boston Soc. Nat. Hist., vol.26, pp.1-17, July 31, 1895.

THE SKUNKS OF THE GENUS MEPHITIS OF EASTERN NORTH AMERICA. Outram Bangs. Proc. Biol. Soc. Washington, vol. 10, pp.139-144, Dec. 28, 1896.

WISCONSIN WILDLIFE FOR BOYS AND GIRLS--ANIMALS. THE SKUNK. N. R. Barger. Wisconsin Conserv. Bull., Madison, vol.13, no.1, pp.16-17, illus., Jan., 1948.

SKUNKS OF NORTH DAKOTA. J.E.Campbell. N. Dakota Outdoors, vol.7, no.10, pp.9-10, Apr., 1945.

HE ALWAYS WALKS TO THE NEAREST EXIT. Rod Cochran. Ohio Cons. Bull., vol.17, no.5, pp.2-3, illus., May, 1953.

ECOLOGY AND MANAGEMENT OF THE PRAIRIE SPOTTED SKUNK IN IOWA. Wilfred D. Crabb. Ecol. Monog., vol.18, no.2, pp.201-232, Apr., 1948.

ECOLOGY AND MANAGEMENT OF THE PRAIRIE SPOTTED SKUNK, SPILOGALE INTERRUPTA (RAFINESQUE), IN SOUTH-EASTERN IOWA. Wilfred D. Crabb. PhD thesis, Iowa State Coll., 1943; Jour. Sci., vol.18, no.1, pp.22-24, Oct., 1943. (Abstract.)

TEXAS SKUNKS. William B. Davis.Texas Game and Fish, vol.3, no.8, pp.8-10, 25-26, July, 1945; vol.9, no.4, pp.18-21, 31, Mar., 1951.

SPOTTED SKUNK OF THE CHANNEL ISLANDS OF SOUTHERN CALIFORNIA. Donald R. Dickey. Proc. Biol. Soc.Washington, vol.42, pp.157-160, Apr. 4, 1929.

A NEW SUBSPECIES OF THE CALIFORNIA SPOTTED SKUNK (SPILOGALE PHENAX MERRIAM). E. Raymond Hall. Jour.Mamm., vol.7, no.1, pp.53-56, figs.2, Feb., 1926.

WINTER ACTIVITY OF THE SKUNK. W.J. Hamilton, Jr. Ecology, vol.18, no.2, pp. 326-327, Apr., 1937.

LITTLE SPOTTED SKUNK, SPILOGALE GRACILIS SAXATILIS, RECORDED FOR MONTANA. William L. Jellison. Jour. Mamm., vol.12, no.3, p.314, Aug., 1931.

NATURAL HISTORY OF THE STRIPED SKUNK IN NORTHEASTERN KANSAS. Forrest H. Jones. MA thesis, Univ.Kansas, 1950.

WINTER STUDIES OF SKUNKS IN PENNSYLVANIA. H.Walter Jones, Jr. Jour. Mamm., vol.20, no.2, pp.254-256, May, 1939.

SPOTTED SKUNK IN PENNSYLVANIA. Roger M. Latham, C.R. Studholme. Jour. Mamm., vol.28, no.4, p.409, Nov. 26, 1947.

STATUS OF THE SKUNK IN NORTH DAKOTA. Wilford L. Miller. N.Dakota Outdoors, Bismarck, vol.9, no.8, p.3, Feb., 1947.

MEXICAN POLECAT, HYDROPHOBIA CAT, SPILOGALE INDIANOLA, OF SOUTHERN TEXAS. J.D. Mitchell. Jour. Mamm., vol. 4, no.1, pp.49-51, Feb. 9, 1923.

ALTITUDINAL RECORD FOR THE SPOTTED SKUNK IN CALIFORNIA. Robert T. Orr. Jour. Mamm., vol.24, no.2, p.270, May, 1943.

EXTENSION OF RANGE OF PUGET SOUND SPOTTED SKUNK (SPILOGALE PHENAX OLYMPICA). Kenneth Racey. Canadian Field-Nat., Sutton West, vol.58, no.3, p.104, May-June, 1944.

WISCONSIN'S FIRST PRAIRIE SPOTTED SKUNK, AND OTHER NOTES. Walter E. Scott. Jour. Mamm., vol.32, no.3, p. 363, Aug. 23, 1951.

LITTLE SPOTTED SKUNK IN NORTHERN MINNESOTA. Gustav Swanson. Jour.Mamm., vol.15, no.4, pp.318-319, Nov., 1934.

BETE PUANTE OF MINNESOTA.(Striped Skunk, With Particular Reference To Its Economic Status.) Sidel B. Swenson. Fins, Feathers, and Fur, no.70, pp.29, 38, Feb., 1929.

FUR-BEARING MAMMALS OF WYOMING. PART 10. (Striped Skunk.) Earl M. Thomas. Wyo. Wildl., vol.16, no.12, pp.32-38, illus., Dec., 1952.

SPOTTED SKUNKS (SPILOGALE) OF EASTERN UNITED STATES. Richard G. Van Gelder. MA thesis, Univ. Ill., 1952.

HOG-NOSED SKUNK (CONEPATUS) IN COLORADO. Edward R. Warren. Jour. Mamm., vol.2, no.2, p.112, May, 1921.

FUR ANIMALS OF TEXAS. (Skunks.) Texas Game and Fish, Austin, vol.2, no. 2, pp.13, 17, illus., Jan., 1944.

(Skunks) Physiology

SOME PHYSIOLOGICAL OBSERVATIONS ON CAPTIVE SKUNKS. M.M. Ellis, O.W. Barlow. Jour. Mamm., vol.6, no.1, pp. 56-57, Feb., 1925.

HIBERNATION OF THE STRIPED SKUNK IN IOWA. Lyle F. Selko. Jour. Mamm., vol.19, no.3, pp.320-324, tbl., Aug., 1938.

(Skunks) Reproductive Biology and Young

A SKUNK HALF-DOZEN. Mary Drake. Nature Mag., Washington, D.C., vol.32, no.9, pp.505-506, illus., Nov., 1939.

JUVENILE SKUNKS. L.T.S. Norris-Elye. Canadian Field-Nat., Ottawa, vol.62, no. 1, pp.41-42, Jan.-Feb., 1948.

CAPTIVE STRIPED SKUNK PRODUCES TWO LITTERS. Albert R. Shadle. Jour. Wildl. Mgt., vol.17, no.3, pp.388-389, July, 1953.

PARTURITION IN A SKUNK, MEPHITIS MEPHITIS HUDSONICA. Albert R. Shadle. Jour. Mamm., vol.37, no.1, pp.112-113, Feb. 28, 1956.

REPRODUCTION IN THE EASTERN SKUNK (MEPHITIS MEPHITIS NIGRA). H.M.Wight. Jour. Mamm., vol.12, no.1, pp.42-47, Feb., 1931.

(Skunks) Taxonomy

FURTHER NOTE ON THE GENERIC NAMES OF THE MEPHITINAE. J.A. Allen. Proc. Biol. Soc. Washington, vol.15, pp.59-60, Mar. 22, 1902.

GENERIC NAMES OF THE MEPHITINAE. J.A. Allen. Bull. Amer. Mus. Nat. Hist., vol.14, pp.325-334, Nov. 12, 1901.

TWO NEW SKUNKS OF THE GENUS CONEPATUS. E.A. Goldman. Jour. Mamm., vol. 3, no.1, pp.40-41, Feb., 1922.

GEOGRAPHIC RANGE OF THE HOODED SKUNK, MEPHITIS MACROURA, WITH DESCRIPTION OF A NEW SUBSPECIES FROM MEXICO. (Mephitis macroura eximius.) E. Raymond Hall, Walter W. Dalquest. Univ. Kansas Publ., Mus. Nat. Hist., Lawrence, vol.1, no.24, pp.575-580, fig.1, Jan. 20, 1950.

REVISION OF THE SKUNKS OF THE GENUS SPILOGALE. Arthur H. Howell. N.Amer. Fauna, no.26, pp.1-55, pls.1-10, Nov. 4, 1906.

CONTRIBUTION TOWARD A REVISION OF THE LITTLE STRIPED SKUNKS OF THE GENUS SPILOGALE. C.Hart Merriam.North Amer. Fauna, no.4, U.S. Dept. Agric., pp.15, tbls., Oct., 1890.

SIX NEW SKUNKS OF THE GENUS CONEPATUS. C. Hart Merriam. Proc. Biol. Soc. Washington, vol.15, pp.161-165, Aug. 6, 1902.

NEW HOG-NOSED SKUNK. Frederic W. Miller. Jour. Mamm., vol.6, no.1, pp. 50-51, pl.5, Feb., 1925.

THE TYPE SPECIMEN OF MEPHITIS FRONTATA COUES. Gerrit S. Miller, Jr. Jour. Mamm., Baltimore, vol.22, no.2, pp.190-192, May 14, 1941.

EXHIBITION OF A REMARKABLY SMALL SKUNK OF THE GENUS SPILOGALE. Oldfield Thomas. Proc. Zool. Soc. London, pp.898-899, Nov. 30, 1897.

(Otters) General

SEA OTTER. J.A. Allen. Amer.Nat., vol. 32, pp.356-358, May, 1898.

CHILDREN OF THE SEA. (History of Sea Otter Since 1742.) C.L. Andrews.Alaska Sportsman, vol.4, no.7, pp.8-9, 27-28, 31-32, July, 1938.

DECLINE OF THE SEA OTTER. C.L. Andrews. Nature Mag., vol.29, no.2, pp. 107-108, illus., Feb., 1937.

WHAT DO YOU KNOW ABOUT THE SEA OTTER? Mary Y. Ayer. Frontiers, Philadelphia, vol.3, no.1, pp.24-26, illus., Oct., 1938.

THE OTTER. Vernon Bailey. Nature Mag., vol.4, no.4, pp.237-238, Oct., 1924.

OTTER. N.R. Barger. Wisconsin Conserv. Bull., Madison, vol.15, no.1, p.33, Jan., 1950.

OTTER'S TRAIL. STRANGE FIDELITY TO ANCIENT RUNWAYS. H. Mortimer Batten. Field, London, vol.155, no.4037, p.692, May 10, 1930.

NOTE ON LUTROGALE PERSPICILLATA (I. GEOFFROY) (MUSTELIDAE). A.C.V. van Bemmel. Treubia, Buitenzorg, vol. 20, pt.2, pp.375-377, Oct., 1949.

TORPEDO IN FUR.(River Otter.) Carl L. Biemiller. Holiday, Philadelphia, vol.9, no.1, pp.13-14, 16, illus., Jan., 1951.

OTTER--PLAYBOY OF STREAMS AND LAKES. G.W. Bradt. Mich. Cons., vol.15, no.6, pp.6-7, July, 1946.

WHAT ABOUT THE OTTER? G.W. Bradt. Mich. Cons., Lansing, vol.14, no.2, pp. 4, 10, illus., Feb., 1945.

(NOTES ON THE OTTER.) Notes sur la Loutre. A. Chaigneau. Mammalia, Paris, vol.2, no.2, pp.99-102, June, 1938.

AMIKUK, THE SEA OTTER. Alan Devoe. Frontiers, Lancaster, vol.8, no.5, pp.138, 158-159, June, 1944.

WINNING WAYS OF THE SEA OTTER.Alan Devoe. Reader's Digest, Pleasantville, vol. 44, no.266, pp.29-31, June, 1944.

SEA BEAVER IS COMING BACK. Ben East. Animal Kingdom, vol.50, no.4, pp.124-129, Aug., 1947.

SEA OTTER, PAST AND PRESENT. Edna M. Fisher. Proc. 6th Pac. Sci. Cong., vol. 3, pp.223-236, 1940.

AGE DETERMINATION, BY USE OF THE BACULUM, IN THE RIVER OTTER, LUTRA C. CANADENSIS SCHREBER. Charles E. Friley, Jr. Jour. Mamm., Baltimore, vol. 30, no.2, pp.102-110, fig.1, pls.2, May 23, 1949.

SEA OTTER. Raymond M. Gilmore. Our Endangered Wildl., Nat. Wildl.Federation, pp.7-8, illus., Jan., 1956.

OTTER IS A GENTLEMAN. Oliver B.Goin. Fauna, Philadelphia, vol.9, no.2, pp.39-41, illus., June, 1947.

OBSERVATIONS ON THE MARGINED-TAILED OTTER (PTERONURA SANDBACHII). John Edward Gray. Proc. Zool. Soc. London, pp.61-66, figs.2, pl.7, 1868.

WHAT IS THE FUTURE OF THE SEA OTTER? Richard E. Griffith. Trans. 18th N. Amer. Wildl. Conf., pp.472-478, 1953.

AGE GROUPS IN MICHIGAN OTTER. Emmet T. Hooper, Burton T. Ostenson.Occas. Papers Mus. Zool., Univ. Michigan, Ann Arbor, no.518, pp.1-22, Mar. 23, 1949.

FETCH, OTTIES! (Otter.) Josef Israels. Saturday Evening Post, Philadelphia, vol. 214, no.33, pp.16-17, 74-76, illus., Feb. 14, 1942.

OTTER, PLAYFELLOW OF THE WILD. H.H.T. Jackson. Home Geographic Monthly, vol.1, no.9, pp.44-48, figs.6, Dec., 1931.

WHAT WE OTTER KNOW. David H.Jenkins. Michigan Cons., Lansing, vol.20, no.2, pp.9-10, 23-24, Mar.-Apr., 1951.

REPORT OF THE SEA OTTER INVESTIGATIONS CONDUCTED DURING 1951. Robert D. Jones, Jr. (In) Science in Alaska 1951, Proc. 2nd Alaskan Sci. Conf., Alaska Div. AAAS, pp.351-355, 1953.

FACTS ABOUT OTTER. E.F. Keith. Outdoorsman, Chicago, vol.86, no.1, whole no.506, pp.26-28, illus., Jan.-Feb., 1944.

OTTER. Phyllis Kelway. Game and Gun and the Angler's Monthly, London, vol.17, no.174, pp.122-125, Mar., 1940.

SEA OTTER. Karl W. Kenyon. Oryx, vol. 4, no.3, pp.153-158, Nov., 1957.

SEA OTTER AND LAND OTTER. Agnes Laut. Forest and Stream, vol.91, pp.8-9, 31, Jan., 1921.

AN OTTER'S STORY. Emil E. Liers. Viking., pp.191, illus., Apr., 1953.

LAST OF THE SEA OTTERS. H.McCracken. Frederick A. Stokes Co., Philadelphia, New York, pp.99, illus., 1942.

MYSTERIOUS SEA OTTER. H.McCracken. Nature Mag., vol.5, pp.169-172, figs.6, pl.1, Mar., 1925.

WHEN THE SEA OTTER FLOURISHED. H. McCracken. Forest and Stream, vol.90, pp.298, 332-333, June 1920.

EMIL LIERS, THE OTTER MAN. Patricia Marr. Nature Mag., Washington, vol.43, no.3, pp.127-129, illus., Mar., 1950.

FATE OF TWO OTTERS. Herbert Maxwell. Scottish Naturalist, no.175, p.7, Jan.-Feb., 1929.

NORTHERN SEA OTTER. Alan G. May. Nat. Hist., New York, vol.52, no. 1, pp. 22-23, 47, illus., June, 1943.

(FROM THE LIFE OF THE SEA OTTER.) Aus dem Leben des Seeotters. Rob.Mertens. Natur und Volk, vol.65, no.9, pp.401-407, figs.7, Sep. 1, 1935.

(FURTHER EXPERIENCES WITH THE PRESENT-DAY MARSH OTTER.) Weitere Erfahrungen in der heutigen Nerzranz. Otto Mertz. Der Deutsche Pelztierzuechter, Jahrg. 1931, Munich, no.11, pp.303-304, June 1, 1931.

OTTER. C.H. Moffat. Irish Naturalists' Jour., vol.1, no.11, pp.209-212, May, 1927.

SEA OTTER--PAST AND PRESENT. M.F. Murphy. Nature Mag., Washington, D.C., vol.32, no.8, pp.425-428, illus., Oct., 1939.

(SOME NOTES ON LUTRA (PTERONURA) PARANENSIS OF THE LOCAL ZOOLOGICAL GARDEN.) Einige Notizen ueber die Lutra (Pteronura) paranensis des hiesigen zoologischen Gartens. Alfred Nehring. Sitz.Ber. Gesell. Naturf. Freunde Berlin, no.4, pp. 133-135, Apr. 16, 1901.

SEA OTTER (ENHYDRA LUTRIS LUTRIS LINN.). W.A. Newcombe. Rep. Prov. Mus. Nat. Hist., Victoria, 1928, pp.f12-f14, pl.5, 1929.

NOTES ON A PREGNANT SEA OTTER. Oliver P. Pearson. Jour. Mamm., vol.33, no.3, p.387, Aug. 19, 1952.

(TRIX, THE OTTER.) Trix, het visottertje. W.G. Pelt. Artis, Amsterdam, vol.1, no.6, pp.126-129, illus., Apr., 1956. (Lutra cincerea).

SCENES IN THE LIFE OF AN OTTER. Oliver G. Pike. Illus. London News, vol. 215, no.5764, p.554, illus., Oct.8, 1949.

(ON THE MARSH OTTER.) Von der Nerzranz. Emil Ruppmann. Der Deutsche Pelztierzuechter, Jahrg.1931, Munich, no.7, p. 180, Apr. 1, 1931.

THE OTTER: PLAYBOY OF NATURE.Archibald Rutledge. Country Life, vol.38,no. 6, pp.106, 110, 112, 114, Oct.,1920.

LUTE, THE OTTER. J.J. Shomon. Va. Wildl., Richmond, vol.10, no.12, pp.16-17, 23, Dec., 1949.

SEA OTTER COMES BACK. Kathryn Sollars. Fauna, Philadelphia, vol.7, no.1, pp.11-13, illus., Mar., 1945.

OTTER RESEARCH. Marie Stephens. Oryx, vol.2, no.5, pp.320-324, Aug., 1954.

PROBLEM OF AQUATIC ADAPTATION IN THE CARNIVORA, AS ILLUSTRATED IN THE OSTEOLOGY AND EVOLUTION OF THE SEA OTTER. Walter P. Taylor. Univ. Calif. Publ. Bull., Dept. Geol., vol.7, no. 25, pp.465-495, figs.15, Jan. 22, 1914.

(MY FRIEND--THE FISH OTTER.) Mein Freund--der Fischotter. H. Utzon. Der Deutsche Pelztierzuechter, Munich, Jahrg.9, no.22, pp.431-435, illus., Nov. 15, 1934.

BULLETS BEYOND THE BREAKERS. (Sea Otter.) Stanley P. Young. Amer. Rifleman, Washington, vol.93, no.6, pp.8-9, 27, illus., June, 1945.

MR. OTTER, NATURE'S PLAYBOY--BUT DON'T GET HIM RILED. Iowa Conservationist, Des Moines, vol.3, no.3, pp.1, 21, Mar. 15, 1944.

"OLD MEN OF THE SEA" ARE READY TO SPREAD AFTER SURVIVING SCOURGE OF HUNTERS. Nat. Humane Review, Albany, vol.38, no.5, pp.9-10, illus., May, 1950. (Sea Otter.)

RETURN OF THE SEA OTTERS. Westways, Beverly Hills, vol.30, no.9, pp.14-15, illus., Sep., 1938.

SAVED ON THE VERGE OF EXTERMINATION: SEA OTTERS, ONCE HUNTED FOR THEIR PELTS. Illus. London News, vol.217, no.5811, p.367, illus., Sep. 2, 1950.

SEA OTTER ON EXHIBIT. Acad. News Letter, Calif. Acad. Sci., San Francisco, no.37, pp.3-4, Jan., 1943.

(Otters) Africa

PARAONYX, A NEW GENUS OF CLAWLESS OTTER DISCOVERED BY CAPT. J. E. PHILIPPS, M.C., IN CENTRAL AFRICA. Martin A.C. Hinton. Ann. and Mag. Nat. Hist., ser.9, vol.7, pp.194-200, Feb., 1921.

NEW SUBSPECIES OF CLAWLESS OTTER (AONYX CAPENSIS CONGICA) FROM LOWER CONGO. Einar Lönnberg. Arkiv f. Zool., Upsala, vol. 7, no.9, pp.1-8, figs. 2, Dec. 15, 1910.

ON THE CLAWLESS OTTER OF CENTRAL AFRICA (LUTRA CAPENSIS HINDEI THOMAS) AND BIOLOGICAL ADAPTATIONS OF AFRICAN CLAWLESS OTTERS. Einar Lönnberg. Arkiv f. Zool., Stockholm, vol. 4, no.12, pp.11, fig.1, pl.1, 1908.

ON CERTAIN AFRICAN AND SOUTH AMERICAN OTTERS. Oldfield Thomas. Ann. and Mag. Nat. Hist., ser.8, vol.1, no.5, pp.387-395, May, 1908.

(Otters) Anatomy

EXTRA PREMOLARS IN THE RIVER OTTER. Lyle C. Dearden. Jour. Mamm., vol. 35, no.1, pp.125-126, Feb. 10, 1954.

AN ANOMALOUS MUSCLE IN THE CALIFORNIA RIVER OTTER. Edna M. Fisher. Science, n.s., vol.82, no.2121, pp.172-173, Aug. 23, 1935.

NOTES ON THE TEETH OF THE SEA OTTER. Edna M. Fisher. Jour. Mamm., vol. 22, no.4, pp.428-433, figs.5, Nov. 14, 1941.

OSTEOLOGY AND MYOLOGY OF THE CALIFORNIA RIVER OTTER. Edna M. Fisher. Stanford Univ. Press, pp.vi+65, figs.37, 1942.

INCISOR TOOTH WEAR IN THE SEA OTTER. Milton Hildebrand. Jour. Mamm., vol.35, no.4, p.595, Nov. 29, 1954.

DESCRIPTION OF THE OSTEOLOGY OF THE SEA OTTER (ENHYDRA MARINA, FLEM.). W. Martin. Proc. Zool. Soc. London, pt.4, pp.59-62, 1836.

ON THE EXTERNAL CHARACTERS OF SOME SPECIES OF LUTRINAE (OTTERS). R.I. Pocock. Proc. Zool. Soc. London, pt.3, pp.535-546, Sep., 1921.

SOME EXTERNAL CHARACTERS OF THE SEA OTTER (ENHYDRA LUTRIS). R. I. Pocock. Proc. Zool. Soc. London, 1928, pt.4, pp.983-991, figs.1-5, Jan. 31, 1929.

SIZE OF OTTERS. H.W. Robinson. Field, London, vol.151, p.614, Apr. 12, 1928.

MEASUREMENTS OF SEA OTTERS FROM WESTERN ALASKA. Victor B. Scheffer. Jour. Mamm., vol.32, no.1, pp.10-14, Feb., 1951.

THE OS CLITORIDIS OF THE PACIFIC OTTER. Victor B. Scheffer. Murrelet, Seattle, vol.20, no.1, pp.20-21, figs.6, Jan.-Apr., 1939.

REFLECTIONS ON THE SKULL OF A SEA OTTER. Victor B. Scheffer. Nature Mag., Washington, vol.43, no.3, pp.151-152, illus., Mar., 1950.

(Otters) Economic Importance

OTTER AS A FUR BEARER. Vernon Bailey. Amer. Breeder's Assoc., vol.5, pp.313-320, figs.2, 1909.

OTTER TRAPPING. Frank Cresap. Trapper, Chicago, vol.1, no.2, p.10, illus., Apr., 1937.

SEA OTTER HUNT. Ben East. Field and Stream, New York, vol.49, no.4, pp.34-36, 63-65, illus., Aug., 1944.

PRICES OF SEA OTTER PELTS. Edna M. Fisher. Calif. Fish and Game, vol.27, no.4, pp.261-264, Oct., 1941.

CHASE LITTLEJOHN, 1854-1943: OBSERVATIONS BY LITTLEJOHN ON HUNTING SEA OTTERS. E. Raymond Hall. Jour. Mamm., vol.26, no.1, pp.89-91, Feb. 23, 1945.

SEA OTTER AND THE COURSE OF EMPIRE. Joel W. Hedgepeth. Frontiers, Philadelphia, vol.7, no.3, pp.69-72, illus., Feb., 1943.

GAME FARM OTTER. Marvin O. Kaukl. Wisc. Cons. Bull., Madison, vol.15, no. 12, pp.21-22, illus., Dec., 1950.

HUNTING WE WILL GO! COLORFUL DAY WITH THE BUCKS OTTER HOUNDS, SHOWING THAT SPORT IS NOT ALWAYS HOSTILE TO CONSERVATION. Robert Cushman Murphy. Nat. Hist., New York, vol.39, no. 4, pp.231-236, illus., Apr., 1937.

CALIFORNIA SEA OTTER TRADE 1784-1848. Adele Ogden. Univ. Calif. Publ. Hist., Berkeley, vol.26, pp.xi+251, illus., col.pl.1, Nov. 15, 1941.

LITTLE IS KNOWN ABOUT BREEDING OTTERS. Fur of Canada, Winnipeg, vol. 10, no.1, p.18, Apr., 1945.

OTTER BREEDING. Amer. Fur Breeder, Duluth, vol.14, no.6, p.36, Dec., 1941.

SEA OTTERS TO BE TRANSPLANTED ALONG ALASKA COAST. Amer. Nat. Fur and Market Jour. Wausau, vol.28, no.9, pp.5-6, 17, illus., Apr., 1950.

(Otters) In Captivity

PET OTTERS. Wendell Chapman, Lucie Chapman. Nature Mag., vol.29, no.3, pp. 140-143, illus., Mar., 1937.

NOTE ON THE BREEDING OF THE OTTER IN CONFINEMENT. James Hunt. Proc. Zool. Soc. London, pt.15, pp.27-28, 1847.

NOTES ON CAPTIVE SEA OTTERS. Charles M. Kirkpatrick et al. Arctic, Ottawa, vol. 8, no.1, pp.46-59, illus., Winter, 1955.

TO THOSE WHO WOULD KEEP AN OTTER. A STORY--AND A WARNING. Francis Pitt. Field, London, vol.163, no.4228, p.21, illus., Jan. 6, 1934.

(INFORMATION ON TAME OTTERS (LUTRA LUTRA L.).) Einiges ueber zahme Fischottern (Lutra lutra L.). Wilhelm Schreitmueller. Zeitschr. f. Saeugetierk., Berlin, vol.17, no.3, pp.172-173, Feb. 19, 1953.

TAME OTTERS. Isaac Wood. Field, London, vol.153, p.73, Jan. 10, 1929.

(Otters) Central and South America

(A NEW OTTER IN CENTRAL AMERICA.) Una nueva nutria de la América Central. (Lontra mesopetes, sp.nov.) Angel Cabrera. Bol. R. Soc. Española Hist. Nat., vol.24, pp.52-53, Feb., 1924.

(OTTER OF CENTRAL AMERICA AND ITS CLOSEST RELATIVES.) Der centralamerikanische Fischotter und seine naechsten Verwandten. C.J. Forsyth Major. Zool. Anzeiger, Leipzig, vol.20, no.529, pp. 136-142, Apr. 26, 1897.

(OCCURRENCE OF GENUS "LONTRA" IN THE LITTORAL FAUNA OF BUENOS AIRES.) La presencia del género "Lontra" en la fauna ensenadense de Buenos Aires. Carlos Rusconi. Anales Soc. Cient. Argentina, Buenos Aires, vol.114, no.3, pp.149-151, fig.1, Sep., 1932.

(Otters) Diseases, Parasites

NEW ASCARID FROM AN OTTER. H.A. Baylis. Ann. and Mag. Nat. Hist., ser.9, vol.11, pp.459-463, figs.3, Apr., 1923.

FRACTURED FEMUR OF THE ALASKAN RIVER OTTER. Edna M. Fisher. Jour. Mamm., vol.14, no.4, pp.362-365, figs. 2, Nov., 1933.

SEA OTTER WITH GASTRIC PERFORATIONS. Edna M. Fisher. Jour. Mamm., Baltimore, vol.21, no.3, pp.357-359, fig. 1, Aug. 14, 1940.

DIPLOSTOMUM FOSTERI N. SP. FROM A PANAMA OTTER, LUTRA REPANDA GOLDMAN. A. McIntosh. Jour. Parasitology, Baltimore, vol.25, suppl., p.25, Dec., 1939.

STUDIES ON THE HELMINTH FAUNA OF ALASKA. XIII. DISEASE IN THE SEA OTTER, WITH SPECIAL REFERENCE TO HELMINTH PARASITES. Robert Rausch. Ecology, Durham, vol.34, no.3, pp.584-604, illus., July, 1953.

STUDIES ON THE HELMINTH FAUNA OF ALASKA. II. ON SOME HELMINTHS PARASITIC IN THE SEA OTTER, ENHYDRA LUTRIS (L.). Robert Rausch, Betty Locker. Proc. Helminth. Soc. Wash., vol.18, no. 1, pp.77-81, illus., 1951.

STUDIES ON THE HELMINTH FAUNA OF ALASKA. XVII. NOTES ON THE INTERMEDIATE STAGES OF SOME HELMINTH PARASITES OF THE SEA OTTER. Everett L. Schiller. Biol. Bull., vol.106, no.1, pp. 107-121, illus., Feb., 1954.

(Otters) Ecology, Habits, Behavior

AN OTTER LOSES HIS DINNER TO AN OSPREY. Frank H. Anderson. Yellowatone Nature Notes, vol.10, nos.1-2, p.7, Jan.-Feb., 1933.

PRECOCIOUS YOUNG OTTER. H.B. Booth. Naturalist, London, no.862, p.324, Nov., 1928.

RIVER OTTER PLAYS ON MOONLIGHT NIGHTS. Una Boyle, Calif. Fish and Game, vol.5, no.2, p.98, Apr., 1919.

SLIDING OTTER. T.W. Burgess. Jour. Mamm., vol.5, no.1, p.76, Feb., 1924.

(OBSERVATIONS DURING THE TAMING OF THE OTTER.) Beobachtungen bei der Zaehmung der Fischotters. F.A. Cerva. Zool. Garten, Leipzig, n.F., vol.3, nos. 11-12, pp.319-323, figs.3, 1930.

AN OTTER TAKES A RIDE. David B. Cook. Jour. Mamm., vol.21, no.2, p.216, May 14, 1940.

SEA OTTERS AND ABALONES. John E. Cushing, Jr. Jour. Mamm., vol.20, no.3, p.371, Aug. 14, 1939.

(ON THE EARLY LIFE OF THE OTTER.) Aus dem Jugendleben des Fischotters. Karl Eckstein. Zeitschr. f. Saeugetierk., vol.5, no.1, pp.40-47, pl.1, Aug. 8, 1930. (Reprint from Aus der Natur, 1912.)

EXPERT DIVER. (Lutra.) Arthur H. Fisher. Nature Mag., Washington, D.C., vol.33, no.1, p.23, illus., Jan., 1940.

NATURE'S EXPERT FISHERMAN. (Otter.) Arthur H. Fisher. Field and Stream, New York, vol.52, no.1, p.52, illus., May, 1947.

EARLY LIFE OF A SEA OTTER PUP. Edna M. Fisher. Jour. Mamm., vol.21, no.2, pp.132-137, figs.6, May 14, 1940.

HABITS OF THE SOUTHERN SEA OTTER. Edna M. Fisher. Jour. Mamm., vol.20, no.1, pp.21-36, Feb., 1939.

YEARLY FOOD HABITS OF THE RIVER OTTER IN THE THOMPSON LAKES REGION, NORTHWESTERN MONTANA, AS INDICATED BY SCAT ANALYSES. Kenneth R. Greer. Amer. Midl. Nat., Notre Dame, vol. 54, no.2, pp. 299-313, illus., Oct., 1955.

FISHING WITH THE OTTER. E.W.Gudger. Amer. Naturalist, Lancaster, vol.61, no. 674, pp.193-225, figs.6, May-June, 1927.

(OTTER IN WINTER SPORT.) Fischotter beim Wintersport. Kathe Hecht. Deutsche Jagd, Berlin, nos.15-16, pp.142-143, illus., July 19, 1940.

OTTERS AND CROCODILES. C.Howson. Jour. Bombay Nat. Hist. Soc., vol.40, no.3, pp.557-558, Dec., 1938.

EARLY SPRING FOOD OF THE OTTER IN MICHIGAN. Karl F. Lagler, Burton T. Ostenson. Jour. Wildl. Mgt., Menasha, vol.6, no.3, pp.244-254, July, 1942.

POSITION OF LIMBS IN THE SLIDING OTTER. Herbert Lang. Jour. Mamm., vol.5, no.3, pp.216-217, illus., Aug. 11, 1924.

MY FRIENDS THE LAND OTTERS. (Behavior of Partly Domesticated Otters.) Emil Liers. Nat. Hist., vol.60, no.7, pp.320-326, Sep., 1951.

NOTES ON THE RIVER OTTER (LUTRA CANADENSIS). Emil Liers. Jour.Mamm., vol.32, no.1, pp.1-9, Feb., 1951.

OTTER TAKING HOOKED TROUT. W. Logan. Irish Nat. Jour., Belfast, vol.8, no.3, p.78, Mar., 1943.

CASE OF THE OTTER. (Food Habits.) David J. Maclay. N.Region News, p.34, Aug., 1937.

NOTES ON THE SEA OTTER. (Habits.) Olaus J. Murie. Jour. Mamm., vol.21, no.2, pp.119-131, May, 1940.

AN OBSERVATION ON OTTER FEEDING. Tony J. Peterle. Jour. Wildl. Mgt., Ithaca, vol.18, no.1, pp.141-142, Jan., 1954.

ANIMALS USING TOOLS. (Sea Otter.) A.L. Rand. Canadian Field-Nat., Sutton West, vol.57, nos.3-4, p.94, Apr.-May, 1943.

FISH PREDATION BY THE OTTER IN MICHIGAN. Richard A. Ryder. Jour. Wildl. Mgt., vol.19, no.4, pp.497-498, Oct., 1955.

OTTERS DIVING TO A DEPTH OF SIXTY FEET. Victor B. Scheffer. Jour. Mamm., vol.34, no.2, p.255, May, 1953.

OTTER TAKING A HERON. C.Schelling. Field, London, vol.152, p.368, Aug. 30, 1928.

OTTER ADVENTURES. Hugo H.Schroder. Nature Mag., Washington, vol.40, no.3, pp.134-136, illus., Mar., 1947.

SWIMMING POWER OF THE CANADIAN OTTER. Walter E. Scott. Jour.Mamm., vol.20, no.3, p.371, Aug. 14, 1939.

SPEED AND GAIT OF AN OTTER. C.W. Severinghaus, J.E. Tanck. Jour.Mamm., vol.29, no.1, p.71, Feb. 13, 1948.

NOTES ON AN OTTER FISHING. Laurence H. Smith. Jour. Mamm., vol.20, no.3, pp.370-371, Aug. 14, 1939.

FLORIDA OTTERS EAT LARGE TERRAPIN. John J. Stophlet. Jour. Mamm., vol.28, no.2, p.183, May 19, 1947.

NOTES ON FOOD OF THE SEA OTTER. Cecil S. Williams. Jour. Mamm., vol.19, no.1, pp.105-107, tbls., Feb. 14, 1938.

OTTERS KILLING SWANS. E.G. Woods. Field, London, vol.151, p.806, May 10, 1928.

(Otters) Eurasia

(RIVERS OF ZAMORA (DATA AND NOTES).) Los rios de Zamora (Datos y notas). Joaquin Aroca. Publ.Fed.Española Pesca, vol.1, pp. 1-30, illus., 1944.

(OTTER AND ITS DISAPPEARANCE.) La loutre et sa disparition. J. Estanove. Mammalia, Paris, vol.16, no.4, pp.256-257, Dec., 1952.

NOTICE OF LUTRONECTES WHITELEYI, AN OTTER FROM JAPAN. J.E. Gray. Proc. Zool. Soc. London, pp.180-182, fig.1, 1867.

OTTERS IN COUNTY DOWN. H.A.C. Griffith. Irish Naturalists' Jour., vol.1, no.14, p.275, Nov., 1927.

NEW RACE OF THE INDIAN SMOOTH-COATED OTTER FROM IRAQ. R.W. Hayman. Ann. and Mag. Nat. Hist., ser.12, vol.9, pp.710-712, Oct., 1956.

THE IRISH OTTER. Martin A.C. Hinton. Ann. and Mag. Nat. Hist., ser.9, vol.5, p.464, June, 1920.

AN OTTER IN BELFAST. J.H.MacLoughlin. Irish Nat. Jour., Belfast, vol.10, no.2, p. 42, Apr., 1950.

SOME NOTES ON THE COMMON INDIAN OTTER (LUTRA LUTRA). C. McCann. Jour. Bombay Nat. Hist. Soc., vol.29, pp.275-276, Apr. 20, 1923.

NOTICE OF A NEW SPECIES OF OTTER FROM THE NORTH OF IRELAND. W. Ogilby. Proc. Zool. Soc. London, pt.2, p.111, 1834.

NOTES ON SOME BRITISH INDIAN OTTERS, WITH DESCRIPTIONS OF TWO NEW SUBSPECIES. R.I. Pocock. Jour. Bombay Nat. Hist. Soc., vol.41, no.3, pp.514-517, Apr., 1940.

OTTERS NEAR HULL. Chas. F. Procter. Naturalist, London, no.855, p.105, Apr., 1928.

LARGE DOG OTTER. H.W. Robinson. Scottish Nat., no.165, p.95, May-June, 1927.

LARGE DOG OTTER. Donald Ross. Scottish Nat., no.164, p.44, Mar.-Apr., 1927.

OTTERS OF NORFOLK. WITH NOTES ON OTTER CUBS BY MISS E.O. TOWNSHEND. S. Shepheard. Trans. Norfolk and Norwich Nat. Soc. 1936, vol.14, pt.2, pp.138-142, pl.5, Mar., 1937.

FISHING WITH THE OTTER IN WEST CHINA. Arthur de C. Sowerby. China Jour., vol.17, no.6, p.315, fig.1, Dec., 1932.

OTTER IN THE REGION OF THE PECHERO-ILYCHSKIY NATURE RESERVE. V. P. Teplov. Bull. Moscow Soc. Nat., n.s., Biol. Sect., vol.58, no.6, pp.7-16, 1953. (In Russian.)

NOTES ON SOME SPECIMENS OF THE BRITISH OTTER. H. Tetley. Proc. Zool. Soc. London, vol.115, pts.1-2, pp.189-193, Oct., 1945.

(Otters) Mortality

DEATH COMES TO A SEA OTTER. Edna M. Fisher. Calif. Fish and Game, San Francisco, vol.26, no.3, pp.278-281, figs.104-107, July, 1940.

PHYSIOLOGICAL INVESTIGATION OF CAPTIVITY MORTALITY IN THE SEA OTTER (ENHYDRA LUTRIS). Donald E. Stullken, Charles M. Kirkpatrick. Trans. 20th N.Amer. Wildl. Conf., Wildl.Mgt. Inst., Washington, pp.476-494, 1955.

(Otters) North America

SEA OTTERS ON SAN MIGUEL! Al.Allanson. Pacific Discovery, Calif. Acad. Sci., vol.8, no.3, pp.24-25, illus., May-June, 1955.

CAROLINA OTTER. Rod Amundson. Iowa Conservationist, Des Moines, vol.9, no.9, pp.65, 69, illus., Sep. 15, 1950.

FUR BEARING ANIMALS OF THE UNITED STATES. Frank G. Ashbrook, Horace J. McMullen. Fur Jour., vol.2, no.1, pp.26-27, illus., Jan., 1928. (Otter.)

REAPPEARANCE OF THE SOUTHERN SEA OTTER ALONG THE CALIFORNIA COAST. Rolf L. Bolin. Jour. Mamm., vol.19, no.3, pp.301-303, Aug., 1938.

NATURAL HISTORY NOTES FROM BAKER LAKE, N.W.T. (Capture of an Otter Reported.) W.O. Douglas. Canadian Field-Nat., vol.42, no.4, p.106, Apr., 1928.

SEA OTTERS IN THE ALEUTIAN ISLANDS. Walter J. Eyerdam. Jour. Mamm., vol.14, no.1, pp.70-71, Feb., 1933.

SEA OTTER IN CALIFORNIA. Edna M. Fisher. Proc. 6th Pacific Sci. Congr., Berkeley, vol.4, pp.231-240, fig.11, 1940.

NEW OTTER FROM LATE CENOZOIC BEDS, SOUTHWESTERN IDAHO. E. L. Furlong. Bull. Geol. Soc. America, vol.44, no.1, p.219, Feb. 28, 1933. (Abstract.)

NEW OTTER FROM KAMCHATKA. E.A. Goldman. Jour. Mamm., vol.17, no.2, p. 164, May 14, 1936.

PLEISTOCENE OTTER FROM IOWA. E.A. Goldman. Papers on Mammalogy. Zool. Ser., Field Mus. Nat. Hist., vol.27, pp. 299-231, fig.45, Dec. 8, 1941.

DISTRIBUTION OF RIVER OTTERS IN CALIFORNIA. WITH DESCRIPTION OF A NEW SUBSPECIES. Joseph Grinnell. Univ. Calif. Publ. Zool., vol.12, no.8, pp.305-310, pl.14, Oct. 31, 1914.

REPORT ON THE SEA-OTTER BANKS OF ALASKA. C.L. Hooper. U.S.Treasury Dept., Doc.no.1977, pp.35, fold.map 1, 1897.

PRESENT STATUS OF THE SEA OTTER IN ALASKA. Robert D. Jones, Jr. Trans. N.Amer. Wildl. Conf., vol.16, pp.376-382, 1951.

AN OTTER CATCH ON THE GILA RIVER IN SOUTHWESTERN NEW MEXICO. Jim McClellan. Jour. Mamm., vol.35, no.3, pp.443-444, Aug. 20, 1956.

PACIFIC PELTS. SEA OTTERS CHOOSE CALIFORNIA COAST. Augustin S. MacDonald. Privately printed, Oakland, Calif., pp.12, illus., 1938.

SOUTHERN SEA OTTER ON PACIFIC COAST. Donald D. McLean. Associated Sportsman, vol.5, no.5, pp.6-7, May, 1938.

NEW SEA OTTER FROM SOUTHERN CALIFORNIA. C. Hart Merriam. Proc. Biol. Soc. Washington, vol.17, pp.159-160, Oct. 6, 1904.

OTTER--PENNSYLVANIA'S RAREST FURBEARER. Earl L. Poole. Penna. Game News, vol.25, no.3, pp. 4-9, illus., Mar., 1954.

NEW JERSEY OTTERS. Samuel N.Rhoads. The Friend, pp.244-245, Feb. 24, 1894.

NEW MAMMAL FOR YOSEMITE. (Records the Otter.) C.P. Russell. Yosemite Nature Notes, vol.7, p.78, Sep., 1928.

RECENT RECORDS OF THE OTTER IN IOWA. Glen C. Sanderson. Iowa Cons., vol.13, no.7, pp.52, 55, July, 1954.

SEA OTTER ON THE WASHINGTON COAST. Victor B. Scheffer. Pac. Northwest Quart., vol.31, no.4, pp.370-388, Oct., 1940.

SEA OTTERS OF CALIFORNIA DID NOT REAPPEAR. W.L. Scofield. Calif.Fish and Game, San Francisco, vol.27, no.1, pp.35-38, Jan., 1941.

ON A NEW SUBSPECIES OF OTTER FROM NEBRASKA. Myron Harmon Swenk. Univ. Studies, Lincoln, Nebraska, 1918, Separate, pp.1-6, pl.1, May 15, 1920.

FURBEARING MAMMALS OF WYOMING. PART 9. OTTER. Earl M. Thomas. Wyo. Wild Life, vol.16, no.11, pp.30-34, illus., Nov., 1952.

CALIFORNIA RIVER OTTER IN YOSEMITE NATIONAL PARK. Gail Whitney. Yosemite Nat. Notes, Stockton, Calif., vol.18, no.2, pp.9-10, Feb., 1939.

OTTERS OF THE DELTA HARDWOOD REGION OF MISSISSIPPI. (Ecology and Management.) Lee E. Yeager. Jour. Mamm., vol.19, no.2, pp.195-201, May, 1938.

THE "EXTINCT" SEA OTTER SWIMS BACK TO LIFE. Life, vol.4, no.25, p.30, fig., June 20, 1938.

MICHIGAN OTTER STILL A PUZZLE. Mich. Cons., vol.10, no.5, p.5, Apr., 1941.

ORPHAN OTTER FOUND ON DeKALB STREAM. Outdoor Georgia, Atlanta, vol.5, no.30, p.7, illus., Apr. 1, 1945.

OTTER TRAPPED IN CHESTERFIELD COUNTY, VIRGINIA. Va. Wildl., Richmond, vol.10, no.4, p.25, Apr., 1949.

REAPPEARANCE OF THE SEA OTTER OFF THE COAST OF CALIFORNIA. Jour. Soc. Preservation Fauna of Empire, Hertford, n.s., pt.35, pp.39-43, Dec., 1938.

(Otters) Taxonomy

REMARKS ON THE GENUS LUTRA, AND ON THE SPECIES INHABITING NORTH AMERICA. George Barnston. Canadian Nat., Montreal, vol.8, no.2, pp.147-158 (1-13), figs.7, June, 1863.

NEW GENUS OF OTTER FROM THE PLIOCENE OF THE NORTHERN GREAT BASIN PROVINCE. (Lutravus; L.halli.) Eustace L. Furlong. Contrib. to Paleont., Carnegie Inst. Washington, Publ.no.418, no.V, pp. 93-103, pls.2, Aug. 3, 1932.

(ON GRAY'S OTTER GENERA LUTRONECTES, LONTRA, AND PTERONURA.) Ueber die Gray'schen Fischotter-Gattungen Lutronectes, Lontra und Pteronura. Alfred Nehring. Sitz. Ber. Gesell. Naturf. Freunde Berlin, no.3, pp.21-25, Mar. 15, 1887.

(SUBFAMILY LUTRINAE (SYSTEMATIC-ZOOGEOGRAPHICAL STUDY OF THE MATERIAL OF THE BERLIN MUSEUM).) Die Unterfamilie der Lutrinae. (Eine systematisch-tiergeographische Studie an dem Material der Berliner Museum.) Hermann Pohle. Archiv f. Naturg., Jahrg.85, 1919, Abt. A, no.9, pp.1-247, figs.19, pls.10, Nov., 1920.

(Review by N. Hollister of) (SUBFAMILY LUTRINAE.) Die Unterfamilie der Lutrinae. Hermann Pohle. Jour. Mamm., vol.2, no.3, pp.177-178, Aug. 19, 1921.

VALIDITY OF THE SUBSPECIES ENHYDRA LUTRIS NEREIS, THE SOUTHERN SEA OTTER. Victor B. Scheffer. Jour. Washington Acad. Sci., vol.40, no.8, pp.269-272, illus., Aug. 15, 1950.

## Viverridae

OBSERVATIONS ON A SPECIES OF PARADOXURUS, PROBABLY PARIPREHENSILIS, GRAY, PRESENTED BY LORD FITZROY SOMERSET. E.T. Bennett. Proc. Zool. Soc. London, pt.2, p.33, 1834.

OBSERVATIONS ON THE GENUS CRYPTOPROCTA. E.T. Bennett. Proc. Zool. Soc. London, pt.2, p.13, 1834.

(ON THE OCCURRENCE OF THE TIGER FITCHET (VORMELA PEREGUSNA GUELD.) IN BULGARIA.) Ueber das Vorkommen des Tigeriltis (Vormela peregusna Gueld.) in Bulgaria. Hans von Boetticher. Zeitschr. f. Saeugetierk., vol.11, no.3, pp.277-278, Dec. 30, 1936.

MONGOOSE ABROAD AND IN THE HOME. Maurice Burton. Illus. London News, vol. 214, no.5729, pp.180-181, illus., Feb. 5, 1949.

(COLOR AND BRIGHTNESS VISION AND INSTINCTS IN VIVERRINES AND FELIDS.) Gerti Duecker. Zool. Beitraege, Berlin, n.s., vol.3, no.1, pp.25-99, 1957. (In German.)

A NOTE ON DOLOGALE DYBOWSKII POUSARGUES. R.W. Hayman. Ann. and Mag. Nat. Hist., London, ser.10, vol.18, no.108, pp.626-638, Dec., 1936.

(KASPAR HAUSER EXPERIMENTS WITH FITCHETS.) Kaspar Hauser Versuche mit Iltissen. Konrad Herter, Margarethe Herter. Zool. Anzeiger, vol.151, nos.7-8, pp.175-185, Oct., 1953.

ON HELOGALE PARVULA, SUNDEVALL. Fredericus Anna Jentink. Notes Leyden Mus., vol.11, no.7, pp.31-33, Nov., 1888.

ON PARADOXURUS ANNULATUS, WAGNER. Fredericus Anna Jentink. Notes Leyden Mus., vol.8, no.16, pp.127-129, pls.4-5, Mar., 1886.

( MID-AGE REPORT ON THE CIVET CAT.) Ein mittelalterlicher Bericht ueber die Zibethkatze. S. Killermann. Zeitschr. f. Saeugetierk., Berlin, vol.6, no.6, pp.235-236, Dec. 15, 1931.

NOTE ON VIVERRA CIVETTINA. Helen M. Lindsay. Jour. Bombay Nat. Hist. Soc., vol.33, no.1, pp.146-148, pl.1, Sep. 30, 1928.

ON THE HIMALAYAN PALM-CIVET (PARADOXURUS GRAYI). S.J. Martin. Jour. Bombay Nat. Hist. Soc., vol.33, no.3, p. 703, May 31, 1929.

(ON WHITE-NOSED MIERKATS.) Ueber die weissnasigen Meerkatzen. Paul Matschie. Sitz. Ber. Gesell. Naturf. Freunde Berlin, no.3, pp.94-101, Mar. 21, 1893.

THE MONGOOSE. J.G. Myers, F.W. Urich. Tropical Agriculture, Trinidad, vol.8, no.4, pp.94-97, 1931.

NATURE'S ORIGINAL COMMANDO. (Mongoose.) E.D. Neff. Nature Mag., Wash., vol.38, no.8, pp.431-432, illus., Oct., 1944.

THE STRIPED-NECKED MONGOOSE (HERPESTES VITTICOLLIS). E.G.Phythian Adams. Jour. Bombay Nat. Hist. Soc., vol. 34, no.4, p.1054, Mar. 2, 1931.

ON THE FEET AND GLANDS AND OTHER EXTERNAL CHARACTERS OF THE VIVERRINAE, WITH THE DESCRIPTION OF A NEW GENUS. R.I. Pocock. Proc. Zool. Soc. London, pt.1, pp.131-149, figs.7, Mar. 26, 1915.

REMARKS ON THE CIVET CATS. Dr. Shortt. Proc. Zool. Soc. London, pt.28, pp.98-99, 1860.

(SWAMP CIVET OPENING NUTS.) Nuesse oeffnender Sumpfichneumon. G.Steinbacher. Zool. Garten, Leipzig, n.F., vol.18, nos. 1-2, p.58, 1951.

(THE CIVET.) La civette. (Viverra civetta.) R. Vandenput. Bull. Agricole du Congo Belge, Bruxelles, vol.28, no.1, pp.135-146, figs.51-60, Mar., 1937.

(OBSERVATIONS ON THE NANDINE (NANDINIA BINOTATA GRAY).) Beobachtungen am Fleckenroller (Nandinia binotata (Gray). J. Vosseler. Zeitschr. f. Saeugetierk., vol.3, pp.80-91, June 11, 1928.

(ON THE BINTURONG (ARCTICTIS BINTURONG RAFFL.).) Vom Binturong (Arctictis binturong Raffl.). J.Vosseler. Zool. Garten, Leipzig, n.F., vol.1, nos. 7-9, pp.296-302, figs.2, Feb., 1929.

CITIZEN MONGOOSE. Lewis W. Walker. Audubon Mag., New York, vol.50, no.2, pp.80-85, illus., Mar.-Apr., 1948.

(TIGER FITCHET (VORMELA PEREGUSNA GUELD.) IN BULGARIA.) Der Tigeriltis (Vormela peregusna Gueld.) in Bulgarien. Heinrich Wolf. Zool. Garten, Leipzig, n.F., vol.12, nos.4-6, pp.322-325, figs.2, Dec., 1940.

PARADOXURUS NIGER AND HERMAPHRODITUS OF BLANFORD. R.C.Wroughton. Jour. Bombay Nat. Hist. Soc., vol.25, no. 1, pp.48-51, Mar. 20, 1917.

MILD-MANNERED MIERKATS. Life, Chicago, vol.30, no.28, pp.53-54, illus., May 28, 1951.

(MISDEEDS OF THE MONGOOSE.) Les méfaits de la mangouste. La Nature, Paris, no.3118, pp.253-254, illus., Aug. 15, 1946.

Africa

(OBSERVATIONS OF SOUTHWEST AFRICAN SURICATES, SURICATA SURICATTA HAHNI THOMAS 1927.) Beobachtungen an suedwestafrikanischen Scharrtieren, Suricata suricatta hahni Thomas, 1927. Lutz Heck, Jr. Saeugetierk. Mitteil., Stuttgart, vol.4, no. 1, pp.33-34, illus., Jan. 1, 1956.

DESCRIPTION OF A NEW WATER MONGOOSE FROM EAST AFRICA. N.Hollister. Proc. Biol. Soc. Wash., vol.25, pp.1-2, Jan.23, 1912.

(NOTES ON THE MAMMALOGY OF NORTH AFRICA: THE GENETS.) Notes de mammalogie Nord-Africaine. Les genettes. Louis Lavauden. Bull. Soc. Hist. Nat. Afrique du Nord, vol.17, no.1, pp.51-54, Jan., 1926.

(DESCRIPTIONS OF SOME NEW MIERKATS OF THE MUSEUM OF THE BELGIAN CONGO.) Beschreibungen einiger neuer Meerkatzen des "Musée du Congo Belge". Paul Matschie. Rev. Zool. Africaine, Bruxsels, vol.1, fasc.3, pp.433-442, figs.1-4, Mar., 1912.

NEW GENUS OF AFRICAN MONGOOSES, WITH A NOTE ON GALERISCUS. R. I. Pocock. Ann. and Mag. Nat. Hist., London, ser.8, vol.17, pp.176-179, Feb., 1916.

THE CIVITS OF NIGERIA. D.R.Rosevear. Nigerian Field, London, vol.4, no.3, pp. 114-122, pls.2, July, 1935.

MONGOOSES OF NIGERIA. D.R.Rosevear. Nigerian Field, London, vol.4, no.4, pp. 165-170, pls.2, Oct., 1935.

ON A NEW MONGOOSE FROM THE CAMEROONS. (Galerella sanguinea mustela.) E. Schwarz. Ann. and Mag. Nat. Hist., London, ser.10, vol.15, no.86, pp.300-301, Feb., 1935.

ON TWO NEW GENETS FROM THE UPPER CONGO. (Genetta genetta hintoni; G.tigrina soror.) E. Schwarz. Ann. and Mag. Nat. Hist., ser.10, vol.3, pp.47-48, Jan., 1929.

DESCRIPTION OF A SECOND SPECIES OF THE CARNIVOROUS GENUS NANDINIA, FROM SOUTHERN NYASSALAND. Oldfield Thomas. Ann. and Mag. Nat. Hist., ser.6, vol.12, no.69, p.205, Sep., 1893.

NEW GENET FROM BRITISH EAST AFRICA. Oldfield Thomas. Ann. and Mag. Nat. Hist., ser.7, vol.9, no.53, pp.365-366, May, 1902.

NEW MONGOOSE FROM NAMAQUALAND. Oldfield Thomas. Ann. and Mag. Nat.Hist., ser.7, vol.12, no.70, pp.465-466, Oct., 1903.

ON A NEW BANDED MONGOOSE FROM SOMALILAND. Oldfield Thomas. Ann. and Mag. Nat. Hist., ser.6, vol.15, no.90, pp.531-532, June, 1895.

ON AFRICAN MONGOOSES. Oldfield Thomas. Proc. Zool. Soc. London, pp.59-93, pl.3, Jan. 3, 1882.

ON THE DWARF MONGOOSE (HELOGALE) OF SOMALILAND. Oldfield Thomas. Ann. and Mag. Nat. Hist., ser.6, vol.20, no. 118, pp.377-379, Oct., 1897.

ON THE EAST-AFRICAN MONGOOSE DESCRIBED AS GALERISCUS JACKSONI. Oldfield Thomas. Ann. and Mag. Nat. Hist., ser.10, vol.1, pp.344-345, Mar., 1928.

TWO NEW S. W. AFRICAN MONGOOSES. Oldfield Thomas. Ann. and Mag. Nat. Hist., ser.10, vol.2, no.11, p.408, Nov., 1928.

DESCRIPTION OF A NEW MONGOOSE FROM WEST AFRICA. W.E. de Winton. Bull. Liverpool Mus., vol.3, no.2, pp.35-37, illus., Mar. 13, 1901.

ON A NEW MONGOOSE FROM MATABELE-LAND BRITISH SOUTH AFRICA. W. E. de Winton. Ann. and Mag. Nat. Hist., ser.6, vol.18, no.108, p.469, Dec., 1896.

ON THE AFRICAN MONGOOSES USUALLY REFERRED TO THE HERPESTES GRACILIS GROUP. R.C. Wroughton. Ann. and Mag. Nat. Hist., ser.7, vol.20, pp.110-121, Aug., 1907.

Anatomy

(ON SOME OSTEOLOGICAL AND OSTEOMETRICAL CHARACTERS OF THE GENET OF THE PYRENEES COMPARED WITH THE GENETS OF WESTERN EUROPE AND THOSE OF FRANCE IN PARTICULAR.) Sur quelques caractères ostéologiques et ostéometriques de la genette des Pyrénées dans le cadre des genettes de l'Europe occidentale et de la France en particulier. E. Bourdelle, M. Deziliere. Bull. Soc. Hist. Nat. Toulouse, vol.86, pp.122-124, 1951.

NOTE ON THE ANATOMY OF THE TWO-SPOTTED PARADOXURE (NANDINIA BINOTATA). William Henry Flower. Proc. Zool. Soc. London, pp.683-684, 1872.

NOTES ON THE ANATOMY OF THE BINTURONG (ARCTICTIS BINTURONG). Alfred Henry Garrod. Proc. Zool. Soc. London, pp.196-202, figs.4, 1873; p.142, 1878.

DESCRIPTION OF AN ADULT SKULL OF EUPLERES GOUDOTI. John Edward Gray. Proc. Zool. Soc. London, pp.824-828, figs. 2, pl., 1870.

ON A SPECIMEN OF HERPESTES SEMI-TORQUATUS GRAY FROM SUMATRA. F.A. Jentink. Notes Leyden Mus., vol.16, no.22, p.210, Dec., 1894.

ON THE FEMALE GENITAL ORGANS OF CRYPTOPROCTA. Einar Lönnberg. Bihang till K. Svenska Vet.-Akad. Handlingar, Stockholm, Bd.28, afd.4, no.3, pp.11, figs. 5, pl., 1902.

NOTES ON THE DISSECTION OF A MANGUE (CROSSARCHUS OBSCURUS, F. CUV.). W. Martin. Proc. Zool. Soc. London, pt.2, pp.113-115, 1834.

(ON THE INDIVIDUAL AND GEOGRAPHICAL VARIATIONS OF THE GENETS.) Ueber die individuellen und geographischen Abaenderungen der Ginsterkatzen. Paul Matschie. Verhandl. V. Internat. Zool. Congr., Berlin, pp.1128-1144, pl.1, (1901) 1902.

SOME OBSERVATIONS ON THE FOETAL MEMBRANES OF THE INDIAN PALM-CIVET, PARADOXURUS HERMAPHRODITUS HERMAPHRODITUS (SCHRATER). M. A. Moghe. Proc. Nat. Inst. Sci. India, pt.B, vol.22, no.1, pp.41-47, Feb.26, 1956.

ON THE ANATOMY OF A FEMALE SURICATE (RYZAENA TETRADACTYLE, ILL.). R. Owen. Proc. Comm. Sci. and Corres. Zool. Soc. London, pt.1, p.39, 1830-1831.

ON THE ANATOMY OF A MALE SURICATE. R. Owen. Proc. Comm. Sci. and Corres. Zool. Soc. London, pt.1, p.51, 1830-1831.

ON SOME EXTERNAL CHARACTERS OF GALIDIA, GALIDICTIS, AND RELATED GENERA. R.I. Pocock. Ann. and Mag. Nat. Hist., London, ser.8, vol.16, pp. 351-356, pls.14-15, Oct., 1915.

ON SOME OF THE EXTERNAL CHARACTERS OF CRYPTOPROCTA. R. I. Pocock. Ann. and Mag. Nat. Hist., London, ser. 8, vol.17, pp.413-425, figs.4, June, 1916.

ON SOME OF THE EXTERNAL CHARACTERS OF CYNOGALE BENNETTII, GRAY. R.I. Pocock. Ann. and Mag. Nat. Hist., London, ser.8, vol.15, pp.351-360, pl.14, Apr., 1915.

ON SOME OF THE EXTERNAL CHARACTERS OF THE GENUS LINSANG, WITH NOTES UPON THE GENERA POIANA AND EUPLERES. R.I. Pocock. Ann. and Mag. Nat. Hist., London, ser.8, vol.16, pp.341-351, pls.12-13, Oct., 1915.

ON SOME OF THE EXTERNAL CHARACTERS OF THE PALM-CIVET (HEMIGALUS DERBYANUS, GRAY) AND ITS ALLIES. R.I. Pocock. Ann. and Mag. Nat. Hist., London, ser.8, vol.16, pp.153-162, pl.8, Sep., 1915.

ON THE EXTERNAL CHARACTERS OF THE MONGOOSES (MUNGOTIDAE). R.I. Pocock. Proc. Zool. Soc. London, pt.2, pp.349-374, figs.10, June 20, 1916.

PERFUME-GLAND OF THE BINTURONG (ARCTICTIS). R.I. Pocock. Jour. Mamm., vol.26, no.4, p.443, Feb.12, 1946.

EXTERNAL GENITALIA AND PERFUME GLAND IN ARCTICTIS BINTURONG. H. Elizabeth Story. Jour. Mamm., vol.26, no.1, pp.64-66, fig.1, pl.1, Feb.23, 1945.

(OBSERVATION ON THE DENTAL FORMULA OF RHYNCOGALES.) Observation sur la formule dentaire des Rhyncogales. R. Thévenin. Bull. Mus. Nat. Hist. Nat., Paris, ser.2, vol.15, no.6, pp.380-381, June, 1943.

Asia

VIVERRIDS FROM ASIATIC EXPEDITIONS. Glover M. Allen. Amer. Mus. Novitates, no.359, pp.1-9, July 15, 1929.

NOTICE OF TWO VIVERRIDAE FROM CEYLON, LATELY LIVING IN THE GARDENS. J.E. Gray. Proc. Zool. Soc. London, pt.19, p.131, 1851.

CIVET CATS OF HONG KONG. G.A.C. Herklots. Hong Kong Nat., vol.5, no.2, pp.91-94, pl.7, June, 1934.

ARCTICTIS OF JAVA. C. Boden Kloss. Treubia, Buitenzorg, vol.10, p.497, June, 1929.

FURTHER NOTES ON THE MONGOOSES OF THE MALAY PENINSULA. C. Boden Kloss. Jour. Fed. Malay States Mus., vol.7, pt.4, p.241, June, 1918.

ON A NEW MONGOOSE FROM SIAM. C. Boden Kloss. Jour. Nat. Hist. Soc. Siam, vol.2, pp.215-217, May, 1917.

ON THE MONGOOSES OF THE MALAY PENINSULA. C. Boden Kloss. Jour. Fed. Malay States Mus., pt.3, pp.123-125, Sep., 1917.

NOTES ON A PARADOXURE FROM CENTRAL BORNEO. Einar Lönnberg. Nyt Mag. for Naturvidensk., vol.62, pp.60-62, Nov. 22, 1924.

CIVET-CATS OF ASIA. R.I. Pocock. Jour. Bombay Nat. Hist. Soc., vol.36, no.2, pp.423-449, figs.4, Apr. 15, 1933; vol.36, no.3, pp.629-656, figs.5, Aug. 15, 1933.

GEOGRAPHICAL RACES OF PARADOXURUS AND PAGUMA FOUND TO THE EAST OF THE BAY OF BENGAL. R.I. Pocock. Proc. Zool. Soc. London, pt.3, pp.613-683, figs. 11, pls.1-2, Sep. 14, 1934.

MONGOOSES OF BRITISH INDIA, INCLUDING CEYLON AND BURMA. R.I. Pocock. Jour. Bombay Nat. Hist. Soc., vol.39, no.2, pp.211-245, figs.2, Apr. 15, 1937.

PALM CIVETS OR "TODDY CATS" OF THE GENERA PARADOXURUS AND PAGUMA INHABITING BRITISH INDIA. R.I. Pocock. Jour. Bombay Nat. Hist. Soc., vol.36, no. 4, pp.855-877, figs.2, Dec.15, 1933; vol. 37, no.1, pp.172-192, figs.3-4, Apr. 15, 1934; vol.37, no.2, pp.314-346, figs.5-7, Aug. 15, 1934.

RARER GENERA OF ORIENTAL VIVERRIDAE. R.I. Pocock. Proc. Zool. Soc. London, pt.4, pp.969-1035, pls.3, figs. 7, Dec., 1933.

ON THE SOUTHERN MALAYAN RACE OF THE WHITE-WHISKERED PALM-CIVET. H.C. Robinson, C.B. Kloss. Jour. Fed. Malay States Mus., vol.7, pt.4, pp.243-244, June, 1918.

EXHIBITION OF SKIN AND SKULL OF A VIVERRINE CARNIVORE FROM TONKIN. Oldfield Thomas. Proc. Zool. Soc. London, no.106, pp.17-18, Mar. 19, 1912. (Abstract.)

MASKED CIVETS (PAGUMA) OF WESTERN CHINA. Oldfield Thomas. Ann. and Mag. Nat. Hist., ser.9, vol.8, pp.617-618, Dec., 1921.

NEW BINTURONG FROM SIAM. Oldfield Thomas. Ann. and Mag. Nat. Hist., ser.8, vol.17, no.99, pp.270-271, Mar., 1916.

SOUTH TENASSERIM RACE OF PAGUMA LEUCOMYSTAX, GRAY. Oldfield Thomas. Ann. and Mag. Nat. Hist., ser.10, vol.2, no.7, pp.101-102, July, 1928.

GEM-FACED CIVET OCCURRING IN THE CENTRAL PART OF HONSHU. T. Udagawa. Misc. Repts. Yamashina's Inst. Ornithol. and Zool., Tokyo, no.4, pp.174-175 (42-43), June, 1954. (In Japanese with English summary.)

NEW PALM-CIVET FROM ASSAM. R.C. Wroughton. Jour. Bombay Nat. Hist. Soc., vol.27, pp.600-601, Mar. 31, 1921.

ON A LOCAL FORM OF THE CHINESE TODDY-CAT TAKEN IN NORTH BURMA BY CAPT. A. W. KEMMIS, BURMA MILITARY POLICE. R.C. Wroughton. Jour. Bombay Nat. Hist. Soc., vol.19, no.4, pp.793-794, Feb. 28, 1910.

SCIENTIFIC RESULTS FROM THE MAMMAL SURVEY. XI. H. THE COMMON INDIAN MONGOOSE. R.C. Wroughton. Jour. Bombay Nat. Hist. Soc., vol.24, pp.50-55, Sep. 30, 1915.

SCIENTIFIC RESULTS FROM THE MAMMAL SURVEY. XI. L. THE BURMESE CIVETS. R.C. Wroughton. Jour. Bombay Nat. Hist. Soc., vol.24, no.1, pp.63-65, Sep. 20, 1915.

Coloration

PROTECTIVE COLOURING IN A GENET. Maurice Burton. Illus. London News, vol. 137, no.3567, p.394, illus., Sep. 3, 1955.

COLOUR MUTANTS OF THE MALAY SHORT-TAILED MONGOOSE, HERPESTES BRACHYURUS GRAY. E. Schwarz. Proc. Zool. Soc. London, vol.117, no.1, pp.79-80, May, 1947.

Diseases and Parasites

ON TENUOSTRONGYLUS CYNICTIS, GEN. ET SP. N., TRICHOSTRONGYLID PARASITIZING THE YELLOW MUNGOOSE (CYNICTIS PENICILLATA). P.L. Leroux. Ann. and Mag. Nat. Hist., ser.10, vol.11, pp.222-228, figs.7, Feb., 1933.

TWO NEW NEMATODES FROM THE SURICAT (VIVERRIDAE). H.O. Monnig. 17th Rep. Director Vet. Serv. and Animal Industry, Union S. Africa, pp.277-282, figs.8, Aug., 1931.

TICKS OF JAMAICA, B. W. I. (THE MONGOOSE (HERPESTES JAVANICUS AUROPUNCTATUS HODGSON)). Gorden B. Thompson. Ann. and Mag. Nat. Hist., London, ser.12, vol.3, no.27, pp.220-229, Mar., 1950.

MONGOOSE RABIES IN PUERTO RICO. Ernest S. Tierkel et al. Public Health Rep., vol.67, no.3, pp.274-278, illus., Mar., 1952.

Ecology, Habits, Behavior

LETTER ON THE HABITS, AND OF CRYPTOPROCTA FEROX, BENN. M.W. Bojer. Proc. Zool. Soc. London, pt.2, p.13, 1834.

HOW THE MONGOOSE COUNTERACTS SNAKE BITE. A.L'E. Brownlow. Jour. Bombay Nat. Hist. Soc., vol.42, no.1, p.183, Dec., 1940.

ONLY MONGOOSES! (Habits of African Herpestes Zebra or Fasciatus.) Hans Coudenhove. Atlantic Monthly, vol.133, pp. 445-456, Apr., 1924.

FIGHT BETWEEN A COBRA AND A MONGOOSE. P.E.P. Deraniyagala. Spolia Zeylanica, Ceylon Jour. Sci., vol.17, pt.1, pp.53-55, pls.9-10, Oct. 11, 1932.

HABITS OF THE GREY MONGOOSE. C.E.C. Fischer. Jour. Bombay Nat. Hist. Soc., vol. 28, p.274, Dec. 30, 1921.

MONGOOSE AND SNAKE WARFARE. J.A. W. Foottit. Field, London, vol.153, p.828, illus., May 24, 1929.

FOOD OF THE SMALL INDIAN CIVET (VIVERRICULA MALACCENSIS) IN CAPTIVITY. Chas. M. Inglis. Jour. Bombay Nat. Hist. Soc., vol.28, pp.265-266, Dec. 30, 1921.

MONGOOSE ATTACKING A DONKEY. E.S. Lewis. Jour. Bombay Nat. Hist. Soc., vol. 41, no.4, p.893, Aug., 1940.

IS THE MONGOOSE A SNAKE KILLER? James A. Oliver. Nat. Hist., vol.64, no. 8, pp.426-429, illus., Oct., 1955.

ON THE HABITS OF THE MONGOOS (HERPESTES GRISEUS). Lieutenant Pegus. Proc. Zool. Soc. London, pt.20, pp.89-90, 1852.

SOME FOOD HABITS OF THE MONGOOSE (HERPESTES BIRMANICUS). C.E. Pemberton. Hawaiian Planters' Rec., vol.37, no.1, pp.12-13, fig.1, 1933.

MONGOOSE LURING GUINEA FOWL. F.W. Preston. Jour. Mamm., vol.31, no.2, p. 194, May 25, 1950.

(NUT-CRACKING MONGOOSES.) Nuesse oeffnender Sumpfichneumon. Georg Steinbacher. Zool. Garten, Leipzig, n.F., vol. 10, nos.5-6, pp.228-229, Jan., 1939.

MONGOOSE. THE FOOD OF THE MONGOOSE IN TRINIDAD. C.B. Williams. Trinidad Tobago Bull., vol.17, no.4, pp. 167-188, 1918.

FOOD OF MONGOOSE (HERPESTES JAVANICUS AUROPUNCTATUS HODGSON) IN ST. CROIX AND PUERTO RICO. George N. Wolcott. Jour. Agric. Univ. Puerto Rico, vol.37, no.3, pp.241-247, illus., 1953.

SNAKE-KILLING MONGOOSE IN ACTION: DUELS TO THE DEATH. Illus. London News, vol.189, no.5091, p.877, Nov.14, 1936. (Mongoose killing cobra.)

Europe

(THE SPANISH GENET.) Sobre las ginetas españolas. Angel Cabrera. Bol. Real Soc. Española Hist. Nat., Madrid, vol.5, no.5, pp.259-267, May, 1905.

(NEW GENETTE CAPTURE IN BELGIUM (GENETTA VULGARIS LESSON).) Une nouvelle capture de la Genette (Genetta vulgaris Lesson) en Belgique. Ch. Dupond. Ann. Soc. R. Zool. Belgique, vol.59, pp. 91-94, (1928) 1929.

(NOTE ON THE GENET IN FRANCE, GENETTA GENETTA RHODANICA MATSCHIE. Note sur la Genette en France, Genetta genetta rhodanica Matschie. A. Hugues. Rev. Française Mammal., ser.1, no.2, pp.52-60, Dec. 7, 1928.

(A GENETTE IN VAUD CANTON.) Une genette dans le canton de Vaud. P. Murisier. Bull. de la Soc. Vaudoise des Sci. Nat., vol.56, no.219, pp.329-331, fig.1, July 25, 1927.

(ETHOLOGY AND DISTRIBUTION OF THE GENET IN FRANCE TODAY.) Ethologie et répartition actuelle de la genette en France. P.L. Niort. Bull. Soc. Hist. Nat. Toulouse, vol.86, pp.133-150, 1951.

(ON THE EXISTENCE OF GENETTA AFRA IN PORTUGAL.) Sur l'existence de la Genetta afra Fr. Cuv. en Portugal. A.F. de Seabra. Bull. Soc. Portugaise Sci. Nat., vol. 2, fasc.1-2, pp.80-81, Nov., 1908.

GENET OF THE BALEARIC ISLANDS. Oldfield Thomas. Ann. and Mag. Nat. Hist., ser.7, vol.10, no.56, pp.162-163, Aug., 1902.

MONGOOSE IN CLYDE AREA. D. Wotherspoon. Scottish Natturalist, no.172, p.121, Aug., 1928.

Fossils

FOSSIL CARNIVORES OF THE TRANSVAAL CAVES: TWO NEW VIVERRIDS, TOGETHER WITH SOME GENERAL CONSIDERATIONS. R.F. Ewer. Proc. Zool. Soc. London, vol.126, no.2, pp. 259-274, pls.2, Apr. 6, 1956.

(PALEONTOLOGICAL EXCAVATIONS MADE IN 1936.) Fouilles paléontologiques faites en 1936. M.C. Lamberton. Bull. Acad. Malgache, n.s., vol.19, pp.1-19, pls.2-4, 1936.

(DESCRIPTION OF A CRANIUM OF A SUB-FOSSIL CRYPTOPROCTA AND REMARKS ON THE AFFINITIES OF THIS GENUS.) Description d'un crâne de Cryptoprocte sub-fossile suivie de remarques sur les affinités du genre Cryptoprocta. G. Petit. Archiv. Mus. Nat. Hist. Nat. Paris, ser.6, vol.12, pp.621-636, figs.7, June, 1935. (Vol.2 du Tricentenaire.) (Cryptoprocta spelaea Grandidier.)

In Captivity, As Pets

CRAB-EATING MONGOOSE (HERPESTES URVA (HODGS.) IN CAPTIVITY. A.L'E. Brownlow. Jour. Bombay Nat. Hist. Soc., vol.41, no.4, pp.893-894, pl., Aug., 1940.

MY MEERKAT. Edward Hall. Field, London, vol.148, p.395, Aug. 26, 1926.

(AN ICHNEUMON AS PET.) Ein Ichneumon als Hausgenosse. Ernst Heller. Zool. Garten, Leipzig, n.F., vol.9, no.5, pp.222-225, Oct., 1937; vol.12, nos.2-3, pp.196-197, July, 1940.

BANDED MONGOOSES AS PETS. Arthur Loveridge. Nat. Hist., New York, vol.53, no.2, pp.82-83, 96, illus., Feb., 1944.

(CRYPTOPROCTA FEROX BENN. IN THE FORMER HAMBURG ZOO.) Cryptoprocta ferox Benn. im ehemaligen Hamburger Zoo. Erna Mohr. Zool. Garten, Leipzig, n.F., vol.14, no.4, pp.210-211, fig.1, 1942.

(CROSSARCHUS OBSCURUS FR. CUV. AS PET.) Ueber Crossarchus obscurus Fr. Cuv. als Hausgenossen. Elis Naundorff. Carnivoren-Studien, vol.2, Kleintier und Pelztier, Leipzig, Jahrg.12, no.8, pp.97-102, Dec., 1936.

INTERESTING ARRIVALS AT THE ZOOLOGICAL GARDENS. (Hemigalus hardwickii.) D. Seth-Smith. Field, London, vol.156, no.4054, p.344, fig.1, Sep. 6, 1930.

Madagascar

NEW SPECIES OF FOSSA FROM CENTRAL MADAGASCAR. G. Dollman. Ann. and Mag. Nat. Hist., London, ser.8, vol.4, pp.306-307, 1909.

DESCRIPTION OF NEW SPECIES OF GALIDICTIS FROM MADAGASCAR. J.E. Gray. Proc. Zool. Soc. London, pt.16, pp.21-23, 1848.

ON THE FOSSANE OF D'AUBENTON (FOSSA D'AUBENTONII). J.E. Gray. Proc. Zool. Soc. London, pp.869-872, figs.3, pl., Dec. 3, 1872.

(ON A NEW MALAGASIAN CARNIVORE OF THE GENUS EUPLERES.) Sur un nouveau Carnivore malgache du genre Eupleres. (Eupleres major.) L. Lavauden. Comptes Rendus Acad. Sci. Paris, vol.189, p.197, 1929.

ON THE SPECIES OF THE MASCARENE VIVERRID GALIDICTIS, WITH THE DESCRIPTION OF A NEW GENUS AND A NOTE ON GALIDIA ELEGANS. R.I. Pocock. Ann. and Mag. Nat. Hist., London, vol. 16, pp.113-124, pl.7, 1915.

NEW GALIDIA (VIVERRIDAE) FROM MADAGASCAR. G.H.H. Tate, A.L. Rand. Amer. Mus. Novitates, New York, no.1112, p.1, May 19, 1941.

LETTERS ACCOMPANYING A PRESENT OF A NEW QUADRUPED FROM MADAGSCAR. C. Telfair. Proc. Zool. Soc. London, pt.1, p.46, 1833.

North America, Hawaii

LIFE HISTORY AND ECONOMIC STATUS OF THE MONGOOSE IN HAWAII. Paul H. Baldwin et al. Jour. Mamm., vol.33, no. 3, pp.335-356, Aug. 19, 1952.

MONGOOSE IN KENTUCKY. H.H.T. Jackson. Jour. Mamm., vol.2, no.4, pp. 234-235, Nov. 29, 1921.

REPRODUCTION AND AGE STRUCTURE OF A MONGOOSE POPULATION IN HAWAII. Oliver P. Pearson, Paul H. Baldwin. Jour. Mamm., vol.34, no.4, pp.436-447, Nov. 13, 1953.

BIOLOGY OF THE INDIAN MONGOOSE IN PUERTO RICO. David Pimentel. Jour. Mamm., vol.36, no.1, pp.62-68, Feb., 1955.

MONGOOSE ARE OUT. Texas Game and Fish, Austin, vol.2, no.12, p.22, Nov., 1944.

Reproductive Biology

BREEDING HABITS OF THE COMMON MONGOOSE (HERPESTES EDWARDSI). A.G. Frere. Jour. Bombay Nat. Hist. Soc., vol.33, no.2, pp.426-428, Feb. 15, 1929.

BREEDING DWARF MONGOOSES. Mrs. S. Taylor. Zoo Life, London, vol.10, no.3, pp.70-72, illus., Autumn, 1955.

Taxonomy

ON THE SPECIES OF THE GENUS VIVERRICULA. J.L. Bonhote. Ann. and Mag. Nat. Hist., ser.7, vol.1, pp.119-122, Feb., 1898.

STATUS OF PRIONAILURUS BENGALENSIS ALLENI SODY. Geo. G. Goodwin. Amer. Mus. Novitates, no.1767, pp.103, Apr.13, 1956.

DESCRIPTIONS OF A NEW SPECIES OF HERPESTES. J.E. Gray. Proc. Zool. Soc. London, pt.17, p.11, 1849.

NOTICE OF HELOGALE, A NEW GENUS VIVERRIDAE. J.E. Gray. Proc. Zool. Soc. London, pt.29, p.308, fig.2, 1861.

ON A NEW SPECIES OF PARADOXURE (PARADOXURUS DERBIANUS), WITH REMARKS ON SOME MAMMALIA RECENTLY PURCHASED BY THE BRITISH MUSEUM, AND CHARACTERS OF THE NEW SPECIES. J.E. Gray. Proc. Zool. Soc. London, pt.5, p.67, 1837.

ON THE FAMILY OF VIVERRIDAE AND ITS GENERIC SUBDIVISIONS; WITH AN ENUMERATION OF THE SPECIES OF PARADOXURUS, AND CHARACTERS OF SEVERAL NEW ONES. J.E. Gray. Proc. Comm. Sci. and Corres. Zool. Soc. London, pt.2, pp.63-68, 1832.

REVISION OF THE GENERA AND SPECIES OF VIVERRINE ANIMALS (VIVERRIDAE), FOUNDED ON THE COLLECTION IN THE BRITISH MUSEUM. J.E. Gray. Proc. Zool. Soc. London, pp.502-510, 1864.

ON THE EVOLUTION AND MAJOR CLASSIFICATION OF THE CIVETS (VIVERRIDAE) AND ALLIED FOSSIL AND RECENT CARNIVORA: A PHYLOGENETIC STUDY OF THE SKULL AND DENTITION. William K. Gregory, Milo Hellman. Proc. Amer. Philos. Soc., Philadelphia, vol.81, no.3, pp.309-392, figs.33, tbls.11, Aug. 31, 1939.

ON THE SPECIFIC DISTINCTION OF VIVERRA RASSA, HORSF., AND VIVERRA INDICA, GEOFFR. T. Horsfield. Proc. Comm. Sci. and Corres. Zool. Soc. London, pt.2, p.22, 1832.

TAXONOMIC STUDY OF CYNICTIS PENICILLATA (G. CUVIER). B.G. Lundholm. Ann. Transvaal Mus., vol.22, no.3, pp. 305-319, Jan. 24, 1955.

DESCRIPTION OF A NEW MAMMAL, (CYNICTIS MELANURUS MART.). W. Martin. Proc. Zool. Soc. London, pt.4, p.55, 1836.

(SOME NEW SPECIES OF GENETS.) Einige neue Arten von Ginsterkatzen. Oscar Neumann. Sitz. Ber. Gesell. Naturf. Freunde Berlin, nos.7-8, pp.181-184, Oct. 21, 1902.

CHARACTERS OF A NEW GENUS OF CARNIVOROUS MAMMALIA FROM THE COLLECTION OF MR. STEEDMAN. W. Ogilby. Proc. Zool. Soc. London, pt.1, p. 48, 1833.

REMARKS UPON THE PROBABLE IDENTITY OF CYNICTIS MELANURUS MART., WITH A SPECIES NOTED BY BOSHMAN UNDER THE NAME OF KOKEBOG. W. Ogilby. Proc. Zool. Soc. London, pt.4, pp.55-56, 1836.

CLASSIFICATION OF THE MONGOOSES (MUNGOTIDAE). R.I. Pocock. Ann. and Mag. Nat. Hist., ser.9, vol.3, pp.515-524, June, 1919.

NOTES ON VIVERRIDAE. H.C. Robinson, C. Boden Kloss. Rec. Indian Mus., vol. 19, pp.175-179, Nov., 1920.

GEOGRAPHICAL RACES OF HERPESTES BRACHYURUS, GRAY. Oldfield Thomas. Ann. and Mag. Nat. Hist., ser.9, vol.8, pp.134-136, July, 1921.

MONGOOSES OF THE HERPESTES SMITHII GROUP. Oldfield Thomas. Jour. Bombay Nat. Hist. Soc., vol.28, pp.23-26, Dec. 30, 1921.

NEW SPECIES OF PARADOXURUS OF THE P. PHILIPPINENSIS GROUP, AND A NEW PAGUMA. Oldfield Thomas. Ann. and Mag. Nat. Hist., ser.8, vol.3, no.16, pp.374-377, Apr., 1909.

ON A NEW MONGOOSE ALLIED TO HERPESTES ALBICAUDATUS. Oldfield Thomas. Proc. Zool. Soc. London, pp. 622-624, pl.62, Dec. 3, 1889.

ON TWO NEW GENERA AND A NEW SPECIES OF VIVERRINE CARNIVORA. Oldfield Thomas. Proc. Zool. Soc. London, pp.498-503, figs.61-63, June, 1912.

TWO NEW RACES OF MONGOOSE. Oldfield Thomas. Ann. and Mag. Nat. Hist., ser.8, vol.10, no.60, pp.588-589, Dec., 1912.

SCIENTIFIC RESULTS FROM THE MAMMAL SURVEY. XXIX. A RENAMING OF "MUNGOS MUNGO ELLIOTI". R.C. Wroughton. Jour. Bombay Nat. Hist. Soc., vol.28, no.1, p.629, Dec. 30, 1921.

Hyaenidae

HYAENAS IN SOMALILAND. R. Drake Brockman. Field, London, vol.156, no. 4035, p.20, July 5, 1930.

NEW PRIMITIVE HYAENA FROM STERKFONTEIN. (Lycyaena silberbergi.) R. Broom. Sambab, S.African Mus. Assoc., Durban, vol.3, no.9, p.273, Mar., 1945.

THE "GADETT" OR BRAIN-EATER. (Killing of Sheep for Brain Alone by Spotted Hyena; Sheep Remain Untouched.) Cara Buxton. Jour. East Africa and Uganda Nat. Hist. Soc., no.15, p.498, Nov., 1919.

HYAENAS IN MESOPOTAMIA. Stewart Capper. Jour. Bombay Nat. Hist. Soc., vol. 27, p.937, July 31, 1921.

JUNGLE IN SUNLIGHT AND SHADOW. PT. 3. FISHING CATS AND RATELS. F.W. Champion. Field, London, vol.162, no. 4207, pp.428-429, figs., Aug. 12, 1933.

IN DEFENSE OF HYENAS. Georgia B. Dittoe. Zoonooz, San Diego, vol.19, no. 7, p.6, July, 1946.

HYAENA NEW TO THE EXHIBITION COLLECTION. J.G. Dollman. Nat. Hist.Mag., London, vol.1, no.3, p.65, fig., July, 1927.

NOTE ON THE YOUNG OF THE SPOTTED HYAENA (CROCUTA MACULATA). John Edward Gray. Proc. Zool. Soc. London, pp. 245-247, figs.3, 1869.

HYAENA BORISSIAKI N. SP. FROM THE RUSILLON FAUNA OF BESSARABIA. I.P. Khomenko. Trav. Inst. paleozool. Acad. Sci. USSR, Leningrad, vol.1, pp.81-136, pls.9, 1932. (In Russian with German summary.)

PERCROCUTA KRETZOI (MAMMALIA, CARNIVORA), A GROUP OF NEOGENE HYENAS. Björn Kurtén. Acta Zool. Cracoviensia, Polska Akad. Nauk, vol. 2, no.16, pp.375-404, Dec. 15, 1957. (In English with Polish and Russian summaries.)

(SPOTTED HYENA OF THE CAMEROONS HINTERLAND.) Die Flecken-Hyaene des Hinterlandes von Kamerun. Paul Matschie. Sitz. Ber. Gesell. Naturf. Freunde Berlin, no.9, pp.211-215, illus., Nov. 20, 1900.

BIONOMICS OF THE SPOTTED HYAENA, CROCUTA CROCUTA ERXL. L. Harrison Matthews. Proc. Zool. Soc. London, vol. 109, ser.A, pt.1, pp.43-56, figs.2, pls.4, May, 1939.

HYAENAS IN SOMALILAND. A.H. Mosse. Field, London, vol.156, no.4058, pp.483-484, Oct. 4, 1930.

HYAENAS IN SOMALILAND. Richard Oakley. Field, London, vol.156, no.4061, p.590, Oct. 25, 1930.

THE KERIT. (Notes on Spotted Hyena.) Richard Oakley. Field, London, vol.149, p.676, Apr. 21, 1927.

HE WHO LAUGHS LAST-. (Hyena) Edalee Orcutt. San Diego Zoonooz, vol.22, no.3, pp.3-4, illus., Mar., 1949.

VITALITY OF A HYAENA (HYAENA STRIATA ). T.J. Phillips. Jour. Bombay Nat. Hist. Soc., Bombay, vol.42, no.2, p.438, Apr., 1941.

THE STORY OF A HYENA. H.E. Pike. Field, London, vol.152, p.1009, illus., Dec. 20, 1928.

COMMENTS ON THE AARDWOLF (PROTELES CRISTATUS, SPARRM.) MENTIONED IN 'A SPORTING TRIP TO SOMALILAND' IN THIS JOURNAL. C.R.S. Pitman. Jour. Bombay Nat. Hist. Soc., vol.33, no.1, p.201, Sep. 30, 1928.

HYAENAS. W.P. Pycraft. Illus. London News, vol.191, no.5138, p.600, figs.4, Oct. 9, 1937.

(CONTRIBUTION TO KNOWLEDGE OF THE STRIPED HYENA.) Ein Beitrag zur Kenntnis der gestreiften Hyaene. Theobald Renner. Annalen Wetterauischen Gesell. Gesammte Naturk., Frankfurt am Main, vol.4 (Neue Annalen, vol.1), no.1, pp. 140-146, 1818.

HYAENAS OF NIGERIA. D.R. Rosevear. Nigerian Field, vol.5, no.1, pp.10-11, figs.2, Jan., 1936.

(OPERATIVE REMOVAL OF A TUMOR THE SIZE OF A HEAD IN A YOUNG SPOTTED HYENA.) Operative Entfernung einer Geschwulst von Kopfgroesse bei einer jungen Fleckenhyaene. W. Schulze. Zool. Garten, Leipzig, vol.21, nos.5-6, pp.385-386, illus., 1956.

HYENAS AND THEIR ALLIES. Ken Stott, Jr. Zoonooz, San Diego, vol.13, no.4, p.6, Apr., 1941.

ON A REMARKABLE INSTANCE OF AFFECTIONATE ATTACHMENT IN THE COMMON HYAENA (HYAENA VULGARIS, CUV.). Lieut.-Col. W.H. Sykes. Proc. Zool. Soc. London, pt.1, p.76, 1833.

STRANGE OCCURRENCE OF AARD WOLF, PROTELES CRISTATUS SPARRMAN, AT SALISBURY, SOUTHERN RHODESIA. J.A. Whellan. Proc. and Trans. Rhodesia Sci. Assoc., vol.44, p.64, 1956.

Anatomy

FEMALE EXTERNAL GENITALIA OF THE SPOTTED HYENA. D. Dwight Davis, H. Elizabeth Story. Fieldiana-Zoology, Chicago Nat. Hist. Mus., vol.31, no.33, pp.277-283, figs.68-69, Aug. 26, 1949.

(ON AN ICTITHERIUM SKULL (FAMILY VIVERRIDAE).) Ueber einen Schaedel von Ictitherium (Fam. Viverridae). W.O. Dietrich. Neues Jahrb. Mineral., Geol. u. Paelaont., Abt. B, vol.57, pp.364-371, pl.1, fig.1, 1927.

SOME ADAPTIVE FEATURES IN THE DENTITION OF HYAENAS. R.F. Ewer. Ann. and Mag. Nat. Hist., London, ser. 12, vol.7, no.75, pp.188-194, Mar., 1954.

ON THE ANATOMY OF THE PROTELES, PROTELES CRISTATUS (SPARRMAN). William Henry Flower. Proc. Zool. Soc. London, pp.474-496, figs.11, pl.36, 1869.

(COMPLEMENTARY REMARKS ON THE FEMALE ORGAN OF HYAENA CROCUTA.) Remarques complémentaires sur l'organe femelle de l'Hyaena crocuta. Henri Neuville. Bull. Mus. Nat. d'Hist. Nat., Paris, ser.2, vol.8, no.1, pp.54-60, figs.4, Jan., 1936.

(THE FEMALE ORGAN OF THE SPOTTED HYENA.) De l'organe femelle de l'hyène tachetée (Hyaena crocuta Erxl.). Henri Neuville. Archiv. Mus. Nat. d'Hist. Nat., Paris, ser.6, vol.12, pp.225-229, figs.2, June, 1935.

ON DENTITION AND EXTREMITIES OF ICTITHERIUM HIPPARIONUM GERVAIS. J.A. Orlov. Comptes Rendus (Doklady) Acad. Sci. USSR, Moscow, n.s., vol.22, no.8, pp.530-532, Mar. 15, 1939.

ON THE STRUCTURE OF EXTREMITIES OF CROCUTA EXIMIA ROTH ET WAGNER. J.A. Orlov. Comptes Rendus (Doklady) Acad. Sci. USSR, Moscow, n.s., vol.22, no.8, pp.533-535, Mar. 15, 1939.

ON SOME OF THE EXTERNAL STRUCTURAL CHARACTERS OF THE STRIPED HYAENA (HYAENA HYAENA) AND RELATED GENERA AND SPECIES. R. I. Pocock. Ann. and Mag. Nat. Hist., London, ser.8, vol.17, pp.330-343, figs.5, Apr., 1916.

TYMPANIC BULLA IN HYAENAS. R. I. Pocock. Proc. Zool. Soc. London, pt.1, pp.303-307, figs.2, Apr. 20, 1916.

ECTOCRANIAL SUTURE CLOSURE IN THE HYAENAS. F.P. Schweikher. Amer. Jour. Anat., vol.45, no.3, pp.443-460, fig. 1, May 15, 1930.

LATER STAGES OF DEVELOPMENTAL GROWTH IN THE HYAENA SKULL. T. Wingate Todd, F.P. Schweikher. Amer. Jour. Anat., vol.52, no.1, pp.81-123, figs. 14, Jan. 15, 1933.

ON THE FEMALE GENERATIVE ORGANS OF HYAENA CROCUTA. M. Watson. Proc. Zool. Soc. London, pt.3, pp.369-379, pls., 1877.

ON THE MALE GENERATIVE ORGANS OF HYAENA CROCUTA. M. Watson. Proc. Zool. Soc. London, pp.416-428, pls.24-25, 1878.

Fossils

ON FOSSIL REMAINS OF A HYAENID FROM JAVA. L.D. Brongersma. Zool. Mededeel., Leiden, vol.20, pp.186-202, pl.13, 1937.

(ICE AGE CAVE HYENA AND ITS LIVING RELATIVES.) Die eiszeitliche Hoehlenhyaene und ihre lebenden Verwandten. Kurt Ehrenberg. Verhandl. Zool. Bot. Gesell. Wien, vol.85, pp.104-115, 1935.

FOSSIL CARNIVORES OF THE TRANSVAAL CAVES. THE HYAENIDAE OF KROMDRAAI. R.F. Ewer. Proc. Zool. Soc. London, vol. 124, pt.3, pp.565-585, pls.1-3, Nov. 15, 1954.

FOSSIL CARNIVORES OF THE TRANSVAAL CAVES. THE HYAENIDAE, OTHER THAN LYCYAENA, OF SWARTKRANS AND STERKFONTEIN. R.F. Ewer. Proc. Zool. Soc. London, vol.124, pt.4, pp.815-837, figs.10, pls.2, Feb. 22, 1955.

FOSSIL CARNIVORES OF THE TRANSVAAL CAVES. THE LYCYAENAS OF STERKFONTEIN AND SWARTKRANS, TOGETHER WITH SOME GENERAL CONSIDERATIONS OF THE TRANSVAAL FOSSIL HYAENIDS. R.F. Ewer. Proc. Zool. Soc. London, vol. 124, pt.4, pp.839-857, pl.1, Feb. 22, 1955.

CAVE HYAENA, CROCUTA CROCUTA SPELAEA (GOLDFUSS), NEW TO THE PLEISTOCENE FAUNA OF THE NETHERLANDS. D.A. Hooijer. Geol. en Mijnbouw, n.s., Jaarg.14, no.11, pp.385-388, Nov., 1952.

TERTIARY CARNIVORA OF WEST SIBERIA. IV. HYAENINAE. TERTIARY MAMMALIA AND THE LOCALITIES OF THEIR REMAINS. J.A. Orlov. Trav. Inst. Paléont., Moscow and Leningrad, vol.8, no.3, pp. 40-59, pls.1-5, 1941. (In Russian with English summary.)

TERTIARY CARNIVORA OF WEST SIBERIA. V. ICTITHERIINAE. TERTIARY MAMMALIA AND THE LOCALITIES OF THEIR REMAINS. J.A. Orlov. Trav. Inst. Paléont., Moscow and Leningrad, vol.8, no.3, pp.61-85, pls.2, 1941. (In Russian with English summary.)

(STUDIES ON THE QUATERNARY FAUNA OF THE LOWER VALLEY OF GARD OR GARDON. III. HYENAS.) Études sur la faune quaternaire de la valée inférieure du Gard ou Gardon.-III. Les hyenes. Marcel Paulus. Bull. Mus. Hist. Nat. Marseille, vol.6, nos.1-2, pp.1-20, pls.2, Jan.-Apr., 1946.

ON A NEW FOSSIL HYAENA. (Crocuta pilgrimina.) C.R. Narayan Rao. Half-Yearly Jour. Mysore Univ., vol.6, no.1, pp.99-103, figs.5, 1932.

HYAENA IN PREHISTORIC CHINA. Arthur de Carle Sowerby. China Jour., Shanghai, vol.25, no.4, pp.238-239, photos, Oct., 1936.

FOSSIL HYENAS OF THE MAKAPANSGIT VALLEY. M.J. Toerien. S.African Jour. Sci., Cape Town, vol.48, no.9, pp.293-300, Apr., 1952.

Habits, Behavior

HYAENAS ATTACKING HUMAN BEINGS. R.W. Burton. Jour. Bombay Nat. Hist. Soc., vol.41, no.1, pp.170-171, 1939.

HABITS OF HYAENAS. Alun R. Hughes. S.African Jour. Sci., vol.51, no.5, pp. 156-158, Dec., 1954.

(THE SEXUAL MIMICRY OF HYAENA CROCUTA.) Sur le Mimétisme sexuel de l'hyaena crocuta. Henri Neuville. Mammalia, Paris, vol.1, no.2, pp.49-58, Dec., 1936.

STRIPED HYAENA AS A MAN-EATER. S.H. Prater. Jour. Bombay Nat. Hist.Soc., vol.39, no.2, pp.388-390, Apr. 15, 1937.

COURAGE AND COWARDICE OF THE HYAENA. C.W. Sanders. Jour. Bombay Nat. Hist. Soc., vol.34, no.4, pp.1055-1056, Mar. 2, 1931.

PERPETUAL APPETITE. (Hyena) Homer F. Snow. Nature Mag., Washington, vol.38, no.1, pp.17-18, illus., Jan., 1945.

60 LB. HYAENA HAD 30 LBS. FOOD IN STOMACH. W. Uthmoeller. Wochenschr. f. Aquarien- u. Terrarienkunde, Braunschweig, Jahrg.36, no.1, p.16, Jan. 3, 1939.

Reproductive Biology

REPRODUCTION IN THE SPOTTED HYAENA, CROCUTA CROCUTA (ERXLEBEN). L. Harrison Matthews. Philos. Trans. Roy. Soc. London, ser.B, Biol. Sci., no.565, vol.230, pp.1-78, figs.34, pls.14, July 5, 1939.

BREEDING OF HYAENAS. R.P. Papillon. Field, London, vol.150, p.1033, Dec. 22, 1927.

(SOME PICTURES OF SPOTTED HYENAS (CROCOTTA CROCUTA) MATING.) Einige Bilder zur Paarung der Fleckenhyaene, Crocotta crocuta Erxl. Karl Max Schneider. Zool. Garten, Leipzig, vol.19, nos.2-4, pp.135-149, illus., 1952.

(ON THE SEX DETERMINATION IN THE SPOTTED HYENA CROCOTTA CROCUTA (ERXLEBEN 1777).) Uber die Geschlechtsbestimmung bei Tuepfelhyaenen, Crocotta crocuta (Erxleben 1777). Heinrich Wickingen. Saeugetierk. Mitteil., Stuttgart, vol.4, no.3, pp.129-130, July 1, 1956.

Taxonomy

STATUS AND AFFINITIES OF HYAENA SINENSIS OWEN AND HYAENA ULTIMA MATSUMOTO. Björn Kurtén. Amer. Mus. Novitates, vol.1764, pp.1-48, illus., Apr. 6, 1956.

TYPE COLLECTION OF ICTITHERIUM ROBUSTUM (GERVAIS, EX NORDMANN) AND THE RADIATION OF THE ICTITHERES. Björn Kurtén. Acta Zool. Fennica, vol.86, pp.1-26, illus., 1954.

(GEOGRAPHICAL FORMS OF THE HYENAS.) Geographische Formen der Hyaenen. Paul Matschie. Sitz. Ber. Gesell. Naturf. Freunde Berlin, no.1, pp.18-58, Jan. 16, 1900.

(NEVER BEFORE DESCRIBED SPECIES OF STRIPED HYENA FROM AFRICA, HYAENA (HYAENA) HIENOMELAS BERGERI SUBSP. NOV.) Eine noch nicht beschriebene Form der Streifenhyaene aus Afrika, Hyaena (Hyaena) hienomelas bergeri subsp. nov. Paul Matschie. Sitz. Ber. Gesell. Naturf. Freunde Berlin, no.8, pp.361-369, June 7, 1910.

(RACE OF HYENA APPARENTLY NEVER BEFORE DESCRIBED.) Eine anscheinend noch nicht beschriebene Rasse des Hyaenenhundes. Paul Matschie. Sitz. Ber. Gesell. Naturf. Freunde Berlin, no.4, pp.250-255, Apr., 1912; no.5, p.311, May, 1912.

SUBSPECIES AND VARIATION OF THE SPOTTED HYAENA, CROCUTA CROCUTA ERXL. L. Harrison Matthews. Proc. Zool. Soc. London, vol.109, ser.B, pt.2, pp.237-260, figs.20, pls.3, Aug., 1939.

RACES OF THE STRIPED AND BROWN HYAENAS. R.I. Pocock. Proc. Zool. Soc. London for 1934, pt.4, pp.799-825, Jan. 14, 1935.

AILURAENA STIRTON AND CHRISTIAN REFERRED TO CHASMAPORTHETES HAY. R.A. Stirton, Wayne G. Christian. Jour. Mamm., vol.22, no.2, p.198, May 14, 1941.

Felidae

ARE THERE TWO TYPES OF LEOPARD? W.G. Adam. Field, London, vol.158, no. 4098, p.56, July 11, 1931.

MY ACQUAINTANCE WITH LIONS. Carl E. Akeley. World's Work, vol.41, pp.277-288, figs.9, Jan., 1921.

BLACK LEOPARDS. Salim A. Ali. Jour. Bombay Nat. Hist. Soc., vol.31, p.1027, Feb. 20, 1927.

CLOUDED LEOPARD--A CAT ARISTOCRAT. Brent Altsheler. Nature Mag., Wash., D.C., vol.33, no.1, pp.24, 55, illus., Jan., 1940.

MONOGRAPH OF NEOFELIS NEBULOSA AND PARDOFELIS MARMORATA OR THE CLOUDED LEOPARD AND THE MARBLED CAT. Brent Altsheler. Nat. Hist. Publ. Co., Louisville, Ky., pp.7, Nov., 1936.

BOBCAT--WILDCAT (LYNX RUFUS RUFUS). N.R. Barger. Wisconsin Conserv. Bull., Madison, vol.13, no.5, pp.29-30, illus., May, 1948.

COUGAR. Lloyd Beebe. Sports Afield, New York, vol.123, no.1, pp.36-39, illus., Jan., 1950.

THE DESERT CAT (ERIMAILURUS THINOBIUS OGNEV, MAMMALIA). St. J. Bilkevič. Trav. Inst. Zool. Acad. Sci. de l'URSS, Leningrad, vol.2, no.1, (1933), pp.1-3, 1934.

DISTURBANCE IN THE NIGHT. (Cougar.) John W. Bingaman. Yosemite Nat. Notes, Yosemite, vol.23, no.3, pp.34-35, Mar., 1944.

SABA: A CIVILIZED OCELOT. Merlys Blakeslee. Nature Mag., vol.27, no.1, pp. 13-14, Jan., 1936.

CARELESS TIGER. N.L. Bor. Jour. Bombay Nat. Hist. Soc., vol.33, no.1, pp.194-195, Sep. 30, 1928.

LYNX AND BOBCAT. G.W. Bradt. Mich. Cons., vol.16, no.8, pp.4-5, Sep., 1947.

TIGER TRACKS. A.A.D. Brander. Jour. Bombay Nat. Hist. Soc., vol.33, no.4, p.972, Oct. 15, 1929.

THE CHEETAH--THE MILDEST CAT. William Bridges. Animal Kingdom, New York Zool. Soc., vol.58, no.5, pp.130-134, illus., Oct., 1955.

THE LYNX--THE OUTLAWED WILD CAT. Maurice Burton. Illus. London News, vol. 219, no. 5855, p. 22, illus., July 7, 1951.

BOOK OF THE TIGER. R. G. Burton. Hutchinson and Co., Ltd., London, pp.287, pls.16, 1933.

HUNTING LEOPARD (CYNAELURUS JUBATUS). R.G. Burton. Jour. Bombay Nat. Hist. Soc., vol.27, pp.397-398, Dec. 20, 1920.

KING OF BEASTS. THE TIGER'S CLAIM TO THE TITLE. R.G. Burton. Field, London, vol.153, p.192, Jan. 31, 1929.

KING OF CATS AND HIS COURT. Victor H. Cahalane. Nat. Geogr. Mag., Wash., D.C., vol.83, no.2, pp.217-259, illus., Feb., 1943.

JUNGLE IN SUNLIGHT AND SHADOW. PT. 1. WHAT IS THE USE OF LEOPARDS? F.W. Champion. Field, Lóndon, vol.162, no.4205, pp.286-288, figs., July 29, 1933.

TIGER TRACKS. F.W. Champion. Jour. Bombay Nat. Hist. Soc., vol.33, no.2, pp. 284-287, pls.4, Feb. 15, 1929.

THE REAL COUGAR. W.B. Conger. Nature Mag., Wash., D.C., vol.31, no.8, pp. 491-492, Oct., 1938.

GREAT CATS. (AND THEIR PAINTERS.) Frank Davis. Illus. London News, vol.216, no.5791, p.594, illus., Apr. 15, 1950.

FELIX (sic) VIVERRINA. H.C. Delsman. Tropische Natuur, Buitenzorg, vol.21, no.11, p.209, Nov., 1932.

(NEW DATA ON THE DESERT CAT FELIS MARGARITA LOCHE.) Nouvelles données sur le chat désertique Felis margarita Loche. G.P. Dementiev. Mammalia, Paris, vol.20, no.3, pp.217-222, Sep., 1956.

NEIGHBORS IN NATURE. (Ocelot, jaguarondi.) Georgia B. Dittoe. San Diego Zoonooz, vol. 18, no.2, pp.5, 6, illus., Feb., 1945.

KING CHEETAH. (Acinonyx rex.) J. G. Dollman. Nat. Hist. Mag., London, vol.2, no. 9, pp.1-6, illus., Jan., 1929.

PERSIAN TIGER AND SOUTH AFRICAN LEOPARD. (Felis tigris virgata.) J.G. Dollman. Nat. Hist. Mag., London, vol.1, no. 5, pp.162-166, illus., Jan., 1928.

SNOW-LEOPARD OR OUNCE. J.G. Dollman. Nat. Hist. Mag., London, vol.1, no. 6, pp.177-178, illus., Apr., 1928.

RACING CHEETAHS: THE GREYHOUNDS OF THE EAST. K.C. Gandar Dower. Indian Wild Life, Lucknow, vol.3, no.2, pp.62-65, Apr.-May-June, 1938.

PANTHER OF THE HEARTH. Frederick B. Eddy. Nat. Geogr. Mag., Washington, vol. 74, no.5, pp.589-634, illus., Nov., 1938. (Including 25 col. photographs by W.R. Culver.)

MONOGRAPH OF THE FELIDAE OR FAMILY OF THE CATS. Danial G. Elliot. Pls. 43, 1883.

ON FELIS PARDINOIDES, J.E. GRAY. Daniel G. Elliot. Proc. Zool. Soc. London, p.203, 1872.

CATS AND ALL ABOUT THEM. L.H. Fairchild. Orang Judd Publ. Co., New York, pp. 243, illus., 1947; 1948 (Revised edition).

(SOME TIGER-LIKE CHARACTERISTICS IN FELIS SPELAEA GOLDF.) Quelques caractères de tigre chez le Felis spelaea Goldf. V. Ferrant, M. Friant. Bull. Mus. Nat. Hist. Nat., Paris, ser.2, vol.11, no.6, pp.508-512, figs.5, Dec., 1939.

THE DOMESTIC CAT. BIRD KILLER, MOUSER AND DESTROYER OF WILD LIFE. MEANS OF UTILIZING AND CONTROLLING IT. Edward Howe Forbush. Mass. State Board Agric. Econ. Biol. Bull., no.2, pp.112, pls.20, illus., 1916.

NOTES ON PANTHERS. E. Brook Fox. Jour. Bombay Nat. Hist. Soc., vol.27, pp.394-397, Dec. 20, 1920.

NOTES ON THE CLOUDED LEOPARD (NEOFELIS NEBULOSA (GRIFFITH).) C.A. Gibson-Hill. Jour. Bombay Nat. Hist. Soc., vol.49, no.3, pp.543-546, Dec., 1950.

THE JAGUAR. E.A. Goldman. (In) North American Big Game. A Book of the Boone and Crocket Club, Compiled by the Committee on Records of North American Big Game. Charles Scribners Sons, New York, pp.421-426, 1939.

THE PUMA. E.A. Godlman. (In) North American Big Game. A Book of the Boone and Crocket Club, Compiled by the Committee on Records of North American Big Game. Charles Scribners Sons, New York, pp.407-414, 1939.

LIONS--THE PROUD, BIG CATS. George G. Goodwin. Animal Kingdom, New York Zool. Soc., vol.56, no.4, pp.119-125, illus., July-Aug., 1953.

WHEN THE LIONS HELPED OUT. Harold T. Green. Frontiers, Lancaster, vol.12, no.3, pp.77-79, 95, 97, illus., Feb., 1948.

STARS IN STRIPES FOREVER. (Tigers) Edalee Harwell. Zoonooz, Zool. Soc. San Diego, vol.25, no.4, pp.2-4, illus., Apr., 1952.

PRELIMINARY STUDY OF THE MOUNTAIN LION (FELIS COUGAR). Frank C. Hibben. MS thesis, Univ. N. Mex., 1936.

THE LION, KING OF BEASTS. John Eric Hill. Nat. Hist., New York, vol.49, no.3, p.155, illus., Mar., 1942.

(FROM THE LIFE OF THE FEARED "STRIPED ONE.") (Tiger.) Uit het leven van den govreesden "Gestreepte." A. Hoogerwerf. Tropische Natuur, Jaarg.28, no.1, pp. 12, figs.6, Nov., 1938.

OUR WORLD CATS. Carra E. Horsfall. Nature Mag., vol.12, pp.353-354, col. illus., Dec., 1928.

(THE PUMA OR COUGAR.) Le puma or cougard. Emile Housse. La Nature, Paris, no.3021, pp.167-170, Mar. 15, 1938.

SOME WILD CATS. C. M. Ingles. Jour. Bengal Nat. Hist. Soc., Darjeeling, vol.25, no.1, pp.1-6, Oct., 1951.

ON FELIS BADIA GRAY. A.F. Jentink. Notes Leyden Mus., vol.23, no.11, pp. 91-93, Nov., 1901.

(THE IMPORTANCE OF THE CARACAL.) Die Bedeutung der Karakul. H. Juhe, J. Langlet. Zeitschr. f. Schafzucht, Hanover, pp.189-205, 213, 1938.

(A MID-AGE REPORT ON THE ZIBET CAT.) Ein mittelalterlicher Bericht ueber die Zibethkatze. S. Killermann. Zeitschr. f. Saeugetierk., vol.6, no.6, pp.235-236, Dec.15, 1931.

WILD AND DOMESTIC CAT COMPARED. John C. Kirk. Scottish Naturalist, Edinburgh, no.216, pp.161-169, figs.3, Nov.-Dec., 1935.

(ESSAY ON THE NATURAL HISTORY OF THE LYNX.) Essai sur l'Histoire Naturelle du Lynx. Louis Lavauden. Bull. Soc. Sci. du Dauphiné, Grenoble, vol.50, pp.108, pls. 6, 1930.

(SOME STUDIES PERTAINING TO THE LYNX.) Några lodjursstudier. (Felis.) Einar Lönnberg. Fauna och Flora, Uppsala, Heft 3, pp.97-104, figs.3, 1940.

AN UNUSUAL TIGER. A.C. Lothian. Jour. Bombay Nat. Hist. Soc., vol.37, no.2, pp. 479-482, Aug. 15, 1934.

NOTES ON PANTHERS. A.G. McArthur. Jour. Bombay Nat. Hist. Soc., vol.27, p.935, July 31, 1921.

HISTORY OF THE LYNX. Colin Matheson. Jour. Soc. Preserv. Fauna Empire, Hertford, pt.58, pp.18-27, Dec., 1947.

(GEOGRAPHICAL DISTRIBUTION OF CATS AND THEIR RELATIONSHIP.) Die geographische Verbreitung der Katzen und ihre Verwandtschaft untereinander. Paul Matschie. Sitz. Ber. Gesell. Naturf. Freunde Berlin, Jahrg.1895, no.10, pp.190-199, Dec. 17, 1905; Bol. Mus. Nac. Rio de Janeiro, vol.4, no.2, pp.49-56, June, 1928. (In Portuguese.)

(ON FELIS NIGRIPES BURCH.) Ueber Felis nigripes Burch. Paul Matschie. Sitz. Ber. Gesell. Naturf. Freunde Berlin, no.10, pp.258-259, Dec. 13, 1894.

THE OCELOT CATS. Edgar A. Mearns. Proc. U.S. Nat. Mus., Wash., D.C., vol. 25, no.1286, pp.237-249, Sep.14, 1902.

SCIENCE AND THE MYSTERY OF THE CAT. I.M. Mellen. New York, pp.275, illus.40, 1949.

THE CAT. AN INTRODUCTION TO THE STUDY OF BACKBONED ANIMALS, ESPECIALLY MAMMALS. St. George Mivart. New York, pp.557, illus.200, 1881.

TALE OF FIVE TIGERS. R.C. Morris. Jour. Bombay Nat. Hist. Soc., vol.35, no.2, pp.405-408, Oct. 15, 1931.

PANTHER AS I HAVE KNOWN HIM. PTS. 3-4. A.H.E. Mosse. Jour. Bombay Nat. Hist. Soc., vol.34, no.3, pp.673-693, Nov. 15, 1930; no.4, 1015-1023, Mar. 2, 1931.

CATS, GOOD AND BAD. William F. Munch. Conservation Volunteer, St. Paul, vol.4, no.21, pp.51-53, June, 1942.

QUESTIONNAIRE ON THE LION (PANTHERA LEO). T.G. Nel. Bull.Nat.Parks Union S. Africa, Pretoria, no.1, p.2, 1951.

(A FEMALE TIGER.) Ein weiber Tiger. Hans Petzsch. Zeitschr. f. Saeugetierk., vol.8, no.6, p.280, Dec. 20, 1933.

BLACK LEOPARDS. R.M. Pizey. Jour. Bombay Nat. Hist. Soc., vol.36, no.1, pp.236-237, Nov. 15, 1932.

CATALOGUE OF THE GENUS FELIS. R.I. Pocock. British Mus., Nat.Hist., London, pp.vii+190, illus., Mar., 1951.

NOTE ON THE SPOTTED LION OF THE ABERDARES. R.I. Pocock. Appendix to "The Spotted Lion," by K.Gandar Dower, publ.by Little, Browne and Co., Boston, Mass., pp.331 (pp.317-321), 1937.

ON PALLAS'S CAT. R.I. Pocock. Proc. Zool. Soc. London, pp.299-306, figs.87-89, Aug. 1, 1907.

TIGERS. R.I. Pocock. Jour. Bombay Nat. Hist. Soc., vol.33, no.3, pp.505-541, col.pl.1, black and white pls.12, May 31, 1929.

SOME FACTS ABOUT THE LION. Pondoro. Field, London, vol.154, no.4008, p.581, Oct. 19, 1929.

PREDATORY ANIMALS--THE MOUNTAIN LION. Charles G. Poole. Pacific Sportsman, vol.2, no.5, pp.7, 34, May, 1926.

SAVAGE FURY. (Snow Leopard.) George H. Pournelle. Zoonooz, Zool. Soc. San Diego, vol.29, no.8, pp.1-4, illus., Aug., 1956.

MY ADVENTURES WITH A TIGRESS. A.V. Pullan. Jour. Bengal Nat. Hist. Soc. Darjeeling, vol.15, no.1, pp.8-10, pls.3, June, 1940.

THE LION. J.W. Rees. Indian Wild Life, Agra, vol.3, no.4, pp.208-212, Oct.-Dec., 1938.

TWO EXPERIENCES WITH PANTHER. L.F. Rusby. Jour. Bombay Nat. Hist. Soc., vol. 36, no.3, pp.743-744, Aug. 15, 1933.

BLACK-OUTS. (Black Leopard.) Jacqueline Schermerhorn. San Diego Zoonooz, vol.18, no.6, pp.6-7, illus., June, 1945.

(PHYLOGENY, KNOWLEDGE OF RACES, AND BREADING SYSTEM IN RELATION TO THE DOMESTIC CATS.) Stammesgeschichte, Rassenkunde, und Zuchtsystem der Hauskatzen. F. Schwangart. Verlag Heber and Co., Leipzig, pp.59, illus., 1929.

(SPECIES OF DOMESTICABLE SMALL CATS.) Domestizierbare Kleinkatzenarten. F. Schwangart. Kleintier u. Pelztier, Leipzig, vol.9, no.7, pp.121-125, figs.12, July 15, 1933.

NOTE ON A SECOND SPECIMENS OF FELIS LANEA. Philip Lutley Sclater. Proc. Zool. Soc. London, pp.655-656, 1878.

BLACK PANTHERS. Ram Singh. Jour. Bombay Nat. Hist. Soc., vol.43, no.3, p.519, Dec., 1942.

WINE-BIBBING PANTHER--AND OTHERS. Ram Singh. Jour. Bombay Nat. Hist. Soc., vol.43, no.3, pp.520-521, Dec., 1942.

CAVE TIGER OF AMOY. W.C.Smith. Nat. Hist., vol.28, no.4, pp.430-438, 1928.

FRUSTRATED BOBCAT. William Stevenson. Yosemite Nat. Notes, Yosemite, vol.23, no.4, pp.43-44, Apr., 1944.

AN INTERESTING PANTHER INCIDENT. C.H. Stockley. Jour. Bombay Nat. Hist. Soc., vol.28, pp.535-536, Mar. 25, 1922.

CATS, LARGE AND SMALL. Ken Stott, Jr. Zoonooz, San Diego Zool. Soc., vol.12, no.7, pp.1-4, July, 1940.

DRAMA IN THE GRASSLANDS. (Leopard.) Hugh Thomason. Fauna, Philadelphia, vol. 7, no.4, pp.99-103, illus., Dec., 1945.

UNKNOWN VISITOR TO A LEOPARD CARCASE. C.H. Tresham. Jour. Bombay Nat. Hist. Soc., vol.42, no.3, pp.656-657, illus., Aug., 1941.

UNUSUAL FIND IN A TIGER'S SKULL. Van Ingen. Jour. Bombay Nat. Hist. Soc., vol.33, no.1, pp.195-196, fig.1, Sep.30, 1928.

THE CAT. F.E.Zeuner. Oryx, Hertford, vol. 1, no.2, pp.65-71, 1951.

THE CAT FAMILY. Nat. Nature News, vol. 2, no.19, pp.3-5, May 9, 1938.

MOUNTAIN LION FELIS CONCOLOR HIPPOLESTES. Wyoming Wild Life, Cheyenne, vol.5, no.1, pp.6, 13, illus., Jan., 1940.

PURRING PUMA. Our Dumb Animals, Norwood, vol.78, no.8, p.150, illus., Aug., 1945.

TRIUMPHANT PANTHER. (Black Leopard) Life, New York, vol.27, no.6, p.29, Aug. 8, 1949.

Africa

(ON FELIS AURATA TEMM., A PECULIAR WEST AFRICAN CAT SPECIES.) Ueber Felis aurata Temm., eine eigenartige westafrikanische Katzenart. F. Baumann. Mitt. Natur. Ges. Bern, vol.8, pp.1-6, 1923.

(THE GOLDEN CATS OF AFRICA AND ASIA.) Les chats dorés d'Afrique et d'Asie. E. Bourdelle. Sommaire Séances Soc. Compte Rendu Biogeogr., Paris, 9me Année, no.78, pp.66-70, (Assemblée générale Dec. 16, 1932) 1933.

(NOTE ON A PARTICULAR FORM OF FELID FROM THE KIVU REGION.) Note sur une forme particulière de Félidé de la Région du Kivu (Felis aurata Temminck= Profelis aurata Pocock). E. Bourdelle. Bull. Mus. Nat. Hist. Nat., Paris, ser.2, vol. 3, no.3, pp.294-297, Mar., 1931.

(MORE ON THE AFRICAN LEOPARDS.) Más sobre los leopardos Africanos. Angel Cabrera. Bol. Real Soc. Española Hist. Nat., Madrid, vol.28, no.1, pp.79-94, Jan., 1928.

RHODESIAN CHEETAH. Abel Chapman. Field, London, vol.151, p.654, Apr. 19, 1928.

(CONSIDERATIONS ON THE CATS OF WESTERN AFRICA.) Considerations sur les chats (Felis libyca Forster) de l'Afrique occidentale. P.L. Dekeyser. Bull. Institut Français d'Afrique Noire, vol.12, no.3, pp. 700-709, July, 1950.

(ON THE CATS OF FRENCH BLACK AFRICA.) A propos des chats de l'Afrique Noire Française. P.L. Dekeyser. Mammalia, Paris, vol.9, no.2, pp.51-60, June, 1945.

(NOTE ON THE WILD CATS OF SOUTHERN TUGO.) Note sur les chats sauvages (Felis lybica Forster) du Sud-Tugo. Jean Dorst. Bull. Mus. Nat. Hist. Nat., Paris, ser.2, vol.22, no.2, pp.204-208, Mar., 1950.

CHEETAHS ON THE UGANDA RAILWAY. E. Holloway, Jour. East Africa and Uganda Nat. Hist. Soc., no.16, pp.58-59, Feb., 1921.

THE LION, PROWLER OF THE VELDT. Hartley H.T. Jackson. Home Geogr. Monthly, vol.2, no.4, pp.19-23, illus., Oct., 1932.

(NORTHERN AFRICA MAMMALOGICAL NOTES. THE CATS.) Notes de mammalogie nord-africaine. Les Chats. L. Lavauden. Bull. Soc. d'Hist. Nat. l'Afrique, Nord, vol.19, pp.255-262, 1928.

MUMMIFIED CATS OF ANCIENT EGYPT. T.C.S. Morrison-Scott. Proc. Zool. Soc. London, vol.121, pt.4, pp.861-867, Feb. 8, 1952.

PRELIMINARY SURVEY OF LIONS (PANTHERA LEO) IN THE PRETORIUS KOP AREA OF THE KRUGER NATIONAL PARK. T.G. Nel. Bull. Nat. Parks Union of S. Africa, Pretoria, no.7, pp.8, tbls.2, map, 1951. (Mimeographed.)

LEOPARDS OF AFRICA. R.I. Pocock. Proc. Zool. Soc. London, no.347, p.33, Apr. 26, 1932 (Abstr.); pt.2, pp.543-591, pls. 1-4, figs.1-9, July, 1932.

NOTES UPON SOME AFRICAN SPECIES OF THE GENUS FELIS, BASED UPON SPECIMENS RECENTLY EXHIBITED IN THE SOCIETY'S GARDENS. R.I. Pocock. Proc. Zool. Soc. London, pp.656-677, pl. 38, Oct. 8, 1907.

ALGERIAN SAND CAT (FELIS MARGARITA LOCHE). R.I. Pocock. Proc. Zool. Soc. London, vol.108, pp.41-46, fig.1, pl.1, Apr., 1938.

WILD CAT (FELIS LYBICA) OF NORTHERN BENGUELLA, ANGOLA. R.I. Pocock. Ann. and Mag. Nat. Hist., London, ser.11, vol. 11, no.74, pp.130-133, Feb., 1944.

RACES OF THE NORTH AFRICAN WILD CAT (FELIS LYBICA). R.I. Pocock. Proc. Zool. Soc. London, vol.114, pts.1-2, pp.65-73, Aug., 1944.

THREE RACES, ONE NEW, OF THE SERVAL (LEPTAILURUS) FROM NORTH AFRICA. R.I. Pocock. Ann. and Mag. Nat. Hist., London, ser.11, vol.11, no.82, pp.690-698, figs.2, Oct., 1944.

SOUTH AFRICAN RACES OF THE WILD CAT (FELIS LYBICA). R.I. Pocock. Proc. Zool. Soc. London, vol.114, pp.297-301, fig.1, pt.3, Dec., 1944.

(A BLACK LEOPARD.) Un léopard noir. H. Schouteden. Rev. Zool. et Bot. Africaines, vol.12, nos.3-4, pp.72-74, figs.2, Dec. 5, 1935.

TRANSVAAL RACE OF THE COMMON SOUTH AFRICAN WILD CAT. Oldfield Thomas. Ann. and Mag. Nat. Hist., ser. 10, vol.1, pp.318-319, Feb., 1928.

(LAST BERBER LIONS AND OTHER LARGE CATS.) Von den letzten Berberloewen und anderen Grosskatzen. F. Werner. Zool.Gartne, Leipzig, n.F., vol.10, nos.5-6, pp. 224-227, Jan., 1939.

(INTERESTING CATS OF EAST AFRICA.) Interessante Katze aus Ostafrika. Heinrich Wolf. Zeitschr. f. Saeugetierk., vol.11, no.3, p.274, Dec. 30, 1936.

WILD LIONS AT NAIROBI, BRITISH EAST AFRICA. Illus. London News, vol.216, no. 5792, p.619, illus., Apr. 22, 1950.

BLACK LEOPARDS. (Abyssinia.) Jour. E. Africa Nat. Hist. Soc., Nairobi, vol.16, nos.4-5 (73-74), pp.223-224, June, 1942.

Anatomy

DIGITAL ABNORMALITIES IN A CAT. Yoshio Abe. Jour.Sci.Hiroshima Univ., ser.B, vol.15, div.1, pp.189-191, illus., Dec., 1954.

NOTE ON A PECULIAR PANCREATIC BLADDER IN THE CAT. Cora Jipson Beckwith. Anat. Rec., vol.18, no.4, pp.363-367, May 20 (June), 1920.

BLOOD VESSELS OF THE ADRENAL GLAND OF THE ADULT CAT. H. Stanley Bennet, Lawrence Kilham. Anat. Rec., Philadelphia, vol.77, no.4, pp.447-471, figs.3, pls.4, Aug. 26, 1940.

LABORATORY ANATOMY OF THE CAT. Ernest S. Booth. Published by the author, College Place, Washington, pp.58, figs. 56, 1944.

A TAIL-LESS PANTHER. D. Ramsay Brown. Jour. Bombay Nat. Hist. Soc., vol.41, no.4, pp.890-891, fig.1, Aug., 1940.

THE 'DEW-CLAWS' OF THE HUNTING LEOPARD OR CHEETAH (ACINONYX JUBATUS (SCHREB.)). R.W.Burton. Jour. Bombay Nat. Hist. Soc., vol.49, no.3, pp.541-543, Dec., 1950.

ON THE RELATIVE FREQUENCY OF VARIANT TYPES OF THE CAVA POSTERIOR IN THE CAT. E.G. Butler et al. Anat. Rec., Philadelphia, vol.94, no.1, pp.93-103, fig. 1, Jan., 1946.

CLAWS OF THE CHEETAH; RETRACTILE WHEN YOUNG. Major A.L. Cooper. Field, London, vol.155, no.4020, p.44, Jan. 11, 1930.

CAROTID CIRCULATION IN THE DOMESTIC CAT. D. Dwight Davis, H.Elizabeth Story. Zool. Ser., Field Mus. Nat. Hist., Chicago, vol.28, no.1, publ.527, pp.1-47, figs.9, Mar. 25, 1943.

MAMMALIAN ANATOMY, WITH SPECIAL REFERENCE TO THE CAT. Alvin Davison. 4th ed., rev. by Frank A. Stromsten. P. Blakiston's Son and Co., Philadelphia, pp. xi+286, illus.123, 1927; 7th ed., pp.xi+ 349, illus.187, figs.92, 1947.

DEVELOPMENT AND MORPHOLOGY OF THE CORPUS LUTEUM OF THE CAT. Alden B. Dawson. Anat. Rec., Philadelphia, vol.79, no.2, suppl.no.1, pp.155-177, pls. 4, Feb., 1941.

POST PARTUM HISTORY OF THE CORPUS LUTEUM OF THE CAT. Alden B.Dawson. Anat. Rec., Philadelphia, vol.95, no.1, pp.29-51, pls.1-3, May, 1946.

SOME EVIDENCE OF SPECIFIC SECRETORY ACTIVITY OF THE ANTERIOR PITUITARY GLAND OF THE CAT. Alden B. Dawson. Amer. Jour. Anat., Philadelphia, vol.78, no.3, pp.347-409, pls.1-4, May, 1946.

PREIMPLANTATION CHANGES IN THE UTERINE MUCOSA OF THE CAT. Alden B. Dawson, Betty Ann Kosters. Amer.Jour. Anat., Philadelphia, vol.75, no.1, pp.1-37, pls.1-5, July, 1944.

LATE DEVELOPMENT OF THE THYMUS IN THE CAT: NATURE AND SIGNIFICANCE OF THE CORPUSCLES OF HASSELL AND CYSTIC FORMATIONS. O.A. Dearth. Amer. Jour. Anat., vol.41, pp.321-351, illus., May 15, 1928.

AN ATLAS OF CAT ANATOMY. Hazel E. Field, Mary E. Taylor. Univ. Chicago Press, pp.75, illus., 1949.

AN HERMAPHRODITE TIGER. C.Fraser. Jour. Bombay Nat. Hist. Soc., vol.43, no. 1, p.99, Apr., 1942.

AMPULLA OF VATER AND THE PANCREATIC DUCTS IN THE DOMESTIC CAT (FELIS DOMESTICA). Simon H. Gage. Amer. Quart. Microscop. Jour., New York, vol.1, pp.1-20, pls.12-14, 1878.

ORIGIN AND DEVELOPMENT OF THE EXTRINSIC OCULAR MUSCLES IN THE DOMESTIC CAT. Perry W. Gilbert. Jour. Morphology, Philadelphia, vol.81, no.2, pp.151-193, pls.1-8, Sep., 1947.

EPITHELIAL CELL SHAPES IN THE FIRST SEGMENT OF THE PROXIMAL TUBULE OF THE CAT NEPHRON, AS DEMONSTRATED BY CHROMESOMESILVER METHOD. Allan L. Grafflin, John J. Foote.Amer. Jour. Anat., Philadelphia, vol.65, no.2, pp. 179-198, pls.3, Sep. 15, 1939.

APLASIA OF THE UMBILICAL CORD.(Cat embryo.) Peter Gruenwald. Jour. Morphol., Philadelphia, vol.73, no.1, pp.103-109, illus., July, 1943.

DEVELOPMENT OF THE AORTIC ARCH BODIES IN THE CAT. Warner S. Hammond. Amer. Jour. Anat., Philadelphia, vol.69, no.2, pp.265-294, illus., Sep. 15, 1941.

SUPRARENALS OF THE LARGER FELIDAE. W.C.O. Hill. Jour. Anat., Cambridge, vol. 72, pt.1, pp.71-82, figs.2, tbls.4, pl.1, Oct., 1937.

CYTOLOGICAL STUDY OF THE CAROTID BODY OF THE CAT. W. Henry Hollinshead. Amer. Jour. Anat., Philadelphia, vol.73, no.2, pp.185-213, pl.1, Sep., 1943.

ATLAS OF CAT ANATOMY. David B.Horsburgh, James P. Heath. Stanford Univ. Press, pp.39, quarto, board covers, no text, 1938.

CASE OF ABNORMALITY IN CATS' PAWS. Freeland Howe, Jr. Amer.Nat., vol.36, no. 427, pp.511-526, figs.1-18, July, 1902.

DEVELOPMENT OF THE VEINS IN THE DOMESTIC CAT (FELIS DOMESTICA) WITH ESPECIAL REFERENCE, (1) TO THE SHARE TAKEN BY THE SUPRACARDINAL VEINS IN THE DEVELOPMENT OF THE POSTCAVA AND AZYGOS VEINS AND (2) TO THE INTERPRETATION OF THE VARIANT CONDITIONS OF THE POSTCAVA AND ITS TRIBUTARIES, AS FOUND IN THE ADULT. George S. Huntington, Charles F. W. McClure. Anat.Rec., vol.20, pp.1-30, figs.12, Dec. 20, 1920.

(OBSERVATIONS OF THE ABDOMEN AND THE INTERCOSTAL MUSCULATURE OF THE LION AND DOMESTIC CAT.) Beobachtungen an der Bauch und Zwischenrippenmuskulatur des Loewen und der Hauskatze. M. John. Anat. Anzeiger, vol.65, pp.145-154, figs.4, Apr. 16, 1928.

NOTES ON THE DISSECTION OF A TIGER. Rymer Jones. Proc. Zool. Soc. London, pt.2, pp.54-56, 1834. (Felis tigris, Linn.)

PRACTICAL ANATOMY OF THE DOGFISH, NECTURUS, AND CAT. George C.Kent, Jr. Wm.C. Brown, Publishers, pp.84, 1948.

ON THE SO-CALLED LARYNGEAL TONSILS OF MAMMALS; WITH SPECIAL REFERENCE TO THEIR STRUCTURE AND DEVELOPMENT IN THE CAT. B.F.Kingsbury. Amer. Jour. Anat., Philadelphia, vol. 72, no.2, pp.171-197, pls.1-3, Mar., 1943.

LYMPHATIC TISSUE AND REGRESSIVE STRUCTURE, WITH PARTICULAR REFERENCE TO DEGENERATION OF GLANDS. (In the Cat.) B.F. Kingsbury. Amer. Jour. Anat., Philadelphia, vol.77, no.2, pp.159-187, pls.1-4, Sep., 1945.

TONSILLAR EPITHELIUM AND THE LYMPHOCYTE: AN EXAMINATION OF THE PALATINE TONSILE OF THE CAT. B. F. Kingsbury. Amer. Jour. Anat., Philadelphia, vol.75, no.2, pp.233-261, pls.1-3, Sep., 1944.

(DEVELOPMENT, STRUCTURE, AND BIOLOGICAL SIGNIFICANCE OF THE ANAL GLANDS IN THE DOMESTIC CAT.) Entwicklung, Bau und biologische Bedeutung der Analbeuteldruesen bei der Hauskatze. O. Kroelling. Zeitschr. f. Anat. u. Entwicklungsgesch., vol.82, pp.22-69, Jan. 27, 1927.

FUNCTIONAL ANATOMY OF THE MAMMAL. A GUIDE TO THE DISSECTION OF THE CAT AND AN INTRODUCTION TO THE STRUCTURAL AND FUNCTIONAL RELATIONSHIP BETWEEN THE CAT AND MAN. William James Leach. 2nd ed., New York, McGraw-Hill, pp.276, illus., 1952.

SEASONAL AND SEXUAL VARIATION IN THE THYROID GLANDS OF CATS. E. Lowe. Quart. Jour. Micr. Sci., vol.73, pp.577-592, pls.2, May, 1930.

ANOMALY IN THE HEPATIC PORTAL SYSTEM OF THE CAT. Joyce M.McChesney, Hobart M. Smith. Ward's Nat. Sci. Bull., Rochester, vol.18, no.2, p.1, Dec., 1944.

(OBSERVATIONS ON THE ABDOMINAL AND INTERCOSTAL MUSCULATURE OF LIONS AND THE DOMESTIC CAT.) Beobachtungen auf der Bauch- und Zwischenrippenmusculatur der Loewen und der Hauskatze. John Manfred. Anat. Anzeiger, vol.65, pp.145-154, text figs.4, 1928.

NOTES OF THE DISSECTION OF A PUMA (FELIS CONCOLOR LINN.). W. Martin. Proc. Zool. Soc. London, pt.1, pp.120-121, 1833.

ON THE ANATOMY OF THE JAGUAR (FELIS ONCA, L.). W. Martin. Proc.Comm., Sci. and Corres. Zool. Soc. London, pt.2, p.7, 1832.

(THE CHROMOSOME FORMULA OF THE DOMESTIC CAT.) La formule chromosomiale du Chat domestique. R. Matthey. Comptes Rendus Soc. Biol., Paris, vol.117, pp.435-436, 1934.

GLANDS IN THE EXTERNAL AUDITORY MEATUS OF THE CAT. William Montagna. Jour. Morphol., Philadelphia, vol.85, no. 3, pp.423-442, pls.2, Nov., 1949.

COMPARATIVE STUDY OF THE MUCOUS MEMBRANES IN THE ORAL CAVITY OF THE CAT. Earl A. Morgan. Wasmann Collector, San Francisco, vol.6, no.1, pp. 1-12, pls.1-3, Apr., 1944.

(ON THE DEVELOPMENT AND FINER STRUCTURE OF THE TAPETUM LUCIDUM OF FELIDAE.) Ueber die Entwicklung und den feineren Bau des Tapetum lucidum der Feliden. E. Murr. Zeitschr. f. Zellforschung u. Mikr. Anat., vol.6, pp.315-336, pl.1, figs.10, Oct. 26, 1927.

ON THE ANATOMY OF THE CHEETAH (FELIS JUBATA, SCHREB.). R. Owen. Proc. Zool. Soc. London, pt.1, p.108, 1833.

AN ABNORMALITY OF THE VENOUS SYSTEM OF THE CAT, WITH SOME CONSIDERATIONS REGARDING ADAPTATION IN TERATOLOGICAL DEVELOPMENT. Raymond Pearl. Archiv. f. Entwicklungsmechanik Organismen, vol.25, no.4, pp. 648-654, May 19, 1908.

ON THE STRUCTURES ON THE HARD PALATE OF FELIS TIGRIS. Chi Ping. Proc. Zool. Soc. London, pt.1, pp.135-139, Apr.6, 1927.

ON THE EXTERNAL CHARACTERS OF THE FELIDAE. R.I. Pocock. Ann. and Mag. Nat. Hist., ser.8, vol.19, pp.113-136, figs.12, Jan., 1917.

ON THE HYOIDEAN APPARATUS OF THE LION (FELIS LEO) AND RELATED SPECIES OF FELIDAE. R.I. Pocock. Ann. and Mag. Nat. Hist., London, ser.8, vol.18, pp.222-229, figs.2, Aug., 1916.

PANTHER WITH ABNORMAL FEET. S.H. Prater. Jour. Bombay Nat. Hist. Soc., vol. 40, no.2, p.321, Sep., 1938.

BREGMATIC FONTANELLE BONES IN THE GENUS LYNX. Loring W. Pratt. Jour. Mamm., vol.23, no.4, pp.411-416, pls. 2, Nov. 14, 1942.

ANATOMY OF THE CAT. J.E.Reighard, H.S. Jenings. 2nd ed., rev., New York, H. Holt and Co., pp.xx+429, 473-498, illus., 1923.

ANATOMICAL STRUCTURE OF THE CEREBRUM IN FELIS CONCOLOR. T.V.Sakharov. Proc. Moscow Zool. Parks, vol.1, pp.64-69, 1940. (In Russian with English summary.)

PRECAVAL ANOMALIES OF THE CAT. J.M. Sanders. Trans. Illinois State Acad. Sci., Springfield, vol.35, no.2, p.216, Dec., 1942.

(MUSCLES OF THE UPPER EXTREMITY OF AN 18-YEAR-OLD LIONESS.) Die Muskeln der oberen Extremitaet einer 18-jaehrigen Loewin. B. Scharlau. Zeitschr.f. Anat. u. Entwicklungsgeschichte, vol.77, pp.187-211, figs.6, Aug. 20, 1925.

(FISSURATION OF THE CORTEX CEREBRI IN AN 18-YEAR-OLD TIGRESS.) Die Furchung der Grosshirnrinde bei einer 18 jaehrigen Tigerin. H. Schewior. Zeitschr. f. Anat. u. Entwicklungsgeschichte, vol.88, pp.469-499, figs.8, 1929.

BLOOD SUPPLY AND INNERVATION OF THE CHOLEDOCHODUODENAL JUNCTION IN THE CAT. John W. Schulze, Edward A. Boyden. Anat. Rec., Philadelphia, vol.86, no.1, pp.15-39, pls.3, figs.4, May, 1943.

ANOMALY IN THE CAT.(Diaphragmatic hernia.) Fae M. Shawhan. Proc. Iowa Acad. Sci., Des Moines, vol.49, pp.523-524, Sep., 1942.

CASE OF HORSESHOE KIDNEY AND ASSOCIATED VASCULAR ANOMALIES IN THE DOMESTIC CAT. H. Elizabeth Story. Anat. Rec., Philadelphia, vol.86, no.3, pp.307-319, figs.3, July, 1943.

SOFT PALATE IN THE DOMESTIC CAT. T.B. Stowell. Proc. Amer. Soc.Microscopists, Columbus, Ohio, vol.10, pp.19, fig.1, 1888.

GUSTATORY ORGANS OF VULPES VULGARIS. Frederick Tuckerman. Jour.Anat. and Physiol., vol.23, pp.201-205, 1889.

(MECHANICS OF TIGER TOES.) Mechanic der Tigerzehen. Hans Virshow. Zeitschr. f. Saeugetierk., vol.1, nos.1-2, pp.64-90, figs.8, pls.3-4, Aug.31 and Dec.24, 1926.

CASE OF AN INCOMPLETE PERICARDIAL CAVITY IN THE CAT. Warren F. Walker, Jules E. Zessman. Anat. Rec., Philadelphia, vol.113, no.4, pp. 459-466, illus., Aug., 1952.

LETTER FROM, ON THE DISSECTION OF FELIS LEO. Anthony White. Proc. Zool. Soc. London, pt.12, p.54, 1844.

ANATOMICAL TECHNOLOGY AS APPLIED TO THE DOMESTIC CAT. AN INTRODUCTION TO HUMAN, VETERINARY, AND COMPARATIVE ANATOMY. B.G. Wilder, S.H. Gage. New York and Chicago, A.S. Barnes and Co., pp.vi+585, illus., pls.4, 1886.

BRAIN OF THE CAT. B.G. Wilder. Proc. Amer. Philos. Soc., Philadelphia, vol.19, no.109, pp.524-562, pls.4, Dec.6, 1881.

ON THE BRAIN OF A CAT LACKING THE CALLOSUM-PRELIMINARY NOTICE.B.G. Wilder. Amer. Jour. Neurology and Psychiatry, New York, pp.1-10, figs.4, Aug., 1883.

HISTOCHEMICAL REACTIONS IN THE PLACENTA OF THE CAT. George B. Wislocki, Edward W. Dempsey. Amer. Jour. Anat., Philadelphia, vol.78, no.1, pp.1-45, pls.1-4, Jan., 1946.

CATS WITH ABNORMALLY ARRANGED VISCERA. Harold E. Wolfe. Trans.Wisc. Acad. Sci., Arts and Letters, Madison, vol. 34, pp.99-102, pls.1-5, 1942.

ON THE CLAW OF THE TIP OF THE TAIL OF THE LION (FELIS LEO, L.). H.Woods. Proc. Comm. Sci. and Corres. Zool. Soc. London, pt.2, p.146, 1832.

STUDY OF THE CYTOGENESIS OF CORTICO-ADRENAL CELLS IN THE CAT. R.M. Wotton, R.L. Zwemer. Anat. Rec., Philadelphia, vol.86, no.3, pp.409-416, figs.23, July, 1943.

RANGE OF VARIATION IN THE LEOPARD. Nature, London, vol.132, no.3329, pp.273-274, Aug. 19, 1933.

As Pets

TIGER AS A PET. F.A.Betterton. Field, London, vol.152, p.705, illus., Nov. 1, 1928.

LYNX IN THE HOME. Isabel Harper Blount. Nat. Hist., New York, vol.47, no.2, pp. 102-109, illus., Feb., 1941.

TIGER IN THE PARLOR. Edwin H. Colbert. Frontiers, Philadelphia, vol.4, no.1, pp. 3-6, Oct., 1939.

BABY PANTHERS FOR PLAYMATES. Wm. L.Finley, Irene Finley.Nature Mag., vol.4, pp.5-7, 63, figs.5, July, 1924.

TOM AND BOB. (Two Pet Wildcats.) Wm. L.Finley, Irene Finley.Nature Mag., vol.5, pp.33-36, 63-64, figs.8, pl.1, Jan., 1925.

HAMPSHIRE REGIMENT ADOPTS ZOO TIGER. James Fisher. Field, London, vol. 176, no.4572, p.194, Aug. 10, 1940.

SONG OF SUSAN, OR BRINGING UP A LIONESS IN AN APARTMENT HOUSE. Lucile Quarry Mann. Nature Mag., vol. 17, no.1, pp.41-43, figs.5, Jan., 1931.

COUGAR IN THE HOUSE. Hazel E.Nelson. Nature Mag., Wash., vol.38, no.3, pp. 146-147, 164, illus., Mar., 1945.

TAMING A WILDCAT. C.C. Presnall. Yosemite Nat. Notes, vol.12, no.6, p.61, June, 1933.

SANDINO--A NICARAGUAN PET. (Habits of Ocelot Kept as Pet.) Louis W. Walker. Nature Mag., vol.14, pp.112-113, illus., Aug., 1929.

BOB-CAT BOARDERS. Hazel E. Wolkenhauer. Nat. Humane Review, Mt.Morris, vol.37, no.5, pp.11, 30, May, 1949.

LIVING WITH LYNXES. Hazel E. Wolkenhauer. Nature Mag., Wash., vol.42, no. 4, pp.176-177, illus., Apr., 1949.

LYNX AS A PET. Hazel E. Wolkenhauer. All-Pets Mag., Fond du Lac, vol.20, no.2, pp.68-70, Feb., 1949.

JUST ONE OF THE FAMILY: A TAME LIONESS, AT HOME. Illus. London News, vol.216, no.5787, p.427, illus., Mar. 18, 1950.

A TIGER IN THE HOUSE. THE EDUCATION OF BLANG, A WAIF FROM THE JUNGLE. Field, London, vol.163, no.4242, p.795, illus., Apr. 14, 1934.

Asia

MAN-EATING LEOPARD OF PUNANAI. R.S. Agar. Loris, Ceylon, vol.1, no.5, pp.268-280, illus., Dec., 1938.

OCCURRENCE OF THE PANTHER IN THE SIND DESERT. Hamid A. Ali.Jour.Bombay Nat. Hist. Soc., vol.35, no.3, p.671, Feb. 15, 1932.

CARACAL (FELIS CARACAL) AND HUNTING LEOPARD (CYNAELURUS JUBATUS) IN MIRZAPUR, U.P. G.O.Allen. Jour. Bombay Nat. Hist. Soc., vol.26, p.1041, Jan. 31, 1920.

MANCHURIAN TIGER. N.A. Baikoff. Special publ. Manchuria Research Soc., Harbin, China, pp.18, col.pl., 1925. (In Russian.)

OCCURRENCE OF TIGER IN SIKKIM.F.M. Bailey. Jour. Bombay Nat. Hist. Soc., vol. 41, no.1, p.166, 1939.

OCCURRENCE OF THE PANTHER (PANTHERA PARDUS LINN.) IN TIBET. R.K.M. Battye. Jour. Bombay Nat. Hist. Soc., vol. 38, no.3, p.609, illus., Apr. 15, 1936.

(REMARKS ON THE PERSIAN LIONS.) Bemerkungen ueber den persischen Loewen. John Becker. Zeitschr. f. Saeugetierk., Berlin, vol.9, nos.1-3, pp.439-440, Dec. 30, 1934.

NOTES ON SOME RECENT AND FOSSIL CATS, CHIEFLY FROM THE MALAY ARCHIPELAGO. L.D. Brongersma. Zool. Mededeel., Leiden, vol.18, nos.1-3, pp. 1-89, pls.11, 1935.

PRESERVATION OF THE WILD LIFE OF INDIA. NO. 5. THE INDIAN LION.Patrick Cadell. Jour. Bombay Nat. Hist. Soc., vol. 37, no.4, suppl., pp.162-166, Apr. 15, 1935.

THE GIR LIONS. Keith Caldwell. Jour.Soc. Preservation Fauna of Empire, Hertford, n.s, pt.34, pp.62-65, Aug., 1938.

OCCURRENCE OF THE LION IN PERSIA. R.N. Champion-Jones. Jour. Bombay Nat. Hist. Soc., vol.45, no.2, p.230, Apr., 1945.

CARACAL IN IRAQ. N.L. Corkhill. Jour. Bombay Nat. Hist. Soc., vol.34, no.1, pp.232-233, photo, Mar. 1, 1930.

ON THE OCCURRENCE OF THE CHEETAH (ACONONYX JUBATUS) IN IRAQ. N. L. Corkill. Jour. Bombay Nat. Hist. Soc., vol. 33, no.3, pp.700-702, photo, May 31, 1929.

THE INDIAN LION (PANTHERA LEO PERSICA). J.C. Daniel. Jour. Bengal Nat. Hist. Soc., vol.28, no.3, pp.81-90, Aug., 1956.

TIGERS IN THE SUNDERBANS. T.V.Dent. Jour. Bombay Nat. Hist. Soc., vol.38, no. 1, p.178, Aug. 15, 1935.

CEYLON LEOPARD, A DISTINCT SUBSPECIES. P.E.P. Deraniyagala. Spolia Zeylanica, vol.28, no.1, pp.115-116, June 25, 1956.

NEW SUBSPECIES OF JUNGLE CAT FROM SOUTH INDIA. P.E.P. Deraniyagala.Spolia Zeylanica, Bull. Nat. Mus. Ceylon, vol. 27, pt.2, p.291, May 25, 1955.

NEW SUBSPECIES OF RUSTY SPOTTED CAT FROM CEYLON. P.E.P.Deraniyagala. Spolia Zeylanica, vol.28, no.1, pp.113-114, June 25, 1956.

YOUNG CHINESE TIGER. J. Guy Dollman. Nat. Hist. Mag., British Mus., vol.2, pp. 81-82, illus., July, 1929.

LEOPARD SHOT NEAR KULING (KIANGSU). John F. Duff. China Jour., vol.18, no.2, p.109, Feb., 1933.

BLACK PANTHER SHOT IN SIND. K. R. Eates. Jour. Bombay Nat. Hist. Soc., vol. 44, no.2, pp.291-292, Dec., 1943.

HUNTING LEOPARD (CYNAELURUS JUBATUS) IN KATHIAWAR. L.L. Fenton. Jour.Bombay Nat.Hist.Soc., vol.27, pp. 398-399, Dec. 20, 1920.

DESCRIPTION OF A NEW SPECIES OF CAT (FELIS BADIA) FROM SARAWAK. John Edward Gray. Proc. Zool. Soc. London, pp. 322-323, pl., 1874.

ON THE STEPPE-CAT OF BOKHARA (CHAUS CAUDATUS). John Edward Gray. Proc. Zool. Soc. London, pp.31-33, pls.6-7, Jan. 6, 1874.

(LIVING ARABIAN SAND CATS (FELIS MARGARITA LOCHE 1858).) Lebende arabische Sandkatze, Felis margarita (Loche 1858). Theodor Haltenorth. Saeugetierk. Mitteil., Stuttgart, vol.1, no.2, pp.71-73, illus., Apr. 1, 1953.

CHINESE SMALL SPOTTED TIGER-CAT. FELIS BENGALENSIS CHINENSIS GRAY. G.A.C. Herklots. Hong Kong Nat., vol. 10, no.2, pp.128-130, pls.13-14, May, 1940.

TIGRESS AT TAI PO. G.A.C. Herklots. Hong Kong Naturalist, vol.1, no.1, p.41, Jan., 1930.

NOTE ON A VARIETY OF FELIS RUBIGINOSA FROM CEYLON. E.W.H. Holdsworth. Proc. Zool. Soc. London, pp.756-758, 1871.

(ON JAVAN TIGER CATS.) Ueber javanische Tigerkatzen. Edward Jacobson. Zool. Garten, Leipzig, n.F., vol.6, nos.10-12, pp.238-244, Dec., 1933.

TIGER, ROYAL BEAST OF INDIAN JUNGLE. Hartley H.T. Jackson. Home Geogr., Monthly, vol.2, no.6, pp.19-24, figs.6, Dec., 1932.

PAST AND PRESENT DISTRIBUTION OF THE LION IN SOUTHEASTERN ASIA.N.B.

Kinnear. Jour. Bombay Nat. Hist. Soc., vol. 27, pp.33-39, July 1, 1920.

NOTES ON FORMOSAN FELIS. Nagamichi Kuroda. Dobutsugaku Zasshi, Zool. Soc. Japan, Tokyo, vol.47, pp.240-244, figs.7, Apr. 15, 1935. (In Japanese.)

OCCURRENCE OF TIGER IN NORTHERN SIKKIM. F.H. Lister. Jour. Bombay Nat. Hist. Soc., vol.40, no.3, p.553, Dec., 1938.

THE INDIAN LION. T.R. Livesey. Jour. Bombay Nat. Hist. Soc., vol.28, p.795, June 30, 1922.

NOTES ON SOME CATS FROM EASTERN ASIA WITH DESCRIPTION OF A NEW SUBGENUS. Einar Lönnberg. Arkiv för Zool., Stockholm, vol.18, no.2, pp.1-22, figs.5, pl.1, 1926.

ON A WILD CAT FROM SZE-CHUEN. Richard Lydekker. Proc. Zool. Soc. London, pp.433-434, Oct., 1908.

LEOPARDS FROM VICINITY OF NAGA HILLS. G.H.L. Marshall. Jour. Bombay Nat. Hist. Soc., vol.40, no.4, p.739, May, 1939.

(AN INTERESTING GEOGRAPHICAL VARIETY OF THE TIGER.) Eine interessante geographische Abart des Tigers. Paul Matschie. Sitz. Ber. Gesell. Naturf. Freunde Berlin, no.2, pp.13-17, Feb. 16, 1897.

RECORDS OF SOME CLOUDED LEOPARD (NEOFELIS NEBULOSA) IN THE DARJEELING DISTRICT. W.H. Matthews. Jour. Bombay Nat. Hist. Soc., vol.37, no.4, pp.946-947, illus., Apr. 15, 1935.

ARE THERE MORE THAN ONE SPECIES OF PANTHER IN INDIA? R.C. Morris. Jour. Bombay Nat. Hist. Soc., vol.33, no.3, pp.697-698, May 31, 1929.

DISTRIBUTION OF THE HUNTING LEOPARD (ACINONYX JUBATUS ERXL.) IN SOUTH INDIA. R.C. Morris. Jour. Bombay Nat. Hist. Soc., vol.38, no.2, pp.386-387, Dec. 1, 1935.

FURTHER RECORDS OF THE DISTRIBUTION OF THE CHEETAH (ACINONYX JUBATUS ERXL.) IN SOUTH INDIA. R.C. Morris. Jour. Bombay Nat. Hist. Soc., vol. 38, no.3, p.610, Apr. 15, 1936.

THE CLOUDED LEOPARD IN WESTERN CHINA. Wilfred H. Osgood. Jour. Mamm., vol.16, no.2, pp.148-149, May, 1935.

TIGER IN THE NEW TERRITORIES. (China.) R.A. Pereira. Hong Kong Nat., vol.5, no.4, pp.322-323, Dec., 1934.

LION IN BALUCHISTAN. R.I. Pocock. Jour. Bombay Nat. Hist. Soc., vol.38, no.2, pp. 381-382, Dec. 1, 1935.

LIONS OF ASIA. R.I. Pocock. Jour. Bombay Nat. Hist. Soc., vol.34, no.3, pp.638-665, pls.1-5, map, Nov. 15, 1930.

MARBLED CAT (PARDOFELIS MARMORATA) AND SOME OTHER ORIENTAL SPECIES, WITH THE DEFINITION OF A NEW GENUS OF THE FELIDAE. R.I. Pocock. Proc. Zool. Soc. London, pt.3, pp.741-766, pls., figs. 5, Sep. 10, 1932.

NEW DESERT CAT (FELIS) FROM NORTH CHINA. R.I. Pocock. Proc. Zool. Soc. London, ser.B, vol.113, pp.172-175, pl.1, Nov., 1943.

ON THE SUMATRAN TIGER. R.I. Pocock. Proc. Zool. Soc. London, pp.890-893, Apr., 1909.

PANTHERS AND OUNCES OF ASIA. R.I. Pocock. Jour. Bombay Nat. Hist. Soc., vol.34, no.1, pp.64-82, pls.1-6, Mar. 1, 1930; no.2, pp.307-336, pls.7-13, July 15, 1930. (New: Panthera pardus sindica.)

PANTHERS OF THE NORTH-WEST FRONTIER. R.I. Pocock. Jour. Bombay Nat. Hist. Soc., vol.36, no.2, pp.489-490, Apr. 15, 1933.

PERSIAN PANTHER (P. PARDUS SAXICOLOR) IN BALUCHISTAN. R.I. Pocock. Jour. Bombay Nat. Hist. Soc., vol.35, no.44, p.886, July 15, 1932.

STORY OF THE INDIAN LION. R.I. Pocock. Asiatic Review, pp.1-9, July, 1935.

THE WILD CAT (FELIS LYBICA) OF PALESTINE. R.I. Pocock. Ann. and Mag. Nat. Hist., London, ser.11, vol.11, no.74, pp. 125-130, Feb., 1944.

NUMBER OF TIGERS SHOT IN RESERVED FOREST IN INDIA AND BURMA DURING THE YEAR 1937-1938. S.H. Prater. Jour. Bombay Nat. Hist. Soc., vol.41, no.4, pp. 881-889, Aug., 1940.

ON THE OCCURRENCE OF TIGERS ON THE ISLANDS OF BOMBAY AND SALSETTE. S.H. Prater. Jour. Bombay Nat. Hist. Soc., vol.33, no.4, pp.973-974, Oct. 15, 1929.

HUNTING LEOPARD (CYNAELURUS JUBATUS) IN THE CENTRAL PROVINCES. J.M. Richardson. Jour. Bombay Nat. Hist. Soc., vol.34, no.2, p.235, Mar. 1, 1930.

CLOUDED LEOPARD IN SARAWAK. E.M. Selous, E. Banks. Sarawak Mus. Jour., Kuching, vol.4, no.14, pp.263-266, pl.19, Dec., 1935.

DO LIONS STILL EXIST IN PERSIA? Ronald Sinclair. Jour. Bombay Nat. Hist. Soc., vol. 35, no.3, p.671, Feb. 15, 1932.

ON THE MANELESS LION OF GUZERAT. Capt. W. Smee. Proc. Zool. Soc. London, pt.1, p.140, 1833.

THE TIGER OF JAVA HEAD. William Lord Smith. Nat. Hist., New York, vol.45, no.2, pp.74-79, Feb., 1940.

THE BALINESE TIGER. PANTHERA TIGRIS BALICA (SCHWARZ). H.J.V. Sody. Jour. Bombay Nat. Hist. Soc., vol.36, no.1, pp. 233-234, Nov. 15, 1932.

(THE FISHING CAT (PRIONAILURUS VIVERRINUS BENN.) ON SUMATRA?) Die Fischkatze (Prionailurus viverrinus Benn.) auf Sumatra? H.J.V. Sody. Zool. Garten, Leipzig, n.F., vol.8, nos.4-6, p.141, Jan., 1936.

NEW CAT FROM WEST CHINA. Arthur de C. Sowerby. China Jour. Sci. and Arts, vol. 2, pp.352-353, July, 1924.

THE TIGER IN CHINA. Arthur de C. Sowerby. China Jour., vol.18, no.2, pp.94-101, 108-109, Feb., 1933.

TIGERS AND LEOPARDS IN NORTH CHINA. Arthur de C. Sowerby. China Jour., vol.17, no.4, p.194, fig.1, Oct., 1932.

TIGER! TIGER! ADVENTURES WITH MAN-EATERS IN THE MALAY JUNGLES. J.B.H. Thurston. Nat. Hist., New York, vol.44, no.4, pp.213-216, 244-245, Nov., 1939.

THE LION OF INDIA. Arthur S. Vernay. Nat. Hist., vol.30, no.1, pp.81-89, Jan.-Feb., 1930.

GIR FOREST AND ITS LIONS. M.A. Winter-Blyth. Jour. Bombay Nat. Hist. Soc., vol. 49, no.3, pp.456-470, Dec., 1950.

(THE FOREST CAT OF THE FAR EAST.) Le chat sylvicole de l'extrême orient Felis (Prionailurus) euptilura microtis Milne-Edwards (1868-1874). M.I. Zoubarovsky. Bull. Soc. Nat. Moscow, sect.biol., n.s., vol.48, nos.2-3, pp.75-81, 1939. (In Russian with French summary.)

(THREE NEW SMALL CAT RACES FROM WESTERN ASIA.) Drei neue Kleinkatzenrassen aus Westasien. Ludwig Zukowsky. Archiv. f. Naturgeschichte, Jahrg.80, Abt. A, Heft 10, pp.124-142, pl.1, 1914.

MAN-EATING TIGERS IN MALAYA. Jour. Soc. Preservation Fauna of Empire, Hertfort, n.s., pt.38, pp.25-26, Dec., 1939.

Attacks on Humans

CAT-BITE WOUND INFECTION. A. E. Allin. Canadian Med. Assoc. Jour., pp.1-7, 1942.

THEY'RE NOT ALL MAN-EATERS. (Tiger) W.J. Banks. Fauna, Philadelphia, vol.10, no.2, pp.35-38, illus., June, 1948.

CLOUDED LEOPARD (FELIS NEBULOSA) ATTACKING MAN. A. Brownlow. Jour. Bombay Nat. Hist. Soc., vol.32, pp.789-790, pl.1, May 31, 1928.

MOUNTAIN LION KILLS BOY IN WASHINGTON. H.C. Bryant. Calif. Fish and Game, vol.11, no.2, pp.89-90, Apr., 1925.

MAN-EATING TIGERS ON SAUGUR ISLAND IN THE 18TH CENTURY. R.G. Burton. Jour. Bombay Nat. Hist. Soc., vol.27, pp.385-386, Dec. 20, 1920.

MAN-EATERS OF KUMAON. Jim Corbett. Field and Stream, New York, vol.51, no. 7, pp.23-27, 59-60, 117-118, illus., Nov., 1946; Oxford Univ. Press, New York, pp. xix+235, illus., 1946.

THE MAN-EATING LEOPARD OF RUDRAPRAYAG. Jim Corbett. Oxford Univ. Press, New York, p.188, illus., 1948.

SOME BOBCATS DO ATTACK! (Instances of unprovoked attacks on human beings.) William Curtis. Outdoor Life, New York, vol.101, no.4, p.119, Apr., 1948.

COUGAR KILLS A BOY. William L. Finley. Jour. Mamm., vol.6, no.3, pp.197-199, Aug., 1925.

DRAGGED FROM A TRAIN BY A LION. Cyril Foley. Field, London, vol.161, no. 4195, p.1138, illus., May 20, 1933.

EFFECTS OF MAULING BY TIGER. H.A. Fooks. Jour. Bombay Nat. Hist. Soc., vol. 41, no.1, pp.169-170, 1939.

NOTES ON AN ENCOUNTER WITH A MAN-EATING TIGER. Ulrich Guehler. Jour. Siam Soc., Nat. Hist. Suppl., vol.10, no.2, pp. 171-174, Nov., 1936.

PENICILLIN IN TREATMENT OF WOUNDS INFLICTED BY A LION. Alexander H. Kemp. Jour. Amer. Med. Assoc., Chicago, vol.137, no.1, p.22, May 1, 1948.

MAN-EATING TIGERS. A.P. Kingloch. Jour. Bombay Nat. Hist. Soc., vol.32, p.209, Aug. 1, 1927.

PANTHER SHOOT AT SEA. (Leopard Gets Aboard 60-ton Boat and Attacks Men at Sea.) N. Kirwan. Jour. Bombay Nat. Hist. Soc., vol.31, pp.808-809, photo, Nov. 1, 1926.

RAVAGES BY TIGER AND INCIDENCE OF MAN-EATERS IN NORTH COIMBATORE BETWEEN 1860 AND 1880. R.C. Morris. Jour. Bombay Nat. Hist. Soc., vol.39, no.2, pp.382-385, Apr. 15, 1937.

NOTES ON MAN-EATING TIGERS. Victor N. Narayan. Jour. Bombay Nat. Hist. Soc., vol.28, p.1124, Dec. 20, 1922.

WHERE MAN-EATING TIGERS OCCUR. E. O'Brien. Jour. Bombay Nat. Hist. Soc., vol.45, no.2, pp.231-232, Apr., 1945.

ATTACKED BY A COUGAR? W.H. Osgood. Jour. Mamm., vol.1, no.5, pp.240-241, Nov., 1920.

MAN-EATING LIONS OF TSAVO. J. H. Patterson. Field Mus. Nat. Hist., Zool. Leaflet, no.7, pp.40, pls.4, Nov., 1925.

PUMA ATTACKS CHILD AND MAN. Sam Peterson. Idaho Wildl. Rev., vol.4, no.3, p.15, illus., Jan.-Feb., 1952.

MAN-EATING PANTHER. (Indian Leopard Attacks Man.) C. Twidale. Field, London, vol.152, p.461, Sep. 20, 1928.

WHERE DID THIS REALLY HAPPEN? E.R. Warren. Science, n.s., vol.79, no.2039, p.79, Jan. 26, 1934. (Concerning the Story of a Jaguar Killing Four People.)

THE MAN EATERS OF LANGTING INDIA. H.S. Wood. Jour. Darjeeling Nat. Hist. Soc., vol.5, no.1, pp.8-15, June, 1930.

MAN-EATING TIGERS. H.S. Wood. Jour. Soc. Preservation Fauna Empire, Hertford, n.s., pt.39, pp.44-45, Apr., 1940.

EFFECTS OF MAULING BY TIGER. W. Workman. Jour. Bombay Nat. Hist. Soc., Darjeeling, vol.41, no.3, p.653, Apr., 1940.

EXPLODING THE MYTH OF THE FEROCIOUS LION: FRIENDLY WILD BEASTS EASILY APPROACHED BY MOTOR-CAR OR ON FOOT. Illus. London News, vol. 182, no.4890, pp.8-9, illus., Jan. 7, 1933.

MAN-EATERS OF TSAVO. Jour. Bombay Nat. Hist. Soc., vol.33, no.2, pp.424-425, pl.1, Feb. 15, 1929.

Breeding in Captivity

REMARKS ON THE BREEDING OF THE LARGER FELIDAE IN CAPTIVITY. A.D. Bartlett. Proc. Zool. Soc. London, pt.29, pp.140-141, pl.22, 1861.

(RAISING LYNXES IN CAPTIVITY.) Zucht von Luchsen in Gefangenschaft. Alarik Behm. Zool. Garten, Leipzig, n.F., vol. 6, nos.7-9, p.196, Oct., 1933.

OUR FAMOUS JAGUAR TWINS. Emily Burlingame. Zoonooz, San Diego, vol.19, no.7, p.7, illus., July, 1946.

(LYNX BREEDING IN THE ZOOLOGICAL GARDEN OF HEIDELBERG.) Luchszucht im Tiergarten Heidelberg. Otto Fehringer. Zool. Garten, Leipzig, n.F., vol.9, nos. 1-2, p.45, illus., Feb., 1937.

LARGE CATS AT THE ZOO. James Fisher. Field, London, vol.176, no.4571, p.166, illus., Aug. 3, 1940.

ZOO LEOPARDS AND JAGUARS. James Fisher. Field, London, vol.176, no.4573, p.224, Aug. 17, 1940.

THE LION HOUSE. Wm.T. Hornaday. Zool. Soc. Bull., N.Y. Zool. Soc., no.8, pp.57-62, illus., Jan., 1903.

LEOPARD CAT (F. BENGALENSIS) IN CAPTIVITY. A.M. Kintoch. Jour. Bombay Nat. Hist. Soc., vol.27, pp.623-624, Mar. 31, 1921.

(THE OUNCES (FELIS UNICA SCHREB.) OF THE DRESDEN ZOOLOGICAL GARDEN.) Die Schneeleoparden (Felis unica Schreb.) des Dresdner Zoologischen Gartens. Ingo Krumbiegel. Zool. Garten, Leipzig, n.F., vol.9, nos.1-2, pp.34-37, illus., Feb., 1937.

(DESERT LYNX: BREEDING AND CARE.) Zucht und Pflege des Wuestenluchses. Hans Petzsch. Zoologische Garten, Leipzig, n. F., vol.11, nos.1-2, pp.23-24, illus., June, 1939.

MODEL OUT-OF-DOORS LION HOUSE IN AUDUBON PARK. William Scheppegrell. Parks and Recreation, vol.11, pp.202-203, illus., Feb., 1928.

WHO'S WHO IN THE ZOO. MATTIE, THE PUMA. Fauna, Philadelphia, vol.5, no.3, p.91, illus., Sep., 1943.

Canada

COUGAR SEEN NEAR MEDICINE HAT, ALBERTA. A.W.A. Brown. Canadian Field-Nat., Sutton West, vol.61, no.5, p.174, 1947.

COUGAR IN SASKATCHEWAN. C.H.D. Clarke. Canadian Field-Nat., Ottawa, vol. 56, no.3, p.45, photo, Mar., 1942.

COUGAR IN VANCOUVER ISLAND. Silver Doctor. Field, London, vol.159, no.4124, p.51, fig.1, Jan.9, 1932.

CANADA LYNX. Stuart C. Downing. Canadian Nature, Toronto, vol.10, no.2, p.62, illus., Mar.-Apr., 1948.

NEW MOUNTAIN LION FROM VANCOUVER ISLAND. (Felis concolor vancouverensis.) E.W. Nelson, E.A. Goldman. Proc. Biol. Soc. Wash., vol.45, pp.105-108, July 15, 1932.

STATUS OF THE LYNX IN CANADA, 1920-1952. A.de Vos, S.E. Matel. Jour. For., vol. 50, no.10, pp.742-745, map, graph, Oct., 1952.

FURTHER NOTES ON THE PANTHER IN THE NORTHEAST. Bruse S. Wright. Canadian Field-Nat., vol.67, no.1, pp.12-28, Jan.-Mar., 1953.

SURVIVAL OF THE NORTHEASTERN PANTHER (FELIS CONCOLOR) IN NEW BRUNSWICK. Bruce S. Wright. Jour. Mamm., vol.29, no.3, pp.235-246, Aug., 1948.

Diseases and Parasites

GENERALIZED LEISHMANIASIS IN A CAT. H. Bosselut. Trop. Disease Bull., London, vol.45, no.9, p.775, Sep., 1948.

RABIES IN TIGER--TWO PROVED INSTANCES. R.W. Burton. Jour. Bombay Nat. Hist. Soc., vol.49, no.3, pp.538-541, Dec., 1950.

ANTI-RABIC TREATMENT OF AN INDIAN LION (PANTHERA LEO PERSICA MEYER). P. R. Cadell. Jour. Bombay Nat. Hist. Soc., vol.38, no.1, p.181, Aug. 15, 1935.

MESOCESTOIDES MANTERI N. SP. FROM A LYNX, WITH NOTES ON OTHER NORTH AMERICAN SPECIES OF MESOCESTOIDES. Asa C. Chandler. Jour. Parasitology, vol. 28, no.3, pp.227-231, June, 1942.

COIN LODGED IN A TIGER'S PALATE. D. Chetwode. Jour. Bombay Nat. Hist. Soc., vol.41, no.1, pp.167-169, 1939.

COMPARATIVE THERAPY OF ENDAMOEBA HISTOLYTICA INFECTIONS IN THE KITTEN. James M. Clampit. Amer. Jour. Trop. Med., Baltimore, vol.28, no.2, pp.289-294, Mar., 1948.

(DISTOME OF A PALPEBRO-ORBITAL ABSCESS IN A PANTHER. POSSIBILITY OF DISTANT AFFINITIES BETWEEN THIS DISTOME AND THE PARAGONIMIDAE.) Distome d'un abcès palpébro-orbitaire chez une panthère. Possibilité d'affinités lointaines entre ce distome et les Paragonimidae. Robert-Ph. Dollfus. Annal. Parasit. Humaine et Comparée, Paris, vol.17, no.3, pp.209-235, illus., 1939.

(ON STRONGYLOIDAL PARASITES IN CATS.) A propos de la strongyloidose des chats. Albert Erhardt, Karl Denecke. Annal Parasit. Humaine et Comparée, Paris, vol.17, no.3, pp.206-208, May, 1939.

(THIOGENE NARCOSIS IN THE PUMA.) Thiogenalnarkose beim Puma. Klaus Gartner. Zool. Garten, Leipzig, vol.21, nos.5-6, pp.382-383, 1956.

THREE NEW SPECIES OF THE GENUS METATHELAZIA (NEMATODA). (Puma, Lynx.) C.B. Gerichter. Jour. Parasitol., Lancaster, vol.34, no.2, pp.75-83, illus., Apr., 1948.

LIPURIA IN TIGERS. T.F. Hewer, Harrison Matthews, T. Malkin. Proc. Zool. Soc. London, vol.118, pt.4, pp.924-928, Feb. 28, 1949.

NEW SPECIES OF FLUKE, PARAMETORCHIS NOVEBORACENSIS, FROM THE CAT IN THE UNITED STATES. See-Lu Hung. Proc. U.S. Nat. Mus., vol.69, art.1, pp.1-2, 1926.

(INTRA-ABDOMICAL THIOGENE NARCOSIS IN AN ADULT TIGER.) Intraabdominale Thiogenalnarkose beim erwachsenen Tiger. Klaus-Peter Jaksztien. Zool. Garten, Leipzig, vol.21, nos.5-6, pp.388-389, 1956.

(EPIDEMIC CAT DISEASES TRANSFERABLE TO RACCOONS.) Auf Waschbaeren uebertragbare Katzenseuche. J. Krembs. Deutsche Pelztierzuechter, Muenchen, vol.14, no.4, pp.77-80, Feb. 15, 1939.

COIN LODGED IN A TIGER'S PALATE. C. McCann. Jour. Bombay Nat. Hist. Soc., vol.43, no.3, p.518, Dec., 1942.

COIN LODGED IN A TIGER'S PALATE. A. St.John MacDonald. Jour. Bombay Nat. Hist. Soc., vol.43, no.1, p.100, Apr., 1942.

ON THE MORBID APPEARANCES OF A LION (FELIS LEO, L.). William Martin. Proc. Comm. Sci. and Corres. Zool. Soc. London, pt.1, p.28, 1830-31.

SEVERE CASE OF DIAPHRAGMATIC HERNIA IN THE DOMESTIC CAT. W. S. Newcomer. Turtox News, Chicago, vol. 27, no.5, pp.117-120, May, 1949.

JOYEUXIA FUHRMANNI BAER, 1924, A HITHERTO UNRECORDED CESTODE PARASITE OF THE DOMESTICATED CAT IN SOUTH AFRICA. R.J. Ortlepp. Onderstepoort Jour. Vet. Sci. and Animal Industry, vol.1, no.1, pp.97-98, 1933.

SPIROCERCA FROM THE SNOW LEOPARD. Lawrence R. Penner. Jour. Mamm., vol.31, no. 4, p.462, Nov. 21, 1950.

NOTOEDRIC MANGE IN THE BOBCAT, LYNX RUFUS. Lawrence R. Penner, W.N. Parks. Jour. Mamm., vol.35, no.3, p. 458, Aug., 1954.

DOUBLE HERNIA OF THE DIAPHRAGM ACCOMPANIED BY HYPERPLAS OF THE BILIARY SYSTEM AND EROSION OF THE THORACIC BODY WALL IN THE DOMESTIC CAT. Charles A. Reed. Jour. Mamm., vol.26, no.3, pp.275-284, figs.2, pl.1, Aug., 1945.

PERICARDIO-PERITONEAL HERNIAE IN MAMMALS, WITH DESCRIPTION OF A CASE IN THE DOMESTIC CAT. Charles A. Reed. Anat. Rec., vol.110, no.1, pp. 113-120, May, 1951.

ON ANEURYSMS IN A TIGER. C.G. Seligmann. Proc. Zool. Soc. London, pp.634-635, Oct. 10, 1906.

RABIES IN A MOUNTAIN LION. Tracy I. Storer. California Fish and Game, vol.9, pp.45-48, Apr. (June 8), 1923.

LYNXRUFUS WILSONI N. G., N. SP. (NEMATODA: METASTRONGYLIDAE) FROM THE LUNGS OF THE BOBCAT, LYNX RUFUS RUFUS (SCHREBER). Betty D. Stough. PhD thesis, Va. Poly. Inst., pp. 34, 1953.

CLINOSTOMUM ABDONI SP. NOV., A TREMATODE PARASITE OF THE CAT IN THE PHILIPPINES. Marcos A. Tubangui, Eusebio Y. Garcia. Philippine Jour. Sci., Manila, vol.70, no.4, pp.397-401, Dec., 1939.

(EAR PARASITES OF THE INDIAN LEOPARD.) Die Ohrenparasiten des Geparden. H. Graf Vitzthum. Der Zoolosche Garten, Leipzig, n.F., vol.2, pts. 4-6, pp.121-122, 1929.

Economic Importance

FUR BEARING ANIMALS OF THE UNITED STATES. THE COUGUAR. Frank G. Ashbrook et al. Fur Jour., vol.2, no.11, pp.36-37, 62, illus., Dec., 1928.

FUR BEARING ANIMALS OF THE UNITED STATES. THE WILD CAT. Frank G. Ashbrook et al. Fur Jour., vol.2, no.10, pp. 12, 35, 41, illus., Nov., 1928.

PROBLEM OF MOUNTAIN LION CONTROL IN CALIFORNIA. Jay Bruce. California Fish and Game, vol.11, pp.1-17, figs.5, Jan., 1925.

THE CAT SPANKER. (Device to Drive Away Cats.) Robert R. Budlong. Natl. Park Serv., Region Three Quart., vol.2, no.4, pp.35-37, Oct., 1940.

USE OF CATS IN FARM RAT CONTROL. C.S. Elton. Brit. Jour. Anim. Behaviour, vol.1, no.4, pp.151-154, Oct., 1953.

ON THE CONSERVATION OF THE LYNX IN SCANDINAVIA. Paul L. Errington. Jour. Mamm., vol.35, no.2, pp.254-255, May, 1954.

CATS, LICENSES, HUNTERS AND CONSERVATION. A.K. Fisher. National Humane Rev., vol.21, no.4, p.4, Apr., 1933.

THE HOUSE CAT. (Account of Destructive Habits.) A.K. Fisher. Outers' Recreation, vol.64, no.2, p.84, Feb., 1921.

THE CASE OF THE COUGAR. (Maintains Cougar Has Been Maligned.) Weldon F. Heald. Nat. Mag., vol.46, no.1, pp.8-12, 50, illus., Jan., 1953.

CATS AND THE LAW. Harry Hibschman. Harper's Mag., vol.173, pp.438-441, Sep., 1936.

FEEDING HABITS AND POPULATION CHARACTERISTICS OF THE HOUSE CAT AS A FACTOR IN WILDLIFE MANAGEMENT. Herman Holbrook. MF thesis, Univ. Mich., 1950.

IN DEFENSE OF THE LION. (Conserving Mountain Lion As Game Animal.) Lloyd G. Ingles. Amer. Forests, Wash., D.C., vol.45, no.1, pp.21-22, Jan., 1939.

BREEDING LYNX. E.H. Johnson. Amer. Fur Breeder, vol.4, no.6, p.36, Dec.. 1931.

UNIFORM BOUNTY SYSTEM FOR MOUNTAIN LION. R.H. Lambeth. Proc. 31st Ann. Conf. Western Assn. State Game and Fish Comm., pp.63-64, Apr. 30 - May 2, 1951.

(THE CAT, ITS USEFULNESS.) Le chat, son utilité. Adrien Loir, Mme Adrien Loir. Baillière, Paris, pp.120, pls.6, 1930.

BOBCAT AS A LABORATORY ANIMAL FOR COURSES IN ZOOLOGY. E.W. Pfeiffer. Jour. Mamm., vol.37, no.4, pp.548-549, Jan. 9, 1957.

ECONOMIC STATUS OF THE BOBCAT. Chas. G. Poole. Monthly Bull. Dept.Agric. Calif., vol.18, no.8, pp.458-460, figs.2, Aug., 1929.

HOW SERIOUS IS THE BOBCAT IN VIRGINIA? Donald R. Progulske. Va. Wildl., vol. 16, no.5, pp.18-20, illus., May, 1955.

HOW TO CONTROL VAGRANT CATS. U.S. Fish and Wildl. Serv., Chicago, Wildl. Leaflet, no.269, pp.1-2, May, 1945.

Europe

(ON FELIS BRACCATA COPE AND OTHER SMALL SCHOENBRUNN CATS.) Ueber Felis braccata Cope und andere Schoenbrunner Kleinkatzen. Otto Antonius. Zool.Garten, Leipzig, n.F., vol.6, nos.1-3, pp. 10-23, May, 1933.

PICTURES OF THE FORMER AND PRESENT ANIMAL STOCK OF SCHOENBRUNN. II) LYNXES.) Bilder aus dem frueheren und jetzigen Schoenbrunner Tierbestand. II. Luchse. Otto Antonius. Zool. Garten, Leipzig, n.F., vol.10, nos.1-2, pp.1-7, illus., May, 1938.

(LYNXES IN BULGARIA.) Luchse in Bulgarien. H. von Boetticher. Zeitschr. f. Saeugetierk., Berlin, vol.13, no.2, pp.242-243, 1939.

WILD CAT IN DUMBARTONSHIRE. George Christie. Scottish Nat., no.166, p.111, July-Aug., 1927.

(LYNX (LYNX LYNX), HISTORY AND OCCURRENCE IN SWEDEN AND THE REST OF EUROPE.) Lons (Lynx lynx) historia och nuvarande förekomst i Sverige och övriga Europa. Kai Curry-Lindahl. Sveriges Natur, Göteborg, pp.122-162, illus., 1951.

BRITISH WILD CAT. NOTES ON STATUS IN SCOTLAND. G. Dent. Jour. Soc.Preservation Fauna of Empire, Hertford, n.s., pt.26, pp.48-51, Sep., 1935.

(LYNX IN SOUTHERN SWEDEN 1937-1947.) Lodjuren i sodre Sverige 1937-1947. Albert Eklundh. Svensk Faunistik Revy, vol.9, no. 2, pp.47-53, 1947.

(PROBLEM OF THE AFFINITIES OF THE BIG CAT OF THE CAVERNS.) Sur la question des affinités du grand chat des Cavernes. M. Friant. Mammalia, Paris, vol.4, nos.3-4, pp.88-93, illus., pl.4, Sep.-Dec., 1940.

(FELIS (CATOLYNX) CHAUS GÜLD. FROM THE TRAVERTINE OF UNTERTÜRKHEIM NEAR STUTTGART.) Felis (Catolynx) chaus Güld. aus dem Travertin von Untertürkheim bei Stuttgart. H. von Helbing. Eclogae geologicae Helvetiae, vol.27, no. 2, pp.443-457, figs.11, 1934.

LYNX REMAINS FROM YORKSHIRE CAVES. J.W. Jackson. Naturalist, London, no.891, pp.115-115, Apr., 1931.

(WILD CAT IN THE DOUBS.) Chat sauvage dans le Doubs. A. Jullien et al. La Terre et Vie, Paris, no.1, pp.17-21, illus., 1956.

(PREGLACIAL FELIDS OF VILLÁNY SOUTHERN HUNGARY.) Die praeglazialen Feliden von Villány (Suedungarn). Th. Kormos. Folia Zool. et Hydrobiol., Riga, vol.4, no.1, pp. 148-161, pl.1, Sep. 3, 1932.

(LYNX (LYNX LYNX L.) IN ETHNOGRAPHIC SLOVENIA.) Ris (Lynx lynx L.) na osemlju etnografske Slovenijo. Fran Kos. Glasnik Muzsjskega drustva za Slovenijo. Bull. de L'Assoc. du Musée de Slovenie Letnik, année X-B, Posebni Odtis -Extrait, Ljubljana, Dec., 1929.

(ON THE WILD CAT OF CORSICA.) Sur le Chat sauvage de la Corse. L. Lavauden. Comptes Rendus Acad. Sci. Pairs, vol.189, p.1023, 1929.

(WILDCATS IN GERMANY.) Wildkatzen in Deutschland. Waldemar Lindemann. Die Umschau, Frankfurt, vol.17, pp.526-527, Sep., 1952.

ON THE LEOPARD OF THE CAUCASUS. R. Lydekker. Proc. Zool. Soc. London, pt.3, pp.795-796, pl.54, Oct. 1, 1899.

ANTIQUITY OF THE LION IN GREECE. A.B. Meyer. Smithsonian Rep., Wash., D.C., Publ.no.1529, pp.661-667, (1903) 1904.

(HOW FAR BACK IN HISTORICAL TIME CAN THE LION IN GREECE BE TRACED?) Bis wie weit in der historischen Zeit zurueck ist der Loewe in Griechenland nachweisbar. A.B. Meyer. Zool. Garten, Leipzig, Jahrg. 44, pp.65-73, 1903.

SOUTHERN MOVEMENT OF THE WILD CAT IN SCOTLAND. John G. Millais. Field, London, vol.148, p.763, Oct. 28, 1926.

(MORE ON THE LYNX OF SARDINIA.) Ancora della lince della Sardegna. Boll. Soc. Zool. Italiana, Rome, ann.1908, fasc.1-2, pp.3, 1908.

(ON A YOUNG WILD CAT, FELIS S. SILVESTRIS (SCHREBER, 1777), FROM THE NORTHERN HARZ MOUNTAIN REGION.) Ueber eine junge Wildkatze, Felis s. silvestris (Schreber, 1777), aus dem Nordharz. D. Mueller-Using. Saeugetierk. Mitteil., vol.1, no.3, pp.122-123, July 1, 1953.

(TWO NEW WILDCAT FINDS IN THURINGIA.) Zwei neue Wildkatzenfunde in Thueringen. Hans Muench. Saeugetierk. Mitteil., Stuttgart, vol.3, no.1, pp.31-32, Jan. 1, 1955.

NEW GENUS AND SPECIES OF CAT FROM THE TRANSCASPIAN REGION. (Eremaelurus thinobius, gen. et sp. nov.) S.I. Ognev. Ann. Mus. Zool. Sci. USSR, vol. 27, pp.356-362, pl.26, 1926. (In Russian.)

ON A NEW FORM OF THE STEPPE CAT FROM THE TRANSCASPIAN REGION. (Otocolobus manul ferrugineus.) S.I. Ognev. Comptes Rendus Acad. Sci. USSR, A., nos.16-17, pp.308-310, 1928. (In Russian.)

(SURVEY OF THE SMALL CATS OF RUSSIA.) Uebersicht der russischen Kleinkatzen. S.I. Ognev. Zeitschr. f. Saeugetierk., vol. 5, nos.1-2, pp.48-85, pls.2-4, Aug.7 and 30, 1930.

(THE DISAPPEARANCE OF THE LYNX.) Au sujet de la disparition du lynx. Victor Piraud. Revue d'Hist. Nat., Pt.1, A, Mammifères, Paris, vol.10, no.7, pp.239-241, July, 1929.

NEW RACE OF THE EUROPEAN WILD CAT (FELIS SILVESTRIS). R.I. Pocock. Ann. and Mag. Nat. Hist., London, ser. 11, vol.10, no.70, pp.701-702, Oct., 1943.

ON ENGLISH DOMESTIC CATS. R.I. Pocock. Proc. Zool. Soc. London, pp.143-168, pls.3, June 12, 1907.

RACES OF THE EUROPEAN WILD CAT (FELIS SILVESTRIS). R.I. Pocock. Jour. Linn. Soc. London, Zool., vol.39, no. 263, pp.1-14, June 14, 1934.

(WILD CAT, FELIS S. SILVESTRIS SCHREB. 1777, IN THE KNÜLL MOUNTAINS OF HESSEN.) Wildkatze, Felis s. silvestris Schreb., 1777, im Knuellgebirge, Hessen. W. Rieck. Saeugetierk. Mitteil., Stuttgart, vol.3, no.1, pp.32-33, Jan. 1, 1955.

NORTHERN LIMIT OF WILD CAT IN SCOTLAND. James Ritchie. Scottish Naturalist, no.175, p.10, Jan.-Feb., 1929.

WILD CATS ON WESTERMORLAND-LANCASHIRE BORDER. H.W. Robinson. London, Naturalist, no.849, p.202, Oct., 1927.

(A WILD CAT OF FRANCE.) Sur un chat sauvage de France. P.Rode, R.Didier. Bull. Mus. Nat. d'Hist. Nat., no.2, pp. 90-94, 1935.

(WILDCATS OF THE BALEARIC ISLES.) Die Wildkatze der Balearen. Ernst Schwarz. Zool. Anzeiger, vol.91, nos.5-8, pp.223-224, Oct. 5, 1930.

THE LYNX POPULATIONS ARE RETREATING. Lauri Siivonen. Suomen Riista, vol. 9, p.184, maps, 1954. (Finnish Eng. abs. on separate, mimeo. sheets.)

THE WILD CAT (FELIS SILVESTRIS) IN GREAT BRITAIN. W.L. Taylor. Jour. Anim. Ecol., London, vol.15, no.2, pp.130-133, Nov., 1946.

ON THE SCOTTISH WILD CAT. H. Tetley. Proc. Zool. Soc. London, vol.111, ser.B, pts.1-2, pp.13-23, Oct., 1941.

(WILDCATS IN AUSTRIA.) Wildkatzen in Oesterreich. E.P. Tratz. Saeugetierk. Mitteil., Stuttgart, vol.1, no.4, p.180, Oct. 1, 1953.

(A MUMMIFIED CAT CARCASS FROM HUNGARY.) Ein Mumifizierter Katzenkadaver aus Ungarn. Julius Vigh. Palaeobiologica, Wien, vol.2, nos.4-5, pp.246-250, fig.1, 1929.

SUPPOSED WILD CAT IN IRELAND. Robert Warren. Irish Nat., Dublin, vol.14, no.6, pp.135-136, June, 1905.

(CONTRIBUTIONS TO THE WILDLIFE BIOLOGY OF THE SOUTHEAST EUROPE LYNX (LYNX l. LYNX LINNÉ 1758).) Beitraege zur Freilandbiologie des suedosteuropaeischen Luchses, Lynx l. lynx (Linné, 1758). Friedrich Karl Werner. Saeugetierk. Mitteil., Stuttgart, vol.1, no.3, pp.104-110, July 1, 1953.

Food Habits

METHOD ADOPTED BY LEOPARDS IN HUNTING MONKEYS. Iftikhar Alikhan. Jour. Bombay Nat. Hist. Soc., vol.40, no.3, pp.555-557, Dec., 1938.

HOW DOES A TIGER MAKE A 'KILL'? R.K.M. Battye. Jour. Bombay Nat. Hist. Soc., vol.36, no.2, pp.488-489, Apr.15, 1933.

FARM CAT AS PREDATOR. G.W. Bradt. Mich. Cons., vol.18, no.4, pp. 23-25, July-Aug., 1949.

HOW TIGERS HUNT. NEW LIGHT ON INDIA'S MOST FEROCIOUS BEAST. MASTER OF THE LION TRIBE, HE FALLS UPON HIS VICTIMS WITH TERRIFIC SPEED AND STRENGTH. R.G. Burton. Forest and Outdoors, vol.30, no.7, pp.561-562, July, 1934.

CANNIBALISM IN PANTHERS. R.W. Burton. Jour. Bombay Nat. Hist. Soc., vol.35, no. 2, pp.440-441, Oct. 15, 1931.

TIGER FEEDING ON A COW WHILE YET ALIVE. R.W. Burton. Jour. Bombay Nat. Hist. Soc., vol.37, no.4, pp.945-946, Apr. 15, 1935.

TIGER'S METHOD OF MAKING A 'KILL.' R.W. Burton. Jour. Bombay Nat. Hist. Soc., vol.33, no.4, pp.974-975, illus., Oct. 15, 1929.

UNUSUAL BEHAVIOR OF A TIGRESS WITH LIVE BAIT. F.O. Cave. Jour. Bombay Nat. Hist. Soc., vol.32, p.587, illus., Jan. 15, 1928.

JUNGLE IN SUNLIGHT AND SHADOW. PT. 5. THE ALLEGED CRUELTY OF TIGERS. F.W. Champion. Field, London, vol.162, no.4209, pp.536-537, figs., Aug. 26, 1933.

TUSSLE BETWEEN TIGER AND BUFFALO BAIT. J. McC. Clive. Jour. Bombay Nat. Hist. Soc., vol.32, p.586, Jan. 15, 1928.

FOOD HABITS AND LIFE HISTORY OF THE MOUNTAIN LION (FELIS CONCOLOR HIPPOLESTES). Edward J. Conolly, Jr. MS thesis, Univ. Utah, 1949.

FOOD HABITS OF THE BOBCAT IN ALABAMA. James R. Davis. MS thesis, Ala. Poly. Inst., pp.xi+79, illus., Mar., 1955.

ABNORMAL FOOD OF CATS. George Dimmock. Amer. Naturalist, vol.18, pp.941-943, Sep., 1884.

FOOD HABITS OF PENNSYLVANIA HOUSE CATS. Thomas Eberhard. Jour. Wildl. Mgt., Ithaca, vol.18, no.2, pp.284-286, Apr., 1954.

CASE OF CANNIBALISM IN CANADA LYNX (LYNX CANADENSIS). C.A. Elsey. Jour. Mamm., vol.35, no.1, p.129, Feb. 10, 1954.

NOTES ON FOOD HABITS OF SOUTHERN WISCONSIN HOUSE CAT. Paul L. Errington. Jour. Mamm., vol.17, no.1, pp.64-65, Feb., 1936.

A LION AND HIS PREY. E.P. Gee. Oryx, London, vol.3, no.4, pp.186-187, illus., May, 1956.

HAIR BALL FROM A LION'S GULLET. S.W.E. Gray. Field, London, vol.151, p.225, illus., Feb. 9, 1928.

CATS AD FISHERMEN. E.W. Gudger. Nat. Hist., vol.25, pp.143-155, Mar.-Apr. (May), 1925.

DOES THE JAGUAR USE HIS TAIL AS A LURE IN FISHING. E.W. Gudger. Jour. Mamm., vol.27, no.1, pp.37-49, figs.2, Mar. 14, 1946.

FALL AND WINTER FOOD HABITS OF VERMONT BOBCATS. W.J.Hamilton, Jr. Jour. Wildl.Mgt., Menasha, vol.3, no.2, pp.99-103, tbl., Apr., 1939.

(DOMESTIC CAT EATS STRAWBERRIES.) Hauskatze nascht Erdbeeren. Victor Hornung. Zool. Garten, Leipzig, vol.21, no.4, p.314.

FOOD HABITS OF FERAL HOUSE CATS IN THE SACRAMENTO VALLEY. Earl L. Hubbs. Calif. Fish and Game, vol.37, no. 2, pp.177-189, Apr., 1951.

FOOD OF THE BOBCAT. H.H. Hunt. Calif. Fish and Game, vol.6, no.1, p.37, Jan., 1920.

HOUSE CAT AS A COLLECTOR OF MAMMALS. O.C. van Hyning. Jour. Mamm., vol.12, no.2, p.164, May, 1931.

FOOD HABITS OF BALTIMORE, MARYLAND, CATS IN RELATION TO RAT POPULATIONS. William B. Jackson. Jour. Mamm., vol.32, no.4, pp.458-461, Nov., 1951.

LIONS AND THEIR PREY. Donald Ker. Field and Stream, vol.42, no.7, pp.32-33, illus., Nov., 1937.

CALIFORNIA MOUNTAIN LION OBSERVED STALKING. Carl B. Koford. Jour. Mamm., vol.27, no.3, pp.274-275, Aug., 1946.

STUDY OF THE POSSIBLE EXTENT OF PREDATION ON HEAVY CONCENTRATIONS OF VALLEY QUAIL WITH SPECIAL REFERENCE TO THE BOBCAT. Howard R. Leach, Walter H. Frazier. Calif. Fish and Game, vol.39, no.4, pp.527-538, illus., 1953.

HOW TIGERS KILL THEIR PREY. T. R. Livesey. Jour. Bombay Nat. Hist. Soc., vol.38, no.1, p.180, Aug. 15, 1935.

TIGERS BURYING THEIR KILL. T. R. Livesey. Jour. Bombay Nat. Hist. Soc., vol.38, no.1, pp.179-180, Aug. 15, 1935.

PANTHER TREEING ITS KILL. W. M. Logan-Home. Jour. Bombay Nat. Hist. Soc., vol.32, pp.209-210, illus., Aug. 1, 1927.

PANTHER IN A TREE WITH A PIG. J. H. Longrigg. Jour. Bombay Nat. Hist. Soc., vol.27, pp.935-936, July 31, 1921.

HUNTING HABITS OF LIONS. Denis D. Lyell. Field, London, vol.152, p.368, Aug. 30, 1928.

FOOD OF FERAL HOUSE CATS IN OKLAHOMA, A PROGRESS REPORT. Frank B. McMurry, Charles C. Sperry. Jour. Mamm., vol.22, no.2, pp. 185-190, May, 1941.

WILD CAT EATS CHICKEN. D. W. Maxey. Calif. Fish and Game, vol.6, no.1, p.37, Jan., 1920.

GREAT BLUE HERON KILLED BY BOBCAT. Gale Monson. Wilson Bull., vol.63, no.4, Dec., 1951.

FEEDING THE SERENGETI LIONS. M.S. Moore. Field, London, vol.161, no.4195, pp.1112-1113, figs.5, May 20, 1933.

CASE OF TIGER EATING SALT-LICK EARTH. R.C. Morris. Jour. Bombay Nat. Hist. Soc., vol.38, no.2, pp.385-386, Dec. 1, 1935.

PANTHERS FEEDING ON TIGER KILLS. R.C. Morris. Jour. Bombay Nat. Hist. Soc., vol.36, no.3, p.742, Aug. 15, 1933.

TIGER KILLING SOLITARY BULL BISON (BIBAS GAURUS). R.C. Morris. Jour. Bombay Nat. Hist. Soc., vol.38, no.1, p.179, Aug. 15, 1935.

WOUNDED PANTHER RETURNING TO 'KILL.' R. C. Morris. Jour. Bombay Nat. Hist. Soc., vol.33, no.4, pp.977-978, Oct. 15, 1929.

WOUNDED TIGER RETURNING TO KILLS. R.C. Morris. Jour. Bombay Nat. Hist. Soc., vol.33, no.2, pp.425-526, Feb. 15, 1929.

STUDY OF THE DOMESTIC CAT IN RELATION TO GAME BIRDS IN THE WILLAMETTE VALLEY, OREGON. Nils N. Nilsson. MS thesis, Oregon State Coll., 1940.

FOOD HABITS OF THE FERAL HOUSE CAT IN EAST-CENTRAL TEXAS. Paul W. Parmalee. Jour. Wildl. Mgt., Ithaca, vol.17, no.3, pp.375-376, July, 1953.

FOOD HABITS OF THE BOBCAT IN THE NEW ENGLAND STATES. E.M. Pollack. Jour. Wildl. Mgt., Menasha, vol.15, no. 2, pp.209-213, Apr., 1951.

BOBCAT IN MASSACHUSETTS. INCLUDING ANALYSES OF FOOD HABITS OF BOBCATS FROM OTHER NORTHEASTERN STATES, PRINCIPALLY NEW HAMPSHIRE. E.M. Pollack, William G. Sheldon. Mass. Div. Fisheries and Game, pp.24, illus., Sep., 1951.

BOBCAT AND ITS RELATION TO PREY SPECIES IN VIRGINIA. Donald R. Progulske. MA thesis, Va. Poly. Inst., 1952.

GAME ANIMALS UTILIZED AS FOOD BY THE BOBCAT IN THE SOUTHERN APPALACHIANS. Donald R. Progulske. Jour. Wildl. Mgt., Ithaca, vol.19, no.2, pp. 249-253, Apr., 1955.

BOBCATS AND WILD TURKEYS. Ernest T. Seton. Jour. Mamm., vol.1, no.3, p. 140, May, 1920.

WINTER PROVIDES FEASTS FOR WILDCATS IN DEER YARDS. Harrison Shobe. W. Va. Conserv., Charleston, vol.12, no.1, pp.17, 21, Apr., 1948.

TIGERS PREFERRING CARRION TO LIVE BAIT. W.H.O. Shortt. Jour. Bombay Nat. Hist. Soc., vol.32, p.370, Oct. 20, 1927.

WILDCAT PREDATION ON DEER. Bertrand E. Smith. Jour. Mamm., vol.26, no.4, pp.439-440, Nov., 1945.

DOES THE PANTHER (FELIS CONCOLOR) GO INTO THE WATER TO KILL FISH? Livingston Stone. U.S. Nat. Mus., Proc., Washington, vol.5, p.570, (1882) 1883.

WHY A LION TURNED CATTLE THIEF. G. Stuart-Watt. Field, London, vol.160, no.4163, p.548, photo, Oct. 8, 1932.

TIGER ATTACKING AN ELEPHANT. I.K. Swaine. Jour. Bombay Nat. Hist. Soc., vol. 36, no.4, pp.983-984, Dec. 15, 1933.

THREE TIGERS AT A KILL. C. Swire. Jour. Bombay Nat. Hist. Soc., vol.34, no. 3, pp.796-797, Nov. 15, 1930.

BUTTERFLIES AND A KITTEN. G.C. Toner. Jour. Mamm., vol.36, no.2, p.290, May 26, 1955.

HOUSE CAT PREDATION ON SMALL ANIMALS. G.C. Toner. Jour. Mamm., vol.37, no.1, p.119, Feb. 28, 1956.

A PAIR OF HUNTING CHEETAHS. Van Ingen. Jour. Bengal Nat. Hist. Soc., Darjeeling, vol.17, no.2, pp.75-76, illus., Oct., 1942.

COUGAR SURPRISED AT WELL-STOCKED LARDER. George M. Wright. Jour. Mamm., vol.15, no.4, p.321, Nov., 1934.

MOUNTAIN LION EATS ITS KITTENS. S.P. Young. Jour. Mamm., vol.8, no.2, pp.158-160, May, 1927.

Fossils

NOTES ON FOSSIL AND PREHISTORIC REMAINS OF "FELIDAE" FROM JAVA AND SUMATRA. L.D. Brongersma. Comptes Rendus 12th Congrès Internat. Zool. Lisbonne 1935, pp.1855-1865, 1937.

MACHAERODUS CATOCOPIS COPE FROM THE PLIOCENE OF TEXAS. William Henry Burt. Univ. Calif. Publ., Bull. Dept. Geol. Sci., vol.20, no.7, pp.261-292, pls.43-50, May 7, 1931.

ON NEW MATERIAL OF SOME MACHAIRODONTS OF PONTIAN AGE FROM SHANSI. Hsi-chih Chang. Vertebrate Palasiatica, vol.1, no.3, pp.193-200, Sep., 1957.

THE TAR PIT TIGER. Edwin H. Colbert. Nat. Hist., New York, vol.46, no.5, pp. 284-287, illus., Dec., 1940.

(SABRE-TOOTH TIGER.) Tigre dos Dentes de Sabre. Carlos de Paula Couto. Rev. Mus. Nac., Rio de Janeiro, Ano 2, no.5, pp.20-22, figs.4, Dec., 1945.

(STUDY OF SOME BONES OF FELIS SPELAEA GOLDFUSS OF THE CAVE OF GONDENANS-LES-MOULINS (DOUBS).) Étude de quelques ossements de Felis spelaea Goldfuss de la grotte de Gondenans-les-Moulins (Doubs). Robert Didier. Mammalia, Paris, vol.6, no.1, pp.13-17, pls. 1-3, Mar., 1942.

JOHN DAY FELIDAE IN THE MARSH COLLECTION. George F. Eaton. Amer. Jour. Sci., ser.5, vol.4, no.24, pp.425-452, figs.12, Dec., 1922.

FOSSIL CARNIVORES OF THE TRANSVAAL CAVES: MACHAIRODONTINAE. R.F. Ewer. Proc. Zool. Soc. London, vol.125, pts.3-4, pp.587-615, pls.1-3, Nov. 23, 1955.

FOSSIL CARNIVORES OF THE TRANSVAAL CAVES: FELINAE. R.F. Ewer. Proc. Zool. Soc. London, vol.126, pt.1, pp.83-85, pls.3, Jan. 11, 1956.

(MACHAIRODUS (MEGANTHEREON) OF THE UPPER VALDERNO.) Machairodus (Megantherean) del Valderno Superiore. Fabrini. Boll. R. Com. Geol. d'Italia, 3a serl., pp.121-144, 1890.

(ON THE QUESTION OF THE AFFINITIES OF THE LARGE CAT OF THE CAVERS.) Sur la question des affinités du grand chat des Cavernes. M. Friant. Mammalia, Paris, vol.4, nos.3-4, pp. 88-93, figs.4, pl.4, Sep.-Dec., 1940.

NEW FELIDS FROM THE UPPER PLIOCENE OF IDAHO. C. Lewis Gazin. Jour. Mamm., vol.14, no.3, pp.251-256, figs.3, Aug., 1933.

TWO NEW GENERA OF FELIDAE FROM THE MIDDLE PLIOCENE OF KANSAS. Claude W. Hibbard. Trans. Kansas Acad. Sci., vol.37, pp.239-255, pls.4-6, 1934.

PLEISTOCENE REMAINS OF PANTHERA TIGRIS (LINNAEUS) SUBSPECIES FROM WANHSIEN, SZECHWAN, CHINA COMPARED WITH FOSSIL AND RECENT TIGERS FROM OTHER LOCALITIES. D.A. Hooijer. Amer. Mus. Novitates, New York, no.1346, pp.1-17, figs.3, May 8, 1947.

AUDITORY REGION IN NORTH AMERICAN FOSSIL FELIDAE: ITS SIGNIFICANCE IN PHYLOGENY. Jean Hough. U.S. Dept. Interior, Geol. Survey Prof. Paper 243-G, pp.95-115, illus., 1953.

SUBSPECIES OF HOPLOPHONEUS: A STATISTICAL STUDY. Jean Hough. Jour. Paleontol., Menasha, vol.23, no.5, pp.536-555, figs.3.

AMERICAN EUSMILOID SABRE-TOOTH CATS OF THE OLIGOCENE EPOCH. Glenn L. Jepsen. Proc. Amer. Philos. Soc., vol.72, no.5, pp.355-369, pls.4, 1933.

OLDEST KNOWN CAT, HOPLOPHONEUS OHARRAI. Glenn L. Jepsen. Black Hills Engineer (S. Dakota School of Mines), vol. 14, no.2, pp.87-92, Mar., 1926.

SABER-TOOTH CAT, SMILODON CALIFORNICUS BOVARD, FROM LOGAN COUNTY, OKLAHOMA. David B. Kitts. Oklahoma Geol. Notes, Oklahoma Geol. Surv., vol.18, no.2, pp.19-23, illus., Feb., 1958.

(NOTE ON THE PAW OF FELIS SPELAEA GOLDF.) Note sur la patte de Felis spelaea Goldf. F. Edouard Koby. Eclogae Geol. Helvetiae, Basel, vol.34, no.2, p.319, Mar. 7, 1942.

(SMILODONTIDION RIGGII, N. GEN. N. SP., A NEW AND SMALL SMILODONTID IN THE PLIOCENE FAUNA OF THE CHAPADMALAL.) Smilodontidion riggii, n.gen.n.

sp., un nuevo y pequeño esmilodente en la fauna pliocena de Chapadmalal. Lucas J. Kraglievich. Rev. Mus. Argentino Cienc. Nat."Bernardino Rivadavia," Buenos Aires, Cienc. Zool., vol.1, no.1, pp.1-44, figs. 10, pls.4, 1948.

DESCRIPTION OF AN EXTINCT SPECIES OF AMERICAN LION: FELIS ATROX. J. Leidy. Trans. Amer. Philos. Soc., ser.2, vol.10, pp.319-321, pl.34, 1852.

NEW FINDS OF PLEISTOCENE JAGUAR SKELETONS FROM TENNESSEE CAVES. Edward McCrady et al. Proc. U.S. Nat. Mus., Wash., vol.101, no.3287, pp.497-511, Oct. 16, 1951.

NEW PSEUDAELARUS FROM THE LOWER SNAKE CREEK FAUNA OF NEBRASKA. J.R. MacDonald. Jour.Paleontol., vol.28, no.1, pp.67-69, illus., Jan., 1954.

NEW SPECIES OF NIMRAVUS FROM THE UPPER OLIGOCENE OF SOUTH DAKOTA. J.R. MacDonald. Jour. Paleontol., vol.24, no.5, pp.601-603, fig.1, Sep., 1950.

NEW SPECIES OF PSEUDAELURUS FROM THE LOWER PLIOCENE OF NEBRASKA. J.R. MacDonald. Univ.Calif.Publ., Bull. Dept. Geol.Sci., Berkeley, vol.28, no.2, pp.45-52, figs.4, Mar. 3, 1948.

DESCRIPTION OF A NEW SPECIES OF THE GENUS FELIS. W. Martin. Proc. Zool.Soc. London, pt.4, p.107, 1836.

ANALYSIS OF MEASUREMENTS IN LENGTH OF THE METAPODIALS OF SMILODON. Henry W. Menard, Jr. Bull.Southern Calif. Acad. Sci., Los Angeles, vol.46, no.3, pp.127-135, pls.5, Apr. 20, 1948.

(THE SMILODON BONAERENSIS (MUNIZ). OSTEOLOGIC AND OSTEOMETRIC STUDY OF THE FOSSIL TIGER OF THE PAMPAS, COMPARED WITH OTHER FELIDS, LIVING AND FOSSIL.) El Smilodon bonaerensis (Muñiz). Estudio osteológico y osteométrico del gran tigre fósil de la pampa comparado con otros félidos actuales y fósiles. Rodolfo Méndez-Alzola. Anal.Mus.Argentino Nat., Buenos Aires, vol.11, no.66, pp.135-252, pls.15, Apr., 1941.

FELIDAE OF RANCHO LA BREA. John C. Merriam, Chester Stock. Publ.422 Carnegie Inst. Wash., pp.xvi+231, figs.152, pls.42, Dec. 16, 1932.

PHENOMENON OF SACRALIZATION IN THE PLEISTOCENE SABRE-TOOTH. Roy L. Moodie. Amer. Jour. Surgery, New York, vol. 10, no.3, pp.587-589, Dec., 1930.

(TERTIARY CARNIVORES OF WESTERN SIBERIA. I. MACHAIRODONTINAE.) J.A. Orlov. Trav. Inst. Paleozool. Acad.Sci. USSR, vol.5, pp.111-152, figs.21, pl.1, 1936. (In Russian.)

(FOSSIL PANTHERS IN THE MALARNAUD REGION (ARIÈGE).) Panthères fossiles de la région de Malarnaud (Ariège). L. Pales. Bull. Soc. Hist. Nat. Toulouse, vol.58, no. 2, pp.235-240, pl.1, figs.3, 1929.

(SABRE-TOOTH TIGER OF BRAZIL.) O "Tigre-dentes-de-sabre" do Brasil. Carlos de Paula Couto. Bol. Conselho Nacional de Pesquisas, no.1, pp.1-30, illus., 1955.

(REMARKS ON THE GENUS PSEUDAELURUS GERVAIS.) Remarques sur le genre Pseudaelurus Gervais. Marguerite Richard. Bull. Soc. Géol. France, Paris, ser.5, vol.5, fasc.6-7, pp.479-482, figs.4, May, 1936.

(NOTICE ON A JUVENILE SKELETON BELONGING TO THE GREAT EXTINCT CARNIVORES, SMILODON BONAERENSIS.) Noticias acerca de un esqueleto juvenil perteneciente a los grandes carnivors extinguidos:"Smilodon bonaerensis". Carlos Rusconi. Anales Soc. Cien. Argentina, Buenos Aires, vol.111, pp.147-156, figs.8, Mar., 1931.

PROBLEMATICAL CAT-LIKE MANDIBLE FROM THE UINTA EOCENE, APATAELURUS KAYI, SCOTT. William Berryman Scott. Ann. Carnegie Mus., vol.27, pp.113-120, pl.7, 1938.

NOTE ON AN OCCURRENCE OF MACHAIRODUS IN KOREA. Tokio Shikama. Proc. Imp. Acad., Tokyo, vol.10, no.8, pp.490-493, figs.2, Oct., 1934.

LARGE PLEISTOCENE FELINES OF NORTH AMERICA. George Gaylord Simpson. Amer. Mus. Novitates, New York, no.1136, pp.1-27, figs.11, Aug. 11, 1941.

SPECIES OF HOPLOPHONEUS. George Gaylord Simpson. Amer. Mus. Novitates, New York, no.1123, pp.21, June 11, 1941.

SKULL OF EUSMILUS. W.J.Sinclair, G.L. Jepsen. Proc. Amer. Phil.Soc., vol.66, pp.391-407, 1927.

IS FELIS ATROX OF RANCHO LA BREA A LION OR A TIGER? Chester Stock. Bull. Geol. Soc. America, vol.43, no.1, p.290, Mar., 1932. (Abstract.)

SKULL AND DENTITION OF THE AMERICAN MIOCENE CAT, PSEUDAELURUS. Chester Stock. Bull. Geol. Soc. America, vol.45, pp.1051-1058, pls.129-130, Dec. 31, 1934.

SKULL AND UPPER DENTITION OF AN AMERICAN SPECIES OF PSEUDAELURUS. Chester Stock. Pan-Amer.Geol., vol.59, no.5, p.376, June, 1933.

ON TWO SKULLS OF MACHAIRODUS FROM THE LOWER PLEISTOCENE BEDS OF CHOUKOUTIEN. P. Teilhard de Chardin. Bull. Geol.Soc. China, Pehpei, Chungking, vol.19, no.3, pp.235-256, figs.6, Dec., 1939.

HOPLOPHONEUS MENTALIS, AND CUSP HOMOLOGIES IN CATS. Elmer Horace Wood 2nd. Jour.Mamm., vol.8, no.4, pp.296-301, Nov., 1927.

SABRE-TOOTH AND LION-LIKE CATS: SKELETONS FOUND IN ASPHALT. Illus. London News, vol.182, no.4896, pp.222-223, illus., Feb. 18, 1933.

## General Habits, Ecology, Behavior

COUGAR WHIPS BEAR IN BLOODY BATTLE ON BIG CREEK FOREST. Jack Anderson. Idaho Wildl. Review, Boise, vol.2, no.4, p.13, Dec., 1949.

JAGUAR AND THE JUNGLE. H.E.Anthony. Nature Mag., vol.6, pp.15-18, figs.4, pl.1, July, 1925.

CAT AND DOG AFFAIR. FEROCITY AND STRENGTH OF THE SCOTTISH WILD CAT. H. Mortimer Batten. Field, London, vol. 156, no.4050, p.204, Aug. 9, 1930.

TIGERS SWIMMING. R.K.M. Battye. Jour. Bombay Nat. Hist. Soc., vol.43, no.3, pp.516-517, Dec., 1942.

PANTHERS AND ARTIFICIAL LIGHT. C.B. Beadnell. Jour. Bombay Nat. Hist. Soc., vol.28, p.265, Dec. 30, 1921.

PANTHER AND FLASHLIGHT. B.A.S. Brunskill. Jour. Bombay Nat. Hist. Soc., vol.32, p.588, pl.1, Jan. 15, 1928.

TIGERS IN TREES. R.G. Burton. Jour. Bombay Nat. Hist. Soc., vol.27, p.164, July 1, 1920; vol.27, pp.383-385, Dec. 20, 1920.

"STRANGE" BEHAVIOR OF A PANTHER. R.G. Burton. Jour. Bombay Nat. Hist.Soc., vol.29, p.1044, May 15, 1924.

ASSOCIATION BETWEEN A LEOPARD AND A TIGRESS. R.G. Burton. Jour.Bombay Nat. Hist. Soc., vol.39, no.3, p.610, Sep. 25, 1937.

DEATH CRY OF TIGER. R.W. Burton. Jour. Bombay Nat. Hist. Soc., vol.49, no. 3, p.538, Dec., 1950.

PANTHER CLIMBING UP TO A MACHAN. R.W. Burton. Jour. Bombay Nat. Hist.Soc., vol.33, no.4, pp.978-979, Oct. 15, 1929.

UNUSEAL BEHAVIOUR OF PANTHERS AND TIGERS. R.W. Burton. Jour. Bombay Nat. Hist. Soc., vol.41, no.1, p.167, 1939.

BATTLES OF THE AFRICAN JUNGLE. PT. 4. THE CUNNING OF THE LEOPARD. W. S. Chadwick. Outdoor Life, vol.67, no.3, pp.32-33, 70-71, Mar., 1931.

TIGER CLIMBING A TREE. G.E.R.Cooper. Jour. Bombay Nat. Hist. Soc., vol.29, pp. 276-277, Apr. 20, 1923.

COOL AND AUDACIOUS TIGER. John Dewar. Jour. Darjeeling Nat. Hist. Soc., vol.12, no. 1, pp.27-28, June, 1937.

COUGAR ENCOUNTERED IN THE OPEN. Joseph S. Dixon. Jour. Mamm., vol.15, no.1, p.71, Feb., 1934.

(OBSERVATIONS ON THE BEHAVIOR OF THE PANTHER AND LION.) Observations sur le comportement de la panthère et du lion. F. Edmond-Blanc. Mammalia, Paris, vol.21, no.4, pp.452-453, Dec., 1957.

PORCUPINE-PANTHER INCIDENT. E. T. Ferguson. Jour. Bombay Nat. Hist.Soc., vol.29, p.550, Aug. 25, 1923.

ARE WILDCATS WILD? William L. Finley. Nature Mag., vol.23, no.4, pp.189-191, illus., Apr., 1934.

STRANGE BEHAVIOUR OF A TIGRESS. E. P. Gee. Jour. Bombay Nat. Hist. Soc., vol.39, no.3, p.614, Sep. 25, 1937.

EXPERIENCE WITH A TIGRESS. S. Hanhart. Jour. Bombay Nat. Hist. Soc., vol.33, no.4, pp.976-977, Oct. 15, 1929.

STRANGE BEHAVIOR OF A PANTHER (F. PARDUS). S. Hanhart. Jour. Bombay Nat. Hist. Soc., vol.29, pp.549-550, Aug. 25, 1923.

COUGAR CHARACTERISTICS. M.E. Hatcher. Outdoor Life, vol.67, no.5, pp. 30-31, 58-59, figs.5, May, 1931.

WHERE A TIGER SHARPENED HIS CLAWS. C.E. Hewetson. Jour. Bombay Nat. Hist. Soc., vol.42, no.4, pp.926-927, photo, Dec., 1941.

MOUNTAIN LION AND ECOLOGY. Frank C. Hibben. Ecology, Brooklyn, vol.20, no. 4, pp.584-586, Oct., 1939.

PRELIMINARY STUDY OF THE MOUNTAIN LION (FELIS OREGONENSIS SUB. SP.) Frank C. Hibben. Univ. N. Mex., Bull.318, pp.59, Dec., 1937.

SOME EFFECTS OF ENVIRONMENT AND HABIT ON CAPTIVE LIONS. N. Hollister. Proc. U.S. Nat. Mus., vol.53, pp.177-193, pls.22-25, June 1, 1917.

SWIMMING CATS. Ernest G. Holt. Jour. Mamm., vol.13, no.1, pp.72-73, Feb., 1923.

BOLDNESS OF PANTHERS. W.M.Logan Home. Jour. Bombay Nat. Hist. Soc., vol.32, pp.588-589, Jan. 15, 1928.

(OBSERVING THE LIVING HABITS OF FELIS MINUTA TEMM.) Beobachtungen ueber die Lebensweise von Felis minuta Temm. E. Jacobson. Notes Leyden Mus., vol.34, note 7, pp.31-36, 1911.

ASSOCIATION BETWEEN A LEOPARD AND A TIGRESS. Iftikhar Ali Khan. Jour. Bombay Nat. Hist. Soc., vol.39, no.1, pp.154-156, Dec. 1, 1936.

THE 'SAMBUR' CALL OF THE TIGER AND ITS EXPLANATION. E.S. Lewis. Jour. Bombay Nat. Hist. Soc., vol.41, no.4, pp.889-890, Aug., 1940.

(THE BEHAVIOR OF CATS (FELIDAE).) Das Verhalten der Katzen (Felidae). P. Leyhausen. Handb. der Zoologie, Berlin, Bd.8, Teil 10, no.21, (Lief.7), pp.1-32, July, 1956.

(THE DISTINGUISHABLE DEVELOPMENT OF SOME TYPES OF BEHAVIOR IN THE FELIDS.) Ueber die unterschiedliche Entwicklung einiger Verhaltensweisen bei den Feliden. P. Leyhausen. Saeugetierk. Mitteil., Stuttgart, vol.4, no.3, pp.123-125, July 1, 1956.

(STUDIES OF CAT BEHAVIOR.) Verhaltensstudien an Katzen. P. Leyhausen. Supplement no.2, to Zeitschr. f. Tierpsychologie, Verlag Paul Parey, Berlin and Hamburg, pp.120, figs.76, July, 1956.

PANTHER INCIDENT. G. de L'Isle Sturm. Jour. Bombay Nat. Hist. Soc., vol.34, no.3, p.798, Nov. 15, 1930.

DRUMMING SOUND MADE BY LEOPARDS. T.R. Livesey. Jour. Bombay Nat. Hist.Soc. vol.34, no.4, pp.1056-1057, Mar. 2, 1931.

SCREAM OF THE MOUNTAIN LION. Robert A. McCabe. Jour. Mamm., vol.30, no.3, pp.305-306, Aug. 17, 1949.

STRANGE BEHAVIOR OF A TIGRESS. A. MacDonald. Jour. Bombay Nat. Hist. Soc., vol.34, no.1, pp.231-232, Mar. 1, 1930.

DOES THE MOUNTAIN LION SCREAM? E.G. Marsh, Jr. Colorado Conserv. Comments, Denver, vol.6, no.4, p. 14, Dec. 15, 1943.

DOMESTIC CAT AS A FACTOR IN URBAN ECOLOGY. Colin Matheson. Jour. Anim. Ecol., London, vol.13, no.2, pp.130-133, Nov., 1944.

PANTHER'S INDIFFERENCE. H.J.C. Millett. Jour. Bombay Nat. Hist. Soc., vol.28, pp.275-276, Dec. 30, 1921.

PANTHER CLIMBING UP TO A MACHAN. R.C. Morris. Jour. Bombay Nat. Hist. Soc., vol.34, no.3, pp.797-798, Nov. 15, 1930.

PANTHER'S STRANGE BEHAVIOUR. R.C. Morris. Jour. Bombay Nat. Hist. Soc., vol. 35, no.2, p.440, Oct. 15, 1931.

TIGER CLAW MARKS ON TREES. R.C. Morris. Jour. Bombay Nat. Hist. Soc., vol.43, no.4, p.656, Apr., 1943.

TWO WARY TIGERS AND TWO OTHERS. R.C. Morris. Indian Wild Life, vol.1, no. 2, pp.82-87, Aug., 1936.

UNUSUAL BEHAVIOUR OF PANTHERS AND TIGERS. R.C. Morris. Jour. Bombay Nat. Hist. Soc., vol.42, no.3, pp.655-656, Aug., 1941.

THE TIGRESS WHICH FACED THE FLASH-LIGHT. E.H. Peacock. Field, London, vol. 160, no. 4161, pp.456-458, illus., Sep. 24, 1932.

ECOLOGY OF THE BOBCAT (LYNX RUFUS RUFUS SCHREBER) IN THE NEW ENGLAND STATES. E. Michael Pollack. MS thesis, Univ. Mass., 1949.

A TIGER FIGHT. W.D. Ritchie. Jour. Bombay Nat. Hist. Soc., vol.49, no.3, p.537, Dec., 1950.

(LION AS AN AMBLER.) Der Loewe als Passgaenger. Karl Max Schneider. Zool. Garten, n.F., vol.12, no.1, pp.55-58, illus., Mar., 1940.

(ON "TWIRLING" IN LARGE CATS.) Ueber das "Drehen" der Grosskatzen. Karl Max Schneider. (Ein Beitrag zur Raubtierzucht.) Zool. Garten, Leipzig, n.F., vol.6, nos. 7-9, pp.173-181, figs.9, Oct., 1933.

TIGERS CLIMBING TREES. Sadeg Z. Shah. Jour. Bombay Nat. Hist. Soc., vol.33, no. 1, p.196, Sep. 30, 1928.

PANTHER COMMITTING SUICIDE. W.H.O. Shortt. Jour. Bombay Nat. Hist. Soc., vol. 32, p.371, Oct. 20, 1927.

DAYS WITHOUT TIME. Edwin Way Teale. Dodd, Mead and Co., New York City, pp. 283, illus., 1948. (Swimming Cats, pp. 45-50.)

NOTES ON TIGERS AND THEIR CALLS. W.S. Thom. Jour. Bombay Nat. Hist. Soc., vol.29, pp.548-549, Aug. 25, 1922.

ANECDOTE ABOUT CATS. (Cat Nursing Young Woodchucks.) Henry Turner. Amer. Naturalist, vol.17, no.2, p.220, Feb., 1883.

VITALITY OF A PANTHER. A.S. Vernay. Jour. Bombay Nat. Hist., vol.33, no.3, pp.698-699, May 31, 1929.

DO CATS SHARPEN THEIR CLAWS? Ole N. de Weerdt. Science, n.s., vol.66, pp. 398-399, Oct. 28, 1927.

(PANTHER EXPERIENCES.) Panther-Erlebnisse. Alfred Weidholz. Der Zoologische Garten, Leipzig, n.F., vol.12, no. 1, pp.20-28, illus., Mar., 1940.

OUR CATS AND ALL ABOUT THEM, THEIR VARIETIES, HABITS, AND MANAGEMENT, AND FOR SHOW, THE STANDARD OF EXCELLENCE AND BEAUTY, DESCRIBED AND PICTURED. Harrison Weir. 1889.

DOES THE PUMA (MOUNTAIN LION) SCREAM? Stanley P. Young. Western Sportsman, Denver, vol.6, no.6, pp.6-9, illus., May, 1941.

ON THE SCREAM OF THE PUMA. Stanley P. Young. Amer. Forests, vol.52, no.9, pp.408-409, 442, Sep., 1946.

HOW ARE LEOPARD CHARGES REVEALED BY REMARKABLE PHOTOGRAPHS. Illus. London News, vol.190, no.5108, p.431, figs.3, Mar. 13, 1937.

LYNX SEEN SWIMMING IN THE LAC LA RONGE AREA. Blue Jay, Saskatchewan Nat. Hist. Soc., vol.14, no.2, p.51, June, 1956.

Heredity

A TWO-FACED KITTEN. Thomas Hume Bissonnette. Jour. Heredity, Wash., D.C., vol.24, no.3, pp.103-104, figs.5-6, Mar., 1933.

WHERE THE CATS CAME FROM. Edwin H. Colbert. Nat. Hist., New York, vol. 46, no.5, pp.288-289, illus., Dec., 1940.

(THE ORIGIN AND DISTRIBUTION OF THE DOMESTIC CAT.) Ueber den Ursprung und die Verbreitung der Hauskatze. H.F. Jaeger. Wuerttemb. Naturw. Jahresheft, no.1, pp.65-74, 1848.

INCIDENCE OF THE GENES FOR COAT COLORS IN JAPANESE CATS. Taku Komai. Annt. Zool. Japonenses, Zool. Soc. Japan Zool. Inst., Tokyo, vol.25, nos.1-2, pp. 209-211, Jan., 1952.

ON THE ORIGIN OF THE TORTOISESHELL MALE CAT - A CORRECTION. Taku Komai. Japan Acad., vol.28, no.3, pp.150-151, 1952.

PRELIMINARY NOTE ON THE OCCURRENCE OF A SEX-LIMITED CHARACTER IN CATS. C.C. Little. Science, Lancaster, n.s., vol. 35, no.907, pp.784-785, May 17, 1912.

EXPERIMENTAL BREEDING. (GENETICS OF THE FELINE.) James D. McCrae. Caribou Publ. Co., Caribou, Maine, pp. 1-131, illus., 1955.

ORIGIN OF THE MEXICAN HAIRLESS CAT. Ida M. Mellen. Jour. Heredity, Wash., D.C., vol.30, no.10, pp.435-436, figs.14, Oct., 1939.

ON THE TABBY CATS AND SOME FEATURES IN THE INHERITANCE OF THEIR COAT PATTERNS AND COLOUR. R. I. Pocock. Mendel Jour., London, vol.1, pp. 53-73, pl.2, Feb., 1911.

(A CASE OF INHERITED PARTIAL ALBINOISM IN THE LION.) Ein Fall von erblichem partiellen Albinismus beim Loewen. Karl Max Schneider. Zool. Garten, Leipzig, n.F., vol.2, nos.10-12, pp.274-278, figs. 1-4, Mar., 1930.

GENETICS OF THE BURMESE CAT. Joseph C. Thompson et al. Jour. Heredity, Wash., D.C., vol.34, no.4, pp.119-123, figs.10-13, Apr., 1943.

INHERITANCE OF WHITE-SPOTTING AND OTHER COLOR CHARACTERS IN CATS. P.W. Whiting. Amer. Nat., vol.53, pp. 473-482, Nov., 1919.

THREE GENERATIONS OF DEAF WHITE CATS. Dorothy Wolff. Jour. Heredity, Wash., D.C., vol.33, no.2, pp.39-43, fig.3, Feb., 1942.

Hunting and Trapping

PURSUIT OF OLD JUAN. (Jaguar, Felis onca.) Mary Ogden Abbott. Nat. Hist., New York, vol.48, no.1, pp.25-27, illus., June, 1941.

LION OF LOS PILARES. Russel Barnett Aitken. Field and Stream, New York, vol. 53, no.1, pp.66-68, 167-171, illus., May, 1948.

CAPTURING A PANTHER. (Felis concolor coryi.) E. Ross Allen. Florida Conservator, Tallahassee, vol.1, no.6, pp.3-4, 10-11, illus., Dec., 1934.

THE BOBCAT. (Trapping) Walter L. Arnold. Fur-Fish-Game, Columbus, vol.95, no. 10, pp.38, 40-42, illus., Oct., 1947.

AN INTERESTING TIGER SHOOT. Bahadursinh. Jour. Bombay Nat. Hist. Soc., vol.44, no.2, p.291, Dec., 1943.

OLD CAP COUGAR. S. Omar Barker. Sports Afield, Minneapolis, vol.119, no.4, pp.62-63, 136-139, illus., Apr., 1948.

DEVIL'S CLAWS. (Canada Lynx.) Edwin J. Becker. Rod and Gun in Canada, Montreal, vol.49, no.10, pp.11-12, 36, illus., Mar., 1948.

NOOSING TIGERS. H.A. Boas. Jour. Bombay Nat. Hist. Soc., vol.32, p.790, May 31, 1928.

THE KNEELING NUN LION! Percy Brown. Outdoorsman, Columbus, vol.90, no.4, pp. 32-33, 66-67, illus., July-Aug., 1948.

MAN-EATING TIGER. (Account of Capture of Tiger.) Frank H. Buck. Parks and Recreation, vol.9, pp.366-371, Feb., 1926.

OLD DECCAN DAYS. MY TIGER-HUNTING JOURNAL IN 1899. R.G. Burton. Jour. Bombay Nat. Hist. Soc., vol.35, no.4, pp.761-770, July 15, 1932.

EXPERIENCES WITH MAN-EATING TIGERS IN CHINA. PART 4. METHODS IN TIGER HUNTING WITH OBSERVATIONS THEREON. Harry R. Caldwell. The National Review, China, Foochow, pp.1-7, 1914.

NATIVE METHODS OF TIGER HUNTING IN FUKIEN. (Shooting With Poisoned Arrows.) Harry R. Caldwell. China Jour., vol.11, no.1, p.48, July, 1929.

COUGAR TRAILS. Bertram Chichester. Rod and Gun in Canada, Montreal, vol.45, no.3, pp.12-13, 27, illus., Aug., 1943.

TIGER SMOKED TO DEATH IN A CAVE. S.A. Christopher. Jour. Bombay Nat. Hist. Soc., vol.39, no.2, pp.385-386, Apr.15, 1937.

THE FASTEST HUNT IN THE WORLD. IN ONE OF THEIR OLDEST AND FAVORITE SPORTS THE PRINCES OF INDIA DEPEND UPON THE FLEETEST-FOOTED ANIMAL ON EARTH, THE CHEETAH OR HUNTING LEOPARD. C. Suydam Cutting. Nat. Hist., New York, vol.41, no.3, pp.179-181, illus., Mar., 1938.

A TIGER HUNT IN NEPAL. C. Suydam Cutting. Nat. Hist., New York, vol.34, no.1, pp.45-52, illus., Jan.-Feb., 1934.

DECOYING TIGER BY SOUND. M.O. Daly. Jour. Bombay Nat. Hist. Soc., vol.33, no. 3, pp.696-697, May 31, 1929.

BEN LILLY FOLLOWED THE LION TRAILS. (Mountain Lion.) J. Frank Dobie. New Mexico, Albuquerque, vol.27, no.2, pp.24, 35-39, illus., Feb., 1949.

IN QUEST OF THE SPOTTED LION. K.C. Gandar Dower. Field, London, vol.166, no. 4306, p.21, illus., July 6, 1935.

WILDCAT IN THE RAIN. Ben East. Field and Stream, New York, vol.49, no.9, pp. 32-34, 70-72, illus., Jan., 1945.

BOBCAT HUNT. Otto Failing. Michigan Conserv., Lansing, vol.18, no.1, pp.21-22, Feb., 1949.

UTAH LION HUNT. Helene Fischer. Field and Stream, New York, vol.51, no.11, pp. 29-31, illus., Mar., 1947.

ON THE TRAIL OF THE LORD TIGER. (Hunting Tiger.) Henry C. Flower, Jr. Asia, vol.20, no.9, pp.893-897, Oct., 1920.

KILLERS OF THE RIMROCK. (Cougar) Monroe H. Goode. Field and Stream, New York, vol.48, no.2, pp.32-34, 75-76; no. 3, pp.35, 60-61, illus., June, July, 1943.

THE REAL COUGAR. Monroe H. Goode. Field and Stream, New York, vol.49, no.4, pp.26-27, 70-72, illus., Aug., 1944.

TIGERLAND. REMINISCENCES OF FORTY YEARS' SPORT AND ADVENTURE IN BENGAL. Charles E. Gouldsbury. London, Chapman and Hall, ltd., pp.xvii+261, illus.24, pls., 1913.

COUGARS FALL FOR PISTOLS. W. J. Grandberg. Outdoor Life, New York, vol. 104, no.4, pp.26-28, 78-79, illus., Oct., 1949.

HUNTING MOUNTAIN LIONS. Lorin Hall. Outdoor Life, vol.68, no.5, pp.18-19, 70-71, figs.3, Nov., 1931.

COUGAR CUNNING. Frank C. Hibben. Field and Stream, New York, vol.50, no.11, pp. 42-43, 124-125, Mar., 1946.

THE EAGLE CAT. (Mountain Lion.) Frank C. Hibben. Field and Stream, New York, vol.54, no.2, pp.50-51, 132-136, illus., June, 1949.

HUNTING AMERICAN LIONS. Frank C. Hibben. T.Y.Crowell, New York, pp.225, illus., 1948.

DANGER ON THE TRAIL. (Mountain Lion) Charles F. Hilder. Outdoorsman, Chicago, vol.86, no.2, whole no.507, pp.14-15, 24, illus., Mar.-Apr., 1944.

TIGER ON THE LOOSE. (Jaguar.) Howard Hill. Field and Stream, New York, vol.54, no.3, pp.54, 55, 115, illus., July, 1949.

TRAPPING BOBCATS IN KAY COUNTY, OKLAHOMA. Wallace Hughes. Oklahoma Game and Fish News, Oklahoma City, vol. 6, no.12, pp.12-13, illus., Dec., 1950.

GREAT LION KILLER. John A. Hunter. Life, Chicago, vol.33, no.3, pp.93-107, illus., July 21, 1952.

SMOKING A PANTHER TO DEATH. Chief Of Ichalkaranji. Jour. Bombay Nat. Hist. Soc., vol.39, no.4, p.850, Dec. 15, 1937.

SOUTH TEXAS BIG GAME HUNT. (Jaguar) Charles G. Jones. Texas Game and Fish, Austin, vol.4, no.4, pp.29, 32, Mar., 1946.

JAGUARS. HUNTING BIG CATS IN CENTRAL AMERICA. Frank Jones. Field and Stream, no.6, pp.28-29, 84-85, Oct., 1929.

LEOPARD HUNTING ON THE CAMPUS OF THE FUKIEN CHRISTIAN UNIVERSITY, FOOCHOW. C.R. Kellogg. China Jour., vol.6, pp.209-210, Apr., 1927.

LADY AND THE LIONS. (Hunting Pumas) Bess Kennedy. McGraw-Hill Book Co., Inc., New York and London, pp.221, illus., 1942.

LION HUNTING: ACE OF SPORTS. (Mountain Lion In Colorado.) William L. Kent. Colorado Outdoors Mag., vol.6, no.1, pp.6-9, Jan., 1957.

LEARNING FROM THE MOUNTAIN LION. William J. Long. Sports Afield, vol.127, no.3, pp.30-31, 63-68, illus., Mar., 1952.

YELLOW SLAYER. (Mountain Lion) Jason Lucas. Sports Afield, Minneapolis, vol.115, no.4, pp.38-39, 60, 63-68, illus., Apr., 1946.

BIG BAD CATS. V.E. Lynch. Fur-Fish-Game (Harding's Mag.), Columbus, vol. 79, no.10, pp.8-9, 28-29, illus., Oct., 1945.

LIONS AS LIVE STOCK. Roman J. Miller. Field and Stream, vol.36, no.4, pp.24-25, 58-59, Aug., 1931.

LION HUNTING IN TANGANYIKA. Walter Mittelholzer. Field, London, vol.159, no. 4123, pp.4-6, figs.3, Jan. 2, 1932.

TIGER HUNTING IN NEPAL. William J. Morden. Nat. Hist., vol.29, pp.339-352, illus., Aug., 1929.

TIGER 'POOKING.' R.C. Morris. Jour. Bombay Nat. Hist. Soc., vol.33, no.1, pp.197-198, Sep. 30, 1928.

USE OF ARTIFICIAL LIGHT IN PANTHER SHOOTING. R.C. Morris. Jour. Bombay Nat. Hist. Soc., vol.35, no.4, pp.887-888, July 15, 1932.

HUNTING WITH CHEETAHS. F.C. O'Rorke. Field, London, vol. 163, no.4240, p.697, illus., Mar. 31, 1934.

TIGER 'POOKING'. E.G. Phythian-Adams. Jour. Bombay Nat. Hist. Soc., vol.43, no.3, p.517, Dec., 1942.

DEATH OF A KILLER. (Leopard) Hugh Prior. Field and Stream, New York, vol.51, no.2, pp.60, 122, June, 1946.

SOME SUGGESTIONS ON PANTHER SHOOTING. Surguha Of Ramanuj. Jour. Bombay Nat. Hist. Soc., vol.35, no.2, pp.411-442, Oct. 15, 1931.

HUNTING THE JAGUAR. Kemit Roosevelt. (In) N.American Big Game. A Book of the Boone and Crocket Club, Compiled by the Committee On Records of N.American Big Game. Charles Scribners Sons, New York, pp.426-431, 1939.

(HUNTING LYNX WITH BEAGLE.) Lojakt med stovare. E. Sandling. Svensk Jakt, Stockholm, vol.87, no.11, pp.339-340, illus., Nov., 1949.

BOBCAT AT BAY. E.J. Sawyer. Western Sportsman, Denver, vol.7, no.5, pp.3-4, Oct., 1941.

WILDCAT HUNTING IN THE MAINE WOODS. Arthur Scribner. Hunting and Fishing, Philadelphia, vol.25, no.2, pp.55, 96, Feb., 1948.

HAND TO CLAW COMBAT. THE THRILL OF HUNTING THE BRAZILIAN JAGUAR WITH A SPEAR. Alejandre Siemel. Sportsman, Concord, N.H., vol.9, no.6, pp.47-48, 86, illus., June, 1931.

HOW TO MAKE A CAT TRAP. James Silver. U.S. Dept. Agric., Leaflet no.50, pp.4, fig.1, Nov., 1929.

KILLER ON THE DOSY. (Cougar) Aubrey F. Taylor. Outdoor Life, New York, vol. 106, no.6, pp.17, 60-63, illus., Dec., 1950.

COUGARS CAN BE SPITEFUL. C. V. Tench. Fur-Fish-Game(Harding's Mag.), Columbus, vol.81, no.3, pp.16-17, illus., Mar., 1946.

TIGER SHOOTING IN BURMA. W.S. Thom. Jour. Bombay Nat. Hist. Soc., vol.37, no.3, pp.573-603, pls.1-2, Dec. 15, 1934.

AN AMATEUR AND A TIGER. Vernon L. Whitney. Field and Stream, no.5, pp.26-27, 71-73, Sep., 1929.

OBSERVATIONS ON LEOPARD OR PANTHER AND ITS SHIKAR. H.S. Wood. Jour. Bengal Nat. Hist. Soc., Darjeeling, vol.17, no.2, pp.59-61, Oct., 1942.

OBSERVATIONS ON THE LEOPARD OR PANTHER AND ITS SHIKAR. H.S. Wood. Jour. Bengal Nat. Hist. Soc., Darjeeling, vol.14, no.4, pp.134-137, Apr., 1940.

OBSERVATIONS ON THE TIGER AND ITS SHIKAR. H.S. Wood. Jour. Bengal Nat. Hist. Soc., Darjeeling, vol.14, no.1, pp.19-24, June, 1939; no.3, pp.92-93, Jan., 1940.

HINTS ON BOBCAT TRAPPING. P. Stanley Young. U.S.Dept. Agric., Leaflet no.78, pp.6, figs.4, June, 1931; U.S.Dept. Interior, Fish and Wildl. Serv., Circ.no.1, pp.6, figs.4, 1941.

HINTS ON MOUNTAIN-LION TRAPPING. P. Stanley Young. U.S. Dept. Agric., Bur. Biol. Surv., Leaflet no.94, pp.8, figs.3, Apr., 1933.

MOUNTAIN LION TRAPPING. P. Stanley Young. U.S. Dept. Interior, Fish and Wildl. Serv., Circ.no.6, pp.7, figs.4, 1945.

BELEAGUERED BOBCAT AROUSES STERLINGITES. Outdoors in Illinois, Springfield, vol.16, no.2, p.14, illus., Spring, 1950.

BIG GAME HUNTING IN NEPAL. "RINGING" TIGERS IN HIGH GRASS. Field, London, vol.155, no.4020, p.45, Jan. 11, 1930.

BOBCAT HUNTERS TEAM UP ON A DEER KILLER. Outdoor Life, New York, vol.103, no.2, pp.51-55, illus., Feb., 1949.

HARK TO 'EM! A JULY HOUND DARES A FLORIDA PANTHER TO CHARGE. Field and Stream, New York, vol.49, no.6, p. 29, illus., Oct., 1944.

PANTHER HUNT IN PENNSYLVANIA. Port Folio, Philadelphia, vol.31, no.266, pp. 494-499, June, 1824.

PHILIP MAN KILLS LYNX WITH A CLUB. S. Dakota Conserv.Digest, Pierre, p.9, Feb., 1940.

QUAIL HUNTER AT HOME, TIGER KILLER IN INDIA. Alabama Conservation, Montgomery, vol.16, no.11, p.9, May, 1945.

Hybrids

TIGER-LION HYBRIDS. C.W.G. Eifrig. Jour. Mamm., vol.18, no.4, p.516, Nov., 1937.

(LEOPARD-PUMA HYBRID.) Ein Leopard-Puma-Bastard. Theodor Haltenorth. Zeitschr. f. Saeugetierk., vol.11, no.3, pp. 285-288, Dec. 30, 1936.

(BACK BREEDING OF A LION-TIGER CROSS WITH A LION IN THE SECOND GENERATION AND VETERINARY OBSERVATIONS DURING THE RAISING OF THE DELICATE YOUNG.) Ueber ein Rueckkreuzung eines Loewen-Tiger-Bastards mit einem Loewen in der zweiten Generation und tieraerztliche Beobachtungen bei der Aufzucht der empfindlichen Jungtiere. Alwin Kemna. Zool. Garten, Leipzig, n.F., vol. 20, nos.2-3, pp.122-126, illus., 1953.

(CONSIDERATIONS ON A PROBLEMATIC CROSS OF FELIDS.) Considerazioni sopra un problematico incrocio di felidi. Pasquale Mola. Boll. Soc. Zool. Italiana, Rome, fasc.1-2, pp.4, illus., 1908.

CROSSING WILD CATS WITH TAME. Frances Pitt. Field, London, vol.163, no. 4252, p.1528, June 23, 1934.

LION-TIGER HYBRID. R.I. Pocock. Field, London, vol.153, p.355, illus., Feb. 28, 1929.

ON A HYBRID WILD CAT. R.I. Pocock. Proc. Zool. Soc. London, pp.749-750, figs.194-195, June 4, 1908.

SKULL OF A LION-TIGER HYBRID. R.I. Pocock. Proc. Zool. Soc. London, pt.3, pp.736-740, figs.2, Sep. 12, 1935.

STRIPED LIONS AND STRIPELESS TIGERS. R.I. Pocock. Field, London, vol.159, no. 4127, p.149, figs.4, Jan. 30, 1932.

(TIGER-LION HYBRID AT THE ZOOLOGICAL PARK OF THE BOIS DE VINCENNES.) Un hybride de Tigre-Lion au parc zoologique du Bois de Vincennes. Ach. Urbain, J. Rinjard. Mammalia, Paris, vol. 14, no.4, pp.103-104, pl.4, Dec., 1950.

FATHER A LION; MOTHER A TIGER. THREE RARE HYBRIDS IN SOUTH AFRICA. Illus. London News, vol.186, no.5004, p. 435, figs.3, Mar. 16, 1935.

Longevity

REMARKABLE AGE ATTAINED BY A BOBCAT. T. Donald Carter. Jour. Mamm., vol. 36, no.2, p.290, May, 1955.

(LONG LIFE SPAN OF A LYNX (LYNX L. LYNX LINNÉ 1758).) Lange Lebensdauer eines Luchses, Lynx l. lynx (Linné, 1758). G. Steinbacher. Saeugetierk. Mitteil., Stuttgart, vol.1, no.2, p.78, Apr. 1, 1953.

Madagascar

(A CURIOUS EXAMPLE OF THE SURVIVAL OF A TYPE OF MAMMAL THROUGH GEOLOGICAL TIMES: THE SMALL AELURICTIS OF MADAGASCAR.) Un curieux exemple de survivance d'un type de mammifère à travers les temps geologiques' le petit Aeluríctis de Madagascar. L. Joleaud. Bull. Soc. Zool. France, vol.49, pp.10-19, 1924.

Measurements, Weights

LENGTH OF TIGERS AND PANTHERS. R.G. Burton. Jour. Bombay Nat. Hist.Soc., vol.27, p.163, July 1, 1920.

NOTE ON THE RECORD INDIAN LION (PANTHERA LEO PERSICA MEYER). P.R. Cadell. Jour. Bombay Nat. Hist. Soc., vol. 38, no.1, p.181, Aug. 15, 1935.

MEASUREMENTS OF TIGERS AND PANTHERS. Stewart Capper. Jour. Bombay Nat. Hist. Soc., vol.27, p.936, July 31, 1921.

VERY SMALL TIGER. Merle Taylor Dunn. Fauna, Philadelphia, vol.2, no.2, pp. 28-31, illus., June, 1940.

THE SIZE OF THE JUNGLE CAT (FELIS CHAUS AFFINIS). E.P. Gee. Jour. Bombay Nat. Hist. Soc., vol.39, no.4, pp. 850-851, illus., Dec. 15, 1937.

WEIGHTS OF EASTERN BOBCATS. W.J. Hamilton, Jr. Jour. Mamm., vol.21, no.2, p. 218, May 14, 1940.

(DETERMINING THE MAXIMAL SIZE OF FELIS SILVESTRIS BRISS.) Zur Festellung der maximalen Groesse von Felis silvestris Briss. H. Helbing. Bericht ueber die 15te Jahresversammlung der Schweizerischen Palaeont. Gesell., Basel (Ecologae geologicae Helvetiae), vol.28, no.2, pp. 577-580, figs.3, 1935.

WHAT IS THE RECORD PANTHER? W.M. Logan Home. Jour. Bombay Nat. Hist. Soc., vol.32, pp.587-588, Jan. 15, 1928.

AN OVERSIZE BOBCAT. Allie I. Libby. Outdoorsman, Chicago, vol.86, no.2, whole no.507, p.7, Mar.-Apr., 1944.

A RECORD PANTHER. E. Limouzin. Jour. Bombay Nat. Hist. Soc., vol.33, no.3, pp.699-700, May 31, 1929.

MEASUREMENTS OF LIONS. Denis D. Lyell. Field, London, vol.167, no.4338, p.459, Feb. 29, 1936.

MEASUREMENTS OF TIGERS IN THE NAGA HILLS, ASSAM. G.H.L. Marshall. Jour. Bombay Nat. Hist. Soc., vol.39, no. 3, p.615, Sep. 25, 1937.

MEASUREMENTS OF TIGERS SHOT IN THE NAGA HILLS. G.H.L. Marshall. Jour. Bombay Nat. Hist. Soc., vol.40, no. 4, p.740, May, 1939. (A Correction.)

PROPORTION OF THE SEXES IN TIGERS. R.C. Morris. Jour. Bombay Nat. Hist. Soc., vol.33, no.4, p.972, Oct. 15, 1929.

TAILLESS TIGER. R.C. Morris. Field, London, vol.164, p.216, illus., July 28, 1934.

RECORD SCOTCH WILD CAT. (Felis silvestris grampia.) R.I. Pocock. Scottish Nat., vol.206, pp.33-39, 1934.

MEASUREMENTS OF PANTHERS. E.G. Pythiam-Adams. Jour. Bombay Nat. Hist. Soc., vol.40, no.3, p.554, Dec., 1938.

MEASUREMENTS OF TIGERS SHOT IN THE NILGIRIS 1925-37. E.G.Pythian-Adams. Jour. Bombay Nat. Hist. Soc., vol.40, no.3, p.553, Dec., 1938.

MEASUREMENTS OF PANTHERS. J. R. Stockley Roper. Jour. Bombay Nat. Hist. Soc., vol.33, no.2, p.426, Feb. 15, 1929.

LARGE PANTHER. Yashodhar Singh. Jour. Bombay Nat. Hist. Soc., vol.41, no.3, p.656, Apr., 1940; vol.42, no.1, pp.183-184, Dec., 1940.

SHORT-TAILED TIGER. Maharaja of Surguja. Jour. Bombay Nat. Hist. Soc., vol. 38, no.2, pp.384-385, Dec. 1, 1935.

WEIGHTS OF LIONS. S.P. Teare. Field, London, vol.167, no.4355, p.1444, June 13, 1936.

Methods, Techniques

DETERMINATION OF THE ABUNDANCE OF COUGAR. Murray L. Johnson, Leo K. Couch. Jour. Mamm., vol.35, no.2, pp. 255-256, May 26, 1954.

RETICULO-SPINAL TRACTS IN THE CAT. MARCHI METHOD. James W. Papez. Jour. Comp. Neur., vol.41, pp.365-400, illus., Aug. 15, 1926.

MEANS OF DISTINGUISHING THE CANADA LYNX FROM THE BAY LYNX. Frederick W. True. Science, vol.7, no.171, pp.428-429, May 14, 1886.

QUICK METHOD OF PRESERVING CATS FOR DISSECTION. Horace Elmer Wood 2nd. Science, n.s., vol.65, p.261, Mar. 11, 1927.

HYPNOTISING A LION AND OTHER ANIMALS: AID FOR ZOO "VETS." Illus. London News, vol.191, no.5149, p.1158, illus., Dec. 25, 1937.

Mexico, Central and South America

NOTES ON THE SYNONYMY AND NOMENCLATURE OF THE SMALLER SPOTTED CATS OF TROPICAL AMERICA. J.A.Allen. Bull. Amer. Mus. Nat. Hist., vol.41, pp. 341-419, figs.1-31, Oct. 3, 1919.

(ALSO IN NORTHEAST PARAGUAY: FELIS BRACCATA.) Felis braccata auch in Nordostparaguay. O. Antonius. Zool. Garten, n. F., Leipzig, vol.6, nos.1-3, p.58, May, 1933.

ON FELIS MELANURA. R. Ball. Proc. Zool. Soc. London, pt.12, p.128, 1844.

(THE LIVING AND EXTINCT JAGUARS OF SOUTH AMERICA.) Los yaguares vivientes y extinguidos de la América austral. A. Cabrera. Notas prelim. Mus. de La Plata, Buenos Aires, vol.3, pp.9-39, pls.1-11, Jan. 31, 1934.

(NOTES ON RECENT PUMAS OF SOUTH AMERICA.) Notas sobre los pumas de la América austral. A. Cabrera. Rev. Chilena Hist. Nat. vol.33, pp.312-320, pl. 19, 1929.

(SYNONYMIC CATALOGUE OF THE SOUTH AMERICAN FELIDAE.) Catálogo sinonimico de los Felidae Sudamericanos. A. Cabrera. Rev. Chilena Hist. Nat., vol. 15, no.1, pp.40-54, Feb., 1911.

RACES OF THE OCELOT AND MARGAY IN MIDDLE AMERICA. E.A. Goldman. Jour. Mamm., vol.24, no.3, pp.372-385, Aug. 17, 1943.

TWO NEW OCELOTS FROM MEXICO. (Felis pardalis nelsoni; F.p.sonoriensis.) E.A. Goldman. Jour. Mamm., vol.6, no. 2, pp.122-124, May, 1925.

NOTICE OF A NEW SPECIES OF JAGUAR FROM MAZATLAN, LIVING IN THE SOCIETY'S GARDENS. John Edward Gray. Proc. Zool. Soc. London, pt.25, p.278, pl.58, 1857.

LION IN THE CARMENS. (Felis concolor stanleyana in Coahuila, Mexico.) Tappan Gregory. Chicago Nat. (Chicago Acad.Sci.), vol.1, no.3, pp.70-81, 110-120, 1938.

TWO NEW SOUTH AMERICAN JAGUARS. N. Hollister. Proc. U.S. Nat. Mus., vol. 48, pp.169-170, pl.5, Dec. 15, 1914.

ONCIFELIS GEOFFROYI IN CHILE. F. Guillermo Mann. Investig. Zool.Chilenas, Univ. Chile, vol.3, nos.8-10, pp.139-140, Oct. 25, 1957. (In Spanish.)

OBSERVATIONS ON THREE SPECIMENS OF THE GENUS FELIS PRESENTED TO THE SOCIETY BY CHARLES DARWIN, ESQ., CORR. MEMB. Z. S. W.Martin. Proc. Zool. Soc. London, pt.5, pp.3-4, 1837.

NEW PUMA FROM BRAZIL. (Felis concolor borbensis.) E.W. Nelson, E.A. Goldman. Jour. Washington Acad. Sci., vol.23, no.11, pp.523-525, Nov. 15, 1933.

NEW PUMA FROM LOWER CALIFORNIA. J.C. Phillips. Proc. Biol. Soc. Washington, vol.25, pp.85-86, pl.5, May 4, 1912.

GROUPS OF THE SMALL AND MEDIUM-SIZED SOUTH AMERICAN FELIDAE. R.I. Pocock. Ann. and Mag. Nat. Hist., London, ser.8, vol.20, pp.43-47, July, 1917.

(SOUTH AMERICAN BUSH, MOUNTAIN, AND STEPPE CATS.) Suedamerikanische Busch-, Berg- und Steppenkatzen. Friedrich Schwangart. Abhandlung der Bayerischen Akademie der Wissenschaften. Math.-Naturwissenschaftliche Abt., n. F., Hft.49, pp.44, illus., pls.7, 1941.

ON A NEW FORM OF PUMA FROM PATAGONIA. Oldfield Thomas. Ann. and Mag. Nat. Hist., ser.7, vol.8, no.45, pp.188-189, Sep., 1901.

Museum Collections

LION GROUP AND ITS CREATION. G. L. Carlisle, Jr. Nat.Hist., New York, vol.37, no.1, pp.16-23, illus., Jan., 1936.

ADDITIONAL OBSERVATIONS ON THE SPECIES OF CATS (FELIDAE) IN THE BRITISH MUSEUM. J.E. Gray. Proc.Zool. Soc. London, pp.874-876, 1867.

NOTES ON CERTAIN SPECIES OF CATS IN THE COLLECTION OF THE BRITISH MUSEUM. J.E. Gray. Proc. Zool. Soc. London, pp.394-405, pls.14-15, 1867.

EXAMPLES OF THE COLOCOLO AND OF THE PAMPAS CAT IN THE BRITISH MUSEUM. R.I. Pocock. Ann. and Mag. Nat. Hist., London, ser. 11, vol.7, pp.257-274, Mar., 1941.

PAIR OF INDIAN LIONS PRESENTED TO THE BRITISH MUSEUM BY H. H. THE NAWAB OF JUNAGADH. R.I. Pocock. Jour. Bombay Nat. Hist. Soc., vol.38, no.2, pp.382-384, Dec. 1, 1935.

A JAGUAR FOR THE MUSEUM. C. V. Whitney. Nat. Hist., New York, vol.48, no.1, p.24, illus., June, 1941.

Neurology

LOCALIZATION IN THE GANGLION SEMILUNARE OF THE CAT. Wm. F. Allen. Jour. Comp. Neur., vol.38, pp.1-26, fig.11, Dec. 15, 1924.

AFFERENT CONNECTIONS OF THE 1ST, 2ND, AND 3RD CERVICAL NERVES IN THE CAT. José Escolar. Jour. Comp. Neurol., Philadelphia, vol.89, no.2, pp. 79-92, Oct., 1948.

NOTES ON THE GOLGI APPARATUS IN SPINAL-GANGLION CELLS OF THE CAT. Benjamin Esterman, Abraham J. Gitlitz. Anat. Rec., vol.36, pp.319-324, illus., Oct. 25, 1927.

NIGROHYPOTHALAMIC FIBERS IN THE CAT. Donald L. Kimmel. Proc. Soc. Exper. Biol. and Med., Utica, vol.52, no.1, pp.51-52, Jan., 1943.

NEURAL MECHANISM OF SEXUAL BEHAVIOR IN THE FEMALE CAT. J. P. Meas. Nature, London, vol.144, no.3648, pp.598-599, Sep. 30, 1939.

STRUCTURE AND FUNCTION OF THE CEREBRAL CORTEX IN THE NEW-BORN CAT (FELIS DOMESTICA). W. Riese. Confinia Neurologica, Basel, vol.7, fasc. 1-2, pp.55-62, fig.1, 1946.

GLOSSO-PHARYNGEAL, THE ACCESSORY AND THE HYPOGLOSSAL NERVES IN THE DOMESTIC CAT. T.B. Stowell. Proc.Amer. Philos. Soc., vol.25, no.127, pp.89-104, pls.3, Mar. 2, 1888.

TRIGEMINUS NERVE IN THE DOMESTIC CAT (FELIS DOMESTICA). T.B.Stowell. Proc. Amer. Philos. Soc., vol.21, pp.459-478, 1886.

VAGUS NERVE IN THE DOMESTIC CAT (FELIS DOMESTICA). T.B.Stowell.Proc. Amer. Philos. Soc., vol.20, pp.123-138, pls.2, July 15, 1881.

DISTRIBUTION AND PROBABLE SIGNIFICANCE OF UNMYELINATED NERVE FIBERS IN THE TRIGEMINAL NERVE OF THE CAT. William F. Windle. Jour.Comp. Neur., vol.41, pp.453-477, illus., Aug. 15, 1926.

North America

FUR BEARING ANIMALS OF THE UNITED STATES. THE CANADA LYNX. Frank G. Ashbrook, Horace J. McMullen. Fur Jour., vol.3, no.1, pp.12, 39-41, illus., Feb., 1929.

NOTES ON THE LYNXES OF EASTERN NORTH AMERICA, WITH DESCRIPTIONS OF TWO NEW SPECIES. Outram Bangs. Proc. Biol.Soc. Washington, vol.11, pp.47-51, figs.1-2, pl.2, Mar. 16, 1897.

PUMAS. Jack Bowman. Texas Game and Fish, Austin, vol.5, no.6, pp.10, 23, illus., May, 1947.

FEW RANDOM NOTES ON WILD CATS. H.H. Brimley. N.Carolina Wildl.Conservation, Raleigh, vol.6, no.9, pp.5-6, 14, illus., Sep., 1942.

KING OF AMERICAN CATS. (Puma) J.B. Burr. Texas Game and Fish, vol.6, no.4, pp.6, 17-18, illus., Mar., 1948.

MOUNTAIN LION: FACT AND FANCY. Bryan L. Denton, William L. Kent. Colorado Outdoors Mag., vol.6, no.1, pp.10-11, Jan., 1957.

MOUNTAIN LION. Stuart Downing. Canadian Nature, Toronto, vol.8, no.5, pp.154-155, col.pl., Nov.-Dec., 1946.

THE BOBCAT--HUNTER AND HUNTED. Otto Failing. Michigan Conservation, Lansing, vol.22, no.1, pp.7-9, illus., Jan., 1953.

JAGUARS OF NORTH AMERICA. E. A. Goldman. Proc. Biol. Soc. Washington, vol. 45, pp.143-146, Sep.9, 1932.

A SEXTET FROM AMERICAN CATDOM. (Jaguar, Puma, Ocelot, Yagouaroundi, Lynx, and Bobcat.) Carra E. Horsfall. Nature Mag., vol.11, pp.145-146, col.illus., Mar., 1928.

MOUNTAIN LION. Jason Lucas. Sports Afield, New York, vol.120, no.6, pp.46-47, 70-74, illus., Dec., 1948.

THE AMERICAN JAGUARS. Edgar A. Mearns. Proc. Biol. Soc. Washington, vol. 14, pp.137-143, Aug. 9, 1901.

DESCRIPTION OF A NEW OCELOT FROM TEXAS AND NORTHEASTERN MEXICO. Edgar A. Mearns. Proc. Biol. Soc. Wash., vol.14, pp.145-148, Aug. 9, 1901.

TWO NEW CATS OF THE EYRA GROUP FROM NORTH AMERICA. Edgar A. Mearns. Proc. Biol. Soc. Wash., vol.14, pp.149-151, Aug. 9, 1901.

SPEAKING OF CATS. (Bobcats.) Bill Nelson. Outdoorsman, Columbus, vol.84, no.1, pp. 12-14, 34-36, illus., Jan., 1942.

OLD FELIS CONCOLOR. AN ARTICLE ON THE HABITS AND THE HUNTING OF THIS LARGE AMERICAN CAT. Jack O'Connor. Field and Stream, vol.41, no.4, pp.36-37, 64-65, illus., Aug., 1936.

PUMA, COUGAR, PANTHER? Edalee Orcutt. San Diego Zoonooz, vol.21, no.8, pp.5-7, illus., Sep., 1948.

SELF-PORTRAIT OF A MOUNTAIN LION. Robert T. Orr. Pacific Discovery, California Acad. Sci., vol.8, no.5, pp.26-27, Sep.-Oct., 1955.

MOUNTAIN LION, OUR LARGEST CAT (COUGAR, PUMA OR PANTHER). Ralph S. Palmer. Bull. to the Schools, Univ. State of New York, vol.40, no.6, p.176, Feb., 1954.

NOTES ON THE BOBCATS (LYNX RUFUS) OF EASTERN NORTH AMERICA WITH THE DESCRIPTION OF A NEW RACE. Randolph L. Peterson, Stuart C. Downing. Contrib. Royal Ontario Mus. Zool. and Palaeontol., Toronto, no.33, pp.1-23, illus., Apr. 8, 1952.

THE AMERICAN COUGAR. Edward A. Preble. Nature Mag., Washington, vol.38, no.3, p.137, illus., Mar., 1945.

LADY OF LEISURE. (Cougar) William M. Rush. Fauna, Philadelphia, vol.6, no.4, pp.114-118, illus., Dec., 1944.

COUGAR: THE GREAT AMERICAN LION. W.J. Schoonmaker. Nat. Humane Review, vol.23, no.3, pp.10-11, illus., Mar., 1935.

CAT THAT NOBODY KNOWS. (Bobcat) Clayt Seagers. New York State Conservationist, Albany, vol.3, no.3, pp.32, Dec., 1948-Jan., 1949.

FELINE FLYING SAUCER. (Cougar) Clayt Seagears. New York State Conservationist, Albany, vol.10, no.3, p.48, Jan., 1956.

MOUNTAIN LION, OCELOTS, LYNXES AND THEIR KIN. (Popular Account of North American Cats.) R.W. Shufeldt. Amer. Forestry, vol.27, pp.629-636, 659, figs.8, Oct., 1921.

PUMA, OR AMERICAN LION; FELIS CONCOLOR OF LINAEUS. Frederick William True. U.S. Nat. Mus., Ann. Rep., Washington, pp.591-608, pl.,(1889) 1891; Science, vol.19, no.417, pp.169-171, Mar. 25, 1892.

GHOST OF NORTH AMERICA: THE STORY OF THE EASTERN PANTHER. Bruce S. Wright. New York, pp.140, photos 23, figs., 1959.

PUMA, MYSTERIOUS AMERICAN CAT. PART I. HISTORY, LIFE HABITS, ECONOMIC STATUS, AND CONTROL. PART II. CLASSIFICATION OF THE RACES OF THE PUMA. Stanley P. Young, Edward A. Goldman. N.Amer. Wildl. Inst., Wash., D.C., pp.xvi+358, figs.6, pls.93, Nov. 16, 1946.

Pelage, Coloration

(A WHITE TIGER.) Ein weisser Tiger. Hans von Boetticher. Zeitschr. f. Saeugetierk., Berlin, vol.7, nos.1-6, p.258, Dec. 15, 1932.

SIAMESE, AN ALBINISTIC COLOR VARIATION IN CATS. W.E. Castle. Amer.Nat., vol.53, pp.265-268, May-June, 1919.

ON A BLACK VARIETY OF FELIS TEMMINCKI FROM SUMATRA. K.W. Dammerman. Treubia, Buitenzorg, vol.12, livr.2, pp.133-134, Oct., 1930.

(A TRICOLORED CAT.) Un chat tricolore. Ed. Dechambre. Mammalia, Paris, vol.15, no.4, p.211, Dec., 1951.

THE KING'S WHITE TIGER. J.G. Dollman. Nat. Hist. Mag., London, vol.1, no.1, pp.22-23, illus., Jan., 1937.

AN UNUSUALLY COLOURED LEOPARD. (Partly White) J.G. Dollman. Field, London, vol.149, p.153, Jan. 27, 1927.

A PALE COLOUR FORM OF THE PANTHER. H.A. Fooks. Jour. Bombay Nat. Hist. Soc., Bombay, vol.42, no.2, pp.435-436, photo, Apr., 1941.

EXHIBITION OF THE SKIN OF A LEOPARD FROM JAPAN. Louis Fraser. Proc. Zool. Soc. London, pt.31, p.510, 1865.

EXHIBITION OF THE SKIN OF A PUMA. Edmund Thomas Higgins. Proc. Zool. Soc. London, p.377, 1868.

HAIRLESS SIAMESE CATS. Etienne Letard. Jour. Heredity, vol.29, no.5, pp.173-175, illus., May, 1938.

DISTRIBUTION AND COLORATION OF THE LYNX (LYNX LYNX). D.G. Lowndes. Jour. Bombay Nat. Hist. Soc., vol.34, no.1, pp. 234-235, Mar. 1, 1930.

ON AN ABNORMAL LEOPARD SKIN. R. Lydekker. Proc. Zool. Soc. London, pp. 1-3, fig.1, June, 1908.

EXHIBITION OF A PHOTOGRAPH OF A CHEETAH SKIN FROM ARABIA. T. C. S. Morrison-Scott. Agenda and Abst. Sci. Meetings Zool. Soc. London, no.1, p.2, Mar. 5, 1951; Proc. Zool. Soc. London, vol.121, pt.1, p.201, May 22, 1951.

(ON THE SOLE COLOR OF THE HIND FEET OF FELIS CATUS, F. CALIGATA, F. MANICULATA, AND F. DOMESTICA.) Ueber die Sohlenfaerbung am Hinterfusse von Felis catus, F. caligata, F. maniculata, und F. domestica. Alfred Nehring. Sitz. Ber. Gesell. Naturf. Freunde Berlin, no.3, pp.26-27, figs.2, Mar. 15, 1887.

OBSERVATIONS ON A COLLECTION OF SKINS FROM SIERRA LEONE, EXHIBITED BY MR. GARNETT. William Ogilby. Proc. Zool. Soc. London, pt.7, p.94, 1839.

(A WHITE TIGER.) Ein weisser Tiger. Hans Petzsch. Zeitschr. f. Saeugetierk., Berlin, vol.8, nos.3-6, p.280, Dec. 20, 1933.

EXHIBITION OF SKIN OF YOUNG CHEETAH (ACINONYX JUBATUS) FROM NORTHERN RHODESIA. R.I. Pocock. Proc. Zool. Soc. London, pt.3, pp.814-816, fig., 1932.

THE LION'S MANE--IS IT LUXURIANT ONLY IN CAPTIVITY? R.I. Pocock. Field, London, vol.158, no.4102, p.208, illus., Aug. 8, 1931.

A REMARKABLE VARIETY OF LEOPARD. (Exhibition of Skin.) R.I. Pocock. Proc. Zool. Soc. London, pt.3, pp.791-795, illus., Sep., 1927.

THE SKIN OF A PERSIAN PANTHER (PANTHERA PARDUS SAXICOLOR). R.I. Pocock. Jour. Bombay Nat. Hist. Soc., vol. 36, no.1, p.236, Nov. 15, 1932.

SKINS OF TWO INTERESTING VARIETIES OF LEOPARD (PANTHERA PARDUS). R.I. Pocock. Proc. Zool. Soc. London, pt.3, pp.733-735, figs.2, Sep. 12, 1935.

THE TRUTH ABOUT THE LION'S MANE. R.I. Pocock. Field, London, vol.155, no. 4034, p.577, Apr. 19, 1930.

VARIATION OF THE PATTERN IN LEOPARDS. R.I. Pocock. Field, London, vol. 148, p.707, Oct. 21, 1926.

BLACK TIGERS. S.H. Prater. Jour. Bombay Nat. Hist. Soc., vol. 39, no.2, pp. 381-382, Apr. 15, 1937.

WHITE TIGERS. F.B. Robinson. Jour. Bombay Nat. Hist. Soc., vol.32, pp.584-585, illus., Jan. 15, 1928.

(COMPARISON OF THE PELAGE OF FELIDS FOUND BY M. G. BABAULT IN THE KIVU REGION (BELGIAN CONGO) WITH THE PELAGE OF GOLDEN CATS OF AFRICA AND ASIA.) Comparison entre le pelage du Félidé trouvé par M. G. Babault dans la région de Kivu (Congo belge), avec les pelages des Chats dorés d'Afrique et d'Asie, étude des poils. M.P. Rode. Bull. Mus. Nat. Hist. Nat. Paris, ser.2, vol.4, no.2, pp.159-161, Feb., 1932.

(ON THE SPOTS OF YOUNG LIONS.) Von der Fleckung junger Loewen. Karl Max Schneider. Zool. Garten, Leipzig, n.F., vol.20, nos.2-3, pp.127-150, illus., 1953.

ON THE CENSUS OF COAT COLORS IN CAT (I). Akio Suzuki. Misc. Repts. Yamashina's Inst. Ornithol. and Zool., Tokyo, no.3, pp.43-44, Dec. 1953. (In Japanese with English summary.)

EXHIBITION OF A SKIN OF A ROYAL TIGER. Robert Swinhoe. Proc. Zool. Soc. London, pt.31, pp.237-239, 1863.

EXHIBITION OF, AND REMARKS UPON, A SKIN OF A MANTCHURIAN TIGER AND CHINESE LEOPARD. Robert Swinhoe. Proc. Zool. Soc. London, pp.3-4, 1870.

ON THE FOETUS OF A PANTHER, EXHIBITING ALL THE MARKINGS OF THE ADULT ANIMAL. Lieut.-Col. W.H. Sykes. Proc. Zool. Soc. London, pt.1, p. 49, 1833.

MELANISM IN THE FELIDAE, WITH SPECIAL REFERENCE TO THE GENUS LYNX. Fred A. Ulmer, Jr. Jour. Mamm., vol.22, no.3, pp.285-288, pl.1, Aug. 14, 1941.

VARIATION IN COLOUR OF TIGERS AND PANTHERS. Van Ingen. Jour. Bombay Nat. Hist. Soc., vol.42, pp.654-655, illus., Aug., 1941.

EXHIBITION OF A TIGER-SKIN (FELIS TIGRIS). Edwin Ward. Proc. Zool. Soc. London, p.102, 1871.

(A BLACK INDIAN GOLDEN-CAT (FELIS TEMMINCKI VIG. HRSF.).) Ein Schwaerzling der indischen Goldkatze (Felis temmincki Vig. Hrsf.). Ad. Wendnagel. Zool. Garten, Leipzig, n.F., vol.10, nos.3-4, pp.114-115, illus., Sep., 1938.

Photography

UNIQUE LION PHOTOGRAPH. Salim A. Ali. Jour. Bombay Nat. Hist. Soc., vol.32, pp. 583-584, pl.1, Jan. 15, 1928.

KING GEORGE THE FIFTH AND THE MUSEUM. (Photographs of Indian Tigers.) Guy Dollman. Nat. Hist. Mag., London, vol.5, no.38, pp.249-255, illus., Apr., 1936.

SOME OF OUR BIG CATS. (Photos of Lion, Tiger, Leopard, Jaguar.) Sam Dunton. Animal Kingdom, New York Zool. Soc., vol. 57, no.2, pp.47-49, Apr., 1954.

TRAILING A COUGAR TO GET HIS PHOTOGRAPH. William L. Finley, Irene Finley. Nat. Mag., vol.4, pp.69-72, illus., Aug., 1924.

TRAILING THE MOUNTAIN LION AND, WHAT'S MORE, MAKING HIM POSE FOR PICTURES. Arthur Newton Pack. Nature Mag., vol.15, no.2, pp.75-81, pl.1, figs. 17, 1930.

THE TRUTH ABOUT 'A UNIQUE LION PHOTOGRAPH.' P. McD. Sanderson et al. Jour. Bombay Nat. Hist. Soc., vol.32, pp.788-789, May 31, 1928.

(SOME PICTURES ON THE RAISING OF A SNOW LEOPARD.) Einige Bilder zur Aufzucht eines Schneeleoparden. Karl Max Schneider. Zool. Garten, Leipzig, n.F., vol.9, nos.1-2, pp.37-39, illus., Feb., 1937.

"CATNIPING" OUR BIG CATS. A FEW DROPS OF "WHAT MAKES THE WILDCAT WILD" SPRINKLED ON A SMALL BALL OF COTTON AND THINGS HAPPEN--FOR THE FIRST TIME MOUNTAIN LION IS LED TO TAKE ITS OWN PHOTOGRAPH--WILDLIFE IS "FRAMED AND HELD

WHERE YOU WANT IT. Stanley P. Young. Western Sportsman, Denver, vol.4, no.6, pp.4-8, illus., May, 1940.

Physiology and Experimental Biology

FUNCTION OF THE CELLS IN THE MOTOR ROOT OF THE NERVUS TRIGEMINUS IN THE CAT. William F. Allen. Jour. Comp. Neur., vol.38, pp.349-368, figs.4, Apr. 15, 1925.

ELECTRICAL STIMULATION OF THE NEURAL MECHANISM REGULATING SPASMODIC RESPIRATORY ACTS IN THE CAT. Herbert Leon Borison. Amer. Jour. Physiol., Baltimore, vol.154, no.1, pp.55-62, July 1, 1948.

EFFECT OF DIISOPROPYLFLUROPHOSPHONATE ON NEUROMUSCULAR TRANSMISSION IN CATS. G.L.Brown et al. Jour. Physiol., London, vol.107, no.3, pp.346-354, June 25, 1948.

UROPEPSIN OUTPUT IN CATS TREATED WITH CAFFEINE AND HISTAMINE. G.R. Bucher. Amer. Jour. Physiol., Baltimore, vol.153, no.3, pp.454-457, June 1, 1948.

MAXIMUM FREQUENCY OF REFLEX RESPONSE IN THE SPINAL CAT. Sybil Cooper, E.D. Adrian. Jour. Physiol., vol. 59, pp.61-81, 1924.

AN EXPERIMENT TESTING THE ABILITY OF A CAT TO MAKE DELAYED RESPONSE AND TO MAINTAIN A GIVEN RESPONSE TOWARD A VARYING STIMULUS. E.A. Cowan. Jour. Comp. Psychol., vol.3, pp.1-9, 1923.

EFFECTS OF LACTATION ON THE POST-PARTUM INVOLUTION OF THE UTERUS OF THE CAT. Alden B. Dawson. Amer. Jour. Anat., Philadelphia, vol.79, no.2, pp.241-265, pls.3, Sep., 1946.

TIME AND SEQUENCE OF PREOVULATORY CHANGES IN THE CAT OVARY AFTER MATING OR MECHANICAL STIMULATION OF THE CERVIX UTERI. Alden B.Dawson, Harry B. Friedgood. Anat. Record, Philadelphia, vol.76, no.4, pp.411-429, pls.2, Apr. 25, 1940.

(THE INTERVENTION OF "ACTIVE SUBSTANCES" AND "VAGAL SUBSTANCES" IN THE WORK OF THE HEART.) A propos de l'intervention des "substances actives" et des "substances vagales" dans le travail du coeur. (Experiments on Cat.) J. Demoor, P. Rylant. Comptes Rendus des Séances de la Soc. de Biol., vol.97, pp.726-729, Aug. 26, 1927.

CONDUCTION RATES AND DORSAL ROOT INFLOW OF SENSORY FIBERS FROM THE KNEE JOINT OF THE CAT. Ernest Gardner. Amer. Jour. Physiol., Baltimore, vol.162, no.2, pp.436-445, Feb. 1, 1948.

MUTUAL INFLUENCE OF SECRETORY STIMULI IN THE SUBMAXILLARY GLAND OF THE CAT. E.E. Goldenberg. Jour. Physiol., vol.58, pp.267-273, Mar., 1924.

SOME EXPERIMENTAL EVIDENCE ON THE CONNECTION OF THE VESTIBULAR MECHANISM IN THE CAT. Lloyd P.Gray. Jour. Comp. Neur., vol.41, pp.319-364, pls.4, Aug. 15, 1926.

PULSATION OF A CAT'S HEART AFTER DEATH. Horace Gunthorp. Science, n.s., vol.53, p.92, Jan. 28, 1921.

ANTIDROMIC ACTION. PART II. STIMULATION OF THE PERIPHERAL NERVES OF THE CAT'S HIND FOOT. J.N.Langley. Jour. Physiol., vol.58, pp.49-69, 1923.

INCREASED SPONTANEOUS ACTIVITY PRODUCED BY FRONTAL LOBE LESIONS IN CATS. Orthello R. Langworthy, Curt P. Richter. Amer. Jour. Physiol., Memphis, vol.126, no.1, pp.158-161, fig.1, May, 1939.

VAGINAL SMEARS AND THE OESTROUS CYCLE OF THE CAT AND LIONESS. H. Liche, Kazimierz Wodzicki. Nature, London, vol.144, no.3640, pp.245-246, Aug. 5, 1939.

(INOCULATION OF THE YELLOW VIRUS IN YOUNG CATS.) Inoculação de virus amarilico em gatos jovens. Herminio Linhares. Mem. Inst. Oswaldo Cruz, Rio de Janeiro, vol.38, no. 2, pp.201-207, Apr., 1943.

SECRETORY INNERVATION OF THE CAT'S FOOTPAD. Harry D. Patton. Jour. Neurophysiology, vol.11, pp.217-228, figs.6, 1948.

ELECTROCARDIOGRAM OF THE BOBCAT. E.W. Pfeiffer. Jour. Mamm., vol.37, no.4, p.549, Jan. 9, 1957.

(ON HOMING ABILITY IN MAMMALS. I. EXPERIMENTS WITH CATS.) Ueber das Heimfinderermoegen von Saeugetieren. I. Versuche an Katzen. H. Precht, E. Lindenlaub. Zeitschr. Tierpsychol., vol.11, no.3, pp.485-494, 1954. (With English summary.)

STUDIES ON MUSCLE TONUS. I. CONTRACTILE AND PLASTIC FACTORS IN DECEREBRATE RIGIDITY. (Work on Cats.) S.W. Ranson. Jour. Comp. Neur., vol.40, pp.1-14, Feb. 15, 1926.

STUDIES ON MUSCLE TONUS. II. COMPARISON OF THE SYNAPSE-BLOCKING ACTION OF NICOTINE AND CHLORAL HYDRATE. (Work on Cats.) S.W. Ranson. Jour. Comp. Neur., vol.40, pp.15-22, Feb. 15, 1926.

STUDIES ON MUSCLE TONUS. III. SUBLAMINAL INJECTION OF CHLORAL HYDRATE IN DECEREBRATED CATS. S.W. Ranson. Jour. Comp. Neur., vol.40, pp. 23-32, Feb. 15, 1926.

REACTIONS OF THE CAT TO HOT ATMOSPHERES. Kathleen Robinson, H.K. Lee Douglas. Proc. Roy. Soc. Queensland, Brisbane, vol. 53, no.10, pp.159-170, figs.5, Dec. 12, 1941.

INFLUENCE OF OVARIAN HORMONES ON THE TRANSMISSION OF THE ACTIVITY OF THE SYMPATHETIC NERVES OF THE CAT. J. Secker. Jour. Physiol., London, vol.107, no.3, pp.265-271, June 25, 1948.

EXPERIMENTAL DEMONSTRATION OF THE ENTIRE COURSE OF FOUR DESCENDING TRACTS BY A SINGLE ALCOHOLIC INJECTION IN THE MID-BRAIN OF THE CAT. A.T. Smussen. Proc. Soc. Exper. Biol. and Medicine, vol.20, pp. 104-107, 1922.

AUTOPLASTIC AND HOMOPLASTIC PARATHYROID TRANSPLANTATION. (Work on Cat.) W.W. Swingle, J.S.Nicholas. Amer. Jour. Anat., vol.36, pp.91-128, figs.4, pl.1, Sep. 15, 1925.

EFFECT OF CASTRATION ON THE SKULL OF THE DOMESTIC CAT, AND THE ESTABLISHMENT OF DIFFERENTIATING CHARACTERS ON THE SKULLS OF THE DOMESTIC CAT AND THE WILD CAT. J. Szunyoghy. Ann. Hist. Nat. Mus. Nat. Hungarici, Budapest, n.s., vol.2, pp.177-181, pls.9-11, 1952.

(ANIMATION EXPERIMENTS WITH A YOUNG LION.) Belebungsversuche an einem jungen Loewen. Wolfgang Ullrich. Zool. Garten, Leipzig, n.F., vol.21, no.3, p. 193, 1955.

ELECTROENCEPHALOGRAMS IN BEHAVIOR CHANGES IN CATS. M.D. Wheatley et al. Proc. Soc. Exp. Biol. Med., Utica, vol.70, no.1, pp.16-19, Jan., 1949.

FETAL RESPIRATORY MOVEMENTS IN THE CAT. W.F. Windle et al. Physiol. Zool., Chicago, vol.11, no.4, pp.425-433, Oct., 1938.

Population Dynamics

TEN-YEAR CYCLE IN NUMBERS OF THE LYNX IN CANADA. Charles Elton, Mary Nicholson. Jour. Animal Ecol., vol.11, no. 2, pp.215-244, Nov., 1942.

STATISTICAL ANALYSIS OF THE CANADIAN LYNX CYCLE. I. STRUCTURE AND PREDICTION. P. A. P. Moran. Aust. Jour. Zool., vol.1, no.2, pp.163-173, 1953.

STATISTICAL ANALYSIS OF THE CANADIAN LYNX CYCLE. II. SYNCHRONIZATION AND METEOROLOGY. P.A.P. Moran. Aust. Jour. Zool., vol.1, no.3, pp.291-298, 1953.

STATISTICAL ANALYSIS OF THE SUNSPOT AND LYNX CYCLES. P.A.P. Moran. Jour. Animal Ecol., vol.18, no.1, pp.115-116, May 1949.

CATS HAVE THEIR CYCLES. (Bobcat.) A.M. Stebler. Mich. Cons., vol.9, no.6, p.11, Mar., 1940.

CYCLES OF LYNX ABUNDANCE. Leonard W. Wing. Jour. Cycle Res., vol.2, no. 2, pp.28-51, graphs, Spring, 1953.

Predators of Felids

SKUNK EATS KITTENS. L.R. Dice. Jour. Mamm., vol.7, no.2, p.131, May, 1926.

Psychology

EXPERIMENTAL STUDIES OF ADAPTIVE BEHAVIOR IN CATS. Donald Keith Adams. Comp. Psych. Monographs, vol.6, no.1, pp.1-168, illus, May, 1929. (Baltimore:The Johns Hopkins Press.)

HOMING POWERS OF THE CAT. Francis H. Herrick. Sci. Monthly, vol.14, pp.525-539, figs.3, 1922.

SHIPS' CATS, AND AN INSTANCE OF THEIR HOMING INSTINCT. John H. Hughes. Jour. Bombay Nat. Hist. Soc., vol.31, pp.1027-1028, Feb. 20, 1927.

(OBSERVATIONS ON A YOUNG SIAMESE CAT IN FORGETTING AND RECALL IN RELATION TO THE ENVIRONMENT.) Beobachtungen an einer jungen Siamkatze ueber Vergessen und Erinnern in Bezug auf die Umgebung. Bruno M. Klein. Zoologische Garten, Leipzig, n.F., vol.11, nos.1-2, pp.24-31, June, 1939.

SENSE OF SMELL IN INDIAN FELIDAE. R.C. Morris. Jour. Bombay Nat. Hist.Soc., vol.33, no.3, p.695, May 31, 1929.

HAVE CATS A LANGUAGE? N. Morrison. Field, London, vol.150, p.626, Oct. 20, 1927.

SENSE OF SMELL IN THE LION. Harry D. Oliver. Jour. Bombay Nat. Hist. Soc., vol. 33, no.4, p.977, Oct. 15, 1929.

PERMANENCE OF THE DOMESTIC INSTINCT IN THE CAT. C.A. White. Amer. Naturalist, vol.18, pp.213-214, Feb., 1884.

(VISUAL BACKGROUND OF THE LION.) Der Augenhintergrund des Loewen. E. Woelfflin. Zeitschr. f. gessammte Anat., vol.69, pp.1-4, 1923.

DO KITTENS INSTINCTIVELY KILL MICE? Robert M. Yerkes, Daniel Bloomfield. Psychol. Bull., Lancaster, vol.7, no.8, pp.253-263, Aug. 15, 1910.

Reproductive Biology

NUMBER OF CUBS IN A TIGER'S LITTER. A.H. Berriff. Jour. Bombay Nat. Hist. Soc., vol.35, no.3, p.670, Feb. 15, 1932.

(ANOMALOUS BIRTH OF A FEMALE LION.) Anomales Werfen einer Loewin. H. Borggreve. Zool. Garten, Leipzig, n.F., vol.2, nos.10-12, p.343, Mar., 1930.

PARTURITION IN A BENGAL TIGRESS. Malcolm Davis. Jour. Mamm., vol.27, no.4, p.393, Nov. 25, 1946.

BREEDING HABITS OF THE PANTHER (FELIS PARDUS). C.H.Donald. Jour.Bombay Nat. Hist. Soc., vol.31, pp.809-810, Nov. 1, 1926.

REPRODUCTION IN THE BOBCAT, LYNX RUFUS. Kenneth L. Duke. Anatomical Record, Philadelphia, vol.120, no.3, pp. 816-817, Nov., 1954. (Abstract.)

REPORT ON THE PERIOD OF GESTATION OF THE PUMA (FELIS CONCOLOR, L.). Devereux Fuller. Proc. Comm. Sci. and Corres. Zool. Soc. London, pt.2, p.62, 1832.

ABDOMINAL PREGNANCY IN A CAT. R.H. Hunter. Jour. Anat., vol.66, pp.261-263, fig.1, 1932.

SUPERFETATION IN CATS, AND SOME OBSERVATIONS ON THE PUBERTAL AGE OF FEMALE CATS. Gunnar Lie. Nytt Mag. Zool., vol.3, pp.66-69, 1955.

REPRODUCTION IN THE SCOTTISH WILD CAT, FELIS SILVESTRIS GRAMPIA MILLER. L.Harrison Matthews. Proc. Zool. Soc. London, vol.111, ser.B, 1941, pts.1-2, pp.59-77, fig.1, pls.3, Oct., 1941.

TIGRESS WITH FIVE CUBS. Randolph C. Morris. Jour. Bombay Nat. Hist. Soc., pp.

810-811, Nov. 1, 1926; Indian Wild Life, vol.1, nos.3-4, pp.105-106, Sep.-Oct., 1936.

BREEDING OF THE OCELOT IN TEXAS. Geo. A. Petrides et al. Jour. Mamm., vol.32, no.1, p.116, Feb. 15, 1951.

(PRESENTATION OF A "KING OF CATS" OBSERVED AT RENNES.) Presentation d'un "Roi de chats" observé a Rennes. (Seven kittens with entangled umbilical cords.) R. Poisson, P. Pesson. Bull. Soc. Sci. Bretagne, Rennes, vol.14, nos.3-4, année 1937, pp.186-188, fig.1, May 30, 1938.

BREEDING HABITS OF THE BOBCAT IN NORTHEASTERN UNITED STATES. E. Michael Pollack. Jour. Mamm., vol.31, no.3, pp.327-330, Aug. 21, 1950.

(ON THE RACE FORMATION AND BREEDING OF THE DOMESTIC CAT (FINDINGS AND PROBLEMS).) Zur Rassenbildung und -zuechtung der Hauskatze (Ergebnisse und Probleme). F. Schwangart. Zeitschr. f. Saeugetierk., Berlin, vol.7, nos.1-6, pp. 73-155, figs.27, pls.6-15, Dec. 15, 1932.

BREEDING OF LIONS IN CAPTIVITY. T.J. Steyn. Fauna and Flora Transvaal, Pretoria, no.2, pp.37-57, illus., 1951.

NUMBER OF CUBS IN A TIGRESS LITTER. C.G. Toogood. Jour. Bombay Nat. Hist.Soc., vol.39, no.1, pp.158-159, Dec. 1, 1936.

Skull, Teeth, Skeleton

DENTICLES IN SHAPE AND ARRANGEMENT SUGGESTIVE OF SELACHIAN TEETH ON THE INNER SURFACE OF THE LIP OF THE CAT. Barry J. Anson. Anat. Record, vol.31, pp.93-115, pls.3, Oct. 25, 1925.

SELACHIAN "DENTICLES" IN THE CAT. Barry J. Anson. Science, n.s., vol.60, pp. 528-529, Dec. 5, 1924.

(ON THE SKULL OF THE PANTHER SAID TO BE FROM MALARNAUD.) A propos du crane de panthère, dit de Marlarnaud. H. Bégouen. Bull. Soc. Hist. Nat. Toulouse, vol.56, no.4, pp.469-474, 1927.

NOTES ON THE MILK DENTITION OF THE LION, LEOPARD AND CHEETAH. R.Broom. Ann. Transvaal Mus., Cambridge, vol.21, pt.2, pp.183-185, illus., May 12, 1949.

(REMARKS ON THE SKELETON OF A WILD CAT (FELIS SYLVESTRIS SCHREB.).) Remarques sur le squelette d'un Chat sauvage Felis sylvestris Schreb. Pierre Cantuel. Mammalia, Paris, vol.19, no.4, pp.470-477, illus., Dec., 1955.

WEARING OF TEETH IN TIGER. Cyril Gore. Jour. Bombay Nat. Hist. Soc., vol.45, no.2, pp.230-231, Apr., 1945.

NOTES ON THE SKULLS OF THE CATS (FELIDAE). J.E. Gray. Proc. Zool. Soc. London, pp.258-277, figs.7, 1867.

(THE POSITION OF THE LARGE CATS ACCORDING TO INTERRELATIONSHIP. 1. DESCRIPTION OF SKULL BONES.) Die verwandtschaftliche Stellung der Grosskatzen zueinander. 1. Beschreibung der Schaedelknochen. Theodor Haltenorth. Zeitschr. f. Saeugetierk., vol.11, no.1, pp.32-104, pls. 21-46, Mar. 13, 1936.

(SUPERNUMERARY INCISORS IN A LYNX (LYNX LYNX LINNÉ 1758).) Ueberzarhlige Schneidezaehne bei einem Luchs, Lynx lynx (Linné, 1758). W. Herold. Saeugetierk. Mitteil., Stuttgart, vol.4, no.2, pp.81-82, Apr. 1, 1956.

PATHOLOGIC SKULLS OF CAPTIVE LIONS. A. Brazier Howell. Jour. Mamm., vol.6, no.3, pp.163-168, Aug., 1925.

MAMMALIAN ANATOMY. A PREPARATION FOR HUMAN AND COMPARATIVE ANATOMY. PART 1. THE SKELETON OF THE CAT, ITS MUSCULAR ATTACHMENTS, GROWTH, AND VARIATIONS COMPARED WITH THE SKELETON OF MAN. Horace Jayne. Lippincott Co., pp.816, illus., 1898.

NOTES ON THE COMPARATIVE OSTEOLOGY OF THE BOBCAT AND THE HOUSE CAT. Keith R. Kelson. Jour. Mamm., vol.27, no. 3, pp.255-264, figs.7, Aug. 14, 1946.

RECORD PANTHER SKULL (F. PARDUS). S. H. Later. Jour. Bombay Nat. Hist. Soc., vol.27, pp.933-934, pl.1, July 31, 1921.

SKULL OF A CAPE LIONESS (FELIS LEO MELANOCHAITUS H. SMITH). B. Lundholm. Ann. Transvaal Mus., vol.22, pt.1, pp.21-24, Nov. 4, 1952.

ON THE DISTINGUISHING PECULIARITIES OF THE CRANIA OF THE LION AND TIGER. R. Owen. Proc. Zool. Soc. London, pt.2, p.1, 1834.

(CONTRIBUTION TO THE OSTEOLOGY OF THE LARGE LIVING FELIDS OF ARGENTINA.) Contribución a la osteologia de los grandes felinos vivientes de la Argentina. Rodolfo Parodi. Physis, Buenos Aires, vol. 10, no.35, pp.74-84, pls.2, figs.2, July 12, 1930.

CAT SKELETON WITH AN ANOMALOUS THIRD HIND LEG AND ABNORMAL VERTEBRAE. Thomas S. Parsons, John M. Stein. Bull. Mus. Comp. Zool., vol.114, no.6, pp.293-317, May, 1956.

ON THE SKELETON OF FELIS TIGRIS. Chi Ping. Contrib. Biol. Lab. Sci. Soc. China, Nanking, vol.2, no.1, pp.1-6, illus., 1926.

RECORD SKULL OF AN INDIAN CLOUDED LEOPARD (NEOFELIS NEBULOSA GRIFFITH). R.I. Pocock. Jour. Bombay Nat. Hist. Soc., Bombay, p.1, Aug., 1943.

SOME DENTAL AND CRANIAL VARIATIONS IN THE SCOTCH WILD CAT (FELIS SYLVESTRIS). R.I. Pocock. Ann. and Mag. Nat. Hist., London, ser.8, vol.18, pp.272-277, fig.1, Sep., 1916.

STRUCTURE OF THE AUDITORY BULLA IN EXISTING SPECIES OF FELIDAE. R.I. Pocock. Ann. and Mag. Nat. Hist., London, ser.8, vol.18, pp.326-334, figs.7, Oct., 1916.

SOME DISTINCTIVE CRANIAL CHARACTERS OF THE CANADA LYNX. Frederick W. True. Proc. U.S. Nat. Mus., vol.10, publ.603, pp.8-9, Apr. 25, 1887.

COMMON-CAT SKULL WITH SUPERNUMERARY PREMOLAR TEETH. Joyce Van Eaton. Amer. Midl. Nat., Notre Dame, vol.38, no. 2, pp.504-505, illus., Sep., 1947.

ON A MESAL CUSP OF THE DECIDUOUS MANDIBULAR CANINE OF THE CAT, FELIS DOMESTICA. Burt G. Wilder. Proc. Amer. Assoc. Adv. Sci., vol.30, p.1, Feb., 1882.

(DESCRIPTION OF THE SKULL OF FELIS CAUDATA MACROTHRIX ZUKOWSKY.) Beschreibung des Schaedels von Felis caudata macrothrix Zukowsky. Ludwig Zukowsky. Archiv. f. Nat., Jahrg.87, Abt.A, Hft.10, pp.175-183, figs.2, Dec., 1921.

Taxonomy

SEVERTZOW'S CLASSIFICATION OF THE FELIDAE. J.A. Allen. Bull. Amer. Mus. Nat. Hist., vol.41, pp.335-340, Sep. 22, 1919.

(GILDED CATS OF AFRICA AND ASIA.) Les chats dorés d'Afrique et d'Asie. E. Bourdelle. Compte Rendu Som. Séances Soc. Biogéogr., année 9, no.78, pp.66-70, 1932.

(SPECIFIC AND SUBSPECIFIC NAMES OF SOME "FELIDAE".) Sobre los nombres especificos y subespecificos de algunos "Felis". Angel Cabrera. Bol.Real.Soc. Española Hist. Nat., Madrid, vol.10, pp. 423-428, Nov., 1910.

REMARKS ON FELIS TIGRINA, ERXL., AND ITS SYNONYMY. Daniel G. Elliot. Proc. Zool. Soc. London, pt.4, pp.704-707, 1877.

REMARKS ON VARIOUS SPECIES OF FELIDAE, WITH A DESCRIPTION OF A SPECIES FROM NORTH-WESTERN SIBERIA. Daniel G. Elliot. Proc. Zool. Soc. London, pp.758-761, pl.76, Dec. 5, 1871.

SUBSTITUTE NAME FOR FELIS CONCOLOR YOUNGI. E.A.Goldman. Proc. Biol. Soc. Washington, vol.51, pp.63-64, Mar. 18, 1938.

TWO NEW RACES OF THE PUMA. E. A. Goldman. Jour. Mamm., Baltimore, vol.24, no.2, pp.228-231, May, 1943.

STATUS OF PRIONAILURUS BENGALENSIS ALLENI SODY. George G. Goodwin. Amer. Mus. Novitates, New York, vol.1767, pp. 1-3, Apr. 13, 1956.

NOTICE OF A COMMUNICATION ON THE SPECIES OF FELINE ANIMALS (FELIDAE). John Edward Gray. Proc. Zool. Soc. London, p.307, 1874.

(INTERRELATIONSHIP OF THE LARGE CATS.) Die verwandtschaftliche Stellung der Grosskatzen zueinander vii. Theodor Haltenorth. Zeitschr.f.Saeugetierk., vol. 12, pp.97-240, pls.4-14, July 1, 1937.

(WILD CATS OF THE OLD WORLD. SURVEY OF SUBGENUS FELIS.) Die Wildkatzen der alten Welt. Eine Uebersicht ueber die Untergattung Felis. Theodor Haltenorth. Akad. Verlagsgesell., Leipzig, pp.117, illus., 1953.

(Review by Randolph L. Peterson of) (WILD CATS OF THE OLD WORLD. SURVEY OF SUBGENUS FELIS.) Die Wildkatzen der alten Welt. Eine Uebersicht ueber die Untergattung Felis. Theodor Haltenorth. Jour. Mamm., vol.35, no.2, pp.271-272, May 26, 1954.

(ON THE MUTUAL RELATIONS AND THE SYSTEMATIC POSITION OF DESERT CATS (EREMAELURUS THINOBIUS OGNEV AND FELIS MARGARITA LOCHE).) Sur les relations mutuelles et la position systématique des chats désertiques Eremaelurus thinobius Ognev et Felis margarita Loche. W. Heptner, G. Dementiev. Mammalia, Paris, vol.1, no. 6, pp.227-242, illus., Dec., 1937.

(THE SYSTEMATIC POSITION OF FELIS SPELAEA GOLDF.) Die systematische Stellung von Felis spelaea Goldf. Zugleich ein Beitrag zur vergleichenden Osteologie von Loewen und Tiger. Max Hilzheimer. Sitz.Ber.Gesell.Nat.Freunde Berlin, pp. 12-24, 1922.

NOMENCLATURE OF THE CHEETAHS. N. Hollister. Proc. Biol. Soc. Washington, vol.24, pp.225-226, Oct. 31, 1911.

NOTES ON SOME NAMES OF LIONS. Ned Hollister. Proc. Biol. Soc. Washington, vol.23, p.123, Sep. 2, 1910.

ON THE SYSTEMATIC NAMES OF THE CHEETAHS. N. Hollister. Proc. Biol. Soc. Washington, vol.27, p.216, Oct. 31, 1914.

NEW NAME FOR FELIS (CATOPUMA) MELLI MATSCHIE, AND NOTE ON THE NOMENCLATURE OF FELIS PARDUS CENTRALIS LÖNNBERG. A. Brazier Howell. Proc. Biol. Soc. Washington, vol. 39, p.143, Dec. 27, 1926.

(PREHISTORIC LIONS IN THE FORMENKREIS OF FELIS SPELAEA.) Praehistorische Loewen aus dem Formenkreis der Felis spelaea. O. Jaekel. Zool.Anzeiger, vol.70, pp.225-236, illus., Mar. 20, 1927.

NOTE ON THE SYSTEMATIC AND EVOLUTIONARY RELATIONSHIPS OF FELIS TEILHARDI PEI. Bjorn Kurtén. Vertebrata Palasiatica, vol.1, no.2, pp.123-128, June, 1957.

MAMMALIAN CLASSIFICATION. THE CAT AND ITS RELATIONS. Frederic A. Lucas. Trans. Rochester Soc. Nat. Sci., no.2, pp. 1-15, 1881.

(ON FELIS JACOBITA, COLOCOLA, AND TWO CATS SIMILAR TO THEM.) Ueber Felis jacobita, colocola und zwei ihnen aehnliche Katzen. Paul Matschie. Sitz.Ber. Gesell. Nat. Freunde Berlin, no.4, pp.255-259, Apr., 1912.

(ON SEVERAL RACES OF THE STEPPES LYNX FELIS (CARACAL) CARACAL (ST. MÜLL.).) Ueber einige Rassen des Steppenluches Felis(Caracal)caracal (St. Müll.). Paul Matschie. Sitz. Ber. Gesell. Nat. Freunde Berlin, no.2a, pp.55-67, 1912.

(ON THE SPECIES OF THE GENUS CARACAL GRAY 1867.) Ueber die Formen der

Gattung Caracal Gray 1867. Paul Matschie. Sitz. Ber. Gesell. Naturf. Freunde Berlin, no.7, pp.113-115, July 19, 1892.

PRELIMINARY REVISION OF THE PUMAS (FELIS CONCOLOR GROUP). Hart C. Merriam. Proc. Wash. Acad. Sci., vol.3, pp. 577-600, Dec. 11, 1901.

LIST OF THE PUMAS, WITH THREE DESCRIBED AS NEW. E. W. Nelson, E. A. Goldman. Jour. Mamm., Baltimore, vol.10, no. 4, pp.345-350, Nov., 1929.

REVISION OF THE JAGUARS. E. W. Nelson, E.A. Goldman. Jour. Mamm., Baltimore, vol.14, no.3, pp.221-240, Aug. 17, 1933.

THREE NEW PUMAS. E. W. Nelson, E. A. Goldman. Jour. Washington Acad. Sci., vol. 21, no.10, pp.209-212, May 19, 1931.

FELIS OCELOT OF HAMILTON SMITH. Wilfred H. Osgood. Jour. Mamm., Baltimore, vol.1, no.2, pp.88-90, Mar. 2, 1920.

CLASSIFICATION OF EXISTING FELIDAE. R.I. Pocock. Ann. and Mag. Nat. Hist., London, ser.8, vol.20, pp.329-350, Nov., 1917.

DESCRIPTION OF A NEW RACE OF PUMA (PUMA CONCOLOR), WITH A NOTE ON AN ABNORMAL TOOTH IN THE GENUS. R.I. Pocock. Ann. and Mag. Nat. Hist., London, ser.11, vol.6, no.33, pp.307-313, Sep., 1940.

DESCRIPTION OF A NEW SPECIES OF CHEETAH (ACINONYX). R.I. Pocock. Proc. Zool. Soc. London, p.18, Feb. 22, 1927; Proc. Zool. Soc. London, pt.1, pp. 245-252, col.pl.1, Apr.6, 1927.

DESCRIPTION OF TWO SUBSPECIES OF LEOPARDS. R.I. Pocock. Ann. and Mag. Nat. Hist., ser.9, vol.20, pp.213-214, Aug., 1927.

KING CHEETAH. R.I. Pocock. Field, London, vol.153, p.903, illus., June 7, 1929.

NEW RACE OF THE SAND-CAT (FELIS MARGARITA). R.I. Pocock. Ann. and Mag. Nat. Hist., London, ser.11, vol.1, pp.472-476, tbl., Apr., 1938.

ON THE TOOTH-CHANGE, CRANIAL CHARACTERS, AND CLASSIFICATION OF THE SNOW-LEOPARD OR OUNCE (FELIS UNICA). R.I. Pocock. Ann.and Mag. Nat. Hist., London, ser.8, vol. 18, pp.306-316, figs.4, Sep., 1916.

THE RACES OF GEOFFROY'S CAT (ONCIFELIS GEOFFROYI). R.I. Pocock. Ann. and Mag. Nat. Hist., London, ser.11, vol. 6, no.34, pp.350-355, Oct., 1940.

RACES OF JUGUAR (PANTHERA ONCA). R.I. Pocock. Novitates Zoologicae, Tring, vol.41, no.4, pp.406-422, figs.306-310, tbls., Oct. 31, 1939.

RACES OF THE OCELOT AND THE MARGAY. R.I. Pocock. Papers on Mammalogy. Zool. Ser., Field Mus. Nat. Hist., vol.27, pp.319-369, Dec. 8, 1941.

SOME NEW GEOGRAPHICAL RACES OF LEOPARDUS, COMMONLY KNOWN AS OCELOTS AND MARGAYS. R.I. Pocock. Ann. and Mag. Nat. Hist., London, ser.11, vol.8, pp.234-239, Sep., 1941.

(WHAT IS FELIS ELATA BRAVARD?) Was ist Felis elata Bravard? S. Schaub. Basel, Eclogae Geol. Helvetiae, vol.32, no.2, pp. 187-193, Apr. 15, 1940.

(THE MANUL, OTOCOLOBUS MANUL PALLAS, IN THE SYSTEM OF FELIDS.) Der Manul, Otocolobus manul (Pallas), im System der Feliden. F. Schwangart. Carnivoren-Studien, vol.2, Kleintier und Pelztier, Leipzig, Jahrg.12, no.8, pp.19-53, figs.21, pls. 4-16, Dec., 1936.

(ON THE TERMINOLOGY OF THE CAT SPECIES.) Zur Terminologie der Katzenarten. B. Shitkov. Bull. Soc. Nat. Moscow, ser.biol., vol.45, no.3, pp.225-232, 1936.

FELIS (MICROFELIS) NIGRIPES THOMASI SUBSP. NOV. G.C. Shortridge. Rec. Albany Mus., Grahamstown, vol.4, no.1, pp.119-121, pl.1, Jan.9, 1931.

(ON TWO NEW SPECIES OF FELIS CAUDATA GRAY.) Ueber zwei neue Formen von Felis caudata, Gray. Ludwig Zukowsky. Archiv f. Naturgeschichte, Jahrg.80, Abt.A, Heft 9, pp.93-101, pl.1, 1914.

United States, Eastern

NOTES ON THE FLORIDA PANTHER, FELIS CONCOLOR CORYI BANGS. Ross Allen. Jour. Mamm., vol.31, no.3, pp.279-280, Aug.21, 1950.

MICHIGAN'S LITTLE LIONS. (Bobcats.) David A. Arnold. Michigan Conserv., Lansing, vol.24, no.1, pp.7-8, Jan., 1955.

VIRGINIA ANIMALS EVERYONE SHOULD KNOW. THE BOBCAT. R.H. Cross, Jr. Va. Wild Life, Richmond, vol.9, no.3, pp.19-20, illus., Mar., 1948.

BALD MOUNTAIN BOBCATS. E.J. Dailey. Fur-Fish-Game, Harding's Mag., Columbus, vol.73, no.1, pp.13, 19, Jan., 1941.

AN OLD RECORD OF THE MOUNTAIN LION IN NEW HAMPSHIRE. Ned Dearborn. Jour. Mamm., vol.8, no.4, pp.311-312, Nov., 1927.

FOOD HABITS AND ACTIVITIES OF THE HOUSE CAT (FELIS DOMESTICUS) IN PENNSYLVANIA. Thomas T. Eberhard. MS thesis, Penna. State Coll., 1950.

RECENT RECORD OF LYNX IN MICHIGAN. Albert W. Erickson. Jour. Mamm., vol.36, no.1, pp.132-133, Feb. 25, 1955.

SEX RATIO AND WEIGHTS OF VERMONT BOBCATS IN AUTUMN AND WINTER. Leonard E. Foote. Jour. Wildl. Mgt., Menasha, vol.9, no.4, pp.326-327, Oct., 1945.

THE DISAPPEARING PANTHER. O. Earl Frye et al. Fla. Wildl., vol.5, no.5, pp. 8-9, 31-32, Oct., 1950.

MOUNTAIN LION KILL IN ST. CLAIR COUNTY, ALABAMA. A.D. Hare. Alabama Conservation, Montgomery, vol.19, no.10, p.11, illus., Apr., 1948.

THE LOUISIANA PUMA. Ned Hollister. Proc. Biol. Soc. Washington, vol.24, pp.175-178, June 16, 1911.

THE WISCONSIN PUMA. Hartley H. T. Jackson. Proc. Biol. Soc. Washington, vol. 68, pp.149-150, Oct. 31, 1955.

THERE AIN'T NO 'PAINTERS' IN WEST VIRGINIA. Harold Lambert. W. Va. Cons., vol.19, no.1, pp.10-12, illus., Mar., 1955.

PANTHER IN EASTERN PART OF PARK. Leo W. Lorenzo. Everglades Nat. Hist., Homestead, Florida, vol.1, no.4, p.189, Dec., 1953.

REPORTS OF COUGAR IN NEW YORK. Richard H. Manville. Jour. Mamm., vol. 32, no.2, p.227, May 21, 1951.

OUR BOBCATS. Bill Nickles. Shenandoah, Luray, vol.2, no.1, pp.11-13, Autumn, 1937.

OBSERVATIONS ON NEW ENGLAND BOBCATS. E. M. Pollack. Jour. Mamm., vol. 32, no.3, pp.356-358, Aug., 1951.

BOBCAT IN MASSACHUSETTS. E.M. Pollack, W. G. Sheldon. Massachusetts Div. Fisheries and Game, pp.24, illus., Sep., 1951.

FELIS CATUS IN PENNSYLVANIA? BEING REPORTS OF THE TAKING OF A GENUINE EUROPEAN WILD CAT IN TINICUM TOWNSHIP, BUCKS COUNTY, JANUARY 16, 1922. Lord Rothschild. Altoona, Penna., published by Times Tribune Co., pp.20, 1922.

STATUS OF THE BOBCAT IN TENNESSEE. Vincent Schultz. Jour. Tennessee Acad. Sci., vol.29, no.1, pp.66-72, Jan., 1954; Rep. Reelfoot L. Biol. Sta., vol.18, pp.66-72, maps, Jan., 1954.

THE LYNX IS BACK. Clayt Seagears. New York State Cons., vol.6, no.3, p.40, illus., Dec.-Jan., 1951-52.

MOUNTAIN LION IN ARKANSAS. John A. Sealander. Jour. Mamm., vol.32, no.3, p.364, Aug. 23, 1951.

THE PANTHER IN PENNSYLVANIA. Henry W. Shoemaker. Penna. Game News, vol. 13, no.11, pp.7, 28, 32, Feb., 1943.

THE PANTHER ON TERRACE MOUNTAIN. Henry W. Shoemaker. Penna. Game News, Harrisburg, vol.20, no.2, pp.8-9, illus., May, 1949.

THE PENNSYLVANIA LION. Henry W. Shoemaker. Penna. Game News, Harrisburg, vol. 17 (18), no.12, pp.6, 27, Mar., 1948.

PENNSYLVANIA LION OR PANTHER. Henry W. Shoemaker. Altoona Tribune Co., pp.47, photos, 1914.

PENNSYLVANIA WILD CATS. Henry W. Shoemaker. Altoona Tribune Co., pp.34, photos, 1916.

DISCOVERY OF JAGUAR BONES AND FOOTPRINTS IN A CAVE IN TENNESSEE. George Gaylord Simpson. Amer. Mus. Novitates, New York, no.1131, pp.1-12, Aug. 6, 1941.

CATAMOUNT IN VERMONT. John Spargo. Bennington Historical Mus. and Art Gallery, pp.24, illus., 1950.

EXTANT NEW YORK SPECIMENS OF THE ADIRONDACK COUGAR. Dayton Stoner. New York State Mus., Albany, Cir.25, pp. 1-34, figs.12, May, 1950.

MOUNTAIN LION COMEBACK IN ALABAMA. J. Fred Thornton. Ala. Cons., vol.25, no.5, pp.30-31, Mar.-Apr., 1954.

LYNX IN THE ADIRONDACKS. John D. Whish. Forest and Stream, vol.89, p.353, July, 1919.

RETURN OF THE INDIAN DEVIL. Stanley P. Young. Penna. Game News, vol.25, no. 12, pp.8-14, illus., Dec., 1954.

MOUNTAIN LIONS? Wisconsin Conserv. Bull., Madison, vol.12, no.3, p.31, Mar., 1947.

PANTHERS IN FLORIDA. Outdoor Florida, Tampa, Fla., vol.1, no.8, p.13, illus., Oct., 1936.

WICKED WILDCAT REPORTED AT LARGE IN FLORIDA. (Jaguarundi.) Science News Letter, Washington, D.C., vol.42, no.7, p. 100, Aug. 15, 1942.

United States, Western

MISSING LYNX. Leon V. Almirall. Western Sportsman, Denver, vol.7, no.2, pp.25, 32, illus., July, 1941.

MOUNTAIN LION IN SOUTHEASTERN TEXAS. Rollin H. Baker. Jour. Mamm., Baltimore, vol.30, no.2, p.199, May 23, 1949.

ARE THERE MOUNTAIN LIONS IN MINNESOTA? Gerald T. Bue, Milton H. Stenlund. Cons. Volunteer, vol.15, no.89, pp. 32-37, Sep.-Oct., 1952.

RECENT RECORDS OF THE MOUNTAIN LION, FELIS, CONCOLOR IN MINNESOTA. Gerald T. Bue. Milton H. Stenlund. Jour. Mamm., vol.34, no.3, pp.390-391, Aug. 14, 1953.

CANADA LYNX IN THE BLUE MOUNTAINS. Leo K. Couch. Murrelet, vol.13, no.3, p. 95, Sep., 1932.

MOUNTAIN LION INCREASE IN COLORADO. George Crowley. Colorado Conserv. Comments, Denver, vol.9, no.1, p.11, Mar. 15, 1946. (Mimeographed.)

TEXAS CATS. W.B. Davis. Texas Game and Fish, vol.3, no.12, pp.21-23, 29, Nov., 1945.

UNUSUAL RECORD OF THE OCELOT IN TEXAS. W.B. Davis. Jour. Mamm., vol. 32, no.3, pp.363-364, Aug. 23, 1951.

AN ARIZONA COUGAR. J. Kenneth Doutt. Jour. Mamm., vol.16, no.1. p.66, Feb., 1935.

MOUNTAIN LION IN YOSEMITE VALLEY. Robert Fitzgerald. Yosemite Nat. Notes, Yosemite, vol.19, no.9, p.71, Sep., 1940.

A NEW PUMA FROM TEXAS. E.A. Goldman. Proc. Biol. Soc. Washington, vol.49, pp.137-138, Aug. 22, 1936.

BAILEY BOBCAT CONTRIBUTES NEW MAMMAL RECORDS. Russell K. Grater. Jour. Mamm., vol.17, no.2, pp.170-171, May, 1936.

LION IN THE CARMENS. Tappan Gregory. Chicago Nat., vol.1, no.3, pp.70-81, no.4, pp.110-120, illus., map, 1938.

REVISION OF THE GENUS LYNX IN CALIFORNIA. Joseph Grinnell, Joseph Dixon. Univ. Calif. Pub. Zool., vol.21, pp.339-354, fig.1, pl.1, Jan. 24, 1924.

SYSTEMATIC STATUS OF THE MOUNTAIN LION OF CALIFORNIA. Joseph Grinnell, Joseph Dixon. Univ. Calif. Pub. Zool., vol. 21, pp.325-332, pls.2, Apr.7, 1923.

RECENT RECORD OF THE YUMA MOUNTAIN LION IN ARIZONA. Arthur F. Halloran. Jour. Mamm., vol.27, no.1, pp.89-90, Mar. 14, 1946.

SOUTHWESTERN EXOTIC FELIDS. Raymond J. Hock. Amer. Midland Nat., Notre Dame, vol.53, no.2, pp.324-328, Apr., 1955.

SPOTTED TIGER-CAT IN TEXAS. N.Hollister. Proc. Biol. Soc. Washington, vol.27, p.219, Oct. 31, 1914.

BOBCAT AT ARCH ROCK. Odin S. Johnson. Yosemite Nat. Notes, Yosemite, vol.23, no.4, p.44, Apr., 1944.

OCCURRENCE OF THE MOUNTAIN LION IN NEBRASKA. J. Knox Jones, Jr. Jour. Mamm., vol.30, no.3, p.313, Aug. 17, 1949.

RECORD OF THE JAGUARUNDI IN ARIZONA. Elbert L. Little. Jour.Mamm., vol.19, no.4, pp.500-501, Nov. 14, 1938.

MOUNTAIN LIONS IN CALIFORNIA. D.C. McLean. California Fish and Game, vol. 40, no.2, pp.147-166, Apr., 1954.

DESCRIPTIONS OF TWO NEW PUMAS FROM THE NORTHWESTERN UNITED STATES. C. Hart Merriam. Proc. Biol. Soc. Wash., vol.11, pp.219-220, July 15, 1897.

IS THE JAGUAR ENTITLED TO A PLACE IN THE CALIFORNIA FAUNA? C. Hart Merriam. Jour. Mamm., vol.1, no.1, pp. 38-40, Nov., 1919.

NEW BOBCAT (LYNX UINTA) FROM THE ROCKY MOUNTAINS. C. Hart Merriam. Proc. Biol. Soc. Wash., vol.15, pp.71-72, Mar. 22, 1902.

OCCURRENCE OF A MOUNTAIN LION IN OKLAHOMA. George C. Merrifield. Proc. Oklahoma Acad. Sci., vol.34, for 1953, p. 75, Jan., 1955.

MOUNTAIN LION IN TEXAS. Ray S. Meschkat. Tex. Game and Fish, vol.11, no.3, pp. 24-26, illus., Feb., 1953.

SOME HABITS OF MOUNTAIN LIONS IN ARIZONA. M.E. Musgrave. Jour. Mamm., vol.7, no.4, pp.282-285, Nov., 1926.

MOUNTAIN LION OBSERVED NEAR WAWONA TUNNEL. Lloyd P. Parratt. Yosemite Nat. Notes, Yosemite, vol.21, no.5, p.48, May, 1942.

COUGAR IN MISSOURI. Dunbar Robb. Mo. Cons., vol.16, no.7, p.14, illus., July, 1955.

HABITS, FOODS, AND PARASITES OF THE BOBCAT IN MINNESOTA. Clair T. Rollings: MS thesis, Univ. Minn., 1942; Jour. Wildl. Mgt., Menasha, vol.9, no.2, pp.131-145, pls.4-5, Apr., 1945.

JAGUAR IN COLORADO. Ernest Thompson Seton. Jour. Mamm., vol.1, no.5, p.241, Nov., 1920.

MOUNTAIN LION VISITS YOSEMITE VALLEY. Lloyd M. Smith. Yosemite Nature Notes, Yosemite, vol.25, no.10, p.123, illus., Oct., 1946.

THE BOBCAT, LYNX RUFUS TEXENSIS, IN DALLAS COUNTY, TEXAS. William B. Stallcup. Field and Laboratory, vol.25, no.1, p.31, Jan., 1957.

DISCUSSION AND CORRESPONDENCE. THE PUMAS OF THE WESTERN UNITED STATES. Witmar Stone. Science, n.s., vol.9, no.210, pp.34-35, Jan. 6, 1899.

RECENT RECORD OF THE JAGUAR IN TEXAS. Walter P. Taylor. Jour. Mamm., vol.28, no.1, p.66, Feb. 15, 1947.

FUR-BEARING MAMMALS OF WYOMING. PART 15. LYNX. Earl M. Thomas. Wyo. Wild Life, vol.17, no.5, pp.12-16, illus., May, 1953.

FUR-BEARING MAMMALS OF WYOMING. PART 16. BOBCAT. Earl M. Thomas. Wyo. Wild Life, vol.17, no.6, pp.10-13, illus., June, 1953.

LIONS OF THE KAIBAB FOREST. Jack Tooker. Outdoor Life, vol.68, no.1, pp. 7-9, 70, figs.3, July, 1931; no.2, pp.13-15, 72, figs.6, Aug., 1931.

NOTES ON THE OCCURRENCE OF THE PUMA (FELIS CONCOLOR L.) IN SOUTHERN NEW MEXICO. Charles Henry Tyler Townsend. Zoe, vol.3, pp.309-311, Jan., 1893.

TRACKING THE CAT FAMILY IN LOWER TENAYA CANYON. C. Dewey Youngblood. Yosemite Nat. Notes, vol.29, no.11, pp. 109-111, Nov., 1950.

OLD BOB: IOWA'S WILD GHOST. Iowa State Conserv. Commission, Iowa Conserv., vol.13, no.9, pp.65, 70, illus., Sep., 1954.

Young

WILD CAT KITTEN. Ralph H. Anderson. Nat. Hist., New York, vol.55, no.9, pp. 430-431, illus., Nov., 1946.

ON THE TYPE OF POSTEMBRYONIC GROWTH OF THE SKELETON IN FELIS CATUS DOMESTICUS L. V.J. Brovar. Comptes Rendus (Doklady) Acad. Sci.USSR, Moscow, vol.34, no.1, pp.27-32, Jan. 10, 1942.

CUBS ARE GROWING UP. (Tiger cubs.) Lee S. Crandall. Animal Kingdom, New York, vol.47, no.4, pp.94-97, illus., July-Aug., 1944.

NEWS FROM THE NURSERY. (Lion, Tiger, Black Leopard Cubs.) Lee S. Crandall. Animal Kingdom, New York, vol.48, no.2, pp.27-31, illus., Mar.-Apr., 1945.

THREE TIGER CUBS. Lee S. Crandall. Animal Kingdom, New York, vol.47, no. 2, pp.46-48, illus., Mar.-Apr., 1944.

DESERTED LEOPARD CUB. C.H.Donald. Field, London, vol.151, May 31, 1928.

ENGATO THE LION CUB. Jack Herbert Driberg. E.P.Dutton and Co., Inc., New York, pp.13-151, pls.2, 1934.

JUNGLE ORPHAN. (Jaguar Kitten.) Tom Gill. Nature Mag., vol.19, no.1, pp.11-15, figs.5, Jan., 1932.

EARLY DEVELOPMENT OF THE CAT. J.P. Hill. Quart. Jour. Micro. Sci., vol. 68, pp.513-602, figs.12, pls.6, Nov., 1924.

CORRELATED STUDY OF THE DEVELOPMENT OF REFLEX ACTIVITY IN FETAL AND YOUNG KITTENS AND THE MYELINIZATION OF TRACTS IN THE CENTRAL NERVOUS SYSTEM. Orthello R. Langworthy. Contrib. to Embryol.Carnegie Inst. Wash. Pub.no.394, vol.20, no.114, pp.127-172, pls. 8, 1929.

SHEBA THE BABY LIONESS. Frank D. McKenney. San Diego Zoonooz, vol.14, no.14, p.6, illus., Feb., 1942.

DESCRIPTION OF A NEWLY-BORN LYNX. LYNX CANADENSIS (DESM.) RAF. C.Hart Merriam. Bull.no.5, Nat. Hist. Soc., New Brunswick, pp.4, illus., Apr., 1886.

(THE YOUNG SWAMP LYNX.) Junge Sumpfluchse. Georg Raak. Zool. Garten, n.F., vol.12, nos.2-3, pp.198-200, illus., July, 1940.

BABY BLACK LEOPARDS. Herbert L. Ratcliffe. Fauna, Philadelphia, vol.2, no.4, pp.85-87, illus., Dec., 1940.

(YOUNG PANTHERS.) Jonge panters. H.P. Rensenbrink. Artis, Amsterdam, vol.1, no. 3, pp.54-58, illus., Oct., 1955.

JUNGLE ORPHANS. (Tigers.) Hugh Thomason. Fauna, Philadelphia, vol.6, no.2, pp. 57-59, illus., June, 1944.

PINNIPEDIA

ORDER OF THE PINNIPEDIA; THE HAIR AND FUR SEALS OF THE WORLD. B.M. Arnold, Jr., H.J. McMullen. Fur Jour., vol. 1, no.5, pp.32-34, 36, 37, Sep., 1927.

ON THE GEOGRAPHICAL DISTRIBUTION OF SEALS. F.H. Balkwill. Zoologist, ser.3, vol.12, pp.401-411, 1888.

PINNIPEDIA. J.G. Bartholomew, et al. (In) Atlas of Zoogeography, Bartholomew's Physical Atlas, vol.5, Edinburgh, Roy.Geogr.Soc., pp.15-16, pls.4, maps 5-6, 1911.

PINNIPEDIA. F.E. Beddard. (In) The Cambridge Natural History, London, Macmillan, vols.10, (vol. 10, pp.446-455) 1895-1909.

WHERE DO SEALS LIVE? Colin Bertram. Discovery, Cambridge, n.s., vol.3, no.22, pp.8-15, Jan., 1940.

BIOLOGY OF THE WEDDELL AND CRABEATER SEALS: WITH A STUDY OF THE COMPARATIVE BEHAVIOUR OF THE PINNIPEDIA. G.C.L. Bertram. British Graham Land Exped. 1934-1937, Sci. Repts., British Mus., Nat.Hist., London, vol.1, no.1, pp. 1-139, figs.42, pls.10, Sep. 14, 1940.

SEALS OF THE EMPIRE. G.C.L. Bertram. Jour. Soc. Preservation Fauna Empire, Hertford, n.s., pt.40, pp.19-28, pl., Aug., 1940.

(GEOGRAPHICAL DISTRIBUTION OF SEALS (PINNIPEDIA).) Die geographische Verbreitung der Robben (Pinnipedia). H. von Boetticher. Zeitschr. f. Saeugetierk., vol.9, pp. 359-368, 1934.

PLEISTOCENE GEOGRAPHY AND THE DISTRIBUTION OF NORTHERN PINNIPEDS. J.L. Davies. Ecology, vol.39, no.1, pp.97-113, Jan., 1958.

(ATTEMPT AT A QUANTITATIVE ESTIMATE OF THE POPULATION OF THE WHITE SEA HERD OF GREENLAND SEALS BY MEANS OF AERIAL PHOTOGRAPHS.) Versuch einer quantitativen Schaetzung des bestandes der Weissmerherde des groenlandischen Seehunds durch aerophotographischen Aufnahmen. S.V. Dorofeiev, S. Freimann. Rept. Sci. Research Inst. Fisheries USSR, Moscow, vol.2, no.4, pp.1-28, 1928. (In Russian with German and Russian titles.)

(ORDER PINNIPEDIA.) Ordre des pinnipedes. S. Frechkop. (In) Traite de zoologie . . . public sous la direction de Pierre-P. Grasse. Paris, Masson, vols.18 (Tome 17, fasc.1, pp.292-340), 1955.

(SEALS.) Phoques. E. Geoffroy Saint-Hilaire, F. Cuvier. (In) Dictionnaire des sciences naturelles, Strasbourg and Paris, vols. 60, atlas of 12 vols., (vol.39, pp.540-559), 1816-1830.

PRODROME OF A MONOGRAPH OF THE PINNIPEDS. T. Gill. Proc. Essex Inst., Salem, Communications, vol.5, pp.3-13, 1866.

(THE PINNIPEDS.) Les pinnipèdes. Agatha Gijzen. Zoo (Soc. Roy. Zool. Anvers), Annee 22, no.1, pp.3-37, 1956.

FIN-FOOTED MARINE MAMMALS, THE PINNIPEDS. George G. Goodwin. Audubon Nature Bull., vol.18, no.6, pp.1-4, Feb., 1948.

(GEOGRAPHICAL DISTRIBUTION OF PINNIPEDIA.) Die geographische Verbreitung der Pinnipedia. C. Greve. Nova Acta Abh. der Kaiserl. Leop.-Carol. Deutschen Akad. der Naturforscher, Bd.66, no.4, pp.287-332, pls.4 (maps in color), 1896.

PAST AND PRESENT STATUS OF THE NORTHERN ELEPHANT SEAL WITH A NOTE ON THE GUADALUPE FUR SEAL. Laurence M. Huey. Jour. Mamm., vol. 11, no.2, pp.188-194, May, 1930.

(ON THE BIOLOGY OF SEALS AND THEIR BEHAVIOR IN CAPTIVITY.) Zur Biologie der Robben und zu ihrer Haltung in Gefangenschaft. Ingo Krumbiegel. Zool.Garten, Leipzig, n.F., vol.6, nos.1-3, pp. 33-44, figs.8, May, 1933.

ON THE SKULL OF A SEAL (OTARIA GILLESPII, M'BAIN) FROM THE GULF OF CALIFORNIA; WITH SOME PRELIMINARY OBSERVATIONS ON THE AMPHIBIOUS CARNIVORA. J. M'Bain. Proc. R. Phys. Soc. Edinb., vol.1, pp.422-428, 1854-1858.

NOTES ON THE PINNIPEDIA. St.G.Mivart. Proc. Zool. Soc. London, pp.484-500, 1885.

(REMARKS ON HARBOR, RINGED, AND HAIR SEALS.) Bemerkungen ueber Seehund, Ringel- und Kegelrobbe. Erna Mohr. Zool. Garten, n.F., vol.12, nos.2-3, pp.173-182, illus., July, 1940.

SEALS AND SNAILS AND SCULPIN TALES. Katherine Brooks Norcross. Audubon Mag., New York, vol.47, no.4, sec.1, pp.194-200, illus., July-Aug., 1945.

LETTER FROM, CONTAINING REMARKS ON THE SEA-LION (OTARIA JUBATA) AND OTHER SEALS. Henry Pain. Proc. Zool. Soc. London, pp.681-682, 1872.

EPILOGUE TO KIPLING'S "WHITE SEAL." Georges Préfontaine. Proc. Royal Canadian Inst., Toronto, ser.3A, vol.14, pp.82-83, 1950.

SEALS, SEA LIONS, AND WALRUSES. (A Review of the Pinnipedia.) Victor B. Scheffer. Stanford Univ. Press, Stanford, Calif., pp.x-179, figs.15, pls.32, Apr. 24, 1958.

SEALS. G. Shaw. (In) General Zoology or Systematic Nat.Hist., London, G.Kearsley, 14 vols. in 28 (vol.1, pt.2, pp.249-273, pls. 4), 1800-1826.

NORTHERN ELEPHANT SEAL AND THE GUADALUPE FUR SEAL. C.H. Townsend. Nat. Hist., vol.24, pp.566-577, 1924.

PELAGIC SEALING, WITH NOTES ON THE FUR SEALS OF GUADALUPE, THE GALAPAGOS, AND LOBOS ISLANDS. C.H. Townsend. Washington, The Fur Seals and Fur-Seal Islands of the N.Pacific Ocean, pt.3, pp.223-274, pls.22-35, chart, 1899.

A RARE SEAL. C.H. Townsend. Bull.Zool. Soc. New York, vol.16, no.60, pp.1050-1051, illus., Nov., 1913.

NOTES ON PINNIPEDIA. E.P. Wheeler. Jour. Mamm., vol.34, no.2, pp.253-255, May, 1953.

POLES APART. (Walrus, Fur Seal, Sea Elephant and Sea Leopard.) Junior Nat.Hist. Mag., New York; vol.5, no.12, pp.4-7, 14, figs.8, Feb., 1941.

(SEAL ISLAND.) Ostrov Tyuleniy. Geografiya v Shkole (Geography in School), no.3, p. 63, 1957. (In Russian.)

SEALS AND THEIR KINDRED. Zoonooz, San Diego, vol.20, no.10, pp.4-7, illus., Oct., 1947.

Anatomy

(ON SOME SEAL SKULLS.) Sur quelques crânes de phoques. H.-M.D. Blainville. J. de Physique, de Chimie, d'Histoire Nat. et des Arts, vol.91, pp.286-300, 1820.

PINNIPEDIA. W.H. Flower. (In) Catalogue of the Specimens Illustrating the Osteology and Dendition of Vertebrated Animals, Mus. of the Roy. College of Surgeons of England, London, J. and A. Churchill, 2 parts (part 2, pp.186-218), 1884.

CONTRIBUTIONS TO THE COMPARATIVE ANATOMY OF THE EARED AND EARLESS SEALS (GENERA ZALOPHUS AND PHOCA). A.B. Howell. Proc. U.S. Nat. Mus., no. 2736, vol.73, art.15, pp.1-142, pl.1, 1929.

PYRAMIDAL TRACT OF AN AQUATIC CARNIVORE (SEAL). A.M. Lassek, P. Karlsberg. Jour. Comp. Neurol., Philadelphia, vol.106, no.2, pp.425-432, Dec., 1956.

SUBSURFACE CRYPTS, OOGENSIS, AND THE CORPUS LUTEUM IN THE OVARIES OF SEALS. L. Harrison Matthews, R.J. Harrison. Nature, London, vol.164, no. 4170, pp.587-588, Oct. 1, 1949.

MYOLOGY OF THE PINNIPEDIA. W.C.S. Miller. (In) Rep. on the Scientific Results of the Voyage of H.M.S. Challenger, Edinburgh, Challenger Office, vol.26, no.2, pp. 139-240, 1880-95.

(SECONDARY GROWTH OF SEAL TEETH.) Sekundaeres Wachstum der Robbenzaehne. Erna Mohr. Sitz. Ber. Gesell. Naturforsch. Freunde, pp.258-260, Mar. 1, 1943.

(ON THE ANATOMY OF THE SEAL HEART.) Zur Anatomie des Robbenherzens. E. Mueller. Gegenbaurs Jahrb., vol.85, pp.59-90, 1940.

(COMMENTS ON PHOCA HISPIDA ANNELATA, ITS SIZE, FOOD, ETC.) Om vikaresalens, Phoca hispida annelata, storlek och foda m.m. Ossian Olofsson. Fauna och Flora, no.1, pp.17-28, illus., 1933.

(HAIR SEAL WITH EXTERNAL EARS.) Eine Kegelrobbe mit Ohrmuscheln. J. Thienemann. Zeitschr. f. Saeugetierk., Berlin, vol.6, no.6, p.225, Dec. 15, 1931.

Australia

PROPOSED DESTRUCTION OF SEALS IN VICTORIAN WATERS. A.F. Basset Hull. Australian Zoologist, Sydney, vol.10, pt.1, p.124, Dec. 19, 1941.

ORDER PINNIPEDIA. T. Iredale, E. LeG. Troughton. (In) A Check-List of the Mammals Recorded from Australia, Mem. Aust. Mus., Sydney, no.6, pp.87-89, 1934.

NOTES ON AUSTRALIAN SEALS. F. Lewis. Vict. Nat., Melb., vol.59, pp.24-26, 1942.

Captivity

ROCKY BASIN OF THE SEALS AND PENGUINS IN THE ZOOLOGICAL GARDEN OF BERLIN.) Das Felsenbecken fuer Robben und Pinguine im Berliner Zoologischen Garten. Ludwig Heck. Der Zool.Garten, n. F., Leipzig, vol.4, nos.10-12, pp.318-362, figs.9, Dec. 16, 1931.

(SOME REMARKS ON SEAL TRAINING.) Einige Bemerkungen zur Robbendressur. Alfred Lehmann. Zool. Garten, Leipzig, vol.22, no.1, pp.47-56, illus., 1955.

(RAISING A SEAL BORN IN CAPTIVITY.) Aufzucht eines in Gefangenschaft geborenen Seehundes. O. Stocker. Zool. Garten, Leipzig, n.F., vol.6, nos.10-12, pp.237-238, Dec., 1933.

FOUR LITTLE SEALS WHO DIDN'T GO TO SEA. NEWCOMERS TO THE ZOO SEEN IN THEIR NEW HOME AT THE OLD OTTER POND, REGENT'S PARK. Illus. London News, vol.215, no.5755, p.187, illus., Aug. 6, 1949.

Economic Importance

SYNOPSIS OF THE PINNIPEDS, OR SEALS AND WALRUSES, IN RELATION TO THEIR COMMERCIAL HISTORY AND PRODUCTS. J.A. Allen. (In) Fur Seal Arbitration, Appendix to the Case of the United States Before the Tribunal of Arbitration to Convene at Paris, Washington, Govt. Print. Off., vol. 1, pp.367-391, 1892?

SOUTH AFRICAN FISH PRODUCTS. M.M. Black, et al. The S.African Seal Fishery, J. Soc. Chem. Ind., London, vol.64, pt. 19, pp.326-331, 1945.

SEAL-HUNTING IN THE STONE AGE OF NORTH-WESTERN EUROPE: A STUDY IN ECONOMIC PREHISTORY. J.G.D. Clark. Proc. Prehistoric Soc., London, n.s., vol. 12, pp.12-48, figs.11, 1946.

SAVING THE SEAL HERDS OF THE ARCTIC SEAS. J.M. Creighton. Travel, vol.41, no.2, pp.21-24, 68, figs.11, June, 1923.

SOUTH AFRICAN SEALING INDUSTRY. Cecil M.P. Cross. Fur Jour., vol.2, no.1, pp.24, 37-39, Jan., 1928.

(RELATIONSHIP OF AGE GROUPS IN SEALS AS INDICATIVE OF THE CONDITION OF THE STOCK.) Vsesoiuznyi nauchno-issledovatel'skii institut morskogo rybnogo khoziaistva i okeanografii SSR. S.W. Dorofejev. Volume in Honor of Sci. Activity of N.M.Knipovich, Inst. Marine Fisheries and Oceanography USSR (VNIRO), People's Commissariat for Food Industry USSR, Moscow and Leningrad, pp. 369-382, 1939. (In Russian with English summary.)

LEATHER AND MEAT AND OIL. Ben East. Beaver, Winnipeg, outfit 270, no.2, pp.40-43, illus., Sep., 1939.

SALMON, SEALS AND SKULLDUGGERY. William L. Finley. Activities of Commissioner of Fisheries Open to Question, Nature, Mag., vol.28, no.5, pp.299-303, illus., Nov., 1936.

INTRODUCING A SERIES OF PHOTOGRAPHS OF BREATHING-HOLE SEALING BY VICOMTE GONTRAN DE PONCINS. Angus Gavin. Beaver, Winnipeg, outfit 270, no.4, pp.26-31, illus., Mar., 1940.

WITH THE NORWEGIAN SEALERS. Per Host. Nat. Hist., New York, vol.51, no.1, pp.6-15, illus., Jan., 1943.

(DRIFT ICE AND SEALING.) Drivis og selfangst. Thor. Iversen. Aarsberetning vedk. Norges Fiskier, hefte 1, pp.1-84, figs.51, 1927. (Notes on Seals and Seal Fisheries.)

HUNTER AGAINST THE SEAL HERDS. Philip Knowling. Carling Conserv.Digest, Toronto, vol.1, no.3, pp.11-12, illus., July, 1947.

NO WONDER THEY WORSHIP THE SEAL. Margaret Lantis. Nat. Hist., New York, vol.48, no.3, pp.166-172, illus., Oct., 1941.

HYPOTHETICAL "SANCTUARY" FOR OCEAN-DWELLING SEALS. C. Hart Merriam. Science, n.s., vol.80, no.2069, pp.186-187, Aug. 24, 1934.

(EXPLOITATION, DESTRUCTION, AND PROTECTION OF THE PINNIPEDS.) Exploitation, destruction et protection des pinnipedes. P. Paulian. La Terre et la Vie, no.1, pp.1-10, 1956.

GOVERNMENT GUANO ISLANDS: BIRDS AND SEALS. R.W. Rand. Union of South Africa Dept. Agric., Pretoria, pp.15, illus., 1950.

SEAL HUNTING ON SLEDGES IN THE WINTER AND SPRING OF 1929. A. N. Roganov. Repts. Astrakhan Sci. Fish. Sta., vol.7, no.2, pp.31-128, 1931. (In Russian.)

SEAL-HUNTING IN THE MANGISHLAK REGION IN 1928-29. P.E. Samofalov.Rept. Astrakhan Sci. Fish. Sta., vol.7, no.2, pp.3-30, 1930. (In Russian.)

SEALING. Johs. Sellaeg. Norsk Hvalfangst-Tidende (Norwegian Whaling Gazette), vol. 44, no.6, pp.316-323, illus., June, 1955.

SEAL FISHERIES. Seton Thompson. (In) Marine Products of Commerce, Donald K. Tressler, James McW. Lemon, Reinhold Publ. Co., New York, ed.2, pp.716-732, illus., 1951.

REPORTS FOR YEARS 1891 AND 1892. W. H. Williams. Seal and Salmon Fisheries and General Resources of Alaska, Wash., vol.1, pp.271, 300, 304, 1898.

SEAL HUNTER. (Eskimo Spearing Seals at Breathing Hole in Ice.) Beaver, Winnipeg, outfit 269, no.1, p.14, illus., June, 1938.

Eurasia

ORDER PINNIPEDIA. G.M. Allen. (In)The Mammals of China and Mongolia, Amer. Mus. Nat. Hist., Nat. Hist. of Central Asia, vols.11, 1932-40 (vol.11, pt.1, pp. 490-493, 1938).

PINNIPEDIA. N.A. Bobrinskoi. (In) Mammals of USSR Moscow, pp.162-168, 1944.

PINNIPEDIA. M. Degerbøl. (In) List of Danish Vertebrates, Copenhagen, Dansk Videnskabs Forlag, p.143, map, 1950. (In English.)

PINNIPEDIA. Maria Manuela da Gama.(In) Mamiferos de Portugal (chaves para a sua determinacao). Mem Mus. Zool.Univ.Coimbra, vol.246, pp.202-206, 1957.

PINNIPEDIA. O. Grimm. (In) Fishing and Hunting on Russian Waters, St.Petersburg, prepared for Internatl. Fish. Exhibn. London, pp.44-47, 1883. (In English.)

(ANOTHER ARCTIC SEAL, PHOCA HISPIDA HISPIDA, FOUND ALONG OUR WEST COAST.) Ännu en arktisk vikare, Phoca hispida hispida, funnen vid var vastkust. Einar Lonnberg. Fauna och Flora, Upsala, no.5, p.235, 1936.

(DISCOVERY OF PHOCA HISPIDA ON THE WEST COAST OF SWEDEN.) Ett fynd av vikare, Phoca hispida, vid var vastkust. Einar

Lonnberg. Fauna och Flora, Stockholm, pt.1, pp.19-24, illus., 1931.

THE SEALS OF THE USSR; THE RAW MATERIAL BASIS OF THE MARINE MAMMAL FISHERY. S.P. Naumov. (In) Economically Exploited Animals of the USSR, ed. by N. A. Bobrinskoi, Moscow and Leningrad, All-Union Cooperative United Publishing House, pp.105, 1933. (In Russian; English transl. in Oxford Bur. Animal Population.)

PINNIPEDIA. S.I. Ognev. (In) The Mammals of Eastern Europe and Northern Asia, Moscow and Leningrad, State Publishing House, vol.1 (1928) to vol.7 (1950). (In Russian.)

(SEALS.) Phocae. P.S. Pallas. (In) Zoogeographia Rosso-Asiatica, sistens omnium animalium in extense imperio Rossico et adjacentibus maribus, Petropoli, in officina Caes. Acad. Scientarum impress, (vols.3) vol.1, pp.99-119, 1811-42.

REVIEW OF RUSSIAN PINNIPEDS. N. A. Smirnov. Mem. Acad. Sci. St.Petersb., ser.8 (phys.-math.), vol.23, no.4, pp. 1-75, pl.1, 1908. (In Russian.)

SEALS AND THE SEAL FISHERY. Thomas Southwell. Trans. Norfolk and Norwich Nat. Soc., Norwich, vol. 3, pp. 482-503, 1883.

SEALS OF NORTHERN HOKKAIDO. F. Wilke. Jour. Mamm., vol.35, pp.218-224, 1954.

Fossils

(FOSSIL SEALS OF THE ANTWERP BASIN.) Les phoques fossiles du bassin d'Anvers. M. P.-J. van Beneden. Bull. Acad. Roy. Belg., vol.41, pp.783-812, pl.1, 1876.

PLIOCENE PINNIPED FROM THE SAN DIEGO FORMATION OF SOUTHERN CALIFORNIA. Gretchen M.L. Burleson. Univ. California Publ. Zool., Berkeley, vol.47, no.10, pp.247-253, illus., Oct. 15, 1948.

NEW PINNIPED (ATOPOTARUS) FROM THE MIOCENE OF SOUTHERN CALIFORNIA, WITH REMARKS ON THE OTARIIDAE. T. Downs. Jour. Paleont., vol.30, pp.115-131, pl.1, 1956.

PINNIPEDIA. O.P. Hay. (In) Second Bibliography and Catalogue of the Fossil Vertebrata of N.America, Publ.Carneg.Inst., vol.2, no.390, pp.555-565, 1929-30.

NEW PINNIPED FROM THE UPPER PLIOCENE OF CALIFORNIA. Remington Kellogg. Jour. Mamm., vol.2, no.4, pp.212-226, Nov., 1921.

NEW PINNIPEDS FROM THE MIOCENE DIATOMACEOUS EARTH NEAR LOMPOC, CALIFORNIA. Remington Kellogg. (In) Additions to the Tertiary History of the Pelagic Mammals on the Pacific Coast of N.America, Contrib.Palaeont.Carneg.Inst., publ.no.348, pt.4, pp.71-95, 1925.

PINNIPEDS FROM MIOCENE AND PLEISTOCENE DEPOSITS OF CALIFORNIA. (Description of a New Genus and Species of Sea Lion from the Temblor Together With Seal Remains from the Santa Margarita and San Pedro Formations and a Resume of Current Theories Regarding Origin of Pinnipedia.) Remington Kellogg. Univ.Calif.Pub.Dept. Geol.Sci., vol.13, pp.23-132, figs.6, Apr. 14, 1922.

FOSSIL PINNIPEDS FROM CALIFORNIA. Remington Kellogg. Carnegie Inst. Wash., publ.348, pp.25-37, figs.8, Nov. 3, 1927.

ON TWO SPECIES OF FOSSIL PINNIPEDIA FROM KAZUSA AND SAGHALIN. H. Matsumoto. Jour. Geol. Soc. Tokyo, vol.32, p.46, pl.3, 1925.

(ON THE REMAINS OF A PRIMITIVE PINNIPED FROM THE NEOCENE DEPOSITS OF WESTERN SIBERIA.) Ueber die Reste eines primitiven Pinnipedier aus den neogenen Ablagerungen Westsibiriens. J.A. Orlov. C.R.Acad.Sci. USSR, ser.A, no. 3, pp.67-70, 1931.

PINNIPED HUMERUS FROM THE ASTORIA MIOCENE OF OREGON. Earl Leroy Packard. Oregon State Monographs, Studies in Geol., Corvallis, no.5, pp.25-28, pl.3, Dec., 1947.

DESCRIPTION OF A NEW GENUS AND SPECIES OF FOSSIL SEAL FROM THE MIOCENE OF MARYLAND. F.W. True. Proc. U.S. Nat. Mus., vol.30, pp.835-840, pls.2, 1906.

(FOSSIL PINNIPEDS.) Pinnipedes fossiles. J. Viret.(In) Traite de Zoologie, public sous la direction de Pierre-P. Grassé, Paris, Masson, vols.18 (Tome 17, fasc.1, pp.336-340), to 1955.

Habits, Behavior

DIET OF SEALS. Frank Greenshields. Nature, London, vol.135, no.3417, p.657, Apr. 27, 1935.

SEAL NAVIGATION. John Eric Hill. Nat. Hist., New York, vol.55, no.3, pp.113, illus., Mar., 1946.

HABITS OF SOME WEST COAST SEALS. A. Brazier Howell. Jour. Mamm., vol.3, no.3, pp.170-172, Aug. 4, 1922.

HABITS OF SEALS. Hiram Ketchom, Jr. Seal and Salmon Fisheries and General Resources of Alaska, Washington, vol.1, pp.4-5, 1898.

SEALS ON THE VICTORIAN COAST AND THEIR FEEDING HABITS. F. Lewis. Australian Mus. Mag., vol.4, no.2, pp.39-44, figs.4, Apr.-June, 1930.

(BEHAVIOR OF PINNIPEDS.) Das Verhalten der Pinnipedier. Erna Mohr. Handbuch der Zoologie, Berlin, vol.8, pt.10, no.22, pp. 1-20, illus., 1956.

(VOICE OF SEALS IN THE EUROPEAN WATERS.) Die Stimme der Robben in den europaeischen Gewaessern. Erna Mohr. Schriften Naturwissenschaft. Vereins Schleswig-Holstein, vol.25, (Karl-Gripp-Festschrift), pp.29-33, 1951.

FOOD OF SEALS. C.E. Radclyffe. Field, London, vol.164, no.4279, p.1517, Dec. 29, 1934.

REPORT OF THE CANADIAN ARCTIC EXPEDITION 1913-1918. VOL. VII. CRUSTACEA. PART E. AMPHIPODS. (Contains Records of Stomach Contents of Seals.) Clarence R. Shoemaker. Ottawa, pp.2-30, Sep. 7, 1920.

ON CALCULATION OF THE KILLING RATE OF PINNIPEDS. N. Smirnov. Bull. Inst.Applied Ichthyol. USSR, Leningrad, vol.8, pp. 5-16, 1928. (In Russiand with English titles.)

Medical Aspects

SEALER'S FINGER OR SPECKFINGER. William L. Jellison. Mimeo.Cir., Rocky Mountain Lab., U.S.Publ. Health Service, pp.4, Dec., 1951.

SEAL FINGER. J.S. Skinner. Amer. Med. Assoc. Arch. Dermatol., vol.75, pp.559-561, 1957.

Methods, Techniques

NEW "EYES" FOR THE SEALING FLEET. (Scouting for Seals by Airplane.) E. L. Chicanot. Scientific American, vol.138, pp.409-411, illus., May, 1928.

SEAL MARKING AT HEARD ISLAND, 1949. R.G. Chittleborough, C.H.M. Ealey. Interim Rep. Australian Nat. Antarctic Res. Exped., no.1, pp.1-30, illus., Oct., 1951.

A. N. A. R. E. BIRD BANDING AND SEAL MARKING. Patricia Howard. Vict. Nat., Melb., vol.71, pp.73-82, 1954.

SEAL-MARKING METHODS. Richard M. Laws. Polar Rec., vol.6, no.43, pp.359-361, Jan., 1952.

HOW TO SKIN A SEAL: IN EIGHT EASY LESSONS. (Eskimo Method.) D.B. Marsh. Beaver, Winnipeg, outfit 272, pp.50-51, illus., Dec., 1941.

EXPERIMENTS IN THE MARKING OF SEALS AND SEA-LIONS. Victor B. Scheffer. Special Sci. Rep. Wildl., Fish and Wildl. Serv., no.2, pp.31, illus., Apr., 1950.

GROWTH LAYERS ON THE TEETH OF PINNIPEDIA AS AN INDICATION OF AGE. Victor B. Scheffer. Science, vol.112, no. 2907, pp.309-311, Sep. 15, 1950.

INSTRUCTION FOR FIELD WORK ON BIOLOGY OF SEALS. N. Smirnov. Vsesoiznyi arkticheskii institute, PRI TSIK SSSR, Leningrad, no.4, pp.58, figs.9, 1934. (Arctic Inst. of USSR.)

Museum Exhibits

HAND-LIST OF SEALS, MORSES, SEA-LIONS, AND SEA-BEARS IN THE BRITISH MUSEUM. J.E. Gray. London, Brit.Mus., pp.44, pls.30, 1874.

PINNIPEDIA. J.E. Gray. (In) Catalogue of Seals and Whales in the British Museum, London, Brit.Mus., pp.1-60, figs.1-18, 1866b.

SEAL COLLECTION, A FEATURE OF THE HALL OF OCEAN LIFE, AMERICAN MUSEUM. Frederic A. Lucas. Nat. Hist., vol. 24, no.5, pp.589-593, Sep.-Oct., 1924.

North and Central America

HISTORY OF NORTH AMERICAN PINNIPEDS, A MONOGRAPH OF THE WALRUSES, SEA-LIONS, SEA-BEARS AND SEALS OF NORTH AMERICA. J.A. Allen. Washington, U.S. Geol. and Geogr. Surv. Terr., Misc. Publ., no.12, pp.16-785, 1880.

SPRING, SUMMER, AND FALL CENSUSES OF THE PINNIPEDS ON SAN NICOLAS ISLAND, CALIFORNIA. George A. Bartholomew. Jour. Mamm., vol.32, no.1, pp.15-21, pl.1, Feb. 15, 1951.

WINTER POPULATION OF PINNIPEDS ABOUT GUADALUPE, SAN BENITO, AND CEDROS ISLANDS, BAJA CALIFORNIA. George A. Bartholomew, Carl. L. Hubbs. Jour. Mamm., vol.33, no.2, pp.160-171, illus., May 16, 1952.

REPORT ON THE SEALS AND SEA LIONS OF CALIFORNIA, 1928. P. Bonnot. Calif. Div. Fish and Game, Fish. Bull., no.14, pp.62, 1929.

KNOCK ON THE DOOR. (Sea Lions, Seals.) Lawrence Carson. Alaska Sportsman, Ketchikan, vol.9, no.11, pp.14-15, 28-35, illus., Nov., 1943.

OBSERVATIONS ON PINNIPEDS OF SAN MIGUEL ISLAND. R.D. Collyer, J. L. Baxter. Calif. Fish Game, no.37, p.511, 1951.

ORDER PINNIPEDIA. D.G. Elliot. (In) A Synopsis of the Mammals of North America and the Adjacent Seas, Publ.Field Mus., Zool. Ser., vol.2, pp.355-365, pls.12, 1901.

PINNIPEDIA. D.G. Elliot. (In) The Land and Sea Mammals of Middle America and the West Indies, Publ. Field Mus.95, Zool. Ser., vol.4, 2 parts (part 2, pp.538-546, pls.53-66), 1904.

(DETAILED DESCRIPTIONS OF THE SEALS ON GREENLAND.) Udfarlig beskrivels over de Gronlandske saele. O. Fabricius. Skrivter af Naturhistorie-Selskabet, Kobenhavn, Bind 1, Hefte 2, pp.73-170, pls.2, 1791.

(SEA LIONS AND SEA ELEPHANTS UNDER NATURAL PROTECTION.) Seelowen und See-Elefanten unter Naturschutz. (Guadalupe Island.) Hans Haerlin. Kosmos, Handweiser fuer Naturfreunde (Gesell.der Naturfreunde), Stuttgart, Jahrg.1932, no.1, pp.3-6, figs.4, Jan., 1932.

HARBOR SEALS AND SEA LIONS IN ALASKA. Ralph H. Imler, Hosea R. Sarber. U.S. Dept. Interior, Fish and Wildl.Serv., Spec. Sci. Rep., no.28, pp.23, Apr., 1947.

PINNIPEDIA. G.S. Miller, Jr. (In) List of North American Recent Mammals, 1923, Bull. U.S.Nat.Mus., no.128, pp.16-673, 1924. (Pinnipedia pp.162-167.)

PINNIPEDIA. G.S. Miller, Jr., R.Kellogg. (In) List of North American Recent Mammals, Bull. U.S. Nat.Mus., no.205, pp. 12-954, 1955. (Pinnipedia pp.782-790.)

SEALS AND SEA LIONS. ORDER PINNIPEDIA. R.S. Palmer. (In) The Mammal Guide, Garden City, New York, Doubleday, pp.148-166, col.pls.2, 1954.

OUTPOSTS OF BAJA CALIFORNIA. (Photographs of Sea-Lions and Sea-Elephants.) Joseph R. Slevin. Nat. Hist., New York, vol.37, no.6, pp.65-73, illus., June, 1936.

NOTES ON PINNIPEDIA ( IN NORTHERN LABRADOR). E.P. Wheeler. Jour.Mamm., vol.34, pp.253-255, 1953.

Northern Waters

PINNIPEDIA FREQUENTING THE SPITZBERGEN AND GREENLAND SEAS. Robert Brown. Proc. Zool. Soc. London, for 1868, pp.405-440, 1868.

PINNIPEDIA OF THE ARCTIC AND SUB-ARCTIC. M.J. Dunbar. Fisheries Res. Bd. Can., Bull.85, pp.22, 1949.

PINNIPEDIA. L. Freund. (In) Die Tierwelt der Nord- und Ostsee, begruendet von G. Grimpe und E. Wagler, Leipzig, Akad. Verlagsgesellschaft, Lief. 24, Teil 12, pp. k2-k83, 1933. (In German.)

PINNIPEDIA OF THE OKHOTSK SEA (CHIEFLY SOUTHERN PART). S.P. Naumov. Uchenye Zapiski Moskovskogo Gosudarstvennogo Pedagogicheskogo Instituta, Tom 24, no.2, pp.19-74, 1941. (In Russian with English summary.)

OBSERVATIONS ON PINNIPEDS OF THE OKHOTSK AND JAPAN SEAS. P.G. Nikulin. Bull. Pacific Sci. Inst. of Fisheries and Oceanography, Vladivostok, vol.10, pp.49-58, 1937. (In Russian with English summary.)

PINNIPEDIA. T.S. Rass, et al. (In) Geographical Distribution of Fishes and Other Commercial Animals of the Okhotsk and Bering Seas, Trudy Inst. Okeanologii, Tom 14, pp.1-120, 1955. (In Russian.)

PINNIPEDIA. B. Saemundsson. (In) Mammalia, The Zoology of Iceland, Copenhagen and Reykjavik, Ejnar Munksgaard, vol.4, part 76, pp.6-14, 1939.

(SEALS OF THE BALTIC SEA AND THEIR CAPTURE.) Die Seehunde der Ostsee und ihr Fang. Otto Schubart. Zool. Garten, Leipzig, n.F., vol.1, nos.7-9, pp.313-324, Feb., 1929.

BIOLOGY OF WALRUS AND SEALS IN THULE DISTRICT. Christian Vibe. Grönlandsposten, Copenhagen, vol.5, pp.281-287, 1946. (In Danish.)

Origins, Relationships, Taxonomy

(ON THE ORIGIN OF THE PINNIPEDS.) De l'origine des pinnipedes. P. Magne de la Croix. An.Soc.Cient.Argent., vol.123, pp.321-328, 1937.

LINGUISTICS. - THE WORD FOR SEAL (PINNIPEDIA) IN VARIOUS LANGUAGES. John P. Harrington. Jour. Wash. Acad. Sci., vol.37, no.4, pp.109-111, Apr. 15, 1947.

SOME NAMES APPLIED TO SEALS BY DYBOWSKI IN 1929. Gerrit S. Miller, Jr. Proc. Biol. Soc. Wash., vol.45, pp.149-150, Sep. 9, 1932.

PINNIPEDIA. H. Winge. (In) The Interrelationships of the Mammalian Genera, transl. from Danish by E. Deichmann, G.M. Allen, Copenhagen, C.A. Reitzel, vols.3, (vol.2, pp.211, 241-249), 1941-1942.

Parasites

REDESCRIPTION OF UNCINARIA LUCASI STILES, A HOOKWORM OF SEALS. H.A. Baylis. Parasitology, London, vol.38, no. 3, pp.160-162, illus., July, 1947.

NOTES ON ANOPLURA INFESTING MARINE CARNIVORES. Willis H. Doetschman. Jour. Parasitol., Lancaster, vol.30, no.3, p.200, June, 1944.

NEW SPECIES OF THE GENUS PARAFILAROIDS DOUGHERTY, 1946. (NEMATODA: METASTRONGYLIDAE), FROM SEA-LIONS, WITH A LIST OF THE LUNGWORMS OF THE PINNIPEDIA. Ellsworth C. Dougherty, Carlton M. Herman. Proc.Helminthol.Soc., Washington, vol.14, no.2, pp.75-77, illus., July, 1947.

PARASITIC HELMINTH AND ARTHROPODS FROM PINNIPEDIA OF THE CANADIAN PACIFIC COAST. L. Margolis. Jour.Fish. Res.Bd.Can., vol.13, pp.489-505, 1956.

PSEUDOPHYLLIDEAN CESTODES FROM ALASKAN PINNIPEDS. Horace W. Stunkard. Jour. Parasitol., Lancaster, vol.34, no.3, pp. 211-228, June, 1948.

LUHE'S "DIPHYLLOBOTHRIUM" (CESTODA). Robert A. Wardle, et al. Jour. Parasitology, vol.33, no.4, pp.319-330, Aug., 1947.

Pelage, Coloration

(CONTRIBUTION TO KNOWLEDGE OF THE SKIN OF SOME PINNIPEDS.) Beitraege zur Kenntnis der Haut einiger Pinnipedier. B. Bergersen. Skrift. Norske Vidensk.-Akad., Oslo, Mat.-Naturvidensk. Klasse, pp.1-179, pls.22, 1931.

(HAIR COVER AND REPLACEMENT IN THE SEALS.) Behaarung und Haarwechsel der Robben. Erna Mohr. Neue Ergebnisse und Probleme der Zoologie (Klatt-Festschrift), Leipzig, pp.602-614, fig.6, 1950.

(SINUS HAIRS OF THE FIN FOOTED ANIMALS.) Sinus Haare der Flossemfuessler. D. Tretjakoff. Zeitschr. Wiss. Zoologie, vol.131, pp.269-292, figs.6, June, 1928.

Physiology

EXPERIMENTS ON THE RELATION BETWEEN BLOOD FLOW AND HEART RATE IN THE DIVING SEAL. S.W. Grinnell, et al. Jour. Cell. and Comp. Physiol., Philadelphia, vol.19, no.3, pp.341-350, figs.4, June 20, 1942.

(OBSERVATIONS AND REFLECTIONS ON THE BREATHING RHYTHM OF PINNIPEDS.) Beobachtungen und Gedanken ueber den Atemrhythmus der Pinnipedier. Otto Harnisch. Zool. Anzeiger, vol.117, nos.9-10, pp.225-232, figs.2, Mar. 1, 1937.

WATER BALANCE OF A MARINE MAMMAL, THE SEAL. L. Irving, et al. Jour. Cell. Comp. Physiol., vol.6, pp.387-391, 1935.

METABOLISM AND INSULATION OF SEALS AS BARE-SKINNED MAMMALS IN COLD WATER. L. Irving, J.S. Hart. Canadian Jour. Zool., Ottawa, vol.35, no.4, pp. 497-511, Aug., 1957.

SIGNIFICANCE OF THE HEART RATE TO THE DIVING ABILITY OF SEALS. L. Irving, et al. Jour. Cell. and Comp. Physiol., Philadelphia, vol.18, no.3, pp.283-297, figs.5, Dec. 20, 1941.

REGULATION OF ARTERIAL BLOOD PRESSURE IN THE SEAL DURING DIVING. L. Irving, et al. Amer. Jour. Physiol., Philadelphia, vol.135, no.3, pp.557-566, Feb., 1942.

OBSERVATIONS ON THE REFRACTION AND VISION OF THE SEAL EYE. G.L. Johnson. Proc. Zool. Soc. London, pp. 719-723, 1893.

(COMPARATIVE PHYSIOLOGICAL INVESTIGATION ON BOARD THE PRINCESS ALICE. OBSERVATIONS AT SPITZBERG ON A YOUNG SEAL. THE SLEEP OF MARINE MAMMALS.) Recherches de Physiologie comparée faites a bord de la Princesse Alice. Varia- Observations faites au Spitzberg sur un jeune phoque. Le sommeil des Mammifères marins. Paul Portier. Resultats Campagnes Sci. accomplies sur son yacht par Albert Prince souverain de Monaco, fasc. 98, pp.81-84, 1938;(TEMPERATURE OF THE PINNIPEDS.) Temperature des pinnipedes. fasc.98, pp.71-72, tbl., 1938.

MUSCLE HEMOGLOBIN OF SEALS AS AN OXYGEN STORE IN DIVING. Douglas Robinson. Science, Lancaster, n.s., vol.90, no. 2334, pp.276-277, tbl.1, Sep. 22, 1939.

AEROBIC AND ANAEROBIC CHANGES IN SEAL MUSCLES DURING DIVING. P.F. Scholander, et al. Jour. Biol. Chemistry, Baltimore, vol.142, no.1, pp.431-440, figs. 4, Jan., 1942.

(ON THE CHEMICAL COMPOSITION OF SEAL MILK.) Ueber die chemische Zusammensetzung von Robbenmilch. Erling Sivertsen. Nyt. Mag. f. Naturvidensk., Oslo, vol.75, pp.183-185, 1936.

Reproductive Biology

SEAL'S BREEDING HABITS. (Weddell, Common, and Eared Seals, and Sea Elephant.) Colin Bertram. Discovery, Cambridge, n.s., vol.3, no.24, pp.130-135, illus., Mar., 1940.

REPRODUCTION IN SOME PINNIPEDIA. R.J. Harrison, L.H. Matthews, J.M. Roberts. Trans. Zool. Soc. London, vol. 27, pp.437-540, pls.4, 1952.

(GESTATION CONDITIONS OF SEALS.) Tragzeitverhaeltnisse der Robben. Erna Mohr. Zool. Anzeiger, Leipzig, vol.139, nos.9-10, pp.176-183, Sep. 19, 1942.

THE BIOLOGY OF REPRODUCTION OF PINNIPEDIA OF THE FAR EAST. M.M. Sleptzov. Zool. Jour. USSR, Moscow, vol. 22, no.2, pp.109-128, figs.9, tbls.7, 1943. (With English summary.)

South America

(OBSERVATIONS ON THE PRESENT CONDITION OF THE PINNIPEDS OF ARGENTINA.) Observaciones sobre el estado actual de las poblaciones de pinnipedos de la Argentina. Italo Santiago Carrara. Republica Argentina, Ministerio de Educacion, Univ. Nac. Eva Peron, Fac.Ciencias Veterinarias, pp.1-17, pls.5, 1954.

(PINNIPEDIA.) C. da Cunha Veira. (In) Lista remissiva dos mamiferos do Brasil, Arch.Zool.S. Paulo, vol.8, p.456, 1955.

(SOME OBSERVATIONS ON THE SEALS OF THE COAST OF URUGUAY.) Algunos observaciones sobre los lobos marinos de la uruguaya. Fernando De Buen. Rev.Soc. Mexicana Hist.Nat., Mexico, vol.8, nos. 1-4, pp.221-227, illus., 1948.

(CHILEAN SEALS IN THE MUSEUM OF SANTIAGO.) Die Chilenischen Seehunde in Museum zu Santiago. R.A. Philippi. Anales del Museo Nacional de Chile, pp. 1-52, 1893.

(CHILEAN SEALS OF THE NATIONAL MUSEUM.) Las Focas Chilenas del Museo Nacional. R.A. Philippi. Anal.del Mus.Nac. de Chile, Publicados por orden del gobierno de Chile, Primera Session: Zoolojia, Santiago, Chile, pp.1-48, pls.23, 1892.

Southern Waters

ROOKERY ISLAND (MACQUARIE). H.F. Doutch. Geogr.Mag., vol.25, pp.224-231, 1952.

SOUTHERN SEALS: POPULATION STUDIES AND CONSERVATION PROBLEMS. R. A. Falla. Proc. 7th Pac. Sci. Congr., vol.4, p.706, 1953.

(FAUNA OF THE ATLANTIC OCEAN LITTORAL: SEA-LIONS AND ELEPHANT SEALS, PENGUINS, AND GUANO BIRDS.) La fauna del litoral Atlantico: lobos y elefantes marinos, pinguinos y aves guaneras. Ruiz Gonzalez. Natura, Buenos Aires, vol.1, pp.121-129, 1955.

SEALS OF THE SOUTHERN HEMISPHERE. J.E. Gray. (In) The Zoology of the Voyage of H.M.S. Erebus and Terror, During the Years 1839 to 1843, ed.by John Richardson, London, vols.2, pp.1-8, pls.1-10, 14-17, 1844; pp.9-12, 1875.

SEALS AND SEALING IN THE FALKLAND ISLANDS AND THEIR DEPENDENCIES. (Elephant, Weddell, Crab-Eating and Leopard Seals; Fur Seal and Sea-Lion.) J. E. Hamilton. Jour. Soc. Preservation Fauna in Empire, Hertford, n.s., pt.34, pp.68-75, Aug., 1938.

SEALS (PINNIPEDIA). J.G. Hayes. (In) Antarctic, a Treatise on the Southern Continent, London, Richards, pp.103-108, 1928.

SEALS OF THE FALKLAND ISLANDS AND DEPENDENCIES. R.M. Laws. Oryx, vol.2, no.2, pp.87-97, Aug., 1953.

STATUS OF SEALING IN THE SUB-ANTARCTIC ATLANTIC. Robert Cushman Murphy. Sci. Monthly, Lancaster, vol.7, no.8, pp.112-119, illus., Aug., 1918.

(OCCURRENCE OF THE HYDRURGA LEPTONYX (BL.) AND ARCTOCEPHALUS GAZELLA (PET.) ON THE ISLANDS OF KERGUELEN AND BIOLOGICAL NOTES ON TWO SEALS.) Sur la presence aux iles kerguelen d'Hydrurga leptonyx (Bl.) et d'Arctocephalus gazella (Pet.) et notes biologiques sur deux Phocidés. Patrice Paulian. Mammalia, Paris, vol.16, no.4, pp.223-227, Dec., 1952.

(NOTES ON THE SEALS ON THE ISLANDS AMSTERDAM AND ST. PAUL.) Note sur les phoques des Iles Amsterdam et Saint-Paul. Patrice Paulian. Mammalia, Paris, vol.21, no.3, pp.210-225, pls.7-8, Sep., 1957.

(PINNIPEDIA OF THE GERMAN SOUTH POLE EXPEDITION 1901-1903.) Die Pinnipedier der Deutschen Suedpolar-Expedition 1901-1903. Hermann Pohle. (In) Erich von Drygalski's Deutsche Suedpolar-Exped. 1901-1903, vol.19 (Zool., vol.11), pp.449-462, Nov., 1927.

PINNIPEDIA. J.R.C. Quoy, J.P.Gaimard. (In) Voyage de la corvette l'Astrolabe exécute, pendant les annees 1826...1829, sous le commandement de J. Dumont d'Urville, Paris, vols.15 in 12, 1830-35; atlas 5 vols. (vol.1, pp.89-99), 1833-34.

ON THE SEALS OF THE FALKLAND ISLANDS. COMMUNICATED, WITH NOTES. Philip Lutley Sclater. Proc. Zool. Soc. London, pp.189-192, 1868.

(PINNIPED MAMMALS.) Mammiferes pinnipedes. E.L. Trouessart. (In) Expedition antarctique Francaise (1903-1905) comandee par le Dr.Jean Charcot, Sciences Naturelles, documents scientifiques, Paris, Masson, pp.1-28, pls.1-4, 1907.

SEALS OF THE SOUTHERN OCEAN. E.G. Turbott. (In) The Antarctic Today. A Mid-century Survey by the New Zealand Antarctic Society. A.H. Wellington and A.W. Reed in conjunction with the Society, pp.389 (pp. 195-215), fold.map, 1952.

REPORT ON THE SEALS COLLECTED DURING THE VOYAGE OF H.M.S. CHALLENGER IN THE YEARS 1873-1876. W. Turner. (In) Rep. on the Scientific Results of the Voyage of H.M.S. Challenger, Edinburgh, Challenger Office, vol.26, no.2, pp.1-240, pls.10; Challenger Zool. Repts., pt.68, 1880-95.

JOINT NORWEGIAN-BRITISH-SWEDISH EXPEDITION IN THE ANTARCTIC, HAULING A SEAL ABOARD FROM THE ICE-FLOE. Illus. London News, vol.216, no.5790, p. 539, illus., Apr.8, 1950.

## Otariidae

### (Eared Seals and Otariidae) General

CLASSIFICATION OF THE EARED SEALS. J.A. Allen. Amer. Nat., Salem, vol.4, pp. 37-42, 1871. (Bound in volume of Theodore Gill, "Pinnipeds and Cetaceans".)

GENERIC AND SPECIFIC NAMES OF SOME OF THE OTARIIDAE. J.A. Allen. Bull. Amer. Mus. Nat. Hist., vol.16, pp.111-118, Mar. 15, 1902.

ON THE EARED SEALS (OTARIADAE), WITH DETAILED DESCRIPTIONS OF THE NORTH PACIFIC SPECIES, TOGETHER WITH AN ACCOUNT OF THE HABITS OF THE NORTHERN FUR SEAL (CALLERHINUS URSINUS), BY CHARLES BRYANT. J.A. Allen. Bull. Mus. Comp. Zool., vol. 2, no.1, pp.1-108, pls.1-3, Aug., 1870.

(Review by Theodore Gill of) MEMOIR ON THE EARED SEALS, OTARIIDAE, WITH DETAILED DESCRIPTIONS OF THE NORTH PACIFIC SPECIES. J. A. Allen. Amer.Nat., Lancaster, vol.4, pp.675-684, Jan., 1871.

MARINE COUSINS OF THE BEARS. Paul Bonnot. Animal Kingdom, New York, vol. 47, no.5, pp.106-110, illus., Sep.-Oct., 1944.

ON THE EARED SEALS OF THE AUCKLAND ISLANDS. J.W. Clark. Proc. Zool. Soc. London, pp.750-760, 1873.

ON THE EARED SEALS OF THE ISLANDS OF ST.PAUL AND AMSTERDAM, WITH A DESCRIPTION OF THE FUR-SEAL OF NEW ZEALAND, AND AN ATTEMPT TO DISTINGUISH AND RE-ARRANGE THE NEW ZEALAND OTARIIDAE. J.W.Cla-k. Proc. Zool. Soc. London, pp.650-677, pls. 3, 1875.

MANDIBLE OF THE SEAL ALLODESMUS KERNENSIS FROM THE KERN RIVER MIOCENE (TEMBLOR) OF CALIFORNIA. T. Downs. Bull. S.Calif. Acad. Sci., vol. 52, pp.93-102, 1953.

OTARIIDAE OF THE GALAPAGOS ISLANDS. Irenäux Eibl-Eibesfeldt. Jour. Mamm., vol. 37, no.4, p.549, Jan. 9, 1957.

CLASSIFICATION OF THE EARED SEALS. T. Gill. Amer. Nat., vol.5, p.6, June, 1871.

NOTES ON THE SKULLS OF SEA-BEARS AND SEA-LIONS (OTARIADAE) IN THE BRITISH MUSEUM. J.E. Gray. Ann. Mag. Nat. Hist., ser.3, vol.18, pp.228-237, 1866.

ON THE SEA-BEAR OF NEW ZEALAND (ARCTOCEPHALUS CINEREUS) AND THE NORTH AUSTRALIAN SEA-BEAR (GYSOPHOCA TROPICALIS). J.E. Gray.Proc. Zool. Soc. London, pp.653-662, figs.6, 1872.

NOTES ON THE FUR SEALS (AND SEA-LION) AT MACQUARIE ISLAND AND HEARD ISLAND. A.M. Gwynn. Interim Repts.Australian Natl. Antarct. Res. Exped., no.4, p.16, 1853b.

EARED SEALS OF SOUTH AUSTRALIA. Frederick Wood Jones. Rec.S.Australian Mus., vol.3, no.1, pp.9-16, June 30, 1925.

DIVING DEPTHS OF THE STELLER SEA LION AND ALASKA FUR SEAL. Karl W. Kenyon. Jour. Mamm., vol.33, no.2, pp. 245-246, May 16, 1952.

OTARTID SEALS OF THE PACIFIC COAST OF AMERICA. J.E. King. Bull., Brit. Mus. Nat. Hist. Zoo., vol.2, no.10, pp.311-337, 1954.

REPORT ON THE EARED SEALS COLLECTED BY THE SOCIETY'S KEEPER FRANCOIS LECOMTE IN THE FALKLAND ISLANDS. James Murie. Proc. Zool. Soc. London, pp.100-109, figs.2, pl.7, 1869.

(PRELIMINARY NOTE ON THE CLASSIFICATION OF SEALS OF AMSTERDAM ISLAND.) Note preliminaire sur la systematique de l'otaries de l'Itle Amsterdam. P. Paulian. Mammalia, Paris, vol.21, no.1, pp.9-15, Mar., 1957.

(ON THE EARED SEALS, OTARIAE, ADDENDUM TO HIS TREATMENT ON THESE ANIMALS READ IN THE PREVIOUS YEAR.) Ueber die Ohrenrobben, Otariae, als Nachtrag zu seiner im vorigen Jahre ueber diese Thiere gelesenen Abhandlung. W.Peters. Monatsber. Koen. Akad. Wiss. Berlin, pp. 505-507, Aug. 9, 1877.

(ON THE EARED SEALS (SEA LIONS AND BEARS), OTARIAE, ESPECIALLY THOSE IN THE COLLECTIONS AT BERLIN.) Ueber die Ohrenrobben (Seeloewen und Seebaeren), Otariae, insbesondere ueber die in den Sammlungen zu Berlin befindlichen Arten. W. Peters. Gesammtsitzung, vol.17, pp. 261-281, pls.4, May, 1866.

(SUPPLEMENT TO HIS TREATMENT OF THE EARED SEALS (OTARIAE).) Nachtrag zu seiner Abhandlung ueber die Ohrenrobben (Otariae). W. Peters. Monatsber. Koen. Akad. Wiss. Berlin, pp.665-672, pl.1, 1866b.

USE OF VERNACULAR NAMES, SEA-LION AND FUR SEAL. Victor B. Scheffer. Jour. Parasitol., Baltimore, vol.34, no.2, p.164, Aug., 1948.

REVIEW OF THE FAMILY OF OTARIIDAE. E. Sivertsen. One-page separate headed "XIV. Intern. Zool. Cong. Copenhagen 1953," 1953b.

SURVEY OF THE EARED SEALS (FAMILY OTARIIDAE) WITH REMARKS ON THE ANTARCTIC SEALS COLLECTED BY M. K. NORVEGIA IN 1928-1929. E.Sivertsen. Norske Videnskaps- Akad. Oslo, Sci.Res. Norwegian Antarctic Exped.1927-1928 et sqq., instituted and financed by Consul Lars Christensen, no.36, pp.1-76, illus., 1954.

### (Fur Seals) General

FAMILY LIFE OF THE FUR SEAL. T. McKean Downs. Frontiers, Lancaster, vol. 10, no.2, pp.35-37, 62-63, illus., Dec., 1945.

(SKETCH OF) ADULT MALE AND FEMALE ALASKA SEALS, AGED THREE, FIVE AND SEVEN YEARS. H.W. Elliot. (Bound in volume of Theodore Gill "Pinnipeds and Cetaceans".) Mar. 1, 1873.

CHARACTERISTICS OF FUR SEALS. S. Falconer. Seal and Salmon Fisheries and General Resources of Alaska, Washington, vol.1, pp.53-61, 1898.

ON THE SEA-BEAR OF FOSTER, THE URSUS MARINUS OF STELLER ARCTOCEPHALUS URSINUS OF AUTHORS. J.E. Gray. Proc. Zool. Soc. London, pt.27, pp.102-103, figs.3, pls., 1859.

SPECIES OF CALLORHINUS OR NORTHERN FUR SEAL. D.S. Jordan, G.A.Clark. (In) The Fur Seals, pt.3, pp.2-4, 1899.

FUR-SEALS. Henry Mygatt. Hunter-Trader-Trapper, vol.74, no.2, pp.13, 16, illus., Feb., 1937.

FACTS ABOUT OUR FUR SEALS. Edward A. Preble. Nat. Humane Rev., vol.21, no. 11, pp.22-23, Nov., 1933.

VITAMIN A IN SELECTED PALE-COLORED LIVERS OF ALASKA FUR SEALS, 1948. V. B. Scheffer et al. U.S. Dept. Interior, Fish and Wildl. Serv., Spec. Sci. Rept., Fisheries 32, pp.8, 1950.

RELATIVE GROWTH IN THE NORTHERN FUR SEAL. V.B. Scheffer, Ford Wilke. Growth, vol.17, pp.129-145, 1953.

STUDIES IN TASMANIAN MAMMALS, LIVING AND EXTINCT. NO. XIV. EARED SEALS OF TASMANIA (PART 2). H.H. Scott, Clive E. Lord. Papers and Proc. Royal Soc. Tasmania, 1925, pp.187-194, pls.6, 1926.

GUARDIANS OF THE HERD. (Fur Seals.) Charles H. Simmons. Hunting and Fishing, Philadelphia, vol.27, no.10, p.22, Oct., 1950.

FUR SEAL OF THE GALAPAGOS ISLANDS. Charles Haskins Townsend. Zoologica, New York, vol.18, no.2, pp.43-56, figs. 15-25, Aug., 1934.

PELAGIC FUR SEAL RESEARCH OFF JAPAN IN 1950. Ford Wilke. Preliminary Study Nat. Resources Sec., Gen. Headquarters, Supreme Commander for Allied-Powers, Tokyo, no.67, pp.35, figs.16, Oct., 1951; U.S. Fish and Wildl.Serv., Wildl. Leaflet no.338, pp.35, illus., Jan., 1952.

### (Fur Seals) Africa

ON THE EARED-SEAL OF THE CAPE OF GOOD HOPE (OTARIA DELALANDII). John E. Gray. Proc. Zool. Soc. London, pt.27, pp.107-110, pls., 1859.

STUDIES ON THE CAPE FUR-SEAL (ARCTOCEPHALUS PUSILLUS, SCHREBER). R.W. Rand. Union S.Africa Dept. Agric., Govt.Guano Islands Admin., Progr. Repts. 1-3, pp.60, tbls., figs., 1950b.

CAPE FUR SEALS. R.W. Rand. Farming in South Africa, Pretoria, vol.25, no.294, pp.305-307, illus., Sep., 1950.

CAPE FUR SEAL ARCTOCEPHALUS PUSILLUS (SCHREBER). ITS GENERAL CHARACTERISTICS AND MOLT. R.W. Rand. Commerce and Industry, Dept. Comm. and Ind. Union of S. Africa, Pretoria, vol.14, no.10, pp.671-721 (reprint paged 1-52), illus., June, 1956.

(SOUTH AFRICAN DWARF SEAL (ARCTOCEPHALUS PUSILLUS SCHREBER).) Von suedafrikanischen Zwergseebaeren (Arctocephalus pusillus Schreber). Karl Max Schneider. Zool. Garten, vol.14, nos.1-2, pp.69-98, illus., 1942.

### (Fur Seals) Alaska and Bering Sea

OBSERVATIONS DURING A CRUISE ON THE SEALING SCHOONER LOUIS OLSEN, AUGUST, 1894. A.B. Alexander. Seal and Salmon Fisheries and General Resources of Alaska, Doc.137, pt.2, vol.4, pp.563-571, 1898.

(SKETCH OF) ALASKA.--THE SEAL ROOKERY ON THE REEF AT ST. PAUL'S ISLAND. Henry W. Elliott. (Bound in volume of Theodore Gill "Pinnipeds and Cetaceans".) Nov. 16, 1872.

MONOGRAPH OF THE SEAL-ISLANDS OF ALASKA. Henry W. Elliott. U.S. Com. Fish and Fisheries, Special Bull.176, pp. 176, pls.29, (Rep. Fisheries Indust. 10th Census), 1882.

SECOND PRELIMINARY REPORT OF THE BERING SEA FUR SEAL INVESTIGATIONS. David Starr Jordan. Doc.U.S. Treas. Dept., no.1994, pp.48, 1898.

DESCRIPTION OF THE SEAL ROOKERIES IN BERING SEA. James B. Morrow. Clipping from Leader, Cleveland, Ohio, pp.3, Feb. 28, 1892.

FUR-SEAL'S TOOTH; A STORY OF ALASKAN ADVENTURE. Kirk Munroe. New York, Harper and Brothers, pp.viii-267, pls., map, 1894.

(Fur Seals) Anatomy

DENTITION OF THE ALASKAN FUR SEAL. R.B. Chiasson. Jour. Mamm., vol.38, pp. 310-319, 1957.

ON THE MILK DENTITION OF THE CAPE FUR SEAL. R.W. Rand. Jour. Dental Assoc. of S.Africa, vol.5, no.10, pp.462-472, illus., Oct. 15, 1950.

CRYPTORCHID FUR SEALS. V.B.Scheffer. Amer. Midland Nat., Notre Dame, vol.46, no.3, pp.646-648, Nov., 1951.

(Fur Seals) California and Lower California Islands

FUR-SEAL OF GUADALUPE ISLAND, OFF LOWER CALIFORNIA. J.A. Allen et al. Fur-Seal Arbitration Proc. Tribunal Arbts. at Paris, Appendix, vol.1, pp.586, 1892.

MALE GUADALUPE FUR SEAL ON SAN NICOLAS ISLAND, CALIFORNIA. G. A. Bartholomew. Jour. Mamm., vol.31, pp. 175-180, 1950.

RECORD OF PLANTS COLLECTED ON GUADALUPE ISLAND IN JUNE, 1897, BY RUFUS L. GREEN, CHARLES B. WING AND WILBUR E. THOBURN. Wm R. Dudley. Fur Seals and Fur Seal Islands of the North Pacific Ocean, pt.3, pp.280-283, 1899.

IS THE GUADALUPE FUR SEAL RETURNING? Andrew Hamilton. Nat. Hist., vol.60, no.2, pp.90-94, Feb., 1951.

BACK FROM OBLIVION. GUADALUPE FUR SEAL: STILL A LIVING SPECIES. Carl L. Hubbs. Pacific Discovery, Calif. Acad. Sci., vol.9, no.6, pp.14-21, illus., Nov.-Dec., 1956.

GUADALUPE FUR SEAL STILL LIVES. Carl L. Hubbs. Zoonooz, Zool. Soc. San Diego, vol.29, no.12, pp.6-9, illus., Dec., 1956.

NEW FUR SEAL OR SEA-BEAR (ARCTOCEPHALUS TOWNSENDI) FROM GUADALUPE ISLAND, OFF LOWER CALIFORNIA. C.H. Merriam. Proc. Biol. Soc. Washington, vol.11, pp.175-178, 1897.

FUR SEAL OF THE CALIFORNIA ISLANDS WITH NEW DESCRIPTIVE AND HISTORICAL MATTER. C.H. Townsend. Zoologica, New York, vol.9, no.12, pp.443-457, figs. 345-354, Apr. 17, 1931.

GUADALUPE FUR SEAL IN 1929. C.H. Townsend. Bull. New York Zool. Soc., vol. 33, no.1, p.32, 1930.

(Fur Seals) Economic Importance

REPORT OF THE FUR SEAL INVESTIGATIONS, 1896-1897. J.A. Allen. Science, n.s., vol.10, pp.885-890, Dec. 15, 1899.

JAPANESE FUR SEALING. Oliver L.Austin, Ford Wilke. Special Sci. Rept. Wildl., Fish and Wildl. Serv., no.6, pp.6-91, figs.15, illus., Sep., 1950.

BERING SEA. DISPUTE: A SETTLEMENT. Geo. Baden-Powell. Fur-Seal Arbitration Proc. Tribunal Arbtr. at Paris, Washin gton, Appendix, vol.1, pp.588-589, 1892.

FUR SEALS OF THE PRIBILOF ISLANDS. Ralph C. Baker. Conservation in Action, U.S. Fish and Wildl. Serv., vol.12, pp. 1-24, 1957.

ALASKA FISHERY AND FUR-SEAL INDUSTRIES IN 1925. FUR-SEAL INDUSTRY. Ward T. Bower. Rep. U.S. Comm. Fisheries 1926, Appendix 3, Bureau Fish. Doc., no. 1008, pp.140-160, Nov., 1926.

ALASKA FISHERY AND FUR-SEAL INDUSTRIES IN 1935. Ward T. Bower. U.S. Bur. Fisheries, Rep. of the Comm. for the fiscal year 1936, Washington, Appendix, pp. 71, 1938. (Whales, p.44; Fur-Seal Industry, p.47 ff; Computation of Fur Seals, Pribilof Islands, 1935, by Harry J. Christoffers, pp. 65-67.)

ALASKA FISHERY AND FUR-SEAL INDUSTRIES IN 1937. Ward T. Bower. U.S. Bur. Fisheries, Admin. Rept., no.31, pp.73-150, 1938.

ALASKA FISHERY AND FUR SEAL INDUSTRIES IN 1941. Ward T. Bower. U.S. Dept. Int., Fish and Wildl. Serv., Stat.Digest, no.5, pp.1-71, 1943.

ALASKA FISHERY AND FUR-SEAL INDUSTRIES IN 1945. Ward T. Bower. U.S.Dept. Interior, Fish and Wildl. Serv., Stat.Digest, no.15, pp.63, 1948.

ALASKA FISHERY AND FUR-SEAL INDUSTRY. PRIBILOF ISLANDS FUR-SEAL INDUSTRY. 1946. Ward T. Bower. U.S.Dept. Interior, Fish and Wildl. Serv., Stat.Digest, no.17, pp.49-70, 1948.

FUR-SEAL INDUSTRY OF THE PRIBILOF ISLANDS, ALASKA. Ward T. Bower. U.S. Fish and Widll. Serv., Chicago, Fishery Leaflet, no.77, pp.1-10, 1944.(Mimeographed.)

SEAL OF APPAREL. ALASKAN SEALSKINS FROM ONE ISLAND AND ONE TRADER. Wayne Brinkerhoff. Monsanto Mag., St. Louis, vol.20, no.1, pp.22-25, figs.6, Feb., 1941.

ALASKA FUR-SEAL INDUSTRY AND CANADA'S INTEREST. G.Clifford Carl. Rept. Provincial Mus. Nat. Hist. and Anthropol., Victoria, 1946, pp.B21-B24, figs.1-12, 1947.

PELAGIC SEALING IN BERING SEA. J. G. Carlisle, et al. Seal and Salmon Fisheries and General Resources of Alaska, Washington, Doc.137, vol.2, House Doc.92, pt.1-2, pp.315-382, 1898.

FUR SEAL CENSUS. Geo. Archibald Clark. Science, Lancaster, n.s., vol.36, no.939, pp.894-897, Dec. 27, 1912.

LIFE OF A SEAL-SKIN COAT. (Fur Seal.) John A. De Lance. N.Dakota Outdoors, Bismarck, vol.8, no.9, p.8, Mar., 1946.

SEAL MANAGEMENT HAS PAID DIVIDENDS. (Pribilof Islands.) Ben East. Animal Kingdom, vol.50, no.6, pp.188-194, Nov.-Dec., 1947.

UNCLE SAM'S PRIZE FUR FACTORY CLOSES DOWN. (Pribilof Islands Fur Seals.) Ben East. Nat. Hist., New York, vol.51, no.4, pp.188-195, illus., Apr., 1943.

AFFAIRS OF NATIVES, SEAL ISLANDS. Henry W. Elliott. Seal and Salmon Fisheries and General Resources of Alaska, Washington, vol.1, pp.51-52, 1898.

ALASKA SEAL QUESTION. Henry W. Elliott. Plain Dealer, Cleveland, pp.8, Sep. 25, 1899.

REPORT ON THE SEAL ISLANDS OF ALASKA. Henry W. Elliott. Seal and Salmon Fisheries and General Resources of Alaska, Washington, Doc.92, vol.3, pp.285, pls.29, 1898.

REPORT UPON THE CONDITION OF THE FUR-SEAL ROOKERIES OF THE PRIBILOF ISLANDS OF ALASKA. Henry W. Elliott. Seal and Salmon Fisheries and General Resources of Alaska, Washington, House Doc. 175, vol.3, pp.313-538, pls.48, 1898.

REPORT UPON THE PRESENT CONDITION OF THE FUR-SEAL ROOKERIES OF THE PRIBILOF ISLANDS OF ALASKA. Henry W. Elliott. 54th Congress (1st Session) House of Representatives, Doc.175, pp.240, 1896.

STATEMENT SUBMITTED IN RE THE FUR-SEAL HERD OF ALASKA, 1913. Henry W. Elliott. Hearings on investigations of fur-seal industry of Alaska Expenditures in Commerce Dept. Committee, House of Representatives, pp.261, 1913.

RESEARCH AN IMPORTANT FACTOR IN FUR SEAL MANAGEMENT. Robert K. Enders. Trans. 10th N. Amer. Wildl.Conf., Washington, pp.92-94, 1945.

NORTHERN FUR-SEAL PROBLEM AS A TYPE OF MANY PROBLEMS IN MARINE ZOOLOGY. Barton Warren Evermann. Sci. Monthly, vol.9 (Sep.), pp.263-282, figs. 10, Aug. 30, 1919; Papers on the Exploration of the N.Pacific Ocean, Bull.Scripps Inst. for Biol. Research, no.9, pp.13-26 (Dec. 15, 1919), 1920.

CLAIM OF THE NORTH AMERICAN COMMERCIAL COMPANY. Charles Foster. Fur-Seal Arbitration Proc. Tribunal Arbtr. at Paris, Washington, Appendix, vol.1, pp. 520-522, 1892.

TREASURY LIST OF RAIDS. Charles Foster. Fur-Seal Arbitration Proc. Tribunal Arbtr. at Paris, Washington, Appendix, vol.1, pp. 519-520, 1892.

CASE OF THE UNITED STATES. John W. Foster. The Seal Arbitration Proc. Tribunal Arbtr. at Paris, Washington, vol.2, pp.303, 1895.

FINAL REPORT OF THE AGENT OF THE UNITED STATES; PROTOCOLS OF THE PROCEEDINGS OF THE TRIBUNAL;AWARD AND DECLARATION. John W. Foster. Fur-Seal Arbitration Proc. Tribunal Arbtr. at Paris, Washington, vol.1, pp.86, 1895.

ST. LOUIS--FUR SEALSKIN MARKET OF THE WORLD. P.B. Fouke. Amer. Nat. Fur and Market Jour., Wausau, vol.27, no.11, pp.13, 76-77, illus., June, 1949.

REPORTS FOR THE YEARS 1882-1884. Henry A. Glidden. Seal and Salmon Fisheries and General Resources of Alaska, Washington, vol.1, pp.152, 157, 164, 167, 1898.

REPORTS FOR YEARS 1889 AND 1890. Charles J. Goff. Seal and Salmon Fisheries and General Resources of Alaska, Washington, vol. 1, pp.214, 228, 230, 1898.

CONTRACT FOR PELAGIC CATCH. Wm. Grant, M.J. Davis. Fur-Seal Arbitration Proc. Tribunal Arbtr. at Paris, Washington, Appendix, vol.1, p.523, 1892.

REPORT ON CONDITION OF THE FUR SEALS OF THE PRIBILOF ISLANDS. Charles S. Hamlin. Seal and Salmon Fisheries and General Resources of Alaska, Washington, vol.1, pp.448-455, Senate Doc.137, pt.1, 1898.

WHY NOT PROTECT THE FUR SEAL HERDS OF THE SOUTHERN HEMISPHERE. G. Dallas Hanna. Australian Zool., vol. 3, pt.1, pp.11-14, Sep., 1922.

OPINION OF MR. JUSTICE HARLAN AT THE CONFERENCE IN PARIS. Justice Harlan. Fur-Seal Arbitration Proc. Tribunal Arbtr. at Paris, Washington, vol.1, pp.3-228, 1893.

SPECIAL INVESTIGATION OF THE ALASKA FUR-SEAL ROOKERIES, 1910. Harold Heath. Bureau of Fisheries, Doc. 748, pp.1-22, 1911.

REPORT TO THE SECRETARY OF TREASURY. C.L. Hooper. Fur-Seal Arbitration Proc. Tribunal Arbtr. at Paris, Washington, Appendix, vol.1, pp.498-504, 1892.

RESCUED SEAL INDUSTRY. W.T. Hornaday. Science, n.s., vol.52, pp.81-82, July 23, 1920; Wisconsin Conservationist, vol.2, no.4, p.2, Sep., 1920.

PROTECTION OF ROOKERIES FROM MARAUDERS. W.A. Howard. Seal and Salmon Fisheries and General Resources of Alaska, Washington, vol.1, p.3, 1898.

STATEMENTS AND LETTERS OF NATURALISTS. T.H. Huxley, et al. Fur-Seal Arbitration Proc. Tribunal Arbtr. at Paris, Washington, Appendix, vol.1, pp.411-433, 1892.

FUR SEAL, AN INVESTMENT IN NATURE. Hartley H.T. Jackson. Home Geographic Mag., vol.1, no.11, pp.43-48, illus., May, 1932.

FUR-SEAL CENSUS, PRIBILOF ISLANDS, 1925. ALASKA FISHERY AND FUR- SEAL INDUSTRIES IN 1925. Edward C. Johnston. Rep. U.S. Comm. Fisheries 1926, Appendix 3, Bureau Fish.Doc.1008, pp.161-166, Nov., 1926.

THE FUR SEALS. David Starr Jordan. Science, n.s., vol.52, p.255, Sep. 3, 1920.

SEAL AND SALMON FISHERIES AND GENERAL RESOURCES OF ALASKA. David Starr Jordan. U.S. Printing Office, vols. 4, maps, illus., 1898.

APPENDIX. David Starr Jordan, Geo. A. Clark. Seal and Salmon Fisheries and General Resources of Alaska, Washington, vol.1, pp.491-501, 1898.

TRUTH ABOUT THE FUR SEALS OF THE PRIBILOF ISLANDS. David Starr Jordan, Geo. A. Clark. Dept. Commerce and Labor Bur. Fisheries, Circ.4, pp.7, Dec. 20, 1912.

REPORTS FOR YEARS 1890-1893. A. W. Lavender. Seal and Salmon Fisheries and General Resources of Alaska, Washington, vol.1, pp.239, 297, 363, 428, 1898.

FUR SEAL PRESERVATION. INTERNATIONAL CONVENTION. INTERESTING REPORT OF THE U. S. FISHERIES COMMISSION. J. Lawrence-Hamilton. Financier, London, p.1, Apr. 15, 1913.

REVIEW OF ALASKA FUR SEAL HISTORY AND SEALING METHODS. Norman O. Levardsen. MS thesis, Cornell Univ., 1946.

REPORT FOR YEAR 1889. A.P. Loud. Seal-Salmon Fisheries and General Resources of Alaska, Washington, vol.1, pp.225-227, 1898.

CONDENSATION OF REPORT FOR 1893. Paul S. Luttrell. Seal and Salmon Fisheries and General Resources of Alaska, Washington, Doc.137, vol.2, House Doc. 92, pt.2-25, pp.397-403, 1898.

FUR-SEAL INDUSTRY OF ALASKA. Bird McGuire, Chas. E. Patton. Rep.500, pt.2, House of Representatives, 63rd Congress, 2nd Session, pp.22, July 27, 1914.

STATISTICS OF FUR-SEAL TRADE FOR 1869. John T. McLean. Seal-Salmon Fisheries and General Resources of Alaska, Washington, vol.1, pp.5-13, 1898.

REPORT FOR YEAR 1889. J.P. Manchester. Seal-Salmon Fisheries and General Resources of Alaska, Washington, vol.1, pp. 227-228, 1898.

HUNTING OF THE SILVER FLEECE:EPIC OF THE FUR SEAL. Fredericka Martin. Greenberg, New York, pp.xxiii-328, illus., 1946.

FUR-SEAL FISHERIES. Washburn Maynard. Seal-Salmon Fisheries and General Resources of Alaska, vol.3, pp.289-309, 1898.

REPORTS OF BERING SEA COMMISSION. C. Hart Merriam, Thomas C. Mendenhall. Seal Arbitration Proc. Tribunal Arbtr. at Paris, Washington, vol.2, pp.307-433, 1895.

CUSTOMS DISTRICT, PUBLIC, SERVICE, AND RESOURCES OF ALASKA. Wm.G. Morris. Seal-Salmon Fisheries and General Resources of Alaska, House Doc.59, Washington, vol.4, pp.3-167, illus.59, 1898.

REPORTS FOR YEARS 1877 AND 1878. J.H. Moulton. Seal-Salmon Fisheries and General Resources of Alaska, Washington, vol.1, pp.96, 98, 110, 113, 131, 1898.

REPORT FOR 1894. Joseph Murray. Seal-Salmon Fisheries and General Resources of Alaska, Washington, Doc.137, vol.2, House Doc.92, pt.2-25, pp.404-435, 1898.

REPORT FOR 1895. Joseph Murray. Seal-Salmon Fisheries and General Resources of Alaska, Washington, Doc.137, vol.2, House Doc.92, pt.2-25, pp.436-459, 1898.

REPORT ON THE SEAL ISLANDS OF ALASKA FOR THE YEAR 1894. Joseph Murray. Seal and Salmon Fisheries and General Resources of Alaska, Washington, Doc.137, vol.2, House Doc. 92, pt.1-2, pp.3-275, 1898.

REPORTS FOR YEARS 1890-1893. Joseph Murray. Seal-Salmon Fisheries and Resources of Alaska, Washington, vol.1, pp.236, 292, 359, 364, 423, 1898.

STATISTICS OF SEALS TAKEN FOR ALL PURPOSES, 1870-1889. Joseph Murray. Seal-Salmon Fisheries and General Resources of Alaska, Washington, vol.1, pp.364-407, 1898.

REPORT OF LEVI W. MYERS, UNITED STATES CONSUL AT VICTORIA, BRITISH COLUMBIA. Levi W. Myers. Fur-Seal Arbitration Proc. Tribunal Arbtr. at Paris, Washington, Appendix, vol.1, pp.507-518, 1892.

FALSE CONSERVATION OF FUR SEALS. Wilfred H. Osgood. Forest and Stream, New York, vol.86, pp.953-955, illus., May, 1916.

REPORT FOR 1892. Max Pracht. Seal-Salmon Fisheries and General Resources of Alaska, Washington, Doc.137, vol.2, House Doc.92, pt.2-25, pp.385-396, 1898.

FUR SEALS. RESEARCH AND MANAGEMENT. R.W. Rand. Commerce and Industry, Official Jour., Dept. Commerce and Industries, Pretoria, S.Africa, vol.11, no.1, pp.35-40, illus., Sep., 1952.

REPORT FOR 1885. T.F. Ryan. Seal-Salmon Fisheries and General Resources of Alaska, Washington, vol.1, pp.183-186, 1898.

CONSERVING THE ALASKA FUR SEALS. Victor B. Scheffer. Proc. 7th Pac. Sci. Congress, no.4, pp.615-619, 1953.

USE OF FUR-SEAL CARCASSES BY NATIVES OF THE PRIBILOF ISLANDS, ALASKA. Victor B. Scheffer. Pacific Northwest Quarterly, Seattle, vol.39, no.2, pp.131-132, fig.1, Apr., 1948.

CONSERVING THE ALASKA FUR SEALS. Victor B. Scheffer. Trans.14th N.Amer. Wildl. Conf., Washington, pp.440-450, 1949.

FUR SEAL HERD COMES OF AGE. Victor B. Scheffer, Karl W. Kenyon. Nat.Geogr. Mag., Washington, vol.101, no.4, pp.491-512, illus., Apr., 1952.

NATURALIST'S VIEW OF THE FUR-SEAL QUESTION. P.L. Sclater. 19th Century, London, pp.1038-1045, June, 1893.

LOG BOOKS OF SEALING VESSELS. L.G. Shepard. Fur-Seal Arbitration Proc. Tribunal Arbtr. at Paris, Washington, Appendix, vol. 1, pp.524-585, 1892.

PRIBILOF SEALS AGAIN UNDER CONSIDERATION. Carl D. Shoemaker. League of Maryland Sportsmen, Rally Sheet, Baltimore, vol.2, no.4, p.6, Apr., 1944.

ECONOMICS AND THE CRUELTIES OF THE FUR SEAL TRADE, WITH BRIEF NOTES ON THE SEAL IN GENERAL. Robert W. Shufeldt. Nat. Humane Review, vol.12, no.5, pp.86, 100, illus., Albany, N.Y., May, 1924.

FUR-SEAL FISHERIES OF ALASKA. Thomas Southwell. Gentleman's Mag., London, vol. 270, no.1923, pp.244-258, Mar., 1891.

PAST AND FUTURE OF THE FUR SEAL. Joseph Stanley-Brown. Seal-Salmon Fisheries and General Resources of Alaska, Washington, Doc.137, vol.2, House Doc. 92, pt.1-2, pp.276-311, 1898.

FUR-SEAL INDUSTRY OF THE COMMANDER ISLANDS, 1897 TO 1922. Leonhard Stejneger. Bull. U.S. Bureau Fish., vol.41, pp.289-332, 1925.

REPORT ON THE ROOKERIES OF THE COMMANDER ISLANDS, SEASON OF 1897. Leonhard Stejneger. Treas. Dept., Doc.1997, Office of Secretary, Special Agents' Div., pp.17, 1897.

REPORT ON THE RUSSIAN FUR-SEAL ISLANDS. Leonhard Stejneger. Seal-Salmon Fisheries and General Resources of Alaska, Washington, Doc.137, pt.2, vol.4, pp.615-757, 1898.

RUSSIAN FUR-SEAL ISLANDS. Leonhard Stejneger. U.S. Fish Comm. Bull., art. 1, pp.1-148, pls.1-66, fold.map, 1896.

ACTUAL STATE OF THE FUR-SEAL FISHERIES IN AMERICA. E.K.Suvorov. Bull. Inst. Applied Ichthyol. USSR., Leningrad, vol.13, no.1, pp.25-44, 1931. (In Russian, with Russian and English titles.)

SEALS IN DANGER. (Pribilof Fur Seals.) Frank Thone. Science News Letter, Washington, D.C., vol.42, no.8, p.124, illus., Aug. 22, 1942.

REPORTS FOR YEARS 1885-1888. Geo.R. Tingle. Seal-Salmon Fisheries and General Resources of Alaska, Washington, vol.1, pp.171, 175, 186, 198, 205, 206, 1898.

REPORT ON THE FUR-SEAL CATCH OF JAPANESE, BRITISH, AND AMERICAN VESSELS SAILING FROM AND WITH HEADQUARTERS AT JAPANESE PORTS IN 1895. C.H. Townsend. Seal-Salmon Fisheries and General Resources of Alaska, Washington, vol.4, pp.603-605, 1898.

REPORTS OF AGENTS, OFFICERS, AND PERSONS, ACTING UNDER THE AUTHORITY OF THE SECRETARY OF THE TREASURY, IN RELATION TO THE CONDITION OF SEAL LIFE ON THE ROOKERIES OF THE PRIBILOF ISLANDS, AND TO PELAGIC SEALING IN BERING SEA AND THE NORTH PACIFIC OCEAN, IN THE YEARS 1893-1895. C.H. Townsend. Part II, 54th Congress, 1st Session, Doc.137, pp.97, 1896.

FROM A REPORT ON THE FUR-SEAL ROOKERIES OF THE PRIBILOF ISLANDS, 1895. F.W. True. Part II, 54th Congress, 1st Session, Doc.137, pp.99-111, 1896.

FISHERY RESOURCES OF THE UNITED STATES OF AMERICA. Lionel A. Walford. U.S.Dept. Interior, Fish and Wildl. Serv., Washington, pp.1-135, illus., 1945. (Fur Seal Resource, pp.37-38.)

REPORT OF INTERVIEW WITH MR. GREBNITZKY, MANAGER OF RUSSIAN SEAL ISLANDS. Geo. Wardman. Seal-Salmon, Fisheries and General Resources of Alaska, Washington, vol.1, pp.162-163, 1898.

CASE OF THE UNITED STATES. Wm.F. Wharton. Fur-Seal Arbitration Proc. Tribunal Arbtr. at Paris, Washington, Appendix, vol. 1, pp.1-364, 1892.

FUR SEAL BLUBBER. Charles G. Wilber. Jour. Mamm., vol.33, no.4, pp.483-485, fig.1, tbl.1, Nov. 19, 1952.

SCIENCE SAVES THE FUR SEAL. Robert Wyndham. Frontiers, vol.23, no.5, pp.131-133, 159, 1959.

ALASKA SEALSKINS. Oil-Power, Socony-Vacuum Oil Co., New York, vol.15, no.9, pp.6, illus., Sep., 1940.

NUMBERS OF SKINS OF FUR SEALS TAKEN ON ST. PAUL AND ST. GEORGE ISLANDS, BERING SEA. Fisheries Serv. Bull., no.50, p.5, July 1, 1919.

SHIPMENT OF MAMMAL BONES FROM THE PRIBILOF ISLANDS SOLD IN SAN FRANCISCO; NOTICE OF INCREASED SEAL KILLINGS AUTHORIZED. Fisheries Serv. Bull., no.51, pp.8, Aug. 1, 1919.

ANNUAL 1919, CENSUS OF FUR-SEALS SHOWS INCREASE OF 10 PER CENT OVER 1918; REPORT OF SKINS TAKEN DURING SEASON. Fisheries Serv. Bull., no.52, p.5, Sep. 2, 1919.

SALE OF SEAL PRODUCTS. (Sale of Oil and Fertilizer, By-Products of Carcasses of Fur Seals Killed for Pelts, on Probilof Islands.) Fisheries Serv. Bull., no.55, p.1, Dec., 1919.

FUR FISHERIES OF THE NORTHWEST SEAS. Forest and Stream, New York, June 13, 1889.

FUR SEAL AGREEMENT. Conservation News, Nat. Wildl. Federation, Washington, pp.3, Mar. 1, 1944.

INTERIM CONVENTION ON CONSERVATION OF NORTH PACIFIC FUR SEALS. U.S. Senate, 85th Congress, 1st Session, executive J, pp.18, 1957.

INVESTIGATION OF THE FUR-SEAL INDUSTRY OF ALASKA. G.P.O., pp.849, 1914.

LETTER FROM C. M. LAMPSON AND CO. Fur-Seal Arbitration Proc. Tribunal Arbtr. at Paris, Washington, vol.1, p.587, 1892.

REPORTS OF AGENTS, OFFICERS AND PERSONS ... IN RELATION TO SEAL LIFE ON THE ROOKERIES OF THE PRIBILOF ISLANDS. U.S. Treasury Dept., Washington, Fur Seal Rookeries, illus., 1896.

RUBBER-COLLARED FUR SEALS BAFFLE BIOLOGISTS. Oklahoma Game and Fish News, Oklahoma City, vol.4, no.12, p.17, Dec., 1948.

(Fur Seals) Exhibits and Zoos

ALASKA FUR SEALS. Zoonooz, San Diego, vol.13, no.12, p.7, Dec., 1941.

SAN DIEGO ZOO AIDS IN RE-DISCOVERY OF RARE FUR SEAL. Belle J. Benchley. Parks and Recreation, vol.11, p.418, illus., Aug., 1928.

CAPTURING FUR SEALS FOR THE SAN DIEGO ZOO. Karl W. Kenyon. San Diego Zoonooz, vol.21, no.12, pp.3-4, illus., Dec., 1948.

NEW HABITAT GROUP SHOWS SEALS AT "UNCLE SAM'S FUR FARM" IN ALASKA. Wilfred H. Osgood. Field Mus. News, Chicago, vol.12, no.1, pp.1-2, Jan., 1941.

NORTHERN FUR SEALS ARRIVE! Ken Stott, Jr. Zoonooz, San Diego, vol.20, no.10, pp.3, 6, illus., Oct., 1947.

(Fur Seals) Habits, Behavior

NOTES ON THE HABITS OF THE NORTHERN FUR SEAL. G.E.H.Barrett-Hamilton. Nat. Sci., vol.15, no.89, pp.17-41, July, 1899.

DURATION OF LIFE AND BEHAVIOR OF ALASKA FUR SEALS IN CAPTIVITY. Kelshaw Bonham. Jour. Mamm., vol. 24, no.4, p.504, Nov. 17, 1943.

OBSERVATIONS ON THE HABITS OF THE FUR SEAL. J.J. Brice. Seal and Salmon Fisheries and General Resources of Alaska, Washington, Doc.137, pt.2, vol.4, pp.609-611, 1898.

ANALYSIS OF STOMACH CONTENTS OF FUR SEALS TAKEN OFF THE WEST COAST OF VANCOUVER ISLAND IN APRIL AND MAY, 1935. W.A. Clemens, et al. Publ. Dept. Fisheries, Ottawa, Canada, pp.20, tbls.2, 1936.

FOOD OF THE FUR SEAL OFF THE COAST OF BRITISH COLUMBIA. W. A. Clemens, G.V. Wilby. Jour. Mamm., vol.14, no.1, pp.43-46, Feb., 1933.

MIGRATION OF THE NORTHERN FUR SEAL, CALLORHINUS URSINUS. K.W. Kenyon, F. Wilke. Jour. Mamm., vol.34, pp.86-98, 1953.

FUR SEALS PREYING ON BLACK-FOOTED ALBATROSS. J.L. McHugh. Jour. Wildl. Mgt., Ithaca, N.Y., vol.16, no.2, p.226, Apr., 1952.

FOOD OF THR FUR SEAL. Franklin H. May. Jour. Mamm., vol. 18, no.1, pp. 99-100, Feb., 1937.

FOOD HABITS OF THE NORTH PACIFIC FUR SEAL IN JAPANESE WATERS, WITH A STUDY OF THE FISHES FOUND ON THE FEEDING GROUNDS. Giles W. Mead, Jr. PhD thesis, Stanford Univ., pp.141, 1953.

LIFE AND HABITS OF THE AMERICAN FUR-SEAL. Wilfred H. Osgood. Hunting and Conservation, the Book of the Boone and Crockett Club, New Haven, Yale Univ. Press, pp.74-137, pls.5, 1925.

FOOD OF THE ALASKA FUR SEAL. Victor B. Scheffer. U.S. Fish and Wildl. Serv., Wildl. Leaflet, no.329, pp.16, illus., June, 1950.

PROBING THE LIFE SECRETS OF THE ALASKA FUR SEAL. Victor B. Scheffer. Pacific Discovery, San Francisco, vol.111, no.5, pp.22-30, illus., Sep.-Oct., 1950.

WINTER INJURY TO YOUNG FUR SEALS ON THE NORTHWEST COAST. Victor B. Scheffer. Calif. Fish and Game, vol.36, no.4, pp.378-379, Oct., 1950.

STOMACH CONTENTS OF FUR SEALS TAKEN OFF THE COAST OF WASHINGTON. Leonard P. Schultz, A.Morris Rafn. Jour. Mamm., vol.17, no.1, pp.13-15, Feb., 1936.

RECORDS OF THE CAPTURE OF FUR SEALS ON LAND IN CALIFORNIA. E. C. Starks. Calif. Fish Game, vol.8, pp.155-160, 1922.

DISTRIBUTION AND FOOD HABITS OF THE FUR SEALS OF THE NORTH PACIFIC OCEAN. REPORT OF COOPERATIVE INVESTIGATIONS BY THE GOVERNMENTS OF CANADA, JAPAN, AND THE UNITED STATES OF AMERICA, FEBRUARY-JULY, 1952. F.H. Taylor, et al. U.S. Fish and Wildl. Serv., pp.x-86, illus., 1955.

CONDITION OF SEAL LIFE ON THE ROOKERIES OF THE PRIBILOF ISLANDS, IN 1893. C.H. Townsend. Seal-Salmon Fisheries and General Resources of Alaska, Washington, House Doc.137, pt.2, vol.4, pp.453-547, 1898.

FOOD OF FUR SEALS IN THE EASTERN BERING SEA. Ford Wilke, Karl W. Kenyon. Jour. Wildl.Mgt., vol.21, no.2, pp.237-238, Apr., 1957.

MIGRATION AND FOOD OF THE NORTHERN FUR SEAL. Ford Wilke, Karl W. Kenyon. Trans. 19th N.Amer. Wildl.Conf., pp.430-439, 1954.

FOOD OF FUR SEALS. U.S. Fisheries Serv. Bull., no.252, pp.6, May, 1936.

(Fur Seals) North America

FUR SEALS OFF CALIFORNIA. Allen Brooks. Jour. Mamm., vol.18, no.1, p. 99, Feb. 14, 1937.

OCCURRENCE OF ZALOPHUS CALIFORNIANUS IN THE GULF OF CALIFORNIA. Robert B. Chiasson. Jour. Mamm., vol.35, no.4, p.596, Nov. 29, 1954.

PRIBILOF FUR SEAL ON CALIFORNIA COAST. E. Raymond Hall. Calif. Fish and Game, San Francisco, vol.26, no.1, pp.76-77, Jan., 1940.

ALASKA FUR SEALS, CALLORHINUS URSINUS, OBSERVED OFF SAN FRANCISCO BAY, CALIFORNIA. G.D. Hanna. Jour. Mamm., vol.32, no.3, pp.364-365, Aug. 23, 1951.

PRIBILOF FUR SEAL TAKEN IN SAN DIEGO COUNTY, CALIFORNIA. L.M. Huey.Jour. Mamm., vol.23, pp.95-96, 1942.

FOURTH RECORD OF THE PRIBILOF FUR SEAL ON THE OREGON COAST. Stanley G. Jewett. Jour. Mamm., vol.14, no.4, p. 369, Nov., 1933.

PRIBILOF FUR SEAL ON THE OREGON COAST. Stanley G. Jewett. Jour. Mamm., vol.2, no.4, p.235, Nov. 1921.

SECOND OCCURRENCE OF THE PRIBILOF FUR SEAL ON THE OREGON COAST. Stanley G. Jewett. Jour. Mamm., vol.6, no.3, p.200, Aug., 1925.

THIRD RECORD FOR THE ALASKA FUR SEAL ON THE OREGON COAST. Stanley G. Jewett. Jour. Mamm., vol.11, no.3, p.314, Aug., 1930.

SPORADIC OCCURRENCE OF AN ALASKAN FUR SEAL. E.H. McEwen. Jour. Mamm., vol.35, no.3, p.444, Aug. 20, 1956.

NORTHERN FUR SEAL IN THE INSIDE COASTAL WATERS OF BRITISH COLUMBIA. J.I. Manzer, I.McT. Cowan. Jour.Mamm., vol.37, no.1, pp.83-86, tbls.2, Feb. 28, 1956.

FUR SEAL IN WILLAPA HARBOR. Victor B. Scheffer. Murrelet, Seattle, vol.20, no. 2, May-Aug., p.43, Aug. 10, 1939.

RECORDS OF THE CAPTURE OF FUR SEALS ON LAND IN CALIFORNIA. Edwin C. Starks. Calif. Fish and Game, San Francisco, vol.8, no.3, pp.155-160, figs. 67-68, July, 1922.

NORTHERN FUR SEAL ASHORE IN SAN DIEGO, CALIFORNIA. Ken Stott, Jr. Jour. Mamm., vol.35, no.2, p.258, May 26, 1954.

(Fur Seals) Parasites

REDESCRIPTION OF UNCINARIA LUCASI STILES, A HOOKWORM OF SEALS. (From Alaskan Fur Seal.) H.A. Baylis.Parasitology, vol.38, no.3, pp.160-162, July, 1947.

MITES ENDOPARASITIC IN THE RESPIRATORY TRACT OF THE CAPE SEA LION (FUR SEAL). W.M. Till. Jour. Ent. Soc. S. Afr., vol.17, pp.266-267, 1954.

(Fur Seals) Physiology

BODY TEMPERATURE IN THE NORTHERN FUR SEAL, CALLORHINUS URSINUS. G.A. Bartholomew, F. Wilke. Jour. Mamm., vol. 37, pp.327-337, 1956.

TEMPERATURE RECORDS OF ALASKA FUR SEALS. G. Dallas Hanna. Amer.Jour. Physiol., vol.68, pp.52-53, Mar., 1924.

(Fur Seals) Population Dynamics

BEHAVIORAL FACTORS AFFECTING SOCIAL STRUCTURE IN THE ALASKA FUR SEAL. Geo. A. Bartholomew, Jr. Trans. 18th N.Amer. Wildl.Conf., Mar. 9, 10, 11, 1953, Washington, D.C., pp.481-502, 1953.

WHAT BECOMES OF THE FUR SEALS. G. Dallas Hanna. Science, n.s., vol.55, pp.505-507, May 12, 1922.

POPULATION STUDY OF THE ALASKA FUR-SEAL HERD. K.W. Kenyon, et al. U.S. Dept. Interior, Fish and Wildl.Serv., Spec.Sci.Rept.Wildl., no.12, pp.77, 1954.

FUR SEAL MORTALITY OF THE PRIBILOF ROOKERIES IN THE ABSENCE OF PELAGIC SEALING. M.C. Marsh. Science, Lancaster, n.s., vol.36, no.939, pp.897-989, Dec.27, 1912.

GROWTH OF THE ALASKAN FUR-SEAL HERD. G.H. Parker. Proc. 3rd Pan-Pacific Sci. Congress, Tokyo, vol.1, pp.1055-1064, (1926) 1928.

BRANDING IN FIELD-WORK ON SEALS. R.W. Rand. Jour. Wildl. Mgt., vol.14, no.2, pp.128-132, Apr., 1950.

STUDIES ON THE CAPE FUR SEAL (ARCTOCEPHALUS PUSILLUS SCHREBER). 1. AGE-GROUPING IN THE FEMALE. R.W. Rand. Progress Rept. Govt. Guano Islands Admin., Union S. Africa Dept. Agric., pp.24, 1950.

STUDIES ON THE CAPE FUR SEAL (ARCTOCEPHALUS PUSILLUS SCHREBER). 2. ATTENDANCE AT THE ROOKERY. R.W.Rand. Progress Rept. Govt. Guano Islands Admin., Union of S. Africa Dept. Agric., pp.22, 1950.

STUDIES ON THE CAPE FUR SEAL (ARCTOCEPHALUS PUSILLUS SCHREBER). 3. AGE GROUPING IN THE MALE. R.W. Rand. Progress Rep., Government Guano Islands Admin., Union of S. Africa Dept. Agric., pp.28, pls.3, 1950.

(Fur Seals) Pribilof Islands

SEAL LIFE ON THE PRIBILOF ISLANDS. OBSERVATIONS DURING A CRUISE ON THE SEALING SCHOONER LOUIS OLSEN, AUGUST, 1894. OBSERVATIONS DURING A CRUISE ON THE DORA SIEWARD, AUG.-SEP., 1895. A.B. Alexander. U.S. Senate Doc.137, pt.2-10, pp.113-150, 1895.

PRIBILOF FUR SEALS. G.C.L. Bertram. Arctic, vol.3, no.2, pp.75-85, Aug., 1950.

FUR-SEALS OF THE PRIBILOF ISLANDS, ALASKA. Ward T. Bower. Fur Jour., vol.1, no.4, pp.28, 40-42, 47, illus., Aug., 1927.

OLD MAN OF THE PRIBILOFS. Albert M. Day. Sci. Monthly, vol.68, no.5, pp.329-337, May, 1949; Fish and Wildl. Serv., Wildl. Leaflet 323, pp.13, illus., July 1949; Amer. Nat. Fur and Market Jour., Wausau, vol.28, no.5, pp.10-11, 25-27, 29, illus., Dec., 1949.

FUR SEAL OF THE PRIBILOF ISLANDS. J.E. Hamilton. Scottish Zoo and Wildl., Edinburgh, vol.1, pt.3, pp.105-108, illus., Oct., 1948.

(IN THE DORADO OF FUR SEALS.) Im Dorado der Seebaeren. Alfred Heinicke. Die Umschau, Frankfurt, a.M., Jahrg.37, no.38, pp.739-741, figs.5, Sep. 16, 1933.

HISTORY, CONDITION, AND NEEDS OF THE HERD OF FUR SEALS RESORTING

TO THE PRIBILOF ISLANDS. D.S. Jordan, G.A. Clark. (In) Fur Seals and Fur-Seal Islands of the North Pacific Ocean, by D.S. Jordan et al., Washington, Govt. Print. Off., Treasury Dept. Doc.2017, pt.1, pp.7-249, pls.12, 1898.

OBSERVATIONS ON THE FUR SEALS OF THE PRIBILOF ISLANDS. PRELIMINARY REPORT. D.S. Jordan et al. Govt.Print. Off., Washington, pp.69, map, 1896.

FUR SEAL AND OTHER LIFE OF THE PRIBILOF ISLANDS, ALASKA, IN 1914. Wilfred H. Osgood et al. Bull. Bur. Fisheries, vol.34, 1914, Doc.no.820, Wash., pp.172, pls.17, maps 24, June 19, 1915.

FUR-SEALS OF THE PRIBILOF ISLANDS. G.H. Parker. Scientific Monthly, pp.385-409, figs.24, May, 1917.

FUR SEALS OF THE PRIBILOF ISLANDS. E.A. Preble. Nature Mag., vol.6, pp.226-230, figs.5, Oct., 1925.

FROM A REPORT ON THE FUR-SEAL ROOKERIES OF THE PRIBILOF ISLANDS, 1895. F.W. True. Seal-Salmon Fisheries and General Resources of Alaska, Wash., pt.2, vol.4, Doc.no.137, pp.549-561, 1898.

FUR SEALS OF THE PRIBILOFS. Violet H. Wilson. Beaver, Winnipeg, Outfit no. 278, pp.43-44, illus., Dec., 1947.

(Fur Seals) Reproductive Biology

REPRODUCTIVE BEHAVIOUR OF THE ALASKA FUR SEAL, CALLORHINUS URSINUS. Geo. A. Bartholomew, Jr., Paul G. Hoel. Jour. Mamm., vol.34, no.4, pp.417-436, illus., Nov. 13, 1953.

FUR SEAL PUP IS BORN. O. Wilford Olsen. Turtox News, Chicago, vol.35, no.1, p.33, illus., Jan., 1957.

FURTHER OBSERVATIONS ON THE REPRODUCTION OF THE ALASKAN FUR SEAL. Anita K. Pearson, Robert K. Enders. Anat. Rec., vol.111, no.4, pp.695-711, illus., Dec., 1951.

REPRODUCTION IN THE FEMALE CAPE FUR SEAL, ARCTOCEPHALUS PUSILLUS (SCHREBER). R. W. Rand. Proc. Zool. Soc. London, vol. 124, pt. 4, pp. 717-740, illus., Feb. 22, 1955.

MYSTERY OF THE ABANDONED WATER BABIES: SEAL PUPS DESERTED BY THEIR PARENTS. Illus. London News, vol.214, no.5745, p.723, illus., May 28, 1949.

(Fur Seals) South America

(ON A FUR SEAL OF RIO DE JANEIRO.) Ueber eine Pelzrobbe von Rio de Janeiro. A. Nehring. S.B.Ges.Naturf.Freunde, Berlin, pp.207-208, 1887c.

(ON A FUR SPECIES OF THE COAST OF SOUTH BRAZIL.) Ueber eine Pelzrobben-Art von der Kueste Sued-Brasiliens. A. Nehring. Arch.Naturgesch., vol.1, pp.75-94, pl.1, 1887a.

(ON THE FUR SEAL OF SOUTHERN BRAZIL.) Ueber die suedbrasilienische Pelzrobbe. A. Nehring. S.B. Ges.Naturf.Freunde, Berlin, pp.142-143, 1887b.

URUGUAYAN FUR-SEAL ISLANDS. Hugh M. Smith. Zoologica, New York, vol.9, no.6, pp.271-294, figs.7, Sep. 30, 1927.

(Fur Seals) Southern Waters

NOTES ON THE SOUTHERN FUR SEAL IN SOUTH GEORGIA. W. Nigel Bonner. Proc. Zool. Soc. London, vol.130, no.2, pp.241-252, pls.1-3, Mar. 13, 1958.

FUR SEALS OFF THE FARALLONES. B. W. Evermann. Science, n.s., vol.54, pp. 547-548, Dec. 2, 1921.

NOTES ON THE FUR SEALS AT MACQUARIE ISLAND AND HEARD ISLAND. A.M. Gwynn. Interim Rept. Australian Nat. Antarctic Research Exped., no.4, pp. 16, illus., Jan., 1953.

(ON THE FUR SEAL OF SAINT PAUL AND AMSTERDAM ISLANDS.) Ueber die Pelzrobbe von den Inseln St. Paul und Amsterdam. W.C. Peters. Monatsber. K.P. Akad. Wissensch. Berlin, pp.315-316, 1876.

NOTES ON THE MARION ISLAND FUR SEAL. R.W. Rand. Proc. Zool. Soc. London, vol.126, pt.1, pp.65-82, pls.2, Jan. 11, 1956.

(Fur Seals) Taxonomy

TYPE SPECIMENS OF THE PRIBILOF FUR SEAL, CALLORHINUS ALASCANUS JORDAN AND CLARK. William V. Mayer. Jour. Mamm., vol.30, no.3, pp.316-317, Aug. 17, 1949.

EARLIEST GENERIC NAME OF THE NORTHERN FUR-SEAL. T.S. Palmer. Proc. Biol. Soc. Washington, vol.14, pp. 133-134, Aug. 9, 1901.

NEW GENERIC NAME FOR THE BERING SEA FUR-SEAL. T.S. Palmer. Proc.Biol. Soc. Washington, vol.7, p.156, July 27, 1892.

(Sea Lions) General

BEARS WHO WENT TO SEA. (Eumetopias jubata and Zalophus californianus.) Paul Bonnot. Nature Mag., vol.14, no.4, pp. 236-238, figs.4, Oct., 1929.

(MARINE BEAR.) L'ours-marin. (Supplement, Tome 6, pp.336-357, pl.47). G.L.L. Buffon. (In) Histoire naturelle, generalle et particuliere, avec la description du cabinet du Roi, Ed.2, Paris, vols.37 and supplement of vols.7, 1774-89.

LIONS OF THE SEA. William L. Finley, Irene Finley. Nat. Mag., vol.4, pp.203-207, 256, illus., Oct., 1924.

SECOND REPORT ON THE SOUTHERN SEA LION, OTARIA BYRONIA (DE BLAINVILLE). J.E. Hamilton. Discovery Repts., Cambridge, vol.19, pp.121-164, figs.6, tbls.14, pls.26-33, 1939.

SOUTHERN SEA-LION. (Otaria byronia.) J.E. Hamilton. Nat. Hist. Mag., British Mus., vol.4, no.26, pp.56-66, figs.1-9, Apr., 1933; Discovery Repts., vol.8, pp.269-318, pls.13, 1934.

SEAL LIONS. Joel W. Hedgpeth. Nature Mag., Washington, vol.37, no.8, pp.443, 445, Oct., 1944.

HYBRID SEA-LION. Geo. Jennison. Proc. Zool. Soc. London, pp.219-220, 1914.

STELLER SEA LION. Karl W. Kenyon. Pacific Discovery, San Francisco, vol.5, no.4, pp.41-43, July-Aug., 1952.

SEA-LION PRIMA DONNAS. Clarissa Lorenz. Nature Mag., Washington, D.C., vol.37, no.5, pp.240-243, illus., May, 1944.

WITH THE SOUTHERN SEA LION. F.A. Lucas. Forest and Stream, New York, pp. 63-64, July 28, 1900.

SEAL IN THE CIRCUS. (California Sea Lion.) Mark McMillin. Frontiers, Philadelphia, vol.6, no.5, pp.141-142, June, 1942.

ON THE CAUSE OF DEATH OF THE SEA-BEAR (OTARIA HOOKERI) LATELY LIVING IN THE SOCIETY'S GARDENS. James Murie. Proc. Zool. Soc. London, pp.243-244, 1867.

"SERGEANT FINNEGAN," A SEA LION. Thurlow Weed. Nature Mag., vol.27, no. 6, pp.343-344, fig., June, 1936.

SEA LIONS. Time, London, vol.30, no. 1, p.43, July 5, 1937.

SEA-LIONS MAY BE FOOD FOR FUR ANIMALS ON LAND. Science News Letter, Washington, D.C., vol.41, no.19, p.296, May 9, 1942.

(Sea Lions) Anatomy

(RESEARCH ON THE NEOPALLIUM OF THE SEA LION.) Recherches sur le neopallium de l'otarie. R. Anthony, M. Friant. Anat. Anz., Jena, vol.85, nos.7-8, pp. 139-158, figs.22, Nov. 1, 1937.

INTESTINAL LENGTH IN STELLER'S SEA LION. E.T. Engle. Jour. Mamm., vol.7, pp.28-30, 1926.

DESCRIPTION OF THE YOUNGER SKULL OF STELLER'S SEA-BEAR (EUMETOPIAS STELLERI.) J.E. Gray. Proc. Zool. Soc. London, pp.737-743, 1872.

(ON THE MORPHOLOGY OF THE M. TRAPEZIUS IN OTARIA STELLERI.) Zur Morphologie des M. trapezius beim Otaria stelleri. W. Kassianenko. Anat. Anzeiger, vol.66, pp.218-221, figs.2, Nov. 3, 1928.

(VOCAL ORGAN OF THE SEA LION (OTARIA JUBATA ( ZALOPHUS).) Das Stimmorgan des Seeloewen (Otaria jubata (· Zalophus). G. Kelemen, A. Hassko. Zeitschr. Anat. Entw. Gesch., vol.95, pp.497-511, 1931.

ON AN ANOMALOUS CONDITION OF THE LEFT ARTICULATING SURFACE OF THE MANIDBLE OF EUMETOPIAS JUBATA, THE STELLER'S SEA LION. Wm. V. Mayer. Proc. Calif. Zool. Club, Stanford Univ., vol.1, no.2, pp.9-12, illus., 1948.

NOTICE OF THE FIRST PORTION OF A MEMOIR ON THE ANATOMY OF THE SEA-BEAR (OTARIA). James Murie. Proc. Zool. Soc. London, p.254, 1868.

NOTICE OF THE SECOND PART OF A MEMOIR ON THE ANATOMY OF THE SEA-LION. James Murie. Proc. Zool. Soc. London, pp.802-803, 1870.

(REPORT ON AN AUTOPSY ON A SEA LION (EUMETOPIAS CALIFORNIANUS LESS.).) Bericht ueber die Obduktion eines Seeloewen (Eumetopias californianus Less). B.Seifert. Zool. Garten, n.F., Leipzig, vol.8, nos. 10-12, p.309, Sep., 1936.

DOUBLE TRACHEA IN PENGUINS AND SEA LIONS. Pearl Zeek. Anat. Rec., vol.111, pp.327-344, 1951.

(Sea Lions) Development of Young

BRINGING UP BENNY. (Sea Lion.) Lee S. Crandall. Animal, Kingdom, New York, vol.49, no.2, pp.61-65, illus., Mar.-Apr., 1946.

WEANING OF "FLIP." Sam Dunton. Animal Kingdom, New York Zool. Soc., vol.57, no. 3, pp.80-82, June, 1954.

BABY SEA LION. C.W. Leister. Bull.New York Zool. Soc., vol.38, no.5, p.182, Sep.-Oct., 1935.

GROWTH AND BEHAVIOR OF YOUNG SEA LIONS. V.B. Scheffer. Jour. Mamm., vol. 26, pp.390-392, 1945.

(CHARACTERISTIC BIRTH OF A SEA LION AND REMARKS ON ITS EARLY DEVELOPMENT.) Eigenartige Geburt eines Seeloewen und Bemerkungen zu seiner Jugendentwicklung. Karl Max Schneider. Zool. Garten, n.F., Leipzig, vol.9, no.6, pp. 290-292, illus., Dec., 1937.

(ON THE REPRODUCTION AND DEVELOPMENT OF THE YOUNG OF THE CALIFORNIA SEA LION.) Zur Fortpflanzung und Jugendentwicklung des kalifornischen Seeloewen. Karl Max Schneider. Zool. Garten, n.F., Leipzig, vol.6, nos.1-3, pp.23-33, figs.7, May, 1933.

FLIPPER, A BABY SEA LION. Ken Stott, Jr. Zoonooz, San Diego, vol.11, no.9, p.7, Sep., 1939.

(Sea Lions) Economic Importance

SEA-LION SLAUGHTER. Clinton G. Abbott. Bird-Lore, New York, vol.41, no.5, pp.265-270, illus., Sep.-Oct., 1939; Conservation, Amer. Forestry Assn., Washington, D.C., vol.5, no.6, pp.18-20, Nov.-Dec., 1939; Parks and Recreation, Rockford, Ill., vol.23, no.6, pp.253-259, illus., Feb., 1940.

(STUDY ON THE PURIFICATION OF THE OIL OF THE SEA LION.) Etude sur la purification de l'huile de loup-marin. L.C. Dugal, A. Cardin. Jour. Fisheries Res. Board Canada, Toronto, vol.7, no.8, pp. 471-489, figs.19, Mar., 1949.

THERE MUST BE A SEA LION INDUSTRY. K. Ruskii. Fishery Industry of the Far East, Vladivostok, nos.3-4, pp.55-56, 1931. (In Russian.)

"LION" HUNTING. (Sea Lion.) Lee Straight. Rod and Gun in Canada, Ottawa, vol.52, no. 11, pp.13, 40-42, Apr., 1951.

DEFENDS THE SEA LION. Lewis Wayne Walker. Outdoor Life, vol.68, no.5, p.32, Nov., 1931.

SEA-LION PERSECUTION. Nature Mag., Washington, D.C., vol.39, no.6, p.313, June-July, 1946.

SEA LION SLAUGHTER. Nature Mag., vol. 41, p.5, 1948.

UTILIZATION OF SEA LIONS STUDIED. Commercial Fisheries Rev., U.S. Fish and Wildl. Serv., vol.18, no.3, p.10, Mar., 1956.

(Sea Lions) Eurasia and Australia

SEA LIONS OF BOGOSLOF. Ben East. Nat. Hist., New York, vol.55, no.10, pp.474-477, illus., Dec., 1946.

(ON THE SEA LION (EUMETOPIA CALIFORNIANUS) "INGE" OF THE BREMERHAVEN ANIMAL GROTTOS.) Ueber die Seelowin (Eumetopias californianus) "Inge" der Tiergrotten Bremerhaven. Kurt Ehlers. Zool. Garten, Leipzig, vol.23, nos.1-3, pp.189-194, 1957.

ADDITIONAL NOTES ON ARCTOCEPHALUS CINEREUS AND ON GYPSOPHOCA. John Edward Gray. Proc. Zool. Soc. London, p. 743, 1872.

ON THE SKULLS OF JAPANESE SEALS, WITH THE DESCRIPTION OF A NEW SPECIES, EUMETOPIAS ELONGATUS. John Edward Gray. Proc. Zool. Soc. London, pp. 776-779, figs.2, Dec. 2, 1873.

REGISTRATION OF THE COASTAL LYING PLACES OF EUMETOPIAS JUBATUS AT THE KURIL ISLANDS, AND A TENTATIVE DETERMINATION OF THEIR NUMBER. S. K. Klumov. Doklady Akad. Nauk SSSR, vol.117, no.2, pp.345-348, 1957. (In Russian with English summary.)

SEA-LION OF THE OKHOTSK SEA AND ITS HUNTING. P.G. Nikulin. Bull.Pacific Sci. Inst. of Fisheries and Oceanography, Vladivostok, vol.10, pp.35-48, 1937. (In Russian with English summary.)

SEA LIONS OF BOGOSLOF. Kathryn Sollars. Fauna, Philadelphia, vol.6, no.3, pp.86-88, figs.33, Sep., 1944.

(Sea Lions) Fossils

FOSSIL SEA LION FROM THE MIOCENE OF THE SAN JOAQUIN HILLS, ORANGE COUNTY, CALIFORNIA. Theodore Downs. Bull. S. Calif. Acad. Sci., vol.54, pt.2, pp.49-56, illus., Oct. 5, 1955.

MIOCENE SEA LION FROM LOMITA, CALIFORNIA. (Pontolis magnus True.) Gretchen M. Lyon. Univ. Calif. Publ. Zool., vol.47, no.2, pp.23-42, figs.2, pls.2-6, Oct. 14, 1941.

FOSSIL SEA LION FROM CAPE BLANCO, OREGON. Earl Leroy Packard. Oregon State Monographs, Studies in Geol., Corvallis, no.5, pp.15-19, pls.2, Dec., 1947.

ON A FOSSIL REMAIN OF SEA-LION, EUMETOPIAS (?) KISHIDAI N. SP. FROM JAPAN. Tokio Shikama. Sci. Rept. Yokohama Nat. Univ., sec.2, no.2, pp.10-14, Mar., 1953.

DIAGNOSIS OF A NEW GENUS AND SPECIES OF FOSSIL SEA-LION FROM THE MIOCENE OF OREGON. Frederick W. True. Smith.Inst., Misc.Coll., vol.48, pt.1, publ.1577, pp.47-49, May 13, 1905.

FURTHER ACCOUNT OF THE FOSSIL SEA LION PONTOLIS MAGNUS, FROM THE MIOCENE OF OREGON. Frederick W.True. U.S. Geol. Survey, Professional Paper 59, pp.143-148, pls.11, 12, 13, 1909.

(Sea Lions) Galapagos Islands and Southern Waters

(SOME REMARKS ON THE GALAPAGOS SEA LION ZALOPHUS WOLLEBAEKI SIVERTSEN 1953.) Einige Bemerkungen ueber den Galapagos-Seeloewen, Zalophus wollebaeki, Sivertsen, 1953. Irenäus Eibl-Eibesfeldt. Saeugetierk. Mitteil., Stuttgart, vol.3, no.3, pp.101-103, July 1, 1955.

(PRELIMINARY NOTE ON THE SYSTEMATICS OF THE SEA LIONS OF THE ISLAND OF AMSTERDAM.) Note préliminaire sur la systématique de l'otarie d l'Ile Amsterdam. P. Paulian. Mammalia, Paris, vol. 21, pp.9-14, 1957a.

(ON A NEW SPECIES OF SEA BEAR, ARCTOPHOCA GAZELLA, FROM KERGUELEN ISLAND.) Ueber eine neue Art von Seebaeren, Arctophoca gazella, von der Kerguelen-Inseln. W.C.H. Peters. Monatsber. K.P. Akad. Wissensch. Berlin, pp.393-399, 1875.

NEW SPECIES OF SEA LION, ZALOPHUS WOLLEBAEKI, FROM THE GALAPAGOS ISLANDS. Erling Sivertsen. Kongel.Norske Videnskab. Selskabs Forhandl., vol.26, no. 1, pp.1-3, illus., 1953.

(Sea Lions) Habits, Behavior

NOTE ON THE FISHING OF THE CALIFORNIA SEA LION. Paul Bonnot. Calif. Fish and Game, vol.18, no.1, pp.98-99, Jan., 1932.

(ETHOLOGICAL STUDIES OF THE GALAPAGOS SEA LION, ZALOPHUS WOLLEBAEKI SIVERTSEN.) Ethologische Studien am Galapagos-Seeloewen, Zalophus wollebaeki Sivertsen. Irenaus Eibl-Eibesfeldt. Zeitschr. Tierpsychol., Berlin, vol.12, no. 2, pp.286-303, illus., Nov., 1955.

(OBSERVATIONS ON THE TERRITORIAL BEHAVIOR AND CARE OF YOUNG IN THE GALAPAGOS SEA LION.) Beobachtungen ueber territoriales Verhalten und Brutpflege des Galapagos-Seeloewen. Irenaus Eibl-Eibesfeldt. Zeitschr. Saeugetierk., Berlin, vol.20, nos.2-3, pp.75-77, Aug. 3, 1955.

NOTES ON BEHAVIOR OF THE CALIFORNIA SEA LION. Clarence W. Fry. Jour. Mamm., vol.24, no.1, pp.101-102, Feb. 20, 1943.

UNDERWATER BEHAVIOR OF THE SOUTHERN SEA LION, OTARIA JUBATA. Chester C. Lindt. Jour. Mamm., vol.37, no.2, pp. 287-288, June 9, 1956.

(CONTRIBUTIONS TO KNOWLEDGE OF SEA LIONS.) Beitraege zur Kenntnis der Maehnenrobben. Erna Mohr. Zool. Garten, vol.19, nos.2-4, pp.98-112, illus., 1952.

NOTE ON THE STELLER SEA LION. C. W. Townsend. Jour. Mamm., vol.6, no.3, pp.199-200, Aug., 1925.

SOMNOLENT SEA-LION. Illus. London News, vol.215, no.5760, p.395, illus., Sep. 10, 1949.

(Sea Lions) North America

SEA LION POPULATION OF SANTA BARBARA ISLAND, CALIFORNIA, IN THE 1950 BREEDING SEASON. Geo.A.Bartholomew, Jr. et al. Calif. Fish and Game, vol.37, no.1, pp.65-68, Jan., 1951.

CALIFORNIA SEA LION CENSUS FOR 1930. Paul Bonnot. Calif. Fish and Game, vol.17, no.2, pp.150-155, figs.5, Apr., 1931.

CALIFORNIA SEA LION CENSUS FOR 1936. Paul Bonnot. Calif. Fish and Game, vol.23, no.2, pp.108-112, fig.1, Apr., 1937.

SEA LION POPULATION OF CALIFORNIA. Paul Bonnot. Calif. Conservationist (State Dept. Nat. Resources), vol.2, no.8, pp. 6, 23, Aug., 1937.

SEA LIONS OF CALIFORNIA. Paul Bonnot. Calif. Fish and Game, vol.14, no.1, pp. 1-16, figs.10, Jan., 1928.

CALIFORNIA SEA LION CENSUS FOR 1938. Paul Bonnot et al. Calif. Fish and Game, vol.24, no.4, pp.415-419, Oct., 1938.

CALIFORNIA SEA LION CENSUS FOR 1947. (Comparison of Populations for Years 1927, 1928, 1930, 1936, 1938, and 1947.) Paul Bonnot, Wm. Ellis Ripley. Calif. Fish and Game, vol.34, no.3, pp.89-92, July, 1948.

THE ANO NUEVO STELLER SEA LION ROOKERY. B.W. Evermann. Jour.Mamm., vol.2, no.1, pp.16-17, pls.3, Feb., 1921.

STELLER SEA LION ROOKERY ON AÑO NUEVO ISLAND, CALIFORNIA, IN 1924. B.W. Evermann, G. D. Hanna. Jour. Mamm., vol.6, no.2, pp.96-99, pls.3, May, 1925.

WINTER INFLUX OF SEA LIONS FROM LOWER CALIFORNIA. Donald H. Fry, Jr. Calif. Fish and Game, San Francisco, vol. 25, no.3, pp.245-250, figs.93-95, tbl., July, 1939.

ON THE SEA-LIONS, OR LOBOS MARINOS OF THE SPANIARDS, ON THE COAST OF CALIFORNIA. J.E. Gray. Proc. Zool. Soc. London, pp.357-361, pl.1, 1859.

EVERY CAST, A STRIKE! (Sea Lions.) D.L. Henning. Alaska Sportsman, Ketchikan, vol.15, no.2, pp.10-13, illus., Feb., 1949.

SEA LION ROOKERIES OF SOUTHERN CALIFORNIA. C.F. Holder. Scientific American, p.411, June 24, 1899.

LIFE HISTORY OF THE SEA-LIONS ON THE CALIFORNIA COAST. John Rowley. Jour. Mamm., vol.10, no.1, pp.1-36, pls. 3, Feb., 1929.

AIRPLANE RECONNAISSANCE OF SEA LIONS IN WASHINGTON. Victor B. Scheffer, Preston P. Macy. Jour. Wildl. Mgt., Menasha, vol.8, no.4, pp.340-341, Oct., 1944.

(SEA LIONS OF NORTH AMERICA.) Die nordamerikanischen Seeloewen. O.Schubart. Zool. Garten, n.F., vol.3, nos.4-8, pp. 173-183, figs.1-8, Aug. 11, 1930.

NEPTUNE'S TROOPERS. (California Sea Lion.) Henrietta Holland. Travel, Baltimore, vol.92, no.3, pp.12-13, Mar. 31, 1949.

CALIFORNIA SEA LION CENSUS FOR 1946. Bureau of Marine Fisheries, Calif. Fish and Game, San Francisco, vol.33, no.1, pp.19-22, Mar. 15, 1947.

OUR SEA LION POPULATION. California Conservationist, vol.3, no.12, pp.7, 22, Dec., 1938.

SEA-LION CENSUS. Calif. Fish and Game, vol.17, p.150, 1931.

(Sea Lions) Parasites

MITES PARASITIC IN THE LUNGS AND AIR PASSAGES OF SEALS WITH SPECIAL EMPHASIS ON THEIR OCCURRENCE IN THE CALIFORNIA SEA LION. Willis H. Doetschman. MA thesis, Univ. S. Calif., 1942.

NEW SPECIES OF ENDOPARASITIC MITE OF THE FAMILY HALARACHNIDAE (ACARINA). Willis H. Doetschman. Trans.Amer. Micros. Soc., vol.63, no.1, pp.68-72, Jan., 1944.

ON A NEW SPECIES OF MITE OF THE FAMILY HALARACHNIDAE FROM THE SOUTHERN SEA LION. Susan Finnegan. Discovery Repts., vol.8, pp.319-328, 1934.

ACANTHOCEPHALA OF THE GENUS CORYNOSOMA FROM THE CALIFORNIA SEA-LION. David Richard Lincicome. Jour. Parasitol., Lancaster, vol.29, no.2, pp. 102-106, figs.9, Apr., 1943.

(Sea Lions) Physiology

ON THE RESPIRATORY FUNCTION OF THE BLOOD OF THE SEA LION. Marcel Florkin, Alfred C. Redfield. Biol. Bull., vol.61, no.3, pp.422-426, Dec., 1931.

THIAMINE DEFICIENCY IN SEA LIONS (OTARIA CALIFORNIANA) FED ONLY FROZEN FISH. R.H. Rigdon, Glenn A. Drager. Jour. Amer. Vet. Med. Assoc., vol.127, no.944, pp.453-455, illus., Nov., 1955.

(Sea Lions) Psychology

(BRIEF CONTRIBUTIONS ON THE PSYCHOLOGY OF THE SEA LION (EUMETOPIAS CALIFORNIANUS) (=ZALOPHUS).) Kleine Beitraege zur Psychologie des Seeloewen (Eumetopias californianus) (=Zalophus). M. Spindler, E. Bluhm. Zeitschr. Vergl. Physiol., vol.21, pp.616-631, 1934.

(Sea Lions) South America

NOTES ON THE PATAGONIAN SEA LION. Fred G. Brandenburg. Jour. Mamm., vol. 19, no.1, pp.44-57, figs.2, Feb. 14, 1938.

(SEA-LIONS, AUKS, AND GUANO PLACES ON THE ARGENTINIAN COAST AND NEARBY ISLANDS.) Lobos marinos, pinquinos y guaneras de las costas del litoral maritmo e islas adyacentes de la Republica Argentina. I. Santiago Carrara. Special Publ. Fac. Cienc. Vet., Univ. Nac. La Plata, pp.191-199, pls.8, 1952.

(GENERAL CHARACTERISTICS OF THE URUGUAYAN ISLANDS INHABITED BY

SEA-LIONS.) Caracteristicas generales de las islas Uruguayas habitadas por lobos marinos. R. Vaz Ferreira. Montevideo, Servicio Oceanografico y de Pesca, Trabajos Sobre Islas de Lobos y Lobos Marinos, no. 1, p.21, 1956a.

(ON A SPECIES OF OTARIA NEW TO CHILE.) Ueber eine fuer Chile neue Art von Otaria. W.C.H. Peters. Monatsber. K.P. Akad. Wissensch. Berlin, pp.558-566, pls.2, 1871.

(ON THE ISLAND OF SEA LIONS.) Auf der Insel der Seeloewen. (Coast of Uruguay.) Eugen Schuhmacher. Naturforscher, Jahrg. 15, no.4, pp.109-114, figs.10, July, 1938.

Odobenidae

THE WALRUS. H.E. Anthony. (In) North American Big Game. A Book of the Boone and Crockett Club, Compiled by the Committee on Records of North American Big Game. Charles Scribners Sons, New York, pp.433-434, 1939.

(THE WALRUS IN ZOOLOGICAL HISTORY.) Valrossen i zoologiens historia. Per Brinck. Zool. Bidrag, Uppsala, vol.25, pp.118-133, figs.7, 1947.

THE WALRUS GETS A REST. Edna Walker Chandler. Alaska Sportsman, Ketchikan, vol.9, no.2, pp.14-15, 18, illus., Feb., 1943.

BIBLIOGRAPHY ON WALRUS. Emma M. Charters. U.S. Dept. Interior, Fish and Wildl.Serv., Wildl. Leaflet 293, pp.14, May, 1947.

THE WALRUS. Stuart C. Downing. Canadian Nat., Toronto, vol.10, no.1, pp.28-29, illus., Jan.-Feb., 1948.

THE WALRUS. J. B. Gilpin. Nova-Scotian Inst.Nat.Sci.Proc. and Trans., vol.2, pt. 3, pp.123-127, pl., 1870.

ON THE ATTITUDES AND FIGURES OF THE MORSE. J.E. Gray. Proc. Zool.Soc. London, pt.21, pp.112-116, figs.10, 1853.

THE WALRUS. R.W. Gray. Naturalist, London, no.991, pp.201-207, Aug., 1939.

(ON THE WALRUS (TRICHECHUS ROSMARUS).) Ueber das Walross (Trichechus rosmarus). Otto Hermes. Sitz. Ber.Gesell. Naturf. Freunde, Berlin, no.4, pp. 67-70, Apr. 15, 1884.

NOTE ON THE OCCURRENCE OF A WALRUS IN THE FIRTH OF CLYDE. John G. Kerr. Glasgow Naturalist, vol.15, pt.3, p.104, Oct., 1949.

NOTICE OF REMAINS OF THE WALRUS DISCOVERED ON THE COAST OF THE UNITED STATES. Joseph Leidy. Trans. Amer. Philos. Soc., vol.11, pp.1-4, 1857.

(ALARIK BEHM ATTRIBUTES THE WALRUS TO GOTLAND.) Alarik Behm hat das Walross der Insel Gotland zugeeignet. Erna Mohr. Zool. Garten, Leipzig, n.F., vol. 6, nos.4-6, pp.83-96, figs.13, 1933.

(WALRUSES AS ERRONEOUS GUESTS IN THE EUROPEAN WATERS.) Walrosse als Irrgaeste in den europaeischen Gewaessern. Erna Mohr. Zool. Anzeiger, Leipzig, vol. 130, nos.9-10, pp.253-255, June 15, 1940.

ON THE MORBID APPEARANCES OBSERVED IN THE WALRUS LATELY LIVING IN THE SOCIETY'S GARDENS. WITH A DESCRIPTION OF A NEW SPECIES OF ASCARIS FOUND IN THE STOMACH, BY DR. BIARD. James Murie. Proc. Zool. Soc. London, pp. 67-71, fig.1, 1868.

(WALRUSES.) Om Walrossen. J.J.S.Steenstrup. Ofvers. Vetensk. Akad. Forh., Stockh., sextonde årgangen, 1859, pp.441-447, 1860.

Anatomy

DENTITION OF THE WALRUS (ODOBENUS OBESUS). W. Montague Cobb. Proc. Zool. Soc. London, pt. 3, pp.645-668, figs.8, pls.6, Sep. 20, 1933.

(THREE CASES OF DOUBLE TUSKS IN THE WALRUS.) Om 3 tilfaelde af dobbelte Stødtaender hos Hvalrossen (Odobenus rosmarus L.). Magnus Degerbøl. Vidensk.Meddel. Dansk. Naturhist. Foren.København, vol. 88, pp.287-292, figs.4, (1929) 1930.

WALRUS SKULL (ODOBENUS) FROM BLUE-HILL BAY, MAINE. Robert L. Dow. Jour. Mamm., vol.35, no.3, p.444, Aug. 20, 1954.

CEREBRAL FISSURES OF THE ATLANTIC WALRUS. P.A. Fish. Proc. U.S.Nat.Mus., Washington, vol.26, pp.675-688, pls.28-29, 1903.

ANCIENT WALRUS SKULL. Birger R.Headstrom. Science, n.s., vol.67, p.608, June 15, 1928.

NOTICE OF A MEMOIR ON THE ANATOMY OF THE WALRUS. James Murie. Proc. Zool. Soc. London, pp.544-545, 1870.

ON THE ANATOMY OF THE WALRUS. R. Owen. Proc. Zool. Soc. London, pt.21, pp.103-106, 1853.

LARGE WALRUS TUSK FROM ST. PAUL ISLAND, ALASKA. Ford Wilke. Murrelet, Seattle, vol.23, no.1, p.17, May 14, 1942.

Atlantic Ocean

WALRUS IN NEW ENGLAND. Glover M. Allen. Bull. Boston Nat. Hist., Soc., no. 47, pp.10-12, illus., Apr., 1928.

STATUS OF THE ATLANTIC WALRUS, ODOBENUS ROSMARUS (L.), IN CANADA. M.J. Dunbar. Arct. Circ., no.8, pp.11-14, 1954; (In) Proc. and Pap. 5th Technical Meeting, Internatl. Union for the Protection of Nature, Copenhagen, 1954, Bruxelles, pub.by the Secretariat, pp.59-61, 1956.

WALRUS IN BRITISH WATERS. H.W. Robinson. Northwestern Nat., Arbroath, vol.11, no.2, p.155, June, 1936.

WALRUS REMAINS FROM NORTHERN NEW ENGLAND. Ralph S. Palmer. Jour. Mamm., vol.25, no.2, p.193, May 25, 1944.

Extinction

SHALL THE WALRUS BECOME EXTINCT? J.A. Allen. Amer. Mus. Jour., vol.13, pp. 38-42, illus., Jan., 1913.

ANIMALS IN DECLINE: 2. WALRUSES. Maurice Burton. Illus. London News, vol. 218, no.5832, p.148, illus., Jan. 27, 1951.

UNUSUAL WALRUS MORTALITY ON ST. LAWRENCE ISLAND, ALASKA. Everett L. Schiller. Jour. Mamm., vol.35, no.2, pp.203-210, illus., May, 1954.

Fossils

PROROSMARUS ALLENI, A NEW GENUS AND SPECIES OF WALRUS FROM THE UPPER MIOCENE OF YORKTOWN, VIRGINIA. E.W. Berry, W. K. Gregory. Amer. Jour. Sci., ser.4, vol.21, pp.444-450, 1906.

FOSSIL WALRUS FROM THE OKHOTSK COAST. A. Borisiak. Ann. Soc. Paléont. Russie, vol.8, pp.1-8, pl.1, (1928-1929) 1930. (In Russian with English summary.)

TRICHECODON HUXLEYI (MAMMALIA: ODOBENIDAE) IN THE PLEISTOCENE OF SOUTHEASTERN UNITED STATES. Clayton R. Ray. Cambridge, Mass., Harvard Univ., Mus.Comp.Zool., Bull., vol.122, no.3, pp.127-142, illus., pls., tbl., 1960.

NOTES ON THE FOSSIL WALRUS OF EASTERN NORTH AMERICA. Samuel N.Rhoads. Proc. Acad. Nat. Sci., Philadelphia, pp. 196-201, May 3 - June 13, 1898.

Habits

HABITS OF THE PACIFIC WALRUS (ODOBENUS DIVERGENS). Grenold Collins.Jour. Mamm., vol.21, no.2, pp.138-144, May, 1940.

REPORT ON PACIFIC WALRUS (ODOBENUS DIVERGENS. (Numbers, Habits, and Utilization.) Grenold Collins. U.S. Dept. Int., Biol. Surv., Alaska Game Comm., pp.11, Sep., 1939.

OLD MAN OF THE ICE FLOES. (Habits, Hunting, Depletion.) J. Lester Minner. Alaska Sportsman, vol.19, no.3, pp.18-21, 38-39, illus., Mar., 1953.

DESCRIPTION OF THE CHUKOTSK WALRUS, ITS HABITS, DISTRIBUTION IN THE CHUKCHI AND BERING SEAS, ITS FOOD AND MIGRATIONS. P.G. Nikulin. Bull. Pacif. Sci. Inst. Fish., Vladivostock, vol. 20, pp.21-59, 1940. (In Russian.)

Hunting

HUNTING THE WALRUS. Robert A. Bartlett. (In) N.Amer. Big Game. A Book of the Boone and Crockett Club, compiled by the Committee on Records of N. Amer. Big Game. New York, Charles Scribners Sons, pp.435-437, 1939.

WALRUS COLLECTING WITH CAPTAIN BOB. ESKIMO HUNTERS AND THE CREW OF THE EFFIE M. MORRISEY COMBINED TO GET FOUR PUPS FOR THE ZOOLOGICAL PARK. Rupert W.Bartlett.Bull. N.Y. Zool. Soc., vol.43, no.5, pp.139-143, figs. 4, Sep.-Oct., 1940.

ON THE ICY TRAIL OF AIVIK. Harold McCracken. Sportsman, vol.6, pp.64-66, 68-69, illus., Aug., 1929.

WALRUSING. HUNTING AND EXPLORING THROUGH POLAR ICE. Harold McCracken. Field and Stream, no.7, pp.42-44, 93, Nov., 1929.

WALRUS HUNT. B.M. May. Beaver, Winnipeg, outfit 273, pp.38-40, illus., Sep., 1942.

WALRUS HUNT. Edward Weyer, Jr. Nat. Hist., New York, vol.65, no.1, pp.28-32, illus., Jan., 1956.

Northern Waters

TO THE ARCTIC FOR WALRUS. H.E. Anthony. Nat. Hist., vol.29, pp.50-64, illus., Feb., 1929.

LOCAL WALRUS PROTECTION IN NORTHEAST SIBERIA. Joseph F. Bernard. Jour. Mamm., vol.4, no.4, pp.224-227, pl.25, Nov., 1923.

WALRUS PROTECTION IN ALASKA. Joseph F. Bernard. Jour. Mamm., vol.6, no.2, pp.100-102, May, 1925.

WALRUS OF THE KARA SEA. K.K.Chapskiy. Trans. Arct. Inst., Leningrad, Tom 67, p. 111, 1936. (In Russian with English summary.)

SMALL CONTRIBUTIONS TO OUR KNOWLEDGE OF DANISH FAUNA. 4. ON A WALRUS (TRICHECHUS ROSMARUS L.) WHICH HAS VISITED DENMARK AND PROBABLY FOUR OTHER EUROPEAN COUNTRIES. Ad. S. Jensen. Vidensk. Medd. fra Dansk Naturh. Foren., Copenhagen, vol.84, pp.189-193, map, 1927.

WALRUS--THE MANY-PURPOSE ANIMAL OF THE ARCTIC. Dorothea C. Leighton. Nature Mag., Washington, D.C., vol.35, no.9, pp.477-479, illus., Nov., 1942.

WALRUS AND ITS VISITS TO THE NORWEGIAN COAST SINCE 1900. Hjalmar Munthe-Kaas Lund. Norsk Hvalfangst-Tidende (Norwegian Whaling Gazette), Sandefjord, vol.43, no.11, pp.639-646, illus., Nov., 1954. (In Norwegian and English.)

WALRUS (ODOBAENUS ROSMARUS L.) OFF THE COAST OF NORWAY IN THE PAST AND AFTER THE YEAR 1900, TOGETHER WITH SOME OBSERVATIONS ON ITS MIGRATIONS AND "CRUISING SPEED". Hjalmar Munthe-Kaas Lund. Astarte, Zool. Dept. Tromsø Mus., no.8, pp.1-2, illus., July 25, 1954.

STRONG CURRENT. (Walrus.) Robert Mayokok. Alaska Sportsman, Ketchikan, vol.15, no.11, pp.18-21, illus., Nov., 1949.

WALRUS WEST OF GREENLAND. C.Vibe. (In) Proc. and Pap. 5th Technical Meeting, Internat. Union for the Protection of Nature, Copenhagen, 1954, Bruxelles, pub. by the Secretariat, pp.79-84, 1956.

MATERIALS ON THE BIOLOGY OF THE WALRUS OF THE FRANZ JOSEPH ARCHIPELAGO. V.I. Zalkin. Bull. Soc. Nat. Moscow, sect.biol., n.s., vol.46, no.1, pp.43-51, 1937. (In Russian with English summary.)

FROM KETCHIKAN TO BARROW. (Walrus.) Alaska Sportsman, Ketchikan, vol.11, no.7, pp.21-23, July, 1945.

Pacific Ocean

CONTRIBUTION TO THE LIFE HISTORY AND ECOLOGY OF THE PACIFIC WALRUS. J.W. Brooks. Alaska Cooperative Wildlife Research Unit (College, Alaska) Spec. Rept., no.1, pp.9-103, 1954.

PACIFIC WALRUS AND ITS IMPORTANCE TO THE ESKIMO ECONOMY. J.W.Brooks. Trans. 18th N. Amer. Wildl. Conf., pp. 503-510, 1953.

NOTES ON IVORY IN HAWAII. (Walrus.) Schuyler Cammann. Jour. Polynesian Soc., Wellington, vol.63, no.2, pp.133-140, pl. 1, Sep., 1954.

HISTORY AND PRESENT STATUS OF THE PACIFIC WALRUS POPULATION. Francis H. Fay. Trans. 22nd N. Amer. Wildl.Conf., Washington, pp.431-445, 1958.

PACIFIC WALRUS. Turtox News, Chicago, vol.25, no.11, p.221, illus., Nov., 1947.

Taxonomy

NAMING OF THE WALRUS. J.Brian Bird. Arctic, Jour. Arctic Inst. N.America, Ottawa, vol.6, no.1, pp.62-63, Mar., 1952.

SECOND REPORT ON THE STATUS OF THE GENERIC NAMES "ODOBENUS" BRISSON, 1762 AND "ROSMARUS" Brunnich, 1771 (CLASS MAMMALIA). F. Hemming. Bull. Zool. Nom., vol.11, pp.196-198, 1955.

SYSTEMATIC NAME OF THE PACIFIC WALRUS. L. Stejneger. Proc. Biol. Soc. Washington, vol.27, p.145, 1914.

Young

(RAISING AND CARING FOR WALRUSES.) Aufzucht und Pflege von Walrossen. Th. Alving. Zool. Garten, Leipzig, n.F., vol. 10, nos.5-6, pp.215-218, figs. 4, tbl.1, Jan., 1939.

HOW "PEE-UK" CAME TO THE ZOOLOGICAL PARK. (Account of Rearing a Baby Walrus.) Jack Angel. Bull. New York Zool. Soc., vol.38, no.5, pp.173-177, illus., Sep.-Oct., 1935.

CAREFREE LIFE OF HERBERT. Sam Dunton. Animal Kingdom, New York Soc., vol.55, no.2, pp.48-50, illus., Mar.-Apr., 1952.

THIS IS HERBERT. Sam Dunton. Animal Kingdom, New York Zool. Soc., vol.54, no.6, pp.175-177, illus., Nov.-Dec., 1951.

(RAISING THREE YOUNG WALRUSES IN THE COPENHAGEN ZOO.) Aufzucht dreier junger Walrosse im Kopenhagener Zoo. Axel Reventlow. Zool. Garten, Leipzig, n.F., vol.10, nos.1-2, pp.50-53, illus., May, 1938.

STORY OF A YOUNG WALRUS WHO TRAVELED FARTHER SOUTH THAN HIS RELATIVES IN BERING STRAIT. Woodbridge Williams. Nat. Hist., New York, vol.47, no.1, pp.42-45, figs.7, Jan., 1941.

A FRIENDLY ... YOUNG WALRUS ... IN THE NEW YORK ZOOLOGICAL PARK. Illus. London News, vol.220, no.5895, pp. 630-631, illus., Apr. 12, 1952.

Phocidae

A RARE SEAL (MONACHUS SCHAUINSLANDI). A.L.C. Atkinson, W.A. Bryan. Bull. N.Y. Zool. Soc., vol.16, pp.1050-1051, 1913.

GREY SEAL. K.M. Backhouse. Univ.Durham Coll. Med. Gaz., vol.48, no.2, pp. 9-16, 1954.

NORTHERN ELEPHANT SEAL. George A. Bartholomew. Zoonooz, San Diego Zool.Soc., vol.28, no.1, pp.6-9, illus., 1955.

LOBODON CARCINOPHAGUS (H.J.) GR. EN EL RIO DE LA PLATA. C. Berg. Comun. Mus. Nac. B. Aires, Tomo 1, p.15, 1898.

RAREST SEAL. (Monachus schauinslandi.) Thomas M. Blackman. Nat. Hist., New York, vol.47, no.3, pp.138-139, illus., Mar., 1941.

ATLANTIC GRAY SEAL. F.F. Darling. Animal Kingdom, vol.55, no.4, pp.122-126, illus., July-Aug., 1952.

LIFE HISTORY OF THE ATLANTIC GREY SEAL. F.F. Darling. (In) Nat. Hist. in the Highlands and Islands. London, Collins, pp. 217-231, 1947.

ON THE BIOLOGY OF THE GREY SEAL (HALICHOERUS GRYPUS FABR.). A.N. Dubrovskii. Priroda, Leningrad, no.2, p. 107, Feb., 1937. (In Russian.)

ON THE ELEPHANT SEAL (MACRORHINUS LEONINUS, LINN.) W.H. Flower. Proc. Zool. Soc. London, pp.145-162, figs.2, Jan. 4, 1881.

PHOCA. C.G. Giebel. (In) Allgemeine Encyclopaedie der Wissenschaften und Kuenste, by J.S. Ersch und J.G. Gruber, Leipzig, sect. 3, pp.284-292, 1848.

NOTES ON THE SEALS (PHOCIDAE), INCLUDING THE DESCRIPTION OF A NEW SEAL (HALICYON RICHARDII), FROM THE WEST COAST OF NORTH AMERICA. J.E. Gray. Proc. Zool. Soc. London, pp. 27-34, 1864.

LEOPARD SEAL HYDRURGA LEPTONYX (DE BLAINVILLE). J.E. Hamilton. Discovery Repts., vol.18, pp.239-264, pls.7, 1939a.

ON THE HISTORY OF THE ELEPHANT SEAL, MIROUNGA LEONINA (LINN.). J.E. Hamilton. Proc. Linnean Soc.London, 152nd Sess.(1939-40), pt.1, pp.33-37, fig. 1, Feb. 9, 1940.

FURTHER STUDIES ON THE GREY SEAL. H.R. Hewer. Proc. Zool. Soc. London, vol. 126, no.3, p.485, May 31, 1956.

MONK SEALS (GENUS MONACHUS). Judith E. King. Bull. British Mus., Nat.Hist., London, Zool., vol.3, no.5, pp.201-256, pls.3-8, Jan., 1956.

(SEAL.) Phoque. R.P. Lesson. (In) Dictionnaire classique d'histoire naturelle, ed. by Baron J.B.G.M. Bory de Saint-Vincent. Paris, Rey et Gravier, vol.13, pp.400-426, Jan., 1828.

HOOD SEAL (CYSTOPHORA CRISTATA). H.R. Lillie. (In) Pap. and Proc. 5th Technical Meeting Internatl. Union for the Protection of Nature, Copenhagen, 1954. Bruxelles, pub.by the Secretariat, pp.62-63, 1956.

NOTES ON THE CRAB-EATER SEAL. Alton A. Lindsey. Jour. Mamm., vol.19, no.4, pp.456-461, figs.2, tbl., Nov. 14, 1938.

ATLANTIC GREY SEAL. R.M. Lockley. Oryx, vol.2, pp.384-387, 1954.

EFFECTS OF A SEAL BITE AT MOULD BAY. S.D. Macdonald. Arctic Cir., vol.6, no.3, pp.34-35, 1953.

GREEN ALGAL GROWTH ON GRAY SEALS. B.A. Mackenzie. Jour. Mamm., vol.35, no.4, pp.595-596, Nov. 29, 1954.

CESTODES OF SEALS FROM THE ANTARCTIC. S. Markowski. Bull. Brit. Mus., Nat. Hist., Zool., vol.1, pp.125-150, 1952.

NATURAL HISTORY OF THE ELEPHANT SEAL. L.H. Matthews. Discovery Repts., vol.1, pp.234-255, pls.6, 1929.

SEA ELEPHANT: THE LIFE AND DEATH OF THE ELEPHANT SEAL. L.H. Matthews. Macgibbon and Kee, pp.190, illus., 1952.

(DATA ON THE RINGED SEAL "HISTRIOPHOCA" FASCIATA ZIMMERMANN 1783.) Zur Kenntnis der Bandrobbe, "Histriophoca" fasciata (Zimmermann 1783). Erna Mohr. Zool. Anzeiger, Leipzig, vol.147, nos.7-8, pp.187-195, illus., 1951.

(THE SEA DOG.) Der Seehund. Erna Mohr. Die neue Brehm-Bucherei, Heft 145, Ziemsen (Wittenberg Lutherstadt), pp.55, figs. 48, 1955.

NOTES ON THE SEA ELEPHANT, MIROUNGA LEONINA (LINNE). R.C. Murphy. Bull. Amer. Mus. Nat. Hist., vol.33, pp. 63-79, pls.7, 1914.

(ON HALICHOERUS GRYPUS FABR.) Ueber Halichoerus grypus Fabr. Alfred Nehring. Sitz. Ber. Gesell. Naturf. Freunde Berlin, no.8, pp.117-127, Oct. 17, 1882.

(ON HARARACHNE HALICHOERI ALLMAN AND SOME HALICHOERUS SKULLS.) Ueber Halarachne halichoeri Allman, sowie ueber einige Halichoerus Schaedel. Alfred Nehring. Sitz.Ber. Gesell. Naturf. Freunde Berlin, no.4, pp.57-67, fig.1, Apr. 15, 1884.

(CONTRIBUTION TO KNOWLEDGE OF ISOLATED FORMS OF RINGED SEALS (PHOCA FOETIDA FABR.).) Beitrag zur Kenntnis der isolierten Formen der Ringelrobbe (Phoca foetida Fabr.). O.Nordquist. Acta Soc. Fauna Flora Fenn., vol.15, pp. 1-44, tbls.1, pls.3, 1899.

NOTES ON THE HOOD SEAL (CYSTOPHORA CRISTATA). J.M. Olds. Jour. Mamm., vol. 31, no.4, pp.450-452, Nov. 21, 1950.

(ANIMALS AND COLD.) Les animaux et le froid. (Phoca vitulina.) A. Rochon-Duvigneaud. La Terre et la Vie, Paris, vol.9, no. 1, pp.27-28, Jan.-Feb., 1939.

MIROUNGA ANGUSTIROSTRIS (GILL). W. Rothschild. Novit.Zool., vol.15, pp.393-394, pls.8, 1908.

NOTES ON SEA ELEPHANTS (MIROUNGA.) W. Rothschild. Novit. Zool., vol.17, pp. 445-446, pls.2, 1910.

CREATURES OF SEA ICE AND TUNDRA BARRENS. (Phoca hispida.) Katharine Sherman, Richard S. Miller. Animal Kingdom, New York Zool. Soc., vol.58, no.2, pp.56-61, illus., Apr., 1955.

(CONTRIBUTIONS TO THE HISTORY OF OUR KNOWLEDGE OF ELEPHANT SEALS.) Beitraege zur Geschichte unserer Kenntnisse vom See-Elefanten. H. Steinmetz. Zool. Garten, Leipzig, vol.21, nos.1-2, pp.24-43, illus., Mar., 1955.

A SEAL'S WORLD. (Harp Seal.) Frank Stuart. McGraw-Hill Book Co., New York, pp.224, illus., May, 1954.

(CONTRIBUTION TO THE STUDY OF THE PINNIPEDS BY WAY OF TWO MEDITERRANEAN SEALS.) Contribution a l'étude des pinnipedes a propos de deux phoques de la Mediterranee. A. Troitzky. Bull.Inst. Oceanogr. Monaco, vol.50, whole no.1032, pp.2-46, 1953.

SEA ELEPHANT IS PECULIAR. Judy Van der Veer, George Lindsay. Nature Mag., Washington, vol.43, no.4, pp.185-188, illus., Apr., 1950.

ELEPHANTS OF THE SEA. (Mirounga.) Lewis W. Walter. Nature Mag., vol.19, no.3, pp.173-174, figs.3, Mar., 1932.

UNUSUAL INJURY TO YOUNG HARBOR SEAL. Ford Wilke. Jour. Mamm., vol. 24, no.3, pp.401-402, Aug. 17, 1943.

JUMBO OF THE DEEP. (Elephant Seals.) Woodbridge Williams. Nat. Hist., New York, vol.48, no.3, pp.144-149, illus., Oct., 1941.

(CONTRIBUTION TO KNOWLEDGE OF PUSA HISPIDA PYGMAEA.) Beitrag zur Kenntnis von Pusa hispida pygmaea. Ludwig Zukowsky. Archiv. fuer Nat., Jahrg. 87, Abt. A, Heft 10, pp.183-199, figs.2, Dec., 1921.

Africa

ELEPHANT SEAL COW AND PUP ON SOUTH AFRICAN COAST. H.B.D. Kettlewell. Nature, vol.175, pp.1000-1001, 1955.

(SAHARAN SEALS.) Phoques Sahariens. Th. Monod. La Terre et la Vie (Revue d'Hist. Nat.), vol.2, no.5, pp.257-261, figs.1-4, May, 1932.

(NOTES ON THE MONK SEALS OF THE SPANISH SAHARA LITTORAL.) Notes sur les phoques-moines (Monachus monachus Herm.) du littoral saharien espagnol. E. Morales-Agacino. Mammalia, Paris, vol. 14, nos.1-2, pp.1-6, pls.2, Mar.-June, 1950.

ASHORE AT CAPE TOWN DURING A STORM; AN ELEPHANT-SEAL WHICH RESTED ON THE ROCKS FOR TWO DAYS BEFORE RETURNING TO THE SEA. Illus. London News, vol.214, no.5746, p.760, illus., June 4, 1949.

Anatomy

REPRODUCTIVE ORGANS OF FOETAL AND JUVENILE ELEPHANT SEALS. W. Nigel Bonner. Nature, London, vol.176, no.4490, pp.982-983, Nov. 19, 1955.

MEASUREMENTS AND WEIGHTS OF ANTARCTIC SEALS. W.S. Bruce. (In) Rept.

on the Scientific Results of the Voyage of S.Y."Scotia"During the years 1902, 1903 and 1904. Edinburgh, Scottish Oceanogr. Lab., pt.11, pp.159-174, pls.2, 1915.

(THE FEMUR OF SCALD SEALS; ITS MORPHOLOGICAL INTERPRETATION.) Le femur des phocides scaldisiens; son interpretation morphologique. Madeleine Friant. Bull. Mus. Roy. Hist. Nat. Belgique, Brussels, vol.20, no.12, pp.1-4, figs.4, June, 1944.

(RESEARCH ON THE FEMUR OF SEALS.) Recherches sur le femur des Phocidae. Madeleine Friant. Bull. Mus. Roy. Hist. Nat. Belgique, Bruxelles, vol.23, no.2, pp.51, figs.20, Mar., 1947.

NOTES ON SEALS (PHOCIDAE) AND THE CHANGES IN THE FORM OF THEIR LOWER JAW DURING GROWTH. J.E. Gray. Ann. Mag. Nat. Hist., ser.4, vol.4, pp. 342-346, 1869.

ON THE VARIATION IN THE TEETH OF THE CRESTED SEAL, CYSTOPHORA CRISTATA, AND ON A NEW SPECIES OF THE GENUS FROM THE WEST INDIES. J.E. Gray. Proc. Zool. Soc. London, pp. 91-93, 1849.

WEIGHT, ETC. OF ELEPHANT SEAL. J.E. Hamilton. Nature, London, vol.163, no.4144, p.536, Apr. 2, 1949.

ON THE VARIATION OF THE SEA-ELEPHANTS. Einar Lonnberg. Proc. Zool.Soc. London, pp.580-588, figs.55-56, Aug., 1910.

ON THE SKULL-CHARACTERS IN THE SOUTHERN SEA-ELEPHANT. R. Lydekker. Proc. Zool. Soc. London, pp.600-606, 1909.

THE 'HOOD' OF THE HOODED SEAL, CYSTOPHORA CRISTATA. C. Hart Merriam. Science, vol.4, no.96, pp.514-516, figs.5, Dec. 5, 1884.

(THE PROBOSCIS OF THE HOOD-SEAL AND HOW IT WORKS.) La "Trompe" du Phoque a capunchon et son fonctionement. Erna Mohr. Mammalia, Paris, vol. 16, no.2, pp.73-76, June, 1952.

ON PHOCA GROENLANDICA, MULL. :ITS MODES OF PROGRESSIO AND ITS ANATOMY. James Murie. Proc. Zool. Soc. London, pp.604-608, pl., 1870 .

TRACHEA OF OGMORHINUS (-HYDRURGA), WITH NOTES ON OTHER SOFT PARTS. R. C. Murphy. Bull. Amer. Nat. Hist., vol.32, pp.505-506, 1913.

ON THE ANATOMY OF THE SEAL (PHOCA VITULINA, LINN.). R. Owen. Proc.Comm. Sci. and Corres. Zool. Soc. London, pt.1, pp.151-154, 1830-1831.

PRESENCE OF THE EXTERNAL PINNA IN THE GREY SEAL (HALICHOERUS GRYPUS). R.I. Pocock. Proc. Zool. Soc. London, pt.2, pp.419-420, fig.1, June 30, 1933.

(ON THE HOODED SEALS FETUS AND ITS MILK TEETH.) Om Klapmydsens ufodte Unge og dens Melketandsaet. J. Reinhardt. Naturhist. Foren. Vidensk, Meddelelser, pp.17, figs., Apr., 1864.

(CRANIAL OBSERVATIONS ON THE SEA-ELEPHANT.) Observaciones craneanas en los elefantes de mar. (Mireunga leonina L.) Carlos Rusconi. Anales Soc. Cient., Argentina, Buenos Aires, pt.4, vol.127, pp.294-305, figs.6, tbl.1, Apr., 1939.

INTERESTING FOETAL COMMON SEAL. A.C. Stephen. Scottish Nat., no.221, p. 140, Sep.-Oct., 1936.

(A GREY SEAL WITH EAR MUSCLES.) Eine Kegelrobbe mit Ohrmuscheln. Dr.J. Thienemann. Zeitschr.f.Saeugetierk., vol. 6, no.6, p.225, Dec. 15, 1931.

ON THE SKELETON OF PHACA (HISTRIOPHOCA) FASCIATA, ZIMMERMAN. F.W. True. U.S. Nat. Mus., Proc., Washington, vol.6, pp.417-426, illus., pls.11-14, 1883.

OSTEOLOGICAL CHARACTERS OF THE GENUS HISTRIOPHOCA. F.W. True. Amer. Nat., Lancaster, vol.17, pt.2, p.798, July, 1883.

Asia and Asian Waters

NOTES ON THE PRESENT STATUS OF THE MONK SEAL IN PALESTINE. G.C.L. Bertram. Jour. Soc. Preservation Fauna Empire, Hertford, n.s., pt.47, pp.20-21, Aug., 1943.

LADOGA LAKE SEAL AND PERSPECTIVE OF ITS CATCHING. K.K. Chapsky. Bull. Inst. Applied Ichthyol. USSR, Leningrad, vol.13, fasc.2, pp.147-157, 1932. (In Russian, with Russian and English titles.)

BIOLOGY OF LAKE BAIKAL. (Mentions Seal.) Theodore D.A. Cockerell. Science, n.s., vol.66, pp.552-554, Dec. 9, 1927.

(CONTRIBUTION TO KNOWLEDGE OF THE SEALS OF SIBERIA.) Contribution a la connaissance des phoques de Sibérie. B. Dybowski. Acad. Polonaise Sci. and Lettr. Comptes Rendus. Mens. Cl. Sci. Math. and Nat., no.8, p.7, (Abstract) Oct., 1929.

(KNOWLEDGE OF THE SIBERIAN SEAL.) Zur Kenntnis der sibirischen Seehunde. B. Dybowski. Bull. Internat. Acad. Polonaise Sci. et Lett., Cl. Sci. Math. et Nat., Ser. B, Sci. Nat. (II) (Zool.), Cracovie, nos.8-10 B II, pp.405-415, pls.3, Oct.-Dec., 1929.

(ON THE BAIKAL SEAL PHOCA BAICALENSIS.) Ueber die Baikal-Robbe, Phoca baicalensis. B. Dybowski. Arch. Anat. Physiol. Wissensch. Medizin, pp.109-125, pls.2, 1873.

HAIR SEALS (AZARASHI) IN OUR NORTHERN WATERS. T. Inukai. Shokubutsu Dobutsu (Botany and Zoology), vol.10, no. 10, pp.927-932; vol.10, no.11, pp.1025-1030, 1942. (In Japanese.)

PRELIMINARY NOTE ON THE RIBBON SEAL, HISTRIOPHOCA FASCIATA (ZIMM.) GILL, FROM THE WATERS OF SAGHALIEN. (Distribution.) T. Inukai. Jour. Faculty Sci., Hokkaido Imp. Univ., Sapporo, vol.7, no. 3, pp.299-303, figs.2, Nov., 1940.

PHOCA RICHARDII PRIBILOFENSIS OBTAINED IN THE ROBBEN IDS., SAGHALIEN. Nagamichi Kuroda. Dobutsugaku Zasshi, Zool. Soc. Japan, Tokyo, vol.47, pp.353-354, June 15, 1935. (In Japanese.)

ON THE OCCURRENCE (sic) OF A HAIR-SEAL, PHOCA RICHARDSI (GRAY), IN THE COAST OF NORTH CHINA. P. Leroy. Bull. Fan Memorial Inst. of Biol., Zool. Ser., no.10, pp.61-68, pl.1, 1940.

SEALS OF NORTHERN HOKKAIDO. Ford Wilke. Jour. Mamm., vol.35, no.2, pp. 218-224, illus., May 26, 1954.

Australia and Pacific Ocean and Islands

THE HAIR SEALS (FAMILY PHOCIDAE) OF THE NORTH PACIFIC OCEAN AND BERING SEA. J.A. Allen. Bull. Amer. Mus. Nat. Hist., vol.16, pp.459-499, text figs. 10, Dec. 12, 1902.

LETTER FROM, RELATING TO A SPECIES OF SEAL (STENORHYNCHUS) CAPTURED IN NEW ZEALAND. Charles Fraser. Proc. Zool. Soc. London, p.2, 1869.

CRABEATER SEALS IN AUSTRALIAN WATERS. T.S. Hall. Nature, no.67, pp.327-328, 1903.

OCCURRENCE OF THE CRAB-EATING SEAL LOBODON CARCINOPHAGA HOMBRON AND JACUINOT (sic), IN NEW SOUTH WALES. A.S. LeSouef. Aus.Zool., no.6, p.99, pl.1, 1929.

(A SEAL OF LAYSAN.) Eine Robbe von Laysan. P. Matschie. Sitz. Ber. Naturf. Freunde Berlin, pp.254-262, 1905.

(A NEW WEST PACIFIC SEAL.) Ein neuer westpazifischer Seehund. Erna Mohr. Zool. Anzeiger, no.133, pp.49-60, 1941.

NOTES ON THE SYSTEMATIC POSITION AND GEOGRAPHIC DISTRIBUTION OF THE PHOCIDAE OF THE NORTH PACIFIC OCEAN. S.P. Naumov, N.A. Smirnov. (In) The Marine Mammals of USSR Far East (resources and commercial use). Trans. Inst. Mar. Fish. USSR. (VNIRO), vol.3, pp.161-184, 1936. (In Russian.)

CRAB-EATING SEAL IN NEW ZEALAND. W.R.B. Oliver. Trans. New Zealand Inst., Wellington, vol.53, p.360, pl.56, Aug. 8, 1921.

HARBOR SEAL OF THE WESTERN PACIFIC. E. Schwartz. Jour. Mamm., vol.23, pp.222-223, 1942.

RECORD OF THE LEOPARD SEAL IN WESTERN AUSTRALIA. D.L. Serventy. W.Aust. Nat., Perth., no.1, p.155, 1948.

OBSERVATIONS ON THE OCCURRENCE OF THE WEDDELL SEAL IN NEW ZEALAND. E.G. Turbott. Rec. Auckland (N.Z.) Inst., no.3, pp.377-379, pl.1, 1949.

LOBODON CARCINOPHAGUS IN TASMANIA. Pap. Roy. Soc. Tasm., 1945, p.165, 1946b.

Captivity

NOTES ON THE KEEPING OF A BABY SEAL (PHOCA VITULINA). J. Bossanyi. Proc. Zool. Soc. London, vol.117, no.4, pp.791-792, Feb. 3, 1948.

(FEEDING AND ACCLIMATIZATION OF SEA ELEPHANTS IN CAPTIVITY AT THE ZOO PARK OF THE BOIS DE VINCENNES.) Alimentation et acclimatement d'elephants de mer (Mirounga leonina L.) en captivite, au parc zoologique du Bois de Vincennes. P. Bullier. Mammalia, Paris, vol.18, no.3, pp.272-276, pl.1, Sep., 1954.

(REARING SEALS IN THE ANIMAL GROTTOS OF THE TOWN OF WESERMUENDE.) Die Aufzucht der Seehunde in den Tiergrotten der Stadt Wesermuende. Hermann Junker. Zool. Garten, n.F., vol.12, nos.4-6, pp.306-315, illus., Dec., 1940.

FOUR BABIES FROM ALASKA. (Harbor Seals and Bald Eagles.) Robert M. McClung. Animal Kingdom, New York Zool. Soc., vol. 57, no.4, pp.120-124, illus., Aug., 1954.

LETTER FROM, AND EXHIBITION OF A YOUNG HARP SEAL (PHOCA GROENLANDICA, MÜLLER) PRESENTED BY E.L. Moore. Proc. Zool. Soc. London, pt.10, p.49, 1842.

REARING OF A GREY SEAL IN CAPTIVITY. Betty June Myers. Canadian Field-Nat., vol. 69, no.4, pp.151-153, Oct.-Dec., 1955.

(ON A SPECIMEN OF HALICHOERUS GRYPUS IN THE BERLIN AQUARIUM.) Ueber ein im Berliner Aquarium befindliches Exemplar von Halichoerus grypus. A. Nehring. Sitz. Ber. Gesell. Naturf. Freunde Berlin, no.1, pp.7-8, Jan. 17, 1888.

(ON THE CAPTIVE LIFE OF THE SEAL (HALICHOERUS GRYPUS NILSS.).) Ueber das Gefangenleben der Kegelrobbe. (Halichoerus grypus Nilss.) A. Nehring. Zool. Garten, vol.28, pp.21, figs.2, 1887.

(NORTHERN ELEPHANT SEALS (MIROUNGA ANGUSTIROSTRIS) IN THE COPENHAGEN ZOOLOGICAL GARDEN.) Noerdliche See-Elefanten (Mirounga angustirostris) im Zoologischen Garten Kopenhagen. Axel Reventlow. Zool. Garten, Leipzig, vol.22, no.1, pp.73-76, illus., 1955.

(SEALS IN THE ZOOLOGIC MUSEUM OF COIMBRA.) As Focas do Museu Zoologico de Coimbra. Antonio Armando Themido. Rev. Faculdade Ciencias, Univ. Coimbra, vol.7, no.1, pp.46-51, 1938.

WEST INDIAN SEAL AT THE AQUARIUM. C.H. Townsend. Science, Lancaster, vol. 30, no.763, p.212, Feb. 16, 1906.

Economic Importance

HAZARDOUS INDUSTRY OF NORTH ATLANTIC SEALING. C.W. Andrews. Animal Kingdom, vol.54, no.3, pp.66-76, 94, May-June, 1951.

SEAL HUNTING OFF JAN MAYEN. O.F. Backer. Nat. Geogr. Mag., no.93, pp.57-72, photos 15 (10 in color), map 1, 1948.

SEALING SAGA OF NEWFOUNDLAND. Robert A. Bartlett. Nat. Geogr. Mag., vol. 56, no.1, pp.91-130, illus., July, 1929. (Methods of Hunting Seals.)

HAIR SEALS IN DANGER. N.J. Berrill. Nat. Mag., vol.46, no.3, pp.146-148, 162, illus., Mar., 1953.

GREAT GREY SEALS PROTECTION ACT. H.B. Booth. Naturalist, London, no.905, p.165, June, 1932.

(CHRONICLES.) Kronoki. (Erignathus barbatus, Phoca fasciata, Phoca vitulina larga,

Phoca hispida.) S. Bormanov. Priroda i Sotsialisticheskoe Khoziaistvo Sbornik, Moscow, vol.6, pp.25-37, 1933. (In Russian.)

NEWFOUNDLAND SEAL FISHERY AND THE SECOND WORLD WAR. J.S. Colman. Jour. Animal Ecol., vol.18, no.1, pp.40-46, May, 1949.

PRESENT STATE OF THE NEWFOUNDLAND SEAL FISHERY. J.S. Colman. Jour. Animal Ecol., vol.6, no.1, pp.145-159, May, 1937.

WILD LIFE CONSERVATION. (Halichoerus grypus.) F. Fraser Darling. Jour. Soc. Preservation Fauna of Empire, Hertford, n.s., pt.34, pp.31-40, illus., Aug., 1938.

GREATEST HUNT IN THE WORLD. (Voyage with Newfoundland Sealers.) George Allen England. Sat. Even. Post., vol.195, no.11, pp.10, 11, 123, 126, 129, 130, 133; figs.13, Sep. 9, 1922.

UTILIZATION OF ATLANTIC HARP SEAL POPULATIONS. H.D. Fisher. Trans. 20th N. Amer. Wildl. Conf., pp.507-518, 1956.

(STATISTICS ON THE TAKE OF SEALS DURING THE YEARS 1909-1918.) Statistik over salfangsten Aren 1909-1918. (Statistics for Baltic Sea.) G. Gottberg. Finlands Fiskerier Utgiven av Byrån for Fiskeriundersok-ningar, vol.8 (Lantbruksstyrelsen Meddelanden, no.167), pp.23-34, 1927.

SEAL HUNTERS OF NEWFOUNDLAND. M. Harvey. Maritime Monthly, no.3, vol.1, pp.249-250, Mar., 1873.

(VALUE OF THE NORWEGIAN HOODED SEAL INDUSTRY ALONG S.E. GREENLAND.) Verdien av den norske Klappmysfangst langs Sydostgrønland. F. Isachsen. Norges Svalbard-og Ishavs-Undersøkelser, Oslo, Meddelelse, no.22, pp.1-24, 1933. (With English summary.)

SLAUGHTER OF SEALS. (North Coast of Cornwall.) C.J. King. Field, London, vol. 164, no.4277, p.1423, Dec. 15, 1934.

SEAL CATCHING IN THE WHITE SEA. A.A. Kirpichnikov. Bull. Inst. Applied Ichthyol. USSR, Leningrad, vol.13, fasc. 2, pp.167-172, 1932. (In Russian with English and Russian titles.)

ELEPHANT SEAL INDUSTRY AT SOUTH GEORGIA. Richard M. Laws. Polar Rec., vol.6, no.46, pp.746-754, illus., July, 1953.

(SEALING IN SWEDEN AND FINLAND DURING 1933.) Salfangsten i Sverige och Finland under ar 1933. Einar Lonnberg. Fauna och Flora, Stockholm, no.6, pp.269-272, 1934.

SEA ELEPHANTS. SAVING THE BIGGEST OF ALL SEALS FROM EXTINCTION. R.I. Pocock. Field, London, vol.159, no.4138, p.577, figs.2, Apr. 16, 1932.

EXPLOITATION AND PROTECTION OF EAST GREENLAND SEAL HERDS. Birger Rasmussen. Norsk Hvalfangst-Tidende (Norwegian Whaling Gazette), vol.46, no. 2, pp.45-59, Feb., 1957.

PROTECTION OF THE GREY SEAL. James Ritchie. Scottish Naturalist, no.182, pp. 33-36, Mar.-Apr., 1930.

SEAL HUNTING ON SLEDGES IN DZHAMBAI (CASPIAN SEA) IN THE WINTER OF 1929. A.N. Roganov. Rept. Astrakhan Sci. Fishery Station, vol.7, no.2, pp.31-68, 1930. (In Russian.)

SPRING SEAL HUNTING IN 1929. A.N. Roganov. Rept. Astrakhan Sci. Fishery Station, vol.7, no.2, pp.69-128, 1930. (In Russian.)

NEWFOUNDLAND SEALING, 1906. Thomas Southwell. Zoologist, London, (ser.4, vol. 10), vol.6, no.784, pp.375-376, Oct., 1906.

SEAL FISHERIES. Captain Temple. International Fisheries Exhibition, London, pp. 22, 1883.

NEWFOUNDLAND SEAL FISHERY. Charles Haskins Townsend. Science, n.s., vol.80, no.2074, p.289, Sep. 28, 1934.

HUNTING SEALS ON ICE FLOES. Harold T. Wilkins. Popular Mechanics Mag., Chicago, vol.45, no.4, pp.595-599, illus., Apr., 1926.

EARLY SEALERS IN WEST ANTARCTICA. Nature, London, vol.143, no.3626, p.731, Apr. 29, 1939.

GREAT SEAL HUNT: ICY SLAUGHTER OFF NEWFOUNDLAND YIELDS MORE THAN 200,000 PELTS. (Phoca groenlandica.) Life, Chicago, vol.28, no.20, pp.59-62, illus., May 15, 1950.

NORTH ATLANTIC HARP SEAL FISHERY. Arctic Cir., vol.5, no.6, p.69, 1952.

Europe and European Waters

PLANNING A CENSUS OF THE HARBOUR SEAL (PHOCA VITULINA L.) ON THE COASTS OF THE NETHERLANDS. A.C.V. Van Bemmel. Beaufortia, Zool. Mus. Amsterdam, vol.5, no.54, pp.121-132, July 31, 1956.

A SEAL IN THE THAMES. A.S. Buckhurst. Nature, London, vol.132, no.3344, p.860, Dec. 2, 1933.

(OBSERVATIONS ON THE OCCURRENCE OF THE MONK SEAL (MONACHUS ALBIVENTER BODD.) IN THE BLACK SEA.) Beobachtungen ueber das Vorkommen der Moenchsrobbe (Monachus albiventer Bodd.) im Schwarzen Meer. H. Caspers. Neue Ergebnisse und Probleme der Zoologie ("Klatt-Festschrift), Leipzig, pp.91-105, figs.3, 1950.

(EVOLUTIONARY HISTORY OF CASPIAN AND BAIKAL SEALS.) K voprosu ob istorii formirovaniya kaspiiskogo i baikalskogo tyulenei. K.K. Chapskii. Trudi Zool.Inst. Akad. Nauk SSSR, vol.17, pp.200-216, 1955.

GREY SEALS OF LUNGA. (Halichoerus grypus.) F. Fraser Darling. Jour. Soc. Preservation Fauna of Empire, Hertford, n.s., pt.33, pp.36-38, Mar., 1938.

I LIVED WITH SEALS. (North Rona Island; Life History Observations on Gray Seal.) F. Fraser Darling. Discovery, Cambridge, England, n.s., vol.2, no.12, pp.112-120, illus., Mar., 1939.

GREY SEAL AT THE ISLES OF SCILLY. J.L. Davies. Proc. Zool. Soc. London, vol.127, no.2, pp.161-166, Oct. 29, 1956.

OBSERVATIONS ON THE GREY SEAL (HALICHOERUS GRYPUS) AT RAMSEY ISLAND, PEMBROKESHIRE. J.L. Davies. Proc. Zool. Soc. London, vol.119, pt.3, pp.673-692, figs.3, pls.2, Nov. 22, 1949.

(CASPIAN SEA DOG AND ITS CAPTURE IN ICE.) Der kaspische Seehund und sein Fang im Eise. S. Dorofeiev, S. Freimann. Rept. Sci. Research Inst. Fisheries USSR, Moscow, vol.3, no.3, pp.1-118, 1928. (In Russian, with German and Russian titles.)

NOTES ON THE FOOD AND PARASITES OF THE GREY SEAL, HALICHOERUS GRYPUS (FABRICIUS), FROM THE ISLE OF MAN. A. Duncan. Proc. Zool. Soc. London, no.126, pp.635-644, 1956.

(SEAL SUMMER AT GOTSKA SANDON.) Salsommar pa Gotska Sandon. Lars Bruno Engstrom. Svensk Jakt, Stockholm, vol.89, no.4, pp.106-107, illus., Apr. 19, 1951.

GREENLAND SEAL IN BRITISH WATERS. H. Fetley. Nature, London, vol.137, no. 3457, p.192, Feb. 1, 1936.

ON THE OCCURRENCE OF THE RINGED OR MARBLED SEAL (PHOCA HISPIDA) ON THE COAST OF NORFOLK, WITH REMARKS ON THE SYNONYMY OF THE SPECIES. William Henry Flower. Proc. Zool. Soc. London, for 1871, pp.506-512, June 6, 1871.

(SEA DOG HUNT ON THE SANDS OF THE NORTH SEA.) Seehundsjagd an den Sanden der Nordsee. Bernnard Freemann. Deutsche Jagd, Berlin, nos.29-30, pp.275-278, illus., Oct. 25, 1940.

SEAL ON CHISWICK EYOT. G. Rostrevor Hamilton. Jour. Soc. Preservation Fauna Empire, Hertford, n.s., pt.45, p.19, Aug., 1942.

NUMBERS OF THE GREAT GREY SEAL (HALICHOERUS GRYPUS) ON ST. KILDA AND NORTH RONA. T.H. Harrisson. Jour. Animal Ecology, vol.1, no.1, p.83, May, 1932.

(SEAL (PHOCA VITULINA L.) IN DUTCH WATERS.) Der Seehund (Phoca vitulina L.) in den Hollaendischen Gewaessern. B. Havinga. Tijdschr. Ned. Dierk. Ver., Ser.3, Aft.2-3, pp.79-111, 1933.

GRAY SEAL IN THE FIRTH OF FORTH. Ian Hay. Scottish Nat., no.206, p.39, Mar.-Apr., 1934.

GREY SEALS OF THE FARNE ISLANDS. Grace Hickling. Trans. Nat. Hist. Soc. Northumb., Durham, and Newcastle upon Tyne, n.s., vol.11, pp.230-244, 1956; vol.12, no.4, pp.93-133, Sep., 1957.

(REPORT ON THE LIVING CONDITIONS AND HUNTING OF NORTHERN SEALS.) Bericht ueber die Lebensverhaeltnisse und den Fang der nordischen Seehunde. Johan Hjort. Copenhagen, A.F. Host and Fils, pp.125, tbls.9, maps 3, 1907.

(THE SEAL OF NARIPIO.) Loytojen elaintieteellinen selvitys. (Phoca groenlandica.) V.A. Korvenkontio. Suomen Museo, Helsinki, vol.43, pp.16-37, figs.11-16, tbls., 1937. (In Finnish, with German summary.)

SCANDINAVIAN SEAL LORE. Alexander H. Krappe. Scandinavian Studies, Menasha, vol.18, no.4, pp.156-162, Nov., 1944.

(SEALS OF THE ADRIATIC SEA.) Die Robben der Adria. Othmar Kuehn. Zool. Garten, Leipzig, vol.2, nos.7-9, pp.194-197, Jan., 1930.

HALICHOERUS GRYPUS. (Grassholm, Wales.) R.M. Lockley. Field, London, vol.172, no.4479, p.1031, illus., Oct. 29, 1938.

SEALS ON THE COAST OF WALES. (Halichoerus grypus.) R.M. Lockley. Field, London, vol.163, no.4231, p.181, illus., Jan. 27, 1934; no.4249, p.1307, illus., June 2, 1934.

GREY SEALS OF TRESNISH ISLANDS. Dugald MacIntyre. Field, London, vol. 155, no.4019, p.13, Jan. 4, 1930.

(SEALS OF THE EUROPEAN WATERS.) Die Robben der europaeischen Gewaesser. Erna Mohr. Frankfurt am Main, Paul Schoeps, Monographien der Wildsaeugetiere, Band 12, pp.283, pls.40, 1952b.

(ON THE SEALS OF THE BALTIC SEA, ESPECIALLY THE RINGED SEAL.) Ueber die Robben der Ostsee, namentlich ueber die Ringelrobbe. A. Nehring. Sitz. Ber. Gesell. Naturf. Freunde Berlin, no.8, pp. 119-124, Oct. 19, 1886.

(SEAL SPECIES OF THE GERMAN COAST.) Die Seehunds-Arten der deutschen Kueste. A. Nehring. Sonder. aus den Mittheilungen, no.2-3-4, pp.16, figs.7, 1887.

CASPIAN SEAL AND SEAL FISHERY. A.N. Roganov. Rept. Astrakhan Sci. Fishery Sta. USSR, Astrakhan, vol.7, no.4, pp.1-28, 1931. (In Russian, with Russian and English titles.)

SEALS ON THE WEST COAST. H. Morrey Salmon. Trans. Cardiff Nat. Soc., vol.68, pp.13-36, pl.1, (1935) 1937.

STATUS OF THE COMMON SEAL (PHOCA VITULINA L.) ON THE EAST ANGLIAN COAST. D.E. Sergeant. Jour. Marine Biol. Assn., no. 29, pp.707-717, 1951.

ON THE BIOLOGY OF THE HARP SEAL, PHOCA GROENLANDICA ERXL. INVESTIGATIONS CARRIED OUT IN THE WHITE SEA, 1925-1937. Erling Sivertsen. Hvalradets Skrifter, no.26, Norske Vidensk.-Akad., Oslo, pp.ix-166, figs.41, pls.11, 1941.

RESULTS OF INVESTIGATIONS CONCERNING THE CASPIAN SEAL AND ITS CATCHINGS IN THE YEAR 1929. N. Smirnov. Bull. Inst. Applied Ichthyol. USSR., Leningrad, vol.13, no.1, pp.13-24, 1931. (In Russian, with Russian and English titles.)

STUDIES ON BIOLOGY OF THE WHITE SEA HARP SEAL (HISTRIOPHOCA GROENLANDICA OCEANICA). N. Smirnov. Bull.

Inst. Applied Ichthyol. USSR., Leningrad, vol.6, no.1, pp.5-27, 1927. (In Russian, with Russian and English titles.)

SEALS (HALICHOERUS GRYPUS) OF CORNWALL COASTS. G.A. Steven. Jour. Marine Biol. Assoc. United Kingdom, vol.20, no. 3, pp.493-506, figs.6, 1936.

SHORT INVESTIGATION INTO THE HABITS, ABUNDANCE, AND SPECIES OF SEALS ON THE NORTH CORNWALL COAST. G.A. Steven. Jour. Marine Biol. Assoc. United Kingdom, vol.19, no.2, pp.489-501, May, 1934.

GREY SEALS OF THE FARNE ISLANDS. Ian M. Telfer, Grace Watt. Trans. Nat. Hist. Soc. Northumberland, Durham and Newcastle upon Tyne, vol.10, no.5, pp. 165-182, July, 1953.

(THE SEAL OF THE PORTUGUESE COAST.) As focas das costas de Portugal. A. A. Themido. Mem. Mus. Zool. Univ. Coimbra, no.179, pp.1-12, pl.1, 1947.

SEALS ON THE COAST OF WALES. Field, London, vol.162, no. 4226, p.1591, Dec. 23, 1933.

Food Habits

ON THE FOOD OF SEALS IN THE CANADIAN EASTERN ARCTIC. M.J. Dunbar. Can. Jour. Res., Sec.D, vol.19, no.5, pp. 150-155, May, 1941.

DIET OF SEALS. (Halichoerus grypus.) R.W. Gray. Nature, London, vol.135, no. 3412, p.473, Mar. 23, 1935.

STOMACH CONTENTS OF ATLANTIC HARBOR SEALS. Donald R. Griffin. Jour. Mamm., vol.17, no.1, pp.65-66, Feb., 1936.

CAPTURE OF AN ELEPHANT SEAL OFF SAN DIEGO, CALIFORNIA, WITH NOTES ON STOMACH CONTENTS. Laurence Huey. Jour. Mamm., vol.11, no.2, pp.229-231, May, 1930.

(THE QUESTION OF THE FOOD OF CASPIAN SEALS.) Bodo Johansen. Zool. Zhurn. (Zool. Jour. USSR), Moscow, vol.13, no.3, pp.584-587, 1934. (In Russian, with German summary.)

(ON THE FOOD OF OUR SEAL SPECIES.) Ueber die Nahrung unserer Robben-Arten. A. Nehring. Deutscher Fischerei Verein, Mittheil. Sec. Kuesten- und Hochseefischerei, Berlin, no.7, pp.101-105, July, 1886.

OSCAR ACHIEVES POSTHUMOUS FAME. (Captive Harbor Seal With Four Pounds of Pennies in its Stomach.) Academy News Letter, Calif. Acad. Sci., San Francisco, no.84, pp.3-4, Dec., 1946.

Fossils

(CASPIAN SEAL FROM LOWER-QUATERNARY DEPOSITS ON THE SHORES OF THE SEA OF AZOV.) Kaspiiskii tyulen iz Nizhnechetvertichnix etlozhenii poberezhbya azovskogo morya. (Fossil Phocidae.) A.A. Kirpichnikov. Dokladi Akademii Nauk SSSR, vol.90, no.5, pp.883-886, 1953.

STENORHYNCHUS VETUS N. SP. J. Leidy. Proc. Acad. Nat. Sci. Philadelphia, no.6, p.377, 1853.

FIRST DISCOVERY OF FOSSIL SEALS IN AMERICA. Frederick W. True. Science, n.s., vol.22, no. 572, p.794, Dec. 15, 1905.

DESCRIPTION OF A NEW GENUS AND SPECIES OF FOSSIL SEAL FROM THE MIOCENE OF MARYLAND. Frederick W. True. Proc. U.S. Nat. Mus., vol.30, publ. 1475, pp.835-840, pls.75-76, June 16, 1906.

(A NOTABLE PHOCID FIND FROM THE TORTON OF THE VIENNA BASIN.) Ein bemerkenswerter Phocidenfund aus dem Torton des Wiener-Beckens. Helmuth Zapfe. Verhandl. Zool.-Bot. Ges. Wien, Jahrg. 1936-37, vols.86-87, pp.271-276, figs.2, 1937.

Growth and Longevity

GROWTH OF THE GREY SEAL (HALICHOERUS GRYPUS) FROM BIRTH TO WEANING. E.C. Amoroso, J.H. Matthews. Jour. Anat., no.85, pp.426-428, 1951.

FLOATING CADAVERS OF THE CASPIAN SEAL. K.K. Chapsky. Bull. Inst. Applied Ichthyol. USSR, Leningrad, vol.13, fasc. 2, pp.159-165, 1932. (In Russian, with Russian and English titles.)

NOTE ON THE POSSIBLE CAUSE OF DEATH IN A YOUNG SEAL. Alfred Henry Garrod. Proc. Zool. Soc. London, pt.4, pp.792-793, 1877.

ELEPHANT SEAL (MIROUNGA LEONINA LINN.) I. GROWTH AND AGE. R.M. Laws. Sci. Repts. Falkland Islands Dependencies Survey, London, no.8, pp.62, illus., 1953.

GROWTH RATES AND AGES OF CRABEATER SEALS, LOBODON CARCINOPHAGUS JACQUINOT AND PUCHERAN. R.M. Laws. Proc. Zool. Soc. London, vol.130, no.2, pp.275-288, pls.1-2, Mar. 13, 1958.

ON THE GROWTH RATES OF THE LEOPARD SEAL, HYDRURGA LEPTONYX (DeBLAINVILLE, 1820). R.M. Laws. Saeugetierk. Mitteil., vol.5, no.2, pp.49-55, Apr. 1, 1957.

MASS DYING OF CRABEATER SEALS, LOBODON CARCINOPHAGUS (GRAY). R.M. Laws, R.J.F. Taylor. Proc. Zool. Soc. London, vol.129, no.3, pp.315-324, pl.1, Nov. 11, 1957.

LONGEVITY IN THE GREY SEAL. Colin Matheson. Nature, London, vol.166, pp. 73-74, July 8, 1950.

INITIATION OF A STUDY OF MORTALITY AND MORBIDITY IN THE FARNE ISLANDS GREY SEALS NURSERIES. A.G. Ogilvie. Trans. Nat. Hist. Soc. Northumberland, Durham and Newcastle upon Tyne, vol.12, no.4, pp.134-136, Sep., 1957.

(ON THE AGE AND GROWTH OF THE SEA LEOPARD HYDRURGA LEPTONYX (BLAINVILLE). Sur l'age et la croissance du leopard de mer, Hydrurga leptonyx ( De Blainville). Patrice Aulian. Mammalia, Paris, vol.19, no.2, pp.347-356, June, 1955.

AGE MARKINGS ON THE SKULL OF SEALS OF THE GENUS PUSA, SCOP. N. Smirnov, K. Chapsky. Bull. Inst. Applied Ichthyol. USSR, Leningrad, vol.13, no.2, pp.133-146, 1932. (In Russian, with Russian and English titles.)

Habits, Behavior

BEHAVIOUR OF THE GREY SEAL (HALICHOERUS GRYPUS FAB.) IN THE SPRING. K.M. Backhouse, H.R. Hewer. Proc. Zool. Soc. London, vol.129, no.3, p.450, pl.1, Nov. 11, 1957.

(THE LIVING CONDITIONS OF SEALS IN HOLLAND.) De levensomstandigheden van den zeehond (Phoca vitulina L.) in Nederland. G.A. Brouwer. De Levende Natuur, vol.33, pp.115-119, 149-153, 185-191, 213-218, 1928.

Methods, Techniques

NOTES ON THE MARKING OF ATLANTIC SEALS IN PEMBROKESHIRE. H.R. Hewer. Proc. Zool. Soc. London, vol.125, no.1, pp.87-93, figs.6, May, 1955.

NEW METHOD OF AGE DETERMINATION IN MAMMALS WITH SPECIAL REFERENCE TO THE ELEPHANT SEAL. R.M. Laws. Sci. Rep. Falkland Islands Dependencies Survey, London, no.2s, pp.11, illus., 1953.

PROCESSING HUDSON SEAL. David L. Levin. Trans. 10th N.Amer. Wildl. Conf., Washington, pp.90-92, 1945.

DETERMINATION OF THE AGES OF SEALS. P. Plehanoff. Abstr. Works Zool. Inst. Moscow State Univ., pp.88-91, figs.3, 1933. (In Russian.)

EXPERIMENT IN MARKING THE GREY SEAL HALICHOERUS GRYPUS. Grace Watt. Nature, vol.169, p.883, May 24, 1952.

FIELD IDENTIFICATION OF THE COMMON GREY SEALS. V.C. Wynne-Edwards. Scottish Nat., no.66, p.192, 1954.

Migrations Movements

UNUSUAL MIGRATION OF THE SPOTTED AND RIBBON SEALS. Alfred M. Bailey. Jour. Mamm., vol.9, no.3, pp.250-251, Aug., 1928.

MIGRATION OF HISTRIOPHOCA GROENLANDICA FABR. S.J. Freimann. Vsesoiznyi nauchno-issledovatel'skii institut morskogo rybnogo khoziaistva i okeanografii SSSR. Volume in honor of sci. activity of N. M. Knipovich, Inst. Marine Fisheries and Oceanography USSR (VNIRO), People's Commissariat for Food Industry USSR, Moscow and Leningrad, pp.353-368, figs.3, 1939. (In Russian with English summary.)

REPORT OF RINGING AND RETURNS OF GREY SEALS: NO.1. SEPTEMBER 1954-AUGUST 1956. Mammal Soc. of the British Isles. Proc. Zool. Soc. London, vol.128, no.4, pp.594-596, July 24, 1957.

North America

TWO NEW SEALS FROM ARCTIC CANADA WITH KEY TO THE CANADIAN FORMS OF HAIR SEALS (FAMILY PHOCIDAE). (Phoca hispida beaufortiana, P.h. soperi.) Rudolph Martin Anderson. Ann. Report Provancher Soc. Nat. Hist. Canada, Quebec, 1942, pp.23-47, Sep., 1943.

ELEPHANT SEAL OFF SANTA CRUZ ISLAND, CALIFORNIA. A.W. Anthony. Jour. Mamm., vol.2, no.2, pp.112-113, May, 1921.

NOTES ON THE PRESENT STATUS OF THE NORTHERN ELEPHANT SEAL, MIROUNGE ANGUSTIROSTRIS. A. W. Anthony. Jour. Mamm., vol.5, no.3, pp. 145-152, pls.17-20, Aug., 1924.

CENSUS OF HARBOR SEALS IN SAN FRANCISCO BAY. George A. Bartholomew, Jr. Jour. Mamm., vol.30, no.1, pp.34-35, Feb., 1949.

REOCCUPATION BY THE ELEPHANT SEAL OF LOS CORONADOS ISLANDS, BAJA CALIFORNIA, MEXICO. George A. Bartholomew, Jr. Jour. Mamm., vol.31, no.1, p. 98, Feb. 21, 1950.

NEWFOUNDLAND SEALS. Robert A. Bartlett. Jour. Mamm., vol.8, no.3, pp.207-212, Aug., 1927; Fur Jour., vol.1, no.6, pp.34-35, 52-55, Oct., 1927.

RECORDS OF HARBOR SEALS IN LAKES WASHINGTON AND UNION, SEATTLE. Kelshaw Bonham. Murrelet, Seattle, vol. 23, no.3, p.76, Feb. 15, 1943.

HARBOR SEAL IN NORTH CAROLINA. H. H. Brimley. Jour. Mamm., vol.12, no.3, p.314, Aug., 1931.

NORTHERN ELEPHANT SEAL (MIROUNGA ANGUSTIROSTRIS) IN BRITISH COLUMBIA WATERS AND VICINITY. Ian McTaggart Cowan, G. Clifford Carl. Canadian Field-Nat., Sutton West, vol.59, no.5, pp.170-171, pl., Sep.-Oct., 1945.

HARBOR SEALS (PHOCA VITULINA RICHARDII) ON THE SKEENA RIVER, B. C. H.D. Fisher. Prog. Rept. Pacific Biol. Sta., Nanaimo, no. 72, pp.36-40, 1947.

SEALS OF THE CANDIAN EAST COAST. H.D. Fisher. Fisheries Res. Bd. Can., Atl. Biol. Sta., Gen. Ser., no.18, pp.4, Sep., 1950.

SOME STUDIES ON THE BIOLOGY OF ATLANTIC COAST SEALS. H.D. Fisher. Can. Jour. Compar. Med. and Vet. Sci., vol.17, no.7, pp.305-313, July, 1953.

STATUS OF THE HARBOR SEAL IN BRITISH COLUMBIA, WITH PARTICULAR REFERENCE TO THE SKEENA RIVER. H.D. Fisher. Bull. Fisheries Research Board Canada, no.93, pp.58, illus., 1952.

ELEPHANT SEAL (MIROUNGA ANGUSTIROSTRIS) IN OREGON. Richard E. Freiburg, Philip C. Dumas. Jour. Mamm., vol.35, no.1, p.129, Feb. 10, 1954.

RIBBON SEAL OF ALASKA. T. Gill. Amer. Nat., no.7, pp.178-179, 1873.

ON THE SEALS OF NOVA SCOTIA. J. Bernard Gilpin. Nova-Scotian Inst. Nat. Sci. Proc. and Trans., vol.3, pp.377-384, 1874.

OCCURRENCE OF A GREY SEAL AT ATLANTIC CITY, N. JERSEY. G.G. Goodwin. Jour. Mamm., vol.14, no.1, p.73, Feb., 1933.

SIGHT RECORDS OF THE WEST INDIAN SEAL, MONACHUS TROPICAL (GRAY), FROM THE TEXAS COAST. Gordon Gunter. Jour. Mamm., vol.28, no.3, pp.289-290, Aug. 19, 1947.

LATE INFORMATION OF THE GUADALUPE ISLAND ELEPHANT SEAL HERD. Laurence M. Huey. Jour. Mamm., vol.6, no.2, pp. 126-127, May, 1925.

LATEST NORTHERN ELEPHANT SEAL CENSUS. Laurence M. Huey. Jour.Mamm., vol.8, no.2, pp.160-161, May, 1927.

ELEPHANT SEALS COME BACK. George Lindsay. Pac. Discovery, vol.4, no.4, pp. 18-24, July-Aug., 1951.

SEAL STRAYS INTO MARYLAND WATERS. R. Mansueti. Maryland Tidewater News, vol.12, no.3, pp.1-3, Aug., 1955.

THE HARP SEAL, A PERMANENT RESIDENT IN THE ST. LAWRENCE ISLAND. C. Hart Merriam. American Naturalist, vol.18, no.12, pp.1227-1231, Dec., 1884.

HOODED SEAL IN FLORIDA. G.S.Miller, Jr. Proc. Biol. Soc. Washington, no.30, p.121, 1917.

ELEPHANT SEALS OFF THE COAST OF CALIFORNIA. John Rowley. Jour. Mamm., vol.2, no.4, pp.235-236, Nov., 1921.

HARBOR SEAL IN WASHINGTON STATE. (Phoca vitulina richardii.) Victor B. Scheffer, John W. Slipp. Amer. Midland Nat., Notre Dame, vol.32, no.2, pp.373-416, figs.17, Sep., 1944.

ACCOUNT OF RECENT CAPTURES OF THE CALIFORNIA SEA ELEPHANT, AND STATISTICS RELATING TO THE PRESENT ABUNDANCE OF THE SPECIES. Charles H. Townsend. Proc. U.S. Nat.Mus., vol.8, pp.90-96, 1885.

NORTHERN ELEPHANT SEAL HERD IN 1929. Charles H. Townsend. Bull. New York Zool. Soc., vol.33, no.1, pp.31-32, fig.1, 1930.

RETURN OF THE SEA ELEPHANT. Lewis W. Walker. Nat. Hist., New York, vol. 56, no.9, pp.408-411, illus., Nov., 1947.

ELEPHANT SEAL IN SOUTHEASTERN ALASKA. G. Willett. Jour. Mamm., vol. 24, no.4, p.500, Nov. 17, 1943.

Northern Waters

MARINE HARE (ERIGNATHUS BARBATUS FABR.) OF THE KARA AND BARENTS SEAS. (Biology and Hunting.) K.Chapsky. Trans. Arctic Inst. Chief Administration Northern Sea Route, Leningrad, vol.123, pp.7-70, figs.90, tbls.23, pls.1-2, 1938. (In Russian.)

RING SEAL OF WESTERN SEAS OF THE SOVIET ARCTIC. THE MORPHOLOGICAL CHARACTERISTIC, BIOLOGY, AND HUNTING PRODUCTION. (Phoca hispida). K. Chapsky. Trans. Arctic Inst. Chief Administration Northern Sea Route, Leningrad and Moscow, vol.145, pp.72, figs.12, pl.1, 1940. (In Russian.)

NORTH RONA: A NORTH ATLANTIC ISLAND. F. Fraser Darling. Nature, London, vol.143, no.3623, pp.585-588, illus., Apr. 8, 1939. (Includes brief account of habits of Atlantic grey seal, Halichoerus grypus.)

NOTES ON THE NORTHERN ELEPHANT SEAL. M.E. McLellan Davidson. Proc. Calif. Acad. Sci., ser.4, vol.18, no.9, pp.229-243, pls.25-26, Apr. 5, 1929.

HARP SEALS OF THE NORTHWEST ATLANTIC. Harold D. Fisher. Fisheries Res. Board Can., Atl. Biol. Sta. Cir., Gen.Ser., no.20, pp.1-4, graphs, map, Sep., 1952.

OBSERVATIONS ON THE NORTHERN ELEPHANT SEAL, MIROUNGA ANGUSTIROSTRIS. John E. Fitch, Robert C. Wilson. Jour. Mamm., Baltimore, vol.30, no.2, pp.192-194, May 23, 1949.

RECENT OBSERVATIONS ON THE NORTHERN ELEPHANT SEAL. Laurence M.Huey. Jour. Mamm., vol.5, no.4, pp.237-242, pls.24-27, Nov. 15, 1924.

THE SAGA OF THE GREY SEAL: INTRODUCING THE NATURAL HISTORY OF THE GREY SEAL OF THE NORTH ATLANTIC. R.M. Lockley. Devin-Adair, pp.149, illus., 1955.

SUMMARY OF THE BIOLOGY OF THE RINGED SEAL IN WATERS OF SOUTHWEST BAFFIN ISLAND. I.A. McLaren. (In) The "Calanus" expeditions in the Canadian Arctic, by M.J. Dunbar. Arctic, no.9, pp.185-186, 1956.

THE NORTHERN ELEPHANT SEAL. C.H. Townsend. Zoologica, vol.1, no.1959, p. 173, 1912.

Pelage, Coloration

(CONTRIBUTIONS TO KNOWLEDGE OF TH' SKIN OF SOME PINNIPEDS. SPECIAL CONSIDERATION THE SKIN OF PHOCA GROENLANDICA. Beitraege zur Kenntnis der Haut einiger Pinnipedien. Unter besonderer Beruecksichtigung der Haut der Phoca groenlandica. Birger Bergersen. Det Norsk Videnskaps-Akad. i. Oslo, I. Mat.-naturv. Kl., 1931, no.5, pp.1-179, figs.92, pls.22, 1931.

PELAGE AND EAR PINNA OF A VERY YOUNG COMMON SEAL (PHOCA VITULINA L.). Lionel F. Cowley. Proc.Zool. Soc.London, vol.110, ser.B, pts.3-4, pp. 183-184, pl.1, Mar., 1941.

RED-HEADED GREY SEAL (HALICHOERUS GRYPUS). H.R. Hewer, K.M. Backhouse. Proc. Zool. Soc. London, vol.128, no.4, p. 592, July 24, 1957 (Abstract).

ON MOLTING OF THE WHITE SEA SEAL (HISTRIOPHOCA GROENLANDICA LEPECHIN). N.M. Kulagin. Comptes Rendus Acad. Sci. USSR., ser.A, 1928, no.20-21, pp.427-430, figs.3, 1928. (In Russian.)

PELAGE AND EAR PINNA OF A NEWLY BORN COMMON SEAL (PHOCA VITULINA L.). L. Harrison Matthews. Proc. Zool. Soc. London, 1936, pt.1, pp.315-316, fig.1, pl.1, Apr., 1936.

(SKIN OF THE RINGED SEAL HISTRIOPHOCA FASCIATA ZIMM.) Ein Fell der Bandrobbe, Histriophoca Fasciata Zimm. Erna Mohr. Zool. Anzeiger, Leipzig, vol. 139, nos.7-8, pp.142-143, figs.2, Dec. 1, 1942.

SPECIALIZATIONS IN THE SKIN OF THE SEAL (PHOCA VITULINA). W. Montagna, R.J. Harrison. Amer. Jour. Anat., no.100, pp.81-114, 1957.

BLACK SEAL ON THE SOUTH COAST. Rohn and Sons. Irish Naturalists' Jour., vol. 1, no.10, p.195, Mar., 1927.

(HAIR SHEDDING IN THE ELEPHANT SEAL.) Der Haarwechsel des See-Elefanten. B. Troll-Obergfell. Anat.Anzeiger, no.65, pp.327-333, 1928.

(ON SOME PECULIARITIES OF THE HAIR OF THE COMMON SEAL (PHOCA VITULINA L.).) Ueber einige Besonderheiten der Haare des gemeinen Seehundes (Phoca vitulina L.). B. Troll-Obergfell. Anat.Anzeiger, vol.69, nos.18-19, pp.404-415, figs.5, 1930.

Physiology, Biochemistry

BODY TEMPERATURE AND RESPIRATORY AND HEART RATES IN THE NORTHERN ELEPHANT SEAL. Geo. A. Bartholomew, Jr. Jour. Mamm., vol.35, no.2, pp.211-218, May 26, 1954.

THE RENAL EXCRETION OF SODIUM, POTASSIUM AND WATER BY THE HARBOR SEAL (PHOCA VITULINA L.): EFFECT OF APNEA; SODIUM, POTASSIUM AND WATER LOADING; PITRESSIN; AND MERCURIAL DIURESIS. S.E. Bradley et al. Jour. Cellular and Comp. Physiol., Philadelphia, vol.43, no.1, pp.1-22, Feb., 1954.

SODIUM AND POTASSIUM CONCENTRATION IN THE BLOOD CELLS AND PLASMA OF THE ELEPHANT SEAL. J.Eadie, R.L. Kirk. Aust. Jour. Sci., vol.15, pp.26-27, 1952.

ELEPHANT SEAL (MIROUNGA LEONINA LINN.). III. THE PHYSIOLOGY OF REPRODUCTION. R.M. Laws. Sci. Repts. Falkland Islands Dependencies Survey, vol.15, pp.1-66, 1956.

INDUSTRIAL FAT OF THE CASPIAN SEAL: PHYSICO-CHEMICAL CONSTANTS. M.P. Osipov. Repts. Astrakhan Volgo-Caspian Sea Sci. Fish. Sta., vol.7, no.4, pp.48-71, 1931. (In Russian.)

EFFECT OF VARIATION IN FILTRATION RATE ON THE URINARY CONCENTRATING MECHANISM IN THE SEAL, PHOCA VITULINA L. Lot B. Page et al. Jour. Cell. and Comp. Physiol., Philadelphia, vol.43, no.3, pp.257-270, June, 1954.

COMPOSITION OF THE BLUBBER FAT OF CRABEATER SEAL. G. Winter, E. Nunn. Jour. Sci. Food Agric., vol.4, pp.439-442, 1953.

Reproductive Biology, Development of Young

DELAYED IMPLANTATION IN THE GREY SEAL, HALICHOERUS GRYPUS (FAB.). K. Backhouse, H.R. Hewer. Nature, vol.178, p.550, 1956.

A NOTE ON SPRING PUPPING IN THE GREY SEAL (HALICHOERUS GRYPUS FAB.). K.M. Backhouse, H.R. Hewer. Proc. Zool. Soc. London, vol.128, no.4, pp.593-594, July 24, 1957.

REPRODUCTIVE AND SOCIAL BEHAVIOR OF THE NORTHERN ELEPHANT SEAL. George A. Bartholomew, Jr. Univ.Calif. Publ. Zool., Berkeley and Los Angeles, vol. 47, no.15, pp.369-472, illus., July 3, 1952.

"LOCH NESS MONSTERS" AT THEIR SOURCE. WHERE THE GREY SEALS ARE BORN. M.G.S. Best. Field, London, vol. 163, no.4232, p.219, illus., Feb. 3, 1934.

AERIAL STUDIES OF A BREEDING COLONY OF GREY SEALS, HALICHOERUS GRYPUS (FAB.), AT GASKER, OUTER HEBRIDES, IN 1955 AND 1956. J. Morton Boyd. Proc. Zool. Soc. London, vol.129, no.3, pp.333-342, pls.1-3, Nov. 11, 1957.

OBSERVATIONS ON THE NEWLY BORN LEOPARD SEAL. K.G. Brown. Nature, vol. 170, pp.982-983, 1952.

ON HALICHOERUS GRYPUS AND ITS BREEDING ON THE FRO ISLANDS OFF TRONDHJEMS-FJORD IN NORWAY. R. Collett. Proc. Zool. Soc. London, pp.380-387, 1881.

COLONY SIZE AND REPRODUCTION IN THE GREY SEAL. J.L. Davies. Proc.Zool. Soc. London, vol.123, pt.2, pp.327-332, Aug. 18, 1953.

OBSERVATIONS ON THE REPRODUCTION PERIOD OF GREENLAND SEALS (HISTRIOPHOCA GROENLANDICA OCEANICA LEPECHIN). S.V. Dorofejev. Compt.Rend. (Doklady) Acad. Sci. USSR, Moscow, n.s., vol.2, no.1, pp.47-48, 1936. (In Russian with English summary.)

ON THE NUPTIAL CRY OF THE BEARDED SEAL (ERIGNATHUS BARBATUS FABR.). A.N. Dubrovskii. Priroda, Leningrad, no.4, p.124, illus., Apr., 1937. (In Russian.)

DELAYED IMPLANTATION IN THE ELEPHANT SEAL. L. Gibbney. Nature, London, vol.172, p.590, Sep. 26, 1953; vol. 173, no.4410, pp.879-880, May 8, 1954.

SEASONAL REPRODUCTIVE CYCLE OF THE FEMALE ELEPHANT SEAL--MIROUNGA LEONINA, LINN.--AT HEARD ISLAND. L. Gibbney. Australian National Antarctic Research Expeditions Reports, Dept. External Affairs, Melbourne, ser.B, vol.1 (Zool.), pp.1-26, Feb., 1957.

NOTE ON THE SIZE OF A SEAL (CALLOCEPHALUS FOETIDUS) AT THE TIME OF BIRTH. John Edward Gray. Proc.Zool. Soc. London, pt.30, p.202, 1862.

BREEDING PLACES OF THE SADDLE OR HARP SEAL. R.W. Gray. Naturalist, London, no.905, pp.183-186, June, 1932.

HEBRIDEAN BREEDING COLONY OF GREY SEALS, HALICHOERUS GRYPUS (FAB.), WITH COMPARATIVE NOTES ON THE GREY SEALS OF RAMSEY ISLAND, PEMBROKESHIRE. H.R. Hewer. Proc. Zool. Soc. London, vol.128, no.1, pp.23-66, pls.1-2, Feb. 14, 1957.

ON A PUP OF THE CRABEATER SEAL LOBODON CARCINOPHAGUS. Judith E.

King. Ann. and Mag. Nat. Hist., ser.12, vol.10, no.116, pp.619-624, Aug., 1957.

BABY WHITECOAT. (Northern Seal.) Edith M. Laing. Nature Mag., Washington,D.C., vol.32, no.10, p.568, Dec., 1939.

ELEPHANT SEAL (MIROUNGA LEONINA LINN.). II. GENERAL, SOCIAL AND REPRODUCTIVE BEHAVIOUR. R.M. Laws. Sci. Repts. Falkland Islands Dependencies Survey, London, no.13, pp.88, illus.,1956.

HYBRID BETWEEN GREY SEAL, HALICHOERUS GRYPUS NILS. AND BALTIC RINGED SEAL, PHOCA HISPIDA ANNELLATA NILS. Einar Lonnberg. Arkiv for Zoologi, vol.21 A., no.5, pp.1-8, figs.1-9, July 22, 1929.

BREEDING BEHAVIOUR AND REPRODUCTIVE CYCLE OF THE WEDDELL SEAL (LEPTONYCHOTES WEDDELLI LESSON). A.W. Mansfield. Falkland Islands Dependencies Survey, Scientific Repts., no. 18.

(YOUNG BEARDED SEAL ERIGNATHUS BARBATUS FABRICUS 1776.) Junge Bartrobben, Erignathus barbatus (Fabricus, 1776). Erna Mohr. Saeugetierk. Mitteil., Stuttgart, vol.1, no.2, pp.67-68, illus., Apr. 1, 1953.

(SOME VARIATIONS OF THE DATE OF GIVING BIRTH OF SEA ELEPHANTS.) Sur quelques variations de la date de mise bas de l'elephant de mer (Mirounga leonina). Patrice Paulian. Mammalia, Paris, vol.18, no.4, pp.375-379, Dec., 1954.

SEALS ASHORE. A VISIT TO THE WELSH CAVES AND ROCKY ISLETS WHERE THE SEAL PUPS ARE BORN. Frances Pitt. Field, London, vol.161, no.4196, p.1215, illus., May 27, 1933.

WHERE THE GREY SEALS BREED. DECEMBER ON THE FARNES. (Halichoerus grypus.) Niall Rankin. Field, London, vol.166, no.4329, pp.1406-1407, illus., Dec. 14, 1935.

MATING BEHAVIOUR OF THE SEAL PHOCA VITULINA IN SHETLAND. U.M. Venables, L.S.V. Venables. Proc. Zool. Soc. London, vol.128, no.3, pp.387-396, June 6, 1957.

OBSERVATIONS ON A BREEDING COLONY OF THE SEAL PHOCA VITULINA IN SHETLAND. U.M. Venables, L.S.V. Venables. Proc. Zool. Soc. London, vol. 125, pts.3-4, pp.521-532, illus., Nov. 23, 1955.

(BIRTH AND EARLY DEVELOPMENT OF THE COMMON SEAL (PHOCA VITULINA L.).) Geburt und Jugendentwicklung beim Seehund (Phoca vitulina L.). Hans Wagner. Zool. Garten, n.F., Leipzig, vol.8, nos. 10-12, pp.258-265, illus., Sep., 1936.

ON AN ISLAND BREEDING PLACE OF THE ATLANTIC GREY SEAL. R.L. Willan, C.A.M. Smith. Illus. London News, vol. 218, no.5851, pp.950-951, illus, June 9, 1951.

ATLANTIC SEALS ON A WELSH BREEDING ISLAND, STUDIES OF SEAL COWS AND CALVES. R.L. Willan, C.A.M. Smith, P. Smith. Illus. London News, vol.222, no. 5935, pp.90-91, illus., Jan. 17, 1953.

BABIES IN THEIR SCOTTISH ROOKERY: LITTLE SEALS OF THE TRESHNISH ISLES. (Grey Seals, Halichoerus grypus.) Illus. London News, vol.189, no.5088, p. 732, Oct. 24, 1936.

Southern Waters

(OBSERVATIONS ON MARINE MAMMALS OF THE KERGUELEN ARCHIPELAGO WITH A DETAILED STUDY OF THE SEA ELEPHANT, MIROUNGA LEONINA (L.).) Observations sur les Mammiféres Marins de l'Archipel de Kerguelen avac une etude detaillee de l'Elephant de mer, Mirounga leonina (L.). Michel Angot. Mammalia, Paris, vol.18, no.1, pp.1-111, illus., Mar., 1954.

(SEA ELEPHANT (MIROUNGA LEONINA (L.). BIOLOGICAL STUDY OF THE SPECIES IN THE KERGUELEN ARCHIPELAGO.) L'elephant de mer (Mirounge leonina (L.). Etude biologique de l'espece dans les possessions Francaises Australes (Archipel. des Kerguelen). Raymond Aretas. Mammalia, Paris, vol.15, no.4, pp.105-117, Dec., 1951.

LEOPARD SEAL AT HEARD ISLAND, 1951-54. K.G. Brown. Interim Rept.Australian Nat. Antarctic Research Expeds., Melbourne, vol.16, pp.1-34, pls.4, Mar., 1957. (Mimeographed.)

BIOLOGY AT EAST BASE, PALMER PENINSULA, ANTARCTICA. Herwil M. Bryant. Proc. Amer. Philos. Soc., Philadelphia, vol.80, no.1, pp.256-269, figs.29, Apr. 30, 1945. (Seals pp.268-269.)

(SOME MEMOIRS ON THE SEALS OF THE ANTARCTIC.) Quelques souvenirs des Phoques de l'Antarctique. J.B. Charcott. La Terre et la Vie (Revue d'Hist.Nat.), vol. 1, no.6, pp.323-328, illus., July, 1931.

VOYAGE OF THE "MARY AND SALLY" TO MACQUARIE ISLAND FOR THE PURPOSE OF OBTAINING SEA ELEPHANT OIL AND SEAL SKINS. (NOVEMBER 16, 1813-MARCH 13, 1814.) W.L. Crowther. Papers and Proc. Roy. Soc. Tasmania, 1932, pp. 39-46, pl.1, May 10, 1933.

ZOOLOGICAL NOTES FROM THE VOYAGE OF PETER MUNDY, 1655-56... SEA ELEPHANT ON ST. HELENA. F.C. Fraser. Proc. Linn. Soc. London, for 1934-35, pp. 32-37, pl.1, 1935.

DESCRIPTION OF A NEW GENUS AND SPECIES OF SEAL(HELIOPHOCA ATLANTICA) FROM MADEIRA. John Edward Gray. Proc. Zool. Soc. London, pt.22, pp.43-44, 1854.

STATUS OF THE LEOPARD SEAL AT HEARD ISLAND AND MACQUARIE ISLAND, 1948-1950. A.M. Gwynn. Interim Rept. Australian Nat. Antarctic Research Exped., no.3, pp.33, illus., Jan., 1953.

ON THE PRESENT STATUS OF THE ELEPHANT SEAL IN SOUTH GEORGIA. J.E. Hamilton. Proc. Zool. Soc. London, vol. 117, pt.1, pp.272-275, May, 1947.

THE WEDDELL SEAL IN THE FALKLAND ISLANDS. J.E. Hamilton. Proc. Zool. Soc. London, vol.114, pt.4, p.549, Mar., 1945.

CONCESSION FOR ELEPHANT SEAL TAKING IN KERGUELEN AND OTHER ISLANDS. Hartley H.T. Jackson. Jour. Mamm., vol.19, no.4, pp.502-503, Nov. 14, 1938.

THE WEDDELL SEAL IN THE BAY OF WHALES, ANTARCTIC. A.A. Lindsey. Jour. Mamm., vol.18, pp.127-144, 1937.

NATURAL HISTORY OF THE ELEPHANT SEAL WITH NOTES ON OTHER SEALS FOUND AT SOUTH GEORGIA. L. Harrison Matthews. Discovery Repts., Government Dependencies Falkland Islands, vol.1, pp. 233-255, pls.6, 1929.

(ON THE PRESENCE IN THE KERGUELEN ISLANDS OF HYDRURGA LEPTONYX (Bl.) AND ARCTOCEPHALUS GAZELLA (PET.) AND BIOLOGICAL NOTES ON TWO PHOCIDS.) Sur la presence aux Iles Kerguelen d'Hydrurga leptonyx (Bl.) et d'Arctocephalus gazella (Pet.) et notes biologiques sur deux phocidés. P. Paulian. Mammalia, Paris, vol.16, pp.223-227, 1952.

BIOLOGY AT LITTLE AMERICA III, THE WEST BASE OF THE UNITED STATES ANTARCTIC SERVICE EXPEDITION 1939-1941. Jack E. Perkins. Proc. Amer. Philos. Soc., Philadelphia, vol.89, no.1, pp.270-284, figs.23, Apr. 30, 1945. (Seals pp.277-281.)

ELEPHANT SEALS OF KERGUELEN LAND. T.P.A. Ring. Proc. Zool. Soc. London, pt. 2, pp.431-443, pls.2, July, 1923.

SEALS OF THE WEDDELL SEA: NOTES ON THEIR HABITS AND DISTRIBUTION. R.N. Rudmose Brown. Edinburgh, Scottish Natl. Antarctic Exped., Sci. Res. Voyage "Scotia," 1902-1904, vol.4(Zool.), pt.13, pp.181-198, pls.9, 1913.

(SEALS OF ADÉLIE LAND.) Les phoques de Terre Adelie. J. Sapin-Jaloustre. Mammalia, vol.16, pp.179-212, pls.5, vol.17, pp.1-20, pls.2, 1952-53.

(ANIMAL LIFE IN THE SOUTH POLE REGION.) Tierleben im Suedpolargebiet.(Weddel Seal, Sea Leopard, Sea Elephant.) A. Schellenberg. Kosmos, Stuttgart, vol.29, no.3, pp.86-88, figs.6-7, Mar., 1932.

ELEPHANT SEALS OF CAMPBELL ISLAND. J.H. Sorensen. N.Z.Dept.Sci. Industr. Res., Wellington, Cape Exped. Series, Bull.6, pp.31, 1950.

(ON THE PRESENCE OF THE ELEPHANT SEAL IN THE VICINITY OF THE MASCARENE ISLANDS.) Sur la présence de l'elephant de mer aux Mascareignes. J. Vinson. Proc. Roy. Soc. Arts Sci. Mauritius, vol.1, pp.313-318, 1956.

ELEPHANT SEALS AT STELLINGEN. Ludwig Zudowsky. Field, London, vol.148, p. 633, Oct. 7, 1926.

Taxonomy

NOTE ON PHOCA NIGRA PALLAS. J.A. Allen. Proc. Biol. Soc. Washington, vol. 16, p.49, Mar. 19, 1903.

ON THE SUBSPECIES OF MONACHUS MONACHUS (LINN.) Outram Bangs. Proc.New England Zool. Club, vol.1, pp.33-37, Mar. 31, 1899.

(NOTES ON THE DISTRIBUTION AND POINTS OF RELATIONSHIP OF THE MONK SEAL (MONACHUS ALBIVENTER BODDAERT).) Notizen zur Verbreitung und ueber die Verwandtschaftsbeziehungen der Mönchsrobbe (Monachus albiventer Boddaert). C.R. Boettger. Zool. Anzeiger, Leipzig, vol.147, pp.303-310, Dec., 1951.

(SYSTEMATICS OF SUBFAMILY PHOCINAE.) Opit peresmotra sitemi i diagnostiki tryulenei podsemeistva Phocinae. K.K. Chapskii. Trudi Zool. Inst. Akad. Nauk SSSR, vol.17, pp.160-199, 1955.

NOTES ON THE NORTHERN ELEPHANT SEAL. (Notes on nomenclature and taxonomic characters.) M.E. McLellan Davidson. Proc. Calif. Acad. Sci., ser.4, vol. 18, pp.229-243, pls.25-26, Apr. 5, 1929.

REVIEW OF THE GENUS PHOCA. J. K. Doutt. Ann. Canegie Mus., Pittsburgh, vol.29, art.4, pp.61-125, figs.11, pls.14, May 12, 1942.

ON A NEW SPECIES OF THE GENUS MACRORHINUS. T. Gill. Proc. Chicago Acad. Sci., vol.1, pp.33-34, 1866b.

PHOCARUM SPECIES DESCRIPTAE. I. Lepechin. Acta Academiae Scientiarum Imperialis Petropolitanae, for 1777, vol. 1, pp.257-266, pls.4, 1778.

(OUTLINE OF A SYSTEMATIC DIVISION AND SPECIAL DESCRIPTION OF THE PHOCIDS.) Entwurf einer systematischen Eintheilung und speziellen Beschreibungen der Phoken. S. Nilsson. Arch. Naturgesch., Jahrg.7, Band 1, pp.301-333, 1841.

(MACRORHINUS OR MIROUNGA?) Macrohinus oder Mirounga? Franz Poche. Zool. Anzeiger, Leipzig, vol.34, no.10, p.1, May 18, 1909.

LITTLE-KNOWN REFERENCE TO NAME OF A HARBOR SEAL. V.B. Scheffer. Jour. Washington Acad. Sci., vol.46, no.11, p. 352, Dec. 10, 1956.

DIAGNOSES OF SOME GEOGRAPHICAL VARIETIES OF THE RINGED SEAL(PHOCA HISPIDA SCHREB.). N. Smirnov. Comptes Rendus Acad. Sci., USSR, A, no.4, pp.94-96, 1929.

DIAGNOSTICAL REMARKS ABOUT SOME SEALS (PHOCIDAE) OF THE NORTHERN HEMISPHERE. N. Smirnov. Tromsø Mus. Årshefter, vol.48, no.5, pp.23, (1925) 1927.

ON THE EASTERN HARP-SEAL PHOCA (PAGOPHOCA) GROENLANDICA VAR. OCEANICA LEPECHIN. N. Smirnov. Tromsø Mus. Årshefter, vol.47, no.2, pp.3-11, 1924.

West Indies

WEST INDIAN SEAL (MONACHUS TROPICALIS). J.A. Allen. Bull. Amer. Mus.

Nat. Hist., vol.2, no.1, pp.1-34, pls.1-4, Apr. 25, 1887.

"SEA WOLVES" OF THE WEST INDIES. Romeo Mansueti. Nat. Mag., vol.47, no. 9, pp.471-472, 500, illus., Nov., 1954.

THE WEST INDIAN SEAL. C.H. Townsend. Jour. Mamm., vol.4, no.1, p.55, Feb., 1923.

ON THE WEST INDIAN SEAL (MONACHUS TROPICALIS, GRAY). Frederick W. True, F.A. Lucas. U.S. Nat. Mus., Ann.Report, Washington, pp.331-335, pl.1, 1885.

NOTES ON THE LIFE-HISTORY OF MONACHUS TROPICALIS, THE WEST INDIAN SEAL. Henry L. Ward. Amer.Naturalist, vol.21, no.3, pp.257-264, Mar., 1887.

## TUBULIDENTATA

### Orycteropodidae

(THE TEETH OF ORYCTEROPUS.) Ueber die Zaehne von Orycteropus. Dr.Adloff. Zeitschr. Anat. u. Entwicklungsgesch., Berlin, vol.102, pp.710-717, figs.8, 1933.

STRUCTURE OF THE STOMACH OF THE SOUTH AFRICAN AARDVARK, ORYCTEROPUS AFER. A.C. Allison. S.African Jour. Sci., Johannesburg, vol.43, pp.204-209, figs.3, July, 1947.

(NEW DATA ON THE EVOLUTION OF THE DENTAL AND CRANIAL MORPHOLOGY OF TUBULIDENTATA (ORYCTEROPUS).) Donnees nouvelles sur l'evolution de la morphologie dentaire et cranienne des Tubulidentata (Orycteropes). R. Anthony. Bull. Soc. Zool. France, Paris, vol.59, pp.256-266, 1934.

AFRICA'S CHAMPION DIGGER. (Ard-Vark.) William Bridges. Animal Kingdom, New York Zool. Soc., vol.61, no.1, pp.20-22, illus., Feb., 1958.

MONOGRAPH OF ORYCTEROPUS AFER--III. THE SKULL. W.E. Clark. SKELETON OF THE TRUNK AND LIMBS. GENERAL SUMMARY. C.F. Sonntag. Proc. Zool. Soc. London, pp.445-485, illus., July, 1926.

PRESENCE OF TUBULIDENTATES IN THE MIDDLE SIWALIK BEDS OF NORTHERN INDIA. Edwin H. Colbert. Amer. Mus.Nov., no.604, pp.10, figs.8, Mar. 30, 1933.

STUDY OF ORYCTEROPUS GAUDRYI FROM THE ISLAND OF SAMOS. Edwin H. Colbert. Bull. Amer. Mus. Nat. Hist., vol.78, art. 4, pp.305-351, figs.25, Aug. 12, 1941.

ANT-BEAR. R.O. Crewe-Read. Jour. East Africa and Uganda Nat. Hist. Soc., no.14, pp.421-422, pl.1, July, 1919.

(HABITS OF ORYCTEROPUS OF ERITREA (ORYCTEROPUS AFER AETHIOPICUS.) L. Fossati. Natura, Milan, vol.28, no.1, pp.16-23, figs.1-2, 1937.

(NOTES ON THE MAMMALS. XXI. ON THE EXTREMITIES OF ORYCTEROPUS.) Notes sur les Mammiferes. XXI. Sur les extremites de l'Orycterope. Serge Frechkop. Bull. Mus. Roy.d'Hist.Nat.Belgique, Bruxelles, vol.13, no.19, pp.21, figs.9, Apr., 1937.

(ON THE TAXONOMY OF TUBULIDENTATA.) Zur Taxonomie der Tubulidentata. H. Frick. Saeugetierk. Mitteil., Stuttgart, vol.4, no.1, pp.15-17, Jan. 1, 1956.

(NEW AARDVARKS (ORYCTEROPUS) FROM GERMAN EAST AFRICA AND THE CAMEROONS.) Neue Erdferkel (Orycteropus) aus Deutsch-Ostafrika und Kamerun. Hermann Grote. Archiv. f. Nat., Jahrg.87, Abt. A, Heft 7, pp.121-127, 1921.

AARDVARK OF THE HAUT-UELE. Robert T. Hatt. Amer. Mus. Novit., no.535, pp.2, June 6, 1932.

(PROBLEM OF THE DENTITION OF ORYCTEROPUS.) Le problème de la dentition de l'orycterope. B. Heuvelmans. Bull. Mus. Royal Hist. Nat. Belgique, vol.15, no.40, pp.1-30, illus., Aug., 1939.

EARLY STAGE OF PLACENTATION IN THE AARDVARK ORYCTEROPUS. C.J. van der Horst. Proc. Zool. Soc. London, vol.119, pt.1, pp.1-18, illus., May 16, 1949.

(ANATOMICAL INVESTIGATION OF ORYCTEROPUS CAPENSIS.) Anatomische Untersuchung des Orycteropus capensis. H. F. Jaeger. Thesis, Stuttgart, pp.22, illus., 1837.

TUBULODON TAYLORI, A WIND RIVER EOCENE TUBULIDENTATE FROM WYOMING. G.L. Jepsen. Proc. Amer.Philos. Soc., Philadelphia, vol.71, no.5, pp.255-274, fig.1, pl.1, Aug., 1932.

(CONTRIBUTION TO KNOWLEDGE OF SUBFOSSIL FAUNA OF MADAGASCAR.) Contribucion à la connaissance de la faune subfossil de Madagascar. Note XV. Plesiorycteropus madagascariensis Filhol. C. Lambertson. Bull. Acad. Malgache, Tananarive, n.s., vol.25, pp.25-53, pls. 4, 1946.

A SKULL OF ORYCTEROPUS PILGRIM. G. Edward Lewis. Amer. Jour. Sci., ser. 5, vol.36, no.216, pp.401-405, figs.4, Dec., 1938.

ON A NEW ORYCTEROPUS FROM NORTHERN CONGO AND SOME REMARKS ON THE DENTITION OF THE TUBULIDENTATA. Einar Lonnberg. Arkiv. f. Zool., Stockholm, vol.3, no.3, pp.35, figs.12, pl.1, 1906.

AARDVARK AND THE ARMISTICE. Arthur Loveridge. Nat. Hist., New York, vol.53, no.1, pp.22-23, illus., Jan., 1944.

ANCYLOSTOMA HESCHELERI N. SP. FROM THE ANTBEAR, ORYCTEROPUS AFER, WITH A NOTE ON A NEW VARIETY A. CANINUM. H.O. Monnig. Vierteljahrsschrift Naturf. Gesell. Zuerich, vol.83, no. 30, Festschrift Karl Hescheler, pp.1-5, Nov. 3, 1938.

FETAL MEMBRANES OF THE AARDVARK. H. W. Mossman. Mitt.Naturf.Gesell. Bern, n.F., vol.14, pp.119-134, Feb., 1957.

SKELETON OF CORYPHODON. Bryan Patterson. Proc. New England Zool. Club, Cambridge, vol.17, pp.97-110, July 10, 1939.

SOME EXTERNAL CHARACTERS OF ORYCTEROPUS. R. O. Pocock. Proc. Zool. Soc. London, pp.697-706, figs.5, Sep., 1924.

DESCRIPTION OF A NEW RACE OF AARDVARK (ORYCTEROPUS AFER KORDOFANICUS). Lionel Walter Rothschild. Ann. and Mag. Nat. Hist., ser.9, vol.19, p.512, Apr., 1927.

(ORYCTEROPUS EXISTS AT LAKE LEOPOLD II.) L'Orycterope existe au Lac Leopold II. H.Schouteden. Rev. Zool. Bot. Afric., vol.24, Suppl., pp.(33)-(34), fig. (-Bull.Cercle Zool. Congol., vol.10, no. 2), Dec. 22, 1933.

(ORYCTEROPUS OF THE LOMAMI.) Un Orycterope du Lomami. H.Schouteden. Rev. Zool. Bot. Afr., vol.26, (Suppl. Bull. Cercle Zool. Congo, vol.11, nos.1-2), pp. 8-9, Nov.-Dec., 1934.

ANT-BEAR OR AARDVARK. V.G.L. van Someren. Jour. East Africa and Uganda Nat. Hist. Soc., no.14, p.421, July, 1919.

MONOGRAPH OF ORYCTEROPUS AFER--I. ANATOMY EXCEPT THE NERVOUS SYSTEM, SKIN,AND SKELETON. Charles F. Sonntag. Proc. Zool. Soc. London, pt.2, pp.331-437, pl.1, July, 1925.

MONOGRAPH OF ORYCTEROPUS AFER--II. NERVOUS SYSTEM, SENSE-ORGANS AND HAIRS. Charles F. Sonntag, H.H. Woollard. Proc. Zool. Soc. London, pt.3, pp.1185-1235, illus., Oct., 1925.

MILK DENTITION IN ORYCTEROPUS. Oldfield Thomas. Proc. Roy. Soc., London, vol.47, pp.246-248, pl.8, Jan., 1890.

NAME OF THE AARDVARK. Oldfield Thomas. Proc. Biol. Soc. Washington, vol. 14, p.24, Apr. 2, 1901.

(DENTITION OF ORYCTEROPUS AETHIOPICUS.) Das Gebiss von Orycteropus aethiopicus. Hans Virchow. Zeitschr. Morphol. u. Anthrop., Stuttgart, vol.34, (Festb. Eugen Fischer), pp.413-435, pls. 19-22, Apr., 1935.

HUNTING THE AARDVARK: AN ANIMAL THAT CAN DIG FASTER THAN A GANG OF MEN. Illus. London News, vol.216, no.5778, pp.54, 55, illus., Jan. 14, 1950.

## PROBOSCIDEA

MASTODON FACTS VS. FUNDAMENTALIST FANCIES. Walter S. Kraatz. Evolution, New York, no.7, p.6, illus., Aug., 1928.

MASTODONS, MAMMOTHS, ELEPHANTS. Helen M. Martin. Michigan Conserv., Lansing, vol.24, no.2, pp.24-26, illus., Mar., 1955.

MAMMOTHS AND MASTODONS. W. D. Matthew. Amer.Mus.Nat.Hist., New York, Guide Leaflet Series, no.43, pp.26, 1915.

RESTORATION OF THE WORLD SERIES OF ELEPHANTS AND MASTODONS. Henry Fairfield Osborn. Bull. Geol. Soc. Amer., Wash., D.C., vol.25, no.3, pp.407-410, figs.2, Sep. 15, 1914.

(Review by Oliver P. Hay of) PAPER ON MASTODONS. Dr. Guenther Schlesinger. Jour. Wash. Acad. Sci., vol.15, no.16, pp.381-387, Oct. 4, 1925.

### Africa

FATE OF THE RASH PLATYBELODON. Roy Chapman Andrews. Nat. Hist., New York, vol.31, no.2, pp.115-128, figs.18, Mar.-Apr., 1931.

SOME EXTINCT ELEPHANTS, THEIR RELATIVES AND THE TWO LIVING SPECIES. P.E.P. Deraniyagala. Ceylon Nat. Mus. Publ., Colombo, pp.161, pls. 48, Aug., 1955.

ON SOME SOUTH AFRICAN FOSSIL PROBOSCIDAE. S.H. Haughton. Trans. Roy. Soc. South Africa, vol.21, no.1, pp.1-18, pls.4, figs.8, Dec., 1932.

MIOCENE AND POST-MIOCENE PROBOSCIDAE FROM EAST AFRICA. D.G. MacInnes. Trans. Zool. Soc. London, vol.25, pt.2, pp.33-106, figs.4, pls.8, map, July 1942.

CONTRIBUTION TO THE KNOWLEDGE OF MOERITHERIUM. H. Matsumoto. Bull. Amer. Mus. Nat. Hist., vol.48, art.4, pp.97-139, figs.11, Sep. 21, 1923.

RESUME ON HEMIMASTODON, A LITTLE-KNOWN GENUS OF FOSSIL PROBOSCIDAE. H. Matsumoto. Vol. Jubilare for Prof. Sadao Yoshida, Osaka, pp.1301-1317, figs.8, Mar., 1939.

MAMMOTH OR "STIFF-LEGGED BEAR". Truman Michelson. Amer. Anthropologist, vol.38, no.1, pp.141-143, Jan.-Mar., 1936.

WHAT IS THE FIRST FOSSIL COLLECTED BY MAN. Louise Sudbury. Science, n.s., vol.68, p.135, Aug. 10, 1928.

DEINOTHERIUM IN THE PLEISTOCENE. E.J. Wayland. Nature, London, vol.129, no.3244, p.24, Jan. 2, 1932.

ANCIENT DEATHTRAP. (Gnathabelodon buckneri Sellards.) Nat. Hist., New York, vol.46, no.2, pp.104-105, illus., Sep., 1940.

### Anatomy

(SCULPTURED RECONSTRUCTION OF A LIVING BUNOLOPHODON ANGUSTIDENS.) Plastische Rekonstruktion des Lebensbildes von Bunolophodon angustidens. O. Abel. Palaeobiol., Wien, vol.1, pp.482-486, pls. 2, 1928.

NOTE ON THE SKULL OF DINOTHERIUM GIGANTEUM IN THE BRITISH MUSEUM. C.W. Andrews. Proc. Zool. Soc. London, pt.3, pp.525-534, Sep., 1921.

ARTICULATED SKELETON OF EUBELODON MORRILLI. E.H. Barbour. Nebraska State Mus., vol.1, Bull.28, pp.243-246, figs.2, Mar., 1932.

MANDIBLE OF AMEBELODON FRICKI. E.H. Barbour. Nebraska State Mus., vol. 1, Bull.15, pp.139-146, figs.93-97, Dec., 1929.

MANDIBLE OF TORYNOBELODON BARNUMBROWNI. E.H. Barbour. Amer. Jour. Sci., vol.24, pp.214-219, figs.3, Sep., 1932.

MANDIBULAR TUSKS OF AMEBELODON FRICKI. E.H. Barbour. Bull. Nebraska

State Mus., Lincoln, vol.1, Bull.14, pp. 135-138, Dec., 1929.

MOUNTED SKELETON OF MEGABELODON LULLI. E.H. Barbour. Nebraska State Mus., vol.1, Bull.39, pp.303-310, figs.177-181, June, 1934.

SKULL AND MANDIBLE OF MASTODON MOODIEI. E.H. Barbour. Nebraska State Mus., vol.1, Bull.29, pp.247-250, figs. 2, Oct., 1932.

(ROUND TUSKS IN A RECENT ELEPHANT.) Kreisfoermige Stosszaehne bei einem rezenten Elefanten. L. Doederlein. Zeitschr. f. Saeugetierk., vol.3, pp.213-230, pls.8-12, June 11, 1928.

FOUR-TUSKED ELEPHANT. Guy Dollman. Proc. Linn. Soc. London, 142nd sess., pp. 74-78, Jan., 1931; Nat. Hist. Mag., London, vol.3, no.21, pp.156-163, figs.3, Jan., 1932.

TOOTH SEQUENCE IN CERTAIN TRILOPHODONT TETRABELODONT MASTODONS. Childs Frick. Bull. Amer. Nat. Hist., vol. 56, art.2, pp.122-178, Apr. 9, 1926.

ON THE SIGNIFICANCE OF THE SUPRASYMPHYSIAL DEPRESSION AND GROOVE IN THE SHOVEL-TUSKED MASTODONTS. William K. Gregory. Jour. Mamm., vol. 15, no.1, pp.4-12, Feb., 1934.

DESCRIPTIONS OF THE INFERIOR MAXILLARY BONES OF MASTODONS, IN THE CABINET OF THE AMERICAN PHILOSOPHICAL SOCIETY, WITH REMARKS ON THE GENUS TETRACULODON, AND C. Isaac Hays. Trans. Amer. Philos. Soc., n.s., vol. 4, pp.1-23, pls.20-29, 1833.

CIRCULAR IN REGARD TO BONES AND TEETH OF THE MASTODON AND MAMMOTH. Frederick A. Lucas. Smiths. Inst., Circ.no.48, pp.1-4, illus., 1897.

(THE MOLARS OF DINOTHERIUM FROM SCANDINAVIA (?) AT THE MUSEUM OF KICHINEFF (BESSARABIA).) Les Molaires de Dinotherium provenant de Scandinavie(?) au Musee de Kichineff (Bessarabie). Nic. N. Morosan. Bull. Soc. Geol. France, Paris, ser.5, vol.6, nos.1-3, pp.209-212, pl.10, Oct., 1936.

(ON SOME DIFFERENTIAL CHARACTERISTICS OF THE CARPEL AND TARSUS OF PROBOSCIDIANS.) Sur quelques caracteres differentiels du Carpe et du Tarse chez les Proboscidiens. Henri Neuville. Mammalia, Paris, vol.10, nos.3-4, pp.122-128, illus., Sep.-Dec., 1946.

REMARKS UPON THE SKULLS OF MOERITHERIUM AND PALAEOMASTODON. B. Petronievics. Ann. and Mag. Nat. Hist., ser.9, vol.12, pp.55-61, pl.1, figs.2, July, 1923.

(ON DENTAL ANOMALIES OBSERVED IN PROBOSCIDIANS.) A propos d'anomalies dentaires observees chez les proboscidiens. Georges Pontier. Ann. Soc. Geol. du Nord, vol.55, pp.2-10, pls.2, 1930.

(STUDY OF THE DEFENSIVE BULB OF DINOTHERIUM GIGANTEUM KAUP.)Etude du bulbe de le defense du Dinotherium giganteum Kaup. George Pontier. Ann.Soc. Geol. du Nord. Lille, vol.58, pp.118-125, figs.2, 1933.

MISCONSTRUCTING A MASTODON. George Gaylord Simpson. Nat. Hist., New York, vol.37, no.2, pp.170-172, illus., Feb., 1926.

(OBSERVATIONS ON SOME TEETH OF MASTODONS OF TURKEY AND CHINA.) Observations sur quelques dents de mastodontes de Turquie et de Chine. J.Viret. Ann. Univ. Lyon, sec.C, vol.7, pp.50-66, illus., 1953.

(ON TWO PICTURES OF ADAMS' MASTODON.) Ueber zwei Bilder des Adamsschen Mammuts. C. Zimmer. Zeitschr.f.Saeugetierk., vol.4, no.2, pp.84-89, pls.11-12, Aug. 6, 1929.

Eurasia

(THE MAMMOTH OF BAULOU.) Le Mammouth de Baulou. Gaston Astre. Bull. Soc. Hist. Nat. Toulouse, vol.58, no.4, pp. 609-633, pls.11-14, 1929.

ABOUT THE REMAINS OF A MASTODON FROM ULAN-TOLOGOI. E.I. Belyaeva. Proc. Paleo. Inst., Acad. Sci. USSR, vol. 41, pp.78-86, illus., 1952.

NEW MASTODON FROM THE LOWER MIOCENE SEDIMENTS OF KAZAKSTAN. (Mastodon (angustidens var.) atavus.) A.A. Borissiak. Comptes Rendus Acad. Sci. USSR, no.1, pp.37-39, 1933.

MASTODON BORSONI LART. FROM THE BALTA DEPOSITS OF THE VILLAGE HOLDASHEVKA, VINNITZA DISTRICT. N.I. Burchak-Abramovich. Jour. Geol., Ukranian Acad. Sci., Kiev, vol.2, no.2, pp.143-144, figs.5, 1935. (In Russian with English summary.)

MIOCENE PROBOSCIDEA FROM BALUCHISTAN. C. Forster Cooper. Proc. Zool.Soc. London, pp.609-626, pls.4, Sep., 1922.

(DEINOTHERIIDS OF MONGOLIA.) Dinotseraty Mongolii. K.K. Flerov. Trudy Paleont. Inst. Akad. Nauk SSSR, vol.67, pp.1-87, 1957.

FOSSIL PROBOSCIDAE FROM THE MALAY ARCHIPELAGO AND THE PUNJAB. D.A. Hooijer. Zool. Verhand. Mus. Leiden, no. 28, pp.1-146, illus., Aug. 31, 1955.

MASTODONT TEETH FROM SZECHWAN, CHINA. D.A. Hooijer, Edwin H. Colbert. Fieldiana, Geology, vol.10, no.12, pp.129-134, Dec. 6, 1951.

FOSSIL PROBOSCIDEA FROM CHINA. A. Tindell Hopwood. Palaeont. Sinica, ser.C, vol.9, no.3, pp.1-108, pls.1-8, Feb., 1935.

NEW MASTODON FINDS IN EUROPEAN TURKEY. George D. Hubbard. Science, vol.73, no.1898, pp.527-528, May 15, 1931.

(A SWIDISH MAMMOTH. WHAT THE FINDINGS AT DOSEBACKA CAN TELL ABOUT OUR ANCIENT WORLD OF ANIMALS.) En Svensk Mammut. Vad benfynden fran Dosebacka ha att fortalja om var forntida djurvarld. L.A. Jagerskiold. Goteborgs Museum Arstryck, pp.3-7, figs. 3, 1932.

(MASTODON LONGIROSTRIS-ARVERNENSIS OF LEOPOLDSDORF IN LOWER AUSTRIA.) Mastodon longirostris-arvernensis von Leopoldsdorf in Niederoesterreich. Hans Klahn. Verhandl. Geol. Bundesanst., Wien, no.12, pp.235-240, figs.5, Dec., 1929.

ON TWO NEW MASTODONTS AND AN ARCHETYPAL STEGODONT OF JAPAN. Hikoshichiro Matsumoto. Sci. Rep. Tohoku Imp. Univ., ser.2 (Geol.), vol. 10, pp.1-11, illus., 1926.

ON THE ARCHETYPAL MAMMOTH FROM THE PROVINCE OF KAZUSA. Hikoshichiro Matsumoto. Sci. Rep. Tohoku Imp. Univ., ser.2, (Geol.), vol.10, no.2, pp.43-50, pls.7, 1926.

SERRIDENTINUS AND BALUCHITHERIUM, LOH FORMATION, MONGONA. Henry Fairfield Osborn. Amer. Mus. Novit., no. 148, pp.1-5, figs.1-2, Nov. 11, 1924.

TRILOPHODON COOPERI, SP. NOV., OF DERA BUGTI, BALUCHISTAN. Henry Fairfield Osborn. Amer. Mus. Novit., no. 585, pp.6, figs.2, Nov. 15, 1932.

PLATYBELODON GRANGERI, THREE GRWOTH STAGES, AND A NEW SERRIDENTINE FROM MONGOLIA. Henry Fairfield Osborn, Walter Granger. Amer. Mus. Novit., New York, no.537, pp.13, figs.8, June 9, 1932.

SHOVEL-TUSKERS, AMEBELODONTINAE, OF CENTRAL ASIA. Henry Fairfield Osborn. Amer. Mus. Novit., no.470, pp.12, figs.3, Apr. 10, 1931.

(MASTODON BORSONI HAYS OF THE VILLAGE GRADESHNITSE (MORIHOVO) IN MACEDONIA.) Mastodon borsoni Hays iz sela gradeshnitse (Morixovo) v Makedoniia. Zhivadin M. Petroniievic. Glasnik Prirodyachkog Museia Srpske Zemle, Belgrade, ser.A, vol.5, pp.243-248, 1952. (In Serbian with French summary.)

(CONTINUATION OF THE STUDY ON THE MOLARS OF QUATERNARY ELEPHANTS OF THE VALLEY OF THE SEINE FROM THE COLLECTION OF EMILE RIVIÈRE.) Suite de l'etude sur les molaires d'elephants quaternaires de la vallee de le Seine provenant de la collection Emile Rivière. Georges Pontier. Bull. Soc. Prehist.France, vol.26, no.1, pp.62-68, fig.1, 1929.

(NEW FINDS OF PROBOSCIDEANS IN STAJERSKO.) O novih majdbah proboscidov na Stjerskem. I. Rakovec. Slovenska Akad. Znan. Umet., Cl IV, Hist. Nat., no.3, pp.331-358, June, 1955. (With English summary.)

ON THE NEW FIND OF MASTODON REMAINS IN SLOVENIA. I. Rakovec. Geologija 2, Ljubljana, pp.94-112, illus., 1954.

(DISCOVERIES OF MASTODON REMAINS NEAR LEON.) Descubrimiento de restos de "Mastodon" en las cercanias de Leon. J. Royo Y Gomez. Bol. Real Soc. Expanola de Hist. Nat., Madrid, vol.30, no.8, pp. 395-396, Oct. 31, 1930.

FIRST DISCOVERY OF PENTALOPHODON FROM JAPAN. Tokio Shikama. Proc. Imp. Acad., Tokyo, vol.12, no.9, pp.292-295, figs.4, Nov., 1936.

(PLIOCENE MAMMALS OF CIMISLIA. III. PROBOSCIDIANS.) Les mammiferes Pliocenes de Cimislia (Roumanie). III. Proboscidiens. I. Simionescu, Virginia I. Barbu. Acad. Romana Publ. Fondului Vasile Adamachi, Bucuresti, vol.9, no.52, pp.1-20, figs.12, pls.3, 1939. (In Roumanian with French summary.)

(ANOTHER MASTODON TOOTH OBTAINED IN THE LISBON TERTIARY.) Mais um dente de Mastodon (Tetrabelodon) angustidens, Cuv., colhido no terciario de Lisboa. A. Torres Sousa. Bol. Mus. Lab. Mineral. e Geol. Univ. Lisboa, ser.2, no. 4, pp.41-44, figs.2, 1935.

PROBOSCIDEANS OF SOUTHWESTERN SHANSI. P. Teilhard de Chardin. Palaeontologia Sinica, ser.C, vol.13, no.1, pp.84, figs.6, pls.13, 1937.

(THE MAMMOTH AND THE IVORY OF SIBERIA.) Le Mammouth et l'ivoire de Siberie. E.L. Trouessart. Bull. Soc. Nat. Acclimat. France, Paris, annee 1898, pp. 12, 1898.

(FIRST NOTE ON FOSSIL MIOCENE VERTEBRATES OF VALLES. THE OCCURRENCE OF DINOTHERIUM GIGANTEUM KAUP VAR. LAEVIUS AT JOURDAN SANT QUIRZE DE GALLINERS.) Primera nota sobre vertebrats fòssils miocènics del Vallès. La presència del Dinotherium giganteum Kaup var. Laevius Jourdan a Sant Quirze de Galliners. J.F. de Villalta Comella, M.Crusafont Pairó. Butll. Inst.Catalana Hist. nat., Barcelona, vol.33, nos.4-5, pp.258-261, pl.11, 1933.

Evolution, Phylogeny

ON A NEW DIRECTION IN THE ADAPTIVE RADIATION OF MASTODONTS. A.Borissiak. Palaeobiologica, vol.2, nos.1-3, pp. 19-33, figs.4, pls.3-5, 1929.

(LIVING ELEPHANTS AND THEIR ANCESTORS. MAPUTO AND IPANA.) Os elefantes actuais e os seus antepassados. A proposito de "Maputo" e de "Ipana". Fernando, Frade. Soc. Sci. Nat. Portucalensis, Lisboa, pp.48, figs.10, 1925.

(EVOLUTION OF THE CARPUS IN THE PROBOSCIDIANS.) Die Evolution des Karpus bei den Proboscidiern. A. Gawrilenko. Anat. Anzeiger, vol.58, pp.218-244, figs. 5, Sep. 15, 1924.

THE EVOLUTION OF THE ELEPHANT. Richard S. Lull. Yale Univ. Peabody Mus. Nat. Hist., Guide no.2, pp.1-44, figs.1-27, charts 1-4, 1908. (Reprinted from the Amer. Jour. of Sci., vol.25, pp.169-212, figs.27, charts 3, Mar., 1908.)

EVOLUTION OF THE ELEPHANTS AND MASTODONS. Richard S. Lull. Special Guide no.2, Peabody Mus. Nat. Hist., Yale Univ., pp.40, figs.33, 1931. (Revised edition.)

ADAPTIVE RADIATION AND CLASSIFICATION OF THE PROBOSCIDAE. Henry Fairfield Osborn. Proc. Nat. Acad. Sci., vol.7, no.8, pp.231-234, Aug. (Dec. 19), 1921.

ADDITIONAL GENERIC AND SPECIFIC STAGES IN THE EVOLUTION OF THE PROBOSCIDEA. Henry Fairfield Osborn. Amer. Mus. Novit., no.154, pp.1-5, figs. 1-2, Dec. 24, 1924.

ANCESTRAL TREE OF THE PROBOSCIDEA. DISCOVERY, EVOLUTION, MIGRATION AND EXTINCTION OVER A 50,000,000 YEAR PERIOD. Henry Fairfield Osborn. Proc. Nat. Acad. Sci. Washington, vol.21, no.6, pp.404-412, figs.5, June, 1935.

BIOLOGICAL INDUCTIONS FROM THE EVOLUTION OF THE PROBOSCIDEA. Henry Fairfield Osborn. Science, n.s., vol.76, no.1979, pp.501-502, Dec. 2, 1932; Proc. Nat. Acad. Sci., vol.19, no.1, pp.159-163, Jan., 1933.

EVOLUTION AND GEOGRAPHIC DISTRIBUTION OF THE PROBOSCIDEA:MOERITHERES, DEINOTHERES AND MASTODONTS. Henry Fairfield Osborn. Jour. Mamm., vol.15, no.3, pp.177-184, Aug., 1934.

EVOLUTION, PHYLOGENY, AND CLASSIFICATION OF THE MASTODONTOIDEA. Henry Fairfield Osborn. Bull. Geol. Soc. Amer., vol.32, pp.327-332, Sep. 1 (Oct. 5), 1921.

EVOLUTION, PHYLOGENY AND CLASSIFICATION OF THE PROBOSCIDEA. Henry Fairfield Osborn. Amer. Mus. Novit., no. 1, pp.1-15, figs.4, Jan. 31, 1921.

FACTORS IN THE EVOLUTION AND PHYLOGENY OF THE PROBOSCIDEA. Henry Fairfield Osborn. Anat. Record, vol.29, pp. 114-115, Dec. 25, 1924.

FINAL CONCLUSIONS ON THE EVOLUTION, PHYLOGENY, AND CLASSIFICATION OF THE PROBOSCIDEA. Henry Fairfield Osborn. Proc. Amer. Philos. Soc., Philadelphia, vol.64, no.1, pp.17-35, figs.3, 1925.

LONG-JAWED MASTODON SKELETON FROM SOUTH DAKOTA AND PHYLOGENY OF THE PROBOSCIDEA. Henry Fairfield Osborn. Bull. Geol. Soc. Amer., Wash., D.C., vol.29, no.1, pp.133-137, Mar. 31, 1918.

MIGRATIONS AND AFFINITIES OF THE FOSSIL PROBOSCIDEANS AND EURASIA, NORTH AND SOUTH AMERICA, AND AFRICA. (Sixth contribution on the evolution of the Proboscidea.) Henry Fairfield Osborn. Amer. Nat., Lancaster, vol.56, pp.448-455, fig.1, Sep.-Oct., 1922.

NEW SUBFAMILY, GENERIC, AND SPECIFIC STAGES IN THE EVOLUTION OF THE PROBOSCIDEA. Henry Fairfield Osborn. Amer. Mus. Novit., New York, no.99, pp.4, Dec. 27, 1923.

PALAEOMASTODON, THE ANCESTOR OF THE LONG-JAWED MASTONDONS ONLY. Henry Fairfield Osborn. Proc.Nat. Acad. Sci., vol.5, pp.265-266, Aug. 26, 1919.

PROBOSCIDEA. MONOGRAPH OF THE DISCOVERY, EVOLUTION, MIGRATION AND EXTINCTION OF THE MASTODONTS AND ELEPHANTS OF THE WORLD. VOL. 1. MOERITHERIOIDEA, DEINOTHERIOIDEA, MASTODONTOIDEA. Henry Fairfield Osborn. Publ. Amer. Mus. Nat. Hist., New York, vol.1, pp.xl-802, figs.680, Aug. 15, 1936.

(Review by A. Smith Woodward of) PROBOSCIDEA. MONOGRAPH OF THE DISCOVERY, EVOLUTION, MIGRATION AND EXTINCTION OF THE MASTODONTS AND ELEPHANTS OF THE WORLD. VOL.1. MOERITHERIOIDEA, DEINOTHERIOIDEA, MASTODONTOIDEA. Henry Fairfield Osborn. Nature, London, vol.138, no.3499, pp.860-862, Nov. 21, 1936.

PROBOSCIDEA. MONOGRAPH OF THE DISCOVERY, EVOLUTION, MIGRATION AND EXTINCTION OF THE MASTODONTS AND ELEPHANTS OF THE WORLD. VOL. 2. STEGODONTOIDEA, ELEPHANTOIDEA. Henry Fairfield Osborn. Amer. Mus. Press, New York, 1942.

(Review by D.M.S. Watson of) PROBOSCIDEA. MONOGRAPH OF THE DISCOVERY, EVOLUTION, MIGRATION AND EXTINCTION OF THE MASTODONTS AND ELEPHANTS OF THE WORLD. VOL. 2, STEGODONTOIDEA, ELEPHANTOIDEA. Henry Fairfield Osborn. Nature, London, vol.153, no.3870, pp.5-7, Jan. 1, 1944.

THIRTY-NINE DISTINCT LINES OF PROBOSCIDEAN DESCENT, AND THEIR MIGRATION INTO ALL PARTS OF THE WORLD EXCEPT AUSTRALIA. Henry Fairfield Osborn. Proc. Amer. Philos. Soc., vol.74, no.4, pp.273-285, figs.4, Aug., 1934.

HISTORY OF ELEPHANT ORDER TRACE IN FOSSIL EXHIBIT. Bryan Patterson. Field Mus. News, Chicago, vol.12, no.5, pp.7-8, fig.1, May, 1941.

(ON THE MORPHOLOGICAL EVOLUTION OF THE MOLARS IN MASTODONS OF THE SERIES OF TETRABOLEDON ANGUSTIDENS G. CUV.) A propos de l'evolution morphologique des molaires chez les Mastodontes de la serie du Tetraboledon angustidens G. Cuv. G.Pontier, R. Anthony. Comptes Rendus Acad. Sci.Paris, vol.198, no.15, pp.1361-1363, figs. Apr.9, 1934.

ANCESTORS OF THE ELEPHANTS. W. Henry Sheak. Bull. Wagner Free Inst.Sci., vol.3, no.5, pp.43-55, Oct., 1928.

EVOLUTION OF THE PROBOSCIDEA. D. M.S. Watson. Biol. Rev. Cambridge Philos. Soc., Cambridge, vol.21, no.1, pp.15-29, figs.1-3, Jan., 1946.

North America

(ON A MASTODON HUNT ON THE YUKON.) Auf der Mammutjagd am Yukon. Benno Alexander. Ueber Land und Meer, Arena 1911-12, no.1, pp.97-105, Sep. 15, 1911.

AMERICAN MASTODON WITH MANDIBULAR TUSKS. E.H. Barbour. Nebraska State Mus., vol.1, Bull.no.19, pp.163-170, figs.103-108, Mar., 1931.

MORNING'S CONSIGNMENT OF PROBOSCIDEAN FREIGHT. E.H. Barbour. Bull. Nebraska State Mus., Lincoln, vol.1, Bull. no.18, pp.159-162, Feb., 1931.

PROBOSCIDEA OF NEBRASKA. E.H.Barbour. Bull. Geol. Soc. America, vol.41, no.1, p.180, Mar., 1930. (Abstract.)

THE THURSTON COUNTY MASTODON, MASTODON GRANGERI, SP. NOV. E. H. Barbour. Nebraska State Mus., vol.1, Bull. no.35, pp.287-290, fig.1, May, 1934.

SHOVEL-TUSKED MASTODON, AMEBELODON FRICKI, FROM KANSAS. E. H. Barbour, Claude W. Hibbard. Bull. Univ. Nebraska State Mus., Lincoln, vol.2, no.4, pp.37-46, Jan., 1941.

TEMPLE HILL (ORANGE COUNTY, N. Y.) MASTODON. Sherman C. Bishop. Science, n.s., vol.54, p.170, Aug. 26, 1921.

HAMPTON TUSK. (Mastodon americanus.) Emmett J. Cable. Proc. Iowa Acad. Sci., Des Moines, vol.41, pp.191-197, figs.4, 1934.

HAMPTON TUSK OF MASTODON. Emmett J. Cable. Pan-Amer. Geol., vol.62, no.3, pp.187-192, pl.1, Oct., 1934.

BLOOMFIELD HILLS MASTODON.(Michigan.) E.C. Case, Geo.M. Stanley. Cranbrook Inst. Sci. Bull., Bloomfield Hills, no.4, pp.8, pls.4, fig.1, Oct., 1935.

MASTODON REMAINS IN WASHINGTON. Harold E. Culver. Science, n.s., vol.66, pp.540-541, Dec. 2, 1927.

NEW MASTODONT FROM THE MIOCENE OF OREGON. Theodore Downs. Univ.Calif. Publ. Geol. Sci., Berkeley, vol.29, no.1, pp.1-20, Sep. 17, 1952.

FINDS OF THE AMERICAN MASTODON (MAMMUT AMERICANUM) IN DELAWARE COUNTY, INDIANA. R.A. Gantz. Proc. Indiana Acad. Sci., vol.34, 1924, p.393, 1925.

GOMPHOTHERIUM FRICKI FROM BIJOU HILLS, SOUTH DAKOTA. Morton Green. Proc. S.Dakota Acad. Sci., vol.36, 1957, pp.139-142, illus., 1958.

AMEBELODON JAW FROM THE TEXAS PANHANDLE. Joseph T. Gregory. Univ. Texas Publ., Austin, no.4401, pp.477-484, fig.1, pl.46, Dec., 1945.

POLLEN ANALYSIS AND THE AGE OF PROBOSCIDIAN BONES NEAR SILVERTON, OREGON. Henry P. Hansen, E.L. Packard. Ecology, Lancaster, vol.30, no.4, pp.461-468, Oct., 1949.

DESCRIPTION OF A NEW SPECIES OF MASTODON, GOMPHOTHERIUM ELEGANS, FROM THE PLEISTOCENE OF KANSES. O.P. Hay. Proc. U.S. Nat. Mus., vol.53, pp.219-221, pl.26, June 1, 1917.

EXTINCT PROBOSCIDEANS OF MEXICO. O.P. Hay. Pan-American Geol., vol.44, pp.21-37, Aug., 1925.

ON REMAINS OF MASTODONS FOUND IN TEXAS, ANANCUS BRASOSIUS AND GOMPHOTHERIUM CIMARRONIS. O.P. Hay. Proc. U.S. Nat. Mus., vol.66, art. 35, pp.1-15, pls.1-4, Apr. 25, 1925.

ON SOME PROBOSCIDEANS OF THE STATE OF NEW YORK. (Records of Fossil Remains of Elephas and Mammut.) O.P. Hay.Science, n.s., vol.49, pp.377-379, Apr. 18, 1919.

IMMATURE MASTODON FROM THE OGALLALA PLIOCENE. Curtis J. Hesse. Jour. Mamm., vol.16, no.1, pp.61-63, Feb., 1935.

A NEW MASTODON, SERRIDENTINUS MEADENSIS, FROM THE MIDDLE PLIOCENE OF KANSAS. (Serridentinus meadensis.) Claude W. Hibbard. Contrib. Mus. Paleontol. Univ. Michigan, Ann Arbor, vol. 9, no.6, pp.217-225, pls.1-4, Dec. 31, 1951.

MASTODON OF THOMAS JEFFERSON. Margaret R. Hitchcock. Jour. Washington Acad. Sci., vol.21, no.5, pp.80-86, figs. 2, Mar. 4, 1931.

NOTES ON UNEARTHING PARTS OF A MASTODON SKELETON. Edward Kintner. Proc. Indiana Acad. Sci., vol.39, pp.237-239, figs.3, (1929) 1930.

FOSSIL REMAINS IN THE LOESS OF EASTERN WASHINGTON. (Fossil Elephant.) Macy H. Lapham. Science, n.s., vol.65, pp.446-447, May 6, 1927.

ON THE FARMINGTON SPECIMEN - MAMMUT AMERICANUM IN CONNECTICUT. Richard S. Lull. Amer. Jour. Science, vol. 37, pp.329-330, Apr., 1914.

INDIANA MASTODONS. M. W. Lyon, Jr. Proc. Indiana Acad. Sci., Indianapolis, vol.48, pp.246-247, figs.4, 1939.

PLIOCENE MASTODON SKULL FROM CALIFORNIA, PLIOMASTODON VEXILLARIUS, N.SP. W.D. Matthew. Univ.Calif. Publ., Bull. Dept. Geol. Sci., vol.19, no. 16, pp.335-348, figs.2, pls.41-44, Nov. 26, 1930.

JACOBS CAVERN MASTODON AGAIN. N.C. Nelson. Science, n.s., vol.66, pp.258-259, Sep. 16, 1927.

PROBOSCIS STATUE FROM THE ISTHMUS OF TEHUANTEPEC. Gladys Ayer Nomland. Amer. Anthropol., vol.34, no.4, pp.591-593, pls.2, 1932.

PROBOSCIDEA OF MARYLAND. T.Milton Oler. Bull. Nat. Hist. Soc. Maryland, vol. 8, no.1, pp.1-5, Sep., 1937.

NEW BEAK-JAWED MASTODONT FROM FLORIDA. Stanley J. Olsen. Jour.Paleontol. Soc. India, Lucknow, vol.2, pp.131-135, 1957.

DIBELODON EDENSIS (FRICK) OF SOUTHERN CALIFORNIA, MIOMASTODON OF THE MIDDLE MIOCENE, NEW GENUS. Henry Fairfield Osborn. Amer. Mus. Nov., New York, no.49, pp.4, fig.1, Oct. 23, 1922.

ELEPHANTS AND MASTODONTS ARRIVE IN AMERICA. Henry Fairfield Osborn. Nat. Hist., New York, vol.25, no.1, pp. 3-23, illus., Jan.-Feb., 1925.

FIRST APPEARANCE OF THE TRUE MASTODON IN AMERICA. Henry Fairfield Osborn. Amer. Mus. Nov., no.10, pp.1-6, figs.1-2, June 15, 1921; Science, n.s., vol. 54, p.108, Aug. 5, 1921.

MASTODONS AND MAMMOTHS OF NORTH AMERICA. Henry Fairfield Osborn. Amer. Mus. Nat. Hist., New York, Guide Leaflet, no.62, pp.46, illus., maps, 1926. (Reprinted from Nat. Hist., vol.23, no.1, 1923; vol.25, no.1, 1925.)

MASTODONS OF THE HUDSON HIGHLANDS. Henry Fairfield Osborn. Nat. Hist., vol.23, pp.3-24, col.pl.,figs., Jan.-Feb., 1923.

SERBELODON BURNHAMI, A NEW SHOVEL-TUSKER FROM CALIFORNIA. Henry Fairfield Osborn. Amer. Mus. Nov., no.649, pp.1-5, figs.2, June 29, 1933.

MASTODON REMAINS IN THE YUKON VALLEY. Wilfred H. Osgood. Proc. Biol. Soc. Washington, vol.18, pp.254-255, Dec. 9, 1905.

GEOLOGICAL SETTING OF THE AURORA MASTODON REMAINS. William E.Powers. Trans. Illinois State Acad. Sci., Springfield, vol.28, no.2, pp.193-194, Dec., 1935.

MASTODON (MAMMUT AMERICANUM) REMAINS IN RIVER GRAVELS AT POINT MARION, PA. Paul H. Price, Dana Wells. W.Virginia Univ. Bull., ser.33, no.15 (Proc. W.Virginia Acad. Sci., vol.6), pp. 81-84, pl.1, Mar., 1933.

POST-GLACIAL OCCURRENCE OF MASTODON REMAINS IN SOUTHWESTERN ONTARIO. Loris S. Russell. Trans. Royal Canadian Inst., Toronto, vol.27, no.57, pp.57-64, figs.4, 1948.

RICHMOND MASTODON. J.T. Sanford. Bull. Geol. Soc. America, vol.44, no.1, p.200, Feb. 28, 1933. (Abstract); Proc. Rochester Acad. Sci., vol.7, no.5, pp. 137-156, figs.8, Mar., 1935.

SURVEY OF VARIOUS LATE CENOZOIC VERTEBRATE FAUNAS OF THE PANHANDLE OF TEXAS. PART II. PROBOSCIDEA. Donald E. Savage. Univ.Calif. Publ. Geol. Sci., vol.31, no.3, pp.51-74, illus., Oct., 1955.

GARRETT MASTODON. Paul F. Simpson. Proc. Indiana Acad. Sci., vol.43, pp.154-155, fig.1, Apr., 1934.

MASTODON AND OTHER FINDS AT AURORA. Clarence R. Smith. Trans Ill. State Acad. Sci., Springfield, vol.28, no. 2, pp.195-196, Dec., 1935.

MASTODON AND OTHER REMAINS AT AURORA, ILLINOIS. Clarence R. Smith. Science, n.s., vol.81, no.2103, pp.379-380, Apr. 19, 1935.

ANOTHER MASTODON FOUND IN OHIO. Karl Ver Steeg. Science, Lancaster, vol. 100, no.2599, p.357, Oct. 20, 1944.

MASTODON DISCOVERED IN OHIO. Karl Ver Steeg. Science, n.s., vol.88, no. 2291, p.498, Nov. 25, 1938.

NEW RECORDS OF MASTODONS AND MAMMOTHS IN CANADA. C.M.Sternberg. Canadian Field-Nat., vol.44, pp.59-65, pl.1, map, Mar., 1930.

A PLIOMASTODON SKULL FROM THE THOUSAND CREEK BEDS, NORTHWESTERN NEVADA. Chester Stock. Carnegie Inst. Washington (Contrib.Palaeont.), Publ.no.473, pp.35-39, pl.1, July 10,1936.

MASTODON REMAINS FOUND IN WEST VIRGINIA. W.J. Sumpstine, B.R. Weimer. Science, Lancaster, n.s., vol.90, no.2345, pp.539-540, Dec. 8, 1939.

ORELETON FARMS MASTODON. Edward S. Thomas. Ohio Jour. Sci., vol.52, no.1, pp.1-5, illus., Jan., 1952.

TOOTH-MARKS ON BONES OF THE ORLETON FARMS MASTODON. Albert E. Wood. Ohio. Jour. Sci., Columbus, vol.52, no.1, pp.27-28, Jan., 1952.

South America

(ON A MASTODON OF BOLIVIA.) Sur un Mastodon de Bolivie. (Teleobunomastodon for Mastodon bolivianus.) Pierre Revilliod. Mem. Soc. Paleont. Suisse, vol.51, pp. 21, figs.9, pls.2, 1931.

MASTODONTS OF BRAZIL. George Gaylord Simpson, Carlos de Paula Couto. Bull. Amer. Mus. Nat. Hist., vol.112, no.2, pp.125-190, pls.23, Apr. 15, 1957.

(LAST MASTODON OF SOUTH AMERICA.) Das letzte Mastodon von Suedamerika.Fr. Spillmann. Bericht Sencken.Naturf.Gesell., vol.59, no.2, pp.119-123, pl.1, fig.4, Feb., 1929.

Taxonomy

AMEBELODON SINCLAIRI SP. NOV. E.H. Barbour. Nebraska State Mus., vol.1, Bull. no.17, pp.155-158, fig.101, Jan., 1930.

MILFORD MASTODON, MASTODON MOODIEI, SP. NOV. A PRELIMINARY REPORT. E.H. Barbour. Nebraska State Mus., vol.1, Bull.no.24, pp.203-210, figs.5, Dec., 1931.

NEW AMEBELODONT, TORYNOBELODON BARNUMBROWNI, SP. NOV. PRELIMINARY REPORT. E.H. Barbour. Nebraska State Mus., vol.1, Bull.no.22, pp.191-198, figs. 123-126, Aug., 1931.

PRELIMINARY NOTICE OF A NEW PROBOSCIDEAN AMEBELODON FRICKI, GEN. ET SP. NOV. E.H. Barbour. Nebraska State Mus., vol.1, Bull.no.13, pp.131-134, figs.3, June, 1927.

TORYNOBELODON LOOMISI, GEN. ET SP. NOV. E.H. Barbour. Nebraska State Mus., vol.1, Bull.no.16, pp.147-153, figs. 3, Dec., 1929.

GNATHABELODON THORPEI, GEN. ET SP. NOV. A NEW MUD-GRUBBING MASTODON. E.H. Barbour. Nebraska State Mus., vol.1, Bull.no.42, pp.395-404, figs.187-191, May, 1935.

NEW REMAINS OF TRILOPHODONT-TETRABELODONT MASTODONS. Childs Frick. Bull. Amer. Mus. Nat. Hist., vol.59, art.9, pp.505-652, figs.38, Mar. 2, 1933.

TWO NEW PLEISTOCENE MASTODENS. (New Species: Mammut francisi and M. oregonense.) Oliver P. Hay. Jour. Washington Acad. Sci., vol.16, no.2, pp.35-41, Jan. 19, 1926.

(REMARKS ON THE CLASSIFICATION AND PHYLOGENY OF SOUTH AMERICAN MASTODONS.) Remarques sur la classification et la phylogenie des Mastodontes sud-americains. Robert Hoffstetter.Bull. Mus. Nat.d'Hist.Nat., Paris, vol.27, ser. 2, pp.484-491, illus., Dec., 1955.

REVISION OF PALAEOMASTODON DIVIDING IT INTO TWO GENERA, AND WITH DESCRIPTIONS OF TWO NEW SPECIES. H. Matsumoto. Bull. Amer.Mus. Nat. Hist., New York, vol.50, art.1, pp. 1-58, figs.48, July 2, 1924.

ADDITIONAL NEW GENERA AND SPECIES OF THE MASTODONTOID PROBOSCIDEA. Henry Fairfield Osborn. Amer. Mus.Nov., no.238, pp.16, illus., Nov. 30, 1927.

NEW EURASIATIC AND AMERICAN PROBOSCIDEANS. Henry Fairfield Osborn. Amer. Mus. Nov., New York, no.393, pp. 23, figs.22, Dec. 24, 1929.

Elephantidae

ELEPHANTS. Carl E. Akeley. World's Work, vol.41, pp.73-92, figs.19, Nov., 1920.

(THE DISTRIBUTION REGION OF ELEPHANTS AT THE BEGINNING OF THE HISTORICAL PERIOD.) Das Verbreitungsgebiet der Elefanten zu Beginn der Historischen Zeit. Rudolf Arnold. Zeitschr. f. Saeugetierk., Berlin, vol.17, no.2, pp.73-82, Feb. 19, 1953.

(Review by Francis Petter of) (A QUATER OF A CENTURY AMONG THE ELEPHANTS.) Un quart de siècle parmi les Elephants. W. Baze. (DISEASES AND ANTHROPOIDS.) Ueber Krankheiten der Menschenaffen. W. Koch, B. Deimel. Mammalia, Paris, vol. 16, no.3, pp.176-177, Sep., 1952.

JUMBO. (Type of Elephas africanus rothschildi Lydekker.) Leonard J. Bolger. Nat. Hist., New York, vol.46, no.1, p.8, fig. 1, June, 1940.

ELEPHANTS IN GENTLER MOOD. Maurice Burton. Illus. London News, vol.137, no. 3571, p.574, Oct. 1, 1955.

ELEPHANTS. Richard Carrington.

(AN ELEPHANT DISAPPEARS.) En elefant forsvinner. Kai Curry-Lindahl. Fauna och Flora, Upsala, pts.1-2, pp.15, illus.,1953.

CASE OF THE MISSING ELEPHANTS. Richard Dempewolff. Science Illus., New York, vol.3, no.6, pp.23-25, 80-81, June, 1948.

PIGMY ELEPHANTS. Guy Dollman. Nat. Hist. Mag. (British Mus.), vol.4, no.31, pp.266-271, figs.1-5, July, 1934.

ALL ABOUT ELEPHANTS. Dorothy Lee Edwards. New York, E.P. Dutton and Co., pp.88, illus., 1941.

(Review by Claude W. Luister of) ALL ABOUT ELEPHANTS. Dorothy Lee Edwards. Animal Kingdom, New York, vol.45, p.80, May-June, 1942.

ELEPHANT DRAINS. Philip Fowke. Loris, Ceylon, vol.2, no.3, pp.159-160, Dec.,1940.

(PRESENTATION OF AN ELEPHAS INDICUS EMBRYO.) Presentation d'un embryon d'Elephas inducus L. M.Friant. Bull. Soc. Zool. France, Paris, vol.62, pp.159-165, 1937.

ELEPHANTS IN AND OUT OF THE ZOO. E. Heller. Bull. Washington Park Zool. Soc., Milwaukee, vol.4, no.1, pp.18, May, 1933; Zoonooz, Zool. Soc. San Diego, vol. 25, no.4, pp.2-5; no.5, pp.5-7; no.6, pp. 5-7, illus., Apr., May, June, 1952.

PYGMY ELEPHANT AND GIANT TORTOISE. Dirk Albert Hooijer. Sci. Monthly, Lancaster, vol.72, no.1, pp.3-8, illus., Jan., 1951.

A BABY ELEPHANT. J.Ibbotson. Jour.Bombay Nat. Hist. Soc., vol.40, no.3, pp.558-559, pl.1, Dec., 1938.

(PYGMY ELEPHANTS.) Elephants nains. L. Joleaud. Bull. Soc. Nat. Acclimat., France, vol.77, no.4, pp.54-57, Apr., 1930.

NATURE'S VACUUM CLEANER. (Elephant.) Winifred E. King. San Diego Zoonooz, vol. 18, no.10, pp.3-5, illus., Oct., 1945.

ELEPHANT MISTAKEN FOR A TIGER. R.C. Morris. Jour. Bombay Nat. Hist. Soc., vol.33, no.4, pp.981-983, Oct. 15, 1929.

ELEPHANTS, IN PARTICULAR. Edalee Orcutt. Zoonooz, San Diego, vol.20, no. 10, pp.3-4, illus., Nov., 1947.

ELEPHANTOGRAPHIA CURIOSA, SEU ELEPHANTI DESCRIPTIO, JUXTA MATHODUM ET LEGES IMPERIALIS ACADEMIAE LEOPOLDINO-CAROLINAE NATURAE CURIOSORUM ADORNATA, MULTISQVE SELECTIS OBSERVATIONIBUS PHYSICIS, MEDICIS ET JUCUNDIS HISTORIIS REFERTA, CUM FIGURIS AENEIS. D. Geo. C. Petrie. Joh.Henrici Groschii, Acad.Typogr. Erfordiae, pp.1-284, pls.255, 1715.

THE EMPIRE'S ELEPHANT COUNTRY. C.R.S. Pitman. Field, London, vol.161, no.4195, pp.1125-1126, illus., May 20, 1933.

WHAT BECOMES OF DEAD ELEPHANTS? R.I. Pocock. Field, London, vol.153, p. 761, illus., May 9, 1929.

CONCERNING ELEPHANTS: THE MOST REMARKABLE OF LIVING MAMMALS. W.P. Pycraft. Illus. London News, vol. 185, no.4972, p.189, figs.3, Aug. 4, 1934.

LIFE WITH ALICE: 40 YEARS OF ELEPHANT ADVENTURES. Richard Richards. Coward-McCann Inc., New York, pp.67, 1944.

JUMBO. John R. Russell. Univ. Rochester Library Bull., vol.3, no.1, pp.12-20, Autumn, 1947.

ELEPHANT BEFORE A.D. C.Davies Sherborn. Ann. and Mag. Nat. Hist., London, ser.10, vol.15, no.88, pp.492-495, Apr., 1935.

(OBSERVATIONS ON KAOKO ELEPHANTS.) Beobachtungen am Kaoko-Elefanten. J.Steinhardt. Zool. Garten, Leipzig, n.F., vol. 4, nos.8-9, pp.294-296, Oct., 1931.

RESUME OF "THE ELEPHANT." Etsuijiro Sunamoto. Published privately. No.6, 5 Chome Kawara-machi, Higachi-Ku, Osaka, Japan, vols.2, pp.2169, pls.263, 1931-32. (In Japanese.)

(THE ELEPHANTS.) Les elephants. Gaston Tournier. Paris, Bibliotheque Generale d'Editions, pp.237, illus., 1909.

AN ELEPHANT AS AN ARCTIC TRAVELER. Frederick W. True. Smiths. Inst., Misc. Coll., Quarterly Issue, vol.47, pp.517-518, May 6, 1905.

(ELEPHANT DOCTORS.) Les elephants médecins. F. Varlet. Notes Africaines, pp.100, 1949.

ELEPHANTS. Herbert S. Zim. New York, Wm. Morrow and Co., pp.63, illus., 1946.

AJANTA: PART THREE. (Outline drawing of a fesco, numerous elephants with mythical giant 6 tusker.) Illus. London News, vol.211, no.5658, p.342, illus., Sep. 27, 1947.

ELEPHANTS IN 16TH CENTURY TAPESTRY. Illus. London News, vol.217, no. 5805, p.122, illus., July 22, 1950.

PRINCELY INDIAN WEDDING.... THE BRIDEGROOM...ON A SPLENDIDLY-CAPARISONED ELEPHANT. Illus. London News, vol.216, no.5795, p.738, illus., May 13, 1950.

Africa

ZOOLOGICAL RESULTS OF THE GEORGE VANDERBILT AFRICAN EXPEDITION OF 1934. PART II. THE FOREST ELEPHANT OF AFRICA. Glover M. Allen. Proc. Acad. Nat. Sci., Philadelphia, vol.88, pp.15-44, fig.1, pls.1-4, Mar. 10, 1936.

ELEPHANT IN THE KABBA PROVINCE. P.A. Allison. Nigerian Field, vol.14, no. 1, pp.5-10, map, Jan., 1949.

(NOTES ON THE MAMMALS OF FRENCH EQUATORIAL AFRICA. THE PYGMY ELEPHANT.) Notes sur les mammiferes de l'Equateur africain francais. L'elephant nain. L. Blancou. Mammalia, Paris, vol. 15, no.3, pp.84-91, Sep., 1941.

(NOTES ON A PYGMY ELEPHANT OF GABON.) Note relative a un éleph ant nain du Gabon. E. Bourdelle, F. Petter. Mammalia, vol.14, no.4, pp.145-153, Dec., 1950.

ELEPHANTS IN THE BELGIAN CONGO. William Bridges. Animal Kingdom, New York, vol.51, no.1, pp.20-28, illus., Jan.-Feb., 1948.

AFRICAN ELEPHANT. PART III. Cuthbert Christy. Jour. African Soc., vol.21, pp. 291-301, July, 1922.

TWO SKULLS OF A SMALL RACE OF ELEPHANT FROM THE CAMEROONS AND FROM SIERRA LEONE. Guy Dollman. Proc. Linnaean Soc. London, 145th Session, pp. 11-13, Jan. 20, 1933.

(CONTRIBUTION TO STUDY OF THE PYGMY ELEPHANTS OF THE SOUTHERN CAMEROUN.) Contribution a l'étude des Elephants nains du Sud-Cameroun. Francois Edmond-Blanc. Mammalia, Paris, vol.19, no.3, pp.428-429, Sep., 1955.

(THE AFRICAN ELEPHANT.) L'elephant africain. F. Fallon. Mem.Inst.Roy. Colonial Belge, Brussels, Sect. Sci. Nat. et Medic., vol.13, fasc.2, pp.1-51, pls. 7, 1944.

(THE ELEPHANTS OF THE REGIONS OF THE NORTHERN CAMEROUN AND BENUE.) Les Elephants des régions du Nord-Cameroun et de la Benoue. P.Flizot. Mammalia, Paris, vol.12, no.4, pp.148-151, Dec., 1948.

(THE AFRICAN ELEPHANT.) L'eléphant d'Afrique. Edouard Foa. Rev. de Paris, 6th année, no.15, pp.611-626, Aug.1, 1899.

(THE ELEPHANTS OF ANGOLA.) Elephants d'Angola. F.Frade. Bull. Soc. Portugaise Sci. Nat., Lisboa, vol.11, no. 30, pp.319-333, pls.20-21, Dec., 1933.

(ELEPHANTS OF MOZAMBIQUE.) Éléphants du Mozambique. F.Frade. Bull.Soc. Portugaise Sci. Nat., Lisboa, vol.11, no. 29, pp.307-318, pls.18-19, Dec., 1933.

(GEOGRAPHIC DISTRIBUTION OF THE AFRICAN ELEPHANTS.) Distribution geographique des elephants d'Afrique. F. Frade. Comptes Rendus, 12th Internat. Congr. Zool. 1935, Lisboa, vol.2, pp. 1191-1202, fig.1, 1936-37.

(THE ELEPAHNTS OF MAURITANIA.) Les eléphants de Mauritanie. G. Grandidier. La Terre et la Vie (Revue d'Hist.Nat.), vol.2, no.3, pp.130-134, illus., Mar., 1932.

THE ADDO BUSH ELEPHANTS. John D. Hamlyn. Hamlyn's Menagerie Mag., vol. 5, no.7, pp.51-55, figs.1-4, Nov., 1919.

FATE OF THE ADDO ELEPHANTS. John D. Hamlyn. Hamlyn's Menagerie Mag., vol.5, no.4, pp.28-30, Aug., 1919.

THE ELEPHANT IN EAST CENTRAL AFRICA. A MONOGRAPH. W.C. Osman Hill et al. London, Rowland Ward, Ltd., pp. 150, pl.1, 1953. (Included Articles: THE EVOLUTION OF THE AFRICAN ELEPHANT, by W.C.Osman Hill; THE ANATOMY OF THE AFRICAN ELEPHANT, by W.C.Osman Hill; THE REPRODUCTION OF THE AFRICAN ELEPHANT, by W.C.Osman Hill; THE ELEPHANT IN THE SUDAN, by W. Barker; THE ELEPHANT IN KENYA, by C.H.Stockley; THE ELEPHANT IN UGANDA, by C.R.S.Pitman; THE ELEPHANT IN THE BELGIAN CONGO, by P.P.M. Offermann; THE ELEPHANT IN TANGANYIKA, by G.G. Rushby; THE AFRICAN ELEPHANT IN HISTORY, by William Gowers.)

OBSERVATIONS ON THE ELEPHANTS OF NORTHERN RHODESIA AND PORTUGUESE EAST AFRICA. Wynant Davis Hubbard. Jour. Mamm., vol.9, no.1, pp. 39-43, Feb., 1928.

(THE ELEPHANT OF AFRICA.) L'elephant d'Afrique. A. Jeannin. Payot, Paris, pp.250, 1947.

(Review by P. Rode of) (ELEPHANT OF AFRICA.) L'elephant d'Afrique. A.Jeannin. Mammalia, Paris, vol.11, no.4, p.167, Dec., 1947.

(THE ELEPHANT OF BARBARY.) L'elephant de Berberie. L. Joleaud. Assoc. Franc. Avanc. Sci. Nancy, 55th Session, pp.478-482, 1931.

(STUDIES OF ZOOGEOGRAPHY ON THE BARBARY. THE PROBOSCIDIANS. I. THE AFRICAN ELEPHANT.) Etudes de geographie zoolegique sur la Berberie. Les proboscidiens. I. L'elephant d'Afrique. L. Joleaud. Bull. Soc. Zool. France, vol. 56, no.6, pp.483-499, Feb. 15, 1932.

(DISCOVERY OF A MOLAR OF AN AFRICAN ELEPHANT NORTHWEST OF OUED EL ANEB (EDOUGH MASSIF, ALGERIA).) Sur la decouverte d'une molaire d'elephant d'Afrique au Nord-Ouest d'Oued el Aneb (massif de l'Edough, Algérie). L. Joleaud, Marcel Roubault. Seances Soc. Geol.France, Paris, no.12, p.207, June 22, 1936.

ELEPHANTS IN UGANDA. Theodore Karam. Field, London, vol.166, no.4331, p.1521, Dec. 28, 1935.

(ELEPHANTS OF CHAD.) Les eléphants du Tchad. R. Malbrant. Bull. Soc. Nat. Acclimat. France, vol.77, no.3, pp.38-40, Mar., 1930. (Abstract.)

(NOTES ON THE ELEPHANTS OF CHAD.) Notes sur les eléphants du Tchad. R.Malbrant. Rev. Hist. Nat., Soc. Nat. Acclimat. France, 1st Partie, A. Mammiferes, vol.11, no.9, pp.281-283, Sep., 1930.

ELEPHANTS IN AFRICA. Frank Melland. Charles Scribner's Sons, New York, pp. xiii-186, illus., 1938.

OCCURRENCE OF THE ELEPHANT (ELEPHAS AFRICANUS) IN SIERRA LEONE. C.B. Mitford. Proc. Zool. Soc. London, pt.1, pp. 2-3, June 1, 1894.

AFRICAN ELEPHANT. B.D. Nicholson. African Wild Life, Johannesburg, vol.10, no.1, pp.25-36, illus., Mar., 1956.

THE KNYSNA ELEPHANTS, BRIEF NOTE ON THEIR HISTORY AND HABITS. J.F.V. Phillips. S.African Jour. Sci., vol.22, pp. 287-293, Nov., 1925.

(NOTES ON AFRICAN ELEPHANTS.) Notizen ueber afrikanische Elephanten. Hermann Pohle. Zeitschr. f. Saeugetierk., vol.1, no.1, pp.58-64, figs.2, pl.1, Aug. 31, 1926.

AFRICAN ELEPHANTS. P.H.G. Powell-Cotton. Field, London, vol.149, p.676, Apr. 21, 1927.

(NOTES ON THE ELEPHANT OF THE ADDO BUSH.) Notizen ueber den Elefanten des Addo-Busches. Ulrich Roeder. Zool.Garten, Leipzig, n.F., vol.5, nos.1-3, pp.59-60, June, 1932.

HOOFED MAMMALS OF NIGERIA. SUB-ORDER PROBOSCIDEA. D.R. Rosevear. Nigerian Field, London, vol.9, no.1, pp. 7-10, Mar., 1940.

(SOME MEETINGS WITH THE ELEPHANTS OF AFRICA.) Quelques recontres avec les elephants d'Afrique. Le Docteur Thibout. La Terre et la Vie (Revue d'Hist.Nat.), vol. 1, no.11, pp.643-656, illus., Dec., 1931.

HUNTED DOWN WIND BY AN ELEPHANT. A THREE-MILE POINT IN THE SUDAN. C. Whitaker. Field, London, vol.164, no. 4260, p.396, illus., Aug. 18, 1934.

WILD AFRICAN ELEPHANTS DRINKING AND BATHING. R.L. Willan. Illus. London News, vol.222, no.5942, p.367, illus., Mar. 7, 1953.

LOXODONTA AFRICANA MOCAMBICUS FRADE. Ludwig Zukowsky. Zool. Garten, Leipzig, n.F., vol.3, nos.9-10, pp.244-246, figs.2, Oct., 1930.

ADDO BUSH ELEPHANTS. (Nearing extinction.) Sambab, S.African Mus. Assoc., Durban, vol.3, no.7, p.193, Sep., 1944.

Anatomy (General)

(OBSERVATIONS ON AN ASIAN ELEPHANT'S BRAIN FIXED IN POSITION IN THE CRANIUM.) Observations sur un encephale d'eléphant d'Asie fixe en position dans le crane. J. Anthony. Ann. Sci. Nat., Paris, ser.11, vol.9, pt.2, pp.253-264, figs.5, Oct., 1948.

ELEPHANT'S HEAD. STUDIES IN THE COMPARATIVE ANATOMY OF THE ORGANS OF THE HEAD OF THE INDIAN ELEPHANT AND OTHER MAMMALS. FIRST PART. THE FACIAL MUSCLES AND THE PROBOSCIS, WITH SEVENTEEN PLATES IN COLOURS. J.E.V.Boas, Simon Paulli. Jena, Gustav Fischer, pp.79, pls. 17, 1908.

(Comments by Nellie B.Eales on) THE ELEPHANT'S HEAD. PART 2. J.E.V. Boas, Simon Paulli. Anat. Anzeiger, vol.61, pp. 361-364, Aug. 14, 1926. (In German.)

(ANATOMICAL STUDIES ON THE SYMPATHETIC NERVOUS SYSTEM OF THE INDIAN ELEPHANT.) Études anatomiques sur le système nerveux sympathique de l'elephant des Indes. M.J. Botar. Bull.Mus. Nat. Hist. Nat., Paris, ser.2, vol.3, no.8, pp.722-726, figs.4, Dec., 1931.

(THE ORIGIN AND MEANING OF THE INTERCROSSING OF THE TUSKS OF SOME ELEPHANTS.) Sobre el origen y significàtion del entrecruzamiento de las defensas en algunos elefantes. Angel Cabrera. Bol. Real Soc. Española Hist. Nat., vol.27, pp.441-449, 1927.

NOTE ON A LOWER JAW OF AN AFRICAN ELEPHANT. C. Forster Cooper. Ann. and Mag. Nat. Hist., ser.9, vol.12, pp.263-264, figs.2, Aug., 1923.

(PECULIARITY OF THE MAMMOTH TAIL OBSERVED IN THE INDIAN ELEPHANT.) Une particularité de la queue de mammouth observee chez l'elephant d l'Inde. Ed. Dechambre. Bull. Mus. Nat. Hist. Nat., Paris, ser.2, vol.18, no.1, pp.43-44, pl.1, Jan., 1946.

DEVELPMENT OF THE MANDIBLE IN THE ELEPHANT. Nellie B. Eales. Proc. Zool. Soc. London, pt.1, pp.115-125, figs. 9, pl.1, Apr. 14, 1931.

EXTERNAL CHARACTERS, SKIN, AND TEMPORAL GLAND OF A FOETAL AFRICAN ELEPHANT. Nellie B. Eales. Proc. Zool. Soc. London, pt.2, pp.445-456, pl.1, July, 1925.

ON THE ANATOMY OF THE AFRICAN ELEPHANT (ELEPHAS AFRICANUS, BLUM). W.A. Forbes. Proc. Zool. Soc. London, no.28, pp.420-435, figs.8, May 6, 1879.

(FIRST TWO VERTEBRAE IN AFRICAN ELEPHANTS.) Les deux premieres vertebres chez les eléphants d'Afrique. F.Frade. Bull. Soc. Portugaise Sci. Nat., Lisboa, vol.11, no.25, pp.277-284, pls.15-16, Dec., 1933.

(THE JAWBONE OF PRESENT-DAY ELEPHANTS.) La mandibule des éléphants actuels. F. Frade. Arquivos Mus.Bocage, Mus. e Labor. Zool. e Antrop., Lisboa, no.4, pp.1-6, figs.2, 1933.

(A CASE OF ENROLLMENT OF TUSKS IN THE AFRICAN ELEPHANT.) Un cas d'enroulement des defenses chez l'eléphant Africain. M. Friant. La Terre et la Vie (Revue d'Hist.Nat.), vol.2, no.2, pp.111-112, 118, illus., Feb., 1932.

(INVESTIGATIONS OF THE BRAIN OF THE ELEPHANT (LOXODONTA AFRICANA BLUM).) Recherches sur le cerveau de l'elephant (Loxodonta africana Blum). M. Friant. Ann. Soc. Roy. Zool. Belgique, vol. 82, no.1, pp.51-66, 1951.

ON THE HYOID BONE OF THE ELEPHANT. Alfred Henry Garrod. Proc. Zool. Soc. London, pp.365-367, fig.1, 1875.

(STRUCTURAL CHANGE IN THE BONES OF PROBOSCIDEANS IN CONNECTION WITH CONDITIONS IN THEIR HABITAT.) Izmenenie Stroeniia Kisti Khobotnykh (Proboscidea) v Sviazi s Usloviiami iu Obitaniia. B.E. Garutt. Doklady Akad. Nauk SSSR, Novaia Serriia, Moscow, vol. 77, no.3, pp.513-515, 1951.

ADAPTIVE SIGNIFICANCE OF THE SHORTENING OF THE ELEPHANT'S SKULL. W.K. Gregory. Bull. Amer. Mus. Nat. Hist., art.9, vol.19, pp.387-394, figs.4, pl.23, July 8, 1903.

NOTE ON THE SPERMATOZOA, AND ON THE ELEVATOR MUSCLES OF THE PENIS, OF THE INDIAN ELEPHANT. George Gulliver. Proc. Zool. Soc. London, pt.15, p. 105, 1847.

EXTERNAL AND RADIOLOGICAL ANATOMY OF A FOETAL ASIATIC ELEPHANT. W.C. Osman Hill. Ceylon Jour. Sci., sect. B. Zool. and Geol., Spolia Zeylanica, vol. 21, pt.1, pp.31-43, figs.5, pls.1-2, Feb. 10, 1938.

STUDIES ON THE CARDIAC ANATOMY OF THE ELEPHANT. I. CORONARY BLOOD VESSELS. W.C. Osman Hill. Jour. Anat., Cambridge, vol.70, pt.3, pp.386-398, pls.3, Apr., 1936.

STUDIES ON THE CARDIAC ANATOMY OF THE ELEPHANT. II. THE HEART AND GREAT VESSELS OF A FOETAL ASIATIC ELEPHANT. W.C. Osman Hill. Ceylon Jour. Sci., sect.B. Zool. and Geol., Spolia Zeylanica, vol.21, pt.1, pp.45-61, fig.1, pls.3-4, Feb. 10, 1938.

(ON THE TACTILE ORGANS OF ELEPHAS INDICUS.) Ueber die Tastorgane von Elephas indicus. W. Kolmer. Anat. Anz. vol.54, no.5, pp.73-77, May 22, 1921.

ELEPHANT WITH EXTRAORDINARY 'GLANDS.' A.S. Laurie. Jour. Bombay Nat. Hist. Soc., vol.32, pp.792-793, pl.1, May 31, 1928.

(DEMONSTRATION OF A FOETUS OF THE WEST AFRICAN ELEPHANT ELEPHAS CYCLOTIS MATSCHIE.) Demonstration eines Foetus vom westafrikanischen Elefanten, Elephas cyclotis Matschie. Einar Lonnberg. Comptes Rendus, 6th Congress Inter. Zool., Berne, 1904, pp.323-326, pl.1, May 25, 1905.

AN ELEPHANT WITH EXTRAORDINARY GLANDS. G. Carmichael Low. Jour.Bombay Nat. Hist. Soc., vol.32, no.3, p.707, May 31, 1929.

WHITE ELEPHANT CALF. D.F. Macfie. Field, London, vol.148, p.1051, Dec.16, 1926; Jour. Bombay Nat. Hist. Soc., vol. 32, p.214, Aug. 1, 1927.

(COMPARATIVE STUDIES ON THE FEMALE ORGANS OF THE ELEPHANTS WITH REMARKS ON THE FORMATION OF THE HYMEN.) Recherches comparatives sur l'organe femelle des elephants avec remarques sur les formations dites hyménales. Henri Neuville. Ann. Sci. Nat., Zool., Paris, ser.10, vol.20, no.2, pp.245-295, figs.11, Dec., 1937.

(REVIEW OF SOME DATA ON THE PLEURA OF PROBOSCIDEANS.) Revision de quelques Donnees sur la Plevre des Proboscidiens. Henri Neuville. Mammalia, vol.8, nos.3-4, pp.81-132, illus., pls.1-4, Sep.-Dec., 1944.

(SECOND PRELIMINARY NOTE ON THE ORGANIZATION OF THE FOOT OF THE ELEPHANT.) Seconde note préliminaire sur l'organisation du pied des Elephants. Henri Neuville. Bull. Mus. Nat. Hist. Nat. Paris, ser.2, vol.5, no.1, pp.63-67, figs.1-2, Jan., 1933.

(SOME DIFFERENTIAL CHARACTERS OF THE CARPUS AND TARSUS AMONG THE PROBOSCIDEANS.) Sur quelques caracteres differentiels du carpe et du tarse chez les proboscidiens. Henri Neuville. Mammalia, Paris, vol.10, nos.3-4, pp.122-128, fig.1, Sep.-Dec., 1946 (1947).

(THIRD PRELIMINARY NOTE ON THE ORGANIZATION OF THE ELEPHANT'S FOOT. THE PRAEPOLLEX AND THE PRAEHALLUX.) Troisieme note preliminaire sur l'organization du pied des éléphants. Le praepollex et le praehallux. Henri Neuville. Bull. Mus. Nat. Hist.Nat., Paris, ser.2, vol.6, no.3, pp.210-217, figs.4, Apr., 1934.

HEADS OF AFRICAN ELEPHANTS. DISPARITY IN SIZE BETWEEN THAT OF THE MALE AND THAT OF THE FEMALE. Henry Fairfield Osborn. Nat. Hist., vol.21, pp. 244-245, figs.2, May-June, 1921.

(OBSERVATIONS ON THE ANATOMY OF THE ADULT AFRICAN ELEPHANT (LOXODON AFRICANUS).) Observations sur l'Anatomie de l'Elephant d'Afrique (Loxodon Africanus) adulte. M. Felix Plateau, M. Valiere Lienard. Bull. Acad. Royal de Belgique, ser.3, vol.1, no.3, pp.1-38, figs.1-2, 1881.

(INVESTIGATIONS OF THE FINE STRUCTURE OF THE TEMPORAL GLAND IN THE AFRICAN AND INDIAN ELEPHANTS, LOXODONTA AFRICANA CUVIER AND ELEPHAS MAXIMUS LINNEAUS.) Untersuchungen ueber den Feinbau der Schlafendruese beim afrikanischen und indischen Elefanten, Loxodonta africana Cuvier und Elephas maximus Linneaus. Rolf Schneider. Acta Anatomica, Basel, vol.28, no.3, pp. 303-312, 1956.

GENITO-URINARY SYSTEM OF THE ELEPHAS INDICUS MALE. T.L. Schulte. Amer. Jour. Anat., Philadelphia, vol.61, no.1, pp. 131-157, pls.1-2, May 15, 1937.

MUSCULATURE OF INDIAN ELEPHANT. PART 1. MUSCULATURE OF THE FORELIMB. PART 2. MUSCULATURE OF THE HINDLIMB. Tokuichi Shindo, Masaru Mori. Okajimas Folia Anat. Japonica, vol.28, nos.1-6, pp.89-147, Sep., 1956.

INNERVATION OF THE TRUNK OF THE INDIAN ELEPHANT. R. Sprinz. Proc.Zool. Soc. London, vol.122, pt.3, pp.621-623, illus., Nov., 1952.

(EXTERNAL MORPHOLOGICAL DIFFERENCES BETWEEN FOETUSES OF ELEPHAS AFRICANUS AND E. MAXIMUS.) Aeussere morphologische Unterschiede zwischen Foeten von Elephas africanus und E. Maximus. Otto Wettstein. Arkiv. f. Zoologi, vol.13, no.15, pp.15, figs.3, Oct. 23, 1920.

Anatomy (Teeth)

(AN ELEPHANT OF AFRICA(LOXODONTA AFRICANA BLUM) WITH A SYMMETRICAL ANOMALY (SPIRAL ENROLLMENT) OF THE TUSKS.) Un éléphant d'Afrique (Loxodonta africana Blum.) présentant une anomalie symetrique (enroulement en spire) des défenses. M.R. Anthony. Bull.Mus. Nat. Hist. Nat., Paris, ser.2, vol.3, no.1, pp.74-76, fig.1, Jan., 1931.

(VESTIGES OF TWO SUCCESSIVE REPLACEMENTS OF THE THIRD MILK MOLAR IN THE ASIAN ELEPHANT.) Vestiges de deux remplacements successifs de la 3ème molaire de lait chez l'elephant d'Asie (Elephas indicus Cuv.). M. R. Anthony. Proc. Zool. Soc. London, pt.3, pp.723-727, figs.1-2, pl.1, Sep., 1931.

(AN AFRICAN ELEPHANT SKULL (LOXODONTA AFRICANA BLUM.) WITH FOUR UPPER INCISORS.) Un crane d'elephant d'Afrique (Loxodonta africana Blum.) a quatre incisives superieures. M.R. Anthony, M.Prouteaux. Archiv.Mus.Hist. Nat., Paris (6), vol.4, pp.15-32, figs.3, map, pl., 1929.

MANDIBULAR TUSKS OF AMEBELODON FRICKI. Erwin Hinckley Barbour.Nebraska State Mus., vol.1, Bull.no.14, pp.135-138, fig.1, Dec., 1929.

(FUNCTION OF THE CHEWING APPARATUS IN THE PROBOSCIDIANS.) Die Funktion des Kauapparates bei den Proboscidien. Hsichih Chang. Palaeobiolgica, vol.2, nos.1-3, pp. 34-48, figs.6, 1929.

AN ELEPHANT WITH FOUR TUSKS. John M. Clark. Science, n.s., vol.50, pp.395-396, fig.1, Oct. 24, 1919.

ABNORMAL TUSKS OF ELEPHANTS. Frank Colyer. Jour. Bombay Nat.Hist.Soc., vol. 34, no.3, pp.694-699, Nov. 15, 1930.

LARGE TUSKS OF INDIAN ELEPHANT (E. MAXIMUS). C.R.T. Congreve. Jour. Bombay Nat. Hist. Soc., vol.29, pp.1044-1045, fig.1, May 15, 1924.

(CONTRIBUTION TO DATA ON ELEPHANT MOLARS.) Beitrag zur Kenntnis des Elefantenmolaren. Fritz Driak. Gegenbaurs Morphol. Jahrb., Leipzig, vol.73, pp.257-288, figs.32, Dec., 1933.

(ABNORMALLY DEVELOPED DECIDUAL INCISOR OF THE ELEPHANT.) Une incisive deciduale d'éléphant anormalement développée. M. Friant. Bull. Mus. Nat. Hist. Nat., Paris, ser.2, vol.3, no.7, pp. 576-578, figs.2, Nov., 1931.

BULLETS AND SPEAR-HEADS EMBEDDED IN THE TUSKS OF ELEPHANTS. E. W. Gudger. Sci. Monthly, vol.35, no.4, pp. 312-327, figs.15, Oct., 1932.

LARGE TUSKER ELEPHANT. A.W.John. Jour. Bombay Nat. Hist. Soc., vol.32, p.596, Jan. 15, 1928.

REMARKABLE DOUBLE TUSKS OF A SUMATRAN ELEPHANT. G.C.A. Junge. Zool. Mededeel., Leiden, vol.23, pp.2, illus., 1941.

EXHIBITION OF A REMARKABLE PAIR OF TUSKS OF THE INDIAN ELEPHANT. Benjamin Leadbeater. Proc. Zool. Soc. London, p.195, 1864.

ABNORMAL ELEPHANT TUSKS (ELEPHAS MAXIMUS). G.D.L. Millar. Jour. Bombay Nat. Hist. Soc., vol.39, no.4, p.854, illus., Dec. 15, 1937.

WEIGHT OF TUSKS OF THE INDIAN ELEPHANT. G.D.L. Millar. Jour. Bombay Nat. Hist. Soc., vol.41, no.1, pp.171-172, 1939.

IVORY, THE PEARL OF THE FOREST. Ernst D. Moore. Scientific American, vol. 144, no.1, pp.9-12, Jan., 1931.

ABORTED TUSKS IN ELEPHANTS. R.C. Morris. Jour. Bombay Nat. Hist. Soc., vol.30, no.1, p.202, Sep. 30, 1928.

ELEPHANT TUSK WEDGED IN A TREE. R.C. Morris. Jour. Bombay Nat. Hist. Soc., vol.34, no.1, p.242, Mar. 1, 1930.

FORMATION AND ABSENCE OF TUSKS IN ELEPHANTS. R.C. Morris. Jour. Bombay Nat. Hist. Soc., vol.38, no.3, pp.615-617, Apr. 15, 1936.

MEASUREMENTS AND WEIGHTS OF ELEPHANT TUSKS. R.C. Morris. Jour.Bombay Nat. Hist. Soc., vol.41, no.3, p.660, Apr., 1940.

UNERUPTED TUSKS OF ELEPHANT. R.C. Morris. Jour. Bombay Nat. Hist. Soc., vol. 35, no.4, pp.889-891, fig.1, July 15, 1932.

NATURALLY SHED ELEPHANT MOLARS. T.C.S. Morrison-Scott. Proc. Linnean Soc. London, sess.149, 1936-37, pt.1, pp.40-42, Feb. 23, 1937.

ON THE OCCURRENCE OF A PRESUMED FIRST MILK-MOLAR (M. M. 1) IN AFRICAN ELEPHANTS. T.C.S. Morrison-Scott. Proc. Zool. Soc. London, 1938, vol.108, ser.B, Syst. and Morphol., pt.4, pp. 711-713, pls. 1-2, Jan., 1939.

REVISION OF OUR KNOWLEDGE OF AFRICAN ELEPHANTS' TEETH, WITH NOTES ON FOREST AND "PYGMY" ELEPHANTS. T.C.S. Morrison-Scott. Proc. Zool. Soc. London, vol.117, pts.2-3, pp. 505-527, fig.1, pls.3, 1947.

(STUDY OF THE DENTITION OF ELEPHAS (ARCHIDISCODON) IMPERATOR LEIDY (1858).) Etude sur la dentition de l'Elephas (Archidiscodon) imperator Leidy (1858). G. Pontier. Ann. Soc. Géol. du Nord, Lille, vol.58, pp.127-134, figs.2, 1933.

(PRESENCE OF A PRE-MOLAR IN ELEPHAS IMPERATOR LEIDY.) Presence d'une premolaire chez l'Elephas imperator Leidy. G. Pontier, R. Anthony. Comptes Rendus Acad. Sci. Paris, vol.196, no.22, pp.1686-1687, May 29, 1933.

ROGUE ELEPHANTS WITH MALFORMED TUSKS. L.L. Reade. Jour. Bombay Nat. Hist. Soc., vol.33, no.4, pp.979-980, illus., Oct. 15, 1929.

EXHIBITION OF, AND REMARKS UPON, A PAIR OF CORRODED TUSKS OF THE INDIAN ELEPHANT. Philip Lutley Sclater. Proc. Zool. Soc. London, p.145, 1871.

A LARGE PAIR OF ELEPHANT'S (ELEPHAS MAXIMUS) TUSKS FROM BURMA. J.K. Stanford. Jour. Bombay Nat. Hist. Soc., vol.37, no.2, pp.486-487, pl., Aug. 15, 1934.

THREE DIFFERENT KINDS OF ODONTOMA FOUND IN THE MOLARS OF ASIATIC FOSSIL ELEPHANTS. Fuyuji Takai. Jour. Geol. Soc. Japan, Tokyo, vol.46, no.554, pp.581-582, pl.28, Nov. 20, 1939.

TOOTH OF ELEPHANT FROM THE SEA-BOTTOM NEAR THE ISLAND OF HAKUREI, KÔKAIDO, KOREA. Fuyuji Takai. Jour. Geol. Soc. Japan, Tokyo, vol.44, no.523, pp.304-305, pl.1, Apr. 20, 1937. (In Japanese.)

MOLAR OF A MAMMOTH (ELEPHAS PRIMIGENIUS?). Arno Viehoever. Jour. Thailand Research Soc. (formerly The Siam Soc.), Bangkok, Nat. Hist. Suppl., vol.12, no.1, p.139, pl.1, Dec., 1939.

LARGE TUSKER FROM SOUTH INDIA. D.R.D. Wadia. Jour. Bombay Nat. Hist. Soc., vol.33, no.2, pp.434-437, pl.1, Feb. 15, 1929.

SOME OBSERVATIONS ON THE TUSKS OF AN INDIAN ELEPHANT--THE INNERVATION OF THE PULP. Harold L. Weatherford. Anat. Record, Philadelphia, vol.76, no.1, suppl.no.1, pp.81-94, pls. 1-2, Jan. 25, 1940.

DESCRIPTION OF ELEPHANTINE MOLARS IN THE MUSEUM OF THE UNIVERSITY. A. Winchell. Canadian Naturalist, pp.1-3, Aug., 1863.

ON THE TEETH OF ELEPHANT FOUND IN THE COURSE OF EXCAVATION OF THE TÔKYÔ SUBWAY. Jour. Geol. Soc. Tokyo, vol.37, no.436, pp.25-26, fig.1, Jan. 20, 1930. (In Japanese.)

RECORD PROBOSCIDEAN TUSK. Jour. Amer. Mus. Nat. Hist., New York, vol.35, no.4, p.357, Apr., 1935.

Asia

WILD ELEPHANTS IN THE UNITED PROVINCES. F.W. Champion. Jour. Bombay Nat. Hist. Soc., vol.32, pp.127-132, pls. 4, Aug. 1, 1927.

THE ELEPHANT AND I. (Indian Elephant.) M.D. Chaturvedi. Nat. Geogr. Mag., Washington, vol.112, no.4, pp.489-507, illus., Oct., 1957.

ELEPHAS MAXIMUS, THE ELEPHANT OF CEYLON. P.E.P. Deraniyagala. Nat. Mus., Ceylon, vol.1, pp.1-48, pls.18, Feb. 12, 1951.

ELEPHAS MAXIMUS, THE ELEPHANT OF CEYLON (PART II). P.E.P. Deraniyagala. Spolia Zeylanica, Bull.Nat.Mus.Ceylon, Colombo, vol.26, pp.161-176, Dec. 20, 1951; vol.27, pt.1, pp.109-124, illus., Oct. 24, 1953.

NAMES OF THE ELEPHANTS OF CEYLON. P.E.P. Deraniyagala. Ann. and Mag. Nat. Hist., London, ser.11, vol.11, no.73, pp. 61-64, Jan., 1944.

SOME ASPECTS OF THE ASIATIC ELEPHANT IN ZOOLOGY AND ETHNOGRAPHY. PART II. P.E.P. Deraniyagala. Jour. Roy. Asiatic Soc., Ceylon, vol.35, no.93, pp. 7-28, figs.5, pl.1, Feb. 10, 1941.

(ELEPHANTS IN BORNEO.) Olifanten in Borneo. D. Habbema. Tropische Natuur, vol.23, no.9, pp.167-171, Sep., 1934.

WILD ELEPHANTS IN ASSAM. J.E. Hall. Jour. Bombay Nat. Hist. Soc., vol.41, no. 3, pp.563-572, pl., Apr., 1940.

MALAYAN ELEPHANT (ELEPHAS MAXIMUS INDICUS). Theodore Hubback. Jour. Bombay Nat. Hist. Soc., vol.42, no.3, pp.483-509, pls.8, Aug., 1941.

"EMPTY TUMMIES." THE CEYLON ELEPHANT IN DUTCH TIMES. M.W. Jurriaanse. Loris, Ceylon, vol.2, no.3, pp. 148-154, illus., Dec., 1940.

MALAY RACE OF THE INDIAN ELEPHANT. (Elephas maximus hirsutus). R. Lydekker. Proc. Zool. Soc. London, pp.285-288, figs. 1-3, June, 1914.

SOME OBSERVATIONS ON WILD ELEPHANTS IN ORISSA. H.F. Mooney. Jour. Bombay Nat. Hist. Soc., vol.33, no.2, pp.430-433, map 1, Feb. 15, 1929.

ENCOUNTERS WITH ELEPHANTS ON THE BILLIGIRIRANGAN HILLS. R.C. Morris. Jour. Bombay Nat. Hist. Soc., vol.34, no. 1, pp.237-242, Mar. 1, 1930.

THE MALAYAN ELEPHANT. R.C. Morris. Jour. Bombay Nat. Hist. Soc., vol.42, no. 4, pp.928-929, Dec., 1941.

OBSERVATIONS ON THE INDIAN ELEPHANT. R.C. Morris. Jour. Bombay Nat. Hist. Soc., vol.34, no.3, pp.800-801, Nov. 15, 1930.

WHERE 500 ELEPHANTS ARE CAUGHT IN A YEAR. LITTLE-KNOWN FACTS ABOUT THE WILD HERDS OF BURMA. E.H. Peacock. Field, London, vol.161, no.4181, pp.252-253, illus., Feb. 11, 1933.

(NOTES ON ELEPHANTS IN SUMATRA. HABITAT, FOOD, AND DAILY ROUTINE.) Ondervindingen en waarnemingen omtrent olifanten in Sumatra. 1. Het woongebied der olifanten. 2. Voedsel en dagverdeeling der olifanten. D. Pieters. Tropische Natuur, Buitenzorg, vol.21, no.4, pp.57-59, fig.1, Apr., 1932; no.9, pp.158-162, fig.1, Sep., 1932.

(NOTES ON ELEPHANTS IN SUMATRA. SENSE ORGANS. VISION POOR, HEARING EXCELLENT, SMELL VERY ACUTELY DEVELOPED.) Ondervindingen en waarnemingen omtrent olifanten in Sumatra. 4. De zintuigen der olifanten. D. Pieters. Tropische Natuur, vol.23, no.6, pp.113-118, fig.1, June, 1934.

SOMETHING ABOUT ELEPHANTS IN SUMATRA. D. Pieters. Dutch East Indies, Department van landbouw, nijverheid en handel (Nature Protection in the Netherlands Indies), Dept. Econ. Affairs, Batavia, pp. 53-54, illus., 1938.

NOTES ON THE ASIATIC ELEPHANT (ELEPHAS MAXIMUS). R.I. Pocock. Ann. and Mag. Nat. Hist., London, ser.11, vol. 10, no.64, pp.273-280, Apr., 1943.

ROGUE ELEPHANTS IN THE KHASI HILLS. L.L. Reade. Jour. Bombay Nat. Hist. Soc., vol.35, no.3, p.674, Feb. 15, 1932.

AN ELEPHANT TREK. E.O. Shebbeare. Malayan Nature Jour., Kuala Lumpur, Selangor, vol.1, no.1, pp.9-14, Aug., 1940.

ELEPHANTS AGAIN. (Notes on habits of Indian elephant.) A.W. Smith. Atlantic Monthly, vol.142, no.5, pp.633-642, Nov., 1928.

(FIFTEEN YEARS OF ELEPHANTS ON SUMATRA (1924-1938).) Vijftien jaren olifanten op Sumatra (1924-1938). H.J.V. Sody. Boschbouwkundig Tijdschrift "Tectona," Buitenzorg, vol.32, pp.745-771, Sep., 1939.

OUR ELEPHANTS. A.C. Tutein-Nolthenius. Loris, Ceylon, vol.1, no.3, pp.133-136, illus., Dec., 1937.

THE JENUT KLEBANG. (Elephants.) D. Vesey-FitzGerald. Malayan Nature Jour., Kuala Lumpur, vol.1, no.4, pp.135-137, July, 1941.

(CEYLON'S WILD AND TAME ELEPHANTS.) Ceylons wilde und zahme Elefanten. Paul Wirz. Sonderabdruck "Geographica Helvetica," vol.2, no.5, pp.81-92, 1950.

Control, Conservation

CONSERVATION OF ELEPHANTS. Keith Caldwell. Jour. Mamm., vol.7, no.4, p. 347, Nov., 1926.

ELEPHANT CONTROL IN EAST AFRICA. A.M.M. Davies. Loris, Colombo, Ceylon, vol.7, no.2, pp.122-124, Dec., 1955.

CONTROL OF WILD ELEPHANTS IN BURMA. E.H. Peacock. Field, London, vol. 162, no.4210, pp.592-593, figs., Sep. 2, 1933.

ELEPHANTS BY THE ACRE. SOME PROBLEMS OF A CONTROL OFFICER. R.J.D. Salmon. Field, London, vol.168, no.4368, pp.618-619, illus., Sep. 12, 1936.

Diseases and Parasites

A FILARIID FROM THE AFRICAN ELEPHANT. H.A. Baylis. Ann. and Mag. Nat. Hist., ser.9, vol.11, pp.208-211, figs.2, Feb., 1923.

DEATH OF AN ELEPHANT FROM RABIES. J. Beckett. Jour. Bombay Nat. Hist. Soc., vol.36, no.1, pp.242-243, Nov. 15, 1932.

TETANUS IN AN ELEPHANT (ELEPHAS MAXIMUS). Leonard J. Goss. Zoologica, New York, vol.27, pt.1, no.2, pp.5-6, Apr. 30, 1942.

PRELIMINARY NOTE ON SOME NEW NEMATODE PARASITES FROM THE ELEPHANT. M. Khalil. Ann. and Mag. Nat. Hist., ser.9, vol.9, pp.212-216, Feb., 1922.

REVISION OF THE NEMATODE PARASITES OF ELEPHANTS, WITH A DESCRIPTION OF FOUR NEW SPECIES. M. Khalil. Proc. Zool. Soc. London, pp.205-279, June, 1922.

DEATH OF 14 ELEPHANTS (ELEPHAS MAXIMUS LINN.) BY FOOD POISONING. R.C. Morris. Jour. Bombay Nat. Hist. Soc., vol.37, no.3, pp.722-723, Dec. 15, 1934.

FOOD POISONING OF ELEPHANTS. R.C. Morris. Field, London, vol.164, no.4254, p.39, July 7, 1934.

PATHOLOGY OF THE ELEPHANT "DJINDAU." N.P. Tsvetaeva. Proc. Moscow Zool. Park, vol.1, pp.362-375, 1940. (In Russian with a resume in English.)

CURIOUS INJURY TO THE TAIL OF AN ELEPHANT. A.J. Yandle. Jour. Bombay Nat. Hist. Soc., vol.41, no.2, pp.418-419, photo, Dec., 1939.

Domestication

(CAPTURE AND TRAINING OF ELEPHANTS OF ASIA AND AFRICA.) La capture et le dressage des elephants d'Asie et Afrique. Guy Barbault. Revue d'Hist. Nat., pt.1, A. Mammiferes, Paris, vol.11, no.7, pp.228-236, July, 1930.

TRAINED TUSKERS OF THE TEAK FORESTS. (Training and working elephants in Siam.) Truman Bailey. Nat. Hist., New York, vol.50, no.5, pp.228-237, illus., Dec., 1942.

DOMESTICATING THE AFRICAN ELEPHANT. Lady Broughton. Field, London, vol.160, no.4165, p.616, illus., Oct. 22, 1932.

(DOMESTICATION OF THE AFRICAN ELEPHANT.) La domestication de l'elephant d'Afrique. A. Dubois. Science and Nature, vol.1, no.8,pp.113-118, Oct. 5, 1907.

(BELGIAN ELEPHANT TAMING STATION GANGALA NA BODIO.) Die belgische Elefanten-Zaehmungsstation Gangala na Bodio. Bernhard Grzimex. Saeugetierk. Mitteil., Stuttgart, vol.4, no.1, pp.1-10, Jan. 1, 1956.

(SOME NOTES ON THE DOMESTICATED ELEPHANTS OF BUTA.)Quelques notes sur les eléphants domestiques de Buta. R. Fr.J. Hutsebout. Rev. Zool. and Bot. Africaines, vol.17, no.4, pp.39-45, figs.4, Feb. 15, 1930.

DOMESTICATION OF THE AFRICAN ELEPHANT. Denis D. Lyell. Field, London, vol.149, p.153, Jan. 27, 1927.

HOW SIR ELEPHANT MASTERED THE HERD. Charles Mayer. Asia, vol.21, pp. 27-32, Jan., 1921.

DOMESTICATING THE AFRICAN ELEPHANT. EXPERIMENTS IN THE BELGIAN CONGO. Paul Philippson. Field, London, vol.163, no.4252, p.1527, illus., June 23, 1934.

TRAINED AFRICAN ELEPHANTS. John C. Phillips. Jour. Mamm., vol.6, no.2, pp. 130-131, May, 1925.

TAMING OF BOLIVAR. (Taming of Indian elephant.) Dallas Lore Sharp. Nature Mag., vol.10, pp.147-150, illus., Sep., 1927.

WILD ELEPHANT AND THE METHOD OF CAPTURING AND TAMING IT IN CEYLON. Emerson Tennent. London, pp.198, illus., 1867.

CONGO ELEPHANTS. FEW OF THEM ARE NOW SUCCESSFULLY TAMED. Life, vol. 4, no.25, pp.42-43, illus., June 20, 1938.

Exhibits

AFRICAN ELEPHANT SCENE. (South African elephant group mounted in British Museum.) J.G. Dollman. Nat. Hist.Mag., London, vol.1, pp.97-99, illus., Oct., 1927.

MOUNTING OF AN ELEPHANT GROUP. Louis Jonas. Publ. Amer. Assoc. Mus., Washington, D.C., n.s., no.11, pp.1-32, figs.42, 1930.

HOW ELEPHANTS ARE MOUNTED. A CHAPTER IN THE HISTORY OF TAXIDERMY. Frederic A. Lucas. Nat. Hist., vol.23, pp.597-605, figs.9, Nov.-Dec., 1923.

(ELEPHANT EXHIBITION IN THE CATHEDRAL AT EXETER.) Die Elefanten-Darstellung in der Kathedrale zu Exeter. Erna Mohr. Zool. Garten, Leipzig, n.F., vol. 3, nos.4-8, pp.213-215, Aug. 11, 1930.

Food Habits

ELEPHANTS FEEDING EACH OTHER. M.C.E. Ashby. Field, London, vol.152, p.420, Sep.13, 1928.

WHY ELEPHANTS VISIT SALT-LICKS. Theodore Hubback. Jour. Bombay Nat.Hist. Soc., vol.40, no.4, p.730, May, 1939.

ELEPHANTS EATING EARTH. Randolph C. Morris. Jour. Bombay Nat. Hist. Soc., vol.36, no.2, pp.496-497, Apr. 15, 1933.

(ECOLOGICAL NOTE ON SOME WATERING PLACES OF ELEPHANTS IN THE BELGIAN CONGO.) Note écologique sur quelques bains d'elephants au Congo belge. W. Robyns. Bull. Inst. Roy. Colonial Belge, Brussels, vol.12, no.2, pp.318-327, figs.1-2, 1941.

(HOW DOES THE ELEPHANT QUENCH HIS THIRST DURING THE DRY SEASON IN THE STEPPE REGIONS?) Wie stillt der Elefant waehrend der Trockenzeit in den Steppengebieten sein Wasserbeduerfnis. Ludwig Schuster. Zool.Garten, Leipzig, n.F., vol.1, nos.7-9, pp.302-304, Feb., 1929.

STRANGE CONTENTS OF ELEPHANTS' STOMACHS. (Pebbles and Stones Eaten.) Jour. Soc. Preservation Fauna of the Empire, Hertford, n.s., pt.37, p.48, Aug., 1939.

Fossils (General)

NATURE'S DEEP FREEZE. (Baby Mammoth.) H.E. Anthony. Nat. Hist., New York, vol.58, no.7, pp.296-301, illus., Sep., 1949.

(ELEPHAS ANTIQUUS WITH A HIGHER LAMINAR FORMULA.) Sur un Elephas antiquus a formule laminaire elevée. Gaston Astre. Bull. Soc. Hist.Nat.Toulouse, vol.71, nos.1-2, pp.26-32, pl.1, June 30, 1937.

(MASTODONTOID CHARACTER OF ELEPHAS MERIDIONALIS DE BRUGES.) Caractère mastodontoide de l'Elephas meridionalis de Bruges. Gaston Astré.Bull. Soc. Hist. Nat. Toulouse, vol.76, fasc.2, pp.93-102, figs.4, June 30, 1941.

ARCHIDISKODON MAIBENI. Erwin H. Barbour. Nebraska State Mus. Bull., vol. 1, no.11, pp.119-122, fig.1, 1926.

RECORD PROBOSCIDEAN TUSK. A.Katherine Barger. Nat. Hist., New York, vol. 35, no.4, p.357, Apr., 1935.

SOME STEGODONT ELEPHANTIDS. P.E.P. Deraniyagala. Spolia Zeylanica, Bull.Nat. Mus. Ceylon, vol.27, pt.2, pp. 215-217, May 25, 1955.

FIFTY THOUSAND YEARS ON ICE.(Mammoth.) Charles W. Gilmore. Nature Mag., vol.21, no.1, p.30, illus., Jan., 1933.

(GEOLOGICAL OBSERVATIONS ON THE SKELETONS OF GENUS ELEPHAS.) Observations tératologiques sur des squelettes du genre Elephas. Louis Giltay. Bull. Mus. Roy. d'Hist. Nat. Belgique, vol.9, no.11, pp.7, figs.6, Apr., 1933.

A FURTHER AND DETAILED DESCRIPTION OF THE TYPE OF ELEPHAS ROOSEVELTI HAY AND DESCRIPTIONS OF THREE REFERRED SPECIMENS. Oliver P. Hay. Proc. U.S. Nat. Mus., vol.66, art.34, pp.1-6, pls.1-4, May 22, 1925.

FURTHER OBSERVATIONS ON SOME EXTINCT ELEPHANTS. Oliver P. Hay. Proc. Biol. Soc. Washington, vol.35, pp. 97-102, Sep. 30, 1922.

OBSERVATIONS ON SOME EXTINCT ELEPHANTS. Oliver P. Hay. Pp.1-19, figs., June 12, 1922.

IDENTITY OF ELEPHAS TROGONTHERII POHLIG. A.T.Hopwood. Bull.Geol. Inst. Univ., Upsala, vol.27, pp.19-24, 1937.

ON LOXODONTA (PALAEOLOXODON) TOKUNAGAI MATSUMOTO, WITH REMARKS ON THE DESCENT OF LOXODONTINE ELEPHANTS. Hikoshichirô Matsumoto. Sci.Reports Tôhoku Imp. Univ.(2), Geol., vol.13, no.1, pp.7-11, pl.7, 1929.

ON PARASTEGODON MATSUMOTO AND ITS BEARING ON THE DESCENT OF EARLIER ELEPHANTS. Hikoshichiro Matsumoto. Sci. Reports Tôhoku Imp. Univ. (2), Geol., vol.13, no.1, pp.13-15, pl.8, 1929.

(CONCLUSION.) Schlusswort. (Remarks on Mammoth.) Joseph Mauz. Senckenbergiana, Frankfurt, a.M., vol.21, no.1, pp. 41-44, Apr. 21, 1939.

MAMMOTH OR "STIFF-LEGGED BEAR." Truman Michelson. American Anthrop., vol.38, no.1, pp.141-143, Jan.-Mar., 1936.

(ON THE EXTINCTION OF THE MAMMOTH.) De l'Extinction du Mammouth. H.Neuville. L'Anthropologie, Paris, vol.29, pp.193-212, figs.1-3, July, 1919; Ann. Rep. Smiths. Inst., for 1919, pp.327-338, pls.3, 1921.

(Review by G.S. Miller of) (ON THE EXTINCTION OF MAMMOTH.) De l'Extinction du Mammouth. H. Neuville. Jour. Mamm., vol.1, no.3, pp.150-151, May, 1920.

(MAMMOTH HUNTING AND FOOD.) Mammutjagd und Mammutkost. Hugo Obermaier. Forsch. u. Fortschr., Berlin, Jahrg.15, no. 10, pp.134-137, Apr. 1, 1939.

PALAEOLOXODON ANTIQUUS ITALICUS SP. NOV., FINAL STAGE IN THE 'ELEPHAS ANTIQUUS' PHYLUM. Henry Fairfield Osborn. Amer. Mus. Novitates, no. 460, pp.24, figs.17, Mar. 10, 1931.

PARELEPHAS IN RELATION TO PHYLA AND GENERA OF THE FAMILY ELEPHANTIDAE. Henry Fairfield Osborn.Amer. Mus. Novitates, no.152, pp.1-7, figs.1-2, Dec. 20, 1924.

ROMANCE OF THE WOOLLY MAMMOTH. Henry Fairfield Osborn. Nat. Hist., New York, vol.30, no.3, pp.226-241, illus., May-June, 1930.

(LARGE EXTINCT ELEPHANT: THE MAMMOTH.) Um grande elephante extincto: O mammuth. Carlos de Paula Couto. Rev. Acad. Colombiana Cienc. Exactas, Fis.y Nat. Bogota, vol.2, no.7, pp.458-464, figs.3, Sep.-Oct., 1938.

CONTRIBUTION TO THE MORPHOLOGY OF THE MAMMOTH, ELEPHAS PRIMIGENIUS BLUMENBACH; WITH AN EXPLANATION OF MY ATTEMPT AT A RESTORATION. E. Pfizenmayer. Ann. Rept. Smiths. Inst., Washington, D.C., for 1906, no.1759, pp.321-333, figs.4, pl.1, 1907.

FOLSOMOID POINT FOUND IN ALLUVIUM BESIDE A MAMMOTH'S BONES. Cyrus N. Ray, Kirk Bryan. Science, n.s., vol.88, no.2281, pp.257-258, Sep. 16, 1938.

(ON ELEPHAS TROGONTHERII POHL.) Ueber Elephas trogontherii, Pohl. O.Schmidtgen. Palaeont. Zeitschr., vol.8, pp.62-70, 1927.

ELEPHAS MAMMONTEUS CUVIER VERSUS E. PRIMIGENIUS BLUMENBACH. A. H. Serebryakov. Bull. Acad. Sci. USSR, Cl. sci. math. et nat., Moscow, nos.5-6, pp. 1063-1068, 1938. (In English with Russian summary.)

ON THE GENUS PARASTEGODON. Tokio Shikama. Jour. Geol. Soc. Japan, Tokyo, vol.43, no.514, pp.557-564, July 20,1936. (In Japanese with English summary.)

MAMMOTH OR "STIFF-LEGGED BEAR." Frank G. Speck. Amer. Anthrop., vol.37, no.1, pp.159-163, Jan.-Mar., 1933.

PALEONTOLOGIC SKETCHES. PART III. THE ELEPHANTS. Arthur Frederic Wark. Florida Nat., n.s., vol.2, pp.52-55, illus., Jan., 1929.

(ON TWO PICTURES OF ADAMS' MAMMOTH.) Ueber zwei Bilder des Adamsschen Mammuts. C. Zimmer. Zeit. f. Saeugetierk., vol.4, pt.2, pp.84-89, pls. 2, Aug. 6, 1929.

AMAZING MAMMOTH FAMILY. Jr.Nat. Hist. Mag., New York, vol.7, no.8, pp. 4-7, illus., Oct., 1942.

Fossils (New World)

NEW MAMMOTH RECORD FOR ILLINOIS. Frank C. Baker. Science, n.s., vol.80, no.2066, p.118, Aug. 3, 1934.

ANCIENT ELEPHANTS OF NEBRASKA. Edwin H. Barbour. Pan-Amer. Geol., vol. 53, no.1, pp.39-40, Feb., 1930.

ANALYSES OF FRAGMENTS FROM THE TUSKS OF FOUR SPECIMENS OF EXTINCT ELEPHANTS FOUND IN KANSAS. H. W. Brubaker. Trans. Kansas Acad. Sci., vol. 37, pp.115-116, 1934.

DISCOVERY OF ELEPHAS PRIMIGENIUS AMERICANUS IN THE BED OF GLACIAL LAKE MOGODORE, IN CASS COUNTY, MICHIGAN. Ermine C. Case, Irving D. Scott. Papers Michigan Acad. Sci. Arts and Letter, Ann Arbor, vol.20, pp.449-454, maps 2, June 24, 1935.

RECENT FIND OF MAMMOTH REMAINS IN THE QUATERNARY OF FLORIDA, TOGETHER WITH ARROW-HEAD. Jack

H. Connery. Science, n.s., vol.75, no. 1950, p.516, May 13, 1932.

MORE EVIDENCE OF MAMMOTHS IN THE HIGH MOUNTAINS OF COLORADO. Harold J. Cook. Science, vol.73, no.1889, pp. 283-284, Mar. 13, 1931.

FOSSIL ELEPHANT OF OKLAHOMA. E.D. Crabb. Yearbook Public Mus. City Milwaukee, vol.3, 1923, pp.173-177, Apr. 29, 1925.

PROBABLE ASSOCIATION OF MAMMOTH AND ARTIFACTS IN THE WILLAMETTE VALLEY, OREGON. L.S. Cressman, W. S. Laughlin. American Antiquity, Menasha, vol.6, no.4, pp.339-342, pls.2, Apr., 1941.

MAMMOTH FOUND IN LOESS OF WASHINGTON. O.W. Freeman. Science, n.s., vol.64, p.477, Nov. 12, 1926.

CONTINUING THE ELEPHANT HUNT. J.W. Gidley. Explorations and Field-Work of the Smiths. Inst. in 1927, Smiths. Inst., Publ. no.2957, pp.11-16, illus., 1928.

ELEPHANT HUNT IN FLORIDA. J.W. Gidley. Explorations and Field-Work Smiths. Inst. in 1926, Smiths. Inst.Misc. Coll., vol.78, no.7, pp.48-51, illus., 1927.

HAIRY MAMMOTH SKELETON IN UTAH. Geo. H. Hansen. Utah Acad. Sci., Provo, vol.6, pp.7-8, July 5, 1929; Science, n.s., vol.68, p.621, Dec. 21, 1928.

DESCRIPTION OF REMAINS OF AN ELEPHANT FOUND AT PORT WILLIAMS, WASHINGTON. Oliver P. Hay. Jour. Washington Acad. Sci., vol.16, pp.154-159, Mar. 19, 1926.

FOSSIL ELEPHANTS OF MANITOBA. Edward I. Leith. Canadian Field-Nat., Ottawa, vol.63, no.4, pp.135-137, pl.1, July-Aug., 1949.

NORTH AMERICAN ELEPHANTIDS. F.A. Lucas. Science, n.s., vol.15, no.379, pp. 554-555, 1902.

CRANIUM OF MAMMUTHUS (ARCHIDISKODON) CF. IMPERATOR FROM NORTHEASTERN SOUTH DAKOTA. J.R. MacDonald. Jour. Mamm., vol.32, no.4, pp.466-467, Nov. 19, 1951.

THE "ELEPHAS MERIDIONALIS" STAGE ARRIVES IN AMERICA. Henry Fairfield Osborn. Proc. Colorado Mus. Nat.Hist., vol.11, no.1, pp.1-3, figs.2, Sep. 7, 1932.

PARELEPHAS FLORIDANUS FROM THE UPPER PLEISTOCENE OF FLORIDA COMPARED WITH P. JEFFERSONII. Henry Fairfield Osborn. Amer. Mus. Novitates, no.443, pp.17, figs.9, Dec. 18, 1930.

SPECIES OF AMERICAN PLEISTOCENE MAMMOTHS. Henry Fairfield Osborn. Amer. Mus. Novitates, no.41, pp.16, figs.12, July 6, 1922. (New Species Elephas jeffersonii.)

AN HISTORICAL DISQUISITION ON THE MAMMOTH, OR GREAT AMERICAN INCOGNITUM, AN EXTINCT, IMMENSE, CARNIVOROUS ANIMAL, WHOSE FOSSIL REMAINS HAVE BEEN FOUND IN NORTH AMERICA. Rembrandt Peale. London, Printed for E. Lawrence, by C. Mercier, pp.v-91, pl., 1803.

ARTEFACTS ASSOCIATED WITH FOSSIL ELEPHANT. E.H. Sellards. Univ. Texas News Letter, Bur. Econ. Geol., p.2, fig.1, Feb. 15, 1938.

FOSSIL ELEPHANTS OF MINNESOTA. Clinton R. Stauffer. Science, n.s., vol. 60, pp.40-41, July 11, 1924.

EXILED ELEPHANTS OF THE CHANNEL ISLANDS, CALIFORNIA. Chester Stock. Sci. Monthly, vol.41, no.3, pp.205-214, figs.10, Sep., 1935.

FOSSIL ELEPHANT SKULL UNEARTHED ON THE NEWLANDS PROJECTS, NEVADA. Chester Stock. New Reclamation Era, vol. 22, no.11, p.252, fig.1, Nov., 1931.

ICE AGE ELEPHANTS OF THE CHANNEL ISLANDS. Chester Stock. Westways, Los Angeles, vol.28, no.6, pp.14-15, figs., June, 1936.

PLEISTOCENE ELEPHANTS OF SANTA ROSA ISLAND, CALIFORNIA. Chester Stock, E.L. Furlong. Science, n.s., vol. 68, pp.140-141, Aug. 10, 1928.

HYPERTROPHY IN THE JAW OF AN OKLAHOMA PROBOSCIDEAN. J.W. Stovall, C.S. Johnston. Amer. Midland Nat., vol.15, no. 5, pp.622-624, figs.2, 1934.

NORTH AMERICAN INDIAN TRADITIONS SUGGESTING A KNOWLEDGE OF THE MAMMOTH. W.D. Strong. Amer.Anthrop., vol.36, no.1, pp.81-88, Jan.-Mar., 1934; Amer. Anthrop., n.s., vol.37, pp.159-163, Feb., 1935.

MAMMOTH FOUND IN PEORIAN LOESS NEAR BELLEVIEW, ILLINOIS. H.B. Wiliman. Amer. Jour. Sci., New Haven, vol.239, no.6, pp.413-416, figs.2, June, 1941.

THERE WERE ELEPHANTS IN ILLINOIS. (Mammoth.) Living Museum, Springfield, vol.8, no.7, pp.145-146, illus., Nov., 1946.

<u>Fossils (Old World)</u>

NOTICE OF A MEMOIR ON THE OSTEOLOGY OF THE MALTESE FOSSIL ELEPHANTS. A. Leith Adams. Proc. Zool. Soc. London, p.557, 1873.

NOTE ON THE SKULL AND MANDIBLE OF A SIBERIAN MAMMOTH EXHIBITED IN THE BRITISH MUSEUM (NATURAL HISTORY). C.W. Andrews. Ann. and Mag. Nat. Hist., ser.9, vol.12, pp.322-325, pl.1, Sep., 1923.

ON A SPECIMEN OF ELEPHAS ANTIQUUS FROM UPNOR. WITH FURTHER NOTES ON THE TEETH AND SKELETON BY CLIVE FORSTER COOPER. C. W. Andrews. Publ. Brit. Mus. Nat. Hist., London, pp. viii-25, figs.5, pls.8, Feb. 25, 1928.

(STRATIGRAPHY OF THE LOWER BASIN OF TROTUSULUI. II. ELEPHAS MERIDIONALIS FROM THE UPPER PLIOCENE OF PRALEA-CAIUTI (DISTR. BACAU). Stratigrafia basinului inferior al Trotusului. II. Elephas meridionalis, din Pliocenul Superior de la Pralea-Caiuti (Distr.Bacau). Sava Athanasiu, D.M. Preda. Annuar.Inst. Geol. Romaniei, vol.13, pp.65-84, fig.1, map, pls.2, (1928) 1929.

(MORPHOLOGICAL STUDIES ON THE FOSSIL ELEPHANTS OF THE DEPARTMENT OF ARDENNES.) Études morphologiques sur les Elephants fossiles du Départment des Ardennes. Osteologie et Dentition. A. Bastir Ann. Soc. Géol. Nord, vol.57, pp.87-101, figs.5, 1932.

DISCOVERY OF A FOSSIL ELEPHANT IN PALESTINE. Dorothea M. Bate. Nature, London, vol.134, no.3380, p.219, Aug. 11, 1934.

ON ELEPHANT REMAINS FROM CRETE, WITH DESCRIPTION OF ELEPHAS CRETICUS SP. N. Dorothea M. Bate. Proc. Zool. Soc. London, pp.238-250, pls.2, Aug.1, 1907.

UPNOR ELEPHANT. F.A. Bather. Nat. Hist. Mag., London, vol.1, pp.99-106, illus., Oct., 1927.

FOSSIL ELEPHANTS OF THE TAMAN PENINSULA, NORTH CAUCASUS. E.I. Beliaeva. Bull. Acad. Sci. USSR, Cl. Sci. Math. et Nat., no.8, pp.1209-1211, 1933. (In Russian with German summary.)

IS THIS THE EARLIEST KNOWN FOSSIL COLLECTED BY MAN? Barnum Brown. Nat. Hist., vol.26, p.535, illus., Sep.-Oct., 1926.

ON A PALAEOLOXODON NAMADICUS MANDIBLE. D.K. Charkavarti. Quart. Jour. Geol., Min. and Metallurg. Soc., Calcutta, vol.10, no.8, pp.143-149, figs. 3, Sep., 1938.

ON A PRIMITIVE LOXODONTINE FORM OF ELEPHANT FROM THE SIWALIKS OF JAMMU. D.K. Charkavarti. Quart. Jour. Geol. Min. Metallurg. Soc. India, Calcutta, vol.9, no.2, pp.39-42, pl.1, June, 1937.

ON A MANDIBLE OF PALAEOLOXODON FROM PEKIN, WITH DISCUSSION ON THE FOSSIL ELEPHANTS OF NAMADICUS GROUP OF CHINA. Minchem M. Chow. Acta Paleontol. Sinica, vol.5, no.2, pp. 283-294, pls.1-3, May, 1957. (In Chinese with English summary.)

NEW FOSSIL ELEPHANT REMAINS FROM THE VICTORIA FALLS, NORTHERN RHODESIA, AND PRELIMINARY NOTE ON THE GEOLOGY AND ARCHAEOLOGY OF THE DEPOSIT. (Palaeoloxodon darti.) H.B.S. Cooke, J. Desmond Clark. Trans. Roy. Soc. South Africa, Cape Town, vol. 27, pt.3, pp.287-319, figs.11, tbl.1, pls. 12-13, Dec., 1939.

(QUATERNARY MAMMALS OF LORRAINE. ELEPHANTIDAE.) Les Mammiferès Quarternaires de Lorraine. Les Eléphantidés. G. Corroy, G. Minoux. Bull. Soc. Géol.France, ser.5, vol.1, nos.8-9, pp.635-653, figs.4, map 1, (1931) 1932.

MAMMOTHS AND MAN IN THE TRANSVAAL. R.A. Dart. Nature, vol.120, suppl. pp.41-48, Dec. 10, 1927.

MAMMOTHS AND OTHER FOSSIL ELEPHANTS OF THE VAAL AND LIMPOPO WATERSHEDS. R.A. Dart. S.African Jour. Sci., vol.26, pp.698-731, figs.1-28, Dec., 1929.

EXTINCT LOXODONTA ELEPHANT OF NORTHERN AFRICA. P.E.P. Deraniyagala. Spoilia Zeylanica, Bull. Nat. Mus.Ceylon, vol.27, pt.1, pp.15-16, illus., Oct. 24, 1953.

(DESCRIPTION OF THE PRE-MOLAR OF ELEPHAS PRIMIGENIUS FOUND AT ST. DRUON, NEAR CAMBRAI.) Description de la molaire de lait d'Elephas primigenius trouvée a St.Druon, pres Cambrai. Georges Dubois. Ann. Soc. Geol. du Nord, vol.53, pp.112-115, pl.1, (1928) 1929.

TRUNK OF MAMMOTH (ELEPHAS PRIMIGENIUS BLUM.) FOUND IN THE KOLYMA DISTRICT (SIBERIA). K. K. Flerov. Bull. Acad. Sci. USSR, Cl. Sci. Math. et Nat., pp.863-870, figs.4, pls. 1-2, 1931. (In English with Russian summary.)

NEW LOCALITY OF STEGODON ORIENTARIS SHADOENSIS MATSUMOTO? H. Fujimoto. Jour. Geol. Soc. Japan, Tokyo, vol.43, no.508, pp.45-46, pl.1, Jan. 20, 1936. (In Japanese.)

HISTORICAL REVIEW OF DISCUSSION ON THE FOSSIL ELEPHANTS FOUND IN JAPAN, IN THE LATE YEDO PERIOD. Bunnosuke Gokan. Jour. Geol. Soc.Japan, Tokyo, vol.45, no.541, pp.773-776, Oct. 20, 1938.

ON DISCOVERY OF REMAINS ELEPHAS PRIMIGENIUS IN MINDEL-REISS AGE. V.I. Gromova. Bull. Acad. Sci. USSR, Cl. Sci. Math. et Nat., Ser.Biol., Moscow, no.1, pp.231-235, figs.3, 1937. (In Russian with English summary.)

(ELEPHAS PRIMEGENIUS (SIC) BLUM. OF THE ENVIRONS OF MONTMEDY (MEUSE).) Elephas primegenius Blum. aux environs de Montmédy (Meuse). Louis Guillaume. Bull. Mensuel Soc. Sci., Nancy, n.s., vol.4, nos.3-4, pp.76-79, illus., Apr.-May, 1939.

ON THE OCCURRENCE OF FOSSIL STEGODON FROM TAIWAN. Ichiro Hayasaka. Jour. Geol. Tokyo, vol.37, no.438, pp.113-118, Mar. 20, 1930. (In Japanese.)

MAMMOTH TEETH FROM NORWAY. A. Heintz. Norsk Geol. Tidsskrift, vol.34, pp.73-104, illus., 1955.

FROZEN MAMMOTH IN SIBERIA. Otto F. Herz. Smiths. Inst., Ann.Rep., Washington, pp.611-625, illus., pl.9, map, 1904.

PALAEOLOXODON CF. NAMADICUS (FALCONER ET CAUTLEY) FROM BORNEO. D.A. Hooijer. Proc. Kon. Nederl. Akad. Wetenschappen, Amsterdam, ser. B, vol.55, no.4, pp.395-398, illus., 1952.

PLEISTOCENE VERTEBRATES FROM CELEBES. VI. STEGODON SPEC. D.A.

Hooijer. Zool. Mededel. Rijksmus. Nat. Hist. Leiden, vol.32, no.11, pp.107-112, pl.5, Oct. 14, 1953.

PLEISTOCENE VERTEBRATES FROM CELEBES. VII. MILK MOLARS AND PREMOLARS OF ARCHIDISKODON CELEBENSIS HOOIJER. D.A.Hooijer. Zool. Mededel. Rijksmus. Nat. Hist. Leiden, vol.32, no.20, pp.221-231, pl.7, Dec. 30, 1953.

PLEISTOCENE VERTEBRATES FROM CELEBES. XI. MOLARS AND A TUSKED MANDIBLE OF ARCHIDISKODON CELEBENSIS HOOIJER. D.A.Hooijer. Zool. Mededel. Rijksmus. Nat. Hist. Leiden, vol. 33, no.15, pp.103-120, pls.20-22, Dec. 24, 1954.

PYGMY STEGODON FROM THE MIDDLE PLEISTOCENE OF EASTERN JAVA. D.A. Hooijer. Zool. Mededel. Rijksmus. Nat. Hist. Leiden, vol.33, no.14, pp.91-102, pl.19, Dec. 24, 1954.

STEGODON FROM FLORES. D.A.Hooijer. Treubia, vol.24, no.1, pp.119-129, pls.2-3, Dec. 15, 1957.

AFRICAN ELEPHANTS AS GEOLOGICAL INDICATORS. Herbert P.T. Hyde. Nature, London, vol.165, no.4191, p.326, Feb. 25, 1950.

(ON A MOLAR OF A YOUNG ELEPHAS PRIMIGENIUS FOUND AT BRIENNE-LE-CHATEAU AND ON THE REMAINS OF ELEPHANTS FOUND IN THE UPPER VALLEY OF THE VOIRE (HAUTE-MARNE.) Sur une molaire d'un jeune Elephas primigenius trouvee a Brienne-le-Chateau (Aube) et sur des restes d'éléphants signales dans la haute vallée de la Voire (Haute-Marne). Paul Jodot. Bull. Soc. Géol. France, Paris, ser.5, vol.3, nos.1-2, pp.45-47, Aug., 1933.

(ELEPHANTS AND PLIOCENE DINOTHERIUMS OF ETHIOPIA. CONTRIBUTION TO PALEOGEOGRAPHIC STUDY OF AFRICAN PROBOSCIDIANS.) Elephants et dinothériums pliocenes de l'Ethiopie: Contribution a l'etude paleogeographique des proboscidiens africains. L. Joleaud. Comptes Rend. Congres. Géol. Internat. Madrid, 14th Sess. en Espagne, 1926, no.3, pp.1001-1007, illus., 1928.

FOSSIL ELEPHAS PRIMIGENIUS AT THE VILLAGE RULIKIV, MOTOVILIVKA, UKRAINE. V. Karavaev. Acad. Sci. Ukraine, Mem. Cl. Sci. Phys. et Math., Trav. Mus. Zool., no.8, vol.15, no.2, pp.331-332, figs.2, 1930. (In Ukrainian with German summary.)

PROBLEMS AND FACTS ABOUT FROZEN SIBERIAN MAMMOTHS (ELEPHAS PRIMIGENIUS) AND THEIR IVORY. Herbert Lang. Zoologica, vol.4, no.2, pp.25-53, illus., Jan. 8, 1925.

(NEW OBSERVATION ON ELEPHAS ANTIQUUS OF SOUTHERN ITALY.) Nuove osservazione sull'Elephas antiquus dell' Italia meridionale. Giuseppe de Lorenzo, Geremia D'Erasmo. Rend.Accad.Sci.fis. e mat. (Cl. Soc. R.Napoli), ser.3, vol.36, p.143, 1931.

NOTES ON A FOSSIL ELEPHANT FROM SAHAMMA, TOTOMI. (Elephas namadicus naumanni.) Jiro Makiyama. Mem. College Sci. Kyoto Imp. Univ., Ser.B, vol.1, no.2, pp.255-265, pls.12-16, June, 1924.

ON A NEW ARCHETYPAL FOSSIL ELEPHANT FROM MT. TOMURO, PROV. KAGA. Hikoshichiro Matsumoto. Sci. Reports, Tohoku Imp. Univ., ser.2 (Geol.), vol.3, no.2, pp.51-56, figs.3, pl.1, 1918.

ON A NEW FOSSIL RACE OF THE ASIATIC ELEPHANT IN JAPAN. Hikoshichiro Matsumoto. Sci. Reports, Tohoku Imp. Univ., ser.2 (Geol.), vol.10, no.3, pp.57-58, 1927.

ON LEITH-ADAMSIA SIWALIKIENSIS, A NEW GENERIC AND SPECIFIC NAME OF ARCHETYPAL ELEPHANTS. Hikoshichiro Matsumoto. Inst. Geol. and Palaeont. Tohoku Imp. Univ., Sendai, p.213, Oct. 14, 1927.

ON LOXODONTA (PALAEOLOXODON) NAMADICA (FALCONER AND CAUTLEY) IN JAPAN. Hikoshichiro Matsumoto. Sci. Reports, Tohoku Imp. Univ. (2), Geol., vol.13, no.1, pp.1-5, pls.1-6, 1929.

ON SOME FOSSIL ELEPHANTS FROM PROVINCES OF KAZUSA, FROM PROVINCE OF SHIMOTSUKE, AND FROM OTHER LOCALITIES. Hikoshichiro Matsumoto. Zool. Mag., Tokyo, vol.51, no.10, pp.701-717, figs.8, Oct., 1939.

ON THE ARCHETYPAL MAMMOTHS FROM THE PROVINCE OF KAZUSA. Hikoshichiro Matsumoto. Sci. Reports, Tohoku Imp. Univ., ser.2 (Geol.), vol.10, pp.43-50, illus., 1926.

TWO SPECIES OF MAMMOTHS FROM OFF ODOMARI AND VICINITY KARAFUTO (SAGHALIN). Hikoshichiro Matsumoto. Zool. Mag. (Japan), vol.49, no.1, pp.9-10, figs.2, Jan., 1937.

(OBSERVATIONS ON THE LAYERS OF ELEPHAS PRIMIGENIUS BLUM. IN BASSE-NORMANDIE.) Observations sur les gisements d'Elephas primigenius Blum., en Basse-Normandie. Jean Mercier. Bull. Soc. Linn. Normandie, ser.8, vol.6, pp. 6-11, (1933) 1934.

(ON THE FOSSIL OF A PACHYODON DISINTERRED IN LEBANON TWO HOURS NORTH-EAST OF BELLUNO IN THE MIDDLE OF THE GREY SANDSTONE.) Sulle relique d'un Pachyodon dissoterrate e Libano due ore Nord-Est di Belluno in mexzo all' arenaria grigia. Raffaele Molin. Sitz. Ber. K. Akad. Wissensch. Wien, Math.-Naturw. Classe, vol.35, no.8, pp. 117-128, 1859.

PRIMITIVE ARCHIDISKODON AND PALAEOLOXODON OF SOUTH AFRICA. Henry Fairfield Osborn. Amer. Mus. Novitates, no.741, pp.15, figs.5, Aug. 24, 1934.

ON THE STRATIGRAPHIC HORIZON OF ELEPHAS FROM MIYAKO IS., TYÜKYÜ ISLANDS, JAPAN. Yanosuke Otuka. Proc. Imperial Acad., Tokyo, vol.17, no.2, pp. 43-47, figs.3, Feb., 1941.

(DISCOVERY OF AN "ELEPHAS TROGONTHERII" OR "ELEPHAS INTERMEDIUS" BETWEEN CHARMES AND SAINT-GEORGES-LES-BAINS (ARDECHE).) Decouverte d'un "Elephas trogontherii" ou "Elephas intermedius" entre Charmes et Saint-Georges-les-Bains (Ardèche). M. Paul Paya. Bull. Soc. Préhist. Française, Paris, vol.36, no.4, pp.203-212, pls.5, Apr., 1939.

(THE FINDING OF A MAMMOTH TUSK IN SARCE.) Nalez mamutiho klu v Sárce. Jar. Petrbok. Veda Přirodni Més. pro Sír. a Pést. Véd. Přir., Prague, vol.8, no.4, pp.106-109, fig.1, 1927.

(THE FINDING OF MAMMOTH BONES IN KUNDRATICE.) Nalez mamuti kosti v Kundraticich. Jar. Petrbok. Véda Přirodni Mes. pro Sir. a Pest. Ved. Prir., Prague, vol.8, no.8, p.238, 1927.

(MAMMOTH FINDS IN SIBERIA.) Mammut Funde in Sibirien. F.W. Pfizenmayer. Natur und Volk, vol.67, no.5, pp.221-232, figs.5, May, 1937; vol.67, no.6, pp.279-288, figs. 6-14, June, 1937.

(ON ELEPHAS MERIDIONALIS, ANTIQUUS OF THE HAMLET OF TORQUATO (ALENQUER).) Sobre "Elephas meridionalis" cfr. "antiquus" do casal do Torquato (Alenquer). R. de Serpa Pinto. Anais Fac. Ciên. Porto, vol.17, no.2, pp.104-106, fig.1, 1932.

NOTE ON THE EXTINCTION OF THE MAMMOTH IN SIBERIA. T.P. Polmachoff. Amer. Jour. Sci., ser.5, vol.15, pp.66-69, July, 1927.

(FOSSIL ELEPHANTS OF ABBEVILLE.) Les éléphants fossiles d'Abbeville. Georges Pontier. Ann. Soc. Géol. du Nord, vol.53, pp.20-46, figs.4, pls.4, (1928) 1929.

(DISCOVERY OF A PYGMY ELEPHANT IN THE PROVINCE OF VALENCE (SPAIN) AND CONSIDERATIONS ON THE QUATERNARY FAUNA OF THIS REGION.) Découverte d'un elephant nain dans la province de Valence (Espagne) et considérations sur la faune quaternaire de cette région. J. Royo Y Gomez. Comptes Rendu Sommaire Séances Soc. Géol. France, no.18, pp.358-360, Dec. 19, 1938.

ON PARELEPHAS PROTOMAMMONTEUS (MATSUMOTO) RECENTLY FOUND IN THE PROVINCE OF KAZUSA. Shirô Saheki. Japanese Jour. Geol. and Geogr., vol.8, no.3, pp.125-129, pl.1, fig.1, Feb., 1931

(PRESENCE OF ELEPHAS (LOXODON) ANTIQUUS IN THE TERRITORY OF BUCOVINEI.) Prezenta lui Elepahs(Loxodon) antiquus pe teritoriul Bucovinei. Emilian Sahleanu. Bul. Fac. Stiinte Cernauti, vol. 7, nos.1-2, pp.146-152, fig.1, (1933)1934. (In Rumanian with German summary.)

ON A OCCURRENCE OF A MAMMOTH TOOTH FROM NOKORO, JAPANESE SAGHALIN. Yasuo Sasa. Jour. Geol. Soc. Japan, Tokyo, vol.44, no.523, pp.368-375, pl.14, Apr. 20, 1937.

MIOCENE STEGOLOPHODON FROM YATUO GROUP IN TAYAMA PREFECTURE. T. Shikama. Trans. Proc. Paleont.Soc.Japan, n.s., vol.24, pp.285-289, illus., Oct.31, 1956.

NOMENCLATIVE NOTES ON PARELEPHAS PROTOMAMMONTEUS (MATSUMOTO). T. Shikama. Japanese Jour. Geol. and Geogr. (Trans. and Abs.), Tokyo, vol.14, nos.3-4, pp.163-166, tbls.2, Oct., 1937.

(ELEPHAS PRIMIGENIUS. FROM THE CAVE DILUVIUM ON STRANSKA ROCK AT BRNO.) Elephas primigenius. Z jeskynniho diluvia na Stranske skále u Brna. Alois Stehlik. Prace. Moravske Přirodovedecke Společnosti, vol. 5, no.1, pp.1-23, figs.7, 1928.

FOSSIL ELEPHANTS FROM TIBA PREFECTURE, JAPAN. Fuyuji Takai. Japanese Jour. Geol. and Geogr., Tokyo, vol.13, nos.3-4, pp.197-203, pl.24, Oct., 1936.

ON A NEW FOSSIL ELEPHANT FROM OKUBO-MURA, AKASHI-GUN, HYOGO PREFECTURE, JAPAN. (Parastegodon akashiensis.) Fuyuji Takai. Proc. Imp. Acad., Tokyo, vol.12, no.1, pp.19-21, figs.2, 1936.

(DISCOVERY OF A FOSSIL ELEPHANT IN THE MID-SAHARA.) Sur la découverte d'un Eléphant fossile au centre du Sahara. Jean Tilho, Camille Arambourg. Comptes Rendus Séanc. Acad. Sci. Paris, vol.206, no.24, pp.1775-1780, figs.2, June 13, 1938.

FOSSIL ELEPHANT TOOTH DISCOVERED IN MIYAKOZIMA, AN ISLAND OF THE RYÛYÛ ARCHIPELAGO, JAPAN. Shigeyasu Tokunaga. Proc. Imper. Acad., Tokyo, vol. 16, no.3, pp.122-124, figs.2, Mar., 1940.

NEW FOSSIL ELEPHANT FOUND IN SHIKOKU, JAPAN. (Parastegodon sugiyamai.) Shigeyasu Tokunaga. Proc. Imp. Acad., Tokyo, vol.11, no.10, pp.432-434, figs.2, 1935.

FOSSIL ELEPHANTS FROM TOTIGI PREFECTURE, JAPAN. Shigeyasu Tokunaga, Fuyuji Takai. Japanese Jour. Geol. and Geogr., Trans. and Abstracts, Tokyo, vol. 15, nos.1-2, pp.69-82, figs.10, pls.5-8, Mar., 1938.

ODONTOMA IN A FOSSIL ELEPHANT FROM THE INLAND SEA OF JAPAN. Shigeyasu Tokunaga, Fuyuji Takai. Jour. Geol.Soc. Japan, vol.44, no.524, pp.444-446, pl.1, May 20, 1937. (In Japanese with English summary.)

ON A FOSSIL ELEPHANT, PALAEOLOXODON AOMORIENSIS, FROM SHICHINOHE, KAMIKITAGUN, AOMORI PREFECTURE, JAPAN. Shigeyasu Tokunaga, Fuyuji Takai. Jour. Geol. Soc. Japan, Tokyo, vol.43, no. 511, pp.254-258, pls.2, Apr. 20, 1936.

ON THE FOSSIL ELEPHANTS FROM TOCHIGI PREFECTURE. Shigeyasu Tokunaga, Fuyuji Takai. Jour. Geol.Soc. Japan, Tokyo, vol.44, no.525, pp.536-537, June 20, 1937. (In Japanese.)

NOTE ON THE EXTINCTION OF THE MAMMOTH IN SIBERIA. T.P. Tolmachoff. Amer. Jour. Sci., ser.5, vol.15, pp.66-69, July, 1927.

MAMMOTH TEETH FROM THE ANIWA BAY IN SAGHALIEN. Tomoye Urita. Jour.

Geol. Soc. Japan, Tokyo, vol.44, no.524, pp.376-382, pls.2, May 20, 1937. (In Japanese with English summary.)

THREE ALLEGED OCCURRENCES OF STEGOLOPHODON LATIDENS (CLIFT) IN JAPAN. Hisakatsu Yabe. Proc. Japan Acad., vol.26 (1950), no.9, pp.61-65, illus., 1951.

ELEPHAS NAMADICUS MAK. FROM SAKU, SHINANO. Teisuke Yagi. Jour. Geogr., Tokyo, vol.43, no.506, pp.217-222, figs. 5, pl.6, Apr., 1931.

MAMMOTH REMAINS FROM IYASAKA-MURA, MANCHURIA, AND THEIR DISTRIBUTION IN SAME COUNTRY. Teisuke Yagi. Jour. Geogr. Tokyo, vol.50, no.596, pp.11-12, pl.4, Oct., 1938. (English abstract.)

MAMMOTH TOOTH FROM NOKORO, SOUTH SAKHALIN. Teisuke Yagi. Jour. Geogr., vol. 50, no.596, pp.12-13, pl.5, Oct., 1938. (English abstract.)

NEW STEGODON FROM KWANGSI. C.C. Young. Bull.Geol.Soc.China, Chungking, vol.18, nos.3-4, pp.219-226, pl.1, Dec., 1938.

General Habits, Behavior

WHY ELEPHANTS TURN 'ROGUES'. S.K. Ghosh. Jour. Bombay Nat. Hist., vol.38, no.3, pp.614-615, Apr. 15, 1936.

GAIT OF THE ELEPHANT. I.V. Gillis. China Jour., vol.25, no.3, pp.172-173, Sep., 1936.

CURIOUS BEHAVIOUR OF ELEPHANTS. F.W. Haswell. Jour. Bombay Nat. Hist. Soc., vol.40, no.3, p.560, Dec., 1938.

A JUNGLE TRAGEDY. (Sequel to Fight Between Two Wild Bull Elephants.) A.P. Mathew. Jour. Bombay Nat. Hist. Soc., vol.33, no.3, pp.707-708, May 31, 1929.

ELEPHANTS LYING DOWN. R.C. Morris. Jour. Bombay Nat. Hist. Soc., vol.42, no.3, p.658, Aug., 1941.

ENCOUNTERS WITH A ROGUE ELEPHANT. R.C. Morris. Indian Wild Life, Agra, vol. 4, no.2, pp.65-68, Apr.-June, 1939.

PECULIAR BEHAVIOUR OF AN ELEPHANT. R.C. Morris. Jour. Bombay Nat. Hist. Soc., vol.39, no.1, pp.164-165, Dec. 1, 1936.

ELEPHANTS ASLEEP. M. Morrison. Field, London, vol.151, p.344, Mar. 1, 1928.

UNUSUAL BEHAVIOUR OF AN ELEPHANT. A.F. Nathan. Field, London, vol.150, p. 319, Aug. 25, 1927.

ELEPHANTS ASLEEP. G.C. Robinson. Field, London, vol.151, p.806, May 10, 1928.

ELEPHANT FIGHT. W.S. Thom. Game and Gun and the Angler's Monthly, London, vol.12, no.122, pp.660-661, illus., Nov., 1935.

Growth

NOTES ON AGE AT SEXUAL MATURITY, GESTATION PERIOD AND GROWTH OF THE INDIAN ELEPHANT, ELEPHAS MAXIMUS. Stanley S. Flower. Proc. Zool. Soc. London, ser.A, vol.113, pp.21-27, fold.tbl., June, 1943.

INDIAN ELEPHANT (E. MAXIMUS): EARLY GROWTH GRADIENT AND INTERVALS BETWEEN CALFING. E.P. Gee. Jour. Bombay Nat. Hist. Soc., vol.53, no.1, pp. 125-128, illus., Aug., 1955.

STATISTICAL RECORD OF GROWTH IN THE INDIAN ELEPHANT (E. MAXIMUS). Gordon Hundley. Jour. Bombay Nat. Hist. Soc., vol.37, no.2, pp.487-488, Aug. 15, 1934.

STATISTICS OF HEIGHT INCREMENTS OF INDIAN CALF ELEPHANTS. Gordon Hundley. Proc. Zool. Soc. London, 1934, pt.3, pp.697-698, Sep., 1934.

SOME OBSERVATIONS ON GROWTH AND TUSK WEIGHT IN MALE AND FEMALE AFRICAN ELEPHANTS. J.S. Perry. Proc. Zool. Soc. London, vol.124, pt. 1, pp.97-104, pl.1, May 27, 1954.

(DATA ON THE RATE OF GROWTH OF THE INDIAN ELEPHANT.) Przycznek de znajomości wzrostu slonia indyjskiego. Adolf Rzasnicki. Ann. Mus. Zool. Polonici, vol.13, no.24, pp.303-313, pls.25-27, July, 13, 1939.

Hunting

ELEPHANTS OF KENYA COLONY. Charles Cottar, Jr. Outdoor Life, vol.68, no.3, pp. 9-11, figs.3, Sep., 1931; no.4, pp.22-23, 70, figs.3, Oct., 1931; no.5, pp.28-29, 46, figs. 4, Nov., 1931.

ELEPHANT SHOOTING. HINTS FOR THE NOVICE. L.M. Dundas. Field, London, vol. 155, no. 4023, p. 160, Feb. 1, 1930.

SHOOTING OF A WILD ELEPHANT IN "MUSTH" IN THE DUARS. G.R. Entwistle. Jour. Bengal Nat. Hist. Soc., Darjeeling, vol.18, no.3, pp.102-103, photo, Jan., 1944.

ADVERSARIA OF ELEPHANT HUNTING (TOGETHER WITH AN ACCOUNT OF ALL THE RITES, OBSERVANCES AND ACTS OF WORSHIP TO BE PERFORMED IN CONNECTION THEREWITH, AS WELL AS NOTES ON VOCABULARIES OF SPIRIT LANGUAGE, FAKE OR TABOO LANGUAGE AND ELEPHANT COMMAND WORDS.) Francis H. Giles. Jour. Siam Soc., vol. 23, pt.2, pp.61-96, Dec., 1929.

ELEPHANT HUNT. Henry Goldstein. Animal Kingdom, New York, vol.52, no.3, pp.77-84, illus., June 1, 1949.

(HUNTING ELEPHANTS WITH GUN AND PHOTOGRAPHIC EQUIPMENT.) L'Elephant sa chasse au fusil et a l'appareil photographique. Gromier. La Terre et la Vie (Revue d'Hist. Nat.), vol.2, no.6, pp.315-337, illus., June, 1932.

(CAPTURE OF ELEPHANTS AT THE NATIONAL PARK OF GARAMBA.) La capture des elephants au Parc National de la Garamba. H. Hediger. Bull. Inst. Roy. Colonia Belge, vol.21, fasc.1, pp. 218-226, 1950.

A TREK AFTER TUSKERS. W.H. Herren. Outdoor Life, vol.68, no.6, pp.22-23, 42-43, figs.4, Dec., 1931.

ELEPHANT SHOOTING. J. De. W. Van Ingen. Jour. Bengal Nat. Hist. Soc., Darjeeling, vol.16, no.2, pp.37-48, pl. 1, Oct., 1941.

ELEPHANT HUNTING IN INDO-CHINA. Livingston Longfellow. Field and Stream, no.4, pp.24-25, 59, 61, Aug., 1929.

HINTS FOR YOUNG BIG GAME HUNTERS IN AFRICA. II. TRACKING AND SHOOTING AN ELEPHANT. Denis D. Lyell. Game and Gun, vol.4, pp.592, 594, 596, Nov., 1927.

BANDALA METHOD OF HUNTING ELEPHANT ON FOOT. J.G.S. MacPhail. Sudan Notes and Records, vol.13, pt.2, pp.279-283, 1930.

ELEPHANT DRIVING. G.K. Maurice. Game and Gun and Anglers Monthly, vol.15, no. 156, pp.528-530, illus., Sep., 1938.

TRAPPING AN ELEPHANT HERD IN TRENGGANU. Charles Mayer. Asia, vol. 20, pp.1055-1058, Dec., 1920.

ELEPHANT CATCHING IN ASSAM. A.J.W. Milroy. Jour. Bombay Nat. Hist. Soc., vol. 29, pp.803-811, Dec. 31, 1923.

ELEPHANT SHOOT ON THE BARAGUR HILLS. R.C. Morris. Jour. Bombay Nat. Hist. Soc., vol.31, pp.720-725, pl.1, 1926.

FURTHER ELEPHANT SHOOT ON THE BARAGUR HILLS. R.C. Morris. Jour. Bombay Nat. Hist. Soc., vol.33, no.4, pp.861-868, Oct. 15, 1929.

ELEPHANT CATCHING SYNDICATE. E.O. Shbbeare. Jour. Bengal Nat. Hist. Soc., Darjeeling, vol.15, no.2, pp.35-46, pls.4, Oct., 1940; no.3, pp.85-93, pls.4-7, Jan., 1941; no.4, pp.120-125, pls.3, Apr., 1941.

LAST OF THE MAMMOTHS. (Hunting African Elephants.) Murray T. Smith. Field and Stream, New York, vol.53, no.2, pp.58-59, 152-155, illus., June, 1948.

HUNTING THE ELEPHANT IN AFRICA, AND OTHER RECOLLECTIONS OF THIRTEEN YEARS' WANDERINGS. C.H. Stigand. Macmillan Co., New York, pp. xv-379, illus., pls., fold.tbl., 1913.

ADVENTURES OF AN ELEPHANT HUNTER. James Sutherland. Macmillan and Co., London, pp.xviii-324, illus., 1912.

ELEPHANT DRIVE. (In the Sudan.) Hugh Thomason. Fauna, Philadelphia, vol.5, no.2, pp.42-45, illus., June, 1943.

Longevity

AN ELEPHANT 170 YEARS OLD. Guy Dollman. Jour. Bombay Nat. Hist. Soc., vol.39, no.3, p.619, Sep. 25, 1937.

FURTHER NOTES ON THE DURATION OF LIFE IN MAMMALS. THE ALLEGED AND ACTUAL AGES TO WHICH ELEPHANTS LIVE. Stanley S. Flower. Proc. Zool. Soc. London, vol.117, no.4, pp. 680-688, 1948.

ON THE HEIGHT AND AGE OF AN ELEPHANT. N.G. Pillai. Jour. Bombay Nat. Hist. Soc., vol.42, no.4, pp.927-928, pl.1, Dec., 1941.

ELEPHANTS--AGE TO WHICH THEY LIVE IN CAPTIVITY. R.D. Richmond. Jour. Bombay Nat. Hist. Soc., vol.36, no.2, pp.494-496, Apr. 15, 1933.

Measurements

HEIGHT IN ELEPHANTS. David Boyle. Jour. Bombay Nat. Hist. Soc., vol.33, no.2, p.437, Feb. 15, 1929.

(MEASUREMENTS OF AN ASIAN ELEPHANT AT BIRTH.) Mensurations d'un elephant d'Asie a la naissance. C. Bressou, G. Vandel. Mammalia, Paris, vol.3, no.2, pp.49-52, pl.3, June, 1939.

(MEASUREMENTS OF AN ASIAN ELEPHANT.) Mensurations d'un elephant d'Asie (Elephas maximus L.). Ed. deChambre. Mammalia, Paris, vol.1, no.4, pp.160-174, pl.8, June, 1937.

LARGE INDIAN ELEPHANT. F.J. Mustill. Jour. Bombay Nat. Hist. Soc., vol.40, no.2, pp.324-325, Sep., 1938.

DISCUSSION ON CERTAIN MEASUREMENTS OF A NUMBER OF ELEPHANTS (L. AFRICANA) OF THE KRUGER NATIONAL PARK. T.G. Nel. Bull. Nat. Parks Union South Africa, Pretoria, no.5, p.1, 1951.

Mortality

YOUNG ELEPHANT KILLED BY A TIGER. C.H. Biddulph. Jour. Bombay Nat. Hist. Soc., vol.39, no.2, pp.387-388, Apr. 15, 1937.

WHERE DO WILD ELEPHANTS DIE? Lieut. Colonel Gordon Casserly. Jour. Mamm., vol.5, no.2, pp.113-116, May, 1924.

ON 'NATURAL DEATHS' IN WILD ELEPHANTS. F.W. Champion. Jour. Bombay Nat. Hist. Soc., vol.33, no.2, pp.433-434, Feb. 15, 1929.

TIGERS KILL AN ELEPHANT. A. A. Dunbar-Brander. Field, London, vol.176, no.4567, p.27, July 6, 1940.

WHAT BECOMES OF DEAD ELEPHANTS? F.W. Frohawk. Field, London, vol.153, p.864, May 31, 1929.

REPORT ON THE INDIAN ELEPHANT WHICH DIED IN THE GARDENS ON JULY 7th, 1875. Alfred Henry Garrod. Proc. Zool. Soc. London, pp.542-543, 1875.

PASSING OF A GRAND OLD LADY. (Elephant.) Wilbur T. Gracey. Fauna, Philadelphia, vol.2, no.3, pp.59-60, Sep., 1940.

(COMMUNICATION ON THE DEATH OF AN ELEPHANT IN THE COLOGNE ZOOLOGICAL GARDEN.) Mitteilung ueber den Tod eines Elefanten im Zoologischen Garten Koeln. J. Kladetzky. Zool. Garten, Leipzig, n.F., vol.20, nos.2-3, p.198, 1953.

TRAGEDY AMONG ROYAL PACHYDERMS IN SIAM. BEING AN ACCOUNT OF THE DEATH OF TWO TUSKERS IN THE ROYAL ELEPHANT STABLES IN BANGKOK UNDER MOST UNUSUAL CIRCUMSTANCES. Edwin

B. McDaniel. Bull. New York Zool. Soc., vol.36, no.2, pp.47-50, illus., Mar.-Apr., 1933.

ELEPHANT GRAVEYARDS. Ernst D. Moore. Reader's Digest, vol.20, no.120, pp.76-78, Apr., 1932. (Condensed from Asia, Oct., 1931.)

DEATH OF AN ELEPHANT (ELEPHAS MAXIMUS LINN.) WHILE CALFING. R.C. Morris. Jour. Bombay Nat. Hist. Soc., vol.37, no.3, p.722, Dec. 15, 1934.

ON 'NATURAL DEATHS' IN WILD ELEPHANTS. R.C. Morris. Jour. Bombay Nat. Hist. Soc., vol.32, pp.794-795, May 31, 1928.

"JESSIE" JOINS HER ANCESTORS. (Elephant age, weight.) Robert A. Patten. Parks and Recreation, Rockford, Ill., vol.23, no.5, pp.200-202, Jan., 1940.

AN ISLAND OF DEATH. HOW FOUR ELEPHANTS PERISHED ON LAKE EDWARD. E.A. Temple Perkins. Field, London, vol. 166, no.4324, p.1075, illus., Nov. 9, 1935.

(PACHYDERM TRAGEDY.) Dickhaeuter-Tragoedie. Joh. Riedel. Zool. Garten, Leipzig, n.F., vol.3, nos.11-12, p.344, 1930.

Photography

UNENDING MINUTES UNDER AN ELEPHANT. A THRILL OF BIG GAME PHOTOGRAPHY. A. Radclyffe Dugmore. Field, London, vol.164, no.4273, p.1160, illus., Nov. 17, 1934.

CAMERA STUDIES OF ELEPHANTS AT HOME. Marcuswell Maxwell. (In) Elephants and other big game studies from the Times. The Times Publ.Co., Ltd., London, pls.28, 1930.

SPECTACULAR RIVER DRIVE OF WILD ELEPHANTS IN MYSORE. The Madras Mail, p.1, Jan. 16, 1939.

Physiology

WHEN AN ELEPHANT SNEEZES. S. Leonard Bastin. Field, London, vol.153, p.895, June 7, 1929.

HEART RATE OF THE ELEPHANT. Francis G. Benedict, Robert C. Lee. Proc. Amer. Philos Soc., vol.76, no.3, pp.335-341, July, 1936.

(ON THE PHYSIOLOGY OF THE ELEPHANT. AFTER A RECENT WORK OF F.G. BENEDICT AND R.C. LEE.) Sur la physiologie de l'éléphant. D'apres un travail recent de F.G. Benedict et R.C. Lee. Ch. Devillers. Mammalia, Paris, vol.2, no.4, pp.187-190, Dec., 1938.

(ON THE SLEEP OF ELEPHANTS.) Ueber den Schlaf der Elefanten. Bernhard Grzimek. Saeugetierk. Mitteil., Stuttgart, vol.4, no. 3, p.130, July 1, 1956.

(ELEPHANT EAR MUSCLES AS WARMTH REGULATORS.) Die Ohrmuscheln des Elefanten als Waermeregulator. Richard Hesse. Zeitschr. Wiss. Zoologie, vol.132, pp.314-328, tbls.6, fig.1, Sep., 1928.

PUSHING POWER OF AN ELEPHANT. W. T. Hornaday. Zool. Soc. Bull., vol.25, pp.112-115, Sep., 1922.

SPEED OF ELEPHANTS. Denis D. Lyell. Field, London, vol.154, no.4008, p.589, Oct. 19, 1929.

Psychology

VIRTUE ASCRIBED TO AN ELEPHANT. A. Kerr. Jour. Siam Soc., vol.23, pt.2, p.123, Dec., 1929.

GAME IN UGANDA. INTELLIGENCE OF ELEPHANTS. Indian Wild Life, Agra, vol.4, no.2, pp.101-102, Apr.-June, 1939.

INTELLIGENCE IN THE ELEPHANT. Amer. Naturalist., vol.17, no.6, p.684, 1883.

Reproductive Biology

BIRTH OF AN ELEPHANT. SOME OBSERVATIONS AT A CEYLON "LODGING-PLACE." W.G. Adam. Field, London, vol.157, no.4095, p.906, June 20, 1931.

MUSTH IN ELEPHANT. N.L. Bor. Jour. Bombay Nat. Hist. Soc., vol.32, pp.594-596, Jan. 15, 1928.

RECORD OF GESTATION PERIODS AND GROWTH OF TRAINED INDIAN ELEPHANT CALVES IN THE SOUTHERN SHAN STATES, BURMA. E.C. Burne. Proc. Zool. Soc. London, vol.113, ser.A, pts.1-2, p. 27, June, 1943.

MATING OF ELEPHANTS. Paul De Launey. Jour. Bombay Nat. Hist. Soc., vol.40, no. 2, pp.323-324, Sep., 1938.

AGE OF PUBERTY IN THE INDIAN ELEPHANT (ELEPHAS MAXIMUS L.). A.E. Foot. Jour. Bombay Nat. Hist. Soc., vol. 38, no.2, p.392, Dec. 1, 1935.

MATING OF ELEPHANTS. J.Gonzalez. Jour. Bombay Nat. Hist. Soc., vol.40, no.4, p.731, May, 1939.

(OBSERVATIONS DURING ELEPHANT BREEDING.) Beobachtungen bei der Elefantenzucht. H. Heck. Der Naturforscher, Jahrg.9, no.11, pp.401-404, pl.85, Feb., 1933.

BREEDING OF ELEPHANTS IN CAPTIVITY. Gordon Hundley. Jour. Bombay Nat. Hist. Soc., vol.28, pp.537-539, Mar.25, 1922.

TWIN CALF ELEPHANTS. Gordon Hundley. Jour. Bombay Nat. Hist. Soc., vol.27, pp. 628-629, Mar. 31, 1921; vol.32, pp.214-215, pl.1, Aug. 1, 1927.

(ON ELLEN, THE INDIAN ELEPHANT, AND HER THREE YOUNG BORN IN CAPTIVITY.) Von der indischen Elefantin Ellen und ihren drei in Gefangenschaft geborenen Jungen. Hans Hvass. Zool.Garten, Leipzig, n.F., vol.5, nos.7-9, pp.191-199, figs.8, 1932.

LETTER FROM SIR WM. F. GOWERS, K.C.M.G., ON THE GESTATION PERIOD OF THE AFRICAN ELEPHANT (ELEPHAS AFRICANUS). P. Chalmers Mitchell. Proc. Zool. Soc. London, pt.3, p.1207, Sep., 1931.

REPRODUCTION OF THE AFRICAN ELEPHANT, LOXODONTA AFRICANA. J.S. Perry. Philos. Trans. Royal Soc. London, ser.B, vol.237, pp.93-149, Feb.10, 1953.

BIRTH OF AN ELEPHANT. F.Popleton. Oryx, vol.4, no.3, pp.180-181, Nov., 1957.

ELEPHANTS BREEDING IN CAPTIVITY. G.C. Robinson. Field, London, vol.150, p.319, Aug. 25, 1927.

TIME OF SEXUAL MATURITY OF THE ELEPHANT (ELEPHAS MAXIMUS L.). G.C. Robinson. Jour. Bombay Nat. Hist. Soc., vol.37, no.4, p.950, Apr. 15, 1935.

(SOME OBSERVATIONS ON THE SEX LIFE OF THE INDIAN ELEPHANT.) Einige Beobachtungen ueber das Geschlechtsleben des indischen Elefanten. Karl Max Schneider. Zool.Garten, Leipzig, n.F., vol.3, nos.11-12, pp.305-314, figs.16, 1930.

LETTER FROM, ON THE BREEDING OF THE ELEPHANT IN CAPTIVITY. C.J. Smith. Proc. Zool. Soc. London, pp.731-732, 1865.

TWIN ELEPHANT CALVES. C.H.Stockley. Jour. Bombay Nat. Hist. Soc., vol.31, pp. 813-814, illus., Nov.1, 1926.

BIRTH OF AN ELEPHANT CALF (ELEPHAS MAXIMUS LINN.). A.C.Tutein-Nolthenius. Jour. Bombay Nat. Hist.Soc., vol.38, no.1, pp.183-184, Aug. 15, 1935.

BREEDING OF ELEPHANTS IN CAPTIVITY. J.C.C. Wilson. Jour. Bombay Nat. Hist. Soc., vol.28, pp.1128-1129, Dec. 20, 1922.

(ELEPHANT BIRTHS IN NORTH AMERICAN ZOOS AND CIRCUS MENAGERIES.) Elefantengeburten in nordamerikanischen Zoos und Zirkusmenagerien. Zool. Garten, Leipzig, n.F., vol.6, nos.7-9, pp.196-197, Oct., 1933.

Taxonomy

EARS AS A RACE-CHARACTER IN THE AFRICAN ELEPHANT. R.Lydekker. Proc. Zool. Soc. London, pp.380-403, Aug. 1, 1907.

(GEOGRAPHICAL VARIANTS OF THE AFRICAN ELEPHANT.) Geographische Abarten des afrikanischen Elefanten. Paul Matschie. Sitz. Ber. Gesell.Naturf. Freunde, Berlin, no.8, pp.189-197, 1900.

RACES OF AFRICAN ELEPHANT. P.H.G. Powell-Cotton. Field, London, vol.148, p.763, Oct. 28, 1926.

NAME FOR A SUPPOSED NEW SUB-SPECIES OF ELEPHANT FROM GERMAN SOUTHWEST AFRICA. (Loxodonta africana zukowskii.) Embrik Strand. Archiv. f. Naturgesch., year 90, Abt.A, Heft 1, p. 68, July, 1924. (Footnote.)

Zoos, Circuses

BELGIUN CONGO'S GIFT TO THE NEW YORK ZOOLOGICAL SOCIETY. (Elephants.) William Bridges. Animal Kingdom, New York, vol.49, no.5, pp.158-164, illus., Sep.-Oct., 1946.

TWELVE ELEPHANTS. THERE HAVE BEEN SOME FAMOUS CHARACTERS IN THE BRONX ZOO'S COLLECTION SINCE GUNDA CAME IN 1904. William Bridges. Bull. New York Zool. Soc., vol.44, no.5, pp.136-152, illus., Sep.-Oct., 1941.

CAPTIVE PIGMY ELEPHANTS IN AMERICA. C. Emerson Brown. Jour. Mamm., vol.15, no.3, pp.248-250, Aug., 1934.

THAT SWEET CANDY! Sam Dunton. Animal Kingdom, New York Zool. Soc., vol.55, no. 5, pp.150-153, illus., Oct., 1952.

FIRST LIVING ELEPHANT IN AMERICA. G.G. Goodwin. Jour. Mamm., vol.6, no.4, pp.256-263, pls.23-25, Nov., 1925.

(ELEPHANTS IN CIRCUS AND ZOO.) Elefanten im Zirkus und Zoo. Lorenz Hagenbeck. Zool. Garten, Leipzig, n.F., vol. 17, nos.1-5, pp.60-66, 1950.

OUR SECOND PYGMY ELEPHANT. (Account of living specimens of West African elephant in New York Zoological Park.) W.T. Hornaday. Zool. Soc. Bull., vol.26, no.1, pp.3-4, fig., Jan., 1923.

ON A YOUNG AFRICAN ELEPHANT IN THE BRONX ZOOLOGICAL PARK. P.Chalmers Mitchell. Proc. Zool. Soc. London, pp.447-448, Oct. 8, 1907.

ELEPHANT TALES. (Stories of zoo and circus elephants for children, with many photographs of African and Indian elephants.) Esse Forrester O'Brien. Steck Co., Austin, pp.x-294, illus., 1941.

("IPANI," THE PORTUGUESE EAST AFRICAN FEMALE ELEPHANT OF THE FRANKFURT ZOO.) "Ipani," die portugiesisch-ostafrikanische Elefantin des Frankfurter Zoo. Kurt Priemel. Zool. Garten, n.F., vol.3, nos.9-10, pp.241-244, figs.1-4, Oct., 1930.

ANNOUNCEMENT OF THE ARRIVAL OF A YOUNG MALE AFRICAN ELEPHANT IN THE SOCIETY'S GARDENS. Philip Lutley Sclater. Proc. Zool. Soc. London, pp.510-511, 1865.

CIRCUS ELEPHANT. D.L. Sharp. Nature Mag., vol.6, pp.79-82, figs.4, Aug., 1925.

ELEPHANT IN CAPTIVITY. W.Henry Sheak. Nat. Hist., vol.22, pp.406-415, figs.6, Sep.-Oct., 1922.

(BIRTH OF AN ASIAN ELEPHANT (ELEPHAS MAXIMUS L.) AT THE ZOOLOGICAL PARK OF THE BOIS DE VINCENNES.) Naissance d'un elephant d'Asie (Elephas maximus L.) au Parc zoologique de Bois de Vincennes. Achille Urbain et al. Mammalia, Paris, vol.9, nos.3-4, pp.92-94, pl.1, Sep.-Dec., 1945.

ACCLIMATIZING ELEPHANTS. San Diego Zoonooz, vol.16, no.7, p.3, illus., July, 1943.

"DUMBO", THE LONDON ZOO'S TWO-YEAR OLD ELEPHANT, HAS A LONG DRINK BEFORE STARTING HER DAILY RATIONS. Illus. London News, London, vol.216, no.5798, p.853, illus., June 3, 1950.

KING OF THE CIRCUS. (Duties of elephants in circuses.) Junior Nat. Hist.Mag., New York, vol.2, no.3, pp.12-13, figs.2, May, 1937.

32-INCH ELEPHANT: SIAMESE ORPHAN THAT LOVES KIDS. Life, Chicago, vol. 29, no.4, pp.47-48, illus., July 24, 1950.

## HYRACOIDEA

### Procaviidae

TRICHODECTIDAE (MALLAPHAGA) PARASITIC ON PROCAVIIDAE. G.A.H. Bedford. Proc. Zool. Soc. London, pt.3, pp.709-730, figs.20, Sep., 1932.

(CHARACTERISTICS IMPORTANT IN DIFFERENTIATING THE SPECIES OF PROCAVIIDAE.) Ueber die sur Unterscheidung der Arten der Procaviiden wichtigen Merkmale. August Brauer. Zeitschr. f. Saeugetierkunde, Berlin, vol.9, nos.1-3, pp.198-206, figs.9, Dec. 30, 1934.

HYRAX: A NATURAL ODDITY. Maurice Burton. Illus. London News, vol.218, no. 5830, p.59, illus., Jan. 13, 1951.

FOSSIL HYRACOIDEA OF THE TRANSVAAL AND TAUNGS DEPOSITS. C.S. Churcher. Annals Transvaal Mus., vol. 22, no.4, pp.477-501, Feb. 16, 1956.

HYRAX--WHAT IS IT? W. Stuart Cramer. Nature Mag., vol.28, no.1, p.18, illus., July, 1936.

GUSTATORY PAPILLAE AND THE STOMACH OF HYRACOIDEA, WITH A DISCUSSION OF THE EVOLUTION OF THE MAMMALIAN TONGUE PAPILLAE. Hans Elias. Jour. Morphol., Philadelphia, vol.79, no. 1, pp.97-111, pls.2, July, 1946.

EXHIBITION OF THE SKULL OF A HYRAX WITH ABNORMAL DENTITION, OBTAINED BY MR. BLANFORD. William Henry Flower. Proc. Zool. Soc. London, pp.603-604, 1869.

SOME NOTES UPON THE NATURE, HEALTH AND MAINTENANCE OF THE HYRAX. Herbert Fox. Proc. Amer. Philos. Soc., Philadelphia, vol.72, no.1, pp.1-24, figs.4, June 2, 1933.

DESCRIPTION OF A NEW SPECIES OF HYRAX, FROM FERNANDO PO. Louis Fraser. Proc. Zool. Soc. London, pt. 20, p.99, pl.33, 1852.

DENDROHYRAX ARBOREUS BRAUERI SUBSP. NOV. Herbert Hahn. Zeitschr. f. Saeugetierkunde, Berlin, vol.8, nos. 3-6, pp.278-279, Dec. 20, 1933.

(FAMILY PROCAVIIDAE.) Die Familie der Procaviidae. Herbert Hahn. Zeitschr. F. Saeugetierk., vol.9, nos.1-3, pp.207-358, figs.60, tbls., pls.13-16, Dec. 12, 1934.

(FAMILY PROCAVIIDAE ONCE AGAIN!) Noch einmal die Familie Procaviidae! Herbert Hahn. Zeitschr. f. Saeugetierk., vol.11, no.3, p.276, Dec. 30, 1936.

ANNOTATED CATALOGUE OF THE HYRACOIDEA IN THE AMERICAN MUSEUM OF NATURAL HISTORY, WITH A DESCRIPTION OF A NEW SPECIES FROM THE LOWER CONGO. Robert T. Hatt. Amer. Mus. Novitates, no.594, p.13, Jan. 26, 1933.

HYRAXES COLLECTED BY THE AMERICAN MUSEUM CONGO EXPEDITION. Robert T. Hatt. Bull. Amer. Mus. Nat. Hist., vol. 72, art.4, pp.117-141, figs.3, pls.18-22, Aug. 28, 1936.

(COMPLEMENTARY NOTE ON THE DAMANS OF AHAGGAR.) Note complementaire sur les Damans de l'Ahaggar. H. Heim de Balsac. Bull. Mus. Nat. Hist. Nat., Paris, ser.2, vol.6, no.3, pp.224-227, Apr., 1934.

(NEW FACTS ON THE DAMANS OF AHAGGAR.) Faits nouveaux concernant les demans de l'Ahaggar. H. Heim de Balsac, Max Bègouen. Bull. Mus. Nat. Hist. Nat., Paris, vol,4, no.5, pp.478-483, 1932.

NEW HYRAX FROM EAST AFRICA. (Heterohyrax brucei albipes.) N. Hollister. Proc. Biol. Soc. Washington, vol.35, pp. 135-136, Oct. 17, 1922.

NOTES ON AFRICAN HAEMAPHYSALIS TICKS. III. THE HYRAX PARASITES, H. BEQUAERTI SP. NOV., H. ORIENTALIS N. AND W., 1915 (NEW COMBINATION), AND H. COOLEYI BEDFORD, 1929 (IXODOIDEA, IXODIDAE). H. Hoogstraal. Jour. Parasitol., vol.42, no.2, pp.156-172, Apr., 1956. (Hyrax distribution pp.168-170.)

LICE OF THE HYRAXES ESPECIALLY PROCAVIA CAPENSIS. G.H.E. Hopkins. Jour. Entom. Soc. South Africa, vol.8, pp.1-12, 1945.

NOTES ON THE MALLOPHAGA OF PROCAVIIDAE. G.H.E. Hopkins. Rev. Brasileira Biol., Rio de Janeiro, vol.2, no.4, pp.391-397, figs.3, Dec., 1942.

ON THE SIZE OF THE LITTER AND THE GESTATION PERIOD OF PROCAVIA CAPENSIS. C.J. van der Horst. Science, Lancaster, n.s., vol.93, no.2418, pp.430-431, May 2, 1941.

ON THE FORM OF THE PLACENTA IN THE CAPE HYRAX. T.H. Huxley. Proc. Zool. Soc. London, pt.31, p.237, 1863.

BOPO THE BOLD. THE ANTICS OF A PET ABYSSINIAN CAVY. Rhea Kimberley Johnson. Nature Mag., vol.16, no.4, pp.224-225, figs.5, Oct., 1930.

(ON THE VERY RECENT MORPHOLOGICAL EVOLUTION OF AN ANCIENT UNGULATE GROUP, THE DAMANS.) Sur l'evolution morphologique très récente d'un groupe d'Ongules archaiques, les Damans. L. Joleaud. Comptes Rendus hebd. Acad. Sci., Paris, vol.204, no.10, pp.791-793, Mar. 8, 1937.

(NEW PROCAVIANS OF THE ALGERIAN SAHARA.) Procavia nouveau du Sahara Algérien. Max Kollmann. Bull. Mus. Nat. Hist. Nat., no.5, pp.281-283, 1912.

NOTES OF A DISSECTION OF THE CAPE HYRAX (HYRAX CAPENSIS, PALL.) W. Martin. Proc. Zool. Soc. London, pt.3, p. 14, 1835.

(CONTRIBUTION TO KNOWLEDGE OF THE LIVING HABITS OF PROCAVIA.) Beitrag zur Kenntnis der Lebensweise von Procavia. Paul Matschie. Sitz. Ber. Gesell. Naturf. Freunde Berlin, no.10, pp.228-231, Dec. 19, 1893.

(DESCRIPTION OF AN APPARENTLY NEW CONY, PROCAVIA KERSTINGI MTSCH.) Beschreibung eines anscheinend neuen Klippschliefer Procavia Kerstingi Mtsch. Paul Matschie. Sitz. Ber. Gesell. Naturf. Freunde Berlin, no.3, pp.59-64, Mar. 21, 1899.

(ON PROCAVIA SYRIACA (SCHREB.).) Ueber Procavia syriaca (Schreb.). Paul Matschie. Sitz. Ber. Gesell. Naturf. Freunde Berlin, no.8, pp.193-194, Oct. 16, 1894.

CONTRIBUTION TO THE KNOWLEDGE OF THE FOSSIL HYRACOIDEA OF THE FAYŬM, EGYPT, WITH DESCRIPTION OF SEVERAL NEW SPECIES. H. Matsumoto. Bull. Amer. Mus. Nat. Hist., vol. 56, art.4, pp.253-350, illus., Dec. 1, 1926.

MEGALOHYRAX ANDREWS AND TITANOHYRAX, G. N. --A REVISION OF THE GENERA OF HYRACOIDS FROM THE FAYUM, EGYPT. H. Matsumoto. Proc. Zool. Soc. London, 1921, pt.4, pp.839-850, Jan., 1922.

(LIST OF THE CONIES BROUGHT BACK BY THE SECOND GERMAN CENTRAL AFRICA EXPEDITION.) Liste der von der Zweiten Deutschen Zentral-Afrika- Expedition mitgebrachten Klippschliefer. Robert Mertens. Senckenbergiana, vol.11, no.3, pp.119-122, Apr. 29, 1929.

ON THE MYOLOGY OF HYRAX CAPENSIS. St. George Mivart, Murie James. Proc. Zool. Soc. London, pp.329-352, figs.13, 1865.

(ON HYRACOIDS.) Ueber Hyraciden. Oscar Neumann. Sitz. Ber. Gesell. Naturf. Freunde Berlin, no.9, pp.238-244, 1901.

ON THE ANATOMY OF THE CAPE HYRAX (HYRAX CAPENSIS, SCHREB.). R. Owen. Proc. Comm. Sci. and Corres. Zool. Soc. London, pt.2, pp.202-207, 1832.

CONIES ARE BUT A FEEBLE FOLK. W.P. Pycraft. Illus. London News, vol.191, no. 5133, p.384, figs.3, Sep. 4, 1937.

(ROCK RABBIT DENDROHYRAX DORSALIS FRASER.) Der Baum- oder Waldschliefer, Dendrohyrax dorsalis (Fraser). U. Rahm. Zool. Garten, Leipzig, vol.23, nos.1-3, pp.67-74, illus., 1957.

NOTE ON THE HABITS OF THE CAPE HYRAX (HYRAX CAPENSIS, PALL.) W.H. Rudston Read. Proc. Zool. Soc. London, pt.3, pp.13-14, 1835.

HOOFED MAMMALS OF NIGERIA: MAMMALS II. SUB-ORDER HYRACOIDEA: HYRAXES AND CONEYS. FAMILY PROCAVIIDAE. D.R. Rosevear. Nigerian Field, London, vol.8, no.4, pp.136-138, Oct., 1939.

(THE DAMANS OF MOUNTAINS.) Les Damans de montagnes. (Dendrohyrax.) H. Schouteden. Rev. Zool. Bot. Afr., vol. 26 (Suppl. Bull. Cercle Zool. Congo., vol. 11, nos.1-2), p.8, illus., Nov.-Dec., 1934.

HYRAX OF THE CENTRAL SAHARA. Ernst Schwarz. Ann. and Mag. Nat. Hist., London, ser.10, vol.12, pp.625-626, Dec., 1933.

EVIDENCE CONCERNING A LARGE FOSSIL HYRAX. J.C. Shaw. Jour. Dental Res., vol.16, no.1, pp.37-40, fig.1, Feb., 1937.

ON THE VAGUS AND SYMPATHETIC NERVES OF HYRAX CAPENSIS. Charles F. Sonntag. Proc. Zool. Soc. London, pt. 1, pp.149-156, Apr., 1922.

(ON NORTH AFRICAN PROCAVIIDAE.) Ueber nordafrikanische Procaviidae. P. Spatz. Zeitschr. f. Saeugetierk., Berlin, vol.12, no.3, pp.325-326, July 15, 1938.

DIAGNOSIS OF A NEW SPECIES OF PROCAVIA. Oldfield Thomas. Annali del Museo Civico di Storià Naturali di Genova, ser.2, vol.10, p.908, 1891.

NEW DASSIE FROM NORTH NYASALAND. Oldfield Thomas. Ann. and Mag. Nat. Hist., ser.7, vol.6, no.3, p.387, Oct., 1900.

ON THE CLASSIFICATION OF THE CAVILS. Oldfield Thomas. Ann. Mag. Nat. Hist., ser.8, vol.18, pp.301-303.

ON THE SPECIES OF THE HYRACOIDEA. Oldfield Thomas. Proc. Zool. Soc. London, pp.50-76, pl.3, Jan. 5, 1892.

AN INTERESTING BIRTH AT THE ZOO. (Tree Hyrax.) C.S. Webb. Zoo Life, London, vol.1, no.1, pp.9-10, illus., Spring, 1946.

ENDOCRANIAL CAST IN RECENT AND FOSSIL HYRAXES (PROCAVIIDAE). L.H. Wells. South African Jour. Sci., Johannesburg, vol.36, pp.365-373, figs.2, pl.1, Dec., 1939.

ON AN UNUSUAL PLACENTAL FORM IN THE HYRACOIDEA: ITS BEARING ON THE THEORY OF THE PHYLOGENY OF THE PLACENTA. G.B. Wislocki. Contrib. to Embryol. Carnegie Inst. Washington, vol. 21, no.122, pls.5, pp.83-95, 1930.

PLACENTATION OF HYRAX (PROCAVIA CAPENSIS). G.B. Wislocki. Jour. Mamm., vol.9, no.2, pp.117-126, pls.5, May, 1928.

PLACENTATION OF PROCAVIA CAPENSIS WITH A DISCUSSION OF THE PLACENTAL AFFINITIES OF THE HYRACOIDEA. G.B. Wislocki. P. van der Westhuysen. Carnegie Inst. Washington, Publ. no.518 (Contrib. to Embryology, vol.28, no.171), pp.65-88, pls.7, Aug. 15, 1940.

## SIRENIA

(CONTRIBUTION TO THE ONTOGENY OF THE SIRENIAN FIN.) Beitraege zur Entwicklungsgeschichte der Sirenenflosse. Hans Joachim Bahrdt. Jenaische Zeitschr. Naturwiss., Jena, vol.68, pp.193-276, figs.35, tbls., 1933-34.

NOTES CONCERNING MANATEES AND DUGONGS. O.W. Barrett. Jour. Mamm., vol.16, no.3, pp.216-220, Aug., 1935.

DUGONGS FROM MAFIA ISLAND AND A MANATEE FROM NIGERIA. Guy Dollman. Nat. Hist. Mag. (British Mus.), London, vol.4, no.28, pp.117-125, figs.7, Oct., 1933.

(STRUCTURE AND DEVELOPMENT OF THE INTEGUMENT OF THE SIRENIANS.) Bau und Entwicklung des Integuments der Sirenen. F. Dosch. Jena, Zeitschr. Naturwiss., vol.53, pp.805-851, Abb.15, 1915.

TWO NOTES ON THE CENTRAL NERVOUS SYTEM OF FOSSIL SIRENIA. T. Edinger. The Fouad I Univ., Bull. Fac. Sci., Cairo, no.19, pp.43-57, pls.3, 1939.

BIBLIOGRAPHY OF THE MAMMALIAN ORDER SIRENIA. L. Freund. Vestn.Ceskol. zool.Spol., XIV, pp.161-181, 1950.

(ON THE STRUCTURE AND DEVELOPMENT OF THE OLFACTORY ORGAN OF THE SIRENIANS.) Ueber den Bau und die Entwicklung des Geruchsorganes der Sirenen. Joachim Genschow. Zeitschr. Wissenschaft. Biol., Abt. A, Zeitschr. Morphol.u.Okol. Tiere, Berlin, vol.28, no.4, pp.402-444, figs.28, May 19, 1934.

ON THE AFFINITIES OF THE SIRENIANS. Theodore Gill. Proc. Acad. Nat. Sci. Philadelphia, pp.262-273, 1873.

MENATEES AND DUGONGS. R. W. Hayman. Zoo Life, London, vol.10, no.4, pp.98-100, illus., Winter, 1955-1956.

(NOTES ON THE DENTITION OF SIRENIANS. IV. THE CASE OF PRORASTOMA VERONENSE.) Notes sur la dentition des siréniens. IV. Le cas de Prorastoma veronense. B. Heuvelmans. Bull. Mus.Roy. Hist. Nat. Belgique, Brussels, vol.18, no. 3, pp.1-6, figs.4, Jan., 1942.

(SIRENIANS OR SEA COWS.) Sirenen oder Seekuehe. M. Hilzheimer. Brehms Tierleben, Aufl.4, Bd.12, pp.580-590, 1915.

ON THE DISTRIBUTION OF SIRENIANS IN THE PACIFIC. Kyosuke Hirasaka. Proc. 5th Pacific Sci. Congress, Canada, 1933, Univ. Toronto Press, pp.4221-4222, 1934.

SIRENS IN FANCY AND IN FACT. A.T. Hopwood. Nat. Hist. Mag., London, vol. 1, no.1, pp.17-21, figs.3, Jan., 1927.

(CONTRIBUTION TO THE STUDY OF RECENT AND FOSSIL SIRENIANS.) Contribution a l'étude des Siréniens actuels et fossiles. Jean Kaltenmark. Mammalia, Paris, vol.6, no.2, pp.53-64, illus., June, 1942; nos.3-4, pp.101-113, illus., Sep.-Dec., 1942; vol.7, no.1, pp.14-25, illus., Mar., 1943.

(MOZAMBIQUE FAUNA. SIRENIANS.) Fauna Mocambicana. Sirenios. Alberto Peao Lopes. Moçambique, Documentario trimestral, Lourence Marques, Ano 2, no.6, pp.27-36, pls.2, June 30, 1936.

SEA COWS, PAST AND PRESENT. F.A. Lucas. Nat. Hist., New York, vol.16, pp.315-318, fig.3, 1916.

MODERN MERMAIDS. F. A. Lucas.Nat. Hist., New York, vol.23, no.2, pp.122-124, figs.3, Mar-Apr., 1923.

(PROPORTIONAL THICKNESS OF SKIN IN MAMMALS IN GENERAL AND THE SIRENIA IN PARTICULAR.) Die Dickenverhaeltnisse der Haut bei den Mammalien im allgemeinen, den Sirenia im besonderen. Ernst Matthes. Zeitschr. Wiss. Zool., vol. 134, pp.345-357, 1929.

NEW SIRENIAN FROM THE TERTIARY OF PORTO RICO, WEST INDIES. W.D. Matthew. Ann. New York Acad. Sci., vol.27, pp.23-29, figs.2, Jan. 28, 1916.

(SIRENIANS, OR SEA COWS.) Sirenen oder Seekuehe. Erna Mohr. (In) Die Neue Brehm Buecherei Series, A.Ziemsen Verlag, Leipzig, 1957.

EOCENE SIRENIANS IN EGYPT. Henry Fairfield Osborn. Science, Lancaster, n.s., vol.16, no.409, p.715, Oct. 31, 1902.

(CLASSIFICATION OF SPECIES, GENUS TRICHECHI.) De specibus systematicum genus Trichechi. N. Ozertskovsky. Nova acta petropolitana, XIII, pp.371-375, fig., 1802.

(THE ORDER SIRENIA.) Ordre des Siréniens. Georges Petit. (In) Grasse, Traité de Zool., XVII, Paris, 1955.

(CONTRIBUTIONS TO KNOWLEDGE OF TERTIARY SIRENIANS. I. THE EOCENE SIRENIANS OF THE MEDITERRANEAN REGION. II. THE SIRENIANS OF THE BELGIAN TERTIARY.) Beitraege zur Kenntnis Tertiaerer Sirenen. I. Die Eozaene Sirenen des Mittelmeergebietes. II. Die Sirenen des Belgischen Tertiaers. Otto Sickenberg. Mem. Mus. Roy. d'Hist.Nat. Belgique, no.63, pp.1-352, figs.52, pls. 11, Dec. 31, 1934.

(INFLUENCE OF LIFE IN THE WATER ON THE INNER SECRETION AND FORM DEVELOPMENT OF THE SIRENIANS.) Die Einfluesse des Wasserlebens auf die innere Sekretion und Formgestaltung der Sirenen. Otto Sickenberg. Forschungen und Fortschritte, Berlin, Jahrg.9, no.29, pp.427-429, Oct. 10, 1933.

MORPHOLOGY AND PHYLOGENY OF THE SIRENIANS. PART I. THE INFLUENCE OF WATER LIFE ON THE INNER SECRETION AND FORM DEVELOPMENT OF THE SIRENIANS.) Morphologie und Stammesgeschichte der Sirenen. I. Teil. Die Einfluesse des Wasserlebens auf die innere Sekretion und Formgestaltung der Sirenen. Otto Sickenberg. Palaeobiologica, Wien und Leipzig, vol.4, nos.6-7, pp.405-444, 1931.

FOSSIL SIRENIA OF FLORIDA AND THE EVOLUTION OF THE SIRENIA. George G. Simpson. Bull. Amer. Mus. Nat. Hist., vol.59, art.8, pp.419-503, figs.23, Sep. 6, 1932.

SEA SIRENS. THE STRANGE MAMMALS RESPONSIBLE FOR THE ANCIENT IDEAS OF MERMAIDS. George G. Simpson.Nat. Hist., vol.30, no.1, pp.40-47, Jan.-Feb., 1930.

MANATEES AND THE ARCTIC SEA COW. Frederick W. True. Fisheries and Fishery Industries of the United States, vol.1, pt. 1, pp.114-136, pls.33-34, 1885.

(ILLNESS AND DEATH OF THE TWO HAMBURG SIRENIANS.) Krankheit und Tod des Hamburger Sirenenpaares. J. Vosseler. Zeitschr. f. Saeugetierk., vol. 5, no.6, pp.362-364, 1930.

Dugongidae

FORMER OCCURRENCE OF THE DUGONG IN CHINESE WATERS. Glover M. Allen. China Jour., vol.22, no.2, pp.79-82, Feb., 1935.

NOTES ON THE SPECIES AND EXTERNAL CHARACTERS OF THE DUGONG (HALICORE DUGONG). N. Annandale. Jour. Asiatic Soc. Bengal, 1905.

ANATOMICAL NOTES ON THE DUGONG. Bunichiro Aoki et al. Lab. Comp.Morph. and Mamm., Zool. Inst., Tailhoku Imperial Univ., Taiwan, Japan, pp.491-518, illus., 1938.

SIREN OF THE SEAS. Marius Barbeau. Beaver, Winnipeg, outfit 275, pp.20-23, illus., Dec., 1944.

NOTE ON THE SEA COW IN THE GULF OF AQABA. G.C.L. Bertram.Jour. Soc. Preservation Fauna Empire, Hertford, n.s, pt.47, pp.21-23, Aug., 1943.

(ON THE SUPPOSED EXISTENCE OF SEALS ON THE ISLAND OF SHADWAN (RED SEA).) Sur la pretendue existence des Phoques dans la région de l'ile Shadwan (Mer Rouge).(The Supposed Seals Were Dugongs.) Paul Budker. Bull. Mus. Nat. Hist. Nat., Paris, ser.2, vol.11, no.5, pp.450-453, June, 1939.

(ON THE BIOLOGY AND MORPHOLOGY OF HALICORE DUGONG.) Zur Biologie und Morphologie von Halicore dugong. H. Dexler, L. Freund. Arh. Naturg. I, pp.77-106, 1906.

ON TWO DUGONGS FROM MAFIA ISLAND. Guy Dollman. Proc. Linnaean Soc. London, 145th Session, pp.16-17, Jan. 20, 1933.

ON THE AUSTRALIAN DUGONG (HALICORE AUSTRALIS). J.K.E. Fairholme. Proc. Zool. Soc. London, pt.24, pp.352-353, 1856.

THE TEETH OF THE DUGONG. V.S.V. Fernand. Ceylon Jour. Sci., vol.25, pt.2, pp.139-147, illus., Oct. 10, 1953.

(ON THE ANATOMY AND HISTOLOGY OF THE DIGESTIVE TRACT OF HALICORE DUGONG ERXL.) Zur anatomie und histologie des Verdauungstraktes von Halicore Dugong Erxl. J.F. Gudernatsch. Morpholog. Jahrbuch, Leipzig, vol.37, no.4, pp.586-613, figs.1-19, pl.14, 1907.

"EUGENIE" THE DUGONG MERMAID. Robert R. Harry. Pacific Discovery, vol. 9, no.1, pp.21-27, illus., Jan.-Feb., 1956.

WHAT ARE DUGONGS? M.A.C. Hinton. Loris, Ceylon, vol.1, no.2, pp. 82-84, illus., June, 1937.

OCCURRENCE OF DUGONG IN FORMOSA. Kyosuke Hirasaka. Mem. Fac. Sci. and Agric. Taihoku Imp. Univ., Formosa, vol. 7, no.1, pp.1-4, pl.1, Oct., 1932.

VESTIGAL LOWER INCISOR IN THE DUGONG. Charles P. Lyman. Jour. Mamm., vol.20, no.2, pp.229-231, fig.1, May, 1939.

(ON TWO DUGONGS (HALICHOERUS GRYPUS) OF THE ZOOLOGICAL GARDEN OF BERLIN.) Ueber zwei Kegelrobben (Halichoerus grypus) des zoologischen Gartens in Berlin. Alfred Nehring. Sitz. Ber. Gesell. Naturf. Freunde Berlin, no. 5, p. 85, May 18, 1886.

ON THE ANATOMY OF THE DUGONG. R. Owen. Proc. Zool. Soc. London, pt. 6, pp.28-46, 1838.

(NOTES ON THE DUGONGS OF THE MADAGASCAR COASTS.) Notes sur les dugongs des cotes de Madagascar. M.G. Petit. Bull. Mus. Nat.Hist.Nat., Paris, anneé 1924, no.2, pp.124-127, 1924.

GUIDE TO THE MAMMALS OF CEYLON. PART 7. SIRENIA. W.W.A. Phillips. Ceylon Jour. Sci., vol.14, pt.1, pp.51-55, Apr. 30, 1927.

SOME NOTES ON THE DUGONG. R.I. Pocock. Ann. and Mag. Nat. Hist., London, ser.11, vol.5, no.28, pp.329-345, figs.3, Apr., 1940.

DUGONG OR SEA-COW. (HALICORE DUGONG.) S.H. Prater. Jour. Bombay Nat. Hist. Soc., vol.33, no.1, pp.84-99, pls. 1-4, Sep. 30, 1928.

HOW THE FEMALE DUGONG CARRIES HER YOUNG. S.H. Prater. Jour. Bombay Nat. Hist. Soc., vol.33, no.4, p.987, Oct. 15, 1929.

EUROPEAN NOTICES OF INDIAN NATURAL HISTORY. 1. THE DUGONG. 2. NEPAL SPECIMENS. J. Robison. Jour. Asiatic Soc. Bengal, pp.100-101, Feb., 1833.

(DESCRIPTION OF THE DUGONG (HALICORE DUGONG) OCCURRING IN THE RED SEA.) Beschreibung des im Roten Meer vorkommenden Dugong (Halicore dugong). E. Ruppell. Mus. Senckenbergianum 1, 1834.

LETTERS ACCOMPANYING A DUGONG (HALICORE DUGONG, ILL.), PRESENTED BY G. SWINTON. G.Swinton. Proc.Comm. Sci. and Corres. Zool. Soc. London, pt.1, p.113, 1830-31.

SEA COWS MAKING COMEBACK. Stephen Trumbull. Audubon Mag., New York, vol. 51, no.5, p.337, Sep.-Oct., 1949.

Extinct Forms, Fossils

ADDITIONAL REMAINS OF THE FOSSIL DUGONG OF FLORIDA. Glover M. Allen. Jour. Mamm., vol.4, no.4, pp.231-239, pl.26, Nov., 1923.

(NOTES ON THE PELVIC BONE OF RHYTINA STELLERI OSER.) Notice sur l'os pelvis du Rhytina stelleri Oser. A. Birula. Comptes Rendus Acad. Sci. USSR, A, no.4, pp.87-90, 1929.

(ON THE SKIN OF THE NORDIC SEA COW (RHYTINA BOREALIS ILLIG.).) Ueber die Haut der nordischen Seekuh (Rhytina borealis Illig.). Al. Brandt. Mem.Sci.St.Petersb., ser.7, t.17, 1871.

(FURTHER PROOF OF THE EXTERMINATION OF THE NORDIC OR STELLER'S

SEA COW (RHYTINA BOREALIS).) Nochmaliger Nachweis der Vertilgung der nordischen oder Steller'schen Seekuh (Rhytina borealis). J.F. Brandt. Bull. no.2, Soc. Imp. Nat., Moscow, pp.26, 1866.

(FEW MORE WORDS ON THE EXTERMINATION OF STELLER'S SEA COW.) Noch einige Worte ueber die Vertilgung der Rhytina. J.F. Brandt. Melanges Biologiques Bull. Acad. Imp. Sci., St. Petersburg, vol. 5, pp.343-366, Oct. 5-17, 1865.

(FEW WORDS ON THE REPLIES CONCERNING THE EXTERMINATION OF THE NORDIC SEA COWS.) Wenige Worte in Bezug auf die Erwiderungen in Betreff der Vertilgung der nordischen Seekuh. J.F. Brandt. Bull. Soc. Imp. Nat. Moscow, no. 4, pp.17, 1868.

(SOME CONCLUDING WORDS AS REGARDS THE EXTERMINATION OF STELLER'S SEA COW.) Einige Schlussworte zum Nachweis der Vertilgung der Rhytina. J.F. Brandt. Bull. no.1, Soc. Imp. Nat., Moscow, pp. 16, 1867.

(SUPPLEMENTARY COMMUNICATIONS ON THE EXPLANATION OF THE DISTRIBUTION AND EXTERMINATION OF STELLER'S SEA COW.) Ergaenzende Mittheilungen zur Erlaeuterung der ehemaligen Verbreitung und Vertilgung der Steller'schen Seekuh. J.F. Brandt. Melanges Biologiques tires du Bull. Acad. Imp. Sci., St. Petersburg, vol.6, pp.223-232, Mar. 28-Apr. 9, 1867.

(ILLUSTRATION OF THE NORDIC SEA COW (RHYTINA GIGAS ZIMM.). WITH SPECIAL CONSIDERATION OF NEWLY FOUND MANUSCRIPT MATERIALS IN HIS MAJESTY'S LIBRARY IN TSARSKOYE SELO.) Die Abbildungen der nordischen Seekuh (Rhytina gigas Zimm.). Mit besonderer Beruecksichtigung neu aufgefundener handschriftlicher Materialien in Seiner Majestaet Hoechst Eigenen Bibliotek zu Zarskoje Sselo. Eug. Buechner. Mem. Acad. Imp. Sci. St. Petersbourg, ser. 7, vol.38, no.7, pp.24, fold. pl., May 29, 1891.

ANIMALS IN DECLINE: 3. STELLER'S SEA-COW. Maurice Burton. Illus. London News, vol.218, no.5833, p.178, illus., Feb. 3, 1951.

(ON STELLER'S SEA COW.) Von der Stellerschen Seekuh. Tilly Edinger. Natur Mus., vol.60, pp.221-225, illus.3, 1930.

THE END OF THE GREAT NORTHERN SEA COW. George G. Goodwin. Nat. Hist., New York, vol.55, no.2, pp.57-61, illus., Feb., 1946.

ROSTRUM OF FELSINOTHERIUM OSSIVALENSE. Joseph T. Gregory. State of Florida, Dept. Conservation, Geol. Surv., Geol. Bull., no.22, pp.29-47, figs.2, pls. 2, 1941.

(CONSTRUCTION AND PECULIARITIES OF THE SKIN OF STELLER'S SEA COW (RHYTINA STELLERI RETZ.), WHICH WAS EXTERMINATED 188 YEARS AGO.) Konstruktion und Eigenschaft der Haut der vor 188 Jahren ausgerotteten Stellerschen Seekuh (Rhytina stelleri Retz.). K. Haffner. Verh. Dtsch. Zool. Ges. Hamburg, (1956) 1957.

(STRUCTURE, CHARACTERISTICS, AND FORMER USE OF THE SKIN OF STELLER'S SEA COW, RHYTINA STELLERI RETZ., EXTINCT SINCE 1768.) Bau, Eigenschaften und ehemalige Verwendung der Haut der seit 1768 ausgerotteten Steller'schen Seekuh (Rhytina stlleri Rets.). K. Haffner. Mitt. Hamburg Zool. Mus. Inst., vol.55, pp.107-136, Sep., 1957.

DESCRIPTION OF A NEW FOSSIL SEA COW FROM FLORIDA, METAXYTHERIUM FLORIDANUM. Oliver P. Hay. Proc. U.S. Nat. Mus., vol.61, art.17, pp.4, pl.1, May 3, 1922.

(ON A SKELETON AND A RECONSTRUCTION OF THE EXTERNAL BODY APPEARANCE OF THE GIANT SEA COW RHYTINA GIGAS ZIMMERMAN 1780.) Ueber ein Skelet und eine Rekonstruktion des aeusseren Habitus der Riesenseekuh Rhytina gigas Zimmerman 1780. Adolf Kleinschmidt. Zool. Anzeiger, Leipzig, vol.146, pp.292-314, May, 1951.

(PIECE OF THE SKIN OF THE STELLER'S SEA COW (RHYTINA GIGAS ZIMM.).) Ein Hautstueck der Stellerschen Seekuh, Rhytina gigas Zimm. Erna Mohr. Zool. Anz., vol.145, pp.181-185, illus.6, 1950.

THE EARLIEST NAME FOR STELLER'S SEA COW AND DUGONG. T.S. Palmer. Science, Lancaster, vol.2, no.40, pp. 449-450, Oct. 4, 1895.

HALITHERIUM SP. Giambattista dal Piaz. Mem. Ist. Geol. R. Univ. Padova, vol.11, pp.1-5, 1937.

NEW GENUS OF SEA COW FROM THE MIOCENE OF COLOMBIA. Roy H. Reinhart. Univ. Calif. Publ., Bull. Dept. Geol. Sci., vol.28, no.9, pp.203-214, figs.2, Feb. 16, 1951.

CONTRIBUTION TO THE HISTORY OF THE COMMANDER ISLANDS. NO. 2. INVESTIGATIONS RELATING TO THE DATE OF THE EXTERMINATION OF STELLER'S SEA-COW. Leonhard Stejneger. Proc. U.S. Nat. Mus., pp.181-189, 1884.

HOW THE GREAT NORTHERN SEA-COW (RHYTINA) BECAME EXTERMINATED. Leonhard Stejneger. Amer. Nat., vol.21, no.12, pp.1047-1054, Dec., 1887.

ON THE EXTERMINATION OF THE GREAT NORTHERN SEA-COW (RHYTINA). Leonhard Stejneger. Amer. Geogr. Soc. Bull., New York, no.4, pp.317-328, 1886.

SKELETONS OF STELLER'S SEA-COW PRESERVED IN THE VARIOUS MUSEUMS. Leonhard Stejneger. Science, Lancaster, vol.21, no.523, p.81, Feb. 10, 1893.

(DESCRIPTION OF THE MANATEE, OR THE SO-CALLED SEA COW.) Beschreibung des Manati, oder der sogenannten Seekuh. G.W. Steller. Hamburger Mag., vol.1, pp.132-187, pl.1, 1753.

Trichechidae

BIRTH OF A MANATEE. Thomas Barbour. Jour. Mamm., vol.18, no.1, pp.106-107, Feb. 14, 1937.

SOME EARLY NOTICES ON AMERICAN MANATEES AND THE MODE OF THEIR CAPTURE. J.L. Baughman. Jour. Mamm., vol.27, no.3, pp.234-239, Aug., 1946.

MANATEE AS A FOOD ANIMAL. William P.B. Beal. Nigerian Field, London, vol. 8, no.3, pp.124-126, July, 1939.

MANATEE IN NORTH CAROLINA. H.H. Brimley. Jour. Mamm., vol.12, no.3, pp.320-321, Aug., 1931.

MANATEES AND THE FLORIDA FREEZE. A.R. Cahn. Jour. Mamm., vol.21, no.2, pp.222-223, May 14, 1940.

BABY MERMAID--A MANATEE AT THE AQUARIUM. Christopher W. Coates. Bull. New York Zool. Soc., vol.42, no.5, pp. 140-148, illus., Sep.-Oct., 1939.

(BIOLOGY OF THE MANATEE IN CAPTIVITY.) Sur la biologie du Lamatin en captivite. Ch. Davilliers. Mammalia, Paris, vol.11, pp.84-88, 1938.

AMEDULLARY BONES OF THE FLORIDA MANATEE (TRICHECHUS LATIROSTRIS). Don W. Fawcett. Amer. Jour. Anat., Philadelphia, vol.71, no.2, pp.271-309, fig.1, pls.9, Sep. 15, 1942.

ON THE AMEDULLARY BONES OF THE FLORIDA MANATEE (TRICHECHUS LATIROSTRIS). Don W. Fawcett. Anat. Record, Philadelphia, vol.82, no.3, pp. 410-411, Mar. 25, 1942. (Abstract.)

(THE MANATEE BRAIN (MANATUS INUNGUIS NATTERER).) Le cerveau du Lamantin (Manatus inunguis Natterer). Madeleine Friant. Vierteljahresschrift Naturf. Gesell. Zurich, vol.99, no.2, pp.129-135, June 30, 1954.

NOTICE OF A MEMOIR ON THE STRUCTURE OF THE MANATEE. Alfred Henry Garrod. Proc. Zool. Soc. London, p.567, 1875.

OBSERVATIONS ON THE SPECIES OF THE GENUS MANATUS. John Edward Gray. Proc. Zool. Soc. London, pt.25, pp.59-61, 1857.

FURTHER MISCELLANEOUS NOTES ON AMERICAN MANATEES. Gordon Gunter. Jour. Mamm., vol.23, no.1, pp.89-90, Feb. 14, 1942.

TEXAS MANATEES. Gordon Gunter. Texas Game and Fish, vol.2, no.9, pp.9, 11, Aug., 1944.

(CONTRIBUTIONS TO KNOWLEDGE OF THE MANATUS SPECIES.) Beitraege zur Kenntnis der Manatus-Arten. Cl. Hartlaub. Zool. Jahrb. Syst., vol.1, pp.1-112, 1886.

AMERICAN MUSEUM CONGO EXPEDITION MANATEE AND OTHER RECENT MANATEES. Robert T. Hatt. Bull. Amer. Mus. Nat. Hist., vol.66, art.4, pp.533-566, figs. 2, pl.27, Sep. 10, 1934.

MANATEE OF ST. HELENA. G.C. Kitching. Nature, London, vol.138, no.3479, pp.33-34, July 4, 1936.

ON A REMNANT OF THE OMPHALO-MESENTERIC ARTERIES IN THE MANATEE. K. Kostanecki. Proc. Zool. Soc. London, pt.2, pp.273-276, July, 1923.

LETTER OFFERING TO FORWARD MANATEES FOR THE SOCIETY'S MENAGERIE. George Latimer. Proc. Zool. Soc. London, pp.167-168, 1864.

POSSIBLE EARLY RECORD OF A MANATEE IN VIRGINIA. W.L. McAtee. Jour. Mamm., vol.31, no.1, pp.98-99, Feb.21, 1950.

OBSERVATIONS OF MANATEES IN AGGREGATIONS. Joseph Curtis Moore. Amer. Mus. Novitates, New York, vol.1811, pp. 1-24, illus., Dec. 23, 1956.

RANGE OF THE FLORIDA MANATEE. Joseph Curtis Moore. Jour. Florida Acad. Sci., vol.14, no.1, pp.1-19, fig.1, Mar., 1951.

STATUS OF THE MANATEE IN THE EVERGLADES NATIONAL PARK, WITH NOTES ON ITS NATURAL HISTORY. Joseph Curtis Moore. Jour. Mamm., vol. 32, no.1, pp.22-36, Feb. 15, 1951.

WANT TO SEE A FLORIDA MANATEE? Joseph Curtis Moore. Animal Kingdom, New York Zool. Soc., vol.57, no.1, pp. 11-13, illus., Feb., 1954.

THE "MANATEE" OF ST. HELENA. Th. Mortensen. Nature, London, vol.133, p. 417, Mar. 17, 1934.

ON THE "MANATEE" OF ST. HELENA. Th. Mortensen. Vidensk. Medd. fra Dansk. naturh. Foren, vol.97, pp.1-9, figs.2, Aug. 19, 1933.

NOTICE OF A MEMOIR ON THE MANATEE. James Murie. Proc. Zool. Soc. London, pp.747-748, 1870.

NOTE ON THE HISTOLOGY AND PHARMACOLOGY OF THE HYPOPHYSIS OF THE MANATEE (TRICHECHUS INUNGUIS). Frances Oldham et al. Anat. Record, vol. 71, no.1, pp.27-32, figs.2, May 25, 1938.

ON THE ANATOMY OF THE MANATEE. D.P. Quiring, Charles F. Harlan. Jour. Mamm., vol.34, no.2, pp.192-203, illus., May 14, 1953.

EXPERIMENTAL INVESTIGATIONS ON THE RESPIRATION AND DIVING OF THE FLORIDA MANATEE. P.F. Scholander, Laurence Irving. Jour. Cell. and Comp. Physiol., Philadelphia, vol.17, no.2, pp.169-191, figs.15, Apr., 1941.

NOTICE OF ADDITIONS TO THE SOCIETY'S MENAGERIE, AND OF THE TRANSMISSION OF A MANATEE TO THE SOCIETY BY MR. G. W. LATIMER, OF PORTO RICO. Philip Lutley Sclater. Proc. Soc. London, p.201, 1866.

(A NEW SPECIES OF PARASITIC TREMATODE IN THE INTESTINES OF THE MANATEE. (SCHIZAMPHISTOMA MANATI).) Una nueva especie de trematodo parasito del intestino del manati. Schizamphistoma manati. Demetrio Sokoloff, Eduardo Caballero. Anal. Inst. Biol., Mexico, D.F., no. 2, pp.163-167, figs.5, 1932.

MYSTERY MAMMAL--THE FLORIDA MANATEE. Alexander Sprunt, Jr. Audubon Mag., New York, vol.51, no.5, pp.286-288, 337, illus., Sep.-Oct., 1949.

(CONTRIBUTIONS TO KNOWLEDGE OF THE AMERICAN MANATEE.) Beitraege zur Kenntnis der amerikanischen Manatie. Hermann Stannius. Rostock, pp.1-57, pls. 2, 1845.

DENTITION OF THE MANATEE. Oldfield Thomas, R. Lydekker. Proc. Zool. Soc. London, p.814, Nov. 16, 1897.

ON THE NUMBER OF GRINDING-TEETH POSSESSED BY THE MANATEE. Oldfield Thomas, R. Lydekker. Proc. Zool. Soc. London, pp.595-600, pl.36, May 18, 1897.

MANATEE ALONG THE GEORGIA COAST. Ivan R. Tomkins. Jour. Mamm., vol.37, no.2, pp.288-289, June 9, 1956.

(CARE AND KEEPING OF THE MANATEE (TRICHECHUS), WITH CONTRIBUTIONS ON ITS BIOLOGY.) Pflege und Haltung der Seekuehe (Trichechus) nebst Beitraegen zu ihrer Biologie. Jul Vosseler. Pallasia, vol.2, pp.58-67, 167-180, 213-230, illus. 2, tbls.2, 1924.

LUNGS OF THE MANATEE(TRICHECHUS LATIROSTRIS) COMPARED WITH THOSE OF OTHER AQUATIC MAMMALS. George B. Wislocki. Biol. Bull., vol.68, no.3, pp. 385-396, pls.1-2, June, 1935.

PLACENTATION OF THE MANATEE. (Trichechus latirostris.) George B. Wislocki. Memoirs Mus. Comp. Zool., Harvard College, vol.54, no.3, pp.177, pls.71, Dec., 1935.

MANATEES AT THE AQUARIUM. Bull. New York Zool. Soc., vol.43, no.3, pp. 99-100, fig., May-June, 1940.

Desmostylidae

DESMOSTYLUS TOOTH DREDGED IN MONTEREY BAY. G.D. Hanna. Bull.Geol. Soc. Amer., vol.43, no.1, p.291, Mar., 1932.

NOTES ON TERTIARY SIRENIANS OF THE GENUS DESMOSTYLUS. Harold Hannibal. Jour. Mamm., vol.3, no.4, pp.238-240, pls.11-12, Nov., 1922.

CONTRIBUTION TO THE KNOWLEDGE OF THE EXTINCT SIRENIAN DESMOSTYLUS HESPERUS MARSH. Oliver P. Hay. Proc. U.S. Nat. Mus., vol.49, pp.381-397, pls. 56-58, Aug. 31, 1915.

NOTES ON THE OSTEOLOGY AND DENTITION OF THE GENERA DESMOSTYLUS AND CORNWALLIUS. Oliver P. Hay. Proc. U.S. Nat. Mus., vol.65, art.8, pp.1-8, pls.1-2, 1924.

ON THE TOOTH-GERM (OR ZAHNKEIM) OF DESMOTHYLUS JAPONICUS TOKUNAGA ET IWASOKI. Shoji Ijiri. Jour. Geol. Soc. Japan, Tokyo, vol.44, no.525, p.532, June 20, 1937. (In Japanese.)

HISTOLOGICAL STUDY OF THE TEETH OF DESMOSTYLUS. Syozi Iziri. Jour. Geol.Soc. Japan, Tokyo, vol.46, no.548, pp.220-230, figs.13, tbl.1, May 20, 1939. (In Japanese with German summary.)

MICROSCOPIC STRUCTURE OF A TOOTH OF DESMOSTYLUS. Syozi Iziri. Proc.Imp. Acad., Tokyo, vol.15, no.5, pp.135-138, figs.6, May, 1939.

CONTRIBUTION TO THE MORPHOLOGY, PALAEOBIOLOGY AND SYSTEMATICS OF DESMOSTYLUS. Hikoshichiro Matsumoto. Sci. Reports, Tohoku Imp. Univ., ser.2 (Geol.), vol.3, no.2, pp.61-74, pl.1, 1918.

CLASSIFICATION AND GEOLOGICAL DISTRIBUTION OF THE DESMOSTYLIDAE. Takumi Nagao. Jour. Geol. Soc. Japan, Tokyo, vol.44, no.525, pp.533-534, June 20, 1937. (In Japanese.)

DESMOSTYLELLA, NEW GENUS OF DESMOSTYLIDAE FROM JAPAN. Takumi Nagao. Proc. Imp. Acad. Tokyo, vol.8, no.3, pp.82-85, figs.5, Mar., 1937.

DESMOSTYLUS MIRABILIS NOV. FROM SAGHALIN. Takumi Nagao. Jour.Geol.Soc. Japan, vol.42, nos.504-507, pp.822-824, (Trans.Proc.Paleont.Soc.Japan, 1935, no. 1). (In Japanese with English summary.)

NEW SPECIES OF DESMOSTYLUS FROM JAPANESE SAGHALIEN AND ITS GEOLOGICAL SIGNIFICANCE. (Desmostylus minor.) Takumi Nagao. Proc. Imp. Acad. Tokyo, vol.13, no.2, pp.46-49, figs.3, Feb., 1937.

NEW OCCURRENCE OF A SMALL DESMOSTYLUS TOOTH IN HOKKAIDŌ. Takumi Nagao. Proc. Imp. Acad. Tokyo, vol.8, no. 4, pp.110-113, figs.9, Apr., 1937.

ON THE TEETH OF DESMOSTYLUS. Takumi Nagao. Jour. Geol. Soc. Japan, Tokyo, vol. 42, no.505, pp.605-614, pls.17-18, Oct.20, 1935. (In Japanese.)

GEOGRAPHICAL DISTRIBUTION OF DESMOSTYLUS. Takumi Nagao, Saburo Oishi. Jour. Geol. Soc. Japan, Tokyo, vol.42, no.497, pp.74-81, Feb. 20, 1935. (In Japanese.)

REMARKABLE NEW MAMMAL FROM JAPAN. ITS RELATIONSHIP TO THE CALIFORNIAN GENUS DESMOSTYLUS, MARSH. Henry Fairfield Osborn. Science, Lancaster, vol.16, no.409, pp.713-714, Oct. 31, 1902.

DISCOVERY OF A TOOTH OF DESMOSTYLUS IN KAMCHATKA. I.B. Pleshakov. Doklady Acad. Sci.USSR, Moscow, n.s., vol.28, no.4, pp.374-376, figs.2, 1940.

DIAGNOSIS OF THE NEW MAMMALIAN ORDER, DESMOSTYLIA. Roy Reinhart. Jour. Geol., Chicago, vol.61, no.2, p. 187, Mar., 1953.

ON THE LOCALITY OF DESMOSTYLUS, SOUTH OF LAKE SINDI. E. Sakai. Jour. Geol. Soc. Japan, Tokyo, vol.42, no.498, pp.161-162, fig.1, Mar. 20, 1935. (In Japanese.)

(IS DESMOSTYLUS A SIRENIAN?) Ist Desmostylus eine Sirene? O.Sickenberg. Palaeobiologica, Wien-Leipzig, vol.6, pt. 2, pp.340-357, 1938.

NEW LOCALITY OF DESMOSTYLUS. Masatosi Tagami. Jour. Geol. Soc. Japan, Tokyo, vol.43, no.508, pp.47-48, figs.2, Jan. 20, 1936. (In Japanese.)

NATURE AND DISTRIBUTION OF DESMOSTYLUS, A MARINE TERTIC MAMMAL. V.L. Vanderhoof. Pan-Amer.Geol., Des Moines, vol.64, no.1, p.80, Aug., 1935.

OCCURRENCE OF THE TERTIARY MARINE MAMMAL CORNWALLIUS IN LOWER CALIFORNIA. V.L. Vanderhoof. Amer. Jour. Sci., New Haven, vol.240, no.4, pp.298-301, pl.1, Apr., 1942.

STUDY OF THE MIOCENE SIRENIAN DESMOSTYLUS. V.L. Vanderhoof. Univ. Calif. Publ., Bull. Dept. Geol. Sci., vol. 24, no.8, pp.169-262, figs.65, maps 2, Oct. 7, 1937.

PERISSODACTYLA

THE MILK-MOLARS OF PERISSODACTYLA, WITH REMARKS ON MOLAR OCCLUSION. P.M. Butler. Proc. Zool. Soc. London, vol. 121, pt.4, pp.777-817, illus., Feb. 8, 1952.

MOLARISATION OF THE PREMOLARS IN THE PERISSODACTYLA. P.M. Butler. Proc. Zool. Soc. London, vol.121, pt.4, pp.819-843, illus., Feb. 8, 1952.

OCCURRENCE OF A MONGOLIAN EOCENE PERISSODACTYLE IN THE RED SANDSTONE OF SICHUAN, S. W. HONAN. P. Teilhard de Chardin. Bull. Geol. Soc.China, Peiping, vol.9, no.4, pp.331-332, fig.1, 1930.

NOTICE OF A NEW SPECIES OF AMERICAN TAPIR, WITH OBSERVATIONS ON THE SKULLS OF TAPIRUS, RHINOCHOERUS, AND ELASMOGNATHUS IN THE COLLECTION OF THE BRITISH MUSEUM. J.E. Gray. Proc. Zool. Soc. London, pp.876-886, figs.2, pl., 1867.

ABSENCE OF THE POLLEX IN PERISSODACTYLA. W.D. Matthew. Bull. Amer. Mus. Nat. Hist., New York, vol.37, art. 21, pp.573-577, Sep. 7, 1917.

SMALLER PERISSODACTYLS OF THE IRDIN MANHA FORMATION, EOCENE OF MONGOLIA. W.D. Matthew, Walter Granger. Amer. Mus. Novitates, no.199, pp.9, illus., Nov. 23, 1925.

TWO NEW PERISSODACTYLS FROM ARSHANTO EOCENE OF MONGOLIA. W.D. Matthew, Walter Granger. Amer. Mus.Novit., no.208, pp.5, illus., Feb. 16, 1926.

PERISSODACTYLS TYPICALLY POLYPHYLETIC. Henry Fairfield Osborn.Science, Lancaster, vol.16, no.409, p.715, Oct. 31, 1902.

TITANOTHERES AND LOPHIODONTS IN MONGOLIA. Henry Fairfield Osborn. Amer. Mus. Nov., New York, no.91, pp. 5, figs.2, Oct. 17, 1923.

PERISSODACTYLS OF THE LOWER MIOCENE WHITE RIVER BEDS. Henry Fairfield Osborn, J.L. Wortman. Bull. Amer. Mus. Nat. Hist., New York, vol.7, art. 12, pp.343-375, figs.12, pls.8-11, Dec. 23, 1895.

PERISSODACTYLA FROM THE SESPE OF THE LAS POSAS HILLS, CALIFORNIA. Chester Stock. Contrib. to Paleont.,Carnegie Inst. Washington, Publ.440, pp.15-28, pls. 4, Nov. 15, 1933.

PERISSODACTYLA OF THE SESPE EOCENE, CALIFORNIA. Chester Stock. Proc. Nat. Acad. Sci., Washington, D.C., vol.22, no. 5, pp.260-265, May, 1936.

MAMMALIAN FAUNA OF THE WHITE RIVER OLIGOCENE. PART 5. PERISSODACTYLA. William Berryman Scott. Trans. Amer. Philos. Soc., Philadelphia, n.s., vol.28, pt.5, pp.i-xvi, 747-980, figs.21, pls.22, June, 1941.

ODD TOES. (Perissodactyla.) Ken Stott, Jr. Zoonooz, San Diego, vol.12, no.3, pp.6-7, Mar., 1940.

PERISSODACTYL SUBORDERS. Horace Elmer Wood. Jour.Mamm., vol.18, no.1, p.106, Feb. 14, 1937.

SOME EARLY TERTIARY RHINOCEROSES AND HYRACODONTS. Horace Elmer Wood. Bull. Amer. Paleontology, vol.13, no.50, pp. 1-104, pls.7, charts, Dec. 3, 1927.

(EQUUS AND OTHER PERISSODACTYLA.) Equus und andere Perissodactyla. Otto Zdansky. Palaeont. Sinica, ser.C, vol.6, no.5, pp.1-54, pls.1-7, Jan., 1935.

Palaeotheriidae

ON THE STRUCTURE AND SHAPE OF PALAEOTHERIUM. Theodore Gill. Bull.Philos. Soc. Washington, 68th meeting, p.99, Apr. 25, 1874.

Equidae

HORSE SECRETS WRITTEN, COMP. AND NOW DISCLOSED. Alexander S. Alexander. Philadelphia, Wilmer Atkinson Co., pp.64, illus., 1913.

(THE DONKEY.) O burro. R. Andrade. Bol. Pecuário, Lisboa, Ano 7, no.1, pp.5-22, figs.73, tbls., 1939.

(MORE PRECISE DATA ON THE TRUE QUAGGA (EQUUS QUAGGA QUAGGA GM.).) Zur genaueren Kenntnis des echten Quaggas (Equus quagga quagga Gm.). Otto Antonius. Zool. Garten, Leipzig, n.F., vol.4, nos. 3-5, pp.103-115, figs.10, May, 1931.

(OBSERVATIONS ON SOLIPEDS IN SCHOENBRUNN. I) THE SYRIAN HALF-ASS.) Beobachtungen an Einhufern in Schoenbrunn. I. Der syrische Halbesel. Otto Antonius. Zool. Garten, vol.1, nos.1-2, pp.19-25, 1928.

(OBSERVATIONS ON SOLIPEDS IN SCHOENBRUNN. II) THE MONGOLIAN WILD HORSES.) Beobachtungen an Einhufern in Schoenbrunn. II. Die mongolischen Wildpferde. Otto Antonius. Zool. Garten, vol. 1, nos.3-4, pp.87-98, 1928.

(OBSERVATIONS ON SOLIPEDS IN SCHOENBRUNN. III) ZEBRAS, PARTICULARLY

BURCHELL'S ZEBRA.) Beobachtungen an Einhufern in Schoenbrunn. III. Ueber Zebras, insbesondere das Burchellzebra. Otto Antonius. Zool. Garten, vol.1, nos.5-6, pp. 165-182, 1928.

(OBSERVATIONS ON SOLIPEDS IN SCHOENBRUNN. V. MOUNTAIN ZEBRA, GRÉVY'S ZEBRA, AND ZEBRULA.) Beobachtungen an Einhufern in Schoenbrunn. V. Bergzebras, Grévyzebras und Zebroide. Otto Antonius. Zool. Garten, Leipzig, n.F., vol.2, nos. 10-12, pp.261-274, figs.1-10, Mar., 1930.

(OBSERVATIONS ON SOLIPEDS IN SCHOENBRUNN. VI. AN INTERESTING FILLY.) Beobachtungen an Einhufern in Schoenbrunn. VI. Ein interessantes Ponyfohlen. Otto Antonius. Zool. Garten, Leipzig, n.F., vol. 4, nos.3-5, pp.158-159, figs.2, May, 1931.

(OBSERVATIONS ON SOLIPEDS IN SCHOENBRUNN. VII. HALF-ASS.) Beobachtungen an Einhufern in Schoenbrunn. VII. Halbesel. Otto Antonius. Zool. Garten, Leipzig, n.F., vol.5, nos.10-12, pp.261-275, figs.9, Dec., 1932.

(OBSERVATIONS OF SOLIPEDS IN SCHOENBRUNN. VIII. PONIES AND DOMESTIC ASSES.) Beobachtungen an Einhufern in Schoenbrunn. VIII. Ponys und Hausesel. Otto Antonius. Zool. Garten, Leipzig, n.F., vol.6, nos.10-12, pp.213-224, figs.8, Dec., 1935.

(OBSERVATIONS OF SOLIPEDS IN SCHOENBRUNN. IX. MORE EXACT INFORMATION ON THE WAHLBERG ZEBRA (EQUUS QUAGGA WAHLBERGI POC.).) Beobachtungen an Einhufern in Schoenbrunn. IX. Zur genaueren Kenntnis des Wahlbergzebras (Equus quagga wahlbergi Poc.). Otto Antonius. Zool.Garten, Leipzig, n.F., vol.7, nos.1-3, pp.16-24, figs.10, May, 1934.

(OBSERVATIONS OF SOLIPEDS IN SCHOENBRUNN. X.ZEBRULA AND MULE. XI. ON THE SECOND SCHOENBRUNN MULE.) Beobachtungen an Einhufern in Schoenbrunn. X.Zebroid und Maulesel.XI.Ueber den zweiten Schoenbrunner Maulesel. Otto Antonius. Zool.Garten, Leipzig, n.F., vol.7, nos.7-9, pp.165-179, illus., Nov., 1934.

(OBSERVATIONS ON SOLIPEDS IN SCHOENBRUNN. XII. ON THE KLADRUB HORSE.) Beobachtungen an Einhufern in Schoenbrunn. XII. Ueber das Kladruber Pferd. Otto Antonius. Zool. Garten, Leipzig, n.F., vol.7, nos.10-12, pp.249-262, illus., Feb., 1935.

(OBSERVATIONS OF SOLIPEDS IN SCHOENBRUNN, XIII AND XIV.) Beobachtungen an Einhufern in Schoenbrunn, XIII und XIV. Otto Antonius. Zool. Garten, Leipzig, vol.8, pts. 4-6, pp.100-113, figs.13, Jan., 1936.

(OBSERVATIONS ON SOLIPEDS IN SCHOENBRUNN. XV) AN ONAGER-ZEBRULA.) Beobachtungen an Einhufern in Schoenbrunn. XV. Ein Onagerzebroid. Otto Antonius. Zool. Garten, n.F., vol.12, nos.2-3, pp.161-165, illus., July, 1940.

(OBSERVATIONS OF SOLIPEDS IN SCHOENBRUNN. XVI. ON THE DAMARA ZEBRA (EQUUS QUAGGA ANTIQUORUM H.SM.).) Beobachtungen an Einhufern in Schoenbrunn. XVI. Ueber das Damarazebra (Equus quagga antiquorum H. Sm.). Otto Antonius. Zool. Garten, Leipzig, n.F., vol.12, nos.4-6, pp.247-257, figs.11, Dec., 1940.

(OBSERVATIONS OF SOLIPEDS IN SCHOENBRUNN. XX. ON NORTHERN SMALL HORSES.) Beobachtungen an Einhufern in Schoenbrunn. XX. Ueber nordische Kleinpferde. Otto Antonius. Zool. Garten, Leipzig, n.F., vol.20, no.1, pp.1-24, illus., 1953.

ON THE GEOGRAPHICAL DISTRIBUTION IN FORMER TIMES AND TODAY OF THE RECENT EQUIDAE. Otto Antonius. Proc. Zool. Soc. London, vol.107, ser.C, no.10, p.43, Oct. 12, 1937. (Abstract); ser.B, vol. 107, pt.4, pp.557-564, Jan., 1938.

WILD HORSES. Belle J. Benchley. Zoonooz, San Diego, vol.12, no.10, pp.1-4, Oct., 1940.

HARTMANN'S ZEBRA. Gilbert Blaine. Jour. Soc. Preserv. Fauna Empire (Great Britain), n.s., pt.22, pp.15-17, May, 1934.

(EQUUS OR REAL HORSES.) Los Equus o verdaderos Caballos. Marcellin Boule. Anales Univer. Central, Quito, vol.58, no. 299, pp.153-156, Jan.-Mar., 1937.

THE TRUE MOUNTAIN ZEBRA. H.A.Bryden. Field, London, vol.152, p.492, illus., Sep. 27, 1928.

A DAZZLE OF ZEBRAS. Maurice Burton. Illus. London News, vol.137, no.3584, p. 1142, illus., Dec. 31, 1955.

QUAGGAS AND ZEBRAS. Maurice Burton. Illus. London News, vol.219, no.5862, p. 292, illus., Aug. 25, 1951.

A QUAGGA CHASE IN SOUTH-WEST AFRICA. Bernard Carp. African Wild Life, Johannesburg, vol.6, no.2, pp.101-105, illus., June, 1952.

A GOOD LONGEVITY RECORD FOR A CHAPMAN'S ZEBRA. L.S. Crandall. Animal Kingdom, New York Zool. Soc., vol.57, no.3, p.94, June, 1954.

EGYPTIAN AND ARABIAN HORSES. E. Prisse D'Avennes. Smiths. Inst. Rept., pp. 457-467, 1904.

A YOUNG GRANT'S ZEBRA. (Distribution and characters of various forms of zebras.) J.G. Dollman. Nat. Hist. Mag., London, vol.2, no.16, pp.260-261, fig.1, Oct., 1930.

'HORSES' NOT HORSES. Theo. Gill. Science, n.s., vol.19, no.488, pp.737-738, May 6, 1904.

HORSE IN THE TIGER'S SKIN. (Account of zebras.) William K. Gregory. Zool.Soc. Bull., vol.29, no.4, pp.111-133, illus., July-Aug., 1926.

(THE KOENIGSBERG QUAGGA.) Das Koenigsberger Quagga. Max Hilzheimer. Zeitschr. f. Saeugetierk., vol.5, no.2, pp.86-95, pl.5, Aug. 30, 1930.

DESERT CANARY. (Burro.) Henrietta Holland. Frontiers, Lancaster, vol.11, no.1, pp.24-26, illus., Oct., 1946.

RARE WILD HORSES. W.T. Hornaday. New York Zool. Soc., Zool. Soc. Bull., no.8, p.64, Jan., 1903.

RESTORE THE BURCHELL ZEBRA. W.T. Hornaday. Zool. Soc. Bull., vol.24, no.1, pp.18-20, Jan., 1921.

(DWARF DONKEYS.) Dwergezeltjes. L.J. de Jong. Artis, Amsterdam, vol.1, no.6, pp. 144-147, illus., Apr., 1956. (Burros.)

(OBSERVATIONS ON ZEBRAS.) Bemerkungen ueber Tigerpferde. E. Kattinger. Zeitschr. f. Saeugetierk., vol.17, no.2, pp.115-122, pls. 12-15, illus., Feb. 19, 1953.

(MEASUREMENTS OF THE HORSE SKELETON AS A CONTRIBUTION TO THE THEORETICAL PRINCIPLE OF JUDGING THE HORSE.) Skelettmessungen am Pferd als Beitrag zur theoretischen Grundlage der Beurteilungslehre des Pferdes. Ludwig Kiesewalter. Inaugural-Dissertation, Univ. Leipzig, pp.1-39, tbls.2, 1888 or 1889.

(THE RHIZOPODA FAUNA OF HORSE FECES.) Die Rhizopodenfauna des Pferdekotes. Karl Krosz. Archiv. f. Protistenkunde, vol.48, pp.316-341, July 15, 1924.

HORSE AND ITS RELATIVES. Richard Lydekker. London, George Allen and Co., Ltd., pp.286, illus., 1912.

EQUUS PENRICEI THOS. Paul Matschie. Sitz. Ber. Gesell. Naturf. Freunde Berlin, no.10, p.231, Dec. 18, 1900.

(ON THE HAFLINGER HORSE.) Vom Haflinger Pferd. Erna Mohr. Zool. Garten, Leipzig, n.F., vol.3, nos.4-8, pp.159-168, figs. 1-10, Aug. 11, 1930.

HORSES OF ANOTHER COLOR. (Zebras.) Edalee Orcutt. San Diego Zoonooz, vol.20, no.1, pp.6-7, illus., Jan., 1947.

WILD HORSES COULDN'T DRAG ME. (Prsewalski horse and wild asses.) Edalee Orcutt. San Diego Zoonooz, vol.20, no.3, pp.6-7, Mar., 1947.

(WHAT IS THE "PANJE HORSE"?) Was ist das "Panjepferd"? F.P. Pritzwald. Zool. Garten, Leipzig, n.F., vol.4, nos.8-9, pp.261-266, figs.4, Oct., 1931.

WILD ASSES. W.P. Pycraft. Illus. London News, vol.192, no.5172, p.1019, photos 3, June 4, 1938.

THE QUAGGA. Graham Renshaw. Jour.Soc. Preservation of Fauna of Empire, Hertford, n.s., pt.26, pp.23-29, Sep., 1935.

(PYGMY AND DWARF HORSES.) Caballos petisos y enanos. Carlos Rusconi. Suelo Argentina, Año 4, no.47, pp.16-18, 20-23, 45, illus., Nov., 1945.

(DATA ON THE GRÉVY ZEBRA AND THE HISTORY OF ITS DISCOVERY.) Zur Kenntnis und zur Entdeckungsgeschichte des Grévy-Zebras. Adolf Rzaśnicki. Zool.Garten, Leipzig, n.F., vol.8, nos.10-12, pp. 283-291, illus., Sep., 1936.

(ZEBRAS AND QUAGGAS.) Adolf Rzaśnicki. Ann. Mus. Zool. Polonici, Warsaw, vol.14, no.16, pp.203-252, pls.19-34, July 30, 1951. (In English with Polish summary.)

PRZEWALSKY'S HORSE. W. Salensky.1907. (Translation.)

A KINGDOM FOR WILD HORSES. Barney Schwartz. Nature Mag., Washington, vol.42, no.1, pp.8-12, 50, illus., Jan., 1949.

HARTMANN'S MOUNTAIN ZEBRA. Guy C. Shortridge. Jour. Soc. Preserv. Fauna Empire (Great Britain), n.s., pt.22, pp.13-15, pl.1, May, 1934.

(THE CELTIC PONY, THE TARPAN, AND THE FJORD HORSE.) Den celtiske pony, tarpanen og fjordhesten. Leonhard Stejneger. Naturen, Kobenhavn, no.647, pp.161-168, June, July, 1904.

LETTER RELATING TO A YOUNG KIANG. Hon. J. Thomason. Proc. Zool. Soc. London, pt. 16, p.62, 1848.

WILD HORSES. Edouard L. Trouessart. Popular Sci. Monthly, vol.37, no.5, pp. 626-631, figs.3, Sep., 1890.

(FURTHER STUDIES ON THE POLISH KONIK (POLISH FARM HORSE).) Weitere Studien ueber den polischen Konik (polisches Landpferd). T. Vetulani. Bull.Acad.Pol.Sci.Lettres, B., pp.835-949, 1927.

(REINTRODUCTION OF THE FOREST TARPAN IN THE VIRGIN FOREST OF BIATOWIEZA.) Die Wiedereinfuehrung des Waldtarpans in den Urwald von Biatowieza (Bialowies). T. Vetulani. Bull.Internat. Acad. Polonaise Sci. et Lettres, Cracovie, nos.3-4, pp.205-214, pl.9, Mar.-Apr., 1936.

(REPORT ON THE DEATH OF TWO ZEBRAS.) J. Vosseler. Zeitschr. f. Saeugetierk., vol.5, no.6, pp.371-373, 1930. (In German.)

TWO "HERDS" OF THREE-TOED HORSES. M.V. Walker. Trans. Kansas Acad. Sci., vol.33, pp.137-143, 1930.

THE ZEBRA IS A DARK HORSE. David P. Willoughby. Fauna, Philadelphia, vol.8, no.3, pp.67-70, illus., Sep., 1946.

## Africa

(ON THE GEOGRAPHICAL DISTRIBUTION OF THE BURCHELL ZEBRA AND THE REAL QUAGGA.) Zur geographischen Verbreitung des Burchellzebras und des echten Quaggas. Otto Antonius. Zool. Garten, Leipzig, n.F., vol.8, nos.1-3, pp.1-7, figs.8, Sep., 1935.

(OCCURRENCE OF THE WILD ASS IN THE WESTERN SAHARA.) Ueber das Vorkommen wilder Esel in der Westsahara. Otto Antonius. Zeitschr. f. Saeugetierk., Berlin, vol.6, no.3, pp.133-136, pl.3, figs.1-3, Dec. 15, 1931.

EARLY HISTORY OF THE CAPE MOUNTAIN ZEBRA. R. Bigalke. African Wild Life, Johannesburg, vol.6, no.2, pp.143-153, illus., June, 1952.

ZOE CAME TO STAY DESPITE ALL THE PESSIMISTS. (Photographs of baby zebra in Kenya.) Violet Campbell. Field, London, vol.175, no.4557, pp.657-658, figs.7, Apr. 27, 1940.

NEW RACE OF WILD ASS FROM THE SUDAN, ASINUS ASINUS DIANAE, SUBSP. NOV. J. Guy Dollman. Proc. Linn. Soc. London, session 1934-35, pt.4, pp.132-134, Oct. 10, 1935.

A QUAGGA INQUIRY. C.H. Hahn. Jour.Soc. Preservation Fauna Empire, Hertford, n.s., pt.39, pp.39-41, Apr., 1940.

NOTE ON SUBFOSSIL TEETH OF EQUUS ZEBRA L. FROM ORANGE FREE STATE. D.A. Hooijer. Zool. Mededeel., Leyden, vol.25, pp.101-108, fig.1, pls.6-8, 1945.

(WILD HORSES OF AFRICA.) Die afrikanischen Wildpferde. Paul Matschie. Naturwissensch. Wochenschr., Bd.10, no.8, pp. 90-94, Feb. 24, 1895.

(AFRICAN WILD HORSES AS REPRESENTATIVES OF ZOOGRAPHICAL SUBREGIONS.) Die afrikanischen Wildpferde als Vertreter zoogeographischer Subregionen. Paul Matschie. Zool. Garten, Jahrg.35, no.2, pp.33-39, Feb., 1894.

(GEOGRAPHICAL DISTRIBUTION OF THE TIGER HORSE AND THE ZENBRA IN THE KAOKO FIELD IN GERMAN SOUTHWEST AFRICA.) Die geographische Verbreitung der Tigerpferde und das Zebra des Kaoko-Feldes in Deutsch-Suedwest Afrika. Paul Matschie. Sitz. Ber. Gesell. Naturf.Freunde Berlin, no.9, pp.169-181, Nov. 15, 1898.

(ON THE AFRICAN WILD ASS.) Ueber afrikanische Wildesel. O. Neumann. Zeitschr. f. Saeugetierk., vol.10, no.1, pp. 152-153, Dec. 31, 1935.

EXTINCT QUAGGAS OF SOUTH AFRICA. W.P. Pycraft. Illus. London News, vol. 197, no.5281, p.8, July 6, 1940.

ON EQUUS QUAGGA OF SOUTH-WESTERN AND EASTERN AFRICA. J.St. Leger. Ann. and Mag. Nat. Hist., ser.10, vol.10, no. 60, pp.587-593, Dec., 1932.

(THE ZEBRAS OF KUNDELUNGU AND THE PROTECTION OF FAUNA IN THE UPPER KATANGA.) Les zèbres des Kundelungu et la protection de la faune dans le Haut-Katanga. J. Schwetz. Annales Comité Belge pour la Protection de la Natur, vol.1, year 1926, pp.63-68, illus., 1928.

EXHIBITION OF, AND REMARKS UPON, A ZEBRA FROM THE HENGA COUNTY, BRITISH CENTRAL AFRICA. Philip Lutley Sclater. Proc. Zool. Soc. London, 1893, pt.4, pp.688-690, Apr. 1, 1896.

ON AN APPARENTLY NEW SPECIES OF ZEBRA FROM THE SEMLIKI FOREST. Philip Lutley Sclater. Proc. Zool. Soc. London, vol.1, pt.1, pp.50-52, fig.7, June 1, 1901.

ON EQUUS PENTICEI, A REPRESENTATIVE OF THE MOUNTAIN ZEBRA (EQUUS ZEBRA L.) DISCOVERED BY MR. W. PENRICE IN ANGOLA. Oldfield Thomas. Ann. and Mag. Nat. Hist., ser.7, vol.6, no.35, pp.465-466, Nov., 1900.

(PRELIMINARY COMMUNICATION ON TWO NEW ZEBRA SPECIES FROM SOUTHWEST AFRICA.) Vorlaeufige Mitteilung ueber zwei neue Zebraformen aus Suedwestafrika. Ludwig Zukowsky. Archiv. f. Naturgesch. year 90, sect.A, vol.1, pp.165-168, July, 1924.

Age Determination

AN INFALLIBLE GUIDE TO DISCOVER THE AGE OF HORSES. Louis Brandt. Indianola, Texas, pp.iv+47, illus., 1860.

AGE OF HORSES BY THEIR TEETH, AND THE MEASUREMENT OF THE KING OF THE TURF AND OTHER NOTED HORSES. Rufus Brown. Buffalo, New York, pp.32, illus., 1880.

TREATISE ON THE AGE OF THE HORSE. INSTRUCTIONS HOW TO TELL HIS AGE, FROM A FOAL TO THE PERIOD OF SIXTEEN YEARS... ALSO, AN ESSAY, ON FOUNDER, CONTRACTION AND RUNNING THRUSH... THE CAUSES, BEST MODE OF TREATMENT, AND CURE BY THE USE OF THE HOT AND COLD BATH. James Carver. Philadelphia, Littell and Henry, pp.93, pls.2, 1818.

TREATISE ON THE TEETH OF THE HORSE, SHEWING ITS AGE BY THE CHANGES THE TEETH UNDERGO, FROM A FOAL UP TO TWENTY-THREE YEARS OLD;ESPECIALLY AFTER THE EIGHTH YEAR. Francois Narcisse Girard. London, Sherwood, Gilbert, and Piper, pp.viii+75, col.pls.2, 1829.

HOW TO TELL THE AGE OF A HORSE. (A pocket manual. A chapter on horse character, or how to determine the disposition of a horse.) John M. Heard. New York, M.T. Richardson, pp.53, illus., 1884.

The Americas

(DWARF HORSES OF THE CANYON OF COLORADO.) Los caballos del Cañon del Colorado. F. Bonet. Ciencia, Mexico, D.F., vol.3, no.1, pp.30-31, Jan. 25, 1942.

(HORSES OF AMERICA.) Caballos de América. Angel Cabrera. Editorial Sudamericana, Buenos Aires, pp.1-405, figs.1-80, Oct. 31, 1945.

(THE PYGMY HORSES OF THE COLORADO CANYON. AN EXAMPLE OF THE EFFECT OF GEOGRAPHICAL ISOLATION.) Los caballos enanos del Cañon del Colorado. Un ejemplo del efecto del aislamiento geografico. Angel Cabrera. Revista Argentina de Zoogeografia, Buenos Aires, vol.1, no.1, pp.3-9, pl.1, 1941.

(THE AMERICAN HORSE.) El caballo americano. Hermano Daniel. Boletin Mus. Hist. Nat. "Javier Prado," Lima, año 5, no.19, pp.488-499, 1941.

THE MUSTANGS. Frank Dobie. Little Brown and Co., A Bantam Book, 1952.

NORTHWARD SPREAD OF HORSES AMONG THE PLAINS INDIANS. Francis Haines. Amer. Anthrop., n.s., vol.40, no.3, pp. 429-437, fig.1, July-Sep., 1938.

WHERE DID THE PLAINS INDIANS GET THEIR HORSES? Francis Haines. Amer. Anthrop., vol.40, no.1, pp.112-117, Jan.-Mar., 1938.

(BIOLOGICAL STUDIES IN SOUTH AMERICA. VI. ON THE HORSES OF THE RAZA CRIOLLA.) Biologische Resiestudien in Suedamerika. VI. Ueber die Pferde der Raza criolla. Hans Krieg. Zeitschr. f. Morph.u. Oekologie der Tiere, vol.4, pp.685-701, figs.2, Oct. 29, 1925.

ZEBRA WAS ORIGINALLY NORTH AMERICAN NATIVE--A MILLION YEARS AGO. Paul O. McGrew. Chicago Nat. Hist. Mus. Bull., vol.15, nos.3-4, pp.1-3, illus., Mar.-Apr., 1944.

THE CRIOLLO HORSE OF SOUTH AMERICA. Emilio Solanet. Jour. Heredity, vol. 21, no.11, pp.449-480, illus., Nov., 1930.

FICTION OF THE AMERICAN HORSE AND THE TRUTH ON THIS DISPUTED POINT. E.L. Trouessart. Science, vol.20, no.504, pp.188-189, Sep. 30, 1892.

SUNSET TRAIL. THE MUSTANG. Wyoming Wild Life, Cheyenne, vol.10, no.6, pp.4-11, 38, illus., June, 1946.

WILD BURROS IN CALIFORNIA. Calif. Dept. of Game and Fish. Outdoor Calif., vol.13, no.25, pp.4-5, June, 1952; Mod. Game Breeding and Hunting Club News, vol.22, no.6, p.15, June, 1952.

Anatomy (General)

(ANDALUSION HORSE OF STRAIGHT PROFILE AND THE ORIENTAL TYPE.) O cavalo andaluz de perfil recto e tipo oriental. Ruy d' Andrade. Boletim Pecuário, Lisboa, no.4, ano 7, pp.16, pls.16, 1939.

(THREE-CHAMBERED HEART OF THE HORSE.) Das dreikammerige Herz des Pferdes. D.M. Awtokratow. Anat. Anzeiger, vol.65, pp.26-266, figs.2, 1928.

(LYMPHATIC VESSELS OF THE FASCIAE OF THE HORSE.) Die Lymphgefaesse der Fascien des Pferdes. H. Baum. Zeitschr.f. Anatomie und Entwicklungsgeschichte, vol. 77, pp.266-274, figs.2, Aug. 20, 1925.

(LYMPHATIC VESSELS OF THE HORSE LIVER.) Die Lymphgefaesse der Leber des Pferdes. H. Baum. Zeitschr. f. Anatomie und Entwicklungsgeschichte, vol. 76, pp.645-652, figs.2, pl.1, June 30, 1925.

(THE LYMPHATIC VESSELS OF THE SHOULDER OF THE HORSE.) Die Lymphgefaesse der Schultergliedmasse des Pferdes. H. Baum. Anat. Anzeiger, vol.63, pp.122-131, pl.1, fig.1, May 25, 1927.

(MORE ON THE JUDGMENT OF THE POLYDACTYLISM OF THE HORSE.) Weiteres zur Beurteilung der Polydactylie des Pferdes. J.E.V. Boas. Zool. Jahrbuecher (Anatomie), vol.51, pp.313-322, figs.9.

(ANATOMICAL NOTES AND ZOOLOGICAL CONSIDERATIONS REGARDING ZEBRAS.) Notes anatomiques et considérations zoologiques sur les zèbres. E. Bourdelle. 67th Congr. Soc. Savantes, pp.99-112, 1934.

(OSTEOLOGIC AND OSTEOMETRIC NOTES ON THE PRZEWALSKI HORSE.) Notes ostéologiques et ostéométriques sur le cheval de Przewalski. E. Bourdelle. Bull. Mus. Nat. Hist. Nat. Paris, ser.2, vol.4, no.7, pp.810-821, Nov., 1932.

(OSTEOLOGIC AND OSTEOMETRIC NOTES ON THE WILD DONKEYS OF AFRICA.) Notes ostéologiques et ostéométriques sur les Anes sauvages d'Afrique. E.Bourdelle. Bull. Mus. Nat. Hist. Nat. Paris, ser.2, vol.7, no.6, pp. 304-314, Nov., 1935.

(THE EXTERNAL MORPHOLOGY OF THE FOOT OF WILD AND DOMESTIC EQUIDAE.) La morphologie extérieure de pied chez les équidés domestiques et sauvages. E. Bourdelle. Mammalia, Paris, vol.4, nos.3-4, pp.73-87, figs.1-6, Sep.-Dec., 1940; vol.5, no.1, pp.1-10, figs.7-12, Mar., 1941.

(SOME ANATOMICAL CHARACTERS OF HARTMANN'S ZEBRA.) Quelques caractères anatomiques du zèbre de Hartmann (Equus zebra hartmannae Matschie). E. Bourdelle. Bull. Mus. Nat. Hist. Nat., Paris, ser.2, vol.8, no.6, pp.473-477, Nov., 1936.

PHYLOGENY AND FUNCTIONS OF THE DIGITAL LIGAMENTS OF THE HORSE. Charles L. Camp, Natasha Smith. Mem. Univ. Calif., Berkeley, vol.13, no.2, pp. 69-124, pls.8-11, figs.41, June 6, 1942.

ANATOMY AND PHYSIOLOGY OF THE HORSE. (With anatomical and questional illustrations. Containing, a series of examinations on equine anatomy and physiology, with instructions in reference to dissection, and the mode of making anatomical preparations. To which is added, glossary of veterinary technicalities, toxicological chart, and dictionary of veterinary science.) George H. Dadd. Boston, J.P. Jewett and Co.; New York, Sheldon, Blakeman and Co., pp.291, pls.20, 1857.

(DEVELOPMENT OF THE EXTREMITIES AND POLYDACTYLY IN HORSES. THE ONTOGENESIS OF THE HAND AND FOOT SKELETON, VARIANTS ON THE CARPUS, AND THE JUDGEMENT OF THE "DEVELOPMENT-DETERMINED" POLYDACTYLY IN EQUUS CABALLUS.) Extremitaetenentwicklung und Polydactylie beim Pferde. Die Ontogenese des Hand- und Fusskeletts, Varianten am Carpus und die Beurteilung der "entwicklungsbedingten" Polydactylie bei Equus caballus. F. Drahn. Berlin, Gebrueder Borntraeger, pp.206, figs.130, 1927.

SIGNIFICANCE OF THE CALLOSITIES ON THE LIMBS OF THE EQUIDAE. R. Lydekker. Proc. Zool. Soc. London, vol.1, pt.2, pp.199-203, Aug. 6, 1903.

POLYDACTYLA HORSES, RECENT AND EXTINCT. O. C. Marsh. Amer. Jour.Sci. and Arts, New Haven, vol.17, pp.497-503, figs.4, June, 1879.

RECENT POLYDACTYLE HORSES. O.C. Marsh. Amer.Jour.Sci., New Haven, ser.3, vol.43, no.143, pp.339-354, figs.21, Apr., 1892.

PRELIMINARY CONTRIBUTION TO THE STUDY OF THE ATRIO-VENTRICULAR SYSTEM OF THE HORSE. R.W.M. Mettam. S.Afr. Jour. Sci., Pretoria, vol.23, pp.556-559, pl.6, Dec., 1926.

PRELIMINARY NOTE ON THE OCCURRENCE OF A MUSCLE OF DOUBTFUL MORPHOLOGY IN THE FOOT OF A HORSE. R.W.M. Mettam. S.Afr.Jour.Sci., vol.22, pp.270-271, Nov., 1925.

PATTERN ON BONE FUSION IN THE EQUINE METACARPUS AND METATARSUS. H.D. Mills. Proc. Zool. Soc. London, vol. 124, pt.4, pp.809-813, illus., Feb. 22, 1955.

(ON THE HIPPARIONLIKE ACCESSORY HOOF OF AN EAST PRUSSIAN HORSE.) Ueber den Hipparion-aehnlichen Nebenhuf eines ostpreussischen Pferdes. Alfred Nehring. Sitz. Ber. Gesell. Naturf. Freunde Berlin, no.4, p.138, Oct. 21, 1884.

ON DIFFERENCES IN THE COMPOSITION OF THE BLOOD OF HORSES, ASSES AND MULES. V.I. Patrushev. Bull.Acad.Sci. USSR, Cl. Sci. Math. et Nat., ser.Biol., Moscow, no.4, pp.929-946, figs.15, tbls. 10, 1938. (In Russian with English summary.)

ANATOMY OF THE HORSE, EMBRACING THE STRUCTURE OF THE FOOT. William Percivall. London, Longman, Rees, Orme, Brown, Green, and Longman, pp.xxiii+454, 1832.

(THE THYROID GLAND OF THE HORSE.) Die Schilddruesse des Pferdes. L. Reisinger. Zool. Anzeiger, vol.79, pp.65-68, Nov. 1, 1928.

(NOTE ON THE NUMERIC VARIATIONS OF THE LUMBAR VERTEBRAE IN EQUUS PRZEWALSKII POLIAKOW.) Note sur les variations numériques des vertèbres lombaires chez Equus przewalskii Poliakow. Lucien R. Richard. Mammalia, Paris, vol. 20, no.3, pp.326-328, Sep., 1956.

(ON THE DEVELOPMENT AND INVOLUTION OF THE MUSCULUS PRONATOR QUADRATUS OF THE HORSE.) Ueber Entwicklung und Rueckbildung des Musculus pronator quadratus des Pferdes. William Schauder. Anat. Anzeiger, vol.61, pp.302-310, illus., July 23, 1926.

(BLOOD GROUPS OF THE HORSE AND THEIR PRACTICAL SIGNIFICANCE.) Die Blutgruppen des Pferdes und ihre praktische Bedeutung. S. Schermer, A.Kaempffer. Tieraerztliche Wochenschrift, no.9, pp. 145-146, fig.1, Feb. 28, 1936.

OSTEOLOGY OF MESOHIPPUS BARBOURI. Erich M. Schlaikjer. Bull. Mus. Comp. Zool., vol.72, no.11, pp.393-410, pls.1-5, June, 1932.

(ON THE BASIC CHARACTERS IN THE SKELETAL STRUCTURE OF DWARF HORSES.) Ueber grundsaetzliche Eigentuemlichkeiten im Skelettbau der Zwergpferde. Anton Schotterer. Zeitschr. f.Saeugetierk., Berlin, vol.6, no.3, pp.85-132, pls.1-3, Dec. 15, 1931.

STRUCTURE AND FUNCTION OF THE HORSE'S FOOT. F. Smith. Roy.Inst.Great Britain, London, meeting of May 3, 1895, pp.1-10, 1895.

(ANKLE JOINT OF THE HORSE WITH SPECIAL CONSIDERATION OF THE PHENOMENON OF THE SPRING.) Das Sprunggelenk des Pferdes mit besonderer Ruecksicht auf das Federungsphaenomen. Gunnar Stranning. Zeitschr. f. Anat. und Entwicklungsgeschichte, vol.92, no.5, pp.622-643, figs.4, 1930.

ON THE DEVELOPMENT OF THE BONES OF THE FOOT OF THE HORSE AND OF DIGITAL BONES GENERALLY; AND ON A CASE OF POLYDACTYLY IN THE HORSE. John Struthers. Jour. of Anat. and Physiology, vol.28, pp.51-62, pl.1, 1893.

ANATOMY OF THE HORSE. George Stubbs. London, printed by J. Purser, reprinted by Gibbings and Co., Ltd., pp.vi+148, pls., 1899.

(ONE A. CRANIO--OCCIPITALIS AND TWO Aa. MENINGEAE MEDIAE IN THE HORSE.) Eine A. Cranio--occipitalis und zwei Aa. meningeae mediae beim Pferde. G. Taran. Anat. Anzeiger, vol.65, pp.266-268, fig.1, May 15, 1928.

AN ASS WITH ABNORMALLY DEVELOPED HOOFS. Frederick W. True. Science, vol. 8, no.191, p.304, Oct. 1, 1886.

(BONY INNER EAR OF THE DOMESTIC ASS (EQUUS ASINUS L.).) Das knoecherne innere Ohr des Hausesels (Equus asinus L.). B.G. Turkewitsch. Zeitschr. f. Saeugetierk., vol.11, no.1, pp.1-15, pls.17-18, Mar. 13, 1936.

MIDDLE EAR OF THE HORSE (EQUUS CABALLUS). H.C. Wilkie. Proc. Zool. Soc. London, pt.1, pp.97-110, figs.12, Apr., 1931.

(CASE OF A VARIATION OF BOTH LEG ARTERIES AND THE SHOULDER ARTERY IN A COLT.) Fall einer gleichzeitigen Variation beider Schenkelarterien und der Schulterarterie bei einem Fohlen. P. P. Winogradow. Ant. Anzeiger, vol.67, pp. 472-475, fig.1, July 20, 1929.

(VARIATIONS OF THE COMMON CRANIAL ARTERIES (Aa. CAROTIDES COMMUNES) IN THE HORSE.) Ueber die Variationen der gemeinschaftlichen Kopfarterien (Aa. carotides communes) beim Pferde. P.P. Winogradow. Anat. Anzeiger, vol.66, pp. 273-280, fig.1, Dec. 5, 1928.

(STIMULUS-CONDUCTION SYSTEM OF THE HEART IN EQUIDS.) Das Reizleitungssystem des Herzens bei Equiden. A. Zimmermann. Verh. Anat. Gissel, Anat. Anz., Ergaenzungsheft zum vol.57, pp.252-258, Dec., 1923.

Anatomy (Skull, Teeth)

(SOME OBSERVATIONS ON THE TEETH OF LIVING HORSES.) Quelques observations sur les dents des équidés actuels. Ruy d'Andrade. Comptes Rendus 12th Cong. Internat. Zool. Lisbonne 1935, pp.696-699, figs.5, pl.34, 1936.

(OBSERVATIONS ON THE NASAL CHAMBERS OF EQUIDAE.) Observations sur les fosses nasales des Équidés. R.Anthony. Archic. Anat. Histol. Embryol. Strasbourg, vol.10, pp.235-270, pls.2, figs.21, 1929.

(CONSIDERATIONS ON THE SKULL OF THE FOA ZEBRA AND ON THE SPECIFIC VALUE OF THE SPECIMEN DESCRIBED UNDER THIS NAME.) Considérations sur la tête osseuse du Zèbre de Foa (Equus quagga foa Praz. et Trt.) et sur la valeur spécifique du spécimen décrit sous ce nom. E. Bourdelle. Bull. Mus. Nat. Hist. Nat., Paris, vol.16, no.6, pp.408-411, 1944.

DENTITION OF EQUUS CAPENSIS BROOM. R. Broom, H. le Riche. S. African Jour.Sci., Johannesburg, vol.33, pp.769-770, fig.1, Mar.. 1937

(COMPARATIVE CRANIOLOGY OF THE DOMESTIC HORSE.) Craneologia comparada del caballo criollo. Angel Cabrera. Revista de la Facultad de Agronomia y Veterinaria, Buenos Aires, ser.2, vol.7, pp.287-327, figs.13, Nov., 1931.

"HORNED" HORSES--THEY WEREN'T EXACTLY UNICORNS BUT OF THE 3300 HORSES EXAMINED 6 HAD THE SKIN-COVERED HORNS WITH RESULT FROM A DISPROPORTIONATE DEVELOPMENT OF THE SKULL BONES. S. Harmsted Chubb. Nat. Hist., New York, vol.39, no.5, pp.357-359, illus., May, 1937.

OCCURRENCE OF A TRUE FOURTH MOLAR IN A MODERN HORSE. Harold J. Cook.Jour. Mamm., vol.10, no.1, pp.82-83, Feb., 1929.

(SOME DATA ON THE CRANIOLOGY OF FAMILY EQUIDAE.) Quelques données sur la craniologie de la fam.Equidae.K.K. Flerov. Comptes Rendus Acad.Sci.USSR, pp.369-272, figs.3, 1931. (In Russian with English summary.)

NOTES ON THE SKULL OF EQUUS HEMIONUS AND EQUUS KIANG. J.E.Gray. Proc. Zool. Soc. London, pt.17, pp.29-30, 1849.

OBSERVATIONS ON A CALVARIUM OF EQUUS SIVALENSIS FALCONER ET CAUTLEY FROM THE SIWALIKS OF THE PUNJAB, WITH CRANIOMETRICAL NOTES ON RECENT EQUIDAE. D.A. Hooijer. Archiv. Neerlandaises Zool., Leiden, vol. 8, livr.3, pp.243-266, figs.2, pl.9, 1949.

NOTE ON THE SKULL AND MARKINGS OF THE QUAGGA. R. Lydekker. Proc. Zool. Soc. London, vol.i, pt.2, pp.426-431, Aug. 2, 1904.

ABNORMAL GROWTH OF THE LEFT GRINDERS IN THE SKULL OF A HORSE IN THE HULL MUSEUM. W. C. M'Intosh. The Naturalist, pp.125-130, pl.6, Mar. 1, 1930.

CRANIOMETRICAL STUDIES ON THE SKULLS OF WILD ASSES FROM WEST MONGOLIA. Heiichiro Motohashi. Mem. Toltori Agric. College, vol.1, pt.1, pp.1-62, 1930.

CRANIOMETRY OF THE EQUIDAE. Henry Fairfield Osborn. Mem. Amer. Mus.Nat. Hist., n.s., vol.1, pt.3, pp.57-100, figs. 17, June, 1912.

INDIVIDUAL VARIATION IN THE CRANIAL AND DENTAL CHARACTERS OF THE BURCHELL'S ZEBRA. J.Walter Paxton. Proc. Geol. Soc. America for 1937, pp. 295-296, June, 1938. (Abstract.)

(Review by E. Bourdelle of) (ANATOMY OF THE MOLARS OF EQUIDAE: HORSE AND DONKEY.) Anatomie des molaires des Equidés: Cheval et âne. Petit Marcel. Lion et fils, Toulouse, vol.1, pp.323, figs. 206, pls.110, 1939; Mammalia, Paris, vol. 3, pp.80-81, June, 1939.

(MOLARS OF THE EQUIDAE.) Les molaires des Équidés. Marcel Petit. Mammalia, Paris, vol.3, nos.3-4, pp.99-108, figs.12, Sep.-Dec., 1939.

(RESEARCH ON THE OSTEOLOGY OF THE HEAD OF EQUIDAE.) Recherches sur l'ostéologie de la tête des Equidés. Pts.1-4. Marcel Petit. Revue Méd. Vét. Toulouse, vol.89, pp.324-346, figs.1-10, tbls.8, June, 1937; Pts.5-11, pp.398-419, figs.11-13, tbls.9-12, July, 1937.

(COMPLEMENTARY OBSERVATIONS ON THE DENTITION OF A ZEBRA SKULL.) Observations complementaires faites sur la dentition d'une tete osseuse de zebra, Equus (Pseudoquagga) boehmi cf. Zambeziensis Prazak. Lucien Richard. Mammalia, Paris, vol.18, no.4, pp.397-404, Dec., 1954.

(NOTE ON THE NUMERIC VARIATION OF THE LUMBAR VERTEBRAE IN EQUUS CABALLUS PRZEWALSKII POLIAKOW.) Note sur les variation numériques des vertèbres lombaires chez Equus caballus Przewalskii Poliakow. Lucien Richard. Mammalia, Paris, vol.20, no.3, pp.326-328, Sep., 1956.

(OSTEOLOGIC AND OSTEOMETRIC OBSERVATIONS ON THE SKULL OF A ZEBRA FROM THE MUSEUM OF NATURAL HISTORY OF ROUEN.) Observations ostéologique et ostéométriques taites sur une tête osseuse de zèbre du Muséum d'Histoire Naturelle de Rouen. Lucien Richard. Mammalia, Paris, vol.6, no.1, pp.27-35, Mar., 1942.

DEVELOPMENT OF CHARACTERS IN HORSE TEETH AND THE DENTAL NOMENCLATURE. R.A. Stirton. Jour.Mamm., vol.22, no.4, pp.434-446, figs.10, Nov.14, 1941.

(HORNLIKE FORMATIONS ON THE FRONTAL BONE OF A HORSE.) Hoernerfoermige Bildungen auf dem Stirnbein eines Pferdes. P.P. Winogradow, A.L. Frolow.Anat.Anzeiger, vol.68, pp.93-94, figs.2, 1929.

Breeding

(BACK BREEDING THE POLISH WILD HORSE.) Die Rueckzuechtung des polnischen Wildpferdes. Otto Antonius. Zool. Garten, Leipzig, n.F., vol.8, nos.7-9, pp.190-200, figs.3, 1936; vol.10, nos.3-4, pp.102-107, figs.10, Sep., 1938.

BREEDING-BACK OF THE TARPAN. Heinz Heck. Oryx, Hertford, vol.1, no.7, pp.338-342, Nov., 1952.

(BACK BREEDING THE FOREST TARPAN IN THE BIALOWIEZA HEATH.) Rueckzuechtung des Waldtarpans in der Bialowiezaer Heide. K. Szczerkowski. Zool. Garten, n.F., Leipzig, vol.8, nos.7-9, pp. 189-190, June, 1936.

(PRELIMINARY COMMUNICATION ON THE BREEDING OF A SO-CALLED WARD ZEBRA.) Vorlaeufige Mitteilung ueber die

Zuechtung eines sogenannten Ward-Zebras. Adolf Rząśnicki. Ann. Mus. Zool.Polonici, Warsaw, vol.13, no.17, pp.197-204, tbl., pls.10-11, July 14, 1938.

(SELECTION OF STUDIES OF HORSE BREEDING.) Seleccion de Estudios de Cria Caballar. Rafael Janini Janini. Valencia, pp.402, illus., 1924.

Coloration, Pelage

(ON THE "TIGER" PATTERN OF THE HORSE, ESPECIALLY THE NORIKER.) Ueber die Tigerfarbe des Pferdes, insbesondere des Norikers. Otto Antonius. Zeitschr. f. Gestuetkunde u. Pferdezucht, Hannover, Jahrg.30, nos.5-6, pp.57-63, illus., May-June, 1935; nos.9-10, pp.131-132, Sep.-Oct., 1935.

CURLY COAT OF HORSES. Leonard H. Blakeslee et al. Jour.Heredity, Wash., D.C., vol.34, no.4, pp.115-118, figs.7-9, Apr., 1943.

GENETICS OF THE PALOMINO HORSE. CONFIRMATION OF THE SALISBURY-BRITTON HYPOTHESIS. W.E. Castle. Jour. Heredity, Washington, vol.37, no.2, pp.34-38, figs.1-2, Feb., 1946.

(PERSISTENCE OF STRIPES IN THE PELAGE OF DOMESTIC HORSES.) Persistance de zébrures sur le pelage d'équidés domestiques. Paul Magne de la Croix. La Terre et la Vie, Rev. d'Hist.Nat., vol.4, no.3, pp. 165-167, illus., Mar., 1934.

LEOPARD SPOTTING AND COLOR ALTERATION IN THAT RECENTLY ESTABLISHED BREED OF HORSES, THE COLORADO RANGERS. Helen Gibbon. Jour. Colorado-Wyoming Acad. Sci., Denver, vol.3, no.1, p.48, Apr., 1941.

COAT COLORS IN HORSES. Fred Gremmel. Jour. Heredity, Wash., D.C., vol.30, no. 10, pp.437-445, figs.15-16, Oct., 1939.

(REMARKS ON THE MANE OF THE PRIMITIVE WILD HORSE.) Bemerkungen ueber die Maehne der Urwildpferde. H. Heck. Zool. Garten, n.F., Leipzig, vol.8, nos. 7-9, pp.179-189, illus., June, 1936.

COAT COLOR AND TEMPERAMENT IN MULES. Clyde E. Keeler. Jour.Heredity, Washington, vol.36, no.8, p.243, Aug., 1945.

THE "PIED" AND "SPLASHED WHITE" PATTERNS IN HORSES AND PONIES. V. Klemola. Jour. Heredity, vol.24, no.2, pp.65-69, figs.4, Feb., 1933.

(SPOTTED FORMS OF ARGENTINIAN HORSES.) Scheckungsformen argentinischer Pferde. Hans Krieg. Zeitschr. f. induktive Abstammungs- u. Vererbungslehre, vol.34, pp.134-139, figs.1-6, 1924.

(UNUSUAL STRIPING IN HORSES.) Ungewoehnliche Streifung bei Pferden. Erna Mohr. Zool. Anzeiger, Leipzig, vol.148, pp.303-305, May, 1952.

DESCRIPTION OF A SKIN RESEMBLING HIPPOTIGRIS ZEBRA FREDERICI TROUESS. FROM THE COLLECTION OF THE POLISH MUSEUM OF ZOOLOGY AT WARSAW. Adolf Rząśnicki. Ann. Mus. Zool. Polonici, Warsaw, vol.9, no.5, pp. 45-55, pls.8-9, Aug. 25, 1930.

(A SHETLAND COLT BEARING THE COLOR OF A WILD HORSE.) Ein wildpferdfarbiges Shetlandponyfohlen. Adolf Rząśnicki. Zool. Garten, Leipzig, n.F., vol.7, nos.4-6, pp.89-92, Aug., 1934.

(DATA ON ASS COLORATION.) Einiges ueber Eselfaerbung. Adolf Rząśnicki, Erna Mohr. Zool. Garten, Leipzig, n.F., vol.12, nos.4-6, pp.299-306, figs.15, Dec., 1940.

INHERITANCE OF EQUINE COAT COLOR. THE BASIC COLORS AND PATTERNS. G. W. Salisbury. Jour. Heredity, Washington, D.C., vol.32, no.7, pp.235-240, July, 1941.

INHERITANCE OF EQUINE COAT COLOR. II. THE DILUTES, WITH SPECIAL REFERENCE TO THE PALOMINO. G.W.Salisbury, J.W. Britton. Jour. Heredity, Wash., D.C., vol.32, no.8, pp.255-260, figs.4, Aug., 1941.

(A HARTMANN ZEBRA, EQUUS ZEBRA HARTMANNAE MATSCHIE 1898, WITH INTERMEDIATE STRIPES.) Ein Hartmann-Zebra, Equus zebra hartmannae Matschie, 1898, mit Zwischenstreifen. Eberhard Trumler. Saeugetierk. Mitteil., vol.5, no. 4, pp.173-174, illus., Dec. 1, 1957.

Diseases, Parasites

EQUINE ENCEPHALOMYELITIS IN AVIAN HOSTS. F.R. Beaudette. Vet. Med., Chicago, vol.35, p.18, Jan., 1940.(Abstract.)

THE EQUINE ENCEPHALOMYELITIS PROBLEM; CLINICAL MANIFESTATIONS OF EQUINE ENCEPHALOMYELITIS. W. L. Boyd. Proc.N.Central States Entom., Lafayette, Ind., vol.18, pp.84-85, 1939. (Mimeographed.)

EQUINE TRYPANOSOMIASIS-"MURRINA" OR "DERRENGADERA". SOME NOTES ON THE DISEASE IN PANAMA. Herbert C. Clark et al. Amer. Vet. Med. Assoc., vol. 83, no.3; n.s., vol.36, pp.358-389, Sep., 1933.

"WOBBLES"--AN HEREDITARY DISEASE IN HORSES. W.W. Dimock. Jour. Heredity, Baltimore, vol.41, no.12, pp.319-323, Dec., 1950.

(PRESENCE OF EQUINE ENCEPHALOMYELITIS-TYPE VIRUS IN THE EPIDEMIC IN THE STATE OF TAMAULIPAS, MEXICO, DURING THE YEAR 1941.) La presencia del virus tipo este de la encefalomielitis equina en la epizootia ocurrida en el Estado de Tamaulipas, Mexico, durante el año de 1941. Alfredo Téllez Girón, Oscar Valdez Ornelas. Revista Soc. Mexicana Hist. Nat., Mexico, D.F., vol.2, no.4, pp.251-259, Dec., 1941.

EQUINE ENCEPHALOMYELITIS. R.Graham, H.R. Hester. Ill.State Acad. Sci. Trans., Springfield, vol.32, pp.205-207, Dec., 1939. (Abstract.)

MELANOMATA OF GREY AND WHITE HORSES. S. Hadwen. Canadian Medical Assoc. Jour., vol.25, pp. 519-530, pls.3, 1931.

TWO CASES OF RHINOSPORIDIOSIS IN EQUINES. G. de Kock. S.Afr. Jour.Sci., Pretoria, vol.23, pp.289-294, pls.7-9, Dec., 1926.

(REMARKS ON A ZEBRA STALLION WITH A VERTEBRAL INJURY.) Bemerkungen ueber einen Zebrahengst mit einer Wirbelverletzung. Hans Kummerloewe. Zool. Garten, Leipzig, n.F., vol.8, nos.7-9, pp.222-223, illus., June, 1936.

EQUINE ENCEPHALOMYELITIS. W.A. Riley. Proc. N.Central State Entom., Lafayette, Ind., vol.18, p.85, 1939. (Mimeographed.)

INFECTIOUS ANEMIA OF HORSES. John W. Scott. Ant. Record, vol.29, p.122, Dec. 23, 1924.

Drawings

(PREHISTORIC EQUIDAE REPRESENTED BY STONE PICTURES AND CARVINGS IN THE CAVES OF EYZIES (DORDOGNE).) Les équidés préhistoriques représentés par les dessins et sculptures rupestres des grottes des Eyzies (Dordogne). E.Bourdelle. Bull. Soc. Nat. Acclimat.France, vol.80, no.12, pp.461-465, 1933.

(PREHISTORIC EQUIDAE DRAWINGS OF GANTIES-MONTESPAN (HAUTE-GARONNE).) Les dessins d'équidés préhistoriques de Ganties-Montespan (Haute-Garonne). E. Bourdelle, F. Trombe. Mammalia, Paris, vol.10, no.1, pp.13-25, figs.1-20, Mar., 1946.

EXHIBITION OF DRAWINGS REPRESENTING THE FOUR KNOWN SPECIES OF WILD ASSES. Philip Lutley Sclater. Proc. Zool. Soc. London, pt.30, pp.163-164, 1862.

PALAEOLITHIC DRAWING OF A HORSE FROM SHERBORNE, DORSET. W. J. Sollas. Nature, London, vol.117, no.2937, p.233, Feb. 13, 1926.

Economic Importance

(ORDER OF DIETYNGE OF HORSES, AS WELL WHEN THEY RESTE, AS WHEN THEY TRAUEL, WHERIN IS CONTEYNED NOT ONLY THE KEPERS OFFICE, BUT ALSO MANY PRECEPTS NECESSARY TOO BEE KNOWEN OF THE FERRER OR HORSELECHE: LATELY SET FORTHE. Thomas Blundeville. London, Imprinted by W.Seres, pp.32, 1565.

RESPITE FOR THE BURRO. Grace S.Davis. Nat. Mag., vol.46, no.7, pp.370-374, illus., Aug.-Sep., 1953.

RUNNING WILD. (Damages by feral burros.) Natt N. Dodge. Parks Mag., vol.25, no.104, pp.10-15, illus., Jan.-Mar., 1951.

HORSE IN BLACKFOOT INDIAN CULTURE, WITH COMPARATIVE MATERIAL FROM OTHER WESTERN TRIBES. John C. Ewers. Smiths. Inst., Bureau of Amer.Ethnology Bull.159, pp.374, pls.17, 1955.

(MULE INDUSTRY AT POITOU.) L'industrie mulassière en Poitou. R. Gouin. Ann. Sci. Agron., année 30 (sér.4, année2), sem.1, pp.161-177, Paris, 1913.

(PONIES IN ENGLISH MINES.) Die Ponys in englischen Bergwerken. Erna Mohr. Zool. Garten, Leipzig, n.F., vol.6, nos. 4-6, p.129, July, 1933.

BELGIAN DRAFT HORSE. George W.Roosevelt. U.S.Consular Repts., Wash., D.C., vol.39, no.142, pp.516-525, illus., 1892.

HORSE MEAT FOR FUR FARM; ITS CHEMICAL COMPOSITION. Sedgwick E. Smith, Chas. F. Bassatt. Amer. Fur Breeder, Duluth, vol.14, no.2, pp.14-16, Aug., 1941.

BREAKING AND TRAINING COLTS. V.G. Stambaugh. Washington, Govt. Print.Off., U.S. Dept. Agriculture, Farmers' Bull., no.667, pp.16, illus., 1915.

(CHANTILLY COURSE UNDER THE JULY MONARCHY.) Les courses de Chantilly sous la monarchie de juillet. Jean Stern. Paris, Calmann-Lévy, pp.vii+420, illus., pls., ports., double plan, 1913.

HORSE, IN THE STABLE AND IN THE FIELD: HIS VARIETIES, MANAGEMENT IN HEALTH AND DISEASE, ANATOMY, PHYSIOLOGY, ETC. John Henry Walsh. London, pp.622, illus., 1880.

THOROUGH-BRED HORSE: ON THE TURF AND ACROSS COUNTRY. George E. Waring. Century Mag., pp.157-171, illus.

CALIFORNIA'S WILD BURROS GIVEN LEGAL PROTECTION. Calif.Dept.of Game and Fish. Outdoor Calif., vol.14, no.20, p.2, Mar., 1953.

Eurasia

MONGOLIAN WILD ASS. THE FLEET-FOOTED "KULON" OF THE DESOLATE PLAINS OF CENTRAL ASIA. Roy Chapman Andrews. Nat. Hist., New York, vol.23, no.1, pp.3-16, illus., Jan-Feb., 1933.

(ZOOLOGICAL CONSIDERATIONS ON LIVING ASIATIC HORSES.) Considérations zoologiques sur les équidés asiatiques actuels. E. Bourdelle. Archiv. Mus. Nat. Hist. Nat., Paris, ser.6, vol.12, pp.475-483, June, 1935.

NATIVE PONY BREEDS OF BRITAIN. Nancy Deed. Jour. Soc. Preservation Fauna Empire, Hertford, n.s., pt.53, pp.56-58, pl.1, June, 1946.

EXMOOR PONIES. Mary G. Etherington. Jour. Soc. Preservation Fauna Empire, Hertford, n.s., pt.53, pp.12-18, pls.3, June, 1946.

IN DEFENSE OF THE HORSES OF T'ANG T'AI TSUNG. Helen E. Fernald. Univ. Mus. Bull., Univ. Penna., Philadelphia, vol.9, no.4, pp.18-28, pls.5-6, June, 1942.

(HISTORY OF HORSES IN THE OLD WORLD.) Istoria loshadei (roda Equus) v starom svete. Vera Gromova. Trudi Paleon. Inst., Akad. Nauk SSSR, Moscow, vol.17, no.1, pp.374, illus., 1949.

NOTES ON THE KIANG OF THIBET (EQUUS KIANG). W.E. Hay. Proc. Zool. Soc. London, pp.353-357, pl.73, 1859.

(NOTES ON THE SOUTHERN RUSSIA WILD HORSE.) Notiz ueber den suedrussischen Tarpan. W. Heptner. Zeitschr. f.Saeugetierk.,

Berlin, vol.9, nos.1-3, pp.431-433, Dec. 30, 1934.

FORMER DISTRIBUTION OF CABALLINE AND ZEBRINE HORSES IN EUROPE AND ASIA. A. Tendell Hopwood. Proc. Zool. Soc. London, for 1936, pt.4, pp.897-912, figs.2, pls.2, Jan., 1937.

(MAMMAL COLLECTION OF THE HOANG HO PAI HO DE TIEN TSIN MUSEUM. ORDER PERISSODACTYLA, FAM. EQUIDAE.) Collection des mammifères du musée Hoang ho Pai ho de Tien Tsin. Ordre Perissodactyla, Fam.Equidae. B.P. Jakovleff. Publ.Mus. Hoang ho Pai ho, Tientsin, no.10, pp.1-7, pl.1, Apr. 15, 1932.

WILD HORSES OF POLAND. T.Janikowski. Nature, London, vol.150, no.3815, pp.681-682, figs.5, Dec. 12, 1942.

TEN SACRIFICED HORSES PRESERVED FOR 2000 YEARS BY THE ETERNAL FROST: A BRONZE AGE BURIAL DISCOVERED IN SIBERIA. Horace H.F. Jayne. Illus. London News, vol.181, no.4868, pp. 205-207, illus., Aug. 6, 1932.

HORSE IN THE LIFE OF THE ORDOS MONGOLS. Joseph Kler. Primitive Man, Washington, vol.20, nos.1-2, pp.15-25, figs.3, Jan.-Apr., 1947.

(ADDITIONAL NOTES. A. BIOLOGY OF ASINUS KIANG MOORCROFT. B. THE HORSE, DONKEY, AND MULE IN CHINA.) Notes additionnelles. A.Biologie de l'Asinus kiang Moorcroft. B.Le cheval, l'ane et le mulet en Chine. E. Licent. Publ.Mus. Hoang ho Pai ho, Tientsin, no.10, pp.8-10, Apr. 15, 1932.

LAST OF SWEDEN'S WILD HORSES. Holger Lundbergh. Nature Mag., vol.23, no.4, p. 169, illus., Apr., 1934.

NOTE ON THE WILD ASS OF MONGOLIA. R. Lydekker. Proc. Zool. Soc. London, vol.i, pt.2, pp.431-432, pls.27-28, Aug. 2, 1904.

THE HORSE IN NORWAY. Fracnis H.A. Marshall. Proc. Roy. Soc. Edinburgh, session 1905-1906, vol.26, pt.1, pp.22-32, pls.2, Feb. 12, 1906.

(DO SEVERAL SPECIES OF WILD HORSES EXIST IN CENTRAL ASIA?) Giebt es in Mittelasien mehrere Arten von echten Wildpferden? Paul Matschie. Naturwissenschaftliche Wochenschrift, n.F., vol.2, (vol.18) no.49, pp.581-583, illus., Sep., 1903.

COMMENTS ON SOME RACES OF THE ASIATIC WILD ASSES (MICROHIPPUS), WITH A DESCRIPTION OF THE SKULL OF THE CHIGETAI. R.I. Pocock. Proc. Zool. Soc. London, vol.117, pt.4, pp.764-767, fig.1, Feb. 3, 1948.

MONGOLIAN WILD HORSE. R.I. Pocock. Field, London, vol.150, p.1071, illus., Dec. 29, 1927.

(NOTE ON THE WILD EQUIDAE ENCOUNTERED IN CENTRAL ASIA BY THE HAARDT-AUDOUIN-DUBREUIL MISSION.) Note sur les équidés sauvages rencontrés en Asie Centrale par la Mission Haardt-Audouin-Dubreuil. A. Reymond. Bull.Mus. Nat.Hist.Nat., Paris, ser.2, vol.4, no.7, pp.807-809, map., Nov., 1932.

ONAGER, WILD ASS OF PERSIA. Ernst Schwarz. Nature Mag., vol.31, no.3, p. 236, Apr., 1938.

(RARE KIANG (EQUUS KIANG) IN THE STEPPES OF HIGH TIBET.) Vom seltenen Kiang (Equus kiang) in den Steppen Hochtibets. Ernst Schafer. Naturforscher, Jahrg. 14, Heft 11, pp.348-352, illus., Feb., 1938.

CRITICAL REMARKS ON THE "FOREST TARPAN." Edward Skorkowski. Kosmos (Bull. Soc. Polonaise Nat. "Kopernik"), ser.A, Memoires, vol.59, pp.197-205, fig. 1, 1934.

THE CELTIC HORSE IN NORWAY. Leonard Stejneger. Science, Lancaster, n.s., vol. 25, no.641, p.582, Apr. 12, 1907.

(THE VESTLAND HORSE FROM A ZOOLOGICAL STANDPOINT.) Om Vestlandshesten fra zoologik standpunkt. Leonhard Stejneger. Norsk Vetern. Tidsskr., vol.21, pp.11-17, 1909.

ON THE IDENTITY OF THE WILD ASS OF CUTCH AND INDUS, WITH THE DZEGGETAI. W.H. Sykes. Proc. Zool. Soc. London, pt.5, p.91, 1837.

(PROBLEM OF THE TARPAN ON THE BASIS OF NEW WORK OF THE ACADEMY OF SCIENCES USSR ON THE HISTORY OF HORSES IN THE OLD WORLD.) Problema tarpana nafone noveyskekh rabot Akademii Nauk SSSR po istorii loshadey v starom svete. Tadeush Vetulyani. Zool. Zhurnal, Moscow, vol.31, no.5, pp.727-735, 1952.

RESULTS OF RESEARCH ON THE SMALL NATIVE POLISH HORSE AND ON THE PROBLEM OF THE TARPAN.) Résultats de recherches sur le petit cheval indigène polonais "Konik polonais" ainsi que sur le problème du Tarpan. T.Vetulani. Mammalia, Paris, vol.3, nos.3-4, pp.89-98, Sep.-Dec., 1939.

(TWO MORE SOURCES AS TO THE QUESTION OF THE EUROPEAN FOREST TARPAN.) Zwei weitere Quellen zur Frage des europaeischen Waldtarpans. T. Vetulani. Zeitschr. f. Saeugetierk., Berlin, vol.8, nos.3-6, pp.281-282, Dec. 20, 1933.

ENGLAND'S WILD MOORLAND PONIES. Nat. Geogr. Mag., Washington, vol.89, no.1, pp.129-136, photos 10, Jan., 1946.

THE HORSE IN MESOPOTAMIA IN 3000 B.C.; AND OTHER KHAFAJE FINDS. Illus. London News, vol.181, no.4877, p. 529, illus., Oct. 8, 1932.

PRESERVATION OF THE INDIAN WILD ASS. Jour. Soc. Preservation Fauna of Empire, Hertford, n.s., pt.34, pp.56-57, Aug., 1938.

WILD ASS OF THE GOBI (EQUUS HEMIONUS). China Jour., vol.11, no.3, p.158, illus., Sep., 1929.

Evolution, History

(CONTRIBUTION TO THE PHYLOGENY OF HORSES: THE PHYLOGENETIC POSITION OF HIPPARION AND NEOHIPPARION.) Ein Beitrag zur Stammesgeschichte der Pferde: die Phylogenetische Stellung von Hipparion und Neohipparion. Othenio Abel. Anzeiger Akad. Wiss. Wien Math. Nat.Kl., vol.65, nos.1-27, pp.28-32, 1928.

(ANCESTRY OF PORTUGUESE DOMESTIC HORSE AND ITS RELATIVES.) Ruy D'Andrade. Bol. Pecuário, Lisboa, vol.6, no.2, pp.1-16, figs.92, 1938.

(CONTROVERSIES AS TO THE PHYLOGENY OF THE EQUIDAE.) Streitfragen zur Phylogenie der Equiden. Otto Antonius. Verhandl. Zool.-Bot. Ges. Wies, vol.78, no.1, pp.4-18, figs.2, Jan., 1928.

(ON THE ORIGIN OF THE DOMESTIC HORSE.) Zur Abstammung des Hauspferdes. Otto Antonius. Zeitschr. f. Zuechtung, Reihe B. Tierzuechtung u. Zuechtungsbiol. einschliesslich Tiernaehrung, Berlin, vol.34, no.3, pp.359-398, figs.13, Mar., 1936.

(ON THE ORIGIN OF THE DOMESTIC HORSE AND ASS.) Zur Abstammung des Hauspferds und Hausesels. Otto Antonius. Verhandl. Zool.-Bot. Ges., Wien, vol.85, nos.1-4, pp.102-104, 1936.

(PREVIOUSLY UNNOTICED MENTION OF THE TIGER HORSE OF ANTIQUITY.)Eine bisher uebersehene Erwaehnung der Tigerpferde aus dem Altertum. Otto Antonius. Zool. Garten, Leipzig, n.F., vol.8, nos. 1-3, pp.31-33, Sep., 1935.

HORSES AND MEN. IT HAS TAKEN ABOUT FIFTY-FIVE MILLION YEARS FOR HYRACOTHERIUM TO EVOLVE INTO THE EQUUS WE KNOW TODAY. William Beebe. Bull. New York Zool. Soc., vol.43, no.6, pp.181-188, figs.5, Nov.-Dec., 1940.

(ORIGIN OF THE HORSE AS A DOMESTIC ANIMAL IN THE LIGHT OF THE LATEST INVESTIGATIONS.) El origen del caballo como animal domestico a la luz de las ultimas investigaciones. Angel Cabrera. Jornadas Agronómicas y Veterinarias, Buenos Aires, pp.125-137 (3-15), figs.3, 1938.

THE STORY OF A HORSE. William Harding Carter. Nat. Geog. Mag., vol.44, pp.455-466, illus., Nov., 1923.

(THE ORIGIN OF THE CREOLE HORSE. REPLY TO A CRITIC.) Origen de caballo criollo. Contestación a una critica. Paul Magne de la Croix. Anales Soc. Cient. Argentina, Buenos Aires, vol.114, pt.2, pp.70-71, Aug., 1932.

(SPANISH HORSES ANCESTORS OF OUR OWN CREOLES.) Los caballos españoles antepasados de nuestros criollos. Paul Magne de la Croix. Cientifica Argentina, Buenos Aires, ser.4, vol.114, pp.201-205, 1932.

EVOLUTION OF THE HORSE BRAIN. Tilly Edinger. Geol. Soc. America Mem., no.25, pp.x+177, figs.24, pls.4, Feb. 16, 1948.

FRONTAL SINUS EVOLUTION (PARTICULARLY IN THE EQUIDAE). Tilly Edinger. Bull. Mus. Comp. Zool., Cambridge, vol. 103, no.8, pp.412-496, 1950.

THE MULTIPLE ORIGIN OF HORSES AND PONIES. J.C. Ewart. Smiths. Inst., Ann. Rep., Washington, 1905.

(ON THE HISTORY OF THE HORSE.) Zur geschichte des Pferdes. Ernst Feige. Aus der Heimat Naturwissensch. Montatsschr. Deutschen Lehrervereins Naturk., Stuttgart, Jahrg.42, no.4, pp.109-116, fig.1, Apr., 1929.

THE "DAWN HORSE" AND ITS PROGENY. (Fossil horses.) H.O. Fletcher. Australian Mus. Mag., Sydney, vol.8, no.4, pp.136-140, illus., June 30, 1943.

THE HORSE: A STUDY IN NATURAL HISTORY. William Henry Flower. New York, D.Appleton and Co., pp.204, illus., 1892.

(INTERPRETATION OF THE UPPER MILK MOLAR OF EOHIPPUS AND CONSIDERATIONS ON THE PHYLOGENY OF EQUIDAE.) Interprétation de la molaire supérieure jeune de l'Eohippust et considerations sur la phylogénie des Équidés. M. Friant. Bull. Mus. Nat. Hist. Nat., Paris, ser.2, vol.8, no.2, pp.200-204, figs.6, Mar., 1936.

WILD ANCESTOR OF MAN'S FAITHFUL BURDEN-BEARER. (African wild ass.) Eric Hardy. Frontiers, Philadelphia, vol. 13, no.4, pp.106-108, illus., Apr., 1949.

THE EVOLUTION OF THE DOMESTIC HORSE. Max Hilsheimer. Antiquity, Gloucester, vol.9, no.34, pp.133-139, pls.9, June, 1935.

HISTORY IN BRIEF OF "LEOPARD" AND "LINDEN," GENERAL GRANT'S ARABIAN STALLIONS, PRESENTED TO HIM BY THE SULTAN OF TURKEY IN 1879, ALSO THEIR SONS "GENERAL BEALE", "HEGIRA", AND "ISLAM". Randolph Huntington, 1885.

HORSEBACK RIDING IN MESOPOTAMIA IN THE THIRD MILLENIUM B.C. Leon Legrain. Univ. Mus. Bull., Philadelphia, vol.11, no.4, pp.27-33, pl.9, Apr., 1946.

EVOLUTION OF THE HORSE. Frederic B. Loomis. Boston, Marshall Jones Co., pp. xvi+233, pls.26, figs.41, June, 1926.

EVOLUTION OF THE HORSE FAMILY. Richard Swann Lull. Amer.Jour.Sci., vol. 23, pp.22, figs.16, Mar., 1907.

(MISCELLANEA FROM THE HISTORY OF THE SOLIPEDS.) Allerlei aus der Geschichte der Einhufer. Paul Matschie. Monatshefte Naturwissenschaftlichen Unterricht aller Schulgattungen, Leipzig, vol.2, no. 7, pp.296-310, June 29, 1909.

EVOLUTION OF THE HORSE. W.D. Matthew. Amer. Mus. Jour., New York, vol.3, no.1, pp.30, illus., Jan., 1903. (Suppl.Guide Leaflet no.9.); Quart.Rev. Biol., vol.1, pp.139-185, pl.1, Apr., 1926.

HORSE AND HIS PROGENITORS. W. D. Matthew. Science Conspectus Soc. Arts. Massachusetts Inst. Tech., Boston, vol. 6, no.1, pp.1-15, illus., 1916.

NEW LINK IN THE HISTORY OF THE HORSE. W. D. Matthew. Amer. Mus. Nov., New York, no.131, pp.2, Sep. 23, 1924.

EVOLUTION OF THE AMERICAN TROTTING HORSE. Francis E. Nipher. Amer. Jour. Sci., Philadelphia, ser.3, vol.26, no.151, pp.20-24, July, 1883.

EQUUS AND HIS FORBEARS. Edalee Orcutt. San Diego Zoonooz, vol.19, no.12, p.4, Dec., 1946.

ORIGIN AND HISTORY OF THE HORSE. Henry Fairfield Osborn. (Address before the New York Farmers, Metropolitan Club, Dec. 19, 1905), New York, pp.16, figs.29, 1905.

EVOLUTION IN THE HORSE'S SKULL. E.C.R. Reeve, P.D.F. Murray. Nature, London, vol.150, no.3805, pp.402-403, illus., Oct. 3, 1942.

HORSE GODS OF GUATEMALA. Dorothy Reynolds. Nat. Hist., New York, vol.49, no.3, pp.177-179, illus., Mar., 1942.

GEOLOGICAL HISTORY AND EVOLUTION OF THE HORSE. Elmer S. Riggs. Field Mus. Nat. Hist., Dept. Geol., Leaflet no. 13, pp.54, pls.19, figs.4, 1932.

STUDY OF MUTATIONS IN EVOLUTION. I. EVOLUTION OF THE EQUINE SKULL. 2. ONTOGENY IN THE EQUINE SKULL. R. Cumming Robb. Jour. Genetics, London, vol.31, no.1, pp.39-52, illus., June 27, 1935.

STUDY OF MUTATIONS IN EVOLUTION. IV. ONTOGENY OF THE EQUINE FOOT. R. Cumming Robb. Jour. Genetics, London, vol.34, no.3, pp.477-486, fig.1, tbl. 1, June, 1937.

ORIGIN OF THE DOMESTIC HORSE. B.F. Rumjahcev. Bull. Acad. Sci. URSS, cl.sci. math. et nat., ser.biol., Moscow, nos. 2-3, pp.415-448, figs.21, 1936.

STORY OF THE HORSE. ALTHOUGH ITS ORIGIN IS HIDDEN IN THE MISTS OF THE PAST, THE HORSE IS BELIEVED TO HAVE COME FROM CENTRAL ASIA. Ernst Schwarz. Nature Mag., vol.31, no.3, pp. 162-163, figs.4, Mar., 1938.

HORSES. THE STORY OF THE HORSE FAMILY IN THE MODERN WORLD AND THROUGH SIXTY MILLION YEARS OF HISTORY. George Gaylord Simpson. Oxford Univ. Press, New York, pp.xxiv+247, pls. 32, 1951

(Review by Claude W. Hibbard of) HORSES. George Gaylord Simpson. Jour. Mamm., vol.33, no.2, pp.262-263, May 16, 1952.

(INVESTIGATION OF THE ORIGIN OF EUROPEAN HORSES.) Badanie pochodzenia kni europejakich. Edward Skorkowsli. Roczniki Nauk Rolniczch i Lésnych, vol.29, no. 1, pp.1-15, 1933.

(REMARKS ON THE QUESTION OF THE DIRECT ASCENDANCE OF THE GENUS EQUUS.) Bemerkungen zu der Frage nach der unmittelbaren Ascendenz des Genus Equus. H.G. Stehlin. Eclogae Geologicae Helvetiae, vol.22, no.2, pp.186-201, figs. 4, Dec., 1929.

COMMENTS ON THE ORIGIN AND GENERIC STATUS OF EQUUS. R.A. Stirton. Jour. Paleontol., Menasha, vol.16, no.5, pp. 627-637, figs.25, Sep., 1942.

NEW EVIDENCE ON THE ANCESTRY OF EQUUS. R.A. Stirton. Proc. Geol. Soc. America 1935, p.395, June, 1936.

PHYLOGENY OF NORTH AMERICAN EQUIDAE. R.A. Stirton. Univ. Calif. Publ. Bull. Dept., Geol. Sci., Berkeley, vol.25, no.4, pp.165-198, figs.52, chart 1, June 14, 1940.

ASCENT OF EQUUS. Chester Stock. Hildegarde Howard. Los Angeles County Mus. Sci Ser., no.8 (Paleontology, no.5), pp.38, figs.15, Mar. 31, 1944.

HISTORY AND ROMANCE OF THE HORSE. Arthur Vernon. Dover Publications, New York, pp.525, 1946.

(ORIGIN AND BREED OF THE HORSE FROM THE BURIAL HILL NEAR WILNO, AS TOLD FROM THE SKULL.) Pochodzenie i przynależność rasowa konia z kurhanu z okolic Wilna, na podstawie charakterystystyki czaszki. T. Vetulani. Roczniki Nauk Rolnicz. i Lésnych (Polish Agric. and Forestal Ann.), vol.27, no.2, pp.263-288, 1932.

(DEVELOPMENT OF THE GERMAN HORSE.) Der Werdegang des deutschen Pferdes. Arthur Weinberg. Natur u. Volk, Frankfurt a.M., vol. 65, no.9, pp.412-448, figs.46, Sep., 1935.

EVOLUTION OF THE SKULL IN HORSES. Nature, London, vol.136, no.3434, p.304, Aug. 24, 1935. (Abstract of "Study of mutations in evolution; ontogeny in equine skull," by R. Cumming Rubb, Jour. Genetics, vol.31, no.1, pp.47-52, June, 1935.)

ORIGIN OF THE DOMESTICATED HORSE. Nature, London, vol.36, no.3429, p.111, July 20, 1935.

Fossils (General)

(HORSES AT THE END OF THE PALEOLITHIC PERIOD AND BEGINING OF THE NEOLITHIC.) Equideos do fim do paleolitico e inicio do neolitico. Ruy d'Andrade. Publ. Inst. de Coimbra, vol.94, pp.1-32, 1939.

CHARACTERS USEFUL IN DETERMINING THE POSITION OF INDIVIDUAL TEETH IN THE PERMANENT CHEEK-TOOTH SERIES OF MERYCHIPPINE HORSES. Francis D. Bode. Bull. Geol. Soc. America, vol.43, no. 1, pp.287-288, Mar., 1932. (Abstract.)

NEW SPECIES OF MERYCHIPPUS. (M. tehachapiensis.) J.P. Buwalda, G.E. Lewis. Prof. Paper U.S. Geol. Surv., no.264-G, pp.147-152, illus., 1955.

HIPPARION (GENUS HIPPARION). Vera Gromova. Proc. Paleo. Inst., Acad. Sci. USSR, vol.36, p.477, illus., 1952.

NOTES ON SOME FOSSIL HORSES, WITH DESCRIPTIONS OF FOUR NEW SPECIES. Oliver P. Hay. Proc. U.S. Nat. Mus., vol. 44, pp.569-594, pls.69-73, Apr. 30, 1913.

NOTES ON THE CRANIOMETRY OF EQUUS SCOTTI GIDLEY. C. Stuart Johnston. Jour. Paleont., vol.11, no.5, pp.459-461, figs.3, July, 1937.

DID THE PLIOCENE HORSE PLIOHIPPUS EAT HACKBERRIES. J.R. MacDonald, Sherril Swenson. Jour. Mamm., vol.37, no.3, p.459, Sep. 11, 1956.

NOTICE OF NEW EQUINE MAMMALS FROM THE TERTIARY FORMATION. O.C. Marsh. Amer. Jour. Sci. and Arts, vol.7, pp.247-258, Mar., 1874.

THREE-TOED HORSES. A FOSSIL RECORD THAT PROVIDES DIRECT EVIDENCE OF EVOLUTION. W.D. Matthew. Nat. Hist., vol.20, pp.473-478, Sep.-Oct., 1920.

FLUORINE CONTENT OF SOME MIOCENE HORSE BONES. Russell Olsen. Science, Lancaster, vol.112, no.2917, pp.620-621, Nov. 24, 1950.

PROGRESS OF THE EXPLORATION FOR FOSSIL HORSES. Henry Fairfield Osborn. Science, Lancaster, vol.16, no.409, p.715, Oct. 31, 1902.

PREORBITAL FOSSA OF HIPPARION. P.L. Pirlot. Amer. Jour. Sci., New Haven, vol. 251, no.4, pp.309-312, Apr., 1953.

LOWER MIOCENE HORSE. (Anchitherium agatense (Osborn).) Alfred S. Romer. Amer. Jour. Sci., ser.5, vol.12, pp.325-335, illus., Oct., 1926.

STUDY OF PARAHIPPUS WYOMINGENSIS AND A DISCUSSION OF THE PHYLOGENY OF THE GENUS. Erich Maren Schlaikjer. Bull. Mus. Comp. Zool. at Harvard College, vol.80, no.5, pp.255-280, p.1, Jan., 1937.

MOUNTED SKELETONS OF EOHIPPUS, MERYCHIPPUS AND HESPEROSIREN. George Gaylord Simpson. Amer. Mus. Novitates, New York, no.587, pp.7, figs. 3, Dec. 15, 1932.

RESURRECTION OF THE DAWN-HORSE. George Gaylord Simpson. Nat. Hist., New York, vol.46, no.4, pp.194-199, illus., Nov., 1940.

(STATE OF OUR KNOWLEDGE OF THE FOSSIL ANCESTORS OF THE HORSE.) État de nos connaissances sur les ancêtres fossiles du cheval. J. Viret. Rev. Gén. Sci. Pures et Appl., vol.41, no. 7, pp. 207-212, figs.3, 1930.

STATISTICAL STUDY OF THE METAPODIALS OF EQUUS OCCIDENTALI LEIDY. David P. Willoughby. Bull. Southern Calif. Acad. Sci., Los Angeles, vol.47, pt.3, pp.84-94, Sep.-Dec., 1948.

Fossils (New World)

(HISTORY OF THE EQUIDAE ON THE SOIL OF NORTH AMERICA.) Die Geschichte der Equiden auf dem Boden Nordamerikas. Othenio Abel. Verh. Zool. Bot Gesell. Wien., vol.74-75, pp.159-164, 1926.

QUANTITAVE STUDY OF THE EQUIDAE OF THE THOMAS FARM MIOCENE. R. S. Bader. Bull. Mus. Comp. Zool., vol. 115, no.2, pp.49-78, Aug., 1956.

METARTARSAL OF EQUUS FROM MARINE PLIOCENE OF NORTH CAROLINA. Charles T. Berry. Pan-American Geologist, vol.56, pp.340-342, pl.22, Dec., 1931.

ANCHITHERIINE HORSES FROM THE MERYCHIPPUS ZONE, NORTH COALINGA DISTRICT, CALIFORNIA. Francis D. Bode. Bull. Geol. Soc. America, vol.44, no.1, p.219, Feb. 28, 1933 (Abstract); Contrib. to Palaeont., Carnegie Inst., Wash., Publ. 440, pp.43-58, pls.5, Nov. 15, 1933.

MERYCHIPPINE SPECIES OF WESTERN UNITED STATES AND THEIR STRATIGRAPHIC RELATIONSHIPS. Francis D. Bode. Pan-Amer. Geol., vol.59, no.5, p. 377, June, 1933; Proc. Geol. Soc. America, for 1933, New York, p.392, June, 1934.

MERYCHIPPUS ZONE FAUNA, COALINGA, CALIFORNIA. Francis D. Bode. Pan Amer. Geol., Des Moines, vol.62, no.1, p.68, Aug., 1934.

TOOTH CHARACTERS OF PROTOHIPPINE HORSES WITH SPECIAL REFERENCE TO SPECIES FROM THE MERYCHIPPUS ZONE, CALIFORNIA. Francis D. Bode. Carnegie Inst. Washington, Publ.453, pp.39-63, figs.6, pls.2, Dec. 20, 1934.

EXPLORATIONS FOR FOSSIL HORSES IN IDAHO. Norman H. Boss. Explorations and Field-Work Smiths. Inst. in 1931, Publ. 3134, pp.41-44, figs.5, 1932.

REMARKS ON THE USE OF THE NAME "VALENTINE." Edwin H. Colbert. Amer. Jour. Sci., New Haven, ser.5, vol.36, no. 213, pp.212-214, Sep., 1938.

LATER TERTIARY EQUIDAE FROM THE TEJON HILLS, CALIFORNIA. Arthur B. Drescher. Contrib. Paleontol., Carnegie Inst. Washington, Publ. 530, pp.25-33, figs.6, pls.3, May 1, 1941.

NOTES ON THE OSTEOLOGY OF THE WHITE RIVER HORSES. Marcus S. Farr. Proc. Amer. Philos. Soc., Philadelphia, vol.35, no.151, pp.147-175, figs.6, pl.13, Sep. 7, 1896.

WESTWARD EXTENSION OF THE KANSAS "EQUUS BEDS." John C. Frye. Jour. Geol., Chicago, vol.51, no.1, pp.33-47, figs.3, Jan.-Feb., 1943. (Mammals pp.44-46.)

EQUUS FROM THE PLEISTOCENE OF ILLINOIS. Edwin C. Galbreath. Jour. Mamm., vol.27, no.1, pp.91-92, Mar. 14, 1946.

STUDY OF THE FOSSIL HORSE REMAINS FROM THE UPPER PLIOCENE OF IDAHO. C. Lewis Gazin. Proc. U.S. Nat. Mus., vol.83, no.2985, pp.281-320, figs.21-24, pls.23-33, June 1, 1936.

CONTINUATION OF THE FOSSIL HORSE ROUND-UP ON THE OLD OREGON TRAIL. James W. Gidley. Explorations and Field-Work, Smiths. Inst. on 1930, Publ.3111, pp. 33-40, figs.27-32, Mar. 26, 1931.

NEW PLIOCENE HORSE FROM IDAHO. James W. Gidley. Jour. Mamm., vol.11, no.3, pp.300-303, pl.18, Aug., 1930.

NEW SPECIES OF PLEISTOCENE HORSE FROM THE STAKED PLAINS OF TEXAS. James W. Gidley. Bull. Amer. Mus. Nat. Hist., art.13, vol.13, pp.111-116, Aug.18, 1900.

EXTENSION OF THE RANGE OF MERYCHIPPUS. Joseph T. Gregory. Proc. Geol. Soc. America, 1937, p.295, June, 1938. (Abstract.)

DESCRIPTION OF A NEW SPECIES OF EXTINCT HORSE, EQUUS LAMBEI, FROM THE PLEISTOCENE OF YUKON TERRITORY. Oliver P. Hay. Proc. U.S.Nat.Mus., vol.53, pp.435-443, pls.56-58, June 5, 1917.

DESCRIPTION OF THE SKULL OF AN EXTINCT HORSE, FOUND IN CENTRAL ALASKA. Oliver P. Hay. Smiths.Inst. Misc.Coll., vol.61, no.2, Publ.2181, pp. 18, figs.8, pls.2, June 4, 1913.

FURTHER COMMENTS ON THE USAGE OF "VALENTINE." F. Walker Johnson. Amer. Jour. Sci., New Haven, ser.5, vol. 36, no.213, pp.215-219, tbl., Sep., 1938.

DESCRIPTION OF A NEW HORSE CALIPPUS REGULUS FROM THE CLARENDON BEDS OF DONLEY COUNTY, TEXAS. C. Stuart Johnston. Amer.Midland Nat., vol. 18, no.5, pp.905-907, fig.1, Sep., 1937.

SKULL OF NANNIPPUS GRATUS (LEIDY) FROM THE LOWER PLIOCENE OF TEXAS. C. Stuart Johnston. Amer.Midland Nat., vol.19, no.1, pp.245-248, figs.3, Jan., 1938.

AMERICAN HYRACOTHERIUM (PERISSODACTYLA, EQUIDAE). David B.Kitts. Bull. Amer. Mus. Nat. Hist., vol.110, no.1, pp.1-60, pls.7, May 21, 1956.

COMMENTARY ON McGREW AND MEADE'S PAPER (ON "VALENTINE" EQUIDS). G. Edward Lewis. Amer. Jour. Sci., New Haven, ser.5, vol.36, no.213, pp.208-211, Sep., 1938.

NEBRASKA STATE GEOLOGICAL SURVEY AND THE "VALENTINE PROBLEM." A.L. Lugn. Amer. Jour. Sci., New Haven, ser.5, vol.36, no.213, pp.220-227, tbls., Sep., 1938.

NOTES ON THE VALENTINE QUESTION. A.L. Lugn. Amer. Jour. Sci., New Haven, vol.237, no.6, pp.433-438, June, 1939.

NEW AND PRIMITIVE EARLY OLIGOCENE HORSE FROM TRANS-PECOS TEXAS. Paul O. McGrew. Fieldana-Geology, Chicago Nat. Hist. Mus., vol.10, no.15, pp.167-171, fig.1, June 19, 1953.

BEARING OF THE VALENTINE AREA IN CONTINENTAL MIOCENE-PLIOCENE CORRELATION. Paul O. McGrew, Gratson E. Meade. Amer. Jour. Sci., New Haven, ser. 5, vol.36, no.213, pp.197-207, chart, Sep., 1938.

FOSSIL HORSES IN AMERICA. O.C. Marsh. Amer. Naturalist, vol.8, pp.288-294, May, 1874.

EQUIDAE FROM THE PLIOCENE OF TEXAS. W.D. Matthew, R.A. Stirton. Univ. Calif. Publ., Bull. Dept. Geol. Sci., vol.19, no. 17, pp.349-396, pls.45-58, Nov. 29, 1930.

GEOLOGIC AGE OF EARLIEST NORTH AMERICAN HIPPARION FAUNAS. John H. Maxson.Bull.Geol.Soc.Amer., pt.2, vol.49, no.12, pp.1916-1917, Dec.1, 1938. (Abstract.)

MERYCHIPPUS ISONESUS (COPE) FROM THE LATER TERTIARY OF THE CROOKED RIVER BASIN, OREGON. John H. Maxson. Contrib. to Paleont., Carnegie Inst. Wash., Publ.393, pp.55-58, fig.1, 1929.

NEW SPECIES OF THE HIPPARION GROUP FROM THE PACIFIC COAST AND THE GREAT BASIN PROVINCES OF NORTH AMERICA. John C. Merriam. Berkeley, Univ. of Calif. Press, Bull. Dept. Geol., vol.9, no.1, pp.1-8, illus., 1915.

PRELIMINARY REPORT ON THE HORSES OF RANCHO LA BREA. John C. Merriam. Univ. Calif. Publ., Berkeley, Bull. Dept. Geol., vol.7, no.21, pp.397-418, figs.14, Dec. 16, 1913.

EQUIDAE OF THE OLIGOCENE, MIOCENE, AND PLIOCENE OF NORTH AMERICA, ICONOGRAPHIC TYPE REVISION. H.F. Osborn. Memoirs, Amer. Mus. Nat.Hist., n.s., vol.2, pt.1, pp.221, pls.54, 1918.

ARE THE EQUIDAE RELIABLE FOR THE CORRELATION OF THE SIWALIKS WITH THE COENOZOIC STAGES OF NORTH AMERICA? (With an appendix by A.T.Hopwood.) Guy E. Pilgrim. Records Geol.Surv. India, Calcutta, vol.73, pt.4, pp.437-482, 1938.

MIOCENE EQUIDAE OF THE TEXAS GULF COASTAL PLAIN. James H. Quinn. Univ. Texas Publ., no.5516, pp.1-102, illus., Nov., 1955.

LOWER PLIOCENE HORSES FROM BLACK HAWK RANCH, MOUNT DIABLO, CALIFORNIA. King A. Richey. Univ.Calif. Publ., Bull. Dept. Geol.Sci., Berkeley, vol. 28, no.1, pp.1-44, figs.13, pls.3, Mar. 3, 1948.

NEW SPECIES OF MERYCHIPPUS FROM THE MIOCENE OF SASKATCHEWAN. (Merychippus praecocidens.) Loris S. Russell. Canadian Field Nat., vol.47, no.1, p. 11, Jan., 1933.

PLEISTOCENE HORSE TEETH FROM SASKATCHEWAN. Loris S. Russell. Jour. Paleontol., Menasha, vol.17, no.1, pp.110-114, figs.13, Jan., 1943.

SIGNIFICANCE OF A FOSSIL HORSE TOOTH FOUND AT MOSCOW, IDAHO. Vernon E. Scheid. Northwest Science, Cheney, vol.14, no.3, pp.56-57, fig.1, Aug., 1940.

DESCRIPTION OF A NEW MESOHIPPUS FROM THE WHITE RIVER FORMATION OF SOUTH DAKOTA. (Mesohippus barbouri.) Erich Maren Schlaikjer. Proc.New England Zool. Club, vol.12, pp.35-38, Jan. 17, 1931.

PLESIPPUS FRANCESCANA (FRICK) FROM THE LATE PLIOCENE, COSO MOUNTAINS, CALIFORNIA, WITH A REVIEW OF THE GENUS PLESIPPUS. J. R. Schultz. Carnegie Inst. Wash. (Contrib.Palaeont.), Publ.453, pp.1-13, figs.3, pls.3, May 21, 1936.

PLESIPPUS FRANCESCANA FROM COSO MOUNTAINS. J.R. Schultz. Pan-Amer. Geol., Des Moines, vol.64, no.1, p.79, Aug., 1935.

(FOSSIL HORSES OF SOUTH AMERICA.) Die fossilen Pferde Suedamerikas. Ivar Sefve. Uppsala, Almqvist and Wiksells boktryckeri-a.-b., pp.185, illus.32, pls. 3, 1912.

MOUNTED SKELETON OF A NEW MESOHIPPUS FROM THE PROTOCERAS BEDS. William J. Sinclair. Proc. Amer. Philos. Soc., vol.64, pp.55-63, illus., 1925.

ARE PETALUMA HORSE TEETH RELIABLE IN CORRELATION? R. A. Stirton. Bull. Amer. Assoc. Petrol. Geol., vol.36, no. 10, pp.2011-2025, illus., Oct., 1952.

TWO NEW SPECIES OF THE EQUID GENUS NEOHIPPARION FROM THE MIDDLE PLIOCENE, CHIHUAHUA, MEXICO. R.A.Stirton. Jour. Paleontol., vol.29, no.5, pp.886-902, illus., Sep., 1955.

CRANIUM OF PLIOHIPPUS FOSSULATUS FROM THE CLARENDON LOWER PLIOCENE FAUNA OF TEXAS. R.A. Stirton, Will Chamberlain. Jour. Palaeontol., Chicago, vol.13, no.3, pp.349-353, figs.4, May, 1939.

ANCHITHERIINE HORSES FROM THE FISH LAKE VALLEY REGION, NEVADA. Chester Stock. Univ. Calif. Publ. Geol., vol.16, no.3, pp.61-68, 1926.

NEOHIPPARION LEPTODE (MERRIAM) FROM THE PLIOCENE OF NORTHWESTERN NEVADA. Chester Stock. Amer.Jour. Sci., New Haven, vol.249, no.6, pp.430-438, figs.2, pls.6, June, 1951.

TOOTH OF HIPPARION MOHAVENSE FROM THE PUENTE FORMATION, CALIFORNIA. Chester Stock. Contrib. Paleont., Carnegie Inst. Washington, Publ.393, pp.49-53, fig. 1, Sep., 1928 (Oct. 24, 1928).

PROTOLOPH-ECTOLOPH ANGLE AND ITS CORRELATION WITH THE GEOLOGIC HORIZON OF FIVE GENERA OF NORTH AMERICAN EQUIDAE. J. Willis Stovall. Jour. Geol., vol.37, no.8, pp.790-794, fig.1, 1929.

SKULL OF PLIOHIPPUS TANTALUS FROM THE LATER TERTIARY OF THE SIERRAN FOOTHILLS OF CALIFORNIA. V.L.Vanderhoff. Univ. Calif. Publ., Bull. Dept. Geol. Sci., vol.23, no.5, pp.183-194, figs. 5, pl.16, Aug. 11, 1933.

SPECIES OF HYRACOTHERIUM AND ALLIED PERISSODACTYLA FROM THE WAHSATCH AND WIND RIVER BEDS OF NORTH AMERICA. J.L. Wortman. Bull. Amer. Mus. Nat. Hist., vol.8, art.6, pp. 81-110, figs.18, pl.2, May 12, 1896.

Fossils (Old World)

(THE HIPPARION FAUNA OF EL-HAMMAM (ALGERIA).) La fauna a Hipparion de l'oued el Hammam (Algerie). C. Arambourg.Assoc. Serv. Geol. Africains, fasc.21, pp.295-302, 1954.

ON FINDS OF ANCHITHERE IN KAZAKHSTAN. E.I. Belyaeva. Proc. Paleo. Inst., Acad. Sci. USSR, vol.47, pp.55-60, illus., 1954.

(ON THE PRESENCE OF "EQUUS HYDRUNTINUS" IN THE QUATERNARY GRAVELS OF THE ANIENE RIVER.) Sulla presenza di "Equus hydruntinus" nelle ghiaie quaternarie del'Aniene. G.A. Blanc. Atti Reale Accad. Naz. dei Lincei, Roma, ser.6, Rendiconti cl. sci. fis. matem. et nat., vol.23, no.11, pp.827-830, figs.2, 1936.

ON PARANCHITHERIUM KARPENSKII GEN. ET SPEC. N.--NEW REPRESENTATIVE OF EQUIDAE FROM THE MIDDLE PLIOCENE DEPOSITS OF THE CAUCASUS. A. Borisiak. Bull. Acad. Sci. USSR, cl. sci.math.et nat., ser.geol., Moscow, no. 4, pp.789-793, figs.2, 1937. (In Russian with English summary.)

ON THE EQUIDAE FROM THE MIDDLE MIOCENE OF NORTHERN CAUCASUS. A. Borisiak. Trudy Paleontologicheskogo Instituta, Moscow, vol.13, pp.1-52, figs. 14, pls.3, 1945.

ON THE REMAINS OF ANCHITHERIUM FROM THE MIDDLE-MIOCENE OF NORTH CAUCASUS. A. Borisiak. Bull. Acad. Sci. USSR, cl.sci. math.et nat., ser.biol., Moscow, no.1, pp.207-218, figs.4, 1938. (In Russian with English summary.)

(THE DISCOVERY OF HIPPARION MOLARS AT THE BASE OF THE LACUSTRIAN SERIES OF SMECTITE ARGIL AT CAMP BERTEAUX (EASTERN MOROCCO).) Sur la découverte de molaires d'Hipparion à la base de la série lacustre à argile smectiques de Camp-Berteaux (Maroc Oriental). Jacques Bourcart. Compte Rendu Sommaire Séances Soc. Géol. France, Paris, nos.7-8, pp.79-80, Apr. 12-19, 1937.

(HORSE CAVE OF LABASTIDE (HAUTES-PYRÉNÉES, FRANCE).) Die Pferdehoehle von Labastide (Htes. Pyrénées, France). Norbert Casteret. Die Umschau, Frankfurt am Main, Jahrg.37, no.10, pp.184-187, figs. 8, Mar. 4, 1933.

OCCURRENCE OF ANCHITHERIUM AURELIANENSE AT FANGSHAN, NANKING. Minchen M. Chow, Hu Chang-Kong. Acta Pal. Sinica, vol.4, no.4, pp.525-533, illus., 1956.

DISTRIBUTIONAL AND PHYLOGENETIC STUDIES ON INDIAN FOSSIL MAMMALS. II. THE CORRELATION OF THE SIWALIKS OF INDIA AS INFERRRED BY THE MIGRATIONS OF HIPPARION AND EQUUS. Edwin H. Colbert. Amer. Mus. Novitates, no.797, pp.15, figs.3, May 8, 1935.

NEW ANCHITHERIINE HORSE FROM THE TUNG GUR FORMATION OF MONGOLIA. (Anchitherium gobiense.) Edwin H.Colbert. Amer. Mus. Novitates, no.1019, pp.1-9, figs.3, tbls., Apr. 12, 1939.

CRITICAL REVISION OF THE QUATERNARY PERISSODACTYLA OF SOUTHERN AFRICA. H.B.S. Cooke. Ann. S.Africa Mus., Cape Town, vol.31, no.4, pp.393-479, Dec., 1950.

GENUS HYRACOTHERIUM. A REVISION AND DESCRIOTION OF NEW SPECIMENS FOUND IN ENGLAND. C. Forster Cooper. Philos. Trans. Roy. Soc. London (B), vol. 221, pp.431-448, figs.3, pls.3, 1932.

(A HORSE FROM THE SWEDISH VIKING AGE.) Ueber ein Pferd aus der swedischen Wikingerzeit. Nils-Gustaf Gejvall. Arkiv. f. Zool., Stockholm, vol.30, no.17, pp. 1-16, figs.2, 1938.

NEW FOSSIL HORSE FROM CENTRAL ASIA. (Equus valeriani.) Vera Gromova. Comptes Rendus (Doklady) Acad. Sci. USSR, Moscow, vol.54, no.4, pp.347-350, Nov. 10, 1946.

HISTORY OF HORSES (GENUS EQUUS) IN THE OLD WORLD. PART I. REVIEW AND ACCOUNT OF FORMS. Vera Gromova. Proc. Paleo. Inst., Acad. Sci. USSR, vol. 17, p.374, illus., 1949.

HISTORY OF HORSES (GENUS EQUUS) IN THE OLD WORLD. PART II. EVOLUTION AND CLASSIFICATION OF THE GENUS. Vera Gromova. Proc. Paleo.Inst., Acad. Sci. USSR, vol.17, p.162, illus., 1949.

A NEW FIND OF ANCHITHERE IN MONGOLIA. Vera Gromova. Proc. Paleo.Inst., Acad. Sci. USSR, vol.41, pp.87-98, illus., 1952.

(ON THE REMAINS OF THE MERCK RHINOCEROS (RHINOCEROS MERKI JAEG.) OF THE LOWER VOLGA.) Vera Gromova. Trudy Paleozoologicheskogo Instituta Akademii Nauk SSSR (Trav.Inst. Paleozool. Acad. Sci. USSR), vol.4, pp. 91-136, figs.4, pls.3, fold.tbl.1, 1935. (In Russian with German summary.)

FOSSIL EQUIDAE OF SOUTH AFRICA. S.H. Haughton. Ann. S. African Mus., vol.28, pt.4, pp.407-427, figs.6, Feb., 1932.

(FOSSIL HORSES FROM CORNELIA.) Fossiele Perde van Cornelia. E.C.N. van Hoepen. Paleont. Navorsing Nasion. Mus. Bloemfontein, vol.2, no.2, pp.13-24, figs.22, Apr. 16, 1930.

(FOSSIL HORSES OF THE ORANGE FREE STATE.) Vrystaatse fossiele Perde. E.C.N. van Hoepen. Paleont. Navorsing Nasion Mus., vol.2, no.1, pp.11, figs.10, Feb. 14, 1930. (With German summary.)

CHINESE HIPPARION FAUNA. Björn Kurtén. Comment. Biol., Soc. Sci. Fennica, vol. 13, no.4, pp.82, 1954.

EQUUS ZEBRA GREATHEADI N. SUBSP. A NEW SOUTH AFRICAN FOSSIL ZEBRA. B. Lundholm. Ann. Transvaal Mus., vol. 22, pt.1, pp.25-27, pl.4, Nov. 4, 1952.

FOSSIL HORSE OF BISHOP'S STORTFORD, WITH REMARKS ON THE FOSSIL HORSES OF EUROPE. E.T. Newton. Essex Nat., Stratford, vol.16, pts.5-6, pp.132-136, Feb., 1911.

(INVESTIGATIONS OF FOSSIL HORSE REMAINS OF BOHEMIA AND THEIR RELATIONSHIP TO SOME RECENT AND FOSSIL HORSE RACES.) Untersuchungen ueber fossile Pferdereste Boehmens und ihre Beziehungen zu einigen rezenten und fossilen Pferderassen. Max Nitsche. Zeitschr. f. Ind. Abstammungs- u. Vererbungslehre, vol.51, pp.146-244, figs.10, tbls.5, 1929.

HIPPARION FAUNA IN THE IRTYSH RIVER (SIBERIS). Iu Orlov. Priroda, Leningrad, no. 1, pp.47-58, figs.5, 1930.

NEW LOCALITY OF HIPPARION-FAUNA AT DJAPARIDZE, EAST GEORGIA. TERTIARY MAMMALIA AND THE LOCALITIES OF THEIR REMAINS. J.A. Orlov. Trav. Inst. Paleont., Moscow, Leningrad, vol.8, no.3, pp.99-101, figs.2, 1941. (In Russian with English summary.)

CABALLINE AND ZEBRINE HORSES IN THE NORFOLK FOREST BEDS. Paul Pirlot. Proc. Zool. Soc. London, vol.118, pt.4, pp.1118-1133, illus., Feb. 28, 1949.

(EUROPEAN FORMS OF THE GENUS HIPPARION.) Les formes europeennes du genre Hipparion. Paul Pirlot. Dip. Prov. Barcelona, Mem. Com. Inst. Geol., no.14, pp.150, 1956.

OBSERVATIONS ON THE FRAGMENT OF A HORSE SKULL FROM AN INTERGLACIAL DEPOSIT NEAR PULAWY, POLAND. R. Prawocheński, B. Kaczkowski. Proc. Roy. Soc. Edinburg, vol.47, pt.3, no.19, pp. 243-251, pl.1, 1926-1927.

(HORSE SKULL FROM A MOUND NEAR SWIECANY (VILNA). CONTRIBUTION TO THE PROBLEM OF THE PRIMITIVE TYPES OF HORSES.) Czaska konia z kurhanu w okolicy Świecian (Wileńskie). Przyczynek do charakterystyki pierwotnych typów koni. R. Prawocheński, Br.Slizyński. Roczniki Nauk Rolnicznych i leśnych, Poznań, vol. 26, pp.1-20, figs.11, 1931.

(ON EUROPEAN FOSSIL HORSES AND THE ORIGIN OF THE DOMESTIC HORSE.) Ueber europaeische fossile Pferde und den Ursprung der Hauspferde. E. Schwarz. Palaeont. Zeitschr. Band 4, Heft 2-3, 1922.

(HIPPARIONS OF NORTHERN CHINA.) Die Hipparionen Nord-Chinas. Ivar Sefve. Palaeontologia Sinica, ser.C, vol.4, fasc.2, pp.1-93, pls.1-7, Feb., 1927.

(HIPPOLOGICAL CORRECTIONS.) Poprawki hipologiczne. Edward Skorkowski. Roczniki Nauk Rolniczych i Leśnych (Polish Agricultural and Forest Annual), Poznań, vol.30, no.3, pp.343-370, figs.10, 1933. (In Polish with English summary.)

(ON A QUATERNARY HORSE FROM TRANSYLVANIA.) Ueber ein Quataerpferd aus Transilvanien, "Equus transilvanicus." N. Teodoreanu. Bull. Sect. Sci. Acad. Roumaine, Bucharest, vol.10, no.2, pp. 17-24, figs.4, 1926.

(NOTES ON A RECENT TEST IN THE GROTTO OF ST. THEODORE IN THE PROVINCE OF MESSINA.) Cenni su un recente assagio nella grotta di S.Teodoro in Provincia di Messina. (Equus hydruntinus.) Giuseppina Tricomi. Boll. Soc. Sci. Nat. ed Economiche Palermo, n.s., vol. 20, pp.29-32, 1928.

FOSSIL HORSE FROM KOFFIEFONTEIN, O.F.S. (Equus fowleri.) L.H. Wells. Trans. Roy. Soc. S. Africa, Cape Town, vol.28, pt.4, pp.301-306, fig.1, pl.1, June, 1941.

Habits, Behavior

(BEHAVIOR OF ICELAND HORSES IN A NORTHERN GERMAN FREE LANDSCAPE.) Verhaltensweisen von Islandpferden in einem nordeutschen Freigelaende. Hermann Ebhardt. Saeugetierk. Mitteil., Stuttgart, vol.2, no.4, pp.145-154, illus., Oct. 1, 1954.

(THREE DIFERENT TYPES OF BEHAVIOR IN ICELAND HORSES IN FREE PRESERVE OF NORTHERN GERMANY.) Drei unterschiedliche Verhaltensweisen von Islandpferden in nord-deutschen Freigehegen. Hermann Ebhardt. Saeugetierk. Mitteil., vol.5, no.3, pp.113-117, Aug. 1, 1957.

(OBSERVATIONS ON ZEBRAS.) Bemerkungen ueber Tigerpferde. E. Kattinger. Zeitschr. f. Saeugetierk., Berlin, vol.17, no.2, pp. 115-122, pls.12-15, Feb. 19, 1953.

(FURTHER OBSERVATIONS ON ZEBRAS, AND SOME DOMESTICATION RESULTS.) Weitere Beobachtungen an Zebras sowie einige Zaehmungserfolge. Adolf Rzasnicki. Zool. Garten, vol.14, no.4, pp.253-261, illus., 1942.

(OBSERVATIONS ON CHAPMAN ZEBRAS.) Beobachtungen an Chapman-Zebras. Adolf Rzasnicki. Zool. Garten, Leipzig, n.F., vol.6, nos.1-3, pp.1-10, figs.14, May, 1933.

(INFORMATION ON THE KIANG (EQUUS KIANG MOORCROFT). Ernst Schaefer. Zool. Garten, Leipzig, n. F., vol.9, nos. 3-4, pp.122-139, illus., May, 1937.

ENERGY COST OF STANDING IN HORSES. C.F. Winchester. Science, Lancaster, n.s., vol.97, no.2505, p.24, Jan. 1, 1943.

Heredity

AN EARLY HORSE SKELETON. Thornton Chart. Jour.Heredity, vol.28, no.9, pp. 317-319, figs.4, Sep., 1937.

THE SEX RATIO IN THE MULE. W.A. Craft. Record of Proc., Ann. Meeting 1932, Amer. Soc. Anim. Protection, pp.2-3; Paper no.149, Dept. Genetics, Wisconsin Agric. Exper. Sta., pp.283-285.

GENETIC ANALYSIS OF THE AMERICAN QUARTER HORSE. J. Lane Fletcher. Jour. Heredity, Washington, vol.36, no.11, pp. 346-352, figs.9-12, Nov., 1945.

STUDIES IN MAMMALIAN SPERMATOGENESIS. V. THE CHROMOSOMES OF THE HORSE. Theophilus S. Painter. Jour. Exper. Zool., vol.39, pp.229-247, Apr. 5, 1924.

DEVELOPMENT OF A SUPERIOR FAMILY IN THE MODERN QUARTER HORSE. A. O. Rhoad, R.J. Kleberg. Jour. Heredity, Washington, vol.37, no.8, pp.226-238, figs.1-9, Aug., 1946.

Hybrids

(WHEN MULES PROPAGATE.) Naar muldyr forplanter sig. (Crosses between mules and both parent forms.) Esben Ditlevsen. Copenhagen, Naturens Verden, vol.23, no.2, pp. 63-74, figs.7, 1939.

TELEGONY EXPERIMENTS: THE BIRTH OF A HYBRID BETWEEN A MALE BURCHELL'S ZEBRA (EQUUS BURCHELLI) AND A MARE (E. CABALLUS). J.C. Ewart. Veterinarian, London, vol.69, pp.755-769, figs.2, illus., Nov., 1896.

(SOME CONSIDERATIONS ON ZEBRAS AND THEIR HYBRIDS.) Alcune considerazioni sulle Zebre e sui loro ibridi. Achille Griffini. Revista mensile Sci. Nat. "Natura" vol.4, pp.5-52, figs.11, 1913.

FERTILE MARE MULE. A.H. Groth. Jour. Heredity, vol.19, pp.413-416, illus., Sep., 1928.

A NEW HYBRID -- PRZEWALSKI'S WILD HORSE X ZEBRA (EQUUS FERUS PALLAS, EQUUS PREZEWALSKII POLIJAK X HIPPOTIGRIS QUAGGA CHAPMANI LAJARD.) A.P. Gunali. Trudy Inst.Sel'skokhoziaistevennoi Gibridizatsii i Akklimatizatsii Zhivotnykh v Askanii-Nova (Bull. Inst. Agric. Hybridization and Acclimatization of Animals), Moscow, vol.1, pp.67-84, figs.14-25, 1933. (In Russian with English summary.)

A MULE COLT FROM NEBRASKA. (Said to have mule mother and jack father.) Erasmus Haworth. Jour. Heredity, vol.19, p.412, illus., Sep., 1928.

(CONTRIBUTION TO KNOWLEDGE OF ZEBRA HYBRIDS.) Przycznek do znajomości mieszańców zebr. Adolf Rząśnicki. Annales Musei Zoologici Polonici, Warsaw, vol.9, no.11, pp.155-160, pls.14-18, 1931.

A SUPPOSED ZEBRA-DONKEY HYBRID. S.P. Teare. Field, London, vol.167, no.4351, p. 1186, illus., 1936.

BACKCROSS OFFSPRING OF THE COMMON MULE. Ernest Warren. Ann. Natal. Mus., vol.7, pt.2, pp.243-247, pl.13, May, 1933.

FERTILE MULE. Ernest Warren. Nature, London, vol.129, no.3247, pp.130-131, Jan. 23, 1932.

LORD MORTON'S QUAGGA-HORSE HYBRID. WAS IT A HYBRID? James Wilson. Sci.Proc. Rov. Dublin Soc., vol.18, n.s., no.41, pp. 485-487, July 25, 1927.

In Captivity, Zoos

(ON ANIMAL GARDEN SPECIMENS OF EQUUS ZEBRA FREDERICI TROUESS.) Ueber Tiergarten-Exemplare von Equus zebra frederici Trouess. Otto Antonius. Zool. Garten, Leipzig, n.F., vol.9, nos. 3-4, pp.145-148, illus., May, 1937.

HORSES, ASSES, AND ZEBRAS AT THE ZOO. James Fisher. Field, London, vol. 175, no.4564, p.930, June 15, 1940.

THE WILD EQUINES OF THE ZOOLOGICAL PARK. Henry Fairfield Osborn. Zool.Soc. Bull., New York, vol.16, no.55, pp.941-948, figs.11, Jan., 1913.

(FAMILY OF WILD HORSES OF THE JARDIN DES PLANTES DE PARIS.) La famille de chevaux sauvages du Jardin des Plantes de Paris. M.V. Parvulescu. Bull. Mus. Nat. Hist. Nat. Paris, vol.1, no.5, pp.298-303, June, 1929.

WILD HORSE FOAL AT THE GARDENS. R.I. Pocock. Field, London, vol.151, p. 961, illus., June 7, 1928.

HOW OUR NEW ONAGER CAME TO THE ZOO. Bronson M. Potter. Animal Kingdom, New York Zool. Soc., vol.59, no.1, pp. 24-28, illus., Feb., 1956.

(A HINNY AT THE WARSAW ZOO.) Ein Maulesel im Warschauer Zoo. A.Rzasnicki. Zool. Garten, Leipzig, n.F., vol.10, nos. 5-6, pp.202-207, illus., Jan., 1939.

(WILD ASS OF SOUTHERN PERSIA IN THE BERLIN ZOOLOGICAL GARDEN.) Ein suedpersischer Wildesel im Berliner Zoologischen Garten. E. Schwarz. Der Zoologische Garten, Leipzig, n.F., vol.2, pts. 4-6, pp.85-94, figs.5, 1929.

EXHIBITION OF A PHOTOGRAPH OF THE FEMALE SPECIMEN OF GRÉVY'S ZEBRA LIVING IN THE JARDIN ZOOLOGIQUE D"ACCLIMATION, PARIS. Philip Lutley Sclater. Proc. Zool. Soc. London, pt.3, pp.713-714, fig.1, Oct. 1, 1899.

GRANT'S ZEBRA, MOTHER AND COLT. Philadelphia Zoo, vol.1, no.4, p.13, illus., Sep., 1938.

Museum Collections

ON A PREPARED SPECIMEN RESEMBLING EQUUS ZEBRA FREDERICI TROUESS. FROM THE COLLECTION OF THE STUTTGART "NATURALIENSAMMLUNG." Cs. G. Anghi. Ann. Mus. Nat. Hungarici, Budapest, vol.29, Pars Zool., pp.166-168, fig.1, June 3, 1935.

(THE ZEBRA OF THE MUSEUM OF NATURAL HISTORY OF ROUEN.) Le Zebre du Museum d'Histoire Naturelle de Rouen. L. Brasil, G. Pennetier. Equus Burchelli Pococki, pp.97-117, pls.6-7, 1909.

NOTES ON THE SPECIMENS OF WILD ASSES IN ENGLISH COLLECTIONS. R. Lydekker. Novitates Zool., vol.11, pp. 583-596, pls.17-20, Sep., 1904.

SPECIMEN OF TYPICAL BURCHELL'S ZEBRA IN THE UNITED STATES NATIONAL MUSEUM. Marcus Ward Lyon, Jr. Proc. U.S.Nat.Mus., vol.32, no.1505, pp.1-3, pls.1-3, Jan., 1907.

(NOTES ON SOME ZEBRAS OF THE BÂLE MUSEUM OF NATURAL HISTORY.) Notes sur quelques zèbres du Muséum d'Histoire naturelle de Bâle. J. Roux. Revue Suisse Zool., Geneve, tome 18, fasc.4, pp.917-927, pl.7, 1910.

COMPLETE LIST OF THE SPECIMENS OF SKELETONS AND SKINS OF EQUUS QUAGGA QUAGGA (GM.) PRESERVED IN THE MUSEUMS OF THE WHOLE WORLD IN 1939. Adolf Rzasnicki. Ann. Mus.Zool. Polonici, Warsaw, vol.14, no.5, pp.69-73, May 31, 1949.

(QUAGGA AND BURCHELL'S ZEBRA OF THE MUSEUM COLLECTION.) Le Couagga et le Zèbra de Burchell de la collection du Muséum. E.L.Trouessart. Bull. Mus. d'Hist. Nat., Paris, no.7, pp. 449-452, 1906.

GUIDE TO THE SPECIMENS OF THE HORSE FAMILY (EQUIDAE) EXHIBITED IN THE DEPARTMENT OF ZOOLOGY, BRITISH MUSEUM (NATURAL HISTORY) 1907. London, pp.1-42, figs.26, 1907; 2nd ed., London, pp.43, illus., 1922.

Psychology

AN INVESTIGATION OF A "MIND-READING" HORSE. J.B.Rhine, L.E.Rhine. Jour. Abnormal and Social Psychol., vol.23, no.4, pp.449-466, Jan.-Mar., 1929.

SECOND REPORT ON LADY, THE "MIND-READING" HORSE. J.B.Rhine, L.E.Rhine. Jour. Abnormal and Social Psychology, vol. 24, no.3, pp.287-292, Oct.-Dec., 1929.

Reproductive Biology

(ON THE FORMATION OF HERDS AND MATING PECULIARTIES AMONG SOLIPEDS.) Ueber Herdenbildung und Paarungseigentuemlichkeiten der Einhufer. Otto Antonius. Zeitschr. f. Tierpsychol., vol.1, pp.259-289, 1937.

OBSERVATIONS ON FOUR MULES IN MILK. Alfred Duges. Proc. U.S.Nat.Mus., vol.5, publ.278, pp.223-225, Aug. 5, 1882.

OESTROUS CYCLE IN THE MARE AND SOME ASSOCIATED PHENOMENA. E. Seaborn. Anat. Record, vol.30, pp.277-288, July 25, 1925.

ON THE PROBLEM OF STUDYING OVULATION IN THE MARE. H.I. Zhivotkov et al. Problems of Animal Husbandry, Moscow, no.3, pp.71-76, fig.1, 1936. (In Russian.)

Taxonomy

(ELEMENTS FOR A CLASSIFICATION OF LIVING EQUIDAE AFTER THEIR CRANIOLOGIC AND DENTAL CHARACTERS.) Éléments pour une classification des équidés actuels, d'après leurs caracterès craniologiques et dentaires. Ruy d'Andrade. Bull. Soc. Portugaise Sci. Nat., Lisbon, vol.12, no.32, pp.267-293, figs.6, tbls.9, pls.28-40, Oct., 1937.

(SOME DENTAL ELEMENTS FOR CLASSIFICATION OF LIVING EQUIDAE.) Alguns elementos dentarios para a classificaçao dos equideos actuais. Ruy d'Andrade. Bull. Soc. Portugaise Sci. Nat., vol.12, no.11, pp.71-85, figs.19, Jan., 1936.

(CLASSIFICATION OF PRESENT-DAY EQUIDAE.) La classification des Equidès actuels. E. Bourdelle, S. Frechkop. Mammalia, Paris, vol.14, no.4, pp.126-139, Dec., 1950.

(ZOOLOGICAL POSITION OF THE"HEMIONUS OF SYRIA" AMONG THE EQUIDAE, MAINLY IN RELATION TO THE HEMIONUS AND PREJEWALSKY'S HORSE, AFTER SKELETAL CHARACTERS.) La position zoologique de l' "hémippe de Syrie, "parmi des équides, principalement par rapport a l'hémione et au cheval de Prejewalski, d'après les caractères du squelette. E. Bourdelle. 66th Congr. Soc. Savantes, Paris, art.35, pp.193-199, 1933.

SUBSPECIFIC AND INDIVIDUAL VARIATION IN THE BURCHELL ZEBRAS. Angel Cabrera. Jour. Mamm., vol.17, no.2, pp.89-112, figs. 22, May 14, 1936.

EXTRACT OF A LETTER FROM E. L. LAYARD TO, ON A NEW ZEBRA. John Edward Gray. Proc. Zool. Soc. London, pp.417-422, 1865.

ON THE TYPE SKULL OF EQUUS LAURENTIUS HAY. Oliver P. Hay. Jour. Washington Acad. Sci., vol.17, pp.5-7, Jan.3, 1927.

REVISION OF THE GENUS OROHIPPUS (PERISSODACTYLA, EQUIDAE). David B. Kitts. Amer. Mus. Novitates, New York, vol.1864, pp.1-40, Dec. 6, 1957.

EXTRACT OF A LETTER FROM, ADDRESSED TO DR. J. E. GRAY, ON A NEW ZEBRA. Edgar Leopold Layard. Proc.Zool. Soc. London, pp.417-422, 1865.

(NEW ZEBRA SPECIES: GREVY'S ZEBRA (EQUUS GREVYI).) Une nouvelle espece de Zebre. Le Zebre de Grevy (Equus Grevyi). E. Oustalet. La Nature, vol.10, no.470, pp.12-14, figs.2, June, 1882.

SPECIES AND SUBSPECIES OF ZEBRAS. R.I. Pocock. Ann. and Mag. Nat. Hist. London, ser.6, vol.20, pp.33-52, illus., July, 1897.

(DESCRIPTION OF A NEW ZEBRA SPECIES (EQUUS FOAI) AND REMARKS ON THE CHARACTERS OF THE SPECIES OF THE SUBGENUS HIPPOTIGRIS.) Description d'une espèce nouvelle de Zèbre (Equus foai) et remarques sur les caractères des especes du sousgenre Hippotigris. J.P. Prazak, E. Trouessart. Bull. Mus.d.Hist. Nat. Paris, no.7, pp.350-354, figs. 2, 1899.

DESCRIPTION OF A NEW ZEBRA. Walter Rothschild. Proc. Zool. Soc. London, p. 691, Oct. 10, 1906.

STUDIES ON THE SYSTEMATICAL POSITION OF SPECIES BELONGING TO THE GENUS EQUUS. Edward Skorkowski. Zoologica Poloniae, vol.6, no.3, pp.283-292, 1955.

(ON THE OSTEOLOGY OF THE CARPUS OF ELASMOTHERIUM CAUCASICUM BORISSIAK.) Zur Osteologie der Handwurzel von Elasmotherium caucasicum Borissiak. W. Slodkewitsch. Ann. Soc.Paleont. Russie, vol.8, pp.83-90, pl.1, (1928-29) 1930.

(ON A NEW VARIETY OF BURCHELL'S ZEBRA (EQUUS BURCHELLI SUBSP. ZAMBESIENSIS).) Sur une variété nouvelle du Zèbre de Burchell (Equus burchelli subsp. zambesiensis). E. Trouessart. Bull. Mus. Hist.Nat.Paris, no.2, pp.63-67, Apr., 1898.

(THE SPECIFIC IDENTITY OF QUATERNARY EQUUS CABALLUS AND STILL LIVING EQUUS PRZJEWALSKII.) Sur l'identité Spécificue de l'Equus Caballus quaternaire et de l'Equus Przjewalskii encore vivant. E. Trouessart. Bull. Mus. Hist. Nat. Paris, no.7, pp.453-454, figs.5, 1906.

Brontotheriidae

THE ARTICULATED SKELETON OF A TITANOTHERIUM. (BRONTOPS DISPAR.) Erwin Hinckley Barbour. Nebraska State Mus., vol.1, bull.26, pp.235-238, fig.1, Jan., 1932.

A NEW TITANOTHERE FROM THE EOCENE OF MISSISSIPPI, WITH NOTES ON THE CORRELATION BETWEEN THE MARINE EOCENE OF THE GULF COASTAL PLAIN AND CONTINENTAL EOCENE OF THE ROCKY MOUNTAIN REGION. (NOTIOTITANOPS, N. MISSISSIPPIENSIS.) C. Lewis Gazin, J. Magruder Sullivan. Smithsonian Misc. Coll., vol. 101, no.13, publ.3679, pp.13, fig.1, pls.3, Apr.23, 1942.

NOTICE OF A NEW PALEOCENE MAMMAL, A POSSIBLE RELATIVE OF THE TITANOTHERES. James Williams Gidley. Proc. U.S. Nat. Mus., Wash., vol.52, pp. 431-435, illus., pl.36, 1917.

A NEW TITANOTHERE GENUS FROM THE UPPER EOCENE OF MONGOLIA AND NORTH AMERICA. (METATELMATHERIUM; M. CRISTATUM.) Walter Granger, William King Gregory. Bull. Amer. Mus. Nat. Hist., vol.74, addendum, pp.435-436, Oct.14, 1938.

A REVISION OF THE MONGOLIAN TITANOTHERES. Walter Granger, William King Gregory. Bull. Amer. Mus. Nat. Hist., New York, vol.80, art.10, pp.349-389, figs.11, pls.2-31, Feb.4, 1943.

EVOLUTIONARY RELATIVE GROWTH IN THE TITANOTHERES. A. H. Hersh. Amer. Nat., vol.68, no.719, pp.537-561, Nov., 1934.

VARIATION IN PALAEOSYOPS. H. H. Lane. Univ. Kansas Sci. Bull., vol.20, nos.7-21, pt.2, pp.319-326, 1932.

PRINCIPAL CHARACTERS OF THE BRONTOTHERIDAE. O. C. Marsh. Amer. Jour. Sci. and Arts, New Haven, vol.11, pp.335-340, figs.2, pls.6, Apr., 1876.

BIOLOGICAL CONCLUSIONS DRAWN FROM THE STUDY OF THE TITANOTHERES. Henry Fairfield Osborn. Science, Lancaster, n.s., vol.33, no.856, pp.825-828, May 26, 1911.

THE CRANIAL EVOLUTION OF TITANOTHERIUM. Henry Fairfield Osborn. Bull. Amer. Mus. Nat. Hist., New York, vol.8, art.9, pp.157-197, figs.13, pls.3-4, July 31, 1896.

EMBOLOTHERIUM, GEN. NOV., OF THE ULAN GOCHU, MONGOLIA. Henry Fairfield Osborn. Amer. Mus. Novitates, no.353, pp.1-20, May 30, 1929.

THE FOUR PHYLA OF OLIGOCENE TITANOTHERES. Henry Fairfeld Osborn. Bull. Amer. Mus. Nat. Hist., New York, vol.16, art.8, pp.91-109, figs.13, Feb.18, 1902.

NEW CONCEPTIONS OF SPECIES AND GENERA, AND OF CLASSIFICATION, DISCOVERED IN THE EVOLUTION OF THE TITANOTHERES. Henry Fairfield Osborn. Jour. Mam., vol.12, no.1, pp.1-12, Feb., 1931.

NEW OR LITTLE KNOWN TITANOTHERES FROM THE EOCENE AND OLIGOCENE.

Henry Fairfield Osborn. Bull. Amer. Mus. Nat. Hist., New York, vol.24, art.32, pp. 599-617, figs.21, Sept.19, 1908.

NEW TITANOTHERES OF THE HUERFANO. Henry Fairfield Osborn. Bull. Amer. Mus. Nat. Hist., vol.41, pp.557-569, figs.1-7, Dec.10, 1919.

RECENT RESULTS IN THE PHYLOGENY OF THE TITANOTHERES. Henry Fairfield Osborn. Bull. Geol. Soc. Amer. Wash., D.C., vol.25, no.3, pp.403-405, fig.1, Sept.15, 1914.

THE TITANOTHERES OF ANCIENT WYOMING, DAKOTA, AND NEBRASKA. Henry Fairfield Osborn. Monograph 55, U.S. Geol. Surv., Dept. Int., vol.1, pp. xxiv, 701, pls.1-42, figs.1-639, colored frontispiece; vol.2, pp.xi, 703-953, pls.45-236, figs.640-676, Jan.31, 1930.

UPPER EOCENE AND LOWER OLIGOCENE TITANOTHERES OF MONGOLIA. Henry Fairfield Osborn. Amer. Mus. Nov., New York, no.202, p.12, Nov.24, 1925.

NEW SPECIES OF THE GENUS TELEODUS FROM THE UPPER UINTA OF NORTH-EASTERN UTAH. (TELEODUS UINTENSIS.) O. A. Peterson. Ann. Carnegie Mus., vol.20, nos.3-4, pp.307-312, pls.4, figs.2, June, 1931.

NEW TITANOTHERES FROM THE UINTA EOCENE IN UTAH. (DIPLACODON PROGRESSUM, STHENODECTES PRISCUS.) O. A. Peterson. Annals Carnegie Mus., vol.22, nos.3-4, pp.351-361, figs.3, pls. 16-18, Apr.10, 1934.

COMPLETE SKULL OF A TITANOTHERE FROM THE LOWER OLIGOCENE OF SASKATCHEWAN. Loris S. Russell. Bull. Geol. Soc. Amer., (Abstracts), vol. 49, no.12, pt.2, p.1920, Dec.1, 1938.

TITANOTHERES FROM THE LOWER OLIGOCENE CYPRESS HILLS FORMATION OF SASKATCHEWAN. Loris S. Russell. Trans. Roy. Soc. Canada, Ottawa, ser.3, sect.4, vol.34, pp.89-100, pls.5, 1940.

AN EOCENE TITANOTHERE FROM SAN DIEGO COUNTY, CALIFORNIA, WITH REMARKS ON THE AGE OF THE POWAY CONGLOMERATE. Chester Stock. Proc. Nat. Acad. Sci., Wash., vol.23, no.2, pp. 48-53, pl.1, Feb., 1937.

TITANOTHERE FROM THE SESPE FORMATION, NORTH OF THE OJAI VALLEY, CALIFORNIA. Chester Stock. Proc. Geol. Soc. Amer., 1937, pp.297-298, June, 1938.

A TITANOTHERE FROM THE TYPE SESPE OF CALIFORNIA. Chester Stock. Proc. Nat. Acad. Sci., Wash., vol.24, no.11, pp. 507-512, figs.2, pl.1, Nov., 1938.

TITANOTHERE REMAINS FROM THE SESPE OF CALIFORNIA. Chester Stock. Proc. Nat. Acad. Sci. Wash., vol.21, no. 7, pp.456-462, pls.2, July, 1935.

TITANOTHERES FROM THE TITUS CANYON FORMATION, CALIFORNIA. Chester Stock. Proc. Nat. Acad. Sci., Wash., vol.22, no.11, pp.656-661, pls.2, Nov.30, 1936.

## Chalicotheriidae

AN AFRICAN CHALICOTHERE. C. W. Andrews. Nature, vol.112, p.696, Nov.10, 1923.

OCCURRENCE OF RUSSIAN CHALICOTHERES IN MONGOLIA. E. I. Belyaeva. Proc. Paleo. Inst., Acad. Sci. USSR, vol. 55, pp.44-84, illus., 1954.

THE CHALICOTHERES AS A BIOLOGICAL TYPE. A. Borissiak. Amer. Jour. Sci., New Haven, vol.243, pp.667-679, figs.4, Dec., 1945.

CHALICOTHERES--PHYLLOTILLON BETPAKDALENSIS (FLEROW) AS A BIOLOGICAL TYPE. A. Borissiak. Zool. Jour. USSR, Moscow, vol.23, no.4, pp.125-134, figs.4, 1944. (English summary.)

A NEW CHALICOTHERE FROM THE TERTIARY OF KAZAKHSTAN. (PHYLLOTILLON BETPAKDALENSIS.) A. A. Borissiak. Akad. Nauk SSSR, Trudy Paleontologicheskii Institut, Moscou, vol. 13, no.3, pp.1-134, figs.37, pls.14, 1946.

OBSERVATIONS ON THE GENUS POSTSCHIZOTHERIUM. T. Chardin. Bull. Geol. Soc. China, vol.19, pp.257-267, 1939.

CHALICOTHERES FROM MONGOLIA AND CHINA IN THE AMERICAN MUSEUM. Edwin H. Colbert. Bull. Amer. Mus. Nat. Hist., vol.67, art.8, pp.353-387, figs.15, Nov.7, 1934.

DISTRIBUTIONAL AND PHYLOGENETIC STUDIES ON INDIAN FOSSIL MAMMALS. III. A CLASSIFICATION OF THE CHALICOTHERIOIDEA. Edwin H. Colbert. Amer. Mus. Novitates no.798, pp.15, May 8, 1935.

(CAN CHALICOTHERIUM AND RELATED GENERA BE RECONSTRUCTED?) Lassen sich Chalicotherium und verwandte Gattungen schon rekonstruieren? W. O. Dietrich. Centralbl. Miner., Geol., Palaeont., vol.6, pp.366-376, 1928.

(MACROTHERIUM OGGENHAUSENSE N. SP.) Macrotherium oggenhausense n. sp. W. O. Dietrich. Separat-Abdruck aus dem Centralblatt f. Min., etc., no.6, pp.190-191, fig.1, 1923.

THE CASE OF THE CURIOUS CLAWS. (CHALICOTHERES) John A. Dorr, Jr. Carnegie Mag., Pittsburgh, vol.26, no.3, pp.98-101, illus., Mar., 1952.

MACROTHERIUM SALINUM, SP. N., A NEW CHALICOTHERE FROM INDIA. C. Forster-Cooper. Ann. and Mag. Nat. Hist., ser.9, vol.10, pp.542-544, figs.3, Nov., 1922.

THE OSTEOLOGY OF THE CHALICOTHEROIDEA, WITH SPECIAL REFERENCE TO A MOUNTED SKELETON OF MOROPUS ELATUS MARSH, NOW INSTALLED IN THE CARNEGIE MUSEUM. William Jacob Holland, O. A. Peterson. Pittsburgh, Board of trustees of the Carnegie Inst., (Memoirs of the Carnegie Mus., vol.3, no.2) pp.189-411, illus., pl.XLVIII-LXXVII, 1913.

A FEMUR OF A (?) CHALICOTHERE FROM THE PLIOCENE OF UPPER BURMA. Dirk Albert Hooijer. Jour. Mam., vol.32, no. 4, pp.467-468, Nov.19, 1951.

ARTIONYX, A NEW GENUS OF ANCYLOPODA. Henry Fairfield Osborn, Jacob L. Wortman. Bull. Amer. Mus. Nat. Hist., New York, vol.5, art.1, pp.1-18, figs.5, Feb., 1893.

OBSERVATIONS ON THE SKELETONS OF MOROPUS COOKI IN THE AMERICAN MUSEUM. Henry Fairfield Osborn. Bull. Geol. Soc. Amer., Wash., D.C., vol.29, no.1, pp.131-133, Mar.31, 1918.

SEVENTEEN SKELETONS OF MOROPUS; PROBABLE HABITS OF THIS ANIMAL. Henry Fairfield Osborn. Proc. Nat. Acad. Sci., vol.5, pp.250-252, July, Aug.26, 1919.

NEW OBSERVATIONS ON THE GENUS POSTSCHIZOTHERIUM VON KOENIGSWALD. P. Teilhard de Chardin. Bull. Geol. Soc. China, Pehpei, Chungking, vol. 19, no.3, pp.257-267, figs.4, Dec., 1939.

NEW REMAINS OF POSTSCHIZOTHERIUM FROM S. E. SHANSI. P. Teilhard de Chardin, E. Licent. Bull. Geol. Soc. China, Nanking, vol.15, no.3, pp.421-427, figs.3, Sept., 1936.

## Helaletidae

A NEW HEPTODON FROM THE WIND RIVER OF WYOMING. (HEPTODON BROWNORUM.) Henry Seton. Proc. New England Zool. Club, vol.12, pp.45-48, May 29, 1931.

## Tapiridae (Extinct and Fossil)

A PRIMITIVE TAPIR-LIKE (MAMMAL) FROM THE PALEOGENE OF MONGOLIA. (ERGILIA, E. PACHYPTERNA.) Vera Gromova. Proc. Paleo. Inst., Acad. Sci. USSR, vol.41, pp.99-119, illus., 1952.

(TAPIR REMAINS FROM THE AQUITANE OF ULM AND MAINZ.) Die Tapirreste aus dem Aquitan von Ulm und Mainz. Ralph Koenigswald. Palaeontographica, Stuttgart, vol.73, pp.1-29, fig.1, 1930.

TAPIR REMAINS FROM LATE CENOZOIC BEDS OF THE PACIFIC COAST REGION. John C. Merriam. Univ. California Publ., Berkeley, Bull. Dept. Geol., vol.7, no.9, pp.169-175, figs.2, Jan.8, 1913.

(ON A CRANIUM OF TAPIRUS (MEGATAPIRUS) AUGUSTUS, GRANGER, FROM YEN-CHING-KAL, SZECHUAN, CHINA.) Ueber einen Schaedel von Tapirus (Megatapirus) augustus, Granger, aus Yen-Ching-Kao, Szechuan, China. Paul V. Rautenfeld. Acta Zoologica, vol.9, pp.425-444, figs.12, 1928.

("LISTRIODON DUPUYI" AND HIS RELATIONS WITH THE TAPIRS.) "Listriodon dupuyi" y sus relaciones con los tapires. Carlos Rusconi. Anal. Soc. Cient. Argentina, Buenos Aires, entrega II, vol.123, pp. 87-88, Feb., 1937.

A NEW TAPIR FROM THE LOWER MIOCENE OF WYOMING. (MIOTAPIRUS M. HARRISONENSIS.) Erich Maren Schlaikjer. Bull. Mus. Comp. Zool., Harvard College, vol.80, no.4, pp.231-251, figs.4, Jan., 1937.

NOTES ON PLEISTOCENE AND RECENT TAPIRS. George Gaylord Simpson. Bull. Amer. Mus. Nat. Hist., New York, vol. 86, art.2, pp.31-81, pls.5-10, Nov.12, 1945.

THE CALIFORNIA TAPIR TAPIRUS HAYSII CALIFORNICUS MERRIAM FROM SANTA BARBARA COUNTY, CALIFORNIA. R. A. Stirton, H. W. Weddle. Univ. Calif. Publ. Bull. Dept. Geol. Sci., vol.18, no.7, pp.225-226, fig.1, 1929.

TAPIRUS HAYSII OF OKLAHOMA. J. Willis Stovall, C. Stuart Johnston. Amer. Midland Nat., Notre Dame, vol.15, no.1, pp.92-93, fig.1, Jan., 1934.

ANCESTORS OF THE TAPIR FROM THE LOWER MIOCENE OF DAKOTA. J. L. Wortman, Charles Earle. Bull. Amer. Mus. Nat. Hist., vol.5, art.11, pp.160-180, figs.7, Aug.18, 1893.

## Tapiridae (Recent)

(MOUNTAIN TAPIR.) Bergtapire. Wilhelm Eigener. Zeitschrift fuer Saeugetierkunde, Berlin, vol.19, no.3, pp.178-180, Dec.31, 1954.

RECENT AND FOSSIL TAPIRS. J. B. Hatcher. Amer. Jour. Sci., New Haven, ser.4, vol.1, no.3, pp.161-180, figs.2, pls.2-5, Mar., 1896.

AMERICA'S LEAST KNOWN BIG GAME ANIMAL, THE GIANT TAPIR. (TAPIRELLA) W. T. Hornaday. Zool. Soc. Bull., vol. 26, no.1, pp.17-19, Jan., 1923.

TAPIRS, SO FAR AS KNOWN. W. T. Hornaday. Bull. New York Zool. Soc., vol.32, no.2, pp.43-53, figs.10, Mar.-Apr., 1929.

(MY ENCOUNTER WITH A MOUNTAIN TAPIR (TAPIRUS PINCHAQUE ROULIN).) Meine Begegnung mit einem Bergtapir (Tapirus pinchaque Roulin). Elisabeth Naundorff. Zool. Garten, Leipzig, N.F., vol.20, no.1, pp.51-52, illus., 1953.

ON THE TAPIR (TAPIR AMERICANUS, GMEL.). R. Owen. Proc. Comm. Sci. and Corres. Zool. Soc. Lond., pt.1, p.94, 1830-1831.

TRUDY THE TAPIR. Ken Stott, Jr. San Diego Zoonooz, vol.17, no.10, pp.3, 4, fig. 1, Nov., 1944.

### Anatomy

(ON THE DENTITION OF TAPIRUS AMERICANUS.) Ueber das Gebiss von Tapirus americanus. Adloff. Anat. Anzeiger, vol.66, pp.132-136, fig.1, Sept. 4, 1928.

EXHIBITION OF THE SKULL OF A TAPIR (ELASMOGNATHUS BAIRDI GILL). W. H. Flower. Proc. Zool. Soc. Lond., p.240, 1867.

SHORT COMPARATIVE NOTES ON THE ANATOMY OF THE INDIAN TAPIR. Arkiv. Zool., Upsala, vol.6, no.15, pp.15, figs.7, June 3, 1910.

(THE RESPIRATORY MECHANISM OF TAPIRUS INDICUS CUV.) Sur l'appareil respiratoire du Tapirus indicus Cuv. M. H. Neuville. Bull. Mus. Nat. Hist. Nat. Paris, ser.2, vol.5, no.5, pp.346-352, June, 1933.

ON THE ANATOMY OF THE AMERICAN TAPIR (TAPIR AMERICANUS, GMEL.). R. Owen. Proc. Comm. Sci. and Corres. Zool. Soc. Lond., pt.1, pp.161-162-163, 1830-1831.

EXHIBITION OF A SKULL OF TAPIRUS BAIRDI FROM NICARAGUA. Philip L. Sclater. Proc. Zool. Soc. Lond., p.473, 1867.

EXHIBITION OF TWO SKULLS OF BAIRD'S TAPIR (TAPIRUS BAIRDI) FROM MEXICO. Philip L. Sclater. Proc. Zool. Soc. Lond., p.89, 1874.

ON THE STRUCTURE OF THE TEETH OF THE AMERICAN AND INDIAN TAPIRS. John Tomes. Proc. Zool. Soc. Lond., pt.19, pp.121-124, 1851.

CONTRIBUTIONS TO THE ANATOMY OF THE TAPIR. H. N. Turner. Proc. Zool. Soc. Lond., pt.18, pp.102-106, figs.2, 1850.

Asia

ON A BLACK VARIETY OF THE MALAY TAPIR (TAPIRUS INDICUS). K. Kuiper. Proc. Zool. Soc. Lond., pp.425-426, pl.1, July, 1926.

NIP AND TUCK AND THEIR PRIMITIVE CLAN. (MALAYAN TAPIR) Edalee Orcutt. San Diego Zoonooz, vol.21, no.5, pp.4-6, illus., May, 1948.

MALAY TAPIR. Colin Campbell Sanborn. Zoonooz, Zool. Soc. San Diego, vol.28, no.5, pp.7-10, illus., May, 1955.

NOTES ON THE MALAY TAPIR AND OTHER GAME ANIMALS IN SIAM. Colin Campbell Sanborn, Rush Watkins. 1950.

NOTES ON THE TAPIRS INTRODUCED INTO JAPAN. Haruo Takashima. Misc. Repts. Yamashina's Inst. Ornithol. and Zool., Tokyo, no.2, pp.78-82, illus., June, 1953. (In Japanese, with English summary.)

THE MALAY TAPIR (TAPIRUS INDICUS.). W. S. Thom. Jour. Bombay Nat. Hist. Soc., vol.38, no.3, pp.479-483, pl.1, Apr.15, 1936.

Early Development

(CONTRIBUTIONS TO THE EARLY DEVELOPMENT OF THE INDIAN TAPIR (RHINOCHOERUS INDICUS CUV.).) Beitraege zur Jugendentwicklung des Schabrackentapirs (Rhinochoerus indicus (Cuv.)). Ingo Krumbiegel. Zool. Garten, n.F., Leipzig, vol.8, pt.4-6, pp.96-99, figs.1-6, Jan., 1936.

(EMBRYONIC ADDITIONS TO "TAPIRUS AMERICANUS.") Anexos Embrionarios do "Tapirus americanus." Jose Oria. Bol. Mus. Nac. Rio de Janeiro, vol.13, nos.1-2, pp.1-61, figs.14, June, 1937.

(REPRODUCTION, BREEDING, AND EARLY DEVELOPMENT OF THE INDIAN TAPIR.) Zur Fortpflanzung, Aufzucht, und Jugendentwicklung des Schabrackentapirs. Karl Max Schneider. Zool. Garten, Leipzig, n.F., vol.8, pts.4-6, pp. 83-96, figs.1-14, Jan., 1936.

PHOTO OF BRAZILIAN TAPIR AND ITS YOUNG. Fauna, Phila., vol.8, no.3, pp. 66, Sept., 1946.

South America

BREEDING OF THE BRAZILIAN TAPIR. A. B. Baker. Jour. Mam., vol.1, no.3, pp.143-144, May, 1920.

COMING FROM ECUADOR: GIANT HUMMERS AND ANOTHER MOUNTAIN TAPIR. Emy Cordier. Animal Kingdom, New York Zool. Soc., vol.55, no.2, pp.51-55, illus., Mar.-Apr., 1952.

TAPIRS: STRANGE MAMMALS NATIVE TO ASIA AND TROPICAL AMERICA FROM MEXICO SOUTH. Philip Hershkovitz. Chicago Nat. Hist. Mus. Bull., vol.20, no. 9, pp.6-7, illus., Sept., 1949.

REMARKS ON THE HAIRY TAPIR (TAPIRUS ROULINI) OF THE COLUMBIAN ANDES. Philip L. Sclater. Proc. Zool. Soc. Lond., pp.51-52, 1870.

LETTERS FROM, CONCERNING THE HAIRY TAPIR (TAPIRUS ROULINI) OF THE HIGHLANDS OF COLUMBIA. Robert B. White. Proc. Zool. Soc. Lond., pp.51-52, 1870.

(TAPIR IN AMERICA.) Tapir de America. Caza, Tiro y Pesca, Mexico, vol.20, nos. 206-207, pp.11-15, illus., Jan.-Feb., 1950.

Taxonomy

A NEW GENERIC NAME FOR THE ASIATIC TAPIR. E. A. Goldman. Proc. Biol. Soc. Wash., vol.26, pp.65-66, Mar. 22, 1913.

TAPIRELLA DOWII A SYNONYM. George O. Goodwin. Jour. Mam., vol.27, no.1, p.91, Mar.14, 1946.

DESCRIPTION OF A YOUNG TAPIR FROM THE PERUVIAN AMAZONS. John E. Gray. Proc. Zool. Soc. Lond., pp.624-625, 1872.

NOTES ON A NEW SPECIES OF TAPIR (TAPIRUS LEUCOGENYS) FROM THE SNOWY REGIONS OF THE CORDILLERAS OF ECUADOR, AND ON THE YOUNG SPOTTED TAPIRS OF TROPICAL AMERICA. John E. Gray. Proc. Zool. Soc. Lond., pp.483-492, fig.1, pls.21-22, Mar.5, 1872.

(A NEW TAPIR FROM BRAZIL AND EASTERN BOLIVIA.) Ein neuer Tapir aus Brasilien und Ostbolivien. (Tapirus anulipes sp. nov.) Rudolf von Hermann. Mitteil. Zool. Mus. Berlin, vol.11, pp.167-168, Feb., 1924.

MAMMALS OF NORTHERN COLOMBIA. PRELIMINARY REPORT NO. 7: TAPIRS (GENUS TAPIRUS), WITH A SYSTEMATIC REVIEW OF AMERICAN SPECIES. Philip Hershkovitz. Proc. U.S. Nat. Mus., Wash., vol.103, no.3329, pp.465-496, illus., May 18, 1954.

Zoo Collections

THE MOUNTAIN TAPIR IN THE BRONX ZOO. Lee S. Crandall. Animal Kingdom, New York, vol.54, no.1, pp.2-8, illus., Jan.-Feb., 1951.

EXHIBITION OF, AND REMARKS UPON, A DRAWING OF A TAPIR LIVING IN THE SOCIETY'S GARDENS. Philip L. Sclater. Proc. Zool. Soc. Lond., pt.3, p.391, pl.23, Oct.1, 1882.

REPORT ON THE ADDITIONS TO THE SOCIETY'S MENAGERIE IN MAY 1878, AND REMARKS ON TAPIRUS ROULINI. Philip L. Sclater. Proc. Zool. Soc. Lond., pp.631-632, pl.39, 1878.

## Hyrachyidae

REVISION OF THE HYRACHYIDAE. Horace Elmer Wood, 2nd. Bull. Amer. Mus. Nat. Hist., vol.67, no.5, pp.181-295, figs.51, pls.20-24, May 26, 1934.

REVISION OF THE HYRACHYIDAE. Horace Elmer Wood, 2nd. Bull. Geol. Soc. Amer., vol.40, no.1, p.221, Mar., 1929.

## Hyracodontidae

NEW MATERIALS ON TERTIARY RHINOCEROS-LIKE (MAMMALS) FROM KAZAKHSTAN. E. I. Belyaeva. Proc. Paleo. Inst., Acad. Sci. USSR, vol.47, pp.24-54, illus., 1954.

PRIMITIVE RHINOCEROS-LIKE (MAMMALS) FROM MONGOLIA. E. I. Belyaeva. Proc. Paleo. Inst., Acad. Sci. USSR., vol.41, pp. 120-143, illus., 1952.

NEW SPECIES OF HYRACODON. Edward L. Troxell. Amer. Jour. Sci., Ser.5, vol. 2, no.7, pp.34-40, figs.5, July, 1921.

HYRACODON PETERSONI, A NEW CURSORIAL RHINOCEROS FROM THE LOWER OLIGOCENE. Horace Elmer Wood. Ann. Carnegie Mus., vol.16, no.2, pp.315-318, fig.1, pl.26, Mar.18, 1926.

## Amynodontidae

METAMYNODON BUGTIENSIS, SP. N. FROM THE DERA BUGTI DEPOSITS OF BALUCHISTAN.--PRELIMINARY NOTICE. C. Forster Cooper. Ann. and Mag. Nat. Hist., ser.9, vol.9, pp.617-620, figs.2, May, 1922.

AMPHIBIOUS RHINOCEROSES (AMYNODONTIDAE) OF MONGOLIA. Vera Gromova. Proc. Paleo. Inst., Acad. Sci. USSR, vol. 55, pp.85-189, illus., 1954.

CADURCOTHERIUM ARDYNENSE, OLIGOCENE, MONGOLIA. Henry Fairfield Osborn. Amer. Mus. Nov., New York, pp.4, figs.3, Nov.11, 1924.

CADURCOTHERIUM FROM MONGOLIA. Henry Fairfield Osborn. Amer. Mus. Nov., no.92, pp.1-2, Oct.19, 1923.

AMYNODON MONGOLIENSIS FROM THE UPPER EOCENE OF MONGOLIA. Henry Fairfield Osborn. Amer. Mus. Nov. , no. 859, pp.9, figs.6, June 8, 1936.

AN AMYNODONT SKULL FROM THE SESPE DEPOSITS, CALIFORNIA. Chester Stock. Proc. Nat. Acad. Sci., vol.19, no. 8, pp.762-767, 1933.

EOCENE AMYNODONTS FROM SOUTHERN CALIFORNIA. Chester Stock. Proc. Nat. Acad. Sci., Wash., vol.25, no.6, pp.270-275, pls.1-2, June, 1939.

NEW AMYNODONTS IN THE MARSH COLLECTION. Edward L. Troxell. Amer. Jour. Sci., N. H., vol.2, no.9, pp.21-34, figs.7, July, 1921.

A NEW, LOWER OLIGOCENE, AMYNODONT RHINOCEROS. Horace Elmer Wood, 2nd. Jour. Mam., vol.18, no.1, pp.93-94, fig.1, Feb.14, 1937.

"ORTHOGENESIS" IN AMYNODONT RHINOCEROSES. Horace Elmer Wood, 2nd. Bull. Geol. Soc. Amer. (Abstracts), vol. 49, no.12, pt.2, p.1924, Dec.1, 1938.

## Rhinocerotidae

NOTES ON RHINOCEROS SUMATRENSIS, CUVIER. John Anderson. Proc. Zool. Soc. Lond., pp.129-132, 1872.

THE LESSER ONE-HORNED RHINOCEROS. Thomas Barbour, Glover M. Allen. Jour. Mam., vol.13, no.2, pp.144-149, pl.11, May, 1932.

THE SONDAICUS RHINOCEROS. A. Katherine Berger. Nat. Hist., New York, vol. 34, no.1, pp.97-99, illus., Jan.-Feb., 1934.

FURTHER NOTES ON RHINOCEROS. Maurice Burton. Illus. London News, vol. 137, no.3566, p.344, illus., Aug.27, 1955.

THE WHITE RHINOCEROS. Edmund Heller. Smithsonian Misc. Coll., publ.2180, vol. 61, no.1, pp.77, pls.31, Oct.11, 1913.

GENE DISPERSAL AND THE ETHOLOGY OF THE RHINOCEROITIDAE. G. E. Hutchinson, S. Dillon Ripley. Evolution, Lancaster, vol.8, no.2, pp.178-179, June, 1954.

RECENT AND HISTORICAL NOTES ON THE SQUARE-LIPPED RHINOCEROS (CERATOTHERIUM SIMUM). Herbert Lang. Jour. Mam., vol.4, no.3, pp.155-163, Aug.10, 1923.

(RHINOCEROSES.) Les rhinoceros. L. Lavauden. La Terre et la Vie (Revue d' Hist. Nat.), vol.2, no.9, pp.507-519, illus., Sept., 1932.

KEEPING PACE WITH A RHINO. Marcuswell Maxwell. Field, London, vol.172, no.4471, pp.552-553, illus., Sept.3, 1938.

(ON RHINOCEROS INERMIS LESSON.) Ueber Rhinoceros inermis Lesson. W. Peters. Nat. Hist., vol.58, 1836; Monats. Koen. Akad. Wiss, Berlin, pp.68-71, pls. 3, Feb.19, 1877.

MONSTER OF THE MIST FORESTS. Ken Stott, Jr. Nat. Hist., New York, vol.59, no.1, pp.20-23, illus., Jan., 1950.

MY FIRST ENCOUNTER WITH A BLACK RHINO. P. D. Swanepoel. African Wildlife, Johannesburg, vol.9, no.3, pp.209-210, illus., Sept., 1955.

A FEW NOTES ABOUT THE FIVE RHINOCEROS OF THE WORLD. W. S. Thom. Jour. Bombay Nat. Hist. Soc., vol.44, no.2, pp.257-274, Dec., 1943.

THE LIVING RHINOCEROSES. Frederick A. Ulmer, Jr. Fauna, Phila., vol.3, no.1, pp.2-11, illus., Mar., 1941.

Africa

(NOTES ON THE OCCURRENCE OF THE RHINOCEROS IN THE OUHAM REGION (UBANGI-SHARI). Notes sur la presence du Rhinoceros dans la region de l'Ouham (Oubangui-Chari). M. Anna. Mammalia, Paris, vol.14, nos.1-2, pp.26-28, Mar.-June, 1950.

(NOTES ON THE MAMMALS OF THE FRENCH AFRICA EQUATOR (A RHINOCEROS OF THE FOREST?).) Notes sur les mammiferes de l'equateur Africain Francais. (Un Rhinoceros de Foret?) L. Blancou. Mammalia, Paris, vol.18, no.4, pp.358-363, Dec., 1954. (English summary.)

(NOTES ON THE MAMMALS OF UBANGI-SHARI. THE RHINOCEROS.) Notes sur les mammiferes de l'Oubangui-Chari. Les rhinoceros. L. Blancou. Mammalia, Paris, vol.2, no.3, pp.111-119, map, Sept., 1938.

THE EXTINCT AND LIVING SUBFAMILIES OF AFRICAN RHINOCEROTIDAE. P.E.P. Deraniyagala. Spolia Zeylanica, Bull. Nat. Mus. Ceylon, vol.27, pt.1, pp.13-14, illus., Oct.24, 1953.

ON THE AFRICAN RHINOCEROSES. W.H. Drummond. Proc. Zool. Soc. Lond., pp. 109-114, 1876.

(A RHINOCEROS FOETUS OF THE SONDE.) Sur un foetus de rhinoceros de la Sonde. Serge Frechkop. Bull. Inst. Roy. Sci. Nat. Belgique, Bruxelles, vol.27, no.2, pp.7, Jan., 1951.

NOTICE OF A PRESUMED NEW SPECIES OF RHINOCEROS FROM SOUTH AFRICA. John E. Gray. Proc. Zool. Soc. Lond., pt.21, pp.46-47, 1853.

ZULULAND'S WHITE RHINOS. H. Grote. Zool. Garten, Leipzig, n.F., vol.2, nos. 10-12, p.342, Mar., 1930.

(RHINOCEROS SIMUS GERMANO-AFRICANUS N. SUBSP. FROM OLDOWAY.) Rhinoceros simus germano-africanus n. subsp. aus Oldoway. Max Hilzhiemer. Aus Wissensch. Ergebnisse der Oldoway-Expedition von Dr. H. Ruk, N.F., Heft 2, pp.47-79, pl.4, 1925.

CONTRIBUTIONS TO THE STUDY OF SOME AFRICAN MAMMALS. (DICEROS BICORNIS (LINNAEUS)) A. Tindell Hopwood. Proc. Linnean Soc. Lond., 150th Sess., pt.1, p. 49, Dec.31, 1937.

CONTRIBUTIONS TO THE STUDY OF SOME AFRICAN MAMMALS. II. THE SUBSPECIES OF THE BLACK RHINOCEROS, DICEROS BICORNIS (LINNAEUS), DEFINED BY THE PROPORTIONS OF THE SKULL. A. Tindell Hopwood. Jour. Linnean Soc. Lond., vol.40, no.273, pp.447-457, tables 4, pls.10-11, 1939.

(ZOOGEOGRAPHICAL STUDIES ON THE BARBARY. THE PERISSADACTYLS. 1. THE RHINOCEROSES. Etudes de géographie zoologique sur la Berbérie. Les Périssadactyles. 1. Les rhinocéros. L. Joleaud. Archiv. Zool. Ital., vol.16, pt.1-2, pp.680-686, 1931.

THE WHITE RHINOCEROS OF THE BELGIAN CONGO. (GENERAL ACCOUNT OF HABITS, PHYSICAL FEATURES, DISTRIBUTION, HABITAT.) Herbert Lang. Zool. Soc. Bull., vol.23, pp.67-92, figs., July, 1920.

WITH THE WHITE RHINOCEROS IN ZULULAND. C. T. Astley Maberly. Jour. Soc. Preservation Fauna of Empire, Hertford, n.s., pt.34, pp.52-55, illus., Aug., 1938.

COMMENTS ON THE BLACK AND SQUARE-LIPPED RHINOCEROS SPECIES IN AFRICA. S. Dillon Ripley. Ecology, 39 (1): 172-174, Jan., 1958.

(THE CONGO RHINOCEROS.) Les rhinoceros congolais. H. Schouteden. Rev. Zool. Africaine, vol.15, fasc.2, Bull. Cercle Zool. Congolais, pp.19-31, illus., June, 1927.

THE BLACK RHINO OF THE LADO. (GENERAL ACCOUNT OF HABITS AND CHARACTERISTICS.) C. H. Stigand. Forest and Stream, vol.89, pp.604-605, 626-627, Nov., 1919.

THE WHITE RHINO OF THE LADO. (HABITS AND CHARACTERISTICS.) C. H. Stigand. Forest and Stream, vol. 89, pp.538-539, Oct., 1919.

THE WHITE RHINOCEROS ON THE UPPER NILE. Oldfield Thomas. Nature, Lond., vol.62, p.599, Oct.18, 1900.

(THE WHITE RHINOCEROS OF THE SUDAN (RHINOCEROS SIMUS COTTONI).) Le Rhinoceros blanc du Soudan (Rhinoceros simus cottoni). E. L. Trouessart. Proc. Zool. Soc. Lond., pp.198-200, pl. 29-31, June, 1909.

Anatomy

(PARTIAL REPRODUCTION IN A HORSE OF THE TYPE OF UPPER TEETH OF RHINOCEROTIDAE.) Reproduction partielle chez un cheval du type dentaire jugal superieur des Rhinocerotidae. J. Anthony. Mammalia, Paris, vol.5, no.3-4, pp.94-98, figs.3, pl. 7, Sept.-Dec., 1941.

NOTES ON THE LESSER ONE-HORNED RHINOCEROS, RHINOCEROS SONDAICUS. 1. A SKULL OF RHINOCEROS SONDAICUS IN THE AMERICAN MUSEUM OF NATURAL HISTORY. T. Donald Carter, John Eric Hill. Amer. Mus. Novitates, New York, no.1206, pp.3, illus., Nov.12, 1942.

THE ANATOMY OF A TWENTY-TWO MILLIMETRE EMBRYO OF THE AFRICAN RHINOCEROS (RHINOCEROS BICORNIS). J. Davies. Proc. Zool. Soc. Lond., vol. 122, pt.3, pp.593-613, illus., pls.6, Nov., 1952.

NOTES ON THE CRANIAL AND DENTAL CHARACTERS OF A SPECIMEN OF RHINOCEROS SONDAICUS DESM. H. H. Finlayson. Proc. Zool. Soc. Lond., vol. 120, pt.1, pp.151-154, May 16, 1950.

ON SOME CRANIAL AND DENTAL CHARACTERS OF THE EXISTING SPECIES OF RHINOCEROSES. William H. Flower. Proc. Zool. Soc. Lond., pp.443-457, figs. 4, May 16, 1876.

ON THE SKULL OF A RHINOCEROS (R. LASIOTIS, SCL.) FROM INDIA. William H. Flower. Proc. Zool. Soc. Lond., pp.634-636, 1878.

ON THE MALE GENERATIVE ORGANS OF THE SUMATRAN RHINOCEROS (CERATORHINUS SUMATRENSIS). W. A. Forbes. Trans. Zool. Soc. Lond., vol.11, pt.4, no. 1, pp.107-109, pl.1, Apr., 1881.

(NOTES ON THE MAMMALS. XXXVIII. A RHINOCEROS FOETUS OF THE SONDE.) Notes sur les mammiferes. XXXVIII. Sur un foetus de rhinoceros de la Sonde. Serge Frechkop. Bull. Inst. Roy. Sci. Nat. Belgique, vol.27, no.2, pp.1-7, pls. 1-4, Jan., 1941.

(INVESTIGATIONS OF THE TELENCEPHALON OF THE RHINOCERIDAE.) Recherches sur le télencéphale des Rhinoceridae. Madeleine Friant. Proc. Zool. Soc. Lond., vol.120, pt.2, pp.337-347, figs.9, Aug.30, 1950.

NOTICE OF A MEMOIR ON THE BRAIN OF THE SUMATRAN RHINOCEROS. Alfred Henry Garrod. Proc. Zool. Soc. Lond., pt. 3, pp.533, 1877.

ON SOME POINTS IN THE VISERAL ANATOMY OF THE RHINOCEROS OF THE SUNDERBUNDS (RHINOCEROS SONDAICUS). Alfred Henry Garrod. Proc. Zool. Soc. Lond., pt.4, pp.707-711, figs.3, 1877.

ON THE DEATH OF A RHINOCEROS IN THE SOCIETY'S GARDENS, AND ON SOME POINTS IN ITS ANATOMY. Alfred Henry Garrod. Proc. Zool. Soc. Lond., p.2, 1874.

ON THE VISCERAL ANATOMY OF THE SUMATRAN RHINOCEROS (CERATORHINUS SUMATRENSIS). Alfred Henry Garrod. Proc. Zool. Soc. Lond., pp.92-104, figs.8, 1873.

ON THE DENTITION OF RHINOCEROSES (RHINOCEROTES), AND ON THE CHARACTERS AFFORDED BY THEIR SKULLS. John E. Gray. Ann. and Mag. Nat. Hist., Lond., ser.4, vol.11, no.65, pp.356-361, May, 1873.

ON THE INCISOR TEETH OF THE AFRICAN RHINOCEROS. John E. Gray. Proc. Zool. Soc. Lond., p.225, 1869.

(STUDIES OF THE UPPER DENTITION OF THE WOOLLY RHINOCEROS RHINOCEROS LENENSIS PALLAS (ANTIQUITATIS BLUMENB.).) Studien am Oberkiefergebiss des wollharigen Nashorns Rhinoceros lenensis Pallas (antiquitatis Blumenb.). E. Jacobshagen. Palaeont. Zeitschr., vol. 15, no.4, pp.246-279, figs.25, Dec.31, 1933.

(ON THE STRUCTURE OF THE RHINOCEROS PENIS.) Zur Gestalt des Nashorn-Penis. Koenraad Kuper, Karl Max Schneider. Zool. Garten, N.F., vol.12, nos.4-6, pp.288-291, illus., Dec., 1940.

THE NASAL SEPTUM IN EXISTING ASIATIC RHINOCEROSES. R. I. Pocock. Ann. and Mag. Nat. Hist., Lond., ser.11, vol.12, no.89, pp.341-344, fig.1, Nov.16, 1945.

THE PREMAXILLAE IN THE ASIATIC RHINOCEROSES. R. I. Pocock. Ann. and Mag. Nat. Hist., Lond., ser.11, vol. 11, pp.834-842, figs.3, Dec., 1944.

A SEXUAL DIFFERENCE IN THE SKULLS OF ASIATIC RHINOCEROSES. R. I. Pocock. Proc. Zool. Soc. Lond., vol.115, pts.3-4, pp.319-322, Feb., 1946.

SOME CRANIAL AND DENTAL CHARACTERS OF THE EXISTING SPECIES OF ASIATIC RHINOCEROSES. R. I. Pocock. Proc. Zool. Soc. Lond., vol.114, pt.4, pp.437-450, figs.5, Mar., 1945.

SOME STRUCTURAL VARIATIONS IN THE SECOND UPPER PREMOLAR OF THE LESSER ONE-HORNED RHINOCEROS (RHINOCEROS SONDAICUS). R. I. Pocock. Proc. Zool. Soc. Lond., vol.115, pts.3-4, pp.306-309, fig.1, Feb., 1946.

EXHIBITION OF A TRACING OF THE OUTLINE OF A SKULL OF THE ADULT MALE RHINOCEROS SUMATRANUS, ON BEHALF OF MR. E. BLYTH, CORR. MEMB. Philip L. Sclater. Proc. Zool. Soc. Lond., pt.30, p.1, 1862.

NOTE ON THE EXTERNAL CHARACTERS OF RHINOCEROS SIMUS. Philip L. Sclater. Proc. Zool. Soc. Lond., pt.2, pp.143-144, figs.2, pl.16, Aug.1, 1886.

(REMARKS ON THE FORE DENTAL FORMULA OF RHINOCEROTIDAE.) Bemerkungen zur Vordergebissformel der Rhinocerotiden. H. G. Stehlin. Ecologae geologicae Helvetiae, Basel, vol.23, no.2, pp.644-648, figs.3, 1930.

Asia

RHINOCEROS SONDAICUS IN WEST-JAVA. E. J. Appelman, P. F. Franck. De Tropische Natuur, Buitenzorg, Jahrg.23, no.4, pp.73-79, figs.2, Apr.19, 1934.

(OLD REPRESENTATIONS OF THE INDIAN RHINOCEROS.) Anciennes figurations du rhinoceros de l'Indie. Christine Coste. Acta Tropica, Basel, vol.3, no.2, pp.116-129, figs.12, 1946.

THE JAVAN RHINOCEROS. J. Guy Dollman. Nat. Hist. Mag., Lond., vol.3, no.24, pp. 273-277, figs.3, Oct., 1932.

LETTER REGARDING THE EXISTENCE OF THE RHINOCEROS IN BORNEO. William T. Fraser. Proc. Zool. Soc. Lond., p.529, 1869.

RHINOCEROS SONDAICUS IN ZUID SUMATRA. J. C. Hazewinkel. Tropische Natuur, Buitenzorg, vol.22, no.6, pp.101-109, figs.3, June, 1933.

THE ASIATIC TWO-HORNED RHINOCEROS. Theodore Hubback. Jour. Mam., vol.20, no.1, pp.1-20, figs.5, Feb.14, 1939.

THE TWO-HORNED ASIATIC RHINOCEROS (DICERORHINUS SUMATRENSIS). Theodore Hubback. Jour. Bombay Nat. Hist. Soc., vol.40, no.4, pp.594-617, pls.1-8, May, 1939.

ON THE RHINOCEROSES FROM THE EAST-INDIAN-ARCHIPELAGO. F. A. Jentink. Notes Leyden Mus., vol.16, no.26, pp.231-233, Dec., 1894.

FURTHER RECORDS OF THE ONE-HORNED RHINOCEROS IN THE MALAY STATES. C. Boden Kloss. Bull. Raffles Mus., Singapore, Straits Settelments, no. 5, p.102, pl.6, Aug., 1931.

THE ONE-HORNED RHINOCEROS IN THE MALAY PENINSULA. C. Boden Kloss. Jour. Federated Malay States Mus., vol. 13, pt.4, pp.207-208, pl.5, Aug., 1927.

RHINOCEROS SONDAICUS. THE JAVAN OR LESSER ONE-HORNED RHINOCEROS AND ITS GEOGRAPHICAL DISTRIBUTION. Charles W. Loch. Jour. Malay Branch Roy. Asiatic Soc., vol.15, pt.2, pp.130-149, tables, pls.3-4, map, Sept., 1937.

NOTE ON THE ALLEGED OCCURRENCE OF THE RHINOCEROS IN BORNEO. Andrew Murray. Proc. Zool. Soc. Lond., pp.440-442, 1868.

ADDITIONAL NOTES ON THE ASIATIC TWO-HORNED RHINOCEROS. S. H. Prater. Jour. Bombay Nat. Hist. Soc., vol.40, no.4, pp.618-627, May, 1939.

EXHIBITION OF A DRAWING OF A SUPPOSED NEW RHINOCEROS FROM THE TERAI OF BHOOTAN. Philip L. Sclater. Proc. Zool. Soc. Lond., p.82, 1875.

REMARKS UPON A TWO-HORNED RHINOCEROS KILLED IN 1876, NEAR COMILLAH, IN TIPPERAH, AND ON A LIVING SPECIMEN OF RHINOCEROS SONDAICUS FROM THE SUNDERBANS. Philip L. Sclater. Proc. Zool. Soc. Lond., pt.2, pp.269-270, 1877.

STATUS OF THE THREE ASIATIC RHINOCEROS. E. O. Shebbeare. Oryx, vol.2, no.3, pp.141-149, Nov., 1953.

THE RHINOCEROS IN CHINA. Arthur deC. Sowerby. China Jour., vol.20, no.2, p.81, Feb., 1934.

A VISIT TO THE GREAT INDIAN RHINO. C. R. Stonor. Jour. Soc. Preservation Fauna Empire, Hertford, n.s., pt.53, pp. 46-48, June, 1946.

JAVA'S ONE-HORNED RHINO. Anton de Vos, A. Hoogerwerf. Nature Mag., Wash., vol.43, no.6, pp.297-298, 332, illus., June-July, 1950.

MEMORANDUM ON THE KAHILU SANCTUARY. (RHINOCEROS FOOTPRINTS.) D'Arcy Weatherbe. Jour. Bombay Nat. Hist. Soc., vol.41, no.3, pp.660-661, Apr., 1940.

Diseases, Parasites

ON THE TAENIA OF THE RHINOCEROS OF THE SUNDERBUNDS (PLAGIOTAENIA GIGANTEA, PETERS). Alfred Henry Garrod. Proc. Zool. Soc. Lond., pt.4, pp.788-789, fig.1, 1877.

NEOPLASM IN AN INDIAN RHINOCEROS (SARCOMA OF HEART AND LUNGS). H. Harold Scott. Proc. Zool. Soc. Lond., pt.3, pp.503-510, pls.2, Sept., 1927.

A NEW OPHRYOSCOLECID CILIATE, ENTODINIUM INSOLITUM, SP. N., FROM THE INDIAN RHINOCEROS. John M. Watson. Proc. Zool. Soc. Lond., vol.114, pt.4, pp.507-522, figs.4, Mar., 1945.

Economic Importance

RHINOCEROS SONDAICUS IN BURMA: THE PROBLEM OF CONSERVATION. H.R. Blanford. Jour. Soc. Preservation Fauna of the Empire, Hertford, n.s., pt.37, pp.27-32, Aug., 1939.

RHINOCEROS IN BORNEO: AND TRADED IN CHINA. Tom Harrisson. Sarawak Mus. Jour., Kuching, 7 (8): 263-274, pls.2-5, Dec., 1956.

THREATENED QUICK EXTINCTION OF THE WHITE RHINOCEROS. W. T. Hornaday. Zool. Soc. Bull., vol.27, pp. 12-15, Jan., 1924.

THREATENED EXTINCTION OF THE WHITE RHINOCEROS (CERATOTHERIUM SIMUM). Herbert Lang. Jour. Mam., vol. 5, no.3, pp.173-180, Aug.11, 1924.

THE BENGAL RHINOCEROS SANCTUARY. E.O. Shebbeare. Jour. Soc. Preservation Fauna in the Empire, n.s., pt.56, pp.33-35, Feb., 1948.

PROTECTING THE GREAT INDIAN RHINOCEROS. A LAST SANCTUARY IN BENGAL. E. O. Shebbeare. Field, Lond., vol.165, no.4299, pp.1229, 1231, illus., May 18, 1935.

THREATENED BY A TSE-TSE-FLY CAMPAIGN: THE RARE WHITE RHINOCEROS. Illus. London News, vol.191, no.5148, p.1117, illus., Dec.18, 1937.

TWILIGHT FOR THE RHINOCEROS. St. Louis Zoo, vol.13, no.2, p.2, June, 1942.

Fossils

A NEW RHINOCEROS MOUNT, TRIGONIAS OSBORNI. E. H. Barbour. Nebraska State Mus., vol.1, bull.38, pp.299-302, figs.2, May, 1934.

ON THE PARACERATHERIUM. A. Borisiak. Comp. Rend. Acad. Sci. URSS, no.1, pp. 1-2, 1927.

BALUCHITHERIUM OSBORNI AND ITS RELATIONS. C. Forster-Cooper. Nature, vol.112, pp.327-328, figs.5, Sept.1, 1923.

INDRICOTHERIUM ASIATICUM BORISS AND ITS TAXONOMIC POSITION. S. A. Gatuev. Bull. Soc. Nat. Moscow, sect. geol., vol. 11, no.2, pp.181-192, 1933. (In Russian.)

BUILDING A SUPER-GIANT RHINOCEROS. (BALUCHITHERIUM.) William K. Gregory. Natural History, New York, vol.35, no.4, pp.338-343, Apr., 1935.

GOBITHERIUM N. G. (MAMM. RHINOC.). M. Kretzoi. Foeldtani Koezloeny, vol.73, nos.1-3, pp.269-272, 1943.

BALUCHITERIUM GRANGERI. A. Le Comte. La Terre et la Vie, vol.7, no. 1, pp.22-26, figs.3, Jan.-Feb., 1937.

A COMPLETE SKELETON OF TELEOCERAS FOSSIGER. NOTES UPON THE GROWTH AND SEXUAL CHARACTERS OF THIS SPECIES. Henry Fairfield Osborn. Bull. Amer. Mus. Nat. Hist., New York, vol.10, art.4, pp.51-59, pls.4-4a, Mar.18, 1898.

THE BALUCHITHERIUM, THE LARGEST LAND MAMMAL THAT EVER LIVED. Arthur deC. Sowerby. China Jour., vol. 11, pp.95-98, pls.4, Aug., 1929.

HAS THE ELASMOTHERIUM BEEN TRIDACTYLOUS? W. A. Teriaev. Ann. Soc. Paleont. Russie, vol.8, pp.77-82, fig.1, (1928-29), 1930.

(DATA ON THE LOWER PLIOCENE DICEROS SPECIES (MAMMALIA, RHINOCEROTIDAE).) Zur Kenntnis der unterpliozaenen Diceros-Arten (Mammalia, Rhinocerotidae). Erich Thenius. Ann. Nat. Hist. Mus. Wien, 60: 202-211, Dec., 1955.

CAENOPUS, THE ANCESTRAL RHINOCEROS. Edward L. Troxell. Amer. Jour. Sci., ser.5, vol.2, no.7, pp.41-51, figs.6, July, 1921.

LOWER OLIGOCENE RHINOCEROSES OF THE GENUS TRIGONIAS. Horace Elmer Wood, 2nd. Jour. Mam., vol.12, no.4, pp.414-428, Nov., 1931.

PROHYRACODON ORIENTALE KOCH, THE OLDEST KNOWN TRUE RHINOCEROS. Horace Elmer Wood, 2nd. Amer. Mus. Novitates, no.395, pp.7, figs.6, Dec.31, 1929; Bull. Geol. Soc. Amer., vol.40, no. 1, p.221, Mar., 1929. (Abstract.)

STATUS OF EPIACERATHERIUM (RHINOCEROTIDAE). Horace Elmer Wood, 2nd. Jour. Mam., vol.13, no.2, pp.169-171, May, 1932.

PALAEOBIOLOGY AND CLIMATE OF THE PAST. (RHINOCEROSES.) Friedrich E. Zeuner. Problems of Paleontology, Publ. Lab. Paleont. Moscow Univ., vol.1, pp.199-216, 1936. (In English with Russian summary.)

Fossils--Africa

(ON THE LONGEVITY OF THE RHINOCEROS GENUS IN NORTHERN AFRICA DURING THE QUATERNARY PERIOD.) Sur la longevite, en Afrique du Nord, du genre Rhinoceros pendant la periode quaternaire. C. Arambourg. Comptes Rendus Acad. Sci., Paris, vol.192, no.17, pp.1044-1046, Apr. 27, 1931.

A HORNLESS RHINOCEROS FROM THE MIO-PLIOCENE DEPOSITS OF EAST AFRICA. P.E.P. Deraniyagala. Spolia Zeylanica, vol.26, pt.2, pp.133-135, pl.1, Dec.20, 1951.

Fossils--Eurasia

NOTES ON SOME OLIGOCENE RHINOCEROSES OF MONGOLIA. E. I. Belyaeva. Proc. Paleo. Inst., Acad. Sci. USSR, vol. 55, pp.190-205, illus., 1954.

(REPORTS ON MAMMAL-BONE FINDS IN THE VIENNA BASIN. REPORT I: A FIND OF RHINOCEROS BONES IN SYHRN NEAR GLOGGNITZ.) Berichte ueber Funde von Saeugetierknochen im Wiener Becken. 1. Fundbericht. Ein Fund von Rhinozerosnochen in Syhrn bei Gloggnitz. Fritz Bodo. Verhandl. Geol. Bundesanst., 1926, pp.105-108, 1926.

A NEW DICEROHINUS FROM THE MIDDLE MIOCENE OF NORTH CAUCASUS. (DICERORHINUS CAUCASICUS.) A. A. Borissiak. Trav. Inst. Paleozool., Moscou and Leningrad, vol.8, no.2, pp.69, figs. 20, pls.2, 1938.

ON THE OLDEST ACERATHERE FROM KAZAKHSTAN. A. A. Borissiak. Proc. Paleo. Inst., Acad. Sci., USSR, vol.47, pp.5-23, illus., 1954.

A NEW RHINOCEROS FROM THE SIWALIK BEDS OF INDIA. (GAINDATHERIUM, G. BROWNI.) Edwin H. Colbert. Amer. Mus. Nov., no.749, pp.13, figs.5, Oct.8, 1934.

(TEETH OF RHINOCEROS. DISCUSSION OF THE TERRACE OF VILLEFRANCHE.) Dents de Rhinoceros. Discussion sur la terrasse de Villefranche. MM.D'Ault du Mesnil, G. de Mortillet, D'Arcy, Tardy. 1896.

(NEW RHINOCEROS REMAINS FROM SWABIA (DIACERATHERIUM TOMERDINGENSIS N.G.N.SP.) Neue Nashornreste aus Schwaben (Diaceratherium tomerdingensis n.g. n. sp.) W. O. Dietrich. Zeitschrift fuer Saeugetierkunde, Berlin, vol.6, no.5, pp.203-220, figs.15, pls.22-23, Dec.15, 1931.

THE EXTINCT RHINOCEROSES OF BALUCHISTAN. C. Forster-Cooper. Philos. Trans. Roy. Soc. Lond., ser.B, vol.223, pp.569-616, figs.21, pls.64-67, Aug.1, 1934.

(A RHINOCERID FIND FROM THE LOWER FRESH WATER MOLASSE OF THE LANGENTHAL AND ITS STRATIGRAPHIC POSITION.) Ueber den Fund eines Rhinoceriden aus der untern Suesswassermolasse von Langenthal und dessen stratigraphische Stellung. Ed Gerber. Ecologae Geol. Helvetiae, vol. 25, no.2, pp.274-275, Dec., 1932.

A SKELETON OF THE FOSSIL RHINOCEROS FOUND IN THE VICINITY OF FULIAERHTZI STATION OF THE HEILUNGCHIANG PROVINCE. T. P. Gordeev, V. N. Jernakov. Vertebrata Palasiatica, 1 (3): 233-246, Sept., 1957. (In Russian, with English summary.)

FURTHER NOTES ON THE GIGANTIC EXTINCT RHINOCEROS, BALUCHITHERIUM, FROM THE OLIGOCENE OF MONGOLIA. Walter Granger, William K. Gregory. Bull. Amer. Mus. Nat. Hist., vol.72, pp.73, figs.47, pls.4, Aug.21, 1936.

A REVISED RESTORATION OF THE SKELETON OF BALUCHITHERIUM, GIGANTIC FOSSIL RHINOCEROS OF CENTRAL ASIA. Walter Granger, William

K. Gregory. Amer. Mus. Nov., no.787, pp.1-3, figs.2, Apr.1, 1935.

ON THE REMAINS OF THE MERCK RHINOCEROS (RHINOCEROS MERCKI JAEG.) FROM THE LOWER VOLGA. Vera Gromova. Trav. Inst. Paleozool. Acad. Sci. URSS, Leningrad, vol.4, pp.91-136, figs.4, pls.3, 1935. (In Russian, with German summary.)

(ON SPECIMENS OF FAMILY INDRICOTHERIIDAE FROM OLIGOCENE DEPOSITS IN GEORGIA.) O predstavitelyax semeistva Indricotheriidae iz oligotsenovix otlojenii gruzii. L. K. Habuniya. Doklady Akad. Nauk SSSR, Moscow, vol.81, no.6, pp.1135-1137, 1951.

(DISCOVERY OF A MOLAR OF COELODONTA ANTIQUITATIS BLUMENBACH IN THE PLEISTOCENE OF THE TROUILLE VALLEY NEAR GIVRY.) Découverte d'une molaire de Coelodonta antiquitatis Blumenbach dans le Pléistocene de la vallée de la Trouille, près de Givry. F. Halet. Bull. Soc. Belge Géol. Paléont. et Hydrol., vol. 47, no.1, pp.80-82, fig.1, table, July 27, 1937.

PREHISTORIC AND FOSSIL RHINOCEROSES FROM THE MALAY ARCHIPELAGO AND INDIA. D. A. Hooijer. E. J. Brill, Leiden, pp.1-138, fig.1, pls. 10, 1946.

(Review by P. Rode of) PREHISTORIC AND FOSSIL RHINOCEROS FROM THE MALAY ARCHIPELAGO AND INDIA. D. A. Hooijer. Mammalia, Paris, 10 (1): 66, Mar., 1946.

RHINOCEROS SONDAICUS DESMAREST FROM KITCHEN-MIDDENS OF BINDJAI TAMIANG, NORTH SUMATRA. D. A. Hooijer. Geologie and Mijnbouw, n.s., vol.10, pp.116-117, 1948.

(BONE FRAGMENTS OF SMALLER VERTEBRATES FOUND IN STARUNIA TOGETHER WITH THE WOOLLY RHINOCEROS.) Knochenfragmente der in Starunia zusammem mit dem Wollnashorn gefundenen kleineren Wirbeltiere. Theodor Kormos. Starunia, Polska Akad. Umiljetności, Kraków, no.5, pp.1-4, figs. 6, 1934.

(RHINOCEROS BRACHYPUS OF SIMORRE.) Rhinoceros brachypus de Simorre. L. Mestre. Bull. Soc. Hist. Nat. Toulouse, vol.66, no.2, pp.309-318, figs.9, Aug.31, 1934.

THE SECOND WOOLLY RHINOCEROS (COELODONTA ANTIQUITATIS BLUM.) FROM STARUNIA, POLAND. J. Nowak, E. Panow, J. Tokarski, W. Szafer, J. Stach. Bull. Internat. Acad. Polonaise Sci. et Lett., Cl. Sci. Math. et Nat., Cracovie, ser.B, Sci. Nat., Bull.3, suppl., pp.1-47, pls.10, 1930.

BALUCHITHERIUM GRANGERI, A GIANT HORNLESS RHINOCEROS FROM MONGOLIA. Henry Fairfield Osborn. Amer. Mus. Nov., New York, no.78, pp.15, figs. 9, May 25, 1924.

THE EXTINCT GIANT RHINOCEROS BALUCHITHERIUM OF WESTERN AND CENTRAL ASIA. Henry Fairfield Osborn. Nat. Hist., vol.23, pp.209-228, figs.17, May-June, 1923.

A NEW PLEISTOCENE RHINOCEROS RELATED TO THE SUMATRAN FORM. Henry Fairfield Osborn. Science, Lancaster, vol.16, no.410, pp.751, Nov.7, 1902.

A NEW RHINOCEROS FROM SOUTHERN BAVARIA. Henry Fairfield Osborn. Science, Lancaster, vol.17, no.425, p. 312, Feb.20, 1903.

(RHINOCEROS FIND AT MIKOVIC.) Nalez nosorozce u Mikovic. (Rhinoceros antiquitalis) Jor Peterbok. Veda Prirodni Mes. pro Sir. a Pest. Ved Prir., Prague, vol.8, no.8, p.253, 1927.

(FOSSIL RHINOCEROSES OF POLAND.) Les rhinoceros fossiles de Pologne. G. Portevin. La Terre et la Vie, Paris, vol. 5, no.1, pp.37-39, Jan., 1935.

COELODONTA MERCKI JAG. FROM THE "DOLARJEVA JAMA" CAVE NEAR LOGATEC. Ivan Rakovec. Prirodoslovne Razprave, vol.2, no.1, pp.5-41, pls.1-4, Apr.13, 1933. (In Jugoslavian, with German summary.)

(RHINOCEROSES OF THE HIPPARION FAUNA OF NORTH CHINA.) Nashoerner der hipparion-fauna Nord Chinas. Torsten Ringstroem. Geological Survey, China, Peking, 1924.

(RHINOCEROS MERCKI IN RUMANIA.) Rhinoceros mercki in Rumaenien. I. Simionescu. Acad. Roumanie, Bull. Sect. Sci., Bukharest, vol.22, no.10, pp. 4, fig.1, pl.1, 1939-1940.

(FINDING OF A DILUVIAL RHINOCEROS JAW-BONE AT ORLOV.) Nalez celisti diluvialniho nosorozce v Orlove. Vaclav Susta. Sbornik Prirodov. Spolecn. v Mor. Ostrave, vol.7, pp.145-152, fig.1, pl.3, 1932.

FOSSILS OF RHINOCEROTIDAE FOUND IN JAPAN. Shigeyasu Tokunaga. Proc. Imp. Acad. Japan, vol.2, no.6, pp.289-291, 1926.

A RHINOCEROS BONE FROM BRIERTON, NEAR WEST HARTLEPOOL. C. T. Trechmann. Proc. Yorkshire Geol. Soc., Wakefield, England, vol.24, pt.2, pp.99-100, pl.13, Nov.30, 1939.

(THE FOSSIL RHINOCERATIDAE OF CHOU-KOU-TIEN.) Die Fossilen Rhinocerotiden von Chou-Kou-Tien. K. M. Wang. Contrib. Nat. Research Inst. Geol., Acad. Sinica, Shanghai, no.1, pp.69-84, pls.4, 1931.

COOPERIA TOTADENTATA, A REMARKABLE RHINOCEROS FROM THE EOCENE OF MONGOLIA. Horace Elmer Wood, 2nd. Amer. Mus. Novitates, no.1012, pp.1-20, figs.7, Dec.30, 1938.

THE RHINOCEROS IN THE PARIS BASIN. Nature, London, vol.143, no.3613, p.174, Jan.28, 1939.

(RHINOCEROS FIND IN EASTERN GALICIA (AUSTRIA).) Nashornfund in Ostgalizien. Naturforscher, Berlin, vol. 6, no.12, p.474, 1930.

Fossils--North America

APHELOPS FROM THE HAWTHRON FORMATION OF FLORIDA. Edwin H. Colbert. Bull.10, Florida State Geol. Suv., Tallahassee, pp.55-58, figs.30, 1932.

NEW RHINOCEROSES FROM THE PLIOCENE OF COLORADO AND NEBRASKA. Harold J. Cook. Proc. Colorado Mus. Nat. Hist., vol.9, no.4, pp.44-51, pls.7, Dec. 15, 1930.

A RHINOCEROS BONE BED. L. M. Cools. Black Hills Engineer, South Dakota School of Mines, vol.14, no.2, pp.95-99, Mar., 1926.

NEW MATERIAL FOR THE STUDY OF INDIVIDUAL VARIATION, FROM THE LOWER OLIGOCENE OF COLORADO. (CHARACTERS OF SPECIES OF TRIGONIAS.) J. D. Figgins. Proc. Colorado Mus. Nat. Hist., vol.13, no.3, pp.7-14, pls.3, Dec.29, 1934.

A SKULL OF TELEOCERAS FOSSIGER COPE, FROM THE CLARENDON BEDS OF DONLEY COUNTY, TEXAS. C. Stuart Johnston. Amer. Midland Nat., vol.18, no.1, pp.152-154, figs.3, Jan., 1937.

A NEW RHINOCEROS FROM KANSAS. (PARAPHELOPS ROOKSENSIS.) H. H. Lane. Univ. Kansas Sci. Bull., vol.17, no.2, pp.297-311, illus., Sept., 1927.

A NEW RHINOCEROS, TRIGONIAS OSBORNI, FROM THE MIOCENE OF SOUTH DAKOTA. Frederic A. Lucas. Proc. U.S. Nat. Mus., vol.23, no.1207, pp.221-223, figs.1-2, Oct.9, 1900.

ACERATHERIUM TRIDACTYLUM FROM THE LOWER MIOCENE OF DAKOTA. Henry Fairfield Osborn. Bull. Amer. Mus. Nat. Hist., vol.5, art.7, pp.85-86, Apr. 29, 1893.

A RHINOCEROS TOOTH FROM THE CLARNO EOCENE OF OREGON. R. A. Stirton. Jour. Paleontol., Menasha, vol. 18, no.3, pp.265-267, fig.1, May, 1944.

AMERICAN OLIGOCENE RHINOCEROSES--A POSTSCRIPT. Horace Elmer Wood, 2nd. Jour. Mam., vol.10, no.1, pp.63-75, Feb., 1929.

A FOSSIL RHINOCEROS (DICERATHERIUM ARMATUM MARSH) FROM GALLATIN COUNTY, MONTANA. Horace Elmer Wood, 2nd. Proc. U.S. Nat. Mus., vol. 82, art.7, pp.1-4, pls.3, Mar.14, 1933.

Habits, Behavior

(THE SPEED OF THE RHINOCEROS (DICEROS BICORNIS L.).) Propos de la vitesse du rhinoceros (Diceros bicornis (L.). Lt. Col. Eble. Mammalia, Paris, 14 (4): 178-179, Dec., 1950.

THE SOUTHERN WHITE RHINOCEROS, ITS HISTORY, PECULARITIES, HABITS AND BEHAVIOUR. 'Mfohloza. Durban, Wild life Protection Society, Natal Branch, pp.14, illus., 1933?

(THE RELATIONS BETWEEN CRANIAL FORM AND HABITS IN RECENT AND FOSSIL RHINOCEROSES.) Die Beziehungen zwischen Schaedelform und Lebensweise bei den rezenten und fossilen Nashoernern. Friedrich Zeuner. Ber. naturf. Ges. Freiburg i. Br., vol.34, no.1, pp.21-80, figs.21, July, 1934.

Horns

THE REGENERATION OF THE ANTERIOR HORN OF THE BLACK RHINOCEROS, DICEROS BICORNIS (LINN.). R. Biglake. Proc. Zool. Soc. Lond., vol.115, pts.3-4, pp.323-326, pls.1-2, Feb., 1946.

RHINOCEROS HORN. Maurice Burton. Illus. London News, vol.219, no.5857, p.108, illus., July 21, 1951.

WEAPONS OF THE GREAT INDIAN RHINOCEROS. Richard Glover. Oryx, London, 3 (4): 197, May, 1956.

RECUPERATIVE POWER OF THE HORN OF THE BLACK RHINOCEROS (RHINOCEROS BICORNIS L.). E. F. Jacobi. Zool. Garten, Leipzig, 23 (1-3): 223-227, illus., 1957.

(HORN OF THE INDIAN RHINOCEROS UNICORNIS.) Das Horn des indischen Rhinoceros unicornis. Erna Mohr. Zool. Garten, Leipzig, 23 (1-3): 37-45, 1957.

WEAPONS OF THE TWO AFRICAN RHINOCEROSES. Charles R. S. Pitman. Oryx, London, 3 (4): 195-196, May, 1956.

RHINOCEROS HORN. Michael L. Ryder. Turtox News, vol.40, no.11, Nov., 1962.

EXHIBITION OF, AND REMARKS ON, A HORN OF THE MALE INDIAN RHINOCEROS (RHINOCEROS UNICORNIS). Philip L. Sclater. Proc. Zool. Soc. Lond., pp. 8-11, figs.2, 1871.

EXHIBITION OF, AND REMARKS ON, THE UPPER HORN OF A TWO HORNED RHINOCEROS FROM THE VALLEY OF THE BRAHMAPOOTRA. Philip L. Sclater. Proc. Zool. Soc. Lond., p.566, 1875.

ON SOME HORNS BELONGING, APPARENTLY TO A NEW FORM OF AFRICAN RHINOCEROS. Philip L. Sclater. Proc. Zool. Soc. Lond., pt.3, pp.514-517, figs.2, Oct.2, 1893.

EXHIBITION OF, AND REMARKS ON, A SERIES OF HORNS OF AFRICAN RHINOCEROSES. Frederick Selous. Proc. Zool. Soc. Lond., p.179, 1876.

TOO MANY HORNS. (RHINOCEROS) Ken Stott. San Diego Zoonooz, vol.21, no. 11, pp.3-4, illus., Nov., 1948.

EXHIBITION OF SOME RHINOCEROS-HORNS OBTAINED BY MR. EVERETT IN BORNEO. Alfred Russell Wallace. Proc. Zool. Soc., Lond., p.498, 1874.

Hunting

LASSOING A RHINOCEROS. Cherry Kearton. Field, London, vol.165, no. 4282, pp.118-119, illus., Jan.19, 1935.

THE HUNT FOR THE ONE-HORNED JAVAN RHINOCEROS: HOW A MAGNIFICENT

SPECIMEN OF ONE OF THE RAREST OF BEASTS WAS SHOT IN THE MALAYAN FORESTS. Florence MacNaught. Illus. London News, vol.181, no.4878, pp.566-567, illus., Oct.15, 1932.

DREADNAUGHT OF THE VELDT. (RHINOCEROS) Hugh Prior. Field and Stream, New York, vol.52, no.6, pp.54-56, 132-133, illus., Oct., 1947.

RHINOCEROS SHOOTING IN BURMA. W. S. Thom. Jour. Bombay Nat. Hist. Soc., vol.38, no.1, pp.137-150, illus., Aug.15, 1935.

OBSERVATIONS ON INDIAN RHINO AND THEIR SHIKAR ON FOOT. H. S. Wood. Jour. Darjeeling Nat. Hist. Soc., vol.4, no.3, pp.59-69, 1930.

CAPTURING A NEPAL RHINO. Field, London, vol.162, no.4213, pp.769-770, figs., Sept.23, 1933.

CATCHING A RARE RHINO. (INDIAN RHINOCEROS) Life, Chicago, vol.32, no.17, pp.131-132, 135, illus., Apr.28, 1952.

In Captivity, Zoos

BABY RHINOCEROS AT CHICAGO ZOOLOGICAL PARK. Ed. H. Bean. Parks and Recreation, Rockford, vol.25, no.3, pp.119-120, illus., Nov., 1941.

(OUR WHITE RHINOCEROS (CERATOTHERIUM SIMUM COTTONI LYDEKKER).) Nos rhinoceros blancs (Ceratotherium simum Lydekker). Walter Van den Bergh. Zool. Garten, Leipzig, N.F., vol.21, no. 3, pp.129-151, illus., 1955.

PRETORIA ZOO HAS A BABY WHITE RHINOCEROS. R. Biglake. Animal Kingdom, New York, vol.50, no.2, pp. 48-55, fig.8, Mar.-Apr., 1947.

OBSERVATIONS ON A JUVENILE FEMALE SQUARE-LIPPED OR WHITE RHINOCEROS (CERATOTHERIUM SIMUM SIMUM (BURCH.)) IN THE NATIONAL ZOOLOGICAL GARDENS OF SOUTH AFRICA. R. Biglake, T. Steyn, D. de Vos, K. de Waard. Proc. Zool. Soc. Lond., vol.120, pt.3, pp. 519-528, pls.2, Nov.30, 1950.

THE FIRST WHITE RHINO IN CAPTIVITY. Robert Broom. Nat. Hist., New York, vol. 55, no.9, pp.432-433, illus., Nov., 1946.

ANNOUNCEMENT OF THE ADDITION TO THE SOCIETY'S COLLECTION OF A FEMALE SUMATRAN RHINOCEROS. Philip L. Sclater. Proc. Zool. Soc. Lond., p.185, 1872.

ANNOUNCEMENT OF THE ARRIVAL IN THE SOCIETY'S MENAGERIE OF A JAVAN RHINOCEROS. Philip L. Sclater. Proc. Zool. Soc. Lond., pp.182-183, pl. 28, 1874.

(THE CAPTIVE LIFE OF A YOUNG RHINOCEROS.) Vom Gefangenleben eines jungen Nashorns. Vera Coenraad Uhlig. Zool. Garten N.F., Leipzig, vol.6, nos. 4-6, pp.114-116, July, 1933.

Museum Collections

OBSERVATIONS ON THE PRESERVED SPECIMENS AND SKELETONS OF THE RHINOCEROTIDAE IN THE COLLECTION OF THE BRITISH MUSEUM AND ROYAL COLLEGE OF SURGEONS, INCLUDING THE DESCRIPTIONS OF THREE NEW SPECIES. John E. Gray. Proc. Zool. Soc. Lond., pp.1003-1030, figs.6, 1867.

ON RHINOCEROS SIMUS, BURCHELL IN THE LEYDEN MUSEUM. F. A. Jentink. Notes Leyden Mus., vol.12, no.41, pp. 241-245, Oct., 1890.

Photography

(PICTURES OF THE FORMER AND PRESENT ANIMAL STOCK OF SCHONBRUNN. 1. RHINOCEROSES.) Bilder aus dem frueheren und jetzigen Schoenbrunner Tierbestand. I. Nashoerner. Otto Antonius. Zool. Garten, N.F., Leipzig, vol.9, nos.1-2, pp.18-26, illus., Feb., 1937.

WITH THE WHITE RHINOCEROS IN UGANDA. THE STORY OF TWO MORNING'S PHOTOGRAPHY. B. H. Bourdillon. Field, London, vol.163, no.4247, p.1170, illus., May 19, 1934.

A CREATURE WHOSE ONLY SERIOUS ENEMY IS MAN: THE GREAT INDIAN RHINOCEROS PHOTOGRAPHED IN ITS NATIVE JUNGLE. H. E. Tyndale. Illus. London News, vol.210, no.5631, pp.300, 301, illus., Mar.22, 1947.

(REMARKABLE PHOTOGRAPHS OF A YOUNG SUMATRA RHINOCEROS (DICERORHINUS SUMATRENSIS CUV.).) Bemerkenswerte Aufnahmen eines jungen Sumatra-Nashorns (Dicerorhinus sumatrensis Cuv.). Wolfgang Ullrich. Zool. Garten, Leipzig, vol.22, no.1, pp.29-33, illus., 1955.

Phylogeny

CONTRIBUTION TO THE PHYLOGENY OF DICERORHINAE. A. Borissiak. Comptes Rendus (Doklady) Acad. Sci. URSS, Moscow, n.s., vol.19, no.9, pp.767-770, illus., 1938.

NOTES ON THE LESSER ONE-HORNED RHINOCEROS, RHINOCEROS SONDAICUS. 2. THE POSITION OF RHINOCEROS SONDAICUS IN THE PHYLOGENY OF THE GENUS RHINOCEROS. Edwin H. Colbert. Amer. Mus. Nov., New York, no.1207, pp.6, figs.3, Nov.12, 1942.

NEW MATERIAL FOR THE STUDY OF EVOLUTION. A SERIES OF PRIMITIVE RHINOCEROS SKULLS (TRIGONIAS) FROM THE LOWER OLIGOCENE OF COLORADO. William K. Gregory, Harold J. Cook. Proc. Colorado Mus. Nat. Hist., vol.8, no.1, pp. 1-32, pls.1-6, Feb.1, 1928; (Abstract), Bull. Geol. Soc. Amer., vol.38, p.235, Mar.30, 1927.

THE EVOLUTION OF THE SKELETON OF RHINOCEROS SONDAICUS DESMAREST. D. A. Hooijer. Proc. K. Nederlandsche Akad. Wetenschappen, Amsterdam, vol.49, no.6, pp.3-8, figs.2, 1946.

CRITICAL OBSERVATIONS ON THE PHYLOGENY OF THE RHINOCEROSES. W. D. Matthew. Univ. Calif. Publ., Bull. Dept. Geol. Sci., vol.20, no.1, pp.1-9, figs.2, Jan.23, 1931; Bull. Geol. Soc. Amer., vol.42, no.1, pp.366-367, Mar., 1931.

PHYLOGENY OF THE RHINOCEROSES OF EUROPE. RHINOCEROS CONTRIBUTIONS, NO.5. Henry Fairfield Osborn. Bull. Amer. Mus. Nat. Hist., vol.13, art.19, pp. 229-267, figs.16, Dec.11, 1900.

TRENDS IN RHINOCEROS EVOLUTION. Horace Elmer Wood, 2nd. Trans. New York Acad. Sci., New York, ser.2, vol.3, no.4, pp.83-96, Feb., 1941.

Reproductive Biology

THE BREEDING OF THE INDIAN RHINOCEROS (RHINOCEROS UNICORNIS) IN CAPTIVITY. Salim A. Ali. Jour. Bombay Nat. Hist. Soc., vol.31, p.1031, Feb.20, 1927.

(BIRTH OF AN INDIAN RHINOCEROS (RHINOCEROS UNICORNIS) IN THE BASEL ZOOLOGICAL GARDEN.) Geburt eines Panzernashorns, Rhinoceros unicornis, im Zoologischen Garten Basel. Ernst M. Lang. Saeugetierk. Mitteil., 5 (2): 69-70, illus., Apr.1, 1957.

TERRITORIAL AND SEXUAL BEHAVIOR IN THE GREAT INDIAN RHINOCEROS, A SPECULATION. S. Dillon Ripley. Ecology, Lancaster, vol.33, no.4, pp.570-573, illus., Oct., 1952.

NOTES ON THE BREEDING OF THE INDIAN RHINOCEROS, RHINOCEROS UNICORNIS, AT WHIPSNADE PARK. E. H. Tong. Proc. Zool. Soc. Lond., 130 (2): 296-299, Mar.13, 1958.

Taxonomy

THE GENERIC STATUS OF ? CAENOPUS PREMITIS. J. D. Figgins. Proc. Colorado Mus. Nat. Hist., vol.13, no.1, p.1, June 23, 1934.

ON A NEW SPECIES OF RHINOCEROS. John E. Gray. Proc. Zool. Soc. Lond., pp.250-251, 1854.

A REVIEW OF THE RHINOCEROSES WITH A DESCRIPTION OF APHELOPS MATERIAL FROM THE PLIOCENE OF TEXAS. W. D. Matthew. Univ. Calif. Publ., Bull. Dept. Geol. Sci., vol.20, no.12, pp.411-480, pls. 61-79, figs.12, Feb.26, 1932.

THE IDENTITY OF THE GENOTYPE OF RHINOCEROS LINN. R. I. Pocock. Ann. and Mag. Nat. Hist. Lond., ser.11, vol. 11, pp.616-618, Sept., 1944.

NOTES ON THE TYPE SPECIMEN OF RHINOCEROS LASIOTIS SCLATER; WITH REMARKS ON THE GENERIC POSITION OF THE LIVING SPECIES OF RHINOCEROS. Oldfield Thomas. Proc. Zool. Soc., Lond., pp.154-158, June 4, 1901.

Young

A YOUNG SUMATRAN RHINOCEROS. (RHINOCEROS SUMATRENSIS.) J. G. Dollman. Nat. Hist. Mag., London, vol. 1, no.7, pp.255-258, illus., July, 1928.

(CONTRIBUTIONS TO THE YOUNG DEVELOPMENT OF RHINOCHEORUS INDICUS CUV.) Beitraege zur Jugendentwicklung des Schabrackentapirs (Rhinochoerus indicus (Cuv.)). Ingo Krumbiegel. Zool. Garten, N.F., Leipzig, vol.8, nos.4-6, pp.96-99, illus., Jan., 1936.

KATHLEEN, THE RHINOCEROS CALF. R. I. Pocock. Field, London, p.203, illus., Aug.2, 1928.

THE SUMATRAN RHINOCEROS. (NEWLY BORN YOUNG RECEIVED BY BRITISH MUSEUM.) R. I. Pocock. Field, London, vol.151, p.338, illus., Feb.23, 1928.

## ARTIODACTYLA

NOTES ON THE MUSK-OX AND THE CARIBOU. R.M. Anderson. (In) Conserving Canada's musk-oxen, being an account of an investigation of Thelma Game Sanctuary 1928-1929, with a brief history of the area and an outline of known facts regarding the musk-ox. By W.H. Hoare. North West Territories and Yukon Branch, Dept. Interior, Ottawa, pp. 49-53, 1930.

(BISON AND ELK. TWO PRIMITIVE HEROES.) Wisent und Elch. Zwei urige Recken. Kurt Floericke. Stuttgart, Kosmos, Gesellschaft der Naturfreunde, pp. 78, figs.15, 1930.

(THE OKAPI AND SOME AFFINITIES OF THE GIRAFFINES AND ANTELOPES.) De l'okapi et des affinites des giraffides avec les antilopes. S. Frechkop. Bull. Mus. Roy. Hist. Nat., Bruxelles, vol.22, no.1, p.1, 1946.

WHERE THE ELK AND THE BUFFALO PLAY. Lyn Harrington. Forest and Outdoors, Montreal, vol.13, pp.51-52, 1947.

NOTES ON THE MUSKOX AND THE CARIBOU. W.H.B. Hoare. Ottawa, 1930.

(ON SUS MARCHEI HUET AND TRAGULUS NIGRICANS THOMAS.) Ueber sus Marchei Huet und Tragulus nigricans Thomas. Alfred Nehring. Sitz. Ber. Gesell. Naturf. Freunde Berlin, Jahrg.1894, nr.9, pp.219-226, figs.2, Nov.20, 1894.

MONOGRAPH ON THE HOLLOW-HORNED RUMINANTS. W. Ogilby. Proc. Zool. Soc. Lond., pt.8, pp.4-5, 1840.

THE DISPERSAL OF THE ARTIODACTYLA. Guy E. Pilgrim. Biol. Reviews, Cambridge, vol.16, no.2, pp.134-163, Apr., 1941.

Africa

WART-HOGS AND BLUE WILDBEESTE AT LARGE IN THEIR NATIVE HAUNTS IN THE TRANSVAAL: STRANGE BEASTS PHOTOGRAPHED TOGETHER AT A DRINKING POOL. B. F. Jearey. Illus. London News, vol.189, no.5082, p.445, fig., Sept. 12, 1936.

(ZOOGEOGRAPHICAL STUDIES ON THE BARBARY.) Etudes de géographie zoologique sur la Berbérie. (On cervids and giraffes.) L. Joleaud. Separate from commemorative volume of Prof. Gorjanović-Krambergera, pp.1-60, 1925.

Anatomy

VENOUS VALVES IN THE GIRAFFE, OKAPI, CAMEL AND OSTRICH. E. C. Amoroso, O. G. Edholm, R. E. Rewell. Proc. Zool. Soc. Lond., vol.117, pts.2-3, pp.435-440, figs.4, Oct.30, 1947.

QUANTITATIVE STUDIES OF THE TESTIS. I. SOME OBSERVATIONS ON THE CRYPT ORCHID TESTES OF SHEEP AND SWINE. K. F. Bascom. Anat. Record, vol.30, pp. 225-241, figs.22, June 25, 1925.

ON THE MEANING OF MOVABLE ATTACHMENT OF THE INCISIVIFORM TEETH IN RUMINANTIA. A. C. V. Van Bemmel. Beaufortia, Amsterdam, no.22, pp.3, Nov. 17, 1952.

(ON SOME PARALLEL VARIATIONS OBSERVED IN THE OSTEOLOGY OF THE HEAD IN SUIDAE AND HIPPOPOTAMIDAE.) Sur quelques variations paralléliques observées dans l'ostéologie de la tête chez les Suidés et les Hippopotamidés. E. G. Dehaut. Bull. Mus. Hist. Nat., Paris, ser.2, vol.11, no.3, pp.282-286, figs.3, Mar., 1939.

(ON THE PROBLEM OF THE COMPARATIVE ANATOMICAL INVESTIGATION OF THE YAK, THE KIRGHIZ NEAT, AND THEIR HYBRIDS.) Zur Frage der vergleichenden anatomischen Untersuchung des Yaks, des kirgisischen Rindes und ihrer Hybriden. A.N. Druzinin, W. W. Iwanowa, I. L. Ljubimow. Bull. Acad. Sci. URSS, Moscow, Cl. Sci., Math., Nat., ser. biol., pp.841-894, 1937.

(TOOTH REPLACEMENT IN RUMINANTS.) Du remplacement des dents chez les ruminants. S. Frechkop. Bull. Mus. Roy. Hist. Nat. Belgique, Bruxelles, vol.24, no. 34, pp.1-8, 1948.

(OBSERVATIONS ON THE SPLEEN IN UNGULATE ARTIODACTYLS.) Observations sur le splenial chez les Ongules artiodactyles. M. Friant. Bull. Soc. Zool. France, vol.63, no.4-5, pp.240-243, figs. 9, 1938.

NOTES ON THE VISCERAL ANATOMY AND OSTEOLOGY OF THE RUMINANTS, WITH A SUGGESTION REGARDING A METHOD OF EXPRESSING THE RELATIONS OF SPECIES BY MEANS OF FORMULAE. Alfred Henry Garrod. Proc. Zool. Soc. Lond., pt.1, pp.2-18, figs.25, tables 3, 1877.

SKELETAL DIFFERENCES BETWEEN DEER, SHEEP, AND GOATS. M. Hildebrand. California Fish and Game, vol.41, no.4, pp.327-346, illus., Oct., 1955.

(THE DEVELOPMENT OF THE DENTINAL SACS IN RUMINANTS.) Die Entwickelung der Zahnsaeckchen der Wiederkaeuer. A. Koelliker. Zeitschr. Wiss. Zool., vol. 12, pp.455-460, 1863.

(COMPARATIVE STUDY OF THE HEART OF AN OKAPI AND OTHER RUMINANTS.) Etude comparative du coeur de l'okapi et d'autres ruminants. Janine Laurent-Combaz. Bull. Mus. Roy. Hist. Nat. Belgique, Bruxelles, vol.20, no.15, pp.19, figs.7, June, 1944.

CONTRIBUTIONS TO KNOWLEDGE OF THE ANATOMY OF THE RUMINANTS. Einar Loennberg. Arkiv Zool., Upsala, vol.5, no.10, pp.1-23, fig.1-10, 1909.

(ON THE MORPHOLOGY AND HISTOLOGY OF THE ARTIODACTYL PENIS.) Zur Morphologie und Histologie des Artiodactylenpenis. C. Mandowsky. Zeitschr. f. Anat. u. Entwicklungsgesch., vol.83, pp.269-326, figs.29, July 11, 1927.

A SECOND INSTANCE OF THE DEVELOPMENT OF RODENT-LIKE INCISORS IN AN ARTIODACTYL. Gerrit S. Miller, Jr. Proc. U.S. Nat. Mus., vol.66, art.8, pp. 1-3, pl.1, Oct.13, 1924.

(ON THE DEVELOPMENT OF THE TAPETUM LUCIDUM FIBROSUM IN THE EYE OF RUMINANTS.) Zur Entwicklung des Tapetum lucidum fibrosum im Auge der Wiederkaeuer. E. Murr. Zeitschr. f. Zellforschung u. Mikroskopische Anat., vol.2, pp.703-740, illus., Nov.23, 1925.

DIFFERENCES BETWEEN CERVIDS AND ANTELOPES IN THEIR MOLAR TEETH. Joji Nagasawa. Jour. Geol. Soc. Tokyo, vol.38, no.451, pp.188-193, Apr.20, 1931. (In Japanese.)

(ON THE OCCURRENCE OF CANINE TEETH IN ANTILOPE SAIGA, CERVUS CAPREOLUS, AND OTHER CERVUS SPECIES.) Das Vorkommen von Eckzaehnen bei Antilope saiga, bei Cervus capreolus und anderen Cervus-Arten. Alfred Nehring. Sitz. Ber. Gesell. Naturf. Freunde. Berlin, Jahrg.1883, no.1, pp.13-19, illus., 1883.

THE EXTERNAL CHARACTERS OF THE PIGMY HIPPOPOTAMUS (CHOEROPSIS LIBERIENSIS) AND OF THE SUIDAE AND CAMELIDAE. R. I. Pocock. Proc. Zool. Soc. Lond., pt.3, pp.531-549, Oct., 1923.

ON THE SPECIALIZED CUTANEOUS GLANDS OF RUMINANTS. R. I. Pocock. Proc. Zool. Soc. Lond., 1910: 840-985, 1910.

ON THE PHALANX OF DEER AND WILD BOAR WITH THE HOLE RESEMBLED TO SOCALLED REINDEER PIPE. Hisashi Suzuki. Zinruigaku Zassi (Jour. Anthrop. Soc. Tokyo), vol.54, no.626, pp.515-521, figs.2, Dec., 1939. (In Japanese.)

(CONTRIBUTIONS TO THE STRUCTURE OF THE LOWER JAW GLANDS OF DOMESTIC RUMINANTS. NEAT, GOAT, SHEEP.) Beitraege zum Bau der Unterkieferdruese der Hauswiederkaeuer. Rind, Ziege und Schaf. H. Ziegler. Zeitschr. f. Anat. u. Entwicklungsgesch., vol.82, pp.73-121, illus., Jan.27, 1927.

Bibliographies

A BIBLIOGRAPHY OF REINDEER, CARIBOU, AND MUSK-OX. Arthème Dutilly. U.S. Dept. Army, Office Quartermaster Gen., Environmental Prot. Sec., Rep.129, pp.462, May, 1949.

Diseases, Parasites

A MONOGRAPH OF THE MELOPHAGINAE, OR KEDFLIES, OF SHEEP, GOATS, DEER AND ANTELOPES (DIPTERA, HIPPOBOSCIDAE). J. Bequaert. Entomologica Amer., N.S., 1 (1-4): 1-220, 1942.

WHERE DEER AND ANTELOPE PLAY: NORTH DAKOTA'S BIG GAME ANIMALS ARE NOT RESERVOIRS OF BRUCELLOSIS. F. M. Bolin, D. F. Eveleth. Bimonthly Bull., 14 (2): 46-47, Nov.-Dec., 1951.

"WATER BLOOM" AS A CAUSE OF POISONING IN LIVESTOCK IN NORTH DAKOTA. T. O. Brandenburg, Fred M. Shigley. Jour. Amer. Vet. Med. Assn., 110 (843): 384-385, June, 1947.

(PATHOLOGIC DENTAL ANOMALIES OF SOME UNGULATES OF THE PAMPAS.) Anomalias patologicas dentarias en algunos ungulados pampeanos. Notas prelim. Angel Cabrera. Mus. de La Plata, Buenos Aires, vol.2, pp.183-185, pls.1-2, 1934.

A REVIEW OF BLOAT IN RUMINANTS. H.H. Cole, C. F. Huffman, Max Kleiber, T. M. Olson, A. F. Schalk. Jour. Anim. Sci., Menasha, vol.4, no.3, pp.183-236, Aug., 1945.

THE AMERICAN CATTLE DOCTOR: A COMPLETE WORK ON ALL THE DISEASES OF CATTLE, SHEEP, AND SWINE, INCLUDING EVERY DISEASE PECULIAR TO AMERICA, AND EMBRACING ALL THE LATEST INFORMATION ON THE CATTLE PLAGUE AND TRICHINA. CONTAINING ALSO A GUIDE TO SYMPTOMS, A TABLE OF WEIGHTS AND MEASURES, AND A LIST OF VALUABLE MEDICINES. George H. Dadd. New York, Orange Judd Co., Cincinnati, R. W. Carroll & Co., pp.13-367, illus., 1880.

HELMINTH PARASITES OF NORTH AMERICAN SEMIDOMESTICATED AND WILD RUMINANTS. G. Dikmans. Proc. Helminth. Soc. Wash., 6 (2): 97-101, July, 1939.

TWO NEW LUNGWORMS FROM NORTH AMERICAN RUMINANTS AND A NOTE ON THE LUNGWORMS OF SHEEP IN THE UNITED STATES. G. Dikmans. Proc. U.S. Nat. Mus., vol.79, art.18, pp.1-4, pls.2, Aug.29, 1931.

KETOSIS IN THE RUMINANT SPECIES. Richard Mather Forbes. Abstracts of Theses, 1942, Cornell Univ., Ithaca, pp. 287-288, 1943.

TUBERCULOSIS IN THE BUFFALO. Seymour Hadwen. Jour. Amer. Vet. Med. Assn., 100 (778): 19-22, Jan., 1942.

FURTHER NOTES ON SELENOMONAS FROM CALIFORNIA MAMMALS. (S. RUMINANTIUM FROM RUMEN OF ANTELOPE, DEER, ELK.) Carlton M. Herman, Kenji Sayama. Trans. Amer. Micros. Soc., 70 (2): 185-187, Apr., 1951.

PARASITE INTERRELATIONSHIPS OF DOMESTIC SHEEP AND COLUMBIAN BLACK-TAILED DEER. William M. Longhurst, James R. Douglas. Trans. 18th N. A. Wildl. Conf., pp.168-188, 1953.

OBSERVATIONS ON THE STABILITY OF THE ERYTHROCYTES OF THE OX, PIG AND SHEEP. Marcus W. Lyon, Jr. Jour. Infectious Diseases, vol.22, no.1, pp.49-52, Jan., 1918.

BANG'S DISEASE IN THE YELLOWSTONE NATIONAL PARK BUFFALO AND ELK HERDS. W. M. Rush. Jour. Mam., vol. 13, no.4, pp.371-372, Nov., 1932.

SOME REMARKS ON THE GEOGRAPHICAL DISTRIBUTION OF CERTAIN CILIATES FOUND IN THE DIGESTIVE TRACT OF RUMINANTS. J.F.M. Schuurman. South Afr. Jour. Sci., Pretoria, vol.23, pp.571-574, Dec., 1926.

INTERNAL METAZOAN PARASITES COLLECTED FROM RUMINANTS IN THE PHILIPPINE ISLANDS. Benjamin Schwartz. Philippine Jour. Sci., vol.26, pp.521-534, Apr., 1925.

(SOME REMARKS ON THE TRICHURIS WORMS OF RUMINANTS.) Einige Bemerkungen ueber die Trichocephalen der Wiederkauer. C. Sprehn. Zool. Anzeiger, vol.70, pp.83-93, illus., Feb.20, 1927.

THE LIFE CYCLE OF FASCIOLOIDES MAGNA (BASSI, 1875), THE LARGE LIVER FLUKE OF RUMINANTS, IN CANADA, WITH OBSERVATIONS ON THE BIONOMICS OF THE LARVAL STAGES AND THE INTERMEDIATE HOSTS, PATHOLOGY OF FASCIOLOIDIASIS MAGNA, AND CONTROL MEASURES. W. E. Swales. Canadian Jour. Research, vol. 12, no.2, pp.177-215, pls.1-5, Feb., 1935.

SKRJABINEMA OREAMI SP. NOV., A NEMATODE PARASITE OF OREAMNOS AMERICANUS AND RANGIFER SP. IN CANADA. W. E. Swales. Canadian Jour. Research, vol.10, no.5, pp.527-531, figs., May, 1934.

ROUTE OF MIGRATING PARASITES IN RUMINANTS. J. H. Tetley. Nature, London, vol.138, no.3497, p.802, Nov.7, 1936.

BRUCELLA INFECTION AMONG EWES, CAMELS AND PIGS IN EGYPT. R. Zaki. Jour. Comp. Path. and Therap., London, vol.58, no.2, pp.145-151, 1948.

Ecology, Habits, Behavior

(ETHOLOGIC NOTES ON SOME AFRICAN MAMMALS. GENERAL NOTES ON THE RUMINANT ARTIODACTYLS OF THE SAVANNAS.) Notes ethologiques sur quelques mammiferes africains. Generalities sur les artiodactyles ruminants des savanes. G. Babault. Mammalia, Paris, vol.13, no.3, pp.57-68, Sept., 1949.

THE ANTELOPE SITUATION. (ANTELOPE-LIVESTOCK RELATIONS IN WESTERN TEXAS.) Helmut K. Buechner. Texas Game and Fish, 6 (5): 5, 12, 17-18, Apr., 1948.

THE RANGE VEGETATION IN KERR COUNTY, TEXAS, IN RELATION TO LIVESTOCK AND WHITE-TAILED DEER. Helmut K. Buechner. MS thesis, A. & M.

Coll., Texas, 1943; Amer. Midland Nat., Notre Dame, vol.31, no.3, pp.697-743, May, 1944.

SHEEP AND DEER FRATERNISING. Jeremiah Colman. Field, London, vol. 148, p.690, Oct.14, 1926.

RANGE COMPETITION BETWEEN MULE DEER, BIGHORN SHEEP, AND ELK IN JASPER PARK, ALBERTA. I. McT. Cowan. Trans. N.A. Wildl. Conf., 12: 223-227, 1947.

SOCIAL LIFE IN UNGULATES. F. Darling. In Structure et Physiologie des Societies Animales, Paris, March (1952), pp.221-225, 1950.

DEER-LIVESTOCK FORAGE STUDIES ON THE INTERSTATE WINTER DEER RANGE IN CALIFORNIA. William Dasmann. Jour. Range Mgt., 2 (4): 206-212, Oct., 1949.

A STUDY OF SOME INTERRELATIONSHIPS OF A NATIVE SOUTH TEXAS RANGE, ITS CATTLE, AND ITS DEER. Richard B. Davis. PhD thesis, A. & M. Coll., Texas, 1952.

THE USE OF RUMEN CONTENTS DATA IN A STUDY OF DEER-CATTLE COMPETITION AND "ANIMAL EQUIVALENCE." Richard B. Davis. Trans. 17th N.A. Wildl. Conf., pp.448-458, illus., 1952.

DEER VERSUS LIVESTOCK ON GULF COAST RANGE. Phil Goodrum, Vincent H. Reid. Presented at 8th Ann. Conf. S.E. Assn. Game and Fish Comm., New Orleans, La., pp.1-6, mimeo, Nov., 1954.

SHEEP FRATERNIZING WITH DEER. H.A. C. Goodwin. Field, London, vol.148, p. 543, Sept.23, 1926.

NORTHERN YELLOWSTONE WINTER RANGE STUDIES. (EFFECT OF BIG GAME ON RANGE VEGETATION.) Rudolf L. Grimm. Jour. Wildl. Mgt., 3 (4): 295-306, Oct., 1939.

THEY DIE YOUNG. (DEER AND LIVESTOCK OVERPOPULATION IN CENTRAL TEXAS.) Henry C. Hahn. Texas Game and Fish 5 (11): 5, 25-26, Oct., 1947.

BIGHORN--DEER FOOD RELATIONSHIPS IN SOUTHERN NEW MEXICO. Arthur F. Halloran, Cecil A. Kennedy. Jour. Wildl. Mgt., 13 (4): 417-419, Oct., 1949.

VIABLE SEED RECOVERED FROM FECAL PELLETS OF SHEEP AND DEER. Harold F. Heady. Jour. Range Mgt., 7 (6): 259-261, Nov., 1954.

MOUNTAIN SHEEP DRIVE MULE DEER FROM FOOD. Gilbert N. Hunter, Robert G. Kinghorn. Jour. Mam., vol.31, no.2, p.193, May 25, 1950.

DEER AND CATTLE RANGE RELATIONS IN UTAH. Odell Julander. For. Sci., 1 (2): 130-139, map, June, 1955.

DEER AND LIVESTOCK COMPETITION IN UTAH. Odell Julander. Proc. 32nd Ann. Conf. Western Assn. State Game and Fish Comm., Glacier Nat. Park, Mont., June 15-17, 1952, pp.79-85, maps, 1953.

ECOLOGY OF DEER-LIVESTOCK FOOTHILL RANGES IN UTAH. Odell Julander. Proc. 34th. Ann. Conf. Western Assn. State Game and Fish Comm., pp.186-194, May, 1954 (1955).

DEER AND CATTLE RANGE RELATIONSHIPS ON OAK CREEK RANGE IN UTAH. Odell Julander, W. Leslie Robinette. Jour. Forestry, Wash., vol.48, no.6, pp. 410-415, illus., June, 1950.

THE KAIBAB NORTH COOPERATIVE DEER-LIVESTOCK FORAGE RELATIONSHIP STUDY. Thomas L. Kimball, Allan G. Watkins. Ariz. Game and Fish Comm., pp. 1-77, illus., 1951.

(ECOLOGIC AND ETHOLOGIC OBSERVATIONS ON THE ANTELOPES AND THE CHEVROTAIN OF THE GABON.) Observations ecologiques et ethologiques sur les antilopes et le chevrotain du gabon. A. R. Maclatchy. Mammalia, Paris, 15 (1-2): 1-10, Mar.-June, 1951.

STATUS OF BROWSE ON RANGES OF EASTERN OREGON AND EASTERN WASHINGTON. (LIVESTOCK HAVE REDUCED WINTER FOOD OF MULE DEER AND ELK.) Glenn E. Mitchell. Jour. Range Mgt., 3 (4): 249-253, July, 1951.

COMPETITION OF ELK AND DOMESTIC LIVESTOCK FOR SUMMER RANGE FORAGE. G. D. Pickford, Elbert H. Reid. Jour. Wildl. Mgt., 7 (3): 328-332, July, 1943.

GAME-LIVESTOCK FORAGE COMPETITION STUDY IN COLORADO. Glenn Rogers. Proc. 32nd. Ann. Conf. Western Assn. State Game and Fish Comm., Glacier Nat. Park, Mont., June 15-17, 1952, pp.228-232, 1953.

(SOME CASES OF DESIRE TO ATTACK IN RUMINANTS.) Ueber einige Faelle von Angriffslust bei Wiederkauern. Ad Schumann. Zool. Garten, Leipzig, n.F., vol.3, nos.1-3, pp.39-42, May, 1930.

EFFECTS OF MULE DEER AND LIVESTOCK UPON A FOOTHILL RANGE IN NORTHERN UTAH. Arthur D. Smith. Jour. Wildlife Mgt., Menasha, vol.13, no. 4, pp.421-423, Oct., 1949.

LIVESTOCK AND DEER GRAZING EFFECT ON UTAH VEGETATION IS POINTED OUT. Arthur D. Smith. Utah Fish and Game Bull., Salt Lake City, vol.6, no.2, pp.1-2, Oct., 1948.

MULE DEER VS. LIVESTOCK. Arthur D. Smith. Utah Fish and Game Bull., 7 (12): 1, 4-5, 7, Mar., 1950.

THE STATUS OF FORAGE PREFERENCE STUDIES OF MULE DEER AND SHEEP GRAZED WITHIN PORTABLE PADDOCKS. Arthur D. Smith. Proc. Ann. Conf. W. Assn. State Game and Fish Comm., 30: 113-116, 1950.

DEER AND SHEEP COMPETITION IN UTAH. Justin G. Smith, Odell Julander. Jour. Wildl. Mgt., 17 (2): 101-112, map and graph, Apr., 1953.

LAND, LIVESTOCK AND DEER IN THE MILFORD-DOYLE AREA OF NORTHEASTERN CALIFORNIA. M. L. Upchurch, T. S. Brown. Calif. Agr. Ext. Serv., pp. 32, illus., Nov., 1951.

THE COMPARATIVE FORAGE UTILIZATION BETWEEN ROCKY MOUNTAIN MULE DEER AND DOMESTIC LIVESTOCK. Clarence Williamson. Wyo. Range Mgt., Issue no. 25, pp.3, July, 1950.

THE COOPERATIVE KAIBAB NORTH LIVESTOCK-DEER FORAGE RELATIONSHIP STUDY. J. T. Wright. Ariz. Game and Fish Comm., Job Compl. Rep. 27-R, pp.iv, 222, map, June, 1952.

Eurasia

PIGS AND DEER FROM ASIATIC EXPEDITIONS. Glover M. Allen. Amer. Mus. Nov., no.430, pp.19, Sept.18, 1930.

DAYS IN THE DAWNA MOUNTAINS IN QUEST OF A RARE BARKING DEER. E. H. Peacock. Field, London, vol.163, no. 4240, pp.693-694, illus., Mar.31, 1934.

(STUDIES ON THE RUMINANTS OF CENTRAL ASIA.) Etude sur les Ruminants de l'Asic centrale. Eugene De Pousargues. Mem. Soc. Zool. France, vol.11, pp.126-224, 1898.

ON THE ARTIODACTYLA-FAUNA IN THE SOUTHERN PART OF YUNNAN-PROVINCE (CHINA). I. I. Sokolov. Zool. Zhurnal, Moscow, 36 (11): 1750-1760, 1957. (In Russian, with English summary.)

(CAMELS AND REINDEER IN THE SOVIET UNION.) Kamele und Rentiere in der Sowjetunion. N. v. Transehe. Zool. Garten, N.F., vol.18, nos.3-4, pp.150-151, 1951.

RED DEER AND CHAMLIS STALKING IN AUSTRIA. Field, London, vol.166, no. 4322, pp.962-963, illus., Oct.26, 1935.

Fossils

BRACHYODUS BORBONICUS CASTELNAU D'ESTRETEFONDS. Gaston Astre. Comptes Rendus Somm. Séance Soc. Géol. France, no.5, pp.63-65, 1929.

STUDIES ON ENDOCRANIAL ANATOMY. II. ON THE ENDOCRANIAL ANATOMY OF OREODON (MERYCOIDODON). Davidson Black. Jour. Comp. Neurology, vol.32, pp.271-327, figs.48, Dec., 1920.

VARIATION IN THE SPECIES OF MERYCOIDODON. Boardman Bump, F. B. Loomis. Amer. Jour. Sci., vol.20, no. 115, pp.17-21, figs.2, July, 1930.

THE OSTEOLOGY AND RELATIONSHIPS OF ARCHAEOMERYX, AN ANCESTRAL RUMINANT. Edwin H. Colbert. Amer. Mus. Nov., New York, no.1135, pp.1-24, figs.6, Aug.7, 1941.

A NEW DICHOBUNID ARTIODACTYL FROM THE UINTA EOCENE. Charles Lewis Gazin. Mus. Comp. Zool., Harvard Univ., Breviora, no.96, pp.6, illus., 1958.

NOTES ON A NEWLY MOUNTED SKELETON OF MERYCOIDODON, A FOSSIL MAMMAL. Charles W. Gilmore. Proc. U.S. Nat. Mus., vol.31, no.1492, pp.513-514, pl.12, 1906.

PLEISTOCENE VERTEBRATES FROM CELEBES. III. ANOA DEPRESSICORNIS (SMITH) SUBSP., AND BABYROUSA BABYRUSSA BERUENSIS NOV. SUBSP. D. A. Hooijer. Proc. Kon. Nederlandsche Akad. Wetenschappen, Amsterdam, vol.51, no.10, pp.3-11, pl.1, 1948.

(THE LABYRINTH AND BRAIN OF CAENOTHERIUM.) Das Labyrinth und das Gehirn von Caenotherium. Joh. Huerzeler. Eclogae geologicae Helvetiae, Basel, vol. 28, no.2, p.590, (1935) Jan.8, 1936.

REPORTS OF THE AWATOVI EXPEDITION, PEABODY MUSEUM, HARVARD UNIVERSITY. REPORT NO.4. PART I. MAMMALS FOUND AT THE AWATOVI SITE. PART II. POST-CRANIAL SKELETAL CHARACTERS OF DEER, PRONGHORN, AND SHEEP-GOAT WITH NOTES ON BOS AND BISON. Barbara Lawrence. Papers Peabody Mus. Amer. Archae. and Ethnol., Cambridge, vol.35, no.3, pp.vii, 43, illus., 1951.

ON A FOSSIL GENUS AND SPECIES OF RUMINANTOID PACHYDERMATA: MERYCOIDODON CULBERTSONII. Joseph Leidy. Proc. Acad. Nat. Sci. Phila., pp. 1-3, figs.5, 1848.

LEPTAUCHENIA AND CYCLOPIDIUS. F. B. Loomis. Amer. Jour. Sci., vol.9, pp.241-249, illus., Mar., 1925.

THE SKELETON OF NANNOTRAGULUS. F. B. Loomis. Amer. Jour. Sci., ser.5, vol.25, no.149, pp.290-398, figs.6, May, 1933.

A SKELETON OF MERYCOIDODON GRACILIS AND ITS ADAPTIVE SIGNIFICANCE. W. D. Matthew. Univ. Calif. Publ. Bull. Dept. Geol. Sci., Berkeley, vol.22, no.2, pp.13-30, pls.2-3, July 12, 1932.

THE SKULL OF HYPISODUS, THE SMALLEST OF THE ARTIODACTYLA, WITH A REVISION OF THE HYPERTRAGULIDAE. W. D. Matthew. Bull. Amer. Mus. Nat. Hist., New York, vol.16, art.23, pp.311-316, figs.4, Sept.25, 1902.

A FOSSIL MAMMAL WITH UNBORN TWINS. Cleophas C. O'Hara. Science, vol.71, no. 1839, pp.341-342, Mar.28, 1930.

ON THE SKULLS OF EARLY TERTIARY SUIDAE, TOGETHER WITH AN ACCOUNT OF THE OTIC REGION IN SOME OTHER PRIMITIVE ARTIODACTYLA. Helga S. Pearson. Philos. Trans. Roy. Soc. Lond., B, vol.215, pp.389-460, Aug.17, 1927.

ANALYSIS OF MERYCOIDODON SKULLS. Fred B. Phleger, Jr., W. S. Putnam. Amer. Jour. Sci., New Haven, vol.240, no.8, pp. 547-566, figs.5, Aug., 1942.

TWO YOUNG MERYCOIDODONTS. Fred B. Phleger, Jr., Frank C. Whitmore, Jr. Amer. Jour. Sci., ser.5, vol.36, pp.377-388, pls.1-2, Nov., 1938.

DESCRIPTION AND FIGURATION OF LOPHIOBUNODON MINERVOISENSIS. Marguerite Richard. Bull. Soc. Hist. Nat., Toulouse, vol.77, fasc.2, pp.141-144, figs.2, Sept.30, 1942.

THREE NEW OREODONTS. (EPOREODON CHEEKI, MESOREODON SCOTTI, PROMERYCOCHOERUS LOOMISI.) Erich Maren Schlaikjer. Proc. Boston Soc. Nat. Hist., vol.40, no.3, pp.219-231, Dec., 1934.

MERYCOCHOERINAE A NEW SUBFAMILY OF OREODONTS. C. Bertrand Schultz, Charles H. Falkenbach. Bull. Amer. Mus. Nat. Hist., New York, vol.77, pp.213-306, figs.18, Oct.23, 1940.

MERYCHYINAE, A SUBFAMILY OF OREODONTS. Bertrand C. Schultz, Charles H. Falkenbach. Bull. Amer. Mus. Nat. Hist., New York, vol.88, art.4, pp.157-286, figs. 17, tables 6, charts 4, Mar.25, 1947.

PHENACOCOELINAE, A NEW SUBFAMILY OF OREODONTS. C. Bertrand Schultz, Charles H. Falkenbach. Bull. Amer. Mus. Nat. Hist., New York, vol.95, art.3, pp. 87-150, illus., Nov.13, 1950.

DESMATOCHOERINAE, A NEW SUBFAMILY OF OREODONTS. C. Bertrand Schultz, Charles H. Falkenbach. Bull. Amer. Mus. Nat. Hist., vol.105, pp.143-256, illus., Dec.6, 1954.

MINIOCHOERINAE AND OREONETINAE, TWO NEW SUBFAMILIES OF OREODONTS. C. Bertrand Schultz, Charles H. Falkenbach. Bull. Amer. Mus. Nat. Hist., 109 (4): 377-482, illus., July 2, 1956.

PROMERYCOCHOERINAE, A NEW SUBFAMILY OF OREODONTS. C. Bertrand Schultz, Charles H. Falkenbach. Bull. Amer. Mus. Nat. Hist., New York, vol. 93, pp.69-198, figs.26, May 20, 1949.

PRELIMINARY NOTE ON THE SELENODONT ARTIODACTYLS OF THE UINTA FORMATION. William B. Scott. Proc. Amer. Philos. Soc., Phila., vol.37, no. 157, pp.73-81, July, 1898.

A SKELETON OF MERYCOIDODON GRACILIS AND ITS ADAPTIVE SIGNIFICANCE. George Gaylord Simpson. Univ. Calif. Publ., Bull. Dept. Geol. Sci., vol. 22, no.2, pp.13-30, pls.2-3, July 12, 1932.

COMMENTS ON THE RELATIONSHIPS OF THE CERVOID FAMILY PALAEOMERYCIDAE. R. A. Stirton. Amer. Jour. Sci., New Haven, vol.242, pp.633-655, figs.2, Dec., 1944.

ADDITIONAL NOTES ON OREODONTOIDEA OREGONENSIS THORPE. Malcolm R. Thorpe. Amer. Jour. Sci., ser.5, vol.7, pp.316-319, figs.3, Apr., 1924.

THE GEOGRAPHIC DISTRIBUTION OF THE MERYCOIDODONTIDAE. Malcolm R. Thorpe. Amer. Jour. Sci., vol.34, no. 199, pp.9-11, July, 1937.

THE GEOLOGICAL DISTRIBUTION OF THE MERYDOIDODONTIDAE. Malcolm R. Thorpe. Amer. Jour. Sci., ser.5, vol.33, no.198, pp.426-429, June, 1937.

THE GEOLOGICAL HISTORY OF THE OREODONTS. Malcolm R. Thorpe. Jour. Mam., vol.6, no.2, pp.69-82, pls.6-7, figs.5, May, 1925.

THE GENERIC DISTINCTIONS BETWEEN MERYCOCHOERUS LEIDY AND PROMERYCOCHOERUS DOUGLASS. Malcolm R. Thorpe. Amer. Jour. Sci., ser.5, vol.7, pp.121-131, Feb., 1924.

HYOID APPARATUS OF MERYCOIDODON. Malcolm R. Thorpe. Amer. Jour. Sci., vol.5, pp.225-228, illus., 1923.

THE MERYCOIDODONTIDAE. AN EXTINCT GROUP OF RUMINANT MAMMALS. Malcolm R. Thorpe. Mem. Peabody Mus. Nat. Hist., New Haven, vol.3, pt.4, pp. xxi, 428, figs.188, pls.50, Mar.31, 1937.

NATURAL BRAIN CASTS OF MERYCOIDODONTS. Malcolm R. Thorpe. Amer. Jour. Sci., vol.21, pp.193-203, figs.4, Mar., 1931.

THE OSTEOLOGY OF EPOREODON SOCIALIS MARSH. Malcom R. Thorpe. Bull. 2 Peabody Mus. Nat. Hist., pp.43, figs.23, pls.2, 1931.

PHYLOGENY OF THE MERYCOIDODONTS. Malcolm R. Thorpe. Amer. Jour. Sci., ser.5, vol.33, no.196, pp.252-259, Apr., 1937.

THE PRIMITIVE, AND CARNIVORE-LIKE CHARACTERS OF THE MERYCOIDODONTIDAE. Malcom R. Thorpe. Amer. Jour. Sci., ser.5, vol.6, no.33, pp.239-246, Sept., 1923.

EARLY MIOCENE ENTELODONTS, TEXAS COASTAL PLAIN. John A. Wilson. Amer. Jour. Sci., 255: 641-649, illus., Nov., 1957.

Fossils--Eurasia

(CAVICORNS OF THE HIPPARION FAUNA OF NORTHERN CHINA.) Cavicornier der hipparion-fauna nord-Chinas. Birger Bohlin. China, Geological Survey, Palaeont. Sinica, Peiping, ser.C, vol.9, fasc.4, pp. 5, 166, pl.1-20, tables, illus., 1935.

PSEUDAMPHIMERYX HANTONENSIS, SP. N., WITH NOTES ON CERTAIN SPECIES OF ARTIODACTYLS FROM THE EOCENE DEPOSITS OF HORDWELL. C. Forster Cooper. Ann. and Mag. Nat. Hist., Lond. (10), vol.2, no.7, pp.49-55, figs.2, pls.3, 1928.

ANTHRACOTHERIIDAE IN CEYLON. P.E. P. Deraniyagala. Nature, London, vol.149, no.3777, p.330, illus., Mar.21, 1942.

(ANTHRACOTERIUM OF SZAPAR.) A Szapári Anthracotherium. J. Ehik. Állattani Koezlemények, vol.24, pp.77-81, illus; pp.116-120 (full résumé in English), 1927.

(REMAINS OF ANTHRACOTHERES OF SOUTHERN AND WESTERN GERMANY.) Reste von Anthracotheriiden aus Sued- und Westdeutschland. R. v. Koenigswald. Centralblatt f. Mineral., Abt.B, no.4, pp. 217-221, 1932.

ON SOME NEW FOSSIL CERVICORNS FROM KAZUSA AND LIUKIN. Hikoshichiro Matsumoto. Sci. Rep. Tohoku Imp. Univ., ser.2 (Geol.), vol.10, pp.17-26, illus., 1926.

THE ARTIODACTYLA OF THE EOCENE OF BURMA. Guy E. Pilgrim. Mem. Geol. Surv. India, Palaeontologia Indica, vol.13, pp.1-39, pl.4, 1928.

(THE RUMINANTS OF THE HUNGARIAN PRE-GLACIAL.) Die Ruminantier des ungarischen Praeglacials. Fritz Schmidt. Ecologae Geologicae Helvetiae, Basel, vol. 25, no.2, pp.319-330, Dec., 1932.

(REMARKS ON THE ANTHRACOTHERIUM OF THE FRENCH OLIGOCENE.) Remarques sur les Anthracotherium de l'Oligocène Francais. Rudolf Sieber. Bull. Soc. Hist. Nat. de Toulouse, vol.70, fasc.1, pp.351-361, Dec.30, 1936.

(ANTHRACOTHERIUM REMAINS FROM PETROSANI.) Aspura unui anthracotherium de la Petrosani. I. Simionescu. Acad. Romana. Mem. Sectiunii Stiintifice, Bucuresti, ser.3, vol.10, pp.1-13, figs.6, pl.1, 1934-35. (In Rumanian, with German summary.)

(PLIOCENE MAMMALS FROM CIMISLIA (BESSARABIA). V. RUMINANTS.) Mamiferele Pliocene dela Cimislia (Basarabia). V. Rumegatoarele. I. Simionescu, Elena Dobrecu. Acad. Romana Publ. Fondului Vasile Adamachi, Bucuresti, vol.9, no.54, pp.1-36, figs.49, pls.3, 1941.

(ARTIODACTYLS WITH FIVE-FINGERED FRONTAL EXTREMITIES FROM THE EUROPEAN OLIGOCENE.) Artiodactylen mit fuenffingriger Vorderextremitaet aus dem europaeischen Oligocaen. H. G. Stehlin. Verhandl. Naturforsch. Ges. Basel, vol.40, pt.2, pp.599-625, figs.13, (1928-1929) 1929.

NEW ENTELODONTIDS FROM MONGOLIA AND KAZAKHSTAN. B. A. Trofimov. Proc. Paleo. Inst., Acad. Sci. USSR, vol. 41, pp.144-154, illus., 1952.

ON THE ARTIODACTYLA FROM THE SINANTHROPUS SITE AT CHOUK'OUTIEN. C. C. Young. Paleontographia Sinica, ser. C, vol.8, no.2, Peiping, pp.158, figs.32, pls.29, 1932.

Fossils--North America

A NEW ANTILOCAPRID AND A NEW CERVID FROM THE LATE TERTIARY OF NEBRASKA. Erwin Hinckley Barbour, C. Bertrand Schultz. Amer. Mus. Nov., no.734, pp.4, fig.1, Aug.3, 1934.

A NEW OREODONT SLAB. Erwin Hinckley Barbour, C. Bertrand Schultz. Bull. Nebraska State Mus., Lincoln, vol.1, no. 31, pp.259-262, fig.162, Oct., 1932.

BRACHYHYOPS, A NEW BUNODONT ARTIODACTYL FROM BEAVER DIVIDE, WYOMING. Edwin H. Colbert. Ann. Carnegie Mus., vol.28, pp.87-108, fig.5, Mar.17, 1938.

NOTICE OF A NEW GENUS AND SPECIES OF ARTIODACTYL FROM THE UPPER EOCENE OF WYOMING. (BRACHYHYOPS, B. WYOMINGENSIS.) Edwin H. Colbert. Amer. Jour. Sci., ser.5, vol.33, no.198, pp.473-474, June, 1937.

A MIOCENE OREODONT FROM JACKSON HOLE, WYOMING. (MERYCHYUS ARENARUM COPE.) Edwin H. Colbert. Jour. Palaeont., Menasha, vol.17, no.3, pp.298-304, figs.3, May, 1943.

NEW ARTIODACTYLS FROM THE OLIGOCENE AND LOWER MIOCENE OF NEBRASKA. Harold J. Cook. Amer. Midland Nat., Notre Dame, vol.15, no.2, pp. 148-164, pls.3-4, Mar., 1934.

A KITCHEN MIDDEN WITH BONES OF EXTINCT ANIMALS IN THE UPPER LAKES AREA. (BONES OF BISON OLIVER-HAYI, ELK AND CARIBOU.) Samuel Eddy, Albert Ernest Jenks. Science, n.s., vol. 81, no.2109, p.535, May 31, 1935.

HORNED RUMINANTS OF NORTH AMERICA. Childs Frick. Bull. Amer. Mus. Nat. Hist., New York, vol.69, pp.xxviii, 669, figs.68, Mar.31, 1937.

A REVIEW OF THE UPPER EOCENE ARTIODACTYLA OF NORTH AMERICA. C. Lewis Gazin. Smithsonian Misc. Coll., Wash., vol.128, no.8, pp.1-96, illus., Sept.28, 1955.

DESCRIPTIONS OF TWO NEW SPECIES OF RUMINANTS FROM THE PLEISTOCENE OF IOWA. Oliver P. Hay. Proc. Biol. Soc. Wash., vol.26, pp.5-8, fig., Jan.18, 1913.

OREODONS OF THE LOWER HARRISON BEDS. F. B. Loomis. Amer. Jour. Sci., ser.5, vol.6, pp.222-228, figs.5, Sept., 1923.

THREE OREODONT SKELETONS FROM THE LOWER MIOCENE OF THE GREAT PLAINS. F. B. Loomis. Bull. Geol. Soc. Amer., vol.44, pp.723-734, figs.9, Aug. 31, 1933.

THE NORTH AMERICAN ANTHRACOTHERES. J. R. Macdonald. Jour. Paleon., 30 (3): 615-645, May, 1956.

ARRETOTHERIUM FRICKI, A NEW MIOCENE ANTHRACOTHERE FROM NEBRASKA. J. R. Macdonald, C. B. Schultz. Bull. Univ. Nebraska State Mus., 4 (3): 52-58, illus., May, 1956.

EXHIBIT SHOWS PIG-LIKE ANIMALS OF THE BAD LANDS 30 MILLION YEARS AGO. Elmer S. Riggs. Field Mus. News, Chicago, vol.12, no.12, pp.4-5, illus., Dec., 1941.

THE MAMMALIAN FAUNA OF THE WHITE RIVER OLIGOCENE, PART IV. ARTIODACTYLA. William Berryman Scott. Trans. Amer. Philos. Soc., Phila., n.s., vol.28, pt.4, pp.363-764, figs.118-136, pls. 36-78, Apr., 1940.

WHITE RIVER ARTIODACTYLA. William Berryman Scott. Science, n.s., vol.88, no. 2291, pp.503-504, Nov.25, 1938.

A REVISION OF THE BUNODONT ARTIODACTYLA OF THE MIDDLE AND LOWER EOCENE OF NORTH AMERICA. William J. Sinclair. Bull. Amer. Mus. Nat. Hist., New York, vol.33, art.21, pp.267-295, figs.28, May 15, 1914.

ARTIODACTYLA FROM THE FOSSIL BEDS OF FISH LAKE VALLEY, NEVADA. R. A. Stirton. Univ. Calif. Publ., Bull. Dept. Geol. Sci., vol.18, pp.291-302, illus., June 1, 1929.

A NEW GENUS OF ARTIODACTYLA FROM THE CLARENDON LOWER PLIOCENE OF TEXAS. R. A. Stirton. Univ. Calif. Publ. Bull. Dept. Geol. Sci., vol.21, no.6, pp.147-168, figs.3, pls.6-11, Feb.26, 1932.

A NEW RUMINANT FROM THE HEMPHILL MIDDLE PLIOCENE OF TEXAS. (PEDIOMERYX, P. HEMPHILLENSIS.) R. A. Stirton. Jour. Paleont., vol.10, no.7, pp. 644-647, fig.1, Oct., 1936.

ARTIODACTYLA FROM THE SESPE OF THE LAS POSAS HILLS, CALIFORNIA. Chester Stock. Publ.453, Carnegie Inst. Wash. (Contrib. Paleont.), pp.119-126, pl.1, July 20, 1935.

HESPEROMERYX, A NEW ARTIODACTYL FROM THE SESPE EOCENE, CALIFORNIA. Chester Stock. Proc. Nat. Acad. Sci., vol. 22, no.3, pp.177-182, pl.1, Mar., 1936.

A HYPERTRAGULID FROM THE SESPE UPPERMOST EOCENE, CALIFORNIA. Chester Stock. Proc. Nat. Acad. Sci., Wash., vol.20, no.12, pp.625-629, pl.1, Dec.15, 1934.

ON THE OCCURRENCE OF AN OREODONT SKELETON IN THE SESPE OF SOUTH MOUNTAIN, CALIFORNIA. Chester Stock. Proc. Nat. Acad. Sci., vol.20, no. 9, pp.518-523, figs.2, pls.2, Sept., 1934.

OREODONTS FROM THE SESPE DEPOSITS OF SOUTH MOUNTAIN, VENTURA COUNTY, CALIFORNIA. Chester Stock. Contrib. to Palaeontology, Carnegie Inst. Wash., Publ.404, pp.27-42, figs.2, pls.1-2, Aug., 1930.

QUATERNARY ANTELOPE REMAINS FROM A SECOND CAVE DEPOSIT IN THE ORGAN MOUNTAINS, NEW MEXICO. Chester Stock. Los Angeles Mus., Publ. ser. no. 2, Paleont. no.2, pp.1-18, figs.3, May 29, 1930.

WHITE RIVER (OLIGOCENE) EPOREODONS. Malcom R. Thorpe. Amer. Jour. Sci., ser. 5, vol.7, pp.219-225, Mar., 1924.

Horns and Antlers

HORNS AND ANTLERS. Belle J. Benchley. Zoonooz, San Diego, vol.16, no.11, pp.3-5, illus., Nov., 1943.

HORNS AND ANTLERS. (WHITETAIL AND MULE DEER, WAPITI, MOOSE, REINDEER, CARIBOU, PRONGHORN, MOUNTAIN GOAT.) Wilfrid S. Bronson. Harcourt, Brace and Co., New York, pp.143, illus., 1942.

(ANTLERS AND HORNS.) Von den Geweihen und Gehornen. Paul Matschie. Emil Regeners "Jagdmethoden und Fanggeheimnisse," Zweiter Abschnitt, pp.301-328, figs. 129-177, 1902.

THE RELATIONSHIP OF CERTAIN VARIANT FOSSIL TYPES OF "HORN" TO THOSE OF THE LIVING PECORA. Guy E. Pilgrim. Ann. and Mag. Nat. Hist., London, ser.11, vol.7, no.38, pp.172-184, Feb., 1941.

DATES ON SHEDDING OF HORNS IN YELLOWSTONE PARK. M. P. Skinner. Jour. Mam., vol.2, no.2, p.116, May, 1921.

HORN SHEDDING IN YELLOWSTONE PARK. M. P. Skinner. Jour. Mam., vol.2, no.3, pp.172-173, Aug., 1921.

Hunting and Trapping

TRAPS AND SNARES FROM UPPER EGYPT. James Hornell. Ethnos, Stockholm, vol.2, no.3, pp.65-73, figs.7, May, 1937.

HUNTING ON THE UPPER KLUTLAN. (HUNTING MOUNTAIN SHEEP, MOOSE, AND CARIBOU NEAR THE ALASKA-YUKON BOUNDARY.) L. Mighell. Forest and Stream, vol.89, pp.265-267, 318, June, 1919.

DATA ON ELK AND ANTELOPE HUNTING. Charles C. Niehuis. Arizona Wildlife and Sportsman, Safford, vol.6, no.10, p.8, Oct., 1944.

GAME WON'T FOLLOW THE RULES. (ELK, ANTELOPE.) Clyde Ormond. Field and Stream, New York, vol.51, no. 3, pp.44-45, 85-86, illus., July, 1946.

WYOMING GAME UTILIZATION. (TAKE OF BIG GAME IN CONNECTION WITH ESTIMATES OF ELK AND DEER ON NATIONAL FORESTS FOR 1938.) Wyo. Wild Life, 4 (8): 1-2, 18-19, Aug., 1939.

Hybrids

A MOOSE-DAIRY COW CROSS? W. W. Green, R. Fenstermacher. Jour. Heredity, Wash., D.C., vol.30, no.10, pp.458-460, figs.21-22, Oct., 1939.

(YAK-NEAT HYBRID.) Ein Bastard zwischen Yak und Rind. H. Peters. Ber. Internat. Ges. Erhaltung des Wisents, Berlin, vol.3, no.3, p.166, pls.12-13, Mar. 1, 1932.

Management

EMERGENCY FEEDING IN '49. (EFFECT OF FEEDING PROGRAM ON ELK, DEER, AND ANTELOPE.) Chester C. Anderson. Wyoming Wild Life, Cheyenne, vol.13, no. 7, pp.4-13, 37-38, illus., Aug., 1949.

LICKS PRESENT INTERESTING PROBLEM. I. V. Anderson. N. Region News, Jan.6, 1942: 26-27, Jan.6, 1942.

THE DISTRIBUTION OF SALT FOR BIG GAME ANIMALS. I. V. Anderson, Raymond M. West. Field Notes on Wildl., 2 (7): 4, Mar., 1941.

REMOVING SURPLUSES OF WILDLIFE FROM THE STANDPOINT OF STATE ADMINISTRATION. Elliott S. Barker. Trans. N. A. Wildl. Conf., 6: 362-367, 1941.

USE OF SALT IN MANAGING MULE DEER AND DOMESTIC ANIMALS ON RANGE LANDS OF CENTRAL OREGON. William D. Barron. MS thesis, Oreg. State Coll., 1953.

BIG GAME TRANSPLANTING EVALUATION. Faye M. Couey, others. Mont. State Fish and Game Dept., pp.94, July-Sept., 1950.

SOME MANAGEMENT ASPECTS OF GAME-LIVESTOCK RELATIONSHIP IN UTAH. Harold S. Crane. Proc. 32nd. Ann. Conf. Western Assn. State Game and Fish Comm., Glacier Nat. Park, Mont., June 15-17, 1952, pp.90-91, 1953.

COLORADO'S 1949 BIG GAME WINTER FEEDING BY AIR. Jack C. Culbreath. Colo. Cons. Comments, 10 (9): 7-8, 30, Mar., 1949.

CONSERVATION. BIALOWIES, THE OLD AND NEW HOME OF THE EUROPEAN BISON. THE WOOD BISON, PLAINS BISON, AND PRONGHORN ANTELOPE IN AMERICA. George G. Goodwin. Nat. Hist., New York, vol.34, no.3, pp.298-301, illus., May-June, 1934.

MANAGEMENT OF DEER AND CATTLE ON THE ARANSAS NATIONAL WILDLIFE REFUGE, TEXAS. Arthur F. Halloran. Jour. Wildl. Mgt., Menasha, vol.7, no. 2, pp.203-216, Apr., 1943.

DEER MANAGEMENT PROBLEMS AS RELATED TO DISEASES AND PARASITES OF DOMESTIC RANGE LIVESTOCK. Carlton M. Herman. Trans. 10th N. Amer. Wildl. Conf., Wash., pp.242-246, 1945.

RANGE MANAGEMENT INCLUDES BIG GAME. G. D. Pickford. Natl. Wool Grower, 33 (3): 18-19, Mar., 1943.

THEODORE ROOSEVELT NATIONAL MEMORIAL PARK AS A GAME SANCTUARY. Russell Reid. N. Dak. Outdoors, 11 (12): 4-5, 12-13, June, 1949.

PRESERVES AND RANGES MAINTAINED FOR BUFFALO AND OTHER BIG GAME. Clara Ruth. U.S. Dept. Agric., Wildl. Research and Mgt., Leaflet BS-95, pp.1-20, figs.12, Sept., 1937.

REINDEER AND MUSK-OX. REPORT OF THE ROYAL COMMISSION UPON THE POSSIBILITIES OF THE REINDEER AND MUSK-OX INDUSTRIES IN THE ARCTIC AND SUB-ARCTIC REGIONS. John Gunion Rutherford, James Stanley McLean, James Bernard Harkin. Ottawa, Dept. of Interior, pp.1-99, illus., 1922.

A FAIR POLICY ON BIG GAME. H. L. Shantz. Natl. Wool Grower, 30 (3): 13-16, Mar., 1940.

HOW BEST TO MANAGE HERDS OF BIG GAME. H. L. Shantz. USDA, Forest Serv., pp.7, 1940.

DEER MANAGEMENT AND RANGE LIVESTOCK PRODUCTION. L. A. Stoddart, D. I. Rasmussen. Utah Agr. Exp. Sta., Cir.121, pp.17, 1945.

WYOMING FEEDS ITS GAME. (DEER, ANTELOPE, AND ELK.) Wyo. Wild Life, 13 (1): 4-7, 37-38, Jan., 1949.

Methods, Techniques

SOME REMARKS CONCERNING THE NORTH DAKOTA BIG GAME SURVEY. (AIRPLANE OBSERVATION AND OTHER METHODS COMPARED AS TO COST AND RESULTS.) Roy N. Bach. N. Dak. Outdoors, 3 (12): 18-22, June, 1941.

PRECIPITIN TEST--A USEFUL TOOL IN GAME-LAW ENFORCEMENT. (DISTINGUISHING VENISON FROM FLESH OF LIVESTOCK.) Allen Brohn, Leroy J. Korschgen. Trans. N. A. Wildl. Conf., 15: 467-476, 1950.

A STUDY OF DEER CENSUS METHODS AND DEER-CATTLE RELATIONSHIPS ON THE ARANSAS NATIONAL WILDLIFE REFUGE. Arthur F. Halloran. MS thesis, A. & M. Coll., Texas, 1941.

AERIAL CENSUS OF BIG GAME IN NORTH DAKOTA. Stanley Saugstad. Trans. N. A. Wildl. Conf., 7: 343-354, 1942.

THE USE OF MOVABLE PADDOCKS IN THE STUDY OF FORAGE PREFERENCES OF MULE DEER AND LIVESTOCK. Arthur D. Smith, David M. Gaufin. Trans. 15th North Amer. Wildlife Conf., Wash., pp. 512-518, 1950.

METHODS USED IN THE KAIBAB (NORTH) LIVESTOCK-DEER FORAGE RELATIONSHIP STUDIES. J. T. Wright. Proc. Ann. Conf. W. Assn. State Game and Fish Comm., 29: 129-134, 1949.

Museum Collections

A PROPOSED STANDARD OF VIEWPOINTS FROM WHICH TO ILLUSTRATE HORNED AND ANTLERED MAMMAL SKULLS. J.D. Figgins. Proc. Colorado Mus. Nat. Hist., vol.10, no.3, p.22, pls.1-3, Sept.26, 1931.

CATALOGUE OF RUMINANT MAMMALIA (PECORA, LINNAEUS) IN THE BRITISH MUSEUM. John E. Gray. London, pp.102, tables 4, 1872.

MUSEUM PRESERVATION OF INCISOR TEETH OF RUMINANTIA. N. Hollister. Jour. Mam., vol.4, no.2, pp.123-125, fig. 1, May, 1923.

(MAMMAL COLLECTION OF THE HOANG PAIHO MUSEUM OF TIEN TSIN. UNGULATA, ORDER ARTIODACTYLA, FAM. BOVIDAE, CERVIDAE AND SUIDAE.) Collection des mammiferes du Musee Hoang Paiho de Tien Tsin. Ungulata, Ordre Artiodactyla, Fam. Bovidae, Cervidae et Suidae. B. P. Jakovleff. Publ. de Musee Hoangho Paiho de Tientsin, no.35, pp.1-31, pls.1-2, Mar., 1935.

CATALOGUE OF THE UNGULATE MAMMALS IN THE BRITISH MUSEUM (NATURAL HISTORY) VOL. 2. ARTIODACTYLA. VOL. 3. ARTIODACTYLA. Richard Lydekker, Gilbert Blaine. 1914.

REMARKS UPON SOME RARE OR UNDESCRIBED RUMINANTS IN THE SOCIETY'S COLLECTION. W. Ogilby. Proc. Zool. Soc. Lond., pt.4, p.119, 1836.

North America

NORTH AMERICAN RUMINANTS. J. A. Allen. Amer. Mus. Jour., vol. 2, pp. 1-29, illus., Mar., 1902.

ANNUAL BIG GAME CENSUS. Roy N. Bach. N. Dak. Outdoors, 7 (10): 12-13, Apr., 1945.

ON THE RUMINATING ANIMALS OF NORTH AMERICA, AND THEIR SUSCEPTIBILITY OF DOMESTICATION. Spencer F. Baird. U.S. Patent Off., Rept., Senate Doc. 118 - House Doc. 102, pp. 104-128, pls. 7, 1851.

THE ANTELOPE AND DEER OF AMERICA. A COMPREHENSIVE SCIENTIFIC TREATISE UPON THE NATURAL HISTORY, INCLUDING THE CHARACTERISTICS, HABITS, AFFINITIES, AND CAPACITY FOR DOMESTICATION OF THE ANTILOCAPRA AND CERVIDAE OF NORTH AMERICA. John Dean Caton. Forest and Stream Publ. Co., New York, 1877.

ANIMALS OF THE PLAINS. (BISON, PRONGHORN ANTELOPE.) Stuart Downing. Canadian Nature, Toronto, vol. 8, no. 5, pp. 152-153, illus., Nov.-Dec., 1946.

REPORT OF THE AMERICAN BISON SOCIETY 1922-23. (TOTAL LIVING AMERICAN BISON, TOTAL LIVING PRONGHORN ANTELOPE.) Martin S. Garretson. Published by the Society, pp. 71, figs. 18, 1923.

HOOFED ANIMALS OF NORTH AMERICA. PT. 2.--ANIMALS WITH HOLLOW HORNS. PT. 3--WILD PIGS. George G. Goodwin. School Nat. League Bull., New York, ser. no. 17, bull. no. 2, pp. 4, illus., Oct., 1946.

NOGLE BETRAKTNINGER OVER FORSKELLIGE FORHOLD I NORDOSTGRONLAND. (MUSK-OX AND REINDEER IN NORTHEAST GREENLAND.) J. G. Jennov. Naturen no. 14, pp. 427-445, illus., 1953.

STATUS OF MEXICAN BIG-GAME HERDS. A. Starker Leopold. Trans. N. A. Wildl. Conf., 12: 437-447, 1947.

CALIFORNIA'S LARGE GAME ANIMALS. (FORMER ABUNDANCE OF BISON, REINDEER, AND VALLEY ELK.) M. Hall McAllister. California Fish and Game, vol. 9, pp. 11-15, fig. 1, Jan., 1923.

OREGON 1947 GAME OUTLOOK. (ELK, MULE DEER, ANTELOPE) John McKean. Oregon Outdoors, Oswego, vol. 4, no. 9, pp. 14-15, 26-29, illus., Sept., 1947.

STATUS OF BIG GAME IN N. D. William T. McKean. N. Dak. Outdoors, 13 (12): 9-11, June, 1951.

COLORADO'S "SPLIT-HOOFED" BIG GAME ANIMALS. Clifford A. Moser, Lyndle Dunn. Colorado Outdoors Mag., 6 (5): 16-17, Sept., 1957.

THE DEER AND ANTELOPE OF NORTH AMERICA. Theodore Roosevelt. In "The Deer Family." 1902.

THE STATUS OF THE DALL SHEEP AND CARIBOU IN ALASKA. Robert F. Scott, Edward F. Chatelain, Winston A. Elkins. Trans. 15th N. A. Wildl. Conf., Wash., pp. 612-626, 1950.

COLORADO. (ELK, DEER, AND MOUNTAIN SHEEP.) Harold Titus. Field and Stream, New York, vol. 48, no. 7, pp. 28-29, 66, illus., Nov., 1943.

(THE PRESENT DISTRIBUTION OF THE LARGER HUNTING MAMMALS IN MEXICO.) (PECCARY AND PRONGHORN ANTELOPE.) Jabalies y berrendos. Distribución actual de los mamíferos de caza mayor en México. Bernardo Villa R. Bol. Divulgación Sec. Agric. y Ganaderia, México, D.F., no. 2, pp. 30, figs. 3, 1951.

SLAUGHTER IN LOWER CALIFORNIA. (MT. SHEEP, ANTELOPE.) Lewis W. Walker. Nat. Hist., New York, vol. 56, no. 9, pp. 385-431, Nov., 1947.

ON THE DISTRIBUTION OF THE DIFFERENT SPECIES OF DEER AND OTHER RUMINANTS IN NORTHERN CALIFORNIA AND OREGON. Thomas Walsingham. Proc. Zool. Soc. Lond., pp. 561-563, 1873.

THE FACE LOOKED FAMILIAR—WHY NOT MAKE SURE? (DEER, MOOSE ELK, MT. SHEEP.) Wyoming Wild Life, Cheyenne, vol. 10, no. 12, pp. 12-17, 38, illus., Dec., 1946.

Phylogeny

(ESSAY ON THE EVOLUTION OF THE MOLAR IN ARTIODACTYL UNGULATES.) Essai sur l'évolution de la molaire chez les Ongulés artiodactyles. R. Anthony, M. Friant. Mem. Mus. Roy. d'Hist. Nat., Belgique, ser. 2, fasc. 3, pp. 489-495, figs. 7, Apr. 30, 1936.

VARIABILITY AND EVOLUTIONARY RATE IN THE OREODONTS. Robert S. Bader. Evolution, Lancaster, vol. 9, no. 2, pp. 119-140, illus., June, 1955.

DISTRIBUTIONAL AND PHYLOGENETIC STUDIES ON INDIAN FOSSIL MAMMALS. IV. THE PHYLOGENY OF THE INDIAN SUIDAE AND THE ORIGIN OF THE HIPPOPOTAMIDAE. Edwin H. Colbert. Amer. Mus. Nov., no. 799, pp. 24, figs. 4, May 8, 1935.

A PHYLOGENETIC CHART OF THE ARTIODACTYLA. W. D. Matthew. Mamm., Balto., vol. 15, no. 3, pp. 207-209, Aug. 10, 1934.

THE ORIGIN OF A MAMMALIAN ORDINAL CHARACTER. Bobb Schaeffer. Evolution, Lancaster, vol. 2, no. 2, pp. 164-175, figs. 5, June, 1948.

Physiology

METABOLISM IN THE RUMEN. E. F. Annison, D. Lewis. 1959.

THE RELATION OF SOILS TO THE COBALT REQUIREMENTS OF RUMINANTS. Kenneth C. Beeson. PhD thesis, Cornell Univ., 1948.

A PHYSICAL DEFICIENCY IN THE RATION OF RUMINANTS. H. H. Cole, S. W. Mead. Science, Lancaster, n.s., vol. 98, no. 2555, pp. 543-544, Dec. 17, 1943.

NUTRITIONAL PHYSIOLOGY OF THE ADULT RUMINANT. E. B. Forbes. Science, Lancaster, n.s., vol. 90, no. 2334, pp. 270-272, Sept. 22, 1939.

CONTINUOUS GASTRIC SECRETION IN THE RUMINANT. K. J. Hill. Quart. Jour. Exper. Physiol., Edinburgh, London, vol. 40, no. 1, pp. 32-39, Jan., 1955.

THE ROLE OF THE RUMEN IN THE NUTRITION OF THE RUMINANT. C. F. Huffman. Sci. Monthly, Lancaster, vol. 66, no. 4, pp. 342-344, Apr., 1948.

DIGESTION IN THE RUMINANT. R. A. McAnally, A. T. Phillipson. Biol. Rev. Cambridge Philos. Soc., London, vol. 19, no. 2, pp. 41-54, Apr., 1944.

OBSERVATIONS ON DIGESTION IN THE RUMINANT. H. E. Magee. Jour. Exper. Biol., vol. 9, no. 4, pp. 409-426, figs. 9, Oct., 1932.

(MOVEMENTS AND INNERVATION OF THE RUMINANT STOMACH.) Bewegungen und Innervation des Wiederkaeuermagens. E. Mangold, W. Klein. George Thieme, Leipzig, pp. 57, figs. 24, 1927.

PHYSIOLOGICAL ASPECTS OF RUMINANT DIGESTION. J. I. Quin. South African Jour. Sci., Johannesburg, vol. 36, pp. 417-423, Dec., 1939.

NOTES ON THE ORIGIN AND FUNCTION OF THE ARTIODACTYL TARSUS. Bobb Schaeffer. Amer. Mus. Nov., New York, no. 1356, pp. 1-24, illus., 1947.

THE PHYSIOLOGY OF DIGESTION IN RUMINANTS, WITH PRACTICAL REMARKS. Henry C. Slee. Jour. Comp. Med. and Surgery, New York, pp. 136-143, July, 1882.

Reproductive Biology

RECORD OF THE PERIOD OF GESTATION OF CERTAIN RUMINANTS WHICH BREED IN THE SOCIETY'S GARDENS. Philip L. Sclater. Proc. Zool. Soc. Lond., pt. 31, pp. 230-231, 1863.

Taxonomy

QUANTITATIVE SEROLOGIC RELATIONSHIPS WITHIN THE ARTIODACTYLA. Joseph G. Baier, Jr., Harold R. Wolfe. Zoologica, New York, vol. 27, pt. 1, no. 4, pp. 17-23, Apr. 30, 1942.

THE NAMES FOR TWO GENERA OF AFRICAN ARTIODACTYLA. N. Hollister. Proc. Biol. Soc. Wash., vol. 34, p. 77, Mar. 31, 1921.

RECLASSIFICATION OF THE ARTIODACTYL FAMILIES. W. D. Matthew. Bull. Geol. Soc. Amer., vol. 40, no. 2, pp. 403-408, June, 1929.

TWO NEW BIGHORNS AND A NEW ANTELOPE FROM MEXICO AND THE UNITED STATES. C. Hart Merriam. Proc. Biol. Soc. Wash., vol. 14, pp. 29-32, Apr. 5, 1901.

ON THE GENERIC CHARACTERS OF RUMINANTS. W. Ogilby. Proc. Zool. Soc. Lond., pt. 4, pp. 131-139, 1836.

SEROLOGIC RELATIONSHIPS AMONG BOVIDAE AND CERVIDAE. Harold R. Wolfe. Zoologica, New York, vol. 24, pt. 3, pp. 309-321, Nov. 2, 1939.

Zoo Collections, Pets

BUCK MEETS NANNETTE. (ROCKY MOUNTAIN GOAT AND PRONG-HORNED ANTELOPE KEPT AS PETS.) William L. Finley, Irene Finley. Nature Mag., vol. 14, pp. 74-79, illus., Aug., 1929.

PRIDE OF THE ANTELOPE HOUSE. "CONGO," THE OKAPI, AND "DOREEN," THE BONGO, ARE STILL GREAT RARITIES BUT THEY LEAD UNEVENTFUL LIVES. Calude W. Leister. Animal Kingdom, New York, vol. 46, no. 1, pp. 15-18, illus., Jan.-Feb., 1943.

BUT ONCE IN A LIFETIME. (BONGO, NYALA, OKAPI.) Ken Stott, Jr. Zoonooz, San Diego, vol. 13, no. 8, pp. 4-5, Aug., 1941.

## Suidae

GRUNT, MY WILD BOAR. Margaret Altmann. Animal Kingdom, New York Zool. Soc., 60 (1): 9-10, illus., Feb., 1957.

(ON SUS CELEBENSIS MUELLER AND SCHLEGEL.) F. J. Appelman. Zool. Garten, Leipzig, n.f., vol. 21, no. 3, pp. 152-156, illus., 1955. (In German.)

TUSKER--A WILD BOAR. Ernest Harold Baynes. Nature Mag., vol. 2, pp. 91-92, figs. 5, Aug., 1923.

(CONTRIBUTION TO KNOWLEDGE OF THE GENUS POTAMOCHOERUS GRAY.) Beitrag zur Kenntniss der Gattung Potamochoerus, Gray. Oscar de Beaux. Zool. Jahrbuecher, Abteil. fuer Systematik, etc., vol. 47, pp. 379-504, figs. 3, pls. 4-6, June 25, 1924.

(RESEARCH ON THE GENUS "HYLOCHOERUS.") G. Bouet, H. Neuville. Archiv. Mus. Nat. d'Hist. Nat., Paris (6), vol. 5, pp. 215-304, figs. 74, pls. 1-4, 1931.

ONE OF MY BEST FRIENDS. (WART HOG.) Emily Burlingame. San Diego Zoonooz, vol. 18, no. 4, p. 4, Apr., 1945.

NOTE ON THE GIANT-FOREST HOG (HYLOCHOERUS MEINERTZHAGENI). W. B. Cotton. Proc. Zool. Soc. Lond., no. 3, pp. 687-688, Sept., 1936.

(THE GEOGRAPHICAL ASPECTS OF SUIDAE.) Sur les facies geographiques des Suides. M. E. G. Dehaut. Bull. Mus. Nat. Hist. Nat., Paris, ser. 2, vol. 11, no. 6, pp. 521-525, figs. 2, Dec., 1939.

A PIG BY ANOTHER NAME. (BABIRUSA.) Georgia Dittoe. San Diego Zoonooz, vol. 18, no. 5, pp. 3-4, illus., May, 1945.

SWEEDY, A CHARACTER STUDY. Georgia Dittoe. San Diego Zoonooz, vol. 18, no. 4, p. 5, Apr., 1945.

(INFORMATION ON THE AFRICAN FOREST SWINE HYLOMEINERTZHAGENI THOS.) Zur Kenntnis des afrikanischen Waldschweines Hylochoerus meinertzhageni Thos. Ch. Graf Doenhoff. Zool. Garten, vol. 14, no. 4, pp. 192-200, illus., 1942.

REPLY TO DR. SCLATER ON THE WART-HOGS. John E. Gray. Ann. and Mag. Nat. Hist., ser.4, vol.6, no.36, pp.455-456, Dec., 1870.

(CONTRIBUTION TO STUDY OF PHACOCHOERUS AETHIOPICUS (PALLAS).) Contribution a l'etude du Phacochoerus aethiopicus (Pallas). M. Guiraud. Mammalia, Paris, 12 (3): 54-66, pl.3, Sept., 1948.

LETTER ON A SINGULAR RACE OF PIGS. Col. Hammal. Proc. Zool. Soc. Lond., pt.1, p.16, 1833.

(GENETIC EXPERIMENTS AND OBSERVATIONS ON SWINE.) Verebungsversuche und -Beobachtungen an Schweinen. C. Kronacher. Zeitschr. Indukt. Abstamm. und Verebungslehre, vol.34, pp.1-120, 1924.

THE WILD PIGS OF THE WORLD. Claude W. Leister. Bull. New York Zool. Soc., vol.42, no.5, pp.131-139, illus., Sept.-Oct., 1939.

CONTRIBUTIONS TO KNOWLEDGE OF THE GENUS POTAMOCHOERUS. Einar Loennberg. Arkiv f. Zool., Stockholm, vol.7, no.6, pp.40, figs.5, 1910.

THE GIANT FOREST PIG. Frederick A. Lucas. Amer. Mus. Jour., vol.12, no.7, p.243, Nov., 1912.

(THE GIANT FOREST SWINE HYLOCHOERUS MEINERTZHAGENI THOS.) Das Riesen-Waldschwein, Hylochoerus meinertzhageni Thos. Erna Mohr. Zool. Garten, vol.14, no.4, pp.177-191, illus., 1942.

(CERTAIN PECULIARITIES OF SUIDS.) De certaines particularites des Suides. M. H. Neuville. Bull. Mus. Nat. Hist. Nat., Paris, ser.2, vol.3, no.7, pp.570-575, figs.5, Nov., 1931.

PREDATION ON THE DOMESTIC PIG BY THE LONG-TAILED WEASEL. Emmett B. Polderboer. Jour. Mam., vol.29, no.3, pp.295-296, Aug.13, 1948.

(BIOLOGY OF THE EUROPEAN WILD HOG SUS SCROFA LINNE 1758.) Zur Biologie des europaeischen Wildschweins, Sus scrofa Linne, 1758. G. Steinbacher. Saeugetierk. Mitteil., Stuttgart, vol.2, no.3, p.126, July 1, 1954.

WARTHOG (PHARCOCHOERUS AETHIOPICUS). Nigerian Field, London, vol.3, no. 1, pp.19-23, pl.1, Jan., 1934.

FISHING PIG. Life, Chicago, vol.32, no. 25, pp.115-116, illus., June 23, 1952.

Africa

THE WEST AFRICAN FOREST PIG (HYLOCHOERUS RIMATOR THOMAS). Glover M. Allen. Proc. Biol. Soc. Wash., vol.23, pp. 49-52, Apr.19, 1910.

(THE GEOGRAPHICAL DISTRIBUTION OF THE AFRICAN WILD SWINE AND ITS ECOLOGICAL BASES.) Die geographische Verbreitung der afrikanischen Wildschweine und ihre oekologischen Grunglagen. Hans von Boetticher. Jenaische Zeitschr. Naturwiss., vol.68, no.2, pp.463-498, maps 2, Dec.20, 1933.

(ON A HYLOCHAERUS OF THE IVORY COAST AND OF LIBERIA (BAS-CAVALLY).) Sur un Hylochaerus de la Côte D'Ivoire et du Liberia (Bas-Cavally). G. Bouet, H. Neuville. Revue Hist. Nat. Soc. Nat. d'Acclimat. France, vol.11, no. 9, pp.284-287, Sept., 1930.

ON THE PAINTED PIG OF THE CAMEROONS(POTAMOCHOERUS PENICILLATUS). John E. Gray. Proc. Zool. Soc. Lond., pt.20, pp.129-132, pl.34, 1852.

(ZOOGEOGRAPHIC STUDIES ON THE BARBARY COAST. THE PACHYDERMS. I. THE WILD BOARS AND WART HOGS.) Études de géographie zoologique sur la Berbérie. Les pachydermes. 1. Les sangliers et les phacochères. L. Joleaud. Revue Geogr. Marocaine, Soc. Geogr. Maroc Casablanca, 17 année, nos.3-4, pp. 177-192, Dec., 1933.

(REMARKS ON THE PIG AND WILD BOAR OF OLD EGYPT.) Remarques sur le Porc et le Sanglier dans l'Egypte ancienne. L. Keimer. Bull. Inst. d'Egypte, sess. 1936-37, Cairo, vol.19, no.2, pp.147-156, figs.6, pls.3, 1937.

A NEW TYPE OF AFRICAN WARTHOG. Denis D. Lyell. Field, London, vol.152, p.157, illus., July 26, 1928.

NEW TYPE OF AFRICAN WARTHOG--A CORRECTION. Denis D. Lyell. Field, London, vol.152, p.420, Sept.13, 1928.

ON THE SPECIES OF POTAMOCHOERUS, THE BUSH-PIGS OF THE EHTOPIAN REGION. C. I. Forsyth Major. Proc. Zool. Soc. Lond., pt.2, pp.359-370, figs. 4, pls.2, Aug.1, 1897.

"WILD PIG" (POTAMOCHOERUS CHOEROPOTAMUS) AT THE KNSYNA: NOTES BY A NATURALIST. John F. V. Phillips. S. Afr. Jour. Sci., Pretoria, vol.23, pp.655-660, Dec., 1926.

(A NEW KIND OF WARTHOG FROM SOUTHWESTERN AFRICA.) Eine neue quartaere Warzenschwein-Art aus Suedwestafrika. Pia Julius. Centralbl. Mineral. Geol. u. Palaeont., Abt.B, 1930, no.2, pp.76-83, figs.2, 1930.

(NOTES ON THE WILD SUIDAE OF GUINEA.) Note sur les suidés sauvages de Guinée. D. Prunier. Mammalia, Paris, vol.10, nos. 3-4, pp.146-148, Sept.-Dec., 1946 (issued in 1947).

ON AFRICAN FOREST-PIGS. Walter Rothschild. Proc. Zool. Soc. Lond., p. 632, Oct.10, 1906.

THE FOREST PIG OF CENTRAL AFRICA. Oldfield Thomas. Nature, vol.70, p.577, Oct.13, 1904.

ON HYLOCHOERUS, THE FOREST-PIG OF CENTRAL AFRICA. Oldfield Thomas. Proc. Zool. Soc. Lond., vol.2, pp.193-199, pls.14-15, Apr.18, 1905.

(COMMUNICATION ON AN APPARENTLY NEW FORM OF HYLOCHOERUS FROM THE WINTER HIGHLANDS, FROM THE MUTJEK MOUNTAINS, AND FROM MERU MOUNTAIN.) Mitteilungen ueber eine anscheinend neue Form von Hylochoerus aus dem Winterhochlande, vom Mutjekgebirge und vom Meru-Berge. Ludwig Zukowsky. Archiv f. Nat., 87 Jahrg., Abt. A, Heft 1, pp.179-191, fig.1, July, 1921.

(FURTHER INFORMATION ON HYLOCHOERUS SCHULZI OF THE MUTJEK MOUNTAINS.) Weitere Mitteilungen ueber Hylochoerus schulzi vom Mutjekgebirge. Ludwig Zukowsky. Archiv. fur Naturgesch., Jahrg.88, Abt.A, no.7, pp. 5, May, 1922.

Anatomy

COMPARATIVE ANATOMY OF THE TUBO-UTERINE JUNCTION. HISTOLOGY AND PHYSIOLOGY IN THE SOW. Dorothy H. Andersen. Amer. Jour. Anat., vol.42, pp. 255-305, illus., Sept.15, 1928.

(MORPHOLOGICAL AND CAUSAL-ANALYTICAL INVESTIGATIONS ON THE DEVELOPMENT OF THE STOMACH REGION IN SUS SCROFA DOMESTICA.) Morphologische und kausalanalytische Untersuchungen ueber die Entwicklung der Magengegend bei Sus scrofa domestica. K. T. Andersen. Zeitschr. Anat. Entw.-Gesch. Berlin, vol.88, pp.652-696, figs. 21, 1929.

EOSINOPHILIC LEUCOCYTES IN THE THYMUS OF POSTNATAL PIGS. J. A. Badertscher. Anat. Rec., vol.18, no.1, pp.23-24, Feb.20 (Mar.), 1920.

ON THE DESCENDED TESTES OF SEX-INTERGRADE PIGS. John R. Baker. Quart. Jour. Micro. Sci., vol.69, pp.689-701, figs.8, Oct., 1925.

THE FOETAL PIG--A MAMMALIAN TYPE. W. J. Baumgartner. School Sci. and Math., Univ. Kansas, vol.25, no.3, pp. 300-301, Mar., 1925.

LABORATORY MANUAL OF THE FOETAL PIG. W. J. Baumgartner. Macmillan Co., New York, pp.57, 1924.

(THE CARPAL GLAND OF PIGS.) La glande carpienne des porcins. E. Bourdelle. Bull. Soc. Zool. France, Paris, vol.55, no.2, pp.136-141, fig.1, 1930.

NOTES ON THE ANATOMY OF THE BABIRUSA. D. Dwight Davis. Zool. Ser. Field Mus. Nat. Hist., Chicago, vol.22, no.5 (publ.477), pp.363-411, figs.14-37, Aug.6, 1940.

THE DESCENT OF THE TESTES IN THE PIG; INTRA-ABDOMINAL PRESSURE SUGGESTED AS A CAUSE. C. D. Day. Jour. Tennessee Acad. Sci., Nashville, vol.9, no.1, pp.18-46, 1934.

HISTOLOGICAL STUDIES OF BOAR TESTES. W. W. Green, L. M. Winters. Jour. Morphol., Phila., vol.75, no.2, pp.291-301, Sept., 1944.

(THE HEART OF THE WILD SWINE. VI. CONTRIBUTION TO THE ANATOMY OF SUS SCROFA L. AND TO THE PROBLEM OF DOMESTICATION.) Das Herz des Wildschweines. VI. Beitrag zur Anatomie von Sus scrofa L. und zum Domestikationsproblem. Theodor Gschwend. Anat. Anz., vol.72, nos.4-5, pp.49-89, figs.8, May 28, 1931.

THE DEVELOPMENT OF THE SHOULDER-GIRDLE OF SUS SCROFA. Frank Blair Hanson. Anat. Rec., vol.18, no.1, pp.1-21, Feb.20 (Mar.), 1920.

THE DEVELOPMENT OF THE STERNUM IN SUS SCROFA. Frank Blair Hanson. Anat. Rec., vol.17, pp.1-23, figs.19, Sept.20, 1919.

GROWTH OF THE MANDIBLE IN THE PIG. H. A. Harris. Nature, London, vol.144, no.3647, pp.552-553, figs.2, Sept.23, 1939.

THE FREEMARTIN CONDITION IN THE SWINE. W. Hughes. Anat. Rec., vol.41, pp.213-245, illus., Jan.25, 1929.

SEX-INTERGRADES IN FOETAL PIGS. W. Hughes. Biol. Bull., vol.52, no.2, pp.121-136, Feb., 1927.

(ON THE ANATOMY OF THE SWINE HEART: INVESTIGATIONS OF THE CHAMBER INTERIOR IN SUS SCROFA DOMESTICUS.) Zur Anatomie des Schweineherzens. Untersuchungen des Kammerinnern bei Sus scrofa domesticus. B. Huwyler. Anat. Anzeiger, vol.61, pp. 49-76, illus., Nov.25, 1926.

(ON THE GROWTH OF THE THORAX AND THORACIC ORGANS (HEART, LUNGS, THYMUS) DURING THE DEVELOPMENT OF THE SWINE.) Ueber das Wachstum des Brustkorbes und der Brustorgane (Herz, Lunge, Thymus) waehrend der Entwicklung beim Schwein. W. Lenkeit. Zeitschr. f. Anat. u. Entwicklungsgesch., vol.82, pp. 605-642, illus., Mar.8, 1927.

THE DEVELOPMENT OF THE TONSIL OF THE DOMESTIC PIG. Paul M. Levin. Anat. Rec., vol.45, no.2, pp.189-197, figs.6, 1930.

(ON PALATE FORMATION IN SUS BARBATUS AND RELATED TYPES IN COMPARISON WITH SUCH FORMATION IN SUS VERRUCOSUS.) Ueber die Gaumenbildung von Sus barbatus und Verwandten im Vergleich mit der von Sus verrucosus. A. Nehring. Sitz. Ber. Gesell. Naturf. Freunde Berlin, Jahrg.1895, no.4, pp.45-49, figs.2, Apr.16, 1895.

ON THE ANATOMY OF THE WART-HOG (PHACOCHOERUS PALLASII, VAN DER HOEVEN). R. Owen. Proc. Zool. Soc. Lond., pt.19, pp.63-69, 1851.

THE EXTERNAL CHARACTERS OF A FOREST HOG (HYLOCHOERUS) AND OF A BABIRUSA (BABIRUSSA) THAT DIED IN THE SOCIETY'S GARDENS. R. I. Pocock. Proc. Zool. Soc., Lond., ser.B, vol.113, pp.36-42, figs.5, July, 1943.

ON THE LATER DEVELOPMENT OF THE AZYGOUS VEINS OF SWINE. Franklin P. Reagan. Anat. Record, vol.17, pp.111-125, figs.16, Nov.20, 1919 (Dec., 1919).

(CASE OF INOSCULATION OF THE RECTUM IN THE VAGINA OF A FEMALE PIG-

LET.) Un cas d'abouchement du rectum dans le vagin chez une porcelette, "Sus scrofa" L. Joaquim dos Santos Junior. Comptes Rendus, 12th Internat. Congr. Zool.1935, Lisboa, vol.2, pp.715-718, pl.37, 1936-37.

EXHIBITION OF DRAWINGS ILLUSTRATIVE OF WART-HOGS. Philip L. Sclater. Proc. Zool. Soc. Lond., p.277, figs.2, 1869.

THE DEVELOPMENT OF THE MUSCULAR ARCHITECTURE OF THE VENTRICLES OF THE PIG'S HEART, WITH A REVIEW OF THE ADULT HEART AND A NOTE ON TWO ABNORMAL MAMMALIAN HEARTS. Ralph F. Shaner. Anat. Rec., vol.39, pp. 1-35, illus., June 25, 1928.

HISTOGENESIS OF THE PIG NEUROHYPOPHYSIS. William M. Shanklin. Amer. Jour. Anat., Phila., vol.74, no.3, pp.327-353, pls.1-5, May, 1944.

OBSERVATIONS ON THE DISTRIBUTION AND FUNCTION OF THE UTERINE CILIATED EPITHELIUM IN THE PIG, WITH REFERENCE TO CERTAIN CLINICAL HYPOTHESES. Franklin F. Snyder, George W. Corner. Amer. Jour. Obstetrics and Gynecol., St. Louis, vol. 3, no.4, p.8, figs.5, Apr., 1922.

REMARKS ON THE STOMACH OF THE POTAMOCHOERUS PENICILLATUS. T. Howard Stewart. Proc. Zool. Soc. Lond., pt.28, pp.194-195, 1806.

HISTOCHEMICAL REACTIONS OF THE PLACENTA OF THE PIG. G. B. Wislocki, E. W. Dempsey. Amer. Jour. Anat., Phila., vol.78, no.2, pp.181-225, pls.1-6, Mar., 1946.

HISTOGENESIS OF THE HEART MUSCLE OF THE PIG IN RELATION TO THE APPEARANCE AND DEVELOPMENT OF THE INTERCALATED DISCS. Lucile Witte. Amer. Jour. Anatomy, vol.25, no. 3, pp.333-347, figs.18, May, 1919.

Anatomy--Defects, Malformations

(ON THE VARIABILITY OF MALFORMATIONS, WITH SPECIAL CONSIDERATION OF INVESTIGATIONS ON SWINE.) Ueber die Variabilitat der Monstrositaten, unter besonderer Beruecksichtigung eigener Untersuchungen am Schwein. F. Alverdes. Anat. Anz., vol.57, pp.1-17, July, 1923.

A DOUBLE MONSTER PIG--CEPHALOTHORCOPAGUS MONOSYMMETROS. William J. Baumgartner. Anat. Rec., vol.37, no.3, pp.303-316, Jan.25, 1928.

NOTICE OF SOME OSTEOLOGICAL PECULIARITIES IN DIFFERENT SKELETONS OF THE GENUS SUS. T. C. Eyton. Proc. Zool. Soc. Lond., pt.3, p.23, 1837.

AN ARTERIAL ANOMALY IN THE FETAL PIG. Robert E. Gregg. Anat. Record, Phila., vol.95, no.1, pp.53-65, figs.1-4, pl.1, May, 1946.

A CASE OF CONJOINED TWINS IN THE PIG. H. O. Hetzer, O. N. Eaton. Anat. Record, Phila., vol.87, no.1, pp.53-65, figs.5, Sept., 1943.

CONGENITAL SKIN, EAR, AND SKULL DEFECTS IN A PIG. J. E. Nordby. Anat. Rec., vol.42, pp.267-280, illus., May 25, 1929.

(PATHOLOGICAL DEFORMATION OF THE FOOT OF A WILD BOAR.) Deformation pathologique d'un pied de sanglier. Ernest Olivier. Bull. Soc. Zool. France, Paris, vol.29, pp.148-150, 1904.

("PIG TAIL" IN A CHILD.) "Queue de cochon" chez une enfant. J. A. Pires de Lima. Bull. et Mém. Soc. Anthrop, Paris, ser.7, vol.8, pp.58-60, figs.1-2, photos, 1927.

DEFORMED TUSK IN A BOAR. Ram Singh. Jour. Bombay Nat. Hist. Soc., vol.43, no. 3, pp.522-523, pl.1, Dec., 1942.

(VARIABILITY AND MALFORMATION IN SWINE HEARTS.) Variabilitaet und Missbildung im Schweineherzen. W. Steger. Anat. Anzeiger, vol.63, pp.145-164, figs.5, June 11, 1927.

(TWO CASES OF HERMAPHRODITISM IN SWINE.) Zwei Faelle von Hermaphroditismus bei Schweinen. P. P. Winogradow. Anat. Anzeiger, vol.67, pp.475-479, fig. 2, July 20, 1929.

Anatomy--Pelage

(THE SKIN AND ANNEXED ORGANS IN THE PIG.) La peau et ses organes annexes chez le porc ou couchon domestique. E. Bourdelle. Revue Hist. Nat. Appliquée, Paris, pt.1, no.12, pp.1-8, 1926.

(HAIR COVER AND SKIN OF THE WILD HOG. VII. CONTRIBUTION TO THE ANATOMY OF SUS SCROFA L. AND TO THE DOMESTICATION PROBLEM.) Haarkleid und Haut des Wildschweines. VII. Beitrag zur Anatomie von Sus scrofa L. und zum Domestikationsproblem. H. Hoefliger. Zeitschr. f. Anat. u. Entwicklungs., vol.96, pp.551-623, figs.31, 1931.

(RECESSIVE WHITE AND STRIPED COATS IN YOUNG OF THE MANGALITZ HOGS.) Rezessives Weiss und Frischlingsstreifung der Mangalitza-Schweine. H. P. Ossent. Der Zuechter, Berlin, Jahrg.1, pt.1, pp.11-13, illus., Apr., 1929.

THE WILD PIG'S SUMMER COAT. A. deC. Sowerby. China Jour., vol.12, no.1, pp.45-46, pl.1, 1930.

Anatomy--Skull and Teeth

AN UNUSUALLY LARGE SKULL OF THE GIANT FOREST HOG (HYLOCHOERUS MEINERTZHAGENI) FROM GILGIL, KENYA COLONY, PRESENTED TO THE BRITISH MUSEUM (NATURAL HISTORY) BY N.R.C. WARWICK, ESQ., M.V.O., O.B.E. (EXHIBIT.). Guy Dollman. Proc. Linn. Soc., London, 149th sess., 1936-37, pt.1, pp.38-40, Feb.23, 1937.

OBSERVATIONS ON PIGS (SUS, LINNAEUS; SETIFERA, ILLIGER) AND THEIR SKULLS, WITH THE DESCRIPTION OF A NEW SPECIES. John E. Gray. Ann. and Mag. Nat. Hist., ser.4, vol.11, no.66, pp.430-439, June, 1873.

ON THE MADAGASCAR RIVER-HOG, (POTAMOCHOERUS) AND ON THE SKULLS OF THE THREE SPECIES OF THE GENUS. John E. Gray. Ann. and Mag. Nat. Hist., ser.4, vol.15, no.85, pp.45-48, pl.4, Jan., 1875.

ON THE SKULL OF THE JAPANESE PIG (SUS PLICICEPS). John E. Gray. Proc. Zool. Soc. Lond., pt.30, pp.13-17, figs.6, 1862.

(THE LACKING TOOTH OF SUS DOMESTICUS, A CONTRIBUTION TO THE DEVELOPMENTAL HISTORY OF THE DENTITION OF SUS DOMESTICUS AND TO KNOWLEDGE OF THE NATURE OF THE DENTITION.) Der Lueckzahn von Sus domesticus, ein Beitrag zur Entwicklungs-geschichte des Gebisses von Sus domesticus und zur Kenntnis des Wesens der Dentitionen. Max Hirsch. Anat. Anz., vol.54, pp.323-330, Oct., 1921.

REMARKS ON SOME WART-HOG SKULLS IN THE BRITISH MUSEUM. Einar Loennberg. Proc. Zool. Soc. Lond., pp.936-940, Apr., 1909.

(MORPHOLOGICAL VARIATIONS OF THE CANINE TOOTH IN THE SUIDAE.) Les variations morphologiques de la canine chez les suidés. P. L. Maronneaud. Mammalia, Paris, vol.10, nos.3-4, pp.105-121, figs.14, Sept.-Dec., 1946 (issued in 1947).

(ON DENTITION DEVELOPMENT IN SWINE, PARTICULARLY PREMATURE AND DELAYED DEVELOPMENT WITH NOTES ON THE SKULL FORM OF PRECOCIOUS AND RETARDED SWINE.) Ueber die Gebissentwicklung der Schweine insbesondere ueber Verfruehungen und Verspaetungen derselben nebst Bemerkungen ueber die Schaedelform fruehreifer und spaetreifer Schweine. A. Nehring. Landwirthsch. Jahrb. Berlin, Jahrg.1888, pp.54, figs.15, 1888.

(ON THE LOWER CANINE TEETH IN WILD HOGS AS WELL AS IN THE SO-CALLED "TORFSCHWEIN" (SUS PALUSTRIS RUTIMEYER).) Ueber die Form der unteren Eckzaehne bei den Wildschweinen, sowie ueber das sog. Torfschwein (Sus palustris Ruetimeyer). A. Nehring. Sitz.-Ber. Gesell. Naturf. Freunde Berlin, Jahrg. 1888, no.2, pp.9-16, figs.12, Feb.21, 1888.

(ON TWO SUS LONGIROSTRIS NEHRING SKULLS FROM BORNEO AND JAVA.) Ueber zwei Schaedel des Sus longirostris Nehring von Borneo und Java. A. Nehring. Sitz.-Ber. Gesell. Naturf. Freunde Berlin, Jahrg.1886, no.5, pp.80-85, figs.3, May 18, 1886.

(ALL ABOUT HOGS.) Allemaal zwijnerij. (Notes on tusks of Sus vittatus and S. verrucosus in Java.) J. Oliver. Tropische Natuur, Buitenzorg, vol.22, no.10, pp.184-188, fig.1, Oct., 1933.

ON THE STRUCTURE AND DEVELOPMENT OF THE SKULL IN THE PIG (SUS SCROFA). W. K. Parker. Philos. Trans. Lond., pp.289-336, pls.28-37, 1874.

CRANIOLOGICAL INVESTIGATIONS OF THE WILD SWINE. Jur Philiptschenko. Trudy Lab. Genet., Akad. Nauk, Leningrad, SSSR, vol.1, pp.157-184, figs.11, 1933.

NOTE ON THE SKULL OF THE RED RIVER-HOG (POTAMOCHOERUS PENICILLATUS). Philip L. Sclater. Proc. Zool. Soc. Lond., pt.28, pp.301-302, figs.2, 1860.

WILD BOAR TUSK MEASUREMENTS. Arthur deC. Sowerby. China Jour., vol. 20, no.5, pp.294-295, May, 1934.

AN ANCIENT BOAR'S TUSKS. J. Lawson Tancred. Field, Lond., vol.164, p.216, July 28, 1934.

THE LATER DEVELOPMENTAL FEATURES IN THE SKULL OF SUS BARBATUS BARBATUS. T. Wingate Todd, Ralph E. Wharton. Proc. Zool. Soc. Lond., pt.3, pp.685-696, figs.7, pl.1, Sept.14, 1934.

NOTE ON A SKULL OF SUS GARGANTUA MILLER IN THE CAMBRIDGE MUSEUM. B. W. Tucker. Proc. Zool. Soc. Lond., pt.2, pp.487-492, pls.1-2, figs.2, June, 1931.

Asia

REPORT OF THE CURATOR, ZOOL. DEPARTMENT. (SUS FROM ANDAMAN AND NICOBAR ISLANDS.) Edward Blyth. Jour. Asiatic Soc. Bengal, vol.27, pp.267-269, 1858.

A FURTHER NOTE ON THE BEARDED PIG IN MALAYA. C. A. Gibson-Hill. Jour. Bombay Nat. Hist. Soc., vol.47, no.4, pp.632-637, map, 1948.

THE BEARDED PIG (SUS BARBATUS) IN THE MALAY STATES. C. Boden Kloss. Bull. Raffles Mus., Singapore, Straits Settlements, no.5, pp.102-105, pl.7, Aug., 1931.

MALAYSIAN BEARDED PIGS. (SUS BARBATUS, SUS OI, AND OTHER WILD PIGS OF BORNEO AND SUMATRA.) C. Boden Kloss. Jour. Straits Branch, Royal Asiatic Soc., no.83, pp.147-150, Apr., 1921.

THE NEW SUMATRAN PIG. SUS OI IN THE RIO-LINGA ARCHIPELAGO. C. Boden Kloss. Jour. Straits Branch Royal Asiatic Soc., no.45, pp.55-60, pls.1-3, 1905.

ON SUS VERRUCOSUS, MUELL. AND SCHLEG., AND ALLIES, FROM THE EASTERN ARCHIPELAGO. C. I. Forsyth Major. Ann. and Mag. Nat. Hist., ser.6, vol.19, pp.521-542, May, 1897.

ON A NEW RACE OF SUS FROM THE TYPE-SITE OF ATSUTEAN. (SUS NIPPONICUS MIYAE.) Hikoshichiro Matsumoto. Sci. Reports Tohoku Imp. Univ. (2), Geol., vol.13, no.3, pp.49-50, pl.16, 1930.

A NEW PIG FROM SUMATRA. Gerrit S. Miller, Jr. Proc. Biol. Soc., Wash., vol. 15, pp.51-52, Mar.5, 1902.

NOTES ON MALAYAN PIGS. Gerrit S. Miller, Jr. Proc. U.S. Nat. Mus., vol. 30, pp.737-758, illus., pls.39-44, June 13, 1906.

PARTIAL DISAPPEARANCE OF THE WILD PIG (SUS CRISTATUS). R. C. Morris.

Jour. Bombay Nat. Hist. Soc., vol.34, no. 1, pp.245-246, Mar.1, 1930.

ON THE PIG OF THE PREHISTORIC AGE IN JAPAN. Nobuo Naora. Jour. Anthrop. Soc. Tokyo, vol.52, no.598, pp.286-296, Aug., 1937. (In Japanese.)

(ON A NEW SPECIES OF WILD SWINE (SUS LONGIROSTRIS NEHRING) FROM SOUTHEAST BORNEO.) Ueber eine neue Art von Wildschweinen (Sus longirostris Nehring) aus Suedost-Borneo. A. Nehring. Zool. Anzeiger, Leipzig, Jahrg.8, no.197, pp.347-353, illus., 1885.

(ON THE JAPANESE WILD SWINE (SUS LEUCOMYSTAX TEMM.).) Ueber das japanische Wildschwein. (Sus leucomystax Temm.) A. Nehring. Zoologische Garten, Frankfurt, Jahrg.26, vol.26, no.11, pp.325-336, Nov., 1885.

CHINESE SWINE AND THEIR PERFORMANCE COMPARED WITH MODERN AND CROSSES BETWEEN CHINESE AND MODERN BREEDS. Ralph W. Phillips, T. Y. Hsu. Jour. Heredity, Wash., vol. 35, no.12, pp.365-379, figs.4-10, Dec., 1944.

THE BEARDED PIG (SUS BARBATUS) IN THE MALAY PENINSULA. H. C. Robinson, J. C. Moulton. Jour. Straits Branch Roy. Asiatic Soc., Singapore, no.85, pp.202-205, Mar., 1922.

(HOW MANY TYPES OR VARIETIES OF HOGS ARE THERE ON JAVA?) Hoeveel soorten of varieteiten van zwijnen zijn er op Java? (Sus verrucosus.) H.J.V. Sody. Nederlandsch-Indische Jager, Buitenzorg, no.8, pp.4, illus., 1939.

A NEW RACE OF SUS VERRUCOSUS FROM MADOERA ISLAND. (SUS VERRUCOSUS OLIVIERI.) H.J.V. Sody. Treubia, Buitenzorg, vol.18, pt.2, pp.393-394, Dec., 1941.

(SOME SUS SCROFA POPULATIONS OF SUMATRA, JAVA AND AMBON.) Enkele Sus scrofa populaties van Sumatra, Java en Ambon. H.J.V. Sody. Ned. Indische Jager, vol.11, p.70, 1941.

(TYPES OF HOGS IN THE SMALL SOENDA ISLANDS.) De zwijnensoort (en) van de Kleine Soenda-Eilanden. H.J.V. Sody. Ned. Indische Jager, pp.1-12, Mar., 1941.

THE WILD BOAR IN CHINA. A. deC. Sowerby. China Jour., vol.12, no.1, pp. 49-50, pl.2, 1930.

SOME NOTES ON BABRISSUA. Oldfield Thomas. Ann. and Mag. Nat. Hist., ser.9, vol.5, pp.185-188, Feb., 1920.

Embryology

TWO PIGS WITHIN A SINGLE CHORION WITH SOME CONSIDERATIONS CONCERNING MONOCHORIONIC TWINS. Mary T. Harman. Trans. Kansas Acad. Sci., vol.36, pp.220-223, 1933.

THE BRANCHIAL VESSELS AND THEIR DERIVATIVES IN THE PIG. C. H. Henser. Carnegie Inst. Wash., publ.332, Contrib. Embryology, no.77, pp.19, pls.4, figs.8, 1924.

EARLY DEVELOPMENT OF PIG EMBRYOS, FROM THE PERIOD OF INITIAL CLEAVAGE TO THE TIME OF THE APPEARANCE OF LIMB-BUDS. C. H. Heuser, G. L. Streeter. Contrib. to Embryol. Carnegie Inst. Wash. Publ.no.394, vol.20, no.109, pp.1-30, pls.12, figs.8, 1929.

TWIN HETEROSEXUAL PIG EMBRYOS (32 MM.) FOUND WITHIN FUSED MEMBRANES. Leigh Hoadley. Anat. Rec., vol.38, pp.177-187, illus., Apr.25, 1928.

THE CHONDROCRANIUM OF AN EMBRYO PIG, SUS SCROFA. Charles Searing Mead. Amer. Jour. Anat., Phila., vol.9, no.2, pp.167-209, pls.4, May, 1909.

(ON THE MESOTHELIAL VILLI OF THE ALLANTOIS IN SWINE EMBRYOS.) Ueber die mesothelialen Zotten der Allantois bei Schweinsembryonen. Charles S. Minot. Anatomischer Anzeiger, vol.18, no.4-5, pp.127-136, figs.2, June, 1900.

ON THE VEINS OF THE WOLFFIAN BODIES IN THE PIG. Charles Sedgwick Minot. Proc. Boston Soc. Nat. Hist., vol.28, no.10, pp.265-274, pl.1, July, 1898.

THE EMBRYOLOGY OF THE PIG. Bradley M. Patten. P. Blakiston's Son Co., Phila., vol.8, pp.323, illus., figs. 372, 1927.

(REVIEW by Paul B. Johnson of) THE EMBRYOLOGY OF THE PIG. Bradley M. Patten. Jour. Mam., vol.8, no.3, pp.253-254, Aug., 1927.

VENOUS SYSTEM ASSOCIATED WITH THE LIVER OF A 6 MM. PIG EMBRYO. C. H. Thienes. Anat. Record, vol.31, pp.149-158, figs.6, Oct.25, 1925.

THE BEGINNING AND DEVELOPMENT OF FUNCTION IN THE SUPRARENAL MEDULLA OF PIG EMBRYOS. Morie F. Weymann. Anatomical Record, vol.24, no.5, pp.299-308, pls.1-2, Dec., 1922.

Europe

ON THE ENDEMIC OCCURRENCE OF SUS SCROFA REISERI BOLKAY IN BOSNIA--HERCEGOVINA. St. J. Bolkay. 10th. Cong. Internat. Zool., sec.8, pp.1382-1385, illus., 1929.

THE EUROPEAN WILD BOAR. William L. Hamnett. Wildlife in North Carolina, Raleigh, vol.11, no.5, p.12, illus., Nov., 1947.

(THE INFLUX OF WILD BOARS IN CENTRAL FRANCE.) Les invasions de sangliers dans le midi de la France. Albert Hugues. Bull. Soc. Nat. Acclimat. France, vol.79, no.10, pp.449-461, Oct., 1932.

WILD BOARS IN RYAZAN REGION. V. V. Kozlov. Zool. Zhurnal, 37 (1): 142-143, Jan., 1958. (In Russian, with English summary.)

(NEW NOTIONS CONCERNING THE BIOLOGY OF THE WILD BOAR OF THE CAUCASUS (SUS SCROFA ATTILA THOMAS).) Nouvelles notions concernant la biologie du sanglier du Caucase (Sus scrofa attila Thomas). W. W. Loguinoff. Bull. Soc. Nat. Moscou, n.s., vol.45, sect. biol., no.1, pp.10-21, 1936. (In Russian with French summary.)

(THE INFLUX OF WILD BOAR IN BAS-LANGUEDOC.) Des infiltrations de sangliers dans le Bas-Languedoc. Edouard Maistre. Bull. Soc. Nat. Acclimat. France, vol.80, no.7, pp.249-258, July, 1933.

(OBSERVATIONS ON THE PRESENCE OF WILD BOAR (SUS SCROFA) IN NORTHWEST ITALY.) Osservazioni sulla presenza del cinghiale (Sus scrofa, L.) nell' Italia nord occidentale. Augusto Toschi. Inst. Zool. Univ. Bologna, Ricerche zool. appl. alla Caccia, Imola, pp.22, pl.1, 1936.

Fossils

A FOSSIL WART-HOG FROM PALESTINE. (PHACOCHOERUS GARRODAE.) Dorothea M.A. Bate. Ann. Mag. Nat. Hist. ser.10, vol.13, pp.120-129, pl.6, Jan., 1934.

A NEW EXTINCT GIANT PIG FROM THE DIAMOND GRAVELS OF WINDSORTON, SOUTH AFRICA. (NOTOCHOERUS PAICEAE.) R. Broom. Rec. Albany Mus., Grahamstown, vol.4, no.1, pp.167-168, fig.1, Jan. 9, 1931.

ON EVIDENCE OF A GIANT PIG FROM THE LATE TERTIARIES OF SOUTH AFRICA. R. Broom. Records of the Albany Mus (Grahamstown), vol.3, pp.307-308, fig.1, Mar.6, 1925.

TH' SKULL AND MANDIBLE OF CONOHYUS, A PRIMITIVE SUID FROM THE SIWALIK BEDS OF INDIA. Edwin H. Colbert. Amer. Mus. Nov., no.621, pp.12, figs.5, May 13, 1933.

AN UPPER MIOCENE SUID FROM THE GOBI DESERT. (LISTRIODON MONGOLIENSIS.) Edwin H. Colbert. Amer. Mus. Nov., no.690, pp.1-7, fig.1, Jan.20, 1934.

THE FOSSIL SUINA OF SOUTH AFRICA. H.B.S. Cooke. Trans. Royal Soc. South Africa, vol.32, no.1, pp.1-44, illus., 1949.

THE FOSSIL PIGS OF FLORISBAD. R. F. Ewer. Navorsinge (Researches) Nasionale Mus., Bloemfontein, 1 (10): 239-257, illus., June 26, 1957.

THE FOSSIL SUIDS OF THE TRANSVAAL CAVES. R. F. Ewer. Proc. Zool. Soc. Lond., 127 (4): 527-544, illus., pls.1-3, Dec.21, 1956.

(WILD WART HOGS OF THE ORANGE FREE STATE.) Vrystaatse wild varke. Ir. E.C.N. van Hoepen, H. E. van Hoepen. Paleont. Navorsing Nas. Mus., Bloemfontein, vol.2, no.4, pp.39-62, figs. 77, Oct.25, 1932.

HYLOCHOERUS GRABHAMI, A NEW SPECIES OF FOSSIL PIG FROM THE WHITE NILE. A. Tindell Hopwood. Ann. and Mag. Nat. Hist., ser.10, vol.4, pp. 289-290, Sept., 1929.

ON THE DISCOVERY OF HYOTHERIUM IN SERBIA. V. Laskarev. Ann. Geol. Peninsule Balkanique, Beograd, vol.14, pp. 87-96, fig.1, 1937. (In Russian, with French summary.)

FOSSIL SUIDAE FROM OLDOWAY. L.S.B. Leakey. Jour. E. Africa Nat. Hist. Soc., Nairobi, vol.16, nos.4-5 (73-74), pp.178-196, figs.2, pls.60-62, June, 1942.

NEW FOSSIL SUIDAE FROM SHUNGURA OMO. L.S.B. Leakey. Jour. East Africa Nat. Hist. Soc., Nairobi, vol.17, nos.1-2 (75-76), pp.45-61, pls.14-20, Mar., 1943.

PRELIMINARY NOTICE OF A NEW SPECIES OF HIPPOHYUS FROM INDIA. (HIPPOHYUS DETERRAI.) G. Edward Lewis. Amer. Jour. Sci., ser.5, vol.27, no.162, pp.457-459, pl.1, June, 1934.

DESCRIPTION OF A JAW OF HYOTHERIUM, FROM THE PLIOCENE OF INDIA. R. Lydekker. Quart. Jour. Geol. Soc., vol. 43, pp.19-22, 1887.

GROWTH CHANGES AND VARIATIONS IN WART HOG THIRD MOLARS AND THEIR PALEONTOLOGICAL IMPORTANCE. Shaw J.C. Middleton. Trans. Roy. Soc. South Africa, Cape Town, vol.27, pt.1, pp.51-94, June, 1939.

THE TEETH OF THE SOUTH AFRICAN FOSSIL PIG (NOTOCHOERUS CAPENSIS SYN. MEADOWSI) AND THEIR GEOLOGICAL SIGNIFICANCE. Shaw J.C. Middleton. Trans. Roy. Soc. South Africa, Cape Town, vol.26, pt.1, pp.25-38, illus., May, 1938.

CHINESE FOSSIL SUIDAE. H. Pearson. Geol. Surv. China, Palaeontol. Sinica, ser.C, vol.5, no.5, pp.1-75, pls.4, figs. 37, 1928.

ON THE SKULLS OF EARLY TERTIARY SUIDAE. H. Pearson. Phil. Trans. Roy. Soc. Lond., B 215, pp.389-460, 1927.

THE FOSSIL SUIDAE OF INDIA. Guy E. Pilgrim. Palaeontologia Indica, vol.8, mem.no.4, pp.1-65, pls.1-20, 1926.

ON THE DOMESTIC PIG OF PREHISTORIC TIMES IN BRITAIN, AND ON THE MUTUAL RELATIONS OF THIS VARIETY OF PIG AND SUS SCROFA FERUS, SUS CRISTATUS, SUS ANDAMANENSIS, AND SUS BARBATUS. George Rolleston. Trans. Linn. Soc. Lond., ser.2, zool., vol.1, no., pp.251-286, pls.41-43, 1876.

GROWTH CHANGES AND VARIATIONS IN WART HOG THIRD MOLARS AND THEIR PALAEONTOLOGICAL IMPORTANCE. J. C. Middleton Shaw. Trans. Roy. Soc. South Africa, Cape Town, vol.27, pt.1, pp.51-94, figs.9, table 1, June, 1939.

THE TEETH OF THE SOUTH AFRICAN FOSSIL PIG (NOTOCHOERUS CAPENSIS SYN. MEADOWSI) AND THEIR GEOLOGICAL SIGNIFICANCE. J. C. Middleton Shaw. Trans. Roy. Soc. South Africa, Cape Town, vol.26, pt.1, pp.25-37, figs. 6, May, 1938.

FOSSIL PIGS OF THE GENUS MICROSTONYX. B. A. Trofimov. Proc. Paleo. Inst., Acad. Sci., USSR, vol.47, pp.61-99, illus., 1954.

Habits, Behavior

THE WAYS OF WILD BOAR. SOCIAL CUSTOMS AMONG THE PIG TRIBES OF CEYLON. W. G. Adam. Field, London, vol.160, no.4154, p.195, figs.3, Aug.6, 1932.

MORE ABOUT THE HABITS OF THE WILD BOAR. Jay Bruce. Calif. Cons., 6 (5): 14, 21, May, 1941.

SOME FIELD NOTES ON THE BEARDED PIG. J. A. Hislop. Malayan Nature Jour., Kuala Lumpur, vol.4, no.2, pp.62-65, June, 1949.

CROCODILE AND WILD BOAR. E. S. Lewis. Jour. Bombay Nat. Hist. Soc., vol.41, no.4, p.903, Aug., 1940.

EXHIBITION OF, AND REMARKS UPON, A MOUNTED SPECIMEN OF THE RIVER-HOG OF MADAGASCAR (POTOMOCHOERUS EDWARDSI), WITH NOTES ON ITS HABITS BY MR. J. T. LAST. Philip L. Sclater. Proc. Zool. Soc. Lond., pt.1, pp.92-94, June 1, 1894.

A STUDY OF THE BEHAVIOR OF THE PIG (SUS SCROFA) BY THE MULTIPLE CHOICE METHOD. Robert M. Yerkes, Charles A. Coburn. Jour. Animal Behavior, vol.5, no.3, pp.185-225, tables 11, figs.2, May-June, 1915.

BEARDED PIG SWIM AGAIN. (MIGRATION OF PIGS IN NORTH BORNEO.) Malayan Nature Jour., Kuala Lumpur, vol.8, no.3, pp.118-120, Dec., 1953.

Heredity

THE INHERITANCE OF PARALYSED HIND LEGS, SCROTAL HERNIA AND ATRESIA ANI IN PIGS. S. Berge. Jour. Heredity, Wash., D.C., vol.32, no.8, pp.271-274, figs.10-13, Aug., 1941.

HYDROCEPHALUS IN SWINE, A NEW LETHAL DEFECT. C. T. Blunn, E. H. Hughes. Jour. Heredity, vol.29, no.5, pp.203-208, May, 1938.

LINKED COLOR FACTORS IN HAMPSHIRE SWINE. LINKAGE OF BLACK AND THE BASIC WHITE OF THE WHITE BELT PATTERN. Ralph J. Bushnell. Jour. Heredity, Wash., vol.34, no.10, pp.302-307, figs. 8-10, Oct., 1943.

(RECESSIVE WHITE IN THE SWINE.) Ein rezessives Weiss beim Schwein. G. K. Constantinescu. Zeitschr. f. Ind. Abstammungs. und Verebungslehre, vol. 47, pp.147-150, figs.4, 1928.

ABORIGINAL PIGS OF CHUVASHIA. J. Havesson. Trudy Lab. Genet., Akad. Nauk, Leningrad, SSSR, vol.1, pp.313-373, figs.22, 1933.

INHERITANCE OF COAT COLOR IN SWINE. H. O. Hetzer. Jour. Heredity, Wash., vol.36, no.4, pp.121-128; no.6, pp.186-192, figs.10-12; no.8, pp.254-256, fig.21; no.10, pp.308-312, fig.9, Apr., June, Aug., Oct., 1945.

INHERITANCE OF COAT COLOR IN SWINE. V. RESULTS OF LANDRACE BY DUROC-JERSEY CROSSES. H. O. Hetzer. Jour. Heredity, Wash., vol.37, no.6, pp.216-224, figs.9-10, July, 1946.

INHERITANCE OF COAT COLOR IN SWINE. VII. RESULTS OF LANDRACE BY HAMPSHIRE CROSSES. H. O. Hetzer. Jour. Heredity, Balto., vol.39, no.4, pp. 123-127, Apr., 1948.

(TRANSMISSION EXPERIMENTS ON SWINE: THE INHERITANCE OF NIPPLE NUMBER.) Vererbungsversuche an Schweinen: Die vererbung der Zitzenzahl. H. Nachtsheim. Zeitschr. Indukt. Abstammung-und Vererbungslehre, vol. 33, pp.307-311, 1924.

AN INHERITED SKULL DEFECT IN SWINE. J. E. Nordby. Jour. Heredity, vol.20, pp. 229-232, May, 1929.

OCCURRENCE OF RED-EYE IN SWINE. E. Roberts. Jour. Heredity, Wash., vol. 36, no.7, pp.207-208, figs.6-7, July, 1945.

INHERITANCE AND HISTOLOGY OF WATTLES IN SWINE. E. Roberts, C.C. Morrill. Jour. Heredity, Wash., vol.35, no.5, pp.149-151, figs.13-14, May, 1944.

MICROPTHALMIA IN SWINE. Lloyd D. Roberts. Jour. Heredity, Balto., vol.39, no.5, pp.146-148, May, 1948.

SOME ANOMALIES IN PIGS. E. J. Warwick, A. B. Chapman, Burr Ross. Jour. Heredity, Wash., vol.34, no.11, pp.349-352, figs.13-14, Nov., 1943.

INHERITANCE OF BLACK IN SWINE. B. L. Warwick. Jour. Heredity, vol.17, no.7, pp.251-255, figs.7-8, July, 1926.

Hunting

WILD PIG HUNTING IN THE KULING FOOTHILLS. John F. Duff. China Jour., vol.20, no.4, pp.204-205, illus., Apr., 1934.

WITH RIFLE, GUN AND ROD IN MANCHURIA. A WILD BOAR HUNT. V. de Franck. China Jour., vol.6, pp.197-201, pl.1, Apr., 1927.

BOAR HUNTING ON SANTA CRUZ. John Edwin Hogg. Outers' Recreation, vol.63, pp.194-196, 238-240, Sept., 1920.

CAPTURING WARTHOGS IN THE ZAMBESI VALLEY. Wynant D. Hubbard. Nature Mag., vol.2, pp.233-236, figs.5, Oct., 1923.

HUNTING THE RUSSIAN BOAR. D. E. Koontz. North Carolina Wildlife Conserv., Raleigh, vol.7, no.9, pp.8-12, illus., Sept., 1943.

PRIMITIVE METHODS OF HUNTING WILD BOAR IN SHANSI. G. D. Wilder. China Jour., vol.21, no.2, pp.80-83, illus., Aug., 1934.

MANIFEST'S TRIPLE CROWN. HOW CAPTAIN TUCK WON THE BLUE RIBBON FOR PIG-STICKING. (INDIA.) Field, London, vol.167, no.4347, pp.894-895, illus., Apr.18, 1936.

Management

GAME HOG MENACE. Leonard E. Foote. Texas Game and Fish, Austin, vol.6, no. 10, pp.6, 17, 18, 19, Sept., 1948.

(SWINE RAISING IN CENTRAL ITALY.) L'elevage du porc dans l'Italie centrale. Guy de Germiny. Revue d'Histoire Naturelle, Pt.1, A, Mammifères, Paris, vol.11, no.11, pp.356-363, figs.3, Nov., 1930.

TELLICO WILDLIFE MANAGEMENT AREA. (WILD BOAR.) L. J. Williams. Southern Sportsman, Austin, vol.7, no. 2, pp.3, 24-25, Sept., 1943.

OUTDOOR WRITERS OF AMERICA TO HOLD SUMMER MEET AT TELLICO PLAINS; TO STUDY MODEL WILDLIFE AREA. (WILD BOAR.) Tennessee Conserv., Nashville, vol.7, no.6, pp.3, 5, 9, illus., June, 1943.

Museum Collections

NOTE ON THE SOLID-HOOFED PIGS IN THE SOCIETY'S COLLECTION. Alfred Henry Garrod. Proc. Zool. Soc. Lond., pt.1, p.33, 1877.

SYNOPSIS OF THE SPECIES OF PIGS (SUIDAE) IN THE BRITISH MUSEUM. John E. Gray. Proc. Zool. Soc. Lond., pp.17-49, 1868.

ON THE MALAYAN AND PAPUAN PIGS IN THE LEYDEN MUSEUM. F. A. Jentink Notes Leyden Mus., vol.13, no.6, pp.85-104, Jan., 1891.

GIANT FOREST HOG--ONCE A 'MYSTERY CREATURE'--SHOWN IN NEW GROUP. Wilfred H. Osgood. Chicago Nat. Hist. Mus. Bull., vol.15, nos.7-8, p.1, illus., July-Aug., 1944.

North America

THE EUROPEAN WILD HOG IN AMERICA. A. C. Shaw. Trans. N. A. Wildl. Conf., 5: 436-441, 1941.

THE EUROPEAN WILD BOAR IN THE CHEROKEE NATIONAL FOREST, TENNESSEE. Leroy C. Stegeman. Jour. Mam., 19 (3): 279-290, Aug., 1938.

THE ORNERY "ROOSHAN." (WILD BOAR.) Carlos Vinson. Outdoors, Dayton, vol.17, no.5, pp.20-21, 50-51, May, 1949.

WILD "ROOSHIANS" OF TENNESSEE. Carlos Vinson. Nature Mag., 39 (8): 405-406, Oct., 1946.

THE WILD RAZORBACK. Louisiana Conservationist, New Orleans, vol.1, no.5, pp.9, illus., Jan., 1949.

Origins, History

ON THE QUESTION OF THE ORIGIN OF DOMESTIC PIGS. G. P. Adlerberg. Trudy Lab. Genet., Akad. Nauk, Leningrad, SSSR, vol.1, pp.185-209, figs.10, 1933.

(STUDY OF THE HISTORY OF THE SWINE RACES, ESPECIALLY THOSE OF SWEDEN.) Studien zur Geschichte der Schweinerassen, insbesondere derjenigen Schwedens. Adolf Pira. Zool. Jahrb., Jena, suppl. Bd.10, pp. 233-426, figs.A-X, 1909.

Parasites

A NOTE ON TWO SPECIES OF THE GENUS MURSHIDIA (NEMATODE, STRONGYLOIDEA) PARASITIC IN THE WARTHOG. R. Daubney. Ann. and Mag. Nat. Hist., ser. 9, vol.11, pp.256-263, figs.10, Feb., 1923.

THE PIG AS A HOST OF PULEX IRRITANS L. (SIPHONAPTERA, PULICIDAE). R. B. Freeman. Entom. Monthly Mag., Lond., vol.82, pp.19-21, 1946.

A COMMENSAL NEMATODE IN THE AFRICAN BUSH PIG. Basil J. G. Marlow. Jour. Mam., 36 (1): 147, Feb.25, 1955.

SUSCEPTIBILITY OF THE DOMESTIC PIG TO CENTRAL ASIATIC TICK RELAPSING FEVER SPIROCHAETE. E. N. Pavlovsky, A. F. Cheskis. Comptes Rendus (Doklady) Acad. Sci. URSS, Moscow, vol.38, no.1, pp.55-56, Jan.10, 1943.

(ON A BALANTIDIUM OF THE WILD SWINE.) Ueber ein Balantidium des Wildschweines. P. P. Popow. Archiv. f. Protistenkunde, vol.64, pp.96-97, fig.1, Oct.26, 1928.

Physiology

(IN WHICH TISSUE STARTS THE ORIGINAL IRRITATION FOR THE BEGINNING OF HORN DEVELOPMENT? II. COMMUNICATION: EXPLORATIVE OPERATIONS ON THE HORN BUDS OF CAPREOLUS CAPREOLUS.) Von welchem Gewebe geht der eigentliche Reiz zur Gewiehentwicklung aus? II. Mitteilung: Operative Eingriffe auf den Rosenstoecken der Rehboecke, Capreolus c. capreolus (L., 1758). Antonin Bubenik, Rudolf Pavlansky. Saeugetierk. Mitteil., Stuttgart, 4 (3): 97-103, July 1, 1956.

VITAMINS REQUIRED BY SWINE FOR GROWTH WITH SOME OBSERVATIONS ON REPRODUCTION. A. G. Hogan, G. C. Anderson. Jour. Nutrition, Phila., vol.36, no.4, pp.437-449, Oct.11, 1948.

PHYSIOLOGICAL INSULATION OF SWINE AS BARE-SKINNED MAMMALS. Laurence Irving. Jour. Applied Physiol., vol.9, no.3, pp.414-420, Nov., 1956.

METABOLISM AND INSULATION OF SWINE AS BARE-SKINNED ANIMALS. Laurence Irving, Leonard J. Peyton, Mildred Monson. Jour. Applied Physiol., vol.9, no.3, pp.421-426, Nov., 1956.

CHOLINE DEFICIENCY IN THE BABY PIG. B. C. Johnson, M. F. James. Jour. Nutrition, Phila., vol.36, no.3, pp.339-349, pls.1-2, Sept.10, 1948.

FURTHER STUDIES ON THE RELATIONSHIP OF NICOTINIC ACID, TRYPTOPHANE AND PROTEIN IN THE NUTRITION OF THE PIG. R. W. Luecke, W. N. McMillen, F. Thorpe, Carolyn Tull. Jour. Nutrition, Phila., vol.36, no.3, pp.417-424, Sept.10, 1948.

FAT OF SOW'S MILK. P.B.D. de la Mare, F. B. Shorland. Nature, London, vol.153, no.3882, p.380, Mar.25, 1944.

THE EFFECT OF IRRADIATION WITH THE CARBON ARC ON PIGS ON A DIET HIGH IN PHOSPHORUS AND LOW IN CALCIUM. J. B. Orr, H. E. Magee, J. M. Henderson. Jour. Physiol., vol.59, pp.25-26, 1924.

REACTIONS OF THE PIG TO HOT ATMOSPHERES. Kathleen Robinson, Douglas H.K. Lee. Proc. Roy. Soc. Queensland, Brisbane, vol.53, no.9, pp.145-158, figs.1-6c, Feb.23, 1942.

THE EFFECT OF VASECTOMY ON SWINE. B. L. Warwick. Anat. Record, vol.31, pp. 19-22, Sept.25, 1925.

Reproductive Biology

(ON THE BREEDING OF SWINE.) O chowie trzody chlewnej. Stanislaw Lodzia Baranowski. W Krakowie , Czcionkami drukarni W.L. Anczyca y spolki, pp.198, illus., 1883.

ON THE SIZE OF LITTERS AND THE NUMBER OF NIPPLES IN SWINE. G. H. Parker, C. Bullard. Proc. Amer. Acad. Arts and Sci., Boston, vol.49, no.7, pp. 399-426, Sept.,1913.

STUDIES ON THE SEX-RATIO AND RELATED PHENOMENA. (4) THE FREQUENCIES OF SEX COMBINATIONS IN PIG LITTERS. A. S. Parkes. Biometrika, vol. 15, pts. 3, 4, pp.373-381, fig.1, Dec., 1923.

STUDIES ON THE SEX-RATIO AND RELATED PHENOMENA. 8. THE SEASONAL SEX-RATIO IN THE PIG. A. S. Parkes. Zeitschr fuer induktive Abstammungs-und Vererbungslehre, vol.40, pp.121-138, 1926.

ON THE CORRELATION BETWEEN THE NUMBER OF MAMMAE OF THE DAM AND SIZE OF LITTER IN MAMMALS. II. INTRA-RACIAL CORRELATION IN SWINE. Raymond Pearl. Proc. Soc. Exper. Biol. and Med., pp.31-32, 1913.

NOTE ON THE REPRODUCTION OF THE RED RIVER-HOG (POTAMOCHOERUS PENICILLATUS) IN THE SOCIETY'S MENAGERIE. Philip L. Sclater. Proc. Zool. Soc. Lond., pt.29, p.63, 1861.

Taxonomy

PRELIMINARY SYNOPSIS OF RUSSIAN AND MONGOLIAN WILD BOARS. G. Adlerberg. Comptes Rendus Acad. Sci. URSS, 1930, pp.91-96, figs.3, 1930.

(DERIVATION, SPECIES, AND RACES OF THE WILD SWINE OF EURASIA.) Abstammung, Arten und Rassen der Wildschweine Eurasiens. Rudolf Amon. Zeitschr. f. Zuechtung, ser.B, Tierzuechtung u. Zuechtungsbiol., Berlin, vol.40, no.1, pp.49-88, figs.5, maps 4, tables 6, Jan., 1938.

(REMARKS ON THE SYSTEMATICS OF REAL SWINE (GENUS SUS LINNE).) Bemerkungen zur Systematik der Echten Schweinen (Gattung Sus Linne). H. von Boetticher. Zeitschr. f. Saeugetierkunde, Berlin, vol.13, no.2, pp.246-254, 1939.

(REVIEW OF THE SPECIES OF THE FAMILY OF SWINE (SETIFERA) KNOWN UP TO THE PRESENT.) Revision der bis jezt bekannt gewordenen arten der familie der Borstenthiere oder Schweine (Setigera). L. J. Fitzinger. Sitz. Akad. Wiss. Wien, vol.50, Bd.L, pp.52, Nov.10, 1864.

(INTRASPECIFIC VARIATION BETWEEN TWO EXTREME TYPES OF PHACOCHERS.) Variation intraspécifique entre deux types extremes de Phacochères. E. Guiraud. Première Conférence Internationale des Africanistes de l'Ouest, Dakar, vol.1, pp. 199-200, 1950.

EUREODON AS THE GENERIC NAME OF THE WARTHOGS. Marcus W. Lyon, Jr. Proc. Biol. Soc. Wash., vol.28, p.141, June 29, 1915.

PRELIMINARY REPORT ON THE SYSTEMATIC POSITION OF THE WILD BOAR OF JUGOSLAVIA. Vladimir Martino. Lovtsa, nos.5-6, pp.1-4, figs.4, May-June, 1937. (Bulgarian)

ON THE TYPE-MATERIAL OF SUS NIPPONICUS SENDAE. Hikoshichiro Matsumoto. Sci. Reports Tohoku Imp. Univ. (2), Geol., vol.13, no.3, p.1, pls.18-29, 1930.

PRELIMINARY DESCRIPTION OF A NEW WARTHOG. (PHACOCHAERUS BARKERI, SP. NOV., FROM SOUTHWEST OF BAHR EL GHAZAL.) Lord Rothschild. Ann. and Mag. Nat. Hist., ser.9, vol.6, p.416, Oct., 1920.

CHOIROPOTAMUS VERSUS KOIROPOTAMUS. Oldfield Thomas. Proc. Biol. Soc. Wash., vol.34, p.135, June 30, 1921.

ON A NEW FOREST-PIG. Oldfield Thomas. Proc. Zool. Soc. Lond., vol.1, pp.2-4, June 7, 1906.

PHACOCHOERUS AS THE GENERIC NAME OF THE WARTHOGS. Oldfield Thomas. Proc. Biol. Soc. Wash., vol.28, p.181, Nov.29, 1915.

SOME NOTES ON BABIRUSSA. Oldfield Thomas. Ann. and Mag. Nat. Hist. (9), vol.5, no.26, pp.185-188, Feb., 1920.

THE RACES OF THE EUROPEAN WILD SWINE. Oldfield Thomas. Proc. Zool. Soc. Lond., pp.390-393, June, 1912.

Zoo Collections

THIS LITTLE PIG. (YOUNG PIGS IN SAN DIEGO ZOO.) Belle J. Benchley. Zoonooz, San Diego, vol.11, no.9, pp.3-6, Sept., 1939.

A RARE SPECIES TO APPEAR AT THE ZOO FOR THE FIRST TIME; GIANT FOREST HOGS IN THEIR NATIVE WILD. S. Lippens, L. Lippens. Illus. London News, vol.190, no.5099, p.61, illus., Jan.9, 1937.

ANNOUNCEMENT OF THE TRANSFER BY HER MAJESTY THE QUEEN OF A SPECIMEN OF PHACOCHOERUS AELIANI TO THE CARE OF THE SOCIETY. Philip L. Sclater. Proc. Zool. Soc. Lond., pt.29, pp.30-31, 1861.

ON THE BABIRUSSA AND OTHER SUIDAE, NOW LIVING IN THE SOCIETY'S MENAGERIE. Philip L. Sclater. Proc. Zool. Soc., Lond., pt.28, p.443, 1860.

Tayassuidae--Extinct and Fossil

ON PLATYGONUS COMPRESSUS: A NEW FOSSIL PACHYDERM. John L. Le Conte. Mem. Amer. Acad. Arts and Sci., vol.3, no., pp.257-274, pls.1-4, 1842.

A NEW FOSSIL PECCARY, PROTHENNOPS NIOBRARENSIS, FROM BROWN COUNTY, NEBRASKA. Edwin H. Colbert. Nebraska State Mus., vol.1, bull.44, pp.419-430, figs.2, June, 1935.

PLIOCENE PECCARIES FROM THE PACIFIC COAST REGION OF NORTH AMERICA. Edwin H. Colbert. Carnegie Inst. Wash., publ.no.487, pp.241-269, figs.4, pls.1-6, tables, May 25, 1938.

AN UPPER TERTIARY PECCARY FROM INDIA. Edwin H. Colbert. Amer. Mus. Nov., no.635, pp.9, figs.5, June 13, 1933.

FOSSIL PECCARY REMAINS FROM THE UPPER PLIOCENE OF IDAHO. C. Lewis Gazin. Jour. Wash. Acad. Sci., vol.28, no.2, pp.41-49, figs.3, Feb.15, 1938.

PLEISTOCENE PECCARIES FROM THE CUMBERLAND CAVE DEPOSIT. James Williams Gidley. Proc. U.S. Nat. Mus., vol.57, pp.651-678, figs.1-13, pls.54-55, 1920.

HESPEROPITHECUS APPARENTLY NOT AN APE NOR A MAN. (PROBABLY A PECCARY.) William K. Gregory. Science, n.s., vol. 66, pp.579-581, Dec.16, 1927.

AN EXTENSION IN THE RANGE OF FOSSIL PECCARIES. C. Stuart Johnston. Amer. Midland Nat., vol.16, no.1, pp.117-119, figs.1-2, Jan., 1935.

A MEMOIR ON THE EXTINCT DICOTYLINAE OF AMERICA. Joseph Leidy. Trans. Amer. Philos. Soc., ser.2, vol. 10, pp.323-343, pls.35-38, 1852.

OBSERVATIONS ON THE EXTINCT PECCARY OF NORTH AMERICA. Joseph Leidy. Trans. Amer. Philos. Soc., vol.11, pp.15-23, 1857.

HESPEROPITHECUS, THE FIRST ANTHROPOID PRIMATE FOUND IN AMERICA. (HESPEROPITHECUS HAROLDCOOKII FROM AGATE, NEBRASKA; PLIOCENE.) Henry Fairfield Osborn. Science, n.s., vol.55, pp.463-465, May 5, 1922.

(ARGENTIEAN SPECIES OF FOSSIL PECCARIES AND THEIR RELATIONS WITH THOSE OF BRAZIL AND NORTH AMERICA.) Las especies fósiles Argentinas de pecaríes ("Tayassuidae") y sus relaciones con las del Brasil y Norte América. Carlos Rusconi. Anales Mus. Nac. Hist. Nat. "Bernardino Rivadavia", Buenos Aires, vol. 36, pp.121-241, figs.32, pls.18, May 21, 1930.

(EXTINCT PECCARIES OF URUGUAY.) Pecaries extinguidos del Uruguay. Carlos Rusconi. Rev. Mus. Hist. Nat. Mendoza, vol.6, nos.1-4, pp.123-128, Dec., 1952.

A PECCARY FROM THE MCKITTRICK PLEISTOCENE, CALIFORNIA. Chester Stock. Contrib. Paleont., Carnegie Inst. Wash., publ.393, pp.23-27, figs.7, Sept., 1928 (Oct.24, 1928).

A PECCARY SKULL FROM THE BARSTOW MIOCENE, CALIFORNIA. Chester Stock. Proc. Nat. Acad. Wash., vol.23, no.7, pp. 398-404, fig.1, pl.1, July, 1937.

A NEW SPECIES OF EXTINCT PECCARY FROM OREGON. M. R. Thorpe. Amer. Jour. Sci., ser.5, vol.7, pp.393-397, figs. 4, May, 1924.

Tayassuidae--Recent

PECCARIES—THE NATIVE PIGS OF AMERICA. Vernon Bailey. National Nature News, vol.2, no.40, pp.3, 5, illus., Oct.17, 1938.

IS THE PECCARY DANGEROUS? J. G. Burr. Texas Game and Fish, Austin, vol.7, no.2, pp.4, 29, illus., Jan., 1949.

WILD PIGS OF THE DESERT. (PECCARY.) William H. Carr. Nat. Hist., New York, vol.55, no.8, pp.352-355, 392, illus., Oct., 1946.

WHITE LIPPED PECCARY. THIS DISTINGUISHED AND GENERALLY FEARED INHABITANT OF TROPICAL AMERICAN FORESTS BECOMES A NEAR NEIGHBOR OF THE NATURALISTS ON BARRO COLORADO ISLAND. Frank M. Chapman. Natural History, New York, vol.38, no.5, pp.408-413, illus., Dec., 1936.

THE WHITE-LIPPED PECCARY IN THE STATE OF VERACRUZ, MEXICO. Walter W. Dalquest. Anal. Inst. Biol., Mexico City, vol.20, nos.1-2, pp.411-413, figs.2, 1949.

(SIGNIFICANCE OF THE TRIPLE GEOGRAPHIC FACIES ON WHICH THE DICOTYLES CUVIER ARE IMPRINTED.) Sur la signification du triple facies geographique dont les Dicotyles, Cuvier sont empreints. E. G. Dehaut. Bull. Mus. Nat. Hist. Nat., Paris, ser.2, vol.17, no.1, pp.32-36, figs.2, Jan., 1945.

PECCARIES ON THE PECK. Cas Edwards. Texas Game and Fish, Austin, vol.6, no.5, pp.4, 13, illus., Apr., 1948.

MORPHOLOGY OF THE SCENT GLAND OF THE JAVELINA. Glenwood P. Epling. Jour. Mam., 37 (2): 246-248, illus., June 9, 1956.

HUNTING ARIZONA JAVELINA. Ralph A. Fisher, Sr. Ariz. Wildl.-Sportsman, vol. 24, no.2, pp.16, illus., Feb., 1953.

NOTE ON THE NAMES OF THE GENERA OF PECCARIES. Theodore Gill. Proc. Biol. Soc. Wash., vol.15, pp.38-39, Mar.5, 1902.

THE COLLARED PECCARIES OF MIDDLE AMERICA. E. A. Goldman. Proc. Biol. Soc. Wash., vol.39, pp.47-50, July 29, 1926.

A NEW PECCARY FROM COSTA RICA. E. A. Goldman. Proc. Biol. Soc. Wash., vol.25, pp.189-190, Dec.24, 1912.

FIVE FETUSES REPORTED FOR PECARI ANGULATUS FROM ARIZONA. Arthur F. Halloran. Jour. Mam., vol.26, no.4, p. 434, Feb.12, 1946.

THE TYPE LOCALITY OF PECARI TAJACU. N. Hollister. Proc. Biol. Soc. Wash., vol. 28, p.69, Mar.12, 1915.

(IMPRINTED JAVELINA.) Le Jabali facétieux (Dicotyles tayacu, Gray). Lucien Iches. Bull. Soc. Nat. Acclimat. France, vol.81, no.4, pp.166-171, Apr., 1934.

THE COLLARED PECCARY IN TEXAS. William S. Jennings, John T. Harris. Tex. Game and Fish Comm., FA Rep. Ser.no. 12, pp.1-31, illus., Dec., 1953.

STATISTICAL REPORT OF THE 1942 JAVELINA HUNT. Theodore Knipe. Ariz. Wildl.-Sportsman, 4 (6): 14, May, 1942.

JAVELINA--MYSTERY PIGS. Carroll Lemon. Ariz. Wildl.-Sportsman, 25 (2): 16-19, 45-49, illus., Feb., 1954.

UNPREDICTABLE PIGS. Carroll Lemon. Ariz. Wildl.-Sportsman, 23 (2): 6-9, 52-55, illus., Feb., 1952.

BREEDING RECORD OF JAVELINA, TAYASSU ANGULATUS, IN SOUTHERN ARIZONA. Clay Y. McCulloch. Jour. Mam., 36 (1): 146, Feb.25, 1955.

THE JAVELINA IN TEXAS. Robert Mauermann. Texas Game and Fish, 2 (1): 5, 23-25, Dec., 1943.

DESCRIPTIONS OF FOUR NEW PECCARIES FROM MEXICO. C. Hart Merriam. Proc. Biol. Soc. Wash., vol.14, pp.119-124, July 19, 1901.

FURTHER NOTES ON THE GENERIC NAME OF THE COLLARED PECCARIES. Gerrit S. Miller, Jr. Proc. Biol. Soc. Wash., vol.27, p.229, Dec.29, 1914.

THE GENERIC NAME OF THE COLLARED PECCARIES. Gerrit S. Miller, Jr. Proc. Biol. Soc. Wash., vol.27, p.215, Oct.31, 1914.

(THE PECCARIES IN THE PERU JUNGLE.) Los pecaris en la selva del Peru. Alvaro Piazza L. Pesca y Caza, Ministerio de Agricultura, Lima, no.4, pp.21-32, 1952.

THE JAVELINA. Aline Rothe. Cattleman, 39: 29, 46, Jan., 1953.

(CRANIODENTAL ANATOMY OF THE LIVING PECCARIES.) Anatomía craneo-dental de los tayassuinos vivientes (pecaríes). Carlos Rusconi. Anales Soc. Cient. Argentina, Buenos Aires, vol.107, pp.1-75, figs.21, pls.9, 1929.

LETTER REFERRING TO A SPECIES OF PECCARY. Robert Temple. Proc. Zool. Soc. Lond., pt.28, pp.206-207, 1860.

JAVELINAS ARE REAL SPORT. Jack Underwood. Arizona Wildlife and Sportsman, Safford, vol.6, no.4, p.4, Apr., 1944.

THESE LITTLE PIGS HAVE A WAY. (NOTES ON JAVELINA TRAITS.) M. V. Walker. Natl. Park Serv., Region Three Quart., 3 (3): 15-18, July, 1941.

FORT HUACHUCA WILDLIFE AREA INVESTIGATIONS. Charles O. Wallmo. Ariz. Game and Fish Comm., pp.100, 1951.

NOTES ON THE FEMALE REPRODUCTIVE TRACT (OVARIES, UTERUS AND PLACENTA) OF THE COLLARED PECCARY (PECARI ANGULATUS BANGSI GOLDMAN). G. B. Wislocki. Jour. Mam., vol. 12, no.2, pp.143-149, pls.2, May, 1931.

JAVELINA WEIGHTS. Ariz. Wildl.-Sportsman, 25 (5): 6-7, May, 1954.

## Hippopotamidae--Extinct and Fossil

(ON THE OCCURRENCE OF THE QUATERNARY HIPPOPOTAMUS IN NORTHEASTERN FRANCE.) Sur la présence de la l'hippipotame quaternaire dans le Nord-Est de la France. A. Bastin. Ann. Soc. Geol. du Nord, Lille, vol.58, pp.92-118, map, pl.6, fig.1, 1933.

THE EXTINCT HIPPOPOTAMUS ANTIQUUS OF EUROPE. P.E.P. Deraniyagala. Spolia Zeylanica, Bull. Nat. Mus. Ceylon, vol.27, pt.2, pp.219-222, May 25, 1955.

SOME HIPPOPOTAMUSES OF CEYLON, WESTERN ASIA, EAST AFRICA AND ENGLAND. P.E.P. Deraniyagala. Spolia Zeylanica, Colombo, vol.26, pp.125-132, Dec.20, 1951.

THE FOSSIL HIPPOPOTAMIDAE OF ASIA, WITH NOTES ON THE RECENT SPECIES. D. A. Hooijer. Zool. Verhandel., Rijksmus, Natuurlijke Hist. Leiden, no.8, pp. 1-124, figs.5, pls.22, Feb.14, 1950.

ON RECENT AND FOSSIL HIPPOPOTAMI. D. A. Hooijer. Archives Néerlandaises Zool., Leyden, vol.7, pp.289-290, 1945.

ON THE NOMENCLATURE OF SOME FOSSIL HIPPOPOTAMI. D. A. Hooijer. Archives Néerlandaises Zool., Leyden, vol.6, livr.2-3, pp.279-282, 1942.

(REMAINS OF A HIPPOPOTAMUS IN SOUTHERN ITALY.) Avanzi di ippopotamo nell'Italia meriodionale. (Hippopotamus amphibius.) Guiseppe de Lorenzo, Geremia D'Erasmo. Atti Reale Acad. Sci. fis. e. mat. Napoli, ser.2, vol.20, no.15, pp.1-17, figs.6, pls.1-2, 1935.

(SOME NEW ELEMENTS CONCERNING HIPPOPOTAMUS IMAGUNCULA HOPWOOD.) Quelques éléments nouveaux concernant Hippopotamus imaguncula Hopwood. Xavier Misonne. Bull. Inst. Royal Sci. Nat. Belgique, Brussels, vol. 28, no.3, pp.1-12, pls.1-3, table, Jan., 1952.

(SKELETON OF A HIPPOPOTAMUS FOUND IN THE VILLAFRANCHIANO IN THE SURROUNDINGS OF PERUGIA.) Scheletro di Ippopotamo rinvenuto nel Villafranchiano dei dintorni di Perugia. G. Ramaccioni. Atti della Soc. Toscana Sci. Nat., proc. Verb., vol.45, no.4, pp.31-34, 1936.

HIPPOPOTAMUS AMPHIBIUS OF MAUER A. D. ELSENZ. J. Voelcker. Heidelberger Akademie der Wiss. Sitz., Mat.-nat. klasse, Jahrg., abh.3, pp.6, 1931.

## Hippopotamidae--Recent

HIPPOS AT HOME AND AT SCHOOL. Maurice Burton. Illus. London News, vol. 137, no.3573, p.664, illus., Oct.15, 1955.

EXHIBITION OF A MOUNTED SKELETON OF A YOUNG HIPPOPOTAMUS. William H. Flower. Proc. Zool. Soc. Lond., p.329, 1871.

(A HIPPOPOTAMUS BIRTH ON LAND.) Eine Nilpferdgeburt an Land. Heinz Heck, Jr. Saeugetierk. Mitteil., Stuttgart, vol. 1, no.1, pp.30-31, Jan.10, 1953.

(A SYMBIOTICLIKE RELATIONSHIP BETWEEN HIPPOPOTAMUS AND FISH.) Ein symbioseartiges Verhaeltnis zwischen Flusspferd und Fisch. H. Hediger. Saeugetierk. Mitteil., Stuttgart, vol.1, no.2, pp.75-76, illus., Apr.1, 1953.

FACT AND FICTION IN HIPPOPOTAMOLOGY. (SAMPLING THE HISTORY OF SCIENTIFIC ERROR.) Dirk Albert Hooijer. Osiris, Bruges, vol.10, pp.109-116, 1952.

HIPPO HUNTING BY NIGHT. Jack Jardine. Uganda Jour., vol.5, no.4, pp.302-303, Apr., 1938.

THE STORY OF THE HIPPOPOTAMUS. Willy Ley. Fauna, Phila., vol.5, no.2, pp.53-55, illus., June, 1943.

DESCRIPTION OF A NEW SPECIES OF HIPPOPOTAMUS. Gerrit S. Miller, Jr. Smithsonian Miscel. Coll., vol.54, no. 7, publ.1927, pp.3, pls.4, Mar.28, 1910.

ON A SUPPOSED NEW SPECIES OF HIPPOTAMUS. Samuel George Morton. Proc. Acad. Nat. Sci., Phila., vol.2, no.1, pp. 14-17, illus., Apr., 1844.

MEMORANDA ON THE HIPPOPOTAMUS AND BALAENICEPS RECENTLY IMPORTED INTO ENGLAND, AND NOW IN THE GARDENS OF THE SOCIETY. John Petherick. Proc. Zool. Soc. Lond., pt. 28, pp.195-199, 1860.

STRANGE ODYSSEY OF THE WILD. (HIPPOPOTAMUS.) Hugh Prior. Nature Mag., Wash., vol.39, no.4, pp.177-180, illus., Apr., 1946.

THE HIPPO CHARMER. Hugh Thomason. Fauna, Phila., vol.8, no.4, pp.108-111, illus., Dec., 1946.

HIPPOPOTAMI IN THE MASS: A MOST REMARKABLE AIR PHOTOGRAPH OF A STARTLED HERD IN FLIGHT. Illus. London News, vol.189, no.5090, pp.816-817, Nov.7, 1936.

HIPPOPOTAMI...SUNK BENEATH THE RIVER...AND RISING OUT OF IT. Illus. London News, vol.221, no.5909, p.111, illus., July 19, 1952.

### Africa

THE HIPPOPOTAMUS IN GAMBIA, WEST AFRICA. John R. Clarke. Jour. Mam., vol.34, no.3, pp.299-315, illus., Aug.14, 1953.

A NEW SPECIES OF HIPPOPOTAMUS FROM POTGIETERSRUST. (HIPPOPOTAMUS MAKAPANENSIS.) J. W. Kitching. South African Jour. Sci., Johannesburg, vol.47, no.7, pp. 209-211, Feb., 1951.

ADDITIONAL OBSERVATIONS ON A LIVING SPECIES OF HIPPOPOTAMUS, OF WESTERN AFRICA (HIPPOPOTAMUS LIBERIENSIS). Samuel George Morton. Jour. Acad. Nat. Sci. Phila., ser.2, vol. 1, pp.3-11, pls.32-34, 1849.

REMARKS ON THE LIBERIAN HIPPOPOTAMUS. Philip L. Sclater. Proc. Zool. Soc., Lond., p.434, 1873.

(ETHOLOGIC MONOGRAPH ON THE HIPPOPOTAMUS.) Monographie ethologique de l'hippopotame (Hippopotamus amphibius Linne). Rene Verheyen. Inst. Parcs Nat. Congo Belge, Explor. Parc National Albert, pp.91, 1954.

DROUGHT VICTIMS. (HIPPOS BOG DOWN AND DIE AS E. AFRICAN LAKE BED DRIES UP.) Life, Chicago, vol.28, no.13, pp.36, 37, illus., Mar.27, 1950.

### Anatomy

THE PLACENTA AND FOETAL MEMBRANES OF THE HIPPOPOTAMUS (HIPPOPOTAMUS AMPHIBIUS L.). E. C. Amoroso, N. A. Hancock. Proc. Zool. Soc. Lond., 126 (3): 486-487, May 31, 1956.

IDENTIFICATION OF A CALCULUS FROM A HIPPOPOTAMUS. F. A. Bannister, M. H. Hey, K. P. Oakley. Nature, London, vol.160, no.4066, p.470, illus., Oct.4, 1947.

NOTE ON THE PLACENTA OF THE HIPPOPOTAMUS. Alfred H. Garrod. Proc. Zool. Soc. Lond., pp.821-822, 1872.

PARTIAL REVERSION TO HEXAPROTODONT DENTITION IN HIPPOPOTAMUS, H. AMPHIBIUS, LINN. R. L. Harger. Jour. East Africa and Uganda Nat. Hist. Soc., 1930-1931, nos.40-41, pp.129-131, figs.2, Apr., 1932.

NOTE ON A DISEASED DENTAL CONDITION IN HIPPOPOTAMUS AMPHIBIUS L. D. A. Hooijer. Proc. Nederl. Akad. van Wetenschappen, vol.44, no.9, pp.1147-1150, fig.5, 1941.

ON THE SUPPOSED HEXAPROTODONT MILK DENTITION IN HIPPOPOTAMUS AMPHIBIUS L. D. A. Hooijer. Zool. Med., Leyden, vol.24, afl.1-2, pp.187-196, figs.2, pls.7-10, 1942.

(CONSIDERATIONS ON THE DENTAL SYSTEM OF HIPPOPOTAMUSES.) Considerations sur le Systeme Dentaire des Hippopotames. L. Joleaud. Bull. Soc. Zool. France, vol.46, nos.1-7, pp.17-22, fig.1, 1921.

ON THE OSTEOLOGY OF THE HEAD OF HIPPOPOTAMUS, AND A DESCRIPTION OF THE OSTEOLOGICAL CHARACTERS OF A NEW GENUS OF HIPPOPOTAMIDAE. Joseph Leidy. Jour. Acad. Nat. Sci., n.s., vol.2, pt.3, pp.207-234, pl.21, May 7, 1852.

(INVESTIGATIONS OF THE HAIRS OF A NEWBORN HIPPOPOTAMUS AND A PYGMY HIPPOPOTAMUS.) Untersuchungen an Haaren eines neugeborenen Nilpferdes und eines Zwergflusspferdes. Th. Lochte. Zool. Garten, Leipzig, n.F., vol.18, nos. 3-4, pp.119-124, 1951.

(THE LARYNX OF HIPPOPOTAMUS AMPHIBIUS.) Der Kehlkopf des Hippopotamus amphibius. R. Luecke. Anat. Anzeiger, vol.67, pp.241-264, figs.4, May 30, 1929.

(ABNORMAL MANDIBULAR CANINES IN THE HIPPOPOTAMUS.) Abnorme Mandibularcanini bei Hippopotamus. Ernst Matthes. Zeitschrift fuer Anatomie u. Entwicklungsgeschichte, Berlin, vol.110, no.2, pp.181-211, figs.28, 1939.

(DIMENSIONS, FORM AND POSITION OF THE LOWER CANINE TEETH OF THE HIPPOPOTAMUS.) Dimensões, forma e posição dos caninos inferiores do hippopótamo. Ernst Matthes. Rev. Faculade de Ciências da Univ. Coimbra, vol.8, no.1, pp.1-26, figs.3, 1939.

(NOTABLE DENTAL ANOMALY IN THE HIPPO.) Sôbre uma notável anomalia dentária no Hipopótamo. Ernst Matthes. Arquivos do Museu Bocage, Lisbon, vol.10, pp.9-14, figs.4, 1939.

(THE BREAST BONE OF THE HIPPOPOTAMUS (CHOEROPSIS LIBERIENSIS.).) Ueber das Brustbein des Hippopotamus (Choeropsis) liberiensis. W. Peters. Monatsbericht der Koenig. Akad. der Wiss. Berlin, vol., no., pp.445-447, 1878.

ON THE BLOOD-COLOURED EXUDATION FROM THE SKIN OF THE HIPPOPOTAMUS. John Tomes. Proc. Zool. Soc. Lond., pt. 18, pp.160-162, 1850.

EXHIBITION OF, AND REMARKS ON, A PAIR OF HIPPOPOTAMUS TEETH. Edwin Ward. Proc. Zool. Soc. Lond., p.381, 1875.

In Captivity

(A HIPPOPOTAMUS BIRTH AND OTHER EVENTS IN THE COPENHAGEN ZOO.) Flusspferdgeburt und andere Ereignisse im Zoo Kopenhagen. Th. Alving. Zool. Garten, Leipzig, n.F., vol.5, nos.1-3, pp.34-37, June, 1932.

REARING HIPPOPOTAMUSES IN CAPTIVITY. C. Emerson Brown. Jour. Mam., vol.5, no.4, pp.243-246, Nov., 1924.

(HABITS, BIRTH, PUBERTY AND LIFE-SPAN OF HIPPOPOTAMUS AMPHIBIUS L.) Over dracht, geboorte, puberteit en levensduur van Hippopotamus amphibius L. C. Kerbert. Bijdragen tot de Dierkunde, Amsterdam, Afl.22, pp.185-191, 1922.

ANNOUNCEMENT OF THE BIRTH OF A HIPPOPOTAMUS IN THE SOCIETY'S GARDENS. Philip L. Sclater. Proc. Zool. Soc. Lond., p.145, 1871; Proc. Zool. Soc. Lond., p.795, 1872.

SOME NOTES ON THE RECENT BIRTH OF A HIPPOPOTAMUS (H. AMPHIBIUS) IN THE GARDENS. G. M. Vevers. Proc. Zool. Soc. Lond., pp.1097-1100, illus., Dec., 1926.

Pygmies

ANOTHER PIGMY HIPPO. William Bridges. Bull. New York Zool. Soc., vol.39, pp.82-83, illus., Mar.-Apr., 1936.

THE PIGMY HIPPOPOTAMUS. J. G. Dollman. Nat. Hist. Mag., London, vol. 3, no.22, pp.203-204, fig.1, Apr., 1932.

TWO SKULLS OF THE PIGMY HIPPOPOTAMUS PRESENTED TO THE BRITISH MUSEUM (NAT. HIST.) BY I.R.P. HESLOP, ESQ., FROM SOUTHERN NIGERIA. Guy Dollman. Proc. Linnean Soc. Lond., 152nd Sess., pt.3, pp.287-288, Aug.21, 1940.

BIRTH OF A PYGMY HIPPOPOTAMUS. William T. Hornaday. Zool. Soc. Bull., vol.23, no.1, pp.10-13, pl.1, Jan., 1920.

PYGMIES AND GIANTS: TWO SPECIES OF HIPPOPOTAMUS. W. P. Pycraft. Illus. London News, vol.193, no.5182, p.273, figs.3, Aug.13, 1938.

THE PIGMY HIPPOPOTAMUS. (CHOEROPSIS LIBERIENSIS.) W. P. Pycraft. Illus. London News, vol.181, no.4871, p.300, illus., Aug.27, 1932.

DISTRIBUTION OF THE PIGMY HIPPOPOTAMUS. James Ritchie. Nature, London, vol. 126, no.3171, pp.204-205, Aug.9, 1930.

(DETAILS ON THE BIRTH OF A PYGMY HIPPOPOTAMUS.) Naeheres zur Geburt eines Zwergflusspferdes. K. M. Schneider. Zool. Garten, Leipzig, n.F., vol.5, nos. 10-12, pp.275-282, figs.11, Dec., 1932.

(ON THE BIRTH OF A PYGMY HIPPOPOTAMUS.) Zur Geburt eines Zwergflusspferdes. K. M. Schneider. Zool. Garten, n.F., vol. 5, nos.4-6, pp.166-167, fig.1, Aug., 1932.

(OBSERVATIONS OF THE DEVELOPMENT OF YOUNG PYGMY HIPPOPOTAMUSES IN THE BERLIN ZOOLOGICAL GARDEN.) Beobachtungen ueber die Entwicklung junger Zwergflusspferde im Zoologischen Garten Berlin. H. Steinmetz. Zool. Garten, Leipzig, n.F., vol.9, no.6, pp. 255-263, Dec., 1937.

HERE AND THERE. NOT A PIG, BUT A PIGMY. (HIPPOPOTAMUS.) San Diego Zoonooz, vol.19, no.6, pp.6-7, June, 1946.

Camelidae

DATA ON THE BIOLOGY AND THE GEOGRAPHIC DISTRIBUTION OF THE WILD CAMEL. A. G. Bannikov. Zool. Jour. USSR, Moscow, vol.24, no.3, pp.190-200, map 1, 1945. (English summary.)

SIX ATTRACTIVE LITTLE COUSINS. (LLAMA, ALPACA, VICUNA, GUANACO, CAMEL.) Belle J. Benchley. San Diego Zoonooz, vol.16, no.4, pp.4-5, illus., Apr., 1943.

STONES FROM THE STOMACH OF A GUANACO. D. S. Bullock. Jour. Mam., vol.10, no.2, pp.170-171, May, 1929.

THE GUANACO. G. Dennler de la Tour. Oryx, vol.2, no.5, pp.273-279, Aug., 1954.

THE VICUNA. (MATING SEASON, FOOD, DISTRIBUTION, AND ESTIMATE OF PRESENT NUMBERS.) G. Dennler de la Tour. Nature, London, vol.175, no.4451, pp.332-333, Feb.19, 1955.

BACTRIAN CAMEL. (CAMELUS BACTRIANUS.) J. G. Dollman. Nat. Hist. Mag., London, vol.1, no.8, pp.273-275, Oct., 1928.

MOUNTAIN CAMEL (LLAMA) Katherine Fields. Our Dumb Animals, Norwood, vol.82, no.4, p.9, illus., Apr., 1949.

CONGENITAL MACROFOLLICULAR CYSTIC GOITER IN A DROMEDARY. Leonard E. Finkelstein. Zoologica, New York, vol.24, pt.3, pp.289-292, pl.1, Nov.2, 1939.

GIFTS OF THE AMERICAS: THE VICUNA. Marjorie Fryckberg. Agriculture in the Americas, Wash., vol.6, nos.6-7, cover p.3, June-July, 1946.

(COMPOSITION OF CAMEL MILK.) Zusammensetzung von Kamelmilch. Bernhard Grzimek. Zool. Garten, Leipzig, 23 (1-3): 247, 1957.

CAMELS AND CARAVANS. Kilroy Harris. Home Geographic Monthly, vol.1, no.9, pp.1-6, figs.8, Dec., 1931.

BUILT-IN KNAPSACK. (THE CAMELS HUMP.) John Eric Hill. Nat. Hist., New York, vol.55, no.8, p.387, illus., Oct., 1946.

CAMELS OF THE CLOUDS. (LLAMA, ALPACA, VICUNA, GUANACO.) W. H. Hodge. Nat. Geogr. Mag., Wash., vol. 89, no.5, pp.641-656, illus., May, 1946.

LLAMAS: NEW WORLD BEASTS OF BURDEN. W. H. Hodge. Illus. London News, vol. 215, no.5769, pp.752-753, illus., Nov.12, 1949.

THE GUANACO. Emile Housse. La Nature, Paris, no.3033, pp.175-179, Sept. 15, 1938. (In French.)

THE VICUNA AND THE PUNA. Carl B. Koford. Ecol. Monog., 27 (2): 153-219, Apr., 1957.

LLAMA, "PERUVIAN SHEEP." Edith M. Laing. Nature Mag., Wash., D.C., vol. 37, no.1, p.35, Jan., 1944.

CAMEL CARAVAN. Claude W. Leister. Fauna, Phila., vol.5, no.4, pp.102-107, illus., Dec., 1943.

AUCHENIA. I. THE GUANACO. A. Leon. La Terre et la Vie, Rev. d'Hist. Nat., vol. 3, no.1, pp.30-38, illus., Jan., 1933. (In French.)

AUCHENIA. II. THE LLAMA. A. Leon. La Terre et la Vie, Rev. d'Hist. Nat., vol.3, no.11, pp.644-653, illus., Nov., 1933.

AUCHENIA. III. THE VICUNA. A. Leon. La Terre et la Vie, vol.4, no.4, pp.195-208, illus., Apr., 1934. (In French.)

NOTES ON GUANACOS. Einar Loennberg. Arkiv. Zool., vol.8, no.19, pp.1-8, figs. 1-4, July 3, 1913.

THE GUANACOS OF CURAMALAL. Emiliano J. MacDonagh. Notas Mus. La Plata, Univ. Nacional La Plata, vol.14, Zool., no.129 bis, pp.505-537, pls.1-3, 1949. (In Spanish.)

COLOUR-FILM SHOTS OF THE WILD CAMEL. Ivor Montagu. Proc. Zool. Soc. Lond., 129 (4): 592-595, pl.1, Dec.17, 1957.

LITTLE CAMEL OF THE SOUTH. (GUANACO) Una G. Nichols. Zoonooz, Zool. Soc. San Diego, vol.28, no.9, pp. 5-7, illus., Sept., 1955.

REMARKABLE CAMEL RECORDS. Ewen K. Patterson. Our Dumb Animals, Norwood, vol.74, no.2, p.25, Feb., 1941.

THE EXAMINATION OF THE CAMEL FOR SOUNDNESS, WITH INDICATIONS AS TO ITS AGE. D. S. Rabagliati. Veterinary Jour., vol.79, nos.11, 12, pp.1-31, figs.20, 1923.

THE VICUNA (AUCHENIA VICUGNA). Cesar A. Ridoutt. Bol. Mus. Hist. Nat. "Javier Prado," Lima, ano 6, nos.22-23, pp.400-409, 1942. (In Spanish.)

(LLAMAS, ALPACAS, AND GUANACOS.) Llamas y Alpacas vicunas y Guanacos. Elias C. Romero. Montevideo, pp.1-208, figs.50, 1927.

KNOTHEAD. (ALPACA.) Jordan S. Roux. San Diego Zoonooz, vol.20, no.6, pp.3-4, illus., June, 1947.

REBELLIOUS LLAMA. Wilbert N. Savage. Our Dumb Animals, Norwood, vol.77, no. 5, p.105, illus., June, 1944.

THE CAMEL BRIGADE. Hobart E. Stocking. Nat. Hist., New York, vol.53, no.9, pp.396-397, 431-433, illus., Nov., 1944.

VICUNA! Dan L. Thrapp. Nature Mag., Wash., vol.39, no.9, pp.469-472, 498, illus., Nov., 1946.

WHAT'S NEW. (BACTRIAN CAMEL.) San Diego Zoonooz, vol.21, no.7, p.7, July, 1948.

Africa

(THE CAMEL OF THE OUED ITEL.) Le dromadaire de l'Oued Itel. G. Cauvet. Bull. Soc. Hist. Nat. Afrique du Nord, Alger, vol.28, no.9, pp.513-525, pls.48-49, Dec., 1937.

(ON THE HISTORY OF THE CAMEL IN NORTH AFRICA.) Zur Geschichte des Kamels in Nordafrika. R. Uhden. Petermanns Mitteil. Justus Perthes' Geogr. Anst., vol.75, nos.11-12, p.307, 1929.

Anatomy

(DROMEDARIES WITH 34 TEETH AND DROMEDARIES WITH 36 TEETH.) Dromadiares a 34 dents et Dromadaires a 36 dents. G. Cauvet. Bull. Soc. Hist. Nat. Afrique Nord, vol.20, no.9, pp.247-256, fig.1, Dec.15, 1929.

(COMPARATIVE OSTEOLOGY OF THE PERU AUCHENIA.) Osteologia comparada de los Auchenidos Peruanos. J. Estruch. Revista Univ. Arequipa, Ano.15, no.18, pp. 113-157, illus., Apr.-July, 1943.

NOTE ON THE SPINAL ACCESSORY NERVE OF LONG-NECKED UNGULATES. (LLAMA.) A. Brazier Howell, William L. Straus, Jr. Proc. Zool. Soc. Lond., pt.1, pp.29-32, Apr., 1934.

THE SPINAL ACCESSORY NERVE OF THE CAMEL. (CAMELUS BACTRIANUS.)

Francis Kiss, S. Zuckerman. Proc. Zool. Soc. Lond., pt.1, pp.⁻⁻-74, fig.1, Apr., 1934.

ON THE LLAMA AND ALPACA IN THEIR SUMMER DRESS. James Murie. Proc. Zool. Soc. Lond., pp. 580-581, pl.XLIV, 1866.

(SOME DENTAL PECULIARITIES OF CAMELIDS.) De certaines particularités dentaires des Camélidés. M. H. Neuville. Bull. Mus. Nat. Hist. Nat., Paris, ser.2, vol.3, no.1, pp.77-81, figs.3, Jan., 1931.

THE DENTITION OF THE CAMEL. D. S. Rabagliati. Government Press, Cairo, pp. i-vii, 1-32, pls.27, 1924.

(NUMERIC DENTAL ANOMALIES IN SOME LIVING GUANACOS (LAMA GUANICOE MUELLER).) Sobre anomalías dentarias numéricas en algunos guanacos vivientes (Lama guanicoe Mueller). Carlos Rusconi. Physis, Buenos Aires, vol.10, no. 35, pp.199-203, figs.3, July 12, 1930.

(NEW CASE OF POLYDACTYLY IN A GUANACO FOUND IN AN INDIAN FUNERAL PILE OF SANTIAGO DEL ESTERO (ARGENTINA).) Un nuevo caso de Polidactilia en un guanaco hallado en un tuemulo indígena de Santiago del Estero (Argentina). Carlos Rusconi. Revista Chilena Hist. Nat., Ano 34, pp.224-227, fig.42, 1930.

(CHESTNUTLIKE FORMATIONS ON THE MEMBERS OF LAMA HUANACHUS.) Ueber kastanienartige Bildungen an den Gliedmasson von Lama huanachus. E. Schuntermann. Anat. Anzeiger, vol.60, pp.87-93, figs.2, Sept.3, 1925.

NOTES OF THE POST-MORTEM EXAMINATION OF A DROMEDARY (CAMELUS DROMEDARIUS, LINN.). Mr. Spooner. Proc. Comm. Sci. and Corres. Zool. Soc., Lond., pt.2, pp.126-127, 1832.

THE EXTRAHEPATIC BILIARY TRACT OF THE CAMEL. Paul H. Stevenson. Anat. Record, vol.22, pp.85-95, Aug., 1921.

Asia

LETTER CONTAINING REMARKS ON THE SUPPOSED EXISTENCE OF THE WILD CAMEL IN CENTRAL ASIA. Otto Finsch. Proc. Zool. Soc. Lond., pp.696-698, 1876.

AUSTRALIAN MOUNTED POLICE ON CAMELS: "MOUNTIES" WITH WIDE POWERS AND DUTIES. Illus. London News, vol.214, no.5740, pp.540-541, illus., Apr. 23, 1949.

Domestication, Naturalization

(THE DOMESTICATION OF THE VICUNA.) La domesticacion de la vicuna. Carlos A. Barreda. Revista Zootenica, Buenos Aires, ano 23, no.236, pp.252-263, July-Aug.-Sept., 1936.

CAMELS AND MEN. DOMESTICATED FOR THOUSANDS OF YEARS, THE DROMEDARY AND BACTRIAN STILL COMPLAIN OF THE BURDENS THEY MUST CARRY. William Beebe. Bull. New York Zool. Soc., vol.48, no.4, pp.117-126, illus., July-Aug., 1940.

(ACCLIMATION OF THE DROMEDARY TO THE INTERIOR OF NORTHERN BRAZIL AND THE CULTIVATION OF THE DATE TREE, WITH TRANSLATION OF THE REPORT MADE BY DR. DARESTE TO THE ZOOLOGIC SOCIETY OF ACCLIMATION OF PARIS.) Aclimatacao do dromadario nos sertoes do norte do Brasil, e da cultura da tamareira, com a traduccao do relatorio de Mr. Dareste apresentada a Sociedade zoologica de aclimatacao de Paris. Frederico Leopoldo Cesar Burlamaqui. Rio de Janeiro, Typographia nacional, pp. 89, 1857.

THE DOMESTICATION OF THE LLAMA. Ned Hollister. Science, n.s., vol.47, p. 461, May 10, 1918.

THE CAMEL IN ANTIQUITY. A. E. Robinson. Sudan notes and Records, vol. 19, pt.1, pp.47-69, 1936.

AN HISTORICAL AND DESCRIPTIVE ACCOUNT OF THE PERUVIAN SHEEP, CALLED CARNEROS DELLA TIERRA; AND OF THE EXPERIMENTS MADE BY THE SPANIARDS TO IMPROVE THE RESPECTIVE BREEDS. TO WHICH IS ADDED, AN ACCOUNT OF A SUCCESSFUL ATTEMPT TO DOMESTICATE THE VICUNA IN ENGLAND, AND A RECOMENDATION OF THIS SPECIES TO CROSS WITH OUR NATIVE FLOCKS. William Walton. London, J. Booth, pp.183, illus., 1818.

A MEMOIR ADDRESSED TO PROPREITORS OF MOUNTAIN AND OTHER WASTE LANDS, AND AGRICULTURISTS OF THE UNITED KINGDOM, ON THE NATURALIZATION OF THE ALPACA. RECOMMENDED BY THE NATURAL HISTORY SOCIETY OF LIVERPOOL AS A NEW BREEDING STOCK NOT LIKELY TO INTERFERE WITH SHEEP PASTURAGE. William Walton. London, Natural Hist. Soc. Liverpool, pp. 44, pls.3, 1841; 2nd ed. Liverpool, Printed for the Nat. Hist. Soc. Liverpool, pp.44, 1843.

Ecology, Habits, Behavior

(OBSERVATIONS ON THE ECOLOGY AND ETHOLOGY OF THE CAMEL IN THE NORTHWESTERN SAHARA.) Quelques observations sur l'ecologie et l'ethologie du dromadaire dans le Sahara nord-occidental. H. Gauthier-Pilters. Mammalia, Pairs, 22 (1): 140-151, Mar., 1958.

(THE BEHAVIOR OF MOTHER ANIMAL AND THE NEWBORN AMONG THE CAMELOIDS.) Das Verhalten von Muttertier und Neugeborenen bei Cameliden. Helmut Kraft. Saeugetierk, Mitteil., 5 (4): 174-175, Dec.1, 1957.

(THE BEHAVIOR OF TYLOPODS.) Das Verhalten der Tylopoden. Hilde Pilters. Handbuch der Zoologie, Berlin, vol.8, pt.10, no.22, pp.1-24, illus., 1956.

(INVESTIGATIONS OF INBORN BEHAVIOR IN TYLOPODS, WITH SPECIAL CONSIDERATION OF THE NEW WORLD FORMS.) Untersuchungen ueber angeborene Verhaltensweisen bei Tylopoden, unter besonderer Beruecksichtigung der neuweltlichen Formen. Hilde Pilters. Zeitschr. Tierpsychol., 11 (2): 213-303, 1954. (With English summary.)

MOVEMENTS OF CAMELS. C. E. Radclyffe. Field, London, vol.172, no. 4483, p.1306, illus., Nov.26, 1938.

Fossils

(NEW REMAINS OF LAMA GUANICOE LONNBERGI (AMEGH.).) Nuevos restos de Lama guanicoe loennbergi (Amegh.). Carlos Ameghino, Carlos Rusconi. La Semana Medica, Buenos Aires, no.1, pp. 11, 1933.

A NEW GIANT CAMEL GIGANTOCAMELUS FRICKI, GEN. ET SP. NOV. E. H. Barbour, C. B. Schultz. Bull. Univ. Nebraska, State Mus., Lincoln, vol.2, no. 2, pp.17-27, figs.5-12, Sept., 1939.

A NEW GIANT CAMEL, TITANOTYLOPUS NEBRASKENSIS, GEN. ET SP. NOV. E. H. Barbour, C. B. Schultz. Nebraska State Mus., vol.1, bull.36, pp.291-294, figs.171-172, May, 1934.

A MIOCENE CAMEL BED-GROUND. Barnum Brown. Nat. Hist., New York, vol.29, no.6, pp.658-662, figs.6, 1929.

A SOUTH DAKOTA CAMEL. (POEBROTHERIUM.) James D. Bump. Black Hills Engineer, Rapid City, vol.21, no.1, pp.28-29, figs.2, Jan., 1933.

ALTICAMELUS ALEXANDRAE, A NEW CAMEL FROM THE BARSTOW UPPER MIOCENE OF THE MOHAVE DESERT. Pirie Davidson. Univ. Calif. Publ. Geol., vol.14, no.12, pp.397-408, figs.16, Nov. 20, 1923.

SKULL AND SKELETAL REMAINS OF THE CAMEL PARATYLOPUS CAMELOIDES (WORTMAN) FROM THE JOHN DAY DEPOSITS, OREGON. Jack F. Dougherty. Carnegie Inst., Wash. publ.no.514, pp. 49-58, pl.1, June 27, 1940.

NOTICE OF THE OCCURRENCE OF A PLEISTOCENE CAMEL NORTH OF THE ARCTIC CIRCLE. James W. Gidley. Smithsonian Misc. Coll., Publ.2173, vol. 60, no.26, pp.2, Mar.21, 1913.

TWO NEW CAMELS FROM THE LATE LOWER PLIOCENE OF SOUTH DAKOTA. Joseph T. Gregory. Jour. Mam., vol.20, no.3, pp.366-368, illus., tables, Aug.14, 1939.

CAMELS OF THE FOSSIL GENUS CAMELOPS. Oliver P. Hay. Proc. U.S. Nat. Mus., vol.46, pp.267-277, pls.25-26, Dec.6, 1913.

AN EXTINCT CAMEL FROM UTAH. Oliver P. Hay. Science, n.s., vol.68, pp.299-300, Sept.28, 1928.

SKULL OF FOSSIL CAMELID FROM AMERICAN FALLS LAKE BED AREA OF IDAHO. Marie L. Hopkins. Jour. Mam., 36 (2): 278-282, pl.1, table 1, May 26, 1955.

TERTIARY CAMELS OF THE EASTERN HEMISPHERE (GENUS PARACAMELUS). Y. I. Khaveson. Proc. Paleo. Inst., Acad. Sci. USSR, vol.47, pp.101-162, illus., 1954.

POEBROTHERIUM. F. B. Loomis. Amer. Jour. Sci., vol.16, no.92, pp.137-142, 1928.

THE SKELETON OF A NEW FOSSIL CAMEL FROM WYOMING. F. B. Loomis. Univ. Wyoming Publ., Laramie, vol.2, nos.5-7, pp.59-64, figs.4, May 1, 1936.

TWO NEW SPECIES OF OXYDACTYLUS FROM THE MIDDLE MIOCENE RUSEBUD FORMATION IN WESTERN SOUTH DAKOTA. William Diller Matthew, J. R. Macdonald. American Mus. Nat. Hist., New York, Amer. Mus. Nov., no.2003, pp.7, illus., 1960.

THE GAZELLE CAMEL, STENOMYLUS. Grayson E. Meade. Texas Tech. College, Lubbock, Research Publ. no.5, pp.1-8, 1942.

A LLAMA FROM THE PLEISTOCENE OF MCKITTRICK, CALIFORNIA. John C. Merriam, Chester Stock. Carnegie Inst. Wash., Contrib. Palaeontol., publ. no.347, pp.37-42, figs.4, Oct.8, 1925.

THE SKULL AND DENTITION OF A CAMEL FROM THE PLEISTOCENE OF RANCHO LA BREA. John C. Merriam. Berkeley, Univ. Calif. Press, Bull. Dept. Geol., vol.7, no.14, pp.305-323, illus., 1913.

(A FOSSIL CAMEL SKULL (CAMELUS KNOBLOCHI) FROM SAREPTA ON THE VOLGA.) Einer fossile Schaedel (Camelus knoblochi) von sarepta an der Wolga. A. Nehring. Sitz. Ber. Gesell. Naturf. Freunde, Berlin, Jahrg., no.5, pp.137-144, May 21, 1901.

FOSSIL CAMELS OF THE OLD WORLD. J. A. Orlov. Trudy Lab. Genet., Akad. Nauk, Leningrad, SSSR, vol.1, pp.211-217, 1933.

(ON THE REMAINS OF A FOSSIL CAMEL FROM THE AKMOLINSK REGION (WESTERN SIBERIA).) Ueber die Reste eines fossilen Kamels aus dem Gouvernement Akmolinsk (Westsibirien). J. A. Orlov. Ann. Mus. Zool. Acad. Sci. URSS, vol.28, pp.496-538, 1927.

(ON THE REMAINS OF FOSSIL CAMELIDAE FROM THE SEMIPALATINSK GOVERNMENT (WEST SIBERIA).) Ueber die Reste der fossilen Camelidae aus dem Gouvernement Semipalatinsk (Westsibirien). J. A. Orlov. Ann. Soc. Paleont. Russie, Leningrad, vol.8, pp.99-116, pls.12-14, 1930.

A RARE CAMELOID FROM THE LATE PLEISTOCENE SANDS OF SOUTHWESTERN KANSAS. E. S. Riggs. Trans. Kansas Acad. Sci., Lawrence, vol.48, no.1, pp. 101-104, figs.2, June, 1945.

A FRESH SKULL OF AN EXTINCT AMERICAN CAMEL. A. S. Romer. Jour. Geol., vol.37, no.3, pp.261-267, 1929.

(DENTITION OF PALAEOLMA IN RELATION TO THAT OF OTHER CAMELIDS.) La dentadura de Palaeolama en relacion a la de Otros camelidos. Carlos Rusconi.

Revista Med. Veterinaria, Buenos Aires, vol.13, no.6, pp.250-273, figs.10, Nov., 1931.

TANUPOLAMA, A NEW GENUS OF LLAMA FROM THE PLEISTOCENE OF CALIFORNIA. Chester Stock. Contrib. Paleont., Carnegie Inst. Wash., Publ.393, pp.29-37, pls.6, Sept., 1928 (Oct.24, 1928).

THE EXTINCT CAMELIDAE OF NORTH AMERICA AND SOME ASSOCIATED FORMS. J. W. Wortman. Bull. Amer. Mus. Nat. Hist., vol.10, art.7, pp.93-142, figs.23, pl.11, Apr.9, 1898.

PERACAMELUS GIGAS SCHLOSSER. Otto Zdansky. Peking, Geol. Survey China, China Geological Survey, pp.6, illus., 1926.

Haematology

THE BLOOD COMPOSITION OF THE CAMELS IN CONNECTION WITH THEIR WORKING ABILITY. H. F. Kushner. Bull. Acad. Sci. URSS, Cl. Sci. Math et Nat., ser. Biol., Moscow, no.4, pp.903-916, figs.6, tables 11, 1938. (In Russian, with English summary.)

COMPOSITION OF BLOOD IN CAMELS IN RELATION TO THE WORKING ABILITY OF THESE ANIMALS. H. F. Kushner. Comptes Rendus Acad. Sci. URSS, vol.18, no.9, pp.681-684, 1938.

ON CERTAIN INDICES IN THE COMPOSITION OF THE BLOOD OF DROMEDARY-BACTRIAN HYBRIDS IN CONNECTION WITH HETEROSIS. V. I. Patrushev. Bull. Acad. Sci. URSS, Cl. Sci. Math. et Nat., ser. Biol., Moscow, no.4, pp.917-928, figs.5, tables 9, 1938. (In Russian, with English summary.)

HAEMATOLOGY OF THE CAMELIDAE. Eris Ponder, J. Franklin Yeager, Harry A. Charipper. Sci. Contrib. New York Zool. Soc., vol.11, no.1, pp.1-7, Dec.5, 1928.

Hybrids

INTERSPECIFIC HYBRIDIZATION OF DROMEDARIES AND BACTRIANS. I. I. Lakoza. Bull. Acad. Sci. URSS, Cl. Sci. Math. et Nat., ser. Biol., Moscow, no.4, pp.885-902, figs.4, tables 1-3b, 1938. (In Russian, with English summary.)

(OBSERVATIONS ON GUANACOS CROSSED WITH LLAMAS AT BARRETO (CORDOBA).) Observaciones sobre guanacos cruzados con llamas en Barreto (Cordoba). Emiliano J. MacDonagh. Revista del Mus. de La Plata, Buenos Aires, n.s., vol.2, zoologia no.10, pp.63-84, illus., 1940.

Introduction into North America

CAMELS IN TEXAS? (U.S. ARMY CAMEL EXPERIMENTS OF THE 1850'S.) Gerry Doyle. San Jacinto Mus. Hist. Assoc., San Jacinto Monument, Texas, pp.12, illus., 1956.

THE USES OF THE CAMEL: CONSIDERED WITH A VIEW TO HIS INTRODUCTION INTO OUR WESTERN STATES AND TERRITORIES. Joseph Warren Fabens. New York, Carleton Publisher, pp.32, 1865.

IMPORTATION OF CAMELS. Gen. Harlan. U.S. Patent Off., Report, Agriculture, Wash., 1853, pp.61-63, 1854.

THE CAMEL: ITS INTRODUCTION AND ACCLIMATION IN THE UNITED STATES BY MAJOR HERBERT C. WAYNE, U.S.A., FOR ARMY TRANSPORTATION PURPOSES IN TEXAS AND ADJACENT TERRITORIES. Sidney Herbert. Southern Cultivator and Dixie Farmer, pp.1-11, May, 1882.

THOSE CAMELS OF ARIZONA. Vic H. Housholder. Arizona Wild Life, vol.3, no.1, pp.4, 31, Dec., 1930.

UNCLE SAM'S CAMELS. THE JOURNAL OF MAY HUMPHREYS STACEY SUPPLEMENTED BY THE REPORT OF EDWARD FITZGERALD BEALE (1857-1858). Lewis Burt Lesley. Cambridge, Harvard Univ. Press, pp.298, pls.2, map, 1929.

THE CAMEL, HIS ORGANIZATION HABITS AND USES CONSIDERED WITH REFERENCE TO HIS INTRODUCTION INTO THE UNITED STATES. Geo. P. Marsh. 1856.

LECTURE ON THE CAMEL: DELIVERED BEFORE THE SMITHSONIAN INSTITUTION. Geo. P. Marsh. 9th Ann. Report Board Regents Smithsonian Inst., Misc. doc.37, 33rd Congress, 2nd Session, Wash., D.C., pp.98-122, 1855.

A "FOSSIL" CAMEL RECENTLY LIVING IN UTAH. Alfred S. Romer, A. H. Sutton. Science, n.s., vol.68, pp.19-20, July 6, 1928.

HOW THE CAMEL CAME TO AMERICA. Zulma Steele. Fauna, Phila., vol.8, no. 3, pp.78-79, illus., Sept., 1946.

REPORTS UPON THE PURCHASE, IMPORTATION, AND USE OF CAMELS AND DROMEDARIES, TO BE EMPLOYED FOR MILITARY PURPOSES. U.S. War Dept., Wash., pp.258, illus., 1857.

WHAT HAPPENED TO AMERICA'S CAMELS? Science Illustrated, Louisville, vol.2, no.7, pp.48-49, illus., July, 1947.

Origins

(THE ORIGIN OF THE ALPACA.) Die Herkunft des Alpakka. Wolf Herre. Saeugetierk. Mitteil., Stuttgart, vol.1, no.4, pp.176-177, Oct.1, 1953.

(ON THE ORIGIN OF THE ALPACA (LAMA PACOS LINNE 1758).) Zur Abstammung des Alpakka, Lama pacos (Linne, 1758). G. Steinbacher. Saeugetierk. Mitteil., Stuttgart, vol.1, no.2, pp. 78-79, Apr.1, 1953.

Physiology

THE DISTRIBUTION OF OXYTOCIN AND VASOPRESSIN (ANTIDIURETIC HORMONE) IN THE NEUROHYPOPHYSIS OF THE CAMEL. K. Adamsons, Jr., S. L. Engel, H. B. van Dyke, B. Schmidt-Nielsen, K. Schmidt-Nielsen. Endocrinology, Springfield, Illinois, vol.58, no.2, pp.272-278, Feb., 1956.

RENAL FUNCTION AND ELECTROLYTES IN THE LLAMA. E. L. Becker, J. A. Schilling, R. B. Harvey. Amer. Jour. Physiol., vol.183, no.2, pp.307-308, Nov., 1955.

(ON THE QUESTION OF THE USE OF CAMEL GASTRIC JUICE.) Zur Frage der Geniessbarkeit der Kamelmagenfluessigkeit. Th. Haltenorth. Saeugetierk., Mitteil., Stuttgart, vol.1, no.2, pp.79-80, Apr.1, 1953.

BODY TEMPERATURE OF THE CAMEL. K. Schmidt-Nielsen, B. Schmidt-Nielsen, T. R. Houpt, S. A. Jarnum. Federation Proc., Wash., vol.14, no.1, pt.1, p.133, Mar., 1955.

BODY TEMPERATURE OF THE CAMEL AND ITS RELATION TO WATER ECONOMY. K. Schmidt-Nielsen, B. Schmidt-Nielsen, S. A. Jarnum, T. R. Noupt. Amer. Jour. Physiol., Wash., 188 (1): 103-112, Jan., 1957.

DEHYDRATION AND REHYDRATION IN THE CAMEL. B. Schmidt-Nielsen, K. Schmidt-Nielsen, S. A. Jarnum, T. R. Houpt. Federation Proc., Wash., vol. 14, no.1, pt.1, p.32, Mar., 1955.

THE QUESTION OF WATER STORAGE IN THE STOMACH OF THE CAMEL. K. Schmidt-Nielsen, B. Schmidt-Nielsen, T. R. Houpt, S. A. Jarnum. Mammalia, Paris, vol.20, no.1, pp.1-15, Mar., 1956.

UREA EXCRETION IN THE CAMEL. B. Schmidt-Nielsen, K. Schmidt-Nielsen, T. R. Houpt, S. A. Jarnum. Amer. Jour. Physiol., Wash., 188 (3): 477-484, Mar., 1957.

WATER BALANCE OF THE CAMEL. B. Schmidt-Nielsen, K. Schmidt-Nielsen, T. R. Houpt, S. A. Jarnum. Amer. Jour. Physiol., 185 (1): 185-194, Apr., 1956.

CAMELS DO NOT STORE WATER IN EITHER HUMP OR STOMACH. Science News Letter, Wash., D.C., p.382, June 14, 1941.

South America

(STUDIES OF THE WILD AND DOMESTICATED TYLOPODS OF SOUTH AMERICA.) Studien ueber die wilden und domestizierten Tylopoden suedamerikas. Wolf Herre. Zool. Garten, Leipzig, vol.19, nos.2-4, pp.70-98, illus., 1952.

GOLDEN FLEECE OF THE ANDES. (VICUNA.) Walter Henricks Hodge. Nat. Hist., New York, vol.59, no.5, pp.200-207, illus., May, 1950.

(CONSIDERATIONS ON THE CAMELIDS OF THE ANDES.) Algunas consideraciones sobre los camelidos de los Andes. J. Alberto Leon. Bol. Mus. Hist. Nat. "Javier Prado", Lima, ano 3, no.11, pp.95-105, illus., 1939.

(THE GUANACOS OF CURAMALAL.) Los guanacos de Curamalal. Emiliano J. MacDonagh. Notas Mus. La Plata, vol. 14, zool., no.129 bis, pp.505-537, pls.1-3, 1949.

(GUANACO COLONIES (LAMA GUANICOE) IN THE NORTHERN DESERTS OF CHILE.) Colonias de guanacos--Lama guanicoe--en el desierto septentrional de Chile. F. Mann, Guillermo, Hilde Zapfe, Ruben Martinez, Gerardo Melcher. Investig. Zool. Chilenas, Santiago, vol.1, fasc.10, pp.11-13, June, 1953.

THE STATUS OF THE VICUNA IN SOUTHERN PERU, 1940. Oliver P. Pearson. Jour. Mam., vol.24, no.1, p.97, Feb.20, 1943.

(THE SOUTH AMERICAN CAMELIDS.) Sobre camelidos sud-americanos. Carlos Rusconi. La Semana Medica, vol.40, no. 2043, pp.856-857, Mar.9, 1933.

SHEEP OF THE ANDES. (ALPACA, LLAMA, GUANACO, AND VICUNA.) Elizabeth P. Tappy. Agriculture in the Americas, Wash., D.C., vol.4, no.3, pp.46-50, illus., Mar., 1944.

SOUTH AMERICA'S WILD CAMELS. (VICUNA.) Dan L. Thrapp. Fauna, Phila., vol.10, no.1, pp.9-13, illus., Mar., 1948.

Young

SPRING NURSERY. (CAMELS.) Belle J. Benchley. Zoonooz, San Diego, vol.12, no.4, pp.6-7, Apr., 1940.

(BOTTLE-FEEDING A YOUNG GUANACO.) Guanaco-baby aan de fles. E. F. Jacobi. "Artis" 3e Jaargang no.6, Maart-Apr., 1958, pp.193-197, illus.4, 1958.

JUST A FEW HOURS OLD: THE ZOO'S BABY CAMEL WITH ITS MOTHER. (BACTRIAN.) Illus. London News, vol.216, no.5787, p.428, illus., Mar.18, 1950.

Tragulidae

ON THE MEANING OF THE NAME CERVUS JAVANICUS OSBECK 1765 (TRAGULIDAE). A.C.V. van Bemmel. Treubia, Buitenzorg, vol.20, pt.2, pp.378-380, Oct., 1949.

(ON THE TRAGULIDAE AND THEIR RELATIONSHIPS TO THE OTHER ARTIODACTYLA.) Ueber die Tragulidae und ihre Beziehungen zu den uebrigen Artiodactyla. Albertina Carlsson. Acta Zoologica, vol. 7, pp.69-100, 1926.

THE DISTRIBUTION OF THE MOUSEDEER (MOSCHIOLA MEMINNA). F. W. Champion. Jour. Bombay Nat. Hist., vol.33, no.4, pp. 985-986, Oct.15, 1929.

(THE MOUSE-DEER.) De kantjil. P.M.W. Dukkus. Tropische Natuur, Buitenzorg, vol.21, no.7, pp.112-115, fig.1, July, 1932.

ON THE GENERIC CHARACTERS OF THE FAM. TRAGULIDAE (MAMM., ARTIODACTYLA). K. K. Flerov. Comptes Rendus Acad. Sci. URSS, pp.75-79, 1931.

MEMOIR ON THE GENUS MOSCHUS OF LINNAEUS, WITH DESCRIPTIONS OF TWO NEW SPECIES. John E. Gray. Proc. Zool. Soc. Lond., pt.4, p.63, 1836.

NOTES ON MALAYAN AND OTHER MOUSE-DEER. C. Boden Kloss. Jour. Fed. Malay States Mus., vol.7, pt.4, pp.245-256, June, 1918.

ON A NEW MOUSE-DEER FROM UPPER SIAM. C. Boden Kloss. Jour. Nat. Hist. Soc., Siam, vol.2, no.2, pp.88-89, Dec., 1916.

ON A NEW PRIMITIVE DEER AND TWO TRAGULOID GENERA FROM THE LOWER MIOCENE OF NEBRASKA. W. D. Matthew. Amer. Mus. Novit., no.215, pp.4, illus., May 10, 1926.

DESCRIPTIONS OF ELEVEN NEW MALAYAN MOUSE DEER. Gerrit S. Miller, Jr. Proc. Biol. Soc., Wash., vol.16, pp.31-44, Mar.19, 1903.

THE MOUSE DEER OF THE RHIO-LINGA ARCHIPELAGO; A STUDY OF SPECIFIC DIFFERENTATION UNDER UNIFORM ENVIRONMENT. Gerrit S. Miller, Jr. Proc. U.S. Nat. Mus., vol.37, no.1695, pp.1-9, figs.1-2, pls.1-3, Sept.1, 1909.

A NEW MOUSE DEER FROM LOWER SIAM. Gerrit S. Miller, Jr. Proc. Biol. Soc., Wash., vol.8, pp.185-186, Dec.21, 1900.

A NEW MOUSE-DEER FROM THE RHIO-LINGA ARCHIPELAGO. Gerrit S. Miller, Jr. Proc. Biol. Soc., Wash., vol.24, pp. 165-166, June 16, 1911.

TWO NEW MALAYAN MOUSE DEER. Gerrit S. Miller, Jr. Proc. Biol. Soc., Wash., vol.15, pp.173-175, Aug.6, 1902.

ON A NEW SPECIES OF MUSK DEER FROM SIERRA LEONE. W. Ogilby. Proc. Zool. Soc. Lond., pt.8, p.35, 1840.

ON CERVULUS FEAE, A NEW SPECIES OF MUNTJAC FROM TENASSERIM. Oldfield Thomas. Proc. Zool. Soc., Lond., p.85, Feb.19, 1889.

ON THE GENERIC NAMES APPLICABLE TO THE CHEVROTIANS (TRAGULIDAE). Oldfield Thomas. Ann. and Mag. Nat. Hist. (8), vol.18, no.103, pp.72-73, July, 1916.

SCIENTIFIC RESULTS FROM THE MAMMAL SURVEY. NO.XXXVIII. THE MOUSE-DEER (TRAGULUS) OF THE MERGUI ARCHIPELAGO. Oldfield Thomas. Jour. Bombay Nat. Hist. Soc., vol.29, no.1, pp. 84-85, Apr.20, 1923.

SCIENTIFIC RESULTS FROM THE MAMMAL SURVEY. XI. E.--THE INDIAN RIBBED-FACED DEER OR MUNTJAC. R. C. Wroughton. Jour. Bombay Nat. Hist. Soc., vol.24, pp.42-46, Sept.30, 1915.

Anatomy

NOTES ON THE VISCERAL ANATOMY OF HYOMOSCHUS AQUATICUS. W. H. Flower. Proc. Zool. Soc. Lond., pp.954-960, figs. 2, 1867.

(THE PELAGE OF THE WATER CHEVROTAIN.) Du pelage de chevrotain aquatique. S. Frechkop. Bull. Mus. Roy. Hist. Nat. Belgique, Bruxelles, vol.24, no.28, pp.1-8, 1948.

ON THE GRAVID UTERUS AND PLACENTA OF HYOMOSCHUS AQUATICUS. Alfred Henry Garrod. Proc. Zool. Soc. Lond., pp.682-686, pl.XLIV, 1878.

ON THE BONY DORSAL SHIELD OF THE MALE TRAGULUS KANCHIL. John E. Gray. Proc. Zool. Soc. Lond., pp.226-227, fig.1, 1869.

NOTE ON THE RED CORPUSCLES OF THE BLOOD OF THE MEMINNA DEER. George Gulliver. Proc. Zool. Soc. Lond., pt.15, p.13, 1847.

(ANATOMICAL, ZOOLOGICAL, AND PALEONTOLOGICAL RESEARCH ON THE FAMILY OF CHEVROTAINS.) Recherches Anatomiques, Zoologiques et Paleontologiques sur las Famille des Chevrotains. Alphonse Milne-Edwards. Ann. des Science, Nat. Paris, 5th ser. Zool., vol.2, p.132, pls.2-11, 1864.

THE DEVELOPMENT OF THE AXIAL VEINS AND LYMPHATICS IN TRAGULUS MEMINNA, ERXLEBEN. Frederick Tilney. Amer. Jour. Anat., vol.13, no.2, pp.193-221, pls.13, May, 1912.

ON THE GRAVID UTERUS AND PLACENTA OF HYOMOSCHUS AQUATICUS. William Turner. Proc. Zool. Soc. Lond., pp.682-686, pl.XLIV, 1878.

## Cervidae

Cervidae--General

(A NEW GENUS FOR THE "STAG" OR "STAG OF THE MARSH.") Um novo genero para o "cervo" ou "veado do pantanal" (Ruminantia, Cervidae). Fernando Dias De Avila-Pires. Bol. Mus. Nacional, Rio de Janeiro, nov. ser., zool., no.153, pp.1-10, Mar.28, 1957.

BIG GAME NEWS. (DEER, CARIBOU.) W. Arthur Benson. Blue Jay, Saskatchewan Nat. Hist. Soc., 14 (1): 26-27, Mar., 1956.

MOOSE AND ELK--GIANTS OF THE ANTLERED WORLD. G. W. Bradt. Michigan Conserv., Lansing, vol.17, no.2, pp.4-5, illus., Feb., 1948.

DEER OF THE WORLD. Victor H. Cahalane. Natl. Geog. Mag., 76 (4): 463-510, Oct., 1939.

(Review by P. Rode of) (THE HABITS OF DEER.) Les Habitudes du Gibier. A. Chaigneau. Mammalia, Paris, 11 (4): 167, Dec., 1947.

MOOSE AND WAPITI. Stuart C. Downing. Canadian Nature, Toronto, vol.9, no.4, pp.126-127, illus., Sept.-Oct., 1947.

(CRITICAL INVESTIGATIONS OF THE SPECIES OF THE NATURAL FAMILY OF DEER (CERVI).) Kritische Untersuchungen ueber die Arten der natuerlichen Familie der Hirsche (Cervi). L. P. Fitzinger. Sitz.-Ber. math.-naturw. Cl. Kais. Akad. Wiss. Wien, vols.69-70, 1874; vol.78, 1878; vol.79, 1879, pp.1-65.

A DEER THAT PAYS A DEBT. Erwin Hein. Nature Mag., Wash., D.C., vol.36, no.6, pp.293-294, illus., June-July, 1943.

(THE DEER OF THE BARBARY.) Le Cerf de Berbérie. L. Joleaud. Bull. Soc. Nat. Acclimat., France, vol.77, no.6, pp.86-87, June, 1930.

(A DEER OF SUBGENUS PUDELLA, NEW TO SCIENCE.) Un venado del subgenero Pudella nueva para la ciencia. (Pudu (Pudella) mephistophiles wetmorei.) V. F. C. Lehman. Rev. Univ. Cauca, Popayán, Colombia, no.6, pp.76-79, pls.2, Mar.30, 1945.

PHYLOGENY OF THE DEER. F. B. Loomis. Amer. Jour. Sci., vol.16, no. 96, pp.531-542, figs.10, 1928.

(IMPORTANCE OF SOME CERVIDS IN THE DIET. INTRODUCTION AND ACCLIMATION OF CERTAIN FOREIGN SPECIES. DOMESTICATION OF ABORIGINES.) Importancia de algunos Cervides en la alimentacion. Introduccion y aclimatacion de ciertas especies exoticas. Domestication de las aborigenes. Carlos Lopez. Estudios Biologicos, Mexico, pp.1-24, figs. 1-24, 1922.

THE DEER OF ALL LANDS: A HISTORY OF THE FAMILY CERVIDAE LIVING AND EXTINCT. Richard Lydekker. 1898.

DEER IN THE MAKING. W. P. Pycraft. Illus. London News, vol.191, no.5144, p. 905, figs.3, Nov.30, 1937.

THE DEER FAMILY. Theodore Roosevelt. N. Y., 1st Ed., pp.345, pls.20, 1902.

(CONTRIBUTION TO A NATURAL HISTORY OF DEER.) Beitraege zu einer Natuerlichen Geschichte der Hirsche. L. Rutimeyer. Abhandl. schweiz. palaeont. Gesell., vol. 8, pp.3-96, pls.3, Zurich, Dec., 1881.

LIVING IN VELVET. (ELK, DEER.) Jacqueline Schermerhorn. San Diego Zoonooz, vol.19, no.5, pp.3-6, illus., May, 1946.

(THE DEER OF MY LIFE.) Der Hirsch meines Lebens. I. Vhilipowicz. Deutsche Jagd, Berlin, nos.44-45, pp.599-601, Feb.2, 1940.

WHEN IS AN ELK NOT AN ELK? (WAPITI AND MOOSE.) Clifford Wilson. Beaver, Winnipeg, outfit 270, no.3, pp.36-37, illus., Dec., 1939.

Cervidae--Anatomy (General)

THE EYE GLANDS IN THE DEER FAMILY. William H.F. Addison. Report Lab. and Mus. Comp. Path., Zool. Soc. Phila., pp. 26-27, 1933.

ON A CASE OF SYNDACTYLOUS ANOMALY IN A SOUTH AMERICAN DEER. Einar Loennberg. Arkiv. foer Zoologi, vol.22, no.8, pp.1-3, figs.4, Dec.19, 1930.

ON THE EXTERNAL CHARACTERS OF ELAPHURUS, HYDROPOTES, PUDU, AND OTHER CERVIDAE. R. I. Pocock. Proc. Zool. Soc. Lond., pt.2, pp.181-207, July, 1923.

BANNER OF DEER TRIBE DISTINCTIVE LABEL. (TAILS OF DEER ILLUSTRATED.) Nat. Nature Notes, Wash., D.C., vol.3, no.7, pp.54-55, illus., Oct.15, 1939.

Cervidae--Anatomy (Skull and Teeth)

HINGED TEETH IN MAMMALS: A STUDY OF THE TUSKS OF MUNTJAKS (MUNTIACUS) AND CHINESE WATER DEER (HYDROPOTES INERMIS). James Aitchison. Proc. Zool. Soc. Lond., vol. 116, pt.2, pp.329-338, figs.3, Nov., 1946.

ON HYDROPOTES INERMIS AND ITS CRANIAL CHARACTERS, AS COMPARED WITH THOSE OF MOSCHUS MOSCHIFERUS. Victor Brooke. Proc. Zool. Soc. Lond., pp.522-525, figs.3, 1872.

CRANIAL AND DENTAL CHARACTERS OF SOME SOUTH AMERICAN CERVIDAE. Angel Cabrera. Papers on mammalogy, zool. ser., Field Mus. Nat. Hist., vol.27, pp.125-135, figs.8, Dec.8, 1941.

(ANOMALIES IN THE DENTITION OF THE CERVIDS.) Anomalien am Gebiss der Cerviden. H. Eidmann. Zool. Anzeiger, Leipzig, vol.137, nos.9-10, pp.151-162, figs.6, Mar.15, 1942.

NOTICE OF A RUDIMENTARY CANINE TOOTH IN A FEMALE OF SPECIES OF DEER FROM SOUTH AMERICA. W. Martin. Proc. Zool. Soc. Lond., pt.4, p. 4, 1836.

SUPPLEMENTS 1, 2, AND 3 TO MY NOTE "ON ACCESSORY COLUMNS, ANTERIOR OUTER FOLDS, AND CUSPS DEVELOPED IN THE MOLAR TEETH OF CERVIDS." Jôji Nagasawa. Jour. Geol. Soc. Tokyo, vol.38, no.449, pp.87-90, Feb.20, 1931; no.455, pp.446-452, Aug.20, 1931; no.459, pp.641-649, pls.4, figs.20, Dec.20, 1931. (In Japanese.)

THE INCISIFORM TEETH OF EUROPEAN AND ASIATIC CERVIDAE. R. I. Pocock. Proc. Zool. Soc. Lond., pt.1, pp.179-194, figs.7, Apr.3, 1935.

(CONTRIBUTIONS TO THE HISTORY OF THE DEER FAMILY. I. SKULL STRUCTURE.) Beitraege zu der Geschichte der Hirschfamilie. I. Schaedelbau. L. Ruetimeyer. Verhandl. Naturf. Gesell. Basel, vol.7, pt.1, pp.1-61, 1882.

Cervidae--Antlers

HORNS AND ANTLERS. THEIR OCCURRENCE, DEVELOPMENT AND FUNCTION IN THE MAMMALIA. PART 2. H. E. Anthony. Bull. New York Zool. Soc., vol. 32, pp.3-24, illus., Feb., 1929.

THE INTERNAL STRUCTURE AND SEASONAL GROWTH-CHANGES IN DEER ANTLERS. H. E. Anthony, C. V. Noback. Bull. N.Y. Zool. Soc., vol.32, no.1, pp. 34-49, illus., Jan.-Feb., 1929.

THE GROWTH OF THE DEER ANTLER. Joseph C. Aub, George B. Wislocki, Charles M. Waldo. New York State Conserv., Albany, vol.4, no.3, pp.4-5, illus., Dec., 1949, Jan., 1950.

(INVESTIGATIONS OF THE CHEMICAL COMPOSITION AND STRUCTURE OF DEER ANTLERS.) Untersuchungen ueber chemische Zusammensetzung und Aufbau des Hirschgeweihes. K. Bernhard, G. Brubacher, H. Hediger, H. Bruhin. Experientia Basel, vol.9, no.4, pp.138-140, illus., 1953.

DATES ON SHEDDING OF ANTLERS. C. Emerson Brown. Jour. Mam., vol.2, no.1, p.39, Feb., 1921.

(STRANGE ANTLER DEVELOPMENT.) Seltsame Geweihentwicklung. E. von

Bruenneck. Deutsche Jagd, Berlin, nos. 21-22, pp.197-200, illus., Aug.30, 1940.

(ON SOME HORNS OF BLASTOCERUS DICHOTOMUS.) Sobre algunas cornamentas de Blastocerus dichotomus. Angel Cabrera. Notas Mus. La Plata, vol.10, zool., no.87, pp.221-231, figs.1-3, Dec.14, 1945.

ABNORMAL ANTLERS IN SOME CEYLON CERVIDAE. P.E.P. Deraniyagala. Spolia Zeylanica, Bull. Nat. Mus. Ceylon, vol. 27, pt.1, p.106, illus., Oct.24, 1953.

SESAME CAKE AND ANTLER GROWTH. J. C. Drummond, Allan W. Greenwood, R. R. Ridgway, Peter Williams. Nature, London, vol.147, no.3714, pp.26-27, Jan.4, 1931.

(CONTRIBUTION TO THE THEORY OF THE OCCURRENCE OF DOE WITH ANTLERS.) Ein Beitrag Zur Lehre Von Dem Vorkommen Gehoernter Weiblicher Rehe. Programm Sr. Koenigl. Hoheit Dem Grossherzoge Von Hessen Und Bei Rhein Ludewig IV Zum 25, Gewidmet Von Rector Und Senat Der Landesuniversitaet, Giessen, pp.3-27, 1886.

NEW YORK'S RECORD HEADS. Pete Fosburgh. New York State Conservationist, Albany, vol.1, no.2, pp.16-17, 30, illus., Oct.-Nov., 1946. (Reprinted in Minnesota Sportsman's Digest, Minneapolis, vol.7, no.5, pp.12-14, illus., Jan.-Feb., 1947.)

(DEER WITH ABNORMAL ANTLER FORMATION.) Hirsch mit abnormer Geweihbildung. Frahne. Deutsche Jagd, Berlin, nos.29-30, p.280, illus., Oct.25, 1940.

ON SOME DEFECTS IN THE GROWTH OF THE ANTLERS, AND SOME RESULTS OF CASTRATION, IN THE CERVIDAE. John S. Gaskoin. Proc. Zool. Soc. Lond., pt. 24, pp.151-159, figs.1-8, 1856.

THE MORPHOLOGY OF THE ANTLERS OF THE CERVIDAE. T. Gill. Bull. Philos. Soc., Wash., 128th meeting, pp.135-136, 1877.

ON THE MORPHOLOGY OF THE ANTLERS AND OTHER CHARACTERS OF THE DEER, WITH REMARKS ON A METHOD OF EXPRESSING THE RELATIONS OF SPECIES BY MEANS OF FORMULAE. T. Gill. Field and Forest, vol.3, no.2, pp.21-28, figs.7-18, Aug., 1877.

(STUDY ON THE DEVELOPMENT OF THE ANTLERS OF DEER OF BRAZIL.) Estudos sobre o desenvolvimento da armacao dos veados calheiros do Brazil (Cervus paludosus, C. campestris, C. Wiegmanni). Emilio A. Goeldi. Mem. Mus. Goeldi, no. 3, pp.1-46, pls.1-4, 1902.

DATES OF SHEDDING OF HORNS. N. Hollister. Jour. Mam., vol.1, no.5, pp. 244-245, Nov., 1920.

THE RELATIVE SIZE OF ANTLERS IN DEER. Julian S. Huxley. Proc. Zool. Soc. Lond., pt.3, pp.819-864, figs.13, tables 16, Sept., 1931.

EFFECT OF UNILATERAL CASTRATION ON ANTLERS GROWTH IN ROE-DEER (CAPREOLUS CAPREOLUS L.) AND COMMON STAG (CERVIS ELAPHUS L.). Zbigniew Jaczewski. Fragmenta Faunistica Mus. Zool. Polonici, Warsaw, vol.6, no.12, pp.199-205, pl.1, July 26, 1952.

THE GROWTH AND SHEDDING OF THE ANTLER OF THE DEER. THE HISTOLOGICAL PHENOMENA AND THEIR RELATION TO THE GROWTH OF BONE. William Macewen. Glasgow, Machlehose, Jackson and Co., publishers to the Univ., pp.i-xvii, 1-109, figs.109, 1920.

(THE NINETEENTH GERMAN EXHIBITION OF ANTLERS AT BERLIN, 1913.) Die neunzehnte deutsche Geweihausstellung zu Berlin 1913. P. Matschie. Veroeffentlichungen Inst. Jagdkunde, Neudamm, vol.2, no.4, pp.97-108, figs.90, 1913.

WHAT BECOMES OF A DEER'S SHED HORNS? Clyde Miller. Outdoor Life, vol.75, no.6, pp.22-23, 88, illus., June, 1935.

HISTOGENESIS OF BONE IN THE GROWING ANTLER OF THE CERVIDAE. Walter Modell, Charles V. Noback. Amer. Jour. Anat., vol.49, no.1, pp.65-86, pls.1-4, figs.2, Sept.15, 1931.

NOTES ON ANTLER GROWTH OF CERVIDAE. William H. Moore. Jour. Mam., vol.12, no.2, pp.169-170, May, 1931.

GROWTH AND SHEDDING OF ANTLERS IN SAMBAR (RUSA UNICOLOR) AND CHEETAL (AXIS AXIS) IN SOUTH INDIA. R. C. Morris. Jour. Bombay Nat. Hist. Soc., vol.37, no.2, p.484, Aug.15, 1934.

(A DEER WITHOUT ANTLERS.) Ueber einen geweihlosen Hirsch. August Pelzeln. Wien Zool. Bot. Verhandl., vol.30, pp.611-614, 1881; Verhandl. K.K. Zool.-Bot. Gesell. Wien, Jahrg.1880, vol.30, pt.2, pp.611-614, 1881.

ON ANTLER GROWTH IN THE CERVIDAE, WITH SPECIAL REFERENCE TO ELAPHURUS AND ODOCOILEUS (DORCELAPHUS). R. I. Pocock. Proc. Zool. Soc. Lond., pp.773-783, figs.108-112, Nov.27, 1912.

THE HOMOLOGIES BETWEEN THE BRANCHES OF THE ANTLERS OF THE CERVIDAE BASED ON THE THEORY OF DICHOTOMOUS GROWTH. R. I. Pocock. Proc. Zool. Soc. Lond., pt.2, pp.377-406, figs.13, June, 1933.

WHY DEER DROP THEIR ANTLERS EACH YEAR. C. C. Presnall. Yosemite Nat. Notes, vol.12, no.6, p.65, June, 1933.

(ON THE DEVELOPMENTAL MECHANICS OF CORKSCREW ANTLER FORMATIONS AND RELATED PHENOMENA.) Zur Entwicklungsmechanik von Korkziehergeweihbildungen und verwandter Erscheinungen. Ludwig Rhumbler. Zeitschr. Wiss. Biol. Abt.D, Roux' Archiv Entwicklungsmech., vol.191 (Festschr.), pp.441-515, figs.49, 1929.

(THE ANTLER COLLECTION OF THE IMPERIAL AGRICULTURAL UNIVERSITY OF BERLIN.) Die Geweihsammlung der koniglichen landwirtschaftlichen Hochschule in Berlin. C. Roerig. Neudamm, pp.90, figs.42, 1896.

THE BUCK AND HIS ANTLERS. W. J. Schoonmaker. Nat. Humane Rev., New York, vol.35, no.2, pp.20-21, illus., Feb., 1947.

MORPHOLOGY OF ANTLERS. Frank Schwarz. Parks and Recreation, vol.16, no.10, pp.477-482, illus., June, 1933.

(HOW AN ANTLER ORIGINATES.) Wie entsteht ein Geweih. Horst Siewert. Der Naturforscher, Jahrg.11, no.12, pp.408-414, figs.7, Mar., 1935.

(ON THE DEER'S USE OF ANTLERS.) Zum Gewiehgebrauch der Hirsche. G. Steinbacher. Saeugetierk. Mitteil., 5 (2): 75, Apr.1, 1957.

(SELECTION OF THE BUCK ANTLER AND DOE HORN COLLECTION OF COUNT GEORGE ALBRECHT ZU ERBSCH-ERBACH.) Selecta der Hirschgeweih- und Rehgehooern-Sammlung des regierenden Grafen George Albrecht zu Erbsch-Erbach. Eduard Stormer, E. R. von Dombrowski. Leipzig, pls.30, 1891.

(ON THE INFLUENCE OF SEX HORMONES ON THE GROWTH OF THE ANTLERS OF CERVIDS.) Ueber den Einfluss der sexualhormone auf das Gewiehwachstum der Cerviden. Rudolf Tachezy. Saeugetierk, Mitteil., Stuttgart, 4 (3): 103-112, July 1, 1956.

SHEDDING ANTLERS. Fay E. Thetford. Outdoorsman, Chicago, vol.86, no.1, whole no.506, pp.38-39, illus., Jan-Feb., 1944.

ANTLERS ARE NOT HORNS. Paul C. Ziemke. Wyoming Wild Life, Cheyenne, vol.11, no.9, pp.25-28, illus., Sept., 1947.

Cervidae--Australia, New Zealand

DEER - NEW ZEALAND'S ENEMY NO. 1. Forest and Bird, 37: 3-5, Aug., 1935.

BIRDS AND BUSH OF THE KAIMANAWAS. (DEER) D. A. Bathgate. Forest and Bird, Wellington, no.91, pp.4-6, Feb., 1949.

A BRIEF ACCOUNT OF THE DEER IN AUSTRALIA. Arthur Bentley. Jour. Wildlife Mgt., 21 (2): 221-225, Apr., 1957.

DEER IDOLATORY: AN AMERICAN VOICE. Forest and Bird, Wellington, vol.85, pp.1-2, illus., Aug., 1947.

FROM ALASKA TO NEW ZEALAND. SUCCESSFUL INTRODUCTION OF WAPITI AND MOOSE. Field, London, vol.161, no.4189, p.741, Apr.8, 1933.

Cervidae--Diseases, Parasites

DEER AS CARRIERS OF ANAPLASMOSIS. William Hutchins Boynton, Grace M. Woods. Science, vol.78, no.2033, pp.559-560, Dec. 15, 1933.

(OSTERTAGIA SCHULZI, N.SP.--A NEW NEMATODE IN A WILD DEER.) Ostertagia schulzi, n.sp.--eine neue Nematode bei einem Wildhirsche. S. A. Rajewskaja. Zool. Anzeiger, vol.90, pp.331-335, Sept. 15, 1930.

CEPHENOMYIA SP. KILLING DEER. C.R. Walker. Science, N.S., vol.69, pp.646-647, June 21, 1929.

Cervidae--Distribution

THE HOME RANGE OF DEER. H. Mortimer Batten. Field, London, vol.151, p. 1040, June 21, 1928.

GEOGRAPHICAL DISTRIBUTION OF THE DEER IN MIDDLE ASIA (WESTERN TURKESTAN). N. Bobrinskoy. Zoologitscheskij Jour., Moscow, vol.12, pt.4, pp.77-86, 1933.

OLD-TIME RANGE OF VIRGINIA DEER, MOOSE, AND ELK. George Bird Grinnell. Nat. Hist., vol.25, pp.136-142, Mar.-Apr. (May), 1925.

(THE DISTRIBUTION OF DEER.) Die Verbreitung der Hirsche. Paul Matschie. Sitz.-Ber. Gesell. Naturf. Freunde Berlin, Jahrg.1899, no.7, pp.130-137, July 18, 1899.

REMARKS ON THE ARRANGEMENT AND DISTRIBUTION OF THE CERVIDAE. Philip L. Sclater. Proc. Zool. Soc. Lond., pp.114-116, 1870.

Cervidae--Ecology, Habits, Behavior

UNWARY DEER. G. G. Baiss. Field, London, vol.148, p.395, Aug.26, 1926.

THE INFLUENCE OF ELK ON DEER POPULATIONS. George Case. Univ. Idaho Bull., 33 (22): 25-27, Dec., 1938.

RELATIONSHIP BETWEEN ELK AND MULE DEER IN THE BLUE MOUNTAINS OF OREGON. Edward P. Cliff. Trans. 4th North Amer. Wildlife Conf., Wash., D.C., pp.560-569, 1939.

SOME NOTES ON THE SOCIAL HABITS OF THE BRITISH DEER. Peter Delap. Proc. Zool. Soc. Lond., 128 (4): 608-612, July 24, 1957.

ELK AND DEER FOODS AND FEEDING HABITS. R. M. DeNio. N. Region News, 31, Mar., 1938.

ELK AND DEER FOODS AND FEEDING HABITS. R. M. DeNio. Trans. N.A. Wildl. Conf., 3:421-427, 1938.

STOMACH ANALYSES OF DEER AND ELK IN NORTHERN IDAHO AND MONTANA. R. M. Denio. Bull. Univ. Idaho, vol.33, no.22 (Bull. School Forestry, no.8), pp. 34-36, Dec., 1938.

ON THE QUESTION OF THE FOOD OF NORTHERN DEER. A. N. Formosov. Moscow Univ. Sbornik Nauchno issledovatel 'skogo inst. Zool. (Abstracts Works Zool. Inst. Moscow State Univ.), no.3, p.114, 1936. (In Russian.)

EFFECTS OF LAND USE ON MOOSE AND CARIBOU IN ALASKA. A. Starker Leopold, F. Fraser Darling. Trans. 18th N. A. Wildl. Conf., pp.553-560, 1953.

(ETHOLOGY OF THE DEER IN TUYU.) La etologia del venado en el Tuyu. (Ozotoceras bezoarticus.) Emiliano J. MacDonagh. Inst. Mus. Univ. Nac. La Plata, Notas del Museo de La Plata, Buenos Aires, vol.5, Zoologia no.33, pp. 49-68, figs.16, pls.3, 1940.

MEASURES OF ASSOCIATION BETWEEN MOOSE AND ELK ON FEEDING GROUNDS. John F. McMillan. Jour. Wildlife Mgt., Ithaca, vol.17, no.2, pp.162-166, Apr., 1953.

MULE DEER AND ELK FOOD HABITS ON THE NATIONAL BISON RANGE. Melvin S. Morris, John E. Schwartz. Jour. Wildlife Mgt., 21 (2): 189-193, illus., Apr., 1957.

WINTER RANGE CONDITIONS IN ROCKY MOUNTAIN NATIONAL PARK. Harold M. Ratcliff. Trans. N. A. Wildl. Conf., 6: 132-139, 1941.

CANADA. THE USE AND MISUSE OF SHRUBS AND TREES AS FODDER, WITH TABLES SHOWING COMPOSITION AND DIGESTIBILITY. E. W. Tisdale, J. A. Campbell. Imp. Agr. Bur., Joint Pub., 10: 177-184, June, 1947.

Cervidae--Eurasia

DEER IN WICKLOW. Peter Delap. Irish Nat. Jour., vol.6, no.4, pp.82-88, pl.4, July, 1936.

THE DEER SITUATION IN SWEDEN. L. von Essen. Pap. Game Res., 8: 158-160, 1952.

DEER FROM NORTH KIUSIU, JAPAN. N. Kuroda. Dobutsugaku Zasshi, pp.439-441, Oct.15, 1924. (Japanese text.)

DEER AND DAUERWALD IN GERMANY. I. HISTORY. Aldo Leopold. Jour. For., 34 (4): 366-375, Apr., 1936.

DEER AND DAUERWALD IN GERMANY. II. ECOLOGY AND POLICY. Aldo Leopold. Jour. For., 34 (5): 460-466, May, 1936.

(DEER IN THE VAL DE FERRET (VALAIS).) Les cerfs dans le Val de Ferret (Valais). L. Luisier. Bull. Murithienne Soc. Valaisanne Sci. Nat., fasc.48, pp.88-93, 1930-1931.

ON AN APPARENTLY NEW DEER FROM NORTH CHINA, IN THE MENAGERIE OF THE DUKE OF BEDFORD AT WOBURN ABBEY. R. Lydekker. Proc. Zool. Soc. Lond., pt.4, pp.930-934, pls.48-49, Dec. 1, 1896.

ROEDEER AND RED DEER IN FINLAND IN THE 16TH AND 17TH CENTURIES. K. R. Melander. Suomen Riista, 9: 27-38, 1954.

BRITISH DEER AND THEIR HORNS. John Guille Millais. H. Sotheran Co., pp.224, pl.10, illus., 1897.

FERAL DEER AT ASHRIDGE. Charles Oldham. Trans. Hertfordshire Nat. Hist. Soc., and Field Club, Hertford, vol.20, pt.5, pp.305-306, Apr., 1938.

WILD DEER IN GALLOWAY. W. T. Palmer. Field, London, vol.164, p.215, July 28, 1934.

THE LARGER DEER OF BRITISH INDIA. R. I. Pocock. Jour. Bombay Nat. Hist. Soc., vol.43, no.3, pp.298-317, figs.8, Dec., 1942.

TWO FINE POLISH TROPHIES. George Potocki. Field, London, vol.164, no.4275, p.1304, illus., Dec.1, 1934. (Carpathian stag and elk.)

NOTICE OF A MEMOIR ON THE DEER OF THE OLD WORLD. Philip L. Sclater. Proc. Zool. Soc. Lond., p.114, 1870.

REPORT ON A COLLECTION OF SKINS SHIPPED BY MR. SWINHOE ON BOARD THE 'HARKAWAY.' Philip L. Sclater. Proc. Zool. Soc. Lond., pt.29, pp.390-391, 1861.

ON CHINESE DEER, WITH THE DESCRIPTION OF AN APPARENTLY NEW SPECIES. Robert Swinhoe. Proc. Zool. Soc. Lond., pp.572-575, 1873.

ON THE CERVINE ANIMALS OF THE ISLAND OF HAINAN (CHINA). Robert Swinhoe. Proc. Zool. Soc. Lond., pp.652-660, figs. 3, 1869.

THE DISTRIBUTION OF WILD DEER IN ENGLAND AND WALES. W. L. Taylor. Jour. Anim. Ecol., Lond., vol.8, no.1, pp.6-9, May, 1939; vol.17, no.2, pp.151-154, Nov., 1948.

THE DISTRIBUTION OF WILD DEER IN SCOTLAND. W. L. Taylor. Jour. Animal Ecol., Lond., vol.18, no.2, pp.187-192, Nov., 1950.

OUR DEER. A. C. Tutein-Nolthenius. Loris, Ceylon, vol.1, no.2, pp.92-96, June, 1937.

CONTRIBUTION OF KNOWLEDGE OF FODDER PLANTS OF THE WILD DAPPLED DEER. O. V. Vendland. Bull. Far Eastern Branch Acad. Sci. USSR, Vladivostock, no.28, pp.134-140, figs.3, 1938.

NOTES ON THE NATURAL HISTORY AND SHIKAR OF INDIAN DEER. H. S. Wood. Jour. Darjeeling Nat. Hist. Soc., vol.5, no.3, pp.61-68; no.4, pp.100-105; vol.6, no.1, pp.20-26; no.2, pp.55-67, 1931; no. 3, pp.103-108; no.4, pp.142-149; vol.7, no. 1, pp.20-24; no.2, pp.45-49, 1932; no.3, pp.103-104; no.4, pp.152-157, pls.4, fig.1, 1933.

POPULATION DENSITY AND CENSUS OF DEERS IN THE CRIMEAN STATE GAME PRESERVE. P. A. Yanushko. Zool. Zhurnal, Moscow, 36 (10): 1565-1570, 1957. (In Russian, with English summary.)

DEER IN BRITAIN. Nature, London, vol. 167, no.4248, p.509, Mar.31, 1951.

A NEW ROCK-SCULPTURE DISCOVERY. (DEER, NORWAY.) Illus. London News, vol.181, no.4878, p.570, illus., Oct.15, 1932.

Cervidae--Extinct and Fossil Forms

(GIANT DEER.) Fynd av jaettehjort i Skane. Herved Berlin. Fauna och Flora, Haft 3, pp.118-124, 1938.

ERRATUM. (STEPHANOCEMAS, TO REPLACE STEPHANOCERAS, PREOCCUPIED.) Edwin H. Colbert. Amer. Mus. Novit. no. 854, p.1, 1936.

A PROBABLE SECOND RECORD OF THE EXTINCT DEER, ODOCOILEUS DOLICHOPSIS (COPE). William L. Engels. Amer. Midland Nat., Notre Dame, Indiana, vol.13, no.1, pp.12-15, pl.3, Jan., 1932.

(THE GIANT DEER.) Der Riesenhirsch. C. Flerov. Kosmos, Stuttgart, vol.27, no.2, p.71, pl.1, 1930.

A NEW GENUS OF FOSSIL DEER FROM THE MIOCENE OF AFRICA. D. G. MacInnes. Jour. Linn. Soc. Lond., vol.39, no.267, pp.521-530, figs.5, Apr.27, 1936.

CERVUS TCHELEKENSIS N. SP. AND ALCES MAEOTICUS N. SP. Marie Pavlow. Ann. Russian Paleont. Soc., vol.4, pp.45-72, fig.1, pl.1, 1917. (In Russian, with French summary.)

MAMMALIA. THE GIANT DEER GROUP. R. F. Scharff. Proc. Roy. Irish Acad., vol.39 B, no.1, p.4, Oct., 1929.

(DICROCEROS ELEGANS LARTET AND ITS ANTLER SHEDDING.) Dicroceros elegans Lartet und sein Geweihwechsel. H. G. Stehlin. Eclogae Geol. Helvetiae, Basel, vol.32, no.2, pp.162-179, figs.11, Apr.15, 1940.

Cervidae--Extinct and Fossil Forms (Americas)

A NOTE ON A FOSSIL ELK'S HEAD. Emmett J. Cable. Proc. Iowa Acad. Sci., Des Moines, vol.39, p.195, fig.1, 1932.

A CONTRIBUTION TO THE PLEISTOCENE FAUNA OF NEW YORK STATE. (RANGIFER.) Donald W. Fisher, John H. Ostrom Amer. Jour. Sci., vol.250, no.8, pp.609-616, Aug., 1952.

A SECOND RECORD OF CERVALCES FROM EAST-CENTRAL ILLINOIS. Edwin C. Galbreath. Jour. Mam., vol.20, no.4, pp. 507-508, Nov.14, 1939.

A CRANIUM OF THE EXTINCT MOOSE, CERVALCES, FROM THE QUATERNARY OF NORTHERN INDIANA. C. Lewis Gazin. Amer. Midland Nat., vol.19, no.3, pp.740-741, figs.1-2, May, 1938.

THE OCCURRENCE OF CERVALCES SCOTTI LYDEKKER IN KANSAS. Claude W. Hibbard. Trans. Kansas Acad. Sci., Topeka, vol.43, pp.411-415, pls.2, Dec. 23, 1940.

REMAINS OF THE BARREN GROUND CARIBOU IN PLEISTOCENE DEPOSITS OF MICHIGAN. Claude W. Hibbard. Papers Mich. Acad. Sci., Arts and Letters, vol. 37, pp.235-237, illus., 1952.

(CONTRIBUTION TO KNOWLEDGE OF THE FOSSIL DEER OF URUGUAY.) Contribución al conocimento de los ciervos fósiles del Uruguay. Lucas Kraglievich. Anales Mus. Hist. Nat. de Montevideo, ser.2, vol.3, pt. 3, pp.355-438, figs.9, pls.60-66, 1932.

ANOTHER FOSSIL CARIBOU FROM NEW YORK STATE. Arthur H. Norton. Jour. Mam., vol.5, no.2, pp.132-133, May, 1924.

OCCURRENCE OF THE EXTINCT MOOSE, CERVALCES, IN INDIANA AND IN ILLINOIS. Elmer S. Riggs. Amer. Midland Nat., vol.17, no.3, p.664, May, 1936.

Cervidae--Extinct and Fossil Forms (Asia)

ON A NEW DEER SPECIES FROM THE TERTIARY BEDS OF MONGOLIA. A. Alekseev. Priorda, Leningrad, no.11, pp.96-98, figs.3, 1937.

A NEW DEER FROM THE SIWALIKS. Barnum Brown. Amer. Mus. Novit. no. 242, pp.6, illus., 1926.

A NEW FOSSIL MUNTJAC FROM CENTRAL SHANSI. Minchen M. Chow. Acta Paeo. Sinica, 4 (2): 229-232, illus., 1956.

SOME CERVID TEETH FROM THE TUNG GUR FORMATION OF MONGOLIA, AND ADDITIONAL NOTES ON THE GENERA STEPHANOCEMAS AND LAGOMERYX. Edwin H. Colbert. Amer. Mus. Novit., New York, no.1062, pp.6, figs.3, table 1, May 1, 1940.

TERTIARY DEER DISCOVERED BY THE AMERICAN MUSEUM ASIATIC EXPEDITIONS. Edwin H. Colbert. Amer. Mus. Novit., no.854, pp.21, figs.10, June 3, 1936.

A NEW PALEOLITHIC REINDEER FROM SIBERIA. C. C. Flerov. Jour. Mam., vol. 15, no.3, pp.239-240, pl.8, Aug., 1934.

TWO NEW DEER FROM THE PLEISTOCENE OF WANHSIEN, SZECHWAN, CHINA. Dirk Albert Hooijer. Amer. Mus. Novit., New York, no.1495, pp.1-18, illus., Mar. 5, 1951.

ON THE "PACHYGENES" OR "PACHYGNATHES" (THICK-JAWED QUATERNARY DEER FROM AFRICA AND ASIA). L. Joleaud. Bull. Geol. Soc. China, Peiping, vol.9, no.3, pp.195-203, 1930.

ON THE DISTRIBUTION OF MEGACEROS IN CHINA. H. D. Kahlke, Changkang Hu. Vertebrata Palasiatica, 1 (4): 273-283, illus., Dec., 1957.

ON A NEW ARCHETYPAL FOSSIL CERVID FROM THE PROVINCE OF MINO. Hikoshichiro Matsumoto. Sci. Reports, Tohoku Imp. Univ., ser.2 (Geol.), vol.3, no.2, pp.75-81, fig.1, pl.1, 1918.

ON SOME FOSSIL ANTLERS OF DEERS FROM THE BASAL CALABRIAN AT NAGAHAMA, MINATO TOWN, PROVINCE OF KAZUSA, JAPAN. Hikoshichiro Matsumoto. Zool. Mag., Tokyo, vol.50, no.3, pp.111-115, figs.3, Mar., 1938.

ON SOME FOSSIL CERVIDS FROM SHANTUNG, CHINA. Hikoshichiro Matsumoto. Sci. Rep. Tohaku Imp. Univ., ser.2 (Geol.), vol.10, pp.27-38, 1926.

FOSSIL PÉRE DAVID'S MILOU DEER FROM PROVINCE OF HARIMA. Jôji Nagasawa. Jour. Geol. Soc. Tôkyô, vol.40, no.475, pp.210-212, fig.1, Apr.20, 1933. (In Japanese.)

ON SOME REMAINS OF CERVUS FOUND IN A FISSURE IN LIMESTONE AT SHIMODA, INABU-MURA, NAGAOKA-GUN, PROVINCE OF TOSA. Jôji Nagasawa. Jour. Geol. Soc. Tôkyô, vol.38, no.456, pp.484-488, pl.1, fig.1, Sept.20, 1931. (In Japanese.)

DEPERÉTIA, A NEW SUBGENUS OF CERVUS, WITH A NOTE ON A NEW SPECIES FROM THE PLEISTOCENE OF JAPAN.

Tokio Shikama. Proc. Imp. Acad., Tokyo, vol.12, no.8, pp.251-254, figs.2, Oct., 1936.

DISCOVERY OF A GIANT FALLOW DEER FROM THE PLEISTOCENE OF JAPAN. Tokio Shikama. Japanese Jour. Geol. and Geogr., Tokyo, Trans and Abstracts, vol.16, nos.1-2, pp.115-122, figs.2, pl.8, July, 1939.

FOSSIL CERVIFAUNA OF SYATIN NEAR TAINAN, SOUTHWESTERN TAIWAN (FORMOSA). Tokio Shikama. Sci. Reports, Tohoku Imp. Univ., Sendai, Japan, ser.2, vol.19, no.1, pp.75-85, figs.2, pl.16, 1937.

ON A NEW SPECIES OF FOSSIL DEER, CERVUS (CFR. ANOGLOCHIS) PRAENIPPONICUS SP. NOV., FROM JAPAN. Tokio Shikama. Jour. Geol. Soc. Japan, Tokyo, vol.43, no.510, pp.168-176, Mar.20, 1936.

THE MIOCENE CERVIDS FROM SHANTUNG. P. Teilhard de Chardin. Bull. Geol. Soc. China, Pehpei, Chungking, vol.19, no.3, pp.269-278, figs.5, Dec., 1939.

A NEW FORM OF CERVUS FROM THE TERTIARY OF SHINANO. S. Tokunaga. Jour. Geol. Soc., Tokyo, vol.33, pp.397-402, pl.1, 1926.

A NEW ROE-DEER, CAPREOLUS (CAPREOLINA) MAYAI, N. SUBGEN. AND N. SP. FROM THE INLAND SEA OF JAPAN. S. Tokunaga, Fuyuji Takai. Jour. Geol. Soc. Japan, Tokyo, vol.43, no.515, pp. 642-646, figs.2, pl.1, Aug.20, 1936.

A STUDY OF METACERVULUS ASTYLODON (MATSUMOTO) FROM THE RYUKYU ISLANDS, JAPAN. S. Tokunaga, Fuyuji Takai. Biogeographica, Trans. Biogeogr. Soc. Japan, Tokyo, vol.3, no.2, pp.221, pls.28, Oct., 1939.

(FOSSIL DEER OF CHINA.) Fossile Hirsche Chinas. O. Zdansky. Palaeontol. Sinica, ser.C, vol.2, fasc.3, pp.1-90, Dec., 1925.

(FURTHER REMARKS ON FOSSIL CERVIDS FROM CHINA.) Weitere Bemerkungen Ueber Fossile Cerviden aus China. O. Zdansky. Palaeontologia Sinica, ser.C, vol.5, no.1, pp.1-19, pl.1, figs.6, 1927.

Cervidae--Extinct and Fossil Forms (Europe)

THE DEER OF THE WEYBORN CRAG AND FOREST BED OF NORFOLK. A. Azzaroli. Bull. British Mus. Nat. Hist., Lond., Geol., vol.2, no.1, pp.96, illus., 1953.

A NEW PLEISTOCENE DEER FROM GIBRALTAR. (CERVUS TARICUS.) Dorothea M. A. Bate. Ann. and Mag. Nat. Hist., Lond., ser.11, vol.10, no. 66, pp.411-426, June, 1943.

(THE FINDING OF A GIANT DEER SKULL WITH FULLY PRESERVED ANTLERS IN THE GRAVELS OF STEINHEIM (MURR).) Fund eines Riesenhirschschaedels mit vollstaending erhaltenem Geweih aus den Schottern von Steinheim (Murr). F. Berckhemer. Aus der Heimat, vol.41, no. 5, pp.140-145, 1928.

"ELK" OUR FOREFATHERS HUNTED. F. W. Frohawk. Field, London, vol.158, no.4121, p.924, illus., Dec.19, 1931.

(ON A BUCK FROM THE GERMAN DILUVIUM.) Ueber einen Damhirsch aus dem deutschen Diluvium. K. Keilhack. Jahr. Koenigl. Preuss. Geol. Landesanstalt, Berlin, pp.283-290, pl.11, 1888.

WHICH IS THE TAXONOMIC POSITION OF THE IRISH GIANT DEER AND ALLIED RACES? Einar Loennberg. Arkiv. Zool., Upsala, vol.3, no.14, pp.1-8, figs.1-2, Aug.2, 1906.

(A NEW FORM OF MUNTJAC FROM THE PLIOCENE DEPOSITS OF THE SOUTHERN USSR.) Novaya forma mundjaka iz pliotsenovix otlojenii yuga USSR. I. H. Pidoplichko. Doklady Akad. Nauk SSSR, Moscow, vol.81, no.4, pp.677-679, 1951.

THE GIANT DEER. A MONOGRAPH OF THE BRITISH PLEISTOCENE. Sidney H. Reynolds. Mammalia, Palaeont. Soc.1927, London, vol.3, pt.3, pp.1-62, figs.31, pls. 1-2, Dec., 1929.

A MONOGRAPH ON THE BRITISH PLEISTOCENE MAMMALIA, VOL.3, PT.4, THE RED DEER, REINDEER, AND ROE. H. Sidney Reynolds. Palaeontograph. Soc., Lond., Monogr.no.85, pp.46, figs.15, pls. 3, July, 1933.

(HALF OF A LOWER JAW FROM A FALLOW BUCK FROM THE SAND OF MOSBACH.) Eine Unterkieferhaelfte vom Damhirsch aus dem Mosbacher Sand. Otto Schmidtgen. Notizbl. Ver. Erdkunde Hess. Geol. Landesandst. Darmstadt, vol.5, no.12, pp.114-118, pl.1, 1930.

CONTRIBUTIONS TO THE QUESTION OF THE LOCATION OF THE DEER WELLS IN THE EUROPEAN PART OF THE URSS. M. S. Shvetzov. Problems Soviet Geol. Moscow, vol.6, no.8, pp.712-713, 1936. (In Russian.)

(REMARKS ON THE DEER OF STEINHEIM-ON-THE-AALBUCH.) Bemerkungen ueber die Hirsche von Steinheim am Aalbuch. H. G. Stehlin. Eclog. Geol. Helv., vol.21, no.1, pp.245-256, 1928.

DID THE GIANT DEER SURVIVE THE LAST GLACIATION IN IRELAND? A. W. Stelfox. Irish Naturalist Jour., Belfast, vol.7, no.3, pp.70-71, Sept., 1938.

IRISH ELK REMAINS IN CO. LIMERICK. A. W. Stelfox. Irish Nat. Jour., vol.4, no.12, pp.243-244, Nov., 1933.

THE PROBLEM OF THE IRISH ELK. A.W. Stelfox. Irish Nat. Jour., vol.5, no.4, pp.74-76, July, 1934.

(NEW STUDY ON THE CERVUS ERTBORNI FROM THE ARGIL OF THE CAMPINE.) Nouvelle etude sur le Cervus ertborni Dub. des Argiles de la Campine. Pierre Teilhard de Chardin, Jean Piveteau. Bull. Mus. Rpy. Hist. Nat. Belgique, Bruxelles, vol.8, no.5, pp.12, figs.5, May, 1932.

A NEW DEER FROM THE MIDDLE PLIOCENE OF MOLDAVIA. (CERVUS (RUSA) MOLDAVICUS.) N.M. Yanovskaya. Proc. Paleo. Inst. Acad. Sci. USSR, vol.47, pp. 163-171, illus., 1954.

A NEW SUBSPECIES OF RED DEER FROM THE UPPER PLEISTOCENE OF JERSEY, CHANNEL ISLANDS. (CERVUS ELAPHUS JERSEYENSIS.) Frederick E. Zeuner. Ann. and Mag. Nat. Hist., Lond., ser.11, vol.5, no.27, pp.326-328, Mar., 1940.

Cervidae--Hunting

ELK AND DEER HUNTING REPORT. O. N. Arrington. Arizona Wildlife and Sportsman, Tucson, vol.9, no.1, p.28, Jan., 1948.

CARIBOU AND MOOSE IN KLAPPAN. (HUNTING IN THE CASSIAR DISTRICT, NORTHERN BRITISH COLUMBIA.) Henry Bannon. Forest and Stream, vol.90, pp. 629-631, 660, 661, Dec., 1920.

(THE DEER (A MONOGRAPHICAL CONTRIBUTION TO HUNTING ZOOLOGY).) Das Reh ein Monographischer Beitrag zur Jagdzoologie. Raoul von Dombrowski. 1887.

THREE DEER, TWO MOOSE, ONE CARIBOU—THAT WAS THE LIMIT! L. D. Lammon. Minnesota Div. Bull. Isaak Walton League, p.19, 4th quarter, 1944.

DEER HUNTING IN SHAKESPEARE'S DAY. C. E. Luard. Jour. Bombay Nat. Hist. Soc., vol.29, pp.217-220, Apr.20, 1923.

THE DEER AND DEER FORESTS OF SCOTLAND: HISTORICAL, DESCRIPTIVE, SPORTING. Alexander Inkson McConnochie. H.F.& G. Witherby, London, pp.336, pls. 14, 1923.

DEER AND ELK KILLS. R. U. Mace. Oregon State Game Comm. Bull., 4 (5): 1, 4-7, May, 1949.

ASPECTS OF DEER FORESTS TO-DAY. Frank Wallace. Field, London, vol.174, no.4527, p.717, Sept.30, 1939.

DEER FORESTS IN 1928: A REVIEW OF THE SEASON. Frank Wallace. Field, London, vol.153, pp.19-22, illus., Jan.3, 1929.

THE STALKING SEASON: 1927. Frank Wallace. Field, London, vol.151, pp.94-96, illus., Jan.19, 1928.

OBSERVATIONS ON DEER KILL UNDER DIFFERENT SYSTEMS OF HUNTING. Kaj Westerskov. Jour. Wildl. Mgt., 15 (1): 27-32, Jan., 1951.

1949 DEER AND ELK KILL. Oregon State Game Comm. Bull., Portland, vol.5, no. 8, p.8, Aug., 1950.

Cervidae--In Captivity, In Zoos

INTRODUCTION TO THE ZOO. (MOOSE AND AMERICAN ELK.) Lee S. Crandall. Animal Kingdom, New York, vol.50, no.2, pp.34-36, 60, illus., Mar.-Apr., 1947.

(DEER AS PETS.) Rehe als Hausgenossen. Kaethe Hecht. Naturforscher, Berlin, vol. 11, no.7, pp.236-243, figs.7, Oct., 1934.

(MATERIALS ON THE DEER RAISING OF THE FORMER HAMBURG ZOO.) Materialien ueber die Hirschzuchten des ehemaligen Hamburger Zoo. E. Mohr. Zool. Garten, Leipzig, n.F., vol.5, nos. 1-3, pp.3-15, figs.1-4, June, 1932.

(THE HOT SEASON AT THE VINCENNES ZOO.) Les grandes chaleurs au zoo de Vincennes. J. Nouvel. La Terre et La Vie, 8 annee, no.5, pp.148-149, illus., Sept.-Oct., 1938.

NOTE ON THE JAPANESE DEER LIVING IN THE SOCIETY'S MENAGERIE. Philip L. Sclater. Proc. Zool. Soc. Lond., pt. 28, pp.375-377, 1860.

RAISING DEER IN CAPTIVITY. U. S. Bur. Biol. Surv., Wildlife Leaflet BS-144, pp.1-6, Aug., 1939.

Cervidae--Management

DEER CONTROL IN THE HOME COUNTIES. Reginald Adcock. Field, 174 (4531): 858-859, Oct.28, 1939.

ARTIFICIAL RESTOCKING OF BIG GAME FEED. (DEER, ELK.) E. K. Brown. Colorado Conservation Comments, Denver, vol.9, no.2, p.23, June 15, 1946.

GAME SALTING NOTES ON THE UPPER SELWAY. George Case. N. Region News, 35-37, May, 1937.

THE USE OF SALT IN CONTROLLING THE DISTRIBUTION OF GAME. George Case. Jour. Wildl. Mgt., 2 (3): 79-81, July, 1938.

THE USE OF SALT IN SPARING WINTER RANGE ON THE SELWAY. George Case. Univ. Idaho Bull., 33 (22): 27-29, Dec., 1938.

RESTORATION; MANAGEMENT BY PUBLIC AGENCIES. Newell B. Cook. Proc. N. A. Wildl. Conf., pp.187-190, 1936.

DEVELOPMENT AND LAND USE ON A PRIVATE GAME PRESERVE IN SOUTHERN TANEY COUNTY, MISSOURI. Paul D. Dalke, David L. Spencer. Jour. Wildl. Mgt., 8 (1): 1-6, Jan., 1944.

SOME OBSERVATIONS ON GAME SALTING. Charles Gallaher. N. Region News, 27-28, Oct., 1938.

ON THE QUESTION OF, "IS IT RIGHT TO PROTECT THE FEMALE OF THE SPECIES AT THE COST OF THE MALE?" E. Raymond Hall. Canadian Field-Nat., vol.43, p.59, Mar., 1929.

ESTABLISHMENT OF THE 1943 DEER AND ELK SEASONS. Gilbert N. Hunter. Colorado Conserv. Comments, Denver, vol.6, no.2, pp.19-21, June 15, 1943.

THE 1943 DEER AND ELK SITUATION. Gilbert N. Hunter. Colorado Conser. Comments, Denver, vol.6, no.4, pp.17-18, Dec.15, 1943.

(THE SEMI-DOMESTICATION OF DEER IN THE MEDITERRANEAN REGION.) La semi-domestication du daim dans les contrees mediterraneennes. M. Joleaud. L'Anthropologie, Paris, vol.32, pp.272-275, 1922.

PLANNING OF MANAGEMENT PROGRAMS FOR WESTERN BIG-GAME HERDS. D. I.

Rasmussen, Everett R. Doman. Trans. N. A. Wildl. Conf., 12: 204-210, 1947.

MANAGING UTAH'S BIG-GAME CROP. (DEER AND ELK.) D. I. Rasmussen. Trees; Ybk. Agr., 1949: 573-580, 1949.

CONTROL OF BIG GAME DEPREDATIONS ON AGRICULTURE. (NEW DEER AND ELK REPELLENT.) O. L. Resner. Game Bull., 1 (1): 5-6, Aug., 1949.

SURVEY OF 1938-1939. Herbert S. Wallace, James M. Coutts, Lucas M. Dargan, Harland Means, William M. Nemanic. Colo. Game and Fish Dept., Deer-Elk Surv., vol.1, pp.ii, 103, pls.3, map 1, graph, July, 1939.

DEER AND THEIR MANAGEMENT IN THE DEER PARKS OF GREAT BRITAIN AND IRELAND. G. Kenneth Whitehead. Country Life, pp.370, illus., 1950.

DEER BREEDING FOR FINE HEADS, WITH DESCRIPTIONS OF MANY VARIETIES AND CROSS-BREEDS. Walter Winans. R. Ward, limited, London, 1913.

BIG GAME WINTER PROBLEMS. (ELK AND DEER.) Oregon State Game Comm. Bull., Portland, vol.4, no.2, pp.1, 3, 10, Feb., 1949.

THE GAME RANGE PROBLEM WHEN WINTER COMES. Colo. Cons. Comments, 10 (13): 10-13, 16-18, Mar., 1950.

Cervidae--Methods, Techniques

THE SEXING OF DEER AND ELK BY AIRPLANE IN COLORADO. Laurence E. Riordan. Trans. N.A. Wildl. Conf., 13: 409-428, 1948.

TAKING PICTURES OF MOOSE AND DEER. Charles M. Whitney. Nature Mag., vol.3, pp.325-331, 376, figs.12, June, 1924.

Cervidae--Mortality

DEER AND WIRE. (LOOSE WIRE ENTANGLES DEER.) H. Mortimer Batten. Field, London, vol.152, p.37, July 5, 1928.

A DEATH TRAP. (ELK, MOOSE AND THE LIKE TRAPPED IN QUAKING BOG SPRING.) F. R. Oberhansley. Nature Notes, Yellowstone Nat. Park, vol.15, nos.5-6, pp.23-24, May-June, 1938.

(A DEER THAT FELL VICTIM TO A REMARKABLE FATAL ACCIDENT.) Ein auf bemerkenswerte Weise verunglucktes Reh. F. Plate. Zool. Garten, N.F., Leipzig, vol.8, nos.7-9, pp.220-221, illus., June, 1936.

Cervidae--North America

WITH THE MOOSE AND CARIBOU IN ALASKA. William N. Beach. Explor. and Field-work Smithsonian Inst., 1937, publ.3480, pp.45-50, figs.49-54, 1938.

MOOSE AND WAPITI IN THE WESTERN UNITED STATES. A. Katherine Berger. Natural History, New York, vol.34, no.8, p.763, Dec., 1934.

CARIBOU, REINDEER AND MOOSE IN ALASKA. F. Fraser Darling. Oryx, vol. 2, no.5, pp.280-285, Aug., 1954.

(DEER AMONG THE ANCIENT SETTLERS OF JALISCO. CONTRIBUTION TO HISTORICAL, ETHNOGRAPHIC, AND FOLKLORE PRE-COLUMBIAN STUDIES OF JALISCO.) El venado entre los antiguos pobladores de Jalisco. Contribucion a los estudios historicos, etnograficos y folkloricos precolombinos Jaliscienses. J. Ignacio Davila Garibi. Mem. y. Rev. Soc. Cient. "Antonio Alzate," vol.49, nos.7-12, pp.447-460, 1928.

HOOFED ANIMALS OF NORTH AMERICA. PART I. ANIMALS WITH ANTLERS--THE DEER. George G. Goodwin. School Nat. League Bull., New York, ser.16, no.9, pp. 4, May, 1946.

AMERICA'S BEST WILDLIFE REFUGE. (HABITS OF MOOSE AND ELK.) Oliver Griswold. Minnesota Conservationist, St. Paul, no.51, pp.12-13, 25, illus., Nov., 1937.

A STUDY OF THE DEER AND ELK HERDS OF ROCKY MOUNTAIN NATIONAL PARK, COLORADO. Fred M. Packard. Jour. Mam., 28 (1): 4-12, Feb., 1947.

THE DEER AND ELK OF THE PACIFIC COAST. T. S. Van Dyke. In "The Deer Family." 1902.

(THE MEXICAN DEER.) Los venados en Mexico. Bernardo Villa R. Secretaria de Agriculturia y Ganaderia, Departamento de Caza, Mexico, Boletin de Divulgación, no.1, pp.132, illus., 1950.

Cervidae--South America

THE GUEMUL OR ROEBUCK OF SOUTHERN PERU. John E. Gray. Proc. Zool. Soc., Lond., pp.496-499, figs.2, 1869.

(JOURNEY IN SOUTH AMERICA FOR THE PURPOSE OF BIOLOGICAL STUDY. V. CHILEAN DEER.) Biologische Reisestudien in Sudamerika. V. Die chilenischen Hirsche. Hans Krieg. Zeitschr. fuer Morph. und Oekologie der Tiere, vol.4, pp.585-597, fig. 7, Sept.16, 1925.

(THE MAMMALS OF THE SOUTH AMERICA EXPEDITIONS OF PROF. DR. KRIEG. 16. SWAMP AND PAMPA DEER.) Die Saeugetiere der Suedamerika-Expeditionen Prof. Dr. Kriegs. 16. Sumpf- und Pampashirsche. Ingo Krumbiegel. Zool. Anzeiger, Leipzig, vol.138, no.3-4, pp. 49-70, figs.14, May 1, 1942.

(THE DEER OF BRAZIL ACCORDING TO THE RONDON COLLECTIONS AND THE VARIOUS MUSEUMS, NATIONAL AND FOREIGN.) Os veados do Brasil segundo as colleccoes Rondon e de varios Museus nacionaes e estrangeiros. Alipio de Miranda Ribeiro. Revista do Museu Paulista, vol.11, pp.209-307, pls.25, map 1, 1919.

FURCIFER ANTISIENSIS. Alfred Nehring. Sitz.-Ber. Gesell. Naturf. Freunde Berlin, Jahrg.1886, no.2, pp.17-18, Feb.16, 1886. (In German.)

(ON THE CERVIDS OF THE ENVIRONS OF PIRACICABA IN BRAZIL.) Ueber die Cerviden der Gegand von Piracicaba in Brasilien. Alfred Nehring. Sitz. Gesell. Naturf. Freunde Berlin, Jahrg.1884, pp. 115-137, illus., Oct.21, 1884.

CERVUS ANTISENSIS, CHILENSIS, BRACHYCEROS. Rudolph Amandus Philippi. Anales Del Museo Nacional De Chile - Publicados Por Orden Del Gobierno De Chile - - Primera Seccion: Zoolojia - entrega 7, pp.5-16, pls.4, Santiago, Chile, 1894.

(THREE DEER OF THE ANDES.) Drei Hirsche Der Anden. Rudolph Amandus Philippi. Aus Den "Anales Del Museo Nacional De Chile." pp.1-15, pls.4, F. A. Brockhaus, Leipzig, 1895.

(ANOMALIES OF THE GUEMAL'S HORNS.) Anomalias en las cornamentas del huemul. Carlos Rusconi. Anal. Soc. Cient. Argentina, vol.122, pp.288-296, figs.9, Nov., 1936.

NOTICE OF A PUDU DEER RECENTLY ADDED TO THE SOCIETY'S MENAGERIE. Philip L. Sclater. Proc. Zool. Soc. Lond., pp.104-105, fig.1, 1866.

Cervidae--Taxonomy

ON THE CLASSIFICATION OF THE CERVIDAE, WITH A SYNOPSIS OF THE EXISTING SPECIES. Victor Brooke. Proc. Zool. Soc. Lond., pp.883-928, figs.19, pl.LV, 1878.

(ON THE SYSTEMATICS OF THE DEER AND ON ITS INDIVIDUAL AND GEOGRAPHIC VARIATION.) Sobre la sistematica del venado y su variacion individual y geografica. Angel Cabrera. Rev. Mus. La Plata, n.s., vol.3, no.18, pp.1-42, figs. 7, pl.1, Feb.5, 1943.

(FAUNA OF USSR. MAMMALS: MUSK DEER AND CERVINES.) Fauna SSR. Mlekopitayushchie: Kabargi i Olyeni. K.K. Flerov. Zool. Inst. Akad. Nauk SSSR, Nov.Ser., no.55, pp.255, 1952.

OBSERVATIONS UPON THE TUFTS OF HAIR OBSERVABLE UPON THE POSTERIOR LEGS OF THE GENUS CERVUS, AS A CHARACTER OF THAT GROUP, AND AS A MEANS OF SUBDIVIDING IT INTO NATURAL SECTIONS. John E. Gray. Proc. Zool. Soc. Lond., pt.4, pp.66-68, 1836.

SYNOPSIS OF THE SPECIES OF DEER (CERVINA), WITH THE DESCRIPTION OF A NEW SPECIES IN THE GARDENS OF THE SOCIETY. John E. Gray. Proc. Zool. Soc. Lond., pt.18, pp.222-240, 1850.

(THE OLFACTORY AREA OF THE BUCK AS AN AID IN THE SYSTEMATIC CLASSIFICATION.) Das Nasenfeld der Hirsche als Hilfsmittel bei der systematischen Bestimmung. E. Mohr. Archiv fuer Naturgeschichte, Jahrg.83 (1917), pp.125-128, pl.1, Nov., 1919.

SOME NAMES OF AMERICAN CERVIDAE. Wilfred H. Osgood. Proc. Biol. Soc. Wash., vol.15, pp.87-88, Apr.25, 1902.

ON CERTAIN OF THE SMALLER S. AMERICAN CERVIDAE. Oldfield Thomas. Ann. and Mag. Nat. Hist. (8), vol.11, no.66, pp.585-589, June, 1913.

Cervidae--Venison

VENISON. (DRESSING AND COOKING, REVISED EDITION.) Paul M. Barrett. Ext. Bull., Michigan State College, East Lansing, no.253, pp.16, illus., Oct., 1948.

VENISON FROM FOREST TO TABLE. Paul M. Barrett. Michigan Conservation, Lansing, vol.12, no.9, pp.6-7, Nov., 1943.

Cervidae--Young

CERVINE FOUNDLINGS. Fauna, Phila., vol.8, no.3, p.65, illus., Sept., 1946.

Axis, Hyelaphus

HERD HABITS OF THE SPOTTED DEER. W. G. Adam. Field, London, vol.160, no. 4172, p.888, illus., Dec.10, 1932.

A FURTHER NOTE ON AXIS (HYELAPHUS) KUHLII (MUELLER AND SCHLEGEL) (UNGULATA, CERVIDAE). A. C. V. van Bemmel. Treubia, Buitenzorg, vol.19, pt. 2, pp.403-406, May, 1948.

ONE OF THE RAREST DEER OF THE WORLD. (HYELAPHUS KUHLII.) A.C.V. van Bemmel. Beaufortia, Zool. Mus. Amsterdam, no.27, pp.1-5, illus., Feb.18, 1953.

THE TAXONOMIC POSITION OF CERVUS KUHLII MUELL. ET SCHL. TREUBIA. A.C.V. van Bemmel. Buitenzorg, vol. "hors serie." pp.149-155, pls.45-46, May 29, 1944.

ASIA'S MOST BEAUTIFUL DEER. A CHITAL STAG ON THE WAY TO WATER. (CERVUS AXIS.) Bengt Berg. Field, London, vol.166, no.4328, p.1345, illus., Dec.7, 1935.

A DOE CHEETAL WITH HORNS. Chandra Chur. Jour. Bombay Nat. Hist. Soc., vol.49, no.3, p.547, Dec., 1950.

DISTRIBUTION OF CHITAL (AXIS AXIS ERXL.) IN ASSAM. R. N. De. Jour. Bombay Nat. Hist. Soc., vol.38, no.2, pp.396-397, Dec. 1, 1935.

(ON THE DEVELOPMENT OF ANTLERS IN THE AXIS DEER (AXIS AXIS ERXL.).) Ueber die Entwicklung des Geweihs beim Axishirsch (Axis axis Erxl.). B. Falkenstein, L. Kreps. Zool. Garten, Leipzig, n.F., vol.4, no.6-7, pp.222-226. figs.1-3 July, 1931.

THE BRAY OF THE CHITAL STAG. W. M. Logan Home. Jour. Bombay Nat. Hist. Soc., vol.32, p.594, Jan.15, 1928.

A BABY HOG DEER IN CAPTIVITY. A. Kennion. Jour. Bombay Nat. Hist. Soc., vol.28, pp.271-273, pl.1, Dec.30, 1921.

MALFORMED HORNS IN THE CHEETAL (AXIS AXIS). B. A. Parr. Jour. Bombay Nat. Hist. Soc., vol.29, pp.1051-1052, fig.1, May 15, 1924.

A CURIOUS CASE OF ABNORMAL ANTLER GROWTH IN A CEYLON SPOTTED DEER (AXIS AXIS CEYLONENSIS). W.W.A. Phillips. Loris, Ceylon, vol.1, no.4, pp. 211-212, illus., June, 1938.

CURIOUS DEATH OF CHEETAL (AXIS AXIS) IN CAPTIVITY. Danushkati Pillai. Jour. Bombay Nat. Hist. Soc., vol.36, no. 4, pp.986-988, Dec.15, 1933.

THE LARGER DEER OF BRITISH INDIA. PART IV. THE CHITAL (AXIS) AND THE HOG-DEER (HYELAPHUS). R. I. Pocock. Jour. Bombay Nat. Hist. Soc., vol.44, no.2, pp.169-178, figs.4-8, Dec., 1943.

HABITS OF THE HOG DEER (HYELAPHUS PORCINUS ZIMM.). J. B. Rowntree. Jour. Bombay Nat. Hist. Soc., vol.38, no. 2, p.396, Dec.1, 1935.

(THE HOG DEER.) Der Schweinshirsch. Karl Max Schneider. Mitteil. Zool. Garten, Leipzig, N.F., 1944/45, no.6, pp.1-7, figs. 6, 1945.

SOME EXPERIMENTS IN ALBINISM. (MATING EXPERIMENTS WITH ALBINO CHITAL.) Ram Singh. Jour. Bombay Nat. Hist. Soc., vol.43, no.3, pp.523-524, pl. 1, Dec., 1942.

MALFORMED CHEETAL HEAD (AXIS AXIS). Surajinal Singh. Jour. Bombay Nat. Hist. Soc., vol.34, no.1, p.245, illus., Mar.1, 1930.

THE SPOTTED DEER. (CHITAL—CERVUS AXIS.) His Highness Maharaj Rana Sir Rajender Singhji. Indian Wild Life, Agra, vol.5, pp.3-7, photos.2, Oct.29, 1940.

EXTRACT OF A LETTER FROM. Robert Swinhoe. Proc. Zool. Soc. Lond., p.510, 1865.

Capreolus (Roe Deer)

("ROE-DEER" IN DENMARK.) "Raavildt" i Danmark. Av. G. Ahlefeldt-Bille. Svensk Jakt, Stockholm, vol.86, no.1, pp.5-10, illus., Jan.20, 1948.

ANALYSIS OF A DANISH ROE-DEER POPULATION (CAPREOLUS CAPREOLUS (L.)) BASED UPON THE EXTERMINATION OF THE TOTAL STOCK. Johs Andersen. Danish Rev. Game Biol., 2 (2): 127-155, illus., 1953. (English.)

(OBSERVATIONS OF THE RANGE OF VARIATION OF CAPREOLUS CAPREOLUS.) Beobachtungen ueber die Variationsbreite von Capreolus capreolus. A. Bachofen-Echt. Zeitschr. f. Saeugetierkunde, Berlin, vol.8 nos.3-6, pp.184-194, fig.1, pls.16-20, Dec.20, 1933.

(THE OCCURRENCE OF CAPREOLUS IN THE PLEISTOCENE OF WUERTTEMBERG.) Das Vorkommen von Capreolus im Plistozaen Wuerttembergs. A. Bachofen-Echt. Palaeontologische Zeitschr., vol.13, no.3, pp.238-251, figs.7, Sept.15, 1931.

THE INTRODUCTION AND EXTERMINATION OF ROE DEER IN IRELAND. Edgar N. Barclay. Nat. Hist. Mag., Lond., vol. 3, no.24, pp.265-267, Oct., 1932.

NOTES ON THE ROE DEER. (COLORATION, LENGTH AND TEXTURE OF COAT, SIZE, AND ANTLERS.) Edgar N. Barclay. Ann. and Mag. Nat. Hist., Lond., ser.10, vol.12, no.67, pp.66-80, July, 1933.

THE ROE-DEER OF EUROPEAN TURKEY. Edgar N. Barclay. Ann. and Mag. Nat. Hist., Lond., ser.10, vol.17, no.99, pp. 404-405, Mar., 1936.

THE ROE-DEER OF KOREA. Edgar N. Barclay. Ann. and Mag. Nat. Hist., Lond., ser.10, vol.15, no.90, pp.626-627, June, 1935.

THE VARIATION OF BRITISH ROEDEER. Edgar N. Barclay. Proc. Zool. Soc. Lond., pt.4, pp.709-716, pls.1-2, 1934.

THE ASTUTENESS OF THE ROE. H. Mortimer Batten. Field, London, vol.150, p.495, Sept.29, 1927.

(SIZE OF THE CENTRAL EUROPEAN DEER (CAPREOLUS CAPREOLUS L.) IN THE ALLUVIAL-PREHISTORIC AND EARLY HISTORIC PERIODS.) Zur Groesse des mitteleuropaeischen Rehes (Capreolus capreolus L.) in alluvial-vorgeschichtlicher und frueher historischer Zeit. Joachim Boessneck. Zeitschr. Saeugetierk., Berlin, 21 (3-4): 121-131, Feb.28, 1957.

(SOME NOTES ON THE LIFE OF THE ROE-DEER THROUGHOUT THE YEAR.) Lidt om Raadyrenes liv aaret rundt. F. W. Braestrup. Dyr i Natur og Museum, Kobenhavn, 1943-1944, pp.9-22, figs.16, 1944.

ROE-DEER IN DORSET. H. A. Bryden. Field, London, vol.151, p.921, May 31, 1928.

ROE DEER RINGS. Anthony Buxton. Oryx, London, 3 (4): 203-204, illus., May, 1956.

NOTE ON THE ROE-DEER OF KURDISTAN. R. C. Cheesman, Martin A. C. Hinton. Ann. and Mag. Nat. Hist., ser.9, vol.12, pp.608-609, Nov., 1923.

THE ILLIK OF THE THIAN SHAN; COLLECTING ROE DEER FOR AN AMERICAN MUSEUM GROUP ON THE GRASSY SLOPES ABOVE TIMBER-LINE OF THE MOUNTAINS OF CENTRAL ASIA. James L. Clark. Nat. Hist., vol.33, no.2, pp.175-186, Mar.-Apr., 1933.

(THE CAPREOLUS OF CENTRAL ITALY.) Il Capriolo dell'Italia centrale. E. Festa. Boll. Mus. Zool. ed Anat. Comp. R. Univ., Torino, vol.40 (paper no.37), pp.1-2, 1925 (1926).

(ON THE DIAGNOSTIC CHARACTERS OF THE GENUS CAPREOLUS FRISCH.) K. K. Flerov. Comptes Rendus Acad. Sci. Union Socialistic Soviet Republics, pp.479-484, 1928. (In Russian, with diagnoses of species and subspecies in English.)

SEASONAL VARIATIONS IN THE HAIR OF THE DEER (CAPREOLUS FRISCH). K. K. Flerov. Comptes Rendus Acad. Sci. USSR, A, no.22, pp.467-469, 1928.

(SOME NEW DATA ON THE ROE (CAPREOLUS FRISCH) OF EASTERN ASIA.) K. K. Flerov. Comptes Rendus Acad. Sci. URSS, pp.429-432, 1929. (In Russian.)

THE ROE DEER IN CUMBERLAND. Ritson Graham. Trans. Carlisle Nat. Hist. Soc., England, vol.5, pp.104-116, 1933.

NOTES ON THE SKULL OF A ROEBUCK IN THE BRITISH MUSEUM. John E. Gray. Proc. Zool. Soc., Lond., pp.601-602, fig. 1, 1871.

A FINE ROEBUCK HEAD. W. Douglas Home. Field, London, vol.156, no.4056, p.414, fig.1, Sept.20, 1930.

(CRANIOMETRIC INVESTIGATION AND PHYLOGENETIC DERIVATION OF DEER (CAPREOLUS H. SMITH).) Kraniometrische Untersuchung und stammesgeschichtliche Ableitung der Rehe (Capreolus H. Smith). A. Jacobi. Jenaische Zeitschr. f. Naturwiss., vol.67, pp.326-345, figs.2, 1932.

THE APPEARANCE OF ROE DEER IN FINLAND AND THE VARIATIONS IN ITS SPREAD IN THE ADJOINING AREAS. O. Kalela. Suomen Riista, Helsinki, vol.3, pp.34-56, figs.2, 1948. (In Finnish, with English summary.)

(ON THE QUESTION OF DEGENERATION AND SUB-NORMAL MODIFICATION IN THE ROE DEER.) Zur Frage der Degeneration und Kuemmermodifikation beim Rehwild. Hans Krieg. Biol. Zentralbatt, vol.57, nos.5-6, pp.225-228, figs.2, May-June, 1937.

THE BRITISH ROE-DEER (CAPREOLUS CAPREOLUS THOTTI), A PRELIMINARY DIAGNOSIS. Einar Loennberg. Ann. and Mag. Nat. Hist., ser.8, vol.6, pp.297-298, Sept., 1910.

ON THE ANTLERS OF MALE ROEBUCK. V. Martino. Lovocki Glasnik, Novi Sad, Febr.-Mar., 1931, Br.2-3, pp.1-4, figs.3, 1931. (In Jugo-Slavian, with diagnoses in German.)

A NEW ROE-DEER FROM CHINA. Gerrit S. Miller, Jr. Proc. Biol. Soc., Wash., vol.24, pp.231-232, Nov.28, 1911.

(THE ABSENCE OF THE FIRST PREMOLARS OF THE LOWER JAW IN THE ROE--A PROGRESSIVE CHARACTER.) Das fehlen des ersten Unterkieferpraemolaren beim Reh--ein progressives Merkmal. Detlev Mueller. Zeitschrift f, Saeugetierkunde, vol.5, no.6, pp.369-371, 1930.

NOTE UPON CANON TRISTRAM'S RECENT DISCOVERY OF THE ROE-BUCK (CERVUS CAPREOLUS) IN PALESTINE. Alfred Newton. Proc. Zool. Soc. Lond., pp.700-701, 1876.

ROEBUCK AT KING'S LANGLEY. Charles Oldham. Trans. Hertfordshire Nat. Hist. Soc. and Field Club, vol.18, no.4, p.216, Apr., 1929.

(THE ROE DEER'S DISTRIBUTION IN NORWAY.) Radyrets (Capreolus capreolus (L.)) utbredelse i Norge. O. Olstad. Statens Viltundersokelser Meddelel., vol.14, p. 1063, 1944.

(SOME REMARKS ON THE ROE-DEER OF JURA.) Quelques remarques au sujet de chevreuils du Jura. A. A. Quartier. Mammalia, Paris, vol.18, no.4, pp.380-388, illus., Dec., 1954.

UNUSUAL DEVELOPMENT OF ROE DEER CALF. James Ritchie. Scottish Nat., no. 170, pp.49-50, Mar.-Apr., 1928.

(THE ROE-DEERS FROM THE COLLECTION OF THE DUC D'ORLEANS MUSEUM.) Les bois de chevreuil de la collection du Musee du Duc d'Orleans. Paul Rode, Robert Didier. Bull. Soc. Nat. Acclimat. France, Paris, pp.187-201, figs.12, 1941.

(METHOD OF AGING THE ROE DEER.) K metodike opredeleniya vozrasta kosuli (Capreolus capreolus L.). I. I. Sokolov. Zool. Zhurnal. Akad. Nauk, SSSR, 35 (8): 1238-1249, 1956.

THE PAST AND PRESENT DISTRIBUTION OF ROE DEER IN NORTHUMBERLAND. H. S. Tegner. Trans. Nat. Hist. Soc. Northumberland, Durham and Newcastle upon Tyne, n.s., vol.11, no.7, pp.164-168, 1955.

NOTE ON THE DISCOVERY OF THE ROEBUCK (CERVUS CAPREOLUS) IN PALESTINE. H. B. Tristram. Proc. Zool. Soc., Lond., pp.420-421, 1876.

NOTES ON SOME FIRST CLASS ROE HEADS. Frank Wallace. Field, London, vol.152, pp.225-227, illus., Aug.9, 1928.

A THREE-HORNED ROE. Frank Wallace. Field, p.1, illus., Mar.6, 1937.

(EXPERIMENTING WITH A NEW TYPE OF MARKING OF WILD ANIMALS.) Versuch einer neuen art von Wildmarkierung. (Marking roe deer fawns for field identification of age classes.) O. Wettstein. Z. Jagdwissensch., 1 (2): 65-69, 1955.

Dama (Fallow Deer)

NOTES ON THE FALLOW DEER OF ASIA MINOR. Edgar N. Barclay. Ann. and Mag. Nat. Hist., vol.14, no.79, pp.157-159, July, 1934.

WILD FALLOW DEER IN NORTH-EAST HERTFORDSHIRE AND THE ADJOINING COUNTIES. Michael F. Berry. Trans. Hertfordshire Nat. Hist. Soc. and Field Club, Hertford, vol.20, pt.5, pp.307-308, Apr., 1938.

SUPPLEMENTARY NOTES ON CERVUS MESOPOTAMICUS. Victor Brooke. Proc. Zool. Soc. Lond., pp.298-303, figs.4, 1876.

SPIKE BUCK OF FALLOW DEER RUNS AMUCK. Walter F. Burton. Murrelet, vol. 11, no.2, p.17, May, 1930.

IS THERE A FALLOW IN YOUR FUTURE? Rush Butcher. W. Va. Cons., 19 (6): 12-13, illus., Aug., 1955.

(SYMBIOSIS BETWEEN ARDEA CINEREA AND DAMA DAMA.) Symbios mellan haeger (Ardea cinerea) och dovhjort (Dama dama). Kai Curry-Lindahl. Var. Fagelvaerld, Goeteborg, vol.15, no.2, pp. 123-126, 1956. (In Swedish, with English summary.)

DEER IN ANCIENT EGYPT. Warren R. Dawson. Jour. Linnaean Soc. Lond., vol. 39, no.264, pp.137-145, illus., Oct.3, 1934.

(HABITAT, LIFE HISTORY, AND DISTRIBUTION OF THE MESOPOTAMIAN FALLOW DEER, CERVUS MESOPOTAMICUS BROOKE, 1875.) Lebensraum, Lebensweise und Vorkommen des Mesopotamischen Damhirsches, Cervus mesopotamicus Brooke, 1875. T. Haltenorth. Saeugetierkundliche Mitteilungen, vol.9, no.1, pp.15-39, Muenchen, 1961.

THE DEVELOPMENT AND GROWTH OF THE PLACENTOMES IN THE FALLOW DEER (DAMA DAMA L.). R. S. Harrison, A. R. Hyett. Jour. Anat., Lond., vol.88, pt.3, pp.338-355, July, 1954.

(DAMA SCHAEFERI HILZH.) Dama schaeferi Hilzh. Max Hilzheimer. Zeitschr. f. Saeugetierkunde, vol.2, no.1, pp.68-73, fig.5, Oct.15, 1927.

RELEASE, DISPERSAL, AND REPRODUCTION OF FALLOW DEER IN NEBRASKA. Robert L. Packard. Jour. Mam., 36 (3): 471-473, fig.1, Aug.30, 1955.

THE PERSIAN FALLOW DEER (DAMA MESOPOTAMICA). R. I. Pocock. Jour. Soc. Preservation Fauna Empire, Hertford, n.s., pt.53, pp.53-55, June, 1946.

ANTLER GROWTH AND SHEDDING IN A CAPTIVE GROUP OF FALLOW DEER (DAMA DAMA) IN NEW ZEALAND. Thane Riney. Trans. Roy. Soc. New Zealand, vol.82, pt.2, pp.569-578, illus., Sept., 1954.

(FOOD OF FALLOW DEER.) Kormlenie lanei (Dama dama L.). G. M. Shakhnazarov, A. D. Obukhova. Trudy Moskovskogo Zooparka (Proc. Moscow Zool. Park), vol. 3, pp.72-82, 1946.

FALLOW DEER IN THE FIJI ISLANDS. R. M. Spencer. Field, London, vol.154, no.4015, p.871, Dec.7, 1929.

EXHIBITION OF, AND REMARKS UPON, TWO DOUBLE HIND FEET OF A FALLOW DEER (CERVUS DAMA). Edwin Ward. Proc. Zool. Soc. Lond., p.90, 1874.

Elaphurus

LETTER FROM, RELATING TO THE HABITAT OF ELAPHURUS DAVIDIANUS, AND TO THE LOCALITIES OF VARIOUS PHASIANIDAE. J. Le Père Armand David. Proc. Zool. Soc. Lond., p.210, 1868.

NOW WE EXHIBIT THE RAREST DEER IN THE WORLD. (Pere David's deer.) Jean Delacour. Animal Kingdom, New York, vol. 50, no.1, pp.3-5, 24, illus., Jan.-Feb., 1947.

(NOTES ON ELAPHURUS DAVIDIANUS, NEW SPECIES OF THE DEER FAMILY.) Note sur L'Elaphurus davidianus espece Nouvelle de la famille des cerfs. Milne Alphonse Edwards. Bull. Nouv. Archiv. der Mus. Paris, vol.2, pp.27-40, pls.4-6, 1866; Nat. Hist., vol.71.

OBSERVATIONS ON THE DEVELOPMENT AND RADIOLOGY OF THE PERE DAVID'S DEER FOETUS (ELAPHURUS DAVIDIANUS). T. W. Glenister. Proc. Zool. Soc. Lond., vol.123, pt.4, pp.757-763, pls.1-2, Feb. 10, 1954.

PLACENTATION IN PERE DAVID'S DEER, ELAPHURUS DAVIDIANUS. W. J. Hamilton, R. J. Harrison. Nature, London, vol.167, no.4246, pp.443-444, Mar.17, 1951.

A CONTRIBUTION TO THE HISTORY AND ANATOMY OF PERE DAVID'S DEER. F. Wood Jones. Proc. Zool. Soc. Lond., vol. 121, pt.2, pp.319-370, pls.1-6, Aug.31, 1951.

(INFORMATION ON THE ELAPHURE.) Einiges von Milu. C. S. Kooi. Zool. Garten, Leipzig, N.F., vol.20, nos.2-3, pp.190-191, illus., 1953.

THE PERE DAVID DEER HERD. John C. Phillips. Jour. Mam., vol.6, no.4, pp. 283-284, Nov., 1925.

ANNOUNCEMENT OF THE ARRIVAL OF A SKIN AND SKELETON OF ELAPHURUS DAVIDIANUS. Philip L. Sclater. Proc. Zool. Soc. Lond., p.531, 1868.

NOTES ON THE ORIGINAL HABITAT OF FATHER DAVID'S DEER. A. deC. Sowerby. Musee Heude, Univ. L'Aurore, Shanghai, no.4, pp.1-19, illus., Jan.14, 1949.

THE RANGE OF FATHER DAVID'S DEER. Arthur deC. Sowerby. Animal Kingdom, New York Zool. Soc., vol.57, no.3, pp. 83-85, illus., June, 1954.

LETTER ON ELAPHURUS DAVIDIANUS, AND ON COLLECTIONS IN HAINAN. Robert Swinhoe. Proc. Zool. Soc. Lond., pp.530-531, 1868.

MISCELLANEOUS REPORTS OF PERE DAVID'S DEER. H. Takashima. Trans. Mamm. Soc. Japan, no.8, pp.68-69, Feb., 1954. (In Japanese.)

THE ROMANCE OF PERE DAVID'S DEER. H. Takashima. Misc. Repts. Yamashina's Inst. Ornithol. & Zool., Tokyo, no.1, pp. 5-14, illus., Dec., 1952. (In Japanese, with English summary.)

WORLD REGISTER OF PERE DAVID'S DEER. E. H. Tong. Proc. Zool. Soc. Lond., 129 (3): 343-349, Nov.11, 1957.

PERE DAVID'S DEER IN THE COLLECTION OF THE ZOOLOGICAL SOCIETY OF LONDON. G. M. Vevers, G. B. Stratton. Proc. Zool. Soc. Lond., vol.121, pt.2, p.325, Aug.31, 1951.

(REMARKS ON ELAPHURUS DAVIDIANUS, IN PARTICULAR ON ANTLER SHEDDING AND THE CHIN CLEFT.) Bemerkungen ueber Elaphurus davidianus, inshesondere ueber den Geweihwechsel und die Kinnspalte. Ludwig Zukowsky. Arkiv fuer Naturgeschichte, vol.88, A, no.7, pp.121-128, May, 1922.

Hydropotes (Chinese Water Deer)

NOTES ON THE ANATOMY OF THE CHINESE WATER-DEER (HYDROPOTES INERMIS). Alfred Henry Garrod. Proc. Zool. Soc. Lond., pt.4, pp.789-792, figs. 2, 1877.

EXHIBITION OF, AND REMARKS UPON, THE SKULL OF A CHINESE DEER (HYDROPOTES INERMIS). Edward Hamilton. Proc. Zool. Soc. Lond., p.702, 1871.

REMARKS ON THE PROLIFIC NATURE OF HYDROPOTES INERMIS. Edward Hamilton. Proc. Zool. Soc. Lond., p.258, 1871.

SIXTEEN DEER FOR LOCAL RESTAURANT. (HYDROPOTES INERMIS.) Arthur deC. Sowerby. China Jour., vol.18, no.3, p. 168, figs.2, Mar., 1933.

Key Deer

CAN WE SAVE THE KEY DEER? Robert P. Allen. Nat. Hist., 60 (2): 79-83, Feb., 1951.

THE KEY DEER: A CHALLENGE FROM THE PAST. Robert P. Allen. Audubon Mag., 54 (2): 76-81, illus., Mar.-Apr., 1952.

THE KEY DEER. Gerald F. Baker. Our Endangered Wildlife, Nat. Wildlife Federation, pp.11-12, illus., Jan., 1956.

THE DIRECTOR REPORTS TO YOU: THOSE SEMINOLE DEER AGAIN. John H. Baker. Audubon Mag., Harrisburg, sec.1, vol.43, no.6, pp.551-553, Nov.-Dec., 1941.

SOUTH TO SEE KEY DEER. Martha Connor, Paul Connor. Everglades Nat. Hist. Homestead, Florida, vol.1, no.3, pp.96-99, illus., Sept., 1953.

WHAT HAS HAPPENED TO THE KEY DEER? Clarence Cottam, Philip A. Dumont. Natl. Parks Mag., 27 (113): 82, Apr.-June, 1953.

THE LAST STAND OF THE KEY DEER. Clarence Cottam, James Silver. Natl. Parks Mag., 24 (102): 100-103, July-Sept., 1950.

AN ECOLOGICAL STUDY OF THE KEY DEER. John D. Dickson, III. Fla. Game and Fresh Water Fish Comm., Tech. Bull. no.3, pp.v, 104, figs.20, Dec., 1955.

KEY DEER GET ANOTHER STAY OF EXECUTION. James Silver. US F&WS, Region 4, Third Progress Rep., pp.2, Aug., 1953.

TINY FLORIDA DEER NEAR EXTINCTION. South Dakota Conserv. Digest, Madison, vol.17, no.5, p.15, May, 1950.

Mazama (Brockets)

NOTES ON AMERICAN DEER OF THE GENUS MAZAMA. J. A. Allen. Bull. Amer. Mus. Nat. Hist., vol.34, pp.521-553, Nov. 2, 1915.

THE NAME MAZAMA. C. Hart Merriam. Mazama, Portland, vol.1, no.2, p.288, Oct., 1897.

A NEW BROCKET FROM YUCATAN. C. Hart Merriam. Proc. Biol. Soc. Wash., vol.14, pp.105-106, July 19, 1901.

A NEW DEER OF THE BROCKET GROUP FROM VENEZUELA. Oldfield Thomas. Ann. and Mag. Nat. Hist. (8), vol.1, no. 3, pp.349-350, Apr., 1908.

CONCERNING A MAZAMA NEMORIVAGA CITA. P. Wagenaar Hummelinck. Arch. Neerland. Zool., Leyden, vol.4, no.2-3, pp.133-138, pl.3, July, 1940.

Moschus (Musk Deer)

ON THE CLASSIFICATION AND THE GEOGRAPHICAL DISTRIBUTION OF THE GENUS MOSCHUS (MAMMALIA, CERVIDAE). K. Flerov. Ann. Mus. Zool. Acad. Sci. URSS, pp.1-20, pls.1-7, 1930.

PRELIMINARY NOTE ON THE DIAGNOSTIC CHARACTERS OF THE GENUS MOSCHUS LINNE (MAMMALIA, CERVIDAE). K. Flerov. Comptes Rendus Acad. Sci. l' URSS, 1928, pp.515-519, 1928.

ON THE STRUCTURE AND AFFINITIES OF THE MUSK-DEER (MOSCHUS MOSCHIFERUS, LINN.). William H. Flower. Proc. Zool. Soc. Lond., pp.159-190, figs. 14, Mar.16, 1875.

NOTES ON THE ANATOMY OF THE MUSK-DEER (MOSCHUS MOSCHIFERUS). Alfred H. Garrod. Proc. Zool. Soc. Lond., pt.2, pp.287-292, figs.4, 1877.

ON THE BLOOD-CORPUSCLES OF THE STANLEY MUSK DEER. George Gulliver. Proc. Zool. Soc. Lond., pt.11, p.66, 1843.

HIS PERFUME STIRS THE WORLD. (MUSK DEER.) Jennie E. Harris. Nat. Hist., New York, vol.56, no.2, pp.68-71, 94, illus., Feb., 1947.

A NEW MUSK-DEER FROM KOREA. Ned Hollister. Proc. Biol. Soc. Wash., vol.24, pp.1-2, Jan.28, 1911.

THE MUSK-DEER IN CHINA. Arthur deC. Sowerby. China Jour. Sci. and Arts, vol. 3, no.12, pp.651-653, pl.1, Dec., 1925.

Muntjacs (Barking Deer)

MUNTIACUS LACRYMANS, THE BARKING DEER OR MUNTJAC. E. A. Aylmer. Hong Kong Nat., vol.3, no.1, pp.69-70, pls.12, 13, Mar., 1932.

PECULIARITIES OF THE BARKING DEER (MUNTIACUS VAGINALIS). T. A. Baldry. Jour. Darjeeling Nat. Hist. Soc., vol.3, no.4, pp.82-85, Apr., 1929.

ON SCLATER'S MUNTJAC AND OTHER SPECIES OF THE GENUS CERVULUS. Victor Brooke. Proc. Zool. Soc. Lond., pp.33-42, figs.5, pls.8-9, 1874.

CLICKING NOISE MADE BY MUNTJAC. R. W. Burton. Jour. Bombay Nat. Hist. Soc., vol.33, no.2, p.439, Feb.15, 1929.

HOOF DISEASE IN THE MUNTJAC (MUNTIACUS MUNTJAC). G.V.R. Frend. Jour. Bombay Nat. Hist. Soc., vol.37, no. 3, p.726, Dec.15, 1934.

ON THE CHINESE DEER NAMED LOPHOTRAGUS MICHIANUS BY MR. SWINHOE. Alfred H. Garrod. Proc. Zool. Soc. Lond., pp.757-765, figs.3, pl.LXXVI, 1876.

A NEW RACE OF BARKING DEER FROM ANNAM. (MUNTIACUS MUNTJAK ANNAMENSIS.) C. Boden Kloss. Ann. and Mag. Nat. Hist., ser.10, vol.1, pp.399-400, Mar., 1928.

THE ICHANG TUFTED DEER. R. Lydekker. Proc. Zool. Soc. Lond., vol.2, pp.166-169, figs.32-33, Oct.1, 1904.

"CLICKING NOISE" MADE BY MUNTJAC. Randolph C. Morris. Jour. Bombay Nat. Hist. Soc., vol.32, p.216, Aug.1, 1927.

HABITS OF THE MUNTJAC (M. MALABARICUS). Randolph C. Morris. Jour. Bombay Nat. Hist. Soc., vol.36, no.2, p.497, Apr. 15, 1933.

ON A NEW SPECIES OF MUNTJAC DEER FROM CHINA. W. Ogilby. Proc. Zool. Soc. Lond., pt.6, p.105, 1838.

CLICKING NOISE MADE BY MUNTJAC. B. B. Osmaston. Jour. Bombay Nat. Hist. Soc., vol.32, p.795, May 31, 1928.

ABNORMAL GROWTH IN THE MUNTJAC (MUNTIACUS VAGINALIS). F. H. Peppe. Jour. Bombay Nat. Hist. Soc., vol.39, no. 4, pp.854-855, illus., Dec.15, 1937.

CLICKING SOUNDS MADE BY MUNTJAC. S. Sundara Raj. Jour. Bombay Nat. Hist. Soc., vol.37, no.2, p.486, Aug.15, 1934.

AN UNUSUAL ALTITUDE RECORD FOR THE BARKING DEER (MUNTIACUS VAGINALIS). A.A.K. Sangster. Jour. Bombay Nat. Hist. Soc., vol.30, no.1, p.201, Sept.30, 1928.

EXHIBITION OF SKINS OF CERVULUS SCLATERI. Robert Swinhoe. Proc. Zool. Soc. Lond., p.519, 1873.

ON A SMALL, TUFTED HORNLESS DEER FROM THE MOUNTAINS NEAR NINGPO. Robert Swinhoe. Proc. Zool. Soc. Lond., pp.452-454, pl.LIX, 1874.

CLICKING NOISE MADE BY MUNTJAC. Charles Theobald. Jour. Bombay Nat. Hist. Soc., vol.32, pp.593-594, Jan. 15, 1928.

TUFTED DEER IN BURMA (ELAPHODUS CEPHALOPHUS MILNE-EDWARDS). U Tun Yin. Jour. Bombay Nat. Hist. Soc., vol.53, no.1, pp.123-125, illus., Aug., 1955.

Cervus--General

(TWO PICTURES OF THE SCHOMBURGK DEER (RUCERVUS SCHOMBURGKI BLYTH) FROM ZOOLOGICAL GARDENS.) Zwei Abbildungen vom Schomburgks-Hirsch (Rucervus schomburgki Blyth) aus Zoologischen Gaerten. Otto Antonius. Zool. Garten, N.F., Leipzig, vol.9, no.5, pp.209-211, illus., Oct., 1937.

BUGLERS OF THE PEAKS. (WAPITI.) Elizabeth Bachmann. Frontiers, Lancaster, vol.10, no.4, pp.102-104, illus., Apr., 1946.

WAPITI--VANISHING MAGNIFICENCE. Elizabeth Bachmann. Conserv. Volunteer, St. Paul., vol.13, no.76, pp.20-24, May-June, 1950.

ELK (CERVUS CANADENSIS CANADENSIS). N. R. Barger. Wisconsin Conserv. Bull., Madison, vol.16, no.1, pp.33-34, illus., Jan., 1951.

NOTES ON THE PONOLIA DEER (CERVUS ELDI). R. C. Beavan. Proc. Zool. Soc. Lond., pp.759-766, 1867.

FRIENDLY FOLKS ON THE DEER MESA. (SIKA DEER.) Belle J. Benchley. Zoonooz, San Diego, vol.15, no.11, pp.3-4, illus., Nov., 1942.

(ON THE NATURAL HISTORY OF THE RED DEER.) Zur Naturgeschichte des Rothirsches. J. Beninde. Leipzig, Monographie der Wildsaeugetiere, no.4, pp.vii, 223, 1937.

NOTES ON THE SCHOMBURGK DEER. Phya Jolamark Bhicharana. Jour. Siam Soc., Nat. Hist. Suppl., vol.8, no.4, pp. 311-313, pl.1, Oct., 1931.

THAMIN (RUCERVUS THAMIN). H. R. Blandford. Jour. Soc. Preservation Fauna, Empire, Hertford, n.s., pt.36, pp.25-27, May, 1939.

ON CERVUS SCHOMBURKI (BLYTH). Victor Brooke. Proc. Zool. Soc. Lond., pp.304-307, figs.2, 1876.

BUGLES IN THE FOREST. (ELK.) R. D. Burroughs. Michigan Conserv., Lansing, vol.24, no.5, pp.33, Oct., 1955.

A VARIETY OF THE THAMIN OR BROW-ANTLERED DEER (RUCERVUS THAMIN). R. W. Burton. Jour. Bombay Nat. Hist. Soc., vol.34, no.4, p.1059, Mar.2, 1931.

THE JUNGLE IN SUNLIGHT AND SHADOW. PART 4.--PHOTOGRAPHING SWAMP DEER AND A RIDDLE OF THE FOREST. F. W. Champion. Field, London, vol.162, no. 4208, pp.482-483, figs., Aug.19, 1933.

A HERD OF RED DEER. A STUDY OF ANIMAL BEHAVIOUR. F. Fraser Darling. Oxford Univ. Press, London, pp.v-viii, 215, figs.10, tables 4, pls.7, map, 1937.

(Review by Canning Suffern of) A HERD OF RED DEER: A STUDY IN ANIMAL BEHAVIOR. F. Fraser Darling. Man, London, vol.38, nos.82-100, p.94, June, 1938.

(THE DEER PSEUDAXIS.) Le Cerf Pseudaxis. J. Delacour. La Terre et la Vie (Revue d'Hist. Nat.), vol.1, no.6, pp. 373-375, illus., July, 1931.

THE RIDDLE OF CERVUS SCHOMBURGKI. Francis H. Giles. Jour. Siam Soc., Nat. Hist. Suppl., Bangkok, vol.10, no.3, pp.1-34, pls.10, Nov., 1937.

NOTES ON THE SIKA DEER. Richard Glover. Jour. Mam., 37 (1): 99-105, Feb.28, 1956.

THE DEER WITH PERSONALITY. (SAMBAR). Roger Good. San Diego Zoonooz, vol.24, no.1, p.5, illus., Jan., 1951.

THE NATURAL HISTORY OF THE ROOSEVELT ELK. William Graf. PhD thesis, Oregon State Coll., 1943.

ON A VERY LARGE ROE DEER (C. LEUCOTIS) IN THE COLLECTION OF THE EARL OF DERBY. John E. Gray. Proc. Zool. Soc. Lond., pt.17, pp.64-65, 1849.

FURTHER EXAMPLES OF THE SCHOMBURGK DEER. Ulrich Guehler. Jour. Siam Soc., Nat. Hist. Suppl., vol.9, no. 1, pp.147-149, fig.1, June, 1933.

(CONTRIBUTION TO THE HISTORY OF CERVUS (RUCERVUS) SCHOMBURGKI BLYTH.) Beitrag zur Geschichte von Cervus (Rucervus) schomburgki Blyth. U. Guehler. Zeitschr. f. Saeugetierkunde, vol.11, no.1, pp.2-31, Mar.13, 1936.

THE ROOSEVLET ELK, CERVUS ROOSEVELTI MERRIAM. E. N. Kavanagh. Jour. Forestry, Wash., vol.28, no.5, pp.659-663, May, 1930.

SOME NOTES ON CERVUS (RUCERVUS) SCHOMBURGKI. P. R. Kemp. Jour. Nat. Hist. Soc. Siam, Bangkok, vol.3, no.1, pp. 1-9, pl.1, Nov.20, 1918.

THE ELK, THEIR HOME AND HABITS. Stephen Nelson Leek. Campbell Art Co., Elizabeth, N.J., 1914.

A HABITAT OF SCHOMBURGK'S DEER (CERVUS SCHOMBURGKI). C. Boden Kloss. Jour. Nat. Hist. Soc. Siam, vol.4, p.105, Mar., 1921.

WHITE PATCH (THE BIOGRAPHY OF AN ELK). S. N. Leek. Zool. Soc. Bull., New York, vol.20, no.3, pp.1481-1489, illus., May, 1917.

THE WAPITI. Robert Page Lincoln. Fur-Fish-Game (Harding's Mag.), Columbus, vol.79, no.10, pp.5-7, 19-20, illus., Oct., 1945.

CERVUS RHENO, BY HOFFBERT, CAROLUS FRID. Carl Linnaeus. Upsala, pp.24, 1754.

(ZOOLOGICAL CONCEPTS: WAPITI-ZYGOMATURUS.) Zoologische Begriffe: Wapiti-Zygomaturus. Paul Matschie. Handwoerterbuch der Zoologie, Anthropologie und Ethnologie, Breslau, Bd.8, Lief.37-38 (Encyklopaedie der Naturwissenschaften, Lief.76-77), pp.512-707, 1900.

THE BIOLOGY OF THE DOMESTICATED DAPPLED DEER. (CERVUS HORTULORUM SWINHOE.) I. I. Miroliubof. Bull. Far Eastern Branch Acad. Sci. USSR, Vladivostok, no.16, pp.155-174, 1934. (In Russian, with English summary.)

(THE FORMER HAMBURG BREEDING OF THE SCHOMBURGK DEER, RUCERVUS SCHOMBURGKI BLYTH.) Die ehemalige Hamburger Zucht des Schomburgk-Hirsches, Rucervus schomburgki Blyth. Erna Mohr. Zool. Anz., Leipzig, vol.142, nos.1-2, pp.30-35, figs.4, Apr.4, 1943.

'STAMPING GROUNDS' AND 'SORE NECK' IN SAMBAR. R. C. Morris. Jour. Bombay Nat. Hist. Soc., vol.40, no.3, pp.560-561, Dec., 1938.

THE FIRING LINE. (ELK.) Olaus J. Murie. Amer. Forests, Wash., vol.53, no.9, pp. 392-394, 422, illus., Sept., 1947.

SPRING ELK OBSERVATIONS. F. R. Oberhansley. Nature Notes, Yellowstone, Nat. Park, vol.15, nos.5-6, pp.21-23, May-June, 1938.

THE NATURE OF THINGS. (ROOSEVELT ELK.) Donald Culross Peattie. Audubon Mag., Harrisburg, sec.1, vol.43, no.5, pp.435-438, illus., Sept.-Oct., 1941.

SIDELIGHTS ON THE WAPITI. Archie Pendergraft. Wyoming Wild Life, Cheyenne, vol.10, no.3, pp.34-35, illus., Mar., 1946.

A SEARCH FOR SCHOMBURGK'S DEER. R. Pigot. Jour. Siam Soc. Nat. Hist. Suppl., vol.8, no.1, pp.51-54, 1929.

SAGA OF THE WILD. (ELK.) William Marshall Rush. Fauna, Phila., vol.4, no.2, pp.53-58, illus., June, 1942.

A-WI-E-GWA, THE ELK. W. J. Schoonmaker. National Humane Review, Albany, vol.31, no.10, pp.24-25, illus., Oct., 1943.

SOME REMARKS ON THE BOKHARA DEER (CERVUS BACTRIANUS LYD.). B. M. Shitkov. Proc. Moscou Zool. Park, vol.1, pp.50-58, 1940. (In Russian, with a resume in English.)

THE WAPITI. Robert W. Shufeldt. Natur und Haus, vol.17, no.17, pp.259-261, June 1, 1909. (In German.)

A CASTRATED ELK. M. P. Skinner. Jour. Mam., vol.4, no.4, p.252, pl.28, Nov., 1923.

THE ELK SITUATION. M. P. Skinner. Jour. Mam., vol.9, no.4, pp.309-317, Nov., 1928.

THOROLD'S DEER. A. deC. Sowerby. China Jour. Sci. and Arts, vol.5, p.155, Sept., 1926.

SORE NECK IN SAMBAR. THE THEORY OF 'ATAVISTIC DEGENERACY'. (RUSA UNICOLOR EQUINUS.) W. S. Thom. Jour. Bombay Nat. Hist. Soc., vol.40, no.4, pp. 733-736, May, 1939.

BABY ELK ARRIVE. George M. Wright. Yosemite Nature Notes, vol.7, p.50, July, 1928.

THOROLD'S DEER. R. I. Pocock. Field, London, vol.147, p.824, May 27, 1926.

THE ROOSEVELT ELK. Acad. News Letter, San Francisco, no.61, pp.3-4, Jan., 1945.

ELK IN THE WINTERTIME. Montana Wildlife Bull., Helena, vol.2, no.1, p.6, illus., Feb., 1945.

HERE COME THE ELK. Nat. Nature Notes, Wash., D.C., vol.1, no.34, pp.1-3, figs.2, Nov.15, 1937.

WAPITI, OR AMERICAN ELK. South Dakota Conservation Digest, Pierre, vol. 11, no.12, p.14, Dec., 1944.

Cervus--Anatomy (General)

THE THYROID AND PARATHYROID GLANDS OF THE BARASINGHA DEER, WITH PARTICULAR REFERENCE TO AUTOFLOURESCENCE, FAT AND PIGMENT. Allan L. Grafflin. Jour. Morph., Phila., vol.65, no.2, pp.297-321, Sept.1, 1939.

ARRANGEMENT OF THE OBTURATOR MUSCLES, WITH NOTES ON THE OTHER MUSCLES OF THE THIGH, IN THE DWARF WAPITI (CERVUS NANNODES MERRIAM). E. Raymond Hall, Alden H. Miller. Jour. Mam., vol.14, no.4, pp.358-361, figs.1-2, Nov.13, 1933.

Cervus--Anatomy (Skull, Teeth)

CRANIOLOGICAL CHARACTERISTICS OF THE DEER CERVUS ELAPHUS BRAUNERI IN COMPARISON WITH C. ELAPHUS MARAL. R. L. Beme. Zool. Zhurnal, Moscow, 36 (10): 1557-1564, 1957. (In Russian, with English summary.)

(THE NORWEGIAN RED DEER (CERVUS ELAPHUS L.), A CRANIOMETRIC INVESTIGATION.) Das norwegische Rotwild (Cervus elaphus L.) eine kraniometrische Untersuchung. Olaf Ingebrigtsen. Bergens Museums Aarbok, 1922-23, Naturvid. raekke, no.7, pp.1-242, pls.1-5, figs.1-11, 1924.

NOTE ON THE ERUPTION AND REPLACEMENT OF THE TEETH OF JAPANESE DEER, CERVUS SIKA. Eisato Kuwanc. Annotat., Zool. Japan, vol.12, pp.105-107, July 25, 1929.

EXHIBITION OF THE SKULL OF AN ELK FROM NOVA SCOTIA. William Ogilby. Proc. Zool. Soc. Lond., pt.7, p.93, 1839.

THE ABNORMAL LAST MOLAR IN THE SAMBAR OF THE BONIN ISLANDS. R. I. Pocock. Ann. and Mag. Nat. Hist., Lond., ser.11, vol.9, p.391, figs.3, May, 1942.

THE SKULL CHARACTERS OF SOME OF THE FORMS OF SAMBAR (RUSA) OCCURRING TO THE EAST OF THE BAY OF BENGAL. R. I. Pocock. Ann. and Mag. Nat. Hist., Lond., ser.11, vol.9, no.55, pp.516-525, figs.2, July, 1942.

THE SKULL-CHARACTERS OF SOME OF THE FORMS OF SAMBAR (RUSA) OCCURRING TO THE EAST OF THE BAY OF BENGAL.--PART II. THE SAMBARS OF LUZON AND BASILAN ISLAND. R. I. Pocock. Ann. and Mag. Nat. Hist., Lond., ser.11, vol.10, no.63, pp.159-167, figs.2, Mar., 1943.

THE SKULL-CHARACTERS OF SOME OF THE FORMS OF SAMBAR (RUSA) OCCURRING TO THE EAST OF THE BAY OF BENGAL.--PART III. RUSA NIGRICANS AND RUSA BONINENSIS. R. I. Pocock. Ann. and Mag. Nat. Hist., London, ser.11, vol.10, no.63, pp.191-196, fig.1, Mar., 1943.

Cervus--Antlers

LARGE ANTLER OF A WELSH STAG. Rhys P. Allaway. Field, London, vol.153, p.798, May 16, 1929.

(IRREGULAR ANTLER FORMATION IN A WAPITI.) Unregelmaessige Geweihbildung bei einem Wapiti. Otto Antonius. Zool. Garten, Leipzig (N.F.), vol.8, nos.4-6, pp.116-122, figs.9, 1936.

A THREE HORNED WAPITI (CERVUS CANADENSIS CANADENSIS). Ralph D. Bird. Jour. Mam., vol.14, no.2, pp.164-166, May, 1933.

LARGE HEAD OF MALAY SAMBHAR (CERVUS UNICOLOR EQUINUS). A. L. Brownlow. Jour. Bombay Nat. Hist. Soc., vol.35, no.1, p.199, June 15, 1931.

ABNORMAL HORNS OF SAMBUR (CERVUS UNICOLOR). R. W. Burton. Jour. Bombay Nat. Hist. Soc., vol.34, no.4, pp.1058-1059, Mar.2, 1931.

GROWTH AND SHEDDING OF ANTLERS IN THE SWAMP DEER (RUCERVUS DUVAUCELLI) IN THE UNITED PROVINCES. F. W. Champion. Jour. Bombay Nat. Hist. Soc., vol.37, no.2, p.485, Aug.15, 1934.

DOUBLE GROWTH OF HORNS IN SAMBHAR. Hugh Copley. Jour. Bombay Nat. Hist. Soc., vol.27, p.938, July 31, 1921.

EXHIBITION, FOR LORD POWERSCOURT, OF AN ENORMOUS PAIR OF ANTLERS WITH FORTY-FOUR POINTS. Louis Fraser. Proc. Zool. Soc. Lond., pt.30, p.142, 1862.

EXHIBITION OF A PAIR OF HORNS OF CERVUS MARIANNUS. Louis Fraser. Proc. Zool. Soc. Lond., pp.367-368, fig. 1, 1866.

ABNORMAL ANTLERS OF A KASHMIR STAG (CERVUS HANGLU). G. M. Gamble. Jour. Bombay Nat. Hist. Soc., vol.33, no. 2, p.438, fig.1, Feb.15, 1929.

GROWTH AND SHEDDING OF ANTLERS IN THE SWAMP DEER (RUCERVUS DUVAUCELLI) IN MANIPUR STATE. C. Gimson. Jour. Bombay Nat. Hist. Soc., vol.37, no.3, p. 726, Dec.15, 1934.

ANCIENT RED DEER ANTLER ON A SOLWAY MARSH. Ritson Graham. North Western Naturalist, vol.9, no.2, p.151, pl. 1, June, 1934.

ANTLERS OF THE MALAYAN SAMBAR. U. L. Guehler. Jour. Thailand Research Soc. (formerly The Siam Soc.), Bangkok, Nat. Hist. Suppl., vol.12, no.1, p.137, illus., Dec., 1939.

A FINE SWAMP DEER HEAD. (CERVUS DUVAUCELI.) J. E. Hall. Jour. Bombay Nat. Hist. Soc., vol.41, no.2, pp.417-418, photo, Dec., 1939.

THE ANNUAL INCREMENT OF THE ANTLERS OF THE RED DEER (CERVUS ELAPHUS). Julian S. Huxley. Proc. Zool. Soc., Lond., no.67, pp.1021-1035, figs.1-3, Dec.30, 1926.

FREE TRANSPLANTATION OF ANTLER IN RED DEER (CERVUS ELAPHUS L.). Z. Jaczewski. Bull. Acad. Polonaise Sci., Cl.II, vol.4, no.2, pp.107-110, 1956.

A PAIR OF ELK ANTLERS FROM ST. JOSEPH COUNTY, INDIANA. Marcus Ward Lyon, Jr. Amer. Midland Nat., vol.12, no.7, pp.213-216, fig., Jan., 1931.

CAUSE OF ONE HORN ON STAG. Vladimir Martino. Lovtsa, nos.5-6, pp.2, fig., May-June, 1936. (In Bulgarian.)

(CAN THE DEER OF THE DANUBE, THE GERMAN COASTAL REGION, AND THE GERMAN INLAND BE DIFFERENTIATED BY THEIR ANTLERS?) Kann man am Geweih den Donauhirsch, den deutschen Kustenhirsch und den deutschen Inlandshirsch unterschieden? Paul Matschie. Deutsche Jaeger-Zeitung, Neudamm, vol.38, no.46, pp.735-739, figs.7; no.47, pp.752-757, figs.15; no.48, pp.771-777, figs.11, Mar.9, 13, 16, 1902.

EARLY DEVELOPMENT OF ANTLERS BY SAMBHUR IN THE BILLIGIRIRANGAN HILLS, SOUTH INDIA. R. C. Morris. Jour. Bombay Nat. Hist. Soc., vol.38, no. 3, p.619, Apr.15, 1936.

SEASON OF HORN DEVELOPMENT IN SAMBHUR. R. C. Morris. Jour. Bombay Nat. Hist. Soc., vol.38, no.4, p.819, Aug., 1936.

ON A CASE OF VARIATION IN THE HORNS OF A PANOLIAN DEER. James Murie. Proc. Zool. Soc., Lond., pp.611-614, fig. 1, 1870.

(WHAT BECOMES OF THE VELVET OF THE RED DEER (CERVUS ELAPHUS LINNE 1758?) Was wird aus dem Gewiehbast des Rothirsches, Cervus elaphus Linne, 1758? F. van Ommen. Saeugetierk, Mitteil, Stuttgart, 3 (1): 34-35, Jan. 1, 1955.

REMOVAL OF THE TESTICLE IN A SIKA DEER FOLLOWED BY DEFORMITY OF THE ANTLER ON THE OPPOSITE SIDE. Charles B. Penrose. Jour. Mam., vol.5, no.2, pp.116-117, pls.3, May, 1924.

GROWTH AND SHEDDING OF ANTLERS OF SAMBAR AND SWAMP DEER IN ASSAM. Ed. de Poncins. Jour. Bombay Nat. Hist. Soc., vol.38, no.1, p.185, Aug.15, 1935.

SWAMP-DEER (RUCERVUS DUVAUCELLI) HEAD WITH NINETEEN POINTS. R. Powell. Jour. Bombay Nat. Hist. Soc., vol.34, no.4, p.1060, Mar.2, 1931.

EXHIBITION, THROUGH MR. FRASER, OF AN ENORMOUS PAIR OF ANTLERS WITH FOURTY-FOUR POINTS. Viscount Powerscourt. Proc. Zool. Soc. Lond., pt. 30, p.142, 1862.

LARGE KASHMIR STAG HEAD (CERVUS CASHMIRIANUS). C. Gilbert Rogers. Jour. Bombay Nat. Hist. Soc., vol.26, pp. 1038-1039, Jan.31, 1920.

ANTLER-BEARING BY A FEMALE SIKA DEER. Jordan S. Roux, Ken Stott, Jr. Jour. Mam., vol.29, no.1, p.71, Feb.13, 1948.

THE GROWTH OF A WAPITI ANTLER. Elwin R. Sanborn. Bull. New York Zool. Soc., vol.32, pp.25-33, illus., Feb., 1929.

A RECORD STAG. Georg Schicht. Field, London, vol.166, no.4329, p.1421, Dec.14, 1935.

EXHIBITION OF, AND REMARKS ON, AN ANTLER OF A RUSA DEER. Philip L. Sclater. Proc. Zool. Soc. Lond., pp.179-180, 1876.

RED DEER ANTLER IN LINCOLNSHIRE FLAT. T. Sheppard. Naturalist, London, no.856, p.158, May, 1928.

MEASUREMENTS OF AN UNUSUAL ELK HEAD. M. P. Skinner. Jour. Mam., vol. 1, no.4, p.186, May, 1920.

(ANTLER USE IN THE RED DEER CERVUS ELAPHUS LINNE 1758.) Zur Gewiehgebrauch beim Rothirsch, Cervus elaphus Linne, 1758. G. Steinbacher. Saeugetierk, Mitteil., Stuttgart, 3 (1): 35, Jan.1, 1955.

SOME NOTES ON THE HORNS OF THE THAMIN (CERVUS ELDI). C. H. Stockley. Jour. Bombay Nat. Hist. Soc., vol.28, pp. 268-271, pl.1, Dec.30, 1921.

DATA FOR A STUDY ON THE HORNS OF THE TRUE DEER (CERVUS ELAPHUS L.). V. J. Tzalkin. Zool. Jour. USSR, Moscow, vol.24, no.4, pp.224-236, figs.14, tables 4, 1945. (English summary.)

A FINE SWAMP DEER HEAD. Van Ingen, Van Ingen. Jour. Bombay Nat. Hist. Soc., vol.42, no.3, p.657, illus., Aug., 1941.

EXHIBITION OF A PAIR OF ANTLERS OF A DEER OBTAINED BY MAJOR CATHCART IN THE CRIMEA. Edwin Ward. Proc. Zool. Soc. Lond., p.206, 1874.

SEASON OF SHEDDING AND GROWTH OF ANTLERS IN THE SWAMP DEER (RUCERVUS DUVAUCELLI) IN ASSAM. D. Moncrieff Wright. Jour. Bombay Nat. Hist. Soc., vol.34, no.1, p.236, Mar.1, 1930.

THE ELK GROWS HIS ANTLERS. Junior Nat. Hist. Mag., vol.3, no.3, pp.4-7, May, 1938.

A HEAD OF THE SHOU (CERVUS AFFINIS HODGS.). Jour. Bengal Nat. Hist. Soc., Darjeeling, vol.17, no.4, pp.140-141, illus., Apr., 1943.

A RECORD STAG FROM BOHEMIA. (MEASUREMENTS AND WEIGHT OF HORNS.) Field, London, vol.166, no.4324, p.1077, illus., Nov.9, 1935.

Cervus--Asia

AN INTERESTING DEER FROM SZECHWAN. Glover M. Allen. Jour. Mam., vol. 8, no.1, pp.62-63, Feb., 1927.

NOTES ON THE SWAMP DEER (RUCERVUS DUVAUCELLI) IN ASSAM. C. A. R. Bhadian. Jour. Bombay Nat. Hist. Soc., vol.37, no.2, p.485, Aug.15, 1934.

REMARKS UPON TWO SPECIES OF DEER OF THE GENUS CERVUS FROM THE PHILIPPINE ARCHIPELAGO. D. G. Elliott. Field Columbian Mus., publ.20, zool.ser., vol.1, no.7, p.159, June, 1897.

THE TURKESTAN STAG OR HANGUL. K. K. Flerov. Trudy Kirgizskoi Kompleksnoi ekspeditsii, 1932-1933, vol.10, pp. 315-343, figs.11, pl.1, 1935. (In Russian.)

NOTICE OF A STAG FROM NORTHERN CHINA, SENT BY MR. SWINHOE TO THE ZOOLOGICAL SOCIETY. John E. Gray. Proc. Zool. Soc. Lond., pt.29, pp.236-238, pl.27, 1861.

ON TWO NEW RACES OF CERVUS NIPPON FROM THE SOUTHERN ISLANDS OF KYUSHU, JAPAN. Nagamichi Kuroda, Yoshikazu Okada. Annot. Zool. Japonenses, Tokyo, vol.24, no.1, pp.59-64, Dec., 1950.

EXHIBITION OF THE HEADS OF THREE STAGS SHOT BY COL. SAREL AT PEKIN. B. Leadbeater. Proc. Zool. Soc. London, pt.29, pp.368-369, 1861.

ON A NEW SPECIES OF INDIAN DEER (CERVUS, L.). W. Ogilby. Proc. Comm. Sci., Corres., Zool. Soc., Lond., pt.1, p.136, 1830-1831.

THE LARGER DEER OF BRITISH INDIA. PART 2. R. I. Pocock. Jour. Bombay

Nat. Hist. Soc., vol.43, no.4, pp.553-572, figs.7, Apr., 1943; Part 3. THE SAMBAR (RUSA). Vol.44, no.1, pp.27-37, figs. 5, Aug., 1943.

ON A RARE STAG (CERVUS WALLICHII) FROM NEPAL RECENTLY PRESENTED TO THE ZOOLOGICAL SOCIETY BY HIS MAJESTY KING GEORGE. R. I. Pocock. Proc. Zool. Soc., Lond., pt.3, pp.558-575, figs.66-71, Aug.29, 1912.

THE STATUS OF THE HIMALAYAN STAGS. R. I. Pocock. Field, London, vol.146, p. 1066, Dec.17, 1925.

NOTICE OF A MANTCHURIAN DEER RECEIVED FROM MR. SWINHOE. Philip L. Sclater. Proc. Zool. Soc. Lond., pp.1-2, 1865.

NOTE ON THE DEER OF FORMOSA. Philip L. Sclater. Proc. Zool. Soc., Lond., pt.30, pp.150-151, pls.16-17, 1862.

HORNS OF A NEW DEER AND OTHER RELICS FROM THE WASTE OF YIN, HONAN, CHINA. (CERVUS (RUCERVUS) MENZIESIANUS. SEMI-FOSSILIZED HORNS OBTAINED FROM PIT.) Arthur deC. Sowerby. China Jour., vol.19, no.3, pp.141-144, figs. 2, Sept., 1933.

THE SIKA, OR SPOTTED DEER OF EASTERN ASIA. Arthur deC. Sowerby. China Jour., vol.11, pp.192-195, pls.3, Oct., 1929.

NOTES ON THE KASHMIR STAG (CERVUS HANGLU). C. H. Stockley. Jour. Bombay Nat. Hist. Soc., vol.31, pp.814-815, illus., Nov.1, 1926.

EXTRACTS FROM HIS LETTER RESPECTING THE FORMOSAN DEER. Robert Swinhoe. Proc. Zool. Soc., Lond., pt.29, p.235, 1861.

EXTRACTS OF LETTERS FROM. Robert Swinhoe. Proc. Zool. Soc., Lond., pp. 667-678, 1865.

LETTER FROM, ON A DEER SEEN IN CAPTIVITY IN SHANGHAI. Robert Swinhoe. Proc. Zool. Soc. Lond., pp.798-799, 1872.

THE MALAYAN OR BURMESE SAMBAR (RUSA UNICOLOR EQUINUS). W. S. Thom. Jour. Bombay Nat. Hist. Soc., vol.39, no. 2, pp.309-319, pl.1, Apr.15, 1937.

Cervus--Coloration

AN ALBINO SAMBAR. H. G. Champion. Jour. Bombay Nat. Hist. Soc., vol.40, no. 2, pp.322-323, Sept., 1938.

ON THE COLOUR-PATTERN OF THE YOUNG MALAY RUSA (CERVUS UNICOLOR EQUINUS). F. N. Chasen. Jour. Malayan Branch Roy. Asiatic Soc., vol. 3, pt.1, pp.89-91, pl.2, Apr., 1925.

ALBINO ELK. Oregon Game Comm. Bull., Portland, vol.1, no.8, p.4, Nov., 1946.

Cervus--Diseases, Parasites

INTERNAL PARASITES OF THE ELK OF WYOMING. Louis E. Alderson. MS thesis, Univ. Wyo., 1949.

OBSERVATIONS ON THE NATURAL HISTORY OF THE SCOTTISH RED DEER. V. ARTHROPOD PARASITES OF THE RED DEER (CERVUS ELAPHUS L.) IN SCOTLAND. A. E. Cameron. Proc. Roy. Phys. Soc. Edinburgh, vol.22, pt.2, pp.81-89, May, 1932.

OBSERVATIONS ON THE NATURAL HISTORY OF THE SCOTTISH RED DEER. VI. SOME NOTES ON THE PARASITIC WORMS OF THE SCOTTISH RED DEER. T.W.M. Cameron. Proc. Roy. Phys. Soc. Edinburgh, vol.22, pt.2, pp.91-97, May, 1932.

PARASITIC GASTRITIS OF ELK. D. F. Eveleth, F. M. Bolin. Jour. Wildlife Mgt., Ithaca, vol.19, no.1, p.152, Jan., 1955.

HEALING OF THE FRACTURED LEG BONE OF AN ELK. Paul F. Gilbert, Ralph R. Hill. Jour. Mam., 37 (1): 129, Feb.28, 1956.

OCCURRENCE OF ECHINOCOCCUS GRANULOSUS IN ELK (CERVUS CANADENSIS NELSONI), BANFF NATIONAL PARK. Hubert U. Green. Canadian Field Nat., Ottawa, vol.63, no.5, pp.204-205, Oct.25, 1949.

CRYPTORCHID ELK (CERVUS CANADENSIS) IN THE BLUE MOUNTAINS OF WASHINGTON. George E. Hudson. Jour. Mam., vol.31, no.4, p.464, Nov.21, 1950.

AN EPIZOOTIC DISEASE OF ELK. Olaus J. Murie. Jour. Mam., vol.11, no.2, pp. 214-222, pls.12-14, May, 1930.

(ON PSEUDOARTHRITIS IN THE RED DEER.) Ueber eine Pseudoarthrose des Rothirsches. N. Peters. Zool. Anzeiger, vol.89, pp.62-64, fig.1, May 20, 1930.

DISEASE KILLS FEEDGROUND ELK. NECROTIC STOMATITIS TAKES TOLL OF JACKSON HERD. Wyoming Wild Life, Cheyenne, vol.9, no.2, pp.1-8, 27, illus., Feb., 1944.

Cervus--Ecology, General Habits, Behavior

PATTERNS OF HERD BEHAVIOR IN FREE-RANGING ELK OF WYOMING, CERVUS CANADENSIS NELSONI. M. Altmann. New York Zool. Soc., Zoologica, vol.41, no.2, pp.65-71, Sep. 17, 1956.

SOCIAL BEHAVIOR OF ELK, CERVUS CANADENSIS NELSONI, IN THE JACKSON HOLE AREA OF WYOMING. M.Altmann. Behaviour, vol.4, no.2, pp.116-143, 1952.

SOCIAL GRACES IN ELK SOCIETY. M. Altmann. Anim. Kingdom., vol.56, no.3, pp.66-72, illus., May-June, 1953.

STAGS FIGHTING. H. Mortimer Batten. Field, London, vol.148, p.1051, Dec. 16, 1926.

STAGS FIGHTING TO A FINISH. H. Mortimer Batten. Field, London, vol.152, p.955, illus., Dec. 13, 1928.

CURIOUS BEHAVIOUR OF THAMIN DEER. F.H. Giles. Jour. Siam Soc., Nat. Hist. Suppl., vol.8, no.1, p.55, 1929.

WAPITI OF THE RIDING MOUNTAIN, MANITOBA. AN ECOLOGICAL STUDY AND COMMENTARY. H.U. Green. Canadian Field-Nat., vol.47, no.6, pp.105-111, Sep., 1933; no.7, pp.122-132, Oct., 1933; no.8, pp.150-157, Nov., 1933; no.9, pp.172-174, Dec., 1933.

TIGER KILLING SWAMP DEER OR GOND (RUCERVUS DUVAUCELLI). L.D.W. Hearsey. Jour. Bombay Nat. Hist. Soc., vol.35, no.4, pp.885-886, July 15, 1932.

ELK SWIM THE COLUMBIA. R.P.Holland. Outers' Recreation, vol.63, p.421, Dec., 1920.

WOUNDED SAMBHUR SEIZED BY A TIGER. Charles W.G. Morris. Jour. Bombay Nat. Hist. Soc., vol.33, no.3, pp.695-696, May 31, 1929.

PECULIAR CRIES EMITTED BY SAMBHUR STAGE FIGHTING. Randolph C. Morris. Jour. Bombay Nat. Hist. Soc., vol.32, pp. 216-217, Aug. 1, 1927.

ELK CALLS. Olaus J. Murie. Jour.Mamm., vol.13, no.4, pp.331-336, Nov., 1932.

MORE ABOUT ELK CALLS. W.M.Rush. Jour. Mamm., vol.14, no.1, p.78, Feb., 1933.

(ON THE QUESTION OF THE INTERRELATION BETWEEN ORGANISM AND ENVIRONMENT. OBSERVATION ON STAGS IN THE LENINGRAD ZOO.) Zur Frage der Wechselbeziehungen zwischen Organismus und Umwelt. Beobachtungen an Hirschen des Leningrad Zoo. A. Stieren. Zool. Garten, Leipzig, n.F., vol.2, nos.7-9, pp.197-199, Jan., 1930.

STAGS "FIGHTING" IN VELVET. H. A. Taylor. Field, London, vol.160, no.4156, p.279, photo, Aug. 20, 1932.

ELK AT PLAY. John Thompson. Yellowstone Nat. Notes, Yellowstone Park, vol. 18, nos.9-10, pp.51-52, Sep.-Oct., 1941.

A STUDY OF THE RANGE HABITS OF ELK ON THE SELWAY GAME PRESERVE. Vernon A. Young, W. Leslie Robinette. Univ. of Idaho Bull., Moscow, vol.34, no.16, pp.47, Dec., 1939.

Cervus--Economic Importance

(ATTEMPT TO USE TWO ELKS AS DRAFT ANIMALS.) Ueber einen Versuch, zwei Elche als Zugtiere zu benuetzen. Peter Krott. Zeitschr. Tierpsychol., vol.11, no. 2, pp.304-318, 1954. (With English summary.)

STOP THE SELLING OF ELK TEETH. A.W. Lewis. Outdoor Life, p.388.

SIKA DEER AND DEER FARMING IN MANCHURIA. A. deC.Sowerby. China Jour., vol. 9, pp.151-152, pls.2, Sep., 1928.

Cervus--Europe

(RED DEER OF THE CAUCASUS. (Cervus elaphus subsp.) Edgar N. Barclay. Proc. Zool. Soc. London for 1934, pt.4, pp.789-798, figs.5, pls.3, Jan., 1935.

(SOME HISTORICAL PARTICULARITIES OF THE RED DEER IN THE NETHERLANDS, AND A CONSIDERATION OF THE DEER OF THE VELUWE DEER AS AN OBJECT OF NATURAL CONSERVATION.) Einige historische bijzonderheden over het edelhert in Nederland en een beschouwing over de veluwse herten als natuurbeschermingsobject. G.A. Brouwer. (In) "In het voetspoor van Thijsse," H.Veenman and Sons, Wageningen, pp.214-248, figs.12, 1949.

(ON THE DEER OF SPAIN.) Sobre los ciervos de España. Angel Cabrera. Bol. Real Soc. Espanola Hist. Nat., Madrid, vol.11, no.10, pp.557-560, Dec., 1911.

WILD RED DEER OF SCOTLAND. Allan Gorden Cameron. Edinburgh and London, William Blackwood and Sons, pp.xvii+248, illus., 1923.

(CONTRIBUTION TO KNOWLEDGE OF NORWAY'S VERTEBRATES IN ANCIENT TIMES. I. THE STAG.) Bidrag til kundskaben om Norges hvirveldyrfauna i ealdre tider. I. Hjorten. James A, Grieg. Bergens Mus. Aarbog, no.7, pp.34, figs.7, 1908.

(A CAPITAL NORWEGIAN STAG.) En kapital norsk hjort. Olaf Ingebrigtsen. Bergens Mus. Arbok, 1935, no.5, pp.7, figs.2, 1936.

(DISTRIBUTION OF THE STAG IN NORWAY.) Hjortens utbredelse i Norge.Olaf Ingebrigtsen. Bergens Mus. Aarbok, 1922-23, Naturvid. Raekke, no.6, pp.1-58, maps 2, July 26, 1924.

(NORWEGIAN RED DEER (CERVUS ELAPHUS L.).) Das norwegische Rotwild (Cervus elaphus L.). Olaf Ingebrigtsen. Bergens Mus. Aarbok, 1922-23, Naturvid. Raekke, no.7, pp.1-242, pls.1-5, figs.1-11, tbls.1-2, 1924.

ON THE GEOGRAPHIC RACES OF RED DEER IN SCANDINAVIA. Einar Lönnberg. Arkiv. Zool., Upsala, vol.3, no.9, pp.1-19, figs.1-5, Jan. 22, 1906.

(OUR RED DEER.) Gedanken um unser Rotwild. H.C. Mueller. Wald und Wild, Hamburg, Jahrg.1, nos.3-4, pp. 3-4, figs. 3, Oct. 15, 1948.

(CRANIUM OF CERVUS EURYCEROS ALDR. WITH IRREGULAR ANTLERS FOUND AT BARYCZ ON SAN.) Edward Lubicz Niezabitowski. Poznańskie Towarzystwo Przyjaciół Nauk Prace Komisji Matematyczno-Przyrodniczej, serja B, vol. 7, no.3, pp.1-5, illus., 1935. (In Polish with French summary.)

OBSERVATIONS ON THE NATURAL HISTORY OF THE SCOTTISH RED DEER. IV. SOME NOTES ON THE NATURAL HISTORY OF THE SCOTTISH RED DEER. I.W. Parnell. Proc. Roy. Phys. Soc. Edinburgh, vol.22, pt.2, pp.75-80, May, 1932.

(CERVUS EURYCERUS ALDR. FOUND IN THE RYAZAN GOVERNMENT.) Cervus eurycerus Aldr. trouvé dans le gouvernement de Riazan. Marie Pavlow. Bull. Soc. Nat. Moscow, 36 (Sect.Géol.), vol.6, no.2, pp. 213-224, pl.I, fig.1, 1928.

PREHISTORIC RED DEER'S ANTLERS IN ROXBURGHSHIRE. James Ritchie. The Scottish Naturalist, no.175, p.8, Jan.-Feb., 1929.

RED-DEER IN SELKIRKSHIRE IN PREHISTORIC TIMES. James Ritchie. Scottish Naturalist, no.165, pp.65-68, May-June, 1927.

RED DEER REMAINS FROM ORKNEY. James Ritchie. Scottish Naturalist, no.184, p.126, July-Aug., 1930.

(STAG AND THE SCOTLAND-NORWAY LANDBRIDGE.) Hjorten og den skotsknorske landbro. Leonhard Stejneger. Bergens Mus. Aarbog, no.14, pp.1-10, 1908.

(ON THE ABORIGINAL STAG OF WESTERN BELORUSSIA.) Ob Aborigennom olene Zapodnoi Belorussii.B.T.Tsalkin.Doklady Akad. Nauk SSSR Novaia Seriia, Moscow, vol.77, no.3, pp.521-523, 1951.

IRISH RED DEER. R.J. Ussher. American Naturalist, vol.21, no.2, pp.188-189, 1887.

Cervus--Food Habits

PRELIMINARY STUDY OF THE FOOD HABITS OF ELK IN VIRGINIA. W.P. Baldwin, C.P. Patton. Trans. 3rd N. Amer. Wildl. Conf., pp.747-755, 1938.

ARE RED DEER CARNIVOROUS? A STAG THAT WENT RABBITING. H. Mortimer Batten. Field, London, vol.155, no.4044, p.954, June 28, 1930.

ELK--FOOD--AND WINTER. Victor H. Cahalane. Outdoor America, Madison, vol. 8, no.3, pp.4-5, 16, illus., Feb., 1943.

EFFECTS OF WINTER ELK BROWSING, SOUTH FORK OF THE FLATHEAD RIVER, MONTANA. William S. Gaffney. Jour. Wildl. Mgt., Menasha, vol.5, no.4, pp. 427-453, illus., Oct., 1941.

RESULTS OF THE COPPER RIDGE BASIN ELK STUDY. (Food preferences.) R.J. Greffenius. Rocky Mt. Region Bull., vol. 21, no.4, pp.14-15, Apr., 1938.

FOOD CONSUMPTION AND WEIGHT RESPONSE OF ELK UNDER WINTER CONDITIONS. Melvin S. Morris, Roger Hungerford. Proc. 32nd Ann. Conf. Western Assn. State Game and Fish Comm., Glacier Nat. Park, Mont., June 15-17, 1952, pp.185-187, 1953.

BROWSING OF THE OLYMPIC PENINSULA ELK IN EARLY WINTER. Milton P. Skinner. Jour. Mamm., vol.17, no.3, pp.253-256, Aug., 1936.

GREYS RIVER ALK WINTER PASTURE. Wyoming Wild Life, Cheyenne, vol.13, no.1, pp.8-11, 37, illus., Jan., 1949.

Cervus--Hunting

ELK IN THE WELKIN. Chester Chatfield. Field and Stream, New York, vol.47, no.8, pp.36-38, 69, illus., Dec., 1942.

ELK HUNT INFORMATION. John M. Hall. Arizona Game and Fish Comm., Arizona Game Surv., Proj. Job Compl. Rep., 1951, Proj. 53 R 1-WP 2-J 2, pp.1-4, illus., Dec., 1951.

HUNTING THE WAPITI. E. Roland Harriman. (In) North American Big Game. A Book of the Boone and Crocket Club, Compiled by the Committee on Records of North American Big Game. Charles Scribners Sons, New York, pp.229-237.

ROPING ELK IN ONTARIO. A.D. Kean. Rod and Gun in Canada, Montreal, vol. 50, no.6, pp.16, 39-40, illus., Nov., 1948.

ALGONQUIN PARK ELK. Cashman Kearney. Rod and Gun in Canada, Montreal, vol.48, no.11, pp.15-19, Mar., 1947.

ELK SEASON--1919 VS. 1920. I.H. Larom. Outers' Recreation, vol.64, no.2, p.84, Feb., 1921.

CALIFORNIA ELK DRIVE. C. Hart Merriam. Sci. Monthly, pp.466-475, Nov., 1921.

ELK TRAPPING IN UTAH. Eugene D. Miner. Utah Fish and Game Bull., vol.9, no.5, pp.7-8, illus., May-June, 1952.

ELK SHOOTING IN GRAND TETON AGAIN. Olaus J. Murie. Natl.Parks Mag., vol.26, no.110, p.118, July-Sep., 1952.

THE FIRING LINE. (Mass Hunting of Elk.) Olaus J. Murie. Amer. Forests, vol.53, no.9, pp.392-394, 422, Sep., 1947.

SAVING MEAT. (Elk.) Clyde Ormond. Field and Stream, New York, vol.48, no.6, pp. 30-31, illus., Oct., 1943.

ELK TRAPPING IN YELLOWSTONE PARK. Edmund B. Rogers. Wyoming Wild Life, Cheyenne, vol.14, no.6, pp.20-22, illus., July, 1950.

AFTER BARASINGH IN KASHMIR--STALKING NEAR THE WARDWAN VALLEY. Salar. Field, London, vol.168, no.4376, pp.1138-1139, illus., Nov. 7, 1936; no.4377, pp.1192-1193, illus., Nov. 14, 1936.

CHARMS OF THE FOREST. POINTS OF VIEW ON STALKING AND DRIVING THE RED DEER. J. Whyte-Melville Skeffington. Field, London, vol.162, no.4213, pp.766-767, figs., Sep. 23, 1933.

WAPITI HUNTING IN MANCHURIA. Arthur De C. Sowerby. China Jour., vol.11, no.4, p.207, Oct., 1929.

PAGES FROM AN ELK HUNTER'S DIARY. Kyle M. Walker. American Field, Chicago, vol.148, no.49, pp.786-787, illus., Dec. 6, 1947.

VIRGINIA ELK HUNTING GROWS IN POPURLARITY. Roy K. Wood. Virginia Wildl., Blacksburg, vol.3, no.3, p.3, Nov., 1939.

ELK PERMIT DRAWING NECESSARY AFTER 466 HUNTERS MAKE APPLICATION FOR LICENSES. S.Dakota Conservation Digest, Pierre, vol.9, no.10, pp.2, 14, Oct., 1942.

GAME COMMISSION TO PERMIT TAKING 150 ELK BY HUNTERS. S.Dakota Conservation Digest, Pierre, vol.9, no.9, p.11, Sep., 1942.

Cervus--Management

EXPERIMENTAL FEEDING OF CALF ELK. Chester C. Anderson. Wyoming Wild Life, Cheyenne, vol.15, no.1, pp.24-27, 38, illus., Jan., 1951.

FEDERAL ELK COMMISSION REPORT. (Northern Yellowstone herd, its artificial feeding since 1895, present numbers, and necessity for and methods of reduction.) George F. Baggley. Trans. Amer. Game Conf., vol.21, pp.184-187, 1935.

FEEDING ELK IN WYOMING. Lester Bagley. Wyoming Wild Life, Cheyenne, vol.4, nos. 2-3, pp.1-2, Feb.-Mar., 1939.

HISTORY OF THE BIG HORN MOUNTAIN ELK HERD. Lester Bagley. Wyoming Wild Life Mag., vol.3, no.11, pp.1-3, Nov., 1938.

THE 1951 SURVEY OF SUMMER ELK RANGE IN THE TETON WILDERNESS AREA. A. A. Beetle. Wyo. Range Mgt., no.51, p.5, Sep., 1952.

(SHALL THE STATE SAVE THE RED DEER?) Skall staten radda kronhjorten? Bengt Berg. Svensk Jakt, Stockholm, vol. 86, no.7, pp.162-166, illus., July 15, 1948.

JACKSON HOLE ELK HERD: ITS HISTORY, RANGE, AND MANAGEMENT. Robert C. Brown. Wyo. Wild Life, vol.11, no.12, pp. 4-11, 29-32, Dec., 1947.

KERN COUNTY ELK REFUGE. Lewis A. Burtch. California Fish and Game, vol.20, no.2, pp.140-147, Apr., 1934.

CONSERVATION SPIRAL. Victor H. Cahalane. Audubon Mag., vol.45, no.1, pp.14-18, Jan.-Feb., 1943.

ELK--FOOD--AND WINTER. Victor H. Cahalane. Outdoor Am., vol.8, no.3, pp. 4-5, 16, Feb., 1943.

ELK MANAGEMENT AND HERD REGULATION. (Yellowstone.) Victor H. Cahalane. Outdoor Am., vol.8, no.5, pp.29-31, Apr.-May-June, 1943; Trans. 8th N.Amer. Wildl. Conf., Wash., D.C., pp.95-101, 1943.

MANAGMENT OF THE YELLOWSTONE ELK. F.W. Childs. Amer. Wildl., vol.24, no.5, pp.69, 77-78, Sep.-Oct., 1935.

ELK MANAGEMENT PROBLEMS. Robert F. Cooney. Jour. Range Mgt., vol.3, no.4, pp.279-280, July, 1951.

ELK PROBLEMS IN MONTANA. Robert F. Cooney. Jour. Range Mgt., vol.5, no.1, pp.3-7, Jan., 1952.

EXPERIENCES IN THE ACQUISITION OF A BIG GAME RANGE AS A MANAGEMENT TOOL. Robert F. Cooney. Proc. Ann.Conf. W. Assn. State Game and Fish Comm., vol.30, pp.141-144, 1950?

ADDITIONAL ELK PLANTING INFORMATION. Leo K. Couch. Murrelet, vol.16, no. 2, p.42, May, 1935.

CHRONOLOGICAL DATA ON ELK INTRODUCTION INTO OREGON AND WASHINGTON. Leo K. Couch. Murrelet, vol.16, no.1, pp.3-10, illus., Jan., 1935.

RESTORATION AND MANAGEMENT OF ELK IN UTAH. Harold S. Crane. Proc. 31st Ann. Conf. Westerm Assn. State Game and Fish Comm., Apr. 30-May 2, 1951, pp.165-167.

VIRGINIA'S ELK HERDS. R.H. Cross. Va. Wildl., vol.11, no.6, pp.10-11, 22, June, 1950.

MORE TULE ELK PLANTED IN OWENS VALLEY. G.W. Dow. California Fish and Game, vol.20, no.3, pp.288-290, fig.112, July, 1934.

PROTECT THE ROOSEVELT ELK. C. N. Edge. Emergency Conserv. Comm., New York, Publ.no.69, pp.8, illus., Mar., 1938.

AN ATTEMPT TO SAVE CALIFORNIA ELK. B.W. Evermann. Calif. Fish and Game, San Francisco, vol.1, no.3, pp.11, figs.19-26, Apr. 10, 1915.

RETURN OF THE WAPITI. William L. Finley, Irene Finley. Nature Mag., vol.5, pp.69-73, figs.7, pls.2, Feb., 1925.

ELK PLANTED ON DEERLODGE FOREST. George M. Fisher. N.Region News, pp.39-40, Mar., 1937.

PENNSYLVANIA ELK COME BACK. Robert Ford. Penna.Game News, Harrisburg, vol. 18, no.7, p.11, illus., Oct., 1947.

OUR NATIONAL ELK HERDS. A PROGRAM FOR CONSERVING THE ELK ON NATIONAL FORESTS ABOUT THE YELLOWSTONE NATIONAL PARK. Henry S. Graves, E.W. Nelson. U.S. Dept. Agriculture, Dept.Circular 51, pp.34, figs.19, June, 1919.

ANNUAL SPRING AND FALL ELK SURVEYS. John M. Hall. Ariz. Game and Fish Comm., Ariz. Game Surv., Proj. Job Compl. Rep., 1951, Proj. 53 R 1-WP 3-J 2, pp. 1-7, June, 1951.

MANAGMENT STUDY OF THE CACHE ELK HERD. Norman V. Hancock. MS thesis, Utah State Agr. Coll., 1955.

WINTER ELK FEEDING. Charles W.Hanscum. Wyo. Wild Life, vol.16, no.10, p.2, Oct., 1952.

TOO MANY ELK. A.B. Hatch. N. Region News, pp.34-35, Oct., 1937.

ELK INTRODUCTION TO ARIZONA. K.C. Kartchner. Ariz. Wildl.-Sportsman, vol.2, no.5, pp.2, 11, Aug., 1940.

TRANSFERS OF ELK FOR RE-STOCKING. Hoyes Lloyd. Canadian Field-Nat., vol.41, no.6, pp.126-127, illus., Sep., 1927.

HOW ARIZONA WAS RESTOCKED WITH ELK. R.N. Looney. Ariz. Wildl. and Sportsman, Phoenix, vol.1, no.3, pp.2, 7, Mar., 1939.

PERSONAL OBSERVATION IN THE CARE AND MANAGEMENT OF AN ELK (WAPITI) HERD AT ELK ISLAND NATIONAL PARK, ALBERTA, CANADA. B.I. Love. Can.Jour. Comp. Med. and Vet. Sci., vol.19, no.6, pp.184-192, diagrams, June, 1955.

MANAGEMENT OF THE YAKIMA ROCKY MOUNTAIN ELK HERD. Gleen E. Mitchell, J. Burton Lauckhart. Trans. 13th N.Amer. Wildl. Conf., Wash., pp. 401-409, 1948.

PENNSYLVANIA'S ATTEMPTS TO STOCK ELK PROVE A FLOP. Johnny Mock. Outdoor Life, New York, vol.101, no.6, pp.124-125, June, 1948.

JACKSON HOLE MONUMENT AND THE ELK. O.J. Murie. Natl. Parks Mag., vol. 83, pp.13-17, Dec., 1945.

NATURAL ELK MANAGEMENT. O.J. Murie. Nature Mag., vol.30, no.5, pp. 293-295, illus., Nov., 1937.

STUDIES IN ELK MANAGEMENT. O.J. Murie. Trans. 20th Amer. Game Conf., Amer. Game Assoc., New York, pp.355-359, 1934.

TETON'S ELK PROBLEM CONTINUES. O.J. Murie. Natl. Parks Mag., vol.27, no.113, pp.56-57, Apr. -June, 1953.

HISTORY AND FUNCTION OF THE WYOMING ELK REFUGE. Almer Nelson. Wyo. Wild Life, Cheyenne, vol.5, no.3, pp.4-5, 18, illus., Mar., 1940.

THE 'FIRING LINE' IN THE MANAGEMENT OF THE NORTHERN ELK HERD. A. L. Olsen. Univ. Idaho Bull., vol.33, no.22, pp.36-42, Dec., 1938.

ELK MANAGMENT. Orange Olsen. Utah Juniper, vol.7, pp.10-15, 1936.

MANAGING NEBO'S WAPITI. Orange Olsen. Trans. 7th N. Amer. Wildl. Conf., Wash., D.C., pp.375-381, 1942.

DO WE WANT TO SAVE OLYMPIC NATIONAL PRIMEVAL PARK? Samuel H. Ordway, Jr. Animal Kingdom, vol.51, no. 1, pp.2-7, Jan.-Feb., 1948.

ELK PROBLEM IN THE SELWAY. Jack Parsell. Univ. Idaho Bull., vol.33, no.22, pp.23-25, Dec., 1938.

TRAGIC TRUTH ABOUT THE ELK. Dick Randall. Emergency Conservation Comm., pp.9, illus., map, Apr., 1934.

SITGREAVES PROBLEM. Charles M. Rapson. Ariz. Wildl.-Sportsman, vol.22, no.5, pp.38-43, 66, May, 1951.

AMERICAN ELK OR WAPITI--TODAY. D.I. Rasmussen. Trans. N.Amer. Wildl. Conf., vol.14, pp.513-526, 1949.

WHAT IS TO BECOME OF OUR NORTHERN ELK HERD? William Rush. Amer. Forests and Forest Life, vol.35, pp.93-95, 125-126, illus., Feb., 1929.

TWO-WAY WASTE. HOW SOLVE THE YELLOWSTONE ELK PROBLEMS OF STARVATION AND RUIN OF THE RANGE? W.M. Rush. Amer. Forests, Wash., D.C., vol.49, no.6, pp.286-289, 318, 320, illus., June, 1943.

PROBLEM OF ANTLER ROOM. Paul M. Scheffer, R.M. Bond. Soil Cons., vol.11, no.7, pp.161-166, Jan., 1946.

RANGE CONDITIONS AND MANAGEMENT OF THE ROOSEVELT ELK ON THE OLYMPIC PENINSULA. John E. Schwartz. U.S. Dept. Agric., Forest Serv., pp.65, figs.18, 1943. (Mimiographed.)

SOUTHERN ELK HERD. John W. Scott. Outdoor Amer., Madison, vol.8, no.5, p. 31, Apr.-June, 1943.

THE CONSERVATION OF THE ELK JACKSON HOLE, WYOMING. Charles Sheldon. Nat. Conf. Outdoor Recreation, Wash., D.C., pp.36, illus., map, July, 1927.

PRESENT PLIGHT OF THE JACKSON HOLE ELK. H.P. Sheldon et al. U.S. Dept. Agric., Biol. Surv., Wildl. Research and Mgt. Leaflet, no.BS 12, July, 1935.

JACKSON HOLE NOT FOR ELK. W.B. Sheppard. The New York Times. Sunday, May 20, 1934, p. E 5.

THE PECOS ELK RANGE. D.A. Shoemaker. New Mexico Conservationist, vol.1, no.3, pp.11-12, Mar., 1928.

PROBLEMS OF SURPLUS ELK IN YELLOWSTONE PARK. Curtis K. Skinner. Wyo. Wild Life, Cheyenne, vol.14, no.6, pp.22-26, July, 1950.

SAVING THE YELLOWSTONE ELK HERDS. Walter P. Taylor. Conservationist, vol.3, no.1, pp.3-6, figs.2, Jan., 1920.

KENTUCKY'S RED DEER PROBLEM. Carlos Vinson. Nature Mag., vol.40, no.3, pp. 153-154, 1947.

KEEPING DOWN THE DEER: A SEASON'S WORK IN THE FORESTS. Frank Wallace. Field, vol.175, no.4562, pp.846-847, June 1, 1940.

FEEDING THE WAPITI AT JACKSON HOLE. Mary Hayden White. Our Dumb Animals, Norwood, vol.75, no.2, p.27, Feb., 1942; Wyo. Wild Life, Cheyenne, vol.7, no.4, p. 19, Apr., 1942.

GRAZING PERMITS AND ELK. D.W. Wingfield. Ariz. Farmer, vol.30, pp.23, 27, Nov. 10, 1951.

DAKOTA ELK TARGET OF GAME MANAGERS. S.Dakota Conservation Digest, Pierre, vol.9, no.10, p.4, illus., Oct., 1942.

JACKSON HOLE ELK HERD RESOLUTION. Jour. Mamm., vol.16, no.3, p.239, Aug., 1935.

NORTHERN YELLOWSTONE ELK HERD. Montana Wildl. Bull., Helena, vol.1, no. 2, p.11, Mar., 1944.

SUBLETTE COUNTY ELK PROBLEM. Wyo. Wild Life, Cheyenne, vol.11, nos.1-2, pp. 8-10, Jan.-Feb., 1947.

TULE ELK TRANSFERRED FROM YOSEMITE. (Moved to Owens Valley Calif.) Park and Recreation, vol.17, no.4, pp.148-149, Dec., 1933.

RESTORING THE WAPITI. Wyo. Wild Life, vol.10, no.3, pp.4-16, Mar., 1946.

WYOMING FEEDS ITS GAME. (Elk.) Wyo. Wild Life, Cheyenne, vol.13, no.1, pp.4-7, 37-38, illus., Jan., 1949.

Cervus--Methods, Techniques

ELK TAGGING IN WYOMING. Warren J. Allred. Wyo. Wild Life, vol.14, no.1, pp. 4-9, 35-38, Feb., 1950.

ELK TAGGING IN WYOMING. Chester C. Anderson. Wyo. Wild Life, vol.17, no.5, pp.4-10, illus., May, 1953.

TECHNIQUES AND RESULTS OF ELK TRAPPING AND TAGGING IN YAKIMA COUNTY, WASHINGTON. Ellsworth R. Brown. Wash. State Game Bull., vol.6, no.3, pp.5, 8-9, 12, illus., July, 1954.

CENSUSING ELK BY AIRPLANE IN THE BLUE MOUNTAINS OF WASHINGTON. Helmut K. Buechner et al. Jour. Wildl. Mgt., Menasha, vol.15, no.1, pp.81-87, 1951.

EAR-TAGGING ELK. Albert J. Cramer. Field Notes on Wildl., vol.1, no.2, p.5, Feb., 1939.

(AGING PHENOMENA ON THE TEETH OF THE RED STAG AS A BASIS FOR DETERMINING EXACT AGE.) Alterserscheinungen am Gebiss des Rothirsches als Gundlage zur exakten Bestimmung des Lebensalters. H. Eidmann. M.and H.Schaper, Hannover, pp.58, figs.34, 1933.

AN ELK TREND SURVEY TECHNIQUE. John Hall. Proc. Ann. Conf. W. Assn. State Game and Fish Comm., vol.30, pp. 145-149, 1950?

ELK CENSUS TECHNIQUES. Charles W. Hanscum. Wyo. Wild Life, vol.13, no.7, pp.28-30, Aug., 1949.

ELK BELOW! TAKING A WINTER CENSUS OF THE JACKSON HOLE HERD FROM THE AIR IS A TOUGH BUT EXCITING JOB. Orang A. Olsen. Amer. Forests, Wash., D.C., vol. 50, no.2, pp.65-67, 94, illus., Feb., 1944.

MANDIBULAR DENTITION AS AN AGE INDICATOR IN ROCKY MOUNTAIN ELK. Don C. Quimby, J.E. Gaab. Jour. Wildl. Mgt., vol.21, no.4, pp.435-451, Oct., 1957.

PRELIMINARY REPORT ON A STUDY OF ELK DENTITION AS A MEANS OF DETERMINING AGE CLASSES. Don C. Quimby, J.E. Gaab. Proc. 32nd Ann. Conf. Western Assn. State Game and Fish Comm., Glacier Nat. Park, Mont., June 15-17, 1952, pp.225-227, 1953.

TECHNIQUE FOR AGE DETERMINATION OF ELK (CERVUS CANADENSIS). Carl V. Swanson. Murrelet, vol.32, no.2, pp.19-22, May-Aug., 1951.

REVEALING ELK SECRETS. Ken Thompson. Amer. Forests, Wash., vol.54, no.5, pp. 214-215, 240, illus., May, 1948.

Cervus--Migration

RE-ESTABLISHMENT OF SEASONAL ELK MIGRATION TROUGH TRANSPLANTING. Warren J. Allred. Trans. N.Amer. Wildl. Conf., vol.15, pp.597-610, 1950; Wyo. Wild Life, Cheyenne, vol.14, no.2, pp.18-19, 32-38, illus., Mar., 1950.

MIGRATION STUDIES OF JACKSON HOLE'S ELK HERD. Chester C. Anderson. Wyo. Wild Life, vol.18, no.4, pp.26-34, illus., Apr., 1954.

MIGRATION STUDY OF THE JACKSON HOLE ELK HERD. Floyd M. Blunt. Wyo. Wild Life, Cheyenne, vol.14, no.2, pp.25-32, illus., Mar., 1950.

ELK MIGRATION PATTERNS, AND SOME OF THE FACTORS AFFECTING MOVEMENTS IN THE GALLATIN RIVER DRAINAGE, MONTANA. Arthur R. Brazda. Jour. Wildl. Mgt., Ithaca, vol.17, no.1, pp.9-23, illus., Jan., 1953.

TRANSPLANTED ELK WANDERS. Hartley H.T. Jackson. Jour. Mamm., vol.22, no.4, p.448, Nov. 14, 1941.

ELK MIGRATION...A COMPLICATING FACTOR IN JACKSON HOLE. Pete Muchmore. Wyo. Wild Life, vol.17, no.1, pp. 14-16, 27, illus., Jan., 1953.

MIGRATION ROUTES OF ALK YELLOWSTONE NATIONAL PARK. M.P. Skinner. Jour. Mamm., vol.6, no.3, pp.184-192, Aug., 1925.

Cervus--Mortality

HEART FAILURE AMONG STAGS. H. M. Batten. Field, London, vol.152, p.92, July 19, 1928.

BULL ELK TRAPPED IN PECULIAR GRANITE STRUCTURE. F.R. Oberhansley. Nature Notes, Yellowstone Nat. Park, vol. 15, nos.5-6, pp.25-26, May-June, 1938.

Cervus--New Zealand

RED DEER PROBLEMS IN NEW ZEALAND. Lord Latymer. Field, London, vol.168, no. 4368, pp.622-623, illus., Sep. 12, 1936.

PRELIMINARY REPORTS OF THE NEW ZEALAND-AMERICAN FIORDLAND EXPEDITION: INVESTIGATIONS IN FIORLAND, NEW ZEALAND, IN 1949. (Wapiti and red deer.) A.L. Poole, compiler. New Zealand Dept. Sci. and Indus. Res., Bull.no.103, pp.1-99, illus., 1951.

EVALUATING CONDITION OF FREE-RANGING RED DEER (CERVUS ELAPHUS), WITH SPECIAL REFFERENCE TO NEW ZEALAND. I:DESCRIPTION OF TECHNIQUES FOR DETERMINATION OF CONDITION OF RED DEER. II:APPLICATION OF CONDITION INDICES TO DEER ECOLOGY AND MANAGEMENT RESEARCH. Thane A. Riney. New Zealand Jour. Sci. and Tech., Sect.B 36, pp.429-463, illus., Mar., 1955.

Cervus--North America

TULE ELK. A.R. Ainsworth. Calif. Fish and Game, vol.18, no.1, pp.81-83, fig.1, Jan., 1932.

WYOMING ELK POPULATION. Lester Bagley. Wyo. Wild Life, Cheyenne, vol.6, no.8, pp.1-2, Aug., 1941.

OUR NOBLEST DEER. (Wapiti.) Vernon Bailey. Nature Mag., vol.30, no.3, pp. 137-139, 188, illus., Sep., 1937.

TYPICAL SPECIMEN OF THE EASTERN ELK FROM PENNSYLVANIA. Vernon Bailey. Jour. Mamm., vol.18, no.1, p.104, Feb. 14, 1937.

YELLOWSTONE ELK HERD. Henry T. Bannon. Outdoor Life, vol.61, no.6, pp. 31, 104-105, June, 1928.

ELK IN DEL NORTE COUNTY. Earl P. Barnes. Calif. Fish and Game, vol.11, no. 2, p.90, Apr., 1925.

JACKSON HOLE ELK HERD: ITS HISTORY, RANGE, AND MANAGEMENT. Robert C. Brown. Wyo. Wild Life, Cheyenne, vol.11, no.12, pp.4-11, 29-32, illus., Dec., 1947.

WILD AND DOMESTICATED ELK IN THE EARLY DAYS OF FRANKLIN COUNTY,

INDIANA. Amos W. Butler. Jour. Mamm., vol.15, no.3, pp.246-248, Aug., 1934.

BIOLOGICAL AND ECONOMIC APPRAISAL OF THE JACKSON HOLE ELK HERD. John J. Craighead. New York Zool. Soc. and Cons. Found., pp.32, illus., Nov., 1952.

UTAH'S ELK HERD PROVIDES INTERESTING HISTORY. Harold S. Crane. Utah Fish and Game Bull., vol.8, no.12, pp.1, 3, 5, Nov., 1951.

OLYMPIC FOREST, LOGGED AND UNLOGGED. (Numbers of Roosevelt elk.) Lois Crisler. Living Wilderness, Wash., vol.12, no.23, pp.7-12, illus., Dec., 1947.

RANGE OF THE ROOSEVELT ELK. F.P. Cronemiller. Living Wilderness, vol.3, no. 3, p.12, Dec., 1937.

THE WAPITI IN ONTARIO. J.R. Dymond. Canadian Field Nat., vol.40, p.140, Oct. 8, 1926.

SUMMARY OF THE HISTORY OF THE YELLOWSTONE ELK HERD. Leon Evans. Yellowstone Nat. Notes, Yellowstone Park, vol.16, nos.1-2, pp.3-13, Jan.-Feb., 1939.

PIGEON RIVER ELK. Otto Failing. Michigan Conserv., Lansing, vol.20, no.5, pp.5-6, 23, illus., Sep., 1951.

ELK IN PENNSYLVANIA. ITS EXTERMINATION AND REINTRODUCTION. Richard Gerstell. Penna. Game News, Harrisburg, vol.7, no.7, pp.6-7, 26, illus., Oct., 1936.

EASTERN ELK ANTLERS FROM PENNSYLVANIA. G.G. Goodwin. Jour. Mamm., vol.21, no.1, p.95, Feb. 14, 1940.

COMPLETE SKELETON OF PENNSYLVANIA ELK FOUND. Hal H. Harrison. Penna. Game News, Harrisburg, vol.19, no.3, p.8, illus., 1948.

WAPITI IN DELAWARE. R.T. Hatt. Jour. Mamm., Baltimore, vol.30, no.2, p.201, May 23, 1949.

HUNTING IN THE HOME. (Elk skeleton found in Belford County Pennsylvania.) Caroline A. Heppenstall. Penna. Game News, Harrisburg, vol.22, no.3, pp.35-37, June, 1951.

ROOSEVELT ELK OF THE OLYMPIC PENINSULA. H.D. Hinkley. Calif. Fish and Game, vol.23, no.1, pp.69-72, Jan., 1937.

EARLY OBSERVATIONS ON THE ELK IN KANSAS. Donald F. Hoffmeister. Trans. Kansas Acad. Sci., Topeka, vol.50, no.1, pp.75-76, 1947.

ELK IN JACKSON HOLE, WYOMING. Hartley H.T. Jackson. Jour. Mamm., vol. 8, no.2, p.175, May, 1927.

THE OLYMPIC ELK. Gardiner F. Jones. Wash. State Game Bull., vol.5, no.4, p. 3, Oct., 1953.

ELK REMAINS IN NORFOLK COUNTY. Monroe Landon. Canadian Field-Nat., vol. 45, no.2, p.40, Feb., 1931.

ELK LIVE HERE! Roger M. Latham. Pa. Game News, vol.25, no.12, pp.15-19, illus., Dec., 1954.

ELK IN SHASTA COUNTY. M. Hall McAllister. Calif. Fish and Game, vol.5, no.2, p.98, Apr., 1919.

CERVUS ROOSEVELTI, A NEW ELK FROM THE OLYMPICS. C.Hart Merriam. Proc. Biol.Soc. Washington, vol.11, pp.271-275, Dec. 17, 1897.

NEW ELK FROM CALIFORNIA, CERVUS NANNODES. C. Hart Merriam. Proc.Biol. Soc. Washington, vol.18, pp.23-26, illus., Feb. 2, 1905.

OBSERVATIONS ON YELLOWSTONE ELK. Harlow B. Mills. Jour. Mamm., vol.17, no.3, pp.250-253, Aug., 1936.

HISTORY OF THE YOSEMITE ELK HERD. James Moffitt. Calif. Fish and Game, vol. 20, no.1, pp.37-51, Jan., 1934.

THE ELK OF JACKSON HOLE. Olaus J. Murie. Nat. Hist., New York, vol.35, no. 3, pp.237-247, illus., Mar., 1935.

ELK OF NORTH AMERICA. Olaus J.Murie. Stackpole, p.376, 1951.

GRAND TETON NATIONAL PARK AND ITS ELK. Olaus J. Murie. Natl.Parks Mag., vol.25, no.107, pp.119-120, 149-150, illus., Oct.-Dec., 1951.

JACKSON HOLE NATIONAL MONUMENT AND THE ELK. Olaus J. Murie. Natl.Parks Mag., Wash., no.83, pp.13-17, illus., Oct.-Dec., 1945.

OUR BIG GAME IN WINTER. Olaus J. Murie. Trans. N.Amer. Wildl.Conf., vol.9, pp.173-176, 1944.

NEW SPECIES OF ELK FROM ARIZONA. E.W. Nelson. Bull. Amer. Mus. Nat. Hist., New York, vol.16, art.1, pp.1-12, figs.7, Jan. 16, 1902.

FLORIDA'S BIG GAME. (Sambar deer.) Coleman Newman. Florida Wildl., Tallahassee, vol.1, no.11, pp.4, 5, 18, illus., Apr., 1948.

ROCKY MOUNTAIN ELK. Nils N.Nilsson. Oregon State Game Comm. Bull., Portland, vol.2, no.2, pp.1, 5-7, illus., Mar., 1947.

ELK SITUATION IN UTAH. Orange A. Olsen. Utah State Agric. College, Logan, Utah, pp.43-45, May, 1933.

NOTES ON THE LIFE-HISTORY OF THE ROOSEVELT ELK IN CALIFORNIA. Robert T. Orr. Jour. Mamm., vol.18, no.1, pp.62-66, Feb. 14, 1937.

REPORT ON CONDITION OF ELK IN JACKSON HOLE, WYOMING, IN 1911. E. A. Preble. U.S. Dept. Agric. Biol. Surv.Bull., Wash., D.C., no.40, pp.23, pls.7, 1911.

WISCONSIN'S ELK HERD. Staber W. Reese. Wisc. Cons. Bull., vol.9, no.4, pp.6-10, Apr., 1944.

SITGREAVES ELK HERD. Paul H. Roberts. Jour. Forestry, Wash., vol.28, no.5, pp. 655-658, May, 1930.

ELK IN COLORADO. Glen Rogers. Colo. Cons. Comments, vol.10, no.3, pp.9-10, Sep., 1947.

THE POPULATION, RANGE, AND PRODUCTIVITY OF THE NORTH NEBO ELK HERD. Merle J. Rognrud. MS thesis, Utah State Agric. Coll., p.168, 1953.

ELK SITUATION IN MONTANA. W.M. Rush. Montana State Fish and Game Dept., Bien. Rept. 1931-1932, p.7.

NORTHERN YELLOWSTONE ELK STUDY. W.M. Rush. Montana Fish and Game Comm., pp.131, figs., map, 1933.

ELK IN EARLY WISCONSIN. A.W.Shorger. Trans. Wisc. Acad. Sci., Arts and Letters, vol.43, pp.5-23, Sep. 15, 1954.

ROOSEVELT ELK ON THE OLYMPIC PENINSULA, WASHINGTON. John E. Schwartz, Glenn E. Mitchell. Jour. Wildl. Mgt., vol.9, no.4, pp.295-319, Oct., 1945.

HOME-COMING OF THE ELK. Grace V. Sharritt. Audubon Mag., vol.48, no.6, pp.348-354, Nov.-Dec., 1946.

THE PRESENT PLIGHT OF THE JACKSON HOLE ELK. H.P. Sheldon. U.S. Dept. Agric., Biol. Surv., Wildl.Leaflet no.12, pp.4, July, 1935.

JACKSON HOLE ELK HERD. Carl D.Shoemaker. Wyo. Wild Life, vol.16, no.11, pp. 4-8, illus., Nov., 1952.

PECOS ELK HERD. D.A. Shoemaker. Jour. Forestry, Washington, vol.28, no.5, pp.648-654, May, 1930.

DISAPPEARANCE OF THE WAPITIS. H. W. Shoemaker. Penna. Game News, Harrisburg, vol.17, no.11, pp.6, 31, Feb., 1948.

ROOSEVELT ELK OF THE OLYMPIC PENINSULA. M.P. Skinner. Murrelet, Seattle, Wash., vol.17, nos.2-3, pp.31-35, illus., Nov. 14, 1936.

STORY OF THE WHITEBAR ELK. THE LIFE HISTORY OF A YELLOWSTONE ELK. M.P. Skinner. Nat. Hist., New York, vol.20, no. 5, pp.577-583, illus., Nov.-Dec., 1920.

SUN RIVER ELK HERD. Glen A. Smith. Jour. Forestry, Wash., vol.28, no.5, pp. 644-647, May, 1930.

MICHIGAN HAS ELK. J.H.Stephenson. Michigan Conserv., Lansing, Mich., vol.5, no.4, p.2, illus., Sep., 1935.

AMERICAN ELK IN MINNESOTA. Gustav Swanson. Cons. Volunteer, vol.1, no.2, pp.5-7, Nov., 1940.

PARTIAL HISTORY OF THE ELK HERDS OF COLORADO. Lloyd W. Swift. Jour. Mamm., vol.26, no.2, pp.114-119, July 15, 1945.

RETURN OF THE OUTCAST ELK. (Tule elk of California.) Dan Lincoln Thrapp. Pacific Discovery, vol.6, no.6, pp.3-7, illus., Nov.-Dec., 1953.

ELK OF THE NORTHERN ROCKY MOUNTAIN REGION. Raymond M. West. Field Notes on Wildl., vol.2, no.9, pp.32, Aug., 1941.

ARCHAEOLOGICAL EVIDENCE OF THE PRESENCE OF THE WAPITI IN SOUTHWESTERN ONTARIO. W.J. Wintemberg. Canadian Field Nat., vol.40, p.58, Mar. 29, 1926.

ELK IN VIRGINIA. Roy Wood. MS thesis, Va. Polytechnic Inst., 1943.

AMERICAN ELK CERVUS CANADENSIS. Wyo. Wild Life, Cheyenne, vol.5, no.2, pp.6, 16, Feb., 1940.

CALIFORNIA'S TULE ELK. Natl.Parks Mag., vol.27, no.112, pp.33-34, illus., Jan.-Mar., 1953.

HERMOSA CREEK ELK HERD. Colo.Conserv.Comments, Denver, vol.7, no.4, p. 5, Dec. 15, 1944.

JACKSON HOLE ELK. Nature Mag., Wash., vol.42, no.7, p.328, Aug.-Sep., 1949.

KING OF WASHINGTON'S WILDLIFE--THE WAPITI. Wash. State Game Bull., vol.4, no.4, pp.11-12, illus., Oct., 1952.

THOSE ELK AGAIN. Nat. Mag., vol.46, no.2, p.89, Feb., 1953.

WHAT OF THE TULE ELK? Nat. Mag., vol.46, no.7, p.369, illus., Aug.-Sep., 1953.

Cervus--Population Dynamics

IRRUPTION OF ELK IN RIDING MOUNTAIN NATIONAL PARK, MANITOBA. A.W.F. Banfield. Jour. Wildl. Mgt., vol.13, no.1, pp.127-134, Jan., 1949.

ANNUAL NORTHERN YELLOWSTONE ELK HERD COUNT. Victor H. Cahalane. Trans. 3rd N.Amer. Wildl.Conf., pp. 388-389, 1938.

COLORADO ELK ON INCREASE. Jack C. Culbreath. Colorado Conserv. Comments, Denver, vol.10, no.6, pp.7-8, 25, June, 1948.

CENSUS OF THE YELLOWSTONE ELK HERD. Francis D. LaNoue. Univ.Idaho Bull., vol.33, no.22, pp.42-43, Dec., 1938.

A POPULATION STUDY OF THE SOUTH CACHE ELK HERD. Jessop B. Low. Quart. Rept. Utah Coop. Wildl. Research Unit, Logan, vol.14, no.3, pp.19-25, July-Sep., 1949.

POPULATION STUDY OF THE SOUTH CACHE ELK HERD. Roger J. McCormack. MS thesis, Utah State Agric.Coll., 1951.

HOW MANY ELK? Grace V. Sharritt. Amer. Forests, Wash., vol.56, no.6, pp.12-13, illus., June, 1950.

THE 1949 ELK CENSUS. Wyo. Wild Life, Cheyenne, vol.13, no.4, pp.23-24, illus., May, 1949.

THIRTY-TWO ELK MULTIPLY TO 500 HEAD IN 20 YEARS. National Nature News, Wash., D.C., vol.2, no.17, p.4, Apr.25, 1938.

Cervus--Psychology

ANIMAL MENTALITY--THE RED DEER. Richard Perry. Illus. London News, vol. 216, no.5788, p.466, illus., Mar. 25, 1950.

Cervus--Reproductive Biology

UNUSUAL BIRTH OF CAPTIVE ELK. V.A. Bower. Rod and Gun in Canada, Montreal, vol.49, no.2, p.12, illus., July, 1947.

INCREASED NATALITY RESULTING FROM LOWERED POPULATION DENSITY AMONG ELK IN SOUTHEASTERN WASHINGTON. Helmut K. Buechner, Carl V.Swanson. Trans. 20th N.Amer. Wildl. Conf., pp.560-567, graph, 1955.

PRODUCTIVITY OF NORTH YELLOWSTONE ELK AS INDICATED BY OVARY ANALYSIS. E.L. Cheatum, J.E. Gaab. Proc. 32nd Ann. Conf. Western Assn. State Game and Fish Comm., Glacier Nat. Park, Mont., June 15-17, 1952, pp.174-177, 1953.

PREGNANT YEARLING COW ELK. A.Lynn Coffin, Jack D. Remington. Jour. Wildl. Mgt., vol.17, no.2, p.223, Apr., 1953.

AGE AT SEXUAL MATURITY IN MALE ELK (CERVUS CANADENSIS). Clinton Conaway. Jour. Wildl. Mgt., Ithaca, vol. 16, no.3, pp.313-315, July, 1952.

(BIRTH OF A SIKA DEER.) Naissance d'un cerf sika. Ed. Dechambre. La Terre et la Vie, vol.7, no.2, pp.63-64, illus., Mar.-Apr., 1937.

UNUSUAL RUTTING OF A CAPTIVE WAPITI STAG. Richard Glover. Jour. Mamm., vol.34, no.1, pp.136-137, Feb. 19, 1953.

PRODUCTIVITY AND SEX SURVIVAL OF ELK IN BANFF NATIONAL PARK, ALBERTA. Hubert U. Green. Canadian Field-Nat., Ottawa, vol.64, no.1, pp.40-42, Jan.-Feb., 1950.

BIOLOGY OF THE ELK CALF, CERVUS CANDENSIS NELSONI. Donald E.Johnson. MS thesis, Mont. State Coll., 1950; Jour. Wildl. Mgt., vol.15, no.4, pp.396-410, Oct., 1951.

REPRODUCTION OF YELLOWSTONE ELK. Walter H. Kittams. Jour. Wildl. Mgt., Ithaca, vol.17, no.2, pp.177-184, Apr., 1953.

MT. NEBO ELK PRODUCTIVITY. Merle J. Rognrud. Utah Fish and Game Bull., vol.9, no.6, pp.1-2, July, 1952.

FETUS IN YEARLING COW ELK, CERVUS CANADENSIS. Jack K.Saunders, Jr. Jour. Mamm., vol.36, no.1, p.145, Feb., 1955.

BIOLOGY OF THE REPRODUCTION OF CERVUS ELAPHUS L. V.I.Zalkin. Zool. Jour. Moscow, vol.23, no.6, pp.369-377, figs.3, 1944. (In Russian with English summary.)

Cervus--Sex Ratios

AN UNUSUAL SEX-RATIO IN RED DEER. Glyn Davies. Nature, London, vol.127, no.3194, p.94, Jan. 17, 1931.

OBSERVATIONS ON THE NATURAL HISTORY OF THE SCOTTISH RED DEER. VII. A PRELIMINARY NOTE UPON THE SEX RATIO OF SCOTTISH RED DEER. Wm.C. Miller. Proc. Roy. Phys. Soc. Edinburgh, vol.22, pt.2, pp.99-101, May, 1932.

Cervus--Taxonomy

NEW NAME FOR THE ROCKY MOUNTAIN ELK. Vernon Bailey. Proc. Biol. Soc.Wash., vol.48, pp.187-190, Nov. 15, 1935.

REVISION OF THE RUSINE DEER IN THE INDO-AUSTRALIAN ARCHIPELAGO . A.C. V. van Bemmel. Treubia, Buitenzorg, vol. 20, pt.2, pp.191-262, pls.2-4, Oct., 1949.

SOME ADDITIONS TO A REVISION OF THE RUSINE DEER IN THE INDO-AUSTRALIAN ARCHIPELAGO. A.C.V. van Bemmel. Treubia, Buitenzorg, vol.21, pt. 1, pp.105-110, illus., Apr. 25, 1951.

MATERIALS FOR THE SYSTEMATICS OF DEER OF THE SUBGENUS CERVUS. N. Bobrinskoy, K. Flerov. Archiv. Mus. Zool. Univ. Moscow, vol.1, pp.15-41, figs. 19, 1934. (In Russian.)

WHITE MUZZLE DEER (CERVUS ALBIROSTRIS PRZEW.) AS THE REPRESENTATIVE OF A NEW GENUS PRZEWALSKIUM. K. Flerov. Comptes Rendus Acad. Sci. USSR, 1930, pp.115-120, 1930.

(TECHNICAL NAME OF THE GERMAN RED DEER.) Der technische Name des deutschen Rothirsches. Ernst Schwartz. Zeitschr. f. Saeugetierk., Berlin, vol.8, nos.3-6, pp.274-276, Dec. 20, 1933.

(CERVUS MEGACEROS MOSBACHENSIS N. SP. AND THE PHYLOGENY OF THE GIANT STAG.) Cervus megaceros mosbachensis n.sp. und die Stammesgeschichte der Riesenhirsche. W. Soergel. Selbstverlag der Senckenbergischen Naturforschenden Gesell., Frankfurt a.M., pp. 365-408, 1927.

SYSTEMATIC NAME OF THE JAPANESE DEER. Leonhard Stejneger. Science, Lancaster, n.s., vol.22, no.561, pp.402-403, Sep. 29, 1905.

(DESCRIPTION OF A NEW SPOTTED DEER OF THE SOUTHERN USSURI, CERVUS DYBOWSKII.) Description d'un nouveau Cerf tacheté du pays d'Ussuri méridional, Cervus dybowskii. L.Taczanowski. Proc. Zool. Soc. London, pp.123-125, fig.1, 1876.

NOMENCLATURE OF THE GEOGRAPHICAL FORMS OF THE PANOLIA DEER (RUCERVUS ELDI AND ITS RELATIVES). Oldfield Thomas. Jour. Bombay Nat.Hist. Soc., vol.25, no.3, pp.363-367, Jan.15, 1918.

Cervus--Weights and Measurements

SUPPOSED GIANT RED DEER. P. C. Mitchell. Proc. Zool. Soc. London, pt. 2, p. 433, July 1934.

VERY LARGE SAMBAR STAG. R. C. Morris. Jour. Bombay Nat. Hist. Soc., vol. 39, no.2, p.390, Apr. 15, 1937.

WEIGHTS AND MEASUREMENTS OF ROCKY MOUNTAIN ELK. Don C. Quimby, Donald E. Johnson. Jour. Wildl.Mgt., Menasha, vol.15, no.1, pp.57-62, Jan., 1951.

LIVE ELK WEIGHTS. Curtis K. Skinner. Wyo. Wild Life, vol.10, no.7, p.32, July, 1946.

(AN ATTEMPT TO EXPLAIN THE BODY-WEIGHT DIFFERENCES OCCURRING IN RED DEER IN WEST GERMANY.) Ein Erklaerungsversuch der bei Rotwild in Westdeutschland anzutreffende unterschiede im Koerpergewicht. E. Ueckermann. Zeitschr. Jagdwissensch., vol.1, no.2, pp.92-98, figs., 1955. (With English summary.)

Odocoileus--General

WHITE-TAILED DEER. Rod Amundson. Wildl. in N.Carolina, Raleigh, vol.14, no. 3, pp.4-7, illus., Mar., 1950.

DEER IN AUTUMN. Alfred M. Bailey. Chicago Nat., vol.2, no. 4, pp.105-108, Dec., 1939.

PINYON BUCKS. (Odocoileus hemionus.) Alfred M. Bailey. Western Sportsman, Denver, vol.5, no.6, pp.13-14, 22-23, illus., Nov., 1940.

WHITE-TAILED DEER. THE VIRGINIA DEER AND ITS SUBSPECIES,AND THE LITTLE FAN-TAIL, OR MEXICAN DEER. Vernon Bailey. Nature Mag., vol.21, no.3, pp.123-126, figs.5, map, Mar., 1933.

DEER DON'T LAUGH. S. Omar Barker. New Mexico Mag., Albuquerque, vol.22, no.11, pp.12-13, 31, 33, 35, illus., Nov., 1944.

ACTAEON--A WHITE-TAILED DEER. Ernest Harold Baynes. Nat.Mag., vol. 3, pp.79-83, 124-126, illus., Aug., 1924.

DON'T MISS THE BOAT. (Deer.) Logan J. Bennett. Penna. Game News, Harrisburg, vol.13, no.9, pp.14-24, Dec., 1942.

MY FRIENDS, THE DEER. T.Brazil. Nature Mag., vol.5, pp.5-10, figs.10, pls.2, Jan., 1925.

TIMELY NATURE LESSON. (New-born fawns should be left undisturbed.) Harold C. Bryant. Yosemite Nature Notes, vol.6, pp.44-45, June, 1927.

PERSISTENT CALLERS. (Deer.) Marion Carr. Jr.Nat.Hist.Mag., Amer.Mus.Nat. Hist., New York, pp.4-7, pls.5, Jan., 1944.

WHITETAILS. William H. Carr. Nat.Hist., New York, vol.53, no.9, pp.420-424, illus., Nov., 1944.

DEER TROUBLE. David B. Cook. Audubon Mag., New York, vol.47, no.2, pp.74-79, illus., Mar.-Apr., 1945.

WHITE-TAIL. Alan Devoe. Audubon Mag., New York, vol.46, no.3, pp.155-159, illus., May-June, 1944; S.Dakota Conservation Digest, Pierre, vol.11, no.10, pp.2-3, 14, illus., Oct., 1944.

REMARKS ON THE ANALYSIS OF KILL-CURVES OF FEMALE DEER. John Gill. Proc. N.E. Sect. Wildl. Soc., 9th Ann. Conf., Bretton Woods, N.H., Sep.20-23, 1953, pp.1-12, graphs.

WHITE-TAILED DEER. James Nelson Gowanloch. Louisiana Conservationist, New Orleans, vol.2, no.2, pp.17-18, 24, illus., Oct., 1949.

DEER AT NIGHT IN THE NORTH WOODS. Tappan Gregory. Charles C.Thomas, Springfield, Ill., pp.221, pls.45, 1930.

(Review by Edward A. Preble of) DEER AT NIGHT IN THE NORTH WOODS. Tappan Gregory. Jour. Mamm., vol.12, no.1, pp. 84-85, Feb., 1931.

BLACK TAILED DEER. Gardiner F.Jones. Wash. State Game Bull., vol.6, no.4, pp. 4-5, illus., Oct., 1954.

KNOW YOUR WHITETAILS. (Deer) Roger M. Latham. Field and Stream, New York, vol.51, no.7, pp.52-53, 100-103, illus., Nov., 1946.

TOO MANY DEER. A. Starker Leopold. Sierra Club Bull., vol.38, no.8, pp.51-57, Oct., 1953; Scientific American, New York, vol.193, no.5, pp.101-108, Nov., 1955.

HERD OF MULE DEER. A RECORD OF OBSERVATIONS MADE ON THE HASTINGS NATURAL HISTORY RESERVATION. Jean M. Linsdale, P. Quentin Tomich. Univ. Calif. Press, pp.xiii+567, illus., 1953.

(Review by W. Robert Eadie of) HERD OF MULE DEER: A RECORD OF OBSERVATIONS MADE ON THE HASTINGS NATURAL HISTORY RESERVATION. Jean M. Linsdale, P. Quentin Tomich. Jour. Mamm., vol.34, no.4, pp.521-522, Nov. 13, 1953.

STUDY OF THE COLUMBIAN BLACK-TAILED DEER, ODOCOILEUS HEMIONUS COLUMBIANUS (RICHARDSON). James S. Lindzey. MS thesis, Oregon State Coll., 1943.

WHITETAIL DILEMMA. J.P. Linduska. Hunting and Fishing, vol.30, no.10, pp. 18-19, 31-35, illus., Oct., 1953.

THE BURRO DEER ODOCOILEUS HEMIONUS EREMICUS. William M. Longhurst, John E. Chattin. Calif. Fish and Game, vol.27, no.1, pp.2-12, Jan., 1941.

(MONOGRAPH OF THE BLACK TAIL DEER.) Monografia del venado bura o cola prieta (Odocoileus hemionus canus Mearns). Carlos López. Univ. Nac., Mexico, pp.1-37, figs.17, 1922.

DEER: THOSE ADAPTABLE ANIMALS. Robert M. McClung. Animal Kingdom, New York Zool. Soc., vol.56, no.2, pp. 34-44, illus., Apr., 1953.

INTRODUCING TO THE EAST AND FAR WEST THE BABY MULE DEER. Lloyd E. McDowell. Living Wilderness, Wash., D.C., vol.9, whole no.10, pp.22-23, illus., May, 1944.

FAWN OBSERVATIONS. Edwin D.McKee. Grand Canyon Nature Notes, vol.8, no.5, pp.181-182, Aug., 1933.

OBSERVATIONS ON A PAIR OF FAWNS. Vincent Mowbray. Yosemite Nat.Notes, Yosemite, vol.19, no.9, pp.69-70, Sep., 1940.

MONARCH OF THE PASS. (Mule deer.) Joyce Muench, Josef Muench. Frontiers, Lancaster, vol.9, no.3, pp.80-82, illus., Feb., 1945.

(Review by Hartley H.T. Jackson of) WHITETAILED DEER. William Montpeny

Newsom. Jour. Mamm., vol.7, no.4, pp. 335-336, Nov. 23, 1926.

FAWN-NAPPERS. THE SCOURGE OF WILD-LIFE. Chas. C. Niehuis. Ariz. Wildl. and Sportsman, Tucson, vol.6, no.13, pp.8-10, Nov., 1945.

THE MULE DEER. Jack O'Connor. Ariz. Wildl. and Sportsman, Safford, vol.6, no. 4, pp.6-7, Apr., 1944.

WHITE-TAILED DEER. Wilfred H. Osgood. Field Mus. Nat. Hist., Chicago, Zool. Dept., Leaflet no.1, pp.12, illus., June, 1922.

WITH THE MULE DEER THROUGH THE SEASONS. Gayle Pickwell. Audubon Mag., Harrisburg, vol.43, no.1, pp.24-30, illus., Jan.-Feb., 1941.

LIVING IN A DEER YARD. Willet Randall. Game Breeder and Sportsman, New York, vol.49, no.4, pp.41-42, Apr., 1944.

STANDARD TERMINOLOGY FOR THE DEER TEETH. Thane Riney. Jour. Wildl. Mgt., Ithaca, vol.15, no.1, pp.99-101, illus., Jan., 1951.

ANY DEER AND LOTS OF SNOW. Dunbar Robb. Mo. Cons., vol.13, no.1, pp.2-3, 13, illus., Jan., 1952.

STALKING DEER AFTER DARK. Hobart B. Roberts. Fauna, Philadelphia, vol.7, no.3, pp.80-81, Sep., 1945.

WHITE-TAILED DEER. Archibald Rutledge. Fauna, Philadelphia, vol.2, no.3, pp.55-58, illus., Sep., 1940.

THE WHITE-TAILED DEER THROUGH THE YEAR. Walter J. Schoonmaker. Nature Mag., Wash., vol.39, no.1, pp.25-30, illus., Jan., 1946.

DIONNE OF THE DEER FAMILY. Joe A. Small. Sports Afield, Minneapolis, vol.116, no.4, pp.32, 75, illus., Oct., 1946.

LET US EXAMINE THE RECORD. (Deer.) Ernest F. Swift. Wisc. Conservation Bull., Madison, vol.9, no.10, pp.12-16, Oct.; Pt. III., no.11, pp.12-15, Nov., 1944.

THE DEER. G.C. Toner. Carling Conserv. Digest, Toronto, vol.1, no.1, pp.10-11, illus., Jan., 1947. (White-tailed, mule.)

DEER RESEARCH. S.C. Whitlock. Michigan Conserv., Lansing, vol.19, no.6, pp.7-8, 25-26, Nov., 1950.

STORY OF TWO BUCKS. S.C. Whitlock. Michigan Conserv., Lansing, vol.21, no.6, pp.29-30, illus., Nov., 1952.

MULE DEER FAWN IN NORTHERN YOSEMITE (PHOTOGRAPH). Cedric Wright. Sierra Club Bull., San Francisco, vol.27, no.4, pl. following p.78, Aug., 1942.

CONCERNING THE DEER. Wyo. Wild Life, Cheyenne, vol.10, no.4, pp.19-23, illus., Apr., 1946.

DEER OBSERVATIONS. Wisc. Conserv. Bull., Madison, vol.11, no.3, pp.22-27, illus., Mar., 1946.

DEER SURVIVAL. New York State Cons., vol.7, no.6, p.15, June-July, 1953.

MASTER WHITETAIL. Texas Game and Fish, Houston, vol.3, no.4, pp.5-6, 14, illus., Mar., 1945.

MORE ABOUT DEER. Penna. Game News, Harrisburg, vol.14, no.12, pp.4-5, 26, illus., Mar., 1944.

PLAINS WHITE-TAILED DEER ODOCOILEUS VIRGINIANUS MACROURUS. Wyo. Wild Life, vol.5, no.3, pp.8, 15, Mar., 1940.

ROCKY MOUNTAIN MULE DEER ODOCOILEUS HEMIONUS. Wyo. Wild Life, Cheyenne, vol.4, no.7, pp.4, 15, illus., July, 1939.

SETBACKS SUFFERED BY DEER AND DOVES. Alabama Conserv., Montgomery, vol.22, nos.1-2, pp.4, 17, illus., July-Aug., 1950.

WHITE-TAILED DEER. Va. Wildl., Richmond, vol.10, no.1, pp.7, 21, illus., Jan., 1949.

Odocoileus--Anatomy

CYCLIC VARIATION IN THE MULE DEER THYMUS. L.G. Browman, H.S. Sears. Proc. Soc. Exper. Biol. and Med., vol.93, no.1, pp.161-162, Oct., 1956.

AGE VARIATION IN THE TEETH AND SKULL OF THE WHITETAIL DEER. Victor H. Cahalane. Cranbrook Inst. Sci., Sci. Publ. no.2, Bloomfield Hills, Michigan, pp.1-14, pls.7, Nov., 1932.

SUPERNUMERARY INCISOR IN THE WHITE-TAILED DEER. C. David Fowle, R.C. Passmore. Jour. Mamm., vol.29, no.3, p.301, Aug. 31, 1948.

NOTE ON THE THYROID AND PARATHYROID GLANDS OF THE VIRGINIA DEER. Allen L. Grafflin. Anat. Record, Philadelphia, vol.75, no.1, pp.27-38, Sep. 25, 1939.

PHYSICAL CHARACTERISTICS OF COLORADO MULE DEER IN RELATION TO THEIR AGE CLASSES. Gilbert N. Hunter. Colorado Game and Fish Dept., Denver, pp.1-38, figs. 23, 1947.

ABNORMAL MANDIBLE IN WHITE-TAILED DEER. Charles E. Johnson. Jour. Mamm., vol.16, no.1, pp.69-70, Feb., 1935.

CHANGES IN HISTOLOGICAL STRUCTURE OF THE LONG BONES OF WHITE-TAILED DEER (ODOCOILEUS VIRGINIANUS) DURING THE GROWTH OF THE ANTLERS. Waldemar W. Meister. Anat. Record, Philadelphia, vol. 124, no.4, pp.709-717, Apr., 1956.

ELK TEETH IN CALIFORNIA DEER. (Odocoileus hemionus.) Gus Nordquist. Calif. Fish and Game, San Francisco, vol.27, no. 1, pp.39-40, Jan., 1941.

NOTES ON TOOTH DEVELOPMENT AND WEAR FOR ROCKY MOUNTAIN MULE DEER. W. Leslie Robinette et al. Jour. Wildl. Mgt., vol.21, no.2, pp.134-153, illus., Apr., 1957.

CANINE TEETH IN A WISCONSIN WHITE-TAILED DEER FAWN. Charles H. Southwick. Jour. Mamm., vol.35, no.3, pp. 456-457, Aug. 20, 1954.

CHARACTERISTICS OF THE PELVIC GIRDLE IN RELATION TO SEX IN BLACK-TAILED AND WHITE-TAILED DEER. R.D. Taber. Calif. Fish and Game, Sacramento, vol.43, no.1, pp.15-21, illus., Jan., 1956.

CANINE TEETH IN WHITE-TAILED DEER. Richard G. Van Gelder, Donald F. Hoffmeister. Jour. Wildl. Mgt., Ithaca, vol. 17, no.1, p.100, illus., Jan., 1953.

FURTHER OBSERVATIONS ON THE HISTOLOGICAL CHANGES ASSOCIATED WITH THE SHEDDING OF THE ANTLERS OF THE WHITE-TAILED DEER (ODOCOILEUS VIRGINIANUS BOREALIS.) George B. Wislocki, Charles M. Waldo. Anat. Record, Philadelphia, vol.117, no.3, pp.353-376, Nov., 1953.

Odocoileus--Antlers

LOSS OF ANTLERS BY DEER. I.H. Bartlett. Oklahoma Game and Fish News, Oklahoma City, vol.3, no.2, pp.6-7, 19, illus., Feb., 1947.

DEER ANTLERS. M.E. Beatty. Yosemite Nat. Notes, Yosemite, vol.22, no.3, pp. 30-31, Mar., 1943.

A "HORNED" BLACKTAIL DOE WITH FAWN. Lester J. Berry. Jour. Mamm., vol.13, no.3, pp.282-283, Aug., 1932.

A HORNED DOE. F.A. Bullard. Calif. Fish and Game, vol.12, no.1, p.47, Jan., 1926.

CHEMICAL ANALYSIS OF DEER ANTLERS. T.T. Chaddock. Wisc. Cons. Bull., vol.5, no.6, p.42, June, 1940.

ANTLERED DOE MULE DEER. Ian McT. Cowan. Canadian Field-Nat., Sutton West, vol.60, no.1, pp.11-12, Jan.-Feb., 1946.

PRELIMINARY NOTE ON THE NUMBER OF TINES IN THE ANTLERS OF THE WHITE-TAILED DEER AS CORRELATED WITH AGE. E.D. Crabb. Proc. Oklahoma Acad. Sci., vol.2, (Univ. Oklahoma Bull., n.s., no.247) pp.12-13, Oct., 1922.

DOES HAVE ANTLERS. F.P. Cronemiller. Calif. Fish and Game, vol.18, no.1, p.83, Jan., 1932.

VIRGINIA DEER WITH FIFTY-FOUR TINES. Ralph W. Dexter. Jour. Mamm., vol.26, no. 3, p.310, illus., Aug., 1945.

HORNED DOES. Joseph Dixon. Jour. Mamm., vol.8, no.4, pp.289-291, pls.29-30, Nov., 1927.

FREAK ANTLERS OF MULE DEER. E. Raymond Hall. Calif. Fish and Game, San Francisco, vol.27, no.1, pp.38-39, figs. 19-20, Jan., 1941.

ANTLERS AWAY! (Growth of antlers in whitetail deer.) Arnold O. Haugen. Alabama Conservation, vol.28, no.5, pp.14-16, illus., Apr.-May, 1957.

DICHOTOMOUS FORKING IN THE ANTLERS OF WHITE-TAILED DEER. A. Starker Leopold. Jour. Mamm., vol.35, no.4, pp. 599-600, illus., Nov., 1954.

ANTLERS--KING SIZE. Harry Livingston. Outdoors, Dayton, vol.16, no.4, p.24, illus., Apr., 1948.

LOPSIDED DOE. (Antlered white-tailed doe.) F. Merner. Sylva, Toronto, vol.4, no.1, p.43, 1948.

REPORT TO THE DEER HUNTERS. (Weights, ages, antlers.) Raymond Moody. La. Cons., vol.7, no.2, pp.2-4, illus., Nov., 1954.

INTERNAL STRUCTURE AND SEASONAL GROWTH-CHANGES OF DEER ANTLERS. Charles V. Noback. Bull. New York Zool. Soc., vol.32, pp.34-40, illus., Feb., 1929.

ANTLERS OF A VIRGINIA DEER AFFECTED BY CANCER. R.I. Pocock. Proc. Zool. Soc. London, pt.1, pp.301-302, Apr. 20, 1916.

ANTLERLESS MULE DEER BUCKS. W. Leslie Robinette, Jay S. Gashwiler. Jour. Mamm., vol.36, no.2, pp.202-205, pl.1, May 26, 1955.

OLD HORNY'S SKULL EXHIBITED. (Three-horned buck skull.) C.P. Russell. Yosemite Nature Notes, vol.7, p.56, July, 1928.

VARIATIONS BY AGE CLASS IN THE ANTLER BEAM DIAMETERS OF WHITE-TAILED DEER RELATED TO RANGE CONDITIONS. C.W. Severinghaus et al. Trans. N. Amer. Wildl. Conf., vol.15, pp.551-568, 1950.

PENNSYLVANIA DEER AND THEIR HORNS. Henry W. Shoemaker. Faust Printing Co., Reading, pp.120, photos, 1915.

BUCK WITH 2 POINTS. Harold Steinhoff. Colorado Outdoors Mag., vol.6, no.5, pp. 28-29, Sep., 1957.

GROWTH OF THE DEER ANTLER. Edgar B. Taft, Thomas C. Hall. New York Conservationist, Albany, vol.10, no.4, pp.4-5, illus., Mar., 1956.

ON A PAIR OF ABNORMAL ANTLERS OF THE VIRGINIA DEER. Frederick W. True. Proc. U.S. Nat. Mus., vol.6, publ. no. 358, p.151, fig.1, Oct. 11, 1883.

(CONTRIBUTION TO KNOWLEDGE REGARDING THE TIME OF SHEDDING AND NEW GROWTH OF HORNS AND FUR IN THE WHITE TAIL DEER.) Contribucion al conocimiento de las epocas de caida y nacimiento de la cornamenta y de su terciopelo en venados cola blanco (Odocoileus virginianus) de san ceyetano, estado de Mexico, Mexico. R. Bernardo Villa. An. Inst. Biol., vol.25, pp.451-461, illus., 1954.

ANTLERS IN FEMALE DEER, WITH A REPORT OF THREE CASES IN ODOCOILEUS. George B. Wislocki. Jour. Mamm., vol.35, no.4, pp.486-495, illus., Nov., 1954.

FURTHER NOTES ON ANTLERS IN FEMALE DEER OF THE GENUS ODOCOILEUS. George B. Wislocki. Jour. Mamm., vol.37, no.2, pp.231-235, illus., June 9, 1956.

STUDIES ON THE GROWTH OF THE DEER ANTLERS. I. ON THE STRUCTURE AND HISTOGENESIS OF THE ANTLERS OF THE VIRGINIA DEER (ODOCOILEUS VIRGINIANUS BOREALIS). George B. Wislocki. Amer. Jour. Anat., Philadelphia, vol.71, no.3, pp. 371-415, figs.1-1a, pls.5, Nov. 16, 1942.

EXIT "OLD HORNY." (Notes on three-antlered deer.) George M. Wright. Yosemite Nature Notes, vol.7, pp.17-18, illus., Mar., 1928.

THE "RHINO BUCK" OF YOSEMITE. George M. Wright. Yosemite Nature Notes, vol.7, p.5, illus., Jan., 1928. (Three-antlered deer.)

ANTLER-SHEDDING TIME. Rod and Gun in Canada, Montreal, vol.48, no.10, p.7, 1947.

ANTLERS ARE NOT HORNS. (Deer.) Texas Game and Fish, Austin, vol.6, no.1, pp.4-5, 27, illus., Dec., 1947.

Odocoileus--Breeding

TRAILSIDE FAWNS. AN ADVENTURE IN ANIMAL UPBRINGING. William H. Carr. Nat. Hist., New York, vol.34, no.2, pp. 151-160, illus., Mar.-Apr., 1934.

BREEDING EXPERIMENTS WITH THE WHITETAIL DEER. Richard Gerstell. Penna. Game News, Harrisburg, vol.6, no.12, pp.4, 20, illus., Mar., 1936.

HOW DEER RESPOND TO KINDNESS IF TAKEN WHEN YOUNG. Alfred Kay. Canadian Field-Nat., vol.46, no.8, p.183, Nov., 1932.

RAISING DEER. (Experiences in breeding white-tailed deer.) L.M. Pickett. Country Life, vol.37, pp.84, 86, 88, 90, Jan., 1920.

HANDS OFF, AND ON. (Adopting deer fawns.) H.H. Sheldon. Nature Mag., Wash., D.C., vol.36, no.1, pp.19-21, illus., Jan., 1943.

Odocoileus--Diseases, Parasites

EFFECTS OF SCREW-WORM ON DEER IN THE SOUTHEAST. George W. Allen. Trans. N.Amer. Wildl. Conf., vol.16, pp.135-143, 1951.

ENLARGED SPLEEN IN WHITETAIL DEER AT GLACIER NATIONAL PARK. John F. Alton. Trans. 3rd N.Amer. Wildl. Conf., pp.890-892, 1938.

NEW RECORD OF A DEER PARASITE FOR CALIFORNIA. R.F. Annereaux. Amer. Jour. Vet. Res., vol.2, no.3, pp.199-201, Apr., 1941.

BLACKLEG IN DEER. H.L. Armstrong, J.K. MacNamee. Jour. Amer. Vet. Med. Assoc., Chicago, vol.117, no.882, pp.212-214, Sep., 1950.

FIBROMA IN A VIRGINIA DEER. E.C. Berry. Jour. Mamm., vol.6, no.2, p.130, May, 1925.

BRUCELLOSIS IN NORTH DAKOTA DEER... A SURVEY. F.M. Bolin et al. Bi-Monthly Bull., Fargo, vol.11, no.3, pp.102-103, illus., Jan.-Feb., 1949.

ANAPLASMOSIS AMONG DEER IN THE NATURAL STATE. W.H. Boynton, G.M. Woods. Science, vol.91, no.2355, p.168, Feb. 16, 1940.

DEER AS CARRIERS OF ANAPLASMOSIS. W.H. Boynton, G.M. Woods. Science, n.s., vol.78, no.2033, pp.559-560, Dec. 15, 1933.

INVESTIGATIONS OF DEER DISEASE IN MENDOCINO COUNTY. H.C. Bryant. Calif. Fish and Game, vol.12, pp.107-108, Apr., 1926.

A "MAD STONE" FROM A DEER. H.C. Bryant. Jour. Mamm., vol.5, no.3, pp. 200-201, Aug., 1924.

CALCULUS FROM THE STOMACH OF A DEER. William H. Burt. Jour. Mamm., vol. 23, no.3, pp.335-336, illus., Aug. 14, 1942.

STUDIES ON THE ENDOPARASITIC FAUNA OF TRINIDAD MAMMALS. I. SOME PARASITES OF TRINIDAD DEER. Thomas W.M. Cameron. Canadian Jour. Sci., vol.13, sec. D, no.5, pp.89-96, figs.1-11, Nov., 1935.

EPITHELIAL PAPILLOMAS REPORTED IN DEER. T.T. Chaddock. Wisc. Cons. Bull., vol.4, no.2, pp.31-32, Feb., 1939.

CONTRIBUTION TO THE LIFE-HISTORY OF THE DEER LUNG-WORM LEPTOSTRONGYLUS ALPENAE (NEMATODA: METASTRONGYLIDEA), WITH OBSERVATIONS ON ITS INCIDENCE AND BIOLOGY. E.L. Cheatum. PhD thesis, Univ. Mich., 1948.

DISEASE IN RELATION TO WINTER MORTALITY OF DEER IN NEW YORK. E.L. Cheatum. Jour. Wildl. Mgt., Menasha, vol. 15, no.2, pp.216-220, Apr., 1951.

NOTES ON THE LIFE HISTORY AND MORPHOLOGY OF CEPHENEMYIA JELLISONI TOWNSEND AND LIPTOTENA DEPRESSA SAY, TWO DIPTEROUS PARASITES OF THE COLUMBIAN BLACK-TAILED DEER (ODOCOILEUS HEMIONUS COLUMBIANUS (RICHARDSON).). Ian McT. Cowan. Canadian Jour. Research, Ottawa, vol.21, no.6, sec.D, pp.171-187, illus., 1943.

PARASITES, DISEASES, INJURIES, AND ANOMALIES OF THE COLUMBIAN BLACK-TAILED DEER, ODOCOILEUS HEMIONUS COLUMBIANUS (RICHARDSON), IN BRITISH COLUMBIA. Ian McT Cowan. Canadian Jour. Research, Ottawa, sec.D, vol.24, no.3, pp. 71-103, fig.7, pls.1-5, June, 1946.

TWO CASES OF PATHOLOGIC SKIN GROWTHS IN DEER OF THE GENUS ODOCOILEUS. Ian McT. Cowan. Murrelet, vol. 15, no.3, pp.81-82, Sep., 1934.

MORE ABOUT DEER DISEASE. B.F. Cox. Wildl. in N.C., vol.14, no.7, pp.19-20, July, 1950.

REPORT ON THE INVESTIGATION OF THE DEAD DEER AT THE RUBY STATE GAME RESERVE AT RUBY, WASHINGTON. Arthur Crews. Murrelet, vol.16, no.2, pp.35-37, May, 1935.

THE FOOT-WORM DISEASE IN DEER OF THE NORTHERN ROCKY MOUNTAIN REGION. R.M. DeNio, Raymond M. West. Field Notes on Widl., vol.2, no.6, p.4, Feb., 1941; Jour. Forestry, vol.40, no.7, pp.540-543, July, 1942.

NEW NEMATODE, SKRJABINEMA PARVA (NEMATODA: OXYUROIDEA), FROM DEER. G. Dikmans. Proc. Helminth. Soc. Wash., vol.9, no.2, pp.66-68, July, 1942.

HELMINTH PARASITES COLLECTED FROM DEER, ODOCOILEUS VIRGINIANUS, IN FLORIDA. A.G. Dinaburg. Proc. Helminth. Soc. Wash., vol.6, no.2, pp.102-104, July, 1939.

NEMATODE LUNGWORMS (SUBORDER STRONGYLINA) OF NORTH AMERICAN DEER OF THE GENUS ODOCOILEUS. E. C. Dougherty. Parasitol., London, vol.36, nos.3-4, pp.199-208, illus., Mar., 1945.

SICKLE CELLS IN THE BLOOD OF WESTERN DEER. R.W. Dougherty. Jour. Wildl. Mgt., vol.3, no.1, pp.17-18, Jan., 1939.

TWO CALCULI FROM MULE DEER. Vergil Draney, Leslie Robinette. Jour. Mamm., vol. 36, no.2, p.308, May 26, 1955.

AUTOPSY FINDINGS OF DEER. R. Fenstermacher. Proc. Minn. Wildl. Cons. Short Course, no.2, pp.42-43, 1940.

DISEASES OF WHITE-TAILED DEER. R. Fenstermacher, et al. Conserv. Volunteer, St. Paul, vol.7, no.39, pp.48-50, Mar.-Apr., 1944.

SOME DISEASES OF WHITE-TAILED DEER IN MINNESOTA. R. Fenstermacher et al. Cornell Veterinarian, Ithaca, vol.33, no.4, pp.323-332, pls.2, Oct., 1943.

PARATYPHOID IN A FAWN. H.C. Gauger, Seth Gordon, Jr. Jour. Amer. Vet. Med. Assn., vol.99, no.772, p.54, July, 1941.

NOTES ON THE ADULTS OF PROTOSTRONGYLUS COBURNI IN THE LUNGS OF WHITE-TAILED DEER. Frans C. Goble. Jour. Parasitology, vol.29, no.2, p.158, Apr., 1943.

TISSUE CHANGES IN WHITE-TAILED DEER (ODOCOILEUS VIRGINIANUS BOREALIS) ACCOMPANYING NATURAL INFECTIONS OF LUNGWORMS (GENERA PROTOSTRONGYLUS AND DICTYOCAULUS). Frans C. Goble. Jour. Wildl. Mgt., Menasha, vol.5, no.2, pp.141-158, pls.9-14, Apr., 1941.

DEGENERATIVE MYOPATHY IN A WHITE-TAILED DEER, ODOCOILEUS VIRGINIANUS. W.J. Hadlow. Cornell Vet., vol.45, no.4, pp.538-547, illus., Oct., 1955.

PSEUDOTUBERCULOSIS OF DEER. H. Hamersland, E.M. Joneschild. Jour. Amer. Vet. Med. Assn., vol.91, no.2, pp.186-192, Aug., 1937.

FLYING STAGE OF THE DEER LOUSEFLY, LIPOTENA DEPRESSA (SAY), IN CALIFORNIA. John E. Hare. Pan-Pac. Ent., vol.21, no.2, pp.48-57, Apr., 1945.

SYMPTOMS OF MALNUTRITION IN DEER. Dave Harris. Jour. Widl. Mgt., Menasha, vol.9, no.4, pp.319-322, Oct., 1945; South Dakota Conserv. Digest, Pierre, vol.13, no. 2, pp.12-13, Feb., 1946.

CEPHENEMYIA JELLISONI TOWNSEND (DIPTERA CUTEREBRIDAE) REARED FROM NASAL BOT OF BLACK-TAILED DEER. Carlton M. Herman. Pan-Pac. Ent., vol.21, no.3, p.120, July, 1945.

EYE WORM (THELAZIA CALIFORNIENSIS) INFECTION IN DEER IN CALIFORNIA. Carlton M. Herman. Calif. Fish and Game, San Francisco, vol.30, no.1, pp.58-60, Jan., 1944.

FURTHER OBSERVATIONS ON DEER FOOT WORM INFECTION. Carlton M. Herman. Calif. Fish and Game, San Francisco, vol. 33, no.1, p.54, Mar. 15, 1947.

NOSE BOT FLY OF DEER. Carlton M. Herman. Calif. Fish and Game, vol.32, no.1, pp.17-18, Jan., 1946.

SOME WORM PARASITES OF DEER IN CALIFORNIA. Carlton M. Herman. Calif. Fish and Game, San Francisco, vol.31, no. 4, pp.201-208, Oct., 1945.

FOOT WORM PARASITE OF DEER. Carlton M. Herman, Arthur I. Bischoff. Calif. Fish and Game, vol.32, no.4, pp.182-190, Oct., 1946.

PAPILLOMA, SKIN TUMORS IN DEER. Carlton M. Herman, Arthur I. Bischoff. Calif. Fish and Game, San Francisco, vol. 36, no.1, pp.10-20, illus., Jan., 1950.

REPAIR OF FRACTURED DEER BONES. William S. Hoar. Acadian Nat., Fredericton, vol.2, no.5, pp.44-46, pl.3, May, 1945.

FREAK DEER HEAD. Ralph F. Honess. Jour. Wildl. Mgt., vol.3, no.4, p.360, Oct., 1939.

NEUROFIBROMATOSIS IN WHITE-TAILED DEER. Earl E. Hoover. Jour. Mamm., vol. 18, no.1, pp.104-105, Feb. 14, 1937.

PARASITE PERILS DEER. J.S. Hunter. Calif. Conservationist, Sacramento, vol.5, no.11, p. 7, Nov., 1940.

EXISTENCE OF TROPICAL VARIETY OF CATTLEFEVER TICK (BOÖPHILUS ANNULATUS VAR. AUSTRALIS) COMPLICATES TICK ERADICATION. J.V. Knapp. Jour. Amer. Vet. Med. Assn., vol.96, no. 758, pp.607-608, May, 1940.

THE DEER FLY. James Lee. New York State Cons., vol.8, no.3, p.32, illus., Dec.-Jan., 1953-54.

SEARCH FOR BANG'S DISEASE IN NORTH DAKOTA DEER. William T. McKean. N. Dakota Outdoors, Bismarck, vol.11, no.8, pp.10, Feb., 1949.

MALIGNANT EDEMA IN DEER. F.D. McKenney. Trans. 3rd N.Amer. Wildl. Conf., pp.886-889, 1938.

SCREW-WORM FLY. Donald D. McLean. Calif. Cons., vol.6, no.2, pp.11, 20-21, Feb., 1941.

WHITE-TAILED DEER, A NEW HOST OF DICROCOELIUM DENDRITICUM (RUDOLPHI, 1819) LOOSS, 1899 (TREMATODA: DICROCOELIIDAE). Cortland R. Mapes, Donald W. Baker. Cornell Vet., vol.40, no.2, pp. 211-212, Apr., 1950.

CALIFORNIA MULE DEER A HOST FOR NEMATODE EYE WORMS IN SEQUOIA NATIONAL PARK. Frank R. Oberhansley. Jour. Amer. Vet. Med. Assn., vol.96, no.757, p.542, Apr., 1940.

WHITE-TAILED DEER AS A RESERVOIR HOST OF THE LARGE AMERICAN LIVER FLUKE. O. Wilford Olsen. Vet. Med., Chicago, vol.44, no.1, pp.26-30, illus., Jan., 1949.

HELMINTHS OF NORTH AMERICAN DEER WITH SPECIAL REFERENCE TO THOSE OF THE WHITE-TAILED DEER (ODOCOILEUS VIRGINIANUS BOREALIS) IN MINNESOTA. O. Wilford Olsen, R. Fenstermacher. Minn. Agr. Exp. Sta., Tech.Bull., no.159, pp.20, 1943.

WELLCOMIA EVAGINATA (SMITH, 1908) (OXYURIDAE: NEMATODE) OF PORCUPINES IN MULE DEER, ODOCOILEUS HEMIONUS, IN COLORADO. O. Wilford Olsen, C.D. Tolman. Proc. Helminth. Soc. Wash., vol. 18, no.2, pp.120-122, July, 1951.

LUNGWORM SITUATION IN THE WHITE-TAILED DEER (ODOCOILEUS VIRGINIANUS BOREALIS) IN MICHIGAN. E.C.O'Roke. Proc. N.Amer. Wildl. Conf., pp.473-478, 1936.

SICKLE-CELL ANEMIA IN DEER. E.C. O'Roke. Proc. Soc. Exp. Biol. and Med., vol.34, pp.738-739, 1936.

EXPERIMENTAL TRANSMISSION OF THE DEER LUNGWORM, LEPTOSTRONGYLUS ALPENAE. E.C. O'Roke, E.L.Chaetum. Cornell Vet., vol.40, no.3, pp.315-323, July, 1950.

HEMORRHAGIC SEPTICEMIA IN MULE DEER. E.R. Quortrup. N. A. Vet., vol. 23, no.1, pp.34-36, Jan., 1942.

TUMORS OF DEER. E.R. Quortrup. Va. Wildl., Richmond, vol.7, no.1, pp.15, 18, illus., July, 1946.

OBSERVATIONS ON HISTOPATHOLOGICAL CHANGES ASSOCIATED WITH STARVATION IN WISCONSIN DEER. Robert Rausch. Jour. Wildl. Mgt., Menasha, vol.14, no.2, pp.156-161, pls.6-7, Apr., 1950.

"PARROT MOUTH" IN ROCKY MOUNTAIN MULE DEER. W. Leslie Robinette, C.M. Aldous. Jour. Mamm., vol.36, no.2, pp. 308-310, May 26, 1955.

PARASITISM IN DEER. H. Van Roekel. Calif. Fish and Game, vol.15, no.4, pp. 309-314, figs. 6, (Oct.) Dec., 1929.

EPIZOOTIC OF FOOT ROT IN CALIFORNIA DEER. Merton N. Rosen et al. Trans.16th N.Amer. Wildl. Conf., pp.164-178, 1951.

RELATION OF HEMATOLOGY TO CONDITION IN CALIFORNIA DEER. Merton N. Rosen, Arthur I. Bischoff. Trans. 17th N. Amer. Wildl. Conf., pp.482-496, illus., 1952.

CONTAGIOUS PANOPHTHALMITIS IN DEER. Irene Rosenfeld, O.A. Beath. Jour. Wildl. Mgt., vol.8, no.3, pp.247-250, July, 1944.

WHAT IS "BLACK TONGUE" AMONG DEER? Frederick J. Ruff. Wildl. in N.C., vol.14, no.6, pp.16-19, June, 1950.

ONCHOCERCIASIS, A NEW DISEASE IN THE WHITE-TAILED DEER OF MONTANA. W. M. Rush. Jour. Mamm., vol.16, no.1, pp. 70-71, Feb., 1935.

CASEOUS LYMPHADENITIS OF DEER (ODOCOILEUS HEMIONUS) IN WASHINGTON. L. Seghetti, F.D. McKenney. Jour. Amer. Vet. Med. Assn., vol.98, no.767, pp.129-131, Feb., 1941.

OCCURRENCE OF A BOTFLY LARVA IN WHITE-TAILED DEER. C.W. Severinghaus. Jour. Mamm., Baltimore, vol.30, no.1, p. 75, Feb. 14, 1949.

DEER IN RELATION TO FEVER TICK ERADICATION IN FLORIDA. J.E. Shillinger. Trans. 3rd N.Amer. Wildl. Conf., pp.882-885, 1938.

INFECTIOUS FIBROMA OF DEER. Richard E. Shope. Proc. Soc. Exp. Biol. and Med., vol.88, no.4, pp.533-535, Apr., 1955.

DEER MORTALITY / EPIZOOTIC HEMORRHAGIC DISEASE OF DEER. Richard E. Shope et al. N. J. Outdoors, vol. 6, no.5, pp.16-21, illus., Nov., 1955.

SURVEY OF BRUCELLOSIS IN WHITE-TAILED DEER IN MISSOURI. M.O.Steen, et al. Jour. Wildl. Mgt., Ithaca, vol.19, no.2, pp.320-321, Apr., 1955.

NEW BACTERIUM, CORYNEBACTERIUM LIPOPTENAS, ASSOCIATED WITH THE LOUSE FLY, LIPOPTENA DEPRESSA SAY. Edward A. Steinhaus. Jour.Parasitology, vol.29, no.1, p.80, Feb., 1943.

SCREW-WORM PROBLEM IN THE OCALA NATIONAL FOREST DEER HERD. Donald D. Strode. Presented at 8th Ann. Conf.S.E. Assn. Game and Fish Comm., New Orleans, La., Nov., 1954, pp.1-19, graph, mimeo.

RESEARCHES ON LIVER FLUKE IN DEER. W.E. Swales. Trans. 21st Amer. Game Conf., Amer. Game Assn., New York, pp. 406-411, 1935.

PARASITISM AND MALNUTRITION OF DEER IN TEXAS. H.L. Van Volkenberg, Arnold Nicholson. Jour. Wildl.Mgt., vol. 7, no.2, pp.220-223, Apr., 1943.

DISEASE IN MICHIGAN DEER. S. C. Whitlock. Michigan Conservation, Lansing, vol. 18, no.6, pp.33-34, Dec., 1949.

PREVALENCE OF DISEASE AND PARASITES IN WHITETAIL DEER. S.C.Whitlock. Trans. 4th N.Amer. Wildl.Conf., pp.244-249, 1939.

DEER LIVER FLUKE COMMON IN THE UPPER PENINSULA. S.C. Whitlock, Carl Gower. Michigan Conservation, vol.8, no.2, p.8, Oct., 1938.

TICK-INFESTED DEER. George M. Wright. Yosemite Nature Notes, vol.7, p.38, May, 1928.

TICKY DEER IN FLORIDA. Fla. Cattleman, vol.2, no.2,pp.11, 14, Nov. 15, 1937.

Odocoileus--Economic Importance

EFFECTS OF DEER ON CONIFER REPRODUCTION IN NORTHWESTERN MONTANA. Lowell Adams. Jour. Forestry, vol.47, no. 11, pp.909-913, Nov., 1949.

CONTROL OF DEER IRRUPTIONS IN NEVADA. C.M. Aldous. U.S.Dept.Interior, Fish and Wildl. Serv., Spec. Sci. Rep., no.57, pp.16, Sep., 1948.

DAMAGE TO NATURAL REPRODUCTION BY DEER BROWSING. Carl Arbogast, Miron L. Heinselman. U.S. Dept. Agric., Lake States Forest Exp. Sta., Tech. Note 332, p.1, Apr., 1950.

THE DEER DAMAGE COMMITTEE. Paul M. Barrett. Mich. Cons., vol.10, no.1, pp.2, 10, Nov., 1940.

DEER-PROOF FENCES. I.H. Bartlett. Mich. Dept. Cons., p.3, 1950.

ZINC DIMETHYLDITHIOCARBAMATE-CYCLOHEXYLAMINE COMPLEX AS A DEER REPELLENT APPLICABLE TO AGRICULTURAL CROPS. Luther L.Baumgartner, Stephen E. Powell. Contrib.Boyce Thompson Inst., vol.15, no.7, pp.411-420, Apr.-June, 1949.

OCTOBER, 1943, SURVEY OF LOSS OF CRANBERRIES AS A RESULT OF DEER DAMAGE. D.O. Boster. Proc. Ann.Meeting Am.Cranberry Grower's Assn., no.74, pp. 12-13, 16, 1944.

ORCHARD DAMAGE. Arlow P. Boyce. Mich. Cons., vol.19, no.6, pp.9-10, 26, Nov.-Dec., 1950.

WHITE-TAILED DEER--BIG BUSINESS IN THE NORTH COUNTRY. G.W.Bradt.Mich. Cons., vol.15, no.10, p.4, Nov., 1946.

FOREST GRAZING PROBLEM CREATED BY DEER IN EASTERN FORESTS. W.C. Bramble, P.F. English. Proc. Soc.Amer. Foresters' Meeting, 1948, pp.257-263, 1949.

DEER DAMAGE CONTROL THROUGH HERD MANAGEMENT. Gardiner Bump. Trans. 14th N.Amer. Wildl. Conf., pp.604-611, 1949.

ELECTRIC FENCES THAT REPEL DEER. J.G. Burr. Science, vol.92, no.2397, pp. 529-530, Dec. 6, 1940.

BROWSING DEER DISCOURAGED BY REPELLENT. E. Garth Champagne. U.S. Forest Serv., Cent.States Forest Exp.Sta., Sta. Notes no.80, pp.2, Sep., 1953.

DEER DAMAGE CONTROL. Floyd B. Chapman. Ohio Conserv. Bull., Columbus, vol. 10, no.9, pp.12-13, illus., Sep., 1946.

BACKYARD BLACKTAILS. Mel Cummings. Oreg.State Game Comm.Bull., vol.10, no. 9, pp.3-4, 7, illus., Sep., 1955.

RED DEER INVADERS. Bonnycastle Dale, Jr. Forest and Outdoors, vol.33, no.5, pp.144-145, May, 1937.

TOO MANY DEER. Bonnycastle Dale, Jr. Rod and Gun in Canada, vol.42, no.1, pp.15-37, June, 1940.

DEER DAMAGE TO FOREST REPRODUCTION SURVEY. Stanley G. DeBoer. Wisc. Cons. Bull., vol.12, no.10, pp.3-23, Oct., 1947.

SURVEY OF DEER DAMAGE TO CONIFEROUS PLANTINGS IN SELECTED PENNSYLVANIA COUNTIES. John S. Detwiler. MS thesis Penna.State Univ., pp.94, 1953.

OUR DEER HERD'S LITTLE DIVIDEND. Robert L. Dunkeson. Mo.Cons., vol.16, no.6, pp.4-6, illus., June, 1955.

THE "NATURAL" CONTROL OF DEER POPULATIONS. C.D. Fowle. Conv.Internat. Assn. Game, Fish and Cons.Comm., vol. 40, pp.56-63, 1950.

ELECTRIC FENCE REPELS DEER. Bill Garrett. Texas Game and Fish, vol.13, no.3, p.9, illus., Mar., 1955.

ELECTRIC FENCING AS A DEER CONTROL AGENCY. Richard Gerstell. Penna. Game News, vol.8, no.12, pp.8-9, 32, Mar., 1938.

ANTLERLESS SEASON CONTROLS DEER DAMAGE. Carl Gower. Mich.Cons., vol. 13, no.7, pp.3, 11, Aug., 1944.

DEER REPELLENT SPRAYS NOT HARMFUL TO FOLIAGE ON TWO-YEAR-OLD TREES. Walter E. Howard, Henry A. Hjersman.Jour. Wildl. Mgt., Ithaca, vol.16, no.3, pp.390-391, July, 1952.

DEER REPELLENTS. Walter E. Howard, Henry A. Hjersman. Univ. Calif.Agric. Exp. Sta., vol.5, no.9, p.7, 1951.

DEER DAMAGE AND CONTROL IN CULTIVATED CROPS AND ORCHARDS IN MAINE. Walter H. Kittams. MS thesis, Univ.Maine, 1941.

DEER DAMAGE TO A JACK PINE PLANTATION IN MICHIGAN. Laurits W. Krefting. U.S. Forest Serv., Lake States Exp.Sta., Tech. Notes no.387, p.1, Jan., 1953.

DEER FARMING IN THE UNITED STATES. David E. Lantz. U.S.Dept.Agric., Farmers' Bull., no.330, pp.20, figs.2, July 29, 1908.

PLANTING TO REDUCE DEER DAMAGE. William M. Longhurst. Calif. Agric., vol. 7, no.2, p.4, illus., Feb., 1953.

INJURIES TO YOUNG TREE TRUNKS FROM ANTLER RUBBING BY DEER. H.J. Lutz, H.H. Chapman. Jour. Wildl. Mgt., vol.8, no.1, pp.80-81, Jan., 1944.

SOME EFFECTS OF HEAVY DEER CONCENTRATIONS IN THE ALLEGHENY NATIONAL FOREST. Randal McCain. Pa. Game News, vol.11, no.10, pp.10, 29, Jan., 1940.

APPRAISAL OF DEER DAMAGE TO NATURAL FOREST REPRODUCTION ON FENCED AND UNFENCED PLOTS IN SELECTED LOCALITIES IN PENNSYLVANIA. James M. McCullough. MS thesis, Penna. State Coll., June, 1952.

DEER DAMAGE STUDY PLOTS IN PENNSYLVANIA. J.C. Middour. Penna. Game News, vol.9, no.9, pp.8-9, 30-31, Dec., 1938.

PROTECTING ORCHARD TREES FROM DEER. E.M. Mills. U.S.Dept.Agric., Bur. Biol. Surv., Wildl. Research and Mgt. Leaflet, no.BS-117, pp.1-5, pl.1, June, 1938.

PROTECTING TREES FROM DEER. E.M. Mills. Penna. Game News, Harrisburg, vol. 7, no.6, pp.20-21, illus., Sep., 1936.

BUSINESS SIDE OF DEER HUNTING. Jerome K. Pasto, D. Woods Thomas. Penna. Game News, vol.26, no.1, pp.23-30, illus., Jan., 1955.

COSTS AND BENEFITS OF THE POTTER AND MONROE COUNTY DEER HERDS.

Jerome K. Pasto, D. Woods Thomas. Penna. Game News, vol.26, no.2, pp.4-12, illus., Feb., 1955.

DEER DAMAGE TO FARM CROPS. Jerome K. Pasto, D. Woods Thomas. Penna. Game News, vol.25, no.11, pp.22-28, illus., Nov., 1954.

DEER ECONOMICS. Jerome K. Pasto, D. Woods Thomas. Penna State Univ., Coll. Agric. Ext. Serv., pp.1-29, illus., 1955.

DOLLAR SIDE OF DEER DAMAGE TO FARM CROPS. Jerome K. Pasto, D. Woods Thomas. Penna. Game News, vol.25, no. 12, pp.37-43, illus., Dec., 1954.

CROP PROTECTION THROUGH A NEW DEER REPELLENT SPRAY. Stephen E. Powell. Trans. 14th N.Amer. Wildl.Conf., pp.567-576, 1949.

WHITE-TAILED DEER. A FOREST CROP IN THE ARKANSAS OZARKS. Ralph A. Read. Southern Lumberman, Nashville, vol.173, pp.141-142, 1946.

ELECTRIC FENCES FOR THE CONTROL OF DEER DAMAGE. Roger A. Seamans. Vt.Fish and Game Serv., State Bull., PR Ser. no.16, pp.1-77, illus., Feb., 1951.

EFFECT OF DEER BROWSING ON REPRODUCTION IN THE NORTHERN HARDWOOD-HEMLOCK TYPE IN NORTHEASTERN WISCONSIN. J.H. Stoeckeler et al. Jour. Wildl. Mgt., vol.21, no.1, pp.75-80, illus., Jan., 1957.

DEER PROOF FENCES IN CALIFORNIA. Tracy I. Storer, Gordon H. True, Jr. Calif. Fish and Game, vol.17, no.3, pp.263-269, July, 1931.

TRADE IN DEER SKINS IN EARLY TEXAS. John K. Strecker. Jour. Mamm., vol.8, no. 2, pp.106-110, May, 1927.

DEER DAMAGE TO FOREST REPRODUCTION SURVEY. Ernest Swift. Conv.Internat.Assn.Game, Fish and Cons.Comm., vol.38, pp.181-203, 1949?

DEER HERD CONTROL METHODS AND THEIR RESULTS. Ernest Swift. 41st Conv. Internat. Assn. Game, Fish and Cons.Comm., Sep. 10-11, 1951, Rochester, N.Y., pp.126-133; Wisc. Cons.Bull., vol. 17, no.1, pp.3-9, Jan., 1952.

WISCONSIN'S DEER DAMAGE TO FOREST REPRODUCTION SURVEY--FINAL REPORT. Ernest Swift. Publ. Wisc.State Conserv. Dept., Madison, no.347, pp.24, illus., 1948.

DEER--OUR UNDEVELOPED ASSET. Lawrence Temple. Oklahoma Game and Fish News, Oklahoma City, vol.6, no.11, pp.3-5, illus., Nov., 1950.

ECONOMIC ANALYSIS OF DEER DAMAGE TO FARM CROPS AND INCOME FROM HUNTERS, POTTER AND MONROE COUNTIES, PENNSYLVANIA. D. Woods Thomas. PhD thesis, Penna. State Univ., 1954. (For 1951.)

DEER REPELLENT TESTS. Donald R. Thompson, John M. Keener. Wisc.Cons. Bull., vol.16, no.10, pp.10-13, Oct., 1951.

DAMAGE BY DEER TO CROPS IN CALIFORNIA. Gordon H. True. Calif. Fish and Game, vol.18, no.2, pp.136-147, Apr., 1932.

REPELLENTS AND DEER DAMAGE CONTROL. Gordon H. True, Jr. Calif.Fish and Game, vol.18, no.2, pp.156-165, Apr., 1932.

SIMPLE DEER REPELLENT FOR CONIFER PLANTATIONS. Siegfried Weiss. Jour. Wildl. Mgt., Menasha, vol.4, no.1, pp.77-79, Jan., 1940.

DEER DAMAGE IN THE BRULE RIVER VALLEY. Stanley Welsh. Wisc.Cons.Bull., vol.4, no.6, pp.41-46, June, 1939.

SUMMARY OF DEER CONTROL STUDIES. Jack F. Welch. Mich. Dept. Cons., p.8, 1948.

ECONOMIC IMPORTANCE OF THE ARKANSAS DEER HERD. Roy Wood. Proc. Ark. Acad. Sci., vol.2, pp.65-68, 1947.

BONE TAR OIL SPRAYS REPEL DEER. Va.Comm. of Game and Inland Fisheries. Va. Wildl., vol.16, no.2, p.25, Feb., 1955.

DEER DAMAGE TO JACK PINE PLANTATION IN MINNESOTA. Forest Res. Dig., pp.4-5, Spring, 1938.

FAWNS ARE SO CUTE. (Deer destroy planted forest seedlings.) Wisc.Conserv.Bull., Madison, vol.14, no.6, p.35, illus., June, 1949.

INCREASING PROBLEM OF DEER DAMAGE. Timberman, vol.56, no.11, pp.48-51, illus., Sep., 1955.

MICHIGAN'S DEER DAMAGE PROBLEM. Mich. Cons., vol.9, no.2, pp.6-7, Nov., 1939.

NEW ELECTRIC DEER FENCE. Va.Wildl., Richmond, vol.9, no.10, pp.23, illus., Oct., 1948.

USEFUL THINGS FROM DEER HIDES AND HORNS. Minnesota Sportsman's Digest, Minneapolis, vol.7, no.5, p.6, illus., Jan.-Feb., 1947.

Odocoileus--Europe

WHITE-TAILED DEER IN FINLAND. A.M. Salmi. Suomen Riista, vol.4, p.124, 1949. (With English summary of a 34-page, illus. article in Finnish.)

Odocoileus--Food Habits

DEER BROWSING ON PONDEROSA PINE. Lowell Adams. Proc. Mont.Acad.Sci., no. 7 and 8, pp.65-68, 1948.

WHITE-TAILED DEER BROWSING ON NATURAL CONIFER SEEDLINGS. Lowell Adams. U.S. Dept. Agric., N.Rocky Mt. Forest and Range Exp.Sta., Res.Note 105, p.3, Sep., 1951.

DEER BROWSE CLIPPING STUDY IN THE LAKE STATES REGION. Shaler E. Aldous. Jour. Wildl. Mgt., Ithaca, vol.16, no.4, pp. 401-409, pl.1, 1952.

PINE IN THE DIET OF THE WHITE-TAILED DEER. Shaler E. Aldous. Jour.Forestry, vol. 37, no.3, pp.265-267, Mar., 1939.

FALL AND WINTER FOOD HABITS OF DEER IN NORTHEASTERN MINNESOTA. Shaelr E. Aldous, Clarence F. Smith. U.S. Dept. Agric., Biol. Survey, Wildl. Leaflet no.137, pp.10, May, 1939; U.S.Dept.Interior, Fish and Wildl. Serv., Wildl. Leaflet no. 310, pp.10, illus., Aug., 1948.

FOOD HABITS OF MINNESOTA DEER AS DETERMINED BY STOMACH ANALYSIS. Shaler E. Aldous, Clarence F. Smith. Trans. 3rd N.Amer. Wildl. Conf., pp.756-767, 1938.

WHITE-TAILED DEER FOODS OF THE UNITED STATES. Earl L. Atwood. Jour. Wildl. Mgt., vol.5, no.3, pp.314-332, July, 1941.

AVAILABILITY OF WHITE-TAILED DEER BROWSE WITHIN THE HATTER CREEK ENCLOSURE. Joseph V. Basile. MS thesis, Univ. Idaho, pp.45, 1954.

SALT USE BY MULE DEER IN THE DESCHUTES NATIONAL FOREST OF CENTRAL OREGON. Hugh C. Black. MS thesis, Oreg. State Coll., pp.xi+143, illus., 1955.

DIET OF DEER INFLUENCED BY RANGE. F.E. Blackstock. Texas. Game and Fish, vol.10, no.8, p.18, July, 1952.

SEASONAL BROWSING OF WOODY PLANTS BY WHITE-TAILED DEER. W.C. Bramble, M.K. Goddard. Penna. Game News, vol. 15, no.4, pp.8-9, 29, July, 1944.

SEASONAL BROWSING OF WOODY PLANTS BY WHITE-TAILED DEER IN THE BEAR OAK FOREST TYPE. W.C. Bramble, M.K. Goddard. Jour. Forestry, vol.41, no.7, pp. 471-475, July 1943.

SEASONAL BROWSING OF WOODY PLANTS BY WHITE-TAILED DEER IN THE RIDGE AND VALLEY SECTION OF CENTRAL PENNSYLVANIA. W.C. Bramble, M.K. Goddard. Jour.Forestry, vol.51, no.11, pp. 815-819, Nov., 1953.

FISH-EATING DEER. Thornton W.Burgess. Jour. Mamm., vol.5, no.1, pp.64-65, Feb., 1924.

FOOD HABITS OF THE WHITE-TAILED DEER, ODOCOILEUS VIRGINIANUS BODDAERT, IN BOONE COUNTY, IOWA. Frank E. Buxton. MS thesis, Iowa State Coll., 1951.

WHAT DEER EAT. BY SPECIES, BY SEASON, BY RANGE AND BY PREFERENCE. Arthur H. Carhart. Amer. Forests, vol.50, no.8, pp. 383-385, Aug., 1944; Amer.Field, Chicago, vol.143, no.2, pp.28-29, illus., Jan.13, 1945.

FOOD PLANTS UTILIZED BY THE DEER IN THE MARIPOSA GROVE. Arthur Carthew. Yosemite Nat. Notes, Yosemite, vol.21, no. 9, p.80, Sep., 1942.

FOOD PREFERENCES TO THE COLUMBIAN BLACK-TAILED DEER, ODOCOILEUS HEMIONUS COLUMBIANUS (RICHARDSON), ON THE TILLAMOOK BURN, OREGON. E.F. Chatelain. MS thesis, Oregon State Coll., 1947.

SUMMER BROWSING BY DEER ON CUT-OVER HARDWOOD LANDS. David B.Cook. Jour. Wildl. Mgt., vol.10, no.1, pp.60-63, Jan., 1946.

NOTES ON MULE DEER FORAGE. Robert F. Cooney. N.Region News, pp.38-39, May, 1937.

DEER BROWSE IN THE MISSOURI OZARKS. Paul D. Dalke. Proc. Missouri Acad. Sci., Columbia, vol.7, no.4, whole no.24, p.95, Jan. 25, 1942. (Abstract.)

DEER FOODS IN THE MISSOURI OZARKS. Paul D. Dalke. Missouri Cons., Jefferson City, vol.8, no.9, pp.4-5, illus., Sep., 1947.

USE AND AVAILABILITY OF THE MORE COMMON WINTER DEER BROWSE PLANTS IN THE MISSOURI OZARKS. Paul D. Dalke. Trans. 6th N.Amer. Wildl. Conf., Wash., D.C., pp.155-160, 1941.

STUDY OF THE FOOD PREFERENCES AND REQUIREMENTS OF THE WHITE-TAILED DEER IN NEW YORK STATE. Robert Darrow. Trans. 21st Amer. Game Conf., Amer. Game Assn., New York, pp.392-396, 1935.

DEER AND FORAGE RELATIONSHIP ON THE LASSEN-WASHOE INTERSTATE WINTER DEER RANGE. William P. Dasmann, James A. Blaisdell. Calif. Fish and Game, vol.40, no.3, pp.215-234, July, 1954.

FIND DEER HAVE MARKED FOOD PREFERENCES. L.A. Davenport. Mich. Cons., vol. 7, no.4, pp.4-6, 11, Dec., 1937.

FOOD HABITS OF WHITE-TAILED DEER ON THE CATTLE STOCKED, LIVEOAK-MESQUITE RANGES OF THE KING RANCH, AS DETERMINED BY ANALYSES OF DEER RUMEN CONTENTS. Richard B. Davis. MS thesis, A. and M. Coll. Texas, pp.97, 1951.

WHAT DEER EAT. Joseph Dixon. Amer. Forests and Forest Life, vol.34, pp.143-145, illus., Mar., 1928.

FEEDING HABITS OF THE WHITE-TAILED DEER, ODOCOILEUS VIRGINIANUS, IN RELATION TO DEER MANAGEMENT IN THE MISSOURI OZARKS. Robert L.Dunkeson. MA thesis, Univ. Mo., 1950.

NOTES ON SUMMER WATER CONSUMPTION BY DESERT MULE DEER. James B. Elder. Jour. Wildl. Mgt., Ithaca, vol.18, no.4, pp. 540-541, Oct., 1954.

DEER MUST EAT, TOO! L.D. Fay, R.A. MacMullan. Michigan Conserv., Lansing, vol.20, no.6, pp.8-10, illus., Nov., 1951.

FOOD HABITS OF A CALIFORNIA DEER HERD. Carol M. Ferrel, Howard R. Leach. Calif. Fish and Game, vol.36, no.3, pp. 235-240, July, 1950.

MOUNTAIN LAUREL AND RHODODENDRON AS FOODS FOR THE WHITE TAILED DEER. E.B. Forbes, S.I. Bechdel. Ecology, vol.12, no.2, pp.323-333, figs.1-4, Apr., 1931.

QUANTITIES OF DEER BROWSE PRODUCED ON RECENTLY CUTOVER ASPEN LAND. Samuel A. Graham, Casey E. Westell, Jr. Mich. Widll., no.1, pp.2, Sep., 1955.

THE DIET OF "WILD DEER." Dorothy Hack. Yosemite Nature Notes, vol.7, p.69, Aug., 1928.

AMMATE IN THE DIET OF DEER. Arnold O. Haugen. Jour. Wildl. Mgt., vol.17, no. 1, pp.33-36, Jan., 1953.

WHAT CONSTITUTES A DEER'S MENU. Ralph Hill. S.Dak.Cons.Dig., vol.9, no. 2, p.3, Feb., 1942.

FOOD PREFERENCES OF BLACK HILLS DEER. Ralph Hill, Dave Harris. Jour.Wildl. Mgt., vol.7, no.2, pp.233-235, Apr., 1943.

NOTES ON WINTER FOODS OF MICHIGAN DEER. William J. Howard. Jour.Mamm., vol.18, no.1, pp.77-80, Feb., 1937.

WATERHOLES FOR WILDLIFE.Carlock E. Johnson. Natl. Park. Serv., Region Three Quart., vol.2, no.2, pp.9-11, Apr., 1940.

FORAGE HABITS OF MULE DEER DURING THE LATE FALL, AS MEASURED BY STOMACH CONTENT ANALYSES. Odell Julander. U.S.Forest Serv., Intermt.Exp. Sta., Res.Note no.2, pp.5, Mar., 1952.

UTILIZATION OF BROWSE BY WILDLIFE. Odell Julander. Trans. 2nd N.Amer. Wildl. Conf., pp.276-287, 1937.

STUDY OF THE FOOD HABITS OF MISSOURI DEER. Leroy J. Korschgen. Mo. Cons. Comm., pp.iii+43, map, July, 1954.

DEER ON REFUGE PREFER PEACH TWIGS ABOVE OTHER BROWSE. M.G. Lewis. Va.Wildl., vol.3, no.3, p.3, Nov., 1939.

STUDIES OF FEEDING HABITS OF MULE DEER IN THE INTERMOUNTAIN REGION. S.B. Locke. Trans. Amer. Game Conf., vol.18, pp.262-266, (1931) 1932.

WINTER DEER FOOD DISTRIBUTION. E.L. Loyster. Wisc.Conserv.Bull., Madison, vol.9, no.2, p.5, Feb., 1944.

FALL AND WINTER FOODS OF NORTH DAKOTA DEER. William T.McKean. N. Dak.Agr. Exp.Sta., Bimonthly Bull., vol. 17, no.1, pp.25-31, Sep.-Oct., 1954.

DEER LICK IN LITTLE YOSEMITE.Donald McLean. Yosemite Nat.Notes, vol.7, p.94, Nov., 1928.

FOOD PREFERENCES AND REQUIREMENTS OF THE WHITE-TAILED DEER IN NEW YORK STATE. L.A. Maynard et al. N.Y. State Cons. Dept. and N.Y.State Coll.Agr., Joint Bull.no.1, pp.35, Jan., 1935.

DIFFERENTIAL BROWSING BY DEER ON PLOTS VARIOUSLY FERTILIZED. H. L. Mitchell, N.W. Hosley. Black Rock Forest Papers, vol.1, no.5, pp.24-27, Apr., 1936.

SAMPLING YIELDS AND UTILIZATION OF BROWSE ON WINTER DEER RANGES IN NORTHERN IDAHO. Allen D. Morton.MS thesis, Univ. Idaho, 1950; Jour.Forestry, vol.48, pp.684, Oct., 1950.

WHITE-TAILS LIKE ACORNS.Allen M. Pearson. Ala.Cons., vol.15, no.6, pp.8-9, 12, Dec., 1943.

DEER FOOD IN THE BLACK WARRIOR NATIONAL FOREST. Allen M. Pearson, Carey S. Burnett. Ala. Game and Fish News, vol.11, no.8, pp.3-4, Feb., 1940.

OBSERVATIONS ON THE RELATIVE IMPORTANCE OF WINTER DEER BROWSE SPECIES IN CENTRAL NEW YORK. George A. Petrides. Jour. Wildl. Mgt., Menasha, vol.5, no.4, pp.416-422, Oct., 1941.

CHAPARRAL CROWN SPROUTS AS BROWSE FOR DEER. Hudson Reynolds, Arthur W. Sampson. Jour. Wildl. Mgt., vol.7, no.1, pp.119-122, Jan., 1943.

PLANTS EATEN BY CALIFORNIA MULE DEER ON THE LOS PADRES NATIONAL FOREST. Cyril S. Robinson. Forestry, Wash., vol.35, no.3, pp.285-292, Mar., 1937.

STUDY OF PLANTS EATEN BY DEER ON THE SANTA BARBARA NATIONAL FOREST. Cyril S. Robinson. U.S.Dept.Agric., Forest Serv., pp.8, 1935.

FOOD HABITS RESEARCH. (Whitetailed deer.) Geo. B. Rossbach. Wisc. Wildl. Research, Quart. Prog. Rept., vol.4, no. 1, pp.19-24, Oct., 1944.

FOOD HABITS RESEARCH PROJECT. Geo. B. Rossbach. Wisc. Wildl. Research, Quart. Prog. Rept., Madison, vol.2, no.1, pp.32-54 (mimeogr.), Apr., 1942. (Food of white-tailed deer, pp.50-54.)

STUDIES ON THE FOOD HABITS OF THE WHITE-TAILED DEER IN ALABAMA. Dyer N. Ruggles. MS thesis, Ala.Polytechnic Inst., 1938.

WHAT'S ON THE MENU FOR NEBRASKA DEER? Geo. Schildman. Outdoor Nebr., vol.32, no.1, p.13, illus., Winter (Jan.), 1954.

CONSUMPTION OF NATIVE FORAGE SPECIES BY CAPTIVE MULE DEER DURING SUMMER. Arthur D. Smith. Jour. Range Mgt., vol.6, no.1, pp.30-37, graph, Jan., 1953.

HOW MUCH WATER DOES A DEER DRINK? Arthur D. Smith. Utah Fish and Game Bull., vol.10, no.9, pp.1, 8, Apr., 1954.

INQUIRIES INTO DIFFERENTIAL CONSUMPTION OF JUNIPER BY MULE DEER. Arthur D. Smith. Utah Fish and Game Bull., Salt Lake City, vol.9, no.5, p.4, Oct., 1950.

SAGEBRUSH AS A WINTER FEED FOR DEER. Arthur D. Smith. Jour. Wildl.Mgt., vol.14, no.3, pp.285-289, July, 1950.

PREFERENCE RATINGS FOR WINTER DEER FORAGES FROM NORTHERN UTAH RANGES BASED ON BROWSING TIME AND FORAGE CONSUMED. Arthur D. Smith, Richard L. Hubbard. Jour. Range Mgt., vol. 7, no.6, pp.262-265, Nov., 1954.

DEER FORAGE OBSERVATIONS IN UTAH. Justin G. Smith. Jour. Wildl. Mgt., vol. 13, no.3, pp.314-315, July, 1949.

FOOD HABITS OF MULE DEER IN UTAH. Justin G. Smith. Jour. Wildl. Mgt., Ithaca, vol.16, no.2, pp.148-155, illus., Apr., 1952.

SOME UNUSUAL FOODS OF OREGON MULE DEER. Clarence A. Sooter. Jour. Mamm., vol.25, no.2, pp.198-199, May, 1944.

FOOD STUDY OF THE WHITE-TAILED DEER. LeRoy C.Stegeman. Trans.2nd N.Amer. Wildl. Conf., pp.438-445, 1937.

DEER SELECT MOST NUTRITIOUS FORAGES. R.W. Swift. Jour. Wildl.Mgt., vol.12, no.1, pp.109-110, Jan., 1948.

DEER HAVE OWN NOTIONS ABOUT WHERE TO FEED. Joseph A. Tarr. Penna. Agr.Exp. Sta., Suppl.no.3 to Bull. 553, pp.4, June, 1953.

DEER FEEDING HABITS. Henry B. Ward. Va. Wildl., vol.3, no.10, p.5, June, 1940.

LOOKING INTO A DEER'S STOMACH. Fran Waugh. Game Breeder and Sportman, New York, vol.47, no.3, pp.49, 58-59, Mar., 1942.

SO I BEGAN ANALYZING DEER STOMACHS. Fran Waugh. S.Dak.Cons.Dig., vol.8, no.6, pp.7-8, June, 1941.

INTERPRETATION OF OVERBROWSING IN NORTHEASTERN FORESTS. (By deer.) William L. Webb. Jour. Wildl. Mgt., vol. 21, no.1, pp.101-103, Jan., 1957.

AVAILABLE BROWSE FOLLOWING ASPEN LOGGING IN LOWER MICHIGAN. Casey E. Westell, Jr. Jour. Wildl. Mgt., vol.18, no.2, pp.266-271, graph, Apr., 1954.

BLACK WARRIOR DEER FOOD. R. J. Wheeler, Jr, F.S. Barkalow, Jr. Alabama Cons., Montgomery, pp.1-3, fig.1, photo, Nov., 1940.

FLORA OF TWO EXPERIMENTAL PLOTS IN MASON COUNTY, TEXAS, WITH SPECIAL REFERENCE TO ITS UTILIZATION BY WHITE-TAILED DEER. Matt H. Whisenhunt. MS thesis, A. and M. Coll., Texas, 1949.

CHICKEN-EATING DEER. Va. Wildl., Blacksburg, vol.2, no.10, p.4, June, 1939.

FIRST WINTER BROWSE STUDY. (Deer.) N.Dakota Outdoors, Grand Forks, vol.11, no.4, p.6, illus., Oct., 1948.

FOOD HABITS OF MINNESOTA DEER. U.S. Dept. Agric., Lake States Forest Exp. Sta., Tech.Note no.133, p.1, Feb., 1938.

## Odocoileus--General Habits, Ecology, Behavior

DEER KILLS RATTLESNAKE. Clarence M. Aldous. Jour. Mamm., vol.19, no.1, p.111, Feb. 14, 1938.

EDGE EFFECT OF THE LESSER VEGETATION OF CERTAIN ADIRONDACK FOREST TYPES WITH PARTICULAR REFERENCE TO DEER AND GROUSE. F.B. Barick. Roosevelt Wildl. Bull., vol.9, no.1, pp.1-146, Aug., 1950.

ESCAPE BEHAVIOR OF THE WHITE-TAILED DEER. Frederick S. Barkalow, Jr., Walter E. Keller. Jour. Wildl. Mgt., Menasha, vol. 14, no.2, pp.246-247, Apr., 1950.

DEER AND SNOW. I.H. Bartlett. Michigan Conserv., Lansing, vol.18, no.1, pp.3-5, 23-25, figs.4, Feb., 1949.

WHERE DO DEER SLEEP? O.P. Brownlow. Calif. Fish and Game, vol.6, no.2, p.88, Apr., 1920.

RANGE OF AN INDIVIDUAL DEER. Harold C. Bryant. Jour. Mamm., vol.5, no.3, pp. 201-202, Aug., 1924.

VARIATIONS IN FERTILITY OF WHITE-TAILED DEER RELATED TO RANGE CONDITIONS. E.L. Cheatum, C.W.Severinghaus. Trans. 15th N.Amer. Wildl.Conf., Wash., pp. 170-190, 1950.

DEER ANTICS. Geo W. Coats. S.Dakota Conservation Digest, Pierre, vol.13, no.7, pp.1, 16, July, 1946.

NOTES ON THE LIFE HISTORY OF THE BLACK-TAILED DEER. J.D. Coffman. Calif. Fish and Game, vol.6, no.1, pp.15-16, Jan., 1920.

ECOLOGICAL RELATIONSHIPS OF THE FOOD OF THE COLUMBIAN BLACK-TAILED DEER, ODOCOILEUS HEMIONUS COLUMBIANUS (RICHARDSON), IN THE COAST FOREST REGION OF SOUTHERN VANCOUVER ISLAND, BRITISH COLUMBIA. Ian McT. Cowan. Ecol. Monographs, Durham, vol.15, no.2, pp.109-139, illus., Apr., 1945.

ECOLOGY AND SOCIAL BEHAVIOR OF A POPULATION OF THE COLUMBIAN BLACK-TAILED DEER IN CALIFORNIA. Raymond F. Dasmann. PhD thesis, Univ.Calif., Berkeley, pp.155, Aug., 1954.

STUDY OF THE CARRYING CAPACITY OF DEER YARDS AS DETERMINED BY BROWSE PLOTS. L.A. Davenport et al. Trans. 9th N.Amer. Wildl. Conf., pp.144-148, 1944.

STUDY OF DEERYARD CARRYING CAPACITY BY CONTROLLED BROWSING. L.A. Davenport et al. Trans. 18th N.Amer. Wildl. Conf., pp.581-596, graphs, 1953.

TEXAS WHITE-TAILS ARE AMPHIBIOUS. J.B. Davis. Texas Game and Fish, Austin, vol.2, no.1, p.19, Dec., 1943.

DEER CARRYING CAPACITY OF PENNSYLVANIA WOODLAND. E.B. Forbes, L. O. Overholts. Ecology, vol.12, no.4, pp.750-752, Oct., 1931.

FOOD PRODUCING CAPACITY OF THE HUNTINGTON FOREST WITH RESPECT TO DEER BROWSE. W.J. Frank. MS thesis, Syracuse Univ., 1940.

TERRITORIALISM IN DEER. William Graf. Jour. Mamm., vol.37, no.2, pp.165-170, June 9, 1956.

CHANGES IN NORTHERN MICHIGAN FORESTS FROM BROWSING BY DEER. Samuel A. Graham. Trans. 19th N.Amer. Wildl. Conf., pp.526-531, 1954.

MOBILITY OF HILL COUNTRY DEER. Henry C. Hahn, Jr. Texas Game and Fish, Austin, vol.3, no.8, p.17, July, 1945.

FACTORS INFLUENCING MULE DEER ON ARIZONA BRUSHLANDS. William R. Hanson, Clay Y. McCulloch. Trans. 20th N.Amer. Wildl.Conf., pp.568-588, graphs, 1955.

CALL OF THE WHITE-TAIL FAWN. Robert T. Hatt. Jour. Mamm., vol.18, no.1, p. 105, Feb. 14, 1937.

SOME WINTER RELATIONS OF THE WHITE-TAILED DEER TO THE FORESTS IN NORTH CENTRAL MASSACHUSETTS. N. W. Hosley, R.K. Ziebarth. Ecology, vol.16, no.4, pp. 535-553, Oct., 1935.

ON THE SUPPOSED RELATION OF DEER TO CEDARS BORDERING CERTAIN ADIRONDACK LAKES. Charles E. Johnson. Jour. Mamm., vol.8, no.3, pp.213-221, pls.20-21, Aug., 1927.

DEER WEIGHTS AND ANTLER MEASUREMENTS IN RELATION TO POPULATION DENSITY AND HUNTING EFFORT. F.W. Johnson. Trans. 2nd N.Amer. Wildl.Conf., pp.446-457, 1937.

WHITE-TAILED DEER. TRAPPING TECHNIQUES, ECOLOGICAL AND LIFE HISTORY NOTES. W.H. Kellogg. Texas Game, Fish and Oyster Comm., Quart.Prog.Rept., Austin, Oct.-Dec., pp.2-6, 1941.

DO DEER SCARE EASILY? Jim Kjelgaard. Field and Stream, New York, vol.52, no. 10, pp.60-61, 107-108, illus., Feb., 1948.

DEER IN COMBAT. Meredith Leitch. Va. Wildl., Richmond, vol.10, no.6, pp.18-20, June, 1949.

DEER IN RELATION TO PLANT SUCCESSION. A. S. Leopold. Trans. 15th N.Amer. Wildl. Conf., Wash., pp.571-580, Mar., 1950; Jour. Forestry, vol.48, no.10, pp. 675-578, Oct., 1950.

ECOLOGICAL ASPECTS OF DEER PRODUCTION ON FOREST LANDS. A. S. Leopold. Proc. United Nations Scientific Conf. on the Conserv. and Utilization of Resources, 17 Aug. - 6 Sep., 1949, vol.7 (Wildl. and Fish Resources) pp.205-207, Aug., 1952.

UNUSUAL "CURIOSITY" BEHAVIOR ON THE PART OF AN ODOCOILEUS HEMIONUS DOE. J.R. MacDonald. Jour.Mamm., vol. 34, no.3, p.397, Aug. 14, 1953.

WARINESS AS AN INFLUENCE ON AGE COMPOSITION OF WHITE-TAILED DEER KILLED BY HUNTERS. H.F. Maguire, C.W. Severinghaus. New York Fish and Game Jour., vol.1, no.1, pp.98-109, Jan., 1954.

DO YOU KNOW? THE FACTS ABOUT WHITE-TAILED DEER. (Life history, habits, laws.) Robert D. McDowell. Pa. Game News, Spec. Issue, vol.1, pp.41-50, Sep., 1950.

EFFECT OF THE QUABBIN RESERVATION ON DEER POPULATIONS IN THE ADJACENT TOWNS. C.L. McLaughlin. Proc. Northeastern Game Conf., pp.38-40, 1948.

WINTER BEHAVIOR OF DEER IN NORTHWESTERN MAINE. Merwin A. Marston. MS thesis, Univ. Maine, 1942.

EFFECT OF DEER BROWSING ON CERTAIN WESTERN ADIRONDACK FOREST TYPES. John Pearce. Bull. New York State Coll. Forestry, Syracuse, vol.10, no.2, (Roosevelt Wildl. Bull., vol.7, no.1), pp. 1-61, figs.25, fold.map, Oct., 1937.

INFLUENCE OF BROWSING BY WHITE-TAILED DEER (ODOCOILEUS VIRGINIANUS BORELIS MILLER) ON WESTERN ADIRONDACK FORESTS. John Pearce. MS thesis, Syracuse Univ., 1935.

SIDELIGHTS ON THE MULE DEER. (Brief account of gaits.) Archie Pendergraft. Wyo. Wild Life, Cheyenne, vol.10, no.2, pp.32-33, illus., Feb., 1946; Texas Game and Fish, Austin, vol.4, no.6, p.17, May, 1946.

FAWN OBSERVED ABOVE TIMBERLINE. Geo. A. Petrides. Yosemite Nat.Notes, Yosemite, vol.19, no.9, p.69, Sep., 1940.

LIFE HISTORY OF THE WHITE-TAILED DEER. Earl L. Poole. Frontiers, vol.2, no.1, p.21, illus., Oct., 1937.

RELATIONSHIPS BETWEEN BIRDS AND DEER. Thane Riney. Condor, Berkeley, vol.53, no.4, pp.178-185, July-Aug., 1951.

TRUCK TRAILS AND FIREBREAKS; THEIR USE BY DEER ON THE SANTA BARBARA NATIONAL FOREST. Cyril S. Robinson. Jour. Forestry, vol.33, no.11, pp.940-942, Nov., 1935.

RELATION OF THE WHITETAIL DEER TO HABITAT IN WINDHAM COUNTY, VT. Roger Seamans. Trans. 3rd N.Amer. Wildl. Conf., pp.243-247, 1938.

SPRINGTIME IN NEW YORK--ANOTHER ANGLE. C.W. Severinghaus. N.Y.State Conserv., vol.7, no.5, pp.2-4, illus., Apr.-May, 1953.

FAWN'S HIDING PLACE. D.C.Smiley. Yosemite Nat.Notes, vol.13, no.11, pp.82-83, Nov., 1934.

TWO LOCKED MULE DEER BUCKS SEPARATED. A.G. Smith. Canadian Field-Nat., vol.41, no.5, p.111, illus., May, 1927.

PLANT COMMUNITIES AND OTHER FACTORS AFFECTING THE DEER AND TURKEY POPULATIONS OF GULF HAMMOCK. David Swindell. MS thesis, Univ. Fla., 1949.

EFFECT OF DEER BROWSING ON QUALITY OF HARDWOOD TIMBER IN NORTHERN MICHIGAN. D.F. Switzenberg et al. For. Sci., vol.1, no.1, pp.61-67, illus., Mar., 1955.

ENVIRONMENTAL ANALYSIS OF A WINTER DEER RANGE. William L. Webb. Trans. 13th N.Amer. Wildl. Conf., pp. 442-449, 1948.

EFFECT OF WHITE-TAILED DEER ON A MATURE NORTHERN HARDWOOD FOREST. William L. Webb et al. Jour.Forestry, vol.54, no.6, pp.391-398, June, 1956.

DEER ATTACKS FOX. Elwood Wolfe. Yosemite Nat. Notes, Yosemite, vol. 20, no.3, p.19, Mar., 1941.

DEER CONDUCTS "BLITZ" ON ITS OLD ENEMY--THE COYOTE. Wyo. Wild Life, Cheyenne, vol.9, no.1, p.9, Jan., 1944.

NATURE ADJUSTS TEXAS DEER HERDS TO FOOD SUPPLY. Outdoor News Bull., Wash., vol.2, no.11, p.3, May 21, 1948.

SPORTSMEN TELL OF AN UNUSUAL SIGHT--COME ACROSS TWO LARGE BUCK DEER WITH HORNS LOCKED IN COMBAT. Maryland Conservationist, Baltimore, vol.19, no.1, p.9, Winter, 1942.

WINTER HABITS OF DEER. Forest Res. Dig., p.6, July, 1935.

Odocoileus--Hunting

DOES AIN'T DEER. Durward L. Allen. Sports Afield, vol.120, no.6, pp.19-21, 90-91, Dec., 1948.

REPORT ON THE 1951 DEER HUNT. John M. Allen. Outdoor Ind., vol.19, no.4, pp. 4-5, 7, illus., Apr., 1952.

MULE DEER MARATHON. S.Omar Baker. Field and Stream, no.4, pp.28-29, 105, Aug., 1929.

DOES ARE DEER. Helmut K. Buechner. Amer. Rifleman, vol.101, no.4, pp.24-27, 65-67, illus., Apr., 1953.

HUNTING NORTH AMERICAN DEER. A. H. Carhart. Macmillan Co., New York, pp.232, pls.16, 1946.

BIG BUCKS OF THE CLEARWATER. (British Columbia.) Bertram Chichester. Rod and Gun in Canada, Montreal, vol.46, no. 4, pp.14-15, 36, illus., Sep., 1944.

JACK-LIGHTING DEER. J.S. Dorland. Syla, Toronto, vol.5, no.1, p.24, 1949.

HUNTING WHITETAILS. F.C.Edminster. Morrow, pp.192, illus., 1954.

COUES DEER. LITTLE-KNOWN SPECIES OF WHITE-TAILED DEER THAT FURNISHED TOP SPORT. Grancel Fitz. Field and Stream, vol.41, no.8, pp.36-38, 87, illus., Dec., 1936.

IT'S TIME TO SCRAP THE BUCK LAW! Arthur Grahame. Outdoor Life, vol.104, no.3, pp.42-44, 102-103, Sep., 1949.

RESULTS OF CONTROLLED DEER HUNTS ON THE TAMARAC NATIONAL WILDLIFE REFUGE. L.W. Krefting et al. Jour.Wildl. Mgt., vol.19, no.3, pp.346-352, July, 1955.

CONCERNING THE DEER SITUATION. (Some Ontario deer kill statistics.) J. Macartney. Sylva, Toronto, vol.3, no.2, pp.17-18, illus., 1947.

HUNTING THE COUES DEER. Jack O'Connor. (In) N.Amer.Big Game. A book of the Boone and Crocket Club, Compiled by the Comm. on Records of N.Amer.Big Game. Charles Scribners Sons, New York, pp.217-224, 1939.

TEXAS AND VERMONT DEER HUNTING COMPARED BY SAN ANTONIO SCRIBE. Harold Scherwitz. Monthly Bull. Texas Game, Fish and Oyster Comm., Austin, vol.4, no.3, p.3, Feb., 1941.

SHOULD DOES BE KILLED? E.A.Sherman, R.R.Hill. Amer. Game, Bull. Amer.Game Protective Assn., vol.17, pp.92-93, illus., Nov., 1928.

WHY NOT SHOOT THEM? Milton H.Stenlund. Outdoor Life, vol.110, no.5, pp.50-51, 102-104, illus., Nov., 1952.

QUEER DEER. Hart Stilwell. Field and Stream, New York, vol.50, no.8, pp.23-25, 86, 89, illus., Dec., 1945.

WHEN DEER HUNTERS DISAGREE. Harold Titus. Field and Stream, New York, vol.47, no.8, pp.24-25, 68-69, illus., Dec., 1942.

HUNTING THE WHITETAIL DEER. J. W. Webb. (In) N.Amer. Big Game. A Book of the Boone and Crocket Club, Compiled by the Comm. on Records of N.Amer.Big Game. Charles Scribners Sons, New York, pp.190-197, 1939.

OBSERVATIONS ON DEER KILL UNDER DIFFERENT SYSTEMS OF HUNTING. Kaj Westerskov. Jour. Wildl. Mgt., Menasha, vol.15, no.1, pp.27-32, Jan., 1951.

Odocoileus--Hunting (Eastern United States)

DEER CENSUS AND KILL RECORDS OF THE LAKE STATES. Harry E. Adams. Trans. 3rd N.Amer. Wildl.Conf., pp.287-295, 1938.

DOES AIN'T DEER. Durward L. Allen. Wisc. Conserv. Bull., Madison, vol.14, no.2, pp.20-23, Feb., 1949; Penna.Game News, Harrisburg, vol.20, no.3, pp.5-8, illus., June, 1949.

NIGHT DEER HUNTER. R.B. Armfield. N.Carolina Wildl.Conserv., Raleigh, vol. 7, no.12, pp.8, 11, Dec., 1943.

PENNSYLVANIA TO KILL DOES AND PROTECT BUCKS. Carlos Avery. Amer. Game, Bull. Amer. Game Protective Assn., vol.17, pp.55-56, 66-67, illus., July, 1928.

DOES MAINE NEED A NEW DEER SEASON? Chester F. Banasiak. Me.Dept. Inl.Fisheries and Game, pp.1-17, mimeo., maps, graphs, Jan., 1955.

BLOOD-STAINED TRAIL OF THE WHITE-TAILED DEER IN WISCONSIN. W. E. Barber. Wisc. Conservationist, vol.3, no.1, pp.1-2, Mar., 1921.

DEER STILL PLENTIFUL IN WISCONSIN. W.E. Barber. Wisc. Conservationist, vol. 3, no.6, p.16, Jan. (Mar.), 1922.

HOW WAS THE DEER SEASON, 1943? N.R. Barger. Wisc.Conserv.Bull., Madison, vol.9, no.4, pp.3-5, illus., Apr., 1944.

DEER HUNTING AT HOLLY SHELTER. F.S. Barkalow, Jr. N.Carolina Wildl. Conserv., Raleigh, vol.6, no.10, pp.3-4, 13, Oct., 1942.

ANTLERLESS DEER SEASON. I.H.Bartlett. Michigan Conserv., Lansing, vol.19, no. 2, pp.9-11, fig.1, Mar., 1950.

COMPARISON OF DEER SEASONS--1919 AND 1943. I.H. Bartlett. Michigan Conserv., Lansing, vol.13, no.10, pp.3, 12, Nov., 1944.

DEER HUNTING IS IMPROVING IN KEWEENAW. I.H. Bartlett. Michigan Conserv., Lansing, vol.15, no.10, pp.7, 13, Nov., 1946.

DEER HUNTING REGULATIONS LIBERALIZED. I.H. Bartlett. Michigan Conserv., Lansing, vol.21, no.6, pp.3-5, Nov., 1952.

DEER SEASON MAY HAVE SET NEW RECORDS. I.H. Bartlett. Michigan Conserv., Lansing, vol.16, no.1, pp.3, 8, Jan., 1947.

DEER SEASON--1948. I.H. Bartlett. Michigan Conserv., Lansing, vol.18, no.1, pp. 26-27, Feb., 1949.

DEER SEASON--1949. I.H. Bartlett. Michigan Conserv., Lansing, vol.18, no.6, pp. 2-7, Nov.-Dec., 1949.

DEER SEASON--1950. I.H. Bartlett. Michigan Conserv., Lansing, vol.19, no.6, pp. 3-6, illus., Nov., 1950.

DEER HUNTING 1950-1951. I.H. Bartlett. Michigan Conserv., Lansing, vol.20, no.6, pp.5-7, 21-23, illus., Nov., 1951.

DEER SEASON PROSPECTS. I.H. Bartlett. Michigan Conserv., Lansing, vol.14, no.11, p.3, Nov., 1945.

HUNTERS AND DEER--1947-1948. I. H. Bartlett. Michigan Conserv., Lansing, vol. 17, no.11, p.3, figs.2, Nov., 1948.

THE 1947 DEER SEASON. I.H. Bartlett. Michigan Conserv., Lansing, vol.17, no.1, pp.3, 12, Jan., 1948.

REPORT TO MICHIGAN DEER HUNTERS. I.H. Bartlett. Michigan Conserv., Lansing, vol.16, no.10, pp.3, 10-11, illus., Nov., 1947.

BOW AND ARROW DEER HUNTING IN WISCONSIN, 1934-1947. Otis S. Bersing. Wisc. Conserv.Bull., Madison, vol.13, no.4, pp.7-16, illus., Apr., 1948.

CONTROLLED DEER HUNTING IN THE NECEDAH REFUGE. Otis S. Bersing. Wisc. Conserv. Bull., Madison, vol.13, no.8, pp.19-22, Aug., 1948.

THE DEER KILL /1950 SEASON. Otis S. Bersing. Wisc. Conserv. Dept., pp.11, 1951.

THE DEER KILL /1951 SEASON. Otis S. Bersing. Wisc. Conserv. Dept., pp.10, 1952.

HUNTER'S OPINION OF AN ANY DEER SEASON. Otis S. Bersing. Wisc.Conserv. Bull., Madison, vol.14, no.9, pp.6-9, illus., Sep., 1949.

HUNTERS' REPORT OF THE 1944 (WISCONSIN) DEER KILL. Otis S. Bersing. Wisc. Conserv. Bull., Madison, vol.10, no.10, pp.3-11, Oct., 1945.

THE 1946 DEER HUNTING SEASON. Otis S. Bersing. Wisc. Conserv.Bull., Madison, vol.12, no.9, pp.4-12, Sep., 1947.

THE 1947 DEER SEASON. Otis S. Bersing. Wisc. Conserv. Bull., Madison, vol.13, no.10, p.11, Oct., 1948.

DEER HUNTING IN SOUTH CAROLINA. Horatio Bigelow. Amer. Field, Chicago, vol.140, no.41, p.347, Oct. 9, 1943.

IMPORTANT SIDELIGHTS ON THE DEER SEASON. I.T. Bode. Missouri Conserv., Jefferson City, vol.5, no.10, pp.2-3, 10, 13, illus., Oct., 1944.

AMERICA'S NO.1, BIG GAME ANIMAL. (Deer.) Stanley T. Bogges. Penna. Game News, New Cumberland, vol.9, no.12, pp.16-17, Mar., 1939.

MAINE DEER KILL, TOWN AND COUNTY TOTALS. W. Earle Bradbury. Me.Dept. Inl. Fisheries and Game, p.1, fold.map, 1952.

THE 1954 DEER KILL IN NEW YORK. A. W. Bromley. N.Y.State Conserv., vol.9, no.5, pp.34-35, Apr.-May, 1955.

GAME REFUGES AND PUBLIC HUNTING GROUNDS IN MICHIGAN. R.D. Burroughs. Jour. Wildl. Mgt., vol.10, no.4, pp.285-296, Oct., 1946.

DEER HUNTING RECORDS FROM CENTRAL BAYFIELD COUNTY, 1930-1946. Irven Buss, Herman E. Buss. Wisc. Conserv. Bull., vol. 12, no.1, pp.5-11, Jan., 1947.

MORE THAN 900 BUCKS TAKEN IN 3-DAY HUNT. Charles Callison. Missouri Conservationist, Jefferson City, vol.6, no.12, pp. 1-3, illus., Dec., 1945.

THE 1947 DEER HUNT AT A GLANCE. F.B. Chapman. Ohio Conserv.Bull., vol.12, no.2, pp.18-19, Feb., 1948.

HUNTERS ENJOY STATE'S GREATEST DEER SEASON. Louis S. Clapper. Tenn. Conserv., vol.20, no.2, pp.6-7, 16, illus., Feb., 1954.

AGAINST THE BUCK LAW. D.H.Clark. Wisc. Conservtionist, vol.3, no.6, p.11, Jan. (Mar.), 1922.

HARVEST OF DEER IN WISCONSIN. H.T. J. Cramer. Trans. 13th N.Amer. Wildl. Conf., pp.492-508, 1948.

104 DEER A MINUTE. Wilbur M. Cramer. Penna. Game News, vol.21, no.3, pp.3, 26-27, June, 1950.

WISCONSIN DEER PROBLEM AND THE 1949 HUNTING SEASON. B.L. Dahlberg. Wisc. Conserv. Bull., vol.15, no.4, pp. 3-7, Apr., 1950.

PRELIMINARY REPORT ON THE 1949 DEER SEASON. B.L. Dahlberg, James B. Hale. Wisc. Conserv. Bull., vol.15, no.1, pp.7-8, Jan., 1950.

DEER HUNTING--THEN AND NOW. Robert W. Darrow. N.Y.State Conserv., vol.10, no.1, pp.19-23, illus., Aug.-Sep., 1955.

DEER HUNTING IN THE ALLEGHANIES. A.B.Davies, Jr. Va. Wildl., Richmond, vol.8, no.2, pp.15-17, Feb., 1947.

THE 1951 DEER SEASON. W.R. DeGarmo. W.Va. Conserv., vol.15, no.11, pp.4-7, illus., Feb., 1952.

RESULTS OF THE SECOND 'ANY DEER' SEASON. W.R. DeGarmo. W.Va.Conserv., vol.16, no.12, pp.34-37, illus., Feb., 1952.

DOE DEER MAY BE HUNTED NEXT SEASON. Sumner Dow. Tenn. Conserv., vol.19, no.6, pp.12-13, illus., June, 1953.

SLAUGHTER OF DEER IN THE SEMINOLE RESERVATION OF FLORIDA. Rosalie Edge. Emergency Conserv. Comm., New York, Letter Dated Nov. 14, 1941, to Amer. Soc. of Mammalogists.

KNOWLEDGE GAINED AT THE BIG LEVELS MANAGED HUNT. J.W. Engle, P.J.Hanlon. Va. Wildl., vol.8, no.5, pp.1-13, illus., May, 1952.

WEATHER AND THE KILL OF WHITE-TAILED DEER IN MAINE. C. B.Fobes. Jour. Wildl. Mgt., vol.9, no.1, pp.76-78, Jan., 1945.

WHY ANTLERLESS DEER SEASON ARE NECESSARY. Richard Gerstell. Penna. Game News, vol.8, no.6, pp.4-5, Sep., 1937.

WANTED: MORE DEER HUNTERS. Merrill C. Gilfillan. Ohio Conserv.Bull., vol. 19, no.3, pp.12-13, graph, Mar., 1955.

THE 1954 DEER SEASON. John Gill. W. Va. Conserv., vol.18, no.12, pp.11-24, Feb., 1955.

RESULTS OF THE 1953 DEER SEASON. John Gill. "Your Deer Herd," Conserv. Comm. W.Va., pp.4-15, illus., Dec. 30, 1953.

WISCONSIN DEER SEASONS: A REVIEW. R.C. Guettinger. Michigan Conserv., Lansing, vol.21, no.6, pp.10-11, Nov., 1952.

ARCHERY HUNTERS KILL SEVEN DEER AT WATOGA. J.W. Handlan. W. Va. Conserv., Charleston, vol.10, no.9, pp. 10-13, 20-21, illus., Jan., 1947.

BOW 'N' ARROW HUNTING--GOOD CONSERVATION. Arnold O. Haugen. Trans. 13th N.Amer. Wildl. Conf., pp.459-464, 1948.

DEER HUNTING, INDIAN STYLE. Arnold O. Haugen. Michigan Conserv., Lansing, vol.15, no.5, pp.8-11, June, 1946.

MORE BUCKS TO HARVEST. (White-tailed deer.) Arnold O. Haugen. Alabama Conserv., vol.27, no.3, pp.16-19, illus., Nov.-Dec., 1955.

GREEN MOUNTAIN WHITETAILS. Sidney C. Hayward. Field and Stream, New York, vol.54, no.9, pp.35-37, 76-77, illus., Jan., 1950.

TRUE TALE OF AN OHIO DEER HUNT. Leroy Hollingsworth. Ohio Conserv.Bull., Columbus, vol.8, no.7, pp.14-15, July, 1944.

DEER KILL, SEASON OF 1948. Arthur W. Holweg. N.Y. State Conserv., vol.3, no.4, pp.24-25, Feb.-Mar., 1949.

PRELIMINARY REPORT ON THE 1950 DEER SEASON. Cyril Kabat, James B. Hale. Wisc. Conserv. Bull., vol.16, no.1, pp.10-12, Jan., 1951.

MARYLAND'S 1951 DEER KILL. Chester M. Kerns. Md. Conserv., vol.29, no.1, pp.5-6, Spring, 1952.

DEER KILL IN MARYLAND--1952. Chester M. Kerns. Md.Conserv., vol.30, no.1, pp. 8-9, illus., Spring, 1953.

DEER KILL IN MARYLAND--1953. Chester M. Kerns. Md. Conserv., vol.31, no.2, pp. 17-18, illus., Mar., 1954.

DEER KILL 1954. Chester M. Kerns. Md. Conserv., vol.32, no.2, pp.7-10, illus., Mar., 1955.

ANOTHER OPPONENT. A.W. Kingsley. Wisc. Conservationist, vol.3, no.6, p.11, Jan. (Mar.), 1922.

RESULTS OF SPECIAL DEER HUNTS ON THE MUD LAKE NATIONAL WILDLIFE REFUGE, MINNESOTA. Laurits Krefting, Arnold B. Erikson. Jour. Wildl.Mgt., vol. 20, no.3, pp.297-302, July, 1956.

FACTS FOR DEER HUNTERS. Roger M. Latham. Penna. Game News, Harrisburg, vol.20, no.8, pp.4-6, 28-29, illus., Nov., 1949.

HARVESTING OUR DEER CROP. Roger M. Latham. Penna. Game News, vol.19, no. 2, pp.4-5, 17, 21, May, 1948.

KILL OF THE DEER IN MARYLAND AND THE WOODMONT ROD AND GUN CLUB, SEASON 1943. E. Lee LeCompte. Md. Conservationist, Baltimore, vol.21, no.2, pp.1-10, illus., Spring, 1944.

WHY SHOOT SPIKES. (White-tailed deer.) Francis X. Lueth. Alabama Conserv., vol. 27, no.3, pp.12-13, 19, 26, illus., Nov.-Dec., 1955.

REMOVING SURPLUS DEER BY HUNTING, ALLEGHENY NATIONAL FOREST, PENNSYLVANIA. Randal McCain. Trans.6th N. Amer. Wildl. Conf., Wash., D.C., pp. 332-338, 1941.

THE 1953 IOWA DEER SEASON. John Madson. Iowa Conserv., vol.13, no.1, pp.1, 5, illus., Jan., 1954.

HOW ABOUR THE BUCK LAW? Deane Mather. Fla. Wildl., vol.5, no.7, pp.16-17, 33, Dec., 1950.

DEER HUNTING WITH BOW AND ARROW. Margaret Maunder. Minnesota Sportsman's Digest, Minneapolis, vol.4, no.4, pp.4, 8-11, Dec., 1943.

PRIME FROM LITTLE ROUND MOUNTAIN. (Deer.)Charles C. Niehuis. Field and Stream, New York, vol.50, no.11, pp.34-35, 81-83, illus., Mar., 1946.

NEW VERSION OF OLD STORY. (Deer hunting over 20 years.) Roy Osmun. Michigan Conserv., Lansing, vol.17, no.2, pp.6, 12, Feb., 1948.

1942--BIGGEST DEER SEASON. OVER 100,000 HUNTERS TOOK TO THE WOODS. Lansing Parker. Conservation Volunteer, St.Paul, vol.6, no.33, pp.32-34, illus., June, 1943.

REPORT ON THE 1950-51 DEER SEASON. Chester F. Phelps. Va.Wildl., Richmond, vol.12, no.3, p.12, Mar., 1951.

IS ILLINOIS READY FOR A DEER SEASON? Lysle R. Pietsch. Outdoors in Ill., vol.17, no.1, pp.4-7, illus., Winter, 1951.

THE DECEMBER DEER HUNT. Dunbar Robb. Missouri Conservationist, Jefferson City, vol.10, no.3, pp.13-14, illus., Mar., 1949.

DIXIE'S DOPE ON DECEMBER'S DEER. Dunbar Robb. Mo. Conserv., vol.14, no.3, pp.1-3, 12, illus., Mar., 1953.

CONSERVE OUR DEER. Valentine Roeth. Wisc. Conservationist, vol.2, no.2, pp. 2-3, July, 1920.

DEER MANAGEMENT DESIGNED TO WIN SUPPORT. (The problem of shooting does.) H.D. Ruhl. Wisc. Conserv. Bull., Madison, vol.14, no.6, pp.27-28, June, 1949.

HUNTING DEER IN DIXIELAND. Archibald Rutledge. Forest and Stream, vol.91, pp. 53-56, 91, Feb., 1921.

RESULTS OF A STUDY OF THE HARVESTING OF WHITETAIL DEER IN THE CHEQUAMEGON NATIONAL FOREST. Roy D. Sanders. Trans. 4th N. Amer. Wildl. Conf., pp.549-553, 1939.

RESULTS OF IOWA'S FIRST DEER SEASON IN RECENT YEARS. Glen C. Sanderson. Proc. Iowa Acad. Sci., vol.61, pp.615-630, map, 1954.

TRENDS IN THE KILL OF WISCONSIN WHITETAIL BUCKS, 1936-1940. William H. Schunke, Irven O. Buss. Jour. Wildl. Mgt., vol.5, no.3, pp.333-336, July, 1941.

DEER HUNTING POSSIBILITIES IN NEW YORK AS INDICATED BY DISTRIBUTION OF HUNTERS, DEER RANGE, AND LEGAL KILL IN 1946. C.W. Severinghaus. N.Y. State Conservationist, Albany, vol.4, no.2, pp.22-25, illus., Oct.-Nov., 1949.

FAWN WEIGHTS IN RELATION TO REGULATIONS FOR TAKING ANTLERLESS DEER. C.W. Severinghaus. N.Y. Fish and Game Jour., vol.2, no.2, p.247, July, (Nov.), 1955.

HAS THE LACK OF A BUCK LAW HARMED NEW HAMPSHIRE'S DEER HERD? Hilbert R. Siegler. Trans. 16th N. Amer. Wildl. Conf., pp.472-491, 1951.

DEER AND THE DEER HUNT. M.O. Steen. Missouri Conservationist, Jefferson City, vol.7, no.10, pp.1-3, 16, illus., Oct., 1946.

WHITE-TAILED DEER BAG CHECKS, GEGOKA MANAGEMENT UNIT, SUPERIOR NATIONAL FOREST. Milton H. Stenlund et al. Jour. Wildl. Mgt., Ithaca, N.Y., vol.16, no.1, pp.58-63, Jan., 1952.

DOES ARE DEER, TOO! F.W. Stuewer. Michigan Conserv., Lansing, vol.18, no. 6, pp.8-11, Dec., 1949.

REVIEW OF DEER SEASON. Ernest F. Swift. Wisc. Conserv. Bull., Madison, vol. 9, nos.8-9, p.10, Aug.-Sep., 1944.

COMMENTS ON THE 1943 ANTLERLESS DEER SEASON. Randolph Thompson. Penna. Game News, Harrisburg, vol.15, no.1, pp. 17, 32, Apr., 1944.

WHAT AILS THE APPALACHIAPS? (Deer.) Harold Titus. Field and Stream, New York, vol.51, no.7, pp.62-63, Nov., 1946.

COOPERATIVE DEER HUNTING. CONTROL OF WILDLIFE HARVEST IMPERATIVE TO GOOD MANAGEMENT. R.E. Trippensee. Amer. Wildl., vol.24, no.6, pp. 87, 92-93, Nov.-Dec., 1935.

DEER-HUNTING TERRITORY. STATEMENT ON THE HUNTING ORDER FOR 1943. Chester S. Wilson. Conservation Volunteer, St. Paul, vol.6, no.37, pp.1-3, Nov.-Dec., 1943.

SOUTHERN MICHIGAN DEER HUNTING. Cash Wonser. Michigan Conserv., Lansing, vol.18, no.6, pp.21-23, Nov.-Dec., 1949.

CAMP AND WARDENS REPORTS INDICATE 3,000 DEER KILLED IN MISSISSIPPI. Miss. Game and Fish Comm., vol.15, no.7, pp. 8-9, Jan., 1952.

DEER HARVEST DROPS TO 27,630 FOR 1952. Wisc. Conserv. Dept., Activities Progress Rep., no.57, pp.11, May, 1953; Wisc. Conserv. Bull., vol.18, no.6, pp. 24-25, June, 1953.

DEER HUNTING INFORMATION. Michigan Conserv., Lansing, vol.15, no.10, p.16, Nov., 1946.

DEER HUNTING LAYOUT IN SOUTHERN OHIO. Ohio Conserv. Bull., Columbus, vol.8, no.11, pp.16-18, illus., Nov., 1944.

DEER KILL TO DROP UNDER BUCK LAW. Wisc. Conserv. Bull., vol.17, no.9, pp. 26-27, Sep., 1952.

FIRST OFFICIAL WISCONSIN CONSERVATION DEPARTMENT REPORT ON THE 1953 DEER HUNTING SEASON CHECK. Wisc. Conserv. Dept., pp.1-42, map, graphs, mimeo., Dec., 1953.

KILL OF DEER IN MARYLAND--SEASON 1942 AND AT THE WOODMONT ROD AND GUN CLUB. Md. Conservationist, Baltimore, vol.20, no.1, pp.1-2, 18-21, 29, Winter, 1943.

MARYLAND DEER KILL RECORD. Md. Conservationist, Baltimore, vol.25, no.1, p.27, Spring, 1948.

NEW JERSEY DEER KILL--1953. New Jersey Dep. of Conserv. and Economic Development. N.J. Outdoors, vol.4, no. 9, p.32, Mar., 1954.

1944 MISSOURI DEER SEASON, NOVEMBER 3-4. Missouri Wildl., St. Louis, vol.6, no. 4, pp.10-11, 13, Oct., 1944.

THE 1951 DEER HARVEST WAS HIGH--129,475. Wisc. Conserv. Dept., Wisc. Conserv. Bull., vol.17, no.5, pp.22-23, May, 1952.

1951 DEER HUNTING INFORMATION. Mich. Dept. Conserv., Game Div. pp.4, graphs, 1952.

THE 1951 DEER TAKE. N.Y. State Conserv., vol.6, no.4, p.33, Feb.-Mar., 1952.

1952 DEER HUNTING INFORMATION AND 1953 DEER HUNTING REGULATIONS. Mich. Dept. Conserv., pp.4, 1953.

1952 TENNESSEE DEER HUNTS HIGHLY SUCCESSFUL. Tennessee Game and Fish Comm., Tenn. Conserv., vol.18, no.2, p.14, illus., Feb., 1953.

OPEN SEASON THIS FALL. (Deer.) Missouri Conservationist, Jefferson City, vol. 5, no.8, pp.1, 11, Aug., 1944.

"RECAP" OF THE 1944 DEER SEASON. Ohio Conserv. Bull., Columbus, vol.9, no.2, pp.4-5, Feb., 1945.

REPORTED DEER TAKE FOR NEW YORK STATE 1949-51. N.Y. Conserv. Dept., Fish and Game News, pp.4-5, Winter, 1952.

THREE NATIONAL FOREST DEER HUNTS. Alabama Conserv., Montgomery, vol.15, no. 5, p.11, Nov., 1943.

TOTAL OF 4,958 BUCKS KILLED. W. Va. Conserv., Charleston, vol.12, no.10, pp. 5-8, 20-21, illus., Jan., 1949.

TWENTY-EIGHT BUCKS FELLED ON FOUR BANKHEAD HUNTS. (White-tailed deer.) Alabama Conserv., Montgomery, vol.19, nos.7-8, pp.9, 23, Jan.-Feb., 1948.

UNOFFICIAL FIGURES LIST 4,479 DEER KILLED LAST SEASON. W. Va. Conserv., Charleston, vol.14, no.10, pp.22-23, 33-34, illus., Jan., 1951.

WEST VIRGINIA SEES RECORD DEER CROP HARVESTED. W. Va. Conserv., Charleston, vol.11, no.9, pp.4-6, 19, Jan., 1948.

WINTER DEER KILL, 1954-55. N.Y. State Conserv., vol.10, no.1, p.39, Aug.-Sep., 1955.

Odocoileus--Hunting (Western United States)

THE WOODS IS FULL OF 'EM! Durward L. Allen. Field and Stream, vol.56, no.7, pp. 32-33, 106-107, Nov., 1951.

DEEP IN THE HEART OF TEXAS. (A deer hunt.) W.E. Anderson. Texas Game and Fish, Austin, vol.5, no.12, pp.8-9, 21-22, illus., Nov., 1947.

317 DEER REMOVED FROM LOWER SOURIS REFUGE DURING 1945 STATE-WIDE OPEN SEASON. Roy N. Bach. North Dakota Outdoors, Grand Forks, vol.8, no. 6, pp.10-11, illus., Dec., 1945.

CALIFORNIA BUCKS. (Deer.) K.M. Bradford. Field and Stream, New York, vol.51, no.4, pp.44-45, 80-83, illus., Aug., 1946.

THE 1952 DEER SEASON. A.R. Brazda. North Dakota Outdoors, vol.16, no.2, p. 12, Aug., 1953.

RESULTS OF THE 1950 SPECIAL DEER HUNT ON MINERAL KING NATIONAL GAME REFUGE. Homer F. Bryan, Walter I. Long. Calif. Fish and Game, vol.38, no.2, pp.235-238, Apr., 1952.

MARCH DEER HUNT FIFTY-EIGHT YEARS AGO. G.W. Coats. South Dakota Conserv. Digest, Pierre, vol.12, no.10, pp.14-15, Oct., 1945.

1950 NORTHERN ARIZONA DEER SEASON, ROCKY MOUNTAIN MULE DEER. P. M. Cosper, Denis J. Illige. Ariz. Game and Fish Comm., Ariz. Game Surv., Proj. Job Compl. Rep., 1951, Proj. 53 R 1 - WP 2 - J 3, pp.1-15, illus., Jan., 1952.

CRIPPLING LOSSES AMONG MULE DEER IN UTAH. R.J. Costley. Trans. 13th N. Amer. Wildl. Conf., pp.451-457, 1948.

DEER HUNT IN THE BLACK HILLS. Ray Frost. Forest and Stream, vol.89, pp.519-521, 554, 556, 558, 560-561, Oct., 1919.

WHAT ABOUT THE DEER SEASON? Vernon E. Gunvalson. Conserv. Volunteer, vol.13, no.76, pp.1-6, May-June, 1950.

THE 1942 DEER SEASON. DEER POPULATION AN ACUTE PROBLEM. Paul R. Highby. Conserv. Volunteer, St. Paul, vol.5, no.27, pp.1-3, Dec., 1942.

DEER HUNTING IN CALIFORNIA. J.S. Hunter. Calif. Fish and Game, vol.10, pp.18-23, Jan., 1924.

DEER KILL RECORDS--A GUIDE TO MANAGEMENT OF DEER HUNTING. F.W. Johnson. Calif. Fish and Game, vol.25, no. 2, pp.96-165, Apr., 1939.

DEER-HARVEST OR STARVE THEM? Odell Julander, W. Leslie Robinette. Utah Fish and Game Bull., Salt Lake City, vol. 8, no.8, pp.3-5, illus., May, 1951.

ONE WAY TO TAKE A WHITETAIL BUCK. R.V. Kessler. Ariz. Wildl. and Sportsman, Safford, vol.6, no.4, pp.5, 10, Apr., 1944.

WHY A LIBERAL DEER SEASON? Thomas L. Kimball. Colorado Outdoors Mag., vol. 7, no.1, pp.1-5, illus., Jan., 1958.

1950 SOUTHERN ARIZONA DEER SEASON, ZONES 2 AND 3, WHITE-TAILED AND DESERT MULE DEER. Theodore Knipe. Ariz. Game and Fish Comm., Ariz. Game Surv., Proj. Job Compl. Rep., 1951, Proj. 53 R 1 - WP 2 - J 4 and 5, pp.1-25, illus., Oct., 1951.

DEER HUNT IN THE BLACK HILLS. E.R. Lamster. South Dakota Conserv. Digest, Pierre, vol.10, no.12, p.1, 14, Dec., 1943.

REPORT ON SOUTHERN CALIFORNIA'S JANUARY DEER SEASON. John Laughlin. Calif. Fish and Game, vol.39, no.4, pp. 507-515, illus., Oct., 1953.

THE 1945 DEER HUNTING SEASON. W.J. Lowe. North Dakota Outdoors, Bismarck, vol.8, no.5, pp.3-4, Nov., 1945.

HARVESTING BIG GAME. W. T. McKean. North Dakota Outdoors, vol.14, no.3, pp. 8-9, 15, Sep., 1951.

SPECIAL REGULATIONS AFFECTING THE 1942 DEER SEASON. Geo. P. Miller. Calif. Fish and Game, San Francisco, vol.29, no. 1, pp.42-43, Jan., 1943.

SUGGESTED DATES OF OPEN SEASON ON DEER IN CALIFORNIA. James Moffitt. Calif. Fish and Game, vol.12, pp.124-127, illus., July, 1926.

DEER HUNTING IN NEBRASKA. Levi L. Mohler. Outdoor Nebraska, Lincoln, vol. 23, no.4, pp.4-7, illus., Spring, 1946.

THREE BUCKS FOR THREE BUCKS. S.C. Pierce. Ariz. Wildl. and Sportsman, Safford, vol.6, no.6, pp.4, 8, June, 1944.

TEXAS HOLDS SECOND ANTLERLESS DEER HUNT. Bob Ramsey. Texas Game and Fish, vol.13, no.8, pp.2-3, 26-27, illus., Aug., 1955.

TAKE 'EM OR LEAVE 'EM. Bob Ramsey, Eugene Walker. Texas Game and Fish, vol.12, no.7, pp.4-6, 20-21, 27-28, illus., June, 1954.

THE 1947 DEER HARVEST IN NORTH DAKOTA. Russell Stuart. North Dakota Outdoors, Bismarck, vol.10, no.11, p.10, May, 1948.

SOME NOTES ON RECENT DEER SEASON IN NORTH DAKOTA. Russell Stuart. North Dakota Outdoors, Grand Forks, vol.10, no. 7, pp.6-7, illus., Jan., 1948.

DEER HUNTING DATA. Lawrence Temple. Oklahoma Game and Fish News, Oklahoma City, vol.5, no.2, pp.12-13, illus., Feb., 1949.

HUNTING THE MULE DEER. F.L.Waugh. Colorado Outdoors Mag., vol.6, no.5, pp. 6-11, Sep., 1957.

OLD SHOOTING BLINDS. John H Wegner. Yosemite Nat. Notes, vol.8, pp.53-54, illus., May, 1929.

DEER AND DEER-HUNTING IN TEXAS. Charles Wright. Amer. Nat., vol.2, no. 9, pp.466-476, Nov., 1868.

CALIFORNIA'S ELEVEN-YEAR DEER HARVEST BY COUNTIES. Calif. Conserv., vol.2, no.11, p.5, Nov., 1937.

DEER SEASON CLOSES WITH ONE FATALITY. North Dakota Outdoors, Bismarck, vol.6, no.6, p.3, Dec., 1943.

HUNTING WITH BOW AND ARROW.(Deer.) North Dakota Outdoors, Grand Forks, vol. 8, no.6, pp.8-9, Dec., 1945.

THIRD DEER HUNT IN THREE YEARS... 68 PER CENT KILL IN '50. Outdoor Nebr., vol.29, no.4, pp.31-34, illus., Fall, 1951.

UNWARRANTED KILLING OF DEER STILL REMAINS A PROBLEM IN THE BLACK HILLS. South Dakota Conserv. Digest, Pierre, vol.9, no.12, p.2, illus., Dec., 1942.

WYOMING'S DEER, TROPHY GAME OF THE WEST. Wyo. Wild Life, Cheyenne, vol.12, no.7, pp.5-11, 36-39, illus., Aug., 1948.

Odocoileus--Hybrids

HYBRID DEER OF THE $F_2$ GENERATION. Hartley H.T. Jackson. Jour. Mamm., vol. 2, no.3, pp.140-143, fig.1, pl.8, Aug.19, 1921.

MULE--WHITETAIL HYBRIDS. North Dakota Game and Fish Dept. N.Dakota Outdoors, vol.15, no.7, p.9, illus., Jan., 1953.

Odocoileus--Longevity

NOTES ON THE ESTIMATION OF SURVIVAL RATES FROM AGE DISTRIBUTIONS OF DEER. Don W. Hayne, Lee Eberhardt. Presented at 14th Midwest Wildl. Conf., Des Moines, Iowa, pp.1-6, graphs 5, Dec.17-19, 1952.

WICONSIN'S OLDEST DEER LIVED TO BE NEARLY 20. Wisc. Conserv.Bull., Madison, vol.15, no.7, pp.21-22, illus., July, 1950.

Odocoileus--Management

MULE DEER PROBLEM AREAS OF THE WESTERN STATES. C.M.Aldous. Trans. 14th N.Amer. Wildl. Conf., pp.502-512, 1949.

DEER RESTORATION IN THE SOUTHEASTERN UNITED STATES. Frank B. Barick. Presented at 5th Ann.Meeting, S.E. Assn. Game and Fish Comm., pp.1-18, illus., Oct., 1951.

CASE FOR DEER HERD MANAGEMENT. I.H. Bartlett. Michigan Conserv., Lansing, vol.23, no.6, pp.2-7, illus., Nov., 1954.

WHERE ARE THE BUCKS? I.H. Bartlett. Michigan Conserv., Lansing, vol.12, no.9, pp.10-11, Nov., 1943.

FALLACIES IN WINTER FEEDING OF DEER. Arthur H. Carhart. Trans. 8th N. Amer. Wildl. Conf., pp.333-337, 1943.

DEER TROUBLE. David B. Cook. Audubon Mag., vol.47, no.2, pp.74-79, Mar.-Apr., 1945; South Dakota Conserv.Digest, Pierre, vol.12, no.9, pp.2-3, 10, Sep., 1945.

THINNING FOR BROWSE. David B. Cook. Jour. Wildl. Mgt., vol.3, no.3, pp.201-202, July, 1939.

PREVENTING DEER CONCENTRATIONS. W.T. Cox. Jour. Wildl. Mgt., vol.2, no. 1, pp.1-2, Jan., 1938.

DEER MANAGEMENT RESEARCH. B.L. Dahlberg. Wisc. Wildl. Research, Quart. Prog. Repts., Madison, vol.6, no.1, pp. 15-23, Apr., 1947; vol.7, no.2, pp.1-13, July, 1948; vol.8, no.4, pp.1-18, Jan., 1950.

WINTER DEER-RANGE CONDITIONS, 1949. B.L. Dahlberg. Wisc. Conserv.Bull., Madison, vol.14, no.6, pp.21-24, illus., June, 1949.

WINTER DEER FEEDING. Robert W. Darrow. N.Y. State Conserv., vol.2, no.4, p.21, Feb.-Mar., 1948.

FARM-LAND DEER. L.A. Davenport. Michigan Conserv., Lansing, vol.17, no. 11, pp.11-12, Nov., 1948.

--AND THE BROWSE CAME BACK. Stanley G. DeBoer. Michigan Conserv.Bull., vol. 18, no.1, pp.3-10, illus., Jan., 1953.

FEED 'EM - WITH AN AXE. Stanley G. DeBoer. Wisc. Conserv. Bull., vol.17, no. 3, pp.3-11, illus., Mar., 1952.

THE DEER PROBLEM IN THE NATIONAL FORESTS. Winston A. Elkins. Abs. Papers Presented at Wildl. Cons.Short Course, Univ. Minn., pp.23-25, May 4, 5, 6, 1939.

DEER MANAGEMENT RESEARCH. W. S. Feeney. Wisc. Wildl.Research, Madison, vol.3, no.1, pp.1-9, Apr., 1943; no.3, pp. 1-14, June, 1944; vol.4, no.1, pp.1-18, Oct., 1944; vol.5, no.3, pp.1-6 (mimeog.), Nov., 1946.

DEER MANAGEMENT RESEARCH PROJECT. W.S. Feeney. Wisc. Wildl. Research, Quarterly Prog. Repts., Madison, vol.1, no.2, pp.1-12, (mimeog.), July 1941; no.4, pp.1-9 (mimeog.), Jan., 1942; vol.2, no.1, pp.1-9 (mimeog.), Apr., 1942.

OPERATION DEER PASTURE. Merrill C. Gilfillan. Ohio Conserv. Bull., vol.15, no. 12, pp.8-9, illus., Dec., 1951.

MANAGEMENT OF OUR DEER HERDS. E.A. Goldman. Trans. 19th Amer Game Conf., 1932, Amer. Game Assn., New York, pp.49-61, 1933.

DEER MANAGEMENT RESEARCH. R. C. Guettinger. Wisc. Wildl. Research, Madison, vol.9, no.2, pp.6-21, July, 1950.

DEER, BRUSH AND THE ITASCA PARK FOREST. Henry L. Hansen, R.M. Brown. Conserv. Volunteer, vol.13, no.78, pp.1-5, Sep.-Oct., 1950.

EFFECT OF FOREST CUTTING PRACTICES ON DEER BROWSE IN THE CHESTNUT OAK, QUERCUS MONTANA, TYPE. John E. Harney. MF thesis, Penna. State Coll., 1948.

ASPEN MANAGEMENT: A PARTIAL SOLUTION TO THE DEER PROBLEM. R. P. Harrison. Wisconsin Conservation Bull., vol.20, no.2, p.18-22, illus., Feb., 1955.

MSC STUDENTS MEASURE LACK OF DEER FOOD. Arnold O. Haugen. Michigan Conserv., Lansing, vol.17, no.12, p.11, Dec., 1948.

OUR DEER MUST BE MANAGED. John V. Hoene. Amer. Forests, Wash., vol.53, no. 10, pp.450-452, illus., Oct., 1947.

EXPERIMENTAL WINTER FEEDING OF MULE DEER UTILIZING BOTH TOTAL WEIGHT CONSUMED AND FEEDING MINUTES AS AN INDICATION OF PREFERENCE. Richard L. Hubbard. MS thesis, Utah State Agr. Coll., 1952.

DEER BROWSE AND RIVER FLOW. J.R. Jacobson. Wisc. Conserv.Bull., Madison, vol.9, no.10, pp.9-11, illus., Oct., 1944.

NEED FOR DEER RANGE MANAGEMENT. John M. Keener. Wisc. Conserv.Bull., vol. 17, no.11, pp.7-10, illus., Nov., 1952.

DEER PROBLEM? WELL, ISN'T IT FOOD PROBLEM? Ford Kellum. Michigan Conserv., Lansing, vol.17, no.11, pp.5, 13, Nov., 1948.

DEER MANAGEMENT STUDIES WITH SPECIAL REFERENCE TO METHODS OF INCREASING BROWSE. Laurits W. Krefting. MS thesis, Univ. Minn., 1938.

EFFECT OF CUTTING MOUNTAIN MAPLE ON THE PRODUCTION OF DEER BROWSE. Laurits W. Krefting. Univ.Minn., Minn. For. Notes, no.21, pp.2, Sep., 1953.

USE OF HERBICIDES IN INDUCING REGROWTH OF MOUNTAIN MAPLE FOR DEER BROWSE. Laurits W. Krefting, et al. Univ. Minn., Minn. For.Notes, no.42, pp. 2, July, 1955.

FUTURE OBJECTIVES OF BIG GAME MANAGEMENT . J. Burton Lauckhart. Proc. 33rd Ann. Conf. Western Assn.State Game and Fish Comm., June 1-3, 1953, pp. 87-92, graph, 1954.

ABOUT KEEPING DEER IN A PEN. Daniel W. Lay. South Dakota Conserv.Digest, Pierre, vol.11, no.11, pp.7, 15, illus., Nov., 1944.

JACK PINE VS. DEER BROWSE. Russell K. LaBarron, Shaler E. Aldous. Conserv. Volunteer, vol.8, no.48, pp.23-24, Sep.-Oct., 1945.

EXCESS DEER PROBLEM. Aldo Leopold. Audubon Mag., New York, vol.45, no.3, pp.156-157, illus., May-June, 1943.

MORTGAGING THE FUTURE DEER HERD. Aldo Leopold. Wisc. Conserv.Bull., Madison, vol.12, no.9, p.3, Sep., 1947.

WHAT NEXT IN DEER POLICY? Aldo Leopold. Wisc. Conserv.Bull., vol.9, no.6, pp.3-4, 18-19, June, 1944.

MANAGING DEER ON PRIVAT LAND. William M. Longhurst, Walter E. Howard. Calif. Agric., vol.10, no.5, pp.4, 10, 1956.

DEER LICK IMPROVEMENTS. James K. McBride. Ohio Conserv. Bull., vol.10, no. 10, pp.20-21, Oct., 1946.

DEER HERD MANAGEMENT . Randal McCain. Oregon Outdoors, Oswego, vol. 4, no.2, pp.10-11, 23-25, illus., Feb., 1947.

DEER - OR TIMBER? J. M. McCullough. Penna. Game News, vol.23, no.6, pp.30-35, illus., Sep., 1952.

EFFECT OF FORESTRY CUTTING PRACTICES ON THE PRODUCTION OF DEER BROWSE IN THE VIRGINIA PINE (PINUS VIRGINIA) TYPE. Burd Sheldon McGinnes. MS thesis, Penna. State Coll., 1949.

WINTER AND THE DEER HERD. Wm.T. McKean. North Dakota Outdoors, Bismarck, vol.10, no.12, pp.5-6, illus., June, 1948.

RESEARCH AND HUNGRY DEER. R. A. MacMullan. Michigan Conserv., Lansing, vol.23, no.6, pp.15-18, illus., Nov., 1954.

FIVE YEAR GAME MANAGEMENT REPORT. THE DEER PROBLEM. L.G. MacNamara. New Jersey Fish and Game Comm., Trenton, pp.1-107, illus., 1940.

HERD MANAGEMENT OF MULE DEER. Glenn E. Mitchell. Trans. 7th N. Amer. Widl. Conf., pp.391-397, 1942.

MANAGEMENT OF WHITE-TAILED DEER AND PONDEROSA PINE. Geo.Neils et al. Trans. 20th N. Amer. Wildl. Conf., pp. 539-551, illus., 1955.

EXPERIMENTAL FEEDING OF DEER. A.A. Nichol. Proc. N.Amer. Wildl. Conf., pp. 403-410, 1936; Univ. Ariz., Tech. Bull., no.75, pp.39, June, 1938.

PETE THINKS ABOUT DEER MANAGEMENT. Jerome K. Pasto, Thomas Woods. Penna. Game News, vol.25, no.10, pp.12-17, illus., Oct., 1954.

FOOD FOR DEER AND FOOD FOR THOUGHT. Galen W. Pike. Wisc.Conserv. Bull., Madison, vol.14, no.7, pp.22-24, July, 1949.

PROBLEM OF "ANTLER ROOM." Paul M. Scheffer. Soil Conserv., Wash., vol.11, no. 7, pp.161-166, illus., Jan., 1946.

MANAGEMENT OF WHITETAIL DEER ON THE PISGAH NATIONAL GAME PRESERVE (SUMMARY OF FIVE-YEAR STUDY). E.A. Schilling. Trans. 3rd N.Amer. Wildl. Conf., pp.248-255, 1938.

TOO MANY DEER? Clay Schoenfeld. Field and Stream, New York, vol.53, no.3, pp. 32-33, 114-116, illus., July, 1948.

FEEDING DEER ON BROWSE SPECIES DURING WINTER. Arthur D. Smith. Jour. Range Mgt., vol.3, no.2, pp.130-132, Apr., 1950.

DEER AS AN OUTDOOR PROBLEM. Ernest Swift. Wisc. Conserv. Bull., Madison, vol.11, no.7, pp.6-10, July, 1946.

PROBLEM OF MANAGING DEER. Ernest Swift. Wisc. Conserv. Bull., vol.4, no.2, pp.8-27, Feb., 1939.

VALUE OF CLEAR-CUTTING IN STRIPS TO PRODUCE BROWSE FOR DEER IN MIXED OAK FORESTS OVER A FOURTEEN YEAR PERIOD. Joseph A. Tarr. MS thesis, Penna. State Coll., Aug., 1952.

THEORETICAL FRAMEWORK FOR UNDERSTANDING THE DEER MANAGEMENT PROBLEM. D. Woods Thomas, Jerome K. Pasto. Jour. Wildl.Mgt., vol.19, no.1, pp. 143-147, graphs, Jan., 1955; Proc. N.E. Sect. Wildl. Soc., 9th Ann. Conf., Bretton Woods, N.H., pp.1-5, graphs, Sep. 20-23 1953.

ARE WE PREPARED TO RESTORE THE WINTER DEER RANGES? Con Tolman. Colo.Conserv., pp.20-22, Dec., 1950.

WE ARE KILLING OUR DEER WITH KINDNESS. Jas. B. Trefethen. Sports Afield, New York, vol.122, no.5, pp.17-19, 90-95, illus., Nov., 1949.

EVALUATING AMOUNTS OF DEER BROWSE ON RECENTLY CUTOVER ASPEN STANDS. Casey E. Westell, Jr. Presented at 15th Midwest Wildl. Conf., Chicago, Ill., pp.1-3, Dec. 9-11, 1953.

TOO LATE TO SAVE CENTRAL AREA DEER? Leslie Woerpel. Wisc. Conserv. Bull., Madison, vol.14, no.3, p.30, Mar., 1949.

AIR-BORNE FODDER FOR SNOWBOUND DEER. Outdoor Life, New York, vol.103, no.3, pp.34-35, illus., Mar., 1949.

THE DEER DEBATE. Wisc. Conserv.Bull., Madison, vol.11, no.6, p.10, June, 1946.

DEER MANAGEMENT MEANS BETTER HUNTING--OR WORSE? Wisc. Conserv. Bull., Madison, vol.14, no.6, p.26, June, 1949.

DEER PROBLEM. Wisc. Conserv.Bull., Madison, vol.11, no.7, p.18, July, 1946.

DEER PROBLEM REVIEWED. Penna.Game News, Harrisburg, vol.18, no.9, pp.14, 30, illus., Dec., 1947.

RESULTS OF NOT FEEDING DEER. Colorado Conserv. Comm., Denver, vol.8, no. 2, pp.13-14, June 15, 1945.

TOO MANY DEER. Wisc. Conserv.Bull., Madison, vol.13, no.12, p.22, Dec., 1948.

WE'VE LED THE NATION IN WASTING DEER. Wisc. Conserv. Bull., Madison, vol.14, no.8, pp.26, Aug., 1949.

Odocoileus--Management (Eastern United States)

DEER MANAGEMENT SUGGESTIONS FOR NORTHERN WHITE CEDAR TYPES. Shaler E. Aldous. Jour. Wildl. Mgt., vol.5, no.1, pp.90-94, Jan., 1941.

EXPERIMENTAL PLANTING OF FOOD AND COVER FOR DEER. Shaler E. Aldous. U.S. Dept. Interior, Fish and Wildl. Serv., Wildl. Leaflet, no.320, pp.9, May, 1949.

WINTER DEER FOOD PROBLEM. Shaler E. Aldous. Conserv. Volunteer, vol.5, no.27, pp.37-39, Dec., 1942.

DEER PROBLEMS / NEW TO ARKANSAS / AN OLD STORY ELSEWHERE. Harold E. Alexander. Ark. Game and Fish Comm., pp.24, illus., 1954.

MANAGEMENT OF GEORGIA DEER. Geo. W. Allen. Jour. Wildl. Mgt., Menasha, vol. 12, no.4, pp.428-432, Oct., 1948.

ONE WILL GET YOU TWENTY! IN NORTH CAROLINA'S BIG GAME RESTORATION PROGRAM. F.B. Barick. Wildl. in N.C., vol.14, no.10, pp.14-17, 19, Oct., 1950.

CEDAR SWAMP MANAGEMENT AND DEER. I.H. Bartlett. Proc. Soc. Amer. Foresters' Meeting, 1947, pp.210-214, 1948.

OUR DEER PROBLEM AND ITS EFFECT ON THE MANAGEMENT OF FOOD AND COVER FOR WILDLIFE. I.H. Barlett. Conv. Internat. Assn. Game, Fish and Conserv. Comm., vol.38, pp.204-214, 1949?

WHITE-TAILS--PRESENTING MICHIGAN'S DEER PROBLEM. I.H. Barlett. Mich.Conserv., vol.8, no.2, pp.4-5, 7 to vol.8, no.7, pp.8, 11, Oct., 1938 to Mar., 1939; Penna. Game News, New Cumberland, vol. 9, no.12, pp.12-14, 29, Mar., 1939.

DEER MANAGEMENT IN MINNESOTA. Frank D. Blair. Wisc. Conserv.Bull., Madison, vol.14, no.4, pp.3-6, Apr., 1949.

WHITETAIL DEER AND ITS MANAGEMENT IN SOUTHEASTERN OHIO. Floyd B. Chapman. Trans. 4th N. Amer. Wildl. Conf., pp.257-267, 1939; Ohio Wildl. Res. Sta., Release 103, pp.10, Sep., 1939.

WINTER DEER FEEDING. Greenleaf Chase, C.W. Severinghaus. N.Y. Conserv. Dept., Fish and Wildl. Inf. Bull., no.3, pp.16, 1949.

ADIRONDACK DEER: A NEW PROPOSAL FOR THEIR MANAGEMENT IN WILDERNESS AREAS. E.L. Cheatum. N.Y.State Conserv., vol.7, no.5, p.5, map, Apr.-May, 1953.

DEER MANAGEMENT PROBLEM IN SOUTHERN NEW YORK. E.L. Cheatum. N.Y. State Conserv., vol.8, no.1, pp.22-23, illus., Aug.-Sep., 1953.

FOREST-CARRYING CAPACITY AND FOOD PROBLEMS OF DEER. Henry E. Clepper. Proc. N. Amer. Wildl. Conf., pp.410-415, 1936.

CRITICAL REVIEW OF WISCONSIN'S DEER PROBLEM. B.L. Dahlberg, R.C.Guettinger. Wisc. Conserv. Bull., vol.14, no.11, pp.6-9, Nov., 1949.

RESULTS OF DEER FEEDING EXPERIMENTS AT CUSINO, MICHIGAN. L. A. Davenport. Trans. 4th N. Amer. Wildl. Conf., pp.268-274, 1939.

DEER RANGE APPRAISAL FOR THE MISSOURI OZARKS. Robert L. Dunkeson.Jour. Wildl. Mgt., vol.19, no.3, pp.358-364, illus., July, 1955.

FOOD FOR DEER--PLANTED WITH AN AX! Robert L. Dunkeson. Missouri Conservationist, Jefferson City, vol.12, no.2, pp.4-5, 13, illus., Feb., 1951.

PROBLEMS OF DEER HERD MANAGEMENT. James W. Engle. Va. Wildl., vol.12, no.5, pp.22-24, May, 1951.

FOREST MANAGEMENT AND DEER REQUIREMENTS ON THE ALLEGHENY NATIONAL FOREST. E.O. Ehrhart. Jour. Forestry, vol.34, no.5, pp.472-474, May, 1936.

MINNESOTA'S DEER PROBLEM. Gordon Fredine. Minnesota Game and Fish, St. Paul, Conserv. Teaching Aid, no.1, pp. 21-27, 1940.

PENNSYLVANIA DEER PROBLEM IN 1938. Richard Gerstell. Penna. Game News, vol. 9, no.5, pp.12-13, 31 to vol.9, no.7, pp. 6-7, 29, Aug. to Oct., 1938.

WHITE-TAILED DEER AND ITS MANAGEMENT IN THE EDWARDS PLATEAU. Henry C. Hahn. Texas Game, Fish and Oyster Comm., Quart. Prog. Repts., Austin, pp. 9-11, Oct.-Dec., 1941.

DEER MANAGMENT IN MISSISSIPPI. Rolland B. Handley. Miss. Game and Fish, vol.16, no.3, pp.3, 8, 10, illus., Oct., 1952.

THE IOWA DEER PROBLEM AND ITS SOLUTION. James R. Harlan. Iowa Conserv., vol.12, no.1, pp.97, 102, illus., Jan., 1953.

COMING CATASTROPHE IN THE FLAGG. Edward N. Hein. Wisc. Conserv. Bull., Madison, vol. 14, no.6, pp.24-25, illus., June, 1949.

DEER MANAGEMENT STUDY: MUD LAKE NATIONAL WILDLIFE REFUGE, HOLT, MINNESOTA. Robley W. Hunt, Lloyd M. Mangus. Jour. Wildl. Mgt., Ithaca, vol.18, no.4, pp.482-495, Oct., 1954.

PLANTING TREES AND SHRUBS FOR WILDLIFE. B.C. Jenkins, H.D. McGinley. Mich. Conserv., vol.17, no.7, pp.10-12, July, 1948.

PENNSYLVANIA'S DEER PROBLEM. Roger M. Latham. Penna. Game News, Special Issue, vol.1, pp.2-40, Sep., 1950.

LOOKING AHEAD TO THE DEAR OLD DAYS. W.E. Laycock. Mich. Conserv., vol.16, no.10, pp. 5, 12, Nov., 1947.

OUR DEER PROBLEM AND ITS EFFECT ON THE MANAGEMENT OF FOOD AND COVER FOR WILDLIFE. Ross L. Leffer. Conv. Internat. Assn. Game, Fish and Conserv. Comm., vol.38, pp.175-179, 1949?; Penna. Game News, Harrisburg, vol.20, no.6, pp.3-5, 32, illus., Sep., 1949.

PENNSYLVANIA'S DEER PROBLEM. R.D. McDowell. Penna. Game News, Harrisburg, special issue, no.1, pp.1-40, illus., Sep., 1950.

MINNESOTA'S DEER PROBLEM. J. Manweiler. Minnesota Conservationist, no.50, pp.3, illus., Oct., 1937.

NEW WILDLIFE ERA: WHAT THE SPOTSMAN'S MONEY IS BUYING ON THE VIRGINIA NATIONAL FORESTS. C.P. Mead. Va. Wildl., vol.9, no.1, pp.16-18, Jan., 1948.

TECHNICIAN'S PLACE IN THIS JOB OF CONSERVATION. Ralph H. Quick. W.Va. Conserv., vol.15, no.3, pp.5-10, 41, June, 1951.

REGULATED WILDLIFE MANAGEMENT AREAS ON THE NATIONAL FORESTS IN THE SOUTH AND SOUTHEAST. E. A. Schilling. Trans. 8th N. Amer. Wildl.Conf., pp.102-108, 1943.

ADMINISTRATOR'S DILEMMA--SPORTSMEN'S BURDEN. (Wisconsin's deer problem.) W.E. Scott. Wisc. Conserv. Bull., Madison, vol.14, no.1, pp.6-10, illus., Jan., 1949.

DEER MANAGEMENT. Roger Seamans. Proc. Northeastern Game Conf., pp.41-43, 1948.

THREATS TO OUR DEER HERDS. C.W. Severinghaus. W.Va. Conserv., vol.14, no.9, pp.11-18, 38-39, Dec., 1950.

WEST VIRGINIA'S DEER PROBLEM. C.W. Severinghaus et al. Conserv. Comm.W.Va., PR-Project 25-R, pp.1-31, illus., 1951.

GRAND TRAVERSE REGION'S DEER PROBLEM. Warren W. Shapton. Michigan Conserv., Lansing, vol.17, no.11, pp.4, 12, figs.2, Nov., 1948.

MANAGEMENT OF WHITETAILED DEER IN MASSACHUSETTS. Samuel P. Shaw, Charles L. McLaughlin. Mass. Div.Fisheries and Game, Res. Bull., no.13, pp.vi+ 59, illus., 1951.

EVALUATION OF THE DEER AND GROUSE MANAGEMENT PRACTICES ON THE JEFFERSON NATIONAL FOREST. Jasper C. Sweet. MS thesis, Va.Polytechnic Inst., 1950.

FEEDING SNOWBOUND DEER. C. Roy Teller. Minn. Conserv., vol.67, pp.8-9, Apr., 1939.

PENNSYLVANIA'S DEER PROBLEM. R.L. Watts. Penna. Game News, Harrisburg, vol.11, no.12, p.25, Mar., 1940.

TOWARD BETTER CONSERVATION OF TREES AND DEER IN STATE PARKS. Chester S. Wilson. Conserv. Volunteer, vol.9, no.54, pp.20-24, Sep.-Oct., 1946.

ADIRONDACK DEER PROBLEM. N.Y. Conserv. Dept., N.Y. State Conserv., vol. 6, no.4, pp.28-29, illus., Feb.-Mar., 1952.

DEER FEEDING. Wisc. Conserv. Bull., vol. 11, no.8-9, pp.28-30, Aug.-Sep., 1946.

UWHARRIE DEER PROJECT. Bull. North Carolina Dept. Conserv. and Development, Raleigh, no.1, pp.1-19, illus., Jan., 1946.

WEST VIRGINIA FACES DEER MANAGEMENT PROBLEM. W.Va. Conserv., Charleston, vol.14, no.1, pp.9-10, Apr., 1950.

Odocoileus--Management (Western United States)

WHITE-TAILED DEER BROWSING ON PONDEROSA PINE PLANTAIONS. Lowell Adams. U.S. Dept. Agric., N.Rocky Mt. Forest and Range Exp. Sta., Res. Note, no.89, pp.5, Feb., 1951.

BIRTH CONTROL ON THE KAIBAB. Ben Avery. Ariz. Wildl. Mag., vol.7, no.7, pp.5, 13, Nov.-Dec., 1937.

MULE DEER PROBLEM OF THE MALHEUR NATIONAL FOREST, OREGON. Dana P. Berghuis. MS thesis, Oregon Sate Coll., 1939.

DEER MANAGEMENT IN THE BLACK HILLS OF SOUTH DAKOTA. Lester M. Berner. S.Dak. Conserv. Digest, vol.20, no.11, pp. 8-13, 16, illus., Nov., 1953; vol.20, no.12, pp.8-12, 16, graphs, Dec., 1953.

DEER MANAGEMENT PROBLEMS AND TECHNIQUES IN THE BLACK HILLS. Lester M. Berner. Presented at 13th Midwest Wildl. Conf., Minneapolis, pp.1-9, graphs, Dec. 12-14, 1951.

DANGER SIGNALS IN BLACK HILLS. (Overbrowsing of range by deer.) Wendell Bever. S.Dak. Conserv. Digest, Pierre, vol.15, no. 8, pp.10, 16, illus., Aug., 1948.

DEER MANAGEMENT ON THE KAIBAB. R.P. Boone. Trans. 3rd N.Amer. Wildl. Conf., pp.368-375, 1938.

KILLING DEER BY KINDNESS. Arthur H. Carhart. Amer.Forests, vol.51, no.1, pp. 13-15, 40, Jan., 1945.

DEER REFUGES UNDER THE BUCK LAW. F.P. Cronemiller. Calif. Fish and Game, vol.29, no.4, pp.180-190, Oct., 1943.

BASIC DEER MANAGEMENT (A STORY WITH PICTURES). William Dasmann. Calif. Fish and Game, vol.36, no.3, pp. 251-284, July, 1950.

NEW TRENDS IN DEER MANAGEMENT IN CALIFORNIA. William Dasmann. Jour. Range Mgt., vol.3, no.4, p.280, July, 1951.

GAME RESEARCH TACKLES BLACK HILLS DEER PROBLEM. Wayne Davis. S.Dak.Conserv.Digest, vol.17, no.9, pp. 8-10, 12, Sep., 1950.

MANAGEMENT STUDY OF THE UTAH-IDAHO INTERSTATE DEER HERD WITH SPECIAL REFERENCE TO THE SUBLETT, BLACK PINE, AND EAST RAFT RIVER MOUNTAIN UNIT. Kennest L. Diem. MS thesis, Utah State Agr. Coll., June, 1952.

STUDIES ON THE CONDITION OF CALIFORNIA MULE DEER AT SEQUOIA NATIONAL PARK. Joseph S. Dixon, Carlton M. Herman. Calif. Fish and Game, vol.31, no.1, pp.3-11, Jan., 1945.

SUPPLEMENTAL WINTER FEEDING OF MULE DEER IN NORTHERN UTAH. E.R. Doman, D.I. Rasmussen. Jour. Wildl.Mgt., vol.8, no.4, pp.317-338, Oct., 1944.

CRUDE PROTEIN DETERMINATION OF DEER FOOD AS AN APPLIED MANAGEMENT TECHNIQUE. Arthur S. Einarsen. Trans. N.Amer. Wildl. Conf., vol.11, pp. 309-312, 1946.

MANAGEMENT OF BLACK-TAILED DEER. Arthur S. Einarsen. Jour. Wildl. Mgt., vol. 10, no.1, pp.54-59, Jan., 1946.

EXPERIMENTAL TRAPPING AND TRANSPLANTING OF MULE DEER. O.F.Etheredge. Texas Game, Fish and Oyster Comm., F A Rep. Ser.5, pp.10, Aug., 1949.

WHY IT BECOMES NECESSARY TO PROPERLY MANAGE DEER HERDS IN SOUTH DAKOTA. Phillips Haas. S.Dakota Conserv. Digest, Pierre, pp.3, 14, illus., Oct., 1942.

SUPPLEMENTAL DEER FEEDING IN THE BLACK HILLS. Dave Harris. S.Dakota Conserv. Digest, vol.19, no.6, pp.6-7, 16, illus., June, 1952.

RESEARCH AT THE CLEMONS TREE FARM. Gardiner F. Jones. Wash.State Game Bull., vol.4, no.4, pp.4-5, 9, illus., Oct., 1952.

DEER RANGE EXPERIMENTS IN THE BLACK HILLS. James E. King. S.Dakota Conserv. Digest, Madison, vol.15, no.9, pp.10, 14-15, Sep., 1948; vol.15, no.10, pp.10, 14, 16, illus., Oct., 1948.

DEER MANAGEMENT IN WASHINGTON. Burton Lauckhart. Game Bull., vol.1, no.1, pp.1, 4, Aug., 1949.

TYPICAL DEER PROBLEM. Daniel W.Lay, Henry C. Hahn. Texas Game and Fish, vol. 3, no.4, p.12, Mar., 1945.

PRELIMINARY REPORT ON THE PROBLEMS OF DEER MANAGEMENT IN CALIFORNIA. A. Starker Leopold. Calif. Fish and Game Comm., pp.16, illus., 1948.

NORTHERN BLACK HILLS DEER FEEDING PROGRAM. Wm.T. McKean. S.Dakota Conserv. Digest, Pierre, vol.12, no.5, pp.10-11, May, 1945.

WINTER DEER PROBLEM. Wm.T. McKean. S.Dakota Conserv. Digest, Pierre, vol.12, no.1, pp.2-3, 6, Jan., 1945.

COMMENTS ON ARTIFICIAL FEEDING. David J. Maclay. N.Region News, pp. 51-52, June, 1937.

DEER MANAGEMENT STUDIES ON THE KAIBAB NATIONAL FOREST. Walter G. Mann. Utah State Agric. Coll., Logan, Utah, Misc. publ.10, pp.38-41, May, 1933.

SURVEY OF THE DEER SITUATION IN ZION CANYON, UTAH. Clifford C.Presnall. Proc. Utah Acad. Sci., Arts and Letters, vol.15, pp.107-110, 1938.

DEER WINTER RANGE STUDIES 1937-1938, MODOC NATIONAL FOREST. Allen C. Randle. U.S. Dept. Agric., Forest Serv., Calif. Region, Leaflet no.73-W-4, pp.17, Sep., 1938.

UTAH'S MULE DEER STUDIES AND MANAGEMENT PROBLEMS. D.I. Rasmussen. Amer. Wildl., vol.28, no. 5, pp.232-240, Sep.-Oct., 1939.

NEW ERA IN DEER MANAGEMENT. J. Clark Salyer II. N.Dakota Outdoors, vol. 10, no.5, p.11, Nov., 1947.

MANAGING UTAH'S DEER HERDS. Arthur D. Smith. Utah Fish and Game Bull., Salt Lake City, vol.4, no.7, pp.1-3, Dec., 1947.

MANAGEMENT OF NATIVE DEER IN NEBRASKA. John H. Wampole, Edson Fichter. Wildl. Mgt. Notes,pts.1-2, vol. 1, nos.4-5, pp.15-22, Mar., 1949.

DEER FEEDING FAILS IN COLORADO. Michigan Conserv., Lansing, vol.12, no.3, p.10, illus., Apr., 1943; Colorado Conserv. Comm., Denver, vol.6, no.1, pp.3, 4, Mar., 1943.

INTERSTATE WINTER DEER RANGE MANAGEMENT PLAN. Calif. Fish and Game, vol.35, no.2, pp.103-114, Apr., 1949.

REHABILITATING THE DEER. Wyo.Wild Life, vol.7, no.8, pp.1-3, Aug., 1942.

RESTORE WHITE-TAIL DEER EAST OF PECOS. New Mexico Mag., Albuquerque, vol.22, no.8, p.29, Aug., 1944.

TEXAS DEER PROBLEM. Wisc. Conserv. Bull., Madison, vol.12, no.9, pp.29-30, Sep., 1947.

Odocoileus--Methods, Techniques

CONDUCTING DEER STUDIES WITH THE USE OF A HELICOPTER. Clarence M. Aldous. Jour. Wildl. Mgt., vol.20, no.3, pp.327-328, July, 1956.

DEER BROWSE SURVEY METHOD. Shaler E. Aldous. Jour. Mamm., vol.25, no.2, pp.130-136, May, 1944.

ART OF TRACKING DEER ON SNOW. L.A. Anderson. Fur-Fish-Game, Harding's Mag., Columbus, vol.79, no.10, pp.12-13, 20, Oct., 1945.

LIMITATIONS OF THE BONE MARROW TECHNIQUE IN DETERMINING MALNUTRITION IN DEER. Arthur I. Bischoff. Proc. 34th Ann. Conf. Western Assn. State Game and Fish Comm., pp.205-210, May, 1954 (1955).

BONE MARROW AS AN INDEX OF MALNUTRITION IN DEER. E. L. Cheatum. N.Y. Conservationist, Albany, vol.3, no.5, pp. 19-22, illus., Apr.-May, 1949.

USE OF CORPORA LUTEA FOR DETERMINING OVULATION INCIDENCE AND VARIATIONS IN THE FERTILITY OF WHITE-TAILED DEER. E.L. Cheatum. Cornell Veterinarian, Ithaca, vol.39, no.3, pp.282-291, illus., July, 1949.

TECHNIQUES USED IN DETERMINING THE PERIOD OF THE RUT AMONG WHITE-TAILED DEER OF NEW YORK STATE. E.L. Cheatum, G.L. Morton. Trans. 7th N.Amer. Wildl. Conf., Wash., D.C., pp.334-342, figs.4, 1942.

DEER MARKING DEVICES. Melvin R. Clover. Calif. Fish and Game, vol.40, no.2, pp.175-181, illus., Apr., 1954.

PREVENTING DEER CONCENTRATIONS. W.T. Cox. Jour. Wildl. Mgt., vol.2, no.1, pp.1-2, Jan., 1938.

NICOTINE SALICYLATE FOR CAPTURING DEER. Jack A. Crockford, Frank A. Hayes. Jour. Wildl. Mgt., vol.21, no.2, pp.213-220, illus., Apr., 1957.

PROBABLE ERRORS IN SAMPLE MEASUREMENTS OF DEER KILL. F.P.Cronemiller. Jour. Wildl. Mgt., vol.11, no.1, pp.103-104, Jan., 1947.

CRITICAL REVIEW OF RANGE SURVEY METHODS AND THEIR APPLICATION TO DEER RANGE MANAGEMENT. William Dasmann. Calif. Fish and Game, vol.34, no.4, pp.189-207, Oct., 1948.

SOME DEER RANGE SURVEY METHODS. William Dasmann. Calif. Fish and Game, vol.37, no.1, pp.43-52, Jan., 1951.

METHODS OF STUDYING BROWSE PREFERENCE OF DEER. J.L. Deen. Trans. 3rd N.Amer. Wildl. Conf., pp.256-260, 1938.

USE OF A DEER CALL AS A MEANS OF LOCATING DEER FAWNS. Kenneth Diem. Jour. Wildl. Mgt., Ithaca, vol.18, no.4, pp.537-538, illus., Oct., 1954.

APPRAISAL OF OVARIAN ANALYSES IN DETERMINING REPRODUCTIVE PERFORMANCE OF BLACK-TAILED DEER. Frank B. Golley. Jour. Wildl. Mgt., vol.21, no.1, pp.62-65, illus., Jan., 1957.

DEER TRAPPING AND TAGGING--. Phillips Haas. S.Dakota Conserv. Digest, Pierre, vol.9, no.4, p.7, illus., Apr., 1942.

PRELIMINARY REPORT ON THE USE OF FLAXEDIL[R] TO PRODUCE PARALYSIS IN THE WHITE-TAILED DEER(ODOCOILEUS VIRGINIANUS BOREALIS). T.C.Hall et al. Jour. Wildl. Mgt., vol.17, no.4, pp.516-520, illus., Oct., 1953.

PRELIMINARY REPORT ON A DEER BROWSE CENSUS BASED ON 100% CLIPPING METHOD. Richard F.Harlow. Presented at 9th Ann. Meeting, S.E. Assn. Game and Fish Comm., pp.1-47, Oct., 1955.

CONTROL OF THE NASAL BOT-FLY. Wm. Hiller. Penna. Game News, vol.9, no.1, p.27, Apr., 1938.

PRELIMINARY REPORT ON A FIELD METHOD OF CAPTURING DEER USING DRUGS. James H. Jenkins et al. Presented at 9th Ann. Meeting, S.E.Assn. Game and Fish Comm., pp.1-7, Oct., 1955.

AGEING THE INYO MULE DEER. Fred L. Jones. Proc. 33rd Ann. Conf. Western Assn. State Game and Fish Comm., pp.209-219, June 1-3, 1953 (1954).

TECHNIQUE FOR EVALUATING DEER BROWSING. Harold C. Jordahl. MF thesis, Univ. Mich., 1950.

METHODS OF INCREASING DEER BROWSE. Laurits W. Krefting. Jour. Wildl. Mgt., vol. 5, no.1, pp.95-102, Jan., 1941.

WHITETAIL TRAPS AND TAGS. Donald Y. McBeath. Mich. Conserv., vol.10, no.11, pp.6-7, 11, Oct., 1941; vol.10, no.12, pp.6-7, Nov., 1941.

METHOD FOR MEASURING DEER RANGE USE. Randal McCain. Trans. 13th N.Amer. Wildl. Conf., pp.431-440, 1948.

REPLACEMENT OF TEETH IN DEER AS A MEANS OF AGE DETERMINATION. Donald D. McLean. Calif. Fish and Game, vol.22, no.1, pp.43-44, figs.20, Jan., 1936.

TECHNIQUE FOR DETERMINING AGE IN BLACK-TAILED DEER. Raleigh Moreland. Proc. 32nd Ann. Conf. Western Assn. State Game and Fish Comm., Glacier Nat. Park, Mont., pp.214-219, graphs, June 15-17, 1952 (1953).

TECHNIQUE FOR REDUCING MAN-POWER IN THE DEER DRIVE CENSUS. Marius Morse. Jour. Wildl. Mgt., vol.7, no.2, pp. 217-220, Apr., 1943.

SIMPLIEFIED METHOD FOR DETERMINING THE CONDITION OF WHITE-TAILED DEER HERDS IN RELATION TO AVAILABLE FORAGE. Barry C. Park, Besse B. Day. U.S. Dept. Agric., Tech. Bull., no.840, pp.60, 1943.

METHOD FOR APPRAISAL OF WINTER RANGE OF DEER. R.C. Passmore, R.L. Hepburn. Ont. Dept. Lands and For., Res. Rep., no.29, pp.7, Jan., 1955.

DETERMINING THE AGE OF DEER. Geo. A. Petrides. S.Dakota Conserv. Digest, Pierre, vol.11, no.10, p.10, illus., Oct., 1944.

SIMPLIFIED METHOD FOR DETERMINING THE AGE OF MULE DEER. W. Leslie Robinette, Wallace Jensen. Utah State Dept. Fish and Game, Dept. Inf. Bull., no.1, pp. 5, Oct., 1950.

AGING A DEER. C.W. Severinghaus. N.Y. State Conserv., vol.5, no.2, pp.8-10, Oct.-Nov., 1950.

ANESTHETIZATION OF WHITETAILED DEER. C.W. Severinghaus. Cornell Vet., vol.40, no.3, pp.275-282, July, 1950.

DEER WEIGHTS AS AN INDEX OF RANGE CONDITIONS ON TWO WILDERNESS AREAS IN THE ADIRONDACK REGION. C.W. Severinghaus. N.Y. Fish and Game Jour., vol.2, no.2, pp.154-160, July (Nov.), 1955.

DEVELOPMENT OF A METHOD FOR DETERMINING THE AGE OF WHITE-TAILED DEER. C.W. Severinghaus. Proc. Northeastern Game Conf., pp.33-37, 1948.

TOOTH DEVELOPMENT AND WEAR AS CRITERIA OF AGE IN WHITE-TAILED DEER. C.W. Severinghaus. Jour. Wildl. Mgt., Menasha, vol.13, no.2, pp.195-216, Apr., 1949.

TRAPPING AND MARKING WHITE-TAILED DEER. William L. Webb. Jour. Wildl. Mgt., Menasha, vol.7, no.3, pp.346-348, July, 1943.

LIFE SAVING ARROWS. J. Martin Young, Jr. Nat. Hist., vol.55, no.9, pp.424-425, Nov., 1946.

Odocoileus--Migrations, Movements

MOVEMENTS OF WHITE-TAILED DEER TAGGED IN MINNESOTA. J.C. Carlsen, Robert E. Farmes. Jour. Wildl. Mgt., vol. 21, no.4, pp.397-401, Oct., 1957.

FACTORS INFLUENCING MOVEMENT OF NON-MIGRATORY DEER. Raymond F. Dasmann. Proc. 33rd Ann. Conf. Western Assn. State Game and Fish Comm., pp. 112-116, June 1-3, 1953 (1954).

DEER MOVEMENTS IN THE EDWARDS PLATEAU. Henry C. Hahn, Walter P. Taylor. Texas Game and Fish, vol.8, no.12, pp.4-9, 31, Nov., 1950.

DEER MIGRATIONS. C.P. Russell. Yosemite Nature Notes, vol.4, pp.20-23, Mar., 1925.

SEASONAL MIGRATION OF MULE DEER. C.P. Russell. Ecological Monographs, no. 2, pp.1-46, figs.5, Jan., 1932.

LOCAL CHANGE IN MIGRATION HABITS OF THE MULE DEER. Winton Weydemeyer. Jour. Mamm., vol.9, no.3, pp.209-212, Aug., 1928.

MIGRATION CENSUS OF MULE DEER IN THE WHITE RIVER REGION OF NORTHWESTERN COLORADO. Edward Wright, Lloyd W. Swift. Jour. Wildl. Mgt., Menasha, vol.6, no.2, pp.162-164, Apr., 1942.

MOVEMENT OF COLUMBIAN BLACK-TAILED DEER IN THE WILLAPA HILLS AREA, WASHINGTON. Fred Zwickel et al. Murrelet, Seattle, vol.34, no.3, pp.41-46, Dec., 1953.

WHITE RIVER DEER MIGRATION. Colorado Conserv. Comm., Denver, vol.9, no. 2, p.27, June 15, 1946.

Odocoileus--Mortality

FAWNS" FATE DEPENDS ON WEATHER. I.H. Bartlett. Mich. Conserv., vol.16, no. 2, pp.3, 6, Feb., 1947.

ICEBOUND. (Doe caught in ice.) Earl L. Bray. Nature Mag., Wash., D.C., vol.32, no.5, p.281, photo 1, May, 1939.

SUMMER MORTALITY OF JUVENILE BLACK-TAILED DEER IN WESTERN WASHINGTON. James H. Brigham. Murrelet, vol.35, no.3, pp.39-42, graph, Sep.-Dec., 1954.

MINNESOTA'S DEER TRAFFIC TOLL. Donald W. Burcalow. Conserv. Volunteer, St. Paul, vol.5, no.25, pp.14-16, Oct., 1942.

ACCIDENTAL DEATH OF A MULE DEER IN IDAHO. Edwin B. Caswell. Jour. Mamm., vol.34, no.4, p.515, Nov. 13, 1953.

SPORTSMEN'S COMMITTEE REPORTS. (Starvation of deer.) Duncan D. DeLaurier, Chairman. Michigan Conserv., Lansing, vol.16, no.10, pp.8, 12-13, Nov., 1947.

MUST THEY STARVE? Ben East. Amer. Forests, vol.42, no.10, pp.463-465, 483, Oct., 1936.

FAMINE STALKS THE DEER. W.S. Feeney. Wisconsin Conserv. Bull., vol.7, no.9, pp. 8-10, Sep., 1942.

WHAT HAPPENED TO YOUR DEER? (Deer mortality causes.) Stanley E. Forbes. Pa. Game News, vol.23, no.9, pp.35-39, illus., Dec., 1952.

CASE OF THE STARVING DEER. Bill Gamble. Ariz. Wildl.-Sportsman, vol. 25, no.3, pp.62-63, Mar., 1954.

WINTER DEER LOSSES. Richard Gerstell. Penna. Game News, vol.8, no.7, pp.18-21, 29, Oct., 1937.

MARSH DEER "DIE-OFF" IN LOUISIANA. Leslie L. Glasgow, Allan Ensminger. Jour. Wildl. Mgt., vol.21, no.2, pp.245-247, Apr., 1957.

STARVING DEER OF THE KAIBAB FOREST. Geo. Bird Grinnell. The Outlook, vol.136, no.5, pp.186-187, Jan. 30, 1924.

DEER DON'T DIE FROM LEAD ALONE! Vernon E. Gunalson. Conserv. Volunteer, vol.15, no.89, pp.45-48, Sep.-Oct., 1952.

TWO INSEPARABLE BUCKS. THE STORY OF A DOUBLE TRAGEDY. C.E. Hagie. Field and Stream, no.6, pp.23, 79, Oct., 1929.

THEY DIE YOUNG. (Deer.) Henry C. Hahn, Jr. Texas Game and Fish, Austin, vol.5, no.11, pp.5, 25-26, illus., Oct., 1947.

BARBED WIRE FENCE CAUSES DEATH OF DEER. E. Raymond Hall. Calif. Fish and Game, vol.12, pp.151-152, July, 1926.

DANGER: DEER CROSSING. (Deer killed by automobiles.) Harold D. Hettrick. Wisc. Conserv. Bull., vol.23, no.3, pp.7-9, Mar., 1958.

MINNESOTA'S DEER PROBLEM. Ralph Hill. Minn. Conserv., vol.57, pp.9, 19, 22-23, May, 1938.

AN UNUSUAL CAUSE OF DEER MORTALITY. Fred L. Jones. Jour. Wildl. Mgt., Ithaca, vol.18, no.1, p.142, Jan., 1954.

MORTALITY STUDIES OF COLUMBIAN BLACK-TAILED DEER IN THE COASTAL REGION OF OREGON. Lee W. Kuhn. MS thesis, Oregon State Coll., 1942.

ROCKY MOUNTAIN MULE DEER INVESTIGATIONS. DEER LOSSES ON THE CACHE DEER HERD. J.B. Lowe. Quart. Rept. Utah Coop. Wildl. Research Unit, Logan, vol.14, no.3, pp.1-8, July-Sep., 1949. (Winter of 1948-1949.)

TO THEM SPRING WILL NOT COME. (Deer.) J.B. Lowe. Utah Fish and Game Bull., Salt Lake City, vol.9, no.5, pp.5-7, Oct., 1950.

BLACK HILLS WINTER DEER LOSS. Wm. T. McKean. S.Dakota Conserv. Digest, vol.11, no.8, p.10, Aug., 1944.

REPORT OF TWO DEER YARDS IN DOUGLAS AND BAYFIELD COUNTIES. (Mortality in northern Wisconsin.) Fred T. Minor et al. Wisc. Conserv. Bull., vol.4, no.5, pp.18-24, May, 1939.

DEATH OF BUCK DEER RESULT OF FIGHTING IN RUT. James Moffitt. Calif. Fish and Game, vol.20, no.1, pp.82-84, Jan., 1934.

LOSS OF DEER IN THE CANAL OF THE WESTERN STATES GAS AND ELECTRIC COMPANY, EL DORADO COUNTY. Geo. Neale. Calif. Fish and Game, vol.10, pp. 115-119, figs.25-27, July, 1924.

LOSSES OF CRIPPLED DEER. Urban C. Nelson. Conserv. Volunteer, St. Paul, vol.7, no.43, pp.34-35, Nov.-Dec., 1944.

DEER MORTALITY FROM GUNSHOT WOUNDS. W. Leslie Robinette. U.S. Dept. Interior, Fish and Wildl. Serv., Wildl. Leaflet, no.295, pp.8, July, 1947.

WINTER MORTALITY AMONG MULE DEER IN THE FISHLAKE NATIONAL FOREST, UTAH. W. Leslie Robinette. U.S. Dept. Interior, Fish and Wildl. Serv., Sp. Sci. Rept. 65, pp.15, Apr., 1949.

DIFFERENTIAL MORTALITY BY SEX AND AGE AMONG MULE DEER. W. Leslie Robinette et al. Jour. Wildl. Mgt., vol.21, no.1, pp.1-16, Jan., 1957.

WINTER MORTALITY OF MULE DEER IN UTAH IN RELATION TO RANGE CONDITION. W. Leslie Robinette et al. Jour. Wildl. Mgt., Ithaca, vol.16, no.3, pp.289-299, July, 1952.

ICE-CLOSED LAKE PROVIDES NATURAL TRAP FOR DEER. Harrison Shobe. West Va. Conserv., Charleston, vol.10, no.10, pp.18-19, Feb., 1947.

DEER STARVE AT FEEDING STATIONS. B.P. Stollberg. Wisc. Conserv. Bull., Madison, vol.14, no.2, pp.18-19, illus., Feb., 1949.

SEX DIFFERENCE IN MORTALITY IN YOUNG COLUMBIAN BLACK-TAILED DEER. Richard D. Taber, Raymond F. Dasmann. Jour. Wildl. Mgt., Ithaca, vol. 18, no.3, pp.309-315, July, 1954.

WHY DEER ARE DYING. Walter P. Taylor. Texas Game and Fish, Astin, vol.5, no.7, p.17, June, 1947.

DIE-OFFS AMONG THE WHITE-TAILED DEER IN THE EDWARDS PLATEAU OF TEXAS. Walter P. Taylor, Henry C. Hahn. Jour. Wildl. Mgt., vol.11, no.4, pp.317-323, Oct., 1947.

DECLINE IN DEER MORTALITIES. L.W. Ward. W.Va. Conserv., vol.12, no.7, pp. 9-10, Oct., 1948.

TECHNICIANS STUDYING DEER MORTALITY PROBLEMS. L.W. Ward. W.Va. Conserv., Charleston, vol.12, no.2, pp.6-7, May, 1948.

BEARDED GRAINS CAUSE DEATH OF DEER. Kenneth B. Winter, Ralph F. Honess. Jour. Wildl. Mgt., Ithaca, N.Y., vol.16, no.1, pp.113-114, pl.4, Jan., 1952.

ANOTHER WINTER IS ON THE WAY. (Deer.) Michigan Conserv., Lansing, vol.12, no.9, p.3, illus., Nov., 1943.

DEER ON NATIONAL FORESTS--DANGER OF STARVATION. Jour. Mamm., vol.10, no.1, pp.99-100, Feb., 1929.

DEER STARVATION 1947. Michigan Conserv., Lansing, vol.16, no.10, p.9, Nov., 1947.

HIGHWAYS TAKE HEAVY DEER TOLL. Wash. State Game Bull., vol.5, no.3, p.8, July, 1953.

MONTHLY SUMMARY OF DEER LOSSES FROM PROTECTOR'S REPORTS 1952. Wash. Dept. Game, pp.12, mimeo., 1953.

ONE OF NATURE'S TRAGEDIES. (Deer.) S.Dakota Conserv. Digest, Pierre, vol.9, no.3, p.3, illus., Mar., 1942.

UTAH DEER LOSS HEAVY DESPITE EMERGENCY FEEDING PROGRAM. Utah Fish and Game Bull., Salt Lake City, vol. 7, no.3, pp.1, 3-6, illus., Apr., 1949.

WINTER DEER LOSSES GREATEST IN UTAH'S HISTORY. Utah Fish and Game Bull., vol.9, no.5, pp.1-2, illus., May-June, 1952.

Odocoileus--North America

NORTH AMERICAN DEER. J.A. Allen. Amer. Nat., vol.36, pp.755-756, Sep., 1902.

BLACKTAIL AND MULE DEER. ATTRACTIVE HORNED MAMMALS OF WESTERN NORTH AMERICA. Vernon Bailey. Nat. Geog. Mag., vol.20, no.2, pp.61-64, illus., Aug., 1932.

WHITE TAILED DEER ODOCOILEUS VIRGINIANUS IN JASPER NATIONAL PARK, ALBERTA. A.W.F. Banfield. Canadian Field-Nat., vol.67, no.1, p.44, Jan.-Mar., 1953.

WHITETAIL DEER--UNITED STATES AND CANADA. I.H. Bartlett. Trans. 14th N. Amer. Wildl. Conf., pp.543-553, 1949.

WHITETAILS OF ONTARIO. N. Edwin Carlson. Outdoorsman, Chicago, vol.86, no.5, whole no.510, pp.14-15, 34, Sep.-Oct., 1944.

WHITE-TAILED DEER OF ONTARIO. E.C. Cross. Rod and Gun in Canada, vol.38, no. 9, pp.14-15, 32, Feb., 1937.

WHITE-TAILED DEER. Stuart C. Downing. Canadian Nature, Toronto, vol.11, no.4, pp.100-101, illus., Sep.-Oct., 1949.

NORTHERN LIMIT OF THE WHITE-TAILED DEER IN ONTARIO. J.R. Dymond. Canadian Field Nat., vol.44, no.4, p.96, Apr., 1930.

HOOFED ANIMALS OF NORTH AMERICA. PART I. ANIMALS WITH ANTLERS--THE DEER. Geo. G. Goodwin. School. Nature League Bull., vol.16, no.9, p.4, May, 1946.

DEER OF THE UNITED STATES. Geo B. Johnson. Va. Wildl., Blacksburg, vol.3, no.3, pp.2, 7, Nov., 1939.

SURVEY OF OVER-POPULATED DEER RANGES IN THE UNITED STATES. Aldo Leopard et al. Jour. Wildl. Mgt., Menasha, vol.11, no.2, pp.162-177, Apr., 1947.

(DEER. DIFFERENT CLASSES. ITS HUNT AND UTILIZATION.) El Venado. Diferentes Clases. Su Cazay Aprovechamiento. (White-tailed deer in Mexico.) Carlos Zinser Lopez. Proteccion a la Naturaleza, Mexico City, vol. 1, no.2, p.13, Nov., 1935.

DEER OF NORTH AMERICA. THE WHITE-TAILED, MULE AND BLACK-TAILED DEER, GENUS ODOCOILEUS. THEIR HISTORY AND MANAGEMENT. Walter P. Taylor (Editor). Stackpole Co., Harrisburg, and Wildl. Mgt. Inst., Washington, pp.668, pls.2 (in color), 1956.

VIRGINIA DEER IN PRINCE EDWARD ISLAND. W.J. Wintemberg. Canadian Field-Nat., Ottawa, vol.53, no.8, p.122, Nov., 1939.

NOTES ON AMERICAN DEER. Owen A. Wyatt. Hunting and Fishing, Philadelphia, vol.27, no.10, pp.23-27, illus., Oct., 1950.

Odocoileus--Pelage and Coloration

WHITE ANTLERED BUCK. N.R. Casilio. Penna. Game News, Harrisburg, vol.13, no.12, pp.4-5, 24-25, illus., Mar., 1943.

THAT ALBINO DEER FAWN. Lee S. Crandall. Animal Kingdom, New York Zool. Soc., vol. 55, no.2, pp.61-62, illus., Mar.-Apr., 1952.

REMEMBER WHITEY? (Albino Deer.) E.N. Gein. Wisc. Conserv. Bull., Madison, vol. 9, no.11, p.11, illus., Nov., 1944.

WOOLLY WHITE-TAILED DEER. Geo. M. Sutton. Jour. Mamm., vol.11, no.1, pp.86-87, Feb., 1930.

ALBINISM IN THE VIRGINIA DEER. Jour. Heredity, Wash., D.C., vol.33, no.8, pp. 274, 284, fig.1, Aug., 1942.

ALBINO DEER SEEN IN HILLS COUNTRY. S.Dakota Conserv. Digest, Pierre, pp.14, Dec., 1939.

Odocoileus--Physiology, Biochemistry

NUTRITIONAL KNOWLEDGE SHORT CUT. Earl L. Atwood. Jour. Wildl. Mgt., vol.12, no.1, pp.1-8, Jan., 1948.

GROWTH OF DEER AFFECTED BY NUTRITION. Wendell Bever. S.Dakota Conserv. Digest, Madison, vol.17, no.5, pp.6, 12, illus., May, 1950.

DIGESTIBILITY OF CERTAIN NATURAL AND ARTIFICIAL FOODS EATEN BY DEER IN CALIFORNIA. Harold D. Bissell et al. Calif. Fish and Game, vol.41, no.1, pp.57-58, illus., Jan., 1955.

CRUDE PROTEIN VARIATIONS IN THE BROWSE DIET OF CALIFORNIA DEER. Harold D. Bissell, Helen Strong. Calif. Fish and Game, vol.41, no.2, pp.145-155, Apr., 1955.

ERYTHROCYTE VALUES, AND ALIMENTARY CANAL pH VALUES IN THE MULE DEER. Ludvig G. Browman. Jour. Mamm., vol.36, no.3, pp.474-476, Aug., 1955.

MULE DEER MILK. Ludvig G. Browman, Howard S. Sears. Jour. Mamm., vol.36, no.3, pp.473-474, Aug., 1955.

NORMAL TEMPERATURE OF THE COLUMBIAN BLACK-TAILED DEER. I. McT. Cowan, A.J. Wood. Jour. Wildl. Mgt., Ithaca, vol.19, no.1, pp.154-155, Jan., 1955.

DEER MEAT INVESTIGATION. H.W. Estill. Calif. Fish and Game, vol.18, no.3, pp. 249-250, July, 1932.

DIGESTIVE CAPACITIES OF THE WHITE-TAILED DEER. E.B. Forbes et al. Jour. Wildl. Mgt., Menasha, vol.5, no.1, pp. 108-114, pl.6, Jan., 1941.

NUTRIENT REQUIREMENTS FOR GRWOTH AND ANTLER DEVELOPMENT IN THE WHITE-TAILED DEER. C.E. French et al. Jour. Wildl. Mgt., vol.20, no.3, pp.221-232, July, 1956.

NUTRITIONAL REQUIREMENTS OF WHITE-TAILED DEER FOR GROWTH AND ANTLER DEVELOPMENT. C.E. French. Bull. Penna. State Univ. Agric. Exper. Sta., nos.600, 600P, pp.50+8, illus., July, 1955.

HOMING INSTINCT OF WHITE-TAILED DEER. W.C. Glazener. Texas Game and Fish, Austin, vol.6, no.8, pp.5, illus., July, 1948.

TOTAL GONADOTROPHIC POTENCY OF MULE DEER PITUITARIES. K.C. Grieser, L.G. Browman. Endocrinology, Springfield, vol.58, no.2, pp.206-211, Feb., 1956.

COMPOSITION OF DEER MILK. Herbert L. Hagen. Calif. Fish and Game, San Francisco, vol.37, no.2, pp.217-218, Apr., 1951.

NUTRITIVE VALUE FOR DEER OF SOME FORAGE PLANTS IN THE SIERRA NEVADA. Herbert Hagen. Calif. Fish and Game, vol. 39, no.2, pp.163-175, Apr., 1953.

AMMATE IN THE DIET OF DEER. Arnold O. Haugen. Presented at the 5th Ann. Meeting, S.E. Assn. Game and Fish Comm., pp.1-7, Oct., 1951; Jour. Wildl. Mgt., Ithaca, vol.17, no.1, pp.33-36, Jan., 1953.

STUDY OF MONTHLY VARIATIONS IN THE NUTRITIVE VALUE OF SEVERAL NATURAL WINTER DEER FOODS. Henry Hellmers. Jour. Wildl. Mgt., vol.4, no.3, pp.315-325, July, 1940.

STUDY OF THE NUTRITIVE VALUE OF SEVERAL OF THE NATURAL WINTER FOODS OF DEER. Henry Hellmers. MS thesis, Penna. State Coll., 1939.

PALATABILITY RATINGS OF BLACK HILLS PLANTS FOR WHITE-TAILED DEER. Ralph R. Hill. Jour. Wildl. Mgt., Menasha, vol.10, no.1, pp.47-54, Jan., 1946.

EFFECT OF AGE AND PLANE OF NUTRITION ON THE BLOOD CHEMISTRY OF THE COLUMBIAN BLACK-TAILED DEER (ODOCOILEUS HEMIONUS COLUMBIANUS). A. PACKED-CELL VOLUME, SEDIMENTATION RATE, AND HEMOGLOBIN. W.D. Kitts. Canadian Jour. Zool., vol.34, no.5, pp. 477-484, Oct., 1956.

RELATIONSHIP OF FOOD INTAKE TO THE NUTRITIONAL STATUS AND ANTLER GROWTH OF THE WHITE-TAILED DEER. Lowell C. McEwen. MS thesis, Penna. State Univ., 1954.

DIGESTIBILITY OF SOME NATIVE FORAGES FOR MULE DEER. Arthur D. Smith. Jour. Wildl. Mgt., Ithaca, vol.16, no.3, pp.309-312, July, 1952.

CHEMICAL COMPOSITION A HERBAGE BROWSED BY DEER IN TWO WILDLIFE MANAGEMENT AREAS. Frank H. Smith et al. Jour. Wildl. Mgt., vol.20, no.4, pp.359-367, Oct., 1956.

VITAMIN EXCRETION BY DEER. A. E. Teeri, et al. Jour. Mamm., vol.36, no.4, pp.553-557, tbls.3, Dec. 14, 1955.

STUDIES ON THE BLOOD OF WHITE-TAILED DEER. S.C. Whitlock. Jour. Wildl. Mgt., Menasha, vol.3, no.1, pp. 14-16, Jan., 1939.

Odocoileus--Population Dynamics and Studies

CONTROVERSIAL DEER POPULATION FIGURES. I.H. Bartlett. Michigan Conserv., Lansing, vol.9, no.2, pp.7, 10, Nov., 1939.

STUDY OF DEER POPULATIONS BY USE OF PELLET-GROUP COUNTS. Logan J. Bennett et al. Jour. Wildl. Mgt., vol.4, no.4, pp.398-403, Oct., 1940.

SOME DYNAMICS OF A MULE DEER POPULATION. F.P. Cronemiller. Jour. Wildl. Mgt., Menasha, vol.15, no.2, pp.206-208, Apr., 1951.

CENSUSING A DEER HERD BY SAMPLING METHODS. F.P. Cronemiller, G.A. Fischer. Trans. 11st N.Amer. Wildl. Conf., pp.349-354, 1946.

METHODS FOR ESTIMATING DEER POPULATIONS FROM KILL DATA. R.F. Dasmann. Calif. Fish and Game, San Francisco, vol.38, no.2, pp.225-233, illus., Apr., 1952.

COMPARISON OF FOUR DEER CENSUS METHODS. R. F. Dasmann, R.D. Taber. Calif. Fish and Game, vol.41, no.3, pp. 225-228, July, 1955.

DETERMINING STRUCTURE IN COLUMBIAN BLACK-TAILED DEER POPULATIONS. R.F. Dasmann, R.D. Taber. Jour. Wildl. Mgt., vol.20, no.1, pp.78-83, Jan., 1956.

NOTES ON A METHOD FOR CENSUSING WHITE-TAILED DEER IN THE SPRING AND SUMMER. Arnold B. Erickson. Jour. Wildl. Mgt., vol.4, no.1, pp.15-18, Jan., 1940.

PELLET-GROUP COUNT METHOD OF CENSUSING MULE DEER IN UTAH. Robert B. Ferguson. MS thesis, Utah State Agr. Coll., 1955.

EXPERIENCES IN DETERMINING ANNUAL HARVEST AND CENSUS METHODS IN UTAH. (Mule deer.) D.M. Gaufin. Proc. Ann. Conf. W. Assn. State Game and Fish Comm., vol.30, pp.89-94, 1950?

COMPARISON OF AIR AND GROUND DEER COUNTS IN COLORADO. Paul F. Gilbert, Jack R. Grieb. Jour. Wildl. Mgt., vol.21, no.1, pp.33-37, Jan., 1957.

OHIO DEER FACTS. HOW FAST DO OHIO DEER INCREASE? Merrill C. Gilfillan. Ohio Conserv. Bull., vol.16, no.8, pp.5, 32, illus., Aug., 1952.

PENNSYLVANIA BAGS 700, 000 DEER IN TEN YEARS. (Fluctuations in numbers and reasons for them.) Seth Gordon. Penna. Game News, vol.13, no.4, pp.3, 26-27, 29, July, 1942.

HUNTING SEASON STATISTICS AS AN INDEX TO RANGE CONDITIONS AND DEER POPULATION FLUCTUATIONS IN MINNE-SOTA. Vernon E. Gunvalson et al. Jour. Wildl. Mgt., Ithaca, N.Y., vol.16, no.2, pp.121-131, illus., Apr., 1952.

METHOD FOR CENSUSING DEER AND ITS APPLICATION IN THE EDWARDS PLATEAU OF TEXAS. Henry C. Hahn. Texas. Game, Fish and Oyster Comm., pp.24, Feb., 1949.

COUNTS OF BUCKS VS. SHED ANTLERS IN ROCKY MOUNTAIN MULE DEER. M.R. Hickel, L.W. Swift. Jour. Wildl.Mgt., vol. 7, no.1, pp.123-124, Jan., 1943.

COMPUTING THE RATE OF INCREASE FOR DEER. Geo. H. Kelker. Jour. Wildl. Mgt., Menasha, vol.11, no.2, pp.177-183, Apr., 1947.

MEASUREMENT AND INTERPRETATION OF FORCES THAT DETERMINE POPULA-TIONS OF MANAGED DEER HERDS. Geo. H. Kelker. PhD thesis, Univ. Mich., 1946.

NOTES ON THE CRUISING METHOD OF CENSUSING WHITE-TAILED DEER IN OKLAHOMA. L.W. Krefting, J.B. Fletscher. Jour. Wildl. Mgt., Menasha, vol.5, no.4, pp.412-415, Oct., 1941.

DETERMINING THE BIG-GAME POPULA-TION FROM THE KILL. Burton Lauckhart. Trans. 15th N.Amer. Wildl. Conf., pp.644-649, 1950.

DEER IRRUPTIONS. Aldo Leopold. Wisc. Conserv.Bull., vol.8, no.8, pp.3-11, Aug., 1943; Trans. Wisc. Acad. Sci., Arts and Letters, vol.35, pp.351-366, 1943.

DEVELOPMENT AND USE OF GAME DRIVES FOR DETERMINING WHITETAIL DEER POPULATIONS ON ALLEGHENY NATIONAL FOREST. Randal McCain. Trans. 4th N.Amer. Wildl. Conf., pp.221-230, 1939.

SIGHT COUNTS AND ROAD DRAGS IN CENSUSING DEER POPULATIONS. P.J. McDermott. Proc. Ann. Conf. W. Assn. State Game and Fish Comm., vol.30, pp.117-120, 1950?

NECEDAH REFUGE DEER IRRUPTION. F.R. Martin, L.W. Krefting. Jour. Wildl. Mgt., Ithaca, vol.17, no.2, pp.166-176, illus., Apr., 1953.

CENSUSING BIG GAME FROM THE AIR. Marius Morse. Conserv.Volunteer, vol.9, no.52, pp.29-33, May-June, 1946.

SOME FACTORS AFFECTING POPULATION CHANGES OF THE DEER HERD ON THE EPHRAIM UNIT OF THE MANTI NATIONAL FOREST. Errol Nielson. MS thesis, Utah State Agric. Coll., 1949.

DEER TAGGING AND POPULATION STUDIES IN MINNESOTA. Herman F. Olson. Trans. 3rd N.Amer. Wildl.Conf., pp.280-286, 1938.

AERIAL DEER COUNTS. Geo. A. Petrides. Jour. Wildl. Mgt., Ithaca, vol.17, no.1, pp.97-98, Jan., 1953.

CENSUS METHODS AND THEIR APPLICA-TION IN THE MANAGEMENT OF MULE DEER. D.I. Rasmussen, Everett R. Doman. Trans. 8th N.Amer. Wildl.Conf., Wash., D.C., pp.369-380, 1943.

REGION 8 TECHNIQUE OF WILDLIFE IN-VENTORY. Frederick J. Ruff. Trans. 4th N.Amer. Wildl. Conf., pp.542-545, 1939.

ROADSIDE DEER COUNTS AS AN EMER-GENCY CENSUS METHOD. Thomas A. Schrader. Trans. 9th N.Amer. Wildl.Conf., pp.150-154, 1944.

ANALYSIS OF VARIANCE APPLICABLE TO TRANSECT POPULATION DATA. Vincent Schultz, Robert J. Muncy. Jour. Wildl. Mgt., vol.21, no.3, pp.274-278, July, 1957.

STUDY OF PRODUCTIVITY AND MOR-TALITY OF CORALLED DEER. C. W. Severinghaus. Jour. Wildl. Mgt., vol.15, no.1, pp.73-80, Jan., 1951.

STUDY OF DEER POPULATIONS ON THE WASATCH GAME PRESERVE, UTAH, 1934-1942. Justin G. Smith. MS thesis, Utah State Agr. Coll., 1942.

WHITE-TAILED DEER CENSUS METHODS. Harold W. Steinhoff. MS thesis, Syracuse Univ., 1947.

USE OF CHECKING STATION DATA IN DETERMINING THE SIZE OF THE NEW HAMPSHIRE DEER HERD. Clark L. Stevens. Proc. N.E. Sect. Wildl.Soc., 9th Ann. Conf., Bretton Woods, N.H., pp.5, graphs, Sep. 20-23, 1953.

DYNAMICS OF THREE NATURAL POPULA-TIONS OF THE DEER ODOCOILEUS HEMIONUS COLUMBIANUS. Richard D. Taber, Raymond F. Dasmann. Ecology, vol.38, no.2, pp.233-246, Apr., 1957.

ESTIMATING DEER POPULATIONS FROM TRACKS: A PRELIMINARY REPORT. Edwin L. Tyson. Presented at 6th Ann. Conf., S. E. Assn. Game and Fish Comm., Savannah, Ga., pp.1-15, graphs, Oct. 19-22, 1952.

MORNING VERSUS EVENING DEER COUNTS. Forest Res. Dig., Jan., 1935.

Odocoileus--Predators

RELATIONSHIP OF PREDATORS TO WHITE-TAIL DEER IN GLACIER NATIONAL PARK. John F. Aiton. Trans. 3rd N. Amer. Wildl. Conf., pp.302-304, 1938.

THE "BLACK KILLER." (Wild "wolf dogs" killing deer.) Albert Anderson. Conserv. Volunteer, St. Paul, vol.4, no.21, p.40, June, 1942.

DESTRUCTION OF DEER BY THE NORTH-ERN TIMBER WOLF. Vernon Bailey. U.S. Dept. Agric., Biol. Survey Circ., no.58, pp.1-2, May 4, 1907.

DEER-COYOTE EPISODE. V.H. Cahalane. Jour. Mamm., vol.28, no.1, pp.36-39, Feb., 1947.

DRAMAS OF THE WILD. (Coyote, deer.) James W. Chapman. Fauna, Philadelphia, vol.8, no.2, pp.37-39, illus., June, 1946.

BOBCAT PREYS ON DEER. Herbert H. Dill. Jour. Mamm., vol.28, no.1, p.63, Feb., 1947.

DOE PURSUES COYOTE. Joseph Dixon. Yosemite Nature Notes, vol.7, p.86, Oct., 1928.

KIPAWA DEER AND THE WOLVES. A. Fraser. Rod and Gun in Canada, Montreal, vol.45, no.8, pp.7, 33, illus., Feb., 1945.

ONE ACT PLAY OF NATURE. (Coyote chasing deer.) Francis D. LaNoue. Yellow-stone Nat.Notes, vol.10, nos.1-2, p.2, Jan.-Feb., 1933.

MOUNTAIN LION FOILED. (Puma chasing deer.) Hamilton MacCaughey. Yosemite Nature Notes, vol.16, no.4, pp.25-27, Apr., 1937.

WINTER RELATIONS OF BOBCATS TO WHITE-TAILED DEER IN MAINE. Merwin A. Marston. Jour. Wildl. Mgt., vol.6, no.4, pp.328-337, Oct., 1942.

CATS KILL DEER. J.R. Matson. Jour. Mamm., vol.29, no.1, pp.69-70, Feb., 1948.

MENACE OF DEER KILLING DOGS. Geo. W. Russell. Oregon Sportsman, vol.1, no. 1, pp.20-21, fig.1, Sep., 1924.

WOLVES TOUGH ON DEER. Ernest E. Shepard. Hunting and Fishing in Canada, Montreal, vol.13, no.10, p.24, 1947.

WILDCAT PREDATION ON DEER. B.E. Smith. Jour. Mamm., vol.26, no.4, pp. 439-440, Feb. 12, 1946.

DEER OR DOGS IN SOUTHERN WEST VIRGINIA? Larry Ward. W.Va.Conserv., vol.18, no.6, pp.3-5, Aug., 1954.

BOBCAT KILLS DEER. S.P. Young. Jour. Mamm., vol.9, no.1, pp.64-65, Feb., 1928.

EAGLE CARRIES OFF FAWN. Washington State Game Bull., Seattle, vol.4, no.3, p. 8, July, 1952.

Odocoileus--Productivity

VERMONT DEER HERD. A STUDY IN PRODUCTIVITY. Leonard E. Foote. Vt. Fish and Game Serv., State Bull., Pittman-Robertson Ser., no.13, pp.125, 1945.

REGIONAL DIFFERENCES IN SIZE AND PRODUCTIVITY OF DEER IN WEST VIRGINIA. John Gill. Jour. Wildl. Mgt., vol.20, no.3, pp.286-292, July, 1956.

PRODUCTIVITY DATA OF ARIZONA MULE DEER. Denis J. Illige. Proc. 33rd Ann. Conf. Western Assn. State Game and Fish Comm., pp.117-127, graphs, June 1-3, 1953.

PRODUCTIVITY IN CALIFORNIA DEER HERDS AS INFLUENCED BY RANGE CONDITION AND HUNTING PRESSURE. William M. Longhurst. Proc. Ann. Conf. Western Assn. State Game and Fish Comm., vol.30, pp.135-140, 1950?

REGIONAL DIFFERENCES IN BREEDING POTENTIAL OF WHITE-TAILED DEER IN NEW YORK. G.H. Morton, E.L. Chaetum. Jour. Wildl. Mgt., vol.10, no. 3, pp.242-248, July, 1946.

PRODUCTIVITY AND YIELD OF THE GEORGE RESERVE DEER HERD. E.C. O'Roke, F.N. Hamerstrom, Jr. Jour. Wildl. Mgt., vol.12, no.1, pp.78-86, Jan., 1948.

STUDIES OF THE PRODUCTIVITY OF MULE DEER IN CENTRAL UTAH. W. Leslie Robinette, Orange A. Olsen. Trans. 9th N. Amer. Wildl. Conf., Washington, pp.156-161, 1944.

PRODUCTION, MORTALITY, AND YIELD OF BLACK-TAILED DEER ON CHAPAR-RAL RANGE. Richard D. Taber. Proc. 33rd Ann. Conf. Western Assn. State Game and Fish Comm., pp.128-131, June 1-3, 1953 (1954).

PRODUCTIVITY OF MULE DEER IN COL-ORADO. Carwin D. Tolman. Trans. 15th N. Amer. Wildl. Conf., Washington, pp. 589-597, 1950.

Odocoileus--Reproductive Biology

FETAL DEVELOPMENT OF THE NORTH-ERN WHITE-TAILED DEER. Ruth Alison Armstrong. MS thesis, Vassar Coll., 1949; Amer. Midland Nat., vol.43, no.3, pp.650-666, May, 1950.

BREEDING HABITS OF MULE DEER. Oscar L. Barnum. Calif. Fish and Game, vol.16, no.2, p.184, Apr., 1930.

DEER FAMILY OF THREE FAWNS. V.G. Baysinger. Yosemite Nature Notes, Stockton, vol.18, no.12, p.124, Dec., 1939.

ABNORMAL FETAL DEVELOPMENT FROM A MULE DEER. Arthur I. Bischoff. Calif. Fish and Game, vol.40, no.3, pp.340-341, July, 1954.

BLESSED EVENT NEAR THE MUSEUM. (Twin fawns.) C. Frank Brockman. Yosemite Nat. Notes, Yosemite, vol.21, no.10, pp. 85-86, Oct., 1942.

DOE WITH THREE FAWNS. W.S. Brown. Calif. Fish and Game, vol.6, no.1, p.37, Jan., 1920.

BREEDING SEASON AND PRODUCTIVITY IN THE INTERSTATE DEER HERD. John E. Chattin. Calif. Fish and Game, vol.34, no.1, pp.25-31, Jan., 1948.

WHITETAIL FERTILITY. E.L.Chaetum. N.Y. State Conserv., vol.1, no.5, pp.18, 32, Apr.-May, 1947.

BREEDING SEASON OF WHITE-TAILED DEER IN NEW YORK. E.L.Chaetum, G.H. Morton. Jour. Wildl. Mgt., Menasha, vol. 10, no.3, pp.249-263, July, 1946.

INITIAL PROOF OF MULE DEER FAWNS BREEDING IS FOUND IN UTAH. Harold S. Crane, Dale A. Jones. Jour. Wildl.Mgt., Ithaca, vol.17, no.2, p.225, Apr.,1953.

LATE BREEDING RECORD FOR THE WHITE-TAILED DEER. Arnold B.Erickson. Jour. Wildl. Mgt., Ithaca, vol.16, no.3, p.400, July, 1952.

BIRTH DATE OF MULE DEER FAWNS. Charles A. Gianini. Jour. Mamm., vol.13, no.1, p.80, Feb., 1932.

SEPTEMBER BIRTH OF A MICHIGAN WHITE-TAILED DEER. Earl J.Gordinier. Jour. Mamm., vol.29, no.2, pp.184-185, May 14, 1948.

BREEDING RECORDS OF WHITETAIL DEER IN THE UPPER PENINSULA OF MICHIGAN. Arnold Haugen, L.A.Davenport. Jour.Wildl. Mgt., vol.14, no.3, pp.290-295, July, 1950.

ANALYSIS OF THE REPRODUCTIVE PATTERN OF WHITETAIL DEER IN SOUTH TEXAS. Denis Illige. Jour. Mamm., vol.32, no.4, pp.411-421, illus., Nov. 19, 1951.

FIELD-LABORATORY STUDIES OF MULE DEER REPRODUCTION IN ARIZONA. Denis Illige, A.C. Edwards. Proc. 31st Ann. Conf. Western Assn. State Game and Fish Comm., pp.195-198, Apr.30-May 2, 1951.

UNUSUAL TWIN FAWNS IN DESERT MULE DEER DOE. Denis Illige, Homer G.Erling. Jour. Mamm., vol.36, no.1, p.145, Feb. 25, 1955.

HIGH REPRODUCTIVE RATE FOR ROCKY MOUNTAIN MULE DEER (ODOCOILEUS H. HEMIONUS). Wallace Jensen, W.Leslie Robinette. Jour. Wildl. Mgt., vol.19, no. 4, p.503, Oct., 1955.

BIRTH DATES OF ALABAMA DEER. Francis X. Lueth. Presented at 9th Ann. Meeting, S.E. Assn. Game and Fish Comm., pp.1-7, graphs, Oct., 1955.

BREEDING SEASON OF THE SONORA WHITE-TAILED DEER. Robert A.McCabe, A.S. Leopold. Jour. Wildl.Mgt., Menasha, vol.15, no.4, pp.433-434, illus., Oct., 1951.

NOTE ON DEER MORTALITY AND REPRODUCTION. William H. Meyer. Jour. Wildl. Mgt., Menasha, vol.5, no.4, p. 472, Oct., 1941.

EARLY BLACK-TAILED DEER BREEDING RECORD. James Moffitt. Calif. Fish and Game, vol.20, no.3, p.291, July, 1934.

RUTTING BEHAVIOR OF THE WHITETAIL DEER (ODOCOILEUS VIRGININIANUS). William O. Pruitt, Jr. Jour.Mamm., vol. 35, no.1, pp.129-130, Feb. 10, 1954.

BREEDING SEASON, PRODUCTIVITY, AND FAWNING PERIOD OF THE MULE DEER IN UTAH. W. Leslie Robinette, Jay S. Gashwiler. Jour. Wildl. Mgt., vol.14, no. 4, pp.457-469, Oct., 1950.

FERTILITY OF MULE DEER IN UTAH. W. Leslie Robinette, Jay S. Gashwiler. Jour. Wildl. Mgt., Ithaca, vol.19, no.1, pp.115-136, illus., Jan., 1955.

AGE AND FECUNDITY OF MULE DEER (ODOCOILEUS HEMIONUS HEMIONUS). Roland Case Ross. Jour. Mamm., vol.15, no.1, p.72, Feb., 1934.

QUADRUPLETS IN MULE DEER. H.S. Sears, L.G. Browman. Anat. Record, vol. 122, no.3, pp.335-340, July, 1955.

SOME OBSERVATIONS ON THE BREEDING BEHAVIOR OF DEER. C.W.Severinghaus. N.Y. Fish and Game Jour., vol.2, no.2, pp. 239-241, July (Nov.), 1955.

WILLINGNESS OF NURSING DEER TO ADOPT STRANGE FAWNS. C.W.Severinghaus. Jour. Mamm., Baltimore, vol.30, no.1, pp.75-76, Feb. 14, 1949.

MATING HABITS OF WHITE-TAILS. Gill Shark. Hunting and Fishing in Canada, Montreal, vol.13, no.2, p.18, 1947.

STUDIES OF BLACK-TAILED DEER REPRODUCTION ON THREE CHAPARRAL COVER TYPES. Richard D. Taber.Calif. Fish and Game, vol.39, no.2, pp.177-186, illus., Apr., 1953.

(NOTE ON THE DURATION OF GESTATION OF A WHITE TAIL DEER OF TEPECUACUILCO.) Nota acerca de la duracion del periodo de gestacion de una venada cola blanca (Odocoileus virginianus mexicanus) de Tepecuacuilco, Gro. R.Bernardo Villa. An. Inst. Biol., vol.24, no.2, pp.459-460, 1953.

TRIPLETS. (White-tailed deer.) Oklahoma Game and Fish News, Oklahoma City, vol. 4, no.11, p.16, illus., Nov., 1948.

## Odocoileus--Sex Ratios

SEX RATIO OF WHITETAIL DEER PROGENY. Richard Gerstell. Penna. Game News, vol.7, no.5, pp.6-9, Aug., 1936.

SEX AND AGE RATIO STUDIES OF WISCONSIN DEER. Ralph C. Guettinger. Presented at 13th Midwest Wildl. Conf., Minneapolis, pp.1-3, Dec. 12-14, 1951.

STATE'S DEER SEX RATIOS. Ernest C. Martin. Alabama Conserv., Montgomery, vol.21, nos.5-7, p.8, illus., Winter issue, 1949-50.

USE OF AGE COMPOSITION DATA FOR DETERMINING SEX RATIOS AMONG ADULT DEER. C.W. Severinghaus, H.F. Maguire. N.Y.Fish and Game Jour., vol. 2, no.2, pp.242-246, July (Nov.), 1955.

SECONDARY SEX RATIO IN ODOCOILEUS. Richard D. Taber. Jour. Wildl. Mgt., Ithaca, vol.17, no.1, pp.96-97, Jan., 1953.

## Odocoileus--Taxonomy

(ON THE ODOCOILEUS OF COLOMBIA.) Sobre los Odocoileus de Colombia. (Key to the subspecies of O.gymnotis.) Angel Cabrera. Bol. Real Soc. Española Hist. Nat., vol.18, pp.300-307, pl.8, June, 1918.

NEW RACE OF DEER FROM EASTERN CALIFORNIA. (Odocoileus hemionus inyoensis.) Ian McT. Cowan. Proc. Biol.Soc. Washington, vol.46, pp.69-70, Apr. 27, 1933.

NEW MULE DEER FROM SONORA. (Odocoileus hemionus sheldoni.) E.A.Goldman. Jour. Mamm., Baltimore, vol.20, no.4, pp.496-497, Nov. 14, 1939.

TEN NEW WHITE-TAILED DEER FROM NORTH AND MIDDLE AMERICA. E.A. Goldman, Remington Kellogg. Proc.Biol. Soc. Washington, vol.53, pp.81-90, June 28, 1940.

TECHNICAL NAME OF THE VIRGINIA DEER WITH A LIST OF THE SOUTH AMERICAN FORMS. P. Hershkovitz.Proc. Biol. Soc. Washington, vol.61, pp.41-48, Apr. 30, 1948.

DESCRIPTION OF A NEW DEER (DORCELAPHUS TEXANUS) FROM TEXAS AND NORTHERN MEXICO. Edgar A. Mearns. Proc. Biol. Soc. Washington, vol.12, pp. 23-26, Jan. 27, 1898.

EARLIEST GENERIC NAME FOR THE NORTH AMERICAN DEER, WITH DESCRIPTIONS OF FIVE NEW SPECIES AND SUBSPECIES. C. Hart Merriam. Proc.Biol. Soc. Wash., vol.12, pp.99-104, Apr. 30, 1898.

NEW WHITE-TAILED DEER FROM LOUISIANA. Frederic W. Miller. Jour. Mamm., vol.9, no.1, pp.57-59, Feb., 1928.

NEW DEER FROM COSTA RICA. Gerrit S. Miller, Jr. Proc. Biol. Soc. Wash., vol.14, pp.35-37, Apr. 25, 1901.

TECHNICAL NAME OF THE VIRGINIA DEER. Gerrit S. Miller, Jr. Proc. Biol. Soc. Wash., vol.15, p.39, Mar. 5, 1902.

ANOTHER "NEW" DEER FOR CALIFORNIA. (Cowan's Odocoileus hemionus fuliginatus, San Diego mule deer.) James Moffitt. Calif. Fish and Game, vol.20, no. 1, p.81, Jan., 1934.

PROPOSED USE OF THE PLENARY POWERS FOR THE PURPOSE OF STABILISING THE NAME FOR THE VIRGINIA DEER. T.C.S. Morrison-Scott. Bull. Zool.Nomencl., vol.9, pt.10, pp.297-298, Dec., 1954.

STATUS OF PENNANT'S "MEXICAN DEER." Wilfred H. Osgood. Jour. Mamm., vol.1, no.2, pp.75-78, pl.4, Mar. 2, 1920.

DESCRIPTION OF A NEW SPECIES OF DEER, CARIACUS CLAVATUS, FROM CENTRAL AMERICA. Frederick W.True. Proc. U.S.Nat.Mus., Washington, vol.11, pp.417-424, 1888 (1889).

## Odocoileus--Trapping, Transplanting

DEER TRAPPING COORDINATED WITH WEATHER. Frank B. Barick. Wildl. in N.C., vol.16, no.10, pp.10-11, 20, illus., Oct., 1952.

PROGRESS REPORT ON BIG GAME RESTORATION. F.B. Barick. Wildl. in N.C., vol.15, no.7, pp.8-10, 22, July, 1951.

178 DEER RELEASED IN STATE. Howell Buntin. Tennessee Conservationist, Nashville, vol.13, nos.7-8, p.3, July-Aug., 1948.

PORTABLE DEER TRAP AND CATCHNET. Melvin R. Clover. Calif. Fish and Game, vol.40, no.4, pp.367-373, illus., Oct., 1954.

WYOMING'S 1953 WHITE-TAILED DEER TRANSPLANT. William T. Crump. Wyo. Wild Life, vol.17, no.6, pp.14-18, illus., June, 1953.

UWHARRIE DEER RESTOCKING.MONTGOMERY AND STANLEY COUNTIES 1944-1945. Lyman De Berry. N.C.Dept.Cons. and Devel., State Bull., PR Ser., vol.1, no.1, Fed. Aid in Wildl. Restoration Proj. 19D, pp.19, Jan., 1946.

INTRODUCTION OF NEW DEER NOT A REMEDY. Don A. Gilchrist. N.Mexico, vol.14, no.8, p.31, Aug., 1936.

OPERATION DEER TRAP. W.C.Glazener. Texas Game and Fish, vol.7, no.10, pp. 6-7, 17, 26, Sep., 1949.

WHITE-TAILED DEER. EFFICIENCY OF NINETY-EIGHT DEER TRAPS ON THE FEDERAL ARANSAS REFUGE. W.C. Glazener. Texas Game, Fish and Oyster Comm., Quart. Prog. Repts., Austin, pp. 6-7, Oct.-Dec., 1941.

THE 1949 WHITE-TAIL TRANSPLANT. James E. Grasse. Wyo. Wild Life, vol. 13, no.2, pp.4-9, Feb., 1949.

RESULTS OF THE 1949-50 DEER TRAPPING SEASON. Rolland B. Handley. Mississippi Game and Fish, Jackson, vol.13, no.10, pp.3-4, Apr., 1950.

TRAPPING AND RESTOCKING WHITE-TAILED DEER IN ARKANSAS. Carl Hunter. Ark. Game and Fish Comm., PR Proj. 17-D, pp.1-17, illus., Oct., 1952.

WINTER DEER TRAPPING. (Transplanting whitetails in Oklahoma.) Juanita Mahaffey. Okla. Game and Fish News, vol.5, no.2, pp.8-10, Feb., 1949.

EFFICIENT HANDLING CRATE FOR WHITETAIL DEER. Edward J. Mikula. Jour. Wildl. Mgt., vol.19, no.4, pp.501-502, illus., Oct., 1955.

DEER TRAPPING ON SWAN ISLAND, RICHMOND, MAINE. Stephen E. Powell. Proc. 8th Ann. N.E. Wildl. Conf., Jackson's Mill, W.Va., pp.1-4, Apr. 1-4, 1952.

TRAPPING DEER ON THE PISGAH NATIONAL GAME PRESERVE, NORTH CAROLINA. Frederick J. Ruff. Jour. Wildl. Mgt., vol. 2, no.3, pp.151-161, illus., July, 1938.

TRAPPING PENNED DEER. Frederick J. Ruff. Jour. Wildl. Mgt., vol.3, no.4, pp. 288-294, Oct., 1939.

YES! WE'RE TRAPPING DEER IN LOUISIANA. Lyle S. St. Amant. La.Conserv., vol.4, no.6, pp.11-15, illus., Feb., 1952.

MASS TRAPPING OF MULE DEER. Gail M. Thomas, Warren J. Allred. Jour.Wildl. Mgt., vol.7, no.4, pp.407-411, Oct., 1943.

"LIVE TRAPPING" DEER. Mel Washburn. Louisiana Conservationist, New Orleans, vol.1, no.5, pp.13-16, 22, illus., Jan., 1949.

TRAP DEER FOR TRANSPLANTING IN SPARSE AREAS. Mel Washburn. Louisiana Conservationist, vol.8, no.12, pp.18-19, illus., Nov., 1956.

ARKANSAS' DEER TRANSPLANTING PROGRAM. Roy Wood. Trans. N.Amer. Wildl. Conf., vol.9, pp.162-167, 1944.

DEER TRAPPING AND TRANSPLANTING. Wildl. in N.Carolina, Raleigh, vol.10, no. 1, pp.10-11, illus., May, 1946.

RELEASE OF 175 PLANNED IN DEER RESTOCKING PROGRAM. W.Va.Conserv., Charleston, vol.7, no.11, pp.5, 16, Feb., 1944.

VIRGINIA'S DEER RESTOCKING PROGRAM. Va. Wildl., Richmond, vol.6, no. 1, pp. 6-8, illus., Fall-Winter, 1942.

Odocoileus--United States, Eastern

HISTORY OF THE VIRGINIA DEER IN NEW ENGLAND. Glover M. Allen. Papers Read at Conf. of Massachusetts Fish and Game Assn. Jan. 11, 1929, pp.19-38, 1929.

LOUISIANA DEER. Glover M. Allen. Amer. Naturalist, vol.35, no.414, pp.449-454, figs.3, June, 1901.

FOUR THOUSAND WHITETAILS CAN BE WRONG. John M. Allen. Outdoor Ind., vol.15, no.2, pp.2-3, Feb., 1948.

3000 WHITE-TAILS CAN BE WRONG. John M. Allen. Presented at 13th Midwest Wildl. Conf., Minneapolis, pp.1-13, map, Dec. 12-14, 1951.

DEER RETURN TO INDIANA! A.E.Andrews. Nature Notes, Peoria, vol.7, no.12, pp.283-286, Dec., 1940.

DEER INVESTIGATIONS IN PENNSYLVANIA. Vernon Bailey. Biennial Rep. Board Game Commissioners, Commonwealth of Penna., Harrisburg, pp.27-34, 1927-1928.

FLORIDA DEER. Outram Bangs. Proc.Biol. Soc. Wash., vol.10, pp.25-28, Feb. 25, 1896.

WHITE-TAILED DEER OF EASTERN UNITED STATES. Thomas Barbour, Glover M. Allen. Jour. Mamm., vol.3, no.2, pp. 65-78, pls.4-5, May, 1922.

NORTHERN VIRGINIA DEER. N.R.Barger. Wisc. Conserv. Bull., Madison, vol.14, no. 1, pp.35-36, illus., Jan., 1949.

WHITETAIL DEER IN NEW HAMPSHIRE. W.C. Barnart. Forest and Stream, pp.581-584, 612-614, Nov., 1920.

WHITE-TAILED DEER IN INDIANA. William B. Barnes. Outdoor Indiana, Indianapolis, vol.12, no.2, pp.4-5, 16, illus., Mar., 1945.

DEER POPULATION IN MICHIGAN. I.H. Bartlett. Papers Michigan Acad. Sci., Arts and Letter, vol.19, pp.567-570, 1933.

DEER REPORT. I.H. Barlett. Michigan Conserv., Lansing, vol.22, no.6, pp.3-4, Nov., 1953.

NORTH MANITOU ISLAND'S DEER HERD. I.H. Bartlett. Mich. Conserv., vol.13, no. 8, p.10, Sep., 1944.

MICHIGAN DEER. I.H. Bartlett. Mich. Dept. Conserv., Game Div., pp.50, June, 1950.

OLD ORDER CHANGES. I.H. Bartlett. Mich. Out-of-Doors, vol.3, no.5, pp.12-17, illus., Oct., 1952.

PROGRESS IN THE MICHIGAN DEERYARD SURVEY. I.H. Bartlett. Mich. Acad.Sci. Arts, Letters, 30-31 Ann.Rept., pp.80-82, 1929.

WISCONSIN DEER / HERD-RANGE-REGULATIONS. I.H. Bartlett, L.A.Davenport. Mich.Dept. Conserv., pp.5, 1948.

PRELIMINARY SURVEY OF DEERYARDS IN THE UPPER PENINSULA OF MICHIGAN. I.H. Bartlett, Joseph H. Stephenson. Papers Mich. Acad. Sci. Arts and Letters, vol. 10, pp.411-416, pl.1, 1929.

ON THE TRAIL OF THE WHITE-TAIL. A.F. Belitz. Wisc. Conservationist, vol. 1, no.5, p.1, Nov., 1919; no.6, pp.5-6, Jan., 1920; vol.2, no.1, pp.33, 34, Mar., 1920; no.3, pp.7, 8, July, 1920.

WINTER USE BY WHITE-TAILED DEER OF RECENTLY CUT OVER JACK PINE AREAS ON THE CLOQUET FOREST EXPERIMENT STATION. Bruno L.Berklund. MS thesis, Univ. Minn., 1947.

WILD DEER ON STATEN ISLAND. Howard H. Cleaves. Proc. Staten Island Inst.Arts and Sci., Lancaster, vol.9, pt.4, pp.145-146, illus., Oct. 7, 1942.

WINTER HABITS OF WHITE-TAILED DEER IN CENTRAL NEW YORK. David B. Cook, W.J. Hamilton, Jr. Jour.Wildl.Mgt., Menasha, vol.6, no.4, pp.287-291, pl.24, Oct., 1942.

DEER HERD IN MAINE. Malcolm W. Coulter. Maine For., pp.62-67 (reprints paged 1-7), 1951.

WINTER DEER-RANGE CONDITIONS, 1949. B.L. Dahlberg. Wisc. Conserv. Bull., vol. 14, no.6, pp.21-24, June, 1949.

WHITE-TAILED DEER IN WISCONSIN. B.L. Dahlberg, R.C.Guettinger. Technical Wildl. Bull., no.14, Wisc. Conserv.Dept., Madison, pp.282, illus., 1956.

WHAT'S HAPPENING TO OUR DEER RANGE? Robert W. Darrow. N.Y. State Conserv., vol.5, no.3, pp.6-8, Dec.-Jan., 1950-1951.

WHITETAIL IN NEW YORK. Robert W. Darrow. Western N.Y. Conservationist, Buffalo, vol.2, no.3, pp.10-13, 1947; N.Y. State Conserv., vol.2, no.3, pp.10-13, Dec.-Jan., 1947-48.

REPORT ON THE GLADES DEER. Stuart P. Davey. Va. Wildl., vol.16, no.9, pp.5-7, 22, illus., Sep., 1955.

FROM BUCKS TO DEER IN WEST VIRGINIA. W.R.DeGarmo. Proc. 8th Ann. N.E. Wildl. Conf., Jackson's Mill, W.Va., pp.1-20, illus., Apr.1-4, 1952.

WHERE TO SEEK FINEST BUCKS. W.R. DeGarmo, Kenneth Chiavetta. W. Va. Conserv., vol.14, no.7, pp.15-23, Oct., 1950.

DEER IN PENNSYLVANIA--PAST AND PRESENT. G.W. Dillin. Penna. Game News, Harrisburg, vol.10, no.9, pp.15-17, Dec., 1939.

DEER OF HIAWATHA'S RIVER. FRIENDLY AND UNAFRAID, THEY CAME BACK YEAR AFTER YEAR TO THE CABIN WHERE SALT--AND PHOTOGRAPHERS--ALWAYS AWAITED THEM. Ben East. Bull. New York Zool. Soc., vol.43, no.1, pp.15-20, photos, Jan.-Feb., 1940.

CONDITIONS INFLUENCING THE PATTERN OF DEER IN OVERPOPULATED AREAS IN VIRGINIA - 1949. James W. Engle. MS thesis, Va.Polytechnic Inst., 1950.

WHITETAIL MAKES A COMEBACK! James W. Engle. Va. Wildl., vol.10, no.12, pp. 18-20, Dec., 1949.

PRESENT STATUS OF WISCONSIN'S DEER HERD AND DEER RANGE. W.S.Feeney. Wisc. Conserv. Bull., Madison, vol.9, no. 6, pp.4-5, June, 1944.

WISCONSIN DEER TODAY AND TOMORROW. W.S. Feeney. Wisc. Conserv. Bull., Madison, vol.8, no.8, pp.11-19, illus., Aug., 1943.

SIZE OF CALVERT COUNTY DEER HERD ESTIMATED. V.F. Flyger. Md.Tidewater News, vol.13, no.3, p.2, Sep.-Oct., 1956.

PENNSYLVANIA DEER. ARE THEY BECOMING GRADUALLY SMALLER? Richard Gerstell. Penna. Game News, vol. 6, no.7, pp.10-11, 18-19, Oct., 1935.

STORY OF THE OHIO DEER AND DEER HUNTING. PART I. Merrill C. Gilfillan. Ohio Conserv. Bull., vol.17, no.8, p.28, Sep., 1953.

WINTER HABITAT STUDY OF DEER IN MAINE. Leslie L. Glasgow. MS thesis, Univ. Maine, 1948; Jour. Forestry, vol.47, no.4, p.299, Apr., 1949. (Abstract.)

WINTER MOVEMENTS AND WINTER FOODS OF WHITE-TAILED DEER IN CENTRAL WISCONSIN. F.N.Hamerstrom, Jr., James Blake. Jour.Mamm., vol.20, no.2, pp.206-215, May, 1939.

STATE HUNTERS MAKE RECORD DEER KILL. J.W. Handlan. W.Va.Conserv., Charleston, vol.10, no.9, pp.4-7, 18-20, illus., Jan., 1947.

PARAGRAPHS FROM FIELD NOTES.(Deer.) R.S. Harris. W.Va.Conserv., Charleston, vol.11, no.5, pp.17-19, Sep., 1947.

WISCONSIN DEER. Edward N. Hein.Wisc. Conserv. Bull., vol.2, no.10, p.3, Oct., 1937.

LAST RECORD OF DEER IN WALWORTH COUNTY WISCONSIN. Ned Hollister.Bull. Wisc. Nat. Hist. Soc., vol.6, pp.143-144, Apr., 1909.

MOUNT DESERT DEER, PAST AND PRESENT. Lawrie Holmes. Pp.36, 1944.

SOME WINTER RELATIONS OF THE WHITE-TAILED DEER TO THE FORESTS IN NORTH CENTRAL MASSACHUSETTS. N.W. Hosley, R.K.Zierbarth. Ecology, vol.16, no.4, pp.535-552, Oct., 1935.

GHOST OF BUCK BONES. (White-tailed deer in North Carolina.) W.W.Huber.Amer. Wildl., Wash., D.C., vol.28, no.4, pp. 188-191, figs.3, July-Aug., 1939.

EXTIRPATION AND RESTORATION OF NORTH GEORGIA DEER--A SIXTY-YEAR HISTORY. James H. Jenkins. Trans. 17th N.Amer. Wildl. Conf., pp.472-476, 1952.

SOME WINTER HABITS OF WHITE-TAILED DEER AND THE DEVELOPMENT OF CENSUS METHODS IN THE FLAG YARD OF NORTHERN WISCONSIN. Cyril Kabat, et al. Wisc. Conserv. Dept., Tech. Wildl. Bull., no.7, pp.1-32, illus., 1953.

ADIRONDACK DEER. Z. Ted de Kalmar. Amer. Game, Bull. Amer. Game Protective Assn., vol.18, no.5, p.85, Aug., 1929.

OUR DEER--PAST, PRESENT AND FUTURE. Roger M. Latham. Penna. Game News, vol.14, no.9, pp.4-5, 26-27, Dec., 1943.

TOO MANY, TOO LONG! Roger M. Latham. Penna. Game News, vol.24, no.2, pp.4-7, illus., Feb., 1953.

TOO MANY DEER--IN 1928. R.L. Leffler. Penna. Game News, vol.22, no.9, pp.21-25, illus., Dec., 1951.

WHITE-TAILED DEER STUDY. THREE YEAR PROGRESS REPORT (1949, 1950 AND 1951 SEASONS). J.R.Longwell et al. Md.Dept. Res. and Educ., Resource Study Rep., no.1, pp.1-9, illus., Oct., 1952.

STATUS OF DEER IN WINDHAM COUNTY, VERMONT, 1938-1942. Robert H.McCauley. Vt. Fish and Game Serv., State Bull., PR Ser., no.9, pp.23, Mar., 1943.

STATUS OF DEER IN WINDHAM COUNTY, VERMONT, 1943. Robert H. McCauley. Vt. Fish and Game Serv., State Bull., PR Ser., no.10, pp.16, Mar , 1944.

WHITE-TAILED DEER IN DELAWARE. Burd S. McGinnes. (Cover title:Deer Management.) Del. Game and Fish Comm., pp.1-12, Dec., 1950.

TO THE CITIZENS OF WISCONSIN INTERESTED IN DEER. H.W.MacKenzie. Wisc. Conserv., vol.2, no.9, pp.3-9, Sep., 1937.

DEER DAMAGE AND MANAGEMENT IN THE PINE REGION OF NEW JERSEY. L.G. MacNamara. N.Eng.Game Conf., pp.6, 1940.

DEER FOR ALL. Frederick Mahan. Wildl. in North Carolina, Raleigh, vol.10, no.3, p.15, Oct., 1946.

HURON MOUNTAIN DEER HERD. Richard H. Manville. Jour. Wildl. Mgt., vol.11, no. 3, pp.263-266, July, 1947.

WHITE-TAILS IN ALABAMA. Geo. C. Moore. Ala. Conserv., vol.15, no.8, pp. 8-9, 12-14, Feb., 1944.

OUTLINE OF DEER INVESTIGATION IN NEW YORK AND THE NORTHEAST. G.H. Morton. N.Eng.Game Conf., pp.3, 1940.

STATUS OF THE WHITE-TAILED DEER IN BATH COUNTY, VIRGINIA. Robert J. Muncy. MS thesis, Va.Poly.Inst., pp.103, June, 1954.

DEER AND TURKEY HABITATS AND POPULATIONS OF FLORIDA. Coleman C. Newman, Edward Griffin. Fla.Game and Fresh Water Fish Comm., Tech.Bull., no.1, pp.30, 1950.

PRODUCTIVITY AND YIELD OF THE GEORGE RESERVE DEER HERD. E.C. O'Roke, F.N. Hamerstrom, Jr. Jour. Wildl. Mgt., Menasha, vol.12, no.1, pp.78-86, Jan., 1948.

WHITETAIL DEER OF TOMHEGAN CAMPS, MAINE, WITH ADDED NOTES ON FECUNDITY. Ralph S. Palmer. Jour. Mamm., vol. 32, no.3, pp.267-280, Aug., 1951.

WHITE-TAILED DEER POPULATIONS IN ILLINOIS. Lysle R. Pietsch. Ill.Nat.Hist. Surv., Biol. Notes, no.34, pp.1-22, illus., June, 1954.

HIGHLIGHTS OF VIRGINIA'S 1952 DEER STUDY. E.V. Richards. Va.Wildl., vol.14, no.10, pp.18-19, 22, illus., Oct., 1953.

HISTORY OF THE WHITE-TAILED DEER IN NEW HAMPSHIRE. Tudor Richards. Proc. N.H. Acad. Sci., vol.1, no.9, pp.46-52, 1949.

QUICK LOOK AT DEER IN ROOSEVELT GAME AREA. Geo. Robey. Ohio Conserv. Bull., Columbus, vol.8, no.1, pp.16-17, 25, illus., Jan., 1944.

WHITE-TAILED DEER ON THE PISGAH NATIONAL GAME PRESERVE, NORTH CAROLINA. Frederick J. Ruff. U.S.Dept. Agric., Forest Serv., S.Region, pp.249, Nov., 1939.

DEER OF COASTAL ISLANDS. (Wild deer along coast of South Carolina and Georgia.) Archibald Rutledge. Country Life, vol.37, pp.70, 72, 74, 76, Feb., 1920.

TOO MANY DEER? Clay Schoenfeld. Wisc. Conserv. Bull., Madison, vol.14, no.3, pp.27-30, Mar., 1949.

NOTES ON THE WHITETAIL DEER IN NEW YORK STATE. W.J. Schoonmaker. Jour. Mamm., vol.19, no.4, pp.503-504, Nov., 1938.

STATUS OF THE WHITE-TAILED DEER IN TENNESSEE. Vincent Schultz. Rep. Reelfoot L. Biol.Sta., no.19, pp.66-75, maps, Jan., 1955; Jour. Tennessee Acad. Sci., vol.30, no.1, pp.66-75, Jan., 1955.

WISCONSIN DEER SITUATION AS OF SEPTEMBER, 1938. Walter E. Scott. Wisc. Conserv. Bull., vol.3, no.10, pp. 4-46, Oct., 1938.

SPECIAL PHASE OF LIFE HISTORY OF DEER IN VERMONT. Roger Seamans. N. Eng.Game Conf., pp.3, 1940.

THE TIME IS NOW! A PICTORIAL STUDY OF VERMONT'S DEER HERD. Roger Seamans. Vt.Fish and Game Ser., State Bull., Pittman-Robertson, Ser., Montpelier, no.15, pp.48, illus., Jan. 1, 1947.

RELATIONSHIP OF WEATHER TO WINTER MORTALITY AND POPULATION LEVELS AMONG DEER IN THE ADIRONDACK REGION OF NEW YORK. C.W.Severinghaus. Trans. 12th N.Amer.Wildl. Conf., pp.212-223, 1947.

WINTER DEER MORTALITY AND THIS FALL'S HUNTING PROSPECTS. C. W. Severinghaus. New York State Conserv., Albany, vol.3, no.1, p.29, Aug.-Sep., 1948.

DEER OF ALLEGANY STATE PARK, NEW YORK. Albert R. Shadle, Donald Stullken. Jour. Wildl. Mgt., vol.6, no.1, pp.27-30, Jan., 1942.

WHITETAIL IN NEW YORK. PART I. J.V. Skiff. N.Y.State Conserv., vol.2, no.2, pp.6-7, Oct.-Nov., 1947.

SOME LATE WINTER AND EARLY SPRING OBSERVATIONS ON THE WHITE-TAILED DEER OF THE ADIRONDACKS. Chas.J. Spiker. Roosevelt Wild Life Bull., Syracuse, vol.6, no.2, pp.327-385, figs.170-227, maps 3-9, Oct., 1933.

WHITE-TAILED DEER (ODOCOILEUS VIRGINIANUS BOREALIS) IN WISCONSIN. Bruce P. Stollberg. Pro Natura, Switzerland, vol.1, no.2, pp.89-91, illus., Oct., 1948.

OCALA DEER HERD. Donald D. Strode. Fla. Game and Fresh Water Fish Comm., Game Publ., no.1, pp.1-42, illus., 1954.

PRESENT DEER SITUATION IN OHIO. J. W. Stuber. Ohio Conserv. Bull., Columbus, vol.7, no.12, pp.4-5, 32, illus., Dec., 1943.

SOME ASPECTS OF THE DEER HERD IN NEW JERSEY ON A REGIONAL BASIS. Jasper C. Sweet, Charles W. Wright. Proc. 8th Ann. N.E. Wildl. Conf., Jackson's Mill, W.Va., pp.1-17, illus., Apr. 1-4, 1952.

DEER AS AN OUTDOOR PROBLEM. Ernest Swift. Wisc. Conserv. Bull., vol.11, no.7, pp.6-10, July, 1946.

HISTORY OF WISCONSIN DEER. Ernest Swift. Wisc. Conserv. Dept., Madison, Publ.no.323, pp.96, illus., Mar., 1946.

STORY OF A PORTAGE COUNTY DEER YARD. Walter R. Sylvester. Wisc.Conserv. Bull., Madison, vol.14, no.5, pp. 13-16, illus., May, 1949.

WHITE-TAILED DEER OF THE ADIRONDACKS. M.T. Townsend, M.W.Smith. Roosevelt Wild Life Bull., Syracuse, vol. 6, no.2, pp.153-326, figs. 75-169, pls.4-5, Oct., 1933.

TOO MANY DEER. Earl C. Tuberson. Penna. Game News, Harrisburg, vol.20, no.2, pp.3, 26, illus., May, 1949.

DEERYARDS OF THE UPPER PENINSULA OF MICHIGAN. Max C. Wakeman. Papers Michigan Acad. Sci., Arts and Letters, vol. 19, pp.333-339, 1933.

MASSACHUSETTS DEER. H.J.Walker. Amer. Field, Chicago, vol.41, no.14, p. 316, Apr. 1, 1944.

WHITE-TAILED DEER IN THE BAKER SANCTUARY AREA. Lawrence H. Walkinshaw. Jack-Pine Warbler, Lansing, vol.30, no.4, pp.138-139, Dec., 1952.

BIOLOGICAL CHARACTERISTICS OF THE WHITE-TAILED DEER HERD AND AN EVALUATION OF THE RANGE IN THE BLUE RIDGE GAME MANAGEMENT AREA. Charles H. Webb. Master of For. thesis, Univ. Ga., Game and Fish Comm., pp.55, illus., mimeo., June, 1954.

MICHIGAN'S DEER HERD. A WINTER DEERYARD STUDY FOR 4-H CLUB MEMBERS. Charles Welch, A.G.Kettunen. Mich. State Coll., Club Bull., no.40, pp.30, Oct., 1939.

WORCESTER COUNTY DEER HERD. K.A. Wilson, E.A. Vaughn. Md.Conserv., vol. 19, no.3, pp.6-8, Summer, 1942.

DEER INVESTIGATION. Donald J. Wooley. Va. Comm. Game and Inl. Fisheries, Investigational Bull., no.2, pp.ii+8, tbls., mimeo., June, 1941.

SURVIVAL OF RESTOCKED DEER IN VIRGINIA. Donald J. Woolley. MS thesis, Va. Polytechnic Inst., 1940.

VIRGINIA ANIMALS EVERYONE SHOULD KNOW. THE WHITE-TAILED DEER. Donald J. Woolley. Va. Wildl., Richmond, vol.7, no.5, pp.6-7, 16, illus., Nov., 1946.

SURVEY OF WHITE-TAILED DEER (ODOCOILEUS VIRGINIANUS SUBSP.) DAMAGE, DAMAGE CONTROL METHODS, AND POPULATION CHARACTERISTICS IN NEW JERSEY. Charles W. Wright. N.J.Div. Fish and Game, Final Rep. Proj. 21-R-2, pp.1-71, graph, Apr., 1950.

NEW JERSEY'S WHITETAIL HERD. Charles W. Wright, Jasper Sweet. N.J.Outdoors, vol. 5, no.6, pp.5-8, illus., Dec., 1954.

SOME WINTER RELATIONS OF THE WHITE-TAILED DEER TO THE FORESTS IN NORTH CENTRAL MASSACHUSETTS. R.K. Ziebarth. MF thesis, Harvard Univ., 1934.

DEER IN MADISON. Outdoor Indiana, Indianapolis, vol.12, no.4, p.15, May, June, 1945.

DEER STATUS - OCTOBER - 1954. Ohio Div. Wildl., Game Surv. News, vol.1, no.10, p.4, map, graph, Oct. 27, 1954.

DEER WERE SCATTERED THROUGH THE WINTER. Wisc. Conserv. Bull., vol.17, no.4, pp.20-21, illus., Apr., 1952.

JACKSON COUNTY, WISCONSIN, DEER SURVEY. Wisc. Conserv. Bull., Madison, vol.13, no.5, pp.3-4, May, 1948.

LOGAN DEER POSES ON TIPPLE ROOF. W. Va. Conserv., Charleston, vol.9, no. 4, p.11, illus., July, 1945.

LOOK AT THE DEER ON FORT BRAGG MILITARY RESERVATION. N.Carolina Wildl. Conserv., Raleigh, vol.8, no.3, pp.8-10, Mar., 1944.

MAINE BOASTS OF GOOD DEER HERD. Wisc. Conserv. Bull., Madison, vol.16, no.3, pp.19-20, Mar., 1951.

WHAT'S YOUR DEER HERD WORTH TO YOU? N.J.Outdoors, vol.3, no.7, pp. 4-5, illus., Jan., 1953.

WHITETAIL CENSUS. Michigan Conserv., Lansing, vol.22, no.3, pp.16-18, illus., May, 1953.

WHITE-TAILED DEER IN PENNSYLVANIA. Penna. Game Comm., Educ.Pamphlet, no. 6, pp.12, 1942.

Odocoileus--United States (Pacific Coastal States)

DISTRIBUTION AND VARIATION IN DEER (GENUS ODOCOILEUS) OF THE PACIFIC COAST REGION OF NORTH AMERICA. I.McT. Cowan. PhD thesis, Univ. Calif., 1935; Calif. Fish and Game, vol.22, no.3, pp.155-246, figs.51-63, July, 1936.

STUDY OF THE OREGON WHITE-TAILED DEER, ODOCOILEUS VIRGINIANUS LEUCURUS (DOUGLAS). Arthur K.Crews. MS thesis, Oregon State Coll., 1939.

CALIFORNIA MULE DEER IN CHAPARRAL FORESTS. F.P.Cronemiller, Paul S. Bartholomew. Calif. Fish and Game, vol.36, no.4, pp.343-365, Oct., 1950.

STUDY OF THE LIFE HISTORY AND FOOD HABITS OF MULE DEER IN CALIFORNIA. Joseph S. Dixon. Calif. Fish and Game, vol.20, no.3, pp.181-282, figs.47-111, July, 1934; no.4, pp.315-354, figs.116-135, Oct., 1934.

WHITE-TAILED DEER IN CALIFORNIA. Joseph S. Dixon. Jour. Mamm., vol.8, no.4, p.308, Nov., 1927.

STUDIES ON THE CONDITION OF CALIFORNIA MULE DEER AT SEQUOIA NATIONAL PARK. Joseph S. Dixon, Carlton M. Herman. Calif. Fish and Game, San Francisco, vol.31, no.1, pp.3-11, illus., Jan., 1945.

1939 WINTER DEER RANGE SURVEY REPORT, MALHEUR NATIONAL FOREST, OREGON. O.T. Edwards. U.S. Dept.Agric., Forest Serv., pp.21, Aug., 1939.

REPORT ON THE 1938 WINTER DEER RANGE SURVEY AND DEER CENSUS, MALHEUR NATIONAL FOREST, OREGON. O.T. Edwards. U.S. Dept. Agric., Forest Serv., pp.31, June, 1938.

SURVEY OF WINTER DEER RANGE, MALHEUR NATIONAL FOREST, OREGON. O.T. Edwards. Jour. Wildl. Mgt., Menasha, vol.6, no.3, pp.210-220, pls.15-16, July, 1942.

NINE-YEAR OBSERVATION OF A DEER PROBLEM AREA. Arthur S. Einarsen. Trans. 12th N.Amer. Wildl. Conf., pp.193-203, 1947.

THE WINTER RANGE OF THE INTERSTATE DEER HERD, MODOC NATIONAL FOREST, CALIFORNIA. Geo. A. Fischer, John C.

Davis. U.S. Forest Serv., Reg.5, San Francisco, pp.20, 1944.

DEER OF CALIFORNIA. E. Raymond Hall. Calif. Fish and Game, vol.13, no.4, pp. 233-259, Oct., 1927.

A CORRECTION. (Corrections to author's "The Deer of California".) E. Raymond Hall. Calif. Fish and Game, vol.14, no.1, pp.30-31, Jan. 30, 1928.

FOOD HABITS, PRODUCTIVITY AND CONDITION OF THE DOYLE MULE DEER HERD. Robert W. Lassen et al. Calif. Fish and Game, vol.38, no.2, pp.211-224, illus., Apr., 1952.

SUPPLEMENTAL DEER REPORT 1940. Burton Lauckhart. Wash. Dept. Game, Biol. Bull., no.4, pp.1-29, mimeo., July, 1940.

JAWBONE DEER HERD. A. Starker Leopold et al. Calif. Div. Fish and Game, Game Bull., no.4, pp.139, 1951.

STATEWIDE SURVEY OF CALIFORNIA DEER RANGES. William M. Longhurst. Proc. Ann. Conf. W. Assn. State Game and Fish Comm., vol.29, pp.117-121, 1949?

SURVEY OF CALIFORNIA DEER HERDS, THEIR RANGES AND MANAGEMENT PROBLEMS. William M. Longhurst et al. Calif. Dept. Fish and Game Bull., no.6, pp.1-126, illus., 1952.

BURRO DEER IN CALIFORNIA. Donald D. McLean. Calif. Fish and Game, vol.16, no.2, pp.119-120, Apr., 1930.

DEER OF CALIFORNIA, WITH PARTICULAR REFERENCE TO THE ROCKY MOUNTAIN MULE DEER. Donald D. McLean. Calif. Fish and Game, San Francisco, vol.26, no. 2, pp.139-166, figs.59-72, Apr., 1940.

OREGON'S MULE DEER RESOURCES. (Cover title: Oregon's Mule Deer.) Robert U. Mace. Oreg. State Game Comm., pp. 1-26, illus., 1953.

MURDERERS CREEK DEER HERD. Glenn E. Mitchell. Trans. 9th N.Amer. Wildl. Conf., pp.167-172, 1944.

MULE DEER STUDY PROGRAM. James Moffitt. Calif. Fish and Game, vol.20, no.1, pp.52-66, Jan., 1934.

DEER RENDEZVOUS. (Mule deer in Oregon.) Janet Moore. Nature Mag., Wash., vol.39, no.10, pp.521, 550, illus., Dec., 1946.

CALIFORNIA MULE DEER. Joyce Muench, Josef Muench. Nat. Hist., New York, vol. 54, no.3, pp.110-112, photos, Mar., 1945.

DEER CENSUS REPORT 1938, INYO NATIONAL FOREST. Reed S. Neilson. U.S. Dept. Agric., Forest Serv., Region 5, Leaflet 42-W-2, pp.14, Aug., 1938.

COLUMBIAN BLACK-TAIL DEER OF THE CALIFORNIA NATIONAL FORESTS. J.W. Nelson. Jour. Forestry, Wash., vol.28, no.5, pp.664-667, May, 1930.

NOTES ON THE DEER OF CALIFORNIA REDWOOD STATE PARK. Robert T. Orr. Calif. Fish and Game, vol.23, no.4, pp. 286-289, Oct., 1937.

WASHINGTON DEER REPORT 1939. Clarence Pautzke et al. Wash. Dept. Game, Biol. Bull., no.1, pp.ix+44, maps, pls.10, July 1939.

BLACK-TAILED DEER INVESTIGATIONS ON A CLOSED AREA IN WESTERN OREGON. Carroll A. Rieck. MS thesis, Oreg. State Coll., 1952.

REPORT OF THE DEER HERDS IN DISTRICT #5. John R. Rogers. Wash. Dept. Game, pp.1-13, mimeo., Mar., 1953.

NEWLY LOCATED HERD OF PACIFIC WHITE-TAILED DEER. Victor B. Scheffer. Jour. Mamm., vol.21, no.3, pp.271-282, Aug., 1940.

DEER OF CALIFORNIA. H.H.Sheldon. Santa Barbara Mus. Nat. Hist., Occas. Papers, no.3, pp.71, pls.19, map, Nov. 1, 1933.

INTRODUCED WHITE-TAILED DEER IN SOUTHEASTERN WASHINGTON. Carl V. Swanson. Murrelet, vol.31, no.3, pp.43-44, Sep.-Dec., 1950.

DEER NUTRITION AND POPULATION DYNAMICS IN THE NORTH COAST RANGE CALIFORNIA. Richard D. Taber. Trans. 21st N.Amer. Wildl. Conf., pp.159-172, 1956.

DEER STATISTICS FOR 1939. Calif. Conservationist, Sacramento, vol.5, no.2, p. 5, Feb., 1940.

DEVILS GARDEN DEER HERD. Interstate Deer Herd Comm. Calif. Fish and Game, vol.37, no.3, pp.233-272, July, 1951.

SECOND PROGRESS REPORT ON THE COOPERATIVE STUDY OF THE INTERSTATE DEER HERD AND ITS RANGE. Interstate Deer Herd Comm. Calif. Fish and Game, San Francisco, vol.33, no.4, pp.287-314, Oct., 1947.

THIRD PROGRESS REPORT ON THE COOPERATIVE STUDY OF THE INTERSTATE DEER HERD AND ITS RANGE. Interstate Deer Herd Comm. Calif. Fish and Game, vol.35, no.2, pp.115-134, Apr., 1949.

FOURTH PROGRESS REPORT ON THE COOPERATIVE STUDY OF THE INTERSTATE DEER HERD AND ITS RANGE. Interstate Deer Herd Comm. Calif. Fish and Game, vol.36, no.1, pp.27-52, Jan., 1950.

EIGHTS PROGRESS REPORT ON THE COOPERATIVE STUDY OF THE DEVILS GARDEN INTERSTATE DEER HERD AND ITS RANGE. Interstate Deer Herd Comm. Calif. Fish and Game, vol.40, no.3, pp.235-266, illus., July, 1954.

Odocoileus--United States, Western

DEER ON FISHER RIVER. Lowell Adams. Outdoor Montana, Helena, vol.2, no.4, pp. 7, 20-21, illus., Aug.-Sep., 1947.

WINTER STUDY OF MULE DEER IN NEVADA. C.M.Aldous. Jour. Wildl. Mgt., vol.9, no.2, pp.145-151, Apr., 1945.

EARLY SUMMER FOODS AND MOVEMENTS OF THE MULE DEER (ODOCOILEUS HEMIONUS) IN THE SIERRA VIEJA RANGE OF SOUTHWESTERN TEXAS. Alfred W. Anderson. Texas Jour. Sci., Huntsville, vol.1, no.4, pp.45-50, Dec., 1949.

WHITE-TAILED DEER IN WYOMING. Chester C. Anderson. Wyo. Wild Life, Cheyenne, vol.13, no.4, pp.20-22, May, 1949.

WHITE-TAILED DEER IN MISSOURI. Earl L. Atwood, A. Steyermark. U.S.Dept. Agric., Forest Serv., Clark Natl.Forest, pp.34, 1937.

NORTH DAKOTA'S VIRGINIA WHITE-TAILED DEER. Roy N. Bach. N.Dakota Outdoors, Bismarck, vol.6, no.5, p.6, Nov., 1943.

NORTHWESTERN WHITE-TAIL DEER. Vernon Bailey. Proc. Biol. Soc. Wash., vol. 45, pp.43-44, Apr.2, 1932.

WHITE-TAIL IN NORTH DAKOTA. Vernon Bailey. N.Dakota Outdoors, Bismarck, vol. 1, no.11, pp.6-7, May, 1939.

DEER IN BLACK CANYON, ARIZONA. E.S. Barker. Outdoor Life, vol. 68, no.5, p.33, Nov., 1931.

ANALYSIS OF ROCKY MOUNTAIN MULE DEER KILL-RECORDS OF FIVE YEAR DEER REMOVAL FROM THE LOGAN RIVER DRAINAGE OF NORTHERN UTAH. Wilmer Bartels. MS thesis, Utah State Agr. Coll., 1941.

WHITETAILS MOVING SOUTH. Robert I. Benson. Conserv. Volunteer, vol.17, no. 101, pp.14-18, illus., Sep.-Oct., 1954.

PROGRESS REPORT ON THE DOYLE DEER HERD. James A. Blaisdell. Proc. 33rd Ann. Conf. Western Assn. State and Fish Comm., pp.132-139, map, June 1-3, 1953 (1954).

AGE COMPOSITION, WEIGHTS, AND PHYSICAL CHARACTERISTICS OF MISSOURI'S DEER. Allen Brohn, Dunbar Robb. Mo.Conserv. Comm., PR Ser., no.13, pp.ii+28, map, graphs, Feb., 1955.

PICEANCE - WHITE RIVER DEER HERD. A RESUME OF THE RECORD ON THIS IMPORTANT DEER HERD, 1939 TO 1943. Arthur H. Carhart. Colo. Game and Fish Dept., Deer-Elk Surv., Suppl. Rep., pp. 20, mimeo., pl.4, Aug., 1943.

STUDY OF THE BEHAVIOR AND MOVEMENTS OF THE TUCSON MOUNTAIN MULE DEER. E. Dan Clark. MS thesis, Univ. Ariz., pp.1-111, 1953.

WHITE-TAILED DEER IN THE GREAT PLAINS REGION. Faxon W. Cook. Jour. Wildl. Mgt., vol.9, no.3, pp.237-242, July, 1945.

UTAH'S DEER HERD REMAINS IN HEALTHY CONDITION. Harold Crane. Utah Fish and Game Bull., Salt Lake City, vol. 7, no.11, pp.1, 5-6, illus., Feb., 1950.

THOSE NEVADA MULE DEER. William Curtis. Outdoorsman, Chicago, vol.86, no. 1, whole no.5-6, pp.12-13, 22, illus., Jan.-Feb., 1944.

FOOD HABITS AND POPULATION STUDIES OF WHITE-TAILED DEER ON THE LIVE OAK-MESQUITE RANGES OF THE KING RANCH. Richard B. Davis. Quart. Rept. Texas Coop. Wildl. Research Unit, Austin, vol.9, no.4, pp.2-6, June-Aug., 1949.

DEER PROBLEM, DEER TRAPPING, AND DEER REMOVAL AT ZION CANYON, UTAH. Joseph S. Dixon, Lowell Sumner. Trans. 4th N.Amer. Wildl. Conf., pp. 231-235, 1939.

ARKANSAS' DEER HERD. David Donaldson et al. Ark. Game and Fish Comm., Fed. Aid Publ., Proj. 17-D and 20-R, pp.1-72, illus., 1951.

CONCERNING MINNESOTA'S DEER HERD. Richard J. Dorer. Minnesota Div.Bull. Isaac Walton League, 4th Quarter, pp.18-19, Dec., 1945.

STATUS OF GAME: 1946. (Deer.) Richard J. Dorer. Conserv. Volunteer, St.Paul, vol. 9, no.51, pp.5-10, Mar.-Apr., 1946.

DEER RANGE APPRAISAL FOR THE MISSOURI OZARKS. Robert L.Dunkeson. Jour. Wildl. Mgt., vol.19, no.3, pp.358-364, graph, July, 1955.

DEER RANGE APPRAISAL IN THE OZARKS. Robert L. Dunkeson. Presented at 13th Midwest Wildl. Conf., Minneapolis, pp.1-10, Dec. 12-14, 1951.

MISSOURI'S DEER HERD / REPRODUCTION AND CHECKING STATION DATA. Robert L. Dunkeson, D.A.Murphy. Presented at 15th Midwest Wildl.Conf., Chicago, Ill., pp.1-5, graphs 2, Dec. 9-11, 1953.

ADDITIONAL MULE DEER RECORDS FOR MINNESOTA. Arnold B.Erickson, G.T. Bue. Jour. Mamm., vol.35, no.3, pp.457-458, Aug., 1954.

ST. CROIX PARK DEER HERD. Arnold B. Erickson, D.W. Burcalow. Conserv. Volunteer., vol.17, no.97, pp.6-17, illus., Jan.-Feb., 1954.

STUDY OF THE LIFE HISTORY OF THE ROCKY MOUNTAIN MULE DEER IN NORTHERN UTAH. Thomas B. Evans. MS thesis, Utah State Agr. Coll., 1941.

DEER SURVEY, 1948. Lester F.Faber. Iowa Conserv., Des Moines, vol.7, no.4, pp.30, illus., Apr. 15, 1948.

DEER INVENTORY STUDIES IN MINNESOTA. Gordon Fredine. Proc. Minn.Acad. Sci., no.8, pp.41-49, 1940.

MINNESOTA'S DEER PROBLEM. Gordon Fredine. Conserv. Volunteer, vol.1, no. 2, pp.18-23, Nov., 1940 ; Proc. Minn. Wildl. Conserv. Short Course, no.2, pp. 36-42, 1940.

SO! YOU BELIEVE IT, EH? (Deer.) Phil. Goodrum. Texas Game and Fish, Austin, vol.2, no.1, pp.7, 18-19, Dec., 1943.

MULE DEER RECORD FOR MINNESOTA. Harvey L. Gunderson. Jour. Mamm., vol. 29, no.2, p.184, May 14, 1948.

HUNTING SEASON STATISTICS AS AN INDEX TO RANGE CONDITIONS AND DEER POPULATION FLUCTUATIONS IN MINNESOTA. Vernon E. Gunvalson et al. Jour. Wildl. Mgt., vol.16, no.2, pp.121-131, illus., Apr., 1952.

DEER IN THE HILL COUNTRY. Henry C. Hahn. Texas Game and Fish, Austin, vol.1, no.5, pp.7, 15, Apr., 1943.

WHITE-TAILED DEER IN THE EDWARDS PLATEAU REGION OF TEXAS. Henry C. Hahn. Texas Game, Fish and Oyster Comm., pp.52, May, 1945.

ANNUAL ROCKY MOUNTAIN MULE DEER SURVEY. John M. Hall. Ariz. Game and Fish Comm., Ariz. Game Surv., Proj. Job Compl. Rep., 1951, Proj. 53 R 1-WP 3-J 3, pp.1-7, illus., Jan., 1952.

DESERT MULES IN YUMA COUNTY.(Mule deer.) Arthur F. Halloran. Ariz. Wildl.-Sportsman, Phoenix, vol.8, no.11, p.21, illus., Dec., 1947.

STATUS OF MINNESOTA DEER. PART 2. Paul Highby, Marius Morse. Conserv. Volunteer, St.Paul, vol.4, no.21, pp.58-64, figs.3, June, 1942.

LIFE HISTORY AND MANAGEMENT OF THE CACHE DEER HERD. Jerry W. Hill. MS thesis, Utah State Agr. Coll., June, 1952.

NEBRASKA'S DEER. Ralph Hill. Outdoor Nebr., vol.22, no.2, pp.7-8, Summer, 1944.

HISTORY OF WHITE-TAILED DEER OF COLORADO 1948. Gilbert N. Hunter.Colo. Game and Fish Dept., pp.10, 1948.

SOUTHWESTERN MULE DEER. Fred W. Johnson. Ariz. Wildl.and Sportsman, Tucson, vol.6, no.9, p.8, July, 1945.

ARIZONA WHITETAIL. Geo. B.Johnson. Field and Stream, pp.84-85, illus., Apr., 1935.

PINES AND BUCKS OF EAST TEXAS. Daniel W. Lay. Texas Game and Fish, Austin, vol.1, no.2, pp.4, 11, Jan., 1943.

LIGHTS IN THE NIGHT. (Deer.) V. W. Lehmann. Texas Game and Fish, Austin, vol.2, no.2, pp.5, 15-17, Jan., 1944.

WHITE-TAILED DEER IN OKLAHOMA, ECOLOGY, AND MANAGEMENT, AND PRODUCTION. James S. Lindzey. PhD thesis, Okla. A. and M. Coll., July, 1951; Okla.Game and Fish Dept., PR Proj.37-R, pp.xiv+105, illus., 1952.

COOPERATIVE DEER RANGE STUDY. William T. McKean. S.Dakota Conserv. Digest, Pierre, vol.13, no.3, pp.2-3, 14, Mar., 1946.

NORTH DAKOTA DEER PASTURES. William T. McKean. N.Dak.Outdoors, vol.13, no.5, pp.4-5, Nov., 1950.

NORTH DAKOTA DEER TRENDS. William T. McKean. N.Dak.Outdoors, vol.15, no. 1, pp.4-5, illus., July, 1952.

WINTER DEER PROBLEM. William T. McKean. S.Dak. Conserv.Digest, vol. 12, no.1, pp.2-3, 6, Jan., 1945.

WHITETAILS ON THE MOVE! Juanita Mahaffey. Oklahoma Game and Fish News, Oklahoma City, vol.1, no.1, pp. 3-6, illus., Jan., 1945.

WHAT HAS HAPPENED TO KAIBAB DEER? Walter G. Mann. Ariz. Wildl. and Sportsman, Tucson, vol.7, no.1, pp.10-12, Jan., 1946.

MINNESOTA'S DEER PROBLEM. J. Manweiler. Minn. Conserv., no.50, pp.7, 20-23, 31, Oct., 1937.

DEER SITUATION IN NORTHERN IDAHO. Fred H. Mass. Univ. Idaho Bull., vol.33, no.22, pp.30-34, Dec., 1938.

DOES SOUTH DAKOTA HAVE TOO MANY DEER? Harland Means. S.Dakota Conserv. Digest, Pierre, vol.14, no.9, pp.10, 12, Oct., 1947.

MULE DEER IN NEBRASKA NATIONAL FOREST. Levi L. Mohler, et al. Jour. Wildl. Mgt., vol.15, no.2, pp.129-157, Apr., 1951.

DEER OVERWINTER WELL. Marius Morse. Conserv. Volunteer, St.Paul, pp.39-40, June, 1942.

STATUS OF MINNESOTA DEER. Marius Morse, Paul R. Highby. Conserv.Volunteer, vol.4, no.20, pp.13-16, May, 1942; vol.4, no.21, pp.58-64, June, 1942.

ARIZONA WHITETAIL. Jack O'Connor. Ariz. Wildl. and Sportsman, Tucson, vol.6, no.4, p.10, Feb., 1945.

DEER TAGGING AND POPULATION STUDIES IN MINNESOTA. Herman F. Olson. Trans. 3rd N.Amer. Wildl.Conf., pp.280-286, 1938.

SUPERIOR FOREST DEER STUDIES. Herman F. Olson. Conserv.Volunteer, vol.3, no.17, pp.52-56, Feb., 1942.

DEER OF THE KAIBAB. T.G.Pearson. Nature Mag., vol.5, pp.158-160, illus., Mar., 1925.

SURVEY OF THE DEER SITUATION IN ZION CANYON, UTAH. C.C.Presnall. Proc. Utah Acad. Sci., Arts and Letters, vol.15, pp.107-110, June, 1938.

MULE DEER RANGE AND POPULATION STUDIES IN UTAH. D.I. Rasmussen. Trans. 4th N.Amer. Wildl. Conf., pp.236-243, 1939.

END OF THE BEGINNING. Dunbar Robb. Mo. Conserv., vol.14, no.10, pp.5-6, 14, illus., Oct., 1953.

MISSOURI'S DEER HERD. Dunbar Robb. Mo. Conserv. Comm., pp.36, 1951.

SOME PROSPECTS ON DEER. Dunbar Robb. Mo. Conserv., vol.13, no.10, pp. 1-3, 12, illus., Oct., 1952.

DEER IN LOUISIANA. Lyle S. St.Amant, Carroll J. Perkins. La.Conserv., vol.5, no.8, pp.2-4, illus., May-June, 1953 ; La. Conserv., vol.5, no.9, pp.14-16, map, July-Aug., 1953.

ECOLOGY AND MANAGEMENT OF THE WHITE-TAILED DEER, ODOCOILEUS VIRGINIANUS (BODDAERT ), IN THE LEDGES STATE PARK REGION, BOONE COUNTY, IOWA. James C. Salinas. MS thesis, Iowa State Coll., 1948.

PRELIMINARY REPORT ON THE STUDY OF WHITE-TAILED DEER IN THE EDWARDS PLATEAU OF TEXAS. Earl Sanders. Jour. Wildl. Mgt., Menasha, vol.5, no.2, pp.182-190, Apr., 1941.

IOWA DEER HERDS--1950. Glen C. Sanderson. Iowa Conservationist, Des Moines, vol.9, no.4, pp.25, 31, Apr. 15, 1950.

MISSOURI'S DEER HERD. C.W.Schwartz. Missouri Conservationist, Jefferson City, vol.9, no.11, p.17, illus., Nov., 1948.

WHITE-TAILED DEER FORMERLY IN THE YELLOWSTONE PARK. M.P. Skinner. Jour. Mamm., vol.10, no.2, pp.101-115, pls.2, May, 1929.

"DEER IN GREAT DROVES..." LET'S BRING 'EM BACK TO MISSOURI. M.O. Steen. Missouri Conservationist, Jefferson City, vol.7, no.2, pp.1-3, Feb., 1946.

MINNESOTA DEER FACTS. Milton H. Stenlund. Conserv. Volunteer. vol.12, no.72, pp.28-32, Sep.-Oct., 1949.

MULE DEER IN ARIZONA CHAPARRAL. W. G. Swank. Ariz. Game and Fish Dept., Wildl. Bull., no.3, pp.1-109, illus., Feb., 1958.

WHITE-TAILED DEER IN COLORADO. C.E. Till. Jour. Mamm., vol.35, no.2, p.269, May 26, 1954.

DEER MAY GET A BREAK. E.C.Walker. Texas Game and Fish, Austin, vol.5, no. 3, pp.13, 26, Feb., 1947.

DEER HERD OF WASHINGTON COUNTY, IOWA. H.O. Weaver. Amer. Field, vol. 119, no.9, p.204, illus., Mar. 3, 1928.

RANGE USE, FOOD HABITS, AND AGRICULTURAL RELATIONSHIPS OF THE MULE DEER, BRIDGER MOUNTAINS, MONTANA. Bruce T. Wilkins. Jour.Wildl. Mgt., vol.21, no.2, pp.159-169, illus., Apr., 1957.

SOME OBSERVATIONS ON A WHITE-TAILED DEER WINTER RANGE IN IDAHO. E.J. Woolfolk. U.S.For.Serv., N.Rocky Mt. Exp. Sta., Res.Note, no.116, pp.1-4, Feb., 1953.

DEER SEEN IN LAKE COUNTY. S.Dakota Conserv. Digest, Pierre, pp.11, June, 1940.

RARE MULE DEER.(First record for Minnesota since 1887.) Conserv.Volunteer, St. Paul, vol.4, no.20, p.49, May, 1942.

SOUTH DAKOTA'S DEER SURVEY. S.Dak. Conserv. Digest, Pierre, vol.8, no.11, pp. 5, 13, 14, illus., Nov., 1941.

UTAH DEER HERDS STILL HEALTHY. Utah Fish and Game Bull., Salt Lake City, vol.6, no.3, pp.7-8, Nov., 1948.

Odocoileus--Weights and Measurements

GROWTH RATE OF THE BLACK-TAILED DEER (ODOCOILEUS HEMIONUS COLUMBIANUS). I.McT. Cowan, A.J. Wood.Jour. Wildl. Mgt., vol.19, no.3, pp.331-336, graph, July, 1955.

DEER AGE AND WEIGHT STUDY DURING 1955 SEASON COMPLETE. V.F.Flyger. Md. Tidewater News, vol.13, no.1, pp.1, 4, June, 1956.

OHIO DEER FACTS. HOW BIG ARE OHIO DEER? Merrill C. Gilfillan. Ohio Conserv. Bull., vol.16, no.9, p.29, illus., Sep., 1952.

WEIGHTS RELATIONSHIPS IN THE GEORGE RESERVE DEER HERD. F.N.Hamerstrom, Jr., F.Camburn. Jour. Mamm., vol.31, no.1, pp. 5-17, Feb., 1950.

HOW MUCH DOES A WILD DEER WEIGH? R.P. Holland. Outers' Recreation, vol.62, p.340, May, 1920.

WISCONSIN'S LARGE DEER OF 1938. R. Hopkins. Wisc. Conserv. Bull., vol.4, no.10, pp.49-51, Oct., 1939.

SURRY COUNTY'S BIG BUCK. Geo. B. Johnson. Va.Wildl., Blacksburg, vol.1, no.11, pp.2-3, July, 1938.

LARGE DEER. SEASON 1941-42. E.L. Loyster. Wisc. Conserv.Bull., Madison, vol.8, no.1, pp.29-30, Jan., 1943.

COMPARATIVE WEIGHT AND MEASUREMENTS OF WHITE-TAILED DEER. A.J. Nicholson. Texas Game, Fish and Oyster Comm., Quart. Prog. Rept., Austin, pp. 7-9, Oct.-Dec., 1941.

DEER WEIGHTS AND MEASUREMENTS ON THE ALLEGHENY NATIONAL FOREST. Barry C. Park. Trans. 3rd N.Amer. Wildl. Conf., pp.261-279, 1938.

SKULL MEASUREMENTS IN THE NORTHERN VIRGINIA DEER. John C. Phillips. Jour. Mamm., vol.1, no.3, pp.130-133, May, 1920.

WEST VIRGINIA DEER. WEIGHTS AND MEASUREMENTS. C.B. Pierle. West Va. Conserv., Charleston, vol.5, no.5, pp. 10-13, 21, Aug., 1941.

SIZE AND WEIGHT OF ADIRONDACK DEER. W.J. Schoonmaker. Jour. Mamm., vol.17, no.1, pp.67-68, Feb., 1936.

DEER WEIGHTS AND MEASUREMENTS. Roger Seamans. Vt.Fish and Game Serv., Bull. no. 3-2, pp.16, Feb., 1941 ; State Bull., PR Ser. no.6, pp.1-27, 1942.

DEER--THE LIVE WEIGHT-DRESSED WEIGHT AND LIVE WEIGHT-EDIBLE MEAT RELATIONSHIPS. C.W.Severinghaus. N.Y.State Conservationist, Albany, vol.4, no.2, p.26, Oct.-Nov., 1949.

MULE DEER. (Measurements and weight, in British Columbia.) Howard J. Smith. Field, London, vol.168, no.4366, p.513, illus., Aug. 29, 1936.

COMPARISON OF WEIGHT AND ANTLER DEVELOPMENT BETWEEN WHITE-TAILED DEER IN NORTHERN AND SOUTHERN NEW JERSEY. J.C. Sweet. N.J. Outdoors, vol.3, no.3, pp.3-8, illus., Sep., 1952.

NORTH DAKOTA HUNTER KILLS WORLD'S LARGEST DEER. (B.A.Sell, Grafton, N.D. sportsman, bags four hundred and seventeen pound whitetail deer.) N.Dakota Outdoors, Bismarck, vol.2, no.10, p.5, Apr., 1940.

Alces--General

(MOOSE (ALCES PALMATA, KLEIN).)Das Elch. (Alces palmata, Klein). Wilhelm Blasius. Raoul Ritter von Dombrowstis "Allgemeine Encyklopaedie der gesammten Forst und Jagdwissenschaften", pp.1-38, 1887.

THE MOOSE. Victor Cahalane. Cranbrook Inst. Sci. News Letter, Bloomfield Hills, vol.14, no.7, pp.70-74, Mar., 1945.

THE ROMANCE OF THE MOOSE. J.K. Doutt. Carnegie Mag., Pittsburgh, vol.14, no.7, pp.205-208, figs.3, Dec., 1940.

(REPLY AND SOME SUGGESTIONS ON THE QUESTION OF THE MOOSE.) En replik och några förslag i älgfragan. Torsten Gardell. Sv. Jagareforb. Tidskr., vol.76, no.5, pp. 129-136, illus., 1938.

MOOSE. Madison Grant. 7th Rep.Forest, Fish and Game Comm., State of New York, pp.225-238, illus., 1903.

(MEETING WITH THE MOOSE.) Möte med älg. S. Kr. Kjeldstad. Svensk Jakt, Stockholm, vol.89, no.6, pp.164-166, illus., June 14, 1951.

REVIEW OF THE LIVING REPRESENTATIVES OF THE GENUS ALCES. Randolph Peterson. Contrib. Royal Ontario Mus. Zool. and Palaeontol., Toronto, no.34, pp. 30, illus., Oct. 15, 1952.

(MOOSE.) Älgjägare. Erik Rooth. Svensk Jakt, Stockholm, vol.87, no.9, pp.250-254, Sep., 1949.

BEAVER BOY STUDIES FLATHORN, THE MOOSE. W.J. Schoonmaker. Nat.Humane Rev., New York, vol.35, no.3, pp.20-21, 33, illus., Mar., 1947.

(THE MOOSE.) Algen. Folke Skuncke. P.A. Norstedt and Sons, Stockholm, pp.400, illus., 1949.

M IS FOR MOOSE. Anton Swanson.Vantage, pp.64, 1954.

Alces--Anatomy

(SNOUT OF THE ELK (ALCES ALCES L.).) Die Nase des Elchs (Alce alces L.). Arnold von Jacobi. Anat. Anzeiger, Jena, vol.52, nos.1-2, pp.41-46, figs.1-5, 1919.

(CONTRIBUTION TO THE DEVELOPMENTAL HISTORY OF THE NASAL REGION OF THE ELK (ALCES ALCES L.).)Beitrag zur Entwicklungsgeschichte der Nasenregion des Elches (Alces alces L.). A. Pinus. Zeitschr. f. Morph. u. Oekologie der Tiere, vol.13, pp.36-64, figs.12, Dec. 22, 1928.

REMARKS ON THE POST MORTEN APPEARANCE OF A MOOSE DEER(CERVUS ALCES, LINN.). Mr. Spooner. Proc. Zool. Soc. London, pt.1, p.46, 1833.

Alces--Diseases and Parasites

TREATMENT OF A SICK MOOSE WITH COBALTOUS CHLORIDE. D.A. Benson. Jour. Wildl. Mgt., vol.16, no.1, pp.110-111, Jan., 1952.

DISEASES AFFECTING MOOSE. R. Fenstermacher. Abs. Papers Presented at Wildl. Cons, Short Course, Univ.Minn., pp.5-6, May, 4, 5, 6, 1939 ; Conserv. Volunteer, vol.5, no.27, pp.46-48, Dec., 1942.

FURTHER STUDIES OF DISEASES AFFECTING MOOSE. R. Fenstermacher. Bull. Univ. Minn. Agric. Exper.Sta., no. 308, pp.26, illus., Sep., 1934.

FURTHER STUDIES OF DISEASES AFFECTING MOOSE III. R. Fenstermacher, O.Wilford Olsen. Cornell Vet., vol.32, no. 3, pp.241-254, July, 1942.

BRUCELLOSIS IN A MOOSE. William L. Jellison, Charles W. Fishel, E.L.Chaetum. Jour. Wildl. Mgt., Ithaca, vol.17, no.2, pp.217-218, Apr., 1953. (Alces americanus.)

SARCOCYSTIS IN THE MOOSE. Arthur L. Kelly. Jour. Mamm., vol.31, no.4, pp.462-263, Nov. 21, 1950.

MOOSE ENCEPHALITIS. Lester S. King. Amer. Jour. Path., vol.15, no.4, pp.445-454, July, 1939.

MAINE MOOSE DISEASE STUDIES. A.L. Lamson. MS thesis, Univ. Maine, 1941.

MOOSE RAMPANT. Percy E. Nobbs. Beaver, Winnipeg, outfit 277, pp.42-44, illus., Sep., 1946.

PARASITES OF MOOSE IN NORTHERN MINNESOTA. O.W. Wilford, R. Fenstermacher. Amer. Jour. Vet. Res., vol.3, no.9, pp.403-408, Oct., 1942.

MOOSE AND TICKS. John E. Peil. Conserv. Volunteer, St.Paul, vol.5, no.26, p. 19, Nov., 1942.

MAD MOOSE. M. Sauerbrei. Sylva, Toronto, vol.4, no.1, p.43, 1948.

SOME NOTES ON MOOSE PARASITES. A.de vos Vos, A.E. Allin. Jour.Mamm., vol.30, no.4, pp.430-431, Nov. 17, 1949.

Alces--Distribution

RANGE OF THE MOOSE EXTENDING NORTHWARD. R.M. Anderson. Canadian Field-Nat., vol.38, pp.27-29, Feb., 1924.

ON THE GEOGRAPHICAL DISTRIBUTION AND SYSTEMATICS OF ELKS OR MOOSE (ALCES GRAY). C.C. Flerov. Comptes Rendus Acad. Sci. USSR, vol.2, no.2, pp. 137-143, Apr. 11, 1934.

Alces--Economic Importance, Management

AERIAL RECONNAISSANCE OF MOOSE IN SUMMER. Robert I. Bowman. Jour.Wildl. Mgt., vol.19, no.3, pp.382-387, illus., July, 1955.

OUR VANISHING MOOSE. Geo.Carpenter. Rod and Gun in Canada, Montreal, vol.50, no.3, pp.11, 42, Aug., 1948.

WINTER RANGE PROBLEMS OF MOOSE IN THE SUSITNA VALLEY. Edward F. Chatelain. (In) Science in Alaska 1951, Proc. 2nd Alaskan Science Conf., Alaska Div. AAAS, pp.343-347, 1953.

SACRED COW. C.H.D. Clarke.Northern Sportsman, vol.7, no.6, pp.10-12, illus., June, 1952.

MOOSE FOR TOMORROW.(Trapping of live moose, to stock other regions.) Ben East. Country Life, New York, vol.76, pp.57, 88-91, illus., June, 1939.

MOOSE HERD IS MOVED. MICHIGAN TRANSFERS THIRTY-EIGHT ANIMALS FROM ISLE ROYALE TO THE UPPER PENINSULA MAINLAND AS A CONSERVATION MEASURE. Ben East. Bull. N.Y. Zool. Soc., vol.39, no.4, pp.141-149, illus., July-Aug., 1936.

AERIAL MOOSE CENSUS. R. Y. Edwards. B.C. Forest Serv. Res. Notes, no.23, p. 9, map, 1952.

COMPARISON OF AN AERIAL AND GROUND CENSUS OF MOOSE. R.Y. Edwards. Jour. Wildl. Mgt., Ithaca, vol.18, no.3, pp.403-404, July, 1954.

TRAPPING THE MOOSE. James E. Grasse. Wyo. Wild Life, vol.14, no.5, pp.12-18, 36-37, June, 1950.

(PROTECTION OF ALCES.) Det Norrländska Älgvårdsproblemet. B. Haglund. Svenska Jagareforbundets Tidskrift, Stockholm, vol. 78, no.7, pp.301-304, July 11, 1940.

PAST AND PRESENT ASPECTS OF THE MOOSE PROBLEM IN CENTRAL BRITISH COLUMBIA. James Hatter. Proc. Ann. Conf. W. Assn. State Game and Fish Comm., vol.30, pp.150-154, 1950?

GUNS A FACTOR IN FUTURE OF MOOSE. (Transferring moose in Michigan.) Paul Hickie. Michigan Conserv., vol.7, no.6, pp.8-9, Feb., 1938.

(ON THE DAMAGE TO THE FORESTS CAUSED BY THE MOOSE, AND ITS SIGNIFICANCE IN THE ECONOMY OF THE FOREST.) Hirven metsässä aikaan saamat tuhot ja niiden metsätaloudellinen merkitys. Esko Kangas. Suomen Riista, Helsinki, no.4, pp.62-90, illus., 1949. (In Finnish with English summary.)

FUTURE OF MINNESOTA MOOSE. IS OUR LARGEST MAMMAL WANING? J.Manweiler. Conserv. Volunteer, St. Paul, vol. 3, no.15, pp.38-43, illus., Dec., 1941.

PROTECTION OF THE MOOSE. W.F.H. Mason. Canadian Field-Nat., vol.43, pp. 107-108, May, 1929.

MANAGEMENT OF MOOSE. R.L.Peterson. Conv. Internat. Assn. Game, Fish and Conserv. Comm., vol.39, pp.71-75, 1949.

MOOSE RESEARCH PROJECT. R.L. Peterson. Carling Conserv. Digest, Toronto, vol.1, no.4, pp.3-4, illus., Oct., 1947.

NORTH AMERICAN MOOSE TRANSPLANTATIONS AND HANDLING TECHNIQUES. D.H. Pimlott, W.J. Carberry. Jour. Wildl.Mgt., vol.22, no.1, pp.51-62, illus., Jan., 1958.

TRAPPING AND TAGGING MOOSE ON WINTER RANGE. R.W. Ritcey, R.Y. Edwards. Jour. Wildl. Mgt., vol.20, no. 3, pp.324-325, July, 1956.

FACT-FINDING HUNTER TAKES BUSH FLIGHT FOR MOOSE. Rob. F. Sanderson. Outdoor Life, New York, vol.104, no.4, pp.46-53, illus., Oct., 1949.

PROGRESS IN THE MANAGEMENT OF THE MOOSE OF SOUTH CENTRAL ALASKA. David L. Spencer, Edward F. Chatelain. Trans. 18th N.Amer. Wildl. Conf., pp. 539-552, 1953.

WHAT SHALL WE DO WITH OUR MOOSE? Thaddeus Surber. Fins, Feathers and Fur, no.70, pp.31, 37, map, Feb., 1929.

DANGER OF OVER PROTECTION.(Moose on Isle Royale.) G.C.Toner. Carling Conserv. Digest, Toronto, vol.1, no.2, p.13, Apr., 1947.

AERIAL CENSUSING OF MOOSE AT BLACK BAY PENINSULA, ONTARIO. A. de Vos, G.C. Armstrong. Tech. Bull.Ontario Dept. Lands and Forests, Fish and Wildl. ser., no.3, pp.1-12, June 3, 1954.

Alces--Eurasia

ELK OF SIBERIA. Edgar N. Barclay. Ann. and Mag. Nat. Hist., London, ser.10, vol. 14, no.82, pp.447-448, Oct., 1934.

ON THE PRESENT CONDITION AND HABITS OF THE ELK IN NORWAY. H.J. Elwes.Proc. Zool. Soc. London, pp.133-151, figs.18-26, Feb. 3, 1903.

ON ONE OF THE OLDEST KNOWN REMAINS OF THE COMMON ELK, ALCES ALCES L., FOUND RECENTLY IN THE NETHERLANDS. D.P. Erdbrink. Geol. Munbouw, n.s., Jaarg.16, pp.301-309, illus., July, 1954.

(PRESENT-DAY STATUS OF THE EUROPEAN ELK (ALCES ALCES L. VAR.).) Der gegenwaertige Stand der Stangenelch-Frage (Alces alces (L) var.). V. Franz. Zool. Anzeiger, Leipzig, vol.125, nos.3-4, pp. 81-87, Feb. 1, 1939.

ELK IN POLAND. Wlodzimierz Korsak. Inst. for the Advancement of Sci., Warsaw, pp.47, figs.22, pl.1, Apr. 19, 1934.

EUROPEAN MOOSE-DEER (ALCES ALCES (L.)) OF POLAND, EAST PRUSSIA, AND BALTIC LANDS. Karel Kostron. Inst. Nat. Agronomique Brno, Bull. 1938: (D25), pp. 99, 1938.

ELK (ALCES MACHLIS, OGILBY) IN THE THAMES VALLEY. Edwin Tulley Newton. Quart. Jour. Geol. Soc. London, vol.59, pt.1, no.253, pp.80-89, pl.51, Feb. 10, 1903.

(ELK IN NORWAY.A STATISTICAL INVESTIGATION.) Elgen i Norge. En statistisk undersøkelse. O.Olstad. Skrifter Norske Vidensk.-Akad., Oslo, mat.-naturvidensk. kl., no.4, pp.1-123, figs.10, map, 1934.

(SIBERIAN ELK.) Sibirische Elche. B. Petri. Naturforscher, vol.9, no.12, pp.458-461, Mar., 1933.

(SKELETON OF ALCES LATIFRONS FROM THE ENVIRONS OF GOETTINGEN.) Ein Skelett von Alces latifrons aus der Gegend von Goettingen. H. Schmidt. Palaeontol. Zeitschr., vol.12, no.2, p.135, 1930.

(ON ELK IN THE USSR.) Ueber den Elch in USSR. B. Shitkov. Zeitschr. f. Saeugetierk., vol.11, no.1, pp.16-19, fig.1, Mar. 13, 1936.

(THE ELK). Älgen. Folke Skuncke. P.A. Norstedt and Sons, Stockholm, pp.400, 1949.

MOOSE IN MANCHURIA. A.de C.Sowerby. China Jour., vol.22, no.4, pp.203-204, illus., Apr., 1935.

SKELETON OF ELK (CERVUS ALCES) FROM NEASHAM NEAR DARLINGTON. C.T. Trechmann. Proc. Yorkshire Geol. Soc., Wakefield, England, vol.24, pt.2, pp.100-102, pl.14, Nov. 30, 1939.

HOW SHALL WE GET OUR MOOSE POPULATION PALMATED IN TYPE? Paavo Voipio. Suomen Riista, vol.7, pp.52-59, illus., 1952. (In Finnish with English summary.)

Alces--Habits, Behavior, Ecology

WINTER BROWSE UTILIZATION AND ACTIVITIES OF MOOSE ON THE SNAKE AND BUFFALO BOTTOMS OF JACKSON HOLE, WYOMING. Neil R. Bassett. MS thesis, Utah State Agr. Coll., 1951.

DIVING MOOSE. A.T. Blake. Field, London, vol.153, p.864, May 31, 1929.

NOTES ON WINTERING MOOSE. Robert C. Brown, James R. Simon. Wyo. Wild Life, vol.11, no.6, pp.4-8, 38, June, 1947.

EFFECT OF FOREST SUCCESSION UPON THE QUANTITY AND UPON THE NUTRITIVE VALUES OF WOODY PLANTS USED AS FOOD BY MOOSE. I. McT. Cowan et al. Can. Jour. Res., Sec.D, vol.28, no.5, pp. 249-271, Oct., 1950.

ECOLOGY, BEHAVIOR AND POPULATION DYNAMICS OF THE WYOMING OR ROCKY MOUNTAIN MOOSE, ALCES ALCES SHIRASI. Rollin H. Denniston II. Zoologica, New York Zool. Soc., vol.41, no.3, pp.105-118, Nov. 23, 1956.

RECORD OF MOOSE SPEED. James S. Findley. Jour. Mamm., vol.32, no.1, p.116, Feb. 15, 1951.

WINTER FOOD HABITS OF MOOSE IN JACKSON HOLE, WYOMING. C.Bryan Harry. Jour. Wildl. Mgt., vol.21, no.1, pp.53-57, Jan., 1957.

THE MOOSE AND ITS ECOLOGY. N.W. Hosley. U.S. Dept. Interior, Fish and Wildl. Serv., Wildl. Leaflet, no.312, pp. 51, Oct., 1949.

CUSINO'S CAPTIVE MOOSE. (Food, weights, and behavior.) Ford Kellum. Mich. Conserv., vol.10, no.7, pp.4-5, June, 1941.

BELLIGERENT MOOSE. Cariboo King. Beaver, Winnipeg, outfit 274, pp.40-41, Sep., 1943.

WINTER FOOD OF THE MOOSE IN FINLAND. Jukka Koskimies. Suomen Riista, vol.8, p.177, 1953. (In Finnish with English summary.)

NOTES ON THE HABITS OF THE MOOSE IN THE FAR NORTH OF BRITISH AMERICA IN 1865. J.G. Lockhart. Proc. Nat. Mus., vol.8, no.827, pp.305-308, 1890.

SOME FEEDING HABITS OF MOOSE IN YELLOWSTONE PARK. John E. McMillan. Ecology, Lancaster, vol.34, no.1, pp.102-110, Jan., 1953.

SUMMER FOOD HABITS OF MOOSE (ALCES AMERICANA SHIRASI NELSON) AND EFFECTS OF VARIOUS FACTORS ON FOOD SUPPLY IN YELLOWSTONE PARK. John F. McMillan. PhD thesis, Univ. Mich., 1950.

PRIVATE LIFE OF ALCES AMERICANUS. William J. McNulty. Forest and Stream, vol.98, no.2, pp.84-85, 122-123, Feb., 1928.

WINTER NOTES ON THE MOOSE. W.M. Newsom. Jour.Mamm., vol.18, no.3, pp. 347-349, Aug. 14, 1937.

(MOOSE AND THE FOREST.) Algen och skogen. Axel Olsson. Svensk Jakt, Stockholm, vol.88, no.9, pp.208-213, illus., Sep. 15, 1950.

LOOKING INTO THE PRIVATE LIFE OF MOOSE. Randolph L. Peterson. Proc.Royal Canadian Inst., Toronto, ser.3A, vol.14, pp.68-69, 1950.

STUDIES OF THE FOOD HABITS AND THE HABITAT OF MOOSE IN ONTARIO. Randolph L. Peterson. Contrib. Royal Ontario Mus. Zool. and Palaeontol., Toronto, no.36, pp. 49, illus., May 30, 1953.

MOOSE, WHERE IT LIVES AND HOW IT LIVES. Andrew J. Stone. (In) The Deer Family. 1902.

LARGEST DEER ON EARTH. (Moose habits and habitat.) William M. Rush. Fauna, vol. 8, no.2, pp.40-43, June, 1946.

MOOSE OBSERVED ON DESERT. Wyo. Wild Life, Cheyenne, vol.8, no.11, p.23, Nov., 1943.

Alces--Hunting

HUNTING THE WYOMING MOOSE. H.E. Anthony. (In) North Amer. Big Game. A Book of the Boone and Crocket Club, Compiled by the Committee on Records of N. Amer. Big Game. Charles Scribners Sons, New York, pp.278-284, 1939.

MOOSE VS THE "IRON HORSE". B.H. Atwood. Outdoor Amer., vol.17, no.2, pp.10-11, illus., Mar.-Apr., 1952.

HUNTING THE ALASKA MOOSE. William N. Beach. (In) N.Amer. Big Game. A Book of the Boone and Crocket Club, Compiled by the Committee on Records of N.Amer. Big Game. Charles Scribners Sons, New York, pp.272-278, 1939.

MOOSE HUNTING IN SWEDEN. Ingmar Bosaeus. N. Dak. Outdoors, vol.15, no.6, pp.6-7, 17, illus., Dec., 1952.

QUARRY OF THE FORESTS. HUNTING THE ELK IN SWEDEN. Patrick R.Chalmers. Field, London, vol.162, no.4211, p.646, figs., Sep. 9, 1933.

LET SLEEPING MOOSE LIE. Alton Cleland. Rod and Gun in Canada, Montreal, vol.45, no.8, pp.14-15, illus., Feb., 1945.

HUNTING MOOSE ON HORSEBACK. Capt.P. A. Curtis. Field and Stream, no.7, pp.30-31, 76-77, Nov., 1929.

LURE OF THE "BARK". MAKING THE BIRCH BARK TALK MOOSE LANGUAGE. B. Dale, Jr. Rod and Gun in Canada, Montreal, vol.45, no.4, pp.14, 24, illus., Sep., 1943.

MOOSE MEETS MAN. Frank Dufresne. Field and Stream, New York, vol.51, no.1, pp.20-21, 94-95, May, 1946.

MOOSE HUNT IN NOVA SCOTIA. G.T. Goldthwaite. Forest and Stream, vol.90, pp.638, 657-659, Dec., 1920.

MOOSE IN THE MUSKEG. Stephen Greenless. Rod and Gun in Canada, Montreal, vol. 45, no.8, pp.8-9, 22, illus., Jan., 1944.

ON THE VERMILION. A MOOSE HUNT IN THE HINTERLANDS OF CANADA. Alfred Horsch. Outdoor Life, vol.67, no.2, pp. 14-15, 78-80, Feb., 1931.

WILY OLD MOOSE. Will A. Johnson. Alaska Sportman, Ketchikan, vol.16, no.2, pp.16-17, illus., Feb., 1950.

OLD ROUND HOOF. (Moose.) Howard D. Kemp. Rod and Gun, Montreal, vol.47, no. 10, pp.14-15, Mar., 1946.

LEARNING FROM THE MOOSE. William J. Long. Sports Afield, New York, vol.123, no. 3, pp.26-27, 62-66, illus., Feb., 1950.

MOOSE IN ONTARIO. E.G.McDougall. Rod and Gun in Canada, vol.36, no.11, p.11, map, Apr., 1935.

BIG GAME HUNTING IN THE WILD WEST. III. MOOSE HUNTING EXPERIENCES. R.B. Marcy. Outing, Albany, vol.11, no.3, pp. 218-224, illus., Dec., 1887.

MOOSE ON THE SKYLINE. Jack O'Connor. Field and Stream, New York, vol.48, no.5, pp.32-33, 68, Sep., 1943.

(LOOKING FOR ELK IN FINLAND.) Auf Elche in Finnland. Fritz Anton Schifferer. Deutsche Jagd, Berlin, nos.50-51, pp. 659-661, Mar. 15, 1940.

HUNTING THE MOOSE IN NORTHERN MINNESOTA. P.E. Sheppard. Outdoor Life, Denver, vol.23, no.4, pp.345-350, photo, Apr., 1909.

(MOOSE HUNTING DAYS.) Algjaktsdagar. B. Stafas. Svensk Jakt, Stockholm, vol.89, no.12, pp.352-353, illus., Dec. 20, 1951.

MOOSE OF THE SUSITNA. Manley Sweazey. Alaska Sportsman, Ketchikan, vol.16, no.9, pp.10-11, 24-28, illus., Sep., 1950.

HUNTING THE CANADA MOOSE. F. C. Walcott. (In) N.Amer. Big Game. A Book of the Boone and Crocket Club, Compiled by the Committee on Records of N.Amer. Big Game. Charles Scribners Sons, New York, pp.266-272, 1939.

MOOSE HUNTING. Chas. C. Ward. N.Y., Scibner's Monthly, vol.15, no.4, pp.449-465, illus., Feb., 1878.

KNOW YOUR BIG GAME.--AMERICAN MOOSE. Walter J. Wilwerding. Sports Afield, Minneapolis, vol.122, no.5, pp. 36-37, illus., Nov., 1949.

MOOSE IN SASKATCHEWAN. Rod and Gun in Canada, Montreal, vol. 48, no.9, p.33, 1947.

MOOSE ON THE BASKATONG. Rod and Gun in Canada, Montreal, vol.50, no.6, pp.11, 22-25, illus., Nov., 1948.

Alces--In Captivity, Zoos

RAISING AND FEEDING OF MOOSE. Robert Bierwirth. Parks and Recreation Mag., vol. 37, no.3, pp.21-22, illus., Mar., 1954.

PROBLEM ANIMAL: THE MOOSE. AFTER MANY ATTEMPTS TO EXHIBIT THE LARGEST MEMBER OF THE DEER FAMILY THE ZOOLOGICAL PARK IS TRYING AGAIN. William Bridges. Animal Kingdom, New York, vol.45, no.6, pp.146-150, illus., Nov.-Dec., 1942.

MOTHERING A MOOSE. Paul Hidey. Our Dumb Animals, Norwood, vol.73, no.10, p.148, Oct., 1940.

Alces--Migrations, Movements

MIGRATION OF MOOSE. John Bauman. Yellowstone Nat. Notes, Yellowstone Park, vol.18, nos.5-6, p.33, May-June, 1941.

MIGRATIONS OF A MOOSE HERD. R. Y. Edwards, R.W. Ritchey. Jour. Mamm., vol. 37, no.4, pp.486-494, Jan. 9, 1957.

MOOSE WANDER FAR. Harry W. Poor. Bull. Massachusetts Audubon Soc., Boston, vol.29, no.1, pp.21-22, illus., Feb., 1945.

Alces--Mortality

TRAGEDY IN A MOOSE FAMILY. Thomas A. Denley. Amer. Game, Bull.Amer.Game Protective Assn., vol.17, p.94, illus., Nov., 1928.

STARVATION STALKS ISLE ROYAL MOOSE. Ben East. Amer. Forests, vol. 41, no.8, pp.370-372, 399, Aug., 1935.

Alces--North America

THE PRESENT STATUS OF MOOSE ON ISLE ROYAL. Shaler E. Aldous. L.W. Krefting. Trans. 11th N.Amer. Wildl.Conf., pp.296-306, 1946.

MOOSE--MAJESTIC ANIMAL OF THE NORTH AMERICAN CONTINENT. Albert Anderson. Minnesota Sportsmen's Digest, Minneapolis, vol.7, no.3, p.5, Sep.-Oct., 1946.

THE MOOSE. H.E. Anthony. (In) N.Amer. Big Game. A Book of the Boone and Crocket Club, Compiled by the Committee on Records of N. Amer. Big Game. Charles Scribners Sons, New York, pp.263-265, 1939.

MOOSE IN COLORADO. Alfred M. Bailey. Jour. Mamm., vol.21, no.1, p.96, Feb. 14, 1940.

OUR NORTH AMERICAN MOOSE. Vernon Bailey. Nature Mag., vol.33, no.5, pp. 269-272, May, 1940.

RECORDS OF MOOSE IN COLORADO. Alfred M. Bailey. Jour. Mamm., vol.25, no.2, pp.192-193, May 25, 1944.

ISLE ROYAL MOOSE HERD. A.K. Berger. Nat. Hist., New York, vol.34, no.7, p. 678, Nov., 1934.

RECORD OF NORTH AMERICA'S MOST WESTERLY MOOSE. James W. Brooks. Jour. Mamm., vol.34, no.3, pp.396-397, Aug. 14, 1953.

DISTRIBUTION AND ABUNDANCE OF MOOSE IN ALASKA. Edward F. Chatelain. (In) Science in Alaska 1952, Proc. 3rd Alaskan Sci. Conf., Alaska Div. AAAS, pp.134-136, Sep., 1954.

CERTAIN ASPECTS OF THE DEVELOPMENT AND BEHAVIOR OF THE WYOMING MOOSE--ALCES AMERICANA SHIRASI. R.H. Denniston. Anat. Record, Philadelphia, vol.105, no.3, pp.25-26, Nov., 1949. (Abstract.)

WOODLAND GIANT. (Moose.) Stuart C. Downing. Canadian Nature, Toronto, vol. 10, no.4, pp.120-121, pl.1, Sep.-Oct., 1948.

TOO MANY MOOSE. Frank Dufresne. Field and Stream, vol.57, no.5, pp.54-57, 115-116, illus., Sep., 1952.

LORD OF THE NORTHERN TRAILS.(Moose.) Ben East. Animal Kingdom, vol.49, no.5, pp.171-176, illus., Sep.-Oct., 1946.

IDENTITY OF THE BOWRON LAKE MOOSE OF BRITISH COLUMBIA. (Alces americana americana.) E.R. Hall. Murrelet, vol.17, no.1, p.17, Jan., 1936.

PRELIMINARY STUDIES ON THE MOOSE OF CENTRAL BRITISH COLUMBIA. James Hatter. MA thesis, Univ. B.C., 1947.

STATUS OF MOOSE IN NORTH AMERICA. James Hatter. Trans. 14th N.Amer. Wildl. Conf., Washington, pp.492-501, 1949.

STUDIES ON MOOSE IN THE INTERIOR OF BRITISH COLUMBIA. James Hatter. Northwest Sportsman, North Vancouver, vol.2, no.2, pp.9-10, Dec., 1946.

ISLE ROYAL MOOSE STUDIES. Paul F. Hickie. Proc. N.Amer. Wildl. Conf., Senate Committee Print, 74th Congress, 2nd Session, Wash., D.C., pp.396-398, GPO 1937.

MICHIGAN MOOSE. Paul F. Hickie. Mich. Dept. Conserv., Game Div., pp.57,

PRELIMINARY REPORT ON THE PAST AND PRESENT STATUS OF THE MOOSE, ALCES AMERICANA (CLINTON), IN MICHIGAN. Paul F. Hickie. Michigan Acad. Sci. Arts and Letters, vol.22, pp.629-639, tbl.1, 1937.

OUR AMERICAN MOOSE. Geo. B. Johnson. Va. Wildl., Blacksburg, vol.3, no.4, p.2, Dec., 1939.

WHAT IS THE FUTURE OF THE ISLE ROYALE MOOSE HERD? L. W. Krefting. Trans. 16th N. Amer. Wildl. Conf., pp. 461-470, 1951.

WHEN MOOSE WERE PLENTIFUL IN MINNESOTA. L.D. Lammon. Minnesota Div. Bull. Isaac Walton League, 4th Quarter, pp.17, Dec., 1945.

SIGHTS AND SOUNDS OF THE NORTH-WOODS. (Notes on the moose in Minnesota, pp.29-32.) D. Lange. The North Woods. Official Bull. Minnesota Forestry Assoc., vol.7, no.10, pp.24-32, Dec., 1919.

AN OLD BULL MOOSE. (In Alberta.) Allan McConnochie. Field, London, vol.161, no. 4192, p.931, fig., Apr. 29, 1933.

ROYALE VACATION. (Moose on Isle Royal.) Nat. W. McKelvey, Helen Hargreaves. American Forests, Wash., vol.54, no.7, pp.306-309, illus., July, 1948.

SOME OBSERVATIONS ON MOOSE IN YELLOWSTONE PARK. John F. McMillan. Amer. Midland Nat., vol.52, no.2, pp. 392-399, Oct., 1954.

A STRAY MOOSE. James W. McNaughton. Wisc. Conservationist, vol.3, no.6, p.12, Jan. (Mar.), 1922.

FUTURE OF MINNESOTA MOOSE. J. Manweiler. Conserv. Volunteer, vol.3, no.15, pp.38-43, Dec., 1941.

MOOSE IN WESTERN MASSACHUSETTS. Clifford B. Moore. Jour. Mamm., vol.25, no.3, p.310, Sep.8, 1944.

MOOSE OF ISLE ROYALE. Adolph Murie. Misc. Publ., Univ. Michigan, Mus.Zool., Ann Arbor, no.25, pp.44, pl.6, July 7, 1934.

MOOSE, OUR LARGEST DEER. Ralph S. Palmer. Bull. to the Schools, Univ.State New York, vol.41, no.7, pp.1-3 of cover, p.260, Mar., 1955.

SIDELIGHTS ON THE MOOSE. Archie Pendergraft. Wyoming Wild Life, Cheyenne, vol.10, no.4, pp.32-33, illus., Apr., 1946.

NORTH AMERICAN MOOSE. Randolph L. Peterson. Univ. Toronto Press, pp.xii+280, illus., 1955.

(Review by W. Robert Eadie of) NORTH AMERICAN MOOSE. Randolph L. Peterson. Jour. Mamm., vol.36, no.4, pp.575-576, Dec. 14, 1955.

(Review by R.Y. Edwards of) NORTH AMERICAN MOOSE. Randolph L. Peterson. Jour. Mamm., vol.36, no.4, 576-578, Dec. 14, 1955.

STUDY OF NORTH AMERICAN MOOSE WITH SPECIAL REFERENCE TO ONTARIO. Randolph L. Peterson. PhD thesis, Univ. Toronto, 1950.

NEWFOUNDLAND MOOSE. Douglas H. Pimlott. Trans. 18th N.Amer.Wildl.Conf., pp.563-579, maps, 1953.

BLACK MOOSE. Henry W. Shoemaker. Penna. Game News, Harrisburg, vol.18, no.7, pp.7, 25, 31, illus., Oct., 1947.

BLACK MOOSE IN PENNSYLVANIA. Henry W. Shoemaker. Altoona Tribune Co., p.45, photos, 1917.

MOOSE BECOMING A COMMON SIGHT IN YELLOWSTONE NATIONAL PARK. M.P. Skinner. Jour. Mamm., vol.8, no.2, p. 163, May, 1927.

MOOSE NOTES. Ken Stott, Jr. San Diego Zoonooz, vol.21, no.7, pp.3-4, illus., July, 1948.

MOOSE RECORDS FOR VERMONT. H.E. Warfel. Jour. Mamm., vol.18, no.4, p.519, Nov., 1937.

MONTANA MOOSE. Montana Wildl. Bull., Helena, vol.1, no.2, p.9, Mar., 1944.

THE MOOSE. Canadian Nature, Toronto, vol.1, no.2, p.29, Nov.-Dec., 1939.

MOOSE? Wisc. Conserv. Bull., Madison, vol.8, no.10, p.15, Oct., 1943.

SHIRAS MOOSE ALCES AMERICANUS SHIRASI. Wyo. Wild Life, Cheyenne, vol. 4, no.9, pp.6, 14, Sep., 1939.

Alces--Photography

FILMING MOOSE ON ISLE ROYALE. S.A. Barrett. Milwaukee Public Mus., Yearbook, vol.4, pp.47-59, illus., Oct. 9, 1926.

STALKING MOOSE. W.L.Finley, Irene Finley. Nature Mag., vol.6, pp.345-348, figs.4, pl.1, Dec., 1925.

TOO MUCH MOOSE. Arthur Newton Pack. Nature Mag., vol.13, pp.223-226, 259, illus., Apr., 1929. (Photographing moose in Glacier National Park.)

MOOSE MINDED. SOME HIGHLIGHTS OF SHOOTING THE ANTLERED MONARCH WITH A CAMERA. Eleanor B. Pack. Nature Mag., vol.22, no.1, pp.23-27, illus., July, 1933.

Alces--Physiology

(THERMOREGULATION IN MOOSE.) Osobyennosti tyermoryegulyatsii u losya. E.P. Knorre, E.K. Knorre. Zool. Zhurnal, Moscow, vol.32, no.1, pp.140-149, 1953.

Alces--Reproductive Biology

(ON THE BIRTH OF AN ELK IN THE BERNE ANIMAL PARK IN 1940.) Zur Elch-Geburt im Berner Tierpark 1940. H. Hediger. Zool. Garten, vol.14, nos.1-2, pp.14-23, illus., 1942.

LATE BREEDING IN MOOSE, ALCES ALCES. Gaston Moisan. Jour. Mamm., vol.37, no.2, p.300, June 9, 1956.

DEPRESSIONS FOUND ON MOOSE TRAILS AND THEIR SIGNIFICANCE. T.L.Tanton. Jour. Mamm., vol.1, no.3, pp.142-143, May, 1920.

OBSERVATIONS OF MOOSE COURTING BEHAVIOR. W.K. Thompson. Jour. Wildl. Mgt., Menasha, vol.13, no.3, p.313, July, 1949.

APPEARANCE OF A MOOSE RUTTING GROUND. Howard E. Woodin. Jour.Mamm., vol.37, no.3, pp.458-459, Sep. 11, 1956.

Alces--Skull and Antlers

(SOME CONTRIBUTIONS TO THE STUDY OF MOOSE ANTLER DEVELOPMENT.) Några bidrag till studiet av älghornens utvekling. Torsten Gardell. Svenska Jägareförbundets Tidskrift, Stockholm, vol.78, no. 8, pp.345-354, illus., 1940.

ANTLERS FOR JEFFERSON. Anna C. Jones. New England Quarterly, Baltimore, vol.12, no.2, pp.333-348, June, 1939.

SKULL AND ANTLERS OF AN ADULT MALE ELK FROM SIBERIA. R. Lydekker. Proc. Zool. Soc. London, vol.1, pt.1, pp. 107-109, fig.16, June, 1902.

ABNORMAL GROWTH OF MOOSE ANTLERS. Olaus J. Murie. Jour. Mamm., vol.9, no.1, p. 65, Feb., 1928.

(ON THREE JAMTLAND ELK ANTLERS IN NATURAL HISTORY MUSEUM AT GÖTEBORG.) Ueber drei jaemtlaendische Elchgeweihe im Naturhistorischen Museum zu Goeteborg. Orvar Nybelin. Zool. Garten, vol.14, nos.1-2, pp.23-25, illus., 1942.

RECORD MOOSE ANTLERS. Nat. Hist., New York, vol.43, no.1, p.51, illus., Jan., 1939.

(UNUSUAL FORM OF A MOOSE HORN.) Egendomlig form på älghorn. Svensk Jakt, Stockholm, vol.78, no.1, p.37, Jan. 15, 1940.

Alces--Taxonomy

REVIEW OF THE ELK OR MOOSE(ALCES GRAY) OF THE OLD WORLD. K.K.Flerov. Comptes Rendus Acad. Sci. USSR, pp.71-74, 1931.

NEW MOOSE FROM ALASKA. Gerrit S. Miller, Jr. Proc. Biol. Soc., Washington, vol.13, pp.57-59, May 29, 1899.

DESCRIPTION OF A NEW SUBSPECIES OF MOOSE FROM WYOMING. E.W.Nelson. Proc. Biol. Soc. Washington, vol.27, pp. 71-74, Apr. 25, 1914.

NEW SUBSPECIES OF MOOSE FROM NORTH AMERICA. (Alces americana andersoni.) Randolph L. Peterson. Occas. Papers Roy. Ontario Mus. Zool., Toronto, no.9, pp.7, May 25, 1950.

(ON ALCES PFIZENMAYERI AND TWO APPARENTLY NEW RACES OF ELK.) Ueber Alces pfizenmayeri und zwei anscheinend neue Rassen des Elches. Ludwig Zukowsky. Archiv f. Naturgesch., Jahrg.80, Abt. A, Heft 9, pp.33-45, pl.1, 1914.

Alces--Weights and Measurements

WEIGHTS OF A MINNESOTA MOOSE. W.J. Breckenridge. Jour. Mamm., vol.27, no.1, pp.90-91, Feb., 1946.

HOW MUCH DOES A MOOSE WEIGH? Geo. H. Lesser. Outdoor Life, New York, vol.103, no.1, pp.19, 88, Jan., 1949.

RECORD ALASKAN MOOSE (ALCES GIGAS). R.C. Morris. Jour. Bombay Nat. Hist. Soc., vol.41, no.2, pp.416-417, illus., Dec., 1939.

(A GIGANTIC ELK.) En jätteälg. Svensk Jakt, Stockholm, vol.78, no.1, pp.36-37, Jan. 15, 1940.

RECORD MOOSE HEAD TAKEN IN WYOMING. Wyo. Wild Life, Cheyenne, vol.6, no.2, p.7, Feb., 1941.

WYOMING HUNTER CLAIMS RECORD MOOSE HEAD. Wyo. Wild Life, Cheyenne, vol.10, no.5, p.22, May, 1946.

Alces--Young

LIFE WITH MOTHER. (Yellowstone moose calf.) Margaret Altmann. Animal Kingdom, New York Zool. Soc., vol.60, no.3, pp. 79-80, June, 1957.

PUGNACIOUS CALF MOOSE. Frank H. Anderson. Yellowstone Nat. Notes, vol. 10, nos.1-2, p.3, Jan.-Feb., 1933.

MOOSE BABIES. B. Dale, Jr. Field and Stream, New York, vol.45, no.12, pp.28-29, 99, illus., Apr., 1941.

TRIPLET ALASKAN MOOSE CALVES. N.W. Hosley, Frank S. Glaser. Jour. Mamm., vol.33, no.2, p.247, May 16, 1952.

(COW MOOSE WITH QUADRUPLETS?) Älgko med frylingar? Svensk Jakt, Stockholm, vol. 78, no.1, pp.35-36, Jan. 15, 1940.

Rangifer--General

PEARY CARIBOU (RANGIFER PEARYI ALLEN ). J.A. Allen. Bull. Amer.Nat. Hist., vol.24, pp.487-493, figs.1-12, May 22, 1908.

BARREN-GROUND CARIBOU. A.W.F.Banfield. Dept. Resources and Development, Ottawa, pp.vi+52, illus., mimeographed, 1951.

PRELIMINARY INVESTIGATION OF THE BARREN GROUND CARIBOU. PART I. FORMER AND PRESENT DISTRIBUTION, MIGRATIONS, AND STATUS. A.W.F. Banfield. Canadian Wildl. Serv., Wildl. Mgt. Bull., ser.1, no.10A, pp.iii+79, illus., 1954.

PROVISIONAL LIFE TABLE FOR THE BARREN GROUND CARIBOU. A.W.F. Banfield. Canadian Jour. Zool., vol.33, no.3, pp.143-147, graph, June, 1955.

SECOND REPORT ON THE BARREN-GROUND CARIBOU INVESTIGATION. A.W. F. Banfield. Arctic Cir., vol.5, no.4, pp. 43-44, 1952.

REINDEER OR CARIBOU OF THE UPPER MACMILLAN BASIN. Edgar N. Barclay. Proc. Zool. Soc. London, pt.2, pp.305-307, pls.2, July 4, 1935.

NOMADS OF THE NORTH. (Caribou.) Edwin J. Becker. Rod and Gun in Canada, Montreal, vol.49, no.2, pp.15-16, 43, 49, illus., July, 1947.

(REINDEER DOMESTICATION AND VARIATIONS.) Le renne, domestication et variations. Ed. Dechambre. Mammalia, Paris, vol.6, no.2, pp.74-81, June, 1942.

(ON THE SUBJECT OF RECENT RESEARCH ON THE ORIGIN OF THE REINDEER.) A propos de recherches récentes sur l'origine des rennes. Ch. Devillers. Mammalia, Paris, vol.5, nos.3-4, pp.110-112, Sep., 1941.

WOODLAND CARIBOU. Stuart C.Downing. Carling Conserv. Digest, Toronto, vol.2, no.1, pp.8-10, illus., First quarter, 1948.

THE CARIBOU. Daniel G. Elliot. (In) The Deer Family. 1902.

WE FLEW BACK 20,000 YEARS. (Barren Ground caribour.) Grancel Fitz. Field and Stream, New York, vol.54, no.1, pp.46-47, 142-145, illus., May, 1949.

MANNA IN THE WILDERNESS.(Caribou.) Philip H. Godsell. Rod and Gun in Canada, Gardenvale, vol.52, no.7, pp.12-13, 27-28, illus., Dec., 1950.

THE CARIBOU. Madison Grant. 7th Ann. Rep. N.Y. Zool. Soc., pp.24, illus., 1902.

IN CARIBOU LAND. Francis Harper. Nat. Hist., New York, vol.58, no.5, pp.224-231, 239-240, illus., May, 1949.

THE WORD CARIBOU. F.W.Hodge.Science, n.s., vol.68, p.513, Nov. 23, 1928.

(DISTRIBUTION OF REINDEER AND CONTINENTAL DRIFT.) Die Verbreitung der Rentiere und die Kontinentenverschiebung. A. Jacobi. X Congrès International de Zoologie tenu à Budapest, Sep.4-10, 1927, pt.2, pp.1372-1381, figs.7, 1929.

(THE REINDEER (A ZOOLOGICAL MONOGRAPH ON THE GENUS RANGIFER).) Das Rentier.(Eine Zoologische Monographie der Gattung Rangifer.) A. Jacobi. Akad. Verlagsgesellschaft m.b.H. Leipzig/1931-Ergaenzungsband zum Zoologischen Anzeiger, Bd.96, pp.1-264, text figs.32, pls. 6, 1931; (Review of this book, by Gerrit S. Miller, Jr., Jour.Mamm., vol.13, no.2, pp.173-174, May, 1932.)

(REINDEER.) Renskötseln. Hilding Johansson. Ymer (Tidsk.Svenska Sällsk.Antropol. Geogr.), Stockholm, nos.3-4, pp.403-420, figs.1-7, 1942.

SANTA CLAUS STUFF. (Reindeer.) D.B. Marsh. The Beaver, Winnipeg, Outfit no. 278, pp.16-18, illus., Dec., 1947.

("CRACKLING" IN A DEAD REINDEER.) "Knacken" beim toten Rentier. Erna W. Mohr. Biol. Zentralblatt, vol.46, pp.231-232, 1926.

BARREN GROUND CARIBOU. Olaus J. Murie. (In) N.Amer. Big Game. A Book of the Boone and Crocket Club, Compiled by the Committee on Records of N.Amer. Big Game. Charles Scribners Sons, New York, pp.239-246, 1939.

(RANGIFER TARANDS AND COMPARABLE TYPES.) Rangifer tarandus et formes rapprochées. M.V. Pavlow. Biulleton' Moskovskogo Obshchestva Ispytatelei Prirody. Otdel Geologicheskii (Bull. Soc. Naturalistes) Moscow, Sect.Geol., vol.5, no.2, pp.137-170, pls.1-2, 1927. (In French with Russian summary.)

ARCTIC CARIBOU. Edward A. Preble. National Nature News, Washington, D.C., vol.3, no.2, p.11, illus., Jan. 9, 1939.

CARIBOU OF THE ARCTIC. Edward A. Preble. Nat. Mag., vol.8, pp.218-222, illus., Oct., 1926.

AMONG THE CARIBOU-EATERS. J.Robinson. Beaver, Winnipeg, Outfit no.275, pp. 38-41, illus., Dec., 1944.

THE REINDEER. Ernst Schwarz. Nature Mag., Wash., D.C., vol.31, no.10, p. 580, Dec., 1938.

REINDEER. Kenneth E. Stager. Los Angelos County Mus. Quarterly, Los Angelos, vol. 5, no.4, pp.12-14, illus., Winter, 1946.

(ON THE DISTRIBUTION OF REINDEER IN THE PRESENT AND PAST ACCORDING TO THE EXTENT OF FOSSIL REMAINS, WITH SPECIAL CONSIDERATION OF GERMAN LOCALITIES WHERE DISCOVERIES HAVE BEEN MADE.) Ueber die Verbreitung des Renthiers in der Gegenwart und in aelterer Zeit nach Maassgabe seiner fossilen Reste unter besonderer Beruecksichtigung der deutschen Fundorte. C. Struckmann. Zeitschr. der Deutschen Geologischen Gesellschaft, pp.728-773, 1880.

WORD CARIBOU. L.B. Walton. Science, n.s., vol.68, pp.352-353, Oct. 12, 1928.

WORD "CARIBOU". A.H. Wright. Jour. Mamm., vol.10, no.4, pp.353-356, Nov., 1929.

REINDEER HERD INCREASING. Nature Notes, Peoria, Ill., vol.6, no.7, p.149, July, 1939.

WOODLAND CARIBOU. Carling Conserv. Digest, Toronto, vol.1, no.4, p.13, Oct., 1947.

Rangifer--Anatomy

(MANDIBLE OF THE REINDEER.) La mandibule du renne. J. Bouchud. Mammalia, Paris, vol.17, no.1, pp.27-49, illus., Mar., 1953.

(ON THE DENTAL DEVELOPMENT AND DETRITION IN THE REINDEER, COMPARED WITH THAT IN SOME OTHER CERVIDS.) Über Zahnentwicklung und Zahnabnutzung beim Rentier vergliechen mit denen bei einigen anderen Cerviden. (Studien an skandinavischen Zahm- und Wildrentieren.) F. Bromée-Skuncke. Arkiv. för Zoologi, Stockholm, n.s., vol.4, no.1, pp.1-43, 1952.

HISTOLOGICAL INVESTIGATIONS OF REINDEER MUSCLES INFECTED WITH SARCOCYSTIS. N.L. Justoff. Arctic Inst. USSR, the Soviet Reindeer Industry, vol. 9, pp.115-118, 1937. (In Russian with English summary.)

EXHIBITION OF HORNS OF THE CARIBOO (TARANDUS RANGIFER). Benjamin Leadbeater. Proc. Zo[illegible]. Soc. London, p.139, 1864.

NOTE ON A REINDEER SKULL FROM NOVAIA ZEMLIA. R. Lydekker. Proc. Zool. Soc. London, 1902, vol.2, pt.2, pp. 360-362, fig.77, Apr., 1903.

DETERMINING THE AGE OF REINDEER BY THE LOWER JAW MOLARS. A.F. Mishin. Sovetskii Sever, nos.7-8, pp.65-68, figs.12, 1930. (In Russian.)

(OBSERVATIONS ON THE SINUS CUTANEUS UNGULARUM IN THE REINDEER.) Beobachtungen ueber den Sinus cutaneus ungularum beim Renntier. V.I. Oksala. Anat.Anzeiger, vol.64, pp.129-139, figs.5, Nov. 15, 1927.

HISTOLOGY AND CYTOCHEMISTRY OF SKIN GLAND AREAS IN THE CARIBOU, RANGIFER. W.B. Quay. Jour. Mamm., vol.36, no.2, pp.187-201, pls.6, May 26, 1955.

ON THE EXTERNAL CHARACTERS OF FEOTAL REINDEER, AND OTHER NOTES. R.W. Shufeldt. Proc. Acad. Nat. Sci. Philadelphia, pp.224-233, figs.2, 1891.

SEXUAL, AGE AND RACIAL VARIATION OF SKULL OF WILD AND DOMESTICATED REINDEER. I.I. Sokolov. Arctic Inst.USSR, the Soviet Reindeer Industry, vol.9, pp.9-100, pls.1-5, 1937. (In Russian with English summary.)

ON THE MORBID APPEARANCES OF A REINDEER (CERVUS TARANDUS LINN.). W. Yarrell. Proc. Comm. Sci. and Corres. Zool. Soc. London, pt.1, p.14, 1830-1831.

Rangifer--Diseases and Parasites

PARASITES OF THE WOODLAND CARIBOU. Arnold B. Erickson, Paul R. Highby. Jour. Parasitology, vol.28, no.5, p.423, Oct., 1942.

(INFECTION OF THE NORTHERN REINDEER OF SAKHALIN BY NASAL GADFLY IN RELATION TO GROWTH OF VIBRISSAE.) Zarazhennost severnikh olenei o-va Sakhalin nosovim ovodom v zavisimosti ot razvitiya vibriss. I.P. Mishin. Zool. Zhurnal, Moscow, vol.33, no.1, pp.162-165, Jan.-Feb., 1954.

ON THE QUESTION OF SARCOCISTYS OF REINDEER. W.L. Yakimoff. Artic Inst. USSR, the Soviet Reindeer Industry, vol. 9, pp.107-113, 1937.

(ON THE PROBLEM OF PIROPLASMOSIS IN THE REINDEER.) Zur Frage ueber die Piroplasmose des Renntieres. W.L. Yakimoff, W.D. Kolmakoff. Archiv. f. Protistenkunde, vol.66, pp.322-328, pl.1, May 24, 1929.

Rangifer--Economic Importance and Management

REINDEER BREEDING ON NOVAYA ZEMLYA AND THE PROSPECTS OF ITS DEVELOPMENT. V.D. Alexandrova. Problemy Arkiki (Problems of the Arctic, Chief Administration of Northern Sea Route, Artic Inst. USSR), Leningrad, no.2, pp.71-87, fig.1, 1937.

CARIBOU CRISIS. A.W.F. Banfield. The Beaver, Canadian Wildl. Serv., pp.3-7, illus., Spring, 1956.

PLIGHT OF THE BARREN GROUND CARIBOU. A.W.F. Banfield. Oryx, Jour. Fauna Preservation Soc., vol.4, no.1, pp.5-20, pls., Apr., 1957.

REINDEER FOR THE ESKIMO. Allen J. Baxter. Forest and Outdoors, Montreal, vol.32, no.9, pp.301-302, illus., Oct., 1936.

REINDEER-BREEDING. ORIGIN, DEVELOPMENT AND PERSPECTIVES. W.Bogoras-Tan. Trudy Lab. Genet., Akad. Nauk, Leningrad, USSR, vol.1, pp.219-251, 1933.

CARIBOU ARE LOSING GROUND. Edna W. Chandler. Alaska Sportsman, Ketchikan, vol.9, no.8, pp.16-17, 28-29, illus., Aug., 943.

CANADA ADOPTS THE REINDEER. NEW SOURCE OF FOOD FOR THE DOMINION.

E.L. Chicanot. Field, London, vol.154, no.4002, p.369, Sep. 7, 1929.

FIGHT FOR THE WOODLAND CARIBOU. W.T. Cox. Amer. Forests, vol.47, no.2, pp.55-57, 93-94, Feb., 1941.

REINDEER FOR THE CANADIAN ESKIMO. O.S. Finnie. Nat. Hist., vol.31, no.4, pp.409-416, illus., July-Aug., 1931.

IMPORTANCE AND DEVELOPMENT OF THE REINDEER INDUSTRY IN ALASKA. Herbert C. Hanson. Jour. Range Mgt., vol. 5, no.4, pp.243-251, illus., July, 1952.

CARIBOU AND THE MEAT SHORTAGE. Wm. H. Hobbs. Science, Lancaster, n.s., vol.97, no.2521, p.377, Apr. 23, 1943.

REPORT ON INTRODUCTION OF DOMESTIC REINDEER INTO ALASKA. Sheldon Jackson. Seal and Salmon Fisheries and General Resources of Alaska, Wash., vol. 3, pp.565-682, 1898; U.S. Bur Educ., Senate Executive Doc., no.70, 53rd Congress, 2nd sess. (Whole no. 215), pp. 1-187, illus., maps, 1894; Senate Doc., no. 111, 54th Cong., 1st sess., pp.144, illus., 1896.

TENTH ANNUAL REPORT ON INTRODUCTION OF DOMESTIC REINDEER INTO ALASKA. Sheldon Jackson. Pp.169, illus., 1901.

TWELFTH ANNUAL REPORT ON INTRODUCTION OF DOMESTIC REINDEER INTO ALASKA. Sheldon Jackson. Pp.144, illus., 1902 (1903).

HISTORY OF THE EVER USEFUL REINDEER. MAN'S SUB-ARCTIC ALLY. F. de Laguna. Frontiers, Philadelphia, vol.3, no. 2, pp.48-54, Dec., 1938.

REINDEER INDUSTRY IN ALASKA. Margaret Lantis. Arctic, vol.3, no.1, pp.27-44, Apr., 1950.

CARIBOU FOR CHIPEWYANS. Douglas Leechman. The Beaver, Winnipeg, Outfit no. 278, pp.12-18, illus., Mar., 1948.

HEARINGS BEFORE THE COMMITTEE ON WAYS AND MEANS, HOUSE OF REPRESENTATIVES, ON REINDEER MEAT, JAN. 21, 1921. Carl J. Lomen. Tariff Information, Wash., Gov. Printing Office, pp.1-25, 1921.

ALL CARIBOU. (Utilization of caribou by Eskimo.) D.B. Marsh. Beaver, Winnipeg, Outfit no.273, pp.18-22, illus., Dec., 1942.

NOTES ON THE DOMESTICATION OF REINDEER. N.T. Mirov. Amer. Anthropol., Menasha, n.s., vol.47, no.3, pp.393-408, map, July-Sep., 1945.

(ON THE USE OF THE REINDEER'S SINEWS.) Om utnyttelse av renens sener. Leif R. Natvig. Tidsshrift Norske Landbruk, Oslo, vol.6, pp.12, figs.7, 1927.

IMPROVED REINDEER HANDLING. L.J. Palmer. Circular no. 82, U.S. Dept. Agric., pp.17, figs.2, Nov., 1929.

RAISING REINDEER IN ALASKA. L.J. Palmer. Misc. Publ. no.207, U.S. Dept. Agric., pp.40, figs.18, Nov., 1934.

PRESERVING THE NORWEGIAN REINDEER. C.V.A. Peel. Field, London, vol.156, no. 4046, p.63, July 12, 1930.

REINDEER INDUSTRY AND THE CANADIAN ESKIMO. Erling Porsild. Geogr. Jour., vol. 88, no.1, pp.1-19, pls.2, map 1, July, 1936.

REINDEER--AN INDIAN SERVICE CONTRIBUTION TO THE WAR. Clifford C. Presnall. Trans. 8th N. Amer. Wildl. Conf., Wash., D.C., pp.110-117, 1943.

REINDEER IN HARNESS. W.P. Pycraft. Illus. London News, London, vol.195, no. 5254, p.956, illus., Dec. 30, 1939.

GIVING THE REINDEER BACK TO THE ESKIMO. C.E. Rachford. Conservation, Amer. Forestry Assn., Wash., D.C., vol. 5, no.4, pp.20-23, July-Aug., 1939.

BASIC PRINCIPLES FOR THE PROTECTION OF THE BARREN GROUND CARIBOU AND REINDEER BREEDING IN QUEBEC. J. Rousseau. Ann. Rept. Prov. Quebec Assoc. Prot. Fish and Game, 1951, pp.28-35, 1953.

(PROBLEMS OF CONSERVATION OF UNGAVA AND LABRADOR.) Les problèmes de conservation de l'ungava et du labrador. J. Rousseau. Comptes Rendus Assn. Can. Cons., pp.51-79, 1952.

DEVELOPMENT OF REINDEER ACTIVITIES IN ALASKA. Albert L. Seeman. Economic Geography, vol.9, no.3, pp.292-302, figs. 13, July, 1933.

USE OF REINDEER ANTLERS FOR FORAGE. V.B. Sochava, L.V. Rosman. Arctic Inst. USSR, the Soviet Reindeer Industry, vol.9, pp.119-124, 1937. (In Russian with English summary.)

REINDEER RECIPES. Louise Stanley. U.S. Dept. Agric., Leaflet 48, pp.8, illus., 1929.

NEWFOUNDLAND CARIBOU LIBERATED IN NOVA SCOTIA. R.W. Tufts. Canadian Field-Nat., Ottawa, vol.53, no.8, p.123, Nov., 1939.

ABOUT THE QUALITY OF LEATHER TANNED OUT OF REINDEER SKINS. A.A. Voskresensky. Artic Inst. USSR, the Soviet Reindeer Industry, vol.9, pp.141-159, 1937. (In Russian with English summary.)

EDUCATION CAN HELP SAVE THE CARIBOU, COMMISSIONER SAYS. H.A. Young. News of the North, vol.6, no.27, p.2, 1950.

Rangifer--Eurasia

(OCCURRENCE OF REINDEER(RANGIFER TARANDUS L.) IN SWEDEN DURING THE POSTARCTIC EPOCH, AND A CONTRIBUTION TO KNOWLEDGE OF THE FIRST APPEARANCE OF MAN IN SWEDEN.) Das Vorkommen des Renntiers (Rangifer tarandus L.) in Schweden waehrend der postarktischen Zeit nebst einem Beitrag zur Kenntniss ueber das dortige erste Auftreten des Menschen. O. Isberg. Arkiv. f. Zoologi, vol. 21, no.12, pp.1-26, 1930.

(REINDEER BREEDING AND REINDEER PARASITES IN NORWAY.) Renntierzucht und Renntierparasiten in Norvegen. Leif Reinhardt Natvig. X Congrès International de Zoologie tenu a Budapest du 4 au 10 Sep. 1927, pp.272-300, illus., 1929.

FUTURE OF REINDEER IN SCOTLAND. M.N.P. Utsi. Oryx. vol.4, no.1, pp.40-42, Apr., 1957.

REINDEER RANGE IN ANADYRLAND. V.N. Vassiliev. Trans. Arctic Inst., Leningrad, vol.62, pp.9-104, figs.17, fold. map, 1936. (In Russian with English summary.)

WILD REINDEER IN NORWAY. Aage Wildhagen. Pap. Game Res., 8: pp.50-57, maps, graphs, 1952. (In Norwegian with English summary.)

SPITSBERGEN REINDEER (RANGIFER TARANDUS SPETSBERGENSIS). Alf Wollebaek. Skrifter om Svalbard og Ishavet, vol.1, no.4, pp.1-71, figs.16, pls.6, map, Apr. 23, 1926.

REINDEER BREEDING AND REINDEER PASTURE ON NOVAYA ZEMLYA. A.I. Zubokov. Trudy Arkticheskogo Instituta (Trans. Artic Inst.), Leningrad, vol.22, pp.7-34, figs.6, 1935. (In Russian with English summary.)

REINDEER OF NOVAYA ZEMLYA. A.I. Zubokov. Trudy Arkticheskogo Instituta (Trans. Arctic Inst.), Leningrad, vol.22, pp.55-61, 1935. (In Russian with English summary.)

Rangifer--Habits, Ecology

SUMMER FOOD OF THE REINDEER ON GUSSINAYA ZEMLYA (NOVAYA ZEMLYA). V.D. Aleksandrova. Trudy Arkticheskogo Instituta (Trans. Arctic Inst.), Leningrad, vol.22, pp.35-50, 1935. (In Russian with English summary.)

WINTER FORAGE OF REINDEER. V.D. Aleksandrova. Artic. Inst. USSR, the Soviet Reindeer Industry, vol.9, pp.127-139, 1937. (In Russian with English summary.)

ENEMIES OF THE CARIBOU. George Anderson. Beaver, Hudson's Bay Co., Winnipeg, Outfit 268, no.1, pp.30-32, illus., June, 1937.

PRELIMINARY INVESTIGATION OF THE BARREN GROUND CARIBOU. PART II. LIFE HISTORY, ECOLOGY, AND UTILIZATION. A.W.F. Banfield. Can. Wildl. Serv., Wildl. Mgt. Bull., Ser.1, no.10B, pp.iii+112, illus., 1954.

REINDEER-PASTURE IN THE CHUKCHEE ANADYR DISTRICT. I.V. Drury. Trans. Arctic Inst., Leningrad, vol.62, pp.105-124, figs.9, 1936. (In Russian with English summary.)

ON THE FOOD OF THE REINDEER. A.N. Formosov, L.N. Formosov. Moscow Univ. Sbornik Nauchno issledovatel'skogo Inst. Zool. (Abstract Works Zool. Inst. Moscow State Univ.), no.3, pp.115-115, 1936. (In Russian.)

REINDEER GRAZING. B.F. Heintzleman. The Western Range, 74th Cong., 2nd Sess., Senate Doc. 199, pp.581-598, 1936.

LICHEN WOODLAND IN LABRADOR AND THEIR IMPORTANCE AS WINTER PASTURES FOR DOMESTICATED REINDEER. Ilmari Hustich. Acta Geog., vol.12, pp.1-48, 1951.

CARIBOU CALVING STUDIES, 1951. John P. Kelsall. Arctic Cir., vol.6, no.1, p.6, 1953.

PROGRESS OF REINDEER GRAZING INVESTIGATIONS IN ALASKA. Lawrence J. Palmer. U.S. Dept. Agric., Dept. Bull., no.1423, pp.36, pls.18, 1926.

STUDY OF ALASKA TUNDRA WITH REFERENCE TO ITS REACTIONS TO REINDEER AND OTHER GRAZING. Lawrence J. Palmer, Charles H. Rouse. U.S. Dept. Interior, Fish and Wildl. Serv., Res. Rep., no.10, pp.48, 1945.

EFFECT OF CLIMATIC CHANGES ON THE REINDEER. G. Panin. Sovetskii Sever, nos. 7-8, pp.60-64, 1930. (In Russian.)

REINDEER AND CARIBOU GRAZING IN CANADA. A.E. Porsild. Trans. 7th N. Amer. Wildl. Conf., Wash., D.C., pp.381-391, 1942.

REINDEER PASTURES AND VEGETATION-COVER OF THE MURMAN DISTRICT. A.S. Salaskin et al. Trans. Arctic Inst., Leningrad, vol.72, pp.313, figs.13, fold. map, 1936. (In Russian with English summary.)

RELATIONS BETWEEN THE REINDEER AND ANIMAL LIFE OF THE TUNDRA AND FOREST. V.M. Sdobnikov. Trans. Arctic Inst., Leningrad, vol.24, pp.5-66, figs., (1934) 1935. (In Russian with English summary.)

Rangifer--Heredity

THE CASE OF AN INHERITED DEFORMITY IN REINDEER. E.V. Schmit. Arctic Inst. USSR, the Soviet Reindeer Industry, vol.9, pp.103-106, 1937. (In Russian with English summary.)

Rangifer--Hunting

REINDEER HUNTING TRIBES OF NORTHERN EUROPE. J.G.D. Clark. Antiquity, London, vol.12, no.46, pp.154-171, pls., June, 1938.

BIG CARIBOU ON THE TIMBERLINE. Paul Gartner. Outdoorsman, Columbus, vol.83, no.6, pp.8-9, 64, illus., Dec., 1941.

CARIBOU HUNT IN NEWFOUNDLAND. Charles B. Kelsey. Amer. Field Publ. Co., Chicago, pp.45, illus., 1910.

LEARNING FROM THE CARIBOU. Wm. J. Long. Sports Afield, Minneapolis, vol. 123, no.4, pp.26-27, 92-99, illus., Apr., 1950.

HUNTING THE MOUNTAIN AND THE BARREN GROUND CARIBOU. Carl. Rungius. (In) N. Amer. Big Game. A Book of the Boone and Crocket Club, Compiled by the Committee on Records of N. Amer. Big Game. Charles Scribners Sons, New York, pp.246-254, 1939.

CARIBOU HUNT ON PEARY'S 1898-1902 EXPEDITION. Clarence F. Wykoff. Arctic, Jour. Arctic Inst. N. Amer., Ottawa, vol.5, no.3, pp.178-182, illus., Oct., 1952.

NEWFOUNDLAND CARIBOU. Hunting and Fishing in Canada, Montreal, vol.13, no. 10, p.26, 1947.

Rangifer--Migrations, Movements

FIRE AND THE DECLINE OF A MOUNTAIN CARIBOU HERD. R.Y. Edwards. Jour. Wildl. Mgt., vol.18, no.4, pp.521-526, Oct., 1954.

MEAT. A STORY OF THE FOUR-YEAR TREK OF THE CANADIAN GOVERNMENT REINDEER HERD. Allen Roy Evans. Beaver, Winnipeg, Outfit 264, no.4, pp. 26-28, 64; Outfit 265, no.1, pp.24-27, ; no.2, pp.14-17, 64, illus., Mar., June, Sep., 1934.

NOTES ON REINDEER NOMADISM. Gudmund Hatt. Amer. Anthropological Assn., Memoirs, vol.6, no.4, pp.75-133, figs.10-11, 1917.

GREAT REINDEER MIGRATION. T.H. Inkster. Nature Notes, Peoria, vol.7, no.2, pp.43-44, Feb., 1940.

BARREN-GROUND CARIBOU MOVEMENTS IN THE CANADIAN ARCTIC. John P. Kelsall. Trans. 20th N. Amer. Wildl. Conf., pp.551-560, map, 1955.

NOTE ON THE MIGRATION OF THE BARREN GROUND CARIBOU. E.M. Kindle. Ottawa Nat., vol.31, pp.107-109, Dec., 1917.

WILD REINDEER OF SAKHALIN. (Movements.) I.P. Mishin. Priroda, no.1, p.120, 1952.

BIG REINDEER SWIM: 2,500 FOLLOW LEADERS ACROSS WIDE LAPLAND FJORD. Life, Chicago, vol.30, no.18, pp.118-119, illus., Apr. 30, 1951.

Rangifer--North America

CARIBOU OF BRITISH COLUMBIA AND ALASKA. J.A. Allen. Outing, pp.555-561, figs., 1902.

MOUNTAIN CARIBOU OF NORTHERN BRITISH COLUMBIA. J.A. Allen. Bull. Amer. Mus. Nat. Hist., vol.13, pp.1-18, figs.1-18, Apr. 3, 1900.

PRESENT STATUS OF NORTH AMERICAN CARIBOU. A.W.F. Banfield. Trans. 14th N. Amer. Wildl. Conf., Wash., pp.477-491, 1949.

REPORT ON CARIBOU INVESTIGATIONS IN THE CANADIAN ARCTIC, 1948-50. A.W.F. Banfield. Polar Record, Cambridge, England, vol.6, no.44, pp.532-534, July, 1952. (Summary.)

STATUS, ECOLOGY, AND UTILIZATION OF THE CONTINENTAL BARREN-GROUND CARIBOU (RANGIFER ARCTICUS ARCTICUS). A.W.F. Banfield. PhD thesis, Univ. Mich., 1951.

DEER OF THE NORTHERN BARRENS. (Reindeer in northern Canada.) W.J. Banks. Fauna, Philadelphia, vol.4, no.4, pp. 122-124, illus., Dec., 1942.

CANADA'S REINDEER FLOURISH. W.J. Banks. Our Dumb Animals, Norwood, vol. 76, no.5, p.86, May, 1943.

ALASKA'S REINDEER-CARIBOU. W.B. Bell. Amer. Forests and Forest Life, vol. 35, no.1, pp.17-20, illus., Jan., 1929.

CANADA'S REINDEER EXPERIMENT. R.H.G. Bonnycastle. Proc. N.Amer. Wildl. Conf., pp.424-427, 1936.

EXTINCT REINDEER OF EAST GREENLAND. RANGIFER TARANDUS EOGROENLANDICUS, SUBSP. NOV. COMPARED WITH REINDEER FROM OTHER ARCTIC REGIONS. Magnus Degerbøl. Acta Arctica, Copenhagen, vol.10, pp.1-66, map, pls.1-11, 1957.

ROMANCE OF THE NEWFOUNDLAND CARIBOU. AN INTIMATE ACCOUNT OF THE LIFE OF THE REINDEER OF NORTH AMERICA. A.R. Dugmore. London, W. Heinemann, pp.viii+191, illus., pls., fold. map, 1913.

CARIBOU OF THE KENAI PENINSULA, ALASKA. D.G. Elliot. Field Col. Mus. Publ., no.59, Zool. Ser., vol.3, no.5, pp.59-62, pls.11-13, July, 1901.

REINDEER IN ALASKA. Gilbert H. Grosvenor. Smiths. Inst., Ann. Rep., Wash., pp.613-623, pl.11, (1902) 1903; National Geographic Mag., vol.14, no.4, Apr., 1903.

REINDEER IN ALASKA. Seymour Hadwen, Lawrence J. Palmer. U.S. Dept. Agric. Bull., no.1089, pp.1-74, pls.1-24, Sep. 22, 1922.

CANADA'S REINDEER RANGE. H.J. Hargrave. Can. Cattlemen, vol.10, no.4, pp.226-227, 254, Mar., 1948; vol.11, no. 1, pp.24-25, 33, June, 1948.

RANGE RESOURCES OF THE FAR NORTH AND THE REINDEER HERD AT AKLAVIK, N.W.T. H.J. Hargrave. Jour. Range Mgt., vol.3, no.4, pp.281-282, July, 1951.

BARREN GROUND CARIBOU OF KEEWATIN. Francis Harper. Misc. Publ. Univ. Kansas Mus. Nat. Hist., Lawrence, no.6, pp.164, illus., Oct. 21, 1955.

REINDEER HERD. Richard N. Hourde. Beaver, Winnipeg, Outfit 267, no.4, pp. 26-29, illus., Mar., 1937.

REPORT ON INTRODUCTION OF DOMESTIC REINDEER INTO ALASKA, WITH MAPS AND ILLUSTRATIONS. Sheldon Jackson. 52nd Cong. 2nd Sess., Senate Misc. Doc., no.22, pp.1-39, illus., 1893.

CAMEL OF THE FROZEN DESERT. (Introduced reindeer in Alaska.) Carl J. Lomen. Nat. Geog. Mag., vol.36, pp.539-556, illus.19, Dec., 1919.

WOODLAND CARIBOU FROM SASKATCHEWAN. J. Manweiler. Parks and Recreation, vol.22, no.3, pp.134-138, Nov., 1938.

WILDS WHERE THE CARIBOU ROAM. Adolph Murie. Audubon Mag., Harrisburg, vol.44, no.1, pp.2-11, illus., Jan.-Feb., 1942.

ALASKA-YUKON CARIBOU. Olaus J. Murie. U.S. Dept. Agric., Biol. Survey, N.Amer. Faune, no.54, p.93, June, 1935.

CARIBOU IN GREENLAND. Alf E. Porsild. Arctic Circ., vol.4, no.4, pp.52-58, 1951.

REPORT OF THE INVESTIGATIONS OF THE ALASKA REINDEER COMMITTEE. C.E. Rachford. 76th Cong., 1st Session, Hearings before the Subcommittee of the Committee on Appropriations, House of Representatives, pt.2, pp.571-619, 1939.

WOODLAND CARIBOU AND --TIME. Paul B. Riis. Parks and Recreation, vol.21, no.10, pp.529-535, illus., June, 1938; vol.21, no.12, pp.639-645, illus., Aug., 1938; vol.22, no.1, pp.23-30, illus., Sep., 1938.

(CARIBOU AND REINDEER IN ARCTIC AND SEMI-ARCTIC QUÉBEC.) Le caribou et le renne dans le Québec arctique et hémiarctique. Jacques Rousseau. Rev. Canadienne Geo., vol.4, nos.3-4, pp.60-89, 1950.

(PROTECTION OF THE CARIBOU AND REARING OF REINDEER IN CANADA.) Protection du caribou et elevage du renne au Canada. Jacques Rousseau. Forêt Cons., vol.21, no.2, pp.12-14, Feb., 1955.

RISE AND FALL OF A REINDEER HERD. (Pribilof Islands.) Victor B. Scheffer. Sci. Monthly, vol.73, no.6, pp.356-362, illus., Dec., 1951.

RANGIFER DAWSONI, PRELIMINARY DESCRIPTION OF A NEW CARIBOU FROM QUEEN CHARLOTTE'S ISLANDS. Ernest Seton-Thompson. Ottawa Nat., vol.13, no.11, pp.257-261, pls.4-5, Feb., 1900.

DOMESTICATED REINDEER IN ALASKA. C.H. Townsend. Bull. Sool. Soc., New York, vol.16, no.60, pp.1045-1046, illus., Nov., 1913.

STATUS OF THE WOODLAND CARIBOU IN ONTARIO. A. de Vos. Sylva, vol.4, no.1, pp.17- 23, 1948.

REVIEW OF THE STATUS OF WOODLAND CARIBOU (RANGIFER CARIBOU) IN ONTARIO. A. de Vos, R.L. Peterson. Jour. Mamm., vol.32, no.3, pp.329-337, Aug., 1951.

CARIBOU INVESTIGATIONS IN THE CANADIAN ARCTIC, 1948-49. Polar Rec., Cambridge, vol.6, no.42, pp.253-255, July, 1951.

Rangifer-Taxonomy

DESCRIPTION OF A NEW CARIBOU FROM NORTHERN BRITISH COLUMBIA, AND REMARKS ON RANGIFER MONTANUS. J.A. Allen. Bull. Amer. Mus. Nat. Hist., vol.16, pp.149-158, figs.6, Apr. 16, 1902.

DESCRIPTIONS OF A NEW SPECIES OF CARIBOU FROM THE REGION OF THE ALASKA-YUKON BOUNDARY. (Rangifer mcguirei.) J.D. Figgins. Proc. Colorado Mus. Nat. Hist., pp.3, pls.2, Dec., 1919

BRIEF OUTLINE OF THE CLASSIFICATION AND GEOGRAPHICAL DISTRIBUTION OF THE REINDEERS OR CARIBOU OF THE OLD WORLD. K.K. Flerov. Publ. Acad. Sci. USSR, Yakutsk Ser., no.4, Leningrad, pp.1-15, figs.13, 1932.

REVIEW OF THE PALAEARCTIC REINDEER OR CARIBOU. K.K. Flerov. Jour. Mamm., vol.14, no.4, pp.328-338, figs.10, Nov., 1933.

GEOGRAPHICAL RACES OF ANIMALS WITH ESPECIAL REFERENCE TO REINDEER. S. Hadwen. Trans. Roy. Soc. Canada, ser.3, vol.26, sec.5, pp.237-256, figs.11, May, 1932.

TAXONOMIC NOTES ABOUT PALEARCTIC REINDEER. Einar Lonnberg. Arkiv. Zool., Upsala, vol.6, no.4, pp.1-18, figs.1-5, 1909.

RANGIFER CARIBOU AND ITS SUBSPECIES. W.C. Motley. Rod and Gun, Woodstock, Ontario, vol.29, pp.967-968, May, 1928.

PRELIMINARY DESCRIPTION OF A NEW CARIBOU. Ernest Seton-Thompson. The Ottawa Nat., vol.13, no.5, pp.129-130, Aug. 11, 1899.

Rangifer--United States

STATUS OF THE MINNESOTA CARIBOU. W.J. Breckenridge. Jour. Mamm., vol.16, no.4, pp.327-328, Nov., 1935.

CARIBOU ANTLER FROM THE LOWER PENINSULA OF MICHIGAN. Wm. H. Burt. Jour. Mamm., vol.23, no.2, p.214, May 14, 1942.

LAST STAND OF WOODLAND CARIBOU. W.T. Cox. Outdoor Amer., vol.2, nos.6-7, pp.4-5, 16, May-June, 1937.

WOODLAND CARIBOU IN MINNESOTA. W.T. Cox. Soil Conserv., vol.5, no.6, pp.138-143, 156, Dec., 1939.

CARIBOU TO MINNESOTA. J. Manweiler. Beaver, Winnipeg, Outfit 270, no.4, pp.14-17, illus., Mar., 1940.

MINNESOTA'S WOODLAND CARIBOU. J. Manweiler. Conserv. Volunteer, St.Paul, vol.1, no.4, pp.33-40, illus., Jan., 1941.

WOODLAND CARIBOU STUDY IN NORTHERN MINNESOTA. J. Manweiler. Parks and Recreation, vol.22, no.2, pp.74-78, Oct., 1938.

WOODLAND CARIBOU IN THE "BIG BOG". J. Manweiler. Minn. Conserv., vol.65, pp.16-17, 23, 30, Feb., 1939.

WOODLAND CARIBOU IN MINNESOTA. Urban C. Nelson. Jour. Wildl. Mgt., Menasha, vol.11, no.3, pp.283-284, July, 1947.

MOUNTAIN CARIBOU(RANGIFER MONTANUS) IN THE STATE OF WASHINGTON. H.C. Nickelsen. Murrelet, vol.19, nos.1-2, p.19, Jan.-May, 1938.

LATE RECORDS OF CARIBOU IN MAINE. Ralph S. Palmer. Jour. Mamm., vol.19, no.1, pp.37-43, Feb. 14, 1938.

RANGIFER CARIBOU IN MAINE IN 1946. Ralph S. Palmer. Jour. Mamm., vol.30, no.4, pp.437-438, Nov. 17, 1949.

WOODLAND CARIBOU AND --TIME. PT.2. HISTORIC AND PRESENT-DAY CARIBOU RANGE IN THE UNITED STATES. Paul B. Riis. Parks and Recreation, vol.21, no.11, pp.594-600, illus., July, 1938.

EARLY WINTER TRIP TO KATAHDIN. Edward S.C. Smith. Bull. Applachachian Mountain Club, vol.20, no.4, pp.493-

496, figs.4, Dec., 1926. (Records and photographs of woodland caribou.)

PRESENT STATUS OF THE WOODLAND CARIBOU IN MINNESOTA. Thaddeus Surber. Fins, Feathers and Fur, no.28, p.6, Dec., 1921.

MINNESOTA CARIBOU HERD. Gustav Swanson. Proc. N. Amer. Wildl. Conf., pp.416-419, 1936.

Giraffidae

(THE SEROLOGICAL RELATIONSHIP BETWEEN THE OKAPI AND THE GIRAFFE.) De la parenté sérologique de l'okapi et de la girafe. L. van den Berghe, G. Boné. Bull. Classe Sci. Acad. Roy. Belgique, Brussels, ser.5, vol.30 (1944), nos.4-6, pp.239-244, 1945.

(FAMILY GIRAFFIDAE, WITH SPECIAL CONSIDERATION OF THE FOSSIL FORMS FROM CHINA.) Die Familie Giraffidae mit besonderer Beruecksichtigung der fossilen Formen aus China. B. Bohlin. Palaeontologia Sinica, ser.C, vol.4, fasc.1, pp.5-178, pls.1-12, Sep., 1926.

SOME REMARKS ON FOSSIL GIRAFFIDAE. Birger Bohlin. Bull. Geol. Soc. China, vol. 14, no.1, pp.83-89, pl.1, Mar., 1935.

DISTRIBUTIONAL AND PHYLOGENETIC STUDIES ON INDIAN FOSSIL MAMMALS. V. THE CLASSIFICATION AND THE PHYLOGENY OF THE GIRAFFIDAE. Edwin H. Colbert. Amer. Mus. Novitates, no.800, pp.15, May 8, 1935.

GIRAFFE AND HIS LIVING ANCESTOR. Edwin H. Colbert. Nat. Hist., New York, vol.41, no.1, pp.47-50, 78, illus., Jan., 1938.

PALAEOTRAGUS IN THE TUNG GUR FORMATION OF MONGOLIA. Edwin H. Colbert. Amer. Mus. Novitates, no.874, pp.17, figs.7, July 24, 1936.

SKULL AND MANDIBLE OF GIRAFFOKERYX PUNJABIENSIS PILGRIM. Edwin H. Colbert. Amer. Mus. Novitates, no.632, pp.14, figs. 6, June 9, 1933.

WAS THE EXTINCT GIRAFFE (SIVATHERIUM) KNOWN TO THE EARLY SUMERIANS? Edwin H. Colbert. Amer. Anthropol., vol.38, no.4, pp.605-608, pls.21-22, Oct., 1936.

FOSSIL MAMMALS FROM THE MAKAPAN VALLEY, POTGIETERSRUST, III. GIRAFFIDAE. H.B.S. Cooke, L.H. Wells. S.African Jour. Sci., Johannesburg, vol.43, pp.232-235, fig.1, July, 1947.

VESTIGIAL METAPODIALS IN THE OKAPI AND GIRAFFE. F.C. Fraser. Proc. Zool. Soc. London, vol.121, pt.2, pp.315-317, pls.2, Aug., 1951.

(NOTES ON THE MAMMALS. 29) ON THE OKAPI AND THE AFFINITIES OF THE GIRAFFINES WITH THE ANTELOPES.) Notes sur les mammifères. 29. De l'Okapi et des affinités des Giraffidés avec les Antilopes. Serge Frechkop. Bull. Mus. Royal Hist. Belgique, Bruxelles, vol.22, no.1, pp.1-28, figs.12, Feb., 1946.

NEW FOSSIL GIRAFFE FROM MONGOLIA. (Samotherium mongoliense.) A. Y. Godina. Proc. Paleo. Inst., Acad. Sci. USSR, vol. 47, pp.172-180, illus., 1954.

(REMARKS ON THE FOSSIL GIRAFFINES OF AFRICA.) Remarques sur les giraffidés fossiles d'Afrique. L. Joleaud. Mammalia, Paris, vol.1, no.3, pp.85-96, illus., Mar., 1937.

ON CERTAIN POINTS IN THE STRUCTURE OF THE CERVICAL VERTEBRAE OF THE OKAPI AND THE GIRAFFE. Ray Lankester. Proc. Zool. Soc. Lond., pp.320-334, Sep., 1908.

CEREBRAL BLOOD SUPPLY IN THE GIRAFFIDAE. W.E. Lawrence, R.E. Rewell. Proc. Zool. Soc. London, vol.118, pt.1, pp. 202-212, May 20, 1948.

NEW BRAMATHERIUM SKULL. G. Edward Lewis. Bull. Geol. Soc. Amer. (Abstract), vol.49, no.12, pt.2, p.1915, Dec. 1, 1938; Amer. Jour. Science, New Haven, vol.237, no.4, pp.275-280, pl.2, Apr., 1939.

ON FOSSIL GIRAFFIDAE. C.J.F. Major. Proc. Zool. Soc. London, pp.319-320, 1891.

GIRAFFE AND OKAPI. "A LIVING SUMMARY OF EVOLUTION". Donald Marcy. Popular Ser., no.6, Dept. Education New York Zool. Soc., pp.8, illus., 1944.

Giraffes--General

DISCOVERY OF THE GIRAFFE IN SOUTH AFRICA. R. Bigalke. Fauna and Flora Transvaal, Pretoria, no.2, pp.24-28, illus., 1951.

(SOME EXPERIENCES ON A GIRAFFE HUNT.) Einige Erfahrungen aus einer Giraffenjagd. Ivar Broman. Zool. Garten, Leipzig, n.F., vol.10, nos.3-4, pp.84-94, figs.5, tbl.1, Sep., 1938.

SOUTH AFRICAN GIRAFFE. J. Guy Dollman. Nat. Hist. Mag., London, vol.2, no.10, pp.64-67, fig.1, Apr., 1929.

FIRST WHITE GIRAFFE SEEN IN KENYA: AN ADULT "ALBINO" BULL. Geo. Goodwin. Illus. London News, vol.194, no.5213, p. 421, illus., Mar. 18, 1939.

(TO AN UNKNOWN MEDAL (MEDALLION) ON THE SUBJECT OF THE GIRAFFE.) A une médaille inconnue au sujet de la girafe. A. Guillaumin. Bull. Mus. Nat. Hist. Nat. Paris, ser.2, vol.18, no.1, pp.41-42, fig.1, Jan., 1946.

THE MASAI GIRAFFE. Edmund Heller. Bull. Wash. Park Zool. Soc., Milwaukee, vol.2, no.1, pp.8-10, photo, Dec., 1931.

SACRED ANIMAL OF THE GOD SET. Ad.S. Jensen. Det. Kgl. Danske Videnskabernes Selskab. Biologiske Meddelelser, vol.11, no.5, pp.19, figs.9, 1934. (The "Set-animal" is identified as the giraffe.)

LONGNECKER FAMILY. (Giraffes.) W.E. King. San Diego Zoonooz, vol.20, no.1, pp.3-4, illus., Jan., 1947.

(HIGHEST ANIMAL OF OUR COLONIES: DRAWINGS AND GEOGRAPHICAL DISTRIBUTION OF THE GIRAFFE.) Vom hoechsten Tier unserer Kolonien: Zeichnungsmuster und geographische Verbreitung der Giraffe. Ingo Krumbiegel. Freude am Leben, Berlin, vol.17, no.2, pp.17-20, illus., May, 1940.

(GIRAFFE CROSSBREEDS.) Giraffenmischlinge. Ingo Krumbiegel. Zool. Garten, Leipzig, n.F., vol.18, nos.3-4, pp.109-114, 1951.

GIRAFFE AT HOME. Arthur Loveridge. Frontiers, Philadelphia, vol.10, no.1, pp.3, 26-27, Oct., 1945.

ON THE SUBSPECIES OF GIRAFFA CAMELOPARDALIS. R. Lydekker. Proc. Zool. Soc. London, vol.1, pt.1, pp.202-227, figs.24-37, pls.9-16, June 9, 1904.

SOME GIRAFFE NOTES AND PROBLEMS. C.T. Astley Maberly. African Life, Johannesburg, vol.9, no.4, pp.330-332, illus., Dec., 1955.

A WHITE GIRAFFE. D.S.A. McDougall. Field, London, vol.174, no.4534, p.1003, Nov. 18, 1939.

ON A YOUNG FEMALE KORDOFAN GIRAFFE. P. Chalmers Mitchell. Proc. Zool. Soc. London, pp.130-134, Sep., 1908.

NOTES ON THE REPRODUCTION OF A BARINGO GIRAFFE. Geo. H. Pournelle. Jour. Mamm., vol.36, no.4, p.574, Dec. 14, 1955.

(EXPERIENCES IN BREEDING GIRAFFES.) Erfahrungen bei der Giraffenzucht. M. Schlott. Zool. Garten, Leipzig, n.F., vol.19, no.5, pp.171-180, 1952.

(MAMMALOGICAL NOTES. THE GIRAFFES.) Notes Mammalogiques. Les girafes. A.F. de Seabra. Bull. Sec., Portugaise Sci. Nat., Lisbonne, vol.5, fasc.1, pp.27-34, figs.9, 1911.

WAS THIS THE OLDEST GIRAFFE? D. Seth-Smith. Field, London, vol.158, no. 4107, p.402, fig.1, Sep. 12, 1931.

SKYSCRAPER OF THE VELD. Ann M. Shire. Our Dumb Animals, Norwood, vol. 82, no.5, p.9, May, 1949.

HIGHBOYS. Ken Stott, Jr. Nat. Hist., New York, vol.59, no.4, pp.164-167, illus., Apr., 1950.

LETTER RELATIVE TO THE CAPTURE OF THE GIRAFFES. M. Thibaut. Proc. Zool. Soc. London, pt.4, p.9, 1836.

ON A NEW SUBSPECIES OF GIRAFFE FROM NIGERIA. Oldfield Thomas. Proc. Zool. Soc. London, pp.39-41, Feb.1, 1898.

EXHIBITION OF THE SKIN OF A GIRAFFE FROM SOMALILAND. Oldfield Thomas. Proc. Zool. Soc. London, pp.135-136, Feb. 20, 1894.

ON THE FIVE-HORNED GIRAFFE OBTAINED BY SIR HARRY JOHNSTON NEAR MOUNT ELGON. Oldfield Thomas. Proc. Zool. Soc. London, pp.474-483, figs.42-48, Nov. 19, 1901.

REMARKS ON THE EXISTING FORMS OF GIRAFFE. W.E. de Winton. Proc. Zool. Soc. London, no.28, pp.273-283, figs.4, Feb. 16, 1897.

EVOLUTION OF THE GIRAFFE. Frederic Wood-Jones. Nature, London, vol.164, no. 4164, p.323, Aug. 20, 1949.

SYMPHONY IN PATCHES. F.J. Worrall. Our Dumb Animals, Boston, vol.78, no.11, p.207, Nov., 1945. (Giraffe.)

Giraffes--Anatomy

ON THE LIVER AND GALL-BLADDER OF THE GIRAFFE. A.J.E. Cave. Proc. Zool. Soc. London, vol.120, pt.2, pp.381-393, figs.5, Aug. 30, 1950.

NOTES ON THE SPERMATOZOA OF THE GIRAFFE. G. Gulliver. Proc. Zool. Soc. London, pt.17, p.7, 1849.

(ORIGIN AND DEVELOPMENT OF THE MOST IMPORTANT MUSCLES OF THE FRONTAL EXTREMITIES OF THE MASSAI GIRAFFE. (GIRAFFA CAMELOPARDIS TIPPELSKIRCHI MTSCH. 1898.) Ursprung und Insertion der wichtigsten Muskeln der Vorderextremitaet der Massaigiraffe. (Giraffa camelopardis tippelskirchi Mtsch. 1898.) Friedrich Kuhlhorn. Anat. Anzeiger, Bd. 101, Heft 16-19, pp.237-242, illus., 1955.

ORIGIN OF THE LATERAL HORNS OF THE GIRAFFE IN FOETAL LIFE ON THE AREA OF THE PARIETAL BONES. E. Ray Lankester. Proc. Zool. Soc. London, pp. 100-115, figs.24-36, June 12, 1907.

PARALLEL HAIR-FRINGES AND COLOUR-STRIPING ON THE FACE OF THE FOETAL AND ADULT GIRAFFES. E. Ray Lankaster. Proc. Zool. Soc. London, pp.115-125, figs. 37-48, pl.5, June 12, 1907.

(MICROSCOPIC PICTURE OF A GIRAFFE HAIR.) Das mikroskopische Bild des Giraffenhaares. Th. Lochte. Zool. Garten, n.F., vol.19, no.5, pp.204-206, 1952.

(THE GLANDULAR URETHRA OF GIRAFFES.) L'urètre glandaire des girafes. Henri Neuville. Bull. Mus. Nat. Hist., Paris, ser.2, vol.7, no.6, pp.333-339, figs.2, Nov., 1935.

NOTES ON THE ANATOMY OF THE NUBIAN GIRAFFE. R. Owen. Proc. Zool. Soc. London, pt.6, pp.6-15, 20-22, 1838.

DESCRIPTION OF THE ORGANS OF DEGLUTITION IN THE GIRAFFE. R. Owen. Proc. Zool. Soc. London, pt.6, p.47, 1838.

EXHIBITION OF PHOTOGRAPHS OF GIRAFFES SHOWING THE DIFFERENCES IN MARKINGS BETWEEN TWO RECOGNIZED FORMS. Philip Lutley Sclater. Proc. Zool. Soc. London, pt.1, p.41, June, 1898.

SPINAL ACCESSORY NERVE OF THE GIRAFFE. S. Zuckerman, Francis Kiss. Proc. Zool. Soc. London, pt.3, pp.767-770, Sep., 1932.

Giraffes--Birth

PARTURITION OF THE NUBIAN GIRAFFE (GIRAFFA CAMELOPARDALIS.) Malcolm Davis. Jour. Mamm., vol.30, no.3, pp. 306-307, Aug. 17, 1949.

(OBSERVATIONS CONCERNING THE BIRTH AND GROWTH OF GIRAFFES.) Quelques observations concernant la naissance et la croissance de girafes (Giraffa camelopardalis antiquorum (Swainson)) au Jardin Zoologique d'Anvers. Agatha Gijzen. Mammalia, Paris, vol.1, pp.112-120, pl.5, Mar., 1958.

BIRTH OF A GIRAFFE. T. Koga. Parks and Recreation, Rockford, Ill., vol.22, no.9, pp.485, May, 1939.

(OBSERVATIONS DURING TWO GIRAFFE BIRTHS.) Beobachtungen waehrend zweier Giraffensgeburten. Ernst M. Lang. Saeugetierk. Mitteil., Stuttgart, vol.3, no.1, pp. 1-5, illus., Jan. 1, 1955.

BREEDING THE GIRAFFE (GIRAFFA CAMELOPARDALIS). Robert A. Patten. Australian Zoologist, Sydney, vol.9, pt.4, pp.452-454, Dec. 9, 1940.

Giraffes--Habits

(GAIT OF THE GIRAFFE, PARTICULARLY THE GALLOP.) Les allures de la girafe en particulier le galop. E. Bourdelle. Bull. Mus. Nat. Hist. Nat. Paris, ser.2, vol.6, no.4, pp.329-339, June, 1934.

DO GIRAFFES LIE DOWN? Estelle Brick. Field, London, vol.167, no.4348, p.956, illus., Apr. 25, 1936.

WHEN GIRAFFES TALK TOGETHER. Maurice Burton. Illus. London News, vol. 137, no.3581, p.1018, illus., Dec. 10, 1955.

FIGHTING BETWEEN BULL GIRAFFES. C.T.Astley Maberly. Field, London, vol. 158, no.4117, p.781, illus., Nov. 21, 1931.

Giraffes--Zoo Collections

(BERLIN ZOOLOGICAL GARDEN: GIRAFFE ACQUISITION AND BREEDING.) Giraffenfang und Giraffenzucht des Berliner Zoologischen Gartens. Lutz Heck. Zool. Garten, n.F., Leipzig, vol.9, no.5, pp.191-204, illus., Oct., 1937.

GIRAFFES IN THE ZOOLOGICAL GARDENS BELLE VUE, MANCHESTER 1929-1954. Gerald T. Iles. Zool. Garten, Leipzig, vol. 23, nos.1-3, pp.162-177, 1957.

(THE FIRST GIRAFFE IN SCHOENBRUNN.) Die erste Giraffe in Schoenbrunn. E.M. Kronfeld. Zool. Garten, n.F., Leipzig, vol.8, nos.7-9, pp.214-220, illus., June, 1936.

REPORT OF THE BIRTH OF A YOUNG MALE GIRAFFE, AND LIST OF GIRAFFES THAT HAVE LIVED IN THE SOCIETY'S GARDENS. Philip Lutley Sclater. Proc. Zool. Soc. London, pp.391-392, 1867.

Okapis--General

THE OKAPI. J.A. Allen. Amer. Mus. Jour., vol.11, no.2, pp.73-75, Mar., 1911.

CRITICAL STUDY OF HELMINTHES (PARASITES) FROM THE OKAPI.) Étude critique des helminthes parasites de l'okapi. Jean G. Baer. Acta Tropica, Basel, vol.7, no.2, pp.164-186, pls.1-5, 1950.

OKAPI EXPERIENCES. William Bridges. Animal Kingdom, New York, vol.50, no. 5, pp.154-157, illus., Sep.-Oct., (Oct.1), 1947.

(OKAPI--BIBLIOGRAPHY.) Okapi--Bibliographie. H. Bruhn. Acta Tropica, Basel, vol.7, no.2, pp.187-192, 1950.

(FIRST LIVING OKAPI IN EUROPE.) El primer okapi vivo en Europa. Angel Cabrera. Bol. Real Soc. española Hist. nat., vol.19, pp.443-445, fig.1, Oct., 1919.

(SOME PICTURES OF THE ANTWERP OKAPI (OKAPIA JOHNSTONI SCLATER).) Einige Bilder vom Antwerpener Okapi, Okapia johnstoni Sclater. Hans Caspary. Zool. Garten, Leipzig, n.F., vol.16, no. 5, pp.180-182, illus., 1950.

PHOTOGRAPHING AN OKAPI. Herbert P. Cinnamond. Field, London, vol.168, no. 4359, p.106, illus., July 11, 1936.

SULLA OKAPIA JOHNSTONI RAY LANKESTER. Giorgio Coen. Boll. Soc. Veneziana Storia Nat., vol.1, no.11, pp.210-214, pl.9, Apr. 16, 1938.

RELATIONSHIPS OF THE OKAPI. Edwin H. Colbert. Jour. Mamm., vol.19, no.1, pp.47-64, figs.3, Feb. 14, 1938.

(THE PHYSIO-PATHOLOGICAL FACTORS INFLUENCING THE ACCLIMATIZATION OF THE OKAPI.) Les facteurs physiopathologiques influencant l'acclimatation de l'okopi. L.M.G. Geurden. Bull. Soc. Roy. Zool. Anvers, no.3, pp.3-21, illus., 1953.

IN QUEST OF THE RARE OKAPI. Herbert Lang. New York Zool. Soc. Bull., vol.21, no.3, pp.1601-1614, May, 1918.

AN OKAPI REARED IN CAPTIVITY. A BELGIAN WOMAN FIRST TO ACHIEVE SUCCESS. Herbert Lang. Zool. Soc. Bull., New York, vol.22, pp.71-73, figs.1-2, July, 1919.

MONOGRAPH OF THE OKAPI: ATLAS. E. Ray Lankester. 1910.

NOTES ON THE GEOGRAPHICAL DISTRIBUTION OF THE OKAPI. Einar Lönnberg. Proc. Zool. Soc. London, vol.2, pp.309-310, Apr. 5, 1906.

(THE OKAPI. A NEW RUMINANT FROM CONGO.) L'okapi. Nouveau ruminant du haut bassin du Congo. A. Menegaux. Rev. des Idées, Paris, ann. 2, no.23, pp.831-838, pls.2, Nov. 15, 1905.

RELATIONS OF OKAPIA. Henry Fairfield Osborn. Science, Lancaster, vol.16, no. 410, pp.751-752, Nov. 7, 1902.

THE OKAPI. R.I. Pocock. Zoo Life, Zoological Society of London, vol.1, no.1, pp.2-7, illus., Spring, 1946.

(SOME IMPRESSIONS OF THE OKAPI (OKAPIA JOHNSTONI SCLATER).) Einige Eindruecke vom Okapi, Okapia johnstoni Sclater. Karl Max Schneider. Zool.Garten, Leipzig, n.F., vol.16, no.5, pp.182-185, 1950.

(THE OKAPI.) Das Okapi. Ernst Schwarz. Zool. Garten, vol.3, nos.4-8, pp.154-158, figs.5, May 2, 1930.

(A CONCISE REVIEW OF THE PRESENT STATUS OF THE OKPAI.) Beknopt overzicht der huidige omtrent de Okapi (okapia Johnstoni ). A. Vandermander. Landbouwkundig Tijdschrift voor Belgish-Congo, vol.39, no.3, pp.677-697, 1948.

(SUCCINCT REVIEW OF OUR PRESENT KNOWLEDGE OF THE OKAPI.) Apercu succint de nos connaissances actuelles au sujet de l'okopi. A. Vandermander. Bull. Soc. Roy. Zool. Anvers, vol.3, pp.22-43, illus., 1953.

ODD OKAPI, RARE RELATIVE OF EQUALLY CURIOUS GIRAFFE. Field Mus. News, Chicago, vol.13, no.4, p.5, illus., Apr., 1942.

Okapis--Africa

OKAPIA. Julien Jean Joseoh Fraipont. Bruxelles (Impr. veuve Monnom) pp.118, map, 1907. (Annales du Musée du Congo, Zoologie, sér.11, Contributions à la faune du Congo, t.1.)

VISIT TO BROTHER JOSEPH. (Missionary who reared okapis in the Belgian Congo.) William Bridges. Animal Kingdom, New York, vol.50, no.2, pp.37-44, illus., Mar.-Apr., 1947.

HUNTING THE RARE OKAPI. IN THE PIGMY COUNTRY WITH THE W.D. CAMPBELL AFRICAN EXPEDITION OF THE AMERICAN MUSEUM OF NATURAL HISTORY. William D. Campbell. Nat. Hist., New York, vol. 39, pp.116-119, illus., Feb., 1937.

CAPTURING OKAPIS. ADVENTURES IN SEARCH OF AFRICA'S RAREST ANIMAL: A QUEST ACHIEVED, WITH THE HELP OF PYGMIES, BY SIMULATING THE FALL OF A GIANT TREE. Attilio Gatti. Illus. London News, vol.185, no.4895, pp.693-736, illus., Nov. 3, 1934.

ON THE TRACK OF THE ONCE "MYSTICAL" OKAPI: ADVENTURES IN EQUATORIAL FORESTS OF AFRICA TO GET FOR THE "ZOO" ITS FIRST OKAPIS; HAUNTS AND HABITS OF AN EXTREMELY ELUSIVE ANIMAL; AND ITS PYGMY HUNTERS. Attilio Gatti. Illus. London News, vol.185, no.4986, pp.747-749, 778, 780, illus., Nov. 10, 1934.

(WITH PYGMIES ON THE OKAPI HUNT.) Mit Pygmäen auf Okapi-Fang. Attilio Gatti. Die Umschau, Frankfurt, Jahrg.39, no.14, pp.260-265, figs.1-7, Apr. 1, 1935.

CONGO OKAPI. Attilio Gatti. Nature Mag., vol.30, no.1, pp.15-18, illus., July, 1937.

OKAPI IN THE BELGIAN CONGO. Ida F. Illingworth. Field, London, vol.168, no. 4378, p.1298, illus., Nov. 21, 1936.

THE OKAPI. NEWLY-DISCOVERED BEAST LIVING IN CENTRAL AFRICA. Harry H. Johnston. McClure's Mag., vol.17, no. 5, pp.497-501, figs., col.pl., Sep., 1901.

Okapis--Anatomy

(PECTORAL MUSCLES OF THE OKAPI.) Les muscles pectoraux de l'Okapi. E. Bourdelle. Bull. Mus. Nat. Hist. Nat., Paris, ser.2, vol.11, no.6, pp.513-518, fig.1, Dec., 1939.

(THE OKAPI EYE.) Das Auge des Okapi. R. Bruckner. Acta Tropica, Basel, vol.7, no.2, pp.123-132, figs.9, tbl.1, 1950.

DESCRIPTION OF THE STOMACH, INTESTINE, LIVER, AND PANCREASE OF THE OKAPI, OKAPIA JOHNSTONI, SCL. R.H. Burne. Proc. Zool. Soc. London, vol.109, ser.B, pts.3-4, pp.451-479, figs.3, pls.2, Dec., 1939.

BRAIN OF THE OKAPI. W.E. Le Gros Clark. Proc. Zool. Soc. London, vol.109, ser.B, Syst. and Morphol., pt.2, pp.153-159, figs. 4, Aug., 1939.

(ANATOMICAL INVESTIGATIONS OF THE OKAPI, OKAPIA JOHNSTONI SCL. III) THE SPLEEN.) Recherches anatomiques sur l'Okapi, Okapia johnstoni Scl. III. La Rate. J.M. Derscheid. (1924) 1925.

(RUDIMENTARY METAPODIALS IN THE OKAPI.) Rudimentaere Metapodien beim Okapi. Walter Koch. Zeitschr. f. Saeugetierk., Berlin, vol.10, pp.148-150, figs.2, 1935.

ON THE EXISTENCE OF RUDIMENTARY ANTLERS IN THE OKAPI. E. Ray Lankester. Proc. Zool. Soc. London, pp.126-135, figs.49-55, pls.6-7, June 12, 1907.

(ANATOMICAL INVESTIGATIONS OF THE OKAPI (OKAPIA JOHNSTONI SCL.).) Recherches anatomiques sur l'Okapi, Okapia johnstoni Scl. H.Neuville, J.M.Derscheid. Rev. Zool. Bot. Afr., vol.16, no.4, pp. 373-419, figs.1-19, Apr. 1, 1929.

PRELIMINARY NOTE ON A NEW POINT IN THE STRUCTURE OF THE FEET OF THE OKAPI. R.I. Pocock. Proc. Zool. Soc. London, pt.2, pp.583-586, figs.2, July 20, 1936.

SOME ADDITIONAL EXTERNAL CHARACTERS OF THE OKAPI (OKAPIA JOHNSTONI) THAT DIED IN THE SOCIETY'S GARDENS. R.I. Pocock. Proc. Zool. Soc. London, ser.B, vol.113, 1943, pp.31-35, figs.3, July, 1943.

Okapis--Habits, Behavior

(BEHAVIOR AND OESTRUS IN OKAPIS IN EPULU.) Haltung und Brunst von Okapia in Equlu. Ernst M. Lang. Saeugetierk. Mitteil., Stuttgart, vol.4, no.2, pp.49-52, illus., Apr. 1, 1956.

(VOCAL CONTACT BETWEEN OKAPIS.) Stimmlicher Kontakt von Okapis untereinander. Ernst M. Lang. Saeugetierk. Mitteil., vol.5, no.4, p.171, Dec. 1, 1957.

(ON THE GENITAL FUNCTION AND BIRTH OF AN OKAPI.) Remarques sur la fonction génitale et la naissance d'un okapi. J. Nouvel. Mammalia, Paris, vol.22, no.1, pp.107-111, Mar., 1958.

Okapis-- Zoo Collections

OKAPI COMES TO THE ZOOLOGICAL PARK. FOR THE FIRST TIME THE NEW WORLD SEES THE LIVING LINK BETWEEN THE EXTINCT SAMOTHERIUM AND THE MODERN GIRAFFE. William Bridges. Bull. New York Zool. Soc., vol. 40, no.5, pp.135-147, figs.13, Sep.-Oct., 1937.

(OKAPI AT THE VINCENNES ZOO.) Un Okapi au zoo de Vincennes. P. Rode. Mammalia, Paris, vol.12, nos.1-2, pp. 45-46, pl.1, Mar.-June, 1948.

AN OKAPI AT THE ZOO. David Seth-Smith. Field, London, vol.166, no.4310, p.257 illus., Aug. 3, 1935.

THE ZOO'S OKAPI. David Seth-Smith. Field, London, vol.166, no.4312, p.385, illus., Aug. 17, 1935.

(ACCLIMATIZATION OF OKAPIS AT LONDON AND COPENHAGEN.) L'acclimatation des okopis a Londres et Copenhague. M.M. C.S. Webb, A.Reventlow. Bull.Soc.Roy. Zool. Anvers, vol.3, pp.45-54, illus., 1953.

FIRST PAIR OF LIVING OKAPIS TO BE SEEN IN EUROPE. Illus. London News, vol.181, no.4878, p.575, illus., Oct. 15, 1932.

ONLY OKAPI PAIR IN EUROPE (LONDON). Illus. London News, vol. 215, no.5754, p. 159, illus., July 30, 1949.

MUYONI, OUR NEW FEMALE OKAPI. Ralph Graham. Animal Kingdom, New York Zool. Soc., vol.59, no.6, pp.162-169, illus., Nov., 1956.

OKAPI. John D. Hamlyn. Hamlyn's Mag., vol.5, no.4, pp.25-27, Aug., 1919.

(FEW OBSERVATIONS ON THE COPENHAGEN OKAPI.) Kleine Beobachtungen am Kopenhagener Okapi. Erna Mohr. Zool. Garten, Leipzig, n.F., vol.20, nos.2-3, pp.73-76, illus., 1953.

CONGO'S OKAPI IS HERE! Geo. H.Pournelle. Zoonooz, Zool. Soc. San Diego, vol.30, no.1, pp.1-5, illus., Jan., 1957.

OUR OKAPI, "CONGO". Claude W.Leister. New York Zool. Park School News, vol.3, no.6, pp.1-2, illus., Nov., 1938.

## Antilocapridae

THE PRONGHORN. H.E. Anthony. (In) N.Amer. Big Game. A Book of the Boone and Crocket Club, Compiled by the Committee on Records of N.Amer. Big Game. Charles Scribners Sons, New York, pp.333-336, 1939.

ANTELOPE--OUR OWN PECULIAR GAME ANIMAL. Will C. Barnes. Producer, Denver, vol.9, no.8, pp.5-8, illus., Jan., 1928.

ANTELOPE AGEING STUDIES IN MONTANA. Sumner A. Dow. Proc. 32nd Ann. Conf. Western Assn. State Game and Fish Comm., Glacier Nat. Park, Mont., June 15-17, 1952, pp.220-224, 1953.

PRONGHORN ANTELOPE AND ITS MANAGEMENT. Arthur S. Einarsen. Wildl. Mgt. Inst., Washington, pp.239, illus., 1948.

PRONGHORN ANTELOPE. Geo. Bird Grinnell. Jour. Mamm., vol.10, no.2, pp.135-141, May, 1929.

AMERICAN PRONG-HORNED ANTELOPE (ANTILOCAPRA AMERICANA) WITH SPECIAL REFERENCE TO THE HISTORY OF A PAIR AND THEIR PROGENY AT THE MILWAUKEE ZOOLOGICAL GARDEN. Edmund Heller. Bull. Wash. Park Zool. Soc. of Milwaukee, vol.1, no.4, pp.1-8, illus., May-June, 1930.

HOW TO DISTINGUISH AN ANTELOPE DOE. Daniel W. Lay. Texas Game and Fish, Austin, vol.3, no.10, pp. 7, 25, illus., Sep., 1945.

ANTELOPES IN RETROSPECT. Claude W. Leister. Bull. New York Zool. Soc., vol. 41, no.3, pp.75-93, illus., May-June, 1938.

PRONGHORN OF NORTH AMERICA. Claude W. Leister. Bull. New York Zool. Soc., vol.35, no.6, pp.183-194, figs., Nov.-Dec., 1932.

FASTEST ON FOUR FEET. (Antelope.) Dan McCowan. Beaver, Winnipeg, Outfit 277, pp.36-39, illus., Mar., 1947.

PRONGHORN ANTELOPE. Donald D. McLean. Colorado Conserv. Comments, Denver, vol.8, no.3, pp.11-12, Sep. 15, 1945.

PRONGHORN OF THE PLAINS. Enos A. Mills. Sat. Even.Post, vol.191, no.45, pp.62, 65, May 10 (8), 1919.

CHOKECHERRY TOXIC TO AN ANTELOPE. Stanley Ogilvie. Jour. Mamm., vol.36, no. 1, p.146, Feb., 1955.

PRONGHORN PROFILE. Stanley Ogilvie. Colorado Conserv., vol.3, no.4, pp.22-24, illus., July, 1954.

SIDELIGHTS ON THE PRONGHORN ANTELOPE. Archie Pendergraft. Texas Game and Fish, Austin, vol.4, no.7, p. 22, illus., June, 1946.

RARITY OF THE RANGE.(Pronghorn.) Jack Richard. Nat. Mag., Wash., D.C., vol.33, no.7, pp.398-400, illus., Aug.-Sep., 1940.

AMERICAN PRONGHORN. William M. Rush. Nat. Hist., New York, vol.53, no.7, pp.321-323, illus., Sep., 1944.

UN-PREDICTABLE PRONGHORNS. John G. Samson. New Mexico Mag., Albuquerque, vol.28, no.10, pp.27, 49-51, illus., Oct., 1950.

PRONGHORN, THE ANTELOPE. W.J. Schoonmaker. National Humane Review, Albany, vol.31, no.12, pp.24-25, illus., Dec., 1943.

NOTICE OF A PRONGHORNED ANTELOPE ADDED TO THE SOCIETY'S MENAGERIE. Philip Lutley Sclater. Proc. Zool. Soc. London, p.60, 1865.

COUNTRY OF THE ANTELOPE. Grace V. Sharritt. Nature Mag., Wash., vol.43, no. 8, pp.405-407, illus., Oct., 1950.

SEE HOW THEY RUN. H.H. Sheldon. Western Sportsman, Denver, vol.7, no.1, pp.24-25, illus., June, 1941.

AMERICAN ANTELOPE. Clarence R. Shoemaker. Amer. Forestry, vol.26, pp. 747-754, figs.13, Dec., 1920.

PRONGHORN. M.P. Skinner. Jour.Mamm., vol.3, no.2, pp.82-105, pls.4, May, 1922.

ACRES OF ANTELOPE. F. Homer Tegler. New Mexico Mag., Santa Fe, vol.18, no. 10, pp.22, 33-34, Oct., 1940.

ANTELOPE. Jay R. Udy. Utah Fish and Game Bull., Salt Lake City, vol.8, no.4, pp.1-3, May, 1949.

AMERICAN ANTELOPE. S.W.Williston. Amer. Nat., vol.11, no.10, pp.599-603, Oct., 1877.

KNOW YOUR BIG GAME. AMERICAN PRONGHORN, ANTILOCAPRA AMERICANA. Walter J. Wilwerding. Sports Afield, Minneapolis, vol.122, no.2, pp. 36-37, illus., Aug., 1949.

ANTILOCAPRA AMERICANA, THE PRONGHORN. Sci. Monthly, Lancaster, vol.77, no.5, p.232, Nov., 1953.

PRONGHORN ANTELOPE ANTILOCAPRA AMERICANA. Wyo. Wild Life, Cheyenne, vol.4, no.8, pp.6, 17, Aug., 1939.

PRONGHORNED ANTELOPE. S.Dakota Conserv. Digest, Pierre, vol.11, no.9, p. 16, illus., Sep., 1944.

### Anatomy

PLACENTATION OF THE PRONGHORNED ANTELOPE (ANTILOCAPRA AMERICANA). Geo. B. Wislocki, D. Fawcett. Bull.Mus. Zool., Cambridge, vol.101, no.5, pp.545-559, illus., 1949.

### Censuses

ANNUAL ANTELOPE CENSUS COMPLETED SEPTEMBER, 1945. Roy N. Bach. N.Dakota Outdoors, Grand Forks, vol.8, no.4, p.8, Oct., 1945.

WYOMINGS'S 1950 ANTELOPE CENSUS. Floyd M. Blunt. Wyo. Wild Life, vol.14, no.4, pp.8-13, 36-37, May, 1950.

CENSUS OF THE PRONGHORN. Claude W. Leister. Bull. New York Zool. Soc., vol. 35, no.6, pp.185-194, figs., Nov.-Dec., 1932.

1950 SUMMER ANTELOPE CENSUS. William T. McKean. N.Dakota Outdoors, Bismarck, vol.13, no.3, p.12, Sep., 1950.

NORTH DAKOTA ANTELOPE CENSUS FOR 1947-1948. William T. McKean. N.Dakota Outdoors, Grand Forks, vol.11, no.7, p.6, Jan., 1949.

AERIAL CENSUS OF INTERSTATE ANTELOPE HERDS OF CALIFORNIA, IDAHO, NEVADA, AND OREGON. Leonard M. Springer. Jour. Wildl. Mgt., vol.14, no.3, pp.295-298, July, 1950.

NORTH DAKOTA ANTELOPE CENSUS FOR 1946. Russell Stuart. N.Dakota Outdoors, vol.9, no.7, pp.13-14, Jan., 1947.

STATE-WIDE RECONNAISSANCE, JULY-AUGUST, 1939. Herbert S. Wallace. Colo. Game and Fish Dept., Antelope Surv., vol.1, pp.ii+33, maps 2, Jan., 1940.

AN ANTELOPE CENSUS. STATUS OF ANTELOPE FOR 1929 AS GIVEN IN LETTERS FROM GAME COMMISSIONERS. Bird Lore, vol.32, no.2, pp.172-174, Mar.-Apr., 1930.

FIELD CREWS COMPLETE 1948 ANTELOPE CENSUS. Wyo. Wild Life, vol.12, no.4, pp.18-25, 35, 37, Apr., 1948.

WYOMING ANTELOPE. 48000 PRONGHORNS COUNTED IN 1946 CENSUS. Wyo. Wild Life, Cheyenne, vol.10, no.5, pp.4-6, 19-21, map, May, 1946.

### Economic Importance, Management

OUT IN THE PRONGHORN COUNTRY. A NATIONAL ANTELOPE REFUGE IS PROPOSED FOR "THE MOST AMERICAN OF AMERICAN BIG GAME ANIMALS". Albert C. Antrei. Bull. New York Zool. Soc., vol. 39, no.1, pp.3-12, illus., Jan.-Feb., 1936.

PREDATOR CONTROL AS A FACTOR IN ANTELOPE MANAGEMENT. O.N.Arrington, Alfred E. Edwards. Trans. N.Amer. Wildl. Conf., 16: pp.179-190, 1951.

ANTELOPE COMEBACK. (Transplanting.) Elliot S. Barker. Field and Stream, vol.53, no.4, pp.26-27, 121-123, Aug., 1948.

ANTELOPE RESTORATION. Gordon Douglas. Quart. Prog. Rept. Colorado Dept. Game and Fish, Denver, pp.17-21, illus., Apr., 1950.

CONSERVATION SUCCESS STORY.(Pronghorn antelope.) S.C. Downing. Carling Conserv.Digest, Toronto, vol.2, no.2, pp. 2-4, illus., Second quarter, 1948.

ANTELOPE TRANSPLANTING PROJECT ON LOST RIVER AND BIRCH CREEK RANGES REMOVES 298 PRONGHORNS. Marshall Edson. Idaho Wildl. Rev., Boise, vol.2, no.4, pp.8-9, illus., Dec., 1949.

ANTELOPE RESTORATION IN COLORADO. Robert R. Elliott. Colo.Conserv.Comments, vol.10, no.5, pp.3-4, 22, Mar., 1948.

CAN THE ANTELOPE AND SAGE GROUSE BE SAVED? Wm.L.Finley, Irene Finley. Nature Mag., vol.3, pp.69-72, figs.8, Feb., 1924.

LIVE TRAPPING TEXAS ANTELOPES. Lee W. Fisher. Jour. Wildl. Mgt., vol.6, no.3, pp.231-236, July, 1942.

TRAPPING THE TEXAS PRONGHORN. Lon Fitzgerald. Texas Game and Fish, Austin, vol.8, no.1, pp.14-17, Dec., 1949.

ANTELOPE SITUATION. Ira N.Gabrielson. Amer. Game, vol.24, no.4, pp.54, 59, July-Aug., 1935.

VANISHING RACE OF PRONGHORN. Edmund Heller, Hilda Hampl. Traval, vol.41, no.2, pp.5-10, 48, figs.10, June, 1923.

VANISHING PRONG-HORNED ANTELOPE. W.T. Hornaday. Zool. Soc. Bull., vol.25, p.111, Sep., 1922.

ANTELOPE SANCTUARY. Hartley H.T. Jackson. Jour. Mamm., vol.9, no.1, pp. 90-91, Feb., 1928.

ANTELOPE MANAGEMENT. Paul V. Jones, Jr. Texas Game and Fish, Austin, vol.7, no.12, pp.4-5, 18-20, 24-25, 28-29, illus., Nov., 1949.

EXPERIMENTAL MANAGEMENT OF ANTELOPE. Paul V. Jones, Jr. Texas Game, Fish and Oyster Comm., F A Rep. Ser.3, pp.31, Aug., 1949.

ANTELOPE SEASON RESEARCH. William McKean. N.Dakota Outdoors, vol.14, no.7, p.17, Jan., 1952.

CAPTURING, TRANSPLANTING, AND CARE OF YOUNG ANTELOPES. A.A.Nichol. Jour. Wildl.Mgt., vol.6, no.4, pp.281-286, Oct., 1942.

RESTORING THE ANTELOPE. A.J.Nicholson. Texas Game and Fish, Austin, vol.1, no.5, pp.5, 17, Apr., 1943.

THE ANTELOPE'S S. O. S. THE EXTINCTION OF THE PRONGHORN ANTELOPE IS A PREVENTABLE MISFORTUNE THAT WE ARE NEGLECTING TO PREVENT. Davis Quinn. The Emergency Conserv. Committee, New York, pp.16, Oct., 1930.

ANTELOPE TRANSPLANTING IS SUCCESS. Paul Russell. N. Mexico, vol.15, no.6, pp. 32-33, June, 1937.

CRISIS OF ANTELOPE MANAGEMENT. Paul Russell. Proc. 31st Ann. Conf. Western Assn. Sate Game and Fish Comm., Apr.30 - May 2, pp.112-116, 1951.

ANTELOPE ROUND UP. Robert M. Rutherford. Outdoors, Dayton, vol.16, no.4, pp. 22-23, 52-53, illus., Apr., 1948.

GRAND CANYON ANTELOPE. HOW THE EXPERIMENT OF STOCKING THE TONTO FLOOR OF THE CANYON IS WORKING OUT. E.T. Scoyen. Nat. Parks Bull., vol. 9, no.53, p.23, July, 1927.

ANTELOPE MANAGEMENT IN CALIFORNIA. James D. Stockes. Proc. 32nd Ann. Conf. Western Assn. State Game and Fish Comm., Glacier Nat. Park, Mont., June 15 - 17, 1952, pp.99-101, 1953.

ANTELOPE: A RANGE ASSET. Charles S. Terwilliger, Jr. Colo. Conserv., vol.2, no.5, pp.24-25, illus., Sep.-Oct., 1953.

AIR-HERDING THE PRONGHORN. Ken Thompson. American Forests, Washington, vol.53, no.8, pp.348-349, 380-381, illus., Aug., 1947.

AIRPLANE ROUNDUPS. (Rounding up pronghorn antelopes.) Frank Thone. Science News Letter, Wash., D.C., vol.42, no.22, p.348, Nov. 28, 1942.

EFFECTS OF PREDATOR CONTROL ON ANTELOPE POPULATIONS. Jay R. Udy. Fed. Aid Div. Utah Dept. Fish and Game, Publ. no.5, pp.1-48, illus., 1954.

OUR DISAPPEARING ANTELOPE. Hardy Ulm. Nature Mag., vol.2, pp.121, 123, figs.3, Aug., 1923.

COMEBACK OF THE ANTELOPE. FROM NEARLY ZERO TO 200,000. THE CURIOSITY OF THIS ANIMAL NEARLY BROUGHT ABOUT ITS EXTINCTION. Stanley P. Young. Western Sportsman, Denver, vol.5, no.4, pp.6-8, 23, 31, photo, map, tbl., Sep., 1940.

ANTELOPE ROUNDUP TIME. Texas Game and Fish, Austin, vol.5, no.5, pp.16-17, illus., Apr., 1947.

ANTELOPE TRAPPED, READY TO SHIP. Utah Fish and Game Bull., Salt Lake City, vol.5, no.9, pp.4-6, illus., Feb.-Mar., 1948.

"COME-BACK" OF ANTELOPE IS STIRRING WYOMING STORY. W.Va. Conserv., Charleston, vol.7, no.4, pp.19-21, July, 1943.

'PHANTOMS OF THE GRASSLAND AND SAGEBRUSH' TRAPPED AND TRANSPLANTED. (Pronghorn antelope.) S.Dakota Conserv. Digest, Pierre, vol.18, no.1, pp.2-5, illus., Jan., 1951.

RANCHER COMMENTS ON ANTELOPE SITUATION--. S.Dakota Conserv. Digest, Pierre, vol.9, no.2, pp.11, 14, Feb., 1942.

REHABILITATING THE PRONGHORN. Wyo. Wild Life, vol.7, no.6, pp.1-3, 17, June, 1942.

TEXAS PRONGHORN PAY THEIR WAY. Texas Game and Fish, Austin, vol.6, no.3, p.22, Feb., 1948.

UTAH ANTELOPE TRANSFER PROVES SUCCESSFUL. Utah Fish and Game Bull., Salt Lake City, vol.6, no.3, pp.1-2, illus., Nov., 1948.

Fossils

REMNANT FROM THE PLEISTOCENE. SOME FACTS ABOUT THE ANTELOPE OF THE PLAINS. Albert C. Antrei. Nature Mag., Wash., D.C., vol.32, no.10, pp.587-589, illus., Dec., 1939.

NEW SPECIES OF SPHENOPHALOS FROM THE UPPER OGALLALA OF NEBRASKA. Erwin H. Barbour, C.B. Schultz. Bull. Univ. Nebraska State Mus., Lincoln, vol.2, no.6, pp.59-62, fig.23, June, 1941.

STUDY OF TETRAMERYX AND ASSOCIATED FOSSILS FROM PAPAGO SPRING CAVE, SONOITA, ARIZONA. Edwin H. Colbert, R.G. Chaffee. Amer. Mus. Novitates, N.Y., no. 1043, pp.21, figs.12, June 26, 1939.

CAPROMERYX TAYLOR FROM THE McKITTRICK PLEISTOCENE, CALIFORNIA. E.L. Furlong. Contrib. Palaeontology, Carnegie Inst. Wash., Publ.404, pp.49-53, figs.2, Aug., 1930.

GENERIC IDENTIFICATION OF THE PLEISTOCENE ANTELOPE FROM RANCHO LA BREA. E.L. Furlong. Carnegie Inst. Wash., Publ.551, pp.135-140, pls.3, Jan. 25, 1946.

NEW MERYCODONTS FROM THE UPPER MIOCENE OF NEVADA. E.L. Furlong. Carnegie Inst. Wash., Publ.453, pp.1-10, pls.5, May 25, 1934.

NEW PLIOCENE ANTELOPE FROM MEXICO WITH REMARKS ON SOME KNOWN ANTILOCAPRIDS. E.L. Furlong. Contrib. Paleontol., Carnegie Inst. Wash., Publ.530, pp.1-23, fig.1, pls.2, May 1, 1941.

OCCURRENCE AND PHYLOGENETIC STATUS OF MERYCODUS FROM THE MOHAVE DESERT TERTIARY. E.L. Furlong. Univ. Calif. Publ. (Bull. Dept. Geol. Sci., Berkeley), vol.17, no.4, pp.145-186, figs.28, pls.24-28, 1927.

OCCURRENCE OF THE PLIOCENE ANTELOPE, ILINGOCEROS, IN NEVADA. E.L. Furlong. Science, Lancaster, n.s., vol.97, no.2516, p.262, Mar. 19, 1943.

PLEISTOCENE ANTELOPE, STOCKOCEROS CONKLINGI, FROM SAN JOSECITO CAVE, MEXICO. E.L. Furlong. Contrib. Paleontol., Carnegie Inst. Wash., Publ.551, pp.1-8, pls. 5, Feb. 3, 1943.

PLIOCENE ANTELOPES OF THE PRONGHORN TYPE. E.L. Furlong. Science, n.s., vol.82, no.2124, pp.250-251, Sep. 13, 1935.

NEW ANTILOCAPRID FROM THE UPPER PLIOCENE OF IDAHO. C. Lewis Gazin. Jour. Paleont., vol.9, no.5, pp.390-393, fig.1, July, 1935.

CAPROMERYX ALTIDENS (MATTHEW) POSSIBLE ANCESTOR OF ANTELOCAPRA (SIC) AMERICANA. Curtis J. Hesse. Pan-Amer. Geol., Des Moines, vol.62, no.1, p.68, Aug., 1934.

NEW EVIDENCE ON THE ANCESTRY OF ANTILOCAPRA AMERICANA. Curtis J. Hesse. Jour. Mamm., vol.16, pp. 307-315, figs.5, Nov., 1935.

ANTILOCAPRID FROM THE LOWER PLIOCENE OF BEAVER COUNTY, OKLAHOMA. Claude W. Hibbard. Trans. Kansas Acad. Sci., Topeka, vol.54, no.3, pp. 387-390, 1951.

BURIED INDIAN WORKSHOP WITH REMAINS OF EXTINCT MAMMAL. William A. Parkes. Bull. Geol. Soc. Amer., vol.36 pp.429-434, June, 1925.

NEW SPECIES OF ANTILOCAPRINE, TETRAMERYX ONUSROSAGRIS, FROM A PLEISTOCENE CAVE DEPOSIT IN SOUTHERN ARIZONA. Quentin Roosevelt, J.W. Burden. Amer. Mus. Novitates, no. 754, pp.4, fig.1, Nov. 17, 1934.

NOTES ON SOME LATE TERTIARY AND PLEISTOCENE ANTILOCAPRIDS. R.A. Stirton. Jour. Mamm., vol.19, no.3, pp. 366-370, tbl., Aug., 1938.

TERTIARY AND PLEISTOCENE ANTILOCAPRIDS AND THEIR APPARENT RELATIONSHIP TO ANTILOCAPRA AMERICANA ORD. R.A. Stirton. Proc. Geol. Soc. America, 1937, p.297, June, 1938. (Abstract.)

QUATERNARY ANTELOPE REMAINS FROM A SECOND CAVE DEPOSIT IN THE ORGAN MOUNTAINS, NEW MEXICO. Chester Stock. Los Angeles Mus., publ.2, pp.18, figs.3, May 29, 1930.

NEW ANTELOPE FROM THE PLEISTOCENE OF RANCHO LA BREA. Walter P. Taylor. Univ. Calif. Publ. Geol., vol.6, no.10, pp. 191-197, figs., July 14, 1911.

Habits, Behavior, Ecology

PRONGHORN WINTER-KILL. Theodore C. Baker. Wyo. Wild Life, vol.18, no.1, pp. 22-23, illus., Jan., 1954.

WHAT ABOUT SOUTH DAKOTA'S SAGEBRUSH? (Relation of sage to antelope and sheep.) Wendell Bever. S.Dakota Conserv. Digest, vol.18, no.1, pp.12-13, Jan., 1951.

NOTES ON THE PRONGHORN. (Numbers, habits, hazards.) Max Bridge. Wyo. Wild Life, vol.7, no.11, pp.20-22, 23, Nov., 1942.

ANTELOPE IN THE SNOW. Harry J. Brockley. Wyo. Wild Life, vol.13, no.4, pp.27-30, May, 1949.

LIFE HISTORY, ECOLOGY, AND RANGE USE OF THE PRONGHORN ANTELOPE. H.K. Buechner. Amer. Midland Nat., vol. 43, pp.257-354, 1950.

RANGE ECOLOGY OF THE PRONGHORN ON THE WICHITA MOUNTAINS WILDLIFE REFUGE. H.K. Buechner. Trans. 15th N. Amer. Wildl. Conf., pp.627-643, 1950.

RANGE USE OF THE PRONGHORNED ANTELOPE IN WESTERN TEXAS. H.K. Buechner. Trans. 12th N. Amer. Wildl. Conf., pp.185-191, 1947.

SPEED OF PRONG-HORN ANTELOPES. Carlyle Carr. Jour. Mamm., vol.8, no.3, pp.249-250, Aug., 1927.

NOTES ON AN ANTELOPE FIGHT. Jim Chapman. Canadian Field-Nat., Ottawa, vol.62, no.5, pp.153-154, Sep.-Oct., 1948.

PRONGHORN ANTELOPE: ITS RANGE USE AND FOOD HABITS IN CENTRAL MONTANA. Glen F. Cole. Bull.516, Montana State Coll. Agric. Exp. Sta., Bozeman, pp.1-63, illus., Feb., 1956.

ANTELOPE FOODS IN SOUTHEASTERN MONTANA. Faye M. Couey. Jour. Wildl. Mgt., Menasha, vol.10, no.4, p.367, Oct., 1946.

FOOD HABITS OF THE PRONG-HORN ANTELOPE OF CALIFORNIA. Carol M. Ferrel, Howard R. Leach. Calif. Fish and Game, vol.36, no.1, pp.21-26, Jan., 1950.

PRONG-HORNED ANTELOPE OF CALIFORNIA WITH SPECIAL REFERENCE TO FOOD HABITS. Carol M. Ferrel, Howard R. Leach. Calif. Fish and Game, vol.38, no.3, pp.285-293, illus., July, 1952.

NOTE ON THE BEHAVIOR OF THE PRONGHORNED ANTELOPE. Stanley G. Jewett. Jour. Mamm., vol.27, no.1, p.84, Mar. 14, 1946.

ANTELOPE REPEL COYOTE ATTACK. Ben Kroll. Fur Jour., vol.2, no.9, p.26, Oct., 1928. (Reprint from "The Service", Amer. Game Protective Assn., July, 1928.)

GOLDEN EAGLE ATTACKING ANTELOPE. Robert W. Lehti. Jour. Wildl. Mgt., Menasha, vol.11, no.4, pp.348-349, Oct., 1947.

FOOD HABITS OF THE HART MOUNTAIN ANTELOPE HERD. Ellis Mason. Proc. 32nd Ann. Conf. Western Assn. State Game and Fish Comm., Glacier Nat. Park, Mont., June 15-17, 1952, pp.95-97, 1953.

THE 1945 STATUS OF THE PRONGHORN ANTELOPE, ANTILOCAPRA AMERICANA (ORD), IN CANADA. A.L. Rand. Ottawa, E. Cloutier, Printer to the King, pp.34, illus., maps, 1947. (Canada, Nat. Mus., Ottawa, Bull. no.106, Biological ser., no. 34.)

NOTES ON WINTER FORAGING HABITS OF ANTELOPES IN OKLAHOMA. Charles H. Rouse. Jour. Mamm., vol.22, no.1, pp. 57-60, Feb., 1941.

ANTELOPE POPULATION AND SOLAR RADIATION. V.E. Shelford. Jour. Mamm., vol.35, no.4, pp.533-538, Nov. 29, 1954.

ANTELOPE WITH LOCKED HORNS. C.C. Spencer. Jour. Mamm., vol.23, no.1, p. 92, Feb. 14, 1942.

ANTELOPE DOE COVERS FAWNS TO CONCEAL THEM. F.R. Starr. Calif.Fish and Game, vol.20, no.3, p.291, July, 1934.

PRONGHORNS BEGIN TO LEARN. Hart Stilwell. Field and Stream, New York, vol. 64, no.10, pp.52-53, 117-118, illus., Feb., 1950.

PREDATION ON ANTELOPE. W.K.Thompson. Jour. Wildl. Mgt., vol.13, no.3, pp. 313- 314, July, 1949.

THE PRONGHORN. (Habits, life history, management.) Michael Throckmorton. Texas Game and Fish, vol.4, no.1, pp. 14, 23-24, Dec., 1945.

ANTELOPE VS. PREDATORS. Ivan T. Wilson. Arizona Wildl. and Sportsman, Safford, vol.6, no.10, p.11, Oct., 1944.

LION KILLS ANTELOPE. New Mexico Mag., Albuquerque, vol.23, no.8, p.27, Aug., 1945.

Horns

OLD AND NEW HORNS OF THE PRONG-HORNED ANTELOPE. Vernon Bailey.Jour. Mamm., vol.1, no.3, pp.128-129, pl.8, May, 1920.

HORN OF THE PRONG-HORN ANTELOPE (ANTILOCAPRA AMERICANA) FOUND AT MOLINE, ILLINOIS. F.M.Fryxell. Jour. Mamm., vol.7, no.4, pp.333-334, Nov., 1926.

NOTICE OF THE HORNS OF THE UNRECORDED SPECIES OF THE PRONGHORN (ANTILOCAPRA), IN THE COLLECTION OF THE DERBY MUSEUM, LIVERPOOL. John Edward Gray. Proc. Zool. Soc. London, pt.23, pp.9-11, figs. 2, 1855.

SHED HORNS OF THE AMERICAN ANTELOPE. Geo. Bird Grinnell. Jour.Mamm., vol.2, no.2, pp.116-117, May, 1921.

HOW THE PRONGHORN GROWS HIS HORNS. C.E. Hagie. Colo.Conserv.Comments, Denver, vol.6, no.3, pp.5-6, Sep. 15, 1943.

DECIDUOUS HORNS OF THE PRONGHORN ANTELOPE, ANTILOCAPRA AMERICANA. Charles Noback. Bull. New York Zool. Soc., vol.35, no.6, pp.195-207, figs.13, Nov.-Dec., 1932.

HORN SHEDDING IN THE YELLOWSTONE PARK. M.P. Skinner. Jour. Mamm., vol. 4, no.3, p.185, Aug., 1923.

Hunting

HUNTING PRONGHORN IN MEXICO FOR A GROUP BY AKELEY: A PAGE OF MUSEUM HISTORY. C.M. Barber. Chicago Nat. Hist. Mus. Bull., vol.17, nos.7-8, p.5, illus., July-Aug., 1946.

ANTELOPE SEASONS PAST AND PRESENT. Lester M. Berner. S.Dakota Digest, vol.21, no.8, pp.2-3, Aug., 1954.

PRONGHORNS HAVE BRAINS. J. Chapman. Outdoorsman, Chicago, vol.89, no.3, (whole no.526), pp.30, 85-87, illus., May-June, 1947.

PRONG-HORNED ANTELOPE CHALLENGE THE HUNTER. Charles Clay. Rod and Gun in Canada, Montreal, vol.51, no.2, pp.17, 48, July, 1949.

ANTELOPE ANTICS. R.F.Duke.Rod and Gun in Canada, Montreal, vol.48, no.8, pp.7, 40, Jan., 1947.

OREGON'S OPEN SEASON ON ANTELOPE IN 1938. Arthur S. Einarsen. Trans.4th N.Amer. Wildl.Conf., Wash., D.C., pp. 216-220, 1939.

THE 1946 ANTELOPE HUNT. O.F.Etheredge, W.C. Glazener. Texas Game and Fish, vol.5, no.6, pp.12-13, May, 1947.

THE 1947 ANTELOPE HUNT. O.F.Etheredge, W.C.Glazener. Texas Game and Fish, Austin, vol.6, no.7, pp.5, 17, June, 1948.

ANTELOPE BUCKS--1946. W.C.Glazener. Texas Game and Fish, Austin, vol.4, no. 10, pp.5, 19, illus., Sep., 1946.

CONDUCTED ANTELOPE HUNTS..WHY? W.C. Glazener. Texas Game and Fish, vol.10, no.1, pp.2-5, illus., Dec., 1951.

WIN, LOSE, OR DRAW--THEY GOT ONLY ONE SHOT EACH! (Antilocapra americana.) Richard Goff. Western Sportsman, Denver, vol.5, no.6, pp.6-7, 17-18, 29, illus., Nov., 1940.

NEXT YEAR'S BUCK. (Antelope.) Geo. W. Grunkemeyer. Field and Stream, New York, vol.51, no.2, pp.52-53, 117-119, illus., June, 1946.

ANTELOPE RIFLES. Duke Lamster. South Dakota Conserv. Digest, Pierre, vol.15, no. 2, pp.6, 12, Feb., 1948.

ANTELOPE HUNT. Daniel W. Lay.Texas Game and Fish, Austin, vol.3, no.1, pp. 4-6, illus., Dec., 1944.

CONTROLLED ANTELOPE HUNTS AND SOME PROBLEMS OF ADMINISTERING PUBLIC HUNTING. Daniel W. Lay.Trans. 11th N. Amer. Wildl. Conf., Wash., pp. 274-279, 1946.

ANTELOPE IN HIGH GEAR. Lester L. Linn. Outdoor Life, New York, vol.102, no.5, p.8, Nov., 1948.

HALF-PINT ANTELOPES. Jack O'Connor. Arizona Wildl. and Sportsman, Tucson, vol.6, no.10, pp.8-9, Aug., 1946.

CURTAINS FOR ANTELOPE! Frank Ramsay. Western Sportsman, Denver, vol.7, no.1, pp. 6-9, illus., June, 1941.

HUNTING ANTELOPE WITH DOGS. A.R. Ross.Colorado Mag., Denver, vol.24, no.4, pp.162-166, July, 1947.

SILHOUETTES IN THE SAGE.(Antelope.) Francis C. Zuiker. Outdoorsman, Chicago, vol.86, no.3, whole no.508, pp.12-13, 48, illus., May-June, 1944.

ANTELOPE HUNT. Texas Game and Fish, Austin, vol.4, no.1, pp.10-11, illus., Dec., 1945.

1946 ANTELOPE SEASON OPENS. Wyo. Wild Life, Cheyenne, vol.10, no.8, pp. 19-22, Aug., 1946.

PUBLIC DRAWING HELD TO AWARD PERMITS FOR FIRST ANTELOPE SEASON. S.Dakota Conserv. Digest, Pierre, vol.9, no.9. pp.3, 11, Sep., 1942.

UTAH'S ANTELOPE HUNT IS HUGE SUCCESS, CLAIM SPORTSMEN. Utah Fish and Game Bull., Salt Lake City, vol.3, no.6, pp.1-2, Sep.-Oct., 1946.

WANNA HUNT AN ANTELOPE? Texas Game and Fish, Austin, vol.2, no.6, p.11, illus., May, 1944.

A WORD OF ADVICE. (Antelope hunting.) Texas Game and Fish, Austin, vol.4, no.1, pp.12-13, illus., Dec., 1945.

Migrations, Movements

ANTELOPE MOVEMENT AND MIGRATION STUDIES. Theodore C. Baker. Wyo. Wild Life, vol.17, no.10, pp.30-36, illus., Oct., 1953.

PRONGHORNS ON THE MOVE. Texas Game and Fish, Austin, vol.7, no.3, pp.22-25, illus., Feb., 1949.

North America

WYOMING ANTELOPE--HISTORY AND WARTIME MANAGEMENT. W.J.Allred. Trans.8th N.Amer.Wildl.Conf., Wash., D.C., pp.117-122, 1943.

PRONGHORN ANTELOPE IN LOS ANGELOS COUNTY. Harvey T. Anderson, Jr. Calif. Fish and Game, vol.20, no.1, pp.91-92, Jan., 1934.

WYOMING'S ANTELOPE. Lester Bagley. Wyo. Wild Life, Cheyenne, vol.12, no.4, p.2, Apr., 1948.

OREGON ANTELOPE. Vernon Bailey.Proc. Biol. Soc. Wash., vol.45, pp.45-46, Apr. 2, 1932.

OLD MAN OF THE PRAIRIE. HISTORY OF THE WESTERN PRONGHORN ANTELOPE OF COLORADO. H.G. Bayne. Colo.Conserv. Comments, Denver, vol.6, no.3, pp. 3-4, Sep.15, 1943.

DISTRIBUTION AND STATUS OF PRONGHORN ANTELOPE IN MONTANA. James Beer. Jour. Mamm., vol.25, no.1, pp.43-46, fig.1, Feb., 1944.

HISTORY OF ANTELOPE IN SOUTH DAKOTA. Wendell Bever. S.Dakota Conserv. Digest, vol.22, no.8, pp.2-3, Aug., 1955.

CENSUS AND MANAGEMENT OF CENTRAL MONTANA ANTELOPE. Don L. Brown.Proc. 34th Ann. Conf. Western Assn.State Game and Fish Comm., pp.211-215, May 1954 (1955).

BIOLOGY OF THE ANTELOPE IN MONTANA. Paul Buck. MS thesis, Mont. State Coll., 1947.

LIFE HISTORY, ECOLOGY, AND RANGE USE OF THE PRONGHORN ANTELOPE IN TRANS-PECOS TEXAS. Helmut K.Buechner. PhD thesis, Okla. A.and M. Coll., 1949; Amer. Midl. Nat., Notre Dame, vol.43, no.2, pp.257-254, figs.12, Mar., 1950.

PRONG-HORNED ANTELOPE IN CALIFORNIA. E.S. Cheney. Calif. Fish and Game, vol.15, no.2, p.175, Apr., 1929.

NEVADA ANTELOPE. S.B.Doten.Official Bull. Nevada State Fish and Game Protective League, vol.1, no.1, p.7, Feb., 1923.

LIFE HISTORY AND MANAGEMENT OF ANTELOPE IN OREGAN. Arthur S.Einarsen. Trans. 3rd N.Amer. Wildl. Conf., pp.381-387, 1938.

ANTELOPE OF LASSEN COUNTY. C.O. Fisher. Calif. Fish and Game, vol.15, no. 4, pp.349-350, (Oct.) Dec., 1929.

PRONGHORN ANTELOPE AND ITS MANAGEMENT IN TEXAS. Lee W. Fisher. Texas Game, Fish and Oyster Comm., Quart. Prog. Rept., Austin, Oct.-Dec., pp.11-13, 1941.

DWARF ANTELOPE OF THE YUMA FLATS. Arthur F. Halloran. Ariz. Wildl.-Sportsman, vol.25, no.4, pp.26-28, illus., Apr., 1954.

SURVEY OF 1941-1942 / LIFE HISTORY, CENSUS, HABITS. Lorin G. Kautz. Colo. Game and Fish Dept., Antelope Surv., vol.2, pp.x+36, graph, tbsl.3, maps 4, Aug., 1942.

WYOMING PRONGHORNS. J.J.King.Kentucky Happy Hunting Ground, Frankfort, vol. 6, no.1, p.6, Jan., 1950.

ANTELOPE NEAR FRESNO. Mrs.Henry Larsen. Calif. Fish and Game, vol.15, no. 4, pp.350-351, (Oct.) Dec., 1929.

ARIZONA ANTELOPE. J.C. McGregor. Mus.Notes, publ.by Northern Ariz.Soc. of Sci. and Art, Inc., vol.8, no.3, pp.13-16, Sep., 1935.

NORTH DAKOTA ANTELOPE SITUATION--1949. William T. McKean. N.Dakota Outdoors, Grand Forks, vol.12, no.4, p.12, Oct., 1949.

PRONG-HORNED ANTELOPE IN CALIFORNIA. Donald D. McLean. Calif.Fish and Game, San Francisco, vol.30, no.4, pp.221-241, maps, Oct., 1944.

PRONGHORN IN ARIZONA. Chuck Mabery. Ariz. Wildl.-Sportsman, vol.23, no.9, pp. 34-48, illus., Sep., 1952.

OREGON'S PRONGHORN ANTELOPE. Robert U.Mace. Oreg.State Game Comm., pp.1-26, illus., revied and enlarged, 1954.

FOOD HABITS AND MEASUREMENTS OF HART MOUNTAIN ANTELOPE. Ellis Mason. Jour. Wildl. Mgt., Ithaca, vol. 16, no.3, pp.387-389, July, 1952.

OREGON ANTELOPE. Ellis Mason. Oregon State Game Comm. Bull., vol.2, no.6, pp. 1, 4, 7, June, 1947.

DISTRIBUTION OF THE PRONGHORNED ANTELOPE IN CALIFORNIA. E.W. Nelson. Calif. Fish and Game, vol.11, no.4, pp.154-157, Oct., 1925.

AMERICAN ANTELOPE IN YELLOWSTONE NATIONAL PARK. M.P.Skinner. Roosevelt Wild Life Forest Experiment Sta., Syracuse, N.Y., pp.1-32, figs.8, col.pl.1, 1924.

HART MOUNTAIN. (Antelope.) Ken Stott. San Diego Zoonooz, vol.21, no.6, pp.6-7, June, 1948.

PRONG-HORNED ANTELOPE IN THE SOUTHWEST. Walter P. Taylor. Proc. N.Amer. Wildl. Conf., Feb. 3-7, 1936, Senate Comm. Print, 74th Congr. 2nd Sess., Wash., pp. 652-655, 1936.

PRONGHORN IN NEW SPAIN. J. Monroe Thorington. Frontiers, Lancaster, vol.12, no.3, pp.67-69, illus., Feb., 1948.

WYOMING ANTELOPE. Robert E. Treman. Field and Stream, vol.42, no.2, pp.30-31, 80, illus., June, 1937.

OREGON'S PRONGHORN ANTELOPE. Oregon State Game Comm., pp.10, illus.

WYOMING ANTELOPE. Wyo. Wild Life, vol.10, no.5, pp.4-5, 19-21, May, 1946.

WYOMING HAS LARGE PRONGHORN ANTELOPE POPULATION. Wyo. Wildl., Laramie, vol.8, no.6, pp.1-3, 10-15, illus., June, 1943.

Parasites

PARASITE FROM ANTELOPE IN CALIFORNIA. John E. Chattin, C.M.Herman. Trans. Amer. Micros. Soc., vol.63, no.1, pp.27-29, Jan., 1944.

INTERNAL PARASITES IN NORTH DAKOTA ANTELOPE. Alice I. Goldsby, D.F.Eveleth. Jour. Parasit., vol.40, no.6, pp.637-648, illus., Dec., 1954.

EIMERIA ANTELOCAPRAE, A NEW COCCIDIUM FROM THE AMERICAN ANTELOPE. Henry Huizinga. Jour.Parasitology, vol.28, no.2, pp.167-168, Apr., 1942.

DISTRIBUTION OF PSEUDOSTERTAGIA BULLOSA AND SOME NEW RECORDS OF NEMATODES FROM PRONGHORN ANTELOPE (ANTILOCAPRA AMERICANA). John T. Lucker, D. Dikemans. Proc. Helminthol. Soc. Wash., Beltsville, vol. 12, no.1, pp.2-4, Jan., 1945.

Photography

RIDING THE RIM ROCKS.(Photographing prong-horn antelope.) William L.Finley. Nature Mag., vol.12, pp.149-154, illus., Sep., 1928.

Reproductive Biology

CALIFORNIA ANTELOPE REPRODUCTIVE POTENTIALS. John E. Chattin, Robert Lassen. Calif. Fish and Game, vol.36, no.3, pp.328-329, July, 1950.

MONTANA RECORDS OF ANTELOPE EMBRYOS AND REPRODUCTIVE TRACTS. Clarence A. Tryon, Jr., Paul David Buck. Jour. Mamm., vol.31, no.2, pp.192-193, May 25, 1950.

Status

STATUS OF SOUTH DAKOTA ANTELOPE. Wendell Bever. S.Dakota Conserv.Digest, Pierre, vol.14, no.8, pp.10, 13-14, illus., Aug., 1947.

STATUS OF THE ANTELOPE HERDS OF NORTHERN ARIZONA. Theodore Knipe. Ariz. Game and Fish Comm., pp.40, 1944.

STATUS OF THE PRONGHORN ANTELOPE, 1922-1924. Edward W. Nelson. U.S.Dept. Agric.,Dept. Bull., no.1346, pp.1-64, pls. 1-6, Aug. 15, 1925.

1945 STATUS OF THE PRONGHORN ANTELOPE, ANTILOCAPRA AMERICANA (ORD), IN CANADA. A.L. Rand. Natl. Mus.Can., Bull.106, pp.34, 1947.

ANTELOPE: THE STATUS OF UTAH'S ANTELOPE. Jay R. Udy. Utah Fish and Game Bull., vol.8, no.4, pp.1-3, May, 1949.

Taxonomy

NEW PRONGHORN ANTELOPE FROM SONORA. (Antilocapra americana sonoriensis.) E.A. Goldman. Proc. Biol.Soc. Wash., vol.58, pp.3-4, Mar. 21, 1945.

REMARKS ON THE HORNS AND ON THE SYSTEMATIC POSITION OF THE AMERICAN ANTELOPE. Marcus W. Lyon, Jr. Proc. U.S. Nat. Mus., vol.34, no.1619, pp.393-402, pls.38-39, Aug. 11, 1908.

## Bovidae

THE CHAMOIS. Margaret Altmann. Animal Kingdom, New York Zool. Soc., vol.59, no. 5, pp.137-141, illus., Oct., 1956.

WHAT IS AN ANTELOPE. H.E.Anthony. Bull. New York Zool. Soc., vol.30, pp.82-112, illus., Aug., 1927.

(ON THE WILD GOATS.) Ueber Steinwild. Otto Antonius. Der Zoologische Garten, Leipzig, n.F., vol.2, pts.4-6, pp.95-106, figs.1-8, 1929.

GIANT SABLE ANTELOPE. Andrey Avinoff. Carnegie Mag., Pittsburgh, vol.7, no.3, pp.82-83, illus., June, 1933.

MOUNTAIN GOAT THAT IS NOT A GOAT. Vernon Bailey. Nature Mag., vol.18, no.3, pp.153-157, figs.6, map 1, Sep., 1931.

BREEDING OF A BUFFALO TEAM. Ernest H. Baynes. Nature Mag., vol.3, pp.267-270, 314, May, 1924.

GOD'S CATTLE. (Water-buffalo.) K.W. Bennett. Fauna, Philadelphia, vol.10, no.3, pp.74-77, illus., Sep., 1948.

(SOME REMARKS ON THE SCRAPING GOAT.) Einige Bemerkungen ueber die scheuernde Ziege Prof. Lakowitz'. J.A. Bierens. Biol. Zentralblatt, vol.47, pp. 627-629, 1927.

BONTEBOK (DAMALISCUS PYGARGUS (PALL.)), WITH SPECIAL REFERENCE TO ITS HISTORY AND PRESERVATION. R. Bigalke. Fauna and Flora, Transvaal, vol.6, for 1955, pp.94-115, illus., 1957.

BUSHCOW. John Blair. Nigerian Field, London, vol.8, no.3, p.132, July, 1939.

GORAL (NEMORHAEDUS CAUDATUS RADDEANUS HEUDE, 1894). G.F.Bromlei. Zool. Zhurnal, vol.35, no.9, pp.1395-1405, 1956.

ON THE ROYAL ANTELOPE, AND ALLIED SPECIES OF THE GENUS NANOTRAGUS. Victor Brooke. Proc. Zool. Soc. London, pp.637-643, fig.1, pl., 1872.

THE TAKIN. H.S. Bryant. Nature Mag., vol. 2, p.367, fig.1, Dec., 1923.

WARD'S REEDBUCK (CERVICAPRA REDUNCA WARDI). H.A. Bryant. Appendix to Great and Small Game of Africa, pp.2.

MUSKOX (OVIBOS MOSCHATUS) LONGEVITY. John L. Buckley, David L. Spencer, Paul Adams. Jour. Mamm., vol.35, no.3, p.456, Aug., 1954.

ANIMALS IN DECLINE: 1. THE MUSK-OX. Maurice Burton. Illus. London News, vol. 218, no.5831, p.108, illus., Jan. 20, 1951.

PROBLEMATIC CHIRU. (Pantholops hodgsoni) Maurice Burton. Illus. London News, vol.221, no.5911, p.188, illus., Aug. 2, 1952.

FIELD NOTES ON THE HARTEBEESTS AND GAZELLES. F.S. Collier. The Nigerian Field, London, vol.7, no.4, pp.149-152, col. pls.2, Oct., 1938.

FIELD NOTES ON WATERBUCK, KOB AND REEDBUCK. F.S.Collier. The Nigerian Field, London, vol.7, no.4, pp.156-157, Oct., 1938.

THE GIANT ELAND (TAUROTRAGUS DERBIANUS). C.B. Cotton. Proc. Zool.Soc. London, pt.4, pp.1037-1038, Dec., 1933.

SITATUNGA (TRAGELAPHUS SPEKII SCLATER). W.B. Cotton. Proc. Zool. Soc. London, pt.1, pp.143-144, Apr., 1935.

THE CHAMOIS, RUPICAPRA RUPICAPRA (L.) M.A.J. Couturier. Grenoble, Arthaud, pp.xi+857, pl.s103, 1938. (In French.)

(Review by P. Rode of) THE CHAMOIS, RUPICAPRA RUPICAPRA (L.). M.A.J. Couturier. Mammalia, Paris, vol.3, no.1, pp.39-40, Mar., 1939.

(Review by P. Rode of) (CONTRIBUTION TO THE NATURAL HISTORY OF THE CHAMOIS.) Contribution à l'Histoire naturelle du Chamois. M.A.J.Couturier. Mammalia, Paris, vol.1, no.6, p.262, Dec., 1937.

NOTES ON THE WILD GOAT, CAPRA AEGAGRUS, GM. Charles G. Danford. Proc. Zool. Soc. London, pp.458-468, figs.2, 1875.

(YELLOW-BACK DUIKERBOK AND JENTINK'S DUIKERBOK.) Cephalophe a dos jaune et cephalophe de Jentink. P.L.Dekeyser, A. Villiers. Notes Africaines, Bull.Inform. et Correspondence Inst. Français Afrique Noire, no.66, pp.54-57, Apr., 1955.

HARNESSED ANTELOPES AND THEIR ALLIES. Raymond L. Ditmars. Bull. New York Zool. Soc., vol.36, no.2, pp.38-45, illus., Mar.-Apr., 1933.

ANTELOPES OF THE GENUS BOÖCERCUS. J.G. Dollman. Nat. Hist. Mag., London, vol.1, no.7, pp.240-242, illus., July, 1928.

BARKER'S BUSHBUCK. J.G. Dollman. Nat. Hist. Mag., British Mus., vol.2, pp.96-101, illus., July, 1929.

GERENUK, OR WALLER'S GAZELLE. J.G. Dollman. Nat. Hist. Mag., London, vol.3, no.22, pp.188-193, fig.1, Apr., 1932.

MAMMALS OF THE MOUNTAINS.(Mountain goat, mountain sheep.) Stuart C. Downing. Canadian Nat., Toronto, vol.9, no.1, pp. 30-31, illus., Jan.-Feb., 1947.

ROCKY MOUNTAIN GOAT. Stuart C. Downing. Canadian Nat., Toronto, vol.8, no.1, pp.14-15, col.pl., Jan., 1946.

TWO VERY DIFFERENT ANTELOPE. THE ORYX AND THE WILDEBEEST. J.R.Dugmore. Field, London, vol.165, no.4293, pp.753-754, illus., Apr. 6, 1935.

WHERE GAUR AND WATER BUFFALO MEET. A.W. Duncan. Field, London, vol. 177, no.4611, pp.388-389, illus., May 10, 1941.

SOME OBSERVATIONS OF THE CHAMOIS. RUPICAPRA RUPICAPRA LINN. (R. TRAGUS GRAY). Alex. S. Gillespie. North-West Naturalist Scotland, vol.5, no.3, pp.148-150, Sep., 1930.

THE MUSKOX (OVIBOS MOSCHATUS). R. Glover. Oryx, vol.2, no.2, pp.76-86, Aug., 1953.

ROCKY MOUNTAIN GOAT. Madison Grant. Ann. Rep. N.Y. Zool. Soc., pp.36, illus., 1905.

YOU CAN'T BLUFF A MOUNTAIN GOAT. Wendell H. Harmon. S. Dakota Conserv. Digest, Madison, vol.16, no.3, pp.2-3, 12-13, Mar., 1949.

(HISTORY OF A BISON AND A NEWLY DISCOVERED HORN OF THE AUROCHS (BOS PRIMIGENIUS).) Die Geschichte eines Wisenthorns und ein neuentdecktes Horn vom Ur (Bos primigenius). Max Hilzheimer. Zeitschr. Wissenschaftliche Zool., Leipzig, Abt. A, vol.150, no.1, pp.97-106, figs.2, Sep., 1937.

THE MARKHOR. Edward Hindle. Zoo Life, London, vol.1, no.1, p.7, Spring, 1946.

GIANT SABLE ANTELOPE. L.Mitchell Hodges. Field, London, vol.161, no.4200, p.1485, illus., June 24, 1933.

CHAMPION MOUNTAIN CLIMBER.(Mountain goat.) Henrietta Holland. Fauna, Philadelphia, vol.9, no.1, pp.13-15, illus., Mar., 1947.

NATURE NOTES (9). (Sitatunga, Nyala.) C.J.P. Ionides. African Wild Life, Johannesburg, vol.9, no.3, pp.229-231, illus., Sep., 1955.

FIGHTING FURY, THE BUSHBUCK. W.T. Jackson. African Wild Life, Johannesburg, vol.9, no.4, pp.335-338, illus., Dec., 1955.

NOTES ON THE SITUTUNGA. M.D.W. Jeffries. Nigerian Field, London, vol.9, no.2, pp.65-68, figs.3, July, 1940.

ON BUBALUS MINDORENSIS HEUDE. F.A. Jentink. Notes Leyden Mus., vol.16, no.20, pp.199-204, pls.8-11, Dec., 1894.

ON CEPHALOPHUS SILVICULTOR (AFZELIUS). F.A. Jentink. Notes Leyden Mus., vol.22, no.14, pp.179-187, pls.1-2, Nov., 1900.

ON STREPSICEROS KUDU AND STREPSICEROS IMBERBIS. F.A. Jentink. Notes Leyden Mus., vol.12, no.37, pp.211-221, pl.9, Aug., 1890.

ON TWO RE-DISCOVERED ANTELOPES. F.A. Jentink. Notes Leyden Mus., vol.7, no.25, pp.269-273, pls.9-10, Sep., 1885.

SPECIES OF THE ANTELOPE-GENUS PEDIOTRAGUS. F.A. Jentink. Notes Leyden Mus., vol.22, no.4, pp.33-43, Feb., 1900.

GOOD NILGIRI TAHR (HEMITRAGUS HYLOCRIUS). A.W. John. Jour.Bombay Nat. Hist. Soc., vol.32, p.597, Jan.15, 1927.

(THE GENUS MATSCHIEA.) Die Gattung Matschiea. Theodor Knottnerus-Meyer. Zool. Garten, Leipzig, n.F., vol.7, nos.1-3, pp.47-48, May, 1934.

(NOTES ON NAMING THE GIRAFFE GAZELLE (LITOCRANIUS WALLERI BROOK).) Notiz zur Benennung der Giraffengazelle (Litocranius walleri Brook). Ingo Krumbiegel. Zool. Garten, Leipzig, n.F., vol.6, nos.4-6, pp.117-118, fig.1, July, 1933.

THE WATER BUFFALO. Edith M. Laing. Nature Mag., Wash., D.C., vol.34, no. 10, p.556, illus., Dec., 1941.

(CONTRIBUTION TO THE NATURAL HISTORY OF BUFFALO.) Contribution à l'Histoire naturelle des Buffles. L. Lavauden. Rev. Franç Mamm., vol.1, pp.10-39, pls.1-5, Dec. 7, 1927.

WILD SHEEP, GOATS AND ROCK ANTELOPES. Claude W. Leister. Bull. New York Zool. Soc., vol.37, no.1, pp.2-26, illus., Jan.-Feb., 1934.

FIELD NOTES ON BUSHCOW. (Syncerus caffer subsp.) K.G. Littlejohn. The Nigerian Field, vol.7, no.1, pp.17-20, Jan., 1938.

THE WHITE-MANED SEROW. R. Lydekker. Proc. Zool. Soc. London, for 1905, vol.2, pp.329-331, pl.8, Apr. 5, 1906.

WILD OXEN, SHEEP, AND GOATS OF ALL LANDS, LIVING AND EXTINCT. Richard Lydekker. 1898.

MARKHOR AND THE SAIGA. Richard H. Manville. Animal Kingdom, New York Zool. Soc., vol.59, no.1, pp.21-23, illus., Feb., 1956.

(FEMALE ANTELOPES.) Die Kuhantilopen. Paul Matschie. Naturwissenschaftliche Wochenschrift, vol.9, no.27, pp.329-330, illus., July, 1894.

(ON THE DISTRIBUTION OF THE ANTELOPES BELONGING TO THE GENUS "ORYX" BLAINV.) Ueber die Verbreitung der zur Gattung "Oryx" Blainv. gehoerigen Antilopen. Paul Matschie. Sitz. Ber.Gesell. Naturf. Freunde, Berlin, Jahrg.1893, no.3, pp.101-104, Mar. 21, 1893.

URUS AND BISON. W.D. Matthew. Nat. Hist., vol.21, pp.598-606, figs.4, Nov.-Dec., 1921.

(DATA ON THE SAIGA (SAIGA TATARICA L.).) Einiges ueber die Saiga, Saiga taterica L. Erna Mohr. Zool. Garten, n.F., vol.15, nos.5-6, pp.175-185, figs.12, 1943.

KAMBING UTAN (CAPRICORNIS SUMATRENSIS BECHST.) Erna Mohr. Zool.Garten, Leipzig, n.F., vol.7, nos.1-3, pp.24-28, May, 1934. (In German.)

(MORE ON THE KAMBING UTAN (CAPRICORNIS SUMATRENSIS BECHST.).) Weiteres vom Kambing oetan (Capricornis sumatrensis Bechst.). Erna Mohr. Zool. Garten, Leipzig, n.F., vol.8, nos.10-12, pp.291-295, illus., Sep., 1936.

ON THE SAIGA ANTELOPE, SAIGA TARTARICA (PALL.) James Murie. Proc. Zool. Soc. London, pp.451-503, figs.13, 1870.

(VARIOUS SPECIES OF KLIPSPRINGER (OREOTRAGUS).) Die verschiedenen Arten des Klippspringers (Oreotragus). Oscar Neumann. Sitz. Ber. Gesell. Naturf. Freunde Berlin, nos.7-8, pp.169-175, Oct. 21, 1902.

(CONTRIBUTIONS TO KNOWLEDGE OF PYGMY ANTELOPES.) Beitraege zur Kenntniss der Zwergantilopen. Fritz Oelckers. Zool. Garten, Leipzig, n.F., vol.17, nos. 1-5, pp.141-152, illus., 1950.

BUSHCOW. R.O. Orekyer. Nigerian Field, London, vol.8, no.3, pp.130-13, July, 1939.

REMARKS ON THE SECRETION IN THE LACHRYMAL SINUS OF THE INDIAN ANTELOPE (ANTILOPE CERVICAPRA, PALL.) WITH A TABULAR VIEW OF THE RELATIONS BETWEEN THE HABITS OF THE SEVERAL SPECIES OF ANTELOPES AND THE SUBORBITAL, MAXILLARY, POST-AUDITORY, AND INGUINAL GLANDS. R. Owen. Proc. Zool. Soc. London, pt.4, p.36, 1836.

NOTE ON THE GORAL (NEMHORAEDUS GORAL). R.H. Paddison. Jour. Bombay Nat. Hist. Soc., vol.29, p.552, Aug. 25, 1923.

CAPRA WALIE RUPPEL. Bruno Pabisi. Atti della Soc. Ital. di Sci. Nat., vol.64, pp. 110-118, pl.3, 1925. (In Italian.)

JUNGLE MEMORIES, PT. VII. WILD GOATS AND SHEEP. E.G. Phythian-Adams. Jour. Bombay Nat. Hist. Soc., vol.49, no.3, pp. 418-426, Dec., 1950.

THE DUKE OF YORK'S GAZELLE. R.I. Pocock. Field, London, vol.151, p.164, illus., Feb. 2, 1928.

THE KUDU. R.I. Pocock. Field, London, vol.153, p.1024, illus., June 29, 1929.

NOTES UPON SOME SPECIES AND GEOGRAPHICAL RACES OF SEROWS (CAPRICORNIS) AND GORALS (NAEMORHEDUS), BASED UPON SPECIMENS EXHIBITED IN THE SOCIETY'S GARDENS. R.I. Pocock. Proc. Zool. Soc. London, pp.173-202, figs.30-38, 1908.

MUSK-OXEN, CATTLE OF THE ARCTIC. E.A. Preble. Nature Mag., vol.7, pp.10-12, figs.5, Jan., 1926.

(GIRAFFE GAZELLE.) Die Giraffengazelle. Kurt Priemel. Zool. Garten, Leipzig, n.F., vol.3, nos.4-8, pp.116-134, figs.1-19, Aug. 11, 1930.

(KLIPSPRINGER IN THE WILD AND IN CAPTIVITY.) Der Klippspringer in Freileben und Gefangenschaft. Kurt Priemel. Zool. Garten, vol.14, no.3, pp.125-138, illus., 1942.

NOTE ON TRAGELAPHUS ANGASII. Mr. Proudfoot. Proc. Zool. Soc. London, pt. 18, pp.199-200, 1850.

THE MUSK-OX: AN ARCTIC RUMINANT. W.P. Pycraft. Illus. London News, vol. 189, no.5090, p.829, illus., Nov. 7, 1936.

WHITE-TAILED GNU. W.P. Pycraft. Illus. London News, vol.189, no.5076, p.210, illus., Aug. 1, 1936.

(THE KLIPSPRINGER.) L'Oreotrague sauteur. G. Remacle. La Nature, Paris, no.3007, p.169, fig.1, Aug. 15, 1937.

BATES'S DWARF ANTELOPE (HYLARNUS BATESI). D.R. Rosevear. Nigerian Field, vol.13, no.1, p.29, Jan., 1948.

NEUMANN'S HARTEBEEST. Walter Rothschild. Novitates Zoologicae, Tring, vol. 4, no.3, p.377, pl.14, Dec., 1897.

ON HYBRID HARTEBEESTS AND ON THE DISTRIBUTION OF THE ALCEPHALUS BUSELAPHUS GROUP. A.E. Ruxton, Ernst Schwarz. Proc. Zool. Soc. London, pt.3, pp.567-583, pls.2, Oct. 16, 1929.

IN QUEST OF THE QUEEN OF SHEBA'S ANTELOPE. I-II. Gertrude Sanford, Sidney Legendre. Nat. Hist., vol.30, no.1, pp. 17-32, Jan.-Feb., 1930; vol.30, no.2, pp. 161, 176, Mar.-Apr., 1930.

(ON THE TAHR (HEMITRAGUS JEMLAICUS SCHAEFERI).) Ueber den Schapi (Hemitragus jemlaicus schaeferi). Dr. Schaefer. Zool. Anzeiger, Leipzig, vol.145, pp.247-260, Nov.-Dec., 1950.

(A BONGO ANTELOPE.) Une Antilope Bongo. (Boocercus euryceros.) H. Schouteden. Rev. Zool. Bot. Afr., vol.26 (Suppl.Bull.Cercle Zool. Congo, vol.11, nos.1-2), pp.14, 16, Nov.-Dec., 1934.

THE KLIPSPRINGER. Ernst Schwarz. Nature Mag., vol.31, no.10, p.592, illus., Dec., 1938.

MENELIK'S BUSHBUCK. Ernst Schwarz. Nature Mag., Wash., D.C., vol.31, no. 5, p.308, May, 1938.

ON IBEX AND WILD GOAT. Ernst Schwarz. Ann. and Mag. Nat. Hist., London, ser. 10, vol.16, no.94, pp.433-437, Oct., 1935.

THE BOOK OF ANTELOPES. P.L. Sclater, Oldfield Thomas. London, R.H. Porter, 7 Prince Street, Cavendish Square, W., vol. 1, pp.xxxv+220, pls.24, 1894-95; vol.2, pp.v+194, pls.25, 1896-97; vol.3, pp.v+ 245, pls.47-75, 1897-98; vol.4, pp.v+242, pls.76-100, 1899-1900.

(Review by C. H. Merriam of) THE BOOK OF ANTELOPES. P.L. Sclater, Oldfield Thomas. Science, New York, n.s., vol. 1, no.14, pp.389-390, Apr. 5, 1895.

DESCRIPTION OF HUNTER'S ANTELOPE. P.L. Sclater. Proc. Zool. Soc. London, pt.3, pp.372-377, figs.3, pl. 42, Oct.1, 1889.

FURTHER NOTES ON TRAGELAPHUS GRATUS. P.L. Sclater. Proc. Zool. Soc. London, pt.1, pp.34-37, pl.8, June 1, 1883.

NOTES ON BAKER'S ANTELOPE (HIPPOTRAGUS BAKERI). P.L. Sclater. Proc. Zool. Soc. London, pp.214-218, pl.16, Mar. 26, 1868.

ON THE LESSER KOODOO, STREPSICEROS IMBERBIS OF BLYTH. P.L. Sclater. Proc. Zool. Soc. London, pt.1, pp.45-48, figs.2, pl.4, June 1, 1884.

REMARKS ON THE VARIOUS SPECIES OF WILD GOATS. P.L. Sclater. Proc. Zool. Soc. London, pt.3, pp.314-318, pls.31-32, Oct. 1, 1886.

ROCKY MOUNTAIN GOAT. Ernest T. Seton. (In) N.Amer. Big Game. A Book of the Boone and Crocket Club, Compiled by the Committee on Records of N.Amer. Big Game. Charles Scribners Sons, New York, pp.319-325, 1939.

THE TAKIN. A. deC. Sowerby. China Jour., vol.9, pp.304-306, pl.1, 1928.

WHITE-MANED SEROW. (Nemorhaedus argyrochaetes.) A. deC Sowerby. China Jour., vol.20, no.6, pp.362-362, June, 1934.

EXPERIENCES WITH BUFFALO IN BURMA AND RHODESIA. Reginald Spencer. Jour. Bombay Nat. Hist. Soc., vol.45, no.2, pp. 232-233, Apr., 1945.

MUSKOX (OVITOS MOSCHATUS) LONGEVITY. David L. Spencer. Jour. Mamm., vol. 35, no.3, p.456, Aug. 20, 1956.

BONGO--WARIEST OF ANTELOPES. C.H. Stigand. Forest and Stream, vol.90, pp. 596-597, Nov., 1920.

THE BOVINE WORLD. Ken Stott, Jr. San Diego Zoonooz, vol.15, no.3, pp.3-4, illus., Mar., 1942.

THE ELANDS. Ken Stott, Jr. Zoonooz, San Diego, vol.12, no.5, pp.10-11, May, 1940.

HARNESSED ANTELOPE. Ken Stott, Jr. Zoonooz, San Diego, vol.11, no.7, pp.4-5, July, 1939.

NOTES ON NANOTRAGUS LIVINGSTONIANUS.) Oldfield Thomas. Proc. Zool. Soc., London, no.17, pp.237-239, fig., Feb. 28, 1893.

ON THE DWARF ANTELOPES OF THE GENUS MADOQUA. Oldfield Thomas. Proc. Zool. Soc. London, pp.323-329, figs. 3, Apr. 3, 1894.

GNARRATION ON GNUS. Jack L. Throp. San Diego Zoonooz, vol.28, no.3, pp.5-6, illus., Mar., 1950.

THE GERENUK. (Litocranius.) N. Tourneur. Nature Mag., Wash., D.C., vol.31, no.2, p.79, Feb., 1938.

(CONTRIBUTION TO THE ETHOLOGY OF THE WATERBUCK AND THE HARNESSED ANTELOPE.) Contribution a l'éthologie du waterbuck Kobus defassa ugandae Neumann et de l'antilope harnachée Tragelaphus scriptus (Pallas). R. Verheyen. Mammalia, Paris, vol.19, no.2, pp.309-319, June, 1955.

ON THE M'HORR ANTELOPE (ANTILOPE MHORR, BENN.) W. Willshire. Proc. Zool. Soc. London, pt.1, p.77, 1833.

(ON THE CHAMOIS.) Von der Gemse. Franz Graf Zedtwitz. Naturforscher, Berlin, Jahrg. 14, no.10, pp.314-318, illus., Jan., 1938.

CLEVER ANIMALS. (Mountain goat.) South Dakota Conserv. Digest, Pierre, vol.9, no. 3, p. 2, illus., Mar., 1942.

FIELD NOTES ON ORIBI. Nigerian Field, London, vol.7, no.3, pp.111-112, July, 1938.

FIELD NOTES ON ROAN. Nigerian Field, London, vol.8, no.1, p.10, col. frontispiece, Jan., 1939.

FIELD NOTES ON WHITE ORYX. Nigerian Field, London, vol.8, no.1, pp.10-11, Jan., 1939.

OXEN OF THE ICE AGE. (Muskox.) Living Mus., Springfield, vol.4, no.4, p.27, Aug., 1942.

Africa

(ON THE BONGO ANTELOPE OF EASTERN AFRICA.) Nagra ord om den ostafrikaniska Bongo-antilopen. Eric Ahlstedt. Fauna och Flora, Uppsala, no.4, pp.163-166, 1933.

WITH "FUZZIES" AFTER IBEX. (Expedition in Sudan for American Museum Natural History.) H.E. Anthony. Scientific American, vol.140, pp.126-129, illus., Feb., 1929.

A FOUR-FOOTED DEMON. C.R. Aschemeier. Nature Mag., vol.5, pp.111-112, illus., Feb., 1925. (Gaboon or West African buffalo.)

PYGMY OR GABOON BUFFALO. C. R. Aschemeier. Jour. Mamm., vol.5, no.2, p. 133, May, 1924.

LECHWE OF SOUTH-CENTRAL AFRICA. Edgar N. Barclay. Ann. and Mag. Nat. Hist., London, ser.10, vol.11, no.63, pp.334-339, Mar., 1933.

(NOTES ON THE BOVIDS OF TOGO. ANTILOPINES, CEPHALOPINES, NEOTRAGINES.) Notes sur les Bovides du Togo. Antilopines, Cephalopines, Neotragines. Paul Baudenon. Mammalia, Paris, vol.16, no.3, pp.109-121, Sep., 1952.

(THE IBEX OF ERITREA.) Lo Stambecco del l'Eritrea. (Capra nubiana.) Oscar de Beaux. Annali Mus. Civ. Stor. Nat. Genova, vol.56, pp.384-394, fig., Mar.9, 1934.

(THE IBEX OF THE ERITREA COLONY.) Lo Stambecco della Colonia Eritrea. Oscar de Beaux. Rassegna Economica delle Colonie, Roma, Anno 12, nos.9-10, pp.5-15, Sep.-Oct., 1934.

NOTES ON THE FORMER AND PRESENT OCCURRENCE OF THE SABLE ANTELOPE IN THE SOUTHERN PART OF THE KRUGER NATIONAL PARK. R. Bigalke. Fauna and Flora, Transvaal, vol.6, for 1955, pp.116-123, 1957.

STATUS OF THE BLACK WILDEBEEST CONNOCHAETES GNOU (ZIMM.) IN THE UNION OF SOUTH AFRICA. R. Bigalke. South African Jour. Sci., Johannesburg, vol.43, pp.213-220, fig.1, July, 1947.

(BUFFALO OF UBANGI-SHARI-CHAD.) Buffles d l'Oubangui-Chari-Tchad. Lucien Blancou. La Terre et la Vie, 2e Sem., no.6, pp.202-207, tbls.2, Dec., 1935.

(NOTES ON THE MAMMALS FROM OUBANGUI-CHARI. THE ELAND FROM DERBY.) Notes sur les mammiféres de l'Oubangui-Chari l'éland de Derby. Lucien Blancou. Mammalia, Paris, vol.2, no.4, pp.167-172, map, Dec., 1938.

ON AFRICAN BUFFALOES. Victor Brooke. Proc. Zool. Soc. London, pp.474-484, figs. 5, pl., 1873.

ON THE ANTELOPE OF THE GENUS GAZELLA, AND THEIR DISTRIBUTION. Victor Brooke. Proc. Zool. Soc. London, pp.535-554, pls., 1873.

SUPPLEMENTARY NOTES ON AFRICAN BUFFALOES. Victor Brooke. Proc. Zool. Soc. London, pp.454-457, pl., 1875.

EXTINCT BLUE BUCK OF SOUTH AFRICA. R. Broom. Nature, London, vol.164, no. 4182, pp.1097-1098, illus., Dec. 24, 1949.

NOTE ON THE BONGO, BOOCERUS EURYCERUS, AND ITS DISTRIBUTION. G.S. Cansdale. Jour. Soc. Preserv. Fauna Empire, vol.55, pp.20-24, 1947.

(NOTE ON THE GAZELLES OF THE TIMBUKTU REGION.) Note sur les gazelles de la région de Tombouctou. M. Carbou. Revue d'Histoire Naturelle, pt.1, A. Mammifères, Paris, vol.11, no.1, pp.26-32, Jan., 1930.

SPEKE'S TRAGELAPH ON THE SESE ISLES OF LAKE VICTORIA. G.D. Hale Carpenter. Proc. Zool. Soc. London, 1925, pt.4, pp.1423-1430, pl.1, Jan., 1926.

DISTRIBUTION OF LIVINGSTONE'S SUNI IN SOUTHERN RHODESIA. (Nesotragus.) J.K. Chorley. Proc. and Trans. Rhodesia Sci. Assoc., vol.44, p.63, 1956.

THE AFRICAN BUFFALOES. C. Christy. Proc. Zool. Soc., London, pp.445-462, pls.4, maps 2, 1929.

GIANT ELAND OF SOUTHERN SUDAN. James L. Clark. Nat. Hist., vol.31, no.6, pp.581-599, illus., Nov.-Dec., 1931.

RANGES OF THE DWARF AND ROYAL ANTELOPES. A.B. Cozens. Nigerian Field, vol.16, no.1, pp.14-19, Jan., 1951.

MIGRATORY SPRINGBUCKS OF SOUTH AFRICA. S.C. Cronwright-Schreiner. London, T. Fisher Unwin, Ltd., pp.140, pls. 5, 1925.

(BUFFALO OF THE BELGIAN CONGO.) Les buffles du Congo Belge. Paul Dalimier. Inst. Parcs Nat. Congo Belge, Explor. Parc National Albert, pp.68, 1956.

ANGOLAN DIK-DIK. J.G. Dollman. Nat. Hist. Mag., London, vol.3, no.24, pp. 253-255, fig.1, Oct., 1932.

CONGO DERBY ELAND. J.G. Dollman. Nat. Hist. Mag., London, vol.2, no.9, pp.28-32, illus., Jan., 1929.

THREATENED EXTERMINATION OF BONGOS IN KENYA. Cyril Foley. Field, London, vol.159, no.4130, p.256, figs.2, Feb. 20, 1932.

CONGO BONGO. Attilio Gatti. Nature Mag., vol.30, no.2, pp.80-82, figs.4, Aug., 1937.

(GENERAL CONSIDERATIONS ON SHEEP AND GOATS, WITH SOME PARTICULAR REFLECTIONS ON THE AFRICAN HARNESSED ANTELOPE.) Considerazioni generali sulle pecore e sulle Capre, con alcune speciali riflessioni sul Muffione Africano (Ovis tragelaphus, auct.). Guiseppe Gene. Ann. Sci. Regno Lombardo-Veneto, vol.3, pp.1-4, 1834.

NOTES ON BUSH-BUCKS (CEPHALOPHORIDAE) IN THE BRITISH MUSEUM, WITH THE DESCRIPTION OF TWO NEW SPECIES FROM GABOON. John Edward Gray. Proc. Zool. Soc. London, pp.588-601, figs.8, pls., 1871.

NEW RACES OF ANTELOPES FROM BRITISH EAST AFRICA. Edmund Heller. Wash., Smiths. Inst., Misc. Coll., vol.61, no.7, pp.13, publ.2231, 1913.

NEW SABLE ANTELOPE FROM BRITISH EAST AFRICA. Edmund Heller. Wash., Smiths. Inst., Misc. Coll., vol.54, pt.6, no.1926, pp.2, 1910.

NEW RACE OF THE COMMON DUIKER, SYLVICAPRA, FROM THE KALAHARI DESERT, SOUTHWESTERN AFRICA. John Eric Hill. Amer. Mus. Novitates, New York, no.1170, p.1, May 4, 1942.

KLIPSPRINGERS OF RHODESIA, ANGOLA, AND NORTHERN NIGERIA. Martin A.C. Hinton. Ann. and Mag. Nat. Hist., ser.9, vol.8, pp.129-133, July, 1921.

FIELD-NOTES ON THE ANTELOPES OF THE MAU DISTRICT, BRITISH EAST AFRICA. WITH REMARKS BY P. L. SCLATER. F.J. Jackson, P.L. Sclater. Proc. Zool. Soc. London, pp.450-456, fig., May 4, 1897.

(GAZELLES OF NORTHERN AFRICA.) Les gazelles Nord-Africaines. L. Joleaud. Revue d'Histoire Naturelle, Pt.1, A. Mammifères, Paris, vol.11, no.3, pp.106-107, Mar., 1930.

(INTERPRETATION OF STONE ENGRAVINGS OF OVIDS AND BOVIDS OF THE NEOLITHIC PERIOD IN NORTHERN AFRICA, AFTER THE PRESENT BERBER MAGIC RAIN RITES.) Interprétation des gravures rupestres d'Ovidés et de Bovidés du Néolithique nord-africain, d'après des rites magiques berbères actuels de la pluie. L. Joleaud. L'Anthropologie, Paris, vol.43, pp.676-677, 1933.

(WILD CATTLE, SHEEP, AND GOATS ON THE BARBARY IN HISTORICAL AND PREHISTORICAL TIMES.) Boeufs, moutons et chévres sauvages de Berbérieaux temps prehistoriques et historiques. L. Joleaud. La Terre et la Vie, Rev. d'Hist. Nat., vol. 3, no.10, pp.579-585, figs.1-6, Oct., 1933.

(ZOOGEOGRAPHICAL STUDIES ON THE BARBARY. THE RUMINANTS. V. THE GAZELLES.) Études de géographie zoologiques sur la Berbérie. Les ruminants. V. Les gazelles. L. Joleaud. Bull. Soc. Zool. France, Paris, vol.54, pp.438-457, 1929.

(ZOOGEOGRAPHICAL STUDIES ON THE BARBARY. THE RUMINANTS. VI. SHEEP AND GOATS.) Études de géographie zoologique sur la Berbérie. Les ruminantes. VI. Les ovins et les Caprins. L. Joleaud. Assoc. Franc. Avanc. Sci. Chambéry, 57th Sess., pp.488-492, 1933.

(THE GAZELLES OF THE CENTRAL SAHARA.) Les gazelles du Sahara central. L. Lavauden. Bull. Soc. Hist. Nat. Afrique du Nord, vol.17, no.1, pp.11-27, Jan., 1926.

(NOTES ON THE MAMMALOGY OF NORTHERN AFRICA. THE RED GAZELLE.) Notes de mammalogie Nord-Africaine. La gazelle rouge. L. Lavauden. Bull. Soc. Zool. France, vol.55, pp.327-332, May, 1930.

ON THE HARNESSED ANTELOPES OF THE CAMEROON TERRITORY WITH SOME REMARKS ON THEIR COLOUR AND HABITS. Einar Lönnberg. Arkiv. f. Zool., Upsala, vol.2, no.15, pp.1-12, Apr. 13, 1905.

NEW SITATUNGA FROM CENTRAL AFRICA. (Limnotragus spekei wilhelmi.) Einar Lönnberg, Nils Gyldenstolpe. Ann. and Mag. Nat. Hist., ser.9, vol.13, pp.196-199, pl., Feb., 1924.

BUFFALO-SKULL FROM EAST CENTRAL AFRICA. R. Lydekker. Proc. Zool. Soc. London, vol.ii, pp.163-165, fig.31, Oct. 1, 1904.

ON A WEST-AFRICAN KOB ANTELOPE. R. Lydekker. Proc. Zool. Soc. London, pt. 3, pp.794-795, pl.53, Oct. 1, 1899.

(THE BUFFALOES OF GABON.) Les buffles du Gabon. A.R. Maclatchy. La Terre et la Vie (Revue d'Hist. Nat.), vol.2, no.10, pp. 584-596, illus., Oct., 1932.

HORNED ROYALTY OF SOUTH AFRICA. A.J. Mallet-Veale. Nature Mag., Wash., D.C., vol.32, no.3, pp.132-134, Mar., 1939.

(ARE THE ANTELOPES OF AFRICA MENACED BY THE HIDE INDUSTRY?) Les antilopes d'Afrique sont-elles menacées par l'industrie des peaux. J.P. Marty. Mammalia, Paris, vol.19, no.2, pp.344-346, June, 1955.

(APPARENTLY NEW ADENOTA FROM THE WHITE NILE.) Eine anscheinend neue Adenota vom weissen Nil. Paul Matschie. Sitz. Ber. Gesell. Naturf. Freunde Berlin, no.1, p.15, 1899.

(ZOOLOGICAL FINDINGS OF THE EXPEDITION OF CAPTAIN AN DEM FROMM TO GERMAN EAST AFRICA (1908-1909). IV) MAMMALIA (GENUS KOBUS).) Zoologische Ergebnisse der Expedition des Herrn Hauptmann a.d. Fromm 1908-1909 nach Deutsch-Ostafrika. 4. Mammalia (Gattung Kobus). Paul Matschie. Mitteil. aus dem Zool. Mus. Berlin, vol.5, no.3, pp. 553-575, 1911.

ZULULAND INYALA. H.C. Maydon. Game and Gun, vol.5, pp.76-80, illus., Feb., 1928.

REMARKS ON AN ANTELOPE FROM THE WHITE NILE, ALLIED TO OR IDENTICAL WITH THE KOBUS SING-SING OF GRAY. James Murie. Proc. Zool. Soc. London, pp.3-8, figs.2, pl.2, 1867.

DISTRIBUTION OF SENEGAL HARTEBEEST AND SENEGAL GAZELLE. T.C. Newton. Nigerian Field, vol.5, no.2, pp.84-85, Apr., 1936.

(ON THE KLIPSPRINGER OF GERMAN SOUTHWEST AFRICA.) Ueber den Klippspringer Deutsch-Suedwestafrikas. G. Niethammer. Zool. Garten, vol.14, no.3, pp.139-149, illus., 1942.

IN THE LAND OF THE GIANT SABLE-AFRICA'S RAREST ANTELOPE. (Hippotragus niger variani.) Herbert Noyes. Field, London, vol.164, no.4254, p.31, illus., July 7, 1934.

ON THE ANTELOPES OF THE AURES AND EASTERN ALGERIAN SAHARA. Alfred E. Pease. Proc. Zool. Soc. London, for 1896, pt.4, pp.809-814, figs.3, Apr. 1, 1897.

NOTE ON NKOSI ISLAND AND ITS SITATUNGA. C.R.S. Pitman. Proc. Zool. Soc. London, pt.2, pp.665-657, July, 1928.

AFRICA UGLIEST BEAST. (African buffalo.) Hugh Prior. Field and Stream, New York, vol.49, no.5, pp.9-11, 57, illus., Sep., 1944; no.6, pp.32-33, 83, illus., Oct., 1944.

(THE ANTELOPES OF KATANGA.) Les Antilopes du Katanga. Jean de Riemaecker. Bull. Cercle Zool. Congol., vol.10, no.3, pp.73-84 (=Rev. Zool. Bot. Afric., vol.23, Suppl.), May 5, 1934.

ANTELOPES OF NIGERIA. D.R. Rosevear. Nigerian Field, vol.6, no.3, pp.106-113, pls.2, July, 1937; vol.7, no.1, pp.16-17, illus., Jan., 1938; no.2, pp.52-53, Apr., 1938; no.3, pp.109-111, July, 1938; no.4, pp.153-155, Oct., 1938; vol.8, no.1, pp. 9-10, Jan., 1930.

ON TWO NEW RACES OF ORYX. (Oryx gazella blainei from Angola, and O.g. subcallotis from British East Africa.) Lord Rothschild. Ann. and Mag. Nat. Hist., ser.9, vol.8, pp.209-210, Aug., 1921.

NEW SITATUNGA FROM THE BAHR-EL-GHAZAL. (Limnotragus spekei larkenii.) J. St. Leger. Ann. and Mag. Nat. Hist., ser.10, vol.8, no.46, pp.420-421, Oct., 1931.

ON TWO "RED DUIKERS" FROM MT. ELGON AND MT. KENYA, EAST AFRICA. (Cephalophus fosteri, Cephalophus hooki.) J. St. Leger. Ann. and Mag. Nat. Hist., London, ser.10, vol.14, pp.382-385, Sep., 1934.

(ANNUAL CYCLE AND SOCIAL BEHAVIOR OF THE CAMARGUE BULL.) Cycle annuel et comportment social du taureau de Camargue. Robert Schloeth. Mammalia, Paris, vol.22, no.1, pp.121-139, illus., Mar., 1958.

(ANTELOPES OF THE STANLEYVILLE REGION.) Les Antilopes de la région de Stanleyville. H. Schouteden. Rev. Zool. Bot. Afr., vol.26, (Suppl. Bull. Cercle Zool. Congo, vol.11, nos.1-2), pp.44-45, Nov.-Dec., 1934.

(TWO NEW ANTELOPES FROM THE BELGIAN CONGO.) Zwei neue Antilopen aus dem belgischen Kongo. (Redunca redunca dianae; Tragelaphus scriptus johannae.) E. Schwarz. Rev. Zool. Bot. Afr., vol.16, no.4, pp.420-424, Apr. 1, 1929.

EXHIBITION OF, AND REMARKS UPON, A DRAWING OF THE GNU OF NYASA-LAND. P.L. Sclater. Proc. Zool. Soc. London, pt.3, pp.616-618, pl.23, Oct. 1, 1896.

ON A NEW ANTELOPE FROM SOMALI-LAND, AND ON SOME OTHER SPECIMENS OF ANTELOPES FROM THE SAME COUNTRY. P. L. Sclater. Proc. Zool. Soc. London, pt.1, pp.98-102, figs.2, pl.5, June 1, 1892.

ON TWO SPECIES OF ANTELOPES FROM SOMALILAND. P.L. Sclater. Proc. Zool. Soc. London, pt.4, for 1886, pp.504-505, pl.51, Apr. 1, 1887.

FIELD NOTES ON TWO LITTLE-KNOWN ANTELOPES: THE DAMARALAND DIKDIK (RHYNCHOTRAGUS DAMARENSIS) AND THE ANGOLAN IMPALA (AEPYCEROS PETERSI). G.C. Shortridge. S. African Jour. Sci., vol.28, pp.412-417, Nov., 1931.

LAST OF THE CAPE REEDBUCK. C.J. Skead. Rept. Dept. Nature Conservation Prov. Admin. Cape of Good Hope, Capetown, no.10, pp.23-26, 1953.

(ON NORTH AFRICAN GAZELLES AND ANTELOPES.) Ueber nordafrikanische Gazellen und Antilopen. P. Spatz. Zeitschr. f. Saeugetierk., vol.2, no.1, pp.27-29, Oct. 15, 1927.

DESCRIPTION OF A NEW DIK-DIK ANTELOPE (MADOQUA) DISCOVERED IN N. E. AFRICA BY MR. H. S. H. CAVENDISH. Oldfield Thomas. Proc. Zool. Soc. London, pp.278-279, Apr. 5, 1898.

DIAGNOSIS OF A NEW SUBSPECIES OF GAZELLE FROM BTITISH EAST AFRICA. Oldfield Thomas. Ann. and Mag. Nat. Hist., ser.6, vol.20, no.119, p.479, Nov., 1897.

NEW BLUE DUIKER FROM NYASALAND. Oldfield Thomas. Ann. and Mag. Nat. Hist., ser.7, vol.9, no.49, pp.58-59, Jan., 1902.

NEW DIK-DIK FROM BRITISH EAST AFRICA. Oldfield Thomas. Ann. and Mag. Nat. Hist., ser.7, vol.10, no.57, pp.242-243, Sep., 1902.

NEW DUIKER FROM WEST AFRICA. Oldfield Thomas. Ann. and Mag. Nat. Hist., ser.7, vol.11, no.63, pp.289-291, Mar., 1903.

NEW DUIKER FROM ZANZIBAR. Oldfield Thomas. Ann. and Mag. Nat. Hist., ser.8, vol.2, no.8, pp.151-152, Aug., 1918.

NEW SABLE ANTELOPE FROM ANGOLA. Oldfield Thomas. Proc. Zool. Soc. London, pp.298-301, fig.1, Mar., 1916.

ON A NEW AFRICAN ANTELOPE. Oldfield Thomas. Proc. Zool. Soc. London, pp.225-226, Aug. 6, 1903.

ON A NEW CEPHALOLOPHUS FROM MOUNT KILIMANJARO. Oldfield Thomas. Ann. and Mag. Nat. Hist., ser.6, vol.11, no.61, pp.48-49, Jan., 1893.

ON A NEW FORM OF NORTH-EAST AFRICAN ANTELOPE. Oldfield Thomas. Proc. Zool. Soc. London, pt.1, pp.4-5, fig.2, June 9, 1904.

ON A NEW PIGMY ANTELOPE OBTAINED BY COL. J.J. HARRISON IN THE SEMLIKI FOREST. Oldfield Thomas. Ann. and Mag. Nat. Hist., ser.7, vol.18, no. 104, pp.148-150, Aug., 1906.

ON A NEW SPECIES OF EAST AFRICAN ANTELOPE. (Oryx callotis.) Oldfield Thomas. Proc. Zool. Soc. London, pp. 195-196, pl.14, Mar. 15, 1892.

ON SOME ANTELOPES COLLECTED IN SOMALILAND BY MR. T. W. H. CLARKE. Oldfield Thomas. Proc. Zool. Soc. London, pp.206-212, pls.21-22, Mar. 17, 1891.

ON SOME GAZELLES BROUGHT BY SIR EDMUND LODER FROM ALGERIA. Oldfield Thomas. Proc. Zool. Soc. Lodon, pp. 467-472, pl.32, figs.2, June 5, 1894.

ON THE SKULL OF A BUFFALO OBTAINED IN ANKOLE, S. W. UGANDA. Oldfield Thomas. Proc. Zool. Soc. London, pt.1, p.371, Aug. 2, 1904.

ON THE 'TOHI' THE EAST-AFRICAN REEDBUCK CURRENTLY KNOWN AS CERVICAPRA BOHOR. Oldfield Thomas. Ann. and Mag. Nat. Hist., ser.7, vol.6, no.33, pp.303-304, Sep., 1900.

ON THE ZULULAND FORM OF LIVINGSTONE'S ANTELOPE. Oldfield Thomas. Ann. and Mag. Nat. Hist., ser.7, vol.2, no.10, p.317, Oct., 1898.

ON TWO NEW CENTRAL-AFRICAN ANTELOPES OBTAINED BY MR. F. J. JACKSON. Oldfield Thomas. Ann. and Mag. Nat. Hist., ser.6, vol.9, no.52, pp.385-388, Apr., 1892.

PRELIMINARY DIAGNOSIS OF A NEW GAZELLE FROM ALGERIA. Oldfield Thomas. Ann. and Mag. Nat. Hist., ser.6, vol.13, no.77, p.452, May, 1894.

ON A NEW ORIBI OBTAINED BY MAJOR POWELL-COTTON IN BRITISH EAST AFRICA. Oldfield Thomas. R.C. Wroughton. Ann. and Mag. Nat. Hist., ser.8, vol.1, no.2, pp.177-178, Feb., 1908.

ON THE GAZELLES OF TUNISIA. Joseph S. Whitaker. Proc. Zool. Soc. London, pt. 4, pp.815-817, 1896.

ON A NEW SPECIES OF PIGMY ANTELOPE OF THE GENUS NEOTRAGUS FROM THE CAMEROONS DISTRICT W. AFRICA. W.E. de Winton. Proc. Zool. Soc. London, vol.1, pp.192-194, pl.19, fig.29, Aug. 6, 1903.

ON SOME LOCAL FORMS OF CEPHALOPHUS NATALENSIS. R.C. Wroughton. Ann. and Mag. Nat. Hist., ser.8, vol.8, pp.277-279, Aug., 1911.

TWO NEW DOIKERS RELATED TO CEPHALOPHUS ABYSSINICUS AND A NEW DENDROMUS FROM MT. ELGON. R.C. Wroughton. Ann. and Mag. Nat. Hist., ser. 8, vol.5, pp.273-275, Mar., 1910.

TWO BONGO FROM SIERRA LEONE. Field, London, vol.159, no.4134, p.409, figs.2, Mar. 19, 1932.

### Anatomy

UTERUS AND FETAL MEMBRANES OF THE INDIAN ANTELOPE (ANTILOPE CERVICAPRA). Charles E. Abromavich, Jr. Anat. Rec., vol.46, no.2, pp.105-124, figs.12, 1930.

INDIVIDUAL VARIATION IN MUSKOXEN. J.A. Allen. IXth Congres International de Zoologie tenu a Monaco, pp.210-215, 1913.

ON THE PROPORTIONS OF THE LEG BONES OF SOME BOVINAE. E.G. Andreeva. Comptes Rendus (Doklady) Acad. Sci. USSR, Moscow, n.s., vol.4, no.1, pp.29-33, figs. 2, 1936.

MALFORMATION IN SKULL OF A THAR (HEMITRAGUS JEMLAICUS). R.K.M. Battye. Jour. Bombay Nat. Hist. Soc., vol. 34, no.4, pp.1057-1058, Mar. 2, 1931.

ANATOMICAL STUDIES, NO. 37: ON A HYBRID DUIKER. R. Bigalke. Union S. Africa, Dept. Agric., Dir. Vet. Serv. and Animal Indust. Rept., no.18, pt.2, pp.1093-1094, fig.1, Aug., 1932.

ABNORMAL IBEX HEAD. R.G. Burton. Jour. Bombay Nat. Hist. Soc., vol.28, p.544, Mar. 25, 1922.

OBSERVATIONS ON THE SKELETON OF AFRICAN DWARF GOATS. Tso Kan Chang, Walter Landauer. Jour. Morphol., Philadelphia, vol.86, no.2, pp.367-379, illus., Mar., 1950.

(ANATOMICAL, PHYSIOLOGICAL, AND ECOLOGICAL PARALLELS BETWEEN THE HOOF OF THE IBEX OF THE ALPS AND THAT OF THE CHAMOIS IN CONNECTION WITH ADAPTATION TO MOUNTAINS OF THESE TWO SPECIES.) Parallèle anatomique, physiologique et écologique entre le pied du bouquetin des Alpes (Capra aegagrus ibex ibex) et celui du chamois (Rupicapra rupicapra) en rapport avec l'adaptation a la montagne de ces deux espèces. Marcel A.J. Couturier. Mammalia, Paris, vol.22, no.1, pp.76-89, pls.1-2, Mar., 1958.

(THE SPERMATOZOID OF THE IBEX OF THE ALPS.) Le spermatozoide de bouquitin des Alpes (Capra ibex ibex L. 1758). Marcel A.J. Couturier. Mammalia, vol.20, no.2, pp.124-127, June, 1956.

(MORPHOLOGY OF THE GOAT UNDER THE INFLUENCE OF DOMESTICATION.) La morphologie de la chevre sous l'influence de la domestication. Paul Dalimier. Bull.

Inst. Royal Sci. Nat. Belgique, Brussels, vol.30, no.13, pp.1-12, illus., Apr., 1954.

(OS METACARPALE 2 IN THE BOVID.) Os metacarpale 2 beim Rind. Hans Demeter. Anat. Anzeiger, vol.65, pp.164-166, figs.2, 1928.

DEVELOPMENT OF AURICULAR 'GLANDULAR' PATCHES IN THE WATERBUCKS. J. Guy Dollman. Proc. Linnean Soc. London, 144th sess., pp.86-87, Sep. 19, 1932.

(OBSERVATIONS ON SOME ORGANIC PECULIARITIES OF THE CHAMOIS AND SOME SHEEP.) Observations sur quelques particularités organiques du chamois et des moutons. Joseph Gene. Mem. R.Acad. Sci., Torino, vol.37, pp.195-206, 1834.

NOTICE OF THE SKULL OF A NEW SPECIES OF BUSH-GOAT (CEPHALOPHUS LONGICEPS), SENT FROM THE GABOON BY M. DU CHAILLU. John Edward Gray. Proc. Zool. Soc. London, pp.204-206, fig., 1865.

ON THE BLOOD-CORPUSCLES OF THE IBEX OF CANDIA (CAPRA CAUCASICA, GULD). Geo. Gulliver. Proc. Zool. Soc. London, pt.10, pp.107-111, 1842.

(BREEDABLE GOAT BUCKS WITH FUNCTIONING MAMMARY GLANDS.) Zuchtfaehige Ziegenboecke mit funktionierenden Milchdruesen. J.W. Harms. Zool. Anzeiger, vol.119, nos.5-6, pp.113-123, figs.6, Aug. 1, 1937.

(LACTIFEROUS CAVITY SYSTEM OF THE GOAT UDDER.) Das milchfuehrende Hohlrausmsystems des Ziegeneuters. Wladislaw Herman. Zeitschr. f. Saeugetierk., vol.5, nos.5-6, pp.314-326, figs.2, pls.3, Dec. 22, 1930.

(NECK VERTEBRAE OF BOS AND BISON.) Die Halswirbelsaeule von Bos und Bison. Max Hilzheimer. Archiv. f. Nat., Jahrg.87, Abt. A, Hft.7, pp.1-63, 1921.

CONTRIBUTIONS TO THE STUDY OF SOME AFRICAN MAMMALS. I. THE HUMERUS AND FEMUR OF CERTAIN EAST AFRICAN ANTELOPES. A. Tindell Hopwood. Jour. Linn. Soc. London, Zool., vol.40, no.269, pp.71-92, figs.6, Nov. 30, 1936.

(ON APPARENT SIGNS OF DOMESTICATION IN THE SKELETON OF BOVINES.) Ueber angebliche Anzeichen von Domestikation am Skelett von Rindern. W. Koch. Zeitschr. f. Morph. u. Okol. der Tiere, pt.A, vol.7, no.3, pp.444-471, figs.6, Mar. 17, 1927.

(ON THE GENESIS OF THE OVARIAN TESTES.) Ueber die Genese der Ovariotestes. (Work on Goat.) G.Krediet. Archiv. f. Entwicklungsmechanik, vol.109, pp.390-410, figs.16, June 21, 1927.

ON THE OCCURRENCE OF UPPER CANINES IN A YOUNG GAZELLA GRANTI BROOKE. Einar Lönnberg. Arkiv. för Zoologie, vol.29B, no.1, pp.1-3, fig.1, Mar. 30, 1936.

STRUCTURE OF THE TAIL OF THE MUSKOX. Einar Lönnberg. Vidensk.Meddel. Danks Naturhist. For. Kobenhavn, vol. 99, pp.29-31, fig.1, July 15, 1935.

ON TWO CHINESE SEROW-SKULLS. R. Lydekker. Proc. Zool. Soc. London, for 1908, pp.940-944, Apr., 1909.

(EXPERIMENTAL MORPHOGENESIS OF THE CRANIUM OF CAVICORNS.) Morfogenesi sperimentale del cranio dei cavicorni. Ezio Marchi. Congresso dei Naturalisti Italiani., Milan, Sep. 15-19, 1906.

SUPERFICIAL FACIALIS MUSCULATURE OF THE GREENLAND MUSK-OX, OVIBOS MOSCHATUS. Thydsen Meinertz. Meddel. om Grønland, vol.107, no.5, pp.60, 1954.

VARIATION IN THE SKULL AND HORNS OF THE ISABELLA GAZELLE. Gerrit Smith Miller, Jr. U.S.Nat.Mus., Proc., Wash., vol.42, pp.171-172, pl.15, 1912.

REMARKS UPON THE LACHRYMAL SINUS IN THE INDIAN ANTELOPE (ANTILOPE CERVICAPRA, PALL.) W. Ogilby. Proc. Zool. Soc. London, pt.4, p.38, 1836.

ANATOMY OF A FETUS OF A CYCLOPEAN GOAT. J.A. Pires de Lima. Anat. Rec., vol. 19, pp.73-81, figs.6, July 20, 1920.

EXTERNAL CHARACTERS OF A BONGO (BOOCERCUS EURYCERUS) THAT DIED IN THE SOCIETY'S GARDENS. R.I. Pocock. Proc. Zool. Soc. London, ser.B, vol.113, 1943, pt.4, pp.201-205, figs.3, Feb., 1944.

(MECHANICS OF THE KNEE JOINT IN BOVINE ANIMALS.) Die Mechanik des Kniegelenkes vom Rinde. R. Reinsfeld. Zeitschr. f. Anat. u.Entwicklungsgesch., vol.97, pp.487-508, figs.7, 1932.

UPPER CANINE TEETH IN THE INDIAN ANTELOPE (ANTILOPE CERVICAPRA ). James Ritschie. Nature, London, vol.145, no.3683, p.859, June 1, 1940.

ON THE EXISTENCE OF CANINE TEETH IN AN ABYSSINIAN ANTELOPE (ANTILOPE MONTANA, RUPP.). Dr.Ruppell. Proc. Zool. Soc. London, pt.4, p.3, 1836.

(REPORT ON POST MORTEM EXAMINATION OF THE GIRAFFE GAZELLE OF FRANKFURT.) Bericht ueber die Obduktion der Frankfurter Giraffengazelle. Hans Schreiber. Zool. Garten, Leipzig, n.F., vol.3, nos.4-8, pp.135-137, figs.1-3, Aug. 11, 1930.

ABNORMAL BLACKBUCK AND A GOOD CHINKARA HEAD FROM BIKANIR. Surajmal Singh. Jour. Bombay Nat. Hist. Soc., vol. 32, p.593, illus., Jan. 15, 1928.

BIOLOGIC-ANATOMICAL INVESTIGATIONS ON THE BIPEDAL GAIT AND UPRIGHT POSTURE IN MAMMALS, WITH SPECIAL REFERENCE TO A LITTLE GOAT, BORN WITHOUT FORELEGS. E.J. Slijper. Proc. Nederl. Akad. Wetenschappen, vol.45, nos.3-4, pp.288-295, 407-415, figs.6, 1942.

NOTES OF THE POST MORTEM EXAMINATION OF A M'HORR ANTELOPE(ANTILOPE MHORR, BENN.). Mr. Spooner. Proc. Zool. Soc. London, pt.1, p.2.

(INVESTIGATIONS OF TWO SKULLS OF CAPRA PRISCA ADAMETZ.) Recherches sur 2 crânes de Capra prisca Adamets. N. Teodoreanu. Acad. Roumaine, Bull. Sec. Scient., IX-ème Année, nos.3-4, pp.21-24, figs.4, 1924.

EXHIBITION OF A MOUNTED MALE AND FEMALE SKULL OF THE EAST AFRICAN REPRESENTATIVE OF THE BONGO ANTELOPE. Oldfield Thomas. Proc.Zool. Soc. London, pp.319-320, Nov. 18, 1902.

EXHIBITION OF SKIN AND SKULL OF FEMALE YELLOW-BACHED DUIKER (CEPHALOPHUS SYLVICULTRIX). Oldfield Thomas. Proc. Zool. Soc. London, pp.1-2, Jan. 14, 1902.

(RESEARCH ON THE CRANIUM AND DENTITION OF SOME SPECIES OF AFRICAN ANTELOPE.) Ricerche sul cranio e sulla dentadura di alcune specie di Antilopi africane. Augusto Toschi. Archiv. Zool. Italiano, Torino, vol.23, pp.121-189, pls.2-3, 1936.

NOTE ON THE SUBORBITAL GLAND OF THE NYLGHAU. H.N.Turner. Proc. Zool. Soc. London, pt.19, p.116, 1851

(ANATOMIC RESEARCH ON THE ROYAL ANTELOPE NEOTRAGUS PYGMAEUS L.) Recherches anatomiques sur l'antilope royale Neotragus (Neotragus) pygmaeus L. Ach. Urbain, M. Friant. Archives Mus. Nat. Hist. Nat., Paris, ser.6, vol.18, pp. 167-179, figs.11, pls.13-14, Feb., 1942.

DETERMINATION OF AGE OF WATER BUFFALOES (BUBALUS BUBALIS LYD.) BY THE ERUPTION OF TEMPORARY AND PERMANENT INCISORS. Valente Villegas. Philippine Agric., vol.18, no.6, pp.371-378, fig.1, Nov., 1929.

(ON THE NORMAL ANATOMY OF THE BUFFALO (BOS BUBALUS).) Zur normalen Anatomie des Bueffels (Bos bubalus). P.P. Vinogradow. Anat. Anzeiger, vol.72, nos. 12-14, pp.241-244, figs.4, July 15, 1931.

(A CASE OF HERMAPHRODITISM IN A KID.) Hermaphroditismusfall bei einem Zicklein. P.P. Vinogradow, A.L. Frolow. Anat. Anzeiger, vol.68, pp.91-92, Oct. 5, 1929.

(LACK OF EARS IN SHEEP AND GOATS.) Ohrlosigkeit bei Schafen und Ziegen. B. Wassin. Zeitschr. f. Ind. Abstammungs- u. Vererbungslehre, vol.49, pp.95-104, figs.10, 1929.

PLACENTATION OF AN ANTELOPE (RHYNCHOTRAGUS KIRKII NYIKAE HELLER). Geo. B. Wislocki. Anat.Rec., Philadelphia, vol.81, no.2, pp.221-241, figs.2, pls.3, Oct. 25, 1941.

Australia, New Zealand

BUFFALO CAMP IN THE NORTHERN TERRITORY OF AUSTRALIA. R. Cardwell. Game and Gun, vol.4, pp.654-658, illus., Dec., 1927.

AUSTRALIA'S ONLY BIG GAME. MIGRATORY BUFFALO. Field, London, vol.161, no. 4181, p.413, illus., Mar. 4, 1933.

IMPORTATION OF THAR AND CHAMOIS INTO NEW ZEALAND. Field, London, vol. 161, no.4180, p.200, Feb. 4, 1933.

Diseases, Parasites

EXPERIMENTAL TRYPANOSOMA VIVAX DISEASE IN SHEEP AND GOATS IN SOUTH AFRICA. H.H. Curson. S.Afr.Jour.Sci., vol.25, pp.265-267, June-July, 1928.

NEW HOST-PARASITE RECORDS.(Helminths from Bos, Ovis, canadensis, and Oreamnos.) G. Dikmans. Proc. Helminthol. Soc. Wash., vol.9, no.2, p.65, July, 1942.

ON LONGISTRONGYLUS MEYERI GEN. AND SP. NOV., A TRICHOSTRONGYLE PARASITIZING THE RED HARTEBEEST BUBALIS CAAMA. P.L. Leroux. Jour. Helminthology, vol.9, no.3, pp.141-146, figs.3, July, 1931.

AGRIOSTOMUM EQUIDENTATUM, N. SP., A HOOKWORM OF THE SPRINGBUCK. H.O. Monnig. 15th Annual Rep. Director Vet. Serv. and Animal Industry, Union S.Africa, pp.311-316, figs.8, Oct., 1929.

NEW SPECIES OF SETARIA FROM ANTELOPES. H.O. Monnig. Jour. S.African Vet. Med. Assoc., vol.4, no.1, pp.1-3, figs.4, 1933.

NEW STRONGYLID NEMATODES OF ANTELOPES (PRELIMINARY NOTES). H.O. Monnig. Jour. S. African Vet. Med.Assoc., vol.3, no.4, pp.1-5, 1932.

WILD ANTELOPES AS CARRIERS OF NEMATODE PARASITES OF DOMESTIC RUMINANTS. H.O. Monnig. Pt.1, 17th Rep. Director Vet. Serv. and Animal Industry, Union S. Africa, pp.233-254, figs. 25, Aug., 1931; Pt.2, 18th Rep. Director Vet. Serv. and Animal Industry, Union S. Africa, pp.153-172, figs.27, Aug., 1932; Pt.3, Jour. Vet. Sci. and Animal Ind., vol.1, no.1, pp.77-92, figs.27, 1933.

(ON THE STRUCTURE OF GIARDIA CAPRAE MIHI.) Über den Bau von Giardia caprae mihi. (Parasite in small intestine of goat.) Otto Nieschulz. Archiv. f. Protistenkunde, vol.49, pp.278-286, figs.4, Nov. 5, 1924.

NEW SPECIES OF TRICHOSTRONGYLID WORM OF THE GENUS COOPERIA FROM THE CARABAO IN THE PHILIPPINE ISLAND, WITH A REVIEW OF THE GENUS. Benjamin Schwartz. Proc. U.S. Nat. Mus., vol.74, art.20, pp.1-5, pl.1, 1928.

NOTE ON THE OCCURRENCE OF TRICHOSTRONGYLUS RETORTAEFORMIS IN THE BLACK BUCK (ANTILOPE CERVICAPRA). J.E.N. Sloan. Proc. Zool. Soc. London, vol.121, pt.3, pp.723-725, Nov., 1951.

ANAPLASMOSIS IN CATTLE.(Reported to affect antelope and buffalo.) G.W.Stiles. U.S. Dept. Agric., Circ.no.154, pp.10, Dec., 1939.

(ON A NONPATHOGENIC TRYPANOSOMA FROM THE GOAT AND ITS TRANSMISSION BY LIPOPTENA CAPRINA AUST.) Ueber ein nicht pathogenes Trypanosoma aus der Ziege und seine Uebertragung durch Lipoptena caprina Aust. O.Theodor. Zeitschr.f.

Parasitenkunde, vol.1, pp.283-330, figs.15, pls.2, Aug. 10, 1928.

(ON THE QUESTION OF PIROPLASMA BIGEMINUM IN THE USSR.) Zur Frage ueber Piroplasma bigeminum in Russland (U.S.S.R.). (A parasite of Bovidae.) W.L. Yakimoff. Archiv. f. Protistenkunde, vol. 70, pp.119-130, pls.3, Apr. 4, 1930.

(BOVINE PIROPLASMOSIS AND ITS PRODUCER IN WHITE RUSSIA.) Die Rinderpiroplasmose und ihre Erreger in Weissrussland. W.L. Yakimoff, W.J.Bourzeff. Archiv. f. Protistenkunde, vol.59, pp.339-349, pl.1, Oct. 17, 1927.

(ON THE QUESTION OF BOVINE COCCIDIA.) Zur Frage ueber Rindercoccidien. W.L. Yakimoff, J.G. Galouzo. Archiv. f. Protistenkunde, vol.58, pp.185-200, figs.15, May 30, 1927.

(ON THE QUESTION OF COCCIDIANS IN GOATS.) Zur Frage ueber Coccidien der Ziege. W.L. Yakimoff, E.F. Rastegaieff. Archiv. f. Protistenkunde, vol.70, pp.185-191, figs.5, Apr. 4, 1930 ; vol.72, pp. 139-140, Nov. 3, 1930.

BRUCELLA ABORTUS INFECTION AMONG BUFFALOES IN EGYPT. R. Zaki. Jour. Comp. Path. and Therap., London, vol.58, no.1, pp.73-79, 1948.

Ecology, Habits, Behavior

HUNTED BY A BUFFALO IN CEYLON. W.G. Adam. Field, London, vol.158, no. 4100, p.126, illus., July 25, 1931.

BLACK BUCK V. MOTOR. John Budden. Jour. Bombay Nat. Hist. Soc., vol.27, p.939, July 31, 1921.

TREE-CLIMBING GOATS. Maurice Burton. Illus. London News, vol.222, no.5936, p. 118, illus., Jan. 24, 1953.

FOOD HABITS OF MOUNTAIN GOATS IN WESTERN MONTANA (ABSTRACT). R. L. Casebeer. Proc. Mont. Acad. Sci., vol.7-8, p.69, 1948.

STUDY OF THE FOOD HABITS OF THE MOUNTAIN GOAT (OREAMNUS AMERICANUS MISSOULAE) IN WESTERN MONTANA. R.L. Casebeer. MS thesis, Mont. State Univ., 1948.

DUIKER AND FRANCOLIN. G.S.Cotterell. Nigerian Field, London, vol.7, no.2, p. 95, illus., Apr., 1938.

METHODS OF ATTACK BY BUFFALO. R.M. Dane. Field, London, vol.158, no. 4102, p.219, fig.1, Aug. 8, 1931.

HABITS OF WILD GOATS IN SCOTLAND. F. Fraser Darling. Jour. Animal Ecol., London, vol.6, no.1, pp.21-22, May, 1937.

DIK-DIKS FIGHTING. L.M. Dundas. Field, London, vol.148, p.205, July 29, 1926.

(ECOLOGY AND OSTEOLOGY OF CAPRA SIBIRICA). Ekologiya sibirskogo gornogo kozla (Capra sibirica Meyer). O.V.Egorov. Trudi Zool. Inst. Akad. Nauk USSR, vol. 17, pp.7-134, 1955.

OVIBOS MOSCHATUS. (Summary of muskox habits.)Richard Glover. Beaver, vol.278, pp. 14-17, Sep., 1947.

NOTES ON MOUNTAIN GOATS IN THE BLACK HILLS. (Habits and management.) Wendell Harmon. Jour.Mamm., vol.25, no.2, pp.149-151, May, 1944.

(PECULIAR BEHAVIOR OF A DOMESTIC GOAT.) Eigenartiges Verhalten einer Hausziege. Viktor Hornung. Zool. Garten, Leipzig, n.F., vol.12, nos.2-3, p.197, July, 1940.

BEHAVIORAL INTERACTIONS IN A HERD OF BARBARY SHEEP (AMMOTRAGUS LERVIA). Irwin Katz. Zoologica, New York, vol.34, pt.1, no.3, pp.9-18, May 16, 1949.

THE ELAND AND ITS BIRD SENTINEL. Herbert Lang. Nat. Hist., vol.24, pp.96-97, fig.1, Jan.-Feb., 1924.

TWO JUNGLE INCIDENTS. (Goral swimming.) W.H. Matthews. Jour. Bengal Nat. Hist. Soc., Darjeeling, vol.20, no.4, pp. 140-141, Apr., 1946.

ON THE HABITS OF THE ROCKY MOUNTAIN GOAT. J.C. Merrill. Proc. U.S.Nat. Mus., Wash., vol.2, pp.283-284, (1879) 1880.

HISTORY AND HABITS OF THE MUSKOX. C.F. Periolat. Privately printed, Chicago, pp.24, illus., 1902.

FOOD HABITS AND RANGE USE OF THE ROCKY MOUNTAIN GOAT IN THE CRAZY MOUNTAINS, MONTANA. Jack K.Saunders. Jour. Wildl. Mgt., vol.19, no.4, pp.429-437, illus., Oct., 1955.

INFORMATION CONCERNING THE ANGORA GOAT. Geo. F.Thompson.U.S. Dept. Agric., Bur.Animal Industry, Bull. 27, pp.94, fig.1, pls.17, 1901.

(CONTRIBUTION TO THE ETHNOLOGY OF THE BLACK BUFFALO, BUBALUS CAFFER (SPARRMAN).) Contribution a l'ethologie du buffle noir Bubalus caffer (Sparrman). R. Verheyen. Mammalia, Paris, vol.18, no. 4, pp.364-370, Dec., 1954.

(CONTRIBUTION TO THE ETHNOLOGY OF THE WATERBUCK KOBUS DEFASSA UGANDAE (NEUMANN) AND THE HARNESSED ANTELOPE TRAGELAPHUS SCIPTUS (PALLAS).) Contribution a l'ethologie du waterbuck Kobus defassa ugandae (Neumann) et de l'antilope harnachée Tragelaphus scriptus (Pallas). R. Verheyen. Mammalia, Paris, vol.19, no.2, pp.309-319, June, 1955.

Economic Importance, Management

(MUSK OX PROTECTION.) Moschusochs-Schutz. Th. Alving. Zool. Garten, Leipzig, n.F., vol.3, nos.11-12, pp.344-346, 1930.

EXPERIMENTS IN RE-ESTABLISHMENT OF MUSK-OXEN IN ALASKA. W.B. Bell. Jour. Mamm., vol.12, no.3, pp.292-297, Aug., 1931.

(CHAMOIS AND ITS PROTECTION IN THE FRENCH PYRENEES.) L'isard et sa protection dans les Pyrénées frncaises. C. Bressou. Bull. Soc. Nat. Acclimat, France, vol.80, no.3, pp.79-89, Mar., 1933.

ANGORA GOAT. S.C. Cronwright Schreiner. London, New York, Longmans, Green, and Co., pp.xiv+296, illus., 1898.

COLORADO'S EXCHANGE OF GAME. Jack S. Culbreath. Colo. Conserv. Comments, vol.10, no.4, pp.3-4, 28, Dec., 1947.

THOSE "CRAZY" MOUNTAIN GOATS! (Successful game mgt.) Joe E. Gaab. Mont. Wildl., vol.5, no.1, pp.15-17, illus., Winter, 1955.

WATER BUFFALO (OFTEN CALLED THE MUS BUFFALO) ITS CHARACTERISTICS AND HABITS TOGETHER WITH A DESCRIPTION OF THE PREPARATION OF ITS HIDE FOR MAKING LOOM PICKERS. H.P. Garland. Garland Manufacturing Co., Saco, Maine, Smith and Porter Press, Boston, pp.51, figs.38, 1922.

EGYPTIAN GAME RESERVE SHELTERING MIGRATORY IBEX. L. Hatton. Field, London, vol.166, no.4331, p.1520, illus., Dec. 28, 1935.

ANGORA GOAT. ITS ORIGIN, CULTURE, AND PRODUCTS. J.L. Hayes. New York, Orange Judd Co., pp.viii+178, 1882.

CONSERVING CANADA'S MUSK-OXEN. BEING AN ACCOUNT OF AN INVESTIGATION OF THELON GAME SANTUARY 1928-1929 WITH A BRIEF HISTORY OF THE AREA AND AN OUTLINE OF KNOWN FACTS REGARDING THE MUSK-OX. W.B. Hoare. North West Terr. and Yukon Branch, Dept. Interior, Ottawa, pp.53, illus.,1930.

SANCTUARY. (Musk-oxen in Thelon Game Sanctuary.) W.B.Hoare. Beaver, Winnipeg, Outfit 270, no.1, pp.38-41, illus., June, 1939.

THE BOOK OF THE GOAT. H.S.Holmes-Pegler. 3rd Ed., London, L.U. Gill , pp. xi+222, illus., pls., 1886.

MOUNTAIN GOATS MOVED TO NEW HOME. L.J. Howard. N. Region News, pp.27-28, June 6, 1941.

CONSERVATION NOTES. CONNOCHAETES GNU. A.H.B. Kirkman. Jour. Soc.Preservation Fauna of Empire, Hertford, n.s., pt. 35, p.50, photo, Dec., 1938.

ANTELOPES IN THE KRUGER NATIONAL PARK. Leo Lownds. African Wild Life, Johannesburg, vol.10, no.1, pp.59-61, illus., Mar., 1956.

ANIMALS THAT GIVE PEOPLE MILK. T.W. McCabe. Nat.Dairy Council, Chicago, pp. 28, 1957.

ROCKY MOUNTAIN GOATS FOR OREGON MOUNTAIN. W.J. O'Connor. Western Outdoors, Oswego, vol.5, no.7, p.14, July, 1948.

(ZOO-TECHNIC SPECIAL. CASHMERE AND ANGORA GOATS. ADVANTAGES IN PROPAGATION IN RIO DE LA PLATA, ESPECIALLY IN URUGUAY. PRACTICAL METHOD FOR RAISING THE GOATS.) Zootécnica especial. Cabras cachemiras y angoras, ventajas de su propagacion en el Rio de La Plata con especialidad en el Uruguay. Método practico de la cria de las cabras. D. Ordoñana. 2nd Ed., Montevideo, 1877.

OPERATION GOAT. (Airplane census of mountain goats.) Ernst C. Peterson. Field and Stream, New York, vol.54, no.3, pp.40, 41, 87, illus., July, 1949.

PRIMITIVE PLOUGHING WITH WATER BUFFALOES. HOW THE NATIVES OF CENTRAL CELEBES DOMESTICATE THIS GREAT BEAST AND MAKE USE OF IT IN THE CULTIVATION OF RICE. H.C. Raven. Nat. Hist., New York, vol.32, no.6, pp.521-528, illus., Nov.-Dec., 1932.

TRAPPED AND TRANSPLANTED. MAINTAINING THE BALANCE OF ROCKY MOUNTAIN SHEEP AND GOATS IN THE DISTRICT (BANFF NATIONAL PARK). W.E. Round. Rod and Gun in Canada, vol.35, no.12, pp.9-10, 33, May, 1934.

TRANSPLANTING ROCKY MOUNTAIN GOATS. (In Montana.) Dale White. Nat. Hist., vol.55, no.1, pp.20-23, Jan., 1946.

CANADA'S FIGHT FOR THE MUSK OXEN. E.R. Yarham. Amer. Forests, vol.47, no. 9, pp.424-425, 448, Sep., 1941.

IN THE GREATEST OF GAME RESERVES: RINGED WATERBUCK ROAMING THE KRUGER NATIONAL PARK. (SOUTH AFRICA.) Illus. London News, vol.181, no.4886, pp.ii-iii, col.pl., Dec. 10, 1932.

MILK GOATS PLAY IMPORTANT RÔLE IN EUROPE. National Nature News, vol.2, no.39, pp.1, 6, 7, illus., Oct. 10, 1938.

SET SPECIAL SEASON ON BARBARY SHEEP. New Mexico Department of Game and Fish. New Mex.Mag., vol.33, no.11, pp.31-33, illus., Nov., 1955.

WYOMING'S MOUNTAIN GOAT EXPERIMENT. Wyo. Game and Fish Commission. Wyo. Wild Life, vol.19, no.9, pp.10-13, illus., Sep., 1955.

Eurasia

NOTES ON THE WILD ANTELOPE OF KHAURISM (ANTILOPE SAIGA, PALL.). James Abbott. Proc. Zool. Soc. London, pt.9, p.70, 1841.

SOLVING THE MYSTERY OF A ROGUE BUFFALO. (In Ceylon.) W.G. Adam. Field, London, vol.161, no.4195, p.1156, illus., May 20, 1933.

(ANTELOPES OF NORTHERN TIBET AND ADJACENT REGIONS.) G. P. Adlerberg. Comptes Rendus Acad. Sci. USSR, ser. A, no.12, pp.321-330, figs.2, 1931.

BOVIDAE FROM THE ASIATIC EXPEDITIONS. Glover M. Allen. Amer. Mus. Novitates, no.410, pp.1-11, Mar. 19, 1930.

DISCOVERY OF THE CHINESE TAKIN. M.P. Anderson. Nat. Hist., vol.20, pp. 428-433, Sep.-Oct., 1920.

THE QUEST OF THE GOLDEN FLEECE. Roy C. Andrews. I. THE WILDS OF SHENSI. Asia, vol.22, no.6, pp.440-446, June, 1922; II. TAKIN ON THEIR RUGGED PEAKS. Asia, vol.22, no.7, pp.515-520, 568, July, 1922.

NEW SPECIES OF SAIGA FROM MONGOLIA. (Saiga mongolica.) A.G. Bannikov. Comptes Rendus (Doklady) Acad. Sci. USSR, Moscow, vol.51, no.5, pp.401-404, figs.2, Feb. 20, 1946.

(HISTORY OF THE REINTRODUCTION OF THE WILD GOAT IN THE SWISS ALPS.) Histoire de la réintroduction du bouquetin dans les Alpes suisses. Maurice Boubier. Bull. Soc. Zool. Génève, vol.3, pp.68-75, 1927.

ORYX IN TRANSJORDAN. Ray Buller. Field, London, vol.156, no.4047, p.99, fig.1, July 19, 1930.

WORLD'S RAREST WILD GOAT. (Agrimi of Crete.) Reg Butler. Outdoor Life, New York, vol.110, no.1, pp.17-19, illus., July, 1952.

ARABIAN ADVENTURE TO THE GREAT NAFUD IN QUEST OF THE ORYX. Douglas Carruthers. Witherby, London, pp.xii+208, illus., 1935.

ON A NEW GAZELLE FROM CENTRAL ARABIA. Douglas Carruthers, Ernst Schwarz. Proc. Zool. Soc. London, pt.1, pp.155-156, pl.1, Apr., 1935.

MISHMI TAKIN (BUDORCAS TAXICOLOR). H.L. Cooper. Jour. Bombay Nat. Hist.Soc., vol.29, pp.550-551, Aug. 25, 1923.

(ON THE TRACKS OF MY 500 CHAMOIS FROM FRANCE.) Sur les traces de mes 500 chamois de France. Marcel Couturier. Arthaud, Paris, pp.272, illus., 1949.

(PROJECT FOR A NATIONAL PARK OF IBEX IN FRANCE.) Projet d'un Parc National a Bouquetins en France. Marcel Couturier. Mammalia, Paris, vol.7, no.2, pp.80-85, fig.1, June, 1943.

ON THE OCCURRENCE OF WILD BUFFALOES IN JAVA AND SUMATRA. K.W. Dammerman. Treubia, vol.14, no.4, pp. 487-494, pls.12-14, Dec., 1934.

SUPPOSED DISCOVERY OF UNICORNS IN TIBET. Warren R. Dawson. Proc. Linnean Soc. London, sess.147, pt.2, pp.41-46, May 10, 1935.

(CURIOUS ASIATIC ANTELOPE.) Une curieuse antilope Asiatique. J. Delacour. La Terre et al Vie (Revue d'Hist.Nat.), vol.1, no.4, p.248, figs.2, May, 1931.

WILD BUFFALO OF CEYLON, A NEW SUBSPECIES. P.E.P. Deraniyagala. Spolia Zeylanica, Bull.Nat. Mus. Ceylon, vol.27, pt.1, pp.103-105, illus., Oct. 24, 1953.

A NEW GAZELLE SHOT BY H.R.H. THE DUKE OF YORK, K.G. (Gazella arabica hanishi.) J.G. Dollman. Nat. Hist. Mag., London, vol.1, no.5, pp.129-131, illus., Jan., 1928.

(INTERESTING REPORT ON THE OCCURRENCE OF MUSK OXEN IN ASIA.) Eine interessante Angabe zum Vorkommen des Moschusochsen in Asien. Julius Ehik. Zeitschr. f. Saeugetierk., vol.7, no.6, pp. 258-259, pl.22, Dec. 15, 1932.

(DISTRIBUTION OF THE MOUFFLON AND CHAMOIS BY ZONES IN THE DIFFERENT PERIODS OF THE YEAR IN TEBERDINSKY RESERVATION.) Raspredelenie turov i sern po zonam v raznie periodo goda na territorii teberdinskogo zapovednika. Z. S. Ekvtimishvili. Soobshcheniya Akad. Nauk Gruzinskoi SSR, vol.14, no.3, pp. 163-166, 1953.

(HERD OF MOUFLON AND CHAMOIS IN TEBERDINSKY PRESERVE.) Stadnost turov i sern na territorii teberdinskogo zapovednika. Z.S. Ekvtimishvili. Soobshcheniya Akad. Nauk Gruzinskoi SSR, vol.14, no.5, pp.303-308, 1953.

NOTES ON THE GORAL FOUND IN BURMA. G.H. Evans. Proc. Zool. Soc. London, vol.2, pp.311-314, Apr. 5, 1906.

CHAMOIS OF THE PYRENEES. V. Forbin. Nat. Hist., vol.23, pp.138-141, figs.3, Mar.-Apr., 1923.

NOTE ON THE "HWANG-YANG", OR YELLOW SHEEP OF MONGOLIA. John Edward Gray. Proc. Zool. Soc. London, pp.244-245, figs.2, 1867.

(ON THE DISTRIBUTION OF THE MUSK OX (OVIBOS MOSCHATUS ZIMM.) IN EASTERN EUROPE AND NORTHERN ASIA.) Vera Gromova. Izvestiia Akad. Nauk SSSR, Otdelenie Matematicheskikh i Estestvennykh Nauk (Bull Acad.Sci. USSR Cl. Sci. Math. et Nat.), no.1, pp. 101-114, 1935. (In Russian with German summary.)

(POPULATION OF THE ALPEN WILD GOAT CAPRA IBEX IBEX LINNÉ 1758.) Bestand des Alpensteinbockes, Capra ibex ibex, Linné, 1758. Th. Halthenorth. Saeugetierk. Mitteil., Stuttgart, vol.1, no.4, pp.173-174, Oct. 1, 1953.

(REPORT ON THE SETTLEMENT OF THE ALPEN WILD GOAT IN THE NATURAL PROTECTIVE REGION OF BERCHTESGADEN.) Bericht ueber die Einbuergerung des Alpensteinbockes im Naturschutzgebiet Berchtesgaden. Lutz Heck. Natur und Volk, Frankfurt am Main, vol.81, no.11, pp.295-297, Nov. 1, 1951.

(ANCIENT BUFFALO OF CELEBES.) Der Urbueffel von Celebes: Anos depressicornis (H.Smith). K.M. Heller. Inaugural-Dissertation, Rostock, pp.39, pls.2, 1889.

SEROW FROM WU-HU. Hsi J. Ho. China Jour., vol.23, no.3, pp.175-176, Sep., 1935.

DESCRIPTION OF A NEW GAZELLE FROM NORTHWESTERN MONGOLIA. N. Hollister. Smiths. Inst., Misc. Coll., vol.60, no.19, pp.1-2, publ.2165, Feb. 8, 1913.

(OCCURRENCE OF RUPICAPRA RUPICAPRA ON MOUNT OLYMPUS (GREECE).) Das Vorkommen von Rupicapra rupicapra auf dem Berge Olymp (Griechenland). Otto Koller. Zool. Anzeiger, vol.83, p.46, June 15, 1929.

SAIGA FROM THE STEPPES OF SIBERIA. Claude W. Leister. Bull. New York Zool. Soc., vol.40, no.1, pp.23-24, illus., Jan.-Fen., 1937.

THE BALTISTAN IBEX (CAPRA SIBERICA WARDI). R. Lydekker. Great and Small Game of India, Burma and Tibet, pp.1-5, fig.1, 1900.

GORALS OF INDIA AND BURMA. R. Lydekker. Zoologist, London, ser.4, vol.9, no.765, pp.81-84, pl.1, Mar., 1905.

NOTE ON THE MARKHOR OF CABUL. R. Lydekker. Proc. Zool. Soc. London, vol.2, pt.2, pp.323-324, pl.27, Apr., 1903.

ON THE BALTISTAN IBEX. R. Lydekker. Rowland Ward, Ltd., "The Jungle" Piccadilly, London, pp.1-5, 1900.

THE SZE-CHUEN AND BHUTAN TAKINS. R. Lydekker. Proc. Zool. Soc. London, for 1908, pp.795-802, Apr., 1909.

(PYRENEAN WILD GOAT.) Der Pyrenaensteinbock. Florentin Mann. Die Umschau, Frankfurt am Main, Jahrg.37, no.42, pp. 819-821, figs.3, Oct., 1933.

(CAUCASIAN WILD GOATS.) Kaukasische Steinboecke. Paul Matschie. Sitz. Ber. Gesell. Naturf. Freunde, Berlin, no.1, pp. 27-31, Jan. 15, 1901; Natur und Haus, Jahrg. 9, Hft.5, pp.171-175, Feb. 1, 1901.

LETTER FROM, CONCERNING THE SUPPOSED EXISTENCE OF THE ANOA (ANOA DEPRESSICORNIS) IN THE PHILIPPINES. A.B. Meyer. Proc. Zool. Soc. London, p. 881, 1878.

NEW CHAMOIS FROM THE APENNINES. Gerrit S. Miller, Jr. Proc. Biol. Soc. Wash., vol.25, pp.131-134, July 31, 1912.

DISTRIBUTION OF SEROW IN BURMA. C.E. Milner. Jour. Bombay Nat. Hist. Soc., vol.28, pp.267-268, Dec. 30, 1921.

(GEOGRAPHICAL DISTRIBUTION OF ANOA SPECIES ON CELEBES.) Die geographische Verbreitung der Anoa-Arten auf Celebes. E. Mohr. Archiv f. Nat., pp.208-214, 1921.

DISTRIBUTION OF WILD BUFFALO IN ORISSA. H.F. Mooney. Jour. Bombay Nat. Hist. Soc., vol.34, no.1, pp.242-244, photo, map, Mar. 1, 1930.

(CHAMOIS OF THE ABRUZZI APENNINES.) Die Gemse der Abruzzen. Oscar Neumann. Ann. Mus. Civ. Stor. Nat. Genova, ser.2, vol.20 (40), pp.347-350, illus., Dec. 20, 1899.

WATER BUFFALO OF INDIA. Ralph W. Phillips. Jour. Heredity, Wash., vol.36, no.3, pp.71-76, figs.3-5, Mar., 1945.

SEROWS, GORALS AND TAKINS OF BRITISH INDIA AND THE STRAITS SETTLEMENTS. R. I. Pocock. Jour. Bombay Nat. Hist. Soc., pt.2, vol.22, no.2, pp.296-319a, pls.7, Sep. 30, 1913.

(ON AN OVIBOS FIND FROM SILESIA.) Ueber einen Ovibus-Fund aus Schlesien. Hermann Pohle. Centralblatt f. Min., Abt. B, no.4, pp.122-125, figs.2, 1925.

(IBEX, ITS EXTINCTION AND RESTOCKING IN SWITZERLAND.) Kozorožec, jeho vymírání a znovuosazování ve Švýc. J.S. Procházka. Alpách. Véda Přírodni Měs. pro Šiř. a Pěst. Věd. Přír., Prague, vol.7, nos. 2-3, pp.51-55, 1926.

(WILD WATER BUFFALO IN THE RESIDENTIAL AREA OF BENKOELEN.) Wilde karbouwen in de Residentie Benkoelen. F. W. Rappard. Tropische Natuur, Batavia, Jaarg. 30, Aflevering 10-11, pp.149-154, figs.7, Oct. 20, 1941. (Bubalus bubalis sondaicus (Schleg. and Muell.).)

(RESETTLEMENT OF THE WILD GOAT.) Die Wiedereinburgerung des Steinbocks. Andrea Rauch. Naturforscher, Jahrg. 15, no. 1, pp.5-8, illus., Apr., 1938.

(WILD GOATS OF JOURA ISLAND.) Die Wildziege der Insel Joura. Anton Reichenow. Zool. Jahrbuecher, Jena, vol.3, no.4, pp. 591-596, May 31, 1888.

(NOTES ON THE GAZELLES FOUND IN CENTRAL ASIA BY THE HAARDT-AUDOUIN-DUBREUIL MISSION.) Note sur les gazelles rencontrees en Asie Centrale par la Mission Haardt-Audouin-Dubreuil. A. Reymond. Bull. Mus. Nat. Hist. Nat. Paris, ser.2, vol.4, no.8, pp. 955-957, Dec., 1932.

(ON THE DWARF BHARAL (PSEUDOIS SPEC. NOV.) AND THE LARGE BHARAL (PSEUDOIS NAHOOR HDGS.) OF TIBET.) Ueber das Zwergblauschaf (Pseudois spec.nov.) und das Grossblauschaf (Pseudois bahoor Hdgs.) in Tibet. Ernst Schaefer. Zool. Garten, Leipzig, n.F., vol.9, no.6, pp.263-278, illus., Dec., 1937.

WOOL MART OF THE INDO-TIBETAN BORDERLAND. H. Lee Shuttleworth. Geogr. Review, vol.13, pp.552-558, figs.5, Oct., 1923.

CHAMOIS IN THE ALPS. F.S. Smythe. Field, London, vol.152, p.471, illus., Sep. 20, 1928.

THE BLUE SHEEP OF KANSU. A. deC. Sowerby. China Jour. Sci. and Arts, vol.1, pp.158-160, Mar., 1923.

GAZELLE IN MANCHURIA. A. deC. Sowerby. China Jour., vol.9, p.258, illus., Nov., 1928.

THE YUNNAN SEROW. A. deC. Sowerby. China Jour., vol.13, no.1, p.43, July, 1930.

ON THE FORMS OF THE HIMALAYAN SEROW CAPRICORNIS SUMATRAENSIS. C.H. Stockley. Jour. Bombay Nat. Hist. Soc., vol.29, pp.824-827, pls.2, Dec. 31, 1923.

SIND IBEX WHICH ARE FAST DISAPPEARING. C.H. Stockley. Field, London, vol. 164, no. 4266, p.739, illus., Sep. 29, 1934.

ON A NEW GAZELLE FROM CENTRAL ARABIA. Oldfield Thomas. Ann. and Mag. Nat. Hist., ser.6, vol.19, no.110, pp.162-163, Feb., 1897.

ON A NEW GAZELLE FROM PALESTINE. Oldfield Thomas. Proc. Zool. Soc. London, vol.2, pp.347-349, fig.90, Apr. 18, 1905.

PRELIMINARY DESCRIPTION OF A NEW GOAT OF THE GENUS HEMITRAGUS, FROM SOUTH-EASTERN ARABIA. Oldfield Thomas. Ann. and Mag. Nat. Hist., ser.6, vol.13, no.76, pp.365-366, Apr., 1894.

(ASIATIC BOVINE COLLECTION OF THE BOIS DE VINCENNES.) La collection des Bovinés Asiatiques du parc zoologique du Bois de Vincennes. Ach. Urbain et al.1939.

DAGHESTAN TOOR (MOUNTAIN GOAT) (CAPRA CYLINDRICORNIS BLYTH.) IN AZERBAIJAN. N. Veretschagin. Akad. Nauk SSSR, Azerbaidzhanskii filial, Trudy Zool. Inst., Baku, vol.9, pt.45, pp.72, figs.31, tbls. 18, 1938.

(LIFE AND HABITS OF CAPRA AEGAGRUS (PALLAS) OF THE TAURUS MOUNTAINS (REGION OF ALAYA). Vie et moeurs des Capra aegagrus (Pallas) des Mts. Taurus (région d'Alaya). Aly Wahby. Archiv. Zool. Italiano, vol.16, nos.1-2, pp.545-549, pl. 1, 1931.

ON THE WILD GOAT IN SCOTLAND. Hugh Boyd Watt. Jour. Animal Ecol., London, vol.6, no.1, pp.15-20, pl.1, May, 1937.

WILD GOAT IN SCOTLAND. Hugh Boyd Watt. Scottish Naturalist, Edinburgh, no. 228, p.178, Nov.-Dec., 1937.

THE MISHMI TAKIN. H. W. Wells. Jour. Bombay Nat. Hist. Soc., vol.29, pp.830-831, Dec. 31, 1923.

(THE PRESENT STATUS OF THE GAZELLE IN THE MIL-KARABAGH STEPPE.) N. K. Werestchaghine. Akad. Nauk SSSR, Izvestiia Azerbaidzhanskogo Filiala, Baku, no.2, pp. 155-174, fold.map, 1938. (In Russian with French summary.)

AFTER TONKIN ON THE BURMESE FRONTIER. G.E. Whittall. Field, London, vol. 165, no.4290, p.567, illus., Mar. 16, 1935.

(WILD MAMMALS OF CRETE.7) NOTES ON THE WILD GOAT OF CRETE.) Die Wildsaeuger von Kreta. 7) Bemerkungen ueber die Wildziege Kretas. Klaus Zimmerman. Zeitschr. f. Saeugetierk., vol.17, no.1, p. 66, pl.10, Feb. 19, 1953.

YUNNAN SEROW. China Jour., vol.12, no. 4, p.218, Apr., 1930.

Fossils

(PLIOCENE GAZELLE NEAR THE MOUTH OF THE ORB.) Une gazelle Pliocene près de l'embouchure de l'Orb. Gaston Astre. Bull. Soc. Hist. Nat. Toulouse, vol.60, pp.343-344, 1930.

MUSK-OXEN OF NEBRASKA. E.H. Barbour. Nebraska State Mus., vol.1, Bull.25, pp. 211-233, figs.15, Dec., 1931.

NEW OVIBOVINE, SYMBOS CONVEXIFRONS, SP. NOV. E.H. Barbour. Nebraska State Mus., vol.1, Bull.37, pp.295-298, figs. 173-174, 1934.

NEW FOSSIL BOVID FROM NEBRASKA WITH NOTICE OF A NEW BISON QUARRY IN TEXAS. (Parabos, P. dodsoni.) E.H. Barbour, C.Bertrand Schultz. Bull. Univ. Nebraska State Mus., Lincoln, vol.2, no. 7, pp.63-68, figs.24-27, Dec., 1941.

FOSSIL ANTELOPES OF PALESTINE IN NATUFIAN (MESOLITHIC) TIMES WITH DESCRIPTIONS OF NEW SPECIES. M.A. Bate. Geol. Mag., London, vol.77, no.6, pp.418-443, figs.9, Nov.-Dec., 1940.

NEW AFRICAN FOSSIL LONG-HORNED BUFFALO. M.A. Bate. Ann. and Mag. Nat. Hist., London, ser.12, vol.2, no.17, pp. 396-398, Aug. 19, 1949.

SOME FOSSIL HIPPOTRAGINE ANTELOPES FROM SOUTH AFRICA. H.B.S. Cooke. South African Jour. Sci., Johannesburg, vol. 43, pp.226-231, figs.2, July, 1947.

(GOAT IN ANTIQUITY.) La chèvre dans l'antiquité. Pierre Crepin. Revue d'Histoire Naturelle, pt.1, A, Mammifères, Paris, vol.10, no.11, pp.362-385, Nov., 1929.

FIND OF A SAIGA ANTELOPE (SAIGA TATARICA (PALL.)) IN DANMARK. Magnus Degerbol. Meddelelser Dansk Geol. Forening, Kobenhavn, vol.8, no. 2, pp.175-184, illus., pl.5, 1932. (In Danish with English summary.)

DISTRIBUTION AND DESCRIPTION OF SKULL REMAINS OF THE PLIOCENE ANTELOPE SPHENOPHALOS FROM THE NORTHERN GREAT BASIN PROVINCE. Eustage L. Furlong. Carnegie Inst. Wash., Publ.418, pp.27-36, fig.1, pls.5, Feb., 1931.

PLEISTOCENE ANTELOPE, STOCKOCEROS CONKLINGI, FROM SAN JOSECITO CAVE, MEXICO. Eustage L. Furlong. Carnegie Inst. Wash., Contrib. Paleontol., Publ.551, pp.1-8, pls.5, Feb. 3, 1943.

PREPTOCERAS, AS NEW UNGULATE FROM THE SAMWEL CAVE, CALIFORNIA. Eustage L. Furlong. Univ. Calif. Publ., Berkeley, Bull. Dept. Geol., vol.4, no.8, pp.163-169, pls.-24-25, July, 1905.

STATUS OF THE EXTINCT AMERICAN "ELAND". C. Lewis Gazin. Jour. Mamm., vol.14, no.2, pp.162-164, May, 1933.

DESCRIPTIONS OF TWO NEW SPECIES OF PLEISTOCENE RUMINANTS OF THE GENERA OVIBOS AND BOÖTHERIUM, WITH NOTES ON THE LATTER GENUS. James W. Gidley. Proc. U.S. Nat. Mus., vol.34, no. 1627, pp.681-684, pls.57-59, Sep. 15, 1908.

EXTINCT AMERICAN ELAND. James W. Gidley. Smiths. Misc. Coll., Publ.2174, vol.60, no.27, pp.1-3, pl.1, Mar. 22, 1913.

(ON A NEW SPECIES OF FOSSIL ANTELOPE (PARABUBALIS CAPRICORNIS) OF TRANSBAIKALIA.) Vera Gromova. Annuaire Mus. Zool. Acad. Sci. USSR, Leningrad, vol.32, no.1, pp.127-134, figs. 2, 1931. (In Russian.)

(ON FINDS OF WILD SHEEP AND GOATS IN THE QUATERNARY DEPOSITS OF THE CRIMEA.) Vera Gromova. Comptes Rendus (Doklady) Acad. Sci. USSR, Moscow, n.s., vol.4, nos.1-2, pp.105-108, 1935.

ON A LONG-KNOWN OCCURRENCE OF A MUSK-OX AT NATCHEZ, MISSISSIPPI. O.P. Hay. Jour. Mamm., vol.11, no.4, pp.505-507, Nov., 1930.

EPILEPTOBOS GEN. NOV. FOR LEPTOBOS GROENEVELDTII DUBOIS FROM THE MIDDLE PLEISTOCENE. D.A. Hooijer. Zool. Med. Mus. Leiden, vol.34, no.17, pp.239-241, May 14, 1956.

FOSSIL GAZELLE (GAZELLA SCHREUDERAE NOV. SPEC.) FROM THE NETHERLANDS. D.A. Hooijer. Zool. Mededeel., Leyden, vol.25, pp.55-64, fig.1, 1945.

PLEISTOCENE VERTEBRATES FROM CELEBES. I. CELEBESHEERUS BECKERENI NOV. GEN. NOV. SPEC. D.A. Hooijer. Proc. Kon. Nederlandsche Akad. Wetenschappen, vol.51, no.8, pp.1024-1032, pl. 1, 1948.

(OVIBOS PALLANTIS HAM. SMITH, THE MUSKOX OF THE OLD WORLD GLACIAL PERIOD ACCORDING TO A THIRD FIND FROM SAXONY.) A. Jacobi. Sitz. Ber. u. Abhandl. Naturwiss. Ges. Isis, Dresden, Jahrg.1932, pp.187-197, figs.2, pl.1, 1933. (In German.)

(ANTELOPES OF SAVANNAHS OF THE PLIO-QUATERNARY OF NORTHERN AFRICA AND ANTELOPES OF THE FOREST OF THE SAHARA QUATERNARY.) Antilopes de Savanes du Plio-Quaternaire Nord-Africain et Antilopes forestières du Quaternaire Saharien. Léonce Joleaud. Comptes Rendus 12th Congrès Internat. Zool. Lisbonne 1935, Lisboa, vol.2, pp.1172-1190, 1936-37.

PLEISTOCENE MUSK-OX FROM NEW YORK AND THE DISTRIBUTION OF THE MUSK-OXEN. David B. Kitts. Amer. Mus. Novitates, New York, no.1607, pp.1-8, Jan. 2, 1953.

(GOATS IN THE HUNGARIAN DILUVIAL EPOCH.) Kecskék a Magyar Diluviumban. M. Kretzoi. Földtani Közlöny, vol.72, pp. 259-262, 353-356, pl.24, 1942.

DESCRIPTION OF A FOSSIL BUFFALO FROM EAST AFRICA. Einar Lonnberg. Arkiv. f. Zoologi, Stockholm, vol.25A, no.17, pp.1-32, figs.2, pls.3, June 15, 1933.

ON THE SKULL OF A CHIRU-LIKE ANTELOPE FROM THE OSSIFEROUS DEPOSITS OF HUNDES (TIBET). R. Lydekker. Quart. Jour. Geol. Soc., vol.57, pp.289-292, figs.1-2, Aug., 1901.

SPECIMEN OF THE EXTINCT MUSK-OX, SYMBOS CAVIFRONS (LEIDY), FROM NORTH LIBERTY, INDIANA. Marcus W. Lyon, Jr. Proc. Indiana Acad. Sci., vol. 35, pp.321-324, illus., 1928?

SKULL OF MUSK-OX, GENUS SYMBOS, FROM MONTGOMERY COUNTY, INDIANA. Marcus W. Lyon, Jr., Fred T. Hall. Amer. Midland Nat., vol.18, no.4, pp.608-609, pls.2, July, 1937.

OVIBUS CAVIFRONS FROM THE LOESS OF IOWA. W.J. McGee. Amer. Jour.Sci., New Haven, ser.3, vol.24, pp.217-220, Sep., 1887.

SUPPOSED OCCURRENCE OF AN ASIATIC GOAT-ANTELOPE IN THE PLEISTOCENE OF COLORADO. Gerrit S. Miller, Jr. Smiths. Inst., Misc. Coll., Wash., D.C., vol.82, no.14, Publ.3180, pp.2, pls.2, Dec. 22, 1930.

SCAPHOCEROS TYRRELLI, AN EXTINCT RUMINANT FROM THE KLONDIKE GRAVELS. W.H. Osgood. Smiths. Inst., Misc. Coll., vol.48, pp.173-185, July 1, 1905.

SYMBOS, A SUBSTITUTE FOR SCAPHOCEROS. W.H. Osgood. Proc. Biol. Soc. Wash., vol.18, pp.223-224, Oct. 17, 1905.

(FINDING OF IBEX (AND OTHER FAUNA) IN THE III. PLEISTOCENE TERRACE OF THE VLTAVA RIVER IN HOLESOVICE.) Nález kozorožce (a ostatni fauny) ve III. plistocaenni terase Vltavy v Holešovicich. Jar Petrbok. Věda Přirodni Měs. pro Šif. a Pěst. Věd.Přir., Prague, vol.9, no.3, p. 94, 1928.

FOSSIL BOVIDAE OF INDIA. Guy E. Pilgrim. Mem. Geol. Surv. India, Palaeontologia Indica, Calcutta, n.s., vol.26, mem.1, pp.iii+356, figs.35, pls.8, 1939.

FOSSIL SKULL OF HEMIBOS FROM PALESTINE. Guy E. Pilgrim. Ann. and Mag. Nat. Hist., London, ser.11, vol. 7, no.40, pp.347-360, figs.3, pl.4, Apr., 1941.

SIWALIK ANTELOPES AND OXEN IN THE AMERICAN MUSEUM OF NATURAL HISTORY. Guy E. Pilgrim. Bull. Amer. Mus. Nat. Hist., vol.72, pp.729-874, figs. 81, Mar. 31, 1937.

TWO NEW SPECIES OF SHEEP-LIKE ANTELOPE FROM THE MIOCENE OF MONGOLIA. Guy E. Pilgrim. Amer. Mus. Novitates, no.716, pp.1-29, figs.12, May 2, 1934.

CATALOGUE OF THE PONTIAN BOVIDAE OF EUROPE IN THE DEPARTMENT OF GEOLOGY. Guy E. Pilgrim, A.T. Hopwood. Publ. Brit. Mus. Nat. Hist., London, pp. vii+106, pls.9, 1928.

(PLEISTOCENE BOVIDAE IN SLOVAKIA.) Pleistocenskih bovidih na Slovenskem. I.O. Rakovec. Slovenska Akad Znan. Umet., Cl. IV. Hist. Nat., no.3, pp.303-328, June, 1955. (With English summary.)

(ON THE OCCURRENCE OF THE MUSK OX (OVIBUS MOSCHATUS) IN THE DILUVIUM OF SILESIA.) F. Roemer. Zeitschr. Deutschen Geol. Gesell., vol.26, no.3, figs.5, pp.600-604, 1874. (In German.)

(RESEARCH ON FOSSIL MUSK-OXEN FROM THE AREA OF POLAND.) Badania nad pizmowolami kopalnymi z terenu Polski. Zbigniew Ryziewcz. Inst. Geol. Badan Czwartorzedu Polsce, vol.5, pp.177-230, 1954. (With English summary, pp.242-252.)

(WILD GOAT OF THE CAPRA PRISCA-GROUP FROM THE PLEISTOCENE OF LOWER AUSTRIA.) Eine Wildziege der Capra prisca-Gruppe aus dem Plistozaen Niederoesterreichs. Otto Sickenberg. Palaeobiologica, vol.3, nos.1-2, pp.92-102, fig.1, pl.12, 1930.

(NEW ASPECTS OF THE ANTELOPES OF TERTIARY TIMES IN THE SOUTHERN USSR.) Noviye vidi antilop tretichnoi fauni yuga SSSR. I.I. Sokolov. Trudi Zool. Inst. Akad. Nauk, SSSR, vol.17, pp.217-223, 1955.

ON THE DISCOVERY OF REMAINS OF "POLOROGS" (BOVIDAE, MAMMALIA) IN LOWER MIOCENE DEPOSITS OF

WESTERN GOBI. I.I. Sokolov. Proc. Paleo. Inst., Acad. Sci. USSR, vol.41, pp.155-158, illus., 1952.

(ON THE SYSTEMATIC POSITION OF GENUS LEPTOBOS.) Ueber die systematische Stellung des Genus Leptobos. H.G. Stehlin. Eclog. geol. Helv., vol.21, no.1, pp.217-218, 1928.

ASSOCIATION OF HORN-CORES AND UPPER MOLARS OF THE ANTELOPE SPHENOPHALOS NEVADANUS FROM THE LOWER PLIOCENE OF NEVADA. R.A. Stirton. Amer. Jour. Sci., ser.5, vol.24, no.139, pp.46-51, figs.3, July, 1932.

NEW MOUNTAIN GOAT FROM THE QUATERNARY OF SMITH CREEK CAVE, NEVADA. (Oreamnos harringtoni.) Chester Stock. Bull. Southern Calif. Acad. Sci., Los Angeles, vol.35, pt.3, pp.149-153, pl.35, Jan. 31, 1937.

QUATERNARY ANTELOPES OF SHELTER CAVE, NEW MEXICO. Chester Stock. Bull. Geol. Soc. America, vol.42, no.1, p.364, Mar., 1931. (Abstract.)

EUCERATHERIUM BIZELLI, A NEW UNGULATE FROM OKLAHOMA. J. W. Stovall. Jour. Paleont., vol.11, no.5, pp.450-455, figs.3, July, 1937.

NEW SPECIMEN OF SYMBOS FROM CHICKASHA, OKLAHOMA. J.W. Stovall, J. T. Self. Jour. Mamm., vol.17, no.4, p.422, Nov., 1936.

(NOTES ON THE OCCURRENCE OF MUSK OXEN (OVIBOS MOSCHATUS) IN THE DILUVIAL RIVER GRAVEL OF HAMELN-ON-THE-WESER.) C. Struckmann. Zeitschr. Deut. Geol. Gesell., pp.601-604, 1887. (In German.)

CAVICORNIA OF SOUTH-EASTERN SHANSI. P. Teilhard de Chardin, M. Trassaert. Palaeontologia Sinica, Nanking, n.s., no.6, pp.1-106, figs.65, pls.1-4, tbls.4, Aug., 1938.

(SET OF HORNS FROM A DILUVIAL RAM OF THURINGIA.) Ein diluviales Steinbockgehoern aus Thueringen. Volker Toepfer. Palaeont. Zeitschr., vol.16, nos.3-4, pp. 276-281, pl.1, Dec. 31, 1934.

(ON THE OVIBUS MOSCHATUS WARDI LYDEKKER FIND IN THE MORAVIAN CHALK FORMATION.) Ueber den Fund von Ovibos moschatus wardi Lydekker in Maehrischen Karste. J. Vanura. Bull. Internat. Acad. Tchèque Sci., Prague, vol. 44 (1943), pp.159-189, figs.11, pls.4, 1944.

BUDORCAS, A NEW ELEMENT IN THE PROTO-HISTORIC ANYANG FAUNA OF CHINA. C. C. Young. Amer.Jour.Sci., vol.246, no.3, pp.157-164, figs.2, 1948.

NEW FINDS OF FOSSIL BUBALUS IN CHINA. C.C. Young. Bull. Geol. Soc. China, vol.15, no.4, pp.505-518, figs.4, pl.1, Dec., 1936.

Heredity

(CAPRA AEGAGRUS AND CAPRA FALCONERI AS DOMESTIC GOATS IN THE CAUCASES (PRELIMINARY WORK ON A GENETIC TREATMENT OF DOMESTIC GOATS.) Ueber Capra aegagrus und Capra falconeri als Hausziegen im Kaukasus, eine Vorarbeit zur genetischen Bearbeitung der Hausziege. Wolfgang Amschler. Wiss. Archiv. Landwirtsch. Abt. B. Tiernaehr. u. Tierzucht, vol.3, no.2, pp. 307-338, figs.13, map, 1930.

INHERITANCE OF COLOR, BEARD TASSELS AND HORNS IN THE GOAT. S.A. Asdell, A.D. Buchanan Smith. Jour. Heredity, vol.19, pp.425-430, illus., Sep., 1928.

THE HEJAZ DWARF GOAT. H. Epstein. Jour. Heredity, Wash., vol.37, no.11, pp. 345-352, figs.12-18, Nov., 1946.

INHERITANCE OF HORNS, WATTLES, AND COLOR IN GRADE TOGGENBURG GOATS. Jayl L. Lush. Jour. Heredity, vol.17, no.3, pp.73-91, illus., Mar., 1926.

Horns, Heads

HORN GROWTH IN NILGAI. E.A.d'Abreu. Jour. Bombay Nat. Hist. Soc., vol.39, no.1, p.171, Dec. 1, 1936.

HORNS AND ANTLERS. THEIR OCCURRENCE, DEVELOPMENT AND FUNCTION IN THE MAMMALIA. PART I. H.E. Anthony. Bull. New York Zool. Soc., vol. 31, pp.178-216, illus., Dec., 1928.

HORNED FEMALE IMPALA. Boje Benzon. Field, London, vol.166, no.4307, p.92, illus., July 13, 1935.

(SOME REMARKS ON THE HORNS OF OVIBOVINAE.) Einige Bemerkungen ueber die Hoerner der Ovibovinae. Birger Bohlin. Bull. Geol. Inst. Univ., Upsapa, vol.27, pp.42-47, figs.7, 1937.

REPLACEMENT OF HORN IN NILGAI. Chandrabhanusinhji. Jour. Bombay Nat. Hist. Soc., vol.39, no.3, pp.618-619, Sep. 25, 1937.

BIG BUFFALO HEAD. (Bubalis bubalis.) S.A. Christopher. Jour. Bombay Nat. Hist. Soc., vol.39, no.2, p.391, Apr. 15, 1937.

(NOTE ON TWO EXCEPTIONAL IZARD TROPHIES.) Marcel Couturier. Mammalia, Paris, vol.16, no.4, pp.253-255, Dec., 1952. (Rupicapra rupicapra pyrenaica.) (In French.)

(RECORD HORNS OF THE IZARD AND CHAMOIS OF FRANCE.) Marcel Couturier. Mammalia, Paris, vol.13, nos.1-2, pp.49-51, Mar.-June, 1949. (In French.)

FEMALE ADDAX HEAD. Guy Dollman. Nat. Hist. Mag. (British Museum), vol.4, no.31, pp.237-238, illus., July, 1934.

EXHIBITION OF A PAIR OF HORNS OF THE SINAITIC IBEX )CAPRA SINAITICA). Henry John Elwes. Proc. Zool. Soc. London, p.530, 1869.

(HOLLOW HORNS.) Hohle Hoerner. G. von Frankenberg. Der Naturforscher, Berlin, vol.16, no.12, pp.288-292, Mar., 1940.

EXHIBITION OF A SECOND PAIR OF HORNS OF BUDORCAS TAXICOLOR, ALSO FROM HIS OWN COLLECTION. Louis Fraser. Proc. Zool. Soc. London, p.377, 1864.

EXHIBITION OF THE HORNS OF BUDORCAS TAXICOLOR, HODGS. Louis Fraser. Proc. Zool. Soc. London, p.168, 1864.

( HORN EXHIBITION AT THE SWEDISH HUNTERS' YEARLY MEETING.) Hornutstallningen vid Svenska Jagareforbundets arsmote. T. Gardell. Svensk Jakt, Stockholm, vol.86, no.2, pp.43-44, Feb. 20, 1948; vol.87, no.2, pp.42-43, Feb. 20, 1949.

MEASUREMENTS OF A BUFFALO-HEAD FROM ASSAM. R.G. Griffith. Jour.Bombay Nat. Hist. Soc., vol.38, no.4, pp.817-818, illus., Aug., 1936.

HORN GROWTH AS OBSERVED IN BLACKBUCK AND NILGAI. J.E. Hall. Jour.Bombay Nat. Hist. Soc., vol.38, no.3, p.618, Apr., 1936.

PAIR OF DEFORMED ROCKY MOUNTAIN GOAT HORNS. William L. Jellison. Jour. Mamm., vol.11, no.4, p.474, pl.21, Nov., 1930.

HORNED FEMALE WATERBUCK. T.A. Jenkins. Field, London, vol.153, p.395, illus., Mar. 7, 1929.

HORN GROWTH AS OBSERVED IN BLACK BUCK AND NILGAI. I. A. Khan. Jour. Bombay Nat. Hist. Soc., vol.39, no.1, pp.170-171, Dec. 1, 1936.

(HORN OF THE IBEX (CAPRA FALCONERI WAGN.).) Das Gehoern der Schraubenziege (Capra falconeri Wagn.). W. Koch. Zool. Anzeiger, vol.93, nos.7-10, pp.275-278, figs.2, Mar. 1, 1931.

GOOD HEAD OF THE GOA OR TIBETAN ANTELOPE (PANTHALOPS HODGSONI.) F. Ludlow. Jour. Bombay Nat. Hist. Soc., vol.27, p.626, Mar. 31, 1921.

(HORNS OF THE IBEX AND THE CHAMOIS.) Corna di stambecco e di camoscio. G.A. Lugano. Tribuna-Sport, Naples, vol.28, no. 8, p.1, Feb. 25, 1900.

(LARGEST HORNS OF IBEX AND CHAMOIS.) Le piu grandi corna di stambecco e di camoscio. G.A. Lugano. Bool. Naturalista, vol.19, no.12, pp.145-147, Dec., 1899.

(EXPERIMENTAL RESEARCH ON THE ORGANOGENESIS OF THE HORNS OF THE CAVICORNS.) Ricerche sperimentali sulla organogenesi delle corna dei Cavicorni. Ezio Marchi. Moderno Zooiatro, Torino, no. 22, 1907.

(SEVENTH GERMAN HORN EXHIBITION AT BERLIN (1901).) Die siebente deutsche Geweihausstellung zu Berlin (1901). Paul Matschie. Waidwerk in Wort und Bild, Neudamm, vol.10, no.11, pp.125-138, figs.1-21, Mar. 1, 1901; no.12, pp.145-158, figs. 22-40, Mar. 15, 1901.

(EIGHTH GERMAN HORN EXHIBITION AT BERLIN (1902).) Die achte deutsche Geweihausstellung zu Berlin (1902). Paul Matschie. Deutsche Jaeger-Zeitung, Neudamm, vol.38, no.39, pp.621-625, Feb. 13, 1902; Waidwerk in Wort und Bild, Neudamm, vol.11, no.12, pp.149-171, figs.1-42, Mar. 15, 1902.

(NINTH GERMAN HORN EXHIBITION AT BERLIN (1903).) Die neunte deutsche Geweihausstellung zu Berlin (1903). Paul Matschie. Waidwerk in Wort und Bild, vol. 12, no.10, pp.145-171, figs.1-44, Feb. 15, 1903.

(TENTH GERMAN HORN EXHIBITION.) Aus der zehnte deutschen Geweihausstellung. Paul Matschie. Deutsche Jaeger-Zeitung, vol.42, no.38, pp.599-602, Feb. 7, 1904; Waidwerk in Wort und Bild, Neudamm, vol.13, no.12, pp.169-200, figs. 1-48, pls.1-4, Mar. 15, 1904.

(ELEVENTH GERMAN HORN EXHIBITION AT BERLIN (1905). Die elfte deutsche Geweihausstellung zu Berlin (1905). Paul Matschie. Waidwerk in Wort und Bild, Neudamm, vol.14, no.11, pp.169-210, figs.1-52, Mar. 1, 1905.

(TWELFTH GERMAN HORN EXHIBITION AT BERLIN (1906).) Die zwoelfte deutsche Geweihausstellung zu Berlin (1906). Paul Matschie. Waidwerk in Wort und Bild, vol. 15, no.13, pp.197-241, figs.1-49, Apr., 1906.

(THIRTEENTH GERMAN HORN EXHIBITION AT BERLIN (1907).) Die dreizehnte deutsche Geweihausstellung zu Berlin(1907). Paul Matschie. Waidwerk in Wort und Bild, vol.16, no.12, pp.181-239, figs.1-69, Mar. 15, 1907.

(FOURTEENTH GERMAN HORN EXHIBITION AT BERLIN (1908).) Die vierzehnte deutsche Geweihausstellung zu Berlin (1908). Paul Matschie. Waidwerk in Wort und Bild, Neudamm, vol.17, no.12, pp. 181-211, figs.1-40; no.14, pp.229-270, figs. 41-83, Mar. 15, Apr. 15, 1908.

(FIFTEENTH GERMAN HORN EXHIBITION AT BERLIN (1909).) Die fuenfzehnte deutsche Geweihausstellung zu Berlin (1909). Paul Matschie. Waidwerk in Wort und Bild, Neudamm, vol.18, no.11, pp.161-191, figs.1-23; no.12, pp.197-238, figs.24-74, Mar. 1, 15, 1909.

(SIXTEENTH GERMAN HORN EXHIBITION AT BERLIN (1910).) Die sechzehnte deutsche Geweihausstellung zu Berlin (1910). Paul Matschie. Waidwerk in Wort und Bild, Neudamm, vol.19, nos.13-14, pp.213-304, figs.1-87, Apr. 1, 15, 1910.

ON A FRONTLET AND HORNS OF THE TAKIN. P. Chalmers Mitchell. Proc. Zool. Soc. London, pp.467-468, Oct. 8, 1907.

(HORN VARIATION IN CERTAIN RACES OF SHEEP AND COMPARATIVE REMARKS ON FORKED-HORN ANTELOPES AND FOUR-HORNED ANTELOPES.) De la variation des cornes dans certains races de moutons et remarques comparatives sur l'antilope Furcifere et l'antilope tetracere. H. Neuville. Ann. Sci. Nat., Bot. Zool., Paris, ser.10, vol.9, pp.269-292, figs.8, 1926.

LARGE HEAD OF THE INDIAN BUFFALO (BOS BUBALIS LINN.). R. E. Parsons. Jour. Bombay Nat. Hist. Soc., vol.41, no.3, p. 659, Apr., 1940.

GOOD FEMALE CHINKARD HEAD (G. BENNETTI). G.B. Powar. Jour. Bombay Nat. Hist. Soc., vol.28, p.266, Dec. 30, 1921.

(ON THE DEVELOPMENT MECHANICS OF CORKSCREW HORN FORMATIONS AND RELATED PHENOMENA.) Ludwig Rhumbler. (In) Wilhelm Roux' Archiv f. Entwicklungsmechanik der Organismen, vol.119, pt.4, pp.439-515, figs.49, 1929. (In German.)

HORNS A'PLENTY. (African mammals, bighorn, tahr goat, ibex, bison, yak, anoa). J. Schermerhorn. San Diego Zoonooz, vol. 20, no.4, pp.3-6, illus., Apr., 1947.

EXHIBITION OF A PAIR OF HORN OF ALCELAPHUS TORA. Philip Lutley Sclater. Proc. Zool. Soc. London, p.729, 1873.

EXHIBITION OF, AND REMARKS UPON, A PAIR OF HORNS OF A MALE LIVINGSTONE'S ELAND OFFERED TO THE SOCIETY BY MR. H. H. JOHNSTON, C.B. Philip Lutley Sclater. Proc. Zool. Soc. London, for 1895, pt.4, pp.690-691, fig.1, Apr. 1, 1896.

EXHIBITION OF, AND REMARKS UPON, A PAIR OF HORNS OF THE SO-CALLED ANTILOPE TRIANGULARIS. Philip Lutley Sclater. Proc. Zool. Soc. London, pt.2, p.506, Aug. 1, 1896.

EXHIBITION OF, AND REMARKS UPON, THE HEAD OF AN ANTELOPE FROM BRITISH EAST AFRICA. Philip Lutley Sclater. Proc. Zool. Soc. London, for 1895, pt.4, pp.868-870, fig.1, Apr. 1, 1896.

REMARKS ON A FINE HEAD OF ALCELAPHUS TORA. Philip Lutley Sclater. Proc. Zool. Soc. London, p.762, illus., 1873.

MEASUREMENTS OF A FINE HEAD OF THE INDIAN GAZELLE. Sardar Shivdev Singh. Jour. Bombay Nat. Hist. Soc., vol. 42, no.4, p.930, Dec., 1941.

RECORD THAKIN HEAD. (Widest spread of horns, 17 inches.) F. W. Smith. Jour. Bombay Nat. Hist. Soc., vol.40, no.4, pp.736-737, photo, May, 1939.

EXHIBITION OF THE HEAD OF SOME RARE ANTELOPES FROM FASHODA AND THE SOBAT RIVER. Oldfield Thomas. Proc. Zool. Soc. London, pp.84-85, Feb. 6, 1900.

EXHIBITION OF A HEAD OF ALCELAPHUS TORA. Edwin Ward. Proc. Zool. Soc. London, p.762, fig.1, 1873.

(EXOTIC TROPHIES IN THE GERMAN HORN EXHIBITION (1910).) Exotische Trophaen in der deutschen Geweihausstellung (1910). Ludwig Zukowsky. Wild und Hund, Berlin, Jahrg. 16, no.12, pp.206-208, illus., Mar. 25, 1910.

Hunting, Trapping

ALIAS THE UNICORN. (Oryx.) R.B.Aitken. Field and Stream, New York, vol.54, no.7, pp.38-39, 113, 115, illus., Nov., 1949.

HUNTING THE AFRICAN BUFFALO. C.E. Akeley. World's Work, vol.41, pp.497-504, figs.8, Mar., 1921.

CHAMOIS HUNT IN SWITZERLAND. Loring Andrews. Forest and Stream, vol.90, pp. 231-233, May, 1920.

HUNTING TAKIN IN THE MOUNTAINS OF SHENSI. R. C. Andrews. Nat. Hist., vol.22, pp.292-300, figs.6, July-Aug., 1922.

TRACKING THE SITUTUNGA. J.C.M. Balders. Field, London, vol.158, no.4108, p.432, fig.1, Sep. 19, 1931.

GOATS ABOVE THE GLACIER. C.Howard Baltzo. Alaska Sportsman, Ketchikan, vol. 11, no.9, pp.18-20, 23-28, illus., Sep., 1945.

INDIAN BUFFALO EMERGING FROM HIGH GRASS. B. Berg. Field, London, vol. 166, no.4329, p.1409, Dec. 14, 1935.

IBEX AND POLI IN HIGH THIAN-SHAN. Benjamin Chew. Hunting Trails on Three Continents, New York, Chap.7, pp.165-183, pls.3, 1933.

(NOTES ON TWO EXCEPTIONAL CHAMOIS TROPHIES.) Marcel A.J. Couturier. Mammalia, Paris, vol.16, no.4, pp.253-255, Dec., 1952. (In French.)

(CHAMOIS TROPHIES OF THE PYRENEES OF FRANCE, SPAIN, AND ANDORRA.) Marcel A.J. Couturier. Mammalia, Paris, vol.21, no.4, pp.381-384, pl.11, Dec., 1957. (In French.)

GIANT SABLE ANTELOPE. Charles P. Curtis. Hunting Trails on Three Cintinents, New York, Chap. 11, pp.237-252, pls.2, 1933.

AFTER BISON AND BUFFALO ON THE HIGH SAL FORESTS. J.A. Duke. Jour. Bombay Nat. Hist. Soc., vol.33, no.2, pp.419-424, Feb. 15, 1929.

AFTER KUDU IN ERITREA. H.A.Freeman. Field, London, vol.166, no.4317, p.648, illus., Sep. 21, 1935.

HUNTING THE MUSKOX. Peter Freuchen. (In) N.Amer. Big Game. A Book of the Boone and Crockett Club, Compiled by the Committee on Records of N.Amer. Big Game. Charles Scribners Sons, New York, pp.348-357, 1939.

LOCAL LEAVE IN NORTHERN GAME COUNTRY. (Syncerus.) H.C. Gill. The Nigerian Field, vol.7, no.1, pp.21-27, illus., Jan., 1938.

GAME-NETTING IN UZIGUA. (Methods employed in hunting the smaller antelopes in German East Africa.) D.K.S. Grant. Jour. East Africa and Uganda Nat. Hist. Soc., vol.14, pp.403-407, July, 1919.

ALONG THE LIVINGSTONE TRAIL. (Sable antelope.) P.N. Gray. Hunting Trails on Three Continents, New York, Chap. 5, pp. 103-143, pls.2, 1933.

SHOOTING WILD BUFFALO IN THE KOSI RIVER SWAMPS. J.E. Hall. Jour. Bombay Nat. Hist. Soc., vol.38, no.3, pp.585-592, pl.1, Apr. 15, 1936.

GEMSBUCK ON THE MOLOPO. Geo. L. Harrison. Hunting Trails on Three Continents, New York, Chap. 8, pp.184-197, 1933.

MY FIRST BUSHCOW. J.C.S.Hughes. Nigerian Field (Jour. Nigerian Field Soc.), vol.20, no.4, pp.182-184, Oct., 1955.

GOATS ARE HARD TO GET. W.H.Jackson. Alaska Sportsman, Ketchikan, vol.9, no.1, pp.16-18, 20-23, illus., Jan., 1943.

TAKIN HUNTERS OF TIBET. WATCHING THE TRAPPERS AT WORK. Ronald Kaulbach. Field, London, vol.165, no.4301, p.1352, illus., June 1, 1935.

BUFFALO HUNTING IN ARNHEM LAND. Frederick D. McCarthy. Australian Mus. Mag., vol.11, no.8, pp.252-256, Dec.15, 1954.

AFTER GOAT IN ALASKA. R.E.McGlashan. Forest and Stream, vol.89, pp.358, 384, July, 1919.

GETTING YOUR GOAT. HUNTING BIG GAME IN ALASKA. Norman Marshall. Field and Stream, no.6, pp.13-15, 17, 73, Oct., 1929.

QUEST OF THE BONGO. E.Percy-Smith. Bull. New York Zool. Soc., vol.36, no.2, pp.27-32, illus., Mar.-Apr., 1933.

QUEST OF THE BONGO: A RARE ANTELOPE TAKEN ALIVE. E. Percy-Smith. Illus. London News, vol.181, no.4871, pp.293-295, illus., Aug. 27, 1932.

SHOOTING IN SIKKIM. Philip Pinckney. Jour. Darjeeling Nat. Hist. Soc., vol.13, no.3, pp.105-114, illus., Jan., 1939.

ON THE TRAIL OF THE AFRICAN BUFFALO. Robert H. Rockwell. Nat. Hist., New York, vol.34, no.1, pp.74-82, illus., Jan.-Feb., 1934.

HUNTING THE TAMARAO. Theodore Roosevelt. Sportsman, Boston, vol.21, no.1, pp. 31-33, 80-81, illus., Jan., 1937.

HEAVY HANDS. (African buffalo.) K.Sergel. Sports Afield, New York, vol.120, no.4, pp.56-57, 82, illus., Oct., 1948.

OLD-WORLD HUNT IN TEXAS. (Blackbuck.) Hart Stilwell. Field and Stream, vol.60, no.1, pp.68-69, 143-146, illus., May, 1955.

IN QUEST OF INDIA'S STRANGEST SPECIES. SHOOTING THE ELUSIVE SEROW IN KUMAON. C.H. Stockley. Field, London, vol.161, no.4180, p.200, Feb. 4, 1933.

NEW TROPHY FOR THE RIFLE. SEASON TO BE DECLARED FOR THE SPANISH IBEX. J.D.U. Ward. Field, London, vol. 159, no.4142, p.733, fig.1, May 14, 1932.

ROCKY MOUNTAIN GOAT. Townsend Whelen. Sports Afield, Minneapolis, vol. 117, no.2, pp.32-33, 70, 73, illus., Feb., 1947.

HUNTING THE ROCKY MOUNTAIN GOAT. Vernon H. Wood. (In) N.Amer. Big Game. A Book of the Boone and Crockett Club, Compiled by the Committee on Records of N. Amer. Big Game. Charles Scribners Sons, New York, pp.325-331, 1939.

MOUNTAIN GOAT HARVESTS IN WASHINGTON. Wash. Dept. of Game. Wash. State Game Bull., vol.6, no.2, p.4, Apr., 1954.

TRACKING AND HUNTING THE BONGO. Field, London, vol.158, no.4117, pp.765-766, illus., Nov. 21, 1931.

Hybrids

(ANTELOPE HYBRIDIZATIONS.) Hybridations d'antilopides. (Taurotragus oryx, Strepsiceros capensis.) P. Boulineau. La Terre et la Vie, Rev. d'Hist. Nat., vol.3, no.11, pp.690-691, illus., Nov., 1933.

WILL THE CATTALO DISPLACE THE BUFFALO? Aubrey Fullerton. Forest and Outdoors, Montreal, vol.6, no.3, pp.91-92, Mar., 1940.

IS A SEBU-CARABAO HYBRID POSSIBLE? B.M. Gonzalez, J.P. Esguerra. Jour. Heredity, vol.18, pp.544-547, illus., Dec., 1927.

(SUPPOSED SHEEP-BOVINE HYBRID (SHEEP-OX) OF HUSUM.) Der angebliche Schaf-Rind-Bastard ("Schafochse") von Husum. Erna Mohr. Der Zool. Garten, vol.3, nos.1-3, pp. 35-39, figs.1-6, Oct. 20, 1929.

BUFFALO X YAK X BEEF BREED = CATTALOS. James Montagnes. Breeder's Gaz., vol.118, p.18, Mar., 1953.

HYBRID AMERICAN BISON AND DOMESTIC COW AT THE MYSORE ZOO. Sadeg Z. Shah. Jour. Bombay Nat. Hist. Soc., vol.37, no.4, p.954, pl.1, Apr. 15, 1935.

HYBRID AMERICAN BISON AND INDIAN DOMESTIC COW. Sadeg Z. Shah. Jour. Bombay Nat. Hist. Soc., vol.41, no.4, pp.894-895, fig.1, Aug., 1940.

ELAND-OX HYBRID. Ernest Warren. Nature, London, vol.129, no.3266, p.828, fig., June 4, 1932.

North America

THE MUSK-OX OF ARCTIC AMERICA AND GREENLAND. J.A. Allen. Bull. Amer. Mus. Nat. Hist., vol.14, pp.69-86, pls.13-17, figs.7, Mar. 27, 1901.

PROBABLE RECENT EXTINCTION OF THE MUSK-OX IN ALASKA. J.A. Allen. Science, n.s., vol.36, no.934, pp.720-722, Nov. 22, 1912.

MOUNTAIN GOAT STUDY / PROGRESS REPORT. Niilo A. Anderson. Wash.Dept. Game, Biol. Bull., no.2, pp.i+21, pls.4, mimeo., June, 1940.

WHITE GOATS OF THE SAWTOOTH MOUNTAINS. H.E. Anthony. Nat. Hist., vol.23, pp.142-154, figs.12, Mar.-Apr., 1923.

THE MUSKOX. H.E. Anthony. (In) N.Amer. Big Game. A Book of the Boone and Crockett Club, Compiled by the Committee on Records of N. Amer. Big Game. Charles Scribners Sons, New York, pp.345-347, 1939.

ALASKA SUMMER. (Mountain goats.) Belle J. Benchley. San Diego Zoonooz, vol. 16, no.7, pp.5-6, illus., July, 1943.

IN THE LAND OF THE MUSKOX. G. H. Blanchet. Canadian geographical Society, Canadian geographical Jour., vol.3, no.6, June, 1934.

LIFE HISTORY AND ECOLOGY OF THE MOUNTAIN GOAT IN DAHO AND MONTANA. Stewart Brandborg. MS thesis, Univ. Idaho, 1950.

ROCKY MOUNTAIN GOAT IN MONTANA. Robert L. Casebeer, et al. Montana Fish and Game Comm., Bull.5, pp.107, 1950.

INTRODUCTION OF THE ASIATIC BUFFALO, THE BRAHMIN OX, AND THE CASHMERE, SCINDE AND MALTA GOATS INTO SOUTH CAROLINA. James B. Davis. U.S. Patent Office, Report, Agric. Dept., Wash., pp.20-22, (1853) 1854.

(FUTURE OF THE GREENLAND MUSKOX.) Die Zukunft der groenlaendischen Moschusochsen. G. Duncker. Zool. Garten, n.F., vol.3, nos.4-8, pp.219-221, figs.1-2, Aug. 11, 1930.

BIGHORN SHEEP AND MOUNTAIN GOAT. F.W. Godden, L.T. Gutzman. Univ.Idaho Bull., vol.33, no.22, pp.43-49, Dec., 1938.

MOUNTAIN GOAT IN SOUTH DAKOTA. Walter O. Hanson. PhD thesis, Univ. Mich., 1950.

TRAILING "GOATS" IN THE BLACK HILLS. (Rocky Mountain goat.) Wendell H.Harmon. S. Dakota Conserv. Digest, Pierre, vol.9, no.4, p.13, Apr., 1942.

PRESENT STATUS OF THE MUSKOX IN ARCTIC NORTH AMERICA AND GREENLAND WITH NOTES ON DISTRIBUTION, EXTIRPATION, TRANSPLANTATION, PROTECTION, HABITS AND LIFE HISTORY. Elisabeth Hone. Special Publ. no.5, Amer. Comm. Internat. Wild Life Protection, pp.1-87, pls.4, maps 3, 1934.

OUR NEW MUSK-OX HERD. (New importation of Greenland musk-oxen.) W.T. Hornaday. Zool. Soc. Bull., vol.26, no. 1, pp.10-11, Jan., 1923.

TWO MUSK-OX CALVES BORN IN NEW YORK. W.T. Hornaday. Jour. Mamm., vol. 7, no.1, p.61, Feb., 1926.

RETURN OF THE VANISHING MUSK OXEN. Hartley H.T. Jackson. Audubon Mag., vol. 58, no.6, pp.262-265, Nov.-Dec., 1956; vol.59, no.1, pp.26-29, Jan.-Feb., 1957.

(MUSK OX IN EASTERN GREENLAND.) Der Moschusochse in Ost-Groenland. J.G. Jennov. Zeitschr. f. Saeugetierk., vol.8, no.2, pp.40-46, pls.6-8, Apr. 24, 1933.

RECONNAISSANCE STUDY OF THE MOUNTAIN GOAT IN ALASKA. David R. Klein. MS thesis, Univ. Alaska, pp.x+121, illus., 1953.

TWO-YEAR STUDY OF THE ROCKY MOUNTAIN GOAT IN THE CRAZY MOUNTAINS, MONTANA. Jack W. Lentfer. Jour. Wildl. Mgt., vol.19, no.4, pp.417-429, figs.3, Oct., 1955.

ROCKY MOUNTAIN GOAT ON VANCOUVER ISLAND, BRITISH COLUMBIA. J.A.Munro. The Canadian Field-Nat., vol.47, no.5, pp.95-96, May, 1933.

(MUSK OX IN EASTERN GREELAND.) Der Moschusochse in Ostgroenland. Alwin Pedersen. Zeitschr. f. Saeugetierk., vol. 9, nos.1-3, p.433, Dec. 12, 1934.

MOUNTAIN GOAT RATIOS IN MONTANA. Geo. A. Petrides. Jour. Mamm., vol.29, no.2, p.185, May 14, 1948.

NOTES ON LIVING AND EXTINCT SPECIES OF NORTH AMERICAN BOVIDAE. Samuel N. Rhoads. Proc. Acad. Nat. Sci., Phila., pp.483-502, pl.12, Jan. 18, 1898.

LAND OF THE WILD MOUNTAIN GOAT. William T. Shaw. Nature Mag., vol.6, pp. 167-169, figs.3, Sep., 1925.

MOUNTAIN GOAT (OREAMNOS MONTANUS MISSOULAE) NOT FOUND IN WYOMING. M.P. Skinner. Jour. Mamm., vol.7, no.4, pp.334-335, Nov., 1926.

MUSK OX IN ARCTIC ISLANDS. Vilhjalmur Stefansson. Nature, vol.112, p.590, Oct. 20, 1923.

ROCKY MOUNTAIN GOATS IN THE BLACK HILLS. Lloyd W. Swift. S.Dakota Conserv. Digest, Pierre, pp.8-9, fig.1, June, 1940; Trans. N.Amer. Wildl. Conf., vol.5, pp. 441-443, 1941.

FACTS ABOUT CANADIAN MUSK-OXEN. J.S. Tener. Trans. 19th N.Amer. Wildl. Conf., pp.504-510, 1954.

PRELIMINARY STUDY OF THE MUSK-OXEN OF FOSHEIM PENINSULA, ELLESMERE ISLAND, N.W.T. J.S.Tener. Can. Wildl. Serv., Wildl.Mgt. Bull., Ser.1, no. 9, pp.1-34, figs.7, Feb., 1954.

MUSK OX IN EAST GREENLAND. Chr.Vibe. Mammalia, Paris, vol.22, no.1, pp.168-174, pl.7, Mar., 1958.

STATUS OF MOUNTAIN GOATS INTRODUCED INTO THE OLYMPIC MOUNTAINS, WASHINGTON. E.B. Webster. Murrelet, vol.13, no.1, p.25, Jan., 1932.

VANISHING MUSK-OX. Julia W. Wolfe. Rod and Gun in Canada, Gardenvale, vol.51, no.6, pp.13, 45, illus., Nov., 1949.

RETURN OF THE MUSK OXEN. Stanley P. Young. Amer. Forests, vol.47, no.8, pp. 368-372, Aug., 1941; Ann. Rept. Smiths. Inst., Wash., D.C., 1942, pp.317-322, pls.6, Sep. 20, 1943.

MOUNTAIN GOATS SHIFT THEIR HOME TO BLACK HILLS. Sci. News Letter, Wash., D.C., vol.42, no.11, p.165, Sep. 12, 1942.

MOUNTAIN GOATS THRIVE IN HILLS. S.Dakota Conserv. Digest, p.7, illus., July, 1938.

MUSK OXEN HERD IN ALASKA SHOWS SATISFACTORY INCREASE. Nat.Humane Review. Mt.Morris, vol.38, no.2, p.28, Feb., 1950.

## Origins, Evolution

(REVIEW OF THE RACE AND DERIVATION QUESTION REGARDING DOMESTIC GOATS.) Wolfgang Amschler. Zeitschr. f. Zuechtungskunde, vol.4, no.10, pp. 465-468, fig.1, 1929. (In German.)

(INVESTIGATIONS OF GOATS (GENUS CAPRA S. ST.) AND HYBRIDS THEREOF. A CONTRIBUTION TO THE PHYLOGENY OF THE DOMESTIC GOATS PARTICULARLY OF CENTRAL ASIA.) Max Hilzheimer. (Wissenschaftl. Archiv. f. Landwirtschaft Abt. B) Archiv f. Tierernaehrung und Tierzucht, Berlin, vol.8, no.3, pp.323-371, figs.19, 1933. (In German.)

(EVOLUTION OF THE BRAIN OF THE PYGMY GOAT.) Sur l'évolution du cerveau de la Chèvre naine. Walther Riese. Bull. Mus. Nat. Hist. Nat. Paris, ser.2, vol.10, no.4, pp.355-360, tbl., May, 1938.

(INVESTIGATIONS ON THE ORIGIN OF THE DOMESTIC GOAT IN RUMANIA.) Recherches sur l'origine de la chevre domestique en Roumanie. N. Teodoreanu. Acad. Roumaine, Bull. Sec. Scient, IX-ème Année, no.5-6, pp.14-27, figs.8, 1925.

## Pelage, Coloration

(CONSIDERATIONS OF THE SPECIFIC VALUE OF THE CHARACTERISTICS OF THE PELAGE OF AN ANTELOPE (TRAGELAPHUS SCRIPTUS PALLAS).) E. Bourdelle. Bull. Mus. Nat. d'Hist. Nat. Paris, vol.1, no.3, pp.177-185, 1929. (In French.)

(STUDY OF THE HAIR OF OREAMNOS AMERICANUS.) Étude du poil de l'Oremnos americanus. Ed Dechambre. Revue d'Hist. Nat., pt.1, A, Mammifères, Paris, vol.11, no.7, pp.221-227, fig.1, July, 1930.

FOETAL AND POST-NATAL COATS OF THE ANTELOPES OF THE SUBFAMILY TRAGELAPHINAE. J. Guy Dollman.Proc. Linnean Soc. London, sess. 147, pt.1, pp. 5-6, Mar. 6, 1935.

COAT OF THE ANGORA GOAT. J.E. Duerden, M.R. Spencer. Bull. no.83, Dept. of Agric., Union of S. Africa, pp. 1-35, pl.1, figs.1-13, 1930.

(ON TWO ALBINO ANTELOPES.) Observations sur deux antilopes albinos. F.Edmond-Blanc. Mammalia, Paris, vol.21, no.4, pp.453-454, Dec., 1957.

(NOTES ON THE MAMMALS. XXXVII) PARTIAL ALBINISM IN AN ANTELOPE.) Serge Frechkop. Bull. Inst. Roy. Sci. Nat. Belgique, Bruxelles, vol.24, no.62, pp.4, illus., Dec., 1950. (In French.)

EXHIBITION OF, AND REMARKS UPON, A PALE-COLOURED SPECIMEN OF THE REED-BUCK (CERVICAPRA ARUNDINUM). R. Lydekker. Proc. Zool. Soc. London, pt. 3, p.555, Oct. 1, 1899.

(THREE-COLOR BOVINE ANIMALS IN THE REGION OF CRACOW.) Erna Mohr. Zool. Anzeiger, vol.109, nos.9-10, pp.266-268, figs.3, Mar. 1, 1935. (In German.)

(SIMILARITY OF BUBALIS JACKSONI THOM. AND ACRONOTUS LELWEL HEUGL. AND THEIR COLORATION.) Oscar Neumann. Sitz. Ber. Gesell. Naturf. Freunde Berlin, no.4, pp.76-79, Apr. 18, 1899. (In German.)

BLACK FOUR-HORNED ANTELOPE. Ramanuj of Surguja. Jour. Bombay Nat. Hist. Soc., vol.35, no.3, p.674, Feb. 15, 1932.

AGE VARIATION OF THE SKIN OF KARAKUL SHEEP. V.A. Sholokhov.Comptes Rendus (Doklady) Acad. Sci. USSR, Moscow, n.s., vol.49, no.1, pp.58-61, Oct. 10, 1945.

CHANGE OF COLOUR IN THE BLACKBUCK (ANTILOPE CERVICAPRA). M.H.Simmonds. Jour. Bombay Nat. Hist. Soc., vol.29, pp. 834-837, Dec. 31, 1923.

ALBINO GORAL (NEMORRHAEDUS GORAL) IN CHAMBA. Ram Singh. Jour. Bombay Nat. Hist. Soc., vol.32, p.373, Oct. 20, 1927.

HAIR-WHORL IN GAZELLA MUSCATENSIS. Oldfield Thomas. Proc. Zool. Soc. London, vol.2, pp.317-318, fig.35, Nov. 17, 1903.

EXHIBITION OF SPECIMENS OF A REMARKABLE PARTIALLY WHITE ANTELOPE OF THE GENUS CERVICAPRA-TRANSVAAL. Oldfield Thomas, F.V. Kirby. Proc. Zool. Soc. London, pp.894-898, Nov. 30, 1897.

ALBINO NILGHAI. T.R. Trivedi. Jour. Bombay Nat. Hist. Soc., vol.42, no.4, pp. 929-930, photo, Dec., 1941.

## Photography

PHOTOGRAPHING IMPALA. A WELL PLACED HIDE IN KENYA. A. Radclyffe Dugmore. Field, London, vol.164, no.4276, p.1361, illus., Dec. 8, 1934.

PHOTOGRAPHING BUSHCOW. NIGERIAN EXPERIMENT. O.R. Jackson. Field, London, vol.168, no.4364, pp.392-393, Aug.15, 1936.

(ANTELOPE PHOTOGRAPHS.) Photos d'Antilopes. (Rhapiceros sharpei.) H.Schouteden. Rev. Zool. Bot. Afr., vol.26 (Suppl.Bull. Cercle Zool. Congo, vol.11, nos.1-2), pp. 13-14, illus., Nov.-Dec., 1934.

AIMING A CAMERA AT A WILD MOUNTAIN GOAT. William T. Shaw. Nat. Hist., vol.24, pp.381-387, illus., May-June, 1924.

HUNTING MOUNTAIN GOATS WITH MINIATURE CAMERA. Henry P. Zuidema. Nat. Hist., New York, vol.52, no.1, pp.38-40, illus., June, 1943.

NEARLY EXTINCT:THE SURE-FOOTED IBEX PHOTOGRAPHED IN ITS MOUNTAIN HOME. Illus. London News, vol.221, no. 5910, pp.152-153, illus., July 26, 1952.

PHOTOGRAPHS OF EAST AFRICAN BONGO. Illus. London News, vol.182, no.4894, p. 148, Feb. 4, 1933.

PICTURES. (Photographs of Rocky Mountain goat, aoudad, Spanish ibex, markhor.) Animal Kingdom, New York, vol.45, no.2, pp.43-46, illus., Mar.-Apr., 1942.

## Physiology, Experimental Biology

EXPERIMENTAL MODIFICATIONS OF THE BREEDING CYCLES IN GOATS. T.H. Bissonnette. Physiol. Zool., vol.14, pp. 379-383, 1941.

EFFECT OF SOME STEROID COMPOUNDS ON OVINE RUMEN FUNCTION. C.C.Brooks et al. Science, vol.120, pp.455-456, Sep. 17, 1954.

EFFECT OF ORALLY ADMINISTERED UREA ON THE AMMONIA AND UREA CONCENTRATION IN THE BLOOD OF

CATTLE AND SHEEP, WITH OBSERVATIONS ON BLOOD AMMONIA LEVELS ASSOCIATED WITH SYMPTOMS OF ALKALOSIS. J.S. Dinnings. Amer. Jour. Physiol., Baltimore, vol.153, no.1, pp. 41-46, Apr. 1, 1948.

NOTES ON THE METABOLISM OF A MOUNTAIN GOAT. Hildur Krog, Mildred Monson. Amer. Jour. Physiol., Wash., vol.178, no.3, pp.515-516, Sep., 1954.

METABOLISM OF THYROXINE IN THE GOAT. R.A. Monroe, C.W. Turner. Amer. Jour. Physiol., Baltimore, vol.154, no.1, pp.5, July 1, 1948.

GROSS COMPOSITION OF MUSK-OX MILK. J.S. Tener. Canadian Jour. Zool., vol.34, no.6, pp.569-571, Dec., 1956.

Predators

BUSHVELD TRAGEDY. (Lions, antelopes.) R. Bigalke. African Wildl., Johannesburg, vol.9, no.3, pp.195-198, illus., Sep., 1955.

TIGER AND GOAT. S.M. Fraser. Jour. Bombay Nat. Hist. Soc., vol.27, p.163, July 1, 1920.

TRAGEDEY AT TIMBERLINE. (Cougar, mountain goat.) Frank Gable. Outdoor Life, New York, vol.105, no.1, pp.16-17, 53, illus., Jan., 1950.

BLACK-BUCK AND JACKAL. L.G.W. Hamber. Jour. Bombay Nat. Hist. Soc., vol.29, p.1050, May 15, 1924.

COYOTES PREY ON GOATS. Albert C. Hawbecker. Jour. Mamm., vol.20, no.3, pp.371-372, Aug., 1939.

PYTHONS AND THEIR PREY. (Python swallows 70-pound bush-buck.) E.Holland. Field, London, vol.150, p.395, illus., Sep. 8, 1927.

JACKAL ATTACKING GOAT. R.M.Simmons. Jour. Bombay Nat. Hist. Soc., vol.36, no.2, pp.490-491, Apr. 15, 1933.

Reproductive Biology

(NOTES ON THE RUT OF THE IBEX, CAPRA I. IBEX LINNÉ 1758.) Notes sur le rut du bouguetin, Capra i. ibex Linné, 1758. Robert Hainard. Saeugetierk. Mitteil., Stuttgart, vol.1, no.1, pp.26-28, illus., Jan. 10, 1953.

OBSERVATIONS ON THE REPRODUCTIVE ACTIVITIES, MEASUREMENTS, AND GROWTH RATE OF THE DIKDIK (RHYNCHOTRAGUS KIRKII THOMASI NEUMANN). L.M. Kellas. Proc. Zool. Soc. London, vol.124, pt.4, pp.751-784, illus., Feb. 22, 1955.

(DIFFICULT BIRTHS IN A YAK AND A WATER BUFFALO.) Schwergeburten bei einer Yakkuh und einer Wasserbueffelkuh. Wilhelm Schulze, Helmut Steuer. Zool. Garten, Leipzig, vol.21, no.4, pp.305-307, 1956.

REMARKS ON THE BREEDING OF THE ELAND IN CAPTAVITY. Philip Lutley Sclater. Proc. Zool. Soc. London, pp.953-954, 1867.

BREEDING SEASONS OF THE GOORAL (NEMORHOEDUS GORAL) AND HIMALAYAN TAHR (HEMITRAGUS JEMLAICUS). E.E. G.L. Searight. Jour. Bombay Nat. Hist.Soc., vol.31, p.812, Nov., 1926.

(CONTRIBUTIONS TO KNOWLEDGE OF THE EMBRYONAL DEVELOPMENT OF THE ALPIN GOAT (RUPICAPRA RUPICAPRA ).) Beitrage zur Kenntnis der embryonalen Entwicklung der Gemse (Rupicapra rupicapra). Edward Paul Tratz. Zool.Garten, Leipzig, vol.23, nos.1-3, pp.195-220, fol. pls.7, 1957.

Taxonomy

CRITICAL REVIEW OF THE GENERA NEMORHAEDUS H. SMITH AND CAPRICORNIS OGILBY. G. Adlerberg. Bull.Acad. Sci. USSR, Math.-Nat., no.2, pp.259-285, figs.6, 1932.

ONTOGENETIC AND OTHER VARIATIONS IN MUSKOXEN, WITH A SYSTEMATIC REVIEW OF THE MUSKOX GROUP, RECENT AND EXTINCT. J.A. Allen. Mem. Amer. Mus. Nat. Hist., n.s., vol.1, pt.4, pp. 101-225, pls.11-18, map, figs.45, Mar., 1913.

(OBSERVATIONS ON BOVIDS IN SCHOENBRUNN. IV) ON THE FURTHER DEVELOPMENT AND SYSTEMATICS OF THE AFRICAN BUFFALO.) Otto Antonius. Zool.Garten, Leipzig, n.F., vol.8, nos.10-12, pp. 265-270, illus., Sep., 1936. (In German.)

(DESCRIPTION OF A NEW SUB-SPECIES OF THE GENUS TRAGELAPHUS (MAMMALS, UNGULATES). TRAGELAPHUS SCRIPTUS REIDAE).) Description d'une nouvelle sous-espece du genre Tragelaphus (Mammifère Ongule). Tragelaphus scriptus reidae. Guy Babault. Bull. Mus. Nat. Hist. Nat., Paris, ser.2, vol.19, no.5, pp.379-380, Oct., 1947.

(SYSTEMATIC POSITION OF THE IBEXES AND LIVING WILD GOATS (CAPRA LINNEO 1758) AND THEIR GEOGRAPHIC DISTRIBUTION.) Posizione sistematica degli stambecchi e capre selvatiche viventi (Capra Linneo 1758) e loro distribuzione geografica. Oscar de Beaux. Atti Accad. Ligure di Sci. e Lettere, Genova, vol.12, no.1, pp.123-228, 1956.

TYPE LOCALITY OF THE BONTBOK, DAMALISCUS PYGARGUS (PALLAS). R. Bigalke. Jour. Mamm., vol.29, no.4, pp.421-422, Dec. 31, 1948.

NEW SUBSPECIES OF CONNOCHAETES TAURINUS. (C.t.mattosi.) Gilbert Blaine. Ann. and Mag. Nat. Hist., ser.9, vol.15, pp.129-130, Jan., 1925.

NOTES ON THE KORRIGUM, WITH A DESCRIPTION OF FOUR NEW RACES. Gilbert Blaine. Ann. and Mag. Nat.Hist., ser.8, vol.13, pp.326-336, Mar., 1914.

THREE NEW RACES OF CEPHALOPHUS MONTICOLA. (New subspecies from Rhodesia and Zululand.) Gilbert Blaine. Ann. and Mag. Nat. Hist., ser.9, vol.9, pp.174-176, Feb., 1922.

(REFLECTIONS ON A NATURAL SYSTEMATIC GROUPING OF THE GAZELLES (GAZELLAE).) Gedanken ueber eine naturliche systematische Gruppierung der Gazellen (Gazellae). Hans von Boetticher. Zeitschr. f. Saeugetierk., Berlin, vol.17, no.2, pp.83-92, Feb. 19, 1953.

SUBSPECIES OF THE SPANISH IBEX. Angel Cabrera. Proc. Zool. Soc. London, pp.963-977, figs., pls.52-54, Dec., 1911.

(TWO NEW ANTELOPES OF THE SUBFAMILY TRAGELAPHINAE.) Dos nuevos antilopes de la subfamilla Tragelaphinae. Angel Cabrera. Bol. Real Soc. española Hist. nat., vol.18, pp.274-277, May, 1918.

NEW RACE OF ARABIAN GAZELLE. J.G. Dollman. Proc. Zool. Soc. London, 1927, pt.4, p.1005, Jan., 1928.

NEW SUBSPECIES OF DIK-DIK (MADOQUA). R.E. Drake-Brockman. Ann. and Mag. Nat. Hist., ser.9, vol.18, pp.212-214, Aug., 1926.

REVIEW OF THE ANTELOPES OF THE GENERA MADOQUA AND RHYNCHOTRAGUS. R.E. Drake-Brockman. Proc. Zool. Soc. London, pt.1, pp.51-57, May, 1930.

DESCRIPTION OF AN APPARENTLY NEW SPECIES OF MOUNTAIN GOAT. (Oreamnus kennedyi.) Daniel G. Elliot. Field Col. Mus., Publ.46, Zool. ser., vol.3, no.1, pp.3-5, pls.1-4, June, 1900.

(GENERA OF THE FAMILY OF ANTELOPES (ANTILOPAE) ACCORDING TO THEIR NATURAL RELATIONSHIPS.) J.Fitzinger. Sitz. Ber. Akad. Wissensch., Vienna, vol. 59, Abt.1, pp.55, Feb., 1869. (In German.)

STATUS OF THE NAME DORCEPHALUS CROOKI MEARNS. E.A. Goldman, Remington Kellogg. Jour. Mamm., Baltimore, vol.20, no.4, p.507, Nov. 14, 1939.

DESCRIPTION OF A NEW SPECIES OF ANTELOPE (ORYX BEATRIX) LATELY LIVING IN THE MENAGERIE OF THE SOCIETY. J.E. Gray. Proc. Zool. Soc. London, pt.25, pp.157-158, pl.5,, 1857.

SYNOPSIS OF THE SPECIES OF ANTELOPES AND STREPSICERES, WITH DESCRIPTIONS OF SOME NEW SPECIES. J.E. Gray. Proc. Zool. Soc. London, pt. 18, pp.111-128, 1850.

NAME OF THE BLESBOK. Francis Harper. Proc. Biol. Soc. Washington, vol.52, pp. 89-91, June 5, 1939.

GENERIC NAMES ANOA AND BUBALUS. N. Hollister. Proc. Biol. Soc. Wash., vol. 32, p.45, Apr. 11, 1919.

TYPE SPECIMEN OF THE WATER BUFFALO, ANOA MINDORENSIS STEERE. Emmet T. Hooper. Occas. Papers Mus. Zool., Univ. Michigan, Ann Arbor, no.443, pp.4, July 18, 1941.

(LIST OF KNOWN AND DESCRIBED SPECIES OF THE FAMILY OF ANTELOPES, PRESENTED BY REGIONS. )Liste des espèces cannues et decrites dans la famille des antilopides présentees par régions. M. Huet. Bull. Soc. nat.d'Acclimat. de France, Paris, pp.1-93, figs. 1-35, Aug., 1887.

(NEW SUBSPECIES OF AMMOTRAGUS.) Sopra una muova sottospecie del Ammotragus. G. Lepri. Atti.Pontificia Accad. Sci. Nuovi Lincei, vol.83, pp.269-271, 1930.

NOTES ON THE MEMBERS OF THE GENERA "CEPHALOPHUS" AND "SYLVICAPRA" IN CONGO MUSEUM. Einar Lönnberg. Rev. Zool. Africaine, vol.7, pp.162-185, 1919.

(NOTE ON THE CLASSIFICATION OF AFRICAN BUFFALOES.) Note au sujet de la classification des buffles africains. R. Malbrant. Bull. Mus. Nat. Hist.Nat., Paris, ser.2, vol.7, no.6, pp.320-332, fig., Nov., 1935.

(PRELIMINARY COMMUNICATION ON A NEW SUBSPECIES OF HIPPOTRAGUS BAKERI HEUGL.) Paul Matschie. Sitz. Ber. Gesell. Naturf. Freunde Berlin, Jahrg. 1898, no.9, pp.181-183, Nov. 15, 1898.(In German.)

(SYSTEMATIC POSITION OF BUDORCAS HODGS.) Die systematische Stellung von Budorcas Hodgs. Paul Matschie. Sitz. Ber. Gesell. Naturf. Freunde Berlin, no.4, pp.30-31, Apr. 19, 1898.

CHARACTERS OF A NEW SPECIES OF ANTELOPE (ANTILOPE ELLIPSIPRYMNA), FROM THE COLLECTION OF MR. STEEDMAN. W. Ogilby. Proc. Zool. Soc. London, pt.1, p.47, 1833.

ON A NEW SPECIES OF ANTELOPE (ANTILOPE CUVIERI). W. Ogilby. Proc. Zool. Soc. London, pt.8, pp.34-35, 1840.

DESCRIPTION OF A NEW SPECIES OF GORAL (NEMORHAEDUS) SHOT BY CAPTAIN F. M. BAILEY. R.I. Pocock. Jour. Bombay Nat. Hist. Soc., vol.33, no.1, pp.32-33, June 30, 1914.

DESCRIPTIONS OF THREE NEW FORMS OF TRAGELAPHUS. R.I. Pocock. Ann. and Mag. Nat. Hist., ser.7, vol.5, pp. 94-96, Jan., 1900.

NEW SPECIES OF DIK-DIK (RHYNCHOTRAGUS). (R.hodsoni.) R. I.Pocock. Ann. and Mag. Nat. Hist., ser.9, vol.17, pp.187-188, Jan., 1926.

(TECHNICAL NAME OF THE WILD GOAT.) Der technische Name der Wildziege.(Capra prisca.) Hermann Pohle. Zeitschr. f.Saeugetierk., Berlin, vol.8, nos.3-6, p.288, Dec. 20, 1933.

ON A NEW RACE OF BHARAL. (Pseudois nahoor szechuanensis). Walter Rothschild. Ann. and Mag. Nat. Hist., ser.9, vol.10, p.231, Aug., 1922.

DESCRIPTION OF A NEW BUSH-BUCK. Walter Rothschild. Proc. Zool. Soc. London, pp.691-692, Oct. 10, 1906.

NOTES ON TRAGELAPHUS SPEKEI SPEKEI AND TRAGELAPHUS SPEKEI GRATUS, WITH DESCRIPTION OF A NEW SPECIES. Walter Rothschild. Novitates Zoologicae, vol.5, no.2, p.206, May, 1898.

ON TWO NEW SPECIES OF ANTELOPES. Walter Rothschild. Novitates Zoologicae, vol.2, no.1, pp.52-53, pl.4, Feb., 1895.

DESCRIPTION OF A NEW SUBSPECIES OF HARTEBEESTE (BUBALIS). A.E. Ruxton. Ann. and Mag. Nat. Hist., ser.9, vol.18, p.215, Aug., 1926.

KEY TO THE SPECIES AND SUBSPECIES OF THE SUBGENUS CEPHALOPHUS. J. St. Leger. Proc. Zool. Soc. London, pt.1, pp.209-228, Apr. 16, 1936.

EXHIBITION OF A SPECIMEN AND DESCRIPTION OF A NEW SPECIES OF REEDBUCK PROPOSED TO BE CALLED CERVICAPRA THOMASINAE. Philip Lutley Sclater. Proc. Zool. Soc. London, pt.3, pp.429-430, pl.26, Oct. 1, 1900.

NAME FOR A SPECIES OF ORYX FROM GERMAN SOUTHWEST AFRICA. Embrik Strand. Archiv f. Naturgesch., year 90, Abt. A, Heft 1, p.146, (footnote), July, 1924.

NAMES FOR TWO SUBSPECIES OF PEDIOTRAGUS FROM GERMAN SOUTHWEST AFRICA. Embrik Strand. Archiv f. Naturgesch., year 90, Abt. A, Heft 1, p.133, (footnote), July, 1924.

ON THE TYPE LOCALITY OF TRAGELAPHUS SCRIPTUS REIDAE BABAULT. G.H. Swynnerton. Ann. and Mag. Nat. Hist., London, ser.12, vol.2, no.14, pp.156-157, June 17, 1949.

ON THE TYPE-LOCALITY OF RAPHICERUS CAMPESTRIS NEUMANNI (MATSCHIE). G.H. Swynnerton, R.W. Hayman. Ann. and Mag. Nat. Hist., London, ser.11, vol.12, no.86, pp.137-139, (Feb., 1945) July 10, 1945.

GENERIC NAME CONNOCHAETES OF LICHTENSTEIN. Oldfield Thomas. Proc. Biol. Soc. Wash., vol.28, p.69, Mar.12, 1915.

ON A NEW ANTELOPE. Oldfield Thomas. Proc. Zool. Soc. London, pp.463-464, pl. 35, Oct. 10, 1906.

ON A NEW BUSH-BUCK. Oldfield Thomas. Proc. Zool. Soc. London, vol.2, pp.180-182, Oct. 17, 1905.

ON A NEW FORM OF GRANT'S GAZELLE. Oldfield Thomas. Proc. Zool. Soc. London, vol.2, pp.119-121, figs.10-11, June 16, 1903.

ON A NEW SUBSPECIES OF HARTEBEEST. Oldfield Thomas. Proc. Zool. Soc. London, pt.1, pp.455-456, Aug. 2, 1904.

ON THE ANTELOPES OF THE GENUS CEPHALOLOPHUS. Oldfield Thomas. Proc. Zool. Soc. London, pp.413-430, May 17, 1892.

ON THE EAST-AFRICAN REPRESENTATIVE OF THE BONGO AND ITS GENERIC POSITION. Oldfield Thomas. Ann. and Mag. Nat. Hist., ser.7, vol.10, no.58, pp.309-310, Oct., 1902.

ON THE GENERIC SUBDIVISION OF THE BOVIDAE OR HOLLOW-HORNED RUMINANTS. H.N. Turner. Proc. Zool. Soc. London, pt.18, pp.164-178, 1850.

Weights, Measurements

(ENORMOUS HEIGHT ATTAIND, AT CAZAVET, BY GUATERNARY BOVINES.) Sur l'énorme taille attainte, à Cazavet, par les Bovidés Quaternaires. Gaston Astre. Bull. Soc. Hist. Nat. Toulouse, vol.71, nos.1-2, pp.171-174, June 30, 1937.

(GREATEST HEIGHT OF CHAMOIS.) Le plus forte taille de l'isard. Gaston Astre. Mammalia, Paris, vol.10, nos.1-2, pp. 55-60, Mar.-June, 1947.

RECORD FEMALE INDIAN GAZELLE (G. BENETTI). R.H. Heath. Jour. Bombay Nat. Hist. Soc., vol.27, p.625, Mar. 31, 1921.

RECORD FOUR-HORNED ANTELOPE (TETRACEROS QUADRICORNIS). C. McCann. Jour. Bombay Nat. Hist. Soc., vol.32, pp.592-593, illus., Jan. 15, 1928.

(MEASURING A BLUE CEPHALOPH FROM THE CAMEROUNE, PHILANTOMBA CAERULA SCHULTZEI SCHWARZ, BORN AT THE ZOOLOGICAL PARK IN THE BOIS DE VINCENNES.) Mensurations d'un Céphalophe bleu du Cameroune, Philantomba caerula Schultzei Schwarz, né au Parc Zoologique du Bois de Vincennes. J. Rinjard. Mammalia, Paris, vol.20, no.3, p.329, Sep., 1956.

MEASUREMENTS AND DESCRIPTION OF BUSHCOW. A.H. Smith. Nigerian Field, London, vol.8, no.1, pp.39-42, Jan., 1939.

Zoo and Museum Collections

(OBSERVATIONS OF BOVINES IN SCHOENBRUNN. III. EAST SUDANESE BUFFALO.) Beobachtungen an Rindern in Schoenbrunn. III. Ostsudanesische Bueffel. Otto Antonius. Zool. Garten, Leipzig, n.f., vol.6, nos.7-9, pp.149-155, figs.5, 1933.

FOUR STUBBORN BABIES FROM GREENLAND. CAPTAIN BOB BARLETT BRINGS US TWO PAIRS OF MUSKOX CALVES, THE FIRST EXHIBITED HERE IN ALMOST TEN YEARS. William Bridges. Bull. New York Zool. Soc., vol.42, no.6, pp.163-171, figs. 7, Nov.-Dec., 1939.

UP-STREAM FOR MOUNTAIN GOATS. AFTER WADING THROUGH FRIGID ALASKAN STREAMS, CLAMBERING UP WATERFALLS, AND SCALING PERILOUS CLIFFS, THE CLARK-KISSEL EXPEDITION SECURED FINE SPECIMENS OF THESE HARDY ANIMALS. H.B. Clark. Nat. Hist., New York, vol.40, no.5, pp. 733-738, 782, illus., Dec., 1937.

GROUP OF SPANISH IBEX: GIFT OF THE KING OF SPAIN. J.G. Dollman. Nat. Hist. Mag., London, vol.1, pp.106-107, illus., Oct., 1927.

(SPECIMEN OF A NORTHERN AFRICA BUFFALO IN THE MUSEUM COLLECTIONS.) A propos d'un spécimen de Bubale d'Afrique du Nord conservé dans les collections du Muséum. Jean Dorst. Bull. Mus. Nat. Hist. Nat. Paris, ser.2, vol.29, no.6, pp.447-450, Feb. 25, 1958.

(NOTES ON THE MAMMALS. XXII. REMARKS ON SPECIMENS OF THE GENUS BUBALIS IN THE MUSEUM COLLECTION.) Notes sur les mammifères. XXII. Remarques au sujet des spécimens du genre Bubalis de la collection du Musée. Serge Frechkop. Bull. Mus. Royal Hist. Nat. Belgique, vol. 13, no.39, pp.1-30, pl.1, Oct., 1937.

FIRST BONGO OF HER KIND KEPT IN CAPTIVITY. A FEMALE OF THE NORTH-EAST CONGO SPECIES, NOW IN THE ROME "ZOO": THE STORY OF HER CAPTURE AND HER LIFE IN AN AFRICAN FOREST CAMP. Attilio Gatti. Illus. London News, vol.188, no.5051, pp.233-235, figs.10, Feb. 8, 1936.

ON THE DUIKER BOKS IN THE SOCIETY'S GARDENS. John Edward Gray. Proc. Zool. Soc. London, pt.25, pp.277-278, pl.57, 1857.

TO AFRICA AND BACK WITH BARBARY SHEEP FOR MUSEUM EXHIBIT. H.T. Green. Frontiers, Philadelphia, vol.16, no.1, pp.12-15, illus., 1951.

THE ANTELOPES IN THE LEYDEN MUSEUM. F.A. Jentink. Notes Leyden Mus., vol.23, no.3, pp.17-31, fig.1, May, 1901.

LETTER FROM, CONCERNING A KOODO (TRAGELAPHUS STREPSICEROS?) AND OTHER ANIMALS DESTINED FOR THE SOCIETY. John Kirk. Proc. Zool. Soc. London, pp.195-196, 1873.

BONGO COMES TO THE ZOOLOGICAL PARK. Claude W. Leister. Bull. New York Zool. Soc., vol.36, no.2, pp.33-37, illus., Mar.-Apr., 1933.

WE EXHIBIT THE RARE NYALA. DISCOVERED IN 1847, THIS IS THE FIRST TIME THE ANTELOPE HAS BEEN SHOWN IN THE UNITED STATES. Claude W. Leister. Bull. New York Zool. Soc., vol.41, no.4, pp.129-130, illus., July-Aug., 1938.

NOTES ON THE MEMBERS OF THE GENERA "CEPHALOPHUS" AND "SYLVICAPRA" IN THE CONGO MUSEUM. Einar Lönnberg. Rev. Zool. Africaine, vol.7, fasc.2, pp.162-185, 1919.

(THE IBEX IN CAPTIVITY.) Bouquetins en captivité. Monique Meyer-Holzapfel. Mammalia, Paris, vol.22, no.1, pp.90-103, pls. 3-4, Mar., 1958.

(EUROPEAN BISON IN THE COLLECTIONS OF THE MUSEUM OF NATURAL HISTORY.) Les bisons Européens des collections du Muséum d'Histoire Naturelle. J. Millot. Mammalia, Paris, vol.9, no.1, pp.1-19, pls.2, Mar., 1945.

TWO "FIRST-TIMERS" FOR THE ZOO. (Gerenuk and lesser kudu.) Oliver Milton. Animal Kingdom, N.Y. Zool. Soc., vol. 60, no.6, pp.166-169, illus., Dec., 1957.

(ON AN OVIBOS MOSCHATUS OF THE LOCAL ZOOLOGICAL GARDEN.) Ueber einen Ovibos moschatus des hiesigen zoologischen Gartens. Alfred Nehring. Sitz. Ber. Gesell. Naturf. Freunde Berlin, no.4, p.135, Apr. 16, 1901.

BLACKBUSH AND CHINKARA, ANTELOPES OF INDIA, MAKE ATTRACTIVE GROUP. Wilfred H. Osgood. Field Mus. Notes, vol.6, no.7, p.1, fig., July, 1935.

FIRST LIVING MALE BONGO KEPT IN A EUROPEAN "ZOO". THE STORY OF HIS CAPTURE IN THE MOUNTAIN FORESTS OF KENYA: WITH AN ENGLISHWOMAN'S ACCOUNT OF HIS ATTACK ON HER, BEFORE HIS REMOVAL TO ROME. Eric Percy-Smith, Mrs. W. Mitton. Illus. London News, vol.184, no.4945, pp.121-123, illus., Jan. 27, 1934.

LORD DERBY'S ELAND. STRIKING EXHIBIT AT THE NATURAL HISTORY MUSEUM. R.I. Pocock. Field, London, vol.153, p.525, illus., Mar. 28, 1929.

EXHIBITION OF A SPECIMEN OF THE WILD IBEX OF CRETE. Philip Lutley Sclater. Proc. Zool. Soc. London, pp.89-90, 1874.

EXHIBITION OF PHOTOGRAPHS OF, AND REMARKS ON, TWO YOUNG MUSK-OXEN LIVING IN THE DUKE OF BEDFORD'S PARK AT WOBURN. Philip Lutley Sclater. Proc. Zool. Soc. London, 1899, pt.4, pp. 985-986, fig.1, Apr. 1, 1900.

THE CAPRA FALCONERI WGN. OF THE MOSCOW ZOOLOGICAL PARK. L. V. Shaposhnikov. Proc. Moscow Zool. Park, vol.1, pp.62-63, 1940.

RAISING ISABELLA GAZELLES. Ken Stott, Jr. Zoonooz, San Diego, vol.12, no. 10, pp.4-5, Oct., 1940.

(COLLECTION OF ASIATIC BOVINES AT THE ZOOLOGICAL PARK OF THE BOIS DE VINCENNES.) La collection des Bovinés asiatiques du parc Zoologique du Bois de Vincennes. Ach. Urbain et al. Mammalia, Pairs, vol.3, nos.3-4, pp.122-125, pls.9, Sep.-Dec., 1939.

(MY TWO GIANT ELANDS (TAUROTRAGUS DERBIANUS CONGOLANUS ROTHSCHILD.) Alfred Weidholz. Zool. Garten, Leipzig, n.F., vol.3, nos.4-8, pp.138-144, figs.3, Aug. 11, 1930. (In German.)

STORY BEHIND BAMBI, BROWNIE, AND BABY. (Arabian gazelles.) Mrs. Frank Zukoski. Animal Kingdom, New York Zool. Soc., vol.54, no.5, pp.146-150, 160, illus., Sep.-Oct., 1951.

DOREEN GROWS UP: THE FIRST BONGO KEPT IN A "ZOO" --A RARE ANTELOPE'S DEVELOPMENT IN CAPTIVITY, FROM YOUTH TO MATURITY. Illus. London News, vol.187, no.5029, p.390, figs.6, Sep. 7, 1935.

EXHIBITED AT THE LONDON ZOO AT LAST: THE BONGO AND ITS CALF. Illus. London News, vol.190, no.5113, p.677, illus., Apr. 17, 1937.

FIRST BONGO--RAREST OF EAST AFRICAN ANTELOPES--KEPT IN CAPTIVITY ABROAD: A YOUNG FEMALE SUCCESSFULLY TAKEN TO NEW YORK BY WAY OF LONDON. Illus. London News, vol.183, no.4931, pp.642-643, illus., Oct. 21, 1933.

FINE MALE AOUDAD FROM THE ZOOLOGICAL PARK HERD. New York Zool. Park School News, vol.4, no.1, p.1, photo, May, 1939.

MICKEY, THE WATER BUFFALO. Fauna, Philadelphia, vol.3, no.4, pp.134-135, illus., Dec., 1941.

NEW AND GRACEFUL ARRIVAL AT THE LONDON ZOO: A LESSER KUDU FROM

KENYA. Illus. London News, vol.210, no. 5644, p.664, illus., June 21, 1947.

NEW ANTELOPE. San Diego Zoonooz, vol. 19, no.11, pp.5, 7, Nov., 1946.

NEW INHABITANT FOR THE LONDON ZOO, A NILGHAI CALF. Illus. London News, vol. 217, no.5810, p.309, illus., Aug. 26, 1950.

RARE ANTELOPE RECEIVED AT THE ZOOLOGICAL GARDENS FROM MR. K. GANDAR DOWER; THE FEMALE BONGO PHOTOGRAPHED IN AFRICA AFTER ITS CAPTURE. Illus. London News, vol.190, no.5099, p.39, illus., Jan. 9, 1937.

TAKIN GROUP AT THE PHILADELPHIA ACADEMY. Sci. Monthly, vol.45, no.1, pp.94-95, illus., July, 1937.

Bison--General

(OBSERVATIONS OF BOVINE ANIMALS IN SCHOENBRUNN. I. THE SCHARI BUFFALO.) Beobachtungen an Rindern in Schoenbrunn. I. Die Schari-Bueffel. Otto Antonius. Zool. Garten, Leipzig, n.F., vol.3, nos.4-8, pp. 145-152, figs.5, Aug.11, 1930.

(CENSUS OF THE WORLD'S BISON.) Le recensement des bisons dans le mode. M. C. Bresson. La Terre et la Vie (Revue d'Hist. Nat.), vol.2, no.9, pp.556-557, Sept., 1932.

BUFFALO AND BISON. Maurice Burton. Illus. London News, vol.219, no.5880, p.1078, illus., Dec.20, 1951.

THE UNVANQUISHED BUFFALO. Henry H. Collins, Jr. Blue Heron Press, pp.15, illus., 1952.

(THE AUROCHS OF GERMANY, AFTER DR. LUTZ HECK.) L'auroch de Germanie d'apres le Dr. Lutz Heck. Paul Cordier-Goni. La Terre et La Vie, 8 Annee, no.3, pp.77-83, illus., May-June, 1938.

(SOME NOTES ON THE AUROCHS.) Quelques notes sur l'aurochs. G. P. Dementiev. Mammalia, Paris, 22 (1): 161-167, Mar., 1958.

(SUMMARY OF THE DIAGNOSTIC CHARACTERS OF THE BISON.) C. C. Flerov. Bull. Acad. Sci. URSS, Cl. Sci. Math. et Nat., pp.1579-1590, figs.8, 1932. (In Russian.)

THE PASSING OF THE BUFFALO. I. William T. Hornaday. Cosmopolitan, New York, vol.4, no.2, pp.84-98, illus., Oct., 1887.

THE BISON AS A FACTOR IN ANCIENT AMERICAN CULTURE HISTORY. Walter Hough. Scientific Monthly, vol.30, pp.315-319, Apr., 1930.

(ANAESTHESIA IN THE EUROPEAN BISON (BISON BONASUS L.) BY CHLORALHYDRATE (CHLORALUM HYDRATUM). Narkoza zuba (Bison bonasus L.) wodnikiem chloralu (Chloralum hydratum). Zbigniew Jaczewski, Krzysztof Swierzynski. Zool. Poloniae, Arch. Soc. Zool. Poloniae, Wroclaw, vol.6, fasc.2, pp.80-87, 1955.

(THE AUROCHS OF 1595.) Der Auerochs von 1595. Johannes Kuehlhorn. Zeitschr. Saeugetierk., Berlin, vol.20, nos.2-3, p. 186, Aug.3, 1955.

BUFFALO DISPOSAL. George W. Miller. Yellowstone Nat. Notes, vol.10, nos.1-2, pp.5-6, Jan.-Feb., 1933.

(THE EUROPEAN BISON OF THE COLLECTIONS OF THE MUSEUM OF NATURAL HISTORY.) Les Bisons Europeens de collections du Museum d'Histoire Naturelle. J. Millot. Mammalia, Paris, 9 (1): 1-19, illus., pl.1, Mar., 1945.

WISENT AND BISON. Richard Rein. Naturforscher, Berlin, vol.12, no.3, pp. 82-87, illus., June, 1935. (In German.)

THE CURLY COWS. (BUFFALO) Charles B. Roth. Sports Afield, Minneapolis, vol. 121, no.1, pp.24-25, 80-82, illus., Jan., 1949.

HUMPBACK, THE BUFFALO. W. J. Schoonmaker. National Humane Review, Albany, vol.31, no.11, pp.24-25, illus., Nov., 1943.

THE BISON AND ITS RELATIONS. Charles M. Sternberg. Canadian Field-Nat., vol. 39, p.111, May 19, 1925.

MODERN BUFFALO HUNT WITH A CAMERA. Harold S. Sykes. Arizona Wildlife and Sportsman, Phoenix, vol.8, no.10, pp.19-20, illus., Oct., 1947.

THE STORY OF THE 'BUFFALO.' John Peter Turner. Geographical Mag., vol.3, no.4, pp.221-234, illus., Aug., 1936.

THE LIPIDS IN BISON BISON. Charles G. Wilber. Jour. Mam., 36 (2): 305-308, May, 1955.

BUFFALO DAYS. Junior Nat. Hist. Mag., New York, vol.3, no.7, pp.4-7, illus., Sept., 1938.

Bison--Anatomy

THE FIRST PREMOLAR AND THE CANINE TOOTH IN BISON. W. A. Fuller. Jour. Mam., 35 (3): 454-456, illus., Aug., 1954.

THE AGE ORDER OF EPIPHYSEAL UNION IN THE SKELETON OF THE EUROPEAN BISON (BOS BONASUS L.). Walter Koch. Anat. Record, vol.61, no.3, pp.371-376, Feb.25, 1935.

(ON GROWTH AND AGE CHANGES IN THE SKELETON OF THE WISENT.) Ueber Wachstums- und Altersveraenderungen am Skelett des Wisents. Walter Koch. Beitraege zur Natur- und Kulturgeschichte Lithauens und angrenzender Gebiete. Abhandl. math.-naturw. Abt. Bayer, Akad. Wiss., Suppl. Bd.15, Abhandl., Muenchen, pp.553-678, figs.44, pls.3, 1932.

("HORN SHEDDING" IN BOVINES.) "Hornwechsel" bei Rindern. Erna Mohr. Natur und Volk, Frankfurt a.M., vol.78, nos.10-12, pp.146-151, Dec.1, 1948.

NOTES ON THE ANATOMY OF THE MALE AUROCHS. Professor Owen. Proc. Zool. Soc. Lond., pt.16, pp.126-133, 1848.

(COMPARATIVE ANATOMICAL INVESTIGATIONS OF THE HEAD OF THE BISON (BISON BONASUS L.). PART I: CAVUM ORIS.) Vergleichend-anatomische Untersuchungen am Kopfe des Wisents--Bison bonasus (L.). Teil I--Cavum oris. Edward Wilkus. Acta Theriologica, Inst. Zool. Polska Akad. Nauk, Warsaw, vol.1, no.7, pp.183-307, pls.1-18, July 5, 1957. (In Polish, with German and Russian summaries.)

Bison--Asia

(THE WISENT IN MESOPOTAMIA.) Der Wisent in Mesopotamien. Max Hilzheimer. Der Naturforscher, vol.1, pp.348-350, Nov., 1924.

HISTORY OF THE BISONS IMPORTED INTO JAPAN. Haruo Takashima. Misc. Repts. Yamashina's Inst. Ornithol. and Zool., Tokyo, no.2, pp.45-54, illus., June, 1953. (In Japanese, with English summary.)

Bison--Breeding

(RAISING AND HYBRIDIZATION OF THE BISON OF CANADA.) L'elevage et l'hybridation du bison au Canada. J. Berlioz. Bull. Soc. Nat. Acclimat. France, vol.80, no.2, pp.47-53, Feb., 1933.

(RAISING THE EUROPEAN BISON IN THE COURSE OF PAST YEARS. ITS PRESENT STATUS.) L'elevage du Bison d'Europe au cours des dernieres annees. Son etat actuel. Erna Mohr. Mammalia, Paris, vol.15, no.4, pp.138-142, illus., Dec., 1951.

BREEDING THE THREE-YEAR OLD FEMALES IN THE JACKSON HOLE WILDLIFE PARK BUFFALO HERD. Norman C. Negus. Jour. Mam., vol.31, no.4, p.463, Nov.21, 1950.

CARE OF BUFFALOES. USDI, F&WS, Wildlife Leaflet 212, pp.8, Feb., 1942.

Bison--Conservation, Management

CONDENSED REPORT OF THE PROGRESS OF THE INTERNATIONAL SOCIETY FOR THE PRESERVATION OF THE WISENT, INCLUDING A RESUME OF THE PAPERS PRESENTED AT THE LAST MEETING IN SEPTEMBER 1925. Theodor G. Ahrens. Bericht. Intern. Gesellsch. Erhaltung des Wisents, vol.1, pt.3, pp.85-91, June, 1926.

PROPOSALS FOR THE PRESERVATION OF THE EUROPEAN BISON, OR WISENT. Theodor G. Ahrens. Zool. Soc. Bull., vol.26, pp.46-50, figs.3, May, 1923.

PROPOSALS FOR THE PRESERVATION OF THE WISENT. Theodor G. Ahrens. Science, n.s., vol.58, p.107, Aug.10, 1923.

RECENT DEVELOPMENTS IN THE PRESERVATION OF THE WISENT IN GERMANY. Theodore G. Ahrens. Jour. Mam., vol.17, no.2, pp.137-138, May, 1936.

REPORT OF THE WISENT RESERVE AT SPRINGE, HANOVER. Theodor G. Ahrens. Jour. Mam., vol.14, no.1, pp.78-80, Feb., 1933.

THERE'S STILL A CHANCE FOR THE WISENT. William Bridges. Animal Kingdom, 54 (3): 77-79, May-June, 1951.

BUFFALO GO WILD. Victor H. Cahalane. Nat. Hist., 53 (4): 148-153, Apr., 1944.

BUFFALO, WILD OR TAME? Victor H. Cahalane. Amer. Forests, 50 (10): 472-475, Oct., 1944.

RESTORATION OF WILD BISON. Victor H. Cahalane. Trans. N. A. Wildl. Conf., 9: 135-143, 1944.

THE MONTANA NATIONAL BISON RANGE. Morton J. Elrod. Jour. Mam., vol.7, no. 1, pp.45-48, pl.10, Feb., 1926.

SAVE OUR BUFFALO HERD. Harry Funk. Arizona Wildlife and Sportsman, Prescott, vol.5, no.9, p.7, Sept., 1943.

THE AMERICAN BISON. THE STORY OF ITS EXTERMINATION AS A WILD SPECIES AND ITS RESTORATION UNDER FEDERAL PROTECTION. Martin S. Garretson. N.Y. Zool. Soc., xii, 254 pp., 1938.

THE REDUCTION OF THE BUFFALO HERDS. W.E.D. Halliday. Forest and Outdoors, 36 (8): 257-258, Aug., 1940.

(REPORT ON THE PROTECTIVE BISON PARK IN SPRINGE.) Bericht ueber den Wisent-Schutzpark in Springe. Lutz Heck. Berichte der Internat. Ges. zur Erhaltung des Wissents, 3 (1): 97-120, tables 4-9, 1932.

THE COMING BACK OF THE BISON. C. Gordon Hewitt. Nat. Hist., vol.19, no. 6, pp.553-565, figs.13, Dec., 1919.

(IS THE WISENT BECOMING EXTINCT?) Sterben die Wisente aus? Theodor Knottnerus-Meyer. Naturforscher, Berlin, vol.9, no.7, pp.265-267, Oct., 1932.

WILL THE WISENT SURVIVE THE WAR? Willy Ley. Fauna, Phila., vol.2, no.2, pp.23-27, illus., June, 1940.

REPORT ON CERTAIN LANDS IN SOUTH DAKOTA SUITABLE FOR A BUFFALO AND GAME RESERVE. J. A. Loring. Maps and Illus, vol.8, pp.31, N.Y., 1911.

SAVING SWEDEN'S WILD FAUNA. Holger Lundbergh. Nature Mag., vol.22, no.3, p.132, illus., Sept., 1933.

(MEASURES AND WORKS ON THE CONSERVATION OF THE BISON.) Massnahmen und Arbeiten zur Erhaltung des Wisents. Erna W. Mohr. Zool. Anzeiger, Suppl. band, vol.1, pp.177-182, 1925.

(WILD SPECIES THAT ARE BECOMING EXTINCT IN CENTRAL EUROPE: THE BISON.) Aussterbende Wildarten in Mitteleuropa: Der Wisent. Erna Mohr. Wild und Hund, Hamburg, Jahrg.51, no.7, pp.152-155, figs.4, Nov., 1948.

(REPORT OF THE INTERNATIONAL SOCIETY FOR THE CONSERVATION OF BISON.) Bericht der Internationalen Gesellschaft zur Ernaitung des Wisents. Hermann Pohle. Gesellschaftmitteilungen, pp.184-230, 1927.

(FIRST ANNUAL REPORT OF THE INTERNATIONAL SOCIETY FOR THE CONSERVATION OF BISON.) Erster Jahresbericht der internationalen Gesellschaft zur Erhaltung des Wisents. Kurt Priemel. pp.22, Aug.,1923-Dec.31, 1924, 1925.

(MEASURES FOR THE CONSERVATION OF BISON.) Massnanhmen zur Erhaltung des Wisents. Kurt Priemel. Zool. palaearctica, vol.1, no.1, pp.1-8, 1923.

(THE POSSIBILITY OF THE CONSERVATION OF THE BISON.) Gedenken ueber die Moeglichkeit der Erhaltung des Wisents. Kurt Priemel. Deutsche Jaeger Zeitung, Band 80, nr.20, pp.289-292, Dec.7, 1922.

(Review by Theodor C. Ahrens of) THE POSSIBILITY OF THE CONSERVATION OF BISON. Gadenken Ueber die moeglichkeit der Erhaltung des Wisents. Kurt Priemel. Jour. Mam., vol.4, no.3, pp.197-199, Aug., 1923.

(REPORT ON THE FOUNDING SESSION OF THE INTERNATIONAL SOCIETY FOR CONSERVATION OF BISON ON 25 AND 26 AUGUST 1923 IN THE BERLIN ZOOLOGICAL GARDEN.) Bericht ueber die Gruendungstagung der Internationalen Gesellschaft zur Erhaltung des Wisents am 25 und 26 August 1923 im Zoologischen Garten, Berlin. Kurt Priemel. Frankfurt am Main, pp.1-23, pl.1, 1923.

MISSING IN ACTION. (WISENT.) Frank Thone. Science News Letter, Wash., vol. 47, no.19, p.301, May 12, 1945.

THE NATIONAL PARK BUFFALO. Frederick W. True. Forest and Stream, vol.27, no.15, p.284, Nov.4, 1886.

A RARE ANIMAL CAREFULLY PRESERVED IN POLAND: EUROPEAN BISON IN THE BIALOVIEZA NATIONAL PARK. H. Frank Wallace. Illus. London News, vol.214, no. 5736, pp.396-397, illus., Mar.26, 1949.

WORK ON RESTITUTION OF THE EUROPEAN BISON. Jan Zabinski. Ochrona Przyrody 19: 101-115, 1950. (In Polish, with English summary.)

BRINGING BACK THE BUFFALO. Canadian National Parks Br., Dept. Interior, Ottawa, pp.4, 1927.

EUROPEAN BISON MAY HAVE CHANCE OF SURVIVAL. Science News Letter, Wash., vol.54, no.8, p.114, Aug.21, 1948.

REPORT OF INTERNATIONAL SOCIETY FOR PRESERVATION OF THE WISENT FOR 1927. Jour. Mam., vol.10, no.1, p. 97, Feb., 1929.

SAVING THE BUFFALO. Beaver, Winnipeg, outfit 279, pp.10-13, illus., June, 1948.

Bison--Diseases, Parasites

TICK PARALYSIS IN THE AMERICAN BUFFALO, BISON BISON (LINN.). Glen M. Kohls, N. J, Kramis. Northwest Science, vol.26, no.2, pp.61-64, illus., June, 1952.

PARASITES OF BISON IN NORTHWESTERN U.S.A. Betty Locker. Jour. Parasit., 39 (1): 58-59, Feb., 1953.

OCCURRENCE OF ASPERGILLUS FUMIGATUS FRESEN, IN THE LUNG OF AN AMERICAN BISON. R. E. Rewell, G. C. Ainsworth. Nature, London, vol.160, no. 4063, pp.362-363, Sept.13, 1947.

ARTHROPOD AND HELMINTH PARASITES OF THE AMERICAN BISON (BISON BISON). Robert L. Roudabush. Jour. Parasit., 22 (5): 517-518, Oct., 1936.

Bison--Ecology, Habits, Behavior

AN ALTITUDINAL RECORD FOR BISON IN NORTHERN COLORADO. Richard G. Beidleman. Jour. Mam., 36 (3): 470-471, Aug., 1955.

BUFFALO (BISON BISON) KILLED BY FIRE. James E. Cole. Jour. Mam., 35 (3): 453-454, Aug., 1954.

A NEW HIGH ALTITUDE LIMIT FOR THE AMERICAN BISON. Fritiof M. Fryxell. Jour. Mam., vol.7, no.2, pp.102-109, May, 1926.

THE WISENT OR EUROPEAN BISON. R Richard Glover. Jour. Mam., 28 (4): 333-342, Nov., 1947.

(ON THE BEHAVIOR OF THE AMERICAN BISON AT BIRTH.) Zum verhalten des amerikanischen Bisons bei der Geburt. H. Hediger. Verhandl schweiz. naturforsch, Ges., 120: 174-6, 1940.

THE ROLE OF THE BISON IN MAINTAINING THE SHORT GRASS PLAINS. Floyd Larson. Ecology, 21 (2): 113-121, Apr., 1940.

BUFFALO--A VERB. (HABITS OF THE AMERICAN BISON.) Smith Riley. Nature Mag., vol.23, no.4, pp.185-186, Apr., 1934.

HISTORY, RANGE, AND HOME LIFE OF THE NORTHERN BISON. (DETAILED ACCOUNT OF THE ECOLOGY AND LIFE HISTORY OF THE BISON OF WOOD BUFFALO PARK, CAN.) J. Dewey Soper. Ecol. Mong., 11 (4): 347-412, Oct., 1941.

ALTITUDE LIMIT OF BISON. Edward R. Warren. Jour. Mam., vol.8, no.1, pp.60-61, Feb., 1927.

BUFFALO RUN. Turtox News, Chicago, vol.24, no.1, pp.20-22, illus., Jan., 1946.

Bison--Europe

THE PRESENT STATUS OF THE EUROPEAN BISON OR WISENT. Theodor G. Ahrens. Jour. Mam., vol.2, no.2, pp.58-62, May, 1921.

(CAUCASIAN WISENT.) Kavkazskii Zubr. Ie. Bashkiov, M. A. Zablotskii. Glavnoe Upravlenie po Zapovednikam, Zooparkam i Zoosadam, SNK RSFSR (Krasnyi proletarii, 1939), Moscow, pp.1-44, illus., 1940.

REMAINS OF THE EUROPEAN BISON, BISON BONASUS (L.), FROM PODHALE IN POLAND. Stefania Bochenek. Acta Theriologica, Inst. Zool. Polska Akad. Nauk, Warsaw, vol.1, no.2, pp.15-25, Jan. 20, 1955. (In Polish, with Russian and English summaries.)

(EXISTENCE OF BISON IN BUCOVINA.) Existenta zimbrului in Bucovina. E. Botezat. Bul. Fac. Stiinte Cernauti, vol. 5, no.2, pp.370-377, fig.1, (1931) 1932.

(THE GRADUAL DYING OUT OF THE BISON (BISON BONASUS LINN.) IN THE FOREST OF BELOVESHA.) Das allmaehliche Aussterben des Wisents (Bison bonasus (Linn.) ) Im forste von Bjelowjesha. Eug. Buechner. Mem. Acad. Imp. Sci. St. Petersbourg, vol.3, no.2, pp.1-30, 1895.

THE BISONS OF THE CAUCASUS. Aleksiei Sergieevich Ermolov. Ann. Rept. Smithsonian Inst., Wash., pp.345-353, illus., pl.2, 1907.

THE EUROPEAN BISON IN SWEDEN. Clyde Fisher. Jour. Mam., vol.8, no.3, pp.231-232, pl.22, Aug., 1927.

(THE AUROCHS OF VIG, INJURED AND KILLED BY FLINT WEAPONS.) Om uroxen fra Vig, Saaret og Draebt Med Flint-vaaben. N. Hartz, Herluf Winge. Aarboger Nordisk Oldynidghed og Hist., pp.225-236, pl.1, figs.3, 1906.

(THIRD CONTRIBUTION TO KNOWLEDGE OF THE BISON.) Dritter Beitrag zur Kenntnis der Bisonten. (Old World species, mostly fossil.) Max Hilzheimer. Arch. f. Naturgesch., Jahrg.84, Abt.A, Heft 6, pp.41-87, figs.1-25, Feb., 1920.

(DISTRIBUTION OF EUROPEAN AND CAUCASIAN AUROCHS.) Verbreitung europaeischer und kaukasischer Auerochsen. Bernh Langkavel. Zool. Garten, Jahrg.35, no.2, pp.43-49, Feb., 1894.

(THE SKULL OF THE BISON PRISCUS BOJANUS FROM GRIZYNA.) Czaska zubra dugorogiego Bison priscus Bojanus z Grizyny. Edward Lubicz-Niezabitowski. Fragmenta Faunistica Mus. Zool. Polonici, Warsaw, vol.5, no.18, pp.305-308, illus., 1948.

THE FATE OF A EUROPEAN BISON HERD. Gerrit S. Miller, Jr. Science, n.s., vol. 4, no.99, pp.744-745, Nov.20, 1896.

THE STATUS OF THE WISENT ON DECEMBER 31, 1932. Erna Mohr. Jour. Mam., vol.14, no.3, pp.260-263, Aug., 1933.

(THE PRESENT STATUS OF THE BISON OF EUROPE.) Lo stato attuale del bisonte d'Europa. Edgardo Moltoni. Riv. Sci. Nat. "Natura", Milano, vol.43, pp.24-26, 1952.

FURTHER NOTE ON THE EUROPEAN WISENT. E. N. Munns. Jour. Mam., 29 (3): 300-301, Aug., 1948.

SURVIVAL OF THE EUROPEAN BISON. J. Y. Peary. Jour. Tennessee Acad. Sci., vol.23, no.2, pp.169-172, Apr., 1948.

(BIOLOGICAL AND MORPHOLOGICAL NOTES ON THE CAUCASIAN WISENT. CONTRIBUTIONS TO THE NATURAL AND CULTURAL HISTORY OF LITHUANIA AND NEIGHBORING AREAS.) Biologische und morphologische Notizen ueber den Kaukasus. Wissenschaftl. Beitraege zur Natur- und Kulturgeschichte Lithauens und angrenzender Gebiete. E. W. Pfizenmayer. Abhandl. math.-naturw. Abt. Bayer. Akad. Wiss., Muenchen, suppl.bd., 11 Abh., pp. 497-504, pls.1-3, 1929.

THE END OF THE CAUCASUS WISENTS (ABSTRACT BY J. G. AHRENS). J. Pujanow. Jour. Mam., vol.10, no.1, pp. 97-98, Feb., 1929.

(THE BISON OF POSEN.) Die Posener Wisente. K. Szczerkowski. Zool. Garten, Leipzig, n.f., vol.3, nos.4-8, pp.153-154, figs.2, Aug.11, 1930.

(MATERIALS ON NATURAL HISTORY AND THE HISTORY OF THE EUROPEAN BISON (BISON BONASUS L.).) Materiaux pour l'histoire naturelle et pour l'histoire du bison d'Europe (Bison bonasus Linn.). Jan Sztolcman. Ann. Zool. Mus. Polonici Hist. Natur., vol.2, pp.49-136, pls.1-3, 1924.

(ON THE HISTORY OF THE LITHUANIAN AUROCHS.) K estoree letovskogo zubra. V. I. Tsalkin. Koklady Akad. Nauk SSSR, . Moscow, vol.77, no.2, pp.349-352, 1951.

THE BISONS OF THE CAUCASUS. A. Yermoloff. Smithsonian Report, publ.no. 1761, pp.345-353, pls.2, 1906.

(THE EUROPEAN BISON IN POLAND.) Le Bison d'Europe en Pologne. J. Zabinski. Bull. Soc. Nation. Acclimation France, no.3-4, pp.103-106 1946.

(PEDIGREE BOOK OF THE EUROPEAN BISON.) Ksiegi rodowodowe zubrow. J. Zabinski. Internat. Soc. Protection European Bison, Warsaw, pp.32, illus., 1947; pp.1-52, map, illus., 1949.

THE EUROPEAN BISON. Jour. Soc. Preservation Fauna Empire, Hertford, n. s., pt.53, pp.52-53, June, 1946.

Bison--Fossils

THE FOSSIL BISONS OF NORTH AMERICA. J. A. Allen. Amer. Nat., vol.33, pp.665-666, Aug., 1899.

THE MOUNTED SKELETON OF BISON OCCIDENTALIS, AND ASSOCIATED DART-POINTS. E. H. Barbour. Nebraska State Mus., vol.1, bull.32, pp.263-270, figs.163-165, Oct., 1932.

A FOSSIL BISON SKULL FROM YUKON TERRITORY. F. H. Clark. Canadian Field Nat., vol.41, no.3, pp.45-47, figs.2, Mar., 1927.

THE OCCURRENCE OF BISON OCCIDENTALIS IN OKLAHOMA. E. D. Crabb. Univ. Oklahoma Bull., Norman, n.s., no. 322 (Univ. Studies, no.21), p.124, pl.5, Dec.1, 1925.

FIRST RECORD OF BISON ALLENI FROM A LATE PLEISTOCENE DEPOSIT IN TEXAS. Walter W. Dalquest. Texas Jour. Sci., 9 (3): 346-354, Sept., 1957.

THE BISON OF DENMARK. A ZOOLOGICAL AND GEOLOGICAL INVESTIGATION OF THE FINDS IN DANISH PLEISTOCENE DEPOSITS. Magnus Degerbol, Johs Iversen. Danmarks Geologiske Undersogelse, Copenhagen, ser.2, no.73, pp.1-62, figs. 13, pls.7, 1945.

DID THE FOLSOM BISON SURVIVE IN CANADA? Loren C. Eiseley. Sci.

Monthly, Lancaster, vol.56, no.5, pp. 468-472, May, 1943.

POST-GLACIAL CLIMATIC AMELIORATION AND THE EXTINCTION OF BISON TAYLORI. Loren C. Eiseley. Science, Lancaster, n.s., vol.95, no.2478, pp.646-647, June 26, 1942.

NEW FINDS OF BISON PRISCUS LONGICORNUS MIHI, AND A CRANIUM WHICH STRONGLY DEVIATES FROM THIS FORM. Vera Gromova. Trav. Inst. Paleozool. Acad. Sci. URSS, Leningrad, vol.4, pp. 137-147, figs.2, 1935. (In Russian, with German summary.)

THE EXTINCT BISONS OF NORTH AMERICA; WITH DESCRIPTION OF ONE NEW SPECIES, BISON REGIUS. Oliver P. Hay. Proc. U.S. Nat. Mus., vol.46, pp.161-200, pls.8-19, Dec.6, 1913.

BISON (GIGANTOBISON) LATIFRONS AND BISON (SIMOBISON) ALLENI IN SOUTHEASTERN IDAHO. Marie L. Hopkins. Jour. Mam., vol.32, no.2, pp.192-197, pl.1, May 21, 1951.

A FOLSOM LOCATION IN THE SAN LUIS VALLEY, COLORADO. C. T. Hurst. Southwestern Lore, Gunnison, vol.7, no.2, pp.31-34, fig.1, pl.1, Sept., 1941.

A MINNESOTA KITCHEN MIDDEN WITH FOSSIL BISON. Albert Ernest Jenks. Science, vol.86, no.2228, pp.243-244, Sept.10, 1937.

ON BISON OCCIDENTALIS LUCAS FROM MANCHURIA. Michio Kawada. Jour. Geol. Soc. Tokyo, vol.39, no.463, pp.5-7, pl.1, Apr.20, 1932.

ON BISON BONASUS HUNGARORUM N. SSP. M. Kretzoi. Ann. Hist.-Nat. Mus. Nat. Hungarici, pars Mineral., Geol. et Palaeont., Budapest, vol.39, nos.5-6, pp. 105-107, 1946.

THE CHARACTERS OF BISON OCCIDENTALIS, THE FOSSIL BISON OF KANSAS AND ALASKA. F. A. Lucas. Kan. Univ. Quar., vol.8, no.1, ser.A, pp.17-18, pls. 8-9, Jan., 1899.

THE FOSSIL BISON OF NORTH AMERICA. F. A. Lucas. Proc. U.S. Nat. Mus., vol. 21, pp.755-771, pls.65-84, 1899.

GIANT BISON FOUND. Bruce A. McCorquodale. Blue Jay, Saskatchewan Nat. Hist. Soc., 15 (1): 42, illus., Mar., 1957.

ON BISON EXIGUUS MATSUMOTO AND ITS ANCESTRY. H. Matsumoto. Sci. Repts. Tohoku Imperial Univ., ser.2 (Geology), vol.10, no.3, pp.51-55, 1927.

ON SOME FOSSIL BISONTINES OF EASTERN ASIA. H. Matsumoto. Sci. Repts., Tohoku Imp. Univ., ser.2 (Geol.), vol.3, no.2, pp.83-102, figs.3, pls.11, 1918.

ASSOCIATION OF AN ARROW POINT WITH BISON OCCIDENTALIS IN NEBRASKA. F. G. Meserve, Erwin H. Barbour. Nebraska State Mus., Bull.27, vol.1, pp.239-242, Feb., 1932.

A SPECIMEN OF BISON OCCIDENTALIS FROM NORTHWEST CANADA. Wilfred H. Osgood. Proc. Biol. Soc. Wash., vol.20, June 12, 1907.

(NOTE ON A RADIUS OF BISON PRISCUS-BOJANUS.) Note sur un radius de Bison priscus-bojanus. Vasile Parvulescu. Bulet. Acad. Inalte Studii Agron. din Cluj, vol.4, no.1, pp.128-130, figs.2, 1933.

(ANOTHER ALLUVIAL AUROCHS FIND FROM THE MARK.) Ein weiterer alluvialer Wisentfund aus der Mark. Hermann Pohle. Berichte der Internat. Ges. zur Erhaltung des Wisents, vol.3, no.2, p.96, Feb.5, 1929.

BISON CRASSICORNIS IN THE LATE PLEISTOCENE OF NEW ENGLAND. Alfred Sherwood Romer. Jour. Mam., vol.32, no.2, pp.230-231, May 21, 1951.

THE GEOLOGIC HISTORY OF THE BISON IN THE GREAT PLAINS. (A PRELIMINARY REPORT.) C. Bertrand Schultz, W. D. Frankforter. Bull. Univ. Nebraska State Mus., Lincoln, vol.3, no.1, pp.1-10, fig.1, Dec., 1946.

FOSSIL BISON AND ASSOCIATED ARTIFACTS FROM PLAINVIEW, TEXAS. E. H. Sellards, Glen L. Evans, Grayson E. Meade. Bull. Geol. Soc. America, Balto., vol.58, pp.927-954, figs.6, pls. 5, Oct., 1947.

THE FOSSIL BISON OF ALASKA AND PRELIMINARY REVISION OF THE GENUS. Morris M. Skinner, Ove C. Kaisen. Bull. Amer. Mus. Nat. Hist., New York, vol.89, art.3, pp.123-256, figs.5, pls.8-26, Oct. 31, 1947.

(Review by Claude W. Hibbard of) THE FOSSIL BISON OF ALASKA AND PRELIMINARY REVISION OF THE GENUS. Morris F. Skinner, Ove C. Kaisen. Jour. Mam., vol. 29, no.2, pp.192-193, May 14, 1948.

(REMARKS ON A BISON FIND OF THE FREIBERGEN (BERN CANTON).) Bemerkungen zu einem bisonfund aus den Freibergen (Kt. Bern). H. G. Stehlin. Eclogae geologicae Helvetiae, Basel, vol. 24, no.2, pp.279-288, figs.3, 1931.

A SKULL OF BISON LATIFRONS FROM THE PLEISTOCENE OF NORTHERN CALIFORNIA. V. L. Vanderhoof. Univ. California Publ., Bull. Dept. Geol. Sci., Berkeley, vol.27, no.1, pp.1-24, figs.5, pls.2, Nov.20, 1942.

THREE SKULLS OF BISON CRASSICORNIS RICHARDSON FROM THE YUKON. M. Y. William. Trans. Roy. Soc. Canada, Ottawa, ser.3, vol.31, sec.4, pp.105-110, pls.1-3, May, 1937.

Bison--Hunting

SABOTAGE ON SPECKLED MOUNTAIN. Russell Barnett Aitken. Field and Stream, New York, vol.53, no.11, pp.38-39, 126-129, illus., Mar., 1949.

BUFFALO HUNT. G. A. Belcourt. Beaver, Winnipeg, outfit 275, pp.12-17, illus., Dec., 1944.

THE HUNTING OF THE BUFFALO. E. Douglas Branch. D. Appleton and Co., New York, London, pp.240, 1929.

LAST BUFFALO HUNT IN STUTSMAN COUNTY. J. E. Campbell. North Dakota Outdoors, Bismarck, vol.6, no.6, pp.13-14, illus., Dec., 1943.

A PAWNEE BUFFALO HUNT. J. S. Clark. Chronicles of Oklahoma, Oklahoma City, vol.20, no.4, pp.387-395, Dec., 1942.

BUFFALO LANCER. Reginaldo Espinaza. New Mexico Mag., Albuquerque, vol.21, no.5, pp.15, 31, illus., May, 1943.

HUNTING WOOD BUFFALO. W. A. Fuller. Blue Jay, Saskatchewan, vol.6, pp.6-7, 1947.

ARIZONA BUFFALO HUNT, 1942. Roy Gambrell. Ariz. Wildl.-Sportsman, 4 (6): 8-10, May, 1942.

THE LAST ROUND-UP. Philip H. Godsell. Forest and Outdoors, 6 (6): 174-175, 194-197, June, 1940.

BUFFALO HUNT—1935. (WOOD BUFFALO IN CANADA.) George G. Goodwin. Nat. Hist., New York, vol.36, no.2, pp.156-164, illus., Sept., 1935.

THE EXTERMINATION OF THE AMERICAN BISON. William T. Hornaday. U.S. Nat. Mus. Rept., 1886-1887.

THE SLAUGHTER OF THE BUFFALO. Ross C. McCluskey. Outdoor Life, New York, vol.102, no.4, pp.36-39, 82, 84-85, illus., Oct., 1948.

BUFFALO BONE DAYS. A SHORT HISTORY OF THE BUFFALO BONE TRADE. A SKETCH OF FORGOTTEN ROMANCE OF FRONTIER TIMES. M. I. McCreight. Nupp Printing Co., Sykesville, Pa., pp.1-40, illus., 1939.

THE KILLING OF THE BUFFALO. Henry Bayne MacDonald. The Beaver, Hudson Bay Co., Outfit 266, no.3, pp.20-25, illus., Dec., 1935.

HOUSE ROCK VALLEY BUFFALO HUNT. Raymond E. Maher. Southern Sportsman, Austin, vol.8, no.1, pp.11, 20, illus., Mar., 1944.

BUFFALO CHIPS. (BUFFALO HUNTING IN EARLY DAYS.) F. H. Mayer Montezuma. Outer's Recreation, vol.61, 1919; chapt.1, pp.17-20, July; chapt.2, pp.91-94, Aug.; chapt.3, pp.179-181, 225, Sept.; chapt.4, pp.263-265, Oct.; chapt.5, pp.330-332, 384, Nov.

THE RED RIVER HUNT. (EXTERMINATION OF BISON ON PLAINS OF CANADA.) F. G. Roe. Trans. Roy. Soc. Canada, sect.2, ser.3, vol.29, pp.171-218, May, 1935.

THE BUFFALO HUNTERS. Mari Sandoz. Hastings, pp.372, illus., 1954.

A PENNSYLVANIA BISON HUNT. H. W. Shoemaker. Middleburg Post, pp.60, illus., 1915.

THE HUNTING OF THE BUFFALO. H. W. Shoemaker. Pennsylvania Game News, Harrisburg, vol.14, no.11, pp.15, 21, illus., Feb., 1944.

THE LAST GREAT BUFFALO DRIVE. WHEN THE SIMPLE SONS OF NATURE MAKE HISTORY IN TRUE HOLLYWOOD FASHION. N. Vernon-Wood. Sportsman, Boston, Mass., vol.7, no.6, pp.75-86, illus., June, 1930.

SURELY ANOTHER BUFFALO "HUNT" CAN BE PREVENTED. Nat. Humane Rev., Albany, vol.35, no.4, p.3, Apr., 1947.

Bison--North America

THE AMERICAN BISONS, LIVING AND EXTINCT. J. A. Allen. Mem. of Geol. Sur., Kentucky, vol.1, pt.2, 1876.

FORMER RANGE OF THE BUFFALO IN VIRGINIA. J. A. Allen. New York Evening Post, Dec.10, 1889.

HISTORY OF THE AMERICAN BISON, BISON AMERICANUS. J. A. Allen. 9th Ann. Rept. U.S. Geol. Surv. Terr., 1875, pp.443-587, June, 1877.

NOTE ON THE WOOD BISON. J. A. Allen. Bull. Amer. Mus. Nat. Hist., vol.13, pp. 63-67, Apr.16, 1900.

HISTORY, RANGE, AND HOME LIFE OF THE NORTHERN BISON. R. M. Anderson. Ecol. Monog., Durham, vol.11, no.4, pp. 347-412, illus., Oct., 1941.

BUFFALO HERD INFORMATION. O. N. Arrington. Ariz. Game and Fish Comm., Ariz. Game Surv., Proj. Job Compl. Rep., 1951, Proj.53 R 1-WP 2-J 8, pp.1-9, Jan., 1952.

BUFFALO IN OREGON. Vernon Bailey. Jour. Mam., vol.4, no.4, pp.254-255, Nov., 1923.

BUFFALO OF THE MALHEUR VALLEY, OREGON. Vernon Bailey. Proc. Biol. Soc., Wash., vol.45, Apr.2, 1932.

THE BISON OF HOUSE ROCK VALLEY. Will C. Barnes. Nature Mag., vol.10, pp.217-220, illus., pl., Oct., 1927.

BISON IN COLORADO. W. H. Bergtold. Jour. Mam., vol.10, no.2, p.170, May, 1929.

THE OCCURRENCE OF THE AMERICAN BISON IN ALABAMA AND FLORIDA. Mark F. Boyd. Science, n.s., vol.84, no.2174, p.203, Aug.28, 1936.

WHEN THE BUFFALO CAME TO FORT UNION (FROM FIELD NOTES OF WILLIAM DE LA M. CARY). Walter S. Brinkmann. Maryland Conservationist, Baltimore, vol. 20, nos.3-4, pp.2-3, fig.1, 1943.

BUFFALO ON THE PUBLIC DOMAIN. H.J. Burback. Our Public Lands, 1: 14, Oct., 1951.

THE AMERICAN BISON. Stuart C. Downings. Canadian Nat., Toronto, vol. 13, no.1, pp.24-25, illus., Jan.-Feb., 1951.

WHERE THE BUFFALO ROAMED. Bemjamin Draper. Pacific Discovery, San Francisco, vol.3, no.2, pp.14-27, illus., Mar.-Apr., 1950.

THE BUFFALO STAGES A COMEBACK. Patrick Duffy. Outdoor Life, vol.67, no. 5, pp.15, 71, figs.3, May, 1931.

THE BISON OF THE WESTERN AREA OF THE MISSISSIPPI BASIN. J. D. Figgins. Proc. Colorado Mus. Nat. Hist., vol.12, no.4, pp.16-33, pls.9, Dec.5, 1933.

THE FORMER RANGE OF THE BISON IN THE ROCKY MOUNTAINS. F. M. Fryxell. Jour. Mam., vol.9, no.2, pp.129-139, May, 1928.

AERIAL CENSUS OF NORTHERN BISON IN WOOD BUFFALO PARK AND VICINITY. W. A. Fuller. J. Wildl. Mgt., 1f (14): 445-451, Oct., 1950.

(THE BISON OF AMERICA.) Les bisons d'Amerique. M. S. Garretson. Payot, Paris, pp.238, figs.14, pls.24, 1939.

A SHORT HISTORY OF THE AMERICAN BISON. M. S. Garretson. Illus. 8 vol., wrs. pp.42, N.Y., 1927.

THE BISON. George G. Goodwin. (In) North American Big Game. A book of the Boone and Crockett Club, compiled by the Committee on Records of North American Big Game. Charles Scribners Sons, New York, pp.359-370, 1939.

CANADA'S WILD BUFFALO. OBSERVATIONS IN THE WOOD BUFFALO PARK. WITH AN APPENDIX A RECONNAISSANCE IN THE HOME OF THE WOOD BUFFALO BY F. V. SIEBERT. Maxwell Graham. Canada Dept. Inter., pp.1-16, illus.9, maps 2, Ottawa, 1923.

FINDING RANGE FOR CANADA'S BUFFALO. Maxwell Graham. Canadian Field-Nat., vol.38, p.189, 1924.

WHERE THE BUFFALO ROAMED. Fred M. Griffin. New Mexico Mag., Albuquerque, vol.25, no.9, pp.22, 51, illus., Sept., 1947.

THE AMERICAN BISON IN 1924. George Bird Grinnell. Hunting and Conservation, the book of the Boone and Crockett Club, Yale Univ. Press, New Haven, pp.356-411, 1925.

REMARKS ON AMERICAN BISON IN LOUISIANA. Gordon Gunter. Jour. Mam., vol.24, no.3, pp.398-399, Aug. 17, 1943.

THE WESTERN LIMITS OF THE BUFFALO RANGE. Francis D. Haines. Pac. Northwest Quart. 31 (4): 389-398, Oct., 1940.

THE BISON RETURNED TO THE PLAINS. Arthur F. Halloran. Animal Kingdom, New York Zool. Soc., 60 (5): 130-134, Oct., 1957.

THE BUFFALO IN WYOMING. Charles W. Hanscum. Wyoming Wildlife, Cheyenne, vol.14, no.3, pp.14-17, 32-33, illus., Apr., 1950.

THE WOOD BUFFALO. Francis Harper. Canadian Field-Nat., vol.39, p.45, Feb., 1925.

(THE GIANT BISON OF MEXICO.) El bisonte gigante de Mexico. Claude W. Hibbard, Bernardo Villa R. Anales Inst. Biol., Mexico, vol.21, no.1, pp.243-254, illus., 1950.

ANOTHER RECORD OF THE BUFFALO IN OREGON. Stanley G. Jewett. Jour. Mam., vol.11, no.3, pp.320-321, Aug., 1930.

THE BUFFALO IN NORTHEASTERN CALIFORNIA. C. Hart Merriam. Jour. Mam., vol.7, no.3, pp.211-214, Aug., 1926.

EARLY RECORDS OF BUFFALO IN "CALIFORNIA" (NEVADA, UTAH AND SOUTH-WESTERN WYOMING). C. Hart Merriam. Jour. Mam., vol.3, no.1, pp. 54-55, Feb., 1922.

HERD OF BUFFALO FOUND IN TEXAS. C. H. Moran. Clipping from The Daily News, Pensacola, Fla., May 2, 1894.

THE BUFFALO IN IOWA. L. H. Pammel. Proc. Iowa Acad. Sci., vol.37, p.397, (1930) 1931.

SOUTH DAKOTA BISON. A. H. Pankow. South Dakota Conserv. Digest, Pierre, pp. 8-9, Feb., 1940.

AMERICA'S GREATEST HOST. (AMERICAN BISON.) Donald Culross Peattie. Nat. Hist., New York, vol.52, no.3, pp.112-114, illus., Oct., 1943.

EVIDENCES OF BISON IN SOUTHWESTERN UTAH. C. C. Presnall. Jour. Mam., vol. 19, no.1, pp.111-112, Feb.14, 1938.

RANGE CONDITIONS IN THE WOOD BUFFALO PARK OF WESTERN CANADA WITH NOTES ON THE HISTORY OF THE WOOD BISON. Hugh M. Raup. Amer. Comm. International Wild Life Prot., Special Publ., vol.1, no.2, pp.1-52, 1933.

BISON BEYOND THE PECOS. Erik K. Reed. Tex. Jour. Sci., 7 (2): 130-135, June, 1955.

DISTRIBUTION OF THE AMERICAN BISON IN PENNSYLVANIA, WITH REMARKS ON A NEW FOSSIL SPECIES. Samuel N. Rhoads. Proc. Acad. Nat. Sciences, Phila., pp.244-248, 1895.

THE NORTH AMERICAN BUFFALO: A CRITICAL STUDY OF THE SPECIES IN ITS WILD STATE. Frank G. Roe. Univ. Toronto Press, pp.vii, 957, 1951.

(Review by William Rowan of) THE NORTH AMERICAN BUFFALO: A CRITICAL STUDY OF THE SPECIES IN ITS WILD STATE. F. G. Roe. Jour. Mam., vol.33, no.1, pp.120-122, Feb.18, 1952.

THE NUMBERS OF THE BUFFALO. Frank G. Roe. Trans. Roy. Soc. Canada, Ottawa, ser.3, vol.31, sec.2, pp.171-203, May, 1937.

THE RANGE OF THE BISON IN WISCONSIN. A. W. Schorger. Trans. Wisconsin Acad. Sci. Arts and Letters, Madison, vol.30, pp.117-130, figs.3, 1937.

SOME NOTES ON CANADA'S SO-CALLED WOOD BUFFALO. Fred V. Seibert. Canadian Field-Nat., vol.39, pp.204-206, Jan.21, 1926.

THE OCCURRENCE OF BISON IN FLORIDA. H. B. Sherman. Quart. Jour. Florida Acad. Sci., vol.17, no.4, pp.228-232, Dec., 1954.

THE PENNSYLVANIA BISON. Henry W. Shoemaker. Pennsylvania Game News, Harrisburg, vol.19, no.4, p.4, illus., July, 1948.

AMERICAN BISON IN LOUISIANA. John R. Swanton. Jour. Mam., vol.22, no.3, p.325, Aug.14, 1941.

AMERICAN BISON IN NORTHERN LOUISIANA. John R. Swanton. Jour. Mam., vol.21, no.2, p.222, May, 1940.

NOTES ON THE OCCURRENCE OF BISON NEAR THE GULF OF MEXICO. John R. Swanton. Jour. Mam., vol.19, no.3, pp. 379-380, Aug., 1938.

A BISON FROM EASTERN WASHINGTON. H. W. Tipper, Z. V. Jizba, R. L. Konizeski. Amer. Jour. Sci., New Haven, vol.249, no. 4, pp.318-322, Apr., 1951.

AMERICAN BUFFALO. Wyoming Wild Life, Cheyenne, vol.4, no.10, pp.6, 16, Oct., 1939.

AMERICAN BISON SOCIETY. Ann. Repts., In 13 vols., vol.8, N. Y., 1908-1931.

BISON INTRODUCED IN UTAH IN 1941 HAVE DONE WELL. Utah Fish and Game Bull., Salt Lake City, vol.9, no.4, pp.1, 4, illus., Sept., 1950.

BUFFALO AT ELK ISLAND. Rod and Gun in Canada, Montreal, vol.48, no.9, p.12, Feb., 1947.

BUFFALOES COMING TO GEORGIA. Outdoor Georgia, Atlanta, vol.12, no.6, p.3, Jan., 1944.

BECOMING EXTINCT, BUT LEAVING A HYBRID RACE: THE "WOOD BUFFALO." Illus. London News, vol.191, no.5148, p. 1116, illus., Dec.18, 1937.

THE RETURN OF THE NATIVE. CANADIAN BUFFALO INCREASING AGAIN. Field, London, vol.161, no.4189, p.740, Apr.8, 1933.

STATUS OF THE AMERICAN BISON IN THE UNITED STATES AND ALASKA, 1939. U. S. Dept. Interior, Bur. Biol. Surv., Wildlife Leaflet BS-148, pp.10, Dec., 1939.

Bison--Pelage, Coloration

AN ALBINO BUFFALO. R. M. Barnes. Ooelogist, vol.50, no.10, pp.138-139, Oct., 1933.

SILK BUFFALO ROBES. K. F. Bascom. Jour. Mam., vol.3, no.4, p.263, Nov., 1922.

THE SACRED WHITE BUFFALO. (ALBINO AMERICAN BISON.) Harold McCracken. Nat. Hist., New York, vol. 55, no.7, pp.304-309, 341, illus., Sept., 1946.

(A WHITE BISON CALF.) Weiss Bisonkalb. E. Mohr. Zool. Garten, n.f., Leipzig, vol.8, nos.4-6, p.141, Jan., 1936.

PHOTOGRAPH OF A WHITE BISON, WITH PINK EYES AND NORMALLY COLORED TOP OF HEAD. W. Peyton Moncure. Nat. Hist., New York, vol.45, no.4, p.193, Apr., 1940.

A "SILK BUFFALO" ROBE. Edward R. Warren. Jour. Mam., vol.2, no.3, pp. 173-174, Aug., 1921.

Bison--Taxonomy

ON THE TYPE OF BISON PRISCUS BOJANUS. V. I. Gromova. Comptes Rendus Acad. Sci. USSR, ser.A, no.17, pp.459-462, fig. 1, 1930. (In Russian.)

THE TYPE LOCALITY OF BISON BISON LINNAEUS. Philip Hershkovitz. Proc. Biol. Soc. Wash., 70: 31-32, June 28, 1957.

BISON ISELINI STEHLIN FOR BUBALUS ISELINI STEHLIN. Max Hilzheimer. Zeitschr. f. Saeugetierkunde, Berlin, vol. 13, pp.254-256, Sept.1, 1939. (In German.)

THE MYTH OF MONTEZUMA'S BISON AND TYPE LOCALITY OF THE SPECIES. Erik K. Reed. Jour. Mam., vol.33, no.3, pp. 390-392, Aug.19, 1952.

(REMAINS OF A BISON COW FROM BUCOVINA; A CONTRIBUTION TO KNOWLEDGE OF PHYLOGENETIC RELATIONS BETWEEN BISON PRISCUS AND BISON BONASUS.) Resturi de zimbru din Bucovina, contributie la cunoatserea legaturii filogenetice intre Bison priscus si Bison bonasus. Emilian Sahleanu. Bul. Fac. Stiinte Cernauti, vol.7, nos.1-2, pp.35-58, figs.2, 1933, 1934. (In Roumainan, with German summary.)

(ON THE NECESSITY OF THE SYSTEMATIC TREATMENT OF BISON FOSSILS.) Ein Wort ueber die Notwendigkeit der systematischen Bearbeitung der Wisentreste. Ludwig Zukowsky. Pallasia, vol.2, no.1, pp.1-11, Apr.1, 1924.

Bos--General

(OBSERVATIONS ON BOVINES IN SCHOENBRUNN.) Beobachtungen an Rindern in Schoenbrunn. Otto Antonius. Zool. Garten N.F., Leipzig, vol.6, nos. 7-9, pp.149-155, Oct., 1933.

(OBSERVATIONS ON BOVINE ANIMALS IN SCHOEBRUNN. II. BANTENG, GAUR, GAYAL.) Beobachtungen an Rindern in Schoenbrunn. II. Banteng, Gaur, Gayal. Otto Antonius. Zool. Garten, Leipzig, n. F., vol.5, nos.7-9, pp.178-191, figs.7, Oct., 1932.

(THE BANTENG (BIBOS SONDAICUS).) Vom Banteng (Bibos sondaicus). F. J. Appelman. Zool. Garten, Leipzig, n.F., vol.19, no.5, pp.189-192, 1952.

ON THE GAUR (BOS GAURUS) AND ITS ALLIES. W. T. Blanford. Proc. Zool. Soc., London, pp.592-599, figs.2, pl.49, Nov.4, 1890.

BOS INDICUS. Paul Boulineau. La Terre et la Vie, Rev. d'Hist. Nat., Paris, vol. 4, no.8, pp.489-493, illus., Aug., 1934.

NEWEST ANIMAL--THE KOUPREY. William Bridges. Animal Kingdom, New

York, vol.46, no.2, pp.43-44, illus., Mar.-Apr., 1943.

THE INDO-CHINESE FOREST OX OR KOUPREY. Harold Jefferson Coolidge, Jr. Mem. Mus. Comp. Zool. Harvard College, Cambridge, vol.54, no.6, pp.417-531, figs. 12, pls.11, Aug., 1940.

(Review by P. Rode of) THE INDO-CHINESE FOREST OX OR KOUPREY. H. J. Coolidge, Jr. Mammalia, Paris, 9 (1): 31, Mar., 1945.

BOS PRIMIGENIUS BOJANUS. Jos Cremers. Oeros, Natuurhist, Maandblad, Limburg, vol.16, no.4, pp.44-45, figs.3, Apr.29, 1927.

A CONTRIBUTION TO THE KNOWLEDGE OF THE CAMBODIAN WILD OX OR KOUPROH. Francois Edmond-Blanc. Jour. Mam., vol.28, no.3, pp.245-248, pl.1, Aug.19, 1947.

DERIVATION OF THE NAME SELADANG. C. Gimson. Jour. Bombay Nat. Hist. Soc., vol.40, no.4, p.733, May, 1939.

THE MITHUN. J. C. Higgins. Jour. Bombay Nat. Hist. Soc., vol.35, no.2, pp.444-445, Oct.15, 1931.

(THE DWARF URE-OX.) Der Zwergur. Max Hilzheimer. Brandenburgia Monatsblatt der Gesellsch. fuer Heimatkunde, Jahrg.34, pp.100-108, 1925.

SELADANG--THE OX OF DISTINCTION. J. A. Hislop. Frontiers, p.138, June, 1959.

THE MALAYAN GAUR OR SELADANG. Theodore R. Hubback. Jour. Mam., vol. 18, no.3, pp.267-279, figs.4, Aug.14, 1937; Jour. Bombay Nat. Hist. Soc., vol. 40, no.1, pp.8-19, pls., Apr., 1938.

THE POSITION OF CATTLE IN INDIA. M. Krishnamurti. Tropical Agric., London, vol.32, no.4, pp.278-289, Oct., 1955.

(NEW INFORMATION ON THE URE OX.) Neues vom Ur. W. La Baume. Die Umschau, Frankfurt a.M., Jahrg.37, no. 25, pp.480-482, figs.8, June 17, 1933.

THE TSAINE (BOS BANTENG). S. H. Later. Jour. Bombay Nat. Hist. Soc., vol.28, pp. 786-788, June 30, 1922.

THE RETURN OF THE URUS. Willy Ley. Fauna, Phila., vol.3, no.4, pp.113-115, illus., Dec., 1941.

THE GAYAL, OR MITHAN (BOS FRONTALIS). T. R. Livesey. Jour. Bombay Nat. Hist. Soc., vol.35, no.1, pp.199-202, pl.1, June 15, 1931.

THE URE-OX. Karol Lukaszewicz. Ochrona Przyrody, 20: 1-33, illus., 1952. (English summary.)

A WORLD DICTIONARY OF BREEDS, TYPES, AND VARIETIES OF LIVESTOCK WITH SUPPLEMENT. Ian Lauder Mason. Commonwealth Agricultural Bureaux, England, pp.272, 52 pp. suppl., 1957.

(CONTRIBUTION TO THE EMBRYOLOGY OF BOS TAURUS L.) Beitrag zur Entwicklungsgeschicte vom Bos taurus L. Eduard Michl. Anat. Anz., vol.53, pp.193-215, Aug.20, 1920.

AGE OF BISON. Randolph C. Morris. Jour. Bombay Nat. Hist. Soc., vol.36, no. 2, pp.493-494, Apr.15, 1933.

(ON BOS PRIMIGENIUS: GIANTS AND PYGMIES.) Ueber Riesen und Zwerge des Bos primigenius. Alfred Nehring. Sitz.-Ber. Gesell. Naturf. Freunde, Berlin, Jahrg., no.1, pp.5-7, Jan.15, 1889.

MALAYAN SELADANG. Charles S. Ogilvie. Animal Kingdom, New York Zool. Soc., vol.58, no.1, pp.2-12, illus., Feb., 1955.

BRAHMAN (ZEBU) CATTLE. Virgil V. Parr. U.S. Dept. Agric. Farmers' Bull. no.1361, pp.1-20, figs.9, Oct., 1923.

(THE WILD YAK (BOS (POEPHAGUS) GRUNNIENS MUTUS PREZ.).) Der wilde Yak (Bos (Poeephagus) grunniens mutus Prez.). Ernst Schafer. Zool. Garten, N.F., Leipzig, vol.9, nos.1-2, pp.26-34, illus., Feb., 1937.

THE DOCTRINE OF AHIMSA AND CATTLE BREEDING IN INDIA. Burch H. Schneider. Sci. Monthly, Lancaster, vol.67, no.2, pp. 87-92, illus., Aug., 1948.

NOTES ON THE TSINE (BOS SONDAICUS). C. H. Stockley. Jour. Bombay Nat. Hist. Soc., vol.28, pp.540-543, pl.1, Mar.25, 1922.

(THE KOUPREY OR WILD CAMBODIAN OX.) Le kouprey ou boeuf sauvage combodgien. A. Urbain. Mammalia, Paris, 1 (6): 257-258, pl.10, Dec., 1937.

A MONOGRAPH OF THE GENUS BOS... BULLS, BISONS, AND BUFFALOES. G. Vasey. London, vol.8, pp.192, illus. 72, 1857.

Bos--Anatomy

INVESTIGATIONS ON THE COURSE AND DISTRIBUTION OF THE NERVES SUPPLYING LEVATOR ANGULI SCAPULI AND RHOMBOIDEUS MUSCLES AND THE FORMATION OF THE PHRENIS NERVE IN THE OX, WITH OBSERVATIONS ON CERTAIN ANATOMICAL DEVIATIONS. H. N. Chelva Ayyangar. Imp. Council Agric. Research India, Sci. Monograph, no.11, Delhi, pp.1-60, pls.1-57, 1937.

OBSERVATIONS ON THE CATTLE PITUITARY. E. G. Bassett, C. P. McMeekan. New Zealand Jour. Sci. and Technol., sec. A, vol.32, no.6, pp.1-13, Apr., 1951.

BODY MEASUREMENTS OF A GAUR (BIBOS GAURUS). I. L. Cameron. Jour. Bombay Nat. Hist. Soc., vol.33, no.4, pp. 983-985, illus., Oct.15, 1929.

A STUDY OF THE MUCOSA OF THE GENITAL TRACT OF THE COW, WITH SPECIAL REFERENCE TO CYCLIC CHANGES. H. H. Cole. Amer. Jour. Anat., vol.46, pp.261-302, pls.5, Sept. 15, 1930.

(WHAT DID THE AUROCHS LOOK LIKE?) Wie sah "der" Ur (Auerochse) aus? Fr. Dettweiler. Aus der Natur (Der Naturforscher), Berlin, Jahrg.15, no.6, pp.188-190, Sept., 1938.

(THE BONY PHALANGES OF BOS TAURUS DOMESTICUS.) Les phalanges osseuses de Bos Taurus domesticus. E. Dottrens. Rev. Suisse Zool., Geneva, vol.53, no.33, pp.739-744, figs.27, Oct., 1946.

(DETERMINATION OF THE BONY PHALANGES OF BOS TAURUS DOM.) Determination des phalanges osseuses de Bos taurus dom. E. Dottrens. Compte Rendu Soc. Phys. et Hist. Nat. Geneve, Geneva, vol.63, no.1, pp.46-49, Jan.-Mar., 1946.

SEXUAL DIFFERENCES IN THE SKULL OF FOSSIL AND RECENT BANTENGS. D. A. Hooijer. Mammalia, Paris, 22 (1): 73-75, Mar., 1958.

THE POSTNATAL HISTORY AND FUNCTION OF THE INTERSTITIAL CELLS OF THE TESTIS OF THE BULL. Charles W. Hooker. Amer. Jour. Anat., Phila., vol. 74, no.1, pp.1-37, fig.1, pls.1-5, Jan., 1944.

THE DEVELOPMENT OF THE HYPOPHYSIS OF THE OX. E. L. House. Amer. Jour. Anat., Phila., vol.73, no.1, pp.1-27, figs. 12, pl.1, July, 1943.

(ON TWO MALE CALVES MIS-FORMED AT THE PELVIS.) Ueber zivey am Becken Verwachsene mannlichen kalber. G. v. Jaeger. Overdrukt uit Verslagen en Mededeelingen der Koninklijke Akad. van Wetenschappen, Afdeelimg Natuurkunde, vol.7, no.155, pp.6, pl.1, 1860.

(ON APPARENT INDICATIONS OF DOMESTICATION IN THE SKELETON OF NEATS.) Ueber angebliche Anzeichen von Domestikation am Skelett von Rindern. W. Koch. Zeitschr. f. Morph. u. Oekologie der Tiere, vol.7, pp.444-471, figs.6, Mar.17, 1927.

(THE DEVELOPMENT OF THE OUTER EAR IN DOMESTIC CATTLE (BOS TAURUS L.).) Die Entwicklung des aeusseren Ohres beim Hausrind (Bos taurus, L.). O. Kroelling. Zeitschr. fuer Anatomie und Entwicklungsgeschichte, vol.76, pp.548-560, figs.11, May 30, 1925.

(CONTRIBUTIONS TO RESEARCH ON THE STRUCTURE OF THE MOLARS OF THE DOMESTIC NEAT (BOS TAURUS L.). THE PREMOLAR AND MOLAR DEVELOPMENT ON THE BASIS OF ROENTGENOLOGICAL, HISTOGENETICAL, AND MORPHOLOGICAL INVESTIGATIONS. THE INTERRELATIONSHIPS OF THE INDIVIDUAL DENTAL CONSTITUENTS AND THEIR CONTRIBUTION TO PHYSIOLOGICAL PERFORMANCE.) Beitraege zur Erforschung der baulichen Struktur der Backenzaehne des Hausrindes (Bos taurus L.). Die Praemolar- und Molarentwicklung auf Grund roentgenologischer, histogenetischer und morphologischer Untersuchungen. Die gegenseitigen Beziehungen der einselnen Gebisskonstituenten und ihre Heranziehung zur physiologischen Leistung. Max Kupfer. Denkschr. Schweizer, Naturforsch, Gesell, vol.70, Abh.1, pp.ix, 218, figs.21, pls.43, 1935.

(THE SKULL OF THE FEMALE URUS (BOS PRIMIGENIUS) IN THE DANZIG MUSEUM.) Die weiblichen Schaedel vom Ur (Bos primigenius) im Danziger Museum. W. La Baume. Schriften der Naturforsch. Ges. Danzig., n.F., vol.19, no.3, pp.10-19, pls.4, 1930-1931.

BIRTH OF FREAK CALF AT INDORE. (CALF WITH BIFURCATED HEAD.) C.E. D. Mears. Jour. Bombay Nat. Hist. Soc., vol.32, pp.597-598, illus., Jan.15, 1928.

(THREE CASES OF POLYDACTYLY IN CATTLE.) Drei Faelle von Polydaktylie beim Rinde. Kurt Moeller. Zeitschrift f. Saeugetierkunde, vol.2, no.3, pp.155-174, 1927.

ACCOUNT OF A CASE OF MALFORMATION IN THE GENERATIVE ORGANS OF A COW. James Murie. Proc. Zool. Soc., Lond., pp.592-600, fig.1, 1866.

(THE ATLAS AND EPISTROPHEUS OF BOS PRIMIGENIUS.) Atlas und Epistropheus des Bos primigenius. A. Nehring. Sitz.-Ber. Gesell. Naturf. Freunde Berlin, Jahrg., 1892, no.8, pp.129-130, Oct.18, 1892.

(ON THE SKULL OF A FRANQUEIRO OX OF BRAZIL.) Ueber den Schaedel eines Franqueiro-Ochsen aus Brasilien. A. Nehring. Sitz. Ber. Gesell. Naturf. Freunde Berlin, Jahrg.1888, no.6, pp.91-99, figs.2, June 19, 1888.

AN ACARDIAC MONSTER FROM A COW. C. W. Ottaway. British Veterinary Jour., vol.105, no.8, pp.318-320, figs.2, Aug., 1949.

(WEIGHT OF THE HEART AND WIDTH OF THE OSTIA ATRIOVENTRICULARIA OF THE BOVINE.) Herzgewicht und Weite der Ostia atrioventricularia des Rindes. A. Palmgren. Anat. Anzeiger, vol.65, pp.333-342, curves 7, June 20, 1928.

(ON THE REPRODUCTIVE ORGANS OF A FREEMARTIN.) Degli organi riproduttori d'una Vacca-toro o free-martin degli Inglesi. Corrado Parona. Atti. Soc. Ital. Sci. Nat., vol.19, pp.1-10, 1877.

NOTES ON THE SKULL OF AN ANCIENT OX FROM ROUSAY, ORKNEY. Margery I. Platt. Scottish Nat., no.199, pp.17-24, Jan.-Feb., 1933.

A DEVELOPMENTAL STUDY OF THE MEDIAL RETROPHARYNGEAL LYMPHATIC NODE OF THE CALF (BOS TAURUS). Julia E. Rothermel. Amer. Jour. Anat., vol.43, pp.461-507, illus., May 15, 1929.

EXHIBITION OF, AND REMARKS UPON, A PHOTOGRAPH OF A YOUNG MALE GAUR OR INDIAN BISON (BOS GAURUS). Philip L. Sclater. Proc. Zool. Soc. Lond., pt.2, pp. 249-250, Aug.1, 1894.

EXHIBITION OF THE HOOF OF A BULL (BOS TAURUS, VAR DOMESTICUS) FROM THE FALKLAND ISLAND, BELONGING TO CAPT. ABBOTT. Philip L. Sclater. Proc. Zool. Soc. Lond., pt.29, p.44, 1861.

(ON THE SYNTHETIC MORPHOLOGY OF THE MAMMARY GLAND.) Sur la morphologie synthetique de la glande mammaire. (Studies on Bos taurus.) Stefan Turnau. Comptes Rendus Seances Soc. Biol., Paris, vol.98, pp.1051-1052, Apr.17, 1928.

A HISTOLOGICAL STUDY OF METRORRHAGIA IN A VIRGIN HEIFER. A. F. Weber, B. B. Morgan, S. H. McNutt. Amer. Jour. Anat., Phila., vol.83, no.2, pp.309-327, pls.1-3, Sept., 1948.

THE AUDITORY ORGAN OF THE OX. H. C. Wilkie. Proc. Zool. Soc. Lond., pt.4, pp.985-1009, figs.18, Jan., 1937.

DUPLICATION OF THE MITRAL VALVE AND A RARE INTERVENTRICULAR FORAMEN IN THE HEART OF A YAK CALF. William A. Wimsatt, F. T. Lewis. Amer. Jour. Anat., Phila., vol.83, no.1, pp.67-106, pl.1, July, 1948.

Bos--Diseases, Parasites

LEPTOSPIROSIS IN CATTLE. J. A. Baker, R. B. Little. Jour. Exper. Med., Balto., vol.88, no.3, pp.295-308, pls.10-12, Sept. 1, 1948.

THE CATTLE GRUBS OR OX WARBLES, THEIR BIOLOGIES AND SUGGESTIONS FOR CONTROL. F. C. Bischopp, E. W. Laake, H. M. Brundrett, R. W. Wells. U. S. Dept. Agric., bull.1369, pp.119, figs.38, Apr., 1926.

INTERRELATIONSHIPS OF THE BLOOD CELLS OF CATTLE IN HEALTH AND FOLLOWING AN INDUCED INFECTION WITH BRUCELLA ABORTUS. L. C. Ferguson, M. R. Irwin, B. A. Beach. Jour. Infectious Diseases, Chicago, vol.82, no. 2, pp.101-108, Mar.-Apr., 1948.

INJURIES TO THE SKULLS AND HORNS OF THE INDIAN BISON OR SELADANG (BOS GAURUS). Theodore R. Hubback. Field, London, vol.152, p.460, Sept.20, 1928.

CILIATES FROM BOS GAURUS H. SMITH. C. A. Kofoid, John F. Christenson. Univ. California Publ. Zool., vol.39, no.17, pp. 341-342, pls.25-29, figs.7, Oct.8, 1934.

EXPERIMENTAL STUDIES OF Q FEVER IN CATTLE. R. R. Parker, E. J. Bell, David B. Lackman. Amer. Jour. Hygiene, Lancaster, vol.48, no.2, pp.191-206, Sept., 1948.

THE RAPID AGGLUTINATION TEST IN THE DIAGNOSIS OF PARATYPHOID INFECTION IN CALVES. E. M. Robinson, D. A. Lawrence. S. Afr. Jour. Sci., vol.25, pp. 246-249, June-July, 1928.

(ON THE FAUNA OF INFUSORIA IN THE STOMACH OF CATTLE (BOS TAURUS L.).) O faunie wymoczkow w zoladku bydla (Bos taurus L.). Paul Wertheim. Ann. Mus. Zool. Polonici, vol.10, no.13, pp.251-266, May 9, 1934.

(ON SPIROCHETOSIS IN CATTLE IN THE USSR.) Ueber die Rinderspirochaetose in Russland (U.S.S.R.). W. L. Yakimoff. Archiv. f. Protistenkunde, vol.66, pp. 311-321, May 24, 1929.

(A CASE OF TRYPANOSOMA (TRYPANOSOMA THEILERI) IN THE NEAT IN THE URAL AREA.) Ein Trypanosemenfall beim Rinde (Trypanosoma theileri) im Uraler Gouverement. W. L. Yakimoff, S. A. Amanshouloff, P. N. Arbouzoff, A. N. Schouwaleff. Archiv. f. Protistenkunde, vol.66, pp.307-310, May 24, 1929.

Bos--Economic Importance

BREEDING BACK THE EXTINCT AUEROCHS. Theodore G. Ahrens. Jour. Mam., vol.17, no.3, pp.266-268, Aug., 1936.

BIGGLE COW BOOK; OLD TIME AND MODERN COW-LORE RECTIFIED, CONCENTRATED AND RECORDED FOR THE BENEFIT OF MAN. Jacob Biggle. 5th ed., 45th thousand, W. Atkinson Co., Phila., 1913.

MODERN BREEDS OF LIVESTOCK. Hilton M. Briggs. Macmillan, New York, pp.xiv, 722, illus., 1949.

THE VALUE OF PHOSPHORUS IN THE CATTLE INDUSTRY OF SOUTH AFRICA. P. J. DuToit. S. Afr. Jour. Sci., vol.26, pp.273-285, Dec., 1929.

BISON AND CULTIVATION. A. P. Kinloch. Jour. Bombay Nat. Hist. Soc., vol.32, p.215, Aug.1, 1927.

(INVESTIGATIONS ON THE ECONOMIC IMPORTANCE OF THE COMMON BUFFALO (BUBALUS INDICUS).) Untersuchungen ueber die wirtschaftliche Bedeutung des gemeinen Bueffels, Bubalus indicus. Oscar Ofner. Inaugural- Dissertation, Friedrichs-Universitaet, Halle - Wittenberg, pp.58, 1887.

THE SELENIUM PROBLEM IN RELATION TO PUBLIC HEALTH. (REFERS TO LIVE-STOCK GENERALLY.) Maurice I. Smith, K. W. Franke, B. B. Westfall. Publ. Health Reports, U.S. Treasury Dept., vol. 51, no.44, pp.1496-1505, pl.1, Oct.30, 1936.

LIVE STOCK POPULATION OF THE GLOBE. L. F. Ward. Chicago Times, 7 pages of clippings, Dec.18, 1880.

THE DOMESTICATION OF THE BANTENG. China Jour., vol.13, no.4, p.231, Oct., 1930.

GERMAN BREEDS OF LIVE STOCK. German Agricultural Soc., Berlin, Deutsche landwirtschaftsgesellschaft, pp.4, pls.53, illus., 1912.

Bos--Eurasia

(LOCALITIES IN THE PYRENEAN LOWLANDS WHERE PRIMITIVE CATTLE ARE FOUND.) Localites sous-pyreneennes du grand boeuf primitif. (Bos primigenius.) Gaston Astre. Bull. Soc. Hist. Nat. Toulouse, vol.58, no.4, p.604, 1929.

NOTES ON THE BOVINE ANIMALS OF THE MALAY PENINSULA. G. Windsor Earl. Proc. Zool. Soc. Lond., pt.21, pp. 29-30, 1853.

(THE COW-HERD "RHODEUS AMARUS" AT GENEVA.) La bouviere "Rhodeus amarus" a Geneve. Victor Fatio. Archiv. Sci. Phys. et nat. Geneve, 110 annee, 4th periode, vol.20, pp.680-686 (pp.7), Melanges zoologiques, 1905.

THE BLIND BISON OF BARBERA. H. A. Fooks. Jour. Bengal Nat. Hist. Soc., Darjeeling, vol.16, no.3, pp.83-85, photo, Jan., 1942.

(THE ORIGINAL HABITAT OF THE EUROPEAN DOMESTIC BOVINE.) Die Urheimath des europaeischen Hausrindes. A. V. Frantzius. Archiv. fur Anthropologie, vol.10, pp.129-137, 1870.

THE BIG BULL OF SEMBUTOLLAVU. C.P. Gouldsbury. Jour. Bombay Nat. Hist. Soc., vol.32, no.4, pp.678-682, May 31, 1928.

CONTRIBUTION TO KNOWLEDGE OF THE URUS (BOS PRIMIGENIUS BOJ.) OF EASTERN EUROPE AND NORTHERN ASIA. Vera Gromova. Annuaire Mus. Zool. Acad. Sci. URSS, Leningrad, vol.32, no.3, pp. 293-364, figs.5, pls.3, map, 1931. (In Russian.)

(FOR 100 HOURS THE "INVISIBLE" GUEST OF THE BANTENG IN OEDJOENG-KOELON.) Honderd uren de "ongeziene" gast der bantengs in Oedjoeng-Koelon. (Bos sondaicus in Javan game preserve.) A. Hoogerwerf. "De Tropische Natuur", jaargang 27, no.2, pp.25-35, figs.7; no.3, pp.39-47, figs.7; no.4, pp.64-72, figs.6; no.5, pp.77-86, figs.6, 1938.

THE WILD OX OF BURMA--A HERD OF SAING PHOTOGRAPHED AT THE EDGE OF THE JUNGLE IN NORTHERN BURMA. E. H. Peacock. Field, London, vol.158, no.4118, p.823, fig., Nov.28, 1931.

THE CATTLE OF INDIA. Ralph W. Phillips. Jour. Heredity, Wash., vol.35, no.9, pp.273-288, figs.4-11, Sept., 1944.

(GEOGRAPHIC DISTRIBUTION OF THE KOUPREY.) Distribution geographique du Kou-Prey (Bibos Sauveli Urb.). R. Sauvel. Mammalia, Paris, vol.13, no.4, pp.144-148, Dec., 1949.

(THE KOU-PREY OR GREY OX OF CAMBODIA.) Le kou-prey ou boeuf gris du Cambodge. R. Sauvel. Terre et Vie, 89-109, 1949.

PRIMITIVE CATTLE OF CORSICA. Ernst Schwarz. Nature Mag., Wash., D.C., vol.32, no.1, p.14, illus., Jan., 1939.

(A NEW VIEW OF THE WILD BULL OF SOUTH-WESTERN ASIA.) O novom vide dikogo bika iz yugo-vostochoi azii. I. I. Sokolov. Zool. Jour. Akad. Nauk SSSR, Moscow, vol.31, no.3, pp.474-475, 1952.

SOME NOTES ON BISON (BIBOS GAURUS) IN BURMA. W. S. Thom. Jour. Bombay Nat. Hist. Soc., vol.37, no.1, pp.106-123, pls.1-2, Apr.15, 1934.

NOTE ON THE GOUWA (BOS FRONTALIS) OF WESTERN INDIA, CALLED "THE BISON" BY ENGLISH RESIDENTS. J. Wycmffe Thompson. Proc. Zool. Soc. Lond., pt.20, pp.96-99, 1852.

(COMPLEMENTARY NOTE ON THE WILD BULL OF COMBODIA (BOS BIBOS) SAUVELI URBAIN.) Note complementaire sur le Boeuf sauvage du Cambodge (Bos (Bibos) sauveli Urbain). Achille Urbain. Bull. Mus. Nat. Hist. Nat., Paris, ser.2, vol.11, no.6, pp.519-520, fig.1, Dec., 1939.

(A NEW SPECIES OF ASIATIC BOVINE.) Une nouvelle espece de bovide asiatique. (Bos (Bibos) sauveli.) Achille Urbain. Comptes Rendus Acad. Sci. Paris, vol.209, pp.1006-1007, 1939.

(A URUS (BOS PRIMIGENIUS) FOUND ON HELGOLAND.) Ein Ur (Bos primigenius) auf Helgoland gefunden. H. Weingold. Centralblatt f. Min., etc., 1925, Abt.B, no.1, p.27, 1926.

(THE "WILD BOVINE" OF THE CHINESE.) Das "Wilde Rind" der Chinesen. H. Weingold. Naturwiss, Korrespondenz, vol.1, no.4-5, p.1, Aug., 1923.

WILD CATTLE OF BRITAIN. E. R. Yarham. Nature Mag., Wash., vol.39, no.5, pp.237-239, photos 2, May, 1946.

BRINGING UP SUPPLIES FOR A FRENCH FLYING COLUMN...A BULLOCK-CART... FORDING A RIVER...IN INDO-CHINA. (ZEBUS.) Illus. London News, vol.210, no. 5623, p.100, illus., Jan.25, 1947.

Bos--Fossils and Extinct Forms

(ON A SMALL QUATERNARY BOVINE RECENTLY DISCOVERED IN THE MOUTIERS (LOIRE-INFERIEURE).) Sur un petit Bovidé quaternaire récemment découvert aux Moutiers (Loire-Inférieure). H. Alimen, A. Caillux. Bull. Soc. Géol. France, Paris, ser.5, vol.7, no.9, pp.555-565, figs.2, pl.26, Apr., 1937.

(REMAINS OF THE GREAT PRIMITIVE OX IN THE ALLUVIUM OF TARN.) Restes du grand boeuf primitif dans les alluvions du Tarn. Gaston Astre. Bull. Soc. Hist. Nat. Toulouse, vol.58, no.1, pp.62-66, 1929.

(DISCOVERIES OF THE URUS, BOS PRIMIGENIUS BOJANUS 1827, IN ALLUVIAL STRATA OF BAVARIA.) Funde des Ures, Bos primigenius Bojanus, 1827, aus alluvialen Schichten Bayerns. Joachim Boseeneck. Saeugetierk. Mitteil., vol.5, no.2, pp.55-69, Apr.1, 1957.

DISCOVERY OF REMAINS OF THE CELTIC SHORT-HORNED OX, BOS LONGIFRONS OWENS, AT WHITEPARK BAY, CO. ANTRIM. J. Wilfrid Jackson. Irish Nat. Jour., Belfast, vol.7, no.6, pp.189-193, illus., June, 1939.

ON THE EXTINCT SPECIES OF AMERICAN OX. Joseph Leidy. Trans. Amer. Philos. Soc., vol.10, pp.3-20, pls.1-5, 1852.

(SKULL OF BOS TAURUS PRIMIGENIUS RUTIM. FOUND IN THE PROSNA RIVER.) Czaszka Bos taurus primigenius Rutim. wydobyta z Prosny. Crane de Bos taurus primigenius Rutim. trouvé dans la riviere Prosna. Edward Lubicz-Niezabitowski. Fragmenta Faunistica Mus. Zool. Polonici,

Warsaw, vol.5, no.16, pp.293-300, illus., 1948.

BOS PRIMIGENIUS FROM THE QUATERNARY OF MOGOSESTI (NOW SATU MARE) AND JIBERT (NOW TARNAVA MARE). WITH A SHORT SURVEY OF ITS GEOGRAPHICAL DISTRIBUTION IN RUMANIA. Al Maxim. Revista Mus. Geol.-Mineral. Univ. Cluj, vol.6, nos.1-2, pp.127-147, figs.1-3, pls.1-2, table 1, 1937. (In Rumanian, with German summary.)

REMAINS OF THE GREAT EXTINCT OX IN PERTSHIRE. James Ritchie. Scottish Nat., no.170, p.38, Mar.-Apr., 1928.

(A HORN OF BOS PRIMIGENIUS FOUND AT SUCEVENI.) Un corn de Bos primigenius gasit la Suceveni. Emilian Sahleanu. Bul. Fac. Stiinte Cernauti, vol.7, nos.1-2, pp. 31-34, figs.2, (1933) 1934. (In Roumanian, with German summary.)

Bos--Habits, Behavior

WHISTLING SOUND MADE BY BISON (BIBOS GAURUS H. SM.). C. H. Biddulph. Jour. Bombay Nat. Hist. Soc., vol.39, no.3, pp.617-618, Sept.25, 1937.

GRAZING HABITS OF RANGE CATTLE. Matt Culley. Cattleman, 24 (9): 19-23, Feb., 1938.

THE WAY SELADANG FIGHT. Theodore R. Hubback, D. Macregor. Field, London, vol.151, p.829, illus., May 17, 1928.

BEHAVIOUR OF GAUR OR INDIAN BISON. R. C. Morris. Jour. Bombay Nat. Hist. Soc., vol.40, no.2, pp.325, Sept., 1938.

GAUR BULLS ATTACKING A WOUNDED BULL. R. C. Morris. Jour. Bombay Nat. Hist. Soc., vol.39, no.2, p.391, Apr.15, 1937.

SOCIAL BEHAVIOR OF BISON (BIBOS GAURUS H. SM.). R. C. Morris. Jour. Bombay Nat. Hist. Soc., vol.38, no.2, p.393, Dec.1, 1935.

SOLITARY BULL BISON (BIBOS GAURUS H. SM.). R. C. Morris. Jour. Bombay Nat. Hist. Soc., vol.39, no.3, p.617, Sept.25, 1937.

SOLITARY COW GAUR. R. C. Morris. Jour. Bombay Nat. Hist. Soc., vol.32, p. 215, Aug.1, 1927.

A SPIRITED OLD BULL BISON (BIBOS GAURUS). R. C. Morris. Jour. Bombay Nat. Hist. Soc., vol.36, no.4, pp.984-985, Dec.15, 1933.

BEHAVIOUR OF GAUR OR INDIAN BISON (BIBOS GAURUS). F. J. Mustill. Jour. Bombay Nat. Hist. Soc., vol.40, no.4, pp.731-733, May, 1939.

THE BEHAVIOUR OF SELADANG (BIBOS GAURUS). C. S. Ogilvie. Oryx, vol.2, no.3, pp.167-169, Nov., 1953; Malayan Nature Jour., Kuala Lumpur, vol.9, no.1, pp.1-10, June, 1954.

BISON EATING BARK. G. H. Ogilvie. Jour. Bombay Nat. Hist. Soc., vol.33, no. 3, pp.706-707, May 31, 1929.

SOUNDS MADE BY GAUR OR INDIAN BISON (BIBOS GAURUS). R. M. Pizey. Jour. Bombay Nat. Hist. Soc., vol.36, no.1, p. 243, Nov.15, 1932.

BEHAVIOUR OF GAUR OR INDIAN BISON (BIBOS GAURUS). H. G. Rossel. Jour. Bombay Nat. Hist. Soc., vol.40, no.2, pp.325-326, Sept., 1938.

CURIOUS BEHAVIOUR OF BISON (BIBOS GAURUS H. SM.). C. G. Toogood. Jour. Bombay Nat. Hist. Soc., vol.39, no.4, pp. 852-853, Dec.15, 1937.

SOCIAL BEHAVIOUR OF BISON (BIBOS GAURUS H. SMITH). J. Williams. Jour. Bombay Nat. Hist. Soc., vol.37, no.3, pp.724-726, Dec.15, 1934.

ARE BISON DANGEROUS? Field, London, vol.164, p.215, July 28, 1934.

Bos--Heads and Horns

NOTICE OF THE HORNS AND SKULL OF THE ARNEE. John E. Gray. Proc. Zool. Soc. Lond., pt.23, pp.17-18, pl.40, 1855.

ON THE HORNS OF THE SANGA, OR GALLA OXEN, OF GIBBA. John E. Gray. Proc. Zool. Soc. London, pt.20, pp.132-133, 1852.

(A HORNLESS YAK.) Ein hornloser Yak. Friedrich Kuehlhorn. Zool. Garten, n.F., vol.18, nos.3-4, p.150, 1951.

LENGTH OF HORNS IN TSINE (BIBOS BANTENG BIRMANICUS LYD.). D. A. de Lastic. Jour. Bombay Nat. Hist. Soc., vol.38, no.2, pp.394-396, Dec.1, 1935.

GAUR-HEADS FROM THE CHIN HILLS. T. R. Livesey. Jour. Bombay Nat. Hist. Soc., vol.38, no.4, p.819, illus., Aug., 1936.

SHREDDED HORNS OF OXEN. Erna Mohr. Jour. Mam., vol.30, no.4, pp.393-395, pls.1, Nov.17, 1949.

WORN DOWN TIPS OF BISON HORNS. Randolph C. Morris. Jour. Bombay Nat. Hist. Soc., vol.32, p.216, Aug.1, 1927.

MEASUREMENTS OF AN INDIAN BISON HEAD (BIBOS GAURUS). S. C. H. Robinson. Jour. Bombay Nat. Hist. Soc., vol.43, no. 1, pp.100-101, Apr., 1942.

Bos--Heredity

BOWED PASTERN IN JERSEY CATTLE. F. W. Atkeson, Franklin Eldridge, Heman L. Ibsen. Jour. Heredity, Wash., vol.34, no. 1, pp.25-26, figs.14-15, Jan., 1943.

INHERITANCE OF AN EPILEPTIC TYPE CHARACTER IN BROWN SWISS CATTLE. F. W. Atkeson, Franklin Eldridge, Heman L. Ibsen. Jour. Heredity, Wash., vol.35, no.2, pp.45-48, fig.5, Feb., 1944.

PREVALENCE OF "WRYTAIL" IN CATTLE. F. W. Atkeson, Franklin Eldridge, Heman L. Ibsen. Jour. Heredity, Balto., vol.35, no.1, pp.11-14, figs.6-7, Jan., 1944.

AN UNUSUAL CASE OF TWINNING IN JERSEY CATTLE. F. W. Atkeson, Franklin Eldridge, H. C. Fryer. Jour. Heredity, Wash., vol.34, no.3, pp.81-82, illus., Mar., 1943.

INHERITANCE OF BLACK AND RED COAT COLORS IN CATTLE. M. H. Campbell. Genetics, vol.9, no.5, pp.419-441, Sept., 1924.

GENE-INTERACTIONS IN CATTLE CROSSES. L. O. Gilmore, W. E. Petersen, J. B. Fitch. Jour. Heredity, Wash., D.C., vol.33, no.12, pp.451-453, figs.14-15, Dec., 1942.

ON THE SEX RATIO IN CATTLE. John W. Gowen. Jour. Heredity, Wash., D.C., vol.33, no.8, pp.299-301, fig.10, Aug., 1942.

A CONGENITAL HEREDITARY EYE DEFECT OF CATTLE. P. W. Gregory, S. W. Mead, W. M. Regan. Jour. Heredity, Wash., D.C., vol.34, no.4, pp.124-128, figs.14-15, Apr., 1943.

HEREDITARY CONGENITAL LETHAL SPASMS IN JERSEY CATTLE. P. W. Gregory, S. W. Mead, W. M. Regan. Jour. Heredity, Wash., vol.35, no.7, pp.195-200, fig.2, July, 1944.

A NEW TYPE OF RECESSIVE ACHONDROPLASIA IN CATTLE. P. W. Gregory, S. W. Mead, W. M. Regan. Jour. Heredity, Wash., D.C., vol.33, no.9, pp.317-322, figs.3-4, Sept., 1942.

CONGENITAL EPITHELIAL DEFECTS OF CALVES. EPITHELIOGENESIS IMPERFECTA NEONATORUM BOVIS--A RECESSIVE BROUGHT TO LIGHT BY INBREEDING. Frederick B. Hadley. Jour. Heredity, vol.18, pp.487-495, illus., Nov., 1927.

HEREDITARY EPITHELIAL DEFECTS IN AYRSHIRE CATTLE. F. B. Hutt, J. N. Frost. Jour. Heredity, Balto., vol.39, no. 5, pp.131-137, May, 1948.

FUSED TEATS. A HEREDITARY DEFECT IN BEEF CATTLE. Leslie E. Johnson. Jour. Heredity, Wash., vol.36, no.10, pp.317-320, figs.13-14, Oct., 1945.

THE INHERITANCE OF SCREW TAIL IN CATTLE. "KINKY-TAIL" DEFECT OF SWINE PARALLELED IN A RECESSIVE VARIATION FOUND IN INBRED RED POLLED CATTLE. Bradford Knapp, Jr., M. W. Emmel, W. F. Ward. Jour. Heredity, vol.27, no.7, pp.269-271, figs. 7-8, July, 1936.

HEREDITARY CONGENITAL FLEXED PASTERNS IN JERSEY CATTLE. S. W. Mead, P. W. Gregory, W. M. Regan. Jour. Heredity, Wash., vol.34, no.12, pp. 367-372, figs.10-12, Dec., 1943.

PROPORTIONATE DWARFISM IN JERSEY COWS. S. W. Mead, P. W. Gregory, W. M. Regan. Jour. Heredity, Wash., D.C., vol.33, no.11, pp.411-416, figs.16-17, Nov., 1942.

A RECURRENT MUTATION OF DOMINANT ACHONDROPLASIA IN CATTLE. S. W. Mead, P. W. Gregory, W. M. Regan. Jour. Heredity, Wash., vol.37, no.6, pp.183-188, figs.6-7, June, 1946.

A STUDY OF OVA FROM THE FALLOPIAN TUBES OF DAIRY COWS, WITH A GENITAL HISTORY OF THE COWS. Fred W. Miller, W. W. Swett, Carl G. Hartman, Warren H. Lewis. Jour. Agric. Research, vol.43, no. 7, pp.627-636, fig.1, Oct.1, 1931.

A NEW SEX-LINKED DEFECT IN CATTLE. E. L. Morrill. Jour. Heredity, Wash., vol.36, no.3, pp.81-82, Mar., 1945.

QUINTUPLET CALVES AND ERYTHROCYTE MOSAICISM. R. D. Owen, H. P. Davis, R. F. Morgan. Jour. Heredity, Wash., vol.37, no.10, pp.290-297, figs.1-4, Oct., 1946.

YAKS AND YAK-CATTLE HYBRIDS IN ASIA. Ralph W. Phillips, Illa A. Tolstoy, Ray G. Johnson. Jour. Heredity, Wash., vol.37, no.6, pp.162-170, figs.1-4; no.7, pp.206-215, figs.6-8, June, July, 1946.

HEREDITARY STRABISMUS IN JERSEY CATTLE. W. M. Regan, P. W. Gregory, S. W. Mead. Jour. Heredity, Wash., vol. 35, no.8, pp.233-234, Aug., 1944.

THE SANTA GERTRUDIS BREED. THE GENESIS AND THE GENETICS OF A NEW BREED OF BEEF CATTLE. A. O. Rhoad. Jour. Heredity, Wash., vol.40, no.5, pp. 114-126, figs.8, May, 1949.

EVALUATION OF SPECIES CROSSES OF CATTLE BY POLYALLEL CROSSING. A STUDY OF ZEBU AND AFRICANDER X ABERDEEN-ANGUS CATTLE UNDER SUB-TROPICAL CONDITIONS. Albert O. Rhoad, Ralph W. Phillips, Walker M. Dawson. Jour. Heredity, Wash., vol.36, no.12, pp. 367-374, fig.7, Dec., 1945.

SHORT HORN COLORS, A STUDY OF THE INHERITANCE OF CERTAIN COLOR CHARACTERS IN THE SHORT HORN BREED OF CATTLE. A. D. B. Smith. Jour. Heredity, vol.16, no.3, pp.73-84, Mar., 1925.

THE BREEDING STRUCTURE OF THE ABERDEEN-ANGUS BREED. H. H. Stonaker. Jour. Heredity, Wash., vol. 34, no.11, pp.322-328, figs.1-3, Nov., 1943.

COMPACT SHORTHORNS. H. H. Stonaker, R. C. Tom. Jour. Heredity, Wash., vol. 35, no.8, pp.247-250, fig.12, Aug., 1944.

CELLULAR ANTIGENS IN CATTLE BLOOD. Clyde Stormont, R. W. Cumley. Jour. Heredity, Wash., D.C., vol.34, no.2, pp. 34-41, figs.5, Feb., 1943.

BULLDOG AND HAIRLESS CALVES. T. C. Surrarrer. Jour. Heredity, Wash., vol.34, no.6, pp.175-178, figs.7-12, June, 1943.

GENETIC HISTORY OF CATTLE IN WISCONSIN. George Walter Wooley. Trans. Wisconsin Acad. Sci. Arts and Letters, Madison, vol.30, pp.131-178, figs.5, 1937.

COLOR SIDED CATTLE, SOME REMARKS CONCERNING THEIR OCCURRENCE AND HEREDITY. Christian Wriedt. Jour. Heredity, vol.16, no.2, pp.51-55, Feb., 1925.

(INHERITANCE OF THE CHARACTERISTIC OF DOUBLING IN CATTLE.) Die Verebung des Doppellender-Charakters bei Rindern. Christian Wriedt. Zeitschr. f. Ind. Aktammungs- u. Verebungslehre, Bd.51, pp.482-486, fig.1, 1929.

Bos--Hunting

(BUFFALO HUNT IN INDOCHINA.) Buffeljakt i Indo-Kina. Bertil Bjorkegren. Svensk Jakt, Stockholm, vol.78, no.11, pp. 487-492, Nov.15, 1940.

BANTIN. (BOS SONDAICUS.) R. Cardwell. Game and Gun, vol.5, pp.126-129, illus., Mar., 1928.

STALKING A HERD OF SAING. E. H. Peacock. Jour. Bombay Nat. Hist. Soc., vol.37, no.2, pp.278-280, pls.1-3, Aug. 15, 1934.

SELADANG HUNTING IN PAHANG. (GAUR.) Pelandok. Malayan Forester, Kuala Lumpur, vol.7, no.2, pp.61-71, figs.7, 1938.

AN OLD TIME BUFFALO HUNT. S. H. Prater. Jour. Bombay Nat. Hist. Soc., vol.27, pp.627-628, Mar.31, 1921.

STALKING TSINE IN BURMA. Arthur S. Vernay. Nat. Hist., vol.24, pp.199-203, figs.4, Mar.-Apr., 1924.

OBSERVATIONS ON THE GAUR AND ITS SHIKAR. H. S. Wood. Jour. Darjeeling Nat. Hist. Soc., vol.12, no.1, pp.7-17, June, 1937.

Bos--Hybrids

BISON (BIBOS GAURUS H. SMITH) AND HYBRIDS IN THE MYSORE ZOO. R. W. Burton. Jour. Bombay Nat. Hist. Soc., vol.37, no.1, pp.215-216, illus., Apr.15, 1934.

(EXPERIMENTS ON CROSSING YAKS WITH KIRGHIZIAN AND BROWN SWISS CATTLE.) V. F. Denisov. Bull. Acad. Sci. URSS, Cl. Sci. Math. et Nat., ser. Biol., Moscow, no.4, pp.863-878, figs.9, tables 15, 1938. (In Russian, with English summary.)

(ON THE PROBLEM OF THE FERTILITY OF MALE HYBRIDS BETWEEN THE YAK AND DOMESTIC CATTLE.) V. V. Ivanova. Bull. Acad. Sci. URSS, Cl. Sci. Math. et Nat., ser. Biol., Moscow, no.4, pp.883-884, figs.2, 1938. (In Russian, with English summary.)

(ON THE WORK OF THE OIRAT EXPERIMENT STATION ON THE HYBRIDIZATION OF THE YAK, (POEPHAGUS GRUNNIENS L.) AND DOMESTIC CATTLE (BOS TAURUS L.).) J. Lyubimov. Bull. Acad. Sci. URSS, Cl. Sci. Math. et Nat., ser. Biol., Moscow, no.4, pp.879-882, fig.1, tables 2, 1938. (In Russian, with English summary.)

NOTICE OF A HYBRID BULL. D. W. Mitchell. Proc. Zool. Soc. Lond., pt.17, p.172, 1849.

ZEBU-YAK HYBRIDS. STERILITY OF BULLS, FERTILITY OF COWS AND MATERIAL ON THE GENETICS OF ZEBU-YAK HYBRIDS. M. M. Zawadowsky. Jour. Heredity, vol.22, no.10, pp.297-319, figs.17, pl.1, Oct., 1931.

Bos--Methods, Techniques

ON DISTINGUISHING BETWEEN MALES AND FEMALES AND OTHER CONTROVERSIAL MATTERS PERTAINING TO THE GAUR (BIBOS GAURUS). R. C. Morris. Jour. Bombay Nat. Hist. Soc., vol.34, no. 3, pp.801-802, Nov.15, 1930.

DATA ON SEX DETERMINATION IN CATTLE. Raymond Pearl, H. M. Parshley. Biol. Bull., vol.24, no.4, pp.205-225, Mar., 1913.

ON THE DISTINCTION BETWEEN INDIAN AND MALAYAN GAUR. R. M. Pizey. Jour. Bombay Nat. Hist. Soc., vol.41, no. 3, pp.657-658, pl.1, Apr., 1940.

Bos--North America

THE TEXAS LONGHORN PRESERVED FROM EXTINCTION. Will C. Barnes. Jour. Heredity, vol.18, pp.443-446, fig. 3, 1927.

THEY HELPED BUILD THE WEST. (LONGHORN CATTLE ON WILDLIFE REFUGES.) Glenn Yerk Williamson. Fauna, Phila., vol.6, no.3, pp.77-79, figs.2, Sept., 1944.

TEXAS LONGHORNS. Stanley P. Young. Zoonooz, Zool. Soc. San Diego, vol.28, no.4, pp.3-5, illus., Apr., 1955.

PROPOSED INTRODUCTION OF THE YAK-OX FROM TARTARY TO THE GREAT PLAINS OF THE WEST. U.S. Patent Office Agri. Rept., 1858, pp.239-241, 1859.

Bos--Pelage, Coloration

BISON--VARIATION IN COLOURATION OF THE EXPOSED PART OF THE SNOUT AND TONGUE. C. H. Biddulph. Jour. Bombay Nat. Hist. Soc., vol.39, no.1, p.165, Dec.1, 1936.

THE COLOUR OF 'WHITE BISON' (BIBOS GAURUS). A. A. Dunbar Brander. Jour. Bombay Nat. Hist. Soc., vol.36, no.4, pp. 985-986, Dec.15, 1933.

COLOURATION OF THE BISON'S SNOUT AND TONGUE. R. C. Morris. Jour. Bombay Nat. Hist. Soc., vol.39, no.3, p.618, Sept.25, 1937.

WHAT COLOR ARE THE GAUR'S EYES? R. C. Morris. Field, London, vol.156, no.4050, p.209, Aug.9, 1930.

'WHITE' BISON. R. C. Morris. Jour. Bombay Nat. Hist. Soc., vol.36, no.2, pp.492-493, Apr.15, 1933; vol.37, no.2, pp.483-484, Aug.15, 1934; vol.38, no.2, pp.393-394, Dec.1, 1935; vol.39, no.1, p. 165, Dec.1, 1936.

(THE COLOR OF THE URE-OX.) Die Farbe des Ures. A. B. Szalay. Zool. Garten, Leipzig, n.F., vol.3, nos.9-10, pp.255-263, Oct., 1930.

WHITE BISON IN SOUTH COIMBATORE. J. Williams. Jour. Bombay Nat. Hist. Soc., vol.39, no.1, pp.166-168, Dec.1, 1936.

Bos--Photography

AFTER BISON WITH CAMERA AND TRIPOD. E. H. Peacock. Field, London, vol.160, no.4166, p.654, illus., Oct.29, 1932.

IN AMBUSH FOR BISON. A BIG GAME PHOTOGRAPHER'S FORTUNE AND MISFORTUNE IN BURMA. E. H. Peacock. Field, London, vol.162, no.4212, pp.714-715, figs., Sept.16, 1933; Jour. Bombay Nat. Hist. Soc., vol.37, no.3, pp.529-531, pls.1-3, Dec.15, 1934.

Bos--Physiology

LABILITY OF THE BASAL METABOLISM OF THE DAIRY COW. Francis G. Benedict, Ernest G. Ritzman. Proc. Nat. Acad. Sci., Wash., vol.21, no.6, pp.304-308, June, 1935.

ON THE OCCURRENCE OF HUMAN-LIKE A-ANTIGENS IN CATTLE. Grethe Hartmann. Kgl. Danske Videnskab. Selskab., Biol. Meddel., Copenhagen, vol. 15, no.10, pp.45, figs.11, Mar.4, 1941.

(INVESTIGATIONS OF THE COLOR CAPACITY OF THE ZEBU.) Untersuchungen ueber das Farbenvermoegen des Zebu. Guenther Hoffmann. Zeitschr. Tierpsych., Berlin, vol.9, no.2, pp.470-479, 1952.

SOME EXPERIMENTS ON THE BRIGHTNESS VALUE OF RED FOR THE LIGHT-ADAPTED EYE OF THE CALF. E. Kittredge. Jour. Comp. Psychol., vol.3, pp.141-145, 1923.

VITALITY OF A COW MAULED BY A TIGER. R. C. Morris. Jour. Bombay Nat. Hist. Soc., vol.35, no.2, pp.439-440, Oct.15, 1931; no.4, pp.888-889, July 15, 1932.

MINERAL METABOLISM STUDIES IN DAIRY CATTLE. J. T. Reid, George M. Ward. Jour. Nutrition, Phila., vol.35, no.5, pp.591-596, May 10, 1948.

ACID AND ALKALINE PHOSPHATASE LEVELS IN CONSECUTIVE SEMEN EJACULATES FROM BULLS. J. T. Reid, G. M. Ward, R. L. Salisbury. Amer. Jour. Physiol., Balto., vol.153, no.2, pp. 235-241, May 1, 1948.

BLOOD GLUTATHIONE IN THE BOVINE. J. T. Reid, G. M. Ward, R. L. Salisbury. Amer. Jour. Physiol., Balto., vol.152, no.3, pp.633-636, Mar.1, 1948.

EFFECTS OF CERTAIN FACTORS UPON THE LEVEL OF THE PLASMA PHOSPHATASES OF BREEDING BULLS. J. T. Reid, G. M. Ward, R. L. Salisbury. Amer. Jour. Physiol., Balto., vol.152, no.2, pp.280-285, Feb.1, 1948.

MINERAL METABOLISM STUDIES IN DAIRY CATTLE. J. T. Reid, G. M. Ward, R. L. Salsbury. Jour. Nutrition, Phila., vol.36, no.1, pp.75-89, July 10, 1948.

WATER EXPENDITURE IN BOS TAURUS AND BOS INDICUS CATTLE IN RELATION TO ADAPTABILITY TO A TROPICAL ENVIRONMENT. Albert O. Rhoad. Proc. 8th Amer. Sci. Congr., Wash., D.C., vol.3, pp.115-123, figs.3, Aug.3, 1942.

NUTRITIONAL PHYSIOLOGY OF THE ADULT RUMINANT. Ernest G. Ritzman, Francis G. Benedict. Carnegie Inst. Wash., publ.494, pp.vi, 200, pls.3, Sept., 1938.

(BIOLOGICAL AND PHYSIOLOGICAL INVESTIGATIONS OF THE SEMEN AND VAGINAL SECRETION OF BOVINES IN REGARD TO ARTIFICIAL INSEMINATION.) Biologische und physiologische Untersuchungen am Sperma und am Scheidensekret des Rindes im Hinblick auf die kuenstliche Besamung. O. Roemmele. Zool. Jahrbuecher, Abteil. f. allg. Zool. u. Physiol., vol.44, pp.85-148, figs.5, 1927.

FETAL RESORPTION IN CATTLE. Charles W. Turner. North Amer. Veterinarian, vol.8, no.11, pp.27-31, 1927.

Bos--Predators, Mortality

A BULL GAUR (B. GAURUS) AND A TIGRESS FIGHT TO DEATH. H. V. Blackburn. Jour. Bombay Nat. Hist. Soc., vol.37, no.4, p.950, Apr.15, 1935.

BEASTS OF PREY IN RHODESIA. (BRIEF NOTE ON LIONS, WILD DOGS, LEOPARDS, AND HYAENAS KILLING CATTLE.) Cecil Browne. Field, London, vol.151, p.164, Feb.2, 1928.

TIGER FEEDING ON A LIVE COW. R. C. Morris. Jour. Bombay Nat. Hist. Soc., vol.38, no.2, p.386, Dec., 1935.

WILD DOGS AND FURTHER JUNGLE TRAGEDIES. R. C. Morris. Jour. Bombay Nat. Hist. Soc., vol.31, pp.811-812, Nov.1, 1926.

WILD DOGS ATTACKING CATTLE. R. C. Morris. Jour. Bombay Nat. Hist. Soc., vol.32, p.211, Aug.1, 1927.

CATTLE ON GRIZZLY BEAR RANGE. Adolph Murie. Jour. Wildlife Mgt., Menasha, vol.12, no.1, pp.57-72, pl.1, Jan., 1948.

COYOTE TOLLING A CALF. Robert W. Nero. Blue Jay, Saskatchewan Nat. Hist. Soc., 16 (1): 32-33, Mar., 1958.

THE STRANGE DEATH OF A BISON. L. Rynjah. Jour. Bombay Nat. Hist. Soc., vol.49, no.3, pp.546-547, Dec., 1950.

WILD DOGS ATTACKING CATTLE. H. G. Gregory Smith. Jour. Bombay Nat. Hist. Soc., vol.33, no.1, p.199, Sept.30, 1928.

Bos--Reproductive Biology

SEASONAL DISTRIBUTION OF TWIN BIRTHS IN CATTLE. L. J. Cole, Augustin Rodolfo. Record of Proc. Amer. Anim. Production Soc., Ann. Meeting, 1924, pp. 116-118, 1926.

NOTES ON MULTIPLE PREGNANCIES IN CATTLE, WITH SPECIAL REFERENCE TO THREE CASES OF PRENATAL TRIPLETS AND THE FREE-MARTINS INVOLVED. Thomas Hume Bissonnette. Amer. Jour. Anat., vol.42, pp.29-73, illus., Sept.15, 1928.

THE PHYSIOLOGY OF REPRODUCTION IN THE COW. John Hammond. Univ. Press, Cambridge, pp.226, pls.33, 1927.

Bos--South America

(ON SOUTH AMERICAN DOMESTIC ANIMALS II. THE BOVINE (WITH CONTRIBUTIONS TO MORPHOLOGY AND THE GENESIS OF SPOTTEDNESS) XIV. CONTINUATION OF "JOURNEYS IN SOUTH AMERICA FOR THE PURPOSE OF BIOLOGICAL STUDY.") Ueber Suedamerikanische Haustiere II. Rind (mit Beitraegen zur Morphologie und Genese der Scheckung) XIV. Fortsetzung der "Biologischen Reisestudien in Suedamerika." Hans Krieg. Zool. Garten, Leipzig, vol.2, nos. 1-3, pp.10-23, figs.1-14, 1929.

ZEBU CATTLE IN BRAZIL. Pastoral Review and Graziers Record, Melbourne, p.1348, 1937.

Bos--Taxonomy, Origins

(THE SEXUAL DIMORPHISM OF THE CRANIUM OF THE URE OX AND ITS CONNECTIONS TO THE RACE AND DESCENT PROBLEM OF DOMESTIC BOVINES.) Der sexuelle Dimorphismus am Schaedel des Urs und seine Beziehungen zum Rassen- und Abstammungsproblem des Hausrindes. Leopold Adametz. Biologia Generalis, vol.6, no.1, pp.1-98, pls.1-18, 1930.

DESCENT AND ORIGIN OF THE AFRIKANDER CATTLE. H. Epstein. Jour. Heredity, vol.24, no.12, pp.449-462, figs., Dec., 1933.

THE VALID NAME OF THE BANTENG: BIBOS JAVANICUS (D'ALTON). D. A. Hooijer. Zool. Mededel. Rijksmus. Nat. Hist. Leiden, vol.34, no.14, pp.223-226, Feb.28, 1956.

THE ORIGIN AND THE GEOGRAPHICAL DISTRIBUTION OF CATTLE. N. N. Kolesnik. Bull. Acad. Sci. URSS, Cl. Sci. math. et nat., ser. biol., Moscow, nos.2-3, pp.374-414, figs.28, 1936. (In Russian, with English summary.)

BEFORE MONTEFIORE JOSAH SUNSHINE... A LONG LINE OF ANCESTORS STRETCHES BACK FROM DOMESTIC CATTLE AND ITS BEGINNING IS LOST IN THE MISTS OF ANTIQUITY. Claude W. Leister. Animal Kingdom, New York, vol.46, no.3, pp.63-70, illus., May, 1943.

(RESEARCH ON THE PHYLOGENY OF THE WHITE COWS OF TRANSYLVANIA.) Vasile Parvulescu. Bulet. Acad. Inalte Studii Agron. din Cluj, vol.4, no.1, pp.45-127, figs.43, 1933. (In Rumanian, with summaries in French, English and German.)

THE ORIGIN OF CATTLE--WILD AND DOMESTICATED. W. P. Pycraft. Illus. London News, vol.190, no.5104, p.248, illus., Feb.13, 1937.

FROM BOS TO BOSSY. Ken Stott, Jr. Zoonooz, San Diego, vol.19, no.8, pp. 3-4, illus., Aug., 1946.

Ovis--General

(GENETIC-GEOGRAPHICAL STUDY OF THE HISSAR SHEEP.) Gengeographische Studie am Hissarschaf. John Wolfgang Amschler. Zeitschrift Zuechtungskunde, vol.4, no.7, pp.336-341, figs.1-2, 1929.

BIGHORNS OF PLAIN AND PEAK. Vernon Bailey. Nature Magazine, vol.18, no.5, pp.279-282, 325-327, illus., Nov., 1931.

OVIS ASTORE, A THREE-COATED SHEEP. Aldred F. Barker. Nature, London, vol. 129, no.3247, pp.128-129, figs.4, Jan.23, 1932.

CHARACTERISTICS AND PRODUCTION OF OLD-TIME NAVAJO SHEEP. Cecil T. Blunn. Jour. Heredity, Washington, vol. 34, no.5, pp.141-152, figs.6-10, Mar., 1943.

MONOGRAPH OF THE SPECIES OF THE GENUS OVIS. E. Blyth. Proc. Zool. Soc. Lond., pt.8, pp.12-13, 1840.

OVIS POLI. Katherine G. Bryant. Nature Mag., vol.6, p.208, fig.1, Oct., 1925.

THE QUEST OF THE SILVER RAM. R.R. M. Carpenter. Frontiers, Phila., vol.5, no.3, pp.67-74, illus., Feb., 1941.

MOUNTAIN SHEEP INCIDENT. C. E. Crabtree. Yosemite Nat. Notes, vol.28, no.10, p.125, Oct., 1949.

(SOME OBSERVATIONS ON THE MOUFLON.) Quelques observations au sujet du mouflon a manchettes. Paul Dalimier. Mammalia, Paris, vol.18, no.3, pp.331-333, pl.1, Sept., 1954. (with English summary)

MOUNTAIN SHEEP. George Bird Grinnell. Jour. Mam., vol.9, no.1, pp.1-9, Feb., 1928.

EXHIBITION OF AND REMARKS UPON THE ORIGINAL DRAWING, BY COLONEL GORDON, FROM WHICH THE PLATE OF OVIS POLII IN THE 'PROCEEDINGS' (1874, PL. LIII) WAS PREPARED. Arthur Grote. Proc. Zool. Soc. Lond., pp.414-415, 1876.

SHEEP. Max Hilzheimer. Gloucester, England, vol.10, no.38, pp.195-206, pls. 8, June, 1936.

THE WIDE-HORNED WHITE MOUNTAIN SHEEP. William T. Hornaday. Zool. Soc. Bull., New York, vol.16, no.51, pp.857-860, illus., May, 1912.

ON OVIS SAIRENSIS. R. Lydekker. Proc. Zool. Soc. Lond., pp.113-114, Feb.20, 1900.

BIG HORN SHEEP. P. J. Moran. Canadian Field Nat., vol.42, pp.12-16, illus., Jan., 1928.

(THE RACE OF KARAKUL SHEEP: CAPACITY AND PRODUCTION.) La race ovine Karakul: Aptitudes et productions. Mohammad Nacer Kechawarz. Mammalia, Paris, 20 (4): 439-466, pls.6-7, Dec., 1956.

(GEOGRAPHICAL DISTRIBUTION OF THE WILD SHEEP OF THE OLD WORLD.) Distribution geographique des moutons sauvages du monde ancien. N. Nasonov. Publ. Russian Acad. Sci., Petrograd (Russian State Printing Office), pp.255, figs.65, pls.20, Jan., 1924.

REMARKS UPON THE BURRHAL SHEEP. W. Ogilby. Proc. Zool. Soc. Lond., pt. 6, p.79, 1838.

THE MOUFLON (OVIS MUSIMON). Paul Palffy. Conseil International de la Chasse, Troisieme session, (Varsovie, 19-22, pp.393-398, Apr., 1934. (In French.)

SIDELIGHTS ON THE BIG HORN SHEEP. Archie Pendergraft. Wyoming Wild Life, Cheyenne, vol.10, no.5, pp.30-31, illus., May, 1946; Texas Game Fish, Austin, vol. 4, no.9, p.19, illus., Aug., 1946.

KARAKUL SHEEP. C. G. Potts. Farmers' Bull. no.1632, U.S. Dept. Agric., pp.9, figs.6, Dec., 1931.

CONCERNING SHEEP. W. P. Pycraft. Illus. London News, vol.194, no.5212, p.368, figs.3, Mar.11, 1939.

EXHIBITION OF ORIGINAL DRAWINGS BY MR. VIGNE OF OVIS CYCLOCEROS. Philip L. Sclater. Proc. Zool. Soc. Lond., pt.29, pp.368-369, 1861.

NOTE ON OVIS POLII OF BLYTH. Philip L. Sclater. Proc. Zool. Soc. Lond., pt.28, pp.443-444, fig.1, 1860.

A PECULIAR LEGLESS SHEEP. Charles R. Stockard. Biol. Bull., vol.13, no.5, pp.288-290, pl.13, figs.2, Oct., 1907.

NOTES ON OORIAL. C. H. Stockley. Jour. Bombay Nat. Hist. Soc., vol.28, pp.1126-1128, Dec.20, 1922.

DESCRIPTION OF THE OVIS POLI OF BLYTH. F. Stoliczka. Proc. Zool. Soc. Lond., pp.425-427, pl.LIII, 1874.

LO, THE GENTLE LAMB. (BIGHORN.) Ken Stott, Jr. San Diego Zoonooz, vol.18, no.3, pp.3-4, Mar., 1945.

ON THE WEIGHTS OF DALL'S SHEEP. Frederick A. Ulmer. Jour. Mam., 22 (4): 448-449, Nov., 1941.

THE SHEEP THAT WAS A LEGEND. (MARCO POLO'S SHEEP.) Richard G. Van Gelder. Animal Kingdom, New York Zool. Soc., 60 (1): 2-5, illus., Feb., 1957.

HUNTING BIGHORN WITH A CAMERA. Milton C. White. Wyoming Wild Life, Cheyenne, vol.10, no.4, pp.17-18, illus., Apr., 1946.

LETTER ACCOMPANYING AN AOUDAD (OVIS TRAGELAPHUS, GEOFF.). W. Willshire. Proc. Zool. Soc. Lond., pt. 3, p.41, 1835.

KNOW YOUR BIG GAME: ROCKY MOUNTAIN BIGHORN SHEEP, OVIS CANADENSIS. Walter J. Wilwerding. Sports Afield, Minneapolis, vol.122, no.6, pp.40-41, illus., Dec., 1949.

KNOW YOUR BIG GAME. WHITE SHEEP. Walter J. Wilwerding. Sports Afield, Minneapolis, vol.123, no.4, pp.38-39, illus., Apr., 1950.

SHEEP. U. S. Patent Office, Rept. pt.II, Agriculture, Washington, 1852, pp.71-75, 1851.

Ovis--Africa

PROGRESS OF SHEEP AND WOOL RESEARCH IN S. AFRICA. J. E. Duerden. S. Africa Jour. Sci., vol.28, pp.302-305, Nov., 1931.

(THE MENDES RAM OR DOMESTIC SHEEP OF ANCIENT EGYPT. ITS RELATIONSHIP TO LIVING AND FOSSIL ANTELOPES. Le Belier de Mendes ou le mouton domestique de l'ancienne Egypte. Ses rapports avec les Antilopes vivantes et fossiles. Claude Gaillard. Soc. Anthropol. Lyon, Seance du, pp.34, figs.9, May 4, 1901.

(NORTHERN AFRICA SHEEP AND THEIR IMPORTANCE AS REGARDS THE SETTLEMENT PROBLEM OF NORTHERN AFRICA.) Nordafrikanische Schafe und ihre Bedeutung fuer die Besiedlungsfrage Nordafrikas. M. Hilzheimer. Zeitsch. f. Saeugetierkunde, vol.3, pp.253-277, pls.4, fig.1, June 11, 1928.

(THE MOUFLON. FROM MOROCCO TO EGYPT.) Le mouflon a manchettes. Du Maroc a l'Egypte. L. Joleaud. La Nature, Paris, no.2949, pp.241-243, figs.3, Mar. 15, 1935.

(ZOOGEOGRAPHIC STUDIES ON THE BARBARY: THE MOUFLON.) Etudes de geographie zoologique sur la Berberie: Le Mouflon a Manchettes. L. Joleaud. Compte Rendus Soc. Biogeogr., Paris, no. 27, pp.43-45, Mar.18, 1927.

ON THE OCCURRENCE OF THE BARBARY SHEEP IN EGYPT. Philip L. Sclater. Proc. Zool. Soc. Lond., pt.1, pp.85-86, June 1, 1895.

Ovis--Anatomy

(A CASE OF HERMAPHRODITISM IN A SHEEP BROUGHT FROM ENGLAND.) Ein Fall von Hermaphroditismus bei einem aus England eingefuehrten Schaf. D. M. Awtokratow. Anat. Anzeiger, vol. 70, pp.373-376, fig.1, Oct.8, 1930.

OCCURRENCE OF UPPER CANINES IN MOUNTAIN SHEEP, OVIS CANADENSIS. Seth B. Benson. Amer. Midland Nat., Notre Dame, vol.30, no.3, pp.786-789, pl.1, Nov., 1943.

THE BLOOD SUPPLY OF THE MESONEPHROS OF THE SHEEP. J. Davies. Proc. Zool. Soc. Lond., vol.120, pt.1, pp.95-112, figs.5, pls.2, May 16, 1950.

THE DEVELOPMENT OF THE MESONEPHROS OF THE SHEEP. J. Davies, D. V. Davies. Proc. Zool. Soc. Lond., vol.120, pt.1, pp.73-93, figs.5, pls.3, May 16, 1950.

TOOTH DEVELOPMENT OF THE NELSON BIGHORN SHEEP. O. V. Deming. California Fish and Game, San Francisco, vol.38, no.4, pp.523-529, illus., Oct., 1952.

A HISTOLOGICAL STUDY OF THE ORGANIZATION OF THE RUMEN EPITHELIUM OF

SHEEP. Marjorie J. Dobson, W.C.B. Brown, A. Dobson, A. T. Phillipson. Quarterly Jour. Exper. Physiol., Edinburgh, 41 (3): 247-253, July, 1956.

THE HISTOGENESIS OF THE PINEAL BODY OF THE SHEEP. H. E. Jordan. Amer. Jour. Anat., Phila., vol.12, no.3, pp.249-275, pls.3, Nov., 1911.

(PRESENTATION OF A HEXADACTYLE LAMB PAW.) Presentation d'une patte hexadactyle d'agneau. Fernand Lataste. Actes Soc. Linn., Bordeaux, vol.76, pp.1-5, figs.1-4, Mar.12, 1924.

THE GROWTH OF THE HEAD IN THYROIDECTOMIZED SHEEP. H. S. Liddell. Anat. Record, vol.30, pp.327-332, figs.8, Aug.25, 1925.

AN ANOMALOUS LAMB. S. L. Loewen, J. Russell Jones. Trans. Kansas Acad. Sci., vol.40, pp.377-384, pl., 1937.

VARIATION IN THE HISTOLOGICAL CONDITION OF THE THYROID GLANDS OF SHEEP WITH REGARD TO SEASON, SEX, AGE, AND LOCALITY. E. Lowe. Quart. Jour. Micr. Sci., vol.73, pp.437-464, pls.2, Feb., 1930.

(THE DEVELOPMENT OF THE HYPOPHYSIS CEREBRI IN SHEEP (OVIS ARIES).) Die Entwicklung der Hypophysis cerebri beim Schaf (Ovis aries). H. W. Lubberhuizen. Zeitschr. f. Anat. u. Entwicklungs., vol. 96, pp.1-53, figs.53, 1931.

VARIATION IN TAIL FORM IN IMERITIAN SHEEP. M. D. Rcheulishvili. Comptes Rendus (Doklady) Acad. Sci. URSS, Moscow, n.s., vol.23, no.6, pp.576-579, fig.1, 1939.

VARIATION OF THE SHAPE OF THE "KURDJUK" AND OF TAIL APPENDIX IN TUSHIN SHEEP. M. D. Rcheulishvili. Comptes Rendus (Doklady) Acad. Sci. URSS, Moscow, n.s., vol.23, no.6, pp.573-575, figs.3, 1939.

ANOTHER LAMB CYCLOPS. A. M. Reese. Anat. Anz., Jena, vol.84, nos.9-11, pp.198-203, figs.5, May 25, 1937.

A CEPHALOPAGUS LAMB. A. M. Reese. Anat. Anz., Jena, vol.89, nos.1-4, pp.20-25, figs.3, Oct.16, 1939.

SEASONAL CHANGES IN THE FORM OF THE ROCKY MOUNTAIN SHEEP. Carl Rungius. Zool. Soc. Bull., New York, vol. 16, no.55, pp.950-952, illus., Jan., 1913.

ON AN ABNORMAL SKULL OF THE DOMESTIC SHEEP. C. G. Seligmann. Proc. Zool. Soc. Lond., pp.903, Apr.11, 1907.

LATER POSTNATAL SKULL GROWTH IN THE SHEEP. Thomas Wingate Todd, Ralph E. Wharton. Amer. Jour. Anat., vol.55, no.1, pp.79-95, figs.11, July 15, 1934.

BEHAVIOR OF ULTIMOBRANCHIAL TISSUE IN THE POSTNATAL THYROID GLAND: EPITHELIAL CYSTS, THEIR RELATION TO THYROID PARENCHYMA AND TO "NEW-GROWTHS" IN THE THYROID GLAND OF YOUNG SHEEP. John H. Van Dyke. Amer. Jour. Anat., Phila., vol.76, no.2, pp.201-251, figs.1-7, pls.1-4, Mar., 1945.

## Ovis--Conservation, Management

CAN WE BRING BACK THE SIERRA BIGHORN? Vernon Bailey. Yosemite Nature Notes, vol.11, no.6, pp.1-3, June, 1932.

MOUNTAIN SHEEP ARE COMING BACK. George E. Barclay. Arizona Wildlife and Sportsman, Phoenix, vol.8, no.10, pp.10-11, 22-23, illus., Oct., 1947.

CONFERENCE ON SIERRA BIGHORN PLANNED. Arthur H. Blake. Sierra Club Bull., San Francisco, vol.25, no.6, p.7, Dec., 1940.

RESULTS OF ARTIFICIAL FEEDING. (SICKNESS OF MOUNTAIN SHEEP IN GLACIER NATIONAL PARK.) R. M. Bond. N. Region News, p.51, June, 1937.

WHAT ABOUT THE BIGHORN? E. K. Brown, G. W. Jones. Colorado Conserv. Comments, Denver, vol.9, no.3, pp.10-11, Sept.15, 1946.

THE BIGHORN SHEEP. Helmut K. Buechner. Our Endangered Wildlife, Natl. Wildlife Federation, pp.29-30, illus., Jan., 1956.

GOODBYE BIGHORN. (MOUNTAIN SHEEP IN DANGER OF EXTINCTION.) Arthur Hawthorne Carhart. Rocky Mountain Sportsman, vol.1, no.3, pp.12-13, 27-28, illus., Aug., 1938.

THE FUTURE OF THE BIGHORN SHEEP. Helmut K. Buechner. Animal Kingdom, New York Zool. Soc., vol.59, no.1, pp.2-10, illus., Feb., 1956.

MAN, THE GREATEST ENEMY OF DESERT BIGHORN MOUNTAIN SHEEP. Richard Carson. Texas Game and Fish, (10): 7, 15-16, Sept., 1943.

ARE THE BIGHORNS DOOMED? Faye Couey. Mont. Wildl., 3 (1): 16-18, illus., Winter (Mar.), 1953.

A WAY TO "BRING BACK" THE NATIVE BIGHORN TO THE YOSEMITE. Joseph Grinnell. Sierra Club Bull., vol.20, no. 1, pp.28-31, illus., Feb., 1935.

DESERT BIGHORN MANAGEMENT. Arthur F. Halloran. Trans. N. A. Wildl. Conf., 14: 527-537, 1949.

WATER DEVELOPMENT FOR DESERT BIGHORN SHEEP. Arthur F. Halloran, Oscar V. Deming. Jour. Wildlife Mgt., 22 (1): 1-9, illus., Jan., 1958.

MOUNTAIN SHEEP ROUND-UP. (TRANSPLANTING IN WYOMING.) B. B. Hume. Outdoor Life, 76 (4): 20-21, 51, Oct., 1935.

BIG PLANS FOR THE BIG HORN. Daniel W. Lay. Texas Game and Fish, Austin, vol.3, no.8, p.23, July, 1945.

THE DESERT BIGHORN PROBLEM. Jack O'Connor. Arizona Wildlife and Sportsman, Tucson, vol.6, no.5, pp.8-9, illus., Mar., 1945.

SAVING THE VANISHING BIGHORN. Randolph Roberts. Travel, New York, vol.76, no.4, pp.28-29, 40, illus., Feb., 1941.

BIGHORNS NEED A BREAK. William M. Rush. Outdoor Life, 85 (1): 38-40, 85, Jan., 1940; Conservation, Amer. Forestry Assoc., Wash., D.C., vol.6, no.1, pp.26-28, Jan.-Feb., 1940.

ARIZONA DESERT BIGHORN SHEEP MANAGEMENT SURVEYS. John P. Russo. Ariz. Game and Fish Comm., 1951, Proj. Job Compl. Rep., pp.20, illus., 1952.

THE BIGHORN AND NATIONAL FORESTS. H. L. Shantz. Cons., 5 (1): 34-36, Jan.-Feb., 1939.

SAVING THE BIGHORNS. Laura Markham Trester. Frontiers, 11 (1): 3-4, 26-27, Oct., 1946.

IS THE BIGHORN DOOMED? William Voigt, Jr. Outdoor America, Chicago, vol.11, no.2, pp.10, 11, illus., Jan.-Feb., 1946.

SHALL WE SAVE THOSE MOUNTAIN SHEEP? Charles T. Vorhies. Arizona Wildlife, vol.7, no.5, pp.11-12, Sept., 1937.

BIGHORN SHEEP MAKING LAST STAND FOR EXISTENCE IN U.S. Amer. Field, Chicago, vol.136, no.27, p.4, July 5, 1941.

## Ovis--Diseases, Parasites

CILIATES FROM THE SIERRA NEVADA BIGHORN, OVIS CANADENSIS SIERRAE GRINNELL. Mildred Bush, C. A. Kofoid. Univ. California Publ. Zool., Berkeley, vol.53, no.6, pp.237-261, illus., Jan.8, 1948.

THE LUNGWORM PROTOSTRONGYLUS RUSHI DIKMANS, 1937, OF THE MOUNTAIN SHEEP, OVIS CANADENSIS. G. Dikmans. Proc. Helminth. Soc. Wash., 10 (1): 8-9, Jan., 1943.

A RECORD OF LUNGWORMS IN OVIS DALLI (NELSON). Frans C. Goble, Adolph Murie. Jour. Mam., vol.23, no. 2, pp.220-221, May 14, 1942.

LUMPY-JAW IN BIG-HORN SHEEP. W. T. Hornaday. Zool. Soc. Bull., New York, vol.16, no.55, p.954, Jan., 1913.

HUNTING AS A TECHNIQUE IN STUDYING LUNGWORM INFESTATIONS IN BIGHORN SHEEP. Gilbert N. Hunter, Richard E. Pillmore. Trans. 19th N.A. Wildl. Conf., pp.117-129, map, 1954.

POSSIBLE DISEASE IN MOUNTAIN SHEEP. Edmund Jaeger. California Fish and Game, vol.13, no.3, p.222, July, 1927.

FAT NECROSIS IN SHEEP. G. De Kock. S. Afr. Jour. Sci., vol.25, pp.270-273, June-July, 1928.

PNEUMONIA IN ROCKY MOUNTAIN BIGHORN SHEEP. Hadleigh Marsh. Jour. Mam., vol.19, no.2, pp.214-219, May 14, 1938.

PATHOLOGIC CHANGES IN SHEEP RESULTING FROM EXPOSURE TO LOW BAROMETRIC PRESSURES. John W. Miller. Public Health Repts., Wash., D.C., vol.59, no.19, pp.618-620, illus., May 12, 1944.

HEMORRHAGIC SEPTICEMIA IN THE BIGHORN OF ROCKY MOUNTAIN NATIONAL PARK. Merlin K. Potts. Jour. Mam., vol. 18, no.1, pp.105-106, Feb.14, 1937.

OBSERVATIONS ON DISEASES OF BIGHORN IN ROCKY MOUNTAIN NATIONAL PARK. Merlin K. Potts. Trans. 3rd North Amer. Wildlife Conf., pp.893-897, 1938.

THE WORM BURDEN OF SHEEP ON IMPROVED AND UNIMPROVED HILL PASTURE. Gwendolen Rees. Jour. Anim. Ecol., London, vol.11, no.2, pp.198-204, pl.4, Nov., 1942.

LUNGWORMS FROM OVIS POLI KARELINI BLYTH. N. G. Schulz. Proc. Moscow Zool. Park, vol.1, pp.235-242, 1940. (In Russian with a resume in English.)

OESTRIS OVIS IN THE ROCKY MOUNTAIN BIGHORN, OVIS CANADENSIS. John W. Scott. Jour. Mam., vol.23, no.3, pp.345-346, Aug.14, 1942.

PARASITIC WORMS OF THE URIAL (OVIS VIGNEI BLYTH) OF THE MOSCOU ZOOLOGICAL GARDENS. V. N. Trofimov. Proc. Moscow Zool. Park, vol.1, pp.232-234, 1940. (In Russian with a resume in English.)

(LIVER ROT IN SHEEP.) Die Leberegelseuche bei den Schafen. Alex Unterberger. Baltischen Wochenshrift, no.16, Jahrg., pp.6-14, 1866.

(ENDOGLOBULAR PARASITES OF SHEEP IN THE NORTHERN CAUCASUS.) Endoglobulare Parasiten der Schafe im Nordkaukasus. W. L. Yakimoff. Archiv. f. Protistenkunde, vol.65, pp.151-164, pl.1, Jan.31, 1929.

## Ovis--Ecology, Habits, Behavior

A STUDY OF THE CRYSTAL CREEK BIGHORN SHEEP RANGE. Warren J. Allred. Wyoming Game and Fish Dept. Bull., Cheyenne, no.1, pp.62-81, figs.20-26, July 1, 1942.

BIOLOGICAL SIGNIFICANCE OF MINERAL LICKS. (BIGHORN SHEEP.) O. A. Beath. Wyoming Game and Fish Bull., no.1, pp.88-94, figs.27-30, July 1, 1942.

UTILIZATION OF NORTHERN UTAH SUMMER RANGE PLANTS BY SHEEP. Clyde J. Cook, W. C. Cook, Lorin E. Harris. Jour. Forestry, 46 (6): 416-425, June, 1948.

SUMMER ACTIVITY OF MOUNTAIN SHEEP ON MT. WASHBURN, YELLOWSTONE NATIONAL PARK. William B. Davis. Jour. Mam., 19 (1): 88-94, Feb., 1938.

NOTES ON BIGHORN FOOD IN THE SONORAN ZONE. Arthur F. Halloran, Harry B. Crandell. Jour. Wildlife Mgt., Ithaca, vol.17, no.3, pp.318-320, July, 1953.

WATER HOLES WITH ROOTS. (MOUNTAIN SHEEP AND PRICKLY POPPY.) Flint Hindman. Fauna, Phila., vol.2, no.4, pp.71-74, illus., Dec., 1940.

THE ECOLOGY OF DOMESTIC ANIMALS ON THE EXAMPLE OF THE KARAKUL SHEEP. D. N. Kashkarov. Priroda, Leningrad, no.9, pp.47-67, figs.18, 1937. (In Russian.)

ECOLOGY OF THE MOUNTAIN SHEEP. Lester J. McCann. Amer. Midland Nat., 56 (2): 297-324, Oct., 1956.

AN ECOLOGICAL STUDY OF THE BIGHORN SHEEP IN ROCKY MOUNTAIN NATIONAL PARK, COLORADO. Fred M. Packard. MA thesis, Univ. Colo., 1942; Jour. Mam., 27 (1): 3-28, Feb., 1946.

SHEEP AT A SALT LICK. Jour. Bombay Nat. Hist. Soc., vol.43, no.4, pp.656-657, Apr., 1943.

### Ovis--Economic Importance, Breeding

ON SHEEP BREEDING. Peter Arrell Browne. U.S. Patent Office, Rept. pt.II, Agriculture, Wash., 1852, pp.75-96, 1851.

(TOWARD FRENCH PRODUCTION OF ASTRAKHAN.) Vers une production francaise de l'astrakan. C. P. d'Aigneaux. Revue d'Histoire Naturelle, Pt.1, A, Mammifères, Paris, vol.11, no.3, pp.81-97, Mar., 1930.

REARING BIGHORN LAMBS IN CAPTIVITY. O. V. Deming. Calif. Fish and Game, 41 (2): 131-143, illus., Apr., 1955.

RESEARCH AND THE MERINO SHEEP BREEDER. V. Bosman. S. African Jour. Sci., vol.28, pp.306-307, Nov., 1931.

ANGORA RAISING AS A BUSINESS. Charles W. Orr. Nat. Fur News, Denver, vol.17, no.7, p.6, Aug., 1945.

KARAKUL FUR SHEEP. J. R. Young. Amer. Fur Breeder, Duluth, vol.12, no. 3, pp.18-20, illus., Sept., 1939.

### Ovis--Eurasia

(GENETIC-GEOGRAPHIC STUDIES ON THE HISSAR SHEEP.) Gengeographische Studie am Hissarschaf. Joh. Wolfg. Amschler. Zeitschr. Zuchtungskunde, vol. 4, no.7, pp.336-341, figs.2, July, 1929.

(ON SCHOENBRUNN WILD SHEEP.) Ueber Schoenbrunner Wildschafe. Otto Antonius. Zool. Garten, N.F., Leipzig, vol.7, nos.4-6, pp.81-89, Aug., 1934.

ON THE BIGHORN OF KAMCHATKA. Yu V. Averin. Bull. Moscow Soc. Nat., Biol. Sect., 56 (1): 15-26, 1951. (Russian.)

THE SHEEP POPULATION OF HIRTA, ST. KILDA, 1955. J. Morton Boyd. Scottish Naturalist, 68: 11-13, 1956.

(THE SHEEP OF BUKHARA.) Le mouton de Boukhara. M. C. Bresson. La Terre et la Vie (Revue d'Hist. Nat.), vol.1, no.5, pp. 259-268, illus., June, 1931.

ON THE LARGE SHEEP OF THE THIAN SHAN, AND THE OTHER ASIATIC ARGALI. Basil Brooke. Proc. Zool. Soc. Lond., pp. 509-526, figs.7, 1875.

THE DISTRIBUTION OF THE GREAT PAMIR SHEEP (OVIS AMMON POLI BLYTH). G.V.B. Gillan. Jour. Bombay Nat. Hist. Soc., vol.37, no.1, pp.216-217, Apr.15, 1934.

(ON THE DISTRIBUTION HISTORY OF OVIS AMMMON IN EUROPE.) Zur Verbreitungsgeschichte von Ovis ammon in Europa. Wolf Herre, Klaus-Deitmar Kesper. Zool. Anzeiger, Leipzig, vol.151, nos.7-8, pp.204-209, illus., Oct., 1953.

NOTE ON THE WILD SHEEP OF THE KOPET-DAGH. R. Lydekker. Proc. Zool. Soc. Lond., vol.1, pt.1, pp.102-103, fig. 10, June, 1903.

THE WILD SHEEP OF THE UPPER ILI AND YANA VALLEYS. R. Lydekker. Proc. Zool. Soc. Lond., vol.12, pt.1, pp.80-85, pls.7-8, figs.14-15, Oct., 1902.

(THE SHEEP OF THE ISLAND OF SOAY (HEBRIDES).) Das Schaf der Insel Soay (Hebriden). Erna Mohr. Zool. Garten, Leipzig, n.F., vol.7, nos.10-12, pp.241-249, figs.13, Feb., 1935.

MARCO POLO'S SHEEP. COLLECTING OVIS POLI IN THE HIGH PAMIRS. AN ACCOUNT OF ONE PHASE OF THE MORDEN-CLARK ASIATIC EXPEDITION OF THE AMERICAN MUSEUM OF NATURAL HISTORY. W. J. Morden. Nat. Hist., vol.28, no.5, pp.486-500, 1928.

NOTES FROM AN EXPEDITION FOR OVIS POLI. W. J. Morden. Jour. Bombay Nat. Hist. Soc., vol.34, no.1, pp.142-148, pls. 1-2, Mar.1, 1930.

(A NEW ARGALI, OVIS JUBATA, FROM THE EASTERN PART OF MONGOLIA, NORTH OF PEKING.) Ueber ein neues Argali-Schaf, Ovis jubata, aus dem oestlichen Theile der Mongolei, im Norden von Peking. W. Peters. Monats. Kon. Akad. Wiss. Berlin, pp.177-188, pls.4, Mar.2, 1876.

THE PRESERVATION OF MOUFLON IN CYPRUS. Thomas Comyn Platt. Jour. Soc. Preservation Fauna of Empire, Hertford, n.s., pt.34, pp.58-62, Aug., 1938.

FOUR-HORNED SHEEP: IMMIGRANTS INTO EUROPE FROM THE EAST. W. P. Pycraft. Illus. London News, vol.189, no.5095, p. 1078, figs.4, Dec.12, 1936.

(ON THE EASTERN TIBET ARGALI (OVIS AMMON SUBSP.). Ueber das osttibetische Argalischaf (Ovis ammon subsp.). Ernst Schaefer. Zool. Garten, N.F., Leipzig, vol.8, nos.10-12, pp.253-258, illus., Sept., 1936.

EXTRACT FROM HIS JOURNAL RELATING TO THE BURRHAL SHEEP. T. Smith. Proc. Zool. Soc. Lond., pt.6, pp.79-80, 1838.

THE WILD SHEEP OF THE OLD WORLD AND THEIR DISTRIBUTION. Peter P. Sushkin. Jour. Mam., vol.6, no.3, pp.145-157, Aug., 1925.

(THE MOUFLON, OVIS MUSIMON SCHREBER 1782, IN SLOVAKIA.) Ueber den Mufflon, Ovis musimon Schreber, 1782, in der Slowakei. F. J. Turcek. Saeugetierk. Mitteil., Stuttgart, 4 (4): 167-171, Oct.1, 1956.

(THE MOUFFLON, OVIS MUSIMON PALLAS 1811, IN THE THURINGIAN FOREST.) Das Mufflon, Ovis musimon Pallas, 1811, in Thueringer Wald. Walter Uloth. Saeugetierk. Mitteil., Stuttgart, 3 (1): 35-36, Jan.1, 1955.

NOTES ON SOME SHEEP SHOT IN LADAKH. J.S.E. Walker. Jour. Bombay Nat. Hist. Soc., vol.28, pp.1123-1124, Dec.20, 1922.

ON A SUPPOSED NEW SPECIES OF WILD SHEEP FROM LADAK. Edwin Ward. Proc. Zool. Soc. Lond., pp.143-145, figs.2, 1874.

THE CYPRUS MOUFLON. Jour. Soc. Preservation Fauna of Empire, Hertford, n.s., pt.36, pp.36-39, May, 1939.

### Ovis--Fossils

(THE EXISTENCE OF A SHEEP IN THE PYRENEES DURING THE MAGDALENIAN PERIOD. PLATES OF THE SCHIST PERIOD.) L'existence d'un mouton dans les Pyrénées au Magdalénien. Les plaques de schiste. Jean Cazedessus. Assoc. Francais Advanc. Sci., 55 Sess. Nancy, pp.288-289, 1931.

A NEW PLEISTOCENE BIGHORN SHEEP FROM ARIZONA. Claude W. Hibbard, Barton A. Wright. Jour. Mam., 37 (1): 105-107, illus., Feb.28, 1956.

THE SUPPOSED OCCURRENCE OF AN ASIATIC GOAT-ANTELOPE IN THE PLEISTOCENE OF COLORADO. Gerrit S. Miller, Jr. Smithsonian Misc. Coll., vol.82, publ.3108, pp.1-2, pls.1-2, Dec. 22, 1930.

A PLEISTOCENE OVIS CANADENSIS FROM NEW MEXICO. J. Willis Stovall. Jour. Paleontol., Menasha, vol.20, no.3, pp. 259-260, figs.2, May, 1946.

### Ovis--Heads and Horns

HORNS IN SHEEP AS A TYPICAL SEX-LIMITED CHARACTER. T. R. Arkell, C. B. Davenport. Science, N.S., vol. 35, no.897, pp.375-377 (pp.1-3), (Mar.8, 1912) Mar.29, 1912.

ONE HORNED BIGHORN. Nedward M. Frost. Wyoming Wild Life, Cheyenne, vol.4, nos.5-6, pp.5, 15, May-June, 1939.

EXHIBITION OF FINE EXAMPLES OF THE HEADS AND HORNS OF OVIS AMMON. B. Leadbeater. Proc. Zool. Soc. Lond., pt.29, p.235, 1861.

SUPERNUMERARY HORNS OF CYPRUS SHEEP. R. J. Roe. Cyprus Agric. Jour., vol.27, pt.1, pp.28-29, figs.2, Mar., 1932.

EXHIBITION OF THE HORNS OF A MALE AND FEMALE ARKAR SHEEP (OVIS ARKAR). Philip L. Sclater. Proc. Zool. Soc. Lond., p.89, 1874.

NOTES ON HORNED MAMMALS, WITH SOME OBSERVATIONS UPON POLICERATE OR MULTIPLE-HORNED SHEEP. R. W. Shufeldt. Jour. Comp. Med. and Surg., vol.10, no.1, pp.30-36, Jan., 1888.

### Ovis--Heredity

THE CHROMOSOME COMPLEX OF DOMESTIC SHEEP (OVIS ARIES). R. O. Berry. Jour. Heredity, Wash., D.C., vol. 32, no.8, pp.261-267, figs.5-9, Aug., 1941.

GENETICS OF HORNS IN SHEEP. W. E. Castle. Jour. Heredity, Wash., D.C., vol.31, no.11, pp.486-487, Nov., 1940.

THE GENETICS OF MULTI-NIPPLED SHEEP, AN ANALYSIS OF THE SHEEP-BREEDING EXPERIMENTS OF DR. AND MRS. ALEXANDER GRAHAM BELL AT BEINN BHREAGH, N.S. W. E. Castle. Jour. Heredity, vol.15, pp.75-84, Feb., 1924.

AN ACEPHALIC LAMB MONSTER IN SHEEP AND ITS RELATION TO SINGLE-EGG TWINNING IN SHEEP. Leon J. Cole, W. A. Craft. Jour. Heredity, Wash., vol. 36, no.1, pp.29-32, figs.19-20, Jan., 1945.

MENDELIAN INHERITANCE IN NEW ZEALAND ROMNEY SHEEP. F. W. Ory, Stewart Fraser, G. M. Wright. Nature, London, vol.160, no.4071, p.646, Nov.8, 1947.

CARACUL A DOMINANT MUTATION. L. C. Dunn. Jour. Heredity, Wash., D.C., vol.28, no.10, p.334, table, Oct., 1937.

QUINTUBLE LAMBS OF WOOLLESS DOMESTIC SHEEP. David H. Johnson. Jour. Heredity, Wash., vol.35, no.8, pp. 251-253, figs.13-14, Aug., 1944.

THE ANCON OR OTTER SHEEP. Walter Landauer, Tso Kan Chang. Jour. Heredity, Balto., vol.40, no.4, pp.105-112, illus., Apr., 1949.

STUDIES ON THE GENETICS OF KHARAKHUL SHEEP. II. THE COMPARATIVE VALUE OF DIFFERENT SIRES AS FUR PRODUCERS. T. Marchlewski. Bull. Internat. Acad. Polonaise Sci. and Lett., Cl. Sci. Math. et Nat., Ser.B, Sci. Nat. (II) (Zool.), Cracovie, nos.8-10, pp.271-281, pl.17, Oct.-Dec., 1929.

THE MULTINIPPLE TRAIT IN SHEEP. Ralph W. Phillips, Ralph G. Schott, Damon A. Spencer. Jour. Heredity, Wash., vol.37, no.1, pp.19-26, figs.8-11, Jan., 1946.

SEVERAL CASES OF SO-CALLED BENT-LEG IN SHEEP. A. D. Thomas. S. Afr. Jour. Sci., vol.25, pp.278-281, June-July, 1928.

(THE ANCON SHEEP.) Das Anconschaf. Chr. Weiedt. Zeitschr. fuer Induktive Abstammungs-und Vererbungslehre, vol. 39, pp.281-286, figs.6, 1925.

ALMOST IDENTICAL TWINS. (SIAMESE TWIN LAMBS.) Jour. Heredity, Wash., vol.37, no.6, p.182, illus., June, 1946.

### Ovis--Hunting, Trapping

THE HORNS. (BIGHORNS.) H. E. Anthony.

The Sportsman, Concord, N.H., vol.13, no.3, pp.33, 62, illus., Mar., 1933.

NINE SHEEP ON THE SUMMIT. Harry D. Barnhart. Alaska Sportsman, Ketchikan, vol.10, no.7, pp.12-13, 31-32, illus., July, 1944.

MOUNTAIN SHEEP TAKEN CAPTIVE. O. P. Brownlow. California Fish and Game, vol.12, pp.106-107, Apr., 1926.

SHOULD WE CRY WOLF? (DALL SHEEP.) Victor H. Cahalane. Field and Stream, New York, vol.51, no.2, pp.37, 103-107, illus., June, 1946.

MOUFLON IN SARDINIA. Winthrop Chanler. Hunting and Conservation, the book of the Boone and Crockett Club, pp.1-28 pl.1, New Haven: Yale Univ. Press, 1925.

RAMS ARE RUGGED. (BIGHORN HUNT.) Frank Gregg. Colo. Cons., 3 (5): 4-8, illus., Sept.-Oct., 1954.

THE TRAPPING AND TRANSPLANTING OF ROCKY MOUNTAIN BIGHORN SHEEP IN COLORADO. Gilbert N. Hunter, Theodor R. Swen, George W. Jones. Trans. 11th North Amer. Wildlife Conf., Wash., pp. 364-373, figs.4, 1946.

DALL'S WHITE SHEEP. Hamilton M. Laing. Game and Gun and Angler's Monthly, vol.15, no.155, pp.461-462, illus., Aug., 1938.

ELUSIVE OVIS DALLI. Hamilton M. Laing. Game and Gun and Angler's Monthly, vol. 15, no.156, pp.526-527, illus., Sept., 1938.

LO, THE BIGHORN. Chuck Mabery. Ariz. Wildl. Sportsman, 24 (3): 24-35, illus., Mar., 1953.

WHEN THE QUARRY IS WILD SHEEP. H. C. Maydon. Field, London, vol.85, no. 4626, pp.243-245, illus., Aug.23, 1941.

MY FIRST MOUNTAIN SHEEP. Jack O'Connor. Field and Stream, New York, vol.50, no.7, pp.32, 98-100, illus., Nov., 1945.

BIGHORN SHEEP HUNT. Fred Patton. New Mex. Mag., 32 (3): 26-27, 48, illus., Mar., 1954.

STALKING THE WILY ARROWI SHEEP. (OVIS LERVIA.) Alfred Pease. Field, London, vol.158, no.4100, p.139, July 25, 1931.

VOLCANO SHEEP. G. D. Pope. Hunting Trails on Three Continents, New York, Chap.9, pp.198-228, 1933.

TRAPPING BIGHORN SHEEP IN WYOMING. Euvern F. Putnam. Wyoming Wildlife, Cheyenne, vol.14, no.8, pp.12-15, illus., Sept., 1950.

SHEEP HUNTING IN MEXICO. E. N. Requa. Forest and Stream, vol.89, pp. 204, 205, 252, May, 1919.

HUNTING, A KEY TO RESEARCH STUDIES OF ARIZONA BIGHORN. John P. Russo. Proc. 34th Ann. Conf. Western Assn. State Game and Fish Comm., pp.195-200, May 1954 (1955).

A WYOMING SHEEP HUNT. Cyrus Thompson. Forest and Stream, vol.89, pp.420, 439, 440, Aug., 1919.

HUNTING THE MOUNTAIN SHEEP. Carrington Weems. (In:) North American Big Game. A book of the Boone and Crockett Club, compiled by the Committee on Records of North American Big Game. Charles Scribners Sons, New York, pp. 291-317, 1939.

Ovis--Hybridization

HYBRIDIZATION BETWEEN WILD MOUNTAIN SHEEP (OVIS POLII KARELINI SEV.) AND FINE-WOOLED SHEEP AND THE PROBLEM OF CREATING A DOMESTIC BREED OF MOUNTAIN SHEEP. N. S. Butarin. Bull. Acad. Sci. URSS, Cl. Sci. Mat. et Nat., ser. Biol., Moscow, no.4, pp.853-862, figs.3, tables 5, 1938. (In Russian, with English summary.)

(THE SUITABILITY OF INDIVIDUAL SHEEP RACES FOR KARAKUL CROSSING.) Die Eignung einzelner Schafrassen zur Karakul-Kreuzung. G. Dennler. Pelztierzucht verb. mit Kleintierzucht, vol.8, no. 4, pp.68-70, fig.1, Apr.20, 1932.

NOTE ON THE BREEDING TOGETHER OF THE MOUFFLON AND DOMESTIC SHEEP. A. P. Palmedo. Proc. Comm. Sci. and Corres. Zool. Soc. Lond., pt.2, p.9, 1832.

BIGHORN CROSS. Richard E. Pillmore, Richard D. Teague. Colo. Cons., 4 (1): 22-26, illus., Jan.-Feb., 1955.

HYBRIDIZATION OF BIGHORN AND DOMESTIC SHEEP. Alvert Van S. Pulling. Jour. Wildlife Mgt., Menasha, vol.9, no.1, pp.82-83, Jan., 1945.

Ovis--Methods, Techniques

HOW TO MAKE SKELETONS. VIII. THE MOUNTING OF A SHEEP SKELETON (CONCLUSION). William A. R. Kruse. Ward's Nat. Sci. Bull., Rochester, vol.20, no.1, pp.9-10, figs.1-6, Sept., 1946.

THE FECAL PELLET GROUP DEPOSITION RATE OF DOMESTIC SHEEP. William M. Longhurst. Jour. Wildlife Mgt., Ithaca, vol.18, no.3, pp.418-419, July, 1954.

Ovis--New Zealand

(DATA ON THE CORRIEDALE SHEEP OF NEW ZEALAND.) Einiges ueber die Corriedale-Schafe Neu Seelands. J. P. Lotsy. Genetica, vol.7, pp.325-353, 1925.

(DATA ON THE CORRIEDALE SHEEP OF NEW ZEALAND.) Einiges ueber die Corriedale-Schafe Neu Seelands. J.P. Lotsy. (Conclusion.) Genetica, vol.7, pp.475-486, 1926.

Ovis--North America

HISTORICAL AND NOMENCLATURAL NOTES ON NORTH AMERICAN SHEEP. J. A. Allen. Bull. Amer. Mus. Nat. Hist., vol.31, pp.1-29, figs.1-4, Mar.4, 1912.

ECOLOGY AND MANAGEMENT OF NELSON'S BIGHORN ON THE NEVADA MOUNTAIN RANGES. Joseph C. Allen. Fourth North Amer. Wildlife Conf. Trans., Balto., pp.253-256, 1939.

MOUNTAIN SHEEP--ARE COMING BACK. George E. Barclay. Ariz. Wildl.-Sportsman, 8 (10): 10-11, 22-23, Oct., 1947.

DISAPPEARANCE OF BIGHORNS A MYSTERY. Elliott S. Barker. New Mexico Mag., Santa Fe, vol.17, no.7, pp.27-28, July, 1939.

MOUNTAIN SHEEP FOUND IN LYELL GLACIER. M. E. Beatty. Yosemite Nature Notes, vol.12, no.12, pp.110-112, fig.1, Dec., 1933.

MOUNTAIN SHEEP FOUND MUMMIFIED IN YOSEMITE GLACIER. M. E. Beatty. California Fish and Game, vol.20, no.1, pp.92-93, Jan., 1934.

A BIGHORN SHEEP OF MAMMOTH TERRACES. Lowell Biddulph. Yellowstone Nat. Notes, Yellowstone Park, vol.18, nos.9-10, p.54, Sept.-Oct., 1941.

SOME RECORDS OF MOUNTAIN SHEEP. Arthur H. Blake. Sierra Club Bull., San Francisco, vol.27, no.4, pp.120-121, Aug., 1942.

THE ROCKY MOUNTAIN SHEEP IN BRITISH COLUMBIA. Allan Brooks. Canadian Field-Nat., vol.37, pp.23-25, map, Feb., 1923.

MOUNTAIN SHEEP SKULL FOUND ON PARSON'S PEAK. H. C. Bryant. Yosemite Nature Notes, vol.8, p.100, Oct., 1929.

FOREST ODDITIES--THE BIGHORNS OF OURAY. Arthur H. Carhart. Amer. Forestry, vol.27, pp.37-38, figs.3, Jan., 1921.

A FIGHT FOR SURVIVAL. (STATUS OF MOUNTAIN SHEEP IN TEXAS.) Burch Carson, Jr. Texas Game and Fish, 4 (1): 20-21, Dec., 1945.

MOUNTAIN SHEEP OF THE SIERRA. Norman Clyde. Westways, Los Angeles, vol.29, no.6, pp.32-33, fig.1, June, 1937.

A MOUNTAIN SHEEP RECORD FOR NEBRASKA. Harold J. Cook. Jour. Mam., vol.12, no.2, pp.170-171, May, 1931.

ROCKY MOUNTAIN BIGHORN SHEEP OF MONTANA. Faye M. Couey. Bull. Montana Fish and Game Comm., Helena, no.2, pp.90, illus., 1950.

DISTRIBUTION AND VARIATION IN THE NATIVE SHEEP OF NORTH AMERICA. Ian McT. Cowan. Amer. Midland Nat., Notre Dame, vol.24, no.3, pp.505-580, pls.4, map 1, Nov., 1940.

THE BIGHORN SHEEP OF TEXAS. William B. Davis, Walter P. Taylor. Jour. Mam., vol.20, no.4, pp.440-455, figs.3, Nov.14, 1939.

THE TEXAS BIGHORN. William B. Davis, Walter P. Taylor. Texas A. and M. Coll., Div. Wildl. Res., Prog. Rep.560, pp.2, 1940.

KARAKUL FUR SHEEP IN AMERICA. F.E. Dawley. Amer. Fur Breeder, vol.2, no.11, pp.22-24, vol.2, no.12, p.42, May-June, 1930.

THE STATUS OF THE SIERRA BIGHORN SHEEP. Joseph S. Dixon. Proc. N. A. Wildl. Conf., pp.641-643, 1936.

A SURVEY OF DESERT BIGHORN IN DEATH VALLEY NATIONAL MONUMENT, SUMMER 1938. Joseph S. Dixon, Lowell Sumner. Calif. Fish and Game, 25 (2): 72-95, Apr., 1939.

THE ROCKY MOUNTAIN BIGHORN. Stuart C. Downing. Canadian Nature, Toronto, vol.12, no.4, p.140, illus., Sept.-Oct., 1950.

A NEW MOUNTAIN SHEEP FROM LOWER CALIFORNIA. (OVIS CANADENSIS WEEMSI.) E. A. Goldman. Proc. Biol. Soc. Wash., vol.50, pp.29-32, Apr.2, 1937.

SO! YOU BELIEVE IT, EH? (MOUNTAIN SHEEP.) Phil Goodrum. Texas Game and Fish, Austin, vol.2, no.6, p.8, May, 1944.

THE BIGHORN SHEEP OF BANFF NATIONAL PARK. H. U. Green. Can. Dept. Resources and Development, Natl. Parks and Historic Sites Serv., pp.53, 1949.

THE BIGHORN OF THE SIERRA NEVADA. Joseph Grinnell. Univ. Cal. Publ. Zool., vol.10, no.5, pp.143-153, fig.4, May 9, 1912.

HISTORY AND PRESENT STATUS OF BIGHORN IN SOUTH-CENTRAL NEW MEXICO. Arthur F. Halloran. Jour. Mam., 25 (4): 364-367, Nov., 1944.

BIGHORNS ON THE BORDER. Arthur F. Halloran. Audubon Mag., 49 (6): 332-337, Nov.-Dec., 1947.

WHY NOT BRING BACK THE BIG HORN? Robert P. Hays. Yosemite Nature Notes, vol.8, p.9, Jan., 1929.

BAA, BAA BLACK SHEEP! THAT PERSIAN MAY BE FROM CALIFORNIA. Henrietta Holland. Frontiers, Lancaster, vol.11, no. 2, pp.47-48, illus., Dec., 1946.

A WYOMING BIGHORN-SHEEP STUDY. Ralph F. Honess, Nedward M. Frost. Wyo. Game and Fish Dept., Bull.1, pp. 126, 1942.

NOTES ON THE MOUNTAIN SHEEP OF NORTH AMERICA, WITH A DESCRIPTION OF A NEW SPECIES. William T. Hornaday. 5th Ann. Rep. New York Zool. Soc., pp.77-122, map, illus., June 1, 1901.

THE MOUNTAIN SHEEP. Hartley H. T. Jackson. (In:) North American Big Game. A book of the Boone and Crockett Club, compiled by the Committee on Records of North American Big Game. Charles Scribners Sons, New York, pp.285-290, 1939.

THE SIERRA NEVADA BIGHORN IN YOSEMITE. Fred L. Jones. Yosemite Nat. Notes, vol.29, no.2, p.13, Feb., 1950.

A SURVEY OF THE SIERRA NEVADA BIGHORN. Fred L. Jones. Sierra Club Bull., 35 (6): 29-76, June, 1950.

A SURVEY OF THE SIERRA NEVADA MOUNTAIN SHEEP. Fred L. Jones. MA thesis, Univ. Calif., 1949.

ANOTHER RECORD OF A MOUNTAIN SHEEP (OVIS CANADENSIS) FROM NEBRASKA. J. Knox Jones, Jr. Nat. Hist. Misc., Chicago Acad. Sci., no.91, p.1, Nov.16, 1951.

BIG HORN SHEEP OF YUMA COUNTY. Edward Kaughphy. Arizona Wildlife and Sportsman, Tucson, vol.7, no.1, pp.4, 8, Jan., 1946.

ROCKY MOUNTAIN SHEEP TRANSFERRED FROM BANFF TO SPENCE'S BRIDGE, B.C. Hoyes Lloyd. Canadian Field Nat., vol.41, no.6, p.140, Sept., 1927.

STATUS OF THE DESERT BIGHORN IN GRAND CANYON NATIONAL PARK. Edwin D. McKee. Grand Canyon Nature Notes, vol.9, no.4, pp.294-300, July, 1934.

DESERT MOUNTAIN SHEEP OF THE INYO MOUNTAINS. D. D. McLean. California Fish and Game, vol.16, no.1, pp.79-82, figs.2, Jan., 1930.

FORMER RANGE OF MOUNTAIN SHEEP IN NORTHERN CALIFORNIA. C. Hart Merriam. Jour. Mam., vol.2, no.4, p. 239, Nov., 1921.

OVIS NELSONI, A NEW MOUNTAIN SHEEP FROM THE DESERT REGION OF SOUTHERN CALIFORNIA. C. Hart Merriam. Proc. Biol. Soc., Wash., vol.11, pp.217-218, July 15, 1897.

MOUNTAIN SHEEP IN YOSEMITE. Richard Michaelis. Yosemite Nature Notes, vol.12, no.2, p.13, Feb., 1933.

A PRELIMINARY STUDY OF THE BIGHORN OF YELLOWSTONE NATIONAL PARK. Harlow B. Mills. Jour. Mam., 18 (2): 205-212, May, 1937.

BATTLE FOR THE BIGHORN. Clifford A. Moser. Colo. Cons., 2 (4): 15-19, illus., July-Aug., 1953.

THE BIGHORN IN COLORADO. Clifford A. Moser. Colorado Outdoors Mag., 5 (5): 18-22, illus., Sept.-Oct., 1956.

MOUNTAIN SHEEP IN NORTH AMERICA. E. W. Nelson. The Sportsman, Concord, N. H., vol.13, no.3, pp.31-33, illus., table, Mar., 1933.

A NEW GEOGRAPHICAL RACE OF THE MOUNTAIN SHEEP (OVIS MONTANA DALLI VAR. NOV.) FROM ALASKA. E. W. Nelson. Proc. U.S. Nat. Mus., pp. 12-13, Dec.22, 1883.

DESERT BIGHORN SHEEP. A. A. Nichol. Ariz. Wildl. Mag., 7 (7): 9, 16, and 7 (8): 3, 12, Nov.-Dec., 1937, Jan.-Feb., 1938.

REINTRODUCTION OF RECENTLY EXTERMINATED SPECIES OF FAUNA AT MESA VERDE. (MOUNTAIN SHEEP, WILD TURKEY.) Jesse L. Nusbaum. Colorado Conservation Comments, Denver, vol.8, no.1, p.1, Mar.15, 1945.

THE MOUNTAIN SHEEP OF CALIFORNIA. E. H. Ober. California Fish and Game, vol.17, no.1, pp.27-39, figs.6, Jan., 1931.

DESERT REVIVAL. THE BIGHORNS ARE BACK! Jack O'Connor. Outdoor Life, 110 (3): 30-31, 92-94, illus., Sept., 1952.

SHEEP OF SHOVEL PASS. Arthur Newton Pack. Nature Mag., vol.17, no.6, pp.363-368, figs.10, June, 1931.

REPORT ON THE BIGHORN. Richard E. Pillmore. Colo. Cons., 3 (1): 19-21, illus., Jan.-Feb., 1954.

NOTES ON THE HABITAT OF THE DESERT BIGHORN IN THE SAN GABRIEL MOUNTAINS OF CALIFORNIA. Cyril S. Robinson, Fred P. Cronemiller. California Fish and Game, vol.40, no.3, pp.267-271, July, 1954.

WHAT ABOUT BIGHORN? John P. Russo. Ariz. Wildl. Sportsman, 23 (12): 8-12, illus., Dec., 1952.

DISTRIBUTION AND ABUNDANCE OF DALL SHEEP IN ALASKA. Robert F. Scott. Science in Alaska, Proc. Second Alaskan Science Conf., 1951, pp.340-343, 1953.

THE BIGHORN SHEEP IN IDAHO / ITS STATUS, LIFE HISTORY, AND MANAGEMENT. Dwight R. Smith. Idaho Dept. Fish and Game, Wildl. Bull. no.1, pp.1-154, illus., 1954.

THE LIFE HISTORY AND ECOLOGY OF THE BIG HORN SHEEP IN IDAHO. Dwight R. Smith. MS thesis, U. Idaho, pp.113, 1951.

IDAHO BIGHORN SHEEP STUDIED. Dwight R. Smith. Idaho Wildl. Rev., 5 (5): 4-7, 10, illus., Mar.-Apr., 1953.

BIGHORNS ON THE MARCH. Clifford Spencer. Amer. Forests, 48 (6): 250-253, 285, June, 1942.

NOTES ON THE LIFE HISTORY OF ROCKY MOUNTAIN BIGHORN SHEEP IN THE TARRYALL MOUNTAINS OF COLORADO. Clifford Spencer. Jour. Mam., 24 (1): 1-11, Feb., 1943.

A DESERT INTERLUDE. (NOTES ON MOUNTAIN SHEEP.) Ken Stott, Jr. San Diego Zoonooz, vol.16, no.5, pp.5-6, May, 1943.

AN AIR CENSUS OF DALL SHEEP IN MOUNT MCKINLEY NATIONAL PARK. Lowell Sumner. Jour. Wildlife Mgt., Menasha, vol.12, no.3, pp.302-304, pl.9, July, 1948.

AMERICA'S SHEEP TRAILS, HISTORY, PERSONALITIES. Edward Norris Wentworth. Iowa State College Press, Ames, Iowa, pp.xxii, 667, figs.138, 1948.

BIGHORN. Claude E. White, Jr. Colo. Cons., 1 (2): 1-4, illus., Mar.-Apr., 1952.

BIG HORN SHEEP. Arizona Wildlife and Sportsman, Phoenix, vol.1, no.1, p.4, Jan., 1939.

BIGHORNS HAVE ALMOST VANISHED IN GUADALUPES. New Mexico Mag., Albuquerque, vol.18, no.3, p.31, Mar., 1940.

THE BIGHORNS OF THE ROCKIES. National Nature News, Wash., D.C., vol.2, no.22, pp.3, 7, May 30, 1938.

THE MOUNTAIN SHEEP SURVEY. Wyoming Wild Life, Cheyenne, vol.6, no.3, illus., Mar., 1941.

THE ROCKY MOUNTAIN BIGHORN IN COLORADO. Colorado Conserv. Comments, Denver, vol.7, no.1, pp.16-17, Mar.15, 1944.

THE ROCKY MOUNTAIN BIGHORN OVIS CANADENSIS. Wyoming Wild Life, Cheyenne, vol.4, nos.5-6, pp.6, 15, May-June, 1939.

## Ovis--Pelage, Coloration

THE ARRANGEMENT OF FIBRE FOLLICLES IN SOME ANIMALS, WITH SPECIAL REFERENCE TO THE OVIDAE. BEING SELECTED AND ILLUSTRATED NOTES MADE BY THE LATE DR. J. E. DUERDEN, EMERITUS PROFESSOR OF RHODES UNIVERSITY, GRAHAMSTOWN; HONORARY WORKER AT THE WOOL INDUSTRIES RESEARCH ASSOCIATION, LEEDS, 1932-1937. COMPILED BY DR. A. B. WILDMAN, WOOL INDUSTRIES RESEARCH ASSOCIATION. F. A. E. Crew. Trans. Roy. Soc. Edinburgh, vol.59, pt.3, sess.1938-39, pp.763-771, figs.5, pls.4, July 11, 1939.

A DOWN PELAGE IN THE OVIDAE. J. E. Duerden. Nature, London, vol.130, no. 3289, pp.736-737, fig.1, Nov.12, 1932.

A BIOMETRICAL ANALYSIS OF MERINO WOOL FIBRES. J. E. Duerden, V. Bosman. S. African Jour. Sci., vol.22, pp.248-262, figs.4, Nov., 1925.

CURL CHARACTERISTICS OF KARAKUL PELTS. Thora M. Plitt Hardy. Nat. Fur News, Denver, vol.20, no.6, pp.13, 28-29, illus., July, 1948.

A STUDY OF THE FLEECE OF THE BIGHORN. Alexander Johnston, Robert H. Burns. Wyoming Game and Fish Dept. Bull., no.1, pp.21-25, figs.8-10, July 1, 1942.

CORRELATION BETWEEN THE SKIN TEXTURE OF KARAKUL LAMBS OF ROBUST CONSTITUTION AND VARIOUS TYPES OF THE KARAKUL CURL. N. B. Popova. Comptes Rendus (Doklady) Acad. Sci. URSS, Moscow, n.s., vol.49, no.1, pp.55-57, Oct.10, 1945.

(RACE ANALYTICAL INVESTIGATIONS OF SHEEP, WITH SPECIAL CONSIDERATION OF SKIN AND HAIR.) Rassenanalytische Untersuchungen an Schafen unter besonderer Beruecksichtigung von Haut und Haar. W. Spoettel, E. Taenzer. Archiv. f. Nat., Abt. A, vol.89, Heft 6, pp.1-242, pls.12, July, 1923.

HOW BLOWFLY MAGGOTS AFFECT THE SKIN AND WOOL OF SHEEP. A.B.M. Whitnall. S. African Jour. Sci., vol.28, pp.313-314, Nov., 1931.

COAT AND FIBRE DEVELOPMENT IN SOME BRITISH SHEEP. A. B. Wildman. Proc. Zool. Soc. Lond., pt.2, pp.257-285, figs.1-9, July, 1932.

NON-SPECIFICITY OF THE TRIO FOLLICLES IN THE MERINO. A. B. Wildman. Nature, London, vol.140, no.3551, pp.891-892, Nov.20, 1937.

BIBLIOGRAPHY ON THE BIOLOGY OF THE FLEECE. Imperial Bureau of Animal Genetics, Edinburgh, 1931.

## Ovis--Physiology

(ON THE BLOOD GROUP CHARACTERISTICS OF SHEEP.) Ueber die Blutgruppeneigenschaften der Schafe. Torben Andersen. Rassenphysiol., Muenchen, vol.7, no.4, pp.167-170.

ADAPTATION OF GUISSAR SHEEP TO ALTITUDE. Z. I. Barbasheva, A. G. Ginezinsky. Bull. Acad. Sci. URSS, Moscow, ser.biol., 1942, no.5, pp.295-302, figs.3, 1942. (In Russian, with English summary.)

THE DEVELOPMENT OF MOVEMENT IN THE FOETUS OF THE SHEEP. Joseph Barcroft, D. H. Barron. (Notice of lecture before) Roy. Soc. London, 1 p., Feb.10, 1938.

THE BLOOD PRESSURE IN THE UMBILICAL VEIN OF THE FOETAL SHEEP. Joseph Barcroft, Donald H. Barron, Peter Forsham. Science, Lancaster, n.s., vol.96, no.2486, pp.179-180, Aug.21, 1942.

ANTIHORMONE PROPERTIES OF UREA-DENATURED SHEEP GONADOTROPIN. Fritz Bischoff. Amer. Jour. Physiol., Balto., vol.153, no.1, pp.21-26, Apr.1, 1948.

COMPARATIVE ANALYSIS OF CONSTITUTION OF DOMESTIC AND WILD SHEEP. S. N. Bogolyubsky. Comptes Rendus (Doklady) Acad. Sci. URSS, Moscow, n.s., vol.25, no.3, pp.253-257, table 1, 1939.

ON INTEGRATION OF THE TOTAL OXYGEN CONSUMPTION OF THE SHEEP FOETUS FROM THAT OF THE TISSUES. A. Carlyle. Jour. Physiol., London, vol. 107, no.3, pp.355-364, June 25, 1948.

NORMAL RECTAL TEMPERATURES OF SHEEP. A. B. Clawson. Amer. Jour. Physiol., vol.85, pp.251-270, June, 1928.

SECRETION BY THE PAROTID GLAND OF THE SHEEP: THE RELATIONSHIP BETWEEN SALIVARY FLOW AND COMPOSITION. D. A. Coats, R. D. Wright. Jour. Physiol., Cambridge, England, 135 (3): 611-622, Mar., 1957.

A COMPARISON BETWEEN THE COLORIMETRIC AND ELECTROMETRIC METHODS OF DETERMINING THE HYDROGEN ION CONCENTRATION OF BLOOD. (EXPERIMENTS ON SHEEP'S BLOOD.) Ruth Conway-Verney, L. E. Bayliss. Jour. Physiol., vol.58, no.1, pp.101-107, 1923.

SWEATING IN SHEEP. J. B. Cragg, Lewis Davies. Nature, London, vol.159, no.4027, pp.34-35, Jan.4, 1947.

ALTERATION OF THE ESTRUAL CYCLE IN SHEEP BY USE OF PROGESTERONE AND ITS EFFECT UPON SUBSEQUENT OVULATION AND FERTILITY. R. H. Dutt, L. E. Casida. Endocrinology, Boston, vol.43, no.4, pp.208-217, Oct., 1948.

FUNCTIONS OF THE OMASUM IN THE STOMACH OF THE SHEEP. F. V. Gray, A. F. Pilgrim, R. A. Weller. Jour. Exper. Biol., Cambridge, England, vol. 31, no.1, pp.49-55, Mar., 1954.

THE RELATIVE RATES OF FORMATION OF ACETIC, PROPRIONIC AND BUTYRIC ACID IN THE RUMEN OF SHEEP. K. Halse, W. Velle. Acta Physiologica Scandinavica, Stockholm, 37 (4): 380-390, Nov., 1956.

A FURTHER NOTE ON DOMSIEKTE, OR FATTY INFILTRATION OF THE LIVER IN PREGNANT EWES. G. de Kock. S. Afri. Jour. Sci., vol.25, pp.274-277, June-July, 1928.

THE COMPOSITION OF THE BLOOD OF SHEEP IN CONNECTION WITH THEIR PRODUCTIVITY. H. F. Kushner. Bull. Acad. Sci. URSS, Cl. Sci. math. et nat., ser. Biol., no.2, pp.469-480, 1937. (English resume, pp.480-483.)

REACTIONS OF THE SHEEP TO HOT ATMOSPHERES. H. K. Douglas Lee, Kathleen Robinson. Proc. Roy. Soc. Queensland, Brisbane, vol.53, no.12, pp.189-200, figs.5, Feb.23, 1942.

DIFFERENCE IN BLOOD VALUE OF KARAKUL SHEEP IN CORRELATION WITH THEIR ORGANIC CONSTITUTION. E. P. Panfilova. Comptes Rendus (Doklady) Acad. Sci. URSS, Moscow, n.s., vol.23, no.6, pp.569-572, tables 4, 1939.

RATE OF SPERM TRAVEL AND TIME OF OVULATION IN SHEEP. Ralph George Schott, Ralph Wesley Phillips. Anat. Record, Phila., vol.79, no.4, pp.531-540, fig.1, Apr.25, 1941.

THE EFFECT OF THYROID DEFICIENCY UPON BODILY GROWTH AND SKELETAL MATURATION IN THE SHEEP. T. Wingate Todd, Ralph E. Wharton, Arthur W. Todd. Amer. Jour. Anat., Phila., vol.63, no.1, pp.37-78, figs.3, charts 2, graphs 2, tables 13, July 15, 1938.

THE EFFECT OF THYROID DEFICIENCY UPON SKULL GROWTH IN THE SHEEP. Thomas Wingate Todd, Ralph E. Wharton. Amer. Jour. Anat., Phila., vol.55, no.1, pp.97-116, figs.11, July 15, 1934.

(RESISTANCE OF ANDEAN SHEEP TO SNAKE VENOM.) Resistance de la moufette andine au venin de serpent. J. Vellard. Travaux de l'Institut Francais d'Etudes Andines, Lima, 2: 19-38, 1950.

## Ovis--Predators

KEA AND SHEEP. Johannes Andersen. Jour. Soc. Preservation Fauna in Empire, Hertford, n.s., pt.34, pp.83-87, Aug., 1938.

GOLDEN EAGLE VS. BIGHORN SHEEP. Faye Couey. Montana Wildlife Bull., Helena, vol.1, no.1, pp.2-3, illus., Jan., 1944.

MOUNTAIN LION PREYS ON BIGHORN. F. P. Cronemiller. Jour. Mam., vol. 29, no.1, p.68, Feb.13, 1948.

GOLDEN EAGLE KILLS BIGHORN LAMB. Cecil A. Kennedy. Jour. Mam., 29 (1): 68-69, Feb., 1948.

THE TRUTH ABOUT KEA. NEW ZEALAND'S FAMOUS PARROT IS NOT THE SHEEP-KILLER IT IS CLAIMED. Sydney Porter. Nature Mag., Wash., D.C., vol.32, no.5, pp.275-277, May, 1940.

## Ovis--Reproductive Biology

GESTATION PERIOD OF BIGHORN SHEEP, OVIS CANADENSIS. Nedward M. Frost. Jour. Mam., vol.23, no.2, pp.215-216, May 14, 1942.

STUDIES IN FERTILITY IN SHEEP. 2. SEMINAL CHANGES AFFECTING FERTILITY IN RAMS. R. M. C. Gunn, R. N. Sanders, W. Granger. Commonwealth of Australia, Council for Scientific and Industrial Research, Melbourne, Bull. no.148, pp.140, figs.39, pls.15, 1942.

FAILING TO REPRODUCE. (DIET IN RELATION TO REPRODUCTION IN KARAKUL EWES.) Carl Jahn. Amer. Fur Breeder, Duluth, vol.15, no.3, pp.20, 22, Sept., 1942.

METEROLOGICAL FACTORS AFFECTING FERTILITY IN SHEEP. J. E. Nichols. Zeitschr. f. induktive Abstammungs- und Verebungslehre, vol.43, pp.313-329, 1927.

NON-BREEDING IN BIGHORN SHEEP. Albert Van S. Pulling. Jour. Wildl. Mgt., 9 (2): 155-156, Apr., 1945.

(AMOROUS MOUFLON BUCKS.) Verliebte Muffonboecke. W. Streitmueller. Zeitschr. f. Saeugetierkunde, Berlin, vol.13, no.2, p.256, 1939.

## Ovis--Taxonomy

A NEW NAME FOR THE WILD SHEEP OF NORTHEASTERN CHINA. N. Hollister. Proc. Biol. Soc. Wash., vol.32, p.46, Apr.11, 1919.

ON A NEW FOSSIL RACE OF BIGHORN SHEEP FROM SHANTUNG, CHINA. (OVIS AMMON SHANTUNGENSIS.) Hikoshichiro Matsumoto. Sci. Rep. Tohoku Imp. Univ., ser.2 (Geol.), vol.10, pp.39-42, illus., 1926.

DATES FOR OVIS CANADENSIS, OVIS CERVINA, AND OVIS MONTANA. Wilfred H. Osgood. Proc. Biol. Soc. Wash., vol. 27, pp.1-3, Feb.2, 1914.

THE NAME OF THE ROCKY MOUNTAIN SHEEP. Wilfred H. Osgood. Proc. Biol. Soc. Wash., vol.26, pp.57-61, Mar.22, 1913.

## Ovis--Zoo and Museum Collections

MOUNTAIN SHEEP FROM THE STATE OF WASHINGTON IN THE COLLECTION OF THE UNIVERSITY OF KANSAS. Walter W. Dalquest, Donald F. Hoffmeister. Trans. Kansas Acad. Sci., Topeka, vol.51, no.2, pp.224-234, 1948.

NOTE ON THE PUNJAB SHEEP LIVING IN THE SOCIETY'S GARDEN. Philip L. Sclater. Proc. Zool. Soc. Lond., pt.28, pp.126-130, 1860.

GEOGRAPHICAL

AEGEAN SEA

(FAUNAL RESEARCH IN THE ITALIAN ISLANDS OF THE AEGEAN SEA. MAMMALS.) Ricerche faunistiche nelle isole Italiane dell'egeo. Mammiferi. Oscar de Beaux. Arch.Zool.Italiano, vol.13, nos. 1-2, pp.5-23, 1929.

SAMOS--ROMANTIC ISLE OF THE AEGEAN. Barnum Brown. Nat.Hist., vol.27, no. 1, pp.19-32, 1927.

(THE MAMMAL WORLD OF THE AEGEAN REGION, WITH A REVISION OF THE RACE DISTRICT OF ERINACEUS EUROPAEUS.) Die Saeugewelt der Ägais, nebst einer Revision des Rassenkreises von Erinaceus europaeus. Otto von Wettstein. Annalen Naturhist. Mus. Vienna, vol.52 (1941), pp. 245-278, pls.13-14, May, 1942.

AFGHANISTAN

ZOOLOGY OF THE AFGHAN DELIMINATION COMMISSION. MAMMALS. Oldfield Thomas. Trans.Linn.Soc., London, ser.2, vol.5, Zool.,(1884-1894), pp.55-56, May, 1889.

(ON THE FAUNA OF AFGHANISTAN.) Zur Fauna Afghanistans. Klaus Zimmermann. Zeitschr.Saeugetierk., Berlin, vol.20, nos. 2-3, pp.189-191, Aug. 3, 1955.

AFRICA

Extinct and Fossil Mammals

FOSSIL HUNTING IN AFRICA. P.E.P. Deraniyagala. Free Lanka Review, Ceylon, vol.1, no.2, pp.2-4, figs.3, June, 1948.

NEW AND LITTLE-KNOWN MAMMALS FROM THE MIOCENE OF AFRICA. A. Tendell Hopwood. Amer. Mus.Novitates, no.344, pp.1-9, figs.6, Mar. 9, 1929.

STONE AGE AFRICA. OUTLINE OF PREHISTORY IN AFRICA. Louis Seymour Bazett Leakey. Oxford Univ. Press, London, pp.vi-218, figs.28, pls.1-13, tbl.1, folded map, 1936.

AFRICA SINCE THE MESOZOIC: WITH PARTICULAR REFERENCE TO CERTAIN BIOLOGICAL PROBLEMS. R.E. Moreau. Proc. Zool. Soc. London, vol.121, pt.4, pp.869-913, fig.1, Feb. 8, 1952.

FOSSIL MAMMALS OF AFRICA. London, printed by order of the Trustees of the British Mus.(Nat.Hist.), no.1, illus., pls., tbls., 1951.

Recent Mammals

IN BRIGHTEST AFRICA. Carl E. Akeley. Garden City, New York, pp.267, illus., 1920.

LIONS, GORILLAS, AND THEIR NEIGHBORS. Carl E. Akeley, Mary L. Jobe. New York, Dodd, Mead and Co., pp.xviii-260, pls.21, 1932.

(Review by A.K.Fisher of) LIONS, GORILLAS, AND THEIR NEIGHBORS. Carl E. Akeley, Mary L. Jobe. Jour. Mamm., vol. 14, no.1, pp.80-81, Feb., 1933.

(Review by A.K.Fisher of) CARL AKELEY'S AFRICA. Carl E. Akeley, Mary L. Jobe. Jour. Mamm., vol.12, no.1, pp.82-83, Feb., 1931.

CONSERVATION EXPANDS IN AFRICA. (Carl Akeley's Dream of Absolute Sanctuary for the Vanishing Wildlife of Africa is Being Realized.) Carl E. Akeley, Mary L. Jobe. Nat. Hist., New York, vol.35, no.5, pp.395-396, May, 1935.

IN THE LAND OF HIS DREAMS. THE LAST CHAPTER OF CARL AKELEY'S 1926 AFRICAN EXPEDITION. Carl E. Akeley, Mary L. Jobe. Nat. Hist., New York, vol.27, pp.525-532, illus., Dec., 1927 (Mar., 1928).

NATIONAL PARKS IN AFRICA. THE EXTENSION OF WILD-LIFE CONSERVATION. Carl E. Akeley, Mary L. Jobe. Science, n.s., vol.74, no.1928, pp.584-588, Dec. 11, 1931.

SWAN SONG OF OLD AFRICA. (Big Game of Africa.) Carl E. Akeley, Mary L. Jobe. Sportsman, vol.5, no.3, pp.52-53, 98, illus., Mar., 1929.

CHECKLIST OF AFRICAN MAMMALS. Glover M. Allen. Bull. Mus. Comp.Zool. Harvard Coll., Cambridge, Mass., vol.83, pp.763, Feb., 1939.

(Review by P. Rode of) CHECKLIST OF AFRICAN MAMMALS. Glover M. Allen. Mammalia, Paris, vol.3, nos.3-4, pp. 132-133, Sep.-Dec., 1939.

WATER HOLE GROUP. (African Mammals.) H.E. Anthony. Nat. Hist., New York, vol. 37, no.1, pp.81-85, Jan., 1936.

(ETHOLOGICAL NOTES ON CERTAIN AFRICAN MAMMALS.) Notes ethologiques sur quelques mammiferes africains. G. Babault. Mammalia, Paris, vol.13, nos. 1-2, pp.1-16, Mar.-June, 1949; no.3, pp. 57-68, Sep., 1949; vol.13, no.4, pp.105-124, Dec., 1949.

(ANIMAL PARADISE AFRICA.) Tierparadies Afrika. Arthur Berger. Muehlhausen, Thuer.-Leipzig, Bergwald-Verlag Walter Paul, pp.227, pls., 2nd ed., 1943.

GAME PRESERVATION AND REGULATIONS IN FRENCH COLONIES (AFRICA). Francois Edmond Blanc. Trans. 11th N.Amer.Wildl. Conf., Washington, pp.17-20, 1946.

GREAT AND SMALL GAME OF AFRICA: AN ACCOUNT OF THE DISTRIBUTION, HABITS, AND NATURAL HISTORY OF THE SPORTING MAMMALS, WITH PERSONAL HUNTING EXPERIENCES. H.A. Bryden. Rowland Ward, Ltd., London, pp. 612, illus., 1899.

(NEW AFRICAN MAMMALS.) Mamiferos Africanos nuevos. Angel Cabrera. Bol.Real. Soc. Espanola Hist. Nat., vol.24, pp.216-223, Apr. 28, 1924.

SAVING GAME IN AFRICA. Keith Caldwell. Jour. Mamm., vol.8, no.1, pp.74-75, Feb., 1927.

SAVING THE ANIMAL LIFE OF AFRICA-A NEW METHOD AND A LAST CHANCE. Henry R. Carey. Jour. Mamm., vol.7, no.2, pp.73-85, May, 1926.

BATTLES OF THE AFRICAN JUNGLE. W.S. Chadwick. Outdoor Life, vol.67, no. 2, pp.26-27, 81-82, Feb., 1931.

BIG GAME AND PYGMIES. Cuthbert Christy. Macmillan and Co., London, pp.325, pls. 57, map 1, 1924.

I'LL BRING BACK A BONGO YET.(Photos Bongo, Giant Pangolin, Aard Vark.) Charles Cordier. American Mag., Springfield, vol. 148, no.5, pp.42-43, 86-90, illus.,Nov., 1949.

(MAMMALS OF FRENCH AFRICA.) Les mammiferes de l'Afrique noire francaise. P. L. Dekeyser. Initiations Africaines I, Dakar, pp.61, figs.47, 1948.

(PROTECTED ANIMALS IN FRENCH AFRICA.) Les Animaux protegés de l'Afrique Noire. P.L. Dekeyser, A. Villiers. Inst. Francais d'Afrique Noire, Dakar, pp.128, illus., 1951.

GREAT GAME ANIMALS OF AFRICA. Guy Dollman. Proc. Linn. Soc. London, 149th sess., pt.1, pp.49-50, Feb. 23, 1937.

PROTECTION OF THE FAUNA AND FLORA OF AFRICA. Guy Dollman. Nat. Hist. Mag. (British Mus.), vol.4, no.29, pp.157-160, illus., Jan., 1934.

A SAFARI IN AFRICA. George Eastman. Nat. Hist., vol.27, pp.533-538, illus., Dec., 1927 (Mar., 1928).

(80,000-KILOMETER HUNT ACROSS AFRICA.) 80,000 kilomètres en chassant a travers l'Afrique. François Edmond-Blanc. La Terre et La Vie, 4e Année, no.7, pp. 413-422, illus., July, 1934.

(MAMMALS.) Mammiferes. S. Frechkop. Brussels, Institut des parcs nationaux du Congo Belge. Exploration du Parc national de la Kagera. Mission, 1938.

NOTES ON THE BIG GAME OF AFRICA AND ITS PRESERVATION. Herbert Friedmann. Jour. Mamm., vol.7, no.4, pp. 305-310, Nov., 1926.

AFRICAN GAME-LANDS, A GRAPHIC ITINERARY. Prentiss N. Gray. Supplement to The Sportsman, Boston, pp.32, illus., 1930.

AFRICAN ANATOMICAL EXPEDITION OF COLUMBIA UNIVERSITY AND THE AMERICAN MUSEUM OF NATURAL HISTORY. W.K. Gregory. Columbia Univ. Quart., vol.23, no.1, pp.79-89, Mar., 1931.

(Review by Francis Petter of) (BIG WILD BEASTS OF AFRICA.) Grands fauves d'Afrique. Tome II. E.Gromier. Mammalia, Paris, vol.15, no.4, p.213, Dec., 1951.

(IN THE AFRICAN BUSH: MEMOIRS AND ZOOLOGICAL OBSERVATION.) En brousse Africaine: Souvenirs et observations zoologiques. E. Gromier. La Terre et la Vie, Rev.d'Hist.Nat., vol.3, no.11, pp.670-680, illus., Nov., 1933.

(LIFE OF WILD ANIMALS OF AFRICA.) La vie des animaux sauvages de l'Afrique. E. Gromier. Preface by Ed.Bourdelle. Payot, Paris, pp.1-343, illus., 1936.

SHALL TSETSE DOOM AFRICAN WILD LIFE? (Topi, Kudu, Gazelle, Impalla, African Buffalo, Zebra.) Eric Hardy. Frontiers, Lancaster, vol.12, no.1, pp. 3-5. 25-26, illus., Oct., 1947.

TYPE-LOCALITIES OF SOME AFRICAN MAMMALS. R.W. Hayman, et al. Proc. Zool. Soc., London, vol.115, pts.3-4, pp.387-447, Feb., 1946.

(CAPTURING LARGE WILD ANIMALS IN AFRICA.) Capture de grands animaux sauvages en Afrique. Lutz Heck. La Terre et la Vie, Rev. d'Hist.Nat., vol.1, no.4, pp.195-204, illus., May, 1931.

NEW GENERA AND RACES OF AFRICAN UNGULATES. Edmund Heller. Smiths. Inst., Washington, Misc. Coll., vol.60, no.8, pp.16, Publication 2148, 1912.

AFRICAN MYSTERY BEASTS. W.Hickens. Discovery, London, vol.18, no.216, pp. 369-373, figs.2, Dec., 1937.

SOME NEW AFRICAN MAMMALS. Martin A.C. Hinton. Ann. and Mag. Nat. Hist., ser.9, vol.7, pp.368-373, Apr., 1921.

DESCRIPTIONS OF A NEW GENUS AND EIGHT NEW SPECIES AND SUBSPECIES OF AFRICAN MAMMALS. Ned Hollister. Smiths. Inst., Washington, Misc. Coll., vol.66, no.1, pp.8, Publication 2406, 1916.

PAPERS ON AFRICAN MAMMALS. Ned Hollister. Smiths. Inst., Washington, Misc. Coll., 1910-1918.

AFRICAN GAME PROTECTION. OUTLINE OF EXISTING GAME RESERVES AND NATIONAL PARKS OF AFRICA WITH NOTES ON CERTAIN SPECIES OF BIG GAME NEARING EXTINCTION, OR NEEDING ADDITIONAL PROTECTION. Elisabeth Hone. Special Publ., Amer. Comm.Internat. Wild Life Protection, Cambridge, vol.1, no. 3, pp.45, 1933.

HUNTER. J.A.Hunter. Harper and Bros., New York, pp.263, illus., 1952.

(AFRICAN FAUNA: BIOLOGY, HISTORY, FOLKLORE, HUNTING.) La faune africaine: biologie, histoire, folklore, chasse.Albert Jeannin. Payot, Paris, pp.242(Bibliotheque scientifique), 1951.

(Review by P. Rode of) (GAME OF FRENCH AFRICA.) Les betes de chasse de l'Afrique française. Albert Jeannin. Mammalia, Paris, vol.10, no.1, pp.67-68, Mar., 1946.

(PROTECTION OF NATURE AND AFRICAN AGRICULTURAL EVOLUTION. SOME RELEVANT PRACTICAL PROBLEMS.) La protection de la nature et l'évolution Agricole Africaine. De quelques problemes pratiques qui s'y rattachent. Albert Jeannin. Mammalia, Paris, vol.8, no.2, pp.33-46, June, 1944.

SKY TRAILS IN AFRICA; THE EQUIPMENT AND PLANS OF THE LATEST MARTIN JOHNSON AFRICAN EXPEDITION. Martin Johnson. Nat. Hist., vol.33, no.2, pp.131-138, illus., Apr., 1933.

AT HOME IN AFRICA. Osa Johnson. Nat. Hist., vol.27, pp.561-569, illus., Dec., 1927 (Mar., 1928).

ANIMALS IN AFRICA. Gamilla Koffler. Harper and Brothers, New York, pp.146, illus., photos, 1956.

VANISHING WILD LIFE OF AFRICA. Herbert Lang. Nat. Hist., vol.24, pp.312-327, illus., May-June, 1924.

(LARGE HUNTING ANIMALS OF FRENCH AFRICA.) Les grands animaux de chasse de l'Afrique Francaise. Louis Lavauden. Faune Colonies Francaises, vol.5, no.7, pp.323-495, figs.3-60, pls.1-20, map, 1934.

(AN ORNITHOLOGIST'S VOYAGE ACROSS AFRICA.) Voyage d'un ornithologiste a travers l'Afrique. Louis Lavauden. (Title on cover of separates given as "Voyage, d'un naturaliste a travers d'Afrique.) Rev. Francaise d'Ornithol., ser.2, 18th year, nos.208-210, pp.311-356, illus.; no.211, pp.428-439, map; no.212, pp.484-509, illus., 1926. (First Part Contains Many Notes on Mammals.)

FOCUS ON AFRICA. (With Photographs by Mary Light.) Richard U. Light. Amer. Geogr. Soc., New York, Special Publ.no.25, pp. xv+228, figs.323, photos, 1941.

DEVELOPMENT AND DISTRIBUTION OF THE AFRICAN FAUNA IN CONNECTION WITH AND DEPENDING UPON CLIMATIC CHANGES. E. Loennberg. Arkiv foer Zoologi, vol.21A, no.4, pp.1-33, Nov. 21, 1929.

GAME ANIMALS OF AFRICA. R. Lydekker. London, pp.484, illus., 1908; Revised ed. by J.C. Dollman, London, Rowland Ward, pp. 483, 1926.

NOTES ON TWO AFRICAN MAMMALS. R. Lydekker. Proc. Zool. Soc. London, for 1907, pp.782-785, May, 1908.

SUPPLEMENT TO THE GAME ANIMALS OF AFRICA. R. Lydekker. Pp.26, illus., 1911.

SMITHSONIAN-CHRYSLER EXPEDITION TO AFRICA TO COLLECT LIVING ANIMALS. W.M. Mann. Explorations and Field-Work Smiths. Inst., 1926, Smiths. Misc. Coll., vol.78, no.7, pp.10-21, illus., 1927.

(ON SOME AFRICAN MAMMALS.) Ueber einige afrikanische Saeugethiere. Paul Matschie. Sitz. Ber. Gesell. Naturf. Freunde Berlin, Jahrg.1892, no.7, pp.110-113, July 19, 1892.

(ON THE DISTRIBUTION OF SOME MAMMALS IN AFRICA.) Ueber die Verbreitung einiger Saeugetiere in Afrika. Paul Matschie. Sitz. Ber. Gesell. Naturf. Freunde Berlin, Jahrg.1892, no.10, pp.223-235, Dec. 20, 1892.

(AFRICAN MAMMALS.) Einige afrikanische Saeugetiere. Paul Matschie. Sitz. Ber. Gesell. Naturf. Freunde Berlin, Jahrg. 1893, no.6, pp.175-178, June 20, 1893.

(TWO MONKEYS DESCRIBED BY SCHREBER AND SOME APPARENTLY NEW MAMMALS OF AFRICA.) Zwei von Schreber beschriebene Affen und anscheinend neue Saeugetiere aus Afrika. Paul Matschie. Sitz. Ber. Gesell. Naturf. Freunde Berlin, Jahrg.1893, no.2, pp.60-68, Feb. 21, 1893.

BIG GAME OF AFRICA. Hubert Conway Maydon. New York, C.Scribner's Sons, pp.viii, 9-254, illus., 1935.

BIG GAME SHOOTING IN AFRICA. Hubert Conway Maydon, et al. London, Seeley, Service and Co., Ltd., pp.445, illus.150, 1932. (The Lonsdale Library, vol.xiv.)

ZOOLOGICAL EXPLORATION IN AFRICA. Gerrit S. Miller, Jr. Smiths. Inst., Misc. Coll., vol.72, no.6, pp.21-31, figs.27-43, May 12, 1921.

ROAMING AFRICA'S UNFENCED ZOOS. W. Robert Moore. Nat. Geogr. Mag., Washington, vol.97, no.3, pp.353-380, illus., Mar., 1950.

TYPE-LOCALITIES OF SOME AFRICAN MAMMALS. R.E. Moreau, et al. Proc. Zool. Soc. London, vol.115, pts.3-4, pp. 387-447, Feb., 1946.

(THREE NEW AFRICAN MAMMALS.) Drei neue afrikanische Saeugethiere. Oscar Neumann. Sitz. Ber. Gesell. Naturf. Freunde Berlin, Jahrg.1899, no.2, pp.15-22, Jan.17, 1899.

VANISHING GAME OF AFRICA. Major Herbert Noyes. Field, London, vol.155, no.4023, p.160, Feb. 1, 1930.

CONGO EXPEDITION OF THE AMERICAN MUSEUM OF NATURAL HISTORY. INTRODUCTION. Henry Fairfield Osborn. Bull. Amer. Mus. Nat. Hist., vol.39, pp. xv-xxvii, Aug. 1, 1919.

VANISHING WILD LIFE OF AFRICA. Henry Fairfield Osborn. Nat. Hist., vol. 27, pp.515-524, illus., Dec., 1927 (Mar., 1928).

OPENING OF THE AFRICAN PLAINS. Henry Fairfield Osborn. Bull. New York Zool. Soc., vol.44, no.3, pp.67-73, figs. 6, May-June, 1941.

NEW AND IMPERFECTLY KNOWN SMALL MAMMALS FROM AFRICA. Wilfred H. Osgood. Zool. Ser., Field Mus. Nat. Hist., (no.375), vol.20, no.21, pp.217-256, Dec. 28, 1936.

LONDON CONFERENCE FOR THE PROTECTION OF AFRICAN FAUNA AND FLORA. J.C. Phillips. Bull. New York Zool. Soc., vol.37, no.1, pp.27-28, Jan.-Feb., 1934.

NATURAL HISTORY ESSAYS. Graham Renshaw. London, Sherratt and Hughes, pp.218, pls., 1904. (Examples of the Mammalian Fauna of Africa.)

ANDREW SMITH'S EARLY DESCRIPTIONS OF ANIMALS. Austin Roberts. Sambab, South African Mus. Assoc., Durban, vol. 3, no.8, pp.238-241, Dec., 1944.

NEW FORMS OF AFRICAN MAMMALS. Austin Roberts. Ann. Transvaal Mus., Pretoria, vol.13, pt.2, pp.82-121, July 6, 1929.

(UNGULATE MAMMALS OF FRENCH AFRICA.) Mammiféres ongulés de l'Afrique noire. Paul Rode. Paris, Libraire Larose, (Faune de l'Empire français, II), pts.2, illus., maps, 1943-44.

AFRICAN GAME TRAILS. Theodore Roosevelt. Scribner's Mag., vol.46, no.4, Oct. 1909 to vol.48, no.3, Sep., 1910.

AFRICAN GAME TRAILS. AN ACCOUNT OF THE AFRICAN WANDERINGS OF AN AMERICAN HUNTER-NATURALIST. Theodore Roosevelt. London, pp.534, illus., 1910.

LIFE HISTORIES OF AFRICAN GAME ANIMALS. Theodore Roosevelt, Edmund Heller. Vols. I and II, 1914.

(Review by N. Hollister of) LIFE HISTORIES OF AFRICAN GAME ANIMALS. Theodore Roosevelt, Edmund Heller. Naturwissenschaften, vol.2, pp.719-720, July 17, 1914.

(Review by Francis H. Herrick of) IN WILDEST AFRICA. C.G. Schillings. Science, Lancaster, n.s., vol.27, no. 691, pp.497-500, Mar. 27, 1908.

AFRICAN NATURE NOTES AND REMINISCENCES. Frederick C. Selous. MacMillan and Co., London, pp.356, illus., 1908.

HUNTER'S WANDERINGS IN AFRICA. (Being a Narrative of Nine Years Spent Amongst the Game of the Far Interior of S. Africa, Containing Accounts of Explorations Beyond the Zambesi, on the River Chobe, and in the Matabele and Mashuna Countries, With Full Notes Upon the Natural History and Present Distribution of All the Large Mammalia. Frederick C. Salous. London, R. Bentley and Son, pp. 455, illus., pls., fold.map, 1895.

AFRICAN ZOOLOGY. Andrew Smith. South African Quarterly Jour., Cape Town, 2nd ser., no.1, pp.145-160, 1833?; no.2, pt.3, pp.169-192, Jan.-Mar., 1834; no.3, pt.1, pp.209-224, Apr.-June 1834; no.3, pt.2, pp. 233-248, Apr.-June, 1834.

MAN AND BEAST IN AFRICA. Francois Sommer. London, Herbert Jenkins, pp. 206, illus., 1953.

LOCALITY RECORDS OF AFRICAN MAMMALS. Ken Stott, Jr. Jour. Mamm., vol. 31, no.2, pp.185-189, May 25, 1950.

DESCRIPTIONS OF NEW MAMMALS FROM MOUNT RUWENZORI. Oldfield Thomas. Ann. and Mag. Nat. Hist., ser.7, vol.18, no.104, pp.136-147, Aug., 1906.

FURTHER NEW AFRICAN MAMMALS. Oldfield Thomas. Ann. and Mag. Nat. Hist., ser.8, vol.5, no.26, pp.191-202, Feb., 1910.

FURTHER NEW AFRICAN MAMMALIA. Oldfield Thomas. Ann. and Mag. Nat. Hist., ser.8, vol.5, no.27, pp.282-285, Mar., 1910.

NEW AFRICAN MAMMALIA OF THE GENERA PETRODROMUS DENDROMYS, MUS, AND LEPUS. Oldfield Thomas. Ann. and Mag. Nat. Hist., ser.7, vol.12, no.69, pp.339-344, Sep., 1903.

NEW AFRICAN MAMMALS. Oldfield Thomas. Ann. and Mag. Nat. Hist., ser.8, vol.4, no.24, pp.542-549, Dec., 1909.

NEW AFRICAN MAMMALS. Oldfield Thomas. Ann. and Mag. Nat. Hist., ser.8, vol.5, no.25, pp.83-92, Jan., 1910.

NEW AFRICAN MAMMALS. Oldfield Thomas. Ann. and Mag. Nat. Hist., ser.8, vol.8, no.45, pp.375-378, Sep., 1911.

NEW AFRICAN MAMMALS IN THE BRITISH MUSEUM. Oldfield Thomas. Ann. and Mag. Nat. Hist., ser.8, vol. 6, no.34, pp.426-432, Oct., 1910.

NEW AFRICAN MAMMALS OF THE GENERA CERCOPITHECUS, SCOTOPHILUS, MINIOPTERUS, CROCIDURA, GEORYCHUS, AND HELIOPHOBIUS. Oldfield Thomas. Ann. and Mag. Nat. Hist., ser. 7, vol.17, no.98, pp.173-179, Feb., 1906.

NEW AFRICAN MAMMALS OF THE GENERA GLAUCONYCTERIS, LUTRA, FUNISCIURUS, ARVICANTHIS, LOPHIOMYS, AND PROCAVIA. Oldfield Thomas. Ann. and Mag. Nat. Hist., ser.7, vol. 15, no.85, pp.77-83, Jan., 1905.

NEW AFRICAN SMALL MAMMALS IN THE BRITISH MUSEUM COLLECTION. Oldfield Thomas. Ann. and Mag. Nat. Hist., ser.8, vol.4, no.20, pp.98-112, Aug., 1909.

ON AFRICAN BATS AND SHREWS. Oldfield Thomas. Ann. and Mag. Nat. Hist., ser.8, vol.11, no.63, pp.314-321, Mar., 1913.

ON FURTHER NEW MAMMALS OBTAINED BY THE RUWENZORI EXPEDITION. Oldfield Thomas. Ann. and Mag. Nat. Hist., ser.7, vol.19, no.109, pp.118-123, Jan., 1907.

A NEW GENUS OF FRUIT-BATS AND TWO NEW SHREWS FROM AFRICA. Oldfield Thomas. Ann. and Mag. Nat. Hist., ser. 8, vol.6, no.31, pp.111-114, July, 1910.

ON SOME AFRICAN BATS AND RODENTS. Oldfield Thomas. Ann. and Mag. Nat. Hist., ser.7, vol.18, no.106, pp.294-299, Oct., 1906.

SOME NEW AFRICAN BATS (INCLUDING ONE FROM THE AZORES) AND A NEW GALAGO. Oldfield Thomas. Ann. and Mag. Nat. Hist., ser.7, vol.8, no.43, pp.27-34, July, 1901.

SOME NEW AFRICAN MAMMALIA. Oldfield Thomas. Ann. and Mag. Nat. Hist., ser.9, vol.17, pp.180-184, Jan., 1926.

RUWENZORI EXPEDITION REPORTS. 17 MAMMALIA. Oldfield Thomas, R.C. Wroughton. Trans. Zool. Soc. London, vol.19, pt.5, pp.481-518, pls.20-24, Mar., 1910.

SOS FOR AFRICAN WILDLIFE. Dan Lincoln Thrapp. Nat. Hist., New York, vol. 58, no.3, pp.104-111, illus., Mar., 1949.

CAMP AND TRAMP IN AFRICAN WILDS. (A Records of Adventures, Impressions, and Experiences During Many Years Spent Among the Savage Tribes Round Lake Tanganyika and in Central Africa, With a Description of Native Life, Character, and Customs.) Emil Torday. Philadelphia, J.B. Lippincott Co.; London, Seeley, Service and Co., Ltd., pp.xvi-315, pls., fold. map, illus.45, 1913.

BEST TROPHIES OF AFRICA. Fred A. Wardenburg. Animal Kingdom, New York, vol.54, no.4, pp.111-114, illus., Aug. 1, 1951.

WILD AFRICAN ANIMALS I HAVE KNOWN. Prince of Sweden William. London, John Lane, The Bodley Head Ltd., pp.315, illus.211, 1923.

DANGEROUS ANIMALS OF AFRICA. W.J. Wilwerding. Fauna, Philadelphia, vol.7, no.3, pp.67-71, illus., Sep., 1945.

WITH AFRICA'S HORNED LEGIONS. W.J. Wilwerding. Fauna, Philadelphia, vol.6, no.1, pp.16-19, illus., Mar., 1944.

FOUR NEW AFRICAN MAMMALS. R.C. Wroughton. Ann. Mag. Nat. Hist., ser.8, vol.3, pp.514-516, June, 1909.

NEW AFRICAN MAMMALS OF THE GENERA CRICETOMYS AND PROCAVIA. R.C. Wroughton. Ann. Mag.Nat. Hist., ser.8, vol.5, pp.106-110, Jan., 1910.

AFRICA. FURTHER CORRESPONDENCE RELATING TO THE PRESERVATION OF WILD ANIMALS IN AFRICA. (In continuation of (Cd.5775) July, 1911.) Presented to both houses of Parliament by command of His Majesty. Great Brit. Foreign Office, London, H.M. Stationery Off., pp.55, Mar., 1913. (Parliament, Papers by Command, Cd.6671.)

ANIMALS PUT IN CLASSES A AND B BY THE INTERNATIONAL CONFERENCE FOR THE PROTECTION OF THE FAUNA AND FLORA OF AFRICA. Illus. London News, vol.187, no.5044, pp.1128-1129, illus., Dec. 21, 1935.

UNSPOILT AFRICA. UNION NATIONAL PARKS. Publ. Nat. Parks Board of Trustees, Pretoria, pp.112, illus., 1937.

AFRICA--LIBYA see LIBYA

AFRICA--SAHARA see SAHARA

AFRICA--SUDAN see SUDAN

## AFRICA, CENTRAL

### Extinct and Fossil Mammals

(GEOLOGIC SKETCH OF THE WESTERN BORDER OF LAKE RUDOLF.) Esquisse geologique de la bordure occidental de Lac Rodolphe. C. Arambourg. Mission Sci. l'Omo 1932-1933, Mus. Nat. d'Hist. Nat., Paris, Geol.-Anthrop., vol.1, no.1, pp.9-16, map, 1935.

REVIEW OF THE FOSSIL MAMMALS OF CENTRAL AFRICA. A.T. Hopwood. Amer. Jour. Sci., vol.17, no.98, pp.101-118, Feb., 1929.

SOME MAMMALIA FROM THE PLIOCENE OF HOMA MOUNTAIN, VICTORIA NYANZA. A.T. Hopwood. Ann. and Mag. Nat. Hist., ser.9, vol.18, pp.266-272, Sep., 1926.

(VARIATIONS OF THE PLEISTOCENE CLIMATE IN CENTRAL AFRICA.) Variations du climat Pleistocene en Afrique Centrale. H. Scaetta. Ann. Geogr., Paris, vol.46, no.259, pp.164-171, 1937.

### Recent Mammals

(PROTECTION OF THE FAUNA OF THE KASAI (BELGIAN CONGO).) La protection de la faune au Kasai (Congo, Belge). L. Achten. Annales Comite Belge pour la Protection de la Nature, vol.1, year 1926, pp.63-68, illus., 1928.

INSECTIVORES, CARNIVORES, PRIMATES OF CONGO. J.A. Allen. Bull. Amer. Mus. Nat. Hist., vol.47, pp.1-524.

ACROSS THE GREAT CRATERLAND TO THE CONGO. (Distribution and Habits of Elephants, Lions, Gorillas, and Other Mammals.) T. Alexander Barns. New York, Alfred A. Knopf, pp.276, pls., maps 2, 1924.

(ON SOME MAMMALS OF THE BELGIAN CONGO, MAMMALS COLLECTED BY DR. A. ROSSI.) Su alcuni mammiferi del Congo Belga raccolti dal Dott. A. Rossi. Oscar de Beaux. Atti Soc. Ital. Sci. Nat., Paris, vol.64, pp.88-96 (3-12), 1925.

(ZOOLOGICAL COLLECTIONS MADE IN UGANDA BY DR. BAYON. XIX. MAMMALS. PART IV. APPENDIX WITH PRIMATES, INSECTIVORA AND CARNIVORA.) Collezioni zoologische fatte nell'Uganda dal Dott. E. Bayon. XIX. Mammiferi. Parte IV. Appendix, cum primatibus, insectivoris carnivorisque. Oscar de Beaux. Ann. Mus. civ.Storia Nat. Genova, vol. 52, pp.100-107, (1925) 1928.

(CONTRIBUTION TO STUDY OF THE WILD FAUNA OF UBANGI-SHARI. MAMMALS AND BIRDS OF THE BASINS OF OUAKA AND KANDJIA (DISTRICT OF OUAKA).) Contribution a l'etude de la faune sauvage de l'Oubanggui-Chari. Mammiferes et oiseaux des bassins de la Ouaka et de la Kandjia (circonscription de la Ouaka). Lucien Blancou. Bull. Soc. Recherches Congolaises, Brazzaville, no.18, pp.23, 1933.

(CONTRIBUTION TO STUDY OF THE WILD FAUNA OF UBANGI-SHARI. MAMMALS AND BIRDS OF THE UPPER BASINS OF OUHAM, NANA BARYA, AND PENDE (DISTRICT OF OUHAM-PENDÉ).) Contribution a l'etude de la faune sauvage de l'Oubangui-Chari. Mammiferes et oiseaux des Bassins superieurs de l'Ouham, de la Nana Barya et de la Pendé (circonscription de L'Ouham-Pendé). Lucien Blancou. Soc. Recherches Congolaises, Brazzaville, pp.36. 1936.

(NOTES ON THE MAMMALS OF FRENCH EQUATORIAL AFRICA.) Notes sur les mammiferes de l'equateur Africain Francais. Lucien Blancou. Mammalia, Paris, vol.18, no.2, pp.170-180, June 1954; no.4, pp.358-363, Dec., 1954.

(NOTES ON THE MAMMALS OF UBANGI-SHARI. SOME GEOGRAPHICAL DATA ON THE SUBJECT OF UNGULATES.) Notes sur les mammiferes de l'Oubangui-Chari. Quelques presisions géographiques au sujet des onguleś. Lucien Blancou. Mammalia, Paris, vol.12, nos.1-2, pp.1-14, Mar.-June, 1948.

(PROTECTION OF NATURE IN FRENCH EQUATORIAL AFRICA.) La protection de la nature en afrique Équatoriale Francaise. Lucien Blancou. La Terre et la Vie, 2e Sem., no.5, pp.1-12 illus., Nov., 1935; Mammalia, Paris, vol.15, no.4, pp. 157-169, Dec., 1951.

(REPORT ON THE MAMMALS OBSERVED BY KING FERDINAND OF BULGARIA ON HIS TRIP TO EQUATORIAL AFRICA IN 1929.) Bericht ueber die Saeugetiere, die auf der Reise Koenigs Ferdinand von Bulgarien nach dem aequatorialen Afrika im Jahre 1929 beobachtet wurden. Hans von Boetticher. Bull. Inst. Roy. Hist. Nat. Sophia, Bulgaria, vol.4, pp.51-60, figs.7, 1931.

ON MAMMALS FROM LULUABOURG, SOUTHERN CONGO. A. Cabrera, A.E. Ruxton. Ann. and Mag. Nat. Hist., ser. 9, vol.17, pp.591-602, May, 1926.

FURTHER NOTES ON THE FAUNA OF NKOSI ISLAND, LAKE VICTORIA, UGANDA, AFRICA. G.D.Hale Carpenter. Proc. Zool.Soc.London, pt.1, pp. 129-132, Apr., 1929.

OUR BELGIAN CONGO EXPEDITION COMES HOME. (List of Mammals Collected and Photos of 8 Species.) Charles Cordier. Animal Kingdom, New York, vol. 52, no.4, pp.99-114, 134-136, illus., July-Aug., 1949.

ECOLOGICAL STUDIES ON MAMMALS, BIRDS, REPTILES AND AMPHIBIANS IN THE EASTERN BELGIAN CONGO. Kai Curry-Lindahl. Ann. Mus. Roy. Congo Belge, Tervuren, ser.8, vol.42, no.1, pp. 1-78, illus., 1956.

(MAMMALS OF FRENCH AFRICA.) Les mammiferes de l'Afrique noire francaise. P.L. Dekeyser. Dakar, Inst. Francais d'Afrique noire, pp.426, illus., 2nd ed., 1955.

(BELGIAN CONGO. LEGISLATION ENACTED IN THE YEARS 1930-1934.) Congo Belge. Legislation edictee durant les années 1930-1934. J.M. Derscheid. Revue Internationale de Législation pour la Protection de la Nature, Bruxelles, pp.20, 1932.

(MISSION IN UBANGI-SHARI.) En mission dans l'Oubangui-Chari. Francois Edmond-Blanc. La Terre et la Vie, Rev.d'Hist.Nat., vol.2, no.12, pp.699-712, figs.16, Dec., 1932.

(AMONG THE ANIMALS OF THE EAST OF THE BELGIAN CONGO (ALBERT NATIONAL PARK).) Parmi les mammifères de l'est du Congo Belge (Parc National Albert) (1). Serge Frechkop. La Terre et la Vie, Paris, vol.97, no.1, pp.15, illus., Jan.-Mar., 1950.

(ANIMALS PROTECTED IN THE BELGIAN CONGO AND THE TERRITORY UNDER RUANDA-URUNDI MANDATE.) Animaus Proteges au Congo Belge et dans le Territoire sou Mandat du Ruanda-Urundi.Serge Frechkop. Brussels, 4th ed., Institut des Parcs Nationaux du Congo Belge, pp.434, illus., map, 1953.

(EXPLORATION OF ALBERT NATIONAL PARK (1933-1935), NO.10. MAMMALS.) Exploration du Parc National Albert.(1933-1935), no.10. Mammifères. Serge Frechkop. Inst. Parcs Nat. Congo Belge, Bruxelles, pp.1-103, figs.5, photos, pls.1-19, fold. map, 1938; (1937-1938), pp.186, pls.30, illus., 1943; pp.56, pls.3, illus., 1944.

(Review by P. Rode of) (EXPLORATION OF ALBERT NATIONAL PARK.(1937-1938). Exploration du Parc National Albert. (1937-1938). Serge Frechkop. Mammalia, Paris, vol.8, no.1, pp.30-31, Mar., 1944.

(MAMMALS AND BIRDS PROTECTED IN THE BELGIAN CONGO.) Mammiferes et Oiseaux proteges au Congo Belge.Serge Frechkop. Publ. Inst. Parcs Nat. Congo Belge, Bruxelles, pp.87, illus., map, 1936. (Mammals pp.10-53.)

(Review by P. Rode of) (MAMMALS AND BIRDS PROTECTED IN THE BELGIAN CONGO.) Mammiferes et Oiseaux protegés au Congo Belge. Serge Frechkop. Mammalia, Paris, vol.1, no.3, p.126, Mar., 1937.

OBSERVATION ON MR. DU CHAILLU'S PAPER ON "THE NEW SPECIES OF MAMMALS" DISCOVERED BY HIM IN WESTERN EQUATORIAL AFRICA. John Edward Gray. Proc. Zool. Soc. London, pt.29, pp. 273-275, 1861.

(LIFE OF THE WILD ANIMALS OF UBANGI-SHARI.) La vie des animaux sauvages de l'Oubangui-Chari. Emile Gromier.Bibliotheque Geographique, Paris, pp.239, illus., 1938.

(Review by P. Rode of) (LIFE OF THE WILD ANIMALS OF UBANGI-SHARI.) La vie des animaux sauvages de l'Oubangui-Chari. Émile Gromier. Mammalia, Paris, vol.2, no.4, p.194, 1938.

ZOOLOGICAL RESULTS OF THE SWEDISH EXPEDITION TO CENTRAL AFRICA 1921. VERTEBRATA 4. A NEW SQUIRREL FROM THE BIRUNGA VOLCANOES, NORTH

OF LAKE KIVU. Nils Gyldenstolpe. Arkiv. for Zool., vol.19B, no.6, pp.1-3, Dec.14, 1927.

ZOOLOGICAL RESULTS OF THE SWEDISH EXPEDITION TO CENTRAL AFRICA 1921. VERTEBRATA 5. MAMMALS FROM THE BIRUNGA VOLCANOES, NORTH OF LAKE KIVU. (Appendix Lists 114 Forms of Mammals Collected in Eastern Belgian Congo and Western Uganda.) Nils Gyldenstolpe. Arkiv for Zool., vol.20A, no.4, pp.1-76, pls.1-4, July 12, 1928.

NATURALIST'S VISIT TO THE PARC NATIONAL ALBERT, BELGIAN CONGO. (Photographs of Gorilla Nests.) M.Hachisuka. Nat. Hist. Mag., Brit.Mus., vol.4, no.25, pp.20-30, illus., Jan., 1933.

LAGOMORPHA AND RODENTIA OTHER THAN SCIURIDAE, ANOMALURIDAE AND IDIURIDAE, COLLECTED BY THE AMERICAN MUSEUM CONGO EXPEDITION. Robert T. Hatt. Bull. Amer. Mus. Nat. Hist., vol.76, pp.457-604, figs.39, pls. 19, maps 2, July 3, 1940.

PANGOLINS AND AARD-VARKS COLLECTED BY THE AMERICAN MUSEUM CONGO EXPEDITION. Robert T. Hatt. Bull. Amer. Mus. Nat. Hist., vol.66, art.7, pp.643-672, figs.2, pls.32-39, Sep. 14, 1934.

TWO NEW MAMMALS FROM THE BELGIAN CONGO. R.W. Hayman. Ann. and Mag. Nat. Hist., London, ser.11, vol.3, no.14, pp.219-224, figs.1-2, Feb., 1939.

(OBSERVATION ON ANIMAL PSYCHOLOGY IN THE NATIONAL PARKS OF THE BELGIAN CONGO.) Observations sur la psychologie animale dans les Parcs Nationaux du Congo Belge. H. Hediger. Inst.Parcs Nat. Congo Belge, Brussels, fasc.1, p.194, 1951.

FOUR NEW SUBSPECIES OF LARGE MAMMALS FROM EQUATORIAL AFRICA. Edmund Heller. Smiths.Inst.Misc.Coll., Publ.2255, vol.61, no.22, pp.1-7, Jan. 26, 1914.

NEW RACES OF CARNIVORES AND BABOONS FROM EQUATORIAL AFRICA AND ABYSSINIA. Edmund Heller. Smiths.Inst. Misc.Coll., Publ.2248, vol.61, no.19, pp. 12, 1913.

NEW RACES OF UNGULATES AND PRIMATES FROM EQUATORIAL AFRICA. Edmund Heller. Smiths.Inst.Misc.Coll., Publ.2245, vol.61, no.17, pp.12, Oct. 21, 1913.

NEW SPECIES OF RODENTS AND CARNIVORES FROM EQUATORIAL AFRICA. Edmund Heller. Smiths. Inst. Misc.Coll., Publ.2006, vol.56, no.17, pp.16, Feb. 28, 1911.

NEW SUBSPECIES OF MAMMALS FROM EQUATORIAL AFRICA. Edmund Heller. Smiths.Inst.Misc.Coll., Publ.2272, vol. 63, no.7, pp.12, June 24, 1914.

(ACROSS PLAINS AND VOLCANOS AT THE ALBERT NATIONAL PARK.) Travers plaines et volcans au Parc National Albert. R. Hoier. Inst. des Parcs Nationaux du Congo Belge, Brussels, pp.1-172, pls. 24, 1950.

(EXPLORATION OF THE ALBERT NATIONAL PARK.) Exploration du Parc National Albert. R. Hoir. Inst. Parcs National Congo Belge, Brussels, pp.172, pls.24, 1950.

(MAMMALS OF ALBERT NATIONAL PARK.) Mammiferes du Parc national Albert. R. Hoier. Bruxelles, Office de publicite, pp.111, illus., 1952.

NOTES ON THE ANTELOPES AND ZEBRA OF NORTHERN RHODESIA AND PORTUGUESE EAST AFRICA. Wynant Davis Hubbard. Jour. Mamm., vol.7, no.3, pp.184-193, Aug., 1926.

(LARGE MAMMAL FAUNA OF THE RWINDI-RUTSHURU PLAIN (LAKE EDWARD). ITS DEVELOPMENT SINCE ITS TOTAL PROTECTION.) La faune des grands Mammifères de la plaine Rwindi-Rutshuru (Lac Edouard). Son evolution depuis sa protection totale. E. Hubert. Brussels, pp. 84, pls.25, chart, 1947.

NOTES ON THE MAMMALS COLLECTED BY DR. H. SCHOUTEDEN IN THE BELGIAN CONGO. P.L. Kershaw. Rev.Zool. Africaine, vol.11, pp.355-368, Dec. 27, 1923.

NOTES ON ANT-EATING MAMMALS IN THE BELGIAN CONGO. Herbert Lang. Bull. Amer. Mus. Nat. Hist., vol.45, pp. 320-329, pls.24-25, 1922.

MAMMALS COLLECTED IN CENTRAL AFRICA BY CAPTAIN E. ARRHENIUS. Einar Lonnberg. Kungl.Svenska Vetenskap. Handl., vol.58, no.2, pp.3-110, pls.1-12, Sep. 1, 1917.

(MAMMALS COLLECTED IN THE REGION OF MOUNT ELGON BY DR. BAYER IN 1914.) Mammiferes recueillis dans la Région du Mont Elgon par le Dr.Bayer, en 1914. Einar Lonnberg. Rev.Zool.Africaine, vol.5, pp.172-192, 1918.

NOTES ON NEW AND RARE MAMMALS FROM CONGO. Einar Lonnberg. Rev. Zool. Africaine, vol.3, fasc.2, pp.273-278, Dec., 1913.

NOTES ON SOME MAMMALS COLLECTED IN THE CONGO FREE STATE BY THE SWEDISH MISSIONARY K.E. LAMAN. Einar Lonnberg. Arkiv. Zool., Upsala, vol.4, no.16, pp.14, Apr. 29, 1908.

REMARKS ON SOME CONGO MAMMALS. Einar Lonnberg. Rev.Zool.Africaine, Bruxelles, vol.7, pp.236-248, 1920.

ZOOLOGICAL RESULTS OF THE SWEDISH EXPEDITION TO CENTRAL AFRICA, 1921. VERTEBRATA 2. PRELIMINARY DIAGNOSES OF SEVEN NEW MAMMALS. Einar Lonnberg, Nils Gyldenstolpe. Arkiv.Zool., vol.17B, no.5, pp.6, May 2, 1925.

ZOOLOGICAL RESULTS OF THE SWEDISH EXPEDITION TO CENTRAL AFRICA, 1921. VERTEBRATA 3. PRELIMINARY DIAGNOSES OF FOUR NEW MAMMALS. Einar Lonnberg, Nils Gyldenstolpe. Arkiv.Zool., vol.17B, no.9, pp.5, May 14, 1925.

(CONTRIBUTION TO KNOWLEDGE OF THE UNGULATES OF CENTRAL AFRICA.) Beitrag zur Kenntnis der Huftiere von Zentralafrika. L. Lorenz-Liburnau. Ann. Nat. Hist. Mus., Wien, vol.36, pp.90-123, illus., 1923.

DESCRIPTIONS OF TWO MAMMALS FROM THE ITURI FOREST. (With a Supplementary Note On the Buffalo of the Semlik District.) Richard Lydekker. Proc. Zool. Soc. London, pp.992-966, pl.70, Apr. 11, 1907.

ON A CENTRAL AFRICAN RATEL AND WATER-CHEVROTAIN. Richard Lydekker. Proc. Zool. Soc. London, vol.1, pp.112-113, pl.7, June 7, 1906.

(NOTES ON THE MAMMALS OF CHAD.) Notes sur les mammiferes du Tchad. L. Malbrant. Rev. d'Hist.Nat., Pt.1, A. Mammiferes, Paris, vol.11, no.11, pp.345-355, Nov., 1930.

(FAUNA OF CENTRAL FRENCH AFRICA (MAMMALS AND BIRDS).) Faune du Centre Africain Francais (Mammiferes et Oiseaux). R. Malbrant. Encylopédie Biologique XV, Paris, pp.i-viii-1-435, figs.77, pls. 28, fold.map, 1936. (Mammals, pp.13-171, figs.2, pls.1-22); 2nd ed., Paris, P. Lechevalier, pp.616, illus., pls.33, fold. map, 1952.

(AUSTRAL AFFINITIES OF THE FAUNA OF THE FRENCH CONGO AND GABON.) Affinites Australes de la Faune du Congo Francais et du Gabon. R. Malbrant, A.R. Maclatchy. Mammalia, Paris, vol.11, no. 4, pp.129-138, Dec., 1947.

(FAUNA OF FRENCH EQUATORIAL AFRICA. VOL. 2. MAMMALS.) Faune de l'Equateur africain francais. Tome 2. Mammiferes. R. Malbrant, A.R.Maclatchy. Paris, Lechevalier, pp.323, pls.28, 1949.

(COMMUNICATIONS ON THE MAMMALS OF UGANDA (LETTERS OF OSCAR NEUMANN CONCERNING HIS TRAVELS IN AFRICA.) Nachrichten ueber Saeugethiere von Uganda nach Briefen des Afrikareisenden Oscar Neumann. Paul Matschie. Sitz.Ber.Gesell.Naturf.Freunde, Berlin, Jahrg.1895, no.1, pp.6, Jan.15, 1895.

(DIAGNOSES OF SOME MAMMALS FROM THE CONGO.) Diagnosen einiger Saeugetiere aus dem Kongostaat. Paul Matschie. Zeitschr.f.Saeugetierk., vol.1, no.2, pp. 110-114, Dec. 24, 1926.

STALKING BIG GAME WITH A CAMERA IN EQUATORIAL AFRICA: WITH A MONOGRAPH ON THE AFRICAN ELEPHANT. Marius Maxwell. The Century Co., New York and London, pp.xx-311, photographs 75, map 1, 1924.

(Review by Salim A. Ali of) STALKING BIG GAME WITH A CAMERA IN EQUATORIAL AFRICA: WITH A MONOGRAPH ON THE AFRICAN ELEPHANT. Marius Maxwell. Jour. Bombay Nat. Hist. Soc., vol.32, pp.571-573, Jan. 15, 1928.

COLLINS-GARNER FRENCH CONGO EXPEDITION. Gerrit S. Miller, Jr. Smiths. Inst. Misc.Coll., vol.70, no.2, pp.31-35, figs.33, July 16, 1919.

PROTECTION OF THE BIG GAME IN THE BELGIAN CONGO. Henry Fairfield Osborn. Annales Comité Belge pour la Protection de la Nature, vol.1, year 1926, pp.58-62, illus., 1928.

(MAMMALS COLLECTED BY DR. G. A. FISCHER ON HIS TRIP TO MASAILAND (UNDER THE AUSPICES OF THE GEOGRAPHICAL SOCIETY OF HAMBURG).) Die von Dr. G.A. Fischer auf der im Auftrage der geographischen Gesellschaft in Hamburg unternommenen Reise in das Massai-Land gesammelten Saeugethiere. Dr.Pagenstecher. Jahrb.Hamburgischen Wissensch.Anstalten, Jahrg.2, pp.31-46, pl.1, 1885.

(CENSUS OF LARGE MAMMALS IN THE PLAIN OF LUAMA.) Recensements de grands mammiferes dans la plaine de la Luama. P. Pirlot. Bull. Agric. Congo Belge, vol.47, no.2, pp.341-366, illus., 1956.

(TRAVEL NOTES ON THE ECOLOGY OF MAMMALS BETWEEM THE LOWER CONGO AND KIVU.) Notes de route sur l'ecologie des mammiferes entre le Bas-Congo et le Kivu. P. Pirlot. Bull. Agric. Congo Belge, Brussels, vol.48, no.2, pp.393-408, 1957.

NOTES ON THE VERTEBRATE FAUNA OF NKOSI ISLAND, LAKE VICTORIA, UGANDA, AFRICA. Capt. C.R.S.Pitman. Proc. Zool. Soc. London, pt.1, pp.133-146, Apr., 1929.

WILD LIFE IN UGANDA. THE CONTROL OF ELEPHANTS AND CENSUS OF WHITE RHINOCEROS. Capt. C.R.S. Pitman. Field, London, vol.154, no.4001, pp.309-310, Aug. 31, 1929.

(STUDY OF THE MAMMALS OF THE FRENCH CONGO.) Etude sur les Mammiferes du Congo Francaise. E. de Pousargues. Ann. Sci.Nat., (Zool.), Paris, vol.3, pp.129-416, 1896; vol.4, pp.1-152, 1897.

ROUGH NOTES ON THE NATURAL HISTORY OF THE COUNTRY WEST OF VICTORIA NYANZA. Lt.Col.C. Deline Radcliffe. Proc. Zool. Soc. London, pp.184-191, 1905.

ON MAMMALS COLLECTED BY CAPTAIN C.R.S. PITMAN, GAME WARDEN, ENTEBBE, UGANDA. A.E. Ruxton. Ann. and Mag. Nat. Hist., ser.9, vol.18, pp.28-33, July, 1926.

AN INTERESTING COLLECTION OF MAMMALS, WITH A REMARKABLE NEW SPECIES OF HARE FROM UGANDA. J. St. Leger. Ann. and Mag. Nat. Hist., ser. 10, vol.4, pp.290-294, Sep., 1929.

ON TWO NEW MAMMALS FROM UGANDA. J. St. Leger. Ann. and Mag. Nat. Hist., ser.10, vol.9, pp.240-242, Mar., 1932.

(NOTES ON SOME MAMMALS FROM FRENCH EQUATORIAL AFRICA.) Notes sur quelques mammifères de l'Afrique Equatoriale Française. Colin Campbell Sanborn. Mammalia, Paris, vol.17, no. 3, pp.164-169, Sep., 1953.

(Review by P. Rode of ) (CATALOGUE OF THE BELGIAN CONGO AND RUANDA-URUNDI. ) Catalogue du Congo Belge et du Ruanda-Urundi. H. Schouteden. Mammalia, Paris, vol.8, no.1, p.30, Mar., 1944.

(FAUNA OF THE BELGIAN CONGO AND THE RUANDA-URUNDI. VOL. I. MAMMALS. ) Faune du Congo Belge et du Ruanda-Urundi, vol.I. Mammiferes. H. Schouteden. Tervuren, Ann.Mus.Congo Belge, pp.viii+331, 1948.

(MAMMALS OF THE BELGIAN CONGO AND RUANDA-URUNDI. ) Les Mammiferes du Congo Belge et du Ruanda-Urundi. I. Primates, Chiroptera, Insectivora, Pholidota. H. Schouteden. Ann. Mus. Congo Belge, Tervueren, ser.2, vol.3, fasc.1, pp.1-168, 1944.

(MAMMALS OF THE BELGIAN CONGO AND RUANDA-URUNDI.) Les Mammiferes du Congo Belge et du Ruanda- Urundi. II. Carnivora, Ungulata. H. Schouteden. Ann. Mus. Congo Belge, Tervueren, ser.2, vol. 3, pp.169-332, 1945.

(Review by P. Rode of) (MAMMALS OF THE BELGIAN CONGO AND RUANDA-URUNDI. ) Mammiferes du Congo Belge et du Ruanda-Urundi. H.Schouteden. Mammalia, Paris, vol.8, nos.3-4, p. 133, Sep.-Dec., 1944.

(Review by P. Rode of) MAMMALS OF THE BELGIAN CONGO AND RUANDA-URUNDI.) De Zoogdieren van Belgisch Congo en van Ruanda-Urundi. H.Schouteden. Mammalia, Paris, vol.11, nos.1-2, p.62, Mar.-June, 1947.

(MAMMALS OF THE NORTHERN SECTOR OF ALBERT NATIONAL PARK (KIVU).) Les mammiferes du Secteur Septentrional du Park National Albert (Kivu). H.Schouteden. Rev. Zool. Bot. Afr., vol.26, no.2, pp.202-210, Jan. 10, 1935.

(SOME TYPES OF CONGO FAUNA.) Quelques types de la faune Congolaise. (Notes on Kob and Gorillas.) H. Schouteden. Rev. Zool. Africaine, vol.14, pp.209-211, pls. 10, 1926.

(COLLECTION OF AFRICAN MAMMALS IN THE CONGO MUSEUM. ) Die Sammlung afrikanischer Saeugetiere im Congo-Museum. (Ginsterkatzen (Gattung Genetta Oken).) Ernst Schwartz. Rev. Zool. and Bot.Afr., vol.19, no.2, pp.275-286, July 30, 1930.

NORTHERN LIMIT OF THE FAUNA OF THE AFRICAN EQUATORIAL FOREST. Ernst Schwarz. Science, Lancaster, vol.110, no. 2848, p.124, July 29, 1949.

EXHIBITION OF, AND REMARKS UPON, SOME SKINS OF MAMMALS FROM THE SHIRÉ HIGHLANDS, BRITISH CENTRAL AFRICAN PROTECTORATE. P.L.Sclater. Proc. Zool. Soc. London, pt.3, pp.506-507, Oct. 2, 1893.

EXHIBITION OF, AND REMARKS UPON, SPECIMENS OF MAMMALS OBTAINED BY SIR HARRY JOHNSTON IN UGANDA. P.L. Sclater. Proc. Zool. Soc. London, vol.1, pt.2, pp.222-223, Aug. 1, 1901.

ON SOME SPECIMENS OF MAMMALS FROM LAKE MWERU, BRITISH CENTRAL AFRICA, TRANSMITTED BY VICE-CONSUL ALFRED SHARPE. P.L. Sclater. Proc. Zool. Soc. London, 1893, pt.4, pp.723-729, fig.1, Apr. 2, 1894.

REMARKS ON THE TWO LIVINGSTONE EXPEDITIONS INTO INNER AFRICA. P.L. Sclater. Proc. Zool. Soc. London, p.819, 1872.

CENTRAL AFRICAN GAME AND ITS SPOOR. C.H. Stigand, D.D. Lyell. Horace Cox, London, pp.315, illus., 1906.

REPORT OF SIX MONTH'S JOURNEY ON THE RIVER CONGO, SOUTHWEST COAST OF AFRICA. E.H. Taunt. Senate, 49th Congress, 2nd sess., Ex.Doc., no.77, pp. 1-42, fold.map, 1887.

VEGETATION OF THE KARAMOJA DISTRICT, UGANDA. A.S. Thomas. Jour. Ecol., vol.31, pp.149-178, 1943.

DIAGNOSES OF TWO NEW CENTRAL-AFRICAN MAMMALIA. Oldfield Thomas. Ann. and Mag. Nat. Hist., ser.5, vol.20, no.120, p.440, Dec., 1887.

LIST OF MAMMALS (EXCLUSIVE OF UNGULATA) COLLECTED ON THE UPPER CONGO BY DR. CHRISTY FOR THE CONGO MUSEUM, TERVUEREN. Oldfield Thomas. Ann. and Mag. Nat. Hist., ser.8, vol.16, no.96, pp.465-481, Dec., 1915.

NEW AFRICAN RODENTS AND INSECTIVORES, MOSTLY COLLECTED BY DR. C. CHRISTY FOR THE CONGO MUSEUM. Oldfield Thomas. Ann. and Mag. Nat. Hist., ser.8, vol.16, no.92, pp.146-152, Aug., 1915.

ON A COLLECTION OF MAMMALS OBTAINED BY DR. EMIN PASHA IN CENTRAL AND EASTERN AFRICA. Oldfield Thomas. Proc. Zool. Soc. London, pp.443-450, pl.40, figs., June 3, 1890.

ON A COLLECTION OF MAMMALS OBTAINED BY EMIN PASHA IN EQUATORIAL AFRICA, AND PRESENTED BY HIM TO THE NATURAL HISTORY MUSEUM. Oldfield Thomas. Proc. Zool. Soc. London, pp.3-17, pls.1-2, Jan. 17, 1888.

ON CAPT. BOTTEGO'S SECOND COLLECTION OF MAMMALS FROM CENTRAL AND SOUTHERN SOMALILAND. Oldfield Thomas. Annali del Museo Civico di Storia Naturale di Genova, ser.2, vol. 17, pp.105-107, Nov. 28, 1896.

ON MAMMALS FROM THE ISLAND OF FERNANDO PO. COLLECTED BY MR. E.SEIMUND. Oldfield Thomas. Proc. Zool. Soc. London, vol.2, pp.183-193, 1904.

ON SMALL MAMMALS OBTAINED IN SANKURU, SOUTH CONGO, BY MR. H. WILSON. Oldfield Thomas. Ann. and Mag. Nat. Hist., ser.8, vol.18, no.104, pp.234-239, Aug., 1916.

ON THE MORE NOTABLE MAMMALS OBTAINED BY SIR HARRY JOHNSTONE IN THE UGANDA PROTECTORATE. Oldfield Thomas. Proc. Zool. Soc. London, pp.85-90, pl.5, May 7, 1901.

ON MAMMALS COLLECTED DURING THE UGANDA BOUNDARY COMMISSION BY THE LATE MR. W.G. DOGGETT, AND PRESENTED TO THE BRITISH MUSEUM BY COL. C. DELME-RADCLIFFE. Oldfield Thomas, Harold Schwann. Proc. Zool. Soc. London, pt.1, pp.459-465, fig.95, Aug. 2, 1904.

NEW MAMMALS FROM LAKE CHAD AND THE CONGO, MOSTLY FROM THE COLLECTIONS MADE DURING THE ALEXANDER GOSLING EXPEDITION. Oldfield Thomas, R.C. Wroughton. Ann. and Mag. Nat. Hist., ser.7, vol.19, no.113, pp.370-387, May, 1907; ser.7, vol.19, no.114, pp. 520-522, June, 1907.

RUWENZORI EXPEDITION REPORT 17, MAMMALIA. Oldfield Thomas, R.C. Wroughton. Trans. Zool. Soc. London, vol.19, pp.481-528, pls., 1909-10.

(ALBERT NATIONAL PARK.) Le Parc National Albert. V. Van Straelen. Bull. Soc. Belge Étude Géogr., Louvain, vol.4, no. 1, pp.20-26, figs.A-B, May, 1934.

(CONTRIBUTION TO ETHOLOGIC STUDY OF THE MAMMALS OF THE NATIONAL PARK OF UPEMBA.) Contribution a l'étude ethologique des mammiferes du Parc National de l'Upemba. R. Verheyen. Bruxelles, Inst. des Parcs Nat. du Congo Belge, pp.161, pls.20, 1951.

(EXPLORATION OF THE NATIONAL PARK OF UPEMBA. CONTRIBUTION TO ETHOLOGIC STUDY OF ITS MAMMALS.) Exploration du Parc National de l'Upemba. Contribution a l'etude ethologique des mammiferes du Parc National de l'Upemba. R. Verheyen. Inst. Parcs Nat. du Congo Belge, Bruxelles, pp.161, pls.20, 1951.

WILD MAMMALS OF TESO AND KARAMOJA--VII. J.M. Watson. Uganda Jour., Kampala, vol.15, no.2, pp.193-202, Sep., 1951.

WILD MAMMALS OF TESO AND KARAMOJA--VIII. J.M. Watson. Uganda Jour., Kampala, vol.16, no.1, pp.89-93, Mar., 1952.

TO LAKE RUDOLPH AND BEYOND. William FitzHugh Whitehouse. Hunting and Conservation, the Book of the Boone and Crockett Club, New Haven, Yale Univ. Press, pp.258-339, pls.14, 1925.

MAMMALS FROM BRITISH CENTRAL AFRICA. W.E. de Winton. Proc. Zool. Soc. London, pp.552-553, May 2, 1899.

ON A COLLECTION OF SMALL MAMMALS FROM UGANDA. W.E. de Winton. Ann. and Mag. Nat. Hist., ser.6, vol.20, pp.316-320, Sep., 1897.

(EXPLORATION OF ALBERT NATIONAL PARK.) Exploration du Park National Albert. (1933-1935). G.F. de Witte. Inst. Parcs Nat. du Congo Belge, Bruxelles, no. 1, pp.1-39, pls.1-32, fold.map, 1937.

NATIONAL PARKS OF BELGIAN CONGO. G.F. de Witte, et al. Inst. Parks Nat. Congo Belge, Brussels, pp.3-40, illus.51, map 1, 1939.

## AFRICA, EASTERN

### Extinct and Fossil Mammals

(MIOCENE MAMMALS OF TURKANA(EAST AFRICA).) Mammifères miocenes du Turkana(Afrique Orientale). C. Arambourg. Ann. Paleontol., Paris, vol.22, nos.3-4, pp. 121-147, pls.2, figs.5, Mar., 1934.

(THE SCIENTIFIC MISSION OF OMO.) La mission scientifique de l'Omo. (Southern Ethiopia.) C. Arambourg, R. Jeannel. Comp. Rendus Acad.Sci.Paris, vol.196, no.25, pp.1902-1904, June 19, 1933.

MAMMALS FROM SINGA AND ABU HUGAR. FOSSIL MAMMALS OF AFRICA. NO. 2. THE PLEISTOCENE FAUNA OF TWO BLUE NILE SITES. Dorothea M.A. Bate. Pub. British Mus., Nat. Hist., London, pp.1-28, illus., 1951.

GEOLOGY AND PALAEONTOLOGY OF THE KAISO BONE-BEDS. FOSSIL MAMMALIA. A.T. Hopwood. Uganda Protectorate, Geol. Sur. Dept., Occ.Papers, no.2, pt.2, pp. 13-36, pls.2-4, Nov., 1926.

NEW AND LITTLE KNOWN FOSSIL MAMMALS FROM THE PLEISTOCENE OF KENYA COLONY AND TANGANYIKA TERRITORY. A.T. Hopwood. Ann. and Mag. Nat. Hist., London, ser.10, vol.17, no. 102, pp.636-641, June, 1936.

NEW FOSSIL MAMMALS FROM OLDUVAI, TANGANYIKA TERRITORY. A.T. Hopwood. Ann. and Mag. Nat. Hist., London, ser.10, vol.14, no.83, pp.546-550, Nov., 1934.

BRITISH-KENYA MIOCENE EXPEDITIONS. L.S.B. Leaker, W. E. le Gross Clark. Nature, London, vol.175, no.4449, p.234, Feb. 5. 1955.

ON FOSSIL MAMMALIAN REMAINS FROM EAST AFRICA. Einar Lonnberg. Arkiv for Zoologi, Stockholm, vol.29A, no.2, pp.1-23, figs.12, May 27, 1936.

(ON JURASSIC AND THE FIRST CRETACEOUS FOSSILS OF GALLALAND.) Ueber Jurassische und die ersten Cretaceischen Versteinerungen aus den Galla-Laendern. Oscar Neumann. Zeitschr.Deutsch.Geol. Gesell., Berlin, pp.101-102, 1901.

(TO THE ROOTS OF THE MAMMALIAN STEM. EXCAVATIONS IN GERMAN EAST AFRICA.) An den Wurzeln des Saeugetierstammes. Grabungen in Deutsch-Ost-Afrika. Ernst Nowack. Freude am Leben, Berlin, vol.17, nos.4-5, pp.67-70, illus., July-Aug., 1940.

COLLECTION OF FOSSILS FROM OLDOWAY GORGE, TANGANYIKA. Jour.East Africa and Uganda Nat. Hist. Soc., Nairobi, vol.16, nos.2-3 (71 and 72), p.138, Feb., 1942.

Recent Mammals

WILD LIFE OF THE WIRRAGOI PLAINS. (Kenya; Photographs of Black Rhinoceros and Cape Buffalo.) B.N. Abbay. Field, London, vol.175, no.4555, p.574, Apr. 13, 1940.

BILL, MY KIKUYU GUN-BEARER, AND SOME OF OUR ADVENTURES TOGETHER IN EAST AFRICA. Carl. E. Akeley. World's Work, vol.41, pp.594-607, figs.18, Apr., 1921.

SCIENTIFIC RESULTS OF AN EXPEDITION TO RAIN FOREST REGIONS IN EAST AFRICA. III. MAMMALS. (With Field Notes by Arthur Loveridge.) Glover M. Allen, Barbara Lawrence. Bull. Mus. Comp. Zool. at Harvard College, vol.79, no.3, pp.31-125, pls.5, Jan., 1936.

MAMMALS FROM THE ULUGURU AND USAMBARA MOUNTAINS, TANGANYIKA TERRITORY. Glover M. Allen. Proc. Boston Soc. Nat. Hist., vol.38, no.9, pp.413-441, Dec., 1927.

REPORTS ON THE SCIENTIFIC RESULTS OF AN EXPEDITION TO THE SOUTHWESTERN HIGHLANDS OF TANGANYIKA TERRITORY. Glover M. Allen, Arthur Loveridge. Bull. Mus. Comp. Zool. at Harvard College, vol.75, no.2, pp.47-140, pl.1, Feb., 1933.

SCIENTIFIC RESULTS OF A FOURTH EXPEDITION TO FORESTED AREAS IN EAST AND CENTRAL AFRICA. I. MAMMALS. Glover M. Allen Arthur Loveridge. Bull. Mus. Comp. Zool. at Harvard College, Cambridge, vol.89, no.4, pp.147-214, pls. 5, Feb., 1942.

MAMMALS FROM BRITISH EAST AFRICA, COLLECTED BY THE TJADOR EXPEDITION OF 1906. J.A. Allen. Bull. Amer. Mus. Nat. Hist., vol.26, pp.147-175, text figs.1-10, Mar. 19, 1909.

MAMMALS FROM BRITISH EAST AFRICA, COLLECTED ON THE THIRD AFRICAN EXPEDITION OF THE AMERICAN MUSEUM BY WILLIAM S. RAINSFORD. J.A. Allen. Bull. Amer. Mus. Nat. Hist., vol.33, pp. 337-344, June 18, 1914.

GLIMPSE ALONG THE WHITE NILE. H.E. Anthony. Nat. Hist., vol.29, pp.410-420, illus., Aug., 1929.

(BEHAVIOR OF THE ANIMALS IN THE PARKS OF KENYA.) Comportement des animaux dans les parcs Kenya. Guy Babault. Mammalia, Paris, vol.21, no.3, pp.306-397, Sep., 1957.

WILD LIFE ALONG THE TSAVO RIVER. Leon Bayer. Bull. New York Zool. Soc., vol.39, no.6, pp.211-218, illus., Nov-Dec., 1936.

WILD LIFE ON AND AROUND MOUNT ELGON, EQUATORIAL EAST AFRICA. Leon Bayer. Zool. Soc. Bull., vol.26, pp.130-140, figs.11, Nov., 1923; vol.27, pp. 2-11, figs.13, Jan., 1924.

(BRIEF NOTES ON SOME MAMMALS OF ERITREA (ARVICANTHIS, LEPUS).) Brevi note su alcuni mammiferi dell'Eritrea (Arvicanthis, Lepus). Oscar de Beaux. Atti. Soc. Ital. Sci. Nat. e Mus. Civ. Storia Nat., vol.69, nos.3-4, pp.218-222, Dec., 1930.

(MAMMALIA. BIOLOGICAL MISSION IN BORANALAND.) Mammalia. Missione Biologica nel paese dei Borana. Oscar de Beaux. Raccolte zoologiche, Reale Accad. Italia centro studi per l'Africa Orientale Italiana, Roma, vol.2, pt.1, pp.15, 1940.

(MAMMALS OF ABYSSINIA COLLECTED BY MR. UGO IGNESTI.) Mammiferi dell' Abissinia, raccolti dal signor Ugo Ignesti addelte alla R. Agenzia Commerciale di Gondar. Oscar de Beaux. Atti della Soc. Italiana di Sci. Nat. (Milan), vol.64, pp. 1-23 (of reprint), pl.5, 1925.

(MAMMALS OF ITALIAN SOMALILAND.) Mammiferi della Somalia Italiana. Oscar de Beaux. Atti Soc. Ital. Sci. Nat., vol. 63, pp.2-9, 1924.

(ZOOLOGICAL EXPEDITION OF THE MARGUM SABERIO PATRIZI IN THE LOWER AND UPPER GIUBA RIVER, JUNE-AUGUST 1934. MAMMALS.) Spedizione del Marchese Saberio Patrizi nel Basso Giuba e nell'Oltregiuba. Giugno-Agosto 1934 XII. Mammiferi. Oscar de Beaux. Annali del Museo Civico di Storia Nat., Genova, vol.58, pp.150-173, pls.9-16, Mar. 10, 1937.

(BEASTS OF PREY AND PACHYDERMS IN GERMAN EAST AFRICA.) Raubwild und Dickhauter in Deutsch-Ostafrika. Hans Besser. Stuttgart, pp.92, illus., 1915.

(WILD MAMMALS OF EASTERN AFRICA AND THEIR ENVIRONMENT.) Les mammiferes sauvages de l'Ouest africain et leur milieu. Jacques Bigourdan. Montrouge (Seine: Imprimerie J. de Rudder, pp.367, illus., maps, pls., 1945.

REPORT OF A ZOOLOGICAL COLLECTION FROM THE SOMALI COUNTRY. Edward Blyth. Jour. Asiatic Soc. Bengal, vol.24, pp.291-306, 1855.

(THE GENUS DENDROMUS A. SMITH ATTEMPT AT A NATURAL GROUPING. (RESULTS OF THE EAST AFRICA 1937 TRIP OF UTHMOELLER-BOHMANN).) Die Gattung Dendromus A. Smith. Versuch einer natuerlichen Gruppierung. (Ergebnisse der Ostafrika-Reise 1937 Uthmoeller-Bohmann. VIII.) Ludwig Bohmann. Zool. Anzeiger, vol.139, nos.3-4, pp.33-53, Aug. 1, 1942.

MAMMALS OF SOMALILAND. Dr. Drake Brockman. 1910?

THROUGH THE LAND OF SHEBA. (Mammals of Abyssinia.) Barnum Brown. Nat. Hist., vol.25, no.6, pp.602-617, Nov.-Dec., 1925 (Jan., 1926).

KENYA AND ITS BIG GAME. Keith Caldwell. Field, London, vol.161, no.4197, pp.1270-1271, illus., June 3, 1933.

THE "KERIT" OF KENYA COLONY. Keith Caldwell. Field, London, vol.146, p.959, Dec. 2, 1926.

ELEVEN WEEKS IN A LION-PASTURE. (Observations on Mammals Made on Expedition to Tanganyika for American Museum of Natural History.) G. Lister Carlisle, Jr. Nat. Hist., vol.29, pp. 169-180, illus., Mar., 1929.

BY MOTOR FROM NAIROBI TO THE NILE. James L. Clark. Nat. Hist., vol.29, pp. 261-272, illus., May, 1929.

GAME ANIMALS OF EAST AFRICA. Hugh Copley. Nairobi, The S.P.C.K. and the C.M.S. Bookshop, pp.35, illus., 1944.

SMALL MAMMALS OF KENYA. Hugh Copley. London, New York, Longmans, Green, pp.viii+96, illus., 1950.

ELEPHANTS, LIONS, AND AIRPLANES. COLLECTING AND STUDYING WILD LIFE IN KENYA AND TANGANGYIKA WITH THE AID OF MAN-MADE WINGS. Frederick Truber Davison. Nat. Hist., New York, vol. 34, no.2, pp.105-116, illus., Mar.-Apr., 1934.

MAMMALS OF SOMALILAND. Ralph E. Drake-Brockman. London, Hurst and Blackett, Ltd., pp.xvii-201, illus., pls., 1910.

LIST OF MAMMALS FROM SOMALILAND OBTAINED BY THE MUSEUM'S EAST AFRICAN EXPEDITION. D.G. Elliot. Chicago, Field Columbian Mus., Publ.19, Zoological ser., vol.1, no.6, pp.109-155, 1897.

(Review by P. Rode of) (EXPLORATION OF THE NATIONAL PARK OF KAGERA. (MISSION FRECHKOP 1938). I. MAMMALS.) Exploration du Parc National de la Kagers (Mission Frechkop 1938). Fasc.I. Mammiferes. Serge Frechkop. Mammalia, Paris, vol.8, nos.3-4. pp.133-134, Sep.-Dec., 1944.

ALBUM OF ABYSSINIAN BIRDS AND MAMMALS FROM PAINTINGS. L.A. Fuertes. Chicago, Field Mus. Nat. Hist., col.pls. 32, 1930.

ON MAMMALS FROM THE EASTERN SLOPES OF MOUNT ELGON, KENYA COLONY. (Mammals Collected by the Swedish Mount Elgon Expedition 1920.) Hugo Granvik. (From the Zoological Inst., Lund) Lund, C.W.F. Gleerup, pp.32, illus., pl., tbls., (Lunds Univ. Arsskrift, n.F., Avd.2, Bd.21, nr.3) 1924.

(THE LIFE OF THE WILD ANIMALS OF KILIMANJARO.) La vie des animaux sauvages du Killimandjaro. E. Gromier. Durel, Paris, 1948.

GAME ANIMALS OF EASTERN AFRICA. Charles Albert Walter Guggisberg. 2nd rev.ed., Nairobi, Patwa News Agency, (a pocket nature guide), pp.64, illus., 1956.

SHINYANGA GAME EXPERIMENT: A FEW OF THE EARLY OBSERVATIONS. (Habits, Food, and Habitats of 10 Species of Ungulates in Tanganyika.) H. Harrison. Jour. Anim. Ecol., vol.5, no.2, pp.271-293, pls.7-8, figs.5, Nov., 1936.

MAMMALS COLLECTED BY THE ROCKEFELLER-MURPHY EXPEDITION TO THE TANGANYIKA TERRITORY AND THE EASTERN BELGIAN CONGO. Robert T. Hatt. Amer. Mus. Novitates, New York, no.1070, pp.8, May 17, 1940.

DESCRIPTIONS OF SEVEN NEW SPECIES OF EAST AFRICAN MAMMALS. Edmund Heller. Smiths. Misc. Coll., vol.56, no. 9, publ.1942, pp.1-5, pls.1-3, July 22, 1910.

FOUR NEW SUBSPECIES OF LARGE MAMMALS FROM EQUATORIAL AFRICA. Edmund Heller. Smiths. Misc. Coll., vol.61, no.22, publ.2255, pp.7, 1914.

MOUNT LOLOLOKWI THE UNKNOWN. (Account of a Trip to Mount Lololokwi and Mount Gargues, British East Africa, in 1911, When Several New Species of Mammals Were Discovered by Author.) Edmund Heller. Harper's Mag., vol.140, pp.147-160, figs.9, Jan., 1920.

NEW ANTELOPES AND CARNIVORES FROM BRITISH EAST AFRICA. Edmund Heller. Smiths. Misc. Coll., vol.61, no.13, pp.1-5, publ.2240, Sep. 16, 1913.

NEW RACES OF CARNIVORES AND BABOONS FROM EQUATORIAL AFRICA AND ABYSSINIA. Edmund Heller. Smiths. Misc. Coll., vol.61, no.19, publ.2248, pp.1-12, Nov. 8, 1913.

NEW RACES OF INSECTIVORES, BATS, AND LEMURS FROM BRITISH EAST AFRICA. Edmund Heller. Smiths. Misc. Coll., vol.60, no.12, publ.2152, pp.1-13, Nov. 4, 1912.

NEW RACES OF UNGULATES AND PRIMATES FROM EQUATORIAL AFRICA. Edmund Heller. Smiths. Misc. Coll., vol. 61, no.17, publ.2245, pp.1-12, 1913.

NEW SUBSPECIES OF MAMMAL FROM EQUATORIAL AFRICA. Edmund Heller. Smiths. Misc. Coll., vol.63, no.7, publ.2272, pp.1-12, 1914.

IDENTIFICATION OF THE SPOOR AND DUNG OF EAST AFRICAN MAMMALS. P.R. Hesse Jour. East Africa Nat. Hist. Soc., vol.22, no.3, pp.107-110, illus., Feb., 1954.

FAUNA OF EAST AFRICA AND ITS FUTURE. (Distribution, Present Abundance, and Probable Future Abundance of Game Mammals.) C.W. Hobley. Proc. Zool. Soc. London, pt.1, pp.1-15, Apr., 1922.

ABSTRACT OF "EAST AFRICAN MAMMALS IN THE UNITED STATES NATIONAL MUSEUM. PART 1." Ned Hollister. Jour. Washington Acad. Sci., vol. 9, p.50, Jan. 19, 1919.

EAST AFRICAN MAMMALS IN THE UNITED STATES NATIONAL MUSEUM. Ned Hollister. Washington, Govt. Print. Off., vols.3, illus., pls., maps, 1918-24. (Smithsonian Inst., U.S. Nat. Mus., Bull.99.) Vol. 1. Insectivora, Chiroptera, and Carnivora. Vol.2. Rodentia, Lagomorpha, and Tubulidentata. Vol.3. Primates, Artiodactyla, Perissodactyla, Proboscidae, and Hyrocoidae.

(Review by W.H. Osgood of) EAST AFRICAN MAMMALS IN THE UNITED STATES NA-

TIONAL MUSEUM. (Bull.99, U.S.Nat.Mus.) Ned Hollister. Jour. Mamm., vol.1, no.1, p.43, Nov. 28, 1919.

MAMMALS COLLECTED BY JOHN JAY WHITE IN BRITISH EAST AFRICA, WITH TWO PLATES. Ned Hollister. Smiths.Misc. Coll., vol.56, no.2, publ.1930, pp.1-12, pls.2, 1910.

REPORT OF PROCEEDINGS IN CONNEXION WITH THE ABYSSINIAN EXPEDITION. William Jesse. Proc. Zool. Soc. London, pp.111-117, 1869.

ON A COLLECTION OF MAMMALS FROM TANGANYIKA TERRITORY. P.S.Kershaw. Ann. and Mag. Nat. Hist., ser.9, vol.11, pp.586-600, May, 1923.

ON SOME NEW SMALL MAMMALS FROM EAST AFRICA. P.S. Kershaw. Ann. and Mag. Nat. Hist., ser.9, vol.8, pp.563-569, Nov., 1921.

ON SOME SMALL MAMMALS FROM TANGANYIKA TERRITORY. P.S.Kershaw. Ann. and Mag. Nat. Hist., ser. 9, vol.12, pp.534-536, Oct., 1923.

ON TWO COLLECTIONS OF MAMMALS: (1) FROM MONGALLA AND BAHR-EL-GHAZAL, (2) FROM LAKE TSANA, ABYSSINIA. P.S. Kershaw. Ann. and Mag. Nat. Hist., ser.9, vol.13, pp.19-29, Jan., 1924.

TWO NEW MAMMALS FROM EAST AFRICA. P.S. Kershaw. Ann. and Mag. Nat. Hist., ser.9, vol.13, pp.79-81, Jan., 1924.

TWO NEW MAMMALS FROM PEMBA ISLAND, EAST AFRICA. P.S. Kershaw. Ann. and Mag. Nat. Hist., ser.9, vol.13, pp. 556-557, May, 1924.

LETTER RELATING TO THE ANIMALS OF ZANZIBAR. John Kirk. Proc. Zool. Soc. London, pp.952-953, 1867.

LIST OF MAMMALIA MET WITH IN ZAMBESIA, EAST TROPICAL AFRICA. John Kirk. Proc. Zool. Soc. London, pp.649-660, 1864.

NOTE ON THE LAND AND FRESHWATER SHELLS OF THE ZAMBESI AND LAKE NYASSA, EASTERN TROPICAL AFRICA, WITH A CORRECTION TO A PREVIOUS COMMUNICATION ON THE MAMMALS OF THE SAME REGION. John Kirk. Proc. Zool. Soc. London, pp.231-234, 1865.

ZOOLOGICAL RESULTS OF A FIFTH EXPEDITION TO EAST AFRICA. I. MAMMALS FROM NYASALAND AND TETE. WITH NOTES ON THE GENUS OTOMYS. Barbara Lawrence. Arthur Loveridge. Bull. Mus. Comp.Zool., Cambridge, vol.110, no.1, pp.1-80, pls.1-3, June, 1953.

MAMMALS COLLECTED BY H. R. H. PRINCE VILHELM'S EXPEDITION TO BRITISH EAST AFRICA 1914. E. Lonnberg. Arkiv. Zool., Upsala, vol.10, no.12, pp.1-32, May 19, 1916

MAMMALS COLLECTED BY THE SWEDISH ZOOLOGICAL EXPEDITION TO BRITISH EAST AFRICA 1911. Einar Lonnberg. Kungl.Svenska, Vetenskap.Handl., vol. 48, no.5, pp.4-188, pls.1-15, 1912.

(SCIENTIFIC RESULTS OF THE EXPEDITION OF THE SWEDISH PROF. DR. YNGVE SJOSTEDT TO KILIMANJARO, MERU AND THE SURROUNDING PLAINS OF GERMAN EAST AFRICA. 1905-06.) Wiss.Ergeb. Schwed.Zool.Exped.Nach. dem Kilimandjaro, dem Meru und den Umgebenden Massaisteppen Deutsch-Ostafrikas 1905-06, unter Leitung von Prof. Yngve Sjostedt. Mammals. Einar Lonnberg. No.2, pp.1-58, pls.7, 1908.

EAST AFRICAN EXPEDITION OF 1926. Arthur Loveridge. Proc. U.S. Nat. Mus., no.2738, vol.73, pp.1-69, 1926.

FIELD NOTES ON VERTEBRATES COLLECTED BY THE SMITHSONIAN CHRYSLER EAST AFRICAN EXPEDITIONS OF 1926. Arthur Loveridge. Proc. U.S. Nat. Mus., vol.73, art.17, pp.1-69, pls.1-4, 1928.

MOUNTAIN SAFARI. (Account of Some Mammals in Uluguru Mountains, East Africa.) Arthur Loveridge. Fauna, Philadelphia, vol.6, no.3, pp.82-85, figs.2, Sep., 1944.

NOTES ON EAST AFRICAN MAMMALIA (OTHER THEN HORNED UNGULATES) COLLECTED OR KEPT IN CAPTIVITY 1915-1919. PART I. Arthur Loveridge. Jour. East Africa and Uganda Nat. Hist. Soc., no.16, pp.38-42, Feb., 1921.

NOTES ON EAST AFRICAN MAMMALIA (OTHER THAN HORNED UNGULATES) COLLECTED OR KEPT IN CAPTIVITY 1915-1919. PART II. Arthur Loveridge. Jour. East Africa and Uganda Nat. Hist. Soc., no.17, pp.39-69, Mar., 1922.

NOTES ON EAST AFRICAN MAMMALS, COLLECTED 1920-1923. Arthur Loveridge. Proc. Zool. Soc. London, pp.685-739, map, Dec., 1923.

(FAUNA OF GERMAN EAST AFRICA.) Zur Faunistik Deutsch-Ost-Afrikas. Paul Matschie. Arch. f. Naturg., Berlin, Bd.1, Hft.1, pp.81-88, 1897.

(MAMMALS OF GERMAN EAST AFRICA.) Saeugethiere Deutsch-Ost-Afrikas. Paul Matschie. Berlin, pp.157, illus., 1895.

(ON A SMALL COLLECTION OF MAMMALS AND REPTILES BROUGHT BACK BY HERR L. CONRADT FROM USAMBARA (GERMAN EAST AFRICA).) Ueber eine kleine Sammlung von Saeugethieren und Reptilien, welche Herr L.Conradt aus Usambara (Deutsch-Ostafrika) heimgebracht hat. Paul Matschie. Sitz.Ber. Gesell.Naturf.Freunde, Berlin, no.7, pp. 101-111, July 19, 1892.

(SOME COMMUNICATIONS ON THE MAMMALS OF THE KENYA REGION AND KARAGWE.) Einige Nachrichten ueber die Saeugethiere des Kenia-Gebietes und von Karagwe. Paul Matschie. Sitz.Ber.Gesell. Naturf.Freunde, Berlin, no.7, pp.138-139, July 18, 1899.

(SOME MAMMALS OF GERMAN EAST AFRICA.) Einige Saeugethiere von Deutsch-Ost-Afrika. Paul Matschie. Sitz.Ber.Gesell.Naturf.Freunde, Berlin, no.8, pp. 130-140, Oct. 18, 1892.

(THREE NEW MAMMALS OF EAST AFRICA (HERPESTES, PEDIOTRAGUS, CHRYSOCHLORIS).) Drei neue Saeugethiere (Herpestes, Pediotragus, Chrysochloris) von Ostafrika. Paul Matschie. Sitz. Ber.Gesell.Naturf.Freunde, Berlin, no.4, pp.121-125, Apr. 17, 1894.

(ZOOGEOGRAPHICAL REGIONS OF ETHIOPIA.) Zoogeographischen Gebiete der aethiopischen Region. Paul Matschie. Sitz. Ber. Gesell. Naturf. Freunde, Berlin, no.7, pp.86-93, July 19, 1898.

DUSK IN KENYA. (Photograph of Two Lions and Herd of Zebra.) Marcuswell Maxwell. Field, London, vol.168, no.4369, p.677, illus., Sep. 19, 1936.

BIG GAME SEEN FROM THE AIR. THE EXPERIENCES OF AN AIR PILOT IN EAST AFRICA. Walter Mittelholser. Field, London, vol.158, no.4122, pp.950-952, illus., Dec. 26, 1931.

(FROM SOMALILAND COAST THROUGH SOUTHERN ETHIOPIA TO THE SUDAN.) Von der Somali-Kueste durch Sued-Aethiopen zum Sudan. Oskar Neumann. Zeitschr.Gesell.f.Erdk., Berlin, no.1, pp.7-32, map, illus., 1902.

(MAMMALS I COLLECTED AND OBSERVED IN THE YEARS 1892-95 IN EAST AND CENTRAL AFRICA, PARTICULARLY IN THE MASSAI LANDS AND THE LANDS ON LAKE VICTORIA.) Die von mir in den Jahren 1892-95 in Ost- und Central-Afrika, Speciell in den Massai-Laendern und den Laendern am Victoria Nyansa gesammelten und beobachteten Saeugethiere. Oskar Neumann. Zool. Jahrb., Abt. Syst.Geog.u.Biol.der Thiere, Jena, vol.13, no.6, pp.529-562, fold.map, Oct. 10, 1900.

(DATA ON THE MAMMAL FAUNA OF EAST AFRICA.) Kenntnis der Saeugetier-Fauna von Ostafrika. Th. Noack. Jahrb. Hamburg Wissensch.Anstalten, vol.9, pp.3-76-160, pls.1-2, 1891.

DIAGNOSIS OF NEW EAST AFRICAN MAMMALS, INCLUDING A NEW GENUS OF MURIDAE. Wilfred Hudson Osgood. Chicago, Field Mus. Nat. Hist., publ.141, Zoological ser., vol.10, no.2, pp.13, 1910.

FURTHER NEW MAMMALS FROM BRITISH EAST AFRICA. Wilfred H. Osgood. Field Mus.Nat.Hist., Chicago, publ.143, Zool. ser., vol.10, no. 3, pp.15-21, Apr. 7, 1910.

(ANIMALS FULLY PROTECTED IN ITALIAN EASTERN AFRICA.) Animali protetti in modo assoluto nell'Africa Orientale Italiana. S. Patrizi. Ministero dell'Africa Italiana, Roma, pp.3-18, illus., 1937.

(ON THE MAMMALS COLLECTED BY DR. G. A. FISCHER ON HIS JOURNEY IN EAST AFRICA, FROM MOMBASA TO POKOMO AND SOUTHERN GALLA, IN 1878.) Ueber die von Hrn.Dr.G.A.Fischer auf einer im Jahre 1878 in Ostafrika, von Mombas bis in das Pokomo-Land und das suedliche Galla-Land, unternommenen Reise eingesammelten Saeugethiere. W. Peters. Sitz.Ber. Akad. Wissensch., Berlin, pp.829-832, pls.1-5, Oct.27, 1879.

KENYA'S WILDLIFE RESOURCE AND THE NATIONAL PARKS. George A.Petrides. Royal Nat.Parks of Kenya, Nairobi, pp.iii-24, Mar. 15, 1955.

MAMMALS COLLECTED BY DR. A. D. SMITH DURING HIS EXPEDITION TO LAKE RUDOLF, AFRICA. Samuel N. Rhoads. Proc. Acad.Nat.Sciences, Philadelphia, pp.517-546, illus., pl.25, Oct., 1896.

LIFE-HISTORIES OF AFRICAN GAME ANIMALS. Theodore Roosevelt, Edmund Heller. New York, C.Scribner's Sons, vols.2, illus., maps, 1914.

MAMMALS. Walter Rothschild. (In) P.H.G. Powell-Cotton, a Sporting Trip Through Abyssinia, London, Appendix 3, pp.453-486, illus., 1902.

MAMMALS COLLECTED BY THE LAKE RUDOLF RIFT VALLEY EXPEDITION, 1934, WITH POSTSCRIPT BY R. W. HAYMAN. Jane St. Leger. Ann. and Mag. Nat. Hist., London, ser.10, vol.19, no.113, pp. 524-531, May, 1937.

ON SOME MAMMALS COLLECTED BY DR. DRAKE-BROCKMAN IN SOMALILAND. Jane St. Leger. Ann. and Mag. Nat. Hist., London, ser.10, vol.15, no.90, pp.666-673, June, 1935.

(Review by Francis H. Herrick of) FLASHLIGHTS IN THE JUNGLE: A RECORD OF HUNTING ADVENTURES AND OF STUDIES IN WILD LIFE IN EQUATORIAL EAST AFRICA. C.G. Schillings. Science, Lancaster, n.s., vol.23, no.588, pp.540-544, Apr.6, 1906.

MAMMALS OF KILIMANJARO. P. L. Sclater. Nat. Science, London, vol.2, no.14, pp.257-268, figs.4, Apr., 1895.

ON SOME MAMMALS FROM SOMALILAND. P.L. Sclater. Proc. Zool. Soc. London, for 1884, pt.4, pp.538-542, pls.49-50, Apr. 1, 1885.

ON THE MAMMALS COLLECTED AND OBSERVED BY CAPT. J. H. SPEKE DURING THE EAST-AFRICAN EXPEDITION; WITH NOTES BY CAPT. J. H. SPEKE. P.L. Sclater. Proc. Zool. Soc. London, pp.98-115, pls.12-13, illus., 1864.

LETTER RELATING TO SOME SPECIMENS OF ANIMALS FROM ZANZIBAR. Capt. J.H. Speke. Proc. Zool. Soc. London, pt.29, p.267, 1861.

NOTES ON THE HABITS OF TWO MAMMALS OBSERVED IN THE SOMALI COUNTRY, EASTERN AFRICA. Capt. J.H. Speke. Proc. Zool. Soc. London, pt.27, p.234, 1859.

BIG GAME IN KENYA. (Photos of Giraffe and Zebra.) C.H. Stockley. Field, London, vol.174, no.4523, p.557, illus., Sep.2, 1939.

AN AFRICAN HOLIDAY. (Big-Game Hunting in East Africa.) Richard L. Sutton. St. Louis, C.V.Mosby Co., pp.180, illus., Oct., 1924.

REVISION OF THE TYPE-LOCALITIES OF MAMMALS OCCURRING IN THE TANGANYIKA TERRITORY. G.H. Swynnerton. Proc. Zool. Soc. London, vol.115, pt.1-2, pp. 49-84, Oct., 1945.

DIAGNOSES OF TWO NEW EAST-AFRICAN MAMMALS. Oldfield Thomas. Ann. and Mag. Nat. Hist., ser.6, vol.15, no.86, pp. 187-188, Feb., 1895.

(EXPLORATION OF THE GIUBA RIVER AND ITS TRIBUTARIES BY CAPT. V. BOTTEGO DURING THE YEARS 1892-93 UNDER THE ANSPICES OF THE ITALIAN GEOGRAPHIC SOCIETY. ZOOLOGICAL RESULTS. MAMMALS.) Esplorazione del Giuba e dei suoi Affuenti compiuta dal Cap. V. Bottego durante gli anni 1892-1893 sotto gli auspicii della Societa Geografica Italiana-Risultati Zoologici. Mammiferi. Oldfield Thomas. Annali del Museo Civ. di Storia Nat. di Genova, ser.2, vol.15, pp.1-4, Mar. 30, 1895.

LIST OF MAMMALS FROM MOUNT KILIMANJARO, OBTAINED BY MR. ROBIN KEMP, AND PRESENTED TO THE BRITISH MUSEUM BY MR. C. D. RUDD. Oldfield Thomas. Ann. and Mag. Nat.Hist., ser.8, vol.6, no.33, pp.308-316, Sep., 1910.

LIST OF MAMMALS OBTAINED BY MR. H. J. MACKINDER DURING HIS RECENT EXPEDITION TO MOUNT KENYA, BRITISH EAST AFRICA. Oldfield Thomas. Proc. Zool. Soc. London, pp.173-180, fig., Feb. 20, 1900.

LIST OF SMALL MAMMALS OBTAINED BY MR. A. E. PEASE, N. P., DURING HIS RECENT EXPEDITION TO ABYSSINIA, WITH DESCRIPTIONS OF THREE NEW FORMS OF MACROSCELIDES. Oldfield Thomas. Ann. and Mag. Nat. Hist., ser. 7, vol.8, no.44, pp.154-156, Aug., 1901.

LYCAON AND PEDETES OF BRITISH EAST AFRICA, AND A NEW GERBILLE FROM N. NYASA. Oldfield Thomas. Ann. and Mag. Nat. Hist., ser.7, vol.9, no.54, pp. 438-442, June, 1902.

NEW AFRICAN MAMMALS. EXHIBITION OF SMALL MAMMALS COLLECTED BY MR. ALEXANDER WHYTE DURING HIS EXPEDITION TO THE NYIKA PLATEAU AND THE MASUKU MOUNTAINS, N. NYASA. Oldfield Thomas. Proc. Zool. Soc. London, pp.430-436, May 4, 1897.

ON A COLLECTION OF MAMMALS FROM ABYSSINIA, INCLUDING SOME FROM LAKE TSANA, COLLECTED BY MR. EDWARD DEGEN. Oldfield Thomas. Proc. Zool. Soc. London, pp.308-316, Nov.4, 1902.

ON A COLLECTION OF MAMMALS OBTAINED IN SOMALILAND BY MAJOR H. N. DUNN, R. A. M. C. WITH DESCRIPTION OF ALLIED SPECIES FROM OTHER LOCALITIES. Oldfield Thomas. Ann. and Mag. Nat. Hist., ser.7, vol.14, no. 80, pp.94-105, Aug., 1904.

ON A COLLECTION OF SMALL MAMMALS MADE BY MR. F. J. JACKSON IN EASTERN AFRICA. Oldfield Thomas. Proc. Zool. Soc. London, pp.181-187, pl.15, fig., Mar. 3, 1891.

ON THE MAMMALS COLLECTED DURING CAPT. BOTTEGO'S LAST EXPEDITION TO LAKE RUDOLF AND THE UPPER SOBAT. Oldfield Thomas. Annali del Museo Civ. di Storia Nat. di Genova, ser. 2, vol.18, pp.676-679, Feb. 21, 1898.

PRELIMINARY DIAGNOSES OF FOUR NEW MAMMALS FROM EAST AFRICA. Oldfield Thomas. Ann. and Mag. Nat. Hist., ser.6, vol.7, no.39, pp.303-304, Mar., 1891.

REPORT ON THE MAMMALS OBTAINED AND OBSERVED BY MR. H. H. JOHNSTON ON MOUNT KILIMANJARO. Oldfield Thomas. Proc. Zool. Soc. London, pp. 219-222, pl.12, Mar.3, 1885.

SOME RARITIES FROM ABYSSINIA WITH THE DESCRIPTION OF A NEW MOLE-RAT (TACHYORYCTES) AND A NEW ARVICANTHIS. Oldfield Thomas. Ann. and Mag. Nat. Hist., ser.10, vol.1, no.2, pp. 302-304, Feb., 1928.

TWO NEW GENERA OF SMALL MAMMALS DISCOVERED BY MRS. HOLMSTARN IN BRITISH EAST AFRICA. Oldfield Thomas. Ann. and Mag. Nat. Hist., ser.7, vol.18, no.105, pp.222-226, Sep., 1906.

WILDLIFE PARKS OF EAST AFRICA. Dan Lincoln Thrapp. Nature Mag., Washington, vol.43, no.1, pp.34-37, 50, illus., Jan., 1950.

(NEW AND LITTLE KNOWN MAMMALS OF EAST AFRICA.) Mammiferi nuovi e poco noti dell'Africa Orientale. Augusto Toschi. Bologna, Univ., Lab. di Zool. Applicata alla Caccia. Supplemento alle Ricerche di zoologia applicata alla caccia vol.2, no.1, pp.10.

(ECOLOGICAL NOTES ON SOME MAMMALS OF OLARGASAILLE (MASAI RESERVE, KENYA).) Note ecologiche su alcuni mammiferi di Olorgasailie (Masai Reserve, Kenya C.). Augusto Toschi. Bologna, Univ., Lab. di Zool. Applicata alla Caccia. Supplemento alle Ricerche di zool. applicata alla caccia, vol.2, no.3, pp.63, 1949.

(ON THE ZOOGEOGRAPHIC INDIVIDUALITY OF THE SUBREGION OF NORTHERN EAST AFRICA.) Sulla individualita zoogeografica della sottoregione dell Africa orientale settentrionale. Augusto Toschi. Rivista di Biol. Coloniale, vol.8, pp.14, 1947.

ANNOTATED CATALOGUE OF THE MAMMALS COLLECTED BY DR. W. L. ABBOTT IN THE KILIMANJARO REGION, EAST AFRICA. F.W. True. Proc. U.S. Nat. Mus., vol.15, no.915, pp.445-480, Oct. 26, 1892.

DESCRIPTION OF TWO NEW SPECIES OF MAMMALS FROM MOUNT KILIMANJARO, EAST AFRICA. F.W. True. U.S. Nat. Mus., Proceedings, Washington 1891, vol. 13, pp.227-229, Sep. 16, 1890.

NOTES ON A SMALL COLLECTION OF MAMMALS FROM TANA RIVER, EAST AFRICA, WITH DESCRIPTIONS OF NEW SPECIES. F.W. True. Proc. U.S. Nat. Mus., vol.16, publ.954, pp.601-603, Oct. 25, 1893.

ON A SMALL COLLECTION OF MAMMALS MADE BY MR. C. V. A. PEEL IN SOMALILAND. W.E. de Winton. Ann. and Mag. Nat. Hist., ser.7, vol.1, pp. 247-251, 1898.

ON THE MAMMALS OBTAINED IN SOUTHERN ABYSSINIA BY LORD LOVAT DURING AN EXPEDITION FROM BERBERA TO THE BLUE NILE. W.E. de Winton. Proc. Zool. Soc. London, pp.79-84, 1900.

SOME SERVALS AND AN OTOMYS FROM EAST AFRICA. R.C. Wroughton. Ann. and Mag. Nat. Hist., ser.8, vol.5, pp. 205-207, Feb., 1910.

(THE ITALIAN COLONY OF DIRETTO DOMINO. FAUNA AND GAME.) Le Colonie Italiane di Diretto Domino. Fauna e Caccia. (Maps and Many Photographs Chiefly of Mammals.) Vittorio Tedesco Zammarano. Rome, Ministero delle Colonie, Ufficio Studi e Propaganda, 1930.

NIGHT WATCH IN KENYA. ELEPHANT AND RHINOCEROS WHILE YOU WAIT. Field, London, vol.162, no.4215, p.921, illus., Oct. 7, 1933.

WILDLIFE OF TANGANYIKA. ATTRACTIVE SCENES OF AFRICA FROM AKELEY AFRICAN HALL. Nat. Hist., New York, vol.51, no.4, pp.186-187, illus., Apr., 1943.

## AFRICA, NORTHERN

### Extinct and Fossil Mammals

(CAVE OF ANGLADE QUARRY AT GUYOTVILLE, ALGERIA.) La grotte de la carriere Anglade a Guyotville (D[r] d'Alger). C. Arambourg. Bull. Soc. Hist. Nat. Afrique du Nord, Alger, vol.26, no.1, pp.15-22, figs.3, pls.2, Jan., 1935.

(FOSSIL MAMMALS OF MOROCCO.) Mammiferes fossiles du Maroc. C. Arambourg. Mem. Soc. Sci. Nat. Maroc, Paris, no.46, pp.1-72, figs.15, pls.9, Dec. 15, 1938.

(PALEONTOLOGY OF VERTEBRATES IN FRENCH NORTH AFRICA.) La paleontologie des vertebres en Afrique du Nord Fancaise. C. Arambourg. Monog. Regionales, 19th Internat. Geol. Congr., pp.5-62, 1952.

(PRELIMINARY NOTE ON A NEW BONE CAVE NEAR ALGIERS.) Note preliminaire sur une nouvelle grotte a ossements des environs d'Alger. C. Arambourg. Bull. Soc. Hist. Nat. Afrique du Nord, vol.23, no.7, pp.154-162, figs.4, July 15, 1932.

(QUATERNARY MAMMALS OF ALGERIA.) Les Mammiferes quaternaires de l'Algerie. C. Arambourg. Bull. Soc. Hist. Nat. Afrique du Nord, vol.20, no.3, pp.63-84, pl.1, 1929.

(PALEOLITHIC CAVES OF BENI SEGOUAL (ALGERIA).) Les Grottes Paleolithiques des Beni-Segoual (Algerie). C. Arambourg, M. Boule, H. Vallois, R. Verneau. Arch. Inst. Paleontol. Humaine, Paris, Mem.13, pp.1-242, figs.48, pls.1-22, Dec., 1934. (Mammals, pp. 29, 36-67.)

(TWO-MONTH EXCURSION THROUGH YEBALA.) Una excursion de dos Meses por Yebala. Angel Cabrera. Bol. R. Soc. Española Hist. Nat., vol.22, pp.101-113, Feb., 1922.

(NEW REMAINS OF MOROCCAN HIPPOPOTAMUSES, RHINOCEROSES, AND ELEPHANTS.) Nouvelles pieces d'hippopotames, de rhinoceros et d'elephants marocains. Emile Ennouchi. Bull. Soc. Sci. Nat. & Phys. Maroc, vol.36, pp.307-317, 1956.

(FAUNA OF THE ROCK ENGRAVINGS OF NORTHERN AFRICA.) La Faune des gravures rupestres nord-africaines. L. Joleaud. XV Cong. Internat. Anthrop. et Archeol. Prehist. (Suite) V Sess. Inst. Internat. Anthrop., Paris, Sep.20-27, 1931. pp.220-227, 1933.

(QUATERNARY MAMMALS OF OUNIANGA KEBIR (SOUTHEAST TIBESTI).) Mammiferes quaternaires d'Ounianga Kebir (Tibesti sud-oriental.) L. Joleaud. Comptes Rendus Acad. Sci., Paris, vol.196, no.7, pp.497-499, Feb. 13, 1933.

(CONDITIONS OF FOSSILIZATION AND BEDS OF SOME QUATERNARY MAMMALS OF OUNIANGA KEBIR (SOUTHEAST TEBESTI).) Conditions de fossilisation et de gisement des mammiferes quaternaires d'Ounianga Kebir (Tibesti sud-oriental.) L. Joleaud, J. Lombard. Bull. Soc. Geol. France, Paris, ser.5, vol.3, nos.3-4, pp. 239-243, map, Dec., 1933.

(PRESENCE OF SIMIA PROINUUS AND BUBALUS ANTIQUUS AT THE GRAND ROCHER PREHISTORIC STATION OF GUYOTVILLE.) Presence de Simia proinuus et de Bubalus antiquus a la station Prehistorique de Grand Rocher de Guyotville. H. Marchand. Bull. Soc. Hist. Nat. Afrique du Nord, vol.21, no. 9, pp.197-199, 1930.

PLEISTOCENE MAMMALS OF ALGERIA. FAUNA OF THE PALEOLITHIC STATION OF MECHTA-EL-ARBI. Alfred S. Romer. Logan Mus. Bull., Beloit, Wisc., vol.1, no.2, pp.79-163, tbls., 1928.

### Recent Mammals

(ADDITIONS TO THE MASTOZOOLOGICAL FAUNA OF IFNI TERRITORY.) Additions a la faune Mastozoologique du territoire d'Ifni. E. Morales Agacino. Mammalia, Paris, vol. 4, no.2, pp.59-62, June, 1940.

(DATA AND OBSERVATIONS ON SOME MOROCCAN MAMMALS.) Datos observaciones sobre algunos Mamiferos Marroquies. E. Morales Agacino. Bol. Soc. Española Hist. Nat., Madrid, vol. 33, pp.257-266, fig.1, 1933.

(MAMMALS OF IFNI.) Mamiferos de Ifni. E. Morales Agocino. Bol. Soc. Espanola Hist. Nat., Madrid, vol.35, no.7, pp. 381-393, fig.1, Aug. 25, 1935.

(AN EXPEDITION OF 2 MONTHS TO YEBALA.) Una excursion de dos meses por Yebala. Angel Cabrera. Bol. Real Soc. Espanola Hist. Nat., Madrid, vol. 22, nos.1-2, pp.101-115, Jan.-Feb., 1922.

(MAMMALS FROM MOGADOR.) Mamiferos de Mogador. Angel Cabrera. Bol. Real Soc. Espanola Hist. Nat., Madrid, vol.6, no.7, pp.357-368, July, 1906.

(MAMMALS OF MOROCCO.) Los mamiferos de Marruecos. Angel Cabrera. Trabajos de Museo Nac. de Ciencias Nat., Madrid, zool. ser.no.57, pp.361, col.pls.12, figs.34, Dec. 30, 1932.

(MAMMALS OF THE ZAIAN COUNTRY (MOROCCO).) Les Mammiferes du pays Zaian (Morocco). C.J. Carpentier. Bull. Soc. Sci. Nat. Maroc., vol.12, nos.1-3, pp.11-22, 1932.

(THE VERTEBRATES OF FORT BOURDONNEAU AT FES, MOROCCO.) Les vertébrés du Fort Bourdonneau a Fés (Maroc). Ch. Depéret. Bull. Soc. Hist. Nat. Toulouse, vol.57, no.3, pp.277-295, pls.4, fig.1, 1928.

ON A COLLECTION OF MAMMALS FROM MOROCCO. W.E. deWinton F.Z.S. Proc. Zool. Soc. London, pp.953-962, 1897.

(BIOGEOGRAPHY OF THE MAMMALS AND BIRDS OF NORTH AFRICA.) Biogeographie des mammifères et des oiseaux de l'Afrique du Nord. Henri Heim de Balsac. Paris, Éditions du Bulletin Biologique de la France et de la Belgique, pp.446, illus., pls., maps, diagrs., 1936.

(NOTES ON THE OCCURRENCE AND DISTRIBUTION OF SOME LARGE MAMMALS IN SOUTHERN ORAN AND EASTERN MOROCCO.) Notes sur la présence et la repartition de quelques grands Mammifères dans le Sud-Oranais et le Maroc oriental. H. Heim de Balsac. Rev. Francaise Mammal., ser.1, no.2, pp.83-92, Dec.7, 1928.

(JOURNEY IN NORTHEAST AFRICA.) Reise in Nordost-Afrika. M.J. v. Henglin. Vol.2, p.80, 1877.

ON A COLLECTION OF MAMMALS FROM THE DINKA COUNTRY, BAHR-EL-DJEBEL. A.C. Martin Hinton, P.S. Kershaw. Ann. and Mag. Nat. Hist., ser.9, vol.6, pp.94-101, July, 1920.

(GENERAL CONSIDERATIONS ON THE MAMMAL FAUNA OF MOROCCO.) Considerations générales sur la faune des mammiferes du Maroc. L. Joleaud. La Terre et la Vie, vol.4, no.5, pp.259-271, figs.1-10, May, 1934.

(REMARKS ON THE ZOOGEOGRAPHY OF EASTERN ALGERIA.) Remarques sur la zoogéographie de l'Algérie orientale. L. Joleaud. Compte rend. Soc. Biogeogr., Paris, no.25, pp.5-8, Jan. 21, 1927.

(ZOOGEOGRAPHICAL REGIONS OF NORTH AFRICA.) Les regions zoogeographiques de l'Afrique du Nord. L. Joleaud. Revue Geogr. Marocaine, Soc. Geogr. Maroc, vol.7, no.7, pp.17-38, 1928.

(MAMMALS FROM TUNIS, COLLECTED BY ALFRED WEIDHOLZ, 1912.) Saeugetiere aus Tunis, gesammelt von Alfred Weidholz, 1912. Otto Koller. Ann. Naturhist. Mus. Wien, vol.44, pp.1-4, 1930.

(CONTRIBUTION TO KNOWLEDGE OF THE VERTEBRATE FAUNA OF MOROCCO (AMPHIBIANS, REPTILES, MAMMALS).) Contribution a la connaissance de la faune des Vertebres du Maroc (Batraciens, Reptiles, Mammiferes.) Paul Laurent. Bull. Soc. Hist. Nat. de l'Afrique du Nord, vol.26, no.9, pp.344-359, Dec., 1935.

(COMPOSITION AND ORIGIN OF THE MAMMAL AND ORNITHOLOGICAL FAUNA OF THE BARBARY.) La composition et les origines de la fauna mammalogique et ornithologique de la Berberie. L. Lavauden. Compte Rendu Congres Assoc. francaise avance. Sci. Constantine, 51 Sess., pp.267-270, 1927.

(NOTES ON NORTH AFRICA MAMMALOGY. CATS.) Notes de mammalogie nord-africaine. Les Chats. L. Lavauden. Bull. Soc. d'Hist. de l'Afrique du Nord, vol.19, pp.255-262, July, 1928.

(NATURAL HISTORY OF ALGERIAN MAMMALS.) Histoire Naturelle des Mammiferes de l'Algerie. Commandant Loche. 1867.

(LIST OF THE MAMMALS COLLECTED IN TUNISIA DURING THE YEARS 1896-1897 ON THE EXPEDITION OF CARLO FREIHERR VON ERLANGER.) Liste der waehrend der Expedition in den Jahren 1896-1897 von Carlo Freiherr von Erlanger in Tunesien gesammelten Saeugetiere. Paul Matschie. Beitraege zur Avifauna Tunesiens II. Kurzer Reisebericht, Beilage zum Jour. f. Ornithologie, pp.62-63, 1899.

(FACTS AND OBSERVATIONS ABOUT SOME MOROCCAN MAMMALS.) Datos y observaciones sobre algunos mamiferos marroquies. Agacino E. Morales. Bol. Soc. Española Hist. Nat., Madrid, vol.33, nos. 6-7, pp.257-266, figs.1, 1933.

(BRIEF COMMUNICATION ON THE ZOOLOGICAL FINDINGS OF MY EXPEDITION THROUGH NORTHEAST AFRICA 1900-1901.) Kurze Mitteilung ueber die zoologischen Resultate meiner Expedition durch Nordost-Afrika 1900-1901. Oscar Neumann. Verhandl. 5th Internat. Zool. Congr. Berlin, Jena, for 1901, pp.8, illus., 1902.

(NEW MAMMALS OF NORTHEAST AND EAST AFRICA.) Neue nordost- und ostafrikanische Saeugethiere. Oscar Neumann. Sitz. Ber. Gesell. Naturf. Freunde, Berlin, no.3, pp.49-59, pl.1, Mar. 18, 1902; no.4, pp.93-102, Apr. 15, 1902.

ON MAMMALS FROM NORTH-EAST AFRICA. Oscar Neumann. Proc. Zool. Soc. London, vol.2, pt.1, pp.142-144, Oct., 1902.

(MATERIALS OF THE MISSION FOR STUDY OF THE BIOLOGY OF ACRIDIENS. VERTEBRATES OF ENNEDI.) Matériaux de la Mission d'Etudes de la Biologie des Acridiens. Vertébrés de l'Ennedi. G. Petit. Bull. Soc. Hist. Nat., Afrique du Nord, Alger, vol.28, no.6, pp.392-405, fig.1, pl.41, June, 1937.

(MAMMALS OF NORTH AFRICA. II.) Les mammiferes de l'Afrique du Nord. II. P. Rode. La Terre et la Vie, Bull. Soc. Nat. D'Acclimatation et de Protection de la Nature, Paris, vol.95, no.3, pp.125-150, figs.8, pl.1, July-Sep., 1948.

(ATLAS OF E. RUEPPELL'S TRAVELS IN NORTH AFRICA. MAMMALS TREATED BY J. CRETZCHMAR, M.D.) Atlas zu der Reise im nordlichen Afrika von E. Rueppell. Saeugethiere Bearbeitet von Dr. Med. Ph. J. Cretzchmar. Eduard Ruppell. Frankfurt am Main, Gedruckt und in Commission bei Heinr. Ludw. Bronner, 1826.

(NOTES ON SOME SMALL MAMMALS OF ATLANTIC MOROCCO.) Notes sur quelques petits mammifères du Maroc atlantique. M.C. Saint-Girons, F. Petter. Mammalia, Paris, vol.17, no.4, pp.318-321, Dec., 1953.

(DOMESTIC ANIMALS ON THE ROCK FORMATIONS OF NORTH AFRICA.) Die Haustiere auf den nordafrikanischen Felsbildern. Adolf Staffe. Forschungen und Fortschritte, Berlin, Jahrg.15, no.27, pp.344-346, Sep. 20, 1939.

LIST OF MAMMALS OBTAINED BY THE HON. WALTER ROTHSCHILD, ERNST HARTERT AND CARL HILGERT IN WESTERN ALGERIA DURING 1913. Oldfield Thomas. Novitates Zoologicae, vol.20, pp.586-591, Oct., 1913.

NEW MAMMALS COLLECTED IN NORTH-EAST AFRICA BY MR. ZAPHIRO AND PRESENTED TO THE BRITISH MUSEUM BY W.N. McMILLAN, ESQ. Oldfield Thomas. Ann. and Mag. Nat. Hist., ser.7, vol.18, no.106, pp.300-306, Oct., 1906.

(NEW MONKEYS AND BATS OF NORTH-EAST AFRICA (SESSION OF THE CLASS OF MATHEMATICS AND NATURAL SCIENCES OF 6 JULY 1916).) Neue Affen und Fledermaeuse aus Nordost-Afrika (Sitzung der mathematisch-naturwissenschaftlichen Klasse vom 6 Juli 1916). Otto von Wettstein. Anzeiger Kais. Akd. Wissensch., Wie, vol. 53, no.18, pp.189-192, 1916.

ON A COLLECTION OF MAMMALS FROM MOROCCO. W.E. de Winton. Proc. Zool. Soc. London, pp.953-962, figs.4, Dec.14, 1897.

## AFRICA, SOUTHERN

### Extinct and Fossil Mammals

AGE OF AUSTRALOPITHECUS. R. Broom. Nature, London, vol.125, no.3161, p.814, May 31, 1930.

NOTICES OF A FEW MORE NEW FOSSIL MAMMALS FROM THE CAVES OF THE TRANSVAAL. R. Broom. Ann. & Mag. Nat. Hist., London, ser.10, vol.20, no. 119, pp.509-514, Nov., 1937.

ON SOME NEW MAMMALS FROM THE DIAMOND GRAVELS OF THE KIMBERLY DISTRICT. R. Broom. Ann. South Afr. Mus., vol.22, no.3, pp.439-444, figs.3, Nov., 1928.

ON SOME NEW PLEISTOCENE MAMMALS FROM LIMESTONE CAVES OF THE TRANSVAAL. R. Broom. S. African Jour. Sci., Johannesburg, vol.33, pp.750-768, figs.8, Mar., 1937.

SOME SOUTH AFRICAN PLIOCENE AND PLEISTOCENE MAMMALS. R. Broom. Ann. Transvaal Mus., Cambridge, vol. 21, pt.1, pp.1-38, illus., Apr. 6, 1948.

FURTHER EXCAVATIONS (1939) AT THE MUMBWA CAVES, NORTHERN RHODESIA. J. Desmond Clark. Trans. Roy. Soc. South Africa, Cape Town, vol.29, pt.3, pp.133-201, figs.17, pls.15-17, Sep., 1942.

FOSSIL MAMMALS OF THE VAAL RIVER DEPOSITS. H.B.S. Cooke. Pretoria Govt. Printer, pp.117, illus., maps, 1949. (South Africa, Geological Survey, Memoir no.35, pt.3.)

ON A COLLECTION OF FOSSIL MAMMALIAN REMAINS FROM THE VAAL RIVER GRAVELS AT PNIEL. H.B.S. Cooke. S. African Jour. Sci., Johannesburg, vol.36, pp.412-416, figs.2, Dec., 1939.

A PRELIMINARY ACCOUNT OF THE WONDERWERK CAVE, KURUMAN DISTRICT. SECT. 2: THE FOSSIL REMAINS. H.B.S. Cooke. S. African Jour. Sci. Johannesburg, vol.37, pp.303-312, figs.2-5, Feb., 1941.

FOSSIL REMAINS FROM CHELMER, NEAR BULAWAYO, SOUTHERN RHODESIA. H.B. S. Cooke, L.H. Wells. S. African Jour. Sci., Johannesburg, vol.47, no.7, pp.205-209, Feb., 1951.

FOSSIL MAN AND CONTEMPORARY FAUNAS IN SOUTHERN AFRICA. R.A. Dart. Pan-Amer. Geol., vol.60, no.5, p.379, Dec., 1933.

NEW FOSSIL MAMMALS AND MAN FROM SOUTH AFRICA. T.F. Dreyer, Alice Lyle. Publ. Fort Hart Native College, Bloemfontain, pp.60, figs.12, 1931.

(SOME ZOOLOGICAL COMMENTS ON TRAVEL IN THE SOUTHERN PART OF THE CAPE OF GOOD HOPE PROVINCE. 1853-1856.) Zoologiska anteckningar under en resa i sodra delarne af Caplandet aren 1853-1855. J.W. Grill. K. Vet. Akad. Handl., vol.2, no.10, pp.1-62, tbl.1, 1858.

NOTES ON SOME FOSSILS FROM THE VAAL RIVER GRAVELS. H. Haughton. Trans. S. African Geol. Soc., vol.24.

A GEO-ARCHAELOGICAL NOTE ON TAUNGS, KROMDRAAI AND STERKFONTEIN. (AGE OF FOSSIL MAMMALS.) C. van Riet Lowe. Sambab, S. African Mus. Assoc., Durban, vol.3, no.10, pp.309-312, June 1945.

PRELIMINARY ACCOUNT OF THE WONDERWERK CAVE, KURUMAN DISTRICT. SECT. 1: SITE AND ARCHAEOLOGY. B.D. Malan.

S.African Jour. Sci., Johannesburg, vol. 37, pp.300-303, fig.1, Feb., 1941.

ROCK ENGRAVINGS OF THE WESTERN TRANSVAAL. Margaret Orford. Trabalhos do 1º Congresso Nacional de Antropologia Colonial, Porto, vol.2, pp.463-497, figs. 14, 1934.

MAMMOTHS AND MAN IN THE TRANSVAAL. Henry Fairfield Osborn. Nature, London, vol.121, no.3052, pp.672-673, illus., Apr. 28, 1928.

FOSSIL MAMMALIAN REMAINS FROM BANKIES, KROONSTAD DISTRICT, O.F.S. M.M.J. Shapiro. S.African Jour. Sci., Johannesburg, vol.39, pp.176-181, Jan., 1943.

(REMAINS OF FRESH-WATER AND LAND-INHABITING VERTEBRATES FROM THE DIAMOND FIELDS OF LITTLE MAMAQUALAND (SOUTHWEST AFRICA).) Reste Suesswasser- und Land-bewohnender Wirbeltiere aus den Diamantfeldern Klein-Namaqualandes (Suedwestafrika). E.Stromer. Sitz.-Ber.Bayer. Akad. Wiss. math-naturw. Abt., Munich, pp.17-47, pls.2, 1931.

(WILD ANIMALS OF OKOVANGGO REGION AND THE CAPRIVI CONCESSION.) Das Wild des Okawangogebiets und des Caprivizipfels. J.H. Wilhelm. Jour.S.W.African Sci. Soc., Windhoek, vol.6, pp.51-74, illus., 1933.

PREHISTORY IN SOUTH AFRICA. Nature, London, vol.141, no.3582, pp.1115-1116, June, 25, 1938.

Recent Mammals

IN SOUTH AFRICA'S WONDERLAND--INTIMATE OBSERVATIONS AMONG THE GREAT GAME HERDS OF THREE OF THE MOST IMPORTANT WILD-LIFE RESERVES IN THE WORLD. Mary L. Jobe Akeley.Nat. Hist., New York, vol.39, pp.106-115, illus., Feb., 1937.

KRUGER NATIONAL PARK OF THE TRANSVAAL. Mary L. Jobe Akeley. Sci.Monthly, vol.45, no.3, pp.207-216, Sep., 1937.

MAMMALS OF SOUTH AFRICA. J.A.Allen. Science, n.s., vol.13, pp.105-106, Jan.18, 1901.

SOME MAMMALS FROM NORTHERN RHODESIA. W.F.H. Ansel. Ann. and Mag.Nat. Hist., ser.12, vol.10, no.115, pp.529-550, July, 1957.

STATUS OF NORTHERN RHODESIAN GAME. (OBSERVATIONS ON THE MAMMALS SCHEDULED UNDER THE GAME ORDINANCE.) W.F.H. Ansel. African Wild Life, Johannesburg, vol.6, no.1, pp.21-29; no.2, pp.108-117, illus., 1952.

QUAGGA (EQUUS QUAGGA). OKAPI (OKAPIA JOHNSTONI). (ELEMENTS FOR ITS RESEARCH AND IDENTIFICATION IN ANGOLA.) Elementos para a sua pesquisa e identificacao em Angola. Frederico Bagorro Sequeira. Luanda, Comissao Central de Caca, pp.16, pls., 1939.

NOTES ON SOUTH AFRICAN WILD LIFE CONSERVATION PARKS AND RESERVES. Thomas Barbour, Margaret Dewar Porter. Special Publ. no.7, Amer. Comm.for International Wild Life Protection, pp.1-34, 1935.

(ANIMAL LIFE IN SPANISH GUINEA.) La vida animal en la Guinea Española. Aurelio Basilio. Madrid, Inst.de Estudios Africanos Consejo Superior de Investigaciones Cientificas, pp.146, illus., 1952.

ADULTERATION OF THE FAUNA AND FLORA OF OUR NATIONAL PARKS. R. Bigalke. S.African Jour.Sci., Johannesburg, vol.43, pp.221-225, July, 1947.

WILD LIFE CONSERVATION IN THE UNION OF SOUTH AFRICA. R. Bigalke. Fauna and Flora Transvaal, Pretoria, no.1, pp.5-42, illus., Apr., 1950.

NOTES ON THE ZEBRAS AND SOME ANTELOPES OF ANGOLA. Gilbert Blaine. Proc. Zool. Soc. London, pp.317-339, pls. 8, June, 1922.

DISTRIBUTION OF SOUTH AFRICAN FAUNA IN RELATION TO PLACE NAMES. C. Graham Botha. S.African Jour.Sci., vol. 22, pp.537-539, Nov., 1925.

DESCRIPTION OF NEW RACES OF KALAHARI BIRDS AND MAMMALS. R.D.Bradfield. Privately Printed, 1935, Reprinted in The Auk, vol.53, no.1, pp.131-132, Jan., 1936.

SOUTH AND EAST AFRICAN YEAR BOOK AND GUIDE. (Sections on Hunting and the Game of East and South Africa.) A.Samler Brown, G.Gordon Brown. 27th ed., Published for the Union-Castle Mail Steamship Co., pp.1-915, maps, 1921.

BIG GAME IN NGAMILAND. H.A.Bryden. Field, London, vol.154, no.4011, p.686, Nov. 9, 1929.

ON THE PAST AND PRESENT GEOGRAPHICAL DISTRIBUTION OF THE LARGE MAMMALS OF SOUTH AFRICA. T.E. Buckley. Proc. Zool. Soc. London, pp. 277-293, 1876.

UNIVERSITY OF CALIFORNIA AFRICAN EXPEDITION--SOUTHERN SECTION. Charles L. Camp. Science, Lancaster, vol. 108, no.2812, pp.550-552, Nov. 19, 1948.

TIMELY ACTION TO SAVE SOUTHERN RHODESIA'S BIG GAME. A.E. Capell. Field, London, vol.161, no.4196, p.1214, illus., May 27, 1933.

(Review by P. Rode of) MAMMALS OF ANGOLA. J.E. Hill, T. Donald Carter. Mammalia, Paris, vol.9, no.2, pp.62-63, June, 1945.

AFRICAN HUNTING AMONG THE THONGAS. George Agnew Chamberlain. Harper and Brothers, pp.286, pls.24, map, May, 1923.

GAME PRESERVATION IN ZULULAND. A.E. Charter. Jour. Soc. Preservation Fauna of Empire, Hertford, n.s., pt.41, pp.31-38, Dec., 1940.

LIST OF VERTEBRATES COLLECTED BY MESSRS. F.P. MENNELL AND E.C. CHUBB IN THE MATOPO HILLS, MATABELELAND. E.C. Chubb. Proc.Rhodesia Sci. Assoc., Grahamstown, vol.8, pt.1, pp.60-63, 1908.

ON SOME LITTLE-KNOWN SOUTH AFRICAN MAMMALS RECENTLY OBTAINED IN RHODESIA. E.C. Chubb. Ann.Report S. African Asso. Adv. Sci., Grahamstown Meeting, pp.4, illus., 1908.

NOTES ON THE MAMMALIAN FAUNA OF UMZUMBE VALLEY, NATAL, SOUTH AFRICA. Raymond B. Cowles. Jour.Mamm., vol.17, no.2, pp.121-130, May, 1936.

ZULU JOURNAL. Raymond B. Cowles. Univ.of Calif. Press, pp.300, illus.

NOTES ON QUANTITATIVE METHODS IN THE OBSERVATION OF BIG GAME IN THE KRUGER NATIONAL PARK. D.H.S. Davis. S.African Jour.Sci., Johannesburg, vol.36, pp.381-385, Dec., 1939.

BUFFALO AND LEOPARD IN SOUTHERN RHODESIA. E. Davison. Field, London, vol.167, no.4343, p.649, illus., Mar.21, 1936.

LARGE GAME AND NATURAL HISTORY OF SOUTH AND SOUTH-EAST AFRICA. W.H. Drummond. Edinburgh, pp.428, illus., map, 1875.

(TAXONOMY OF MAMMALS OF THE UNION OF SOUTH AFRICA.) Die taksonomie van die soogdiere van die Unie van Suid-Afrika. John R. Ellerman. Annale van die Univ. van Stellenbosch, jaarg.30, reeks A, no.1, pp. 125, 1954.

SOUTHERN AFRICAN MAMMALS 1758-1951: A RECLASSIFICATION. J.R. Ellerman, et al. London, Brit. Mus., Nat.Hist., pp.363, maps 2, 1953.

(Review by Charles O. Handley of) SOUTHERN AFRICAN MAMMALS 1758-1951. J.R. Ellerman, et al. Science, vol.119, no. 3101, p.82, June 4, 1954; Jour.Mamm., vol.35, no.3, pp.460-461, Aug. 20, 1954.

(ANGOLA AS VIEWED WITH RIFLE AND CAMERA.) Angola en el visor del rifle y de la camera. Jose Fenykovi. Published by Author, Madrid, pp.427, illus., 1953.

NATURAL HISTORY OF SOUTH AFRICA. F.W.Fitzsimons. (Mammals.) London, Longmans, Green and Co., vol.I, pp.i-xix, 1-178, pls.51; vol.II, pp.i-xi, 1-195, pls.48; vol.III, pp.i-xiii, 1-278, pls.47, vol.IV, pp.i-xix, 1-271, pls.30, 1919-1920.

(Review by N. Hollister of) NATURAL HISTORY OF SOUTH AFRICA. (Mammals.) F.W. Fitzsimons. Jour. Mamm., vol.2, no.1, pp.41-42, Feb., 1921.

CONSERVATION OF WILD LIFE IN SOUTH AFRICA. Alwin K. Haagner. S.African Jour. Industries, pp.1-15 (of reprint), pls.4, Dec., 1925.

SOUTH AFRICAN MAMMALS. SHORT MANUAL FOR THE USE OF FIELD NATURALISTS, SPORTSMEN AND TRAVELLERS. Alwin K. Haagner. London, H.F. and G.Whitherby, pp.i-xx, 1-248, illus., 1920.

PORTRAITS OF THE GAME AND WILD ANIMALS OF SOUTHERN AFRICA. DELINEATED FROM LIFE IN THEIR NATIVE HAUNTS, DURING A HUNTING EXPEDITION FROM THE CAPE COLONY AS FAR AS THE TROPIC OF CAPRICORN, IN 1836 AND 1837, WITH SKETCHES OF THE FIELD SPORTS. W. Cornwallis Harris.London, Pub.for the Proprietor by W.Pickering, and to be had of P.and D.Colnaghi, pp.175, col.pls., 1840.

NOTES ON SOME ANGOLAN MAMMALS. R.W. Hayman. Publicacoes Culturais da Companhia de Diamantes de Angola, Lisbon, no.11, pp.31-36, July 26, 1951.

GUIDE TO THE VERTEBRATE FAUNA OF THE EASTERN CAPE PROVINCE. John Hewitt. Albany Mus., Grahamstown, (Mammal pt.) pp.1-55, illus., 1931.

A COLLECTION OF MAMMALS FROM DONDI, ANGOLA. WITH FIELD NOTES BY THE REVEREND KENNETH H. PRIOR. John Eric Hill. Jour. Mamm., Baltimore, vol.22, no.1, pp.81-85, Feb. 14, 1941.

SCIENTIFIC RESULTS OF THE VERNAY-LANG KALAHARI EXPEDITION. LARGER MAMMALS OF BECHUANALAND PROTECTORATE. John Eric Hill. Bull. Amer. Mus. Nat. Hist., New York, vol.79, art. 5, pp.367-390, pls.36-43, map 1, July 7, 1942.

MAMMALS OF ANGOLA, AFRICA. John Eric Hill, T.Donald Carter. Bull. Amer. Mus. Nat. Hist., New York, vol.78, pp. 1-211, figs.36, June 25, 1941.

THREE NEW MAMMALS FROM NORTHERN RHODESIA. (Mimetillus thomasi, Kerivoula lucia, and Zelotomys shortridgei.) Martin A. C. Hinton. Ann. and Mag. Nat. Hist., ser.9, vol.6, pp.239-242, Aug., 1920.

(PRELIMINARY DESCRIPTION OF THE MAMMALS OF THE ORANGE FREE STATE.) Voorlopige Beskrywing van Vrystaatse Soogdiere. E.C.N.van Hoepen. Paleont.Navorsing Nasionale Mus., Bloemfontaine, vol.2, pp.63-65, Nov. 6, 1932.

VANISHING GAME OF SOUTH AFRICA. A WARNING AND AN APPEAL. William T. Hornaday, Alwin K. Haagner. Perm. Wild Life Protect. Fund. Bull.10, pp.1-55, numerous cuts, Sep. 1, 1922.

BIG GAME IN RHODESIA. Wynant Davis Hubbard. Jour. Mamm., vol.4, no.4, pp. 228-230, Nov., 1923.

FURTHER NOTES ON THE MAMMALS OF NORTHERN RHODESIA AND PORTUGUESE EAST AFRICA. Wynant Davis Hubbard. Jour. Mamm., vol.10, no.4, pp.294-297, Nov., 1929.

NETTING GAME IN NORTHERN RHODESIA. EXCITING CAPTURE ALIVE OF THIRTEEN ORIBI, THREE REEDBUCK, AND A FINE, FAT ZEBRA MARE. Wynant Davis Hubbard. The Sportsman, Boston, vol.7, no.6, pp.72, 73, 92, 94, illus., June, 1930.

NOTES ON THE ANTELOPE AND ZEBRA OF NORTHERN RHODESIA AND PORTUGUESE EAST AFRICA. Wynant Davis Hubbard. Jour. Mamm., vol.7, no.3, pp. 184-193, Aug., 1926.

ON A COLLECTION OF MAMMALS FROM SOUTH AFRICA. H.L. Jameson. Ann. and Mag. Nat. Hist., ser.8, vol.4, pp. 455-473, Nov., 1909.

ON MAMMALS FROM MOSSAMEDES. F.A. Jentink. Leyden Mus, vol.9, no. 14, pp.171-180, Feb., 1887.

ON SOME MAMMALS FROM CAHAMA. F.A. Jentink. Notes Leyden Mus., vol. 15, no.37, pp.262-265, pls.4-6, Apr., 1893.

FIELD NOTES ON THE MFOLOZI GAME RESERVE. C.C. Kent. S.African Jour. Nat. Hist., vol.6, pp.38-48, June, 1926.

ON A COLLECTION OF MAMMALS FROM CHIROMO AND CHOLO, RUO, NYASALAND, MADE BY MR. RODNEY C. WOOD, WITH FIELD-NOTES BY THE COLLECTOR. P.S. Kershaw. Ann. and Mag. Nat. Hist., ser.9, vol.10, pp.177-192, Aug., 1922.

ON A COLLECTION OF MAMMALS OBTAINED BY CAPT. G. C. SHORTRIDGE IN NORTHERN RHODESIA, WITH FIELD-NOTES BY THE COLLECTOR. P. S. Kershaw. Ann. and Mag. Nat. Hist., ser. 9, vol.10, pp.99-111, July, 1922.

ON THE COLLECTION OF SOUTH AFRICAN MAMMALS IN THE DURBAN MUSEUM. P.S. Kershaw. Ann. Durban Mus., vol.3, pt.1, pp.27-38, Jan. 31, 1921.

PRELIMINARY REPORT ON THE DISTRIBUTION OF CERTAIN SPECIES OF GAME IN THE TRANSVAAL (1954). W.K.Kettlitz. Fauna and Flora, Transvaal, vol.6, for 1955, pp.124-151, 1957.

(ON THE PRESENT STATUS OF WILD LIFE CONSERVATION IN BRITISH SOUTH AFRICA.) Ueber den gegenwartigen stand des Wildschutzes in Britisch-Suedafrika. H. Kummerloewe. Zool. Garten, Leipzig, n.F., vol.4, nos.3-5, pp.172-173, May, 1931.

SOUTH AFRICA'S BIG GAME AND OTHER ANIMALS (WITH TWO MAPS) GLIMPSES FROM KRUGER NATIONAL PARK AND OTHER RESERVES WITHIN THE UNION. Herbert Lang. Johannesburg and Cape Town, The Central News Agency, pp.32, illus., pls., 1944?

MAMMALS FROM NYASALAND AND TETE, WITH NOTES ON THE GENUS OTOMYS. Barbara Lawrence, Arthur Loveridge. The Museum, Cambridge (Zoological Results of a 5th Expedition to East Africa, 1), Bull. of the Mus.of Comparative Zoology at Harvard College, vol.110, no.1, pp.80, illus., map, 1953.

GAME SANCTUARIES OF NATAL. C.N. Ledward. Publ.Natal Prov.Admin., Pietermaritzburg, pp.32, map, illus., 1936.

(NEW SUBSPECIES OF MAMMALS FROM SOUTH-WEST AFRICA.) Neue Saeugetierrassen aus Suedwestafrika. Ernst von Lehmann. Bonner Zool. Beitraege, vol.6, nos. 3-4, pp.171-172, Dec., 1955.

DESCRIPTIONS OF NEW MAMMALS. B.G. Lundholm. Ann. Transvaal Mus., vol.22, no.3, pp.279-305, Jan. 24, 1955.

BIG GAME AT PEACE WITH MAN. OPPORTUNITIES FOR OBSERVING WILD BEASTS AT CLOSE QUARTERS IN THE KRUGER NATIONAL PARK. C.T.A. Maberly. Field, London, vol.155, no.4033, p.547, Apr. 12, 1930.

CORRECTION TO "THE MAMMALS OF SOUTH AFRICA." J. Meester. Jour. Mamm., vol.34, no.4, pp.418-519, Nov. 13, 1953.

MAMMAL SURVEY OF THE S.A. LOMBARD NATURE RESERVE (1954). J. Meester. Fauna and Flora, Transvaal, vol.6, for 1955, pp.44-57, 1957.

RESEARCH ON THE MAMMALS OF SOUTH AFRICA. J. Meester. Nature, London, vol. 174, no.4442, pp.1148-1149, Dec. 18, 1954.

SOME ASPECTS OF THE MATOPOS. PART III. F.P. Mennell. Proc. Rhodesia Sci. Assoc., vol.8, pt.1, pp.50-60, illus., Grahamstown, 1908.

(SWISS SCIENTIFIC MISSION IN ANGOLA. SCIENTIFIC FINDINGS. PART I. UNGULATES.) Mission Scientifique Suisse dans l'Angola. Résultats scientifiques. Mammiferes. Part I. A. Monard. Soc.Neuchateloise Sci. Nat.Bull., vol.54, n.s., vol.31,) pp.73-102, for 1929, 1930.

(SWISS SCIENTIFIC MISSION IN ANGOLA. SCIENTIFIC FINDINGS. MAMMALS. CHIROPTERS, RODENTS, UNGULATES.) Mission Scientifique Suisse dans l'Angola. Resultats Scientifiques.Mammiferes.A. Monard. Soc.Neuchateloise Sci.Nat.Bull. Centenaire, pt.2, vol.57, (n.s., vol.16) annee 1932, pt.5, Chiropteres, pp.45-53; pt.6 Rongeurs, pp.53-63; pt.7, Ongules, pp.64-66, figs.10, 1933.

SPECIFIC OBSERVATIONS IN CONNECTION WITH ANIMAL MOVEMENTS ON PART OF THE LOWER SABI ROAD. T.G. Nel. Bull. Nat. Parks Union S.Africa, Pretoria, no.6, p.1, 1951.

(CONTRIBUTION TO KNOWLEDGE OF THE MAMMAL FAUNA OF SOUTH AND SOUTH-WEST AFRICA.) Beitraege zur Kenntnis der Saeugethierfauna von Sued- und Sued-west-Afrika. Th. Noack. Zool. Jahrb., Jena, Abt.f. Syst. Geog. u. Biol. Thiere, vol.4, no.1, pp.94-261, pls.5, Feb. 28, 1889.

ON A COLLECTION OF MAMMALIA PROCURED BY CAPT. ALEXANDER DURING HIS JOURNEY INTO THE COUNTRY OF THE DAMARAS, ON THE SOUTH-WEST COAST OF AFRICA. W. Ogilby. Proc. Zool. Soc. London, pt.6, pp.5-6, 1838.

(NATURAL SCIENCE TRIP TO MOZAMBIQUE CARRIED OUT BY ORDER OF HIS MAJESTY, KING FREDERICK WILLIAM IV IN THE YEARS 1842-48. I: MAMMALS.) Naturwissenschaftliche Reise nach Mossambique auf Befehl Seiner Majestaet des Koenigs Friedrich Wilhelm IV in den Jahren 1842-48 Ausgefuehrt. I: Saeugethiere. Wilhelm C. H. Peters. 1852.

NOTE ON A COLLECTION OF SMALL MAMMALIA MADE BY MR. MONTEIRO IN ANGOLA. William C.H. Peters.Proc. Zool. Soc. London, pp.363-364, 1872.

REPORT ON A FAUNAL SURVEY OF NORTHERN RHODESIA WITH ESPECIAL REFERENCE TO GAME, ELEPHANT CONTROL, AND NATIONAL PARKS. C.R.S. Pitman. Govt.Northern Rhodesia, Livingstone, Pt.B, Check lists of the Vertebrate Fauna, pp.xii-500, maps A-K, 1934. (Mammals pp.157-175.)

SURVEY OF NORTHERN RHODESIA'S FAUNA. C.R.S. Pitman. Field, London, vol.161, no.4191, p.867, Apr. 22, 1933; no.4192, p.917, illus., Apr. 29, 1933.

CUTTHROAT OF THE VELDT. (Wild Dogs, Koodoos.) Hugh Prior. Field and Stream, New York, vol.53, no.10, pp. 32-33, 102-103, illus., Feb., 1949.

BECHUANALAND'S BIG GAME. C. F. Rey. Field, London, vol.161, no.4200, p.1480, June 24, 1933.

BIRDS AND MAMMALS FROM SOUTH-WEST AFRICA. Austin Roberts. Ann.Transvaal Mus., vol.12, pt.4, pp.289-329, 1928.

BIRDS AND MAMMALS IN SOUTH-WEST AFRICA DURING DROUGHT CONDITIONS. Austin Roberts. S.African Biol.Soc.Pamphlet, Pretoria, no.12, p.43, 1944. (A Summary.)

DESCRIPTION OF SOME NEW SUBSPECIES OF SOUTH AFRICAN MAMMALS. Austin Roberts. Ann. Transvaal Mus., vol.19, pt.1, pp.99-103, Nov. 8, 1937.

DESCRIPTIONS OF NEW FORMS OF MAMMALS. Austin Roberts. Ann. Transvaal Mus., vol.2, pt.2, pp.231-245, Oct. 31, 1938.

DESCRIPTIONS OF NUMEROUS NEW SUBSPECIES OF MAMMALS. Austin Roberts. Ann. Transvaal Mus., Cambridge, vol.20, pt.4, pp.303-328, Oct. 18, 1946.

DESCRIPTIONS OF SOME NEW MAMMALS. (New Form Each of Cistugo, Eptesicus, Chrysochloris, Mungos, and Otomys, from South Africa.) Austin Roberts. Ann.Transvaal Mus., vol.6, pp.112-115, Apr., 1919.

DESCRIPTIONS OF SOME NEW SUBSPECIES OF MAMMALS. (Cercopithecus mitis stevensoni, Genetta tigrina methi, Petromyscus collinus namibensis, Leo leo vernayi.) Austin Roberts. Ann. Transvaal Mus., vol.21, pt.1, pp.63-69, fold.tbl., Apr.6, 1948.

ELEVEN NEW FORMS OF SOUTH AFRICAN MAMMALS. Austin Roberts. Ann.Transvaal Mus., vol.15, pt.2, pp.265-270, Aug. 1, 1933.

MAMMALS OF SOUTH AFRICA. Austin Roberts. Distributed by Cent.News Agency S.Africa, pp.xlviii-700, illus., 1951; 2nd ed., Johannesburg, Trustees of the "Mammals of South Africa" Book Fund, distributed by Central News Agency, pp.xlviii+700, pls.(part col.), map, diagrs., tbls., 1954.
(Review by Henry W.Setzer of) MAMMALS OF SOUTH AFRICA. Austin Roberts.Jour. Mamm., vol.34, no.1, pp.140-141, Feb. 19, 1953.

NEW FORMS OF AFRICAN MAMMALS. Austin Roberts. Ann. Transvaal Mus., vol.13, pt.2, pp.82-121, 1929.

NEW FORMS OF SOUTH AFRICAN MAMMALS. Austin Roberts. Ann. Transvaal Mus., vol.14, pt.3, pp.221-236, pls.3-8, 1931.

NEW SOUTH AFRICAN MAMMALS. Austin Roberts. Ann. Transvaal Mus., vol.18, pt.3, pp.253-254, 1936.

OLD SURVIVING TYPES OF MAMMALS FOUND IN THE UNION. Austin Roberts. S.African Jour Sci., Johannesburg, vol.34, pp.73-88, figs.8, Nov., 1937.

PRELIMINARY DESCRIPTION OF FIFTY-SEVEN NEW FORMS OF SOUTH AFRICAN MAMMALS. Austin Roberts. Ann. Transvaal Mus., Pretoria, vol.15, pt.1, pp.1-19, 1932.vol.16, pt.2, pp.265-270, 1933.

REPORT UPON A SURVEY OF THE HIGHER VERTEBRATES OF NORTH-EASTERN ZULULAND. Austin Roberts. (Mammals Collected in Zululand, in 1928, 1929 and 1933.) Ann. Transvaal Mus., vol.18, pt.3, pp.222-251, 1936. (See also, pp.170-173.)

SCIENTIFIC RESULTS OF THE VERNAY-LANG KALAHARI EXPEDITION, MARCH TO SEPTEMBER, 1930. MAMMALS. Austin Roberts. Ann. Transvaal Mus., vol.16, pt.1, pp.187-249, pls.2-5, map, Feb. 21, 1935.

SOME ADDITIONS TO THE LIST OF SOUTH AFRICAN MAMMALS. Austin Roberts. Ann. Transvaal Mus., vol.10, pt.2, pp.59-76, Jan. 31, 1924.

SOME NEW SOUTH AFRICAN MAMMALS AND SOME CHANGES IN NOMENCLATURE. Austin Roberts. Ann. Transvaal Mus., vol.11, pt.4, pp.245-263, Sep. 14, 1926.

DESCRIPTION OF SOME NEW MAMMALS FROM SOUTHWESTERN AFRICA. J.St. Leger. Ann. and Mag. Nat. Hist., ser.10, no.55, pp.84-87, July, 1932.

DR. KARL JORDAN'S EXPEDITION TO SOUTH-WEST AFRICA AND ANGOLA: MAMMALS. J. St.Leger. Novitates Zool., vol.40, no.1, pp.75-81, Aug. 25, 1936.

MAMMALS FROM ANGOLA, INCLUDING A NEW SPECIES OF CLAVIGLIS AND A NEW RACE OF ZELOTOMYS. J. St.Leger. Ann. and Mag. Nat. Hist., London, ser. 10, vol.17, no.100, pp.464-472, Apr., 1936.

ON MAMMALS FROM NORTH-WEST DAMARALAND, SOUTH-WEST AFRICA, OBTAINED DURING CAPTAIN SHORTRIDGE'S SIXTH PERCY SLADEN AND

KAFFRARIAN MUSEUM EXPEDITION. J.St. Leger. Proc. Zool. Soc. London, pp. 957-974, pl.1, Jan. 6, 1933.

TWO NEW SUBSPECIES OF MAMMALS FROM ANGOLA. J. St. Leger. Novitates Zoologicae, vol.39, pp.251-252, 1935.

LIST OF THE MAMMALS OBTAINED BY MRS. R. B. WOOSNOM AND R. E. DOUT IN BECHUANALAND. Harold Schwann. Proc. Zool. Soc. London, vol.1, pp.101-111, 1906.

LIST OF MAMMALIA COLLECTED BY MR. J. J. MONTEIRO IN ANGOLA. Philip Lutley Sclater. Proc. Zool. Soc. London, pt.28, pp.245-247, 1860.

MALS BROUGHT BY MR. A. SHARP FROM NYASSALAND. Philip Lutley Sclater. Proc. Zool. Soc. London, pt.1, pp.97-98, June 1, 1892.

THE MAMMALS (FAUNA) OF SOUTH AFRICA. William Lutley Sclater. London, R.H. Porter, vols.2, illus., fold.map, 1900-01. Vol.I-Primates, Carnivora and Ungulata. Vol.II-Rodentia, Chiroptera, Insectivora, Cetacea and Edentata.

SOUTH AFRICAN SWAN SONGS. (Game Animals.) Ken Scott, Jr. San Diego Zoonooz, vol.19, no.12, pp.5-6, illus., Dec., 1946.

FIELD NOTES ON THE FIRST AND SECOND EXPEDITIONS OF THE CAPE MUSEUM'S MAMMAL SURVEY OF THE CAPE PROVINCE; AND DESCRIPTIONS OF SOME NEW SUBGENERA AND SUBSPECIES. G.C. Shortridge. Ann. South African Mus., Edinburgh, vol.36, pt.1, pp.27-100, pls.6-7, Sep., 1942.

MAMMALS OF SOUTH WEST AFRICA; A BIOLOGICAL ACCOUNT OF THE FORMS OCCURRING IN THAT REGION, BY CAPT. G. C. SHORTRIDGE. G.C. Shortridge. London, W. Heinemann, Ltd., vol.2, pls.. maps, 1934.

NEW GENUS AND NEW SPECIES AND SUBSPECIES OF MAMMALS FROM LITTLE NAMAQUALAND AND THE NORTH-WEST CAPE PROVINCE;AND A NEW SUBSPECIES OF GERBILLUS PAEBA FROM THE EASTERN CAPE PROVINCE. G.C. Shortridge. Ann. S. African Mus., Cape Town, vol.32, pt. 4, pp.281-291, July, 1938.

WILD ANIMALS IN THEIR NATURAL HAUNTS; KRUGER NATIONAL PARK, SOUTH AFRICA, THE WORLD'S LARGEST GAME SANCTUARY. C.W. Simons. Illus. London News, vol.181, no.4873, pls.3-4, Sep. 10, 1932.

EXHIBITION OF SOME SMALL QUADRUPEDS COLLECTED IN SOUTH AFRICA. A.Smith. Proc. Zool. Soc. London, pt.5, p.69, 1837.

ILLUSTRATIONS OF THE ZOOLOGY OF SOUTH AFRICA. A. Smith. (Mammals.) Pls.44, 1845.

(ZOOLOGICAL DISSERTATION - ENUMERATION OF MAMMALS OF THE CAPE OF GOOD HOPE; TRIBES OF NEARBY PLAINS.) Dissertatio zoologica, enumerationem mammalium capensium continens; tribus tabulis adjunctis. Jan Smuts. Leidae, apud J.C. Cyfveer, pp.108, pls., 1832.

KRUGER NATIONAL PARK. J.Stevenson-Hamilton. Illus. London News, vol.171, no. 4616, pp.vi-vii, 630, illus., Oct. 8, 1927. Jour. Soc. Preservation Fauna Empire, Hertford, n.s., pt.39, pp.21-28, Apr., 1940.

OVERGRAZING OF THE VELD. EXTRACT FROM THE WARDEN'S REPORT FOR 1939 ON THE KRUGER NATIONAL PARK. J. Stevenson-Hamilton. Jour. Soc. Preservation Fauna Empire, Hertford, n.s,, pt.40, pp.15-16, Aug., 1940.

SANCTUARY FOR SOUTH AFRICAN BIG GAME. THE KRUGER NATIONAL PARK. J. Stevenson-Hamilton. Field, London, vol.153, p.573, illus., Apr.4, 1929.

SOUTH AFRICAN EDEN. FROM SABI GAME RESERVE TO KRUGER NATIONAL PARK. J.Stevenson-Hamilton. Cassel and Co., Ltd., London, pp.xxi-311, illus.26, map, 1937.

NOTES ON FAUNA. I. MAMMALS. G.H. Swynnerton. Ann. Rept. Tanganyika Game Dept., for 1954, pp.22-30, illus., 1955.

ON A COLLECTION OF MAMMALS FROM BRITISH NAMAQUALAND. Oldfield Thomas. Proc. Zool. Soc. London, vol.1, p.171, 1904.

ON A SECOND COLLECTION OF MAMMALS SENT BY MR. H. H. JOHNSTON, C. B. FROM NYASALAND. Oldfield Thomas. Proc. Zool. Soc. London, pp.500-504, May 16, 1893.

ON A SMALL COLLECTION OF MAMMALS FROM LUMBO, MOZAMBIQUE. Oldfield Thomas. Ann. and Mag. Nat. Hist., ser.9, vol.4, pp.29-34, July, 1919.

ON A SMALL COLLECTION OF MAMMALS OBTAINED BY MR. ALFRED SHARPE, C. B., IN NYASALAND. Oldfield Thomas. Proc. Zool. Soc. London, pp.391-394, May 17, 1898.

ON MAMMALS FROM THE GOBABIS DISTRICT, EASTERN DAMARALAND, SOUTH-WEST AFRICA, OBTAINED DURING CAPT. SHORTRIDGE'S FOURTH PERCY CLADEN AND KAFFRARIAN MUSEUM EXPEDITION. WITH FIELD NOTES BY THE COLLECTOR. Oldfield Thomas. Proc. Zool. Soc. London, pt.2, pp.371-398, July 12, 1927.

ON MAMMALS FROM THE KAOKO-VELD, SOUTHWEST AFRICA, OBTAINED DURING CAPT. SHORTRIDGE'S FIFTH PERCY SLADEN AND KAFFRARIAN MUSEUM EXPEDITION. Oldfield Thomas. Proc. Zool. Soc. London, pt.1, pp.99-111, Apr. 30, 1929.

ON MAMMALS FROM THE GOBABIS DISTRICT, EASTERN DAMARALAND, SOUTH KAFFRARIAN MUSEUM EXPEDITION. Oldfield Thomas. Proc. Zool. Soc. London, pt.2, pp.371-398, July 12, 1927.

ON MAMMALS FROM OVAMBOLAND AND THE CUNENE RIVER, OBTAINED DURING CAPT. SHORTRIDGE'S THIRD PERCY SLADEN AND KAFFRARIAN EXPEDITION. Oldfield Thomas. Proc. Zool. Soc. London, pt.1, pp.99-111, Apr. 30, 1929.

ON MAMMALS FROM NORTHERN ANGOLA COLLECTED BY DR. W. J. ANSORGE. Oldfield Thomas. Ann. and Mag. Nat. Hist., ser.7, vol.13, no.78, pp.405-421, figs., June, 1904.

ON MAMMALS FROM NYASALAND. Oldfield Thomas. Proc. Zool. Soc. London, pp.546-554, Nov. 1, 1892.

ON SOME NEW MAMMALS FROM NORTHERN NYASALAND. Oldfield Thomas. Proc. Zool. Soc., London, pp.118-121, Feb.18, 1902.

ON THE MAMMALS OBTAINED BY MR. A. WHYTE IN NYASALAND, AND PRESENTED TO THE BRITISH MUSEUM BY SIR H. H. JOHNSTON, K. C. B.; BEING A FIFTH CONTRIBUTION TO THE MAMMAL-FAUNA OF NYASALAND. Oldfield Thomas. Proc. Zool. Soc. London, pp.925-939, pl.54, Dec. 14, 1897.

ON THE MAMMALS OF MNYSALAND: THIRD CONTRIBUTION. Oldfield Thomas. Proc. Zool. Soc. London, pp.136-146, Feb. 20, 1894.

ON THE MAMMALS OF NYASALAND: FOURTH NOTICE. Oldfield Thomas. Proc. Zool. Soc. London, pp.788-798, pls.38-39, Nov. 17, 1896.

ON MAMMALS COLLECTED BY CAPT. SHORTRIDGE DURING THE PERCY SLADEN AND KAFFRARIAN MUSEUM EXPEDITION TO THE ORANG RIVER. Oldfield Thomas, M.A.C. Hinton. Proc. Zool. Soc. London, pp.383-499, Sep., 1923; pt.3, pp.483-499, Oct., 1923.

ON MAMMALS COLLECTED IN 1923 BY CAPT. SHORTRIDGE DURING THE PERCY SLADEN AND KAFFRARIAN MUSEUM EXPEDITION TO SOUTH-WEST AFRICA. Oldfield Thomas, M.A.C. Hinton. Proc. Zool. Soc. London, pt.1, pp.221-246, Apr. 3, 1925.

ON A COLLECTION OF MAMMALS FROM BRITISH NAMAQUALAND, PRESENTED TO THE NATIONAL MUSEUM BY MR. C. D. RUDD. Oldfield Thomas, Harold Schwann. Proc. Zool. Soc. London, pt.1, pp.171-183, pl.6, June 9, 1904.

THE RUDD EXPLORATION OF SOUTH AFRICA. II. LIST OF MAMMALS FROM THE WAKKERSTROOM DISTRICT SOUTH-EASTERN TRANSVAAL. Oldfield Thomas, Harold Schwann. Proc. Zool. Soc. London, vol.1, pp.129-138, June 1, 1905.

THE RUDD EXPLORATION OF SOUTH AFRICA. III. LIST OF THE MAMMALS OBTAINED BY MR. GRANT IN ZULULAND. Oldfield Thomas, Harold Schwann, Proc. Zool. Soc. London, vol.1, pp.254-276, pl.16, Aug. 10, 1905.

THE RUDD EXPLORATION OF SOUTH AFRICA. IV. LIST OF MAMMALS OBTAINED BY MR. GRANT AT KNYSNA. Oldfield Thomas, Harold Schwann. Proc. Zool. Soc. London, vol.1, pp.159-168, June 7, 1906.

THE RUDD EXPLORATION OF SOUTH AFRICA. V. LIST OF MAMMALS OBTAINED BY MR. GRANT IN N. E. TRANSVAAL. Oldfield Thomas, Harold Schwann. Proc. Zool. Soc. London, pt.2, pp.575-591, Oct. 10, 1906.

THE RUDD EXPLORATION OF SOUTH AFRICA. VI. LIST OF MAMMALS OBTAINED BY MR. GRANT IN THE EASTERN TRANSVAAL. Oldfield Thomas, Harold Schwann. Proc. Zool. Soc. London, pp.774-782, pt.2, Apr.11, 1907.

THE RUDD EXPLORATION OF SOUTH AFRICA. VII. LIST OF MAMMALS OBTAINED BY MR. GRANT AT COGUNO, INHAMBANE. Oldfield Thomas, R. C. Wroughton. Proc. Zool. Soc. London, pt.1, pp.285-299, Aug. 1, 1907.

THE RUDD EXPLORATION OF SOUTH AFRICA. VIII. LIST OF MAMMALS OBTAINED BY MR. GRANT AT BEIRA. Oldfield Thomas, R.C. Wroughton. Proc. Zool. Soc. London, pp.774-782, May, 1908.

THE RUDD EXPLORATION OF SOUTH AFRICA. IX. LIST OF MAMMALS OBTAINED BY MR. GRANT ON THE GORONGOZA MOUNTAINS, PORTUGUESE S.E. AFRICA. Oldfield Thomas, R.C. Wroughton. Proc. Zool. Soc. London, pp.164-173, Sep., 1908.

THE RUDD EXPLORATION OF SOUTH AFRICA. X. LIST OF MAMMALS COLLECTED BY MR. GRANT NEAR TETTE, ZAMBESIA. Oldfield Thomas, R.C. Wroughton. Proc. Zool. Soc. London, pp.535-553, Oct., 1908.

MAMMALS FROM BEIRA (AFRICA). Oldfield Thomas, R.C. Wroughton. Proc. Zool. Soc. London, pp.774-782, 1907.

ON A SECOND COLLECTION OF MAMMALS OBTAINED BY DR. W. J. ANSORGE IN ANGOLA. Oldfield Thomas, R.C. Wroughton. Ann. and Mag. Nat. Hist., ser.7, vol.16, no.92, pp.169-178, Aug., 1905.

(MAMMALS OF THE CAPE OF GOOD HOPE REVIEWED AND ILLUSTRATED.) Mammalia capensia, recensita et illustrata. C.P. Thunberg. Mém. Acad. Sci. St.-Péterb., Tome 3, pp.299-232, 1811.

(WILD ANIMALS AND THEIR RELATION TO THE SANITATION PROBLEMS IN SOUTH ANGOLA.) Animais bravos nas suas relacoes com os problemas sanitários do sul de Angola. Francisco Venancio da Silva. Notas compiladas para o Congresso de medicina de Lourenço Marques. Luanda, Imprensa nacional, pp. 70, pls.2, 1939.

ANGOLA AS A GAME COUNTRY. Arthur S. Vernay. Nat. Hist., vol.27, pp.588-594, illus., Dec., 1927 (Mar., 1928).

ASSOCIATED FAUNA AND CULTURE OF THE VLAKKRAAL THERMAL SPRINGS, O. F. S. L.H. Wells, et al. Trans. Roy. Soc. S. Africa, Cape Town, vol.29, pt.3, pp.203-233, figs.12, Sep., 1942.

HUNTING IN SOUTH AFRICA. J.W.H. Wilson. Science, n.s., vol.88, no. 2291, p.499, Nov. 25, 1938.

NYASALAND AND ITS FAUNA. Rodney C. Wood. Field, London, vol.161, no.4198, p.1332, illus., June 10, 1933.

LIST OF MAMMALS COLLECTED BY MR. C. F. M. SWYNNERTON IN NORTHERN GAZALAND (PORTUGUESE EAST AFRICA) AND THE MELSETTER DISTRICT OF RHODESIA. R.C. Wroughton. Ann. Mag. Nat. Hist., ser.8, vol.1, pp.303-307, Apr., 1908.

ON A COLLECTION OF MAMMALS MADE BY MR. S. A. NEAVE IN RHODESIA, NORTH OF THE ZAMBESI, WITH FIELD NOTES BY THE COLLECTOR. R.C. Wroughton. Manchester Lit. and Philos. Soc. Mem. and Proc., vol.51, no.5, pp.39, 1907.

(CONTRIBUTION TO KNOWLEDGE OF THE MAMMALS OF THE NORTHERN PARTS OF GERMAN SOUTHWEST AFRICA, WITH SPECIAL CONSIDERATION OF LARGE GAME.) Beitrag zur Kenntnis der Saeugetiere der noerdlichen Teile Deutsch-Suedwestafrikas unter besonderer Beruecksichtigung des Grosswildes. Ludwih Zukowsky. Wiegmann's Archiv fuer Naturgesch. Jahr 90, Abt. A, Heft 1, pp.29-164, July, 1924.

(SCIENTIFIC REMARKS ON THE GAME OF THE KAUKAU VELD, TAKING INTO CONSIDERATION THE DRAWINGS AND THE COLLECTION OF CAPT. AN DEM STEINHARDT.) Wissenschaftliche Bemerkungen ueber das Wild des Kaokofeldes unter Beruecksichtigung der Aufzeichnung und der Sammlung des Herrn Hauptmann a.D. Steinhardt. Ludwig Zukowsky. (In) Wahrhaften Riesen und seinem Reiche, 2 Auflage, pp.15, illus., Oct. 1, 1921.

ASHORE AT CAPE TOWN DURING A STORM. Illus.London News, vol.214, no. 5746, p.760, 1949.

GREAT NATIONAL PARK. PRESERVING SOUTH AFRICA'S DISAPPEARING BIG GAME ANIMALS. Field, London, vol. 161, no.4193, pp.976-977, figs.5, May 6, 1933.

SOUTH AFRICA'S EXAMPLE TO THE WORLD IN THE PRESERVATION OF WILD ANIMALS: RARE AND INTERESTING SPECIES IN THE KRUGER NATIONAL PARK AND OTHER RESERVES. Illus. London News, vol.182, no.4900, pp.388-389, illus., March 18, 1933.

## AFRICA, WESTERN

MAMMALS OF LIBERIA. THE AFRICAN REPUBLIC OF LIBERIA AND THE BELGIAN CONGO. G.M. Allen, Harold J. Coolidge. Cambridge, Harvard Univ.Press, pp.569-622, figs.444-453, 1930.(Based on the Observations Made and Material Collected During the Harvard African Expedition 1926-27.)

(WILD ANIMALS IN SPANISH GUINEA.) La vida animal en la Guinea Espanola. R.P. Aurelio Basilio. Inst. Estudios Africanos, Madrid, pp.146, pls., 1952.

CHARACTERS OF TWO SPECIES OF MAMMALIA (ONE CONSTITUTING A NEW GENUS) FROM SIERRA LEONE. E.T.Bennett. Proc. Comm. Sci. and Corres. Zool. Soc. London, pt.1, p.109, 1830-1831.

(WILD MAMMALS OF WESTERN AFRICA AND THEIR ENVIRONMENT.) Les mammifères sauvages de l'Ouest africain et leur milieu. Jacques Bigourdan. Montrouge (Seine) Imprimerie J. de Rudder, pp.367, illus., maps, pls., 1945.

(Review by P. Rode of) (WILD MAMMALS OF WESTERN AFRICA AND THEIR ENVIRONMENT.) Les mammifères sauvages de l'Ouest africain et leur milieu. Jacques Bigourdan. Mammalia, Paris, vol.1, no.5, p.219, Sep., 1937.

(PROTECTION OF WILD FAUNA IN FRENCH EQUATORIAL AFRICA.) La protection de la faune sauvage en Afrique equatoriale francaise. L. Blancou. Mammalia, Paris, vol.15, no.4, pp.157-169, Dec., 1951.

REPORT ON THE MAMMALS COLLECTED BY MR. HARRY MADSEN DURING PROFESSOR O. OLUFSEN'S EXPEDITION TO FRENCH SUDAN AND NIGERIA IN THE YEARS 1927-28. F. Wimpffen Braestrup. Vidensk.Medd.fra Dansk Naturh.Foren., vol.99, pp.73-130, Sep. 11, 1935.

(DESCRIPTIVE CATALOG OF THE MAMMALS OF SPANISH GUINEA.) Catalogo descriptivo de los mamiferos de la Guinea Española. Angel Cabrera. Mem.R.Soc. Española Hist. Nat., Madrid, vol.16, Mem. 1a, pp.121, July 10, 1929.

(LIST OF THE MAMMALS OF THE SPANISH POSSESSIONS OF THE GULF OF GUINEA.) Lista de los mamiferos de las posesiones Españolas del Golfo de Guinea. Angel Cabrera. Mem.R. Soc. Espanola Hist. Nat., Madrid, vol.1, art.25, pp.435-456, 1908.

(MAMMALS OF SPANISH GUINEA.) Mamiferes de la Guinea Española. Angel Cabrera. Mem.R.Soc.Española Hist. Nat., Madrid, vol.1, art.1, pp.1-60, pls. 1-4, 1903.

VOYAGES OF CADAMOSTO, AND OTHER DOCUMENTS ON WESTERN AFRICA IN THE SECOND HALF OF THE FIFTEENTH CENTURY. Alvise Cadamosta. Hakluyt Society Works, London, ser.2, vol.80, pp.xlv+159, maps, 1937.

ANIMALS OF WEST AFRICA. George S. Cansdale. Longmans, Green and Co., London - New York - Toronto.

PROVISIONAL CHECK LIST OF GOLD COAST MAMMALS. George S. Cansdale. Accra, Printed by the Govt.Print.Dept., pp.15, 1948.

REGIONAL ACCOUNT OF THE MAMMALS OF THE GOLD COAST. George S. Cansdale. Jour. Soc. Preservation Fauna Empire, Hertford, n.s., pt.47, pp.8-13, illus., Aug., 1943.

SOME GOLD COAST ANIMALS. George S. Cansdale. Nigerian Field, London, vol.9, no.2, pp.56-65, figs.12, July, 1940.

FIELD NOTES ON NIGERIAN MAMMALS. (Red River Hog, Wart Hog, Hippopotamus, Rhinoceros, Forest Hyrax, Rock Hyrax, and Elephant.) F.S. Collier. Nigerian Field, London, vol.9, no.1, pp.10-16, figs. 3, col.pl.1, Mar., 1940.

NOTES ON THE PRESERVATION OF THE FAUNA OF NIGERIA. F.S. Collier. Nigerian Field, London, vol.4, no.1, pp.3-12, Jan., 1935; no.2, pp.51-62, Apr., 1935; no.3, pp.101-113, July, 1935.

(Criticism by W.T.Shorthose of) NOTES ON THE PRESERVATION OF THE FAUNA OF NIGERIA. F.S. Collier. Nigerian Field, London, vol.5, no.2, pp.60-68, illus., Apr., 1936.

A SHOOTING TRIP TO TERMITT. F.S. Collier. Nigerian Field, London, vol.8, no.1, pp.14-20, figs.8, Jan., 1939.

(LARGE AND SMALL GAME IN FRENCH WEST AFRICA.) Gros et petit gibier en Afrique Occidentale Française. F. de Coutouly. Bull. Comite d'Études Hist.et Sci. de l'Afrique Occidentale Française, vol.8, no.2, pp.217-261, pl.1, June, 1925; no.4, pp.559-605, 1926.

CONTRIBUTION TO THE FAUNA OF OWERRI PROVINCE. A.B. Cozens, S. Marchant. Nigerian Field, vol.17, no.3, pp.116-130, July, 1952.

(MAMMALS OF FRENCH BLACK AFRICA.) Les mammiferes de l'Afrique Noire Francaise. P.L. Dekeyser. Inst.Francaise d'Afrique Noire, Initiation's Africaines, vol.1, ed.2, pp.426, 1955.

(CAMEROONS UNDER FRENCH MANDATE 1916-1924.) Cameroun, Sous Mandat Francais, 1916-1924. J.M. Derscheid. Revue Internationale de Legislation pour la Protection de la Nature, Brussels, pp.37, 1931.

(CONTRIBUTION TO THE MAMMAL FAUNA OF MOUNT CAMEROON AND THE DISTRIBUTION OF SPECIES AT THE VARIOUS LEVELS.) Beitrag zur Saeugetierfauna des Kamerungebirges und Verbreitung der Arten in den verschiedenen Hoehenstufen. M. Eisentraut. Zool. Jahrb., vol.85, no.6, pp.619-672, Dec. 18, 1957.

EXHIBITION OF NEW SPECIES OF QUADRUPEDS COLLECTED AT FERNANDO PO. L. Fraser. Proc. Zool. Soc. London, pt.10, p.124, 1842.

(THE CAMEROONS UNDER FRENCH MANDATE. LEGISLATION PUT THROUGH DURING THE YEARS 1925-29. INTERNATION REVIEW OF LEGISLATION FOR THE PROTECTION OF NATURE. LAWS AND RULES CONCERNING HUNTING, FISHING, ADMINISTRATION OF FORESTS, NATIONAL PARKS, NATURAL RESERVES, AND THE PROTECTION OF FAUNA, FLORA, AND NATURAL SITES.) Cameroun sous Mandat Francais. Legislation edictee durant les annees 1925-29. Revue Internationale de Legislation pour la Protection de la Nature. Lois et reglements concernant la chasse, la peche, l'administration des forets, les parcs nationaux, les reserves naturelles et la protection de la faune, de la flore et des sites naturels. Tordis Graim. Office International pour la Protection de la Nature, Bruxelles, pp.42, 1930.

LIST OF MAMMALIA FROM THE CAMEROON MOUNTAINS, COLLECTED BY CAPT. BURTON, H. M. CONSUL, FERNANDO PO. John Edward Gray. Proc. Zool. Soc. London, pt.30, pp.180-181, pls., 1862.

NOTES ON SOME MAMMALIA, WITH THE DESCRIPTION OF A NEW GOLUNDA, FROM WEST AFRICA. John Edward Gray. Proc. Zool. Soc. London, pp.55-58, illus., 1864.

(LIFE OF THE WILD ANIMALS OF CAMEROUN.) La vie des animaux sauvages du Cameroun. Emile Gromier. Payot, Paris, pp.274, illus., 1937.

(Review by P. Rode of) (LIFE OF THE WILD ANIMALS OF CAMEROUN.) La vie des animaux sauvages du Cameroun. Emile Gromier. Mammalia, Paris, vol. 1, no.6, p.264, Dec., 1937.

MAMMALS OF SIERRA LEONE. R. W. Hayman. Zoo Life, London, vol.10, no.1, pp.2-6, illus., Spring, 1955.

ON A COLLECTION OF MAMMALS FROM THE GOLD COAST. (With a Note on the Leopards by R.I.Pocock.) R.W. Hayman. Proc. Zool. Soc. London, for 1935, pt.4, pp.915-937, pl.1, Jan. 10, 1936.

NIGERIA AND ITS ANIMAL LIFE. A.H.W. Haywood. Field, London, vol.161, no.4199, p.1405, illus., June 17, 1933.

PRESERVATION OF WILD LIFE ON THE GOLD COAST. A.H.W.Haywood. Field, London, vol.161, no.4190, pp.804-805, illus., Apr. 15, 1933.

NAMES OF MAMMALS IN THREE NIGERIAN LANGUAGES. I.R.P. Heslop. Jour. Soc. Preservation Fauna and Empire, Hertford, n.s., pt.34, pp.88-90, Aug., 1938.

ON THE MAMMALS OF THE GOLD COAST. C.M. Ingoldby. Ann. and Mag. Nat. Hist., London, ser.10, vol.3, no.17, pp.511-529, 1929.

(WILD MAMMALS OF CAMEROUN.) Les mammifères sauvages du Cameroun. Albert Jeannin. Paris, P. Lechevalier, pp.iii-255, pls., map, 1936.

(MAMMALS OF CAMEROUN.) Les Mammifères du Cameroun. Albert Jeannin. Bull. Soc.Nat.Acclimat., vol.77, no.4, pp. 56-57, Apr., 1930.

(NOTES ON THE MAMMALS OF CAMEROUN.) Notes sur les mammifères du Cameroun. Albert Jeannin. Revue d'Histoire Naturelle, pt.1, A, Mammifères, Paris, vol.11, no.5, pp.161-165, May, 1930.

ZOOLOGICAL RESEARCHES IN LIBERIA. A LIST OF MAMMALS, COLLECTED BY J. BUTTIKOFER, C.F. SALA AND F.X. STAMPFLI, WITH BIOLOGICAL OBSERVA-

TIONS. F.A. Jentink. Notes Lyden Mus., vol.10, no.1, pls.1-4, Dec., 1887.

LIBERIA. Harry Johnston. Dodd Mead and Co., vol.II, 1906.

NOTES ON THE MAMMALS AND BIRDS OF LIBERIA. Harry Johnston. Proc. Zool. Soc. London, pp.197-210, 1905.

(FAUNAL PRESERVES OF CAMEROUN.) Les reserves de faune du Cameroun. Ch. Kieffer. Mammalia, Paris, vol.17, no.4, pp.270-274, Dec., 1953.

(ON THE MAMMAL FAUNA OF FERNANDO PO.) Zur Kenntnis der Saeugetierfauna von Fernando Po. Ingo Krumbiegel. Archiv f. Naturgesch., Leipzig, n.F., vol.11, no.4, pp.305-349, figs.13, Jan. 31, 1943.

COLLECTING LIVE ANIMALS IN LIBERIA. William M. Mann, Lucile Q. Mann. Explor. and Field-work Smiths. Inst., for 1940, publ. no.3631, pp.13-20, illus., Apr. 3, 1941.

ASPECTS OF THE FAUNA OF THE OWERRI PROVINCE. S. Marchant. Nigerian Field, vol.14, no.2, pp.47-51, Apr., 1949.

BRIEF FAUNAL SURVEY OF NORTH-WESTERN BENIN. P.F. Mason. Nigerian Field, London, vol.9, no.1, pp.17-22, Mar., 1940.

(ORYCTEROPUS, HYSTRIX, PHACOCHOERUS, AND SOME OTHER MAMMALS OF THE HINTERLAND OF TOGO IN GERMAN WEST AFRICA.) Orycteropus, Hystrix, Phacochoerus und einige andere Saeugethiere aus dem Hinterlande von Togo in Deutsch-West-Afrika. Paul Matschie. Sitz. Ber. Gesell. Naturf. Freunde, Jahrg.1900, no.3, pp. 100-106, Mar. 20, 1899.

(SOME MAMMALS OF THE CAMEROONS AND ITS HINTERLAND.) Ueber einige Saeugetiere von Kamerun und dessen Hinterlande. Paul Matschie. Archiv. f. Naturgesch., Jahrg.57, 1891, vol.1, no.3, pp.351-356, 1892.

(SOME MAMMALS OF THE HINTERLAND OF THE CAMEROONS.) Einige Saeugethiere aus dem Hinterlande von Kamerun. Paul Matschie. Sitz. Ber. Gesell. Naturf. Freunde, Berlin, Jahrg. 1900, no.3, pp.87-100, Mar. 20, 1902.

(SOME WEST AFRICAN MAMMALS OF THE SENCKENBERG MUSEUM.) Einige westafrikanische Saeugethiere des Senckenbergischen Museums. Paul Matschie. Sitz. Ber. Naturf. Freunde, Berlin, Jahrg.1893. no.10, pp.252-257, Dec. 19, 1893.

(INSECTIVORES AND CARNIVORES OF WESTERN AND CENTRAL AFRICA.) Insectivoren und carnivoren aus west- und Zentral-Afrika. Robert Mertens. Senckenbergiana, vol.7, no.34, pp.65-74, Apr. 20, 1925.

COLLECTION OF SMALL MAMMALS FROM MOUNT COFFEE, LIBERIA. Gerrit S. Miller, Jr. Washington, Acad. Sci., vol.2, pp.631-649, figs.39-43, Dec. 28, 1900.

(RESULTS OF THE SCIENTIFIC MISSION OF DR. MONRAD IN PORTUGUESE GUINEA 1937-1938.) Resultats de la Mission Scientifique du Dr. Monard en Guinee Portugaise 1937-38. X. Rongeurs. Albert Monard. Arquivos Mus. Bocage, Lisbon, no.12, pp. 7-16, 1941.

DESCRIPTIONS OF MAMMALIA AND BIRDS FROM THE GAMBIA. W. Ogilby. Proc. Zool. Soc. London, pt.3, p.97, 1835.

(IN THE DIDESSA RESERVE (GALLA SIDAMO).) Nella riserva del Didessa (Galla Sidamo). Saverio Patrizi. Boll. Idrobiol., Caccia e Pesca Africa Occid. Italiana, Addis Abeba, anno 1, no.1, pp.57-69, illus., 1940.

NIGERIA. A.S. Pearse. Science Monthly, vol.25, pp.228-239, illus., Sep., 1927.

(MAMMALS OF CAMEROUN FROM THE COLLECTION OF J. L. PERRET.) Mammiferes du Cameroun de la collection J. L. Perret. J. L. Perret, V. Aellen. Suisse Zool., vol.63, no.26, pp.395-450, Sep., 1956.

(ON A NEW SPECIES OF BAT, PROMOPS BONARIENSIS AND LOPHUROMYS, A RODENT GENUS OF WEST AFRICA.) Ueber eine neue Art von Flederthiere, Promops bonariensis und ueber Lophuromys, eine Nagergattung von West-Afrika. W. Peters. Monatsber. K. Preussischen Wiss. Berlin, pp.232-234, pl.1, Mar. 18, 1874.

REPORT UPON A SMALL COLLECTION OF MAMMALIA BROUGHT FROM LIBERIA BY MR. LEONARD LEIGHTON. R.I. Pocock. Proc. Zool. Soc. London, for 1907, pp.1037-1046, pls.54, May, 1908.

(DENSITY AND DISTRIBUTION OF LARGE WILD MAMMALS IN GUINEA.) Densite et répartition des gros mammiferes sauvages en Guinee. R. Pruniere. Premiere Conference Internationale des Africanistes de l'Ouest, Dakar, vol.1, pp.228-232, 1950.

(MAMMALIAN HABITAT ZONES IN FRENCH WESTERN AFRICA.) Les zones d'habitat des mammiferes en Afrique Occidentale Française. R. Pruniere. La Terre et La Vie, Paris, no.3, pp.83-93, figs.8, map, May-June, 1939.

(MAMMALS OF THE MISSION DAKAR-DJIBOUTI (MISSION GRAULE).) Les mammiferes de la Mission Dakar-Djibouti (Mission Griaule). M.P. Rode. Bull. Mus. Nat. d'Hist. Nat., Paris, ser.2, vol.5, no.5, pp.353-359, June, 1933.

(STUDY OF A COLLECTION OF MAMMALS FROM WESTERN AFRICA.) Etude d'une collection de mammifères de l'Afrique Occidentale. M.P. Rode. Bull. Mus. Nat. Hist. Nat., Paris, ser.2, vol.9, no.4, pp. 234-246, June, 1937.

CHECKLIST AND ATLAS OF NIGERIAN MAMMALS, WITH A FOREWORD ON VEGETATION. D.R. Rosevear. Lagos, Pub. under authority of Nigerian Government, pp.131, pls.40, fold. maps 2, 1953.

(Review by Charles O. Handley of) CHECK-LIST AND ATLAS ON NIGERIAN MAMMALS, WITH FOREWORD ON VEGETATION. D.R. Rosevear. Jour. Mamm., vol. 35, no.2, pp.269-270, May 26, 1954.

HOOFED MAMMALS OF NIGERIA. D.R. Rosevear. Nigerian Field, London, vol.8, no.3, pp.104-107, July 1939.

HOOFED MAMMALS OF NIGERIA: UNGULATES, 1. D.R. Rosevear. Nigerian Field, London, vol.8, no.2, pp.48-51, Apr., 1939.

NIGERIAN ANIMALS THAT DON'T EXIST. D.R. Rosevear. Nigerian Field, vol.13, no.1, pp.6-14, figs.7, Jan., 1948.

COLLECTION OF SMALL MAMMALS FROM NORTHERN NIGERIA. J. St. Leger. Ann. and Mag. Nat. Hist., ser.10, vol.3, pp. 387-388, Apr., 1929.

(NOTES ON SOME MAMMALS OF FRENCH EQUATORIAL AFRICA.) Notes sur quelques mammiferes de l'Afrique equatoriale française. Colin Campbell Sanborn. Mammalia, Paris, vol.17, no.3, pp.164-169, Sep., 1953.

GREAT FORESTS. I.T. Sanderson. The Atlantic Monthly, Boston, vol.160, no.3, pp.290-299, Sep., 1937. (Field Notes on Mammals of British Cameroons, West Africa.)

MAMMALS OF THE NORTH CAMEROONS FOREST AREA. I.T. Sanderson. Trans. Zool. Soc. London, vol.24, pp.623-725, pls.1-22, 1940.

PERCY SLADEN ZOOLOGICAL EXPEDITION TO BRITISH CAMEROONS, 1932-33. I.T. Sanderson. Proc. Linn. Soc. London, sess.147, pt.2, pp.25-29, May 10, 1935.

EXHIBITION OF, AND REMARKS UPON, SOME SPECIMENS OF MAMMALS FROM THE GAMBIA, WITH A LIST OF THE ANTELOPE KNOWN FROM THAT COLONY. P.L. Sclater. Proc. Zool. Soc. London, pt. 3, pp.349-350, fig.1, Oct. 1, 1898.

(UNGULATES OF WEST AND CENTRAL AFRICA. FINDINGS OF THE SECOND GERMAN CENTRAL AFRICA EXPEDITION 1910-11.) Huftiere aus West- und Zentralafrika. Ergebnisse der Zweiten Deutschen Zentral-Afrika-Exped.1910-11. Ernst Schwarz. Zoologie, vol.1, pp.831-1044, pls.33-48, June, 1920.

(MAMMALS AND BIRDS CAPTURED BY DR. PEREIRA DO NASCIMENTO IN WESTERN AFRICA.) Mammifères et oiseaux captures par le Dr. Pereira do Nascimento dans l'Afrique Occidentale. A.F. de Seabra. Bull. Soc. Portugaise Sci. Nat., Lisbonne, vol.2, fasc.1-2, pp.41-44, Nov., 1908.

(NOTES ON SOME MAMMALS FROM WESTERN AFRICA CAPTURED BY FR. NEWTON IN 1905 IN POSSESSION OF THE NATURAL HISTORY MUSEUM OF PORTO.) Note sur quelques mammiferes de l'Afrique occidentale captures par Fr. Newton em 1905 et appartenant au Muséum d'Historie Naturelle de Porto. A.F. de Seabra. Annaes Acad. Polytech. Porto, vol.4, pp.3, 1909.

(MAMMALS FROM THE CAMEROONS, WESTERN AFRICA.) Saeugetiere aus Kamerun, West-Afrika. Yngve Sjostedt. Bihang Till K. Svenska Vet.-Akad. Handlingar, Stockholm, vol.23, pt.4, no.1, pp.3-50, col. pl.1, Jan. 13, 1897.

(MAMMALS OF THE NORTHWESTERN CAMEROONS REGIONS.) Saeugethiere des nordwestlichen Kamerungebietes. Yngve Sjöstedt. Mitteil. deutsch. Schutzgebietes, Berlin, vol.10, no.1, pp.1-22, 1897.

WILD LIFE IN SIERRA LEONE. W.B. Stanley. Field, London, vol.161, no. 4194, p.1045, fig.1, May 13, 1933.

LIST OF A THIRD COLLECTION OF MAMMALS FROM PANYAM, N. NIGERIA, PRESENTED BY THE REV. G. T. FOX. Oldfield Thomas. Ann. and Mag. Nat. Hist., ser.8, vol.9, no.54, pp.683-686, June, 1912.

LIST OF MAMMALS FROM THE CAMEROONS MOUNTAIN, COLLECTED BY MR. H. H. JOHNSTON. Oldfield Thomas. Proc. Zool. Soc. London, p.121, Feb. 1, 1887.

LIST OF SMALL MAMMALS OBTAINED BY MR. G. FENWICK OWEN ON THE UPPER GAMBIA AND IN FOUTA DJALLON. Oldfield Thomas. Ann. and Mag. Nat. Hist., ser.8, no.43, pp.117-124, July, 1911.

MAMMALS FROM THE ISLAND OF FERNANDO PO, COLLECTED BY MR. E. SEIMUND. Oldfield Thomas. Proc. Zool. Soc. London, vol.2, pp.183-193, pl.13, Apr. 18, 1905.

MAMMALS FROM JA RIVER, CAMEROONS. Oldfield Thomas. Ann. and Mag. Nat. Hist., ser.8, vol.10, no.55, pp.41-43, July, 1912.

MAMMALS OF THE PANYAM PLATEAU, NORTHERN NIGERIA. II. Oldfield Thomas. Ann. and Mag. Nat. Hist., ser.8, vol.9, no.50, pp.269-274, Feb., 1912.

NOTES ON THE MAMMALS OF SOUTHERN CAMEROONS AND THE BENITO. Oldfield Thomas. Proc. Zool. Soc. London, vol.1, pp.65-85, June 1, 1905.

ON MAMMALS COLLECTED BY THE REV. G. T. FOX IN NORTHERN NIGERIA. Oldfield Thomas. Ann. and Mag. Nat. Hist., ser.8, vol.7, no.41, pp.457-463, May, 1911.

THREE NEW WEST AFRICAN MAMMALS. Oldfield Thomas. Ann. and Mag. Nat. Hist., ser.8, vol.5, no.28, pp.351-354, Apr., 1910.

TWO NEW WEST-AFRICAN MAMMALS. Oldfield Thomas. Ann. and Mag. Nat. Hist., ser.8, vol.10, no.57, pp.280-282, Sep., 1912.

CAPTAIN ANGUS BUCHANAN'S AIR EXPEDITION. I. ON A SERIES OF SMALL MAMMALS FROM KANO. Oldfield Thomas, M.A.C. Hinton. Novitates Zoologicae, vol. 27, pp.315-320, June, 1920.

ON A SERIES OF SMALL MAMMALS FROM KANO. Oldfield Thomas, M.A.C. Hinton.

Novitates Zoologicae, vol.27, pp.315-320, June, 1920.

PROVISIONAL LIST OF MAMMALS. U.S. SCIENTIFIC EXPEDITION TO WEST AFRICA, 1889. David P. Todd, Director. Bull. no.7, pp.1-4, Nov. 15, 1889. (U.S.S. "Pensacola", print.)

DESCRIPTIONS OF NEW SPECIES OF QUADRUPEDS COLLECTED BY MR. FRASER AT FERNANDO PO. G.R. Waterhouse. Proc. Zool. Soc. London, pt.10, pp.124-127, 1842.

ON SOME MAMMALS COLLECTED BY MR. ROBIN KEMP IN S.NIGERIA. R.C. Wroughton. Ann. and Mag. Nat. Hist., ser.7, vol.17, pp.375-379, Apr., 1906.

ON SOME NEW SPECIES OF MAMMALIA FROM FERNANDO PO. G.R. Waterhouse. Proc. Zool. Soc. London, pt.6, pp.57-61, 1838.

(MAMMALS OF WEST AFRICA.(COLLECTED BY ALFRED WEIDHOLZ.).) Saeugetiere Westafrikas. (Gesammelt von Alfred Weidholz.) Rudolf Zimara. Sitz.Ber.Akad.Wiss., math.-naturw.Kl., Abt.1, vol.144, nos.1-2, pp.7-18, 1935.

## ALASKA

### Extinct and Fossil Mammals

MAMMAL REMAINS FROM AN ALEUT STONE AGE VILLAGE. Walter J.Eyerdam. Jour. Mamm., vol.17, no.1, p.61, Feb.14, 1936.

SMITHSONIAN EXPLORATION IN ALASKA IN 1907 IN SEARCH OF PLEISTOCENE FOSSIL VERTEBRATES. Charles Whitney Gilmore. Washington, Smiths. Inst., pp. 38, illus., pls.13 (incl. 2 fold. maps), Smiths. Inst. Miscellaneous Collections, part of vol.LI, 1908.

BEFORE WINTER CAME TO ALASKA. (Extinct Mammals.) Ella Wilson Hill. Scientific America, vol.151, no.6, pp. 290-292, illus., Dec., 1934.

SMITHSONIAN EXPLORATION IN ALASKA IN 1904, IN SEARCH OF MAMMOTH AND OTHER FOSSIL REMAINS. A.G. Maddren. Smiths. Misc. Coll., vol.49, pp.5-117, 1905.

### Recent Mammals

OBSERVATIONS DURING A CRUISE ON THE DORA SIEWERD, AUGUST-SEPTEMBER, 1895. A.B. Alexander. Seal & Salmon Fisheries and General Resources of Alaska, House Doc.137, part.II, Wash., vol.IV, pp.573-600, 1898.

LIST OF MAMMALS COLLECTED IN ALASKA BY THE ANDREW J. STONE EXPEDITION OF 1901. J.A. Allen. Bull. Amer.Mus. Nat. Hist., vol.16, pp.215-230, July 12,1902.

(SUMMARY OF REPORT ON A MISSION TO THE PRIBILOF ISLANDS. (FUR SEALS.).) Compte-rendu sommaire d'une mission aux Iles Pribilof. Raymond Aretas. Bull. Mus. Nat. Hist. Nat., Paris, ser.2, vol.23, no. 6, pp.596-601, 1951.

BIRDS OF CAPE PRINCE OF WALES, ALASKA. (Notes on walrus, seals, and other mammals.) A.M. Bailey. Proc. Colorado Mus. Nat.Hist., Denver, vol.18, no.1, pp.113, illus., Feb. 1, 1943.

NOTES ON THE MAMMALS OF NORTHWESTERN ALASKA. A.M. Bailey, R.W. Hendee. Jour. Mamm., vol.7, no.1, pp. 9-28, pls.2-4, Feb., 1926.

MAMMALS TAKEN ALONG THE ALASKA HIGHWAY. Rollin H. Baker. U.Kans.Publ., Mus.Nat. Hist., vol.5, no.9, pp.87-117, illus., Nov., 1951.

MAMMALS FROM SOUTHEASTERN ALASKA. Rollin H. Baker, James S. Findley. U.Kansas Publ., Mus. Nat. Hist., Lawrence, vol.7, no.5, pp.473-477, Apr. 21, 1954.

MAMMALS OF NORTHERN ALASKA ON THE ARCTIC SLOPE. James W. Bee. U. Kansas publ., Mus.Nat. Hist., Lawrence, pp.309, illus., charts, 1956. (1.Mammals-Alaska. 2.Mammals - Arctic regions.)

ALASKA FISHERY AND FUR-SEAL INDUSTRIES IN 1923. Ward T. Bower. Appendix III to the Report of the U.S.Commissioner of Fisheries for 1924, pp.47-140, U.S. Bureau of Fisheries Doc.no.973, 1925.

ALASKA FISHERY AND FUR-SEAL INDUSTRIES IN 1936. (Arctic Foxes, Sea Otter, Reindeer, and Whaling.) Ward T. Bower. U.S. Dept. Com., Bur.Fisheries, Admin. Rep.28, pp.279-347,1938.

ALASKA FISHERY AND FUR-SEAL INDUSTRIES IN 1937.(Protection of Walruses and Sea-Lions, Take of Whales, and Status of Blue Foxes and Reindeer.) Ward T. Bower. U.S. Dept. Com., Bur.Fisheries, Admin.Rep.31, p.150, 1938.

ALASKA FISHERY AND FUR-SEAL INDUSTRIES IN 1938. Ward T. Bower. U.S. Dept. Com., Bur.Fisheries, Admin.Rep.36, pp. 85-168, 1940.

ALASKA FISHERY AND FUR-SEAL INDUSTRIES IN 1939.(Foxes and Reindeer on Pribilof Islands.) Ward T. Bower. U.S.Dept. Interior, Bur.Fisheries, Admin.Rep.40, pp. 159-184, 1941.

ALASKA FISHERY AND FUR-SEAL INDUSTRIES IN 1941. (Foxes and Reindeer on Pribilof Islands.) Ward T. Bower. U.S.Dept. Interior, Fish and Wildl.Serv., Statis.Dig. 5, p.71, 1943.

ALASKA FISHERY AND FUR-SEAL INDUSTRIES IN 1944. Ward T. Bower. U.S.Dept. Interior, Fish and Wildl.Serv., Statis.Dig. 13, pp.1-79, illus., 1946.

HUNTING IN THE NUTZOTINS. John B. Burnham. Hunting and Conservation, the book of the Boone and Crockett Club, New Haven, Yale Univ. Press, pp.412-437, pl. 1, 1925.

HARRIMAN ALASKA EXPEDITION. John Burroughs, and others. New York, vols.2, pp.420, col.pls.39, photogravure pls., figs.180, maps 5, 1901.

REPORT FROM THE SERVICES. PVT. DONAHUE FINDS PLENTY OF LIFE IN THE BARREN ALEUTIANS. Cpl.Earl Chase, Pvt.Ralph Donahue. Animal Kingdom, New York, vol.47, no.1, pp.11-13, Jan.-Feb., 1944.

BEAR-MOOSE RELATIONSHIPS ON THE KENAI PENINSULA. Edward F.Chatelain. Trans. 15th N.Amer. Wildl.Conf., Wash., pp.224-234, 1950.

ALEUTIAN ISLANDS:THEIR PEOPLE AND NATURAL HISTORY (WITH KEYS FOR THE IDENTIFICATION OF THE BIRDS AND PLANTS). Henry B. Collins, Jr., Austin H. Clark, Egbert H. Walker.Smiths. Inst., War Background Studies, Wash., no. 21, pp.1-131, illus., Feb. 5, 1945. (Mammals, pp.48-54.)

WHAT'S HAPPENING IN ALASKA? F.Darling, A. S.Leopold. Animal Kingdom, vol. 55, no.6, pp.170-174, illus., Nov.-Dec., 1952.

WHITE SHEEP AND GRIZZLY BEAR. A.V. Denman. Alaska Sportsman, Ketchikan, vol.7, no.1, pp.12-13, 30-32, Jan., 1941.

LAND VERTEBRATE ASSOCIATIONS OF INTERIOR ALASKA. Lee Raymond Dice. Occasional Papers Mus.Zool.Univ.Michigan, no.85, pp.24, pls.4, May 25, 1920.

NOTES ON THE MAMMALS OF INTERIOR ALASKA. Lee Raymond Dice. Jour.Mamm., vol.2, no.1, pp.20-28, Feb., 1921.

BIRDS AND MAMMALS OF MT. MCKINLEY NATIONAL PARK, ALASKA. Joseph S. Dixon. Fauna Nat. Parks U.S., Fauna ser.3, U.S.Dept. Interior, Nat.Parks Serv., pp.1-236, figs.85, Aug., 1934. (Mammals, pp. 133-231, figs.40-85.)

FAUNA OF THE NATIONAL PARKS OF THE UNITED STATES. BIRDS AND MAMMALS OF MOUNT MCKINLEY NATIONAL PARK, ALASKA. Joseph S. Dixon. U.S. Govt.Print. Off., Wash., pp.xii+236, illus.(incl.map), pl., 1938. (U.S. Nat.Park Serv., Fauna Series, no.3.)

ALASKA'S ANIMALS AND FISHES. Frank Dufresne. New York, A.S.Barnes and Co., pp.xviii+297, illus.(col.pls.13), 1946; 2nd Ed., Portland, Or., Binfords & Mort, pp. 297, illus., 1955.

MAMMALS AND BIRDS OF ALASKA.(Accounts of Important Game and Fur-Bearing Animals, with Distribution Maps and Measurements of some Record Game Trophies.) Frank Dufresne. U.S.Dept. Interior, Fish and Wildl.Serv., Circular no.3, pp.37,figs. 35, 1942.

ISLANDS OF MIST. (Sea Lion, Seal, Walrus, Arctic Fox, on Pribilof Island.) Ben East. Fauna, Philadelphia, vol.10, no.3, pp.69-73, illus., Sep., 1948.

SPORTSMEN: WE MUST NOT LET ALASKA'S GAME DIE OUT! Ben East. Outdoor Life, New York, vol.101, no.5, pp.24-25, 116-118, illus., May, 1948.

(ALASKA: ITS MAMMALS AND THEIR PURSUIT.) L'Alaska ses mammiferes et leurs chasses. Francois Edmond-Blanc. La Terre et La Vie, 8 Année, no.5, pp. 131, 147, illus., Sep.-Oct., 1938.

NEEDED RESEARCH ON ALASKAN FUR ANIMALS. W.A. Elkins. Science in Alaska, Proc. Second Alaskan Science Conf., 1951, pp.355-362, 1953.

PRESSING PROBLEMS IN ADMINISTRATION OF WILDLIFE RESOURCES IN ALASKA. W.A. Elkins. Science in Alaska, Special Publ. Arctic Inst.N.Amer., Wash., no.1, pp.268-281, June, 1952.

I MARRIED A HEAD HUNTER. (Hunting in Alaska.) Niska Elwell. Outdoorsman, Chicago, vol.87, no.2 (whole no.513), pp.16-17, 49, illus., Mar.-Apr., 1945.

FISHERY AND FUR INDUSTRIES OF ALASKA IN 1912. B.W. Evermann. U.S. Bur. Fish., Doc.780, pp.123, tbls., 1913.

ALASKA'S FROZEN FAUNA. Childs Frick. Nat. Hist., vol.30, no.1, pp.71-80, photos 9, Jan.-Feb., 1930.

TROUBLE IN ALASKA. (Moose, Caribou, Wolves, Coyotes, Dall Sheep.) Chas. E. Gillham. Outdoors, Dayton, vol.16, no.5, pp.18-19, 56-57, illus., May, 1948.

CONDITION OF WILD LIFE IN ALASKA. Madison Grant. Smiths. Inst., Annual Rep., 1909, Wash., pp.521-529, pl.,1910.

BIRDS AND MAMMALS OF THE 1907 ALEXANDER EXPEDITION TO SOUTHEASTERN ALASKA. Joseph Grinnell. Berkeley, Univ. Press, pp.264, illus.4, pls.25-26 (incl.map), 1909.

MAMMALS COLLECTED BY CHARLES D. BROWER AT POINT BARROW, ALASKA. E. Raymond Hall. Univ. Calif. Publ. Zool., vol.30, no.14, pp.419-425, Mar.19, 1929.

NEW MAMMALS FROM ST. LAWRENCE ISLAND, BERING SEA, ALASKA. E.Raymond Hall. Univ. Calif.Publ.Zool., vol. 38, no.9, pp.391-404, pls.5-6, fig.1, Sep. 17, 1932.

MAMMALS OF THE ST. MATTHEW ISLANDS, BERING SEA. G.D. Hanna. Jour. Mamm., vol.1, no.3, pp.118-122, May, 1920.

RARE MAMMALS OF THE PRIBILOF ISLANDS, ALASKA. G.D. Hanna. Jour. Mamm., vol.4, no.4, pp.209-215, pl.23, Nov., 1923.

MAMMALS OF THE 1908 ALEXANDER ALASKA EXPEDITION, WITH DESCRIPTIONS OF THE LOCALITIES VISITED AND NOTES ON THE FLORA OF THE PRINCE WILLIAM SOUND REGION. Edmund Heller. Berkeley, Univ. Press, pp.360, pl., map, 1910.

NEW GAME ACT FOR ALASKA FOR THE BETTER PROTECTION AND MORE RATIONAL UTILIZATION OF ALASKA'S GAME ANIMALS. William T.Hornaday. Permanent Wild Life Protection Fund Bull. no.6, pp.1-45, pls.5, New York, Feb.15, 1920.

EXPLORATION OF MUMMY CAVES IN THE ALEUTIAN ISLANDS. PART II. FURTHER EXPLORATION. Ales Hrdlicka. Sci. Monthly, Lancaster, vol.52, no.2, pp.113-130, illus., Feb., 1941.

FUR FARMING IN ALASKA. Charles E. Kellogg. Fur of Canada, Winnipeg, vol. 11, no.1, p.30, Oct., 1945.

MAMMALS FROM A NATIVE VILLAGE SITE ON KODIAK ISLAND. Remington Kellogg. Proc. Biol. Soc. Washington, vol.49, pp.37-38, Mar. 9, 1936.

NOTES ON MAMMALS OF THE UPPER CHITINA RIVER REGION, ALASKA. Hamilton M. Laing, Rudolph M. Anderson. Nat. Mus. Canada, Bull.56, pp.96-107, 1929.

BIG LAND, BIG GAME. (Grizzly Bear, Mountain Goat.) Ran Lake. Alaska Sportsman, Ketchikan, vol.11, no.10, pp.14-15, 29-33, illus., Oct., 1945.

WILDLIFE IN ALASKA, AN ECOLOGICAL RECONNAISSANCE. A. Starker Leopold, F. Fraser Darling. Ronald Press, New York, pp.140, illus., 1953.

(Review by Ralph S. Palmer of) WILDLIFE IN ALASKA. A. Starker Leopold, F.Fraser Darling. Jour. Mamm., vol.35, no.3, pp. 463-464, Aug. 20, 1954.

METHODS OF SAVING ALASKA GAME. Walter L. Lodge. Forest and Stream, vol.91, pp.156, 157, 188, Apr., 1921.

NOTES ON THE MAMMALS AND BIRDS OBSERVED IN ALASKA; NOTES ON THE DESTRUCTION OF GAME IN ALASKA. J. Loring. New York, Office of the New York Zoological Soc., pp.21, 1902.

BIOLOGICAL SURVEY OF THE PRIBILOF ISLANDS, ALASKA. 1. BIRDS AND MAMMALS. 2. INSECTS, ARCHNIDS, AND CHILOPODS, BY VARIOUS ENTOMOLOGISTS, WITH AN INTRODUCTION BY W. L. MCATEE. W.L. McAtee, Edward A. Preble. U.S. Dept. Agric., Div. Biol. Surv., N.Amer. Fauna no.46, pp.244, pls.15, June 20, 1923.

STAKING OUT THE SPORTSMAN'S CLAIMS IN ALASKA. Harry McGuire. Outdoor Life, vol.67, no.2, pp.12-13, 83-84, Feb., 1931.

MANAGEMENT OF AFFAIRS ON ST. GEORGE ISLAND. Wm.J. McIntyre. Seal and Salmon Fisheries and General Resources of Alaska, Wash., vol.I, pp. 76, 80-81, 1898.

ALASKA GAME LAW AND REGULATIONS OF THE DEPARTMENT OF AGRICULTURE, 1908. C. Hart Merriam. U.S. Dept. Agric., Bur. Biol. Surv., Circular no.66, pp.8, Sep. 3, 1908.

ALASKA SHEEP AND WOLVES, A TIMELY TALK. E.G. Moore. Outdoor Life, vol.70, no.1, pp.16-17, 68-70, July, 1932.

NATURALIST IN ALASKA. (Wolves, Bears, Caribou, Foxes, Ravens, Eagles, and others.) Adolph Murie. New York, pp.320, photos 10, many text drawings, 1960.

WILDLIFE OF MOUNT MCKINLEY NATIONAL PARK. Adolph Murie. Nat. Geogr. Mag., Wash., vol.104, no.2, pp.249-270, illus., Aug., 1953.

ALASKA. (Caribou, Bear, etc.) O.J.Murie. Living Wilderness, Wash., vol.10, whole no.12, pp.3-8, illus., Feb., 1945.

NOTES ON THE MAMMALS OF ST. LAWRENCE ISLAND (app.3, pp.335-346). O.J. Murie. (In) Archaeological Investigations at Kukulik by O.W.Geist, F.G.Rainey.Misc. Publs. Univ. Alaska, vol.2, 1936.

PLANNING FOR ALASKA'S BIG GAME. O.J. Murie. Science in Alaska, Special Publ. Arctic Inst. N.Amer., Wash., no. 1, pp.258-267, June,1952.

WILDLIFE INTRODUCTIONS IN ALASKA. O.J. Murie. Trans. N.Amer. Wildl.Conf., vol.5, pp.432-436, 1941.

BIG GAME OF ALASKA. E.W. Nelson. Bull. Amer. Game Protective Ass., Apr., 1921. Reprint, pp.1-7, figs.6, 1921. (Address before the Seventh Nat. Game Conf., New York City, Jan., 1921.

DECREASE OF FUR-BEARING ANIMALS IN ALASKA. E.W. Nelson. Nat. Hist., vol.22, p.83, Jan.-Feb., 1922.

NOTES ON THE WILD FOWL AND GAME ANIMALS OF ALASKA. E.W. Nelson. Nat. Geog. Mag., Wash., D.C., vol.9, no.4, pp.121-132, illus., Apr., 1898.

MAMMALS OF NORTHERN ALASKA. PT. 2. REPORT UPON NATURAL HISTORY COLLECTIONS MADE IN ALASKA BETWEEN THE YEARS 1877 AND 1881. E.W. Nelson, F.W. True. No.3, Arctic Series of Publications Issued in Connection with the Signal Corps, U.S. Army, pp.229-293, 1887.

IMPRESSIONS OF ALASKA --WHERE EAST AND WEST APPROXIMATE. (Notes on Cetaceans and Seals.) J.T. Nichols. Nat. Hist., vol.26, pp.605-613, illus., Dec., 1926.

LIFE ON THE NAHA. (Black Bear, Black-Tailed Deer, Beaver.) Alda Orton. Alaska Sportsman, Ketchikan, vol.12, no.2, pp. 12-13, 29-31, Feb., 1946.

BIG GAME OF ALASKA. Wilfred H. Osgood. Nat. Geogr. Mag., Wash., D.C., vol.20, no.7, pp.624-636, illus., July, 1909.

BIOLOGICAL RECONNAISSANCE OF THE BASE OF THE ALASKA PENINSULA. Wilfred H. Osgood. N.Amer. Fauna, vol.24, pp.1-86, pls.7, 1904.

COLLECTION OF MAMMALS FROM THE REGION OF MOUNT MCKINLEY, ALASKA. Wilfred H. Osgood. Proc. Biol. Soc. Washington, vol.20, pp.59-64, Apr. 18, 1907.

GAME RESOURCES OF ALASKA. Wilfred H. Osgood. Yearbook U.S. Dept. Agric., Wash., D.C., 1907, pp.469-482, figs. 49-51, pls.56-57, 1908.

LIST OF MAMMALS OF THE ALASKA PENINSULA. Wilfred H. Osgood. N.Amer. Fauna, no.24, pp.27-50, Nov. 23, 1904.

NATURAL HISTORY OF THE COOK INLET REGION, ALASKA. Wilfred H. Osgood. N. Amer. Fauna, no.21, pp.51-81, pls.6, 7, Sep.26, 1901.

REPORTS FOR YEARS 1879-1882. Harrison G. Otis. Seal and Salmon Fisheries and General Resources of Alaska. Wash., vol. I, pp.114, 116, 125, 127, 128, 132, 141, 152, 1898.

ANIMAL AND PLANT RESOURCES OF ALASKA. L.J. Palmer. U.S. Dept.Interior, Fish and Wildl. Serv., Wildl.Leaflet 176, pp.1-12, Jan., 1941.

STUDY OF THE ALASKA TUNDRA WITH REFERENCE TO ITS REACTIONS TO REINDEER AND OTHER GRAZING. L.J. Palmer. U.S. Dept. Interior, Fish and Wildlife Serv., Research Rept.10, pp.48, figs. 20, 1945.

ALASKA AS A SPORTSMAN'S PARADISE. C.F. Periolat. Nat. Sportsman, Boston, pp.15-21, illus., Dec., 1901.

BIRDS AND MAMMALS OF THE PRIBILOF ISLANDS, ALASKA. Edward A. Preble. Washington Govt. Print.Off., pp.255, pl., maps 3, 1923.

MAMMALS OF THE PRIBILOF ISLANDS. Edward A. Preble. N.Amer. Fauna, no.46, pp.102-120, pl., June 20, 1923.

(Review by Clifford C. Presnall of) WILDLIFE IN ALASKA. Jour. Forestry, vol.52, no.2, pp.137-138, Feb., 1954.

OBSERVATIONS ON MAMMALS OF THE SEWARD PENINSULA, ALASKA. (Distribution, Life History, and Ecology.) W.B. Quay. Jour. Mamm., vol.32, no. 1, pp.88-99, Feb., 1951.

SOUTHERN HALF OF THE ALASKA HIGHWAY AND ITS MAMMALS. Austin Loomer Rand. Ottawa, E.Cloutier, pp.50, illus., map, 1944. (Canada, Nat. Mus., Ottawa, Bull.no.98, Biological Ser.no.27.)

NOTES ON THE NUNAMIUT ESKIMO AND MAMMALS OF THE ANAKTUVUK PASS REGION, BROOKS RANGE, ALASKA. Robert Rausch. Arctic, Jour.Arctic Inst. North America, Montreal, vol.4, no.3, pp.147-195, illus., Dec., 1951.

ON THE LAND MAMMALS OF ST. LAWRENCE ISLAND, ALASKA. Robert Rausch. Murrelet, Seattle, vol.34, no.2, pp.18-26, Oct. 5, 1953.

ALASKA'S FISH AND WILDLIFE. Clarence J. Rhode, Will Barker. Circular U.S. Fish and Wildl. Serv., no.17, pp.60, illus., 1953.

MAMMALS OF THE KATMAI NATIONAL MONUMENT ALASKA. Everett L. Schiller, Robert Rausch. Arctic, Jour.Arctic Inst. N.Amer., vol.9, no.3, pp.191-201, 1956.

PROTECTION OF ALASKA GAME. Charles Sheldon. Forest and Stream, vol.90, pp. 107, 158, 159, Mar., 1920.

WILDERNESS OF DENALI. EXPLORATIONS OF A HUNTER-NATURALIST IN NORTHERN ALASKA. Charles Sheldon. New York, Chas. Scribner's Sons, pp.25+412, illus., 1930.

(Review by E.A. Goldman of) WILDERNESS OF DENALI. Charles Sheldon. Jour.Mamm., vol.12, no.1, pp.80-81, Feb., 1931.

PROBLEM OF ALASKAN DEVELOPMENT. Harry Slattery. U.S. Dept. Interior, pp.94, July, 1939.

FAUNA AND FLORA OF ALASKA. A. de C.Sowerby. China Jour., vol.18, no.6, pp. 371-374, figs.8, June 1933.

REPORT FOR 1892. J. Stanley-Brown. Seal and Salmon Fisheries and General Resources of Alaska, Wash., vol.I, pp.316-364, 1898.

(FROM THE FAR EAST. JOURNEY NOTES OF LEONHARD STEYNEGER. II. FOURTEEN MORE DAYS IN KAMCHATKA.) Fra det yderste osten. Rejsebreve fra Leonhard Stejneger. II. Andre fjorten Dage i Kamschatka. Leonhard Stejneger. Naturen, vol. 8, no.1, pp.5-10, Jan., 1884.

REPORT ON THE BIRDS AND MAMMALS, OBTAINED BY THE MCILHENNY EXPEDITION TO PT. BARROW, ALASKA. Witmer Stone. Proc. Acad. Nat. Sci., Philadelphia, pp.4-49, Mar. 24, 1900.

NOTES ON MAMMALS FROM ALASKA. Robert L. Strecker, Fred A. Ryser, William J. Tietz, Peter R. Morrison. Jour. Mamm., vol.33, no.4, pp.467-480, fig. 1, Nov. 19, 1952.

SOME GAME TRAILS OF ALASKA. Hudson Stuck. Country Life, vol.40, no.3, pp.35-39, col.pls.3, figs.6, July, 1921.

YOUR STAKE IN ALASKA'S WILDLIFE AND WILDERNESS. Lowell Sumner. Sierra Club Bull., San Francisco, vol.41, no.10, pp.54-71, pls.16, Dec., 1956.

BIRDS AND MAMMALS OF THE 1909 ALEXANDER ALASKA EXPEDITION. Harry Schelwald Swarth. Berkeley, Univ. Press, pp.172, pls.6, fold.map, 1911. (Univ. California Publ. in Zoology, vol.7, no.2.)

ORIGINS OF THE FAUNA OF THE SITKAN DISTRICT, ALASKA. Harry Schelwald Swarth. Proc. Calif. Acad. Sci., ser.4, vol.23, no.3, pp.59-78, fig.1, June 19, 1936. (Mammals, pp.71-76.)

REPORT BY PROFESSOR D'ARCY THOMPSON ON HIS MISSION TO THE BEHRING SEA IN 1896, DATED MARCH 4, 1897. D'Arcy Thompson. Pp.1-39, 1897.

ALASKA FISHERY AND FUR-SEAL INDUSTRIES IN 1947. Seton H. Thompson. U.S. Dept. Interior, Fish and Wildl. Serv., Statis. Dig.20, pp.78, 1950.

MANAGEMENT OF THE MARINE RESOURCES OF ALASKA. Seton H.Thompson. Science in Alaska, Special Publ.Arctic Inst. N.Amer., Wash., no.1, pp.282-291, June, 1952.

NOTES ON THE NATURAL HISTORY AND ETHNOLOGY OF NORTHERN ALASKA. Charles Haskins Townsend. U.S. Revenue Cutter Ser., Rep. of the Cruise of the Revenue Marine Steamer Corwin in the Arctic Ocean in the Year 1885.

ANNUAL REPORT OF THE GOVERNOR OF ALASKA. John W. Troy. Pp.44, 1936.

(Value of Alaska's Fur and Game Resources.)

ANNOTATED LIST OF THE MAMMALS COLLECTED BY THE LATE MR. CHARLES L. MCKAY IN THE VICINITY OF BRISTOL BAY, ALASKA. Frederick William True. U.S. Nat. Mus., Proceedings, Washington, vol.9, pp.221-224, 1886.

MAMMALS OF THE PRIBILOF ISLANDS. (Extracted from the Fur Seals and Fur-Seal Islands of the North Pacific Ocean, Part III, pp.345-354.) Frederick W. True. Publ. by Govt. Print. Off., Wash., D.C., 1899.

CONTRIBUTION TO THE NATURAL HISTORY OF ALASKA. Lucien Meshan Turner. Govt. Print. Off., Washington, pp.226, pls. 26, 1886.

ALASKA: AMERICA'S CONTINENTAL FRONTIER OUTPOST. (Photographs and Brief Accounts of Economically Important Mammals.) Ernest P. Walker. Smiths. Inst. War Background Studies, Washington, D.C., no.13, pp.v+57, figs.2, pls.21, July 8, 1943.

MAMMALS OF THE KNIK RIVER VALLEY, ALASKA. Charles G. Wilber. Jour. Mamm., vol.27, no.3, pp.213-216, pl.1, Aug. 14, 1946.

ALASKAN ADVENTURE. (Experiences with Wildlife in Southeastern Alaska.) Jay P. Williams. Stackpole Co., Harrisburg, pp. xiii+299, pls.20, Apr. 15, 1952.

ALASKA'S GAMELANDS. Walter J. Wilwerding. Sports Afield, Minneapolis, vol. 121, no.4, pp.32-33, illus., Apr., 1949.

ALASKAN FURS. S.Dakota Conservation Digest, Pierre, vol.9, no.4, p.16, Apr., 1942.

ALASKA DEPARTMENT OF FISHERIES. Annual Report for 1955, Juneau, Rept.7, p.152, 1956.

DISTRIBUTION OF GAME AND LAND FUR-BEARING ANIMALS IN ALASKA 1938. Alaska Game Commission. U.S. Dept. Agric., Biol.Survey, maps 25, 1939.

FROM KETCHIKAN TO BARROW. (Fur Seal, Sea Otter, Buffalo.) Alaska Sportsman, Ketchikan, vol.14, no.2, pp.18-22, Feb., 1948.

REPORT ON THE POPULATION, INDUSTRIES, AND RESOURCES OF ALASKA. Seal and Salmon Fisheries and General Resources of Alaska, (from the 10th Census), Wash., vol.iv, pp.167-450, pls.8, 1898.

SALE OF FURS FROM PRIBILOF ISLANDS. Fisheries Service Bulletin no.53, Oct., 1919.

ALEUTIAN ISLANDS see ALASKA

## ANTARCTIC REGIONS

(HIGHER ANIMAL LIFE IN THE ANTARCTIC REGION. SCIENTIFIC FINDINGS OF THE SWEDISH SOUTH POLE EXPEDITION, 1901-1903.) Das hoehere Tierleben im antarktischen Gebiete. Wissensch. Ergeb. der Schwedischen Suedpolar-Exped. 1901-1903. K.A. Andersson. Stockholm, Band 5 (zool.), Lief.2, pp.1-58, pls.10, maps 2, 1908.

(OBSERVATIONS ON THE MARINE MAMMALS FROM THE KERGUELEN ARCHIPELAGO.) Observations sur les mammiferes marins de l'archipel de Kerguelen. M. Angot. Mammalia, vol.18, pp.1-111, pls.6, maps 2, 1954.

(FLORA AND FAUNA OF THE KERGUELEN ISLANDS.) La flore et la faune des Isles Kerguelen. E. Aubert de la Rue. La Terre et la Vie (Revue d'Hist.Nat.), vol.2, no.1, pp.29-51, illus., Jan., 1932.

REPORT ON THE COLLECTIONS OF NATURAL HISTORY MADE IN THE ANTARCTIC REGIONS DURING THE VOYAGE OF THE "SOUTHERN CROSS." G.E.H. Barrett-Hamilton. London, Brit. Mus. (Nat.Hist), pp.66, pl.1, 1902.

THREE ANTARCTIC YEARS. BRITISH GRAHAM LAND EXPEDITION OF 1934-1937. Launcelot Fleming, Colin Bertram, Brian Roberts. Canadian Geogr. Jour., Ottawa, vol.22, no.1, pp.2-39, illus., Jan., 1941.

KERGUELEN ISLAND--ITS ANIMALS AND PLANTS. H.O. Fletscher. Australian Mus. Mag., vol.4, no.12, pp.401-407, figs.9, Oct. 16, 1932.

ZOOLOGY. SEALS AND CETACEANS. William Henry Flower. Rep. of the British "Transit of Venus" Expedition (to Kerguelen Island) 1874-1875, pp.1-6. Philos. Trans., London, vol.168 (extra vol.), pp.95-100, 1879.

ANTARCTICA: A VANISHED AUSTRAL LAND. Henry G. Forbes. Smiths. Inst. Annual Rep. for 1894. pp.297-316, 1896.

NOTES ON MAMMALS OBSERVED IN THE PERRY RIVER DISTRICT, QUEEN MAUD SEA. Angus Gavin. Jour. Mamm., vol.26, no.3, pp.226-230, Aug., 1945.

U. S. NAVAL ASTRONOMICAL EXPEDITION TO THE SOUTHERN HEMISPHERE, DURING 1849-50-51-52. J.M. Gilliss. (Mammals by Spencer F. Baird.) House of Representatives, 33rd Congress, 1st Session, Ex.Doc.no.121, vol.2, pp.1-300, illus., 1855.

CRUCIAL EVIDENCE FOR ANTARCTIC RADIATION. L. Harrison. Amer. Nat., vol.60, no.669, pp.374-383, 1926.

THE WHITE CONTINENT. T.R. Henry. London, Eyre and Spottiswoode, pp.13-211, 1951.

(VOYAGE TO THE SOUTH POLE AND IN OCEANIA ON THE CORVETTES "ASTROLABE" AND "ZELEE" MADE DURING 1837-40 UNDER THE COMMAND OF J. DUMONT D'URVILLE.) Voyage au Pole Sud et dans l'Oceanie sur les corvettes l'Astrolabe et la Zelee, execute... pendant...1837-1840 sous le commandement de J. Dumont d'Urville. C.H. Jacquinot. Paris, vols.30, atlas, 1842-54.

CONTRIBUTION TO THE NATURAL HISTORY OF KERGUELEN ISLAND, MADE IN CONNECTION WITH THE UNITED STATES TRANSIT-OF-VENUS EXPEDITION, 1874-75. MAMMALS. J.H. Kidder. Bull. U.S. Nat. Mus., no.3, pp.38-41, 1876.

HEARD ISLAND. P.G. Law, T.Burstall. Interim Repts. Australian Nat. Antarctic Res. Exped., no.7, p.32, 1953.

BRITISH ANTARCTIC "TERRA NOVA" EXPEDITION, 1910. NATURAL HISTORY REPORT. CETACEA. D.G. Lillie. Brit. Mus.(Nat.Hist.), London, Zool., vol.1, no.3, pp.85-124, illus., pls.1-8, 1915.

(CETACEANS OF THE ANTARCTIC. 2ND FRENCH ANTARCTIC EXPEDITIONS, 1908-1910.) Cetaces de l'Antarctique. Deux. Exped. Antarct. Francaise, 1908-1910. J. Liouville. Sciences Naturelles:Documents Scientifiques. Cetaces de l'Antarctique, pp.1-171, pls.1-15, 1913.

DISTRIBUTION OF THE PACK-ICE IN THE SOUTHERN OCEAN. N.A. Mackintosh, H.F.P. Herdman. Discovery Repts., vol. 19, pp.285-296, pls.27, 1940.

(BIOGEOGRAPHICAL PROBLEMS OF CHILEAN ANTARCTICA.) Problemas biogeograficos de la Antarctica Chilena. Guillermo Mann Fischer. Rev. Geogr. Chile, Santiago, no.1, pp.101-108, illus., Sep., 1948.

(BIOLOGY OF SOUTH AMERICAN ANTARCTICA. STUDIES REALIZED DURING THE CHILEAN ANTARCTIC EXPEDITION, 1947.) Biologia de la Antarctica Suramericana. Estudios realizados durante la Expedición Antárctica Chilena, 1947. Guillermo Mann Fischer. Publ. Inst. Geogr. Univ. Chile, Santiago, no.2, pp.364, figs. 115, pls.46, maps 2, 1948.

ANTARCTIC FISHERIES. Douglas Mawson. Fisheries Newsletter, Ministry Post War Reconstruction, Cronulla, vol.5, no.1, pp. 6-7, figs.2, Feb., 1946.

THE B. A. N. Z. ANTARCTIC RESEARCH EXPEDITION, 1929-31. Douglas Mawson. Geogr. Jour., London, vol.80, no.2, pp. 101-131, illus., map., Aug., 1932.

ANTARCTIC ZOOGEOGRAPHY AND SOME OF ITS PROBLEMS. Robert Cushman Murphy. Amer. Geog. Soc. special publ. no.7, pp. 355-379, 1928.

SCIENTIFIC ADVANTAGES OF AN ANTARCTIC EXPEDITION. John Murray, and others. Ann. Rept. Smiths. Inst., 1897, publ.1150, pp.413-436, 1898.

NOTES ON FOSSILS FROM THE FALKLAND ISLANDS BROUGHT HOME BY THE SCOTTISH NATIONAL ANTARCTIC EXPEDITION IN 1904. E.T. Newton. Proc. Roy. Phys. Soc. Edinburgh, vol.16, no.6, pp.248-257, pls.10, 1906.

AT THE EDGE OF THE ANTARCTIC ICE. (Includes Notes on Various Species of Cetaceans and Pinnipeds.) John T. Nichols. Nat. Hist., vol.29, pp.129-142, illus., Mar., 1929.

RATS AND REINDEER IN THE ANTARCTIC. O. Olstad. Det Norske Videnskaps-Adad. i Oslo. Sci. Results Norwegian Antarctic Exped. 1927-1928 and 1928-1929, instituted and financed by Consul Lars Christensen, Oslo, vol.1, no.4, pp.1-20, figs.7, May 20, 1930.

ANIMAL LIFE IN THE ANTARCTIC. Earle B. Perkins. Proc. of the American Philos. Soc., vol.82, no.5, 1940.

BIOLOGY AT LITTLE AMERICA III, THE WEST BASE OF THE UNITED STATES ANTARCTIC SERVICE EXPEDITION 1939-1941. J. Perkins. Proc. Amer. Phil. Soc., vol.89, pp.270-284, 1945.

(WHALE HUNTING AND ANIMAL LIFE IN THE ANTARCTIC OCEAN.) Ueber Hochseewalfang und Tierleben im Suedlichen Eismeer. Nicolaus Peters. Zeitschr. "Der Fischmarkt", Cuxhaven, nos. 7-8, pp.28, figs.14, 1937.

(Review by Chr.Jouanin of) ANTARCTIC ISLE. Niall Rankin. Mammalia, Paris, vol.16, no.1, p.42, Mar., 1952.

CHRONOLOGICAL LIST OF ANTARCTIC EXPEDITIONS WITH BRIEF NOTES ON EACH, 1502-1948(p.6-25). B.B.Roberts. (In) The Antarctic Pilot. Ed.2, London, Admiralty, Hydrographic Dept., pp.42-371, maps, 1948.

"SOUTH", THE STORY OF SHACKELTON'S LAST EXPEDITION. E.H. Shackelton. 1920.

WILD LIFE IN THE SUBANTARCTIC. J.H. Sorensen. Whitecomb & Tombs Ltd., Wellington, pp.85, illus., 1951.

ANTARCTIC EXPLORATION. Thomas Southwell. Nat. Science, vol.6, no.36, pp.97-107, illus., Feb., 1895.

NORWEGIAN-BRITISH-SWEDISH SCIENTIFIC EXPEDITION TO THE ANTARCTIC 1949-52. H.U. Sverdrup. Norsk Hvalfangst-Tidende (Norwegian Whaling Gazette), Sandefjord, vol.39, no.3, pp.100-106, illus., Mar., 1950.

VOYAGE TOWARDS THE SOUTH POLE, PERFORMED IN THE YEARS 1822-24. J. Weddell. London, Longman, pp.6+276, maps 5, 1825.

MAMMALIA (Whales and Seals) (pp.ix-xii, 1-69, pls.4). E.A. Wilson. (In) Nat. Ant-Arctic Expedition 1904-04. Nat.Hist.Vol.2, Zoology (Vertebrata, Mollusca, Crustacea). London, Brit. Mus.

ANTARCTIC CRUISE OF THE ROYAL RESEARCH SHIP, DISCOVERY II, OPERATING UNDER DIRECTION OF THE FALKLAND ISLANDS GOVERNMENT. Science, n.s., vol.76, no.1968, p.253, Sep. 16, 1932.

THE ANTARCTIC PILOT. Admiralty, Hydrographic Department. Ed. 2, London, pp. 42-370, fold.maps 3, 1948.

ANTILLES see WEST INDIES

ARABIA

PROBLEMS OF ANIMAL DISTRIBUTION IN ARABIA. F.S. Bodenheimer. Proc. Linnean Soc. London, 150th Sess. (1937-38), pt.1, pp.47-49, Dec. 31, 1937.

ON THE MAMMALS COLLECTED IN THE DESERT OF CENTRAL ARABIA BY MAJOR R.E. CHEESMAN. R.E. Cheesman, Martin A.C. Hinton. Ann. and Mag. Nat. Hist., ser.9, vol.14, pp.548-558, Nov., 1924.

TRAVELS IN ARABIA DESERTS. Charles Montagu Doughty. Random House, New York, pp.696, illus., 1947.

ON A COLLECTION OF MAMMALS FROM OMAN, ARABIA, WITH THE DESCRIPTION OF TWO NEW BATS. David L. Harrison. Ann. Mag. Nat. Hist., ser.12, vol.8, no. 96, pp.897-910, Dec., 1955.

EXPEDITION TO SOUTH-WEST ARABIA. 1937-38. 1. MAMMALIA: CHIROPTERA. R.W. Hayman. British Mus. Nat. Hist., London, vol.1, nos.1-8, pp.1-2, Feb. 22, 1941.

NOTES ON SOME MAMMALS NEWLY RECORDED FROM ARABIA. R.W. Hayman, D.L. Harrison. Ann. Mag. Nat. Hist., London, ser.12, vol.3, no.29, pp.417-419, May, 1950.

(ON SOME MAMMALS, REPTILES, AND AMPHIBIANS COLLECTED AND OBSERVED NEAR ADEN BY OSCAR NEUMANN.) Ueber einige von Herrn Oscar Neumann bei Aden gesammelte und beobachtete Saeugethiere, Reptilien und Amphibien. Paul Matschie. Sitz.Ber. Gesell.Naturf.Freunde, Berlin, no. 1, pp.24-31, Jan. 17, 1893.

SOME ARABIAN MAMMALS COLLECTED BY MR. H. ST. J. PHILBY, C.I.E. T.C.S. Morrison-Scott. Novitates Zoologicae, Tring, vol.41, no.3, pp.181-211, figs.125-127, appendices 4, Aug. 31, 1939.

MAMMALS COLLECTED IN S. E. ARABIA BY MR. BERTRAM THOMAS AND MR. H. ST. J. PHILBY. R.I. Pocock. Ann. Mag. Nat. Hist., London, ser.10, vol.15, no.88, pp.441-467, Apr., 1935.

PRELIMINARY DIAGNOSES OF SOME NEW RACES OF SOUTH ARABIAN MAMMALS. R.I. Pocock. Ann. Mag. Nat. Hist., London, ser.10, vol.14, no.84, pp.635-636, Dec., 1934.

SOME MAMMALS OF YEMEN AND THEIR ECTOPARASITES. Colin Campbell Sanborn, Harry Hoogstraal. Fieldiana-Zool., Chicago Nat.Hist.Mus., vol.34, no.23, pp.229-252, Dec. 30, 1953.

ON FIVE NEW MAMMALS FROM ARABIA AND PERSIA. Oldfield Thomas. Ann.Mag. Nat. Hist., London, ser.7, vol.10, no.60, pp.487-491, Dec., 1902.

ON SOME SPECIMENS OF MAMMALS FROM OMEN, S. E. ARABIA. Oldfield Thomas. Proc. Zool. Soc., London, pp.448-455, pl. 31, May 1, 1894.

ON THE MAMMALS OBTAINED IN SOUTH-WESTERN ARABIA BY MESSRS. PERCIVAL AND DODSON. Oldfield Thomas. Proc. Zool. Soc., London, pp.95-104, Feb. 6, 1900.

ON THE MAMMALS OF ADEN. Oldfield Thomas, J.W. Yerbury. Proc. Zool.Soc., London, pp.542-555, June, 1895.

ON THE MAMMALS OF ADEN. J.W. Yerbury, Oldfield Thomas. Proc. Zool.Soc., London, pp.542-555, June, 1895.

ARCTIC REGIONS

ANDREW J. STONE EXPLORATIONS IN ARCTIC AND SUBARCTIC AMERICA. J.A. Allen. Amer.Mus.Nat.Hist., pp. i-xvi, 1-38, illus.55, 1905.

MAMMALS OF THE EASTERN ARCTIC AND HUDSON BAY... ARCTIC FLORA... Rudolph Martin Anderson. Ottawa, pp.67-137, illus., maps, 1934.

SERVICING ARCTIC AIRBASES. (Walrus, White Whale, Polar Bear.) Robert A. Bartlett. Nat. Geogr.Mag., Washington, vol.89, no.5, pp.602-608, illus., May, 1946.

NOTES ON THE ANIMAL ECOLOGY OF BEAR ISLAND. G.C.L. Bertram, David Lack. Jour.Animal Ecol., Cambridge, vol. 7, no.1, pp.27-52, fig.1, pls.3-4, May, 1938.

NANOOK OF SHUGLIAK. (Walrus, Greenland Whale, Polar Bear.) E.C. Boyer. Field and Stream, New York, vol.53, no.4, pp. 22-23, 119-121, illus., Aug., 1948.

ORIGIN OF ARCTIC FAUNA. DISCOVERIES OF RUSSIAN ZOOLOGISTS. Malcolm Burr. Field, London, vol.172, no.4483, p.1294, Nov. 26, 1938; no.4484, p.1352, illus., Dec. 3, 1938.

ACROSS ARCTIC CANADA, 1925-1926. (Contains Notes on Distibution of Seals, White Whales, Polar Bear, Musk Oxen, and Caribou.) L.T. Burwash. Geogr.Jour., London, vol.74, no.6, pp.553-568, map, 1929.

TACTICS AND TECHNICS OF THE HUNTING FROM VESSELS IN THE ARCTIC REGIONS OF USSR. HUNTING OF WALRUS, BEARDED SEAL AND POLAR BEAR IN THE KARA SEA. K.K.Chapskii. Vsesoiuznyi Arkticheskii Institut Materialy po Izucheniiu Arktiti (Inst.Arctic USSR, Materials for the study of the Arctic), Leningrad, no.5, pp. 1-123, figs.35, 1934.

CANADIAN ARCTIC WILD LIFE ENQUIRY, 1937-38. Dennis Chitty. Jour. Anim. Ecol., London, vol.8, no.2, pp.247-260, Nov., 1939.

CANADIAN ARCTIC WILD LIFE ENQUIRY, 1935-36. Dennis Chitty, Charles Elton. Jour. Animal Ecology, Cambridge, vol.6, no.2, pp.368-385, figs.4, tbls.3, Nov., 1937.

CANADIAN ARCTIC WILD LIFE ENQUIRY, 1940-41. Dennis Chitty, Mary Nicholson. Jour. Anim. Ecol., London, vol.11, no.2, pp.270-287, pls.6-7, Nov., 1942.

CANADIAN ARCTIC WILD LIFE ENQUIRY, 1941-42. Helen Chitty. Jour. Anim. Ecol., London, vol.12, no.2, pp.163-172, maps 4, Nov., 1943.

CANADIAN ARCTIC WILD LIFE ENQUIRY, 1942-43. Helen Chitty, Dennis Chitty. Jour. Anim. Ecol., London, vol.14, no.1, pp. 37-45, May, 1945.

CANADIAN ARCTIC WILD LIFE ENQUIRY, 1943-49: WITH A SUMMARY OF RESULTS SINCE 1933. Helen Chitty. Jour. Anim. Ecol., London, vol.19, no.2, pp.180-193, Nov., 1950.

NOTES ON THE STATUS AND DISTRIBUTION OF CERTAIN MAMMALS AND BIRDS IN THE MACKENZIE RIVER AND WESTERN ARCTIC AREA IN 1942 AND 1943. C.H.D. Clarke. Canadian Field-Nat., Sutton West, vol.58, no.3, pp.97-103, May-June, 1944.

ARCTIC HUNTING. Charles Clay. Rod & Gun in Canada, Montreal, vol.50, no.7, pp.15, 32, Dec., 1948.

FIELD WORK IN THE LOWER ARCTIC ZONE. James C. Critchell-Bullock. Canadian Field-Nat., Ottawa, vol.39, no.8, pp.181-183, Nov., 1925.

REPORT OF THE CANADIAN ARCTIC EXPEDITION, 1913-18. VOL. VIII: MOLLUSKS, ECHINDODERMS, COELENTERATES, ETC. PART A: MOLLUSKS, RECENT AND PLEISTOCENE. William Healey Dall. Southern Party 1913-16, pp.1-30A, Ottawa, Sep. 24, 1919; VOL. VII: CRUSTACEA. PART A: DECAPOD CRUSTACEANS. Southern Party 1913-16, pp.1-14D, Ottawa, Aug. 18, 1919; VOL. VII: CRUSTACEA. PART E: AMPHIPODS. Ottawa, pp.2-30, Sep. 7, 1920.

DOUBLE TROUBLE IN THE ARCTIC. (Conservation in Alaska.) Albert M. Day. Sports Afield, Minneapolis, vol.125, no. 2, pp.44-45, 85-88, illus., Feb., 1951.

MAMMALS. PART I. SYSTEMATIC NOTES. M. Degerbøl. PART II. FIELD NOTES AND BIOLOGICAL OBSERVATIONS, P. Freuchen. (In) Report of the Fifth Thule Expedition 1921-24. Copenhagen, Nordisk Forlag. The Danish Expedition to Arctic America in Charge of Knud Rasmussen, Ph.D., vol.2, nos.4-5, pp.278, figs., pls., map, 1935.

ARCTIC AND SUBARCTIC MARINE ECOLOGY. IMMEDIATE PROBLEMS. (Includes Whales and Seals.) M.J. Dunbar. Arctic, vol.6, no.2, pp.75-90, illus., July, 1953.

ARCTIC MAMMALOGY (pp.35-43). Raymond M. Gilmore. (In) A Program of Desirable Scientific Investigations in Arctic North America. The Arctic Inst. of N. America, Montreal, Bull.no.1, pp.1-65, Mar., 1946.

8000 MILES OF NORTHERN WILDERNESS. AN EXCITING EXPEDITION IN THE BARREN LANDS, THE ARCTIC COAST, AND UP THE SWIFT NAHANNI RIVER, WHICH BROUGHT BACK NEW KNOWLEDGE OF THE GREAT ANIMALS OF THE NORTHWEST. George G. Goodwin. Nat. Hist., New York, vol.37, no.5, pp.421-434, illus., May, 1936.

SOUTHERN RECORDS FOR ARCTIC MAMMALS AND A NORTHERN RECORD FOR ALFARO'S RICE RAT. George G. Goodwin. Jour. Mamm., vol.35, no.2, p.258, May 26, 1954.

ARCTIC EXPLORATION, WITH REFERENCE TO GRINNELL LAND. A.W. Greely. Proc. Roy. Geogr. Soc. and Monthly Record of Geogr., London, pp.20, Mar., 1886.

OBSERVATIONS ON SEALS (PINNIPEDIA) AND WHALES (CETACEA) MADE ON THE DENMARK EXPEDITION 1906-1908. Frits Johansen. Danmark-Ekspeditionen til Grønlands Nordøstkyst 1906-1908. vol. 5, no.2, pp.203-224, figs.1-9, 1910.

PRELIMINARY ECOLOGICAL STUDIES OF MICROCLIMATES INHABITED BY THE SMALLER ARCTIC AND SUBARCTIC MAMMALS. H.M. Johnson. (In) Science in Alaska 1951, Proceedings 2nd Alaskan Sci. Conf., Alaska Div. AAAS, pp.125-131, graphs, 1953.

(CATALOG OF MAMMALS DESCRIBED FROM THE PALEARCTIC FAUNA REGION.) Katalog der aus dem palaarktischen Faunengebiet beschriebenen Saeugetiere. W. Kobelt. Ber. Senckenbergische Naturforsch. Gesell., Frankfurt a.M., pp.73-103, 1896.

CONTRIBUTIONS TO THE NATURAL HISTORY OF ARCTIC AMERICA, MADE IN CONNECTION WITH THE HOWGATE POLAR EXPEDITION, 1877-78. Ludwig Kumlin. Washington, Govt.Print.Off., pp. 179, 1879. (Bull. of the U.S. Nat.Mus., no. 15.) (Issued also as vol.23, art.5, of the Smiths.Misc.Coll., Smiths.Inst. Publication 342.)

AN ACCOUNT OF A VOYAGE TO SPITZBERGEN; CONTAINING A FULL DESCRIPTION OF THAT COUNTRY, OF THE ZOOLOGY OF THE NORTH, AND OF THE SHETLAND ISLES; WITH AN ACCOUNT OF THE WHALE FISHERY. John Laing. J. Mawman, London, pp.171, 1815.

(ZOOGEOGRAPHICAL CONSIDERATIONS OF THE MAMMALS OF THE OLD WORLD OF THE NORTH.) Zoogeographische Betrachtungen ueber die Saeugethiere der noerdlichen alten Welt. Paul Matschie. Archiv f. Naturgesch., Beiheft 67, pp.307-328, pls.10, 1901.

(CONTRIBUTIONS TO THE ZOOGEOGRAPHY OF THE RUSSIAN NORTHERN SEAS.) Beitraege zur Zoogeographie der russischen noerdlichen Meere. I.I. Messjatzev. Ber. des Wissenschaftlichen Meeresinstitutes, Moscow, Lief.13, pp.1-26, fold.map, 1923. (In Russian, with German summary and subtitle.)

HUNTING AND ADVENTURE IN THE ARCTIC. F. Nansen. New York, Duffield, pp.3+ 462, pls., 1925.

(ANIMAL HISTORY OF THE NORTHERN POLAR LANDS.) Thiergeschichte der noerdlichen Polarlaender. (Translated from the English.) Thomas Pennant. Leipzig, S.L. Crusuis, vol.2, pl., 1787.

ARCTIC ZOOLOGY. Thomas Pennant. London, Printed by Henry Hughs, vol.2, pl., 1784-85.

(SECOND GERMAN NORTH POLE VOYAGE IN THE YEARS 1869 AND 1870 UNDER THE DIRECTION OF CAPTAIN KARL KOLDEWEY. II. ZOOLOGY. PART 2. MAMMALS AND FISHES.) Die zweite Deutsche Nordpolfahrt in den Jahren 1869 und 1870 unter Fuehrung des Kapitan Karl Koldewey. II. Zoologie. Pt.2, Saeugethiere und Fische. W. Peters. Leipzig, E.A.Brockhaus, vol. 2, pp.157-174, pls.2, 1874.

(MAMMALS OF THE ARCTIC REGION.) Die Saeugetiere des arktischen Gebietes (Band 6, Lief.2, pp.67-80). H.Pohle.(In) Fauna Arctica, Jena, G.Fischer, vols.6, 1900-1933.

NOTES ON DISTRIBUTION OF SOME ARCTIC MAMMALS. Robert Rausch. Jour. Mamm., vol.31, no.4, pp.464-466, Nov. 21, 1950.

ON THE STATUS OF SOME ARCTIC MAMMALS. Robert Rausch. Artic, Jour. Arctic Inst. N.Amer., Ottawa, vol.6, no.2, pp.91-148, illus., July, 1953.

BIRDS AND MAMMALIA COLLECTED DURING THE LAST ARCTIC LAND EXPEDITION UNDER SIR JOHN FRANKLIN. J. Richardson. Proc. Comm. Sci. & Corres. Zool. Soc. London, pt.1, p.132, 1830-1831.

FAUNA BOREALI-AMERICAN; OR THE ZOOLOGY OF THE NORTHERN PARTS OF BRITISH AMERICA: CONTAINING DESCRIPTIONS OF THE OBJECTS OF NATURAL HISTORY COLLECTED ON THE LATE NORTHERN LAND EXPEDITIONS, UNDER COMMAND OF CAPTAIN SIR JOHN FRANKLIN, R.N. PART 1. QUADRUPEDS. J. Richardson. London, John Murray, pp.xlvi-300, pls.28, 1829.

GAME CONSERVATION IN ARCTIC CANADA. Brian Roberts. Polar Record, Cambridge, vol.3, no.23, pp.499-509, map, Jan., 1942.

BIRD AND MAMMAL OBSERVATIONS ON ELLEF RINGNES ISLAND IN 1960. Douglas Barton Osborne Savile. Ottawa, pp.6, tbls., 1961. (Canadian Nat. Mus., Nat. Hist. Papers, no.9.)

GEOGRAPHY OF MAMMALS. NO.VI. THE NEARCTIC REGION. W.L. Sclater. Geogr. Jour., London, vol.9, no.1, pp.67-76, map, Jan., 1897.

ARCTIC PRAIRIES. E.T. Seton. New York, Scribner's Sons, pp.12-308, 1923.

ARCTIC MAMMALS. T.M. Shortt. Canadian Nature, Toronto, vol.2, no.5, pp.10-11, illus., Nov.-Dec., 1940; vol.8, no.1, pp.12-13, Jan., 1946.

(ANIMALS OF THE ARCTIC.) Zveri Arktiki. Nestor Aleksandrovich Smirnov. Leningrad, Glavsevmorputi Press, pp.579, illus., 1935.

PROTECTION OF ARCTIC ANIMALS. (pp. 55-56). R. Sparck. (In) Proc. and Pap.5th Technical Meeting, Internatl. Union for the Protection of Nature, Copenhagen, 1954. Brussels, 1956, pub.by the Secretariat, 1954.

ARCTIC MANUAL. V. Stefansson. New York, Macmillan, pp.16-556, 1945.

THE FRIENDLY ARCTIC. V. Stefansson. New York, Macmillan, pp.38-812, 1943.

ARCTIC WILDERNESS. (Otter, Dall Sheep, Caribou, Grizzly and Polar Bears.) Lowell Sumner, George L. Collins. Living Wilderness, Washington, vol.18, no.47, pp.5-15, illus., Winter, 1953-54.

SOME ZOOLOGICAL ASPECTS OF THE CANADIAN ARCTIC EXPEDITION OF 1929. (Notes on Muskox, Walrus, and Polar Bear.) P. A. Taverner. Canadian Field-Nat., vol.44, no.2, pp.25-27, pl.1, Feb. 1, 1930.

ARCTIC INSTITUTE. A. L. Washburn. Beaver, Winnipeg, outfit 277, pp.45-48, illus., Sep., 1946.

(ATLAS OF THE ICE CONDITIONS OF THE NORTH ATLANTIC AND GENERAL MAPS OF THE ICE CONDITIONS OF THE NORTH AND SOUTH POLE REGIONS.) Atlas der Eisverhaeltnisse des Nordatlantischen Ozeans und Uebersichtskarten der Eisverhaeltnisse des Nord- und Suedpolargebietes. German Hydrographical Institute, Hamburg, Atlas no.2335, pp.24, pls.28, 1950.

## ASIA

### Extinct and Fossil Mammals

PLEISTOCENE FAUNAS OF ASIA AND THEIR RELATIONSHIPS TO EARLY MAN. Edwin H. Colbert. Trans. New York Acad. Sci., Lancaster, ser.2, vol.5, no.1, pp. 1-10, Nov., 1942.

REMAINS OF UNGULATA FROM BET-PAK-DALA. K.K. Flerov. Comptes Rendus (Doklady) Acad. Sci. USSR, Moscow, n. s., vol.23, nos.1-2, pp.94-96, 1938.

CENTRAL ASIA IN CRETACEOUS TIME. Frederick K. Morris. Bull.Geol.Soc.Amer., vol.47, pp.1477-1534, figs.5, pls.1-2, Sep. 30, 1936.

PALAEONTOLOGICAL EXPEDITION TO BET-PAK-DALA, 1936. TERTIARY MAMMALIA AND THE LOCALITIES OF THEIR REMAINS. J.A. Orlov. Trav.Inst.Paléont., Moscow and Leningrad, vol.8, no.3, pp. 87-98, figs.9, 1941. (In Russian with English summary.)

### Recent Mammals

NEW ASIATIC MAMMALS. (Crocidura lar, Rhinolophus blythi parcus, R.lanosus spurcus, and Coelops sinicus.) Glover M. Allen. Amer. Mus. Novitates, no.317, pp. 5, May 19, 1928.

PRIMATES AND PANGOLINS FROM THE ASIATIC EXPEDITIONS. Glover M.Allen. Amer. Mus. Novitates, no.429, pp.7, Sep. 8, 1930.

MAMMAL AND BIRD COLLECTIONS OF THE ASIATIC PRIMATE EXPEDITION. Glover M. Allen, Harold J. Coolidge, Jr. Bull. Mus. Comp. Zool., Cambridge, vol. 87, no.3, pp.131-166, Dec., 1940.

WILDLIFE AND WEATHER IN THE ASIATIC WAR ZONE. Harold E.Anthony. Nat.Hist., New York, vol.52, no.5, pp. 204-217, illus., Dec., 1943.

(SCIENTIFIC FINDINGS OF N. M. PRZEWALSKI'S JOURNEYS TO CENTRAL ASIA.) Wissenschaftliche Resultate der von N.M. Przewalski nach Central-Asien Unternommenen Reisen.(Mammalia of Central Asia.) Eug. Bucher. Band I, Saeugethiere, Lieferung I-V, St.Petersburg, 1888.

BEYOND THE CASPIAN. A NATURALIST IN CENTRAL ASIA. Douglas Carruthers. Edinburgh and London, Oliver and Boyd, pp.xx-290, pls.22, figs.2, map 1, 1949.

(Review by Francis Harper of) BEYOND THE CASPIAN. A NATURALIST IN CENTRAL ASIA. Douglas Carruthers. Jour. Mamm., vol.31, no.4, p.468, Nov. 21, 1950.

NEW LIGHT ON THE MOST ANCIENT EAST. V.G. Childe. 4th ed. London, Praeger, pp.255, illus., 1953.

(NEW MAMMAL FORMS OF NORTHERN ASIA.) Neue Saeugetierformen aus Nordasien. (Canis lupus dybowskii, Kolonocus sibiricus coreanus, and Mustela punctata.) Janusz Domaniewski. Ann. Zool. Mus. Polonici Hist. Nat., vol.5, pp.52-56, illus., 1926.

(EXPEDITIONS OF THE AMERICAN MUSEUM OF NATURAL HISTORY IN CENTRAL ASIA.) Expeditionen des American Museum of Natural History in Zentralasien. Fritz Drevermann. Natur und Museum, vol.57, no.12, pp.553-567, Dec., 1927; vol.58, no. 1, pp.22-31, figs.19, Jan., 1928.

(NOTES ON THE MAMMALS. XVI. MAMMALS BROUGHT BACK IN 1932 FROM THE FAR EAST BY PRINCE LEOPOLD OF BELGIUM.) Notes sur les Mammiferes. XVI. Les mammiferes rapportes, en 1932, de l'Extreme-Orient par S.A.R. le Prince Leopold de Belgique. Serge Frechkop. Bull. Mus. Roy. d'Hist.Nat. Belgique, Brussels, vol.10, no.14, pp.37, figs.3, pl.1, Apr., 1934.

CAMPS IN THE ALTAI. N. Hollister. Canadian Alpine Jour., vol.5, pp.73-81, May, 1914.

FIVE NEW MAMMALS FROM ASIA. N. Hollister. Proc. Biol. Soc. Wash., vol.25, pp.181-184, Dec. 24, 1912.

MAMMALS COLLECTED BY THE SMITHSONIAN-HARVARD EXPEDITION TO THE ALTAI MOUNTAINS, 1912. N. Hollister. Proc. U.S. Nat. Mus., vol.45, pp.507-532, pls.37-42, June 21, 1913.

NEW ASIATIC MAMMALS COLLECTED BY F. R. WULSIN. (Selenarctos thibetanus wulsini, Ochotona alpina argentata, O. erythrotis vulpina, and Pseudois nayaur caesia.) A. Brazier Howell. Proc. Biol. Soc. Washington, vol.41, pp.115-120, June 29, 1928.

(CONTRIBUTIONS TO MAMMALIAN FAUNA OF THE ALTAI.) A.M. Kolossov. Priroda i sotsialisticheskoe khoziaistvo, Sbornik, vol. 6, pp.110-121, 1933. (In Russian.)

MAMMALS COLLECTED BY DR. W. L. ABBOTT ON ISLANDS IN THE SOUTH CHINA SEA. Gerrit Smith Miller, Jr. Proc.Washington Acad. Sci., vol.2, pp. 203-246, illus., 1900.

ANCIENT VERTEBRATE LIFE OF CENTRAL ASIA. DISCOVERIES OF THE CENTRAL ASIATIC EXPEDITIONS OF THE MUSEUM OF NATURAL HISTORY IN THE YEARS 1921-1929. Henry Fairfield Osborn. Extrait du Livre Jubilaire publié a l'occasion du Centenaire de la Société Géologique de France 1830-1930, Paris, pp.519-543, figs.8, 1930.

ARREST OF GEOLOGIC, ARCHEOLOGIC AND PALEONTOLOGIC WORK IN CENTRAL ASIA. Henry Fairfield Osborn. Science, n.s., vol.74, no.1910, pp.139-142, Aug. 7, 1931.

INTERRUPTION OF CENTRAL ASIATIC EXPLORATION BY THE AMERICAN MUSEUM OF NATURAL HISTORY. Henry Fairfield Osborn. Science, vol.70, no. 1813, pp.291-294, Sep. 27, 1929.

REVIVAL OF CENTRAL ASIATIC LIFE. Henry Fairfield Osborn. Nat. Hist., vol. 29, pp.3-16, illus., Feb., 1929.

WHY CENTRAL ASIA? Henry Fairfield Osborn. Nat. Hist., New York, vol.26, no.3, pp.263-269, illus., May-June, 1926.

MAMMALS OF THE KELLEY-ROOSEVELTS AND DELACOUR ASIATIC EXPEDITIONS. Wilfred H. Osgood. Field Mus.Nat.Hist., Publ.312, Zool.Ser., vol.18, no.10, pp.193-339, figs.2, pls.9-11, Aug. 19, 1932.

CENTRAL ASIATIC EXPEDITION. Sin Pingch'ang. Science, vol.71, no.1831, pp. 129-130, Jan. 31, 1930.

(NOTES ON THE MAMMALS FROM THE EXPEDITION OF M. CHAFFANJON IN CENTRAL ASIA.) Note sur les Mammiferes provenant de l'expedition de M.Chaffanjon dans l'Asie centrale. E. de Pousargues. Bull.Mus.Hist.Nat., Paris, vol.1, no.7, pp.265-267, 1895.

GEOGRAPHY OF MAMMALS. NO. 5. THE ORIENTAL REGION. W.L. Sclater.Geogr. Jour., London, vol.8, no.4, pp.378-389, map, Oct., 1896.

THREE NEW MAMMALS FROM ASIA. (Rattus melanurus, R.perasper, Lepus europaeus cinnamomeus.) H. Harold Shamel. Jour. Mamm., vol.21, no.1, pp.76-78, Feb. 14, 1940.

FAUNA OF SMALL MAMMALS OF THE VALLEY OF THE GREAT ALMATINKA RIVER, SEMIRETSHJE, CENTRAL ASIA. V.N. Shnitnikov. Zashchita rastenii ot vreditelei (Defense des plantes, Bull.Bur. permanent des Congres entomophytopathologiques de Russie), Leningrad, vol.6, nos. 3-4, pp.417-425, Oct., 1929.

(NOTES ON THE BIOLOGY OF SOME HARMFUL VERTEBRATES OF CENTRAL ASIA.) L.V. Sokolova. Uzbekistan Plant Protection Exper. Sta., Tashkent, vol.12, pp.1-19, figs.2, 1928. (In Russian.)

OUTLINES OF THE HISTORY OF THE RECENT FAUNA OF PALAEARCTIC ASIA. Peter Sushkin. Proc. Nat. Acad. Sci., vol.II, no.6, pp.299-302, June, 1925.

SUMMARY OF THE MAMMALIAN FAUNAE OF EASTERN ASIA AND THE INTERRELATIONSHIPS OF CONTINENTS SINCE THE MESOZOIC. Fuyuji Takai. Japanese Jour. Geol. and Geogr., vol.22, pp.169-205, 1952.

LIST OF THE MAMMALS OF THE JAPANESE WAR AREA. G.H.H. Tate. Amer. Mus.Nat.Hist., New York, pts.1-4, pp. 1-22, 1-19, 1-11, 1-18, 1944.

MAMMALS OF EASTERN ASIA. G.H.H. Tate. New York, Macmillan Co., pp.366, illus., 1947.

(Review by Emmet T. Hooper of) MAMMALS OF EASTERN ASIA. G.H.H. Tate. Jour. Mamm., vol.29, no.1, p.78, Feb. 13, 1948.

DIAGNOSES OF THREE NEW ORIENTAL MAMMALS. Oldfield Thomas. Ann. and Mag.Nat.Hist., ser.5, vol.17, no.97, p. 84, Jan., 1886.

DUKE OF BEDFORD'S ZOOLOGICAL EXPLORATION IN EASTERN ASIA. I. LIST OF MAMMALS OBTAINED BY MR. M.P. ANDERSON IN JAPAN. Oldfield Thomas. Proc.Zool.Soc. London, vol.2, pp.331-363, pl.9, Apr. 5, 1906.

DUKE OF BEDFORD'S ZOOLOGICAL EXPLORATION IN EASTERN ASIA. II. LIST OF SMALL MAMMALS FROM KOREA AND QUELPART. Oldfield Thomas. Proc. Zool.Soc. London, pp.858-865, Apr. 11, 1907.

DUKE OF BEDFORD'S ZOOLOGICAL EXPLORATION IN EASTERN ASIA. IV. LIST OF SMALL MAMMALS FROM ISLANDS OF SAGHALIEN AND HOKKAIDO. Oldfield Thomas. Proc.Zool.Soc.London, pp.404-414, Aug.1, 1907.

DUKE OF BEDFORD'S ZOOLOGICAL EXPLORATION IN EASTERN ASIA. V. SECOND LIST OF MAMMALS FROM KOREA. Oldfield Thomas. Proc.Zool.Soc.London, pp. 462-466, Oct. 8, 1907.

DUKE OF BEDFORD'S ZOOLOGICAL EXPLORATION IN EASTERN ASIA. VI. LIST OF MAMMALS FROM THE SHANTUNG PENINSULA, N. CHINA. Oldfield Thomas. Proc.Zool.Soc.London, vol.1, pp.5-10, June, 1908.

DUKE OF BEDFORD'S ZOOLOGICAL EXPLORATION IN EASTERN ASIA. VII. LIST OF MAMMALS FROM THE TSUSHIMA ISLAND. Oldfield Thomas. Proc.Zool. Soc.London, pp.47-54, June, 1908.

DUKE OF BEDFORD'S ZOOLOGICAL EXPLORATION IN EASTERN ASIA. IX. LIST OF MAMMALS FROM THE MONGOLIAN PLATEAU. Oldfield Thomas. Proc.Zool. Soc.London, pp.103-110, June, 1908.

DUKE OF BEDFORD'S ZOOLOGICAL EXPLORATION IN EASTERN ASIA. X. LIST OF MAMMALS FROM THE PROVINCES OF CHIH-LI AND SHAN-SI, N. CHINA. Oldfield Thomas. Proc.Zool.Soc.London, pp.635-646, pl.32, Oct., 1908.

DUKE OF BEDFORD'S ZOOLOGICAL EXPLORATION IN EASTERN ASIA. XI. ON MAMMALS FROM THE PROVINCES OF SHAN-SI AND SHEN-SI, N. CHINA. Oldfield Thomas. Proc.Zool.Soc.London, pp. 963-983, Apr., 1909.

DUKE OF BEDFORD'S ZOOLOGICAL EXPLORATION OF EASTERN ASIA. XIII. ON MAMMALS FROM THE PROVINCES OF KAN-SU AND SZE-CHWAN, W. CHINA. Oldfield Thomas. Proc.Zool.Soc.London, pp.158-180, Mar., 1911.

DUKE OF BEDFORD'S ZOOLOGICAL EXPLORATION OF EASTERN ASIA. XV. ON MAMMALS FROM THE PROVINCES OF SZE-CHWAN AND YUNNAN, W. CHINA. Oldfield Thomas. Proc.Zool.Soc.London, pp.127-141, Mar., 1912.

NEW ASIATIC APODEMUS, EVOTOMYS, AND LEPUS. Oldfield Thomas. Ann.Mag. Nat. Hist., ser.8, vol.1, no.5, pp.447-450, May, 1908.

NEW ASIATIC MAMMALS OF THE GENERA KERIVOULA, ELIOMYS, LEPUS. Oldfield Thomas. Ann.Mag.Nat.Hist., ser.7, vol. 17, no.100, pp.423-426, Apr., 1906.

NEW MAMMALS FROM CENTRAL AND WESTERN ASIA, MOSTLY COLLECTED BY MR. DOUGLAS CARRUTHERS. Oldfield Thomas. Ann.Mag.Nat.Hist., ser.8, vol.8, no.48, pp.758-762, Dec., 1911.

ON MAMMALS FROM CENTRAL ASIA, COLLECTED BY MR. DOUGLAS CARRUTHERS. Oldfield Thomas. Ann.Mag. Nat.Hist., ser.8, vol.9, no.51, pp.391-408, Apr., 1912.

ON SMALL MAMMALS FROM DJARKENT, CENTRAL ASIA. Oldfield Thomas. Ann. Mag.Nat. Hist., ser.8, vol.13, no.78, pp. 563-573, June 1914.

THREE NEW ASIATIC MAMMALS. Oldfield Thomas. Ann.Mag.Nat.Hist., ser. 8, vol.5, no.30, pp.534-536, June, 1910.

WORKS OF THE ZOOLOGICAL INSTITUTE ON THE STUDY OF MAMMALS OF MIDDLE ASIA. B.S. Vinogradov. Bull. Acad. Sci. USSR (Cl.Sci., Math., et Nat.), Ser.biol., Moscow, no.4, pp.1143-1148, 1937. (In Russian with English summary.)

BOOK OF SER MARCO POLO, THE VENETIAN, CONCERNING THE KINGDOMS AND MARVELS OF THE EAST. Marco Polo. 3rd ed. Yule Henry Ed., vol.2, 1903.

## ASIA MINOR

ON THE MAMMALS OF ASIA MINOR. Edward R. Alston, Charles G. Danford. Proc. Zool. Soc. London, for 1877, pt.2, pp.270-281, pls.31, 1877.

(NOTES ON THE MAMMALS BROUGHT BACK FROM ASIA MINOR BY M. GADEAU OF KERVILLE.) Note sur les mammifères rapportés d'Asie Mineure par M. Gadeau de Kerville. Max Kollmann. Bull. Mus. Hist. Naturelle, no.4, pp.201-204, 1918; Voyage Zoologique d'Henri Gadeau de Kerville en Asie-Mineure (Apr.-May 1912), vol.2, pp. 145-150, 1928.

TWO NEW MAMMALS FROM ASIA MINOR. Gerrit S. Miller, Jr. Ann.Mag. Nat. Hist., ser.8, vol.1, pp.68-70, Jan., 1908.

## ATLANTIC OCEAN

FAUNA OF TRISTAN DA CUNHA. H.F.I. Elliot. Oryx, vol.2, pp.41-53, 1953.

(MAMMALIAN FAUNA OF THE LITTORAL ATLANTIC ISLANDS.) Faune mammalienne des iles littorales atlantiques. Henri Heim de Balsac. Comptes Rendus Acad.Sci., Paris, vol.211, no.11, pp.212-214, 1940.

(MAMMALIAN POPULATION OF THE FRENCH ATLANTIC ISLANDS.) Peuplement mammalien d'iles atlantiques francaises. Henri Heim de Balsac. Comptes Rendus Acad.Sci., Paris, vol.211, no.15, pp.296-298, 1940.

(NATURAL HISTORY OF THE NORTH ATLANTIC WHALES AND SEALS.) Naturgeschichte der nordatlantischen Wale und Robben. E. Hentschel. Handbuch der Seefischerei Nordeuropas, herausgegeben von H. Luebbert und E. Ehrenbaum, Stuttgart, vol.3, no.1, pp.5-54, figs.56, pls. 10, 1937.

GOUGH ISLAND SCIENTIFIC SURVEY, 1955-56. M.W. Holdgate, R.W. LeMaitre, M.K. Swailes, N.M. Wace. Nature, vol. 178, pp.234-236, 1956.

CONTRIBUTION TO THE NATURAL HISTORY OF THE BERMUDAS. John Matthew Jones. Washington, Govt. Print. Off., pp. xxiii-353, pls.12 (incl.fold.map), 1884. (Bull.of the U.S.Nat.Mus., no.25.) (Smithsonian Inst. Publication 495.)

(MAMMAL FAUNA OF WANGEROOGE, WITH REMARKS ON THE OTHER EAST FRISIAN ISLANDS.) Die Saeugetierfauna von Wangerooge, mit Bemerkungen ueber die uebrigen ostfriesischen Inseln. Ingo Krumbiegel. Saeugetierk. Mitteil., Stuttgart, vol.3, no.1, pp.12-18, Jan. 1, 1955.

WANDERING AMONG FORGOTTEN ISLES. WITH A CHAPTER ON THE SCIENTIFIC RESULTS OF THE CRUISE BY ROBERT CUSHMAN MURPHY. (Collecting Three Specimens of the Rare Monk Seal, Monachus monachus, on the Desertas Islands, with Notes on the Habits of the Species.) Jesse Metcalf. New York, J.H.Sears and Co., pp.306, pls.15, Nov., 1927.

(LAND MAMMALS OF THE SCHLESWIG-HOLSTEIN NORTH SEA ISLANDS.) Die Landsaeugetiere der schleswigholsteinischen Nordsee-Inseln. Erna Mohr. Schriften Natur. Vereins f. Schleswig-Holstein, vol.19, no.1, pp.59-72, pls.12-13, 1929.

(EXURSION TO THE ISLAND OF HELGOLAND IN SEPTEMBER 1879.) Excursion a l'ile d'Helgoland en Septembre 1879. M.Edm. de Selys Longchamps. Bull. Soc. Zool. de France, pp.32, 1882.

SOME OBSERVATIONS ON THE SHORT-TERM FLUCTUATIONS IN NUMBERS OF MAMMALS AND BIRDS IN THE SPHERE OF THE NORTHERNMOST ATLANTIC. Lauri Siivonen. Riistatieteelisia Julkaisuja, Paper on Game Research, Helsinki, no.4, pp.31, illus., 1950.

(ISLAND FAUNA.) Le Faune Insulari. (St. Helena, Tristan da Cunha, Sandwich Ids., Madagascar, New Zealand, etc.) I. de Stefani. L'Universo Florence, vol.10, no. 4, pp.24, illus., Apr., 1929.

## AUSTRALASIA

MAMMALS OF AUSTRALASIA. R.W. Hayman. Zoo Life, London, vol.9, no.2, pp. 44-51, illus., Summer, 1954.

WILD ANIMALS OF AUSTRALASIA. EMBRACING THE MAMMALS OF NEW GUINEA AND THE NEARER PACIFIC ISLANDS. WITH A CHAPTER ON THE BATS OF AUSTRALIA AND NEW GUINEA BY ELLIS LE G. TROUGHTON. A.S. LeSouef, Harry Burrell. London and Sydney, George G. Harrap and Co., Ltd., pp.388, figs.105, 1926.

PREHUMAN ISOLATIONISTS. (Australasian Fauna.) M.Graham Netting. Fauna, Philadelphia, vol.4, no.4, pp.98-102, illus., Dec., 1942.

ON SOME AUSTRALASIAN MAMMALS. Oldfield Thomas. Ann.Mag.Nat.Hist., ser.7, vol.16, pp.422-428, 1905.

## AUSTRALIA

### Extinct and Fossil Mammals

FOSSIL MAMMALS OF AUSTRALIA. C. Anderson. Proc. Linnean Soc. New South Wales, vol.58, pts.1-2, pp.ix-xxv, 1933.

ORIGIN OF AUSTRALIAN MAMMALS. C. Anderson. Australian Mus. Mag., vol.6, no.4, pp.133-137, Oct.-Dec., 1936.

WELLINGTON CAVES. (Notes on Recent and Fossil Mammals.) C. Anderson. Australian Mus. Mag., vol.2, pp.367-374, illus., July, 1926.

PREHISTORIC ANIMALS OF AUSTRALIA. F.S. Colliver. Victorian Nat., Melbourne, vol.59, no.12, pp.198-200, Apr., 1943.

DISTRIBUTION OF THE TASMANIAN DEVIL THE TASMANIAN WOLF, AND THE DINGO IN S.E. AUSTRALIA IN QUATERNARY TIME. Edmund D. Gill. Victorian Naturalist Melbourne, vol.70, no.5, pp.86-90, Sep., 1953.

(ON THE PHYLOGENY OF THE AUSTRALIAN FAUNA.) Zur Phylogenie der australischen Fauna. Ernst H.P.A. Haeckel. Abdruck aus Semon, Zoologische Forschungsreisen in Australien und dem Malayischen Archipel. Jena, G. Fischer, 1893.

AUSTRALIAN VERTEBRATA--FOSSIL AND RECENT. Gerard Krefft. Gov't.Printer, Sydney, pp.1-96, 1871.

PALAEONTOLOGICAL NOTES. Heber A. Longman. Mem.Queensland Mus., vol.9, pt.3, pp.247-251, pl.29, June 29, 1929.

REPORT ON THE EXTINCT MAMMALIAN REMAINS AT LAKE MENINDEE, NEW SOUTH WALES. Richard H. Tedford. Rec. South Australian Mus., vol.11, no.3, pp. 299-305, Feb. 28, 1955.

TANTANOOLA CAVES, SOUTH-EAST OF SOUTH AUSTRALIA: GEOLOGICAL AND PHYSIOGRAPHICAL NOTES. (Remains of Marsupials, Rodents, and Dingo.) N.B. Tindale. Trans.and Proc.Roy.Soc.S.Australia, Adelaide, vol.57, pp.130-142, figs. 7, Dec. 23, 1933.

MAMMAL BONE BEDS OF PROBABLE PLEISTOCENE AGE, ROCKY RIVER KANGAROO ISLAND. N. B. Tandale, et al. Trans. and Proc. Roy.Soc.S.Australia, Adelaide, vol.59, pp.103-106, figs.3, Dec. 23, 1935.

Recent Mammals

VERTEBRATE FAUNA OF HAUTMAN'S ABROLHOS (ABROLHOS ISLANDS), WESTERN AUSTRALIA. (Includes Notes on a Few Mammals.) W.B. Alexander. Jour. Linn. Soc. London, vol.34, pp.457-486, Feb. 16, 1922.

AUSTRALIAN FAUNA. C. Anderson. Jour. and Proc.Roy.Soc.New South Wales, vol. 59, pp.15-34, June 30, 1925.

AUSTRALIA'S "WILD ZOO." Charles Barrett. Bull.New York Zool.Soc., vol.40, no. 1, pp.15-20, Jan.-Feb., 1937.

RARE AND DISAPPEARING MAMMALS IN THE STATE OF VICTORIA. James Barrett. Jour.Soc.Preservation Fauna of Empire, Hertford, n.s., pt.33, pp.34-36, Mar., 1938.

SOME CENTRAL AUSTRALIAN MAMMALS. H.C. Barry. Australian Mus.Mag., vol.5, no.6, pp.194-198, illus., Apr. 16, 1934.

RESULTS OF THE ARCHBOLD EXPEDITIONS. NO. 68. SUMMARY OF THE 1948 CAPE YORK (AUSTRALIA) EXPEDITION. WITH NOTES ON THE MAMMALS OF CAPE YORK PENINSULA BY G. H. H. TATE. L.J. Brass. New York, pp.139-205, map, pls., 1953. (Amer. Mus. of Nat. Hist., New York, Bulletin, vol.102, art.2.)

MAMMALS OF VICTORIA AND THE DENTAL CHARACTERISTICS OF MONOTREMES AND AUSTRALIAN MARSUPIALS. Charles Walter Brazenor. Melbourne, Brown, Prior, Anderson, pp.125, illus.(part col.), 1950. (Victoria, Australia, Nat.Mus., Melbourne, Handbook no.1.)

AUSTRALIAN FAUNAL REGIONS. A.G. Campbell. Emu, Melbourne, vol.42, pt.4, pp.242-245, Apr., 1943.

AUSTRALIAN CAVE FAUNAS. F.Chapman. Victorian Naturalist, vol.47, no.6, pp.99-100, Oct., 1930.

FURTHER ADDITIONAL FAUNA OF THE COMBOYNE PLATEAU. E.C. Chisholm. Australian Zool., vol.5, pt.4, pp.333-336, Mar. 24, 1929.

INJURIES AND DISEASES IN AUSTRALIA ATTRIBUTABLE TO ANIMALS (INSECTS EXCEPTED). SERIES V: MAMMALS, FISH, SPIDERS, MITES AND TICKS ETC., SHELL FISH, SPONGES, PROTOZOA. J. Burton Cleland, M.D. Univ. of Adelaide Collected Papers no.390. (Reprinted from The Medical Jour. of Australia, p.313, Oct. 3, 1942.)

ON A COLLECTION OF MAMMALS FROM NORTH AND NORTH-WEST AUSTRALIA. R. Collett. Proc.Zool.Soc.London, pp. 317-336, pl.23, Mar. 16, 1897.

CAVE HUNTING IN VICTORIA. F.S.Colliver. Victorian Nat., Melbourne, vol.54, no.10, pp.152-155, figs.2, Feb., 1938.

STRANGE LIVING FOSSILS OF AUSTRALIA. (Colored Photos of Monotremes and Marsupials.) John Dominis. Life, vol.42, no.1, pp.40-49, Jan. 7, 1957.

NOTES ON SOME SOUTH AND CENTRAL AUSTRALIAN MAMMALS. PT. 1. H.H. Finlayson. Trans.and Proc.Roy.Soc.South Australia, vol.54, pp.177-180, Dec. 20, 1930.

NOTES ON SOME SOUTH AND CENTRAL AUSTRALIAN MAMMALS. H.H. Finlayson. Trans.and Proc.Roy.Soc.South Australia, vol.55, pp.161-162, Dec. 24, 1931.

NOTES ON SOME VICTORIAN MAMMALS. H.H. Finlayson. Trans.and Proc.Roy.Soc. South Australia, Adelaide, vol.59, pp.221-226, pl.1, Dec. 23, 1935.

ON MAMMALS FROM THE DAWSON VALLEY, QUEENSLAND. H.H. Finlayson. Trans. and Proc.Roy.Soc.South Australia, vol.55, pp.67-90, pls.3, figs.4, Dec. 24, 1931.

ON MAMMALS FROM THE DAWSON AND FITZROY VALLEYS, CENTRAL COASTAL QUEENSLAND. PT. 2. H.H. Finlayson. Trans.and Proc.Roy.Soc.South Australia, Adelaide, vol.58, pp.218-231, Dec. 22, 1934.

ON MAMMALS FROM THE LAKE EYRE BASIN. PT. II. THE DIPROTODONT MARSUPIALS AND ORNITHODELPHIA. H. H. Finlayson. Trans.Roy.Soc.South Australia, Adelaide, vol.60, pp.157-161, 1936.

ON MAMMALS FROM THE LAKE EYRE BASIN. PT. III. THE DIPROTODONT MARSUPIALS AND ORNITHODELPHIA. H. H. Finlayson. Trans.Roy.Soc.South Australia, Adelaide, vol.60, pp.157-161, 1936.

ON MAMMALS FROM THE LAKE EYRE BASIN. IV. THE MONODELPHIA. H. H. Finlayson. Trans.Roy.Soc.South Australia, Adelaide, vol.63, pt.1, pp.88-118, pls.4-5, July 28, 1939.

ON MAMMALS FROM THE LAKE EYRE BASIN. PT. V. H.H. Finlayson. Trans. Roy.Soc.South Australia, Adelaide, vol. 63, pt.2, pp.348-353, fig.1, Dec. 22, 1939.

PRELIMINARY DESCRIPTIONS OF TWO NEW MAMMALS FROM SOUTH AUSTRALIA. H.H. Finlayson. Trans.and Proc.Roy. Soc.South Australia, vol.56, pp.168-171, Feb. 16, 1932.

THE RED CENTRE. MAN AND BEAST IN THE HEART OF AUSTRALIA. H. H. Finlayson. Angus and Robertson, Ltd., Sydney, pp.1-153, illus.57, 1943.

(DESCRIPTIONS OF ANIMALS WHICH MIGRATED TO LANDS FROM AUSTRALIAN WATERS DURING THE YEARS 1772-1774.) Descriptiones animalium quae in itinerere ad maris australis terras per annos (1772-1774) suscepto... ed.Henrico Lichtenstein. J.R. Forster. Berolini, Koeniglich-Preussische Akad.d.Wissenschaften, pp.13-424, 1844.

LANDING ON PEDRA BRANCA. S.Fowler. Proc.Roy.Zool.Soc.New South Wales, 1946-1947, pp.22-26, 1947.

LETTER FROM, DESCRIBING THE HABITS OF SOME MAMMALIA AND AVES OF WESTERN AUSTRALIA. Mr.Gilbert. Proc. Zool.Soc.London, pt.12, pp.33-37, 1844.

ZOOLOGICAL NOTES ON THE NORTHERN TERRITORY (JUNE 1944 TO SEPTEMBER 1945). I. SAVANNAH WOODLAND. (Brief Notes on Mammals.) Lionel Gilbert. Victorian Nat., Melbourne, vol.64, no.12, pp. 96-102, Aug., 1948.

INTRODUCTION TO THE MAMMALS OF AUSTRALIA. John Gould. London, Printed for the Author by Taylor and Francis, pp. xii-51, 1863.

MAMMALS OF AUSTRALIA. John Gould. London, Printed by Taylor and Francis, Pub.by the Author, vol.3, col.pls.182, 1863.

ON NEW SPECIES OF MAMMALIA AND BIRDS FROM AUSTRALIA. John Gould. Proc.Zool.Soc.London, pt.17, pp.109-112, 1849.

ON SOME NEW SPECIES OF AUSTRALIAN MAMMALS. John Gould. Proc.Zool.Soc. London, pt.10, pp.10-11, 1842.

NOTES ON SOME MAMMALIA FROM PORT ALBANY (CAPE YORK PENINSULA), NORTH AUSTRALIA, WITH THE DESCRIPTIONS OF SOME NEW SPECIES. John Edward Gray.Proc. Zool.Soc.London, for 1866, pp.219-222, pl. 25, 1866.

CONTACT OF AMERICAN WHALERS, SEALERS AND ADVENTURERS WITH THE NEW SOUTH WALES SETTLEMENT.Gordon Greenwood. Jour.and Proc.Royal Australian Hist.Soc., Sydney, vol.29, pt.3, pp.133-156, 1943.

AUSTRALIA, THE LAND OF LIVING FOSSILS. AS EXEMPLIFIED IN THE PROPOSED AUSTRALIAN EXHIBITION, AMERICAN MUSEUM. William K. Gregory. Nat. Hist., vol.24, pp.4-15, illus.11, Jan.-Feb., 1924.

AUSTRALIA--THE STORY OF A CONTINENT. (Kangaroo, Koala, Platypus.) William K. Gregory. Nat.Hist., New York, vol. 53, no.8, pp.360-370, illus., Oct., 1944.

ON THE BUFFALO PLATEAU. (Few Notes on Mammals.) L.L.Hodgsen. Victorian Nat., vol.44, no.7, pp.188-196, Nov., 1927.

PRESENT STATUS OF THE AUSTRALIAN MAMMAL FAUNA. Chas.M. Hoy. Jour. Mamm., vol.4, no.3, pp.164-166, Aug., 1923.

OUR NATIVE FAUNA--A WASTED ASSET. A.F. Basset Hull. Australian Zool., vol. 6, no.1, pp.6-13, 1929.

BROINOWSKI'S BIRDS AND MAMMALS OF AUSTRALIA. Tom Iredale. Proc.Royal Soc. New South Wales, 1954-1955, pp.14-16, Apr. 10, 1956.

CHECK-LIST OF THE MAMMALS RECORDED FROM AUSTRALIA. Tom Iredale, E.Le G.Troughton. Australian Mus., Sydney, mem.6, pp.xi-122, May 4, 1934.

SOME BIRDS AND MAMMALS OF THE GLASSHOUSE MOUNTAINS DISTRICT. N. Jack. Queensland Nat., Brisbane, vol.11, no.6, pp.127-132, Aug., 1941.

FLORA AND FAUNA OF NUYTS ARCHIPELAGO AND THE INVESTIGATOR GROUP. NO. 2.-THE MONODELPHIAN MAMMALS. F. Wood Jones. Trans.Roy.Soc.South Australia, vol.46, pp.181-193, figs.11, 1922.

FLORA AND FAUNA OF NUYTS ARCHIPELAGO AND THE INVESTIGATOR GROUP. NO. 6.-THE DIDELPHIAN MAMMALS. F. Wood Jones. Trans.Roy.Soc.South Australia, vol.47, pp.82-94, figs.9, 1923.

FLORA AND FAUNA OF NUYTS ARCHIPELAGO AND THE INVESTIGATOR GROUP. NO. 15.-THE PEARSON ISLAND RAT AND THE FLINDERS ISLAND WALLABY. F.Wood Jones. Trans.Roy.Soc.South Australia, vol. 48, pp.10-14, 1924.

MAMMALS OF SOUTH AUSTRALIA. PART 1. THE MONOTREMES AND THE CARNIVOROUS MARSUPIALS. F. Wood Jones. Handbooks of Flora and Fauna of South Australia, British Science Guild (South Australian Branch), Adelaide, pp.1-131, figs.88, 1923.

MAMMALS OF SOUTH AUSTRALIA. PART 2. CONTAINING THE BANDICOOTS AND THE HERBIVOROUS MARSUPIALS ( THE SYNDACTYLOUS DIDELPHIA). F. Wood Jones. Handbooks of Flora and Fauna of South Australia, issued by the British Sci. Guild (South Australia Branch), Adelaide, pp.133-270, figs.89-190, 1924.

MAMMALS OF SOUTH AUSTRALIA. PART 3. MONODELPHIA. F. Wood Jones. Handbooks of Flora and Fauna of South Australia, British Science Guild (South Australian Branch), Adelaide, pp.271-458, figs.191-311, Dec. 21, 1925.

PEARSON ISLAND RAT AND THE FLINDERS ISLAND WALLABY. F. Wood Jones. Trans. and Proc.Royal Soc.South Australia, vol. 48, pp.10-14, Dec. 24, 1924.

NOTES ON THE NATIONAL PARK, WILSON'S PROMONTORY. J.A. Kershaw. Victorian Nat., vol.44, no.11, pp.300-302, Mar., 1928.

AUSTRALIAN NATURAL HISTORY. MAMMALS OF AUSTRALIA AND THEIR CLASSIFICATION. PART I. ORNITHODELPHIA AND DIDELPHIA. Gerard Krefft. N.S.W. Roy.Soc.Jour.(Trans.), ser.7, pp.1-13, Nov., 1873.

MAMMALS OF AUSTRALIA. WITH A SHORT ACCOUNT OF ALL THE SPECIES HITHERTO DESCRIBED. Gerard Krefft. Sydney, T. Richards, Government Printer, pp.33, pls. 16, 1871.

NOTES ON THE MAMMALS AND BIRDS OF CAPE YORK, WITH DESCRIPTIONS OF TWO NEW RODENTS OF THE GENUS HAPALOTIS. Gerard Krefft. Proc.Zool. Soc.London, for 1867, pp.316-319, figs. 7, 1867.

AUSTRALIAN NATIVE ANIMALS. HOW THEY STAND TO-DAY, AND THE CAUSE OF THE SCARCITY OF CERTAIN SPECIES. A.S. LeSouef. Australian Zool., vol.3, pt.3, pp.108-111, pl.1, June 7, 1923.

HOW AUSTRALIAN FAUNA FARES. A.S. LeSouef. Jour.Soc.Preservation of Fauna of Empire, n.s., pt.26, pp.45-48, Apr., 1932.

HOW THE AUSTRALIAN FAUNA IS FARING. A.S. LeSouef. Jour.Soc.Preserv. Fauna Empire, n.s., vol.54, pp.34-36, 1946.

NOTES ON SOME MAMMALS FROM BASS STRAIT ISLANDS, INCLUDING A NEW SUBSPECIES OF PSEUDOCHIRUS. A. S. LeSouef. Australian Zool., Sydney, vol. 5, pt.4, pp.329-332, pl.36, Mar. 24, 1929.

NUMBERS AND DISTRIBUTION OF MAMMAL SPECIES IN THE AUSTRALIAN REGION. A.S. LeSouef. Rept.Australian Assoc.Adv.Sci., vol.19, pp.245-248, (1928) 1929.

WILD ANIMALS OF AUSTRALIA. A.S. LeSouef, Harry Burrell. (Embracing the Mammals of New Guinea and the Nearer Pacific Islands. With a Chapter on the Bats of Australia and New Guinea by Ellis W.G.Troughton.) London and Sydney, pp.388, figs.105, 1926.

MAMMALS OF AUSTRALIA IN THE ZOOLOGICAL PARK. W.H.D. LeSouef. Zoologica, vol.2, no.6, pp.167-201, figs.32-68, Jan., 1919.

BUSH BY NIGHT. R. T. Littlejohns. Victorian Naturalist, Melbourne, vol.55, no.1, pp.3-11, illus., pl., May, 1938.

VERTEBRATE FAUNA OF QUEENSLAND. Heber A. Longman. Pp.63-70, 1927?

RESULTS OF DR. E. MJOBERG'S SWEDISH SCIENTIFIC EXPEDITION TO AUSTRALIA 1910-1913, MAMMALS FROM QUEENSLAND. Einar Lonnberg, E.Mjoberg. Kungl. Svenska Vetenskap.Handl., vol.52, no.2, pp.3-20, pl.1, figs.1-6, 1916.

ANIMALS OF AUSTRALIA. MAMMALS, REPTILES AND AMPHIBIANS. A.H.S. Lucas, W.H. Dudley LeSouef. Melbourne, pp.327, illus., 1909.

NOTES UPON SOME MAMMALS RECENTLY DISCOVERED IN QUEENSLAND. Carl Lumholtz. Proc.Zool.Soc.London, pp.406-409, June 3, 1884.

ADDITIONS TO KNOWLEDGE OF THE RANGES OF WESTERN AUSTRALIAN MAMMALS. Ernest Lundelius, Jr. Western Austr. Nat., vol.5, no.7, pp.173-182, Mar. 8, 1957.

SOME FURRED NATIVES OF OUR COASTAL REGION. A.J. Marshall. Australian Mus.Mag., vol.4, no.8, pp.273-278, figs., Oct. 16, 1931.

PASSING OF A FAUNA. Colin Matheson. Jour.Soc.Preservation Fauna Empire, Hertford, n.s., pt.46, pp.12-23, Dec., 1942.

AUSTRALIAN EXPEDITION. EXPLORATION AND FIELD-WORK OF THE SMITHSONIAN INSTITUTION IN 1919. Gerrit S. Miller, Jr. Smiths.Misc.Coll., vol.72, no.1, pp.28-32, figs.30-32, 1920.

AUSTRALIAN EXPEDITIONS. Gerrit S. Miller, Jr. Smiths.Miscel.Coll., vol. 72, no.6, pp.39-43, figs.50-55, May 12, 1921.

SPINIFEX TOWN. (Animals of the Australian Desert.) Charles P. Mountford. Nat. Hist., New York, vol.55, no.2, pp.62-68, illus., Feb., 1946.

ADVANCE COPY OF PORTION OF HAND-LIST OF AUSTRALIAN MAMMALS. J. Douglas Ogilby. Australian Mus., Sydney, Printed by Order of the Trustees, pp.16, illus., 1891.

CATALOGUE OF AUSTRALIAN MAMMALS, WITH INTRODUCTORY NOTES ON GENERAL MAMMALOGY. J. Douglas Ogilby. Australian Mus., Sydney, Printed by Order of the Trustees, pp.xvi-142, 1892.

(VOYAGE OF DISCOVERIES TO THE AUSTRALIAN LANDS DURING THE YEARS 1800-1804.) Voyage de découvertes aux terres australes, exécuté...pendant les années 1800-1804. F. Péron. Paris, Imprimerie Royale, vols.2, atlas, 1807-16.

BUSH ANIMALS OF AUSTRALIA. NOTES ON BIRDS AND REPTILES BY J. R. KINGHORN, C. M. Z. S. NOTES ON THE FURRED ANIMALS BY ELLIS TROUGHTON, C. M. Z. S., F. R. Z. S. Axel Poignant. The Shepherd Press, Sydney, pp.40, illus., 1949.

REVIEW OF MYXOMATOSIS, 1950-1955. F.N. Ratcliffe. Jour.Australian Inst. Agric.Sci., vol.21, no.3, pp.130-133, Sep., 1955.

GLIMPSES OF MAMMALIAN LIFE IN AUSTRALIA AND TASMANIA. AN ACCOUNT OF PART OF THE WORK CARRIED ON BY THE FIRST AUSTRALIAN EXPEDITION OF THE AMERICAN MUSEUM. H.C. Raven. Nat. Hist., vol.24, pp.16-28, figs.16, Jan.-Feb., 1924.

REVIEWS OF THE RECENT WORK OF AUSTRALIAN MAMMALOGISTS. H.C. Raven. Nat.Hist., vol.25, no.6, pp. 618-621, Nov.-Dec., 1925 (Jan., 1926).

STRANGE ANIMALS OF THE ISLAND CONTINENT. (The First of Two Articles Descriptive of the Many Unique Animals of the Australian Region.) H.C. Raven. Nat.Hist., New York, vol.29, no.1, pp. 83-94, illus., Feb., 1929.

STRANGE ANIMALS OF THE ISLAND CONTINENT. (A Second Article Under the Same Title. Notes on the Echidna, Duck-Billed Platypus, Bandicoot, Tasmanian Devil, Wombat, and Tasmanian Wolf.) H.C. Raven. Nat.Hist., vol.29, pp.200-207, illus., Mar., 1929.

UNIQUE MAMMALS OF AUSTRALIA. H.C. Raven. Fauna, Philadelphia, vol.4, no.4, pp.104-108, illus., Dec., 1942.

STRANGE MAMMALS FROM AUSTRALIA. (Photographs of Platypus, Flying Foxes, Echidna, and Flying Opossum.) Edward Samuel. Discovery, London, vol.17, no. 202, pp.303-307, figs.6, Oct., 1936.

QUEST FOR STRANGE ANIMALS ENDS WITH AUSTRALIAN MAMMALS. Wilbert N. Savage. Frontiers, Lancaster, vol.8, no.5, pp.134-135, illus., June, 1944.

NOTICE OF THE EXISTENCE IN QUEENSLAND OF AN UNDESCRIBED SPECIES OF MAMMALS. Philip Lutley Sclater.Proc. Zool.Soc.London, for 1871, pp.629-630, 1871.

GEOGRAPHY OF MAMMALS. NO. II. THE AUSTRALIAN REGION. W.L. Sclater. Geogr.Jour., London, vol.4, no.1, pp.35-52, map, July, 1894.

RECENT INCREASE OF THE RARER NATIVE MAMMALS. D. L. Serventy and others. West.Australian Nat., Perth, vol.4, no.6, pp.128-141, Sep. 15, 1954.

NOTE ON THE AUTHORS OF THE SPECIFIC NAMES IN JOHN WHITE'S JOURNAL OF A VOYAGE TO NEW SOUTH WALES, 1790. C. Davies Sherborn. Ann.and Mag. Nat.Hist., London, ser.6, vol.7, no.42, p.535, June, 1891.

ACCOUNT OF THE GEOGRAPHICAL DISTRIBUTION OF THE MARSUPIALS AND MONOTREMES OF SOUTH-WEST AUSTRALIA, HAVING SPECIAL REFERENCE TO THE SPECIMENS COLLECTED DURING THE BALSTON EXPEDITION OF 1904-1907. G.C. Shortridge. Proc.Zool.Soc.London, for 1909, pp. 803-848, figs.244-278, Apr., 1910.

FIELD NOTES (HITHERTO UNPUBLISHED) ON WESTERN AUSTRALIAN MAMMALS SOUTH OF THE TROPIC OF CAPRICORN (EXCLUSIVE OF MARSUPIALIA AND MONOTREMATA), AND RECORDS OF SPECIMENS COLLECTED DURING THE BALSTON EXPEDITIONS (NOVEMBER 1904 TO JUNE 1907). G.C. Shortridge. Proc.Zool.Soc.London, for 1936, pt.3, pp.743-749, fig.1, Sep., 1936.

ACROSS THE OWEN STANLEY RANGE. (Brief Notes on Mammals.) C.C. Simpson. Victorian Nat., Melbourne, vol.59, no.6, pp.98-104, Oct., 1942.

MAMMALS OF AUSTRALIA. Arthur de Carle Sowerby. China Jour., vol.26, no. 3, pp.143-147, illus., Mar., 1937.

GIANTS AND PIGMIES OF THE DEEP. A STORY OF AUSTRALIAN SEA DENIZENS. David G. Stead. Shakespeare Head Press, Sydney, pp.108, illus., 1933.

TRAGEDIES OF AUSTRALIAN ACCLIMATISATION. WITH SPECIAL REFERENCE TO RECENT PROPOSALS. (Rabbits, Hares, Foxes, Domestic Dogs and Cats.) David G. Stead. Australian Wild Life, Sydney, vol.1, no.4, pp.45-57, illus., Jan., 1938.

TWENTY-FIFTH ANNUAL REPORT. WILD LIFE PRESERVATION SOCIETY OF AUSTRALIA. David G. Stead. Australian Wild Life, Sydney, vol.1, no.2, pp.1-20, illus., Oct., 1935.

ANIMALS OF AUSTRALIA IN COLOUR. Lyla Stevens. Illustrated by Deidre East, Melbourne, Whitcombe and Tombs, pp. 62, illus., 1956.

MAMMALS OF CAPE YORK PENINSULA, WITH NOTES ON THE OCCURRENCE OF RAIN FOREST IN QUEENSLAND. G. H.H. Tate. Bull.Amer.Mus.Nat.Hist., New York, vol.98, art.7, pp.567-616, Mar. 25, 1952.

NOTES ON THE MAMMALS OF CAPE YORK PENINSULA. G.H.H. Tate. Bull. Amer. Mus.Nat.Hist., vol.102, art.2, pp.199-203, June 16, 1953.

RESULTS OF THE ARCHBOLD EXPEDITIONS. NO. 66. MAMMALS OF CAPE YORK PENINSULA, WITH NOTES ON THE OCCURRENCE OF RAIN FOREST IN QUEENSLAND. G.H.H. Tate. Bull.Amer. Mus.Nat.Hist., New York, vol.98, art.7, pp.563-616, illus., Mar. 25, 1952.

AUSTRALIAN FURRED ANIMALS, THEIR PAST, PRESENT, AND FUTURE. Ellis Troughton. Australian Zoologist, vol.7, no.3, pp.173-193, Sep. 15, 1932.

AUSTRALIAN MAMMALS: THEIR PAST AND FUTURE. Ellis Troughton. Jour. Mamm., vol.19, no.4, pp.401-411, Nov. 14, 1938.

FURRED ANIMALS OF AUSTRALIA. Ellis Troughton. Angus and Robertson Ltd., Sydney, 2d (revised) ed., pp.xxvii+374,col. pls.25, Nov., 1943; 4th (revised) ed., 1951.

FURRED ANIMALS OF AUSTRALIA. Ellis Troughton. New York, Charles Scribner's Sons, pp.xxvii+374, col.pls.25 (by Neville W.Cayley), vol.8, 1947.

(Review by E.A.Briggs of) FURRED ANIMALS OF AUSTRALIA. Ellis Troughton. Australian Mus. Mag., Sydney, vol.7, no.11, p.387, Dec., 1941 - Feb., 1942.

(Review by David H. Johnson of) FURRED ANIMALS OF AUSTRALIA. Ellis Troughton. Jour.Mamm., vol.30, no.3, p.321, Aug. 17, 1949.

(Review by C.P. Morrison of) FURRED ANIMALS OF AUSTRALIA. Ellis Troughton. Victorian Nat., Melbourne, vol.58, no.11, p.184, Mar., 1942.

HABITS AND FOOD OF SOME AUSTRALIAN MAMMALS. Ellis Troughton. Australian Zool., vol.7, pt.1, pp.77-83, Aug. 24, 1931.

NOTES ON AUSTRALIAN MAMMALS. NO. 1. Ellis Troughton. Rec. Australian Mus., vol.13, no.3, pp.118-122, figs.1-6, Dec. 4, 1920.

ANIMALS OF THE AUSTRALIAN BUSH. Donald F. Thomson. Nature Mag., vol.26, no.3, pp.137-140, 189, illus., Sep., 1935.

GODMAN EXPLORATION FUND: LIST OF MAMMALS FROM NORTH QUEENSLAND COLLECTED BY MR. T. V. SHERRIN. Oldfield Thomas. Ann.and Mag.Nat.Hist., ser.9, vol.11, pp.170-178, Jan., 1923.

LIST OF FURTHER COLLECTIONS OF MAMMALS FROM WESTERN AUSTRALIA, INCLUDING A SERIES FROM BERNIER ISLAND, OBTAINED FOR MR. W. E. BALSTON; WITH FIELD NOTES BY THE COLLECTOR, MR. G. C. SHORTRIDGE. Oldfield Thomas. Proc. Zool.Soc.London, pp.763-776, Apr., 1907. (Nov. 13, 1906.)

NEW MAMMALS FROM THE AUSTRALIAN REGION. Oldfield Thomas. Ann.and Mag. Nat.Hist., ser.7, vol.17, no.99, pp.324-332, Mar., 1906.

NEW SPECIES OF PTEROPUS, MUS, AND POGONOMYS FROM THE AUSTRALIAN REGION. Oldfield Thomas. Novitates Zoologicae, vol.11, pp.597-600, Sep., 1904.

ON A COLLECTION OF MAMMALS MADE BY MR. J. T. TUNNEY IN ARNHAM LAND, NORTHERN TERRITORY OF SOUTH AUSTRALIA. Oldfield Thomas. Novitates Zoologicae, vol.11, pp.222-229, Mar., 1904.

ON MAMMALS COLLECTED IN SOUTH-WEST AUSTRALIA FOR MR. W. E. BALSTON. Oldfield Thomas. Proc.Zool.Soc. London, pp.468-478, Oct. 10, 1906.

ON MAMMALS FROM NORTHERN AUSTRALIA PRESENTED TO THE NATIONAL MUSEUM BY SIR WM. INGRAM, BT., AND THE HON. JOHN FORREST. Oldfield Thomas. Proc.Zool.Soc.London, pp.536-543, pl.37, Oct. 10, 1906.

ON THE RING-TAILED PHALANGER OF SOUTH AUSTRALIA, AND A NEW RAT FROM NORTH QUEENSLAND. Oldfield Thomas. Ann.and Mag.Nat.Hist., ser.9, vol.12, no.67, pp.158-160, July, 1923.

ON VARIOUS MAMMALS OBTAINED DURING CAPT. WILKIN'S EXPEDITION IN AUSTRALIA. Oldfield Thomas. Ann.and Mag.Nat. Hist., ser.9, vol.17, pp.625-635, June, 1926.

SOME MAMMALS FROM N. E. KIMBERLEY, NORTHERN AUSTRALIA. Oldfield Thomas. Ann.and Mag.Nat.Hist., ser.8, vol.3, no. 14, pp.149-152, Feb., 1909.

TWO NEW AUSTRALIA MAMMALS. Oldfield Thomas. Ann.and Mag.Nat.Hist., ser.8, vol.11, no.61, pp.79-80, Jan., 1913.

TWO NEW AUSTRALIAN SMALL MAMMALS. Oldfield Thomas. Ann.and Mag. Nat.Hist., ser.7, vol.10, no.60, pp.491-492, Dec., 1902.

TWO NEW MAMMALS FROM NORTH AUSTRALIA. Oldfield Thomas. Ann.and Mag. Nat.Hist., ser.8, vol.4, no.21, pp.197-198, Sep., 1909.

MAMMALS FROM INKERMAN, NORTH QUEENSLAND, PRESENTED TO THE NATIONAL MUSEUM BY SIR WILLIAM INGRAM, BT., AND THE HON. JOHN FORREST. Oldfield Thomas, Guy Dollman. Proc.Zool.Soc.London, for 1908, pp.788-794, Apr., 1909.

LADY JULIA PERCY ISLAND. REPORTS OF THE EXPEDITION OF THE McCOY SOCIETY FOR FIELD INVESTIGATION AND RESEARCH. PT. 24. MAMMALIA. J.A. Tubb, C.W. Brazenor. Proc.Roy. Soc.Victoria, vol.49, n.s., pt.2, pp. 435-437, pl.26, fig.2, July 19, 1937.

VERMIN FENCES OF WESTERN AUSTRALIA. Arthur W. Upfield. Australian Geographical Mag. ("Walkabout"), Melbourne, vol.15, no.5, pp.17-20, illus., May 1, 1949.

(DISPLACEMENTS WITHIN THE FAUNA OF AUSTRALIA AND THEIR EFFECTS ON THE ANIMAL TRADE.) Verschiebungen innerhalb der Landesfauna Australiens und ihre Auswirkungen auf den Tiehandel. Helm. Otto Wagner. Zool. Garten, Leipzig, n.F., vol.12, nos.2-3, pp.123-153, figs.20, July, 1940.

MAMMALIA. Edgar R. Waite. Trans.Roy. Soc.South Australia, vol.38, pp.2, 1914.

MAMMALS, REPTILES AND AMPHIBIANS (AUSTRALIA). Edgar R. Waite. Reprinted from Handbook of Sydney and the County of Cumberland, pp.53-67, Jan., 1898.

FAUNA OF THE LAMINGTON NATIONAL PARK. Edgar J. Young. Queensland Nat., vol.10, no.3, pp.50-59, Aug., 1937.

AUSTRALIA--LAND OF QUEER CREATURES. Jr.Nat.Hist.Mag., New York, vol.7, no.1, pp.4-7, 16, illus., Mar., 1942.

BIBLIOGRAPHY OF PUBLICATIONS CONCERNING MYXOMATOSIS IN AUSTRALIA. Jour. Australian Inst.Agr.Sci., vol.21, no. 4, pp.254-255, Dec., 1955.

INTRUDERS: THE CUSCUS AND OTHER FAUNA OF CAPE YORK PENINSULA. Illus.London News, vol.193, no.5181, p. 233, Aug.6, 1938.

AUSTRIA

RECORDS OF SMALL MAMMALS AND THEIR FLEAS FROM EASTERN NORTH TYROL, AUSTRIA. G.M. Dunnet. Ann. and Mag.Nat.Hist., London, vol.8, no. 89, pp.385-389, May, 1955.

(NEW EXCAVATIONS IN AUSTRIAN CAVES.) Neue Ausgrabungen in oesterreichischen Hoehlen. Kurt Ehrenberg. Verhandl.Zool.Bot.Ges.Vienna, vol.79, nos.2-4, pp.71-75, (1929), Oct., 1930.

(CONTRIBUTION TO KNOWLEDGE OF THE SMALL MAMMAL FAUNA OF THE TYROL.) Beitrag zur Kenntnis der Kleinsaeugefauna Tirols. Helmut Schaefer.Zeitschr.f.Saeugetierk., vol.10, no.1, pp.154-155, Dec. 31, 1935.

(FIRST REMAINS OF LAND MAMMALS FROM THE LINZ SANDS.) Erste Reste von Landsaeugetieren aus den Linzer Sanden. Otto Sickenberg. Verhandl. Geol. Bundesanstalt 1934, nos.4-5, pp.60-63, 1934.

(LOWER PLIOCENE WARM SPRINGS ON THE VIENNESE WARM SPRINGS LINE NEAR LEOBERSDORF IN LOWER AUSTRIA.) Eine unterpliozaene Therme auf der Wiener Thermenlinie bei Leobersdorf in Niederoesterreich. Otto Sickenberg. Akad. Wiss. Wiener Anzeiger, no. 17, pp.1-2, 1929.

(NEW ANTELOPE AND OTHER MAMMAL REMAINS FROM THE UPPER MIOCENE OF LOWER AUSTRALIA.) Eine neue Antilope und andere Saeugetierreste aus dem Obermiozaen Niederoesterreichs. Otto Sickenberg. Palaeobiologica, vol.2, nos. 1-3, pp.62-86, figs.4, pls.7-8, 1929.

(NEW VERTEBRATE FINDS FROM THE OLDEST PLEISTOCENE OF LOWER AUSTRIA.) Neue Wirbeltierfunde aus dem Aeltest-Pleistozaen von Niederoesterreich. Erich Thenius. Jahrb.Geol.Bundesanst., IC (2), pp.259-271, illus., 1956.

(ON THE DEVELOPMENT OF THE YOUNG TERTIARY MAMMAL FAUNA OF THE VIENNA BASIN.) Zur Entwicklung der jungtertiaeren Saeugetierfaunen des Wiener Beckens. Erich Thenius. Pal.Zeit., vol.29, pp.21-26, illus., Mar., 1955.

(KNOWLEDGE OF THE FAUNA OF A XEROTHERMIC LOCALITY IN LOWER AUSTRIA (LOWER KAMPTAL).) Zur Kenntniss der Fauna einer xerothermischen Lokalitaet in Nieder-Oesterreich (unteres Kamptal). F. Werner. Zeitschr.f.Morph. u. Oekologie der Tiere, vol.9, pp.1-96, figs.18, Oct. 1, 1927.

(DILUVIAL SMALL MAMMAL REMAINS FROM THE DRAGON CAVERN NEAR MIXNITZ IN STEIERMARK.) Diluvialen Kleinsaeugerreste aus der Drachenhoehle bei Mixnitz in Steiermark. Otto Wettstein-Westersheim. Palaeont.Zeitschr., vol.7, no.1, pp.55-56, 1925.

(ON RECENT FOSSIL BONES FROM THE DRAGON CAVERN NEAR MIXNITZ IN STEIERMARK.) Ueber rezente Knochenreste aus der Drachenhoehle bei Mixnitz in Steiermark. Otto Wettstein-Westersheim. (Sitzung der mathematischen-naturwissenschaftlichen Klasse vom 24 Nov.1921.) Anzeiger Kais.Akad.Wissenschaft, Vienna, pp.1-3, 1921.

(THREE NEW FOSSIL BATS, AND THE DILUVIAL SMALL MAMMAL FOSSILS IN GENERAL, FROM THE DRAGON CAVERN NEAR MIXNITZ IN STEIERMARK.) Drei neue fossile Fledermaeuse und die diluvialen Kleinsaeugerreste im Allgemeinen aus der Drachenhoehle bei Mixnitz in Steiermark. Otto Wettstein-Westersheim. Sitz. der mathematischen-naturwissenschaftlichen Klasse Vienna, vol.8, pp.1-3, Mar., 1923.

BAHAMA ISLANDS

NOTES ON THE MAMMALS OF THE BAHAMAS WITH SPECIAL REFERENCE TO THE BATS. Karl F. Koopman, Max K. Hecht, Emanuel Ledecky-Janecek. Jour.Mamm., vol.38, no.2, pp.164-174, May, 1957.

MAMMALS OF THE BAHAMA ISLANDS. Gerrit S. Miller, Jr. Geog.Soc.Baltimore, pp.371-384, pls.62-64, Feb. 18, 1905.

BALI

(MAMMALS OF BALI, LOMBOK, SUMBAWA, AND FLORES.) Die Saeugetiere der Inseln Bali, Lombok, Sumbawa und Flores. Robert Mertens. Zool.Jahrb. (Abt.Syst.Oekol.u. Geogr.-Tiere), Jena, vol.68, nos.4-5, pp. 273-324, pls.5-6, Mar. 8, 1936.

FOUR NEW MAMMALS FROM BALI AND SOEMBA. H.J.V. Sody. Natuurkundig Tijdschrift voor Nederlandsch-Indië, Batavia, vol.92, no.2, pp.334-340, 1932.

ON THE MAMMALS OF BALI (WITH A NOTE ON THE RACES OF CALLOSCIURUS NOTATUS OF JAVA.). H.J.V. Sody. Natuurk.Tijdschr.Nederlandsch-Indië, Batavia, vol.93, no.1, pp.56-95, 1933.

SOME NOTES ON TRACHYPITHECUS PYRRHUS, PRESBYTIS AYGULA, AND CUON JAVANICUS FROM BALI, JAVA AND SUMATRA. H.J.V. Sody. Proc.Zool.Soc. London, 1937, vol.107, ser.B, Syst.and Morphol., pt.2, pp.257-261, fig.1, July, 1937.

BALKAN PENINSULA

ADDITIONS TO THE MAMMALIAN FAUNA OF THE BALKAN PENINSULA. St.J.L. Bolkay. Sarajevo, Drzavna Stamparija, pp.21, illus., 1926. (Deals with Mammals in the Bosnian-Hercegovinian State Museum in Sarajevo.)

FURTHER CONTRIBUTIONS TO THE MAMMALIAN FAUNA OF THE BALKAN PENINSULA. St.J.L. Bolkay. Sarajevo, Drzavna Stamparija, pp.10, illus., 1927.

PRELIMINARY NOTES ON A NEW MOLE (TALPA KERCEGOVINENSIS N. SP.) FROM CENTRAL HERCEGOVINA AND DIAGNOSES OF SOME NEW MAMMALS FROM BOSNIA AND HERCEGOVINA. St.J.L. Bolkay. Novitates Musei Sarajevoensis, no.1, pp. 16, illus., June 29, 1925.

CONTRIBUTION TO OUR KNOWLEDGE OF THE MAMMALS OF MACEDONIA AND THESSALY. J.L. Chaworth-Musters. Ann. and Mag.Nat.Hist., ser.10, vol.9, pp.166-171, Feb., 1932.

BELGIUM

OCCURRENCE OF ELEPHAS PRIMIGENIUS AND HUMAN INDUSTRIES IN THE PLEIS-

TOCENE AND HOLOCENE SEDIMENTS IN THE VALLEY OF THE ESCOUT AT ANTOING.) Présence d'Elephas primigenius et d'industries humaines dans les sediments pleistocenes et holocenes dans la vallee de l'Escaut a Antoing. J. Baudet. Bull.Soc. Belge Géol., Paléontol.et Hydrol., vol.52, no.2, pp.193-199, fig.1, pl.1, map, 1943.

(ON SOME NEW MAMMALS OF THE TERTIARY OF BELGIUM.) Sur quelques mammifères nouveaux du Tertiaire de la Belgique. P. Teilhard De Chardin. Acad. Roy.Belgique Bull.Cl.Sci., vol.12, nos. 4-5, pp.210-215, figs.2, 1926.

(COMPARATIVE OBSERVATIONS ON THE MOST FREQUENT SMALL MAMMALS OF THE HOHE VENN MOUNTAINS.) Vergleichende Beobachtungen an den haeufigsten Kleinsaeugern des Hohen Venns. Ernst von Lehmann. Bonner Zool.Beitraege, Heft 1-2, pp.17-20, 1953.

(INSECTIVORES, BATS, AND RODENTS OF THE CAVERNS OF GOYET (BELGIUM).) Die Insektenfresser, Fledermaeuse und Nagetiere der Hoehlen von Goyet (Belgien). O. von Sickenberg. Bull.Mus.Roy.Hist. Nat.Belgique, Bruxelles, vol.15, no.19, pp.23, Apr., 1939.

(REPRESENTATIONS OF QUATERNARY MAN AND ANIMALS DISCOVERED IN BELGIUM.) Les representations de l'homme et des animaux quaternaires decouvertes en Belgique. François Twiesselmann. Mem. Inst.Royal Sci.Nat.Belgique, no.113, pp. 28, pls.10, Apr.30, 1951.

## BORNEO

BORNEAN MAMMALS. E. Banks. Kuching Press, Kuching, Sarawak, pp.83, illus., map 1, 1949.

COLLECTION OF MONTANE MAMMALS AND BIRDS FROM MULU IN SARAWAK. E. Banks. Sarawak Mus.Jour., Kuching, vol.4, no.14, pp.327-341, Dec., 1935.

DISTRIBUTION OF MAMMALS AND BIRDS IN SARAWAK AND ADJACENT PARTS OF BORNEO. E. Banks. Proc.Zool.Soc.London, 1933, pt.2, pp.273-282, pl.1, June, 1933.

NATURALIST IN SARAWAK. E. Banks. Kuching Press, Kuching, pp.125, maps, 1949.

POPULAR ACCOUNT OF THE MAMMALS OF BORNEO. E. Banks. Jour.Malayan Branch Roy.Asiatic Soc., Singapore, vol. 9, no.2, pp.1-139, map, pls.9, Nov.,1931.

NOTES ON BORNEAN MAMMALS. F.N. Chasen. Bull.Raffles Mus., Singapore, no.8, pp.195-198, Dec., 1933.

ON SOME MAMMALS FROM THE KARIMATA ISLANDS AND DUTCH WEST BORNEO. F.N. Chasen. Treubia, Buitenzorg, vol.15, no.1, pp.1-7, June, 1935.

TWO NEW MAMMALS FROM BORNEO. F.N. Chasen. Bull.Raffles Mus., Singapore, Straits Settlements, no.13, pp.80-81, Aug., 1937.

ON A COLLECTION OF MAMMALS FROM THE LOWLANDS AND ISLANDS OF NORTH BORNEO. F.N. Chasen, C. Boden Kloss. Bull.Raffles Mus., Singapore, Straits Settlements, no.6, pp.82, pl.1, Dec.,1931.

ON SOME CARNIVORA, RODENTIA AND INSECTIVORA PRINCIPALLY FROM EASTERN BORNEO. F.N. Chasen, C. Boden Kloss. Jour.Malayan Branch Royal Asiatic Soc., vol.6, pt.1, pp.38-49, map 1, Mar., 1928.

MAMMALS OF THE KELABIT PLATEAU, NORTHERN SARAWAK. Delbert Dwight Davis. Chicago Nat.Hist.Mus., Chicago, pp.119-147, illus., map, 1958. (Chicago Nat.Hist.Mus.Publication no.840.) (Series: Chicago Nat.Hist.Mus., Fieldiana:Zoology, vol.39, no.15.)

UP MOUNT KINABALU. John A. Griswold, Jr. Sci.Monthly, Lancaster, Pa., vol.48, no.5, pp.401-414, May, 1939.

REMARKS ON SOME INDIAN AND, MORE ESPECIALLY, BORNEAN MAMMALS. Albert Gunther. Proc. Zool.Soc.London, 1876, pp.424-428, pls.36-37, 1876.

ON A COLLECTION OF MAMMALS MADE IN EASTERN AND CENTRAL BORNEO BY MR. CARL LUMBHOLTZ. Nils Gyldenstolpe. Stockholm, Kungl.Svenska Vet.-Akad.Handl., vol.60, no.6, pp.62, figs.4, pls.6, 1919.

NAMES OF MAMMALS IN THE DUSUN LANGUAGE OF NORTH BORNEO. J.L. Harrison, Robert Traub. Malayan Nature Jour., Kuala Lumpur, vol.8, no.3, pp. 120-128, Dec., 1953.

LARGE MAMMALS OF BORNEO. Tom Harrison. Malayan Nature Jour., Kuala Lumpur, vol.4, no.2, pp.70-76, June, 1949.

MAMMALS OF BORNEO. Charles Hone. London, 1893.

CONTRIBUTION TO THE ZOOLOGY OF MANGALUM ISLAND, NORTH-WEST BORNEO. MAMMALS. C. Boden Kloss. Bull.Raffles Mus., Singapore, Straits Settlements, no.5, pp.88-89, Aug., 1931.

MAMMALS COLLECTED IN WESTERN BORNEO BY DR. W. L. ABBOTT. Marcus Ward Lyon. U.S.Nat.Mus., Proceedings, Washington, 1908, vol.33, pp.547-571, illus., map.

MAMMALS COLLECTED BY DR. W. L. ABBOTT ON BORNEO AND SOME OF THE SMALL ADJACENT ISLANDS. Marcus Ward Lyon. U.S.Nat.Mus., Proceedings, Washington, 1911, vol.40, pp.53-146, pls.7 (1 col.), maps 2.

ZOOLOGICAL EXPEDITION TO MT. KINABALU BRITISH NORTH BORNEO (1929). H.M. Pendleburg, F.N. Chasen. Jour.Fed. Malay States Mus., vol.17, pt.1, pp.1-38, pls.1-8, Sep., 1932.

LIST OF THE MAMMALS OF THE JAPANESE WAR AREA. PT. 4. BORNEO AND THE ISLANDS OF THE CHINA SEA. G.H. H. Tate. Amer.Mus.Nat.Hist., New York, pp.18, 1944.

DESCRIPTIONS OF NEW BORNEO AND SUMATRAN MAMMALS. Oldfield Thomas. Ann.and Mag.Nat.Hist., ser.7, vol.2, pp.245-251.

DESCRIPTIONS OF TWO NEW NORTH-BORNEAN MAMMALS. Oldfield Thomas. Ann.and Mag.Nat.Hist., ser.6, vol.12, no.69, pp.230-232, pl.7, Sep., 1893.

ON SOME MAMMALS FROM MOUNT DULIT, NORTH BORNEO. Oldfield Thomas. Proc.Zool.Soc.London, no.16, pp.221-227, pls.18-19, Mar. 15, 1892.

ON SOME NEW BORNEAN MAMMALIA. Oldfield Thomas. Ann. and Mag. Nat.Hist., ser.6, vol.11, no.65, pp.341-347, May, 1893.

## BRITISH ISLES

### Extinct and Fossil Mammals

LATE GLACIAL DEPOSITS AT NAZEING IN THE LEA VALLEY, NORTH LONDON. (With a Report on Small Mammalia, by M.A.C.Hinton.) Jean Allison. London, Cambridge Univ. Press, pp.169-240, illus., pls., diagrs., tbls., 1952. (Royal Society of London, Philosophical Transactions, ser.B., vol.236, no.632.)

NOTE ON THE FAUNA OF THE ATHLIT CAVES. Dorothea M.A. Bate. Jour.Roy. Anthrop.Inst., London, vol.62, pp.277-279, (July-Dec., 1932) 1933.

CORRELATION OF THE QUATNERNARY DEPOSITS OF THE BRITISH ISLES WITH THOSE OF THE CONTINENT OF EUROPE. Charles E. P. Brooks. Ann. Rep. Smiths. Inst., 1917, pp.277-375, 1919.

HYAENODON AIMI, SP.N., AND A NOTE ON THE OCCURRENCE OF ANTHRACOTHERIUM MINUS FROM THE HEADON BEDS AT HORDLE. C.Forster Cooper.Ann. and Mag.Nat.Hist., ser.9, vol.18, pp.370-373, illus., Oct., 1926.

ON SOME MAMMALIAN REMAINS FROM THE LOWER EOCENE OF THE LONDON CLAY. C.Forster Cooper. Ann. and Mag. Nat.Hist., ser.10, vol.9, no.53, pp.458-467, figs.2, pls.2, May, 1932.

BRITISH PLEISTOCENE MAMMALIA. W. Boyd Dawkins. London, Printed for the Palaeontographical Society, illus., pls., 1866.

MAMMALIA FOUND AT WINDY KNOLL. W. Boyd Dawkins. Quart. Jour. Geol. Soc., pp.246-255, figs.3, May, 1875.

ON THE DISTRIBUTION OF THE BRITISH POSTGLACIAL MAMMALS. W. Boyd Dawkins. London, pp.217, 1869.

NOTES ON THE HOLE OF HORCUM, SALTERSGATE, NORTH YORKSHIRE. VI. THE MAMMALIA, REPTILIA, AND BATRACHIA. Robert F. Flintoff, David Harrison, Charles Mackley. Northwestern Nat. Arbroath, vol.13, no.2, pp.83-92, June, 1938.

BRITISH ANIMALS EXTINCT WITHIN HISTORIC TIMES; WITH SOME ACCOUNT OF BRITISH WILD WHITE CATTLE.James Edmund Harting. London, Trubner and Co., pp.vii-258, illus., 1880. (Bear, Beaver, Reindeer, Wild Boar, Wolf, Wild White Cattle.)

EXCAVATIONS AT BRUNDON, SUFFOLK (1935-37). PART 2. FOSSIL MAMMALS. A. Tindell Hopwood. Proc. Prehistoric Soc. Cambridge, n.s., vol.5, pt.1, pp.13-29, figs.15-18, 1939.

BRITISH MAMMALS; AN ATTEMPT TO DESCRIBE AND ILLUSTRATE THE MAMMALIAN FAUNA OF THE BRITISH ISLANDS FROM THE COMMENCEMENT OF THE PLEISTOCENE PERIOD DOWN TO THE PRESENT DAY. Harry H. Johnston. London, Hutchinson and Co., pp.xvi-405, illus. (incl.maps), pls.32, col.pls.16, 1903.

NOTES ON THE FOSSIL VERTEBRATES OF THE HAMSTEAD BEDS. R. F. Moorman. Wight Nat. Hist. and Archaeol. Soc., Newport, vol.3, pt.1, pp.81-85, Aug. 10, 1939.

ADDITIONAL NOTES ON THE VERTEBRATE FAUNA OF THE ROCK-FISSURE AT IGHTAM (KENT). E. T. Newton. Quart. Jour. Geol. Soc., London, vol.55, pt.3, no.219, pp.419-429, pl.28, Aug. 12, 1899.

NOTE ON THE MAMMALIAN FAUNA OF THE MIDDLE GRAVELS OF THE BARNFIELD PIT. K.P. Oakley. Jour. Roy. Anthropol. Inst. Great Britain and Ireland, London, vol.68, p.28, Jan.-June, 1938.

REPORT ON EXAVATIONS AT JAYWICK SANDS, ESSEX (1934), WITH SOME OBSERVATIONS ON THE CLACTONIAN INDUSTRY, AND ON THE FAUNA AND GEOLOGICAL SIGNIFICANCE OF THE CLACTON CHANNEL. K.P. Oakley, Mary Leakley. Proc. Prehist.Soc. Cambridge for 1937 (July-Dec.), n.s., vol.3, pt.2, pp.217-260, figs.11, pl.19, 1938. (Mammalian Fauna, pp.243-251.)

PLIOCENE (TERTIARY) AND EARLY PLEISTOCENE (QUATERNARY) MAMMALIA OF EAST ANGLIA, GREAT BRITAIN, IN RELATION TO THE APPEARANCE OF MAN. Henry Fairfield Osborn. Geol. Mag., London, vol.59, no.700, pp.433-441, tbl., Oct., 1922.

HISTORY OF BRITISH FOSSIL MAMMALS AND BIRDS. Richard Owen. London, J.Van Voorst, pp.560, illus., tbl., 1846.

ON THE PLEISTOCENE SUCCESSION OF THE BRISTOL DISTRICT. L.S. Palmer. Proc. Geologists' Assoc., vol.42, no.4, pp.345-361, 1931.

SOME INTERESTING MEDIAEVAL ANIMAL RELICS. R.I. Pocock. Field, London, vol.152, p.37, illus., July 5, 1928.

FAUNA OF SCOTLAND DURING THE ICE AGE. PRESIDENTIAL ADDRESS. James Ritchie. Proc. Roy. Phys. Soc., Edinburgh, vol.21, pt.4, pp.185-194, Feb., 1929.

SCOTLAND IN THE DAYS OF THE MAMMOTH AND AFTER. James Ritchie. The Scottish Naturalist, no.177, pp.65-68, May-June, 1929.

MAMMALIAN REMAINS FROM HOLDERNESS GRAVELS. T. Sheppard. Naturalist, London, no.849, p.297, Oct., 1927.

THE CRAG MAMMALIA. H.E.P. Spencer. Trans. Suffolk Nat. Soc., vol.8, pt.3, pp. 153-155, 1954. (Fossils)

ELEPHAS-ANTIQUUS BED OF CLACTON-ON-SEA (ESSEX) AND ITS FLORA AND FAUNA. Samuel H. Warren. Quart. Jour. Geol.Soc.London, vol.79, pp.606-619, Dec. 29, 1923.

COMPARISON OF THE PLEISTOCENE OF EAST ANGLIA WITH THAT OF GERMANY. Friedrich E. Zeuner. Proc. Prehistoric Soc. for 1937 (Jan.-June), n.s., vol.3, pt.1, pp. 136-157, fig.1, 1937.

Recent Mammals

GREAT PLAGUE OF LONDON IN LITERARY AND MEDICAL WRITINGS OF THE PERIOD. Barry J. Anson. Quart. Phi Beta Pi, vol.41, no.1, pp.19, figs.11, Mar., 1944.

ADDITION TO THE LIST OF BRITISH BOREAL MAMMALS. G.E.H.Barrett-Hamilton. Proc. Roy. Irish Acad., vol. 24, sec.B, pt.4, pp.315-319, 1903.

HISTORY OF BRITISH MAMMALS. G.E.H. Barrett-Hamilton. London, Gurney and Jackson, illus., pls.(partly col.), 1910. Vol. 1. Chiroptera, vol. 2. Insectivora, vol. 3. Lagomorpha, vol. 4. Rodentia.

ON A COLLECTION OF MAMMALS FROM THE INNER HEBRIDES. G.E.H. Barrett-Hamilton, Martin A.C. Hinton. Proc.Zool. Soc., London, pp.821-839, figs.136-138, pl.84, Sep., 1913.

STUDIES ON THE BIOLOGY OF THE BRISTOL CHANNEL. XVI. THE FAUNA OF SKOMER ISLAND, A PRELIMINARY SKETCH. (Vole, Seals, Porpoises.) R. Bassindale. Proc. Bristol Nat. Soc., vol. 27, pt.2, pp.109-120, map, July 1, 1946.

BRITISH WILD ANIMALS. H. Mortimer Batten. London, C.Arthur Pearson, Ltd., pp.156, pls.8, 1924.

BRITISH WILD ANIMALS. (An Authoritative Description Based on a Lifetime's Study and Observation of the Habits and Characteristics of Britain's Wild Animals.) H. Mortimer Batten. London, Odhams Press, pp.256, illus., 1952.

HISTORY OF THE BRITISH LAND MAMMALS. Bryan P. Beirne. Ann. and Mag. Nat.Hist., London, ser.11, vol.14, no. 115, pp.501-514, July, 1947 (Apr. 2, 1948).

ORIGIN AND HISTORY OF THE BRITISH FAUNA. Bryan P. Beirne. Methuen and Co., London, pp.x-164, 1952.

HISTORY OF BRITISH QUADRUPEDS, INCLUDING THE CETACEA. Thomas Bell. London, J. Van Voorst, pp.xviii-526, illus., 1837; 2nd ed., pp.xviii-474, illus., 1874.

SUFFOLK MAMMALS. W. Bingley. Trans. Suffolk Nat.Soc., Norwich, vol.4, pt.4, pp.289-290, Dec., 1941. (Excerpts from "Memoirs of British Quadrupeds", 1809.)

MAMMALS IN BRITAIN. Michael Blackmore. London, Collins, pp.128, illus., 1948.

SMALL MAMMAL POPULATIONS AT SILWOOD PARK FIELD CENTRE, BERKSHIRE, ENGLAND. L.E. Brown. Jour. Mamm., vol.35, no.2, pp.161-176, map, graphs., May, 1954.

MAMMALS ON HAVERGATE ISLAND AFTER THE FLOOD. H.G. Brownlow. Trans. Suffolk Nat.Soc., vol.8, pt.3, pp.110-111, 1954.

BRITAIN'S UNOBTRUSIVE MAMMALS. Maurice Burton. Illus.London News, vol. 220, no.5895, p.632, illus., Apr. 12, 1952.

BRITISH MAMMALS. Maurice Burton. London, Oxford Univ.Press, pp.64, illus., 1958.

FUR FARM IN NORFOLK. P.E.T.Carill-Worsley. Trans.Norfolk and Norwich Nat. Soc., vol.13, no.2, pp.105-115, pls.3, (1930-31) 1932.

BRITISH MAMMALS: MAMMALS IN HAMPSHIRE. P.H. Carne. Oryx, London, vol.3, no.4, pp.200-202, May, 1956.

ANNOTATED LIST OF VERTEBRATA OCCURRING ABOUT EUSTON BESIDE THE SUFFOLK BRECKLAND. Redmond B.Caton. Trans.Suffolk Naturalist's Soc., vol.1, pt. 3, pp.162-177, Dec., 1931.

BRITISH ANIMAL TRACKS. J.S.R. Chard. London, pp.80, 1936.

ON THE VOLE AND SHREW OF THE ORKNEY ISLANDS... WITH A REPORT BY PROF. O. CHARNOCK BRADLEY. Wm.Eagle Clarke. Ann. Scottish Nat. Hist., Edinburgh, pp.1-8, figs.2, Jan., 1905.

PRELIMINARY SURVEY OF THE WILD LAND MAMMALS OF THE HASTINGS DISTRICT. L.R. Conisbee. Hastings and East Sussex Naturalist, vol.8, no.4, pp. 108-124, 1955.

MAMMALS OF THE BRITISH ISLES. Harper Cory. London, New York, T.Nelson and Sons, pp.vii-292, illus., pls., 1941.

SOME NOTES ON THE MAMMALS OF LUNDY. T. Coward. Manchester Lit.and Philos.Soc.Mem.and Proc., Manchester, vol.52, no.6, pp.14, 1908.

WILD LIFE OF BRITAIN. F.F. Darling. London, Collins, pp.48, 1947.

SMALL MAMMALS CAUGHT NEAR LONDON. R.A. Davis. London Naturalist, pp. 88-89, 1955.

SURVEY OF THE MAMMAL POPULATION OF RICKS IN ENGLAND AND WALES, 1955-1956. R.A. Davis. Proc.Zool.Soc.London, vol.128, no.4, pp.604-606, July 24, 1957.

SMALL MAMMALS OF A DUMBARTONSHIRE OAKWOOD. M.J. Delany. Glasgow Naturalist, vol.17, no.6, pp.272-278, Oct., 1957.

NATURAL HISTORY OF BRITISH QUADRUPEDS. E. Donovan. London, Printed for the Author, and F.C. and J.Rivington, vols.1-3, col.pl., 1820.

BEASTS OF THE CHASE. Lionel Edwards. London, Putnam, pp.xi-49, illus.(part col.), 1950.

OUR BRITISH BIRDS AND BEASTS. Norman Ellison. Manchester, Open Air Publications, pp.190, illus., 1947.

BIRDS, BEASTS AND FISHES OF THE NORFOLK BROADLAND. Peter Henry Emerson. London, David Nutt, pp.xv-396, illus., pls., 1895.

STUDIES OF A SMALL MAMMAL POPULATION IN BAGLEY WOOD, BERKSHIRE. F.C. Evans. Jour. Anim.Ecol., London, vol.11, no.2, pp.182-197, Nov., 1942.

THE MAMMALIAN FAUNA OF THE EDINBURGH DISTRICT WITH RECORDS OF OCCURRENCES OF THE RARER SPECIES THROUGHOUT THE SOUTH-EAST OF SCOTLAND GENERALLY. William Evans. Edinburgh, pp.123, 1892.

ANIMAL LIFE ROUND LONDON. R.S.R. Fitter. Field, London, vol.174, no.4523, p.555, figs.3, Sep. 2, 1939. (Brown Rat, Gray Squirrel, and Stoat Photographs.)

CKECK-LIST OF THE MAMMALS, REPTILES, AND AMPHIBIA OF THE LONDON AREA, 1900-1949. R.S.R. Fitter. London Nat., vol.28, (1948), pp.98-115, 1949.

CONTRIBUTION TO THE BIBLIOGRAPHY OF THE NATURAL HISTORY OF THE LONDON AREA. I. MAMMALS, REPTILES, AND AMPHIBIA. R.S.R. Fitter. London, Nat., no.27, (1947), pp.76-78, 1948.

A HISTORY OF BRITISH ANIMALS. J. Fleming. Edinburgh, vols.2, 1828.

WILD LIFE IN THE WESTERN HIGHLANDS. (Foxes and Wild Cats Increasing in Absence of Hunters.) Seton Gordon. Nature, London, vol.150, no.3792, pp.12-13, July 4, 1942.

FAUNA OF AN IPSWICH MEADOW. Charles Edward Green. Trans.Suffolk Nat.Soc., Norwich, vol.5, pt.4, pp.177-180, Dec., 1945.

CHANGES IN THE BRITISH FAUNA AND FLORA DURING THE PAST FIFTY YEARS. (1) MAMMALS. M.A.C. Hinton. Proc.Linn. Soc.London, 148th sess.(1935-36), pt.1, pp.33-34, Dec. 23, 1935.

MAMMALS AND REPTILES OF THE BRITISH ISLES. N.Barrie Hodgson. Bognor Regis, Sussex, J. Crowther, pp.69, illus., 1945. (Guide to the Identification, Habits and Characteristics of British Mammals and Reptiles, Together with Lists of their Comparative Sizes.)

NATURAL HISTORY OF HERTFORDSHIRE. Frank W. Jane. Trans.Hertfordshire Nat. Hist.Soc.and Field Club, Hertford, vol.22, pt.4, pp.142-159, Aug., 1946. (Mammals: pp.155-156.)

MAMMALS IN CARLISLE. B.Johnston. Trans.Carlisle Nat.Hist.Soc., England, vol.5, pp.26-30, 1933.

HEDGE FOLKS IN TWILIGHT. Phillis Kelway. 1936.

ECOLOGY OF BARDSEY ISLAND: TOPOGRAPHY AND TYPES OF ENVIRONMENT. F. Loxham Kidd, K.A. Pyefinch, P.M. Butler. Jour.Anim.Ecol., London, vol.4, no.2, pp.231-243, pls.7-8, map 1, Nov., 1935.

WILD MAMMALS AND THE LAND. F. Howard Lancum. Great Brit.Ministry Agr. and Fisheries Bull., no.150, pp.1-60, illus., 1951.

ON NEW MAMMALIA FROM THE RED CRAG. E. Ray Lankester. Ann. and Mag. Nat.Hist., vol.14, pp.353-360, pl.viii, 1864.

OFF THE ROAD. (Brief Notes on English Mammals.) Hermann Lea. Field, London, vol.152, p.74, illus., July 12, 1928.

NOTES ON MAMMALS OBSERVED AT LUNNA, SHETLAND. T.G. Longstaff. Scottish Nat., no.219, p.92, May-June, 1936.

HANDBOOK OF THE BRITISH MAMMALIA. Richard Lydekker. London, pp. 339, 1895. (Allen's Naturalist's Library.)

HANDBOOK TO THE BRITISH MAMMALIA. Richard Lydekker. Lloyd's Natural History (Mammals). 1896.

BRITISH QUADRUPEDS. William Macgillivray. Edinburgh, W.H.Lizars, pp.310, illus., col.pls.34, 1838; London, H.G. Bohn, pp.309, illus., col.pls.34, 1848 and 1866.

NOTES FROM THE GATTY MARINE LABORATORY, ST. ANDREWS. Prof.M'Intosh. (Includes Notes on Rabbits and Whales.) Ann. and Mag. Nat. Hist., ser.9, vol.12, pp.65-94, pls.2, July, 1923.

WAR AND SCOTLAND'S GAME. Dugald MacIntyre. Field, London, vol.174, no. 4531, p.860, Oct. 28, 1939.

SOME ASPECTS OF URBAN ZOOLOGY IN GREAT BRITAIN. Colin Matheson. Sci. Monthly, Lancaster, vol.76, no.1, pp.29-32, Jan., 1953.

BRITISH MAMMALS. L. Harrison Matthews. London, Collins, pp.410, 1952.

NOTE ON CROCIDURA RUSSULA AND OTHER MAMMALS IN ALDERNEY, CHANNEL ISLANDS. L. Harrison Matthews. Jour. Animal Ecology, Cambridge, England, vol. 16, no.2, p.225, Nov., 1947.

STUDIES ON THE BIOLOGY OF THE BRISTOL CHANNEL. VI. THE MARINE MAMMALS OF THE BRISTOL CHANNEL. L. Harrison Matthews. Proc. Bristol Nat.Soc., 4th ser., pt.2, pp.231-250, 1940.

LITTLE ANIMALS OF THE COUNTRYSIDE. Eileen Mayo. London, Pleiades Books, pp. 32, illus.(part col.), 1945.

PERIODIC FLUCTUATIONS IN BRITISH GAME POPULATIONS. A. D. Middleton. Jour.Animal Ecology, vol.3, no.2, pp. 231-249, Nov., 1934.

MAMMALS OF GREAT BRITAIN AND IRELAND. J.G. Millais. Longman's Green and Co., New York and Bombay, vol.1, pp.xx-365, illus., 1904; vol.2, pp.xi-299, illus., 1905; vol.3, pp.xii-384, illus., 1906.

ON A FURTHER COLLECTION OF MAMMALS FROM THE INNER HEBRIDES. Ivor G. Montagu. Proc. Zool. Soc. London, pp. 929-941, fig.1, Dec., 1922.

MAMMALS OF SUFFOLK. 2. MARINE SPECIES. Claude Moreley. Trans. Suffolk Naturalists' Soc., vol.2, no.1, pp.28-33, 1932.

LIST OF BRITISH MAMMALS. T.C.S. Morrison-Scott. British Mus.(Nat.Hist.), London, pp.24, Apr. 18, 1952.

ANIMALS THAT MOVE IN THE NIGHT. Ernest Neal. Illus.London News, vol. 216, no.5782, p.220, illus., Feb. 11, 1950. (British Mammals.)

WILD ANIMAL FRIENDS. B. Nicholas. London and Redhill, Lutterworth Press, pp.104, pls., 1946.

PRESERVATION OF THE EXISTING FAUNA OF GREAT BRITAIN IN A WILD STATE AFTER THE WAR. (The Earl of) Onslow. Proc.Roy.Inst., London, vol.32, pt.1, pp. 1-9, 1942.

SOME OBSERVATIONS ON THE ECOLOGY OF SCOTTISH HERBIVORES AND CARNIVORES. I.W. Parnell, T.W.M.Cameron. Scottish Nat., no.203, pp.139-145, Sep.-Oct., 1933.

LIST OF THE MAMMALS OF SOUTHWEST SUFFOLK. W.H. Payne. Trans.Suffolk Nat.Soc., vol.9, no.4, pp.309-312, 1956.

WILD ANIMALS IN BRITAIN. Frances Pitt. London, B.T. Batsford, Ltd., pp.viii-120, col.front., illus., pls.(part col.), 1938.

HISTORY OF THE WHALE AND SEAL FISHERIES OF THE PORT OF ABERDEEN. James Pyper. Scottish Naturalist, no.176, pp.39-50, Mar.-Apr., 1929; no.177, pp. 69-80, May-June, 1929; no.180, pp.103-108, July-Aug., 1929.

NOTES ON SMALL MAMMALS OF THE WESTERN ISLES. L.P.W. Renouf.Glasgow Nat., vol.9, p.65, (1919-1930) 1931.

WILD ANIMALS OF BRITAIN. William K. Richmond. London, Oxford Univ.Press, pp.viii-176, illus., 1946.

GOVERNMENT AND NATURAL HISTORY. James Ritchie. Scottish Nat., no.180, pp.165-167, 1929.

INFLUENCE OF MAN ON ANIMAL LIFE IN SCOTLAND; A STUDY IN FAUNAL EVOLUTION. James Ritchie. Univ.Press, Cambridge, pp.xvi-550, figs.90, maps 8, 1920.

MAN AND SCOTTISH ANIMAL LIFE. James Ritchie. Nature, vol.112, pp.169-170, Aug. 4, 1923.

ST. KILDA AND THE SIGNIFICANCE OF SOME OF ITS ANIMAL INHABITANTS. James Ritchie. Scottish Nat., no.183, pp. 69-74, May-June, 1930.

EAST YORKSHIRE MAMMALS. T.Sheppard. Naturalist, London, no.846, pp. 193-199, July, 1927.

BRITISH LAND MAMMALS AND THEIR HABITS. Alexander Nicol Simpson. London, A. and C. Black, pp.viii-88, pls. 15 (part col.), 1911.

FAUNA AND FLORA OF NORFOLK. ADDITIONS TO PART I, MAMMALIA (THIRD LIST). Thomas Southwell. Trans.Norfolk and Norwich Nat.Soc., vol.5, pp.632-634, 1894.

MAMMALIA OF NORFOLK. (ADDITIONS TO PART I OF THE FAUNA OF NORFOLK.) Thomas Southwell. Trans. Norfolk and Norwich Nat.Soc., vol.3, pp.657-675, 1884.

SEALS AND WHALES OF THE BRITISH SEAS. Thomas Southwell. London, pp. 128, illus., 1881.

LIST OF THE MAMMALS OF THE OLDHAM DISTRICT. Frederick J. Stubbs. Oldham Micros.Soc.Report, 1905-06-07, pp.8.

MAMMALS OF THE LONDON DISTRICT. Frederick J. Stubbs. School Nat. Study, pp.15, 1917.

CONSERVATION OF NATURE IN ENGLAND AND WALES. Report of the Wildlife Conservation Special Committee (England and Wales). Presented by the Minister of Town and Country Planning to Parliament by Command of His Majesty July 1947. A. G. Tansley, and others. London, His Majesty's Stationary Office, Cmd.7122, pp.v-139, maps 2, July, 1947.

A SUMMARY OF OUR KNOWLEDGE OF YORKSHIRE MAMMALS, 1881-1955. E. Wilfred Taylor. The Naturalist, no.857, pp.37-44, Apr.-June, 1956.

NOTES ON THE MARINE MAMMALS OF THE NORTH-EAST OF SCOTLAND. William Taylor. Ann.Scottish Nat.Hist., Edinburgh, no.34, pp.65-69, Apr., 1900.

GERALD EDWIN HAMILTON BARRETT-HAMILTON. AN APPRECIATION. A HISTORY OF BRITISH MAMMALS. Oldfield Thomas. London, Gurney and Jackson, part xv,pp.103, Mar., 1914.

TECHNICAL NAMES OF BRITISH MAMMALS. Oldfield Thomas. The Zoologist, ser.4, vol.2, no.681, pp.97-103, Mar., 1898.

BRITISH MAMMALS. Archibald Thorburn. London, New York, Longmans, Green and Co., vols.2, illus., col.pls., 1920-21; Parker and Son, Ltd., Oxford, vols.2, col. pls.50, text figs.18, 1931.

MAMMALS OF SUFFOLK. Claud B. Ticehurst. Trans. Suffolk Naturalists' Soc., vol.2, pt.1, pp.13-33, Dec., 1932.

NATURALIST IN UNIFORM SEES ENGLAND. Frederick A. Ulmer, Jr. Fauna, Philadelphia, vol.7, no.2, pp.50-53, illus., June, 1945.

BIRDS AND MAMMALS OF SHETLAND. L.S.V. Venables. Edinburgh, Oliver and Boyd, pp.391, illus., 1955.

BRITISH GAME. Brian Vesey-Fitsgerald. Collins, Toronto, pp.240, illus., 1946.

FAUNA OF THE OUTER HEBRIDES. Radclyffe Walters. Zoologist, ser.3, vol.20, pp.139-140, Apr., 1896.

LIST OF THE REPTILES AND LAND MAMMALS OF THE ISLE OF COLONSAY, INNER HEBRIDES. Tom Warwick. Scottish Naturalist, Edinburgh, no.237, pp.75-76, May-June, 1939.

NOTES ON MAMMALS OF THE ISLES OF BARRA, MINGULAY, AND BERNERAY, OUTER HEBRIDES. Tom Warwick. Scottish Nat., no.230, pp.57-59, Mar.-Apr., 1938.

BRITISH MAMMALS. W.Percival Westell. London, Chapman and Dodd, pp.1-127, figs.26, col.pls.2, 1923.

NATURAL HISTORY AND ANTIQUITIES OF SELBORNE. Gilbert White. London, pp.591, 1875.

ON TWO SPECIES OF MAMMALIA NEW TO BRITAIN; ONE OF THEM ALSO NEW TO SCIENCE. W. Yarrell. Proc. Comm. Sci. and Corres. Zool. Soc. London, pt. 2, p.109, 1832.

BRITISH MAMMALS. Sixty Photographs from Life, by Oxley Grabham, M.A., T.A. Metcalfe, Sydney H. Smith, and Charles Kirk. London, Gowans and Gray, Ltd., pp.69, pls., 1907.

MAMMALS IN HIGH SUFFOLK. Trans. Suffolk Nat. Soc., Norwich, vol.4, pt. 4, p.287, Dec., 1941. (Red Squirrel and Fox.)

RECENT ADDITIONS TO BRITISH MAMMALS. Nature, London, vol.147, no.3716, p.83, Jan. 18, 1941. (Edible Dormouse, Squirrel-Tailed Dormouse, Small Japanese Deer, 'Wild' Goats.)

UNWELCOME "SQUATTERS" AND THEIR HOSTS: FOXES IN BADGERS' SET (EARTH) IN AN OXFORD WOOD. Illus.London News, vol.215, no.5772, p.867, illus., Dec. 3, 1949.

BRITISH ISLES--IRELAND see IRELAND

## BULGARIA

(MAMMALS IN BULGARIA.) Bozainitsite v Bulgariia. Georgi Nelkov Markov. Sofia, Nauka i izkustvo, pp.155, illus., 1959.

ZOOGEOGRAPHIC POSITIONS OF THE MOUNTAINOUS RIDGE OF BISTRA. V.E. Martino. Zapiski Russkago Nauchnago Inst. Belgrade, no.10, pp.81-91, fig.1, tbl.1, 1934. (In Bulgarian with English summary.)

WILD LIFE AND SPORT IN BULGARIA. Henry W. Shoemaker. Hunting Trails on Three Continents, New York, chap.12, pp. 280-302, 1933.

## BURMA

MAMMALS COLLECTED BY THE VERNAY-CUTTING BURMA EXPEDITION. H.E. Anthony. Papers on Mammalogy. Zool. Ser., Field Mus.Nat.Hist., vol.27, pp. 37-123, figs.5, pls.2-5, Dec. 8, 1941.

CATALOGUE OF MAMMALS AND BIRDS OF BURMA. Edward Blyth. Hertford, Printed by S. Austin and Sons, pp.xxiv-167, 1875. (Jour.of the Asiatic Soc. of Bengal vol.43, pt.II, Aug., 1875.)

MAMMALS OF THE VERNAY-HOPWOOD CHINDWIN EXPEDITION, NORTHERN BURMA. T. Donald Carter. Bull. Amer. Mus. Nat.Hist., New York, vol.82, art. 4, pp.95-114, pls.26-32, map, Dec. 30, 1943.

THREE NEW MAMMALS OF THE GENERA CROCIDURA, CALLOSCIURUS AND PTEROMYS FROM NORTHERN BURMA. T. Donald Carter. Amer.Mus.Novitates, New York, no.1208, pp.2, Nov. 12, 1942.

PLEISTOCENE VERTEBRATES COLLECTED IN BURMA BY THE AMERICAN SOUTH-EAST ASIATIC EXPEDITION. Edwin H. Colbert. Trans.Amer.Philos.Soc., Philadelphia, vol.32, pt.3, pp.395-429, figs.79-99, pls.19-32, 1943.

MAMMALS COLLECTED BY LORD CRANBROOK AND CAPTAIN F. KINGDON WARD IN UPPER BURMA. Guy Dollman. Proc. Linnaean Soc. London, 145th session, pp. 9-11, Jan. 20, 1933.

FAUNA OF BURMA AND ADJACENT LANDS. J.P. Harding. Discovery, London, vol.6, no.7, pp.216-220, figs.1-6; no.8, pp.244-250, figs.7-14, July-Aug., 1945.

NOTE ON SOME NATURAL BARRIERS IN BURMA. J.M.D. Mackenzie. Jour.Bombay Nat.Hist.Soc., vol.51, no.1, pp.189-199, map, Dec., 1952.

TUSK AND FANG IN BURMA. Edison Marshall. Field and Stream, New York, vol.48, no.11, pp.9-11, 54-56, illus., Mar., 1944.

VERNAY-HOPWOOD UPPER CHINDWIN EXPEDITION. R.C. Morris. Jour. Bombay Nat.Hist.Soc., vol.38, no.4, pp.647-671, pls.6, Aug. 25, 1936.

CONSERVING WILD LIFE IN BURMA. E.H. Peacock. Field, London, vol.161, no.4187, pp.616-617, illus., Mar. 25, 1933.

SHWE-U-DAUNG GAME SANCTUARY, UPPER BURMA, WITH A NOTE ON THE ASIATIC TWO-HORNED RHINOCEROS(R. SUMATRENSIS). E.H. Peacock. Jour.Bombay Nat. Hist.Soc., vol.35, no.2, pp.446-448, Oct. 15, 1931.

WHERE BIG GAME "TAKE THE WATERS." A HIDDEN WATCHER AT A BURMESE "SALT-LICK." E.H. Peacock. Field, London, vol.162, no.4216, pp.970-971, illus., Oct. 14, 1933; Jour.Bombay Nat.Hist.Soc., vol.37, no.4, pp.780-783, pls.1-3, Apr. 15, 1935.

ON SOME MAMMALIA COLLECTED BY CAPT. A. C. BEAVAN, C. M. Z. S., AT MOULMEIN, BURMAH. William Peter. Proc.Zool.Soc.London, for 1866, pp.426-427, pl.35, 1866.

ANNUAL REPORT ON GAME PRESERVATION IN BURMA (INCLUDING A NOTE AS TO THE POSITION IN THE FEDERATED SHAN STATES) FOR THE YEAR ENDING 31ST MARCH 1935. H.C. Smith. Supt. Govt.Printing and Stationery, Rangoon, Burma, pp.iii-40, 1935.

SOME EXPERIENCES AMONGST ELEPHANT AND OTHER BIG GAME OF BURMA FROM 1887 TO 1931. W.S. Thom. Jour. Bombay Nat.Hist.Soc., vol.36, no.2, pp.321-333, pls.2, Apr. 15, 1933.

DIAGNOSES OF THREE NEW MAMMALS COLLECTED BY SIGNOR L. FEA IN THE CARIN HILLS, BURMA. Oldfield Thomas. Annali del Museo Civico di Storia Naturale di Genova, ser.2, vol. 10, p.884, June, 1891.

ON SMALL MAMMALS FROM THE KACHIN PROVINCE, NORTHERN BURMA. Oldfield Thomas. Jour.Bombay Nat.Hist.Soc., vol. 27, pp.499-505, Mar. 31, 1921.

ON THE MAMMALIA COLLECTED BY SIGNOR LEONARDO FEA IN BURMA AND TENASSERIM. Oldfield Thomas. Annali del Museo Civico di Storia Naturali de Genova, ser.2, vol.10, pp.913-949, pls. 10-11, 1892.

BURMA'S DECREASING WILD LIFE. D'Arcy Weatherbe. Jour. Bombay Nat.Hist.Soc., vol.42, no.1, pp.148-160, pls.2, Dec., 1940.

## CANADA

### Extinct and Fossil Mammals

FOSSIL AND SUBFOSSIL MAMMALS FROM THE QUATERNARY OF BRITISH COLUMBIA. Ian McTaggart Cowan. Trans.Royal Soc.Canada, Ottawa, ser. 3, sect.4, vol. 35, pp.39-50, pls.4, 1941.

EARLY VERTEBRATE FAUNA OF THE BRITISH COLUMBIA COAST. Edna M. Fisher. Bur.Amer.Ethnol., Bull.133, Anthrop.Paper no.20, Appendix A, 1943, pp.133-142, 1943.

OBSERVATIONS ON SOME FOSSIL BONES FOUND IN NEW BRUNSWICK, DOMINION OF CANADA. J. Bernard Gilpin. Nova-Scotian Inst.Nat.Sci.Proc. and Trans., vol.3, pp.400-404, 1874.

PAST VERTEBRATE LIFE OF CANADA. Lawrence M. Lambe. Trans.Roy.Soc. Canada, ser.3, vol.5, sec.4, pp.3-15, 1912.

CRETACEOUS MAMMALS OF ALBERTA. L.S. Russel. Nat.Mus.Canada Bull.126 (Ann.Rept.1950-1951), pp.110-119, illus., 1952.

CRETACEOUS-TERTIARY TRANSITION OF ALBERTA. (Faunal Lists Include Mammalian Forms.) L.S. Russel. Trans. Roy. Soc. Canada, Ottawa, ser.3, sec.4, vol. 26, pp.121-156, 1932.

EARLY TERTIARY MAMMAL TRACKS FROM ALBERTA. L.S. Russel. Trans. Roy.Canadian Inst., vol.17, pt.2, pp. 217-221, pls.7-11, 1930.

MAMMALIAN FAUNA OF THE KISHENEHN FORMATION, SOUTHEASTERN BRITISH COLUMBIA. L.S. Russel. Ann.Rept.Nat. Mus.Canada, Bull.no.132, pp.92-111, illus., Oct. 15, 1954.

MIDDLE EOCENE MAMMAL FROM BRITISH COLUMBIA. (Tillodont.) L.S. Russel. Amer. Jour.Sci., ser.5, vol.29, no.169, pp.54-55, figs.3, Jan., 1935.

NEW AND INTERESTING MAMMALIAN FOSSILS FROM WESTERN CANADA. L.S. Russel. Trans.Roy.Soc.Canada, Ottawa, ser.3, vol.30, sec.4, (geol.sci.), pp.75-80, pl.1, (May, 1936) Jan. 5, 1937.

NEW DATA ON THE PALEOCENE MAMMALS OF ALBERTA, CANADA. L. S. Russel. Jour. Mamm., vol.13, no.1, pp. 48-54, Feb., 1932.

PALEOCENE MAMMAL TEETH FROM ALBERTA. L. S. Russel. Bull. Nat. Mus.Canada, Ann.Rept.1955-1956, vol. 147, pp.96-103, illus., 1958.

PALEOCENE VERTEBRATES FROM ALBERTA. L.S. Russel. Amer. Jour.Sci., vol.17, pp.162-178, Feb., 1929.

REVISION OF THE LOWER OLIGOCENE VERTEBRATE FAUNA OF THE CYPRESS HILLS, SASKATCHEWAN. L. S. Russel. Trans. Roy. Canadian Inst., vol.20, pt. 1, pp.49-67, pls.7-10, 1934.

TERTIARY GRAVELS OF SASKATCHEWAN. (Lists of Mammals.) L.S. Russel. Trans. Roy.Soc.Canada, vol.44, ser.3, sec.4, pp.51-59, June, 1950.

UPPER EOCENE VERTEBRATE FAUNA FROM SASKATCHEWAN. L.S. Russel, R.T.D. Wickenden. Trans. Roy.Soc. Canada, Ottawa, ser.3, sec.4, vol.27, pp.53-65, fig.1, pl.1, Nov.4, 1933.

MAMMALIAN FAUNA AND CORRELATION OF THE PASKAPOO FORMATION OF ALBERTA. George Gaylord Simpson. Amer.Mus.Novitates, no.268, pp.10, Apr. 30, 1927.

MIOCENE GRAVELS IN SOUTHERN SASKATCHEWAN. (Fossil Mammals from the Wood Mountain Gravels.) C. M. Sternberg. Trans. Roy. Soc. Canada, sec. iv, pp.29-30, 1930.

NOTES ON THE EDMONTON FORMATION OF ALBERTA. C. M. Sternberg. Canadian Field-Nat., vol.40, pp.102-104, May 14, 1926.

WHITE WHALE AND OTHER PLEISTOCENE FOSSILS FROM THE OTTAWA VALLEY. C. M. Sternberg. Nat. Mus. Canada Bull., Ottawa, no.123, pp.259-261, illus., 1951.

LAWSON PREHISTORIC VILLAGE SITE, MIDDLESEX COUNTY, ONTARIO. W.J. Wintemberg. Nat.Mus.Canada, Dept. Mines and Resources, Mines and Geology Br., Ottawa, Bull.94, Anthropol.ser.25, pp.1-104, figs.7, pls.1-18, 1939. (Artifacts Made from Bones and Teeth of Mammals, pls.10-12, 17-18.)

### Recent Mammals

BUSINESS OF FUR HUNTING IN CANADA AS AN EXAMPLE OF AN EXTRACTIVE INDUSTRY. John Q. Adams. Jour. Geog., vol.25, pp.303-306, Nov., 1926.

CATALOGUE OF CANADIAN RECENT MAMMALS. R. M. Anderson. Bull. Nat. Mus. Canada, Ottawa, no.102 (Biol.Ser., no.31), pp.vi-238, fig.1, Jan. 24, 1947.

(Review by E.Raymond Hall of) CATALOGUE OF CANADIAN RECENT MAMMALS. R.M. Anderson. Jour. Mamm., vol.28, no.3, p.304, Aug. 19, 1947.

FAUNAS OF CANADA. R. M. Anderson. Dominion Bureau Statistics, Ottawa, Canada Year Book, 1937, pp.29-52, illus., May 28, 1937.

FIELD STUDY OF LIFE-HISTORIES OF CANADIAN MAMMALS. R. M. Anderson. Canadian Field-Nat., vol.33, Nov., 1919, pp.86-90, Jan., 1920.

PRESENT STATUS AND DISTRIBUTION OF THE BIG GAME MAMMALS OF CANADA. R. M. Anderson. Trans. 3rd N. Amer. Wildl.Conf., pp.390-406, 1938.

PRESENT STATUS AND FUTURE PROSPECTS OF THE LARGER MAMMALS OF CANADA. R.M. Anderson. Scottish Geog.Mag., vol.40, pp.321-331, Nov., 1924.

SURVEY OF CANADIAN MAMMALS OF THE NORTH. R. M. Anderson. Prov. Que.Assn. for Prot. Fish and Game, Ann. Rep. 89, pp.9-17, Apr., 1948. (History and Present Status of the Bears, Bison, Caribou, Moose, Muskox, Walrus, Seals, and Sea-Lion.)

CANADA'S GRASSLANDS. (Contains Some Live-Stock Grazing Statistics.) E. S. Archibald. Canadian Nature, Toronto, vol. 10, no.2, pp.68-71, illus., Mar.-Apr., 1948.

IN BIRDLAND. (Few Mammal Records.) James L. Baillie. Evening Telegram, Toronto, Ontario, June 3, 1939.

FUR FARMING CONDITIONS IN WESTERN CANADA. David Borenstein. Fur of Canada, Winnipeg, vol.10, no.12, p.6, Sep., 1945.

CANADIAN FUR FARMING SCENE. E. Rendle Bowness. Nat. Fur News, Denver, vol.20, no.10, pp.37, 88-89, Nov., 1948.

(HUNTING ANIMALS IN CANADA.) La chasse des animaux a fourrure au Canada. Benoit Brouillette. Libraire Gallimard, Paris, pp.205, maps 14, illus., 1934.

CANADA'S WILD FUR CROP. L.Butler. Beaver, vol.281, pp.26-31, Dec., 1950.

NATURE OF CYCLES IN POPULATIONS OF CANADIAN MAMMALS. L. Butler. Canadian Jour. Zool., Ottawa, vol.31, no.3, pp.242-262, June, 1953.

CANADIAN MAMMALS. Austin W.Cameron. Minister of Northern Affairs and National Resources, Ottawa, pp.81, illus., 1958.

GUIDE TO EASTERN CANADIAN MAMMALS. Austin W. Cameron. Nat.Mus. of Canada, Ottawa, pp.v-72, illus., 1956.

(MAMMALS OF CANADA.) Les mammiferes du Canada. Austin W. Cameron. Ministere du Nord Canadien et des Ressources Nationales, Ottawa (Musee Nat. du Canada), pp.89, illus., maps, 1960.

MAMMALS OF THE ISLANDS IN THE GULF OF ST. LAWRENCE. Austin W. Cameron. Superintendent of Publications, Queen's Printer, Ottawa, pp.165, illus., maps, 1958. (Nat.Mus.of Canada Bull. no.154, Biological Series no.53.)

BIOLOGICAL INVESTIGATION OF THE THELON GAME SANCTUARY. C.H.D. Clarke. Bull.96, Biol.Ser.no.25, Canada Dept. of Mines and Resources, pp.135, pls.25, figs.4, 1940; Nat. Mus. of Canada, Bull.no.96, pp.iv-135, 1940.

SOME FIELD NOTES ON THE ABUNDANCE OF SMALL MAMMALS. C. H. D.Clarke. Canadian Field-Nat., vol.47, no.4, pp. 73-74, Apr., 1933.

FUR PRODUCTION OF CANADA, 1923-1924. R. H. Coats. Nat. Asso. Fur Industry, Yearbook, 1925, pp.55-58, 60, 84, Oct., 1925.

SOME VITAL STATISTICS OF BIG GAME ON OVERSTOCKED MOUNTAIN RANGE. I. McT. Cowan. Trans. N. Amer. Wildl. Conf., vol.15, pp.581-588, 1950.

WILDLIFE CONSERVATION IN CANADA. I. McT. Cowan. Forestry Chronicle, Oshawa Ontario, vol.25, no.4, pp.315-318, Dec., 1949; Jour. Wildl.Mgt., Ithaca, vol.19, no.2, pp.161-176, Apr., 1955.

CANADA'S NATIONAL PARKS--A RATIONAL SYSTEM OF PROTECTION FOR WILD LIFE. Geoffrey D'Egville. Field, London, vol.158, no.4109, p.468, illus., Sep. 26, 1931.

CANADIAN BIOTIC PROVINCE WITH SPECIAL REFERENCE TO THE MAMMALS. Lee R. Dice. Ecology, vol.19, no.4, pp.503-514, fig.1, Oct., 1938.

MAMMALS OF AN EASTERN FARMER'S FIELD. S.C. Downing. Canadian Nature, Toronto, vol.13, no.2, pp.67-69, Mar.-Apr., 1951.

(MAMMALS OF MY COUNTRY.) Les mammiferes de mon pays. Rolland Dumais. Éditions Courvilliennes, Quebec, pp.189, illus., 1955.

CANADIAN CONSERVATION PROBLEMS. J.R. Dymond. Part 1. Bird-Lore, New York, vol.41, no.3, pp.141-146, May-June, 1939.

FLUCTUATIONS IN ANIMAL POPULATIONS WITH SPECIAL REFERENCE TO THOSE OF CANADA. J.R. Dymond. Trans. Roy. Soc. Canada, Ottawa, sec.5, vol.41, pp. 1-34, 1947.

LIST OF MAMMALS OBTAINED BY THADDEUS SURBER, COLLECTOR FOR THE MUSEUM, IN THE PROVINCES OF NEW BRUNSWICK AND QUEBEC, CANADA. D.G. Elliot. Chicago, pp.29, 1901. (Field Columbian Mus., Publication no.54, Zoological Series, vol.iii, no.3.)

TRAPPING IN CANADA. C. W. Godfrey. Game and Gun and Angler's Monthly, London, vol.17, no.176, pp.211-212, illus., May, 1940.

MAMMAL SURVEY ALONG THE INTERNATIONAL BOUNDARY IN CANADA. William C. Grimm, Harvey A. Roberts. Jour. Mamm., vol.27, no.2, pp.127-153, May, 1946.

NATIONAL PARKS OF CANADA. REPORT OF THE COMMISIONER, YEAR ENDING MARCH 31, 1927. J.B. Harkin. Dept. Interior, Ottawa, Canada, pp.25, illus., 1928.

REPORT OF THE COMMISSIONER OF CANADIAN NATIONAL PARKS FOR THE YEAR ENDING MARCH 31, 1922. (Numerous Notes On Big Game.) J.B. Harkin. Ottawa, pp.52, illus., 1923.

(Review by Charles C. Adams of) THE CONSERVATION OF WILD LIFE IN CANADA. Hewitt. Science, n.s., vol.59, pp.279-281, Mar. 21, 1924.

HUNTING IN CANADA. C.K. Howard. Canadian Natl.Railways, pp.5-136, illus., 1930.

FUR-TRADE OF CANADA. H.A. Innis. Univ. of Toronto Studies, History and Economics, Toronto, Oxford Univ.Press, Canadian Branch, vol.8, pp.172, Nov., 1927.

FUR FARMING IN CANADA. J. Walter Jones. 1913.

CANADA NORTH OF FIFTY-SIX DEGREES. THE LAND OF LONG SUMMER DAYS. (Includes Notes on Mammals.) E. M. Kindle. Canadian Field-Nat., vol.42, no.3, pp.53-86, figs.31, Mar., 1928.

CORRECTION CONCERNING THE LIFE ZONES OF CANADA. A.Brooker Klugh. Biol.Bull., vol.41, pp.272-275, Nov., 1921 (Jan., 1922).

BIBLIOGRAPHY OF CANADIAN ZOOLOGY FOR 1910 (EXCLUSIVE OF ENTOMOLOGY). Lawrence M. Lambe. Trans. Roy. Soc. Canada, Ottawa, ser.3, vol.5, sec.4, pp. 155-163, 1912.

MANAGEMENT OF CANADA'S WILDLIFE RESOURCES. Harrison F. Lewis. Trans. 11th N.Amer. Wildl.Conf., Washington, pp.11-17, 1946.

CANADA'S FUR RESOURCES. Hoyes Lloyd. Proc. N. Amer. Wildl. Conf., pp.628-630, 1936.

ANIMALS OF THE CANADIAN ROCKIES. Dan. McGowan. Dodd, Mead and Co., New York, pp.302, illus. 26, 1936.

NATURALIST IN CANADA. (Chapters On Pronghorn Antelope, Mole, Wood Rat, Bats.) Dan McGowan. Macmillan Co., Toronto, pp.xii-284, illus., 1941.

WHAT CANADA IS DOING FOR THE HUNTING INDIANS. T.R.L. MacInnes. Proc.N. Amer.Wildl.Conf., pp.229-232, 1936.

FUR GOODS AND FUR DRESSING INDUSTRIES OF CANADA, 1926. James Malcolm. Fur Jour., vol.2, no.1, pp.58-63, Jan., 1928.

NOTES ON THE COUNTRY, BIRDS AND MAMMALS WEST OF HUDSON BAY BETWEEN REINDEER AND BAKER LAKES. T.H. Manning. Canadian Field-Nat., Ottawa, vol.62, no.1, pp.1-28, Jan.-Feb., 1948.

FUR FARMING SITUATION IN CANADA. Hugh J. Montgomery. Nat.Fur News, Denver, vol.19, no.9, pp.21, 50-52, Oct., 1947.

POPULATION STUDIES ON SOME SMALL FOREST MAMMALS IN EASTERN CANADA. R. F. Morris. Jour. Mamm., vol.36, no.1, pp.21-35, graphs, Feb., 1955.

(IN CANADAS' PRIMITIVE FORESTS AND PRAIRIES.) In Kanadas Urwaelder und Praerien. (Account of Mammals, Particularly Wapiti, Bear and Wolf.) Max Otto. Paul Parey, Berlin, pp.327, illus., 1926.

MAMMALS OF THE EASTERN ROCKIES AND WESTERN PLAINS OF CANADA. A.L. Rand. Ottawa, E.Cloutier, King's Printer, pp.237, illus., maps., 1948. (Canada, Nat.Mus., Ottawa, Bull.no.108, Biological Series, no.35.)

SOME CANADIAN FUR BEARERS. A.L. Rand. Nat.Mus.Canada, Dept.Mines and Resources, Ottawa, Sp.Contrib.no.46-1, pp.20, 1946.

SOUTHERN HALF OF THE ALASKA HIGHWAY AND ITS MAMMALS. A.L. Rand. Ottawa, Edmond Cloutier Printer to the King's Most Excellent Majesty, pp.50, illus., map, 1944. (Nat.Mus., Ottawa, Canada, Bull.no.98, Biological Series no.27.)

CANADIAN FUR INDUSTRY. W.M. Ritchie. Fur of Canada, Winnipeg, vol.11, no.1, p.6, Oct., 1945.

BIG GAME OF CANADA. W. Rowan. Country Life, vol.52, pp.137-139, Aug. 5, 1922.

CANADA'S PREMIER PROBLEM OF ANIMAL CONSERVATION. A QUESTION OF CYCLES. W. Rowan. New Biology, Penguin Books, London, no.9, pp.38-57, Oct., 1950.

COMING PEAK OF THE TEN-YEAR CYCLE IN CANADA. W. Rowan. Trans. 15th N. Amer. Wildl. Conf., Washington, pp.379-383, 1950.

TEN-YEAR CYCLE; OUTSTANDING PROBLEM OF CANADIAN CONSERVATION. W. Rowan. Dept. of Extension, Univ.Alberta, Edmonton, pp.16, illus., Aug., 1948. (2nd. Ed.)

OUR NOTEBOOK. (Porcupine, Snowshoe Rabbit.) R. C. Rowe. Rod and Gun in Canada, Montreal, vol.50, no.11, p.18, Apr., 1949.

UNUSUAL ANIMALS OF THE BEECHY DISTRICT. Dave Santy. Blue Jay, Saskatchewan Nat.Hist.Soc., vol.16, no.1, pp.36-37, Mar., 1958.

WILD LIFE IN THE CANADIAN NATIONAL PARKS. R.E. Turnbull. Field, London, vol. 152, p.298, illus., Aug. 23, 1928.

DESCRIPTION OF A NOTABLE JOURNEY OF 4,600 MILES THROUGH NORTHERN CANADA, MADE 42 YEARS AGO. James Tyrrell. Ann. Rep.Assoc.Ontario Land Surveyors, Toronto, no.57, pp.116-138, 1942. (Muskox, Caribou, Moose, Bear.)

CATALOGUE OF THE MAMMALIA OF CANADA EXCLUSIVE OF THE CETACEA. James Tyrrell. Toronto, pp.28, 1888.

WINTER IN CANADA. Ernest Voorhis. Nat. Resources Intelligence Serv., Dept.Interior, Ottawa, Canada, pp.12, illus.

SIBLEY PROVINCIAL PARK. A. de Vos. Sylva, Toronto, vol.4, no.6, pp.15-21, illus., 1948.

CATALOGUE OF CANADIAN PINNIPEDIA, CETACEA, FISHES AND MARINE INVERTEBRATA EXHIBITED BY DEPARTMENT FISHERY, DOMINION GOVERNMENT. J.F. Whiteaves. Colonial and Indian Exhibition, Ottawa, pp.42, 1886.

NOTES ON THE VERTEBRATES OF THE SOUTHERN PLAINS OF CANADA, 1923-1926. M.Y. Williams. Canadian Field-Nat., Sutton West, vol.60, no.3, pp.47-60, May-June, 1946.

CANADA 1948; THE OFFICIAL HANDBOOK OF PRESENT CONDITIONS AND RECENT PROGRESS. Dominion Bureau of Statistics. Can.Dept.Trade and Com., pp.266, (Includes Statistics on Fisheries and Furs.)

CANADA'S FUR BEARERS, CONTAINING NOTES ON THE PRINCIPAL FUR BEARING ANIMALS OF CANADA, TRAPPING AND THE PREPARATION OF FURS FOR THE MARKET. Hudson's Bay Co., Winnipeg, pp.63, map, illus., 1933.

(FAUNA OF THE NATIONAL PARKS.) La faune des parc nationaux. Le Nat.Canadien, Quebec, vol.65 (ser.3, vol.9), nos.8-9, pp.237-238, Aug.-Sep., 1938.

GUIDE TO EASTERN CANADIAN MAMMALS. Nat.Mus., Ottawa, Canada, pp. 72, 1956.

## CANADA -- ALBERTA

ADDITION TO LIST OF MAMMALS OF JASPER PARK, ALBERTA. Rudolph Martin Anderson. Canadian Alpine Jour., vol.10, p.69, 1919.

MAMMALS OF BANFF NATIONAL PARK, ALBERTA. A.W.F. Banfield. Ottawa, Canada Dept. of Northern Affairs and National Resources, pp.53, illus., 1958. (Nat.Mus. of Canada, Bulletin no.159, Biological Series, no.57.)

MAMMALS OF WATERTON LAKES NATIONAL PARK. A.W.F. Banfield. Wildl. Mgt. Bull., Canadian Wildl.Serv., Ottawa, ser.1, no.1, pp.43, Apr., 1950.

BIGGEST BIG GAME PRESERVE.(Jasper National Park.) Lorine L. Butler. American Forests, vol.44, no.9, pp.402-405, 428-429, illus., Sep., 1938.

CHANGES IN THE STATUS OF CERTAIN ANIMALS AND BIRDS DURING THE PAST FIFTY YEARS IN CENTRAL ALBERTA. Frank L. Farley. Canadian Field-Nat., vol.39, pp.200-202, Jan. 21, 1926.

NOTES ON A SMALL COLLECTION OF MAMMALS FROM THE CROW'S NEST PASS REGION OF ALBERTA. Bris Foster. Intermediate Naturalist, Toronto, no.8, pp.20-22, 1953.

CHANGES IN THE NATURAL HISTORY OF THE HIGH RIVER DISTRICT, ALBERTA Roy L. Fowler. Canadian Field-Nat., vol. 51, no.2, pp.15-16, Feb., 1937.

WILD LIFE OF JASPER PARK. (Contains Notes On Mammals.) E.M. Kindle. Canadian Field-Nat., vol.42, pp.111-118, illus., May, 1928.

OBSERVATION ON THE ARLY AUTUMN FAUNA OF SOUTHERN ALBERTA. (Antelope, Coyotes, Gophers, Weasels.) Lt. A.S. Lockley. Canadian Field-Nat., Sutton West, vol.57, nos.7-8, p.132, Oct.-Nov., 1943.

MAMMAL TRACKS FROM THE PASKAPOO BEDS OF ALBERTA. R.L. Rutherford, L.S. Russel. Amer.Jour.Sci., vol.15, no.87, pp.262-264, fig.1, Mar., 1928.

CLEANINGS FROM THE CANADIAN WEST. PART II. MAMMALIAN FAUNA OF ISLAY, ALBERTA. J. Dewey. Soper. Canadian Field-Nat., vol.35, pp.102-111, (Sep., 1921) Feb. 3, 1922.

MAMMAL NOTES FROM THE GRAND PRAIRIE - PEACE RIVER REGION, ALBERTA. J. Dewey Soper. Jour.Mamm., vol.29, no.1, pp.49-64, fig.1, pl.1, Feb. 13, 1948.

MAMMALS OF THE ELK ISLAND NATIONAL PARK, ALBERTA, CANADA. J.Dewey Soper. Can.Widl.Ser., Wildl.Mgt.Bull., ser.1, no.3, pp.1-24, illus., 1951.

MAMMALS OF WOOD BUFFALO PARK, NORTHERN ALBERTA AND DISTRICT OF MACKENZIE. J. Dewey Soper. Jour. Mamm., vol.23, no.2, pp.119-145, May, 1942.

NOTES ON THE FAUNA OF THE FORMER NEMISKAM NATIONAL PARK AND VICINITY, ALBERTA. J. Dewey Soper. Canadian Field-Nat., Ottawa, vol.63, no.5, pp.167-182, figs.4, Oct. 25, 1949.

OBSERVATION ON MAMMALS AND BIRDS IN THE ROCKY MOUNTAINS OF ALBERTA. J. Dewey Soper. Canadian Field-Nat., Sutton West., vol.61, no.5, pp.143-173, figs. 5, 1947.

BIG GAME IN THE PEACE RIVER COUNTRY. Norm. Stabeck. Hunting and Fishing, Philadelphia, vol.25, no.1, pp.43-44, 56-57, illus., Jan., 1948.

FISH AND GAME IN ALBERTA. N.E.Tanner. Fur of Canada, Winnipeg, vol.9, no.2, pp. 20-21, 24, Nov., 1943.

TRAPPING THE ATHABASCA. PART 3. Raymond Thompson. Fur-Fish-Game, Harding's Mag., Columbus, vol.73, no. 1, pp.10-12, Jan., 1941.

CANADA -- ARCTIC REGION see ARCTIC REGIONS

CANADA -- BAFFIN ISLAND

MAMMALS FROM THE MACMILLAN EXPEDITION TO BAFFIN LAND. Glover M. Allen, Manton Copeland. Jour. Mamm., vol.5, no.1, pp.7-12, Feb., 1924.

NOTES ON THE MAMMALS OF SOUTH AND CENTRAL WEST BAFFIN ISLAND. T.H. Manning. Jour. Mamm., vol.24, no. 1, pp.47-59, fig.1, Feb. 20, 1943.

FAUNAL INVESTIGATION OF SOUTHERN BAFFIN ISLAND. J. Dewey Soper. Nat. Mus.Canada, Bull.53, pp.1-143, pls.1-7, fold.map 1, 1928.

MAMMALS OF SOUTHERN BAFFIN ISLAND, NORTHWEST TERRITORIES, CANADA. J. Dewey Soper. Jour. Mamm., vol.25, no.3, pp.221-254, figs.2, pls.2, maps 2, Sep. 8, 1944.

CANADA -- BRITISH COLUMBIA

LIST OF MAMMALS COLLECTED BY MR. CLARK P. STREATOR IN BRITISH COLUMBIA, WITH DESCRIPTIONS OF TWO NEW SUBSPECIES OF SCIURUS. Joel Asaph Allen. (In) Amer.Mus.of Nat.Hist., New York, Bull., vol.iii, pp.161-168, 1891.

FIVE NEW MAMMALS FROM BRITISH COLUMBIA. R.M. Anderson. Ann. Rep., 1931, Nat.Mus. of Canada, Ottawa, Bull. 70, pp. 99-119, pl.5, Nov. 24, 1932.

GAME RANGES OF KLAPPAN. (Account of the Hunting Grounds South of the Stikine River.) Henry Bannon. Forest and Stream, vol.90, pp.485-487, 513-518, Sep., 1920.

PAST AND PRESENT BIG-GAME CONDITIONS IN BRITISH COLUMBIA AND THE PREDATORY MAMMAL QUESTION. Allen Brooks. Jour. Mamm., vol.7, no.1, pp.37-40, Feb., 1926.

NATURAL HISTORY OF THE FORBIDDEN PLATEAU AREA, VANCOUVER ISLAND, BRITISH COLUMBIA. G. Clifford Carl. Rept.Provincial Mus.Nat.Hist. and Anthrop. 1943, Victoria, pp.18-40, pl.1, map, 1944.

NOTES ON THE FLORA AND FAUNA OF BUNSBY ISLANDS, B. C. G. Clifford Carl, Charles J. Guiguet. Rept. Mus.Nat.Hist. and Anthropol., Victoria, British Columbia, 1955: D31-D44, illus., 1956. (Mammals, pp.D38-D41.)

BIOLOGY OF THE SCOTT ISLAND GROUP, BRITISH COLUMBIA. G.Clifford Carl, C.J. Guiguet, George A. Hardy. Rept.Provincial Mus.Nat.Hist. and Anthropol., Victoria, British Columbia, 1950, pp.B21-B63, illus., 1951.

NATURAL HISTORY SURVEY OF THE MANNING PARK AREA, BRITISH COLUMBIA. G. Clifford Carl, C.J. Guiguet, George A. Hardy. Occas.Papers British Columbia Prov.Mus., Victoria, no.9, pp.1-130, illus., July, 1952. (Mammals, pp.61-80.)

FLORA AND FAUNA OF THE PARADISE MINE AREA, BRITISH COLUMBIA. G. Clifford Carl, George A. Hardy. Rept. Prov.Mus.Nat.Hist. and Anthrop. for year 1944, Victoria, pp. C18-C38, pl.1, 1945. (Mammals, pp.C32-C35.)

REPORT ON A COLLECTING TRIP TO THE LAC LA HACHE AREA, BRITISH COLUMBIA. G.Clifford Carl, George A. Hardy. Rept.Provincial Mus.Nat.Hist.and Anthrop., Victoria, B.C., 1942, pp.HH25-HH49, pls. 2, 1943. (Contains Annotated List of Mammals.)

MAMMALS OF POINT GREY. Ian McTaggart Cowan. Canadian Field-Nat., vol.44, no.6, pp.133-134, Sep. 2, 1930.

TWO MAMMALS NEW TO THE KNOWN FAUNA OF BRITISH COLUMBIA. Ian McTaggart Cowan. Murrelet, Seattle, vol. 21, no.1, p.9, Jan.-Apr., 1940.

VERTEBRATE FAUNA OF THE PEACE RIVER DISTRICT OF BRITISH COLUMBIA. Ian McTaggart Cowan. Occas.Papers British Columbia Provincial Mus., Victoria, no.1, pp.1-102, maps 2, pls.1-5, June 1, 1939. (Mammals, pp.67-91.)

MAMMALS OF BRITISH COLUMBIA. Ian McTaggart Cowan, Charles J. Guiguet. British Columbia Provincial Mus., Victoria, Handbook no.11, pp.413, illus., Feb., 1956.

BIRDS AND MAMMALS OF REVELSTOKE NATIONAL PARK. I.McTaggart Cowan, J.A. Munro. Canadian Alpine Jour., Winnipeg, vol.29, no.1, pp.100-121, 1945.

CONSERVATION ECHOES IN BRITISH COLUMBIA. R.Y. Edwards. Michigan Conservation, Lansing, vol.22, no.6, pp.10-12, Nov., 1953.

FUR PRODUCTION OF THE BOREAL FOREST REGION OF BRITISH COLUMBIA. R.Y. Edwards, I.McT.Cowan. Jour.Wildl.Mgt., vol.21, no.3, pp.257-267, July, 1957.

FUR RESOURCE MANAGEMENT IN BRITISH COLUMBIA. Carl R. Eklund. Jour. Wildl.Mgt., Menasha, vol.10, no.1, pp.29-33, Jan., 1946.

NOTES ON MAMMALS OF THE UPPER LIARD AND FRANCES RIVERS. Charles Elton. Canadian Field-Nat., vol.49, no. 7, pp.120-123, Oct., 1935.

CASSIAR HUNT IN NINETEEN-SIX. (Observations to the Southward of Telegraph Creek, and in the Dease Lake Region.) Harry L. Ferguson. Forest and Stream, vol.90, pp.5-8, Jan., 1920.

RELATION OF THE MARINE FAUNA TO THE PHYSIOGRAPHY OF THE WEST COAST OF THE QUEEN CHARLOTTE ISLANDS. C.McLean Fraser. Canadian Field-Nat., vol.52, no.6, pp.88-93, Sep., 1938.

ECOLOGICAL STUDY OF GOOSE ISLAND, BRITISH COLUMBIA, WITH SPECIAL REFERENCE TO MAMMALS AND BIRDS. C.J. Guiguet. Occas.Papers British Columbia Provincial Mus., Victoria, no.10, pp.77, illus., Mar., 1953.

STATUS OF BIRDS AND MAMMALS OF THE OSOYOOS AREA IN MAY, 1951. C.J. Guiguet. Rept.Provincial Mus.Nat.Hist. and Anthropol., Victoria, British Columbia, 1951, pp.B25-B38, 1952.

MAMMALS COLLECTED BY T. T. AND E. B. McCABE IN THE BOWRON LAKE REGION OF BRITISH COLUMBIA. E.Raymond Hall. Univ. Calif.Publ.Zool., vol. 40, no.9, pp.363-386, fig.1, Nov. 5, 1934.

REMARKS ON THE AFFINITIES OF THE MAMMALIAN FAUNA OF VANCOUVER ISLAND, BRITISH COLUMBIA, WITH DESCRIPTIONS OF NEW SUBSPECIES. E. Raymond Hall. Univ. Calif. Publ.Zool., vol.38, no.12, pp.415-423, Nov. 8, 1932.

VARIATION AMONG INSULAR MAMMALS OF GEORGIA STRAIT, BRITISH COLUMBIA. E. Raymond Hall. Amer. Nat., Lancaster, vol.72, no.742, pp.453-463, figs.2, Sep. 10, 1938.

NATURAL HISTORY OF THE FORBIDDEN PLATEAU AREA, VANCOUVER ISLAND, BRITISH COLUMBIA. G.A. Hardy. Rept. Provincial Mus. Nat.Hist. and Anthropol., Victoria, British Columbia, 1954, pp.B24-B63, map, 1955. (Mammals, pp.B61-B62.)

NOTES ON THE FLORA AND FAUNA OF THE BLENKINSOP LAKE AREA ON SOUTHERN VANCOUVER ISLAND, BRITISH COLUMBIA. G.A. Hardy. Rept.Provincial Mus.Nat.Hist. and Anthropol., Victoria, British Columbia, 1956, pp.25-66. (Mammals, pp.58-59.)

MAMMALS OF THE ALPINE CLUB EXPEDITION TO THE MOUNT ROBSON REGION. Ned Hollister. (In) Alpine Club of Canada, Canadian Alpine Jour., Special Number, Winnipeg, pp.1-44, pl.13, 1912.

MEET THE ANIMALS OF CENTRAL B. C. Neil McKelvie. Rod and Gun in Canada, Montreal, vol.48, no.11, pp.10-11, 1947.

BIRDS AND MAMMALS FROM THE KOOTENAY VALLEY, SOUTHEASTERN BRITISH COLUMBIA. Joseph Mailliard. Proc. Calif.Acad.Sci., ser.4, vol.20, pp. 269-290, Jan. 8, 1932.

MAMMALS OF BANKS ISLAND. Thomas Henry Manning. Montreal, pp.74, illus., map, 1958. (Arctic Inst. of N.America, Technical Paper no.2.)

BATS OF QUEEN CHARLOTTE ISLANDS, BRITISH COLUMBIA. C. Hart Merriam. Amer. Naturalist, pp.860-861, Sep. 1, 1895.

ADDITIONAL OBSERVATIONS OF BIRDS AND MAMMALS IN THE VANDERHOOF REGION, BRITISH COLUMBIA. J.A. Munro. Amer.Midland Nat., Notre Dame, vol.53, no.1, pp.56-60, Jan., 1955.

BIRDS AND MAMMALS OF THE CRESTON REGION, BRITISH COLUMBIA. J. A.Munro. Occas.Papers British Columbia Prov.Mus., no.8, pp.1-90, figs.16, Aug., 1950.

BIRDS AND MAMMALS OF THE VANDERHOOF REGION, BRITISH COLUMBIA. J.A. Munro. Amer. Midland Nat., Notre Dame, vol.41, no.1, pp.1-138, illus., Jan., 1949.

OBSERVATIONS OF BIRDS AND MAMMALS IN CENTRAL BRITISH COLUMBIA. J.A. Munro. Occas.Papers British Columbia Prov. Mus., Victoria, no.6, pp.165, Jan., 1947. (Mammals, pp.109-164.)

PRELIMINARY REPORT ON THE BIRDS AND MAMMALS OF GLACIER NATIONAL PARK, BRITISH COLUMBIA. J. A. Munro. Canadian Field-Nat., Sutton West, vol.59, no.6, pp.175-190, pls.2, Nov.-Dec., 1945.

PRELIMINARY REPORT ON THE BIRDS AND MAMMALS OF KOOTENAY NATIONAL PARK, BRITISH COLUMBIA. J.A. Munro, I.McTaggart Cowan. Canadian Field-Nat., Sutton West, vol.58, no.2, pp.34-51, Mar.-Apr., 1944.

MAMMALS OF THE QUEEN CHARLOTTE ISLANDS. Wilfred H. Osgood. N.Amer. Fauna, no.21, pp.25-37, pls.4-5, Sep.26, 1901.

NATURAL HISTORY OF THE QUEEN CHARLOTTE ISLANDS, BRITISH COLUMBIA. Wilfred H. Osgood. U.S. Dept.Agric., Div.Biol.Surv., N.Amer.Fauna no.21, pp. 50, pls.5, Sep. 26, 1901.

NATURE LOVER IN BRITISH COLUMBIA. H.J. Parkham. H.F. and G.Witherby, London, pp.292, pls.21, 1937.

BIOLOGICAL EXPLORATION OF BANKS AND VICTORIA ISLANDS. A. E. Porsild. Arctic, Montreal, vol.3, no.1, pp.45-54, illus., Apr., 1950.

FUR RESOURCES OF A WILDERNESS REGION IN NORTHERN BRITISH COLUMBIA. Horace F. Quick. Ann.Arbor, Univ. Microfilms, no.18, 640, 1956.

SMALL MAMMAL POPULATION IN NORTHERN BRITISH COLUMBIA. Horace F. Quick. Canadian Field-Nat., vol.68, no.3, pp.95-102, July-Sep., 1954.

NOTES ON SOME MAMMALS OF THE CHILOCOTIN, BRITISH COLUMBIA. Kenneth Racey. Canadian Field-Nat., vol. 50, no.2, pp.15-21, Feb., 1936.

MAMMALS OF THE ALTA LAKE REGION OF SOUTHWESTERN BRITISH COLUMBIA. Kenneth Racey, Ian McTaggart Cowan.Rep. Prov.Mus.Nat.Hist.for 1935, Victoria, B.C., pp.H15-H29, pls.5, 1936.

SOUTHERN HALF OF THE ALASKA HIGHWAY AND ITS MAMMALS. Austin Loomer Rand. Ottawa, Edmond Cloutier Printer to the King's Most Excellent Majesty, pp.50, illus., map, 1944. (Nat.Mus., Ottawa, Bull. no.98, Biological Series no.27.)

ADDITIONS TO THE MAMMAL FAUNA OF BRITISH COLUMBIA. Samuel N. Rhoads. Amer. Naturalist, pp.940-942, Oct. 1, 1895.

MAMMALS COLLECTED OR OBSERVED IN THE VICINITY OF LAURIER PASS, B. C. W.G.Sheldon. Jour. Mamm., vol.13, no.3, pp.196-203, Aug., 1932.

NATURALISTS IN THE WILDS OF BRITISH COLUMBIA. I. OUR WILDERNESS HOME

AND LIFE IN WINTER. John F. Stanwell-Fletcher, Theodora C. Stanwell-Fletcher. Sci.Monthly, Lancaster, vol.50, no.1, pp.17-32, illus., Jan., 1940.

NATURALISTS IN THE WILDS OF BRITISH COLUMBIA. II. THE ENDING OF WINTER AND THE COMING OF SPRING. John F. Stanwell-Fletcher, Theodora C. Stanwell-Fletcher. Sci. Monthly, Lancaster, vol. 50, no.2, pp.125-141, illus., Feb., 1940.

NATURALISTS IN THE WILDS OF BRITISH COLUMBIA. III. THE SUMMER AND PREPARATIONS FOR OUR SECOND WINTER. John F. Stanwell-Fletcher, Theodora C. Stanwell-Fletcher. Sci.Monthly, Lancaster, vol.50, no.3, pp.210-224, illus., Mar., 1940.

SOME ACCOUNTS OF THE FLORA AND FAUNA OF THE DRIFTWOOD VALLEY REGION OF NORTH CENTRAL BRITISH COLUMBIA. John F. Stanwell-Fletcher, Theodore C. Stanwell-Fletcher. Occas. Papers British Columbia Provincial Mus., Victoria, no.4, pp.97, pls.5, map, May, 1943.

BIRDS AND MAMMALS OF THE SKEENA RIVER REGION OF NORTHERN BRITISH COLUMBIA. Harry S. Swarth. Univ.Calif. Pub.Zool., vol.24, pp.315-394, pls.3, Jan. 24, 1924.

(Review by R.M. Anderson of) BIRDS AND MAMMALS OF THE SKEENA RIVER REGION OF NORTHERN BRITISH COLUMBIA. Harry S. Swarth. Canadian Field-Nat., vol. 39, pp.87-88, Apr., 1925.

MAMMALS OF THE ATLIN REGION, NORTHWESTERN BRITISH COLUMBIA. Harry S. Swarth. Jour. Mamm., vol.17, no.4, pp.398-405, Nov., 1936.

REPORT ON A COLLECTION OF BIRDS AND MAMMALS FROM THE ATLIN REGION, NORTHERN BRITISH COLUMBIA. Harry S. Swarth. Univ. Calif. Publ.Zool., no.4, pp.51-162, pls.4-8, Sep. 24, 1926.

NOTES ON THE MAMMALS OF THE LOWER CHILCOTIN RIVER REGION, CARIBOO DISTRICT, B.C. G.C.Toner. Canadian Field-Nat., Sutton West, vol.60, no.4, pp.86-89, Mar. 17, 1947.

CHECK-LIST OF THE MAMMALS AND SUMMER BIRDS OF YOHO PARK. Titus Ulke. Canadian Alpine Jour., vol.23, pp. 76-81, pl.1, June, 1936.

OCCURRENCE AND DISTRIBUTION OF MAMMALS IN YOHO PARK, BRITISH COLUMBIA. Titus Ulke. Canadian Field-Nat., vol.37, pp.62-64, Apr., 1923.

BIG GAME'S CHANCES IN CANADA. BRITISH COLUMBIA AND YUKON. Bryan Williams, G.G. Jeckell. Field, London, vol. 163, no.4242, pp.796-797, illus., Apr. 14, 1934.

GAME OF BRITISH COLUMBIA WITH A LIST OF BIRDS AND MAMMALS. Bureau of Provincial Information. Victoria, Printed by R. Wolfenden, Printer to the King's Most Excel.Majesty, Bull.no.17, pp.32, pls., 1903.

CANADA -- HUDSON BAY

TIMBER WOLF AND MOOSE. George M. (Jim) Battey. Field, London, vol.156, no. 4050, p.207, fig.1, Aug. 9, 1930.

HUDSON'S BAY CO. AND FUR CONSERVATION. R.H.G. Bonnycastle. Proc. N. Amer. Wildl.Conf., pp.625-628, 1936.

HUDSON'S BAY CO. CANADA'S FUR TRADE. R.H.G. Bonnycastle. Trans.3rd. N.Amer. Wildl.Conf., pp.531-537, 1938.

EXPEDITION TO HUDSON BAY. J.Kenneth Doutt. Carnegie Mag., Pittsburgh, vol.12, no.8, pp.227-236, illus., Jan., 1939.

OBSERVATIONS ON MAMMALS ALONG THE EAST COAST OF HUDSON BAY AND THE INTERIOR OF UNGAVA. J. Kenneth Doutt. Ann.Carnegie Mus., Pittsburgh, vol. 33, art.14, pp.235-249, Nov.4, 1954.

BIRD AND MAMMAL NOTES FROM THE EAST SIDE OF HUDSON BAY. T.H.Manning. Canadian Field-Nat., Sutton West, vol.60, no.4, pp.71-85, figs.4, map, Mar. 17, 1947.

REMARKS ON THE PHYSIOGRAPHY, ESKIMO, AND MAMMALS OF SOUTHAMPTON ISLAND. T.H. Manning. Canadian Geogr. Jour., Montreal, vol.24, no.1, pp. 16-33, illus., Jan., 1942.

BIOLOGICAL INVESTIGATION OF THE HUDSON BAY REGION. Edward A. Preble. U.S. Dept. Agric., Div.Biol.Surv., N. Amer.Fauna no.22, pp.134, pls.14, Oct. 31, 1902.

EXPLORATION OF SOUTHAMPTON ISLAND, HUDSON BAY. George M. Sutton. Mem. Carnegie Mus., vol.12, pt.1, pp.75, pls.5, Mar. 28, 1932.

MAMMALS OF SOUTHAMPTON ISLAND. George M. Sutton, W.J. Hamilton, Jr. Mem.Carnegie Mus, vol.12, pt.2, sec.1, pp.9-111, pls.6-10, Aug. 4, 1932.

MILESTONES IN THE PROGRESS OF THE HUDSON'S BAY CO. Clifford Wilson. Beaver, Winnipeg, outfit 272, pp.27-34, illus., Dec., 1941.

CANADA -- LABRADOR

LIST OF THE MAMMALS OF LABRADOR. Outram Bangs. Amer.Nat., vol.32, no.379, pp.489-507, July, 1898.

NOTES ON SOME MAMMALS FROM BLACK BAY, LABRADOR. Outram, Bangs. Proc.New Eng.Zool.Club, vol.1, pp.9-18, Feb. 28, 1899.

ON SMALL COLLECTION OF MAMMALS FROM HAMILTON INLET, LABRADOR. Outram Bangs. Proc. Biol.Soc.Washington, vol.11, pp.235-240, fig.13, pl.4, Sep. 17, 1897.

(SOME OBSERVATIONS ON THE HABITS OF CERTAIN ANIMALS FROM LABRADOR.) Quelques observations sur les habitudes de certains animaux du Labrador. E.Bruet. Mammalia, Paris, vol.7, no.1, pp.26-37, illus., Mar., 1943.

LABRADOR. William Brooks Cabot. Boston, Small, Maynard and Co., vol.8, pp.xiii-354, illus., 1921.

(Review by Glover M. Allen of) LABRADOR. William Brooks Cabot. Jour. Mamm., vol. 3, no.1, pp.56-57, Feb., 1922.

(INFORMATION ON THE MAMMAL FAUNA OF SOUTHERN LABRADOR. 2. CONTRIBUTION TO KNOWLEDGE OF THE FAUNA OF SOUTHERN LABRADOR.) Zur Kenntnis der Saeugetierfauna von Suedlabrador. 2.Beitrag zur Kenntnis der Fauna von Suedlabrador. H. Eidmann. Zeitschr.f. Saeugetierkunde, vol.10, no.1, pp.39-61, figs.8, pl.2, fig.1, Dec. 31, 1935.

LABRADOR WINTER NOTES, 1950. (Decline of Seals and Caribou, Disease of Dogs and Foxes.) John E. Frazer. Arctic, Montreal, vol.3, no.2, p.126, Aug., 1950.

CONTRIBUTIONS TO THE KNOWLEDGE OF EXTREME NORTHEASTERN LABRADOR. Bernhard Hantzsch. (Translated by M.B.A. Anderson.) Canadian Field-Nat., vol.46, no.1, pp.7-12, Jan., 1932; no.2, pp.34-36, Feb., 1932.

NOTES ON THE MAMMALS OF SOUTHERN LABRADOR. C.F. Jackson. Jour.Mamm., vol.19, no.4, pp.429-434, Nov., 1938.

NOTES ON THE NATURAL HISTORY OF LABRADOR. W.A. Stearns. Proc. U.S. Nat. Mus., vol.6, no.8, pp.111-137, Aug. 1, 1883.

NOTES ON MAMMALS OF THE LABRADOR INTERIOR. William Duncan Strong. Jour. Mamm., vol.11, no.1, pp.1-10, Feb., 1930.

JOURNEYS ABOUT NAIN. WINTER HUNTING WITH THE LABRADOR ESKIMO. E.P. Wheeler, 2nd. Geogr.Rev., New York, vol. 20, no.3, pp.454-468, figs.8, map 1, July, 1930.

CANADA -- MANITOBA

SURVEYS OF ELK AND OTHER WILDLIFE IN RIDING MOUNTAIN NATIONAL PARK, MANITOBA, 1950-1951, AND 1952. D. G. Colls. Wildl.Mgt.Bull., Canadian Wildl. Serv., Ottawa, ser.1, no.6, pp.25, illus., Dec., 1952.

ANNOTATED LIST OF THE MAMMALS OF AWEME, MANITOBA. Stuart Criddle. Canadian Field-Nat., vol.43, no.7, pp. 155-159, Oct. 1, 1929.

FEW RECORDS OF MAMMALS FROM MANITOBA. Stuart Criddle. Canadian Field-Nat., vol.46, no.8, p.188, Nov., 1932.

MEMOIRS OF THE EIGHTIES. (Notes On Former Abundance of Mammals and Birds.) Norman Criddle. Canadian Field-Nat., vol. 43, pp.176-181, Nov. 1, 1929.

SURVIVAL OF FAUNA IN MANITOBA. A.G. Cunningham. Field, London, vol.163, no. 4243, p.879, illus., Apr. 21, 1934.

MAMMALS OF THE RIDING MOUNTAIN NATIONAL PARK, MANITOBA. H.U. Green. Canadian Field-Nat., vol.46, no.7, pp.149-152, Oct., 1932.

NEW MAMMAL RECORD FOR THE RIDING MOUNTAIN NATIONAL PARK LIST. H.U. Green. Canadian Field-Nat., vol.48, no.3, pp.50-51, Mar., 1934.

FUR AND GAME RESOURCES OF MANITOBA. V.W. Jackson. Winnipeg, Industrial Development Board of Manitoba, pp.56, pls. 10, 1926.

MANUAL OF VERTEBRATES OF MANITOBA. V.W. Jackson. Univ.Manitoba, Winnipeg, pp.42, illus., 1935.

FUR REHABILITATION IN NORTHERN MANITOBA. John S. McDiarmid. Trans. 7th N. Amer. Wildl. Conf., Washington, D.C., pp.481-484, 1942.

DISTRIBUTIONAL NOTES ON SMALL MAMMALS IN NORTHERN MANITOBA, CANADA. W.B. Quay. Jour. Mamm., vol.36, no.1, p. 123, Feb. 25, 1955.

MR. W. H. BRYENTON'S NOTES ON MANITOBA OF THE HERB LAKE--FLIN FLON AREA. A.L. Rand. Canadian Field-Nat., Ottawa, vol.62, no.5, pp.140-150, Sep.-Oct., 1948.

LIFE-HISTORIES OF NORTHERN ANIMALS; AN ACCOUNT OF THE MAMMALS OF MANITOBA. VOL. 1. GRASS EATERS. VOL. 2. FLESH EATERS. Ernest Thompson Seton. New York City, C.Scribner's Sons, illus., pls., maps, 1909.

LIST OF MAMMALS OF MANITOBA. Ernest Thompson Seton. Toronto, Printed at The Oxford Press, pp.26, 1886. (Transactions of the Manitoba Scientific and Historical Society, no.23, May, 1886.)

TUNDRA ANIMAL COMMUNITIES IN THE VICINITY OF CHURCHILL, MANITOBA. V.E. Shelford, A.C. Twomey. Ecology, Brooklyn, vol.22, no.1, pp.47-69, Jan., 1941.

MAMMALS OF RIDING MOUNTAIN NATIONAL PARK, MANITOBA, CANADA. J. Dewey Soper. Can. Wildl.Serv., Wildl. Mgt.Bull., ser.1, no.7, pp.1-34, illus., 1953 (titlepage), Dec., 1952 (cover).

CANADA -- NEW BRUNSWICK

NOTES ON MAMMALS FROM NEW BRUNSWICK, WITH DESCRIPTION OF A NEW SPECIES OF EVOTOMYS. J.A. Allen. Bull. Amer.Mus.Nat.Hist., vol.6, pp.99-106, Apr. 14, 1894.

NOTES ON THE MAMMALS OF GRAND MANAN, N.B., WITH A DESCRIPTION OF A NEW SUBSPECIES OF WHITE-FOOTED MOUSE. Manton Copeland, Morton L. Church. Proc. Biol. Soc. Washington, vol.19, pp.121-126, Sep. 6, 1906.

LIST OF MAMMALS OBTAINED BY THADDEUS SURBER, COLLECTOR FOR THE MUSEUM, IN THE PROVINCES OF NEW BRUNSWICK AND QUEBEC, CANADA. Daniel Giraud Elliot. Chicago, pp.29, 1901. (Field Columbian Mus., Publication 54, Zoological Series, vol. III, no.3.)

LAND MAMMALS OF NEW BRUNSWICK. William H. Moore. Rod and Gun and Canadian Silver Fox News, vol.30, pp. 238-240, Aug., 1928.

LAND MAMMALS OF NEW BRUNSWICK. R.F.Morris. Jour.Mamm., vol.29, no.2, pp.165-176, May 14, 1948.

SMALL FOREST MAMMALS OF NEW BRUNSWICK AND THE GASPE. R.F. Morris. Acadian Naturalist (Bull.Nat. Hist.Soc.New Brunswick), Fredericton, vol.1, no.1, pp.27-42, May, 1943.

CHANGES IN MAMMAL POPULATION IN NEW BRUNSWICK. W. Austin Squires. Acadian Nat., Fredericton, vol.2, no.7, pp.26-44, May, 1946.

WILDERNESS DWELLERS. (Observation and Phtographing of Moose, Deer, and Other Animals in the Tobique Region, New Brunswick.) Thomas Travis. Forest and Stream, vol.90, pp.130, 132, 148, 149, Mar., 1920; pp.202, 204, 206, Apr., 1920; pp. 260, 275-277, May, 1920; pp.316-318, 337, June, 1920; pp.388, 390, 409, July, 1920; pp.452, 454, 458, Aug., 1920; pp.506, 508, 510, 512, Sep., 1920; pp.554, 556, 558, 560, Oct., 1920; pp.602-604, 606, 608, Nov., 1920; pp.650, 652, 654, 656, Dec., 1920.

## CANADA -- NEWFOUNDLAND

LAND MAMMALS OF NEWFOUNDLAND. Outram Bangs. Bull.Mus.Comp.Zool. Harvard Coll., vol.54, no.18, pp.509-516, July, 1913.

GUIDE TO EASTERN CANADIAN MAMMALS. Austin W. Cameron. Ottawa, Dept. of Northern Affairs and National Resources, National Parks Branch, National Mus. of Canada, pp.72, 1956.

MAMMALS OF THE ISLANDS IN THE GULF OF ST. LAWRENCE. Austin W. Cameron. Ottawa, The Queen's Printer, pp.iii-165, illus., maps, diagrs., tbls., 1958. (Canada Nat.Mus., Ottawa, Biological Series no.53.)

RABBIT AND MOOSE IN NEWFOUNDLAND. Allen A. Gillis. Field, London, vol.148, p.959, Dec. 2, 1926.

EXPLORATIONS IN NEWFOUNDLAND AND LABRADOR IN 1887, MADE IN CONNECTION WITH THE CRUISE OF THE U.S. FISH COMMISSION SCHOONER GRAMPUS. Frederic A. Lucas. Report Nat.Mus., 1888-89, pp.709-728, pl.106, 1891.

BIG GAME PRESERVATION IN NEWFOUNDLAND. CAN THE CARIBOU HOLD ITS OWN? J. Gordon Muir. Field, London, vol. 164, no.4263, p.574, illus., Sep. 8, 1934.

## CANADA -- NORTHWEST TERRITORY

MAMMALS FROM THE ATHABASCA-MACKENZIE REGION OF CANADA. J.A. Allen. Bull.Amer.Mus.Nat.Hist., vol. 28, pp.7-11, Jan. 5, 1910.

ON MAMMALS FROM THE NORTHWEST TERRITORY COLLECTED BY MR. A.J. STONE. J.A. Allen. Bull.Amer.Mus.Nat. Hist., vol.12, pp.1-9, Mar. 4, 1899.

MAMMALS AND BIRDS OF THE WESTERN ARCTIC DISTRICT, NORTHWEST TERRITORIES, CANADA. R.M.Anderson. Canada's Western Northland, Land, Parks and Forests Branch, Ottawa, pp.97-122, figs.5, map 1, July 9, 1937.

NOTES ON MAMMALS OF THE MACKENZIE DISTRICT, NORTHWEST TERRITORIES. A.W.F. Banfield. Arctic, Jour. Arctic Inst.N.Amer., Ottawa, vol.4, no. 2, pp.113-121, illus., Sep., 1951.

EXPLORATION INTO THE NORTHERN PLAINS NORTH AND EAST OF GT.SLAVE LAKE, INCLUDING THE SOURCE OF THE COPPERMINE RIVER. G.H.Blanchet. Canadian Field-Nat., vol.38, pp.183-187; vol.39, pp.12-16, 30-34, 52-54, figs.8, Dec., 1924, to Mar., 1925.

CONSERVATION OF FUR IN THE NORTHWEST TERRITORIES OF CANADA. T. Cameron. Proc.N.Amer.Wildl.Conf., pp. 621-625, 1936.

ORDINANCE RESPECTING THE EXPORTATION OF FURS FROM THE NORTH WEST TERRITORIES PASSED BY THE NORTH WEST TERRITORIES COUNCIL IN THE YEAR 1929. W.W. Cory. Ottawa, pp.5, 1929.

SOME OBSERVATIONS ON MAMMALS IN THE AREA BETWEEN COPPERMINE AND POND INLET, N.W.T., DURING 1954 AND 1955. Derek V. Ellis.Canadian Field-Nat., vol.71, no.1, pp.1-6, 1957.

NOTES ON MAMMALS AND BIRDS FROM GREAT SLAVE LAKE. H.W. Fairbairn. Canadian Field Nat., vol.45, no.7, pp. 158-162, map, Oct., 1931.

MAMMAL OBSERVATIONS AT LOWER BACK RIVER, NORTHWEST TERRITORIES, CANADA. H.L. Gunderson, et al. Jour. Mamm., vol.36, no.2, pp.254-259, May, 1955.

GEOGRAPHY, BIRDS, AND MAMMALS OF THE PERRY RIVER REGION. Harold Carston Hanson. Arctic Inst. of North Amer., pp.96, illus., maps, tbls., 1956. (Arctic Inst.of N.Amer., Special Publication no.3.)

MAMMALS OF KEEWATIN. Francis Harper. Lawrence, Univ. of Kansas, pp. 94, illus., 1956. (Univ. of Kansas, Mus. of Nat. Hist., Miscellaneous Publication no.12.)

MAMMALS OF THE ATHABASKA AND GREAT SLAVE LAKES REGION. Francis Harper. Jour. Mamm., vol.13, no.1, pp. 19-36, pls.3-5, Feb. 9, 1932.

PHYSIOGRAPHIC AND FAUNAL AREAS IN THE ATHABASKA AND GREAT SLAVE LAKES REGION. Francis Harper. Ecology, vol.12, no.1, pp.18-32, figs.1-5, Jan., 1931.

WILD LIFE IN THE THELON RIVER AREA, NORTHWEST TERRITORIES, CANADA. John Hornby. Canadian Field-Nat., vol. 48, no.7, pp.105-111, Oct., 1934.

NOTES ON MAMMALS COLLECTED AND OBSERVED IN THE NORTHERN MACKENZIE RIVER DISTRICT, NORTHWEST TERRITORIES OF CANADA, WITH REMARKS ON EXPLORERS AND EXPLORATIONS OF THE FAR NORTH. Roderick Ross MacFarlane. Govt.Print.Off., Washington, pp.673-764, illus., pl., 1905; Smiths.Inst.Publ., no.1405.

BIRDS AND MAMMALS OF ADELAIDE PENINSULA N.W.T. A.H.Macpherson. Ottawa, Queen's Printer, pp.iii-63, illus., map, tbls., 1959. (Canada, Nat. Mus., Ottawa, Biological Series no.59.)

THROUGH THE MACKENZIE BASIN; A NARRATIVE OF THE ATHABASCA AND PEACE RIVER TREATY EXPEDITION OF 1899. (With a Map of the Country Ceded and Numerous Photographs of Native Life and Scenery; Also Notes on the Mammals and Birds of Northern Canada.) Charles Mair. London, Simpkin, Marshall, Hamilton, Kent and Co., Ltd., pp.149-1-151-494, pls., map., 1908.

NOTES ON THE COASTAL DISTRICT OF THE EASTERN BARREN GROUNDS AND MELVILLE PENINSULA FROM IGLOOLIK TO CAPE FULLERTON. (Contains List of Mammals and Notes on Their Relation to the Eskimo.) T.H. Manning. Canadian Geogr.Jour., Montreal, vol.26, no.2, pp. 84-105, illus.

SURVEY OF THE MAMMALS OF BYLOT ISLAND, NORTHWEST TERRITORIES. Richard S. Miller. Arctic, Ottawa, vol. 8, no.3, pp.167-176, illus., 1955.

MAMMALS OF THE MACKENZIE DELTA. A.E. Porsild. Canadian Field-Nat., Sutton West, vol.59, no.1, pp.4-22, (Jan.-Feb.) Aug. 16, 1945.

BIOLOGICAL INVESTIGATION OF THE ATHABASKA-MACKENZIE REGION. Edward A. Preble. U.S.Dept.Agric., Div. Biol.Surv., N.Amer.Fauna, no.27, pp. 557, pls.25, Oct. 26, 1908.

MAMMALS OF KEEWATIN. Edward A. Preble. N.Amer.Fauna, no.22, pp.39-73, Oct. 31, 1902.

MAMMALS OF THE ATHABASKA-MACKENZIE REGION. Edward A. Preble. N.Amer. Fauna, no.27, pp.126-251, figs.10-13, pls. 19-22, Oct. 26, 1908.

MAMMAL INVESTIGATIONS ON THE CANOL ROAD, YUKON AND NORTHWEST TERRITORIES, 1944. Austin Loomer Rand. Ottawa, E.Cloutier, Printer to the King, pp.52, illus., map, 1945. (Canada, Nat. Mus., Ottawa, Bulletin no.99, Biological Series no.28.)

MACKENZIE PARK AS A FIELD FOR SURVEY, EXPLORATION, LITERATURE AND ART. Harlan I. Smith. Science, n.s., vol. 62, pp.211-212, Sep. 4, 1925.

MELLON CARNEGIE MUSEUM EXPEDITION TO THE MACKENZIE DELTA. Arthur C. Twomey. Carnegie Mag., Pittsburgh, vol. 17, no.4, pp.99-110, Sep., 1943; no.6, pp. 179-187, Nov., 1943.

BIOLOGICAL NOTES, COVERING PARTS OF THE PEACE, LIARD, MACKENZIE, AND GREAT BEAR RIVER BASINS. M.Y. Williams. Canadian Field-Nat., vol.47, no.2, pp.23-31, Feb., 1933. (Mammals, pp.30-31.)

## CANADA -- NOVA SCOTIA

BIG GAME IN NOVA SCOTIA. G.H.Allen. Field, London, vol.163, no.4246, p.1064, illus., May 12, 1934.

ON THE MAMMALIA OF NOVA SCOTIA. Bernard J. Gilpin. Trans.Nova Scotian Inst.Nat.Sci., vol.1, pt.3, art.1, pp.8-15, 1867; vol.1, pt.2, pp.58-69, 1868; vol.2, pt.1, pp.8-16, 1870; vol.2, pt.2, pp.58-69, 1870; vol.2, pt.3, pp.8-18, 1870; vol. 2, pt.4, pp.8-17, 83-93, 1870; vol.3, pp. 109-126, 1871; vol.3, pt.1, pp.46-61, 1874; vol.3, pt.2, pp.109-126, 1874.

NOVA SCOTIA MAMMAL NOTES. V.E. Gould. Canadian Field-Nat., vol.50, no.6, pp.103-104, Sep., 1936.

DESCRIPTIVE CATALOGUE OF THE FISHES OF NOVA SCOTIA. Thomas F. Knight. Pub.by Direction of the Provincial Government, Halifax, A.Grant, pp.54, 1866. (Supplementary Paper On Sea-Mammals and Shell-Fish, pp.37-54.)

NOTES ON THE MAMMALS OF THE INTERIOR OF WESTERN NOVA SCOTIA. A.L. Rand. Canadian Field-Nat., vol.47, no.3, pp.41-50, Mar., 1933.

RECENT STATUS OF NOVA SCOTIA FUR BEARERS. A.L. Rand. Canadian Field-Nat., Ottawa, vol.58, no.3, pp.85-96, May-June, 1944.

MAMMALS OF LAKE KEDGEMAKOOGE AND VICINITY NOVA SCOTIA. Carolyn Sheldon. Jour.Mamm., vol.17, no.3, pp. 207-215, map, Aug., 1936.

LAND MAMMALS OF NOVA SCOTIA. Ronald W. Smith. Am.Midland Nat., vol.24, no.1, pp.213-241, July, 1940.

## CANADA -- ONTARIO

SOME ADDITIONS TO THE VERTEBRATE FAUNA OF DARLINGTON TOWNSHIP, DURHAM COUNTY, ONTARIO. (Otter, Deer, Red Fox.) A.E. Allin. Canadian Field-Nat., Ottawa, vol.56, nos.8-9, p.140, Nov.-Dec., 1942.

VERTEBRATE FAUNA OF DARLINGTON TOWNSHIP, DURHAM COUNTY, ONTARIO. A.E. Allin. Trans.Roy.Canadian Inst., Toronto, vol.23, pt.1, no.49, pp.83-118, Oct., 1940. (Mammals, pp.86-90.)

MAMMALS OF RENFREW COUNTY, ONTARIO. N.R. Brown, R.G.Lanning. Canadian Field-Nat., vol.68, no.4, pp.171-180, Oct.-Dec., 1954 (Sep., 1955).

MAMMALS OF THE QUETICO PROVINCIAL PARK OF ONTARIO. Alvin R. Cahn. Jour. Mamm., vol.18, no.1, pp.19-30, Feb. 14, 1937.

MAMMALS OF THE MAZINAN LAKE REGION OF ONTARIO, THEIR REPRODUCTION AND POPULATION DYNAMICS. John J.Christian. Ann.Carnegie Mus.Pittsburgh, vol.31, art.18, pp.339-386, Feb. 19, 1951.

GLEANINGS FROM THE NATURAL HISTORY OF HURON COUNTY, ONTARIO. (Coyote, Porcupine, Varying Hare, European Hare, Elk, White-Tailed Deer.) C.H.D. Clarke. Canadian Field-Nat., Sutton West, vol.58, no.3, pp.82-84, May-June, 1944.

STUDY OF THE MAMMAL POPULATION OF THE VICINITY OF PANCAKE BAY, ALGOMA DISTRICT, ONTARIO. C.H.D. Clarke. Bull.88, Nat.Mus.Canada (Biol. Series no.23), pp.141-152, 1938.

FURTHER NOTES ON THE AMPHIBIA AND MAMMALIA OF THE TEMAGAMI DISTRICT, ONTARIO. A.F. Coventry. Canadian Field-Nat., vol.46, no.7, pp.147-149, Oct., 1932.

CHAPLEAU CROWN GAME PRESERVE. V. Crichton. Sylva, vol.3, no.1, pp.33-42, 1947.

MAMMALS OF ONTARIO. E.C.Cross. Roy.Ontario Mus.Zool., Handbook no. 1, pp.1-56, illus., 1929.

PROVISIONAL CHECK-LIST OF THE MAMMALS OF ONTARIO. S.C. Downing. Roy. Ontario Mus.Zool., Toronto, misc.publ. no.2, pp.1-11, 1948.

MAMMALS OF THE LAKE NIPIGON REGION. J.R. Dymond. Trans.Roy.Canadian Inst., vol.16, pt.2, pp.239-250, 1928.

ABUNDANCE OF CERTAIN MAMMALS OF THE GERALDTON FOREST DISTRICT, ONTARIO. C.A. Elsey. Canadian Field-Nat., Ottawa, vol.64, no.5, pp.159-163, Sep.-Oct., 1950.

WILDLIFE RESEARCH IN ALGONQUIN PARK. C. David Fowle. Sylva, Toronto, vol.4, no.1, pp.51-58, illus., 1948.

TRAPPER'S RECORD OF ANIMAL ABUNDANCE IN THE OBA-HEARST AREA OF ONTARIO FOR THE YEARS 1931-1944. Quimby F. Hess. Canadian Field-Nat., Sutton West, vol.60, no.2, pp.31-32, map, Mar.-Apr., 1946.

BOTANICAL INVESTIGATIONS IN BATCHAWANA BAY REGION, LAKE SUPERIOR. Robert Christie Hosie. Ottawa, J.O.Patenaude, Printer to the King's Most Excellent Majesty, pp.v-152, illus., map, 1938. (Canada, Nat.Mus., Ottawa, Bulletin no. 88, Biological Series no.23.)

NOTES ON THE HABITS AND SIPHONAPTEROUS PARASITES OF THE MAMMALS OF WELLAND COUNTY, ONTARIO. E.W. Jameson, Jr. Jour. Mamm., vol.24, no.2, pp.194-197, May, 1943.

MAMMALS OF THE WANAPITEI PROVINCIAL FOREST, SUDBURG DISTRICT, ONTARIO. D.A. MacLulich. Canadian Field-Nat., vol.50, no.4, pp.56-58, Apr., 1936.

NOTES ON THE MAMMALS OF ONTARIO. Gerrit S. Miller, Jr. Proc.Boston Soc., Nat. Hist., vol.28, no.1, pp.1-44, Apr., 1897.

FUR RESOURCES OF CHAPLEAU DISTRICT, ONTARIO. Randolph Peterson, Vincent Crichton. Canad.Jour.Res., Ottawa, sect.D, vol.27, no.2, pp.68-84, figs.7, Apr., 1949.

LESSER KNOWN OTTAWA MAMMALS. A.L. Rand. Canadian Field-Nat., Sutton West, vol.59, no.4, pp.133-135, July-Aug., 1945.

MAMMALS OF THE OTTAWA DISTRICT. A.L. Rand. Canadian Field-Nat., Sutton West, vol.59, no.4, pp.111-132, July-Aug., 1945.

NOTES ON THE MAMMALS OF ONTARIO. William E. Saunders. Trans.Roy.Canadian Inst., vol.18, pt.2, no.40, pp.271-309, July, 1932.

NOTES ON THE WHITE LIPPED SHREW AND OTHER SPECIES IN THE PARRY SOUND DISTRICT. W.E. Saunders. Canadian Field-Nat., vol.43, pp.207-208, Dec. 2, 1929.

FAUNAL INVESTIGATION OF KING TOWNSHIP, YORK COUNTY, ONTARIO. 2. THE MAMMALS OF KING TOWNSHIP. L. L. Snyder. Trans.Roy.Canadian Inst., vol.17, pt.2, pp.173-182, 1930.

MAMMALS OF THE LAKE ABITIBI REGION. A FAUNAL INVESTIGATION OF THE LAKE ABITIBI REGION, ONTARIO. L. L. Snyder.(Contrib.Roy.Ontario Mus. Zool., no.2.) Univ. Toronto Studies, Biol. Series no.32, pp.1-46, figs.2, map, 1928.

FAUNAL INVESTIGATION OF WESTERN RAINY RIVER DISTRICT, ONTARIO. L.L. Snyder. Trans.Roy.Canadian Inst., Toronto, vol.22, pt.1, no.47, pp.157-213, Oct., 1938. (Mammals, pp.165-180.)

(Review by R.M.Anderson of) FAUNAL INVESTIGATION OF WESTERN RAINY RIVER DISTRICT, ONTARIO. L. L. Snyder. Canadian Field-Nat., Ottawa, vol.53, no.7, p.110, 1939.

MAMMALS OF THE LAKE ABITIBI REGION. L. L. Snyder. Univ.Toronto Studies, Biol.Series no.32, pp.7-15, 1928.

MAMMALS OF PRINCE EDWARD COUNTY, ONTARIO. L.L. Snyder. Univ.Toronto Studies, Biol.Series no.48, pp.12-24, 1941.

NOTES ON THE BIRDS AND MAMMALS OF BRENT AND VICINITY, ALGONQUIN PARK, ONTARIO, JULY AND AUGUST, 1922. L.L. Snyder, J.L. Baillie. Canadian Field-Nat., vol.37, pp.89-94, map 1, May, 1923.

FAUNAL INVESTIGATION OF LONG POINT AND VICINITY, NORFOLK COUNTY, ONTARIO. I. GENERAL INTRODUCTION. L.L. Snyder, E.B.S.Logier. Trans.Roy.Canadian Inst., vol.18, pt.1, no.39, pp.117-236; II. THE MAMMALS OF LONG POINT AND VICINITY, pp.127-138, Sep., 1931.

FAUNAL INVESTIGATION OF THE SAULT STE.MARIE REGION, ONTARIO. L. L. Snyder, et al. Trans. Roy. Canadian Inst., Toronto, vol.24, pt.1, pp.99-165, 1942.

MAMMALS OF WELLINGTON AND WATERLOO COUNTIES ONTARIO. J. Dewey Soper. Jour.Mamm., vol.4, no.4, pp.244-252, Nov., 1923.

GAME MANAGEMENT IN ONTARIO. (Introduced European Hare.) D.J. Taylor.Trans. 7th N. Amer. Wildl.Conf., Wash., D.C., pp.361-365, 1942.

SOME NUMBERS FOR BIG GAME IN ONTARIO. G.C. Toner. Jour.Mamm., vol. 37, no.1, pp.119-120, Feb. 28, 1956.

ADDITIONAL NOTES ON THE FAUNA OF KING TOWNSHIP, YORK COUNTY, ONTARIO. R.D. Ussher. Canadian Field-Nat., Ottawa, vol.53, no.7, pp.101-110, Oct., 1939. (Mammals, p.102.)

NOTES ON THE MAMMALS OF LION'S HEAD, BRUCE PENINSULA, ONTARIO. Fred Warburton. Canadian Field-Nat., Ottawa, vol.63, no.1, pp.34-36, Jan.-Feb., 1949.

NOTES ON THE VERTEBRATES, EXCEPT FISHES, OF THE SAULT STE.MARIE REGION OF ONTARIO. Fred Warburton. Canadian Field-Nat., Ottawa, vol.64, no. 6, pp.192-200, Nov.-Dec., 1950.

NOTES ON THE FAUNA OF BRUCE PENINSULA, MANITOULIN AND ADJACENT ISLANDS. M.Y. Williams. Canadian Field-Nat., Ottawa, vol.56, no.6, pp.92-93, Sep., 1942.

MAMMALS OF THE MAZINAW LAKE AREA. Monty Wood. Frontenac Co., Ont. Intermediate Naturalist, Totonto, no.8, pp.14-18, 1953.

CANADA -- QUEBEC

(MAMMALS OF THE PROVINCE OF QUEBEC.) Mammiferes de la Province de Quebec. Rudolph Martin Anderson. Societe Provancher, Rapport Annuel 1939, pp.37-111, 1940. (Revision, in French, of Anderson, 1938.)

NINE ADDITIONS TO THE LIST OF QUEBEC MAMMALS WITH DESCRIPTIONS OF SIX NEW FORMS. Rudolph Martin Anderson. Ann.Report Provancher Soc.Nat.Hist. Canada, Quebec, 1942, pp.49-77, Sep., 1943.

SIX ADDITIONS TO THE LIST OF QUEBEC MAMMALS WITH DESCRIPTIONS OF FOUR NEW FORMS. Rudolph Martin Anderson. Ann.Report Provancher Soc.Nat.Hist. Canada, Quebec, 1941, pp.31-43, 1942. (French translation, pp.45-57.)

ON A SMALL COLLECTION OF MAMMALS FROM LAKE EDWARD, QUEBEC. Outram Bangs. Proc.Biol.Soc.Washington, vol.10, pp.45-52, Mar.9, 1896.

OBSERVATIONS ON THE NATURAL HISTORY OF THE LEAF BAY-FORT CHIMO REGION, UNGAVA, QUEBEC. Bob Bateman. Intermediate Naturalist, Toronto, no.8, pp. 1-7, 1953.

MAMMALS OF SOUTHEASTERN QUEBEC. Austin W. Cameron. (In) The Provancher Soc.of Nat.Hist.Canada, 1950-51, Publ.by the Soc., 1954, pp.20-86, illus.

MAMMALS OF THE TROIS PISTOLES AREA AND THE GASPE PENINSULA, QUEBEC. Austin W. Cameron. Nat.Mus.Canada Bull.128, pp.168-188, map, 1953.

MAMMALS OF THE LAKE MISTASSINI AND LAKE ALBANEL REGIONS, QUEBEC. Austin W. Cameron, William A.Morris. Bull.Nat.Mus.Canada, Ottawa, no.123, pp.120-130, 1951.

MAMMALS OF THE LAKE ST.JOHN REGION, QUEBEC. Austin W.Cameron, Phillip A. Orkin. Bull.Nat.Mus.Canada, no.118, Ann.Report 1948-49, pp.95-108, 1950.

SOME NOTES ON MAMMALS, BIRDS AND FERNS OF KAZABAZUA DISTRICT, QUEBEC. Eli Davis. Canadian Field-Nat., vol. 45, no.8, pp.193-194, Nov., 1931.

(MAMMALS OF THE PROVINCE OF QUEBEC.) Les mammiferes de la province Quebec. C.E. Dionne. Quebec, Dussault and Proulx, pp.vii-285, illus.34, 1902.

OBSERVATIONS ON MAMMALS ALONG THE EAST COAST OF HUDSON BAY AND THE INTERIOR OF UNGAVA. J. Doutt. Pittsburgh, Carnegie Inst., Mus., Annals, vol.33, art.14, 1954.

MAMMALS OF THE CASCAPEDIA VALLEY, QUEBEC. George G. Goodwin. Jour. Mamm., vol.10, no.3, pp.239-246, Aug., 1929.

MAMMALS OF THE GASPE PENINSULA, QUEBEC. George G. Goodwin. Jour.Mamm., vol.5, no.4, pp.246-257, pls.28-29, Nov., 1924.

EARLY FUR TRADE IN NEW FRANCE AND NEW NETHERLAND. Jean E. Murray. Canadian Hist.Rev., Toronto, vol.19, no. 4, pp.365-377, Dec., 1938.

(LATIN, FRENCH, AND ENGLISH NOMENCLATURE OF MAMMALS OF THE PROVINCE OF QUEBEC.) Nomenclature latine, francaise et anglaise des mammifères de la province de Québec. Walter F. Venner. Quebec, Impr.par la compagnie d'imprimerie "Le Soleil," pp.18, 1902.

FUR FARMING STATISTICS FOR THE WESTERN PROVINCES AND QUEBEC. Fur of Canada, Winnipeg, vol.11, no.8, pp.12, 21, May, 1946.

CANADA - ROCKY MOUNTAINS

COLLECTING HABITAT GROUP MATERIAL IN THE CANADIAN ROCKIES. W.L.Brown. Explor.and Field-Work Smiths.Inst. 1940, publ.no.3631, pp.31-34, illus., Apr.3, 1941.

NATURAL GAME LICKS IN THE ROCKY MOUNTAIN NATIONAL PARKS OF CANADA. I.McT.Cowan, V.C. Brink. Jour. Mamm., vol.30, no.4, pp.379-387, illus., Nov.17, 1949.

NOTES ON MAMMALS OF THE SOUTHERN CANADIAN ROCKY MOUNTAINS. Peter E. Crown. Bull.Amer.Mus.Nat.Hist., New York, vol.80, art.11, pp.391-410, pls.32-34, map 1, Feb. 4, 1943.

FOUR NEW MAMMALS FROM THE CANADIAN ROCKIES. Ned Hollister. Smiths.Misc. Coll., vol.56, no.26, pp.1-4, Dec. 5, 1911.

MAMMALS OF THE EASTERN ROCKIES AND WESTERN PLAINS OF CANADA. A.L.

Rand. Nat.Mus.Canada Bull.no.108 (Biol. Series no.35), Ottawa, pp.vii-237, figs. 88, 1948.

NOTES ON SOME OF THE MORE COMMON ANIMALS AND BIRDS OF THE CANADIAN ROCKIES. (Bears, Marmots, Ground-Squirrels, Pikas, Wood Rats, Chipmunks, and Squirrels.) William Spreadborough. Canadian Alpine Jour., vol.10, pp.51-68, 1919.

CANADA -- SAINT LAWRENCE GULF

MAMMALS OF THE ISLANDS IN THE GULF OF ST. LAWRENCE. Austin W. Cameron. Ottawa, Queen's Printer, pp.iii-165, illus., maps, diagrs., tbls., 1958. (Canada, Nat. Mus., Ottawa, Biological Series no.53.)

RECORDS OF THE ATLANTIC WALRUS AND THE POLAR BEAR IN OR NEAR THE NORTHERN PART OF THE GULF OF ST. LAWRENCE. Harrison F. Lewis, J. Kenneth Doutt. Jour. Mamm., vol.23, no.4, pp. 365-375, fig.1, Nov. 14, 1942.

MAMMALS ON ANTICOSTI ISLAND. William Monypeny Newsom. Jour.Mamm., vol.18, no.4, pp.435-442, Nov., 1937.

NOTES ON THE MAMMALS OF PRINCE EDWARD ISLAND. Robert T. Young. Amer. Naturalist, vol.34, no.402, pp.483-486, June, 1900.

CANADA -- SASKATCHEWAN

NOTES ON SASKATCHEWAN MAMMALS. Frank A. Banfield. Canadian Field-Nat., Ottawa, vol.55, no.8, pp.117-123, illus., Nov., 1941.

SOME NOTES ON NEWLY-DISCOVERED FUR POSTS ON THE SASKATCHEWAN RIVER. O.C. Furniss. Canadian Hist. Rev., Toronto, vol.24, no.3, pp.266-272, illus., Sep., 1943.

MAMMALS FROM TOUCHWOOD HILLS, SASKATCHEWAN. E. Raymond Hall. Canadian Field-Nat., vol.52, no.7, pp.108-109, Oct., 1938.

SASKATCHEWAN FUR FARMS' REPORT ON DISEASE CONTROL. R.J. Kirk. Fur of Canada, Winnipeg, vol.12, no.11, pp. 27-28, Aug., 1947.

MAMMALS OF PRINCE ALBERT NATIONAL PARK, SASKATCHEWAN, CANADA. J. Dewey Soper. Can. Wildl. Serv., Wildl. Mgt. Bull. Ser. 1, no.5, pp.1-48, illus., June, 1952.

CANADA -- VANCOUVER ISLAND

MAMMALS OF VANCOUVER ISLAND. G. Clifford Carl. Victoria Nat., vol.4, pp.4-9, 1947.

NATURAL HISTORY OF THE FORBIDDEN PLATEAU AREA, VANCOUVER ISLAND, BRITISH COLUMBIA. G. Glifford Carl. Rept. Provincial Mus. Nat. Hist. and Anthrop. 1943, Victoria, pp. 18-40, pl.1, map, 1944.

REMARKS ON THE AFFINITIES OF THE MAMMLIAN FAUNA OF VANCOUVER ISLAND, BRITISH COLUMBIA, WITH DESCRIPTIONS OF NEW SUBSPECIES. E. Raymond Hall. Univ.Calif. Publ. Zool., vol.38, no.12, pp.415-423, Nov. 8, 1932.

NATURAL HISTORY OF THE FORBIDDEN PLATEAU AREA, VANCOUVER ISLAND, BRITISH COLUMBIA. G.A. Hardy. Rept. Provincial Mus. Nat. Hist. and Anthrop., Victoria, British Columbia, 1954, pp.B24-B63, map, 1955. (Mammals, pp.B61-B62.)

NOTES ON THE FLORA AND FAUNA OF THE BLENKINSOP LAKE AREA ON SOUTHERN VANCOUVER ISLAND, BRITISH COLUMBIA. G. A. Hardy. Rept. Provincial Mus. Nat. Hist. and Anthrop., Victoria, British Columbia, 1956, pp.25-66, 1957. (Mammals, pp.58-59.)

REPORT ON A STUDY OF JORDAN MEADOWS, VANCOUVER ISLAND. G.A. Hardy. Provincial Mus. Nat. Hist. and Anthrop., Victoria, pp.K-20-K-46, figs.8, 1948.

INTRODUCTION OF THE MUSKRAT AND THE ROCKY MOUNTAIN GOAT IN VANCOUVER ISLAND. Hoyes Lloyd. Canadian Field-Nat., vol.39, pp.151-152, Sep. 30, 1925.

SPORTS IN VANCOUVER AND NEWFOUNDLAND. John G. Rogers. New York, E.P. Dutton and Co., pp.xii-275, pls.20, maps 2, 1912. (Hunting.)

REPORT ON A COLLECTION OF BIRDS AND MAMMALS FROM VANCOUVER ISLAND. Harry S. Swarth. Univ. Calif. Publications in Zoology, vol.10, no.1, pp.1-124, pls.4, Feb. 13, 1912.

CANADA -- YUKON

MAMMALS OBSERVED IN THE YUKON TERRITORY, CANADA, IN THE SUMMER OF 1949. W. W. Judd. Jour.Mamm., vol.31, no.3, pp.360-361, Aug. 21, 1950.

MAMMALS OF THE YUKON REGION. Wilfred H. Osgood. N.Amer. Fauna, no. 19, pp.21-45, figs.2, pls.5-7, Oct. 6, 1900.

RESULTS OF A BIOLOGICAL RECONNAISSANCE OF THE YUKON RIVER REGION. 1. GENERAL ACCOUNT OF THE REGION, pp.7-20. 2. ANNOTATED LIST OF MAMMALS, pp.21-45. Wilfred H. Osgood. U.S.Dept.Agric., Div.Biol. Surv., N.Amer.Fauna, no.19, pp.96, pls. 7, Oct. 6, 1900.

MAMMAL INVESTIGATIONS ON THE CANOL ROAD, YUKON AND NORTHWEST TERRITORIES, 1944. A.L. Rand. Bull.99 (Biol.Ser.no.28), Nat.Mus.Canada, Ottawa, pp.1-52, fig.1 (map), pls. 20, 1945.

MAMMALS OF YUKON, CANADA. A. L. Rand. Bull.100 (Biol.Ser.no.29), Nat. Mus.Canada, Ottawa, pp.1-93, figs.27, 1945.

NOTES ON THE MAMMALS OF THE LOWER YUKON REGION. A.H. Twitchell. Jour.Mamm., vol.2, no.1, pp.40-41, Feb., 1921.

CELEBES

RESULTS OF THE ARCHBOLD EXPEDITIONS, NO.1. A NEW GENUS AND SPECIES OF SQUIRREL FROM CELEBES. R. Archbold, G.H.H. Tate. Amer. Mus. Novitates no.801, pp.6, figs.7, May 17, 1935.

ON PREHISTORIC MAMMALS FROM SOUTH CELEBES. K.W. Dammerman. Treubia, Buitenzorg, vol.17, no.1, pp. 63-72, 1939.

NEW GENUS OF FRUIT-BAT AND A NEW SQUIRREL, FROM CELEBES. R.W. Hayman. Ann. and Mag.Nat.Hist., London, ser.11, vol.12, no.93, pp.569-578, Sep., 1945 (Published July 10, 1946.)

MAN AND OTHER MAMMALS FROM TOALIAN SITES IN SOUTH-WESTERN CELEBES. D.A. Hooijer. Verhandl.Kon. Nederlandsche Akad. Wetensch., Afd. Natuurkunde, Amsterdam, sec.2, vol. 46, no.2, pp.1-158, pls.3, 1950.

PLEISTOCENE VERTEBRATES OF SOUTHERN CELEBES. D.A. Hooijer. Chronica Naturae, Batavia, vol.105, no.5, pp.148-150, May, 1949.

SOME REMARKS ON THE SUBSPECIES OF PHALANGER URSINUS (TEMMINCK) AND OF LENOMYS MEYERI (JENTINK) FROM CELEBES. D.A. Hooijer. Zool. Mededel. Rijksmus.Nat. Hist. Leiden, vol.31, no.21, pp.233-246, July 11, 1952.

LIST OF LAND MAMMALS OF NEW GUINEA, CELEBES AND ADJACENT ISLANDS, 1758-1952. Eleanor M. Laurie. London, Printed by Order of the Trustees of the British Museum, pp.175, map, pls., 1954.

(MAMMALS OF THE CELEBES AND PHILLIPINE ARCHIPELAGO I.) Saeugethiere vom Celebes- und Philippinen-Archipel. I. A.B. Meyer. Abhandl. Ber. K. Zool. Anthropol. Ethno. Mus. Dresden, vol.6, no.6, pp.1-36, pls.1-15, 1896.

TWENTY NEW MAMMALS COLLECTED BY H. C. RAVEN IN CELEBES. Gerrit S. Miller, Jr., N. Hollister. Proc.Biol.Soc. Washington, vol.34, pp.93-104, June 30, 1921.

CELEBETIAN CELEBRITIES. Ken Stott, Jr. Zoonooz, San Diego, vol.11, no.8, pp.6-7, Aug., 1939.

MAMMALS FROM CELEBES, BORNEO, AND THE PHILIPPINES RECENTLY RECEIVED AT THE BRITISH MUSEUM. Oldfield Thomas. Ann. and Mag. Nat.Hist., ser.6, vol.18, no.105, pp.241-250, Sep., 1896.

CENTRAL AMERICA

BIOLOGIA CENTRALI-AMERICANA MAMMALIA; OR CONTRIBUTIONS TO THE KNOWLEDGE OF THE FAUNA AND FLORA OF MEXICO AND CENTRAL AMERICA. Edward R. Alston. London, Pub. for the Editors by R.H. Porter, pp.xx-220, pls.22, 1879-82.

LEAVES OUT OF A JUNGLE. (Notes on Three-Toed Sloth and Photograph of Prehensile-Tailed Porcupine at Barro Colorado Island.) T.H. Eaton, Jr. Chicago Nat., vol.5, no.3, pp.47-52, illus., Oct., 1942.

LAND AND SEA MAMMALS OF MIDDLE AMERICA AND THE WEST INDIES. Daniel Giraud Elliot. Chicago, pp.309, pls., 1904. Publication of the Field Col. Mus., Zool. Series, vol.IV. Part 1. MARSUPIALS TO RODENTS, pp.439. Part 2. CARNIVORA TO PRIMATES, pp.441-850.

CHANGES OBSERVED IN THE MAMMAL FAUNA OF BARRO COLORADO ISLAND, 1929-1937. Robert K. Enders. Ecology, Brooklyn, vol.20, no.1, pp.104-106, Jan., 1939.

MAMMALIAN LIFE-HISTORIES FROM BARRO COLORADO ISLAND. Robert K. Enders. Panama, Bull. Mus. Comp. Zool., vol.78, pp.385-502, pls.5, 1935.

BARRO COLORADO ISLAND LABORATORY. David Fairchild. Jour. Heredity, vol.15, no.3, pp.98-112, figs.12, Mar., 1924.

JUNGLE LABORATORY. COMPANIONS OF THE WILD AT BARRO COLORADO ISLAND. Alfred O. Gross. Nature Mag., vol.15, no.1, pp.11-15, figs.19, Jan., 1930.

BARRO COLORADO, TROPICAL ISLAND LABORATORY. Lloyd Glenn Ingles. Smithsonian Inst., Annual Rep., 1953, Washington, pp.361-366, pls., 1954. (Reprinted from Pacific Discovery, vol.6, no. 4, July-Aug., 1953.)

CHECKLIST OF MAMMALS OF BARRO CA

CHECKLIST OF MAMMALS OF BARRO COLORADO ISLAND. Carl B. Koford. Smithsonian Inst. (SIL-109), pp.3, Sep., 1957. (Mimeog.)

LIST OF MAMMALS OBTAINED BY MR. G. F. GAUMER ON COZUMEL AND RUATEN ISLANDS. GULF OF HONDURAS. Oldfield Thomas. Proc. Zool. Soc., London, no.9, pp.129-135, pls.5, Feb. 21, 1888.

CEYLON

FAUNA OF BRITISH INDIA, INCLUDING CEYLON AND BURMA. W.T. Blanford. Mammalia, 1888-91.

GAME SANCTUARY IN CEYLON. R. W. Burton. Jour. Bombay Nat. Hist. Soc., vol. 38, no.1, pp.20-25, Aug. 15, 1935.

RATNAPURA (SHIVALIK) FOSSILS OF CEYLON. P.E.P. Deraniyagala. Spolia Zeylanica, Bull. Nat. Mus. Ceylon, vol. 27, pt.2, pp.223-225, May 25, 1955.

SOME MAMMALS OF THE EXTINCT RATNAPURA FAUNA OF CEYLON. P.E.P. Deraniyagala. Spoila Zeylanica, vol.24, no.1, pp.19-56, pls.4, figs.12, 1944; vol.24, pt.3, pp.161-171, pls.21-23, Nov. 8, 1946; vol.26, pt.2, pp.117-124, Dec. 20, 1951.

SOME MIOCENE AND UPPER SIWALIK VERTEBRATES FROM CEYLON. P.E.P. Deraniyagala. Spolia Zeylanica, Ceylon Jour.Sci., sec.B (Zool. and Geol.), vol. 20, pt.2, pp.191-198, figs.4, pls.5-6, Apr. 15, 1937.

CEYLON, RECORDS OF BIG GAME. D.J.G. Hennessy. Loris, Ceylon, vol.2, no.2, pp.137-139, June, 1940.

REVISED CHECK-LIST OF THE MAMMALS OF CEYLON. W.C. Osman Hill. Ceylon Jour.Sci.sect.B, Zool.and Geol., vol.21, pt.2, pp.139-184, Feb. 10, 1939.

CATALOGUE OF THE MAMMALIA OF CEYLON. Dr.Kelaart. Proc.Zool.Soc. London, pt.18, pp.155-158, 1850.

NOTES ON FAUNA PROTECTION IN CEYLON. A.B. Lushington. Loris, Ceylon, vol.1, no.1, pp.11-16, Nov., 1936.

CHECK LIST OF THE MAMMALS OF CEYLON. W.W.A. Phillips. Ceylon Jour.Sci., sect.B, Zool. and Geol. Spolia Zeylanica, vol.15, no.2, pp.119-152, col.map 1, May 20, 1929.

GUIDE TO THE MAMMALS OF CEYLON. PART 6. UNGULATA. W.W.A.Phillips. Ceylon Jour.Sci., vol.14, pt.1, pp.1-50, pls.1-5, Apr. 30, 1927.

LIST OF THE MORE IMPORTANT ANIMALS, BIRDS, AND REPTILES OF CEYLON, WITH THE SINHALESE AND TAMIL NAMES OF EACH. W.W.A. Phillips. Loris, Ceylon, vol.2, no.2, pp.140-144, June, 1940.

MANUAL OF THE MAMMALS OF CEYLON. W.W.A. Phillips. Publ.Ceylon Jour.Sci., pp.xxvii-373, figs.55, pls.38, 1935; London, Dulau and Co., Ltd., 1935.

PRESENT STATE OF THE GAME AND WILD LIFE IN CEYLON. W.W.A.Phillips. Jour.Bombay Nat.Hist.Soc., vol.33, no.4, pp.942-946, pls.1-5, Oct. 15, 1929.

SURVEY OF THE DISTRIBUTION OF MAMMALS IN CEYLON. W.W.A. Phillips. Spolia Zeylanica, Ceylon Jour.Sci., vol. 16, pt.3, pp.337-351, Mar. 18, 1932; vol. 17, pt.2, pp.127-138, Nov.3, 1932; vol. 17, pt.3, pp.237-242, May 19, 1933; vol. 18, pt.1, pp.133-142, Dec. 22, 1933; vol. 19, pt.3, pp.315-329, Feb. 18, 1936; vol. 20, pt.2, pp.199-206, Apr. 15, 1937.

FAUNA OF BRITISH INDIA, INCLUDING CEYLON AND BURMA, MAMMALIA, VOL. 1, PRIMATES AND CARNIVORA (IN PART), FAMILIES FELIDAE AND VIVERRIDAE. R. I. Pocock. London, pp.xxxiii-463, figs.106, pls.31, map, Mar. 31, 1939.

FAUNA PRESERVATION IN CEYLON. (Elephants.) R.L. Spittel. Jour.Soc. Preservation Fauna of Empire, Hertford, n.s., pt.35, pp.16-19, photos 3, Dec., 1938.

NATURAL HISTORY OF THE MAMMALIA OF INDIA AND CEYLON. Robert Armitage Sterndale. London, W.Thacker and Co., 1884.

NATURAL HISTORY OF CEYLON. Emerson Tennent. London, 1861.

ON SOME CEYLON MAMMALS. Oldfield Thomas. Ann. and Mag.Nat.Hist., ser. 9, vol.13, pp.239-242, Feb., 1924.

EXPLOITATION OF WILD LIFE (CEYLON). A.C. Tutein-Nolthenius. Jour. Bombay Nat. Hist. Soc., vol.37, no.1, pp.219-220, Apr., 1934.

MEASUREMENTS AND NOTES ON SOME LITTLE-KNOWN CEYLON MAMMALS. A.C. Tutein-Nolthenius. Jour.Bombay Nat.Hist.Soc., vol.35, no.3, pp.606-614, Feb. 15, 1932.

SOME ADVENTURES OF A NATURALIST IN THE CEYLON JUNGLE. (Notes on Water Buffalo, Elephant, Bear, and Leopard.) Casey A. Wood. Ann.Rept.Board Regents Smithsonian Inst., 1928, publ. 2981, pp.525-539, pls.6, Nov. 18, 1929.

## CHINA

### Extinct and Fossil Mammals

CAVE AND ROCK-SHELTER DEPOSITS IN YUNNAN. M.N. Bien, L.P. Chia.Bull. Geol.Soc.China, Chunking, vol.18, nos. 3-4, pp.325-347, figs.12, pl.1, Dec., 1938.

RHINOCEROS AND WILD OX IN ANCIENT CHINA. Carl Whiting Bishop. China Jour., vol.18, no.6, pp.322-330, figs., June, 1930.

RECENT DISCOVERIES AT CHOUKOUTIEN. UPPER PALAEOLITHIC CULTURE IN "UPPER CAVE" SEDIMENTS. Davidson Black. Nature, London, vol.133, no.3351, pp.89-90, Jan. 20, 1934.

FOSSIL MAMMALS FROM THE TERTIARY DEPOSIT OF TABENBULUK, WESTERN KANSU. Birger Bohlin. Stockholm, illus., pl., map, diagrs., 1942.

NOTES ON SOME REMAINS OF FOSSIL MAMMALS FROM CHINA AND MONGOLIA. Birger Bohlin. Bull. Geol.Soc.China, Nanking, vol.15, no.3, pp.321-330, pl.1, Sep., 1936.

SOME MAMMALIAN REMAINS FROM SHIH-EHR-MA-CH'ENG, HUI-HUI-P'U AREA, WESTERN KANSU. Birger Bohlin. Stockholm, pp.46, illus., 1951. (Reports from the Scientific Expedition to the North-Western Provinces of China Under Leadership of Dr.Sven Hedin. The Sino-Swedish Expedition. Publication 35, vi. Vertebrate Palaeontology, 5.)

(PALEOLITHIC OF CHINA.) Le Paleolithique de la Chine. M. Boule, et al. Arch. Inst.Pal. Humaine Mem.4, pp.138.

BONE AND ANTLER INDUSTRY OF THE CHOUKOUTIEN SINANTHROPUS SITE. Henri Breuil.Palaeontologia Sinica, Peiping, new ser., D, no.6, (whole ser., no.117), pp.iv-192, pls.26, 1939.

ON THE QUESTION OF THE EXISTENCE OF ELEPHANTS AND RHINOCEROS IN NORTH CHINA IN HISTORICAL TIMES. H.T. Chang. Bull. Geol.Soc. China, vol.5, pp.99-106, 1926.

NOTES ON THE HUMAN AND SOME OTHER MAMMALIAN REMAINS FROM CHANG-YANG, HUPEI. Lan-po Chia. Vertebrata Palasiatica, vol.1, no.3, pp.247-258, Sep., 1957. (In Chinese, with English Summary.)

QUATERNARY MAMMALIAN FOSSILS FROM CHIHCHENG, HOPEI. Lan-po Chia, Jen-Chieh Chai. Vertebrata Palasiatica, vol. 1, no.1, pp.47-56, pls.3, Mar., 1957.

(ANCIENT ANIMALS OF MY COUNTRY.) Ming-chen Chou. The China Youth Publishing Corporation, Peiping, pp.114, illus., 1956. (Science Booklets for Youths.)

NOTES ON A SMALL COLLECTION OF PLEISTOCENE MAMMALIAN FOSSILS FROM TUNGNAN, SZECHUAN. Minchen M. Chow. Vertebrata Palasiatica, vol.1, pp.57-58, pl., Mar., 1957.

NOTES ON SOME MAMMALIAN FOSSILS FROM THE LATE CENOZOIC OF SINKIANG. Minchen M. Chow. Vertebrata Palasiatica, vol.1, no.1, pp.33-41, Mar., 1957.

ON SOME EOCENE AND OLIGOCENE MAMMALS FROM KWANGSI AND YUNNAN. Minchen M. Chow. Vertebrata Palasiatica, vol.1, no.3, pp.201-214, Sep., 1957.

TWO SPECIMENS OF MAMMALIAN COPROLITE FROM THE SANMEN RAPIDS, SHANSI AND SINGTSAI, HONAN. Minchen M. Chow. Acta Paleo. Sinica, vol.3, no.4, pp.283-286, illus., 1955.

VILLAFRANCHIAN MAMMALS FROM TONGSHANCHEN BASIN, SOUTHERN SHANSI. Minchen M. Chow. Acta Paleontol.Sinica, vol.3, pp.333-342, illus., 1954. (New: Axis rugosus.)

PLEISTOCENE MAMMALS FROM THE MA KAI VALLEY OF NORTHERN YUNNAN, CHINA. Edwin H. Colbert. Amer.Mus. Novitates, New York, no.1099, pp.10, figs. 6, Dec. 31, 1940.

PLEISTOCENE MAMMALS FROM THE LIMESTONE FISSURES OF SZECHWAN, CHINA. Edwin Harris Colbert, Dirk Albert Hooijer. Bull. Amer. Mus. Nat.Hist., New York, vol.102, art.1, pp.1-134, illus., June 12, 1953.

MAMMALIAN FOSSILS FROM THE PLEISTOCENE CAVE DEPOSITS OF CHIHCHIN, NORTHWESTERN KWEICHOW. Yu-hsiuan Hsu, et al. Acta Paleont.Sinica, vol.5, no.2, pp.343-350, pl., May, 1957.

ANTLER FRAGMENT OF STEPHANOCEMAS AND SOME TEETH OF ACERATHERIUM FROM LINCHU, SHANTUNG. Chang-kang Hu. Vertebrata Palasiatica, vol.1, no.2, pp. 163-166, pl., June, 1957. (With English Summary.)

(A MAMMAL FOSSIL ASSOCIATED WITH SIMIA FROM SOUTH CHINA.) Eine fossile Saeugetierfauna mit Simia aus Suedchina. G.H.R. von Koenigswald. Proc.Sect.Sci. Kon.Akad. van Wetenschappen te Amsterdam, vol.38, nos.6-10, pp.872-879, pl., 1935.

(KNOWLEDGE OF MAMMALS IN ANCIENT CHINA.) Saeugetierkenntnisse im altesten China. J. Krumbiegel. Zeitschr.f. Saeugetierk., vol.2, p.198, Apr. 29, 1929.

CHINESE HIPPARION FAUNA; QUANTITATIVE SURVEY WITH COMMENTS ON THE ECOLOGY OF THE MACHAIRODONTS AND HYAENIDS AND THE TAXONOMY OF THE GAZELLES. Bjorn Kurtén. Helsingfors, pp.82, illus., map, diagrs., 1952.(Societas Scientiarum Fennica, Commentationes Biologicae, xiii, 4.)

NAN YE LI SANMENIAN FOSSILIFEROUS DEPOSIT. F.E. Licent. Bull.Geol.Soc. China, vol.9, no.2, pp.101-104, figs.2, 1930.

ON SOME FOSSIL MAMMALS FROM HONAN, CHINA. Hikoshichiro Matsumoto. Sci.Reports, Tohoku Imp.Univ., ser.2, (Geol.), vol.3, no.1, pp.29-38, pls.5, 1915.

ON SOME FOSSIL CERVIDS FROM SHANTUNG, CHINA. Hikoshichiro Matsumoto. Sci.Reports, Tohoku Imp. Univ., ser.2, (Geol.), vol.10, no.2, pp.27-37, pls.4, 1926.

ON SOME FOSSIL MAMMALS FROM SZECHUAN, CHINA. Hikoshichiro Matsumoto. Sci. Reports, Tohoku Imp. Univ., ser.2, (Geol.), vol.3, no.1, pp.1-28, text figs. 4, pls.10, 1915.

NEW FOSSILS FROM THE PLIOCENE OF SZE-CHUAN, CHINA. Matthew, Granger. Amer. Mus. Nat. Hist. Bull., vol.48, pp. 563-598, 1923.

AGE OF CHOUKOUTIEN FOSSILIFEROUS DEPOSIT: A TENTATIVE DETERMINATION BY COMPARISON WITH OTHER LATER CENOZOIC (PSYCHOZOIC) DEPOSITS IN CHINA. W.C. Pei. Reprint from Bull.Geol.Soc.China, vol.10, pp.165-178, fig., tbls.2, 1931.

FOSSIL MAMMALS FROM THE KWANGSI CAVES. W.C. Pei. Bull.Geol.Soc.China, vol.14, no.3, pp.413-425, figs.6, 1935.

MAMMALIAN REMAINS FROM LOCALITY 5 AT CHOUK'OUTIEN. W.C. Pei. Palaeontologia Sinica, Peiping, ser.C, vol.7, fasc.2, pp.18, fig., pl., 1931.

NEW FOSSIL MATERIAL AND ARTIFACTS COLLECTED FROM THE CHOUKOUTIEN REGION DURING THE YEARS 1937 TO 1939. W.C. Pei. Bull. Geol. Soc. China, Pehpei, Chungking, vol.19, no.3, pp.207-234, figs. 11, pl.1, Dec., 1939.

NOTE ON COLLECTION OF MAMMAL FOSSILS FROM TANYANG IN KIANGSU PROVINCE. W.C. Pei. Bull. Geol. Soc. China, Szechuan, vol.19, no.4, pp.379-392, figs.8, Mar., 1940.

ON A MESOLITHIC INDUSTRY OF THE CAVE OF KWANGSI. W.C. Pei. Reprint from Bull. Geol. Soc. China, vol.9, no.3, pp.393-408, figs.13, pls.1-2, 1935.

ON THE MAMMALIAN REMAINS FROM LOCALITY 3 AT CHOUKOUTIN. W. C. Pei. Palaeontologia Sinica, ser.C, vol.7, no.5, pp.120, figs.59, pls.6, 1936. (New: Crocidura Wongi, Microtus Complicidens.)

ON A COLLECTION OF MAMMALIAN FOSSIL FROM CHIACHIASHAN NEAR TANGSHAN. W.C. Pei. Bull.Geol.Soc. China, Peiping, vol.9, no.4, pp.371-377, figs.5, 1930.

ON THE UPPER CAVE INDUSTRY. W.C. Pei. Peking Nat.Hist. Bull., vol.13, pt.3, pp.175-179, pls.3, Mar., 1939.

PRELIMINARY REPORT ON THE LATE PALAEOLITHIC CAVE OF CHOUKOUTIEN. W.C. Pei. Bull. Geol. Soc. China, vol.13, no.3, pp.327-358, figs.10, pls.4, 1934. (Lists Mammals Found in the Cave.)

REPORT ON THE EXCAVATION OF THE LOCALITY 13 IN CHOUKOUTIEN. W.C. Pei. Bull. Geol. Soc. China, vol.13, no.3, pp.359-367, figs.4, 1934. (List of Species of Mammals.)

SIR GRAFTON ELLIOT SMITH AND WORK ON EARLY MAN IN CHINA. W.C. Pei. Nature, London, vol.139, no.3509, pp.192-193, Jan. 30, 1937.

THE UPPER CAVE INDUSTRY OF CHOU-KOUTIEN. W.C.Pei.Palaeontologia Sinica, Peiping, n.s. D, no.9, whole ser.no.120, pp.58, pls.8, Dec., 1939.

ZOOGEOGRAPHICAL DIVISIONS OF QUATERNARY MAMMALIAN FAUNAS IN CHINA. W.C. Pei. Vertebrata Palasiatica, vol.1, no.1, pp.9-24, Mar., 1957.

ON A COLLECTION OF MAMMALIAN FOSSILS FROM LIUHSIA, HONGCHOW, CHEKIANG, CHINA. W.C. Pei, Chung-lang Chiu. Vertebrata Palasiatica, vol.1, no.1, pp.42-46, Mar., 1957.

DISCOVERY OF TRIASSIC SAURISCHIAN AND PRIMITIVE MAMMALIAN REMAINS AT LUFENG, YUNNAN. Mei-nien Pien. Microfilm copy made by Microfilms, Inc. Positive. Collation of the original, as determined from the film, pp.226-234, pl. Reprinted from the Bull.Geol.Soc.China, vol.xx, nos.3-4, 1940.

FOSSIL ANIMALS FROM CHINA AND MON-GOLIA. Arthur de Carle Sowerby. China Jour., Shanghai, vol.25, no.6, illus., Dec., 1936.

(WILD ANIMALS' LIVING HISTORY.) Pang-chieh T'an. Peiping, The China Book Co., pp.236, illus., 1955.

(DESCRIPTION OF THE TERTIARY MAMMALS OF CHINA AND MONGOLIA.) Description de mammiferes tertiaires de Chine et de Mongolie. P. Teilhard de Chardin. Ann. Paleontologie, vol.15, no.1, pp.1-52, pls.1-5, Apr., 1926.

FOSSIL MAMMALS FROM LOCALITY 9 OF CHOUKOUTIEN.P.Teilhard de Chardin. Palaeontologie Sinicia, Nanking, ser.C, vol. 7, no.4, pp.1-70, figs.30, pls.4, tbls., June, 1936.

FOSSIL MAMMALS FROM THE LATE CENOZOIC OF NORTHERN CHINA. P. Teilhard de Chardin. Peiping (Peking), Geological Survey of China, pp.88, illus., pl., map, 1931. (China, Geol.Surv., Palaeontologia Sinica, ser.C, vol.9, fasc. 1.)

FOSSILS FROM THE LOCALITY 12 OF CHOUKOUTIEN. P. Teilhard de Chardin. Palaeontologia Sinica, Nanking, n.s.C, no.5, pp.1-50, figs.36, pl.1, Aug.,1938.

FOSSILS FROM LOCALITY 18 NEAR PEKING. P. Teilhard de Chardin.Palaeontologia Sinica, n.s.C, no.9, whole series 124.

NEW DISCOVERIES IN CHOUKOUTIEN 1933-1934. P. Teilhard de Chardin. Bull. Geol. Soc. China, vol.13, no.3, pp. 369-389, pls.3, figs.9, Sep., 1934.

ON THE MAMMALIAN REMAINS FROM THE ARCHAEOLOGICAL SITE OF ANYANG. P. Teilhard de Chardin. Nanking, Geological Survey of China, pp.78, illus., pls., 1936. (China, Geol.Surv., Palaeontologia Sinica, ser.C, vol.12, fasc.1.)

PLEISTOCENE OF CHINA STRATIGRAPHY AND CORRELATIONS. P. Teilhard de Chardin. Early Man, edited by G.G.Mac Curdy, Lippincott & Co., London, pp.211-220, figs.31-32, 1937.

POST-VILLAFRANCHIAN INTERVAL IN NORTH CHINA. P. Teilhard de Chardin. Bull. Geol.Soc.China, Peking, vol.17, no.1, pp.169-176, 1937.

(FOSSIL MAMMALS OF NIHOWAN, CHINA.) Les Mammiferes Fossiles de Nihowan, Chine. P. Teilhard de Chardin, Piveleau. Ann. de Palaeontologia Paris, vol.19, pp. 3-134, 1930.

CENOZOIC SEQUENCE IN THE YANGTZE VALLEY. P. Teilhard de Chardin, C.C. Young. Bull. Geol.Soc. China, vol.14, no. 2, pp.161-178, figs.12, June, 1935.

PRELIMINARY REPORT ON THE CHOU KOU TIEN FOSSILIFEROUS DEPOSIT. P. Teilhard de Chardin, C.C. Young. Bull. Geol.Soc.China, vol.8, no.3, pp.171-202, figs.10, 1929.

ON THE CENOZOIC FORMATIONS OF KWANGSI AND KWANGTUNG. P. Teilhard de Chardin, et al. Bull. Geol.Soc. China, vol.xiv, no.2, pp.179-210, figs. 14, pls.2, 1935.

ON SOME TRACES OF VERTEBRATE LIFE IN THE JURASSIC AND TRIASSIC BEDS OF SHANSI AND SHENSI. P. Teilard de Chardin, C.C. Young. Bull.Geol. Soc. China, vol.8, no.2, pp.131-133, July, 1929.

UPPER CAVE OF CHOUKOUTIEN. Frank Weidenreich, W.C. Pei. Science, Lancaster, Penna., n.s., vol.89, no.2306, pp.12, 14, Mar. 3, 1939.

EARLY TERTIARY VERTEBRATE FAUNA FROM YUANCHU. C.C. Young. Bull.Geol. Soc. China, Nanking, vol.17, nos.3-4, pp. 413-438, figs.16, Dec., 1937.

MISCELLANEOUS MAMMALIAN FOSSILS FROM SHANSI AND HONAN. C.C. Young. Palaeontologia Sinica, Peiping, ser.C, vol. 9, fasc.2, pp.56, figs.13, pls.7, 1935.

NEW FOSSILS FROM WANHSIEN (SZE - CHUAN). C.C. Young. Bull.Geol.Soc. China, Pehpei, Chungking, vol.19, no.3, pp.317-331, figs.7, Dec., 1939.

NOTES ON THE MAMMALIA REMAINS FROM KWANGSI. C.C. Young. Bull. Geol. Soc. China, vol.8, no.2, pp.125-130, pl. 1, July, 1929.

ON A MIOCENE MAMMALIAN FAUNA FROM SHANTUNG. C.C. Young. Bull. Geol.Soc. China, Nanking, vol.17, no.2, pp.209-238, figs.17, pls.1-3, 1937.

ON SOME FOSSIL MAMMALS FROM YUN-NAN. C.C. Young. Bull.Geol. Soc. China, vol.11, no.4, pp.383-393, 1932.

ON THE FOSSIL VERTEBRATE REMAINS FROM LOCALITIES 2, 7 AND 8 AT CHOU-KOUTHEN. C.C. Young. Palaeontologia Sinica, Peiping, ser.C, vol.7, fasc.3, pp. 24, figs.7, pl.1, 1932.

ON THE INSECTIVORA, CHIROPTERA, RODENTIA AND PRIMATES OTHER THAN SINANTHROPUS FROM LOCALITY 1 AT CHOUKOUTIN. C.C. Young.Palaeontologia Sinica, Peiping, ser.C, vol.8, fasc.3, pp. 160, figs.51, pls.10, Mar. 31, 1934.

ON THE MAMMALIAN REMAINS FROM CHI KU SHAN NEAR CHOU KOU TIEN. C.C. Young. Palaeontologia Sinica, Geol. Surv.China, ser.C, vol.7, no.1, pp.1-19, pls.1-2, 1930.

PLEISTOCENE STRATIGRAPHY AND NEW FOSSIL LOCALITIES OF SHIHHUNG AND WUHO, NORTHERN ANHWEI. C.C. Young. Acta Palaeontologia Sinica, vol.3, no.1, pp.47-54, 1955.

(REMARKS ON SOME ABNORMAL FOSSIL FORMS AND THE DEGREE OF PETRIFACTION OF THE BONE DEPOSITS OF CHOU KOU TIEN.) Bemerkungen ueber einige abnormale Formen von fossilen und den versteinerungsgrad der Knochenablagerung von Chou Kou Tien. C.C. Young. Bull. Geol.Soc.China, vol.9, no.2, pp.183-188, figs.5, July, 1930.

REVIEW OF THE EARLY TERTIARY FORMATIONS OF CHINA. C.C. Young. Bull. Geol.Soc.China, vol.13, no.3, pp.469-503, figs.17, pl.1, 1934.

CENOZOIC GEOLOGY OF THE KAOLAN-YOUNGTENG AREA OF CENTRAL KANSU. C.C. Young, M.N. Bien. Bull. Geol. Soc. China, Nanking, vol.16, pp.221-260, figs. 7, pls.1-8, Apr., 1937. (List of Fossil Mammals, pp.228-231.)

CENOZOIC GEOLOGY OF THE WENHO-SSUSHUI DISTRICT OF CENTRAL SHAN-TUNG. C.C. Young, M.N. Bien. Bull. Geol.Soc.China, vol.14, no.2, pp.221-246, figs.8, pls.4, June, 1935.

ON A MIOCENE MAMMALIAN FAUNA FROM SHANTUNG. C.C. Young. Bull. Geol.Soc.China, Nanking, vol.17, no.2, pp.209-238, figs.17, pls.1-3, June, 1937.

SOME NEW OBSERVATIONS ON THE CENOZOIC GEOLOGY NEAR PEIPING. C.C. Young, M.N. Bien. Bull. Geol.Soc. China, vol.15, no.2, pp.207-216, figs.5, June, 1936.

SOME OLIGOCENE MAMMALS FROM LINGWU, N. KANSU. C.C. Young, M.M. Chow. Acta Pal.Sinica, vol.4, no.4, pp. 447-459, illus., 1956.

ON THE CENOZOIC GEOLOGY BETWEEN LOYANG AND SIAN. (Occurrences of Fossil Mammals.) C.C. Young, W.C. Pei. Bull. Geol. Soc. China, vol.13, no.1, pp. 73-90, figs.8, map, 1933.

ON THE FISSURE DEPOSITS OF CHINGH-SINGHSIEN WITH REMARKS ON THE CENOZOIC GEOLOGY OF THE SAME AREA. C.C. Young. W.C. Pei. Bull. Geol.Soc. China, vol.13, no.1, pp.63-71, figs.4, 1933.

(MAMMALS OF THE QUATERNARY FAUNA OF CHOU-KOU-TIEN.) Saeugetiere der Quataerfauna von Chou-Kou-Tien. Otto Zdansky. Peking, Published by the Geol. Surv. of China, pp.146, illus., tbls., diagrs., pl., 1928. (China, Geol.Surv., Palaeontologia Sinica, ser.C, vol.5, fasc. 4.)

(OLD TERTIARY MAMMALS OF CHINA, WITH STRATIGRAPHICAL REMARKS.) Alttertiaere Saeugetiere Chinas nebst stratigraphischen Bemerkungen. Otto Zdansky. Peiping, Geol.Surv. of China, pp.87, illus., tbls., pls., 1930. (China, Geol. Surv., Palaeontologia Sinica, ser.C. vol.6, fasc. 2.)

ANIMALS CONTEMPORARY WITH "PEKING MAN." (Lists 55 Mammals.) China Jour., vol.12, no.3, pp.164-166, 1930.

Recent Mammals

MAMMALS FROM YUNNAN AND TONKIN. Glover M. Allen. Proc. Biol.Soc.Wash., vol.25, pp.177-180, Dec. 24, 1912.

MAMMALS OF CHINA AND MONGOLIA. PART 1. NATURAL HISTORY OF CENTRAL ASIA. Glover M. Allen. Amer. Mus. Nat. Hist., New York, vol.xi, pt.1, pp.xxv+620, pls.9, figs.23, 1938.

(Review by Wilfred H. Osgood of) MAMMALS OF CHINA AND MONGOLIA. PART 1. Glover M. Allen. Jour, Mamm., vol.20, no. 1, pp.113-114, Feb. 14, 1939.

MAMMALS OF CHINA AND MONGOLIA. PART 2. Glover M. Allen. Publ. Amer.Mus. Nat. Hist., New York, Central Asiatic Expeditions, vol.11, pp.xxvi-(2)-621-1350, figs.24-75, pls.10-20, Sep. 3, 1940.

SOME CHINESE VERTEBRATES. Glover M. Allen. Mem.Mus.Com.Zool., vol.40, no.4, pp.201-247, Aug., 1912.

ZOOLOGICAL RESULTS OF THE SECOND DOLAN EXPEDITION TO WESTERN CHINA AND EASTERN TIBET, 1934-1936. PART 3.

MAMMALS. Glover M. Allen. Proc. Acad. Nat.Sci. Philadelphia, vol.90, pp.261-294, folded map, pls.21-24, Feb. 3, 1939.

ZOOLOGICAL RESULTS OF THE SECOND DOLAN EXPEDITION TO WESTERN CHINA AND EASTERN TIBET, 1934-1936. PART 4. MAMMALS. Glover M. Allen. Proc. Acad. Nat. Sci. Philadelphia, vol.90, pp.261-294, pls., May 3, 1939.

FURTHER NOTES ON MAMMALS FROM THE ISLAND OF HAINAN, CHINA. J.A. Allen. Bull. Amer. Mus. Nat.Hist., vol. 26, pp.239-242, Apr. 17, 1909.

MAMMALS FROM SHEN-SI PROVINCE, CHINA. J.A. Allen. Bull. Amer. Mus. Nat.Hist., vol.26, pp.425-430, Oct. 21, 1909.

MAMMALS FROM THE ISLAND OF HAINAN, CHINA. J.A. Allen. Proc. Biol. Soc. Wash., vol.22, pp.463-490, pl.19, Dec. 17, 1906.

ANATOMICAL AND ZOOLOGICAL RESEARCHES COMPRISING AN ACCOUNT OF THE TWO EXPEDITIONS TO WESTERN YUNNAN IN 1868 AND 1875, AND A MONOGRAPH OF THE TWO CETACEAN GENERA PLATANISTA AND ORCELLA. John Anderson. London, vol.I and II, pls., 1878 (1879).

(CLIMATE CHANGE IN NORTHERN CHINA.) Nordkinesiska klimatvaxlingar. (Seven Tropical Genera of Mammals.) J.G. Anderson. Ymer (Tidsk. Svenska Sällsk Anthropol. Geogr.), Stockholm, no.2, pp.82-100, 1943.

EXPLORATIONS IN CHINA. Roy Chapman Andrews. Science, vol.70, no.1822, pp. 531-532, Nov. 29, 1929.

ON A SMALL COLLECTION OF MAMMALS OBTAINED BY CAPTAIN DEASY IN SOUTH CHINESE TURKESTAN AND WESTERN TIBET. G.E.H. Barrett-Hamilton. Proc. Zool.Soc. London, pp.196-197, Mar. 6, 1900.

SCIENTIFIC RESULTS OF THE SECOND YARKAND MISSION; BASED UPON THE COLLECTIONS AND NOTES OF THE LATE FERDINAND STOLICKZA, PHD. MAMMALIA. William Thomas Blanford. Published by Order of the Government of India, Calcutta, Office of the Superintendent of Government Printing, pp.iv-94, pls.29(part col.), 1879.

ZOOLOGICAL RESULTS OF THE SECOND DOLAN EXPEDITION TO WESTERN CHINA AND EASTERN TIBET, 1934-1936. PART I. INTRODUCTION. Brooke Dolan, II. Proc. Acad. Nat. Sci., Philadelphia, vol.90, pp. 159-184, map, pls.13, May 3, 1939.

(OBSERVATIONS ON SOME MAMMALS OF THE NORTH OF CHINA.) Observations sur Quelques mammiferes du nord de la Chine. Alphonse Milne Edwards. Ann. Sci.Nat., Paris (Zool.), ser.5, vol.8, no.6, pp.374-376, 1867.

(ON THE LARGE MAMMALS OF SZECHWAN, SIKONG, AND EASTERN TIBET.) Ueber die Grossaeuger Szetschwans, Sikongs und Osttibets. Carlheinrich Engelmann. Zeitschr.f.Saeugetierk., vol.13, Sonderheft, pp.1-76, pls.36, July 22, 1938.

(FAUNA OF CHAN-TOUNG.) La faune du Chan-Toung. A. Fauvel. Rev.Quest.Sci., vol.I, p.463, 1892.

(SCIENTIFIC FINDINGS OF THE FILCHNER EXPEDITION TO CHINA AND TIBET (1903-1905).) Wissenschaftliche Ergebnisse der Expedition Filchner nach China und Tibet 1903-1905. Wilhelm Filchner. Band X, Teil I, 1908.

CONTRIBUTIONS TOWARD A LIST OF CHINESE MAMMALS. N. Gist Gee. Peking Soc. Nat.Hist.Bull., 1929-30, vol.4, pt.3, pp.49-91, 1930.

DEVELOPMENT OF THE NATURAL SCIENCES IN CHINA. Amadeus William Grabau. Science, n.s., vol.85, no.2215, pp.551-553, June 11, 1937.

SUMMER COLLECTING TRIP AMONG THE CH'IANG PEOPLE. D.C. Graham. Jour. West China Border Research Soc., Chengtu, vol.6, pp.24-27, pls.2, 1935.

CHARACTERS OF THREE NEW GENERA, INCLUDING TWO NEW SPECIES OF MAMMALIA FROM CHINA. J.E. Gray. Proc. Comm.Sci. and Corres. Zool. Soc. London, pt.I, p.94, 1830-31.

STUDY OF SOME MAMMALS FROM SZECHUAN. Hsi J. Ho. Contr. Biol. Lab. Sci. Soc. China, vol.11, no.5, pp.123-164, 1935.

STUDY OF THE MAMMALS OF NANKING AND ITS VICINITY. Hsi J. Ho. Contr. Biol. Lab. Sci. Soc. China, Nanking, vol.10, zool.ser., nos.4-5, pp.245-287, figs.14, pls.4, 1934.

MAMMALS FROM CHINA IN THE COLLECTIONS OF THE UNITED STATES NATIONAL MUSEUM. A. Brazier Howell. Proc. U.S. Nat. Mus., vol.75, art.1, pp. 1-82, pls.1-10, June 7, 1929.

NEW CHINESE MAMMALS. A. Brazier Howell. Proc. Biol. Soc. Washington, vol. 41, pp.41-43, Mar. 16, 1928.

THREE NEW MAMMALS FROM CHINA. A. Brazier Howell. Proc. Biol. Soc. Washington, vol.39, pp.137-140, Dec. 27, 1926.

NOTES ON A SMALL COLLECTION OF MAMMALS FROM THE PROVINCE OF KAN-SU, CHINA. Marcus Ward Lyon, Jr. Smiths. Inst. Misc. Coll., vol.50 (Quarterly Issue, vol.iv), pp.133-138, pls.15-16, July 9, 1907.

GAME IN THE SHAKSGAM VALLEY. K. Mason. Field, London, vol.149, p.686, Apr. 21, 1927.

BIOLOGICAL EXPLORATIONS IN THE YANG-TZE VALLEY, CHINA. Gerrit S. Miller, Jr. Smiths. Inst. Misc. Coll., vol.76, no.10, pp.30-35, figs.32-35, Mar. 31, 1924.

EXPLORATION IN CHINA. Gerrit S. Miller, Jr. Smiths. Inst. Misc. Coll., vol.66, no. 17, pp.35-36, Apr. 27, 1917.

EXPLORATIONS IN CHINA AND MANCHURIA. Gerrit S. Miller, Jr. Smiths. Inst. Misc. Coll., vol.66, no.3, pp.44-46, fig. 58, May 27, 1916.

FOUR NEW CHINESE MAMMALS. Gerrit S. Miller, Jr. Proc. Biol. Soc. Washington, vol.24, pp.53-56, Feb. 24, 1911.

(OBSERVATIONS ON SOME MAMMALS FROM THE NORTH OF CHINA.) Observations sur quelques mammiferes du Nord de la Chine. Alphonse Milne-Edwards. Nat. Hist., vol.21, 1867.

MAMMALS FROM SIKANG, CHINA. Robert T. Orr. Proc. California Acad. Sci., ser.4, vol.23, no.22, pp.307-310, Sep. 1, 1938.

EXPLORATIONS OF THE AMERICAN MUSEUM OF NATURAL HISTORY IN CHINA AND MONGOLIA. Henry Fairfield Osborn. Proc. Amer. Philos. Soc., vol.62, no.3, pp.90-95, 1923.

(ON THE MAMMAL FAUNA OF SZECHUAN AND ON AN ASIATIC SPECIES OF THE GENUS ZAPUS.) Sur la faune mammalogique du Setchuan et sur une espèce Asiatique du genre Zapus. E. de Pousargues. Bull. Mus. Hist. Nat., Paris, vol.2, no.1, pp.11-16, figs.3, 1896.

CHINESE MATERIA MEDICA. ANIMAL DRUGS. II. WILD ANIMALS. II. RODENTIA. IV. MONKEYS AND SUPERNATURAL BEINGS. V. MAN AS A MEDICINE. Bernard E. Read. Peking Nat. Hist. Bull., vol.6, pt.2, pp.1-102, Sep., 1931. (Use of Mammals in Medicine by the Chinese.)

MANUAL OF THE VERTEBRATE ANIMALS OF NORTHEASTERN AND CENTRAL CHINA EXCLUSIVE OF BIRDS. Cora Daisy Reeves. Chung Hwa Book Co., Ltd., Shanghai, pp.i-xxxi, 1-806, figs.169, 1933.(Mammals, pp.709-783, figs.163-169.)

SMALL COLLECTION OF MAMMALS FROM NORTHEASTERN CHINA. Samuel N.Rhoads. Proc. Acad. Nat. Sci., Philadelphia, pp.120-125, Apr. 5, 1898.

NOTE ON THE MAMMALS FROM SOUTHWESTERN HUNAN. Chausu McAmicus Shih. Bull. Dept. Biol. no.9, College Sci., Sun Yatsen Univ., Canton, China, pp.4, 1930.

PRELIMINARY REPORT ON THE MAMMALS FROM YAOSHAN, KWANGSI, COLLECTED BY THE YAOSHAN EXPEDITION, SUN YATSEN UNIVERSITY, CANTON, CHINA. Chausu McAmicus Shih. Bull.Dept. Biol. no.4, College Sci, Sun Yatsen Univ. Canton, China, pp.10, 1930.

FUKIEN SCIENTIFIC EXPEDITION. Floyd Tangier Smith. China Jour. Sci. and Arts, vol.5, pp.128-131, pls.5, Sep., 1926.

BIG GAME ANIMALS OF THE CHINESE TIBETAN BORDERLAND. Arthur de Carle Sowerby. China Jour., vol.25, no.5, pp. 285-296, illus., Nov., 1936.

CHINA'S FUR TRADE AND FUR-BEARING ANIMALS. Arthur de Carle Sowerby. China Jour., vol.20, no.5, pp.286-288, May, 1934.

FAUNA OF THE SHANGHAI AREA. Arthur de Carle Sowerby. China Jour., vol.16, no. 5, pp.275-287, figs., May, 1932.

FURTHER REVIEW OF THE MAMMALS OF CHINA AND MONGOLIA. Arthur de Carle Sowerby. China Jour., Shanghai, vol. 34, no.1, pp.26-37, illus., Jan., 1941.

MAMMALS RECORDED FROM OR KNOWN TO OCCUR IN THE SHANGHAI AREA. Arthur de Carle Sowerby. Musee Heude, Notes de Mammalogie, Shanghai, no.2, pp.15, pls.3, Apr. 4, 1943.

NATURAL HISTORY OF CHINA. Arthur de Carle Sowerby. Smiths. Inst. Rep. for 1923, pp.351-368, pls.4, June, 1925. (Reprinted from Jour. N.China Branch Royal Asiatic Soc., vol.53, 1922.)

NATURAL HISTORY OF WEST CHINA. Arthur de Carle Sowerby. China Jour., vol.26, no.4, pp.198-209, illus., Apr., 1937.

RECENT RESEARCH UPON THE MAMMALIA OF NORTH CHINA. Arthur de Carle Sowerby. Jour. N.China Branch Royal Asiatic Soc., Shanghai, vol.47, pp.53-82, 1916.

RODENTS AND LAGOMORPHS OF CHINA. Arthur de Carle Sowerby. China Jour., vol. 19, no.4, pp.189-207, figs., Oct., 1933.

SOME REMARKABLE ANIMALS OF CHINA. Arthur de Carle Sowerby. Jour. N.China Branch Royal Asiatic Soc., Shanghai, vol. 71, pp.3-21, illus., 1940.

SPORT AND SCIENCE OF THE SINO- MONGOLIAN FRONTIER. Arthur de Carle Sowerby. London, Andrew Melrose, Ltd., pp. 295, illus., 1918.

ZOOLOGICAL EXPLORATION IN CHINA. Arthur de Carle Sowerby. N. China Branch Royal Asiatic Soc., Shanghai, vol.72, pp. 19-29, 1947.

CATALOGUE OF THE MAMMALS OF CHINA (SOUTH OF THE RIVER YANGTSZE) AND OF THE ISLAND OF FORMOSA. Robert Swinhoe. Proc. Zool. Soc. London, pp.615-653, figs.8, 1870.

EXTRACTS FROM HIS LETTER RELATING TO SPECIMENS SENT FROM CHINA. Robert Swinhoe. Proc. Zool. Soc. London, pt.29, pp.390, 1861.

NOTES ON CHINESE MAMMALIA OBSERVED NEAR NINGPO. Robert Swinhoe. Proc. Zool. Soc. London, pp.813-818, 1872.

ON THE MAMMALS OF HAINAN. Robert Swinhoe. Proc. Zool. Soc. London, pp.224-239, figs.4, pl., 1870.

ZOOLOGICAL NOTES OF A JOURNEY FROM CANTON TO PEKIN AND KALGAN. Robert Swinhoe. Proc. Zool. Soc. London, pp.427-451, 1870.

COLLECTION OF SMALL MAMMALS FROM CHINA. Oldfield Thomas. Proc. Zool. Soc. London, pp.635-638, Oct., 1910.

DUKE OF BEDFORD'S ZOOLOGICAL EXPLORATION OF EASTERN ASIA. XIV. ON MAMMALS FROM SOUTHERN SHEN-SI, CENTRAL CHINA. Oldfield Thomas. Proc. Zool. Soc. London, pp.687-695, pl.29, Sep., 1911.

MAMMALS COLLECTED IN THE PROVINCES OF KAN-ZU AND SZE-CHWAN, WESTERN CHINA, BY MR. MALCOLM ANDERSON, FOR THE DUKE OF BEDFORD'S EXPLORATION OF EASTERN ASIA. Oldfield Thomas. Abstract of Proc. Zool. Soc. London, no.90, pp.3-5, Feb. 7, 1911.

MAMMALS COLLECTED IN THE PROVINCES OF SHAN-SI, NORTHERN CHINA, BY MR. M. P. ANDERSON, FOR THE DUKE OF BEDFORD'S ZOOLOGICAL EXPLORATION OF EASTERN ASIA. Oldfield Thomas. Abstract of Proc. Zool. Soc. London, pp.44-45, Dec. 15, 1908.

MAMMALS COLLECTED IN THE PROVINCES OF SZE-CHWAN AND YUNNAN, W. CHINA, BY MALCOM ANDERSON, FOR THE DUKE OF BEDFORD'S EXPLORATION OF EASTERN ASIA. Oldfield Thomas. Abstract of Proc. Zool. Soc. London, no. 100, pp.48-50, Oct. 24, 1911.

MAMMALS FROM THE PROVINCES OF SZE-CHWAN AND YUNNAN, WESTERN CHINA. Oldfield Thomas. Proc. Zool. Soc. London, pp.127-141, 1912.

NEW SPECIES OF CROCIDURA AND PETAURISTA FROM YUNNAN. Oldfield Thomas. Ann. and Mag. Nat. Hist., ser. 8, vol.9, no.54, pp.686-688, June. 1912.

ON A COLLECTION OF SMALL MAMMALS FROM THE TSIN-LING MOUNTAINS, CENTRAL CHINA, PRESENTED BY MR. G. FENWICK OWEN TO THE NATIONAL MUSEUM. Oldfield Thomas. Ann. and Mag. Nat. Hist., ser.8, vol. 10, no.58, pp.395-403, Oct., 1912.

ON INSECTIVORES AND RODENTS COLLECTED BY MR. F. KINGDOM WARD IN N. W. YUNNAN. Oldfield Thomas. Ann. and. Mag. Nat. Hist., ser.8, vol.9, no.53, pp.513-519, May, 1912.

ON MAMMALS COLLECTED BY J. D. LA TOUCHE AT KUATUN, N. W. FOKIEN, CHINA. Oldfield Thomas. Proc. Zool. Soc. London, pp.769-775, Nov. 15, 1898.

ON MAMMALS FROM THE LI-KIANG RANGE, YUNNAN, BEING A FURTHER COLLECTION OBTAINED BY MR. GEORGE FORREST. Oldfield Thomas. Ann. and Mag. Nat. Hist., ser.9, vol.11, no.66, pp.655-663, June, 1923.

ON MAMMALS FROM THE YUNNAN HIGHLNDS COLLECTED BY MR. GEORGE FORREST AND PRESENTED TO THE BRITISH MUSEUM BY COL. STEPHENSON R. CLARKE, D. S. O. Oldfield Thomas. Ann. and Mag. Nat. Hist., ser.9, vol.10, pp.391-406, Oct., 1922.

ON TWO NEW MAMMALS FROM CHINA. Oldfield Thomas. Ann. and Mag. Nat. Hist., ser.7, vol.10, no.56, pp.163-166, Aug., 1902.

SECOND LIST OF SMALL MAMMALS FROM WESTERN YUNNAN COLLECTED BY MR. F. KINGDOM WARD. Oldfield Thomas. Ann. and Mag. Nat. Hist., ser.8, vol.14, no.84, pp.472-475, Dec., 1914.

BRIEF HISTORY OF NATURAL SCIENCES IN THE CHINESE REPUBLIC. Minoru Tokuda, P'Eng Feng-T'An. Shokubutsu oyobi dobutsu (Botany and Zoology), Tokyo, vol.4, nos.8-9, pp.101-106, figs.4, Aug.-Sep., 1936.

BIG GAME OF CENTRAL AND WESTERN CHINA. Harold Frank Wallace. 1913.

NEW VERTEBRATE HORIZONS IN CHINA. C.C. Young. Bull. Geol. Soc. China, Peking, vol.17, nos.3-4, pp.269-287, 1937.

NOTE ON A MAMMALIAN MICROFAUNA FROM YENCHINGKOU NEAR WANHSIEN, SZECHUAN. C.C. Young. Bull. Geol. Soc. China, vol.14, no.2, pp.247-248, June, 1935.

EXPLORATION IN CHINA. Science, vol. 70, no.1822, pp.531-532, Nov. 29, 1929.

(NOTES ON MAMMALS.) Notes de mammalogie. Shanghai, Univ. l'Aurore, Musee Heude, no.1, illus., pls., maps., 1943.

ROOSEVELTS' EXPEDITION IN WEST CHINA. (Capture of Giant Panda.) China Jour., vol.11, no.2, pp.93-94, Aug., 1929.

CORSICA

(CONTRIBUTIONS TO THE STUDY OF INSULAR VERTEBRATE LIFE IN THE WESTERN MEDITERRANEAN REGION, PARTICULARLY ON SARDINIA AND CORSICA.) Contributions a l'Etude de la Vie Vertebree Insulaire dans la Region Mediterraneenne Occidentale et particulierement en Sardaigne et en Corse. (Number of Articles Wholly or Partly on Mammals.) E.G. Dehaut. Paris, Paul Leehevalier, pp.1-95, pls.1-3, text figs. 1-27, 1920.

(ON THE POSSIBILITIES OF ESTABLISHING BIOLOGICAL RESERVES ON CORSICA.) Sur les possibilites d'établissement de réserves biologiques en Corse. J. Leandri. Bull. Mus. Nat. Hist. Nat., Paris, ser.2, vol.18, no.1, pp.45-49, Jan., 1946.

COSTA RICA

(MAMMALS OF COSTA RICA.) Mamiferos de Costa Rica. Anastasio Alfaro. Study Corrected and Augmented by Prof. J. A. Allen. Printed for the First Central American Exposition National Museum of Costa Rica. San Jose, Costa Rica, Tipografia Nacional, pp.51, 1897.

ADDITIONAL NOTES ON COSTA RICA MAMMALS, WITH DESCRIPTION OF NEW SPECIES. J.A. Allen. Bull. Amer. Mus. Nat. Hist., vol.9, pp.31-43, pl.1, Mar. 11, 1897.

FURTHER NOTES ON COSTA RICA MAMMALS, WITH DESCRIPTION OF A NEW SPECIES ORYZOMYS. J.A. Allen. Bull. Amer. Mus. Nat. Hist., vol.5, pp.237-240, Sep. 22, 1893.

NOTES ON A COLLECTION OF MAMMALS FROM COSTA RICA. J.A. Allen. Bull. Amer. Mus. Nat. Hist., vol.3, pp.203-218, Apr. 17, 1891.

(MAMMALS OF COSTA RICA: CONTRIBUTION TO KNOWLEDGE OF THE GEOGRAPHICAL DISTRIBUTION OF THE MAMMALS OF AMERICA.) Saeugethiere Costaricas, ein Beitrag zur Kenntnis der geographischen Verbreitung der Saeugethiere Amerikas. Alexander von Frantzius. Archiv. f. Naturg., Berlin, Jahrg.35, vol.1, pp. 247-325, 1869.

(MAMMALS OF COSTA RICA. CONTRIBUTION TO KNOWLEDGE OF THE GEOGRAPHICAL DISTRIBUTION OF THE MAMMALS OF AMERICA.) Los mamiferos de Costa-Rica. Contribucion a conocimiento de la extension geografica de los mamiferos de América. Alexander von Frantzius. San Jose de Costa-Rica, pp.376-442, (Translated from the German) 1881.

FOUR NEW MAMMALS FROM COSTA RICA. George G. Goodwin. Amer. Mus. Novitates, no.987, pp.1-5, May 13, 1938.

MAMMALS OF COSTA RICA. George G. Goodwin. Bull. Amer. Mus. Nat. Hist., New York, vol.87, art.5, pp.271-474, figs. 1-50, pl.17, map, Dec. 31, 1946.

FOUR NEW MAMMALS FROM COSTA RICA. William P. Harris, Jr. Occas.Papers Mus. Zool., Univ. Michigan, no.248, pp.1-6, Aug. 4, 1932.

LIST OF MAMMALS FROM COSTA RICA. William P. Harris, Jr. Univ. Michigan, Mus. Zool.Ann Arbor, Occas.Papers no.476, pp. 1-15, Oct. 8, 1943.

NEW TREE SQUIRREL AND A NEW COTTONTAIL RABBIT FROM COSTA RICA. William P. Harris, Jr. Occas.Papers Mus. Zool. Univ. Michigan, no.266, pp.4, June 28, 1933.

(MAMMALS OF COSTA RICA.) (A ZOOGEOGRAPHICAL CONTRIBUTION). Saeugetiere von Costa Rica. (Ein tiergeographischer Beitrag.) Otto Koller. Sitz.-Ber.Akad.Wiss. Wien, math.-naturw.Klasse, Abt.1, vol. 143, nos.5-7, pp.169-194, 1934.

SOME OBSERVATIONS ON THE NATURAL HISTORY OF COSTA RICA. Robert Ridgway. Ann. Rep. Simths. Inst., 1921, pp.303-324, pls.5, 1923.

CRETE

ON THE MAMMALS OF CRETE. Dorothy M.A. Bate. Proc. Zool. Soc. London, vol. 2, pp.315-323, Apr. 5, 1906.

(WILD MAMMALS OF CRETE. 1) INTRODUCTION. Die Wildsaeuger von Kreta. 1) Einleitung. Klaus Zimmerman. Zeitschr. f. Saeugetierk., Berlin, vol.17, no.1, pp. 1-3, pl.1, Feb. 19, 1953.

(WILD MAMMALS OF CRETE. 8) SURVEY OF THE MAMMALIAN FAUNA OF CRETE.) Die Wildsaeuger von Kreta. 8) Das Gesamtbild der Saeuger-Fauna Kretas. Klaus Zimmerman. Zeitschr.f. Saeugetierk., Berlin, vol.17, no.1, pp.67-72, Feb. 19, 1953.

CUBA

FOSSIL MAMMALS FROM CUBA. Glover M. Allen. Bull. Mus. Comp. Zool., Harvard College, vol.62, no.4, pp.133-148, pl.1, May, 1918.

NEW FOSSIL MAMMALS FROM CUBA. Glover M. Allen. Bull. Mus. Comp. Zool., Harvard College, vol.61, no.1, pp.1-12, Jan., 1917.

MAMMALS COLLECTED IN EASTERN CUBA IN 1917. WITH DESCRIPTIONS OF TWO NEW SPECIES. H.E. Anthony. Bull. Amer. Mus. Nat. Hist., vol.41, pp.625-645, pls.35-37, Dec. 30, 1919.

MAMMALS OF PORTO RICO, LIVING AND EXTINCT--CHIROPTERA AND INSECTIVORA. H. E. Anthony. Scientific Survey of Porto Rico and the Virgin Islands, vol.9, pt.1, pp.1-96, pls.1-15, map, Publ. by New York Acad.Sci., Dec., 1925.

MAMMALS OF PORTO RICO, LIVING AND EXTINCT--RODENTIA AND EDENTATA. H.E. Anthony. Scientific Survey of Porto Rico and the Virgin Islands, vol.9, pt.2, pp.97-241, pls.16-54, Publ. by New York Acad. Sci., Jan., 1926.

(PRESENT STATE OF THE PROBLEM OF THE ORIGIN OF CUBAN FAUNA.) Estado actual del problema sobre el origen de la fauna cubana. Carlos Guillermo Aguayo Castro. Proc. 8th Amer. Sci. Congr., Wash., vol.3, pp.475-476, Aug. 3, 1942.

NOTES ON BIRDS AND MAMMALS OBSERVED NEAR TRINIDAD, CUBA, WITH REMARKS ON THE ORIGIN OF WEST INDIAN BIRD-LIFE. Frank Michler Chapman. Amer. Mus. Nat. Hist., New York, Bull., vol.4, pp.279-330, illus., 1892.

(CONTRIBUTION TO THE STUDY OF AQUATIC MAMMALS OBSERVED ON THE CUBAN COAST.) Contribution al estudio de mamiferos acuaticos observados en las costas de Cuba. Luis A. Cuni. Rev. Facultad de Letras, Ciencias, Habana, pp.43, illus., pls.3, 1910.

(ON THE EXISTENCE OF GREAT MAMMAL FOSSILS ON THE ISLE OF CUBA.) De la existencia de grandes mamiferos fosiles en la isla de Cuba. Manuel Fernandez de Castro. Habana, El Iris, vol.1 and 2, illus., pl., 1865-71.

(CATALOGUE OF CUBAN MAMMALS.) Catalogo de los mamiferos Cubanos. Johannes Gundlach. Anales Soc. Hist. Nat., Madrid, vol.1, pp.231-258, Dec., 1872.

(CONTRIBUTIONS TO THE CUBAN MAMMALIA.) Contribucion à la mamalogia cubana. Johannes Gundlach. Habana, Impr. de G. Montiel y comp., pp.53, 1877.

NOTES ON CUBAN MAMMALS. Johannes Grundlach. Abstract of Proc. Linn. Soc., New York, no.7, pp.13-20, July 15, 1895.

(REVIEW AND CATALOG OF THE CUBAN MAMMALS.) Revista y catalogo de los mamiferos cubanos. Johannes Gundlach. Repertorio fisico-naturale de la isla de Cuba, Habana, pp.40-56, 1865-66.

CAVE-FOSSIL VERTEBRATES FROM CAMAGUEY, CUBA. Karl F. Koopman, Rudolfo Ruibal. Breviora Mus. Comp. Zool., no.46, pp.1-8, June 24, 1955.

BONES OF MAMMALS FROM INDIAN SITES IN CUBA AND SANTO DOMINO. Gerrit S. Miller, Jr. Smiths. Inst. Misc. Coll., vol. 66, no.12, pp.1-10, pl.1, Dec. 7, 1916.

THE ASCENT OF THE TURQUINO, THE HIGHEST MOUNTAIN IN CUBA. Fred W. Ramsden. Lancaster, Torreya, vol.16, no. 10, pp.211-225, Oct., 1916.

(PHYSICAL, POLITICAL AND NATURAL HISTORY OF THE ISLAND OF CUBA.) Histoire physique, politique et naturelle de l'ile de Cuba. Ramon de la Sagra. Mammiferes, Paris, A. Bertrand, pp.18, atlas of col.pls.8, 1840.

NOTES ON CUBAN FOSSIL MAMMALS. T. Wayland Vaughan. Science, n.s., vol.15, no.369, pp.148-149, Jan. 24, 1902.

CZECHOSLOVAKIA

VAST PREHISTORIC "POMPEII" REVISITED: FURTHER DISCOVERIES IN MORAVIA, AT VESTONICE AND THE PEKARNA CAVE: THE PALAEOLITHIC ART AND INDUSTRY AMONG THE MAMMOTH-HUNTERS OF CENTRAL EUROPE 30,000 YEARS AGO. Karl Absolon. Illus. London News, vol.188, no.5057, pp.499-504, illus., Mar. 21, 1936.

(ON THE OCCURRENCE OF SOME MAMMALS IN THE HIGH TATRA.) Zum Vorkommen einiger Saeuger in der Hohen Tatra. Heinrich Dathe. Leipziger Vierteljahresschrift f. Suedosteuropa, Leipzig, no.2, pp.75-76, July, 1937.

(SURVEY OF SLOVAK MAMMALS AND REMARKS CONCERNING THEIR LOCAL OCCURRENCE.) Prehled slovenskych ssavcu s poznamkami o jejich mistnim vyskytu. Jos. Jirsik. Pp. 1-8, 1925.

(CONTRIBUTIONS TO KNOWLEDGE OF THE VERTEBRATE FAUNA OF THE BOHEMIAN QUATERNARY.) Beitraege zur Kenntnis der Wirbeltierfauna des boehmischen Quataers. Adalbert Liebus. Lotos, Prag, vol. 81, pp.17-34, pls.3, 1933.

(BATS, INSECTIVORES, RODENTS, AND PREDATORS AT ORAVA.) Letouni, hmyzozravci, hlodavci a selmy no Orave. (37 Species of Mammals Listed, Including Bats, Insectivores, Rodents, and Carnivores.) Jos. Melichar. Veda Prirodni Mes. pro Sir. a Pest. Ved. Prir., Prague, vol. 9, no.10, pp.289-304, figs.7, 1928.

(NEW FINDS OF MAMMALS IN THE CZECH PLEISTOCENE.) Nove nalezy ssavcu v ceskem plistocaenu. Jar. Patrbok. Veda Prirodni Més. pro Šir. a Pest. Véd. Prir., Prague, vol.9, no.1, pp.5-7, 1928.

(CONTRIBUTION TO KNOWLEDGE OF THE MAMMALIAN FAUNA OF BOHEMIA, ESPECIALLY THE NORTHEASTERN REGION.) Beitrag zur Kenntnis der Saeugethier-Fauna Boehmens, besonders der nordoestlichen Gebiete des Landes. J.P. Prazak. Mittheilungen Naturwissensch. Vereines Univ. Wien, pp.20, 1896.

(DATA ON THE MAMMAL FAUNA OF THE BOHEMIAN LIGNITE FORMATION.) Zur Kenntnis der Saeugethierfauna der boehmischen Braunkohlenformation. Max Schlosser. Prague, Calve, pp.43, illus., pl., 1901.

(DILUVIAL FAUNA OF MORAVIA.) Moraviae fauna diluvialis. (A.Mammalia.) (Occurrences Listed Alphabetically Under Each of the 125 Recognized Species.) J. Skutil, A. Stehlik. Sbornik klubu Prir.Brno, Brunn, vol.14, pp.102-178, figs.7, (1931) 1932.

(FOSSILS OF THE MAMMALS FROM STRANSKA SKALA NEAR BRNO.) Fossilini ssavci ze Stránske skály u Brna. Al. Stehlik. Prace Moravske prirodovědecké společnosti Brno, vol.9, no.6, pp. 1-94, figs.1-6, tbls.1-49, pls.1-6, 1934. (With German summary.)

CONTRIBUTION TO THE ECOLOGY OF SOME SMALL MAMMALS IN SLOVAKIA. F.J. Turcek. Vestnik Cs. Zool., vol.15, pp.515-553, illus., 1951. (With English summary.)

EFFECT OF INTRODUCTIONS ON TWO GAME POPULATIONS IN CZECHOSLOVAKIA. F.J. Turcek. Jour. Wildl.Mgt., Menasha, vol.15, no.1, pp.113-114, Jan., 1951.

(SOME DATA ON THE OCCURRENCE OF SOME SMALL MAMMALS IN SLOVAKIA.) Poznamky k vyskytu niektorych foriem drobných savcov na Slovensku. F.J.Turcek. Přirodavedesky Sbornik Ostravského Kraje, vol.12, no.4, pp.495-502, 1951.

DENMARK

(BRIEF CONTRIBUTIONS TO DENMARK'S PREHISTORIC FAUNA. 2. HAVE OTHER DOMESTIC ANIMALS BESIDES THE DOG BEEN FOUND FROM THE OLDER STONE AGE?) Mindre Bidrag til Danmarks forhistoriske Dyreverden. 2. Sind andere Haustiere als der Hund aus der aelteren Steinzeit Daenemarks gefunden worden? Magnus Degerbøl. Videnskabeliga Meddelelser fra Dansk Naturhist. Forening, vol.86, pp. 83-92, 1928.

(DENMARK'S MAMMALS IN THE PAST AND COMPARISON WITH RECENT FORMS.) Danmarks Pattedyr i Fortiden i Sammenligning med recente Former. Magnus Degerbøl. I.Vidensk.Meddel. Dansk Naturh.Forening, Copenhagen, vol. 96, Festskrift 2, pp.357-641, figs.21, pls. 12-24, tbls.12, 1933.

RECENT DISCOVERIES OF REMAINS OF MAMMALS FROM GLACIAL DEPOSITS IN DENMARK, DICERORHINUS KIRCHGERGENSIS (JÄGER), NEW TO THE FAUNA OF DENMARK, MEGALOCEROS GIGANTEUS (BLUMENBACH) AND BISON PRISCUS (H.V.MEYER). Magnus Degerbøl. Copenhagen, pp.26, illus., tbls., 1952. (K.Danske Videnskabernes Selskab, Copenhagen, Biologiske skrifter, bd.6, nr.8.)

(MAMMALS IN THY PROVINCE (JUTLAND).) Saeugetiere in der Landschaft They (Juetland). Erna Mohr. Schrift.Naturw. von Schleswig-Holstein, Bd.xxi, Heft 3, pp.427-439, figs.6, 1936.

(PRESERVATION OF NATURE IN DENMARK AND GREENLAND.) Naturfredning i Dansk Grønland. Morten P. Porsild. Meddelelser om Grønland, Copenhagen, vol.51, pp.253-263, figs.2, 1915.

ZOOGEOGRAPHICAL REMARKS ON THE MAMMALS OCCURRING ON THE ISLANDS SOUTH OF FUNEN (DENMARK). Erik Ursin. Vidensk. Medd. Dansk Naturh. Foren., vol. 112, pp.35-62, illus., 1950.

(ON SOME MAMMALS IN DENMARK.) Om nogle Pattedyr i Danmark. Herluf Winge. Vidensk.Meddel.Naturh. Forening, Copenhagen, vol.1, pp.283-316, 1899.

(ON SOME SMALL MAMMALS IN DENMARK.) Herluf Winge. Vidensk.Meddel. Naturh. Forening, Copenhagen, pp.12, 1882.

(DENMARK'S MAMMALS.) Danmarks Pattedyr. Jul Wulff. Copenhagen, pp.164, illus., 1881.

DOMINICAN REPUBLIC see HISPANIOLA

EAST INDIES

WHAT OF EAST INDIES WILDLIFE? Anthony De Vos. Nature Mag., Washington, vol.37, no.3, pp.125-128, illus., Mar., 1944.

MAMMALS OF BANKA, MENDANAU, AND BILLITON ISLANDS, BETWEEN SUMATRA AND BORNEO. Marcus Ward Lyon. U.S. Nat. Mus., Proceedings, Washington, vol. 31, pp.575-612, illus., map, 1907.

NATIONAL GEOGRAPHIC SOCIETY-SMITHSONIAN EXPEDITION TO THE EAST INDIES. W.M. Mann. Explor. and Fieldwork Smiths. Inst.1937, publ.3480, pp.35-40, figs.37-44, 1938.

LIGHT AND DARKNESS IN A TROPICAL FOREST. (Includes Notes on Nocturnal Habits of Certain East Indian Mammals.) H.C. Raven. Nat. Hist., vol.27, pp.474-484, illus., Sep.-Oct., 1927 (Jan., 1928).

ANIMAL AND PLANT LIFE OF THE EAST INDIES. Arthur de C. Sowerby. China Jour., vol.13, no.4, pp.216-224, figs.15, Oct., 1930.

NEW MAMMALS FROM THE EAST INDIAN ARCHIPELAGO. Oldfield Thomas. Ann. and Mag. Nat. Hist., ser.8, vol. 5, no.28, pp.383-387, Apr., 1910.

ON THE NEW GENUS AND SPECIES OF SHREW, AND SOME NEW MURIDAE FROM THE EAST INDIAN ARCHIPELAGO. Oldfield Thomas. Ann. and Mag. Nat. Hist., ser.9, vol.7, no.39, pp.243-249, Mar., 1921.

EGYPT

Extinct and Fossil Mammals

PRELIMINARY NOTE ON SOME NEW MAMMALS FROM THE UPPER EOCENE OF EGYPT. Charles William Andrews. Cairo, Nat. Print. Department, pp.9, pls.2, 1902.

SMALL COLLECTION OF MAMMALIAN REMAINS SECURED BY THE UNIVERSITY OF MICHIGAN EGYPTIAN EXPEDITION. Robert K. Enders. Paper Michigan Acad. Sci., Arts and Letters, vol.7, pp.293-298, 1926.

(CONTRIBUTION TO STUDY OF THE PREHISTORIC FAUNA OF EGYPT.) Contribution a l'étude de la faune prehistorique de l'Egypt. Claude Gaillard. Archiv. Mus. d'Hist. Nat. Lyon, vol.14, mem.3, pp. 125, figs.55, pls.12, 1934.

(Review by R. Vaufrey of ) (CONTRIBUTION TO STUDY OF THE PREHISTORIC FAUNA OF EGYPT.) Contribution a l'etude de la faune prehistorique de l'Egypt. Claude Gaillard. L'Anthropologie, Paris, année 1935, vol.35, pp.142-143, 1935.

HORNED EOCENE UNGULATE FROM EGYPT. Henry Fairfield Osborn. Science, Lancaster, n.s., vol.17, no.425, pp. 313-314, Feb. 20, 1903.

NEW FOSSIL MAMMALS FROM THE FAYUM OLIGOCENE, EGYPT. Henry Fairfield Osborn. Bull. Amer. Mus. Nat.Hist., New York, vol.24, art.16, pp.265-272, figs.6, Mar. 25, 1908.

Recent Mammals

ZOOLOGY OF EGYPT. MAMMALIA. John Anderson. London, H. Rees, Ltd., pp. 374, illus., pls.66 (part double, part col.), map, 1902.

ON A FURTHER COLLECTION OF MAMMALS FROM EGYPT AND SINAI. J. Lewis Bonhote, M.A., F.L.S. Proc. Zool. Soc. London, pp.224-231, 1912.

UNIVERSITY OF CALIFORNIA AFRICAN EXPEDITION: PART 1, EGYPT. Henry Field. Amer. Anthropologist, Menasha, vol.50, no.3, pt.1, pp.479-493, July-Sep., 1948.

NOTES ON THE RECENT MAMMALS OF EGYPT, WITH A LIST OF THE SPECIES RECORDED FROM THAT KINGDOM. Major Stanley S. Flower. Proc. Zool. Soc. London, pt.2, pp.369-450, July, 1932.

NEW MAMMAL RECORDS FOR THE WESTERN DESERT OF EGYPT. Harry Hoogstraal, et al. Bull. Zool. Soc. Egypt, no. 12 (1954), pp.7-12, Aug. 31, 1955.

RESULTS OF THE NAMRU-3 SOUTH-EASTERN EGYPT EXPEDITION, 1954. 1. INTRODUCTION, ITINERARY, AND ENVIRONMENTAL CONDITIONS. Harry Hoogstraal, et al. Bull. Zool. Soc. Egypt, vol.13, pp.1-12, maps 3, Mar. 11, 1957.

RESULTS OF THE NAMRU-3 SOUTH-EASTERN EGYPT EXPEDITION, 1954. 6. OBSERVATIONS ON NON-DOMESTICATED MAMMALS AND THEIR ECTO-PARASITES. Harry Hoogstraal, et al. Bull. Zool. Soc. Egypt, vol.13, pp.52-76, Mar. 11, 1957.

RECENT DISCOVERIES IN THE EGYPTIAN FAIYUM AND SINAI. Wendell Phillips. Science, Lancaster, n.s., vol. 107, no.2791, pp.666-670, June 25, 1948.

(DESCRIPTION OF MAMMALS FOUND IN EGYPT.) Description des Mammifères qui se trouvent en Egypte. Etienne Geoffroy Saint-Hilaire. France Commission de Monuments d'Egypte, Histoire Naturelle, vol.2, Mammifères, pls.7, 1828 (?).

NOTES ON MAMMALS FROM THE NILE DELTA REGION OF EGYPT. Henry W. Setzer. Proc. U.S. Nat. Mus., Wash., vol.102, no.3305, pp.343-369, Apr. 2, 1952.

ON SOME SMALL MAMMALS COLLECTED BY MR. A. M. MACKILLIGIN IN THE EASTERN DESERT OF EGYPT. Oldfield Thomas. Ann. and Mag. Nat. Hist., ser.7, vol.14, no.80, pp.155-159, Aug., 1904.

MAMMALS OF SOUTH SINAI, EGYPT. Kamal Wassif, Harry Hoogstraal. Proc. Egyptian Acad. Sci., Cairo, vol.9, pp. 63-79, 1954.

LIST OF MAMMALS OBTAINED BY THE HON. N. CHARLES ROTHSCHILD AND THE HON. FRANCIS R. HENLEY IN THE NATRON VALLEY, EGYPT. W.E. de Winton. Novitates Zool., vol.x, pp.279-285, pls.7-8, Aug., 1903.

EL SALVADOR

FOSSIL VERTEBRATES FROM EL SALVADOR. R.A. Stirton, William K.Gealey. Jour. Paleontol., Menasha, vol.17, no.3, p.309, May, 1943.

RECONNAISSANCE GEOLOGY AND VERTEBRATE PALEONTOLOGY OF EL SALVADOR, CENTRAL AMERICA. R. A. Stirton, William K. Gealey. Bull. Geol. Soc. Amer., vol.60, pp.1731-1754, illus., Nov., 1949.

EURASIA

(ON SOME HISTORICAL AND GEOGRAPHICAL VARIATIONS OF EURASIAN UNGULATES.) Sur quelques variations historiques et geographiques des ongules eurasiatiques. C.C. Flerov. Comptes Rendus Acad. Sci. USSr, Leningrad, vol.4, no.3, pp.167-171, Oct. 21, 1934.

PAPERS ON EURASIAN MAMMALS. N. Hollister. Govt. Print. Off., Wash., 1910-1918.

TRANSPLANTATION OF GAME IN EUROPE AND ASIA. W. Lindemann. Jour. Wildl. Mgt., vol.20, no.1, pp.68-70, Jan., 1956.

(WILD ANIMALS OF THE U. S. S. R. AND ADJACENT COUNTRIES; WILD ANIMALS OF EASTERN EUROPE AND NORTHERN ASIA.) Zveri SSSR i prilezhashchukh stran; zveri vostochnoy Yevropi i severnoy Azii. S. I. Ognev. VOL. 1, INSECTIVORA AND CHIROPTERA, pp. 1-631, maps 5, figs.279, 1928; VOL. 2. CARNIVORA (FISSIPEDIA), pp.777, maps 3, pls.5, figs. 199, 1931; VOL. 3. FISSIPEDIA, PINNIPEDIA, 1935; VOLS. 4-7. RODENTIA, 1940-1950. Moscow, Acad. of Sci. USSR Pres.

(Review by W.B. Quay of) (WILD ANIMALS OF THE U. S. S. R. AND ADJACENT COUNTRIES; WILD ANIMALS OF EASTERN EUROPE AND NORTHERN ASIA.) S. I. Ognev. Jour. Mamm., vol.32, no.4, pp. 472-474, Nov. 19, 1951.

(ALBUM OF SOME MAMMALS OF EASTERN EUROPE, WESTERN SIBERIA AND TURKESTAN.) M.K. Serebrennikov. Zeitschrift f. Saeugetierk., (I), vol.5, pp.96-104, no.2, pls.6-14, Aug. 7, 1930; (II), vol.6, no.3, pp.160-163, Dec., 15, 1931; (III), vol.8, no.2, pp.33-40, pls.1-5, Apr. 24, 1933. (In German.)

EUROPE

Extinct and Fossil Mammals

(ANIMAL LIFE IN THE GLACIAL EPOCH IN THE DRAGON CAVE AT MIXNITZ IN STYRIA.) La vie des animaux de l'epoque glaciaire dans la Caverne des Dragons a Mixnitz, en Styrie. Othenio Abel. La Terre et la Vie (Revue d'Hist.Nat.), vol.2, no.1, pp.3-24, figs.1-18, Jan., 1932.

PLEISTOCENE MAMMALS AND THEIR RELATIONS TO THE RELIGION OF THE PALAEOLITHIC MAN OF EUROPE.Othenio Abel. Proc. Linn. Soc. London, session 1934-35, pt.3, pp.58-68, 1935.

(TERNIFINE LAYER: RESULTS OF THE 1955 EXCAVATION AND DISCOVERY OF NEW REMAINS OF ATLANTHROPUS.) Le gisement de Ternifine: Resultats des fouilles de 1955 et decouverte de nouveaux restes d'Atlanthropus. C.Arambourg, Robert Hoffstetter. Comptes Rendus Acad. Sci., Paris, vol.241, pp.431-433, July, 1955.

(PLEISTOCENE CAVE FAUNA FROM THE MOUNTAINOUS REGION OF THE EASTERN ALPS.) Eine Plistozaene Hoehlenfauna aus der Hochgebirgsregion der Ostalpen. Kurt Ehrenberg, O. Sickenberg. Palaeobiologica, vol.2, nos.6-7, pp.303-364, figs. 5, pls.35-42, 1929.

(BASIC TASKS OF THE STUDY OF THE QUATERNARY PERIOD IN EUROPE.) Grundaufgaben des Studiums der Quataerablagerungen. J. Gubkin. (Deposits containing Elephas, Bos, Rhinoceros, Elasmotherium, and Equus.) Trans. II Internat. Conf. Assoc. Study Quaternary Period in Europe, United Geol. and Prosp. Serv. USSR, Leningrad, fasc.1, pp.16-27, pl., 1932.

(EXTINCTION OF THE LARGE MAMMALS OF CENTRAL EUROPE AT THE END OF THE ICE AGE.) Das Aussterben der grossen Saeugetiere Mitteleuropas am Ende der Eiszeit. Max Hilzheimer. Forschungen und Fortschritte, Berlin, Jahrg.9, no.14, pp. 204-205, May 10, 1933.

(REMAINS OF FOSSIL MAMMALS OF SOUTHERN BESSARABIA.) Restes de mammiferes fossiles de la Bessarabie meridionale. Gh. Nic. Macarovici. Annales scientifiques, Univ. de Jassy, Jassy, vol.22, pp.349-367, pls.9-13, Feb.,1936.

PALEOCENE AND LOWER EOCENE MAMMALS OF EUROPE. George Gaylord Simpson. Amer. Mus. Novitates, no.354, pp.1-17, June 5, 1929.

(THE SUIDAE AND TAYASSUIDAE OF THE TERTIARY OF STEYR.) Die Suiden und Tayassuiden des steierischen Tertiars.Erich Thenius. Sitzungsber. Akad. Wiss. Wien, Math.-naturw.Kl., vol.165, nos. 4-5, pp. 337-382, illus., 1956.

PLEISTOCENE CHRONOLOGY OF CENTRAL EUROPE. Friedrich E. Zeuner. Geol.Mag., London, vol.72, no.854, pp.350-376, folding tbl.1, Aug., 1935.

Recent Mammals

AIMS AND STATUS OF PLANT AND ANIMAL PRESERVE WORK IN EUROPE, WITH SPECIAL REFERENCE TO GERMANY, INCLUDING A LIST OF THE MOST IMPORTANT PUBLICATIONS ON THE PRESERVES. Theodor G. Ahrens. Roosevelt Wild Life Bull., vol.1, no.1, pp.83-94, Dec., 1921.

(METHODIC CATALOGUE OF EUROPEAN MAMMALS.) Catalogo metodico dei Mammiferi Europei. C.L.J.L. Bonaparte, Prince de Canino. Milano, pp.32, 1845.

(Review by P. Rode of) (GAME AND HUNTS OF EUROPE.) Gibiers et chasses d'Europe. A. de la Chevasnerie. Bibliotheque geographique, Payot, Paris, vol.1, pp.271, figs. 11, photos 21, 1939; Mammalia, Paris, vol.3, no.2, p.82, June, 1939.

GUIDE TO THE QUADRUPEDS AND REPTILES OF EUROPE; WITH DESCRIPTIONS OF ALL THE SPECIES. Thomas F. Clermont. London, J. van Voorst, pp.viii-277, 1859.

(LIST OF FRENCH AND SPANISH NAMES OF EUROPEAN MAMMALS.) Liste des noms francais et espagnols des mammiferes d'Europe. J. Dorst, et al. Mammalia, Paris, vol.21, no.3, pp.258-266, Sep., 1957.

(MAMMALS FROM KURLAND, LIVONIA, AND ESTONIA.) Saeugetiere Kur-Liv-Estlands. Karl Grevé. Riga., 1909.

(WILD MAMMALS OF EUROPE. I. INSECTIVORES, CHIROPTERS, CARNIVORES.) Les mammiferes sauvages d'Europe. I. Insectivores, Cheiropteres, Carnivores. R. Hainard. Neuchatel, Paris, pp.268, pls.20, 1948.

(WILD MAMMALS OF EUROPE. II. PINNIPEDS, RODENTS, UNGULATES, CETACEANS.) Les mammiferes sauvages d'Europe. II. Pinnipedes, Rongeurs, Ongules, Cetaces. Robert Hainard.Delachaux and Niestle, Paris, pp.274, pls.28, 1949.

(ZOOGEOGRAPHICAL STUDIES OF THE GAME OF STEIERMARK.) Zoogeographische Studien am jagdbaren Wilde Steiermarks. Wilhelm Hoffer. Mitteil.Naturwiss. Ver. Steiermark, vol.68, pp.51-82, maps 8, 1931.

(ON THE SECULAR RHYTHM OF CHANGES IN THE HABITAT OF EUROPEAN BIRDS AND MAMMALS, WITH SPECIAL CONSIDERATION OF WINTERING CONDITIONS AS A CAUSAL FACTOR.) Zur saekularen Rhythmik der areal Veraenderungen Europaeischer Voegel und Saeugetiere, mit besonderer Beruecksichtigung der Ueberwinterungsverhaeltnisse als Kausalfaktor. Olavi Kalela. Ornis Fennica, Helsinki, vol.27, no.1, pp.1-30, illus., 1950.

(DRAFT OF A DEVELOPMENTAL HISTORY AND NATURAL SYSTEM OF THE EUROPEAN ANIMAL WORLD.) Skizzirte Entwicklungs-Geschichte und Naturliches System der Europaeischen Thierwelt. Jakob Kaup. 1829.

(VERTEBRATES OF EUROPE.) Wirbelthiere Europas. Graf A. Keyserling, J.H.Blasius. Braunschweig, pp.248, 1840.

(PROTECTION OF THE ANIMALS OF THE MOUNTAINS OF EUROPE.) La protection des animaux de montagne en Europe. L. Lavauden. La Terre et la Vie, Paris, vol. 4, no.9, pp.543-552, illus., Sep., 1934.

(CAREFREE HOURS.) Sorglose Stunden. (European Game Animals.) Arthur Lindgens. Frank'sche Verlagshandlung, Stuttgart, pp.269, illus., 1948.

ZOOLOGICAL GARDENS AND ESTABLISHMENTS OF GREAT BRITAIN, BELGIUM, AND THE NETHERLANDS. Gustave Loisel. Smiths. Inst., Annual Rep., 1907, Wash., pp.407-448, illus., pl.8, 1908.

(SOME COMMENTS AND NOTES ON THE MAMMALS OF LAPLAND AND SPITSBERGEN.) Iakttagelser och anteckningar till Finnmarkens och Spetsbergens Daggdjursfauna. A.J. Malmgren. Ofvers. of K. Vet.-Akad. Forh., no.2, pp.127-155, 1863.

(REMARKS ON PROF. TROUESSART'S FAUNE DES MAMMIFERES D'EUROPE (MAMMALIAN FAUNA OF EUROPE).) Bemerkungen zu Prof. Trouessart's "Faune des mammiferes d'Europe". L. von Meholy. Archiv. f. Naturgesch., Berlin, Jahrg.76 (1910), pp.52-60, 1911.

CATALOGUE OF THE MAMMALS OF WESTERN EUROPE (EUROPE EXCLUSIVE OF RUSSIA) IN THE COLLECTION OF THE BRITISH MUSEUM. Gerrit S. Miller, Jr. London, Printed by Order of the Trustees, British Mus. (Nat.Hist.) Dept. of Zoology, pp. xv-1019, illus., 1912.

DESCRIPTIONS OF SIX NEW EUROPEAN MAMMALS. Gerrit S. Miller, Jr. Ann. and Mag. Nat. Hist., ser.8, vol.6, pp.458-461, Nov., 1910.

SOME NEW EUROPEAN INSECTIVORA AND CARNIVORA. Gerrit S. Miller, Jr. Ann. and Mag. Nat. Hist., ser.7, vol. 20, pp.389-398, Nov., 1907.

TWELVE NEW EUROPEAN MAMMALS. Gerrit S. Miller, Jr. Ann. and Mag. Nat. Hist., ser.8, vol.3, pp.415-422, May, 1909.

(ON THE DISTRIBUTION AND PROTECTION OF SOME MAMMALS OF ESTONIA, ACCORDING TO DATA OF AN INVESTIGATION OF THE NATURAL PROTECTION SECTION OF THE NATURE RESEARCH SOCIETY OF THE UNIVERSITY OF TARTU.) Ueber Verbreitung und Schutz einiger Saeugetiere Estlands, nach Daten einer Enquete der Naturschutzsektion der Naturforscher-Gesellschaft der Universitaet Tartu (Dorpat). Edwin Reinwaldt. Loodusuurijate Seltsi Looduskaitse Sektsiooni toim, Tartu, no.1, pp.1-19, figs.7, 1927.

(STUDIES OF CENTRAL EUROPEAN SMALL MAMMALS, WITH SPECIAL CONSIDERATION OF THE FORMATION OF RACES.) Studien an mitteleuropaeischen Kleinsaeugern, mit besonderer Beruecksichtigung der Rassenbildung. Helmut Schaefer. Archiv. f. Naturgesch., Leipzig, Abt.B., n.F., vol. 4, no.4, pp.390-535, map, figs.20, 1935.

A VISIT TO THE GREAT SAINT BERNARD, 1925, WITH SOME NOTES ON ITS SURVIVING WILD LIFE. Henry W. Shoemaker. Pennsylvania Alpine Club, Wild Life Bull., no.6, pp.30, illus., 1926.

DECLINE IN NUMEROUS MAMMAL AND BIRD POPULATIONS IN NORTHWESTERN EUROPE DURING THE 1940'S. Lauri Siivonen. Papers on Game Research, Game Research Inst., Helsinki, no.2, pp.26, illus., 1948.

(CONTRIBUTION TO KNOWLEDGE OF SOME CENTRAL EUROPEAN MAMMALS.) Beitraege zur Kenntnis einiger mitteleuropaeischer Saeuger. G. Stein. Mitteil.Zool. Mus. Berlin, vol.17, no.2, pp.273-298, 1931.

SCHARFF'S HISTORY OF THE EUROPEAN FAUNA. Leonhard Stejneger. Amer. Nat., Boston, vol.35, no.410, pp.87-116, Feb., 1901.

CONSPECTUS MAMMALIUM EUROPAE. (MAMMALIAN FAUNA OF EUROPE.) Faune des mammiferes d'Europe. Edouard Louis Trouessart. Berlin, Friedlaender und Sohn, pp.xvii-266, 1910.

ZOOGDIERENGIDS. (A FIELD GUIDE TO THE MAMMALS OF EUROPE WEST OF 30 DEGREES E. LONGITUDE.) F. H. Van den Brink. Elsevier, Amsterdam, pp.321, illus., 1955. (In Dutch.)

(CONTRIBUTION TO EUROPEAN MAMMALOGY.) Beitraege zur Saeugetierkunde Europas. Otto Wettstein-Westersheim. Archiv f. Naturgesch., Abt.A, (I), vol.91, pp.139-163, Jan., 1926; (II), vol.92, no.3, pp.64-146, 1926; Zeitschr. f. Saeugetierk., Berlin, (III), vol.8, nos.1-2, pp.113-122, Apr. 24, 1933.

(CRITICAL REMARKS ON HANS REBEL'S (THE FREE-LIVING MAMMALS OF AUSTRIA AS PRECURSORS OF A DOMESTIC MAMMALIAN FAUNA.)) Kritische Bemerkungen zu: Hans Rebel, die freilebenden Saeugetiere Oesterreichs als Prodromus einer heimischen Mammalienfauna (Oesterreichischer Bundesverlag, Wien, 1933). Otto Wettstein-Westersheim. Zeitschr.f. Saeugetierk., vol.8, no.6, pp.286-288, Dec. 20, 1933.

(FIVE NEW EUROPEAN MAMMAL FORMS.) Fuenf neue europaeische Saeugetierformen. Otto Wettstein-Westersheim. (Sitzung der mathematisch-naturwissenschaftlichen Klasse vom 13.Jaenner 1927.) Anzeiger Kais. Akad. Wissenschaften Wien, no.1, pp.1-5, 1927.

(FAUNAL MIXTURE ALONG THE SOUTHERN RIM OF THE ALPS.) Faunenmischung am Suedrand der Alpen. F. Zschokke. Verhandl. der Naturforsch.Gesellschaft in Basel, vol.38, pp.12-28, 1927.

FAROE ISLANDS

MAMMALIA. Magnus Degerbøl. Zoology of the Faroes, Copenhagen, vol.3, pt.2, fasc.65, pp.1-132, figs.17, 1940.

NARRATIVE OF THE CRUISE OF THE YACHT MARIA AMONG THE FEROE ISLANDS IN THE SUMMER OF 1854. London, pp.89, illus., 1855.

FINLAND

NOTES ON THE OCCURRENCE OF INJURIOUS ANIMALS ON CULTIVATED PLANTS IN NORTHERN FINLAND (trans.title.). Yrjo Hukkinen. Maatalouskoelaitos, Tieteellisiä julkaisuja no.25, pp.164, maps 15, Helsinki, 1925. (In Finnish with German summary. Brief mention of mammals.)

SILVA FENNICA 40. FINNISH GAME AND HUNTING. V.M. Klemola. Suomen Metsatieteellinen Seura-Finska Forstsamfundet (Soc.Forestry in Suomi), Helsinki, pp.27, 1937.

(RESULTS OF MARKING OF GAME ANIMALS DURING THE YEARS 1947-1949.) Tuloksia riistaelainten merkitsemisesta suomessa vv. 1947-49. Jukka Koskimies. Suomen Riista Finnish Foundation for Game Preservation, Helsinki, no.5, pp. 134-143, illus., 1950. (In Finnish with English summary.)

TOPICAL HABITAT PROBLEMS FOR FOREST WILDLIFE IN FINLAND. Jukka Koskimies. Papers on Game Research, Helsinki, vol.8, pp.36-41, illus., 1952.

(ON THE MICROMAMMALOGY OF CENTRAL FINLAND.) Bidrag till mellersta Finlands micromammalogi. Carl Lundahl. Foredr. for Vet. Soc., pp.287-299, Nov. 10, 1851.

(GREAT BOOK OF MAMMALS.) Suuri Nisakaskirja. Lauri Siivonen. Otava Publishing Co., Helsinki, pp.800, illus., 1956.

REPORT OF THE ACTIVITY OF THE GAME-RESEARCH INSTITUTE OF THE FINISH FOUNDATION FOR GAME-PRESERVATION DURING THE 5-YEAR PERIOD 9/11/1943-9/11/1948. Lauri Siivonen. Suomen Riista, Helsinki, vol.3, pp.7-33, figs.6, 1948. (In Finnish with English summary.)

(SURVEY OF GAME IN FINLAND.) En oversikt over villebradet i Finland. Lauri Siivonen, Suomen Riista, Helsinki, no. 4, pp.125-170, illus., 1949. (In Finnish with English summary.)

(THE TASKS OF GAME RESEARCH IN THE IMPROVING OF OUR GAME-ECONOMY. THE FINNISH FOUNDATION FOR GAME-PRESERVATION AS THE CENTRAL ORGAN OF GAME-RESEARCH IN FINLAND.) Riistantutkimuksen tehtavat riistataloutemme kohottamisessa. Suomen Riistanhoito-Saatio maamme riistantutkimuksen keskuselimena. Lauri Siivonen. Suomen Riista, Suomen Riistanhoito-Saatio, Riistantutkimuslaitos(Finnish Foundation for Game, Preservation, Game Research Inst.), Helsinki, vol.1, pp.7-30, 1946. (In Finnish with English summary.)

BIOLOGICAL ZONATION OF FINLAND AS REFLECTED IN ZOOTAXONOMY. P. Voipio. Ann. Zool. Soc. "Vanamo," Helsinki, vol.18, pp.1-36, 1956.

FORMOSA

SYNOPSIS OF THE VERTEBRATES OF TAIWAN. Johnson T.F. Chen. Taiwan K'ai Ming Bookshop, Taipei, pp.619, Jan., 1956. (In Chinese. Mammals, pp. 513-562.)

MATERIAL FOR THE STUDY OF THE FORMOSAN MAMMALS. Y. Horikawa. 3. Trans. Nat. Hist. Soc. Formosa, vol. 19, no.103, pp.357-363, 1929. (In Japanese.)

FORMOSAN MAMMALS PRESERVED IN THE COLLECTION OF MARQUIS YAMASHINA. Nagamichi Kuroda. Jour. Mamm., vol.16, no.4, pp.277-291, Nov., 1935.

GEOGRAPHICAL DISTRIBUTION OF MAMMALS IN THE ISLAND OF BOTEL TOBAGO OR KOTOSHO, NEAR FORMOSA. Nagamichi Kuroda. Bull. Biogeogr. Soc. Japan, vol.2, no.2, pp.122-134, figs.3, pl.13, July, 1931. (In Japanese with English summary.)

MAMMALOGICAL HISTORY OF FORMOSA WITH ZOOGEOGRAPHY AND BIBLIOGRAPHY. Nagamichi Kuroda. Quart. Jour. Taiwan Mus., Taipei, vol.5, no.4, pp. 267-304, Dec., 1952.

ON A COLLECTION OF MAMMALS FROM FOROMSA. Nagamichi Kuroda. Dobutsugaku Zasshi, vol.37, no.435, pp.1-16, Jan. 15, 1925. (In Japanese.)

EXHIBITION OF THE SKINS OF AN OTTER FROM AMOY, AND OF A HARE FROM THE ISLAND OF FORMOSA, FORWARDED BY MR. SWINHOE. Philip Lutley Sclater. Proc. Zool. Soc. London, pt.29, pp.389-391, 1861.

ON THE MAMMALS OF THE ISLAND OF FORMOSA. Robert Swinhoe. Proc. Zool. Soc. London, pt.30, pp.347-365, fig.1, pls., 1862.

MODE OF OCCURRENCE OF THE FOSSIL MAMMAL FROM TAIKEI, FORMOSA. Jour. Geol. Soc. Tokyo, vol.36, no.433, pp. 462-463, Oct. 20, 1929. (In Japanese.)

FRANCE

Extinct and Fossil Mammals

(PRELIMINARY NOTE ON A RUMINANT OF THE LOWER PLIOCENE OF ROUSSILLON.) Note préliminaire sur un Ruminant du Pliocene inférieur du Roussillon. C. Arambourg, Jean Piveteau. Comptes Rendus Somm. Séance Géol. France, nos.10-11, pp.144-146, 1929.

(FAUNA WITH BONY BRECCIA FROM THE WOODS OF THE HOSPITAL NEAR MONTPELLIER.) Faune de la brèche osseuse du bois de l'hopital prés de Montpellier. Gaston Astre. Bull. Soc. Hist. Nat. Toulouse, vol.66, nos.3-4, pp.367-368, Dec. 30, 1934.

(FAUNA OF LOS MORTS GROTTO AT MONTSÉGUR-LE CHATEAU.) Faune de la Grotte de Los Morts a Montségur-Le Chateau. Gaston Astre. Bull. Soc. Hist. Nat. Toulouse, vol.77, fasc.4, pp.282-286, Dec. 30, 1942.

(PLEISTOCENE FAUNA OF THE CHAMBERS OF BERNICAUT AT SOREZE.) Faune pleistocene des chambres de Bernicaut a Soreze. Gaston Astre. Bull. Soc. Hist. Nat. Toulouse, vol.78, fasc.1, pp.17-22, May 10, 1943.

(PALEONTOLOGICAL STUDY OF THE FAUNA OF ISTURITZ.) Etude paleontologique de la faune d'Isturitz. Jean Bouchud. Mammalia, Paris, vol.15, no.4, pp.184-203, Dec., 1951.

(OBSERVATIONS CONCERNING SOME NEW FOSSIL MAMMALS OF QUERCY.) Observations concernant quelques mammiferes fossiles nouveaux du Quercy. Henri Filhol. Paris, Annales des sciences naturelles, zoologie et paleontologie, ser.7, vol.16, pp.129-150, 1894.

(NEW MAMMALS IN THE MIOCENE DEPOSITS OF THE GRIVE ST. ALBAN(ISERE).) Nouveaux Mammiferes dans les depots miocenes de la Grive St. Alban (Isere). Claude Gaillard. Bull. Soc. Nat. et Arch. de l'Ain, pp.1-17, figs.1-7, 1929.

(PREHISTORIC RESEARCH IN THE VALLEY OF FONTECHEVADE.) Recherches prehistoriques dans la vallee de Fontechevade. Germaine Henri-Martin. Bull. Soc.Préhist. Francaise, Paris, vol.36, no.4, pp. 196-199, Apr., 1939.

(STATISTICS OF FINDINGS OF QUATERNARY ELEPHANTS AND RHINOCEROSES IN LORRAINE.) Statistique des trouvailles d'eléphants et de rhinocéros quaternaires en Lorraine. E. Linkenheld. Bull. Assoc. Philom. d'Alsace et de Lorraine, vol.7, no.2, pp.92-103, 1926 (1927).

(PRESENTATION OF BONES FROM THE MOUSTIERIEAN LAYER IN ORIGNY-BENOITE (AISNE).) Présentation d'ossements provenant d'un gisement Moustiérien à Origny-Benoite (Aisne). M. G. Mathieu. Soc. Géol. du Nord, Lille, vol.57, pp.36-37, 1932.

(STRATUM OF BONES OF THE "RENNE AGE" IN PROVENCE.) Un gisement d'ossements de l'"âge du Renne" en Provence. H. Parent. Comptes Rendus Somm.Séance Soc. Géol. France, no.17, pp.286-288, 1928.

(PICTURES OF DISAPPEARED WORLDS. AN EPISODE OF THE HISTORY OF MAMMALS IN THE PARIS BASIN.) Images de mondes disparus. Un épisode de l'Histoire des mammiferes dans le Basin de Paris. Jean Pivetean. La Nature, Paris, no.3191, pp.72-76, Mar., 1951.

(NEW FOSSIL MAMMALS IN THE UPPER LUDIEN OF PONT D'ASSOU.) Nouveaus mammiferes fossiles dans le Ludien superieur de Pont d'Assou. Marguerite Richard. Bull. Soc. Hist. Nat. Toulouse, vol.75, pp.252-259, figs.2, Dec. 30, 1940.

(ANIMALS THAT HAVE DISAPPEARED FROM THE FAUNA OF ALSACE.) Animaux disparus de la faune d'Alsace.Paul Scherdlin. Bull. Assoc. Philom. d'Alsace et de Lorraine, vol.7, no.2, pp.55-59, 1926 (1927).

(ON THE PLIOCENE AGE OF THE FAUNA IN THE CAVES OF LAZARET (SETE, HÉRAULT).) Sur l'age pliocene de la faune des grottes du Lazaret (Sete, Hérault). Louis Thaler. Comptes Rendus Acad. Sci., Paris, vol.241, pp.433-435, July 25, 1955.

(Review by P. Rode of) (VANISHED FAUNA OF FRANCE.) Le Faune disparue de France. R. Thevenin. Mammalia, Paris, vol.8, no. 2, p.77, June, 1944.

(ON THE OLIGOCENE FAUNA OF CODERET, NEAR BRANSSAT (ALLIER).) Sur la faune oligocène de Coderet, pres Branssat (Allier). J. Viret. Comptes Rendus Acad. Sci.Paris, vol.186, no.19, pp.1309-1311, May 7, 1928.

Recent Mammals

(FAUNA OF FRANCE: MAMMALS.) Faune de France; Mammiferes. Alexander Acloque. Paris, pp.84, illus., 1900.

(NOTES ON CAPTURES IN THE NORTH OF THE DEPARTMENT OF HAUTE-VIENNE OF THREE MERIDIONAL MICROMAMMALS.)Note sur les captures dans le nord du department de la Haute-Vienne de trois micromammiferes meridonaux. Rene d'Abadie. Mammalia, Paris, vol.12, no.4, pp.155-157, Dec., 1948.

(WILD ANIMALS OF FRANCE.) Fauves de France. Jean Émile Bénech. Paris, Stock, pp.176, 1954. (Les Livres de nature, 68.)

(JARDIN DES PLANTES; DESCRIPTION AND HABITS OF MAMMALS OF THE MENAGERIE AND THE MUSEUM OF NATURAL HISTORY, PRECEDED BY A HISTORICAL, DESCRIPTIVE, AND PICTORIAL INTRODUCTION BY M.J. JANIN.) Le Jardin des plantes; description et moeurs des mammiferes de la Menagerie et du Museum d'histoire naturelle, precede d'une introduction historique, descriptive et pittoresque par M.J. Janin. Pierre Boitard. Paris, J.J. Dubochet et Co., pp.472, illus., pls.(part col.), fold.plan., 1842.

AMERICAN MAMMALS INTRODUCED INTO FRANCE IN THE CONTEMPORARY PERIOD, ESPECIALLY MYOCASTER AND ONDATRA. E. Bourdelle. Jour. Mamm., vol.20, no.3, pp.287-291, Aug. 14, 1939.

(NOTES ON SOME MAMMALS WHOSE EXISTENCE IS MENACED IN FRANCE.) Note sur quelques mammiferes dont l'existence est menacée en France. E. Bourdelle. Mammalia, Paris, vol.4, no.1, pp.11, Mar., 1940.

(PROTECTION OF MAMMALS IN THE FRENCH COLONIES.) La protection des mammiferes dans les colonies Francaises. E. Bourdelle. Revue d'Histoire Naturelle, Pt.1, A. Mammiferes, Paris, vol.11, no.3, pp.108-110, Mar., 1930.

(PRESENT DISTRIBUTION AND DENSITY OF CARNIVORES IN THE DEPARTMENT OF DEUX-SEVRES AND THE NEIGHBORING REGIONS.) Repartition et densite actuelle des Carnivores dans le Department des Deux-Sevres et les régions voisines. A. Brosset. Mammalia, Paris, vol.18, no.2, pp.216-218, June, 1954.

(THE MAMMALS OF CANTAL.) Les mammiferes du Cantal. P. Cantuel. Mammalia, Paris, vol.2, no.3, pp.125-134, map, Sep., 1938.

(REPRODUCTION PERIOD AND NUMBER OF FOETUSES OF SOME MICROMAMMALS OF THE FAUNA OF FRANCE.) Periode de reproduction et nombre de foetus de quelques micromammiferes de la faune de France. P. Cantuel. Mammalia, Paris, vol.10, nos.3-4, pp.140-144, Sep.-Dec., 1946 (issued in 1947).

(REMARKS ON THE FAUNA OF VOEGTLINSHOFEN (HAUT-RHIN).) Remarques sur la faune de Voegtlinshofen (Haut-Rhin). Georges Dubois. Comptes Rendus Somm. Seance Soc. Géol. France, no.12, pp.176-177, 1929.

(SOME MAMMALS OF THE MASSIF CENTRAL (SOUTHERN FRANCE).) Einige Saeugetiere aus dem Zentralmassiv, Suedfrankreich. H. Felten, C. Koenig. Senckenbergiana Biologica, Frankfurt a.M., vol.36, nos.3-4, pp.267-269, July 15, 1955.

(NOTES ON MAMMALS. XLIII. SOME MAMMALS OF EASTERN PYRENEES.) Notes sur les mammiferes. XLIII. De quelques mammiferes des Pyrenees Orientales. Serge Frechkop. Bull. Inst. Roy. Sci. Nat. Belgique, vol.31, no.70, pp.15, Nov., 1955.

(MAMMALOGY OF SARTHE.) Mammalogie de la Sarthe. A. Gentil. Bull. Soc. Agric., Sci. et arts de la Sarthe, ser.2, vol.20, pp.15-58, 1881.

(NOTE ON THE FAUNA OF MICROMAMMALS IN THE DOMAIN OF L'ETOILE DE CHOISY (VERSAILLES).) Note sur la faune des micromammiferes du domaine de l'Etoile de Choisy (Versailles). J. Giban. Mammalia, Paris, vol.21, no.1, pp.77-89, Mar., 1957.

(MAMMALS OF ALSACE.) Les Mammiferes d'Alsace. M. Francois Gouin. Mus. Zool. Strasbourg, pp.29, figs.11, 1950.

(NOTE ON THE SMALL MAMMALS OF THE PYRENEES.) Note sur les petits Mammiferes des Pyrenées. Maurice Gourdon. Bull. Soc. Sci. Nat. Ouest France, Nantes, ser.4, vol.10, nos.1-4, pp.15-29, Apr.30, 1931.

(UNPUBLISHED ECOLOGICAL CHARACTERS AND DISTRIBUTIONS OF SOME MICROMAMMALS IN THE SOUTHEAST OF FRANCE.) Caracteres ecologiques et répartitions inédits de quelques micromammiferes dans le Sud-Est de la France. Henri Heim de Balsac. Comptes Rendus Acad.Sci., Paris, vol.240, no.2, pp.238-240, Jan., 1955.

(BOTANIC AND ZOOLOGIC RESEARCH REALIZED IN 1926 AND 1927 IN THE ESPINGO CIRCLE AND THE UPPER PART OF THE VALE OF THE PORT OF VENASQUE.) Recherches botaniques et zoologiques effectuées en 1926 et 1927 dans le cirque d'Espingo et la partie superieure du val du port de Venasque (Canton de Bagneres-de-Luchon, Haute-Garonne). Henri Gadeau de Kerville. Bull. Soc. Amis Sci. Nat. Rouen (annees 1926 et 1927), pp.139-203, pls.4, 1928. (Mammals, pp.173-174.)

(PROVISIONAL CATALOGUE OF THE NON-MARINE WILD MAMMALS OF THE DEPARTMENT OF GIRONDE.) Catalogue provisoire des mammiferes sauvages non marins du department de la Gironde. F. Lataste. Actes Soc. Linn. Bordeaux, vol. 38, pp.1-37, 1884.

(NOTES ON SOME SMALL MAMMALS FROM THE SOUTH OF FRANCE.) Note sur quelques petits mammiferes du midi de la France. Edm. de Selys Longchamps. Revue Zool. Soc. Cuvierienne, 6th Annee, no.5, pp.1-3, May, 1843.

(Review of) (UNCOMMON GAME OF FRANCE.) Gibiers rares de France. Paul Megnin. Mammalia, Paris, vol.6, nos. 3-4, p.127, Sep.-Dec., 1942.

(FAUNA OF THE MAINE AND LOIRE.) Faune de Maine et Loire. P.A. Millet. Paris, vols. 1 and 2, 1828.

(NOTES ON THE MAMMALS OF PROVENCE.) Note sur les mammiferes de la Provence. J.F.M. Réguis. Marseille, pp. 70, 1880.

(ATLAS OF THE MAMMALS OF FRANCE.) Atlas des mammiferes de France. Paul Rode, R. Didier. Editions N. Boubee & Cie., Paris, pp.219, figs.114, pls.12 (col.), 1946.

(Review of) (ATLAS OF THE MAMMALS OF FRANCE.) Atlas des mammiferes de France. Paul Rode, R. Didier. Jour. Mamm., vol.28, no.1, p.69, Feb. 15, 1947.

(Review by E. Schwarz of) (MAMMALS OF FRANCE.) Les Mammiféres de France. Paul Rode, R. Didier. Zool. Garten, n.F., Leipzig, vol.8, nos.4-6, pp.160-161, Jan., 1936.

(FAUNA OF MAMMALS OF BURDIGALINE DE LA ROMIEU (GERS).) La faune de mammiferes du Burdigaline de La Romieu (Gers). Frederic Roman, Jean Viret. Mem. Soc. Geol. France, Paris, n.s., vol.9, nos.2-3, mem.21, pp.1-67, figs.25, pls., 1934.

(ECOLOGY OF THE TERRESTRIAL MAMMALS IN THE NORTH OF BASSE-LOIRE.) Ecologie des mammiferes terrestres du nord de la Basse-Loire. H. Saint Girons, M.C. Saint Girons. Mammalia, Paris, vol.10, nos.1-2, pp.44-49, Mar.-June, 1947; vol. 11, nos.1-2, pp.44-49, Mar.-June, 1948.

(CATALOG OF THE MAMMALS OF THE PYRENEES.) Catalogue des mammiferes des Pyrenees. Eugene Trutat. Bull. Soc. Hist. Nat. Toulouse, vol.12, pp.95-122, 1878.

(NATIONAL PARK OF PELVOUX AND THE QUESTION OF MOUNTAIN RESERVES.) Le Parc National du Pelvoux et le question des reserves de Montagne. Charles Valois. La Terre et la Vie (Revue d'Hist.Nat.), vol.2, no.2, pp.85-106, illus., Feb.,1932.

(FRENCH REVIEW OF MAMMALOGY.) Revue Francaise de Mammalogie. Ser.1, nos.1-2, pp.96, illus., 1927-1928.

GALAPAGOS ISLANDS

ON A SMALL COLLECTION OF MAMMALS FROM THE GALAPAGO ISLANDS, COLLECTED BY DR. G. BAUR. J.A. Allen. Bull. Amer. Mus. Nat. Hist., vol.4, pp.47-50, Mar. 25, 1892.

HANCOCK EXPEDITION OF 1933 TO THE GALAPAGOS ISLANDS. G.H. Banning. General Rep. Bull.Zool. Soc. San Diego, Calif., vol.10, pp.1-30, map, 1933.

MAMMALS OF THE GALAPAGOS ARCHIPELAGO, EXCLUSIVE OF THE CETACEA. E. Heller. Pap. Hopkins Stanford Galapagos Exped., 1898-1899. Proc. Calif. Acad. Sci., ser.3, (zool.), vol.3, pp.233-250, pl.1, 1904.

EQUATORIAL WONDERLAND. GALAPAGOS. J.R. Slevin. Nat. Hist., New York, vol.36, pp.374-388, 1935.

GALAPAGOS AS THEY WERE IN 1817. Illus. London News, vol.188, no.5061, p. 687, illus., Apr. 18, 1936.

GERMANY

Extinct and Fossil Mammals

(STEINHEIM PRIMITIVE MAN AND THE ANIMAL WORLD OF HIS RANGE.) Der Steinheimer Urmensch und die Tierwelt seines Lebensgebietes. F. Berckhemer. Aus der Heimat, Naturw.Monatsschr., Stuttgart, Jahrg. 47, no.4, pp.101-115, figs. 9, pls.21-24, Apr., 1934.

(BREAKDOWN OF THE EARLY TERTIARY MOLASSE IN SOUTHERN GERMANY ACCORDING TO MAMMALS.) Gliederung der jungtertiaren Molasse in Sueddeutschland nach Saeugetieren. Richard Dehm. Neues Jahrb. Geol. und Palaontol., pp.140-152, illus., 1951.

(REPORT ON UPPER EOCENE MAMMALS OF THE ALPS NEAR ULM.) Bericht ueber die oberozaenen Saugetiere der Ulmer Alp. W.O. Dietrich. Palaeontologische Zeitschrift, vol.11, no.3, pp.258-261, Nov. 21, 1929.

(A SABERTOOTH TIGER AND A LARGE ANTHROPOID (?) FROM THE SANDS OF MAUER A. D. ELSENZ.) Ein Saebeltiger und ein grosser Anthropoide (?) aus den Sanden von Mauer a.d. Elsenz. Wilhelm Freudenberg. Zeitschr. Deutsch. Geol. Ges., vol.81, no.6, p.291, 1929.

(A FOREST-BED-FAUNA FROM THE SACKDILLINGER CAVE (UPPER PALATINATE).) Eine Forest-Bed-Fauna aus der Sackdillinger Hoehle (Oberpfalz). Florian Heller. Neues Jahrb. f. Mineral. Geol. und Palaont., Stuttgart, vol.63 B, pp.247-298, 1930.

(ANIMAL REMAINS FROM THE STONE AGE FINDS IN THE SATRUPHOLM MOOR IN SCHLESWIG-HOLSTEIN.) Tierreste aus steinzeitlichen Fundstellen des Satrupholmer Moores in Schleswig-Holstein. Wolf Herre. Schriften Naturwiss. Vereins Schleswig-Holstein, Band 24, Heft 1, pp. 53-58, 1949.

(QUATERNARY MAMMAL REMAINS FROM THE BARRANDE GROTTO.) Quataere Saeugetierreste aus der Barrande-Grotte. Adalbert Liebus. Zeitschrift Lotos, vol.76, nos.8-12, pp.347-350, fig.1, Aug.-Dec., 1928.

(BIOLOGICAL INVESTIGATIONS IN THE SEGEBERG CAVE.) Biologische Untersuchungen in der Segeberger Hoehle. Erna Mohr. Schriften Natur. Vereins f. Schleswig-Holstein, vol.19, no.1, pp.1-25, pls. 1-11, 1929.

(AN OLD PALEOLITHIC HUNTING GROUND NEAR WALLERTHEIM IN RHINE-HESSE.) Eine altpalaeolithische Jagdstelle bei Wallertheim in Rheinhessen. O. Schmidtgen, W. Wagner. Notizblatt Ver. Erdkunde Hessischen Geol. Landesanstalt Darmstadt, vol.5, no.11, pp.59-89, 1928 (1929).

(MAMMAL FINDS IN THE DILUVIUM OF BAVARIA. 2. AN OVIBUS SKULL IN THE OLD DILUVIUM OF BAVARIAN SWABIA.) Saeugetierfunde im diluvium Bayerns. 2. Ein Ovibos-Schaedel im Altdiluvium bayrisch Schwabens. Ernst Stromer. Centralblatt Mineral. Geol. und Palaont., Abt. B, no.11, pp.594-600, figs.2, 1928.

(VERTEBRATES IN THE UPPER MIOCENE SIDERITE OF MUNICH.) Wirbeltiere im obermiocaenen Flinz Muenchens. Ernst Stromer. Abhandl. Bayerischen Akad. Wiss. Math.-Nat. Abt., vol.32, no.1, pp.1-71, figs.3, pls.3, 1929.

(ON THE FOSSIL AND SUBFOSSIL REMAINS OF QUATERNARY MAMMALS PREVIOUSLY FOUND IN THE PROVINCE OF HANNOVER.) Ueber die bisher in der Provinz Hannover aufgefundenen fossilen und subfossilen Reste quataerer Saeugethiere. C. Struckmann. Jahresbericht Naturhistorischen Gesellschaft, Hannover, vol.33-34, pp.36, 1884.

(CONTRIBUTIONS TO KNOWLEDGE OF HEPPENLOCH FAUNA AND THE FAUNA OF THE SANDS OF FRANKENBACH.) Beitraege zur Kenntnis der Heppenloch-fauna und der Fauna der Frankenbacher Sande. Otto Thies. Jahrb. Preuss. Geol. Landesanst., vol.46, pp.576-615, (1925) 1926.

SKULL OF A GERMAN WILD BOAR FROM BADEN AND OF A HUNGARIAN WILD BOAR FROM KOLOZVAR. Oldfield Thomas. Abstract of Proc. Zool. Soc. London, no. 105, pp.13-14, Mar. 5, 1912.

(EARLY TERTIARY VERTEBRATES OF HOEWENEGG-HEGAU.) Jungtertiaere Wirbeltiere vom Hoewenegg-Hegau. Umschau, Frankfurt a.M. H.Tobien. Jahrg. 54, Heft 18, pp.559-561, illus., Sep.15, 1954.

(CONTRIBUTIONS TO THE SMALL MAMMAL FAUNA OF LUENEBURG.) Beitraege zur Kleinsaeugerfauna Lueneburgs. R. O. Wedemeyer. Zeitschr. f. Saeugetierkunde, Berlin, vol.16, pp.271-288, figs.11, pls. 7-8, 1942.

FIRST PALEOCENE MAMMALIAN FAUNA IN GERMANY. Johannes Weigelt. Research and Progress, Berlin, vol.6, no.3, pp.117-122, figs.4, May-June, 1940.

Recent Mammals

(STUDIES ON THE ECOLOGY AND ZOOGEOGRAPHY OF BOGS.) Studien zur Oekologie und Tiergeographie der Moore. Otto Amisch. Zool. Jahrbuecher, Abt.f. Systematik, etc., vol.51, pp.1-166, figs. 10, 1925. (Contains Brief Note on Mammals of Peat Bogs, p.115.)

RELATIONS OF WILD LIFE TO FORESTRY PRACTICE IN GERMANY. Theodor G. Arrens. Parks and Recreation, vol.9, no.4, pp.439-444, illus., Apr., 1926.

(VERTEBRATES OF BADEN IN THEIR RELATIONSHIP TO THE SURROUNDINGS AND THE TYPE OF LANDSCAPE.) Die Wirbeltiere Badens in ihrer Beziehung zur Umwelt und zur Landschaftsform. M. Auerbach. Beitraege Naturk. Forschung Suedwestdeutschland, Karlsruhe, vol.5, pp.1-54, 1940.

(GENERAL NATURAL HISTORY OF GERMANY IN RELATION TO ALL THREE KINGDOMS. A HANDBOOK FOR CLEARER AND MORE COMPLETE SELF-INSTRUCTION, INTENDED PARTICULARLY FOR FORESTERS, TEACHERS OF YOUNG PEOPLE, AND ECONOMISTS.) Gemeinnuetzige Naturgeschichte Deutschlands nach allen drei Reichen. Ein Handbuch zur deutlicheren und vollstaendigeren Selbstbelehrung besonders fuer Forstmaenner, Jugendlehrer und Oekonomen. Johann Matthaeus Bechstein. Leipzig, Bey S. L. Crusius, 5 pts. in 4 vols., pls.112, 1789.

(LIVING CONDITIONS AND CARE OF OUR WILDLIFE IN THE FOREST.) Die Lebensbedingungen und Pflege unseres Wildes im Walde. Forstmeister Bindseil. Deutsche Jagd, Berlin, nos.33-34, pp.306-307, Nov. 22, 1940.

(NATURAL HISTORY OF MAMMALS OF GERMANY AND THE BORDERING COUNTRIES OF CENTRAL EUROPE.) Naturgeschichte der Saeugethiere Deutschlands und der angrenzenden Laender von Mitteleuropa. Johann Heinrich Blasius. Brunswick, f. Vieweg und Sohn, pp.vi-549, illus., 1857.

(ANIMAL WORLD OF SCHLESWIG-HOLSTEIN. III. MAMMALIA.) Die Tierwelt Schleswig-Holsteins. III. Die Saeugetiere. Friedrich Dahl. Die Heimat, Hamburg, vol. 4, nos.5-6, pp.113-141, figs.14-32, May-June, 1894.

(ANIMALS FROM FOREST AND FIELD.) Tiere aus Wald und Feld. Artur Eickhorn. Plochingen-Neckar, E.Driess, pp.61, illus., 1950.

(FAUNA OF THE WENDISH FORTRESS "POZTUIPIMI" (POTSDAM).) Fauna der wendischen Burg "Poztupimi" (Potsdam). Hans Enderlein. Zeitschr. f. Saeugetierk., vol.5, nos.5-6, pp.241-333, pls.20-23, Dec. 22, 1930.

(MAMMALS OF THE GERMAN FOREST.) Die Saeugetiere des Deutschen Waldes. Kurt Ehrenreich Floericke. Stuttgart, Kosmos, Gesellschaft der Naturfreunde, pp. 106, illus., 8.Aufl., 1908.

(ON GERMAN MAMMAL NOMENCLATURE.) Zur deutschsprachigen Nomenklatur der Saeuger. H.A. Freye. Zeitschr. f. Saeugetierk., vol.21, nos.1-2, pp.53-57, 1956.

(GERMAN NAMES OF GERMAN MAMMALS.) Deutsche Namen der deutschen Saeugetiere. H.A. Freye, et al. Saeugetierk. Mitteil., Stuttgart, vol.4, no.4, pp.171-174, Oct. 1, 1956.

(ON THE GERMAN NOMENCLATURE OF THE MAMMALS, ESPECIALLY THE MAMMALS OF GERMANY.) Ueber die Deutschsprachige nomenklatur der Saeugetiere, insbesondere der Deutschen. Guenter Gaffrey. Abh. Ber. Staatl. Mus. Tierk., Forschungsstelle, Dresden, vol.22, no.2, pp.185-205, 1955.

BIG GAME HUNTING IN GERMANY. Harold W. Glassen. Michigan Conservation, Lansing, vol.21, no.6, pp.6-9, illus., Nov., 1952.

(REMARKS ON SOME SILESIAN MAMMALS -SOREX PYGMAEUS LAXM. ET PALL., SOREX ETRUSCUS SAVI, AND LUTRA LUTREOLA. ILL. ALSO A FEW WORDS ON THE SEA OTTER, LUTRA MARINA AUCT., AS TYPE OF A CHARACTERISTIC GENUS.) Bemerkungen ueber ein Paar schlesische Saeugethierarten, Sorex pygmaeus Laxm. et Pall., Sorex etruscus Savi und Lutra Lutreola Ill. Nebst einigen Worten ueber die Meer-Otter, Lutra marina auct. als Typus einer eigenen Gattung. C.Gloger. Acad. Caes. Leop., Nova Acta, vol.13, pp.484-512, pls.2, 1826.

(ON THE VERTEBRATES IN AND AROUND BERLIN.) Von den Wirbeltieren in und um Berlin. Konrad Herter. Verlag Naturkundliche Korrespondenz, Berlin-Kleinmachnow, pp.40, figs.7, 1947.

(CONTRIBUTION TO THE MAMMAL FAUNA OF THE IMMEDIATE ENVIRONS OF LEIPZIG.) Ein Beitrag zur Saeugetierfauna der naeheren Umgegend von Leipzig. Erich Hesse. Sitz. Naturforsch. Gesellsch., Leipzig, vol.36, pp.21-31, 1909 (1910).

(CONTRIBUTIONS TO KNOWLEDGE OF THE FAUNA OF THE MARK. 1) WILD MAMMALS.) Beitraege zur Kenntnis der Maerkischen Fauna. 1. Die wildlebenden Saeugethiere. Ernst Huth. Sammlung Naturwissensch. Vortraege, Berlin, vol.2, no.5, pt.1, pp.1-15, 1888.

(LIST OF THE VERTEBRATES OF UPPER SWABIA.) Verzeichniss der Wirbelthiere Oberschwabens. Richard Koenig-Warthausen. 1.Abteilung, Saeugethiere, Stuttgart, pp.1-143, 1875.

(MAMMALIA (IN) BIOLOGY OF THE ANIMALS OF GERMANY.) Mammalia. (In) Biologie der Tiere Deutschlands. I. Krumbiegel. Parts 31 and 32, pp.377, 1930-31.

(MAMMALS AND BIRDS (OF THE NATURAL PARK OF KIPSHAGEN).) Saeugetiere und Voegel (des Naturschutzgebietes Kipshagen). Heinz Kuhlmann. Naturwissenschaftlicher Verein Bielefeld u. Umgegend, Ber., no.6, pp.251-256, Jan. 29, 1933.

(CONTRIBUTION TO THE MAMMAL FAUNA OF THE FEDERSEE REGION (WITH A FIRST INDICATION FOR WUERTTEMBERG).) Beitrag zur Saeugetierfauna des Federseegebiets. (Mit einem Erstnachweis fuer Wuerttemberg.) Hans Lohrl. Jahresheft Ver. Vaterl. Naturk. Wuerttemberg, Stuttgart, Jahrg. 90 (Veroeffentl.Staatl.Stelle f. Naturschutz beim Wuertt, Landesamt f. Denkmalpflege), pp.103-104, (1934) 1935.

(ECOLOGICAL AND PHYSIOLOGICAL STUDIES OF GERMAN MURINES AND SORICIDS.) Oekologische und physiologische Studien an einheimischen Muriden und Soriciden. Hans Lohrl. Zeitschr. f. Saeugetierk., vol.13, pp.114-160, pls.37-38, Aug. 1, 1938.

(MAMMALS OF THE DANZIG REGION AND THE FORMER PROVINCE OF WEST PRUSSIA. I. THE INSECTIVORES.) Die Saeugetiere des Danziger Gebietes und der frueheren Provinz Westpreussen. I. Die

Insektenfresser. Hans Luettschwager. Schriften der Naturforsch. Ges. Danzig, n.F., vol.19, no.3, pp.21-36, 1930-31.

(INTRODUCTION. ZOOLOGY: GERMANY AND HER COLONIES.) Einleitung. Zoologie - Deutschland und seine Kolonien. Paul Matschie. Pp.38, figs.51, 1897.

(MAMMAL WORLD OF GERMANY: YESTERDAY AND TODAY.) Deutschlands Saeugetierwelt einst und jetzt. Paul Matschie. Natur und Haus, Jahrg. 5, no.17, pp.261-267, 1897.

(MAMMAL WORLD OF GERMANY TODAY AND YESTERDAY IN ITS RELATIONSHIP TO ANIMAL DISTRIBUTION.) Die Saeugetierwelt Deutschlands, einst und jetzt, in ihren Beziehungen zur Tierverbreitung. Paul Matschie. Zeitschr. Gesell. f. Erdkunde, Berlin, no.6, pp.473-497, Mar. 17, 1902.

(MAMMALS OF SCHLESWIG-HOLSTEIN.) Die Saeugetiere Schleswig-Holsteins. Erna Mohr. Altona-Elbe, pp.136, figs.74, 1931.

(WILD MAMMALS IN THE VICINITY OF ALTONA.) Wildlebende Saeugetiere in der Umgebung Altonas. (Der Aufsatz beruecksichtigt auch den Kreis Pinneberg.) Erna Mohr. Vor den Toren der Grosstadt III, pp. 20, illus., 1930.

(CONTRIBUTION TO THE HISTORY OF GAME AND THE HUNT IN EAST PRUSSIA.) Beitraege zur Geschichte des Wildes und der Jagd in Ostpreussen. H. Mueller, A. Olberg. Zeitschr. Forst- u. Jagdwesen, Berlin, vol.66, no.1, pp.43-53, Jan.; no. 2, pp.94-109, Feb.; no.6, pp.325-332, June; no.8, pp.436-445, Aug.; no.9, pp. 494-499, Sep.; no.10, pp.545-555, Aug., 1934.

(VERTEBRATE FAUNA OF SILESIA: FAUNAL AND ZOOGEOGRAPHICAL INVESTIGATIONS IN THE ODER REGION.) Wirbeltierfauna von Schlesien faunistische und tiergeographische Untersuchungen im Odergebiet. F. Pax. Berlin, Gebr. Borntraeger, pp.558, figs.105, 1925.

(MAMMAL FAUNA OF NORTHWESTERN GERMANY.) Zur Saeugethier-Fauna des nordwestlichen Deutschland. S.A. Poppe. Abhandl. Naturw. Ver. Bremen, vol.10, pp.301-310, 1889.

(ADDENDUM TO THE MAMMAL FAUNA OF NORTHWESTERN GERMANY.) Nachtrag zur Saeugetier-Fauna des nordwestlichen Deutschland. S.A. Poppe. Abhandl. Naturw. Ver. Bremen, vol.10, p.566, 1889.

(GAME MANAGEMENT IN GERMANY.) Das Jagdwesen in Deutschland. Scherping. Zeitschr. f. Weltforstwirtschaft, Neudamm u. Berlin, vol.3, nos.11-12, pp.856-867, figs.10 (Sonderheft Deutschland), Aug.-Sep., 1936.

(CONTRIBUTION ON THE SMALL MAMMAL FAUNA OF THE EASTERN ERZ MOUNTAINS.) Beitrag zur Kleinsaeugetierfauna des oestlichen Erzgebirges. Richard Schlegel. Zool. Garten, Leipzig, vol.2, nos.10-12, pp.303-308, Mar., 1930.

(MICROFAUNA OF STEINKIRCHE NEAR SCHARZFELD AM HARZ.) Mikrofauna der Steinkirche bei Scharzfeld am Harz. Max Schlosser. Centralblatt f. Min., Abt. B, no.5, pp.174-176, 1926.

(NOTE ON A SCIENTIFIC VOYAGE IN GERMANY, AUSTRIA, AND HUNGARY IN 1876.) Note sur un voyage scientifique fait en Allemagne, en Autriche et en Hongri en 1876. Edm. de Selys-Longchamps. Ann. Soc. Entomol. Belgique, Bruxelles, vol. 19, pp.lxvi-lxxi, 1876.

(BIOLOGICAL STUDIES OF SMALL GERMAN MAMMALS.) Biologische Studien an deutschen Kleinsaeugern. Georg H. W. Stein. Archiv. f. Naturg., Zeitschr. f. Syst. Zool., Leipzig, n.F., vol.7, pp. 477-513, figs.8, Dec. 30, 1938.

(SMALL MAMMALS OF THE EAST GERMAN PLAINS.) Kleinsaeuger ostdeutscher Ackerflaechen. Georg H. W. Stein. Zeitschr. Saeugetierk., Berlin, vol.20, nos. 2-3, pp.89-113, Aug. 3, 1955.

HUNTING SEASONS IN GERMANY. Tracy I. Storer. California Fish and Game, vol. 24, no.4, pp.350-353, figs.114-115, Oct., 1938.

(EXCURSION FAUNA OF GERMANY. VERTEBRATES.) Exkursionsfauna von Deutschland. Wirbeltiere. E. Stresemann, (Editor). Volk und Wissen Verlag, Berlin, pp.xii-340, figs.250, tbls.46, 1955.

(REMARKS ON THE HISTORY OF THE GERMAN MAMMAL FAUNA.) Bemerkungen zur Geschichte der deutschen Saeugetierfauna. Ernst Stromer. Die Umschau, Frankfurt, no.41, pp.1-5, figs.3, 1937.

(OTTER (LUTRA LUTRA LINNE 1758) AND MUSKRAT (ONDATRA ZIBETHICA LINNE 1766) IN THE UPPER WERRA VALLEY.) Fischotter, Lutra lutra (Linne, 1758), und Bisamratte, Ondatra zibethica (Linné, 1766), im oberen Werratal. Walter Uloth. Saeugetierk. Mitteil., Stuttgart, vol.4, no.1, p.32, Jan. 1, 1956.

(NEW RESEARCH ON THE BIOLOGY OF THE DORMOUSE (GLIS GLIS GLIS LINNÉ), ON THE BASIS OF RANGE MARKING IN DEISTER, LOWER SAXONY, AND ON OBSERVATIONS IN HANNOVERSCH-MUENDEN.) Neuere Untersuchungen ueber die Biologie des Siebenschlaefers, Glis glis glis (Linne, 1758), auf Grund von Freilandmarkierungen im Deister, Niedersachsen, und Beobachtungen in Hannoversch-Muenden. Arnold Freiherr von Vietinghoff-Riesch. Saeugetierk. Mitteil., Stuttgart, vol.3. no.3, pp.113-121, July 1, 1955.

(GERMAN FAUNA, OR BRIEF SUMMARY OF THE NATURAL HISTORY OF THE ANIMALS OF GERMANY. PART ONE: MAMMALS AND BIRDS.) Deutsche Fauna, oder Kurzgefasste Naturgeschichte der Thiere Deutschlands. Erster Teil. Saeugethiere und Voegel. Moriz Balthaser Vorkhausen. (In) Cetolog. Extract from the literature of cetology. 1797.

(ON THE FAUNA OF SYLT.) Zur Fauna von Sylt. Klaus von Zimmerman. Schriften des Naturwiss. Vereins fuer Schleswig-Holstein, vol.21, no.2, pp.274-278, tbl. 1, Dec. 10, 1935.

(ON THE SMALL MAMMAL FAUNA OF BELLINCHEN-ON-THE-ODER.) Zur Kleinsaeuger-Fauna von Bellinchen a.O. Klaus von Zimmerman. Maerkische Tierwelt, Berlin, vol.2, no.1, pp.60-64, illus., 1936.

(ON SOME RARE AND LITTLE-KNOWN MAMMALS OF SOUTH EASTERN GERMANY.) Ueber einige seltene und wenig bekannte Saeugethiere des suedoestlichen Deutschlands. 4th Programm d. noe. Landes-Ober-Realschule in St. Poelten, pp.61, 1867.

## GREECE

NEW INSECTIVORES AND VOLES COLLECTED BY MR. A. ROBERT NEAR TREBIZOND. Oldfield Thomas. Ann. and Mag. Nat. Hist., ser.7, vol.17, no.100, pp.415-421, Apr., 1906.

(MAMMALS FROM GREECE COLLECTED BY L. MUNTER. WITH REMARKS ON FAMILIES SORICIDAE, MUSTELIDAE, MURIDAE, AND MYOXIDAE.) Om Graeske Pattedyr, samlede af L. Munter. Med Bemaerkninger om Familierne Soricidae, Mustelidae, Muridae og Myoxidae. Herluf Winge. Vidensk. Meddel. Naturh. Foren, Copenhagen, vol.1, pp.55, 1881.

(FOSSIL BONES OF PIKERMI, GREECE.) Fossilen Knochenueberreste von Pikermi in Griechenland. Abhandl. K. Bayr. Akad., Muenchen, cl.2, vol.7, no.2, pp.3-94, pls.7-14, 1854.

(NEW CONTRIBUTIONS TO KNOWLEDGE OF THE FOSSIL MAMMAL REMAINS OF PIKERMI.) Neue Beitraege zur Kenntniss der fossilen Saeugethierueberreste von Pikermi. Abhandl. K. Bayr. Akad. Muenchen, cl.2, vol.8, no.1, pp.3-50, 1857.

## GREENLAND

GREENLAND EXPEDITION OF 1940. Robert A. Bartlett. Explor. and Field-work Smiths. Inst. 1940, publ.no.3631, pp.47-52, illus., Apr.3, 1941.

ON THE MAMMALIAN FAUNA OF GREENLAND. Robert Brown. Proc. Zool. Soc. London, pp.330-362, 1868.

ANIMAL BONES FROM KING OSCAR FJORD REGION IN EAST GREENLAND. Magnus Degerbol. Meddelelser om Grønland, København, vol.102, no.2, pp.93-97, tbl., Dec., 1935.

ANIMAL REMAINS FROM THE WEST SETTLEMENT IN GREENLAND WITH SPECIAL REFERENCE TO LIVESTOCK. Magnus Degerbol. Meddelelser om Grønland, København, vol.88, no.3, pp.1-54, figs.9, pl.1, tbls., 1936.

CONTRIBUTION TO THE INVESTIGATION OF THE FAUNA OF THE BLOSSEVILLE COAST, EAST GREENLAND, WITH SPECIAL REFERENCE TO ZOOGEOGRAPHY. Magnus Degerbol. Meddelelser om Grønland, København, vol.104, no.19, pp.1-36, tbls., fig.1, pl.1, 1937.

REGULATIONS CONCERNING WILDLIFE PROTECTION IN EAST GREENLAND NORTH OF SCORESBYSUND, 1950. Erik Eriksen. Polar Record, Cambridge, England, vol.6, no.44, pp.547-548, July, 1952.

(GREENLAND FAUNA.) Fauna Groenlandica. Otho Fabricius. (In) Extracts from the literature of cetology, pp.29-51, 1780.

ON THE MAMMALIA OF NORTH GREENLAND AND GRINNELL LAND. H. W. Feilden. The Zoologist, London, ser.3, vol.1, no.9, pp.353-360, Sep., 1877.

NOTES ON A VOYAGE TO THE GREENLAND SEAS IN 1886. Robert Gray. The Zoologist, London, pp.32, pl.2, Apr., 1887.

FAUNA OF GREENLAND. A.S. Jensen. Greenland, vol.1, pp.319-355, illus., 1928.

BIRDS AND MAMMALS OF PEARY LAND IN NORTH GREENLAND, INCLUDING NOTES FROM NORTHEAST GREENLAND. Palle Johnsen. Copenhagen, C.A. Reitzel, pp.135, illus., maps, 1953.

(NOTES ON THE BIOLOGY OF SOME MAMMALS OF SPITZBERGEN AND GREENLAND.) Notizen zur Biologie einiger Saeugetiere von Spitzbergen und Groenland. Ingo Krumbiegel. Zool. Garten, Leipzig, n.F., vol.9, no.5, pp.214-219, figs.5, Oct., 1937.

AN ECOLOGICAL RECONNAISSANCE IN WEST GREENLAND. T.G. Longstaff. Jour. Anim. Ecology, vol.1, no.2, pp. 119-142, pls.6-9, Nov., 1932.

TERRESTRIAL MAMMALS AND BIRDS OF NORTH-EAST GREENLAND. A.L.V. Manniche. Danmark-Ekspeditionen til Grønlands Nordøstkyst 1906-1908, København, Bd.5, nr.1 (Meddelelser om Grønland, no.45), pp.200, figs.20, pls.7, 1910.

(CONTRIBUTIONS TO KNOWLEDGE OF THE MAMMALS AND BIRD FAUNA OF THE EASTERN COAST OF GREENLAND.) Beitraege zur Kenntnis der Saeugetier-und Vogelfauna der Ostkueste Groenlands. Alwin Pederson. Meddelelser om Grønland, vol. 68, pp.150-250, illus., 1926.

(CONTINUED CONTRIBUTIONS TO KNOWLEDGE OF THE MAMMAL AND BIRD FAUNA OF THE EASTERN COAST OF GREENLAND.) Fortgesetzte Beitraege zur Kenntnis der Saeugetier-und Vogelfauna der Ostkueste Groenlands. Alwin Pedersen. Meddelelser om Grønland, København, vol.77, pp. 343-507, figs.60, pl.26, 1930.

(MAMMALS AND BIRDS.) Saeugetiere und Voegel. Alwin Pedersen. Copenhagen, C.A. Reitzel, pp.119, illus., maps, 1942.

(SOME MAMMALS AND BIRDS FROM WESTERN GREENLAND.) Om nogle Vestgrønlandske pattedyr og fugle. Morten P. Porsild. Meddelelser om Grønland, Copenhagen,

Arbejder fra den Danske Arktiske Station Paa Disko, no.10, vol.56, pp.54, figs.5, 1916.

(NEWS OF GREENLAND'S ANIMALS.)Neues von groenlaendischen Tieren. Karl Max Schneider. Zool. Garten, Leipzig, n.F., vol.4, nos.1-2, pp.60-62, 1931. (Abstract of A. Pedersen, 1930, Der Scoresbysund. Drei Jahre Forschungsreisen an der Ostkueste Groenlands, (Three years of journeys to investigate the eastern coast of Greenland), Berlin, pp.157, figs.56, map 1. (Contains description, based on Eskimo accounts, of method of eating young seal by walrus.)

(ANIMAL PARADISE - EASTERN GREENLAND.) Tierparadies Oestgroenland. Curt Teichert. Natur und Museum, vol.63, no. 6, pp.199-209, figs.11, June, 1933.

MARINE MAMMALS AND THE MARINE FAUNA IN THE THULE DISTRICT (NORTHWEST GREENLAND) WITH OBSERVATIONS ON ICE CONDITIONS IN 1939-41. Christian Vibe. Meddelelser om Grønland, Copenhagen, vol.150, no.6, pp.116, illus., 1950.

(GREENLAND'S MAMMALS.) Gronlands Pattedyr. Herluf Winge. Meddelelser om Grønland, Copenhagen, vol.21, pp.319-521, fold.map, 1902.

(FLOWERING DEVELOPMENT OF PAST AND PRESENT GREENLAND FISHERY.) Bloeyende Opkomst der Aloude en Hedendaagsche Greenlandsche Visschery. C. G. Zorgdragers. Amsterdam, pp.330, illus., 1720.

GUADALUPE ISLAND

EXPEDITION TO GUADALUPE ISLAND, MEXICO, IN 1922. THE BIRDS AND MAMMALS. A.W. Anthony. Proc. California Acad. Sci., vol.14, no.13, pp.277-320, Sep. 5, 1925.

NOTES ON GUADALUPE ISLAND. Edward L. Greene. Bull. California Acad. Sci., vol.1, pp.214-220, 1886.

EXPEDITION TO GUADALUPE ISLAND, MEXICO IN 1922. General Report Proc. California Acad. Sci., 4th Ser., vol.14, no.13, pp.217-275, Sep. 5, 1925.

TO GUADALUPE ISLAND. (900 Elephant Seals Counted.) John Thomas Howell. Science, n.s., vol.75, no.1934, pp.97-98, Jan.22, 1932.

MY VISIT TO GUADALUPE ISLAND. Carl L. Hubbs. Leaf. West. Bot., vol.3, pp. 36-41, 1941.

GUADALUPE ISLAND: AN OBJECT LESSON IN MAN-CAUSED DEVASTATION. (Destruction of Fauna of Island.)Laurence M. Huey. Science, n.s., vol.61, pp.405-407, Apr. 17, 1925.

A TRIP TO GUADALUPE, THE ISLE OF MY BOYHOOD DREAMS. Laurence M. Huey. Nat. Hist., vol.24, no.5, pp.579-588, Sep.-Oct., 1924.

GUADALUPE ISLAND, A PROBLEM IN CONSERVATION (MANUSCRITO). George Lindsay. 1955.

GUADALUPE ISLAND. Reid Moran, George Lindsay. Dess. Plant Life Mag., vol.22, pp.3-9, 1950.

GUATEMALA

MAMMALS COLLECTED BY A. W. ANTHONY IN GUATEMALA, 1924-1928. George G. Goodwin. Bull. Amer. Mus. Nat. Hist., vol.68, art.1, pp.1-60, pls. 5, Dec. 12, 1934.

MAMMALS FROM GUATEMALA, WITH THE DESCRIPTION OF A NEW LITTLE BROWN BAT. George G. Goodwin. Amer. Mus. Novitates, New York, no.1744, pp. 1-5, Aug. 12, 1955.

TWO NEW MAMMALS FROM GUATEMALA. George G. Goodwin. Amer. Mus. Novitates, no.528, pp.1-2, May 23, 1932.

SPECIMENS OF MAMMALIA FROM COBAN IN CENTRAL AMERICA. J.E. Gray. Presented by Proc. Zool. Soc. London, pt.11, p. 79, 1843.

GAME MAMMALS OF GUATEMALA. Charles O. Handley, Jr. Special Sci. Rept. Wildlife, U.S. Fish and Wildlife Service, Wash., no.5, pp.141-162, June, 1950.

MAMMALS FROM GUATEMALA AND BRITISH HONDURAS. Adolph Murie. Univ. Michigan Mus. Zool., Misc. Publ.26, pp. 30, pl.1, map 1, July 15, 1935.

(CATALOGUE OF THE GENERA AND SPECIES OF ANIMALS OF GUATEMALA.) Catalogo de los generos y especies de los animales que se encuentran en Guatemala. Juan J. Rodriguez. Primera clase: Mammalia. El Renacimiento, Guatemala, pp. 14, 1885.

NEW MAMMALS FROM GUATEMALA AND HONDURAS. Colin Campbell Sanborn. Zool. Ser. Field Mus. Nat. Hist., vol.20, no.11, pp.81-85, May 15, 1935.

FISH AND WILDLIFE SURVEY OF GUATEMALA. George B. Saunders, et al. U.S. Dept. Interior, Fish and Wildl.Serv., Special Scientific Report, Wildlife no.5, pp.162, 1950.

REPORT OF A COLLECTION OF MAMMALS MADE BY OSBERT SALVIN ESQ., F.Z.S., AT DUENAS, GUATEMALA, WITH NOTES ON SOME OF THE SPECIES BY MR. FRASER. Robert F.Tomes. Proc. Zool. Soc. London, pt.29, pp.278-288, pl.xxxi, 1861.

HAITI see HISPANIOLA

HAWAIIAN ISLANDS

NATURAL HISTORY OF HAWAII. BEING AN ACCOUNT OF THE HAWAIIAN PEOPLE, THE GEOLOGY AND GEOGRAPHY OF THE ISLANDS, AND THE NATIVE AND INTRODUCED PLANTS AND ANIMALS OF THE GROUP. William Alanson Bryan. Hawaiian Gazette Co., Ltd., Honolulu, pp.596, illus., 1915.

NOTES ON IVORY IN HAWAII. Schuyler Cammann. Jour. Polynesian Soc., Wellington, vol.63, no.2, pp.133-140, pl.1, Sep., 1954. (Walrus.)

REPORT OF AN EXPEDITION OF LAYSAN ISLAND IN 1911. Pt. II. (Parts 1 and 2.) Homer R. Dill, Wm.Alanson Bryan. Biol. Survey Bull., Washington, no.42, pp.3-30, pls.9, May 21, 1912.

GEOGRAPHICAL AFFINITIES OF THE MAMMALS OF THE HAWAIIAN ISLANDS AND OF NEW ZEALAND. David H. Johnson. Jour. Mamm., vol.25, no.4, pp.333-336, Dec. 12, 1944.

(THREE MONTHS ON A CORAL ISLAND (LAYSAN).) Drei Monate auf einer Koralleninsel (Laysan). H.H. Schauinsland. Bremen, Max Noessler, pp.104, 1899.

RECONNAISSANCE OF THE GAME BIRDS OF HAWAII. Charles W. Schwartz, Elizabeth Schwartz. Board Comm. Agric. and Forestry, Div. Fish and Game, Terr.Hawaii, pp.168, illus., maps 9, 1949.(Mammalian predators, pp.137-140.)

ANIMALS OF HAWAII. NATURAL HISTORY OF THE AMPHIBIANS, REPTILES AND MAMMALS LIVING IN THE HAWAIIAN ISLANDS. Spencer Wilkie Tinker. Nippu Jini Co., Ltd., Honolulu, pp.188, illus., 1938.

HIMALAYAN REGION

ZOOLOGICAL RESULTS OF THE "DAILY MAIL" HIMALAYAN EXPEDITION 1954. FOUR NEW MAMMALS FROM KHUMBA, EASTERN NEPAL. Biswamoy Biswas, H. Khajuria. Proc. Zool. Soc., Calcutta, vol. 8, no.1, pp.25-30, Mar., 1955.

BIG GAME HUNTING IN THE HIMALAYAS AND TIBET. Major Gerald Burrard. London, Herbert Kenkins, pp.320, illus., maps, 1931.

ILLUSTRATIONS OF THE BOTANY AND OTHER BRANCHES OF THE NATURAL HISTORY OF THE HIMALAYAN MOUNTAINS, AND OF THE FLORA OF CASHMERE. John Forbes Royle. London, W. H. Allen and Co., pp.472, pls.100 (part col.), 1839.

"THE PALE WEASEL" OF BLANFORD'S "MAMMALIA" AND A NEW HIMALAYAN VOLE. R.C. Wroughton. Jour. Bombay Nat. Hist. Soc., vol.20, no.4, pp.930-932, May 20, 1911.

HISPANIOLA

MAMMALS FROM BRITISH HONDURAS, MEXICO, JAMAICA AND HAITI. Philip Hershkovitz. Chicago, Nat. Hist. Mus., Fieldiana: Zoology, vol.31, no.47, 1951.

ARCHEOLOGICAL AND HISTORICAL INVESTIGATIONS IN SAMANÁ, DOMINICAN REPUBLIC. Herbert W. Krieger. U.S. Nat. Mus. Bull.147, pp.1-91, pls. 27, Sep. 9, 1929.

EXPLORATION OF HAITIAN CAVES. Gerrit S. Miller, Jr. Smiths. Inst. Misc. Coll., Washington, vol.78, no.1, pp. 36-40, figs. 37-42, Apr. 8, 1926.

REMAINS OF MAMMALS FROM CAVES IN THE REPUBLIC OF HAITI. Gerrit S. Miller, Jr. Smiths. Inst. Misc. Coll., Washington, vol.74, no.3, pp.1-8, Oct. 16, 1922.

SECOND COLLECTION OF MAMMALS FROM CAVES NEAR ST. MICHEL, HAITI. Gerrit S. Miller, Jr. Smiths.Inst. Misc. Coll., Washington, vol.81, no.9, pp.1-30, pls.1-10, Mar. 30, 1929.

THREE SMALL COLLECTIONS OF MAMMALS FROM HISPANIOLA. (Nesophontes in Owl Pellets.) Gerrit S. Miller, Jr.Smiths. Inst. Misc. Coll., Washington, vol.82, publ.3109, pp.1-10, pls.1-2, Dec. 24, 1930.

EXPEDITION TO SAMANÁ PROVINCE, DOMINICAN REPUBLIC. Gerrit S. Miller, Jr., Herbert W. Krieger. Explor. and Field-Work Smiths. Inst. in 1928, publ. no.3011, pp.43-54, figs.12, 1929.

FURTHER EXPLORATION OF HAITTIAN CAVES. (Search Made Particularly for Mammalian Remains.) Arthur J. Poole. Explorations and Field-Work Smiths. Inst. in 1928, Smiths. publ. no.3011, pp.55-62, illus., Apr., 1929.

CRUISE OF THE ESPERANZA TO HAITI. Alex. Wetmore, Watson M. Perrygo. Explorations and Field-Work of the Smiths. Inst. in 1930, pp.59-66, figs.50-57, 1931.

HOLLAND

(CATALOG OF MAMMALS OF THE NETHERLANDS FOUND IN THE WILD.) Catalogue des mammiferes des Pays-Bas trouves a l'etat sauvage. F.H. van den Brink. Bull. Soc. Zool. France, vol.56, no.2, pp.163-190, 1931.

(DISTRIBUTION OF WILD MAMMALS IN THE NETHERLANDS.) De Verbreiding der in Nederland in Het wild Voorkomende Zoogdier-Soorten. F.H. van den Brink. Nederlandsche Jager, vol.35, no.24, pp. 293-296, Dec. 14, 1929.

(LIST OF DUTCH VERTEBRATES.)Lijst van Nederlandsche Vertebrata. F.H. van den Brink. Martinus Nijhoff, The Hague, pp.56, 1943. (Mammals, pp.48-56.)

(MAMMALOGICAL OBSERVATIONS IN THE NETHERLANDS.) Observations Mammalogiques dans les Pays-Bas. F.H. van den Brink. I.Tijdschrift der Ned.Diekunde Vereeniging Leiden, ser.3, vol.2, pt.1, pp.43-46, 1930.

(MAMMALS CROSS OUR PATH.) Zoogdieren kruisen ons pad. Fop Brouwer. Met tekeningen van Ali Brouwer-Beiboer. Amsterdam, J. Veen, pp.157, illus., 1948.

(DUTCH MAMMALS.) De Nederlandsche zoogdieren. C. Eykman. Rotterdam, De Vereeniging tot oprichting en instandhouding van een Natuurhistorisch Museum, 2 vols. in 1, illus., 1937.

(FOSSIL AND SUBFOSSIL HORSES OF HOLLAND.) Les chevaux fossiles et subfossiles des Pays-bas. P.J. van der Feen. Mammalia, Paris, vol.22, no.1, pp.69-72, Mar., 1958.

(VERTEBRATES FROM THE HEKELINGEN EXCAVATIONS (HOLLAND).)Les vertébreés de fouilles de Hekelingen (Pays-bas). P.J. van der Feen. Kortenbout van der Sluys. Mammalia, Paris, vol.17, no.4, pp.346-353, Dec., 1953.

NOTES ON SOME FOSSIL MAMMALS OF THE NETHERLANDS. D.A. Hooijer. Archiv. Mus. Teyler, Haarlem, ser.3, vol.10, no.1, pp.33-51, pl.1, 1947.

ON DREDGED SPECIMENS OF ANANCUS, ARCHIDISKODON, AND EQUUS FROM THE SCHELDE ESTUARY, NETHERLANDS. D.A. Hooijer. Leidse Geol. Mededel., vol. 17, pp.185-202, pls.1-2, 1953.

PROTOHISTORIC MAMMALS FROM THE LINDERBEEK, PROVINCE OF OVERIJSSL, THE NETHERLANDS. D.A. Hooijer. Proc. Kon. Nederlandsche Akad. van Wetenschappen, vol.50, no.2, pp.1-15, pl.1, 1947.

(FAUNAL FACTS ON MAMMALS OF SOUTH LIMBURG.) Faunistische gegevens over de zoogdieren van Zuid-Limburg. A.M. Husson. Natuurhist. Maandblad, Natuurhist. Geonootschape Limburg, vol.46, nos.5-6, pp.61-68, June 28, 1957.

(MAMMALS OF THE NETHERLANDS.) De zoogdieren van Nederland. Marius Anton Ijsseling, A. Scheygrond. Zutphen, W.J. Thieme, vol.2, pp.viii-530, illus., pls. 79, figs.294, 1943; 2nd ed., revised, pp. 544, pls.84, figs., 1950.

PROTECTION OF NATURE IN THE NETHERLANDS. Lucie A. Pluygers. Department of Nature Protection, Royal Dutch Touring Club, pp.29, illus., May, 1946.

(NEW FIND OF QUATERNARY MAMMALS IN HOLLAND. II. EQUUS CABALLUS L., E. ROBUSTUS POMEL, ASINUS HEMIONUS FOSSILIS OWEN AND MEGACEROS EURYCEROS LATIFRONS SUBSP. NOV.) Neue Funde quataerer Saeugetiere in den Niederlanden. II. Equus caballus L., E.robustus Pomel, Asinus hemionus fossilis Owen und Magaceros euryceros latifrons subsp.nov. Th. Raven. Proc. Kon. Akad. Wet. Amsterdam, vol.38, no.3, pp.290-296, Mar., 1935.

TEGELEN FAUNA, WITH A DESCRIPTION OF NEW REMAINS OF ITS RARE COMPONENTS (LEPTOBOS, ARCHIDISKODON MERIDIONALIS, MACACA, SUS STROZII). A. Schreuder. Archiv. Neerlandaises Zool., Leyden, vol.7, livr.1-2, pp.153-204, figs. 13, pl., 1945.

(CONTRIBUTION TO KNOWLEDGE OF THE MAMMALS OF BIESBOSCH, THE ISLAND OF DORBRECHT, AND VICINITY.) Contribution a la connaissance des mammifères du Biesbosch, de l'ile de Dorbrecht et des environs. C.J. Verhey. Mammalia, Paris, vol.18, no.4, pp.405-419, Dec., 1954.

POSSIBILITIES FOR THE DEVELOPMENT OF A MAMMAL FAUNA IN THE FUTURE SOUTHERN IJSSELLAKE POLDERS. A. van Wijngaarden, B.M. Lensink. Versl. & Meded. Plantenziektenkundige Dienst, vol.130 (1956), pp.186-211, 1957. (In Dutch with English summary.)

HONDURAS

BIRDS AND MAMMALS FROM HONDURAS. Outram Bangs. Bull. Mus. Comp. Zool., Harvard College, vol.39, no.6, pp.141-159, July, 1903.

TWO NEW MAMMALS FROM HONDURAS. E.A. Goldman. Proc. Biol. Soc. Wash., vol.45, pp.121-124, July 30, 1932.

MAMMALS OF HONDURAS. George G. Goodwin. Bull. American Mus.Nat.Hist., New York, vol.79, art.2, pp.107-195, May 29, 1942.

MAMMALS FROM BRITISH HONDURAS, MEXICO, JAMAICA AND HAITI. Philip Hershkovitz. Fieldiana-Zool., Chicago Nat. Hist. Mus., vol.31, no.47, pp.547-569, July 10, 1951.

FIELD MUSEUM PALEONTOLOGICAL EXPEDITION TO HONDURAS. (Pliocene and Pleistocene Mammals Collected.) Paul O. McGrew. Science, Lancaster, n.s., vol.96, no.2482, p.85, July 24, 1942.

NUMEROUS FOSSILS COLLECTED BY HONDURAS EXPEDITION. (Pliocene and Pleistocene Mammals.) Paul O. McGrew. Field Mus. News, Chicago, vol.13, no.6, p.3, June, 1942.

LIST OF MAMMALS AND BIRDS COLLECTED BY MR. JOSEPH LEYLAND IN HONDURAS, BELIZE, AND GUATEMALA. Thomas J. Moore. Proc. Zool. Soc. London, pt.27, pp.50-65, 1859.

MAMMALS FROM GUATEMALA AND BRITISH HONDURAS. Adolph Murie. Univ. Michigan Mus. Zool. Misc. Publ. 26, pp. 30, pl.1, map 1, July 15, 1935.

PLIOCENE MAMMALIAN FAUNA FROM THE REPUBLIC OF HONDURAS. Everett C. Olson. Paul O. McGrew. Bull. Geol. Soc. Amer. (Abstracts), vol.49, no.12, pt.2, p.1895, Dec. 1, 1938.

NEW MAMMALS FROM GUATEMALA AND HONDURAS. Colin Campbell Sanborn. Chicago, pp.81-85, 1935. (Field Mus.Nat. Hist., Publ.no.340.)

ON THE MAMMALS COLLECTED IN EASTERN HONDURAS IN 1887 BY MR. CHARLES H. TOWNSEND, WITH A DESCRIPTION OF A NEW SUBSPECIES OF CAPROMYS FROM LITTLE SWAN ISLAND. Frederick William True. U.S. Nat. Mus., Proceedings, Washington, vol.11, pp.469-472, 1889.

HUNGARY

(HISTORY OF 70 YEARS OF PALEOTOLOGICAL EXCAVATIONS AT BALTAVAR (1856-1926).) A Baltavári oslénytani ásatások 70 éves története 1856-1926. László Benda. Szombathely, Dunántuli nyomdavállalat részvénytársaság, pp.80, illus., pl., diagrs., 1927.

(FAUNAL FINDINGS OF EXCAVATIONS IN THE HERMAN OTTO CAVE.) Die faunistischen Resultate der Grabungen in der Herman Otto-Hoehle. J. Ehik. Barlangkutatas, Budapest, vol.4, no.1, pp.24-48, figs.2, 1916. (With German summary.)

NEW VOLE FROM HUNGARY AND AN INTERESTING BAT NEW TO THE HUNGARIAN FAUNA. J. Ehik. Ann. Mus. Nation. Hungarici, vol.21, pp.159-162, 1924.

(RECENT ADDITIONS TO THE HUNGARIAN MAMMAL FAUNA.) Ujabb adatok magyarorszag emlosfaunajának ismeretéhez. J. Ehik. Allattani Közlemenyek, vol.25, nos.1-2, pp.54-57, 98-99, Apr., 1928.

(RESULTS OF THE HUNGARIAN FAUNA EXPLORATION IN 1943.) A magyar faunakutatas 1943. Evi eredmenyei. J. Ehik. Ann. Mus. Nat. Hungarici, Budapest, vol. 1, pp.1-5, 1944.

(SOME DATA ON THE STUDY OF HUNGARY'S MAMMAL FAUNA.) Néhany adat Magyarország emlosfaunájának ismeretéhez. J. Ehik. Ann. Mus. Nat.Hungarici, vol.25, pp.195-203, 1928.

(RARE MAMMALS FROM THE LATE PLEISTOCENE AT DOROG AND MARIAREMETE. (SICISTA, APODEMUS, ASINUS.)) Ritkabb emlósok a dorogi es mariaremetei kesoi pleisztocenból. D. Janossy. Földtani Kozlony, Budapest, vol.83, pp.419-436, illus., 1953.

(FOSSIL BONES OF THE NEOLITHIC SETTLEMENT OF HÓDMEZOVASARHELY.) Knochenreste der neolithischen Ansiedlung von Hódmezővasárhely. Stephan von Gaál. Ann. Hist.-Nat.Mus.Nat.Hungarici, Budapest, vol.27, pp.259-277, 1931.

(GEOLOGICAL CONDITIONS OF THE MUSSOLINI CAVE.) Mussolini-barlang foldtani viszonyai. O. Kadic. Foldtani Kozlony, Budapest, vol.63, nos.7-12, pp.177-182, map 1, 1933. (In German with Hungarian summary.)

(CONTRIBUTION TO PREGLACIER FAUNA OF THE SOMLYO MOUNTAIN NEAR PUSPOKFURDO.) Beitraege zur Praglazierfauna des Somlyoberges bei Puspokfurdo. Theodor Kormos. Jour. Trimestriel Publié Sect.Zool.Soc.Royal Sci. Nat.Hongrie, Budapest, vol.27, nos.1-2, pp.40-62, 1930. (In Hungarian with German summary.)

(FOSSIL MAMMAL REMAINS FROM BETFIA.) Osemlosmaradvanyok Betfiarol. M. Kretzoi. Földtani Közlony, Budapest, vol. 71, nos.7-12, pp.235-261, July-Dec., 1941.

(MAMMALIAN FAUNA OF THE LOWER PLEISTOCENE OF BETFIA NEAR NAGYVARAD.) Die unterpleistozaene Saeugetierfauna von Betfia bei Nagyvárad. M. Kretzoi. Foldtani Közlony, Budapest, vol.71, no.7-12, pp.308-335, fold.tbl., 1941.

(PALEOVERTEBRATE REMAINS KNOWN FROM THE CAVES IN OUR COUNTRY AND THE HISTORY OF THEIR EXPLORATION.) Hazánk barlangjaibol ismeretes osgerinces maradványok és kutatásuk története. Andreás Kubacska. Acta biologica, Szeged, vol.1, no.2, pp.115-126, pls.7-10, 1929.

(HUNGARIAN ZOOLOGY; HISTORY OF ANIMALS, THE GREATER PART OF WHICH INHABIT HUNGARY.) Tentamen Zoologiae Hungaricae, sev.Historiae Animalium quorum magnam partem alit Hungaria. Ioannis Severini.1779.

IBERIAN PENINSULA

EXCAVATION OF A MOUSTERIAN ROCK-SHELTER AT DEVIL'S TOWER, GIBRALTAR. THE ANIMAL REMAINS. Dorothea M.A. Bate. Jour. Roy. Anthrop. Inst., vol.58, pp.92-113, June, 1928.

(MAMMALS. IBERIAN FAUNA.) Mamiferos. Fauna iberica. A. Barera. Madrid, pp.xviii-441, pls.12, 1914.

(MAMMAL FAUNA OF IBERIA.) Fauna mastodologica iberica. Mariano de la Paz Graells. R. Acad. de ciencias, exactas, fisicas y naturales de Madrid, Memoria, t.xvii, pp.806, pls., maps 2, 1897.

SOME CONSIDERATIONS ON THE ZOOGEOGRAPHY OF THE IBERIAN MAMMALS.) Algunas consideraciones sobre la zoogeografia de los mamiferos Ibericos. Agacino E. Morales. Bol. Soc. Espanola Hist. Nat. Madrid, vol.37, pp.21-28, pl.1, Apr., 1938.

CHRONOLOGY OF THE MOUSTERIAN AT GORHAM'S CAVE, GIBRALTAR. F. E. Zeuner. Proc. Prehist. Soc., vol.19, pt.2, pp.180-188, 1953.

ICELAND

MAMMALIA. WITH AN APPENDIX ON THE FIELD MOUSE BY M. DEGERBØL. Bjarni Saemundsson. The Zoology of Iceland, Copenhagen, vol.4, pt.76, pp.1-52, map 1, Mar. 1, 1939.

INDIA

Extinct and Fossil Mammals

DISTRIBUTIONAL AND PHYLOGENETIC STUDIES ON INDIAN FOSSIL MAMMALS. Edwin H. Colbert. I. Amer.Mus. collecting localities in Northern India. Amer. Mus. Novitates, no.796, pp.20, figs.12, May 8, 1935.

SKULL OF DISSOPSALIS CARNIFEX PILGRIM, A MIOCENE CREODONT FROM INDIA. Edwin H. Colbert. Amer. Mus. Novitates, no.603, pp.8, figs.4, Mar.28, 1933.

NOTE ON THE PLIO-PLEISTOCENE BOUNDARY IN THE SIWALIK SERIES OF INDIA AND IN JAVA. Dirk A. Hooijer,

Edwin H. Colbert. Amer. Jour. Sci., New Haven, vol.249, pp.533-538, July, 1951.

NEW SIWALIK CORRELATION. (Lists Fossil Mammals and Discusses Faunal Assemblages.) G. Edward Lewis. Amer. Jour. Sci., ser.5, vol.33, no.195, pp. 191-204, figs.2, Mar., 1937.

NOTICE OF THE DISCOVERY OF PLESIOGULO BRACHYGNATHUS IN THE SIWALIK MEASURES OF INDIA. G.Edward Lewis. Amer. Jour. Sci., vol.26, no.151, p.80, July 1933.

CORRELATION OF OSSIFEROUS SECTIONS IN THE UPPER CENOZOIC OF INDIA. Guy E. Pilgrim. Amer. Mus. Novitates, no.704, pp.1-5, Mar. 15, 1934.

MIDDLE EOCENE MAMMALS FROM NORTH-WEST INDIA. Guy E. Pilgrim. Proc. Zool. Soc. London, vol.110, ser.B, pts.1-2, pp.127-152, figs.3, pl.1, July, 1940.

DINOSAURIAN AND MAMMALIAN REMAINS IN SOUTH INDIA. C.R.Narayan Rao. Nature, London, vol.124, p.227, fig. 1, Aug. 10, 1929.

LATE CENOZOIC HISTORY IN INDIA. H. de Terra. Nature, London, vol.137, no. 3469, pp.686-688, Apr. 25, 1936.

OBSERVATIONS ON THE UPPER SIWALIK FORMATION AND LATER PLEISTOCENE DEPOSITS IN INDIA. H. de Terra, P. Teilhard de Chardin. Proc. Amer. Philos. Soc., vol.76, no.6, pp.791-822, figs.14, 1936.

Recent Mammals

BIG GAME OF BALTISTAN AND LADAKH. A SUMMER IN HIGH ASIA, BEING A RECORD OF SPORT AND TRAVEL IN BALTISTAN AND LADAKH. F.E.S. Adair. London, W. Thacker and Co., pp.xii-285, illus., pls., fold.map, 1899.

REMARKS ON THE HABITS AND HAUNTS OF SOME OF THE MAMMALIA FOUND IN VARIOUS PARTS OF INDIA AND THE WEST HIMALAYAN MOUNTAINS (COMMUNICATED BY MESSRS. T.J. AND F. MOORE). A. Leith Adams. Proc. Zool. Soc. London, pt.26, pp.512-531, 1858.

MOGHUL EMPERORS OF INDIA AS NATURALISTS AND SPORTSMEN.Salim A. Ali. Jour. Bombay Nat. Hist. Soc., vol.31, pp.833-861, pls.3; vol.32, pp. 34-63, pls.4; vol.32, pp.264-273, 1927.

PRESERVATION OF WILD LIFE IN INDIA. NO. 8, HYDERABAD STATE.Salim A. Ali. Jour. Bombay Nat. Hist. Soc., vol.38, no.2, pp.231-240, Dec. 1, 1935.

ANIMAL LIFE OF THE GANGES. N.Annandale. Jour. Bombay Nat. Hist. Soc., vol.29, pp.633-642, Dec. 31, 1923.

REMARKS ON SOME MAMMALIA FROM TRAVANCORE, INCLUDING A NEW SPECIES OF HERPESTES (HERP. VITTICOLLIS). E.T. Bennett. Proc. Zool. Soc. London, pt.3, pp.66-67, 1835.

FAUNA OF BRITISH INDIA, INCLUDING CEYLON AND BURMA. William T. Blanford. London, Pur. Wesley and Son, pp. 8, 248, 1916.

LIST OF MAMMALIA COLLECTED BY THE LATE DR.STOLICZKA WHEN ATTACHED TO THE EMBASSY UNDER SIR D. FORSYTH IN KASHMIR, LADA'K, EASTERN TURKESTAN, AND WAKHA'N, WITH DESCRIPTIONS OF NEW SPECIES. W.T. Blanford. Jour. Asiatic Soc.Bengal, vol.15, pt.2, pp.1-8, 105-112, 1875.

MAMMALIA. W.T. Blanford. London, Taylor and Francis, illus., 1888.

NOTICE OF A COLLECTION OF MAMMALIA, BIRDS AND REPTILES PROCURED AT OR NEAR THE STATION OF CHERRA PUNJI IN THE KHASIA HILLS, NORTH OF SYLHET. Edward Blyth. Jour. Asiatic Soc. Bengal, pp.517-524, 1851.

WILD ANIMALS IN CENTRAL INDIA. A. A. Dunbar Brander. London, E. Arnold and Co., Demy 8 vol., pp.xv-296, pls.16, 1923.

BIBLIOGRAPHY OF BIG GAME HUNTING AND SHOOTING IN INDIA AND THE EAST. R.W. Burton. Jour. Bombay Nat. Hist.Soc., vol.49, no.2, pp.222-241, Aug., 1950.

GAME ANIMALS OF INDIA. R.W. Burton. Jour. Bombay Nat. Hist. Soc., vol.28, pp. 1120-1121, Dec. 20, 1922.

ON THE BANKS OF THE NARBADA. PT.2. (Tiger, Panther, Jackal, Sambur and Bear.) R.W. Burton. Jour. Bombay Nat. Hist. Soc., vol.43, no.1, pp.48-59, pls.4, Apr., 1942.

ELEPHANT-FEARING GOND; MALIGNED RATEL; AND "ANIMATED FIR-CONE": REMARKABLE NATURE STUDIES FROM INDIA. F.W. Champion. Illus. London News, vol.181, no.4874, pp.420-421, illus., Sep. 17, 1932.

MONKEYS AND CARNIVORA. F.W. Champion. Jour. Bombay Nat. Hist. Soc., vol.33, no.2, p.424, Feb. 15, 1929.

PRESERVATION OF WILD LIFE IN INDIA. NO. 4. THE UNITED PROVINCES. F. W. Champion. Jour. Bombay Nat. Hist. Soc., vol.37, no.1, (suppl.), pp.105-111, Apr.15, 1934.

PRESERVATION OF WILD LIFE IN THE UNITED PROVINCES OF INDIA. F. W. Champion. Field, London, vol.161, no. 4185, pp.478-479, illus., Mar. 11, 1933.

SIWALIK MAMMALS IN THE AMERICAN MUSEUM OF NATURAL HISTORY. Edwin H. Colbert. Amer. Philos. Soc., n.s., vol.26, pp.x-401, figs.198, map 1, Oct., 1935.

ON THE FAUNA OF THE STATE OF HYDERABAD AND ITS PRINCIPAL TYPES. Basonto Das. Comptes Rendus XII Congrès Internat. Zool. Lisbonne 1935, Lisboa, vol. 2, pp.1203-1207, pls.50-51, 1936-37.

PRESERVATION OF WILD LIFE IN INDIA. NO. 1. THE CENTRAL PROVINCES. A.A. Dunbar-Brander. Jour. Bombay Nat. Hist. Soc., vol.36, no.4, (suppl.), pp.40-45, Dec. 15, 1933.

CHECKLIST OF PALAEARCTIC AND INDIAN MAMMALS 1758 TO 1946. John Reeves Ellerman. London, Printed by Order of the Trustees of the British Museum, pp. 810, fold. map, 1951.

CATALOGUE OF THE SPECIES OF MAMMALIA, FOUND IN THE SOUTHERN MAHRATTA COUNTRY; WITH THEIR SYNONYMES IN THE NATIVE LANGUAGES IN USE THERE. Walter Elliot. Madras, J. B. Pharoah, pp.43, pls.4, 1840.

PRINCE OF WALES' SHOOTING IN INDIA IN 1921 AND 1922. PART 3. B.C.Ellison. Jour. Bombay Nat. Hist. Soc., vol.29, pp.179-208, pls.7, map 1, diagrs.4, Apr. 20, 1923.

PRINCE OF WALES' SHOOTS IN INDIA IN 1921-1922. B.C. Ellison. Jour. Bombay Nat. Hist. Soc., vol.28, pp.675-697, map 1, pls.9, pp.1091-1106, pls.3, 1922.

SOME NATURAL HISTORY NOTES CONNECTED WITH THE PRINCE OF WALES' TOUR IN INDIA. B.C. Ellison. Jour. Bombay Nat. Hist. Soc., vol.29, pp.271-274, Apr. 20, 1923.

DISAPPEARANCE OF WILD LIFE IN INDIA. J.C. Faunthorpe. Nat. Hist., vol. 24, pp.204-207, fig.1, Mar.-Apr., 1924.

JUNGLE LIFE IN INDIA, BURMA AND NEPAL. SOME NOTES ON THE FAUNTHORPE-VERNAY EXPEDITION OF 1923. J.C. Faunthorpe. Nat. Hist., vol.24, pp. 174-198, figs.21, Mar.-Apr., 1924.

STERNDALE'S MAMMALIA OF INDIA. Frank Finn. New and Abridged Ed., throughly rev., Calcutta, Thacker, Spink, pp.347, 1929.

COLLECTION OF MAMMALS MADE BY R. STEVENS, IN THE DARJEELING DISTRICT. T.B. Fry. Jour. Bombay Nat. Hist. Soc., vol.29, pp.90-92, Apr. 20, 1923.

BOMBAY NATURAL HISTORY SOCIETY'S MAMMAL SURVEY OF INDIA, BURMA AND CEYLON. REPORT NO. 46. ON A COLLECTION FROM TOUNGOO, BURMA. T.B. Fry. Jour. Bombay Nat. Hist. Soc., vol.32, no.3, pp.545-547, Jan. 15, 1928.

BOMBAY NATURAL HISTORY SOCIETY'S MAMMAL SURVEY OF INDIA, BURMAH, AND CEYLON. REPORT NO. 46 (SUPPLEMENTARY) ON THE SECOND, THIRD AND FOURTH COLLECTIONS FROM TOUNGOO, BURMAH, MADE BY MR. J. M. D. MACKENZIE, I. F.S. BETWEEN DATES FEBRUARY 9, 1927 TO MARCH 2, 1928. T.B. Fry. Jour. Bombay Nat. Hist. Soc., vol.33, no.3, pp.636-652, 1929.

INDIAN FAUNA DURING 1943-44. A. K. Ghosh. Current Science, Bangalore, vol.14, no.9, p.240, Sep., 1945.

ILLUSTRATIONS OF INDIA ZOOLOGY, 1830-32. J.E. Gray.

ILLUSTRATIONS OF INDIAN ZOOLOGY; CHIEFLY SELECTED FROM THE COLLECTION OF MAJOR-GENERAL HARDWICKE. J.E. Gray. Pl.6, 1832.

OBSERVATIONS ON SOME RARE INDIAN MAMMALIA. J.E. Gray. Proc.Zool. Soc. London, pt.21, pp.190-192, pls.35-38, 1853.

FORTY YEARS AMONG THE WILD ANIMALS OF INDIA FROM MYSORE TO THE HIMALAYAS. F.C. Hicks. Allahabad, The Pioneer Press, pp.667, illus.(part col.), maps, plans, diagrs., 1910.

THE GAME BIRDS AND ANIMALS OF THE MANIPUR STATE WITH NOTES OF THEIR NUMBERS, MIGRATION AND HABITS.J.C. Higgins. Jour. Bombay Nat. Hist. Soc., vol.37, no.2, pp.298-309, Aug. 15, 1934.

BOMBAY NATURAL HISTORY SOCIETY'S MAMMAL SURVEY OF INDIA BURMA AND CEYLON. REPORT NO. 37, NEPAL. Martin A.C. Hinton, T.B. Fry. Jour. Bombay Nat. Hist. Soc., vol.29, pp.399-428, Aug. 25, 1923.

READERS' VIEWS ON 'GAME PRESERVATION IN INDIA.' W.M. Logan Home. Jour. Bombay Nat. Hist. Soc., vol.32, pp.581-583, Jan. 15, 1928.

CATALOGUE OF A COLLECTION OF MAMMALIA FROM NEPAL, SIKIM, AND TIBET, PRESENTED TO THE HON. EAST INDIA COMPANY BY B. H. HODGSON. Thomas Horsfield. Proc. Zool. Soc. London, pt.24, pp.393-406, pls.47-50, 1856.

NOTES UPON CERTAIN INDIAN MAMMALS. Capt. Thomas Hutton. Proc. Zool. Soc. London, for 1869, pp.58-59, 1869.

MAMMALS OF INDIA; A NATURAL HISTORY OF ALL THE ANIMALS KNOWN TO INHABIT CONTINENTAL INDIA. Thomas Claverhill Jerdon. London, J. Wheldon, pp.xxxi-335, 1874.

MAMMALIAN FAUNA OF THE SEMI-ARID TRACTS OF THE DECCAN AND ITS BEARING ON THE APPEARANCE OF ARIDITY IN THE REGION. H. Khajuria.Science and Culture, vol.21, no.6, pp.293-295, Dec., 1955.

LARGER MAMMALS OF THE NELLIAMPATHY HILLS. A.P. Kinloch. Jour. Bombay Nat. Hist. Soc., vol.29, pp.552-554, pl.1, Aug. 25, 1923.

TREE-SHREWS, TSINE AND SEROWS. C. Boden Kloss. Jour. Bombay Nat. Hist. Soc., vol.29, pp.555, Aug. 25, 1923.

BOMBAY NATURAL HISTORY SOCIETY'S MAMMAL SURVEY OF INDIA, BURMA AND CEYLON. SUPPLEMENT TO REPORT NO. 23, A SMALL COLLECTION OF MAMMALS MADE BY COL. F. M. BAILEY. H.M. Lindsay. Jour. Bombay Nat. Hist. Soc., vol.31, pp.612-613, Nov., 1926.

BOMBAY NATURAL HISTORY SOCIETY'S MAMMAL SURVEY OF INDIA, BURMA AND CEYLON. REPORT NO. 31A, SUPPLEMENT TO REPORT NO. 31, ON A COLLECTION OF SPECIMENS FROM THE NILGIRIS. H.M. Lindsay. Jour. Bombay Nat. Hist. Soc., vol.31, pp.613-614, Nov., 1926.

BOMBAY NATURAL HISTORY SOCIETY'S MAMMAL SURVEY OF INDIA, BURMA AND CEYLON. REPORT NO. 38. SIND. H.M.

Lindsay, et al. Jour. Bombay Nat. Hist. Soc., vol.31, no.1, pp.40-42, 1926.

BOMBAY NATURAL HISTORY SOCIETY'S MAMMAL SURVEY OF INDIA, BURMA AND CEYLON. REPORT NO. 39. MERGUI ARCHIPELAGO. H.M. Lindsay, et al. Jour. Bombay Nat. Hist. Soc., vol.31, no.1, pp.42-48, 1926.

BOMBAY NATURAL HISTORY SOCIETY'S MAMMAL SURVEY OF INDIA, BURMA AND CEYLON. REPORT NO. 40. GWALIOR STATE. H.M. Lindsay. Jour. Bombay Nat. Hist. Soc., vol.31, no.2, pp.379-382, 1926.

BOMBAY NATURAL HISTORY SOCIETY'S MAMMAL SURVEY OF INDIA, BURMA AND CEYLON. REPORT NO. 41. ASSAM AND MISHMI HILLS. H.M. Lindsay, et al. Jour. Bombay Nat. Hist. Soc., vol. 31, no.2, pp.383-403, 1926.

BOMBAY NATURAL HISTORY SOCIETY'S MAMMAL SURVEY OF INDIA, BURMA AND CEYLON. REPORT NO. 42. KASHMIR AND PUNJAB. H.M. Lindsay, et al. Jour. Bombay Nat. Hist. Soc., vol.31, no.2, pp.403-407, 1926.

BOMBAY NATURAL HISTORY SOCIETY'S MAMMAL SURVEY OF INDIA, BURMA AND CEYLON. REPORT NO. 43. NELLIAMPATHY PLATEAU AND PALNI HILLS. H.M. Lindsay, et al. Jour. Bombay Nat. Hist. Soc., vol.31, no.3, pp.591-597, 1926.

BOMBAY NATURAL HISTORY SOCIETY'S MAMMAL SURVEY OF INDIA, BURMA AND CEYLON. REPORT NO. 44. JANGRA AND CHAMBA. H.M. Lindsay, et al. Jour. Bombay Nat. Hist. Soc., vol.31, no.3, pp. 597-606, 1926.

BOMBAY NATURAL HISTORY SOCIETY'S MAMMAL SURVEY OF INDIA, BURMA AND CEYLON. REPORT NO. 45. PUNJAB SALT RANGE. H.M. Lindsay, et al. Jour. Bombay Nat. Hist. Soc., vol.31, no.3, pp.606-614, 1926.

SCIENTIFIC RESULTS FROM THE MAMMAL SURVEY NO. 46. H.M. Lindsay. Jour. Bombay Nat. Hist. Soc., vol.31, no.2, pp.239-240, Aug., 1926.

CATALOGUE OF THE HEADS AND HORNS OF INDIAN BIG GAME BEQUEATHED BY A. O. HUMS... TO THE BRITISH MUSEUM (NATURAL HISTORY). R. Lydekker. London, Printed by Order of the Trustees, pp. xvi-48, illus., 1913.

GREAT AND SMALL GAME OF INDIA, BURMA, AND TIBET. R. Lydekker. London, R. Ward, Ltd., pp.xviii-416, illus., col.pls.9, 1900.

GAME ANIMALS OF INDIA, MALAYA, AND TIBET; BEING A NEW AND REVISED EDITION OF "GREAT AND SMALL GAME OF INDIA, BURMA, AND TIBET." R. Lydekker. London, R. Ward, Ltd., pp.xiii-408, illus., fold.pls.4, 1907.

GAME PRESERVATION IN ASSAM. A.J.W. Milroy. Jour. Soc. Preservation Fauna Empire, Hertford, n.s., pt.xvi, pp.28-40, 1932.

PRESERVATION OF WILD LIFE IN INDIA. A.J.W. Milroy. Jour. Bombay Nat. Hist. Soc., vol.37, no.1, Appendix, pp.97-111, Apr., 1934; no.3. Assam, vol.37, no.1, (suppl.), pp.97-104, Apr. 15, 1934.

PRESERVATION OF WILD LIFE IN INDIA. NO. 2. THE BOMBAY PRESIDENCY. G. Monteath. Jour. Bombay Nat. Hist. Soc., vol.36, no.4, (suppl.), pp.46-58, Dec.15, 1933.

RECORD OF BIG GAME SHOT IN THE NILGIRI AREA 1905-1931. R. Morris. Jour. Bombay Nat. Hist. Soc., vol.36, no.1, pp.252-253, Nov. 15, 1932.

SITUATION OF BIG GAME IN SOUTHERN INDIA. R. Morris. Field, London, vol.161, no.4188, pp.681-682, Apr. 1, 1933.

ON THE RANN OF CUTCH. (Notes on Speed of Gazelle, Black Buck and Wild Ass.) A.H. Mosse. Jour. Bombay Nat. Hist. Soc., vol. 29, pp.274-275, pls.2, Apr. 20, 1923.

ON A COLLECTION OF MAMMALS FROM CHOTA NAGPUR, BIHAR. Bhola Nath. Records Indian Mus., Calcutta, vol.48, pt.1, pp.29-44, Mar., 1950.

BEYOND THE PIR PANJAL: LIFE AMONG THE MOUNTAINS AND VALLEYS OF KASHMIR. Ernest F. Neve. London, Leipsic, T.F. Unwin, pp.xvi, 17-320, pls., maps, 1912.

HUNTING WITH THE PRINCE OF WALES--INDIAN TIGER, RHINO AND BEARS IN THE NEPAL TERAI. Frederick O'Connor. Field, London, vol.158, no.4107, pp.396-397, illus., Sep. 12, 1931.

SUPPOSED OCCURRENCE OF THE ERMINE IN INDIA. B.B. Osmaston. Jour. Bombay Nat. Hist. Soc., vol.29, p.277, Apr. 20, 1923.

GAME PRESERVATION IN THE NILGIRIS. E.G. Phythian-Adams. Jour. Bombay Nat. Hist. Soc., vol.32, pp.339-343, Oct. 20, 1927.

GAME PRESERVATIONS IN THE NILGIRIS IN 1929. E.G. Phythian-Adams. Jour. Bombay Nat. Hist. Soc., vol.33, no.4, pp.947-951, Oct. 15, 1929.

PRESERVATION OF WILD LIFE IN INDIA. NO. 9, MYSORE. E.G. Phythian-Adams. Jour. Bombay Nat. Hist. Soc., vol.38, no. 2, pp.241-245, Dec. 1, 1935.

SHOOTING IN SIKKIM. Philip Pinckney. Jour. Bengal Nat. Hist. Soc., Darjeeling, vol.14, no.1, pp. 13-18, June, 1939.

FAUNA OF BRITISH INDIA, INCLUDING CEYLON AND BURMA. MAMMALIA.-- Vol. 1. PRIMATES AND CARNIVORA (FELIDAE AND VIVERRIDAE). R. I. Pocock. London, Taylor and Francis, Ltd., pp.463, illus., map 1, Mar. 31, 1939.

(Review by P. Rode of) FAUNA OF BRITISH INDIA, INCLUDING CEYLON AND BURMA. MAMMALIA. Vol.1. PRIMATES AND CARNIVORA (FELIDAE AND VIVERRIDAE). R.I. Pocock. London, Taylor and Francis, vol.1, pp.463, figs.106, pls.31, map 1, 1939. Mammalia, Paris, vol.3, no.2, pp. 81-82, June, 1939.

FAUNA OF BRITISH INDIA, INCLUDING CEYLON AND BURMA. MAMMALIA.-- Vol. 2. CARNIVORA (SUBORDERS AELUROIDAE (PART) AND ARCTOIDAE.) R. I. Pocock. London, Taylor and Francis, Ltd., pp.503, illus., map 1, Sep. 15, 1941.

(Review by S.H. Prater of) FAUNA OF BRITISH INDIA, INCLUDING CEYLON AND BURMA. MAMMALIA. Vol.2. CARNIVORA (SUBORDERS AELUROIDAE (PART) AND ARCTOIDAE). R.I. Pocock. Jour. Bombay Nat. Hist. Soc., vol.43, no. 2, pp.246-249, Aug., 1942.

(Review by D. Seth-Smith of) FAUNA OF BRITISH INDIA, INCLUDING CEYLON AND BURMA. MAMMALIA. Vol.2. CARNIVORA (SUBORDERS AELUROIDAE (PART) AND ARCTOIDAE). R. I. Pocock. Nature, London, vol.149, no.3770, pp. 122-123, Jan. 31, 1942.

LETTER ACCOMPANYING A COLLECTION OF MAMMALIA, BIRDS, AND REPTILES, OBTAINED IN THE TRAVANCORE COUNTRY. P. Poole. Proc. Zool. Soc. London. pt.3, pp.66-67, 1835.

LIST OF THE MAMMALS OF THE RAJASTHAN DESERT. Ishwar Prakash. Jour. Bengal Nat. Hist. Soc., vol.28, no.1-2, pp.1-7, Apr., 1956.

BOOK OF INDIAN ANIMALS. Stanley Henry Prater. Bombay Nat. Hist. Soc., pp.xxxii-262, illus.(part col.), fold. col.map, (Indian Nat. Hist. Series, vol.2) 1947.

ROLE OF DOMESTICATED ANIMALS IN INDIAN HISTORY. M.S. Ranhawa. Science and Culture, Calcutta, vol.12, no.1, pp. 5-14, figs.4, July, 1946.

PRESERVATION OF WILD LIFE IN INDIA. NO. 7, THE MADRAS PRESIDENCY. R.D. Richmond. Jour. Bombay Nat. Hist. Soc., vol.38, no.2, pp.220-224, Dec. 1, 1935.

CONTRIBUTIONS TO THE FAUNA OF MANIPUR STATE, ASSAM. PT. III. M.L. Roonwal. Records Indian Museum, Calcutta, vol.47, pt.1, pp.1-64, Mar., 1949.

SYSTEMATICS, ECOLOGY AND BIONOMICS OF MAMMALS STUDIED IN CONNECTION WITH TSUTSUGAMUSCHI DISEASE (SCRUB TYPHUS) IN THE ASSAM-BURMA WAR THEATER DURING 1945. M.L. Roonwal. Trans. Nat. Inst. Sci. India, Delhi, vol.3, pp.67-122, 1948.

BOMBAY NATURAL HISTORY SOCIETY'S MAMMAL SURVEY OF INDIA. REPORT NO. 10. KATHIAWAR. Kathleen V. Ryley. Jour. Bombay Nat. Hist. Soc., vol.22, no.3, pp.464-486, illus., Dec. 20, 1913; REPORT NO. 11. COORG. Jour. Bombay Nat. Hist. Soc., vol.22, no.3, pp.486-513, illus., Dec. 20, 1913; REPORT NO. 12. PALANPUR AND MOUNT ABU. Jour. Bombay Nat. Hist. Soc., vol.22, no.4, pp. 684-699, Mar. 31, 1914; REPORT NO. 13. S. CEYLON. Jour. Bombay Nat. Hist. Soc., vol.22, no.4, pp.700-710, Mar. 31, 1914; REPORT NO. 14. N. SHAN STATES, BURMA. Jour. Bombay Nat. Hist. Soc., vol.22, no. 4, pp.710-725, Mar. 31, 1914.

SCIENTIFIC RESULTS FROM THE MAMMAL SURVEY. V. Kathleen V. Ryley. Jour. Bombay Nat. Hist. Soc., vol.22, no.3, pp.434-443a, Dec. 20, 1933.

SCIENTIFIC RESULTS FROM THE MAMMAL SURVEY. VI. Kathleen V. Ryley. Jour. Bombay Nat. Hist. Soc., vol.22, no.4, pp.658-664, Mar. 31, 1914.

MAMMALS OF THE SUYDAM CUTTING SIKKIM EXPEDITION. Colin Campbell Sanborn. Jour. Bombay Nat. Hist. Soc., vol.36, no.1, pp.181-187, Nov. 15, 1932.

SHOOTING TRIP TO LADAKH. PART III. THE AMMON GROUND. T.A. Shorten. Jour. Bengal Nat. Hist. Soc., Darjeeling, vol.17, no.4, pp.128-132, Apr., 1943.

HAILEY NATIONAL PARK. A. Kirke Smith. Indian Wild Life, vol.2, no.4, pp.397-405, Oct.-Dec., 1937.

PRESERVATION OF THE WILD LIFE IN INDIA. NO. 6. WILD LIFE PROTECTION IN BURMA. H.C. Smith. Jour. Bombay Nat. Hist. Soc., vol.37, no.4 (suppl.), pp.167-188, Apr. 15, 1935.

HAILEY NATIONAL PARK. E.A.Smithies. Indian Wild Life, Agra, vol.3, no.1, pp. 16-20, pls., Jan.-Mar., 1938.

GAME PRESERVATION IN INDIA. Reginald Spencer, et al. Jour. Bombay Nat. Hist. Soc., vol.32, pp.359-365, Oct. 20, 1927.

MAMMALIA OF INDIA AND CEYLON. Robert A. Sterndale. Thacker, Spink and Co., Calcutta, pp.540, illus., 1884.

STERNDALE'S MAMMALIA OF INDIA. (A new and abridged ed., thoroughly revised and with an appendix on the Reptilia by Frank Finn.) Robert A. Sterndale. Calcutta and Simla, Thacker, Spink and Co., pp.vii-347, illus., 1929.

BIG GAME IN LADAK. C.H. Stockley. Field, London, vol.163, no.4239, pp.626-627, illus., Mar. 24, 1924.

NOTES ON LYDEKKER'S "GAME ANIMALS OF INDIA." C.H. Stockley. Jour. Bombay Nat. Hist. Soc., vol.28, pp.529-533, pl. 1, Mar. 25, 1922.

WILD LIFE OF AN INDIAN SWAMP - I. C.H. Stockley. The Field, London, vol. 175, no.4553, pp.498-500, Mar. 30, 1940.

CATALOGUE OF THE MAMMALIA OF DUKHUN (DECCAN); WITH OBSERVATIONS ON THEIR HABITS AND CHARACTERS OF NEW SPECIES. W.H. Sykes. Proc. Comm. Sci. and Corres. Zool. Soc. London, pt.1, p.99, 1830-1831.

NEW AND INTERESTING MAMMALS FROM THE MISHMI HILLS. Oldfield Thomas. Jour. Bombay Nat. Hist. Soc., vol.28, pp.428-431, Mar. 25, 1922.

SCIENTIFIC RESULTS OF THE MAMMAL SURVEY. NO. 7. Oldfield Thomas. Jour. Bombay Nat. Hist. Soc., vol.23, pp.23-31, June 30, 1914.

SCIENTIFIC RESULTS FROM THE MAMMAL SURVEY. XX. Oldfield Thomas.

Jour. Bombay Nat. Hist. Soc., Oct. 20, 1919.

SCIENTIFIC RESULTS OF THE MAMMAL SURVEY. NO. XXI. (A) SOME NEW MAMMALS FROM BALUCHISTAN AND NORTH-WEST INDIA (pp.933-938); (B) TWO NEW SPECIES OF CALOMYSCUS (pp.938-940). Oldfield Thomas. Jour. Bombay Nat. Hist. Soc., vol.26, no.4, pp.933-940, Jan. 31, 1920.

SCIENTIFIC RESULTS OF THE MAMMAL SURVEY. NO. XXXII. (A) NEW AND INTERESTING MAMMALS FROM THE MISHMI HILLS. Oldfield Thomas. Jour. Bombay Nat. Hist. Soc., vol.28, no.2, pp.428-431, Mar. 25, 1922.

SOME NEW MAMMALS FROM BALUCHISTAN AND NORTH-WEST INDIA. Oldfield Thomas. Jour. Bombay Nat. Hist. Soc., vol.26, pp.933-938, Jan., 1920.

ON NATIVE IMPRESSIONS REGARDING THE NATURAL HISTORY OF CERTAIN (INDIAN) ANIMALS. H. Torrens. Proc. Zool. Soc. London, pt.23, pp.129-131, 1855.

NOTES ON MAMMALS OF BALTISTAN AND THE VALE OF KASHMIR, PRESENTED TO THE NATIONAL MUSEUM BY DR. W. L. ABBOT. Frederick William True. (In) U.S. Nat. Mus., Proceedings, Washington, vol. 17, pp.1-16, May 8, 1894.

BIG GAME SHOOTING OF KASHMIR AND ADJACENT HILL PROVINCES. A.E. Ward. Jour. Bombay Nat. Hist. Soc., vol. 28, pp.45-49, pls.2, Dec. 30, 1921.

GAME ANIMALS OF KASHMIR AND ADJACENT HILL PROVINCES. A.E. Ward. Jour. Bombay Nat. Hist. Soc., vol.28, pp.334-344, pls.2, pp.595-609, pl.1;pp. 874-882, map 1, pl., 1922; vol.29, pp. 318-323, pls.4, Aug.25, 1923; vol.32, no. 4, pp.711-716, May 31, 1928.

MAMMALS AND BIRDS OF KASHMIR AND THE ADJACENT HILL PROVINCES. A.E. Ward. Jour. Bombay Nat. Hist. Soc., vol.29, pp.879-887, pls.7, figs. 4, May 15, 1924.

EXHIBITION OF SOME HEADS OF MAMMALS FROM IADAKH. Edwin Ward. Proc. Zool. Soc. London, p.145, 1871.

SOME OBSERVATIONS ON THE BIRDS AND MAMMALS OF IMAW BUM. F. Kingdom Ward. Jour. Bombay Nat. Hist. Soc., vol.27, pp.754-758, July 31, 1921.

MEMORANDUM ON THE KAHILU SANCTUARY. D'Arcy Weatherbe. Jour. Bombay Nat. Hist. Soc., vol.41, no.1, pp.146-160, 1939.

FIELD NOTES ON THE MAMMALS OF SOUTH TINNEVELLY, SOUTH INDIA. C.G. Webb-Peploe. Jour. Bombay Nat. Hist. Soc., vol.46, no.4, pp.629-644, pl.1, Apr., 1947.

KASHMIR AND ITS BIG GAME. R. G. Wreford. Field, London, vol.161, no. 4186, pp.546-548, illus., Mar. 18, 1933.

BOMBAY NATURAL HISTORY SOCIETY'S MAMMAL SURVEY OF INDIA, BURMA AND CEYLON. REPORT NO.15. INDIA, KUMAON DIVISION, WESTERN BOUNDARY OF NEPAL. R.C. Wroughton. Jour. Bombay Nat. Hist. Soc., vol.23, no.2, pp.282-301, Nov. 20, 1914.

BOMBAY NATURAL HISTORY SOCIETY'S MAMMAL SURVEY OF INDIA, BURMA AND CEYLON. REPORT NO.16. DRY ZONE OF UPPER BURMA AND MT. POPA. R.C. Wroughton. Jour. Bombay Nat. Hist. Soc., vol.23, no.3, pp.460-480, Feb. 2, 1915.

BOMBAY NATURAL HISTORY SOCIETY'S MAMMAL SURVEY OF INDIA, BURMA AND CEYLON. REPORT NO.17. SOUTHERN PORTION OF PROVINCE OF BURMA. R.C. Wroughton. Jour. Bombay Nat. Hist. Soc., vol.23, no.4, pp.695-720, May 25, 1915.

BOMBAY NATURAL HISTORY SOCIETY'S MAMMAL SURVEY OF INDIA, BURMA AND CEYLON. REPORT NO.23. SIKKIM AND BENGAL TERAI. R.C. Wroughton. Jour. Bombay Nat. Hist. Soc., vol.24, pp.468-493.

BOMBAY NATURAL HISTORY SOCIETY'S MAMMAL SURVEY OF INDIA, BURMA AND CEYLON. REPORT NO.24. SIND. R.C. Wroughton. Jour. Bombay Nat. Hist. Soc., vol.24, no.4, pp.749-758, Oct.25, 1916.

BOMBAY NATURAL HISTORY SOCIETY'S MAMMAL SURVEY OF INDIA, BURMA AND CEYLON. REPORT NO.25. CHIN HILLS. R.C. Wroughton. Jour. Bombay Nat. Hist. Soc., vol.24, no.4, pp.758-773, Oct. 25, 1916.

BOMBAY NATURAL HISTORY SOCIETY'S MAMMAL SURVEY OF INDIA, BURMA AND CEYLON. REPORT NO.26. DARJILING DISTRICT. R.C. Wroughton. Jour. Bombay Nat. Hist. Soc., vol.24, no.4, pp.773-782, Oct. 25, 1916.

BOMBAY NATURAL HISTORY SOCIETY'S MAMMAL SURVEY OF INDIA, BURMA AND CEYLON. REPORT NO.27. BHUTAN DUARS. R.C. Wroughton. Jour. Bombay Nat. Hist. Soc., vol.25, no.1, pp.63-71, Mar. 20, 1917.

BOMBAY NATURAL HISTORY SOCIETY'S MAMMAL SURVEY OF INDIA, BURMA AND CEYLON. REPORT NO.28. KALIMPONG (DARJILING). R.C. Wroughton. Jour. Nat. Hist. Soc., vol.25, no.2, pp. 274-278, Sep. 15, 1917.

BOMBAY NATURAL HISTORY SOCIETY'S MAMMAL SURVEY OF INDIA, BURMA AND CEYLON. REPORT NO.29. PEGU. R.C. Wroughton, Winifred M. Davidson. Jour. Bombay Nat. Hist. Soc., vol.25, no.3, pp.472-481, Jan.15, 1918.

BOMBAY NATURAL HISTORY SOCIETY'S MAMMALS SURVEY OF INDIA, BURMA AND CEYLON. REPORT NO.30. DEKHAN (POONA DISTRICT), AND REPORT NO. 31. NILGIRIS. R.C. Wroughton, Winifred M. Davidson. Jour. Bombay Nat. Hist. Soc., vol.26, pp.1025-1035, Jan. 31, 1920.

BOMBAY NATURAL HISTORY SOCIETY'S MAMMAL SURVEY OF INDIA, BURMA AND CEYLON. REPORT NO.32. BALUCHISTAN. R.C. Wroughton. Jour. Bombay Nat. Hist. Soc., vol.27, pp.314-322, Dec. 20, 1920.

BOMBAY NATURAL HISTORY SOCIETY'S MAMMAL SURVEY OF INDIA, BURMA AND CEYLON. REPORT NO.33. HIGH WAVY MOUNTAINS, MADURA DISTRICT.) R.C. Wroughton. Jour. Bombay Nat. Hist. Soc., vol.27, pp.545-554, Mar. 31, 1921.

BOMBAY NATURAL HISTORY SOCIETY'S MAMMAL SURVEY OF INDIA, BURMA AND CEYLON. REPORT NO.34. TRAVANCORE. R.C. Wroughton. Jour. Bombay Nat. Hist. Soc., vol.27, no.3, pp.549-554, Mar. 31, 1921.

FURTHER NOTES ON SOME MAMMALS FROM LOWER SIND. R.C. Wroughton. Jour. Bombay Nat. Hist. Soc., vol.21, no.1, pp.175-177, Oct. 31, 1911.

PROGRESS OF THE MAMMAL SURVEY OF INDIA, BURMA AND CEYLON. R.C. Wroughton. Jour. Bombay Nat. Hist. Soc., vol.22, no.3, pp.616-618, fold.map, Dec. 20, 1913.

PROGRESS OF THE MAMMALS SURVEY OF INDIA, BURMA AND CEYLON. R.C. Wroughton. Jour. Bombay Nat. Hist. Soc., vol.22, no.4, pp.785-787a, Mar. 31, 1914.

PROGRESS OF THE MAMMAL SURVEY. R.C. Wroughton. Jour. Bombay Nat. Hist. Soc., vol.23, no.2, pp.341-342a, map, Nov. 20, 1914.

PROGRESS OF THE MAMMAL SURVEY. R.C. Wroughton. Jour. Bombay Nat. Hist. Soc., vol.23, no.4, pp.758-762, May 25, 1915.

SUMMARY OF THE RESULTS FROM THE INDIAN MAMMAL SURVEY. A SHORT HISTORY OF INDIAN MAMMALOGY. PT.1. R.C. Wroughton. Jour. Bombay Nat. Hist. Soc., vol.25, no.4, pp.547-598, June 10, 1918; vol.26, no.1, pp.20-58, Dec. 20, 1918; vol.26, no.2, pp.338-379, May 20, 1919; vol.26, no.3, pp.776-802, Oct.20, 1919; vol.27, no.4, pp.955-967, Jan.31, 1920; vol.27, no.1, pp.57-85, July 1, 1920; vol.27, no.2, pp.301-313, Dec. 20, 1920.

SUMMARY OF THE RESULTS FROM THE INDIAN MAMMAL SURVEY. R.C. Wroughton. Bombay Nat. Hist. Soc., vol.26, pp. 955-967; vol.27, pp.57-85; pp.303-313, 1920; vol.27, pp.520-534, Mar. 31, 1921.

NOTES UPON CERTAIN INDIAN MAMMALS. Proc. Zool. Soc. London, pp.58-59, 1869.

WILD ANIMALS OF THE INDIAN EMPIRE AND THE PROBLEM OF THEIR PRESERVATION. Pt.1. Jour. Bombay Nat. Hist. Soc., vol.36, no.4, suppl., pp.1-39, pls. 1-14, col.pl.1, Dec. 15, 1933. Pt.2, Ibid., vol.37, no.1, suppl., pp.59-96, pls.15-36, col.pls.2-12, Apr. 15, 1934. Pt.3, Ibid., vol.37, no.4, suppl., pp.112-161, pls.37-52, col.pls.13-15, Apr. 15, 1935.

WILD ANIMALS OF THE INDIAN EMPIRE AND THE PROBLEM OF THEIR PRESERVATION. Pt.2. Jour. Bombay Nat. Hist. Soc., vol.37, no.1, suppl., pp.59-96, pls.16-36, Apr. 15, 1934.

WILDLIFE IN INDIA. Indian Wild Life, vol.1, no.2, pp.60-64, Aug., 1936.

## INDIAN OCEAN

NOTES ON THE NATURAL HISTORY OF ALDABRA, ASSUMPTION, AND GLORIOSO ISLANDS, INDIAN OCEAN. W. L. Abbott. Proc. U.S. Nat. Mus., no.973, vol.16, pp.759-764; Smiths. Inst., 1894.

REPORT OF THE CURATOR, ZOOLOGICAL DEPARTMENT. (Mammals from Andaman Island and Other Malayan Regions.) Edward Blyth. Jour. Asiatic Soc. Bengal, vol.28, pp.271-298, 1859.

NOTES ON THE FAUNA OF CHRISTMAS ISLAND, INDIAN OCEAN. F.N. Chasen. Bull. Raffles Mus., Singapore, Straits Settlements, no.8, pp.51-54, Dec., 1933.

NOTE ON THE MAMMALS OF CHRISTMAS ISLAND. C.A. Gibson-Hill. Bull. Raffles Mus., Singapore, no.18, pp.166-167, Oct., 1947.

MAMMALS OF ENGANO ISLAND, WEST SUMATRA. Gerrit Smith Miller. U.S. Nat. Mus., Proceedings, vol.30, pp.819-825, Washington, 1906.

MAMMALS OF THE ANDAMAN AND NICOBAR ISLANDS. Gerrit Smith Miller. U.S. Nat. Mus., Proc., Washington, vol.24, pp.751-795, illus.1, pls.2, 1902.

(NOTES ON THE CROZET ISLANDS.) Notes sur les Iles Crozet. E.A. de la Rûe. Bull. Mus. Hist. Nat., Paris, vol.22, pp.197-203, 1950.

ON THE MAMMALS OF ENGGANO. H.J.V. Sody. Treubia, Buitenzorg, vol.17, no.4, pp.391-401, pl.1, Apr., 1940.

ON SOME MAMMALS COLLECTED BY DR. E. MODIGLIANI IN SIPORIA, MENTAWEI ISLANDS. Oldfield Thomas. Annali del Museo Civico di Storia Naturale di Genova ser.2, vol.14, pp.660-672, Jan. 7, 1895.

ON SOME MAMMALS FROM ENGANO ISLAND, WEST OF SUMATRA. Oldfield Thomas. Annali del Museo Civico di Storia Naturali di Genova, ser.2, vol.14, pp.105-110, Apr. 10, 1894.

ON THE MAMMALS OF CHRISTMAS ISLAND. Oldfield Thomas. Proc. Zool. Soc. London, pp.532-534, Dec. 4, 1888.

REPORT ON A ZOOLOGICAL COLLECTION MADE BY THE OFFICERS OF THE H. M. S. 'FLYING-FISH' AT CHRISTMAS ISLAND, INDIAN OCEAN. MAMMALIA. Oldfield Thomas. Proc. Zool. Soc. London, pp.511-514, pls.41-42, June 23, 1887.

DIAGNOSES OF NEW MAMMALS COLLECTED BY MR. H. C. ROBINSON IN THE ISLANDS OF THE STRAITS OF MALACCA. Oldfield Thomas, R.C. Wroughton. Ann. and Mag. Nat. Hist., ser.8, vol.4, no.24, pp.534-536, Dec., 1909.

INDO-AUSTRALIAN ARCHIPELAGO

CONTRIBUTION TO THE KNOWLEDGE OF THE GENERA MUNTIACUS AND ARCTOGALIDIA IN THE INDO-AUSTRALIAN ARCHIPELAGO (MAMMALIA, CERVIDAE AND VIVERRIDAE). A.C.V. van Bemmel. Beaufortia, Zool. Mus. Amsterdam, no.16, pp.1-50, illus., fold. tbls., May 7, 1952.

OCCASIONAL NOTES. SOME RARE AUSTRALIAN AND NEW GUINEA MAMMALS WITH NOTES ON THEIR HABITS. A.S. Le Souef. Australian Zool., vol.6, no.2, p.110, 1930.

DISCONTINUOUS DISTRIBUTION OF CERTAIN INDO-MALAYAN MAMMALS, AND ITS ZOOGEOGRAPHICAL SIGNIFICANCE. M.L. Roonwal, Bhola Nath. Proc. Nat. Inst. Sci. India, Delhi, vol. 15, no.8, pp.375-377, figs.3, Nov.-Dec., 1949.

NOTES ON SOME PRIMATES, CARNIVORA, AND THE BABRIRUSA FROM THE INDO-MALAYAN AND INDO-AUSTRALIAN REGIONS (WITH DESCRIPTIONS OF 10 NEW SPECIES AND SUBSPECIES). H.J.V.Sody. Treubia, Buitenzorg, vol.20, pt.2, pp. 121-190, fold.tbl., Oct., 1949.

NOTES ON THE TYPES OF CERTAIN EARLY DESCRIBED SPECIES OF MONOTREMES, MARSUPIALS, MURIDAE, AND BATS FROM THE INDO-AUSTRALIAN REGION. G.H.H. Tate. Amer. Mus. Novitates, New York, no.1061, pp.1-10, May 1, 1940.

RESULTS OF THE ARCHBOLD EXPEDITIONS, NO. 2. TWELVE APPARENTLY NEW FORMS OF RATTUS FROM THE INDO-AUSTRALIAN REGION. G.H.H. Tate, Richard Archbold. Amer. Mus. Novitates, no.802, pp.10, May 18, 1935.

DESCRIPTIONS OF THREE NEW MAMMALS FROM THE EAST INDIAN ARCHIPELAGO AND AUSTRALIA. Oldfield Thomas. Novitates Zoologicae, vol.5, pp.1-4, Mar., 1898.

INDOCHINA

(GENERAL INVENTORY OF INDOCHINA. THE FAUNA OF INDOCHINA. VERTEBRATES. MAMMALS.) Inventaire Général de l'Indochine. La Faune de l'Indochine. Vertebres. Mammiferes. Rene Bourret. Societé de Géographie de Hanoi, fasc.3, pp.7-80, pls.3, 1927.

(THE MAMMALS OF INDOCHINA.) Les mammiferes d l'Indochine. René Bourret. Hanoi, col.pls., col.map, 1947?

(MAMMALS OF THE COLLECTION OF THE ZOOLOGICAL LABORATORY OF THE HIGHER SCHOOL OF SCIENCES.) Les mammiferes de la collection du Laboratoire de Zoologie de l'Ecole Supérieure des Sciences. René Bourret. Notes & Travauxc École Supérieure Sciences, Univ. Indochinoise, Hanoi, no.1, pp.1-44, pls. 2, Dec., 1942.

(Comments by A.Brazier Howell on) INDO-CHINA EXPEDITION. James L. Clark. Jour. Mamm., vol.17, no.2, p.195, May, 1936.

(PROVISIONAL LIST OF THE MAMMALS OF FRENCH INDOCHINA.) List provisoire des mammiféres de l'Indochine Française. J. Delacour. Mammalia, Paris, vol.4, no. 1, pp.20-29, Mar. 1940; no.2, pp.46-58, June, 1940.

(WILD FAUNA OF CAMBODIA; HABITS AND HUNTING.) La faune sauvage du Cambodge; moeurs et chasse. Charles Dumas. Pnompenh, Aymonier, pp.280, 1944.

BIG-GAME HUNTING IN INDO-CHINA. Clarence E. Fronk. Pan-Pacific, Hawaii, vol.2, no.3, pp.47, 48, 58, Oct.-Dec., illus., 1938.

LIST OF MAMMALIA, TORTOISES, AND CROCODILES COLLECTED BY M. MOUHOT IN CAMBOJA. Dr. John Edward Gray. Proc. Zool. Soc. London, pt.29, pp.135-140, pl.xxi, 1861.

ON A SMALL COLLECTION OF MAMMALS FROM CAMBODIA. C. Boden Kloss. Jour. Nat. Hist. Soc. Siam, vol.4, pp.99-102, Mar., 1921.

ADVENTURES ON HUNTING TRAILS OF INDO-CHINA. Sidney J. Legendre. Nat. Hist., New York, vol.32, no.5, pp.481-496, illus., Sep.-Oct., 1932.

(LARGE WILD ANIMALS OF ANNAM, THEIR HABITS, HUNTING AND SHOOTING.) Les grands animaux sauvages de l'Annam, leurs moeurs, leur chasse et leur tir. Fernand Victor Millet. Paris, Plon, pp.374, illus., pls., fold.map, 1930.

MAMMALS OF THE KELLEY-ROOSEVELTS AND DELACOUR ASIATIC EXPEDITIONS. Wilfred Hudson Osgood. Chicago, pp.193-339, illus.1, pls.10-11, map, 1932. (Field Mus. of Nat. Hist., Publication 312, Zoological Series, vol.18, no.10.)

(COMPARISON OF THE MAMMALIAN FAUNA OF LANG SON (TONKIN) AND SE TCHOUEN.) Comparaison des faunes de mammiferes de Lang Son (Tonkin) et du Se Tchouen. Etienne Patte. Bull. Soc. Géol. France, Paris, ser.4, vol.28, nos. 1-2, pp.55-63, figs.3, Feb., 1928.

NEW MAMMALS FROM FRENCH INDO-CHINA AND SIAM. Herbert C. Robinson, C. Boden Kloss. Ann. and Mag. Nat. Hist., ser.9, vol.9, pp.87-99, Jan., 1922.

(HUNTING IN INDOCHINA.) La chasse en Indochine. Lucien Roussel. Paris, Plon-Nourrit et cie, pp.318, pls., 1913.

BIG-GAME HUNTING IN FRENCH INDO-CHINA. THE GOLDEN GATE INTERNATIONAL EXPOSITION OF SAN FRANCISCO, 1939. Omer Sarraut. G.Taupin & Cie, Hanoi, French Indo-China, pp. v-xi - 1-43, illus., fold.map, 1939.

DELACOUR EXPLORATION OF FRENCH INDO-CHINA. MAMMALS. Oldfield Thomas. Proc. Zool. Soc. London, PART I., pp.41-58, pls.2, Apr.6, 1927; PART II. ON THE MAMMALS COLLECTED DURING THE WINTER OF 1926-27, pt.1, pp.139-150, Apr., 1928; PART III. MAMMALS COLLECTED DURING THE WINTER OF 1927-28, pt.4, pp.831-841, Jan. 31, 1929.

MAMMALS OBTAINED BY MR. HERBERT STEVENS ON THE SLADEN-GODMAN EXPEDITION TO TONKIN. Oldfield Thomas. Proc. Zool. Soc. London, 1925, pp.496-506, July, 1925.

WITH A CAMERA IN INDO-CHINA. (Photographs of Tigers, Buffalo, and Elephant.) Field, London, vol.167, no.4350, pp. 1068-1069, illus., May 9, 1936.

IRAQ see MESOPOTAMIA

IRELAND

CLARE ISLAND SURVEY - MAMMALIA. G.E.H. Barrett-Hamilton. Proc. Roy. Irish Acad., vol.31, pt.17, pp.1-14, Sep., 1912.

IRISH MAMMALS. G.E.H. Barrett-Hamilton. Irish Naturalist, vol.4, no.3, pp.65-72 (1-15), Mar., 1895.

EXCAVATION OF WHITE PARK BAY KITCHEN MIDDEN SITE. (Remains of Several Prehistoric Mammals.) Alex H. Davison, et al. Irish Naturalists' Jour., vol.1, no.14, pp. 280-284, pl.1, fig.1, Nov., 1927.

PREHISTORIC MAMMALS OF IRELAND.III. H.E. Forrest. Irish Naturalists' Jour., vol. 1, no.9, pp.171-174, Jan., 1927.

PREHISTORIC MAMMALS OF IRELAND.IV. H.E. Forrest. Irish Naturalists' Jour., vol.1, no.11, pp.215-219; vol.1, no.12, pp.234-236, 1927.

REMARKS ON THE DATE OF EXTINCTION OF THE MOLE AND WEASEL IN IRELAND. Arthur E. Knox. Proc. Zool. Soc. London, pt.31, p.510, 1863.

MAMMALS OF IRELAND. C.B. Moffat. Proc. Roy. Irish Acad., vol.44, sect.B, no.6, pp.61-128, Jan., 1938.

NOTES ON THE MAMMALS OF THE NORTH BULL, DUBLIN BAY. Eugene O'Mahony. Irish Nat.Jour., vol.3, pp.199-201, May, 1931.

REPORT ON SKELETAL REMAINS FOUND AT BALLOO BAY, CO. DOWN. Marie E. Rea. Irish Naturalists' Jour., vol.3, no. 8, pp.166-170, figs.3, Mar., 1931.

(MAMMALS OF IRELAND AFTER THE RECENT WORK OF C.B. MOFFAT.) Les mammifères de l'Irlande d'après le travail recent de C.B. Moffat. P. Rode. Mammalia, Paris, vol.3, no.2, pp.76-78, June 1939.

REPORT ON EXCAVATIONS IN IRELAND IN 1928. E.K. Tratman. Proc.Spelaeolog. Soc.Univ.Bristol, vol.3, no.3, pp.109-125, figs.4, pls.3, (1928) 1929.

ITALY

(MAMMALS OF THE QUATERNARY OF ZANDOBBIO NEAR TRESCORRE BALNEARIO (PROVINCE OF BERGAMO).) Mammiferi del Quaternario di Zandobbio presso Trescorre Balneario (Prov. di Bergamo). Carlo Airaghi. Natura, Milano, vol.25, fasc.2, pp.63-67, figs.2, 1934.

(THE ORIGINS OF THE PARK AND THE FIRST WORKS.) Le origini del parco ed i primi lavori. (Notes on Mammals.) Giorgio Anselmi. Il Parco Nazionale del Gran Paradiso, pp.7-25; Comm.Reale del Parco, Torino, 1925.

(ITALIAN EXPEDITION TO THE CARASORUM HEADED BY THE DUKE OF SPOLETO (1929). MAMMALS.) Spedizione Italiana al Carasorum comandata da S.A.R. il Duca di Spoleto (1929). Mammiferi. Oscar de Beaux. Atti della Società Ligustica di Scienze e Lettere di Genova, vol.14, fasc.1, pp.61-84, 1935.

(MAMMALS COLLECTED BY THE MUSEUM OF NATURAL HISTORY OF VENEZIA TRIDENTINA IN TRENTO DURING THE YEAR 1929.) Mammiferi racolti dal Museo di Storia Naturale della Venezia Tridentina in Trento durante l'anno 1929. (VII-VIII). Oscar de Beaux. 2.Studi Trentini Sci. Nat., vol.12, no.1, pp.37-48, 1931.

(MAMMALS COLLECTED BY THE MUSEUM OF NATURAL HISTORY OF VENEZIA TRIDENTINA IN TRENTO DURING THE YEARS 1930-31.) Mammiferi raccolti dal Museo di Storia Naturale della Venezia Tridentina in Trento durante gli anni 1930-31 (VIII-X). Oscar de Beaux. 3.Studi Trentini Sci. Nat., vol. 13, nos.3-4, pp.177-197, 1932.

(MAMMALS COLLECTED BY THE MUSEUM OF NATURAL HISTORY OF VENEZIA TRIDENTINA IN TRENTO DURING THE YEARS 1932-33.) Mammiferi raccolti dal Museo di Storia Naturale della Venezia Tridentina in Trento durante gli anni 1932-33 (XI-XII). Oscar de Beaux. Studi Trentini di Sci.Nat., Trento, Ann.20, pp.1-14, 1939.

(PALEONTOLOGY OF THE PALAFITTES OF LAKE LEDRO.) Paleontologia delle palafitte del Lago di Ledro. Richard Camillo. Mem. Mus. Stor. Nat. Venezia Tridentina, Trento, Anno 1, fasc.1-2, pp.67-82, pls.6, Sep., 1931.

(DESCRIPTIVE CATALOGUE OF MAMMALIA OBSERVED UP TO NOW IN ITALY.) Catalogo descrittivo dei mammiferi osservati fino ad ora in Italia. Emilio Cornalia. Milano, F. Vallardi, pp.97, 1870.

(NEW REMAINS OF VERTEBRATES DISCOVERED IN THE "VELIKA JAMA" IN FRIULI.) Nuovi resti di vertebrati scoperti nella "Velika Jama" in Friuli. Ramiro Fabiani. Mondo Sotterraneo, Revista di speleologia e idrologia, Anno 8, nos.1-2, pp.12, pl.1, illus., 1912.

(FIRST CONTRIBUTION TO KNOWLEDGE OF THE FAUNA OF THE PARK.) Primo contributo alla conoscenza della Fauna del Parco. E. Festa. Il Parco Nazionale del Gran Paradiso, vol.2, pp.61-65, photos, 1931.

(SECOND CONTRIBUTION TO KNOWLEDGE OF THE FAUNA OF THE PARK.) Secondo contributo alla conoscenza della Fauna del Parco. E. Festa. Parco Nazionale del Gran Paradiso, Torino, vol.3, pp.81-86, photos, 1932.

(GRAN PARADISO NATIONAL PARK OF TORINO.) Il parco nazionale del Gran Paradiso, Torino. E. Festa. Torino, vol. 3, pp.81-86, figs., 1932.

(NOTES ON THE FAUNA.) Cenni sulla fauna. E. Festa. Il Parco Nazionale del Gran Paradiso, pp.47-55; Comm. Reale del Parco, Torino, 1925.

(ZOOLOGICAL EXCURSIONS IN THE MOUNTAINS OF THE SANGRO VALLEY (ABRUZZI).) Escursioni Zoologiche nei monti della vallata del Sangro (Abruzzi). E. Festa. Boll.Mus. Zool. ed Anat.comp. R.Univ.Torino, vol.30, no.692, pp.12, illus., Feb. 27, 1915.

(NOTES ON THE FAUNA OF VALTELINE VERTEBRATES.) Note sulla fauna dei vertebrati Valtellinesi. B.Galli-Valerio. Riv. Ital. Sci. Nat. Siena, Anno 30, no. 9, pp.4, 1910.

(FAUNAL AND SYSTEMATIC RESEARCH ON THE GAME MAMMALS OF ITALY.) Ricerche Faunistiche e sistematiche sui Mammiferi d'Italia che Formano oggetto di Caccia. A. Ghigi. Rev.mensile Sci. Nat. "Natura" Pavia, vol.2, pp.5-52, 1911.

ANIMALS FOR SHOW AND PLEASURE IN ANCIENT ROME. George Jennison. Univ. Manchester Publ.no.258, pp.vii-xiv-1-209, illus., 1937.

(NEW TRACES OF FOREST BED FAUNA IN THE ADRIATIC REGION.) Nuove tracce di una "Forest bed" fauna nella regione Adriatica. Theodor Kormos. Le Grotte d'Italia, Rivista Ist.Italiano di Speleologia, vol.11, pp.2-4, figs.3, Apr.-June, 1933.

(FELIS SILVESTRIS AND SOME NEW MICRO-MAMMALS IN THE CAVERNA DELL' ORSO OF GABROVIZZA IN THE CARSO GORIZIANO - TRIESTINO.) Il Felis silvestris ed alcuni nuovi micromammiferi nella Caverna dell'Orso di Gabrovizza nel Carso Goriziano - Triestino. Cesare Lomi. Bol. Soc. Adriatica Sci. Nat.Trieste, Udine, vol.36, pp.173-178, illus.1, 1938.

(REMAINS OF AN ELEPHANT AND A HIPPOPOTAMUS IN THE SELE VALLEY.) Avanzi di elefante e di ippopotamo nella valle del Sele. G. de Lorenzo, G.d'Erasmo. Societa reale di Napoli, Rendiconto, Accad. Napoli, Sci. Fis. e matem., ser.4, vol.8 (year 77), p.176, Nov. 29, 1938.

(FIRST REPORTS ON THE FOSSILS FOUND BETWEEN THE CONSTANTINIANA BASILICA AND THE COLOSSEUM.) Prime notizie sui fossili rinvenuti fra la Basilica Constantiniana ed il Colosseo. G. de Angelis D'Ossat. Atti Pontificia Accad.Sci.Nuovi Lincei, vol.85, no.7, pp.373-376, fig.1, 1932.

(THE OSSEOUS BRECCIO OF VALDIPORRO IN THE SURROUNDINGS OF VERONA.) Le brecce ossifere di Valdiporro nel Veronese. Angelo Pasa. Mem. Mus. Civico Storia Nat. Verona, vol.1, pp.165-175, illus., 1949.

(ZOOLOGICAL RESEARCH ON THE MASSIF OF POLLINO. X. MAMMALS.) Ricerche zoologiche sul massiccio del Pollino. X. Mammiferi. Angelo Pasa. Ann. Inst. Mus. Zool. Univ. Napoli, vol.7, no.7, pp.1-8, July, 1955.

(MAMMALS OF THE VENETIAN OLIGOCENE.) I mammiferi dell'Oligoceno Veneto. (Archaeopteropus transiens.) Giambattista dal Piaz. Mem. Ist. Geol. R. Univ. Padova, vol.11, pp.8, figs.3, pl.1, 1937. (Chiroptera.)

(STRATIGRAPHY OF THE RIVER-LAKE LANDS OF THE UPPER VALDARNO.) Stratigrafia dei terreni fluvio-lacustri del Valdarno superiore. (Lists Mammals.) A. Sestini. Atti. Soc. Toscana Sci. Nat., proc. verb., vol.45, no.5, pp.37-41, Nov. 16, 1936.

(MAMMAL FAUNA OF LEFFE (BERGAMO PROVINCE).) Saeugetierfauna von Leffe (Prov.Bergamo). H.G. Stehlin. Eclogae geologicae Helvetiae, Basel, vol.23, no.2, pp.648-681, figs.9, 1930.

(MATERIALS ON THE FAUNA OF VALTELINE VERTEBRATES.) Materiali per la Fauna dei Vertebrati Valtellinesi. R.Bruno Galli Valerio. Sondrio, Stab. Tipografico E. Quadrio, p.179, 1890.

JAMAICA

NEW MAMMALS FROM JAMAICA. H.E. Anthony. Bull. Amer. Mus. Nat. Hist., vol.42, art.12, pp.469-475, pl.33, Dec. 11, 1920.

ZOOLOGIST IN JAMAICA. H.E.Anthony. Nat. Hist., vol.20, pp.156-168, Mar.-Apr., 1920.

MAMMALS FROM BRITISH HONDURAS, MEXICO, JAMAICA AND HAITI. Philip Herskovitz. Chicago Nat. Hist. Mus., Fieldiana: Zoology, vol.31, no.47, map, 1951.

RATS AND THE MONGOOSE IN JAMAICA. C.B. Lewis. Oryx, vol.2, no.3, pp.170-172, Nov., 1953.

COLLECTING IN THE CAVES AND KITCHENMIDDENS OF JAMAICA. Gerrit S. Miller, Jr. Explorations and Field-Work of the Smithsonian Institution in 1931, Washington, pp.65-72, figs.60-71, Apr. 22, 1932.

NOTES ON A COLLECTION OF MAMMALS MADE BY THE LATE MR. OSBURN IN JAMAICA. Robert F. Tomes. Proc. Zool. Soc. London, pt.29, pp.63-69, pl. 13, 1861.

JAPAN

Extinct and Fossil Mammals

PLIO-PLEISTOCENE VERSUS LOWER PLIOCENE AGE FOR THE TATUNOKUTI BEDS DEVELOPED IN SENDAI AND ITS ENVIRONS, RIKUZEN PROVINCE, NORTH-EAST HONSYU, JAPAN. Kotora M. Hatai. Japanese Jour. Geol. and Geogr., Nat. Res. Council Japan, Tokyo, vol.16, nos. 3-4, pp.239-243, Dec., 1939.

NOTE ON SOME RECENT DISCOVERIES OF FOSSIL MAMMALS IN JAPAN. Ichiro Hayasaka. Proc. Fourth Pacific Sci. Congress Java, Batavia-Bandoeng, 1929, vol.3, Biol. Papers, pp.405-412, 1930.

BRIEF NOTES ON SOME JAPANESE FOSSIL MAMMALS. Hikoshichiro Matsumoto. Zool. Mag., Tokyo, vol.50, no.12, pp. 481-487, fig.1, Dec., 1938.

EVIDENCES OF THE POST-GLACIAL CYCLE OF CLIMATIC CHANGE IN NORTH-EASTERN JAPAN, BASED UPON A STUDY OF THE MARINE MOLLUSCS AND MAMMALS FROM THE SITES AT DAIGI, MIYAGI DISTRICT, AT HIBIKU, MONO DISTRICT, AND AT MIYATO ISLAND, DITTO, ALL, PROVINCE OF RIKUZEN. Hikoshichiro Matsumoto. Sci.Reports Tohoku Imp. Univ. (2), Geol., vol.13, no.3, pp.35-43, pls.11-15, 1930.

ON TWO SPECIES OF FOSSIL MAMMALS FROM KAZUSA. Hikoshichiro Matsumoto. Zool. Mag., Tokyo, vol.51, no.5, pp. 257-266, figs.2, May, 1939.

REPORT OF THE MAMMALIAN REMAINS OBTAINED FROM THE SITES AT AOSHIMA AND HIBIKU, PROVINCE OF RIKUZEN. Hikoshichiro Matsumoto. Sci. Reports, Tôhuku Imp. Univ., ser.2, Geol., vol.13, no.3, pp.59-93, pls.9, 1930.

UPPER MIOCENE VERTEBRATES FROM KUMANODÔ, NATORI DISTRICT, PROVINCE OF RIKUZEN. Hikoshichiro Matsumoto. Zool. Mag., Japan, vol.48, nos. 8-10, pp.475-480, Oct., 1936. (In Japanese.)

ON THE PLEISTOCENE MAMMALS AND HUMAN ARTIFACTS UNEARTHED AT TWO LOCALITIES ALONG THE TOMAN RIVER. T. Mori. Jour. Geol. Soc.Japan, Tokyo, vol.42, no.501, pp.364-365, June 20, 1935. (In Japanese.)

JAPANESE QUATERNARY, ITS OUTLINE AND HISTORICAL REVIEW. (List of Pleistocene Mammals.) Tokio Shikama. Sci. Rept. Yokohama Nat. Univ., sec.2, no.1, pp.29-51, 1952.

PLEISTOCENE PROBLEMS IN JAPAN AND VICINITY; SOME TENTATIVE CONSIDERATIONS IN PALAEOMAMMALOGY. Tokio Shikama. Translation Prepared by Engineer Intelligence Division, Office of the Engineer, Hq. U.S. Army Forces, Far East, Tokyo, 1956. (From Manchuria, Central National Museum, Hsinkihg, Bulletin no.6, tbls., diagrs., 1943.)

SHORT NOTES ON THE EXCAVATION OF THE OSSIFEROUS FISSURES AND CAVES IN KUZUU DURING THE YEARS 1931 TO 1936. Tokio Shikama. Jour. Geol. Soc. Japan, Tokyo, vol.44, no.524, pp. 405-420, May 20, 1937. (In Japanese, with English summary.)

AN ADDITION TO THE MAMMALIAN FAUNA OF THE JAPANESE MIOCENE. Fuyuji Takai. Jour. Faculty Sci. Univ. Tokyo, sec.2, vol.9, no.2, pp.331-335, Oct. 31, 1954.

AMYNODON WATANABEI FROM THE LATEST EOCENE OF JAPAN WITH A BRIEF SUMMARY OF THE LATEST EOCENE MAMMALIAN FAUNULE IN EASTERN ASIA. Fuyuji Takai. Rept. Geol. Survey Japan, no.131, pp.1-14, pl.1, July 30, 1950.

CENOZOIC MAMMALIAN FAUNA OF THE JAPANESE EMPIRE (A PRELIMINARY NOTE). Fuyuji Takai. Jour. Geol. Soc. Japan, Tokyo, vol.45, no.541, pp.745-763, Oct. 20, 1938.

EOCENE MAMMALS FOUND FROM THE HÔSAN COAL-FIELD, TYÔSEN. Fuyuji Takai. Jour. Geol. Soc. Japan, Tokyo, vol.46, no.555, p.615, Dec. 20, 1939.

MAMMALIAN REMAINS FROM SAIHANA SHELL-MOUNTD, TANABEMATI, AOMORI PREFECTURE. Fuyuji Takai. Jour. Geol. Soc. Japan, Tokyo, vol.43, no.517, pp. 805-806, Oct. 20, 1936. (In Japanese.)

ON SOME CENOZOIC MAMMALS FROM JAPAN (Part I). Fuyuji Takai. Jour. Geol. Soc. Japan, Tokyo, vol.46, no.552, pp. 481-489, Sep. 20, 1939. (In Japanese, with English summary.)

FOSSIL OF LAND MAMMALS IN JAPAN. Shigeasu Tokunaga. Pan-Amer.Geologist, Des Moines, vol.69, no.1, p.71, Feb., 1938.

Recent Mammals

HAND LIST OF JAPANESE AND FORMOSAN MAMMALS. B. Aoki. Annot. Zool. Japon., vol.8, pt.2, pp.261-353, 1913.

JAPANESE ORNITHOLOGY AND MAMMALOGY DURING WORLD WAR II. Oliver L. Austin. Rept. Nat. Resources Sec., Supreme Commander Allied Powers, Tokyo, no.102, pp.47, 1948.

(REMARKS ON THE GEOGRAPHICAL DISTRIBUTION OF THE MAMMALS OF JAPAN.) Bemerkungen ueber die Geographische Verbreitung der Saeugethiere Japans. D. Brauns. Mitt. Ver. f. Erdkunde zu Halle a.S., pp.3-32, 1884.

(FURTHER ADDITIONS TO REMARKS ON THE GEOGRAPHICAL DISTRIBUTION OF THE MAMMALS OF JAPAN.) Fernere Nachtraege zu den Bemerkungen ueber die geographische Verbreitung der Saeugetiere Japans. D. Brauns. Vergl. Mitt. Ver. f. Erdkunde zu Halle a. S., pp.85-87, 1884; pp.24-26, 1885.

FUR FARMING IN JAPAN. Howard J. Cook. Amer. Fur Breeder, Duluth, vol.19, no.2, p.16, Aug., 1946.

NATURAL HISTORY OF JAPANESE MAMMALS. Yoshinori Imaizumi. Tokyo, Yoyo shobo, pp.xiv-348, 1949. (In Japanese.)

PRELIMINARY NOTE ON CHANGES OF MAMMALIAN FAUNA SINCE THE SETTLEMENT OF HOKKAIDO. Tetsuo Inukai. Proc. Imp. Acad., Tokyo, vol.8, no.10, pp.524-527, Dec., 1932.

MAMMALS FROM SADO ISLAND, JAPAN, WITH COMMENTS ON THE STATUS OF APODEMUS ARGENTEUS. J. Knox. Jones, Jr., Yoshinori Imaizumi. Jour. Mamm., vol.37, no.2, pp.272-274, June 9, 1956.

FURTHER NOTES ON THE EFFECT OF SOME EXOTIC ANIMALS UPON THE FAUNA OF JAPAN. Tokio Kaburaki. Proc. 6th Pacific Sci. Congr., Berkeley, vol.4, pp.229-230, 1940.

PRESERVATION OF ZOOLOGICAL NATURAL MONUMENTS IN JAPAN. Tokio Kaburaki. Proc. 5th Pacific Sci. Congress, Canada, 1933, Univ. Toronto Press, vol. 5, pp.4183-4188, 1934. Proc. 6th Pacific Sci. Congress, Berkeley, vol.4, pp.225-227, 1940.

DISTRIBUTION OF MAMMALS IN THE JAPANESE EMPIRE. Nagamichi Kurida. Jour. Mamm., vol.20, no.1, pp.37-50, Feb. 14, 1939.

GEOGRAPHICAL DISTRIBUTION OF MAMMALS IN THE BONIN ISLANDS. Nagamichi Kuroda. Bull. Biogeogr. Soc. Japan, Tokyo, vol.1, no.3, pp.81-88, fig.1, pl.9, June, 1930. (In Japanese with English summary.)

GLIMPSE OF THE ANIMALS AND PLANT LIFE AT SHIOBARA, HONDO, JAPAN, I-III. Nagamichi Kuroda. Syokukutu oyobi Dobutu (Botany and Zoology), Tokyo, vol. 4, no.1, pp.71-76; no.2, pp.395-401; no. 3, pp.551-560, illus., 1935-1936.

LIST OF THE JAPANESE MAMMALS. Nagamichi Kuroda. Privately Published, Tokyo, pp.1-122, June, 1938.

MAMMALS OF JAPAN. Nagamichi Kuroda. Jour. Mamm., 1954.

MONOGRAPH OF THE JAPANESE MAMMALS. Nagamichi Kuroda. Tokyo and Osaka, Sanseido Co., pp.16-311, col.pls. 48, 1940. (In Japanese with Latin and English names of mammals.)

NEW LOCALITIES OF SMALL JAPANESE MAMMALS. Nagamichi Kuroda. Jour. Mamm. Soc. Japan, vol.1, no.4, pp.73-74, June, 1957. (In Japanese.)

NOTES ON THE MAMMAL FAUNA OF TSUSHIMA AND IKI ISLANDS, JAPAN. Nagamichi Kuroda. Jour. Mamm., vol. 3, no.1, pp.42-45, Feb. 9, 1922.

ON A COLLECTION OF JAPANESE AND FORMOSAN MAMMALS. Nagamichi Kuroda. Annot. Zool. Japonenses, vol. 9, pt.5, pp.599-611, tbls., 1920.

ON THREE NEW MAMMALS FROM JAPAN. Nagamichi Kuroda. Jour. Mamm., vol.2, no.4, pp.208-211, Nov. 29, 1921.

PRESENT STATUS OF THE INTRODUCED MAMMALS IN JAPAN. Nagamichi Kuroda. Jour. Mamm. Soc. Japan, vol.1, no.2, pp. 13-18, Feb., 1955.

(ON THE BADGERS, WOLVES, DEER, AND WILD SWINE OF JAPAN.) Ueber Dachs, Wolf, Hirsch und Wildschwein Japans. Alfred Nehring. Sitz. Ber. Gesell. Naturf. Freunde Berlin, no.7, pp.137-143, July 21, 1885.

CATALOGUE OF VERTEBRATES OF JAPAN. Yaichiro Okada. Maruzen Co., Ltd., Tokyo, pp.iv-412, Oct., 1938. (Mammalia, pp.1-25.)

NOTES ON THE MIXED FAUNA OF TROPICAL AND BOREAL ANIMALS IN HONSYU, JAPAN. Yaichiro Okada, Kazuo Koba. Proc. Imp. Acad. Tokyo, vol.9, no.8, pp.443-445, 1933.

NATIONALISTIC ZOOLOGY. Wilfred H. Osgood. Field Mus. News, Chicago, vol. 13, nos.8-9, p.7, Aug.-Sep., 1942.

EXHIBITION OF A COLLECTION OF MAMMALS AND BIRDS FROM JAPAN. Philip Lutley Sclater. Proc. Zool. Soc. London, pp.80-81, 1866.

FAUNA JAPONICA SIVE DESCRIPTIO ANIMALIUM, QUAE IN ITINERE PER JAPONIAM, JUSSU ET AUSPICIIS SUPERIORUM, QUI SUMMUM IN INDIA BATAVA IMPERIUM TENENT, SUSCEPTO, ANNIS 1823-1830 COLLEGIT, NOTIS OBSERVATIONIBUS ET ADUMBRATIONIBUS ILLUSTRAVIT PH. FR. VON SIEBOLD. CONJUNCTIS STUDIIS C.J. TEMMINCK ET H. SCHLEGEL PRO VERTEBRATIS ATQUE W. DE HAAN PRO INVERTEBRATIS ELABORATA. REGIS AUSPICIIS EDITA. Lugduni Batavorum, A.Arnz et socios, pp.24, pls.10 (part.col.), 1842 (first part of vol. 3 of set, which contains 4 vols.)

CLOSE RELATIONSHIP BETWEEN THE JAPANESE AND CHINESE MAMMALIA. Arthur de C. Sowerby. China Jour., vol.13, no.6, p.336, pls.2, Dec., 1930.

MAMMALS OF THE JAPANESE ISLANDS. Arthur de C. Sowerby. Musee Heude, Notes de Mammalogie, Shanghai, no.1, pp.66, pls.9, Feb. 21, 1943.

CONSIDERATIONS ON THE CHANGE OF ANIMAL LIFE IN JAPAN (1). Haruo Takashima. Misc. Repts. Yamashina's Inst. Ornithol. and Zool., Tokyo, no.3, pp.5-17, illus., Dec., 1953. (In Japanese with English summary.)

CONSIDERATIONS ON THE CHANGE OF ANIMAL LIFE IN JAPAN (2). Haruo Takashima. Misc. Repts. Yamashina's Inst. Ornithol. and Zool., Tokyo, no.4, pp.146-155 (14-23), June, 1954. (In Japanese with English summary.)

HAND-LIST OF JAPANESE MARINE MAMMALS. Haruo Takashima. Trans. Nat. Hist. Soc. Formosa, vol.23, nos.126-127, pp. 249-258, Aug., 1933.

STANDARD JAPANESE NAMES FOR THE MAMMALS OF JAPAN (1). Haruo Takashima. Trans. Nat. Hist. Soc. Formosa, vol.20, no.109, pp.195-217, Aug., 1930.

(INTRODUCTION TO THE FAUNA OF JAPAN. FAUNA OF THE ISLAND OF SONDE.) Discours préliminaire destine a servir d'introduction a la Faune du Japon. Coup d'oeil sur la faune des iles de la Sonde et de l'Empire du Japon. C.J. Temminck. 1836.

LIST OF MAMMALS OBTAINED BY MR. M.P. ANDERSON IN JAPAN. Oldfield Thomas. Proc. Zool. Soc. London, pp.331-363, 1905.

ON COLLECTIONS FROM THE ISLANDS OF OKI, YAKUSHIMA, AND TANEGASHIMA. Oldfield Thomas. Proc. Zool. Soc. London, vol.2, pp.357-363, Nov. 28, 1905.

ON MAMMALS AND BIRDS FROM JAPAN. Oldfield Thomas. Proc. Zool. Soc. London, vol.2, pp.182-183, Oct. 17, 1905.

ON SOME NEW JAPANESE MAMMALS PRESENTED TO THE BRITISH MUSEUM BY R. GORDON SMITH. Oldfield Thomas. Ann. and Mag. Nat. Hist., ser.7, vol. 15, no.89, pp.487-495, May, 1905.

ON SOME SMALL MAMMALS COLLECTED ON THE ISLANDS OF OKI. Mitosi Tokuda. Annotationes Zoologicae Japonenses, vol. 13, no.5, pp.577-585, pl.35, Dec. 10, 1932.

PRELIMINARY NOTES ON SOME SMALL MAMMALS FROM SADO ISLAND. Mitosi Tokuda. Annotationes Zool. Japonenses, Tokyo, vol.14, no.2, pp.235-240, pl.11, Oct. 25, 1933.

A BAT AND A NEW SHREW FROM KOTOSHO (BOTEL-TOBAGO). Mitosi Tokuda, Tadao Kano. Annotations Zool. Japonenses, vol.15, no.4, pp.427-432, figs.2, tbls., Dec. 1, 1936.

PRESENT CONDITION OF THE PROTECTION OF BIRDS AND MAMMALS IN JAPAN. Seinosuke Uchida. Tokyo, Dept.of Animal Industry, Ministry of Agriculture and Forestry, 1927.

FUR FARMING IN JAPAN. Ford Wilke. Fur Breeder, Duluth, vol.23, no.2, pp.18, 37, illus., Aug., 1950; American Nat. Fur and Market Jour, Wausau, vol.28, no. 7, pp.6-7, 21, Feb., 1950; Fur of Canada, Winnipeg, vol.16, no.1, p.18, Oct., 1950.

INVESTIGATION ON SEA OTTER AND FUR SEAL. Publ. Fisheries Society of Japan, Dept. Agriculture and Commerce, Tokyo, pp.104, pls.6, 1894. (In Japanese.)

## JAVA

(SOME NOTES ON THE DISTRIBUTION AND LIVING HABITS OF JAVAN MAMMALS.) Zur Kenntnis der Verbreitung und der Lebensweise javanischer Saeugetiere. M. Bartels. Treubia, vol.16, pp.149-164, 1937.

RECENT DISCOVERIES OF SKULLS AND PLEISTOCENE STONE IMPLEMENTS IN JAVA. P.V. van Stein Callenfels. Man, vol.36, no.274-292, pp.209-210, Dec., 1936.

FOUR NEW MAMMALS FROM JAVA. (Petinomys bartelsi, Otomops formosus, Glischropus javanus, and Rhinolophus importunus.) F.N. Chasen. Treubia, Buitenzorg, vol.17, no.3, pp.185-188, Aug., 1939.

ON PREHISTORIC MAMMALS FROM THE SAMPOENG CAVE, CENTRAL JAVA. K.W. Dammerman. Treubia, vol.14, no.4, pp. 477-486, pl.11, Dec., 1934.

ON THE ZOOGEOGRAPHY OF JAVA. I. A LIST OF THE MAMMALS KNOWN FROM JAVA. K.W. Dammerman. Treubia, vol. 11, pt.1, pp.33-39, 1929.

(HUNTING AND NATURE CONSERVATION ON JAVA DURING THE JAPANESE OCCUPATION.) Jacht en natuurbescherming op Java gedurende de japansche bezetting. A. Hoogerwerf. Natuur. Tijdschrift Nederlandsch-Indie, Batavia, vol.102, no.9, pp.205-208, Dec. 1, 1946.

CORRELATION OF FOSSIL MAMMALIAN FAUNAS AND THE PLIO-PLEISTOCENE BOUNDARY IN JAVA. D.A. Hooijer. Kon. Ned. Akad. Wet., Amsterdam, vol.60, no.1, pp.1-10, 1957.

FOSSIL MAMMALS AND THE PLIO-PLEISTOCENE BOUNDARY IN JAVA. D.A. Hooijer. Proc. Kon. Ned. Akad. Wetenschappen, Amsterdam, ser.B, vol.55, no.4, pp.436-443, 1952.

(MAMMALS OF JAVA.) De zoogdieren van Java. Jacob Christiaan Koningsberger. G. Kolff and Co., Batavia, pp.75, pls.111, 1902.

(FOSSIL MAMMALS OF JAVA.) Fossilen Saeugetierfaunen Javas. G.H.R. von Koenigswald. Proc. Kon. Akad. Wetenschappen, Amsterdam, vol.38, no.2, pp. 188-198, Feb., 1935.

(FOSSILS FROM CHINESE DRUGSTORES IN WEST JAVA.) Fossilen iut Chineesche Apotheken in West-Java. G.H.R. von Koenigswald. De Mijningenieur, Bandoeng, 12e Jaargang, no.11, pp.189-192, figs.1-5, Nov., 1931.

(OBSERVATIONS ON JAVA'S FOSSIL MAMMALS.) Bemerkungen zur fossilen Saeugetierfauna Javas (1). G.H.R. von Koenigswald. Ingenieur Nederlandsche-Indie, Jaarg. 2, no.7, pp.67-70, figs.4, July, 1935.

(OBSERVATIONS ON JAVA'S FOSSIL MAMMALS.) Bemerkungen zur fossilen Saeugetierfauna Javas (2). G.H.R. von Koenigswlad. Ingenieur Nederlandsch-Indie, Jaarg. 2, no.10, pp.75-88, figs.3, Oct., 1935.

(ON SOME FOSSIL MAMMALS OF JAVA.) Over enkele fossiele zoogdieren van Java. G.H.R. von Koenigswald. Tijdschrift Koninklijk Nederlandsch Aardrijkskundig Genootschap, Leiden, ser.2, vol.52, pp. 539-543, figs.4, 1935.

CONTRIBUTION TO KNOWLEDGE OF THE FOSSIL MAMMALIAN FAUNA OF JAVA. F.H. van der Maarel. Dutch East Indies Dienst van den Mijnbouw, Wettenschapplijke Medeelingen, Weltevreden, no.15, pp.4-208, figs.27, pls.20, tbls.A-Z, 1932.

NOTES ON HORSFIELD'S "ZOOLOGICAL RESEARCHES IN JAVA." Harry C. Oberholser. Proc. Biol. Soc. Washington, vol. 34, pp.163-166, Dec. 21, 1921.

ON FIVE NEW MAMMALS FROM JAVA. Herbert C. Robinson, C. Boden Kloss. Ann. and Mag. Nat. Hist., ser.9, vol.4, pp. 374-378, Dec., 1919.

(LIST OF JAVANESE MAMMALS WITH DUTCH AND VERNACULAR NAMES.) Lijst van de Zoogdieren van Java (met Hollandsche en Inlandsche namen). H.J.V. Sody. Boschbouwkundig Tijdschrift "Tectona," Buitenzorg, vol.31, pp.741-764, Sep.-Oct., 1938.

(LIST OF JAVANESE MAMMALS. WITH SHORT DESCRIPTIONS OF TWO NEW SUBSPECIES.) Naamlijst van de Zoogdieren van Java. Met korte beschrijvingen van twee nieuwe subspecies. H.J.V. Sody. Natuurkundig Tijdschr. Nederlandsch-Indie, vol.89, no.2, pp.160-166, 1929.

(NOTES ON THE TRACKS OF JAVANESE MAMMALS.) Over de sporen der Javaansche zoogdieren. H.J.V. Sody. Boschbouwkundig Tijdschrift "Tectona," Buitenzorg, vol.30, pp.724-730, Sep., 1937.

ON SOME NEW OR INSUFFICIENTLY KNOWN MAMMALS FROM JAVA, BORNEO AND CELEBES. H.J.V. Sody. Natuurkundig Tijdschrift Nederlandsch-Indie, vol. 90, no.2, pp.258-273, pl.1, 1930.

ON THE MAMMALS OF BALI (WITH A NOTE ON THE RACES OF CALLOSCIURUS NOTATUS OF JAVA). H.J.V. Sody. Natuurkundig Tijdschrift voor Nederlandsch-Indie, Deel XCIII, Afl.1, pp.56-95, 1933.

(SOME FIRST OBSERVATIONS OF THE TRACKS OF JAVANESE MAMMALS.) Enkele Eerste Aanteekeningen over de Sporen der Javaansche Zoogdieren H.J.V. Sody. Boschbouwkundig Tijdschrift "Tectona," vol.29, pp.1-51, figs.35, Apr., 1936.

(TWO LISTS OF JAVANESE MAMMALS.) Twee zoogdierlijsten van Java. H. J. V. Sody. Natuurkundig Tijdschrift Nederlandsch-Indie, vol.90, pp.274-289, 1930.

ON A COLLECTION OF MAMMALS FROM WESTERN JAVA PRESENTED TO THE NATIONAL MUSEUM BY MR. W.E. BALSTON. Oldfield Thomas, R.C. Wroughton. Proc. Zool. Soc. London, pp.371-392, Aug., 1909.

## KOREA

MAMMALS COLLECTED IN KOREA. J.A. Allen. Bull. Amer. Mus. Nat. Hist., vol. 32, pp.427-436, Sep. 2, 1913.

EXPLORATION OF NORTHEASTERN KOREA. Roy C. Andrews. Amer. Mus. Jour., vol.12, no.7, pp.259-270, illus., 1912.

BIG GAME IN CHOSEN. G.V. Hett. Field, London, vol.167, no.4336, pp.226-227, illus., Feb. 1, 1936.

KOREAN MAMMALS PRESERVED IN THE COLLECTION OF MARQUIS YAMASHINA. Nagamichi Kuroda. Jour. Mamm., vol. 15, no.3, pp.229-239, Aug., 1934.

TWO NEW AND RARE MAMMALS FROM KOREA. Nagamichi Kuroda, Tamezo Mori. Jour. Mamm., vol.4, no.1, pp.27-28, Feb., 1923.

ON SOME NEW MAMMALS FROM KOREA AND MANCHURIA. T. Mori. Ann. and Mag. Nat. Hist., ser.9, vol.10, pp.607-614, Dec., 1922.

ON TWO NEW MAMMALS FROM KOREA. (Crocidura longicauda and Mustela nivalis mosanensis.) Tamezo Mori. Jour. Chosen Nat. Hist. Soc., no.5, pp.1-2, June, 1927.

MAMMALS FROM KOREA. Oldfield Thomas. Proc. Zool. Soc. London, pp.858-865, 1906; pp.462-466, 1907.

LIST OF THE FOSSIL LAND MAMMALS OF JAPAN AND KOREA WITH DESCRIPTIONS OF NEW EOCENE FORMS FROM KOREA. Shigeyasu Tokunaga. Amer. Mus. Novitates, no.627, pp.7, figs.2, May 27, 1933.

ON THE GEOLOGICAL AGE OF HOZAN COAL FIELD, CHOSEN. Shigeyasu Tokunaga. Jour. Geol. Soc. Japan, Tokyo, vol.40, no. 475, pp.179-182, fig.1, pl.8, Apr. 20, 1933. (List of Fossil Mammals. In Japanese.)

REPORT OF DIGGINGS AT DOKANTIN, THE COAST OF THE RIVER TOMAN, KOREA. REPORT OF DIGGINGS AT TAMALUKOU, PROVINCE CHIEN-TAO, MANCHOUKUO. Shigeyasu Tokunaga, Tamezo Mori. Rept. 1st. Sci. Exped. Manchoukuo, sect.2, pt.4, pp.1-43-1-5, pls.6, Mar., 1939.

## LEVANT

NOTE ON SMALL MAMMALS FROM THE LEBANON MOUNTAINS, SYRIA. Dorothea M.A. Bate. Ann. and Mag. Nat. Hist., London, ser.11, vol.12, pp.141-158, figs. 2, Mar. (Aug.15), 1945.

(MAMMALS OF SOUTH-EAST TURKEY AND NORTHERN SYRIA.) Mammiferes de la Turquie sud-orientale et du nord de la Syrie. Xavier Misonne. Mammalia, Paris, vol.21, no.1, pp.53-68, Mar., 1957.

## LIBYA

ARMSTRONG COLLEGE ZOOLOGICAL EXPEDITION TO SIWA OASIS (LIBYAN DESERT) 1935. MAMMALIA. R.W. Hayman. Proc. Egyptian Acad. Sci., Cairo, vol.4, pp.38-42, 1948.

ARMSTRONG COLLEGE ZOOLOGICAL EXPEDITION TO SIWA OASIS (LIBYAN DESERT) 1935. GENERAL REPORT. J. Omer-Cooper. Proc. Egyptian Acad. Sci., Cairo, vol.3, pp.51, pls.16, 1948.

REVIEW OF LIBYAN MAMMALS. Henry Setzer. Jour. Egyptian Public Health Assoc., Cairo, vol.32, no.2, pp.41-82, 1957.

ON THE MAMMALS COLLECTED DURING THE WHITAKER EXPEDITION TO TRIPOLI. Oldfield Thomas. Proc. Zool. Soc. London, pp.2-13, pl.1, May 6, 1902.

(MAMMALS OF LIBYA.) Mammiferi della Libia. Augusto Toschi. Lab. Zool. Appl. Cascia, vol.2, no.5, pp.137-177, Oct., 1951.

(PRELIMINARY CHECKLIST OF MAMMALS OF LIBYA.) Elenco preliminare dei mammiferi della Libia. Augusto Toschi. Suppl. Ricerche Zool. Applic. Caccia, Univ. Bologna, vol.2, no.7, pp.241-273, Dec., 1954.

ANIMALS OF THE LIBYAN DESERT. A GROUP PORTRAYING THE LANDSCAPE AND WILD LIFE SOUTH OF THE EGYPTIAN WAR FRONT, ON DISPLAY IN THE AMERICAN MUSEUM. Nat. Hist., New York, vol.50, no.3, pp.138-139, illus., Oct., 1942.

## LOWER CALIFORNIA

ON A COLLECTION OF MAMMALS FROM THE SAN PEDRO MARTIR REGION OF LOWER CALIFORNIA, WITH NOTES ON OTHER SPECIES, PARTICULARLY OF THE GENUS SITOMYS. J.A. Allen. Bull. Amer. Mus. Nat. Hist., vol.5, pp.181-202, Aug. 18, 1893.

(THE FUR SEAL, THE SEA-LION AND THE GRAY WHALE IN LOWER CALIFORNIA, AND THEIR CONSERVATION PROBLEM.) La foca fina, el elefante marino y la ballena gris en Baja California, y el problema de su conservacion. J. Berdegué. Ediciones del Instituto Mexicano de Recursos Naturales Renovables, A.C., no. 14, p.38, 1956.

(A SCIENTIFIC EXPEDITION TO GUADALUPE ISLAND, LOWER CALIFORNIA.) Una excursión cientifica a la Isla de Guadalupe, Baja California. Eduardo Caballero. Memorias de la Academia "Antonio Alzate," Mexico, vol.55, pp.117-125, figs.4, Nov. 9, 1936.

LIST OF MAMMALS COLLECTED BY EDMUND HELLER, IN THE SAN PEDRO MARTIR AND HANSON LAGUNA MOUNTAINS AND THE ACCOMPANYING COAST REGIONS OF LOWER CALIFORNIA, WITH DESCRIPTIONS OF APPARENTLY NEW SPECIES. D.G. Elliot. Chicago, (Field Columbian Mus., Publication no.79, Zoological series, vol.III, no.12) pp.199-203, pls.5, map, 1903.

RECENT SCIENTIFIC EXPEDITION TO THE ISLANDS OFF THE WEST COAST OF LOWER CALIFORNIA. (Notes on Elephant Seal, Guadalupe Fur Seal, and Sea Otter.) G. Dallas Hanna. Science, n.s., vol.56, pp.503-504, Nov. 3, 1922.

CRUISE AMONG DESERT ISLANDS. (Notes and Photographs of Mammals of Islands off Coast of Lower California.) G. Dallas Hanna, A.W. Anthony. Nat. Geog. Mag., vol.44, pp.71-99, illus., July, 1923.

DISCUSSION OF THE ZONAL STATUS OF THE SIERRA SAN PEDRO MARTIR, LOWER CALIFORNIA, MEXICO, WITH DESCRIPTIONS OF A NEW KANGAROO RAT AND A NEW WOODPECKER FROM THAT REGION. Laurence M. Huey. Trans. San Diego Soc. Nat. Hist., vol.5, no.1, pp.10, pl.1, Feb. 20, 1927.

NEW KANGAROO RAT AND A NEW BRUSH RABBIT FROM LOWER CALIFORNIA, MEXICO. Laurence M. Huey. Trans. San Diego Soc. Nat. Hist., vol.5, no.5, pp. 65-68, July 6, 1927.

MAMMALS OF SAN JOSE ISLAND, BAY OF PANAMA. Remington Kellogg. Washington, Smithsonian Institution, Smiths. Misc. Coll., vol.106, no.7, pp.4, publication 3851, 1946.

FAUNA AND FLORA OF ISLANDS OFF THE COAST OF SOUTHERN AND LOWER CALIFORNIA, INCLUDING THE GULF OF CALIFORNIA. Edgar A. Mearns. Science, n.s., vol.3, no.76, p.879, June 12, 1896.

LAND OF DROUGHT AND DESERT--LOWER CALIFORNIA. TWO THOUSAND MILES ON HORSEBACK THROUGH THE MOST EXTRAORDINARY CACTI FORESTS IN THE WORLD. E.W. Nelson. Nat. Geogr. Mag., Washington, D.C., vol.22, no.5, pp.443-474, illus., May, 1911.

LOWER CALIFORNIA AND ITS NATURAL RESOURCES. (Many References to Mammals; Maps and Definitions of Life Zones.) E.W. Nelson. Mem. Nat. Acad. Sci., vol.16, no.1, pp.1-194, pls.34, fold. map, 1921.

ELEVEN NEW MAMMALS FROM LOWER CALIFORNIA. E.W. Nelson, E.A. Goldman. Proc. Biol. Soc. Washington, vol. XXII, pp.23-28, Mar. 10, 1909.

EXPEDITIONS OF THE CALIFORNIA ACADEMY OF SCIENCES TO THE GULF OF CALIFORNIA IN 1921. (Includes Notes on Mammals.) Joseph R. Slevin. Proc. California Acad. Sci., ser.4, vol.12, pp.55-72, map, 1923.

TO BAJA BY AIR. (Deer, Sheep, Goats, Mountain Lion, Wildcat.) Ormal I. Sprungman. Sports Afield, New York, vol.120, no. 4, pp.44-45, illus., Oct., 1948.

ON A COLLECTION OF BIRDS AND MAMMALS FROM THE COLORADO DELTA, LOWER CALIFORNIA. Witmer Stone, S.N. Rhoads. Proc. Acad. Nat. Sci. Phila., pp. 676-690, Sep., 1905.

EXHIBITIONS OF PARTIALLY WHITE ANTELOPE, NEW SKUNK OF GENUS SPILOGALE, AND A BADGER FROM LOWER CALIFORNIA. Oldfield Thomas. Zool. Soc. London, Abstract of Meeting of 30th Nov., 1897, pl.1, Dec. 1, 1897.

MAMMALS COLLECTED IN LOWER CALIFORNIA, WITH DESCRIPTIONS OF NEW SPECIES. Charles H. Townsend. Bull. Amer. Mus. Nat. Hist., vol.31, art.13, pp.117-130, pls.8-9, June 14, 1912.

VOYAGE OF THE 'ALBATROSS' TO THE GULF OF CALIFORNIA IN 1911. Charles H. Townsend. Bull. Amer. Mus. Nat. Hist., vol.35, art.24, pp.399-476, figs.45, Aug. 2, 1916.

LUXEMBOURG

(FAUNA OF THE GRAND DUCHY OF LUXEMBOURG. PART 4: MAMMALS.) Faune du Grand-Duche de Luxembourg. Quatrieme partie: Mammiferes. Victor Ferrant. Imprimerie P. Worre-Mertens: Luxembourg, pp.115, 1931.

(PLEISTOCENE FAUNA OF OETRANGE (GRAND DUCHY OF LUXEMBOURG). VI. THE PROBOSCIDEA. VII. PERISSODACTYL UNGULATES.) La Faune pléistocene d'Oetrange (Grand-Duche de Luxembourg). VI. Les Proboscidiens. VII. Les Ongulés perissodactyles. V. Ferrant. Bull. Mensuels Soc. Nat. Luxembourgeois, n.s., 31st Année, no.4, pp.45-80, figs.16-39, Apr. 28, 1937.

(ANALYSES OF HAIR BALLS AND THE DISTRIBUTION OF THE SMALL MAMMALS OF LUXEMBOURG.) Gewoelle-Analysen und die Verbreitung der Kleinsaeuger von Luxemburg. A.M. Husson. Bull. Ligue luxembourgeoise Prot. Oiseaux, vol.28, Dec., 1948.

(A RECTIFICATION AND A CONTRIBUTION (WITH REMARKS ON THE SMALL MAMMALS OF LUXEMBOURG).) Eine rektification und ein Beitrag (mit Bemerkungen ueber die Kleinsaeuger von Luxemburg). A.M. Husson. Bull. Ligue luxembourgeoise Prot. Oiseaux, vol.28, ser.3, no.6, pp.82-92, 1948.

MADAGASCAR

Extinct and Fossil Mammals

(CONTRIBUTION TO KNOWLEDGE OF THE SUBFOSSIL FAUNA OF MADAGASCAR. NOTE IX. EAR BONE OF LEMURIDS.) Contribution a la connaissance de la faune subfossile de Madagascar. Note IX. Oreille osseuse des lémuriens. C. Lamberton. Mem. Acad. Malgache, Tananarive, fasc.35, pp. 134, pls.10, 1941.

(CONTRIBUTION TO KNOWLEDGE OF THE SUBFOSSIL FAUNA OF MADAGASCAR.) Contribution a la connaissance de la faune subfossile de Madagascar. C. Lamberton. Ext. du Bull. de l'Acad. Malgachia, n.s., vol.25, 1942-1943.

(ON THE PERIOD OF THE SEPARATION OF MADAGASCAR FROM THE ETHIOPIAN CONTINENT.) Ueber die Zeit der Abtrennung Madagaskars vom aethiopischen Festlande. Georg Pfeffer. Jenaische Zeitschr. Naturwiss., vol.67, pp.80-90, 1932.

MADAGASCAR

Recent Mammals

BEVATO, -- A CAMP IN MADAGASCAR. Experieences of a Collector in an Island Forest. Richard Archbold. Nat. Hist., vol.30, no.6, pp.645-652, Nov.-Dec., 1930.

A NEW LEMUR FROM MADAGASCAR. R. Archbold. Amer. Mus. Nov., New York, no.518, p.1, 1932.

(MADAGASCAR AT THE BEGINNING OF THE 20TH CENTURY.) Madagascar an debut du XXe siécle. Rapharl A.E., Blanchard, et al. Paris, 1902.

(ZOOLOGICAL FRANCO-ANGLO-AMERICAN MISSION TO MADAGASCAR.) La mission zoologique Franco-Anglo-Americaine à Madagascar. Jean Delacour. Bull. Mus. Nat. Hist. Nat., Paris, ser.2, vol.4, no. 3, pp.212-221, Apr., 1932.

(ANATOMICAL OBSERVATION ON SOME MAMMALS OF MADAGASCAR. ON THE ORGANIZATION OF CRYTOPRESTA FEREX.) Observation anatomiques sur quelques mammiferes de Madagascar. De l'organisation du Crytoprecta ferex. Milne Alph Edwards, Alf Grandidier. Ann. Sci. Nat. Paris, vol.7, pp.314-338, pls.4, 1867.

(PHYSICAL, NATURAL AND POLITICAL HISTORY OF MADAGASCAR.) Histoire physique naturelle et politique de Madagascar. A. Grandidier. (Mammals by A. Milne-Edwards.) Vols.6, 9-10, 1875-1897.

(ALPHABETICAL LIST OF THE MALGACHE NAME OF ANIMALS.) List alphabetique des noms Malgaches d'Animaux. G. Grandidier. Revue Madagascar, Paris, pp.1-81, 1908.

(NEW MADAGASCAR MAMMALS.) G. Grandidier. Bull., Acad. Malgache, pp. 85-107, pls., 1928.

(NEW MAMMALS OF THE DIEGO-SUAREZ REGION (MADAGASCAR).) Mammiferes nouveaux de la region de Diego-Suarez (Madagascar). G. Grandidier. Bull. Mus. Hist. Nat., Paris, vol.9, no.6, pp.347-353, figs.6, Nov., 1937.

(ZOOLOGY OF MADAGASCAR.) Zoologie de Madagascar. G. Grandidier, G. Petit. Societe d'Editions Geographiques Maritimes et Coloniales, Paris, 1932.

ADDITIONAL NOTES ON THE GENERA EUPLERES AND GALIDIA, AND NOTE ON LEMUR RUBER. John Edward Gray. Proc. Zool. Soc. London, pp.297-298, 1871.

NOTES ON SOME MAMMALS FROM MADAGASCAR. Albert Gunther. Proc. Zool. Soc. London, pp.78-80, figs.3, pls.15-16, 1875.

(MAMMALS FROM MADAGASCAR.) Saeugetiere aus Madagaskar. W. Kaudern. Ark. Zool., Stockholm, vol.9, no.18, pp.1-101, tbls.1-4, 1915.

(MAMMALS FROM MADAGASCAR AND ZANZIBAR.) Saeugetiere von Madagascar und Sansibar. L. von Lorenz-Liburnau. (In) Voeltzkow's Wiss. Ergeb. der Reisen in Madagascar und Ost-Afrika. Abh. Senckenb. Ges., vol.29, pp.445-469, 1898.

ON THE GENERAL RESULTS OF A ZOOLOGICAL EXPEDITION TO MADAGASCAR IN 1894-96. C.I. Forsyth Major. Proc. Zool. Soc. London, for 1896, pp.971-981, Apr. 1, 1897.

LETTER FROM, RELATING TO M. GRANDIDIER'S DISCOVERIES IN MADAGASCAR. Alphones Milne-Edwards. Proc. Zool. Soc. London, p.1, 1869.

(ANATOMICAL OBSERVATIONS ON SMALL MAMMALS FROM MADAGASCAR.) Observations anatomiques sur quelques mammiferes de Madagascar. Nat. Hist., vol.71, 1867.

LIST OF ANIMALS COLLECTED AT MOHAMBO, MADAGASCAR, BY MR. W.T. GERRARD. Alfred Newton. Proc. Zool. Soc. London, pp.832-837, 1865.

MADAGASCAR, LAND OF THE MAN-EATING TREE. (Chapters on the Animal Life and Hunting Wild Cattle.) Chase Salmon Osborn. Republic Publ. Co., New York, pp.443, pls.24, maps 2, 1924.

(COMMUNICATION ON A NEW GENUS AND TWO NEW SPECIES OF MAMMALS FROM MADAGASCAR.) Eine Mittheilung ueber eine neue Gattung und zwei neue Arten von Saeugethiere aus Madagaskar. W. Peters. Nat. Hist., vol.20, 1874.

(ON A NEW GENUS AND TWO NEW SPECIES OF MAMMALS OF MADAGASCAR.) Ueber eine neue Gattung und zwei neue Arten von Saeugethieren aus Madagaskar. W. Peters. Monatsber. Koen. Akad. Wiss. Berlin, pp.690-694, pls.2, Nov. 12, 1874.

(CONTRIBUTION TO FAUNAL STUDY OF THE NATURAL RESERVE OF MANAMPETSA, MADAGASCAR.) Contribution a l'etude faunistique de La Reserve Naturelle du Manampetsa (Madagascar). G. Petit. Ann. des Sci. Nat., Zool., Paris, ser.10, vol.18, pp.423-481, 1935. (Mammals, pp.474-476.)

MADAGASCAR. G. Petit. Paris, Editions Arts et Metiers Graphiques, 1934.

(MAMMALIA. CONTRIBUTION TO STUDY OF THE FAUNA OF MADAGASCAR.) Mammalia. Contribution a l'etude de la faune de Madagascar. Pt.3. G. Petit. Faune Colonies Franc., Paris, vol.4, no. 5, pp.559-589, 1934.

ON THE HABITS OF SOME MADAGASCAR MAMMALS. A.L. Rand. Jour. Mamm., vol.16, no.2, pp.89-104, May, 1935.

REVISION OF THE GENERA AND SPECIES OF MADAGASCAR LEMURIDAE. E. Schwarz. Proc. Zool. Soc. London, pp. 399-428, 1931.

ON THE MAMMALS AND BIRDS COLLECTED IN MADAGASCAR BY DR. C. MELLER. Philip Lutley Sclater. Proc. Zool. Soc. London, pt.31, pp.160-161, 1863.

REPORT ON A COLLECTION OF ANIMALS FROM MADAGASCAR, TRANSMITTED TO THE SOCIETY BY MR. J. CALDWELL. Philip Lutley Sclater. Proc. Zool. Soc. London, pp.467-470, pl.28, 1865.

ARTICLE ON MADAGASCAR. J. Sibree. Encyclopaedia Brittanica, 14th ed., pp. 932-937, Bibliography pp.938-939.

THE GREAT AFRICAN ISLAND (MADAGASCAR). J. Sibree. 1880.

MAMMALS OF MADAGASCAR. J. Sibree. Antanan. Ann., vol.V, pp.67-84, 1893; pp.267-280, 1895.

NATURALIST IN MADAGASCAR. J. Sibree. Pp.330, illus. 52, maps 3, 1915.

ON SOME SMALL MAMMALS FROM MADAGASCAR. Oldfield Thomas. Ann. and Mag. Nat. Hist., ser.9, vol.17, pp.250-252, Feb., 1926.

MADAGASCAR. Ellwood A. Welden. Wash., Govt. Printing Office, Trade Information Bull. no.163, Suppl. to Commerce Reports, 1923.

THEY LIVE IN MADAGASCAR. (Mammals.) Fauna, Philadelphia, vol.4, no.2, p.59, illus., June, 1942.

MALAY ARCHIPELAGO

MAMMALS FROM SOUTH JOHORE AND SINGAPORE COLLECTED BY MR. C.B. KLOSS. Lewis Bonkote. Proc. Zool. Soc. London, vol.1, pp.4-11, 1906.

HANDLIST OF MALAYSIAN MAMMALS. A SYSTEMATIC LIST OF THE MAMMALS OF THE MALAY PENINSULA, SUMATRA, BORNEO AND JAVA, INCLUDING THE ADJACENT SMALL ISLANDS. F.N. Chasen. Bull. Raffles Mus., Singapore, no.15, pp. xx+209, Apr., 1940.

MAMMALS OF THE NETHERLANDS INDIAN MT. LEUSER EXPEDITION 1937 TO NORTH SUMATRA. F.N. Chasen. Treubia, Buitenzorg, vol.17, no.5, pp.479-502, Dec., 1940.

THREE NEW MALAYSIAN MAMMALS. (Rattus mülleri otiosus, Tragulus kanchil klossi, Lariscus insignis saturatus.) F.N. Chasen. Bull. Raffles Mus., Singapore, Straits Settlements, no.9, pp.98-100, Dec., 1934.

(FAUNA OF BURU. MAMMALIA.) Fauna Buruana. Mammalia. K.W. Dammerman. Treubia, Buitenzorg, Suppl., vol.7, no.4, pp.149-164, Dec., 1929.

ON JALORENSIS-RATS AND OTHER MAMMALS FROM THE KRAKATAU ISLANDS. K.W. Dammerman. Treubia, Buitenzorg, vol.16, no.4, pp.421-443, Nov., 1938.

ON THE MAMMALS OF SUMBA. K.W. Dammerman. Treubia, vol.10, pp.299-315, 1928.

(ON THE DISTRIBUTION OF SOME MAMMALS IN THE MALAYO-PAPUAN ARCHIPELAGO.) A propos de la repartition de quelques mammiferes dans l'Archipel Malayo-Papou. Jean Dorst. Mammalia, Paris, vol.17, no.4, pp.306-317, Dec., 1953.

SUPPLEMENT TO CHASEN (1940) HANDLIST OF MALAYSIAN MAMMALS, CONTAINING A GENERIC SYNONYMY AND

A COMPLETE INDEX. J.R. Ellerman, T.C.S. Morrison-Scott. British Museum (Natural History), London, pp.66, Mar. 26, 1955.

(MAMMALIA OF SOEMBA.) Mammalia von Sumba. Lothar von Forcart. Verhandl. Nat. Gessell., Basel, vol.63, no.1, pp. 176-186, 1952.

AMONG RHINO AND JAVANESE WILD OX (BANTENG) IN THE OEDJOENG KOELON GAME RESERVE. A. Hoogerwerf. Dutch East Indies, Department van landbouw, nijverheid en handel (Nature Protection in the Netherlands Indies), Dept. Econ. Affairs, Batavia, pp.8-14, illus., 1938.

ON A COLLECTION OF MAMMALS FROM BILLITON. F.A. Jentink. Notes Leyden Mus., vol.12, no.22, pp.149-154, pl.7, Mar., 1890.

SOME ADDITIONS TO THE MAMMALIAN FAUNA OF BILLITON. F.A. Jentink. Notes Leyden Mus., vol.13, no.31, pp.207-209, July, 1891.

NATURE PROTECTION IN THE NETHERLANDS INDIES. C.H.M.H. Kies, et al. Spec. Publ. Amer. Comm. Internat. Wild Life Protection, no.8, pp.1-73, map, 1936.

MAMMALS FROM PULO CONDORE, WITH DESCRIPTIONS OF TWO NEW SUBSPECIES. C. Boden Kloss. Jour. Siam Soc. Nat.Hist. Suppl., vol.4, pp.357-359, Mar., 1926.

PULO CONDORE GROUP AND ITS MAMMALS. C.Boden Kloss. Jour. Nat. Hist. Soc., Siam, vol.4, no.2, pp.73-83, Mar., 1921.

SEVEN NEW MALAYSIAN MAMMALS. C. Boden Kloss. Jour. Fed. Malay States Mus., vol.10, pt.3, pp.229-234, 1921.

ADDITIONAL NOTES ON MAMMALS OF THE RHIO-LINGA ARCHIPELAGO, WITH DESCRIPTION OF NEW SPECIES AND A REVISED LIST. Marcus Ward Lyon. U.S. Nat.Mus., Proc., Washington, vol.36, pp. 479-491, pl., 1909.

MAMMALS OF BANKA, MENDANAU, AND BILLITON ISLANDS, BETWEEN SUMATRA AND BORNEO. Marcus Ward Lyon. U.S. Nat. Mus., Proc., vol.31, pp.575-612, Washington, 1907.

MAMMALS OF BATAM ISLANDS, RHIO ARCHIPELACO. Marcus Ward Lyon.U.S. Nat. Mus., Proc., vol.31, pp.653-657, Washington, 1907.

(REMARKS ON THE MAMMALS OF LOMBOK, SUMBAWA, AND FLORES ISLANDS.) Bemerkungen ueber die Saeugetiere der Inseln Lombok, Sumbawa und Flores. Robert Mertens. Zool. Garten, Leipzig, vol.2, nos.1-3, pp.23-29, Sep., 1929.

FIFTY-ONE NEW MALAYAN MAMMALS. Gerrit Smith Miller. Washington, Smiths. Inst., Misc. Coll., vol.61, no.21, 1913. (Publication 2252.)

MAMMALS COLLECTED BY DR. W. L. ABBOTT IN RHIO-LINGA ARCHIPELAGO. Gerrit Smith Miller. U.S.Nat.Mus., Proc., Washington, vol.31, pp.247-286, map, 1907.

MAMMALS COLLECTED BY DR. W. L. ABBOTT IN THE KARIMATA ISLANDS, DUTCH EAST INDIES. Gerrit Smith Miller. U.S. Nat. Mus., Proc., vol.31, pp.55-66, Wash., July 23, 1906.

MAMMALS COLLECTED BY DR. W. L. ABBOTT ON ISLANDS IN THE NORTH CHINA SEA. Gerrit Smith Miller. Washington, D.C., The Academy, Proceedings of the Wash., Acad. of Sci., vol.II, pp.203-246, illus., 1900.

MAMMALS COLLECTED BY DR. W. L. ABBOTT ON THE NATUNA ISLANDS. Gerrit Smith Miller. Proc. of the Wash. Acad.of Sci., vol.3, pp.111-138, 1901.

SEVENTY NEW MALAYAN MAMMALS. Gerrit Smith Miller. Smiths. Inst., Misc. Coll., Quarterly Issue, vol.I, pp.1-73, illus., pl.xix, 1903.

(NOTES ON THE MAMMALIAN POPULATION OF THE ISLANDS OF FLORES, KOMODO AND RINTJA (SMALL ISLANDS OF THE SONDE).) Notes sur le peuplement mammalien des iles de Florès, Komodo et Rintja (petites iles de la Sonde). Pierre Pfeffer. Mammalia, Paris, vol.21, no.4, pp.405-419, Dec., 1957.

ZOOLOGY OF KOH SAMUI AND KOH PENNAN. I. INTRODUCTION. II. MAMMALS. H.C. Robinson. Jour. Fed. Malay States Mus., vol.5, no.3, pp.128-152, Mar., 1915.

NOTES ON SOME MAMMALS FROM SUMATRA, JAVA, BURU AND NEW GUINEA. H.J.V. Sody. Temminckia, vol.2, pp.211-220, 1937.

ON THE MAMMALS OF BANKA. H.J.V. Sody. Temminckia, Leiden, vol.2, pp.221-250, tbls., 1937.

SEVENTEEN NEW GENERIC, SPECIFIC, AND SUBSPECIFIC NAMES FOR DUTCH EAST INDIAN MAMMALS. H.J.V.Sody. Natuurk. Tijdschrift, vol.96, no.1, pp. 42-55, 1936.

TEN NEW MAMMALS FROM THE DUTCH EAST INDIES. H.J.V. Sody. Ann. Mag. Nat. Hist., ser.10, vol.12, no.70, pp.430-442, Oct., 1933.

(FIRST OLD TERTIARY REMAINS OF MAMMALS OF THE SUNDA ISLANDS.) Ersten alttertiaeren Saeugetier-Reste aus den Sunda-Inseln. E. Stromer. Wetenschappelijke Mededeelingen van den Dienst van den Mijnbouw in Nederlandsch-Indie, no.17, pp.11-14, pl.1, figs.6a-7b, 1931.

LIST OF THE MAMMALS OF THE JAPANESE WAR AREA. PART 3. LESSER SUNDA ISLANDS, MOLUCCAS, CELEBES. G.H.H. Tate. Amer. Mus. Nat. Hist., New York, pp.11, 1944.

LIST OF THE MAMMALS OF THE JAPANESE WAR AREA. PART 2.THE GREATER SUNDA AREA (ISLANDS OF THE NORTHEAST MARGIN OF THE INDIAN OCEAN: ANDAMANS, NICOBARS, SUMATRA, JAVA, BALI). G.H.H.Tate. Amer.Mus.Nat.Hist., New York, pp.19, 1944.

ON A COLLECTION OF RATS AND SHREWS FROM THE DUTCH EAST INDIAN ISLANDS. Oldfield Thomas. Treubia, vol. 2, pp.109-114, 1921.

ON MAMMALS FROM CERAM. Oldfield Thomas. Ann. and Mag. Nat. Hist., ser. 9, vol.6, pp.422-431, Oct., 1920.

ON SOME MAMMALS FROM SIMALUR ISLAND, WEST OF SUMATRA, COLLECTED BY MR. E. JACOBSON. Oldfield Thomas. Ann. and Mag. Nat. Hist., ser.9, vol.12, pp.591-593, Nov., 1923.

FIRST GLIMPSES OF THE ZOOLOGY OF THE NATUNA ISLANDS. III. LIST OF THE FIRST COLLECTION OF MAMMALS FROM THE NATUNA ISLANDS. Oldfield Thomas, E. Hartert. Novitates Zoologicae, vol.1, pp.652-660, Sep., 1894.

DIAGNOSES OF NEW MAMMALS COLLECTED BY MR. H. C. ROBINSON IN THE MALAY PENINSULA AND RHIO ARCHIPELAGO. Oldfield Thomas, R.C.Wroughton. Ann. and Mag. Nat. Hist., ser.8, vol.3, no. 17, pp.439-441, May, 1909.

(NOTES ON MAMMALS OF THE INDIAN ARCHIPELAGO.) Notizen ueber Saeugethiere des Indischen-Archipels. Max Weber. Extract from Zoologische Ergebnisse einer Reise in Niederlandisch Ost-Indien, vol.3, pp.260-268, 1893.

MALAY PENINSULA

REPORT ON THE MAMMALS. J. Lewis Bonhote. Fasciculi Malayenses, Zool., vol. 1, pp.1-45, pls.1-4, Oct., 1903.

REPORT ON THE MAMMALS. Report on the Gunong Tahan Expedition, May-Sep., 1905.) J. Lewis Bonhote. Jour. Fed. Malay States Mus., vol.3, pp.1-11, pl.1, Feb., 1908.

EARLY DAYS IN MALAYA. (Tiger, Panther, Elephant, Rhinoceros, Gaur, Serow, and Wild Pig.) H.E. Burgess. Jour. Bombay Nat. Hist. Soc., vol.38, no.2, pp.241-257, Dec. 1, 1935.

SOME NOTES ON THE FAUNA OF MALAYA. H.E. Burgess. Jour. Bombay Nat. Hist. Soc., vol.39, no.4, pp.856-861, Dec. 15, 1937.

PRELIMINARY REPORT ON CAVE EXPLORATION, NEAR LENGGONG, UPPER PERAK. Ivor H.N. Evans. Jour. Fed. Malay States Mus., Singapore, vol.7, pt. 4, pp.227-234, June, 1918.

ON THE MAMMALIA OF SIAM AND THE MALAY PENINSULA. Stanley Smith Flower. Proc. Zool. Soc. London, pp.306-379, 1900.

BIG GAME OF MALAYA: THEIR TYPES DISTRIBUTIONS AND HABITS. E.C. Foenander. London, The Batchworth Press, pp.xvi-208, illus., 1952.

MAMMAL NOTES FROM PAHANG. E.C. Foenander. Malayan Nature Jour., Kuala Lumpur, vol.10, no.2, pp.83-85, Dec., 1955.

ON BIRDS AND MAMMALS FROM THE MALAY PENINSULA. Nils Gyldenstolpe. Arkiv. Zool., Stockholm, vol.10, no.26, pp.31, tbls., Feb. 8, 1917.

RODENTS AND INSECTIVORES FROM SELANGOR, MALAYA. J.L. Harrison. Jour. Mamm., vol.31, no.3, pp.337-346, Aug. 21, 1950.

SOME MAMMALS OF THE TREES. J.L. Harrison. Malayan Nature Jour., Kuala Lumpur, vol.4, no.2, pp.66-69, June, 1949.

NEW MAMMALS FROM THE MALAY PENINSULA REGION. C. Boden Kloss. Jour. Fed. Malay States Mus., vol.2, pp.143-147, Sep., 1908.

ON MAMMALS AND BIRDS FROM THE HILLS OF NEGRI SEMBILAN. C.Boden Kloss. Jour. Fed. Malay States Mus., vol.4, nos.3-4, pp.219-229, Oct., 1911.

ON MAMMALS AND BIRDS FROM THE LOWLANDS OF PAHANG. C.Boden Kloss. Jour. Fed. Malay States Mus., vol.4, no. 2, pp.144-166, Feb., 1911.

ON MAMMALS AND BIRDS FROM TRENGGANU. C. Boden Kloss. Jour. Fed. Malay States Mus., vol.4, no.2, pp.135-143, Feb., 1911.

PRIMATES, CARNIVORES AND UNGULATES OF THE PENINSULAR REGION. C.Boden Kloss. Jour. Straits Branch Royal Asiatic Soc., no.53, pp.1-47, 1909.

PROVISIONAL LIST OF MAMMALS OF THE PENINSULA REGION (MALAY PEN.). C. Boden Kloss. Jour. Fed. Malay States Mus., vol.2, no.3.

TRAPPING WILD ANIMALS IN MALAY JUNGLES. 3RD IMPRESSION. Charles Mayer. London, T.Fisher Unwin, Ltd., vol.8, pp.223, 1923.

FIFTY-ONE NEW MALAYAN MAMMALS. Gerrit S. Miller, Jr. Smiths. Inst., Misc. Coll., vol.61, no.21, publ.2252, pp.30, Dec. 29, 1913.

SEVENTY NEW MALAYAN MAMMALS. Gerrit S. Miller, Jr. Smiths. Inst., Misc. Coll., vol.45, no.1420, pp.1-73, pls.1-19, Nov. 6, 1903.

(JOURNEY OF DR. ELIO MODIGLIANI IN THE MALAY STATES. GENERAL RESUME OF THE ZOOLOGICAL RESULTS.) Viaggio del Dott. Elio Modigliani in Malesia. Riassunto generale del risultati zoologici. Elio Modigliani. Genoa, pp.65, 1909.

(ON THE MAMMAL FAUNA OF MALAYA.) Ueber die Malayische Saeugethier-Fauna. August von Pelzeln. Festschr.Zool.Bot. Gesell., pp.51-74, map, Wien, 1876.

LIST OF A SMALL COLLECTION OF BIRDS AND MAMMALS FROM GUNONG KERBAU, PERAK. H.S. Robinson. Jour. Fed.Malay States Mus., Kuala Lumpur, vol.5, no.2, pp.23-27, Feb., 1914.

ON THREE NEW RACES OF MALAYAN MAMMALS. (New: Nycticebus coucang insularis, Lariscus insignis fornicatus, Tomeutes tenuis tiomanicus.) H.C. Robinson. Jour. Fed. Malay States Mus., Singapore, vol.7, pt.3, pp.101-105, Sep., 1917.

LIST OF A SMALL COLLECTION OF MAMMALS AND BIRDS FROM THE KRAU RIVER, WESTERN PAHANG. H.C. Robinson, C. Boden Kloss. Jour. Fed. Malay States Mus., vol.5, no.4, pp.169-175, Mar., 1915.

NATURAL HISTORY OF KEDAH PEAK. H.C. Robinson, C. Boden Kloss. Jour. Fed. Malay States Mus., Kuala Lumpur, vol.6, pt.4, pp.219-244, Feb., 1916.

ON A FURTHER COLLECTION OF MAMMALS AND BIRDS FROM THE HILLS OF NEGRI SEMBILAN. H.C. Robinson, C. Boden Kloss. Jour. Fed. Malay States Mus., Kuala Lumpur, vol.5, no.2, pp.51-57, Feb., 1914.

ON NEW MAMMALS, MAINLY FROM BANDON AND THE ADJACENT ISLANDS, EAST COAST OF THE MALAY PENINSULA. H.C. Robinson, C. Boden Kloss. Ann. and Mag. Nat. Hist., London, ser.8, vol.8, pp.223-234, Feb., 1914.

ON SIX NEW MAMMALS FROM THE MALAY PENINSULA AND ADJACENT ISLANDS. H.C. Robinson, C. Boden Kloss. Jour. Fed. Malay States Mus., vol.4, no. 2, pp.169-174, 1911.

MALAYAN MAMMALS. (Gibbons, Macaques, Leaf Monkeys.) E.O. Shebbeare. Malayan Nature Jour., Kuala Lumpur, Selangor, vol. 1, no.2, pp.54-59, figs.5, Dec., 1940.

DIAGNOSES OF FOUR NEW MAMMALS FROM THE MALAYAN REGION. Oldfield Thomas. Ann. and Mag. Nat. Hist., ser.6, vol.2, no.11, pp.407-409, Nov., 1888.

ON MAMMALS FROM THE MALAY PENINSULA AND ISLANDS. Oldfield Thomas. Ann. and Mag. Nat. Hist., ser.8, vol.2, no.9, pp.301-306, Sep., 1908.

TWO NEW MAMMALS FROM THE MALAY PENINSULA. Oldfield Thomas. Ann. and Mag. Nat. Hist., ser.8, vol.5, no.29, pp.424-426, May, 1910.

ON MAMMALS FROM THE RHIO ARCHIPELAGO AND MALAY PENINSULA COLLECTED BY MESSRS. H. C. ROBINSON, C. BODEN KLOSS, AND E. SEIMUND, AND PRESENTED TO THE NATIONAL MUSEUM BY THE GOVERNMENT OF THE FEDERATED MALAY STATES. Oldfield Thomas, R.C. Wroughton. Jour. Federated Malay States Museums, Kuala Lumpur, vol.4, no.1, pp.99-129, Dec., 1909.

MALAYAN ANIMAL LIFE. M.W.F. Tweedie, J.L. Harrison. Longmans, Green and Co., London, New York, Toronto.

LIST OF A SMALL COLLECTION OF MAMMALS AND BIRDS FROM THE MOUNTAINS OF ULU LANGAT, SELANGOR. Jour. Federated Malay States Museums, Kuala Lumpur, vol.4, nos.3-4, pp.235-241, 1913.

FATE OF A FAUNA. (Speculations on Effects of War in Malay Peninsula and East Indies.) Fauna, Philadelphia, vol.4, no. 1, pp.12-14, 24, map, illus., Mar., 1942.

## MANCHURIA

(WILD ANIMALS OF MANCHURIA.) Les bêtes sauvages de la Mandchourie. Nicolas Baikov. Payot, Paris, pp.270, illus., 1939.

MAMMAL FAUNA OF MANCHOUKUO PRESERVED IN THE COLLECTION OF MARQUIS YAMASHINA. Nagamichi Kuroda. Bull. Biogeogr. Soc. Japan, Tokyo, vol.9, no.1, pp.1-50, Jan., 1939.

ON THE FORMS OF MURIDAE AND SORICIDAE FOUND IN THE FENG TSIEN PROVINCE, MANCHOUKUO. Nagamichi Kuroda, Heiki Gen. Syokukutu oyobi Dobutu (Botany and Zoology), vol.6, no.8, pp.53-60 (1383-1390), map, tbl., Aug.1, 1938. (In Japanese.)

MAMMALS FOUND ON THE TERRITORY OF GREATER HARBIN. A.S. Loukashkin. Rpt. Inst. Sci. Research, Manchoukuo, vol.2, no.2, pp.111-122, figs.3, map, pls. 1-6, Aug., 1938.

MAMMALS OF NORTH MANCHURIA. A.S. Loukashkin. Jour. Mamm., vol.18, no.3, pp.327-332, map, Aug. 14, 1937.

POST-TERTIARY FAUNA OF NORTH MANCHURIA CONTEMPORARY WITH PRIMITIVE MAN. A.S. Loukashkin. Pan-Amer. Geol., vol.60, no.5, p.379, Dec., 1933; Report Internat. Geol. Congr., 16th sess., U.S.A., 1933, vol.2, pp.799-805, fig.1, 1936.

RECENT DISCOVERIES OF REMAINS OF PLEISTOCENE MAMMALS IN NORTHERN MANCHURIA. A.S. Loukashkin. China Jour., vol.16, no.6, pp.345-350, illus., June, 1932.

RECENT DISCOVERIES OF REMAINS OF POST-TERTIARY MAMMALS IN NORTHERN MANCHURIA. A.S. Loukashkin. Annual Club Nat. Sci. and Geogr. of the Y.M.C.A., Harbin, vol.1, pp.125-130, maps 2, pls.8, 1934. (In Russian.)

SOME OBSERVATIONS ON THE REMAINS OF A PLEISTOCENE FAUNA AND OF THE PALAEOLITHIC AGE IN NORTHERN MANCHURIA. A.S. Loukashkin. Early Man, edited by G.G. MacCurdy, Lippincott and Co., London, pp.327-340, figs. 53-54, pl.22, 1937.

FUR TRADE OF NORTH MANCHURIA. (Lists 37 Fur Bearers, With the Chinese Names.) A.S. Loukashkin, V.N. Jernakov. China Jour., vol.21, no.5, pp.227-244, illus., Nov., 1934; no.6, pp.293-303, illus., Dec., 1934.

HAND-LIST OF THE MANCHURIAN AND EASTERN MONGOLIAN VERTEBRATA. Tamezo Mori. Privately Printed, pp.186, July, 1927.

ON FOUR NEW SMALL MAMMALS FROM MANCHURIA. (Meriones kurauchii, Phodopus praedilectus, Cricetulus manchuricus, Microtus dolichocephalus.) Tamezo Mori. Annot. Zool. Japonenses, vol.12, no.2, pp. 417-420, Apr. 7, 1930.

ON THREE NEW MAMMALS FROM MANCHURIA. (Petaurista watasei, Myospalax komurai, Hemiechinus manchurious.) Tamezo Mori. Annot. Zool. Japonenses, vol.2, no.2, pp.107-109, July 31, 1927.

TEILHARDOSAURUS AND ENDOTHERIUM, NEW JURASSIC REPTILIA AND MAMMALIA FROM THE HUSIN COAL-FIELD, SOUTH MANCHURIA. Tokio Shikama. Proc. Japan Acad., vol.23, no.71, pp.76-84, 1947.

NATURALIST IN MANCHURIA. Arthur de Carle Sowerby. Privately Printed, vol.1, 1922; vols.2 and 3 (bound together), 1923, pp.191, illus.

COLLECTION OF MAMMALS FROM NORTHERN AND CENTRAL MANCHURIA. Oldfield Thomas. Ann. and Mag. Nat. Hist., ser.8, vol.4, no.24, pp.500-505, Dec., 1909.

BRIEF REPORT OF THE RESULTS OF THE SECOND EXCAVATION AT KU-HSIANG-TUNG NEAR HARBIN, MANCHOUKUO. Shigeyasu Tokunaga, Nobuo Naora. Proc. Imp. Acad. Tokyo, vol. 10, no.10, pp.654-657, figs.5, Dec., 1934.

FOSSIL MAMMALS AND HUMAN ARTIFACTS EXCAVATED NEAR HARBIN, MANCHUKUO. Shigeyasu Tokunaga, Nobuo Naora. Proc. Imp. Acad. Tokyo, vol.9, no.8, pp.404-406, figs.6, Oct., 1933.

FOSSIL REMAINS EXCAVATED AT KU-HSIANG-TUNG NEAR HARBIN, MANCHUKUO. Shigeyasu Tokunaga, Nobuo Naora. Rept. 1st. Sci. Exped. Manchukuo, sect. 2, pt.4, pp.1-229, figs.23, pls.22, Mar., 1939.

REPORT OF DIGGINGS AT HO-CHIA-KOU, KU-HSIANG-TUNG, KIRIN, MANCHOUKOU. Shigeyasu Tokunaga, Nobuo Naora. Rept. 1st. Sci. Exped. Manchukuo, Tokyo, sect.2, pt.1, pp.119-7, pls.42, figs.17, July, 1934. (In Japanese with English summary.)

SUMMARY REPORT OF THE MAMMALIAN FOSSILS OF HARBIN. Shigeyasu Tokunaga, Nobuo Naora. Jour. Geol. Soc. Japan, Tokyo, vol.44, no.525, pp.536-537, June 20, 1937. (In Japanese.)

PLEISTOCENE FAUNA OF MANCHURIA. China Jour., vol.16, no.6, pp.353-354, June, 1932.

## MEDITERRANEAN SEA

(REMARKS ON SOME MAMMAL SKULLS OF SARDINIA.) Bemerkungen ueber einige Saeugetierschaedel von Sardinien. H.O. Antonius. Proc. Koninklijke Akademie van Wetenschappen to Amsterdam, vol.23, no. 1, pp.37-43, 1920.

MAMMALS OF CYPRUS. Dorothea M.A. Bate. Proc. Zool. Soc. London, for 1903, vol.2, pp.341-348, Apr. 1, 1904.

NOTE ON A NEW VOLE AND OTHER REMAINS FROM THE GHAR DALAM CAVERN, MALTA. Dorothea M. A. Bate. Geol. Mag., vol.57, pp.208-211, fig.1, May, 1920.

TWO NEW MAMMALS FROM THE PLEISTOCENE OF MALTA, WITH NOTES ON THE ASSOCIATED FAUNA. (Nesolutra, N. euxena, Pitymys pauli.) Dorothea M.A. Bate. Proc. Zool. Soc. London for 1935, pt.2, pp.247-264, figs.2, July 4, 1935.

(ON OLD PLEISTOCENE MAMMAL FAUNA OF PIANOSA ISLAND.) Ueber eine altpleistocaene Saeugetierfauna von der Insel Pianosa. H.G. Stehlin. Eclog. geol. Helv., vol.21, no.2, pp.435-460, 1928.

ON MAMMALS FROM GORGONA ISLAND, WITH THE DESCRIPTION OF A NEW SLOTH. Oldfield Thomas. Ann. and Mag. Nat. Hist., ser.9, vol.17, pp.309-311, Mar., 1926.

ON THE MAMMALS OF THE BALEARIC ISLANDS. Oldfield Thomas. Proc. Zool. Soc. London, pp.35-44, Feb. 5, 1901.

(NOTES ON VERTEBRATES OF THE ISLAND OF MONTECRISTO.) Note sui vertebrati dell Isola di Montecristo. Augusto Toschi. Ricerche Zool. Applicata alla Caccia, Inst. Zool. Univ. Bologna, vol.23, pp. 1-52, illus., 1953.

(ZOOLOGICAL EXCURSIONS ON THE ISLE OF RHODES BY DR. ENRICO FESTA.) Escursioni zoologiche nell'Isola di Rodi del Dr. Enrico Festa. Edoardo Zavattari. Boll. Mus. Zool. ed Anat. comp. R. Univ. Torino, vol.28, no.670, pp.2, June 30, 1913.

## MESOPOTAMIA

BIBLIOGRAPHY ON THE VERTEBRATE FAUNA OF IRAQ AND NEIGHBOURING COUNTRIES. I. MAMMALS. Bashir E. Allouse. Publ. Iraq Nat. Hist. Mus., no. 4, pp.1-31, 1954.

REPORT ON THE MAMMALS OF MESOPOTAMIA COLLECTED BY MEMBERS OF THE MESOPOTAMIAN EXPEDITIONARY FORCE, 1915 TO 1919. R.E. Cheesman. Jour. Bombay Nat. Hist. Soc., vol.27, pp.323-346, Dec. 20, 1920.

MAMMALS FROM KURDISTAN, IRAQ, WITH DESCRIPTION OF A NEW BAT. David L. Harrison. Jour. Mamm., vol. 37, no.2, pp. 257-263, illus., June 9, 1956.

MAMMALS OF IRAQ. Robert Torrens Hatt. Ann Arbor, Michigan, Univ., Mus. of Zoology, Misc. Publication, no.106, pp.113, pls., map, tbls., 1959.

NOTES ON MESOPOTAMIAN MAMMALS. C.R.S. Itman. Jour. Bombay Nat. Hist. Soc., vol.28, pp.474-480, Mar.25, 1922.

MAMMALS FROM IRAQ. Colin Campbell Sanborn. Anthropology of Iraq, Anthrop. Ser., Field Mus. Nat. Hist., Chicago, vol.30, pt.1, no. 1, pp.156-162, May 31, 1940.

SOME NEW MAMMALS FROM MESOPOTAMIA. Oldfield Thomas. Jour. Bombay,

Nat. Hist. Soc., vol.26, no.3, pp.745-749, Oct. 20, 1919.

NOTES ON IRAQ INSECTIVORA AND CHIROPTERA. Neal A. Weber. Jour. Mamm., vol.36, no.1, pp.123-126, Feb. 25, 1955.

MEXICO

FURTHER NOTES ON MAMMALS COLLECTED IN MEXICO BY DR. AUDLEY C. BULLER, WITH DESCRIPTIONS OF NEW SPECIES. J.A. Allen. Bull. Amer. Mus. Nat. Hist., vol.9, pp.47-58, Mar. 15, 1897.

BIOLOGIA CENTRALI-AMERICANA; OR CONTRIBUTIONS TO THE KNOWLEDGE OF THE FAUNA AND FLORA OF MEXICO AND CENTRAL AMERICA. Edward R. Alston. London, Pub. for the Editors by R.H. Porter, pp.xx-220, pls.22 (20 col.), 1879-82.

MAMMALS COLLECTED IN MEXICO FROM 1951 TO 1956 BY THE WALLA WALLA COLLEGE MUSEUM OF NATURAL HISTORY. Ernest S. Booth. Walla Walla College Publ., Dept. Biol. Sci. and Biol. Sta., vol.20, pp.1-19, July 10, 1957.

PRESENT DISTRIBUTION AND AFFINITIES OF MEXICAN MAMMALS. William H. Burt. Annals Assoc. Amer. Geographers, vol.39, no.3, pp.211-218, Sep., 1949.

NOTES ON MEXICAN MAMMALS. William B. Davis. Jour. Mamm., vol.25, no.4, pp. 370-403, fig.1, Dec. 12, 1944.

DESCRIPTIONS OF APPARENTLY NEW SPECIES AND SUBSPECIES OF MAMMALS FROM MEXICO AND SAN DOMINGO. D.G. Elliot. Proc. Biol. Soc. Washington, vol. 18, pp.233-236, Dec. 9, 1905.

LIST OF A COLLECTION OF MEXICAN MAMMALS, WITH DESCRIPTIONS OF SOME APPARENTLY NEW FORMS. D.G. Elliot. Chicago, Field Columbian Mus., Publication no.71, Zoological ser., vol. III, no.8, pp.141-149, 1903.

CATALOGUE OF ANIMALS COLLECTED BY THE GEOGRAPHICAL AND EXPLORING COMMISSION OF THE REPUBLIC OF MEXICO. Fernando Ferrari-Perez. U.S. Nat. Mus., Proc., Washington 1887, vol. 9, pp.125-199, 1886.

NOTES ON THE OCCURRENCE OF MAMMALIAN REMAINS IN THE PLEISTOCENE OF MEXICO, WITH DESCRIPTION OF A NEW SPECIES CAPROMERYX MEXICANA. Eustace Leopold Furlong. Berkeley, Univ. of Calif., Publications in Geol.Sciences, vol.15, no.5, pp.137-152, illus., 1925.

BIOLOGICAL INVESTIGATIONS IN MEXICO. Edward A. Goldman. Smiths. Inst. Misc. Coll., Washington, vol.115, pp. xiii-476, pls.71, July 31, 1951.

DESCRIPTIONS OF NEW MAMMALS FROM PANAMA AND MEXICO. Edward A. Goldman. Smiths. Inst. Misc. Coll., Wash., Publication 2168, vol.60, no.22, pp.20, 1913.

BIOTIC PROVINCES OF MEXICO. Edward A. Goldman, Robert T. Moore. Jour. Mamm., vol.26, no.4, pp.347-360, Feb. 12, 1946.

MAMMALS FROM MEXICO COLLECTED BY MARIAN MARTIN FOR THE AMERICAN MUSEUM OF NATURAL HISTORY. George G. Goodwin. Amer. Mus. Novitates, New York, no.1689, pp.1-16, Nov. 12, 1954.

SEVEN NEW MAMMALS FROM MEXICO. George G. Goodwin. Amer. Mus.Novitates, New York, no.1791, pp.1-10, Sep. 28, 1956.

TWO NEW MAMMALS FROM MEXICO. George G. Goodwin. Amer. Mus.Novitates, no.1871, pp.1-3, Feb. 26, 1958.

MAMMALS FROM BRITISH HONDURAS, MEXICO, JAMAICA AND HAITI. Philip Hershkovitz. Chicago Nat. Hist. Mus., Publication no.670, pp.547-569, map, 1951.

PLEISTOCENE VERTEBRATES FROM THE UPPER BECERRA (BECERRA SUPERIOR) FORMATION, VALLEY OF TEQUIXQUIAC, MEXICO, WITH NOTES ON OTHER PLEISTOCENE FORMS. Claude W. Hibbard. Contrib. Mus. Paleontol. Univ. Michigan, vol.12, no.5, pp.47-96, pls.9, Feb. 18, 1955.

NEW MAMMALS FROM COSTA RICA AND MEXICO. N. Hollister. Proc. Biol. Soc. Washington, vol.27, pp.209-210, Oct.31, 1914.

NOTES ON MEXICAN MAMMALS. Emmet T. Hooper. Jour. Mamm., vol.28, no.1, pp.40-57, Feb. 15, 1947.

RECORDS OF MEXICAN MAMMALS. Emmett T. Hooper. Occas. Papers Mus. Zool. Univ. Michigan, vol.586, pp.1-9, Apr. 30, 1957.

PRESIDENT OBREGON PROTECTS BIG GAME OF MEXICO. W.T. Hornaday.Zool. Soc. Bull., vol.26, no.1, pp.8-9, Jan., 1923.

SAVING THE BIG GAME OF MEXICO. W.T. Hornaday. Nat. Mag., vol.4, pp.213-219, 236, illus., Oct., 1924.

STATUS OF MEXICAN BIG-GAME HERDS. A. Starker Leopold. Trans. 12th N.Amer. Wildl.Conf., pp. 437-438, 1947.

WILDLIFE OF MEXICO. A. Starker Leopold. Univ. of California Press, Berkeley, pp.576.

(MEXICAN HUNTING.) Caza mexicana. (Accounts of Fur-Bearing and Game Mammals of Mexico.) Carlos M. Lopez.Bouret, Paris and Mexico, pp.629, illus., 1923.

WILDLIFE CONDITIONS IN MEXICO. A. Luis Macias. Trans. 13th N.Amer. Wildl. Conf., Wash., pp.6-10, 1948.

(FIRST MUSEUM OF NATURAL HISTORY IN MEXICO.) El primer museo de historia natural en Mexico. K.Manuel Maldonado. Rev. Soc. Mexicana Hist. Nat., Mexico, D.F., vol.2, nos.2-3, pp.211-219, pls. 12-13, Sep., 1941.

MEXICAN NATURAL HISTORY. Edgar A. Mearns. Newport Daily News, p.5, Oct. 24, 1899.

FIVE NEW MAMMALS FROM MEXICO. C. Hart Merriam. Proc. Biol. Soc. Washington, vol.15, pp.67-69, Mar.22, 1902.

FOUR NEW MAMMALS, INCLUDING A NEW GENUS (TEANOPUS), FROM MEXICO. C. Hart Merriam. Proc. Biol. Soc. Washington, vol.16, pp.79-82, May 29, 1903.

SEVEN NEW MAMMALS FROM MEXICO, INCLUDING A NEW GENUS OF RODENTS. C. Hart Merriam. Proc. Washington Acad. Sci., vol.3, pp.559-563, Nov. 29, 1901.

NEW CARNIVORES AND RODENTS FROM MEXICO. E.W. Nelson, E.A. Goldman. Mammalia, vol.113, no.5034.

(NOTES ON SOME MAMMALS OF MEXICO.) Note sur quelques mammiferes du Mexique. H. L. F. de Saussure. Paris, Imp. de Mme Ve Bouchard-Huzard, pp. 82, pls.4 (2 col.), 1860.

STRANGE PLEISTOCENE FOSSIL LOCALITY IN MEXICO. Helmut de Terra. Science, vol.118, no.3077, pp.748-749, Dec. 18, 1953.

UNSOLVED PROBLEMS CONCERNING WILDLIFE IN MEXICAN NATIONAL PARKS. William Vogt. Trans. 10th N.Amer. Wildl. Conf., Washington, pp.355-358, 1945.

(FOREST FAUNA IN THE MEXICAN REPUBLIC.) Fauna silvestre de la Republica Mexicana. Juan Zinser. Proc. 8th Amer. Sci. Congr., Wash., D.C., vol.5, pp. 275-278, 1942.

MEXICO--LOWER CALIFORNIA see LOWER CALIFORNIA

MEXICO, CENTRAL

FURTHER NOTES ON MAMMALS FROM NORTHWESTERN DURANGO. J.A. Allen. Bull. Amer. Mus. Nat. Hist., vol.20, pp.205-210, May 28, 1904.

NOTES ON COLLECTIONS OF MAMMALS MADE IN CENTRAL AND SOUTHER MEXICO, BY DR. AUDLEY C. BULLER, WITH DESCRIPTIONS OF NEW SPECIES OF THE GENERA VESPERTILIO, SCIURUS, AND LEPUS. J.A. Allen. Bull. Amer. Mus.Nat. Hist., vol.3, pp.175-194, Dec. 10, 1890.

(MAMMAL FIND IN THE LOWER CENOZOIC OF THE GUANAJUATO RED CONGLOMERATE.) El hallazgo de mamiferos del Cenozoico inferior en el conglomerado rojo de Guanajuato. A.R.V. Arellano. Bol. Asoc. Mexicano Geologous Petroleros, vol.4, nos.1-2, pp.63-64, 1952.

MAMMALS OF THE GUADIANA LAVA FIELD, DURANGO, MEXICO. Rollin Harold Baker. East Lansing, Michigan, State Univ. of Agriculture and Applied Science, Mus., Publications, Biological Series, vol.1, no.9, pp.303-327, map, diagrs., tbl., 1960.

(MAMMALS REGISTERED FOR THE FIRST TIME IN HIDALGO STATE.) Mamiferos registrados por primera vez en el estado de Hidalgo. Rollin H. Baker. Villa R. Bernardo. Rev. Soc. Mexicana Hist.Nat., vol.14, nos.1-4, pp.149-150, Dec., 1953.

MAMMALS OF THE MEXICAN STATE OF SAN LUIS POTOSI. Walter W. Dalquest. Louisiana State Univ. Studies Biol. Sci. Ser. no. 1, pp.229, Dec. 28, 1953.

RECORDS OF MAMMALS FROM THE MEXICAN STATE OF SAN LUIS POTOSI. Walter W. Dalquest. Occas. Papers Mus. Zool., Louisiana State Univ., Baton Rouge, no.23, pp.1-15, figs.2, July 10, 1950.

SIX NEW MAMMALS FROM THE STATE OF SAN LUIS POTOSI, MEXICO. Walter W. Dalquest. Jour. Washington Acad. Sci., vol.41, no.11, pp.361-364, Nov., 1951.

TWO NEW MAMMALS FROM CENTRAL MEXICO. Walter W. Dalquest. Proc.Biol. Soc. Washington, vol.64, pp.105-108, Aug. 24, 1951.

MAMMALS OF THE MEXICAN STATE OF MOREOLOS. W.B. Davis, R.J. Russell. Jour. Mamm., vol.35, no.1, pp.63-80, Feb. 10, 1954.

EARLY CENOZOIC VERTEBRATES IN THE RED CONGLOMERATE AT GUANAJUATO, MEXICO. Carl Fries, Jr., et al. Smiths. Inst. Misc. Coll., vol.123, no.7, pp.1-25, illus., Feb. 17, 1955.

MAMMALS OF THE MEXICAN STATE OF MORELOS. Robert J. Russel. Master's thesis, A. and M. Coll., Texas, 1952.

ON A SMALL COLLECTION OF MAMMALIA FROM CENTRAL MEXICO. Oldfield Thomas. Proc. Zool. Soc. London, pp.371-372, Apr. 18, 1882.

NEW RECORDS OF MAMMALS FROM JALISCO, MEXICO, FROM BARN OWL PELLETS. John W. Twente, Rollin H. Baker. Jour. Mamm., vol.32, no.1, pp. 120-121, Feb. 15, 1951.

(WILD MAMMALS FROM THE VALLEY OF MEXICO.) Mamiferos silvestres del Valle de Mexico. R. Bernardo Villa. Anales Inst. Biol., Mexico, vol.23, nos. 1-2, pp.269-492, 1952.

MEXICO, EASTERN

ON A COLLECTION OF MAMMALS FROM JALAPA AND LA VIGAS, STATE OF VERA ORUS, MEXICO. J.A. Allen. Bull. Amer. Mus. Nat. Hist., vol.9, pp.197-208, June 16, 1897.

MAMMALS FROM OWL PELLETS TAKEN IN COAHUILA, MEXICO. Rollin H.Baker. Trans. Kansas Acad. Sci., Topeka, vol. 56, no.2, pp.253-254, 1953.

MAMMALS FROM TAMAULIPAS, MEXICO. Rollin H. Baker. Univ. Kansas Publ., Mus. Nat. Hist., Lawrence, vol.5, no.12, pp. 207-218, Dec. 15, 1951.

MAMMALS OF COAHUILA, MEXICO. Rollin H. Baker. Univ. Kansas Publ., Mus. Nat. Hist., vol.9, no.7, pp.125-335, June 15, 1956.

MAMMALS OF THE SAN CARLOS MOUNTAINS AND VICINITY. THE GEOLOGY AND BIOLOGY OF THE SAN CARLOS MOUNTAINS, TAMAULIPAS, MEXICO. Lee R. Dice. Univ. Michigan Studies, Sci.Ser., vol.12, pp.245-268, pls.28-30, 1937.

REPORT ON A COLLECTION OF MAMMAL BONES FROM ARCHEOLOGIC CAVE-SITES IN COAHUILA, MEXICO. Raymond M. Gilmore. Jour. Mamm., vol.28, no.2, pp.147-165, figs.3, pl.1, May 19, 1947.

NEW SHORT-TAILED SHREW AND A NEW FREE-TAILED BAT FROM TAMAULIPAS, MEXICO. (Cryptotis mexicana madrea, Tadarida laticaudata ferruginea.) George G. Goodwin. Amer. Mus. Novitates, New York, no.1670, pp.1-3, June 28, 1954.

MAMMALS OF THE GULF OF MEXICO. ITS ORIGIN, WATERS, AND MARINE LIFE. (West Indian Seal, Manatee, and Cetaceans.) Gordon Gunter. U.S. Fish and Wildl. Serv., Fishery Bull. no.89, 1954. (In) Gulf of Mexico, pp.543-551.

MAMMALS OBTAINED BY DR. CURT VON WEDEL FROM THE BARRIER BEACH OF TAMAULIPAS, MEXICO. E. Raymond Hall. Univ. Kansas Publ., Mus. Nat.Hist., Lawrence, vol.5, no.4, pp.33-47, illus., Oct. 1, 1951.

NOTES ON MAMMALS OF TAMAULIPAS, MEXICO. Emmet T. Hooper. Occas. Papers Mus. Zool. Univ. Michigan, Ann Arbor, no.544, pp.12, Mar. 25, 1953.

AN ANNOTATED LIST OF MAMMALS COLLECTED IN NUEVO LEON, MEXICO, IN 1938. E. J. Koestner. Great Basin Nat., Provo, vol.2, no.1, pp.9-15, Feb. 20, 1941.

POPULATIONS OF SMALL MAMMALS ON CERRO POTOSI, NEUVO LEON, MEXICO. E.J. Koestner. Jour. Mamm., vol.25, no. 3, pp.284-289, pl.1, Sep. 8, 1944.

ON A COLLECTION OF MAMMALS FROM CENTRAL VERA CRUZ, MEXICO. Oldfield Thomas. Proc. Zool. Soc. London, pp.71-76, pls.6-7, Feb. 4, 1890.

MEXICO, NORTHERN

LIST OF MAMMALS AND BIRDS COLLECTED IN NORTHEASTERN SONORA AND NORTHWESTERN CHIHUAHUA, MEXICO, ON THE LUMHOLTZ ARCHAEOLOGICAL EXPEDITION, 1890-92. J.A. Allen. Bull. Amer. Mus. Nat. Hist., vol.5, art.3, pp.27-42, Mar. 16, 1893.

LIST OF MAMMALS COLLECTED BY DR. EDWARD PALMER IN NORTHEASTERN MEXICO, WITH FIELD NOTES BY THE COLLECTOR. J.A. Allen. Bull. Mus.Comp. Zool., vol.8, no.9, pp.183-189, Mar., 1881.

VERTEBRATES FOUND IN OWL-PELLETS FROM NORTHEASTERN CHIHUAHUA. Sydney Anderson, Philip W. Ogilvie. Southwestern Naturalist, vol.2, no.1, pp.33-37, Oct., 15, 1957.

(SEAS AND ISLANDS IN THE NORTHWEST OF MEXICO.) Mares e islas del Noroeste de México. C.A. Berzunza. Resultado de la Expedición Cientifico-Militar de la Escuela Superior de Guerra, México, pp.70-90, 1949.

FAUNAL RELATIONSHIPS AND GEOGRAPHIC DISTRIBUTION OF MAMMALS IN SONORA, MEXICO. William H. Burt. Misc. Publ.no.39, Mus. Zool. Univ. Michigan, Ann Arbor, pp.1-77, maps 26, tbl.1, Feb. 14, 1938.

NOTES ON MAMMALS FROM SONORA AND CHIHUAHUA, MEXICO. William H. Burt, Emmet T. Hooper. Occas.Papers Mus. Zool. Univ. Michigan, Ann Arbor, no.430, pp.7, May 27, 1941.

SONORAN BIOTIC PROVINCE. Lee R. Dice. Ecology, Brooklyn, vol.20, no.2, pp.118-129, fig.1, Apr., 1939.

NOTES ON A COLLECTION OF MAMMALS FROM THE SIERRA MADRES OF CHIHUAHUA, MEXICO. Irving W. Knobloch. Jour. Mamm., vol.23, no.3, pp. 297-298, Aug. 14, 1942.

BIG GAME OF CHIHUAHUA, MEXICO, 1898-1902. Charles Sheldon. Hunting and Conservation, the Book of the Boone and Crockett Club, New Haven, Yale Univ. Press, pp.138-181, 1925.

LAND OF ETERNAL SUMMER. (Sonora, Mexico.) Ken Stott, Jr. San Diego Zoonooz, vol.15, no.4, pp.5-7, illus., Apr., 1942.

MEXICO, SOUTHERN

VERTEBRATA FROM YUCATAN. MAMMALIA. Glover M. Allen. Bull. Mus. Comp. Zool., Harvard College, vol.50, no.5, pp.101-109, Nov., 1906.

NOTES ON A COLLECTION OF MAMMALS FROM SOUTHERN MEXICO, WITH DESCRIPTIONS OF NEW SPECIES OF THE GENERA SCIURUS, TAMIAS, AND SIGMODEN. J.A. Allen. Bull. Amer. Mus. Nat. Hist., vol.2, pp.165-191, Oct. 21, 1889.

ON MAMMALS FROM YUCATAN, WITH DESCRIPTIONS OF NEW SPECIES. J.A. Allen. Bull. Amer. Mus. Nat. Hist., vol. 9, pp.1-12, Feb. 23, 1897.

(WILD ANIMALS FROM CHIAPAS.) Animales silvestres de Chiapas. Toro del Alvarez. Ediciones del Gobierno del Estado, Tuxtla Gutierrez, Chiapas, pp.247, illus., 1952.

BIOLOGICAL INVESTIGATIONS IN THE SELVA LACANDONA, CHIAPAS, MEXICO: MAMMALS COLLECTED AT LAGUNA OCOTAL. Frances L. Burnett, C.P. Lyman. Bull. Mus. Comp. Zool., vol.116, no.4, pp.290-298, Apr., 1957.

(MONOGRAPH ON THE MAMMALS OF THE YUCATAN.) Monografia de los mamiferos de Yucatan. George F. Gaumer. México, Departamento de talleres gráficos de la Secretaria de fomento, pp.xxxviii+331, pls. 58, fold.map, 1917.

PRELIMINARY REPORT ON THE MAMMALS COLLECTED BY THOMAS MAC DOUGALL IN SOUTHEASTERN OAXACA, MEXICO. George G. Goodwin. Amer.Mus. Novitates, no.1757, pp.15, Mar. 8, 1956.

ANNOTATED CHECK LIST OF THE MAMMALS OF MICHOACAN, MEXICO. E.Raymond Hall, R.Bernardo Villa. Univ.Kansas Publ., Mus. Nat. Hist., Lawrence, vol.1, no.22, pp.435-472, Dec. 27, 1949; Anales Inst. Biol., Mexico, vol.21, no.1, pp.159-214, illus., 1950. (In Spanish.)

COLLECTORS' DAYS AND NIGHTS IN YUCATAN. Robert T. Hatt. Nat. Hist., vol.30, no.6, pp.617-626, Nov.-Dec., 1930.

NOTES CONCERNING MAMMALS COLLECTED IN YUCATAN. Robert T. Hatt. Jour. Mammals, vol.19, no.3, pp.333-337, Aug., 1938.

FAUNAL AND ARCHEOLOGICAL RESEARCHES IN YUCATAN CAVES. Robert T. Hatt et al. Bull. Cranbrook Inst. Sci., Bloomfield Mills, Michigan, no.33, pp. 119, pls.12, Mar., 1953.

(OBSERVATIONS ON SOME MAMMALS FROM YUCATAN AND QUINTANA ROO.) Observaciones sobre algunos mamiferos de Yucatan y Quitana Roo. Robert T.Hatt, Bernardo Villa. Anales Inst. Biol., Mexico, vol.21, no.1, pp.214-240, illus., 1950.

NOTES OF MAMMALS FROM NORTHERN CHIAPAS, MEXICO. Merle L. Kuns, Richard E. Tashian. Jour. Mamm., vol. 35, no.1, pp.100-103, Feb. 10, 1954.

(BIOLOGICAL RESORTS OF GUERRA, WITH SPECIAL REFERENCE TO HUNTING MAMMALS AND BIRDS.) Los recurses biologicos de Guerra, file referencia especial a los mamiferes y aves de caza. A.Starker Leopold, Hernandez M. Leopoldo. Anuario 1944, Comision Impulsora y Coordinadora de la Investigacion Cientifica, Mexico, pp. 361-390, illus., 1944.

DESCRIPTIONS OF NINE NEW MAMMALS COLLECTED BY E. W. NELSON IN THE STATES OF COLIMA AND JALISCO, MEXICO. C. Hart Merriam. Proc. Biol. Soc., Washington, vol.7, pp.164-174, Sep. 29, 1892.

PRELIMINARY DESCRIPTIONS OF FOUR NEW MAMMALS FROM SOUTHERN MEXICO, COLLECTED BY E. W. NELSON. C. Hart Merriam. Proc. Biol. Soc., Wash., vol.8, pp.143-146, Dec. 29, 1893.

SIX NEW MAMMALS FROM COZUMEL ISLAND, YUCATAN. C. Hart Merriam. Proc. Biol. Soc., Washington, vol.14, pp.99-104, July 19, 1901.

(LOCALITIES VISITED AND ROUTES TAKEN BY E. W. NELSON IN THE STATE OF OAXACA.) Localidades visitadas y rutas recorridas por E. W.Nelson en el estado de Oaxaca. C.V. Morton, Richard Evans Schultes. Anales Inst. Biol., Univ. Nac.Mexico, Mexico, D.F., vol.13, no. 1, pp.47-51, illus., 1942.

FAUNA OF THE CAVES OF YUCATAN. A.S. Pearse. Carnegie Inst. Washington, Publ.no.491, pp.iii-304, figs.78, June 15, 1938.

"TOP OF THE WORLD" IN YUCATAN. DIGGING FOR FOSSIL MAMMALS IN THE LAND OF THE MAYA. Marcelle Roigneau. Nat. Hist., vol.30, no.3, pp.267-275, May-June, 1930.

LATE MIOCENE MAMMALS FROM OAXACA, MEXICO. R.A. Stirton. Amer. Jour. Sci., vol.252, pp.634-638, figs.2, Oct., 1954.

(MAMMALS OF SOCONUSCO, CHIAPAS.) Mamiferos del Soconusco, Chiapas. R. Bernardo Villa. Anales Inst. Biol., Mexico, D.F., vol.19, no.2, pp.485-528, June 30, 1949.

MEXICO, WESTERN

DESCRIPTIONS OF NEW MAMMALS FROM WESTERN MEXICO AND LOWER CALIFORNIA. J.A. Allen. Bull. Amer. Mus. Nat. Hist., vol.10, pp.143-158, Apr.12, 1898.

MAMMALS FROM THE STATES OF SINALOA AND JALISCO, MEXICO, COLLECTED BY J. H. BATTY DURING 1904 AND 1905. J.A. Allen. Bull. Amer. Mus. Nat. Hist., vol.22, pp.191-262, pls.20-23, text figs.3, July 25, 1906.

DESCRIPTIONS OF HERETOFORE UNKNOWN MAMMALS FROM ISLANDS IN THE GULF OF CALIFORNIA, MEXICO. William Henry Burt. Trans. San Diego Soc. Nat. Hist., vol.7, no.16, pp.161-182, Oct. 31, 1932.

NOTES ON MAMMALS OF WESTERN MEXICO. Emmet T. Hooper. Occas. Papers Mus. Zool. Univ. Michigan, Ann Arbor, no.565, pp.1-26, Mar. 31, 1955.

MAMMALS OF TRES MARIAS ISLANDS, OFF WESTERN MEXICO. C. Hart Merriam. Proc. Biol. Soc. Washington, vol. 12, pp.13-19, Jan. 27, 1898.

NATURAL HISTORY OF THE TRES MARIAS ISLANDS, MEXICO. E.W. Nelson, et al. U.S. Dept. Agr., Div. Biol. Surv., North Amer. Fauna, no. 14, pp.97, figs.2, pl.1, Apr. 29, 1899.

ON NEW MAMMALS FROM WESTERN MEXICO AND LOWER CALIFORNIA. Oldfield Thomas. Ann. and Mag. Nat. Hist., ser.7, no.1, pp.40-46, Jan., 1898.

MICRONESIA

ON THE RODENTS AND MARSUPIALS COLLECTED BY THE REV. G. BROWN IN DUKE-OF-YORK ISLAND, NEW BRITAIN, AND NEW IRELAND. Edward R. Alston. Proc. Zool. Soc. London, pp.123-126, pls.18-19, 1877.

SUPPLEMENTARY NOTE ON RODENTS AND MARSUPIALS FROM DUKE-OF-YORK ISLAND AND NEW IRELAND. Edward R. Alston. Proc. Zool. Soc. London, pt.4, pp.743-744, 1877.

SOME EFFECTS OF THE WAR ON THE WILDLIFE OF MICRONESIA. Rollin H.

Baker. Trans. 11th N.Amer.Wildl. Conf., Wash., pp.205-213, figs.3.

(ON A COLLECTION FROM THE ISLAND OF BOUGAINVILLE.) Sur une collection provenant de l'ile de Bougainville. S.Frechkop. Bull. Mus. Roy. Hist. Nat. Belgique, Bruxelles, vol.24, no.13, pp.1-12, 1948.

MAMMALS COLLECTED BY MR. MONUYAMA FROM MICRONESIA. Nagamichi Kuroda. Dobutsugaku Zasshi, vol.32, no. 380, pp.199-208, 1920. (In Japanese.)

(NOTES ON THE ZOOGEOGRAPHY OF WESTERN MICRONESIA.) Bemerkungen zur Zoogeographie des westlichen Mikronesiens. Paul Matschie. Jour. f.Ornithol., Jahrg.49, Hft.1, pp.109-114, 1901.

ON MAMMALS FROM MANUS ISLAND ADMIRALTY GROUP, AND RUK ISLAND, BISMARCK ARCHIPELAGO. Oldfield Thomas. Ann. and Mag. Nat. Hist., ser. 8, vol.13, no.76, pp.434-439, Apr., 1914.

MAMMALIAN FAUNA OF BOUGAINVILLE ISLAND, SOLOMONS GROUP. Ellis Le G. Troughton. Records Australian Mus., Sydney, vol.19, no.5, pp.341-353, Apr. 7, 1936.

## MONGOLIA

### Extinct and Fossil Mammals

MONGOLIAN COLOSSUS. Roy Chapman Andrews. Saturday Evening Post, vol.201, no.25, pp.8-9, 138, 140-141, 145, illus., Dec. 8, 1928.

(ADVANCES OF MAMMAL PALEONTOLOGY: THE DISCOVERIES OF THE AMERICANS IN MONGOLIA.) Fortschritte der Saeugetierpalaeontologie. Die Entdeckungen der Amerikaner in der Mongolei. W.O. Dietrich. Sitz. Gesell. Naturforsch.Freunde, pp.45-79, Oct. 20, 1928.

APPARENTLY NEW FAMILY OF AMBLYPOD MAMMALS FROM MONGOLIA. Walter Granger, William K. Gregory.Amer. Mus. Novitates, no.720, pp.1-8, figs.4, tbl., May 4, 1934.

MONGOLIAN MAMMALS OF THE "AGE OF REPTILES." William K. Gregory. Sci. Monthly, vol.24, pp.225-235, illus., Mar., 1927.

CRETACEOUS MAMMAL SKULLS FROM MONGOLIA. William K. Gregory, G. G. Simpson. Amer. Mus. Novitates, no.225, pp.20, illus., Oct. 8, 1926.

FAUNA AND CORRELATION OF THE GASHATO FORMATION OF MONGOLIA. W.D. Matthew, W. Granger. Amer. Mus. Novitates, no.189, pp.12, figs.14, Oct. 7, 1925.

MOST SIGNIFICANT FOSSIL FINDS OF THE MONGOLIAN EXPEDITION. W.D. Matthew, W. Granger. Nat. Hist., vol. 26, pp.532-534, Sep.-Oct., 1926.

NEW CREODONTS AND RODENTS FROM THE ARDYN OBO FORMATION OF MONGOLIA. W.D. Matthew, W.Granger. Amer. Mus. Novitates, no.193, pp.7, figs.9, Oct. 27, 1925.

NEW INSECTIVORES AND RUMINANTS FROM THE TERTIARY OF MONGOLIA, WITH REMARKS ON THE CORRELATION. W.D. Matthew, W.Granger. Amer. Mus. Novitates, no.105, pp.107, figs.1-3, Jan. 18, 1924.

NEW MAMMALS FROM THE IRDIN MANHA EOCENE OF MONGOLIA. W.D. Matthew, W. Granger. Amer. Mus. Novitates, no. 198, pp.10, illus., Nov. 21, 1925.

NEW MAMMALS FROM THE SHARA MURUN EOCENE OF MONGOLIA. W.D. Matthew, W. Granger. Amer. Mus. Novitates, no.196, pp.11, illus., Nov.20, 1925.

NEW UNGULATES FROM THE ARDYN OBO FORMATION OF MONGOLIA, WITH FAUNAL LIST AND REMARKS ON CORRELATION. W.D. Matthew, W.Granger. Amer. Mus. Novitates, no.195, pp.12, illus., Nov. 19, 1925.

ADDITIONS TO THE FAUNA OF THE GASHATO FORMATION OF MONGOLIA. W.D. Matthew, et al. Amer. Mus. Novitates, no.376, pp.12.

PALEOCENE MULTITUBERCULATES FROM MONGOLIA. W.D. Matthew, et al. Amer. Mus. Novitates, no.331, pp.4, Oct. 30,1928.

REVISED DETERMINATIONS OF SOME TERTIARY MAMMALS FROM MONGOLIA. Gerrit Smith Miller. Peking, Geological Survey of China, Palaeontologia Sinica, ser.C, vol.5, fasc.2, pp.3-20, 1927.

ANCIENT FAUNA OF MONGOLIA DISCOVERED BY THE THIRD ASIATIC EXPEDITION OF THE AMERICAN MUSEUM OF NATURAL HISTORY. Henry Fairfield Osborn. Science, n.s., vol.57, pp.729-732, June 29, 1923.

DISCOVERY OF CRETACEOUS AND OLDER TERTIARY IN MONGOLIA. Henry Fairfield Osborn. Science, n.s., vol.56, pp.291-293, Sep. 15, 1922.

EUDINOCERAS, UPPER EOCENE AMBLYPOD OF MONGOLIA. Henry Fairfield Osborn. Amer. Mus. Novitates, no.145, pp. 5, figs.2, Nov. 10, 1924.

SERRIDENTINUS AND BALUCHITHERIUM, LOH FORMATION, MONGOLIA. Henry Fairfield Osborn. Amer. Mus. Novitates, no.148, pp.5, figs.2, Nov. 11, 1924.

THREE NEW THEROPODA, PROTOCERATOPS ZONE, CENTRAL MONGOLIA. Henry Fairfield Osborn. Amer. Mus.Novitates, no.144, pp.12, figs.8, Nov. 7,1924.

TITANOTHERES AND LOPHIODONTS IN MONGOLIA. Henry Fairfield Osborn.Amer. Mus. Novitates, no.91, pp.5, figs.2, Oct. 17, 1923.

CORYPHODONTS AND UINTATHERES FROM THE MONGOLIAN EXPEDITION OF 1930. Henry Fairfield Osborn. Amer. Mus. Novitates, no.552, pp.16, figs.17, Aug. 17, 1932.

CORYPHODONTS OF MONGOLIA, EUDINOCERAS MONGOLIENSIS OSBORN, E. KHOLOBOLCHIENSIS SP. NOV. Henry Fairfield Osborn, W. Granger. Amer.Mus. Novitates, no.459, pp.13, figs.11, Mar.4, 1931.

PLATYBELODON GRANGERI, THREE GROWTH STAGES, AND A NEW SERRIDENTINE FROM MONGOLIA. Henry Fairfield Osborn. Amer. Mus.Novitates, no.537, pp.13, figs.8, June 9, 1932.

SUMMARY OF DISCOVERIES IN VERTEBRATE PALEONTOLOGY IN THREE SEASONS OF FIELD EXPLORATIONS IN MONGOLIA (1922-1923 AND 1925.) ABSTRACT. Henry Fairfield Osborn, W.D. Matthew. Bull. Geol. Soc. Amer., vol. 37, pp.157-158, Mar., 1926.

MONGOLIAN PALEONTOLOGICAL EXPEDITION OF THE ACADEMY OF SCIENCES OF THE USSR DICOVERED IN 1946-1949 ON THE TERRITORY OF MPR SOME RICH LOCALITIES OF FOSSIL VERTEBRATES OF CENOZOIC AGE.A.K. Rozhdestvensky. Vert.Palasiatica, vol.1, no.3, pp.169-183, Sep., 1957. (In Russian with English summary.)

FURTHER NOTES ON MONGOLIAN CRETACEOUS MAMMALS. George Gaylord Simpson. Amer. Mus. Novitates, no.329, pp.14, figs.7, 1928.

MESOZOIC MAMMAL SKULL FROM MONGOLIA. George Gaylord Simpson. Amer. Mus. Novitates, no.201, pp.11, figs.7, Nov. 24, 1925.

### Recent Mammals

MAMMALS OF CHINA AND MONGOLIA. Glover M. Allen. (In) Natural History of Central Asia, vol.xi, pt.1, pp.579-620, illus., maps, pls., American Museum of Natural History, New York, 1938; pt. 2, pp.621-1350, illus., maps, pls., 1940.

(Review by Wilfred H. Osgood of) MAMMALS OF CHINA AND MONGOLIA, PT. 1. Glover M. Allen. Jour. Mamm., vol.20, no.1, pp.113-114, Feb. 14, 1939.

IN MONGOLIA AND NORTH CHINA. (Collecting Mammals on the American Museum Asiatic Expedition.) Roy Chapman Andrews. Nat. Hist., vol.20, pp.356-373, Sep.-Oct., 1920.

LIVING ANIMALS OF THE GOBI DESERT. Roy Chapman Andrews. Nat. Hist., vol.24, pp.150-159, figs.9, Mar.-Apr., 1924.

(NOTES ON THE MAMMALS OF NORTH-EASTERN MONGOLIA ACCORDING TO THE COLLECTIONS OF THE MONGOLIAN EXPEDITION OF THE ACADEMY OF SCIENCES OF THE USSR IN 1928.) Anatol I. Argyropulo. Zeitschr.Aserbeidschaner Inst. Microbiol., vol.5, no.1, pp. 245-264, fig.1, 1935. (In Russian with German summary.)

(GEOGRAPHICAL DISTRIBUTION AND BIOLOGY OF THF WILD HORSE AND MONGOLIAN CAMEL.) Distribution geographique et biologie du cheval sauvage et du chameau de Mongolie (Equus przewalskii et Camelus bactrianus). A. G. Bannikov. Mammalia, Paris, vol.22, no. 1, pp.152-160, pls.6, Mar., 1958.

(ON THE MAMMALS OF NORTHERN MONGOLIA.) Ueber die Saeugetiere der Noerdlichen Mongolei. (Forty-four Forms Listed.) A.N. Formozow. Folia Zoologica et Hydrobiologica, vol.3, no.1, pp.41-78, June 13, 1931.

CAMP LIFE ON THE GOBI DESERT. INCIDENTS AND EXPERIENCES IN THE DAILY LIVES OF THE MEN OF THE AMERICAN MUSEUM CENTRAL ASIATIC EXPEDITIONS IN MONGOLIA. Walter Granger.Nat. Hist., vol.31, no.4, pp.359-373, illus., 1931.

APPARENTLY NEW FAMILY OF AMBLYPOD MAMMALS FROM MONGOLIA. Walter Granger, William K. Gregory. Amer. Mus. Novitates, no.720, pp.8, figs.4, May 4, 1934.

MONGOLIA THE NEW WORLD. William K. Gregory. Scientific Monthly, vol.24, pp.5-14, photos, Jan., 1927.

MONGOLIAN LIFE RECORD. William K. Gregory. Scientific Monthly, vol.24, pp. 169-181, Feb., 1927.

(ON SOME MAMMALS COLLECTED BY DR. HOLDERER IN THE SOUTHERN GOBI AND IN TIBET.) Ueber einige von Herrn Dr. Holderer in der suedlichen Gobi und in Tibet gesammelte Saeugetiere. Paul Matschie. Durch Asien, Berlin, Zoologie (Nachtrag), vol.3, no.5, pp.1-29, 1911.

DISCOVERIES DURING THE SEASON OF 1923 BY THE THIRD ASIATIC EXPEDITION IN MONGOLIA. Henry Fairfield Osborn. Proc. Nat. Acad. Sci., vol.10, no.1, pp. 23-24m Jan., 1924.

(OBSERVATIONS ON THE FLORA AND FAUNA OF MONGOLIA AND SINKIANG (CHINESE TURKESTAN).) Observations sur la flore et la faune de Mongolie et du Sin-Kiang (Turkestan Chinois). Andre Reymond. La Terre et la Vie, vol.4, no. 5, pp.288-296, illus., May, 1934.

MONGOLIAN MAMMAL NAMES. George Gaylord Simpson. Amer. Mus. Novitates, no.980, pp.1-26, May 11, 1938.

## NEOTROPICAL REGION

MAMMALS FROM SOUTHERN MEXICO AND CENTRAL SOUTH AMERICA. J.A. Allen. Bull. Amer. Mus. Nat. Hist., vol.20, pp.29-80, Feb. 29, 1904.

MAMMALS FROM MEXICO AND SOUTH AMERICA. H.E. Anthony. Amer. Mus. Novitates, no.54, pp.10, figs.2, Jan.17, 1923.

NEW RABBIT AND A NEW BAT FROM NEOTROPICAL REGIONS. H.E. Anthony. Bull. Amer. Mus. Nat. Hist., New York, vol. 37, pp.335-337, pls.34, 1917.

NEW RODENTS AND NEW BATS FROM NEOTROPICAL REGIONS. H.E.Anthony. Jour. Mamm., vol.1, no.2, pp.81-86, figs.1-4, Feb., 1920.

THREE NEW MAMMALS FROM CENTRAL AND SOUTH AMERICA. E.A. Goldman. Proc. Biol. Soc. Washington, vol.24, pp. 237-240, Nov. 28, 1911.

GEOGRAPHIC CLASSIFICATION OF NEOTROPICAL MAMMALS. Philip Hershkovitz. Chicago, Nat. Hist. Mus., Publication no. 845, pp.581-620, maps, tbls., 1958.(Fieldiana:Zoology, vol.36, no.6.)

DESCRIPTIONS OF FOUR NEW MAMMALS FROM TROPICAL AMERICA. N. Hollister. Proc. Biol. Soc. Washington, vol.27, pp. 141-144, July 10, 1914.

FOUR NEW MAMMALS FROM TROPICAL AMERICA. N. Hollister. Proc. Biol. Soc. Washington, vol.27, pp.103-106, May 11, 1914.

(EXPLANATIONS OF THE COMMUNICATIONS OF FRANC. HERNANDEZ ON THE QUADRUPEDS OF NEW SPAIN.) Erlaeuterungen der Nachrichten des Franc.Hernandez von den vierfuessigen Thieren Neuspaniens. Karl Martin Heinrich Lichtenstein. Abhandl. Akad. Wiss. Phys. Klasse, Berlin, pp.89-127, 1827.

FIVE NEW MAMMALS FROM TROPICAL AMERICA. Gerrit S. Miller, Jr. Proc.Biol. Soc. Washington, vol.26, pp.31-34, Feb. 8, 1913.

GEOGRAPHY OF MAMMALS. NO.III. THE NEOTROPICAL REGION. W.L. Sclater. Geogr. Jour., London, vol.5, no.5, pp.471-483, map, May, 1895.

DESCRIPTIONS OF NEW NEOTROPICAL MAMMALS. Oldfield Thomas. Ann. and Mag. Nat. Hist., ser.7, vol.4, no.22, pp.278-288, Oct., 1899; ser.7, vol.5, no. 26, pp.217-222, Feb., 1900; ser.7, vol.5, no.27, pp.269-274, Mar., 1900.

NEW FORMS OF SAIMIRI, SACCOPTERYX, BALANTIOPTERYX, AND THRICHOMYS FROM THE NEOTROPICAL REGION. Oldfield Thomas. Ann. and Mag. Nat. Hist., ser.7, vol.13, no.76, pp.250-255, Apr., 1904.

NEW MYOTIS, ARTIBEUS, SYLVILAGUS, AND METACHIRUS FROM CENTRAL AND SOUTH AMERICA. Oldfield Thomas. Ann. and Mag. Nat. Hist., ser.7, vol.7, no.42, pp.541-545, June, 1901.

NEW NEOTROPICAL CHROTOPTERUS, SCIURUS, NEACOMYS, COENDOU, PROECHIMYS, AND MARMOSA. Oldfield Thomas. Ann. and Mag. Nat. Hist., ser. 7, vol.16, no.93, pp.308-314, 1905.

NEW NEOTROPICAL MAMMALS, WITH A NOTE ON THE SPECIES OF REITHRODON. Oldfield Thomas. Ann. and Mag. Nat. Hist., ser.7, vol.8, no.45, pp.246-255, Sep., 1901.

NEW NEOTROPICAL MOLOSSUS, CONEPATUS, NECTOMYS, PROECHIMYS AND AGOUTI, WITH A NOTE ON THE GENUS MESOMYS. Oldfield Thomas. Ann. and Mag. Nat. Hist., ser.7, vol.15, no.90, pp.584-591, June, 1905.

NOTES ON NEOTROPICAL MAMMALS OF THE GENERA FELIS, HAPALE, ORYZOMYS, AKADON, AND CTENOMYS, WITH DESCRIPTIONS OF NEW SPECIES. Oldfield Thomas. Ann. and Mag. Nat. Hist., ser.7, vol.12, no.68, pp.234-243, Aug., 1903.

ON NEOTROPICAL MAMMALS OF THE GENERA CALLICEBUS (GRISON), REITHRODONTOMYS, CTENOMYS, DASYPUS, AND MARMOSA. Oldfield Thomas. Ann. and Mag. Nat. Hist., ser.7, vol.20, no. 116, pp.161-168, Aug., 1907.

ON NEW SMALL MAMMALS FROM THE NEOTROPICAL REGION. Oldfield Thomas. Ann. and Mag. Nat. Hist., ser.6, vol.18, no.106, pp.301-314, Oct., 1896.

ON TWO NEW NEOTROPICAL MAMMALS. Oldfield Thomas. Ann. and Mag. Nat.Hist., ser.6, vol.13, no.77, pp.436-439, May, 1894.

NEW GUINEA

WHAT I DID AND WHAT I SAW (NEW GUINEA). L.M. d'Albertis. London, vol.1, pp. iii-x, 1-424, figs., pls., 1880.

(Comments by A.Brazier Howell on) SOUTH NEW GUINEA EXPEDITION. Richard Archbold. Jour. Mamm., vol.17, no.2, p.195, May, 1936.

RESULTS OF THE ARCHBOLD EXPEDITIONS. NO.7. SUMMARY OF THE 1933-1934 PAPUAN EXPEDITION. Richard Archbold, A.L. Rand. Bull. Amer. Mus. Nat. Hist., New York, vol.68, art.8, pp.527-579, pls.29-46, Nov. 8, 1935.

WITH PLANE AND RADIO IN STONE AGE NEW GUINEA. Richard Archbold, A.L. Rand. Nat. Hist., New York, vol.40, no. 3, pp.566-576, illus., 1937.

RESULTS OF THE ARCHBOLD EXPEDITIONS, NO.41. SUMMARY OF THE 1938-1939 NEW GUINEA EXPEDITION. Richard Archbold, et al. Bull. Amer. Mus. Nat. Hist., New York, vol.79, no.3, pp.197-288, pls.35, maps 3, June 26, 1942.

RESULTS OF THE ARCHBOLD EXPEDITIONS, NO.75. SUMMARY OF THE FOURTH ARCHBOLD EXPEDITION TO NEW GUINEA (1953). L. J. Brass. Bull. Amer. Mus. Nat. Hist., vol.111, no.2, pp.77-152, pls.10-21, Sep. 17, 1956.

NEW MAMMALS FROM DUTCH NEW GUINEA. Guy Dollman. Proc. Zool. Soc. London, pt.4, pp.1082-1084, 1932.

ON MAMMALS OBTAINED BY MR. SHAW MAYER IN NEW GUINEA, AND PRESENTED TO THE BRITISH MUSEUM BY MR. J. SPEDAN LEWIS. Guy Dollman. Proc.Zool. Soc. London, pp.429-435, pls.1-4, Aug. 14, 1930.

(NOTES ON SOME NEW MAMMALS FROM NEW GUINEA.) Note sur quelques mammiferes nouveaux provenant de la Nouvelle-Guinée. Alphonse Milne Edwards. Comptes Rendus Acad. Sci. Paris, vol. 85, pp.1079-1081, 1877.

CATALOGUE OF THE MAMMALIA AND BIRDS OF NEW GUINEA, IN THE COLLECTION OF THE BRITISH MUSEUM. John Edward Gray, George Robert Gray. British Mus., Nat. Hist., London, Printed by Order of the Trustees, pp.63, illus., tbls., 1859.

(TWO NEW MARSUPIALS FROM GERMAN NEW GUINEA, AND AN ENUMERATION OF KNOWN PAPUAN MAMMALS.) Zwei neue Beutelthiere aus Deutsch Neu Guinea nebst einer Aufzaehlung der bekannten papuanischen Saeugethiere. K.M. Heller. Abhandl. Ber. K.Zool. Anthropol.Ethnoge. Mus. Dresden, 1896-1897, vol.6, no.8, pp.1-7, Feb. 27, 1897.

NOTES ON THE MAMMALS COLLECTED BY THE SWEDISH NEW GUINEA EXPEDITION 1948-1949. A.M. Husson. Nova Guinea, n.s., vol.6, pt.2, pp.283-306, pls.25-28, Dec. 15, 1955.

(TABLE OF THE DETERMINATION OF LAND MAMMALS OF NETHERLANDS NEW GUINEA.) Tabel voor het determineren van de landzoogdieren van Nederlands Nieuw-Guinea. A.M. Husson. Zool. Bijdr. Rijksmus. Nat. Hist. Leiden, no. 1, pp.1-35, illus., Nov. 7, 1955.

MAMMALS COLLECTED BY THE DUTCH NEW GUINEA EXPEDITIONS 1907. F. A. Jentink. Nova Guinea, vol.9, pp.1-14, pl.1, 1907?

MAMMALS COLLECTED BY THE DUTCH NEW GUINEA EXPEDITION 1909-1910. F.A. Jentink. Nova Guinea, Résultats de l'Expedition Scientifique Néerlandaise a la Nouvelle-Guinee, Zool. vol.9, no.2, pp. 165-183, pls.7, Leiden, 1911.

NEW AND INTERESTING MAMMALS OF DUTCH NEW GUINEA EXPEDITION TO THE SNOW-MOUNTAINS. F.A. Jentink. Notes Leyden Museum, vol.33, pp. 233-238, 1911.

MAMMALS COLLECTED BY MR. SHAW MAYER IN NEW GUINEA 1932-1949. Eleanor M.O. Laurie. Bull. British Mus., Nat. Hist., London, Zoology, vol.1, no. 10, pp.269-318, Dec., 1952.

LIST OF LAND MAMMALS OF NEW GUINEA, CELEBES AND ADJACENT ISLANDS. 1758-1952. (With Descriptions of Two New Subgenera by J.R. Ellerman.) Eleanor M. O. Laurie. British Mus., Nat. Hist., London, pp.175, pls.3, June 30, 1954.

(REPORT ON THE LAND, INHABITANTS, AND PRODUCTS OF SOME VILLAGES ON THE NEW GUINEA COAST.) Verslag van het land, de bewoners en voortbrengselen van eenigen plaatsen op de kust van Nieuw Guinea. H. Macklot. Bijdr.Nat.Wet., vol.5, pp.142-182, 1830.

(ZOOLOGY OF NEW GUINEA.) Tierwelt Neu-Guineas. Paul Matschie. (In) M.Krieger, Neu-Guinea. Bibliothek der Laenderkunde, Berlin, Bd.5-6, pp.73-112, illus., 1899.

NOTES ON ZOOLOGY OF THE MACLAY-COAST IN NEW GUINEA. N. de Miklouho-Maclay. Proc. Linn. Soc. New S. Wales, vol.9, pp.713-720, pl.38, 1884.

(ADDITIONS TO KNOWLEDGE OF NEW GUINEA.) Bijdragen tot de kennis van Nieuw-Guinea. S. Mueller. Earste afdeeling. Physische gesteldheid, in C.J.Temminck, Verh. Nat. Gesch. Overz.Bezitt, Land- en Volkenkunde, pp.13-30, 1840.

(DIAGNOSIS OF THREE NEW MAMMALS OF NEW GUINEA AND KEY ISLANDS.) Dianosi di tre nuovi mammiferi della nuova Guinea ed isole key. W. Peters. Ann. del Mus. Civ. di St. Nat. di Genova., vol.6, p.303, 1874.

(ENUMERATION OF MAMMALS COLLECTED IN NEW GUINEA.) Enumerazione dei Mammiferi Raccolti nella Nuova Guinea. W. Peters, G. Doria. Ann. del Mus. Civ. di St. Nat. di Gen., vol.16, pp.29-31, Marzo, 1881.

(ENUMERATION OF MAMMALS COLLECTED BY O. BECCARI, L.M. D'ALBERTS AND A.A. BRUIJN IN NEW GUINEA.)Enumerazione dei mammiferi raccolti da O. Beccari, L.M. d'Alberts ed A.A. Bruijn nella Nuova Guinea propriamente detta. W. Peters, G. Doria. Ann. Mus. Civ. Stor. Nat. Genova, vol.16, pp.665-707, pls.5-18, 1881.

RESULTS OF THE ARCHBOLD EXPEDITIONS. NO.29. SUMMARY OF THE 1936-1937 NEW GUINEA EXPEDITION. A.L. Rand, L.J. Brass. Bull. Amer. Mus. Nat. Hist., New York, vol.77, art.7, pp.341-380, pls.21-42, Nov. 29, 1940.

NEW MAMMALS FROM DUTCH NEW GUINEA. Lord Rothschild, Guy Dollman. Proc. Zool. Soc. London, pt.3, pp.1082-1084, Sep. 10, 1932.

ON MAMMALS COLLECTED IN DUTCH NEW GUINEA BY MR. F. SHAW MAYER IN 1930. Lord Rothschild, Guy Dollman. Proc. Zool. Soc. London, pt.1, pp.211-219, pls.1-4, Mar. 31, 1933.

(FURTHER REMARKS ON THE SYSTEMATICS OF PAPUAN MAMMALS.) Weitere Mitteilungen sur Systematik papuanischer Saeuger. Georg Stein. Zeitschr.f. Saeugetierk., Berlin, vol.8, nos.1-2, pp.87-95, pl.14, Apr. 24, 1933.

(NOTES ON THE BIOLOGY OF PAPUAN MAMMALS.) Notizen zur Biologie papuanischer Saeuger. Georg Stein. Zeitschr. f. Saeugetierk., Berlin, vol.8, nos.1-2, pp.123-126, Apr.24, 1933.

LIST OF THE MAMMALS OF THE JAPANESE WAR AREA. PT.1. NEW GUINEA AND EASTWARD. G.H.H. Tate. Amer. Mus. Nat. Hist., New York, pp.22, 1944.

RESULTS OF THE ARCHBOLD EXPEDITIONS, NO.4. AN APPARENTLY NEW RACE OF WALLABIES FROM SOUTHERN NEW GUINEA. G.H.H. Tate, Richard Archbold. Amer. Mus. Novitates, no.804, pp.2, May 21, 1935.

RESULTS OF THE ARCHBOLD EXPEDITIONS, NO.31. NEW RODENTS AND MARSUPIALS FROM NEW GUINEA. G.H.H. Tate. Amer. Mus. Novitates, no.1101, pp. 9, Jan. 30, 1941.

NEW MAMMALS FROM BRITISH NEW GUINEA. Oldfield Thomas. Proc. Zool. Soc. London, pp.196-202, pl.23, Apr.1, 1904 (Nov. 3, 1903).

NEW MAMMALS FROM NEW GUINEA AND NEIGHBORING ISLANDS. Oldfield Thomas. Ann. and Mag. Nat. Hist., ser. 9, vol.9, pp.261-265, Mar., 1922.

NEW SMALL MAMMALS FROM NEW GUINEA. Oldfield Thomas. Ann. and Mag. Nat. Hist., ser.9, vol.6, no.36, pp.533-537, Dec., 1920.

ON MAMMALS COLLECTED BY C. KEYSSER IN THE SARUWAGED AND RAWLINSON MOUNTAINS REGION OF N. E. NEW GUINEA. Oldfield Thomas. Ann. and Mag. Nat. Hist., ser.9, vol.9, no.54, pp.669-676, June, 1922.

ON NEW MAMMALS OBTAINED BY THE UTAKWA EXPEDITION TO DUTCH NEW GUINEA. Oldfield Thomas. Ann. and Mag. Nat. Hist., ser.8, vol.12, no.68, pp.205-212, Aug., 1913.

ON THREE NEW MAMMALS FROM BRITISH NEW GUINEA. Oldfield Thomas. Ann. and Mag. Nat. Hist., ser.7, vol.20, no.115, pp.70-74, July, 1907.

REPORT ON THE MAMMALS COLLECTED BY THE BRITISH ORNITHOLOGIST'S UNION EXPEDITION AND THE WOLLASTON EXPEDITION TO DUTCH NEW GUINEA. Oldfield Thomas. Trans. Zool. Soc. London, vol.20, pt.9, pp.315-324, May, 1914.

THREE NEW MAMMALS FROM DUTCH NEW GUINEA. Oldfield Thomas. Ann. and Mag. Nat. Hist., ser.8, vol.7, no.40, pp.384-387, Apr., 1911.

DESCRIPTIONS OF SOME NEW GUINEA MAMMALS. E. Throughton. Records Australian Museum, vol.20, no.2, pp.117-127, Aug. 27, 1937.

FURRED ANIMALS OF NEW GUINEA. E. Troughton. Australian Mus. Mag., Sydney, vol.8, no.3, pp.82-90, illus., Mar. 30, 1943.

POST MORTEM STUDIES OF SOME MAMMALS OF THE HOLLANDIA AREA, NETHERLANDS NEW GUINEA. Donald B. Vogtman, Wm.D. Fitzwater, Jr. Jour. Mamm., vol.32, no.2, pp.211-215, May 21, 1951.

(OBSERVATIONS OF MAMMALS OF NEW GUINEA.) Beobachtungen an Saeugetieren aus Neu-Guinea. Rudolf Zimara. Anzeiger Akad. Wiss., Wien, Math.Naturwiss.Kl., vol.74, pp.35-36, 1937.

## NEW ZEALAND

MAMMALS. H.L. Botting. Wellington, School Publications Branch, New Zealnd Education Dept., (Primary School Bull.) pp.31, illus.

GAME ANIMALS OF NEW ZEALAND; AN ACCOUNT OF THEIR INTRODUCTION, ACCLIMATIZATION, AND DEVELOPMENT. T.E. Donne. London, J.Murray, pp.xviii-322, pls., fold.map, 1924.

LETTER FROM, CONTAINING REMARKS ON A LETTER OF DR. HAAST. George Grey. Proc. Zool. Soc. London, pp.116-117, 1870.

LIST OF SEALS, WHALES, AND DOLPHINS OF NEW ZEALAND. J.E. Gray. Trans. New Zealand Inst., vol.6, pp.87-89, 1874.

ECOLOGY OF RABBITS IN NEW ZEALAND COMPARED WITH CALIFORNIA RODENTS. Walter E. Howard. Proc. New Zealand Ecol. Soc., no.5, pp.13-14, Dec., 1957.

(THE "WAITOREKI", AN APPARENTLY NEW MAMMAL OF NEW ZEALAND.) Das "Waitoreki", ein angeblich neues Saeugetier von Neuseeland. Ingo Krumbiegel. Zeitschr.f. Saeugetierk., vol.18, no.2, pp.110-115, Sep. 28, 1952.

BIG GAME IN NEW ZEALAND. THE HOME OF SCOTTISH DEER AND HIMALAYAN THAR. (Lord) Latymer. Field, London, vol.163, no.4247, pp.1149-1150, illus., May 19, 1934.

IMPACT OF MAN UPON NATURE IN NEW ZEALAND. Robert Cushman Murphy. Proc. Amer. Philos. Soc., Philadelphia, vol.95, no.6, pp.569-582, illus., Dec. 21, 1951.

PRELIMINARY REPORTS OF THE NEW ZEALAND-AMERICAN FIORDLAND EXPEDITION INVESTIGATIONS IN FIORDLAND, NEW ZEALAND, IN 1949. A.J. Poole, et al. Bull. New Zealand Dept. Sci. and Industrial Research, Wellington, no.103, pp.99, illus., map, 1951. (Articles dealing with mammals: Introduction, by A.L. Poole; Establishment of red deer in Fiordland, by B. Wisely and R. I. Kean; Distribution and numbers of wapiti, by O.J. Murie; Distribution of red deer, by O.J.Murie; Environmental aajustments and mortality of wapiti, by O.J. Murie; Collecting in the field, by B. Wisely and R.I.Kean; Hybridization, by O.J. Murie; Parasites of the wapiti, compiled from notes of L.J.Dumbleton and P.C. Bull; Deer and the vegetation: Field evidence, by A.L.Poole and J.T. Holloway; Deer stomach-contents, by R.Mason;Comparison of food habits of wapiti in New Zealand and in America, by O.J.Murie; Carrying capacity of Fiordland, by R.I.Kean; Summary and recommendation for the management of wapiti, by O.J. Murie; The small mammals of the Caswell and George Sounds area, by K.A. Wodzicki and P.C.Bull.)

IDENTIFICATION OF BIG GAME ANIMALS IN NEW ZEALAND. Thane Riney. Dominion Mus.Handbook, Wellington, no.4, pp.26, illus., Feb., 1955.

NEW ZEALAND WILDLIFE PROBLEMS AND STATUS OF WILDLIFE RESEARCH. Thane Riney. New Zealand Sci. Rev., Wellington, vol.10, no.3, pp.26-32, 1952.

WILD LIFE IN NEW ZEALAND. PART 1. MAMMALIA. George M. Thomson. New Zealand Board of Sci. and Art, Manual no. 2, pp.112, illus., 1921.

INTERIM REPORT ON WILD LIFE PROBLEMS IN NEW ZEALAND. Kasimierz Wodzicki. Dept. Sci. and Indus.Research, Wellington, Wildlife Sec.Rept. no.1, vols. 3, pp.244, illus., Dec., 1947.

INTRODUCED MAMMALS OF NEW ZEALAND. AN ECOLOGICAL AND ECONOMIC SURVEY. Kasimierz Wodzicki. Bull. Dept. Sci. and Indus.Research, Wellington, no. 98, pp.x+255, illus., 1950.

(Review by W.J.Hamilton Jr. of) INTRODUCED MAMMALS OF NEW ZEALAND. Kasimierz Wodzicki. Jour. Wildl.Mgt., Ithaca, vol.16, no.3, pp.382-383, July, 1952.

SMALL MAMMALS OF THE CASWELL AND GEORGE SOUNDS AREA. Kasimierz Wodzicki, P.C. Bull. New Zealand-American Fiordland Expedition, Dept. Sci. and Indus. Research Bull. no.103, pp. 1-8, 1951.

ANIMALS IN NEW ZEALAND FORESTS. G.F. Yerex. Forest and Bird, Wellington, no.94, pp.12-13, Nov., 1949.

HOW GAME HAS PROSPERED IN NEW ZELAND. MOOSE, WAPITI, AND SCOTCH SALMON. Field, London, vol.155, Empire Suppl., pp.7, 17, May 24, 1930.

## NICARAGUA

MAMMALS. G.M.Allen. (In) Vertebrates from the Corn Islands (Off Nicaragua). Bull. Mus. Comp.Zool. Harvard, vol.69, no.7, pp.129-130, Apr., 1929.

ADDITIONAL MAMMALS FROM NICARAGUA. J.A. Allen. Bull. Amer. Mus. Nat. Hist., vol.28, pp.87-115, Apr. 30, 1910.

MAMMALS FROM NICARAGUA. J.A. Allen. Bull. Amer. Mus. Nat. Hist., vol. 24, pp.647-670, text figs.1-12, Oct. 13, 1908.

## NORTH AMERICA

### Extinct and Fossil Mammals

FURTHER ADVENTURES OF THE AMERICAN MEN OF THE DRAGON BONES. Roy Chapman Andrews. Nat. Hist., vol.29, no.2, pp.114-128, 1929.

ARDYNOMYS AND DESMATOLAGUS IN THE NORTH AMERICAN OLIGOCENE. J.J. Burke. Ann. Carnegie Mus., vol.25, pp.135-154, figs.7, Dec. 12, 1936.

AFTONIAN AGE OF THE AFTONIAN MAMMALIAN FAUNA. Samuel Calvin. Iowa Acad. of Sci. Proc., vol.17, pp. 177-180, Des Moines, 1910.

MASTODON AND EARLY MAN IN AMERICA. Loren C. Eiseley. Science, Lancaster, n.s., vol.102, no.2640, pp.108-110, Aug. 3, 1945.

NOTES ON PALEOCENE AND LOWER EOCENE MAMMAL HORIZONS OF NORTHERN NEW MEXICO AND SOUTHERN COLORADO. Walter Granger. Bull. Amer. Mus. Nat. Hist., New York, vol. 37, art.32, pp.821-830, fig.1, pls.97-98, Dec. 5, 1917.

STUDIES OF TERTIARY AND QUATERNARY MAMMALS OF NORTH AMERICA. E.R. Hall. Washington, Carnegie Inst. of Washington, pp.119, illus., map, pls., diagr., 1936.

A CENSUS OF THE FOSSIL VERTEBRATA OF NORTH AMERICA. Oliver P. Hay. Science, n.s., vol.10, no.254, pp.681-684, Nov. 10, 1899.

CONTRIBUTION TO THE KNOWLEDGE OF THE MAMMALS OF THE PLEISTOCENE OF NORTH AMERICA. Oliver P. Hay. U.S. Nat. Mus., Proc., Washington, vol.48, pp.515-575, illus., pls.30-37, 1915.

ON THE NAMES OF CERTAIN NORTH AMERICAN FOSSIL VERTEBRATES. Oliver P. Hay. Science, n.s., vol.9, no. 225, pp.593-594, Apr. 21, 1899.

PLEISTOCENE OF NORTH AMERICA AND ITS VERTEBRATED ANIMALS FROM THE STATES EAST OF THE MISSISSIPPI RIVER AND FROM THE CANADIAN PROVINCES EAST OF LONGITUDE 95°. Oliver P. Hay. Publ. 322 Carnegie Inst. Washington, pp. i-viii, 1-499, pls.41, figs.25, Feb., 1923.

PLEISTOCENE OF THE MIDDLE REGION OF NORTH AMERICA AND ITS VERTEBRATED ANIMALS. Oliver P. Hay. Carnegie Inst. Washington, publ.322A, pp.1-385, pls.1-29, Oct. 15, 1924.

REVISION OF THE PLEISTOCENE PERIOD IN NORTH AMERICA, BASED ESPECIALLY ON GLACIAL GEOLOGY AND VERTEBRATE PALEONTOLOGY. Oliver P. Hay. Jour. Wash. Acad. Sci., vol.15, no.6, pp. 126-133, Mar. 19, 1925.

SECOND BIBLIOGRAPHY AND CATALOGUE OF THE FOSSIL VERTEBRATA OF NORTH AMERICA. Oliver P. Hay. Carnegie Inst. of Wash., publ.no.390, vol.1, pp.916, Aug., 1929; vol.2, pp. 1074, Jan. 27, 1930.

(Review by Gerrit S. Miller, Jr. of) SECOND BIBLIOGRAPHY AND CATALOGUE OF THE FOSSIL VERTEBRATA OF NORTH AMERICA. Oliver P. Hay. Jour. Mamm., Baltimore, vol.11, no.2, pp.246-247, May 9, 1930.

PLEISTOCENE VERTEBRATE PALEONTOLOGY IN NORTH AMERICA. Claude W. Hibbard. Bull. Geol. Soc. Amer., vol.60, pp.1417-1428, figs.2, Sep., 1949.

SUMMARY OF NORTH AMERICAN PLEISTOCENE MAMMALIAN LOCAL FAUNAS. Claude W. Hibbard. Papers Michigan Acad. Sci., Arts and Letters, vol.43, for 1957, pp.3-32, Mar. 20, 1958.

MEN AND ELEPHANTS IN AMERICA. Ludwell H. Johnson, III. Scientific Monthly, Lancaster, vol.75, no.4, pp.215-221, illus., Oct., 1952.

ADDITIONS TO THE TERTIARY HISTORY OF THE PELAGIC MAMMALS ON THE PACIFIC COAST OF NORTH AMERICA. Remington Kellogg. Washington, Carnegie Inst. of Wash., pp.iii-120, illus., pls. 14, 1925.

AMERICAN INDIAN DISCOVERIES OF VERTEBRATE FOSSILS. E.M. Kindle. Jour.Paleont., vol.9, no.5, pp.449-452, July, 1935.

EXTINCT MAMMALIAN FAUNA OF DAKOTA AND NEBRASKA. (Including an Account of Some Allied Forms From Other Localities, Together With a Synopsis of the Mammalian Remains of North America. Preceded With An Introduction On the Geology of the Tertiary Formations of Dakota and Nebraska, Accompanied With a Map.)Joseph Leidy. Philadelphia, F.V.Hayden, pp.vii-478, col.map, pls.30, 1869. ( Jour. of the Acad. of Nat.Sci. of Philadelphia, vol.vii-second series.)

EARLY FOSSIL HUNTING IN THE ROCKY MOUNTAINS. R.S. Lull. Nat. Hist., vol. 26, pp.455-461, Sep.-Oct., 1926.

TYPICAL ORNITHOPODA OF THE AMERICAN JURASSIC. O.C. Marsh. Amer. Jour. Sci., vol.48, pp.85-90, pls.4-7, July, 1894.

PLEISTOCENE HISTORY OF TEMPERATE BIOTAS IN MEXICO AND EASTERN UNITED STATES. Paul S. Martin, Bryon E. Harrell. Ecology, vol.38, no.3, pp.468-480, illus., July, 1957.

FAUNAL LIST OF THE TERTIARY MAMMALIA OF THE WEST. William Diller Matthew. Dept. Interior, U.S.Geological Survey, bull.361, pp.91-138, 1909.

RELATIONSHIPS OF PLIOCENE MAMMALIAN FAUNAS FROM THE PACIFIC COAST AND GREAT BASIN PROVINCES OF NORTH AMERICA. John C.Merriam. Berkeley, Univ. of Calif. Press, Bull. of the Dept. of Geology, vol.10, no.22, pp.421-443, map, 1917.

AMERICAN EOCENE PRIMATES, AND THE SUPPOSED RODENT FAMILY MIXODECTIDAE. Henry Fairfield Osborn. Bull. Amer. Mus. Nat. Hist., New York, vol.16, art.17, pp.169-214, figs.40, June 28, 1902.

CENOZOIC MAMMAL HORIZONS OF WESTERN NORTH AMERICA. Henry Fairfield Osborn. (With Faunal Lists of the Tertiary Mammalia of the West.) Washington Govt. Print.Off., U.S.Geol. Survey, Bull.361, pp.138, illus., pls.3, maps 2, 1909.

CLOSE OF THE CRETACEOUS AND OPENING OF EOCENE TIME IN NORTH AMERICA. Henry Fairfield Osborn. Bull. Geol. Soc. Amer., Wash., D.C., vol.25, no.3, pp.321-323, Sep. 15, 1914.

THE RISE OF THE MAMMALIA IN NORTH AMERICA. Henry Fairfield Osborn. Boston, Ginn and Co., New York, G.E.Stechert, pp.45, illus., pl., 1893. (Studies from the Biological Laboratories of Columbia College, Zoology, vol.1, no.2.)

TERTIARY MAMMAL HORIZONS OF NORTH AMERICA. Henry Fairfield Osborn. Bull. Amer. Mus. Nat. Hist., New York, vol.23, art.11, pp.237-253, figs.2, Mar. 30, 1907.

SOME FOSSORIAL MAMMALS FROM THE TERTIARY OF WESTERN NORTH AMERICA. Charles A. Reed. Jour.Paleontol., vol. 28, no.1, pp.102-111, illus., Jan., 1954.

DEVELOPMENT OF AMERICAN PALAEONTOLOGY. (History of Vertebrate Palaeontology in North America.) W.B. Scott. Proc. Amer. Phil. Soc., vol.66, pp.409-427, 1927.

EARLY MAN IN AMERICA. (Lists extinct mammals found with man.) E.H. Sellards. Univ. Texas Press, Austin, pp.211, illus., 1952.

AMERICAN MESOZOIC MAMMALIA. George Gaylord Simpson. New Haven, Yale Univ. Press, London, H.Milford, Oxford Univ. Press, (Memoirs of the Peabody Mus. of Yale Univ., vol.3, pt.1,) pp.xv-235, illus., maps, pls., 1929.

(Review by Remington Kellogg of) AMERICAN MESOZOIC MAMMALIA. George Gaylord Simpson. Jour. Mamm., vol.11, no.2, pp.245-246, May, 1930.

DISCOVERY OF FOSSIL VERTEBRATES IN NORTH AMERICA. George Gaylord Simpson. Jour. Paleontol., Menasha, vol.17, no.1, pp.26-38, figs.2, Jan., 1943.

GLOSSARY AND CORRELATION CHARTS OF NORTH AMERICAN TERTIARY MAMMAL-BEARING FORMATIONS. George Gaylord Simpson. Bull. Amer. Mus. Nat. Hist., New York, vol.67, art.3, pp.79-121, figs.8, Nov. 25, 1933.

MESOZOIC MAMMALIA. PART I. AMERICAN TRICONODONTS. George Gaylord Simpson. Amer. Jour. Sci., vol.10, no.56, pp. 145-165, illus., Aug., 1925. PART II. AMERICAN TRICONODONTS. Amer. Jour. Sci., vol.10, no. 58, pp.334-358, illus., Oct., 1925.

SUCCESSION OF NORTH AMERICAN CONTINENTAL PLIOCENE MAMMALIAN FAUNAS. R.A. Stirton. Pan-Amer.Geol., Des Moines, vol.64, no.1, p.78, Aug., 1935; Amer. Jour. Sci., ser.5, vol.32, no.189, pp.161-206, Sep., 1936.

DISCOVERY OF UPPER EOCENE LAND MAMMALS ON THE PACIFIC COAST. Chester Stock. Science, n.s., vol.74, no.1927, pp.577-578, Dec. 4, 1931.

EOCENE LAND MAMMALS ON THE PACIFIC COAST. Chester Stock. Proc. Nat. Acad. Sci., vol.18, no.7, pp.518-523, figs.4, July, 1932.

PUSHING BACK THE HISTORY OF LAND MAMMALS IN WESTERN NORTH AMERICA. Chester Stock. Bull. Geol. Soc. America, vol.59, no.4, pp.327-332, figs. 3, Apr., 1948.

SUCCESSION OF MAMMALIAN FORMS WITHIN THE PERIOD IN WHICH HUMAN REMAINS ARE KNOWN TO OCCUR IN AMERICA. Chester Stock. Amer. Nat., vol.70, no.729, pp.324-331, July-Aug., 1936.

GEOLOGICAL BACKGROUND OF THE FAUNA OF NORTH AMERICA. M.Y. Williams. Murrelet, Seattle, vol.23, no. 1, pp.3-4, May 14, 1942.

(Review by O.P.Hay of) AMERICAN PERMIAN VERTEBRATES. S.W. Williston. Amer. Nat., vol.46, no.549, pp.561-565, Sep., 1912.

SOME TERTIARY MAMMALS AND BIRDS FROM NORTH AMERICA. Robert W. Wilson, et al. Washington, Carnegie Inst. of Wash., Publ.no.584, pp.iii-244, illus., 1949.

NOMENCLATURE AND CORRELATION OF THE NORTH AMERICAN CONTINENTAL TERTIARY. Horace E. Wood, 2nd, et al. Bull. Geol. Soc. Amer., New York, vol. 52, pp.1-48, pl.1, Jan. 1, 1941.

Recent Mammals

VANISHING AMERICANS. (Grizzly Bear, Woodland Caribou.) Jacob Bates Abbott. Pennsylvania Game News, Harrisburg, vol.17, no.1, pp.6-7, 30, illus., Apr., 1946; South Dakota Conserv. Digest, Pierre, vol.13, no.7, pp.12-13, July, 1946.

SUGGESTIONS FOR RESEARCH ON NORTH AMERICAN BIG GAME AND FUR-BEARING ANIMALS. Charles C. Adams. Roosevelt Wild Life Bull., vol.1, no.1, pp.35-41, Dec., 1921.

DESCRIPTIONS OF FIVE NEW NORTH AMERICAN MAMMALS. J.A. Allen. Bull. Amer. Mus. Nat. Hist., vol.6, pp.347-350, Dec. 7, 1894.

DESCRIPTIONS OF NEW AMERICAN MAMMALS. J.A. Allen. Bull. Amer. Mus. Nat. Hist., New York, vol.7, pp.327-340, 1895.

DESCRIPTIONS OF TEN NEW NORTH AMERICAN MAMMALS, AND REMARKS ON OTHERS. J.A. Allen. Bull. Amer. Mus. Nat. Hist., New York, vol.6, pp.317-332, 1894.

GEOGRAPHICAL DISTRIBUTION OF NORTH AMERICA MAMMALS. J. A. Allen. Bull. Amer. Mus. Nat. Hist., New York, vol.4, pp.199-243, pls.5-7, fold.maps, 1892. (Read before the New York Acad. of Sci., Jan. 26, 1891. In revising for publication some new matter has been added.)

LIST OF MAMMALS COLLECTED BY J. H. BATTY IN NEW MEXICO AND DURANGO, WITH DESCRIPTIONS OF NEW SPECIES AND SUBSPECIES. J.A. Allen. Bull.Amer. Mus. Nat. Hist., New York, vol.19, pp. 587-612, Nov. 13, 1903.

MAMMALS COLLECTED IN ALASKA AND NORTHERN BRITISH COLUMBIA BY THE ANDREW J. STONE EXPEDITION OF 1902. J.A. Allen. Bull. Amer. Mus. Nat. Hist., New York, vol.19, art.xxi, pp.521-567, 1903.

MILLER'S KEY TO THE LAND MAMMALS OF EASTERN NORTH AMERICA. J. A. Allen. Amer. Nat., vol.35, pp.59-61, Jan., 1901.

NOTES ON NEW OR LITTLE-KNOWN NORTH AMERICAN MAMMALS, BASED ON RECENT ADDITIONS TO THE COLLECTION OF MAMMALS IN THE AMERICAN MUSEUM OF NATURAL HISTORY. J.A. Allen. Bull. Amer. Mus. Nat. Hist., New York, vol.3, pp.263-310, illus., 1891.

ON A COLLECTION OF MAMMALS FROM ARIZONA AND MEXICO, MADE BY MR. W. W. PRICE, WITH FIELD NOTES BY THE COLLECTOR. J.A. Allen. Bull. Amer. Mus. Nat. Hist., New York, vol.7, pp.193-258, illus., 1895.

ON A COLLECTION OF MAMMALS FROM SOUTHERN TEXAS AND NORTHEASTERN MEXICO. J. A. Allen. Bull. Amer. Mus. Nat. Hist., New York, vol.3, pp.219-228, 1891.

RECENT WORK IN NORTH AMERICAN MAMMALOGY. J.A. Allen. Trans.New York Acad. Sci., vol.10, no.5, pp.71-85, 1891.

REMARKS ON A SECOND COLLECTION OF MAMMALS FROM NEW BRUNSWICK, AND ON THE REDISCOVERY OF THE GENUS NEOTOMA IN NEW YORK STATE. J.A. Allen. Bull. Amer. Mus. Nat. Hist., New York, vol.6, pp.359-364, 1894.

SOME RESULTS OF A NATURAL HISTORY JOURNEY TO NORTHERN BRITISH COLUMBIA, ALASKA, AND THE NORTHWEST TERRITORY, IN THE INTEREST OF THE AMERICAN MUSEUM OF NATURAL HISTORY. J.A. Allen. Bull.Amer. Mus. Nat. Hist., New York, vol.13, pp. 31-62, Apr. 6, 1900.

DISTRIBUTION, ABUNDANCE, AND ECONOMIC IMPORTANCE OF THE GAME AND FURBEARING MAMMALS OF WESTERN NORTH AMERICA. R.M. Anderson. Proc. 5th Pacific Science Congress, Victoria and Vancouver, B.C., 1933, Univ. of Toronto Press, pp.4055-4073, maps 13, 1934.

ANIMALS OF AMERICA, "MAMMALS OF AMERICA". H.E. Anthony. Garden City, New York, Garden City Publishing Co., Inc., pp.xxiii-335, illus., maps, col.pls., diagrs., 1937.

DESCRIPTION AND DISTRIBUTION. (Wapiti, Moose, Pronghorn, Muskox, Walrus.) HORNS AND ANTLERS. H.E. Anthony. (In) North American Big Game. A book of the Boone and Crockett Club, compiled by the Committee on Records of North American Big Game. New York, Charles Scribners Sons, pp.225-237, 1939.

FIELD BOOK OF NORTH AMERICAN MAMMALS. (Descriptions of Every Mammal Known North of the Rio Grande, Together With Brief Accounts of Habits, Geographical Ranges, etc.) H.E. Anthony. New York, London, G.P. Putnam's Sons, pp.xxv-625, illus., pls.(part col.), maps, 1928.

(Review by Hartley H.T. Jackson of) FIELD BOOK OF NORTH AMERICAN MAMMALS. H.E. Anthony. Jour. Mamm., vol.9, no.3, p.257, Aug., 1928.

MAMMALS OF AMERICA. H.E. Anthony. New York, The Univ. Society Inc., pp.xxii-335, illus., maps, pls., diagrs., 1917. (Nature Lover's Library, vol.4.)

AUDUBON'S ANIMALS: THE QUADRUPEDS OF NORTH AMERICA. John James Audubon. New York, Studio Publications in Assoc. with Crowell, pp.222, illus.(part col.), 1951. (Originally Published Under Title: The Viviparous Quadrupeds of North America.)

FAVORITE ANIMALS OF AMERICA. John James Audubon. New York, Grosset and Dunlap, illus., 1951. (Engravings Selected from J.J. Audubon's The Viviparous Quadrupeds of North America.)

QUADRUPEDS OF NORTH AMERICA. (First Issued (1845-1848) as "The Viviparous Quadrupeds of North America" in 3 folio vols. containing 150 pls. and a separate text (1846-1853) of 3 quarto vols.;combined as "The Quadrupeds of North America" of 3 royal octavo vols.) John James Audubon, J. Bachman. New York, V.G. Audubon, vols.3, pls.155.

THE VIVIPAROUS QUADRUPEDS OF NORTH AMERICA. John James Audubon, J.Bachman. New York, 1845.

MAXIMILIAN'S TRAVELS IN THE INTERIOR OF NORTH AMERICA, 1832 TO 1834. Vernon Bailey. Nat. Hist., vol.23, pp.337-343, figs. 4, July-Aug., 1923.

CATALOGUE OF NORTH AMERICAN MAMMALS, CHIEFLY IN THE MUSEUM OF THE SMITHSONIAN INSTITUTION. Spencer F. Baird. Washington, Smiths. Inst., Publication 105, pp.21, 1857. Reprinted from U.S. War Dept. Rep.of Explorations and Surveys for a Railroad from the Mississippi River to the Pacific Ocean, vol.8, pp.xix-xlviii.

MAMMALS OF NORTH AMERICA. (The Descriptions of Species Based Chiefly on the Collections in the Museum of the Smiths. Inst.) Spencer F. Baird. Philadelphia, J.B. Lippincott and Co., Parts I-III, pp.764, illus.(part col.), 1857-59.

MAMMALS TAKEN ALONG THE ALASKAN HIGHWAY. Rollin H. Baker. Univ. Kansas Publ., Mus. Nat. Hist., Lawrence, vol.5, no.9, pp.87-117, Nov. 28, 1951.

FAMILIAR ANIMALS OF AMERICA. Will. Barker. New York, Harper, pp.300, illus., 1956.

PETER KALM'S TRAVELS IN NORTH AMERICA. (The English Version of 1770, With a Translation of New Material From Kalm's Diary Notes.) (Travels in Pennsylvania, New York, New Jersey, and Southern Canada in 1748-1751, With Many References to Mammals.) Adolph B. Benson. New York, Wilson-Erickson Inc., vol.1, pp.xviii-1-380; vol.2, pp.381-797, illus., 1937.

AT THE CROSSROADS. (Hunting Conditions in America.) J. Hammond Brown. Texas Game and Fish, Austin, vol.9, no. 2, pp.10-11, 29, Jan., 1951.

EDGE OF THE DESERT. Vinson Brown. Pacific Discovery, San Francisco, vol.1, no.2, pp.7-13, illus., Mar.-Apr., 1948.

PROVISIONAL DESCRIPTIONS OF SUPPOSED NEW MAMMALS FROM CALIFORNIA AND LOWER CALIFORNIA. Walter E. Bryant. Proc. Calif. Acad. of Sci., ser.2, vol.2, pp.25-27, 1889.

RECENT ADDITIONS TO THE NORTH AMERICAN LAND MAMMAL FAUNA. Walter E. Bryant. Zoe, vol.3, no.3, pp. 201-223, Oct., 1892.

FIELD GUIDE TO THE MAMMALS, GIVING FIELD MARKS OF ALL SPECIES FOUND NORTH OF THE MEXICAN BOUNDARY. William H. Burt. Houghton Mifflin, pp.xxiii-200, illus., 1952.

(Review by W.J. Hamilton, Jr. of) FIELD GUIDE TO THE MAMMALS. William H. Burt. Jour. Mamm., vol.34, no.1, pp.139-140, Feb. 19, 1953.

MAMMALS OF NORTH AMERICA. Victor Harrison Cahalane. New York, The Macmillan Co., pp.x-682, illus., 1947.

(Review by Acker E. Young, Stanley P. Young of) MAMMALS OF NORTH AMERICA. Victor Harrison Cahalane. Amer.Midland Nat., Notre Dame, vol.39, no.1, p.256, Jan., 1948.

NORTH AMERICAN CENSUS OF SMALL MAMMALS. John B. Calhoun. Annual Rep. of Census Made in 1948. Baltimore, Johns Hopkins Univ. Press, Release no.2, pp. 67, tbls., forms, Mar. 2, 1949.

NORTH AMERICAN CENSUS OF SMALL MAMMALS. John B. Calhoun. Annual Rep. of Census Made in 1949. Maine, Bar Harbor, Release no.3, pp.90, tbls., Apr., 1950.

NORTH AMERICAN CENSUS OF SMALL MAMMALS. John B. Calhoun. Annual Rep. of Census Made in 1950. Release 4, pp. 136, June, 1951.

TO WHOM DOES AMERICAN WILD LIFE BELONG? Henry R. Carey. Amer. Forests and Forest Life, vol.32, pp.579-582, 620, Oct., 1926.

DESERT PARADE: A GUIDE TO SOUTHWESTERN DESERT PLANTS AND WILDLIFE. (Treats of 29 Mammal Species; Photographs by Marvin H. Frost.) William H. Carr. Viking Press, New York, pp.96, illus., 1947.

WESTERN WILD LIFE. Allen Chaffee. Caxton Printers, Ltd., Caldwell, Idaho, pp.205, 1945.

WILD LIFE'S CHANCES IN CANADA. ALBERTA AND THE MIDDLE WEST. S.M. Clark. Field, London, vol.163, no.4243, p.878, illus., Apr.21, 1934.

ANIMAL TALES OF THE ROCKIES. Albert Benjamin Cunningham. New York, Abingdon Press, pp.122, pls.4, 1925.

MERRIAM'S LIFE ZONES IN NORTH AMERICA. Rexford F. Daubenmire. Quart. Rev. Biol., vol.13, no.3, pp.327-332, Sep., 1938.

WILDLIFE AND THE AMERICAN INDIAN. Albert M. Day. Sports Afield, Minneapolis, vol.116, no.4, p.17, Oct., 1946.

BIOTIC PROVINCES OF NORTH AMERICA. Lee R. Dice. Univ. of Michigan Press, pp.viii-78, 1943.

STUDIES OF THE ECOLOGY AND GENETICS OF NORTH AMERICAN MAMMALS. Lee R. Dice. Carnegie Inst. Washington Year Book no.33, p.268, Dec. 14, 1934; Year Book no.34, pp.278-280, Dec. 13, 1935; Year Book no.35, pp.287-289, Dec. 11, 1936; Year Book no.36, pp.296-298, Dec. 10, 1937; Year Book no.37, pp.302-303, Dec. 9, 1938.

STUDIES OF MAMMALIAN ECOLOGY IN SOUTHWESTERN NORTH AMERICA WITH SPECIAL ATTENTION TO THE COLORS OF DESERT MAMMALS. Lee R. Dice, Philip M. Blossom. Carnegie Inst. Wash., publ.485, pp.129, figs.7, pls.8, Oct. 1, 1937.

MARK TRAIL'S BOOK OF NORTH AMERICAN MAMMALS. Edward Dodd. 1st ed. New York, Hawthorn Books, pp.242, illus., 1955.

(ILLUSTRATED ANIMAL LIFE. FOR SCHOOL AND HOME. WITH SPECIAL CONSIDERATION OF THE AMERICAN ANIMALS.) Illustrirtes Thierleben. Fuer Schule und Haus. Mit besonderer Beruecksichtigung der amerikanischen Thiere. Hermann Duemling. Milwaukee, G.Brumder, pp.xvi-349, pls.14 (part col.), 1875.

CHECK LIST OF MAMMALS OF THE NORTH AMERICAN CONTINENT, THE WEST INDIES AND NEIGHBORING SEAS. Daniel Giraud Elliot. Amer. Mus. Nat. Hist., New York, vols.2, pp.953, 1917.

DESCRIPTIONS OF APPARENTLY NEW SPECIES AND SUBSPECIES OF MAMMALS FROM CALIFORNIA, OREGON, THE KENAI PENINSULA, ALASKA, AND LOWER CALIFORNIA, MEXICO. Daniel Giraud Elliot. Chicago, Field Columbian Mus., Publication no.74, Zoological Series, vol.3, no.10, pp.153-173, illus., 1903.

DESCRIPTIONS OF APPARENTLY NEW SPECIES OF MAMMALS OF THE GENERA HETEROMYS AND URSUS FROM WASHINGTON AND MEXICO. Daniel Giraud Elliot. Field Col. Mus. Publication no.80, Zoological Series, vol.3, no.13, pp.233-237, June, 1903.

LIST OF THE LAND AND SEA MAMMALS OF NORTH AMERICA NORTH OF MEXICO. Daniel Giraud Elliot. Chicago Field Columbia Mus., Publication no.57, Zoological Series, vol.2, no.2, pp.477-522, pls., 1901.

SYNOPSIS OF THE MAMMALS OF NORTH AMERICA AND THE ADJACENT SEAS. Daniel Giraud Elliot. Chicago, Field Columbian Mus., Zoological Series, vol.2, pp.xiv-471, illus., 1901.

(Review by Gerrit S. Miller Jr. of) SYNOPSIS OF THE MAMMALS OF NORTH AMERICA AND ADJACENT SEAS. Daniel Giraud Elliot. Science, n.s., vol.14, no. 340, pp.25-27, July 5, 1901.

NORTH AMERICAN BIG GAME. Alfred Ely, et al. (In) Book of the Boone and Crockett Club compiled by the Committee on Records of North American Big Game. New York, Charles Scribner's Sons, pp.xxii-533, 1939.

(Review by Stanley P. Young of) NORTH AMERICAN BIG GAME. Alfred Ely, et al. Jour. Mamm., vol.21, no.1, pp.96-98, Feb. 14, 1940.

MAMMALS OF THE MOUNTAIN-TOPS. William L. Finley, Irene Finley. Scribner's Mag., vol.80, pp.433-439. Oct., 1926.

NORTH AMERICAN HEAD HUNTING. (Big Game Trophy Hunting.) Grancel Fitz. New York, Oxford Univ. Press, pp.xxvi-188, illus., 1957.

WILD ANIMALS OF THE FIVE RIVERS COUNTRY. Geo. C. Franklin. Boston, Houghton Mifflin Co., pp.271, illus., 1947.

MATERIAL FOR A BIBLIOGRAPHY OF NORTH AMERICAN MAMMALS. Theodore Nicholas Gill, Elliot Coues. Washington, Govt.Print. Off., pp.951-1081, 1877. (From Coues and Elliot Monographs of North American Rodentia. Survey of the U.S. Geological Survey of the Territories, vol. 11.)

KEY TO THE SKULLS OF NORTH AMERICAN MAMMALS. Bryan P. Glass. Burgess Publishing Co., Minneapolis, pp.116, illus., 1951.

IN SAGUARO LAND. AN ACCOUNT OF THE OFFIELD-BEATY EXPEDITION OF THE CHICAGO ACADEMY OF SCIENCES MAY-JUNE, 1940. Howard K. Gloyd. Chicago Nat., vol.3, no.3, pp.67-78, illus., Oct., 1940.

AMERICAN NATURAL HISTORY. PART I. MASTOLOGY. John D. Godman. Philadelphia, H.C. Carey and I. Lea, vols.3, pl., 1826-28; 2nd ed., Philadelphia, Key and Mielkie, vols.3, pls., 1831; 3rd ed., Philadelphia, Hogan and Thompson, vols.2, illus., pls., 1836; 3rd ed., Philadelphia, U. Hunt and Son, vols.2 in one, pls., 1846.

FIVE NEW MAMMALS FROM MEXICO AND ARIZONA. E.A. Goldman. Proc. Biol. Soc. Washington, vol.28, pp.133-138, June 29, 1915.

NEW MAMMALS FROM NORTH AND MIDDLE AMERICA. E.A. Goldman. Proc. Biol. Soc. Washington, vol.30, pp.107-116, May 23, 1917.

ORIGIN AND RELATIONSHIP OF THE LARGE MAMMALS OF NORTH AMERICA. Madison Grant. New York, reprinted from the Eighth Annual Report of the New York Zoological Society, pp.30, 1904.

NORTH AMERICAN BIG GAME. OFFICIAL MEASUREMENT RECORDS. Prentiss N. Gray. Published by Remington Arms Co., Inc., Bridgeport, Conn., Form no.437, pp. 48, figs.23, 1934.

RECORDS OF NORTH AMERICAN BIG GAME. (Brief Accounts of Thirteen Kinds of Big Game By As Many Authors; Measurements of Heads and Horns.) Prentiss N. Gray. New York, The Derrydale Press, pp. viii-178, illus.60, Dec., 1932.

AMERICAN BIG GAME IN ITS HUNTS. George Bird Grinnell. The Book of the Boone and Crockett Club. 1904.

VERTEBRATE FAUNA OF THE PACIFIC COAST. Joseph Grinnell. Nature and Science on the Pacific Coast, San Francisco, p. 11, pls.12-14, 1915.

WILD ANIMALS OF NORTH AMERICA. (Intimate Studies of Big and Little Creatures of the Mammal Kingdom, by Edward W. Nelson.) Joseph Grinnell. Science, n.s., vol.48, no.1248, pp.547-549, Nov. 29, 1918.

ARCTIC TO TROPICS IN AMERICA. E. Raymond Hall. Proc. XIV Internat.Congr. Zool., Copenhagen 1953, p.125, 1956. (Summary.)

VERNACULAR NAMES FOR NORTH AMERICA MAMMALS NORTH OF MEXICO. E. Raymond Hall. Univ. Kansas, Mus. Nat. Hist., Misc.Publ.no.14, pp.1-16, June 19, 1957.

COMMENTS ON THE TAXONOMY AND GEOGRAPHIC DISTRIBUTION OF SOME NORTH AMERICAN MARSUPIALS, INSECTIVORES, AND CARNIVORES. E. Raymond Hall, Keith R. Kelson. Univ. Kansas Publ., Mus.Nat. Hist., Lawrence, vol.5, no.25, pp.319-341, Dec. 5, 1952.

COMMENTS ON THE TAXONOMY AND GEOGRAPHIC DISTRIBUTION OF SOME NORTH AMERICAN RODENTS. E. Raymond Hall, Keith R. Kelson. Univ.Kansas Publ., Mus. Nat. Hist., vol.5, no.26, pp.343-371, Dec., 1952.

MAMMALS OF NORTH AMERICA. E.Raymond Hall, Keith R. Kelson. New York, Ronald Press Co., vol.2, illus., maps, 1959.

AMERICAN MAMMALS: THEIR LIVES, HABITS, AND ECONOMIC RELATION. W.J. Hamilton, Jr. New York, McGraw-Hill Book Co., Inc., pp.xii-434, illus.92, 1939.

(Review by Remington Kellogg of) AMERICAN MAMMALS. W.J. Hamilton, Jr. Lancaster, Scientific Monthly, vol.52, no.6, (no.309), pp.566-567, June, 1941.

MAMMALOGY IN NORTH AMERICA. W.J. Hamilton, Jr. (In) A Century of Progress in the Natural Sciences, California Acad. Sci., San Francisco, pp.661-688, 1955.

FAUNA AMERICANA: BEING A DESCRIPTION OF THE MAMMIFEROUS ANIMALS INHABITING NORTH AMERICA. Richard Harlan. Philadelphia, A.Finley, pp.318, 1825.

BIRDS AND MAMMALS OF THE 1907 ALEXANDER EXPEDITION TO SOUTH-EASTERN ALASKA. THE MAMMALS. Edmund Heller. Univ. Calif. Publ.Zool., vol.5, no.2, pp.245-264, Feb. 18, 1909.

MAMMALS OF THE 1908 ALEXANDER ALASKA EXPEDITION, WITH DESCRIPTIONS OF THE LOCALITIES VISITED AND NOTES ON THE FLORA OF THE PRINCE WILLIAM SOUND REGION. Edmund Heller. Berkeley, Univ. of Calif. Press, publ. in Zoology, vol.5, no.11, pp. 321-360, pls.31-32, map, 1910.

ANIMAL BOOK. AMERICAN MAMMALS NORTH OF MEXICO. Dorothy Childs Hogner, Nils Hogner. New York, Oxford Univ. Press, pp.223, illus., 1942.

NEW MAMMALS FROM CANADA, ALASKA, AND KAMCHATKA, WITH THREE PLATES. Ned Hollister. Washington, Smiths. Inst., Misc. Coll., Publication no.2072, vol.56, no.35, pp.8, pls.3, 1912.

SHEEP AND BEAR TRAILS. HUNTER'S WANDERINGS IN ALASKA AND BRITISH COLUMBIA. John P. Holman. Frank Walters, Grand Central Palace, New York, pp.xvi+211, pls.43, 1933.

AMERICAN NATURAL HISTORY. (A Foundation of Useful Knowledge of the Higher Animals of North America.) William Temple Hornaday. New York, C. Scribner's Sons, vols.4, maps, pls. (part col.), 1914. (Contents: Vol.I Mammals; Vol.II. Mammals(concluded), Birds; Vol.III. Birds (concluded); Vol.IV. Reptiles, Amphibians and Fishes.)

EARLIEST AMERICANS. Edgar B. Howard. Frontiers, Philadelphia, vol.1, no.2, pp. 39-41, Nov., 1936.

MAMMAL COLLECTIONS OF NORTH AMERICA. A. Brazier Howell. Jour.Mamm., vol.4, no.2, pp.113-120, May, 1923.

GIANT CACTUS FOREST AND ITS WORLD. Paul Griswold Howes. New York, Little Brown, Boston, pp.xxx-258, pls.52, figs. 30, 1954.

DESCRIPTIONS OF NEW MAMMALS FROM ARIZONA AND SONORA, MEXICO. Laurence M. Huey. Trans. San Diego Soc. Nat. Hist., vol.8, no.25, pp.349-360, pl.23, June 15, 1937.

AN EARLIER AMERICAN MAMMAL SOCIETY. Hartley H.T. Jackson. Jour.Mamm., vol.29, no.1, pp.1-4, Feb. 13, 1948.

OUR DESERT NEIGHBORS. Edmund C. Jaeger. Stanford Univ. Press, pp.239, illus., 1951.

FIRST SCIENTIFIC EXPLORATION OF RUSSIAN AMERICA AND THE PURCHASE OF ALASKA. (Transcriptions of Journals of Robert Kennicott and Henry M. Bannister, With Many References to Wildlife.) James Alton James. Northwestern Univ.Studies in Social Sciences, Chicago, no.4, pp. xii+276, illus., 1942.

RODENTS, RABBITS, AND TULAREMIA IN NORTH AMERICA: SOME ZOOLOGICAL AND EPIDEMIOLOGICAL CONSIDERATIONS. W.L. Jellison, R.R. Parker. Amer. Jour. Tropical Med., Baltimore, vol.25, no.4, pp.349-362, maps 5, July, 1945.

HAMMOND'S NATURE ATLAS OF AMERICA. (48 Species of Mammals, pp.126-151, illus. by Walter Ferguson.) E.L. Jordan. New York, C.S. Hammond and Co., pp. 256, illus., 1952.

(IN THE AMERICAN BUSH; HUNTING AND FOREST TRIPS OF HANNS MARIA VON KADICH.) Im amerikanischen Busch; Jagd- und Waldfahrten von Hanns Maria von Kadich. Hanns Maria Kadich. Neudamm, J.Neumann, pp.274, 1913.

SEALS, SEA-LIONS, AND SEA OTTER OF THE PACIFIC COAST. Karl W. Kenyon, Victor B. Scheffer. Wildl.Leaflet U.S. Fish and Wildl. Serv., no.344, pp.28, illus., Feb., 1953; no.32, pp.34, illus., Apr., 1955.

WILD ANIMALS OF NORTH AMERICA. Edward Knobel. New York, The Authors and Newspapers Assoc., pt.9, illus., 1908.

QUADRUPEDS OF NORTH AMERICA. Thomas Landseer. London, J. Murray, pls.28 (part col.), 1829.

(COMMENTS ON RARE NORTH AMERICAN MAMMALS.) Nagra ord om Nordamerikas sallsynta daggdjur. Einar Lonnberg. Fauna och Flora, Uppsala, no.4, pp.163-172, 1941.

IN THE ALASKA-YUKON GAMELAND. (Account of Hunting Trip to White River, Alaska-Yukon Boundary, On Which Type Specimen of Rangifer mcguirei Figgins Was Obtained. Introduction by William T. Hornaday.) J.A. McGuire. Cincinnati, Stewart and Kidd Co., pp.1-215, pls.16, 1921.

AMERICAN WILDLIFE AND PLANTS. Alexander C. Martin, et al. New York, McGraw-Hill Book Co., pp.ix+500, 1951.

(Review by Emmet T. Hooper of) AMERICAN WILDLIFE AND PLANTS. Alexander C. Martin, et al. Jour. Mamm., vol.33, no.3, pp.400-401, Aug. 19, 1952.

(LIST OF MAMMALS OBSERVED ON HIS TRAVELS IN NORTH AMERICA.) Verzeichniss der aus seiner Reise durch Nord-Amerika beobachteten Saeugethiere. Maximilian. Berlin, pp.240, pls.4, 5, 6, 8, 1862.

DESCRIPTIONS OF SIX NEW MAMMALS FROM NORTH AMERICA. Edgar Alexander Mearns. U.S.Nat. Mus., Proc., Wash., vol.19, pp.719-724, 1897.

DESCRIPTION AND DISTRIBUTION. C. Hart Merriam. (In) N.American Big Game. A. Book of the Boone and Crockett Club compiled by the Commitee on Records of N.American Big Game. New York, Charles Scribners Sons, pp.371-378.

DESCRIPTIONS OF A NEW GENUS AND TWO NEW SPECIES OF NORTH AMERICAN MAMMALS. C. Hart Merriam. U.S. Dept. Agric., Div. Orinth. and Mamm., N.Amer. Fauna, no.5, pp.115-117, July 30, 1891.

DESCRIPTIONS OF FOURTEEN NEW SPECIES AND ONE NEW GENUS OF NORTH AMERICAN MAMMALS. C. Hart Merriam. Wash., Govt. Print. Off., U.S. Dept. Agric., Div. of Orinth. and Mamm., N.Amer.Fauna, no.2, pp.52, illus., pls.viii, 1889.

DESCRIPTIONS OF TWENTY-SIX NEW MAMMALS FROM ALASKA AND BRITISH NORTH AMERICA. C. Hart Merriam. Washington Acad. of Sci., pp.30, 1900.

DESCRIPTIONS OF TWENTY-SIX NEW SPECIES OF NORTH AMERICAN MAMMALS. C. Hart Merriam. U.S. Dept. Agric., Div. of Orinth. and Mamm., N. Amer. Fauna, no.4, pp.60, pls.3, fold. tbls., 1890.

GEOGRAPHIC DISTRIBUTION OF ANIMALS AND PLANTS IN NORTH AMERICA. C. Hart Merriam. Yearbook, U.S.Dept. Agric., pp.203-214, figs.20, 1895.

GEOGRAPHIC DISTRIBUTION OF LIFE IN NORTH AMERICA, WITH SPECIAL REFERENCE TO THE MAMMALIA. C. Hart Merriam. Smiths. Inst., Ann. Rep., Wash., pp.365-415, tbls., 1893. (From the Proc.Biolog.Soc., Wash., vol.7, pp.1-64.)

ON A COLLECTION OF MAMMALS FROM ARIZONA AND MEXICO MADE BY W. W. PRICE, WITH FIELD NOTES BY THE COLLECTOR. C. Hart Merriam. Science, n.s., vol.2, no.39, pp.417-418, Sep. 27, 1895.

PAPERS FROM THE HARRIMAN ALASKA EXPEDITION. I. DESCRIPTIONS OF TWENTY-SIX NEW MAMMALS FROM ALASKA AND BRITISH NORTH AMERICA. C. Hart Merriam. Proc. Washington Acad. Sci. vol.2, pp.13-30, Mar. 14, 1900.

KEY TO THE LAND MAMMALS OF NORTHEASTERN NORTH AMERICA. Gerrit S. Miller, Jr. Bull. New York State Mus., no. 38, vol.8, pp.61-160, Nov. 21, 1900.

LIST OF NORTH AMERICAN LAND MAMMALS IN THE UNITED STATES NATIONAL MUSEUM, 1911. Gerrit S. Miller, Jr. Washington, Govt. Print. Off., Smiths. Inst., U.S.Nat. Mus. Bull. no.79, pp.xiv+455, 1912.

LIST OF NORTH AMERICAN RECENT MAMMALS 1923. Gerrit S. Miller, Jr. Washington, Govt. Print. Off., Smiths. Inst., U.S. Nat. Mus. Bull.no.128, pp. xvi+673, 1924; Bull.no.205, pp.xii-954, 1955.

SYSTEMATIC RESULTS OF THE STUDY OF NORTH AMERICAN LAND MAMMALS TO THE CLOSE OF THE YEAR 1900. Gerrit S. Miller, Jr., J.A.G. Rehn. Proc. Boston Soc. Nat. Hist., vol.30, no.1, pp.352, Dec. 27, 1901.

SYSTEMATIC RESULTS OF THE STUDY OF NORTH AMERICAN LAND MAMMALS DURING THE YEARS 1901 AND 1902. Gerrit S. Miller, Jr., J.A.G. Rehn. Proc.Boston Soc. Nat. Hist., vol.31, no.3, pp.61-145, Aug., 1903.

BIG-GAME RESOURCE. Gleen E. Mitchell. Trans. 14th N.Amer. Wildl. Conf., Wash., pp.538-543, 1949.

COMPARISON OF NORTH AMERICAN SMALL-MAMMAL CENSUSES. Carl O. Mohr. Amer. Midland Nat., vol.29, no. 3, pp.545-587, May, 1943.

TABLE OF EQUIVALENT POPULATIONS OF NORTH AMERICAN SMALL MAMMALS. Carl O. Mohr. Amer. Midland Nat., Notre Dame, vol.37, no.1, pp.223-249, Jan., 1947.

NORTH AMERICAN MAMMALS. Charles E. Mohr. Prepared with the cooperation of the Nat.Audubon Soc. Garden City, New York, N.Doubleday, pp.56, illus., 1958. (Nature Program.)

FOREST TREE-SEED-EATERS AND METHODS USED TO MEASURE THEIR POPULATIONS IN THE PACIFIC NORTHWEST DOUGLAS FIR REGION. A.W.

Moore. Univ. Wash. Forest Club Quart., Seattle, vol.23, no.1, pp.7-11, 25, illus., 1949-50.

AMERICAN GAXETTEER, EXHIBITING A FULL ACCOUNT OF THE CIVIL DIVISIONS, RIVERS, HARBOURS, INDIAN TRIBES, ETC. OF THE AMERICAN CONTINENT, ALSO OF THE WEST INDIA AND OTHER APPENDANT ISLANDS; WITH A PARTICULAR DESCRIPTION OF LOUISIANA. Jedidiah Morse. Boston, illus., 1804.

MANAGING QUETICO-SUPERIOR'S WILDLIFE. Olaus J. Murie. Nature Mag., Wash., vol.42, no.5, pp.234-235, May, 1949. (Moose, Fisher.)

OUR BIG GAME IN WINTER. Olaus J. Murie. Trans. 9th N. Amer. Wildl. Conf., Wash., pp.173-176, 1944.

DESCRIPTIONS OF TWO NEW SUBSPECIES OF NORTH AMERICAN MAMMALS. E.W. Nelson. Proc. Biol. Soc. Wash., vol.20, pp.87-88, Dec. 11, 1907.

LARGER NORTH AMERICAN MAMMALS. E.W. Nelson. Washington, Nat. Geographic Soc., pp.385-472, illus.(part col.), 1916. (An Intimate Study of the Larger Wild Animals of North America by the Foremost Authorities.)

SMALLER NORTH AMERICAN MAMMALS. E.W. Nelson. Washington, Nat. Geographic Soc., pp.371-493, illus.(part col.), 1918. (An Intimate Study of the Wild Animals of North America by the Foremost Authorities.)

WILD ANIMALS OF NORTH AMERICA. E.W. Nelson. Wash. Nat. Geographic Soc., p.254, illus.(part col.), fold.col. pl., 1930. (Intimate Studies of Big and Little Creatures of the Mammal Kingdom.)

(Review by J.A. Allen of) WILD ANIMALS OF NORTH AMERICA. E.W. Nelson. Nat. Hist., vol.19, no.3, pp.330-333, Mar., 1919.

(Review by E.A. Goldman of) WILD ANIMALS OF NORTH AMERICA. E.W. Nelson. Jour. Mamm., vol.12, no.3, p.322, Aug., 1931.

ANIMALS OF THE SOUTHWESTERN DESERTS. George Olin. S. W. Monuments Assoc., Pop.Ser.no.8, pp.1-112, maps, sketches, 1954.

REPRINT OF THE NORTH AMERICAN ZOOLOGY. (Being an exact reproduction of the part originally compiled by Mr. Ord for Johnson and Warner, and first publ. by them in their 2d American ed. of Guthrie's geography, in 1815. Taken from Mr. Ord's private, annotated copy. To which is added an appendix on the more important scientific and historic questions involved.) George Ord. Haddonfield, N.J., Pub. by the Editor, 189?

PRESERVATION OF THE WILD ANIMALS OF NORTH AMERICA. Henry Fairfield Osborn. Address before the Boone and Crockett Club, Washington, pp.27, illus., Jan.23, 1904.

RISE OF THE MAMMALIA IN NORTH AMERICA. Henry Fairfield Osborn. Address by Vice-President of the American Assoc. for the Advancement of Sci., Section of Zoology, Madison, Wisc., Aug. 17, 1893; Boston, Ginn and Co., New York, G.E. Stechert, pp.45, illus., pl., 1893.

BIOLOGICAL INVESTIGATIONS IN ALASKA AND YUKON TERRITORY. 1. EAST CENTRAL ALASKA. 2. THE OGILVIE RANGE, YUKON. 3. THE MACMILLIAN RIVER, YUKON. Wilfred H. Osgood. U.S. Dept. Agric., Div. Biol. Surv., N. Amer. Fauna, no.30, pp. 92, pls.5, Oct. 7, 1909.

RESULTS OF A BIOLOGICAL RECONNOISSANCE OF THE YUKON RIVER REGION. GENERAL ACCOUNT OF THE REGION. ANNOTATED LIST OF MAMMALS. ANNOTATED LIST OF BIRDS. Wilfred H. Osgood. Wash., Govt. Print. Off., U.S. Dept. Agric., Div. Biol. Surv., N. American Fauna no.19, pp. 100, pls.7, map, 1900.

MAMMAL GUIDE; MAMMALS OF NORTH AMERICA NORTH OF MEXICO. Ralph Simon Palmer. New York, Doubleday, pp. 384, illus., col.pls.40, maps, 1954.

(Review by Robert T. Orr of) MAMMAL GUIDE. Ralph Simon Palmer. Jour. Mamm., vol.36, no.1, pp.147-148, Feb.25, 1955.

SOUTHERN HALF OF THE ALASKA HIGHWAY AND ITS MAMMALS. A.L. Rand. Nat. Mus. Canada, Ottawa, Bull.no.98, Biol.ser.27, pp.50, fig.1, pls.21, 1944.

DESCRIPTION OF NEW SPECIES OF NORTH AMERICAN MAMMALS WITH REMARKS ON SPECIES OF THE GENUS PEROGNATHUS. Samuel N. Rhoads. Proc. Acad. Nat. Sci., Philadelphia, for 1893, pp.404-406, figs.2, Jan. 27, 1894.

WILD ANIMALS OF THE ROCKIES. (Observations in Story Form.) William M. Rush. Harper, pp.xxiii-296, 1942.

HOW TO KNOW THE AMERICAN MAMMALS. Ivan T. Sanderson. Boston, Little, Brown, pp.164, illus., 1951, New York, Mentor Books, pp.171, illus., July, 1951.

MARINE MAMMALS OF THE NORTHWESTERN COAST OF NORTH AMERICA, DESCRIBED AND ILLUSTRATED: TOGETHER WITH AN ACCOUNT OF THE AMERICAN WHALE-FISHERY. Charles M. Scammon. San Francisco, John H. Carmany and Co., pp.319, 1874.

CACTUSLAND CREATURES. (Skunk, Kangaroo Rat, Pocket Mouse, Wood Rat, Ringtailed Cat.) W.J. Schaldach, Jr. Nat. Mag., Washington, vol.41, no.8, pp.405-408, Oct., 1948.

LIST OF THE MARINE MAMMALS OF THE WEST COAST OF NORTH AMERICA. Victor B. Scheffer. Murrelet, vol.23, no.2, pp.42-47, May-Aug., 1942.

HOMES AND HABITS OF WILD ANIMALS. (North American Mammals.) Karl Patterson Schmidt. Chicago, New York, M.A. Donohue and Co., pp.64, illus., col.pls., 1934.

ON THE QUADRUMANA FOUND IN AMERICA NORTH OF PANAMA. Philip Lutley Sclater. Proc. Zool. Soc. London, pp.2-8, figs.2, pls.1-2, 1872.

METHODS OF CONTROLLED PUBLIC HUNTING IN THE UNITED STATES AND CANADA. Walter E. Scott. Jour. Wildl. Mgt., Menasha, vol.12, no.3, pp.236-240, July, 1948.

ANIMALS, SELECTED FROM "LIFE HISTORIES OF NORTHERN ANIMALS." (Arranged by Robert M. McCurdy; with Paragraphs on Classification from Stone and Cram's "American Animals" as Indicated; 48 illustrations in full color.) Ernest Thompson Seton. New York, Doubleday, Page and Co. for Nelson Doubleday, Inc., pp.xiii-299, col.pls., (The Nature Library) 1926.

LIST OF RESERVES THAT MAY SERVE AS NATURE SANCTUARIES OF NATIONAL AND INTERNATIONAL IMPORTANCE, IN CANADA, THE UNITED STATES, AND MEXICO. V.E. Shelford. Ecology, Brooklyn, vol.22, no.1, pp.100-110, Jan., 1941.

NATURALIST'S GUIDE TO THE AMERICAS. V.E. Shelford. (Editor of the Mammals, Lee R. Dice.) Baltimore, The Williams and Wilkins Co., vol.8, pp.xv-761, pl.1, maps 16, Mar., 1926.

THE ANIMALS OF NORTH AMERICA. H. Beaumont Small. 1864.

MAMMALS OF THE NORTHERN GREAT PLAINS ALONG THE INTERNATIONAL BOUNDARY IN CANADA. J. Dewey Soper. Jour. Mamm., vol.27, no.2, pp.127-153, fig.1, pl.1, May 14, 1946.

SOME RESULTS OF A NATURAL HISTORY JOURNEY TO NORTHERN BRITISH COLUMBIA, ALASKA, AND THE NORTHWEST TERRITORY, IN THE INTEREST OF THE AMERICAN MUSEUM OF NATURAL HISTORY. A.J. Stone. Bull. Amer. Mus. Nat. Hist., vol.13, art.5, pp.31-62, figs.5, Apr. 6, 1900.

AMERICAN ANIMALS. (A Popular Guide to the Mammals of North America North of Mexico, with Intimate Biographies of the More Familiar Species.) Witmer Stone, William Everett Cram. New York, Doubleday, Page and Co., pp.xxiii-318, illus., pls.(part col.), 1902. 2nd ed., 1920.

BIRDS AND MAMMALS OF THE STIKINE RIVER REGION OF NORTHERN BRITISH COLUMBIA AND SOUTHEASTERN ALASKA. (Notes on 34 Species of Mammals.) H.S. Swarth. Univ. Calif. Pub. Zool., vol.24, pp.125-314, pl.8, figs.34, June 17, 1922.

SOME ANIMALS OF THE AMERICAN WILDERNESS. Walter P. Taylor. Living Wilderness, Washington, D.C., vol.8, whole no.9, pp.21-30, illus., Oct., 1943.

DESCRIPTIONS OF NEW BATS AND RODENTS FROM AMERICA. Oldfield Thomas. Ann. and Mag. Nat. Hist., ser.6, vol.20, no.120, pp.544-553, Dec., 1897.

DIAGNOSES OF NEW NORTH AMERICAN MAMMALS. Frederick William True. U.S. Nat. Mus., Proc., Washington, vol.17, pp.241-243, Nov. 15, 1894.

PROVISIONAL LIST OF THE MAMMALS OF NORTH AND CENTRAL AMERICA, AND THE WEST INDIAN ISLANDS. Frederick William True. U.S. Nat. Mus., Proc., Washington, vol.7, pp.587-611, 1884.

HOW TO HUNT AMERICAN GAME. (A Grass-Roots Guide to American Hunting.) Robert B. Vale. Military Service Pub. Co., Harrisburg, pp.199, illus., 1946.

COMMON WILD ANIMALS AND THEIR YOUNG. Rita Vandivert. New York, Dell Pub. Co., pp.126, illus., (Dell Laurel Edition, LC105) 1957.

(CONTRIBUTIONS TO KNOWLEDGE OF THE MAMMALS OF AMERICA.) Beitraege zur Kenntnis der Saeugethiere Amerikas. J.A. Wagner. Munich, 1847.

MOST INTERESTING WILD ANIMALS IN AMERICA. Edward R. Warren. Sci. Monthly, pp.33-41, photos, July, 1928.

RECORDS OF NORTH AMERICAN BIG GAME. S.B. Webb, et al. Scribner's Sons, pp.174, illus., 1952.

AMERICAN ANIMAL NAMES. Wilkins W. Wheatly. Audubon Mag., New York, vol. 53, no.1, pp.18-23, illus., Jan.-Feb., 1951.

(LIST OF THE MAMMALS OBSERVED ON HIS TRIP TO NORTH AMERICA.) Verzeichnis der auf seiner Reise nach Nord-Amerika beobachteten Saeugethiere. Maximilian von Wied. Berlin, Nicolaische Verlagsbuchhandlung (G. Parthey), pp.240, pls., 1862.

ERNEST THOMPSON SETON'S AMERICA. Farida A. Wiley, Editor. New York, Devin-Adair Co., pp.xxiii-413, illus., 1954.

NOTES ON THE LIFE ALONG THE YUKON-ALASKA BOUNDARY. M.Y. Williams. Canadian Field-Nat., vol.39, pp.69-72, Apr., 1925.

FOUR-FOOTED AMERICANS AND THEIR KIN. Mabel Wright. New York, Macmillan Co., pp.xv-432, illus., pls., 1898.

CONTRIBUTION TOWARD A BIBLIOGRAPHY ON NORTH AMERICAN FUR ANIMALS. Lee E. Yeager. Illinois Nat. Hist. Surv., Springfield, Biol. Notes, no.16, pp.iv-209, Dec., 1941. (Mimeogr.)

EARLY WILDLIFE AMERICANA. Stanley P. Young. Amer. Forests, Washington, D.C., vol.49, no.8, pp.387-389, 414, illus., Aug., 1943.

SKETCHES OF AMERICAN WILDLIFE. Stanley P. Young. Monumental Press, Baltimore, pp.xii-143, illus., 1946.

MAMMALS. (A Guide to Familiar American Species. 218 Animals in Full Color.) Herbert Spencer Zim, Donald F. Hoffmeister. Sponsored by the Wildlife Management Institute. New York, Simon and Schuster, pp.160, illus., (A Golden Nature Guide) 1955.

NORTH AMERICAN CENSUS OF SMALL MAMMALS. Release no.1. Baltimore, Rodent Ecology Project, Johns Hopkins Univ., maps, tbls., Jan., 1948. (Mimeogr.)

RECORDS OF NORTH AMERICAN BIG GAME. Rod and Gun in Canada, Montreal, vol.48, no.8, p.21, 1947.

RECORDS OF NORTH AMERICAN BIG GAME. Compiled and Edited by the Committee on Records of North American Big Game of the Boone and Crockett Club. Scribner's, pp.xiii-174, illus., 1952.

WILD ANIMALS OF NORTH AMERICA. Nat. Geographic Soc., Washington, D.C., (Nat.Sci.Library), Edited and Prepared by the Nat. Geographic Book Service, pp.400, illus.(part col.), 1960.

NORWAY

(COMMUNICATIONS ON NORWAY'S MAMMALS IN THE YEARS 1876-1881.) Meddelelser om Norges Pattedyr i aarene 1876-1881. Robert Collett. Saerskilt aftryk af Nyt magazin for naturvidenskaberne, bind xxvii, pp.217-260.

(MAMMALS OF NORWAY.) Norges Pattedyr. Robert Collett. Oslo, 1911-12.

(REMARKS ON NORWAY'S MAMMALS.) Bemaerkninger til Norges pattedyrfauna. Robert Collett. Kistiania, B.M.Bentzens bogtrykkeri, pp.116, 1876.

FUR BREEDING INDUSTRY IN NORWAY. O. Brager Larsen. Conservation, Wash., D.C., vol.6, no.5, pp.35-36, Sep.-Oct., 1940.

SOME NORWEGIAN SMALL MAMMAL FAUNAS; A STUDY BASED ON TRAPPINGS IN WEST AND NORTH NORWAY. Ian Linn. Oikos, Acta Oecologica Scandinavica, Copenhagen, vol.5, fasc.1, pp.1-24, 1954.

FUR FARMING IN THE STAVANGER CONSULAR DISTRICT-NORWAY. U.S. Consul Orr. American Fur Breeder, vol.3, no.4, p.37, Oct., 1930.

(NORWAY'S NATURAL HISTORY.) Norges Naturlige Historie. Erich Pontoppidan. 1752.

(NEW STONE FOR THE SCOTLAND-NORWAY LAND BRIDGE.) En ny sten til den skotsk-norske landbro. Leonhard Stejneger. Naturen, Kobenhavn, vol.38, pp.50-52, Feb., 1914.

(NORWEGIAN MAMMALS: A SHORT DESCRIPTION OF THE TYPES OF MAMMALS FOUND IN NORWAY.) Norsk mastozoologisk ekskursjonsfauna. Kort bestrivelse af de i Norge iagttagne arter pattedyr. Leonhard Stejneger. Kristiana, Forlagt af Alb. Cammermayer, pp.vii-31, 1874.

ORIGIN OF THE SO-CALLED ATLANTIC ANIMALS AND PLANTS OF WESTERN NORWAY. Leonhard Stejneger. Smiths. Inst., Misc. Coll., Washington, vol.xlviii (Quart.issue, vol.III), pp.458-513, illus., pls., fold.map, 1699.

(WHENCE CAME NORWAY'S CHARACTERISTIC ANIMALS AND PLANTS?) Hvorfra kom Vestnorges eiendommelige dyr og planter? Leonhard Stejneger. Naturen, Kobenhavn, pp.193-202, Juli-August, 1908; Sept. Heft. pp.269-277.

NOTES ON A COLLECTION OF SMALL MAMMALS FROM WESTERN NORWAY. D.M. Steven. Univ. Bergen Arbok 1952, Naturvitenskanelig Bekke, no.6, pp.1-13, 1953.

FUR FARMING IN NORWAY. Amer. Nat. Fur and Market Jour., Wausau, vol.28, no.9, pp.7, 21, Apr., 1950.

(NOTES ON THE FISHERIES OF NORWAY.) Notices sur les Pecheries de la Norwege. Catalogue Special del la Norwege a L'Exposition Universelle, Paris, Christiania, pp.70, fold.map, 1878.

PACIFIC OCEAN

LIFE ON MACQUARIE ISLAND. (In) Home of the Blizzard, by D.Mawson. G.F.Ainsworth. Abridged pop.ed. London, Hodder and Stoughton, pp.334-356, 1934.

NOTES ON A SMALL COLLECTION OF MAMMALS FROM THE LIU KIU ISLANDS. Outram Bangs. Amer. Nat., Boston, vol. 35, no.415, pp.561-562, July, 1901.

CHRONOLOGICAL HISTORY OF THE DISCOVERIES IN THE SOUTH SEA OR PACIFIC OCEAN. J. Burney. London, Luke Hansard, vols.5, 1803-1817.

(MAMMALS OF THE PACIFIC EXPEDITION UNDERTAKEN BY A COMMISSION OF NATURALISTS SENT OUT BY THE SPANISH GOVERNMENT IN 1862-65.) Mammiferos del Viaje al Pacifico. Verificado de 1862 a 1865 por una comision de naturalistas enviada por il Gobierno Espanol. Angel Cabrera. Trabajos Mus. Nat. Cienc. Nat. Madrid Ser. Zool., no.31, pp.62, Oct. 28, 1917.

ANIMALS OF THE PACIFIC WORLD. T. Donald Carter, et al. Infantry Jour., Wash., Fighting Forces Series, pp.xxiv-195, figs. 78, 1944.

MAMMALS OF THE PACIFIC WORLD. T. Donald Carter, et al. Macmillan Co., New York, pp.xvi-227, figs.69, 1945.

(Review by William H. Elder of) MAMMALS OF THE PACIFIC WORLD. T. Donald Carter, et al. Ecology, Lancaster, vol.27, no.2, p. 191, Apr., 1946.

(Review by P. Roder of) MAMMALS OF THE PACIFIC WORLD. T. Donald Carter, et al. Mammalia, Paris, vol.10, no.1, p.66, Mar., 1946.

ISLANDS WEST OF SOUTH AMERICA. J.P. Chapin. Nat. Hist., New York, vol. 38, pp.31-55, 1936.

VOYAGE TO THE PACIFIC OCEAN UNDERTAKEN, BY THE COMMAND OF HIS MAJESTY, FOR MAKING DISCOVERIES IN THE NORTHERN HEMISPHERE - 1776-1780. J. Cook. London, G.Nicol and T. Cadell, vol. 1 and 2 by Cooke, vol.3 by James King, 1785.

SCIENTIFIC AND ECONOMIC PROBLEMS OF THE MAMMALS AND BIRDS OF THE NORTH PACIFIC. B.W. Evermann. Papers on the Exploration of the North Pacific Ocean, Bull Scripps Inst.for Biol.Research, no.9, pp.27-34 (dated Dec. 15, 1919), 1920.

WHY NOT SAVE THE MARINE MAMMALS OF THE PACIFIC. B.W. Evermann. Bull. Pan-Pacific Union, n.s., no.34, pp.12-16, Aug., 1922.

EXPEDITION TO THE REVILLAGIGEDO ISLANDS, MEXICO, IN 1925. GENERAL REPORT. G. Dallas Hanna. Proc. Calif. Acad. Sci., ser.4, vol.15, no.1, pp.1-113, pls.1-10, figs.1-7, Mar. 30, 1926.

(NOTES ON SOME ANIMALS AND PLANTS FOUND IN THE SOUTHERN SEAS AND IN THE ISLANDS OF THE GREAT OCEAN; CONSIDERED FROM THE POINT OF VIEW OF THEIR CLASSIFICATION AND RELATIONS WITH INDUSTRY.) Notes sur quelques animaux et quelques vegetaux recontres dans les mers Australes et dans les Iles du Grand-Ocean, consideres au points de vue de leur classification et de leurs rapports avec l'industrie. Henri Jouan. Cherbourg, pp.129-264, 1874.

COASTAL LYING PLACES OF CALLORHINUS URSINUS AND LIVING PLACES OF ENHYDRALUTRIS AT THE KURIL ISLANDS, AND A TENTATIVE DETERMINATION OF THEIR RESPECTIVE NUMBER. S.K. Klumov. Doklady Akad. Nauk USSR, vol. 117, no.1, pp.153-156, 1957. (In Russian, with English summary.)

SOME RESULTS OF THE EXPEDITION TO THE BERING SEA AND TO THE KURILE ISLANDS. S.K. Klumov. Vestnik Akad. Nauk SSSR, vol.5, pp.32-37, map, 1956.

GEOGRAPHICAL DISTRIBUTION OF MAMMALS IN THE KURILE CHAIN. Nagamichi Kuroda. Bull. Biogeogr.Soc. Japan, vol.3, no.3, pp.151-167, Nov., 1933. (In Japanese with English summary.)

MAMMAL FAUNA OF SAKHALIN. Nagamichi Kuroda. Jour. Mamm., vol.9, no.3, pp.222-229, Aug., 1928.

MAMMALS COLLECTED IN THE ISLANDS OF OKINAWA AND YAYEYAMA IN THE RYUKYU ISLANDS. Nagamichi Kuroda. Trans. Biogeogr. Soc. Japan, vol.3, no.1, pp.65-69, (Feb.) Mar. 8, 1938.

MAMMALS OF THE NORTHERN KURILE ISLANDS. Nagamichi Kuroda. Bull.Biogeogr. Soc. Japan, Tokyo, vol.4, no.1, pp.47-50, Oct., 1933.

ON NEW MAMMALS FROM THE RIU KIU ISLANDS AND THE VICINITY. Nagamichi Kuroda. Privately Printed, Tokyo, pp.1-14, Sep. 3, 1924.

LIST OF LAND MAMMALS OF NEW GUINEA, CELEBES AND ADJACENT ISLANDS, 1758-1952. Eleanor M. Laurie, J.E. Hill. London, Printed by Order of the Trustees of the British Museum, British Museum, Nat. Hist., pp.175, pls., map, 1954.

EXPEDITION TO THE REVILLAGIGEDO ISLANDS, MEXICO, IN 1925. VI. THE BIRDS AND MAMMALS. (16 Forms of Mammals Listed.) M.E. McLellan. Proc.Calif. Acad.Sci. fourth series, vol.15, no.11, pp. 279-322, May 20, 1926.

VERTEBRATE ECOLOGY OF ARNO ATOLL, MARSHALL ISLANDS. Joe T. Marshall, Jr. Atoll Res.Bull., Pacific Sci.Board, Wash., no.3, pp.1-42, illus., Oct. 15, 1951.

MACQUARIE ISLAND AND ITS FUTURE. Douglas Mawson. Australian Zoologist, vol.3, pt.3, pp.92-102.

(MAMMALS OF THE SOUTH SEAS EXPEDITION OF THE HAMBURG SCIENTIFIC INSTITUTION 1908-1909.) Die Saeugetiere der Suedsee-Expedition der Hamburgischen wissenschaftlichen Stiftung 1908-1909. Erna Mohr. Mitt. Zool. Inst. Mus. Hamburg, vol.40, pp.7-18, 1923.

PRELIMINARY REPORT ON LAND ANIMALS AT ONOTOA ATOLL, GILBERT ISLANDS. Edwin T. Moul. Atoll Res. Bull., Pacific Sci. Board, Washington, no. 28, pp.28, May 31, 1954.

TERRESTRIAL AND FRESH-WATER FAUNA OF THE MARQUESAS ISLANDS. Edward Philpott Mumford. Ecology, vol. 17, no.1, pp.143-157, Jan., 1936.

MAMMALS OF THE TRES MARIAS ISLANDS. E.W. Nelson. (In) Natural History of the Tres Marias Islands, Mexico, N.Amer.Fauna, no.14, pp.15-19, 1899.

HUNTING IN NEW CALEDONIA. A.J. Nicholson. Texas Game and Fish, Austin, vol.2, no.12, pp.5, 18, Nov., 1944.

DISTRIBUTION OF THE MORE IMPORTANT MARINE MAMMALS OF THE PACIFIC OCEAN, AS IT AFFECTS THEIR CONSERVATION. Robert T. Orr. Trans. Sixth Pacific Sci. Congress, vol.3, Oceanography and Marine Biology, pp.217-222, Apr. 17, 1941.

("QUADALUPE ISLAND" IN "SEAS AND ISLANDS FROM THE NORTHEAST OF MEXICO" RESULTS OF THE SCIENTIFIC-MILITARY EXPEDITION OF THE SUPERIOR SCHOOL OF WAR.) "Isla Guadalupe" en "Mares e Islas del Noroeste de México" Resultado de la expedicion Cientifico-militar de la Escuela Superior de Guerra. Bibiano F. Osorio-Tafall. Mexico, pp.70-90, 1949.

GEOGRAPHICAL DISTRIBUTION OF FISH AND OTHER ECONOMIC ANIMALS OF THE OKHOTSK AND BERING SEAS. T.S. Rass, et al. Trudy Inst. Okeanologii, Akad. Nauk SSSR, Moscow, vol.14, pp. 1-120, illus., 1955. (Part 3. Cetaceans; Part 4. Pinnipeds; in Russian.)

(MAMMALS OF NEW CALEDONIA AND THE LOYALTY ISLANDS.) Les mammiferes de la Nouvelle-Calédonie et des iles Loyalty. Pierre Revilliod. (In) F. Sarasin and J. Roux: Nova Caledonia, Zoologie, vol.1, pt.4, no.9, pp.341-365, pls., 1914.

WILD LIFE DISAPPEARING FROM CEDROS. Joseph R. Slevin. Bull. New York Zool. Soc., vol.43, no.6, pp.192-196, illus., Nov.-Dec., 1940.

"A VISIT AT PITCAIRN'S ISLAND." EXTRACTS FROM THE JOURNAL OF JOHN A. STATES, STONINGTON, CONN., ON A WHALING VOYAGE, 1844-46. John A. States. Publ.Marine Hist. Assoc., Inc., Mystic, Conn., vol.1, no.4, pp.55-60, illus., Nov. 20, 1931.

(FROM THE VERY FAR EAST. JOURNEY NOTES OF LEONHARD STEJNEGER. V. A BOAT TRIP AROUND BERING'S ISLAND.) Fra det yderste østen. Rejsebreve af Leonhard Stejneger. V. En Baadtur rundt Beringsøen. Leonhard Stejneger. Naturen, vol.9, no.10, pp.150-157, Oct., 1885.

CONSPICUOUS MAMMALS OF THE SOUTH PACIFIC. Ken Stott, Jr. Bull. Zool. Soc. San Diego, no.20, pp.39, illus., Apr. 1, 1944.

CONTRIBUTION TO THE NATURAL HISTORY OF THE HAWAIIAN AND FANNING ISLANDS AND LOWER CALIFORNIA, MADE IN CONNECTION WITH THE UNITED STATES NORTH PACIFIC SURVEYING EXPEDITION, 1873-75. Thomas Hale Streets. Washington, Govt.Print.Off., Bull. of the U.S.Nat.Mus., no.7, pp.172, 1877; Smiths.Inst., Misc.Coll., Publication no. 303, vol.8, art.7.

LIST OF THE MAMMALS OF THE JAPANESE WAR AREA. George Henry Hamilton Tate. New York, Amer. Mus. of Nat.Hist., maps, 194?

ON MAMMALS COLLECTED BY MR. ALBERT MEEK ON WOODLARK ISLAND, AND ON KIRIWINA IN THE TROBRIAND GROUP. Oldfield Thomas. Novitates Zoologicae, vol.3, pp.526-529, Dec., 1896.

ON SOME MAMMALS COLLECTED BY MR. ALBERT MEEK ON FERGUSSON ISLAND, D'ENTRECASTEAUX GROUP. Oldfield Thomas. Novitates Zoologicae, vol.2, pp.163-166, June, 1895.

ON SOME MAMMALS FROM THE NEW HEBRIDES. Oldfield Thomas. Ann. and Mag. Nat. Hist., ser.9, vol.16, pp.240-241, Aug., 1925.

REPORT ON THE ZOOLOGICAL COLLECTIONS MADE IN THE INDO-PACIFIC OCEAN DURING THE VOYAGE OF H. M. S. ALBERT.-MAMMALS. Oldfield Thomas. 1884.

A BAT AND A NEW SHREW FROM KOTO-SHO (BOTEL-TOBAGO). Mitosi Tokuda, Tadao Kano. Annotations Zool.Japonenses, vol.15, no. 4, pp.427-432, figs.2, tbls., Dec. 1, 1936.

FOSSIL LAND MAMMALS FROM THE RIUKIU ISLANDS. Shigeyasu Tokunaga. Proc. Imp. Acad., Tokyo, vol.12, no.8, pp.255-257, illus., Oct., 1936.

DIAGNOSES OF NEW MAMMALS FROM THE SOUTH-WEST PACIFIC. Ellis Troughton. Records Australian Mus., Sydney, vol. 21, no.6, pp.373-375, June 25, 1945.

MAMMALS, REPTILES, AND FISHES OF FUNAFUTI. Edgar R. Waite. Memmoirs Australian Mus., vol.3, pp.165-177, pls. 8, 1896.

PACIFIC MARINE MAMMALS: WAYS OF OCEAN DENIZENS. Lewis Wayne Walker. Nat. Humane Rec., Albany, vol.34, no. 3, pp.22-24, Mar., 1946.

PACIFIC OCEAN--MICRONESIA see MICRONESIA

PALAEARCTIC REGION

CHECKLIST OF PALAEARCTIC AND INDIAN MAMMALS, 1758-1946. J.R. Ellerman, T.C.S. Morrison-Scott. British Mus., Nat. Hist., London, pp.810, map, Nov. 19, 1951.

CHECKLIST OF PALAEARCTIC AND INDIAN MAMMALS--AMENDMENTS. J. R. Ellerman, T.C.S. Morrison-Scott. Jour. Mamm., vol.34, no.4, pp.516-518, Nov. 13, 1953.

CHECKLIST OF PALAEARCTIC AND INDIAN MAMMALS--NEW NAME. J. R. Ellerman, T.C.S. Morrison-Scott. Jour. Mamm., vol.33, no.3, p.399, Aug. 19, 1952.

PLAN FOR A BIOLOGICAL SURVEY OF THE PALEARCTIC REGION. Gerrit S. Miller, Jr. Carnegie Inst., Year Book, no. 1, pp.240-266, Jan., 1903.

THREE NEW PALEARCTIC MAMMALS. Oldfield Thomas. Ann. and Mag. Nat. Hist., ser.7, vol.18, no.105, pp.220-222, Sep., 1906.

PALESTINE

(MAMMALS FROM PALESTINE.) Saeugetiere Palaestinas. J. Aharoni. Zeitschr.f. Saeugetierk., vol.5, nos.5-6, pp.327-343, Dec. 22, 1930.

(ZOOGEOGRAPGICAL DATA ON THE FAUNA OF PALESTINE AND ADJACENT COUNTRIES AND THEIR AFFINITIES TO THAT OF THE IBERIAN PENINSULA.) Donnees zoogeographiques sur la Faune de la Palestine et des Contrees adjacentes par rapport a celle de la Peninsule Iberique. I. Aharoni. Comptes Rendus XII Congres Internat. Zool. Lisbonne 1935, pp.1132-1137, 1936.

MAMMALS OBTAINED BY THE PHILLIPS PALESTINE EXPEDITION. Glover M. Allen. Bull. Mus. Comp. Zool. Harvard College, Cambridge, vol.59, no.1, pp.3-14, Feb., 1915.

THE FOSSIL FAUNA OF THE WADY EL-MUGHARA CAVES. Dorothea M.A. Bate. The Stone Age of Mount Carmel--Excavations at the Wady el-Mughara, vol.1, (Palaeontology pt.2), pp.137-240, figs.8, chart 1, 1937.

NEW PLEISTOCENE MAMMALS FROM PALESTINE. Dorothea M.A. Bate. Ann. and Mag. Nat. Hist., London, ser.10, vol. 20, no.117, pp.397-400, Sep., 1937.

ON THE ANIMAL REMAINS FROM THE MUGHARET-EL-ZUTTIYEH IN 1926. (Researches in Prehistoric Galilee 1925-26 by F. Turville-Petre, Brit.School.) Dorothea M.A. Bate. Archaeol.Jerusalem, pp.35-52, figs.10, pls.17, 1927.

ON THE ANIMAL REMAINS OBTAINED FROM THE MUGHARET-EL-ZUTTIYEH IN 1925. (Researches in Prehistoric Galilee 1925-26 by F. Turville-Petre, Brit.School.) Dorothea M.A. Bate. Archaeol.Jerusalem, pp.27-34, figs.25, 1927.

TWO ADDITIONS TO THE PLEISTOCENE CAVE FAUNA OF PALESTINE (TRIONYX AND CROCODILUS). (Includes Summary of the Succession of Mammalian Faunas.) Dorothea M.A. Bate. Ann. and Mag. Nat. Hist., London, ser.10, vol.14, no.82, pp. 474-478, pls.13, Oct., 1934.

ANIMAL LIFE IN PALESTINA. Friedrich Simon Bodenheimer. Jerusalem, 1935.

STONE AGE OF MOUNT CARMEL. H. Breuil. Nature, London, vol.145, no.3683, pp.837-839, June 1, 1940.

(OBSERVATIONS ON THE MICROMAMMALS FOUND IN THE PELLETS OF THE FRIGHTENED SCREECH-OWL (TYTO ALBA) IN PALESTINE.) Observations sur les Micromammiferes trouves dans les pelotes de la Chouette effraye (Tyto alba) en Palestine. M. Dor. Mammalia, Paris, vol.11, nos.1-2, pp. 50-54, Mar.-June, 1947.

BONE-BEARING BEDS OF BETHLEHEM: THEIR FAUNA AND INDUSTRY. Elinor W. Gardner, Dorothea M.A. Bate. Nature, vol. 140, no.3540, pp.431-433, Sep. 4, 1937.

NEAR EAST AS A GATEWAY OF PREHISTORIC MIGRATION. A.E. Garrod. Amer. School of Prehistoric Research, Old Lyme, Bull.no.13, pp.17-21, May, 1937.

RECENT EXCAVATIONS IN THE NEAR EAST. (Report of Paper Read by Miss Garrod Before Sect.H. of B.A. at Leicester in Regard to Palaeanthropus palestinus and Other Prehistoric Mammals.) A.E. Garrod. Nature, London, vol.132, no.3348, pp.1010-1011, Dec. 30, 1933.

PREHISTORIC RESEARCH IN THE NEAR EAST. (Human Skeletons from Palestine.) George Grant Maccurdy. Proc. Amer. Philos. Soc., vol.72, no.3, pp.121-135, figs.1-12, 1933.

(NOTES ON MAMMALS OF PALESTINIAN COASTAL REGION.) Beleshke o fauni sisara peshchanikh dina palestinskog obalskog podruchya i blije okoline. Pavle Roter. Bull. Mus. Hist. Nat. Pays Serbe, ser.B, liv.5-6, pp.487-492, 1953. (In Russian with English summary.)

A NEW SHREW AND TWO NEW FOXES FROM ASIA MINOR AND PALESTINE. Oldfield Thomas. Ann. and Mag. Nat. Hist., ser.9, vol.5, pp.119-122, Jan., 1920.

WILD ANIMALS OF THE HOLY LAND. Edward Thompson. Jour. Mamm., vol.10, no.2, pp.186-188, May, 1929.

SURVEY OF WESTERN PALESTINE. THE FAUNA AND FLORA OF PALESTINE. H. B. Tristram. London, 1884.

ANCIENT FAUNA AND EARLY MAN AT BETHLEHEM. Nature, London, vol.140, no.3540, p.381, Sep. 4, 1937.

FAUNA AND FLORA OF PALESTINE. Nature, London, vol.161, no.4101, p.902, June 5, 1948.

PANAMA

BIRDS AND MAMMALS OF THE WESTERN SLOPE OF THE AZUERO PENINSULA (REPUBLIC OF PANAMA). John Warren Aldrich, Benjamin Patterson Bole, Jr. Sci. Publ. Cleveland Mus. Nat. Hist., vol.7, pp.5-139, 189-196, pls.8, map, Aug. 31, 1937.

MAMMALS FROM DARIEN. Glover M. Allen, Thomas Barbour. Bull. Mus. Comp. Zool., vol.65, pp.259-274, Feb., 1923.

PANAMA MAMMALS COLLECTED IN 1914-1915. H.E. Anthony. Bull. Amer. Mus.Nat. Hist., vol.35, art.20, pp.357-376, June 9, 1916.

CHIRIQUI MAMMALIA. Outram Bangs. Mus. of Comp. Zoo. Bull., Harvard College, Camb., vol.39, pp.15-51, 1902.

VERTEBRATA FROM THE SAVANNA OF PANAMA. INTRODUCTION. MAMMALIA. Outram Bangs. Bull. Mus. Comp.Zool., Harvard College, vol.46, no.12, pp.211-213, Jan., 1906.

MAMMALS AND BIRDS OF THE PEARL ISLANDS, BAY OF PANAMA. Outram Bangs, John E. Thayer. Bull.Mus.Comp.Zool., Harvard College, vol.46, no.8, pp.137-159, Sep., 1905.

ANNOTATED LIST OF MAMMALS OF THE MARIATO RIVER DISTRICT OF THE AZUERO PENINSULA. B.P. Bole, Jr. Sci. Publ. Cleveland Mus. Nat. Hist., vol.7, pp.140-188, Aug. 31, 1937.

HUNTING IN CHIRIQUI. E.R. Cuthbert. Zool. Soc. Bull., vol.26, no.1, pp.4-7, figs.8, Jan., 1923.

MORNING ON BARRO COLORADO. Paul Russel Cutright. Fauna, Philadelphia, vol. 2, no.3, pp.47-52, illus., Sep., 1940.

CHANGES OBSERVED IN THE MAMMAL FAUNA OF BARRO COLORADO ISLAND, 1929-1937. Robert K. Enders. Ecology, Brooklyn, vol.20, no.1, pp.104-106, Jan., 1939.

MAMMALIAN LIFE HISTORIES FROM BARRO COLORADO ISLAND, PANAMA. Robert K. Enders. Bull. Mus. Compar. Zool. Harvard College, vol.78, no.4, pp. 385-502, pls.5, Oct., 1935.

(Review by A. Brazier Howell of) MAMMALIAN LIFE HISTORIES FROM BARRO COLORADO ISLAND, PANAMA. Robert K. Enders. Jour. Mamm., vol.17, no.1, pp.69-70, Feb., 1936.

NOTES ON SOME MAMMALS FROM BARRO COLORADO ISLAND, CANAL ZONE. Robert K. Enders. Jour. Mamm., vol.11, no.3, pp.280-292, pl.16, Aug., 1930.

DESCRIPTIONS OF FIVE NEW MAMMALS

FROM PANAMA. Edward Alphonso Goldman. Smiths.Inst., Misc. Coll., Wash., Publication no.2266, vol.63, no.5, pp.7, 1914.

DESCRIPTIONS OF NEW MAMMALS FROM PANAMA AND MEXICO. Edward Alphonso Goldman. Smiths.Inst., Misc.Coll., Wash., Publication no.2168, vol.60, no.22, pp.20, 1913.

DESCRIPTIONS OF TWELVE NEW SPECIES AND SUBSPECIES OF MAMMALS FROM PANAMA. Edward Alphonso Goldman. Smiths.Inst., Misc.Coll., Publication no.2073, vol.56, no.36, pp.11, 1912.

MAMMALS OF PANAMA. Edward Alphonso Goldman. Smiths. Inst., Misc. Coll., Publication no.2498, vol.69, no.5, pp.309, illus., pls.39, fold.map, 1920.

NEW MAMMALS FROM EASTERN PANAMA. Edward Alphonso Goldman. Smiths. Inst., Misc.Coll., Publication no.2142, vol.60, no.2, pp.18, 1912.

OBSERVATIONS ON BARRO COLORADO ISLAND MAMMALS. Lloyd G. Ingles. Jour. Mamm., vol.34, no.2, pp.266-268, May 14, 1953.

MAMMALS OF SAN JOSE ISLAND, BAY OF PANAMA. Remington Kollogg. Smiths.Inst., Misc.Coll., Publication no.3851, vol.106, no.7, pp.4, 1946.

THREE NEW MAMMALS FROM THE PEARL ISLANDS, PANAMA. (Mazama permira, Dasyprocta punctata bellula, Proechimys semispinosus ignotus.) Remington Kellogg. Proc.Biol.Soc.Wash., vol.59, pp.57-62, Mar. 11, 1946.

COLLECTING ANIMALS AND PLANTS IN PANAMA, 1937. Gerrit S. Miller, Jr. Explor. and Field-Work Smiths.Inst.1937, Publ.3480, pp.27-30, figs.27-32, 1938.

LIST OF MAMMALS AND BIRDS COLLECTED BY MR. BRIDGES IN THE VICINITY OF THE TOWN OF DAVID IN THE PROVINCE OF CHIRIQUI, IN THE STATE OF PANAMA. Philip L. Sclater. Proc. Zool. Soc. London, pt.24, pp. 138-143, 1856.

MAMMALS AND BIRDS OF THE PEARL ISLANDS, BAY OF PANAMA. John E. Thayer, Outram Bangs. Bull. Mus. Comp. Zool., Harvard College, Cambridge, vol. 46, no.8, pp.137-160, Sep., 1905.

NEW MAMMALS FROM CHIRIQUI. Oldfield Thomas. Ann. and Mag. Nat. Hist., ser.7, vol.11, no.63, pp.376-382, Apr., 1903.

ON A COLLECTION OF MAMMALS FROM THE SMALL ISLANDS OFF THE COAST OF WESTERN PANAMA. Oldfield Thomas. Novitates Zoologicae, vol.10, pp.39-42, Apr., 1903.

ON SOME MAMMALS FROM COIBA ISLAND, OFF THE WEST COAST OF PANAMA. Oldfield Thomas. Novitates Zoologicae, vol.9, no.1, pp.135-137, Apr. 10, 1902.

## PERSIA

FOSSIL BONES IN A PERSIAN GARDEN. (Maragha Mammals.) O. Barten. Nat.Hist., vol.29, no.2, pp.143-154, 1929.

EASTERN PERSIA, AN ACCOUNT OF THE JOURNEYS OF THE PERSIAN BOUNDARY COMMISSION 1870-72. VOL. II. ZOOLOGY AND GEOLOGY. Blanford. London, 1876.

REPORT ON A COLLECTION OF MAMMALS MADE BY COL. J. E. B. HOTSON IN SHIRAZ, PERSIA. R.E. Cheesman. Jour. Bombay Nat. Hist. Soc., vol.27, pp.573-581, Mar. 31, 1921.

CAVE EXPLORATIONS IN IRAN 1949. Carleton S. Coon. Univ. Mus., Univ.Pennsylvania, Philadelphia, pp.124, pls.15, 1951.

(SKELETAL MATERIAL COLLECTED DURING THE EXCAVATIONS OF DR. T.J.ARNE IN SHAH TEPE AT ASTRABAD-GORGAN IN IRAN.) Tierreste der Ausgrabungen von dem Grossen Koenigshuegel, Shah Tepé, in Nord-Iran, von J. Wolfg.Amschler. Stockholm, Bokforlags aktiebolaget Thule, pp.129, pls. 26, fold.tbls., diagrs., 1939. (Reports from the Scientific expedition to the northwestern provinces of China under the leadership of Dr. Sven Hedin. The Sino-Swedish expedition. Publication no.9. VII.Archaeology. 4)

FIVE NEW RODENTS FROM THE EASTERN ELBURZ MOUNTAINS AND A NEW RACE OF HARE FROM TEHERAN. George G.Goodwin. Amer. Mus. Novitates, New York, no. 1050, pp.1-5, Dec. 1, 1939.

MAMMALS COLLECTED BY THE LEGENDRE 1938 IRAN EXPEDITION. George G. Goodwin. Amer. Mus. Novitates, New York, no.1082, pp.1-17, July 18, 1940.

HUNTING IN PERSIA. G. Barney Harris. Field and Stream, New York, vol.50, no.3, pp.30-32, 78-81, illus., July, 1945.

(COMMENTS ON SOME MAMMALS OF PERSIA. III. AM EXCERPT FROM "FAUNA AND FLORA".) Om några daggdjur fran Persien. III. Sartryck ur Fauna och Flora". Einar Lonnberg. Popular Tidskrift for Biologi, Haft 2, pp.49-68, 1925.

ON A COLLECTION OF MAMMALS FROM PERSIA AND ARMENIA PRESENTED TO THE BRITISH MUSEUM BY COL. A. C. BAILWARD. Oldfield Thomas. Proc. Zool. Soc. London, vol.2, pp.519-527, pls.16, Apr. 5, 1906.

ON MAMMALS FROM NORTHERN PERSIA, PRESENTED TO THE NATIONAL MUSEUM BY COL. A. C. BAILWARD. Oldfield Thomas Ann. and Mag. Nat. Hist., ser. 7, vol.20, no.117, pp.196-202, Sep., 1907.

## PHILIPPINE ISLANDS

MAMMALS FROM PALAWAN ISLAND, PHILIPPINE ISLANDS. J.A. Allen. Bull. Amer. Mus. Nat. Hist., vol.28, pp.13-17, Jan. 5, 1910.

COLLECTIONS FROM THE PHILIPPINE ISLANDS. Thomas Barbour, et al. Bull. Mus. Comp. Zool. Harvard College, Cambridge, vol.86, no.2, pp.25-128, Nov., 1939. (Mammals by Barbara Lawrence, pp.28-73.)

PRELIMINARY NOTES ON THE BIRDS AND MAMMALS COLLECTED BY THE MENAGE SCIENTIFIC EXPEDITION TO THE PHILIPPINE ISLANDS. Frank Swift Bourns, Dean C. Worcester. Minneapolis, The Academy of Natural Sciences, Occasional Papers, vol.1, no.1, pp.64, 1894.

GEOGRAPHIC NAMES IN THE PHILIPPINE ISLANDS. Henry Gannett. Special Report of the U.S. Board on Geographic Names, pp.59, May, 1901.

REPORT ON SOME OF THE ADDITIONS TO THE COLLECTION OF MAMMALIA IN THE BRITISH MUSEUM. Albert Günther. Proc. Zool. Soc. London, pp.735-751, figs. 9, pls., 1876.

LIST OF THE MAMMALS OF THE PHILIPPINE ISLANDS, EXCLUSIVE OF THE CETACEA. Ned Hollister. Philippine Jour. Sci., Manila, vol.7, no.1, pp.1-64, Feb., 1912.

MAMMALS OF THE PHILIPPINE ISLANDS. Ned Hollister. Philippine Jour. Sci., Manila, vol.7, sec.D, no.1, Feb., 1912.

REVIEW OF THE PHILIPPINE LAND MAMMALS IN THE UNITED STATES NATIONAL MUSEUM. Ned Hollister. U.S. Nat. Mus., Proc., Washington, vol.46, pp.299-341, pls.27-29, 1914.

PHILIPPINE ZOOLOGICAL EXPEDITION 1946-1947. NARRATIVE AND ITINERARY. Harry Hoogstraal. Fieldiana, Zoology, Chicago, vol.33, no.1, pp.1-86, pls.1-7, Apr. 18, 1951.

ON TWO MAMMALS FROM THE CALAMIANES ISLANDS. F.A. Jentink. Notes Leyden Mus., vol.17, pp.41-48, 1895.

COLLECTIONS FROM THE PHILIPPINE ISLANDS. MAMMALS. Barbara Lawrence. Bull. Mus. Comp.Zool., Cambridge, vol. 86, no.2, pp.28-73, Nov., 1939.

MAMMALIA FROM MOUNT MURUD AND THE KALABIT COUNTRY. E. Lonnberg, E. Mjoberg. Ann. and Mag. Nat. Hist., vol.16, ser.9, pp.508-513, pl.27, Nov., 1925.

(MAMMALS OF THE PHILIPPINES.) Saeugethiere von den Philippinen. Paul Matschie. Sitz.Ber.Gesell.Naturf.Freunde Berlin, Jahrgang 1898, no.5, pp.38-43, May 17, 1898.

DESCRIPTIONS OF NEW GENERA AND SPECIES OF MAMMALS FROM THE PHILIPPINE ISLANDS. Edgar Alexander Mearns. U.S. Nat. Mus., Proc., Wash., vol.28, pp.425-460, May 13, 1905.

(MAMMALS OF CELEBES AND THE PHILIPPINE ARCHIPELAGO.) Saeugethiere vom Celebes- und Philippinen- Archipel. A. B. Mayer. Abhandl. and Ber. K.Zool. Anthropol.Ethno. Mus. Dresden, 1898-1899, vol.7, no.7, pp.1-55, pls.11, 1899.

DESCRIPTIONS OF TWO NEW GENERA AND SIXTEEN NEW SPECIES OF MAMMALS FROM THE PHILIPPINE ISLANDS. Gerrit Smith Miller, Jr. U.S. Nat. Mus., Proc., Washington, vol.38, pp.391-404, pls.18-20, 1911.

(MAMMALS OF THE PHILIPPINES, ESPECIALLY OF THE PALAWAN GROUP.) Saeugethiere von den Philippinen, namentlich von der Palawan-Gruppe. Alfred Nehring. Sitz.Ber.Gesell.Naturf.Freunde Berlin, no. 8, pp.179-193, figs.2, Oct. 16, 1894.

TWO NEW MAMMALS FROM NEGROS ISLAND, PHILIPPINES. (Dobsonia viridis chapmani: Crocidura nearina.) Dioscoro S. Rabor. Nat. Hist., Misc., Chicago, no. 96, pp.7, Feb. 8, 1952.

MAMMALS. Colin Campbell Sanborn. Chicago Nat. Hist. Mus., Publication 701, Fieldiana, Zoology, vol.33, no.2, pp.89-158, illus., 1952.

MAMMALS FROM MINDANAO, PHILIPPINE ISLANDS, COLLECTED BY THE DANISH PHILIPPINE EXPEDITION 1951-1952. Colin Campbell Sanborn. Vidensk.Meddelelser Dansk Naturhist. Forening, Copenhagen, vol.115, pp.283-288, pl.1, Nov. 28, 1953.

PHILIPPINE ZOOLOGICAL EXPEDITION 1946-1947. MAMMALS. Colin Campbell Sanborn. Fieldiana, Zool., Chicago Nat. Hist. Mus., vol.33, no.2, pp.89-158, Nov. 28, 1952.

"FIRST-TIMERS" FROM THE PHILIPPINES. (Tarsier, Tree Shrew, Giant Rats.) Karl P. Schmidt. Anim. Kingdom, New York, vol. 50, no.5, pp.139-144, 165-166, illus., Sep.-Oct. (Oct.1), 1947.

LIST OF THE BIRDS AND MAMMALS COLLECTED BY THE STEERE EXPEDITION TO THE PHILIPPINES, WITH LOCALITIES AND WITH BRIEF PRELIMINARY DESCRIPTIONS OF SUPPOSED NEW SPECIES. J.B. Steere. Courier Office, Ann Arbor, pp.1-30, (Mammals pp.28-30) July 14, 1890.

PHILIPPINE LAND MAMMALS. Edward H. Taylor. Monograph 30, Bureau of Science, Dept. Agric. and Commerce, Manila, pp. 548, pls.25, June 30, 1934.

DUKE OF BEDFORD'S ZOOLOGICAL EXPLORATION IN EASTERN ASIA. III. ON MAMMALS OBTAINED BY MR. M. P. ANDERSON IN THE PHILIPPINE ISLANDS. Oldfield Thomas. Proc. Zool. Soc. London, pp.140-142, June 12, 1907.

ON THE MAMMALS OBTAINED BY MR. JOHN WHITEHEAD DURING HIS RECENT EXPEDITION TO THE PHILIPPINES. Oldfield Thomas. Trans. Zool. Soc. London, vol.14, pt.6, pp.377-412, pls.30-33, June, 1898.

PRELIMINARY DIAGNOSES OF NEW MAMMALS FROM NORTHERN LUZON, COLLECTED BY MR. JOHN WHITEHEAD. Oldfield Thomas, Ann. and Mag. Nat. Hist., ser.6, vol.16, no.92, pp.160-164, Aug., 1895.

SEEKING MINDANAO'S STRANGEST CREATURES. (Tarsier, Three Shrew, Flying Lemur, Cloud Rat.) Charles Heizer Wharton. Natl. Geogr.Mag., Washington, vol.94, no.3, pp.388-408, illus., Sep., 1948.

POLAND

PRESERVATION OF NATURE IN POLAND. Julian Borucki. Jour. Soc. Preservation Fauna Empire, Hertford, n.s., pt.45, pp. 10-14, Aug., 1942.

PRESERVATION OF NATURE IN PRE-WAR POLAND. Julian Borucki. Bull. British Ornithol. Club, London, vol.62, no.440, pp.19-27, Dec. 31, 1941.

(PRESENT STATE OF OUR KNOWLEDGE OF THE QUATERNARY IN POLAND.) L'etat actuel de notre connaissance du Quaternaire en Pologne. (Elephas trogontherii.) B. Halick. Trans. II Internat. Confer. Assoc. Study Quaternary Period in Europe, United Geol. and Prosp. Serv. USSR, Leningrad, fasc.1, pp.45-51, pl., 1932.

(SUPPLEMENTARY LIST OF THE MAMMAL FAUNA OF POLAND.) Uzupelnienie do listy ssakow ziem Polski. Jan J. Karpinski. PART I.(SORICIDAE, INSECTIVORA.) Sorex macropygmaeis Mill. Fragmenta Faunistica Musei Zoologici Polonici, Warsaw, vol.5, no.8, pp.2, 1947; PART II. (LIST OF FAUNA MAMMALS OF POLAND.) Liste supplémentaire a la faune des Mammiferes de la Pologne. Vol.5, no.9, pp.3, 1947.

EARLY PLEISTOCENE FAUNA OF SMALL MAMMALS FROM THE KADZIELNIA HILL OF KIELCE (POLAND). Kazimierz Kowalski. Acta Palaeontol. Polonica, vol.3, no.1, pp.1-47, 1958.

INSECTIVORES,BATS AND RODENTS FROM THE EARLY PLEISTOCENE BONE BRECCIA OF PODLESICE NEAR KROCZYCE (POLAND). Kazimierz Kowalski. Acta Palaeontol. Polonica, Polska Akad. Nauk, vol.1, no.4, pp.331-394, pls.1-4, 1956.

(INVESTIGATIONS ON THE ECOLOGY OF FOREST SMALL MAMMALS IN THE NEIGHBOURHOOD OF KRAKOW.) Badania nad ekologią drobnych ssaków, leśnych w okolicy Krakowa. Kazimierz Kowalski. Materialy do Fizjografii Kraju, Polska Akad. Umiejetności, Krakow, no.22, pp.18, illus., 1950. (In Polish with English summary.)

(COMMUNICATIONS ON THE SYSTEMATICS AND GEOGRAPHIC DISTRIBUTION OF SOME MAMMALS OF THE POLISH FAUNA.) Mitteilungen ueber die Systematik und geographische Verbreitung einiger Saeugetierarten der polnischen Fauna. Roman Kuntze. Zeitschr.f. Saeugetierk., vol.10, no.1, pp.62-72, figs.2, Dec. 31, 1935.

(NOTES ON MAMMALS OF SOUTHERN POLAND.) Przyczynek do znajomosci fauny Ssakow poludniowej Polski. Roman Kuntze. Kosmos, Lwów, vol.55, nos.1-2, pp.219-232, fig.1, 1930. (In Polish with German summary.)

(REPORT ON THE MAMMALS OF POLAND AND THEIR GEOGRAPHICAL DISTRIBUTION.) Bericht ueber die Saeugetiere Polands und ihre geographische Verbreitung. Edouard de Lubicz Niezabitowski. Zeitschr. f. Saeugetierk., vol.9, pp.188-197, Dec. 30, 1934.

(SURVEY OF THE MAMMAL FAUNA OF POLAND.) Revue de la faune des mammifères en Pologne. Edouard de Lubicz Niezabitowski. Bull. Soc. Amis Sci. de Poznan, Sci. math. et nat., livr.6, pp. 11, 1934.

(SOME RARER OR LESSER KNOWN MAMMALS FROM THE NIDA VALLEY.) Janina Serafińska, Wlodzimierz Serafinski. Acta Zool. Cracoviensia, Polska Acad. Nauk, vol.2, no.9, pp.208-217, Aug. 31, 1957. (In Polish with German and Russian summaries.)

(FOSSIL REMNANTS OF TALPA EUROPAEA L. AND ARVICOLA TERRESTRIS L. FOUND IN GLACIAL FORMATIONS NEAR TCZEW.) Szczatki kopalne kreta (Talpa europaea L.) i karczownika ziemnowodnego (Arvicola terrestris L.) znalezione w utworach lodowcowych pod tczewem. Wacław Skuratowicz. Inst. Geol. Badan Czwartorzedu Polsce, vol.5, pp.253-257, 1954. (In Polish with English summary.)

(SMALL MAMMALS OF THE ENVIRONS OF LOSIC (SIEDLICE DISTRICT).) Drobne zwierzeta ssacc Łosic i okolocy (powiat Siedlce). Wacław Skuratowicz. Fragmenta faunistica musei zoologici Polonici, vol.5, no.9, pp.141-154, 1947.

(STUDIES OF THE MAMMAL FAUNA OF THE ENVIRONS OF ZAMOSC.) Badania nad fauna ssakow Zamojszczyzny. Wacław Skuratowicz. Fragmenta Faunistica Musei Zool. Polonici, Warsaw, vol.5, no.15, pp. 233-292, 1948.

(WILD ANIMAL POPULATION OF POLAND.) Der Wildbestand Polands. Der Naturforscher, vol.6, no.9, p.338, Dec., 1929.

PORTUGAL

(SYNOPTIC CATALOGUE OF MAMMALS OF PORTUGAL.) Catálogo sinótico dos Mamíferos de Portugal. Bernardo Ayres. Coleccao do Museu Zoológico da Universidade de Coimbra, pp.1-46, 1914.

(MARINE FAUNA OF PORTUGAL.) Fauna marinha de Portugal. A.F. De Seabra, A.A. Themido. Mem. Estudos Mus. Zool. Univ. Coimbra, ser.1, no.108, pp.1-49, illus., 1938.

ON THE CAVES OF ESTREMADURA. H. Gadow. Proc. Zool. Soc. London, p.1, Mar. 3, 1896.

(MAMMALS OF PORTUGAL (WITH KEYS FOR DETERMINATION).) Mamiferos de Portugal (chaves para a sua determinacào). Maria Manuela Da Gama. Mem. Estudos Mus. Zool. Univ. Coimbra, vol.246, pp. 1-246, 1957.

(MARINE FAUNA OF PORTUGAL. SECOND ADDENDUM. MAMMALS. CETACEANS.) Fauna marinha de Portugal. 2 Aditamento. Mamiferos. Cetaceos. Augusto Nobre. Mem. e Estudos Mus. Zool. Univ. Coimbra, ser. 1, no.108, p.1, 1938.

(MARINE FAUNA OF PORTUGAL. I. VERTEBRATES (MAMMALS, REPTILES, FISHES).) Fauna marinha de Portugal. I. Vertebrados (Mammiferos, Reptise, Peixes). Augusto Nobre. Descricào dos mammiferos marinhos de Portugal, pp.1-21, figs.9; Pòrto, pp.lxxxix-547, figs.141, 1935.

(CATALOGUE OF THE MAMMALS OF PORTUGAL.) Catalogo dos mammiferos de Portugal. Manoel Paulino d'Oliveira, A.X. Lopes Vieira. Coimbra, pp.28, 1896.

(DICHOTOMIC TABLE FOR DETERMINATION OF THE MAMMALS OF PORTUGAL.) Tabella dichotomica para a determinacào dos mammiferos de Portugal. Manoel Paulino d'Oliveira. Coimbra, pp.10, 1895.

(SYSTEMATIC CATALOGUE OF THE VERTEBRATES OF PORTUGAL: MAMMALS.) Catalogue systematique des vertébrés du Portugal: Mammiferes. A.F. de Seabra. Bull. Soc. Portugaise Sci. Nat., Lisbonne, vol.4, fasc.3, pp.91-114, 1910.

(LIST OF MAMMALS OF PORTUGAL.) Liste des Mammiferes du Portugal. Antonio Armando Themido. Mem. e Estudos Mus. Zool. Univ. Coimbra, ser.1, no.50, pp. 1-7, 1931.

(DISCOVERY OF A NEW STRATA OF LAND VERTEBRATES IN THE NEOGEAN IN THE PROXIMITIES OF LISBON.) Decouverte de nouveaux gisements de Vertebres terrestres dans le Néogene des environs de Lisbonne (Portugal). Georges Zbyszewski. Comptes Rendus Acad. Sci. Paris, vol.205, no.24, pp.1241-1243, Dec. 13, 1937.

PUERTO RICO

INDIGENOUS LAND MAMMALS OF PORTO RICO, LIVING AND EXTINCT. H. E. Anthony. Memoirs, Amer. Mus. Nat. Hist., n.s., vol.2, pt.1, pp.394-435, figs.55, pls.55-74, Oct. 12, 1918.

(Review by Roy L. Moodie of) INDIGENOUS LAND MAMMALS OF PORTO RICO, LIVING AND EXTINCT. H.E. Anthony. Science, n.s., vol.50, p.91, July 25, 1919.

MAMMALS OF PORTO RICO, LIVING AND EXTINCT - CHIROPTERA AND INSECTIVORA. H.E. Anthony. Scientific Survey of Porto Rico and the Virgin Islands, vol. 9, pt.1, pp.238, figs.28, pls.54, fold. map, 1925.

PRELIMINARY REPORT ON FOSSIL MAMMALS FROM PORTO RICO, WITH DESCRIPTIONS OF A NEW GENUS OF GROUND SLOTH AND TWO NEW GENERA OF HYSTRICOMORPH RODENTS. H.E. Anthony. New York Acad. Sci. Annals, vol.27, pp. 193-203, pls.8, 1916.

FIELD WORK IN PUERTO RICO. Gerrit S. Miller, Jr. Explorations and Field-Work of the Smiths. Inst. in 1932, Publ. no.3213, pp.25-28, May 4, 1933.

WILDLIFE CONSERVATION IN PUERTO RICO. Jose A. Ramos. Rev. Agricultura, Industria, y Conercio de Puerto Rico, San Juan, vol.33, no.4, pp.611-612, Oct.-Dec., 1941.

CAVE FAUNULE FROM WESTERN PUERTO RICO WITH A DISCUSSION OF THE GENUS ISOLOBODON. Thomas E. Reynolds, et al. Breviora, Mus. Comp. Zool., Cambridge, no.12, pp.1-8, illus., Apr. 23, 1953.

RUMANIA

(LIST AND BIBLIOGRAPHY OF THE MAMMALS OF RUMANIA.) Verzeichnis und Bibliographie der Saeugetiere Rumaeniens. R.J. Calinescu. Zeitschr. f. Saeugetierk., Berlin, vol.6, no.2, pp.78-84, Dec.15, 1931.

(MAMMALS OF RUMANIA: DISTRIBUTION AND BIOGEOGRAPHICAL AND ECONOMIC CONSIDERATIONS.) Mamiferele Romaniei repartitia si problemele lor biogeografice-Economice. Raul I. Calinescu. Bul. Minist. Agric. si Domeniilor, Bucuresti, no.251, vol.1, pp.103, figs.28, 1931.

(SOME RUMANIAN MAMMALS.) Von einigen Saeugetieren Rumaeniens. Raul I. Càlinescu. Zeitschr. f. Saeugetierk., Berlin, vol.5, no.6, pp.364-366, 1930.

(EXTINCT AND VANISHING MAMMALS OF TRANSYLVANIA.) Erdely kihalt es kihalofelben levo emlosallatai. Sandor Ferenczi. Erdelyi Muz-Egyesulet Tizenkettedik Vandorgyulesenek Emlekkonyve (Mém. douzieme Congres ambulant Soc. Mus. Transylvanie), for year 1933, pp.119-126, figs. 4, 1934.

(ON MAMMAL FOSSILS OF GIURCANI (FALCIN). Sur les mammiferes fossiles de Giurcani (Dep. Fálciu). Nic Macarovici. Ann. Sci. Univ. Jassy, pt.2 (Sci.Nat.), vol.24, no.2, pp.403-408, fig.1, 1938.

(RUMANIAN MAMMALS.) Rumanische Saeugetiere. Paul Matschie. Sitz.Ber. Gesell. Naturf. Freunde, Berlin, Jahrg. 1901, no.9, pp.220-238, Nov. 19, 1901.

NEW LOCALITY FOR FOSSIL MAMMALS IN RUMANIA. N.N. Morosan. Notationes Biol., Bucharest, vol.2, no.1, pp.1-24, figs.2, 1934.

(QUATERNARY MAMMALS FROM TECUCI.) Mamifere quaternare de la Tecuci (Colectia M: Dumitriu-Tecuci). Virginia Nicolaescu-Barbu, Emil Pappadopol. Notationes Biol., Bucharest, vol.1, no.3, pp.109-114, figs. 6, Oct. 15, 1933.

(EXTINCT MAMMALS OF BUKOWINA.) Mamiferele stinse din Bucovina. Emilian Sahleanu. Bull. Fac. Stiinte Cernáuti, vol.5, no.2, pp.357-369, figs.8, (1931) 1932.

(MARINE MAMMALIA OF THE SARMATICUL OF BALCIC.) Mamifere marine din Sarmaticul dela Balcic. I. Simionescu. Acad. romàna, Memoriile, Sectiunea Stiintifica, Bucharest, ser.3, vol.8, no.2, pp. 1-13, figs.14, 1931.

(PLIOCENE MAMMALS OF CIMISLIA RUMANIA. I. CARNIVORES.) Les mammiferes pliocenes de Cimislia (Roumanie). 1. Carnivores. I. Simionescu. Acad. Romàna

Publ. Fondului Vasile Adamachi, Bucharest, vol.9, no.50, pp.1-30, figs.25, pls.3, 1938.

(PLIOCENE VERTEBRATES OF MALUSTENI (COVURLUI).) Vertebratele Pliocene dela Malusteni (Covurlui), I. Simionescu. Acad. Romană, Publ. Fondului Vasile Adamachi Bucharest, vol.9, no.49, pp.83-151, pls.5, figs.81, 1930.

RUSSIA

MODE OF OCCURRENCE OF THE BONES OF THE UPPER SARMAT VERTEBRATES OF THE ELDAR STEPPE. (Abundance of the Upper Miocene Fossil Mammals.) K. Andrianov, N. Laryn. Bull.Soc.Nat.Moscow, n.s., vol.43, sect.geol., vol.13, pp.559-569, figs.2, 1935. (In Russian with English summary.)

KEY TO THE MAMMALS OF THE USSR. N.A. Bobrinskii, et al. State Publ.House, Moscow, pp.368, illus., 1944. (Sections include: General Notes on Systematics, Mammalia; Insectivora; Bats; Carnivora; Pinnipeds; Cetacea; Ungulata; and Rodentia.)

(Review by Harteley H.T. Jackson of) KEY TO THE MAMMALS OF THE USSR. N.A. Bobrinskii, et al. Jour. Mamm., vol.29, no.3, p.303, Aug. 31, 1948.

PALEOLITHIC IN THE UNION OF SOVIET SOCIALIST REPUBLICS. (Mammals mentioned.) G. Boncho-Osmolovsky, V.Gromov. Report Internat. Geol. Congr., 16th sess., U.S.A., 1933, vol.2, pp.1291-1312, figs.7, pls.1-27, 1936.

BRACHYPOTHERIUM AURELIANENSE NONEL, VAR. NOV. GAILITI FROM THE MIOCENE DEPOSITS OF THE TARGAI REGION. A. Borisyak. Bull. Acad.Sci. Leningrad, pp.273-286, 1927.

(SKETCH OF THE LOCATIONS OF TERTIARY TERRESTRIAL MAMMALS OF THE USSR.) Obzor mestonakhozhdenii tretichnykh nazemnykh mlekopitaiushchikh Soiuza SSR. (k 25-letiiu Sovetskoi paleontologii.) A. Borisyak. Frunze, Kirgizgosizdat, pp.42, 1943.

(LOCATIONS OF TERTIARY TERRESTRIAL MAMMALS THROUGHOUT THE USSR.) Mestonaxojdeniya tretichnex nazemnex mlekopitayushchix na territorii SSSR. A.Borisyak, E.I. Belyaeva. Trudi Paleon.Inst., Akad. Nauk SSSR, Moscow, vol.15, no.3, p.116, 1948.

(CONTRIBUTIONS TO GREATER KNOWLEDGE OF RUSSIA'S MAMMALS.) Beitraege zur naeheren Kenntnis der Saeugethiere Russlands. J.F. von Brandt. St.Petersbourg, De l'imprimerie de L'Acad. Imp. des Sci., pp.365, pls.19 (col.4), 1855.

(BIOLOGY OF FOREST ANIMALS AND BIRDS.) Biologiia lesnykh zverei i ptits. G. Doppel'mair. Moscow, Coslesbumizdat, pp.361, 1951.

(STUDIES ON THE ECOLOGY OF TERRESTRIAL VERTEBRATES IN THE TUNDRAS OF SOUTHERN YAMAL. CONTRIBUTION TO KNOWLEDGE OF THE FAUNA AND FLORA OF THE USSR.) Études sur l'écologie des vertebres terrestres dans les tundras du yamal meridional. Contributions a la connaissance de la fauna et la flore de L'URSS. T.Dunaeva, V.Kutcheruk.Soc. Nat.Moscow, vol.19, no.4, pp.1-80, figs. 11, tbls.20, 1941.

RUSSIAN FUR TRADE. Raymond H.Fisher. Univ. Calif. Publ. Hist., Berkeley, vol.31, pp.1-275, map, 1943.

STUDY OF TRADE ANIMAL QUANTITY OSCILLATIONS AND THE ORGANIZATION OF "HARVEST PROGNOSIS" FOR THE HUNT ECONOMY OF USSR DURING THE PERIOD 1917 TO 1942. A.N. Formozov. Zool. Jour. USSR, Moscow, vol.21, no.6, pp.251-258, figs.2, 1942.

(ANIMAL WORLD IN FIELD-PROTECTIVE FOREST PLANTINGS.) Zhivotnyi mir polezashchitnykh lesonansazdenii. V.G.Geptner. Vserossiiskoe ob-vo okhrany prirody, pp.55, 1949.

(CONTRIBUTIONS TO KNOWLEDGE OF RUSSIAN FAUNA AND FLORA.) Moskovskoe obshchestvo ispytatelei prirody. V.G. Geptner. Moscow, n.s., section Zoologique, pp.174, illus., maps, 1947.

(HARMFUL AND HELPFUL ANIMALS IN AREAS OF FIELD-PROTECTIVE CULTIVATION.) Vrednye i poleznye zveri raionov polezashchitnykh nasazhdenii. V.G.Geptner. Moskovskii universitet, pp.451, 1950.

(MAMMALS IN THE PROTECTIVE FOREST ZONE. GEOGRAPHICAL DISTRIBUTION, LIVING HABITS, ECONOMIC IMPORTANCE.) Die Saeugetiere in der Schutzwaldzone; Geographische Verbreitung, Lebensweise und wirtschaftliche Bedeutung. V.G. Geptner. Berlin, Deutscher Verlag der Wissenschaften, pp.xii+343, illus., maps, 1956.

(RUSSIAN LITERATURE IN THE YEAR 1933.) Russische Literatur im Jahre 1933. V.G. Geptner. Zeitschr.f. Saeugetierk., vol.9, nos.1-3, pp.35-46, Dec. 30, 1934.

(SYSTEMATIC AND ZOOGEOGRAPHIC NOTES ON SOME RUSSIAN MAMMALS.) Systematische und tiergeographische Notizen ueber einige russische Saeuger. V.G. Geptner. Folia Zoologica et Hydrobiologica, Riga, vol.6, no.1, pp.17-24, Aug. 30, 1934.

TWENTY YEARS' WORK ON THE SYSTEMATICS AND GEOGRAPHICAL DISTRIBUTION OF MAMMALS IN THE USSR. (1917-1937). V.G. Geptner. Zool.Zh., vol. 16, pp.902-915, 1937.

TWENTY-FIVE YEARS OF STUDY OF THE QUATERNARY OF THE USSR. V. Gromov. Amer. Jour. Sci., New Haven, vol.243, no.9, pp.492-516, Sep., 1945.

(ON THE PRESENT SITUATION REGARDING THE RAISING OF FUR-BEARING ANIMALS IN RUSSIA.) Ueber den gegenwaertigen Stand der Pelztierzucht in Russland. H. Grote. Zool. Garten, Leipzig, n.F., vol.3, nos.1-3, pp.67-68, May, 1930.

CONTRIBUTION TO THE QUESTION OF THE ORIGIN OF ANIMAL BREEDING IN USSR. V.V. Holmsten. Trudy Lab.Genet., Akad.Nauk, Leningrad, USSR, vol.1, pp. 79-107, 1933.

(ROLE OF A REGIME OF SNOW COVER IN THE LIFE OF HOOFED ANIMALS IN THE TERRITORY OF THE USSR.) Rol' rezhima snezhnogo pokrova v zhizni kopytnykh zhivotnykh. A.A. Nasimovich. Moscow, Acad. of Sci. USSR Press, pp. 401, illus., 1955.

PLAN FOR THE STUDY OF TERRESTRIAL VERTEBRATES IN THE USSR TO BE CARRIED OUT BY PLANT PROTECTION INSTITUTIONS. S.I. Obolenskii. Bull.Plant Protection, vol.4, no.1, pp.95-101, 1931. (In Russian with English summary.)

THE MAMMALS OF USSR AND ADJACENT COUNTRIES. (Mammals of eastern Europe and northern Asia.) (Carnivora, Fissipedia and Pinnipedia.) S.I. Ognev. Moscow and Leningrad, vol.3, pp.752, figs.299, maps 19, pls.8, 1935.

(Review by P.Rode of) THE MAMMALS OF USSR AND ADJACENT COUNTRIES. S.I. Ognev. Mammalia, Paris, vol.9, nos. 3-4, p.104, Sep.-Dec., 1945.

(JOURNEYS THROUGH RUSSIA AND IN THE CAUCASUS MOUNTAINS.) Reisen durch Russland und im Caucasischen Gebirge. P.G. Pallas. St. Petersburg, vol.2, pp.1-552, illus., 1791.

CONTRIBUTION TO THE HISTORY OF THE FAUNA OF THE USSR. I.G. Pidoplitshka. Comptes Rendus (Doklady) Acad. Sci. USSR, Moscow, n.s., vol. 23, no.6, pp.609-612, 1939.

(ANIMALS AND BIRDS OF OUR COUNTRY.) Zveri i pitsy nashei strany. V.N.Shnitnikov. Moscow, Molodaya gvardiya, pp.252, illus., 1957.

(SOME NEW PALEOLITHICAL FINDS FROM THE UKRAINE, RUSSIA, AND SIBERIA.) Nektere nové palaeolithicke nalezy z Ukrajiny, Ruska a Sibiře. Joseph Skutil. Czech.Véda. Přirodni Mês.pro Sir. a Pest.ved Prir, Prague, vol.8, nos.9-10, pp.298-302, 1927.

FAUNA OF THE USSR. A.A.Stackelberg, compiler. Mammals. Moscow, 1937, Zoological Inst. of the Acad. of Sci.USSR, n.s., no.13, illus., vol.3, no.4, 1937. (Summary in English.)

(WILD ANIMALS OF THE USSR AND NEIGHBORING COUNTRIES.) Zveri SSSR i prilezhashchikh stran. A.G. Tomilin. Tom IX. Kitoobraznye. Moscow, Izdatel'stvo Akademii Nauk USSR, pp.756, illus., col.pls., tbls., 1957.

OBSERVATIONS ON THE STATUS OF LARGE MAMMAL PROTECTION IN USSR. Ed. Paul Tratz. Saeugetierkundliche Mitteilungen, Bd.3, Hft.4, pp.172-174, Oct. 1, 1955.

(REPORT ON THE STATUS OF MAMMAL RESEARCH AND THE MOST IMPORTANT MAMMAL SPECIES IN THE SOVIET UNION.) Bericht ueber den Stand der Saeugetierforschung und der wichtigsten Saeugetierarten in der Sowjetunion. Ed. Paul Tratz. Saeugetierk. Mitteil., Stuttgart, vol.3, no.3, pp.126-128, July 1, 1955; vol.3, no.4, pp.172-174, Oct. 1, 1955.

ANIMALS OF THE USSR. G.M. Vevers. William Heinemann, London, pp.xiv-95, illus. 97, 1948.

BRIEF REVIEW ON INVESTIGATIONS PERFORMED ON MAMMALS IN USSR FOR 20 YEARS (1917-1937). B.S.Vinogradov, et al. Bull. Acad. Sci. USSR Cl. Sci.Math. et Nat., Moscow, ser.biol., no.5, pp.1503-1513, 1937. (In Russian with English summary.)

(Review by P. Rode of) MAMMAL FAUNA OF THE USSR. B.S. Vinogradov, A.I. Argyropoulo. Mammalia, Paris, vol.2, no. 1, pp.53-54, Mar., 1938.

SHORT ESSAY ON THE PROGRESS OF SOVIET THEROLOGY (MAMMALOGY) FOR TWENTY-YEARS. B.S. Vinogradov. Priroda, Leningrad, no.10, pp.180-183, 1937. (In Russian.)

(FAUNA OF USSR MAMMALS.) (Familie Dipodidae.) B.S. Vinogradov. Inst. Zool. Acad. Sci. USSR, n.s., Moscow and Leningrad, no.13, pp.viii-197, figs.69, 1913.

INJURIOUS INSECTS AND OTHER ANIMALS IN USSR IN THE YEARS 1921-1924. B.S. Vinogradov, S. Obolensky. Under direction of learned specialist I.N. Filipjew. No.3, Rodents, State Inst. Exper.Agronomy, Works on applied Entomology, vol.XIII, pp.177-221, map, 1926.

ZOOGEOGRAPHICAL STUDY OF THE FAUNA OF ECONOMIC IMPORTANCE. B.M. Zhitkov. Zool. Zhurn., Moscow, vol.11, no.2, pp.3-22, maps 5, 1932.

(ON THE BIRDS AND ANIMALS OF OUR HOMELAND; FOR OUT-OF-CLASS READING IN THE MIDDLE GRADE.) O ptitsakh i zveriakh nashei rodiny. M.D. Zverev. Moscow, pp.172, illus., 1956.

RUSSIA--SIBERIA see SIBERIA

RUSSIA, ASIATIC

(USEFUL AND HARMFUL ANIMALS OF KAZAKHSTAN; SUMMARIES.) Poleznye i vrednye zveri Kazakstana. Aleksandr V. Afanas'ev. Alma-Ata, Acad. of Sci. Kazakh SSR, pp.71, illus., 1955.

MAMMALS OF THE COMMANDER ISLANDS AND THE SURROUNDING SEA. I.Barabash-Nikiforov. Jour. Mamm., vol.19, no.4, pp. 423-429, Nov., 1938.

(PRELIMINARY REPORT ON THE MAMMALS IN A STATION OF MAN OF THE STONE AGE ON MOUNT VERKHOLENSK NEAR IRKUTSK.) Rapport preliminaire sur les mammiferes d'une station de l'homme de l'age de la Pierre sur le mont Verkholensk pres Irkoutsk. A. Birula. Comptes Rendus Acad.Sci. URSS, A, no.4, pp.91-93, 1929.

VERTEBRATE FAUNA OF RUSSIAN TURKESTAN, ITS INVESTIGATIONS AND ACTUAL PROBLEMS. N.Bobrinskoy. Proc.Sci.Invest.Institute of Zoology, Moscow, vol.3, no.2, pp.1-137, map, 1929. (In Russian with English summary.)

(ON THE MAMMALS OF THE LAKE BAYKAL REGION.) Ueber die Saeugetiere des Baikalseegebietes. H.von Boetticher. Zeitschr. f.Saeugetierk., Berlin, vol.13, no.2, pp.189-191, 1939.

QUATERNARY (INTERGLACIAL) FAUNA ON THE APSHERON PENINSULA. V.V. Bogachev. Comp.Rendus (Doklady) Acad. Sci. USSR, Moscow, n.s., vol.23, no.3, pp.315-318, 1939.

MARINE MAMMALIA OF USSR FAR EAST. RESOURCES AND COMMERCIAL USE. S.W.Dorofeiev, S.J.Freimann. Trans.Inst. Fisheries and Oceanography USSR, Moscow, vol.3, pp.1-276, figs.1-69, 1936. (In Russian with English and Russian titles.)

SURVEY OF THE MAMMALS OF THE IL'MEN STATE RESERVATION (SOUTHERN URALS). N.M. Dukelskaia. Trans. Study Reservations, Moscow, vol.10, pp.1-31, 1928.

BRIEF PRELIMINARY LIST OF MAMMALS INHABITING THE RESERVE GROUND OF THE MOUNTAIN TAIGA STATION OF THE FAR EASTERN BRANCH OF THE ACADEMY OF SCIENCES, USSR. A.A. Emel'ianov (A.A. Yemelianof). Trudy Gornotaezhnoi Stantsii Dal'nevostochnogo Filiala Akademii Nauk SSSR (Taiga Station of the Far Eastern Branch Acad.Sci.), vol.1, pp.265-266, 1926. (In Russian with English summary.)

(EDUARD EVERSMANN'S JOURNEY FROM ORENBURG TO BUKHARA (WITH A WORD LIST FROM THE AFGHAN LANGUAGE, A NATURAL HISTORY APPENDIX, AND A PREFACE.) Reise von Orenburg nach Buchara von Eduard Eversmann nebst einem Wortverzeichniss aus der Afghanischen Sprache, begleitet von einem naturhistorischen Anhang und einer Vorrede. Eduard Eversmann, H. Lichtenstein. Berlin, 1823.

(REVIEW OF THE MAMMALS OF THE URAL REGION OF WEST KAZAKHSTAN OBLAST.) Obzor fauny mlekopitayeshchix Priuralnovo raiona Zapadno-Kazakhstanskoi oblasti. V.A. Fokanov. Trudy Zool.Inst. Akad.Nauk USSR, Moscow, vol.11, pp.204-213, 1952.

(VERTEBRATE FAUNA OF BADKHYZ (SOUTHERN TURKMENISTAN).) Fauna pozvonochnykh zhivotnykh Badkhyza (IUshnyi Turkmenistan). V.G. Geptner. Acad. of Sci. Turkmen, SSR Press Ashkhabad, pp.333, illus., pls., diagrs., 1956.

(MATERIAL ON THE MAMMAL FAUNA OF THE MIDDLE AND LOWER AMU DARYA.) Materialien zur Kenntnis der Saeugetierfauna der mittleren und unteren Amu-Daria. N.A. Gladkov, G.V.Nikolskij. Sbornik Trudov Gosudarstvennogo Zoologicheskogo Muzeia (Archiv.Mus.Zool. Univ.Moscow), no.2, pp.3-16, 1935. (In Russian with German summary.)

MAMMALS COLLECTED IN KAZAKSTAN, CENTRAL ASIA, BY THE MORDEN-GRAVES NORTH ASIATIC EXPEDITION, WITH THE DESCRIPTION OF A NEW GROUND SQUIRREL. (Citellus pygmaeus kazakstanicus.) G.G. Goodwin. Amer. Mus. Novitates, no.769, pp.15, Jan. 24, 1935.

TWO NEW MAMMALS FROM KAZAKSTAN. (Crocidura suaveolens mordeni, Microtus gravesi.) G.G. Goodwin. Amer.Mus. Novitates, no.742, pp.2, Aug. 27, 1934.

MAMMALIAN REMAINS OF THE QUATERNARY DEPOSITS IN THE LOWER PART OF THE OBI AND IRTISH RIVERS. V.I. Gromov. Bull. Soc. Nat. Moscow, n.s., vol.45, (sect.geol.vol.15, no.2,) pp.154-156, 1937. (In Russian.)

(REVIEW OF THE MAMMAL FAUNA OF THE PAMIR REGION.) Uebersicht ueber die Saeugetierfauna des Pamirgebietes. Hermann Grote. Zool. Garten, Leipzig, n.F., vol.18, nos.3-4, pp.142-145, 1951.

ECOLOGICAL SURVEY OF THE ENVIRONMENTS OF THE LAKES BEELY-KUL, AK-KUL, AND ASHY-KUL, DISTRICT AULEA-ATA, TURKESTAN. D.N. Kashkarov.Acta Univ.Asiae Mediae, ser.VIII-a, Zool.fasc.2, pp.1-54, pl.1, 1928.(In Russian with English summary.)

PRELIMINARY ECOLOGICAL SURVEY OF THE VERTEBRATE FAUNA OF THE CENTRAL KARA-KUM DESERT IN WESTERN TURKESTAN. D. N. Kashkarov, Victor Kurbaton. Ecology, vol.11, no.1, pp.35-60, figs.11, Jan., 1930.

RESULTS ALTAI ZOOL. EXPEDITION, 1898. N. Th. Kastschenko. Tomsk, pp. 1-158, pls.1-4, 1899. (Inserted also in Bull. Tomsk Imp.Univ., vol.16, year 1900.) New: Mus musculus tomensis, p. 46; Mus Tscherga, p.46; Microtus strelzovi, p.50; Lepus Lugubris, p.57.

(OBSERVATIONS ON THE MARINE MAMMALS IN THE SOUTH EAST PART OF THE KARA SEA.) A.Kirpitchnikoff. Bull. Soc.Nat., Moscow, sect.biol., n.s., vol. 46, no.4, pp.213-217, 1937. (In Russian with French summary.)

(NOTES ON THE MAMMAL FAUNA OF THE LOWER COURSE OF THE EMBA RIVER.) A.M. Kolossow. Bull. Soc. Nat. Moscow, sect.biol., n.s., vol.44, nos.7-8, pp.374-385, 1935. (In Russian with German summary.)

SOME DATA ON THE COMMERCIAL FAUNA OF BEGICHEVA ISLAND. V.N. Koshkin. Problemy Arktiki (Problems of the Arctic, Chief Administration of Northern Sea Route, Arctic Inst. USSR), Leningrad, no.2, pp.89-101, fig.1, 1937. (In Russian with English summary.)

MAMMALS OF THE ALAI VALLEY. B. Kuznetzov. Bull. Soc. Nat. Moscow, sect.biol., n.s., vol.46, no.2, pp.126-132, 1937. (In Russian with English summary.)

(MAMMALS OF THE STEPPE REGION OF THE MID-URALS.) Mammiferes de la region des steppes de l'Oural meridional. B. Kuznetzov. Bull. Soc. Nat. de Moscow, Sect. Biol., n.s., vol.37, livr.3-4, pp. 250-311, figs.12, 1928. (In Russian with French summary.)

(CONTRIBUTION TO THE CLASSIFICATION AND GEOGRAPHICAL DISTRIBUTION OF THE MAMMALS OF THE KIRGHIZ STEPPE.) Contribution a la classification et a la distribution geographique des mammiferes de la Steppe des Kirguises. V. Martino, E.Martino. Part 2. Ann.Mus. Zool.Acad.Sci., Petrograd, vol.24, pp. 19-31, 1923; Part 3. Ann.Mus.Zool.Acad. Sci., Leningrad, vol.31, no.2, pp.207-211, 1930.

ABOUT THE FAUNA OF MAMMALS OF THE DISTRICT OF TUNGUSKI. N. P. Naumov. Empire Med.Publ. Moscow Leningrad, pp.7-12, 1933.

MAMMALIAN FAUNA OF THE TUNGUS DISTRICT. N.P. Naumov. Abstr.works zool.inst.Moscow State Univ., pp.72-79, 1933. (In Russian.)

(MAMMALS OF CENTRAL TIEN-SHAN. CONTRIBUTIONS TO KNOWLEDGE OF THE FAUNA AND FLORA OF THE USSR.) Les Mammifères du Thian-Chan central. Contributions a la Connaissance de la Faune et Flore de L'URSS. S.I. Ognev. Soc.Nat. Moscow, vol.18, no.3, pp.1-85, figs.14, tbls.7, pls.3, 1940.

MAMMALS OF THE SHANTAR ISLANDS. S.I. Ognev. Bull. Pac. Sci. Fishery Res. Sta., Vladivostok, vol.2, pt.5, pp.42, 1929. (In Russian with English summary.)

MAMMALS OF THE MIDDLE KOPET-DAGH MOUNTAINS AND THE ADJACENT PLAIN (RUSSIAN TURKESTAN). S. I. Ognev, V.G. Heptner. Trans. Sci. Res. Inst. Zool., Moscow, vol.3, no.1, pp. 47-171, figs.23, pls.3, 1929. (In Russian with English summary.)

(SOME COMMUNICATIONS ON THE MAMMALS OF THE CENTRAL KOPET DAGH AND THE ADJACENT PLAIN (RUSSIAN TURKESTAN).) Einige Mitteilungen ueber die Saeugetiere des mittleren Kopet-Dag und der anliegenden Ebene (Russisch-Turkestan). S.I. Ognev, W.G. Heptner. Zool.Anzeiger, vol.75, nos.11-12, pp. 258-266, Mar. 1, 1928.

TERTIARY MAMMALS OF KAZAKHSTAN. J.A. Orlov. Jour. Mamm., vol.19, no.4, pp.475-477, fig.1, Nov. 14, 1938.

(MAMMALS OF THE TRANSCASPIAN REGION.) Saeugethiere Transkaspiens. G. Radde, A. Walter, W.Blasius. Zool.Jahrb., Abt.f.Syst.Geogr. und Biol.Thiere, Jena, vol.4, no.5, pp.993-1094, pls.28, Dec.27, 1889.

(ATTEMPT AT A ZOOGEOGRAPHICAL CLASSIFICATION OF THE PAMIRS.) Versuch einer zoogeographischen Gliederung des Pamir-Gebietes. W.P. Reinig. Zool. Jahrb. Abteil.f. Systematik, etc.vol.59, pp.447-504, figs.6, maps 7, diagrs.2, 1 profile and 3 charts, July 3, 1930.

MAMMALS OF BALKHASH PART OF TURKESTAN-SIBERIAN RAILWAYS. V.N. Shnitnikov. Bull. Plant Protection, Leningrad, The Lenin Acad. Agric. Sci. in USSR., vol. 4, no.2, pp.101-110, 1932.

(ON SOME INTERESTING MAMMALS OF THE NARYM REGION.) Ueber einige interessante Saeugetiere des Narymgebietes. (Talpa altaica, Mustela martes, Alopex lagopus, and Lupus (Canis) lupus.) W.N. Skalon. Zool.Anzeiger, vol.77, nos.11-12, pp.307-318, July 15, 1928.

CONTRIBUTIONS TO THE HISTORY OF THE COMMANDER ISLANDS. NO. 1. NOTES ON THE NATURAL HISTORY, INCLUDING DESCRIPTIONS OF NEW CETACEANS. Leonard Stejneger. Proc. U.S.Nat. Mus., vol.6, no.5 and 6, June 22, 1883.

COMMANDER ISLANDS IN 1922. (Fur-Seal Herds.) E.K. Suvorov. Bull.Bur.Applied Ichthyology, Leningrad, vol.6, pp.216-232, 1927. (In Russian with English summary.)

ON MAMMALS COLLECTED IN TURKESTAN BY MR. DOUGLAS CARRUTHERS. Oldfield Thomas. Ann.Mag.Nat.Hist., ser.8, vol.3, no.15, pp.257-266, Mar., 1909.

(MATERIALS ON THE BIOLOGY AND ECOLOGY OF THE MAMMALS ON THE ISLAND OF BARASA-KELMES IN THE ARAL SEA IN CONNECTION WITH THE ACCLIMATIZATION OF THE YELLOW GROUND SQUIRREL (CITELLUS FULVUS LICHT.) ON THIS ISLAND.) V.K. Timofeev. Zoologicheskii Zhurnal (Zool.Jour.USSR), Moscow, vol.13, no.4, pp.731-758, figs.7, map, 1934. (In Russian with German summary.)

(MATERIALS FOR STUDY OF THE MAMMAL FAUNA OF THE REGION OF BARGUZIN (NE BAIKAL).) Materiaux pour l'étude de la faune des mammifères de la region de Barguzin (Baical N.E.). S.B. Turov. Arch.Mus.Zool. Univ.Moscow, vol.3, pp.25-40, 1936. (In Russian with French summary.)

MAMMALS OF THE APSHERON PENINSULA. N. Veretschagin. Azerbaijan branch of the Acad. of Sci. USSR, Pub. by AzFAN, Baku, pp.1-33, 1938.

MAMMALS OF TADJIKISTAN, THEIR LIVES AND IMPORTANCE. B.S.Vinogradov, et al. Trudy Tadzhikistanskoy Bazy (Proc. Tadjikistan Foundation), Akad.Sci.USSR, Moscow and Leningrad, pp.276, figs.91, 1935.

(MAMMALS OF THE KRASNOVODSK REGION OF WESTERN TURKMENISTAN.) Mlekopitayushchie krasnovoskovo raiona zapadnoi Turkmenii. B.S. Vinogradov. Trudy Zool.Inst. Akad. Nauk SSSR, Moscow, vol.10, pp.7-44, 1952.

MAMMALS OF THE IMAN RIVER BASIN (USSURI LAND). AFTER THE MATERIALS OF THE EXPEDITION OF THE FAR EASTERN BRANCH OF THE ACADEMY OF SCIENCE USSR IN 1934, AND THE COLLECTIONS OF THE ZOOLOGICAL

INSTITUTE OF THE ACADEMY OF SCIENCE USSR. N.T. Zolotarev. Thesis Biol.Sci., publ.Acad.Sci.USSR, Far Eastern Branch, Moscow and Leningrad, pp.133, figs.32, 1936.

MAMMALS IN THE AREA OF THE NORTHERN PART OF THE TURKESTAN-SIBERIAN RAILWAY. M.D. Zverev. Bull.Plant Protection, Leningrad, The Lenin Acad. Agric.Sci.in USSR, vol.4, no.2, pp.87-100, 1932. (In Russian with English summary.)

RUSSIA, EUROPEAN

MAMMALS OF THE PLAINS SOUTHEAST OF SAMARAN BAY. V.S. Bashanov. Archaeology, History, Ethnography, and Natural History Soc. at Samara, no.5, pp.18-25, Aug., 1928.

OUTLINE OF THE TRAPPING INDUSTRY OF TARTARY. Iv. Bashkirov, N.D. Grigorjev. Raboty Volzhsko-Kamskoi Krajevoi Promyslovoi Biologicheskoi Stansii (Works of Volga-Kama Region Industrial Biological Station), Kazan, no.1, pp.13-89, figs.11, 1931. (In Russian with English summary.)

(FOSSIL MAMMALS OF SEVASTOPOL.) Mammifères fossiles de Sebastopol. A.A. Borissiak. St. Petersbourg, Memoires du Comité geologique, nouvelle serie, livr. 87, illus., pls., 1914.

(NOTES ON THE VERTEBRATA OF THE NORTH OF THE EUROPEAN PART OF RUSSIA, IN PARTICULAR OF THE NORTHERN URALS. A CONTRIBUTION TO MORE DETAILED DATA ON THE ZOOGEOGRAPHY OF NORTHEAST EUROPE.) Bemerkungen ueber die Wirbelthiere des noerdlichen europaeischen Russlands, besonders des noerdlichen Urals. Ein Beitrag zur naeheren zoologisch-geographischen Kenntnis Nordost-Europas. J.F. Brandt. Pp.75.

(NOTES ON THE MAMMAL FAUNA OF THE KYJIWER DISTRICT.) Materialien zur Fauna der Saeugetiere des Kyjiwer Gebietes. M. Charlemagne. Inst.Recherches Zool. et Biol.Acad.Sci. d'Ukr., Trav.Mus. Zool. Kyiv, no.12, pp.57-73, 1933. (In Russian with German summary.)

MAMMALS OF THE VICINITY OF KIEV. E.W. Charleman. Kiev Mat. pozn.faun. j-z, vol.1, pp.26-94, 1915.

CHANGES IN THE FAUNA OF PESTS IN THE PODZOL ZONE (KIROV REGION) IN THE CASE OF VIRGIN SOIL GOING INTO CULTIVATION. Z. Durnovo, et al. Vsesoiuznaia akad. sel'skokhoziaistvennykh nauk imeni V.I. Lenina, Vsesoiuznyi institut zashchity rastenii. Itogi (Summary Sci. Research Work Inst. Plant Protect. for the year 1935), Leningrad, pp.88-90, 1936.

(NOTICES ON THE MAMMAL FAUNA OF THE VALLEY OF THE TCHOROKH RIVER (WESTERN CAUCASUS).) Notices sur la faune des Mammiferes de la vallee du fleuve Tchorokh (Caucase occid.). K.K. Flerov. Ann. Mus. Zool. Acad. Sci., USSR, vol.28, no.1, pp.63-71, 1927.

(ON THE MAMMAL FAUNA OF THE KARADAG (CRIMEA).) Sur la faune de Mammiferes du Karadagh (Crimee). K.K. Flerov. Ann. Mus. Zool. Acad. Sci., USSR, vol.30, pp.371-404, 1929. (In Russian.)

NOTES ON MAMMALS OF NORTH CAUCASUS. A.N. Formozov. Bull. Sci. de l'Institut de l'Exploration Regional du Caucase du Nord, vol.1, pp.73-89, pls.2, 1926. (In Russian with English summary.)

ON THE GENERAL PLAN OF THE RESTORATION OF THE GAME FAUNA OF THE EUROPEAN PART OF THE USSR AND THE UKRAINE. B. Fortunatov. Priroda i sotsialisticheskoe khoziaistvo, Sbornik, vol.6, pp.90-109, 1933. (In Russian.)

(NOTES ON THE GERBILLIDAE (MAMMALIA, GLIRES). VIII. GERBILLIDAE OF THE CAUCASUS AND THE KALMUCK STEPPES.) Notizen ueber die Gerbillidae (Mammalia, Glires). VIII. Gerbillidae der Kaukasuslaender und der Kalmuecken-steppe. V. G. Gebtner. Folia Zoologica et Hydrobiologica, Riga, vol.6, no.2, pp.179, 268, figs.2, pls.7-11, Oct. 10, 1934.

(NEW MAMMALS FROM DAGHESTAN (EASTERN CAUCASUS).) Neue Saeugetiere aus Dagestan (Ost-Kaukasus). V.G. Gebtner, A. N. Formozoff. Zool. Anzeiger, vol.77, pp.273-280, July 15, 1928.

(SHORT LIST OF THE MAMMALS OF DAGESTAN.) Kratkiy opredlitel' mlekopitayushchikh Dagestana. V.G. Geptner. Makhach-Kala, pp.58, illus., 1926.

(CONTRIBUTION TO THE MAMMAL FAUNA OF SOUTHEASTERN KARELIA.) Beitraege zur Saeugetierfauna von Suedost-Karelien. Friedrich Goethe. Zeitschr. f. Saeugetierk., vol.17, no.2, pp.102-114, pls.11, Feb. 19, 1953.

OLD STONE AGE IN EUROPEAN RUSSIA. (Lists Mammals Found at Collecting Sites.) Eugene A. Golomshtok. Trans. Amer. Philos. Soc., n.s., vol.29, pt.2, pp.vii-191-468, figs.100, pls.37, Mar., 1938.

(ON A FIND OF PLEISTOCENE MAMMALIAN FAUNA IN THE GOVERNMENT OF KOSTROMA.) Ueber einen Fund der Pleistozaenen Saeugetierfauna im Gouvernement Kostroma. V. Gromova. Bull. Acad. Sci., USSR, ser.7, no.3, pp.475-476, pls. 2, 1935. (In Russian with German summary.)

REMAINS OF MAMMALS OF THE STONE AGE IN TRANSCAUCASIA. V. Gromova. Ann. Mus. Zool. Acad. Sci., USSR, vol. 30, no.3, pp.427-446, pls.3, 1929. (In Russian.)

(THE HUNTING FAUNA OF THE CENTRAL STATE NATURAL CONSERVATION REGION.) Die Jagdfauna des Staatlichen Zentralen Naturschutzgebietes. P.W.Jurgenson. Priroda i Sotsialisticheskoe Khoziaistvo (Natur- und sozialistische Wirtschaft), Moscow, vol.5, (1932), pp.212-216, 1933. (In Russian.)

MAMMALS OF THE DONETS DISTRICT, NORTHERN CAUCASUS. N.I. Kalabukhov, V.V. Raevskii. Bull. N.Caucas. Plant Prot. Station, vol.5, pp.129-148, 1930.

REMAINS OF QUATERNARY MAMMALS FROM THE EMBA RIVER, TURGAI, AND FROM THE ALLUVIA OF THE KUBAN RIVER. I.P. Khomenko. Vestnik Geol. Komit. (Bull.Com.Geol., Leningrad, vol. 46), 1927, no.7, pp.33-34, 1927. (In Russian.)

POST-TERTIARY FOSSILS OF THE LOWER VOLGA. A. Kireev. Saratov. Nizhne-Volzhskii Kraevoi Muzei (Jour.), pp.76-98, figs.4, 1932. (In Russian.)

MAMMALS OF THE BLACK AND AZOVSK SEAS. (Biology of Monachus, Delphinus, Phocaena, and Tursiops.) S.E. Kleynenberg. Acad. Sci., USSR, Moscow, pp.285, 1956. (In Russian.)

(STATUS AND RANGES OF MAMMALS OF EASTERN PODOLIA, RUSSIA.) Obecny stan wiadomosci o faunie ssakow i ptakow wschodniego Podola. Roman Kuntze. Kosmos, Lwów, vol.53, no.4, pp.685-698, (1928) 1929.

ON A CERTAIN REGULARITY IN THE DISTRIBUTION OF MAMMALS OVER THE EUROPEAN PART OF THE USSR. B.A. Kuznetzov. Zool. Zhurnal, Moscow, vol.16, no.1, pp.165-182, tbls., 1937. (In Russian with English summary.)

(ON SOME REGULARITIES OF MAMMAL DISTRIBUTION IN THE EUROPEAN PART OF THE USSR.) Ueber einige Gesetzmaessigkeiten der Saeugetierverbreitung im europaeischen Teil des UdSSR. B.A. Kuznetzov. Zool. Zhurnal, Moscow, vol.15, no.1, pp.96-127, maps 7, 1936. (In Russian.)

(ON THE NORTHERN LIMIT OF THE MEDITERRANEAN ELEMENT IN THE FAUNA AND FLORA OF THE CRIMEA.) Ueber die Nordgrenze des mediterranen Elemente in der Fauna und Flora der Krim. B.A. Kuznetznov. Biol. Zentralblatt, vol. 50, pp.422-445, 1930.

NEW DATA ON THE MAMMALS OF THE CRIMEAN MOUNTAINS. V. Martino, E. Martino. Jour. Crimean Soc. Nat. and Nature Lovers, vol.7, pp.1-2 (of reprint), 1917.

REMARKS ON THE SYSTEMATIC RELATIONS AND GEOGRAPHIC DISTRIBUTION OF SOME CRIMEAN ANIMALS. V. Martino, E. Martino. Jour. Crimean Soc. Nat. and Nature Lovers, vol.7, pp.1-7 (of reprint), 1917. (In Russian.)

NEW DATA ON BIRDS AND MAMMALS OF THE PENZA GOVERNMENT (CENTRAL RUSSIA.) A.A. Medvedev. Bull. Soc. Nat. Moscow, Sect.Biol., vol.41, nos.1-2, pp.121-124, 1932. (In Russian.)

(MATERIALS ON THE STUDY OF MAMMALS IN THE SOUTHEAST REGION OF WHITE RUSSIA.) Materialien zum Studium der Saeugetierfauna im Suedoestlichen Gebiet Weissrusslands. V.A. Melander. Univ. Smolensk Wissenschaftl. Mitt., vol.6, no. 1, pp.1-32, 1930. (In Russian with German summary.)

MAMMALS OF THE UKR. SSR (DATA ON THE FAUNA). O. Migulin. Kiev, Ukr. SSR Acad. of Sci. Press, pp.421, 1938. (With English summary. Institute of Zoology and Biology (Akademiia Nauk URSR. Institut Zoologii ta Biologii.)

CONTRIBUTION TO THE CLASSIFICATION OF THE MAMMALS OF THE CAUCASUS. L. Morosova-Turova. Bull. Soc. Na. Moscow, sect.biol., n.s., vol. 48, nos.2-3, pp.98-106, figs.2, 1939.

COLLECTION OF THE SMALL MAMMALS FROM BUKEIEVSKAIA STEPPE (S. E. RUSSIA). S.I. Obolensky. Materials Contr. Fauna Lower Volga Region, Saratow, vol.1, pp.27-28, 1927. (In Russian with English summary.)

(ANIMALS OF EASTERN EUROPE AND NORTHERN ASIA.) Zveri Vostochnoi Evropy i Severnoi Azii. S.Ognev. Moscow, vols.1-7, 1928.

(CONTRIBUTION TO KNOWLEDGE OF THE MAMMALS OF THE CAUCASUS.) Beitraege zur Kenntnis der Saeugetiere Kaukasus. S. Ognev. Bull. Sci. Inst. Explor. Reg. Caucase du Nord, vol.1, pp.31-56, 1926. (In Russian with German summary.)

(MAMMALS FROM SAMARA AND URAL.) Mammiferes du gnt. de Sumara et de la province de l'Oural. S. Ognev. Bull. Soc. Nat. Moscow, sect.Biol., n.s., vol.33, nos.1-2, pp.1-47, figs.4, 1925. (In Russian with French summary.)

A REMARKABLE SMALL MAMMAL. S. Ognev. Priroda i Okhota na Ukraine (Nature and Hunt in Ukraine), Kharkov, vols.1-2, pp.2, illus., 1924. (In Russian.)

TRIP TO THE DELTA OF THE VOLGA. S. Ognev. (In) A Report on the Acclimatization of Animals and Plants Read at a Session of the Imperial Russian Society, Nov. 20, 1912. Trans. (Trudy) Russian Soc. Acclimatization Animals and Plants, Moscow, pp.85-102, 1913. (In Russian.)

FAUNA OF THE TERRESTRIAL VERTEBRATES OF THE GOVERNMENT OF WORONESH. (Describes a number of new subspecies and "forms" and one new genus: Sylvaemus, type species Mus sylvaticus Linnaeus.) S. Ognev, K. A. Worobiev. Moscow, pp.xii-254, (1923) 1924. (In Russian.)

(THE ORIGIN OF FAUNA ON THE CRIMEAN PENINSULA.) Die Entstehung der Fauna auf der Halbinsel Krim. S.J. Paramonow. Ann. Hist. Nat. Mus. Nat. Hungarici, Budapest, pars zool., vol.37, pp.131-151, pls.3, 1944.

(MAMMALIAN DISTRIBUTION IN ARCHANGEL DISTRICT.) Zametki o rasprostranenii nekotorykh mlekopitayushchikh v Arkhangelskoi Oblasti. B.Y.Parovshchikov. Zool. Zhurnal, Moscow, vol.35, no.11, pp.1738-1742, 1956.

SPORT IN THE CRIMEA AND CAUCASUS. Clive Phillipps-Wolley. London, R.Bentley and Son, pp.x-370, 1881.

(MAMMALOGICAL NOTES. ON THE DISTRIBUTION OF SOME WESTERN EUROPEAN MAMMALS IN THE UKRAINE.) Mammologische Notizen. Zur Verbreitung einiger westeuropaeischer Saeugetiere in der Ukraine. I. Pidoplitshka. Trav. Mus. Zool., Kiev, vol.3, pp.185-192, 1927. (In Russian with German summary.)

MATERIALS FOR THE STUDY OF THE FOSSIL FAUNA OF THE UKR. SSR. PT.1. A SURVEY OF PALEONTOLOGICAL FINDS 1917 TO 1937. I. Pidoplitshka. Acad. Sci. Ukr. SSR., Inst. Zool. and Biol., Vidavniststvo Akad. Nauk URSR, Kiev, pp.97-176, figs.11, tbls., 1938.

MATERIALS FOR THE STUDY OF THE FOSSIL FAUNA OF THE UKR. SSR.PT.1. THE UPPER QUATERNARY FAUNA OF NOVGOROD-SEVERSK. I. Pidoplitshka. Acad. Sci. Ukr. SSR., Inst. Zool. and Biol., Vidavniststvo Akad. Nauk URSR, Kiev, pp.3-96, figs.25, pls.9, tbls., 1938.

(NEW DATA ON THE DISTRIBUTION OF SOME MAMMALS IN THE UKRAINE.) Neue Nachrichten ueber die Verbreitung einiger Saeugetiere in der Ukraine. I. Pidoplitshka. Trav.Mus.Zool., Kiev, vol.1, pp.105-108, 1926. (In Russian with German summary.)

(SURVEY OF THE MAMMALS AND BIRDS OF KOLA PENINSULA.) Uebersicht der Saeugethiere und Voegel der Kola-Halbinsel. Theodor Pleske. St. Petersburg, K. Akad. der Wissenschaften, vols.1-2, col.pls., 1884-86.

(MAMMALS OF ADJACENT REGIONS AND DISTRICTS OF EREVAN.) Mlekopitaiushchiesia blizlezhashchikh raionov i okrestnostei Erevana. A.R. Pogosian. Erevan, Erevanskii Universitet, pp.73, 1954. (In Armenian.)

(SUMMARY OF THE MAMMALS OF THE UPPER VOLGA.) Uebersicht der Saeugetiere der oberer Volga. W.W. Rajewski, L.G. Kaplanoff. Zool. Anzeiger, vol.84, pp.140-151, Aug. 10, 1929. (Lists 52 Forms, One of Which is New: Evotomys rutilus volgensis.)

(FAUNISTIC INVESTIGATIONS IN THE VOLGA-URAL SANDY REGIONS (MAMMALIA).) Faunistische Forschungen im Wolga-Ural-Sandgelande (Mammalia). J.M. Rall. Comptes Rendus (Doklady) Acad. Sci. USSR, Moscow, vol.3 (8), no.7 (67), pp.329-332, map 1, 1935.

IDENTIFICATION OF RODENTS AND OTHER ANIMALS OF THE VOLGA-URAL SANDY STEPPE BY THEIR TRACES. U. Rall. Problems of Ecology and Biocenology, Leningrad, pp.37-73, figs.15, 1935. (In Russian with English summary.)

(ANIMALS OF VOLODGA OBLAST'.)Zveri Vologodskoi oblasti. V.A. Savinov. Vologda, Vologodskoye knezhnoye izd-vo, pp.206, illus., 1958.

(INFORMATION ON MAMMALS FROM VORKUTA, NORTHERN RUSSIA.) Saeugetierkundliches aus Workuta, Nordrussland. Helmut Schaefer. Saeugetierk. Mitteil., vol.5, no.4, pp.165-168, Dec. 1, 1957.

GEOGRAPHICAL DISTRIBUTION OF MAMMALS IN THE REGION OF MEZEN, NORTHERN RUSSIA. A.M. Sergeev. Zool.Zhurnal, Moscow, vol.13, no.4, pp.759-761, 1934.

(MAMMALS OF THE BELORUSSIAN SSR.) Mlekopitaiushchie Belorusskoi SSR. I.N. Serzhanin. Minsk, Izd-vo Akad. Nauk Belorusskoi SSR, pp.310, illus., 1955.

(NOTES ON THE FAUNA (MAMMALS AND BIRDS) OF THE CHERNIGOV REGION.) Materialy do fauny zviriv. N.V. Sharleman'. Kiev, Acad. of Sci. Ukr. SSR, pp.112, illus., 1936.

(MAMMAL FAUNA OF THE VALDAI HILLS. S.U. Stroganov. Zool. Zhurnal, vol.15, pp. 520-559, maps, 1936.

(MAMMALS OF THE IRRIGATED LANDS AND FOREST PLANTINGS OF THE VALUISKY EXPERIMENTAL STATION.) Fauna mlekopitayushchix oroshaemyx zemel i lesnyx nasazhdenii Valuiskoi opytnomeliorativnoi stantsii. A.S. Stroganov. (Stalingradskaya obl.). Trudy Zool.Inst. Akad. Nauk USSR, Moscow, vol.11, pp. 214-234, 1952.

(ATTEMPT AT A SYSTEMATIC SUMMARY OF THE MAMMALS OF OSSETIA (NORTHERN CAUCASUS).) Versuch einer systematischen Uebersicht der Saeugetiere von Ossetien (Nordkaukasus). S. Turov. Bull. Scientifique de l'Inst. de l'Explor.Regional du Caucase du Nord, vol.1, pp.311-337, 1926. (In Russian with German summary.)

MAMMAL FRAGMENTS FROM THE LOWER QUARTER OF THE TAMANSK PENINSULA LAYER. N.K. Vereshchagin. Trudy Zool. Inst. Akad. Nauk USSR, vol. 22, pp.9-74, 1957. (In Russian with English summary.)

(REMAINS OF A DOG AND BEAVERS (MAMMALIA: CANIS, CASTOR, TROGONTHERIUM) FROM THE LOWER PLEISTOCENE OF WESTERN CAUCASUS.) Ostatki sobaki i bobrov (Mammalia; Canis, Castor, Trogontherium) iz nijnego pleistotsena zapadnogo Kavkaza. N.K. Vereshchagin. Doklady Akad. Nauk USSR, Moscow, vol. 80, no.5, pp.821-824, 1951.

(ON THE HISTORY OF VERTEBRATES ALONG THE LOWER COURSE OF THE URAL RIVER.) K istorii fauny pozvonochnyx raiona nizhnego techniya reki Ural. N.K. Vereshchagin, I.M.Gromov.Trudy Zool. Inst. Akad. Nauk SSSR, Moscow, vol.9, pp.1226-1269, 1952.

(SHORT SUMMARY OF THE MAMMALS ALONG THE LOWER COURSE OF THE URAL RIVER AND ADJACENT AREAS.) Kratkii obzor fauny mlekopitayushchix doliny nizhnevo techeniya r. Urala i prilezhashchix raionov. B.S. Vinogradov. Trudy Zool. Inst. Akad. Nauk SSSR, Moscow, vol.11, pp.190-203, 1952.

(NOTES ON THE MAMMALS OF KERCH PENINSULA.) Notizen ueber die Saeugetiere der Halbinsel von Kertsch. B. Woljansky. Acad. Sci. Ukraine, Mem.Cl. Sci. Phys. et Math., (Trav.Mus.Zool. no.7), vol.13, no.1, pp.27-34, 1929.(In Russian with German summary.)

MORTALITY OF VOLES (MICROTUS ARVALIS) IN NATURAL CONDITIONS IN THE STEPPE DISTRICTS OF CISCAUGASIA AND THE EXTENT TO WHICH IT IS AFFECTED BY PREDATORS. P.A.Yanushko. Zool.Zh., vol.17, no.1, pp.102-111, 1938.

(WORKS OF VOLGA-KAMA REGION INDUSTRIAL BIOLOGICAL STATION.) Raboty Volzhsko-Kamskoi Krajevoi Prolyslovoi Biologicheskoi Stantsii. Kazan, no.1, 1931. (In Russian with Tartar summar.)

## SAHARA

(AUGIERAS-DRAPER SAHARA MISSION, 1927-28. MAMMALS.) Mission Saharienne Augieras-Draper 1927-28. Mammiferes. H. Heim de Balsac. Bull. Mus. Nat.d'Hist. Nat., Paris, ser.2, vol.7, no.6, pp.482-489, Nov., 1934.

REMARKS ON FAUNAL EXCHANGE THROUGH THE SAHARA. F.W. Braestrup. Vidensk.Medd.fra Dansk naturh. Foren., Copenhagen, vol.110, pp.1-15, fig.1, Nov., 1947.

(MAMMALOGICAL NOTES FROM THE CENTRAL SAHARA.) Notes de Mammalogie au Sahara Central. Ch.Devillers. Mammalia, Paris, vol.4, nos.3-4, pp.118-121, Sep.-Dec., 1940.

(GEOGRAPHICAL EVOLUTION OF THE MAMMALS OF THE CENTRAL SAHARA DURING THE PRESENT-DAY PERIOD OF DRYNESS.) Evolution geographique de la faune des mammiferes du Sahara Central pendant la periode actuelle de dessèchement. L.Joleaud. Comptes Rendus Soc. Biogeogr., 13th annee, no.108, pp.21-23, 1936.

(VERTEBRATES OF THE SAHARA.) Les vertebres du Sahara. Louis Lavauden. Librairie Tournier, Tunis, France, pp. 200, illus., 1926.

(OBSERVATIONS ON THE PRESENT DISTRIBUTION AND HABITS OF SOME LARGE MAMMALS OF TOUAREG.) Observations sur la repartition actuelle et les Moeurs de quelques grands mammiferes du Pays Touareg. H. Lhote. Mammalia, Paris, vol. 10, no.1, pp.26-56, illus., Mar., 1946.

(ON THE DENSITY OF THE ANIMAL SPECIES IN THE SAHARA REGIONS AND SOME OBSERVATIONS MADE ON THEIR HABITAT.) Sur la densite des Especes animales dan les regions Sahariennes et quelque observations faites sur leur habitat. Henri Lhote. Mammalia, Paris, vol.7, nos.3-4, pp.102-109, Sep.-Dec., 1943.

(Review by P. Rode of) (CONTRIBUTION TO STUDY OF THE WESTERN SAHARA. I. ENGRAVINGS, PAINTINGS, AND ROCK INSCRIPTIONS.) Contribution a l'etude du Sahara occidental. Fasc.I: Gravures, Peintures et Inscriptions rupestres.Th. Monod. Mammalia, Paris, vol.3, nos. 3-4, p.133, Sep.-Dec., 1939.

(DATA AND OBSERVATIONS ON CERTAIN MAMMALS OF THE WESTERN SAHARA.) Datos y observaciones sobre ciertos mamiferos del Sahara Occidental. E.Morales-Agacino. Premiere Conference Internationale des Africanistes de l'Oest, Dakar, vol.1, pp.217-227, 1950.

( DATA AND OBSERVATIONS ON CERTAIN MAMMALS OF THE WESTERN SAHARA AND IFNI.) Datos y observaciones sobre ciertos mamiferos del Sahara occidental e Ifni. E. Morales-Agacino. Bol. Real.Soc. Espanola Hist. Nat., vol.47, pp.13-44, illus., Dec. 15, 1949.

(MAMMALS COLLECTED BY THE L. LOZANO EXPEDITION IN THE SPANISH SAHARA.) Mamiferos colectados por la expedición L.Lozano en e Sáhara Espanol. E. Morales-Agacino. Bol.Soc.Espanola Hist. Nat., Madrid, vol.34, pp.449-456, pls.35-38, 1934.

(MY TRIP TO RIO DE ORO. REPORT ON THE TRIP AND OBSERVATIONS ON MAMMALS.) Meine Reise nach Rio de Oro. Reisebericht und Beobachtungen an Saeugetieren. P. Spatz. Zeitschr. f. Saeugetierk., vol.1, no.1, pp.23-28, figs.2, Aug. 31, 1926.

ERNST HARTERT'S EXPEDITION TO THE CENTRAL WESTERN SAHARA. MAMMALS. Oldfield Thomas. Novitates Zoologicae, Tring, vol.20, pp.28-33, Feb., 1913.

ON A SMALL COLLECTION OF MAMMALS FROM THE RIO DE ORO, WESTERN SAHARA. Oldfield Thomas. Novitates Zoologicae, vol.10, pp.300-302, Aug., 1903.

ON THE MAMMALS (OTHER THAN RUMINANTS) COLLECTED BY CAPTAIN ANGUS BUCHANAN DURING HIS SECOND SAHARAN EXPEDITION, AND PRESENTED BY HIM TO THE NATIONAL MUSEUM. Oldfield Thomas. Ann. and Mag. Nat. Hist., ser.9, vol.16, pp.187-197, July, 1925.

CAPTAIN ANGUS BUCHANAN'S AIR EXPEDITION. II. ON THE MAMMALS (OTHER THAN RUMINANTS) OBTAINED DURING THE EXPEDITION TO AIR (ASBEN). Oldfield Thomas, M.A.C. Hinton. Novitates Zoologicae, vol.28, pp.1-13, May, 1931.

EXHIBITION OF SOME MAMMALS, REPTILES, BATRACHIANS, AND FISHES COLLECTED IN THE ALGERIAN SAHARA. Rev. H.B. Tristram. Proc. Zool. Soc. London, pt.27, p.353, 1859.

SCANDINAVIA

(THE MAMMALS OF SCANDINAVIA.) Les Mammiferes de Scandinavie. J. Berlioz. Revue d'Histoire Naturelle, Pt.1, A.Mammiferes, Paris, vol.10, no.1, pp.3-141, Jan., 1929.

SYNOPSIS FAUNAE SCANDINAVIAE. MAMMALIA. G.J. Billberg. Vol.1, pt.1, pp.56, x, 1828.

(THE LAPLAND WILDERNESS.) Das Lapplaendische Wildern. Hans von Boetticher. Zool. Garten, vol.14, nos.1-2, pp.99-103, 1942.

DISTINCTNESS OF THE EREMIAN FAUNAL REGION. F. Wimpffen Braestrup. Proc. "Nordiska (19. skandinaviska) naturforskarmotet i Helsingfors, 1936," pp.2, Nov., 1936.

(ANIMAL BONES OF LANGOFUNDET FROM THE OLDER STONE AGE.) Dyreknogler i Langøfundet fra den aeldre Stenalder. M. Degerbøl. Aarbøger for Nordisk Oldkyndighed og Historie, pp.1-11 (of reprint), 1928.

(MAMMALS OF SCANDINAVIA.) Skandinaviens Daggdjur. August Emil Holmgren. Stockholm, P.A. Norstedt and Söner, pp.431, illus., 1865.

(MAMMALS.) Daggande djuren. S.Nilsson. (In) Skandinavisk fauna, en handbok for jagare och zoologer, Lund, vols.1-3, 1820-1842. (Mammals, vol.1, pp.66-419.)

SKANDINAVISK FAUNA. I. DAGGDJUREN. S. Nilsson. Lund, 2nd ed., pp.656, 1847.

(SCANDINAVIAN FAUNA. I. MAMMALS.) Skandinavisk Fauna. I. Daggdjuren. S. Nilsson. Lund, pp.656, 1847.

SOME OBSERVATIONS ON THE SHORT-TERM FLUCTUATIONS IN NUMBERS OF MAMMALS AND BIRDS IN THE SPHERE OF THE NORTHERNMOST ATLANTIC. Lauri Siivonen. Helsinki, pp.31, diagrs., tbls., 1950. (Suomen Riistanhoito-Saatio. Riistantutkimuslaitos. Riistatieteellisia julkaisuja.Papers on Game Res. no.4.)

SMALL MAMMAL COMMUNITIES OF THE NORTH SCANDINAVIAN BIRCH FOREST. D.M. Steven. Jour. Animal Ecol., Cambridge, vol.24, no.2, pp.403-411, illus., Nov., 1955.

SIAM

ON A COLLECTION OF MAMMALS FROM SIAM MADE BY MR. T.H. LYLE. J.Lewis Bonhote. Proc. Zool. Soc. London, pp.191-196, 1900.

ON MAMMALS FROM SIAM. F.N.Chasen. Jour. Siam Soc. Nat. Hist., Supplement, vol.10, no.1, pp.31-57, tbls., Dec., 1935.

ON MAMMALS FROM THE RAHENG DISTRICT, WESTERN SIAM. F.N. Chasen, C. Boden Kloss. Jour. Siam Soc., Nat. Hist. Suppl., vol.8, no.2, pp.61-78, Nov., 1930.

ON THE MAMMALIA OF SIAM AND THE MALAY PENINSULA. Stanley S. Flower. Proc. Zool. Soc. London, pp.306-377, 1900.

LIST OF MAMMALS AT PRESENT KNOWN TO INHABIT SIAM. (304 Forms Listed, With Original References and Notes on Occurrence.) Nils Gyldenstolpe. Jour. Nat. Hist. Soc. Siam, vol.3, pp.127-175, Aug. 1, 1919.

MAMMALS COLLECTED, OR OBSERVED BY THE SWEDISH ZOOLOGICAL EXPEDITION TO SIAM, 1911-1912. Nils Gyldenstolpe. Arkiv. Zool., Uppsala and Stockholm, vol.8, no.23, Apr.2, 1914.

ZOOLOGICAL RESULTS OF THE SWEDISH ZOOLOGICAL EXPEDITIONS TO SIAM, 1911-1912 AND 1914-1915, V. MAMMALS II. Nils Gyldenstolpe. Kungl.Svenska Vetenskaps-akademiens Handligar. Band 57, no.2, Stockholm, pp.3-58, pls.vi, 1916.

MAMMALS AND BIRDS FROM THE HILLS OF NAKON SRI TAMARAT, PENINSULAR SIAM. C. Boden Kloss, H.C. Robinson. Jour. Fed. Malay States Mus., vol.xi, pt. 1, Apr., 1923.

ON A COLLECTION OF MAMMALS FROM SIAM. C. Boden Kloss. Jour. Nat. Hist. Soc. Siam, vol.2, no.1, pp.1-32, June, 1916.

ON A COLLECTION OF MAMMALS FROM THE COAST AND ISLANDS OF SOUTH-EAST SIAM. WITH AN ACCOUNT OF THE FRUITBATS, BY DR. KNUD ANDERSON, F.Z.S. C.Boden Kloss. Proc. Zool. Soc. London, pp.27-75, figs.2, pl.1, Mar., 1916.

ON A COLLECTION OF MAMMALS FROM THE SIAMESE PROVINCE OF BANDON, NORTH-EAST MALAY PENINSULA. C. Boden Kloss, H.C. Robinson. Jour. Fed. Malay States Mus., vol.5, no.3, Mar., 1915.

ON A FOURTH COLLECTION OF SIAMESE MAMMALS. C. Boden Kloss. Jour. Nat. Hist. Soc. Siam, vol.3, no.2, pp. 49-69, Feb. 25, 1919.

ON A THIRD COLLECTION OF SIAMESE MAMMALS. C. Boden Kloss. Jour. Nat. Hist. Soc. Siam, vol.2, pp.288-318, Dec., 1917.

ON FIVE NEW MAMMALS FROM SIAM. C. Boden Kloss. Jour. Nat. Hist. Soc. Siam, vol.2, pp.282-287, Dec., 1917.

ON MAMMALS COLLECTED IN SIAM. (Report on 340 Specimens Collected in 1916.) C. Boden Kloss. Jour. Nat. Hist. Soc. Siam, vol.3, pp.334-407, pls.7-8, Dec. 31, 1919.

ON SOME SIAMESE MAMMALS. C.Boden Kloss. Jour. Nat. Hist. Soc. Siam, vol.2, no.2, pp.77-87, Dec., 1916.

THREE NEW MAMMALS FROM SIAM. C. Boden Kloss. Jour. Nat. Hist. Soc. Siam, vol.3, no.2, pp.73-77, Feb. 25, 1919.

ZOO-GEOGRAPHICAL DIVISIONS FOR SIAM. C. Boden Kloss. Jour. Nat. Hist. Soc. Siam, vol.1, no.4, pp.250-251, 1915.

ZOOLOGICAL RESULTS OF THE THIRD DE SCHAUENSEE SIAMESE EXPEDITION, IV. MAMMALS. Wilfred H. Osgood. Proc. Acad. Nat. Sci. Philadelphia, vol.86, pp. 311-315, June 13, 1934.

MAMMALS OF THE RUSH WATKINS ZOOLOGICAL EXPEDITION TO SIAM. (With a Note On Collecting Localities and Tapirs by K.G. Gairdner.) Colin Campbell Sanborn. Nat. Hist. Bull. Siam Soc., Bangkok, vol. 15, pt.1, pp.1-20, Sep., 1952.

JOURNEY TO SIAM AND BACK. PART 1. C.H. Stockley. Jour. Bombay Nat. Hist. Soc., vol.29, pp.169-178, pls.2, Apr.20, 1923, PART 2., vol.29, pp.378-387, pls. 2, Aug. 25, 1923; PART 3., vol.29, pp. 718-722, pls.2, Dec. 31, 1923; PART 4., vol.29, pp.974-981, pls.2, May 15, 1924.

FAUNA OF THAILAND. (Mammals pp. 522-602.) Chote Suvatti. Dept. of Fisheries, Bangkok, pp.ii-1100, 1950.

NEW MONKEY AND A NEW SQUIRREL FROM THE MIDDLE MEKONG, ON THE EASTERN FRONTIER OF SIAM. (Pithecus laotum and Dremomys rufigenis laomache.) Oldfield Thomas. Ann. and Mag. Nat.Hist., ser.9, vol.7, pp.181-183, Feb., 1921.

SIBERIA

NOTES ON THE BIRDS AND MAMMALS OF THE ARCTIC COAST OF EAST SIBERIA. MAMMALS. Glover M. Allen. Proc. New England Zool. Club, vol.5, pp.49-66, Apr. 9, 1914.

REPORT ON THE MAMMALS COLLECTED IN NORTHEASTERN SIBERIA BY THE JESUP NORTH-PACIFIC EXPEDITION, WITH ITINERARY AND FIELD NOTES BY N. G. BUXTON. J.A. Allen. Bull. Amer. Mus. Nat. Hist., vol.19, pp.101-184, 195, 196, May 9, 1903.

NEW DATA ON THE QUATERNARY MAMMALS OF WEST SIBERIA. (Two Quaternary Faunas Found in Irtysh Region of West Siberia.) E.I. Beliaeva. Bull. Acad. Sci. USSR. Cl. Sci. Math. et Nat., no.8, pp. 1205-1207, 1933. (In Russian with German summary.)

ACCLIMATIZATION OF FUR-ANIMALS IN WEST SIBERIA. N.Berger. Zool.Jour. USSR, Moscow, vol.23, no.5, pp.267-274, map, 1944. (With English summary.)

ESTABLISHMENT OF NEW FUR-BEARING ANIMALS IN WEST SIBERIA. N. Berger. Zool. Zhurnal, vol.23, pp.267-274, 1944.

(CONSIDERATIONS ON THE VERTEBRATE ANIMALS OF WESTERN SIBERIA.) Considerations sur les animaux vertebres de la Siberie occidentale. F. Brandt. Pp.51, 1845.

THE RIM OF MYSTERY - A HUNTER'S WANDERINGS IN UNKNOWN SIBERIAN ASIA. John B. Burnham. New York, G.P. Putnam's Sons, vol.8, pp.xv-281, illus. 60, map, 1929.

(Review by E.W. Nelson of) THE RIM OF MYSTERY- A HUNTER'S WANDERINGS IN UNKNOWN SIBERIAN ASIA. John B. Burnham. Jour. Mamm., vol.10, no.2, pp.172-173, May, 1929.

PROGRAMS AND INSTRUCTIONS FOR THE STUDY OF HUNTING FUR-BEARING ANIMALS IN YAKUTSK, SIBERIA. G. G. Doppelmair. Materiaux de la Commission pour l'Etude de la Republique Autonome Sovietique Socialiste Iakoute, livr.7, pp.1-25, 1926.

(DATA ON THE MAMMAL FAUNA OF WESTERN SIBERIA.) Zur Kenntnis der Saeugetier-Fauna West Siberiens.N.M. Dukelsky. Zool. Anzeiger, vol.88, pp. 75-84, Apr.1, 1930.

(MATERIAL ON THE MAMMAL FAUNA OF THE YAKUTIA REGION (NORTHEAST SIBERIA).) Materialien ueber die Saeugetier Fauna des Jakutien-Gebietes (Nordost-Sibirien. N.M. Dukelski. Zool. Anzeiger, vol.78, pp.102-107, Sep. 1, 1928.

MAMMALS OF THE NORTHERN URALS AND WESTERN SIBERIA. K.K.Flerov. Bull. Acad. Sci. USSR.Cl.Sci.Math.et Natur., no.3, pp.445-470, figs.12, pls.2, 1933.(In Russian with German summary.)

(ON THE BIOLOGY OF THE MAMMALS OF THE NORTHERN URALS AND WESTERN SIBERIA.) Zur Biologie der Saeugetiere des Noerdlichen Urals und Westsibiriens. K.K. Flerov. Bull. Acad. Sci. USSR.Cl. Sci. Math. et Nat., pp.445-470, figs.12, pls.2, 1933.

(NOTES ON THE MAMMALS OF DICKSON ISLAND, THE PARTS NORTHWEST OF TAIMYR, AND THE KARA SEA.) W.G. Geptner. Archiv. Zool. Mus. Univ., Moscow, vol.3, pp.1-23, 1936. (In Russian.)

MAMMALS COLLECTED IN THE MARITIME PROVINCE OF SIBERIA BY THE MORDEN-GRAVES NORTH ASIATIC EXPEDITION, WITH THE DESCRIPTION OF A NEW HARE FROM THE AMUR RIVER. (Lepus timidus mordeni.) G.G.Goodwin. Amer. Mus.Novitates, no.681, pp.18, Dec. 30, 1933.

FAUNA OF THE UPPER PALEOLITHIC SQUATTING PLACE OF MALTA, NEAR IRKUTSK, SIBERIA. (Several Species of Mammals.) Vera Gromova. Comptes Rendus (Doklady) Acad. Sci. USSR, Moscow, n.s., vol.33, no.1, pp.94-96, 1941.

(ON THE MAMMAL AND BIRD FAUNA OF THE GYDANSKIY PENINSULA (NORTH-WESTERN SIBERIA).) Ueber die Saeugetier- und Vogelfauna der Gyda-Halbinsel (Nordwest-Sibirien). Herman Grote. Zool. Garten, Leipzig, n.F., vol.8, nos.1-3, pp.52-59, Sep., 1935.

NEW MAMMALS FROM THE HIGHLANDS OF SIBERIA. N. Hollister. Smiths. Inst., Misc. Coll., vol.60, no.14, publ.2157, pp. 6, Nov. 29, 1912.

TWO NEW MAMMALS FROM THE SIBERIAN ALTAI. N. Hollister. Smiths. Inst., Misc. Coll., vol.60, no.24, publ.2171, pp.1-3, Mar. 13, 1913.

ZOOLOGICAL EXPEDITION OF DR. THEODORE LYMAN TO THE ALTAI MOUNTAINS, SIBERIA AND MONGOLIA. N. Hollister.

Smiths. Inst., Misc. Coll., vol.60, no.30, July, 1913.

SURVEY OF THE HUNTING AND TRAPPING INDUSTRY IN NORTH-EASTERN YAKUTIA. N.M. Mikhel. Arctica, Arctic Inst. USSR, Leningrad, vol.5, pp.153-231, figs.8, tbls., 1937. (In Russian with English summary.)

WORK BY COPLEY AMORY, JR., IN EASTERN SIBERIA. Gerrit S. Miller, Jr. Smiths. Inst., Misc. Coll., vol.66, no.3, pp.46-51, figs.59-66, May 27, 1916.

ECONOMICALLY IMPORTANT MAMMALS OF THE TURUKHAN REGION, SIBERIA. N.P. Naumov. Soviet North, Moscow, no.3, pp.36-55, map, 1930.

(MAMMALS AND BIRDS OF GYDANSKIY PENINSULA (NORTHWEST SIBERIA).) Mlekopitaiushchie i ptitsy Gydanskogo poluostrova (Severo-Zapadnaia Sibir). S.P. Naumov. Akad. Nauk, Poliarnaia komissiia, Trudy, no.4, pp.106, 1931.

(NOTES AND STUDIES OF THE SIBERIAN COASTAL FAUNA OF MAMMALS.) Anteckningar och Studier till Sibiriska Ishafskustens Daggdjursfauna. Oscar Nordquist. Vega-Expeditionens Vetenskapliga Takttagelser, vol.2, 1883.

MATERIALS FOR THE QUATERNARY FAUNA OF MAMMALS IN SIBERIA. S.I. Obolensky. Doklady Akad. Nauk SSSR (Comptes Rendus Acad. Sci. USSR), Leningrad, pp.35-38, Mar., 1926.

EXHIBITION OF TYRRHAPTES PARADOXUS AND FIVE MAMMALS FROM THE ALTAI MOUNTAINS OF SIBERIA. William Ogilby. Proc. Zool. Soc. London, pt.13, p.75, 1845.

MAMMALS OF NORTHEASTERN SIBERIA. S.I. Ognev. Vladivostok, pp.200, 1926. (In Russian.)

(TRIPS IN THE SOUTH OF EASTERN SIBERIA IN 1855-1859, BY ORDER OF THE IMPERIAL GEOGRAPHICAL SOCIETY, CARRIED OUT BY GUSTAV RADDE.) Reisen im Sueden von Ost-Sibirien in den Jahren 1855-1859, incl., im Auftrage der Kaiserlichen Geographischen Gesellschaft ausgefuehrt von Gustav Radde. Gustav Radde. St. Petersburg, Buchdruckerei der K. Akad. der Wissenschaften, vols.1-2, col. pls.29, maps 4, 1862-63. (Vol. 1. Mammal Fauna. Vol.2. Continental Ornis of Southeastern Siberia.)

(MAMMALS OF THE NORTHEASTERN PART OF THE NEW SIBERIAN DISTRICT.) Saeugetiere des nordoestlichen Teiles des Neusibirischen Kreises. N.N. Scalon. Zeitschr. f. Saeugetierk., vol.6, nos.1-6, pp.221-224, Dec. 15, 1931.

(RESULTS OF EXCAVATIONS OF QUATERNARY MAMMALS IN THE CAVE OF NIJNEOUDINSK (EASTERN SIBERIA).) Resultats des fouilles de mammiferes quaternaires dans la grotte de Nijneoudinsk (Siberie orientale). W.S. Slodkewitsch. Trav. Inst. Paleozool. Acad. Sci. USSR, vol.5, pp. 235-241, illus., pl., 1936. (In Russian with French summary.)

CARCASSES OF THE MAMMOTH AND RHINOCEROS FOUND IN THE FROZEN GROUND OF SIBERIA. I.P. Tolmachoff. Trans. Amer. Philos. Soc., n.s., vol.23, pt.1, art.1, pp.x-74, 1929.

SMALL MAMMALS FROM MINUSINSK DISTRICT AND URJANKHAI. B. Vinogradov. Ann. Russian Mus. of N M. Martjanov, Minusinsk, Siberia, vol.5, pp.33-50, 1927.

SICILY

NOTES ON SOME PONTIAN MAMMALS FROM SICILY, FIGURED BY SEGUENZA. D.A. Hooijer. Archives Néerlandaises Zool., vol.7, livr.3-4, pp.301-333, figs. 2, 1946.

SOME OVERLOOKED NAMES OF SICILIAN MAMMALS. Gerrit S. Miller, Jr. Proc. Biol. Soc., Washington, vol.26, pp.79-82, Mar. 22, 1913.

SINAI

ZOOGEOGRAPHY OF THE SINAI PENINSULA. Fritz Bodenheimer. Comptes Rendus, 12th Internat. Congr. Zool. for 1935, Lisboa, vol.2, pp.1138-1164, 1936-1937.

ON A COLLECTION OF MAMMALS FROM NORTHERN SINAI. Kamal Wassif. Bull. Inst. Desert Egypte, vol.3, no.1, pp.107-118, map, Sep., 1954.

SOLOMON ISLANDS

MAMMALS OF RENNELL ISLAND. J. E. Hill. The Natural History of Rennell Island, British Solomon Islands, Copenhagen, vol. 1, no.6, pp.73-84, Nov. 28, 1956.

DIAGNOSES OF SIX NEW MAMMALS FROM THE SOLOMON ISLANDS. Oldfield Thomas. Ann. and Mag. Nat. Hist., ser.6, vol.1, no. 2, pp.155-158, Feb., 1888.

MAMMALS OF THE SOLOMON ISLANDS, BASED ON THE COLLECTIONS MADE BY C. M. WOODFORD DURING HIS SECOND EXPEDITION TO THE ARCHIPELAGO. Oldfield Thomas. Proc. Zool. Soc. London, pp.470-484, pls.20-22, Dec. 4, 1888.

SOUTH AMERICA

Extinct and Fossil Mammals

(FIRST CONTRIBUTION TO KNOWLEDGE OF THE MAMMAL FAUNA OF THE COLPODON BEDS.) Premiere contribution á la connaissance de la fauna mammalogique des couches a Colpodon. Florentino Ameghino. Buenos Aires, Impr. Coni Frères, pp.70, 1902.

(FIRST CONTRIBUTION TO KNOWLEDGE OF THE MAMMAL FAUNA OF THE PYROTHERIUM BEDS.) Premiere contribution á la connaissance de la faune mammalogique des couches a pyrotherium. Florentino Ameghino. Extrait du Boletin del Instituto geografico argentino, tome xv, cahiers 11 et 12, Buenos-Ayres, P.E.Coni et fils, pp.60, 1895.

BONE-DIGGER IN A LOST WORLD. HOW GEORGE GAYLORD SIMPSON GATHERED NEW EVIDENCE OF SOUTH AMERICA'S MUCH DISPUTED GEOLOGICAL HISTORY AND RESCUED SOME OF THE EARLIEST ANIMAL ANCESTORS FROM OBLIVION. D.R. Barton. Nat. Hist., New York, vol. 46, no.4, pp.244-246, Nov., 1940.

GEOLOGY AND PALEONTOLOGY OF LAKE TACARIGUA, VENEZUELA. (Mammals, pp.566-568.) Edward W. Berry. Proc. Amer. Philos. Soc., Philadelphia, vol.81, no.4, pp.547-568, figs.4, pls.7, Sep., 1939.

(THE REMAINS OF MAMMALS OF THE CONTINENTAL POST-PATAGONIAN SERIES OF MESETA DEL CASTILLO.) Los restos de mamiferos de la serie continental postpatagoniana de la Meseta del Castillo. A. F. Bordas. Physis, Buenos Aires, vol.14, no.46, pp.435-446, figs.7, pls.2, Mar., 1939.

(GREAT FRIASENSE MAMMALS.) Sobra dos grandes mamiferos Friasenses. Angel Cabrera. Inst. Mus. Univ. Nac. La Plata, Notas Mus. La Plata, vol.5, Paleont. no. 24, pp.241-250, figs.3, pl.1, 1940.

(VERTEBRATE FOSSILS OF THE PLIOCENE OF ADOLFO ALSINA.) Sobre vertebrados fosiles del Plioceno de Adolfo Alsina. Angel Cabrera. Rev. Mus. La Plata, Buenos Aires, n.s., vol.2, sec. Paleont., pp.3-35, Apr. 10, 1939.

(REVISIONS OF THE EXTINCT FORMS OF THE PAMPAS.) Revision de las formas extinguidas pampeanas. Eduardo Carette. Cérvidos actuales y fósiles de sud America. (Recent and fossil cervids of South America.) Rev. Mus. La Plata, Buenos Aires, vol.26, ser.4, no.2, pp. 393-472, figs.7, 1922.

(FOSSIL MAMMALS OF SOUTH AMERICA.) Les mammiferes fossiles de l'Amérique du Sud. H. Gervais, F. Ameghino. Buenos Aires and Paris, pp.12-225, 1880. (Alternate p. in Spanish and French.)

TERTIARY, QUATERNARY, AND RECENT MARINE MAMMALS OF SOUTH AMERICA AND THE WEST INDIES. Remington Kellogg. Proc. 8th Amer. Sci. Congr., Wash., D.C., vol.3, pp.445-473, Aug. 3, 1942.

(PLIOCENE ANTIQUITY OF THE FAUNAS OF MONTE HERMOSO AND CHAPADMALAL, DEDUCTED FROM COMPARISON WITH THOSE PRECEDING AND THOSE SUCCEEDING.) La antiguedad pliocena de las faunas de Monte Hermoso y Chapadmalal, deducidas de su comparacion con las que le precedieron y sucedieron. Lucas Kraglievich. With foreword by G.F.C., s.j., and complete bibliography of Kraglievich. El Siglo Ilustrado, Montevideo, pp.1-136, fig.1, pl.1, 1934.

(GREAT FOSSIL MAMMALS OF THE REGION OF BARQUISIMETO.) Los grandes mamiferos fósiles de la region de Barquisimeto. Hermano Nectario Maria. Bol.geol. y mineria, Caracas, Venezuela, vol.1, nos.2-4, pp.301-317, figs.A-B, map, 1937.

EARLY EXPLORERS OF SOUTHERN SOUTH AMERICA FROM THE UNITED STATES. Lawrence Martin. Nature, London, vol.146, no.3694, pp.238-239, Aug. 17, 1940.

REVISION OF THE PUERCO FAUNA. W.D. Matthew. Bull. American Mus. Nat. Hist., New York, vol.9, art.22, pp.259-323, figs. 20, Nov. 16, 1897.

(CONTRIBUTION TO KNOWLEDGE OF THE REGION OF BARUTA-EL HATILLO. 3rd PART.) Contribucion al conocimiento de la region de Baruta-El Hatillo. Tercera Parte. Zoologia. José Luis Méndez. Mem.Soc. Ciencias Naturales La Salle, Caracas, vol. 11, no.30, pp.203-236, Sep.-Dec., 1951.

FOSSIL MAMMALS OF THE PUERCO BEDS. COLLECTION OF 1892. Henry Fairfield Osborn, Charles Earle. Mus. Nat. Hist., New York, vol.7, art.1, pp.70, figs.21, Mar. 8, 1895.

TWO TERTIARY MAMMALS FROM NORTHERN SOUTH AMERICA. Bryan Patterson. Amer. Mus. Novitates, New York, no.1173, pp.7, figs.2, June 17, 1942.

(FOSSILS FROM THE PAMPAS, SOUTH AMERICA; SECOND CATALOGUE.) Fossiles de la Pampa, Amérique du Sud; 2nd catalogue. Santiago Roth. San Nicolás, Imp. y lit. de el Centinela del norte, pp. 10, photos 6, 1882.

(CHRONOLOGY OF THE NEO-TERTIARY TERRAINS OF ARGENTINA IN RELATION TO MAN.) Cronologia de los terrenos neoterciarios de la Argentina en relacion con el hombre. Carlos Rusconi. Bol.Acad. Nac. Cienc. Cordoba, vol.35, entr.2a-3a, pp.151-181, 1941.

(NEW REMAINS OF SCALABRINITHERIUM OF THE TERTIARY OF THE PARANA AND NOTES RELATIVE TO CRANIAL ANATOMY.) Nuevos restos de Scalabrinitherium del Terciario de Paraná y apuntes relativos a su Anatomia craneana. Carlos Rusconi. Rev. Med. y Veterinaria, Buenos Aires, vol.15-19, nos.2-6, pp.131-146, figs.5, Mar.-Dec., 1932.

(PRELIMINARY DATA ON THE PUELCHENSE SANDS AND ITS FAUNA.) Apuntes preliminares sobre las arenas puelchenses y su fauna. Carlos Rusconi. Anales Soc. Cient. Argentina, Buenos Aires, vol.116, no.4, pp.169-193, figs.8, Oct., 1933.

(PUELCHENSE FOSSILS OF THE DISTRICT OF MATANZAS.) Fosiles puelchenses del partido de Matanzas. Carlos Rusconi. Anales Soc. Cient. Argentina, pt.2, vol.127, pp. 144-149, map, Feb., 1939.

(VARIOUS BONE REMAINS OF THE ENSENADENSE FAUNA.) Sobre varios restos de osos de la fauna Ensenadense. Carlos Rusconi. Anales Soc. Cient. Argentina, Buenos Aires, entr.3, vol.126, pp.227-237, figs.4, tbls., Sep., 1938.

(SIXTH NOTICE ON THE FOSSIL VERTEBRATES OF THE PUELCHENSE OF VILLA

BALLESTER.) Sexta noticia sobre los vertebrados fosiles del puelchense de Villa Ballester. Carlos Rusconi. Anales Soc. Cient. Argentina, vol.117, no.4, pp.177-186, figs. 1-7, Apr., 1934.

(SOME VEGETABLE REMAINS (LIGNITIFEROUS) IN VILLA BALLESTER.)Restos de vegetales (lignitiferos) en Villa Ballester. Carlos Rusconi. Bol. Paleontol., Buenos Aires, no.2, pp.1-2, Dec. 31, 1934.

(THIRD NOTICE ON THE VERTEBRATE FOSSILS OF THE PUELCHENSE SANDS OF VILLA BALLESTER.) Tercera noticia sobre los vertebrados fósiles de las arenas puelchenses de Villa Ballester. Carlos Rusconi. Anales Soc. Cient. Argentina, Buenos Aires, vol.117, no.1, pp.19-37, figs.6, Jan., 1934.

(THREE NEW SPECIES OF MAMMALS OF THE PUELCHENSE OF VILLA BALLESTER.) Tres nuevas especies de mamiferos del peulchense de Villa Ballester. Carlos Rusconi. Bol. Paleont. de Buenos Aires, no.5, pp.1-4, figs.4, June 10, 1935.

LATER CENOZOIC MAMMALIAN FAUNAS OF SOUTH AMERICA. William Berryman Scott. Proc. 8th Amer. Sci. Congr., Wash., D.C., vol.4, pp.333-357, Aug. 3, 1942.

ADDITIONS TO THE PUERCO FAUNA, LOWER PALEOCENE. George Gaylord Simpson. Amer. Mus. Novitates, no.849, pp.11, figs.6, May 18, 1936.

BEGINNING OF THE AGE OF MAMMALS IN SOUTH AMERICA. PART I. INTRODUCTION. SYSTEMATICS: MARSUPIALIA, EDENTATA, CONDYLARTHRA, LITOPTERNA, AND NOTIOPROGONIA. George Gaylord Simpson. Bull. Amer. Mus. Nat. Hist., New York, vol.91, art.1, pp.1-232, illus., 1948.

DESCRIPTIONS OF THE OLDEST KNOWN SOUTH AMERICAN MAMMALS, FROM THE RIO CHICO FORMATION. George Gaylord Simpson. Amer. Mus. Novitates, no.793, pp.25, figs.24, Apr. 15, 1935.

EARLY CENOZOIC MAMMALS OF SOUTH AMERICA. George Gaylord Simpson. Proc. 8th Amer. Sci. Congr., Washington, D.C., vol.4, pp.303-332, Aug. 3, 1942.

NOTES ON THE MAMMAL-BEARING TERTIARY OF SOUTH AMERICA. George Gaylord Simpson. Proc. Amer. Philos. Soc., Philadelphia, vol.86, no.3, pp.403-404, July 8, 1943.

ORIGIN OF THE SOUTH AMERICAN FAUNA. George Gaylord Simpson. Amer. Mus. Publ.

PROVISIONAL CLASSIFICATION OF EXTINCT SOUTH AMERICAN HOOFED MAMMALS. George Gaylord Simpson. Amer. Mus. Novitates, no.750, pp.21, Oct. 9, 1934.

REVIEW OF THE MAMMAL-BEARING TERTIARY OF SOUTH AMERICA. George Gaylord Simpson. Proc. Amer. Philos.Soc., Philadelphia, vol.83, no.5, pp.649-709, figs.4, Oct. 31, 1940.

SUPPOSED OCCURRENCES OF MESOZOIC MAMMALS IN SOUTH AMERICA. George Gaylord Simpson. Amer. Mus. Novitates, no.530, pp.9, fig.1, May 28, 1932.

FIRST LOWER OLIGOCENE VERTEBRATE FAUNA FROM NORTHERN SOUTH AMERICA. R.A. Stirton. Compilacion de Estudios Geologicos Oficiales en Colombia, Ministerio de Minas Petroleos, Serv. Geol. Nac., Bogota, vol.7, pp.325-341, pls.3, 1946.

(CAVERNS OF OJO DE AGUA AND LAS HACHAS. GEOLOGICAL HISTORY OF THE LA BRAVA REGION IN RELATION TO THE EXISTENCE OF PREHISTORIC MAN.) Las cavernas de Ojo de Agua y Las Hachas. Historia geologica de la region de La Brava en relacion con la existencia del hombre prehistorico. Augusto Tapia. Republica Argentina, Ministerio de Agricultura de la Nacion, Direccion de Minas y Geologia, Buenos Aires, bol.no. 43, pp.122, illus., maps, pls.26, 1937. (Mammals pp.108-113.)

EARLY MAMMALS OF SOUTH AMERICA. Nature, London, vol.146, no.3695, p.270, Aug. 24, 1940.

Recent Mammals

NEW SOUTH AMERICAN BATS AND A NEW OCTODONT. J.A. Allen. Bull.Amer. Mus. Nat. Hist., vol.33, pp.381-389, pls. 28, July 9, 1914.

NEW SOUTH AMERICAN MAMMALS. J.A. Allen. Bull. Amer. Mus. Nat. Hist., vol. 34, pp.625-634, Dec. 30, 1915. vol.35, pp. 83-87, Apr. 28, 1916.

BEFORE MAGELLAN. (Mammals of Tierra del Fuego.) Junius Bird. Natural History, New York, vol.41, no.1, pp.16-28, 77, 79, illus., Jan., 1938.

(DESCRIPTION OF FAUNA.)Descripcion de la fauna. (Edentata, Ungulata.) W. Branco. Anal. Univ. Central Ecuador, Quito, publ. trimestral, vol.61, no.305, pp.398-556, July-Sep., 1938.

(CATALOGUE OF SOUTH AMERICAN MAMMALS.) Catalogo de los mamiferos de América del Sur. I (Metatheria-Unguiculata-Carnivora). Angel Cabrera. Rev. Mus.Argentino Ciencias Naturales "Bernardino Rivadavia," Cienc. Zool., vol.4, no.1, pp.1-307, Mar. 27, 1958, Buenos Aires, Impr. y Casa Editora Coni.

(SOUTH AMERICAN MAMMALS. LIFE, HABITS, AND DESCRIPTIONS.) Mamiferos sud-americanos. Vida, costumbres y descripcion. Angel Cabrera, J. Yepes. Buenos-Aires, Comp. Argentina de Editores, pp.370, col.pls. 78, 1940.

(CURIOUS ANIMALS.) Animales curioses. Roger Conant. Fauna, Philadelphia, vol.5, no.3, pp.66-72, illus., Sep., 1943.

(NEW OR RARE ANIMALS COLLECTED ON THE EXPEDITION IN THE CENTRAL PARTS OF SOUTH AMERICA.) Animaux nouveaux ou rares recueillis pendant l'expedition dans les parties centrales de l'Amerique du Sud. Mammals (Mammifères). Paul Gervais. Castelnau, F.L. de Laporte Comte de. Expeditions dans les parties centrales de l'Amerique du Sud, pt.7, Zoologie, vol.1, no.2, pp.116, pl.20, 1855.

(FAUNA AND ETHNOZOOLOGY OF SOUTH AMERICA. Raymond M. Gilmore. Bur. Amer. Ethnol. Bull. 143 (Handbook of South American Indians), Washington, vol.6, pp. 345-364, pls.36-47, Dec., 1950.

SOUTH AMERICAN ZOO. (Popular Accounts of Animals.) Victor W. Von Hagen. Julian Messner, Inc., New York, pp.182, illus., 1946.

CRUISE AMONG DESERT ISLANDS. G. Dallas Hanna, A.W. Anthony. Nat. Geog. Mag., vol.44, no.1, pp.74-99, 1923.

ON THREE RARE SOUTH-AMERICAN MAMMALS. F.A. Jentink. Notes Leyden Mus., vol.9, no.28, pp.223-228, pl.3, May, 1887.

PAST AND PRESENT STATUS OF THE MARINE MAMMALS OF SOUTH AMERICA AND THE WEST INDIES. Remington Kellogg. Smiths. Rept. for 1942, Wash. D.C., publ.3719, pp.299-316, Sep.20, 1943.

TERTIARY, QUATERNARY, AND RECENT MARINE MAMMALS OF SOUTH AMERICA AND THE WEST INDIES. Remington Kellogg. Proc. 8th Amer. Sci. Congr., Washington, vol.3, pp.445-473, 1940.

(ON HUMANS AND ANIMALS IN INNER SOUTH AMERICA.) Von Menschen und Tieren im inneren Suedamerikas. Hans Krieg. Die Umschau, Frankfurt, no.47, pp.1-5, 1933.

(ZOOPSYCHOLOGICAL OBSERVATIONS IN SOUTH AMERICA.) Tierpsychologische Beobachtungen in Suedamerika. Hans Krieg. Veroeffent. Zool. Staatssammlung Muenchen, vol.1, pp.63-96, Jan.1, 1950.

(MAMMALS OF THE SOUTH AMERICAN EXPEDITIONS OF PROF. DR. KRIEG.) Die Saeugetiere der Suedamerika-Expeditionen Prof. Dr. Kriegs. Ingo Krumbiegel. Zool. Anzeiger, Leipzig, vol.132, nos. 9-10, pp.223-238, pls.7, Dec. 15, 1940, vol.137, nos.1-2, pp.18-29, figs.7, Jan. 15, 1942.

NOTES ON SOME SOUTH-AMERICAN MAMMALS. Einar Lonnberg. Arkiv for Zool., Stockholm, vol.29A, no.19, pp.1-29, fig.1, Aug. 9, 1937.

(NOTES ON MAMMALS OF THE HIGH PLATEAUS OF SOUTH AMERICA.) Notes sur les Mammiferes des hauts plateaux de l'Amerique du Sud. M.Neveu-Lemaire, G. Grandidier. Mission Scientifique G.de Crequi Montfort et E. Senechal de la Grange, Paris, pp.127, figs.18, pls.7, 1911.

ALONG DARWIN'S TRAIL IN SOUTH AMERICA. Wilfred H. Osgood. Scientific Monthly, vol.40, no.1, pp.73-77, Jan., 1935.

MAMMALS FROM THE COAST AND ISLANDS OF NORTHERN SOUTH AMERICA. Wilfred H. Osgood. Field Mus. Nat. Hist., Chicago, Zool. Ser., vol.10, no.4, publ.149, pp.23-32, pls.2-3, Oct. 20,1910.

MAMMALS OF THE COLLINS-DAY SOUTH AMERICAN EXPEDITION. Wilfred H. Osgood. Field Mus. Nat. Hist., Chicago, Zool. Ser., vol.10, no.14, publ.189, pp. 199-216, pls.6-7, Oct. 31, 1916.

(ZOOLOGICAL PROBLEMS ON THE SOUTH AMERICAN WEST COAST, PARTICULARLY REGARDING THE MASS DEATHS IN THE PACIFIC.) Zoologische Probleme an der suedamerikanischen Westkueste besonders ueber das Massensterben im Pazifik. Gilbert Rahm. Comptes Rendus, 12th Internat. Congr. Zool., 1935, Lisboa, vol.2, pp.1237-1247, 1936-1937.

NATURALIST'S GLIMPSE OF THE ANDES. Karl P. Schmidt. Scientific Monthly, Lancaster, vol.60, no.5, whole no.356, pp. 335-346, illus., May, 1945.

HISTORY OF THE FAUNA OF LATIN AMERICA. George Gaylord Simpson. Amer. Scientist, Easton, vol.38, no.3, pp.361-389, illus., July, 1950; Science in Progress.Yale Univ. Press, ser.7, pp.369-408, illus., 1951.

TURTLES AND THE ORIGIN OF THE FAUNA OF LATIN AMERICA. George Gaylord Simpson. Amer. Jour. Sci., New Haven, vol.241, no.7, pp.413-429, July, 1943.

VERNACULAR NAMES OF SOUTH AMERICAN MAMMALS. George Gaylord Simpson. Jour. Mammalogy, vol.22, p.12.

RANDOM OBSERVATIONS ON HABITS OF SOUTH AMERICAN MAMMALS. G.H.H. Tate. Jour. Mamm., vol.12, no.3, pp. 248-256, Aug., 1931.

(SOUTH AMERICAN MAMMALS--IN HISTORICAL PERSPECTIVE.) Los mamiferos suramericanos--en perspectiva historica. Erich Thenius, Hans Burgl. Rev. Acad. Colombiana, Cien. Exactas, Fisicas y Nat., vol.10, no.39, pp.123-130, Oct., 1957.

DESCRIPTIONS OF FOUR SMALL MAMMALS FROM SOUTH AMERICA, INCLUDING ONE BELONGING TO THE PECULIAR MARSUPIAL GENUS "HYRACODON", TOMES. Oldfield Thomas. Ann. Mag. Nat. Hist., ser.6, vol,16, pp. 367-370. Nov., 1895.

DESCRIPTIONS OF FOUR NEW SOUTH AMERICAN MAMMALS. Oldfield Thomas. Ann. and Mag. Nat. Hist., ser.6, vol.20, no.116, pp.218-221, Aug., 1897.

DESCRIPTIONS OF NEW MAMMALS FROM SOUTH AMERICA. Oldfield Thomas. Ann. and Mag. Nat. Hist., ser.7, vol.2, no.9, pp.265-275, Sep., 1898.

NEW BATS AND RODENTS FROM SOUTH AMERICA. Oldfield Thomas. Ann. and Mag. Nat. Hist., ser.8, vol.10, no.58, pp.403-411, Oct., 1912.

NEW CALLICEBUS AND EUMOPS FROM SOUTH AMERICA. Oldfield Thomas. Ann. and Mag. Nat. Hist., ser.8, vol.13, no.77, pp.480-481, May, 1914.

NEW CENTRONYCTERIS AND CTENOMYS FROM SOUTH AMERICA. Oldfield Thomas. Ann. and Mag. Nat. Hist., ser.8, vol.10, no.60, pp.638-640, Dec., 1912.

NEW FORMS OF SCIURUS, OXYMYCTERUS, KANNABATEOMYS, PROECHIMYS, DASYPROCTA, AND CALUROMYS FROM S. AMERICA. Oldfield Thomas. Ann. and Mag. Nat. Hist., ser.7, vol.11, no.65, pp.487-493, May, 1903.

NEW MAMMALS FROM SOUTH AMERICA. Oldfield Thomas. Ann. and Mag. Nat.Hist., ser.8, vol.12, no.72, pp.567-574, Dec., 1913.

NEW MAMMALS FROM TROPICAL SOUTH AMERICA. Oldfield Thomas. Ann. and Mag. Nat. Hist., ser.8, vol.7, no.41, pp. 513-517, May, 1911.

NEW NASUA, LUTRA, AND PROECHIMYS FROM SOUTH AMERICA. Oldfield Thomas. Ann. and Mag. Nat. Hist., ser.8, vol.14, no.79, pp.57-61, July, 1914.

NEW SOUTH AMERICAN MAMMALS. Oldfield Thomas. Ann. and Mag. Nat. Hist., ser.7, vol.5, no.25, pp.148-153, Jan., 1900.

NEW SOUTH AMERICAN SCIURI, HETEROMYS, CAVIA AND CALUROMYS. Oldfield Thomas. Ann. and Mag. Nat. Hist., ser.7, vol.7, no.38, pp.192-196, Feb., 1901.

NEW SOUTH AMERICAN SMALL MAMMALS. Oldfield Thomas. Ann. and Mag. Nat. Hist., ser.9, vol.13, no.74, pp.234-237, Feb., 1924.

NEW SPECIES OF ORYZOMYS, PROECHIMYS, CAVIA, AND SYLVILAGUS FROM SOUTH AMERICA. Oldfield Thomas. Ann. and Mag. Nat. Hist., ser.7, vol.8, no.48, pp.536-539, Dec., 1901.

NEW SPECIES OF SACCOPTERYX, SCIURUS, RHIPIDOMYS, AND TATU FROM SOUTH AMERICA. Oldfield Thomas. Ann. and Mag. Nat. Hist., ser.7, vol.7, no. 40, pp.366-371, Apr., 1901.

NOTES ON SOME SOUTH AMERICAN MAMMALS, WITH DESCRIPTIONS OF NEW SPECIES. Oldfield Thomas. Ann. and Mag. Nat. Hist., ser.8, vol.4, no.21, pp.230-242, Sep., 1909.

NOTES ON SOUTH AMERICAN MONKEYS, BATS, CARNIVORES, AND RODENTS WITH DESCRIPTIONS OF NEW SPECIES. Oldfield Thomas. Ann. and Mag. Nat.Hist., ser.7, vol.12, no.70, pp.455-464, Oct., 1903.

ON NEW SMALL MAMMALS FROM SOUTH AMERICA. Oldfield Thomas. Ann. and Mag. Nat. Hist., ser.7, vol.3, no.14, pp. 152-155, Feb., 1899.

ON SMALL MAMMALS FROM NICARAGUA AND BOGOTA. Oldfield Thomas. Ann. and Mag. Nat. Hist., ser.6, vol.16, no.91, pp. 55-60, July, 1895.

ON VARIOUS SOUTH AMERICAN MAMMALS. Oldfield Thomas. Ann. and Mag. Nat. Hist., ser.8, vol.13, no.75, pp.345-363, Mar., 1914.

SMALL MAMMALS FROM SOUTH AMERICA. Oldfield Thomas. Ann. and Mag. Nat. Hist., ser.8, vol.10, no.55, pp.44-48, July, 1912.

THREE SMALL MAMMALS FROM SOUTH AMERICA. Oldfield Thomas. Ann. and Mag. Nat. Hist., ser.8, vol.9, no.52, pp.408-410, Apr., 1912.

THREE NEW SOUTH AMERICAN MAMMALS. Oldfield Thomas. Ann. and Mag. Nat. Hist., ser.8, vol.7, no.37, pp.113-115, Jan., 1911, ser.8, vol.13, no.78, pp. 573-575, June, 1914.

TWO NEW MAMMALS FROM SOUTH AMERICA. Oldfield Thomas. Ann. and Mag. Nat. Hist., ser.7, vol.13, no.74, pp.142-144, Feb., 1904.

A NATURALIST IN THE STRAITS OF MAGELLAN. Charles H. Townsend. Popular Science Monthly, vol.77, no.1, illus., pp.5-18, July, 1910.

SOUTH AMERICAN LAND MAMMALS AND THEIR LICE. P.E. Vanzolini, L.R. Guimarães. Evolution, Lancaster, vol.9, no. 3, pp.345-347, Sep., 1955.

(NEW CONTRIBUTIONS TO KNOWLEDGE OF THE MAMMALS OF RIO JURUA.) Nova contribuicao ao conhecimento dos mammiferos do Rio Jurua. Carlos O. C. Vieira. Bol. Mus. Paraense E.Goeldi, Belem do Pará, vol.10, pp.239-274, 1948.

(JUNGLE AND STEPPE ANIMALS.) Animales de la selva y estepa. Ernesto Vollmer. Buenos Aires, Editorial Jupiter, pp. 73, illus., 1942.

(COMMENTARIES ON 100 LOCALITIES NEW FOR SOUTH AMERICAN MAMMALS.) Comentarios sobre cien localidades nuevas para mamiferos sudamericanos. Jose Yepes. Rev. Argentina Zoogeogr., Buenos Aires, vol.4, nos.1-2, pp.59-71, 1945.

(NATIONAL COMMISSION FOR PROTECTION OF SOUTH AMERICAN FAUNA.) La Comision Nacional Protectora de la Fauna Sudamericana. Jose Yepes. Rev. Argentina Zoogeogr., Buenos Aires, vol. 2, no.3, pp.163-165, Dec. 31, 1942.

(REGIONAL PHYSIOGRAPHY AND GEOGRAPHIC DISTRIBUTION OF SOME OF OUR MAMMALS.) La fisiografia regional y la distribucion geografica de algunos de nuestros mamiferos. Jose Yepes. Revista del Centro de Estudiantes del Doctorado en Ciencias Naturales, Buenos Aires, vol. 2, no.4, pp.29-52, pls.9, Apr., 1938.

(ECOLOGIC OBSERVATIONS REGARDING MAMMALS OF THE LOMAS.) Observaciones ecológicas sobre los mamiferos de las lomas. Enrique Zuñiga. Bol. Mus. Hist. Nat. "Javier Prado," Lima, año 6, nos.22-23, pp.392-399, 1942.

## SOUTH AMERICA -- AMAZONIA

OBSERVATIONS ON THE LIFE-HABITS OF SOME BATRACHIANS AND REPTILES FROM THE LOWER AMAZON: AND A NOTE ON SOME MAMMALS FROM MARAJO ISLAND. (Notes on Bats, Hydrochoerus, and Didelphis.) Hugh B. Cott. Proc. Zool. Soc. London, pt.4, pp.1159-1178, pls.6, Dec., 1926.

MAMMALS OF AMAZONIA. Eladio da Cruz Lima. Contribution from the Museu Paraense Emilio Goeldi de Historia Nat. e Etnografia. Regular ed. Rio de Janeiro, Distributed by Livraria Agir, col.pls., 1945. (A translation of the original Portuguese text.)

(MEMORIES OF THE MONKEYS OF THE AMAZON REGIONS AND NEW GRANADA.) Memorias sobre los monos de las regiones Amazonicas y de Nueva Granada. Alexander de Humboldt. Rev. Acad. Colombiana Cienc. Exact., Fis. y Nat., Bogota, vol.5, no.20, pp.506-527, col.pls.4, Aug., 1944.

(THE AMAZON BASIN (CONTINUATION).) La Hoya Amazonica (Continuacion). D.O. Ricaurte. Bol. Soc. Geogr. Colombia, Bogota, vol.4, no.1, pp.8-32, illus., Apr. 1937. (Mammals pp.24-32); no.3, pp.168-181, illus., Dec., 1937.

NEW SPECIES OF OECOMYS, AND MARMOSA FROM AMAZONIA. Oldfield Thomas. Ann. and Mag. Nat. Hist., ser.8, vol.3, no.16, pp.378-380, 1909.

ON MAMMALS FROM THE LOWER AMAZONS IN THE GOELDI MUSEUM, PARA. Oldfield Thomas. Ann. and Mag. Nat.Hist., ser.9, vol.6, pp.266-283, Sep., 1920.

ON SMALL MAMMALS FROM THE LOWER AMAZON. Oldfield Thomas. Ann. and Mag. Nat. Hist., ser.8, vol.9, no.49, pp.84-90, Jan., 1912.

ON SOME MAMMALS FROM THE MIDDLE AMAZONS. Oldfield Thomas. Ann. and Mag. Nat. Hist., ser.9, vol.17, no.102, pp.635-639, June, 1926.

THREE NEW MAMMALS FROM THE LOWER AMAZONS. Oldfield Thomas. Ann. and Mag. Nat. Hist., ser.8, vol.7, no. 42, pp.606-608, June, 1911.

## SOUTH AMERICA -- ARGENTINA

### Extinct and Fossil Mammals

(CONTRIBUTION TO KNOWLEDGE OF FOSSIL MAMMALS IN THE REPUBLIC OF ARGENTINA. WORK DONE UNDER THE AUSPICES OF THE NATIONAL SCIENCE ACADEMY OF ARGENTINA TO BE PRESENTED AT THE UNIVERSAL EXPOSITION IN PARIS IN 1889.) Contribucion al conocimiento de los mamiferos fosiles de la Republica Argentina. Obra escrita bajo los auspicios de la Academia nacional de ciencias de la Republica Argentina para ser presentada a la Exposicion universal de Paris de 1889. Florentino Ameghino. Buenos Aires, Impr. de P.E. Coni é hijos, pp.xxxii-1027, illus., atlas, 1889. (Added: Actas de la Academia nacional de ciencias de la Republica Argentina en Cordoba, t. VI.)

(FOSSIL MAMMALS OF THE ARGENTINE REPUBLIC.) Mamiferos fosiles de la Republica Argentina. Florentino Ameghino. Edicion Oficial de la Obras y Correspondencia Cientifica de Florentino Ameghino, La Plata, vol.10, atlas, pls.98, 1932.

(NEW SPECIES OF MAMMALS, CRETACEOUS AND TERTIARY, OF THE REPUBLIC OF ARGENTINA.) Nuevas especies de mamiferos, cretaceos y terciarios de la Republica Argentina. Florentino Ameghino. Buenos Aires, Coni hermanos, pp.142, 1904.

A NEW FOSSIL PERISSODACTYL FROM PERU. (Griphodon peruvianus, new genus and species.) H.E. Anthony. Amer. Mus. Nov., no.111, pp.3, fig.1, Apr. 21, 1924.

(PRESENT STATE OF THE QUESTION OF THE CRETACEOUS-TERTIARY LIMIT IN ARGENTINA FROM THE PALEONTOLOGIC POINT OF VIEW.) Estado actual de la cuestion del limite Cretaceo-Terciario en la Argentina desde el punto de vista paleontológico. Angel Cabrera. Inst. Mus. Univ. Nac. La Plata, Obra del Cincuentenario, Buenos Aires, pp.1-22, 1935.

(NOTES ON MAMMALS OF MISIONES NEW FOR ARGENTINA.) Nota sobre mamiferos de Misiones nuevos para Argentina. Jorge A. Crespo. Buenos Aires, Impr. y Casa Editora "Coni", Argentina Republic, Instituto Nacional de Investigacion las Ciencias Naturales. Comunicaciones. Ciencios Zoologicas, t.1, no.14, pp.14, illus., tbls., 1950.

(MANUAL OF PALEONTOLOGY OF RIO DE LA PLATA. COMPARATIVE OSTEOLOGY OF THE MAMMALS.) Manual de paleontologia rioplatense. Osteologia comparada de los mamiferos. Kraglievich. Obras de Geologia y Paleontologia, Ministerio de Obras Publicas de la Provincia de Buenos Aires, La Plata, vol.3, pp. 797-850, 1940.

(PREVIOUS DESCRIPTION OF THE NEW FOSSIL UNGULATES AND MARSUPUALS OF THE ARGENTINE PLIOCENE AND EOQUATERNARY.) Descripcion privia de nuevos ungulados y marsupiales fosiles del Plio ceno y del Eocuartario argentinos. Osvaldo A. Reig. Rev. Mus. Municipal Ciencias Nat. y Tradic Mar del Plata, vol. 1, ent.1, pp.119-129, illus., Dec., 1952.

STRATIGRAPHY OF LATE MIOCENE AND PLIOCENE DEPOSITS OF THE PROVINCE OF CATAMARCA (ARGENTINA) WITH NOTES ON THE FAUNAE. Elmer S.Riggs, Bryan Patterson. Physis, Buenos Aires, vol. 16, no.48, pp.143-162, Mar., 1939.

(ANIMAL LIFE AT THE END OF THE UPPER TERTIARY IN BUENOS AIRES.) La vida animal a fines del terciario superior en Buenos Aires. Carlos Rusconi. El Monitor de la Educacion Comun, Buenos Aires, pp.65, figs.31, Aug., 1933.

(CONTRIBUTION TO KNOWLEDGE OF THE GEOLOGY OF THE CITY OF BUENOS AIRES AND ITS SURROUNDINGS, AND REFERENCE TO ITS FAUNA.) Contribucion al conocimiento de la geologica de la ciudad de Buenos Aires y sus alrededores y referencia de su fauna. Carlos Rusconi. Actas Acad. Nac. Cienc.Cordoba, vol.10, entra.3a, pp.177-294, figs.53, 1937.

(LIST OF FOSSIL ORGANISMS OF THE PUELCHENSE OF BUENOS AIRES.) Lista de los organismos fosiles del puelchense de Buenos Aires. Carlos Rusconi. Anal. Soc. Argentina Estud. Geog., Buenos Aires, vol.5, pp.79-89, 1937.

(LIST OF MIOCENE MAMMALS OF HUAYQUERIAS DE MENDOZA.) Lista de los mammiferos miocenicos de las Huayquerias de Mendoza. Carlos Rusconi. Physis, Buenos Aires, vol.14, no.46, pp.461-471, Mar. 31, 1939.

(NEW MAMMAL SPECIES FROM THE PUELCHENSE OF BUENOS AIRES.) Especies nuevas de mamiferos del puelchense de Buenos Aires. Carlos Rusconi. Bol.Paleontol. Buenos Aires, no.16, pp.4, figs.2, Feb. 15, 1944.

(MORE BONE REMAINS OF THE PRE-HISPANIC TOMBS OF SANTIAGO DEL ESTERO.) Mas restos oseos de los tumulos prehispanicos de Santiago del Estero. Carlos Rusconi. Anal. Soc. Cient. Argentina, Buenos Aires, entr.3, vol.144, pp.379-406, figs. 20, 1947.

(PRESENCE OF TERTIARY MAMMALS IN SAN JUAN.) Presencia de mamiferos terciarios en San Juan. Carlos Rusconi. Publ. Inst. Fisiogr. y Geol., Univ. Nac. Litoral, Rosario, pp.11, figs.3, 1946.

(PUELCHENSE OF BUENOS AIRES AND ITS FAUNA (MIDDLE PLIOCENE) (FIRST PART).) El Puelchense de Buenos Aires y su fauna (Plioceno medio) (Primora parte). Carlos Rusconi. Publ. Inst. de Fisiografia y Geologia, Univ. Nacional del Litoral, Republica Argentina, no.33, pp.99, illus., 1948. (SECOND PART). (Segunda parte). Publ. Inst. de Fisiografia y Geologia, Univ. Nacional del Litoral, Republica Argentina, no.36, pp.100-242, pls.1-17, 1949.

(REMAINS OF TERTIARY MAMMALS OF SAN LUIS.) Restos de mamiferos terciarios de San Luis. Carlos Rusconi. Bol. Paleontol. Buenos Aires, no.6, pp.1-4, figs. 2, June 25, 1936.

(SOME TERTIARY FOSSILS OF THE GOVERNMENT OF THE ARGENTINE PAMPAS.) Algunos fosiles terciarios de la Gobernacion de la Pampa Argentina. Carlos Rusconi. Revista Chilena Hist. Nat., ano 38 (1934), pp.104-107, figs.25, 1934.

NATURE AND ORIGIN OF THE SANTA CRUZ FAUNA. WITH ADDITIONAL NOTES ON THE ENTELONYCHIA AND ASTRAPOTHERIA. PART 3. William B. Scott. Reports Princeton Univ. Exped.Patagonia, 1896-1898, vol.7, pp.193-238, pls.A-K, 1932.

EARLY AND MIDDLE TERTIARY GEOLOGY OF THE GAIMAN REGION.CHUBUT, ARGENTINA. George Gaylord Simpson. Amer. Mus. Novitates, New York, no.775, pp.29, figs.13, Jan. 29, 1935.

NEW ADIANTHINE LITOPTERN AND ASSOCIATED MAMMALS FROM A DESEADAN FAUNULE IN MENDOZA, ARGENTINA. George Gaylord Simpson. Amer. Mus. Nat. Hist., New York, Amer. Mus. Novitates, no.1434, pp.27, illus., map, 1949.

SANTA CRUZ TYPOTHERIA. William J. Sinclair. Proc. Amer. Philos. Soc., vol. 47, no.188, pp.64-78, figs.10, Apr., 1908.

(ANIMAL LIFE AT THE END OF THE UPPER TERTIARY AGE IN BUENOS AIRES.) La vida animal a fines del terciario superior en Buenos Aires. Monitor Educ. Comun, Buenos Aires, numero de Agosto, vol.52, no.728, pp.1-65, figs.31, Aug., 1933.

Recent Mammals

(TWO MICROMAMMALS OF NORTHERN ARGENTINA. PRELIMINARY NOTES.) Dos nuevos micromamiferos del Norte Argentino. (Graomys hypogaeus, Marmosa janetta pulchetta.) Angel Cabrera. Notae prelim. Mus. de La Plata, vol.3, no.1a, pp.123-128, fig.1, May 28, 1934.

(SUB-SOIL OF ROSARIO.) El subsuelo de Rosario. Alfredo Castellanos. Anal. Soc. Cient. Argentina, Buenos Aires, vol.127, entr.1, pp.3-13, illus., Jan., 1939.

(NOTE ON MAMMALS OF MISIONES NEW FOR ARGENTINA.) Nota subre mamiferos de Misiones nueves para Argentina. Jorge A. Crespo. Comunic. Inst. Nac. Investig. Cien. Nat., Mus. Argentino Cien. Nat. "Bernardino Rivadavia," Buenos Aires, Cien. Zool., vol.1, no.14, pp.1-14, illus., Dec., 1950.

(INDIGENOUS NAMES IN GUARANI OF THE MAMMALS OF ARGENTINA AND NEIGHBORING COUNTRIES AND THEIR IMPORTANCE FOR SYSTEMATICS.) Los nombres indigenas en guarani de los mamiferos de la Argentina y paises limitrofes y su importancia para la sistematica. Jorge G. Dennler. Physis, Buenos Aires, vol.16, no.48, pp. 225-244, May, 1939. (Vernacular Names.)

NOTES ON SOME OF THE SMALLER MAMMALS OF THE ARGENTINE REPUBLIC. Henry Durnford. Proc. Zool. Soc. London, pt.1, pp.32-33, 1877.

ON MAMMALIA FROM THE NEIGHBORHOOD OF CONCORDIA, IN NEW GRANADA. J.E. Gray. Ann. and Mag. Nat. Hist., London, ser.4, vol.11, no.66, pp.468-469, June, 1873.

(ENUMERATION AND ZOOGEOGRAPHY OF THE MAMMALS OF THE ARGENTINE REPUBLIC.) Enumeracion y zoogegrafia de los mamiferos de la Republica Argentina. Fernando Lahille. Pp.40, 1914.

(ESSAY ON THE GEOGRAPHIC DISTRIBUTION OF THE MAMMALS OF THE REPUBLIC OF ARGENTINA. Ensayo sobre la distribucion geografica de los mamiferos en la Republica Argentine. Fernando Lahille. La Plata, pp.42, fold.map, 1900.

ON SOME MAMMALS FROM THE ARGENTINA CHACO. (New Forms of Mazama and a New Cerdocyon.) Einar Lonnberg. Arkiv. for Zoologi, vol.12, no.10, pp.1-20, figs. 1-5, 1919.

(HEURISTIC BIBLIOGRAPHY OF THE MAMMALS, THE HUNT, AND FISHING;CONTRIBUTIONS TO STUDY OF THE ARGENTINE FAUNA.) Bibliografia euristica de los mamiferos, de caza y caza maritima; contribuciones al estudio de la fauna argentina. Carlos A. Marelli. La Plata, Taller de impresiones oficiales, pp.189, 1936.

(ORGANIZATION FOR THE PROTECTION OF THE SPECIES OF ARGENTINA.) La organización de la proteccion de las especies en la Argentina. Carlos A. Marelli. Proc. 8th Amer. Sci. Congr., Washington, D.C., vol.3, pp.101-102, 1942.

(SYSTEMATIC LIST OF THE FAUNA OF THE PROVINCE OF BUENOS AIRES (PROTOCHORDATES AND VERTEBRATES).) Elenco Sistematico de la Fauna de la Provincia de Buenos Aires (Procordados y Vertebrados). Carlos A. Marelli. Mem. Ministerio Obras Publicas, Buenos Aires, 1922-1923. (Mammals, pp.666-682, 1924.)

(MAMMALS COLLECTED AND OBSERVED IN ARGENTINA BY HERR PAUL HEUMANN.) Die von Herrn Paul Neumann in Argentinien gesammelten und beobachteten Saeugethiere. Paul Matschie. Sitz.Ber. Gesell. Naturf. Freunde, Berlin, no.2, pp.57-64, Feb. 20, 1894.

COLLECTION OF MAMMALS FROM EASTERN BUENOS AIRES, WITH DESCRIPTIONS OF RELATED NEW MAMMALS FROM OTHER LOCALITIES. Oldfield Thomas. Ann. and Mag. Nat. Hist., ser.8, vol.5, no.27, pp.239-247, Mar., 1910.

FURTHER COLLECTION OF MAMMALS FROM JUJUY. Oldfield Thomas. Ann. and Mag. Nat. Hist., ser.9, vol.5, pp.188-196, Feb., 1920.

LIST OF MAMMALS FROM THE HIGHLANDS OF JUJUY, NORTH ARGENTINA, COLLECTED BY SIR E. BUDIN. Oldfield Thomas. Ann. and Mag. Nat. Hist., ser. 9, vol.4, no.21, pp.128-135, Sep., 1919.

NEW RHIPIDOMYS, AKODON, CTENOMYS, AND MARMOSA FROM THE SIRRA SANTA BARBARA, S.E. JUJUY. Oldfield Thomas. Ann. and Mag. Nat. Hist., ser.9, vol.7, no.38, pp.183-187, Feb., 1921.

ON A FURTHER COLLECTION OF MAMMALS FROM JUJUY OBTAINED BY SIR E. BUDIN. Oldfield Thomas. Ann. and Mag. Nat. Hist., ser.9, vol.8, no.48, pp.608-617, Dec., 1921.

ON MAMMALS COLLECTED AT CRUZ DEL EJE, CENTRAL CORDOVA, BY MR. P.O. SIMONS. Oldfield Thomas. Ann. and Mag. Nat. Hist., ser.7, vol.9, no. 52, pp.237-245, Apr., 1902.

ON MAMMALS FROM NEAR TINOGASTA, CATAMARCA, COLLECTED BY SIR E. BUDIN. Oldfield Thomas. Ann. and Mag. Nat. Hist., ser.9, vol.6, no.31, pp.116-120, July, 1920.

ON MAMMALS FROM THE PROVINCE OF SAN JUAN, WESTERN ARGENTINA. Oldfield Thomas. Ann. and Mag. Nat. Hist., ser.9, vol.8, no.44, pp.214-221, Aug., 1921.

ON SOME ARGENTINE MAMMALS. Oldfield Thomas. Ann. and Mag. Nat. Hist., ser.9, vol.15, pp.582-586, May, 1925.

ON SMALL MAMMALS COLLECTED IN JUJUY BY SIR E. BUDIN. Oldfield Thomas. Ann. and Mag. Nat. Hist., ser.8, vol.11, no.61, pp.136-143, Jan., 1913.

ON SMALL MAMMALS FROM "OTRO CERRO," NORTHEASTERN RIOJA, COLLECTED BY SIR E. BUDIN. Oldfield Thomas. Ann. and Mag. Nat. Hist., ser.9, vol.3, pp.489-500, May, 1919. (Nine New Species of Neotropical Mammals.)

ON SMALL MAMMALS FROM SALTA AND JUJUY COLLECTED BY SIR E. BUDIN. Oldfield Thomas. Ann. and Mag. Nat. Hist., ser.9, vol.1, no.2, pp.186-193, Feb., 1918.

ON SMALL MAMMALS FROM THE DELTA OF THE PARANA. Oldfield Thomas. Ann. and Mag. Nat. Hist., ser.8, vol.20, no. 115, pp.95-100, July, 1917.

ON SMALL MAMMALS FROM THE FAMATINA CHAIN, NORTHWESTERN RIOJA. Oldfield Thomas. Ann. and Mag. Nat. Hist., ser.9, vol.6, pp.417-422, Oct., 1920.

ON SOME SMALL MAMMALS FROM CATAMARCA. Oldfield Thomas. Ann. and Mag. Nat. Hist., ser.9, vol.3, no.13, pp.115-118, Jan., 1919.

ON SOME SMALL MAMMALS FROM SALTA N. ARGENTINA. Oldfield Thomas. Ann. and Mag. Nat. Hist., ser.6, vol.20, no. 116, pp.214-218, Aug., 1897.

SPEDAN LEWIS SOUTH AMERICAN EXPLORATION.-III. ON MAMMALS COLLECTED BY SIR E. BUDIN IN THE PROVINCE OF TUCUMAN. Oldfield Thomas. Ann. and Mag. Nat. Hist., ser.9, vol.17, pp.602-609, May, 1926.

SPEDAN LEWIS SOUTH AMERICAN EXPLORATION.-IV. LIST OF MAMMALS OBTAINED BY SIR E. BUDIN ON THE BOUNDARY BETWEEN JUJUY AND BOLIVIA. Oldfield Thomas. Ann. and Mag. Nat. Hist., ser.9, vol.18, pp.193-195, Aug., 1926.

TWO NEW MAMMALS FROM NORTH ARGENTINA. Oldfield Thomas. Ann.and Mag. Nat. Hist., ser.9, vol.17, no.99, pp.311-312, Mar., 1926.

SPEDAN LEWIS SOUTH AMERICAN EXPLORATION. V. MAMMALS OBTAINED BY SIR E. BUDIN IN NEUQUEN. Oldfield Thomas, J. St. Leger. Ann. and Mag. Nat. Hist., ser.9, vol.18, no.108, pp. 635-641, Dec., 1926.

(GENERALITIES AND TAXONOMY OF THE ARGENTINE MAMMALS. PART I. RESUME OF THE CONFERENCES DICTATED IN OCTOBER, 1934.) Generalidades y Taxonomia de los Mammiferos argentinos. Pt.1. Resumen de las conferencias dictadas en octubre de 1934. (Marsupialia and Chiroptera.) Jose Yepes. Rev. Centro Estud.

Doctorado Cienc. Nat., Buenos Aires, vol. 1, no.1, pp.30-48, May, 1935.

(MAMMALS COLLECTED IN THE COMECHINGONES REGION (CORDOBA OESTE) AND ZOO-GEOGRAPHIC CONSIDERATIONS DERIVED FROM ITS STUDY (SUMMARY).) Mamiferos coleccionados en la region de Comechingones (Cordoba Oeste) y consideraciones zoogeograficas que de su estudio se desprenden (Resumen). Jose Yepes. Physis, Buenos Aires, vol.16, no.48, p.291, May, 1939.

(MAMMALS OF MENDOZA AND THEIR RELATION TO THE BOUNDING FAUNAS.) Los mamiferos de Mendoza y sus relaciones con las faunas limitrofes. Jose Yepes. Univ. Buenos Aires, Mision de Estudios de Patologia Regional Argentina Jujuy. Novena Reunion Soc. Argentina de Patologia Regional Filiales y Afiliades, Buenos Aires, vol.2, pp.689-725, pls.3, map, 1937.

(TYPES OF DISTRIBUTION IN THE ZOOGEOGRAPHY OF ARGENTINA.) Tipos de distribucion en la zoogeografia argentina. José Yepes. Rev. Argentina Zoogeog., Buenos Aires, vol.1, no.1, pp.39-58, May, 1941.

SOUTH AMERICA -- BOLIVIA

(BIOLOGICAL STUDIES IN THE BOLIVIAN CHACO. III. CONTRIBUTION TO THE BIOLOGY OF THE MAMMAL FAUNA.) Biologische Studien im bolivanischen Chaco. III. Beitrag zur Biologie der Saeugetierfauna. M. Eisentraut. Zeitschr.f. Saeugetierk., Berlin, vol.8, nos.1-2, pp.47-69, pls.9-11, Apr. 24, 1933.

(ECOLOGICAL SCHEME OF THE BOLIVIAN JUNGLE, SAVANNAH, AND CORDILLERA.) Esquema ecologico de selva, sabana y cordillera en Bolivia. F. Guillermo Mann. Publ. Inst. Geografia, Facultad de Filosofia, Univ. de Chile, Santiago, no.3, pp.236, illus., 1951.

ON MAMMALS COLLECTED BY MR. PERRY O. SIMONS IN THE SOUTHERN PART OF THE BOLIVIAN PLATEAU. Oldfield Thomas. Ann. and Mag. Nat. Hist., ser.7, vol.9, no. 51, pp.222-230, Mar., 1902.

ON MAMMALS FROM COCHABAMBA, BOLIVIA, AND THE REGION NORTH OF THAT PLACE. Oldfield Thomas. Ann. and Mag. Nat. Hist., ser.7, vol.9, no.50, pp. 125-243, Feb., 1902.

ON SOME NEW MAMMALS FROM THE NEIGHBORHOOD OF MOUNT SAHAMA, BOLIVIA. Oldfield Thomas. Ann. and Mag. Nat. Hist., ser.7, vol.1, no.4, pp. 277-283, Apr., 1898.

ON THE SMALL MAMMALS COLLECTED BY DR. BORELLI IN BOLIVIA AND NORTHERN ARGENTINA. Oldfield Thomas. Bollettino di Musei di Zoologia ed Anatomia comparata della R. Universita di Torino, vol.13, no.315, pp.1-4, Apr. 18, 1898.

SPEDAN LEWIS SOUTH AMERICAN EXPLORATION. I. ON MAMMALS FROM SOUTHERN BOLIVIA. Oldfield Thomas. Ann. and Mag. Nat. Hist., ser.9, vol.15, pp.575-582, May, 1925.

SPEDAN LEWIS SOUTH AMERICAN EXPLORATION. II. ON MAMMALS COLLECTED IN THE TARIJA DEPARTMENT, SOUTHERN BOLIVIA. Oldfield Thomas. Ann. and Mag. Nat. Hist., ser.9, vol. 17, pp.318-328, Mar., 1926.

SOUTH AMERICA -- BRAZIL

Extinct and Fossil Mammals

(NEW FOSSIL REMAINS OF OLIGOCENE MAMMALS, COLLECTED BY PROF. PEDRO SCALABRINI AND BELONGING TO THE PROVINCIAL MUSEUM OF PARANA CITY.) Nuevos restos de mamiferos fósiles oligocenos, recogidos por el profesor Pedro Scalabrini y pertenecientes al Museo provincial de la ciudad del Parana. Florentino Ameghino. Buenos Aires, Impr. de P.E. Coni, Articulo publicado en el Boletin de la Academia nacional de ciencias de Cordoba, tome VIII, pag.5 y sig., pp.205, 1885.

ON THE OCCURRENCE OF FOSSIL REMAINS OF MAMMALS IN THE INTERIOR OF THE STATES OF PERNAMBUCO AND ALAGOAS, BRAZIL. John C. Branner. Amer. Jour. of Sci., New Haven, vol.13, pp.133-137, illus., pl., 1902.

(RACE OF LAGOA SANTA AND THE AMERICAN PLEISTOCENE.) A raca da Lagoa Santa e o pleistocene americano. Arnaldo Cathoud. Bibliotheca mineira de cultura, Bello Horizonte, Edicões Apollo, pp.122, pls., diagrs., 1935.

(BRAZILIAN PALEONTOLOGY; MAMMALS.) Paleontologia brasileira; mamiferos. Carlos de Paula Couto. Rio de Janeiro, Biblioteca cientifica brasileira, ser.A, 1, pp.xvi+516, illus., maps, 1953.

(BRAZIL AND ITS GEOLOGICAL EVOLUTION.) Arqui-Brasil e sua evolucao geologica. (List Cenozoic Mammals.) Djalma Guimarães. Agric. Republica Brasil, no. 88, pp.314, illus., 1951.

(PALEONTOLOGIC PROBLEMS OF BRAZIL.) Problemas de paleontologia brasileira. Anibal Mattos. Sao Paulo Companhia editora nacional, pp.291, illus., maps, pls., ports., 1939. (Biblioteca pedagocia brasileira, ser. 5a, Brasiliana, vol.148.)

FOSSIL MAMMALS FROM THE BEGINNING OF THE CENOZOIC IN BRAZIL;CONDYLARTHRA, LITOPTERNA, XENUNGULATA AND ASTRAPOTHERIA. Carlos de Paula Couto. Amer. Mus. Nat. Hist., New York, Bulletin, vol.99, art.6, pp.359-394, illus., pls., tbls., 1952; Amer. Mus. Novitates, New York, no.1568, pp.16, illus., June 6, 1952.

(GLYPTODONT REMAINS FOUND IN BRAZILIAN CAVES, AND A NEW FORM BELONGING TO THE FOSSORIAL EDENTATA.) De i Brasiliens Knoglehuler fundne Glyptodont-Levninger og en ny, til de gravigrade Edentater horende Slaegt. J. Reinhardt. Vidensk. Med. naturhist. Foren. Kjoben., nos.9-15, pp.3-74, pls.4, 1875.

(CACIMBAS FORMATION AND THE APODI GROUP.) A formacao Cacimbas e o grupo Apodi. Vingt-un Rosado. Mossoro, Composto e impresso na Editora Comercial, Colecão mossoroense, ser.B, Folhetos, no. 34, pp.21, 1957.

(FOSSIL AND EXTINCT UNGULATA FROM LAGOA SANTA, MINAS GERAIS, AND BRAZIL.) Jordfundne og nulevende Hovdyr (Ungulata) fra Lagoa Santa, Minas Gerais, Brasilien. Herluf Winge. E. Museo Lundil, Kjobenhavn, vol.3, pt.1, pp.239, pls.9, 1906.

Recent Mammals

(ON A NEW COLLECTION OF MAMMAL FOSSILS GATHERED BY PROF. SCALABRINI IN THE GORGES OF THE PARANA.) Sobre una nueva colección de mamiferos fósiles, recogidos por el profesor Scalabrini en las barrancas del Parana. Florentino Ameghino. Buenos Aires, Imprenta de P.E. Coni, pp.104, 1883. (Publicado en el Bol. de la Acad. nacional de ciencias, t.v, entrega III.)

(ENVIRONMENTAL CHANGE AND SPECIES TRANSFORMATION AMONG BRAZILIAN MAMMALS.) Umweltaenderung und Artumwandlung bei brasilianischen Saeugethieren. Hans Boker. Naturwiss., Berlin, vol.20, no.12, pp.201-205, Mar. 18, 1932.

(MAMMALIAN OBSERVATIONS AND INVESTIGATIONS WHILE ON A BIOLOGICAL-ANATOMICAL TRIP TO BRAZIL IN 1928.) Beobachtungen und Untersuchungen an Saeugetieren waehrend einer biologisch-anatomischen Forschungsreise nach Brasilien im Jahre 1928. Hans Boker. Gegenbaurs Morphol. Jahrb., Leipzig, vol.70, pp.1-66, figs.42, Apr., 1932.

(ANIMALS OF BRAZIL. FIRST PART. MAMMALS.) Thiere Brasiliems. I Theil (Mammals). H. Burmeister. Berlin, vol.8, pp. 431, 1854.

(SOME MAMMALS FROM WESTERN ACRE.) Alguns mamiferos do Acre Ocidental. Cory T. de Carvalho. Bol. Mus. Paraense Emilio Goeldi, nova serie, zool., vol.6, pp.1-22, Aug., 1957.

ANNUAL CYCLE OF PLANTS, MOSQUITOS, BIRDS, AND MAMMALS IN TWO BRAZILIAN FORESTS. David E. Davis. Ecol., Monographs, Durham, vol.15, pp.243-295, figs.24, July, 1945.

NOTES ON THE LIFE HISTORIES OF SOME BRAZILIAN MAMMALS. David E. Davis. Bol. Mus. Nac., Rio de Janeiro, n.s., Zool., no.76, pp.1-8, Apr. 30, 1947.

(CONTRIBUTION TO KNOWLEDGE OF THE ZOOGEOGRAPHICAL HISTORY OF BRAZIL.) Contribuiçao ao conhecimento da historia da zoogegrafia do Brazil. Jose Lacerda de Araujo Feio. Publ. Avulsa Mus. Nac., Univ. Brasil, Rio de Janeiro, Brasil, no.12, pp.3-22, 1953.

(MAMMALS OF BRAZIL.) Os mammiferos do Brazil. Emil August Goeldi. Rio de Janeiro, Livraria classica de Alves & c., pp.181, fold.tbls.2, 1893. (Monographias brazileiras, no.1.) (Literatura sobre os mammiferos do Brasil, pp.155-160.)

NATURALIST IN BRAZIL. THE FLORA AND FAUNA AND THE PEOPLE OF BRAZIL. Konrad Guenther. London, George Allen and Unwin, Ltd., pp.400, pls.32, illus.71, figs.40, 1931.

(CONTRIBUTIONS TO KNOWLEDGE OF THE MAMMALS OF SOUTHERN BRAZIL.) Beitraege zur Kenntniss der Saeugethiere Sued-Brasiliens. Reinhold Hensel. Berlin, pp.130, 1872.

(MAMMALS OF RIO GRANDE DO SUL.) Os mammiferos do Rio Grande do Sul. Hermann von Ihering. Annuario do Estado do Rio Grande do Sul, de Graciano A. de Azambuja, pp.96-123, 1893.

(MAMMALS OF SAO PAULO.) Os mammiferos de S. Paulo - Catalogo. Hermann von Ihering. Typ. do (Diario Official) Sao Paulo, 25 de Janciro de 1894.

WILD LIFE IN BRAZIL. Bertha Lutz. Nat. Hist., New York, vol.32, no.6, pp.539-550, illus., Nov.-Dec., 1932.

SURVIVAL OF BRAZILIAN MAMMALS. Luiz Carlos de Mesquite Meia. Jour. Mamm., vol.33, no.3, pp.389-390, Aug. 19, 1952.

(ANIMALS OF THEREZOPOLIS. I. PRODROMOS.) Fauna de Therezopolis. I. Prodromos. Alipio de Miranda-Ribeiro. Bol. Mus. Nac., Rio de Janeiro, vol.11, nos.3-4, pls.16, maps 2, Sep.-Dec., 1835.

(SOME MAMMALS COLLECTED IN THE NORTHEAST OF BRAZIL, WITH A DESCRIPTION OF TWO NEW SPECIES AND FIELD NOTES.) Alguns mamiferos colecionados no nordeste do Brasil com a descricão de duas especies novas e notas de campo. Joao Moojen. Bol. Mus. Nacional, Rio de Janeiro, n.s., Zoologia, no.1, pp.1-14, pls.1-3, Feb. 25, 1943.

(VOYAGE OF ZOOLOGIC RESEARCH NEAR THE JURDA RIVER, STATE OF AMAZONAS, BRAZIL.) Um viaje a pesquizas zoologicas hacia el Rio Jurúa, Estado del Amasonas, Brasil-1936. A.M. Olalla. Notas de campo. Observaciones biologicas. Rev. Mus. Paulista, Sao Paulo, vol.23, pp.233-297, 1938.

NEW MAMMALS FROM BRAZIL AND PERU. Wilfred H. Osgood. Field Mus. Nat. Hist., Chicago, Zool. ser., vol. 10, no.13, pp.187-198, publ.185, Oct. 22, 1915.

(BRAZILIAN MAMMALS. FINDINGS OF JOHANN NATERER'S TRAVELS IN THE YEARS 1817-1835.) Brasilische Saeugethiere. Resultate von Johann Natterers Reisen in den Jahren 1817 bis 1835. August von Pelzeln. Herg. von der K.K. Zoologischenbotanischen Gesell., Beiheft zu Bd. 33, Wien, A. Hoelder, 2 vols. in 1, 1883.

(ON THE MAMMALS (EXCEPTING RODENTS) COLLECTED BY PROF. BRESSLAU IN BRAZIL (FINDINGS OF PROF. DR. E. BRESSLAU'S JOURNEY TO BRAZIL FOR THE PURPOSE OF ZOOLOGICAL INVESTIGATION (1913-1914). ) Ueber die von Prof. Bresslau in Brasilien gesammelten Saeugetiere (ausser den Nagetieren). (Ergebnisse einer zoologischen Forschungsreise in Brasilien 1913-1914 von Prof. Dr. E. Bresslau.) Hermann Pohle. Abhandl. d. Senckenbergischen Naturforschenden Gesellschaft, vol.40, no.3, pp.239-247, Frankfurt a.M., 1927.

THROUGH THE BRAZILIAN WILDERNESS. ANIMALS OF CENTRAL BRAZIL. Theodore Roosevelt. New York, 1914.

LIST OF THE MAMMALS OBTAINED BY DR. G. FRANCO GRILLO IN THE PROVINCE OF PARANA, BRAZIL. Oldfield Thomas. Annali del Museo Civico di Storia Naturale di Genova, ser.2, vol.20, pp. 346-349, July 4, 1900.

NEW CALLITHRIX, MIDAS, FELIS, RHIPIDOMYS, AND PROECHIMYS FROM BRAZIL AND ECUADOR. Oldfield Thomas. Ann. and Mag. Nat. Hist., ser.7, vol.14, no.81, pp.188-196, Sep., 1904.

ON MAMMALS COLLECTED IN CEARA, N. E. BRAZIL, BY FRAULEIN DR. SNETHLAGE. Oldfield Thomas. Ann. and Mag. Nat. Hist., ser.8, vol.6, no.35, pp.500-503, Nov., 1910.

ON MAMMALS FROM THE LOWER AMAZONS IN THE GOELDI MUSEUM, PARA. Oldfield Thomas. Ann. and Mag. Nat. Hist., ser.9, vol.6, no.33, pp. 266-283, Sep., 1920.

ON MAMMALS FROM THE SERRA DO MAR OF PARANA COLLECTED BY MR. ALPHONSE ROBERT. Oldfield Thomas. Ann. and Nat. Hist., ser.7, vol.9, no.49, pp.59-64, Jan., 1902.

ON MAMMALS OBTAINED BY MR. ALPHONSE ROBERT ON THE RIO JORDAO, S. W. MINAS GERAIS. Oldfield Thomas. Ann. and Mag. Nat. Hist., ser.7, vol. 8, no.48, pp.526-536, Dec., 1901.

ON SOME RARE AMAZONIAN MAMMALS FROM THE COLLECTION OF THE PARA MUSEUM. Oldfield Thomas. Ann. and Mag. Nat. Hist., ser.8, vol.11, no.61, pp. 130-136, 1913.

TWO NEW MAMMALS FROM MARAJO ISLAND. Oldfield Thomas. Ann. and Mag. Nat. Hist., ser.9, vol.12, pp.341-342, Sep., 1923.

(REPORT ON THE FIFTH EXCURSION OF THE OSWALDO CRUZ INSTITUTE MADE TO THE ZONE OF THE NORTH-WEST RAILROAD OF BRAZIL IN JANUARY 1941. II. PARASITOLOGIC RESEARCH.) Relatorio da quinta excursao do Instituto Oswaldo Cruz, realizada a zona da Estrada de Ferro Noroeste do Brasil, em Janeiro de 1941. II. Pesquisas parasitológicas. Lauro Travassos, J.F. Teixeira de Freitas. Mem. Inst. Oswaldo Cruz, Rio de Janeiro, vol. 36, no.3, pp.272-295, Nov., 1941. (Mammals pp.274-276.)

( A MAMMAL COLLECTION OF ALAGOAS STATE.) Sobre uma colecão de mamiferos do Estado de Alagoas. C. Vieira. Arquivos Zool., Sao Paulo, vol.8, pp.209-223, 1955.

(MAMMALS OF MONTE ALGRE.) Mamiferos de Monte Alegre. C. Vieira. Papeis Avyksis di Dept. Zool., Brasil, vol.6, no. 11, pp.127-134, Nov. 30, 1944.

(REMISSIVE LIST OF MAMMALS OF BRAZIL.) Lista remissiva dos mamiferos do Brasil. C. Vieira. Arquivos Zool., Sao Paulo, vol.8, pp.341-464, 1955.

(RODENTS AND LAGOMORPHS OF SAO PAULO STATE.) Roedores e lagomorfos do Estado de Sao Paulo. C. Vieira. Arquivos Zool., Sao Paulo, vol.8, pp.129-166, illus., 1955.

PRESENT OF SOME SPECIMENS OF QUADRUPEDS FROM MINAS GERAES. John Wray. Proc. Zool. Soc. London, pt.7, p.75, 1839.

BRAZIL--LAND OF BEAUTY AND STRANGE BEASTS. Jr. Nat. Hist. Mag., New York, vol.7, no.10, pp.4-7, 16, illus., Dec., 1942.

SOUTH AMERICA -- CHILE

(OBSERVATIONS ON SOME MARINE MAMMALS ON THE COASTS OF CHILE AND PERU.) Osservazioni su alcuni mammiferi marini sulle coste del Cile e del Peru. G. Bini. Bol. Pesca Piscic. Idrobiol., Roma, anno 27, vol.6, n.s., fasc.1, pp.79-93, 1951.

(ECOLOGICAL REGION OF TARAPACA.) Regiones ecologicas de Tarapaca. Guillermo Mann. Rev. Geogr. Chile, Santiago, no.2, pp.51-63, illus., Dec., 1949.

(MAMMALS OF TARAPACA. OBSERVATIONS MADE DURING AN EXPEDITION TO THE HIGH NORTH OF CHILE.) Mamiferos de Tarapaca. Observaciones realizadas durante una expedicion al alto Norte de Chile. Guillermo Mann. Biologica, Santiago, fasc.2, pp.23-98, figs.44, pls.37, July, 1945.

(NEW MAMMALS OF TARAPACA.) Nuevos mamiferos de Tarapaca. Guillermo Mann. Investigaciones Zoologicas Chilenas, fasc. 2, pp.4-6, Dec., 1950.

(KEY TO IDENTIFICATION OF THE MAMMALS OF CHILE.) Clave de determinacion para las especies de mamiferos de Chile. Guillermo Mann. Investigaciones Zoologicas Chilenas, vol.4, pp.89-126, Dec. 30, 1957.

(THE MAMMALS OF CONCEPION PROVINCE IN RELATION TO AGRICULTURE.) Los mamiferos de la provincia de Concepcion en relacion con la agricultura. Carlos Oliver Schneider. Concepcion de Chile, Escuela de artes y oficios, Museo de Concepcion, publicaciones del servicio de extension y vulgarizacion cientifica, no.1, pp.16, illus., 1923.

MAMMALS OF CHILE. Wilfred H. Osgood. Zool. Ser. Field Mus. Nat. Hist., Chicago, vol.30, pp.268, figs.33, maps 10, Dec. 28, 1943.

(Review by E. Raymond Hall of) MAMMALS OF CHILE. Wilfred H. Osgood. Jour. Mamm., vol.26, no.1, pp.97-98, Feb., 1945; Zool. Ser., Field Mus. Nat. Hist., vol.30, publ.no.542, pp.268, Dec. 28, 1943.

(DESCRIPTION OF THE MAMMALS BROUGHT IN THE EXPLORATION TRIP TO TARAPACA. MADE BY ORDER OF THE GOVERNMENT, DURING THE SUMMER OF 1884 TO 1885. (BY FEDERICO PHILIPPI).) Descripcion de los mamiferos traidos del viaje de esploracion a Tarapaca, hecho por orden del gobierno en el verano de 1884 a 1885 (por Federico Philippi). Rudolph Amandus Philippi. Anales del Museo Nacional de Chile - Publicados por orden del gobierno de Chile - Primera Seccion; Zoolojia, entrega 13a, pp.5-24, pls.7, 1896.

(FOSSIL MAMMALS OF CHILE. ADDITIONS AND CORRECTIONS TO THE PRELIMINARY LIST.) Mamiferos fosiles de Chile. Adiciones y correcciones a una lista preliminar. C.O. Schneider. Rev. Chilena Hist. Nat. Pura y Aplicada, Santiago, vol.39, pp.297-304, 1935.

(CHILEAN MARINE VERTEBRATES.) Vertebrados marinos Chilenos. A. Parmenio Yanez. Rev. Biol. Mar., Univ. Chile, vol. 1, no.2, pp.103-123, Sep., 1948.

SOUTH AMERICA -- COLOMBIA

Extinct and Fossil Mammals

SURVIVAL OF PRIMITIVE NOTOUNGULATES AND CONDYLARTHS INTO THE MIOCENE OF COLOMBIA. Malcolm McKenna. Amer. Jour. Sci., vol.254, pp.736-743, illus., Dec., 1956.

(EXTINCT FOSSIL SPECIES RECOVERED IN THE PLAINS OF BOGOTA.) Especies extinguidas hallazgos fosiles en la Sabana de Bogota. (Proboscideans and Horses.) Luis Cuervo Marquez. Rev. Acad. Colombiana Cienc. Exactas, Fisicas y Naturales, Bogota, vol.11, no.5, pp.38-42, figs.23, Jan.-Feb.-Mar., 1938.

(VERTEBRATES OF THE COLOMBIAN CONTINENTAL TERTIARY.) Los vertebrados del Terciario continental colombiano. Jose Royo y Gomez. Rev. Acad. Colombiana Cien. Exactas, Fisicas y Naturales, Bogota, vol.6, no.24, pp.496-512, figs.7, pls.5, Sep., 1945 - Mar., 1946.

REPORT ON FOSSIL VERTEBRATES FROM THE UPPER MAGDALENA VALLEY, COLOMBIA. Donald E. Savage. Science, Lancaster, vol.114, no.2955, pp.186-187, Aug. 17, 1951.

RODENT AND A PECCARY FROM THE CENOZOIC OF COLOMBIA. R.A. Stirton. Compilacion de Estudios Geologicos Oficiales en Colombia, Ministerio de Minas y Petroleos, Serv. Geol. Nac., Bogota, vol.7, pp.317-324, pl.83, 1947.

VERTEBRATE PALEONTOLOGY AND CONTINENTAL STRATIGRAPHY IN COLOMBIA. R.A. Stirton. Bull. Geol. Soc. Amer., vol.64, pp.603-622, illus., June, 1953.

Recent Mammals

MAMMALS FROM WESTERN COLOMBIA. J.A. Allen. Bull. Amer. Mus. Nat. Hist., vol.31, pp.71-95, Apr. 19, 1912.

NEW MAMMALS FROM COLOMBIA AND ECUADOR. J.A. Allen. Bull. Amer. Mus. Nat. Hist., vol.32, pp.469-484, text figs. 1-18, Sep. 25, 1913.

REPORT ON MAMMALS FROM THE DISTRICT OF SANTA MARTA, COLOMBIA, COLLECTED BY MR. HERBERT H. SMITH, WITH FIELD NOTES BY MR. SMITH. J.A. Allen. Bull. Amer. Mus. Nat. Hist., vol. 20, pp.407-468, text figs.1-4, Nov. 28, 1904.

DESCRIPTIONS OF SOME NEW MAMMALS FROM THE SIERRA NEVADA DE SANTA MARTA, COLOMBIA. Outram Bangs. Proc. Biol. Soc. Washington, vol.12, pp.161-165, Aug. 10, 1898.

LIST OF THE MAMMALS COLLECTED IN THE SANTA MARTA REGION OF COLOMBIA BY W. W. BROWN, JR. Outram Bangs. Proc. New England Zool. Club, vol.1, pp. 87-102, pl.1, Feb. 23, 1900.

MAMMALS OF NORTHERN COLOMBIA. P. Hershkovitz. 1947.

MAMMALS FROM WESTERN VENEZUELA AND EASTERN COLOMBIA. Wilfred Hudson Osgood. Field Mus. Nat. Hist., Chicago, publ.155, Zoological ser., vol.10, no.5, pp.33-66, pls.4-5, map, 1912.

NEW CRYPTOTIS, THOMASOMYS, AND ORYZOMYS FROM COLOMBIA. Oldfield Thomas. Ann. and Mag. Nat. Hist., ser. 9, vol.8, pp.354-357, Sep., 1921.

SOUTH AMERICA -- ECUADOR

HUMID FOREST TO SNOW-CAPPED HEIGHT IN ECUADOR. (Many Notes on Mammals.) H.E. Anthony. Nat. Hist., vol.21, pp.459-473, figs.13, Sep.-Oct., 1921.

HIGH ANDES OF ECUADOR; EPISODES IN THE TRAVELS OF A MAMMALOGIST. H.E. Anthony. Nat. Hist., vol.24, no.4, pp.429-441, photos 24, 1924.

PRELIMINARY REPORT ON ECUADOREAN MAMMALS. H.E. Anthony. Amer. Mus. Novitates, NO. I, no.20, pp.1-6, Nov. 3, 1921; NO. II, no.32, pp.1-6, map, Mar. 4, 1922; NO. III, no.55, pp.1-14, figs.4, Jan. 31, 1923; NO. IV, no.114, pp.1-6, May 29, 1924; NO. V, no.120, pp.1-3, June 21, 1924; NO. VI, no.139, pp.1-9, Oct. 20, 1924; NO. VII, no.240, pp.1-6, Dec. 4, 1926.

(COMMENTS ON SOME MAMMALS OF ECUADOR.) Nagra ord om en samling daggdjur fran Ecuador. Einar Lonnberg. Fauna och Flora, Stockholm, no.1, pp. 1-8, pl.1, 1914.

MAMMALS FROM ECUADOR AND RELATED FORMS. Einar Lonnberg. Arkiv for Zool., Upsala, vol.8, no.16, pp.1-36, pl.1, fig.1, July 12, 1913.

NOTES ON SOME MAMMALS FROM ECUADOR. Einar Lonnberg. Jour. Mamm., vol.6, no.4, pp.271-275, Nov., 1925.

SECOND CONTRIBUTION TO THE MAMMALOGY OF ECUADOR WITH SOME REMARKS ON CAENOLESTES. Einar Lonnberg. Arkiv for Zool., vol.14, no.4, pp.1-104, pl.1, figs.8, 1921.

THIRD CONTRIBUTION TO THE MAMMALOGY OF ECUADOR. Einar Lonnberg. Archiv for Zool., vol.14, no.20, pp.1-23, figs.3, 1922.

(ON A SHIPMENT OF MAMMALS AND BIRDS FROM ECUADOR.) Ueber eine Sendung von Saeugethieren und Voegel aus Ecuador. August Pelzeln. Verhandl. K.K. Zool. Bot. Gesell. in Wien, Jahrg. 1882, vol.32, pt.2, pp.443-448, Mar., 1883.

(STUDY OF A COLLECTION OF MAMMALS OF EASTERN ECUADOR (FLORNOY MISSION).) Etude d'une collection de mammiferes de l'Ecuador oriental (Mission Flornoy). P. Rode. Bull.Paris Mus. Nat. d'Hist.Nat., ser.2, vol.9, no.6, pp.342-346, Nov., 1937; vol.10, pp.243-346, 1938.

ON A SPECIES OF QUADRUMANA COLLECTED BY MR. BUCKLEY IN ECUADOR. P.L. Sclater. Proc. Zool. Soc. London, pl.54, May 21, 1872.

ON A COLLECTION OF MAMMALS FROM ECUADOR. Witmer Stone. Acad. of Nat. Sci. of Philadelphia, Proc., vol. 66, pp.9-19, 1914.

NEW GENUS OF PHYLLOSTOME BATS AND A NEW RHIPIDOMYS FROM ECUADOR. Oldfield Thomas. Ann. and Mag. Nat. Hist., ser.8, vol.16, no.94, pp.310-312, Oct., 1915.

ON MAMMALS FROM ECUADOR. Oldfield Thomas. Proc. Zool. Soc. London, pp.393-402, pl.38, figs.3, May 4, 1880.

ON SEVEN NEW SMALL MAMMALS FROM ECUADOR AND VENEZUELA. Oldfield Thomas. Ann. and Mag. Nat. Hist., ser.7, vol.1, no.6, pp.451-457, June, 1898.

NOTES ON A COLLECTION OF MAMMALIA MADE BY MR. FRASER AT GUALAQUIZA. Robert F. Tomes. Proc. Zool. Soc. London, pt.26, pp.546-549, 1858.

NOTES ON A SECOND COLLECTION OF MAMMALIA MADE BY MR. FRASER IN THE REPUBLIC OF ECUADOR. Robert F. Tomes. Proc. Zool. Soc. London, pt. 28, pp.211-221, 1860.

NOTES ON A THIRD COLLECTION OF MAMMALIA MADE BY MR. FRASER IN THE REPUBLIC OF ECUADOR. Robert F. Tomes. Proc. Zool. Soc. London, pt.28, pp.260-268, figs.4, 1860.

ON SOME MAMMALS FROM ECUADOR. W.E. de Winton. Proc. Zool. Soc. London, pp.507-513, pls.19-20, Apr. 21, 1896.

SOUTH AMERICA -- GRAN CHACO

(THE GRAN CHACO AS A ZOOGEOGRAPHICAL PROBLEM.) Der Gran Chaco Chaco als tiergeographisches Problem. Hans Krieg. Comptes Rendus, 12th Internat. Congr. Zool. 1935, Lisboa, vol.2, pp.1229-1236, fig.1, 1936-37.

(IN THE LAND OF THE MANED WOLF. NOTES FROM A CAMP IN THE GRAN CHACO.) Im Lande des Maehnenwolfes. Notizen von einem Standlager im Gran Chaco. Hans Krieg. Zool. Garten, Leipzig, n.F., vol.12, nos.4-6, pp.257-269, figs.8, Dec., 1940.

(ZOOGEOGRAPHICAL PROBLEMS OF THE GRAN CHACO (SOUTH AMERICA).) Die tiergeographischen Probleme des Gran Chaco (Suedamerika). Hans Krieg. Zool. Anzeiger, vol.74, pp.271-283, figs.2, Dec. 5, 1927.

SOUTH AMERICA -- GUIANA

MAMMALS COLLECTED BY WILLIAM BEEBE AT THE BRITISH GUIANA TROPICAL RESEARCH STATION. H.E. Anthony. Zoologia, vol.3, no.13, pp. 265-285, pls.2, Dec. 24, 1921.

NEW MAMMALS FROM BRITISH GUIANA AND COLOMBIA. H.E. Anthony. Amer. Mus. Novitates, no.19, pp.1-7, Oct. 26, 1921.

ANIMAL COLLECTING IN BRITISH GUIANA. (Capybara, Anteater, Tree Porcupine, Sloth, Manatee.) David Attenborough. Illus. London News, vol.137, no.3568, pp.421-424, illus., Sep. 10, 1955.

EXPEDITION TO BRITISH GUIANA.(Sloth, Anteater, Capybara.) David Attenborough. Zoo Life, London, vol.10, no.4, pp.109-116, illus., Winter, 1955-1956.

HIGHER VERTEBRATES OF BRITSH GUIANA. WITH SPECIAL REFERENCE TO THE FAUNA OF BARTICA DISTRICT. William Beebe. Zoologica, vol.2, no.7, pp.205-227, May, 1919.

SURVEY OF NOCTURNAL VERTEBRATES IN THE KARTABO REGION OF BRITISH GUIANA. Stanton C. Crawford. Jour.Anim. Ecol., vol.2, no.2, pp.282-288, Nov., 1933.

(NOTES ON THE MAMMALS BROUGHT BY EMILE DEPLANCHES FROM CAYENNE.) Notice sur des mammiferes rapportes de Cayenne par M. Emile Deplanches. Eudes-Deslongchamps. Bull. Soc. Linn. de Normandie, vol.2, pp.14, illus., 1857.

INTO THE INTERIOR OF BRITISH GUIANA. Herbert Lang. Nat. Hist., vol.24, pp.467-478, figs.14, July-Aug., 1924.

NOTES AND OBSERVATIONS ON ANIMAL LIFE IN BRITISH GUIANA, 1907-1941; A POPULAR GUIDE TO COLONIAL MAMMALIA. Vincent Roth. Georgetown, British Guiana, Daily Chronicle, pp.ii-164-xv, illus., port., 1941 (1943). (The "Daily Chronicle's" Guiana edition of reprints and original works dealing with all phases of life in British Guiana, no.3.)

BRIEF REVIEW OF THE MAMMALS OF SURINAME (DUTCH GUIANA), BASED UPON A COLLECTION MADE IN 1938. Ivan T. Sanderson. Proc. Zool. Soc. London, vol.119, pt.3, pp.755-789, pls.7, Nov. 22, 1949.

A ZOOLOGIST'S "EL DORADO"; TERRITORY WHICH POSSESSES A REMARKABLE VARIETY OF FAUNA, SHOWING SOME OF THE GREATEST EXTREMES IN ANIMAL LIFE THAT CAN BE SEEN IN THE WORLD TODAY. Ivan T. Sanderson. Illus. London News, vol.194, no.5217, pp.620-623, illus., Apr. 15, 1939.

LIFE ZONES AT MOUNT RORAIMA. G.H. H. Tate. Ecology, vol.13, no.3, pp.235-257, figs.12, July, 1932.

MAMMALS OF THE GUIANA REGION. G. H.H. Tate. Bull. Amer. Mus. Nat. Hist., New York, vol.76, art.5, pp.151-229, Oct. 20, 1939.

NOTES ON THE MOUNT RORAIMA REGION. G.H.H. Tate. The Geographical Review, vol.20, no.1, pp.53-68, figs. 10, fold.map, 1930.

MAMMALS FROM THE RIVER SUPINAAM, DEMERARA, PRESENTED BY MR. F. V. MCCONNELL TO THE BRITISH MUSEUM. Oldfield Thomas. Ann. and Mag. Nat. Hist., ser.8, vol.6, no.32, pp.184-189, Aug., 1910.

ON A COLLECTION OF MAMMALS FROM THE KANUKU MOUNTAINS, BRITISH GUIANA. Oldfield Thomas. Ann. and Mag. Nat. Hist., ser.7, vol.8, no.44, pp.139-154, Aug., 1901.

ON A SMALL MAMMALIA COLLECTION IN DEMERARA BY MR. W. L. SCLATER. Oldfield Thomas. Proc. Zool. Soc. London, pp.150-153, pls.19, Feb. 15, 1887.

SOUTH AMERICA -- MATTO GROSSO

(MAMMALOGICAL STUDIES FROM THE SOUTHERN MATTO GROSSO.) Saeugetierkundliche Studien aus Sued-Mattogrosso. Friedrich Kuehlhorn. Saeugetierk. Mitteil., Stuttgart, vol.1, no.3, pp.115-122, July 1, 1953; Part 2: Edentata, Rodentia, vol.2, no.2, pp.66-72, illus., Apr. 1, 1954; Part 3: Carnivora, Perissodactyla, vol.3, no.2, pp.77-82, Apr.1, 1955; Part 4: Artiodactyla, Primates, vol.3, no.4, pp.156-164, Oct. 1, 1955.

NOTES ON SOME MAMMALS OF SOUTHERN MATTO GROSSO, BRAZIL. Frederic Walter Miller. Jour. Mamm., vol.11, no. 1, pp.10-22, pls.1-2, 1930.

ON THE MAMMALS COLLECTED BY MR. A. ROBERT AT CHAPADA, MATTO GROSSO (PERCY SLADEN EXPEDITION TO CENTRAL BRAZIL). Oldfield Thomas. Proc. Zool. Soc. London, pt.2, pp.232-244, pl. 27, Apr. 1, 1904.

(NOTES ON THE MAMMALS OBTAINED BY THE INSTITUTO BUTANTA AO RIO DAS MORTES E SERRA DO RONCADOR EXPEDITION.) Notas sobre os mamiferos obtenidos pela expedicao do Instituto Butanta ao Rio das Mortes e Serra do Roncador. C. Vieira. Papeis Avulsos Dept. Zool., Sec. Agric., Sao Paulo, vol.10, no.4, pp.105-125, Aug. 25, 1951.

(OBSERVATIONS ON THE FAUNA OF THE SALOBRA REGION, MATO GROSSO STATE.) Algumos observacoes sobre a fauna da regiao de Salobra, Estado de Mato Grosso. C. Vieira. Mem. Inst. Oswaldo Cruz, Rio de Janeiro, vol.35, no.3, pp.557-567, Apr. 1941.

(ON A MAMMAL COLLECTION FROM THE MOTO GROSSO.) Sôbre uma coleçao de mamiferos de Mato Grosso. C. Vieira. Arquivos Zool. Estado Sao Paulo, Sao Paulo, vol.4, art. 10, pp.395-429, Aug., 1945.

SOUTH AMERICA -- PARAGUAY

(ESSAYS ON THE NATURAL HISTORY OF THE QUADRUPEDS OF PARAGUAY.) Essais sur l'histoire naturelle des quadrupedes de la Province du Paraguay. Felix de Azara. Privately printed, vol.2, pp.499, 1801.

NATURAL HISTORY OF THE QUADRUPEDS OF PARAGUAY AND THE RIVER LA PLATA. Felix de Azara. Edinburgh, A. and C. Black, pp.xxxii-340, fold.map, 1838. (Tr.from the Spanish of Felix de Azara. With a memoir of the author, a physical sketch of the country, and numerous notes. by W.Perceval Hunter.)

(NOTES ON THE NATURAL HISTORY OF THE QUADRUPEDS OF PARAGUAY AND RIO DE LA PLATA.) Apuntamientos para la historia naturale de los quadrupedos del Paraguay y Rio de la Plata. Felix de Azara. Madrid, En la impr. de la viuda de Ibarra, vol.2, 1802.

SELECTIONS FROM THE NATURAL HISTORY OF THE QUADRUPEDS OF PARAGUAY AND THE RIVER LA PLATA. Felix de Azara. London, A.J. Valpy, pp.xix-288, 1837. (Tr. from the Spanish. With notes by W. Perceval Hunter.)

(SYSTEMATIC CATALOGUES OF THE VERTEBRATES OF PARAGUAY.) Catalogos sistematicos de los vertebrados del Paraguay. A. de Winkelried Bertoni. Rev.Soc. Cient. Paraguay, Asuncion, vol.4, no.4, pp.3-60, May 14, 1939. (Mammals pp.5-14.)

(CROP-FOLLOWING ANIMALS IN SOUTH AMERICA (ARGENTINA, NORTHERN CHACO, EASTERN PARAGUAY).) Kulturfolgende Tiere in Suedamerika. (Argentinien, noerdl. Chaco, Ostparaguay). Hans Krieg. Zoogeographica, Jena, vol.1, no.4, pp. 602-608, 1933.

ZOOLOGIST IN THE PANTANAL OF THE UPPER PARAGUAY. James A.G. Rehn.

Scientific Monthly, vol.39, no.1, pp.20-39, figs.14, July, 1934.

(NATURAL HISTORY OF THE MAMMALS OF PARAGUAY.) Naturgeschichte der Saeugethiere von Paraguay. Johann Rudolph Rengger. Basel, Schweighausersche Buchhandlung, pp.394, 1830.

SOUTH AMERICA -- PATAGONIA

Extinct and Fossil Mammals

(SEDIMENTARY FORMATIONS OF PATAGONIA.) Formaciones sedimentarias de Patagonia. Florentino Ameghino. (Edited by Alfredo J. Torcelli.) Obras completas y correspondencia cientifica de Florentino Ameghino, La Plata, vol.13, pp.993, figs., 1932.

(SYNOPTIC ENUMERATION OF THE SPECIES OF FOSSIL MAMMALS OF THE EOCENE FORMATIONS OF PATAGONIA.) Enumeration synoptique des especes de mammiferes fossiles des formations éocènes de Patagonie. Florentino Ameghino. Buenos Aires, Imp. de P.E. Coni e hijos, pp.196, illus., pl., 1894.

DESEADAN VERTEBRATE FAUNA OF THE SCARRITT POCKET, PATAGONIA. Robert G. Chaffee. Bull. Amer. Mus. Nat. Hist., New York, vol.98, art.6, pp. 503-562, pls.6-17, illus., Mar. 12, 1952.

ON A NEWLY DISCOVERED EXTINCT UNGULATE MAMMALS FROM PATAGONIA, HOMALODONTOTHERIUM CUNNINGHAMI. William Henry Flower. Philos. Trans. London, pp.173-182, pl., 1874.

NEW PROTYPOTHERE FROM THE SANTA CRUZ FORMATION OF PATAGONIA. (Protypotherium martini.) H.H. Lane. Univ. Kansas Sci. Bull., vol.17, no.3, pp.313-317, illus., Sep., 1927.

(NEW REMAINS OF MAMMALS OF PAMPA FAUNA (IN PATAGONIA.) Sobre nuevos restos de mamiferos de la fauna pampeana en Patagonia. Lorenzo J. Parodi. Physis, Buenos Aires, vol.10, no.35, pp.21-34, pls. 5, fig.1, 1930.

NEW ARGYROHIPPUS FROM THE DESEADO BEDS OF PATAGONIA. (Argyrohippus praecox.) Bryan Patterson. Geol. Ser. Field Mus. Nat. Hist., vol.6, no.12,, pp.161-166, figs.34-35, May 15, 1935.

TRACHYTHERUS, A TYPOTHERID FROM THE DESEADO BEDS OF PATAGONIA. Bryan Patterson. Geol. Ser. Field Mus. Nat. Hist., publ.334, vol.6, no.8, pp. 119-139, figs.24-28, Dec. 31, 1934.

DESCRIPTION OF SOME NOTOUNGULATES FROM THE CASAMAYOR (NOTOSTYPLOS) BEDS OF PATAGONIA. Elmer S. Riggs, Bryan Patterson. Proc. Amer. Philos. Soc., Philadelphia, vol.75, no.2, pp.163-215, figs.4, pls.5, June, 1935.

FOSSIL HUNTING IN PATAGONIA. Elmer S. Riggs. Nat. Hist., vol.26, pp.536-544, Sep.-Oct., 1926.

PARTIAL SKELETON OF HOMALODONTOTHERIUM FROM THE SANTA CRUZ BEDS OF PATAGONIA. William Berryman Scott. Field Mus. Nat. Hist., Geol. Mém., vol. 1, no.1, pp.7-34, pls.1-7, 1930.

AN ANIMAL FROM A LOST WORLD. THE SCARRITT EXPEDITIONS UNEARTH RELICS OF THE MOST ANCIENT SOUTH AMERICAN MAMMALS IN PATAGONIA FOSSIL FIELDS. (Thomashuxleya.) George Gaylord Simpson. Natural Hist., New York, vol.36, no.4, pp.316-318, illus., Nov., 1935.

COCHILIUS VOLVENS FROM THE COLPODON BEDS OF PATAGONIA. George Gaylord Simpson. Amer. Mus. Novitates, no.577, pp.13, figs.6, Nov. 4, 1932.

A DAY IN PATAGONIA. COLLECTING REMAINS OF PREHISTORIC ANIMALS IN SOUTHERNMOST SOUTH AMERICA. George Gaylord Simpson. Natural Hist., vol.33, no.2, pp.187-198, Mar.-Apr., 1933.

EOCENE OF PATAGONIA. George Gaylord Simpson. Amer. Mus. Novitates, New York, no.1120, pp.15, June 9, 1941.

NEW NOTOUNGULATE FROM THE EARLY TERTIARY OF PATAGONIA. (Scarrittia, S.canguelensis.) George Gaylord Simpson. Amer. Mus. Novitates, no.735, pp.1-3, Aug. 3, 1934.

NEW OR LITTLE-KNOWN UNGULATES FROM THE PYROTHERIUM AND COLPODON BEDS OF PATAGONIA. George Gaylord Simpson. Amer. Mus. Novitates, no.576, pp.13, figs.9, Nov. 3, 1932.

OCCURRENCE AND RELATIONSHIPS OF THE RIO CHICO FAUNA OF PATAGONIA. George Gaylord Simpson. Amer. Mus. Novitates, no.818, pp.21, figs.7, Aug. 15, 1935.

SKELETAL REMAINS AND RESTORATION OF EOCENE ENTELONYCHIA FROM PATAGONIA. George Gaylord Simpson. Amer. Mus. Novitates, New York, no. 826, pp.12, figs.2, Mar. 14, 1936.

SKULL OF THE EXTRAORDINARY PATAGONIAN EOCENE UNGULATE, TRIGONOSTYLOPS. George Gaylord Simpson. Bull. Geol. Soc. America, vol.44, no.1, p.198, Feb. 28, 1933. (Abstract.)

SKULLS AND BRAINS OF SOME MAMMALS FROM THE NOTOSTYLOPS BEDS OF PATAGONIA. George Gaylord Simpson. Amer. Mus. Novitates, no.578, pp.11, figs.6, Nov. 4, 1932.

SOME NEW OR LITTLE-KNOWN MAMMALS FROM THE COLPODON BEDS OF PATAGONIA. George Gaylord Simpson. Amer. Mus. Novitates, no.575, pp.12, figs.8, Oct. 22, 1932.

STRATIGRAPHIC NOMENCLATURE OF THE EARLY TERTIARY OF CENTRAL PATAGONIA. George Gaylord Simpson. Amer. Mus. Novitates, no.644, pp.13, figs.2, July 5, 1933.

SUPPOSED ASSOCIATION OF DINOSAURS WITH MAMMALS OF TERTIARY TYPE IN PATAGONIA. George Gaylord Simpson. Amer. Mus. Novitates, no.566, p.21, figs. 7, Sep. 21, 1932.

Recent Mammals

MAMMALIA OF SOUTHERN PATAGONIA. J.A. Allen. Repts. Princeton Univ. Exped. Patagonia, 1896-1899, vol.3 (zool), no.1, pp.210, pls., 1905.

(MAMMALS OF PATAGONIA.) Los mamiferos de la Patagonia. Augusto C. Llanos. Nature, vol.1, no.2, pp.167-177, 1955.

REPORTS OF THE PRINCETON UNIVERSITY EXPEDITIONS TO PATAGONIA, 1896-1899. William Berryman Scott. Proc. Amer. Philos. Soc., vol.67, no.2, pp.119-122, 1928.

ATTENDING MARVELS. A PATAGONIAN JOURNAL. George Gaylord Simpson. The Macmillan Co., pp.296, illus. 16, May, 1934.

CHILDREN OF PATAGONIA. PLAYMATES OF THE FIELD AND CAMP ON DESERT WASTES. (Popular Account of Some Patagonia Mammals.) George Gaylord Simpson. Nat. Hist., vol.32, no.2, pp.135-147, figs.15, Mar.-Apr., 1932.

A DAY IN PATAGONIA. George Gaylord Simpson. Nat. Hist., New York, vol.33, no.2, pp.187-198, illus., Mar.-Apr., 1933.

PATAGONIAN OASIS. George Gaylord Simpson. Nat. Hist., New York, vol.34, no.6, pp.541-553, figs., 1934.

ACCOUNT OF THE ZOOLOGICAL COLLECTIONS MADE DURING THE SURVEY OF H. M. S. 'ALERT' IN THE STRAITS OF MAGELLAN AND ON THE COAST OF PATAGONIA. MAMMALIA. Oldfield Thomas. Proc. Zool. Soc. London, pp.3-6, figs.2, Jan. 4, 1881.

MAMMALS OF SEÑOR BUDIN'S PATAGONIAN EXPEDITION. Oldfield Thomas. Ann. and Mag. Nat. Hist. London, ser.10, vol. 4, no.19, pp.35-45, July, 1929.

ON A FURTHER COLLECTION OF MAMMALS MADE BY SR. E. BUDIN IN NEUQUEN, PATAGONIA. Oldfield Thomas. Ann. and Mag. Nat. Hist., ser.9, vol.19, pp.650-658, June, 1927.

ON FURTHER PATAGONIAN MAMMALS FROM NEUQUEN AND RIO COLORADO COLLECTED BY SR. E. BUDIN. Oldfield Thomas. Ann. and Mag. Nat. Hist., ser.9, vol.20, pp.199-205, Aug., 1927.

ON SMALL MAMMALS COLLECTED BY SR. E. BUDIN IN NORTH-WESTERN PATAGONIA. Oldfield Thomas. Ann. and Mag. Nat. Hist., ser.9, vol.3, no.14, pp. 199-212, Feb., 1919.

ON SOME MAMMALS OBTAINED BY THE LATE MR. HENRY DURNFORD IN CHUBUT, E. PATAGONIA. Oldfield Thomas. Proc. Zoöl. Soc. London, pp.210-212, Mar. 15, 1898.

SOUTH AMERICA -- PERU

EXPLORATION OF LAKE TITICACA, BY ALEXANDER AGASSIZ AND S. W. GARMAN. III. LIST OF MAMMALS AND BIRDS BY J. A. ALLEN, WITH FIELD NOTES BY MR. GARMAN. J.A. Allen. Bull. Mus. Comp. Zool., vol.3, nos.15-16, pp.349-359, July, 1876.

ON A SMALL COLLECTION OF MAMMALS FROM PERU, WITH DESCRIPTIONS OF NEW SPECIES. J.A. Allen. Bull. Amer. Mus. Nat. Hist., vol.9, pp. 115-119, Apr. 26, 1897.

ON A FURTHER COLLECTION OF MAMMALS FROM SOUTHEASTERN PERU, COLLECTED BY H. H. KEAYS, WITH DESCRIPTIONS OF NEW SPECIES. J.A. Allen. Bull. Amer. Mus. Nat. Hist., vol. 14, pp.41-46, Jan. 31, 1901.

ON MAMMALS COLLECTED IN SOUTHEASTERN PERU BY H. H. KEAYS, WITH DESCRIPTIONS OF NEW SPECIES. J. A. Allen. Bull. Amer. Mus. Nat. Hist., vol. 13, pp.219-227, Nov. 16, 1900.

REPORT ON THE REMAINS OF MAN AND OF LOWER ANIMALS FROM THE VICINITY OF CUZCO, PERU. George F. Eaton. Amer. Jour. Sci., vol.33, no.196, pp.325-333, figs.14-15, Apr., 1912.

(OBSERVATION ON LOBOS ISLAND.) Observaciones sobre la Isla de Lobos. Paul Vaz Ferreira. Univ. de la Republica, Montevideo, pp.145-175, figs.22, 1950.

NOTES ON COLLECTION OF PERUVIAN MAMMALS. Gerrit S. Miller, Jr. Proc. U.S. Nat. Mus., vol.58, pp.217, 225, Nov. 10, 1920. (Footnotes to Paper by Oldfield Thomas.)

(LIFE IN THE PERUVIAN SEAS.) La vida en los mares del Peru. Carlos Morales Macedo. Bol. Mus. Hist. Nat. "Javier Prado," Lima, vol.10, nos.1-2, pp.3-31, illus., 1946.

BIRD ISLANDS OF PERU. Robert Cushman. Murphy. New York and London, G.P. Putnam's Sons, vol.8, pp.xx-362, pls.32, 1925.

EQUATORIAL VIGNETTES. IMPRESSIONS OF THE COASTS OF PERU AND ECUADOR, 1925. Robert Cushman Murphy. Nat. Hist., New York, vol.25, no.5, pp.431-449, illus., Sep.-Oct., 1925.

SEACOAST AND ISLANDS OF PERU. (Relation of Ocean Currents to the Distribution of Pinnipeds and Other Marine Vertebrates. Maps on Range of Fur-Seals, Sea-elephants, and Sea-Lions.) Robert Cushman Murphy. Part I. Brooklyn Mus. Quart., vol.7, pp. 69-95, figs.6, Apr., 1920.

MAMMALS OF AN EXPEDITION ACROSS NORTHERN PERU. Wilfred Hudson Osgood. Field Mus. Nat. Hist., Chicago, Publication 176, Zoological ser., vol.10, no.12, pp.143-185, 1914.

NEW MAMMALS FROM BRAZIL AND PERU. Wilfred Hudson Osgood. Field Mus. Nat. Hist., Chicago, Publication 185, Zool. ser., vol.10, no.13, pp.187-198, 1915.

NEW PERUVIAN MAMMALS. Wilfred Hudson Osgood. Field Mus. Nat. Hist., Chicago, Publication 168, Zoological ser., vol.10, no.9, pp.93-100, 1913.

ADDITIONS TO THE MAMMALIAN FAUNA OF PERU AND NOTES ON SOME OTHER PERUVIAN MAMMALS. Oliver P. Pearson. Breviora Mus. Comp.Zool., vol.73, pp.1-7, Mar. 29, 1957.

MAMMALS IN THE HIGHLANDS OF SOUTHERN PERU. Oliver P. Pearson. Bull. Mus. Comp. Zool., Harvard Coll., vol.106, no. 3, pp.117-174, pls.8, June, 1951.

(MONOGRAPH ESSAY ON THE PROVINCE OF BOLOGNESI.) Ensayo monografico de la provincia de Bolognesi. Part 3. Alberto Carrillo Ramirez. (Includes Lists of Mammals.) Bol. Soc. Geogr. Lima, vol.57, nos.1-2, pp.14-29, 1940.

MAMMALS FROM MARCAPATA, SOUTHEASTERN PERU. Colin Campbell Sanborn. Publ. Mus. Hist. Nat. "Javier Prado", ser. A, Zool., no.6, pp.1-26, Oct., 1951.

MAMMALS FROM THE DEPARTMENT OF CUZCO AND PUNO, PERU. Colin Campbell Sanborn. Publ. Mus. Hist.Nat. "Javier Prado", Lima, ser.A, Zool., no. 12, pp.1-8, Nov., 1953.

TWO NEW MAMMALS FROM SOUTHERN PERU. (Caluromysiops, C.irrupta, Peropterux kappleri intermedius.) Colin Campbell Sanborn. Fieldiana, Zoology, Chicago, vol.31, no.44, pp.473-477, illus., Feb. 23, 1951.

DESCRIPTION OF TWO NEW MURINES FROM PERU AND A NEW HARE FROM VENEZUELA. Oldfield Thomas. Ann. and Mag. Nat. Hist., ser.7, vol.5, no. 28, pp.354-357, Apr., 1900.

GODMAN-THOMAS EXPEDITION TO PERU. I. ON MAMMALS COLLECTED BY MR. R. W. HENDEE NEAR LAKE JUNIN. Oldfield Thomas. Ann. and Mag. Nat. Hist., ser.9, vol.17, no.99, pp. 313-318, Mar., 1926.

GODMAN-THOMAS EXPEDITION TO PERU. II. ON MAMMALS COLLECTED BY MR. R. W. HENDEE IN NORTH PERU BETWEEN PACASMAYO AND CHACHAPOYAS. Oldfield Thomas. Ann. and Mag. Nat. Hist., ser.9, vol.17, no. 101, pp.610-616, May, 1926.

GODMAN-THOMAS EXPEDITION TO PERU. III. ON MAMMALS COLLECTED BY MR. R. W. HENDEE IN THE CHACHAPOYAS REGION OF NORTH PERU. Oldfield Thomas. Ann. and Mag. Nat. Hist., ser.9, vol.18, no.103, pp.156-167, June, 1926.

GODMAN-THOMAS EXPEDITION TO PERU. IV. ON MAMMALS COLLECTED BY MR. R. W. HENDEE NORTH OF CHACHAPOYAS, PROVINCE OF AMAZONAS, NORTH PERU. Oldfield Thomas. Ann. and Mag. Nat. Hist., ser.9, vol. 18, no.106, pp.345-349, Oct., 1926.

GODMAN-THOMAS EXPEDITION TO PERU. V. ON MAMMALS COLLECTED BY MR. R. W. HENDEE IN THE PROVINCE OF SAN MARTIN, NORTH PERU, MOSTLY AT YURAC YACU. Oldfield Thomas. Ann. and Mag. Nat. Hist., ser.9, vol.19, no.111, pp.361-375, Mar., 1927.

GODMAN-THOMAS EXPEDITION TO PERU. VI. ON MAMMALS FROM THE UPPER HUALLAGA AND NEIGHBORING HIGHLANDS. Oldfield Thomas. Ann. and Mag. Nat. Hist., ser.9, vol.20, pp.594-608, Dec., 1927.

GODMAN - THOMAS EXPEDITION TO PERU. VII. MAMMALS OF THE RIO UCAYALI. Oldfield Thomas. Ann. and Mag. Nat. Hist., ser.10, vol.2, no.9, pp.249-265, Sep., 1928.

GODMAN-THOMAS EXPEDITION TO PERU. VIII. ON MAMMALS OBTAINED BY MR. HENDEE AT PEBAS AND IQUITOS, UPPER AMAZONS. Oldfield Thomas. Ann. and Mag. Nat. Hist., ser.10, vol.2, no.9, pp.285-294, Sep., 1928.

NEW CALLICEBUS, CONEPATUS, AND OECOMYS FROM PERU. Oldfield Thomas. Ann. and Mag. Nat. Hist., ser.9, vol.14, pp.286-288, Sep., 1924.

NEW MAMMALS FROM PERU AND BOLIVIA, WITH A LIST OF THOSE RECORDED FROM THE INAMBARI RIVER, UPPER MADRE DE DIOS. Oldfield Thomas. Ann. and Mag. Nat. Hist., ser.7, vol.7, no.38, pp.178-190, Feb., 1901.

NEW PERUVIAN SPECIES OF CONEPATUS, PHYLLOTIS, AND AKODON. Oldfield Thomas. Ann. and Mag. Nat. Hist., ser.7, vol.6, no.35, pp.466-469, Nov., 1900.

ON A COLLECTION OF MAMMALS MADE BY MR. LATHAM RUTTER IN THE PERUVIAN AMAZONS. Oldfield Thomas. Ann. and Mag. Nat. Hist., ser.9, vol.13, no. 77, pp.530-538, May, 1924.

ON SOME MAMMALS FROM CENTRAL PERU. Oldfield Thomas. Proc. Zool. Soc. London, pp.333-341, pls. 28-29, Apr. 18, 1893.

ON SOME SMALL MAMMALS FROM THE DISTRICT OF CUZCO, PERU. Oldfield Thomas. Ann. and Mag. Nat. Hist., ser. 7, vol.3, no.13, pp.40-44, Jan., 1899.

PRELIMINARY DIAGNOSES OF NEW MAMMALS OBTAINED BY THE YALE-NATIONAL GEOGRAPHIC SOCIETY PERUVIAN EXPEDITION. Oldfield Thomas. Smiths. Inst., Misc. Coll., vol.68, publ.2447, pp.1-3, Apr. 10, 1917.

REPORT ON THE MAMMALIA COLLECTED BY MR. EDMUND HELLER DURING THE PERUVIAN EXPEDITION OF 1915 UNDER THE AUSPICES OF YALE UNIVERSITY AND THE NATIONAL GEOGRAPHIC SOCIETY. Oldfield Thomas. Proc. U.S. Nat. Mus., vol.58, no.2333, pp.217-249, pls. 14-15, Nov. 10, 1920.

THREE NEW MAMMALS FROM PERU. Oldfield Thomas. Ann. and Mag. Nat. Hist., ser.9, vol.12, no.72, pp.692-694, Dec., 1923.

(INVESTIGATIONS OF PERU FAUNA.) Untersuchungen ueber die Fauna Peruana. J.J. von Tschudi. Therologie, St.Gallen, Druck und Verlag von Scheitlin und Zollikofer, pp.xxx+262, col.pls.xviii, issued in 6 parts, 1844-46.

## SOUTH AMERICA -- URUGUAY

FIELD NOTES ON THE MAMMALS OF URUGUAY. O.V. Aplin. Proc. Zool.Soc. London, pp.297-315, 1894.

(MAMMALS OF URUGUAY.) Mamiferos del Uruguay. Garibaldi J. Devincenzi. Anal. Mus. Hist. Nat. Montevideo, ser. 2, vol.4, no.10, pp.96, figs.5, pls.12, 1935.

(NEW STUDIES ON THE GEOLOGY AND PALEONTOLOGY OF URUGUAY.) Nuevos apuntes para la geologia y paleontologia Uruguayas. Lucas Kraglievich. Anales Mus. Hist. Nat. de Montevideo, ser.2, vol.3, pt.3, pp.257-321, figs.12, pls.46-56, 1932.

(GEOLOGIC OBSERVATIONS AND NEW REMAINS OF FOSSIL MAMMALS OF URUGUAY.) Observaciones geológicas y nuevos restos de mamiferos fósiles del Uruguay. Carlos Rusconi. Anal.Mus. Hist. Nat. Montevideo, ser.2, vol.4, no. 6, pp.1-12, Aug., 1934.

THE LAND MAMMALS OF URUGUAY. Colin Campbell Sanborn. Field Mus. Nat. Hist., Zool.ser., Publ.265, vol.17, no.4, pp.147-165, Oct. 24, 1929.

(CONTRIBUTION TO STUDY OF THE GEOLOGY AND PALEONTOLOGY OF THE EASTERN REPUBLIC OF URUGUAY.) Contribución al Estudio de la Geologia y de la Paleontologia de la Republica Oriental del Uruguay. (Mammals pp.38-53.) Augusto Teisseire. Region de Colonia. Montevideo, pp.157, pls.12, maps 2, figs.27, 1930.

## SOUTH AMERICA -- VENEZUELA

MAMMALS OF MARGARITE ISLAND, VENEZUELA. Glover M. Allen. Proc. Biol. Soc. Washington, vol.15, pp.91-97, Apr. 25, 1902.

LIST OF MAMMALS FROM VENEZUELA COLLECTED BY MR. SAMUEL M. KLAGES. J.A. Allen. Bull. Amer. Mus. Nat. Hist., vol.20, pp.337-345, Oct. 8, 1904.

MAMMALS FROM THE CAURA DISTRICT OF VENEZUELA, WITH DESCRIPTIONS OF A NEW SPECIES OF CHROTOPTERUS. J.A. Allen. Bull. Amer. Mus. Nat. Hist., vol.28, pp. 145-149, May 27, 1910.

MAMMALS FROM VENEZUELA COLLECTED BY MR. M. A. CARRIKER, JR., 1909-1911. J.A. Allen. Bull. Amer. Mus. Nat. Hist., vol.30, pp.239-273, Dec. 2, 1911.

NEW MAMMALS FROM VENEZUELA AND COLOMBIA. J. A. Allen. Bull. Amer. Mus. Nat. Hist., vol.20, pp.327-335, Oct. 8, 1904.

LETTER DESCRIBING CERTAIN ZOOLOGICAL SPECIMENS OBTAINED IN AND AROUND CARACAS. A. Ernst. Proc. Zool. Soc. London, pp.2-3, 1870.

DESCRIPTION OF TWO SPECIES OF MAMMALIA FROM CARACAS. J.E. Gray. Proc. Zool. Soc. London, pt.16, p.138, 1848.

(BIOLOGY OF THE PLAINS OF VENEZUELA.) Biologia de la llanura venezolana. Juan Iturbe. Proc. 8th Amer. Sci. Congr., Washington, D.C., vol.3, pp.65-82, Aug. 3, 1942. (Mammals pp.72-73.)

(CONTRIBUTION TO KNOWLEDGE OF THE BARUTA-EL HATILLO REGION. THIRD PART. ZOOLOGY STUDY OF THE MAMMALS COLLECTED.) Contribución al conocmiento de la región de Baruta-El Hatillo. Tercera parte. Zoologia. Estudio de los mamiferos colectados. José Luis Mendez. Mem. Soc. Ciencias Naturales La Salle, Caracas, vol.11, no.30, pp. 203-236, Sep.-Dec., 1951.

(LA SALLE SOCIETY OF THE NATURAL SCIENCE IN THE PERIJA REGION. PART V. ZOOLOGY. STUDY OF THE MAMMALS COLLECTED.) La Sociedad de Ciencias Naturales La Salle en la Region de Perija. Parte V. Zoologia. Estudio de los mamiferos colectados. José Luis Mendez. Mem. Soc. Ciencias Nat. La Salle, Caracas, vol.13, no.34, pp.81-120, illus., Jan.-Apr., 1953.

FOUR NEW MAMMALS FROM VENEZUELA. Wilfred H. Osgood. Field Mus. Nat. Hist., Zool. ser., vol.10, no.11, publ. 175, pp.135-141, Apr. 8, 1914.

MAMMALS FROM WESTERN VENEZUELA AND EASTERN COLOMBIA. Wilfred H. Osgood. Field Mus. Nat. Hist., Chicago, Zool. ser., vol.10, no.5, publ.155, pp.33-66, pls.4-5, Jan. 10, 1912.

(STUDIES OF VENEZUELAN FAUNA. PROVISIONAL LIST OF THE MAMMALS OBSERVED IN THE COUNTRY.) Sobre fauna Venezolana. Lista provisional de los mamiferos observada en el Pais. R. Pittier, H.H. Tate. Bol. Soc. Venezolana Cienc.Nat., Caracas, no.7, pp. 249-278, 1932.

AN ANNOTATED LIST OF MAMMALS COLLECTED IN THE VICINITY OF LA GUAIRA, VENEZUELA. Wirt Robinson, Lyon Marcus Ward. U.S. Nat. Mus., Proc., vol.24, pp.135-162, Washington, 1902. (Bibliographical references with individual species.)

(DESCRIPTIVE FAUNA OF VENEZUELA (VERTEBRATES).) Fauna descriptiva de Venezuela (Vertebrados). Eduardo Rohl. Tipografia Americana, Caracas, ed.2, pp. xxxvi+495, illus., 1949. (Mammals pp. 4-140.)

(VENEZUELAN MAMMALS.) Mamiferos venezolanos. Ernst Schafer. Revista Shell, Caracas, vol.4, no.17, pp.36-40, illus., Dec., 1955.

(MAMMAL FINDS FROM VENEZUELA AND TRINIDAD.) Saeugetierfunde aus Venezuela und Trinidad. S. Schaub. Abhandl. Schweizerischen Palaeont. Gesell., Basel, vol.55, pp.21, figs.3, pls.1-2, 1935.

(MAMMALS FOSSIL LOCALES IN VENEZUELA AND TRINIDAD.) Saeugetierfundstellen in Venezuela und Trinidad. S. Schaub. Verhandl. Schweizerischen Naturforsch. Gesell., Aarau, 112 Jahresversammlung, pp.326-327, 1931; Act. Soc. Helvet, Sci. Nat. vol.112, Sess. Aarau, pp.326-327, 1931.

RESEARCH IN VENEZUELA. George Gaylord Simpson. Science, Lancaster, n.s., vol.90, no.2331, pp.210-211, Sep. 1, 1939.

AUYANTEPUI. NOTES ON THE PHELPS VENEZUELAN EXPEDITION. G. H.H. Tate. Geog. Review, vol.28, no.3, pp. 452-474, figs.1-17, July, 1938.

LIST OF THE MAMMALS COLLECTED AT RANCHO GRANDE, IN A MONTANE CLOUD FOREST OF NORTHERN VENEZUELA. G. H.H. Tate. Zoologica, New York, vol.32, pt.1, no.7, pp.65-66, May 8, 1947.

CERRO DUIDA REGION OF VENEZUELA. G.H.H. Tate, C.B. Hitchcock. Geogr. Review, New York, vol.20, no.1, pp.31-52, figs.20, Jan., 1930.

FOUR NEW SMALL MAMMALS FROM VENEZUELA. Oldfield Thomas. Ann. and Mag. Nat. Hist., ser.8, vol.14, no. 83, pp.410-414, Nov., 1914.

NEW SCIURUS, RHIPIDOMYS, SYLVILAGUS, AND CALUROMYS FROM VENEZUELA. Oldfield Thomas. Ann. and Mag. Nat. Hist., ser.7, vol.14, no.79, pp. 33-37, July, 1904.

## SPAIN

(DATA AND OBSERVATIONS ON SOME MARROQUI MAMMALS.) Datos y observaciones sobre algunos mamiferos Marroquies. E. Morales Agacino. Bol. Soc. Espan. Hist. Nat., Madrid, vol. 33, pp.257-266, fig.1, 1933.

(OBSERVATIONS ON SOME SPANISH MAMMALS.) Observaciones sobre algunos mamiferos espanoles. E. Morales Agacino. Bol. Soc. Espan. Hist. Nat., Madrid, vol. 35, nos.9-10, pp.435-439, Nov.-Dec., 1936.

(NEW MAMMALS OF THE SPANISH NEOCENE.) Los nuevos mamiferos del neogeno de España. Pairo M. Crusafont, J.F. de Villata. Notas y Comunicaciones del Inst. Geol. and Minero España, no.22, pp.1-25, illus., 1951.

RECORDS OF SMALL MAMMALS AND THEIR FLEAS FROM REINOSA, SANTANDER, SPAIN. G.M. Dunnet. Ann. and Mag. Nat. Hist., London, vol.8, no. 90, pp.445-448, June, 1955.

(MAMMALS OF THE PROVINCE OF SORIA.) Mamiferos de la provincia de Soria. Leoncio Gomez Vinuesa. Bol. Soc. Espan. Hist. Nat., Madrid, vol.32, no.4, pp.231-235, May 15, 1932.

(GREAT BEASTS OF THE PALEONTOLOGIC DEPOSITS OF CONCUD (TERUEL).) Las grandes fieras de los yacimientos paleontológicos de Concud (Teruel). Ed. Hernández-Pacheco. Bol. Real Soc. Españ. Hist. Nat., Madrid, vol.30, no.3, pp. 149-158, figs.12, Mar. 15, 1930.

(MAMMAL FAUNA OF THE PITYUSAE (SPAIN).) Die Saeugetierfauna der Pityusen (Spanien). Otto Koller. Akad. Wiss. Wien, Math.-Nat.Kl., Sitz.-ber. Abt.1, Mineral., Biol., Erdk., vol.140, nos. 1-2, pp.57-65, 1931.

(NEW DISCOVERIES OF FOSSIL REMAINS IN A GYPSUM QUARRY OF LLAMAQUIQUE, OVIEDO.) Neuvos hallazgos de restos fosiles en la cantera de yeso de Llamaquique, en Oviedo. T.G. Llarena, J. Royo, Gomez. Bol. Real Soc. Española de Hist. Nat., Madrid, vol.27, no.10, p.421, Dec. 31, 1927.

(OBSERVATIONS ON SOME SPANISH MAMMALS.) Observaciones sobre algunos maiferos espanoles. E. Agacino Morales. Bol. Soc. Española Hist. Nat., Madrid, vol.36, nos.9-10, pp.435-439, Feb. 15, 1937.

(THE ANIMAL RACES IN RELATION TO THE ETNOLOGY OF CATALUNA.) Las razas animales en relación con la etnologia de Cataluña. Pedro M. Rossell Y Vila. Mem. R. Acad. Cien. y Artes, Barcelona, vol.22, no.1, pp.1-29, Apr., 1930.

(SOME FOSSIL VERTEBRATES OF THE DUERO BASIN.) Algunos vertebrados fósiles de la cuenca del Duero. José Royo Gomez. Bol.Soc.Espanola Hist.Nat., vol. 34, no.10, pp.505-511, pls.45-48, fig.1, Dec., 1934.

(DEPOSIT OF PLEISTOCENE MAMMALS IN OLAZAGUTIA, NAVARRE.) Un yacimiento de mammiferos pleistocénicos en Olazagutia (Navarra). Máximo Ruiz de Gaona. Bol. R. Soc. Española Hist. Nat., Santiago, vol.39, nos.3-4, pp.155-160, 1941.

(THE CAVE OF PRADENA (SEGOVIA).) La cueva de Pradena (Segovia). V. Sos. Bol. Soc. Española Hist. Nat., vol.32, no.5, pp.261-263, 1932. (Cave deposit with Pleistocene mammals.)

(MAMMALS OF THE PROVINCE OF SORIA.) Mamiferos de la provincia de Soria. L. G. Vinuesa. Bol. Soc. Española, vol.32, no. 4, pp.231-235, 1932.

## SUDAN

MAMMALS FROM THE BLUE NILE VALLEY. G.M. Allen. Bull. Mus. Comp. Zool., Harvard College, vol.58, no.7, pp.305-357, figs.3, July, 1914.

BIG GAME'S CHANCES IN THE SUDAN. H.C. Brocklehurst. Field, London, vol.161, no.4189, p.740, illus., Apr. 8, 1933.

GAME ANIMALS OF THE SUDAN, THEIR HABITS AND DISTRIBUTION; A HANDBOOK FOR HUNTERS AND NATURALISTS. H.C. Brocklehurst. London, Gurney and Jackson, pp.xix-170, illus., pls.(part col.), fold.map, 1931.

THE BEACH ANGLO-EGYPTIAN SUDAN EXPEDITION. EXPLORATIONS AND FIELDWORK OF THE SMITHSONIAN INSTITUTION IN 1928. W.L. Brown. Smiths. Inst., Publ.3011, pp.63-70, illus., Apr., 1929.

SAVAGE SUDAN; ITS WILD TRIBES, BIG GAME, AND BIRD-LIFE. Abel Chapman. London, Gurney and Jackson, pp.i-xx, 1-452, illus., 1921.

RIVER CRUISE THROUGH SOUTHERN SUDAN. SEEING UNCIVILIZED AFRICA IN COMFORT. C.W. Domville-Fife. Field, London, vol.168, p.1461, illus., Dec. 5, 1936.

(MAMMALS IN THE RELIGION OF THE DOGONS (FRENCH SUDAN).) Les mammifères dans la religion des Dogons (Soudan francais). Marcel Griaule. Mammalia, Paris, vol.5, nos.3-4, pp.104-109, illus., Sep.-Dec., 1941.

FAR AWAY UP THE NILE. John G. Millais. London and New York, Longmans, Green and Co., pp.12-254, pls.49, map, 1924.

PROTECTION OF GAME IN THE SUDAN. Sayyid Ahmed Abdel Nabi. Sudan Notes and Records, vol.37, pp.119-121, 1956.

EXHIBITION OF, AND REMARKS UPON, A SKULL AND HORNS OF THE SQUARE-MOUTHED RHINOCEROS AND MOUNTED HEADS OF TWO ANTELOPES, OBTAINED BY MAJOR A. ST. H. GIBBONS ON THE UPPER NILE. Philip Lutley Sclater. Proc. Zool. Soc. London, for 1900, pt.4, pp. 949-950, Apr. 1, 1901.

FOUR NEW MAMMALS FROM THE ANGLO-EGYPTIAN SUDAN. Henry W. Setzer. Jour. Washington Acad. Sci., vol.43, no.10, pp.333-335, Oct. 22, 1953.

MAMMALS OF THE ANGLO-EGYPTIAN SUDAN. Henry W. Setzer. Proc. U.S. Nat. Mus., vol.106, no.3377, pp.447-587, Nov. 28, 1956.

LIST OF MAMMALS OBTAINED BY DR. DONALDSON SMITH DURING HIS RECENT JOURNEY FROM LAKE RUDOLF TO THE UPPER NILE. Oldfield Thomas. Proc. Zool. Soc. London, pp.800-807, Nov. 20, 1900.

ON A COLLECTION OF SMALL MAMMALS FROM THE UPPER NILE OBTAINED BY MR. R.M. HAWKER. Oldfield Thomas. Ann. and Mag. Nat.Hist., ser.7, vol.8, no.46, pp.273-278, Oct., 1901.

ON SOME MAMMALS COLLECTED BY CAPT. H. L. DUNN, R.A.M.C., IN THE SUDAN. Oldfield Thomas. Proc. Zool. Soc. London, pp.294-301, Aug. 6, 1903.

ON THE MAMMALS OBTAINED IN DARFUR BY THE LYNES-LOWE EXPEDITION. Oldfield Thomas, Martin A.C. Hinton. Proc. Zool. Soc. London, pt.2, pp.247-271, July, 1923.

(NEW RODENTS AND A NEW CONY FROM KORDOFAN.) Neue Nager und ein neuer Klippschliefer aus Kordofan. Otto von Wettstein. (Sitz. der math.-naturwissensch.Kl. vom 15. Juni 1916.) Anzeiger Kais. Akad. Wissensch. Wien, vol.53, no.15, pp.160-162, 1916.

(SCIENTIFIC FINDINGS OF F. WERNER'S ZOOLOGICAL EXPEDITION TO THE ANGLO-EGYPTIAN SUDAN (KORDOFAN) UNDER THE AUSPICES OF THE IMPERIAL ACADEMY OF SCIENCES OF VIENNA AND FINANCED BY THE TREITL FUND (1914). II) TREATMENT OF THE BIRDS AND MAMMALS COLLECTED DURING THE EXPEDITION.) Wissenschaftliche Ergebnisse der mit Unterstuetzung der kaiserlichen Akademie der Wissenschaften in Wien aus der Erbschaft Treitl von F. Werner unternommenen Zoologischen Expedition nach dem Anglo-Ägyptischen Sudan. (Kordofan) 1914. II. Bearbeitung der auf der Expedition Gesammelten Voegel und Saeugetiere. Otto von Wettstein. Denkschriften der kaiserlichen Akademie der Wissenschaften in Wien, Mathematisch-Naturwissenschaftliche Klasse, vol.94, pp.139, pls.4, map 1, 1917.

SOUTHERN SUDAN GAME AND ITS HABITAT. R.C.R. Whalley. Sudan Notes and Records, vol.15, pt.2, pp.261-267, 1932.

LIST OF A COLLECTION OF MAMMALS MADE BY MR. A. L. BUTLER ON THE UPPER NILE. R.C. Wroughton. Ann. and Mag. Nat. Hist., ser.8, vol.8, pp. 458-462, Oct., 1911.

LIST OF A COLLECTION OF SMALL MAMMALS MADE BY MR. A. L. BUTLER IN THE BAHR-EL-GHAZAL. R.C. Wroughton. Ann. and Mag. Nat. Hist., ser.7, vol.20, pp.500-504, Dec., 1907.

WILDLIFE OF THE UPPER NILE AND SUDAN. Nat. Hist., New York, vol.50, no.4, pp.194-195, illus., Nov., 1942.

## SUMATRA

SURVEY OF WILD LIFE CONDITIONS IN ATJEH, NORTH SUMATRA, WITH SPECIAL REFERENCE TO THE ORANG-UTAN. C.R. Carpenter. Communications no.12, Netherlands Comm. Internat. Nature Protection, Amsterdam, pp.34, maps 3, photo, 1938.

MAMMALS OF PULAN BERHALA. F.N. Chasen, C. Boden Kloss. Misc. Zoologica Sumatrana (Medan, Sumatra), no.27, pp. 1-2, 1928.

(NOTES ON MAMMALS. VII. REMARKS ON SOME MAMMALS FROM ATJEH (SUMATRA).) Notes sur les Mammifères. VII. Remarques sur quelques Mammifères provenant d'Atjeh (Sumatra). Serge Frechkop. Bull. Mus. Roy. d'Hist.Nat.Belgique, Bruxelles, vol.7, no.28, pp.1-6, Oct., 1931.

NOTES ON SOME MAMMALS FROM SUMATRA. (Notes on the Harem Tiger,

Leopard, and Other Species.) E.Jacobson. Jour. Fed. Malay States Mus., vol.10, pt.3, pp.235-240, 1921.

LIST OF SPECIES OF MAMMALS FROM WEST-SUMATRA AND NORTH-CELEBES, WITH DESCRIPTIONS OF UNDESCRIBED OR RARE SPECIES. F.A. Jentink. Notes, Leyden Mus., vol.5, no.16, pp.170-181, Apr., 1883.

ADDITIONAL NOTES ON MAMMALS OF THE RHIO-LINGA ARCHIPELAGO, WITH DESCRIPTIONS OF NEW SPECIES AND A REVISED LIST. Marcus Ward Lyon. U.S. Nat. Mus., Proc., Washington, vol. 36, pp.479-491, pl.39, 1909.

MAMMALS COLLECTED BY DR. W. L. ABBOTT ON THE CHAIN OF ISLANDS LYING OFF THE WESTERN COAST OF SUMATRA, WITH DESCRIPTIONS OF TWENTY-EIGHT NEW SPECIES AND SUBSPECIES. Marcus Ward Lyon. U.S. Nat. Mus., Proc., Washington, vol.52, pp.437-462, 1917.

MAMMALS COLLECTED IN EASTERN SUMATRA BY DR. W. L. ABBOTT DURING 1903, 1906, AND 1907, WITH DESCRIPTIONS OF NEW SPECIES AND SUBSPECIES. Marcus Ward Lyon. U.S. Nat. Mus., Proc., Wash., vol.34, pp.619-679, 1908.

TWO NEW MAMMALS FROM SUMATRA. Marcus Ward Lyon. Proc. Biol. Soc. Wash., vol.29, pp.209-211, Sep. 22, 1916.

MAMMALS COLLECTED BY DR. W. L. ABBOTT IN THE REGION OF THE INDRAGIRI RIVER, SUMATRA. Gerrit Smith Miller. Proc. Acad. Nat. Sci. Philadelphia, pp.143-159, June 11, 1902.

MAMMALS COLLECTED BY DR. W. L. ABBOTT IN THE RHIO-LINGA ARCHIPELAGO. Gerrit Smith Miller. U.S. Nat. Mus., Proc., Washington, vol.31, pp.247-286, Sep. 11, 1906.

MAMMALS COLLECTED BY DR. W. L. ABBOTT ON THE COAST AND ISLANDS OF NORTHWEST SUMATRA. Gerrit Smith Miller. U.S. Nat. Mus., Proc., Washington, vol.26, pp.437-484, 1903.

MAMMALS OF ENGANO ISLAND, WEST SUMATRA. Gerrit Smith Miller. U.S. Nat. Mus., Proc., Washington, vol.30, pp.819-825, 1906.

ZOOLOGICAL RESULTS OF THE GEORGE VANDERBILT SUMATRAN EXPEDITION, 1936-1939. PART V. MAMMALS COLLECTED BY FREDERICK A. ULMER, JR. ON SUMATRA AND NIAS. Gerrit S. Miller. Proc. Acad. Nat. Sci., Philadelphia, vol. 94, pp.107-165, pls.3-6, Nov. 13, 1942.

EXPEDITION TO KORINCHI PEAK, SUMATRA (1914). H.M. Pendlebury. Jour. Fed. Malay States Mus., vol.8, pt.1, pp.31, pls.15, map, July, 1936.

DESCRIPTIVE CATALOGUE OF A ZOOLOGICAL COLLECTION, MADE ON ACCOUNT OF THE HONORABLE EAST INDIAN CO., IN THE ISLAND OF SUMATRA AND ITS VICINITY. Thomas S. Raffles. Linn. Soc. London, Transactions, vol.13, pt.1, pp.239-274, 1820; pt.2, pp. 277-340, 1821.

THE GAME RESERVE SOUTH SUMATRA I. Ir. F.W. Rappard, A. Hoogerwerf. Dutch East Indies, Department van landbouw, nijverheid en handel (Nature Protection in the Nederlands Indies), Dept. Econ. Affairs, Batavia, pp.49-52, illus., 1938.

ON A COLLECTION OF MAMMALS FROM THE BENCOOLEN AND PALEMBANG RESIDENCES, SOUTH WEST SUMATRA. H.C. Robinson, C. Boden Kloss. Jour. Fed. Malay States Mus., vol.7, pt.4, pp.257-291, pls.5, fig.1, Dec., 1919.

ON MAMMALS, CHIEFLY FROM THE OPHIR DISTRICT, WEST SUMATRA. H.C. Robinson, C. Boden Kloss. Jour. Fed. Malay States Mus., vol.7, pt.4, pp.299-323, Dec., 1919.

PRELIMINARY DIAGNOSES OF SOME NEW SPECIES AND SUBSPECIES OF MAMMALS AND BIRDS OBTAINED IN KORINCHI, WEST SUMATRA, FEBRUARY TO JUNE 1914. H.C. Robinson, C. Boden Kloss. Jour. Straits Branch Roy. Asiatic Soc., Singapore, no. 73, pp.269-275, July 1916.

RESULTS OF AN EXPEDITION TO KORINCHI PEAK, SUMATRA. PART 2. VERTEBRATES. I. MAMMALS. H.C. Robinson, C. Boden Kloss. Jour. Fed. Malay States Mus., vol.8, pp.1-72, pl.1, June, 1918; PART 2. VERTEBRATES. V. ADDENDA. vol.8, pp.311-319, pls.2-3, Nov., 1923.

(NOTES ON WILDLIFE IN THE RANAU AREA.) Over den wildstand in het Ranaugebied. (II). W.F. Rudin. De Tropische Natuur, Jahrg.24, no.9, pp.151-156, Sep., 1935.

NOTES ON SOME MAMMALS FROM SUMATRA, JAVA, BALI, BURU AND NEW GUINEA. H.J.V. Sody. Temminckia, Leiden, vol.2, pp.211-220, 1937.

SIX NEW MAMMALS FROM SUMATRA, JAVA, BALI AND BORNEO. H.J.V.Sody. Natuurkundig Tijdschr. Nederlandsch Indie, vol.91, no.3, pp.349-360, 1931.

SOME NOTES ON TRACHYPITHECUS PYRRHUS, PRESBYTIS AYGULA, AND CUON JAVANICUS FROM BALI, JAVA, AND SUMATRA. H.J. V. Sody. Proc. Zool. Soc. London, series B, pt.2, pp.257-261, fig.1, July 15, 1937.

COLLECTION OF MAMMALS FROM SUMATRA, WITH A REVIEW OF THE GENERA NYCTICEBUS AND TRAGULUS. Witmar Stone, J.A.G. Rehn. Proc. Acad. Nat.Sci. Phila., pp.127-142, Mar., 1902.

DESCRIPTIONS OF NEW BORNEAN AND SUMATRAN MAMMALS. Oldfield Thomas. Ann. and Mag. Nat. Hist., ser.7, vol.2, no.9, pp.245-251, Sep., 1898.

(FINDINGS OF JOURNEYS MADE IN SUMATRA FOR THE PURPOSE OF ZOOLOGICAL INVESTIGATIONS.) Ergebnisse zoologischer Forschungsreisen in Sumatra. Oldfield Thomas. Zoologischer Anzeiger, vol.27, nos.23-24, pp.722-724, July 12, 1904.

RED-LETTER DAY. (Collecting in Mountains of Northern Sumatra.) George Vanderbilt. Frontiers, Philadelphia, vol.4, no.5, pp.146-150, June, 1940.

SWEDEN

(CALVES AND BREEDING ANIMALS.) Kalvkor och avelstjurar. Kare Backstrom. Sevensk Jakt, Stockholm, vol.86, no.10, pp.256-258, illus., Oct. 17, 1948.

(INFORMATION ON SWEDISH MAMMALS.) Meddelanden om svenska daggdjur. John Bernström. Fauna och Flora, Uppsala, no. 4, pp.173-176, 1941.

(HUNTING AND FISHING IN NORRLAND IN OLD TIMES.) Jakt och fiske i Norrland i aldre tid. Bertil Boëthius. Ymer (Tidsk. Svenska Sallsk. Antropol. Geogr.), Stockholm, nos.3-4, pp.421-448, 1942.

ARCTIC VERTEBRATES THREATENED WITH EXTINCTION IN SWEDEN. Kai Curry-Lindahl. Proc. and Papers 5th Tech. Meeting International Union for the Protection of Nature, pp.66-68, 1956.

(BIOTOPES, DISTRICTS, MIGRATION, AND PERIODICITY OF SOME SMALLER MAMMALS.) Biotoper, revir, vandringar och periodicitet hos några smaol daggdjur. Kai Curry-Lindahl. Fauna och Flora, Uppsala, nos.5-6, pp.193-218, 1956.

(THE NEW HUNTING SEASON.) De nya jakttiderna. Bertil Haglund. Svensk Jakt, Stockholm, vol.88, no.7, pp.161-162, July, 1950.

(DEAD OR ALIVE.) Döda eller inte doda. N. Larsson. Svensk Jakt, Stockholm, vol. 86, no.5, pp.114-116, illus., May 20, 1948.

(SWEDEN'S AND NORWAY'S CHORDATE ANIMALS.) Sveriges och Norges Ryggradsdjur. W. Lillueborg. Vols. I-II, Uppsala, 1874.

(SWEDISH FAUNA.) Fauna Svecica. Linnaeus. (In) Cetology. Extracts from the literature of cetology, pp.98-100, 1746.

(THE PRESENT DISTRIBUTION IN SCANIA OF SOME BREEDS OF WILD ANIMALS.) Nagra villebradsarters nutida utbredning i Skane. Einar Lonnberg. Pp.16, figs.4. 1908?

(SWEDISH ANIMALS.) Svenska djur; daggdjuren. Gosta Notini. Stockholm, Norstedt, pp.651, 1948.

(HUNTING ON THE HALLEBERG AND HUNNEBERG MOUNTAINS.) Frank jakterna på Halle-och Hunneberg. Axel Olsson. Svensk Jakt, Stockholm, vol.88, no.11, pp.269-273, illus., Nov., 1950.

ON BONE DEPOSITS IN THE CAVE "STORA FORVAR" ON THE ISLE OF STORA KARLSO, SWEDEN. (Seals, Dogs, Goats, Sheep, and Oxen.) Adolf Pira. Acta Zoologica, vol.7, pp.123-217, illus., 1926.

(WITH CANOE AND HARPOON.) Med kanot och harpun. Erik Rooth. Svensk Jakt, Stockholm, vol.88, no.12, pp. 293-296, illus., Dec., 1950.

(ZOOLOGICAL IMPRESSIONS GATHERED ON A TRIP TO SWEDEN.) Zoologische Reiseneindrueke aus Schweden. Gerhard Wulker. Natur und Museum, vol.58, no. 1, pp.37-40, no.2, pp.78-87, 1928.

SWITZERLAND

Extinct and Fossil Mammals

(FAUNA OF TICINO. X. ARVICOLA NIVALIS. MART. AND SOREX ALPINUS SCHINZ ON THE BANKS OF THE CERESIO RIVER. XI. PACHYURA ETRUSCA SAVI IN THE CERESIO RIVER BASIN.) Fauna ticinese. X. Arvicola nivalis. Mart. e Sorex alpinus Schinz sulle rive del Ceresio. XI. La Pachyura etrusca Savi, nel bacino del Ceresio. Angelo Ghidini. Boll. Soc. ticinese sci.nat. Locarno, Anno 7, no.1, pp.48-53, Dec., 1911.

(FROM THE PREHISTORY OF THE MAMMALS OF SWITZERLAND.) Aus der Vorgeschichte der Saeugetiere der Schweiz. K. Hescheler. Jahrb. St.Gallischen Naturwiss. Gesell., vol.65, pp.17-46, 1930.

(CONTRIBUTIONS TO KNOWLEDGE OF THE MAMMALIAN FAUNA OF SWITZERLAND SINCE THE NEOLITHIC.) Beitraege zur Kenntnis der Saeugetierfauna der Schweiz seit dem Neolithikum. Emil Kuhn. Rev. Suisse Zool., vol.39, no.18, pp.531-768, 1932; Vierteljahrsschrift Naturforschenden Gesellsch. Zuerich, Jahrg. 78, pt.1, pp.15-26, June 30, 1933.

(NEW FOSSIL FINDS OF GREAT UNGULATES FROM THE DILUVIUM OF THE ENVIRONS OF LIESTAL.) Neue Funde von Resten grosser Huftiere aus dem Dilivium der Umgebung von Liestal. F. Leuthardt. Verhandl. Schweizer. Naturforsch. Gesell., vol.110, pp.191-192, 1929.

(ON BONE REMAINS (KITCHEN MIDDEN) FROM THE IRON AGE FOUND IN SISSACHERFLUH (BASELLAND).) Ueber eisenzeitliche Knochenreste (Kuechenabfaele) von der Sissacherfluh (Baselland). F. Leuthardt. Eclogae Geologicae Helvetiae, vol.23, no.2, pp.588-593, Dec., 1930.

(THE SMALLER VERTEBRATES OF THE PREHISTORIC STATION "BSETZI" NEAR THAYNGEN, SWITZERLAND (SCHAFFHAUSEN CANTON).) Die kleineren Wirbelthiere der praehistorischen Station "Bsetzi" bei Thayngen (Kanton Schaffhausen) Schweiz. E.V. Mandach. Ber. Naturforsch. Gesellsch. zu Freiburg i. Br., vol.27, no.2, pp.1-47, illus., 1927

(AN INTERESTING PHASE IN THE WANDERINGS OF OUR PLEISTOCENE MAMMAL FAUNA.) Eine interessante Phase in den Wandlungen unserer pleistocaenen Saeugetierfauna. H.G. Stehlin. Eclogae Geol. Helvetiae, Basel, vol.34, no.2, pp.287-291, Mar. 7, 1942.

(MAMMALS OF THE EOCENE IN SWITZERLAND. CRITICAL CATALOG OF MATERIALS.) Die Saeugetiere des schweizerischen Eocaens. Critischer Catalog der Materialien. H.G. Stehlin. Abhandl. schweiz.palaeontol. Gesell., vol.41, pp.1-1552, figs.82, tbls.2, 1916.

Recent Mammals

(FREE-LIVING MAMMALS OF SWITZERLAND.) Die Freilebenden Saeugetiere der Schweiz. F. Baumann. Verlag Hans Huber, Bern, pp.xiv+492, illus., 1949.

(PRELIMINARY LIST OF MAMMALS IN VIEW OF A GENERAL SUPPLEMENT TO THE VERTEBRATE FAUNA OF SWITZERLAND.) Liste préliminaire de mammiferes en vue d'un supplement général a la faune des vertébres de la Suisse. Victor Fatio. Archiv., Sci. phys. et nat. Geneva, annee 110, 4th periode, vol.19, pp.5, May, 1905.

(SOME RARITIES FOR SWITZERLAND.) Quelques raretes pour la Suisse. Victor Fatio. Arch. Sci. phys. et nat., vol.31, pp. 91-94, Jan., 1894.

(VERTEBRATE FAUNA OF SWITZERLAND.) Faune des vertebres de la Suisse. Victor Fatio. Geneva and Bale, H. Georg, Libraire-Editeur, 1869-1904, vols.5, col.pls. (Vol. 1. Mammals, 1869; Vol.2. Birds, pts.1-2, 1899-1904; Vol.3. Reptiles and Batrachia, 1872; Vols.4-5. Fishes, pts.1-2, 1882-1890.)

(SWISS FAUNA ... MAMMALS.) Fauna helvetica ... Mammiferes. H. Fischer-Sigwart. (In) Fauna helvetica. Dr. T. Studer, with the cooperation of the Swiss Zoological Society, Berne, pp.104, 1900.

(NOTES ON THE GEOGRAPHICAL DISTRIBUTION OF VERTEBRATES IN THE VALAIS ALPS.) Notes sur la distribution geographique des vertebres dans les alpes valaisannes. B. Galli-Valerio. Bull. de la Murithienne, vol.44, pp.94-123, 1927. (Mammals pp.95-101; Notes on 25 Species.)

(ZOOLOGICAL ZIGZAGS IN THE VALAIS ALPS.) Zigzags zoologiques dans les Alpes du Valais. B. Galli-Valerio. Bull. Murithienne Soc. Valais, Sci.Nat., no.46, pp.52-62, 1929.

(WORKS PERTAINING TO THE FAUNA OF TICINO.) Lavori interessanti la fauna ticinese. A. Ghidini. Boll. Soc. ticinese sci. nat. Locarno, Anno 8, no.1, pp.9, 1912.

(HUNTING ZOOLOGY; ALSO FOR NON-HUNTERS.) Jagdzoologie, auch fuer Nichtjaeger. Heini Hediger. Basel, F. Reinhardt, pp.212, illus.76, 1951.

(REVISION OF THE SPECIES AND SUBSPECIES OF MAMMALS OF SWITZERLAND.) Révision des especes et sous-especes de mammiferes suisses decrites par Fatio de 1862 a 1905. Charles Mottaz. Bull. Soc. Zool. Geneve, vol.1, fasc.8, pp.148-171, Nov. 15, 1908.

(SOME INTERESTING CAPTURES OF SMALL MAMMALS.) Quelques interessantes captures de petits mammiferes. Charles Mottaz. Bull. Soc. Zool. Geneve, vol.1, fasc.9, pp.178-180, Jan. 15, 1909.

(CONTRIBUTION TO STUDY OF THE MAMMALIA FAUNA OF THE CANTON OF VAUD.) Contribution a l'etude de la faune des mammiféres du Canton de Vaud. P. Narbel. Bull. Soc. Vaudoise Sci.Nat., ser.4, vol.37, no.139, pp.99-125, Mar., 1901.

(CHANGES IN THE ANIMAL WORLD OF SWITZERLAND SINCE THE COMING OF MAN.) Die Veraenderungen der Thierwelt in der Schweiz seit Anwesenheit des Menschen. L. Ruetimeyer. Basel, pp.99, figs., 1875.

PROTECTION OF WILD LIFE IN SWITZERLAND AND THE SWISS NATIONAL PARK. Carl Schroeter. South African Jour. Nat.Hist., vol.6, pp.83-88, Feb., 1927.

TASMANIA

PRESENT STATUS OF SOME TASMANIAN MAMMALS IN RELATION TO THE FUR INDUSTRY OF TASMANIA. Eric R. Guiler. Papers and Proc. Royal Soc. Tasmania, vol.91, pp.117-128, 1957.

DESCRIPTIONS OF HITHERTO UNDESCRIBED ANTECHINI AND MURIDAE INHABITING TASMANIA. E.T. Higgins, W. F. Petterd. Papers and Proc. Royal Soc. Tasmania, Hobart, pp.171-176, pl.1, 1882.

STUDIES IN TASMANIAN MAMMALS, LIVING AND EXTINCT. H.H. Scott, C. Lord. Papers and Proc. Royal Soc. Tasmania, 1921, pp.13-15 pls.5, Feb. 28, 1922; No.12. CERTAIN TASMANIAN MARSUPIALS. Papers and Proc. Royal Soc. Tasmania, 1924, pp.53-58, Mar.4, 1925; Nos. 13 and 14. THE EARED SEALS OF TASMANIA. Papers and Proc. Royal Soc. Tasmania, 1925, pp.75-78, 187-194, pls.16-21, 1926.

SYNOPSIS OF THE VERTEBRATE ANIMALS OF TASMANIA. H.H. Scott, C. Lord. (Account of Mammals, Including Descriptions and Brief Accounts of Habits, pp.232-318.) Hobart, Oldham, Beddome and Meredith, pp.340, illus., 1924.

TIBET

ZOOLOGICAL RESULTS OF THE SECOND DOLAN EXPEDITION TO WESTERN CHINA AND EASTERN TIBET, 1934-1936. PART III. MAMMALS. Glover Morrill Allen. Acad. Nat. Sci., Proc., Philadelphia, vol.xc, pp. 261-294, 1939.

ON A SMALL COLLECTION OF MAMMALS OBTAINED BY CAPTAIN DEASY IN SOUTH CHINESE TURKESTAN AND WESTERN TIBET. G.E.H. Barrett-Hamilton. Proc. Zool. Soc. London, pp.196-197, 1900.

ON A COLLECTION OF MAMMALS BROUGHT HOME BY THE TIBET FRONTIER COMMISSION. J. Lewis Bonhote. Proc. Zool. Soc. London, pp.302-307, 1905.

ZOOLOGICAL RESULTS OF THE SECOND DOLAN EXPEDITION TO WESTERN CHINA AND EASTERN TIBET, 1934-1936. PART I. INTRODUCTION. Brooke Dolan, II. Proc. Acad. Nat. Sci. Philadelphia, vol.90, pp. 159-184, pls., map, May 3, 1939.

(ON THE LARGE MAMMALS OF SZECHWAN, SIKONG, AND EAST TIBET.) Ueber die Grossaeuger Szetschwans, Sikongs und Osttibets. C. Engelmann. Zeitschr.f. Saeugetierk., Berlin, vol.13, Sonderheft, pp.1-76, figs.113, pls.1-36, 1938.

SOME TIBETAN ANIMALS. Richard Lydekker. Smiths. Inst., Annual Report, for 1904, Washington, pp.429-435, illus., 1905. (Reprinted from Knowledge and Illustrated Scientific News, London, Sep., 1904.)

(SUMMARY OF SOME SCIENTIFIC RESULTS OF THE SECOND DOLAN EXPEDITION (ACADEMY OF NATURAL SCIENCES, PHILADELPHIA) TO EAST AND CENTRAL TIBET.) Zusammenfassung einiger wissenschaftlicher Ergebnisse der zweiten Dolan-Expedition (Academy of Natural Sciences, Philadelphia), nach Ost- und Zentraltibet. Ernst Schaefer. Forschungen und Fortschritte, Berlin, Jahrg.14, no.4, pp.43-45, figs.6, Feb. 1, 1938.

ON SMALL MAMMALS COLLECTED IN TIBET AND THE MISHMI HILLS BY CAPT. F.M. BAILEY. Oldfield Thomas. Jour. Bombay Nat. Hist. Soc., vol.23, no.2, pp.230-233, Nov. 20, 1914.

MAMMALS OF THE 1921 MOUNT EVEREST EXPEDITIONS. (Pikas Seen at Altitude of 20,100 Feet. New Species of Cricetulus, Phaiomys, and Ochotona.) Oldfield Thomas, Martin A.C. Hinton. Ann. and Mag. Nat. Hist., ser.9, vol.9, pp.178-186, Feb., 1922.

MAMMALS OF THE SUB-HIMALAYAS OR SEWALIKS AND OF TIBET. Calcutta Jour. Nat.Hist., vol.8, pp.100-107, 1948.

WITH LENS AND SHUTTER AMONG THE WILD LIFE OF NORTHERN TIBET. China Jour. Sci. and Arts, vol.3, pp.595-600, pls.2, Nov., 1925.

TRINIDAD

ON A COLLECTION OF MAMMALS FROM THE ISLAND OF TRINIDAD, WITH DESCRIPTIONS OF NEW SPECIES. Joel Asaph Allen, Frank M. Chapman. Amer. Mus. Nat. Hist., New York, Bulletin, vol.5, pp.203-234, 1893.

INTRODUCTION TO THE ECOLOGY OF THE ARIMA VALLEY, TRINIDAD, B.W. I. (19 Species of Mammals pp.181-182.) Williams Bebbe. Zoologica, New York Zool. Soc., vol.37, pt.4, art.13, pp.157-184, pls.1-5, Dec. 31, 1952.

PRELIMINARY LIST OF THE MAMMALS OF TRINIDAD. Oldfield Thomas. Jour. Trinidad Field Naturalists Club, no.7, vol.1, pp.158-168, Apr., 1893.

TRINIDAD MAMMALS. (Lists 70 Species.) Desmond Vesey-Fitzgerald. Tropical Agriculture, vol.13, no.6, pp.161-165, pl., June, 1936.

UNITED STATES

Extinct and Fossil Mammals

DESCRIPTION OF SOME REMAINS OF AN EXTINCT SPECIES OF WOLF AND AN EXTINCT SPECIES OF DEER FROM THE LEAD REGION OF THE UPPER MISSISSIPPI. J.A. Allen. Amer. Jour. Sci., ser.3, vol.11, no.61, pp.47-51, Jan., 1876.

EXTIRPATION OF THE LARGER INDIGENOUS MAMMALS IN THE UNITED STATES. J.A. Allen. Penn.Monthly, pp.794-806, Oct., 1876.

OUR VANISHED HERDS. Edwin H.Colbert. Frontiers, Philadelphia, vol.6, no.1, pp. 8-10, illus., Oct., 1941.

RODENTS AND LAGOMORPHS OF THE RANCHO LA BREA DEPOSITS. Lee Raymond Dice. Carnegie Inst. Washington, publ. no.349, pp.119-130, Sep., 1925.

REMAINS OF LAND MAMMALS FROM THE MIOCENE OF THE CHESAPEAKE BAY REGION. C. Lewis Gazin, R. Lee Collins. Smiths. Inst., Misc. Coll., vol. 116, no.2, pp.1-21, figs.7, Oct. 12, 1950.

MULTITUBERCULATES IN THE WASATCH FORMATION. Walter Granger, George Gaylord Simpson. Amer. Mus. Novitates, no. 312, pp.4, illus., May 14, 1928.

VERTEBRATE FOSSILS FROM McPHERSON EQUUS BEDS. H.J. Harnly. Trans. Kansas Acad. Sci., vol.37, p.151, 1934.

DESCRIPTIONS OF SOME PLEISTOCENE VERTEBRATES FOUND IN THE UNITED STATES. Oliver Hay. Proc. U.S. Nat. Mus., vol.58, pp.83-146, pls.3-11, Oct. 12, 1920.

PALEONTOLOGY: ON THE FOSSIL MAMMALIA OF THE FIRST INTERGLACIAL STAGE OF THE PLEISTOCENE OF THE UNITED STATES. Oliver Hay. Jour. Washington Acad. Sci., vol.20, no.21, pp.501-509, Dec. 19, 1930.

VERTEBRATE FAUNA FROM THE TYPE LOCALITY OF THE OGALLALA FORMATION. Curtis J. Hesse. Bull. Univ.Kansas (Univ.Kansas Sci.Bull., vol.22, no.5), vol. 36, no.5, pp.79-117, pls.15-22, Apr. 15, 1935.

SAW ROCK CANYON FAUNA AND ITS STRATIGRAPHIC SIGNIFICANCE. Claude W. Hibbard. Papers Michigan Acad. Sci., Arts and Letters, vol.38 (1952), pp.387-411, illus., Apr. 27, 1953.

PLEISTOCENE HISTORY OF THE MISSISSIPPI RIVER. William Herbert Hobbs. Science, Lancaster, vol.111, no.2880, pp.260-262, Mar. 10, 1950.

NEW EVIDENCE OF THE AGE OF THE JOHN DAY FORMATION. Edwin T.Hodge. Bull. Geol. Soc. America, vol.43, no.3, pp.695-702, Sep. 30, 1932.

PRELIMINARY REPORT ON THE LATE MIDDLE PLIOCENE, AXTEL LOCALITY, AND THE DESCRIPTION OF A NEW MEMBER OF THE GENUS OSTEOBORUS.(Osteoborus hilli.) C. Stuart Johnston. Amer.Jour. Sci., New Haven, vol.237, no.12, pp.895-898, pl.1, Dec., 1939.

MAMMALS FOUND AT THE AWATOVI SITE. (Post-Cranial Skeletal Characters of Deer, Pronghorn, and Sheep-Goat, With Notes on Bos and Bison.) Barbara Lawrence. Rep. Awatovi Exped., Peabody Mus., Cambridge, Harvard Univ., Report no.4, vol. 35, no.3, pp.vii-43, 1951.

PLEISTOCENE LAKE IN THE WHITE RIVER VALLEY. Paul MacClintock, et al. Amer. Nat., vol.70, pp.346-360, illus., July-Aug., 1936.

NOTE ON THE AGE OF THE TRUCKEE FORMATION. J.R. MacDonald. Amer. Jour. Sci., New Haven, vol.248, pp.581-583, Aug., 1950.

BLANCAN FAUNAS, THEIR AGE AND CORRELATION. Paul O. McGrew. Bull. Geol. Soc. Amer., Baltimore, vol.59, no.6, pp. 549-552, fig.1, June, 1948.

SORICID AND TWO ERINACEIDS FROM THE WHITE RIVER OLIGOCENE. (Netacodon mellingeri, Ankylodon, A.annectens.) Paul O. McGrew. Geol. Ser. no.401, Field Mus. Nat. Hist., vol.6, no.18, pp.245-272, figs.60-74, tbls., Dec. 28, 1937.

CANNONBALL LANCE FORMATION. W.D. Matthew. Science, n.s., vol.54, pp.27-29, July 8, 1921.

NEW FOSSIL MAMMALS FROM THE SNAKE CREEK QUARRIES. (Sthenictis bellus, Cynarctus mustelinus, Mesmathyus validus, Gaillardia, G. thomsoni.) W.D. Matthew. Amer. Mus. Novitates, no.540, pp.8, figs. 7, June 16, 1932.

THIRD CONTRIBUTION TO THE SNAKE CREEK FAUNA. W.D. Matthew. Bull. Amer. Mus. Nat. Hist., vol.50, art.2, pp.59-210, figs.63, July 3, 1924.

AGE OF THE TYPICAL JUDITH RIVER BEDS. Henry Fairfield Osborn. Science, Lancaster, n.s., vol.17, no.426, pp.356-357, Feb. 27, 1903.

FOSSIL MAMMALS OF THE LOWER MIOCENE WHITE RIVER BEDS. COLLECTION OF 1892. Henry Fairfield Osborn, J.L. Wortman. Bull. Amer. Mus. Nat. Hist., vol.6, art.7, pp.199-228, figs.8, pls.2, July 28, 1894.

MAMMALIAN FAUNA OF THE WHITE RIVER OLIGOCENE. PART 1. INSECTIVORA AND CARNIVORA. William Berryman Scott, Gleen Lowell Jepsen. Trans. Amer.Philos. Soc., n.s., vol.28, pt.1, pp.153, figs.7, pls.22, Apr., 1936.

(Review by Curtis J. Hesse of) MAMMALIAN FAUNA OF THE WHITE RIVER OLIGOCENE. William Berryman Scott, Glenn Lowell Jepson. PART 4. ARTIODACTYLA. W.B. Scott. PART 5. PERISSODACTYLA. W.B. Scott. Jour. Paleontol., Menasha, vol. 16, no.2, pp.274-277, Mar., 1942.

REMARKS UPON EXTINCT MAMMALS OF THE UNITED STATES. R.W. Shufeldt. Amer. Field, Chicago, vol.32, nos.17-22, pp.38, illus., pls., 1889.

AGE OF THE MORRISON FORMATION. (Strategraphic Implications of the Fauna, Especially Mammals.) George Gaylord Simpson. Amer. Jour. Sci., vol.12, no. 69, pp.198-216, 1926.

FAUNA OF QUARRY NINE. George Gaylord Simpson. Amer. Jour. Sci., vol.12, no.67, pp.1-11, 1926.

MESOZOIC MAMMALIA. George Gaylord Simpson. VI. GENERA OF MORRISON PANTOTHERES. Amer. Jour. Sci., vol. 13, no.77, pp.409-416, 1927; VII. TAXONOMY OF MORRISON MULTITUBERCULATES. Amer. Jour. Sci., vol.14, no.79, pp. 36-38, 1927; VIII. GENERA OF LANCE MAMMALS OTHER THAN MULTITUBERCULATES. Amer. Jour. Sci., vol.14, no. 80, pp.121-130, 1927.

NOTES ON THE CLARK FORK, UPPER PALEOCENE, FAUNA. George Gaylord Simpson. Amer. Mus. Novitates, no.954, pp.1-24, figs.6, Oct. 14, 1937.

SOME CRETACEOUS MAMMALS FROM THE LANCE FORMATION. George Gaylord Simpson. Ann. Carnegie Mus., vol. 19, no.2, pp.107-113, figs.6, May, 1929.

TIFFANY FAUNA, UPPER PALEOCENE. I. MULTITUBERCULATA, MARSUPIALIA, INSECTIVORA, AND CHIROPTERA. George Gaylord Simpson. Amer. Mus. Novitates, no.795, pp.19, figs.6, Apr. 20, 1935. III. PRIMTATES, CARNIVORA, CONDYLARTHRA, AND AMBLYPODA. Amer. Mus. Novitates, no.817, pp.28, figs.14, Aug. 16, 1935.

MULTITUBERCULATES IN THE WASATCH FORMATION. George Gaylord Simpson, W. Granger. Amer. Mus. Novitates, no. 312, pp.4, figs.2, May 14, 1928.

NEW OR IMPERFECTLY KNOWN RODENTS AND UNGULATES FROM THE JOHN DAY SERIES. William J. Sinclair. Bull. Dept. Geol., Univ. California Publ., vol.4, no.6, pp.125-143, pls.14-18, July, 1905.

CRITICAL REVIEW OF MINT CANYON MAMMALIAN FAUNA AND ITS CORRELATIVE SIGNIFICANCE. R.A.Stirton. Pan-Amer.Geol., Des Moines, vol.59, no.5, p.377, June, 1933; Amer. Jour.Sci., vol.26, pp.569-576, Dec., 1933; Proc. Geol. Soc. Amer. for 1933, New York, p. 392, June, 1934.

SESPE FAUNAS. Chester Stock. Proc. Geol. Soc. Amer. for 1935, p.337, June, 1936.

AGE OF THE RINGOLD FORMATION. (List of Associated Mammals.) Jesse R. Strand, Jean Hough. Northwest Science, vol.26, no.4, pp.152-154, Nov., 1952.

ARCHEOLOGICAL RECONNAISSANCE IN THE MISSOURI VALLEY. William Duncan Strong. Explorations Field-Work Smiths. Inst. in 1931, pp. 151-158, figs.146-151, 1932.

PRELIMINARY ANALYSIS OF THE FOSSIL VERTEBRATES OF THE CANYON FERRY RESERVOIR AREA. Theodore E. White. Proc. U.S. Nat. Mus., Washington, vol.103, no.3326, pp.395-438, illus., map, May 28, 1954.

PRELIMINARY ANALYSIS OF THE VERTEBRATE FOSSIL FAUNA OF THE BOYSEN RESERVOIR AREA. Theodore E. White. Proc. U.S. Nat. Mus., Washington, vol.102, no.3296, pp.185-207, Apr. 2, 1952.

RODENTS AND LAGOMORPHS OF THE UPPER SESPE. Robert W. Wilson. Carnegie Inst., Washington, Publ.no.584, pp.51-65, fig.1, pl.1, June 22, 1949.

Recent Mammals

OUR WILDLIFE LEGACY. Durward L. Allen. New York, Funk and Wagnalls Co., pp.x-422, illus., 1954.

OUR RARER MAMMALS. Glover M. Allen. Audubon Mag., Harrisburg, vol.43, no.2, pp.151-160, illus., Mar.-Apr., 1941.

FAUNA OF THE PRAIRIES. J.A. Allen. The American Naturalist, vol.5, pp.4-9, Mar., 1871.

ANNUAL FUR CATCH OF THE UNITED STATES. Frank G. Ashbrook. U.S. Dept. Interior, Fish and Wildl.Serv., Wildl. Leaflet no.298, pp.24, Sep., 1947;no.315, pp.24, Nov., 1948; no.315, pp.23, Feb., 1950; no.315, pp. 25, June 1951; no.346, pp.24, July, 1953; no.362, pp.24, July, 1954; no.367, pp. 24, July, 1955.

RESULTS OF THE CLARK NATIONAL FOREST FUR-BEARER SURVEY. Earl L. Atwood, Jr. Jour.Wildl.Mgt., vol.2, no.1, pp.20-26, Jan., 1938.

(Review by Hartley H.T. Jackson of) DELINEATIONS OF AMERICAN SCENERY AND CHARACTER. WITH AN INTRODUCTION BY FRANCIS HOBART HERRICK. John James Audubon. Jour. Mamma., vol. 8, no.1, p.63, Feb. 9, 1927.

OUR FUR BEARING ANIMALS. Vernon Bailey. The American Humane Assoc., Albany, pp.8, 1940; National Humane Review, Albany, vol.28, no.7, pp.6-7, illus., July, 1940.

ANIMAL FRIENDS OF THE HIGH SIERRA. Vernon Bailey. Sierra Club Bulletin, vol. 17, no.1, pp.12-24, Feb., 1932.

SUMMER VERTEBRATES OF MARIPOSA GROVE. AN ANNOTATED CHECK LIST. Richard G. Beidleman. Yosemite Nat. Notes, vol.29, no.5, pp.43-50, illus., May, 1950.

VERTEBRATES OF THE UNITED STATES. W. Frank Blair, et al. McGraw-Hill Book Co., Inc., New York, pp.x-819, illus., Aug. 29, 1957.

NATURAL HISTORY OF A WASATCH SUMMER. Claude T. Burnes. The Ralton Co., Salt Lake City, Utah, pp.100, 1957.

GAME ABUNDANT WHEN MEARNS MADE SURVEY. J.G. Burr. Texas Game and Fish, Austin, vol.7, no.12, pp.9, 26, Nov., 1949.

SEEING AMERICA'S WILDLIFE IN OUR NATIONAL REFUGES. Devereux Butcher. Devin-Adair, New York, pp.338, illus., 1955.

MEETING THE MAMMALS. (With Drawings by Walter A. Weber.) Victor H. Cahalane. New York, Macmillan Co., pp.ix-133, illus., 1943.

STATUS OF MAMMALS IN THE U.S. NATIONAL PARK SYSTEM, 1947. Victor H. Cahalane. Jour. Mamm., vol.29, no.3, pp.247-259, fig.1, Aug. 31, 1948.

ONE DAY AT TETON MARSH. Sally Carrighar. Knopf, New York, pp.vii-239, illus., 1947.

(FAUNA CONSERVATION IN THE UNITED STATES.) La conservation de la fauna en los Estados Unidos de America. R. L. Carson. La Conservacion en Accion, no. 5-S, U.S. Dept. Interior, Fish and Wildl. Service, Washington, D.C., pp.1-46, illus., 1948.

MISSOURI RIVER BASIN DEVELOPMENT. Clarence Cottam. North Dakota Outdoors, Grand Forks, vol.10, no.1, pp.12-14, July, 1947.

TEN YEARS OF BIOLOGY IN THE MOUNTAINS. (Jackson Hole Biological Research Station.) Gordon Cuyler. Animal Kingdom, New York Zool. Soc., vol.60, no.5, pp. 138-141, Oct., 1957.

TRAPPING THE DEAD-CREEK REGION. E.J. Dailey. Fur-Fish-Game (Harding's Mag.), Columbus, vol.79, no.9, pp.8-10, 35-36, illus., Sep., 1945.

LIFE ZONE PROBLEM IN THE NORTHERN INTERMOUNTAIN REGION. R.F. Daubenmire. Northwest Science, Cheney, vol.20, no.2, pp.28-38, fig.1, May, 1946.

FAUNA OF THE NATIONAL PARKS OF THE UNITED STATES. BIRDS AND MAMMALS OF MOUNT McKINLEY NATIONAL PARK, ALASKA. Joseph Scattergood Dixon. Washington, U.S. National Park Service, U.S. Govt. Print. Off., Fauna series, no.3, pp.xii-236, illus., map, pl., 1938.

NAME THAT ANIMAL. A GUIDE TO THE IDENTIFICATION OF THE COMMON LAND AND FRESH-WATER ANIMALS OF THE UNITED STATES, WITH SPECIAL REFERENCE TO THE AREA EAST OF THE ROCKIES. Ernest C. Driver. Northampton, E.C. Driver, Smith Coll., pp. 527, 1942.

(Review by D.B.O. Savile of) NAME THAT ANIMAL. A GUIDE TO THE IDENTIFICATION OF THE COMMON LAND AND FRESH-WATER ANIMALS OF THE UNITED STATES, WITH SPECIAL REFERENCE TO THE AREA EAST OF THE ROCKIES. Ernest C. Driver. Canadian Field-Nat., Sutton West, vol.58, no.2, p.70, Mar.-Apr., 1944.

DESCRIPTION OF APPARENTLY NEW SPECIES AND SUBSPECIES OF MAMMALS FROM THE INDIAN TERRITORY. D.G. Elliot. Chicago, Field Columbian Mus.,

Publication no.38, Zoological series, vol. 1, no.15, pp.285-288, 1899.

MEMOIRS OF ESTES PARK. (Gives Some Early Records of Mammals.) Milton Estes. Colorado State College Library, Fort Collins, Library Bull., no.6, pp.1-14, 1939.

MORE BIG GAME. Watson Fenimore. Pathfinder, Washington, vol.53, no.32, p.48, Oct. 23, 1946.

LETTER OF DR. DIEGO ALVAREZ CHANCA, DATED 1494, RELATING TO THE SECOND VOYAGE OF COLUMBUS TO AMERICA. (Being the First Written Document on the Natural History, Ethnography and Ethnology of America.) A.M. Fernandez de Ybarra. Smiths.Inst., Misc.Coll., (Quart.Issue), vol.48, pt.4, no.1698, pp.428-457, pl.66, fig.124, May 4, 1907.

MAMMALS ON THE MOUNTAIN TOPS. William L. Finley. Murrelet, vol.14, no.1, pp.9-12, Jan., 1933.

OUR NATIONAL WILDLIFE REFUGES. PART 2. Ira N. Gabrielson. Field and Stream, New York, vol.47, no.8, pp.16-17, 72-73, 83, illus., Dec., 1942.

BIG GAME OF THE UNITED STATES AND ITS CONSERVATION. E.A. Goldman. Sci. Monthly, vol.22, pp.239-242, Mar., 1926.

BEGINNINGS OF NATURAL HISTORY IN AMERICA. G.B. Goode. Proc. Biol. Soc. Washington, vol.3, pp.35-105, 1886.

AMERICAN GAME PROTECTION, A SKETCH. George Bird Grinnell. Hunting and Conservation, the Book of the Boone and Crockett Club, pp.201-257, pl.1, New Haven, Yale Univ. Press, 1925.

VERTEBRATE ANIMALS OF POINT LOBOS RESERVE, 1934-1935. Joseph Grinnell, Jean M. Linsdale. Carnegie Inst. Wash., Publication no.481, pp.vi-159, pls.39, Dec. 10, 1936.

CONSERVATION IN THE UNITED STATES. A.F. Gustafson, et al. Comstock Publishing Co., Inc., Ithaca, New York, vol.8, pp.xi-445, text figs.232, maps, graphs, Apr., 1939; (Third Edition) pp.534, illus., 1949.

(Review by Hartley H.T. Jackson of) CONSERVATION IN THE UNITED STATES. A.F. Gustafson, et al. Jour. Mamm., vol. 20, no.4, pp.509-510, Nov., 1939.

OUR FUR-BEARERS--A VANISHING NATIONAL RESOURCE. W.J. Hamilton, Jr. Bull. New York Zool. Soc., vol.41, no.3, pp.94-101, illus., May-June, 1938.

INVENTORY OF BIG-GAME ANIMALS OF THE UNITED STATES, 1952. Paul Hickie. U.S. Fish and Wildl. Serv., Washington, Leafl., no.348, p.1, fold. tbl., Aug., 1953; no.364, pp.3, Sep., 1954.

HUNTERS' BAG FOR 1945. UPLAND GAME DOWN, DEER AND WATERFOWL UP. Paul R. Highby. Conservation Volunteer, St. Paul, vol.9, no.53, pp.15-19, July-Aug., 1946.

VALUE OF 1945 FUR CATCH TOPS ALL RECORDS. Paul R. Highby. Conservation Volunteer, St. Paul, vol.9, no.55, pp.45-49, Nov.-Dec., 1946.

UNION BAY: THE LIFE OF A CITY MARSH. Harry W. Higman, Earl J. Larrison. Seattle Univ. of Washington Press, pp.x-315, 1951.

LETTERS TO THE EDITOR. SPECIAL WILDLIFE AREAS IN THE UNITED STATES NATIONAL FORESTS. Emmet T. Hooper. Jour. Mamm., vol.27, no.4, pp.410-411, Nov., 1946.

HISTORY OF BIG GAME IN THE UNITED STATES. Neil W. Hosley. Internat. Tech. Conf. on Protection Nature, UNESCO, IUPN, Conf.2, Misc.23, Lake Success, pp.6 (mimeographed), Aug., 1949.

NOTES ON MAMMALS OF THE MIDDLE MISSISSIPPI VALLEY, WITH DESCRIPTION OF A NEW WOODRAT. A.H. Howell. Proc. Biol. Soc. Washington, vol.22, pp.23-25, Mar. 23, 1910.

ANIMALS IN FUR. Clarence John Hylander. New York, Macmillan (The Young Naturalist Series), pp.206, illus., 1956.

BIG-GAME RESOURCES OF THE UNITED STATES, 1937-1942. Hartley H.T. Jackson. U.S. Dept. Interior, Fish and Wildl.Serv., Research Rept., no.8, pp.1-56, figs.31, (1944) Jan., 1945.

PRELIMINARY RECONNAISSANCE OF THE LAND VERTEBRATES OF THE ARCHER AND ANNA HUNTINGTON WILD LIFE FOREST STATION. PART 1. Chalres E.Johnson. Bull. New York State College Forestry, vol. 10, no.1, (Roosevelt Wild Life Bull., vol. 6, no.4), pp.556-609, figs.285-300, fold. map, Jan., 1937. (Mammals pp.598-609).

MANUAL OF THE VERTEBRATE ANIMALS OF THE NORTHEASTERN UNITED STATES INCLUSIVE OF MARINE SPECIES. David Starr Jordan. 1929.

WILDLIFE CONSERVATION AT GRAND PORTAGE. Laurits Krefting, Alton Bramer. Indians at Work, U.S. Dept. Interior, Chicago, vol.12, no.3, pp.19-21, illus., Sep.-Oct., 1944; Conservation Volunteer, St. Paul, vol.8, no.45, pp. 16-18, Mar.-Apr., 1945.

MAMMALS AND PLAGUE DISTRIBUTION IN THE UNITED STATES. Willard H. Lahnum. U.S. Naval Med. Bull., Wash., vol.46, no.5, pp.782-785, May, 1946.

FUR TRADE OF AMERICA. Agnes C.Laut. Macmillan Co., New York, pp.341, illus., Feb., 1921.

HUNTING STATISTICS IN THE UNITED STATES, 1936 VS. 1946. Daniel L. Leedy. Trans. 14th N.Amer. Wildl.Conf., Wash., pp.411-423, 1949.

WILDLIFE MANAGEMENT IN THE AMERICAS. Frederick C. Lincoln. Agriculture in the Americas, U.S. Dept. Agric., Wash., D.C., vol.4, no.1, pp.13-17, Jan., 1944.

FRANCES SIMES HASTINGS NATURAL HISTORY RESERVATION, 1937-1947. Jean M. Linsdale. Pp.23, 1947.

CULTURE OF THE KEYSER FARM SITE. Carl Manson, et al. Papers Michigan Acad. Sci., Arts and Letters, Ann Arbor, vol.29, pp.375-418, figs.3, pls.13, 1943.

AMERICAN WILDLIFE AND PLANTS. Alexander C. Martin, et al. New York, McGraw-Hill Book Co., pp.ix-500, figs., maps.

REPORT OF THE DIRECTOR OF THE NATIONAL PARK SERVICE TO THE SECRETARY OF THE INTERIOR FOR THE FISCAL YEAR ENDED JUNE 30, 1921, AND THE TRAVEL SEASON 1921. Stephen T. Mather. Washington, pp.306, map, 1921.

ARTICLE XVI. DESCRIPTION OF A NEW SUBSPECIES OF THE EASTERN CHIPMUNK, FROM THE UPPER MISSISSIPPI REGION, WEST OF THE GREAT LAKES. ARTICLE XVII. DESCRIPTION OF A NEW SPECIES OF WEASEL, AND A NEW SUBSPECIES OF THE GRAY FOX, FROM ARIZONA. ARTICLE XVIII. OBSERVATIONS ON THE NORTH AMERICAN BADGERS, WITH ESPECIAL REFERENCE TO THE FORMS FOUND IN ARIZONA, WITH DESCRIPTION OF A NEW SUBSPECIES FROM NORTHERN CALIFORNIA. ARTICLE XIX. NOTES ON THE OTTER (LUTRA CANADENSIS) AND SKUNKS (GENERA SPILOGALE AND MEPHITIS) OF ARIZONA. Edgar Alexander Mearns. New York, Amer. Mus. Nat. Hist., vol.3, no.2, pp.229-262, 1891.

EIGHT NEW MAMMALS FROM THE UNITED STATES. C. Hart Merriam. Proc. Biol. Soc. Washington, vol.16, pp.73-78, May 29, 1903.

LIFE ZONES AND CROP ZONES OF THE UNITED STATES. C. Hart Merriam. U.S. Dept. Agric. Division of Biological Survey, Bull. no.10, pp.1-79, fold.map, 1898.

MAMMALS OF SHASTA. C. Hart Merriam. N.American Fauna, no.16, pp.87-107, figs. 31-35, Oct. 28, 1899.

REPORT ON THE MAMMALS AND BIRDS OF THE EXPEDITION. C. Hart Merriam. (In) U.S. Geological and Geographical Survey of the Territories, Annual Report, no.6, pp.661-715, illus., 1873.

FAUNA OF MUSKEGET ISLAND-A PROTEST. Gerrit S. Miller, Jr. The Auk, vol. 15, pp.75-77, Jan., 1898.

AMERICAN FUR POLICY. David C. Mills. Proc. N. Amer. Wildl. Conf., pp.637-638, 1936.

WILDLIFE WONDERLAND. (Jackson Hole National Monument.) Lorus J. Milne, M. J. Milne. Nature Mag., Washington, vol. 42, no.5, pp.211-214, 242, illus., May, 1949.

OUR WILD ANIMALS. Edwin Lincoln Moseley. New York and London, D.Appleton and Co., vol.8, pp.x-310, illus., Jan., 1928.

GREAT AMERICAN SNOUT COUNT. (Account of big-game estimates in United States and biographical notes on H.H.T. Jackson.) Richard L. Neuberger. Saturday Evening Post, Philadelphia, vol.218, no.51, pp.28-29, 92, 94, illus., June 22, 1946.

OUR FUR-BEARERS. E. Laurence Palmer. Nature Mag., Washington, D.C., vol.33, no.10, pp.581-588, illus., Dec., 1940.

FAUNA AND FLORA OF THE BIG THICKET AREA. H.B. Parks, et al. State Teachers' College, Huntsville, Texas, pp.51, 1938.

REPORT ON GAME CONDITIONS IN SUPERIOR NATIONAL FOREST. A.S. Peck. Fins, Feathers and Fur, no.30, pp.1-3, June, 1922.

BOOK OF SMALL MAMMALS. Theodore S. Pettit. New York, Garden City, Garden City Books, pp.56, illus., 1958.

CONSERVATION OF OUR MAMMALS AND BIRDS. J.C. Phillips. Hunting and Conservation, the Book of the Boone and Crockett Club, New Haven, Yale Univ. Press, pp.29-65, pl. 1, 1925.

(SOME COMMENTS ON THE REGULATION OF HUNTING AND THE PROTECTION OF GAME IN THE U. S. A. ) Quelques commentaires sur la reglementation de la chasse et la protection du gibier aux Etats-Unis d'Amerique. J.C. Phillips. Conseil International de la Chasse, 3rd session (Varsovie 19-23, Apr., 1934), Paris, pp.311-319, 1934.

MANUAL OF LAND AND FRESH WATER VERTEBRATE ANIMALS OF THE UNITED STATES (EXCLUSIVE OF BIRDS). Henry S. Pratt. Philadelphia, P. Blakiston's Sons and Co., pp.xv-422, figs.184, 1923.

OUR DISAPPEARING FUR BEARERS. Edward A. Preble. Nature Mag., vol.10, pp. 375-381, illus., Dec., 1927; reprinted as booklet, pp.24, 1928.

MAMMALS OF ZION-BRYCE AND CEDAR BREAKS. C.C. Presnall. Zion-Bryce Mus. Bull., no.2, pp.20, illus., Jan., 1938.

PRESENT STATUS OF EXOTIC MAMMALS IN THE UNITED STATES. C.C. Presnall. Jour. Wildl.Mgt., vol.22, no.1, pp.45-50, Jan., 1958.

WOODLAND BOOK. Elmer Inglesby Ransom. New York, Howell, Soskin, pp.109, col. pls., 1945.

NATIONAL PARK WILDLIFE RANGES. Harold M. Ratcliff, Lowell Sumner. Trans. 10th N. Amer. Wildl. Conf., Washington, pp.246-250, 1945.

DESCRIPTIONS OF NEW MAMMALS FROM FLORIDA AND SOUTHERN CALIFORNIA. Samuel N. Rhoads. Proc. Acad. Nat. Sciences, Philadelphia, pp.32-37, 1895.

WILD LIFE IN OUR NATIONAL PARKS. Paul B. Riis. Parks and Recreation, vol. 17, no.4, pp.141-148, figs., Dec., 1933.

THE WILDERNESS HUNTER: AN ACCOUNT OF THE BIG GAME OF UNITED STATES AND ITS CHASE WITH HORSE, HOUND, AND RIFLE. Theodore Roosevelt. 1893.

AMERICAN BIG-GAME HUNTING-THE BOOK OF THE BOONE AND CROCKET CLUB. Theodore Roosevelt, George Bird

Grinnell. New York Forest and Stream Publishing Co., 1901.

HOW TO KNOW THE AMERICAN MAMMALS. Ivan T. Sanderson. Little Brown, pp.1-164, illus., 1951.

ZOOLOGICAL CONTRIBUTIONS OF THE LEWIS AND CLARK EXPEDITION. Henry W. Setzer. Jour. Washington Acad. Sci., vol.44, no.11, pp.356-357, Nov. 22, 1954.

AMERICA'S WILDLIFE. (Review of Forest Service big-game estimates for 1939 and outline of Forest Service wildlife policies.) H.L. Shantz. Penna. Game News, vol.10, no.9, pp.11, 27, Dec., 1939.

WETLANDS OF THE UNITED STATES. THEIR EXTENT AND THEIR VALUE TO WATERFOWL AND OTHER WILDLIFE. Samuel P. Shaw, C. Gordon Fredine. U.S. Dept. Interior, Fish and Wildl.Service, Circular 39, pp.67, illus., map 1, 1956.

HISTORY AND SIGNIFICANCE OF AMERICAN WILDLIFE. H.P. Sheldon. U.S.Dept. Agric., Wildl.Research and Management, Leaflet BS-108, pp.1-8, Mar., 1938, Penna. Game News, New Cumberland, vol.10, no. 5, pp.7, 30, Aug., 1939.

GAME MAMMALS OF THE UNITED STATES. R.W. Schufeldt. Shooting and Fishing, vol.30, no.25, p.489, Oct.3, 1901.

(GAME MAMMALS OF THE UNITED STATES OF AMERICA. 1. SURVEY OF CLASS MAMMALIA (CONCLUSION).) Die jagdbaren Saeugetiere der Vereinigten Staaten von Amerika. 1. Allgemeiner Ueberblick ueber die Klasse der Saeugetiere. (Schluss.) Robert W. Shufeldt. Natur and Haus, vol.16, no.15, pp.231-234, May 1, 1908.

(GAME MAMMALS OF THE UNITED STATES OF AMERICA. 2. GEOGRAPHICAL DISTRIBUTION OF EXTANT AND EXTINCT MAMMALS.) Die jagdbaren Saeugetiere der Vereinigten Staaten von Amerika. 2. Die geographischen Verbreitung der jetzt lebenden und der ausgestorbenen Saeugetiere. Robert W. Shufeldt. Natur und Haus, vol. 16, no.18, pp.278-281, June, 1908.

NATURAL HISTORY AND THE AMERICAN MIND. William Martin Smallwood, Mabel Sarah Smallwood. New York, Columbia Univ. Press, pp.xiii+445, pls.10, 1941.

OUR SMALL NATIVE ANIMALS, THEIR HABITS AND CARE. Robert Snedigar. New York, Random House, pp.308, 1939.

AMERICAN ANIMALS: POPULAR GUIDE TO THE MAMMALS OF NORTH AMERICA NORTH OF MEXICO, WITH INTIMATE BIOGRAPHIES OF THE MORE FAMILIAR SPECIES. Witmar Stone, William Everett Cram. New York, Doubleday, Page and Co., pp.318, illus., 1902.

MAMMALS OF COOK FOREST. George Miksch Sutton. Cardinal (Sewickley, Pa.), vol.2, pp.76-81, illus., Jan., 1928.

OUR NATIONAL FORESTS AS A HOME FOR WILDLIFE. (Bear, Deer, Mountain Sheep.) Lloyd W. Swift. Audubon Mag., New York, vol.47, no.5, sec.1, pp.288-295, illus., Sep.-Oct., 1945.

NATIONAL WILDLIFE SURVEY. Walter P. Taylor. Amer. Wildl., Washington, vol.25, no.5, pp.69, 77, illus., Sep.-Oct., 1936.

STATE PARKS AND RECREATIONAL USES OF STATE FORESTS. (Contains a Few Notes on Mammals.) Raymond H. Torrey. Washington, National Conference on State Parks, pp.259, illus., 1926.

HOW DO YOU KNOW WHERE TO LOOK FOR THEM? S.P. Welles. Plateau, Mus. Northern Arizona, Flagstaff, vol.20, no. 3, pp.41-50, Jan., 1948.

MAMMALS AND BIRDS OF "ROCK CITY." L.D. Wooster. Trans. Kansas Acad. Sci., vol.40, pp.197-201, pl., 1938.

BIG GAME OF OUR NATIONAL PARKS. George M. Wright. Scientific Monthly, pp. 141-147, illus., Aug., 1935.

FAUNA OF THE NATIONAL PARKS OF THE UNITED STATES. A PRELIMINARY SURVEY OF FAUNAL RELATIONS IN NATIONAL PARKS. George M. Wright, et al. Contrib. Wild Life Surv., Fauna ser.no.1, Nat. Park Serv., U.S. Dept. Interior, pp.iv-157, figs.56, (May, 1932) 1933.

FAUNA OF THE NATIONAL PARKS OF THE UNITED STATES. WILDLIFE MANAGEMENT IN THE NATIONAL PARKS. George M. Wright, Ben H. Thompson. Contrib. Wildlife Div. Fauna ser.no.2, U.S.Dept. Interior, National Park Service, pp.viii-142, figs.61, July, 1934.

REPORT ON THE CURRENT STATUS OF LARGE MAMMALS IN THE NATIONAL PARKS. George M. Wright, Ben H. Thompson. Fauna Nat'l Parks U.S. Dept.Interior, Fauna ser.no.2, pp.59-74, figs.19-23, 1935.

FOUR-FOOTED AMERICANS AND THEIR KIN. Mabel Osgood Wright. New York, The Macmillan Co., pp.xv+432, illus., pls., 1898.

MAMMALS: A GUIDE TO FIMILIAR AMERICAN SPECIES. Herbert S. Zim, Donald F. Hoffmeister. Simon and Schuster, New York, pp.160, illus., 1955.

ANNUAL FOR CATCH OF THE UNITED STATES. U.S. Dept.Interior, Fish and Wildl.Service, Wildl.Leaflet no.170, pp. 21, Oct., 1940; Wildl.Leaflet no.232, pp.22, Feb., 1943; Wildl.Leaflet no.253, pp.21, July, 1944; Wildl.Leaflet no.276, pp.22, July, 1945; Wildl.Leaflet no.290, pp.22, Aug., 1946.

BIG-GAME INVENTORY OF THE UNITED STATES, FOR 1937. U.S. Dept. Agric., Wildl.Research and Management Leaflet no.BS-122, pp.1-13, tbls.17, Jan.1939; FOR 1938. U.S. Bur.Biol.Surv., Wild-Life Leaflet no.BS-142, pp.11, tbls.17, Aug., 1939; FOR 1939. U.S.Dept.Interior, Fish and Wildl.Service, Wildl.Leaflet no.175, pp.11, Nov., 1940; FOR 1940. Wildl. Leaflet no.207, pp.10, Jan., 1942; FOR 1943. Wildl.Leaflet no.283, pp.11, Feb., 1946; FOR 1946. Wildl.Leaflet no.303, pp.13, Mar., 1948; FOR 1947. Wildl. Leaflet no.321, pp.3, May, 1949.

ESTIMATE OF FUR-BEARING ANIMALS ON NATIONAL FORESTS. (For 1935 and 1936.) U.S. Dept. Agric., Forest Service, p.1, 1937; (In 1936.) U.S. Dept. Agric., Forest Service, pp.6, 1937.

ESTIMATED NUMBERS OF RELATIVE ABUNDANCE OF MAMMALS. (In National Parks, National Monuments, etc.) U.S. National Park Service, Washington, D.C., 1948.

THE GAME INCREASE. Amer.Cattle Prod., vol.26, no.8, p.10, Jan., 1945.

INVENTORY OF BIG-GAME ANIMALS OF THE UNITED STATES, 1949. U.S. Dept. Interior, Wildl.Leaflet, Fish and Wildl. Service, no.321, pp.3, Oct., 1951; FOR 1950 AND 1951. Wildl.Leaflet no.324, pp. 2, Oct., 1952.

STATUS OF WILDLIFE IN THE UNITED STATES. Report of the Special Committee on the Conservation of Wildlife Resources, Washington, D.C., 76th Congr., 3rd sess. Rept.no.1203, pp.457, illus., 1940.

SURVEY OF THE ANNUAL FUR CATCH OF THE UNITED STATES. U.S. Bur. Biol.Surv., Wildlife Research and Management Leaflet, no.BS-140, pp.19, tbls., June, 1939.

WILDLIFE CONDITIONS IN NATIONAL PARKS, 1939. U.S. Dept. Interior, Nat. Park Service, Conserv.Bull.no.3, pp. 38, illus., Jan. 8, 1940 (Mimeogr.); FOR 1941. U.S. Dept. Interior, Nat. Park Serv., pp.58, illus., May, 1943.

WILD LIFE HANDBOOK. U.S. Dept.Agric., Forest Service, Region 9, North Central region, multigraphed, pp.xx-1-297-1-81, Nov., 1935.

UNITED STATES, EASTERN

Extinct and Fossil Mammals

VANISHED MAMMALS. (Wolverine, Fisher, Marten, Cougar, Lynx, Bison, Caribou.) G.W. Bradt. Michigan Conserv., Lansing, vol.17, no.7, pp.4-5, illus., July, 1948.

BEGINNING OF THE PLEISTOCENE IN EASTERN UNITED STATES. Richard Foster Flint. Bull. Geol. Soc. America, Baltimore, vol.59, no.6, pp.543-548, June, 1948.

KINGSTON VILLAGE SITE. A.M.Simpson. Peoria, Ill., Acad. Sci., Archaeol.Sect., pp.15, illus., Apr., 1939. (Mammals p. 15.)

Recent Mammals

SWAN CREEK WILDLIFE EXPERIMENT STATION. Durward L. Allen. Michigan Conservation, Lansing, vol.8, no.10, pp.8-9, 11, June, 1939.

WILDLIFE VISTAS OF THE EASTERN HIGHLANDS. Victor H. Cahalane. Audubon Mag., Harrisburg, vol.44, no.2, pp.101-111, illus., Apr., 1942.

DELAWARE FURBEARERS. Henry P. Cofer. Del. Game and Fish Comm., pp.1-4(text), pp.1-6(bibliog.), Apr., 1950.

FUR-BEARER INVESTIGATIONS. Arthur H. Cook. New York Cons. Dept., Final Rept., PR Proj.1-R, Suppl.G, p.57, May, 1949.

ESTIMATING ACORN CROPS FOR WILD LIFE IN THE SOUTHERN APPALACHIANS. Albert A. Downs. Jour.Wildl.Mgt., Menasha, vol.8, no.4, pp.339-340, Oct., 1944.

OCCURRENCE AND LAST RECORDS OF BIG GAME ANIMALS EAST OF MISSISSIPPI RIVER. G.G. Goodwin. Jour.Mamm., vol.14, no.2, p.182, May, 1933.

MAMMALS OF EASTERN UNITED STATES. AN ACCOUNT OF RECENT LAND MAMMALS OCCURRING EAST OF THE MISSISSIPPI. William J. Hamilton, Jr. Handbooks Amer.Nat.Hist., Comstock Publishing Co., Ithaca, vol.2, pp.432, figs. 184, 1943.

(Review by Jean M. Linsdale of) MAMMALS OF EASTERN UNITED STATES. William J. Hamilton, Jr. Amer.Midland Nat., Notre Dame, vol.30, no.1, pp. 269-270, July, 1943.

THOSE LITTLE MAMMALS. (Field Mice, Shrews, Moles.) William J. Hamilton, Jr. New York State Conservationist, Albany, vol.1, no.6, pp.16-17, June-July, 1947.

PARAGRAPHS FROM FIELD NOTES. (Bobcat, Black and Albino Deer.) R.S. Harris. West Virginia Conservation, Charleston, vol.10, no.4, pp.8-9, 15, illus., Aug., 1946.

RELATION OF THE MEADOW MOUSE MICROTUS P. PENNSYLVANICUS TO THE BIOTA OF A LAKE CHAMPLAIN ISLAND. Robert T. Hatt. Ecology, vol.9, pp.88-92, Jan., 1928.

DEER AND RABBIT BROWSING AND AVAILABLE WINTER FORAGE IN ALLEGHENY HARDWOOD FORESTS. A.F. Hough. Jour. Wildl.Mgt., Menasha, vol.13, no.1, pp. 135-141, Jan., 1949.

NOTES ON THE DISTRIBUTION OF CERTAIN MAMMALS IN THE SOUTHEASTERN UNITED STATES. Arthur H. Howell. Proc. Biol.Soc. Washington, vol.22, pp.55-68, Apr. 17, 1909.

WILDLIFE UNDERGROUND. (Animals found in caves, including bats and rodents.) H.W. Jackson. Virginia Wildlife, Richmond, vol.9, no.10, pp.5-7, 26, illus., Oct., 1948.

PROGRESS REPORT ON SOUTHEASTERN MAMMAL STUDIES. E.V. Komarek. Jour. Mamm., vol.20, no.3, pp.292-299, Aug. 14, 1939.

BEASTS OF CAROLINA. CHAPTER III. John Lawson. N.Carolina Wildlife Conserv., Raleigh, vol.8, no.6, pp.3-6, 11-13, June, 1944.

REPORT ON A GAME SURVEY OF THE NORTH CENTRAL STATES. Aldo Leopold. Madison, Wisconsin, pp.299, maps 21, figs.4, 1931.

RED BAT AND SPOTTED PORPOISE OFF THE CAROLINAS. J.T. Nichols. Jour. Mamm., vol.1, no.2, p.87, Feb., 1920.

LIVING COMMUNITY. (Ground Squirrel, Beaver, Deer.) Paul W.Sundheimer. Virginia Wildlife, Richmond, vol.8, no.6, pp.18-20, illus., June, 1947.

ALLEGHENY FUR TRAILS. V.E.Tringley. Fur-Fish-Game (Harding's Mag.), Columbus, vol.79, no.1, pp.30-31, Jan., 1946.

ANIMAL TRACKS ARE STUDIED BY WINTER HIKERS AT STATE PARKS AND MAKE AN INTERESTING HOBBY. Outdoor Indiana, Indianapolis, vol.8, no.12, pp.16-17, illus., Jan., 1942.

## UNITED STATES, WESTERN

### Extinct and Fossil Mammals

ARCHAEOLOGY OF THE UPPER COLUMBIA REGION. Donald Collier, et al. Univ. Washington Publ.Anthropol., Seattle, vol. 9, no.1, pp.1-178, Sep., 1942. (17 species of mammals listed on pp.126-127, including a specimen record of Bison from Washington.)

COLLECTING IN THE UINTA BASIN. J. Kenneth Doutt. Carnegie Mag., vol.11, no.8, pp.233-238, illus., Jan., 1938.

OUTLINE OF THE GEOLOGY AND PALEONTOLOGY OF SCOTTS BLUFF NATIONAL MONUMENT AND THE ADJACENT REGION. William L. Effinger. Dept. Interior, Nat.Park Serv., Field Div. of Education, Berkeley, Calif., pp.37, pls., tbls., 1934. (Mimeographed.)

HUNTING FOR FOSSIL MAMMALS IN THE NAVAJO COUNTRY. C. Lewis Gazin. Explor.and Field-work Smiths.Inst.1936, publ. 3407, pp.19-22, figs.13-16, Apr.2, 1937.

AN OLD-TIME BONE HUNT. AN ACCOUNT OF THE EXPEDITION UNDERTAKEN BY PROF. O. C. MARSH IN 1870 TO THE THEN WILD WEST. George Bird Grinnell. Nat. Hist., vol.23, pp.329-336, figs.2, July-Aug., 1923.

FOSSIL MAMMALS OF THE PUERCO BEDS. Henry Fairfield Osborn, Charles Earle. Amer. Mus. Nat. Hist., New York, Bulletin, vol.7, pp.1-70, illus., 1895. (Collection of 1892.)

FOSSIL MAMMALS OF THE UINTA BASIN. EXPEDITION OF 1894. Henry Fairfield Osborn. Amer. Mus. Nat. Hist., New York, Bulletin, vol.7, pp.71-105, illus., 1895.

ARCHAEOLOGICAL OCCURRENCES OF PRONGHORN ANTELOPE, BISON, AND HORSE IN THE COLUMBIA PLATEAU. Douglas Osborne. Sci.Monthly, vol.77, no.5, pp.260-269, illus., Nov., 1953.

NEW SPECIES FROM THE OLIGOCENE OF THE UINTA. O. A. Peterson.Annals Carnegie Mus., Pittsburgh, vol.21, pp. 61-78, figs.12, pl.1, Dec. 19, 1931; vol. 21, no.2, pp.61-78, pl.1, Apr., 1932.

EXHIBIT SHOWS VARIED ANIMALS THAT INHABITED THE BAD LANDS 25,000,000 YEARS AGO. Elmer S. Riggs. Field Mus. News, Chicago, vol.13, no.6, pp.4-5, illus., June, 1942.

PALEONTOLOGICAL EVIDENCE FOR THE ANTIQUITY OF THE SCOTTSBLUFF BISON QUARRY AND ITS ASSOCIATED ARTIFACTS. C.Bertrand Schultz, Loren Eiseley. Amer. Anthrop., n.s., vol.37, pp.306-319, pls.8-9, Apr., 1935.

ADDITIONS TO THE PUERCO FAUNA, LOWER PALEOCENE. George Gaylord Simpson. Amer. Mus. Novitates, no. 849, pp.11, figs.6, May 18, 1936.

BONES IN THE BREWERY. PALEONTOLOGIST'S RENDEZVOUS WITH HISTORY AND PREHISTORY IN ST. LOUIS. George Gaylord Simpson. Nat. Hist., New York, vol.55, no.6, pp.252-259, illus., June, 1946.

FOSSIL DEPOSIT IN A CAVE IN ST. LOUIS. George Gaylord Simpson. Amer. Mus. Novitates, New York, no.1408, pp.1-46, figs.16, Feb. 4, 1949.

DISCOVERY OF UPPER EOCENE LAND MAMMALS ON THE PACIFIC COAST. Chester Stock. Science, n.s., vol.74, no.1927, pp.577-578, Dec. 4, 1931.

DALLAS AND HOOD RIVER FORMATIONS, AND THE COLUMBIA RIVER GORGE. Chester Stock. Contrib. to Palaeontology, Carnegie Inst. Washington, Publ.404, pp. 11-26, Aug., 1930.

CONTRIBUTIONS TO PALEONTOLOGY, FROM CARNEGIE INSTITUTION OF WASHINGTON. Carnegie Inst. of Wash., publication no.404, pp.112, illus., tbls., pls.8, 1930.

### Recent Mammals

RESULTS OF THE CLARK NATIONAL FOREST FURBEARER SURVEY.(Missouri.) Earl L. Atwood. Jour. Wildl. Mgt., vol.2, no.1, pp.20-26, Jan., 1938.

CHARACTERISTICS OF SOME NEW SPECIES OF MAMMALIA, COLLECTED BY THE U. S. AND MEXICAN BOUNDARY SURVEY, MAJOR W. H. EMORY, U. S. A. COMMISSIONER. Spencer F. Baird. Proc. Acad. Nat. Sci. Philadelphia, vol. 7, pp.331-333, Apr., 1855.

GENERAL REPORT UPON THE ZOOLOGY OF THE SEVERAL PACIFIC RAILROAD ROUTES. PART 1. MAMMALS. Spencer F. Baird. Ann. and Mag. Nat. Hist., vol. 1, no.5, ser.3, pp.369-374, 1858.

MAMMALS OF THE (MEXICAN) BOUNDARY. Spencer F. Baird. Washington, pp. 62, litho pls.27, 1859.

REPORTS OF EXPLORATIONS AND SURVEYS FOR A RAILROAD FROM MISSISSIPPI RIVER TO PACIFIC OCEAN. PART 1. MAMMALS. Spencer F. Baird. Senate, 33rd Congress, 2nd sess., Ex. Doc.78, vol.8, part 1, pp.xxv-xlvii, 1-737, pls.60, 1857.

OUR PUBLIC LANDS PROBLEMS IN THE WEST--WHAT IS THEIR CURRENT STATUS? Elliott S. Barker. Wyoming Wild Life, Cheyenne, vol.12, no.10, pp.12-17, 38, illus., Nov., 1948; vol.12, no. 11, pp.14-17, 28-30, illus., 1948.

BIG GAME ANIMALS OF THE WEST AND THEIR RELATION TO RANGE MANAGEMENT. Carlton J. Blades. MS thesis, Univ. Michigan, 1936.

UNIFORM TRAPPING SEASON. Arthur L. Clark. Missouri Conservationist, Jefferson City, vol.4, no.9, pp.2-3, Dec., 1943.

SURVEY SHOWS FUR BEARERS DECREASING. Dean Coleman. Colorado Conserv. Comments, Denver, vol.10, no.8, pp.17-18, 29, illus., Dec., 1948.

MISSOURI RIVER BASIN DEVELOPMENT: ITS EFFECTS ON FISH AND WILDLIFE. Clarence Cottam. Outdoor America, Madison, vol.12, no.3, pp.4-8, illus., Feb., 1947; North Dakota Outdoors, Grand Forks, vol.10, no.1, pp.12-14, July, 1947.

MISSOURI RIVER BASIN EFFECTS ON WILDLIFE. Clarence Cottam. Wisconsin Conserv.Bull., Madison, vol.12, no.11, pp.16-20, Nov., 1947.

WILDLIFE PORTFOLIO OF THE WESTERN NATIONAL PARKS. Joseph S. Dixon. U.S.Nat.Park Service Washington, D.C., pp.xii-121, illus., 1942.

MAMMALS OF THE NAVAJO COUNTRY. Theodore H. Eaton, Jr. National Youth Administration (Project 6677-Y), Berkeley, Calif., pp.1-46, figs.34, map, 1937.

LIST OF SPECIES OF MAMMALS, PRINCIPALLY RODENTS, OBTAINED BY W. W. PRICE, DR. S. E. MEEK, G. K. CHERRIE, AND E. S. THOMPSON IN THE STATES OF IOWA, WYOMING, MONTANA, IDAHO, NEVADA AND CALIFORNIA, WITH DESCRIPTIONS OF NEW SPECIES. Daniel Giraud Elliot. Chicago, Field Columbian Mus., Publication 27, Zoological series, vol.1, no.10, pp.193-221, 1898.

TRAPPING IS BIG BUSINESS. FURS YIELD OVER $5,000,000 IN 1943. Arnold B. Erickson, Thomas A. Schrader. Conserv. Volunteer, St. Paul, vol.7, no.41, pp.1-6, July-Aug., 1944.

COLORADO RIVER AS A BARRIER IN MAMMALIAN DISTRIBUTION. E.A. Goldman. Jour. Mamm., vol.18, no.4, pp.427-435, Nov., 1937.

BIG GAME ANIMALS IN THE NORTHEASTERN UNITED STATES. George H. Goodwin. Jour. Mamm., vol.17, no.1, pp.48-50, Feb., 1936.

SURVEY OF FUR-BEARER POPULATIONS AND OF THEIR PRESENT AND POTENTIAL HABITAT. James E. Grasse. Wyo. Wild Life, vol.15, no.8, pp.10-11, 37, Aug., 1951.

ZOOLOGICAL REPORT. MAMMALS. G. B. Grinnell. (In) Wm.Ludlow, 1876, Rep. of a reconnaissance from Carroll, Montana Territory, on the upper Missouri, to the Yellowstone National Park in 1875, pp.79-84.

ANNUAL REPORT TO THE CHIEF OF THE FOREST SERVICE OF THE PACIFIC NORTHWEST FOREST AND RANGE EXPERIMENT STATION FOR THE CALENDAR YEAR 1950. J. Alfred Hall. U.S.Dept.Agric., Pac.Northwest Forest and Range Exp.Sta., pp.62, Mar., 1951.

THE 1941 FUR CATCH. (Minnesota.) Paul R. Highby. Cons.Volunteer, vol.5, no.28, pp.40-43, Jan., 1943.

VALUE OF 1945 FUR CATCH TOPS ALL RECORDS. Paul R. Highby. Cons. Volunteer, vol.9, no.55, pp.45-49, Nov.-Dec., 1946.

ON THE FAUNAL POSITION OF THE PACIFIC COAST OF THE UNITED STATES. A. Brazier Howell. Ecology, vol.8, pp.18-26, Jan., 1927.

PRAIRIE DWELLERS.... ANIMALS OF THE AMERICAN WEST. (Photos of Prairie Dog, Ground Squirrel, Jack Rabbit, Pronghorn, and Mule Deer.) J.W. Jackson. Philadelphia, Fauna, vol.5, no.1, pp.16-17, illus., Mar., 1943.

DENIZENS OF THE MOUNTAINS. Edmund Carroll Jaeger. Springfield, Ill., Baltimore, Md., C.C. Thomas, pp.xiii-168, illus., 1929. (Life History Sketches of Some of the More Familiar and Interesting Mammals and Birds of the Mountains of the Western United States.)

DICHOTOMOUS KEY TO THE SKULLS OF THE RECENT LAND MAMMALS OF THE SOUTHEASTERN UNITED STATES.James H. Jenkins. MS thesis, Univ. Ga., 1949.

BADLANDS SAFARI, 1928. G.L. Jepson. Princeton Alumni Weekly, vol.29, no.10, pp.303-305, Nov. 30, 1928.

MANUAL OF THE VERTEBRATE ANIMALS OF THE NORTHEASTERN UNITED STATES. David Starr Jordan. Yonkers, New York, World Book Co., vol.8, pp.xxxi-446, 1929. (Mammals pp.367-408.)

SEALS, SEA-LIONS, AND SEA OTTER OF THE PACIFIC COAST. Karl W.Kenyon, Victor B. Scheffer. U.S.Dept.Interior, Fish and Wildl.Serv., Circular 32, pp.34, illus., Apr., 1955.

THREAT TO OUR WESTERN RANGES. A. Starker Leopold. Pacific Discovery, San Francisco, vol.1, no.1, pp.28-29, illus., Feb., 1948.

WILDLIFE AND LIVESTOCK ON WESTERN RANGES. Albert L. Linger. Trans. 8th N. Amer. Wildlife Conf., Washington, D.C., pp.62-66, 1943.

ENVIRONMENTAL RESPONSES OF VERTEBRATES IN THE GREAT BASIN. Jean M. Linsdale. Amer.Midland Nat., vol.19, no. 1, pp.1-206, figs.12, Jan., 1938.

RANGE CONDITIONS AS AN INFLUENCE ON BIG GAME PRODUCTIVITY. William M. Longhurst. Proc. 31st Ann. Conf. Western Assn. State Game and Fish Comm., pp.190-194, Apr.30 - May 2, 1951.

MAMMALS OF THE MEXICAN BOUNDARY OF THE UNITED STATES. ( Descriptive Catalogue of the Species of Mammals Occurring in the Region; With a General Summary of the Natural History, and a List of Trees.) Edgar Alexander Mearns. PART 1. FAMILIES DIDELPHIIDAE TO MURIDAE. Washington, Govt.Print. Off., Smiths.Inst., U.S.Nat.Mus., Bulletin 56, pp.xv-530, illus., pls., fold.maps 2, diagrs., 1907.

PRELIMINARY DIAGNOSES OF NEW MAMMALS FROM THE MEXICAN BORDER OF THE UNITED STATES. Edgar Alexander Mearns. Proc. U.S. Nat. Mus., vol.18, no.1075, pp.1-4, Mar.25, 1896; vol.18, pp.443-447, May 23, 1896; vol.19, no.1103, pp.137-140, May 25, 1896; vol.19, pp.137-140, Dec. 21, 1896.

PRELIMINARY DIAGNOSES OF NEW MAMMALS OF THE GENERA MEPHITIS, DORCELAPHUS, AND DICOTYLES, FROM THE MEXICAN BORDER OF THE UNITED STATES. Edgar Alexander Mearns. Govt. Print.Off., Washington, Proc.U.S.Nat. Mus., vol.xx, no.1129, pp.467-471, 1897.

ANIMALS OF THE SOUTHWEST DESERT. George Olin. Globe, Arizona, Southwestern Monuments Assoc., Popular Series, no.8, pp.112, illus., map, 1954.

RESOLUTIONS OF WESTERN ASSOCIATION OF STATE GAME AND FISH COMMISSIONERS NOVEMBER 1, 1930. Roland G. Parvin. Jour. Mamm., vol.12, no.1, pp.96-97, Feb., 1931.

FUR RESOURCES AND BEAR STUDIES. Jack D. Remington. Colo.Game and Fish Dept., Final Rep.Invest.Proj., no.W-61-R, pp.1-85, mimeo., pls., Apr., 1955.

FURS--A MILLION DOLLAR RESOURCE IN AN AGRICULTURAL STATE. Sylvan T. Runkel. Soil Cons., vol.7, no.10, p.237, Apr., 1942.

BIG GAME AND LIVESTOCK ON THE WESTERN RANGE. H.E. Schwan. Trans.10th N. Amer. Wildl. Conf., Washington, pp.219-224, 1945.

ANIMAL COMMUNITIES IN TEMPERATE AMERICA, AS ILLUSTRATED IN THE CHICAGO REGION; A STUDY IN ANIMAL ECOLOGY. Victor Ernest Shelford. Chicago, Ill., Pub.for the Geographic Soc. of Chicago by the Univ. of Chicago Press, Bulletin no. 5, pp.xiii-362, illus., maps 2, diagrs., 1913.

TRAMPS THROUGH THE GULF STATES-I. (Photographs of the Texas Armadillo.) R.W. Shufeldt. Amer. Forestry, vol.26, pp.489-496, Aug., 1920.

BIG GAME--RANGE LIVESTOCK COMPETITION ON WESTERN RANGES. L.A. Stoddart, D.I. Rasmussen. Trans. 10th N.Amer. Wildl.Conf., Washington, pp.251-256, 1945.

SEE FOR YOURSELF. (Wild Life, western U.S.) Ken Stott, Jr. Zoonooz, San Diego, vol.13, no.9, pp.3-7, illus., Sep., 1941.

WILD ANIMALS OF THE FAR WEST. Adrien Stoutenburg. Berkeley, Calif. Parnassus Press, pp.150, illus., 1958.

CHAPTER ON THE NATURAL HISTORY OF THE GREAT BASIN, 1800 TO 1855 (1). Vasco M. Tanner. Great Basin Nat., Provo, vol.1, no.2, pp.33-62, Jan. 28, 1940.

RESEARCH AS A BASIS FOR WILD LIFE MANAGEMENT IN THE SOUTHWESTERN UNITED STATES. Walter P. Taylor. Jour. Forestry, Washington, vol.28, no.5, pp. 637-643, May, 1930.

LARGER GAME ANIMALS REPORTED IN TALES FROM VARIOUS PARTS OF STATE. Outdoor Indiana, Indianapolis, vol.7, no.7, pp.19, 30, Aug., 1940.

UNITED STATES--ALABAMA

STATUS OF GAME BIRDS AND MAMMALS IN ALABAMA. Frank Selman. Publ.Alabama Cooperative Wildlife Research Unit, Dept. Conservation, Montgomery, pp.38, maps 17, Sep., 1939

GAME INVENTORY OF ALABAMA. Frederick S. Barkalow, Jr. Alabama Dept.Cons., Game, Fish and Seafoods Div., Pittman-Robertson Projects, Montgomery, pp.x-140, figs.66, 1949. (Mammals pp.73-108.)

BIOLOGICAL SURVEY OF ALABAMA. I. PHYSIOGRAPHY AND LIFE ZONES. II. THE MAMMALS. Arthur H. Howell. North Amer. Fauna, no.45, pp.1-88, pls.11, col.zone map, text figs.10, Oct. 28, 1921. (Lists 65 Forms of Mammals from the State.)

THE SIZE AND VALUE OF ALABAMA FUR CROP. Earl F. Kennamer. Jour. Wildl. Mgt., Ithaca, vol.18, no.4, p.539, Oct., 1954.

VALUE OF FURBEARERS IN ALABAMA. Earl F. Kennamer. Master's thesis, Ala. Poly.Inst., 1952.

WILD FURBEARER AND ECONOMIC IMPORTANCE IN ALABAMA. Earl F. Kennamer. Presented at 5th Ann.Meeting, S.E. Assn. Game and Fish Comm., pp.1-4, Oct., 1951.

CAHABA RIVER BASIN. (Wildlife potentialities.) George C. Moore. Alabama Conservation, Montgomery, vol.16, no.9, pp.9, 14, illus., Mar., 1945.

UNITED STATES--ARIZONA

CHECK-LIST OF THE MAMMALS OF THE BOULDER DAM NATIONAL RECREATIONAL AREA. Gordon C. Baldwin. U.S. Dept. Interior, National Park Service, Lake Mead National Recreational Area, Boulder City, Nevada, pp.7, 1944?

VERTEBRATE FOSSILS AND THEIR ENCLOSING DEPOSITS FROM THE SHORE OF PLEISTOCENE LAKE COCHISE, ARIZONA. Kirk Bryan, J.W. Gidley. Amer. Jour. Sci., vol.11, pp.477-488, June, 1926.

ADDITIONAL NOTES ON THE MAMMALS OF SOUTHERN ARIZONA. William Henry Burt. Jour. Mamm., vol.14, no.2, pp.114-122, May, 1933.

MAMMALS OF THE CHIRICAHUA MOUNTAINS. COCHISE COUNTY, ARIZONA. Victor H. Cahalane. Jour. Mamm., vol. 20, no.4, pp.418-440, Nov., 1939.

TRAP-REMOVAL CENSUS STUDY OF SMALL MAMMALS. (A Kill-Trapping Study of Rodents in 3 Habitats in Southeastern Arizona.) Victor H. Cahalane. Jour. Wildl. Mgt., vol.5, no.1, pp.42-67, Jan., 1941.

RECENT MAMMALS OF ARIZONA: THEIR TAXONOMY AND DISTRIBUTION. E. Cockrum. Tucson, Univ. of Arizona Press, pp. viii-276, maps, 1960.

ECOLOGICAL STUDIES OF ARIZONA MAMMALS. Lee R. Dice. Carnegie Inst., Year Book no.31, pp.298-299, Dec.9, 1932.

SYSTEMATIC STUDY OF A COLLECTION OF MAMMALS FROM SOUTHERN ARIZONA. J. Kenneth Doutt. Ann.Carnegie Mus., vol.23, pp.241-274, pls.27-38, Aug.4, 1934.

MAMMALS OF THE NAVAJO COUNTRY. Theodore Hildreth Eaton. Berkeley, Nat. Youth Administration, pp.46, 1937.

LATE CENOZOIC VERTEBRATE FAUNAS FROM THE SAN PEDRO VALLEY, ARIZONA. C. Lewis Gazin. Proc. U.S.Nat. Mus., vol.92, no.3155, pp.475-518, figs. 39-47, pls.42-43, Dec. 10, 1942.

FOSSIL PROBOSCIDAE AND EDENTATA OF THE SAN PEDRO VALLEY, ARIZONA. James W. Gidley. U.S. Geol. Surv., prof. paper 140-B, pp.83-95, illus., 1926.

PRELIMINARY REPORT ON FOSSIL VERTEBRATES OF THE SAN PEDRO VALLEY, ARIZONA. (With Descriptions of New Species of Rodentia and Lagomorpha.) James W. Gidley. U.S. Geol. Sur., prof. paper 131-E, pp.119-128, pls.2, Dec. 26, 1922.

MEMORIES OF THE ARIZONA GAME COUNTRY AS I KNEW IT. C.E. Gilham. Arizona Wildlife and Sportsman, Tucson, vol.6, no.10, pp.5, 20, Aug., 1945.

FIVE NEW MAMMALS FROM ARIZONA AND COLORADO. E.A. Goldman. Proc. Biol. Soc., Washington, vol.31, pp.21-26, May 16, 1918.

NEW MAMMALS FROM ARIZONA, NEW MEXICO, AND COLORADO. E.A. Goldman. Jour. Washington Acad. Sci., vol. 23, no.10, pp.463-473, Oct. 15, 1933.

ACCOUNT OF THE MAMMALS AND BIRDS OF THE LOWER COLORADO VALLEY, WITH ESPECIAL REFERENCE TO THE DISTRIBUTIONAL PROBLEMS PRESENTED. Joseph Grinnell. Berkeley, Univ. of California Press, Publications in Zoology, vol.12, no.4, pp.51-294, diagrs., pls.3-13, pls., map, 1914. (Contribution from the Museum of Vertebrate Zoology of the University of California.)

GAME-LIVESTOCK RELATIONSHIP STUDIES IN ARIZONA. John M. Hall. Proc.32nd Ann.Conf. Western Assn.State Game and Fish Comm., Glacier Nat.Park, Mont., June 15-17, 1952, pp.86-89, 1953.

FISH AND WILDLIFE SERVICE REFUGES IN SOUTHWESTERN ARIZONA. Arthur H. Halloran. Arizona Wildl. and Sportsman, Tucson, vol.6, no.13, pp.8-9, 13, Dec., 1945.

MAMMALS FROM SOUTH-CENTRAL ARIZONA. Donald M. Hatfield. Bull. Chicago Acad. Sci., vol.6, no.8, pp.143-157, figs. 8, Jan.12, 1942.

MAMMALS OF THE GRAHAM (PINALENO) MOUNTAINS, ARIZONA. Donald F. Hoffmeister. Amer. Midland Nat., vol.55, no. 2, pp.257-288, Apr., 1956.

OBSERVATIONS ON MAMMALS IN SOUTHEASTERN ARIZONA. Donald F. Hoffmeister. Nat. Hist. Misc., Chicago Acad. Sci., no.129, p.1, Feb. 1, 1954.

MAMMALS OF THE HUACHUCA MOUNTAINS, SOUTHEASTERN ARIZONA. Donald F. Hoffmeister, Woodrow W. Goodpaster. Illinois Biol.Monographs, Univ. Illinois, Urbana, vol.24, no.1, pp. 1-152, illus., Dec. 31, 1954.

DESCRIPTIONS OF NEW MAMMALS FROM ARIZONA AND SONORA, MEXICO. Laurence M. Huey. Trans. San Diego Soc.Nat. Hist., vol.8, no.25, pp.349-360, pl.23, June 15, 1937.

VERTEBRATE FAUNAL SURVEY OF THE ORGAN PIPE CACTUS NATIONAL MONUMENT, ARIZONA. Laurence M. Huey. Trans. San Diego Soc. Nat. Hist., vol.9, no.32, pp.353-376, Feb. 17, 1942.

WILDLIFE IN THE WHITE MOUNTAINS OF ARIZONA IN PIONEER DAYS. Sylvester Hulsey. Arizona Wildl. and Sportsman, Safford, vol.6, no.5, pp.6, 10, illus., May, 1944.

DESCRIPTION OF SUPPOSED NEW SPECIES AND SUBSPECIES OF MAMMALS FROM ARIZONA. Edgar A. Mearns. Bull. Amer. Mus. Nat. Hist., New York, vol.2, no.4, art.20, pp.277-307, Feb. 21, 1890.

LIFE HISTORY NOTES ON THE BANNER-TAILED KANGAROO RAT, MERRIAM'S KANGAROO RAT, AND THE WHITE-THROATED WOOD RAT IN ARIZONA AND NEW MEXICO. Gale Monson, Wayne Kessler. Jour. Wildl.Mgt., vol.4, no.1, pp. 37-43, Jan., 1940.

ANCIENT LIFE OF YUMA COUNTY, ARIZONA. Roy L. Moodie. Scientific Monthly, vol.31, no.5, pp.401-407, figs.9, Nov., 1930.

BIOTIC COMMUNITIES OF KAIBAB PLATEAU, ARIZONA. D. Irvin Rasmussen. Ecological Monographs, Durham, vol.11, no.3, pp.229-275, July, 1941.

PRELIMINARY ANNOUNCEMENT OF A NEW MAMMALIAN FOSSIL LOCALITY IN THE PLIOCENE OF ARIZONA. Charles A. Reed. Plateau, Mus. Northern Arizona, vol.22, no.4, pp.75-77, Apr., 1950.

FAUNA OF PAPAGO SPRINGS CAVE, ARIZONA, AND A STUDY OF STOCKOCEROS; WITH THREE NEW ANTILOCAPRINES FROM NEBRASKA AND ARIZONA. Morris

F. Skinner. Bull. Amer. Mus. Nat. Hist., New York, vol.80, art.6, pp.143-220, figs. 19, Nov. 6, 1942.

RESULTS OF A BIOLOGICAL SURVEY OF THE SAN FRANCISCO MOUNTAIN REGION AND DESERT OF THE LITTLE COLORADO, ARIZONA. 5. ANNOTATED LIST OF REPTILES AND BATRACHIANS, WITH DESCRIPTIONS OF NEW SPECIES. Leonhard Stejneger. U.S. Dept.Agric., Div.Ornith. and Mamm., North Amer. Fauna, no.3, pp.136, pls.13, maps 5, Sep.11, 1890.

FAUNAL AREAS OF SOUTHERN ARIZONA: A STUDY IN ANIMAL DISTRIBUTION. Harry S. Swarth. Proc. California Acad. Sci., 4th series, vol.18, no.12, pp.267-383, pls.27-32, Apr. 26, 1929.

PRELIMINARY STUDY OF THE FAUNA OF RAMPART CAVE, ARIZONA. Robert W. Wilson. Carnegie Inst.of Washington Publ., no.530, Contrib.Paleontol., pp.169-185, fig.1, pls.4, Jan. 19, 1942.

REPORT OF ACTIVITIES OF ARIZONA GAME AND FISH COMMISSION, 1941-1942. Arizona Game and Fish Commission; Phoenix, pp.39, illus., 1943.

UNITED STATES--ARKANSAS

MAMMALS OF NORTHWESTERN ARKANSAS. J.D. Black. Jour. Mamm., vol.17, no.1, pp.29-35, Feb., 1936.

CONSERVATION OF WILD ANIMALS IN ARKANSAS. S.C. Dellinger. Arkansas' Natural Resources--their Conservation and Use, Little Rock, pp.289-350, illus., 1942.

NOTES ON ARKANSAS MAMMALS. S.C. Dellinger, J.D. Black. Jour. Mamm., vol. 21, no.2, pp.187-191, May 14, 1940.

NEW MAMMAL RECORDS FOR ARKANSAS. John A. Sealander, Jr. Jour.Mamm., vol.35, no.3, pp.430, Aug. 20, 1954.

PROVISIONAL CHECK-LIST AND KEY TO THE MAMMALS OF ARKANSAS (WITH ANNOTATIONS). John A. Sealander, Jr. Amer. Midland Nat., vol.56, no.2, pp. 257-296, Oct., 1956.

UNITED STATES--ATLANTIC COAST

WILDLIFE OF THE ATLANTIC COAST SALT MARSHES. W.L. McAtee. U.S. Dept.Agric., Bureau of Biol.Survey, Wildlife Research and Management Leaflet, no.BS-17, pp. 22, (Mammals pp.20-21) Sep., 1935; U.S. Dept. Agric. Circ., no. 520, pp.28, figs.10, pls.1-6, Mar., 1939.

VERTEBRATE LIFE OF OKEFINOKEE SWAMP IN RELATION TO THE ATLANTIC COASTAL PLAIN. A.H. Wright. Ecology, vol.7, pp.77-95, pls.2-6, Jan., 1926.

UNITED STATES--CALIFORNIA

Extinct and Fossil Mammals

FAUNA OF THE MERYCHIPPUS ZONE, NORTH COALINGA DISTRICT, CALIFORNIA. Francis D. Bode. Publ.453, Carnegie Inst. Washington (Contrib.Paleont.), pp. 65-96, figs.10, pls.2, July 20, 1935.

NEW MAMMALIAN FAUNAS FROM MIOCENE SEDIMENTS NEAR TEHACHAPI PASS IN THE SOUTHERN SIERRA NEVADA. John P. Buwalda. Univ. Calif., Bull. Dept. of Geol., vol.10, no.6, pp.75-85, 1916.

NEW MIOCENE MAMMALIAN FAUNA FROM CALIENTE MOUNTAIN, CALIFORNIA. Jack F. Dougherty. Carnegie Inst. Washington, Publ. no.514, pp.109-143, pls. 7, June 27, 1940.

EXTINCT VERTEBRATE FAUNAS OF THE BADLANDS OF BAUTISTA CREEK AND SAN TIMOTEO CAÑON, SOUTHERN CALIFORNIA. Childs Frick. Univ. California Pub.Geol., vol.12, no.5, pp.277-424, pls. 43-50, figs.165, Dec. 28, 1921.

TERTIARY MAMMALIAN FAUNA FROM THE UPPER CUYAMA DRAINAGE BASIN, CALIFORNIA. Charles L. Gazin. Bull. Geol. Soc. America, vol.41, no.1, p.214, Mar., 1930. (Abstract.) Carnegie Inst. Washington, publ.no.404, pp.55-76, figs. 1-5, pls.1-4, 1930.

RODENTS AND LAGOMORPHS FROM THE BARSTOW BEDS OF SOUTHERN CALIFORNIA. E. Raymond Hall. Univ. Calif.Publ., Bull. Dept. Geol.Sci., vol.19, no.13, pp. 313-318, figs.7, Nov. 25, 1930.

MIOCENE VERTEBRATES IN KERN CO., CALIFORNIA. G. Dallas Hanna. Science, vol.61, pp.71-72, Jan. 16, 1925.

TERTIARY MAMMALIAN FAUNA FROM THE AVAWATZ MOUNTAINS, SAN BERNARDINO COUNTY, CALIFORNIA. Paul C. Henshaw. Carnegie Inst.Wash., Publ.no.514, pp.1-30, figs.3, pls.6, May 18, 1939.

STRATIGRAPHY OF THE EASTERNMOST VENTURA BASIN, CALIFORNIA, WITH A DESCRIPTION OF A NEW MIOCENE MAMMALIAN FAUNA FROM THE TICK CANYON FORMATION. Richard H. Jahns. Carnegie Inst. Washington, Publ.no.514, pp.145-194, figs.9, pls.3, June 27, 1940.

PELAGIC MAMMALS FROM THE TEMBLOR FORMATION OF THE KERN RIVER REGION, CALIFORNIA. R. Kellogg. Proc. Calif.Acad.Sci., ser.4, vol.19, no.12, pp. 217-397, Jan.30, 1931.

VAQUEROS FORMATION, LOWER MIOCENE OF CALIFORNIA. I. PALEONTOLOGY. (Occurrence of Fossil Pelagic Mammals.) Wayne Loel, W.H.Corey. Univ. Calif. Publ., Bull.Dept.Geol.Sci., vol. 22, no.3, pp.31-410, pls.4-65, maps 2, Dec. 31, 1932.

NOTES ON THE GEOLOGIC SECTION NEAR COLUMBIA, CALIFORNIA, WITH SPECIAL REFERENCE TO THE OCCURRENCE OF FOSSILS IN THE AURIFEROUS GRAVELS. George D. Louderback.Carnegie Inst., Washington, Publ.no.440, pp.9-14, Mar., 1934.

PINNIPEDS AND A SEA OTTER FROM THE POINT MUGU SHELL MOUND OF CALIFORNIA. Gretchen M. Lyon. Publs.Univ. Calif., Los Angeles, Biol.Sci., vol.1, no. 8, pp.133-168, figs.11, Mar. 23, 1937.

SOME MARINE MAMMALS FROM A SOUTHERN CALIFORNIA SHELLMOUND. Gretchen M. Lyon. Jour. Mamm., vol.16, no.2, pp.151-152, May, 1935.

FAUNA FROM THE TYPE LOCALITY OF THE MONTEREY SERIES IN CALIFORNIA. Bruce Martin. Berkeley, Univ. of Calif., Publ. Bull. of the Dept. of Geol., vol.7, no.7, pp.143-150, 1912.

ASPHALT GROUP OF FOSSIL SKELETONS. THE TAR-PITS OF RANCHO-LA-BREA, CALIFORNIA. W.D. Matthew. Amer. Mus. Jour., New York, vol.13, pp.290-298, illus., Nov., 1913.

TERTIARY MAMMALIAN FAUNA FROM THE MINT CANYON FORMATION OF SOUTHERN CALIFORNIA. John H. Maxson. Bull. Geol.Soc. America, vol.41, no.1, pp.214-215, Mar., 1930. (Abstract.) Contrib. to Paleontology, Carnegie Inst. Washington, Publ.no.404, pp.77-112, figs. 18, Aug., 1930.

COLLECTION OF MAMMALIAN REMAINS FROM TERTIARY BEDS OF THE MOHAVE DESERT. John C. Merriam. Berkeley, Univ. of Calif. Publ., Bull.of the Dept.of Geol., vol.6, no.7, pp.167-169, pl.29, 1911.

FAUNA OF RANCHO LA BREA. John C. Merriam. Mem. Univ. Calif., vol.1, no.2, pp.199-213, fig.1, pls.5, 1911.

MAMMALIAN REMAINS FROM THE CHANAC FORMATION OF THE TEJON HILLS, CALIFORNIA. John C. Merriam. Berkeley, Univ. of Calif. Publ., Bull. of the Dept. of Geol., vol.10, no.8, pp.111-127, illus., 1916.

NEW MAMMALIA FROM RANCHO LA BREA. John C. Merriam. Berkeley, Univ. of Calif. Publ., Bull. of the Dept. of Geol., vol.5, no.25, pp.391-395, 1910.

PECULIAR HORN OR ANTLER FROM THE MOHAVE MIOCENE OF CALIFORNIA. John C. Merriam. Univ.Calif.Publ., Bull. of the Dept. of Geol., vol.7, no.16, pp.335-339, figs.4, Sep. 19, 1913.

REMAINS OF LAND MAMMALS FROM MARINE TERTIARY BEDS IN THE TEJON HILLS, CALIFORNIA. John C. Merriam. Berkeley, Univ. of Calif. Publ., Bull. of the Dept. of Geol., vol.8, no.18, 1915.

TERTIARY MAMMALIAN FAUNAS OF THE MOHAVE DESERT. John C. Merriam. Univ. of Calif. Publ., Bull. Dept. of Geol., vol. 11, no.5, pp.436a-437e, 438-585, figs.253, 1919.

VERTEBRATE FAUNA OF THE ORINDAN AND SIESTAN BEDS IN MIDDLE CALIFORNIA. John C. Merriam. Univ. Calif. Publ., Bull. of the Dept. of Zool., vol.7, no.19, pp.373-385, figs.9, June 28, 1913.

OCCURRENCE OF PLEISTOCENE VERTEBRATES IN AN ASPHALT DEPOSIT NEAR McKITTRICK, CALIF. John C. Merriam, Chester Stock. Science, n.s., vol.54, pp. 566-567, Dec. 9, 1921.

TERTIARY MAMMALS FROM THE AURIFEROUS GRAVELS NEAR COLUMBIA, CALIFORNIA. John C. Merriam, Chester Stock. Contrib. to Paleont., Carnegie Inst. Washington, Publ.no.440, pp.1-6, figs.2, Nov. 15, 1933.

OCCURRENCE OF LATE PLEISTOCENE MAMMALS IN THE SAN FRANCISCO PENINSULA. Frank E. Peabody. Jour. Paleontol., vol.19, no.1, pp.60-63, fig. 1, Jan., 1945.

VERTEBRATE FAUNA FROM A NEW PLIOCENE FORMATION IN NORTHERN CALIFORNIA. R.D. Russell, V.L.Vander Hoof. Univ.Calif.Publ., Bull.Dept.Geol.Sci., vol.20, no.2,pp.11-21, figs.7, Feb.5,1931.

LATE CENOZOIC VERTEBRATES OF THE SAN FRANCISCO BAY REGION. Donald E. Savage. Univ.Calif.Publ., Bull.Dept.Geol. Sci., vol.28, no.10, pp.215-314, figs.51, Mar.23, 1951.

NONMARINE LOWER PLIOCENE SEDIMENTS IN CALIFORNIA. (Geochronologic-stratigraphic classification.) Donald E. Savage. Berkeley, Univ.Calif.Publ., Bull. Geol.Sci., vol.31, no.1, pp.26, illus., maps, 1955. (A Contribution from the Univ. of Calif. Mus. of Paleontology.)

CENOZOIC LAND LIFE OF SOUTHERN CALIFORNIA. Donald E. Savage, Theodore Downs. Geol. of S. Calif., Chapter 3, Historical Geol., Bull.170, State of Calif. Dept.Nat.Resources, pp.43-58, illus., 1954.

LATE CENOZOIC VERTEBRATE FAUNA FROM THE COSO MOUNTAINS, INYO COUNTY, CALIFORNIA. John R.Schultz. Carnegie Inst.Washington, Publ.487, pp. 75-109, figs.5, pls.8, Sep. 25, 1937.

LATE QUATERNARY MAMMAL FAUNA FROM THE TAR SEEPS OF McKITTRICK, CALIFORNIA. John R. Schultz. Carnegie Inst.Washington, Publ.487 (Contrib.Palaeon.) pp.113-215, figs.12, tbls.28, pls.1-17, July 6, 1938.

NEW MAMMALIA FROM THE QUATERNARY CAVES OF CALIFORNIA. William J. Sinclair. Univ.Calif.Publ., Berkeley, Bull.Dept.Geol., vol.4, no.7, pp.145-161, pls.19-23, July, 1905.

EXTINCT ANIMALS OF CALIFORNIA. Charles H. Sternberg. Scientific America, vol.139, pp.225-227, illus., Sep., 1928.

CENOZOIC MAMMAL REMAINS FROM THE SAN FRANCISCO BAY REGION. R.A.Stirton. Univ.Calif.Publ., Berkeley, Bull.Dept. Geol., Sci., vol.24, no.13, pp.339-410, figs. 95, tbl.1, July 26, 1939.

IRVINGTON PLEISTOCENE FAUNA FROM CALIFORNIA. R.A. Stirton. Proc. Geol. Soc. America for 1937, p.297, June, 1938. (Abstract.)

SIGNIFICANCE OF TERTIARY MAMMALIAN FAUNAS IN HOLARCTIC CORRELATION WITH ESPECIAL REFERENCE TO THE PLIOCENE IN CALIFORNIA. R.A.

Stirton. Jour. Paleont., Menasha, Wisc., vol.13, no.1, pp.130-137, figs.2, Jan., 1939.

FOSSIL VERTEBRATES FROM THE SUPERJACENT DEPOSITS NEAR KNIGHTS FERRY, CALIFORNIA. R.A. Stirton, H.F. Goeriz. Univ. Calif. Publ., Berkeley, Bull. Dept. Geol., Sci., vol.26, no.5, pp.447-472, figs.8, July 21, 1942.

ADDITIONS TO THE MAMMALIAN FAUNA FROM THE TECUYA BEDS, CALIFORNIA. Chester Stock. Contrib.to Paleont., Carnegie Inst. Washington, Publ.no.418, no.IV, pp. 87-92, pl.1, Aug.3, 1932.

CANID AND PROBOSCIDEAN REMAINS FROM THE RICARDO DEPOSITS, MOHAVE DESERT, CALIFORNIA. Chester Stock. Contrib. Paleont., Carnegie Inst. Washington, Publ.no.393, pp.39-47, fig.1, pls.4, Sep., 1928 (Oct.24, 1928).

CENSUS OF THE PLEISTOCENE MAMMALS OF RANCHO LA BREA, BASED ON THE COLLECTIONS OF THE LOS ANGELES MUSEUM. Chester Stock. Jour. Mamm., vol.10, no.4, pp.281-289, Nov., 1929.

DEEP-WELL RECORD OF FOSSIL MAMMAL REMAINS IN CALIFORNIA. Chester Stock. Bull. Assoc. Petroleum Geol., vol. 19, no.7, pp.1064-1068, figs.2, July, 1933.

EARLY TERTIARY VERTEBRATE FAUNA FROM THE SOUTHERN COAST RANGES OF CALIFORNIA. Chester Stock. Univ. Calif. Publ., Berkeley, Bull. Dept. Geol., vol.12, no.4, pp.267-276, illus., map, 1920.

FINDING OF PLEISTOCENE MATERIAL IN AN ASPAHLT PIT AT CARPINTERIA, CALIFORNIA. PLEISTOCENE FAUNA AND FLORA. Chester Stock. Science, n.s., vol.64, pp.155-156, Aug. 12, 1927.

MAMMALIAN FAUNA FROM THE TITUS CANYON FORMATION CALIF. Chester Stock. Carnegie Inst. Wash., Publ.no.584, pp.229-244, figs.4, pls.3, June 22, 1949.

MICROSYOPSINAE AND HYOPSODONTIDAE IN THE SESPE UPPER EOCENE, CALIFORNIA. Chester Stock. Proc. Nat. Acad. Sci., vol.20, no.6, pp.349-354, pl.1, June 15, 1934.

PLEISTOCENE FAUNA OF HAWVER CAVE. Chester Stock. Univ. Calif. Publ., Berkeley, Bull. Dept. Geol., vol.10, no.24, pp.461-515, illus., 1918.

RANCHO LA BREA; A RECORD OF PLEISTOCENE LIFE IN CALIFORNIA. Chester Stock. Los Angeles Mus. of Hist., Sci. and Art, California, Publ.no.1, Science Ser.no.1, Paleontology no.1, pp.11-82, illus., diagrs., 1930; 5th Ed., Los Angeles County Mus., Sci. Series, no.15, Paleontology, no. 9, pp.81, illus., diagrs., 1953.

SIGNIFICANCE OF ABRADED AND WEATHERED MAMMALIAN REMAINS FROM RANCHO LA BREA. Chester Stock. Bull. Southern Calif., Acad. Sci., vol.28, no.1, pp.1-5, pls.2, 1929.

TARSID PRIMATE AND A MIXODECTID FROM THE POWAY EOCENE, CALIFORNIA. Chester Stock. Proc. Nat. Acad. Sci. Washington, vol.24, no.7, pp.288-293, pl.1, July, 1938.

UPPER EOCENE MAMMALS FROM THE SESPE, NORTH OF THE SIMI VALLEY, CALIFORNIA. Chester Stock. Bull. Geol. Soc. America, vol.44, no.1, p.158, Feb. 28, 1933. (Abstract.)

UPPER OLIGOCENE MAMMALIAN FAUNA FROM SOUTHERN CALIFORNIA. Chester Stock. Proc. Nat. Acad. Sci., vol.18, no. 8, pp.550-554, figs.2, Aug., 1932.

UPPER OLIGOCENE MAMMALIAN FAUNA FROM THE SESPE OF THE LAS POSAS HILLS, CALIFORNIA. Chester Stock. Bull. Geol. Soc. America, vol.44, no.1, p.158, Feb. 28, 1933. (Abstract.)

WHEN TITANS ROAMED PREHISTORIC DEATH VALLEY. Chester Stock. Westways, Los Angeles, vol.28, no.3, pp.28-29, figs., Mar., 1936.

OCCURRENCE OF LOWER OLIGOCENE MAMMAL-BEARING BEDS NEAR DEATH VALLEY, CALIFORNIA. Chester Stock, Francis D. Bode. Proc. Nat. Acad. Sci., Washington, vol.21, no.10, pp.571-579, pls.3, Oct., 1935.

NEW CANID AND RHINOCEROTID REMAINS FROM THE RICHARDO PLIOCENE OF THE MOHAVE DESERT, CALIFORNIA. Chester Stock, E.L. Furlong. Univ. Calif. Publ., Bull. Dept. Geol., vol.16, no.2, pp. 43-60, 1926.

SKULL AND SKELETAL REMAINS OF A RUMINANT OF THE PREPTOCERAS-EUCERATHERIUM GROUP FROM THE McKITTRICK PLEISTOCENE, CALIFORNIA. Chester Stock, E.L. Furlong. Univ. Calif. Publ., Bull. Dept. Geol., vol.16, no. 10, pp.409-434, 1927.

ADDITIONS TO THE FAUNA OF THE TEHAMA UPPER PLIOCENE OF NORTHERN CALIFORNIA. V.L. Vander Hoof. Amer. Jour. Sci., New Haven, vol.25, pp.382-384, May, 1933.

PLIOCENE VERTEBRATE FAUNA FROM SIERRA FOOTHILLS OF CENTRAL CALIFORNIA. V.L. Vander Hoof. Pan-Amer. Geol., vol.59, no.5, p.376, June, 1933.

MIOCENE MARINE MAMMALS FROM THE BAKERSFIELD REGION, CALIFORNIA. Leslie E. Wilson. Peabody Mus. Nat. Hist., Bull., no.4, pp.143, figs.23, Sep. 9, 1935.

NEW MIDDLE PLIOCENE RODENT AND LAGOMORPH FAUNAS FROM OREGON AND CALIFORNIA. Robert W. Wilson. Carnegie Inst. Washington, Publ.no.487, pp.1-19, tbls., pls.1-3, June 30, 1937.

RODENTS AND LAGOMORPHS OF THE LATE TERTIARY AVAWATZ FAUNA, CALIFORNIA. Robert W. Wilson. Carnegie Inst. Washington, Publ.no.514, pp. 31-38, pl.1, May 18, 1939.

ADDITIONAL MATERIAL FROM THE TERTIARY OF THE CUYAMA BASIN OF CALIFORNIA. Albert Elmer Wood. Amer. Jour. Sci., New Haven, ser.5, vol.33, no.193, pp.29-43, figs.21, Jan., 1937.

NOTES ON THE PLEISTOCENE FOSSILS OBTAINED FROM RANCHO LA BREA ASPHALT PITS. L.E. Wyman. Mus. Hist. Sci. Art, Los Angeles, Dept. Nat. Sci., Misc. Publ., no.1, pp.35, figs.22, photo, 1918.

PAPERS CONCERNING THE PALEONTOLOGY OF CALIFORNIA, ARIZONA, AND IDAHO. Washington, Carnegie Inst., Contributions to Paleontology, Publ.no.440, pp.135, illus., maps, pls., 1934.

Recent Mammals

ON MAMMALS FROM THE SANTA CRUZ MOUNTAINS, CALIFORNIA. J.A. Allen. Bull. Amer. Mus. Nat. Hist., vol.8, pp. 263-270, Dec. 4, 1896.

WILDLIFE IN AND NEAR THE VALLEY OF THE MOON. (Sonoma County, California.) H.H. Arnold. Nat. Geogr. Mag., Washington, vol.97, no.3, pp.401-414, illus., Mar., 1950.

MAMMALS OF THE SAN FRANCISCO BAY REGION. William D. Berry, Elizabeth Berry. Univ. Calif. Press, Calif. Nat. Hist. Guides, Berkeley, no.2, pp.70, illus., 1959.

MANAGEMENT OF CHAMISE BRUSHLANDS FOR GAME IN THE NORTH COAST REGION OF CALIFORNIA. H.H. Biswell et al. California Fish and Game, San Francisco, vol.38, no.4, pp.453-383, illus., Oct., 1952.

THREE NEW MAMMALS FROM SALT MARSH AREAS IN SOUTHERN CALIFORNIA. (Sorex ornatus salicornicus, Reithrodontomys megalotis limicola, Microtus californicus stephensi.) Jack C. von Bloeker, Jr. Proc. Biol. Soc. Washington, vol.45, pp. 131-138, Sep. 9, 1932.

SOME ALTITUDE RECORDS FOR MAMMALS IN THE INYO-WHITE MOUNTAINS OF CALIFORNIA. B.P. Bole, Jr. Jour. Mamm., vol.19, no.2, pp.245-246, May 14, 1938.

SEA LIONS, SEALS AND SEA OTTER OF THE CALIFORNIA COAST. Paul Bonnot. California Fish and Game, vol.37, no.4, pp.371-389, Oct., 1951.

SALTON SEA REGION, CALIFORNIA. J.S. Brown. U.S.G.S. Water-supply Paper no. 497, 1923. (Fauna pp.19-21.)

CALIFORNIA'S FUR BEARING MAMMALS. Harold C. Bryant. California Fish and Game, vol.1, no.3, pp.12, figs.27-28, Apr. 10, 1915.

OUTDOOR HERITAGE. Harold C. Bryant. San Francisco, Los Angelos, Chicago, Powell Publ.Co., vol.8, pp.465, illus.14, 1929.

VERTEBRATE FAUNA OF THE SAN JOAQUIN EXPERIMENTAL RANGE. Henry E. Childs, Jr., Walter E. Howard. Misc. Paper Calif. Forest and Range Exper. Sta., vol.19, pp.1-20, Feb., 1955.

(PORT SAN FRANCISCO AND HIS INHABITANTS.) Port San-Francisco et ses habitants. L. Choris. (In) Voyage pittoresque autour du monde, Paris, pp.1-10, pls.1-14, 1822.

CONTRIBUTIONS FROM THE LOS ANGELES MUSEUM-CHANNEL ISLANDS BIOLOGICAL SURVEY. 33. BRIEF NOTES ON THE EXPEDITIONS CONDUCTED BETWEEN MARCH 16, 1940 AND DECEMBER 14, 1941. John A. Comstock. Bull. Southern Calif. Acad. Sci., vol.45, pt.2, pp.94-107, May-Aug., 1946.

LARGE WILD MAMMALS OF CALIFORNIA. A.E. Culbertson. Sci. Guide for Elementary Schools, Calif. State Dept. Education, vol. 5, no.3, pp.1-26, Oct., 1938.

CATALOGUE OF MAMMALS COLLECTED BY E. HELLER IN SOUTHERN CALIFORNIA. D. G. Elliot. Chicago, Field Columbian Mus., Publ.91, Zoological Series, vol. 3, no.16, pp.271-321, pls.39-49, 1904.

LIST OF MAMMALS OBTAINED BY E. HELLER, COLLECTOR FOR THE MUSEUM, FROM THE COAST REGION OF NORTHERN CALIFORNIA AND OREGON. D.G. Elliot. Chicago, Field Columbian Mus., Publ.76, Zoological Series, vol.3, no.11, pp.175-197, 1903.

DENIZENS OF THE NIGHT. Willis A. Evans. Yosemite Nat. Notes, vol.21, no. 2, pp.17-19, Feb., 1942.

BIOLOGICAL SURVEY OF PARTS OF CALIFORNIA, NEVADA, ARIZONA, AND UTAH. PART II. A.K. Fisher. U.S. Dept. Agric., Div. Orinth. and Mamm., North Amer. Fauna, no.7, pp.393, pls.14, maps 5, May 31, 1893.

EARLY FAUNA OF THE MONTEREY REGION, CALIFORNIA. Edna M. Fisher. Jour. Mamm., vol.15, no.3, p.253, Aug., 1934.

EARLY FAUNA OF THE SANTA BARBARA, REGION CALIFORNIA. Edna M. Fisher. Jour. Mamm., vol.11, no.2, pp.223-224, May, 1930.

EARLY FAUNA OF SANTA CRUZ ISLAND, CALIFORNIA. Edna M. Fisher. Jour. Mamm., vol.11, no.1, pp.75-76, Feb., 1930.

GAME IN THE SAN JOAQUIN VALLEY IN 1853. Andrew J. Grayson. California Fish and Game, vol.6, no.3, pp.104-107, July, 1920.

ACCOUNT OF THE MAMMALS AND BIRDS OF THE LOWER COLORADO VALLEY, WITH ESPECIAL REFERENCE TO THE DISTRIBUTIONAL PROBLEMS PRESENTED. Joseph Grinnell. Univ. Calif. Publ., Berkeley, Bull. Dept. Zoology, vol.12, no.4, pp.51-294, diagrs., pls.3-13, fold. map, 1914.

ACCOUNT OF THE BIRDS AND MAMMALS OF THE SAN JACINTO AREA OF SOUTHERN CALIFORNIA WITH REMARKS UPON THE BEHAVIOR OF GEOGRAPHIC RACES OF THE MARGINS OF THEIR HABITATS. Joseph Grinnell, H.S. Swarth. Univ. Calif. Publ., Berkeley, Bull. Dept. Zoology, vol. 10, no.10, pp.197-406, pls.6-10, Oct. 31, 1913.

ANALYSIS OF THE VERTEBRATE FAUNA OF THE TRINITY REGION OF NORTHERN CALIFORNIA. Joseph Grinnell. Univ.Calif. Publ., Berkeley, Bull. Dept.Zoology, vol. 12, no.14, pp.399-410, 1916.

BIOTA OF THE SAN BERNARDINO MOUNTAINS. Joseph Grinnell. Univ.Calif.Publ., Bull.Dept.Zoology, vol.5, no.1, pp.170, pls.24, Dec. 31, 1908.

DISTRIBUTIONAL LIST OF THE MAMMALS OF CALIFORNIA. Joseph Grinnell. Proc. Calif. Acad. Sci., 4th Series, vol. 3, pp.265-390, pls.15, 16, Aug. 28, 1913.

MAMMALS OF DEATH VALLEY. Joseph Grinnell. Proc. Calif. Acad. Sci., 4th Series, vol.23, no.9, pp.115-169, Aug. 7, 1937.

(Review by Harold C. Bryant of) MAMMALS OF DEATH VALLEY. Joseph Grinnell. Jour. Mamm., vol.19, no.3, pp.381-382, Aug., 1938.

REVIEW OF THE RECENT MAMMAL FAUNA OF CALIFORNIA. Joseph Grinnell. Univ. Calif.Publ., Bull. Dept. Zoology, vol.40, no.2, pp.71-234, Sep. 26, 1933.

REVISED LIFE-ZONE MAP OF CALIFORNIA. Joseph Grinnell. Univ.Calif.Publ., Bull. Dept. Zoology, vol.40, no.7, pp.327-330, map 1, Jan. 16, 1935.

SIX NEW MAMMALS FROM THE MOHAVE DESERT AND INYO REGIONS OF CALIFORNIA. Joseph Grinnell. Univ.Calif.Publ., Bull.Dept.Zoology, vol.17, no.14, pp.423-430, tbls.4, Apr.25, 1918.

SYSTEMATIC LIST OF THE MAMMALS OF CALIFORNIA. Joseph Grinnell. Univ. Calif.Publ., Bull. Dept.Zoology, vol.21, no.10, pp.313-324, Jan. 27, 1923.

FUR-BEARING MAMMALS OF CALIFORNIA. THEIR NATURAL HISTORY, SYSTEMATIC STATUS, AND RELATIONS TO MAN. Joseph Grinnell et al. Univ. Calif. Press, Berkeley, vol.1, pp.xii-375, figs. 138, pls.7; vol.2, pp.xiv-377-777, figs. 139-345, pls.8-13, Aug. 16, 1937.

(Review by Richard S. Croker of) FUR-BEARING MAMMALS OF CALIFORNIA. THEIR NATURAL HISTORY, SYSTEMATIC STATUS, AND RELATIONS TO MAN. Joseph Grinnell et al. California Fish and Game, San Francisco, vol.23, no.4, pp.337-338, Oct., 1937.

VERTEBRATE NATURAL HISTORY OF A SECTION OF NORTHERN CALIFORNIA THROUGH THE LASSEN PEAK REGION. Joseph Grinnell et al. Univ. Calif. Publ., Bull.Dept.Zoology, vol.35, pp.v-594, figs.181, Oct., 1930.

LIFE-ZONE INDICATORS IN CALIFORNIA. Joseph Grinnell, Harvey Monroe Hall. Proc. Calif. Acad. Sci., 4th Series, vol.9, no.2, pp.37-67, June 16, 1919.

(Review by Walter P. Taylor of) LIFE-ZONE INDICATORS IN CALIFORNIA. Joseph Grinnell, Harvey Monroe Hall. Jour.Mamm., vol.1, no.5, p.245, Nov., 1920.

DIAGNOSES OF SEVEN NEW MAMMALS FROM EAST-CENTRAL CALIFORNIA. Joseph Grinnell, Tracy I. Storer. Univ.Calif. Publ., Bull.Dept.Zoology, vol.17, no.1, p.8, fig.1, Aug. 23, 1916.

PROFESSOR OSBORN ON THE MAMMALS AND THE BIRDS OF THE CALIFORNIA TAR POOLS. Oliver P. Hay. Science, n.s., vol.64, pp.426-427, Oct. 29, 1926.

HOST-PARASITE-DISEASE RELATIONSHIPS IN A MAMMALIAN COMMUNITY IN THE CENTRAL COAST RANGE OF CALIFORNIA. R. Holdenried et al.Ecol. Monogr., Durham, vol.21, pp.1-18, illus., Jan., 1951.

SOME CALIFORNIA WILDLIFE-FOREST RELATIONSHIPS. E.E. Horn. U.S.Bur. Biol.Surv., Wildl.Research and Mgt.Leaflet, no.BS-132, pp.1-5, Apr., 1939.

CORRECTED TYPE LOCALITIES OF SOME CALIFORNIA MAMMALS. A. Brazier Howell. Jour. Mamm., vol.4, no.4, p.266, Nov. 1, 1923.

MAMMALS OF MAMMOTH, MONO COUNTY, CALIFORNIA. A. Brazier Howell. Jour. Mamm., vol.5, no.1, pp.25-36, Feb. 9, 1924.

VERTEBRATE ANIMALS OF FRIANT RESERVOIR BASIN WITH SPECIAL REFERENCE TO THE POSSIBLE EFFECTS UPON THEM OF THE FRIANT DAM. Douglass H. Hubbard. California Fish and Game, San Francisco, vol.27, no.4, pp.198-215, illus., Oct., 1941.

SO YOU THINK THAT HALF DOME IS BARREN. (Citellus lateralis, Marmota flaviventris, Neotoma cinerea, Ochotona schisticeps.) Earl L. Hubbs. Yosemite Nat.Notes, vol.28, no.1, pp.6-7, Jan., 1949.

MAMMALS OF CALIFORNIA. Lloyd G. Ingles. Stanford Univ. Press, pp.258, pls. 42, figs.57, 1947; Rev.Ed., Stanford, Calif., Stanford Univ.Press, pp.xiii-396, illus., 1954.

SMALL WILD MAMMALS OF CALIFORNIA. (Key to Genera; Popular Account of Representative Species.) Lloyd G. Ingles. Calif. State Dept.Educ., Sci.Guide for Elem. Schools, vol.3, no.1, pp.44, Aug., 1936.

VERTEBRATE ANIMALS OF THE PROVIDENCE MOUNTAINS AREA OF CALIFORNIA. David H. Johnson et al. Univ. Calif.Publ.in Zool., Berkeley, vol.48, no. 5, pp.217-375, illus., Aug. 20, 1948.

REPORT UPON MAMMALS AND BIRDS FOUND IN PORTIONS OF TRINITY, SISKIYOU AND SHASTA COUNTIES, CALIFORNIA. Louise Kellogg. Univ. Calif. Publ.in Zool., vol.12, no.13, pp. 335-398, pls.15-18, Jan. 27, 1916.

GAME BIRDS AND MAMMALS OF CALIFORNIA; A LABORATORY SYLLABUS. Aldo Starker Leopold. Berkeley, Calif. Book Co., pp.125, 1951.

NOTICE OF A COMMUNICATION CONTAINING NOTES ON THE MAMMALS AND BIRDS OF CALIFORNIA. W. N. Lockington. Proc. Zool. Soc. London, p. 129, 1874.

MAMMALS OF NAPA COUNTY, CALIFORNIA. William M. Longhurst. California Fish and Game, San Francisco, vol.26, no.3, pp.240-270, figs.2, July, 1940.

BIRDS AND MAMMALS OF MODOC COUNTY, CALIFORNIA. GENERAL ACCOUNT OF THE MAMMALS. Joseph Mailliard. Proc. Calif. Acad. Sci., 4th Series, vol. 16, pp.341-359, Apr. 27, 1927.

FIELD WORK AMONG THE BIRDS AND MAMMALS OF THE NORTHERN COAST OF CALIFORNIA IN 1921. Joseph Mailliard. Proc. Calif. Acad. Sci. 4th Series, vol.12, pp.1-26, Jan. 26, 1923.

FURTHER NOTES ON THE BIRDS AND MAMMALS OF SISKIYOU COUNTY, CALIFORNIA. Joseph Mailliard. Proc. Calif. Acad. Sci., 4th Series, vol.13, no. 3, pp.7-28, 1923.

NOTES ON THE BIRDS AND MAMMALS OF SISKIYOU COUNTY, CALIFORNIA. Joseph Mailliard. Proc. Calif. Acad. Sci., 4th Series, vol.11, no.5, pp.73-94, 1921.

FUR BRIGADE TO THE BONAVENTURA. JOHN WORK'S CALIFORNIA EXPEDITION OF 1832-33 FOR THE HUDSON'S BAY COMPANY. Alice Bay Maloney.Calif. Hist.Soc.Quart., San Francisco, vol.22, no.3, pp.193-222, map, Sep., 1943; (continued), vol.22, no.4, pp.323-348, Dec., 1943; vol.23, no.1, pp.19-40, Mar., 1944; vol.23, no.2, pp.123-146, June, 1944.

CALIFORNIA GAME "MARKED DOWN". William B. May. Southern Pacific Co., San Francisco, pp.64, illus., 1896.

HAIR OF CALIFORNIA MAMMALS WITH KEYS TO THE DORSAL GUARD HAIRS OF CALIFORNIA MAMMALS. William V. Mayer. Amer. Midland Nat., vol.48, no.2, pp.480-512, Sep., 1952.

BIOLOGICAL SURVEY OF PARTS OF CALIFORNIA, NEVADA, ARIZONA, AND UTAH. PART II. 7. REPORT ON DESERT CACTUSES AND YUCCAS. C. Hart Merriam. U.S. Dept. Agr., Div. Ornith.and Mamm., North Amer. Fauna, no.7, pp.393, pls. 14, maps 5, May 31, 1893.

DEATH VALLEY EXPEDITION. BIOLOGICAL SURVEY OF PARTS OF CALIFORNIA, NEVADA, ARIZONA, AND UTAH. C. Hart Merriam. North Amer.Fauna, no.7, pp.393, fig.1, pls.14, maps 5, May 31, 1893.

DESCRIPTIONS OF TWO NEW MAMMALS FROM CALIFORNIA. (Sciuropterus oregonensis stephensi, Procyon pallidus.) C. Hart Merriam. Proc. Biol.Soc.Washington, vol.13, pp.151-152, June 13, 1900.

RESULTS OF A BIOLOGICAL SURVEY OF MOUNT SHASTA, CALIFORNIA. C.Hart Merriam. U.S.Dept.Agric., Div.Biol.Surv., N.Amer.Fauna, no.16, pp.9-179, figs.46, pls.5, Oct. 28, 1899.

VERTEBRATE INHABITANTS OF THE PINON ASSOCIATION IN THE DEATH VALLEY REGION. Alden H. Miller. Ecology, Brooklyn, vol.27, no.1, pp.54-60, Jan., 1946.

PART 4. ZOOLOGICAL REPORT, NO.2. REPORT UPON THE ZOOLOGY OF THE ROUTE. CHAP.1. REPORT UPON THE MAMMALS. (pp.35-72, pls.1, 3, 29). ROUTES IN CALIFORNIA AND OREGON EXPLORED BY LIEUT. R.S. WILLIAMSON, CORPS TOPOGRAPH. ENGINEERS, AND LIEUT. HENRY L. ABBOT, CORPS TOPOGRAPH. ENG. IN 1855. J.S. Newberry. Reports Expl. and Surv.R.R.Route from Mississippi River to Pacific Ocean, 1854-1855, vol.6, 1857.

TRAPPING CENSUS REPORT 1938. INYO NATIONAL FOREST. Reed S. Nielson. U.S.Dept.Agric., Forest Service, Region 5, Leaflet 49-W-3, pp.5, Aug., 1938.

EARLY RECORDS OF CALIFORNIAN MAMMALS. Robert T. Orr. Jour. Mamm., vol. 31, no.3, p.362, Aug. 21, 1950.

MAMMALS OF LAKE TAHOE. Robert T. Orr. California Acad. Sci., San Francisco, pp.127, illus., Mar. 15, 1949.

(Review by Gordon L. Bolander of) MAMMALS OF LAKE TAHOE. Robert T. Orr. California Fish and Game, San Francisco, vol.35, no.4, p.334, Oct., 1949.

MAMMALS OF MOUNT TAMALPAIS. Robert T. Orr. Reprinted from Tamalpais--Enchanted Mountain, Roxburgh Club of San Francisco, 1946.

MAMMALS AND BIRDS OF THE CALIFORNIA TAR POOLS. Henry Fairfield Osborn. Nat. Hist., vol.25, no.6, pp.527-543, col.pl., Nov.-Dec., 1925 (Jan., 1926).

BIOLOGICAL SURVEY OF PARTS OF CALIFORNIA, NEVADA, ARIZONA, AND UTAH. PART II. 8. LIST OF LOCALITIES (pp.361-384.) T.S. Palmer. U.S. Dept.Agric., Div. Ornith. and Mamm., North Amer.Fauna, no.7, pp.393, pls.15, maps 5, May 31, 1893.

FRIENDS THAT COME IN THE NIGHT. (Jumping Mouse and Spotted Skunks.) Jeannette Parkinson. Yosemite Nature Notes, vol.7, p.106, Dec., 1928.

REPORT ON THE BIOTA OF THE SANTA ANA MOUNTAINS. Willis E. Pequegnat. Jour. Entom. and Zool., Claremont, vol. 27, no.4, pp.85-96, 1946.

CALIFORNIA'S MAMMALS--PAST AND PRESENT. Edward A. Preble. Nature Mag., vol.12, pp.259-261, 275, illus., Oct., 1928.

NOTES ON A COLLECTION OF MAMMALS FROM THE SIERRA NEVADA MOUNTAINS. W.W. Price. Zoe, vol.4, no.4, pp.315-332, Dec. 21, 1893.

MAMMALS OF THE SAN FRANCISCO MOUNTAIN REGION, NO.2. Charles W. Quaintance. Northern Arizona Soc.Sci. and Art, Inc., vol.7, no.9, pp.37-40, Mar., 1935.

NOTES FROM A RANGER'S DIARY. (Bear, Marmot, Porcupine, Cony, Pine Marten, Weasel, Deer.) Clyde E. Quick. Yosemite Nature Notes, vol.24, no.11, pp.109-111, illus., Nov., 1945.

PLANT SUCCESSION ON BURNED CHAPAR RAL LANDS IN NORTHERN CALIFORNIA. Arthur W. Sampson. Univ. Calif.Agric. Exper.Sta., Berkeley, Bull.865, pp.1-144, figs.46, 1944.

ANNOTATED LIST OF THE MAMMALS OF SAN DIEGO COUNTY, CALIFORNIA. F. Stephens. Trans. San Diego Soc. Nat. Hist., vol.3, no.3, pp.41-56, Apr. 20, 1921.

CALIFORNIA MAMMALS. F. Stephens. San Diego, Calif., The West Coast Publ. Co., West Coast Nature Series, pp.351, illus., pls., map, 1906.

DESCRIPTIONS OF TWO NEW MAMMALS FROM SOUTHERN CALIFORNIA. F. Stephens. Proc. Biol.Soc. Washington, vol. 13, p.153, June 13, 1900.

LAND MAMMALS OF SAN DIEGO COUNTY, CALIFORNIA. F. Stephens. West American Scientist, vol.7, whole no.52, pp.36-39, Aug., 1890.

NOTES ON A COLLECTION OF CALIFORNIA MAMMALS. Witmer Stone. Proc.Acad. Nat.Sci., Philadelphia, pp.586-591, July, 1904.

ON A COLLECTION OF BIRDS AND MAMMALS FROM MOUNT SANHEDRIN, CALIFORNIA, WITH FIELD NOTES BY A. S. BUNNELL. Witmer Stone. Proc. Acad. Nat.Hist.Sci., Philadelphia, pp.576-585, July, 1904.

ECONOMIC EFFECTS OF INTRODUCING ALIEN ANIMALS INTO CALIFORNIA. Tracy I. Storer. Reprint from Proc. 5th Pacific Science Congress, Vancouver, vol. 1, pp.779-784, 1933.

FACTORS INFLUENCING WILD LIFE IN CALIFORNIA, PAST AND PRESENT. Tracy I. Storer. Ecology, vol.13, no.4, pp.315-327, Oct., 1932.

BIRDS AND MAMMALS OF THE SIERRA NEVADA; WITH RECORDS FROM SEQUOIA AND KINGS CANYON NATIONAL PARKS. Lowell Sumner, Joseph S.Dixon. Univ.Calif.Press, Berkeley, pp. xvii-484, illus.(part.col.), fold.maps, 1953.(Prepared Under the Auspices of the National Park Service, U.S.Dept.Interior.)

(Review by E.W. Jameson of) BIRDS AND MAMMALS OF THE SIERRA NEVADA; WITH RECORDS FROM SEQUOIA AND KINGS CANYON NATIONAL PARKS. Lowell Sumner, Joseph S. Dixon. Jour. Mamm., vol.34, no.4, pp.519-520, Nov. 13, 1954.

NOTES ON MAMMALS COLLECTED PRINCIPALLY IN WASHINGTON AND CALIFORNIA BETWEEN THE YEARS 1853 AND 1874 BY DR. JAMES GRAHAM COOPER. Walter P. Taylor. San Francisco, Proc.Calif.Acad.Sci., 4th Series, vol.9, no.3, pp.69-121, 1919. (Printed from the John W.Hendric Publ.Endowment.)

SYNOPSIS OF THE RECENT CAMPAIGN FOR THE CONSERVATION OF WILD LIFE IN CALIFORNIA. Walter P.Taylor. The Condor, vol.15, pp.125-128, May, 1913.

FIELD NOTES ON THE MAMMALS, BIRDS AND REPTILES OF NORTHERN CALIFORNIA. Charles Haskins Townsend. U.S. Nat.Mus., Proc., Washington, vol.10, pp. 159-241, illus., pls.5, tbls., 1888.

FUR CATCH IN CALIFORNIA, 1940-1941. Howard Twining. California Fish and Game, San Francisco, vol.30, no.4, pp.242-246, Oct., 1944.

MAMMALS OF THE SAN GABRIEL MOUNTAINS OF CALIFORNIA. Terry A. Vaughan. Univ.Kansas, Mus.Nat.Hist., vol.7, no.9, pp.513-582, illus., Nov. 15, 1954.

FAUNAL CHANGES IN LOS ANGELES COUNTY. George Willett. Los Angeles County Mus. Quart., vol.1, no.4, pp. 19-23, illus., Oct., 1941.

MAMMALS OF LOS ANGELES COUNTY, CALIFORNIA. George Willett. Los Angeles County Mus., Sci.Ser., no.9, (Zool.no.4), pp.34, Oct., 1944.

TWO RODENTS AND A LAGOMORPH FROM THE SESPE OF THE LAS POSAS HILLS, CALIFORNIA. Robert W. Wilson.Carnegie Inst. Washington, Publ.453, pp.11-17, fig. 1, pl.1, July 14, 1934.

NATURE NOTELET. (Chickaree and Weasel.) E.K. Wolfe. Yosemite Nat.Notes, Yosemite, vol.20, no.11, p.99, Nov., 1941.

UNITED STATES--COLORADO

LIST OF MAMMALS COLLECTED BY MR. CHARLES P. ROWLEY IN THE SAN JUAN REGION COLORADO, NEW MEXICO AND UTAH, WITH DESCRIPTIONS OF NEW SPECIES. J.A. Allen. Amer. Mus.Nat. Hist., New York, Bull., vol.5, pp.69-84, 1893.

MAMMALS OF COLORADO. J.A. Allen. Science, n.s., vol.32, no.814, pp.178-179, 1910.

MAMMALS OF THE GRAND MESA, COLORADO. Sydney Anderson. Kansas, Univ., Mus.Nat.Hist., Publ., vol.9, no.16, pp. 405-414, map, 1959.

MAMMALS OF MESA VERDE NATIONAL PARK, COLORADO. Sydney Anderson.Univ. of Kansas, Lawrence, Univ.Mus.Nat.Hist., Publ., vol.14, no.3, pp.29-67, pls.2, maps, 1961.

HIGH COUNTRY OF COLORADO. (Wildlife.) Alfred M. Bailey. Nat. Geogr.Mag., Wash., vol.90, no.1, pp.43-72, illus., col.pls.12, July, 1946.

HUNTING SEASON OF 1806. (Game Killed by Pike's Expedition in Colorado.) Richard G. Beidleman. Colorado Outdoors Mag., vol.6, no.2, pp. 26-30, Mar.-Apr., 1957.

MANAGEMENT OF FUR RESOURCES IN COLORADO. E.K. Brown. Proc. Ann.Conf. W. Assn.State Game and Fish Comm., vol. 30, pp.105-108, 1950?

BIOLOGICAL SURVEY OF COLORADO. Merritt Cary. U.S. Dept. Agric., Bur. Biol.Surv., N.Amer.Fauna, no.33, pp. 256, figs.39, Aug. 17, 1911.

ZOOLOGY IN COLORADO. Theodore D.A. Cockerell. Univ.Colorado Semicentennial Series, vol.3, pp.7-262, illus., Boulder, Colorado, Univ.of Colorado, Aug., 1927. (Mammals pp.15-55; Resume of Both Fossil and Recent Mammals of Colorado.)

OCCURRENCE OF MAMMOTH AND GIANT BISON IN GLACIAL MORAINES IN THE HIGH MOUNTAINS OF COLORADO. Harold J. Cook. Science, vol.72, no.1855, p.68, July 18, 1930.

COLORADO'S 1949 BIG GAME WINTER FEEDING BY AIR. Jack Culbreath.Colorado Conserv. Comments, Denver, vol.10, no. 9, pp.7-8, 30, illus., Mar., 1949.

SMALL MAMMALS OF MOUNT SANITAS, COLORADO. Norman Wester Dondelinger. MA thesis, Univ.Colorado, 1941.

MAMMALS OF THE NAVAJO COUNTRY. Theodore Hildreth Eaten. Berkeley, National Youth Administration, pp.46, 1937.

ZOOGEOGRAPHY OF THE MONTANE MAMMALS OF COLORADO. James S. Findley, Sydney Anderson. Jour. Mamm., vol.37, no. 1, pp.80-82, Feb., 1956.

NOTES ON THE MAMMALS OF THE GOTHIC REGION, GUNNISON COUNTY, COLORADO. James S. Findley, Norman C.Negus. Jour. Mamm., vol.34, no.2, pp.235-239, May, 1953.

NOTIOSOREX CRAWFORDI AND ANTROZOUS PALLIDIS FROM SOUTHEASTERN COLORADO. Robert B. Finley, Jr. Jour. Mamm., vol.35, no.1, pp.110-111, Feb. 10, 1954.

CONTRIBUTION TO THE TERTIARY GEOLOGY AND PALEONTOLOGY OF NORTHEASTERN COLORADO. Edwin C. Galbreath. Univ.Kansas Paleont.Contrib.Vertebrata, art.4, pp.1-120, pls.2, figs.26, Mar., 1953.

PALEOCENE MAMMALS FROM THE DENVER BASIN, COLORADO. C.Lewis Gazin. Jour. Washington Acad.Sci., Menasha, vol. 31, no.7, pp.289-295, figs.2, July 15, 1941.

BLACK CANYON OF THE GUNNISON RIVER. Russell K. Grater. Nature Notes, Peoria, Ill., vol.6, no.6, pp.124-128, June, 1939.

ACCOUNT OF THE MAMMALS AND BIRDS OF THE LOWER COLORADO VALLEY. J.Grinnell. Univ.Calif.Pub.Zool., vol.12, no.4, pp.51-294, illus., Mar.20, 1914.

(Review by N.Hollister of) ACCOUNT OF THE MAMMALS AND BIRDS OF THE LOWER COLORADO VALLEY WITH ESPECIAL REFERENCE TO THE DISTRIBUTIONAL PROBLEMS PRESENTED. J.Grinnell. Naturwissenschaften, vol.2, p.721, July 17, 1914.

GREEN BOOK OF COLORADO, 1947--A LEGAL HANDBOOK FOR THE STOCKMAN. Billie Hallen. Denver, H.E.Green, pp.370, 1947.

FOSSIL VERTEBRATES COLLECTED NEAR, OR IN ASSOCIATION WITH, HUMAN ARTIFACTS AT LOCALITIES NEAR COLORADO, TEXAS; FREDERICK, OKLAHOMA; AND FOLSOM, NEW MEXICO. Oliver P. Hay, Harold J. Cook. Proc. Colorado Mus.Nat. Hist., vol.9, no.2, pp.40, figs.4, pls.1-14, Oct. 20, 1930.

COLORADO BIG GAME KILL REPORT, 1946-1947. Gilbert N. Hunter. Current Rept. Colorado Dept. Game and Fish, Denver, no. 23, pp.80, maps, 1948.

BIG GAME KILL 1944. Gilbert N. Hunter. Colorado Game and Fish Dept., pp.15, 1945.

"UNCONTROLLED" BIG-GAME HUNTING. Gilbert N. Hunter. Conv.Internat.Assoc. Game, Fish and Cons.Comm., vol.39, pp. 77-83, 1949.

RESUME OF 1945 BIG GAME SEASON. Gilbert N. Hunter. Colorado Cons. Comments, Denver, vol.8, no.4, p.26, Dec. 15, 1945.

BIG GAME MANAGEMENT IN COLORADO. Gilbert N. Hunter, Lee E. Yeager. Jour. Wildl.Mgt., vol.13, no.4, pp.392-411, Oct., 1949.

FOSSIL BIRDS AND MAMMALS OF COLORADO. Harold E. Koerner. Univ.Colorado Studies, vol.18, no.3, pp.163-176, Apr., 1931.

FAUNISTIC STUDY OF MAMMAL DISTRIBUTION IN COLORADO. Robert B. Lewis. MA thesis, Univ.Colorado, 1952.

AGE OF THE FOUR MILE LOCAL FAUNA, NORTHEAST SAND WASH BASIN, COLORADO. Malcolm C. McKenna. Wyoming Geol.Assoc.Guidebook, 10th Ann.Field Conf., pp.105-107, illus., 1955.

EARLIEST EOCENE VERTEBRATES FROM THE SAND WASH BASIN, NORTHWESTERN COLORADO. Malcolm C. McKenna. Guidebook to the Geology of Northwestern Colorado, Joint Field Conf. Intermountain Assoc. Petroleum Geologists and Rocky Mountain Assoc.Geologists, pp.41-43, illus., 1955.

THE GRAY BULL MAMMALS FROM THE KNIGHT FORMATION IN MOFFAT COUNTY, COLORADO. Malcolm C. McKenna. Jour. Mamm., vol.35, no.4, p.581, Nov. 29, 1954.

FOSSIL MAMMALS OF THE TERTIARY OF NORTHEASTERN COLORADO. William Diller Matthew. Amer.Mus.Collection of 1898, New York, Amer.Mus.Nat.Hist., vol.1, pt.7, pp.353-447, illus., pls.,1902?

SKETCH OF THE PISGAH NATIONAL GAME PRESERVE. M.A. Mattoon. Jour.Forestry, Washington, vol.28, no.5, pp.675-678, May, 1930.

COLORADO'S MAMMALS. Frederic W.Miller. Nature Mag., vol.19, no.5, pp.297-299, 322-323, figs.4, May, 1932.

TWO NEW COLORADO MAMMALS. (Conepatus mesoleucus fremonti, Neotoma albigula laplataensis.) Frederic W. Miller.Proc. Colorado Mus.Nat.Hist., vol.12, no.1, pp. 1-2, July 22, 1933.

SURVEY OF 1940 STATEWIDE; RAW FUR CROP. William M. Nemanic. Colorado Game and Fish Dept., Fur Resources Surv., vol.1, pp.i-7, maps, Dec., 1940.

SURVEY OF 1941 STATEWIDE; RAW FUR CROP. William M. Nemanic. Colorado Game and Fish Dept., Fur Resources Surv., vol.2, pp.iv-6, tbls., graphs, Jan., 1942.

HUERFANO LAKE BASIN, SOUTHERN COLORADO, AND ITS WIND RIVER AND BRIDGER FAUNA. Henry Fairfield Osborn. Bull.Amer.Mus.Nat.Hist., New York, vol. 9, art.21, pp.247-258, Oct. 20, 1897.

HOW COLORADO'S BIG GAME CONTRIBUTES TO THE WAR EFFORT. Barry C. Park. Colorado Conserv.Comments, Denver, vol.7, no.2, pp.3-5, June 15, 1944.

EXPEDITION TO WESTERN COLORADO OF THE FIELD COLUMBIAN MUSEUM. Bryan Patterson. Science, Lancaster, Pa., n.s., vol.90, no.2334, p.266, Sep. 22, 1939.

NEW PANTODONTA AND DINOCERATA FROM THE UPPER PALEOCENE OF WESTERN COLORADO. Bryan Patterson. Field Mus. Nat.Hist., Geol.Ser., vol.6, no.24, pp.351-384, figs.100-111, Mar. 24, 1939.

NEW SPECIES OF THE AMBLYPOD TITANOIDES FROM WESTERN COLORADO. (Titanoides faberi.) Bryan Patterson. Amer. Jour.Sci., ser.5, vol.25, no.149, pp.415-425, figs.4, May, 1933.

NOTES ON COLORADO PHENACOMYS AND PIKAS. William O. Pruitt, Jr. Jour.Mamm., vol.35, no.3, pp.450-452, Aug. 20, 1954.

FUR BEARERS OF COLORADO. Jack D. Remington. Colorado Game and Fish Dept., Educ. Pam., no.4, pp.1-18, illus., 1953.

FURTHER INVESTIGATIONS AT A FOLSOM CAMP SITE IN NORTHERN COLORADO. Frank H.H. Roberts, Jr. Explor. and Field-Work Smiths.Inst.in 1935, publ. 3382, pp.69-74, figs.74-79, Apr. 20, 1936.

GUIDE TO THE MAMMALS OF COLORADO. H.G. Rodeck. Leaflet Univ.Colorado Mus., Boulder, no.10, pp.72, Sep., 1952.

(Review by Jean Dorst of) GUIDE TO THE MAMMALS OF COLORADO. H.G. Rodeck. Mammalia, Paris, vol.17, no.2, p.127, June, 1953.

SOREX MERRIAMI AND MICROTUS MEXICANUS IN COLORADO. H.G. Rodeck. Jour. Mamm., vol.37, no.3, p.436, Sep. 11, 1956.

WILDLIFE OF MESA VERDE NATIONAL PARK. Keneth I. Ross. Colorado Conserv. Comments, Denver, vol.8, no.1, p.3, Mar. 15, 1945.

DEER-ELK-BEAR INVESTIGATIONS. L. W. Searle. Quart.Progress Rept., Game Mgt. Div., Federal Aid Section, Colorado Dept. Game and Fish, pp.25-59, figs.17, 1949.

VERTEBRATE LOCALITIES IN SOUTH PARK, COLORADO. J.T. Stark et al. Science, n.s., vol.83, no.2153, pp.327-328, Apr. 3, 1936.

RELATION OF THE UNCOMPAHGRE IN COLORADO TO PUBLIC LAND USE. T.R. Swem. Colorado Conserv.Comments, Denver, vol.7, no.2, pp.5-7, June 15, 1944.

ADDITIONAL NOTES ON THE DISTRIBUTION OF COLORADO MAMMALS. Edward R. Warren. Proc.Biol.Soc.Washington, vol. 26, pp.9-11, Jan. 18, 1913.

FURTHER NOTES ON THE MAMMALS OF COLORADO. Edward R. Warren. Colorado Coll.Publ., vol.1, no.4, ser.no.33, pp. 59-90, Jan., 1908.

LITTLE MOUNTAINEERS IN FUR. (Popular Account of Some Colorado Mammals.) Edward R. Warren. Trail and Timberline, Denver, no.117, pp.2-3, July, 1928.

MAMMALS OF COLORADO. Edward R. Warren. Colorado Coll.Publ., Gen.Ser. no.19, vol.11, Sci.Ser.no.46, pp.225-274, Jan., 1906.

MAMMALS OF COLORADO. AN ACCOUNT OF THE SEVERAL SPECIES FOUND WITHIN THE BOUNDARIES OF THE STATE, TOGETHER WITH A RECORD OF THEIR HABITS AND THEIR DISTRIBUTION. Edward R. Warren. New York, Putnam, pp. xxxiv-300, illus., fold.maps 3, 1910. 2d rev.ed., Norman, Univ. of Oklahoma Press, pp.xviii-330, pls., 1942.

NOTES ON THE DISTRIBUTION OF SOME COLORADO MAMMALS. Edward R. Warren. Proc. Biol.Soc.Washington, vol.25, pp.3-8, Jan.23, 1912.

SMALL MAMMALS OF COLORADO. Edward R. Warren. Colorado Mountain Club, pub.no.7, pp.31, figs.21, June, 1921.

DISTRIBUTION OF MICE AND SHREWS IN A COLORADO MONTANE FOREST. Olwen William. Jour. Mamm., vol.36, no.2, pp.221-231, illus., May, 1955.

SURVEY OF THE COLORADO FUR RESOURCE. Lee E. Yeager et al. Game Management Div., Colorado Game and Fish Dept., rept.25, pp.ix-67, figs.16, Sep., 1949.

SURVEY OF THE COLORADO FUR RESOURCES AND RESULTANT MANAGEMENT IMPLICATIONS. Lee E. Yeager, E.K. Brown. Proc. Ann. Conf. W.Assoc. State Game and Fish Comm., vol.29, pp. 189-195, 1949?

WILD FURS, AN ECONOMIC ASSET IN COLORADO. Lee E. Yeager. Colorado Cons., pp.7-10, Mar., 1951.

NOTES ON THE DISTRIBUTION OF COLORADO MAMMALS, WITH A DESCRIPTION OF A NEW SPECIES OF BAT (EPTESICUS PALLIDUS) FROM BOULDER. Robert T. Young. Acad.Nat.Sci. Philadelphia, Proc., vol.60, pp.403-409, 1909.

COLORADO GAME AND FISH DEPARTMENT BIENNIAL REPORT, 1941-1943. Colorado Game and Fish Comm. Colorado Conserv.Comments, Denver, vol. 7, no.1, pp.23-29, Mar. 15, 1944.

1947 BIG GAME SEASON NEARLY UP TO 1946 ALL TIME RECORD. Colorado Conserv.Comments, vol.10, no.4, pp.17-18, 26, Dec., 1947.

## UNITED STATES--CONNECTICUT

MAMMALS OF CONNECTICUT. George G. Goodwin. State of Connecticut, State Geol. and Nat.Hist.Surv., Hartford, Bull.53, pp. 221, figs.19, pls.33, 1935.

(Review by A. Brazier Howell of) MAMMALS OF CONNECTICUT. George G.Goodwin. Jour. Mamm., vol.17, no.2, p.177, May, 1936.

NEW RECORDS AND SOME OBSERVATIONS ON CONNECTICUT MAMMALS. George G. Goodwin. Jour. Mamm., vol. 13, no.1, pp.36-40, Feb., 1932.

NOTES ON THE MAMMALS OF THE VICINITY OF STAMFORD, CONNECTICUT, PAST AND PRESENT. Paul Griswold Howes. The Oologist, Albion, N.Y., vol.54, no. 12, pp.146-171, Dec., 1937.

STRANGERS IN OUR MIDST. QUIETLY AND UNOBTRUSIVELY, A SURPRISING NUMBER OF FORMS OF ANIMAL LIFE HAVE BEEN EXTENDING THEIR RANGES INTO CONNECTICUT. Paul Griswold Howes. Animal Kingdom, New York, vol.45, no.4, pp.84-90, illus., Aug. 4, 1942.

## UNITED STATES--FLORIDA

### Extinct and Fossil Mammals

TWO PLEISTOCENE MAMMALIAN FAUNAS FROM ALACHUA COUNTY, FLORIDA. Robert S. Bader. Bull. Florida State Mus., Biol.Sci., vol.2, no.5, pp.53-75, 1957.

FOSSIL MAN AND PLEISTOCENE VERTEBRATES IN FLORIDA. Wythe Cooke. Amer. Jour.Sci., vol.12, pp.441-452, Nov., 1926.

ANNOTATED LIST OF FOSSIL MAMMALIA ASSOCIATED WITH HUMAN REMAINS AT MELBOURNE, FLORIDA. Lewis C. Gazin. Jour. Washington Acad. Sci., vol. 40, no.12, pp.397-404, Dec. 22, 1950.

DESCRIPTIONS OF SOME MAMMALIAN AND FISH REMAINS FROM FLORIDA OF PROBABLY PLEISTOCENE AGE. Oliver P. Hay. Proc. U.S.Nat.Mus., vol.56, pp.103-112, pls.3, Mar.15, 1920.

ON THE GEOLOGICAL AGE OF THE PLEISTOCENE FOUND AT VERO AND MELBOURNE, FLORIDA. (Mentions Several Species of Fossil Mammals.) Oliver P. Hay. Jour.Washington Acad.Sci., vol.16, pp.387-392, Aug. 19, 1926.

QUATERNARY DEPOSITS AT VERO, FLORIDA, AND THE VERTEBRATE REMAINS CONTAINED THEREIN. Oliver P. Hay. Jour. Geol., Chicago, vol.25, no.1, pp.52-55, Jan.-Feb., 1917.

REMARKS ON DR. GEORGE G. SIMPSON'S WORK ON THE PLEISTOCENE PALEONTOLOGY OF FLORIDA. Oliver P. Hay. Jour. Washington Acad.Sci., vol.20, no.14, pp. 331-340, Aug. 19, 1930.

VERTEBRATA MOSTLY FROM STRATUM NO. 3, AT VERO, FLORIDA, TOGETHER WITH DESCRIPTIONS OF NEW SPECIES. Oliver P. Hay. 9th Ann.Rept., Florida State Geol.Surv., pp.43-68, pl.3, 1917.

BIRDS AND MAMMALS FROM THE PLEISTOCENE OF WILLISTON, FLORIDA. J. Alan Holman. Gainesville, Univ.Florida, State Mus., Bull., Biological Sciences, vol. 5, no.1, pp.24, illus., tbls., 1959.

ANIMAL REMAINS FROM FOUR PRECERAMIC SITES IN FLORIDA. W.T.Neill et al. Amer. Antiquity, vol.21, no.4, pp. 383-395, Apr., 1956.

ADDITIONS TO THE PLEISTOCENE MAMMALIAN FAUNA FROM MELBOURNE, FLORIDA. Clayton E. Ray. Cambridge, Bull.Mus.Comparative Zool. at Harvard College, vol.119, no.7, pp.419-449, illus., 1958.

LIST, BIBLIOGRAPHY, AND INDEX OF THE FOSSIL VERTEBRATES OF FLORIDA. Clayton E. Ray. Special Publ. Florida Geol. Surv., Tallahassee, no.3, pp.1-175, 1957.

FOSSIL MAMMALS OF THOMAS FARM, GILCHRIST COUNTY, FLORIDA. Alfred Sherwood Romer. Quart.Jour.Florida Acad. Sci., Gainesville, vol.10, no.1, pp.1-11, Mar., 1948.

HUMAN REMAINS AND ASSOCIATED FOSSILS FROM THE PLEISTOCENE OF FLORIDA. E.H. Sellards. 8th Ann.Rept.Florida State Geol.Surv., pp.121-160, figs.15, pls. 15-31, 1916.

ON THE ASSOCIATION OF HUMAN REMAINS AND EXTINCT VERTEBRATES AT VERO, FLORIDA. E.H. Sellards. Jour. Geol., Chicago, vol.25, no.1, pp.4-24, figs.4, Jan.-Feb., 1917.

LIST AND BIBLIOGRAPHY OF THE MAMMALS OF FLORIDA, LIVING AND EXTINCT. H.B. Sherman. Quart.Jour.Florida Acad.Sci., vol.15, no.2, pp.86-126, June, 1952.

ADDITIONS TO THE PLEISTOCENE OF FLORIDA. George Gaylord Simpson. Amer. Mus.Nov., no.406, pp.14, figs.7, Mar.17, 1930.

EXTINCT LAND MAMMALS OF FLORIDA. George Gaylord Simpson. 20th Ann.Rept. Florida State Geol.Surv., pp.229-279, illus., 1929.

HUNTING EXTINCT ANIMALS IN FLORIDA. DIFFICULT SCIENCE OF FINDING THE REMAINS OF ANIMALS OF AGES LONG PAST, AND THE RECONSTRUCTION OF PICTURES OF THOSE AGES. George Gaylord Simpson. Nat.Hist., New York, vol.29, no.5, pp.506-518, illus., Sep.-Oct., 1929.

MIOCENE LAND MAMMALS FROM FLORIDA. George Gaylord Simpson. Bull.10, Florida State Geol.Surv., Tallahassee, pp. 7-41, figs.23, 1932.

PLEISTOCENE MAMMALIAN FAUNA OF THE SEMINOLE FIELD, PINELLAS COUNTY, FLORIDA. George Gaylord Simpson. Bull.Amer.Mus.Nat.Hist., vol.56, no. 8, pp.561-599, figs.22, Feb.19, 1929.

PLEISTOCENE MAMMALS FROM A CAVE IN CITRUS COUNTY, FLORIDA. George Gaylord Simpson. Amer. Mus.Nov., no. 328, pp.1-16, figs.11, Oct. 26, 1928.

TERTIARY LAND MAMMALS OF FLORIDA. George Gaylord Simpson. Bull.Amer. Mus.Nat.Hist., vol.59, pp.149-211, figs. 31, June 5, 1930.

PLEISTOCENE EXPLORATION AND FOSSIL EDENTATES IN FLORIDA. George Gaylord Simpson, Walter W. Holmes. Bull. Amer. Mus. Nat. Hist., New York, vol.59, art.7, pp.383-418, figs.21, June 13, 1931.

MIOCENE VERTEBRATES FROM FLORIDA. MIOCENE LAND MAMMALS FROM FLORIDA. George Gaylord Simpson. NEW HETEROMYID RODENTS FROM THE MIOCENE OF FLORIDA. Albert Elmer Wood. APHELOPS FROM THE HAWTHORN FORMATION OF FLORIDA. Edwin H. Colbert. Tallahassee, Published for the State Geol. Surv., Bull.10, pp.58, illus., 1932.

ADDITIONS TO THE FAUNA OF THE FLORIDA PLIOCENE. Theodore E. White. Proc. New England Zool. Club, Cambridge, vol. 18, pp.67-70, pls.10-12, Sep. 9, 1941.

ADDITIONS TO THE MIOCENE FAUNA OF FLORIDA. Theodore E. White. Proc. New England Zool. Club, Cambridge, vol.18, pp.91-98, Oct. 4, 1941.

ADDITIONS TO THE MIOCENE FAUNA OF NORTH FLORIDA. Theodore E. White. Bull. Mus. Comp. Zool., Cambridge, vol.99, no. 4, pp.497-515, illus., 1947.

LOWER MIOCENE MAMMAL FAUNA OF FLORIDA. Theodore E. White. Bull. Mus. Comp. Zool., Cambridge, vol.92, no.1, pp.1-49, pls.1-14, Nov., 1942.

Recent Mammals

MAMMALS OF FLORIDA. J.A. Allen. Amer. Nat., vol.33, pp.433-436, June, 1898.

ON THE MAMMALS AND WINTER BIRDS OF EAST FLORIDA, WITH AN EXAMINATION OF CERTAIN ASSUMED CHARACTERS IN BIRDS, AND A SKETCH OF THE BIRD-FAUNA OF EASTERN NORTH AMERICA. J.A. Allen. Bull. Mus. Comp. Zool., vol.2, pp.161-450, pls.8, 1870-71.

CORRECTING INACCURATE RANGES OF CERTAIN FLORIDA MAMMALS AND OTHERS OF VIRGINIA AND THE CAROLINAS. Harold H. Bailey. The Bailey Mus and Library Nat. Hist., Miami, Bull. 5, pp.4, Dec. 1, 1930.

LAND MAMMALS OF PENINSULAR FLORIDA AND THE COAST REGION OF GEORGIA. Outram Bangs. Proc. Boston Soc. Nat. Hist., vol.28, no.7, pp.157-235, Mar., 1898.

THAT VANISHING EDEN. NATURALIST'S FLORIDA. Thomas Barbour. Little, Brown and Co., Boston, pp.x-250, illus., 1944.

MAMMALS OF A NORTH FLORIDA FLATWOODS. Burness Austin Barrington, Jr. PhD thesis, Univ. Florida, 1949.

ECOLOGICAL CROSS-SECTION OF THE LOWER PART OF FLORIDA BASED LARGELY UPON ITS MOLLUSCAN FAUNA. Paul Bartsch. Excerpt from Report of Comm. Paleoecology, 1936-1937, National Research Council, Div. Geol. and Geog., Washington, pp.11-25, 1936-1937.

WILDLIFE OF EVERGLADES NATIONAL PARK. Daniel B. Beard. Nat. Geogr. Mag., Washington, vol. 95, no.1, pp.83-116, illus., Jan., 1949.

MAMMALS OF A FLORIDA HAMMOCK. W. Frank Blair. Jour. Mamm., vol. 16, no.4, pp.271-277, map, Nov., 1935.

SOME MAMMALS OF SOUTHERN FLORIDA. W. Frank Blair. Amer. Midland Nat., Notre Dame, vol.16, no.5, pp.801-804, Sep., 1935.

EVERGLADES--YESTERDAY, TODAY AND TOMORROW. Victor H. Cahalane. Nat. Mag., Washington, vol.40, no.10, pp.513-517, 550, illus., Dec., 1947.

DESCRIPTION OF TWO RACES OF MAMMALS FROM FLORIDA, WITH REMARKS ON SITOMYS NIVEIVENTRIS CHAPMAN. Frank Michler Chapman. Amer. Mus. Nat. Hist., New York, Bull., vol.5, pp.339-341, 1893.

REMARKS ON CERTAIN LAND MAMMALS FROM FLORIDA, WITH A LIST OF THE SPECIES KNOWN TO OCCUR IN THE STATE. Frank Michler Chapman. Amer. Mus. Nat. Hist., New York, Bull., vol.6, pp.333-346, 1894.

HUNTING AND FISHING IN FLORIDA, INCLUDING A KEY TO THE WATER BIRDS KNOWN TO OCCUR IN THE STATE. C.B. Cory. 2nd ed., Boston, Estes and Lauriat, pp.304, illus., pl., 1896.

A LIST OF MAMMALS OBTAINED BY T. SURBER, IN NORTH AND SOUTH CAROLINA, GEORGIA AND FLORIDA. D.G. Elliott. Field Col. Mus., Publ.58, Zool. Ser., vol.3, no.4, pp.31-57, pls.5-10, June, 1901.

INDIAN KEY BIRD REFUGES OF TAMPA BAY, FLORIDA. William G. Fargo. Florida Naturalist, vol.3, no.1, pp.1-10, illus., Oct., 1929. (Mammals p.9.)

NOTES ON SOME MAMMALS OF LEE COUNTY, FLORIDA. W.J. Hamilton, Jr. Amer. Midland Nat., Notre Dame, vol. 25, no.3, pp.686-691, fig.1, May, 1941.

NATURAL RESOURCES OF SOUTHERN FLORIDA. Roland M. Harper. Florida State Geol. Surv., 18th Ann. Rept., pp.25-206, figs.2-58, 1927. (Mammals pp.143-144.)

DESCRIPTIONS OF FIVE NEW MAMMALS FROM FLORIDA. Arthur H. Howell. Jour. Mamm., vol.20, no.3, pp. 363-365, Aug. 14, 1939.

FLORIDA'S MAMMALS. Arthur H. Howell. Nature Mag., vol.14, no.6, pp.338-340, 378-379, fig.9, Dec., 1929.

MAMMALS, EXCLUDING BATS, OF PALM VALLEY, FLORIDA. R.D. Ivey. MS thesis, Univ. Florida, 1947.

CATALOGUE OF THE MAMMALS OF FLORIDA, WITH NOTES ON THEIR HABITS, DISTRIBUTION, ETC. C.J. Maynard. Bull. Essex Inst., vol.4, nos.9-10, pp.1-16, 1872.

BIOLOGICAL FIELD WORK IN FLORIDA. Gerrit S. Miller, Jr. Misc. Coll., Smiths. Inst., publ.2912, vol.78, no.7, pp.67-71, figs.72-77, Apr. 21, 1927.

MAMMALS OF THE FLORIDA KEYS. Gerrit S. Miller, Jr. Explor. and Field Work, Smiths. Inst. in 1935, publ.3382, pp.19-22, figs.17-22, Apr. 20, 1936.

DISTRIBUTION OF MARINE MAMMALS TO FLORIDA WATERS. Joseph C. Moore. Amer Midland Nat., Notre Dame, vol.49, no.1, pp.117-158, Jan., 1953.

MAMMALS FROM WELAKA, PUTNAM COUNTY, FLORIDA. Joseph C. Moore. Jour. Mamm., vol.27, no.1, pp.49-59, fig.1, Mar. 14, 1946.

PUTNAM COUNTY AND OTHER FLORIDA MAMMAL NOTES. Joseph C. Moore. Jour. Mamm., Baltimore, vol.30, no.1, pp.57-66, illus., Feb.14, 1949.

SURVEY OF THE MAMMALS OF THE UNIVERSITY OF FLORIDA CONSERVATION RESERVE. Joseph C. Moore. MS thesis, Univ. Florida, 1942; Jour. Mamm., vol.27, p.49, 1946.

GUIDE TO FLORIDA ANIMALS. William Alphonso Murrill. Published by the Author, Gainesville, Florida, pp.93, 1945.

MAMMALS OF GULF HAMMOCK, LEVY COUNTY, FLORIDA. Paul G. Pearson. Amer. Midland Nat., vol.51, no.2, pp. 468-480, map, Apr., 1954.

MAMMALS OF THE NORTH FLORIDA SWAMP. G.H. Pournelle. Jour. Mamm., vol.31, no.3, pp.310-319, fig.1, Aug.21, 1950.

MAMMALS OF A SWAMP REGION NEAR GAINESVILLE, FLORIDA. G.H. Pournelle. MS thesis, Univ. Florida, 1947.

NOTES ON MAMMALS OF ANASTASIA ISLAND, ST. JOHNS COUNTY, FLORIDA. G.H. Pournelle, B.A. Barrington. Jour. Mamm., vol.34, no.1, pp.133-135, Feb. 19, 1953.

TWO NEW MAMMAL RECORDS FROM THE VICINITY OF WELAKA, PUTNAM COUNTY, FLORIDA. G.H. Pournelle. Jour. Mamm., vol.31, no.3, pp.361-362, Aug. 21, 1950.

RESULTS OF THE ARCHBOLD EXPEDITIONS. NO. 45. MAMMAL NOTES FROM HIGHLAND COUNTY, FLORIDA. A.L. Rand, Per Host. Bull. Amer. Mus. Nat. Hist., New York, vol.80, art.1, pp.21, fig.1, Aug. 12, 1942.

CONTRIBUTIONS TO THE MAMMALOGY OF FLORIDA. Samuel N. Rhoads. Proc. Acad. Nat. Sciences, Philadelphia, pp. 152-161, 1894.

NATURAL HISTORY OF PARADISE KEY AND THE NEARBY EVERGLADES OF FLORIDA. W.E. Safford. Ann. Rep. Smiths. Inst., for 1917, pp.377-434, pls.1-64, figs., 1919. (Brief Account of Mammals pp.423-424.)

LAND MAMMALS OF SOUTHERN FLORIDA AND THE UPPER FLORIDA KEYS. Albert Schwartz. PhD thesis, Univ. Mich., pp.189, 1952.

GENERAL BIOTIC RELATIONS OF THE FLORIDA MAMMAL FAUNA. H.B. Sherman. Quart. Jour. Florida Acad. Sci., vol.20, no.3, pp.149-173, 1957.

LIST OF THE RECENT LAND MAMMALS OF FLORIDA. H.B. Sherman. Proc. Florida Acad. Sci. 1936, vol.1, pp.102-128, 1936.

NOTES ON SOME FLORIDA MAMMALS. H.B. Sherman. Jour. Mamm., vol.10, no. 3, pp.258-259, Aug., 1929.

RECENT LITERATURE AND SOME NEW DISTRIBUTION RECORDS CONCERNING FLORIDA MAMMALS. H.B. Sherman. Proc. Florida Acad. Sci., Gainesville, vol.7, nos.2-3, pp.199-202, 1944 (1945).

NEW MIOCENE VERTEBRATES FROM FLORIDA. Theodore E. White. Proc. New England Zool. Club, Cambridge, vol.18, pp.31-38, June 22, 1940.

EVERGLADES NATIONAL PARK. Jour. Mamm., vol.17, no.3, p.297, Aug., 1936.

UNITED STATES--GEORGIA

DIARY OF A JOURNEY THROUGH THE CAROLINAS, GEORGIA, AND FLORIDA FROM JULY 1, 1765 TO APRIL 10, 1766. John Bartram. Trans. Amer. Philos. Soc., Philadelphia, n.s., vol.33, pt.1, pp.iv-120, pls.22, Dec., 1942.

TRAVELS IN GEORGIA AND FLORIDA, 1773-74, A REPORT TO DR. JOHN FOTHERGILL. William Bartram. Trans. Amer. Philos. Soc., Philadelphia, n.s., vol.33, pt.2, pp. 121-242, pls.26, Nov., 1943.

MAMMAL NOTES FROM RANDOLPH COUNTY, GEORGIA. Francis Harper. Jour. Mamm., vol.10, no.1, pp.84-85, Feb.11, 1929.

MAMMALS OF THE OKEFINOKEE SWAMP REGION OF GEORGIA. Francis Harper. Proc. Boston Soc. Nat. Hist., vol.38, no.7, pp.191-396, pls.4-7, Mar., 1927.

OKEFINOKEE SWAMP AS A RESERVATION. (Contains a Few Notes on Mammals.) Francis Harper. Nat. Hist., vol.20, pp.28-41, Jan.-Feb., 1920.

TALES OF THE OKEFINOKEE. Francis Harper. American Speech, vol.1, pp.407-420, May, 1926.

FORTY-FIVE YEARS WITH THE OKEFENOKEE SWAMP 1900-1945. John M. Hopkins. Bull. Georgia Soc. Naturalists, Atlanta, no.4, pp.5-1-69, photos 24, 1947? (Pelts of Fur-Bearers p.43; Bear and Deer p.58.)

AMPHIBIANS AND REPTILES OF A FIFTEEN-ACRE TRACT IN GEORGIA. (Some Mammals Mentioned.) Wilfred T. Neill. Amer. Midland Nat., Notre Dame, vol.45, no.1, pp.241-244, Jan., 1951.

NOTES ON MAMMALS OF THOMAS COUNTY, GEORGIA, WITH TWO STATE RECORDS. W.B. Quay. Jour. Mamm., Baltimore, vol.30, no.1, pp.66-68, Feb. 14, 1949.

OKEFENOKEE, A NATIONAL WILDLIFE REFUGE. J. Clar Salyer, II, Frank Dufresne. U.S. Dept. Interior, Conserv. in Action, no. 6, pp.10, illus., 1948.

HABITATS AND COMPOSITION OF THE VEGETATION OF OKEFINOKEE SWAMP, GEORGIA. A.H. Wright, A.A. Wright. Ecological Monographs, vol.2, no.2, pp. 109-232, figs.75, Apr., 1932.

UNITED STATES--GRAND CANYON REGION

SCIENTIST DESCRIBES VISIT TO UNKNOWN ISLAND IN THE SKY. PLATEAU IN GRAND CANYON NEVER BEFORE VISITED BY WHITE MAN CONTAINS WILD LIFE ISOLATED FROM THEIR KIND. Harold E. Anthony. Sci. News Letter, vol.32, no.862, pp.245-247, figs.3, Oct. 16, 1937.

MAMMALS OF THE GRAND CANYON REGION. Vernon Bailey. Grand Canyon Nat. Hist.Assoc., Nat.Hist. Bull., no.1, pp. 42, illus., June, 1935.

STATUS OF BIG GAME IN GRAND CANYON NATIONAL PARK. H.C. Bryant. Arizona Wildlife and Sportsman, Tucson, vol.6, no. 9, p.11, July, 1945.

FOSSIL FOOTPRINTS FROM THE GRAND CANYON. Charles Whitney Gilmore. Smiths. Inst., Misc.Coll., Washington, vol.77, no. 9; vol.80, nos.3-8, illus., pls., 1926-28.

MAMMALS NEW TO GRAND CANYON NATIONAL PARK, ARIZONA. Donald F. Hoffmeister. Plateau, Mus.Northern Arizona, vol.28, no.1, pp.1-7, July, 1955.

(GRAND CANYON: A BARRIER TO LIFE.) Grand Canyon: Eine Schranke des Lebens. Edwin McKee. Natur und Volk, vol.65, no.1, pp.23-27, figs.1-3, Jan., 1935.

PRELIMINARY CHECK LIST OF MAMMALS, GRAND CANYON. Edwin McKee. U.S.Dept. Interior, Nat. Park Service, pp.11, 1929? (Mimeographed.)

UNITES STATES--GREAT LAKES REGION

MAMMALS OF THE GREAT LAKES REGION. William Henry Burt. Univ. Michigan Press, Ann Arbor, pp.xv-246, figs.54, maps 77, May 31, 1957.

FISH AND GAME IN THE SUPERIOR. C.A. Dahlgren. Parks and Recreation, vol.7, no. 6, pp.629-634, July-Aug., 1924.

KITCHEN MIDDENS WITH BONES OF EXTINCT ANIMALS IN THE UPPER LAKES AREA. Samuel Eddy, Albert E.Jenks. Sciences, n.s., vol.81, no.2109, p.535, May 31, 1935.

ISLAND LIFE: A STUDY OF THE LAND VERTEBRATES OF THE ISLANDS OF EASTERN LAKE MICHIGAN. Robert T. Hatt et al. Bull. Cranbrook Inst.Sci., Bloomfield Hills, Michigan, no.27, pp.xi-179, figs.43, map 1, tbls.15, June 30, 1948.

(Review by Richard H. Manville of) ISLAND LIFE: A STUDY OF THE LAND VERTEBRATES OF THE ISLANDS OF EASTERN LAKE MICHIGAN. Robert T. Hatt et al. Jour. Mamm., Baltimore, vol.30, no.2, pp.203-204, May 23, 1949.

MAMMALS OF THE LAKE STATES. Edward Allen Hyer. Nature Mag., vol.15, no. 5, pp.302-304, 340-341, figs.12, May, 1930.

MAMMAL BONES FROM DUNES SOUTH OF LAKE MICHIGAN. A.L. Rand, S. Stanley. Amer. Midland Nat., Notre Dame, vol.46, no.3, pp.649-659, Nov., 1951.

EXTINCT AND ENDANGERED MAMMALS AND BIRDS OF THE UPPER GREAT LAKES REGION. A.W. Shorger. Trans.Wisconsin Acad.Sci., Arts and Letters, Madison, vol. 34, pp.23-44, 1942.

WILD LIFE OF LAKE SUPERIOR, PAST AND PRESENT. (Deer, Moose, Wolves, Beavers, and Muskrats.)Geo. Shiras 3rd. Nat.Geog.Mag., vol.40, no.2, pp.114-204, illus.76, Aug., 1921.

RESULTS OF THE MERSHON EXPEDITION TO THE CHARITY ISLANDS, LAKE HURON. N.A. Wood. Michigan Acad.Sci., pp.131-134, 1911.

UNITED STATES--GREAT PLAINS REGION

PROPOSED GREAT PLAINS NATIONAL MONUMENT. Victor H. Cahalane. Sci. Monthly, Lancaster, vol.51, no.2, pp. 125-139, illus., Aug., 1940.

PLEISTOCENE OF THE GREAT PLAINS. INTRODUCTION. Edwin H. Colbert. Bull. Geol.Soc. Amer., Baltimore, vol.59, no. 6, pp.541-542, June, 1948.

BLANCAN AS A TIME TERM IN THE CENTRAL GREAT PLAINS. Maxim K.Elias et al. Science, Lancaster, vol.101, no.2620, pp.270-271, Mar. 16, 1945.

CORRELATION OF THE TERTIARY FORMATIONS OF THE GREAT PLAINS. W.D. Matthew. Bull. Geol. Soc. Amer., vol.35, no.4, pp.743-754, Dec. 30, 1924.

HOW ARE THE GREAT PLAINS SHELTERBELTS? E.N.Munns, Joseph H.Stoeckeler. Jour.Forestry, Washington, vol.44, no.4, pp.237-257, illus., Apr., 1946. (Rodents, Rabbits.)

PLEISTOCENE MAMMALS AND TERRACES IN THE GREAT PLAINS. C.Bertrand Schultz, Thompson M. Stout. Bull. Geol.Soc.Amer., Baltimore, vol.59, no.6, pp.553-588, figs. 4, pl.1, June, 1948.

LARGE MAMMALS OF THE GREAT PLAINS. V.E. Shelford. Science, Lancaster, n.s., vol.90, no.2347, pp.591-592, Dec. 22, 1939.

SMALLER ANIMALS OF THE GREAT PLAINS. V.E. Shelford. Science, Lancaster, n.s., vol.91, no.2355, pp.167-168, Feb.16, 1940.

DEVELOPMENT OF FEDERAL REFUGES IN THE GREAT PLAINS REGION WITH EMERGENCY RELIEF FUNDS. M.O.Steen. Trans. 3rd N.Amer.Wildl.Conf., pp.628-632, 1938.

UNITED STATES--GREAT SMOKY MOUNTAINS

GREAT SMOKY MOUNTAINS, WILDERNESS THRONE OF THE EAST. Newton B. Drury. Living Wilderness, Washington, D.C., vol. 7, no.7, pp.3-5, illus., Mar., 1942.

MAMMALS OF THE GREAT SMOKY MOUNTAINS. Edwin V. Komarek, Roy Komarek. Bull. Chicago Acad. Sci., vol.5, no.6, pp. 137-162, figs.6, fold.map, Aug. 15, 1938.

REMARKS ON THE FAUNA OF THE GREAT SMOKY MOUNTAINS: WITH DESCRIPTION OF A NEW SPECIES OF RED-BACKED MOUSE (EVOTOMYS CAROLINENSIS). C. Hart Merriam. Amer. Jour. Science, vol. 36, pp.458-460, Dec., 1888.

UNITED STATES--IDAHO

MAMMALS OF THE ROSS EXPEDITION (1824) IN IDAHO. William B. Davis. Murrelet, vol.16, no.1, pp.7-10, Jan., 1935.

RECENT MAMMALS OF IDAHO: DISTRIBUTIONAL AND BIONOMIC STUDY. William B. Davis. PhD thesis, Univ.Calif., 1938; Caxton Printers, Ltd., Caldwell, Idaho, pp.400, Apr. 5, 1939.

(Review by R.M. Anderson of) RECENT MAMMALS OF IDAHO: DISTRIBUTIONAL AND BIONOMIC STUDY. William B. Davis. Canadian Field-Naturalist, Ottawa, vol.54, no.4, pp.60-61, Apr., 1940.

(Review of) RECENT MAMMALS OF IDAHO: DISTRIBUTIONAL AND BIONOMIC STUDY. William B. Davis. Jour. Mamm., vol.20, no.3, pp.389-390, Aug. 4, 1939.

SOME MAMMALS FROM WESTERN MONTANA AND EASTERN IDAHO. William B. Davis. Murrelet, Seattle, vol.18, pp.22-27, Jan.-May (Sep.4), 1937.

MAMMAL AND BIRD SURVEY OF IDAHO. Ralph Ellis, Jr. Jour.Mamm., vol.11, no. 3, p.433, Aug., 1930.

ANNOTATED LIST OF PLEISTOCENE MAMMALIA FROM AMERICAN FALLS, IDAHO. C. Lewis Gazin. Jour.Washington Acad. Sci., vol.25, no.7, pp.297-302, July 15, 1935.

FOSSIL HUNTING IN SOUTHERN IDAHO. C. Lewis Gazin. Explor.and Field-Work Smiths.Inst., for 1934, pp.9-12, illus., Apr. 23, 1935.

REMAINS FROM THE LATE PLIOCENE AND PLEISTOCENE OF IDAHO. C.Lewis Gazin. Jour. Mamm., vol.16, no.1, pp. 52-60, figs.7, Feb., 1935.

MAMMALS OF THE POCATELLO REGION OF SOUTHEASTERN IDAHO. E. Raymond Hall, Wayne B. Whitlow. Univ. Calif. Publ. Zool., vol.40, no.3, pp.235-276, figs.3, Sep. 30, 1933.

WINTER BROWSE ON THE POCATELLO BIG GAME RANGE IN SOUTHEASTERN IDAHO. Leonard W. Hoskins, Paul D. Dalke. Jour. Wildl.Mgt., Ithaca, vol.19, no.2, pp.215-225, Apr., 1955.

IDAHO'S FOREST TRAPPERS. William H. Marshall. Michigan Forester, Ann Arbor, vol.23, pp.50-52, 68-69, 1942.

MAMMALS OF IDAHO. C. Hart Merriam. N.Amer. Fauna, no.5, pp.31-87, figs.4, July 30, 1891.

RESULTS OF A BIOLOGICAL RECONNOISSANCE OF SOUTH-CENTRAL IDAHO. C. Hart Merriam. Washington Govt.Print. Off., U.S. Dept.Agric., Div.Ornith.and Mammalogy, N.Amer.Fauna, no.5, pp. 132, illus., pls.4, 1891.

NEW MAMMALIA FROM THE IDAHO FORMATION. John Campbell Merriam. Berkeley, Univ.Calif.Press, Bull.of the Dept.Geol., vol.10, no.26, pp.523-530, illus., 1918.

MAMMALS OF THE CLEARWATER MOUNTAINS, IDAHO. Robert T. Orr. Proc.Calif. Acad.Sci., San Francisco, ser.4, vol.23, no.35, pp.511-536, pls.45-47, Aug. 18, 1943.

CONDITIONS INFLUENCING EROSION ON THE BOISE RIVER WATERSHED. F.G. Renner. U.S.Dept.Agric., Tech.Bull., no. 528, pp.32, Oct., 1936.

WILDLIFE OF IDAHO. William H. Rush. Idaho Fish and Game Commission, Boise, pp.299, 1942.

MAMMALS OF NORTHERN IDAHO. Henry Judson Rust. Jour. Mamm., vol.27, no.4, pp.308-327, fig.1, Nov. 25, 1946.

EARLY PLEISTOCENE MAMMAL FAUNA FROM THE VICINITY OF GRAND VIEW, ADA AND OWYHEE COUNTIES, IDAHO. John R. Schultz. Proc. Geol.Soc.Amer., for 1937, p.297, June, 1938.(Abstract.)

RESULTS OF A BIOLOGICAL RECONNOISSANCE OF SOUTHCENTRAL IDAHO. 4. ANNOTATED LIST OF REPTILES AND BATRACHIANS. Leonhard Stejneger. U.S. Dept.Agric., Div.Orinth.and Mammalogy, N.Amer.Fauna, no.5, pp.113, July 30, 1891.

SPECIAL GAME PROBLEMS IN THE NATIONAL FORESTS OF SOUTHERN IDAHO. I.M. Varner. Bull. Univ.Idaho, vol. 33, no.22 (Bull.School Forestry, no.8), pp.9-11, Dec., 1938.

MAMMALS OF THE POCATELLO REGION OF SOUTHEASTERN IDAHO. Wayne B. Whitlow, E. Raymond Hall. Univ.Calif. Publ.in Zool., vol.40, no.3, pp.235-276, figs.3, Sep. 30, 1933.

UNITED STATES--ILLINOIS

SHIFTING OF MAMMALIAN FAUNAS, AS SHOWN BY THE PLEISTOCENE REMAINS OF ILLINOIS. L.A. Adams. Trans. Ill. State Acad. Sci., vol.16, pp.140-144, 1923.

MAMMALS OF FULTON COUNTY, ILLINOIS. Elsie P. Anderson. Bull. Chicago Acad. Sci., vol.9, no.9, pp.153-158, illus., Oct. 12, 1951.

LIST AND BIBLIOGRAPHY OF THE FOSSIL MAMMALS OF ILLINOIS. Robert Smith Bader. Chicago Acad. Sci., Nat. Hist. Misc., no.172, pp.8, 1959.

REMAINS OF ANIMAL LIFE FROM THE KINGSTON KITCHEN MIDDEN SITE NEAR PEORIA, ILLINOIS. Frank Collins Baker. Trans. Ill. State Acad. Sci., vol.29, no.2, pp.243-246, Dec., 1936.

RELATIVE VALUES OF DRAINED AND UNDRAINED BOTTOMLAND IN ILLINOIS. Frank C. Bellrose, Jr. Jour. Wildl. Mgt., Menasha, vol.9, no.3, pp.161-182, July, 1945.

INTRODUCTION OF WILD LIFE INTO SOUTHERN ILLINOIS. Clarence Bonnell. Trans. Illinois State Acad. Sci., Springfield, vol.34, no.2, pp.216-217, Dec., 1941. (Abstract.)

SURVEY OF THE ILLINOIS FUR RESOURCE. Louis G. Brown, Lee E. Yeager. Ill. Nat. Hist. Survey Bull., vol.22, art.6, pp.433-504, Sept., 1943.

ILLINOIS GAME HARVEST. William E. Cloe. Illinois Conservation, Springfield, vol.8, no.4, p.19, Winter Issue, 1943.

MAMMALS OF ILLINOIS AND WISCONSIN. Charles Barney Cory. Chicago, Publ. of the Field Mus. Nat. Hist., Zoological Series, vol.11, pp.505, illus., maps, 1912.

ILLINOIS MAMMALS, TODAY AND YESTERDAY. Virginia Louise (Snider) Eifert. Rev. Springfield, Story of Illinois Series, no.2, pp.38, illus., 1951.

POST-GLACIAL FOSSIL VERTEBRATES FROM EAST-CENTRAL ILLINOIS. Edwin C. Galbreath. Field Mus. Nat. Hist., Geol. ser., Chicago, vol.6, no.20, pp.303-313, figs.81-82, Apr. 29, 1938.

MAMMALS OF THE CHICAGO REGION. Tappan Gregory. Progr. Activities Chicago Acad. Sci., vol.7, nos.2-3, pp.15-75, illus., July, 1936.

ZOOGEOGRAPHICAL RELATIONSHIPS OF THE MAMMALS OF ILLINOIS. D.F. Hoffmeister. Trans. Illinois Acad. Sci., vol. 46, pp.212-215, 1953.

DISTRIBUTION OF SOME ILLINOIS MAMMALS. D.F. Hoffmeister. Nat. Hist. Misc., Chicago Acad. Sci., no.128, pp.4, Feb. 10, 1954.

FIELDBOOK OF ILLINOIS MAMMALS. D.F. Hoffmeister, C.O. Mohr. Manual 4, Nat. Hist. Surv. Div., Urbana, pp.xi-233, figs.119, col. pl.1, maps 19, June, 1957.

QUADRUPEDS OF ILLINOIS, INJURIOUS AND BENEFICIAL TO THE FARMER. Robert Kennicott. U.S. Patent Off., Rep., Agric., Washington, pp.52-110, 1856; pp.72-107, 1857; pp.241-256, 1858.

MAMMAL POPULATIONS AND TERRITORIES IN AN ELM-MAPLE FOREST OF EAST-CENTRAL ILLINOIS. E.J. Koestner. Thesis, Univ. Ill., 1939.

NOTEWORTHY RECORDS OF OCCURRENCE OF MAMMALS IN CENTRAL ILLINOIS. E.J. Koestner. Trans. Illinois State Acad. Sci., Springfield, vol.34, no.2, pp.227-229, Dec., 1941.

SOME RECENT RECORDS OF CENTRAL ILLINOIS MAMMALS. E.J. Koestner. Jour. Tennessee Acad. Sci., Nashville, vol.16, no.1, pp.46-47, Jan., 1941.

MAMMAL SURVEY OF THE CHICAGO REGION. E.V. Komarek, D.A. Spencer. Program of Activities Chacago Acad. Sci., vol. 2, no.1, p.7, Jan., 1931.

FLUCTUATIONS IN THE ABUNDANCE OF SMALL MAMMALS IN EAST-CENTRAL ILLINOIS, 1936-1939. (Woodmouse and Shrew.) Robert G. Lindeborg. Ecology, vol. 22, no.1, pp.96-99, Jan., 1941.

THOSE WE'VE HAD. (Elk, Bison, Black Bear, Panther, Timber Wolf.) Francis X. Lueth. Illinois Conserv., Springfield, vol. 9, no.1, pp.14-15, illus., Spring Issue, 1944.

KANKAKEE AREA--ITS PAST AND PRESENT. Marcus Ward Lyon, Jr. Chicago Nat., vol.5, no.3, pp.43-46, illus., Oct., 1942.

CHECK-LIST OF THE MAMMALS OF ILLINOIS. C.A. Mohr. Getting at Nature, Its Mystery and Its Message, Springfield, vol. 1, no.1, pp.11-13, illus., 1939.

DISTRIBUTION OF ILLINOIS MAMMALS. Carl O. Mohr. Trans. Illinois State Acad. Sci., Springfield, vol.34, no.2, pp.229-232, maps 4, Dec., 1941.

DISTRIBUTION OF THE PRAIRIE MOLE AND POCKET GOPHER IN ILLINOIS. Carl O. Mohr. Jour. Mamm., vol.27, no. 4, pp.390-392, figs.2, Nov. 25, 1946.

ILLINOIS FURBEARER DISTRIBUTION AND INCOME. Carl O. Mohr. Bull. Ill. Nat. Hist. Surv., Urbana, vol.22, art.7, pp.505-537, figs.26, pl.1, Sep., 1943.

ILLINOIS TRAPPER'S AVERAGE REVEAL COON AND POSSUM DISTRIBUTION. Carl O. Mohr. Illinois Conservation, vol.2, no. 4, pp.3-4, figs.4, Dec., 1937.

MAJOR FLUCTUATIONS OF SOME ILLINOIS MAMMAL POPULATIONS. Carl O. Mohr. Trans. Illinois State Acad. Sci., vol.40, pp.197-204, illus., 1947.

TRAPPERS' REPORTS REVEAL FURBEARER FLUCTUATIONS IN ILLINOIS. Carl O Mohr. Illinois Conservation, vol. 4, no.1, pp.4-5, Midwinter, 1938-39.

CHECK LIST OF MAMMALS OF THE CHICAGO REGION. Walter L. Necker. Chicago Acad. Sci. Leaflet, no.9, pp.4, July 21, 1939.

MAMMALS OF ILLINOIS. AN ANNOTATED CHECK LIST WITH KEYS AND BIBLIOGRAPHY. Walter L. Necker, Donald M. Hatfield. Bull. Chicago Acad. Sci., vol.6, no. 3, pp.17-60, May, 1941.

(Errata to) MAMMALS OF ILLINOIS. Walter L. Necker, Donald M. Hartfield. Bull. Chicago Acad. Sci., vol.6, p.1, 1942.

ADDITIONAL RECORDS OF ILLINOIS MAMMALS. R.M. Wetzel. Trans. Ill. Acad. Sci., vol.40, pp.228-233, 1947. (Supplement to Necker and Hatfield, 1941.)

ONE SQUARE MILE--NATURE'S INTRICATE CYCLES IN KENNICOTT'S GROVE, ILLINOIS, REVEAL PROBLEMS FULLY AS ENTHRALLING AS ANY THE NATURALIST MIGHT MEET AT THE ENDS OF THE EARTH. Donald Culross Peattie. Nat. Hist., New York, vol.40, no.2, pp.465-470, figs.17, Sep., 1937.

MAMMALS OF THE CHICAGO AREA. C.C. Sanborn. Chicago, Field Mus. Nat. Hist., Zoology Leaflet, no.8, pp.23, illus., pls., 1925.

ANIMAL COMMUNITIES OF AN ILLINOIS PRAIRIE. (Few Mammals Listed.) M.W. Shackleford. Ecology, vol.10, pp.126-154, figs., pl.1, Jan., 1929.

FLUCTUATION OF FOREST ANIMAL POPULATIONS IN EAST CENTRAL ILLINOIS. V.E. Shelford. Ecological Monographs, vol. 21, pp.183-214, Apr., 1951.

POPULATION SURVEY OF SMALL MAMMALS IN SOUTHWESTERN ILLINOIS. Julius Swayne. MS thesis, S. Ill. Univ., 1949.

STUDY OF THE MAMMALS OF CHAMPAIGN COUNTY, ILLINOIS. Frank Elmer Wood. Illinois State Lab. of Nat. Hist., Bull., vol.8, pp.501-613, illus.12, pls.2, map.

CAPACITY OF ILLINOIS LAND TYPES TO PRODUCE FURS. Lee E. Yeager. Trans. 10th N. Amer. Wildl. Conf., Washington, pp.79-86, 1945.

FUR PRODUCTION AND MANAGEMENT OF ILLINOIS DRAINAGE SYSTEM. Lee E. Yeager. Trans. 8th N. Amer. Wildl. Conf., Washington, pp.294-301, 1943.

UNITED STATES--INDIANA

SPORTSMEN'S QUESTIONNAIRE METHOD OF ESTIMATING THE GAME KILL IN INDIANA. Wm.B. Barnes. Trans. 11th N. Amer. Wildl. Conf., Washington, pp.339-348, figs. 2, 1946.

ACCOUNT OF THE MAMMALIAN FAUNA OF THE POST-PLIOCENE DEPOSITS IN THE STATE OF INDIANA. Edward Drinker Cope. Indiana, Dept. Geol. and Nat. Hist., Ann. Rept., Indianapolis, pt.2, pp.4-62, pls.6, 1884.

NOTES ON THE MAMMALS OF ST. JOSEPH COUNTY, INDIANA. William L. Engels. Amer. Midland Nat., Notre Dame, Ind., vol. 14, no.1, pp.1-16, figs.3, Jan., 1933.

BIBLIOGRAPHY OF INDIANA MAMMALS. PRELIMINARY LIST OF INDIANA MAMMALS. Barton Warren Evermann, A.W. Butler. Proc. Indiana Acad. Sci., pp.120-139, Aug., 1894.

LAKE MAXINKUCKEE. A PHYSICAL AND BIOLOGICAL SURVEY. Barton Warren Evermann, Howard Walton Clark. Pub. by Dept. of Conservation, Indiana, vol.1, pp.1-660; vol.2, pp.1-512, illus. (List of Mammals pp.452-480 of vol.1.)

NOTES ON THE MAMMALS OF THE LAKE MAXINKUCKEE REGION. Barton Warren Evermann. Baltimore, Md., Williams and Wilkins Co., Proc. of the Washington Acad. of Sci., vol.13, no.1, pp.34, 1911.

MAMMALS OF INDIANA, A DESCRIPTIVE CATALOGUE OF THE MAMMALS OCCURRING IN INDIANA IN RECENT TIMES. Walter Louis Hahn. Indiana, Dept. Geol. and Nat. Resources, Ann. Rep., Indianapolis, pp.417-654, illus., 1909.

NOTES ON MAMMALS OF THE KANKAKEE VALLEY. Walter Louis Hahn. Proc. U.S. Nat. Mus., Washington, vol.32, pp.455-464, 1907.

NOTES ON THE MAMMALS AND COLD-BLOODED VERTEBRATES OF THE INDIANA UNIVERSITY FARM, MITCHELL, INDIANA. Walter Louis Hahn. Proc. U.S. Nat. Mus., Washington, vol.35, pp.545-581, 1909.

SOME NOTES ON INDIANA MAMMALS. Chas. M. Kirkpatrick, Clinton H. Conaway. Amer. Midland Nat., Notre Dame, vol.39, no.1, pp.128-136, Jan., 1948.

MAMMALS FOUND AT THE PRESENT TIME IN FRANKLIN COUNTY. Gilbert M. Levette. Indiana, Geol. Survey, Ann. Rep., Indianapolis, pp.203-208, 1869.

MAMMALS OF INDIANA. Marcus Ward Lyon, Jr. Univ. Press, Notre Dame, Indiana, pp.384, illus., Jan., 1936.

(Review by W.J. Hamilton, Jr. of) MAMMALS OF INDIANA. Marcus Ward Lyon, Jr. Jour. Mamm., vol.17, no.2, p.177, May, 1936.

ADDITIONS TO THE "MAMMALS OF INDIANA." Marcus Ward Lyon, Jr. Amer. Midland Nat., Notre Dame, vol.27, no.3, pp.790-791, May (July), 1942.

NEW RECORDS OF INDIANA MAMMALS. Marcus Ward Lyon, Jr. Proc. Indiana Acad. Sci., vol.33, for 1923, pp.284-285, 1924.

NOTES ON THE MAMMALS OF THE DUNE REGION OF PORTER COUNTY, INDIANA. Marcus Ward Lyon, Jr. Proc. Indiana Acad. Sci., for 1922, pp.209-221, figs.3, 1923.

ORIGINS OF INDIANA'S MAMMALS. Marcus Ward Lyon, Jr. Proc. Indiana Acad. Sci., vol.43, pp.27-43, Apr., 1934.

SMALL COLLECTION OF PLEISTOCENE MAMMALS FROM LAPORTE COUNTY, INDIANA. Marcus Ward Lyon, Jr. The Amer. Midland Naturalist, Notre Dame, vol.12, no.10, pp.406-410, figs.2, July, 1931.

LIST OF THE MAMMALS, REPTILES AND BATRACHIANS OF MONROE COUNTY, INDIANA. W.L. McAtee. Proc. Biol. Soc. Washington, vol.20, pp.1-16, Feb. 25, 1907.

GEOLOGICAL HISTORY OF THE VERTEBRATES OF INDIANA AND THEIR POSITION IN THE ANCIENT NORTH AMERICAN FAUNA. Roy L. Moodie. Dept. of Conservation, State of Indiana, Publ., no. 90, pp.115, figs.95, 1929.

NOTES ON THE MAMMALS OF JACKSON COUNTY, INDIANA. Russel E. Mumford, Charles O. Handley, Jr. Jour. Mamm., vol.37, no.3, pp.407-412, Sep. 11, 1956.

FOSSIL MAMMALS OF THE POST-PLIOCENE IN INDIANA. Maurice Thompson. Indiana, Dept. Geol.and Nat.Hist., Ann. Rept., Indianapolis, pp.283-285, 1886.

HOOSIERS FINDING ANIMAL TRACKS AN INTERESTING PART OF OUTDOOR TRIPS. Outdoor Indiana, Indianapolis, vol.10, no. 9, pp.5, 16, illus., Oct., 1943.

INDIANA FUR VALUE SHOWN IN INVOICE LEFT BY VIGO OF VINCENNES THREE LIFETIMES AGO. Outdoor Indiana, Indianapolis, vol. 10, no.10, pp.3, 15, Nov., 1943.

LARGER SPECIES OF WILD ANIMALS ARE REPORTED AS INCREASING IN INDIANA. Outdoor Indiana, Indianapolis, vol.10, no.8, p.4, Sep., 1943.

UNITED STATES--IOWA

NOTES ON THE MAMMALS OF IOWA. Joel A. Allen. Proc. Boston Soc. Nat. Hist., vol.13, pp.178-194, 1869.

IOWA FURS MAKE HIGH QUALITY GARMENTS. Ree M. Berry. Iowa Conservationist, Des Moines, vol.5, no.11, pp.81, 83-84, illus., Nov. 15, 1946.

LIST OF SPECIES OF MAMMALS, PRINCIPALLY RODENTS, OBTAINED BY W. W. PRICE, DR. S. E. MEEK, G. K. CHERRIE, AND E. S. THOMPSON IN THE STATES OF IOWA, WYOMING, MONTANA, IDAHO, NEVADA AND CALIFORNIA, WITH DESCRIPTIONS OF NEW SPECIES. D.G.Elliot. Chicago, Field Col.Mus., Publ.27, Zoological Series, vol.1, no.10, pp.193-221, 1898.

ADDENDUM TO THE SPECIAL REPORT ON THE CASE HISTORY OF THE GOOSE LAKE OBSERVATIONAL AREA. Paul L. Errington. Iowa Coop. Wildl. Research Unit, Quart.Rept., Ames, pp.16-28, Jan.-Mar., 1948.

RECORDS OF MAMMALS FROM SOUTHWESTERN IOWA. James S. Findley, J. Knox Jones, Jr. Trans. Kansas Acad.Sci., vol.57, no.2, pp.212-213, 1954.

'44 FUR HARVEST $2, 000, 000. (IOWA.) James R. Harlan. Iowa Conservation Notes, State Conservation Comm., Des Moines, Mar.8, 1945.

FUR-BEARERS AND GAME MAMMALS OF IOWA. Ellis A. Hicks, George O.Hendrickson. Iowa Agr.Exp.Sta., Bull., no.P3,n.s., pp.115-145, Feb., 1940.

ECOLOGICAL DISTRIBUTION OF MAMMALS IN NORTHEASTERN IOWA. Sherman A. Hoslett. PhD thesis, Univ. Mich., 1940.

ANNOTATED CATALOGUE OF THE RECENT MAMMALS OF IOWA. T. van Hyning, F.C. Pellett. Proc. Iowa Acad. Sci., pp. 211-218, 1910.

NOTES ON THE MAMMALS OBSERVED IN MARSHALL COUNTY, IOWA. Ira N. Gabrielson. Iowa Acad. Sci., vol.28, pp.147-149, 1921.

PRESENT STATUS OF SYSTEMATIC MAMMALOGY IN IOWA WITH SOME NOTES ON RECENT MAMMAL COLLECTING WITHIN THE STATE. Lowell S. Miller. Proc.Iowa Acad.Sci., vol.61, pp.556-560, Dec. 4, 1954.

SOME MAMMAL LOCALITY RECORDS FROM IOWA. Lowell S. Miller. Jour. Mamm., vol.36, no.1, pp.121-122, Feb. 25, 1955.

PARTIAL CATALOGUE OF THE ANIMALS OF IOWA, REPRESENTED IN THE COLLECTIONS OF THE DEPARTMENT OF ZOOLOGY AND ENTOMOLOGY OF THE IOWA AGRICULTURAL COLLEGE. Herbert Osborn. Ames, Iowa, pp.39, 1892.

LATE PLEISTOCENE MATERIAL FROM THE DES MOINES AREA. Harris Palmer. Proc. Iowa Acad. Sci., Des Moines, vol. 60, pp.399-402, illus., Feb., 1954.

CHECK LIST OF MAMMALS OF PRESENT OCCURRENCE IN IOWA WITH NOTES ON NEW ADDITIONS AND DISTRIBUTION SINCE 1937. Emmett Polder. Proc. Iowa Acad. Sci., Des Moines, vol.60, pp.716-724, Feb., 1954.

FIELD IDENTIFICATION OF IOWA MAMMALS. Thos.G. Scott. Nature Notes, Peoria, vol.8, no.6, pp.163-176, figs.5, June, 1941.

MAMMALS OF IOWA. Thos.G. Scott. Iowa State College Jour.Sci., vol.12, no.1, pp.43-97, Oct., 1937.

NOTEWORTHY ADDITIONS TO THE COLLECTION OF MAMMALS FROM IOWA IN 1938. Thos. G. Scott. Iowa State College Jour. Sci., Ames, vol.13, no.3, pp.239-241, Apr., 1939.

WHAT MAMMAL IS THAT? (Opossum, Mole, Shrew.) Thos. G. Scott. Iowa Conservationist, Des Moines, vol.5, no.8, pp.57, 60, 64, illus., Aug. 15, 1946; vol.5, no.9, pp.65, 68-69, 71, Sep., 1946.

MAMMALS OF THE LAKE REGION OF IOWA. T.C. Stephens. Bull.Okoboji Protective Assoc., pp.47-64, June, 1922.

WILDLIFE RESOURCES OF IOWA. Bruce F. Stiles et al. Publ.by State of Iowa, Des Moines, pp.41, illus., 1946.

SESPE FAUNAS. Chester Stock. Pan-Amer. Geol., Des Moines, vol.63, no.4, p.315, May, 1935.

NOTES ON SOME MAMMALIAN REMAINS REPORTED IN IOWA DURING THE PAST YEAR. A.O. Thomas. Iowa Acad.Sci. Proc., vol.29, p.129, 1922.

MAMMALS OF IOWA. PRELIMINARY ANNOTED CATALOGUE OF THE RECENT MAMMALS OF IOWA. T. Van Hyning. Des Moines, Extracted from Proc. of the Iowa Acad.Sci., pp.211-218, 1910.

IOWA TRAPPERS NET TWO AND ONE-HALF MILLION DOLLARS. Iowa Conservationist, Des Moines, vol.5, no.4, pp.25, 28-29, Apr. 15, 1946.

15 YEARS OF IOWA TRAPPING. Iowa State Conservation Comm., vol.14, no.9, pp. 164-165, illus., Sep., 1955.

1951-52 TRAPPING RESULTS. Iowa State Conservation Comm., vol.11, no.8, p.58, Aug., 1952.

UNITED STATES--KANSAS

Extinct and Fossil Mammals

PLIOCENE AND PLEISTOCENE STRATIGRAPHY AND PALEONTOLOGY OF THE MEADE BASIN, SOUTHWESTERN KANSAS. John C. Frye, Claude W. Hibbard. Univ. Kansas Publ., State Geol.Surv.Kansas, Lawrence, Bull.38, pp.389-424, illus., Dec. 5, 1941.

STRATIGRAPHY AND PALEONTOLOGY OF A NEW MIDDLE AND UPPER PLIOCENE FORMATION OF SOUTH-CENTRAL KANSAS. John C. Frye, Claude W. Hibbard. Jour. Geol., Chicago, vol.49, no.3, pp. 261-278, figs. 6, Apr.-May, 1941.

WESTWARD EXTENSION OF THE KANSAS "EQUUS BEDS". John C. Frye et al. Jour. Geol., Chicago, vol.51, no.1, pp.33-47, figs.3, Jan.-Feb., 1943.

STRATIGRAPHY OF THE OGALLALA FORMATION (NEOGENE) OF NORTHERN KANSAS. John C. Frye et al. Kansas Geol. Survey, Bull.118, pp.1-92, illus., Mar., 1956.

VERTEBRATE FOSSILS FROM McPHERSON EQUUS BEDS. H.J. Harnly. Trans.Kansas Acad.Sci., vol.35, p.209, 1932.

ON A COLLECTION OF FOSSIL VERTEBRATES MADE BY DR. F. W. CRAGIN FROM THE EQUUS BEDS OF KANSAS. Oliver P. Hay. Kansas Univ.Sci.Bull., vol.10, no.4, pp.51, pls.3, Jan., 1917.

ADDITIONAL FAUNA OF EDSON QUARRY OF THE MIDDLE PLIOCENE OF KANSAS. Claude W. Hibbard. Amer.Midland Naturalist, vol.18, no.3, pp.460-464, figs.4, May, 1937.

BORCHERS FAUNA, A NEW PLEISTOCENE INTERGLACIAL FAUNA FROM MEADE COUNTY, KANSAS. Claude W. Hibbard. State Geol.Surv.Kansas, Lawrence, Bull. 38, Reports of Studies, pt.7, pp.197-220, pls.2, July 14, 1941.

CONTRIBUTION TO THE REXROAD FAUNA. Claude W. Hibbard. Trans. Kansas Acad. Sci., Topeka, vol.55, no.2, pp.196-208, June 18, 1952.

EQUUS (ASINUS) COLOBATUS TROXELL AND ASSOCIATED VERTEBRATES FROM THE PLEISTOCENE OF KANSAS. Claude W. Hibbard. Trans.Kans.Acad.Sci., vol. 56, no.1, pp.111-126, illus., Mar., 1953.

ETADONOMYS, A NEW PLEISTOCENE HETEROMYID RODENT, AND NOTES ON OTHER KANSAS MAMMALS. Claude W. Hibbard. Trans.Kans.Acad.Sci., Topeka, vol.46, pp.185-191, pl.1, 1943.

JINGLEBOB INTERGLACIAL (SANGAMON?) FAUNA FROM KANSAS AND ITS CLIMATIC SIGNIFICANCE. Claude W. Hibbard. Contrib.Mus.Paleontol.Univ.Michigan, vol. 12, no.10, pp.179-228, pls.2, figs.8, chart 1, Sep. 1, 1955.

LATE CENOZOIC CLIMATE CONDITIONS IN THE HIGH PLAINS OF WESTERN KANSAS. Claude W. Hibbard. Bull.Geol.Soc. Amer., Baltimore, vol.59, no.6, pp.592-597, June, 1948.

MAMMALS OF THE REXROAD FAUNA FROM THE UPPER PLIOCENE OF SOUTHWESTERN KANSAS. Claude W. Hibbard. Trans.Kansas Acad.Sci., Lawrence, vol. 44, pp.265-313, pls.4, 1941.

MAMMALS OF THE REXROAD FORMATION FROM FOX CANYON, KANSAS. Claude W. Hibbard. Contrib. Mus. Paleont. Univ. Michigan, Ann Arbor, vol.8, no.6, pp.113-192, figs.23, pls.5, June 29, 1950.

NEW MAMMALS FROM THE REXROAD FAUNA, UPPER PLIOCENE OF KANSAS. Claude W. Hibbard. Amer.Midland Nat., vol.26, no.2, pp.337-368, figs.12, pls. 3, Sep., 1941.

NEW PLEISTOCENE FAUNA FROM MEADE COUNTY, KANSAS. Claude W. Hibbard. Trans.Kansas Acad.Sci., Topeka, vol.43, pp.417-425, pls.2, Dec.23, 1940.

NOTES ON ADDITIONAL FAUNA OF EDSON QUARRY OF THE MIDDLE PLIOCENE OF KANSAS. Claude W. Hibbard. Trans.Kans.Acad.Sci., Topeka, vol.42, pp.457-462, figs.6, 1939.

NOTES ON SOME MAMMALS FROM THE PLEISTOCENE OF KANSAS. Claude W. Hibbard. Trans.Kans.Acad.Sci., Topeka, vol.42, pp.463-479, pls.5, tbls., 1939.

NOTES ON SOME VERTEBRATES FROM THE PLEISTOCENE OF KANSAS. Claude W. Hibbard. Trans.Kans.Acad.Sci., vol.40, pp.233-234, pl.1, 1937.

PALAEOECOLOGY AND CORRELATION OF THE REXROAD FAUNA FROM THE UPPER PLIOCENE OF SOUTHWESTERN KANSAS, AS INDICATED BY THE MAMMALS. Claude W. Hibbard. Univ.Kans. Sci.Bull., Lawrence, vol. 27, no.6, pp. 79-104, Nov. 1, 1941.

PLEISTOCENE MAMMALS FROM KANSAS. Claude W. Hibbard. State Geol.Surv. Kansas, Bull.41, 1942 Rep.of Studies, pt. 6, pp.261-269, pl.1, Aug. 3, 1942.

PLEISTOCENE STRATIGRAPHY AND PALEONTOLOGY OF MEADE COUNTY, KANSAS. Claude W. Hibbard. Contrib.Mus.Paleontol., Univ.Michigan, Ann Arbor, vol.7, no.4, pp.63-90, figs.2, pl.1, Mar. 2, 1949.

PLIOCENE SAW ROCK CANYON FAUNA IN KANSAS. Claude W. Hibbard. Contrib.Mus. Paleontol., Univ.Michigan, Ann Arbor, vol. 7, no.5, pp.91-105, figs.2, Mar.2, 1949.

REZABEK FAUNA, A NEW PLEISTOCENE FAUNA FROM LINCOLN COUNTY, KANSAS. Claude W. Hibbard. Univ.Kans.Sci. Bull., Lawrence, vol.29, pt.2, no.2, pp. 235-247, figs.3, pl.19, Oct. 15, 1943.

SECOND CONTRIBUTION TO THE REXROAD FAUNA. Claude W. Hibbard. Trans.

Kans.Acad.Sci., vol.57, no.2, pp.221-237, illus., Aug. 2, 1954.

STRATIGRAPHY AND VERTEBRATE PALEONTOLOGY OF PLEISTOCENE DEPOSITS OF SOUTHWESTERN KANSAS. Claude W. Hibbard. Bull.Geol.Soc.America, Wash., vol.55, pp.707-754, June, 1944.

TWO NEW MAMMALS FROM THE MIDDLE PLIOCENE OF SEWARD COUNTY, KANSAS. Claude W. Hibbard. Univ.Kans.Sci. Bull., Lawrence, vol.30, pt.1, no.10, pp. 107-114, pl.10, 11, May 15, 1944.

UPPER PLIOCENE FAUNA FROM MEADE COUNTY, KANSAS. Claude W. Hibbard. Trans.Kans.Acad.Sci., vol.40, pp.239-265, figs.2, pls.5, 1937.

VERTEBRATE FOSSILS FROM LATE CENOZOIC DEPOSITS OF CENTRAL KANSAS. Claude W. Hibbard. Univ.Kans.Paleont.Contrib.Vertebrata, art.2, pp.1-14, illus., Mar. 20, 1952.

VERTEBRATE FOSSILS FROM THE MEADE FORMATION OF SOUTHWESTERN KANSAS. Claude W. Hibbard. Pap.Michigan Acad.Sci., Arts and Letters, vol.41, pp. 145-204, illus., Apr.11, 1956.

VERTEBRATE FOSSILS FROM THE PLEISTOCENE STUMP ARROYO MEMBER, MEADE COUNTY, KANSAS. Claude W. Hibbard. Contrib. Mus. Paleontol.Univ. Michigan, Ann Arbor, vol.9, no.7, pp. 227-245, pls.1-6, Dec. 31, 1951.

RECONNAISSANCE OF PLEISTOCENE DEPOSITS IN NORTH-CENTRAL KANSAS. Claude W. Hibbard et al. Univ.Kans. Publ., Lawrence, State Geol.Surv.Kansas, Bull.52, pt.1, pp.28, figs.2, pls.2, Feb. 20, 1944.

UPPER PLIOCENE VERTEBRATES FROM KEEFE CANYON, MEADE COUNTY, KANSAS. Claude W. Hibbard, Elmer S. Riggs. Bull. Geol.Soc.Amer., vol.60, pp.829-860, figs.11, pls.5, May, 1949.

SURVEY OF THE FOSSIL VERTEBRATES OF KANSAS. PART 5. MAMMALIA. H.H. Lane. Trans.Kans.Acad.Sci., Topeka, vol. 50, no.2, pp.130-161, figs.5, 1947; vol.50, nos.3-4, pp.273-314, figs.9, 1947; vol.51, no.1, pp.29-76, figs.15, 1948.

FOOTPRINTS OF VERTEBRATES IN THE COAL MEASURES OF KANSAS. O.C. Marsh. Amer.Jour.Sci., vol.48, pp.81-84, pls.2-3, July, 1894.

ADDITIONAL MAMMALS FROM THE REXROAD FAUNA. Thomas M. Oelrich. Jour. Mamm., vol.34, no.3, pp.373-378, illus., Aug. 14, 1954.

NEW TESTUDO FROM THE UPPER PLIOCENE OF KANSAS WITH ADDITIONAL NOTES ON ASSOCIATED REXROAD MAMMALS. Thomas. M. Oelrich. Trans.Kansas Acad.Sci., Topeka, vol.55, no.3, pp.300-311, illus., 1952.

FOSSIL MAMMAL TRACKS IN GRAHAM COUNTY, KANSAS. George M. Robertson, George F. Sternberg. Trans.Kans.Acad. Sci., Lawrence, vol.45, pp.258-261, figs. 5, 1942.

Recent Mammals

LIST OF MAMMALS COLLECTED IN THE BLACK HILLS REGION OF SOUTH DAKOTA AND IN WESTERN KANSAS BY MR. WALTER W. GRANGER, WITH FIELD NOTES BY THE COLLECTOR. J.A. Allen. Amer.Mus. Nat.Hist., New York, Bull., vol.7, pp.259-274, 1895.

NOTES ON THE MAMMALS OF PORTIONS OF KANSAS, COLORADO, WYOMING AND UTAH. J.A. Allen. Bull.Essex Inst., vol. 6, pp.43-66, Mar.-Apr., 1874.

KANSAS MAMMALS. Paul Allen. Kansas State Teachers College of Emporia. Topeka, Printed by Kans.State Printing Plant, W.C. Austin, State Printer, Bull.of Information, vol.20, no.5, pp.62, 1940.

MAMMALS OF KANSAS. J.D. Black. 30th Biennial Rep.Kans.State Board Agric., Topeka, pp.116-217, figs.17-36, 1938.

ECOLOGICAL SURVEY OF THE FORT LEAVENWORTH MILITARY RESERVATION. Malcolm J. Brumwell. Amer. Midland, Notre Dame, vol.45, no.1, pp.187-231, Jan., 1951.

HISTORY OF CHANGES IN POPULATION OF CERTAIN MAMMALS IN WESTERN KANSAS. Floyd K. Carter. MS thesis, Ft. Hays Kansas State College, 1939.

MAMMALS OF KANSAS. E. Cockrum. Univ. of Kansas Publ., Lawrence, Mus.Nat.Hist., vol.7, no.1, pp.303, maps, tbls., diagrs., 1952.

(Review by Robert W. Eadie of) MAMMALS OF KANSAS. E. Cockrum. Jour.Mamm., vol.34, no.3, pp.400-401, Aug. 14, 1953.

NOTES ON SOME MAMMALS OF FILEY COUNTY, KANSAS. Lee Raymond Dice. Jour. Mamm., vol.4, no.2, pp.107-112, May, 1923.

NOTES ON THE COMMUNITIES OF THE VERTEBRATES OF RILEY COUNTY, KANSAS, WITH ESPECIAL REFERNCE TO AMPHIBIANS, REPTILES, AND MAMMALS. Lee Raymond Dice. Ecology, vol.4, pp.40-53, Jan. (Feb.), 1923.

FOREST HABITAT OF THE KANSAS NATURAL HISTORY RESERVATION. Henry S. Fitch, Ronald L. McGregor. Univ.Kans. Publ., Mus.Nat.Hist., vol.10, no.3, pp. 77-127, Dec. 31, 1956.

FIVE-YEAR REPORT ON THE KANSAS SMALL MAMMAL CENSUS. H.T. Gier, G.V.R. Bradshaw. Trans. Kans.Acad.Sci., vol.60, no.3, pp.259-272, Oct. 22, 1957.

HANDBOOK OF MAMMALS OF KANSAS. Eugene Raymond Hall. Univ.Kans.Mus. Nat.Hist., Misc.Publ., no.7, pp.303, illus., maps, 1955.

CHECKLIST OF KANSAS MAMMALS, 1943. Claude W. Hibbard. Trans.Kans.Acad.Sci., Lawrence, vol.47, no.1, pp.61-88, Sep., 1944.

OCCURRENCE OF ERETHIZON EPIXANTHUM BRUNERI AND MUSTELA NIGRIPES IN KANSAS. Claude W. Hibbard. Jour. Mamm., vol.15, no.1, pp.70-71, Feb., 1934.

REVISED CHECK LIST OF KANSAS MAMMALS. Claude W. Hibbard. Trans.Kans. Acad.Sci., vol.36, pp.230-249, 1933.

ADDITIONAL RECORDS OF THE SPOTTED GROUND SQUIRREL AND BLACK-FOOTED FERRET IN KANSAS. J. Knox Jones, Jr., Richard B. Loomis. Trans. Kans. Acad.Sci., vol.56, no.1, p.107, 1953.

KANSAS MAMMALS IN THEIR RELATIONS TO AGRICULTURE. D.E. Lantz. Bull. Exper.Station Kans.State Agric.College, Manhattan, no.129, pp.331-402, Dec., 1904.

WICHITA WONDERLAND! Juanita Mahaffey. Oklahoma Game and Fish News, Oklahoma City, vol.1, no.6, pp.6-8, 16, illus., June, 1945.

VERTEBRATE REMAINS IN BARN OWL PELLETS FROM STANTON COUNTY, KANSAS. Robert M. Petitt. Trans. Kans. Acad. Sci., Topeka, vol.54, no.3, p.395, 1951.

DISTRIBUTIONAL RECORDS FROM KANSAS. James M. Sprague. Jour. Mamm., vol.19, no.2, p.246, May 14, 1938.

MAMMAL DISTRIBUTIONAL RECORDS FOR KANSAS. James M. Sprague. Jour. Mamm., Baltimore, vol.20, no.1, pp. 102-103, Feb. 14, 1939.

FURBEARERS IN KANSAS. (Guide to Trapping.) Howard J. Stains, Rollin H. Baker. State Biol.Surv., Mus.Nat.Hist., Univ. Kans., Misc.Publ., no.18, pp.100, illus., 1958.

AMPHIBIANS, REPTILES, AND MAMMALS OF THE MEADE COUNTY STATE PARK. Joe A. Tihen, James M. Sprague. Trans. Kans.Acad.Sci., Topeka, vol.42, pp.499-512, fig.1, pls.2-3, 1939. (Mammals pp. 505-509.)

ECOLOGICAL EVALUATION OF PREDATEES ON A MIXED PRAIRIE AREA IN WESTERN KANSAS. L.D. Wooster. Trans. Kans.Acad.Sci., Topeka, vol.42, pp.515-517, figs.2, tbl.1, 1939.

KANSAS MAMMALIA. Trans.Kans.Acad. Sci., vol.4, pp.18-22, 1875.

UNITED STATES--KENTUCKY

CAVE LIFE OF KENTUCKY. Vernon Bailey. Amer.Midland Nat., Notre Dame, vol.14, no.5, pp.385-635, figs.90, 1933; I. INTRODUCTION. HISTORY AND PREHISTORY OF MAMMOTH CAVE. II. MAMMALS OF THE MAMMOTH CAVE REGION. Univ.Press, Notre Dame, Indiana, pp.1-256, figs.90, 1933.

CHECKLIST AND KEY TO THE MAMMALS OF KENTUCKY. Roger W. Barbour. Dept. Zoology, Univ.Kentucky, Lexington, pp.331, 1955?

MAMMALS OF BIG BLACK MOUNTAIN, HARLAN COUNTY, KENTUCKY. Roger W. Barbour. Jour. Mamm., vol.32, no.1, pp. 100-110, Feb., 1951.

THREE NEW MAMMAL RECORDS FROM KENTUCKY. Roger W. Barbour. Jour.Mamm., vol.22, no.2, pp.195-196, May 14, 1941.

SOME MAMMALS FROM HART COUNTY, KENTUCKY. Roger W. Barbour, Bernice L. Barbour. Jour. Mamm., vol.31, no.3, pp.359-360, Aug. 21, 1950.

WILD LIFE IN KENTUCKY. W.D. Funkhouser. Kentucky Geol.Surv., Frankfort, Kentucky, pp.385, illus., 1925. (Mammals pp.307-353.)

FUR HARVEST IN KENTUCKY INCREASED BOTH IN TOTAL NUMBERS AND VALUE LAST SEASON. Larry R. Gale. Kentucky Happy Hunting Ground, vol.9, no.6, p.14, illus., Nov., 1953.

KENTUCKY'S FUR YIELD ALMOST MILLION DOLLARS FOR 12 MONTHS. Larry R. Gale. Kentucky Happy Hunting Ground, Frankfort, vol.6, no.4, p.16, illus., July, 1950.

FUR HARVEST SHOWS SHARP DECLINE. Larry R. Gale. Kentucky Happy Hunting Ground, vol.11, no.2, p.28, illus., Mar., 1955.

MORE FURS TAKEN, BUT VALUE DOWN LAST SEASON. Larry R. Gale. Kentucky Happy Hunting Ground, vol.8, no.4, p.8, illus., July, 1952.

TOTAL FUR VALUE FOR KENTUCKY UP. Larry R. Gale. Kentucky Happy Hunting Ground, vol.11, no.4, p.18, illus., July, 1955.

SURVEY OF RECENT MAMMALS OF THE INNER BLUEGRASS REGION OF KENTUCKY. William L. Gault. MS thesis, Univ.Kentucky, 1952.

NOTES ON THE MAMMALS OF BREATHITT COUNTY, KENTUCKY. W.J. Hamilton, Jr. Jour. Mamm., vol.11, no.3, pp.306-311, Aug., 1930.

NEW MAMMAL RECORDS FOR MAMMOTH CAVE NATIONAL PARK, KENTUCKY. C. W. Hibbard. Jour. Mamm., vol.16, no.4, p.329, Nov., 1935.

MAMMOTH CAVE OF KENTUCKY. H. C. Hovey, R.E. Call. (With Historical Notes, Scenic Accounts and Descriptive and Scientific Matters of Interest to Visitors, Based Upon New and Original Explorations.) Louisville, J.P.Morton and Co., pp.111, pls.13, fold.map, 1887.

BIG BONES AT LOWER BLUE LICKS. (Notes On the History, Geology and Paleontology Of a Famous Kentucky Fossil Locality.) Willard Rouse Jillson. Louisville, Ky., The Standard Printing Co., pp.10, 1946.

DISCOVERY OF PLEISTOCENE VERTEBRATES AT LOWER BLUE LICKS, 1785-1946; PRESENTED BEFORE THE KENTUCKY ARCHAEOLOGICAL SOCIETY AT THE UNIVERSITY OF KENTUCKY, MAY 20, 1949. Willard Rouse Jillson. Frankfort, Roberts Print.Co., pp.30, 1949. (His Transylvania Series, no.6.)

SOME NOTES ON THE MAMMALS OF MAMMOTH CAVE, KENTUCKY. Samuel N. Rhoads. Jour. Cincinnati Soc.Nat. Hist., vol.19, no.2, pp.53-61, Mar.24, 1897.

KENTUCKY'S RESOURCES. THEIR DEVELOPMENT AND USE. Earl Wallace. Bull.Bur.School Service, Lexington, vol. 18, no.2, pp.351, illus., Dec., 1945.

NOTES ON THE MAMMALS OF ROWAN AND ADJACENT COUNTIES IN EASTERN KENTUCKY. Wilfred A. Welter, Dwight E. Sollberger. Jour. Mamm., vol.20, no.1, pp.77-81, Feb. 14, 1939.

UNITED STATES--LOUISIANA

FUR ANIMALS OF LOUISIANA. Stanley C. Arthur. Bull. Dept.Conservation State of Louisiana, no.18, pp.1-433, illus., Nov., 1928;Revised, pp.1-444, illus., Jan., 1931.

LOUISIANA'S FUR INDUSTRY. Armand P. Daspit. Louisiana Conservationist, New Orleans, vol.1, no.2, pp.16-18, illus., Oct., 1948.

LOUISIANA'S PICTURESQUE WILD LIFE NAMES. James Nelson Gowanloch. Louisiana Conservation Review, Dept.Conservation, New Orleans, vol.10, no.1, pp. 30-34, 37, illus., 1941.

STATISTICAL SUMMARY OF NATURAL RESOURCES OF LOUISIANA. James P. Guillot et al. Louisiana Cons.News, vol. 5, no.3, pp.3-8, July, 1936.

MAMMALS OF NATCHITOCHES PARISH. Horace Hays. MS thesis, Louisiana State Univ., 1941.

FUR SITUATION IN LOUISIANA. C. E. King. Proc. N.Amer.Wildl.Conf., pp.630-632, 1936.

CHECKLIST OF THE MAMMALS OF LOUISIANA AND ADJACENT WATERS. George H. Lowery, Jr. Occas.Papers Mus.Zool., Louisiana State Univ., Baton Rouge, no.13, pp.213-257, figs.5, Nov. 22, 1943.

DISTRIBUTION OF LOUISIANA MAMMALS WITH RESPECT TO THE PHYSIOGRAPHY OF THE STATE. George H. Lowery, Jr. Proc. Louisiana Acad.Sci., vol.8, pp.63-73, figs.2, Dec., 1944.

PRELIMINARY REPORT ON THE DISTRIBUTION OF THE MAMMALS OF LOUISIANA. George H. Lowery, Jr. Proc.Louisiana Acad.Sci., vol.3, no.1, pp.39, pls. 4, map, Mar., 1936.

PRELIMINARY REPORT ON THE MAMMALS OF LOUISIANA. George H. Lowery, Jr. MS thesis, Louisiana State Univ., 1936.

NEW PALEOCENE MAMMAL FROM A DEEP WELL IN LOUISIANA. (Anisonchus fortunatus.) George G. Simpson. Proc.U.S. Nat.Mus., vol.82, art.2, pp.1-4, fig.1, Nov. 5, 1932.

PRELIMINARY LIST OF THE MAMMALS OF CADDO AND DE SOTO PARISHES, LOUISIANA. John K. Strecker. Contrib. Baylor Univ.Mus. (Waco, Texas), no.15, pp.10-15, July, 1928.

UNITED STATES--MAINE

STATUS OF BIG GAME AND FUR ANIMALS IN MAINE. C.M. Aldous, Howard L. Mendall. Maine Coop. Wildl. Res. Unit, pp.24, Sep., 1941.

BIOTIC SUCCESSION ON KATAHDIN. I.H. Blake. Appalachia, vol.18, no.4, pp.409-424, pls.2, Dec., 1931.

SOME SMALL MAMMALS OF MOUNT DESERT ISLAND, MAINE. Manlif Lelyn Branin. Occas.Papers Boston Soc.Nat. Hist., vol.8, pp.311-320, map, Jan. 6, 1939.

BIG GAME AND FUR-BEARING ANIMALS OF MAINE. Malcolm W. Coulter. Univ. Maine, Agr.Ext.Bull., no.425, pp.1-32, illus., Dec., 1952.

MICROSOREX, SOREX PALUSTRIS, AND MICROTUS CHROTORRHINUS FROM MT. KATAHDIN, MAINE. Gerd H. Heinrich. Jour. Mamm., vol.34, no.3, p.382, Aug. 14, 1953.

DR. YOUNG'S BOTANICAL EXPEDITION TO MOUNT KATAHDIN. (Few Mammal Records.) J.K. Laski. Maine Nat., vol. 7, no.2, pp.38-62, June, 1927.

NOTES ON THE MAMMALS OF MOUNT DESERT ISLAND, MAINE. Richard H. Manville. Jour. Mamm., vol.23, no.4, pp.391-398, Nov. 14, 1942.

MAMMALS OF PORTLAND, MAINE, AND VICINITY. Arthur H. Norton. Proc. Portland Soc. Nat. Hist., vol.4, pt.1, pp.1-151, map, 1930.

UNITED STATES--MARYLAND

ANCIENT INHABITANTS OF SOUTHERN MARYLAND. (Fossils from Calvert Cliffs.) Charles T. Berry.Nature Mag., Wash., D.C., vol.32, no.5, pp.259-261, photos3, May, 1939.

MAMMALS OF A LIMITED AREA IN MARYLAND. ECOLOGICAL STUDY IN THE BARE HILLS-LAKE ROLAND AREA. Joseph A. Bures. Maryland Nat., Baltimore, vol.18, no.4, pp.58-68, illus., Fall, 1948.

LIST OF MARYLAND MAMMALS. PART I. MARSUPIALS AND INSECTIVORES. M.C. Gardner. Proc. Biol. Soc. Washington, vol. 63, pp.65-68, May 25, 1950; PART II. BATS. Proc.Biol.Soc. Washington, vol.63, pp.111-114, Dec. 29, 1950.

PLEISTOCENE CAVE DEPOSIT OF WESTERN MARYLAND. J.W. Gidley. Ann. Rep. Smiths.Inst., 1918, pp.281-287, pls.1-6, 1920.

PRELIMINARY REPORT ON A RECENTLY DISCOVERED PLEISTOCENE CAVE DEPOSIT NEAR CUMBERLAND MARYLAND. J.W. Gidley. Proc. U.S.Nat.Mus., vol.46, no.2014, pp.93-102, figs.8, Aug. 23, 1913.

NEW MAMMALIA IN THE PLEISTOCENE FAUNA FROM CUMBERLAND CAVE. J.W. Gidley, C. Lewis Gazin. Jour.Mamm., vol. 14, no.4, pp.343-357, figs.9, Nov., 1933.

PLEISTOCENE VERTEBRATE FAUNA FROM CUMBERLAND CAVE, MARYLAND. J.W. Gidley, C. Lewis Gazin. U.S. Nat. Mus. Bull., no.171, pp.1-99, figs.50, pls. 1-10, tbls.25, May 5, 1938.

NATURAL HISTORY OF PLUMMERS ISLAND, MARYLAND. IX. MAMMALS. E.A. Goldman, H.H.T. Jackson. Proc. Biol.Soc. Washington, vol.52, pp.131-134, Oct. 11, 1939.

NOTES ON THE MAMMALS OF THE PATAPSCO STATE PARK. Irving E. Hampe. Bull. Nat. Hist. Soc. Maryland, Baltimore, vol.10, no.1, pp.4-7, Sep., 1939.

DATA CONCERNING RACCOONS AND MUSKRATS ON TIDAL MARSHES IN MARYLAND. Van T. Harris, David E. Davis.Proc. 8th Ann. N.E.Wildl.Conf., Jackson's Mill, W.Va., pp.1-10, Apr. 1-4, 1952.

EXTINCT OCEAN-LIVING MAMMALS FROM MARYLAND. Remington Kellogg. Explorations and Field Work of the Smiths. Inst. in 1928, Smiths. Publ., no.3011, pp. 27-32, illus., Apr., 1929.

SEARCH FOR EXTINCT MARINE MAMMALS IN MARYLAND. Remington Kellogg. Explorations and Field Work of the Smiths. Inst. in 1933, Smiths.Publ., no.3235, pp. 15-17, figs.19-20, Mar. 20, 1934.

OBSERVATIONS IN THE VICINITY OF LOCH RAVEN. MAMMALS. C. Haven Kolb, Jr. Bull.Nat.Hist.Soc.Maryland, vol.9, no.1, pp.1-5, Sep., 1938.

EXTINCT AND VANISHING MAMMALS OF MARYLAND AND DISTRICT OF COLUMBIA. Romeo Mansueto. Maryland Nat., Nat.Hist. Soc.Maryland, Baltimore, vol.20, nos.1-2, pp.2-48, illus., 1950.

RECENT PALEONTOLOGICAL DISCOVERIES FROM CUMBERLAND BONE CAVE. Brother G. Nicholas. Sci.Monthly, Lancaster, vol.76, no.5, pp.301-305, illus., May, 1953.

FUR TAKE IN MARYLAND. Frank Woodfield. Maryland Cons., vol.31, no.3, pp. 9-12, illus., May, 1954.

FUR RESOURCES DECLINE. Maryland Cons., Baltimore, vol.25, no.1, pp.12-13, illus., Spring, 1948.

UNITED STATES--MASSACHUSETTS

CATALOGUE OF THE MAMMALS OF MASSACHUSETTS: WITH A CRITICAL REVISION OF THE SPECIES. (CETACEA). J.A. Allen. Bull.Mus.Comp.Zool., vol.1, no.8, pp.202-207, 1869. (Typewritten copy.)

IMPORTANT ADDITION TO THE FAUNA OF MASSACHUSETTS. Outram Bangs.Proc. Boston Soc.Nat.Hist., vol.27, pp.159-161, Oct., 1896.

POCKET LIST OF THE MAMMALS OF EASTERN MASSACHUSETTS, WITH ESPECIAL REFERENCE TO ESSEX COUNTY. C. Emerson Brown. Peabody Acad. Sci., pp.53, pls.4, 1913.

NOTES ON THE MAMMALS OF MOUNT GREYLOCK, MASSACHUSETTS. Manton Copeland. Proc.Biol.Soc. Washington, vol. 25, pp.157-162, Dec. 4, 1912.

MAMMALS OF HAMPSHIRE COUNTY, MASSACHUSETTS. Jocelyn Crane. Jour.Mamm., vol.12, no.3, pp.267-273, Aug., 1931.

REPORT ON THE QUADRUPEDS OF MASSACHUSETTS. Ebenezer Emmons. Zool. and Botanical Survey, Cambridge, Mass., pp.1-80, 1840.

MAMMALIAN GEOGRAPHY OF WORCESTER COUNTY, MASSACHUSETTS. Harry C. Parker. MS thesis, Clark Univ., 1938.

PRELIMINARY LIST OF THE MAMMALS OF WORCESTER COUNTY, MASSACHUSETTS. Harry C. Parker. Proc.Boston Soc. Nat.Hist., vol.41, no.7, pp.403-416, Jan., 1939.

UTILIZATION OF MARINE LIFE BY THE WAMPANOAG INDIANS OF MASSACHUSETTS. Frank G. Speck. Jour.Washington Acad.Sci., vol.38, no.8, pp.257-265, figs.3, Aug. 15, 1948.

NOTES ON SOME MAMMALS OF WESTERN MASSACHUSETTS. H.E. Warfel. Jour. Mamm., vol.18, no.1, pp.82-85, Feb. 14, 1937.

REPORTS ON THE HERBACEOUS PLANTS AND ON THE QUADRUPEDS OF MASSACHUSETTS. Massachusetts, Zoological and Botanical Survey. Cambridge, Folsom, Wells amd Thurston, Printers, pp.viii-277, 1840.

UNITED STATES--MICHIGAN

NOTES ON ISLE ROYALE MAMMALS AND THEIR ECOLOGICAL RELATIONS. Chas. C. Adams. An Ecological Survey of Isle Royale, Lake Superior, Univ.Michigan Mus., State Biol.Surv., 1908, Lansing, pp.389-422, 1909.

ECOLOGICAL STUDIES ON THE VERTEBRATE FAUNA OF A 500-ACRE FARM IN KALAMAZOO COUNTY, MICHIGAN. Durward L. Allen. Ecological Monographs, vol.8, pp.347-436, July, 1938.

TWO RECENT MAMMAL RECORDS FROM ALLEGAN COUNTY, MICHIGAN. Durward L. Allen. Jour. Mamm., vol.21, no.4, pp. 459-460, Nov. 14, 1940.

THOSE MICHIGAN BOW HUNTERS. I.H. Bartlett. Michigan Conserv., Lansing, vol. 19, no.5, pp.15-17, 29-30, illus., Sep., 1950.

FOURTEEN YEARS' WILD-FUR HARVEST. Luther L. Baumgartner. Michigan Conserv., vol.11, no.11, pp.4-5, Dec., 1942.

POPULATION DENSITY, LIFE SPAN, AND MORTALITY RATES OF SMALL MAMMALS IN THE BLUE-GRASS MEADOW AND BLUE-GRASS FIELD ASSOCIATIONS OF SOUTHERN MICHIGAN. W. Frank Blair. Amer. Midland Nat., Notre Dame, vol.40, no.2, pp.395-419, figs.2, Sep., 1948.

SMALL MAMMAL POPULATION OF A HARDWOOD FOREST IN NORTHERN MICHIGAN. W. Frank Blair. Contrib. Lab. Vert. Genetics., Univ. Michigan, Ann Arbor, no.17, pp.10, Nov., 1941.

SOME DATA ON THE HOME RANGES AND GENERAL LIFE HISTORY OF THE SHORT-TAILED SHREW, RED-BACKED VOLE,

AND WOODLAND JUMPING MOUSE IN NORTHERN MICHIGAN. W. Frank Blair. Amer. Midland Nat., Notre Dame, vol.25, no.3, pp.681-685, May, 1941.

MICHIGAN WILDLIFE SKETCHES: BETTER KNOWN MAMMALS OF MICHIGAN'S FORESTS, FIELDS, AND MARSHES. Glenn W. Bradt. Lansing, Education Division, Michigan Dept. of Conserv., pp.24, illus., 1947; Revised and enl.Ed., pp.62, illus., 1955.

ANALYSIS OF HUNTING RECORDS FOR THE PRAIRIE FARM PROJECT, SAGINAW COUNTY, MICHIGAN, 1937. R.D.Burroughs. Jour.Wildl.Mgt., Menasha, Wisc., vol.3, no.1, pp.19-25, Jan., 1939.

GAME REFUGES AND PUBLIC HUNTING GROUNDS IN MICHIGAN. R.D.Burroughs. Jour.Wildl.Mgt., Menasha, vol.10, no.4, pp.285-296, Oct., 1946.

HUNTING RECORDS FOR THE PRAIRIE FARM, SAGINAW COUNTY, MICHIGAN, 1937-1939. R.D. Burroughs, Laurence Dayton, Jour. Wildl. Mgt., Menasha, vol.5, no.2, pp.150-167, Apr., 1941.

CHANGES IN THE NOMENCLATURE OF MICHIGAN MAMMALS. William Henry Burt. Univ. Michigan Mus. Zool., Occas. Papers, no.481, Ann Arbor, pp.1-9, Nov. 10, 1943.

ECONOMIC VALUE OF WILD MAMMALS IN MICHIGAN. William Henry Burt. Detroit, Metropolitan Detroit Sci.Rev., vol.7, no.4, pp.26-27, 1947.

LIST OF THE MAMMALS OF MICHIGAN. William Henry Burt. Ann Arbor, Univ.Mus., Univ. of Michigan, pp.4, illus., 1950?

MAMMALS OF MICHIGAN. William Henry Burt. Univ. Michigan Press, Ann Arbor, pp.xv-288, 1946; Revised, xv-288, figs. 107, maps 67, pls.13, 1948.

(Review by Remington Kellogg of) MAMMALS OF MICHIGAN. William Henry Burt. Amer.Midland Nat., Notre Dame, vol.39, no.1, p.254, Jan., 1948.

TERRITORIAL BEHAVIOR AND POPULATIONS OF SOME SMALL MAMMALS IN SOUTHERN MICHIGAN. William Henry Burt. Misc.Publ.Mus.Zool.Univ.Michigan, Ann Arbor, no.45, pp.58, figs.8, pls.2, May 8, 1940.

THE MOOSE (ALCES AMERICANUS) AND THE WATER SHREW (SOREX PALUSTRIS HYDROBADISTES), RARE MAMMALS OF THE SOUTHERN PENINSULA OF MICHIGAN. Charles W. Creaser. Papers Michigan Acad. Sci., Arts and Letters, Ann Arbor, vol.20, pp.597-598, June 24, 1935.

MAMMAL FAUNA OF A WOODED LOT IN SOUTHERN MICHIGAN. Charles M. Davis, Jr. Papers Michigan Acad. Sci., Arts and Letters, vol.5, pp.425-428, Jan., 1926.

MAMMALS OF MARION ISLAND, GRAND TRAVERSE COUNTY, MICHIGAN. L.R. Dice. Univ. Michigan, Occas. Papers Mus. Zool., no.160, pp.1-8, pl.1, May 27, 1925.

MAMMALS OF WARREN WOODS, BERRIEN COUNTY, MICHIGAN. L.R. Dice. Occas. Papers Mus. Zool. Univ. Michigan, no.86, pp.20, pls.2, June 24, 1920.

MANUAL OF THE RECENT WILD MAMMALS OF MICHIGAN. L.R. Dice. Ann Arbor, Univ.Mus., Univ.of Michigan, Michigan Handbook Series, no.2, pp.62, illus., 1927.

PRELIMINARY CLASSIFICATION OF THE MAJOR TERRESTRIAL ECOLOGIC COMMUNITIES OF MICHIGAN, EXCLUSIVE OF ISLE ROYALE. L.R. Dice. Michigan Acad. Sci. Arts and Letters, Papers, vol. 16, pp.217-239, Mar., 1932.

SURVEY OF THE MAMMALS OF CHARLEVOIX COUNTY, MICHIGAN, AND VICINITY. L.R. Dice. Univ. Michigan, Occas.Papers Mus. Zool., no.159, pp.1-33, pls.3, Apr. 11, 1925.

ZOOLOGICAL RESOURCES OF MICHIGAN. THE BIRDS AND MAMMALS. L.R. Dice. Michigan Acad.Sci., Arts and Letters, 27-28th Ann. Rep., pp.74-80, Nov. 15, 1926.

NOTES ON THE MAMMALS OF GOGEBIC AND ONTONAGON COUNTIES, MICHIGAN, 1920. L.R. Dice, H.B. Sherman. Occas. Papers Mus.Zool., Univ.Michigan, no.109, pp.1-46, pls.3, Feb. 25, 1922. (Lists 42 Species.)

ISLE ROYALE, THE NEXT NATIONAL PARK. Ben East. (Notes on Mammals, Especially Caribou and Moose.) Bull.New York Zool.Soc., vol.39, no.2, pp.47-59, illus., Apr., 1936.

NOTES ON SOME MAMMALS OF MONTMORENCY COUNTY, MICHIGAN. Morris M. Green. Jour.Mamm., vol.6, no.3, pp. 173-178, Aug., 1925.

MARINE MAMMALS IN MICHIGAN PLEISTOCENE BEACHES. Charles O. Handley, Jr. Jour. Mamm., vol.34, no.2, pp.252-253, May 14, 1953.

THE MAMMALS. William P. Harris, Jr. (In) The Book of Huron Mountain. Huron Mountain Club (Marquette County, Michigan), pp.191-212, illus., 1929.

LAND VERTEBRATE COMMUNITIES OF WESTERN LEELANAU COUNTY, MICHIGAN, WITH AN ANNOTATED LIST OF THE MAMMALS OF THE COUNTY. Robert T. Hatt. Papers Michigan Acad. Sci., Arts and Letters, vol.3, pp.369-402, pls.3, 1924.

MICHIGAN TRAPPERS. D.W. Hayne. Michigan State College, Agric.Exper.Sta., Special Bull., no.307, East Lansing, pp.34, figs.6, June, 1941.

ECOLOGICAL DISTRIBUTION OF THE MAMMALS OF THE CRANBROOK AREA. Harold J. Leraas. Cranbrook Inst.Sci., Bull.no.13, pp.20, pls.2, Aug., 1938.

ECOLOGY AND LAND-USE RELATIONSHIPS OF SMALL MAMMALS ON A MICHIGAN FARM. J.P. Linduska. PhD thesis, Michigan State College, 1949; Lansing, Game Division, Dept. Conserv., pp.ix-144, illus., 1950.

EDGE EFFECT AS IT APPLIES TO SMALL MAMMALS ON SOUTHERN MICHIGAN FARMLAND. J.P. Linduska. Trans. 11th N.Amer.Wildl.Conf., Washington, pp.200-204, fig.1, 1946.

GAME. P.S. Lovejoy. (In) Fourth Biennial Rep.Michigan Dept. Conservation, 1927-28, pp.217-275, illus., 1929.

MAMMALS OF DRUMMOND ISLAND, MICHIGAN. Richard H. Manville. Jour.Mamm., vol.31, no.3, pp.358-359, Aug. 21, 1950.

STUDY OF SMALL MAMMAL POPULATIONS IN NORTHERN MICHIGAN. Richard H. Manville. Mus. Zool. Univ. Michigan, Misc. Publ., no.73, pp.83, pls.4, Aug. 16, 1949.

VERTEBRATE FAUNA OF THE HURON MOUNTAINS, MICHIGAN. Richard H. Manville. Amer. Midland Nat., Notre Dame, vol.39, no.3, pp.615-640, May, 1948.

REPORT ON THE QUALIFICATIONS AND DEVELOPMENT OF ISLE ROYALE AS A NATIONAL PARK. Adolph Murie. Privately Printed, pp.4, June 13, 1935.

ADDITIONAL ANIMAL REMAINS FROM UNDER SLEEPING BEAR DUNE, LEELANAU COUNTY, MICHIGAN. William O.Pruitt, Jr. Papers Michigan Acad. Sci., Arts and Letters, vol.39, pp.253-256, 1954.

MAMMALS OF THE CHASE S. OSBORN PRESERVE, SUGAR ISLAND, MICHIGAN. William O. Pruitt, Jr. Jour.Mamm., vol. 32, no.4, pp.471-472, Nov. 19, 1951.

MICROCLIMATES AND LOCAL DISTRIBUTION OF SMALL MAMMALS ON THE GEORGE RESERVE, MICHIGAN. William O. Pruitt, Jr. Ann Arbor, Mus. Zoology, Univ. of Michigan, Misc. Publ., no.109, pp.27, diagrs., 1959.

CARRYING CAPACITY OF SOUTHERN MICHIGAN GAME RANGE. H.D. Ruhl. Trans. 6th N.Amer.Wildl.Conf., Wash., D.C., pp.126-132, 1941.

FUR BEARERS IN MICHIGAN'S FOREST AREAS. H.D. Ruhl. Papers Michigan Acad. Sci., Arts and Letters, vol.15, pp.261-266, (1931) 1932.

GAME DIVISION. SEVENTH BIENNIAL REPORT OF THE DEPARTMENT OF CONSERVATION. H.D. Ruhl. Michigan Dept. of Conserv., 7th Biennial Rep. 1933-34, pp. 157-188, illus., 1935.

LAND-ECONOMIC SURVEY IN MICHIGAN. R.A. Smith. Roosevelt Wild Life Bull., vol. 3, no.4, pp.679-692, 1927.

SOME REMARKS ON THE NATURAL HISTORY OF BEAVER ISLANDS, MICHIGAN. James Jesse Strang. Smiths.Inst., Ann. Rep., for 1854, pp.282-288, 1855.

ANNOTATED CHECK LIST OF MICHIGAN MAMMALS. Norman A. Wood. Occas. Papers of the Mus. of Zool., no.4, pp.1-13, Apr. 1, 1914.

MAMMALS OF WASHTENAW COUNTY, MICHIGAN. Norman A. Wood. Occas. Papers Mus.Zool.Univ.Michigan, no.123, pp.23, July 10, 1922.

NOTES ON THE MAMMALS OF BERRIEN COUNTY, MICHIGAN. Norman A. Wood. Occas. Papers Mus. Zool., Univ.Michigan, no.124, pp.4, July 10, 1922.

RECORDS OF THE DISTRIBUTION OF MICHIGAN MAMMALS. Norman A. Wood, L.R. Dice. Papers Michigan Acad. Sci., Arts and Letters, vol.3, pp.425-469, 1924.

MICHIGAN WILDLIFE SKETCHES: THE BETTERKNOWN MAMMALS OF MICHIGAN'S FORESTS, FIELDS AND MARSHES. Michigan Dept. of Conserv., Lansing, pp. 62, 1950.

UNITED STATES--MINNESOTA

MINNESOTA BIG GAME ANIMALS. Shaler E. Aldous. Abs. Papers Presented at Wildl. Cons.Short Course, Univ.Minn., May 4, 5, 6, 1939, pp.15-18, 1939.

MAMMALS OF SHERBURNE COUNTY, MINNESOTA. Bernard Bailey. Jour.Mamm., vol. 10, no.2, pp.153-164, May, 1929.

SOME RANDOM NOTES ON MAMMALS OF MINNESOTA. Bernard Bailey. Jour.Mamm., vol.3, no.4, p.259, Nov., 1922.

TWO NEW LOCALITY RECORDS FOR MAMMALS IN MINNESOTA. James R.Beer. Jour. Mamm., vol.34, no.3, pp.384-385, Aug. 14, 1953.

SMALL MAMMAL POPULATIONS ON THE ISLANDS OF BASSWOOD LAKE, MINNESOTA. James R. Beer, Paul Lukens, David Olsen. Ecology, Durham, vol.35, no.4, pp.437-445, illus., Oct., 1954.

CENTURY OF MINNESOTA WILDLIFE. (Beaver, Buffalo, Antelope.) W.J. Breckenridge. Conserv. Volunteer, St.Paul, vol. 12, no.72, pp.36-41, Sep.-Oct., 1949.

MAMMALS OF ITASCA COUNTY, MINNESOTA. Alvin R. Cahn. Jour.Mamm., vol. 2, no.2, pp.68-74, May, 1921.

TAXONOMIC KEYS TO THE COMMON ANIMALS OF MINNESOTA EXCLUSIVE OF THE PARASITIC WORMS, INSECTS, AND BIRDS. Samuel Eddy, Alex C. Hodson. Burgees Publ.Co., Minneapolis, pp.114, 1947.

MAMMALS OF CEDAR CREEK FOREST, ANOKA COUNTY, MINNESOTA. Harvey L. Gunderson. Flicker, Minneapolis, vol. 21, no.4, pp.96-100, Dec., 1949.

STUDY OF SMALL MAMMAL POPULATIONS AT CEDAR CREEK FOREST, ANOKA COUNTY, MINNESOTA. Harvey L. Gunderson. MS thesis, Univ. Minnesota, 1949; Minn.Mus.Nat.Hist., Occas.Papers, no.4, pp.49, Oct., 1950.

MAMMALS OF MINNESOTA. Harvey L. Gunderson, James R. Beer. Univ. Minn. Press, Minneapolis, pp.196, illus., 1953.

(Review by W.J. Hamilton of) MAMMALS OF MINNESOTA. Harvey L. Gunderson, James R. Beer. Jour.Mamm., vol.35, no. 2, p. 270, May 26, 1954.

MINNESOTA FUR-BEARERS--AN UNDEVELOPED ASSET. Donald M. Hatfield. Proc. Minn. Wildl.Cons.Short Course, vol. 2, pp.32-36, 1940.

SOME REMARKS ON THE NATURAL HISTORY OF THE COUNTRY ABOUT FORT RIPLEY, MINNESOTA. John Frazier Head. Smiths. Inst., Ann. Rep., 1854, pp.291-293, 1855.

MAMMALS OF MINNESOTA. SCIENTIFIC AND POPULAR ACCOUNT OF THEIR FEATURES AND HABITS. Clarence Luther Herrick. Minneapolis, Harrison and Smith, State Printers, pp.299, figs.23, pls.8, 1892. (Minnesota, Geological and Natural History Survey, Bull.no.7.)

BRIEF DESCRIPTIVE LIST OF MINNESOTA MAMMALS. Charles E. Johnson. Fins, Feathers and Fur, no.8, pp.1-8, illus., Dec., 1916.

NOTES ON THE MAMMALS OF NORTHERN LAKE COUNTY, MINNESOTA. Charles E. Johnson. Jour. Mamm., vol.3, no.1, pp.33-39, Feb., 1922.

RECOLLECTIONS OF THE MAMMALS OF NORTHWESTERN MINNESOTA. Charles E. Johnson. Jour.Mamm., vol.11, no.4, pp. 435-452, Nov., 1930.

SOME RECENT OBSERVATIONS ON WILD LIFE CONDITIONS IN THE SUPERIOR GAME REFUGE. (Notes on Game and Fur-Bearing Mammals in Minnesota.) Charles E. Johnson. Fins, Feathers and Fur, no.24, pp.1-4, Dec., 1920.

COMMON INJURIOUS MAMMALS OF MINNESOTA. Maynard S. Johnson. Univ. of Minnesota Agric.Exper.Sta., Bull.no.259, p.67, Jan., 1930.

NOTES ON MAMMALS FROM WEST-CENTRAL MINNESOTA. Harold J. Leraas. Jour. Mamm., vol.23, no.3, pp.343-345, Aug. 14, 1942.

MINNESOTA FUR-BEARERS AND PROBLEMS OF USING THEM PROPERLY. J. Manweiler. Abs.Papers Presented at Wildl. Cons.Short Course, Univ.Minn., May 4, 5, 6, 1939, pp.49-54, 1939.

OPOSSUM AND SPOTTED SKUNK IN BLUE EARTH COUNTY, MINNESOTA. Carl Mohr. Jour. Mamm., vol.12, no.2, pp.162-163, May, 1931.

BIG GAME IN MINNESOTA. Marius Morse. Conservation Volunteer, St.Paul, vol.3, no. 15, pp.52-56, Dec., 1941.

VANISHED MAMMALS OF MINNESOTA. Thos. S. Roberts. (In) The Mammals of Minnesota, by T.Surber. Minnesota Game and Fish Department, St.Paul, pp.3-13, illus., 1932.

SMALL MAMMALS OF NORTHEASTERN LAKE COUNTY, MINNESOTA. William N. Rom. The Flicker, Minneapolis, vol. 12, no.3, pp.29-32, Oct., 1940.

SOME PLEISTOCENE MAMMALIAN INHABITANTS OF MINNESOTA. Clinton R. Stauffer. Proc. Minnesota Acad.Sci., Minneapolis, vol.13, pp.20-44, 1945.

ADDITIONS TO THE MAMMALIAN FAUNA OF MINNESOTA. Thaddeus Surber. Fins, Feathers and Fur, no.18, p.6, June, 1919.

MAMMALS OF MINNESOTA. (With a chapter on the vanished mammals of Minnesota, by Thos. S. Roberts.) Thaddeus Surber. Bull. Minnesota Dept. Conservation, Div. Game and Fish, St.Paul, pp.84, figs., 1932.

PINE COUNTY GAME REFUGE AS A PLAYGROUND. (Notes on Game and Other Mammals.) Thaddeus Surber. Fins, Feathers and Fur (Official Bull., Minn. Game and Fish Dept.), no.18, pp.1-4, June, 1919.

MINNESOTA'S FOSSIL MAMMALS. Gustav Swanson. Conservation Volunteer, St.Paul, vol.8, no.45, pp.22-25, illus., Mar.-Apr., 1945.

MAMMALS OF MINNESOTA. Gustav Swanson. Minnesota Dept. Conservation, St.Paul, Tech.Bull., no.2, pp.108, illus., 1945.

UNITED STATES--MISSISSIPPI

EXPLORATIONS FOR A RAILROAD ROUTE FROM THE MISSISSIPPI TO THE PACIFIC. VOL. VIII. MAMMALS. Spencer F. Baird. (Data on thousands of collected speciemens.) Washington, pp.805, pls.60, 1857.

FUR-BEARING ANIMALS IN MISSISSIPPI WITH SPECIAL REFERENCE TO THEIR BIOLOGY AND ECONOMIS IMPORTANCE. Rita Brignac. MS thesis, Miss.State Coll., 1941.

FUR RESOURCES OF MISSISSIPPI. F.A. Cook. Miss. Game and Fish Comm., Survey Bull., pp.100, 1945.

GAME ANIMALS OF MISSISSIPPI. F.A. Cook. Survey Bull. Mississippi State Game and Fish Comm., Jackson, pp.v+42, 1943. (Mimeographed.)

ANIMALS BONES. Henry W. Setzer. (In) "Archeology of the Bynum Mounds, Mississippi," by John L. Cotter, John M.Corbett. Archeological Res.Series, Nat.Park Serv., Washington, no.1, p.49, 1951.

TRAPPERS AND FUR ANIMALS OF THE ORIGINAL DELTA REGION OF MISSISSIPPI. Lee E. Yeager. Jour.Mamm., vol.22, no.4, pp.364-378, figs.2, Nov. 14, 1941.

MISSISSIPPI FUR TRAPPERS TAKE FOR 1947-48 WORTH $1,179,000. Mississippi Game and Fish, Jackson, vol.11, no.10, p.4, 1948.

REPORT GIVES ESTIMATED HUNTER KILL FOR 1947-48. Mississippi Game and Fish, Jackson, vol.11, no.12, pp.5-7, tbls. 2, June, 1948.

UNITED STATES--MISSOURI

PRELIMINARY LIST OF THE MAMMALS OF MISSOURI. (Excepting the Chiroptera or Bats.) Rudolf Bennitt. Columbia, pp.3, 1939.

WILDLIFE RESEARCH IN MISSOURI. Rudolf Bennitt. Missouri Wildlife, Springfield, vol. 1, no.7, pp.9, 13-14, Feb., 1939.

SURVEY OF THE RESIDENT GAME AND FUR BEARERS OF MISSOURI. Rudolf Bennitt, Werner O. Nagel. Univ. Missouri Studies, vol.12, no.2, pp.215, figs.8, maps 10, Apr. 1, 1937.

PRELIMINARY STUDY OF THE TAXONOMY AND DISTRIBUTION OF THE MAMMALS OF NORTHWESTERN MISSOURI. Allen Brohn. AM thesis, Univ. Missouri, 1947.

DEVELOPMENT AND LAND USE ON A PRIVATE GAME PRESERVE IN SOUTHERN TANEY COUNTY, MISSOURI. Paul D. Dalke, David L. Spencer. Jour.Wildl. Mgt., Menasha, vol.8, no.1, pp.1-6, Jan., 1944.

MAMMAL DISTRIBUTION IN SALINE AND CAMDEN COUNTIES, MISSOURI. Robert K. Enders. Amer.Midland Nat., Notre Dame, Indiana, vol.13, no.3, pp.114-123, May, 1932.

NOTES ON THE MAMMALS OF SOUTHWESTERN MISSOURI. Hartley H.T. Jackson. Proc. Biol. Soc. Washington, vol.20, pp.71-74, June 12, 1907.

SOME MAMMALS OF OZARK COUNTY, MISSOURI. A. Starker Leopold, E. Raymond Hall. Jour.Mamm., vol.26, no.2, pp.142-145, July 15, 1945.

FUR AS A CROP ON MISSOURI FARMS. W.O. Nagel. Missouri Conserv.Comm., Jefferson City, Conserv.Bull., no.3, pp. 1-12, illus., 1944.

HARVESTS, ECONOMIC VALUES, AND SOIL-FERTILITY RELATIONSHIPS OF MISSOURI FURBEARERS. W.O. Nagel. Missouri Conserv.Comm., pp.1-42, graphs, Aug., 1953.

LATE PLEISTOCENE FAUNA FROM HERCULANEUM, MISSOURI. Everett Claire Olson. Jour.Geol., Chicago, vol.48, no.1, pp.32-57, pl.1, figs.10, Jan.-Feb., 1940.

MISSOURI WILDLIFE SCENES. (Opossum, Beaver, Raccoon, Deer.) Rex Gary Schmidt. Missouri Conserv., Jefferson City, vol.5, no.3, pp.8-9, illus., Mar., 1944.

WILD MAMMALS OF MISSOURI. Charles Walsh Schwartz, Elizabeth R. Schwartz. Columbia, Univ.Missouri Press and Missouri Conserv. Comm., pp.viii+341, illus., maps, 1959.

MAMMALS OF MISSOURI. Frank Schwarz. Bull. Saint Louis Nat.Hist.Mus.Assoc., vol.1, pp.38-44, June, 1920.

FEDERAL-AID WILDLIFE PROGRAM IN MISSOURI. Paul Tulenko. Missouri Conservationist, Jefferson City, vol.7, no.7, pp.4-5, 14-15, illus., July, 1946.

MISSOURI FURBEARERS. Reed Twichell. Missouri Conserv.Comm., pp.1-20, illus., July, 1951.

EXCAVATIONS IN THE MATTHEWS SITE, NEW MADRID COUNTY, MISSOURI. (Remains of Mammals p.92.) Winslow M. Walker, Robert McCormick. Trans.Acad. Sci., Saint Louis, vol. 31, no.4, pp.75-120, pls.19, June 30, 1946.

NOTES FROM THE FIELD. Missouri Conservationist, Jefferson City, vol.9, no.2, p.11, Feb., 1948.

WILDLIFE AND FORESTRY CODE OF THE STATE OF MISSOURI 1944. Missouri Conservation Comm., Jefferson City, pp.110, illus., 1944.

UNITED STATES--MONTANA

Extinct and Fossil Mammals

PALEOCENE AND EOCENE STRATA IN THE BEARPAW MOUNTAINS, MONTANA. Roland W. Brown, William T. Pecora. Science, Lancaster, vol.109, no.2837, pp. 487-488, May 13, 1949.

FOSSIL FOOTPRINTS FROM THE FORT UNION (PALEOCENE) OF MONTANA. Charles Whitney Gilmore. U.S.Nat.Mus., Proc., Washington, vol.74, art.5, pp.4, illus.1, pls.3, 1929.

NEW EVIDENCE OF THE LOWER MIOCENE AGE OF THE BLACKTAIL DEER CREEK FORMATION IN MONTANA. Claude W.Hibbard, Kendall A. Keenmon. Contrib.Mus. Paleont.Univ.Michigan, Ann Arbor, vol.8, no.7, pp.193-204, figs.3, map 1, July, 28 1950.

UPPER EOCENE FAUNA FROM THE SAGE CREEK AREA, BEAVERHEAD COUNTY, MONTANA. Jean Hough. Jour. Paleontol., vol.29, no.1, pp.22-36, pls.7-8, Jan., 1955.

GEOLOGY AND VERTEBRATA PALEONTOLOGY OF THE FORT LOGAN AND DEEP RIVER FORMATIONS OF MONTANA. PART 1. NEW VERTEBRATES. Harold E.Koerner. Amer.Jour.Sci., New Haven, vol.238, no. 12, pp.837-862, pls.7, Dec., 1940.

FAUNA OF THE TITANOTHERIUM BEDS AT PIPESTONE SPRINGS, MONTANA. W. D. Matthew. Bull.Amer.Mus.Nat.Hist., New York, vol.19, art.6, pp.197-226, figs. 19, May 9, 1903.

NEW FOSSIL MAMMALS FROM THE DEEP RIVER BEDS OF MONTANA. W.D.Matthew, C.C.Mook. Amer.Mus.Novitates, no.601, pp.7, figs.2, Mar. 22, 1933.

BASAL EOCENE MAMMALIAN FAUNA IN THE FT. UNION BEDS OF MONTANA. Henry Fairfield Osborn. Science, Lancaster, vol. 17, no.425, pp.312-313, Feb. 20, 1903.

ADDITIONS TO THE UPPER PALEOCENE FAUNA OF THE CRAZY MOUNTAIN FIELD. George Gaylord Simpson. Amer. Mus.Novitates, no.940, pp.1-14, figs.4, Aug. 18, 1937.

COLLECTION OF PALEOCENE MAMMALS FROM BEAR CREEK, MONTANA. George Gaylord Simpson. Ann.Carnegie Mus., vol. 19, no.2, pp.115-122, figs.4, May, 1929.

FORT UNION OF THE CRAZY MOUNTAIN FIELD, MONTANA AND ITS MAMMALIAN FAUNAS. George Gaylord Simpson. U.S. Govt.Print.Off., Washington, Smiths.Inst., U.S.Nat.Mus., Bull.169, pp.x+287, illus., pls.10, fold.map, diagrs., 1937.

MAMMALIAN FAUNA OF THE HELL CREEK FORMATION OF MONTANA. George Gaylord Simpson. Amer. Mus. Novitates, no.267, pp.7, illus., Apr. 30, 1927.

NEW FAUNA FROM THE FORT UNION OF MONTANA. George Gaylord Simpson. Amer.

Mus.Novitates, no.873, pp.27, figs.16, July 13, 1936.

NEW MAMMALIAN FAUNA FROM THE FORT UNION OF SOUTHERN MONTANA. George Gaylord Simpson. Amer.Mus. Novitates, no.297, pp.15, illus., Feb. 2, 1928.

NEW PALEOCENE MAMMALS FROM THE FORT UNION OF MONTANA. George Gaylord Simpson. U.S.Nat.Mus., Proc., Washington, vol.83, pp.221-244, 1937.

THIRD CONTRIBUTION TO THE FORT UNION FAUNA AT BEAR CREEK, MONTANA. George Gaylord Simpson. Amer. Mus. Novitates, no.345, pp.1-12, figs.5, 1929.

CONTINENTAL CENOZOIC AT THREE FORKS MONTANA. Horace E.Wood 2nd. Proc. Geol. Soc. America, 1937, pp.291-292, June, 1938.

Recent Mammals

WILD ANIMALS OF GLACIER NATIONAL PARK. THE MAMMALS, WITH NOTES ON PHYSIOGRAPHY AND LIFE ZONES. Vernon Bailey. Dept.Interior, pp.102, figs. 18, 1918; Washington Govt.Print.Off., pp. 210, illus., pls.36, 1918.

SOME MAMMALS FROM WESTERN MONTANA AND EASTERN IDAHO. William B. Davis. Murrelet, Jan.-May, 1937, vol.18, pp.22-27, Sep. 4, 1937.

MAMMALS ASSOCIATIONS AND HABITATS OF THE FLATHEAD LAKE REGION, MONTANA. Lee R. Dice. Ecology, vol.4, pp. 247-260, figs.3, July, 1923.

NOTES ON A FEW MAMMALS AT MISSOULA, MONTANA, 1917-1918. Lee R. Dice. Jour.Mamm., vol.3, no.4, pp.262-263, Nov., 1922.

NOTES ON ANIMAL HABITATS AT MISSOULA, MONTANA. Lee R. Dice.Ecology, vol.3, no.1, p.86, Jan., 1922.

ANCENEY LOCAL MAMMAL FAUNA, LATEST MIOCENE, MADISON VALLEY FORMATION, MONTANA. John A.Dorr, Jr. Jour.Paleontol., vol.30, no.1, pp.62-74, illus., Mar., 1956.

GAME ANIMALS IN GLACIER NATIONAL PARK. Morton J. Elrod. Big Horn, Missoula, Montana, vol.3, no.2, pp.1-2, May, 1926.

MAMMALS OF BITTERROOT VALLEY, MONTANA, IN THEIR RELATION TO SPOTTED FEVER. Henry W. Henshaw, Clarence Birdseye. U.S. Dept.Agr., Bur.Biol.Surv., Circ.no.82, pp.24, figs.12, Aug. 3, 1911.

SPOTTED SKUNK AND FERAL NUTRIA IN MONTANA. William L. Jellison. Jour. Mamm., vol.26, no.4, p.432, Feb. 12,1946.

BIG GAME IN MONTANA FROM EARLY HISTORICAL RECORDS. Elers Koch.Jour. Wildl.Mgt., Menasha, vol.5, no.4, pp.357-370, Oct., 1941.

MAMMALS OF GLACIER NATIONAL PARK. R.R. Lechleitner. Glacier Nat.Hist.Assoc., West Glacier, Montana, no.6, pp.92, illus., Aug., 1955.

STUDY OF BIG GAME IN THE CONTINENTAL AND ADJACENT UNITS. Merle Rognrud. Mont.State Fish and Game Dept., pp.188, 1949.

SMALL MAMMALS FROM SILVER BOW COUNTY, MONTANA. Robert J. Russel. Murrelet, Seattle, vol.37, no.1, pp.2-3, May 24, 1956.

EARLY TRADE VALUE OF SKINS IN MONTANA. Tracy I. Storer. Jour. Mamm., vol. 12, no.1, pp.77-78, Feb., 1931.

UNITED STATES--MOUNT RAINIER NATIONAL PARK

ITEMS OF INTEREST FROM MOUNT RAINIER--PACIFIC BEAVER, YELLOW-HAIRED PORCUPINE, PUGET SOUND STRIPED SKUNK. C. Frank Brockman. Murrelet, Seattle, vol.20, no.3, pp.70-71, Sep.-Dec., 1939.

NOTES ON MAMMALS COLLECTED AT MOUNT RAINIER, WASHINGTON. Marcus Ward Lyon. Smiths.Inst., Smiths.Misc. Coll., Washington, vol.L (Quarterly Issue, vol.IV), Publ.no.1713, pp.89-92, June 27, 1907 (1908).

SOME NOTES ON THE ANIMAL LIFE OF MOUNT RAINIER NATIONAL PARK, WASHINGTON. Preston P. Macy. Murrelet, vol. 15, no.2, pp.46-48, May, 1934.

MAMMALS OF MOUNT RAINIER NATIONAL PARK. Merlin K. Potts, Russell K. Grater. Mount Rainier Nat.Hist.Assoc., Longmire, pp.86, illus., 1949.

OUR GREATEST MOUNTAIN: HANDBOOK FOR MOUNT RAINIER NATIONAL PARK. F.W. Schomoe. New York and London, G.P. Putnam's Sons, vol. 8, pp.xii-366, illus. 64, map 1, 1925.

(Review by Hartley H.T. Jackson of) OUR GREATEST MOUNTAIN: HANDBOOK FOR MOUNT RAINIER NATIONAL PARK. F.W. Schomoe. Jour. Mamm., vol.8, no.2, pp. 166-168, May 11, 1927.

DISTRIBUTIONAL AND ECOLOGICAL STUDY OF MOUNT RAINIER, WASHINGTON. Walter P. Taylor. Ecology, vol.3, pp.214-236, July, 1922.

SOME BIRDS AND MAMMALS OF MOUNT RAINIER. Walter P. Taylor. The Mountaineer, Seattle, vol.14, no.1, pp.27-35, figs.5, Nov., 1921.

MAMMALS AND BIRDS OF MOUNT RAINIER NATIONAL PARK. Walter P.Taylor, William T. Shaw. Washington, U.S.Govt. Print.Off., pp.x-249, illus., fold.map, 1927.

(Review by R.M. Anderson of) MAMMALS AND BIRDS OF MOUNT RAINIER NATIONAL PARK. Walter P. Taylor, William T. Shaw. Canadian Field-Nat., vol.42, no.7, pp.180-182, Oct., 1928.

UNITED STATES--NEBRASKA

Extinct and Fossil Mammals

MAMMALIAN FOSSILS FROM DEVIL'S GULCH. Erwin H. Barbour. Nebraska, Univ. Studies, Lincoln, vol.14, no.2, pp. 185-202, pls.14, 1914.

EARLY PLEISTOCENE FAUNA FROM NEBRASKA. Erwin H. Barbour, C.Bertrand Schultz. Amer. Mus.Novitates, no. 942, pp.10, figs.4, Sep. 10, 1937.

MAMMALIAN FAUNAS OF THE LATE CENOZOIC OF NEBRASKA. Erwin H.Barbour, C. Bertrand Schultz. Proc.Geol.Soc. America for 1937, pp.268-269, June, 1938. (Abstract.)

PLEISTOCENE AND POST-GLACIAL MAMMALS OF NEBRASKA. Erwin H. Barbour, C.Bertrand Schultz. Early Man, edited by G.G.MacCurdy, Lippincott and Co., London, pp.185-192, figs.26, pls.13-15, 1937.

SCOTTSBLUFF BISON QUARRY AND ITS ARTIFACTS. Erwin H. Barbour. Nebraska State Mus., vol.1, Bull.no.34, pp.283-286, fig.169, Dec., 1932.

NEBRASKA--FIFTEEN MILLION YEARS AGO. Edwin H. Colbert. Nat.Hist., New York, vol.35, no.1, pp.37-46, illus., Jan., 1935.

CORRELATION OF THE PLEISTOCENE DEPOSITS OF NEBRASKA. George Evert Condra et al. Rev., Lincoln, Univ. of Nebraska Conservation and Survey Division, Geol.Surv., Bull.no.15-A, pp.74, illus., pl., maps, tbls., 1950.

FAUNAL LISTS OF THE TERTIARY VERTEBRATA OF NEBRASKA AND ADJACENT AREAS. H.J. Cook, Margaret C. Cook. Nebraska Geol.Surv., Paper no.5, pp.1-58, 1933.

FOSSIL BEDS OF NORTHWESTERN NEBRASKA AS OBSERVED ON THE McPHERSON COLLEGE 1937 SUMMER BIOLOGY TREK. Philip Bruce Davis. Trans.Kansas Acad.Sci., Topeka, vol.41, pp.199-200, 1938.

PLEISTOCENE GEOLOGY OF THE MIDDLE PORTION OF THE ELKHORN RIVER VALLEY. W.D. Frankforter. Univ. Nebraska Studies, Lincoln, n.s., no.5, pp.46, figs. 15, map 1, July, 1950. (Lists Fossil Mammals.)

CHADRON MAMMALIAN FAUNA FROM NEBRASKA. Jean Hough, Raymond Alf. Jour. Paleontol., vol.30, no.1, pp.132-140, illus., Mar., 1956.

ANCIENT FAUNA OF NEBRASKA: OR, A DESCRIPTION OF REMAINS OF EXTINCT MAMMALIA AND CHELONIA, FROM THE MAUVAISES TERRES OF NEBRASKA. Joseph Leidy. Washington, Smiths.Inst., Contribution to Knowledge, vol.6, art.7, Publ.no.58, pp.126, illus., pls., map, 1953.

DESCRIPTION OF THE REMAINS OF EXTINCT MAMMALIA AND CHELONIA, FROM NEBRASKA TERRITORY, COLLECTED DURING THE GEOLOGICAL SURVEY UNDER THE DIRECTION OF DR. D.D. OWEN. Joseph Leidy. (In) D.D. Owen, 1807-1860. Report of a Geological Survey of Wisconsin, Iowa, and Minnesota; and Incidentally of a Portion of Nebraska Territory. Philadelphia, pp.533-572, 1852.

EXTINCT MAMMALIAN FAUNA OF DAKOTA AND NEBRASKA, INCLUDING AN ACCOUNT OF SOME ALLIED FORMS FROM OTHER LOCALITIES, TOGETHER WITH A SYNOPSIS OF THE MAMMALIAN REMAINS OF NORTH AMERICA. Joseph Leidy. (Preceded With an Introduction, On the Geology of the Tertiary Formations of Dakota and Nebraska, Accompanied With a Map.) Jour. Acad. Nat. Sci., Philadelphia, vol.7, 2nd Series, pp.7-472, col.map, pls. 30, 1869.

NEBRASKA IN RELATION TO THE PROBLEMS OF PLEISTOCENE STRATIGRAPHY. A.L. Lugn. Amer. Jour. Sci., New Haven, vol.237, no.12, pp.851-884, figs.7, Dec., 1939. (Fossil Mammals p.879.)

PLEISTOCENE GEOLOGY OF NEBRASKA. A.L. Lugn. Nebraska Geol.Surv., ser.2, Bull.no.10, pp.223, figs.38, pls.2, 1935.

BURGE FAUNA, A LOWER PLIOCENE MAMMALIAN ASSEMBLAGE FROM NEBRASKA. Paul O. McGrew. Univ.Calif. Publ., Bull.Dept.Geol.Sci., vol.24, no. 11, pp.309-328, figs.12, Aug.3, 1938.

AN EARLY PLEISTOCENE (BLANCAN) FAUNA FROM NEBRASKA. Paul O. McGrew. Chicago Nat.Hist.Mus., Publ. no.546, Geol.Ser., vol.9, no.2, pp.37, illus., Jan. 20, 1944.

PRELIMINARY NOTICE ON THE MIOCENE AND PLIOCENE. MAMMALIAN FAUNAS NEAR VALENTINE, NEBRASKA. Paul O. McGrew, R.A. Stirton. Amer.Jour. Sci., Ser.5, vol.29, no.170, pp.125-132, figs.3, Feb., 1935.

CONTRIBUTION TO THE SNAKE CREEK FAUNA, WITH NOTES UPON THE PLEISTOCENE OF WESTERN NEBRASKA. W.D. Matthew. Amer.Mus.Expedition of 1916. Bull.Amer.Mus.Nat.Hist., New York, vol. 38, art.7, pp.183-229, figs.20, pls.4-10, Apr. 18, 1918.

FOSSIL BONES IN THE ROCK. FOSSIL QUARRY NEAR AGATE, SIOUX COUNTY, NEBRASKA. W.D. Matthew. Nat. Hist., vol.23, pp.358-369, figs.11, July-Aug., 1923.

LIST OF THE PLEISTOCENE FAUNA FROM HAY SPRINGS, NEBRASKA. W.D. Matthew. Bull. Amer.Mus.Nat.Hist., New York, vol. 16, art.24, pp.317-322, Sep. 25, 1902.

TERTIARY GEOLOGY OF NEBRASKA. Grayson Meade. Compass, Univ.Missouri, Columbia, vol.17, no.2, pp.76-87, figs. 3-10, Jan., 1937.

ASSOCIATION OF ARTIFACTS AND EXTINCT MAMMALS IN NEBRASKA. Bertrand Schultz. Nebraska State Mus., vol.1, Bull.no.33, pp.271-282, figs.166-168, Nov., 1932.

GEOLOGY AND MAMMALIAN FAUNA OF THE PLEISTOCENE OF NEBRASKA. PART

2. THE PLEISTOCENE MAMMALS OF NEBRASKA. Bertrand Schultz. Nebraska State Mus., vol.1, Bull.no.41, pp.357-393, tbl.1, Oct., 1934.

MIOCENE OF WESTERN NEBRASKA. Bertrand Schultz. Amer. Jour. Sci., Ser.5, vol. 35, no.210, pp.441-444, June, 1938.

GRAPHIC RESUME OF THE PLEISTOCENE OF NEBRASKA, WITH NOTES ON THE FOSSIL MAMMALIAN REMAINS. Bertrand Schultz, Gilbert C. Lueninghoener, W.D. Frankforter. Bull.Univ.Nebraska State Mus., Lincoln, vol.3, no.6, pp.41, figs.11, July, 1951.

PRELIMINARY REMARKS ON THE OLIGOCENE OF NEBRASKA. Bertrand Schultz, Thompson M. Stout. Bull.Geol.Soc.Amer. (Abstract), vol.49, no.12, pt.2, p.1921, Dec. 1, 1938.

MEDIAL PLEISTOCENE FOSSIL VERTEBRATE LOCALITIES IN NEBRASKA. Bertrand Schultz, Lloyd G. Tanner. Bull. Univ.Nebraska State Mus., vol.4, no.4, pp.59-81, Sep., 1957.

ADDITIONS TO THE FAUNA OF THE LOWER PLIOCENE SNAKE CREEK BEDS. (Results of the Princeton University 1914 Expedition to Nebraska.) William J. Sinclair. Proc. Amer.Philos.Soc., vol.54, no .217, pp.73-95, figs.18, May-July, 1915.

PRELIMINARY NOTICE ON THE MIOCENE AND PLIOCENE MAMMALIAN FAUNAS NEAR VALENTINE, NEBRASKA. R.A. Stirton, Paul O.McGrew. Amer. Jour.Sci., Ser.5, vol.29, no.170, pp.125-132, Feb., 1935.

Recent Mammals

FACTS ABOUT NIOBRARA BIG GAME RESERVE. Geno A. Amundson. Outdoor Nebraska, vol.11, no.1, pp.4, 12, Feb. 15, 1936.

PRELIMINARY STUDY OF THE ANIMAL ECOLOGY OF THE NIOBRARA GAME PRESERVE. Watson E. Beed. Bull.10, Conserv.Dept., Conserv.and Surv.Div., Univ.Nebraska, pp.3-33, figs.3, Oct., 1936.

NEBRASKA TRAPPER'S GUIDE, A HANDBOOK ON THE TAKING OF MUSKRAT, MINK, BEAVER, AND COYOTE, AND THE HANDLING OF PELTS. Edson Fichter, George Hytrex. Nebraska Game, Forestation and Parks Comm., pp.46, illus., 1948.

CHECKLIST OF MAMMALS OF NEBRASKA. J. Knox Jones, Jr. Trans. Kansas Acad.Sci., vol.60, no.3, pp.273-282, Oct. 22, 1957.

DISTRIBUTION OF SOME NEBRASKAN MAMMALS. J. Knox Jones, Jr. Univ.Kansas Publ., Mus.Nat.Hist., Lawrence, vol. 7, no.6, pp.479-487, Apr. 21, 1954.

NOTES ON MAMMALS FROM RICHARDSON COUNTY, NEBRASKA. J. Knox Jones, Jr. Jour. Mamm., vol.30, no.3, pp.312-313, Aug. 17, 1949.

PROVISIONAL CHECK-LIST OF THE MAMMALS OF NEBRASKA. William F. Rapp, Jr. Div. Sanitation, Nebraska State Dept.Health, Lincoln, pp.16, mimeographed, 1957.

FORT NIOBRARA GAME PRESERVE, NEBRASKA. Clara Ruth. U.S.Dept.Agric. Widl.Res. and Mgt., Leaflet no.BS-109, pp.1-7, pls.1-2, Apr., 1938.

PRELIMINARY REVIEW OF THE MAMMALS OF NEBRASKA. Myron Harmon Swenk. Lincoln, Nebr., under the direction of H.B. Ward, Studies Zool. Lab., Univ.Nebraska, Published conjointly by the Univ.Nebr.and the Nebr.Acad.Sci., no.89, pp.88, 1908.

MAMMALS FROM EASTERN NEBRASKA. Ralph Velich. Jour. Mamm., vol.37, no. 2, pp.271-272, June 9, 1956.

NOTES ON MAMMALS FROM EASTERN NEBRASKA. Ralph Velich. Jour. Mamm., vol.35, no.3, pp.429-430, Aug. 20, 1954.

SOME MAMMALS OF AN EASTERN NEBRASKA PRAIRIE. Don B. Whelan. Trans. Kansas Acad.Sci., vol.39, pp.365-366, 1937.

UNITED STATES--NEVADA

Extinct and Fossil Mammals

CRITICAL COMMENTS ON MAMMALS FROM UTAH, WITH DESCRIPTIONS OF NEW FORMS FROM UTAH, NEVADA AND WASHINGTON. E.R. Hall.Berkeley, Calif., Univ.Calif.Press, Publ.Zool., vol.37, no.1, pp.13, tbl., 1931.

RODENTS AND LAGOMORPHS FROM THE LATER TERTIARY OF FISH LAKE VALLEY, NEVADA. E. R. Hall. Univ.Calif. Publ., Bull.Dept.Geol.Sci., vol.19, no.12, pp.295-312, figs.29, pls.37, Nov. 25, 1930.

TERTIARY MAMMALIAN FAUNA FROM THE SAN ANTONIO MOUNTAINS NEAR TONOPAH, NEVADA. Paul C. Henshaw. Carnegie Inst. Washington, Publ.no.530, Contrib.Paleontol., pp.77-168, figs.7, pls. 11, lithoprinted, Jan. 15, 1942.

BLANCAN MAMMALIAN FAUNA FROM WICHMAN, NEVADA. J.R. MacDonald. Jour.Paleontol., vol.30, no.1, pp.213-216, illus., Mar., 1956.

NEW CLARENDONIAN FAUNA FROM NORTHEASTERN NEVADA. J.R.MacDonald. Berkeley, Univ.Calif.Press, Bull.Dept.Geol. Sci., vol.28, no.7, pp.173-194, 1940.

NEW CLARENDONIAN MAMMALIAN FAUNA FROM THE TRUCKEE FORMATION OF WESTERN NEVADA. (Pseudaplodon occidentale: Aepycamelus, A.bradyi.)J.R. Mac Donald. Jour.Paleontol., vol.30, no.1, pp. 186-202, illus., Mar., 1956.

OCCURRENCE OF MAMMALIAN REMAINS IN A PLEISTOCENE LAKE DEPOSIT AT ASTOR PASS, NEAR PYRAMID LAKE, NEVADA. John Campbell Merriam. Berkeley, Univ.Calif.Press, Bull.Dept.Geol., vol.8, no.21, pp.377-382, 1915.

OCCURRENCE OF TERTIARY MAMMALIAN REMAINS IN NORTHEASTERN NEVADA. John Campbell Merriam. Berkeley, Univ.C Calif.Press, Bull.Dept.Geol., vol.8, no.12, pp.275-281, 1914.

TERTIARY MAMMAL BEDS OF VIRGIN VALLEY AND THOUSAND CREEK IN NORTHWESTERN NEVADA. 1. GEOLOGIC HISTORY. 2. VERTEBRATE FAUNAS.John Campbell Merriam. Berkeley, Univ.Calif. Press, Dept. Geol., vol.6, nos.2, 11, illus., pls., 1910-11.

FURTHER CONTRIBUTION TO THE MAMMALIAN FAUNA OF THE THOUSAND CREEK PLIOCENE, NORTHWESTERN NEVADA. John Campbell Merriam. Contrib. Paleont.Carnegie Inst.Washington, Publ. no.393, pp.5-21, pls.3, figs.14, 1929.

NEVADA FAUNA OF PLEISTOCENE TYPE AND ITS PROBABLE ASSOCIATION WITH MAN. George G. Simpson. Amer. Mus. Novitates, no.667, pp.10, figs.5, Oct. 23, 1933.

CORRELATION OF THE FISH LAKE VALLEY AND CEDAR MOUNTAIN BEDS IN THE ESMERALDA FORMATION OF NEVADA. R.A. Stirton. Science, n.s., vol.76, no. 1959, pp.60-61, July 15, 1932.

NEVADA MIOCENE AND PLIOCENE MAMMALIAN FAUNAS AS FAUNAL UNITS. R.A. Stirton. Proc.6th Pacific Sci.Congress, Berkeley, pp.627-640, Sep., 1940.

EXPLORATION OF GYPSUM CAVE, NEVADA. Chester Stock. Bull.Geol.Soc.Amer., vol.42, no.1, p.364, Mar., 1931. (Abstract.)

Recent Mammals

HARMFUL AND BENEFICIAL MAMMALS OF THE ARID INTERIOR, WITH SPECIAL REFERENCE TO THE CARSON AND HUMBOLDT VALLEYS, NEVADA. Vernon Bailey. U.S. Dept.Agric., Farmers Bull., no.335, pp.2-31, figs.1-9, Oct. 21, 1908.

CHECK LIST OF THE MAMMALS OF THE BOULDER DAM NATIONAL RECREATIONAL AREA. Gordon C. Baldwin. U.S. Dept. Interior, Nat.Park Service, Lake Mead Nat. Recreational Area, Boulder City, Nevada, pp.7, 1944.

MAMMALS FOUND NEAR JARBIDGE, ELKO COUNTY, NEVADA. Adrey E. Borell.Jour. Mamm., vol.15, no.1, pp.72-73, Feb., 1934.

MAMMALS OF THE RUBY MOUNTAINS REGION OF NORTHEASTERN NEVADA. Adrey E. Borell, Ralph Ellis. Jour.Mamm., vol.15, no.1, pp.12-44, pls.1-6, Feb., 1934.

MAMMALS OF SOUTHERN NEVADA. William Henry Burt. Trans.San Diego Soc.Nat. Hist., vol.7, no.36, pp.375-427, map, May 31, 1934.

REPORT UPON THE COLLECTIONS OF MAMMALS MADE IN PORTIONS OF NEVADA, UTAH, CALIFORNIA, COLORADO, NEW MEXICO, AND ARIZONA, DURING THE YEARS 1871, 1872, 1873, AND 1874. Elliot Coues, H.C. Yarrow. U.S.Geographical Survey West of the 109th Meridian, Report, Washington, vol.5, pp.35-129, 1875-89.

MAMMALS OF NEVADA. E.Raymond Hall. Berkeley and Los Angeles, Univ.Calif.Press, pp.xi-710, illus., maps (part.col.), pls.11, tbls., diagrs., 1946.

(Review by Richard J. Costley of) MAMMALS OF NEVADA. E. Raymond Hall. Jour.Forestry, Washington, vol.44, no.12, pp.1102-1103, Dec., 1946.

(Review by Paul L. Errington of)MAMMALS OF NEVADA. E. Raymond Hall. Ecology, Lancaster, vol.28, no.1, pp.82-83, Jan., 1947.

(Review by Carl L. Hubbs of) MAMMALS OF NEVADA. E. Raymond Hall. Amer.Nat., Lancaster, vol.80, no.794, pp.584-586, Sep.-Oct., 1946.

(Review by T.C.Morrison-Scott of) MAMMALS OF NEVADA. E.Raymond Hall. Nature, London, vol.158, no.4026, pp. 926-927, Dec. 28, 1946.

(Review by P.Rode of) MAMMALS OF NEVADA. E. Raymond Hall. Mammalia, Paris, vol.10, nos.3-4, pp.155-156, Sep.-Dec., 1946.

NEW MAMMAL RECORDS FOR NEVADA. Ned K. Johnson. Jour. Mamm., vol.35, no.4, pp.577-578, Nov. 29, 1954.

SIERRA OUTPOST. (Accounts of Coyotes and Other Wild Animals.) Lila Lofberg, David Malcolmson. Dunn, Sloan and Pearce, New York, pp.253, 1941.

MAMMALS OF LAKE TAHOE. Robert T. Orr. San Francisco, Calif.Acad.Sci., pp. 127, 1949.

BIG GAME TRENDS IN NEVADA. J.C.Rabb. Proc. Ann.Conf.W.Assn.State Game and Fish Comm., vol.30, pp.155-163, 1950?

NEVADA MAMMAL RECORDS. Frank Richardson. Jour. Mamm., vol.35, no.4, pp.578-579, Nov. 29, 1954.

MAMMALS OF THE ALEXANDER NEVADA EXPEDITION OF 1909. Walter Penn Taylor. Berkeley, Univ.Press, Publ.Zool., vol.7, no.7, pp.205-307, 1911.

CONSERVING NEVADA FISH AND WILDLIFE. Sessions S. Wheeler. Conserv. and Nevada, State Dept. Public Instruction, Carson City, pp.89-126, illus., 1949.

UNITED STATES--NEW ENGLAND

FAUNA OF NEW ENGLAND. PART 3. LIST OF THE MAMMALIA. Glover Morrill Allen. Boston, Printed for the Society of Nat.Hist., Occasional Papers, no.7, pt.3, pp.35, 1904.

SOME FACTS IN REGARD TO THE DISTRIBUTION OF CERTAIN MAMMALS IN NEW ENGLAND AND NORTHERN NEW YORK. Charles F. Batchelder. Proc.Boston Soc.Nat.Hist., vol.27, pp.185-193, map, Oct., 1896.

LAND MAMMALS OF NEW ENGLAND. THESIS FOR AN ADVANCED DEGREE. Alice Albur (Hicks) Black. Maine State College, '87. Portland, Me., Dec., 1890. Augusta, Burleigh and Flynt, Printers to the State, Ann. Rep., pp.48, pls.5, 1891.

LITTLE BEASTS OF FIELD AND WOOD. William Everett Cram. Boston, Small, Maynard and Co., pp.xx-261, pls., 1899.

NEW ENGLAND'S LAND MAMMALS. Francis Harper. Nature Mag., vol.13, pp. 311-314, 345, illus., May, 1929.

WILD ANIMAL DAMAGE TO NEW ENGLAND FORESTS. N.W. Hosley. (Committee Report.) Jour. Forestry, vol.29, no.5, pp.700-703, May, 1931.

MAMMALOGY AND ORNITHOLOGY OF NEW ENGLAND WITH REFERENCE TO AGRICULTURAL ECONOMY. Edward A. Samuels. U.S. Dept.Agric., Rep., Wash., pp.265-286, 1863.

UNITED STATES--NEW HAMPSHIRE

LIST OF NEW HAMPSHIRE MAMMALS AND THEIR DISTRIBUTION. Ralph G. Carpenter 2nd, Hilbert R. Siegler. N.H. Fish and Game Dept., pp.11, 1945.

NOTES ON NEW HAMPSHIRE MAMMALS. C.F. Jackson. Jour. Mamm., vol.3, no. 1, pp.13-15, Feb., 1922.

ON A COLLECTION OF SMALL MAMMALS FROM THE NEW HAMPSHIRE MOUNTAINS. Gerrit S. Miller, Jr. Proc. Boston Soc. Nat.Hist., vol.27, pp.177-197, pls.3-4, Mar. 24, 1894.

LAND MAMMALS OF NEW HAMPSHIRE. Norman A. Preble. PhD thesis, Ohio State Univ., 1942.

HISTORY OF NEW HAMPSHIRE GAME AND FURBEARERS. Helenette Silver. New Hampshire Fish and Game Dept., Surv.Rept., no.6, pp.xiv-466, illus., May, 1957.

MAMMALS AT BRETTON WOODS. Agnes Waterman. Audubon Soc. New Hampshire Bull., vol.18, no.1, pp.3-6, Spring, 1947.

UNITED STATES--NEW JERSEY

ECOLOGICAL DISTRIBUTION OF SOME SMALL MAMMALS IN A NEW JERSEY PINE BARRENS AREA. Paul F. Connor. Master's thesis, Cornell Univ., 1952.

NOTES ON THE MAMMALS OF NEW JERSEY PINE BARRENS AREA. Paul F. Connor. Jour.Mamm., vol.34, no.2, pp.227-235, May 14, 1953.

SYNOPSIS OF THE EXTINCT MAMMALIA OF NEW JERSEY. Edward Drinker Cope. Geol.Survey, Geology of New Jersey, Newark, pp.739-742, 1868.

CHECK LIST OF THE CRETACEOUS AND TERTIARY VERTEBRATES OF NEW JERSEY. Halsey W. Miller, Jr. Jour.Paleontol., vol.29, no.5, pp.903-914, Sep., 1955.

CONTRIBUTION TO THE MAMMALOGY OF NORTHERN NEW JERSEY. Samuel N. Rhoads. Proc.Acad.Nat.Sci.Philadelphia, pp.23-33, Feb. 23, 1897.

MAMMALS OF PENNSYLVANIA AND NEW JERSEY. (A Biographic, Historic and Descriptive Account of the Furred Animals of Land and Sea, Both Living and Extinct, Known to Have Existed in These States.) Samuel N. Rhoads. Philadelphia, Privately Published, pp.266, pls.9, fold.map, 1903.

MAMMALS OF NEW JERSEY. Witmar Stone. Ann.Rept., N.Jersey State Mus., part 2, pp.33-110, 1907.

SEEDLING REPRODUCTION OF OAK IN SOUTHERN NEW JERSEY. O.M. Wood. Ecology, vol.19, no.2, pp.276-293, Apr., 1938. (Destruction of Acorns and Seedlings by Squirrels and other Animals .)

UNITED STATES--NEW MEXICO

Extinct and Fossil Mammals

REPORT ON THE EXCAVATION OF JEMEZ CAVE, NEW MEXICO. Hubert G. Alexander, Paul Reiter. Monograph Univ.New Mexico School Amer.Research, Santa Fe, pp.67-iii, figs.17, pls.20, 1935. (List of Mammals pp.35-36.)

OCCURRENCE OF FLINTS AND EXTINCT ANIMALS IN PLUVIAL DEPOSITS NEAR CLOVIS, NEW MEXICO. PART II. AGE OF THE CLOVIS LAKE CLAYS. Ernst Antevs. Proc.Acad.Nat.Sci.Philadelphia, vol.87, pp.304-312, 1936.

PREHISTORIC QUARRIES AND IMPLEMENTS OF PRE-AMERINDIAN ASPECT IN NEW MEXICO. Kirk Bryan. Science, Lancaster, Penna., n.s., vol.87, no. 2259, pp.343-346, Apr. 15, 1938.

RECENT BONE-CAVERN FIND AT BISHOP'S CAP, NEW MEXICO. (Bones of Horse, Cave Bear, Camel and Sloth.) William Alanson Bryan. Science, n.s., vol.70, pp.39-41, July 12, 1929.

OCCURRENCE OF FLINTS AND EXTINCT ANIMALS IN PLUVIAL DEPOSITS NEAR CLOVIS, NEW MEXICO, PART 6. REPORT ON FIELD SEASON OF 1937. John Lambert Cotter. Proc. Acad.Nat.Sci., Philadelphia, vol.90, pp.113-117, May 3, 1939; PART 4. REPORT ON EXCAVATION AT THE GRAVEL PIT, 1936. Introduction by Edgar B. Howard. Proc. Acad.Nat.Sci.Philadelphia, vol.89, pp.1-16, fig.1, pls.10, Mar. 12, 1937.

CONTRIBUTIONS TO THE GEOLOGY AND PALEONTOLOGY OF SAN JUAN COUNTY, NEW MEXICO : 2. VERTEBRATE FAUNAS OF THE OJO ALAMO, KIRTLAND AND FRUITLAND FORMATIONS. Charles W. Gilmore. U.S. Geol.Surv., Prof.Paper, no. 98-Q, pp.279-302, figs.42, pls.6, 1916.

EVIDENCE OF EARLY OCCUPATION IN SANDIA CAVE, NEW MEXICO. AND OTHER SITES IN THE SANDIA-MANZANO REGION. Frank C. Hibben. Smiths. Inst., Misc.Coll., vol.99, no.23, pp.1-44, figs.7, pls.15, Oct. 15, 1941.

PLEISTOCENE STRATIFICATION IN THE SANDIA CAVE, NEW MEXICO. Frank C. Hibben. Proc. 8th Amer. Sci. Congr., Washington, D.C., vol.2, pp.45-48, 1942.

ASSOCIATION OF ARTIFACTS WITH MAMMOTH AND BISON IN EASTERN NEW MEXICO. Edgar B. Howard. Science, Lancaster, n.s., vol.78, no.2031, p.524, Dec. 1, 1933.

OCCURRENCE OF FLINTS AND EXTINCT ANIMALS IN PLUVIAL DEPOSITS NEAR CLOVIS, NEW MEXICO. PART 1. INTRODUCTION. Edgar B. Howard. Proc.Acad. Nat.Sci.Philadelphia, vol.87, pp.299-303, Oct. 10, 1935.

BONES FROM THE GOVERNADOR AREA. Barbara Lawrence. (In) Edward T. Hall, Jr. Early Stockaded Settlements in the Governador, New Mexico. Columbia Studies Archeology and Ethnology, New York, vol. 2, pt.1, appendix C, pp.73-78, 1944.

MAMMAL REMAINS FROM TWO PREHISTORIC VILLAGE SITES IN NEW MEXICO AND ARIZONA. Marcus W. Lyon. Proc. U.S.Nat.Mus., vol.31, no.1500, pp. 647-649, Dec. 18, 1906.

PALEOCENE FAUNAS OF THE SAN JUAN BASIN, NEW MEXICO. William Diller Matthew. Trans.Amer.Philos.Soc.Philadelphia, n.s., vol.30, pp.viii-510, figs. 81, pls.65, Feb., 1937.

(Review by C. Forster Cooper of) PALAEOCENE FAUNAS OF THE SAN JUAN BASIN, NEW MEXICO. William Diller Matthew. Nature, London, vol.140, no.3532, pp.46-47, fig.1, July 10, 1937.

PLEISTOCENE CLIMATE AND THE FAUNA OF BURNET CAVE, NEW MEXICO. Keith F. Murray. Ecology, vol.38, no.1, pp.129-132, Jan., 1957.

NEW GENUS AND SPECIES OF CERATOPSIA FROM NEW MEXICO, PENTACERATOPS STERNBERGII. Henry Fairfield Osborn. Amer. Mus.Novitates, New York, no.93, pp.3, fig.1, Oct. 18, 1923.

ARCHEOLOGICAL AND GEOLOGICAL INVESTIGATIONS IN THE SAN JON DISTRICT, EASTERN NEW MEXICO. Frank H.H. Roberts. Smiths. Inst., Misc.Coll., Wash., D.C., vol.103, no.4, publ.no.3692, pp.30, figs.3, pls.9, Oct. 12, 1942. (List of Mammals pp.4-5.)

FAUNA OF BURNET CAVE, GUADALUPE MOUNTAINS, NEW MEXICO. C.Bertrand Schultz, Edgar B. Howard. Proc.Acad.Nat. Sci.Philadelphia, vol.87, pp.273-298, pls. 11-16, Oct. 4, 1935.

FOSSIL MAMMALS FROM THE TYPE AREA OF THE PUERCO AND NACIMIENTO STRATA, PALEOCENE OF NEW MEXICO. George Gaylord Simpson. Amer.Mus.Nat. Hist., New York, Amer.Mus.Novitates, no.1957, pp.22, illus., diagr., tbls., 1959.

HAYDEN, COPE, AND THE EOCENE OF NEW MEXICO. George Gaylord Simpson. Proc. Acad.Nat.Sci.Philadelphia, vol.103, pp.1-21, pls.5, Apr.25, 1951.

OCCURRENCE OF FLINTS AND EXTINCT ANIMALS IN PLUVIAL DEPOSITS NEAR CLOVIS, NEW MEXICO. PART III. GEOLOGY AND VERTEBRATE PALEONTOLOGY OF THE LATE QUATERNARY NEAR CLOVIS, NEW MEXICO. Chester Stock, Francis D. Bode. Proc. Acad.Nat.Sci.Philadelphia, vol. 88, pp.219-241, figs.6, pls. 5-10, June 15, 1936.

PRELIMINARY SURVEY OF A PALEOCENE FAUNULE FROM THE ANGELS PEAK AREA, NEW MEXICO. Robert W. Wilson. Univ.Kansas Publ., Mus.Nat.Hist., Lawrence, vol.5, no.1, pp.1-11, fig.1, Feb.24, 1951.

Recent Mammals

LIST OF MAMMALS COLLECTED BY MR. CHARLES P. ROWLEY IN THE SAN JUAN REGION OF COLORADO, NEW MEXICO AND UTAH, WITH DESCRIPTIONS OF NEW SPECIES. J.A. Allen. Bull.Amer. Mus.Nat.Hist., vol.5, pp.69-84, Apr.28, 1893.

LIST OF MAMMALS COLLECTED BY MR. WALTER W. GRANGER, IN NEW MEXICO, UTAH, WYOMING AND NEBRASKA, 1895-96, WITH FIELD NOTES BY THE COLLECTOR. J.A. Allen. Bull.Amer. Mus.Nat.Hist., vol.8, pp.241-258, Nov. 25, 1896.

ANIMAL LIFE OF THE CARLSBAD CAVERN. Vernon Bailey. Williams and Wilkins, Baltimore, Maryland, pp.195, illus., Feb., 1928.

LIFE ZONES AND CROP ZONES OF NEW MEXICO. Vernon Bailey. N.Amer.Fauna, no.35, U.S.Dept.Agric., pp.100, figs.6, pls.26, Sep. 5, 1913.

MAMMALS OF NEW MEXICO. Vernon Bailey. N.Amer.Fauna, no.53, Bureau Biol.Surv., U.S.Dept.Agric., Washington, pp.412, figs.58, pls.22, Dec., 1931 (Mar. 1, 1932).

TEN NEW MAMMALS FROM NEW MEXICO. Vernon Bailey. Proc.Biol.Soc.Washington, vol.26, pp.129-134 May 21, 1913.

NOTES ON LITTLE KNOWN NEW MEXICAN MAMMALS AND SPECIES APPARENTLY NOT RECORDED FROM THE TERRITORY. G.M.Barber. Proc. Biol.Soc. Washington, vol.15, pp.191-193, Oct. 10, 1902.

ANNOTATED LIST OF MAMMALS OF THE TULAROSA BASIN, NEW MEXICO. W. Frank Blair. Amer.Midland Nat., Notre Dame, vol.26, no.1, pp.218-229, July, 1941.

ECOLOGICAL DISTRIBUTION OF MAMMALS IN THE TULAROSA BASIN, NEW MEXICO. W. Frank Blair. Contrib.Lab. Vert.Biol., Univ.Michigan, Ann Arbor, no. 20, pp.24, map 1, Feb., 1943.

POPULATIONS OF THE DEER-MOUSE AND ASSOCIATED SMALL MAMMALS IN THE MESQUITE ASSOCIATION OF SOUTHERN NEW MEXICO. W. Frank Blair. Contrib. Lab.Vert.Biol.Univ.Michigan, Ann Arbor, no.21, pp.40, figs.2, Mar., 1943.

MAMMALS OF THE MALPAIS, AN AREA OF BLACK LAVA ROCK IN THE TULAROSA BASIN, NEW MEXICO. G.W.Bradt. Jour.Mamm., vol.13, no.4, pp.321-328, Nov., 1932.

MAMMAL DISTRIBUTION IN THE ALAMOGORDO REGION, NEW MEXICO. Lee

R. Dice. Occasional Papers Mus.Zool., Univ.Michigan, no.213, pp.32, pls.3, Apr.24, 1930.

TULAROSA MALPAIS. Lee R. Dice. Lancaster, Scientific Monthly, vol.50, pp.419-424, map, illus., May, 1940.

MAMMALS OF THE NAVAJO COUNTRY. Theodore H. Eaton. Berkeley, Nat. Youth Administration, pp.46, 1937.

NEW MAMMALS FROM ARIZONA, NEW MEXICO, AND COLORADO. E.A. Goldman. Jour. Washington Acad.Sci., vol.23, no.10, pp.463-473, Oct. 15, 1933.

BIG GAME IN THE GILA FOREST. L.S. Gordon. New Mexico Mag., vol.32, no.12, pp.35, 37, illus., Dec., 1954.

NOTE ON NEOTOMA AND SYLVILAGUS IN NEW MEXICO. Arthur F. Halloran. Jour. Mamm., vol.25, no.4, p.410, Dec. 12, 1944.

NOTES ON MAMMALS OF NORTHEASTERN NEW MEXICO. John Eric Hill. Jour. Mamm., vol.23, no.1, pp.75-82, fig.1, Feb. 14, 1942.

FIELD STUDY OF WILD MAMMALS AND FLEAS OF SANTA FE COUNTY, NEW MEXICO. R. Holdenried, Harvey B. Morlan. Amer.Midland Nat., vol.55, no.2, pp.369-381, Apr., 1956.

MAMMALS OF THE LAVA FIELDS AND ADJOINING AREAS IN VALENCIA COUNTY, NEW MEXICO. Emmet T. Hooper. Misc. Publ., Mus.Zool., Univ.Michigan, no.51, pp.47, pls.3, June 14, 1941.

WILD LIFE IN THE NATIONAL FORESTS. John D. Jones. New Mexico, Sunshine States Recreational and Highway Mag., vol.10, no. 11, pp.17-19, 47, Nov., 1932.

PINERIES AND DEER ON THE GILA. Aldo Leopold. New Mexico Conservationist, vol. 1, no.3, p.3, Mar., 1928.

GAME RANGES AND REFUGES. J.Stockley Ligon. New Mexico, Sunshine States Recreational and Highway Mag., vol.10, no. 10, pp.27-28, 44-47, Oct., 1932.

WILD LIFE OF NEW MEXICO, ITS CONSERVATION AND MANAGEMENT; BEING A REPORT ON THE GAME SURVEY OF THE STATE, 1926 AND 1927. J. Stockley Ligon. Publ.by State Game Comm., Santa Fe, New Mexico, pp.212, illus., map, 1927.

EFFECT OF RODENTS, RABBITS, AND CATTLE ON TWO VEGETATION TYPES IN SEMIDESERT RANGE LAND. J.J. Norris. New Mexico Agric.Exp.Sta., Bull. no.353, pp.23, Jan., 1950.

TWO RECORDS FOR NEW MEXICO. Ernest Thompson Seton. Jour. Mamm., vol.12, no.2, p.166, May, 1931.

ON THE TERRESTRIAL VERTEBRATES OF PORTIONS OF SOUTHERN NEW MEXICO AND WESTERN TEXAS. Witmar Stone, J.A.G. Rehn. Proc. Acad. Nat. Sci.Phila., pp.15-34, Jan., 1903.

UNITED STATES--NEW YORK

PLANTS AND ANIMALS OF MOUNT MARCY, NEW YORK. Chas.C. Adams et al. Ecology, vol.1, pt.1, pp.71-94, (Apr.) Aug.; pt.2, pp.204-233, (July) Oct.; pt.3, pp.274-288, (Oct.) Nov., 1920.

PRELIMINARY LIST OF THE MAMMALS OF NEW YORK. J.A. Allen. Amer.Nat., vol.34, pp.316-318, Apr., 1900.

STUDIES OF SMALL MAMMALS ON ABANDONED FARM LAND IN SOUTHCENTRAL NEW YORK. Kile R. Barbehenn. PhD thesis, Cornell Univ., pp.102, 1955.

MAMMALS AND SIPHONAPTEROUS PARASITES OF RENSSELAER COUNTY, NEW YORK. Allen H. Benton, Richard F.Krug. Albany, New York State Univ., State Mus. and Sci.Service, Bull.no.353, pp.22, illus., 1956.

PRELIMINARY WILD LIFE AND FOREST SURVEY OF SOUTHWESTERN CATTARAUGUS COUNTY, NEW YORK. (Notes on Several Species of Mammals.) Victor H.Caffalane. Roosevelt Wild Life Bull., New York State College of Forestry, vol. 5, no.1, pp.1-144, illus., maps 6, Mar., 1928.

SMALL MAMMALS OF OTSEGO AND SCHOHARIE COUNTIES, NEW YORK. Paul F. Connor. Albany, New York State Univ., State Mus. and Sci.Service, Bull.no.382, pp.84, illus., tbls., 1960.

SURVIVAL AND GROWTH OF SHRUBS PLANTED FOR WILDLIFE IN NEW YORK. David B. Cook, Frank C. Edminster. Jour. Widl.Mgt., Menasha, vol.8, no.3, pp.185-191, July, 1944.

MAMMALIA. (Part 1, pp.16-146, pls.33). J.E. DeKay. (In) Zoology of New York, or the New York Fauna, Albany, Thurlow Weed, Printer to the State, vols.5, 1842.

MAMMALS OF SING SING, NEW YORK. A.K. Fisher. Observer, Portland, Conn., vol.7, no.5, pp.193-200, May, 1896.

HABITS OF MAMMALS AT AN ADIRONDACK CAMP. (Detailed Account of Habits of Chipmunk Tamias; Briefer Notes on Habits of Porcupine, Mink and Raccon, and Some of Mice and Shrews.) Lucy B. Fraleigh. New York State Mus.Handbook, no.8, pp.119-169, illus., May 1929.

FUR-BEARERS OF NEW YORK STATE. W.J. Hamilton, Jr. Scientific Monthly, vol.40, pp.182-187, illus., Feb., 1935.

FUR-BEARERS OF NEW YORK IN THEIR RELATION TO AGRICULTURE. W.J. Hamilton, Jr. New York State College Agric.at Cornell Univ., Ithaca, Bull.no. 319, pp.25, figs.9, Mar., 1935.

NEW YORK'S FUR CROP. W.J.Hamilton, Jr. Bull.Farm Research, Geneva, New York, pp.16, July, 1953.

NOTES ON MAMMALS OF THE ADIRONDACKS. (List 41 Forms With Notes on Distribution and Habits.) Francis Harper. New York State Mus.Handbook, no.8, pp.51-118, illus., May, 1929.

ANIMAL HABITATS IN CERTAIN PORTIONS OF THE ADIRONDACKS. Francis Harper, Jean Sherwood Harper. Albany, State Univ., New York State Mus., Handbook 8, pp.176, illus., 1929.

MASTODONS, MAMMOTHS, AND OTHER PLEISTOCENE MAMMALS OF NEW YORK STATE, BEING A DESCRIPTIVE RECORD OF ALL KNOWN OCCURRENCES. C.A. Hartnagel, Sherman C. Bishop. New York State Mus.Bull., no.241-242, pp.110, pls. 25, (Jan.-Feb., 1921) 1922.

RELATION OF MAMMALS TO THE HARVARD FOREST. Robert T. Hatt. Bull. New York State Coll.of Forestry, vol.3, no.2c, pp.625-671, figs.191-213, Aug., 1930.

NOTES ON THE MAMMALS OF LONG ISLAND, NEW YORK. Arthur H. Helme. Proc. Linn.Soc.New York, nos.13-14, pp. 19-30, 1902.

NOTES ON ADIRONDACK MAMMALS WITH SPECIAL REFERENCE TO THE FUR-BEARERS. Madison Grant. 8th and 9th Reports of the Forest, Fish and Game Comm., Albany, N.Y., pp.319-334, pls.23, 1906.

CHAPTER OF HISTORY AND NATURAL HISTORY IN OLD NEW YORK. (Includes a Few Mammal Notes.) George Bird Grinnell. Nat.Hist., vol.20, pp.23-27, Jan.-Feb., 1920.

SOME FACTORS INFLUENCING THE LOCAL DISTRIBUTION AND ABUNDANCE OF WOODLAND SMALL MAMMALS IN CENTRAL NEW YORK. E.W.Jameson, Jr. PhD thesis, Cornell Univ., 1948; Jour. Mamm., vol.30, no.3, pp.221-235, pls. 2, illus., Aug. 17, 1949.

MAMMALS OF ALLEGHANY STATE PARK REGION. Irving W. Knobloch. St.Bonaventure Coll.Sci.Studies, St.Bonaventure, vol. 12, no.1, pp.5-11, Nov., 1943; vol.12, no.2, pp.13-23, Jan., 1944.

NOTES ON THE MAMMALS OF THE CATSKILL MOUNTAINS, NEW YORK, WITH GENERAL REMARKS ON THE FAUNA AND FLORA OF THE REGION. Edgar A.Mearns. Proc. U.S. Nat.Mus., vol.21, no.1147, pp. 341-360, Nov. 4, 1898.

STUDY OF THE VERTEBRATE FAUNA OF THE HUDSON HIGHLANDS, WITH OBSERVATIONS ON THE MOLLUSCA, CRUSTACEA, LEPIDOPTERA, AND THE FLORA OF THE REGION. Edgar A.Mearns. Bull. Amer.Mus.Nat.Hist., vol.10, art. 16, pp. 303-352, Sep. 9, 1898.

TRANSACTIONS OF THE LINNAEAN SOCIETY OF NEW YORK. VOL.1. VERTEBRATES OF THE ADIRONDACK REGION, NORTHEASTERN NEW YORK. (General Introduction--Mammalia, Carnivora.) Clinton Hart Merriam. VOL. 2. THE VERTEBRATES OF THE ADIRONDACK REGION, NORTHEASTERN NEW YORK.(Mammalia, Concluded.) New York, Press of L.S. Foster, 1882-84.

PRELIMINARY LIST OF THE MAMMALS OF NEW YORK. Gerrit S. Miller. Albany, New York State Univ., State Mus., Bull., vol.6, no.29, pp.273-390, 1899.

POPULAR GUIDE TO THE NATURE AND THE ENVIRONMENT OF THE FOSSIL VERTEBRATES OF NEW YORK. Roy L. Moodie. New York State Mus., Albany, Handbook no 12, pp.121, figs.49, 1933.

MERRIAM'S LIFE ZONE CONCEPT AND THE DISTRIBUTION OF CERTAIN SMALL MAMMALS IN CENTRAL NEW YORK. Oliver S. Owen. Jour. Mamm., vol.35, no.4, pp.479-581, Nov. 29, 1954.

WILD LIFE VISTAS ALONG CENTRAL PARK. Russell Owen. New York Times Mag., New York, p.19, illus., Mar. 29, 1942.

POPULATION LEVELS OF SMALL MAMMALS IN VARIOUS HABITATS OF CENTRAL NEW YORK. Ralph Banner Priddy. Abstracts of Thesis, 1942, Cornell Univ., Ithaca, pp.325-328, 1943.

GAME LAWS OF THE STATE OF NEW YORK, REVISED TO 1887. E.W.Rankin. Pp.105, 1887.

VERTEBRATES OF THE CAYUGA LAKE BASIN, NEW YORK. Hugh D. Reed, Albert H. Wright. Proc.Amer.Philos.Soc Phila., vol.48, no.193, pp.369-459, pls.17-20, 1909.

RECIPE FOR HAPPINESS. (Beavers and Other Mammals in New York State.) D. Richardson. Audubon Mag., New York, vol.45, no.3, pp.165-169, illus., May-June, 1943.

FUR--NEW YORK'S FIRST INDUSTRY. C. Seagears. New York State Cons., vol. 1, no.3, pp.16-17, 30, Dec.-Jan., 1946-47.

FURS OF NEW YORK, PAST AND PRESENT. C. Seagears. New York State Conservationist, Albany, vol.4, no.3, pp.20-21, illus., Dec.-Jan., 1949-50.

ANIMAL TRACKS ON STATEN ISLAND. (Sketch of Gray Squirrel.) Ernest Thompson Seton. News Bull. Staten Island Zool. Soc., vol.7, no.1, pp.2-4, illus., Jan., 1940.

WHEN WINTER COMES TO JACKSON HOLE WILDLIFE PARK. (Buffalo, Elk, Antelope, Moose, Mule Deer.) James R. Simon. Animal Kingdom, New York, vol.52, no.1, pp. 10-14, illus., Feb.15, 1949.

RECENT FINDS OF QUATERNARY MAMMALS AT SYRACUSE, NEW YORK. Burnett Smith. New York State Mus., Albany, Bull. no.281, pp.21-23, fig.12, 1929.

BIOLOGY OF A SMALL MAMMAL COMMUNITY IN A CENTRAL NEW YORK WOODLOT. Ralph Albert Smith. Abstract of Thesis, 1942, Cornell Univ., Ithaca, pp.338-342, 1943.

STUDIES ON SOME OF THE SMALL MAMMALS OF CENTRAL NEW YORK. M.T. Townsend. Bull.New York State College Forestry at Syracuse Univ. (Roosevelt Wild Life Annals, vol.4, no.1), vol.8, no.2, pp.120, figs.22, Dec., 1935.

MAMMALS OF THE THOUSAND ISLANDS REGION, NEW YORK. William E. Werner.

Jr. Jour.Mamm., vol.37, no.3, pp.395-406, illus., Sep. 11, 1956.

BEAVER AND OTTER TAKE, SPRING 1952. New York State Conservation Department, vol.6, no.6, pp.31, June-July, 1952.

MAMMALS OF WESTCHESTER COUNTY, NEW YORK. Abstract Proc. Linn. Soc. New York, nos.13-14, pp.31-60, 1902.

1954 BEAVER AND OTTER HARVEST. New York State Conservation Department, vol. 8, no.6, pp.30, June-July, 1954.

WILD ANIMALS OF THE HUDSON HIGHLANDS. Natural History, New York, vol. 35, no.5, pp.405-410, illus., May, 1935.

UNITED STATES--NORTH CAROLINA

MAMMALS OF NORTH CAROLINA. C.S. Brimley. N.Carolina State Mus., pp.36.

OUR RATS, MICE AND SHREWS. C. S. Brimley. Jour. of Elisha Mitchell Scient. Soc., pp.55-60, Oct., 1919.

LIST OF MAMMALS OBTAINED BY THADDEUS SURBER, IN NORTH AND SOUTH CAROLINA, GEORGIA AND FLORIDA. D.G. Elliot. Field Columbian Mus., Chicago, Publ.no.58, Zool.Series, vol.3, no.4, pp. 31-57, pls.5-10, 1901.

VERTEBRATE FAUNA OF NORTH CAROLINA COASTAL ISLANDS. A STUDY IN THE DYNAMICS OF ANIMAL DISTRIBUTION. I. OCRACOKE ISLAND. William L. Engels. Amer. Midland Nat., Notre Dame, vol.28, no.2, pp.273-304, figs. 11, Sep., 1942; II. SHACKLEFORD BANKS. Amer.Midland Nat., Notre Dame, vol.47, no.3, pp.702-742, May, 1952.

NOTES AND BLOOD DATA ON SOME SMALL MAMMALS OF DURHAM COUNTY, NORTH CAROLINA. Charles W. Foreman. Jour.Mamm., vol.37, no.3, pp.427-428, Sep. 11, 1956.

MAMMALS OF THE GREAT SMOKY MOUNTAINS. Edwin V. Komarek, Roy Komarek. Bull.Chicago Acad.Sci., vol.5, no.6, pp. 137-162, figs.2, fold.map, 1938.

SMALL MAMMALS OF THE HIGHLANDS (NORTH CAROLINA) PLATEAU. Eugene P. Odum. Jour. Mamm., Baltimore, vol. 30, no.2, pp.179-192, fig.1, pl.1, illus., May 23, 1949.

HUNTING IN NORTH CAROLINA. Wade H. Phillips. N.Carolina Dept.Conservation and Development, Bull.no.36, pp.1-45, several Photos, June, 1928.

$1, 240, 000 FUR CROP IN NORTH CAROLINA 1940-1941. J.C. Rabb. N.Carolina Wildl.Conservation, vol.6, no.4, pp.3-4, 12-13, Apr., 1942.

NOTES ON A COLLECTION OF SMALL MAMMALS FROM NORTHEASTERN NORTH CAROLINA. Samuel N. Rhoads. Proc.Acad.Nat.Sciences, Philadelphia, pp.303-312, 1897.

FUR RESOURCES OF NORTH CAROLINA. Kenneth A. Wilson. N.Carolina Wildl. Resources Comm., Fed.Aid Proj., W-6-R, pp.1-59, illus., July, 1955.

NORTH CAROLINA'S FUR RESOURCES. (Muskrat, Mink.) Kenneth A. Wilson. Wildl. in N.Carolina, Raleigh, vol.13, no.3, pp. 8-11, illus., Mar., 1949.

STATE-WIDE FUR SURVEY. Kenneth A. Wilson. Wildl. in N.Carolina, vol.15, no. 8, pp.8-11, 17, Aug., 1951.

BIG GAME POPULATION STILL INCREASING. Wildl. in N.Carolina, Raleigh, vol.12, no.3, p.17, May, 1948.

CURRITUCK'S FUR RESOURCES. N.Carolina Wildl.Conservation, Raleigh, vol.9, no.1, pp.3-7, illus., Jan.-Feb., 1945.

UNITED STATES--NORTH DAKOTA

NATURAL HISTORY NOTES: MOUNTAIN LION (FELIS HIPPOLESTES) IN NORTH DAKOTA; SUMMER ANTELOPE SURVEY; THE KANGAROO RAT. Roy N. Bach. North Dakota Outdoors, Bismarck, vol.6, no.2, pp.14-15, illus., Aug., 1943.

USE OF THE AIRPLANE IN BIG GAME MANAGEMENT IN NORTH DAKOTA. Roy N. Bach. N.Dakota Outdoors, Bismarck, vol.6, no.10, p.10, Apr., 1944.

BIOLOGICAL SURVEY OF NORTH DAKOTA. 1. PHYSIOGRAPHY AND LIFE ZONES. 2. THE MAMMALS. Vernon Bailey. N.Amer. Fauna, U.S.Dept.Agric., no.49, pp.226, pls.21, Dec., 1926.

PRELIMINARY REPORT ON THE MAMMALS IN NORTH DAKOTA. Vernon Bailey et al. N.Dakota Agric.Exper.Sta., Circ. no.3, pp.1-20, Dec., 1914.

NORTH DAKOTA FUR HARVEST REPORT 1948-49. Charles Hargrave. N.Dakota Outdoors, Grand Forks, vol.12, no.3, pp.10, Sep., 1949.

THEODORE ROOSEVELT NATIONAL MEMORIAL PARK AS A GAME SANCTUARY. Russell Reid. N.Dakota Outdoors, Bismarck, vol.11, no.12, pp.4-5, 12-13, illus., June, 1949.

SULLYS HILL NATIONAL GAME PRESERVE, NORTH DAKOTA. C.Ruth. U.S. Dept.Agric., Wildl.Research and Mgt. Leaflet, no.BS-61, pp.3, pls.1-2, June, 1937.

AERIAL CENSUS OF BIG GAME IN NORTH DAKOTA. Stanley Saugstad. Trans.7th N. Amer.Wildl.Conf., Washington, D.C., pp. 343-356, figs.2, 1942.

NORTH DAKOTA FUR HARVEST REPORT--1947-1948. Nels J. Struwing. N. Dakota Outdoors, Bismarck, vol.11, no.2, p.11, Aug., 1948.

REPORT ON NORTH DAKOTA FUR HARVEST. Nels J. Struwing. N.Dakota Outdoors, Bismarck, vol.8, no.1, p.11, July, 1946.

ANNUAL BIG GAME SURVEY--WINTER 1948. Russell W. Stuart. N.Dakota Outdoors, Bismarck, vol.10, no.12, pp.12-13, June, 1948.

FURBEARERS IN NORTH DAKOTA. North Dakota Outdoors, Bismarck, vol.13, no.8, p.19, illus., Feb., 1951.

NORTH DAKOTA BIG GAME AERIAL SURVEY COMPLETE. N.Dakota Outdoors, Bismarck, vol.9, no.12, p.5, June, 1947.

WILDLIFE IN NORTH DAKOTA. N.Dakota Outdoors, Bismarck, vol.1, no.7, pp.27-30, Jan., 1939.

UNITED STATES--OHIO

Extinct and Fossil Mammals

ANIMAL REMAINS FROM THE ANDERSON VILLAGE SITE, FORT ANCIENT, OHIO, George W. Brainerd. Abstract Doctor's Dissert., Ohio State Univ., no.24, pp.13-19, tbls., 1937.

ANIMAL REMAINS FROM A PREHISTORIC OHIO INDIAN SITE. Robert M. Goslin. Ohio India Relic Coll.Soc., Columbus, Bull. no.25, pp.16-21, Sep., 1950.

ANIMAL REMAINS FROM OHIO ROCK SHELTERS. Robert M. Goslin. Ohio Jour. Sci., vol.55, no.6, pp.358-362, Nov., 1955.

OHIO CAVE SURVEY. Philip M. Smiths. Ohio Jour.Sci., vol.53, no.6, p.325, Nov., 1953.

THE NUMERICAL STATUS OF SOME MAMMALS THROUGHOUT HISTORIC TIME IN THE VICINITY OF BUCKEYE LAKE, OHIO. (Dates of Extinction of Larger Mammals.) Milton B. Trautman. Ohio Jour.Sci., Columbus, vol.39, no.3, pp.133-143, May, 1939.

Recent Mammals

BIOLOGICAL SURVEY OF THE BOGS AND SWAMPS IN NORTHEASTERN OHIO. John W. Aldrich. Amer.Midland Nat., Notre Dame, vol.30, no.2, pp.346-402, figs.21, Sep., 1943.

THE 1941 FUR CROP IN OHIO. J.R. Benjamin. Ohio Wildl.Research Sta., Release 168, pp.9, Dec., 1941.

ADDITION TO THE KNOWN LIST OF OHIO MAMMALS. (Reithrodontomys humulis merriami.) B.P. Bole, Jr. Ohio Jour.Sci., vol. 32, no.4, p.402, July 1932.

OHIO RECENT MAMMAL COLLECTION IN THE CLEVELAND MUSEUM OF NATURAL HISTORY. B.P. Bole, Jr., Philip N. Moulthrop. Sci.Publ.Cleveland Mus.Nat. Hist., vol.5, no.6, pp.83-181, Sep. 11, 1942.

REPORT ON THE MAMMALIA OF OHIO. A.W. Brayton. Ohio, Geol.Survey, vol.4, pp.1-185, 1882.

HOW MANY MAMMALS IN OHIO. Lou Campbell. Ohio Conserv.Bull., Columbus, vol.11, no.3, p.10, Mar., 1947.

BIG GAME POLICY FOR OHIO. (Deer and Black Bear.) Floyd B. Chapman. Ohio Div. Cons.and Nat.Resources, Bull.no.160, pp. 4, 1940.

CONTROLLED SQUIRREL AND RABBIT HUNTING ON STATE HUNTING PRESERVES, 1936. Floyd B. Chapman. Ohio Wildl. Res. Sta., Release 37, pp.11, June, 1937.

REPORT ON STATE HUNTING PRESERVES, 1935. (Squirrels and Rabbits.) Floyd B.Chapman. Ohio Div.Conservation, Bull. no.97, pp.9, 1936.

RELATIVE IMPORTANCE OF HUNTING RESTRICTIONS AND LAND USE IN MAINTAINING WILDLIFE POPULATIONS IN OHIO. Chas.A. Dambach. Ohio Jour.Sci., Columbus, vol.48, no.6, pp.209-229, illus., Nov., 1948.

TEN-YEAR ECOLOGICAL STUDY OF ADJOINING GRAZED AND UNGRAZED WOODLANDS IN NORTHEASTERN OHIO. Chas.A. Dambach. Ecol.Monogr., Durham, vol.14, no.5, pp.255-270, illus., July, 1944.

THE 1949-1950 OHIO FUR CROP. Eugene H. Dustman. Ohio Conservation Bull., vol.15, no.7, pp.30-32, July, 1951.

OHIO'S 1948-1949 FUR CROP. Eugene H. Dustman. Ohio Conservation Bull., vol.14, no.7, pp.4-5, July, 1950.

SOME FACTORS INFLUENCING THE DISTRIBUTION OF MAMMALS IN OHIO. R.K. Enders. Occasional Papers Mus. Zool., Univ.Michigan, no.212, pp.27, map 1, Apr. 23, 1930.

TWO NEW RECORDS FOR OHIO. R.K. Enders. Jour. Mamm., vol.9, no.2, p.155, May, 1928.

MAMMALS OF SOUTHWESTERN OHIO. Woodrow Goodpaster. Jour.Cincinnati Soc. Nat. Hist., Cincinnati, vol.22, no.3, pp. 41-47, June, 1941.

TWO MAMMALS NEW FOR OHIO. W.F. Henninger. Jour. Mamm., vol.2, no.4, p.239, Nov., 1921.

STATUS OF GAME MAMMALS IN OHIO. Lawrence E. Hicks. Trans. 3rd N. Amer. Wildl.Conf., pp.415-420, 1938; Ohio Wildl. Res.Sta., Release 73, pp.6, Feb., 1938.

KEY TO THE MAMMALS OF OHIO. David T. Katz. Ohio Wildl.Res.Sta., Ohio State Univ., Columbus, Release 158, pp.1-34, mimeog., June 1, 1941.

PRELIMINARY GENERAL SURVEY OF THE MACROFAUNA OF MIRROR LAKE ON THE OHIO STATE UNIVERSITY CAMPUS. (Occurrence of Muskrat and Norway Rat.) Walter C. Kraatz. Ohio Jour.Sci., vol.21, no.5, pp.137-184, Mar., 1921.

MAMMALIA OF THE VICINITY OF CINCINNATI, LIST OF SPECIES WITH NOTES. Frank W. Langdon. Jour. Cincinnati Soc. Nat.Hist., vol.3, no.4, pp.297-313, Jan., 1881.

FURTHER OBSERVATIONS ON THE OHIO GAME KILL AND WILDLIFE ECONOMICS, 1947. Daniel L. Leedy. Ohio Conserv.Bull., Columbus, vol.12, no.8, pp.4-5, 29, Aug., 1948.

OHIO'S FUR CROP. Daniel L. Leedy. Ohio Cons.Bull., vol.12, no.2, pp.14-15, Feb., 1948.

OHIO'S 1947-1948 FUR CROP. Daniel L. Leedy. Ohio Cons.Bull., Columbus, vol.

12, no.11, pp.30-31, Nov., 1948.

OHIO'S STATUS AS A GAME AND FUR PRODUCING STATE. Daniel L. Leedy. Ohio Jour. Sci., Columbus, vol.50, no.2, pp.88-94, Mar., 1950.

SOME OBSERVATIONS ON OHIO'S FUR CROP. Daniel L. Leedy. Ohio Cons.Bull., vol.11, no.2, pp.4-5, 20, Feb., 1947.

SPERMOPHILES AND BADGERS MOVE EASTWARD IN OHIO. Daniel L. Leedy. Jour. Mamm., vol.28, no.3, pp.290-292, Aug., 1947.

EVALUATION OF OHIO'S WILDLIFE RESOURCES. Daniel L. Leedy, C. Dambach. Ohio Wildl.Cons.Bull., Columbus, no.6, pp.16, illus., 1948.

NOTES ON MAMMALS OF PERRY COUNTY, OHIO. Brice Metzger. Jour. Mamm., vol. 36, no.1, pp.101-105, Feb. 25, 1955.

NOTES ON THE MAMMALS OF MORROW COUNTY, OHIO. Norman A. Preble. Jour. Mamm., vol.23, no.1, pp.82-86, Feb.14, 1942.

STUDY OF SOME SMALL MAMMALS OF CENTRAL OHIO. C.E. Smith. MS thesis, Ohio State Univ., 1940.

KNOWING OHIO WILDLIFE. Ohio Cons. Bull., Columbus, vol.8, no.11, pp.27-28, illus., Nov., 1944.

RAW FUR PRICE TRENDS IN OHIO. Ohio Cons.Bull., Columbus, vol.8, no.1, p.12, Jan., 1944.

STATUS OF THE WHITE-TAILED DEER, BADGER, AND BEAVER IN OHIO. Ohio Cons.Bull., Columbus, vol.11, no. 12, p. 15, Dec., 1947.

## UNITED STATES--OKLAHOMA

### Extinct and Fossil Mammals

PRELIMINARY DESCRIPTIONS OF FOSSIL MAMMALS RECENTLY DISCOVERED IN OKLAHOMA, TEXAS AND NEW MEXICO. Oliver P. Hay, Harold J. Cook. Proc. Colorado Mus. Nat.Hist., vol.8, no.2, pt.1, p.33, Feb.2, 1928.

LOWER PLIOCENE VERTEBRATE FOSSILS FROM THE OGALLALA FORMATION (LAVERN ZONE) OF BEAVER COUNTY, OKLAHOMA. Curtis J. Hesse. Carnegie Inst. Washington, (Contrib.Palaeont.), publ.476, pp.47-71, figs.10, Oct. 30,1936.

PLIOCENE VERTEBRATE FAUNA FROM OPTIMA, OKLAHOMA. Curtis J. Hesse. Univ. Calif. Publ., Bull. Dept. Geol. Sci., vol.24, no.3, pp.57-70, figs.5, Dec. 2, 1936.

NEW PLIOCENE VERTEBRATE FAUNA FROM OKLAHOMA. Claude W. Hibbard. Papers Michigan Acad. Sci., Arts and Letters, vol.39, pp.339-359, illus., Apr., 1954.

CENOZOIC OF ROGER MILLS COUNTY. (Cenozoic Geology of Northern Roger Mills County, Oklahoma, D.B. Kitts. A Pliocene Vertebrate Local Fauna from Roger Mills County, Oklahoma, D.B.Kitts, C.C.Black.) David B. Kitts. Norman, Oklahoma, Geol. Survey, Circular 48, pp.47, illus., maps, tbls., 1959.

PLIOCENE VERTEBRATE FAUNA FROM ELLIS COUNTY, OKLAHOMA. David B. Kitts. Circular Oklahoma Geol. Survey, vol.45, pp.1-27, illus., Aug., 1957.

EARLY PLEISTOCENE VERTEBRATE FAUNA FROM FREDERICK, OKLAHOMA. Grayson E. Meade. Jour. Geol., vol.61, no.5, pp.452-460, illus., Sep., 1953.

INVESTIGATION ON THE RED RIVER MADE IN CONNECTION WITH THE OKLAHOMA-TEXAS BOUNDARY SUIT. E.H. Sellards, B.C. Tharp, R.T.Hill. Univ. of Texas Bull., no.2327, July 15, 1923. (Fossil Bison pp.61-64.)

PLEISTOCENE MAMMALS OF THE BERENDS FAUNA OF OKLAHOMA. Andrew Starrett. Jour. Paleontol., vol.30, no.5, pp. 1187-1192, Oct. 22, 1956.

NEW PLEISTOCENE FAUNA FROM HARPER COUNTY, OKLAHOMA. Dwight W. Taylor, C.W. Hibbard. Circular Oklahoma Geol. Survey, no.37, pp.23, illus., 1955.

### Recent Mammals

THE BIG LITTLE MOUNTAINS. WICHITA--OKLAHOMA'S FAMOUS FOREST AND PRESERVE. Will C. Barnes. Nature Mag., Washington, D.C., vol.14, no.4, pp.215-218, illus., Oct., 1929.

BIG GAME IN EARLY OKLAHOMA. J.L. Baugman. Oklahoma Game and Fish News, Oklahoma City, vol.3, no.4, pp.4-5, 17, illus., Apr., 1947.

ECOLOGICAL RELATIONSHIPS OF THE MAMMALS OF THE BIRD CREEK REGION, NORTHEASTERN OKLAHOMA. W.F. Blair. Amer.Midland Nat., vol.20, no.3, pp.473-526, figs.12, tbls.3, Nov., 1938; PhD thesis, Univ.Michigan, 1938.

FAUNAL RELATIONSHIPS AND GEOGRAPHIC DISTRIBUTION OF MAMMALS IN OKLAHOMA. W.F. Blair. Amer.Midland Nat., Notre Dame, vol.22, no.1, pp.85-133, fig. 1, tbls.2, July, 1939.

BIOTIC DISTRICTS OF OKLAHOMA. W.F. Blair, T.H. Hubbell. Amer.Midland Nat., vol.20, no.2, pp.425-454, fig.1, tbl.1, Sep., 1938. (Mammals pp.448-451.)

TWO SPECIES OF MAMMALS FROM CIMARRON COUNTY NEW FOR OKLAHOMA. H.D. Chase. Proc. Oklahoma Acad. Sci., Guthrie, vol.19, p.69, 1939.

SURVEY OF THE GAME AND FUR-BEARING ANIMALS OF OKLAHOMA. L.G. Duck, Jack B. Fletcher. State Fish and Game Comm., Oklahoma City, Pittman-Robertson Series 2, pp.1-144, illus., 1945.

DESCRIPTION OF APPARENTLY NEW SPECIES AND SUBSPECIES OF MAMMALS FROM OKLAHOMA TERRITORY. D. G. Elliot. Field Columbian Mus., Chicago, Publ.no.37, Zool.Series, vol.1, no.14, pp. 279-282, 1899.

LIST OF MAMMALS OBTAINED BY THADDEUS SURBER, COLLECTOR FOR THE MUSEUM, CHIEFLY IN OKLAHOMA AND INDIAN TERRITORIES. D.G. Elliot. Field Columbian Mus., Chicago, Publ.no.40, Zool.Series, vol.1, no.16, pp.291-303, pls. 4, 1899.

NOTES ON THE OCCURRENCE OF MAMMALS IN THE REGIONS ADJACENT TO THE SALT PLAINS OF NORTHWESTERN OKLAHOMA. H.H.T. Jackson, H. E. Warfel. Biol.Surv., Publ.Univ.Oklahoma, Norman, vol.5, nos.1-4, pp.65-72, figs.42-49, (Dec.30, 1933) Feb. 28, 1934.

FUR REPORT FOR OKLAHOMA. Glenn Jones. Oklahoma Game and Fish News, vol.8, nos.7-8, p.15, July-Aug., 1952.

ECOLOGICAL RELATIONSHIPS OF THE MAMMALS OF BRYAN COUNTY, OKLAHOMA. W. H. McCarley. Texas Jour.Sci., San Marcos, vol. 4, no.1, pp.102-112, illus., Mar. 30, 1952; MA thesis, Univ. Texas, 1950.

NO. 1. HOWARD ATWOOD KELLY. A.I. Ortenburger, R.D. Ortenburger. NO. 2. DECAPOD CRUSTACEANS OF OKLAHOMA. E.P. Creaser, A.I. Ortenburger. NO. 3. ECOLOGY OF THE WESTERN OKLAHOMA SALT PLAINS. A.I. Ortenburger, R.D.Bird. NO. 4. NOTES ON THE OCCURRENCE OF MAMMALS IN THE REGIONS ADJACENT TO THE SALT PLAINS OF NORTHWESTERN OKLAHOMA. H.H.T.Jackson, H.E. Warfel. Norman, Univ.of Oklahoma Press, Publ.of the Univ.of Oklahoma, Biol.Survey, vol.5, no.1, 2, 3, 4, pp.87, illus., pls., maps, diagrs., 1933.

WILDLIFE OCCURRENCE AND HABITAT CONDITIONS IN ROBER MILLS AND CUSTER COUNTIES, OKLAHOMA. Ben Osborn, W.H. Kellogg. Proc. Oklahoma Acad.Sci., Guthrie, vol.33, pp.41-44, 1943.

WILDLIFE ON THE T-5 AND SPADE RANCHES. Ralph H. Records. Chronicles of Oklahoma, Oklahoma City, vol.21, no.3, pp.280-299, Sep., 1943.

MAMMALS OF PAYNE COUNTY, OKLAHOMA. Robert R. Schendel. Proc. Oklahoma Acad. Sci., Oklahoma City, vol.22, pp.75-76, 1942.

WICHITA MOUNTAINS WILDLIFE REFUGE. Robert S. Sturgis. Chicago Nat., vol.2, no.1, pp.9-20, illus., 1939.

OKLAHOMA CLIMAGRAPHS AND BIOTIC REGIONS. A.O. Weese. Proc. Oklahoma Acad. Sci., vol.5, 1925, pp.91-95, Mar., 1926.

FUR BEARERS AND GAME MAMMALS OF OKLAHOMA. Oklahoma Game and Fish Dept., Oklahoma City, 2nd ed., pp.43, illus., 1948; 3rd ed., pp.43, illus., June, 1951; 4th ed., pp.34, 1952.

OKLAHOMA FUR HARVEST DOWN 70 PER CENT. Oklahoma Game and Fish Dept., Oklahoma Game and Fish News, vol.9, no.5, p.8, May, 1953.

SURVEY OF THE GAME AND FURBEARING ANIMALS OF OKLAHOMA. Oklahoma Game and Fish Comm., Pittman-Robertson Series no.2, State Bull.no.3, pp.144, 1945?

## UNITED STATES--OREGON

### Extinct and Fossil Mammals

PLEISTOCENE MAMMALS OF FOSSIL LAKE, OREGON. Herbert O. Alftman. Amer.Mus.Novitates, no. 481, pp.1-21, July 14, 1931.

MASCALL FAUNA FROM THE MIOCENE OR OREGON. Theodore Downe. Univ.Calif. Publ. Geol. Sci., vol.31, no.5, pp.199-354, illus., Jan. 12, 1956.

MIOCENE MAMMALIAN FAUNA FROM SOUTHEASTERN OREGON. C. Lewis Gazin. Bull. Geol.Soc.America, vol.42, no.1, p.367, Mar., 1931. (Abstract);Publ. 418 Carnegie Inst. Washington, pp.37-86, figs.20, pls.6, May 10, 1932.

HUNTING FOSSILS ON THE OLD OREGON TRAIL. James W. Gidley. Expl.and Field-Work Smiths.Inst. 1929, Publ.no.3060, pp. 31-36, figs.4, 1930.

PLIOCENE RATTLESNAKE FORMATION AND FAUNA OF EASTERN OREGON, WITH NOTES ON THE GEOLOGY OF THE RATTLESNAKE AND MASCALL DEPOSITS. John C. Merriam, et al. Carnegie Inst.Washington, Contrib.Palaeontol., Publ.no.347, pp. 43-92, figs.45, Oct. 8, 1925.

MIOCENE MAMMALIAN FAUNA FROM SUCKER CREEK, SOUTHEASTERN OREGON. David W. Scharf. Carnegie Inst.Washington, Contrib. Palaeontol., Publ.no.453, pp.97-118, figs.11, pl.1, July 20, 1935.

MIOCENE MAMMALIAN FAUNA FROM BEATTY BUTTES, OREGON. Robert E. Wallace. Contrib.Palaeontol., Carnegie Inst. Washington, Publ.no.551, pp.113-134, fig.1, pls.6, Jan. 25, 1946.

NEW MIDDLE PLIOCENE RODENT AND LAGOMORPH FAUNAS FROM OREGON AND CALIFORNIA. Robert W. Wilson. Carnegie Inst. Washington, Publ.no.487, pp.1-19, tbls., pls.1-3, June 30, 1937.

### Recent Mammals

SMALL MAMMALS FROM GILLIAM COUNTY, OREGON. Sydney Anderson. Murrelet, Seattle, vol.36, no.2, pp.26-27, Aug., 1955.

MAMMALS OF NORTHERN MALHEUR COUNTY, OREGON. H.E. Anthony. Bull. Amer.Mus.Nat.Hist., vol.32, art.1, pp. 1-27, pls.1-2, Mar. 7, 1913.

MAMMALS AND LIFE ZONES OF OREGON. Vernon Bailey. U.S. Dept.Agric., N.Amer.Fauna, no.55, pp.416, figs.102, pls.52, June, 1936.

LIST OF MAMMALS OBTAINED BY EDMUND HELLER, COLLECTOR FOR THE MUSEUM, FROM THE COAST REGION OF NORTHERN CALIFORNIA AND OREGON. Daniel G. Elliot. Field Columbian Mus., Chicago, Publ.no.76, Zool.Series, vol.3, no.11, pp.175-197, 1903.

U. S. FISH COMMISSION INVESTIGATIONS AT GRATER LAKE. Barton Warren Evermann. Mazama, Portland, vol.1, no.2, pp. 230-238, pls.22, 27-28, Oct., 1897.

GAME DAMAGE IN OREGON. Austin F. Hamer. Bull. Oregon State Game Comm., Portland, vol.3, no.3, pp.1, 6-7, illus., Mar., 1948.

FREE-TAILED BATS, AND MELANISTIC MICE IN OREGON. Stanley C. Jewett. Jour. Mamm., vol.36, no.3, pp.458-459, Aug. 30, 1955.

HART MOUNTAIN ANTELOPE REFUGE. Stanley G. Jewett. U.S.Dept.Agric., Misc. Publ., no.355, pp.26, June, 1939.

OREGON'S FUR RESOURCES. Chester E. Kebbe. Bull. Oregon State Game Comm., Portland, vol.1, no.8, pp.1, 6-7, Nov., 1946.

OREGON 1947 GAME OUTLOCK. John McKean. Oregon Outdoors, vol.4, no.9, pp.14-15, 26-29, Sep., 1947.

CONTROL OF BIG GAME CONFLICTS ON EASTERN OREGON RANGES. R.U. Mace. Proc. Ann.Conf. W.Assoc.Sate Game and Fish Comm., vol.29, pp.85-95, 1949?

CURRENT BIG GAME SITUATION. R.U. Mace. Oregon State Game Comm. Bull., vol.6, no.6, pp.1, 4-8, June, 1951.

HARVESTING OREGON'S BIG GAME CROPS. R.U. Mace. Bull. Oregon State Game Comm., Portland, vol.5, no.6, pp.6-8, illus., June, 1950.

MAMMALS OF MOUNT MAZAMA, OREGON. C. Hart Merriam. Mazama, Portland, vol.1, no.2, pp.204-230, pls.16, 21, 23, 26, 30, map, Oct., 1897.

MAMMALS OF THE OREGON CAVES AREA, JOSEPHINE COUNTY. Aryan I. Roest. Jour. Mamm., vol.32, no.3, pp.345-351, Aug.23, 1951.

HEMPHILLIAN MAMMALIAN ASSEMBLAGE FROM NORTHEASTERN OREGON. J. A. Shotwell. Bull. Geol. Soc. Amer., vol.67, pp.717-738, June, 1956.

FUR CATCH REPORT, 1951-52 TRAPPING SEASON. Oregon State Game Comm. Bull., vol.7, no.7, p.7, illus., July, 1952.

FUR CATCH REPORT, 1952-53 TRAPPING SEASON. Oregon State Game Comm. Bull., vol.8, no.7, p.6, July, 1953.

FUR CATCH REPORT, 1953-54 TRAPPING SEASON. Oregon State Game Comm. Bull., vol.9, no.7, p.7, July, 1954.

FUR CATCH REPORT, 1954-55 TRAPPING SEASON. Oregon State Game Comm. Bull., vol.10, no.7, p.6, July, 1955.

## UNITED STATES--PENNSYLVANIA

### Extinct and Fossil Mammals

MAMMALS IN ARCHEOLOGICAL COLLECTIONS FROM SOUTHWESTERN PENNSYLVANIA. Raymond M. Gilmore. Jour. Mamm., vol.27, no.3, pp.227-234, map, Aug. 14, 1946.

ANIMALS REMAINS FROM AN INDIAN VILLAGE SITE, INDIANA COUNTY, PENNSYLVANIA. John E. Guilday. Penna. Archaeologist, vol.25, no.2, pp.142-147, Aug., 1945.

BONES OF MAMMALS COLLECTED BY BAIRD IN PENNSYLVANIA CAVES. Gerrit S. Miller, Jr. Jour. Mamm., vol.21, no. 3, pp.319-322, Aug. 14, 1940.

FOSSILS OF THE FRANKSTOWN CAVE, BLAIR COUNTY, PENNSYLVANIA. Olaf August Peterson. Ann. Carnegie Mus., vol. 16, pp.249-348, illus., Mar. 18, 1926.

EXTINCT PENNSYLVANIA ANIMALS. PART I. THE PANTHER AND THE WOLF. Henry W. Shoemaker. Altoona Tribune Publ. Co., Altoona, Penna., pp.134, illus., 1917.

### Recent Mammals

FUR ON THE CREEK. (Trapping in Central County, Pennsylvania.) Dale Arner. Maryland Conservationist, Baltimore, vol.25, no.2, pp.12-13, Fall, 1948.

RECONNAISSANCE OF THE MAMMALS IN THE VICINITY OF SEWICKLEY, PENNSYLVANIA. Vernon Bailey. Cardinal, Publ. Audubon Soc. Sewickley Valley, Penna., no.18, pp.1-8, pl.1, July, 1926.

CHAPTER ON THE ORNITHOLOGY OF LANCASTER COUNTY, PENNSYLVANIA, WITH SUPPLEMENTARY NOTES ON THE MAMMALS. Herbert Huebner Beck. Reprinted from "Lancaster County, Penna.- A History", pp.39, map, 1924.

NOTES ON SOME PENNSYLVANIA MAMMALS. N.R. Casillo. Penna. Game News, Harrisburg, vol.17 (18), no.12, pp.4-5, 24, illus., Mar., 1948.

PROPOSED MANAGEMENT OF FORESTED GAME LANDS IN PENNSYLVANIA. C. C. Freeburn. Trans. 10th N. Amer. Wildl. Conf., Washington, pp.112-118, 1945.

MAMMAL SURVEY OF SOUTH CENTRAL PENNSYLVANIA. Clay L. Gifford, Ralph Whitebread, Final Rep., Pittman-Robertson Project 38-R, Penna. Game Comm., Harrisburg, pp.75, 1951.

CONTRIBUTION TO THE MAMMALOGY OF THE NORTH MOUNTAIN REGION OF PENNSYLVANIA. Morris M. Green. Ardmore, Penna., Privately Published, pp. 19, color pl., Mar. 31, 1930.

PRIMENESS OF FUR ANIMALS IN NORTHWESTERN PENNSYLVANIA. William C. Grimm. Penna. Game News, Harrisburg, vol. 13, no.9, pp.15, 25, Dec., 1942.

MAMMAL SURVEY OF SOUTHWESTERN PENNSYLVANIA. William C. Grimm, H. A. Roberts. Penna. Game Comm., Final Rep., pp.99, maps, 1950.

MAMMAL SURVEY OF NORTHEASTERN PENNSYLVANIA. William C. Grimm, R. Whitebread. Final Rep., Pittman-Robertson Prokect 42-R, Penna. Game Comm., pp.82, illus., 1952.

DEER AND RABBIT BROWSING AND AVAILABLE WINTER FORAGE IN ALLEGHENY HARDWOOD FORESTS. A.F. Hough. Jour. Wildl. Mgt., vol.13, no.1, pp.135-141, Jan., 1949.

WORK WITH VERTEBRATE ANIMALS ON THE HASTINGS NATURAL HISTORY RESERVATION. Jean M. Linsdale. Amer. Midland Nat., Notre Dame, vol.30, no. 1, pp.254-267, fig.7, July, 1943.

INTRODUCTION TO THE MAMMALS OF PENNSYLVANIA. Leo A. Luttringer, Jr. Bull. no. 15, issued by the Board of Game Commissioners of Penna., pp.66, 1931.

PENNSYLVANIA CAVE FAUNA. Charles E. Mohr. Penna. Caves, Penna. Geol. Surv. Ser.4, Bull. G 3, pp.135-143, pl.1, 1932.

PRELIMINARY REPORT ON THE MAMMALS OF PENNSYLVANIA. Charles E. Mohr. Proc. Penna. Acad. Sci., Harrisburg, vol.5, pp.17-27, 1931.

SMALL MAMMALS FOUND TO BE PRESENT IN THE BARRENS GROUSE STUDY AREA, CENTRE COUNTY, PENNSYLVANIA. Lawrence H. Myers. MS thesis, Penna, State College, Jan., 1952.

PENNSYLVANIA WILDLIFE AND ITS TRACKS. E. Laurence Palmer. Penna. Game News, Harrisburg, vol.21, no.9, pp.16, illus., Dec., 1950.

OWL PREDATION IN PENNSYLVANIA, WITH NOTES ON THE SMALL MAMMALS OF DELAWARE COUNTY. Oliver P. Pearson, Anita K. Pearson. Jour. Mamm., vol.28, no.2, pp.137-147, fig. 1, illus., 1947.

SURVEY OF THE MAMMALS OF BERKS COUNTY, PENNSYLVANIA. Earl L. Poole. Reading Public Mus. and Art Gallery, Bull. 13, pp.74, figs., 1932.

CONTRIBUTION TO THE MAMMALOGY OF CENTRAL PENNSYLVANIA. Samuel N. Rhoads. Proc. Acad. Nat. Sci., Philadelphia, pp.204-226, Apr., 1897.

MAMMALS OF PENNSYLVANIA AND NEW JERSEY. BIOGRAPHIC, HISTORIC AND DESCRIPTIVE ACCOUNT ON THE FURRED ANIMALS OF LAND AND SEA, BOTH LIVING AND EXTINCT, KNOWN TO HAVE EXISTED IN THESE STATES. Samuel N. Rhoads. Philadelphia, Privately Published, pp.266, pls.9, fold.map, 1903.

NOTES ON THE MAMMALS OF MONROE AND PIKE COUNTIES, PENNSYLVANIA. Samuel N. Rhoads. Proc. Acad. Nat.Sci. Philadelphia, pp.387-396, 1894.

PENNSYLVANIA MAMMAL SURVEY. Neil D. Richmond. Penna. Game News, vol.19, no.6, pp.7, 26, 30, 32, Sep., 1948.

MAMMAL SURVEY OF NORTHWESTERN PENNSYLVANIA. Neil D. Richmond, Harry R. Rosland. Final Rep., Pittman-Robertson Project 20-R, Penna. Game Comm., pp.67, illus., 1949.

MAMMAL SURVEY OF SOUTHEASTERN PENNSYLVANIA. Harvey A. Roberts, Robert C. Early. Final Rep., Pittman-Robertson, Project 43-R, Penna. Game Comm., pp.70, illus., 1952.

MAMMAL SURVEY OF NORTHCENTRAL PENNSYLVANIA. Harry R. Roslund. Final Rep., Pittman-Robertson Project 37-R, Penna. Game Comm., pp.55, illus., 1951.

CHESTER COUNTY--A HUNDRED YEARS AGO. H.W. Shoemaker. Penna. Game News, Harrisburg, vol.19, no.3, p.4, illus., June, 1948.

STORIES OF GREAT PENNSYLVANIA HUNTERS. H. W. Shoemaker. Altoona Tribune Co., pp.54, illus., photos, 1913.

STORIES OF PENNSYLVANIA ANIMALS. H.W. Shoemaker. Altoona Tribune, pp.32, illus., 1913.

PENNSYLVANIA CAVES. (Mentions Mammals Found in Caves.) Ralph W. Stone. Penna. Geol. Surv., ser.4, Bull. G 3, pp. 1-63, figs.1-34, 1930.

MAMMALS OF DELAWARE COUNTY, PENNSYLVANIA, AND ADJACENT COUNTIES. Edward T. Stuart, Jr. A resumé. Oologist, vol.43, pp.130-136, Oct.(Dec.), 1926.

MAMMALS OF COOK FOREST. George M. Sutton. Cardinal, Sewickley, Penna., vol.2, pp.76-81, Jan., 1928.

ECONOMIC SURVEY AND GENERAL INVENTORY OF NATIVE PENNSYLVANIA FUR-BEARERS. Douglas E. Wade. Trans. 4th N. Amer. Wildl. Conf., Washington, D.C., pp.250-252, 1939; Penna. Game News, New Cumberland, vol.10, no.1, p. 10, Apr., 1939.

MAMMALIAN FAUNA OF PENNSYLVANIA. Samuel H. Williams. Annals Carnegie Mus., vol.19, no.4, pp.225-234, pl.14, June 30, 1930.

MAMMALS OF PENNSYLVANIA, WITH A DISCUSSION OF THE BIOLOGY OF MAMMALS IN GENERAL, INCLUDING KEYS TO THE ORDERS AND FAMILIES, AND WITH DETAILED ACCOUNTS OF ALL SPECIES INDIGENOUS TO PENNSYLVANIA. Samuel H. Williams. Pittsburgh, pp.163, illus., 1928.

MAMMAL SURVEY OF PENNSYLVANIA. FINAL REPORTS, 1949-52. Harrisburg, Penna., Penna. Game Comm., pt.6, illus., maps, tbls., 1949-52. Contents.-Richmond and Rosland, Mammal Survey of Northwestern Pennsylvania, 1949.- Grimm and Roberts, Southwestern Pennsylvania, 1950.- Roslund, Northcentral Pennsylvania, 1951.- Gifford, Whitebread, Southcentral Pennsylvania, 1951.- Grimm, Whitebread, Northeastern Pennsylvania, 1952.- Roberts, Early, Southeastern Pennsylvania, 1952.

UNITED STATES--RHODE ISLAND

NOTES ON THE MAMMALS OF BLOCK ISLAND, RHODE ISLAND. Outram Bangs. Proc. New England Zool.Club, vol.4, pp. 19-21, pl.1, Mar. 6, 1908.

MAMMALS OF RHODE ISLAND. Edgar A. Mearns. Newport Herald, vol.9, no.2, p.5, Mar. 27, 1900.

NATIVE MAMMALS OF RHODE ISLAND. Edgar A. Mearns. Newport Nat.Hist.Society, Circular, no.1, pp.4, 1900.

LAND MAMMALS OF RHODE ISLAND. Bull. Audubon Society, Rhode Island, vol.13, no. 5, pp.6-8, Dec.-Jan., 1952-53.

UNITED STATES--ROCKY MOUNTAIN REGION

ECOLOGICAL RECONNAISSANCE IN THE MEDICINE BOW MOUNTAINS. Irving H. Blake. Ecological Monographs, Durham, vol.15, no.3, pp.207-242, figs.6, July, 1945.

LORDS OF THE ROCKIES. (Moose, Elk, Mule Deer, Pronghorn, Bison, Mountain Sheep, and Bear.) Wendell Chapman, Lucie Chapman. Nat.Geogr., Washington, D.C., vol.76, no.1, pp.87-129, col.photographs 28, July, 1939.

ACROSS THE WIDE MISSOURI. (Rocky Mts. Fur Trade.) Bernard DeVoto. Houghton Mifflin, p.483, 1947.

PRINCIPAL FACTORS CONTROLLING BIG GAME POPULATIONS IN THE CENTRAL ROCKY MOUNTAIN REGION. L.H.Douglas. Trans. 3rd N.Amer. Wildl.Conf., pp.296-301, 1938.

ANNOTATED LIST OF NATURAL HISTORY WORKS, ESPECIALLY USEFUL TO ROCKY MOUNTAIN STUDENTS. I. THE VERTEBRATES. J. Henderson. Univ.Colorado Studies, vol.5, no.2, pp.101-109, Feb., 1908.

MAMMALS OF ROCKY MOUNTAIN NATIONAL PARK AND THE COLORADO ROCKIES. D.J. Obee. Published by the Author, Colorado Springs, pp. 29, illus., 1945.

WINTER RANGE CONDITIONS IN ROCKY MOUNTAIN NATIONAL PARK. Harold M. Ratcliff. Trans. 6th N.Amer. Wildl.Conf., Washington, D.C., pp.132-139, 1941.

WILD ANIMALS OF THE ROCKIES. ADVENTURES OF A FOREST RANGER. W. M. Rush. Harper and Brothers, New York, pp.xxiii+296, illus., 1942.

ZOOLOGY OF ROCKY MOUNTAIN NATIONAL PARK. Baxtor L. Smith. Nat.Park Service, Field Div. Education, U.S.Dept. Interior, Berkeley, pp.xxiv, mimeographed, 1935.

SPORTING EXCURSIONS IN THE ROCKY MOUNTAINS, INCLUDING A JOURNEY TO THE COLUMBIA RIVER, AND A VISIT TO THE SANDWICH ISLANDS, CHILI. John K. Townsend. London, H. Colburn, "Catalogue of Quadrupeds, Found in the Territory of the Oregon", vol.2, pp.247-278, 1840; 1st ed., Boston, publ. under title: Narrative of a Journey Across the Rocky Mountains, 1839.

UNITED STATES--SOUTH CAROLINA

SOUTH CAROLINA MAMMALS. E.B.Chamberlain. S.Carolina Vertebrate Fauna, publ. by N.Gist Gee, Dept.Biol., Lander Coll., Greenwood, S.C., pp.4, Nov. 20, 1936.

SOME MAMMAL NOTES FROM SOUTH CAROLINA. Robert H. Coleman. Jour. Mamm., vol.29, no.3, pp.293-294, Aug. 31, 1948.

LIST OF MAMMALS OBTAINED BY THADDEUS SURBER, IN NORTH AND SOUTH CAROLINA, GEORGIA AND FLORIDA. D.G. Elliot. Field Columbian Mus., Publ. no.58, Zool.Series, vol.3, no.4, pp.31-57, pls.5-10, Chicago, 1901.

LAND ANIMALS FROM THE SEA. (Fossil Mammals from Edisto Beach State Park South Carolina.) H.S. Ladd. Regional Review, Nat.Park Service, Region one, Richmond, vol.3, no.3, pp.2-7, illus., Sep., 1939.

TWO MAMMAL RECORDS FOR SOUTH CAROLINA. A.L. Nelson. Jour. Mamm., vol.15, no. 3, pp.253-254, Aug., 1934.

DISTRIBUTION AND BIBLIOGRAPHY OF THE MAMMALS OF SOUTH CAROLINA. J.T. Penney. Jour. Mamm., vol.31, no.1, pp.81-89, Feb., 1950.

COLLECTING BIRDS AND MAMMALS IN SOUTH CAROLINA. W.M. Perrygo. Explor. and Fieldwork Smiths.Inst.1940, Publ.no. 3631, pp.27-30, illus., Apr. 3, 1941.

MAMMALS OF UPPER SOUTH CAROLINA. A.L. Pickens. Jour. Mamm., vol.9, no. 2, pp.155-157, May, 1928.

DAMMING THE SANTEE. Archibald Rutledge. Frontiers, Philadelphia, vol.4, no.2, pp.35-38, Dec., 1939.

PLANTATION GAME TRAILS. (Accounts of Hunting White-Tailed Deer Near Mouth of Santee River, South Carolina. Notes on Habits of Deer, Otter, Fox Squirrel.) Archibald Rutledge. The Riverside Press, Cambridge, Mass., pp.300, pls.12, Feb., 1921.

VENDETTAS OF THE MARSH. (Notes on Habits of the Raccoon and White-Tailed Deer.) Archibald Rutledge. Outlook, vol. 127, pp. 379-382, Mar. 9, 1921.

SOME MAMMALS OF WESTERN SOUTH CAROLINA. Frank Sherman. Jour. Mamm., vol.18, no.4, pp.512-513, Nov., 1937.

LIST OF THE VERTEBRATE ANIMALS OF SOUTH CAROLINA. CHAPTER X. SOUTH CAROLINA, RESOURCES AND POPULATIONS, INSTITUTION AND FISHERIES. Frederick W. True. State Board of Agric. of S. Carolina, Charleston, S.C., pp.209-264, 1883.

ON THE DIVISION OF THE WHITE RIVER OR LOWER MIOCENE OF DAKOTA. J.L. Wortman. Bull. Amer. Mus. Nat. Hist., vol.5, art.9, pp.95-105, June 27, 1893.

UNITED STATES--SOUTH DAKOTA

Extinct and Fossil Mammals

LOWER PLIOCENE OGALLALA--WOLF CREEK VERTEBRATE FAUNA, SOUTH DAKOTA. Morton Green. Jour.Paleontol., vol.30, no.1, pp.146-169, illus., Mar., 1956.

PLIOCENE VERTEBRATES FROM BIG SPRING CANYON, SOUTH DAKOTA. Joseph Tracy Gregory. Univ. Calif. Publ., Bull. Dept.Geol.Sci., Berkeley, vol.26, no.4, pp.307-446, pls.49-51, figs.54, July 31, 1942.

FOSSIL COLLECTING IN THE BADLANDS. G.L. Jepsen. Black Hills Engineer, South Dakota School of Mines, vol.14, no.2, pp. 77-86, Mar., 1926.

NOTES ON THE MAMMALS OF FORT SISSETON, DAKOTA. Charles E. McChesney. Annotated by Dr. Elliott Coues. (In) U.S. Geol. and Geographical Surv. of the Territories. Bull., Washington, Govt.Print.Off., vol.4, no.1, art.8, pp.201-218, tbls., 1878.

ADDITIONS TO THE WHITNEYAN FAUNA OF SOUTH DAKOTA. J.R. MacDonald. Jour. Paleontol., Menasha, vol.25, no.3, pp.257-265, illus., May, 1951.

NOTICE OF TWO GENERA OF MAMMALS FROM THE OLIGOCENE OF SOUTH DAKOTA. W.D. Matthew. Bull.Amer.Mus. Nat.Hist., New York, vol.21, pp.21-26, figs.6, Feb. 14, 1905.

FOSSIL MAMMALS OF THE LOWER MIOCENE WHITE RIVER BEDS. COLLECTION OF 1892. Henry Fairfield Osborn. Amer. Mus. Nat.Hist., New York, Bull., vol.6, pp.199-228, illus., pls.2-3, 1894.

FOSSIL HUNTING IN THE WHITE RIVER BAD LANDS, SOUTH DAKOTA. Geo. H. Richardson. North Western Nat., Arbroath, Scotland, vol.14, no.2, pp.85-94, illus., June, 1939.

HITHERTO UNDESCRIBED COPROLITE FROM THE WHITE RIVER BADLANDS OF SOUTH DAKOTA. J. Willis Stovall, W. S. Strain. Jour. Mamm., vol.17, no.1, pp. 27-28, Feb., 1936.

PALEONTOLOGY OF THE AREA. (Fossil Mammals from Titanotherium, Oreodon, and Protoceras Beds of Badlands.) Walter Carl Toepelman. S.Dakota Geol. and Nat. Hist.Survey, Bull.no.11, pp.62-73, Aug., 1922.

STRATIGRAPHY OF THE WHITE RIVER BEDS OF SOUTH DAKOTA. (Information on Mammalian Paleontology.) Harold R. Wanless. Proc. Amer. Philos.Soc., vol. 62, no.4, pp.190-269, figs.10, pls.9, Oct. 18, 1923.

Recent Mammals

LIST OF MAMMALS COLLECTED IN THE BLACK HILLS REGION OF SOUTH DAKOTA AND IN WESTERN KANSAS BY MR. WALTER W. GRANGER, WITH FIELD NOTES BY THE COLLECTOR. J.A. Allen. Bull.Amer.Mus.Nat.Hist., vol.7, pp.259-274, Aug. 21, 1895.

(Review by C. Hart Merriam of) LIST OF MAMMALS COLLECTED IN THE BLACK HILLS REGION OF SOUTH DAKOTA AND IN WESTERN KANSAS BY WALTER W. GRANGER, WITH FIELD NOTES BY THE COLLECTOR. J.A. Allen. Science, New York, vol.11, no.41, p.490, Oct. 11, 1895.

OUR BIG GAME HARVEST IN 1948. Lester M. Berner. S.Dakota Conservation Digest, Pierre, vol.16, no.2, pp.10, 14, 16, Feb., 1949.

SOME OBSERVATIONS ON WILDLIFE IN THE BLACK HILLS DURING THE PAST SIXTY-FIVE YEARS. G.W. Coats. S. Dakota Conservation Digest, Pierre, vol. 12, no.11, pp.10-11, 15, Nov., 1945.

SOUTH DAKOTA PEOPLE FAIL TO RECOGNIZE THE VALUE OF THE STATE'S FUR RESOURCES. Ury Dahling. S.Dakota Conservation Digest, Pierre, vol.10, no.2, pp.3, 7, illus., Feb., 1943.

DISTRIBUTION OF SOME SOUTH DAKOTA MAMMALS. James S. Findley. Nat.Hist. Misc., Chicago Acad.Sci., no.155, pp. 1-2, Apr. 30, 1956.

NOTES ON THE MAMMALS OF FORT SISSETON DAKOTA. C.E. McChesney. Annotated by Dr. Elliot Coues. Bull.U.S. Geol. and Geographical Survey of the Territories, vol.4, no.1, pp.201-218, 1878.

MAMMALS OF SOUTH DAKOTA. William H. Over, E.P. Churchill. Mus. and Dept. Zool., Univ. S. Dakota, Vermillion, pp. 1-56, mimeogr., 1941.

ECOLOGICAL STUDY OF THE MAMMALS OF THE BADLANDS AND THE BLACK HILLS OF SOUTH DAKOTA AND WYOMING. A.M. Stebler. Ecology, Brooklyn, vol.20, no.3, pp.382-393, July, 1939.

GAME KILLED DURING 1947 SEASON. South Dakota Conservation Digest, Pierre, vol.15, no. 7, p.5, July, 1948.

HISTORY OF THE FUR INDUSTRY IN SOUTH DAKOTA. S.Dakota Conservation Digest, Pierre, pp.9-10, Dec., 1939.

UNITED STATES--TENNESSEE

FUR BUSINESS IN TENNESSEE. Earl R. Cady. Tennessee Conservationist, Nashville, vol.13, nos.9-10, p.4, Sep.-Oct., 1948.

TENNESSEE WILDLIFE. John C. Caldwell et al. State Dept. Conserv., Nashville, Educational Service Bull., no.4, pp.1-32, illus., 1938, 1940, and later reprints.

DISTRIBUTION AND FOOD HABITS OF MAMMALS IN THE VICINITY OF THE REELFOOT LAKE BIOLOGICAL STATION. PARTS 1, 2. John B. Calhoun. Jour. Tennessee Acad. Sci., Nashville, vol.16, no.

1, pp.177-185, Jan., 1941; no.2, pp.207-225, figs.2, Apr., 1941.

OBSERVATIONS ON THE MAMMALS OF JOHNSON AND CARTER COUNTIES, TENNESSEE, AND AVERY COUNTY, NORTH CAROLINA. C.H. Conaway, J.C.Howell. Jour. Tennessee Acad. Sci., vol.28, no. 1, pp.53-61, Jan., 1953; Rep.Reelfoot L. Biol.Sta., vol.17, pp.53-61, Jan., 1953.

BREEDING BIRDS OF THE UNICOI MOUNTAINS. (Includes a List of 12 Species of Mammals.) Albert F. Ganier, A. Clebsch. Migrant, Nashville, vol.17, no.4, pp.53-59, map, Dec., 1946.

NOTES ON THE MAMMALS OF WESTERN TENNESSEE. Woodrow W. Goodpaster, Donald F. Hoffmeister. Jour. Mamm., vol. 33, no.3, pp.362-371, Aug. 19, 1952.

OBSERVATIONS ON THE MAMMALS OF THE CUMBERLAND MOUNTAINS OF TENNESSEE. J.C. Howell, C.H.Conaway. Jour. Tennessee Acad. Sci., Nashville, vol. 27, no.2, pp.153-158, Apr., 1952.

ANNOTATED LIST OF TENNESSEE MAMMALS. Remington Kellogg. Proc. U.S. Nat.Mus., vol.86, no.3051, pp.245-303, Feb. 14, 1939.

THE 1953-1954 FUR TAKE REPORT. Eugene Legler, Jr. Tenn.Game and Fish Comm., Tech.Game Leafl., no.2, pp.1-5, July, 1954.

TENNESSEE--LAND OF BEAUTIFUL FORESTS, PLENTY OF GAME BIRDS, ANIMALS, AND DELIGHTFUL HUNTING. Paul S. Mathes. Tenn.Conservationist, Nashville, vol.9, no.8, pp.3, 19, Aug-Sep., 1944.

COLLECTING BIRDS AND MAMMALS IN TENNESSEE. Watson M. Perrygo. Explor. and Fieldwork Smiths.Inst.1937, Publ.no. 3480, pp.31-34, figs.33-36, 1938.

CONTRIBUTIONS TO THE ZOOLOGY OF TENNESSEE. NO. 3. MAMMALS. Samuel N. Rhoads. Proc. Acad. Nat. Sci., Phila., pp.175-200, Apr.21, 1896; pp.201-205, May 12, 1896.

STATEWIDE WILDLIFE SURVEY OF TENNESSEE. STUDY OF THE LAND WILDLIFE, FARMER, HUNTER AND TRAPPER. FINAL REPORT. Vincent Schultz, et al. Tenn.Game and Fish Comm., Nashville, pp.506, mimeogr., 1954.

STATUS OF THE BEAVER AND OTTER IN TENNESSEE. Vincent Schultz. Jour.Tenn. Acad.Sci., vol.29, no.1, pp.73-81, Jan., 1954; Rep.Reelfoot L.Biol.Sta., vol.18, pp.73-81, Jan., 1954.

STATUS OF THE SPOTTED SKUNK, COMMON SKUNK, AND WOODCHUCK IN TENNESSEE. Vincent Schultz. Jour. Tenn.Acad. Sci., vol.29, no.4, pp.305-314, Oct., 1954.

NOTES FROM THE BACKGROUND OF OUR KNOWLEDGE OF THE ZOOLOGY OF TENNESSEE. C.S. Shoup. Jour.Tenn.Acad.Sci., Nashville, vol.19, no.2, pp.126-136, Apr., 1944.

NEW FOSSIL VERTEBRATE FIND NEAR GASSAWAY, CANNON COUNTY, TENNESSEE. (Mastodon, Sabretooth Tiger.) Geo.I. Whitlatch, D.D. Arden, Jr. Jour.Tenn.Acad. Sci., Nashville, vol.17, no.2, pp.224-228, Apr., 1942.

GAME SURVEY IN NORTHEASTERN TENNESSEE. Leonard Wing. Jour.Tenn.Acad. Sci., Nashville, vol.15, no.3, pp.309-320, July, 1940.

NOTICE OF FOSSIL BONES FROM THE NEIGHBORHOOD OF MEMPHIS, TENNESSEE. Jeffries Wyman. Amer. Jour.Sci. Arts, ser.2, vol.10, pp.1-9, 1850.

UNITED STATES--TEXAS

Extinct and Fossil Mammals

ARCHAEOLOGICAL AND FAUNAL MATERIAL FROM WILLIAMS CAVE, GUADALUPE MOUNTAINS, TEXAS. Mary Youngman Ayer. Proc. Acad. Nat. Sci. Philadelphia, pp.599-618, 1937.

BIG GAME IN EARLY TEXAS. (Fossils.) J.L. Baughman. Texas Game and Fish, Austin, vol.4, no.5, pp.4-5, illus., Apr., 1946.

APPARENTLY EXTINCT EUGLANDINA FROM TEXAS. T.D.A. Cockerell. Proc. Colorado Mus. Nat. Hist., vol.9, no.5, pp.52-53, Dec. 16, 1930.

COLLECTION OF PLEISTOCENE VERTEBRATES FROM SOUTHWESTERN TEXAS. Oliver P. Hay. Proc. U.S. Nat. Mus., vol. 68, art.24, pp.1-18, pls.8, 1926.

DESCRIPTION OF SOME FOSSIL VERTEBRATES FROM THE UPPER MIOCENE OF TEXAS. Oliver P. Hay. Proc. Biol.Soc. Washington, vol.37, pp.1-20, pls.6, Jan. 29, 1924.

PRELIMINARY DESCRIPTIONS OF FOSSIL MAMMALS RECENTLY DISCOVERED IN OKLAHOMA, TEXAS, AND NEW MEXICO. Oliver P. Hay, Harold J. Cook. Proc. Colorado Mus. Nat. Hist., vol.8, p.33, Feb. 2, 1928.

PLIOCENE VERTEBRATE FAUNA FROM HIGGINS, LIPSCOMB COUNTY, TEXAS. Curtis J. Hesse. Univ. Texas Publ., Austen, no.3945, pp.671-698, figs.105-112, June, 1940.

PRELIMINARY REPORT ON THE MIOCENE VERTEBRATE FAUNAS OF SOUTHEAST TEXAS. Curtis J. Hesse. Trans. Texas Acad. Sci., Houston, vol.26, pp.157-178, figs.2, 1943.

TRACKS FROM THE PLIOCENE OF WEST TEXAS. (Mastodon, Extinct Felids and Canids.) C. Stuart Johnston. Amer. Midland Nat., vol.18, no.1, pp.147-152, pls.3, Jan., 1937.

SURVEY OF VARIOUS LATE CENOZOIC VERTEBRATE FAUNAS OF THE PANHANDLE OF TEXAS. PART I. INTRODUCTION, PRELIMINARY FAUNAL LISTS. C. Stuart Johnston, D.E. Savage. Univ. Calif. Publ. Geol. Sci., vol.31, no.2, pp. 27-50, illus., Oct., 1955.

FAUNA OF THE DALLAS SAND PITS. Richard Swann Lull. Amer. Jour. Sci., vol.2, pp.159-176, figs.5, Sep., 1921.

EARLY CRETACEOUS MAMMALS FROM NORTHERN TEXAS. Bryan Patterson. Amer. Jour. Sci., Chicago, vol.249, pp.31-46, illus., Jan., 1951.

RECENT AND PLEISTOCENE MAMMALIAN FAUNA OF BRAZOS COUNTY, TEXAS. R. L. Peterson. Jour. Mamm., vol.27, no.2, pp.162-169, figs.5, May 14, 1946.

VERTEBRATE FAUNA AND GEOLOGIC AGE OF TRINITY RIVER TERRACES IN HENDERSON COUNTY, TEXAS. J. Willis Stovall, William N. McAnulty. Amer. Midland Nat., Notre Dame, vol.44, no.1, pp.211-250, pls.2, July, 1950.

MIOCENE FORMATIONS AND VERTEBRATE BIOSTRATIGRAPHIC UNITS, TEXAS COASTAL PLAIN. John A. Wilson. Bull. Amer. Assoc. Petrol. Geol., vol.40, no.9, pp.2233-2246, illus., Sep., 1956.

DAEMONHELIX IN THE PLEISTOCENE OF TEXAS. Horace Elmer Wood 2nd. Jour.Geol., vol.41, no.8, pp.824-833, figs.5, Nov.-Dec., 1933.

MID-TERTIARY VERTEBRATES FROM THE TEXAS COASTAL PLAINS: FACT AND FABLE. Horace Elmer Wood 2nd. Amer. Midland Nat., vol.18, no.1, pp. 129-146, figs.4, pl.1, Jan., 1937.

DISCOVERY OF EARLY CRETACEOUS MAMMALS AND FROGS IN TEXAS. Rainer Zangerl, Robert H. Denison. Science, Lancaster, vol.112, no.2898, p.61, July 14, 1950.

Recent Mammals

ON MAMMALS COLLECTED IN BEXAR COUNTY, TEXAS, BY MR. H. P. ATTWATER, WITH FIELD NOTES BY THE COLLECTOR. J.A. Allen. Bull.Amer. Mus. Nat. Hist., vol.8, pp.47-80, Apr. 22, 1896.

ON THE MAMMALS OF ARANSAS COUNTY, TEXAS, WITH DESCRIPTIONS OF NEW FORMS OF LEPUS AND ORYZOMYS. J.A. Allen. Bull. Amer. Mus. Nat. Hist., vol. 6, pp.165-198, May 31, 1894.

BIOLOGICAL SURVEY OF TEXAS. 1. LIFE ZONES WITH CHARACTERISTIC SPECIES OF MAMMALS, BIRDS, REPTILES, AND PLANTS. 2. REPTILES, WITH NOTES ON DISTRIBUTION. 3. MAMMALS, WITH NOTES ON DISTRIBUTION, HABITS, AND ECONOMIC IMPORTANCE. Vernon Bailey. N.Amer. Fauna, no.25, U.S.Dept.Agric., pp.216, pls.26, Oct. 24, 1905.

MAMMALS OF THE LONE-STAR STATE. Vernon Bailey. Nature Mag., vol.16, no.6, pp.363-365, 386, figs.8, Dec., 1930.

SEVEN NEW MAMMALS FROM WESTERN TEXAS. Vernon Bailey. Proc. Biol. Soc. Washington, vol.15, pp.117-120, June 2, 1902.

NOTES ON SMALL MAMMALS OF EASTERN TEXAS. Rollin H. Baker. Jour. Mamm., vol.23, no.3, p.343, Aug. 14, 1942.

REMARKS ON THE FORMER DISTRIBUTION OF ANIMALS IN EASTERN TEXAS. Rollin H. Baker. Texas Jour. Sci., vol.8, no.3, pp.356-359, Sep., 1956.

TEXAS FUR ANIMALS AND THEIR FUTURE. Rollin H. Baker. Texas Game and Fish, Austin, vol.1, no.3, pp.5, 13, Feb., 1943.

NOTES ON THE MAMMALS OF GALVESTON AND MUSTANG ISLANDS, TEXAS. Rollin H. Baker, Daniel W. Lay. Jour. Mamm., vol.19, no.4, p.505, Nov. 14, 1938.

BIG GAME IN EARLY TEXAS. J.L.Baughman. Texas Game and Fish, Austin, vol. 4, no.5, pp.4-5, 22, illus., Apr., 1946.

BIOTIC PROVINCES OF TEXAS. W.Frank Blair. Texas Jour Sci., San Marcos, vol.2, no.1, pp.93-117, Mar. 31, 1950.

CONTRIBUTION TO THE ECOLOGY AND FAUNAL RELATIONSHIPS OF THE MAMMALS OF THE DAVIS MOUNTAIN REGION, SOUTHWESTERN TEXAS. W.Frank Blair. Misc. Publ.Mus. Zool., Univ. Michigan, Ann Arbor, no.46, pp.7-39, pls.1-3, June 28, 1940.

EXTENSIONS OF THE KNOWN RANGES OF THREE SPECIES OF TEXAS MAMMALS. W. Frank Blair. Jour. Mamm., Baltimore, vol.30, no.2, pp.201-202, May 23, 1949.

MAMMALS OF THE MESQUITE PLAINS BIOTIC DISTRICT IN TEXAS AND OKLAHOMA, AND SPECIATION IN THE CENTRAL GRASSLANDS. W. Frank Blair. Texas Jour. Sci., vol.6, no.3, pp.235-264, Sep., 1954.

MAMMALS OF THE TAMAULIPAN BIOTIC PROVINCE IN TEXAS. W. Frank Blair. Texas Jour. Sci., San Marcos, vol.4, no. 2, pp.230-250, illus, June 30, 1952.

NEW MAMMALS FROM TEXAS AND OKLAHOMA, WITH REMARKS ON THE STATUS OF THOMOMYS TEXENSIS BAILEY. W. Frank Blair. Occas.Papers Mus. Zool., Univ. Michigan, Ann Arbor, no.403, pp.2-7, June 16, 1939.

MAMMALS OF THE SIERRA VIEJA REGION, SOUTHWESTERN TEXAS, WITH REMARKS ON THE BIOGEOGRAPHIC POSITION OF THE REGION. W. Frank Blair, Clay E. Miller, Jr. Texas Jour. Sci., San Marcos, vol.1, no.1, pp.67-92, Mar. 31, 1949.

MAMMALS OF THE BIG BEND AREA OF TEXAS. Adrey E. Borell, Monroe D. Bryant. Univ.Calif.Publ.Zool., Berkeley, vol.48, no.1, pp.1-62, fig.1, pls.1-5, Aug. 7, 1942.

FIELD INVESTIGATIONS PERTINENT TO BULLIS FEVER. PRELIMINARY REPORT ON THE SPECIES OF TICKS AND VERTEBRATES OCCURRING AT CAMP BULLIS, TEXAS. James M. Brennan. Texas Rep. on Biology and Medicine, vol.3, no.1, pp.112-121; no.2, pp.204-226, 1945.(Mammalian Hosts pp.218-219.)

WILDLIFE THRIVES IN BIG BEND AREA. J.G. Burr. Texas Game and Fish, Austin, vol.7, no.6, pp.4-5, 20-22, illus., May, 1949.

MAMMALS OF THE GUADALUPE MOUNTAINS OF WESTERN TEXAS. W.B.Davis. Occas.Papers Mus.Zool., Louisiana State Univ., University, no.7, pp.69-84, fig.1, July 10, 1940.

MAMMALS OF CULBERSON COUNTY, TEXAS. W.B. Davis, J.L.Robertson, Jr. Jour. Mamm., vol.25, no.3, pp.254-273, figs.2, pl.1, Sep. 8, 1944.

NATURE TERRESTRIAL COMMUNITIES OF BREWSTER COUNTY, TEXAS AND ADJACENT AREAS, WITH SPECIAL REFERENCE TO THE DEGREE OF RESTRICTION OF CERTAIN SMALL MAMMALS TO PARTICULAR COMMUNITIES. Helen A. Denyes. Ann Arbor, Univ.Microfilms, Univ. of Michigan, Publ.no.2581, pp.xxv-272, illus., maps, tbls.. 1951.

NATURAL TERRESTRIAL COMMUNITIES OF BREWSTER COUNTY, TEXAS, WITH SPECIAL REFERENCE TO THE DISTRIBUTION OF THE MAMMALS. Helen A. Denyes. Amer. Midland Nat., vol.55, no. 2, pp.289-320, Apr., 1956.

FUR RESOURCES AND FUR ANIMALS OF TEXAS. O. Earl Frye, Daniel W. Lay. Bull.Game Fish and Oyster Commission, Austin, no.25, pp.42, illus., Dec., 1942.

CENTURY OF SCIENTIFIC EXPLORATION IN TEXAS. PART 1: 1820-1880. S.W.Geiser. Field Lab., vol.4, no.2, pp.41-55, Apr., 1936.

WILDLIFE TRANSPLANTING FOR 1948-49. W.C. Glazener. Texas Game and Fish, Austin, vol.8, no.7, pp.18-19, illus., June, 1950.

MAMMALS OF THE STOCKTON PLATEAU OF NORTHEASTERN TERRELL COUNTY, TEXAS. Jack A. Hermann. Texas Jour. Sci., vol.2, no.3, pp.368-393, Sep., 1950.

GAME IN THE BIG BEND. Grady Hill.Texas Game and Fish, Austin, vol.3, no.8, pp.11, 22, illus., July, 1945.

ECOLOGICAL RECONNAISSANCE OF THE MAMMALS OF THE TEXAS HIGH PLAINS REGION. Milton F. Landwer. PhD thesis, Univ. Michigan, 1940.

FUR RESOURCES OF EASTERN TEXAS. Daniel W. Lay. Texas Game, Fish and Oyster Comm., Austin, Bull.no.15, pp.7, Feb., 1939.

MANAGEMENT OF FUR-BEARING ANIMALS ON TEXAS FARMS AND RANCHES. Daniel W. Lay. Texas Game, Fish and Oyster Comm., Bull.no.19, pp.8, 1940.

FUR RESOURCES AND FUR ANIMALS OF TEXAS. Daniel W. Lay, O. Earle Frye. Texas Game, Fish and Oyster Comm., Bull.no.25, pp.42, Dec., 1942.

WILDLIFE ASPECTS OF CUTOVER PINE WOODLAND IN WESTERN TEXAS. Daniel W. Lay, Walter P. Taylor. Jour.Forestry, Washington, D.C., vol.41, no.6, pp.446-448, June, 1943.

NEW LOCALITY RECORDS FOR SOME MAMMALS OF EASTERN TEXAS. W.H. McCarley, W.N. Bradshaw. Jour.Mamm., vol.34, no.4, pp.515-516, Nov. 13, 1953.

GAME RESTORATION IN TEXAS.(Deer, Antelope, Beaver, Raccoon, Muskrat, Javelina.) A.J. Nicholson. Texas Game and Fish, Austin, vol.4, no.9, pp.4-5, 20-21, illus., Aug., 1946.

CERTAIN RECENT GEOLOGICAL AND BIOLOGICAL CHANGES IN SOUTH TEXAS, WITH CONSIDERATIONS OF PROBABLE CAUSES. (Spreading of Ranges of Armadillo, Coati, Covote, Jackrabbit, and Prairie Dog.) W. Armstrong Price, Gordon Gunter. Trans. Texas Acad. Sci., Houston, vol.26, pp. 138-156, figs.2, 1943.

MAMMAL NOTES FROM SULPHUR RIVER, BOWIE COUNTY, TEXAS. John K. Strecker, Walter J. Williams. Jour. Mamm., vol.10, no.3, p.259, Aug., 1929.

MAMMALS FROM COOKE COUNTY, TEXAS. Robert J. Russell. Texas Jour. Sci., vol.5, no.4, pp.454-464, Dec., 1953.

GAME AND FUR-BEARING ANIMALS OF HARRIS COUNTY, TEXAS. Tarleton F. Smith. MS thesis, A. and M. Coll. Texas, 1942.

NOTES ON MAMMALS OF DALLAS COUNTY, TEXAS. William B. Stallcup. Field and Laboratory, Dalla, vol.24, no.3, pp.96-101, June, 1956.

MAMMALS OF NORTHWESTERN TEXAS FOUND IN BARN OWL PELLETS. William H. Stickel, Lucille F. Stickel. Jour. Mamm., vol.29, no.3, pp.291-293, illus., Aug. 31, 1948.

ANIMALS AND STREAMS. CONTRIBUTION TO THE STUDY OF TEXAS FOLK NAMES. John K. Strecker. Baylor Univ., Waco, Texas, Contribution to Folk-Lore, no.2, pp.1-23, Apr. 15, 1929. (Study of Creeks with Animal Names. Also, Information on Distribution of Certain Mammals.)

CHECK LIST OF THE MAMMALS OF TEXAS, EXCLUSIVE OF THE SIRENIA AND CETACEA. John K. Strecker. Baylor Bull., Baylor Univ., Waco, Texas, vol.29, no.3, pp.1-48, Aug., 1926.

CHRONICLES OF GEORGE BARNARD, THE INDIAN TRADER OF THE TEHUACANA, AND OTHER BITS OF TEXAS HISTORY. (Historical Notes on Mammals.) John K. Strecker. Baylor Bull., Baylor Univ., Waco, Texas, vol.31, no.3, pp.1-58, pl.1, Sep., 1928.

MAMMALS OF McLENNAN COUNTY, TEXAS. John K. Strecker. (1st and 2nd Papers.) Baylor Bull., Baylor Univ., Mus. Waco, Texas, vol.27, no.3, pp.3-20, Sep., 1924; no.9, pp.15, Oct. 15, 1926.

NOTES ON THE MAMMALS OF WEST FRIO CANYON, REAL COUNTY, TEXAS. John K. Strecker. (In) Notes on the Zoology of Texas.(From the Unpublished Manuscripts of John K. Strecker). Baylor Bull., Baylor Univ., Waco, Texas, vol.38, no.3, pp.1-69, Aug., 1935.

NOTES ON THE ZOOLOGY OF TEXAS. John K. Strecker. Baylor Bull., Waco, Texas, vol.38, no.3, pp.69, Aug., 1935.

MAMMALS OF TWO AREAS IN THE BIG BEND REGION OF TRANS-PECOS, TEXAS. J.R. Tamsitt. Texas Jour. Sci., vol. 6, no.1, pp.33-61, Mar., 1954.

BIG BEND. Walter P. Taylor. Amer.Forests, Washington, vol.52, no.7, pp.304-306, 343-344, illus., July, 1946.

GEOGRAPHIC DISTRIBUTION OF TEXAS WILDLIFE. Walter P. Taylor. Texas Geogr. Mag., Dallas, vol.9, no.1, pp.1-12, Spring, 1945.

MAMMALS OF TEXAS. Walter P. Taylor. Texas Game, Fish and Oyster Comm., Austin, Div. of Widl. Restoration, Bull. no.27, pp.79, tbls., pls., 1947.

RESEARCH POINTS THE WAY TO MORE GAME IN TEXAS. Walter P. Taylor. Game, Fish and Oyster Comm., Ann.Rept. 1936-1937, Austin, pp.8, illus., 1938.

VANISHING SPECIES OF WILDLIFE IN TEXAS. Walter P. Taylor. Texas Game and Fish, Austin, vol.2, no.5, pp.3, 7, Apr., 1944.

MAMMALS OF TEXAS. Walter P. Taylor, W. Davis. Texas Game, Fish and Oyster Comm., Div. Widl.Restoration, Austin, Bull.no.27, pp.1-79, illus., 1947.

ON THE SMALL MAMMALS OF DUVAL COUNTY, SOUTH TEXAS. Oldfield Thomas. Proc. Zool. Soc. London, pp.443-450, Nov. 20, 1888.

MAMMALS OF BRAZOS COUNTY, TEXAS. Michael Throckmorton. MS thesis, A. and M. Coll. Texas, 1946.

DESCRIPTION OF GEOMYS PERSONATUS AND DIPODOMYS COMPACTUS, TWO NEW SPECIES OF RODENTS FROM PADRE ISLAND, TEXAS. Frederick W. True. Proc. U.S. Nat. Mus., vol.11, Publ.no.699, pp. 159-160, Jan. 5, 1889.

SOILS VEGETATION AND ECOLOGICAL SUCCESSION IN WALKER COUNTY, TEXAS, AS RELATED TO WILDLIFE. S. R. Warner. Trans. Texas Acad. Sci., Houston, vol.26, pp.83-97, 1943.

BIOGEOGRAPHIC REGIONS OF TEXAS AND OKLAHOMA. William L. Webb. Ecology, Lancaster, vol.31, no.3, pp.426-433, illus., July, 1950.

NOTES ON THE ZOOLOGY OF TEXAS. (From the Unpublished Manuscripts of John K. Strecker.) Walter J. Williams. Baylor Bull., vol.38, no.3, pp.1-69, Baylor Univ., Waco, Texas, Aug., 1935.

ECOLOGY OF FURBEARERS IN THE UPLAND POST OAK REGION OF EASTERN TEXAS. John E. Wood. PhD thesis, A. and M. Coll., Texas, 1952.

EFFECTS OF AGRICULTURE (RANCHING AND FARMING) ON THE HABITAT AND FOOD SUPPLY OF FURBEARERS IN THE POST OAK REGION OF TEXAS. John E. Wood. Trans. 17th N.Amer. Wildl. Conf., pp.427-437, illus., 1952.

PHYSICAL AND VEGETATIONAL BASIS FOR ANIMAL DISTRIBUTION IN THE SIERRA VIEJA RANGE OF SOUTHWESTERN TEXAS. Christopher L. York. Texas Jour.Sci., San Marcos, vol.1, no.3, pp. 46-62, Sep. 30, 1949.

FUR ANIMALS OF TEXAS. (Bobcat, Muskrat.) Texas Game and Fish, Austin, vol.2, no.4, p.10, Mar., 1944.

FUR ANIMALS OF TEXAS. (Beaver, Jack Rabbit.) Texas Game and Fish, Austin, vol.2, no.5, pp.6-7, Apr., 1944.

FUR RESOURCES OF EASTERN TEXAS. Texas Game, Fish and Oyster Comm., Austin, Bull.no.15, pp.7, Feb., 1939.

SHORT LIST OF WILDLIFE PUBLICATIONS WITH SPECIAL REGARD TO TEXAS. Game, Fish and Oyster Comm., Austin, Bull.no. 14, pp.31, Oct., 1938. (Revised June, 1939.)

## UNITED STATES--UTAH

### Extinct and Fossil Mammals

PLEISTOCENE MAMMOTHS IN UTAH AND VICINITY. Elliot Blackwelder. Amer. Jour. Sci., New Haven, vol.237, no.12, pp.890-894, pl.1, Dec., 1939.

PRELIMINARY REPORT ON FOSSIL MAMMALS FROM THE GREEN RIVER FORMATION IN UTAH. J.J. Burke. Ann.Carnegie Mus., vol.25, pp.13-14, Nov.25, 1935.

FURTHER CONTRIBUTION TO THE DRAGON PALEOCENE FAUNA OF CENTRAL UTAH. C. Lewis Gazin. Jour.Washington Acad.Sci., vol.29, no.7, pp.273-286, figs.10, July 15, 1939.

MAMMALIAN FAUNAS OF THE PALEOCENE OF CENTRAL UTAH, WITH NOTES ON THE GEOLOGY. C. Lewis Gazin. Proc. Nat.Mus., Washington, vol.91, pp.1-53, illus., pls.3, 1943.

PALEOCENE MAMMALIAN FAUNA FROM CENTRAL UTAH. C. Lewis Gazin. Jour. Washington Acad. Sci., vol.28, no.6, pp. 271-277, figs.3, June 15, 1938.

PALEOCENE MAMMALS FROM UTAH. C. Lewis Gazin. Proc. Geol. Soc. America for 1937, p.278, June, 1938. (Abstract.)

TERTIARY FORMATIONS OF THE UINTA BASIN, UTAH. J. Leroy Kay. Ann.Carnegie Mus., vol.23, pp.357-371, pls.45-49, Oct. 15, 1934.

LIST OF SPECIES AND DESCRIPTION OF NEW MATERIAL FROM THE DUCHESNE RIVER OLIGOCENE, UINTA BASIN, UTAH. O.A. Peterson. Ann. Carnegie Mus., vol. 23, pp.373-389, figs.8, Nov. 19, 1934.

MAMMALIA OF THE DUCHESNE RIVER OLIGOCENE. William B. Scott. Trans. Amer. Philos.Soc., Philadelphia, n.s., vol.34, pt.3, pp.209-253, pls.8, Mar., 1945.

Recent Mammals

MAMMALS FROM BEAVER COUNTY, UTAH, COLLECTED BY THE MUSEUM EXPEDITION OF 1904. Joel Asaph Allen. New York, Macmillan Co. for the Brooklyn Inst. of Arts and Sci., Sci.Bull., vol.1, no.5, pp.117-122, 1905.

MAMMALS OF UTAH. Claude T. Barnes. Kaysville, Utah, Inland Printing Co., Bull. Univ. Utah, vol.12, no.15, pp.166, illus., maps, 1922.

UTAH MAMMAL LIST. Claude T. Barnes. Jour. Mamm., vol.4, no.3, p.194, Aug., 1923.

UTAH MAMMALS. Claude T. Barnes. Bull. Univ. Utah., vol.17, no.12, pp.1-183, maps 32, pl.1, June, 1927.

BIOLOGICAL RECONNAISSANCE OF NAVAJO MOUNTAIN, UTAH. Seth B. Benson. Univ. Calif. Publ. in Zool., vol.40, no.14, pp.439-456, Dec. 31, 1935.

INTERESTING FACTS ABOUT THE ANTELOPE AND GOLDEN-MANTLED GROUND SQUIRREL. Jack H. Berryman. Utah Fish and Game Bull., Salt Lake City, vol.7, no.10, pp.2-3, Jan., 1950.

SERIES OF ARTICLES PRESENTS INTERESTING INFORMATION CONCERNING IMPORTANT MAMMALS OF UTAH. Jack H. Berryman. Utah Fish and Game Bull., Salt Lake City, vol.5, no.12, pp.3-5, illus., July-Aug., 1948.

COMPARATIVE STUDY OF THE VEGETATION OF GRAZED AND UNGRAZED CANYONS OF THE WASATCH RANGE, UTAH. Walter P. Cottam, Frederick R. Evans. Ecology, Lancaster, vol.26, no.2, pp.171-181, Apr., 1945.

COLLECTING IN THE UINTA BASIN. J. Kenneth Doutt. Carnegie Mag., vol.11, no. 8, pp.233-238, illus., Jan., 1938.

THE MAMMALS OF UTAH, TAXONOMY AND DISTRIBUTION. Stephen D. Durrant. PhD thesis, Univ. Kansas, 1950; Univ. Kansas Publ., Mus. Nat.Hist., vol.6, pp. 549, maps, 1952.

(Review by David H. Johnson of) THE MAMMALS OF UTAH, TAXONOMY AND DISTRIBUTION. Stephen D. Durrant. Science, vol. 117, no.3042, p.428, Apr. 17, 1953.

(Review by W. Robert Eadie of) THE MAMMALS OF UTAH, TAXONOMY AND DISTRIBUTION. Stephen D. Durrant. Jour. Mamm., vol.34, no.3, pp.401-402, Aug. 14, 1953.

ADDITIONAL RECORDS AND EXTENSIONS OF KNOWN RANGES OF MAMMALS FROM UTAH. Stephen D. Durrant, M. Raymond Lee, Richard M. Hansen. Univ. Kansas Publ., Mus. Nat. Hist., vol.9, no.2, pp. 69-80, Dec. 10, 1955.

MAMMALS OF THE NAVAJO COUNTY. Theodore H. Eaton. Berkeley, National Youth Administration, pp.46, 1937.

BIOTIC COMMUNITIES OF THE NORTHERN DESERT SHRUB BIOME IN WESTERN UTAH. Reed W. Fautin. Ecological Monograph, Durham, vol.16, no.4, pp.251-310, figs.19, Oct., 1946.

RANGE FOR BIG GAME AND LIVESTOCK IN UTAH. D.M. Gaufin, et al. Utah State Dept. Fish and Game, Bull.no.2, pp.24, 1950.

DIGEST OF 1948 BIG GAME KILL. D.M. Gaufin. Utah Fish and Game Bull., Salt Lake City, vol.8, no.4, pp.1-2, May, 1949.

NINE NEW MAMMALS FROM ISLANDS IN GREAT SALT LAKE, UTAH. E. A. Goldman. Jour. Mamm., vol.20, no.3, pp.351-357, Aug. 14, 1939.

CRITICAL COMMENTS ON MAMMALS FROM UTAH, WITH DESCRIPTIONS OF NEW FORMS FROM UTAH, NEVADA, AND WASHINGTON. E. Raymond Hall. Univ. Calif. Publ. Zool., vol.37, no.1, pp.1-13, Apr. 10, 1931.

THREE NEW MAMMALS (MICROTUS AND OCHOTONA) FROM UTAH. E. Raymond Hall. Great Basin Nat., Provo, vol. 2, no.2, pp.105-107, June 30, 1941.

MAMMALS FROM MILLARD COUNTY, UTAH. E. Raymond Hall, David H. Johnson. Utah Acad. Sci., Arts and Letters, Salt Lake City, vol.15, pp.121-122, 1938.

DISCOVERING AND CONSERVING THE BIOLOGICAL RESOURCES OF UTAH. Ross Hardy. Proc. Utah Acad. Sci., Arts and Letters, Salt Lake City, vol.21, pp. 67-70, 1944.

INFLUENCE OF SOIL TYPE AND OF BARRIERS ON THE LOCAL DISTRIBUTION OF SOME MAMMALS IN SOUTHWESTERN UTAH. Ross Hardy. PhD thesis, Univ.Michigan, 1944.

INFLUENCE OF TYPES OF SOIL UPON THE LOCAL DISTRIBUTION OF SOME MAMMALS IN SOUTHWESTERN UTAH. Ross Hardy. Ecol.Monogr., Durham, vol.15, pp.71-108, figs.19, Jan., 1945.

LOCATION OF BRIGG'S MEADOWS, BEAVER MOUNTAINS, UTAH. Ross Hardy. Jour. Mamm., vol.26, no.4, p.432, Feb. 12, 1946.

NOTES ON MAMMALS FROM ARIZONA, NEVADA, AND UTAH. Ross Hardy. Jour. Mamm., vol.30, no.4, pp.434-435, Nov. 17, 1949.

BIBLIOGRAPHY OF UTAH MAMMALOGY; INCLUDING REFERNCES TO NAMES AND TYPE LOCALITIES APPLIED TO UTAH MAMMALS. C. Lynn Hayward. Proc. Utah Acad. Sci., Arts and Letters, vol.13, pp.121-146, 1936.

BIBLIOGRAPHY OF UTAH MAMMALOGY; INCLUDING REFERENCES TO NAMES AND TYPE LOCALITIES (FIRST SUPPLEMENT). C. Lynn Hayward. Great Basin Nat., Provo, vol.2, no.4, pp.125-136, Dec. 31, 1941.

BIOTIC COMMUNITIES OF THE WASATCH CHAPARRAL, UTAH. C. Lynn Hayward. Ecol. Monographs, Durham, vol.18, no.4, pp.473-508, Oct., 1948.

REVIEW OF UTAH'S BIG GAME, LIVESTOCK, AND RANGE RELATIONSHIPS PROBLEMS. Odell Julander, et al. U.S. Dept.Agric., Intermountain Forest and Range Exp. Sta., Res.Paper, no.24, pp. 53, Sep., 1950.

UTAH'S BIG GAME, LIVESTOCK, AND RANGE RELATIONSHIP RESEARCH PROJECT. Odell Julander. Jour. Range Mgt., vol.4, no.5, pp.330-334, Sep., 1951.

FLUCTUATIONS IN POPULATION OF SMALL MAMMALS IN UTAH. Keith R. Kelson. Jour. Mamm., vol.32, no.1, pp. 113-114, Feb., 1951.

NOTES ON THE LIFE HISTORIES OF SOME UTAH MAMMALS. W.S. Long. Jour. Mamm., vol.21, no.2, pp.170-180, May 14, 1940.

GAME AND MICE COMPETE FOR FORAGE ON UTAH RANGES. Jessop B. Low. Utah Fish and Game Bull., Salt Lake City, vol.4, no.8, pp.1-4, illus., Jan., 1948.

SURVEY OF THE MAMMALS OF THE ISLANDS IN GREAT SALT LAKE, UTAH. William H. Marshall. Jour. Mamm., vol. 21, no.2, pp.144-160, pls.2, map, May 14, 1940.

SIX UTAH MAMMAL RECORDS. A.W. Moore. Jour. Mamm., vol.11, no.1, pp. 87-88, Feb., 1930.

SOME NOTES UPON UTAH MAMMALS. A.W. Moore. Jour. Mamm., vol.10, no.3, pp.259-260, Aug., 1929.

BIG GAME IN MULTIPLE LAND USE IN UTAH. Orange A. Olsen. Jour. Forestry, Washington, D.C., vol.41, no.11, pp.792-797, Nov., 1943; Wisconsin Conserv. Bull., Madison, vol.9, no.2, pp.11-16, Feb., 1944.

GAME MANAGEMENT PROBLEMS OF UTAH NATIONAL PARKS. Thomas C. Parker. Utah State Agric. College, Logan, Misc.Publ., no.10, pp.32-34, May, 1933.

RANGES AND RELATIONSHIPS OF CERTAIN MAMMALS IN SOUTHWESTERN UTAH. C.C. Presnall, E. Raymond Hall. Utah Acad. Sci., Arts and Letters, vol.13, pp.211-213, May 22, 1936.

MAMMALS OF ZION-BRYCE AND CEDAR BREAKS. C.C. Presnall. Zion Nat.Park, Utah, Zion-Bryce Mus.Bull., no.2, pp.20, illus., map, diagr., 1938.

MANAGING UTAH'S BIG-GAME CROP. D. Irvin Rasmussen, David M. Gaufin. Trees, Yearbook Agric., 1949, U.S.Dept. Agric., Washington, pp.573-580, 1949.

WHAT IS THE FUTURE OF UTAH'S FUR RESOURCES? Edwin V. Rawley. Utah Fish and Game Bull., vol.11, no.5, pp.2, 6-7, graphs, Feb., 1955.

NOTES ON THE MAMMALS OF SOUTHERN UTAH. A.L. Siler. Amer.Nat., Lancaster, vol.14, no.9, pp.673-674, Sep., 1880.

ECOLOGICAL DISTRIBUTION OF MAMMALS OF THE NORTH SLOPE OF THE UINTA MOUNTAINS. Ruth D. Svihla. Ecol. Monographs, vol.2, no.1, pp.47-81, figs.7, Jan., 1932.

MAMMALS OF THE UINTA MOUNTAIN REGION. Ruth D. Svihla. Jour. Mamm., vol.12, no.3, pp.256-266, pl.11, fig.1, Aug., 1931.

BIOTIC STUDY OF THE KAIPAROWITS REGION OF UTAH. Vasco M. Tanner. Great Basin Nat., Provo, vol.1, nos.3-4, pp.97-125, illus., June 30, 1940.

SOME OF THE SMALLER MAMMALS OF MOUNT TIMPANOGOS, UTAH. Vasco M. Tanner. Jour. Mamm., vol.8, no.3, pp. 250-251, Aug., 1927.

BIG GAME IN UTAH. Ernest Winkler. Jour. Forestry, Washington, vol.28, no.5, pp. 668-674, May, 1930.

BIOTIC RELATIONSHIPS OF ZION CANYON, UTAH, WITH SPECIAL REFERENCE TO SUCCESSION. Angus M. Woodbury. Ecol. Monographs, no.3, pp.147-246, figs.29, Apr., 1933.

UNITED STATES--VERMONT

ANALYSIS OF VERMONT FUR DEALER REPORTS. Geo. W. Davis. Trans. 3rd. N. Amer. Wildl.Conf., pp.504-507, 1938.

HISTORY OF WILD GAME IN VERMONT. Leonard E. Foote. Vermont Fish and Game Serv., State Bull., Pittman-Robertson Series, no.11, Montpelier, pp.51, figs.20, Nov. 1, 1944. (Fed.Aid in Wildl.Restoration Project no. 1-R; 2nd ed., revised.) (3rd ed., revised, Jan., 1946.)

VERMONT'S WILD GAME RESOURCE. A STUDY OF THE VERMONT HUNTER. Leonard E. Foote. Vermont Fish and Game Serv., State Bull., Pittman-Robertson Series, no.14, Montpelier, pp.48, figs. 16, Apr. 1, 1946.

MAMMALS OF VERMONT. Frederick L. Osgood, Jr. Jour.Mamm., vol.19, no.4, pp.435-441, Nov. 14, 1938.

UNITED STATES--VIRGINIA

BIRD AND MAMMAL NOTES FROM VIRGINIA AND FLORIDA. H.H. Bailey. Bailey Mus. and Library Nat. Hist., Miami, Bull. no.16, pp.3, Dec., 1945.

CORRECTING INACCURATE RANGES OF CERTAIN FLORIDA MAMMALS AND OTHERS OF VIRGINIA AND THE CAROLINAS. H.H. Bailey. Bailey Mus. and Library Nat. Hist., Bull. no.5, Dec. 1, 1930.

MAMMALS OF VIRGINIA. (An Account of the Furred Animals of Land and Sea Known to Exist in this Commonwealth With a List of the Fossil Mammals from Virginia.) John Wendell Bailey. Privatley Printed, Richmond, pp.xvi-416, figs.96, Dec., 1946.

(Review by W.J. Hamilton of) MAMMALS OF VIRGINIA. John Wendell Bailey. Jour. Mamm., vol.29, no.2, pp.190-191, May 14, 1948.

(Review by Lowell S. Miller, Donald F. Hoffmeister of) MAMMALS OF VIRGINIA. John Wendell Bailey. Jour. Wildl. Mgt., vol.12, no.2, pp.217-218, Apr., 1948.

GOVERNMENT REPORT OF GAME SURVEY IN BATH AND HIGHLAND COUNTIES. Vernon Bailey. Game and Fish Conserv., Richmond, Va., vol.9, no.1, pp.3-6, June, 1929.

ILLUSTRATED SKULL KEY TO THE RECENT LAND MAMMALS OF VIRGINIA. G.H. Brown. Va. Cooperative Wildl. Research Unit, Blacksburg, Release no.52-2, pp. 75, illus., mimeogr., Apr., 1952.

TRAIL BLAZERS OF SOUTHWEST VIRGINIA. (Hunting Conditions in the Eighteenth Century.) D.A. Cannaday. Va. Wildl., Richmond, vol.11, no.2, pp.10-12, 23, illus., Feb., 1950.

SOME PLEISTOCENE MAMMALS FROM WARREN COUNTY, VIRGINIA. Austin H. Clark. Science, n.s., vol.88, no.2273, p.82, July 22, 1938.

COOPERATIVE WILDLIFE MANAGEMENT IN VIRGINIA. Cecil F. DeLaBarre. Trans. 11th N.Amer. Wildl. Conf., Washington, pp.313-323, 1946.

WILD MAMMALS OF VIRGINIA. Charles O. Handley, Jr., Clyde P. Patton. Comm. Game Inland Fisheries, Richmond, Va., pp.1-220, illus., maps, 1947.

(Review by W.J. Hamilton, Jr. of) WILD MAMMALS OF VIRGINIA. Charles O. Handley, Jr., Clyde P. Patton. Jour. Mamm., vol.29, no.2, pp.191-192, May 14, 1948.

(Review by Richard L. Hoffman of) WILD MAMMALS OF VIRGINIA. Charles O. Handley, Jr., Clyde P. Patton. Amer. Midland Nat., Notre Dame, vol.39, no.1, pp. 255-256, Jan., 1948.

(Review by Donald F. Hoffmeister of) WILD MAMMALS OF VIRGINIA. Charles O. Handley, Jr., Clyde P. Patton. Jour. Wildl. Mgt., Menasha, vol.12, no.3, pp.335-336, July, 1948.

NOTES ON CERTAIN MAMMALS OF THE MOUNTAINS OF SOUTHWESTERN VIRGINIA. Emmet T. Hooper, Earl R. Cady. Jour. Mamm., vol.22, no.3, pp.232-325, Aug. 14, 1941.

COMPARATIVE STUDY AT COBB'S ISLAND, VIRGINIA. Alfred B. Howell. Auk, vol.28, no.4, pp.449-453, Oct., 1911.

VIRGINIA WAS ONCE ENGLAND'S WILD WEST. Gordon W. Jones. Nature Mag., Washington, vol.38, no.6, pp.317-320, 332, illus., June-July, 1945.

MAMMALS OF AMELIA COUNTY, VIRGINIA. John B. Lewis. Jour. Mamm., Baltimore, vol.21, no.4, pp.422-428, Nov. 14, 1940.

NATURALIST WRITES OF DISMAL SWAMP. (Bear, Deer, Wildcat, Opossum, Raccoon, Mink, Rabbit, Otter.) John B. Lewis. Va. Wildl. Blacksburg, vol.2, no.7, p.2, Mar., 1939.

MAMMALS OF SHENANDOAH NATIONAL PARK. Richard H. Manville. Bull. Shenandoah Nat. Hist. Assoc., vol.2, pp.1-69, illus., 1956.

BRIEF REPORT ON THE 1952 BIG LEVELS REFUGE HUNT. Henry S. Mosby. Va. Wildl., vol.14, no.3, pp.18-19, map, Mar., 1952.

NOTES ON SMALL MAMMAL POPULATIONS AT MOUNTAIN LAKE, VIRGINIA. Eugene P. Odum. Jour. Mamm., vol.25, no.4, pp. 408-410, Nov., 1944.

DISTRIBUTION NOTES ON CERTAIN VIRGINIA MAMMALS. C.P. Patton. Jour. Mamm., vol.20, no.1, pp.75-77, Feb.14, 1939.

PRELIMINARY DISTRIBUTION OF THE MAMMALS OF VIRGINIA. C.P. Patton. MS thesis, Va. Polytechnic Inst., 1938.

DEER AND THE RABBIT HUNTING DRIVE IN VIRGINIA AND THE SOUTHEAST. Frank G. Speck, Claude E. Schaeffer. Southern Indian Studies, Chapel Hill, vol.2, no.1, pp.3-20, illus., Apr., 1950.

FOOD OF SNAKES OF THE GEORGE WASHINGTON NATIONAL FOREST, VIRGINIA. F.M. Uhler, et al. Trans. 4th N. Amer. Wildl. Conf., Washington, D.C., pp.605-622, 1939. (Several Species of Small Mammals, Including First Virginia Record of Parascalops breweri.)

GAME BIRDS, MAMMALS, FISH OF VIRGINIA. Comm. of Game and Inland Fisheries, Richmond, pp.62, illus., 1948.

UNITED STATES--WASHINGTON

FIELD KEY TO THE MAMMALS OF WASHINGTON. Ernest S. Booth. Walla Walla College, pp.72, 1941.

SYSTEMATIC REVIEW OF THE LAND MAMMALS OF WASHINGTON. Ernest S. Booth. PhD thesis, State Coll. Wash., 1947.

WILDLIFE PICTURE OF OLYMPIC NATIONAL PARK. Victor H. Cahalane. Natl. Parks Bull., vol.14, no.66, pp.20-24, Dec., 1938.

ECOLOGIC RELATIONSHIPS OF FOUR SMALL MAMMALS IN WESTERN WASHINGTON. Walter W. Dalquest. Jour. Mamm., vol.22, no.2, pp.170-173, May 14, 1941.

MAMMALS OF WASHINGTON. Walter W. Dalquest. Univ. Kansas Publ., Mus. Nat. Hist., vol.2, pp.1-144, figs.140, Apr. 9, 1948.

(Review by Earl J. Larrison of) MAMMALS OF WASHINGTON. Walter W. Dalquest. Murrelet, Seattle, vol.29, no.1, pp.13-14, Aug. 20, 1948.

MAMMALS OF WASHINGTON STATE. Walter W. Dalquest. Ecology, Lancaster, vol.29, no.4, pp.525-526, Oct., 1948.

DISTRIBUTION OF THE LAND VERTEBRATES OF SOUTHEASTERN WASHINGTON. Lee R. Dice. Univ. Calif. Publ. Zool., vol.16, no.17, pp.293-348, pls. 24-26, June 23, 1916.

MAMMALS COLLECTED BY F. M. GAIGE IN 1919 AT LAKE CUSHMAN AND VICINITY, OLYMPIC PENINSULA, WASHINGTON. Lee R. Dice. Murrelet, vol.13, no.2, pp. 47-49, Mar. 31, 1932.

MAMMALS OF SOUTHEASTERN WASHINGTON. Lee R. Dice. Jour. Mamm., vol.1, no.1, pp.10-22, pls.2, Nov., 1919.

MEGAFAUNAL ZONES OF THE OLIGOCENE OF NORTHWESTERN WASHINGTON. J. Wyatt Durham. Univ. Calif. Publ., Bull. Dept. Geol. Sci., Berkeley, vol.27, no.5, pp.101-211, Nov. 14, 1944.

WILD ANIMAL POPULATION OF THE MOUNT BAKER NATIONAL FOREST, WASHINGTON. J.M. Edson. Murrelet, vol.11, no. 2, pp.14-15, May, 1930.

CATALOGUE OF MAMMALS FROM THE OLYMPIC MOUNTAINS, WASHINGTON, WITH DESCRIPTIONS OF NEW SPECIES. D.G. Elliot. Field Columbian Mus., Chicago, Publ. no.32, Zool. Series, vol. 1, no.13, pp.241-276, illus., pls., 1899.

A JOHN DAY VERTEBRATE FOSSIL DISCOVERED IN THE KEECHELUS SERIES OF WASHINGTON. Robert Y. Grant. Amer. Jour. Sci., New Haven, vol.239, no.8, pp.590-593, figs.2, pl.1, Aug., 1941.

ON THE OCCURRENCE OF CERTAIN MAMMALS IN EXTREME SOUTHWESTERN WASHINGTON. E. Raymond Hall. Murrelet, vol.12, no.1, pp.22, Jan., 1931.

HISTORICAL RESUME OF EXPLORATION AND SURVEY--MAMMAL TYPES AND THEIR COLLECTORS IN THE STATE OF WASHINGTON. F.S. Hall. Murrelet, vol. 13, no.3, pp.1-63, Sep., 1932.

MAMMALS OF THE GRAND COULEE, WASHINGTON. Murray L. Johnson. Murrelet, vol.31, no.3, pp.39-42, Sep.-Dec., 1950.

CHECK LIST OF MAMMALS OF THE OLYMPIC PENINSULA. Murray L. Johnson, Sherry Johnson. Murrelet, vol.33, no.3, pp.32-37, Sep.-Dec., 1952.

EARLY SPRING RECONNAISSANCE OF THE BIRDS AND MAMMALS OF NORTHRUP CANYON, UPPER GRAND COULEE, WASHINGTON--PART I. Earl J. Larrison. Murrelet, Seattle, vol.24, no.3, pp.35-46, Sep.-Dec., 1943. (Actual date of publication, Feb. 15, 1944.) Murrelet, Seattle, vol.25, no.3, pp.25-42, Sep.-Dec. (Dec. 20), 1944.

MISCELLANEOUS DISTRIBUTIONAL NOTES FOR WASHINGTON. Earl J. Larrison. Murrelet, Seattle, vol.28, no.1, pp.11-13, Jan.-Apr., 1947.

NOTES ON MAMMALS COLLECTED AT MT. RAINIER, WASHINGTON. Marcus W. Lyon. Smiths. Inst., Misc. Coll., Wash., Publ. no.1713, (Quarterly Issue, vol.IV), vol. L, pp.89-92, 1908.

STUDY OF THE FUR RESOURCES IN THE STATE OF WASHINGTON. Raleigh Moreland. MS thesis, State Coll. Wash., 1941.

DO WE WANT TO SAVE OLYMPIC NATIONAL PRIMEVAL PARK? Samuel H. Ordway, Jr. Anim. Kingdom, New York, vol.51, no.1, pp.2-7, illus., Jan.-Feb., 1948.

AN 1884 LIST OF THE BIRDS AND MAMMALS OF WASHINGTON. Victor B. Scheffer. Murrelet, Seattle, vol.26, no.2, pp.29-30, May-Aug. (Aug.10), 1945.

FIELD CONDITIONS ON MOUNT BAKER, WASHINGTON, DURING THE SEASON 1933-1934: A COMPARISON. W.T. Shaw, W.C. Moore. Murrelet, vol.15, no.2, p. 54, May, 1934.

ANNOTATED LIST OF MAMMALS OF WHITMAN COUNTY, WASHINGTON. Arthur Svihla, Ruth D. Svihla. Murrelet, Seattle, vol.21, no.3, pp.53-58, Sep.-Dec., 1940.

MAMMALS OF CLALLAM COUNTY, WASHINGTON. Arthur Svihla, Ruth D. Svihla. Murrelet, vol.14, no.2, pp.37-41, May, 1933.

NOTES ON MAMMALS COLLECTED PRINCIPALLY IN WASHINGTON AND CALIFORNIA BETWEEN THE YEARS 1853 AND 1874 BY DR. JAMES GRAHAM COOPER. Walter Penn Taylor. Proc. Calif. Acad. Sci., 4th Series, vol.9, no.3, pp.69-121, 1919.

PROVISIONAL LIST OF LAND MAMMALS OF THE STATE OF WASHINGTON. Walter P. Taylor, Wm.T. Shaw. Occas. Papers Chas. R. Conner Mus., State College of Wash., no.2, pp.32, Dec., 1929.

KING OF THE OLYMPICS; THE ROOSEVELT ELK AND OTHER MAMMALS OF THE OLYMPIC MOUNTAINS. Edward B. Webster. Port Angeles, Wash., pp.227, pls., 1920.

HISTORY OF THE STUDY OF MAMMALOGY IN THE STATE OF WASHINGTON. Ray D. Wiseman. MS thesis, Coll. Puget Sound, 1952.

COMPARATIVE FUR CATCHES IN WASHINGTON. Washington State Game Comm., Wash. State Game Bull., vol.6, no.4, p.5, Oct., 1954.

WILD GAME CENSUS IN COLVILLE NATIONAL FOREST, NORTHEASTERN WASHINGTON. Murrelet, vol.12, no.1, p.26, Jan., 1931.

UNITED STATES--WASHINGTON, D. C.

LIST OF MAMMALS IN THE DISTRICT OF COLUMBIA. Vernon Bailey. Proc. Biol. Soc. Washington, vol.10, pp.93-101, May 28, 1896.

MAMMALS OF THE DISTRICT OF COLUMBIA. Vernon Bailey. Proc. Biol. Soc. Wash., vol.36, pp.103-138, May 1, 1923.

MAMMALS OF THE VICINITY OF WASHINGTON. Vernon Bailey. Jour. Wash. Acad. Sci., vol.16, pp.441-445, Oct. 4, 1926.

ON THE GEOLOGICAL AGE OF THE WALKER HOTEL SWAMP DEPOSIT, IN

WASHINGTON, D.C., AND ON THE ORIGIN AND THE AGES OF THE COASTAL PLAIN TERRACES IN GENERAL. Oliver P. Hay. Jour. Washington Acad. Sci., vol.14, pp.255-264, June 19, 1924.

EXTINCT AND VANISHING MAMMALS OF MARYLAND AND DISTRICT OF COLUMBIA. Romeo Mansueti. Md.Nat., vol.20, no.1-2, pp.2-48, Winter-Spring, 1950.

MAMMALS OF THE NATIONAL CAPITAL PARKS AND THE DISTRICT OF COLUMBIA REGION. George A. Petrides, Jr. U.S. Dept. Interior, Nat. Park Service, Wash., D.C., pp.4, Apr., 1943.

## UNITED STATES--WEST VIRGINIA

NOTES ON MAMMALS FROM WEST VIRGINIA. Roger W. Barbour. Jour. Mamm., vol.32, no.3, pp.368-371, Aug. 23, 1951.

BIOTIC SUCCESSION ON KATAHDIN. Irving H. Blake. Appalachia, vol.18, no.4, pp. 409-424, pls.2, Dec., 1931. (Mammals pp. 421-422.)

NOTES ON EXTINCT AND LIVING MAMMALS OF WEST VIRGINIA. A.B. Brooks. West Virginia Univ.Bull., Proc. West Va. Acad.Sci., vol.4, no.2, pp.57-60, Oct., 1930.

MUSKEG FARTHEST SOUTH. (Small Mammals.) Maurice Brooks. Audubon Mag., New York, vol.47, no.4, sec.1, pp.216-223, illus., July-Aug., 1945.

THREE NEW MAMMAL RECORDS FROM THE NORTHERN PANHANDLE OF WEST VIRGINIA. Karl Haller. West Va. Univ. Bull., Morgantown, ser.40, no.5 (Proc. W.Va.Acad.Sci., vol.12), pp.67-68, Nov., 1939.

FOOTPRINTS FROM THE PERMIAN OF WEST VIRGINIA. Stafford Happ. Jour.Geol., vol.42, no.7, pp.753-755, fig.1, Nov., 1934.

PARAGRAPHS FROM FIELD NOTES. (Deer, Weasel, Muskrat.) R.S. Harris. W. Virgnia Conservation, Charleston, vol.11, no.9, pp.15-16, Jan., 1948.

ANNOTATED LIST OF WEST VIRGINIA MAMMALS. Remington Kellogg. Proc.U.S. Nat.Mus., vol.84, no.3022, pp.443-479, Oct. 7, 1937.

ECOLOGY AND DISTRIBUTION OF THE MAMMALS OF WEST VIRGINIA. Sturgis McKeever. PhD thesis, N.C.State Coll., pp.335, 1955; Univ.Microfilms, Ann Arbor, Mich., Publ.no.16,313, 1956.

SURVEY OF WEST VIRGINIA MAMMALS. Sturgis McKeever, et al. Cons. Comm. W.Va., Final Rep. PR Proj., no.22-R, pp. v-126, maps (also appendix: pp.iii-53, maps), mimeo., 1951 (Jan., 1952).

COLLECTING BIRDS AND MAMMALS IN WEST VIRGINIA. Watson M. Perrygo. Explor. and Field-work Smiths.Inst.for 1936, pp.31-34, figs.25-28, 1937.

FAUNA OF WEST VIRGINIA CAVES. A.M. Reese. Proc. W.Va.Acad.Sci., vol.7 (West Va.Univ.Bull., ser.34, no.15), pp.39-53, Mar., 1934.

INTRODUCTION TO THE MAMMALS OF WEST VIRGINIA. L. Wayne Wilson. Div. Education and Publicity, W.Va. Conserv. Comm., Charleston, pp.ii-20, Dec., 1948.

MAMMALS OF WEST VIRGINIA. I. SHREWS AND MOLES. 2. BATS. L. Wayne Wilson. W.Va.Conservation, Charleston, vol.9, no. 11, pp.10, 20-21, Feb., 1946; no.12, pp.8-9, 15-16, Mar., 1946.

MAMMALS OF WEST VIRGINIA. III. THE CARNIVORES. IV. THE SQUIRRELS. L. Wayne Wilson. W.Va.Conservation, Charleston, vol.10, no.1, pp.9-10, 1921; no.2, pp. 6, 17-18, Apr., May, 1946.

MAMMALS OF WEST VIRGINIA. VII. HARES, RABBITS AND DEER. L. Wayne Wilson. West Va. Conserv., Charleston, vol.10, no.4, pp. 14-15, Aug., 1946.

LIST OF MAMMALS COLLECTED IN WEST VIRGINIA. L. Wayne Wilson, J.E.Friedel. Proc. W.Va. Acad. Sci., 1941, Philippi, vol.15 (W.Va.Univ.Bull., ser.42), no.8-11, pp.85-92, Feb., 1942.

## UNITED STATES--WISCONSIN

AGAIN, OUR FUR-BEARING ANIMALS. (Fur-Bearing Animals in Wisconsin, Excepting Skunk, Reduced to Danger Line.) W.E. Barber. Wisconsin Conservationist, vol.4, no.1, p.11, Mar. (May 11), 1922.

COMMISSION'S STATE-WIDE HEARINGS. W.E. Barber. Wisconsin Conservationist, vol.2, no.4, p.5, Sep., 1920. (Methods of Protecting the Muskrat, Mink and Deer.)

WISCONSIN MAMMALS. N. R. Barger. Wisconsin Cons. Dept. Publ., no.351-51, pp.1-54, illus., 1951?

MAMMALS OF ILLINOIS AND WISCONSIN. Charles B. Cory. Field Mus. Nat. Hist., Publ.no.153, vol.11, Zool.Ser., pp.492, illus., 1912.

GAME MANAGEMENT IN WISCONSIN. W.F. Grimmer. Wisconsin Conserv.Bull., Madison, vol.13, no.6, pp.61-66, illus., June, 1948.

SMALL MAMMAL CENSUS NEAR PRAIRIE DU SAC, WISCONSIN. Harold Carsten Hanson. Wisconsin Acad. Sci., Arts and Letters, Trans., Madison, Wis., vol.36, pp.105-129, tbls., 1944.

WILDLIFE HISTORY OF FAVILLE GROVE, WISCONSIN. Arthur S. Hawkins. Trans. Wisconsin Acad. Sci., Arts and Letters, Madison, vol.32, pp.29-65, 1940.

CHECK-LIST OF WISCONSIN MAMMALS. Ned Hollister. Bull. Wisconsin Nat. Hist. Soc., vol.8, no.1, pp.21-31, May 7, 1910.

NOTES ON WISCONSIN MAMMALS. Ned Hollister. Bull. Wisconsin Nat. Hist.Soc., vol.6, nos.3-4, pp.137-142, Apr., 1909.

DISTRIBUTION OF CERTAIN WISCONSIN MAMMALS. Hartley H.T. Jackson. Bull. Wisc. Nat.Hist. Soc., vol.8, no.2, pp. 86-90, Apr., 1910.

LAND VERTEBRATES OF RIDGEWAY BOG, WISCONSIN: THEIR ECOLOGICAL SUCCESSION AND SOURCE OF INGRESSION. Hartley H.T. Jackson. Bull. Wisc. Nat. Hist. Soc., vol.12, nos.1-2, pp.4-54, figs. 1-9, Oct. 31, 1914.

MAMMALS OF WISCONSIN. Hartley H.T. Jackson. Madison, Univ. of Wisc. Press, pp.xii-504, illus., maps, 1961.

PRELIMINARY LIST OF WISCONSIN MAMMALS. Hartley H.T. Jackson. Bull. Wisc. Nat. Hist. Soc., vol.6, nos.1-2, pp.13-34, pl.3, Apr., 1908.

GAME CYCLE IN WISCONSIN. Cyril Kabat. Wisc. Conserv. Bull., Madison, vol.15, no. 11, pp.3-8, illus., Nov., 1950.

WINTER WILDLIFE CENSUS IN NORTHEASTERN WISCONSIN. George Hills Kelker. Jour. Wildl. Mgt., Menasha, vol. 7, no.2, pp.133-141, Apr., 1943.

REPORT OF THE FUR COMMITTEE TO THE WISCONSIN CONSERVATION CONGRESS, JUNE 6, 1949. Harry Klemme.

NOTES ON MAMMALS OF MENOMINEE INDIAN RESERVATION, WISCONSIN. E.V. Komarek. Jour. Mamm., vol.13, no.3, pp. 203-209, Aug., 1932.

PHENOLOGICAL RECORD FOR SAUK AND DANE COUNTIES, WISCONSIN, 1935-1945. A. Leopold, Sara E. Jones. Ecol.Monog., Durham, vol.17, no.1, pp.81-122, Jan., 1947.

WILDLIFE FOOD PATCHES IN SOUTHERN WISCONSIN. A. Leopold, et al. Jour. Wildl. Mgt., Menasha, vol.3, no.1, pp.60-69, 1939.

NOTES ON WISCONSIN MAMMALS. A.L. Nelson. Jour. Mamm., vol.15, no.3, pp. 252-253, Aug., 1934.

CHANGING WILDLIFE CONDITIONS IN WISCONSIN. A.W. Shorger. Wisc.Conserv. Bull., Madison, vol.13, no.6, pp.53-60, illus., 1948.

PUBLIC'S PART IN WISCONSIN CONSERVATION HISTORY. W.E. Scott. Wisc.Cons. Bull., Madison, vol.13, no.6, pp.84-90, June, 1948.

RARE AND EXTINCT MAMMALS OF WISCONSIN. W.E. Scott. Wisc.Cons.Bull., Madison, vol.4, no.10, pp.21-28, Oct., 1939.

MILLION DOLLAR TRAPPING INCOME. (Data on 1936-37 Wisconsin Fur Harvest.) Wisc.Cons.Bull., vol.3, no.2, p.33, Feb., 1938.

WISCONSIN MAMMALS SCARCE. Outdoor Life, Denver, vol.85, no.4, p.99, Apr., 1940.

## UNITED STATES--WYOMING

### Extinct and Fossil Mammals

EARLY LOWER EOCENE MAMMALS FROM THE WIND RIVER BASIN, WYOMING. R.H. Denison. Proc. New England Zool. Club., vol.16, pp.11-14, fig.1, Jan. 22, 1937.

EARLY CENOZOIC STRATIGRAPHY AND VERTEBRATE PALEONTOLOGY OF THE HOBACK BASIN, WYOMING. John A.Dorr, Jr. Bull. Geol. Soc. Amer., Washington, vol. 63, pp.59-94, figs.7, pls.7, Jan., 1952.

FOSSIL MAMMALIA FROM THE ALMY FORMATION IN WESTERN WYOMING. C.Lewis Gazin. Jour. Washington Acad. Sci., vol.32, no.7, pp.217-220, figs.2, July 15, 1942.

GEOLOGY AND VERTEBRATE PALEONTOLOGY OF UPPER EOCENE STRATA IN THE NORTHEAST PART OF THE WIND RIVER BASIN, WYOMING. PART 2. MAMMALIAN FAUNA OF THE BADWATER AREA. C. Lewis Gazin. Smiths. Inst., Misc.Coll., Washington, vol.131, no.8, pp.1-35, pls.1-3, Oct. 30, 1956.

LOWER EOCENE KNIGHT FORMATION OF WESTERN WYOMING AND ITS MAMMALIAN FAUNAS. C. Lewis Gazin. Smiths. Inst., Misc. Coll., Publ.no.4097, vol.117, no.18, pp.vi-82, illus., map, 1952.

OCCURRENCE OF PALEOCENE MAMMALIAN REMAINS IN THE FOSSIL BASIN OF SOUTHWESTERN WYOMING. C. Lewis Gazin. Jour.Paleontol., vol.30, no.3, pp. 707-711, May, 1956.

PALEOCENE MAMMALIAN FAUNAS OF THE BISON BASIN IN SOUTH CENTRAL WYOMING. C. Lewis Gazin. Smiths.Inst., Misc.Coll., Publ.no.4229, vol.131, no.6, pp.iv-57, pls.16, map, diagrs., 1956.

TAENIODONT SKULL FROM THE LOWER EOCENE OF WYOMING. C. Lewis Gazin. Proc. Amer. Philos. Soc., Philadelphia, vol.76, no.5, pp.597-612, figs.2, pls.5, 1936.

TRAILING EXTINCT ANIMALS IN CENTRAL UTAH AND THE BRIDGER BASIN OF WYOMING. C. Lewis Gazin. Explor. and Field-work Smiths.Inst.for 1940, Publ. no.3631, pp.5-8, illus., Apr.3, 1941.

UPPER PALEOCENE MAMMALIA FROM THE ALMY FORMATION IN WESTERN WYOMING. C. Lewis Gazin. Smiths.Inst., Misc.Coll., Publ.no.4252, vol.131, no.7, pp.iii-18, pls.2, 1956.

FOSSIL HUNTING IN THE BRIDGER BASIN OF WYOMING. Charles W. Gilmore. Exploration and Field-work Smiths.Inst. in 1930, Publ.no.3111, pp.13-20, figs.11-16, Mar. 26, 1931.

NEW VERTEBRATE FOSSILS FROM THE LOWER EOCENE OF THE BIGHORN BASIN, WYOMING. G.L. Jepsen. Proc. Amer. Philos. Soc., vol.69, no.4, pp.117-131, pls.1-4, 1930.

PALEOCENE FAUNAS OF THE POLECAT BENCH FORMATION, PARK COUNTY, WYOMING. PART 1. G.L. Jepsen. Proc. Amer.Philos.Soc., Philadelphia, vol.83, no.2, pp.217-334, figs.22, pls.5, Aug.15, 1940.

STRATIGRAPHY AND PALEONTOLOGY OF THE PALEOCENE OF NORTHWESTERN PARK COUNTY, WYOMING. G.L.

Jepsen. Proc. Amer. Philos.Soc., vol.69, no.7, pp.463-528, figs.4, pls.1-10.

EOCENE MAMMALS FROM THE LYSITE MEMBER, WIND RIVER FORMATION OF WYOMING. Dana R. Kelley, Albert E. Wood. Jour. Paleontol., vol.28, pp.337-366, illus., June, 1954.

GEOLOGY AND PALEONTOLOGY OF THE ELK MOUNTAIN AND TABERNACLE BUTTE AREA, WYOMING. Paul O. McGrew. New York, Bull. Amer. Mus. Nat. Hist., vol.117, art.3, pp.121-176, illus., fold.map, tbls., 1959.

EOCENE FAUNA FROM THE CATHEDRAL BLUFFS TONGUE OF THE WASHAKIE BASIN, WYOMING. William J. Morris. Jour. Paleontol., vol.28, pp.195-203, illus., Apr., 1954.

FOSSIL MAMMALS OF THE WAHSATCH AND WIND RIVER BEDS. COLLECTION OF 1891. Henry Fairfield Osborn, J.L. Wortman. Bull. Amer. Mus. Nat. Hist., New York, vol.4, pp.81-147, illus., pl., 1892.

CONTRIBUTION TO THE STRATIGRAPHY AND PALEONTOLOGY OF THE GOSHEN HOLE AREA, WYOMING. III. A NEW BASAL OLIGOCENE FORMATION. Erich M. Schlaikjer. Bull. Mus. Compar. Zool. at Harvard College, vol.76, no.3, pp.71-93, figs.10, pls.8, Jan., 1935.

CONTRIBUTION TO THE STRATIGRAPHY AND PALEONTOLOGY OF THE GOSHEN HOLE AREA, WYOMING. IV. NEW VERTEBRATES AND THE STRATIGRAPHY OF THE OLIGOCENE AND EARLY MIOCENE. Erich M. Schlaikjer. Bull. Mus. Compar. Zool. at Harvard College, vol.76, no.4, pp.97-189, figs.13, pls.41, May, 1935.

PRELIMINARY ACCOUNT OF THE FOSSIL MAMMALS FROM THE WHITE RIVER AND LOUP FORK FORMATION, CONTAINED IN THE MUSEUM OF COMPARATIVE ZOOLOGY. PART II. THE CARNIVORA AND ARTIODACTYLA. THE PERISSODACTYLA. W.B.Scott, Henry Fairfield Osborn. Bull. Mus. Compar. Zool., Princeton, vol.20, pp.65-100, illus., pls.3, 1890-1891.

GEOLOGY AND VERTEBRATE PALEONTOLOGY OF UPPER EOCENE STRATA IN THE NORTHEASTERN PART OF THE WIND RIVER BASIN, WYOMING. PART 1. GEOLOGY. Harry A. Tourtelot. Smiths. Inst., Misc.Coll., Washington, Publ.no. 4269, vol.134, no.4, pp.1-27, pl.1, Mar. 27, 1957. (List of Fossil Species p.17.)

STRATIGRAPHY OF THE WILLWOOD AND TATMAN FORMATION IN NORTHWESTERN WYOMING. (References to Occurrence of Mammals.) Franklyn B. Van Houten. Bull. Geol. Soc. Amer., vol.55, no.2, pp.165-210, pls.7, Feb., 1944.

SMALL MAMMALS FROM THE UPPERMOST EOCENE (DUCHESNIAN) NEAR BADWATER, WYOMING. Albert E. Wood. Jour. Paleontology, Menasha, vol.23, no.5, pp.556-565, figs.24, Sep., 1949.

NOTES ON MAMMALS FROM THE UPPER CRETACEOUS LANCE FORMATION OF WYOMING. Albert E. Wood, John B.S. Ormsbee. Jour. Paleontology, vol.28, no.1, pp.26-31, illus., Jan., 1954.

Recent Mammals

WILD LIFE RESTORATION IN WYOMING. Lester Bagley. Wyoming Wild Life, Cheyenne, vol.5, no.3, pp.1-2, 16-18, Mar., 1940.

ECONOMIC ASPECTS OF THE WYOMING FUR TRADE. Lester Bagley, Nedward M. Frost. Wyoming Wild Life, vol.7, no.11, pp.1-8, 17-19, Nov., 1942.

WYOMING'S BIG GAME SURVEY.(Antelope, Elk.) Floyd M. Blunt. Wyoming Wild Life, Cheyenne, vol.15, no.2, pp.4-9, 35-36, illus., Feb., 1951.

LIFE ZONE INVESTIGATIONS IN WYOMING. Merritt Cary. U.S. Dept. Agric., Bur. Biol. Surv., N.Amer. Fauna, no.42, pp.95, figs.17, Oct. 3, 1917.

CONGRESS AND JACKSON HOLE MONUMENT. Laurette S. Collier. Living Wilderness, Washington, vol.10, whole no.12, pp. 28-31, Feb., 1945.

LISTS OF SPECIES OF MAMMALS, PRINCIPALLY RODENTS, OBTAINED BY W. W. PRICE, S. E. MEEK, G. K. CHERRIE, AND E. S. THOMPSON IN THE STATES OF IOWA, WYOMING, MONTANA, IDAHO, NEVADA AND CALIFORNIA, WITH DESCRIPTIONS OF NEW SPECIES. Daniel G. Elliot. Field Columbian Mus. Publ., no.27, Zool.Series, vol.1, no.10, pp.193-221, Mar., 1898.

WYOMING FURS AND FUR BEARERS.James E. Grasse. Wyoming Wild Life, Cheyenne, vol.6, no.11, pp.10-14, 19, illus., Nov., 1941.

GAME-LIVESTOCK RELATIONSHIPS IN WYOMING. Charles W. Hanscum.Proc. 32nd Ann. Conf. Western Assoc. State Game and Fish Comm., Glacier Nat.Park, Mont., June 15-17, 1952, pp.92-94, 1953.

RARE MAMMALS. A.A. McCutchen. Wyoming Wild Life, Cheyenne, vol.4, no.7, p.7, July, 1939.

JACKSON HOLE NATIONAL MONUMENT CONTROVERSY. Leslie A. Miller. Outdoor America, Madison, vol.8, no.6, pp. 4-6, illus., July-Aug., 1943.

FENCED WILDLIFE FOR JACKSON HOLE. O.J. Murie. National Parks Mag., Washington, no.84, pp.8-11, illus., Jan.-Mar., 1946.

SPIRIT OF JACKSON HOLE. O.J. Murie. Living Wilderness, Washington, D.C., vol. 9, whole no.10, pp.18-20, May, 1944.

PURPOSE OF THE JACKSON HOLE WILDLIFE PARK. Fairfield Osborn. Nat. Parks Mag., Washington, D.C., no.86, pp.35-37, July-Sep., 1946.

BIG GAME HUNTING IN THE HIGH COUNTRY. Barry C. Park. Colorado Conserv. Comments, Denver, vol.8, no.3, pp.7-8, Sep. 15, 1945.

WYOMING FUR: NEGLECTED RESOURCE. Archie Pendergraft. Wyoming Wild Life, Cheyenne, vol.11, no.5, pp.12-15, illus., May, 1947.

TRAPPER TRAILS TO THE SISK-KE-DEE. Carl P. Russell. Ann. Wyoming, Cheyenne, vol.17, no.2, pp.88-105, maps 2, July, 1945.

MAMMALS AND BIRDS. LIST OF MAMMALS AND BIRDS COLLECTED IN WYOMING TERRITORY, BY MR. H. D. SMITH AND MR. JAMES STEVENSON, DURING THE EXPEDITION OF 1870. James Stevenson. U.S. Geol. and Geographical Survey of the Territories, Ann. Rep., 4th, pp. 461-466, 1871.

WYOMING FUR-BEARERS. Earl M.Thomas. Wyoming Game and Fish Comm. Bull., no. 7, pp.100, 1954. (Reprint of Series of 23 Articles.)

NOTES ON SMALL MAMMALS OBSERVED IN THE TOWER FALLS REGION, YELLOWSTONE NATIONAL PARK, WYOMING. Otis Wade. Murrelet, vol.12, no.3, pp.76-78, Sep., 1931.

MAMMAL POPULATIONS OF THE LARAMIE AREA. Walter J. Wenzel. MS thesis, Univ. Wyoming, 1949.

BIG GAME HARVEST IN 1950. Wyoming Wild Life, vol.15, no.6, pp.10-15, 34-36, June, 1951.

BIG GAME HUNTING OUTLOOK GOOD. Colorado Conserv. Comments, Denver, vol.10, no.7, pp.5-6, illus., Sep., 1948.

GAME HARVEST CONTINUES RISE. Wyoming Wildlife, Cheyenne, vol.12, no. 3, pp.4-11, illus., Mar., 1948.

GAME HARVEST IS HEAVY. MORE THAN HALF OF 31, 297 ANIMALS TAKEN IN 1945 WERE ANTELOPE. Wyoming Wild Life, Cheyenne, vol.10, no.4, pp.5-15, 34-36, Apr., 1946.

1941 BIG GAME KILL SETS RECORDS. Wyoming Wild Life, vol.7, no.3, pp.11-18, Mar., 1942.

1943 GAME HARVEST SETS RECORD 33, 696 ANIMALS OF ALL SPECIES TAKEN. Wyoming Wild Life, Cheyenne, vol.9, no.2, pp.13-22, Feb., 1944.

1946 WAS RECORD GAME YEAR. Wyoming Wild Life, Cheyenne, vol.11, no.8, pp.4-18, illus., Aug., 1947.

1947 HUNTING REGULATIONS. Wyoming Game and Fish Comm., Wyoming Wild Life, vol.11, no.7, pp.4-7, May, 1947.

1948 HUNTING HARVEST. Wyoming Wild Life, Cheyenne, vol.13, no.3, pp.4-15, 38, illus., Apr., 1949.

1949 BIG GAME HARVEST. Wyoming Wild Life, Cheyenne, vol.14, no.7, pp.4-11, 32-33, illus., Sep., 1950.

WILD LIFE IN RETROSPECT. Wyoming Wild Life, Cheyenne, vol.4, no.9, pp. 17-18, Sep., 1939.

WILDLIFE NEWS ROUNDUP. Wyoming Wild Life, Cheyenne, vol.11, no.5, pp. 28-31, illus., May, 1947.

WYOMING GAME SPECIES DISTRIBUTION. Wyoming Wild Life, Cheyenne, vol.7, no. 9, pp.9-11, Sep., 1942.

UNITED STATES--YELLOWSTONE NATIONAL PARK

ANIMAL LIFE OF YELLOWSTONE NATIONAL PARK. Vernon Bailey. Publ. by Chas.C. Thomas, Baltimore, Md., or Springfield, Ill., pp.3-231, figs.70, 1930.

(Review by Edward A. Preble of) ANIMAL LIFE OF YELLOWSTONE NATIONAL PARK. Vernon Bailey. Jour. Mamm., vol. 12, no.1, p.85, Feb., 1931.

ANIMAL LIFE OF YELLOWSTONE PARK. Vernon Bailey. Sierra Club Bull., vol.12, no.4, pp.333-345, pls.99-104, Mar., 1927.

WILD ANIMALS OF YELLOWSTONE NATIONAL PARK. (A Presentation of General Information on Many of the Mammals Most Commonly Seen in Yellowstone; Illustrated With Drawings of Many of the Species Described.) Harold J. Brodrick. Yellowstone Park, Wyoming, Yellowstone Interpretive Series, no.1, pp.vi-69, illus., map, 1954.

WINTER IN YELLOWSTONE. (Habits of Some of the Mammals in Yellowstone Park.) Wendell Chapman, Lucie Chapman. Nat.Hist., New York, vol.35, no.2, pp. 107-120, illus., Feb., 1935.

NORTHERN YELLOWSTONE WINTER RANGE STUDIES. Rudolf L. Grimm.Jour. Wildl.Mgt., Menasha, vol.3, no.4, pp. 295-306, pls.18-21, Oct., 1939.

BIG GAME ANIMALS OF YELLOWSTONE NATIONAL PARK. Edmund Heller. Roosevelt Wild Life Bull., vol.2, no.4, pp.405-467, pls.25-26, Feb., 1925.

YELLOWSTONE AND THE GAME SUPPLY. E.W. Nelson. U.S.Dept.Interior, Nat.Park Service, Washington, D.C., pp.7, 1917. (Address Delivered at the Nat.Parks Conf. at Washington, D.C., Jan.4, 1917.)

YELLOWSTONE NATURE NOTES. Edmund J. Sawyer. Parks and Recreation, vol.9, pp. 556-562, June, 1926; vol.10, pp.70-74, Oct., 1926; vol.10, pp.183-187, Dec., 1926; vol.11, pp.215-220, illus., Jan.-Feb., 1928.

PREDATORY AND FUR-BEARING ANIMALS OF THE YELLOWSTONE NATIONAL PARK. Milton P. Skinner. Roosevelt Wild Life Bull., vol.4, no.2, pp.156-281, figs. 23-51, maps 1-2, 1927.

MAMMALS OF THE YELLOWSTONE NATIONAL PARK. Ernest Seton Thompson. Recreation, vol.8, no.5, pp.365-371, May, 1898.

OUR WILDERNESS NEIGHBORS. A SYMPATHETIC DESCRIPTION OF THE MOST INTERESTING ANIMALS IN YELLOWSTONE NATIONAL PARK. Dorr G. Yeager. A.C. McClurg and Co., Chicago, pp.160, map, pls.19, 1931.

GENERAL INFORMATION REGARDING YELLOWSTONE NATIONAL PARK.SEASON OF 1912-1919. Washington, Govt.Print.Off.,

Dept. Interior, Nat. Park Service, illus., maps, 1912-1919.

UNITED STATES--YOSEMITE REGION

CAMPING IN YOSEMITE. A.E. Borell. Yosemite Nature Notes, vol.13, no.2, pp. 14-15, Feb., 1934.

RARE FUR-BEARING MAMMALS IN YOSEMITE. A.E. Borell. Yosemite Nature Notes, vol.12, no.6, pp.62-63, June, 1933.

NATURE PRESERVE FOR YOSEMITE. Harold C. Bryant. Yosemite Nature Notes, vol.6, pp.46-48, June, 1927.

1950 WILDLIFE CENSUS OF YOSEMITE VALLEY. Wayne W. Bryant. Yosemite Nature Notes, vol.29, no.8, pp.79-81, illus., Aug., 1950.

RECOMMENDATIONS CONCERNING THE TREATMENT OF LARGE MAMMALS IN YOSEMITE NATIONAL PARK. J.Grinnell. Jour. Mamm., vol.9, no.1, p.76, Feb., 1928.

ANIMAL LIFE IN THE YOSEMITE. (An Account of the Mammals, Birds, Reptiles, and Amphibians in a Cross-Section of the Sierra Nevada.) J. Grinnell, T.I.Storer. Univ.Calif.Press, pp.i-xviii, 1-752, pls. 60 (12 col.), maps 2, figs.65, Apr. 17, 1924.

(Review by C.C. Adams of) ANIMAL LIFE IN THE YOSEMITE. J.Grinnell, T.I.Storer. Ecology, vol.6, pp.312-315, July, 1925.

(Review by A.Brazier Howell of) ANIMAL LIFE IN THE YOSEMITE. J.Grinnell, T.I. Storer. Jour. Mamm., vol.5, no.3, pp. 207-208, Aug., 1924.

SOME MAMMALS OF THE YOSEMITE NATIONAL PARK. J. Grinnell, T.I.Storer. Hall's Handbook of Yosemite National Park, G.P. Putnam's Sons, pp.155-173, pls.4, 1921.

THE SLAUGHTER OF THE TRUSTING. (Recommends Game Preserve Around Yosemite National Park.) C.H.Oneal. Yosemite Nature Notes, vol.7, pp.101-102, Dec., 1928.

MAMMALS OF THE YOSEMITE NATIONAL PARK. Harry C. Parker. Yosemite Nature Notes, vol.31, no.6, pp.51-105, illus., June, 1952.

DAY ON SNOWSHOES. (Animals and Birds Seen in Yosemite National Park.) C.C. Presnall. Yosemite Nature Notes, vol.12, no.3, pp.22-23, Mar., 1933.

WEST INDIES

(NATURAL AND MORAL HISTORY OF THE INDIES, IN WHICH NOTABLE THINGS OF THE SKY, ELEMENTS, METALS, PLANTS, ANIMALS, RITES AND CEREMONIES, LAWS AND GOVERNMENT, WARS WITH THE INDIANS ARE DISCUSSED.) Historia natural y moral las Indias, en que se tratan las cosas notables del cielo, y elementos, metales, plantas y animales dellas: y los ritos, y ceremonias, leyes y gobierno, y guerras de los Indios. Joseph de Acosta. Fondo de Cultura Economica, Mexico, D.F., pp. lxxxv-638, 1940. (Mexican ed. prepared by Edmundo O'Gorman, of Acosta's work originally published in 1589. Mammals and Birds pp.317-343, chapters 33-42 of Book 4.)

MAMMALS OF THE WEST INDIES. Glover M. Allen. Bull. Mus. Comp. Zool.Harvard College, vol.54, no.6, pp.175-263, July, 1911.

SUMMARY OF THE FOSSIL LAND MAMMALS OF THE WEST INDIES. Harold E. Anthony. Proc. 8th Amer. Sci. Congr., Washington, D.C., vol.4, pp.359-363, Aug. 3, 1942.

CONTRIBUTION TO THE ZOOGEOGRAPHY OF THE WEST INDIES, WITH ESPECIAL REFERENCE TO AMPHIBIANS AND REPTILES. Thomas Barbour. Mem.Mus.Comp. Zool. Harvard College, vol.44, no.2, pp. 209-359, pl.1, Mar., 1914.

TWO INTERESTING MAMMALS FROM THE ISLAND OF TOBAGO, WEST INDIES. Austin H. Clark. Ann. and Mag. Nat.Hist., London, ser.8, vol.13, pp.68-70, Jan., 1914.

LAND AND SEA MAMMALS OF MIDDLE AMERICA AND THE WEST INDIES. D.G. Elliot. Publ. Field Columbian Mus., Zool. Series, vol.4, pt.1-2, vol.2, pp.309, pls., 1904.

MAMMALS FROM BRITISH HONDURAS, MEXICO, JAMAICA AND HAITI. Philip Hershkovitz. Chicago, Nat. Hist. Mus., Fieldiana, Zoology, vol.31, no.47, pp. 547-569, map, 1951.

MAMMALS OF THE ISLE OF PINES. W.J. Holland. Ann. Carnegie Mus., vol.11, nos. 3-4, pp.356-358, 1917.

WILD LIFE IN DOMINICA. Paul Griswold Howes. Nat.Hist., vol.30, no.1, pp.90-103, Jan.-Feb., 1930.

STUDIES ON THE FAUNA OF CURACAO, ARUBA, BONAIRE AND THE VENEZUELAN ISLANDS. P. Wagenaar Hummelinck. Utrecht, pp.130, pls.16.

(MAMMALS OF THE NETHERLANDS ANTILLES.) De zoogdieren van de Nederlandsc Antillen. A.M. Husson. Uitgaven van de Natuurwetenschappelijke Werkgroep Nederlandse Antillen, no.12, pp.viii-170, illus., pls., diagrs., 1960.

ROBINSON CRUSOE'S TWO ISLANDS (JUAN FERNANDEZ AND TOBAGO). H. Luke. Geogr.Mag., vol.26, pp.291-297, 1953.

AFFINITIES AND ORIGIN OF THE ANTILLEAN MAMMALS. W.D. Matthew. Bull. Geol. Soc. Amer., Washington, D.C., vol. 29, no.4, pp.657-666, Dec. 30, 1918.

LETTER ON HISTORY OF WEST INDIAN MAMMAL FAUNA. Gerrit S. Miller, Jr. Bull. Geol. Soc. Amer., vol.29, p.627, Dec. 30, 1918.

MAMMALS AND REPTILES COLLECTED BY THEODOOR DE BOOY IN THE VIRGIN ISLANDS. Gerrit S. Miller, Jr. Proc.U.S. Nat. Mus., vol.54, pp.507-511, pl.81, Oct. 15, 1918.

VISIT OF MR. GERRIT S. MILLER, JR., TO THE LESSER ANTILLES. Gerrit S. Miller, Jr. Smiths. Inst., Misc. Coll., vol.77, no.2, pp.36-43, figs.40-54, Apr. 17, 1925.

REPORT UPON THE FOSSIL MATERIAL COLLECTED IN 1913 BY THE MESSRS. LINK IN A CAVE IN THE ISLE OF PINES. O.A. Peterson. Ann.Carnegie Mus., Pittsburgh, vol.11, nos.3-4, pp.359-361, pl.36, Nov. 5, 1917.

CARIBBEAN TREASURE. Ivan Terrance Sanderson. New York, The Viking Press, pp.292, illus.32, 1939.

MONGOOSE AND CARIBBEAN WILDLIFE. G.A. Seaman. Trans. 17th N.Amer. Wildl. Conf., pp.188-197, 1952.

ZOOGEOGRAPHY OF WEST INDIAN LAND MAMMALS. George Gaylord Simpson. Amer. Mus.Nov., New York, no.1759, pp.28, Mar. 8, 1956.

COMPENDIUM AND DESCRIPTION OF THE WEST INDIES. (Translation of Manuscript Written ca. 1628; References to Mammals.) Antonio Vásquez de Espinosa. Translated by Charles Upson Clark. Smiths. Inst., Misc. Coll., Washington, D.C., vol.102, pp.xii-862, Sep. 1, 1942.

YUGOSLAVIA

ON SOME REMARKABLE MAMMALIAN REMAINS FROM NORTH BOSNIAN PREHISTORIC SETTLEMENTS. St.J.Bolkay. Novitates Musei Sarajevoensis, no.5, pp. 1-3, pls.1-2, Dec. 31, 1927.

(CONTRIBUTION TO THE VERTEBRATE FAUNA OF DALMATIA.) Ein Beitrag zur Wirbeltierfauna Dalmatiens. Heinrich Dathe. Zool. Garten, n.F., Leipzig, vol. 7, nos.4-6, pp.108-130, Aug., 1934.

(I. THE MAMMALS OF THE NORTH DALMATIAN ISLANDS.) I.Die Saeugetiere der norddalmatinischen Inseln. Otto Koller. Ann.Naturhist. Mus. Wien, vol.43, pp. 193-196, 1929.

(REPORT ON THE GEOGRAPHICAL DIVISION OF JUGOSLAVIA ON THE BASIS OF THE DISTRIBUTION OF THE MAMMALS.) Opit zoogeograficeskago dielenia Jugoslavii a osnovanii rasprostranienia mliekopitaiuscich. Vladimir Martino. Proc. 4th Congr. Russian Academical Foreign Extralimital Organizations, Part 2, Russian Sci. Inst.Belgrade, pp.121-127, 1929.

MATERIALS FOR THE ECOLOGY AND ZOOGEOGRAPHY OF THE MAMMALS OF S. SERBIA. Vladimir Martino, E.Martino. Zapiski Russkago Nauchnago Institut, Belgrade, no.14, pp.85-106, 1939. (In Bulgarian with English summary.)

NOTES ON THE ECOLOGY OF SOME MAMMALS FROM JUGOSLAVIA. Vladimir Martino, E. Martino. Jour.Russian Scient. Inst. Belgrade, pt.2, pp.53-65, 1930. (In Russian with English summary.)

ON SOME MAMMALS FROM SERVIA. Vladimir Martino, E. Martino. Ann.Mus. Nat. Hungarici, vol.23, pp.165-168, 1926.

PRELIMINARY NOTES ON FIVE NEW MAMMALS FROM JUGOSLAVIA. Vladimir Martino, E. Martino. Ann. and Mag.Nat. Hist., London, ser.11, vol.5, no.30, pp. 493-498, June, 1940.

ON SOME MAMMALS FROM JUGOSLAVIA. Ivor G.S. Montagu. Proc. Zool. Soc. London, pp.865-870, Dec., 1923.

(Review by Fran Kos of) ON SOME MAMMALS FROM JUGOSLAVIA. Ivor G.S. Montagu. Separatni odisek iz "Glasnika Muzejakega drustva za Slovenijo", Letnik IV, V in VI, Prirodoslovni del, 1924-1925.

NEW FACTS CONCERNING THE DISTRIBUTION OF SOME MAMMALS IN JUGOSLAVIA. B.M. Petrov. Zapiski Russkago Nauchnago Instituta Bielgradie, no.14, Belgrade, pp.77-83, tbls., 1939. (In Russian with English summary.)

DEVELOPMENT OF PLEISTOCENE IN SLOVENIA. I. Rakovec. Prvi Jugoslovanski Geol. Kongr. Bledu, 1954, pp.59-72, 1956.

(FAUNA OF DALMATIA. II. MAMMALIA.) Fauna Dalmatiens. II. Saeugetiere. Otto Wettstein. Zool. Jahrbuch, vol.42, pp.192-194, 1919.

GENERAL

ANATOMY

PRESENCE OF A NUCLEUS OF BELLONCI IN REPTILES AND MAMMALS. J. L. Addens. Proc. Kon. Nederl. Akad. Wetensch., Amsterdam, vol.41, no.10, pp.1134-1145, figs.5, Dec., 1938. (Mammals, pp.1140-1144, figs. 4-5.)

(MORPHOLOGICAL PROOF FOR THE PRESENCE OF INTRAVITAL COMMUNICATION BETWEEN THE CAVITIES OF THE PLEURAL-SACS IN A GROUP OF MAMMALS.) Morphologische Beweise fuer das Vorhandensein intravitaler Kommunikationen zwischen den Kavitaeten der Pleurasaecke bei einer Reihe von Saugetieren. E. Agduhr. Anat. Anz., vol.64, pp.276-298, figs.11, Dec. 1, 1927.

STRUCTURE OF THE METAPODII OF SOME WILD AND DOMESTIC ANIMALS. E. Andreewa. Trudy Lab. Genet., Akad. Nauk, Leningrad, USSR, vol.1, pp.263-311, figs.43, 1933.

(CRITICAL REMARKS ON THE ANATOMY OF THE HYOID BONE.) Kritisches zur Anatomie des Zungenbeins. J. Andres. Anat. Anz., vol.60, pp.289-309, illus., Dec. 16, 1925.

SENILE CHANGES IN THE LIVER OF MOUSE AND MAN, WITH SPECIAL REFERENCE TO THE SIMILARITY OF THE NUCLEAR ALTERATIONS. Warren Andrew, Harry Marshall Brown, James Bluford Johnson. Amer. Jour. Anat., Philidalphia, vol. 72, no.2, pp.199-221, pls.1-4, Mar., 1943.

SENILE CHANGES IN THE PANCREAS OF WISTAR INSTITUTE RATS AND OF MAN, WITH SPECIAL REGARD TO THE SIMILARITY OF LOCULE AND CAVITY FORMATION. Warren Andrew. Amer. Jour. Anat., Philadelphia, vol.74, no.1, pp.97-127, pls.1-6, Jan., 1944.

COMPARATIVE ANATOMY OF THE LIPS AND LABIAL VILLI OF VERTEBRATES. B. J. Anson. Jour. Morphol. and Physiol., vol.47, pp.335-394, text figs.5, pls.9, 1929.

DETERMINATION OF THE DIAMETERS OF VENTRICULAR MYOCARDIAL FIBERS IN MAN AND OTHER MAMMALS. Laurence M. Ashley. Amer. Jour. Anat., Philadelphia, vol.77, no.3, pp.325-363, fig.1, pls.1-2, Nov., 1945.

(ORGANS OF THE BODY OF MAMMALS AND THEIR FUNCTIONS.) Organy tela mlekopitaiushchikh i ikh rabota. Lev Petrovich Astanin. Moscow, Sovetskaya nauka, pp.351-349, 1958.

HEREDITARY ABNORMALITIES OF THE VISCERA. I. A MORPHOLOGICAL STUDY WITH SPECIAL REFERENCE TO ABNORMALTIES OF THE KIDNEYS IN THE DESCENDANTS OF X-RAYED MICE. Halsey J. Bagg. Amer.Jour.Anat., vol.36, pp. 275-303, figs.3, pls.4, Nov. 15, 1925.

ROTATORY MOBILITY OF THE FIBULA IN EUTHERIAN MAMMALS. C.H.Barnett, J.R. Napier. Jour. Anat., Cambridge, England, vol.87, pt.1, pp.11-21, Jan., 1953.

SOME FACTORS INFLUENCING ANGULATION OF THE NECK OF THE MAMMALIAN TALUS. C. H. Barnett. Jour. Anat., Cambridge, England, vol.89, pt.2, pp.225-230, Apr., 1955.

A STUDY OF THE HISTOLOGICAL STRUCTURE OF THE RESPIRATORY PORTION OF THE LUNGS OF AQUATIC MAMMALS. Leonard F. Belander. Amer. Jour. Anat., Philadelphia, vol.67, no.3, pp.437-469, pls.4, Nov. 15, 1940.

(RELATION BETWEEN THE ANATOMICAL FORMS OF THE METACARPAL AND METATARSAL BONES OF DOMESTICATED ANIMALS TO THE HISTOLOGICAL AND PHYSICAL-CHEMICAL TRAITS OF THE SAME.) Der Zusammenhang der anatomischen Formen der Metacarpal- und Metatarsalknochen der Haustiere mit dem histologischen Bau und den chemischphysikalischen Eigenschaften derselben. N. Bogdaschew. Anat. Anz., vol.70, nos.6/7, pp.143-154, figs.6, 1930.

(CONSIDERATIONS OF SOME ASPECTS OF THE GENERAL MORPHOLOGY AND ORGANIZATION OF THE MAMMALIAN APPARATUS.) Considérations sur quelques aspects de la morphologie et de l'organisation generale de l'appariel mammaire. E. Bourdelle. Volume Jubilaire en l'Honneur du Professeur Charles Porcher pour son soixantieme anniversaire, Chambery, pp.1-15, 1932.

(GENERAL AND REGIONAL MORPHOLOGY OF MAMMALS.) La morphologie generale et regionale des mammiferes. E. Bourdelle. Mammalia, Paris, vol.6, no.1, pp.1-12, figs. 1-7, Mar., 1942; vol.6, no.3-4, pp.89-100, figs.8-18, Sep.-Dec., 1942; vol.7, no.1, pp. 1-13, figs.19-26, Mar., 1943; vol.7, no.2, pp.41-55, figs.27-35, June, 1943.

MAMMALIAN ADRENAL GLAND. Geoffrey Bourne. Oxford, Clarendon, pp. 239, 1949.

GLANDULAR AREAS OF SOME AUSTRALIAN JERBOA MICE, AND REMARKS ON NYCTINOMUS AND MYRMECOBIUS. Geoffrey Bourne, Mem.Nat.Mus.Melbourne, no.8, pp.90-93, fig.1, Sep., 1934.

STUDIES ON THE GOLGI APPARATUS IN GLAND-CELLS. III. LACHRYMAL GLANDS AND GLANDS OF THE MALE REPRODUCTIVE SYSTEM. Robert H. Bowen. Quart. Jour. Micro. Sci., vol.70, pp.395-418, pls. 25-28, Sep. 1926.

STUDIES ON THE GOLGI APPARATUS IN GLAND-CELLS. IV. CRITIQUE OF THE TOPOGRAPHY, STRUCTURE, AND FUNCTION OF THE GOLGI APPARATUS IN GLANDULAR TISSUE. Robert H. Bowen. Quart. Jour.Micro.Sci., vol.70, pp.420-449, illus., Sep., 1926.

CLASSIFICATION OF THE UPPER LIP IN MAMMALS. J. D. Boyd. Jour. Anat., vol.67, pt.3, pp.409-416, pl.1, Apr., 1933.

EFFECT OF NATURAL FOOD ON THE DISTENTION OF THE GALL-BLADDER, WITH A NOTE ON THE CHANGE IN PATTERN OF THE MUCOSA AS IT PASSES FROM DISTENTION TO COLLAPSE. Edward A. Boyden. Anat. Rec., vol.30, pp.333-356, fig.1, pls. 3, Aug. 25, 1925.

PROBLEM OF THE PANCREATIC BLADDER. CRITICAL SURVEY OF SIX NEW CASES, BASED ON NEW HISTOLOGICAL AND EMBRYOLOGICAL OBSERVATIONS. Edward A. Boyden. Amer. Jour. Anat., pp.151-176, figs.6, pls.2, Sep. 15, 1925.

(ON THE CAUSES OF THE ASYMMETRY OF THE LUNGS AND POSITION OF THE HEART IN MAMMALS.) Ueber die Ursachen der Assymmetrie der Lungen und der Herzlage bei den Saeugetieren. Ivar Broman. Anat. Anz., vol.57, pp.95-101, Sep., 1923.

(OBSERVATION ON THE COATING OF THE LUNG ALVEOLUS IN THE MAMMALS.) Observaciones sobre el revestimiento del alveolo pulmonar en los mamiferos. W. Buño. Arch. Soc. Biol. Montevideo, vol.10, no.4, pp.295-297, fig.1, Sep., 1942.

TAILS. CAUDAL APPENDAGES ADAPTED BY NATURE TO THE NEEDS OF HER CREATURES. Charles E. Burt. Nat. Hist., vol.30, no.6, pp.653-660, Nov.-Dec., 1930.

SEXUAL VARIATIONS IN THE PELVIS. W.E. Caldwell, H.C. Moloy. Science, n.s., vol. 76, no.1958, pp.37-40, July 8, 1932.

BONE MARROW OF HORSES AND CATTLE. Lois Calhoun. Science, Lancaster, vol.104, no.2705, p.423, Nov. 1, 1946.

(ON THE MORPHOLOGY OF RENAL CALYCES AND THE PELVIS. COMPARATIVE ANATOMY RESEARCH.) Sulla morfologia della pelvi e dei calici renali. Ricerche anatomocomparative. Andrea Caponneto. Archiv. Italiano Anat.e.Embriol., Firenze, vol.34, fasc.3, pp.293-339, figs.38, May 10, 1935.

DISTRIBUTION OF BRUNNER'S GLANDS IN THE DUODENUM OF MAMMALS. Alice Carleton. Proc. Zool. Soc. London, pt.2, pp.385-390, pl.1, July, 1935.

ON THE VERTEBRAL EPIPHYSES OF MAMMALIA. A. J. E. Cave. Proc. Zool. Soc. London, pt.2, pp.225-233, figs.3, July 1934.

(RIB CURVATURE IN THE MAMMALS.) Die Kruemmung der Rippenbogen bei den Saeugetieren. A. Cedarbaum. Comptes Rendus Soc. Sci. et Lettr. Varsovie 1935, annee 28, cl. IV, nos.1-6, pp.68-85, tbl.5, 1935. (In Polish, with German summary.)

VESTIGIAL CLAVICLES AND RUDIMENTARY SESAMOIDS. THEIR DEVELOPMENT AND FUNCTIONS IN MAMMALS. S. H. Chubb. Amer. Nat., vol.66, no.705, pp. 376-381, figs.2, July-Aug., 1932.

MICROSCOPIC OBSERVATIONS ON NEW FORMATION OF CARTILAGE AND BONE IN THE LIVING MAMMAL. Eliot R. Clark, Eleanor Linton Clark. Amer. Jour. Anat., Philadelphia, vol.70, no.2, pp.167-200, figs.17, Mar. 16, 1942.

MASTER KEYS TO ANATOMY: PRELIMINARY NOTES. Montague W. Cobb. Jour. Nat. Medical Assoc., Tuskegee, vol.35, no.3, pp.75-86, May, 1943.

MORPHOGENESIS. Frank J. Daniel. Univ. Calif. Zool., vol.36, no.12, pp.299-324, figs.2, pls.29-32, 1932.

(GROWTH AND OSSIFICATION OF A SKELETON OF THE LIMB UNDER EXPERIMENTALLY CHANGED CONDITIONS OF WEIGHT.) Rost i okostyenyeniye skyelyeta konyechnostyei usloviyakh ekspyerimentalno izmyenyennoi nagruzki. E. I. Danilvoa, A. I. Sviridov. Zool. Zhurnal, Moscow, vol.32, no.4, pp.780-786, 1953.

UNILATERIAL RENAL AGENESES: ANATOMICAL DESCRIPTION OF A SPECIMEN. Edward H.Daseler, Barry J.Anson. Jour. Urology, Baltimore, vol.50, no.2, pp.155-163, figs.5, Aug., 1943.

ANIMAL MORPHOLOGY IN ITS RELATION TO OTHER SCIENCES. C. B. Davenport. Science, n.s., vol.20, no.517, pp.697-706, Nov. 25, 1904.

PODOLOGY AND PODONYMY. SOME SUGGESTIONS IN THE TERMINOLOGY OR THE NOMENCLATURE OF FEET AND FOOT-SCIENCE. William H.Davis. Med.Rev. of Reviews, pp.4, May, 1932.

MAMMALIAN ANATOMY, WITH SPECIAL REFERENCE TO THE CAT. Alvin Davison. 2d ed., rev., illus.114, pp.246, 1910; 4th ed., rev., illus.123, pp.286, 1923; 7th ed, illus.187, fig.92, pp.349, 1947, Philadelphia, Blakiston Co.

(STUDIES ON NEWBORN MAMMALS (EXTERIOR FORM.) Studien ueber neugeborene Saeugetiere (aeussere Form.) O.DeBeaux. Zool.Jahrbuch, Abteil.f.Systematik etc., vol.54, pp.1-38, pl.1, figs.16, 1927.

(POLYMORPHISM AND MONOMORPHISM IN REINDEER AND DOGS.) A propos du chien et du renne du polymorphisme au monomorphisme. Ed. Dechambre. Mammalia, Paris, vol.8, no.1, pp.19-28, Mar., 1944.

THE SPLEEN IN RUMINANTS AND EQUINES. G. De Kock. S. Afr. Jour. Sci., vol.26, pp. 423-430, Dec., 1929.

(NECK RIBS IN BOVINE ANIMALS AND REDUCED BREAST RIBS IN HORSES AND THEIR IMPORTANCE IN COMPARATIVE ANATOMY.) Halsrippen beim Rind und reduzierte Brustrippen beim Pferd in ihrer vergleichend-anatomischen Bedeutung. Fritz Drahn. Zeitschr. f. Saeugetierkunde, vol. 1, no.2, pp.121-140, figs.16, Dec. 24, 1926.

ON THICKNESS AND SOLIDITY OF BONES IN LARGE AND SMALL ANIMALS.) Ueber die Dicke und Festigkeit der Knochen bei grossen und kleinen Tieren. R.DuBois-Reymond. Zeitschr. Wiss.Zoologie, vol. 132, pp.1-36, figs.2, Sep., 1928.

ADAPTIVE CHIN. Lloyd E. DuBrul, Harry Sicher. Charles C. Thomas, Springfield, Illinois, IX plus, pp.97, figs.47, 1954.

MODIFICATIONS OF THE SHOULDER GIRDLE RELATED TO REACH AND STRIDE IN MAMMALS. Theodore H. Eaton, Jr. Jour. Morphol., Philadelphia, vol.75, no.1, pp. 167-171, July, 1944.

COMPARATIVE HISTOLOGY OF DOMESTIC ANIMALS. I. DIGESTIVE SYSTEM. 1. ORAL CAVITY. Hans Elias. Middlesex Veterinarian, Waltham, vol.4, no.1, pp.18-22, fig.1, pls.2, Winter, 1944.

COMPARATIVE HISTOLOGY OF DOMESTIC ANIMALS. I. DIGESTIVE SYSTEM. 2. THE STOMACH OF DOMESTIC MAMMALS. Hans Elias. Middlesex Veterinarian, Waltham, vol.4, no.2, pp.66-69, pl.1, Spring-Summer, 1944.

COMPARATIVE HISTOLOGY OF DOMESTIC ANIMALS. I. DIGESTIVE SYSTEM. 3. THE OESOPHAGUS AND STOMACH OF DOMESTICATED BIRDS. Hans Elias. Middlesex Veterinarian, Waltham, vol.4, no.3, pp.1-6, figs. A-D, pl.1, Winter, 1945.

(HANDBOOK OF THE COMPARATIVE ANATOMY OF DOMESTIC ANIMALS.) Handbuch der vergleichenden Anatomie der Haustiere. W. Ellenberger, H. Raum. 16 Auflage, Berlin, Julius Springer, 1926.

(ON THE CONSTANT FATTY COMPOUND IN SOME VERTEBRATES.) Ueber einen konstanten Fettkoerper bei einigen Vertebraten. Desider Engel. Zeitschr. f. Zellforschung und Mikro. Anatomie, vol.2, pp. 585-592, figs.7, Sep. 14, 1925.

COMPARATIVE HISTOLOGICAL STUDY OF FOSSIL AND RECENT BONE TISSUES. Donald H. Englow, Sidney O. Brown. Part II, Texas Jour. Sci., vol.9, no.2, pp.186-214, June, 1957.

STUDIES OF FEMORAL DEFORMATION. Gaynor F. Evans. Stanford Med. Bull., vol. 6, no.3, pp.374-381, illus., Aug., 1948.

(CONTRIBUTION TO THE ANATOMY OF MAMMALIAN TONSILS.) Contribution a l'anatomie de l'amygdale chez les mammiferes. Pol Florentin. Nancy, Impr. G. Thomas, 3p. l., (9)-197, (1) p., illus., 1936.

INTRODUCTION TO THE OSTEOLOGY OF THE MAMMALIA. William Henry Flower, 1870.

OSTEOLOGY OF THE MAMMALIA. William Henry Flower. London, 1870.

COMPARATIVE HISTOLOGY OF FEMORAL BONES. J.S.Foote. Trans.Amer.Microscop. Soc., vol.30, no.2, pp.87-140, pls. A, 1-4, Apr., 1911.

COMPARATIVE HISTOLOGY OF THE FEMUR. J. S. Foote. Smithsonian Miscel. Coll., vol. 61, no.8, publ. 2232, pp.9, pls.3, Aug. 22, 1913.

CONTRIBUTION TO THE COMPARATIVE HISTOLOGY OF THE FEMUR. J. S. Foote. Smithson. Contrib. to Know., vol.35, no.3, pp.1-242, pls.38, 1916.

ANATOMICAL QUALITIES OF THE LIVER DURING THE VARIOUS STAGES OF ITS FUNCTIONAL ACTIVITIES. E. Forsgren. Jour. Morphol. and Physiol., vol.47, pp. 519-529, figs.8, 1929.

AVAILABLE MATERIAL IN COMPARATIVE ANATOMY AND PATHOLOGY. Herbert Fox. Science, n.s., vol.66, pp.541, Dec. 2, 1927.

(SKELETON OF THE LIMBS IN MAN AND IN VERTEBRATES, PHYLOGENY AND ONTOGENY.) Lo scheletro degli arti nell'uomo e nei vertebrati, filogenesi ed ontogenesi. Fabio Frassetto. Bologna, pp.158, figs.96, 1915.

(CONCERNING THE MECHANICAL ASPECT OF THE MAMMAL HEART.) De l'aspect mecanique du coeur mammalien. Serge Frechkop. Bull. Inst. Roy. Sci. Nat. Belgique, vol.32, no.27, pp.1-15, Apr., 1956.

(NOTES ON THE MAMMALS. XXV. THE BIPED STANCE AND THE POSITION OF THE HEART.) Notes sur les mammiferes. XXV. L'allure bipede et la position du coeur. Serge Frechkop. Bull. Mus. roy. Hist. Nat. Belgique, Brussels, vol.15, no.44, pp.7, figs.4, Aug., 1939.

(NOTES ON THE MAMMALS. 30. ON THE FORM OF THE PELVIS OF UNGULATES.) Notes sur les mammiferes. 30. De la forme du bassin des Ongules. Serge Frechkop.Bull. Mus. Roy. Hist. Nat. Belgique, Brussels, vol.23, no.32, pp.10, Dec., 1947.

(ON THE QUESTION OF THE RIGHT HANDEDNESS OF HUMANS AND THE ASYMMETRY OF THE BODY MEMBERS OF THE PRIMATES.) Zur Frage der Rechtshaendigkeit des Menschen und der Gliedmassenasymmetrie der Primaten. Wilhelm Freudenberg. Zeitschrift f. Saeugetierk., vol.4, no.1, pp.36-46, pl.1, fig.1, July 6, 1929.

(CONTRIBUTIONS TO THE MORPHOLOGY OF THE UROGENITAL SYSTEM OF THE MAMMALS.) Beitraege zur Morphologie des Urogenitalsystems der Saeugetiere. I and II. L. Freund. Zeitschr. Morph. u. Oekol. Tiere, vol.17, pp.417-440, figs.8, Mar. 24, 1930.

(MORPHOLOGY OF THE HEART.) Morphologie des Herzens. H. Frick. Handbuch der Zoologie, Berlin, Bd.8, Teil 5, no.5, (Lief. 7), pp.1-48, July, 1956.

ELEMENTS OF COMPARATIVE ANATOMY. Carl Gegenbaur. Macmillan & Co., London, pp.645, illus., 1878.

UNIFORMITY IN THE DIVISION OF THE ABDOMINAL REGIONS. THE NEED OF AGREEMENT ON THE LIMITS OF THE ABDOMINAL REGIONS, AND A PROPOSITION FOR A NEW METHOD OF DIVISION. F. H. Gerrish. Boston Med. and Surg. Jour., Boston, pp.10, July 6, 1893.

ON THE CHARACTERISTICS OF THE PRIMARY GROUPS OF THE CLASS OF MAMMALS. Thoedore Nicholas Gill. Cambridge Mass., pp.284-306, 1872.

LENGTH OF LACUAE AND NUMBER OF CANALICULI IN BONES OF SEVERAL MAMMALS. Donald J. Gray. Anat. Record, Philadelphia, vol.81, no.2, pp.163-169, Oct. 25, 1941.

NOTES ON THE FOETUS OF AN ELEPHANT AND OF A HIPPOPOTAMUS IN THE COLLECTION OF THE BRITISH MUSEUM. John Edward Gray. Proc. Zool. Soc. London, pp.491-492, figs.2, 1868.

NOTICE OF COMMUNICATIONS ON THE VERY YOUNG OF THE JAGUAR, ON THE YOUNG OF THE BOSCH VARK, AND ON THE SKULLS OF THE LEOPARD IN THE BRITISH MUSEUM. John Edward Gray. Proc. Zool. Soc. London, pp.206, 1874.

THE BRIDGE-THAT-WALKS. K. Gregory. Nat. Hist., New York, vol.39, pp.33-48, illus., Jan., 1937.

HABITUS FACTORS IN THE SKELETON OF FOSSIL AND RECENT MAMMALS. K. Gregory. Proc. Amer. Philos. Soc., vol. 76, no.4, pp.429-444, figs.14, 1936.

PELVIS FROM FISH TO MAN: STUDY IN PALEOMORPHOLOGY. K. Gregory. Amer. Naturalist, vol.69, pp.193-210, figs.12, May-June, 1935.

STUDIES ON COMPARATIVE MYOLOGY AND OSTEOLOGY. K. Gregory, C. L. Camp. No. III. Bull. Amer. Mus. Nat. Hist. New York, vol. XXXVIII, art XV, pp.447-563, figs.16, pls.39-50, Dec. 31, 1918.

SOME EARLY AND LATE ILLUSTRATIONS OF COMPARATIVE OSTEOLOGY. E. W. Gudger. Annals Med. Hist., N.S., vol.1, no.3, pp.334-355, figs.15, 1929.

ANIMAL MICROLOGY. PRACTICAL EXERCISES IN ZOOLOGICAL MICROTECHNIQUE. Micn

ANIMAL MICROLOGY. PRACTICAL EXERCISES IN ZOOLOGICAL MICROTECHNIQUE. Michael F. Guyer. 4th ed., pp.I-XVI, 1-331, Univ. of Chicago Press, Chicago, 1936.

(Review by I. Gersh of) ANIMAL MICROLOGY. Michael F. Guyer. Jour. Mamm., vol. 17, no.3, p.298, Aug., 1936.

(CREATION AND ESSENCE OF THE FORM OF ORGANISMS.) Schoepfung und Wesen der Organismenform. Wilhelm Haacke. Naturwissensch. wochenschr., Bd.9, no.34, pp. 409-416, Aug. 26, 1894.

ON THE ORIGIN OF THE CELLS LINING THE LIVER SINUSOIDS IN THE CAT AND THE RAT. Warner Smith Hammond. Amer. Jour. Anat., Philadelphia, vol.65, no.2, pp.199-227, pls.5, Sep. 15, 1939.

ANTOGENY AND PHYLOGENY OF THE STERNUM. Frank Blair Hanson. Amer. Jour. Anat., vol.26, pp.41-115, Sep. 15, 1919.

PROBLEM OF THE CORACOID. Frank Blair Hanson. Anat. Rec., vol.19, pp.327-345, figs., Nov. 20, 1920.

INORGANIC CONSTITUTION OF BONE. Sterling B. Hendricks. Science, Lancaster, n.s., vol.96, no.2489, pp.255-257, fig.1, Sep. 11, 1942.

COMPARATIVE STUDY OF THE PANCREAS. Osman W. C. Hill. Proc. Zool. Soc. London, pp.581-631, illus., July, 1926.

CAECUM OF MONOTREMES AND MARSUPIALS. Osman W. C. Hill, R. E. Rewell. Trans. Zool. Soc. London, vol.28, pt.2, pp.185-240, pls.1-8, Jan., 1954.

(HARD MATERIALS FROM MAMMALS.) Hartstoffe von Saeugetieren. Max Hilzheimer. Die Rohstoffe des Tierreichs, Berlin, pt.12, pp.1436-1531, figs.700-741, Feb. 15, 1935.

(HISTOPHYSIOLOGICAL STUDIES OF PANETH CELLS.) Histophysiologische Studien an den Panethsche Zellen. E. Hintzsche, P. Anderegg. Zeitschr. f. Mikroskp. Anat. Forschung, Leipzig, vol.43, pp.143-152, figs.2, Jan. 11, 1938.

(PANETH CELLS OF MAMMALS AND THE PROBLEM OF THEIR BIOLOGICAL EXPLANATION.) Die Panethschen Zellen der Saeugetiere and das Problem ihrer biologischen Deutung. E. Hintzsche, P. Anderegg. Bio-Morphosis, Basel, vol.1, fasc.1, pp. 96-108, figs.3, Apr., 1938.

ON THE ORIGINAL MAMMALIAN CARPAL PATTERN. Nils Holmgren. Acta Zoologia, Stockholm, vol.36, no.3, pp.329-330, 1955.

THE FEMORAL TROCHANTERS. PAPERS ON MAMMALOGY. A.Brazier Howell. Zool. Ser., Field Mus.Nat.Hist., Chicago, vol. 27, pp.279-291, figs.54-55, Dec. 8, 1941.

MORPHOGENESIS OF THE SHOULDER ARCHITECTURE. A.Brazier Howell. PART I. GENERAL CONSIDERATIONS. Quart. Rev.Biol., vol.VIII, no.3, pp.247-259, figs.1-4, Sep., 1933.

MORPHOGENESIS OF THE SHOULDER ARCHITECTURE. A. Brazier Howell. PART V. MONOTREMATA. Quart. Rev. Biol., vol.12, no.2, pp.191-205, June, 1927.

MORPHOGENESIS OF THE SHOULDER ARCHITECTURE. A. Brazier Howell. PART VI. THERIAN MAMMALIA. Quart. Rev. Biol., vol.12, no.4, pp.440-463, Dec., 1937.

PRIMITIVE CARPUS. A. Brazier Howell. Jour. Morphology, vol.57, no.1, pp.105-112, fig.1, Mar., 1935.

MORPHOLOGICAL METHOD AND RECENT PROGRESS IN ZOOLOGY. George Bond Howes. Smithsonian Institution Annual Report 1902, Washington, 1903.

CONTRIBUTION TO THE OSTEOLOGY OF RIBS. Ales Hrdlicka. Proc. Assoc. Amer. Anatomists, 14th ann.sess. pp.61-69, figs., 1900.

THE HUMERUS: SEPTAL APERTURES. Ales Hrdlicka. Anthropologie, Prague, vol. 10, pp.31-96, pls.4-7, 1932.

TYPICAL FORMS OF SHAFT OF LONG BONES. Ales Hrdlicka. Proc. Assoc. Amer. Anatomists, 14th ann.sess. pp.55-60, figs., 1900.

ANATOMICAL NOTES ON PINNIPEDIA AND CETACEA. Ernst Huber. Carnegie Inst. Wash., Publ., no.447, pp.105-136, figs.1-12, Jan. 20, 1934.

(ON THE SIGNIFICANCE OF EXPERIMENTAL METHODS IN FACIALIS INVESTIGATION, AND REMARKS ON THE PHYLOGENIC DEVELOPMENT OF FACIALIS MUSCULATURE IN THE VERTEBRATES.) Ueber die Bedeutung der experimentellen Methode in der Facialisforschung, nebst Betrachtungen ueber die phylogenetische Entwicklung der Facialismuskulatur in der Vertebraten-Reihe. Ernst Huber. Anat.Anz., Jena, vol.58, pp.177-205, 1924.

ON THE RELATION OF THE CHORDA DORSALIS TO THE ANLAGE OF THE PHARYNGEAL BURSA OR MEDIAN PHARYNGEAL RECESS. Gotthelf Carl Huber. Baltimore, Waverly Press, pp.373-404, illus., 1912.

EPARTERIAL BRONCHIAL SYSTEM OF THE MAMMALIA. G. S. Huntington. Ann. N. Y. Acad. Sci., Lancaster, vol.11, pp.127-176, pls.15-28, May 17, 1898.

STUDIES ON HETEROGONIC GROWTH. (IV) THE BIMODAL CEPHALIC HORN OF XYLOTRUPES GIDEON. Julian S. Huxley. Jour. Genetics., Cambridge, vol.18, no.1, pp.45-53, figs.1-2, Mar., 1927.

MANUAL OF THE ANATOMY OF VERTEBRATED ANIMALS. T. H. Huxley. New York, pp.431, 1898.

ON THE CHARACTERS OF THE PELVIS IN THE MAMMALIA, AND THE CONCLUSIONS RESPECTING THE ORIGIN OF MAMMALS WHICH MAY BE BASED ON THEM. T. H. Huxley. Proc. Roy. Soc. London, vol.28, pp. 395-405, pl.8, Mar. 6, 1879.

COMPARATIVE VERTEBRATE ANATOMY. Libbie Henrietta Hyman. Univ. Chicago Press, Chicago, 2nd ed., pp.xx-544, figs. 136, 1942.

(Review by Brazier A. Howell of) COMPARATIVE VERTEBRATE ANATOMY. Libbie Henrietta Hyman. Science, Lancaster, n.s., vol.97, no.2516, pp.263-264, Mar. 19, 1943.

UN-DESCENDED SCAPULA WITH AN OMOVERTEBRAL BONE AND WITHOUT SPINAL DEFECTS. Byron H. Jackson. Moses Taylor Hosp. Bull., vol.1, no.9, pp.8-26, figs.1-11, Dec., 1927.

(SNOUT FORMATION IN MAMMALS OF THE PRESENT AND OF ANTIQUITY.) Die Ruesselbildung bei Saeugetieren der Gegenwart und Vorzeit. Arnold Jacobi. Jenaische Zeitschr. f. Nat., 57 Bd., Neue Folge, 50 Bd., pp.199-218, figs.8, 1921.

(BASIC FORMS OF THE VERTEBRATE BODY.) Die Grundformen des Wirbeltierkoerpers. Otto Jaekel. Mitt. Nat. Ver. Neuvorpommern Ruegen, Jahrg.50-51, pp.11-14, 1925.

NOTES ON THE HISTOLOGY AND PHYSIOLOGY OF THE PLACENTA IN THE UNGULATA. J. W. Jenkinson. Proc. Zool. Soc. London, vol.1, pp.73-96, pl.1-3, June 7, 1906.

(COMMENTS ON THE SCENT AND SCENT GLANDS OF DANISH MAMMALS.) Lidt om Pattedyrs Faert og Faertorganer. Poul Valentin Jensen. Naturens Verden, Copenhagen, vol.25, no.6, pp.241-266, figs.24, 1941.

SOME READAPTATIONS OF THE MAMMALIAN PES IN RESPONSE TO ARBOREAL HABITS. Wood F. Jones. Proc. Zool. Soc. London, vol.123, pt.1, pp.33-41, illus., June 10, 1953.

THE ADRENAL CORTEX. Chester I. Jones. New York, Cambridge Univ. Press. X plus, pp.316, figs.35, pl.9, 1957.

DESCRIPTIVE ANATOMY OF THE HUMAN HEART. William Keiller. Amer. Jour. Med. Sci., pp.1-8, figs.1-5, Apr., 1898.

DIVERTICULUM OF THE LARYNX. Harry H. Kerr, Thomas Bradley. Surgery, St. Louis, vol.2, no.4, pp.3-11, figs.4, Oct., 1937.

COMPARATIVE STUDY OF THE VAS SUBINTESTINAL IN THE VERTEBRATES. Pauline Kimball. Amer. Jour. Anat., vol.42, pp.371-398, illus., Nov. 15, 1928.

REGRESSIVE STRUCTURES AND THE LYMPHOCYTE. THE PLASMA CELL; ITS ORIGIN AND DEVELOPMENT. A STUDY OF THE MAMMALIAN NICTITATING MEMBRANE. D. W. Kingsley. Anat. Record, vol.29, pp.1-18, pl.1, figs.6, Nov. 25, 1924.

(ON THE DEVELOPMENT OF THE ENTOTYMPANICUM.) Ueber die Entwicklung des entotympanicums. O. J. van der Klaauw. E. J. Brill, Leiden, pp.50, pls.3, 1922.

(ANATOMICAL GROUPING OF THE TONSILS OF MAMMALS AND PHYLOGENETIC JUDGMENT OF SUCH GROUPING, TAKING INTO CONSIDERATION PARALEL DEVELOPMENT.) Anatomische Reihen der Gaumenmandeln der Saugetiere und die phylogenetische Beurteilung solcher Reihen unter Beruecksichtigung der Parallel-Entwicklung. Adolf Kleinschmidt. Anat. Anz., Jena, vol. 88, nos.4-6, pp.49-91, figs.6, tbls.2, Apr. 3, 1939.

(CEPHALIC JOINT OF AQUATIC MAMMALS.) Das Kopfgelenk der aquatilen Saeugetiere. Karl Heinrich Knese. Gegenbaurs Morphologisches Jahrbuch, Leipzig, vol.78, no.3, pp.134-376, figs.46, Oct., 1936.

(MECHANICAL CONDITIONALITY IN THE DEVELOPMENT OF ORGANISMS.) Mechanische Bedingtheit in der Entwicklung der Organismen. Hans Krieg. Die Naturwissenschafte, Berlin, 25. Jahrg. no.47, pp.757-762, figs.6, 1937.

LIFE HISTORIES RECORDED IN SKELETONS. Wilton Marion Krogman. Amer. Anthropologist, Lancaster, vol.37, no.1, pp.92-105, fig.1, pls.1-2, Jan.-Mar., 1935.

(CONTRIBUTIONS TO ZOOLOGY AND COMPARATIVE ANATOMY.) Beitraege zur Zoologie und vergleichenden Anatomie. Heinrich Kuhl. Frankfurt a.M., pp.212, pls.9, 1820.

(ADAPTATION PHENOMENA IN THE CHEWING APPARATUS OF MAMMALS DIFFERING AS TO KINDS OF FOOD EATEN.) Anpassungserscheinungen am Kauapparat bei ernaehrungsbiologisch verschiedenen Saeugetieren. Friedrich Kuehlhorn. Zool. Anzeiger, vol.121, nos. 1-2, pp.1-17, 1938.

(RIBS AND BREAST BONE IN THEIR FUNCTIONAL CONNECTIONS.) Rippen und Brustbein in ihren funktionellen Verknuepfungen. Karl Heinz Lange. Gegenbaurs Morphol. Jahrbuch, Leipzig, vol.73, pp.355-384, figs.15, Apr., 1934.

(INITIAL ORIENTATION OF THE POSTERIOR MEMBER OF VERTEBRATES.) Orientation initiale du membre postérieur des vertebres. Fernand Lataste. Compt. Rend. Soc. Biol., vol.90, pp.1010-1012, 1924.

FUNCTIONAL ANATOMY OF THE MAMMAL. James W. Leach. McGraw-Hill Book Co., New York, pp.viii-231, 1946.

FUNCTIONAL ANATOMY OF THE MAMMAL. James W. Leach. Second edition. McGraw-Hill Book Co., New York, pp.x-276, illus., 1952.

(MORPHOLOGICAL-GEOGRAPHICAL FORM SERIES IN THE MAMMALS.) Morphologisch-geographische Formenreihen bei den Saeugetieren. Wilhelm Leche. Lunds Univ. Arsskrift, vol.16, no.10, pp.1-76, figs.11, 1921.

(HAND SKELETON AS A WHOLE.) Handskelett als Ganzes. Rudolf Lips. Zeitschr. f. Saeugetierkunde, vol.5, nos.3-4, pp.112-114, Nov. 10, 1930.

ANATOMICAL NOTES ON MAMMALS OBTAINED IN BRITISH EAST AFRICA BY THE SWEDISH ZOOLOGICAL EXPEDITION 1911. Einar Loennberg. Kungl. Svenska, Vetenskap. Handl., vol.49, no.7, pp.3-33, pls.1-2, 1912.

OBSERVATION ON THE MAMMALIAN INGUINAL REGION. H. F. Lunn. Proc. Zool.Soc. London, vol.118, pt.2, pp.345-355, figs.1-6, Aug. 18, 1948.

THE TRUE CORACOID. R. Lydekker. Proc. Zool. Soc. London, pp.235-237, figs.1-2, June, 1915.

TWO CASES OF CONGENITAL ABSENCE OF ONE KIDNEY. Marcus W. Lyon, Jr. Jour. Amer. Med. Assoc., vol.67, p.1524, Nov. 18, 1916.

RELATION OF MITOCHONDRIA AND OTHER CYCTOPLASMIC CONSTITUENTS TO THE FORMATION OF SECRETION GRANULES. Wen-Chao Ma. Amer. Jour. Anat., vol.41, pp.51-62, pl.1, Mar. 15, 1928.

NOTE ON THE ELASTIC MEMBRANE OF THE BRONCHIAL TREE OF MAMMALS WITH AN INTERPRETATION OF ITS FUNCTIONAL SIGNIFICANCE. Charles C. Macklin. Anat. Rec., vol.24, pp.119-135, Oct., 1922.

COMPARATIVE STUDY OF THE ANATOMY OF THE SPHINCTER AT THE DUODENAL END OF THE COMMON BILE-DUCT WITH SPECIAL REFERENCE TO SPECIES OF ANIMALS WITHOUT A GALL-BLADDER. F. C. Mann. Anat. Rec., vol.18, no.4, pp.355-360, May 20 (June), 1920.

EXTRAHEPATIC BILIARY TRACT IN COMMON DOMESTIC AND LABORATORY ANIMALS. F. C. Mann, S. D. Brimhall, J. P. Foster. Anat. Rec., vol. 18, no.1, pp.47-66, Feb. 20 (Mar.), 1920.

(CRANIUM AND VISCERAL SKELETON. GENERAL.) Kranium und Visceralskelett. Allgemeine Probleme. Wilhelm Marinelli. Handbuch der vergleichenden Anatomie, vol. 4, pp.207-232, illus., 1936.

(ON HISTOLOGY AND A NEW CLASSIFICATION OF THE TISSUES OF THE HUMAN BODY.) Ueber histologie und eine neue Eintheilung der Gewebe des menschlichen Koerpers. C. Mayer. In Isis. no.6, pp.669-672, 1823.

(ASYMMETRIC CHARACTERISTICS IN FREE-LIVING MAMMALS.) Ueber asymmetrische Zeichnungen bei wildlebenden Saeugern. R. Mertens. Saeugetierkunde Mitteil., Stuttgart, vol.2, no.1, pp.32-33, Jan. 1, 1954.

OBSERVATIONS UPON THE ARRANGEMENT OF THE AXILLARY ARTERY AND BRACHIAL PLEXUS. Ruth A. Miller. Amer. Jour. Anat., Philadelphia, vol.64, no.1, pp.143-163, Jan. 15, 1939.

ON MACROPHAGAL FOCI ("MILKY SPOTS") IN THE PLEURA OF DIFFERENT MAMMALS, INCLUDING MAN. Russell L. Mixter. Amer. Jour. Anat., Philadelphia, vol.69, no.2, pp.159-186, illus., Sep. 15, 1941.

(COMPARATIVE ANATOMIC AND HISTOLOGICAL INVESTIGATIONS OF THE REGIO ANALIS AND THE RECTUM OF DOMESTIC MAMMALS.) Vergleichende anatomische und histologische Untersuchungen ueber die Regio analis und das Rectum der Haussaeugetiere. Ljubomir Mladenowitsch. Inaugural-Dissertation, Univ. Leipzig, pp.152, figs.22, 1907.

REMARKS ON THE MINOR CHARACTERS OF MAMMALIA. Andrew Murray. Proc. Zool. Soc. London, pp.146-147, 1866.

FUSION OF PARALLEL LONG BONES AND THE FORMATION OF SECONDARY CARTILAGE. P. D. F. Murray. Australian Jour. Zool., vol.2, no.3, pp.364-380, pls.1-4, 1954.

(DEVELOPMENT OF THE POSITION OF THE ESOPHAGUS AND TRACHEA IN SOME MAMMALS.) Die Lageentwicklung der Speise- und Luftroehre bei einigen Saeugern. E. Th. Nauck. Morphol. Jahrb., vol.61, pp.315-379, text figs.63, 1929.

COMPARATIVE ANATOMY AND PHYSIOLOGY OF THE LARYNX. V. E. Negus. London, Heinemann, pp.20-230, 1949.

ANOMALOUS PATELLAE. Bruno Oetteking. Anat. Rec., Philadelphia, vol.23, no.4, pp. 269-278, figs.4, Apr. 4, 1922.

ON THE MORPHOLOGICAL SIGNIFICANCE OF CERTAIN CRANIO-VERTEBRAL VARIATIONS. Bruno Oetteking. Anat. Rec., Philadelphia, vol.25, no.6, pp.339-353, figs.14, July, 1923.

OBSERVATIONS UPON THE OPPOSABLE POWER OF THE THUMB IN CERTAIN MAMMALS, CONSIDERED AS A ZOOLOGICAL CHARACTER, AND ON THE NATURAL AFFINITIES WHICH SUBSIST BETWEEN THE BIMANA, QUADRUMANA, AND PEDIMANA. W. Ogilby. Proc. Zool. Soc. London, pt.4, p.25, 1836.

DOLICHOCEPHALY AND BRACHYCEPHALY IN THE LOWER MAMMALS. Henry Osborn. Bull. Amer. Mus. Nat. Hist., New York, vol.16, art.7, pp.77-89, figs.5, Feb. 3, 1902.

ADAPTIVE MODIFICATIONS OF THE LIMB SKELETON IN AQUATIC REPTILES AND MAMMALS. Raymond C. Osburn. Ann. New York Acad. Sci., vol.16, pt.3, pp.447-480, pls.7-9, Mar., 1906.

ON THE ANATOMY OF VERTEBRATES. R. Owen. Vol. II, London, 1866.

ON THE ANATOMY OF VERTEBRATES. R. Owen. Vol. III. MAMMALS. Longmans, Green, & Co., London, pp.915, illus., 1868.

PRINCIPAL FORMS OF THE SKELETON AND OF THE TEETH. R. Owen. Privately printed, pp.329, figs.76, 1854.

COMPARATIVE STUDY OF THE UMBILICAL SPHINCTER. Helen J. A. Parry. Proc. Zool. Soc. London, vol.124, pt.3, pp.595-604, pls. 1-3, Nov. 15, 1954.

(ON THE EXTERIOR FORM OF A MAMMAL CYCLOPS.) Ueber die aeussere Form eines Saeugetier-Cyklops. L. Plate. Verhandl. der Deutschen Zoologischen Gesell., pp.139-143, figs.1-6, 1903.

EXTERNAL AND CRANIAL CHARACTERS OF SOME RARE ASIATIC MAMMALS RECENTLY EXHIBITED BY THE SOCIETY. R. L. Pocock. Proc. Zool. Soc. London, vol.115, pts.3-4, pp.310-318, figs., Feb., 1946.

(HYPOTHESES ON THE STRUCTURE OF THE LONG BONES OF MAMMALS.) Études théoriques sur la structure des os longs des mammifères. R. Poplewski. Comptes Rendus Seances Soc. Sci. et Lett. Varsovie, cl.IV, Annee 26, nos.7-8, pp.81-94, figs. 5, 1934.

(VARIATIONS IN THE LIVER IN THE PRINCIPAL SPECIES OF DOMESTIC ANIMALS.) Variations de la masse du foie chez les principales espèces domestiques. A. Porcherel. Comptes Rendus des Séances Soc. Biol., vol.93, no.21, pp.87-89, June. 1925.

POLYDACTYLISM IN MAN AND THE DOMESTIC ANIMALS, WITH ESPECIAL REFERENCE TO DIGITAL VARIATIONS IN SWINE. C. W. Prentiss. Bull. Mus. Comp. Zool., Cambridge, vol.40, no.6, pp.246-314, figs.26, pls.22, April, 1903.

(FEATURES WHICH FAVOR FECUNDATION IN MAMMALS. (MORPHOLOGICAL RESEARCH ON DOMESTIC MAMMALS).) I dispositivi che favoriscono la fecondazione nei Mammiferi (Ricerche morfologiche sui Mammiferi domestici.) Silvio Ranzi. Publ. Stazione Zool. Napoli, vol.16, no.2, pp.198-211, figs.7, Aug. 31, 1937.

SO-CALLED HIBERNATION GLAND. A. T. Rasmussen. Jour. Morphol., vol.38, no.1, pp.147-205, pl.8, Sep., 1923.

CONTRIBUTION TO OUR KNOWLEDGE OF THE STRUCTURE OF THE PLACENTA OF MUSTELIDAE, URSIDAE, AND SCIURIDAE. Subba A. Rau. Proc. Zool. Soc. London, pl.3, pp.1027-1069, Oct., 1925.

(ANATOMY OF MAMMALS. PART I. CETACEA AND PACHYDERMATA.) Anatomia mammalium. pars 1. Cetacea et pachydermata. H. G. L. Reichenbach. Lipsiae, 1845.

VERTEBRAL LEVEL OF TERMINATION OF THE SPINAL CORD WITH REPORT OF A CASE OF SACRAL CORD. Arthur F. Reimann, Barry J. Anson. Anat. Rec., Philadelphia, vol.88, no.1, pp.127-138, figs.7, Jan., 1944.

COMPARISON OF MAMMALIAN AND REPTILIAN CORCACOIDS. A. S. Romer. Anat. Rec., vol.24, pp.39-53, Sep., 1922.

LESSER TROCHANTER OF THE MAMMALIAN FEMUR. A. S. Romer. Anat. Rec., vol.28, pp.95-102, figs.3, June 25, 1924.

THE PES OF DIATECTES: NOTES ON THE PRIMITIVE TETRAPOD LIMB. A. S. Romer. Palaeobiologica, Vienna, vol.4, pp.25-48 figs.9, 1931.

THE VERTEBRATE BODY. A. S. Romer. W. B. Saunders Co., New York, pp.viii-643, figs.363, 1949.

(NOTES ON SOME ANALOGIES OF THE HUMAN TYPE WITH THE VERY ANCIENT MAMMALS.) Note sur quelques analogies du type humain avec cellui des tres-anciens mammiferes. Anatole Roujou. Paris, pp. 799, 8, 1872.

(ON THE OSTEOLOGY OF THE FIRST TWO NECK VERTEBRAE OF MAMMALS.) Zur Osteologie der beiden ersten Halswirbel der Saeugetiere. Jakob Rueger. Vierteljahrschrift Naturforsch. Gessel. Zuerich, Jahrg.83, Beiblatt (Festsch'r. Karl Heschler), pp.25-56, figs.10, tabls., Nov. 3, 1938.

THE OS PRIAPI: A STUDY IN BONE DEVELOPMENT. Elbert B. Ruth. Anat. Rec., vol.60, no.2, pp.231-244, pls.1-3, Sep. 25, 1934.

STUDY OF THE DEVELOPMENT OF THE MAMMALIAN PELVIS. Elbert B. Ruth. Anat. Rec., vol.53, no.2, pp.207-221, pls.2, July 25, 1932.

THE OS EPIPYRAMIS OR EPITRIQUETRUM. R. L. Saunders. Anat. Rec., Philadelphia, vol.84, no.1, pp.17-22, figs.2, Sep. 25, 1942.

CONGENITAL MALFORMATIONS OF THE KIDNEY IN REPTILES, BIRDS, AND MAMMALS. Harold H. Scott. Proc. Zool. Soc. London, 1925, pt.4, pp.1259-1270, pls.5, Jan., 1926.

CERVICAL RIBS. Francis J. Shepherd. Amer. Jour. Med. Sci., Philadelphia, n.s., vol.85, pp.5, figs.2, Jan., 1883.

SKETCH OF THE EARLY HISTORY OF ANATOMY. Francis J. Shepherd. Canada Med. and Surg. Jour., Montreal, vol.14, pp.385-398, Feb., 1886; pp.649-660, June, 1886.

(OBSERVATIONS REGARDING CERTAIN FISH AND MAMMALS IN BRAZIL, PARTICULARLY REGARDING THEIR OSTEOLOGY.) Observacoes sobre certos peixes e mammiferos do Brazil mais particularmente sobre a sua osteologia. R. W. Shufeldt. Revista do Museu Paulist, vol.14, pp.501-561, pls.1-23, 1926.

PROBLEM FOR SOLUTION IN THE FIELD OF COMPARATIVE ANATOMY OF AMERICAN VERTEBRATES. R. W. Shufeldt. Pacific Med. Jour., San Francisco, vol.56, no.7, pp.382-385, (separate pp.1-4) July, 1913.

WHERE WE STAND IN COMPARATIVE OSTEOLOGY. R. W. Shufeldt. Nyt Mag. f. Naturvidensk., Christiania, pp.89-95, Mar. 19, 1912.

(ON THE QUESTION OF THE SPECIFIC ASPECT OF THE VERTEBRAL COLUMN OF ANIMALS.) K voprosu o spetsifike vida u pozvonochnikh zhivotnikh. S. S. Shvartz. Zool. Zhurnal, Moscow, vol.33, no.3, pp. 507-524, May-June, 1954.

ANATOMY OF THE DOMESTIC ANIMALS. Septimus Sisson. Privately printed, pp.930, figs.725, 1927.

ON THE EARLIEST LIVER ANLAGEN IN VERTEBRATES AND ON THE ORIGIN AND DEVELOPMENT OF THE GALL BLADDER. S. A. Siwe. Archives de Biologie, vol.39, pp.467-510, pls.3, 1929.

OSTEOLOGICAL NOTES. Daniel Denison Slade. Science, vol.21, no.523, pp.76-79, Feb. 10, 1893.

COMPARATIVE BIOLOGIC-ANATOMICAL INVESTIGATIONS ON THE VERTEBRAL COLUMN AND SPINAL MUSCULATURE OF MAMMALS. E. J. Slijper. Verhandl. Kon. Nederlandsche Akad. Wetenschappen, afd. Natuurkunde, Amsterdam, sect.2, vol.42, no.5, pp.1-128, figs.125, folding tabls.8, 1946.

OBSERVATIONS ON THE VERTEBRAL COLUMN OF THE DOMESTIC ANIMALS. E. J. Slijper. The Veterinary Jour., London, vol.103, no.11, pp.376-387, figs.9, Nov., 1947.

(Review of) FUNCTIONAL ANATOMY OF THE MAMMAL. Hobart M. Smith. Jour. Mammalogy, vol.28, no.3, pp.301-302, Aug. 19, 1947.

SO-CALLED HIBERNATING GLAND. A. T. Smussen. Jour. Morphology, vol.38, pp. 147-205, pls.8, Sep., 1923.

COMPARATIVE ANATOMY OF THE TONGUES OF THE MAMMALIA. VII. CETACEA, SIRENIA, AND UNGULATA. Charles F. Sonntag. Proc. Zool. Soc. London, pp.639-657, Sep., 1922.

COMPARATIVE ANATOMY OF THE TONGUES OF THE MAMMALIA. IX. EDENTATA, DERMOPTERA, AND INSECTIVORA. Charles F. Sonntag. Proc. Zool. Soc. London, pt.3, pp.515-529, Oct., 1923.

COMPARATIVE ANATOMY OF THE TONGUES OF THE MAMMALIA. X. RODENTIA. XI. MARSUPIALIA AND MONOTREMATA. Charles F. Sonntag. Proc. Zool. Soc. London, pp.725-755, figs.14, Sep., 1924.

COMPARATIVE ANATOMY OF THE TONGUES OF THE MAMMALIA. XII. SUMMARY, CLASSIFICATION, AND PHYLOGENY. Charles F. Sonntag. Proc. Zool. Soc. London, part 2, pp.701-762, July, 1925.

ON CERTAIN SIMILARITIES BETWEEN SLOTHS AND SLOW LEMURS. William L. Straus, Jr., George B. Wislocki. Bull. Mus. Comp. Zool. at Harvard College, vol.74, no.3, pp.45-56, Sep., 1932.

(GOETHE AS MORPHOLOGIST.) Goethe als Morphologe. Fritz Strauss. Schweizerischen Med. Wochenschrift, Jahrg.76, no. 42, pp.1092, (reprint paged 1-11), 1946.

(GOETHE'S MORPHOLOGICAL INVESTIGATIONS.) Goethes Forschungen zur Morphologie. Fritz Strauss. Verlag Paul Haupt Bern, pp.67-116, figs.5, pls.3, 1949.

(THEODOR LANGHANS AND PLACENTOLOGY.) Theodor Langhans und die Placentologie. Fritz Strauss. Mitteil. Naturf. Gesell. Bern, neue Folge, vol.14, pp.33-48, 1957.

CASE OF SUBDIVISION OF THE SCAPHOID CARPAL BONE. John Struthers. Jour. Anat. and Physiol., vol.8, pp.113-114, 1873.

(STUDY OF THE MORPHOLOGY OF THE ELBOW IN MAMMALS.) Contribution a l'etude de la morphologie du coude chez les mammiferes. Barbosa M. B. Sueiro. Arquivos Mus. Bocage, Lisboa, vol.5, pp.111-120, tables, 1934.

COMPARISON OF LYMPHOID CELLS OF BONE MARROW AND LYMPH NODES OF RABBITS AND GUINEA PIGS. Dorothy R. Sundberg, Hal Downey. Amer. Jour. Anat., Philadelphia, vol.70, no.3, pp.455-497, pls.2, May 15, 1942.

SKELETAL CHANGES ASSOCIATED WITH INCREASING BODY SIZE. Alfred Taylor. Jour. Morph., Philadelphia, vol.57, no.1, pp.253-274, figs.2, tbls.7, Mar. 5, 1935.

FUNCTIONAL MAMMALIAN ANATOMY. William T. Taylor, Richard J. Weber. Van Nostrand Co., New York, pp.575, illus., 1951.

PARALLELISM OF VARIATION IN A MAMMALIAN SERIES. R. J. Terry. Anat. Rec., vol.26, pp.171-174, chart, Sep., 1923.

COMPARATIVE HISTOLOGICAL STUDIES ON HAIRLESS MAMMALS, WITH SOME GENETIC NOTES. Lorna W. Thigpen. Univ. Pittsburgh Bull., vol.27, no.3, pp.191-197, 1930.

ON THE CAVUM SEPTI PELLUCIDI. I. MacLaren Thompson. Journ. Anat., Cambridge, vol.67, pt.1, pp.59-77, figs.2, Oct., 1932.

OBSERVATIONS FROM A STUDY OF THE COMPARATIVE ANATOMY OF THE EXTRAHEPATIC BILIARY TRACT. Stewart C. Thomson. Trans. Illinois State Acad. Sci., Springfield, vol.34, no.2, pp.241-243, Dec., 1941.

STUDIES OF THE ANATOMY OF THE EXTRAHEPATIC BILIARY TRACT IN MAMMALIA. Stewart C. Thomson. Zool. Ser. Field Mus. Nat. Hist., Chicago, (Publ. 481), vol.22, no.6, pp.415-430, Oct. 31, 1940.

(SPLEEN.) Milz. Friedrich Tischendorf. Handbuch der Zoologie, Berlin, vol.8, no. 5, pp.1-32, Mar., 1956.

ANATOMICAL FEATURES OF EPIPHYSIAL UNION. Wingate T. Todd. Child Development, vol.1, no.3, pp.186-194, Sep., 1930.

FACIAL GROWTH AND MANDIBULAR ADJUSTMENT. Wingate T. Todd. Internat. Jour. Orthodontia, Oral Surgery Radiogr., vol.XVI, no.12, pp.1243, figs.19, Dec., 1930.

INTEGRAL GROWTH OF THE FACE. I. THE NASAL AREA. Wingate T. Todd. Internat. Jour. Orthodontia and Oral Surgery, St. Louis, vol.22, no.4, pp.321-332, figs.11, Apr., 1936.

NUMERICAL SIGNIFICANCE IN THE THORACICOLUMBAR VERTEBRAE OF THE MAMMALIA. Wingate T. Todd. Anat. Rec., vol.24, pp.261-286, Dec., 1922.

PROGNATHISM: A STUDY IN DEVELOPMENT OF THE FACE. Wingate T. Todd. Jour. Amer. Dental Assocn., vol.19, pp. 2172-2184, figs.7, Dec., 1932.

EPIPHYSIAL UNION PATTERN OF THE UNGULATES WITH A NOTE ON SIRENIA. Wingate T. Todd, Arthur W. Todd. Amer. Jour. Anat., vol.63, no.1, pp.1-36, charts 12, July 15, 1938.

(ON THE MAMMAL PREHALLUX: A THIRD CONTRIBUTION ON THE PHYLOGENESIS OF THE MAMMALIAN FOOT.) Ueber den Saeugetier-Praehallux. Ein dritter Beitrag zur Phylogenese des Saeugetierfusses. Gustav Tornier, Archiv. f. Naturgesch., Berlin, pp. 1-92, pls.7, 1891.

PEDAL BONE VARIATION: CAUSES AND CONSEQUENCES (PRELIMINARY COMMUNICATION).) Fussknochen-Variation, ihre Entstehungsursachen und Folgen (vorlaeufige Mittheilung). Gustav Tornier. Sitz.-Ber. Gesell. Naturforsch. Freunde, Berlin, no.1, pp.23-30, Jan. 16, 1894.

(THE PHYLOGENESIS OF THE TERMINAL SEGMENT OF MAMMALIAN HINDQUARTERS.) Die Phylogenese des terminalen Segmentes der Saeugethier-Hintergliedmassen. Gustav Tornier. Morphol. Jahrbuch, vol.16, pp.401-483, pls.17-18, 1890.

LABORATORY STUDIES IN COMPARATIVE VERTEBRATE ANATOMY. Theodore W. Torrey. Dept. Zool. Indiana Univ., Bloomington, pp.67, 1946.

(THE EPIDURAL ADIPOSE TISSUE.) Das epidurale Fettgewebe. D. Tretjakoff. Zeitschr. f. Anat. u. Entwicklungsgeschichte, vol.79, pp.100-111, illus., May 5, 1926.

A TASK FOR ANATOMISTS. Frederick W. True. Science, vol.7, no.171, pp.428-429, May 14, 1886.

INCIDENCE AND SIZE OF THE MODERATOR BAND IN MAN AND IN MAMMALS. R. C. Truex, L. J. Warshaw. Anat. Rec., Philadelphia, vol.82, no.3, pp.361-372, figs.3, Mar. 25, 1942.

ON THE GUSTATORY ORGANS OF SOME OF THE MAMMALIA. Frederick Tuckerman. Jour. Morphol., vol.4, no.2, pp.151-193, 1890.

OBSERVATIONS ON THE DISTINCTION BETWEEN THE CERVICAL AND DORSAL VERTEBRAE IN THE CLASS MAMMALIA. H. N. Turner. Proc. Zool. Soc. London, pt.15, pp.110-114, 1847.

NOTES ON THE DISSECTION OF THE PARADOXURUS TYPUS AND OF DIPUS AEGYPTIUS. H. N. Turner. Proc. Zool. Soc. London, pt.17, pp.24-28, 1849.

(CONTRIBUTION TO THE STUDY OF THE HISTOGENESIS OF THE PANCREAS IN SOME MAMMALS.) Contribution a l'étude de l'histogenese du pancreas chez quelque mammiferes. E. Van Campenhout. Archives de Biologie, vol.37, pp.121-172, pls.2, June 15, 1927.

(WHAT THE NATURAL SCIENCES OWE TO GOETHE.) Was die Naturwissenschaften Goethe verdanken. Gerhard Venzmer. Pt.1, Kosmos, Stuttgart, vol.29, no.3, pp.77-83, figs.6, March; Pt.2, Kosmos, Stuttgart, vol.29, no.4, pp.111-115, figs. 7-10, Apr., 1932.

(ON THE QUESTION OF THE MORPHOLOGICAL DIVERGENCE OF CLOSELY RELATED FORMS OF MAMMALS.) K boprocu o morfologicheskoi divergentsii blizkix form mlekopitayushchix. B. S. Vinogradov. Trudi Zool. Inst. Akad. Nauk SSSR, Moscow, vol. 8, no.1, pp.89-104, 1946. (English summary.)

ON THE USE OF BOTH CATS AND RABBITS IN THE COMPARATIVE ANATOMY LABORATORY. Warren F. Walker, Jr. Turtox News, Chicago, vol.29, no.1, pp.35-36, Jan., 1951.

VERTICAL AXES OF THE FEMUR AND THEIR RELATIONS. A CONTRIBUTION TO THE STUDY OF THE ERECT POSITION. Thomas Walmsley. Jour. Anat., vol.67, pt. 2, pp.284-300, figs.16, Jan., 1933.

EARLY DEVELOPMENT OF THE MAMMALIAN HEART. Katherine M. Watson. Jour. Anat., vol.58, p.105, 1924.

(ON THE ENAMEL OF VERTEBRATES AND ITS RELATIONSHIP TO THE HYOID BONE. (BONE STUDIES, PT. V.).) Ueber den Schmelz der Wirbeltiere und seine Beziehungen zum Zahnbein. (Knochenstudien, Vter Teil.) F. Weidenreich. Zeitschr. f. Anat. u. Entwicklungsgeschichte, vol.79, pp.292-351, illus., July 5, 1926.

(ON THE SPREADING FOOT OF MAMMALS.) Ueber den Spreizfuss der Saeugetier. M. Westenhoefer. Zeitschr. f. Saeugetierkunde, Berlin, vol.12, no.3, pp.329-331, pls.24-26, July 15, 1938.

(ON THE RELATIONSHIPS BETWEEN BRAIN AND SKULL DEVELOPMENT.) Ueber die Beziehungen zwischen Hirn- und Schaedelentwicklung. Wilhelm Weygandt. Zeitschr. ges. Neurologie u. Psychiatrie, Berlin, vol.142, pp.678-698, figs.10, 1932.

(HYPOTHESES CONCERNING THE APPEARANCE OF CERTAIN GROUP SPECIFIC CHARACTERISTICS IN THE DIFFERENT SPECIES OF ANIMALS.) Eine Voraussetzung fuer das Auftreten gruppenspezifischer Eigenschaften bei den verschiedenen Tierarten. Wichels. Biol. Zentralblatt, vol.50, pp.327-329, 1930.

(OUTLINE OF THE COMPARATIVE ANATOMY OF VERTEBRATES.) Grundriss der Vergleichenden Anatomie der Wirbelthiere. Robert Ernst Eduard Wiedersheim. Verlag von Gustav Fischer, Jena, p.695, illus., 1893.

(NOTES ON THE SKELETONS OF SMALL MAMMALS.) Over het skeletteren van kleine zoogdieren. A. van Wijngaarden, H. De Vries. De Levende Natuur, vol.59, no.6, pp.138-143, 1956.

FUNDAMENTAL PRINCIPLES OF ANATOMICAL NOMENCLATURE. Burt G. Wilder. Medical News, pp.8, Dec. 19, 1891.

ON MORPHOLOGY AND TELEOLOGY, ESPECIALLY IN THE LIMBS OF MAMMALS. Burt G. Wilder. Mem. R. Boston Soc. Nat. Hist., vol.1, no.1, pp.1-35, 1865.

LABORATORY STUDIES IN MAMMALIAN ANATOMY. Inez Wilder. 2d rev.ed. Philadelphia, P. Blakiston's Son & Co., XI, pp. 157, 1923.

LATER DEVELOPMENT OF THE NOTOCHORD IN MAMMALS. Leonard W. Williams. Amer. Jour. Anat., vol.8, no.3, pp.251-284, figs., Oct., 1908.

(CONTRIBUTION ON LARYNX DEVELOPMENT IN THE NEAT AND HORSE.) Beitrag zur Kehlkopfentwicklung bei Pferd und Rind. H. Wilmes. Anat. Anz., vol.69, nos.4/6, pp.122-135, figs.8, 1930.

IS THE ADRENAL CORTEX ESSENTIAL FOR LIFE? R. L. Zwemer. Anat. Rec., vol.29, p.103, Dec. 25, 1924.

STEATOPYGY AND ACROMEGALY. Amer. Jour. Phys. Anthrop., Philadelphia, vol.14, no.1, pp.79-81, figs.3, Jan.-Mar., 1930.

## ANATOMY -- HEMATOLOGY, CIRCULATORY SYSTEM

INCIDENCE OF BILATERAL ANTERIOR VENAE CAVAE IN A SERIES OF EUTHERIAN FOETUSES. E. C. Amoroso, A. E. Barclay, K. J. Franklin, M. M. L. Prichard. Proc. Zool. Soc., London, ser. B., vol.113, pp. 43-53, fig.1, July 1943.

THROTTLING VEINS IN THE LIVERS OF CERTAIN MAMMALS. Leslie B. Arey. Anat. Record, Philadelphia, vol.81, no. 1, pp.21-33, pl.1, Sep. 25, 1941.

(Review by D. V. Davies of) FOETAL CIRCULATION AND CARDIO-VASCULAR SYSTEM AND THE CHANGES THAT THEY UNDERGO AT BIRTH. Alfred E. Barclay, Kenneth J. Franklin, Marjorie M. L. Prichard. Nature, London, vol.155, no.3939, pp. 494-496, Apr. 28, 1945.

SPIRAL STRUCTURES WITHIN THE HEPATIC PORTAL VEIN OF MAMMALS. C. H. Barnett. Proc. Zool. Soc. London, vol.123, pt.4, pp.747-751, pl.1, Feb. 10, 1954.

(LYMPHATIC VESSELS IN THE NASAL MUCOUS MEMBRANE OF THE HORSE, NEAT, SWINE, AND DOG, AND THEIR COMMUNICATION WITH THE NASAL CAVITIES.) Die Lymphgefaesse in der Nasenschleimhaut des Pferdes, Rindes, Schweines und Hundes, und ihre Kommunikation mit der Nasenhoehle. H. Baum, A. Trautmann. Anat. Anzeiger, vol.60, pp.161-181, pls.2, Oct. 12, 1925.

ARTERIAL SUPPLY OF THE SMALL INTESTINE. Lindsay E. Beaton, Barry J. Anson. Quart. Bull., Northwestern Univ. Med. School, Chicago, vol.16, no.2, pp. 1-9, pls.2, 1942.

EFFERENT VESSELS OF THE RENAL GLOMERULI OF MAMMALS AS A MECHANISM FOR THE CONTROL OF GLOMERULAR ACTIVITY AND PRESSURE. Robert D. Bensley. Amer. Jour. Ant., vol.34, pp. 141-170, figs.8, 1929.

FIFTY YEARS OF SYSTEMATIC SEROLOGY. Alan Boyden. Systematic Zool., Washington, vol.2, no.1, pp.19-30, illus., Mar., 1953. (Dasypus, Manis, Orycteropus)

SEROLOGY AND ANIMAL RELATIONSHIP. Alan Boyden. Trans. New York Acad. Sci., ser.2, vol.2, no.8, pp.195-201, June, 1940.

AN INQUIRY INTO THE PHYLOGENETIC BASIS OF THE FLEXUOUS ARTERIA CAROTIS INTERNA OF MAN (THE ARTERIAL CAROTIDS OF THE SEAL). Cerson A. Carmel. Anat. Rec., vol.39, pp.343-347, illus., Aug. 25, 1928.

VISCERAL BRANCHES OF THE ABDOMINAL AORTA: TOPOGRAPHICAL RELATIONSHIPS. Earl W. Cauldwell, Barry J. Anson. Amer. Jour. Ant., Philadelphia, vol.73, no.1, pp. 27-57, July, 1943.

TOPOGRAPHY AND FUNCTION OF THE MESENTERIC CAPILLARY CIRCULATION. Robert Chambers, B.W. Zweifach. Amer. Jour. Anat., Philadelphia, vol.75, no.2, pp.173-205, figs.1-2, pls.1-3, Sep., 1944.

CALIBER CHANGES IN MINUTE BLOOD-VESSELS OBSERVED IN THE LIVING MAMMAL. Eliot R. Clark, Eleanor Linton Clark. Amer. Jour. Anat., Philadelphia, vol.73, no.2, pp.215-250, figs.1-7, Sep., 1943.

BLOOD VOLUME OF MAMMALS AS DETERMINED BY EXPERIMENTS UPON RABBITS, GUINEA-PIGS AND MICE; AND ITS RELATIONSHIP TO THE BODY WEIGHT AND TO THE SURFACE AREA EXPRESSED IN A FORMULA. George Dreyer. Roy. Soc. of London, Philos. trans. v.201, ser.B, pp. 133-160, London, 1910.

FURTHER EXPERIMENTS UPON THE BLOOD VOLUME OF MAMMALS AND ITS RELATION TO THE SURFACE AREA OF THE BODY. George Dreyer. Roy. Soc. of London, Philos. trans. v.202, Ser.B. pp.191-212, London, 1912.

CORONARY SYSTEM OF VEINS OF HEART OPENING INTO LEFT ATRIUM BY A NORMAL THEBESIAN ORIFICE. Thomas H. Evans. Jour. Mamm., vol.27, no.2, pp. 176-177, May 14, 1946.

CIRCULATORY SYSTEM IN BONE. J. S. Foote. Smithson. Misc. Coll., vol.72, no. 10, pp.1-20, pls.6, Aug. 20, 1921.

STRUCTURE OF THE THORACIC INFERIOR VENA CAVA IN THE RABBIT AND IN THE CAT, AND ITS FUNCTIONAL SIGNIFICANCE. K. J. Franklin. Jour. Anat., vol. 66, pp.76-79, figs.3, 1931.

SURVEY OF THE GROWTH OF KNOWLEDGE ABOUT CERTAIN PARTS OF THE FOETAL CARDIO-VASCULAR APPARATUS; AND ABOUT THE FOETAL CIRCULATION, IN MAN AND SOME OTHER MAMMALS. PART 1: GALEN TO HARVEY. K. J. Franklin. Ann. Sci., London, vol.5, no.1, pp. 57-89, figs.4, Aug. 15, 1941.

DUCTUS ARTERIOSUS AND ITS LIGAMENTOUS REMNANT IN THE ADULT. Wallace H. Greig, Barry J. Anson, David K. McAfee, LeRoy E. Kurth. Quart. Bull., Northwestern Univ. Med. School, Chicago, vol.28, no.1, pp.1-10, illus., 1954.

ADDITIONAL MEASUREMENTS OF BLOOD-CORPUSCLES OF MAMMALIA AND AVES. George Gulliver. Proc. Zool. Soc. London, pt.12, pp.7, 145, 1844.

ADDITIONAL MEASUREMENTS OF THE BLOODCORPUSCLES OR RED PARTICLES OF MAMMALIA AND BIRDS. George Gulliver. Proc. Zool. Soc. London, pt.10, pp. 190-196, 1842.

ADDITIONAL MEASUREMENTS OF THE RED CORPUSCLES OF THE BLOOD OF VERTEBRATA. George Gulliver. Proc. Zool. Soc. London, pt.16, pp.36-38, 1848.

ON THE RED CORPUSCLES OF THE BLOOD OF VERTEBRATA, AND ON THE ZOOLOGICAL IMPORT OF THE NUCLEUS, WITH PLANS OF THEIR STRUCTURE, FORM, AND SIZE (ON A UNIFORM SCALE) IN MANY OF THE DIFFERENT ORDERS. George Gulliver. Proc. Zool. Soc. London, pt.30, pp.91-100, 1862.

ON THE SIZE OF THE RED CORPUSCLES OF THE BLOOD IN THE VERTEBRATA, WITH COPIOUS TABLES OF MEASUREMENTS. George Gulliver. Proc. Zool. Soc. London, pt.13, pp.93-102, 1845.

ON THE SIZE OF THE RED CORPUSCLES OF THE BLOOD OF MOSCHUS, TRAGULUS, ORYCTEROPUS, AILURUS, AND SOME OTHER MAMMALIA, WITH HISTORICAL NOTICES. George Gulliver. Proc. Zool. Soc. London, pp.93-98, figs.4, 1870.

COMPARATIVE ANATOMY OF THE BLOOD-SUPPLY OF THE MAMMALIAN TESTIS. R. G. Harrison. Proc. Zool. Soc. London, vol.119, pt.2, pp.325-344, illus., Aug. 17, 1949.

VASCULAR PATTERNS OF THE MAMMALIAN TESTIS AND THEIR FUNCTIONAL SIGNIFICANCE. R. G. Harrison, J. S. Weiner. Jour. Exper. Biol., London, vol.26, no.3, pp.304-316, pls.9-10, Oct., 1949.

OBSERVATION ON THE VENOUS SYSTEM IN CERTAIN PINNIPEDIA AND CETACEA. R. J. Harrison, J. D. W. Tomlinson. Proc. Zool. Soc. London, vol.126, pt.2, pp.205-233, pls.4, Apr. 6, 1956.

PHAGOCYTIC CELLS (V. KUPFFER) IN THE LIVER OF COMMON LABORATORY ANIMALS. George M. Higgins, George T. Murphy. Anat. Rec., vol.40, pp.15-39, illus., Sep. 25, 1928.

MORPHOLOGY OF THE PULMONARY ARTERY IN THE MAMMALIA. George S. Huntington. Anat. Rec., vol.17, pp.165-201, figs.7 (5 colored), Dec. 20, 1919 (Jan., 1920).

CHANGES IN THE BLOOD FLOW THROUGH THE BRAIN AND MUSCLES DURING THE ARREST OF BREATHING. Laurence Irving. Amer. Jour. Physiol., Baltimore, vol.122, no.1, pp.207-214, figs.6, Apr., 1938.

DIAMETERS OF MAMMALIAN ERYTHROCYTES. C. H. N. Jackson, F. L. Vanderplank. Proc. Zool. Soc. London, vol.112, ser.A, pts.1-2, pp.57-60, Sep., 1942.

NOTE ON THE ANATOMY OF THE PULMONARY OF MAMMALS. H. E. Jordan. Anat. Rec., Philadelphia, vol.5, no.10, pp.467-460, figs.2, Oct., 1911.

SIGNIFICANCE OF HEMAL NODES. H. E. Jordan. Jour. Morph. and Physiol., vol.44, pp.89-115, figs.11, June 5, 1927.

COURSE OF THE BLOOD FLOW THROUGH THE FETAL MAMMALIAN HEART. Howard B. Kellogg. Amer. Jour. Anat., vol.42, pp. 443-465, Nov. 15, 1928.

FOETAL HAEMOGLOBIN. J. C. Kendrew. Endeavour, London, vol.8, no.30, pp.80-85, figs.12, Apr., 1949.

BLOOD SUPPLY OF THE ENAMEL ORGAN IN DEVELOPING MOLAR TEETH OF MAMMALS. H. M. Kingery. Amer. Jour. Anat., vol.33, pp.175-196, pls.2, May 15, 1924.

RATIO OF THE CROSS-SECTION OF THE AORTA TO THAT OF ITS BRANCHES IN MAN AND THE SILVER FOX. Marcus A. Krupp. Jour. Mamm., vol.24, no.1, pp. 82-90, Feb. 20, 1943.

PRELIMINARY NOTE ON THE SUPERIOR VENA CAVA OF THE CAT. W. F. Lanchester, A. G. Thacker. Proc. Cambridge Philos. Soc., vol.20, pt.2, pp.227-230, 1920.

(COURSE OF THE BLOOD VESSELS OF THE LUNGS (ESPECIALLY OF THE LOBE) IN MAN AND SOME MAMMALS.) Verlauf der Lungengefaesse besonders des Lobulus beim menschen und bei einigen Saeugetieren. Folke Linell, Olov Loefgren. Lunds Univ. Arsskr., N. F., Avd.2, Bd.36, Nr.6, pp. 1-15, Bild 5, Apr., 1940.

(ON THE SPECIFIC ADAPTATION OF TISSUE COAGULANTS IN MAMMAL ERYTHROCYTES.) Ueber die spezifische Adaptierung der in den Saeugetier-Erythrocyten vorhandenen Gewebskoaguline. Leo Loes, Moyer S. Fleisher. Biochem. Zeitschr., Berlin, vol.28, nos.3-4, pp.169-175, 1910.

ANOTHER DIAGRAM FOR BLOOD-GROUPING. Marcus W. Lyon, Jr. Jour. Amer. Med. Assoc., vol.73, p.498, Apr. 16, 1919.

VARIATION IN THE POINT OF BIFURCATION OF THE COMMON CAROTID ARTERY. David K. McAfee, Barry J. Anson, Joseph J. McDonald. Quart. Bull. Northwestern Univ. Med. School Chicago, vol.27, no.3, p.226, Fall quarter 1953.

SO-CALLED HEMAL NODES OF THE WHITE RAT, GUINEA-PIG, AND SHEEP: STUDY OF THEIR OCCURRENCE, STRUCTURE, AND SIGNIFICANCE. Ruth E. Macmillan. Anat. Rec., vol.39, pp.155-175, illus., July 25, 1928.

(BLOOD GROUPS IN UNGULATES.) Les groupes sanguins chez les ongulés. Pierre Millot. Mammalia, Paris, vol.22, no.1, pp.58-68, Mar., 1958.

VASCULAR ARRANGEMENT OF THE MAMMALIAN SPLEEN. Edward S. Mills. Quart. Rev. Exper. Physiol., vol.16, pp.301-319, illus., 1927.

CIRCULATORY CYCLES IN THE VERTEBRATES. H. W. Mossman. Biol. Rev., Cambridge Univ. Press, London, vol.23, no.3, pp.237-255, July, 1948.

HEMATOLOGICAL STUDIES ON MAMMALS FROM ALASKA. X. J. Musacchia, C. G. Wilber, T. W. Gorski. Jour. Mamm., vol.36, no.3, pp.362-368, tbls.2, Aug. 30, 1955.

SOME OBSERVATIONS ON THE REACTION BETWEEN HORSE SERUM AND A POOL OF RABBIT ANTIHORSE SERUM. I. THE RELATIVE INHIBITORY EFFECT OF EXCESS ANTIGEN AND EXCESS ANTISERUM. G. R. E. Naylor. Jour. Hygiene, London, vol.46, no.2, pp.129-135, July, 1948.

BLOOD VESSELS OF THE JEJUNUM AND ILEUM: COMPARATIVE STUDY OF MAN AND CERTAIN LABORATORY ANIMALS. Rudolf J. Noer. Amer. Jour. Anat., Philadelphia, vol.73, no.3, pp.293-334, figs. 1-5, pls.1-8, Nov., 1943.

SHAPE OF THE MAMMALIAN ERYTHROCYTE AND ITS RESPIRATORY FUNCTION. Eric Ponder. Journ. Gen. Physiol., vol.9, pp.197-204, figs.3, Nov. 20, 1925; vol.9, pp.625-629, fig.1, May 20, 1926.

(STRUCTURE AND DEVELOPMENT OF THE VENOUS SYSTEM OF VERTEBRATES.) Ueber den Bau und die Entwicklung des Venensystems der Wirbelthiere. Heinrich Rathke. 3rd. Ber. Naturwiss. Seminar Univ. Koenigsberg, pp.1-23, 1838.

CENTURY OF STUDY UPON THE DEVELOPMENT OF THE EUTHERIAN VENA CAVA INFERIOR. F. P. Reagan. Quart. Rev. Biol., vol.4, pp.179-212, text figs.26, 1929.

(BLOOD GROUPS IN WILD MAMMALS. INITIAL FINDINGS.) Les groupes sanguins des Mammifères sauvages. Premiers résultats. M. P. Rode. Bull. Mus. Nat. Hist. Nat., Paris, ser.2, vol.6, no.3, pp.218-223, Apr., 1934.

(STUDY OF THE BLOOD GROUPS OF MAMMALS. SEROLOGY IN RELATION TO SYSTEMATICS.) Étude des groupes sanguins chez les Mammiferes. La sérologie dans ses relations avec la systématique. P. Rode. Comptes Rendus Soc. Biol., Paris, vol.115, no.1, pp.27-30, 1934.

(SYSTEMATIC SEROLOGY. ITS PURPOSE METHODS, AND FUTURE.) La serologie systématique. Son but, ses methodes, son avenir. P. Rode. Mammalia, Paris, vol.9, nos.3-4, pp.95-102, Sep.-Dec., 1945.

ARTERIES AND VEINS IN THE MAMMALIAN BRAIN. Ernst Scharrer. Anat. Rec., Philadelphia, vol.78, no.2, pp.173-196, Oct. 25, 1940.

BLOOD SUPPLY OF MYSTACIAL VIBRISSAE. M. G. Scott. Nature, London, vol.175, no. 4452, pp.395-396, Feb. 26, 1955.

(CONTRIBUTION TO THE STUDY OF THE PHYSICAL CHEMISTRY OF THE BLOOD OF MAMMALS.) Contribution à l'étude de la physico-chimie du sang des mammifères. J. L. Tremblay, R. Bernard. Le Natur. Canadien, Quebec, vol.66, (ser.3, vol.10), no.5, pp.129-164, May, 1939.

(CRYOSCOPIC POINT OF THE SERUM OF VARIOUS MAMMALS.) Point cryoscopique du serum de divers mammiferes. Achille Urbain, Raymond Cahen, Jean Servier. Comptes Rendus Seances Acad. Sci., Paris, vol. 206, no.21, pp.1596-1597, table, May 23, 1938.

ON THE NUMBER, SHAPE, STRUCTURE, AND SURFACE AREA OF THE GLOMERULE IN THE KIDNEYS OF MAN AND MAMMALS. B. Vimtrup. Amer. Jour. Anat., vol.41, pp.123-151, illus., Mar. 15, 1928.

AGGLUTININS AND AGGLUTINOGENS IN THE BLOOD OF WILD ANIMALS. Henry Vogel. Zoologica, New York Zool. Soc., vol.36, pt.3, no.15, pp.203-211, Oct. 20, 1951.

WORKING MODEL OF THE CROSSING CAVAL BLOOD STREAMS IN THE FETAL RIGHT ATRIUM. W. H. Whitehead. Anat. Rec., Philadelphia, vol.82, no.3, pp.277-280, Mar. 25, 1942.

ON THE BLOOD VASCULAR BUNDLES IN THE LIMBS OF CERTAIN EDENTATES AND LEMURS. George B. Wislocki, William L. Straus, Jr. Bull. Mus. Comp. Zool. at Harvard College, Cambridge, vol.74, no.1, pp.3-15, pls.1-4, Apr., 1932.

APPLICATION OF PHOTOGRAPHY TO MICROMETRY, WITH SPECIAL REFERENCE TO THE MICROMETRY OF BLOOD IN CRIMINAL CASES. J. J. Woodward. Microscop. Jour., London, vol.16, pp.144-153, 1876.

MAMMALIAN LYMPHOCYTE. J. M. Yoffey. Biol. Rev., London, vol.25, no.3, pp.314-343, July, 1950.

## ANATOMY -- MYOLOGY

ON THE TEMPORAL AND MASSETER MUSCLES OF MAMMALS. Harrison Allen. Proc. Acad. Nat. Sci., Philadelphia, vol.32, pp.385-400, figs.1-2, 1880.

ON THE MORPHOLOGY OF THE CERVICO-COSTO-HUMERALIS MUSCLE OF GRUBER. A.B. Appleton. Jour. Anat. London, vol.63, pp.437-446, figs.2, 1929.

(RELATIONS OF THE MUSCULATURE AND THE PAPILLAE OF THE TONGUE IN REPTILES AND MAMMALS.) Les relations de la musculature et des papilles de la langue chez les reptiles et les mammiferes. W. Besnard, G. Petit. Archiv. Mus. Nat. Hist. Nat., Paris, ser.6, vol.9, pp.95-132, figs.35, June, 1932.

NOTES ON THE FORM AND FUNCTION OF THE GOLGI APPARATUS IN STRIATED MUSCLE. Robert H. Bowen. Biol. Bull., vol.50, pp.108-116, fig.1, Feb., 1926.

M. RETRACTOR BULBI (OCULI) IN CARNIVORA AND UNGULATA. Charnock O. Bradley. Jour. Anat., Cambridge, vol.68, pt.1, pp.65-68, figs.3-12, Oct., 1933.

COMPARATIVE MYOLOGY OF THE FORELIMB OF THE HIPPOPOTAMUS, PIG AND TAPIR. Berry Campell. Amer. Jour. Anat., vol.59, no.2, pp.201-247, figs.7, July 15, 1936.

REGENERATION OF MAMMALIAN STRIATED MUSCLE. W. E. Le Gros Clark. Nature. London, vol.156, no.3952, p.109, July 28, 1945.

CRANIAL MUSCLES OF VERTEBRATES. F. H. Edgeworth. Cambridge: Univ. Press, pp.ix-493, figs.841, 1935 (after July, 1935).

ON THE MUSCLES USED IN SHUTTING AND OPENING THE MOUTH. F. H. Edgeworth. Proc. Zool. Soc. London, 1931, pt.3, pp.817-818, Sep., 1931.

(HISTOGENESIS AND IMPORTANCE OF THE STRIATED MUSCULAR FIBER IN THE MAMMALS.) Histogenesis y significado de la fibra muscular estriada en mamiferos. W. Fernández Ballas, C. Oberti S. Biologica, Trab. Inst. Biol. "Juan Noe" Univ. Chile, Santiago, fasc.14-15, pp.15-27, illus., 1952.

ATTACHMENT OF SKELETAL MUSCLE FIBERS. C. M. Goss. Amer. Jour. Anat., Philadelphia, vol.74, no.2, pp.259-289, fig.1, pls.3, Mar., 1944.

(Review by N. Hollister of) STUDIES IN COMPARATIVE MYOLOGY AND OSTEOLOGY, William K. Gregory. Jour. Mamm., vol.2, no.2, pp.118-119, May, 1921.

OBSERVATIONS ON THE MUSCULAR FIBRES OF THE OESOPHAGUS AND HEART IN SOME OF THE VERTEBRATE ANIMALS. G. Gulliver. Proc. Zool. Soc. London, pt. 10, pp.63-72, 1842.

OBSERVATIONS ON THE MUSCULAR FIBRES OF THE OESOPHAGUS AND HEART IN SOME OF THE MAMMALIA. G. Gulliver. Proc. Zool. Soc. London, pt.7, pp.124-129, 1839.

FLEXOR MUSCLES OF THE FOREARMS AND HAND IN LIZARDS AND MAMMALS. Wheeler R. Haines. Jour. Anat., London, vol.84, pt.1, pp.13-29, figs.12, Jan., 1950.

SOME MUSCULAR CHANGES IN THE TAIL AND THIGH OF REPTILES AND MAMMALS. Wheeler R. Haines. Jour. Morph., vol.58, no.2, pp.355-383, figs.8, Dec. 5, 1935.

INVESTIGATIONS ON THE STRUCTURE AND FUNCTION OF LIVING, ISOLATED, CROSS STRIATED MUSCLE FIBRES OF MAMMALS. Poul Honcke. Aarhus, Aarhuus stiftsbogtrykkerie, pp.230, illus., 1947.

(ON THE MORPHOLOGY OF THE M. AURICULOMANDIBULARIS OF MAMMALS.) Zur Morphologie des M. auriculomandibularis der Saeugetiere. Das Experiment als Stuetze der morphologischen Muskelforschung. Ernst Huber. Anat. Anzeiger, vol.58, pp.8-26, figs.8, July 1, 1924.

EXTENSOR MUSCLES OF THE HINDER FOOT IN MAMMALS. Richard H. Hunter. Proc. Zool. Soc. London, part 2, pp.457-494, July, 1925.

COMPARATIVE MICROSCOPIC STUDY OF THE INTERCALATED DISCS OF VERTEBRATE HEART MUSCLE. H. E. Jordan, K. B. Steele. Amer. Jour. Anat., Philadelpia, vol.13, no.2, pp.151-173, figs. 23, May, 1912.

HOMOLOGIES AND NOMENCLATURE OF THE THIGH MUSCLES OF THE OPOSSUM, CAT, RABBIT AND RHESUS MONKEY. N. S. Kerr. Anat. Rec., Philadelphia, vol. 121, no.3, pp.481-494, Mar., 1955.

(ON THE MM. SUBCOSTALES OF THE MAMMALS.) Ueber die Mm. subcostales der Saeugetiere. Wladimir Was Kolesnikow. Zeitschr. f. Anat. u. Entwicklungsges., vol. 92, no.1, pp.1-19, figs.18, 1930.

(MYOLOGICAL NOMENCLATURE.) Myolo gische Nomenclatur. W. Krause. Goettingen, pp.1-4, 1891.

ON THE LOCATION OF THE CANALIS SEMICIRCULARIS LATERALIS IN MAMMALS.) Ueber die lage des Canalis semicircularis lateralis bei Saeugern. S. Lebedkin. Anat. Anzeiger, vol.58, pp.449-460, figs.4, Nov. 25, 1924.

PROBABLE HOMOLOGUES. STUDY OF THE COMPARATIVE ANATOMY OF THE MANDIBULAR AND HYOID ARCHES AND THEIR MUSCULATURE. Pt. 1. COMPARATIVE MYOLOGY. G. H. S. Lightoller. Trans. Zool. Soc. London, vol.24, pt.5, pp.349-445, figs.2, tbls.7, pls.9, Sep., 1939.

(MATERIAL FOR THE STUDY OF THE MM. SERRATI DORSALES OF MAMMALS.) Material zum Studium der Mm. serrati dorsales der Saeugetiere. A. Maximenko. Zeitschr. f. Anat. u. Entwicklgesch., vol.92, no.2, pp. 151-177, figs.14, 1930.

(ON THE MORPHOLOGY OF THE M. OBLIQUUS ABDOMINIS INTERNUS OF SOME MAMMALS.) Zur Morphologie des M. obliquus abdominis internus einiger Saeugetiere. A. Maximenko. Anat. Anzeiger, vol.64, pp.358-371, figs.13, Jan. 2, 1928.

(COMPARATIVE INVESTIGATIONS OF THE HARDNESS OF THE SKELETAL MUSCLES OF WARM- AND COLD-BLOODED ANIMALS AFTER DEATH AND DURING RIGOR MORTIS.) Vergleichende Untersuchungen ueber die Haerte der Skelettmuskeln beim Warm- und Kaltblueter, nach dem Tode and waehrend der Totenstarre. H. Meltzer. Zeitschr. f. Vergleichende Physiologie, vol.8, pp.78-88, Aug. 25, 1928.

(ON THE DEVELOPMENT OF THE M. HYOEPIGLOTTICUS AND THE M. GLOSSOEPIGLOTTICUS IN SOME MAMMALS.) Ueber die Entwicklung des M. hyoepiglotticus und des M. glossoepiglotticus bei einigen Saeugern. W. A. Mijsberg. Zeitschr. f. Anat. u. Entwicklungsgesch., vol.84, pp. 206-217, figs.8, Oct. 8, 1927.

MUSCULAR COATS OF THE OESOPHAGUS OF THE DOMESTICATED ANIMALS. Leonard Pearson. Proc. Ann. Soc. of Micros., vol.10, pp.59-72; pp.128-129, 1888.

DEGENERATION OF ADULT MAMMALIAN SKELETAL MUSCLE IN VITRO. Irene A. Pogogeff, Margaret R. Murray. Science, Lancaster, n.s., vol.101, no.2616, p.174, Feb. 16, 1945.

GENERAL PHARMACOLOGY OF RYANODINE IN THE MAMMAL WITH SPECIAL REFERENCE TO SKELETAL MUSCLE. Leonard Procita. Ann. Arbor, Michigan, Univ., vol. 15, no.4, p.606, 1955.

CHANGES IN ELASTICITY OF MAMMALIAN MUSCLE UNDERGOING RIGOR MORTIS. E. C. Bate Smith. Jour. Physiology, London, vol.96, no.2, pp.176-193, figs.6, tbls.3, 1939.

ANATOMY -- NEUROLOGY

ON THE INNERVATION OF THE PLATYSMA AND THE MANDIBULO-AURICULARIS. S. B. Adams, J. F. G. Wheeler, F. H. Edgeworth. Jour. Anat. London, vol.63, pp.242-252, figs.3, 1929.

(IS THERE A SATISFACTORY ANATOMIC MEANS TO EXPLAIN THE DEGREE OF CEREBRAL ORGANIZATION OF MAMMALS? I. THE PRINCIPAL METHODS USED UP TO THIS TIME.) Existe-t-il un moyen anatomique satisfaisant d'exprimer le degré d'organisation cerebrale des mammiferes? I.-Les principales methodes employées jusqu'a présent. J. Anthony. Mammalia, Paris, vol.15, no.3, pp.53-68, Sep., 1951.

(IS THERE A SATISFACTORY ANATOMIC MEANS TO EXPLAIN THE DEGREE OF CEREBRAL ORGANIZATION OF MAMMALS? II.) Existe-t-il un moyen anatomique satisfaisant d'exprimer le degré d'organisation cérébrale des mammiferes? (II). J. Anthony. Mammalia, Paris, vol.15, no.4, pp.124-137, Dec., 1951.

(NOTE ON THE TYPE OF ENDING OF THE ANTERIOR PNEUMOGASTRIC NERVE IN SOME MAMMALS.) Note sur le mode de terminaison du pneumogastrique anterieur chez quelques mammiferes. J. Botar. Bull. Mus. Nat. Hist. Nat. Paris, ser.2, vol.5, no.4, pp.269-276, figs.1-7, Apr., 1933.

NOTE ON THE CONNECTION, IN THE MAMMALIAN MYENTERIC PLEXUS, BETWEEN THE ENTERIC NEURONES AND EXTRINSIC NERVE FIBERS. F. W. Carpenter. Anat. Rec., vol.28, pp.149-156, July 25, 1924.

SUPERFICIAL HEPATIC BRANCHES OF THE VAGI AND THEIR DISTRIBUTION TO THE EXTRAHEPATIC BILARY TRACT IN CERTAIN MAMMALS. Stanley L. Chiu. Anat. Rec., Philadelphia, vol.86, no.2, pp.149-155, fig.1, June, 1943.

NISSL GRANULES OF PRIMARY AFFERENT NEURONS. Sam L. Clark. Jour. Comp. Neur., vol.41, pp.423-452, pl.1, Aug. 15, 1926.

NERVOUS CONNECTIONS OF THE MAMMALIAN SPLEEN, INCLUDING AN ACCOUNT OF CERTAIN VISCEROMOTOR AND OTHER ABDOMINAL REFLEXES. J.G. P. Cleland, John Tait. Quart. Jour. Exper. Physiol., London, vol.17, no.26, pp.176-204, figs.1-8, June, 1927.

(Review by P. Rode of) (TERMINATION OF THE PNEUMOGASTRIC NERVES AND THEIR VARIATIONS. STUDY OF DESCRIPTIVE ANATOMY COMPARED IN MAN AND THE SERIES OF VETEBRATES.) La terminaison des nerfs pneumogastriques et ses variations. Etude d'anatomie descriptive comparee chez l'homme et dans la serie des Vertebres, P. Coulouma. Mammalia, Paris, vol.1, no.4, p.182, June, 1937.

(FORM AND DIMENSION OF THE HEAD, AND COEFFICIENT OF CEPHALIZATION.) Forma e dimensoes da cabeca e coefficiente de cephalizacao. Bastos De Avila. Bol. Mus. Nac. Rio de Janiero, vol.7, no.4, pp.257-282, tabls.1-15, Dec., 1931.

(ON THE INNERVATION OF THE MACULA SACCULI IN MAMMALS.) Zur Innervation der Macula sacculi bei Saeugetieren. H. M. De Burlet. Anat. Anzeiger, vol.28, pp.26-32, figs.4, July 1, 1924.

EVOLUTION AND ANATOMY OF THE CEREBELLUM. Robert S. Dow. Biol. Rev. Cambridge Philos. Soc. London, vol.17, no.3, pp.179-220, figs.12, July, 1942.

ON THE BRAIN QUANTITY OF SPECIALIZED GENERA OF MAMMALS. Eug Dubois. Konik. Akad. Wetensch. Amsterdam, Proc., vol.27, pp.430-437, 1924.

(FOSSIL BRAINS.) Die fossilen Gehirne. Tilly Edinger. Julius Springer: Berlin, pp.1-249, 1929.

(FOSSIL BRAINS.) Die fossilen Gehirne. Tilly Edinger. Zeitschr. f. ges. Anat. Abt. III. Ergeb. d. Anat. u. Entwickges., vol.28, pp.1-221, figs.203, 1929.

ON THE COMMISSURES OF THE CEREBRAL HEMISPHERES OF THE MARSUPIALIA AND MONOTREMATA AS COMPARED WITH THOSE OF THE PLACENTAL MAMMALS. William Henry Flower. Philos. Trans., London, vol.155, pp.633-651, pls.36-38, 1865.

ON THE POSTERIOR LOBES OF THE CEREBRUM OF THE QUADRUMANA. William Henry Flower. Philos. Trans., London, pp.185-201, pls.2, 1862.

(MORPHOLOGY AND DEVELOPMENT OF THE BRAIN IN EUTHERIAN MAMMALS. I. INSECTIVORE AND CARNIVORE SERIES.) Morphologie et developpement du cerveau des mammiferes eutheriens. I. Series des insectivores et des carnassiers. Madeleine Friant. An. Soc. Zool. Belg. Tome 86, 1955-56, Fasc.2:249-279.

(MORPHOLOGY AND DEVELOPMENT OF THE BRAIN IN EUTHERIAN MAMMALS AND MAN. II. PRIMATE SERIES.) Morphologie et developpement du cerveau des mammiferes eutheriens et de l'homme, II. Serie des Primates. Madeleine Friant. Ann. Soc. Roy. Zool. Belgique, vol.87, no.1, pp.91-150, 1957.

(THE PRINCIPAL CHARACTERISTICS OF THE BRAIN OF EXISTING ORDERS OF UNGULATES.) Les principales caracteristiques du cerveau des Ordres actuel d'Ongules. Madeleine Friant. Comptes Rendus Acad. Sci., Paris, vol.239, no.16, pp.1004-1006, Oct. 18, 1954.

ON THE RELATIVE POSITION OF THE HIPPOCAMPUS AND THE CORPUS CALLOSUM IN PLACENTAL MAMMALS. F. Goldby. Jour. Anat., Cambridge, vol.74, pt.2, pp.227-238, figs.2, pls.3, Jan., 1940.

(ON THE FORMATION OF THE HYPOPHYSIS IN MAMMALS.) Ueber die Bildung der Hypophyse bei Saeugetieren. Haller, Graf, O. Mori. Zeitschr. f. Anat. und Entwicklungsgesch., vol.76, pp.159-187, figs.24, Apr. 5, 1925.

HYPOPHYSES IN A TIGER (FELIS TIGRIS) AND AN INDIAN ELEPHANT (ELEPHAS MAXIMUS). B. Hanstroem. Lunds. Univ. Arsskrift, Lund, n.f., avd.2, vol.42, no. 8, pp.1-24, figs.13, pl.1, 1946

HYPOPHYSIS IN A WALLABY, TWO TREE-SHREWS, A MARMOSET, AND AN ORANG-UTAN. B. Hanstroem. Arkiv. Zool., Stockholm, vol.6, no.6, pp.97-154, illus., Mar. 17, 1954.

HYPOPHYSIS IN SOME SOUTH-AFRICAN INSECTIVORA, CARNIVORA, HYRACOIDEA, PROBOSCIDEA, ARTIODACTYLA, AND PRIMATES. B. Hanstroem. Arkiv. Zool., Stockholm, vol.4, no.3, pp.187-294, Jan. 21, 1953.

BRAINS OF RATS AND MAN. Judson C. Herrick. Chicago: Univ. Press, pp.xiii-382, 1926.

BRAIN CHORIOID PLEXUSES OF MAMMALS. William A. Hilton. Bull. Southern California Acad. Sci., vol.54, pt.3, pp. 116-125, Sep.-Dec., 1955.

NERVE AND MUSCLE. Marton Hines. Quart. Rev. Biol., vol.2, no.2, pp.149-180, illus., June, 1927.

POINTS OF VIEW CONCERNING FORE-BRAIN MORPHOLOGY IN HIGHER VERTEBRATES. Nils Holmgreen. Acta Zoologica, vol.6, pp.415-477, figs.54, 1925.

NOTE ON THE SPINAL ACCESSORY NERVE OF LONG-NECKED UNGULATES. A.Brazier Howell, William Straus, Jr. Proc. Zool. Soc. London, pp.29-32, Apr. 5, 1934.

BRAINS AND BRAIN PRESERVATIVES. Ales Hrdlicka. Proc. U. S. Nat. Mus., vol.30, pp.245-320, figs.1-27, 1906.

PHYLOGENETIC ASPECT OF THE MOTOR CORTEX OF MAMMALS. Ernst Huber. Quart. Rev. Biol., vol.9, no.1, pp.55-91, figs.20, Mar., 1934.

ON THE BULBUS OLFACTORIUS AND BULBUS OLFACTORIUS ACCESSORIUS OF SOME MAMMALS. Hieronim Jawlowski. Ann. Univ. Mariae Curie-Sklodowska, Lublin, sec. C, vol.10, no.3, pp.67-86, Oct. 10, 1956.

(BRAIN OF AQUATIC MAMMALS: AN ANATOMICAL INVESTIGATION.) Das Gehirn der Wassersaeugetiere: eine anatomische Untersuchung. G. Jelgersma. Privately printed, pp.1-238, figs.188, 1934.

RESULTS OF RECENT STUDIES OF THE MAMMALIAN EPIPHYSIS CEREBRI. H. E. Jordan. Trans. Amer. Microscop. Soc., vol.31, no.4, pp.231-242, Oct., 1912.

(ON THE INTRAEPITHELIAL NERVES AND THEIR ENDINGS IN MAN AND THE MAMMALS.) Ueber die intraepithelialen Nerven und ihre Endigungen beim Menschen und bei den Saeugetieren. D. Kadanoff. Zeitschr. f. Zellforschung u. Mikroskopische Anatomie, vol.7, pp.553-576, figs.18, Aug.23, 1928.

(ON THE ORIGIN OF THE BASAL GANGLIA OF THE CEREBRUM.) Ueber den Ursprung der Basalganglien des Grosshirns. H. Kuhlenbeck. Anat. Anzeiger, vol.58, pp.49-74, figs.8, July 22, 1924.

(REMARKS ON THE DIENCEPHALON STRUCTURE OF MAMMALS.) Bemerkungen ueber den Zwischenhirnbauplan bei Saeugetieren, insbesondere beim Menschen. H. Kuhlenbeck. Anat. Anz., vol.70, nos.6/7, pp.122-142, figs.14, 1930.

DEVELOPMENT OF THE SYMPATHETIC NERVOUS SYSTEM IN MAMMALS. Albert Kuntz. Philadelphia? pp.(211)-258, illus., 1910. Thesis (Ph.D.) State Univ. of Iowa. Reprinted from the Journal of Comparative Neurology and Psychology, vol.20, no.3, June, 1910.

MAMMALIAN ENDBRAIN. I. THE SEPTUM. Yu-Tao Loo. Contrib. Biol. Lab. Sci. Soc. China, Shanghai, vol.15, zool. ser., no.3, pp.29-68, figs.41, 1941.

MAMMALIAN ENDBRAIN. II. THE STRIO-AMYGDALOID COMPLEX. Yu-Tao Loo. Shanghai, China, Sci. Soc. of China, pp. 1-25, illus., 1941. (Biological laboratory Contributions. Zoological series, vol.XVI, no.1.)

PARAPHYSIS IN ADULT MAMMALIAN BRAINS. Yu-Tao Loo. Contrib. Biol. Lab. Sci. Soc. China, Shanghai, vol.15, zool. ser., no.4, pp.71-76, figs.2, 1941.

NERVE FIBER CONSTITUTION OF THE NERVES OF THE EYE. M. Nakanishi. Jour. Physiol., vol.58, pp.310-313, Mar., 1924.

SOME RESULTS OF A STUDY OF VARIATION AND CORRELATION IN BRAIN-WEIGHT. Raymond Pearl. Jour. Comp. Neurol. and Psych., vol.15, no.6, pp.467-481, 1905.

CRANIAL SUBDURAL SPACE. Wilder G. Penfield. Anat. Rec., vol.28, pp.173-175, July 25, 1924.

(PURKINJE CELLS OF THE CEREBELLUM IN THE MAMMALS (ACCORDING TO STUDIES OF BIRDS.) Les cellules de purkinje du cervelet chez les mammiferes (d'apres leur etude chez les oiseaux). Andre Pezard. Mammalia, Paris, vol.5, no.1, pp.18-23, fig.1, pl.1, Mar., 1941.

ON SOME POINTS CONCERNING THE FUNCTIONS OF THE MAMMALIAN CEREBRAL CORTEX. Chi Ping. Contrib. Biol. Sci. Soc. China, Nanking, Zool. Ser., vol.12, no.7, pp.107-129, 1937.

COMPARATIVE STUDY OF THE ANTERIOR SUPERIOR DENTAL NERVE. L. J. Ray. Proc. Zool. Soc. London, vol.119, pt.1, pp. 115-120, figs.7, May 16, 1949.

(INNERVATION OF THE MUSCULUS BRACHIALIS OF DOMESTIC ANIMALS.) Die Innervation des Musculus brachialis der Haustiere. Hans Reimers. Anat. Anzeiger, vol. 59, pp.289-301, fig.1, Mar. 14, 1925.

(THE PLEXUS BRACHIALIS OF DOMESTIC MAMMALS: A COMPARATIVE ANATOMICAL STUDY.) Der Plexus brachialis der Haussaeugetiere. Eine vergleichend-anatomische Studie. Hans Reimers. Zeitschr. f. Anatomie u. Entwicklungsgeschichte, vol. 76, pp.653-753, figs.13, June 30, 1925.

HAND AND FOOT PATTERNS OF LOW ELECTRICAL SKIN RESISTANCE: THEIR ANATOMICAL AND NEUROLOGICAL SIGNIFICANCE. Curt P. Richter, Bettye G. Woodruff, Billie C. Eaton. Jour. Neurophysiol., Springfield, vol.6, pp.417-424, figs.4, 1943.

PRINCIPLE OF INTEGRATION. ITS HISTORY AND ITS NATURE. W. Riese. Jour. Nervous and Mental Disease, Chicago, vol. 96, no.3, pp.296-312, Sep., 1942.

STRUCTURE AND FUNCTION OF THE MAMMALIAN CEREBRAL CORTEX AT THE TIME OF BIRTH. W. Riese. Virginia Med. Month., vol.71, pp.134-139, Mar., 1944.

METOPIC FONTANELLE, FISSURE, AND SUTURE. Adolph H. Schultz. Amer. Jour. Anat., vol.44, pp.475-499, figs.10, 1929.

OBSERVATIONS ON CEREBRAL LOCALIZATION. James Rollin Slonaker. Proc. Indiana Acad. Sci., 25th Annual meeting, pp.1-8, figs.5, 1909.

(MORPHOGENESIS OF THE MYELIN OF THE PERIPHERAL NERVE FIBERS IN MANY VERTEBRATES AND IN MAN.) Die Morphogenese der Markscheide der peripherischen Nervenfasern bei manchen Wirbeltieren und beim Menschen. D. Sokolansky. Anat. Anz., vol.69, nos.7/12, pp.161-184, figs.11, 1930.

ON THE PRESENCE OR ABSENCE OF NERVES IN THE UMBILICAL BLOOD VESSELS OF MAN AND GUINEA PIG. Mary Spivack. Anat. Rec., Philadelphia, vol.85, no.1, pp.85-109, figs.6, Jan., 1943.

(INVESTIGATIONS ON THE ORIGIN OF PURKINJE'S SYSTEM IN THE MAMMAL HEART.) Recherches sur l'origine du système purkinien dans le coeur des mammifères. Leon Stenon. Archives de Biologie, vol.35, pp.89-115, pl.5, 1925.

CONCEPT OF NERVE-MUSCLE SPECIFICITY. William L. Straus, Jr. Biological Rev., Cambridge, England, vol.21, pp.75-91, 1946.

SPINAL ACCESSORY NERVE AND ITS MUSCULATURE. William L. Straus, Jr., A. Brazier Howell. Quart. Rev. of Biology, vol.11, no.4, pp.376-405, Dec., 1936.

MAMMALIAN CEREBELLUM. PART I. THE DEVELOPMENT OF THE CEREBELLUM IN MAN AND THE CAT. Bert Brenette Stroud. Jour. Compar. Neur., vol.5, pp.71-118, pls. 1-8, July, 1895.

(BRACHIAL PLEXUS IN MAMMALS.) Le plexus brachial chez les Mammiferes. L. Thomas. Bull. Soc. Hist. Nat. Toulouse, vol.60, pp.5-216, figs.83, 1930.

(Review by William K. Gregory of) BRAIN FROM APE TO MAN, Prof. Frederick Tilney. Nat. Hist., vol.29, no.2, pp.215-217, 1929.

(ON THE NERVE ENDINGS IN THE PERITONEUM AND DIAPHRAGM OF MAMMALS.) Ueber die Nervenendigung im Bauchfelle und in dem Diaphragma der Saeugethiere. D. A. Timofejew. Archiv. f. mikroskop. Anat. und Entwicklungsgeschichte, Bonn, vol.59, pp.629-646, pl.30, 1902.

(MACROSCOPIC-ANATOMIC INVESTIGATIONS OF ELEPHANT AND HIPPOPOTAMUS HEARTS. A CONTRIBUTION TO THE COMPARATIVE ANATOMY OF THE STIMULUS-CONDUCTION SYSTEM OF THE MAMMAL HEART.) Makroskopisch-anatomische Untersuchungen an Elefanten- und Nilpferdherzen. Ein Beitrag zur vergleichenden Anatomie des Reizleitungs-systems des Saeugetierherzens. E. Vermes. Anat. Anzeiger, vol.60, pp.241-263, figs.7, Nov. 21, 1925.

NERVE ENDINGS IN MAMMALIAN SKIN. G. Weddell, E. Palmer, W. Pallie. Biol. Reviews, Cambridge, England, vol.30, no.2, pp.159-195, May, 1955.

RELATION OF THE THALAMUS TO THE PARACOELE (LATERAL VENTRICLE). Burt G. Wilder. Jour. Nervous and Mental Disease, pp.436-443, fig.1, July, 1889.

NON-BIFURCATING NERVE FIBERS OF THE TRIGEMINAL NERVE. William F. Windle. Jour. Comp. Neur., vol.40, pp. 229-240, figs.7, Feb. 15, 1926.

TOPOGRAPHY OF THE HYPOPHYSIS IN THE ELEPHANT, MANATEE AND HYRAX. George B. Wislocki. Anat. Rec., Philadelphia, vol.77, no.4, pp.427-445, fig.1, pls.3, Aug.26, 1940.

PERIVASCULAR SPACES OF THE MAMMALIAN CENTRAL NERVOUS SYSTEM. D. H. M. Wollam, J. W. Millen. Biol. Rev., Cambridge, England, vol.29, no.3, pp.251-283, Aug., 1954.

## ANATOMY -- PELAGE, SKIN, COLORATION

ADAPTIVE COLOURATION OF DESERT ANIMALS. Salim Ali. Jour. Bombay Nat. Hist. Soc., vol.43, no.3, pp.510-512, Dec., 1942.

DISTRIBUTION OF THE COLOR-MARKS OF THE MAMMALIA. Harrison Allen. Proc. Acad. Nat. Sci., Philadelphia, pp. 84-105, Feb. 28, 1888.

CUTICLE OF MAMMALIAN HAIR. H. M. Applegard, C. M. Greville. Nature, London, vol.166, no.4233, p.1031, Dec. 16, 1950.

EFFECT OF GROUND CONTACT ON FUR. Fred W. Ashley. Nat. Fur News, Denver, vol.20, no.7, p.24, Aug., 1948.

X-RAY STUDIES OF THE STRUCTURE OF HAIR, WOOL, AND RELATED FIBRES. III. CONFIGURATION OF THE KERATIN MOLECULE AND ITS ORIENTATION IN THE BIOLOGICAL CELL. W. T. Astbury, W. A. Sisson. Proc. Roy. Soc. London, ser. A, vol.150, no.871, pp.533-551, figs. la-7b, pls.11-13, July, 1935.

OBSERVATIONS ON THE INFLUENCE OF SOIL AND CLIMATE UPON WOOL. Robert Bakewell. London, J. Harding, pp.1-157, 1808.

COLOR NOMENCLATURE. Claude T. Barnes. Jour. Mammalogy, vol.30, no.1, pp.81-82, Feb. 14, 1949.

ABSTRACT OF A PHYSIOLOGICAL HYPOTHESIS TO EXPLAIN THE WINTER WHITENING OF MAMMALS AND BIRDS INHABITING SNOWY COUNTRIES AND THE MORE STRIKING POINTS IN THE DISTRIBUTION OF WHITE IN VERTEBRATES GENERALLY. G. E. H. Barrett-Hamilton. Proc. Roy. Irish Acad., vol.24, sec.B, pt.4, pp.303-314, 1903.

ANIMAL COLORATION. Frank Evers. London, pp.1-288, illus., 1892.

STUDY OF THE BRANCHED CELLS OF THE MAMMALIAN EPIDERMIS WITH SPECIAL REFERENCE TO THE FATE OF THEIR DIVISION PRODUCTS. R. E. Billingham, P. B. Medawas. Philos. Trans. Roy. Soc., London, ser.B., vol.237, no. 644, pp.151-171, Mar. 10, 1953.

ON COLORATION IN MAMMALS AND BIRDS. J. L. Bonhote. Jour. Linnean Soc. Zool., vol.29, no.190, pp.185-187, Nov. 1, 1904.

STUDY OF METHODS OF COLOR DETERMINATION. Darl E. Bowers. Systematic Zool., vol.5, no.4, pp.147-160, 182, Dec., 1956.

MICROSCOPY OF MAMMALIAN HAIR FOR ANTHROPOLOGISTS. Martin F. Brown. Proc. American Philos. Soc., Philadelphia, vol. 85, no.3, pp.250-274, figs.1-127, Feb. 25, 1942.

(ON THE VARIATIONS OF PIGMENT AND THEIR SIGNIFICANCE FOR THE VARIATION OF HAIR COLOR.) Ueber die Variationen des Pigments und ihre Bedeutung fuer die Variation der Haarfarbe. W. W. Bunak. Biol. Zhurnal, Moscow, vol.6, no.3, pp. 589-600, 1937.

ADAPTIVE COLOURATION OF DESERT ANIMALS. T. W. Burdon. Jour. Bombay Nat. Hist. Soc., vol.43, no.2, pp.250-252, Aug., 1942.

SOME SPECULATIONS ON THE COLORATION OF ANIMALS. J. C. Carothers. Jour. East Africa and Uganda Nat. Hist. Soc., Nairobi, vol.16, nos.2 and 3 (71 and 72), pp.109-118, Feb., 1942.

SCALINESS OF ANIMAL FIBERS. N. H. Chamberlain, J. B. Speakman. Nature, London, vol.150, no.3810, p.546, illus., Nov. 7, 1942.

CHANGES IN THE SKIN IN RELATION TO THE HAIR GROWTH CYCLE. H. B. Chase, W. Montagna, J. D. Malone. Anat. Rec., Philadelphia, vol.116, no.1, pp.75-82, May, 1953.

ACCOUNT OF SOME PHYSICAL PROPERTIES OF CARIBOU AND SEAL SKINS. K. E. Conroy. Can. Defence Res. Board, Chem. Lab. Rep., no.68, leaves ii-16, illus., 1951.

ADAPTIVE COLORATION IN ANIMALS. H. B. Cott. London, pp. XXXII-508, pls.48, 1940.

(CONTRIBUTION TO STUDY OF THE FUR OF DOMESTIC RUMINANTS.) Contribution a l'étude de la fourrure des ruminants domestiques. Pierre Crepin. Revue d'Histoire Naturelle, Pt.1, A, Mammiferes, Paris, vol.11, no.5, pp.145-160, figs.2, May, 1930.

RELATION OF SOME OBSERVATIONS UPON PREDATION TO THEORIES OF PROTECTIVE COLORATION. John E. Cushing, Jr. Condor, Santa Clara, Calif., vol.41, no.3, pp.100-111, May, 1939.

CAMOUFLAGE - IN WILDLIFE. J. B. Davis. Texas Game and Fish, Austin, vol.2, no.7, pp.4-5, 23, illus., June, 1944.

SECTIONS AID IN IDENTIFYING HAIR. Ned Dearborn. Jour. Mamm., vol.20, no. 3, pp.346-348, fig.1, Aug. 14, 1939.

(STUDIES ON THE COLORATION OF ANIMALS.) Études sur la coloration des animaux. G. Dementiev, W. Larionov. Zool. Jour. USSR, Moscow, vol.23, no.5, pp. 189-197, 1944. (French summary)

(MONOGRAPH ON THE FUR AND CONFIGURATION OF THE PELAGE OF SOUTH AMERICAN MAMMALS.) Monografia de los pelos y la configuración del pelaje de mamiferos sudamericanos. Jorge G. Dennler. Physis, Buenos Aires, vol.16, no.48, pp. 207-223, figs.18, May, 1939.

ALBINO VERTEBRATES. John S. Dexter. Science, n.s., vol.52, pp.130-131, Aug. 6, 1920. (Record of albino Citellus richardsoni from Saskatchewan.)

THE TULAROSA MALPAIS. Lee R. Dice. Scientific Monthly, Lancaster, vol.50, no. 5, pp.419-424, illus., May, 1940.

AN EXHIBITION OF VARIATIONS IN HAIR. J. K. Doutt. Carnegie Mag., Pittsburgh, vol. 8, no.9, p.281, Feb., 1935.

SEASONAL VARIATION IN THE COAT OF SOME DOMESTIC MAMMALS. J. E. Duerden. South African Jour. Sci., vol.27, pp. 521-545, Nov., 1930.

WHY NATURE USES HER PAINT BRUSH. IS PROTECTIVE COLOURATION A FALLACY? Radclyffe A. Dugmore. Field, London, vol.167, no.4334, pp.128-129, illus., Jan. 18, 1936.

ALBINO ANIMALS OF THE NORTH. Niska Elswell. Field and Stream, New York, vol. 49, no.9, pp.86-87, illus., Jan., 1945.

INHIBITORY ACTION OF EXTRACTS OF MAMMALIAN SKIN ON PIGMENT FORMATION. Peter Flesch. Proc. Soc. Exp. Biol. Med., Utica, vol.70, no.1, pp.136-140, Jan., 1949.

ROLE OF COPPER IN MAMMALIAN PIGMENTATION. Peter Flesch. Proc. Soc. Exp. Biol. Med., Utica, vol.70, no.1, pp.79-83, Jan., 1949.

FRESH HYPOTHESIS IN REGARD TO PROTECTIVE COLOURATION IN ANIMALS. W. Forsyth. Jour. Bombay Nat. Hist. Soc., vol.29, pp.829-830, Dec. 31, 1923.

(BLONDNESS AND ALBINISM IN MAN AND ANIMAL.) Blondheit und Albinismus bei Menschen und Tieren. H. Friedenthal. Sitz.-Ber. Gesell. Naturforsch. Freunde Berlin, 1932, pt.3, pp.453-470, illus. Mar. 15, 1933.

NATURAL-HISTORY BACKGROUND OF CAMOUFLAGE. Herbert Friedmann. Smiths. Inst. War Background Studies, Washington, D.C., no.5, pp.1-17, pls.16, Dec. 11, 1942.

(HISTOLOGY OF MAMMAL SKINS.) Gistologiia kozhnogo pokrova mlekopitaiushchikh. Evgenii Vasil'evich Gaevoi. Tsentrossoiuz, pp.1-101, 1957.

(INVESTIGATIONS OF THE TACTILE HAIR OF SOME MAMMALS.) Untersuchungen ueber die tasthaare einiger Saeugethiere. C. Gegenbaur. Zeitschr. f. Wiss. Zool. (von Siebold u. Koelliker) vol.3, pt.1, pp. 1-13, pl.1, 1850.

GRAYING OF THE HAIR. Owen S. Gibbs. Science, Lancaster, n.s., vol.95, no.2475, p.576, June 5, 1942.

STUDY OF HAIRS AND WOOLS BELONGING TO THE MAMMALIAN GROUP OF ANIMALS, INCLUDING A SPECIAL STUDY OF HUMAN HAIR CONSIDERED FROM THE MEDICO-LEGAL ASPECT. John Glaister. Egyptian Univ., Faculty of Med., Publ.2, Misr.Press., Cairo, p.188, pls.145, 1931.

(Review by Charles C. Sperry of) A STUDY OF HAIRS AND WOOLS BELONGING TO THE MAMMALIAN GROUP OF ANIMALS, INCLUDING A SPECIAL STUDY OF HUMAN HAIR CONSIDERED FROM THE MEDICO-LEGAL ASPECT, John Glaister, Jr. Jour. Mamm., vol.15, no.1, pp.74-75, Feb.,1934.

ABOUT THE ALBINOS. Lillian S. Graham, Marjorie Wackerbarth. Frontiers, Lancaster, vol.9, no.4, pp.105-106, 120, illus. Apr., 1945.

COLOR AND PRIMENESS IN VARIABLE MAMMALS. Charles Kenneth Gunn. Amer. Nat., vol.66, no.707, pp.546-559, figs.4, Nov.-Dec., 1932.

PHENOMENA OF PRIMENESS. Charles Kenneth Gunn. Canadian Jour. Research Nat. Res. Council Canada, vol.6, no.4, pp.387-397, figs.6, pls.2, Apr., 1932.

THE GROWTH, REPLACEMENT, AND TYPES OF HAIR. J. B. Hamilton, and others. Ann. New York Acad. Sci., vol.53, (art.3) pp.461-752, Mar., 1951.

ROBERT RIDGWAY'S COLOR STANDARDS. D. H. Hamly. Science, Lancaster, vol.109, no.2842, pp.605-608, June 17, 1949.

THERMAL PROPERTIES OF FUR. H. T. Hammel. Amer. Jour. Physiol., vol.182, no.2, pp.369-376, Aug., 1955.

DIFFERENTIATION OF MAMMALIAN EPIDERMIS IN TISSUE CULTURE. Jean Hanson. Jour. Anat., London, vol.84, pt. 1, pp.30-36, Jan., 1950.

"PARTICLES" AND THEIR RELATIONSHIP TO THE STRUCTURE OF ANIMAL FIBERS. J. I. Hardy, Thora M. Plitt. Jour. Agric. Research, Washington, D. C., vol.63, no. 5, pp.295-303, Sep. 1, 1941.

TYPES OF FUR FIBERS. J. I. Hardy, Thora M. Plitt. Jour. Heredity, Washington, D. C. vol.33, no.5, pp.191-199, figs.11-15, May, 1942.

SEASONAL CHANGES IN INSULATION OF THE FUR. J. S. Hart. Canadian Jour. Zool., vol.34, no.1, pp.53-57, Feb., 1956.

COLOR VARIETIES OF LONG ISLAND MAMMALS. Robert T. Hatt. Jour. Mamm., vol.11, no.3, pp.322-323, Aug. 9, 1930.

APPLIED MICROSCOPY OF HAIR. Leon Augustus Hausman. Sci. Mo., Lancaster, vol.59, no.3, whole no.348, pp.195-202, illus., Sep., 1944.

CORTICAL FUSI OF MAMMALIAN HAIR SHAFTS. Leon Augustus Hausman. Amer. Nat., vol.66, no.706, pp.461-470, figs.14, Sep.-Oct., 1932.

FURS UNDER THE MICROSCOPE. Leon Augustus Hausman. Nature Mag., Washington, D. C., vol.32, no.9, pp.501-503, Nov., 1939.

FURTHER STUDIES OF THE RELATIONSHIPS OF THE STRUCTURAL CHARACTERISTICS OF MAMMALIAN HAIR. Leon Augustus Hausman. Amer. Nat., vol.58, pp.544-557, figs.1-9, pl.1, tbl.1, Nov., 1924.

HAIR COLORATION IN ANIMALS. Leon Augustus Hausman. Scient. Monthly, vol. 11, pp.215-222, Mar., 1921.

HAIRS THAT MAKE FABRICS. THE MICROSCOPIC IDENTIFICATION OF MAMMAL HAIRS USED IN THE TEXTILE INDUSTRY. Leon Augustus Hausman. Sci. Amer., vol.122, no.8, pp.184, 200, 202, 204, Feb. 21, 1920.

MAMMAL FUR UNDER THE MICROSCOPE. Leon Augustus Hausman. Nat. Hist., vol. 20, no.4, pp.434-444, figs., 1920.

MICROSCOPIC IDENTIFICATION OF COMMERCIAL FUR HAIRS. Leon Augustus Hausman. Sci. Mo., pp.70-78, figs.1-27, Jan., 1920.

RECENT STUDIES OF HAIR STRUCTURE RELATIONSHIPS. Leon Augustus Hausman. Sci. Mo., vol.30, no.3, pp.258-277, figs. 19, 1930.

STRUCTURAL CHARACTERISTICS OF THE HAIR OF MAMMALS. Leon Augustus Hausman. Amer. Nat., vol.54, pp.496-523, figs. 199, Nov.-Dec. (Dec. 6), 1920.

WINTER COATS. John Eric Hill. Nat. Hist., New York, vol.52, no.4, p.171, illus., Nov., 1943. (Raccoon, rabbit, weasel, fox, squirrel.)

RHINOGLYPHICS: EPITHELIAL SCULPTURE OF THE MAMMALIAN RHINARIUM. W. C. Osman Hill. Proc. Zool. Soc., London, vol. 118, pt.1, pp.1-35, figs.33, May 20, 1948.

SOME STUDIES OF HAIR OF MAMMALS NATIVE TO MINNESOTA. Laurence E. Hiner. MS thesis, Univ. Minn., 1938.

STRUCTURE OF THE WOOL FIBER AS REVEALED BY THE MICROSCOPE. Charles W. Hock. Sci. Monthly, Lancaster, vol.55, no.6, (whole no.327), pp.527-531, figs.7, Dec., 1942.

ALBINISTIC ANIMALS. Wallace Hughes. Oklahoma Game & Fish News, Oklahoma City, vol.4, no.2, p.6, Feb., 1948.

(MELANISM IN SMALL DOMESTIC MAMMALS (NEOMYS FODIENS AND CRICETUS CRICETUS).) Melanismen einheimischer Kleinsaeuger (Neomys fodiens und Cricetus cricetus.) A. Jacobi. Zeitschr. f. Saeugetierkunde, vol.2, no.1, pp.82-87, Oct.15, 1927.

ON THE CAUSATION OF CERTAIN HAIR TRACTS. Frederic Wood Jones. Jour. Anat., vol.59, pt.1, pp.72-79, figs.1-4, Oct., 1924.

COLOR VARIATIONS IN WILD ANIMALS. Sarah V. H. Jones. Jour. Mamm., vol.4, no.3, pp.172-177, Aug., 1923.

PROTECTIVE COLOURATION IN WILD ANIMALS. Kunhi K. Kannan. Jour.Bombay Nat. Hist. Soc., vol.29, p.1043, May 15, 1924.

NOTES ON THE COLOR OF WEST COAST MAMMALS. Charles A. Keeler. Zoe, vol.2, no.3, pp.203-216, Oct., 1891.

(DERMAL GLANDS AND THEIR SIGNIFICANCE IN THE LIFE OF OUR GAME ANIMALS.) Kozne zlazy a ich vysnam v zivote nazej zveri. Karel Kostron. Polovnicky obzor, vol.3, nos.20-22, pp.1-8, illus., 1949.

(ON PIGMENT CENTERS IN MAMMALS.) Ueber Pigmentzentren bei Saeugetieren. H. Krieg. Anat. Anz., vol.54, pp.353-365, Oct. 15, 1921.

(ON THE FORMATION OF STRIPED MARKS IN MAMMALS.) Ueber die Bildung von Streifenzeichnungen bei Saeugetieren. H. Krieg. Anat. Anz., vol.54, pp.33-40, 1921.

(ON MODIFIABILITY IN MAMMALIAN SPOTTEDNESS.) Ueber die Modifikabilitaet der Saeugerscheckung. Friedrich Kroening. Zeitschr. f. induktive Abstammungs-und Vererbungslehre, vol.35, pp. 113-138, pl.5, figs.21, 1924.

ON THE INTERESTING FUNCTION OF WHITE COLORATION. A. V. Lablokov. Nature, Moscow, no.6, pp.92-94, June, 1956. (In Russian.)

ON THE HAIR DIRECTION IN MAMMALS. Walter Landauer. Jour. Mamm., vol.6, no. 4, pp.217-232, pl.19, Nov., 1925.

WHEN THE FURBEARER CHANGES ITS COAT. Neil M. Landsay. Pt. I. Fur-Fish-Game, Columbus, vol.95, no.10, pp.7-9, illus., Oct., 1947.

(ON THE STRUCTURE AND RECOGNITION OF ANIMAL HAIR, WITH SPECIAL CONSIDERATION OF COMMERCIAL HIDES AND FURS.) Ueber den Bau und die Erkennung von Tierhaaren, mit besonderer Beruecksichtigung der Handelsfelle und - pelze. F. M. Litterscherd, C. Abeler. Zool. Jahrbuecher, Abt. f. Systematik, etc., vol.50, pp.377-450, pls.9-18, 1925.

(ATLAS OF HUMAN AND ANIMAL HAIRS.) Atlas der menschlichen und tierischen Haare. Theodore Lochte. Leipzig, Verlag Dr. Paul Schops, pp.xi-306, figs.506, 1938.

NATURE AND PROPERTIES OF WOOL. John Luccock. Printed by E. Baines, pp. 360, fold.tab.2, 1805.

OBSERVATIONS ON THE SURFACE STRUCTURE OF THE HAIRS OF TASMANIAN MONOTREMES AND MARSUPIALS. A. G. Lyne, T. S. McMahon. Proc. Roy. Soc. Tasmania, Hobart, pp.71-83, Dec. 15, 1951.

COLOR CHANGES AND WEATHER. Dugald MacIntyre. Field,London, vol.163, no.4242, p.802, illus., Apr. 14, 1934. (Arctic hare and stoat.)

WOOL - ITS STRUCTURE AND STRENGTH. W. McMurtrie. 13th Rept. Board of Trustees, Univ. Illinois, pp.223-254, 1887.

DICTIONARY OF COLOR. A. Maez, M.Rea Paul. New York, McGraw-Hill Book Co., pp. vii-207, pls.56, 1930.

ORIGIN OF COLOR IN ANIMALS. Paul M. Marchal. Popular Sci. Mo., pp.94-99, 1885.

ON THE CHANGES IN THE COLOUR OF THE PELAGE OF JUGOSLAVIAN MAMMALS. V. Martino. Zapiski Russkago Naucnago Instituta v Belgrade, 4th Issue, pp.219-232, 1931. (Notes of the Russian Educational Institute in Belgrade; In Russian, with English summary.)

"PROTECTIVE COLORATION" IN MUSEUMS. Colin Matheson. Museums Jour., London, vol.41, no.12, pp.289-291, Mar., 1942.

KEY TO HAIRS OF THE MAMMALS OF SOUTHERN MICHIGAN. Harold A. Mathiak. Jour. Wildl. Mgt., Menasha, vol.2, no.4, pp.251-268, figs.38, Oct., 1938.

HAIR: ITS CHEMICAL NATURE. M. Mattikow. Fur Jour., vol.1, no.4, pp.26, 60-62, Aug., 1927.

COMPARATIVE ANATOMY OF THE HAIRS OF CALIFORNIA MAMMALS. William V. Mayer. PhD thesis, Stanford Univ., 1950.

HAIR OF CALIFORNIA MAMMALS WITH KEYS TO THE DORSAL GUARD HAIRS OF CALIFORNIA MAMMALS. William V. Mayer. Amer. Midland Nat., Notre Dame, vol.48, no.2, pp.480-512, illus., Sep., 1952.

(HAIR OF MAMMALS, ESPECIALLY ITS ARRANGEMENT.) Over de haren der zoogdieren; in 't bijzonder over hunne wijze van rangschikking. Johannes Cornelis Hendrik de Meijere. Leiden, E. J. Brill, pp.147, 1893.

ON SOME FOETAL AND POST-FOETAL CHARACTERS OF MAMMALS AND BIRDS: CONCERNING SCALES, HAIRS, AND FEATHERS. Alipio De Miranda-Ribeiro. Proc. Zool. Soc. London for 1934, pt.3, pp.573-582, pls.1-4, Sep., 1934; Proc. Zool. Soc. London for 1935, pp.741-772, pls.5-9, Jan., 1936.

PIGMENTATION IN BRISTLE AND HORSEHAIR. Sanford B. Newman. Jour. Res. Nat. Bur. Standards, Washington, vol.48, no.4, pp.287-297, illus., Apr., 1952.

GHOSTS IN THE WOODS. Mary Lou Norwood. Florida Wildlife, Tallahassee, vol.9, no.8, pp.14-15, illus., Jan., 1956.

("MECHANISM OF DEVELOPMENT OF PROTECTIVE SEASONAL COLORATIONS".) B. G. Novikov, G. I. Blagodatskia. Doklad. Akad. Nauk. SSSR, vol.61, pp.577-580, 1948. (in Russian.)

STUDY OF THE STRUCTURE OF HAIR AS A MEANS OF MAMMAL IDENTIFICATION. Earl R. Oyer. MS thesis, Ft. Hays Kansas State Coll., 1939.

TUFTED TITMICE PULL HAIRS FROM LIVING MAMMALS. Fred M. Packard. Jour. Mamm., vol.30, no.4, p.432, Nov. 17, 1949.

CONCISE COLOR STANDARD. Ralph S. Palmer. E. M. Reilly, Jr. Amer. Ornithol. Union Handbook Fund, pp.1-8, chart, Oct. 19, 1956.

(ON THE SKIN ADAPTATION OF THE MAMMALS.) Ueber die Hautanpassung der Saeugetiere. Hermann Paul. Jena, Frommannsche Buchdruckerei (Hermann Pohle) pp.1-72, 1884.

(ON THE MECHANISMS OF THE DEVELOPMENT OF THE SKIN DERIVATION IN VERTEBRATES.) Ueber die Mechanismen der Entwicklung der Hautderivate bei Wirbeltieren. A. A. Peredelsky. Comptes Rendus (Doklady) Acad. Sci., URSS, Moscou, n.s., vol.32, no.3, pp.223-226, 1941.

MICROSCOPIC IDENTIFICATION OF FUR HAIRS. Ethel L. Phelps. Amer. Fur Breeder, vol.3, no.4, p.20, Oct., 1930.

PROBLEMS IN FUR FIBER RESEARCH. Thora M. Plitt. Amer. Fur Breeder, Duluth, vol.13, no.2, pp.14-15, figs.4, Aug., 1940.

ANIMALS AT THE ZOOLOGICAL GARDENS IN WINTER AND SUMMER. R. I. Pocock. Field (London), vol.150, p.967, illus. Dec. 15, 1927.

ON THE FACIAL VIBRISSAE OF MAMMALIA. R. I. Pocock. Proc. Zool. Soc. London, pt.3, pp.889-912, figs.13, Sep. 7, 1914.

ALBINISM. Earl L. Poole. Pennsylvania Game News, Harrisburg, vol.17, no.4, pp. 11-26, illus., July, 1946.

CHANGES OF RAIMENT, AND THEIR MEANING. W. P. Pycraft. Illus. London News, vol.192, no.5150, p.32, Jan. 1, 1938.

PIEBALD ANIMALS. W. P. Pycraft. Illus. London News, vol.193, no.5181, p.228, figs.3, Aug. 6, 1938. (Phalanger maculatus, lycaon pictus.)

DETERMINATION OF HAIR STRUCTURE. I. PRODUCTION OF WAVED HAIR FROM GENETICALLY NON-WAVED CELLS. Sheldon C. Reed. Jour. Exper. Zool., Philadelphia, vol.79, no.3, pp.347-354, 1938.

COLOR STANDARDS AND NOMENCLATURE. Robert Ridgway. 1912.

ALBINO MAMMALS AND BIRDS IN PERTHSHIRE MUSEUM. John Ritchie. Scottish Naturalist, no.185, p.153, Sep.-Oct., 1930.

WOOL COVERING ON FACE, EARS AND LEGS. E. G. Ritzman. Technical Bull. Durham, New Hampshire Agric. Exper. Sta., no.37, pp.1-35, pls.4, June, 1928.

LIFE OR LASTING QUALITIES OF A MOUNTED MAMMAL SKIN. Robert H. Rockwell. Proc. Amer. Assoc. Mus., Charleston, vol. 16, pp.20-21, 1912.

STRUCTURE OF THE HAIR CUTICLE. K. M. Rudall. Proc. Leeds Philos. and Literary Soc., Scientific Sec., vol.4, pt.1, pp.13-18, figs., pls.2, July, 1941.

(DERMAL GLANDS OF MAMMALS.) Die Hautdruesenorgane der Saeugetiere. J. Schaffer, Vienna and Berlin, 1940.

PROTECTIVE COLORATION. Cleland Scott. Indian Wild Life, Agra, vol.3, no.4, pp.201-207, Oct.-Dec., 1938.

ON THE EPITHELIAL FIBRES IN THE SKIN OF MAMMALS. Boris Shapiro. Quart. Jour. Micros. Sci., vol.68, pp.101-145, figs.17, pl.3, Apr., 1924.

CHANGES IN COLOR OF HAIR DUE TO FOOD. P. G. Shipley. Jour. Mamm., vol. 5, no.3, p.203, Aug., 1924.

FIELD KEY TO GUARD HAIRS OF MIDDLE WESTERN FURBEARERS. Howard J. Stains. Jour. Wildlife Management, vol.22, no.1, pp.95-97, Jan., 1958.

BIOLOGICAL SIGNIFICANCE OF MAMMALIAN HAIR. J. L. Stoves. Proc. Leeds Philos. and Liter. Soc., Sci. sect., vol.4, pt.2, pp.84-86, pls.1-2, July, 1943.

STRUCTURE OF KERATIN FIBRES. J. L. Stoves. Nature, London, vol.151, no.3828, pp.304-305, figs.2, Mar. 13, 1943.

CAUSES OF WHITENESS IN HAIR AND FEATHERS. R. M. Strong. Science, n.s., vol.54, p.356, Oct. 14, 1921.

COLOR OF THE SKIN AND CORIUM PIGMENTATION. R. M. Strong. Archives Pathology Lab. Medicine, vol.3, pp.938-946, figs.3, June, 1927.

TEST OF THE POSSIBLE EFFECTS OF VISUAL STIMULI UPON THE HAIR COLOR

OF MAMMALS. Francis B. Summer. Proc. Nat. Acad. Sci., vol.20, no.6, pp.397-402, June 15, 1934.

SUPPOSED EFFECTS OF THE COLOR TONE OF THE BACKGROUND UPON THE COAT COLOR OF MAMMALS. Francis B. Sumner, Harry S. Swarth. Jour. Mamm., vol.5, no. 2, pp.81-113, pls.7, May, 1924.

RELATION OF COLORATION IN MAMMALS TO LOW TEMPERATURE. Arthur Svihla. Jour. Mamm., vol.37, no.3, pp. 378-381, Sep. 11, 1956.

PROTECTIVE COLOURATION IN WILD ANIMALS. Bruce P. Tailyour. Jour.Bombay Nat. Hist. Soc., vol.29, pp.469-473, Aug. 25, 1923.

MICROSCOPICAL EXAMINATION OF THE LEATHER OF AQUATIC ANIMALS. Arata Terao. Bull. Japanese Soc. Sci. Fisheries, Tokyo, vol.8, no.6, pp.343-346, Mar., 1940. (In Japanese with English summary. Includes Zalophus, Delphinus, Physeter, and Balaenoptera.)

ARRAIGNMENT OF THE THEORIES OF MIMICRY AND WARNING COLOR. Abbott H. Thayer. Popular Sci. Mo., pp.550-570, figs.12, Dec. 1909.

LAW WHICH UNDERLIES PROTECTIVE COLORATION. Abbott H. Thayer. Printed in the Auk, vol.XIII, Apr. and Oct., 1896; Smithsonian Inst. Annual report. Washington, pp.477-482, 1898.

COMPARATIVE HISTOLOGICAL STUDIES ON HAIRLESS MAMMALS, WITH SOME GENETIC NOTES. Lorna Woodward Thigpen. Univ. of Pittsburgh bulletin, vol.27, no.3, Nov., 1930.

NATURE POINTS THE WAY TO WARTIME CAMOUFLAGE. Edward S. Thomas. Fauna, Philadelphia, vol.4, no.2, pp.35-40, illus., June, 1942.

(STRUCTURE AND NATURAL COLORATION OF THE FUR OF WILD MAMMALS.) Aufbau und natuerliche Faerbung des haarkleides der Wildsaeugetiere. Karl Toldt. Leipzig, Deutsche gesellschaft fuer kleintier- und pelztierzucht g.m.b.h. & co., illus. (part col.), 1935.

(ON THE WINTER DECOLORATION OF THE COATS OF THE MAMMALS.) Sur la Decoloration Hivernale du Pelage des Mammiferes. E. L. Trouessart. Comptes rendus Soc. Biol., Paris, vol.60, pp.271-273, Feb., 1906.

ON VARIOUS SKINS OF MAMMALIA FROM CHILE, WITH NOTES RELATING TO THEM BY MR. THOMAS BRIDGES. Mr. Waterhouse. Proc. Zool. Soc. London, pt.12, pp.153-155, 1844.

A REVERSIBLE CONTRACTION PHENOMENON IN ANIMAL HAIRS. C. S. Whewell. H. J. Woods. Nature, London, vol. 154, no.3913, p.546, Oct. 28, 1944.

INEFFICACY OF PANTOTHENIC ACID AGAINST THE GRAYING OF FUR. R. R. Williams. Science, Lancaster, vol.92, no. 2398, pp.561-562, Dec. 13, 1940.

DETERMINATION OF HAIRS BY IMPRESSIONS. V. H. H. Williamson. Jour. Mamm., vol.32, no.1, pp.80-84, figs.2, Feb. 15, 1951.

FIBRE FORMS IN ANIMAL HAIRS. H. J. Woods. Nature, London, vol.136, no.3433, p.262, Aug. 17, 1935.

LITTLE KNOWN FACTS ABOUT FUR. Stanley P. Young. Amer. Forests, Washington, D. C., vol.49, no.4, pp.166-167, 189-190, illus., Apr., 1943.

ANIMAL CAMOUFLAGE. Mus. Leaflet, Santa Barbara, vol.18, no.7, pp.75-79, Oct., 1943.

## ANATOMY -- REPRODUCTIVE ORGANS AND SEX CELLS

ACCESSORY REPRODUCTIVE TRACT IN MAMMALIAN TRUE HERMAPHRODITES, AN EFFECT OF POSITION. S. A. Asdell. Amer. Nat., Lancaster, vol.76, no.762, pp.75-84, Jan., 1942.

QUANTITATIVE STUDIES OF THE TESTICLE. II. PATTERN AND TOTAL TUBULE LENGTH IN THE TESTICLES OF CERTAIN COMMON MAMMALS. K. F. Bascom, H. L. Osterud. Anat. Rec., vol. 31, pp.159-169, Oct. 25, 1925.

QUANTITATIVE STUDIES OF THE TESTIS. III. NUMERICAL TREATMENT OF THE DEVELOPMENT OF THE PIG TESTIS. K. F. Bascom, H. L. Osterud. Anat. Rec., vol.37, pp.63-82, Nov. 25, 1927.

STUDIES ON THE GOLGI APPARATUS OF THE MAMMARY GLAND. H. W. Beams. Science, n.s., vol.66, p.306, Sep. 30, 1927.

MAMMALIAN SPERMATOZOA. M. W. H. Bishop, C. R. Austin. Endeavor, vol.16, no.63, pp.137-150, July, 1957.

PRIMORDIAL MAMMALIAN EGG. F. S. Bodenheimer. Proc. Zool. Soc. London, vol.127, no.1, pp.143-144, Sep. 28, 1956.

MAMMARY APPARATUS OF THE MAMMALIA IN THE LIGHT OF ONTOGENESIS AND PHYLOGENESIS. Ernst Bresslau. Methuen & Co., London, pp.i-vii, 1-145, illus.47, 1920.

(PENILE BONE: DESCRIPTIVE AND COMPARATIVE STUDY.) L'os penien: etude descriptive et comparative. J. Chaine. Actes Soc. Linn. Bordeaux, vol.78, pp.5-195, figs.133, 1925.

COMPARATIVE MORPHOLOGY OF THE ERECTILE TISSUE OF THE PENIS WITH ESPECIAL EMPHASIS ON THE PROBABLE MECHANISM OF ERECTION. L. J. Deysach. Amer. Jour. Anat., Philadelphia, vol.64, no.1, pp.111-131, pls.2, Jan. 15, 1939.

COPULATION PLUG AND THE ACCESSORY GENITAL GLANDS OF MAMMALS. Earl Theron Engle. Jour. Mamm., vol.7, no.2, pp.119-126, May, 1926.

(REMARKS ON THE STRUCTURE OF THE MAMMAL PENIS.) Bemerkungen ueber den Bau des Saeugerpenis. L. Freund. Zool. Anz., vol.75, pp.140-142, Feb. 1, 1928.

(GLANDS ATTACHED TO THE GENITAL APPARATUS IN THE MAMMALS: HOMOLOGIES AND CLASSIFICATION.) Les glandes annexees a l'appareil genital chez les mammiferes: homologies et classification. Rene Godet. Mammalia, Paris, vol.16, no.1, pp. 24-36, illus., Mar., 1952.

OBSERVATIONS ON THE SEMEN AND SEMINAL TUBES OF MAMMALIA AND BIRDS. George Gulliver. Proc. Zool. Soc. London, pt.10, pp.95-102, 1842.

SUB-SURFACE CRYPTS IN THE CORTEX OF THE MAMMALIAN OVARY. R. J. Harrison, L. Harrison Matthews. Proc. Zool. Soc. London, vol.120, pt.4, pp.699-712, fig.1, pls.1-2, Feb. 6, 1951.

HOW LARGE IS THE MAMMALIAN EGG? C. G. Hartman. Quart. Rev. Biol., vol.4, pp.373-388, 1929.

(ON THE PENILE BONE OF SOME FUR-BEARING ANIMALS.) Ueber den Rutenknochen einiger Pelztiere. Eduard Heidegger. Der Deutsche Pelztierzuechter, Jahrg. 1931, Muenchen, no.16, pp.444-445, fig., Aug. 15, 1931.

(ON THE ANATOMY OF THE MALE ELEPHANT, TAPIR, AND HIPPOPOTAMUS GENITALS.) Zur Anatomie des maennlichen Elefanten-, Tapir-, und Hippopotamus-Gentale. Lotar Hofmann. Zool. Jahrb., Abt. f. Anat. und Ontog., Bd.45, pp.161-212, pls. 7-10, 1923.

SUGGESTED HOMOLOG OF THE OS PENIS OR BACULUM OF MAMMALS. W. L. Jellison. Jour. Mamm., vol.26, no.2, pp.146-147, July 15, 1945.

(ON THE STRUCTURE OF THE SEX ORGANS OF THE STALLION AND BULL.) Zur Struktur der maennlichen Geschlechtsorgane von Pferd und Rind. Anton Kircher. Zeitschr. f. Saeugetierkunde, vol.4, no.2, pp.90-91, pls.4, figs.4, Aug. 6, 1929.

QUANTITATIVE STUDY OF THE TESTES OF CERTAIN MAMMALS. Thomas H. Knepp. Zoologica, New York, vol.24, pt. 3, pp.329-332, figs.2, Nov. 2, 1939.

(MAMMAL INTERSEXUALITY.) Zoogdierintersexualiteit. Gerrit Krediet. Gorinchem (J. Noorduijn) pp.1-135, illus., 1942.

ANOVULAR GRAAFIAN FOLLICLES IN MAMMALIAN OVARIES. Bessie League, C. G. Hartman. Anat. Rec., vol.30, pp. 1-9, pls.2, Apr. 25, 1925.

(ACCESSORY SEX GLANDS OF THE MAMMALS.) Die Accessorischen Geschlechtsdruesen der Saeugethiere. J. Th. Oudemans. Haarlem: Natuurk. Verhandl. Hollandsche Maatschappij der Wetenschappen, 3de Verz., Deel V, 2de Stuk., pp.1-96, pls.16, 1892.

NOTE ON THE NOMENCLATURE OF THE SEXUAL ORGANS IN PLANTS AND ANIMALS. Jeffery T. Parker. Proc. Australian Assoc. for Advancement of Science, pp.1-338, 1888.

HEAD LENGTH DIMORPHISM OF MAMMALIAN SPERMATOZOA. A. S. Parkes. Quart. Jour. Micro. Sci., vol.67, pp.617-625, figs.3, Dec., 1923.

HISTOCHEMICAL STUDIES OF THE INTERSTITIAL CELLS OF THE TESTIS. William F. Pollock. Anat. Rec., Philadelphia, vol. 84, no.1, pp.23-29, pl.1, Sep. 25, 1942.

STRUCTURES CONNECTED WITH THE OVARIAN OVUM OF MARSUPIALIA AND MONOTREMATA. Edward B. Poulton. Quart. Jour. Microsc. Sci., London, n.s., vol.24, pp.118-128, pl.5, Jan., 1884.

(NOTES ON MAMMAL OVARIES.) Notizen ueber die Eierstoecke der Saeugethiere. H. Quincke. Zeitschr. Wissensch. Zool., Leipzig, vol.12, no.4, pp.483-485, pl.43B, Jan. 20, 1863.

(ON THE GENITAL APPARATUS OF SOME RODENTS AND INSECTIVORES,PARTICULARLY THEIR ACCESSORY GENITAL GLANDS.) Ueber den Genitalapparat einiger Nager und Insektivoren, insbesondere die akzessorischen Genitaldruesen. Max Rauther. Inaugural-Dissertation, Univ. Jena, pp.1-97, figs.9, 1903.

(ON THE LENGTH OF THE UMBILICAL CORD OF MAMMALS.) Ueber die Laenge der Nabelschnur bei Saeugetieren. Dietrich Starck. Zeitschr. Saeugetierk., vol.22, no.1-2, pp.77-86, 1957.

NOTES ON MAMMAL SPERMS. Irving L. Towers. Maryland, Baltimore, vol.14, no. 4, pp.83-90, Oct., 1944.

MAMMALIAN GERM CELLS. G. E. Wolstenholm, (editor). Little, Brown & Co., New York, pp.xvi-302, illus., 1953.

(BODY SIZE AND SPERM SIZE. COMPARATIVE INVESTIGATION OF THE SIZE OF THE SPERM OF SPERM WHALES, HORSES, AND RABBITS.) Koerpergroesse und Spermiengroesse. Eine vergleichende Untersuchung ueber die Groesse der Spermien beim Pottwal, Pferd und Kaninchen. Jinshin Yamane. Zeitschr. f. Zuechtung, Reihe B, Tierzuechtung und Zuechtungsbiologie einschliesslich Tierernaehrung, Berlin, vol.34, no.1, pp.105-109, fig.1, tbl.4, Jan., 1936.

## ANATOMY -- SKULL, JAWS, TEETH

NOMENCLATURE OF THE TEETH. Harrison Allen. Dental Cosmos, Philadelphia, pp.1-7, figs.21, Dec., 1874.

ON THE TYPES OF TOOTH STRUCTURE IN MAMMALIA. Harrison Allen. Amer. Nat., vol.20, no.3, pp.295-297, Mar., 1886.

NOTES ON THE TEMPORAL BONE IN MAMMALIA, (Chiefly in Primates). Richard J. Anderson. Verhandl. d. VIII Internat. Zool.-Kong. zu Gres, pp.907-914, Aug. 15-20, 1910.

NOTE ON THE SKULLS FROM WHICH THE ENDOCRANIAL CASTS DESCRIBED BY DR. DART WERE TAKEN. C. W. Andrews. Proc. Zool. Soc. London, pt.3, pp.648-652, Oct., 1923.

HORNS AND ANTLER. THEIR OCCURRENCE, DEVELOPMENT AND FUNCTION

IN THE MAMMALIA. H. E. Anthony. Bull. New York Zool. Soc., vol.32, no.1, pp.3-33, illus., Jan.-Feb., 1929.

(PRINCIPLES AND GENERAL OUTLINE OF A DENTAL THEORY OF MAMMALS.) Les principes et les grandes lignes d'une theorie dentaire des mammiferes. R. Anthony. Bull. Soc. Fribourgeoise Sci. nat. C. R. 1934-35 et 1935-36, Fribourg, vol.33, pp.115-124, 1937.

(THEORY OF MAMMALIAN DENTITION.) Theorie de la dentition mammalienne. R. Anthony. Comptes Rendus XII Congres Internat. Zool. Lisbonne 1935, Lisboa, vol.1, pp.154-173, figs.15, 1936.

ON THE IDENTIFICATION OF MECKELIAN AND MYLOHYOID GROOVES IN THE JAWS OF MESOZOIC AND RECENT MAMMALIA. Benjamin Arthur Bensley. (Toronto) Univ. Library, pp.1-9, pl., 1902.

NEW OUTLINES ON COMPARATIVE ODONTOLOGY. L. Berner. Canadian Field-Nat., vol.69, no.4, pp.140-144, Oct.-Dec., 1955.

(Review by P. Rode of) (BUCCODENTAL ANATOMY AND PHYSIOLOGY.) Anatomie et physiologie bucco-dentaires, E.Bourdelle, Ch. Bennejeant. Mammalia, Paris, vol.1, no.4, pp.182-183, June, 1937.

HORNS AND ANTLERS. Wilfred S. Bronson. Harcourt, Brace & Co., New York, pp.1-143, illus., 1942.

FURTHER CONTRIBUTION TO OUR KNOWLEDGE OF THE STRUCTURE OF THE MAMMALIAN BASICRANIAL AXIS. R. Broom. Ann. Transvaal Mus., vol.18, pt.1, pp.33-36, figs.2, Oct. 1, 1935.

ON THE MAMMALIAN PRESPHENOID AND MESETHMOID BONES. R. Broom. Proc. Zool. Soc. London, pp.257-264, Apr. 29, 1926.

SOME FURTHER POINTS ON THE STRUCTURE OF THE MAMMALIAN BASICRANIAL AXIS. R. Broom. Proc. Zool. Soc. London, pt.1, pp.233-244, Apr. 6, 1927.

VOMER-PARASPHENOID QUESTION. R. Broom. Ann. Transvaal Mus., vol.18, pt. 1, pp.23-31, figs.3, Oct. 1, 1935.

ILLUSTRATED SKULL KEY TO THE RECENT LAND MAMMALS OF VIRGINIA. Gordon H. Brown. Coop. Wildl. Res. Unit., Blacksburg, Virginia, no.52-2, pp.1-75, illus., Apr., 1952.

(ON THE BIOLOGY OF FOREHEAD ATTACHMENTS IN UNGULATES.) Zur Biologie der Stirnaufsaetze bei Huftieren. H. Bruhin. Physiol. Comp. & Oecol., vol.3, pt.1, pp.63-92; pt.2, pp.93-127, 1953. (In German, with French and English summaries.)

PATTERN CORRELATION OF MAMMALIAN TEETH AS A MEANS OF IDENTIFICATION. Charles Buck. MS thesis, Mont.State, Coll., 1939.

ONTOGENY OF MOLAR PATTERN. P. M. Butler. Biol. Rev. Cambridge Phil. Soc., vol.31, no.1, pp.30-70, Feb., 1956.

STUDIES OF THE MAMMALIAN DENTITION. II. DIFFERENTIATION OF THE POSTCANINE DENTITION. P. M. Butler. Proc. Zool. Soc. London, vol.108, ser. C, no.10, pp.37-38, Oct. 11, 1938.

STUDIES OF THE MAMMALIAN DENTITION. DIFFERENTIATION OF THE POSTCANINE DENTITION. P. M. Butler. Proc. Zool. Soc. London, vol.109, ser.B. pt.I, pp.1-35, 1939.

TEETH OF THE JURASSIC MAMMALS. P. M. Butler. Proc. Zool. Soc. London, vol. 109, ser.B. pts.3-4, pp.329-356, figs.12, Dec., 1939.

PROBLEM OF UNERUPTED MOLARS IN ITS RELATION TO THE "SUCCESSIONAL" THEORY OF TOOTH-REPLACEMENT. Gordon F. Cawston. South African Dental Jour., Port Elizabeth, vol.15, no.12, pp. 375-376, Dec., 1941.

CRANIO-FACIAL UNION AND THE MAXILLARY TUBER IN MAMMALS. Montague W. Cobb. Amer. Jour. Anat., Philadelphia, vol.72, no.1, pp.39-111, pls.6, Jan., 1943.

ABNORMAL CONDITIONS OF THE TEETH OF ANIMALS IN THEIR RELATIONSHIP TO SIMILAR CONDITIONS IN MAN. Frank Colyer. (Four lectures.) Publ. by Dental Board of the United Kingdom, London, pp. xi-167, figs.217, June 12, 1931.

VARIATIONS AND DISEASES OF THE TEETH OF ANIMALS. Frank Colyer. London: John Bale, Sons & Danielsson, Ltd., pp.viii-750, figs.1007, 1936.

(MAMMALIAN TEETH CONSIDERED AS ZOOLOGICAL CHARACTERS.) Des Dents des Mammiferes, considerees Comme Caracteres Zoologiques. M. F. Cuvier. Paris, pp.1-259, illus., 1825.

(ON CORRELATIONS IN THE PHYLOGENETIC DEVELOPMENT OF THE CRANIAL FORM. I. CONNECTIONS BETWEEN TRUNK AND CRANIAL FORM.) Ueber die Korrelationen in der phylogenetischen Entwicklung der Schaedelform. I. Die Beziehungen zwischen Rumpf und Schaedelform. A. Dabelow. Gegenbaur's Morphol. Jahrb., Leipzig, vol. 63, pp.1-49, figs.27, 1929.

ABNORMAL MAMMAL SKULLS FROM WASHINGTON. Walter W. Dalquest. Murrelet, Seattle, vol.20, no.1, p.19, Jan.-Apr., 1939.

DEVELOPMENT OF THE VERTEBRATE SKULL. G. R. de Beer. Oxford Univ. Press, pp.I-XXIII, 1-552, pls.143, 1937.

STUDIES ON THE VERTEBRATE HEAD. II. ORBITO-TEMPORAL REGION OF THE SKULL. G. R. de Beer. Quart. Jour. Micro. Sci., vol.70, pp.263-370, figs.133, Apr., 1926.

(LOCATION OF THE MACULA ACUSTICA IN THE SKULL OF MAN AND SOME MAMMALS.) Die Stellung der Maculae acustica im Schaedel des Menschen und einigen Saeugetiere. H. M. de Burlet. Morphol. Jahrb., vol.64, no.2, pp.377-393, 1930.

(ON SOME GENERAL CHARACTERISTICS OF THE MAMMAL SKULL.) Ueber einige allgemeine Zuege des Saeugetierschaedels. G. A. Dschawaschischwili. Bull. Mus. Georgie, Tbilissi, vol.10-A, pp.1-70, 1940.

NOTES ON THE FIRST OR MILK DENTITION OF THE MAMMALIA. William Henry Flower. Trans. Odontograph. Soc. Great Britain, vol.3, pp.211-232 (1-22), May 1,1871.

(THE CRANIUM OF MAN AND THAT OF MAMMALS.) Le crane de l'homme en tant que crane de mammifere. Serge Frechkop. Bull. Inst. Roy. Sci. Nat. Belgique, Brussels, vol.25, no.23, pp.12, figs.7, Aug., 1949.

(NOTE ON THE MAMMALS. XIII. PRELIMINARY NOTE ON THE SIMILARITY OF THE SUPERIOR AND INFERIOR MOLARS.) Notes sur les Mammifêres. XIII. Note prèliminaire sur la similitude des molaires superieúres et inferieures. Serge Frechkop. Bull. Mus. Roy. Hist. Nat. Belgique, Bruxelles, vol.9, no.7, pp.1-11, figs.6, Mar., 1933.

(NOTES ON THE MAMMALS. XV. THE RELATIONS BETWEEN THE ANTAGONIST MOLAR TEETH IN THE VEGETARIAN MAMMALS.) Notes sur les Mammiferes. XV. Les relations entre les molaires antagonistes chez les Mammiferes vegetariens. Serge Frechkop. Bull. Mus. Roy. Hist. Nat. Belgique, Bruxelles, vol.9, no.41, pp.1-35, figs.19, Dec., 1933.

(NOTES ON THE MAMMALS. XIX. THE HAMSTER SHOWING THE FUNDAMENTAL DIFFERENCE BETWEEN THE MOLARS OF RODENTS AND THOSE OF UNGULATES.) Notes sur les mammiferes. XIX. Le Hamster montrant la difference fondamentale entre les molaires des Rongeurs et celles des Ongules. Serge Frechkop. Mus. Roy. d'Hist. Nat. Belgique, vol.12, no.18, pp.1-8, figs. 4, June, 1936.

(ON SOME CHARACTERISTICS OF THE CRANIUM OF UNGULATES.) Sur quelques caracteres du crane chez les Ongules. Serge Frechkop. Bull. Mus. Roy. Hist. Nat., Brussels, vol.24, no.15, pp.1-8, 1948.

SOME PECULIAR AUDITORY OSSICLES. Clay B. Freudenberger. Science, n.s., vol.65, pp.450-451, May 6, 1927.

(INFLUENCE OF SIZE ON THE MORPHOLOGY OF THE TEETH IN MAMMALS.) L'influence de la taille sur la morphologie des dents chez les mammiferes. M. Friant. La Terre et la Vie (Revue d'Hist. Nat.), vol. 2, no.3, pp.135-143, figs.9, Mar., 1932.

(ODONTOGRAPHY: COMPARATIVE REPRESENTATION OF THE DENTAL SYSTEM OF LIVING AND FOSSIL VERTEBRATES.) Vergleichende darstellung des Zahnsystemes der Lebenden und Fossilen Wirbelthiere. Christoph G. Giebel. 1855.

KEY TO THE SKULLS OF NORTH AMERICAN MAMMALS. Bryan P. Glass. Minneapolis, Burgess Pub. Co., pp.541, illus., 2d printing, 1951.

STUDIES IN COMPARATIVE MYOLOGY AND OSTEOLOGY; NO. V. ON THE ANATOMY OF THE PREORBITAL FOSSAE OF EQUIDAE AND OTHER UNGULATES. K. Gregory. Bull. Amer. Mus. Nat. Hist., vol. 42, pp.265-284, pl.1, figs.26, Dec. 4, 1920.

ORIGIN OF THE MAMMALIAN ALISPHENOID BONE. W. K. Gregory, G. K. Noble. Jour. Morph. and Physiol., vol.39, pp.435-464, figs.14, Dec. 5, 1924.

INTERORBITAL SEPTUM IN MAMMALS. Wheeler R. Haines. Jour. Linnean Soc. London, Zool., vol.41, no.282, pp.585-607, figs.40, Mar. 17, 1950.

SUPERNUMERARY AND MISSING TEETH IN WILD MAMMALS OF THE ORDERS INSECTIVORA AND CARNIVORA, WITH SOME NOTES ON DISEASE. Raymond E. Hall. Jour. Dental Research, Baltimore, vol.19, no.2, pp.103-143, pl.12, Apr., 1940.

DIMENSION VERSUS FORM IN TEETH AND THEIR BEARING ON THE MORPHOLOGY OF THE DENTAL ARCH. Milo Hellman. Internat. Jour. Orthodontia and Oral Surgery, vol.5, no.11, pp.3-39 of reprint, figs.1-22, Nov., 1919.

(CRANIOLOGICAL STUDIES.) Craniologische Studien. Reinhold Hensel. Nova Acta der Ksl. Leop.-Carol.-Deutschen Akad. der Naturforscher, Bd.XLII, no.4, 1881.

(ON THE HOMOLOGIES AND VARIANTS IN THE DENTAL FORMULAS OF SOME MAMMALS.) Ueber Homologien und Varianten in den Zahnformeln einiger Saeugethieren. Reinhold Hensel. Morpholog. Jahrbuch., vol.5, pp.529-561, 1878.

(OBSERVATIONS ON PRIMITIVE MAMMAL DENTITIONS.) Beobachtungen an primitiven Saeugetiergebissen. Mathilde Hertz. Zeitschr. f. Morph. und Oekologie der Tiere, vol.4, pp.540-584, pl.13, figs. 45, 1925.

ASYMMETRY IN THE SKULLS OF MAMMALS. A.Brazier Howell. Proc. U.S. Nat. Mus., vol.67, art.27, pp.1-18, pls.1-8, Dec. 31, 1925.

CAUSES OF MALOCCLUSION. Ales Hrdlicka. Dental Cosmos, May, 1922.

DIVISION OF THE PARIETAL BONE IN MAN AND OTHER MAMMALS. Ales Hrdlicka. Bull. Amer. Mus. Nat. Hist., vol.19, art.8, pp.231-286, figs.1-39, pls. 7-22, July 11, 1903.

THE FOREHEAD. Ales Hrdlicka. Proc. Amer. Philos. Soc., vol.72, no.5, pp. 315-324, 1933.

FURTHER INSTANCES OF MALAR DIVISION. Ales Hrdlicka. Amer. Nat., vol.38, no.449, pp.361-366, figs.1-5, May, 1904.

FURTHER INSTANCES OF PARIETAL DIVISION. Ales. Hrdlicka. Amer. Nat., Lancaster, vol.38, no.448, pp.301-309, figs.1-4, Apr., 1904.

SHOVEL-SHAPED TEETH. Ales Hrdlicka. Amer. Jour. Phys. Anthr., vol.3, pp.429-465, Dec., 1920.

ON THE STRUCTURE AND DEVELOPMENT OF THE ENAMEL IN MAMMALS. G. Jasswoin. Quart. Jour. Micro, Sci., vol.69, pp. 97-118, pl.6, figs.2, Dec., 1924.

REPORT ON THE DENTAL PATHOLOGY FOUND IN ANIMALS THAT DIED IN THE NEW YORK ZOOLOGICAL PARK IN 1938. Theodore Kazimiroff. Zoologica, New York, vol.24, pt.3, pp.297-304, pls.9, Nov. 2, 1939.

AUDITORY BULLA IN SOME FOSSIL MAMMALS. WITH A GENERAL INTRODUCTION TO THIS REGION OF THE SKULL. C. J. van der Klaauw. Bull. Amer. Mus. Nat. Hist., vol.62, pp.352, figs.18, 1931.

ON MAMMALIAN AUDITORY BULLAE SHOWING AN INDISTINCTLY COMPLEX STRUCTURE IN THE ADULT. C. J. van der Klaauw. Jour. Mamm., vol.11, no.1, pp.55-60, pl.3, Feb. 11, 1930.

SIZE AND POSITION OF THE FUNCTIONAL COMPONENTS OF THE SKULL. C. J. van der Klaauw. Arch. Neerlandaises Zool., Leiden, vol.9, nos.1-2, pp.1-176, 1948; vol.9, no.4, pp.369-559, 1952.

(STRUCTURE AND DEVELOPMENT OF THE AUDITORY OSSICLES.) Bau und Entwicklung der Gehoerknoechelchen. C. J. van der Klaauw. Ergebnisse Anat. und Entwicklungsgesch., vol.25, pp.565-622, 1924.

EFFECT OF TOPICALLY APPLIED SODIUM FLUORIDE ON DENTAL CARIES EXPERIENCE. John W. Knutson. Publ. Health Repts., Washington, D. C., vol.58, no. 47, pp.1701-1715, Nov. 19, 1943.

RACIAL AND INDIVIDUAL VARIATION IN CERTAIN FACIODENTAL RELATIONSHIPS. Wilton Marion Krogman. Jour. Dental Res., vol.14, no.4, pp.277-296, figs.4, Aug., 1934.

(SO-CALLED LAW OF COMPENSATION OF GOETHE IN CONNECTION WITH THE CORRELATION OF ANTLERS AND UPPER TEETH.) Das sog. Kompensationsgesetz Goethes betr. Korrelation von Kopfwaffen und Oberzaehnen. Ingo Krumbiegel. Zu Goethes 100 Todestag am 22.3.1932. Zeitschr. f. Saeugetierkunde, Berlin, vol.6, no.5, pp. 186-202, figs.4, pl.21, figs.5-6, Dec. 15, 1931.

(ADAPTATION PHENOMENA IN THE CHEWING APPARATUS OF MAMMALS BIOLOGICALLY DIFFERING AS REGARDS NUTRITION.) Anpassungserscheinungen am Kauapparat bei ernaehrungsbiologisch verschiedenen Saeugetieren. Friedrich Kuhlhorn. Zool. Anz., Leipzig, vol.121, nos. 1-2, pp.1-17, figs.3, tbl.1, Jan.1, 1938.

OBSERVATION ON ALLOMETRY IN MAMMALIAN DENTITIONS; ITS INTERPRETATION AND EVOLUTIONARY SIGNIFICANCE. Bjorn Kurten. Acta Zool. Fennica, vol.85, pp.1-13, illus., 1954.

(INVESTIGATIONS ON THE DEVELOPMENT OF THE OCCIPITAL BONE OF MAMMALS.) Recherches sur le developpement de l'occipital des mammiferes. Nouvelles observations sur l'evolution embryologique de l'ecaille occipitale de l'homme. A. Lacoste, A. Baudrimont. Comptes Rendus Seances Soc. Biol., Paris, vol.98, pp.955-957, Apr. 17, 1928.

(CONSIDERATIONS ON THE TWO DENTITIONS OF THE MAMMALS.) Considerations sur les deux dentitions des mammiferes. Fernand Lataste. Jour. Anat. & Phys., Paris, vol.25, pp.200-222, 1889.

(DEVELOPMENT OF THE DENTAL SYSTEM OF MAMMALS.) Die Entwicklung des Zahnsystems der Saeugethiere. Wilhelm Leche. Compte-Rendu Seances Troisieme Cong. Int. Zool., Leyden, pp.279-289, Sep. 16-21, 1895.

(ON DENTAL VARIATION IN FULLY DEVELOPED MAMMALS.) Ueber zahnwechsel bei Saeugetieren im erwachsenen Zustand. Wilhelm Leche. Zool. Anz., vol.27, nos.7-8, pp.219-222, figs.3, Jan. 26, 1904.

(ON THE QUESTION OF DENTITIONS.) Zur Dentitionenfrage. Wilhelm Leche. Anat. Anz., Jena, vol.11, no.9, pp.270-276, 1895.

(ON THE QUESTION OF THE PHYLOGENIC SIGNIFICANCE OF THE DECIDUOUS TEETH IN MAMMALS. FIRST COMMUNICATION.) Zur Frage nach der stammesgeschichtlichen Bedeutungen des Milchgebisses bei den Saeugetieren. 1. Mitteilung. Wilhelm Leche. Zool. Jahrb., Abt. Syst. Geog., Biol. der Tiere, vol.28, no.4, pp.449-456, pl.9, 1909.

(STUDIES OF THE DEVELOPMENT OF THE DENTAL SYSTEM OF MAMMALS.) Studien ueber die Entwicklung des Zahnsystems bei den Saeugethieren. Wilhelm Leche. Leipzig, pp.47, 1892; Separat-abdruck aus Morpholog. Jahrb. Bd.19, Heft 3, pp.502-547; Nachtraege zu "Studien ueber die Entwicklung des Zahnsystems bei den Saeugethieren." Leipzig, pp.30, 1893; Separat-abdruck, aus Morpholog. Jahrb. Bd.20, Heft 2, pp.113-142, figs.1-12, 1893.

MOLAR TEETH AND OTHER REMEINS OF MAMMALIA. Richard Lydekker. Calcutta, Office of superintendent of government printing, pp.iv-69, pl.iv-x, 1876.

(OUTLINE OF A FUNCTIONAL ANALYSIS OF THE TETRAPOD SKULL.) Grundriss einer funktionellen Analyse des Tetrapodenschaedels. W. Marinelli. Palaeobiologica, vol.2, pp.127-142, pls.11-14, 1929.

GRAPHIC REPRESENTATION OF THE INSIDE OF THE SKULL WITH SPECIAL REFERENCE TO THE PITUITARY FOSSA. Jindrich Matiegka. Amer. Jour. Phys. Anthrop., Philadelphia, vol.3, no.4, pp. 397-402, figs.2, Oct.-Dec., 1920.

ADAPTIVE MODIFICATIONS OF OCCIPITAL CONDYLES IN MAMMALIA. Charles S. Mead. Amer. Nat., Boston, vol.40, no. 475, pp.475-483, figs.12, July, 1906.

COMPARATIVE CHART OF THE VERTEBRATE SKULL. Charles S. Mead. Contrib. from the Zool. laboratory of Ohio State Univ., no.15, pp.52-55, tbls., 1904; Reprint from Ohio Naturalist, vol.IV, no.3, Jan., 1904.

ON ABNORMAL TEETH IN CERTAIN MAMMALS, ESPECIALLY IN THE RABBIT. W.C. M'Intosh. Trans. Roy. Soc. Edinburgh, vol. 56, pt.2, no.16, pp.333-407, figs.103, 1929.

ORBITOTEMPORAL REGION OF THE SKULL OF THE MAMMALIA. Johanna Muller. Archiv. Neerlandaises de Zool., Leiden, vol.1, nos. 1-2, pp.118-259, figs.114, 1934.

(NOTES ON THE MORPHOLOGY AND PHYLOGENY OF THE VERTEBRATES. 6) ON THE PHYLOGENY OF MAMMALIAN MOLARS.) Notizen zur Morphologie und Stammesgeschichte der Wirbeltiere. 6. Zur Stammesgeschichte der Saeuger-Molaren. A. Naef. Biol. Zentralblatt, vol.45, pp.668-676, figs.5, 1925.

(NOTES ON THE MORPHOLOGY AND PHYLOGENY OF THE VERTEBRATES. 11) ON A NEW THEORY OF THE DEVELOPMENT OF THE MAMMAL DENTITION.) Notizen zur Morphologie und Stammesgeschichte der Wirbeltiere. 11. Ueber eine neue Theorie der Entwicklung des Saeugetiergebisses. A. Naef. Biol. Zentralblatt, vol.46, pp. 306-314, fig.1, 1926.

TEXT-BOOK OF DENTAL HISTOLOGY AND EMBRYOLOGY INCLUDING LABORATORY DIRECTIONS. Frederick Bogue Noyes, Isaac Schour, Harold Judd Noyes. Lea & Febiger, Philadelphia, pp.1-445, figs.284, pls.11, 1938.

CALCULATION OF THE AVERAGE AGE OF SHEDDING AND ERUPTION OF TEETH. H. Cl. Nybølle. Meddelelser om Danmarks Anthrop., vol.3, no.2, pp.331-352, tbls., 1931. (In Danish, with English summary.)

ODONTOGRAPHY; OR, A TREATISE ON THE COMPARATIVE ANATOMY OF THE TEETH; THEIR PHYSIOLOGICAL RELATIONS, MODE OF DEVELOPMENT, AND MICROSCOPIC STRUCTURE IN THE VERTEBRATE ANIMALS. R. Owen. London, vol.1, pp.ix-xix, i-lxxiv, 1-655; vol. 2, pp.7-37, pls.1-150, 1840 1845.

ON THE STRUCTURE AND DEVELOPMENT OF THE SKULL IN THE MAMMALIA. William Kitchen Parker. London, 1874-85, pts. 3; from the Philosophical transactions of the Roy. Soc., vol.164, pp.289-376, 1874, vol. 176, pp.1-120, 121-275, 1885. (Pt.1 has title: On the structure and development of the skull in the pig (Sus scrofa).)

FURTHER NOTES ON TOOTH-REPLACEMENT. F. R. Parrington. Ann. and Mag. Nat. Hist., London, ser.10, vol.18, no.103, pp.109-116, figs.3, July, 1936.

ON A COLLECTION OF RHAETIC MAMMALIAN TEETH. F. R. Parrington. Proc. Zool. Soc. London, vol.116, pts.3-4, pp. 707-728, pl.1, figs.8, Feb. 28, 1947.

IDENTIFYING TOOTH MARKS OF SOME NORTH-EASTERN ANIMALS ON FOREST VEGETATION. John Pearce. Trans. N. A. Wildl. Conf., vol.3, pp.690-694, 1938.

HINDER END OF THE SKULL IN MERYCOPOTAMUS AND IN HIPPOPOTAMUS MINUTUS. Helga S. Pearson. Jour. Anat., vol.63, no.2, pp.237-241, figs.4, 1929.

PICTURES OF IVORY AND OTHER ANIMAL TEETH, BONE AND ANTLER, WITH A BRIEF COMMENTARY ON THEIR USE IN IDENTIFICATION. T. K. Penniman. Pitt Rivers Mus., Occas. Pap. Tech., vol. 5, p.40, pl.20, 1952.

ESSAY IN COMPARATIVE DENTAL ANATOMY. Viger Plamondon. Annual Rept. 1946, Provancher Soc. Nat. Hist. Canada, Quebec, pp.50-60, figs.13, 1946; pp.50-66, figs.13, 1948.

(STUDIES OF THE PHYLOGENY OF THE HUMAN CANINE TOOTH.) Studien ueber die Phylogenie des menschlichen Eckzahns. A. Remane. Zeitschr. Anat. u. Entwicklungsgesch., vol.82, pp.391-481, 1927.

REVISION OF DENTAL SYMBOLS. Elmer S. Riggs. Science, Lancaster, n.s., vol. 89, no.2310, pp.315-316, Apr.7, 1939.

MAMMALIAN LOWER JAW. (ABSTRACT.) W. H. Ruddick, J. S. Kingsley. Biol. Bull. Boston, vol.2, no.6, p.339, June, 1901.

(CONSIDERATIONS ON THE HOMOLOGY OF THE LACHRYMAL BONE IN THE HIGHER VERTEBRATES.) Considerations sur l'homologie de l'os lacrymal chez les vertebrés superieurs. M. I. Salomon. Acta Zoologica, vol.11, pp.15-183, figs.27, 1930.

EFFECTS OF HIBERNATION ON TOOTH DEVELOPMENT. Bernhard G. Sarnat. Anat. Rec., Philadelphia, vol.83, no.4, pp.471-493, figs.4, pl.1, Aug. 25, 1942.

EAR REGION AND THE FORAMINA OF THE CYNODONT SKULL. George Gaylord Simpson. Amer. Jour. Sci., ser.5, vol.26, no.153, pp.285-294, figs.5, Sep., 1933.

"PLAGIAULACOID" TYPE OF MAMMALIAN DENTITION. George Gaylord Simpson. Jour. Mamm., vol.14, no.2, pp.97-107, May, 1933.

STUDIES OF THE EARLIEST MAMMALIAN DENTITIONS. George Gaylord Simpson. Dental Cosmos, Philadelphia, vol.78, no.9, pp.940-953, figs.10, Sep., 1936.

ON CERTAIN VACUITIES OR DEFICIENCIES IN THE CRANIA OF MAMMALS. D. D. Slade. Cambridge, pp.241-246, pls.2, 1888; Bull. Mus. comp. zool., vol.13, 1886-1888.

SIGNIFICANCE OF THE JUGAL ARCH. D. D. Slade. Proc. Amer. Philos. Soc., Philadelphia, vol.34, pp.1-17, illus., May 15, 1895.

(CRANIAL ASYMMETRY AS A RESULT OF ONE-SIDED CHEWING-MUSCLE ACTIVITY.) Schaedelassymmetrie als Folge einseitiger Kaumuskeltaetigkeit. W. Spoettel. Zool. Anz., vol.71, pp.303-331, figs.5, May 28, 1927.

BEASTLY DENTISTRY. Q. M. Stephen-Hassard. Zoonooz Zool. Soc. San Diego, vol.28, no.12, pp.5-7, illus., Dec., 1955.

MICROSCOPIC OBSERVATION OF THE LIVING TOOTH PULP. Cecil A. Taylor. Science, Lancaster, vol.111, no.2872, pp. 1-40, Jan. 13, 1950.

(ON THE QUESTION OF THE CONTINUOUS GROWTH OF MOLAR TEETH IN HOOFED ANIMALS.) Zur Frage ueber das fortdauernde Wachsen der Kauzaehne bei Huftieren. V. A. K. Teriajev. Biulleten' Moskovskogo Obshchestva Ispytatelei Prirody, Otdel Geologicheskii (Bull. Soc. Nat. Moscow, sect.géol.), vol.10, no.1, pp.170-192, figs. 17, 1932.

OBSERVATION ON THE DEVELOPMENT OF THE MAMMALIAN VOMER. Robert J. Terry. Anat. Rec., Philadelphia, vol.3, no.10, pp.525-529, figs.2, Oct., 1909.

X-RAY EXAMINATION OF TOOTH STRUCTURE. J. Thewlis. Nature, London, vol. 137, no.3472, p.828, May 16, 1936.

NOTES ON A STRIKING INSTANCE OF CRANIAL VARIATION DUE TO AGE. Oldfield Thomas. Proc. Zool. Soc., London, pp.125-127, pl.11, Feb. 16, 1886.

NOTES ON DR. W. KUKENTHAL'S DISCOVERIES IN MAMMALIAN DENTITION. Oldfield Thomas. Ann. Mag. Nat. Hist., (6), vol.9, no.52, pp.308-313, Apr. 1892.

(REMARKS ON DR. SCHLOSSER'S "ON THE SIGNIFICANCE OF THE DECIDUOUS DENTITION OF THE MAMMALS".) Oldfield Thomas. Zoologisches Centralblatt, vol.10, no.7, pp.216-219, May 15, 1890.

SUGGESTIONS FOR THE NOMENCLATURE OF THE CRANIAL LENGTH MEASUREMENTS AND OF THE CHEEK-TEETH OF MAMMALS. Oldfield Thomas. Proc. Biol. Soc., Washington, vol.18, pp.191-196, Sep. 2, 1905.

INTRODUCTION TO THE MAMMALIAN DENTITION. Thomas Wingate Todd. St. Louis, C. V. Mosby Co., pp.11-290, illus., 1918.

DESCRIPTION OF AN ODONTOME. Charles S. Tomes. Trans. Odontological Soc. Great Britain, London, pp.1-8, figs.4, 1872.

(INVESTIGATIONS OF PHILOGENETIC MORPHOLOGY OF THE UPPER MOLARS OF THE UNGULATES.) Investigaciones de Morfologia Filogenetica en los Molares Superiores de los Ungulados. Alfredo J. Torcelli. Obras Completas y Correspondencia cientifica de Florentino Ameghino, vol. 9, pp.1-619, figs.631, 1933.

STUDIES IN FUNCTIONAL AND ANALYTICAL CRANIOLOGY. R. Tucker. I-VI. Australian Jour. Zool., vol.2, no.3, pp.381-430, Nov., 1954.

ON THE EVIDENCES OF AFFINITY AFFORDED BY THE SKULL IN THE UNGULATE MAMMALIA. H. N. Turner. Proc. Zool. Soc. London, pt.17, pp.147-157, 1849.

(HISTOGENESIS OF THE FUNDAMENTAL SUBSTANCE OF MAMMAL DENTITION.) La histogenésis de la substancia fundamental de la dentina de los mamiferos. Carlos von Korff. Sem. Med. (Buenos Aires), vol. 34, pp.311-313, illus., 1927.

ANTERIOR PROCESS AND THE OSSIFICATION OF THE MALLEUS IN MAMMALS. Kamal Wassif. Science, vol.113, no.2937, pp.486-487, Apr. 27, 1951.

(ON THE STRUCTURE AND DEVELOPMENT OF THE DENTINE IN THE VERTEBRATES.) Ueber den Bau und die Entwicklung des Zahnbeins in der Reihe der Wirbeltiere. F. Weidenreich. Zeitschr. f. Anat. u. Entwicklungsgesch., vol.76, pp.218-260, figs.23, Apr. 5, 1925.

SHIFTING OF THE MOLAR ROW WITH REGARD TO THE ORBIT IN EQUUS AND GIRAFFA. Maria C. A. Willemse. Zool. Mededel. Rijksmus. Nat. Hist. Leiden, vol.30, no.23, pp.311-326, June 17, 1950.

RELATIONSHIP BETWEEN THE LENGTH OF THE JAW AND THE LENGTH OF THE MOLAR SERIES IN SOME EUTHERIAN MAMMALS. G. Williams. Proc. Zool. Soc. London, vol.126, pt.1, pp.51-64, Jan.11, 1956.

TWO CASES OF DENTAL ANOMALY IN EARLY TERTIARY MAMMALS. Robert W. Wilson. Trans. Kansas Acad. Sci., vol.58, no.4, pp.514-518, Jan. 23, 1956.

ON DIFFERENCES IN THE LOWER JAW OF ANIMALIVOROUS AND HERBIVOROUS MAMMALS. Mrs. E. Arendsen de Wolff-Exalto. I. Proc. Kon. Nederlandse Akad. Wetenschappen, Amsterdam, vol.54, no. 3, pp.237-246, May-June, 1951.

CAUSAL FACTORS IN SHORTENING TOOTH SERIES WITH AGE. Horace Elmer Wood 2nd. Jour. Dental Res., Baltimore, vol.17, no.1, pp.1-13, figs.5, Feb., 1938.

COMPARATIVE ANATOMY OF THE TEETH OF THE VERTEBRATA. Jacob L. Wortman. Reprinted from the American System of Dentistry, pp.351-503, illus., pls.6, 1886.

ON SOME HITHERTO UNRECOGNIZED REPTILIAN CHARACTERS IN THE SKULL OF THE INSECTIVORA AND OTHER MAMMALS. Jacob L. Wortman. Proc. U. S. Nat. Mus., vol.57, pp.1-52, figs.1-16, 1920.

LONDON SKULL. Matthew Young. Biometrika Univ. College, London, vol.229, pts. 3-4, pp.277-321, figs.1-7, tbls.3, pls.1-3, Feb., 1938.

(CONTRIBUTION TO KNOWLEDGE OF THE FINER STRUCTURE OF DENTINAL TUBULES.) Beitrag zur Kenntnis des feineren Baues der Dentinkanaelchen. Rainer Zangerl. Schweizerische Monatsschrift f. Zahnheilkunde, Zuerich, vol.43, no.12, pp.1-10, figs.2, pls.1-2, 1933.

(STUDIES ON THE DEVELOPMENT OF THE DENTAL SYSTEM IN THE MAMMALS.) Studien ueber die Entwicklung des Zahnsystems bei den Saeugethieren. Anat. Anz., Jahrg.7, pp.502-547, figs.1-20, 1882.

## ANATOMY -- WEIGHTS AND MEASUREMENTS

GEOGRAPHICAL VARIATION AMONG NORTH AMERICAN MAMMALS, ESPECIALLY IN RESPECT TO SIZE. J. A. Allen. Bull. U.S. Geol. Surv. Terr., vol.2, no.4, pp.309-344, July 1, 1876.

(PRELIMINARY NOTES ON THE WEIGHT OF NEWBORN AS COMPARED TO THAT OF ADULTS IN SOME MAMMALS.) Note preliminaire sur le poids du nouveau-ne compare a celui de l'adulte chez quelques mammiferes. R. Anthony. Bull. et Mem. Soc. d'Anthorp. Paris, ser.7, vol.5, pp. 52-58, 1924.

(CONCERNING THE WEIGHT OF MICROMAMMALS.) A propos du poids des micromammiferes. P. Cantuel. Mammalia, Paris, vol.16, no.2, p.98, June, 1952.

(LEAST WEIGHTS OF SOME SMALL MAMMALS OF THE FRENCH FAUNA.) Poids Moyens de quelques Micromammifères de la Faune francaise. P. Cantuel. Mammalia, Paris, vol.4, nos.3-4, pp.113-116, tbl.1, Sep.-Dec., 1940.

RELATION OF ADRENAL WEIGHT TO BODY WEIGHT IN MAMMALS. John J. Christian. Science, vol.117, no.3030, pp. 78-80, graph., Jan. 23, 1953.

RECORD OF THE BODY WEIGHT AND CERTAIN ORGAN AND GLAND WEIGHTS OF 3690 ANIMALS. George Chile, Daniel P. Quiring. Ohio Jour. Sci., Columbus, vol.40, no.5, pp.210-259, Sept., 1940. (Mammals, pp.227-233, 238-243, 245-259.)

QUESTIONS OF CUBITS. III. THE GAME OF NORTH AMERICA. Paul Curtis. Field, London, vol.167, no.4340, p.457, illus., Feb.29, 1936.

DRESSED WEIGHTS OF MUSKRATS, BEAVERS AND JACK RABBITS. Joseph Dixon. Jour. Mamm., vol.7, no.2, pp.133-134, May, 1926.

(RATIO OF WEIGHT OF BRAIN TO SIZE OF BODY IN MAMMALS.) De verhouding van het gewicht der hersenen tot de grootte van het lichaa, bij de zoogdieren. Eugene Dubois. Amsterdam, J. Mueller, pp.1-41, 1897.

(INVESTIGATIONS OF BODY SIZE AND BONE STRUCTURE IN MAMMALS.) Untersuchungen ueber Koerpergroesse und Knochenstruktur bei Saeugetieren. Wolfgang Ertelt. Zool. Jahrb., vol.74, no.4, pp.588-638, Dec. 30, 1955.

(CONSIDERATIONS ON THE RELATIONSHIP BETWEEN BODY WEIGHT AND ORGAN WEIGHT.) Betrachtungen ueber die Beziehungen zwischen Koerpergewicht und Organgewicht. H. Frick. Zeitschr. Saeugetierk., Berlin, vol.22, nos.3-4, pp.193-207, 1957.

DRESSED WEIGHTS OF SOME GAME MAMMALS. W. J. Hamilton, Jr. Jour. Wildl. Mgt., vol.11, no.4, pp.349-350, Oct., 1947.

NORMAL WEIGHT. John Eric Hill. Nat. Hist., New York, vol.53, no.4, p.186, Apr., 1944.

(RELATIONS BETWEEN CLIMATE AND BODY SIZE AND SURFACE PROPORTIONS IN AUSTRALASIAN MAMMALS.) Koerpergroesse und Oberflaechenverhaeltnisse bei australasiatischen Saeugetieren in ihrer Abhaengigkeit vom Klima. Heinrich Jansen. Zool. Jahrb. (Systematik), vol.58, pp.381-458, maps 12, Dec. 15, 1929.

WEIGHTS OF BIG GAME. G. W. R. LeMare. Field, London, vol.166, no.4316, p.601, Sep. 14, 1935.

QUESTIONS OF CUBITS-NO. 1. MEASURING AFRICAN ANIMALS. Mannlicher. Field, London, vol.167, no.4338, p.349, illus., Feb. 15, 1936.

QUALITY IN LARGE PACKAGES. Alexander C. Martin. Sports Afield, vol.131, no.2, pp. 23-29, Feb., 1954.

SMALL ONLY IN SIZE. Alexander C. Martin. Sports Afield, vol.130, no.3, pp.25-31, illus., Sep., 1953.

MEASUREMENTS OF BIG GAME. R. Meinertzhagen. Field, London, vol.166, no.4326, p.1239, Nov. 23, 1935.

SOME WEIGHTS AND MEASUREMENTS OF LARGE MAMMALS. R. Meinertshagen. Proc. Zool. Soc. London, ser.A, vol.108, pt.3, pp.433-439, Sep. 28, 1938.

(TAIL MEASUREMENTS IN GROWING MAMMALS.) Schwanzmessungen bei wachsenden Saeugetieren. Erna Mohr. Zeitschr. f. Saeugetierk., vol.2, no.1, pp.74-77, figs.7, Oct. 15, 1927.

MEASUREMENTS OF TIGER, PANTHER, BISON, AND SAMBHUR. R. C. Morris. Jour. Bombay Nat. Hist. Soc., vol.40, no. 3, p.555, Dec., 1938.

MEASURING MAMMALS' TAILS. T. C. S. Morrison-Scott. Ann. Mag. Nat. Hist., London, ser.11, vol.3, no.14, pp.216-219, figs. 3, Feb., 1939.

(WEIGHTS AND MEASUREMENTS OF LARGE MAMMALS ACCORDING TO COL. R. MEINERTZHAGEN.) Mensurations et poids des gros mammiferes d'apres le Colonel R. Meinertzhagen. P. Rode. Mammalia, Paris, vol.3, nos.3-4, pp.126-131, Sep.-Dec., 1939.

BODY SIZE WITH RELATION TO POPULATION DENSITY IN MAMMALS. V. B. Scheffer. Jour. Mamm., vol.36, pp.493-515, 1955.

HOW HEAVY IS YOUR GAME? Walter J. Schoonmaker. Field & Stream, vol.41, no. 4, p.72, Aug., 1936.

(ON THE VARIATIONS IN SIZE OF MAMMALS AND THE SOREX MACROPYGMAEUS MILL. PROBLEM IN FENNOSCANDIA.) Ueber die Groessenvariationen der Saeugetiere und die Sorex macropygmaeus Mill.-Frage in Fennoskandien. Lauri Siivonen. Suomalaisen Tiedeakatemian Toimitaksia, Ann. Acad. Sci. Fennicae, ser.A, no.21, pp.1-24, 1954.

QUESTIONS OF CUBITS IV. INDIAN HEADS-KASHMIR TO COCHIN. C. H. Stockley. Field, London, vol.167, no.4341, pp.517-518, illus., Mar. 7, 1936.

SOME MEASUREMENTS OF BIG GAME. C. H. Stockley. Jour. Bombay Nat. Hist. Soc., vol.28, p.543, Mar. 25, 1922.

## ANNUAL ZOOLOGICAL REPORTS

REPORT OF THE DIVISION OF WILD LIFE. Stanley C. Arthur. Seventh Biennial Rep. Dept. Conservation State of Louisiana, pp.62-176, illus., July, 1926; 8th Biennial

Rep. Dept. Conservation State of Louisiana, 1926-1928, pp.226, 324, illus., May, 1928.

REPORT OF THE CURATOR, ZOOL. DEPARTMENT. Edward Blyth. Jour. Asiatic Soc. Bengal, pp.341-361, Apr., 1852; vol. 25, pp.1-10, 1856.

ANNUAL REPORT OF THE ZOOLOGICAL SOCIETY OF PHILADELPHIA. C. E. Brown. pp.1-60, illus., photos, 1931; pp.1-42, photos, 1933.

FIFTIETH ANNUAL REPORT OF THE BOARD OF DIRECTORS OF THE ZOOLOGICAL SOCIETY OF PHILADELPHIA. Williams B. Cadwalader. Pp.1-52, 1922.

FIFTY-FIRST ANNUAL REPORT OF THE BOARD OF DIRECTORS OF THE ZOOLOGICAL SOCIETY OF PHILADELPHIA. Williams B. Cadwalader. Pp.1-52, 1923.

FIFTY SECOND ANNUAL REPORT OF THE BOARD OF DIRECTORS OF THE ZOOLOGICAL SOCIETY OF PHILADELPHIA. Williams B. Cadwalader. Pp.38, pls.2, 1924.

ANNUAL REPORT OF THE ZOOLOGICAL SOCIETY OF PHILADELPHIA. Radcliffe Cheston, Jr. pp.1-55, figs., year ending Feb. 29, 1932.

ANNUAL REPORT OF THE DIRECTOR TO THE BOARD OF TRUSTEES FOR THE YEAR 1924. D. C. Davies. Field Mus. Nat. Hist., publ.227, report series vol.6, no.4, pp.269-383, pls.47-62, 1925.

ANNUAL REPORT LAKE STATES FOREST EXPERIMENT STATION, 1950. E. L. Demmon. USDA, Lake States Forest Exp. Sta., pp.1-31, 1950?

DIVISION OF MAMMALS. REPORT OF THE DIRECTOR OF THE MUSEUM OF ZOOLOGY TO THE BOARD OF REGENTS. Lee R. Dice. Univ. Michigan Official Publ., vol.30, no.16, pp.16-18, 1928.

REPORT OF THE DIRECTOR OF THE MUSEUM FOR THE YEAR 1923. Barton Warren Evermann. Proc. California Acad. Sci., ser.4, vol.12, pp.1232-1285, pls. 89-92, Oct. 10, 1924.

ZOOLOGICAL GARDENS, GIZA, NEAR CAIRO. REPORT FOR THE YEAR 1904 (SIXTH ANNUAL REPORT). S. S. Flower. Public Works Dept., Gov't Egypt, Cairo, pp.30, 1905.

REPORT ON THE ZOOLOGICAL SERVICE FOR THE YEAR 1920 IN WHICH IS INCLUDED THE 22nd ANNUAL REPORT OF THE GIZA ZOOLOGICAL GARDENS. S. S. Flower. Ministry of Public Works, Egypt, Zool. Service Pub., no.34, pp.1-20, Cairo, 1921.

REPORT ON THE ZOOLOGICAL SERVICE FOR THE YEAR 1922 IN WHICH IS INCLUDED THE 24th ANNUAL REPORT OF THE GIZA ZOOLOGICAL GARDENS. S. S. Flower. Pp.1-26, Cairo, Government press, 1923.

REPORT OF THE LABORATORY AND MUSEUM OF COMPARATIVE PATHOLOGY OF THE ZOOLOGICAL SOCIETY OF PHILADELPHIA. Herbert Fox. Pp.1-33, figs.12, 1924.

ANNUAL REPORT OF THE ZOOLOGICAL SOCIETY OF SCOTLAND FOR THE YEAR ENDING 31st MARCH, 1920. T. H. Gillespie. Pp.1-20, 1920.

ANNUAL REPORT OF THE ZOOLOGICAL SOCIETY OF SCOTLAND FOR THE YEAR ENDING 31st MARCH, 1923. T. H. Gillespie. Pp.1-24, pls.8, 1923.

ANNUAL REPORT OF THE ZOOLOGICAL SOCIETY OF SCOTLAND FOR THE YEAR ENDING 31st MARCH, 1924. T. H. Gillespie. Pp.1-74, pls.8, 1924.

NATIONAL ZOOLOGICAL GARDENS OF SOUTH AFRICA. REPORT FOR THE YEAR 1921. A. K. Haagner. Pretoria, pp.1-28, fig. 1, 1922.

REPORT OF THE COMMISSIONER OF DOMINION PARKS FOR THE YEAR ENDING MARCH 31, 1921. J. B. Harkin. Dept. of Interior, Ottawa, pp.1-70, numerous halftones, 1922.

REPORT OF WASHINGTON PARK ZOOLOGICAL SOCIETY FOR YEAR ENDING OCT. 1, 1927. Edmund Heller. Seventeenth annual report on the activities of the Washington Park Zoological Society, Milwaukee, Rep. of the director of the zoo, pp.1-87, 1927.

REPORT OF THE SUPERINTENDENT OF THE NATIONAL ZOOLOGICAL PARK FOR THE FISCAL YEAR ENDING JUNE 30, 1917. Ned Hollister. Ann. Rep. Smithsonian Inst., 1917, reprint Feb.7, pp.1-87, illus., 1918.

REPORT OF THE SUPERINTENDENT OF THE NATIONAL ZOOLOGICAL PARK FOR THE FISCAL YEAR ENDING JUNE 30, 1921. N. Hollister. Ann. Rep. Smithsonian Inst., pp.84-99, Dec., 1921.

REPORT OF THE SUPERINTENDENT OF THE NATIONAL ZOOLOGICAL PARK FOR THE FISCAL YEAR ENDING JUNE 30, 1923. N. Hollister. Ann. Rep. Smithsonian Inst., pp.87-104, Dec., 1923.

REPORT ON THE NATIONAL ZOOLOGICAL PARK FOR THE YEAR ENDING JUNE 30, 1918. N. Hollister. Ann. Rep. Smithsonian Inst., pp.66-81, Dec. 12, 1918. (Issued as separate with date 1919; reprinted in Smithsonian Rep. for 1918, Sep. 28, 1920.)

REPORT ON THE NATIONAL ZOOLOGICAL PARK FOR THE YEAR ENDING JUNE 30, 1919, N. Hollister. Ann. Rep. Smithsonian Inst., pp.68-81, Dec. 11, 1919. (Issued as separate with date 1920; reprinted in Smiths. Rep. for 1919, Sep. 30, 1921.)

REPORT ON THE NATIONAL ZOOLOGICAL PARK FOR THE YEAR ENDING JUNE 30, 1920. N. Hollister. Ann. Rep. Smithsonian Inst., pp.75-89, Dec. 9, 1920. (Issued as separate with date 1920; reprinted in Smithsonian Rep. for 1920, May 18, 1922.

REPORT ON THE NATIONAL ZOOLOGICAL PARK. N. Hollister. Smithsonian Rep., pp. 88-103, Dec., 1922.

REPORT OF THE CURATOR OF BIRDS AND MAMMALS. Laurence M. Huey. Ann. Rept. San Diego Soc. Nat. Hist., 1925, pp.17-19, 1926.

REPORT OF THE PROVINCIAL MUSEUM OF NATURAL HISTORY FOR THE YEAR 1921. Francis Kermode. Mammals. Rept. Provincial Mus. (British Columbia), 1921, pp.8-9, 1922.

(REPORT OF THE MUNICIPAL NATURAL HISTORY MUSEUM OF BERNE, SUPPLEMENT.) Berichte Stadt. Naturhist. Mus. Bern, Beilage. W. Kuenzi. Pp.1-4, figs.2, 1925.

REPORT OF THE DIRECTOR OF THE NATIONAL ZOOLOGICAL PARK FOR THE YEAR ENDED JUNE 30, 1931. W. M. Mann. Smithsonian Rep. for 1931, pp.86-116, 1931.

REPORT OF THE SUPERINTENDENT OF THE NATIONAL ZOOLOGICAL PARK FOR THE YEAR ENDED JUNE 30, 1925. W. M. Mann. Ann. Rep. Smithsonian Inst., 1925, appendix 6, pp.87-100, 1926.

(REPORT ON THE SCIENTIFIC WORK ACCOMPLISHED IN MAMMALIAN NATURAL HISTORY IN THE YEAR 1893.) Bericht ueber die wissenschaftlichen Leistungen in der Naturgeschichte der Saeugethiere waehrend des Jahres 1893. Paul Matschie. Archiv Naturg. Jahrb, Berlin, Bd.2, Heft 1, pp.141-258, 1895.

MAMMAL PORTION OF REPORT OF ORNITHOLOGIST AND MAMMALOGIST, U.S. DEPT. AGRIC., FOR 1886. Hart C. Merriam. Ann. Rep. of Commissioner of Agric., for 1886, pp.252-258, July, 1887.

REPORT OF THE ORNITHOLOGIST FOR THE YEAR 1886. Hart C. Merriam. Ann. Rep. of Dept. Agric., author's edition, pp.227-258, illus., folded map, 1887.

REPORT OF THE ORNITHOLOGIST AND MAMMALOGIST FOR THE YEAR 1887. C. Hart. Merriam. Ann Rep., Dept. Agric., pp.430-456, illus., 1888.

REPORT OF THE ORNITHOLOGIST AND MAMMALOGIST FOR THE YEAR 1888. C. Hart. Merriam. Ann. Rep., Dept. Agric., author's edition, pp.477-536, illus., 1889.

REPORT OF THE ORNITHOLOGIST AND MAMMALOGIST FOR THE YEAR 1889. C. Hart. Merriam. Ann. Rep., Dept. Agric., author's edition, pp.563-376, pls.2, 1890.

REPORT OF THE ORNITHOLOGIST AND MAMMALOGIST FOR THE YEAR 1890. C. Hart. Merriam. Ann. Rep., Dept. Agric., author's edition, pp.277-285, 1891.

REPORT OF THE ORNITHOLOGIST AND MAMMALOGIST FOR THE YEAR 1892. C. Hart. Merriam. Ann. Rep., Dept. Agric., pp.1-200, pls.4, 1893.

REPORT OF THE ORNITHOLOGIST AND MAMMALOGIST FOR THE YEAR 1893. C. Hart. Merriam. Ann. Rep., Dept. Agric., pp.227-234, folded map, 1894.

MAMMALOGY AND THE SMITHSONIAN INSTITUTION. Cerrit S. Miller, Jr. Ann. Rept. Board Regents Smithson. Inst. for 1928, publ.2981, pp.391-411, pls.1-3, Nov. 18, 1929.

REPORT ON THE DEPARTMENT OF BIOLOGY. REPORT ON THE PROGRESS AND CONDITION OF THE UNITED STATES NATIONAL MUSEUM FOR THE YEAR ENDING JUNE 30, 1922. Gerrit S. Miller, Jr. Pp.49-73, Dec. 20, 1922.

REPORT OF THE COUNCIL AND AUDITORS OF THE ZOOLOGICAL SOCIETY OF LONDON FOR THE YEAR 1924. P. Chalmers Mitchell. Pp.79, 1925.

REPORT OF THE COUNCIL AND AUDITORS OF THE ZOOLOGICAL SOCIETY OF LONDON, FOR THE YEAR 1929, WITH AN APPENDIX ON THE CENTENARY CELEBRATIONS. Chalmers P. Mitchell. London, pp.1-119, 1930.

REPORT OF CHIEF OF BUREAU OF BIOLOGICAL SURVEY. E. W. Nelson. Dept. Agr., Wash., D.C., pp.1-34, 1921.

REPORT OF CHIEF OF BUREAU OF BIOLOGICAL SURVEY. E. W. Nelson. Dept. Agr., Wash., D.C., pp.1-39, Dec., 1922.

REPORT OF CHIEF OF BUREAU OF BIOLOGICAL SURVEY. E. W. Nelson. Dept. Agr., Wash., D.C., pp.1-44, 1923.

REPORT OF CHIEF OF BUREAU OF BIOLOGICAL SURVEY. E. W. Nelson. Dept. Agr., Wash., D.C., pp.1-39, Dec. 2, 1924.

REPORT OF CHIEF OF BUREAU OF BIOLOGICAL SURVEY. E. W. Nelson. Dept. Agr., Wash. D. C., pp.1-28, Dec. 1, 1925.

REPORT OF CHIEF OF BUREAU OF BIOLOGICAL SURVEY. E. W. Nelson. Dept. Agr., Wash. D.C., pp.1-20, Dec. 1, 1926.

FIFTY-SIXTH ANNUAL REPORT OF THE TRUSTEES FOR THE YEAR 1924, THE AMERICAN MUSEUM OF NATURAL HISTORY. Henry Fairfield Osborn. Pp.1-305, pls.18, map 1, May, 1925.

REPORT OF THE CHIEF OF BUREAU OF BIOLOGICAL SURVEY. Paul G. Redington. Dept.Agric., Wash., D.C., pp.1-27, Nov. 21, 1927.

REPORT OF THE CHIEF OF BUREAU OF BIOLOGICAL SURVEY. Paul G. Redington. Dept. Agric., Wash., D.C., pp.1-34, Nov. 26, 1928.

REPORT OF THE CHIEF OF BUREAU OF BIOLOGICAL SURVEY. Paul G. Redington. Dept. Agric., Wash., D.C., pp.1-63, Nov. 25, 1931.

REPORT OF THE DIRECTOR OF THE MUSEUM OF ZOOLOGY TO THE BOARD OF REGENTS, JULY 1, 1923, TO JUNE 30, 1924. Alexander G. Ruthven. Univ. Michigan, Univ. Bull., n.s., vol.26, no. 15, pp.1-40, illustr., Oct. 11, 1924.

REPORT OF THE DIRECTOR OF THE MUSEUM OF ZOOLOGY TO THE BOARD OF REGENTS, JULY 1, 1925, TO JUNE 30, 1926. Alexander G. Ruthven. Univ. Michigan, Univ. Bull., n.s., vol.28, no. 10, pp.1-51, pl.1, Sep. 4, 1926.

REPORT ON THE SARAWAK MUSEUM FOR 1903. R. Shelford. Sarawak Gazette Office, pp.1-24, 1903.

ANNUAL REPORT OF THE DIRECTOR TO THE BOARD OF TRUSTEES FOR THE YEAR 1928. Stephen C. Simms. Field Mus. Nat. Hist., publ.256, rep.ser.vol.7, no. 3, pp.381-600, pls.42-61, Jan., 1929.

REPORT OF FIELD MUSEUM OF NATURAL HISTORY FOR THE YEAR 1930. Stephen C. Simms. Field Mus. Nat. Hist., publ.287, rep.ser.vol.8, no.2, pp.1-274, illus., Jan., 1931.

REPORT OF FIELD MUSEUM OF NATURAL HISTORY FOR THE YEAR 1932. Stephen C. Simms. Field Mus. Nat. Hist., publ.318, rep.ser.vol.9, no.2, pp.1-298, Jan., 1933.

TENTH BIENNIAL REPORT OF THE FISH AND GAME WARDEN OF THE STATE OF IDAHO. R. E. Thomas. Pp.1-205, illus., 1925.

ACCOUNT OF THE UNITED STATES NATIONAL MUSEUM. Frederick W. True. Ann. Rep. Board Regents Smiths. Inst. for the year ending June 30, 1896. Rep. of the U.S. Nat. Mus., pp.281-324, Feb. 13, 1899.

REPORT ON THE DEPARTMENT OF BIOLOGY FOR THE YEAR 1897-1898. Frederick W. True. Ann. Rep. Board of Regents Smiths. Inst. for the year ending June 30, 1898. Rep. of the U.S. Nat. Mus., pp.35-44, Aug. 10, 1900.

REPORT ON THE DEPARTMENT OF BIOLOGY FOR THE YEAR 1898-1899. Frederick W. True. Ann. Rep. Board of Regents Smiths. Inst. for the year ending June 30, 1899. Rep. of the U.S. Nat. Mus., pp.25-35, Apr. 18, 1901.

REPORT ON THE DEPARTMENT OF BIOLOGY FOR THE YEAR 1899-1900. Frederick W. True. Ann. Rep. Board of Regents Smiths. Inst. for the year ending June 30, 1900. Rep. of the U.S. Nat. Mus., pp.31-44, July 3, 1902.

REPORT ON THE DEPARTMENT OF BIOLOGY FOR THE YEAR 1900-1901. Frederick W. True. Ann. Rep. Board of Regents Smiths. Inst. for the year ending June 30, 1901. Rep. of the U.S. Nat. Mus., pp.63-80, Oct. 6, 1903.

REPORT OF THE DEPARTMENT OF BIOLOGY FOR THE YEAR 1901-1902. Frederick W. True. Ann. Rep. Board of Regents Smiths. Inst. for the year ending June 30, 1902. Rep. of the U.S. Nat. Mus., pp.59-76, Mar. 12, 1904.

REPORT OF THE DEPARTMENT OF BIOLOGY FOR THE YEAR 1902-1903. Frederick W. True. Ann. Rep. Board of Regents Smiths. Inst. for the year ending June 30, 1903. Rep. of the U.S. Nat. Mus., pp.61-82, May 17, 1905.

REPORT ON THE DEPARTMENT OF BIOLOGY FOR THE YEAR 1903-1904. Frederick W. True. Ann. Rep. Board of Regents Smiths. Inst. for the year ending June 30, 1904. Rep. of the U.S. Nat. Mus., pp.77-95, Mar. 13, 1906.

REPORT ON THE DEPARTMENT OF COMPARATIVE ANATOMY IN THE U.S. NATIONAL MUSEUM, 1885. Frederick W. True. Ann. Rep. Board Regents Smiths. Inst., 1885, pp.99-102, 1886.

REPORT ON THE DEPARTMENT OF COMPARATIVE ANATOMY IN THE U.S. NATIONAL MUSEUM FOR THE YEAR ENDING JUNE 30, 1886. Frederick W. True. Ann. Rep. Board Regents Smiths. Inst.for 1886, pt. 2, pp.209-213, 1889.

REPORT ON THE DEPARTMENT OF COMPARATIVE ANATOMY IN THE U.S. NATIONAL MUSEUM, 1888. Frederick W. True. Ann. Rep. Board Regents of Smiths. Inst. for 1888, Rep. of the U.S. Nat. Mus., pp.181-182, 1890.

REPORT ON THE DEPARTMENT OF COMPARATIVE ANATOMY IN THE U.S. NATIONAL MUSEUM, 1889. Frederick W. True. Ann. Rep. Board Regents Smiths. Inst. for 1889. Rep. of the U.S. Nat. Mus., pp.387-390, Jan. 13, 1892.

REPORT ON THE DEPARTMENT OF COMPARATIVE ANATOMY IN THE U.S. NATIONAL MUSEUM, 1890. Frederick W. True. Ann. Rep. Board Regents Smiths. Inst. for 1890. Rep. of the U.S. Nat. Mus., pp.231-232, Jan. 27, 1893.

REPORT ON THE DEPARTMENT OF MAMMALS IN THE U.S. NATIONAL MUSEUM FOR THE YEAR ENDING JUNE 30, 1886. Frederick W. True. Ann. Rep. Board Regents Smiths. Inst. for 1886, pt.2, pp.147-152, 1889.

REPORT ON THE DEPARTMENT OF MAMMALS IN THE U.S. NATIONAL MUSEUM, 1887. Frederick W. True. Ann. Rep. Board Regents Smiths. Inst. 1887, pt.2, pp.87-94, 1889.

REPORT ON THE DEPARTMENT OF MAMMALS IN THE U.S. NATIONAL MUSEUM, 1889. Frederick W. True. Ann. Rep. Board Regents Smiths. Inst. for 1889. Rep. of the U.S. Nat. Mus., 1888-89, pp.349-355, Jan. 13, 1892.

REPORT ON THE DEPARTMENT OF MAMMALS IN THE U.S. NATIONAL MUSEUM, 1890. Frederick W. True. Ann. Rep. Board Regents Smiths. Inst. for 1890. Rep. of the U.S. Nat. Mus., pp.189-193, Jan. 27, 1893.

REPORT ON THE DEPARTMENT OF MAMMALS IN THE U.S. NATIONAL MUSEUM, 1891. Frederick W. True. Ann. Rep. Board Regents Smiths. Inst. for 1891. Rep. of the U.S. Nat. Mus., pp.199-205, June 6, 1893.

REPORT ON THE DEPARTMENT OF MAMMALS IN THE U.S. NATIONAL MUSEUM, 1892. Frederick W. True. Ann. Rep. Board Regents Smiths. Inst. for 1892. Rep. of the U.S. Nat. Mus., pp.143-145, July 12, 1894.

REPORT OF THE REPRESENTATIVE OF THE SMITHSONIAN INSTITUTION AND NATIONAL MUSEUM, PAN-AMERICAN EXPOSITION, BUFFALO, NEW YORK, 1901. Frederick W. True. Ann. Rep. Board of Regents Smiths. Inst. for the year ending June 30, 1902, pp.110-115, Mar. 12, 1904.

REPORT OF THE REPRESENTATIVE OF THE SMITHSONIAN INSTITUTION AND NATIONAL MUSEUM, TRANS-MISSISSIPPI AND INTERNATIONAL EXPOSITION, OMAHA, NEBRASKA, 1898. Frederick W. True. Ann. Rep. Board of Regents Smiths. Inst. for the year ending June 30, 1899, pp.82-87, 1901.

EIGHTH ANNUAL REPORT, ZOOLOGICAL PARK OF SAINT LOUIS. George P. Vierheller. Ann. Rep. Div. Parks and Recreation of the Dept. Public Welfare, City of St. Louis, for year ending April, 1925, pp. 53-79, 1925.

NINTH ANNUAL REPORT ZOOLOGICAL BOARD OF CONTROL AND OFFICERS OF ST. LOUIS ZOOLOGICAL PARK, APRIL, 1925 TO APRIL, 1926. George P. Vierheller. Ann. Rep. Div. Parks and Recreation, Dept. Publ. Welfare, St. Louis, for year 1926, pp. 48-64, Nov., 1926.

REPORT FOR YEAR 1936. Zoological Soc. of London, 1937.

(ANNUAL OF THE INSTITUTE FOR THE SCIENCE OF HUNTING.) Jahrbuch des Instituts fuer Jagdtkunde. Neudamm, vol.1, pp.1-226, illus., 1912.

ANNUAL REPORT 1935-36. Bureau of Animal Population, Univ. Oxford, pp.1-48, 1935-36; pp.1-38, 1936-37.

## APPARATUS (CAGES, LABORATORY DEVICES, ETC.

SAN DIEGO'S NEW GROUP OF BURROWING ANIMAL CAGES. Richard A. Addison. Parks and Recreation, vol.9, no.4, pp.452-455, illus., Apr., 1926.

DEN AND RUNWAY SYSTEM FOR WEASELS AND OTHER SMALL MAMMALS IN THE LABORATORY. Thomas Hume Bissonnette, Earl E. Bailey. Amer. Midland Nat., Notre Dame, vol.24, no.3, pp.761-763, fig.1, Nov., 1940.

SCREEN WIRE CONTAINER FOR THE SHIPMENT OF LIVE SMALL MAMMALS. Philip M. Blossom. Jour. Mamm., vol.19, no.1, pp.85-88, figs.1, Feb. 14, 1938.

SIMPLE RESPIROMETER FOR SMALL ANIMALS. Edward G. Boettiger. Nature, vol.142, no.3586, pp.151-152, July 23, 1938.

RAMPS FOR ESCAPE OF WILDLIFE FROM STOCK-TROUGHS. Richard M. Bond. Jour. Wildlife Management, Menasha, vol.7, no.1, p.123, Jan., 1943.

REPORT ON THE USE OF THE PHOTON-REFLECTOMETER IN SEROLOGICAL COMPARISON. Alan Boyden, Ralph J. De Falco. Physiol Zool., Chicago, vol.16, no.3, pp.229-241, July, 1943.

NEW DEVICE FOR FILING MICROSCOPE SLIDES. Howard J. Brown. Science, n.s., vol.65, pp.501-502, May 20, 1927.

REFLECTOMETER FOR MEASURING COLORS OF ANIMALS. Floyd E. Durham. Jour. Mamm., vol.22, no.2, pp.199-201, figs., May 14, 1941.

DROPPING BOARDS FOR POPULATION STUDIES OF SMALL MAMMALS. John T. Emlen, Jr., Ruth L. Hine, William A. Fuller, Pablo Alfonso. Jour. Wildlife Management, vol.21, no.3, pp.300-314, July, 1957.

SIMPLE APPARATUS FOR DEGREASING BONES FOR MUSEUM PURPOSES. H. H. Finlayson. Trans. & Proc. Roy. Soc. South Australia, vol.57, pp.172-174, figs., Feb. 16, 1932.

LLOYD'S DEGREASING APPARATUS. J.H. Fleming. Jour. Mamm., vol.7, no.1, p.62, Feb., 1926.

USEFUL TYPE OF MACHAN. W. Forsyth. Jour. Bombay Nat. Hist. Soc., vol.35, no. 3, p.672, Feb. 15, 1932.

METABOLISM CAGE FOR SMALL ANIMALS. B. K. Harned, Raymond W. Cunningham, Edna R. Gill. Science, Lancaster, vol.109, no.2837, pp.489-490, illus., May 13, 1949.

APPARATUS FOR RAISING THE BODY TEMPERATURE OF SMALL ANIMALS. Wm. A. Hiestand, Walter C. Randall. Amer. Midland Nat., Notre Dame, vol. 22, no.1, pp.214-215, July, 1939.

SIMPLE MEMBRANE MANOMETER. Arthur D. Hirschfelder, Raymond L. Gregory. Science, n.s., vol.61, pp.368-370, Apr. 3, 1925.

NEW CRANIOMETER FOR CARNIVORE AND OTHER MAMMALIAN CRANIA. Elizabeth B. Horner. Jour. Mamm., vol. 25, no.1, pp.71-77, figs.7, Feb., 1944.

STANDARD APPARATUS FOR THE STUDY OF ANIMAL MOTIVATION. T. N. Jenkins, L.H. Warner, C.J. Warden. Jour. Comp. Psych., vol.6, no.5, pp.361-382, 1926.

NEW TYPE OF CAGE FOR RECORDING DAILY ACTIVITY RHYTHMS OF SMALL ANIMALS. Eskil L. Karlson. Jour. Mamm., vol.31, no.4, pp.416-420, Nov. 21, 1950.

DEVICE FOR SAFE HANDLING OF WILD MAMMALS IN THE LABORATORY. Lawrence Kilham, James H. Belcher. Jour. Wildl. Mgt., vol.18, no.3, p.402, illus., July, 1954.

NEW MOISTURE-CONSERVING DISSECTING TABLE. S. I. Kornhauser, S. E. Johnson. Anat. Rec., vol.41, pp.177-179, illus., Jan. 25, 1929.

APPARATUS FOR MEASURING THE TORSION ANGLE IN LONG BONES. Vernon E. Krahl. Science, Lancaster, n.s., vol.99, no.2581, p.498, fig.1, June 16, 1944.

(NEW INSTRUMENT FOR CRANIOMETRICAL MEASUREMENTS.) Un nouvel appareil pour les mesures craniométriques. Ch. Lamberton. Bull. Acad. Malgache, Tananarive, n.s., vol.26, Annees 1944-45, pp.143-144, pl.1, 1947.

NEW TYPE FOX PELT DRYING-BOARD. W. C. Liddell. Amer. Natl. Fur & Market Jour., Wausau, vol.26, no.3, pp.5-6, 17-18, Oct., 1947.

CONVENIENT CONTAINERS FOR SPECIMEN MATERIAL. S. B. Locke. Jour. Mamm., vol.11, no.4, p.507, Nov., 1930.

RAT CAGES OF SIMPLIFIED CONSTRUCTION. J. A. Long. Anat. Rec., vol.28, pp.119-206, figs., Aug. 25, 1924.

APPARATUS FOR MEASURING METABOLISM AND ACTIVITY IN WILD ANIMALS. William H. Long. Univ. Michigan, School Forestry and Conserv., Ann Arbor, Circ. no.5, pp.1-35, 1939.

EASILY FILLED CAPSULE FOR COLLECTING BLOOD. Marcus W. Lyon, Jr. Jour. Amer. Med. Assoc., vol.65, p.1813, Nov. 20, 1915.

PARAFFINE BATH HEATED BY ELECTRICITY. E. L. Mark. Contrib. Zool. Lab. Mus. Comp. Zool. Harvard Coll., Cambridge, no. 139 (from Amer. Nat., vol.37, no.434, pp. 115-119, figs.3, Feb., 1903.)

(HYDROTHERMOSTAT AND OTHER DEVICES FOR BONE MACERATION WITHOUT GAS, WITH REMARKS ON AN IMPROVED MACERATION PROCESS.) Ein Hydrothermostat und andere Vorrichtungen zum Knochenmazerieren ohne Gas, mit Bemerkungen ueber ein verbessertes Mazerations verfahren. N. Mechanik. Anat. Anz., vol.60, pp.225-234, figs.3, Nov.2, 1925.

SIMPLE ACTIVITY CAGE FOR SMALL MAMMALS. R. F. Morris. Acadian Nat., vol.1, no.4, pp.153-156, Nov., 1944.

PLASTIC VIALS FOR STORING SMALL SKULLS. Ralph S. Palmer. Jour. Mamm., vol.27, no.3, pp.276-277, Aug. 14, 1946.

APPARATUS FOR COLLECTION OF ECTOPARASITES FROM MAMMALS. R. E. Ryckman, C. T. Ames. Calif. Fish & Game, vol.40, no.1, pp.75-76, Jan., 1954.

(MEASUREMENT TOOL FOR THE MACROSCOPIC MEASUREMENT OF SMALL ANIMALS.) Messwerkzeug zu makroskopischen Messungen an Kleintieren. Karl Saller. Anat. Anz., vol.60, pp.58-67, figs. 3, Aug. 3, 1925.

MICRO-GAS-ANALYZER. P. F. Scholander. Rev. Sci. Instruments, Menasha, vol.13, no.6, pp.264-266, figs.2, June, 1942.

VOLUMETRIC MICRORESPIROMETER FOR AQUATIC ORGANISMS. P. F.Scholander. G. A. Edwards. Rev. Sci.Instruments, Menasha, vol.13, no.7, pp.292-295, fig.1, July, 1942.

A VOLUMETRIC RESPIROMETER FOR AQUATIC ANIMALS. P. F. Scholander, Niels Haugaard, Laurence Irving. Rev. Sci. Instruments, Menasha, vol.14, no.2, pp. 48-51, Feb., 1943.

OAK BARRELS FOR THE STORAGE OF LARGE ALCOHOLIC SPECIMENS. Leonard P. Schultz, Earl D. Reid. Turtox News, Chicago, vol.17, no.2, pp.1-2, figs.2, Feb., 1939.

METAL RESTRAINING TUBE FOR ANIMALS. Albert R. Shadle, Wm R. Ploss. Jour. Mamm., vol.23, no.4, pp.441-443, Nov., 1942.

ZIPPER TUBE FOR HOLDING SMALL LIVE ANIMALS. Albert R. Shadle, Irene Skarupinski. Science, Lancaster, n.s., vol.82, no.2127, p.335, figs2, Oct. 4, 1935.

DEGREASING APPARATUS. Harley B. Sherman. Jour. Mamm., vol.6, no.3, pp. 182-184, Aug., 1925.

DESCRIPTION OF AN APPARATUS FOR RECORDING THE ACTIVITY OF SMALL MAMMALS. James Rollin Slonaker. Anat. Rec., Philadelphia, vol.2, no.3, pp.116-120, figs.7, June,1908.

NEW APPARATUS FOR LONG TERM MEASUREMENT OF OXYGEN CONSUMPTION IN SMALL MAMMALS. Elizabeth Smith. Proc. Soc. Exper. Biol. & Med., New York, vol.89, no.4, pp.499-501, Aug., 1955.

APPARATUS FOR THE STUDY OF SENSORY DISCRIMINATION IN MAMMALS. Karl Ulrich Smith. Science, Lancaster, n. s., vol.82, no.2131, pp.423-425, diagr.1, Nov.1, 1935.

NEW PERMANENT SOLUTION FOR THE PRESERVATION OF ANATOMIC PREPARATIONS, THE SOUCHON SOLUTION OF CALCIUM CHLORIDE. Edmont Souchon. Anat. Rec., vol.18, no.4, p.361, May 20 (June), 1920.

ELECTRIC FENCE FOR USE IN CHECKING PORCUPINE AND OTHER MAMMALIAN CROP DEPREDATIONS. Donald A. Spencer. Jour. Wildl. Mgt., Menasha, vol.12, no.1, pp.110-111, Jan., 1948.

ELECTRICAL RECORDING OF THE ACTIVITIES OF SMALL MAMMALS. Donald A. Spencer. J. Mamm., vol.20, no.4, pp.479-485, Nov., 1939.

IMPROVED LABORATORY TABLE FOR GROSS ANATOMY. R. J. Terry. Anat. Rec., Philadelphia, vol.29, no.4, pp. 315-318, fig.1, Feb. 25, 1925.

CHEST FOR DERMESTID CLEANING OF SKULLS. Charles T. Vorhies. Jour. Mamm., vol.29, no.2, pp.188-189, May 14, 1948.

RABBIT-EAR CAGE FOR BLOOD-SUCKING ARTHROPODS. Paul A. Woke. U.S. Publ. Health Repts., Washington, vol.66, no. 15, pp.464-471, illus., Apr.14, 1951.

"BONE BOARD" FOR BIG-GAME FIELD WORKERS. Lee E. Yeager. Jour. Wildl. Mgt., vol.17, no.2, pp.223-224, illus., Apr., 1953.

AQUATIC MAMMALS see MARINE AND AQUATIC MAMMALS

## BEHAVIOR

HAND TO HAND WITH A LEOPARD AND SOME EXPERIENCE WITH RHINOS. Carl E. Akeley. World's Work, vol.41, pp.393-402, figs.8, Feb., 1921.

JACKAL AND HARE. Salim A. Ali. Jour. Bombay Nat. Hist. Soc., vol.31, p.812, Nov.1, 1926.

(DOMINANCE AND HIERARCHY IN SOCIETIES OF VERTEBRATES.) In Structure et physiologie des sociétés animales. W. C. Allee. Paris, pp.157-181, pls.IV-VII, Mar., 1950 (1952).

SOCIAL LIFE OF ANIMALS. W. C. Allee. New York, W. W. Norton and Co., Inc., pp. 1-293, 1938.

BEHAVIOR OF MAMMALIAN HERDS AND PACKS. Friedrich Alverdes. Clark Univ. Press, Worcester, Mass., 1935. (Chapter 6, pp.185-203, a handbook of social psychology.)

WILD ANIMALS LEARN THE HARD WAY. Russell Annabel. Sports Afield, Mt.Morris, vol.118, no.1, pp.22-23, illus., July, 1947.

DOG AND THE RABBIT. Harold E. Anthony. Nat. Hist., New York, vol.46, no.5, p.293, Dec., 1940.

(SYMBOLIC ACTIONS AND RELATED THINGS IN MAMMALS.) Ueber Symbolhandlungen und Verwandtes bei Saeugetieren. O. Antonius. Zeitschr. f. Tierpsychol., vol.3, pp.263-278, 1939.

ANTING NOT EXCLUSIVELY AN AVIAN TRAIT. Aaron M. Bagg. Jour. Mamm., vol.33, no.2, p.243, May 16, 1952.

DEFENSE IN THE ANIMAL WORLD. W.J. Banks. Our Dumb Animals, Norwood, vol.75, no.4, p.67, illus., Apr., 1942.

HOW ANIMALS KEEP FIT. W. J. Banks. Our Dumb Animals, Boston, vol.75, no.10, p.187, Oct., 1942.

ARMADILLO HABIT. Harold Bastin. Illus. London News, vol.211, no.5661, p.440, illus., Oct. 18, 1947.

WEASELS AND RATS. Mortimer H. Batten. Field, London, vol.152, p.603, Oct. 11, 1928.

CURRENT CONCEPTS OF PLAY IN ANIMALS. Frank A. Beach. Amer. Nat., Lancaster, vol.79, no.785, pp.523-541, Nov.-Dec., 1945.

(THE JARDIN DES PLANTES; DESCRIPTION AND HABITS OF MAMMALS OF THE MENAGERIE.) Le Jardin des plantes; description et moeurs des mammifères de la Ménagerie. Pierre Boitard. Paris, p.472, illus., 1845.

(THE JARDIN DES PLANTES; DESCRIPTION AND HABITS OF MAMMALS FROM THE MENAGERIE AND THE MUSEUM OF NATIONAL HISTORY.) Le Jardin des plantes; description et moeurs des mammiferes de la Menagerie et du Museum d'Histoire Naturelle. Pierre Boitard. Paris, G. Barba, pp. 308, illus., 1842.

(LIFE AND HABITS OF MAMMALS.) Vie et moeurs des mammifères. Francois Bourlière. Paris, Payot, pp.249, illus., 1951.

(THE WORLD OF MAMMALS, WITH DRAWINGS, 86 HELIOGRAVURE PLATES, AND 16 FULL-PAGE PLATES IN COLOR.) Le monde des mammiferes, avec des dessins, 86 planches en héliogravure et 16 hors-texte en couleurs. Francois Bourliere. Paris, Horizons de France, pp.221, illus., 1954.

ANIMAL FACTS AND FALLACIES. Osmond P. Breland. Harper & Bros., New York, pp. 1-268, illus., 1948.

RELICS IN ANIMAL BEHAVIOR. Maurice Burton. Illus. London News, vol.221, no.5916, pp.1-376, illus., Sep.6, 1952.

FIGHTS BETWEEN WILD BEASTS. R. G. Burton. Field, London, vol.158, no.4117, p.773, illus., Nov. 21, 1931.

HOW ANIMALS SPEND THE WINTER. Charles L. Cadieux. North Dakota Outdoors, Grand Forks, vol.13, no.6, pp.6-7, Dec., 1950.

TWENTY-FOUR HOUR PERIODICITIES IN THE ANIMAL KINGDOM. Part I. THE INVERTEBRATES. Part II. THE VERTEBRATES. John B. Calhoun. Jour. Tennessee Acad. Sci., vol.19, no.2, pp.179-200, Apr., 1944; vol.19, no.3, pp.252-262, July, 1944; vol.20, no.2, pp.228-232, Apr., 1945; vol.20, no.3, pp.291-308, July, 1945; vol.20, no.4, pp.373-378, Oct., 1945; vol.21, no.2, pp.208-216, Apr., 1946; vol.21, no.3, pp. 281-282, July, 1946.

STRANGE HABITS OF ANIMALS IN GETTING THEIR BEAUTY SLEEP. Jewell Casey. Our Dumb Animals, Norwood, vol. 82, no.2, p.9, Feb., 1949.

(HABITS OF GAME.) Les habitudes du Gibier. A. Chaigneau. Paris, Payot, pp.300, 1947.

MAMMALS CAUGHT IN POST HOLES. John J. Christian. Jour. Mamm., vol.17, no.4, p.416, Nov., 1936.

TOOLS FOR CARPENTRY VERSUS COMBAT. Harmsted S. Chubb. Nat. Hist., New York, vol.52, no.4, pp.168-170, illus., Nov., 1943.

AGGRESSIVE BEHAVIOR AMONG VERTEBRATE ANIMALS. Nicholas E. Collias. Physiological Zool., Chicago, vol.17, no.1, pp.83-123, Jan., 1944.

SURVIVAL CURVES OF MAMMALS IN CAPTIVITY. A. Comfort. Proc. Zool Soc. London, vol.128, no.3, pp.349-364, June 6, 1957.

MICE AND MOLES. Lee K. Couch. Jour. Mamm., vol.5, no.4, p.264, Nov., 1924.

HABITS AND CHARACTERISTICS OF NOCTURNAL ANIMALS. Stanton C. Crawford. Quart. Rev. Biol., vol.9, no.2, pp.201-214, June, 1934.

WHEN IS A CHARGE? Paul Curtis. Field, London, vol.174, no.4523, p.556, fig.1, Sep. 2, 1939.

RELEASE FROM WINTER'S BONDAGE. Bonnycastle Dale, Jr. Rod & Gun in Canada, Montreal, vol.46, no.9, pp.10-11, illus., Mar., 1945.

SWIMMING ABILITY OF TWO SMALL MAMMALS. William B. Davis. Jour. Mamm., vol.23, no.1, p.99, Feb. 14, 1942.

(OBSERVATIONS ON THE HABITS OF A HARE AND A PALM SQUIRREL.) Observations sur les Moeurs d'un Lievre et d'un Ecureuil Palmiste. Solange De Ganay. Mammalia, Paris, vol.5, no.1, pp.24-28, Mar., 1941.

HUMAN SIDE OF ANIMALS. Royal Dixon. New York, pp.273, col.pl.1, photos 33, 1918.

JACKRABBIT AND RACCOON. Stuart C. Downing. Canadian Nature, Toronto, vol.11, no.4, pp.98-99, illus., Sep.-Oct., 1949.

RESPECT THESE MAMMALS. Stuart C. Downing. Canadian Nature, Toronto, vol.9, no.2, pp.46-47, illus., Mar.-Apr., 1947.

ANIMAL BEHAVIOR DURING AIR-RAIDS. Barraclough H. Fell. Science, Lancaster, n.s., vol.93, no.2403, pp.61-62, Jan. 17, 1941.

(OBSERVATIONS ON THE MARKING BEHAVIOR OF SOME MAMMALS.) Beobachtungen zum Markierungsverhalten einiger Saeugetiere. Walter Fiedler. Zeitschr.Saeugetierk., vol.22, no.1-2, pp.57-76, pls.5-6, 1957.

RABBIT AND STOAT. Calvert C. Fisher. Field, London, vol.164, p.216, July 28, 1934.

RHYTHM IN NATURE. Frederic William Flattely. Smiths. Inst. Annual Rep., 1920, Washington, pp.389-397, 1922. (Reprinted from Science progress, vol.14, no.55, Jan., 1920.)

(ON SWIMMING IN THE SQUIRREL, SCIURUS VULGARIS FUSCOATER, FIELD HARE, LEPUS E. EUROPAEUS, AND ROE, CAPREOLUS C. CAPREOLUS.) Ueber das Schwimmen von Eichhorn, Sciurus vulgaris fuscoater, Feldhase, Lepus e. europaeus, und Reh, Capreolus c. capreolus. Wolfgang Gewalt. Saeugetierk. Mitteil., vol.5, no.4, pp.162-164, Dec. 1, 1957.

CARIBOU AND FOX. Charles A. Gianini. Jour. Mamm., vol.4, no.4, pp.253-254, Nov., 1923.

HOW DANGEROUS ARE ANIMALS? George G. Goodwin. Nat. Hist., New York, vol.59, no.3, pp.130-135, illus., Mar., 1950.

PRESENCE AND ABSENCE OF ANIMALS. Joseph Grinnell. Univ. Calif. Chronicle, pp.429-450, Oct., 1928.

ANIMALS AND OIL TRAPS. G. D. Hanna. Wasmann Collector, San Francisco, vol.7, no.4, p.138, Dec., 1948.

ANIMALS IN AN AIR RAID. Eric Hardy. Nat. Hist., New York, vol.46, no.5, pp.274-275, 293, Dec., 1940.

FREEDOM OF THE ZOO. Stephen Haweis. Nat. Mag., vol.10, pp.281-285, illus., Nov., 1927.

(CONTRIBUTION TO MAMMALIAN SOCIOLOGY.) Beitraege zur Saeugetier-Sociologie. H. Hediger. In Structure et physiologie des societes animals. Paris, pp.297-321, pls. XIV-XVI, March 1950 (1952).

WILD ANIMALS IN CAPTIVITY: AN OUTLINE OF THE BIOLOGY OF ZOOLOGICAL GARDENS. H. Heidiger. London, Butterworths, pp.ix-207, 1950. (English translation, revised, of the German edition of 1942; bibliography.)

(ZOOLOGICAL GARDEN BIOLOGY AND COMPARATIVE BEHAVIOR RESEARCH.) Tiergartenbiologie und vergleichende Verhaltensforschung. H. Hediger. Zeitschr. Saeugetierk., vol.21, no.1-2, pp.1-28, pls.1-4, 1956.

(LION AND MOUSE.) Loewe und Maus. Erich Hesse. Zeitschr. Saeugetierk., Berlin, vol.13, no.2, p.256, 1939.

WINTER SPORTS. John Eric Hill. Nat. Hist., New York, vol.51, no.1, p.50, illus., Jan., 1943.

IS NATURE CRUEL? Crowther J. Hirst. G. Bell and Sons, London, pp.61, 1926.

TENTATIVE CLASSIFICATION OF THE FORMS OF ANIMAL BEHAVIOR. Samuel J. Holmes. Jour. Comp. Psychol., vol.2, pp.173-186, June (Aug.), 1922.

ABUNDANCE OF DESERT ANIMALS INDICATED BY CAPTURE IN FRESH ROAD TAR. Carl L. Hubbs, Boyd W. Walker. Ecology, Lancaster, vol.28, no.4, pp. 464-466, Oct., 1947.

BRITISH INSTITUTE FOR THE STUDY OF ANIMAL BEHAVIOR. Julian S. Huxley. Science, vol.83, no.2164, p.590, June 19, 1936.

PERMANENCE OF MAMMAL DENS. Lloyd G. Ingles. Jour. Mamm., vol.26, no.3, p.307, Aug., 1945.

(BURROWS OF SOME TRANSBAIKAL MAMMALS IN SCHEMATIC REPRESENTATION.) Die Bauten einiger transbaikalischer Saeugetiere in schematischer Darstellung. H. M. Jettmar. Zeitschr. f. Saeugetierk., vol.1, no.1, pp.13-22, Aug. 31, 1926.

TERM "CRIME" APPLIED TO ANIMALS. Julius M. Johnson. Jour. Mamm., vol.8, no.2, p.173, May, 1927.

MAMMALIAN TOILET AND SOME CONSIDERATIONS ARISING FROM IT. Frederic Wood Jones. The R.M. Johnston Memorial Lecture, 1925. Royal Soc. Tasmania, Papers and Proc., pp.14-62, illus., July, 1925.

SHREWS AND WEASELS. George L. Kirk. Jour. Mamm., vol.2, no.2, p.111, May, 1921.

RIGHT AND LEFT IN ANIMALS. Frank W. Lane. Zoo Life, London, vol.1, no.1, pp. 30-31, Spring, 1946.

MECHANISM SHOWING A REMARKABLE CORRELATION BETWEEN STRUCTURE AND FUNCTION IN CONNECTION WITH THE NURSING REFLEX IN THE YOUNG MAMMAL. H. H. Lane. Kansas Univ. Sci. Bull., vol.15, no.3, pp.249-253, Dec., 1924 (1925).

ARE WILD ANIMALS FEROCIOUS? Tony Lascelles. Forest & Outdoors, Montreal, vol.13, pp.24, 31, 1947.

(OBSERVATIONS ON THE BEHAVIOR OF SMALL MAMMALS IN CAPTIVITY (CONTINUATION).) Observations sur le comportement des petits mammifères en captivité (suite). P. Laurent. Mammalia, Paris, vol.8, no.1, pp.7-15, fig.1, Mar., 1944.

(OBSERVATIONS ON THE BEHAVIOR OF SMALL WILD MAMMALS IN CAPTIVITY.) Observations sur le comportment des petits mammiferes sauvages en captivite. P. Laurent. Mammalia, Paris, vol.2, no.1, pp.12-28, Mar., 1938.

CAN A WEASEL CATCH A RABBIT? Joseph W. Lippincott. Outdoors in Illinois, Springfield, vol.14, no.1, pp.1-15, illus., Spring and Summer, 1949.

KING SOLOMON'S RING. Konrad Z. Lorenz. New York, pp.1-221, numerous illus., 1952.

"SQUEAKING"ANIMALS. Alden J. Loring. Nat. Mag., Washington, vol.39, no.8, pp.430-432, illus., Oct., 1946.

ANIMALS IN CAPTIVITY. William M. Mann. Smiths. Inst. Radio Program, The World is Yours, no.7, p.11, Nov.12, 1939.

RABBIT AND STOAT. J. H. Marples. The Field, London, vol.149, p.677, Apr. 21, 1927.

ANIMAL HOMES. George F. Mason. Wm. Morrow Co., New York, pp.96, illus., 1947.

ANIMALS DO NOT SPARE THE ROD. W.L. McAtee. Nat. Mag., Washington, D.C., vol.33, no.2, pp.113-114, Feb., 1940.

(PLAY IN THE MAMMALS.) Das Spiel bei Saeugetieren. Monika Meyer-Holzapfel. Handb. der Zoologie, Berlin, vol.8, pt.10, no.5, pp.1-36, illus., 1956.

TIGERS AND ELEPHANTS. A. J. W. Milroy. Jour. Bombay Nat. Hist. Soc., vol.32, p. 370, Oct. 20, 1927.

WAYS OF MAMMALS IN FACT AND FANCY. Clifford B. Moore. Ronald Press, New York, pp.273, 1953.

(Reviw by W. J. Hamilton, Jr. of) WAYS OF MAMMALS IN FACT AND FANCY. Clifford B. Moore. Jour. Mamm., vol.35, no.2, pp.270-271, May 26, 1954.

SAMBHAR AND WILD DOG. R. C. Morris. Jour. Bombay Nat. Hist. Soc., vol.33, no.1, p.198, Sep. 30, 1928.

COMMENT ON "TIGERS AND ELEPHANTS" AND NOTES ON TIGERS AND BUFFALOES. Victor Narayen. Jour. Bombay Nat. Hist. Soc., vol.31, p.1025, Feb. 20, 1927.

COMPARISON OF BEHAVIOR DEVELOPMENT IN SNOWSHOE HARES AND RED SQUIRRELS. Margaret M. Nice, Constance Nice, Dorothea Ewers. Jour. Mamm., vol. 37, no.1, pp.64-74, Feb. 28, 1956.

(WHAT I'VE SEEN AMONG THE BEASTS.) Ce que j'ai vu chez les bêtes. Paul Noel. Préface de G. Colomb, Paris, A. Colin, pp.343, illus., 1913.

WILD ANIMALS IN CAPTIVITY. John Fortune Nott. Dodd, Mead & Co., New York, pp.ix-155, pls.41, 1887.

BURROWING HABITS OF SOME SOUTH AFRICAN MAMMALS. Austin Roberts. South African Jour. Nat. Hist., Pretoria, vol.4, no.3, pp.187-208, Sep., 1923.

BEHAVIOR OF ORGANISMS. Tilden W. Roberts. Ecol. Monographs, Durham, vol. 12, no.4, pp.339-412, Oct., 1942.

BEHAVIOUR OF GAUR AND ELEPHANT. H. J. Rossel. Jour. Bombay Nat. Hist. Soc., vol.41, no.3, pp.656-657, pl.1, Apr., 1940.

(ON THE AGGRESSIVENESS OF LARGE INDOCHINESE MAMMALS.) De l'agressivité des grands animaux indochinois. Omer Sarraut. La Terre et la Vie, Paris, vol.5, no.1, pp.27-35, Jan., 1935; no.2, pp.71-80, Feb., 1935; no.3, pp.125-131, illus., Mar., 1935.

(ANIMAL PLAY.) Das Tier in seinen Spielen. Bastian Schmid. Nature und Volk, Frankfurt a.M., vol.69, no.1, pp.1-10, Jan.1, 1939.

NOTICES OF ANIMALS OBSERVED IN SEVERAL CONTINENTAL ZOOLOGICAL GARDENS. Philip Lutley Sclater. Proc. Zool. Soc. London, pp.676-677, 1865.

OBSERVATIONS ON SOME OF THE ANIMALS IN THE ZOOLOGICAL GARDENS OF AMSTERDAM, ROTTERDAM, AND ANTWERP. Philip Lutley Sclater. Proc. Zool. Soc. London, pt.31, pp.224-225, 1863.

ANIMAL BEHAVIOR. John Paul Scott. Pp.250, illus., Nov., 1957.

NATIONAL ZOO AT WASHINGTON, A STUDY OF ITS ANIMALS IN RELATION TO THEIR NATURAL ENVIRONMENT. Ernest Thompson Seton. Smiths. Inst., Annual Rep., 1901, Washington, pp.697-716, pls.XIII, 1902. (Reprinted from the Century Mag., vol.LIX, Mar., 1900; vol. LX, May, 1900.)

QUAINT BEASTS AND QUEER HABITS. C. H. Stockley. Jour. Bombay Nat. Hist. Soc., vol.28, pp.204-209, Dec. 30, 1921.

DETERMINATION OF HOLE SIZES WHICH EXCLUDE CERTAIN PREDATORY MAMMALS. Donald E. Stullken, Charles M. Kirkpatrick. Jour. Wildl. Mgt., Ithaca, vol.17, no.2, pp.124-128, Apr., 1953.

ANIMALS IN MENAGERIES. William Swainson. The Cabinet Cyclopaedia, London, pp.373, illus., 1838.

(THE RELATIONSHIP OF SEX AND SAVAGENESS IN MAMMALS.) K voprosu o sootnoshenii polov u dikikh mlekopitayushchikh. V. P. Teplov. Zool. Zhurnal, Moscow, vol.33, no.1, pp.174-179, Jan.-Feb., 1954.

PLAYTIME IN THE WILDERNESS. John K. Terres. Outdoor Life, New York, vol.101, no.5, pp.26-27, 92-95, illus., May, 1948.

SWIMMING HABITS OF MAMMALS. Stuart L. Thompson. Canadian Field-Nat., vol. 51, no.1, pp.5-6, Jan., 1937.

SOCIAL BEHAVIOR IN ANIMALS, WITH SPECIAL REFERENCE TO VERTEBRATES. N. Tinbergen. John Wiley & Sons, New York, pp.150, 1953.

ON THE DIGGING-HABITS OF SOME FOSSORIAL MAMMALS OF THE DANUBE-DAM IN SOUTHERN SLOVAKIA. F. J. Turcek. Saeugetirk. Mitteil., Stuttgart, vol.4, no.2, pp.61-63, Apr. 1, 1956.

( ON THE QUESTION OF MAMMALS SPITTING ON THEMSELVES.) Zur Frage des Sichselbstbespuckens bei Saeugetieren. Wolfgang Ulbrich. Zeitschr. Tierpsychol., vol.11, no.1, pp.150, 1954. (With English summary.)

(FORTRESS OF TALPA EUROPAEA L. AND THE NEST OF ARVICOLA SCHERMAN

SHAW.) Die Burg von Talpa europaea L. und das Nest von Arvicola scherman Shaw. St. Vásárhelyi. Allattani Koezlemenyek, Budapest, vol.27, nos.3-4, pp.173-181, figs.4, 1930. (Hungarian, with German summary.)

SOME NOTES ON FLIGHT. Allen Waldo. Yosemite Nat. Notes, vol.29, no.11, pp. 107-109, illus., Nov., 1950.

ANIMAL BEHAVIOR. Ernest P. Walker. Smiths. Rep. for 1940, publ.3616, pp.271-312, pls.18, 1941.

EYES THAT SHINE AT NIGHT. Ernest P. Walker. Smiths. Rep. for 1938, publ.3507, pp.349-360, pl.1, 1939.

MORE ABOUT ANIMAL BEHAVIOR. Ernest P. Walker. Smiths. Rep. for 1949, publ.4006, pp.261-292, pls.16, 1949.

GROUND SQUIRRELS AND WEASELS. Edward R. Warren. Jour. Mamm., vol.5, no.4, pp.265-266, Nov. 1924.

(ON THE FLIGHT INSTINCT OF VARIOUS STEPPE MAMMALS.) Ueber den Fluchtinstinkt verschiedener Steppensaeuger. Alfred Weidholz. Zool. Garten, Leipzig, NF, vol.16, no.5, pp.205-207, 1950.

DIURNAL RHYTHMS. John H. Welsh. Quart. Rev. Biol., vol.13, no.2, pp.123-139, June, 1938.

POPULAR HISTORY OF MAMMALIA; COMPRISING A FAMILIAR ACCOUNT OF THEIR CLASSIFICATION AND HABITS. Adam White. Reeve, Benham, and Reeve, London, 1850.

POLYGAMY AND THE GREGARIOUS HABIT. J. M. Winterbottom. Naturalist, London, no.830, pp.331-333, Nov., 1927.

SOME HABITS OF SOUTHERN FUR-BEARERS AS INDICATED BY TRAPPING. Lee E. Yeager. Amer. Midland Nat., vol.18, no.6, pp.1072-1078, Nov., 1937.

(OBSERVATIONS FROM THE ZOOLOGICAL GARDENS OF BERLIN.) Beobachtungen aus dem Zoologischen Garten Berlin. Franz Xaver Zedtwitz. II. Zool. Garten, Leipzig, n.F., vol.3, nos.9-10, pp.250-255, figs.3, Oct., 1930.

(OBSERVATIONS IN THE BERLIN ZOOLOGICAL GARDEN.) Beobachtungen im Zoologischen Garten Berlin. Franz Xaver Zedtwitz. Zool. Garten, Leipzig, vol.2, nos.10-12, pp.278-285, figs.3, Mar., 1930.

INTERPRETATION OF ANIMAL BEHAVIOR. S. Zuckerman. Science Progress, London, no.116, pp.639-649, Apr., 1935.

SOME OBSERVATIONS AND STUDY ON THE LIFE OF WILD ANIMALS IN CAPTIVITY. Indian Wild Life, vol.1, no.2, pp.70-76, Aug., 1936.

WHERE ARE THEY NOW? Jr. Nat. Hist. Mag., New York, vol.7, no.12, pp.4-7, 16, illus., Feb., 1943.

## BIOCHEMISTRY

MARINE OILS WITH PARTICULAR REFERENCE TO THOSE OF CANADA. B. E. Bailey. Bull. Fish. Res. Bd. Can., vol.89, p.413, 1952.

EFFECTS OF HIGH LEVEL X-IRRADIATION ON THE BIOCHEMISTRY OF MAMMALIAN TISSUES. John Christian Ballin. Library, Dept. of Photographic Reproduction, Univ. of Chicago, vol.57, illus., tbls., 1956.

COMPARISON OF THE ACTIVITY AND DISTRIBUTION OF IODINE, IN REPTILIAN AND MAMMALIAN THYROIDS. Emil J. Baumann, Nannette Metzger, David Marine. Proc. Soc. Exper. Biol. and Med., Utica, vol.51, no.1, pp.110-111, Oct., 1942.

(OCCURRENCE OF CREATINE AND CREATININE IN THE BODIES OF MAMMALS.) Het voorkomen van kreatine en kreatinine in het lichsam van zoogdieren. Johan Cornelis Beker. Utrecht, A. Oosthoek, incl. tbls., 1913.

RÔLE OF INOSITOL AND P-AMINOBENZOIC-ACID IN NORMAL LACTATION. David R. Climenko, Evan W. McChesney. Proc. Soc. Exper. Biol. and Med., Utica, vol.51, no.1, pp.157-159, fig.1, Oct., 1942.

LIVER VITAMIN A RESERVES OF SOME BRITISH WILD ANIMALS. A. W. Davies, Alastair N. Worden. Proc. Zool. Soc. London, vol.123, pt.4, pp.739-746, Feb. 10, 1954.

CYTOCHEMICAL SURVEY OF PHOSPHATASES IN MAMMALIAN LIVER, PANCREAS AND SALIVARY GLANDS. Helen Wendler Deane. Amer. Jour. Anat., Philadelphia, vol.80, no.3, pp.321, 359, figs.42, May, 1947.

MECHANISM OF VITAMIN $B_1$ DESTRUCTION BY A FACTOR IN RAW SMELT. H. F. Deutsch, G. L. Ott. Proc. Soc. Exper. Biol. and Med., Utica, vol.51, no.1, pp.119-122, Oct., 1942.

REPLENISHMENT OF DEPLETED SKELETAL RESERVES OF MAGNESIUM. J. Duckworth, W. Godden. Biochemical Jour., Cambridge, England, vol.37, no.5, pp.595-598, 1943.

TRYPTOPHANE AS PRECURSOR OF NICOTINAMIDE IN MAMMALS. P. Ellinger, M. M. Abdel Kader. Nature, London, vol.160, no.4072, pp.675-676, Nov. 15, 1947.

BIOCHEMICAL ASPECTS OF MAMMARY GLAND FUNCTION. S. J. Folley. Biol. Rev., London, vol.24, no.3, pp.316-354, July, 1949.

(FATS OF NONMARINE WILD MAMMALS.) Fette der nicht-marinen Wildsaeuger. Ludwig Freund. Die Rohstoffe des Tierreichs, Berlin, pt.1, pp.139-151, 1930.

ON THE MELTING POINTS OF ANIMAL FATS IN COLD CLIMATES. Laurence Irving, Knut Schmidt-Nielsen, Norman S. B. Abrahamsen. Physiological Zoology, vol.30, no. 2, pp.93-105, Apr., 1957.

WATER CONTENT OF TISSUES OF SOME DESERT REPTILES AND MAMMALS. Fouad Khalil, Guirguis Abdel-Messeih. Jour. Exper. Zool., Philadelphia, vol.125, no.3, pp.407-414, Apr., 1954.

AN ANTIRACHITIC ACTION OF SEA FAT. E. M. Lepsky. Repts. Astrakhan Volgo-Caspian Sea Sci. Fish Sta., vol.7, no.4, pp.72-74, 1931. (In Russian.)

AN ANTIRACHITIC VITAMIN D AND ITS OCCURRENCE IN THE FAT OF SEA MAMMALS AND FISHES. S. N. Matsko. Repts. Astrakhan Volgo-Caspian Sea Sci. Fish Sta., vol.7, no.4, pp.75-87, 1931. (In Russian.)

COMPARATIVE COMPOSITION OF HUMAN MILK AND OF COW'S MILK. Edward B. Meigs, Howard L. Marsh. Jour. Biol. Chemistry, vol.16, no.1, pp.147-168, figs.2, Oct., 1913.

(FATS OF MARINE MAMMALS.) Fette mariner Saeuger. Erna Mohr. Die Rohstoffe des Tierreichs, Berlin, pt.1, pp.152-164, figs.59-66, 1930.

RECENT DEVELOPMENT IN THE CHEMISTRY OF PERFUMES. R. F. Moncrief. Endeavour, London, vol.8, no.30, pp.92-95, Apr., 1949.

THIAMINASE IN AQUATIC ANIMALS FROM NOVA SCOTIA. J. B. Neilands. Jour. Fish. Res. Bd., Canada, vol.7, no.2, pp.94-99, 1947.

(STUDIES ON THE OILS OF SOME MARINE ANIMALS.) Estudios acerca de algunos aceites de animales marinos. Aenlle Enrique Otero. Notas y Resumenes Inst. Español Oceanogr., Madrid, vol.115, pp.1-86, illus., 1943.

AMINO ACIDS - THE BUILDING BLOCKS OF PROTEINS. W. L. Roberts. Amer. Fur Breeder, Duluth, vol.21, no.11, pp.10-12, May, 1949.

VITAMIN A CONTENT AND TOXICITY OF BEAR AND SEAL LIVER. K. Rodahl, T. Moore. Biochemical Jour., London, vol.37, no.2, pp.155-168, July, 1943.

MICROGASOMETRIC DETERMINATION OF NITROGEN IN BLOOD AND SALIVA. P. F. Scholander. Rev. Sci. Instruments, Menasha, vol.13, no.8, pp.362-364, fig.1, Aug., 1942.

CHEMICAL COMPOSITION OF NEWLY BORN MAMMALS. E. M. Widdowson. Nature, London, vol.166, no.4224, pp. 626-628, Oct. 14, 1950.

LIPIDS IN BISON BISON. Charles G. Wilber, Theodore W. Gorski. Jour. Mamm., vol. 36, no.2, pp.305-308, tbls.2, May 26, 1955.

COMPARATIVE STUDY OF LIPIDS IN ARCTIC MARINE MAMMALS. Charles G. Wilber, X. J. Musacchia. Jour. Mamm., vol.31, no. 2, pp.162-167, May 25, 1950.

TOXICITY OF POLAR-BEAR AND SEAL LIVER. Polar Rec., Cambridge, vol.4, no. 28, p.188, July, 1944.

## BODY WEIGHTS AND MEASUREMENTS

see ANATOMY -- WEIGHTS AND MEASUREMENTS

## CAGES

see APPARATUS (CAGES, LABORATORY DEVICES, ETC.)

## CAPTIVE MAMMALS -- BEHAVIOR

see BEHAVIOR

## CAPTIVE MAMMALS -- CARE AND MAINTENANCE

(CONTRIBUTION TO RATIONAL FEEDING OF CAPTIVE MAMMALS, MAINTAINING QUANTITATIVE FEED NORMS.) Beitraege zur rationellen Fuetterung in Gefangenschaft gehaltener Saeugetiere bei Einhaltung der quantitativen Futternormen. Csaba Ceyza V. Anghi. Der Zoologische Garten, Leipzig, n.F., vol.12, no.1, pp.32-38, Mar., 1940.

(STUNNING ZOO ANIMALS.) Betaeubung von Zootieren. E. Berge. Zool. Garten, n. F., Leipzig, vol.10, nos.1-2, pp.33-36, illus., May, 1938.

MEDICAL CARE OF ANIMALS IN THE ZOO. Reid W. Blair. Scientific Monthly, vol.35, no.5, pp.454-457, Nov., 1932.

(FEEDING WILD ANIMALS THEN AND NOW.) Wildfuetterung einst und jetzt. Bonin-Ponitz. Naturforscher, Jahrg. 13, Heft 10, pp.345-348, figs.4, pl.1, Jan., 1937.

(CARE AND PRESENTATION OF MAMMALS IN MODERN ZOOLOGICAL GARDENS.) La conservation et la présentation des mammifères dans les jardins zoologiques modernes. E. Bourdelle. Revue d'Histoire Naturelle, Pt.1, A. Mammifères, Paris, vol.11, no.5, pp.172-174, May, 1930.

FEEDING THE ANIMALS. William Bridges. Bull. New York Zool. Soc., vol.40, no.3, pp.74-84, illus., May-June, 1937.

PROTECTION OF CAPTIVITY. Emerson C. Brown. Nature Mag., vol.2, pp.69-75, figs.13, Aug., 1923.

TAMING WILD APPETITES. Alice Spencer Cook. Nature Mag., Washington, vol.39, no.2, pp.93-96, Feb., 1946.

ANIMAL COLONY MAINTENANCE. E.J. Farris et al. New York Acad. of Sci., New York, vol.46, art.1, pp.1-126.

(DOCTOR'S PRACTICE IN ARTIS. III. MONKEYS.) Dokterspraktijk in Artis. III. Apen. C. J. Folmer. Artis, Amsterdam, vol.1, no.3, pp.62-63, illus., Oct., 1955.

(BRIEF ARTICLE ON THE TREATMENT OF CHIMPANZEES, OSTRICHES, AND INDIAN LEOPARDS IN THE FRANKFURT ZOO.) Kurze Mitteilung ueber die Behandlung von Schimpansen, Straussen und Geparden im Frankfurt Zoo. Bernhard Grzimek. Zool. Garten, Leipzig, n.F., vol.20, nos. 2-3, pp.191-193, 1953.

(METHODICAL STRUGGLE AGAINST DISEASE AND FOR PREVENTION IN ZOO ANIMALS.) Metodische Krankheit- Bekaempfung und-Verhuetung bei Zootieren. E. Jacob. Zool. Garten, Leipzig, n.F., vol.19, no.5, pp.243-248, 1952.

ANIMAL RESTAURANT. Winifred E. King. San Diego Zoonooz, vol.19, no.7, pp.3-5, no.8, pp.6-7, illus., July, Aug., 1946.

(HOW SHOULD I FEED CAPTIVE ANIMALS? A LIST OF FEEDS FOR ALL ANIMAL GROUPS.) Wie fuettere ich gefangene Tiere? Eine Zusammenstellung der Nahrungsmittel fuer saemtliche Tiergruppen. I. Krumbiegel. Akademische Verlagsgesellschaft m.b.H., Leipzig, pp.viii-93, 1933.

(HOW SHOULD I FEED CAPTIVE ANIMALS?) Wie fuettere ich gefangene Tiere? I. Krumbiegel. Verlag Naturkunde, Berlin, pp.131, 1949.

(CONTRIBUTION TO THE FEEDING, KEEPING, AND BREEDING OF PLANT-EATING WILD ANIMALS IN CAPTIVITY. PART I. FEEDS.) Ein Beitrag zur Ernaehrung, Haltung und Zucht pflanzenfressender Wildtiere in Gefangenschaft. 1.Teil. Futtermittel. Gustav Lederer. Zool. Garten, Leipzig, n.F., vol.20, no.1, pp.32-44, 1953; vol.21, no.4, pp.282-302, 1956.

FEEDING LABORATORY ANIMALS. J. K. Loosli. Ann. New York Acad. Sci., vol.46, art.1, pp.45-75, June 15, 1945.

SOME CONSIDERATIONS REGARDING THE HEALTH OF WILD ANIMALS IN CAPTIVITY. G. Martinaglia. S. African Jour. Sci., Johannesburg, vol.33, pp.833-844, Mar., 1937.

WILD BEASTS IN CAPTIVITY. HOW THEY ARE WATERED AND FED; THE SPECIAL DANGERS IN HANDLING THEM. Cleveland Moffett. McClure's Mag., New York, vol.3, pp.71-88, June, 1895.

ZOO VETERINARIAN'S WORK VARIED AND INTERESTING. Patricia O'Connor. News Bull. Staten Island Zool. Soc., New York, vol.10, pp.3-4, illus., Mar., 1943.

DIETS FOR A ZOOLOGICAL GARDEN: SOME RESULTS DURING A TEST PERIOD OF FIVE YEARS. Herbert L. Ratcliffe. Zoologica, Sci. Contrib. New York Zool. Soc., New York, vol.25, pt.4, no.28, pp. 463-472, Dec. 31, 1940.

NEW DIETS FOR THE ZOO. Herbert L. Ratcliffe. Fauna, Philadelphia, vol.2, no.3, pp.62-65, Sep., 1940.

SCIENTIFIC DIETS FOR THE ZOO. Herbert L. Ratcliffe. Fauna, Philadelphia, vol.9, no.1, pp.26-28, illus., Mar., 1947.

(ON THE CARE AND MAINTENANCE OF SWIMMING AND BATHING TROUGHS IN THE BERLIN ZOO.) Ueber die Pflege und Behandlung der Schwimm- und Badebecken im Berliner Zoo. H. Steinmetz. Zool. Garten,n.F., Leipzig, vol.6, nos.10-12, pp. 259-264, Dec., 1933.

(DISINFECTION AND DEODORIZATION IN THE ZOOLOGICAL GARDEN.) Desinfektion und Desodorisation in Zoologischen Garten. K. Wache. Zool. Garten,n.F., Leipzig, vol. 7, nos.1-3, pp.50-51, May, 1934.

CARE OF CAPTIVE ANIMALS. Ernest P. Walker. Ann. Rept. Smithsonian Inst., Washington, D.C., 1941, pp.305-366, pls. 12, 1942.

FIRST AID AND CARE OF SMALL ANIMALS. Ernest P. Walker. Animal Welfare Inst., pp.1-46, illus., 1955.

## CENSUSES, MAMMAL

PURPOSES OF MAMMAL POPULATION STUDIES. Durward L. Allen. Jour. Mamm., vol.30, no.1, pp.18-21, Feb., 1949.

USE OF BAG RECORDS OF BIG GAME TO DETERMINE SEX RATIOS AND POPULATION DENSITIES. Rollin H. Baker, Hilbert R. Siegler. Jour. Wildl. Mgt., Menasha, vol.7, no.1, pp.11-13, Jan., 1943.

AERIAL SURVEY TECHNIQUE FOR NORTHERN BIG GAME. A. W. F. Banfield, D. R. Flook, J. P. Kelsall, A. G. Loughrey. Trans. 20th N.A. Wildl. Conf., pp.519-532, graph., 1955.

METHODS IN WILDLIFE CENSUSES. W. B. Bell. Jour. Amer. Statistical Assoc., vol.32, pp.537-542, Sep., 1937.

PRACTICAL APPLICATION OF MAMMALIAN POPULATION STUDIES. Victor H. Cahalane. Pa. Game News, vol.14, no.9, pp.10-11, Dec., 1943.

TRAP-REMOVAL CENSUS STUDY OF SMALL MAMMALS. Victor H. Cahalane. Jour. Wildl. Mgt., Menasha, vol.5, no.1, pp.42-67, pls.2, Jan., 1941.

BIG GAME CENSUS TECHNIQUES IN MONTANA. Faye M. Couey. Proc. 31st. Ann. Conf. Western Assn. State Game & Fish Comm., pp.153-157, Apr. 30, May 2,1951.

GAME COUNTS CAN BE MADE FROM THE AIR. L. A. Davenport. Michigan Conserv., Lansing, vol.17, no.1, pp.7, 14-15, Jan., 1948.

METHODS FOR ESTIMATING POPULATIONS OF MAMMALS. Lee R. Dice. Jour. Wildl. Mgt., Menasha, vol.5, no.4, pp.398-407, Oct., 1941.

METHODS OF INDICATING THE ABUNDANCE OF MAMMALS. Lee R. Dice. Jour. Mamm., vol.12, no.4, pp.376-381, Nov., 1931.

SOME CENSUS METHODS FOR MAMMALS. Lee R. Dice. Jour. Wildl. Mgt., vol.2, no. 3, pp.119-130, July, 1938.

ESTIMATION OF THE NUMBER OF SPECIES PRESENT ON A GIVEN AREA. F. C. Evans, P. J. Clark, R. H. Brand. Ecology, vol.36, no.2, pp.342-343, Apr., 1955.

FORMULA FOR TAKING A CENSUS OF MAMMALS BY THEIR TRACKS. A. N. Formozov. Zool. Zh. vol.11, no.2, pp. 66-69, 1932.

INTERSECTION METHOD OF COUNTING ANIMALS. Samuel A. Graham. Jour. Wildl. Mgt., Menasha, vol.4, no.3, pp.313-314, July, 1940.

TAKING A WILDLIFE CENSUS. Russell K. Grater. Natl. Park Serv., Region Three Quart. vol.1, no.2, pp.17-21, Oct., 1939.

METHOD FOR DETERMINING THE NUMERICAL STATUS AND POPULATION LEVEL OF SMALL MAMMALS IN FORESTED REGIONS. W. J. Hamilton, Jr. Bull. Ecol. Soc. America, Tucson, vol.20, p.38, Dec., 1939.

EXAMINATION OF THE STRIP CENSUS METHOD FOR ESTIMATING ANIMAL POPULATIONS. Don W. Hayne. Jour. Wildl. Mgt., Menasha, vol.13, no.2, pp.145-157, fig.1, Apr., 1949.

TWO METHODS FOR ESTIMATING POPULATION FROM TRAPPING RECORDS. Don W. Hayne. Jour. Mamm., vol.30, no.4, pp.399-411, figs.3, illus., Nov., 17, 1949.

FOREST WILDLIFE CENSUS METHODS APPLICABLE TO NEW ENGLAND CONDITIONS. N. W. Hosley (Chairman), et al. Jour Forest., vol.34, no.5, pp.467-471, May, 1936.

AIR CENSUS TECHNIQUE AND TREND STUDIES IN RELATION TO BIG GAME. Gilbert N. Hunter. Colorado Conserv. Comments, Denver, vol.7, no.2, pp.17-18, June 15, 1944.

METHODS OF DETERMINING TRENDS IN BIG GAME NUMBERS AND RANGE CONDITIONS. Gilbert N. Hunter. Trans. N.A. Wildl. Conf. vol.10, pp.234-241, 1945.

ON THE METHODS OF TAKING A CENSUS OF THE FURBEARER POPULATION. A.V. Kosmarkow. Zool. Jour., Moscow, vol.17, no.4, pp.602-609, tbls.3, 1938. (In Russian, with English summary.)

GAME CENSUS DRIVE. John Langenbach. Pennsylvania Game News, New Cumberland, vol.9, no.12, p.9, fig.1, Mar., 1939.

DETERMINING THE BIG-GAME POPULATION FROM THE KILL. J. B. Lauckhart. Trans. 15th North Amer. Wildlife Conf., Washington, pp.644-650, 1950.

EVALUATION OF BIG GAME CENSUS TECHNIQUES. J. B. Lauckhart. Proc. 31st Ann. Conf. Western Assn. State Game & Fish Comm., pp.151-152, Apr. 30, May 2, 1951.

PRELIMINARY RESULTS OF WILDLIFE CENSUS BASED ON ACTUAL COUNTS AS COMPARED TO PREVIOUS ESTIMATES ON NATIONAL FORESTS, REGION 2. A.A. McCutchen. Trans. 3rd. North Amer., Wildl. Conf., pp.407-414, 1938.

COUNTING OUR GAME. AN ACCOUNT OF THE METHODS USED IN TABULATING CERTAIN SPECIES OF CALIFORNIA WILDLIFE. Donald D. McLean. California Conservationist, Sacramento, vol.5, no.1, pp. 18, 23, Jan., 1940.

NEW TECHNIQUE OF ANIMAL CENSUS, WITH EXAMPLES. D. A. MacLulich. Jour. Mamm., vol.32, no.3, pp.318-328, illus., Aug. 23, 1951.

COMPARISON OF NORTH AMERICAN SMALL-MAMMAL CENSUSES. C. O. Mohr. American Midland Nat., Notre Dame, vol.29, no.3, pp.545-587, May, 1943.

TABLES OF EQUIVALENT POPULATIONS OF NORTH AMERICAN MAMMALS. C. O. Mohr. American Midland Nat., Notre Dame, vol.37, pp.223-249, 1947.

CENSUSING BIG GAME FROM THE AIR. Marius A. Morse. Conservation Volunteer, St. Paul, vol.9, no.52, pp.29-33, May-June, 1946.

TAKING THE WILDLIFE CENSUS. W. O. Nagel, H. V. Terrill. Missouri Conservationist, Jefferson City, vol.7, no.3, pp.2-3, 10-11, Mar., 1946.

ESTIMATED NUMBERS OR RELATIVE ABUNDANCE OF MAMMALS. National Park Service, pp.4, 1954.

(METHODS OF QUANTITATIVE CENSUS OF FOREST MICROMAMMALIA.) K metodike Kolichestvennogo ucheta Micromammalia. E. I. Orlov, G. K. Lonzinger. Uchenie Zapiski Sgu, Biolog. Ser., vol.1, no.14, pp.167-174, 1937.

CALCULATING THE NUMBERS OF MAMMALS BY THE RINGING METHOD. V. V. Raevskii. Zool. Zh. vol.13, pp.90-96, 1937.

WILDLIFE CENSUS. COUNTING BIG GAME HAS ITS UNCERTAINTIES- BUT HERE'S THE WAY IT'S DONE. William Marshall Rush. Amer. Forests, Washington, D. C., vol.48, no.1, pp.20-23, 48, Jan., 1942.

WILDLIFE SURVEYS- A DISCUSSION OF SAMPLING PROCEDURE AND A SURVEY DESIGN. Vincent Schultz. Tennessee Game and Fish Commission, Nashville, pp.153, mimeog., 1954.

BIG GAME CENSUS. Ernest E. Shepard. Hunting & Fishing in Canada, Montreal, vol.13, no.6, p.50, 1947.

VALUE AND PRACTICABILITY OF WILDLIFE CENSUSES ALONG HIGHWAYS. Hilbert R. Siegler, C. Newman Coleman. Jour. Wildl. Mgt., Menasha, vol.8, no.2, pp.93-99, Apr., 1944.

(Review by Don W. Hayne of) ESTIMATING GAME FROM LICENSE REPORTS. William J. Sondrini. Jour. Wildl. Mgt., vol.15, no.3, pp.325-326, July, 1951.

EXPERIMENTAL ANALYSIS OF METHODS FOR MEASURING SMALL MAMMAL POPULATIONS. Lucille F. Stickel. Jour. Wildl. Mgt., vol.10, no.2, pp.150-159, figs.3, tbls.3, Apr., 1946.

TRAP LINE AS A MEASURE OF SMALL MAMMAL POPULATIONS. Lucille F. Stickel. Jour. Wildl. Mgt., vol.12, no.2, pp.154-161, figs.2, Apr., 1948.

SOME CENSUS METHODS FOR GAME. Allen T. Studholme. Pennsylvania Game News, Harrisburg, vol.13, no.12, pp.10-11, 26-27, 31, illus., Mar., 1943.

BIG GAME CENSUS. Cleland Van Dresser. Amer. Forests, Washington, D. C., vol. 45, no.11, pp.562-563, illus., Nov., 1939.

CIRCULATORY SYSTEM see ANATOMY -- HEMATOLOGY, CIRCULATORY SYSTEM

COLORATION see ANATOMY -- PELAGE, SKIN, COLORATION

## COMMON NAMES

TRADE NAMES IN THE FUR INDUSTRY. Frank J. Ashbrook. Jour. Mamm., vol.4, no.4, pp.216-220, Nov., 1923.

NAMES OF ANIMALS. Alan A. Brown. Our Dumb Animals, Norwood, vol.77, no.8, p. 149, illus., Aug., 1944.

COMMON NAMES OF MAMMALS. Lee R. Dice. Jour. Mamm., vol.18, no.2, pp.223-225, May 14, 1937.

PARTIAL LIST OF MOKI ANIMAL NAMES. A. K. Fisher. American Anthropol., p.174, May, 1896.

THE NAME MAMMAL AND THE IDEA EXPRESSED. Theodore Gill. Smiths. Inst. Ann. Rept. 1903, pp.537-544, 1904.

THE STORY OF A WORD -- MAMMAL. Theodore Gill. Popular Science Monthly, pp.434-438, Sep., 1902.

VERNACULAR NAMES OF MAMMALS. J. L. Harrison. Malayan Nature Jour., vol. 8, no.1, pp.37-40, June, 1953.

ROMANCE IN FURS. Ellis A. Hicks. Texas Game and Fish, Austin, vol.4, no.6, pp.19-26, May 1946.

PLEA FOR UNIFORMITY OF COMMON NAMES OF MAMMALS. Donald F. Hoffmeister. Jour. Mamm., vol.34, no.2, p.285, May, 1953.

(OLD ENGLISH MAMMAL NAMES.) Die altenglischen Saeugetiernamen. Richard Jordan. C. Winter, Heidelberg, 1902.

(ESSAY ON THE ORIGIN AND ETYMOLOGY OF THE NAMES OF THE MAMMALS OF FRANCE.) Essai sur l'origine et l'etymologie des noms des Mammiferes de la France. L. Lavauden. Rev. Francaise Mammal., ser. 1, no.2, pp.64-82, Dec. 7, 1928.

UNIFORMITY OF COMMON NAMES OF MAMMALS. Hugo G. Rodeck. Jour. Mamm., vol.35, no.1, pp.142-144, Feb.1954.

ENGLISH NAMES OF MAMMALS. Ernest Thompson Seton. Jour. Mamm., vol.1, no. 2, pp.104-105, Feb., 1920.

MONGOLIAN MAMMAL NAMES. George Gaylord Simpson. Amer. Mus. Novitates, no.980, pp.1-26, May 11, 1938.

SOME CARIB INDIAN MAMMAL NAMES. George Gaylord Simpson. Amer. Mus. Novitates, New York, no.1119, pp.1-10, June 6, 1941.

(FAMILIES OF ANIMALS.) Familias de Animales. Joaquin Antonio Uribe. El Nino Naturalista, Medellin, pp.379-410, 1935.

CONSERVATION, WILDLIFE

RELATION OF WILD LIFE TO THE PUBLIC IN NATIONAL AND STATE PARKS. Charles C. Adams. Roosevelt Wild Life Bull., vol. 2, no.4, pp.371-401, Feb., 1925.

HOW MAY OUR LARGE MAMMALS BE PROTECTED? H. P. Kjerschow Agersborg. Jour. Mamm., vol.8, no.2, pp.123-132, May, 1927.

FARMER AND WILDLIFE. Durward L. Allen. Wildl. Mgt. Inst., Washington, pp.84, illus., 1949.

RECENT TRENDS IN FARM WILDLIFE MANAGEMENT. Durward L. Allen. Trans. 14th North Amer. Wildl. Conf., Washington, pp.253-260, 1949.

CONSERVING NATURAL RESOURCES AND PRACTICE IN A DEMOCRACY. Shirley W. Allen. McGraw Hill, New York, IX plus pp. 347, figs.169, 1955.

ANIMAL ACTIVITIES OF THE GAME RANCH. C. L. Anderson. Yellowstone Nature Notes, vol.10, nos.1-2, pp.4-5, Jan.-Feb., 1933.

REFUGE AS A GAME MANAGEMENT FACTOR IN MONTANA. I. V. Anderson. Field Notes on Wildl. vol.2, no.10, p.7, Dec., 1941.

SOIL CONSERVATION INCREASES WILDLIFE. Wallace L. Anderson. Conserv. Volunteer, St. Paul, vol.11, no.60, pp.7-12, Jan.-Feb., 1948.

WILDLIFE REFUGE. R. B. Armfield. Wildlife in North Carolina, Raleigh, vol.10, no. 1, pp.12-13, May, 1946.

CONSERVATION AND THE MOLT CYCLE. Frank G. Ashbrook. Jour. Tech. Assoc. Fur Indust., vol.5, no.2, pp.39-69, June, 1934.

FUR SCARCITY THROUGH OVERTRAPPING IMPENDS; CONSERVATION NEEDED. Frank G. Ashbrook. USDA, Ybk. Agr., pp.218-220, 1935.

POSITION OF FUR RESOURCES IN THE SCHEME OF WILDLIFE MANAGEMENT. Frank G. Ashbrook. Trans. 6th N. Amer. Wildlife Conf., Washington, D.C., pp. 326-331, 1941.

NATIONAL WILDLIFE REFUGE OBJECTIVES. Earl L. Atwood. Kentucky Happy Hunting Ground Frankfort, vol.4, no.4, pp. 4, 25, July-Aug., 1948.

MORE DISCRETIONARY POWER IN GAME ADMINISTRATION. Carlos Avery. Fur Jour., vol.2, no.7, pp.18, 53-59, Aug., 1928.

BETTER MANAGEMENT OF PREDATORY AND FUR BEARING MAMMALS. Vernon Bailey. Nature Mag., vol.31, no.3, pp.159-161, figs.4, Mar., 1938.

REPORT OF THE COMMITTEE ON WILD LIFE SANCTUARIES INCLUDING PROVISION FOR PREDATORY MAMMALS. V. Bailey, J. Dixon, E. A. Goldman, E. Heller, C. C. Adams. Jour. Mamm., vol.9, no.4, pp.354-357, Nov., 1928.

USE OF BAG RECORDS OF BIG GAME TO DETERMINE SEX RATIOS AND POPULATION DENSITIES. Rollin H. Baker, Hilbert R. Siegler. Jour. Wildl. Mgt., vol.7, no.1, pp.11-13, Jan., 1943.

MANAGEMENT FOR MAXIMUM PRODUCTION. Elliott S. Barker. Trans. 8th N. Amer. Wildlife Conf., Washington, D.C., pp.122-131, 1943.

REMOVING SURPLUSES OF WILDLIFE FROM THE STANDPOINT OF STATE ADMINISTRATION. Elliot S. Barker. Trans. 6th N. Amer. Wildlife Conf., Washington, D. C., pp.362-368, 1941.

HANDBOOK FOR RANGE MANAGERS, REGION 5. R. W. Beeson, and others. USDA, Forest Serv., pp.212, 1940.

HOW SOIL CONSERVATION AIDS WILDLIFE. Hugh H. Bennett. Audubon Mag., New York, vol.46, no.2, pp.76-86, illus., Mar.-Apr., 1944.

SOIL CONSERVATION IS AID TO WILDLIFE. Hugh H. Bennett. South Dakota Conserv. Digest, Pierre, vol.11, no.4, pp.2, 13, Apr., 1944.

SOIL CONSERVATION MEASURES ASSIST IN RETURN OF WILDLIFE. Hugh H. Bennett. Tennessee Conservationist, Nashville, vol. 9, no.7, pp.4, 14, July, 1944.

ECOLOGY IN WILDLIFE MANAGEMENT. Rudolf Bennitt. Outdoor America, Chicago, vol.4, nos.7-8, pp.4-6, 9, illus., May-June, 1939.

BIG GAME MANAGEMENT ON STATE PARKS. Lester M. Berner. S. Dakota Conserv. Digest, vol.19, no.11, pp.11-13, 16, Nov., 1952.

OUR GROWING NEED: A PLACE TO PRODUCE AND HARVEST WILDLIFE. Jack H. Berryman. Jour. Wildl. Mgt., vol.21, no.3, pp.319-323, July, 1957.

LIMITATION OF COLLECTING EXPEDITIONS AS A FACTOR FOR NATURE CONSERVATION. K. W. L. Bezemer. Proc. Fourth Pacific Sci. Congress Java, Batavia-Bandoeng, 1929, vol.3, Biol. Papers, pp. 127-130, 1930.

EXPERIMENTAL CONTROL OF SEXUAL PHOTO PERIODICITY IN ANIMALS AND POSSIBLE APPLICATIONS TO WILD LIFE MANAGEMENT. Thomas Hume Bissonnette. Jour. Wildl. Mgt., vol.2, no.3, pp.104-118, July, 1938.

BIOLOGICAL CONSERVATION WITH PARTICULAR EMPHASIS ON WILDLIFE. John D. Black. Blakiston, New York, pp.XIV 328, figs.75, 1954.

CENTURY OF WILDLIFE. W. J. Breckenridge. Conserv. Volunteer, St. Paul, vol. 7, no.73, pp.37-43, illus., Nov.-Dec., 1949.

GRAZING AND GAME MANAGEMENT. L. R. Brooks. Arizona Wildlife and Sportsman, Prescott, vol.5, no.6, pp.8, 11, June, 1943.

(WILDLIFE FEEDING IN WINTER.) Die Wildfuetterung im Winter. Hans Bruns. Deutsche Jagd, Berlin, nos.40-41, pp.561-562, Jan. 5, 1940.

USE OF THE HELICOPTER IN WILDLIFE WORK. Helmut K. Buechner. Jour. Wildl. Mgt., vol.14, no.4, pp.472-473, Oct., 1950.

FUR CYCLES AND CONSERVATION. L. Butler. Trans. 7th N. Amer. Wildlife Conf., Washington, D.C., pp.463-472, figs.2, 1942.

(PROTECTION AND CONSERVATION OF FAUNA AND NATURAL HABITATS.) Proteccion y conservacion de faunas y de ambientes naturales. Angel Cabrera. Rev. Argentina Zoogeogr., Buenos Aires, vol.1, no.3, pp.173-179, 1942.

(PROTECTION AND PSEUDOPROTECTION OF FAUNA.) Proteccion y pseudoproteccion de la fauna. Angel Cabrera. Revista Argentina de Zoogeografia Buenos Aires, vol.1, no.3, pp.173-179, 1941.

PREDATORS AND PEOPLE. Victor H. Cahalane. Nat. Parks Mag., Washington, vol.22, no.95, pp.5-12, illus., Oct.-Dec., 1948.

PROGRAM FOR RESTORING EXTIRPATED MAMMALS IN THE NATIONAL PARK SYSTEM. Victor H. Cahalane. Jour. Mamm., vol.32, no.2, pp.207-210, May, 1951.

SHALL WE SAVE THE LARGER CARNIVORES? Victor H. Cahalane. Living Wilderness, Washington, vol.11, no.17, pp. 17-22, illus., June, 1946.

WILDLIFE MANAGEMENT IN THE NATIONAL PARK SYSTEM. Victor H. Cahalane. Yosemite Nat. Notes, Yosemite, vol. 26, no.5, pp.66-70, May, 1947.

WILDLIFE SURPLUSES IN THE NATIONAL PARKS. Victor H. Cahalane. Trans. 6th N. Amer. Wildlife Conf., Washington, D. C., pp.355-361, 1941.

YOUR NATIONAL PARKS - AND YOU. Victor H. Cahalane. Nat. Mag., Washington, D.C., vol.33, no.5, pp.257-265, illus., May, 1940.

REPORTS CONCERNING WILD LIFE RESTORATION. Arno B. Cammerer. Fauna Natl. Parks U.S., Dept. Interior, Fauna ser. no.2, pp.75-133, figs.24-61, 1935.

NATURAL RESOURCES AND THEIR CONSERVATION. Charles Camsell. Canadian Geog. Jour., Ottawa, vol.25, no.1, pp.3-11, illus., July, 1942. (Mammals, pp.8-10.)

IF THIS BE CONSERVATION. Arthur H. Carhart. Outdoor America, Madison, Wis., vol.1, no.1, pp.6-8, 18, illus., Nov., 1935.

LIVE GAME AND FOREST RECREATION. Arthur H. Carhart. Amer. Forestry, vol.26, pp.723-727, figs.9, Dec., 1920.

USE OF SALT IN SPARING WINTER RANGE IN THE SELWAY. George Case. Bull. Univ. Idaho, vol.33, no.22, (Bull.School Forestry, no.8), pp.27-29, Dec., 1938.

SOME BEHAVIOR CHARACTERISTICS OF MAMMALS USEFUL IN MANAGEMENT. Floyd B. Chapman. Jour. Wildl. Mgt., vol. 20, no.3, pp.293-297, July, 1956.

FORESTRY AND GAME MANAGEMENT. Herman H. Chapman. U.S. Dept. Agric., Wildlife Research and Management, Leaflet BS-33, pp.4, Jan., 1936.

GAME PROTECTION AND PROPAGATION IN AMERICA; A HANDBOOK OF PRACTICAL INFORMATION FOR OFFICIALS AND OTHERS INTERESTED IN THE CAUSE OF CONSERVATION OF WILD LIFE. Henry Chase. Philadelphia & London, J.B. Lippincott Co., 1913.

RECENT ADVANCES IN FOREST GAME MANAGEMENT. Warren W. Chase. Trans. 14th North Amer. Wildlife Conf., Washington, pp.233-238, 1949.

OUTLINE OF THE MANAGEMENT OF FUR ANIMALS. Warren W. Chase, Elizabeth B. Beard. Overbeck, pp.48, 1948.

INDIAN AS CONSERVATIONIST. C. H.D. Clarke. Canadian Field-Nat., Ottawa, vol. 56, nos.8-9, pp.127-128, Nov.-Dec., 1942.

IS WILDLIFE CONSERVATION WORTH THE TROUBLE? Justus H. Cline. Virginia Wildlife, Richmond, vol.6, no.1, pp.35-37, Fall-Winter, 1942.

CONVENTION AND DOCUMENTARY MATERIAL ON NATURE PROTECTION AND WILD LIFE PRESERVATION IN THE WESTERN HEMISPHERE. José L. Colom. Pan Amer. Union, Div. Agric. Cooperation, Washington, D.C., pp.1-72, Apr., 1943.

PRESERVATION OF GAME. SOME MORAL REFLECTIONS. Robert Colville. Field, London, vol.172, no.4473, p.653, illus., Sep. 17, 1938.

MANAGEMENT OF BIG GAME THROUGH SPECIAL SEASONS. Newell B. Cook. California Fish & Game, San Francisco, vol.23, no.1, pp.17-21, Jan., 1937.

NEW HORIZONS IN INTERNATIONAL CONSERVATION. Harold J.Coolidge.Trans.13th. N. Amer. Wildl. Conf., Washington, pp.142-159, 1948.

REPORT OF THE AMERICAN COMMITTEE FOR INTERNATIONAL WILDLIFE PROTECTION ACTIVITIES FOR THE SOCIETY OF MAMMALOGISTS, PITTSBURGH, 1946. Harold J. Coolidge. Jour. Mamm., vol.27, no.4, pp.407-409, Nov., 1946.

SALT AS A MANAGEMENT TOOL. Robert F. Cooney. Proc. 31st Ann. Conf. Western Assn. State Game & Fish Comm., pp.99-105, Apr. 30, May 2, 1951.

WILD LIFE IN THE VILLAGE: AN APPEAL. J. Corbett. Indian Wild Life, vol.1, no.2, pp. 67-70, Aug., 1936.

COORDINATION OF MOSQUITO CONTROL WITH WILDLIFE CONSERVATION. Clarence Cottam. U.S. Biol. Surv. Wildlife Research and Management Leaflet B. S-119, pp.6, Sep., 1938.

DOES STOCKING PAY? Clarence Cottam. Wildlife in North Carolina, Raleigh, vol. 13, no.5, pp.18-20, illus., May, 1949.

REVIEW OF COOPERATIVE WILDLIFE MANAGEMENT RESEARCH. Leo K. Couch. Amer. Wildlife, Washington, D.C., vol.28, no.4, pp.172-177, July-Aug., 1939.

SOME VITAL STATISTICS ON BIG GAME ON OVER-STOCKED MOUNTAIN RANGE. I. McT. Cowan. Trans. 15th N. Amer. Wildlife Conf., Washington, pp.581-588, 1950.

WILD LIFE 80 YEARS AGO - AND NOW. T.A. Coward. Field, London, vol.160, no.4161, p.448, illus., Sep. 24, 1932.

CONTROLLED HUNTS FOR BETTER BIG GAME MANAGEMENT. Harold S. Crane. Proc. 33rd Ann. Conf. Western Assn. State Game & Fish Comm., pp.205-208, June 1-3, 1953. (1954.)

WILDLIFE SAMPLING BY SOIL TYPES. Bill T. Crawford. Trans. 11th North Amer. Wildl. Conf., Washington, pp.357-364, 1946.

WHERE THE DEER AND THE ANTELOPE PLAY. CAN WILDLIFE SURVIVE AGAINST MODERN TECHNOLOGY? Alfred Crofts. Wyoming Wild Life, Cheyenne, vol.12, no.11, pp.4-7, 33-35, Dec., 1948.

WORK OF THE COOPERATIVE WILDLIFE RESEARCH UNIT. Paul D. Dalke. Missouri Conservationist,Jefferson City, vol.4, no.6, pp.2-3, 14, Sep., 1943.

SOME BIOLOGIC AND ECONOMIC ASPECTS OF FIELD BORDER MANAGEMENT. Charles A. Dambach. Trans. 10th N. Amer. Wildl. Conf., Washington, pp.169-184, 1945.

POVERTY OR CONSERVATION -- YOUR NATIONAL PROBLEM. J. N. Darling. North Dakota Outdoors, Bismarck, vol.7, no.3, pp.20-23, Sep., 1944; Pennsylvania Game News, Harrisburg, vol.15, no.7, pp.6-7, 27-28, illus., Oct., 1944; Bull. Massachusetts Audubon Soc., Boston, vol.28, no.6, pp.1-30, Oct., 1944.

POVERTY OR CONSERVATION. III. J.N. Darling. Conservation Volunteer, St. Paul, vol.8, no.45, pp.44-48, Mar.-Apr., 1945.

WHICH WILL IT BE ? POVERTY OR CONSERVATION. J. N. Darling. Texas Game and Fish, Austin, vol.3, no.1, pp.8, 14-15, Dec., 1944.

GAME MANAGEMENT ON THE FARM. J. N. Darling, H. P. Sheldon, Ira N. Gabrielson. U.S. Dept. Agric., Farmers' Bull. no. 1759, pp.22, figs.14, Oct., 1936.

ENVIRONMENTAL CONSERVATION. Raymond F. Dasmann. Humboldt State College. Pp.307, 1959.

MALTHUS - A REVIEW FOR GAME MANAGERS. David E. Davis. Jour. Wildl. Mgt., Menasha, vol.14, no.2, pp.180-183, Apr., 1950.

ROLE OF INTRASPECIFIC COMPETITION IN GAME MANAGEMENT. David E. Davis. Trans. 14th N. Amer. Wildl. Conf., Washington, pp.225-231, 1949.

FALSE PRINCIPLES DELAY ADVANCEMENT IN WILDLIFE TECHNIQUES. Verne E. Davison. Jour. Wildl. Mgt., Menasha, vol. 10, no.4, pp.296-299, Oct., 1946.

FEDERAL AID IN WILDLIFE RESTORATION. GENERAL INFORMATION. A. M. Day. Wildl. Circ.3, Bur. Biol. Surv., U.S. Dept. Agric., pp.11, Apr., 1940.

FEDERAL AID TO WILDLIFE RESTORATION ACT. A. M. Day. U.S. Dept. Agric., Wildl. Research & Management Leaflet BS-105, pp.1-4, Feb., 1938.

HOW THE PITTMAN-ROBERTSON ACT WILL OPERATE TO RESTORE WILDLIFE IN THE STATES. A. M. Day, A. Willis Robertson, W. C. Adams. Trans. 3rd N. Amer. Wildl. Conf., pp.56-66, 1938.

IS THE PITTMAN-ROBERTSON ACT FUNCTIONING PROPERLY FOR WILDLIFE? A.M. Day, Carl D. Shoemaker, P. J. Hoffmaster. Trans. 4th N. Amer. Wildl. Conf., pp.12-24, 1939.

LOADS FOR DEER AND VERMIN. Maurice H. Decker. Fur-Fish-Game (Harding's Mag.) Columbus, vol.79, no.1, pp.14-17, Jan., 1946.

DIRECTORY OF OFFICIALS AND ORGANIZATIONS CONCERNED WITH THE PROTECTION OF BIRDS AND GAME. Talbott Denmead, Frank L. Earnshaw. U.S. Dept. Agric., Dept. circular 360, pp.1-11, Oct., 1925

DIRECTORY OF OFFICIALS AND ORGANIZATIONS CONCERNED WITH THE PROTECTION OF BIRDS AND GAME. Talbott Denmead. U.S. Dept. Agric., Misc. publ. no.6, pp.12, Sep., 1927.

DIRECTORY OF OFFICIALS AND ORGANIZATIONS CONCERNED WITH THE PROTECTION OF BIRDS AND GAME. Talbott Denmead, Frank G. Grimes. U.S. Dept. Agric., misc. publ., no.30, pp.1-12, Sep., 1928.

DIRECTORY OF OFFICIALS AND ORGANIZATIONS CONCERNED WITH THE PROTECTION OF BIRDS AND GAME. Talbott Denmead, Frank G. Grimes. U.S. Dept. Agric., misc. publ., no.57, pp.1-12, Sep., 1929.

(ARTIFICIAL AND INDUSTRIAL RAISING CANNOT BE A SUBSTITUTE IN RELATION TO WILD FAUNA.) La cria artificial e industrial no puede substituir a la fauna silvestre. Jorge Dennler. Rev. Argentina Zoogeogr., Buenos Aires, vol.1, no.3, pp.155-164, 1942.

(THE PROTECTION OF NATURE IN THE WORLD.) La protection de la nature dans le monde. J. M. Derscheid. La Terre et la Vie, Paris, vol.1, n.s., no.1, pp.45-55, illus., Feb., 1931.

RIVER DEVELOPMENT PROGRAMS AND THEIR RELATIONSHIP TO FISH AND WILDLIFE RESOURCES. Rudolph Dieffenbach. Jour. Wildl. Mgt., Menasha, vol.12, no.1, pp.96-104, Jan., 1948.

WILD-LIFE PROBLEM OF THE NATIONAL PARK SYSTEM. J. Dixon, G. M. Wright, B. H. Thompson. Science, vol.74, no.1926, p.540, Nov. 27, 1931.

HOW TO ATTRACT WILDLIFE. Richard J. Dorer. Conservation Volunteer, St. Paul, vol.7, no.38, pp.14-18, Jan., Feb., 1944.

GUN CLUBS AND FARMERS. Frank Dufresne. Virginia Wildlife, Richmond, vol.9, no.10, p.12, illus., Aug., 1948.

REMOVING SURPLUSES FROM NATIONAL WILDLIFE REFUGES. Philip A. DuMont, William Krummes. Wildl. Conf., Washington, D. C., pp.348-355, 1941.

CANADIAN CONSERVATION PROBLEMS. PART 2. J. R. Dymond. Bird-Lore, New York, vol.41, no.4, pp.233-237, July-Aug., 1939.

PROBLEMS IN THE CONSERVATION OF GAME AND FUR-BEARING MAMMALS. J. R. Dymond. Proc. 5th Pacific Sci. Congress, Canada, 1933, Univ. Toronto Press, vol.5, pp.4077-4078, 1934.

WILDLIFE MANAGEMENT. J. R.Dymond. Canadian Nature, Toronto, vol.9, no.4, pp.113-121, illus., Sep.-Oct., 1947.

WILDLIFE CONSERVATION AND SCIENCE. Samuel Eddy. S. Dakota Conservation Digest, Pierre, vol.13, no.3, pp.1, 10, Mar., 1946; N. Dakota Outdoors, Bismarck, vol.8, no. 11, pp.8-9, May, 1946.

CONSERVATION -- UP AND DOING. Rosalie Edge. Emergency Conserv. Committee, New York, no.92, pp.18, illus., 1945.

FIGHTING THE GOOD FIGHT. AN ACCOUNT OF MILITANT CONSERVATION IN DEFENSE OF WILD LIFE. Rosalie Edge. Emergency Conserv. Committee, New York, pp.20, illus., Feb. 20, 1935.

ANALYSIS OF THE VALUE OF REFUGES FOR CYCLIC GAME SPECIES. Frank C. Edminster. Jour. Wildl. Mgt., vol.1, nos. 1-2, pp.37-41, July, 1937.

USE OF SHRUBS IN DEVELOPING FARM WILDLIFE HABITAT. Frank C. Edminster. Trans. 15th N. Amer. Wildl. Conf., Washington, pp.519-550, 1950.

HUNTER'S CHOICE IN BIG GAME MANAGEMENT. Marshall Edson. Proc. Ann. Conf. W. Assn. State Game and Fish Comm., vol. 29, pp.122-128, 1949.

ON THE NATURE OF COVER. Charles Elton. Jour. Wildl. Mgt., Menasha, vol. 3, no.4, pp.332-338, Oct., 1939.

FUR ANIMAL REPRODUCTIVE CYCLES AND THEIR RELATION TO MANAGEMENT. Robert K. Enders. Trans. 3rd N. Amer. Wildl. Conf., pp.515-517, 1938.

FORESTRY AND WILDLIFE MANAGEMENT. P. F. English. Amer. Field, Chicago, vol. 140, no.28, pp.28-29, July 10, 1943.

FORESTRY AND WILDLIFE MANAGEMENT. P. F. English. Pennsylvania Game News, Harrisburg, vol.15, no.3, pp.6-7, illus., June, 1944.

PUBLICATION STANDARDS IN WILDLIFE MANAGEMENT. Paul L. Errington. Jour. Wildl. Mgt., Menasha, Wisc., vol.3, no. 2, pp.162-165, Apr., 1939.

THE SIGNIFICANCE OF FOOD HABITS RESEARCH IN WILD LIFE MANAGEMENT. Paul L. Errington. Science, n.s., vol.81, no.2103, pp.378-379, Apr. 19, 1935.

CONSERVING THE REMNANTS. Hal G. Evarts. Sat. Even. Post., vol.197, no.10, pp.7, 141, 145, 146, 149, 150, illus., Sep. 6, 1924.

CONSERVATION OF THE MARINE LIFE OF THE PACIFIC. Barton Warren Evermann. Mid-Pacific Mag., vol.25, pp.303-328, figs. 22, Apr., 1923.

WHY NOT SAVE THE MARINE MAMMALS OF THE PACIFIC? Barten Warren Evermann. Bull. Pan-Pacific Union, n.s., no.34, pp. 12-16, Aug., 1922.

FOREST WILDLIFE AND NATIONAL FOREST LAND MANAGEMENT PRACTICES. Theodore C. Fearnow. Trans. 10th N. Amer. Wildl. Conf., Washington, pp.104-111, 1945.

FEDERAL ENCROACHMENT ON GAME MANAGEMENT. C. N. Feast. Colorado Conserv. Comments, Denver, vol.7, no. 2, p.8, June 15, 1944.

WILDLIFE AT THE CROSSROADS. Wilson B. Fiske. Nature Mag., Washington, D.C., vol.33, no.5, pp.298-299, illus., May, 1940.

BULLDOZER A TOOL OF WILDLIFE MANAGEMENT. Stanley E. Forbes, John E. Harney, Jr. Final Rept., Pittman-Robertson Project 31-R, Pennsylvania Game Comm., Harrisburg, pp.136, illus., 1952.

RATIONAL METHODS FOR THE PROTECTION OF USEFUL AQUATIC ANIMALS AND PLANTS OF THE PACIFIC. C. McLean Fraser. Proc. Third Pan-Pacific Sci. Congr., Tokyo, vol.1, pp.1064-1071, (1926) 1928.

CHANGING CONCEPTS OF WILDLIFE MANAGEMENT. Ira N. Gabrielson. Michigan Conservation, Lansing, vol.16, no.6, pp. 3, 10, July, 1947.

CORRELATION OF FORESTRY AND WILDLIFE MANAGEMENT. Ira N. Gabrielson. U.S. Dept. Agric. Wildl. Research and Management, Leaflet BS-37, pp.8, Feb., 1936; Jour. Forestry, vol.34, no.2, pp.98-103, Feb., 1936.

FISH AND WILDLIFE SERVICE. A SUMMARY OF RECENT WORK. Ira N. Gabrielson. Sci. Monthly, Baltimore, vol.65, no.3, pp.181-198, Sep., 1947.

FUTURE FOR CONSERVATION. Ira N. Gabrielson. Trans. 6th N. Amer. Wildl. Conf. Washington, D.C., pp.27-36, 1941.

GAME MANAGEMENT. Ira N. Gabrielson. California Fish and Game, vol.23, no.1, pp.59-66, Jan., 1937.

OUR NATIONAL WILDLIFE REFUGES. Ira N. Gabrielson. Maryland Conservationist, Baltimore, vol.19, no.4, pp.14-16, Fall, 1942.

PRESCRIPTION FOR WILDLIFE. Ira N. Gabrielson. Pennsylvania Game News, Harrisburg, vol.17, 18, no.12, p.11, Mar., 1948.

RANGE RESTORATION. Ira N. Gabrielson. Bird-Lore, New York, vol.41, no.2, pp.63-66, Mar.-Apr., 1939.

WHAT IS COMING FOR WILDLIFE? Ira N. Gabrielson. Trans. 11th N. Amer. Wildl. Conf., Washington, pp.28-35, 1946.

WHAT IS WRONG WITH WILDLIFE ADMINISTRATION? Ira N. Gabrielson. Wisc. Conserv. Bull., Madison, vol.13, no.12, pp.3-7, Dec., 1948.

WILDLIFE CONSERVATION. Ira N. Gabrielson. Macmillan Co., New York, pp.xv-250, figs.24, pls.32, 1941.

(Review by Richard S. Croker of) WILDLIFE CONSERVATION. Ira N. Gabrielson. California Fish & Game, San Francisco, vol.27, no.4, pp.274-275, Oct., 1941.

WILDLIFE MANAGEMENT. Ira N. Gabrielson. Texas Game & Fish, Austin, vol.6, no.2, pp.4, 11, 18, Jan., 1948.

(Review by A. Starker Leopold of) WILDLIFE MANAGEMENT. Ira N. Gabrielson. Jour. Wildl. Mgt., vol.15, no.4, Oct., 1951.

WILDLIFE REFUGES. Ira N. Gabrielson. Macmillan Co., New York, pp.xiii-257, figs.17, pls.32, 1943.

PLACE OF WINTER FEEDING IN PRACTICAL WILD-LIFE MANAGEMENT. Richard Gerstell. Pennsylvania Game Comm., Harrisburg, Research Bull. no.3, pp.1-121, illus., 1942.

CONSERVING OUR WILD ANIMALS AND BIRDS. E. A. Goldman. Yearbook U.S. Dept. Agric., 1920, separate 836, pp.159-174, 1921.

SURPLUS GAME: A PROBLEM IN ADMINISTRATION. E. A. Goldman. Amer. Game, Bull. Amer. Game Protective Assoc., vol. 15, pp.29-31, Apr., 1926.

CONSERVATION MADNESS. Seth Gordon. Country Gentleman, vol.107, no.5, pp. 16-17, 91-92, May, 1937.

KAIBAB! PISGAH! WHERE NEXT? Seth Gordon. Conservation, Washington, D.C., vol. 6, no.2, pp.30-31, Mar.-Apr., 1940.

FOREST FIRES ARE KILLING OUR GAME. Arthur Grahame. Conservation, Amer. Forestry Assoc., Washington, D.C., vol.6, no.1, pp.36-38, Jan, -Feb., 1940.

LEGUMES FOR SOIL AND WILDLIFE CONSERVATION. Edward H. Craham. Trans. 4th N. Amer. Wildl. Conf., Washington, D.C., pp.501-507, 1939.

NATURAL PRINCIPLES OF LAND USE. Edward H. Graham. Oxford Univ. Press, New York, pp.XII-274, pls.32, 1944.

FEEDING WILDLIFE IN WINTER. Wallace B. Grange. U.S. Dept. Agric., Farmer's Bull., no.1783, pp.21, illus., Nov., 1937.

WAY TO GAME ABUNDANCE: WITH AN EXPLANATION OF GAME CYCLES. Wallace B. Grange. Charles Scribner's Sons, New York, pp.365, illus., 1949.

WILDLIFE CONSERVATION--ITS PAST, ITS PRESENT, AND ITS FUTURE. William Grimm. Pennsylvania Game News, Harrisburg, vol.14, no.8, pp.18-19, 24, 31, Nov., 1943; vol.14, no.10, pp.5, 27, 31, Jan., 1944; vol.14, no.11, p.14, Feb., 1944; vol.14, no.12, pp.10, 31, illus., Mar., 1944; vol.15, no.1, pp.12, 31, illus., Apr., 1944.

CONSERVATIONIST'S CREED AS TO WILDLIFE ADMINISTRATION. Joseph Grinnell. Science, n.s., vol.62, pp.437-438, Nov. 13, 1925.

WILD ANIMAL LIFE AS A PRODUCT AND AS A NECESSITY OF NATIONAL FORESTS. Joseph Grinnell. Jour. Forestry, vol.22, pp.837-845, Dec., 1924.

CEDAR IMPORTANT TO WILDLIFE. Henry C. Hahn, Jr. Texas Game and Fish, Austin, vol.3, no.12, pp.27-28, 1945.

FOREST AND THE GAME. Albert G. Hall. F. F. Weight. New York State Cons., vol. 10, no.1, pp.30-31, illus., Aug.-Sep., 1955.

CONSERVATION OF THE NATION'S FUR RESOURCES. W. J. Hamilton, Jr. Trans. 3rd N. Amer. Wildl. Conf., pp.518-523, 1938.

COMMISSION AT WORK UPON FARM GAME SURVEY. John W. Hanlan. West Virginia Conservation, Charleston, vol.7, no.7, pp. 10-11, Nov., 1942.

GAME-LIVESTOCK RELATIONSHIPS. Charles W. Hanscum. Wyo. Wild Life, vol.16, no.8, pp.4-9, illus., Aug., 1952.

ANIMALS IN PERIL. Eric Hardy. Frontiers, Philadelphia, vol.15, no.4, pp.107-108, 126, Apr., 1951.

BIG GAME MANAGEMENT. A. B. Hatch. Bull. Univ. Idaho, vol.33, no.22, (School Forestry Bull. 8), pp.49-54, Dec., 1938.

RECREATION AND WILDLIFE CONSERVATION. Joseph M. Heiser, Jr. Texas Game and Fish, Austin, vol.2, no.2, pp.10-18, Jan., 1944.

VALUE OF WILDLIFE CONSERVATION. W. C. Henderson. Am. Planning and Civic Ann., pp.40-41, 1935.

KNOWLEDGE, ABILITIES AND TECHNIGUES NEEDED BY A WILDLIFE MANAGER. George O. Hendrickson, and others. Jour. Wildl. Mgt., Menasha, vol.9, no.4, pp.323-324, Oct., 1945.

OBSERVATION ON THE INCOMPATIBILITY OF WOOD AND GAME PRODUCTION. Paul A. Herbert. Trans. 10th N. Amer. Wildl. Conf., Washington, pp.119-125, 1945.

RATIONAL METHODS FOR THE PROTECTION OF USEFUL AQUATIC ANIMALS OF THE PACIFIC. Albert W. Herre. Proc. Third Pan-Pacific Sci. Congress, Tokyo, vol.1, pp.1072-1074, (1926) 1928.

WHAT HAPPENS DURING A GAME HARVEST? Lawrence E. Hicks. Trans. 6th N. Amer. Wildl. Conf., Washington, D.C., pp.338-347, 1941.

WILDLIFE: CONSERVE, MANAGE, OR LAMENT? Milton Hildebrand. Sierra Club Bull., San Francisco, vol.33, no.3, pp. 11-18, Mar., 1948.

PRODUCING WILDLIFE BY GOOD FARM LAND USE. R. G. Hill, G. W. Bradt. Ext. Bull. Mich. State College, East Lansing, no.218, pp.22, figs.13, June, 1948.

UNIFORMITY OF EXPRESSION IN GAME MANAGEMENT. Ralph R. Hill, Jas. W. Kimball. Jour. Wildl. Mgt., Menasha, vol. 12, no.3, pp.232-236, July, 1948.

CONSERVATION OF WILD LIFE. C. W. Hobley. Pt.2. Jour. Soc. Preservation Fauna Empire, Hertford, n.s., pt.33, pp.39-65, Mar., 1938.

BIG GAME FEEDING VS. FOREST FIRES. Chas. Hogeland. Pennsylvania Game News, Harrisburg, vol.14, no.12, pp. 13, 32, illus., Mar., 1944.

SANCTUARY WITHIN A SANCTUARY. Ned Hollister. Bird Lore, vol.20, pp.158-159, Apr., 1918.

BIRDS AND BEASTS AID EROSION CONTROL. Ernest G. Holt. Conservation, Amer. Forestry Assoc., Washington, D.C., vol. 5, no.3, pp.23-26, May-June, 1939.

WHAT IS A BIOLOGICALLY BALANCED FARM. Ernest G. Holt. Virginia Wildlife, Richmond, vol.7, no.2, pp.5-6, 11, Aug., 1946.

WILDLIFE AND LAND USE PATTERNS. Ernest G. Holt, William R. van Dersal. U.S. Dept. Agric., Misc. Publ. no.444, pp.1-73, illus., Apr., 1942.

ACTIVITIES OF THE AMERICAN COMMITTEE FOR INTERNATIONAL WILD LIFE PROTECTION DURING 1932-33. Elizabeth Hone. Jour. Mamm., vol.14, no.3, pp.286-289, Aug., 1933.

AMERICAN WILD LIFE INSTITUTE "RESTORING" VANISHED GAME. W. T. Hornaday. Year Book Emergency Conservation Committee, Pub.53, pp.20-22, Jan., 1936.

CROWD THE "VERMIN" AND BLAME EVERYTHING BUT GUNS! W. T. Hornaday. Parks and Recreation, vol.12, pp.316-317, Aug., 1929.

RATIONAL USE OF GAME ANIMALS. W.T. Hornaday. Reprinted from Wild Life; its Conservation and Protection, of the Commission of Conservation, Canada, pp.1-11, 1919.

WILL OUR VANISHING GAME BE SAVED? W. T. Hornaday. Fins, Feathers and Fur, no.27, pp.1-2, Sep., 1921; Wisconsin Conservationist, vol.3, no.6, p.7, Jan. (Mar.), 1922.

COMMENTS ON INTERNATIONAL WILD LIFE PROTECTION. A. B. Howell. Jour. Mamm., vol.17, no.4, p.438, Nov., 1936.

WILDLIFE RESTORATION AND CONSERVATION. (PROCEEDINGS OF N. AMERICAN WILDLIFE CONFERENCE CALLED BY PRESIDENT ROOSEVELT, FEBRUARY 3-7, 1936.) A. B. Howell. Jour. Mamm., vol. 18, no.2, p.245, May 14, 1937.

HEARING BEFORE A SPECIAL COMMITTEE ON WILD LIFE RESOURCES. A. B. Howell, Lewis Radcliffe, R. Kellogg, T. S. Palmer. United States Senate, Seventy-Second Congr., first session. On the Conservation of Whales and other Marine Mammals. Washington, D.C., pp.1-20, Mar. 20, 1931.

PRESERVATION OF WILD LIFE. Theodore Hubback. Game and Gun, vol.6, pp.84-85, Feb., 1929.

PRINCIPLES OF WILD LIFE CONSERVATION. Theodore Hubback. Game and Gun Ltd., London, 24 pp. illus.

PRINCIPLES OF WILD LIFE CONSERVATION: 1936. Theodore Hubback. Indian Wild Life, vol.2, no.1, pp.208-218, Jan.-Mar., 1937.

THOSE PUBLIC GRAZING LANDS. R. H. Hubbard. Colo. Cons. Comments, vol.10, no.3, pp.12-13, Sep., 1947.

APPLICATION OF PRACTICAL BIG GAME MANAGEMENT TECHNIQUES. Gilbert N. Hunter. Trans. 17th N. Amer. Wildl. Conf., pp.437-447, illus., 1952.

UTILITY OF PERSONAL INTERVIEWS IN OBTAINING INFORMATION ON GAME AND FISH RESOURCES. Gilbert N. Hunter. Trans. 14th N. Amer. Wildl. Conf., pp.239-252, 1949.

WAR TIME PROBLEMS IN BIG GAME MANAGEMENT. Gilbert N. Hunter. Colorado Conservation Comments, Denver, vol.6, no.3, pp.12-13, Sep. 15, 1943.

CONSERVING ENDANGERED WILDLIFE SPECIES. Hartley H. T. Jackson. Trans. Wisconsin Acad. Sci., Arts and Letters, Madison, vol.35, pp.61-89, (1943) 1944.

CONSERVING ENDANGERED WILDLIFE SPECIES. Hartley H. T. Jackson. Annual Report Smiths. Inst., Washington, 1945, pp.247-272, figs.4, pls.13, 1946.

RECENT LITERATURE. ECOLOGICAL SOCIETY OF AMERICA, COMMITTEE ON PRESERVATION OF NATURAL CONDITIONS. Hartley H. T. Jackson. Jour. Mamm., vol.7, no.3, p.231, Aug. 9, 1926.

SOME LESSONS FROM EUROPE IN FOREST-BIG GAME MANAGEMENT. F. W. Johnson, Lowell Adams. Jour. For., vol. 53, no.6, pp.436-438, illus., June, 1955.

RECREATION CONSIDERATIONS OF WESTERN BIG GAME HUNT MANAGEMENT. F.W. Johnson, D. I. Rasmussen. Jour. Forestry, vol.44, no.11, pp.902-906, Nov., 1946.

BIG GAME, LIVESTOCK, AND PROPER LAND USE. Harlan G. Johnson. Arizona Wildlife and Sportsman, Safford, vol.6, no.5, p.11, May, 1944.

GAME MANAGEMTN. Harlan G.Johnson. Arizona Wildlife and Sportsman, Phoenix, vol.1, no.8, pp.5, 9, Aug., 1939.

OPERATIONS AGAINST BIRDS AND MAMMALS. E. R. Kalmbach. Trans. 13th N. Amer. Wildl. Conf., Washington, pp.113-120, 1948.

STATE-SPORTSMAN-LANDOWNER TRIANGLE. George H. Kelker. Jour. Wildl. Mgt., Menasha, vol.7, no.1, pp.7-10, Jan., 1943.

YIELD TABLES FOR BIG GAME HERDS. George H. Kelker. Jour. Forestry, vol.50, no.3, pp.206-207, Mar., 1952.

ADVANCEMENTS IN WILDLIFE MANAGEMENT ON INDIAN LANDS. Laurits W. Krefting. Trans. 11th N. Amer. Wildl. Conf., Washington, pp.434-441, 1946.

MORE GAME FARMS - OR LAND MAN AGEMENT? Roger M. Latham. Outdoorsman, Columbus, vol.90, no.20, pp.69-71, Mar.-Apr., 1948.

ARE WE ADEQUATELY HARVESTING OUR BIG GAME? J. Burton Lauckhart. Proc. 34th Ann. Conf. Western Assn. State Game & Fish Comm., pp.75-77, May, 1954 (1955).

AERIAL PHOTOGRAPHS, THEIR INTERPRETATION AND SUGGESTED USES IN WILDLIFE MANAGEMENT. Daniel L. Leedy. Jour. Wildl. Mgt., Menasha, vol.12, no.2, pp.191-210, illus., Apr., 1948.

WILDLIFE PROBLEMS. Ross L. Leffler. Pennsylvania Game News, Harrisburg, vol. 15, no.6, pp.6-7, 28, illus., Sep., 1944.

WILDLIFE MANAGEMENT IN WARTIME. Ross Leonard. Trans. 8th N. Amer. Wildl. Conf., Washington, D.C., pp.89-94, 1943.

CONSERVATION OF GAME. A. S. Leopold. Missouri Conservationist, Jefferson City, vol.5, no.2, pp.4-5, 14, illus., Feb., 1944.

CONSERVATION OF WILDLIFE. A. S. Leopold. A Century of Progress in the Natural Sciences, California Acad. Sci., San Francisco, pp.795-807, 1955.

PREDATOR IN WILDLIFE MANAGEMENT. A. S. Leopold. Sierra Club Bull., vol.39, no.6, pp.34-38, June, 1954.

GAME MANAGEMENT. Aldo Leopold. New York, pp.512, pls.5, figs.32, tbls.53, 1933.

WILDLIFE RESEARCH- IS IT A PRACTICAL AND NECESSARY BASIS FOR MANAGEMENT? Aldo Leopold, W. P. Taylor, R. Bennitt, H. H. Chapman. Trans. 3rd N. Amer. Wildl. Conf., pp.42-55, 1938.

CONSERVATION OR DESOLATION? J. Stockley Ligon. New Mexico, Albuquerque, vol. 24, no.7, pp.29-30, 47, 49, illus., July, 1946.

FROM THE FACTS TO ACTION. Hoyes Lloyd. Trans. 13th N. Amer. Wildl. Conf., Washington, pp.10-17, 1948.

BIG GAME MEAT CONSUMPTION IN UTAH AND ITS RELATION TO CONSUMPTION OF MEAT FROM COMMERCIAL LIVESTOCK. Russell D. Lloyd. Jour. Range Mgt. vol.8, no.5, pp.214-217, graphs., Sep., 1955.

TEACHING CONSERVATION OF WILDLIFE THROUGH 4-H CLUBS. Ruth Lohmann. U.S. Dept. Agric., Misc. Publ. no.291, pp.1-34, figs.4, Feb., 1938.

GAME DIVISION. P. S. Lovejoy. Mich. Dept. Conservation, 5th biennial rept., 1929-30, pp.237-304, illus., 1931.

JURISDICTION OVER FEDERAL CONSERVATION AREAS. William Lovell. Wisconsin Conservation Bull., Madison, vol.4, no.11, pp.36-45, Nov., 1939.

PLACE OF BURNING IN MANAGEMENT OF THE GULF COAST WILDLIFE REFUGES. John J. Lynch. Jour. Wildl. Mgt., Menasha, vol.5, no.4, pp.454-457, Oct., 1941.

CONSERVATION FROM THE NATURALIST'S POINT OF VIEW. Marcus Ward Lyon, Jr. Indiana Audubon Soc., Inc., Year Book, Crawfordsville, pp.8, 1939.

BIOLOGIC BALANCE ON THE FARM. W.L. McAtee. Soil Conservation, Washington, D.C., vol.5, no.4, pp.97-99, Oct., 1939.

CONSERVATION OF GAME OR OF WILD LIFE - WHICH? W. L. McAtee. Scientific Monthly, vol.38, pp.165-169, Feb., 1934.

ELECTRIC FENCE IN WILDLIFE MANAGEMENT. W. L. McAtee. Jour. Wildl. Mgt., Menasha, Wisc., vol.3, no.1, pp. 1-13, Jan., 1939.

GROUPS OF PLANTS VALUABLE FOR WILDLIFE UTILIZATION AND EROSION CONTROL. W. L. McAtee. U.S. Dept. Agric., circular no.412, pp.12, pls.7, Oct., 1936.

PLANTS VALUABLE FOR WILDLIFE UTILIZATION AND FOR EROSION CONTROL. W. L. McAtee. U.S. Dept. Agric., Wildl. Research and Mgt. Leaflet BS-19, pp.11, Oct., 1935.

WILDLIFE IN LAND PLANNING. W. L. McAtee. Conservation, Washington, D.C., vol.6, no.3, pp.44-46, May-June, 1940.

WILDLIFE IN LAND PLANNING. W. L. McAtee. U.S. Dept. Agric., Wildl. Research and Mgt., Leaflet BS-71, pp.6, Nov., 1936.

WILDLIFE TECHNOLOGY. W. L. McAtee. U.S.Dept.Agric., Wildl. Research and Mgt. Leaflet BS-67, pp.5, Oct., 1936.

EXPERIENCE SHOWS ARTIFICIAL FEEDING HAS MANY DETRIMENTAL EFFECTS ON GAME. P. J. McDermott. Idaho Wildl. Rev., vol.4, no.4, pp.8-9, illus., Mar.-Apr., 1952.

BIG GAME MANAGEMENT. H. H. MacDonald. Publ. Biological Ciné, Dallas, Texas, pp.183, illus., 12 mo.1934.

IMPORTANCE OF FUR RESOURCES IN WILDLIFE ADMINISTRATION. Alexander T. MacLeod. Trans. N. Amer. Wildl. Conf., vol.6, pp.68-72, 1941.

GAME MANAGEMENT. J.C. McNelty. Arizona Wildl. and Sportsman, Prescott, vol.5, no.12, pp.6-7, Dec., 1943.

WILD LIFE PRESERVATION. HANDBOOK OF A TEMPORARY EXHIBITION OCTOBER 1951 TO FEBRUARY 1952. Colin Matheson. National Mus. of Wales, Cardiff, pp.11, 1951.

DIRECTORY OF OFFICALS AND ORGANIZATIONS CONCERNED WITH THE PROTECTION OF BIRDS AND GAME, 1909. C. Hart Merriam. U.S. Dept. Agric., Bur. Biol. Surv., Cir. no.70, pp.16, Aug. 16, 1909.

CONSERVATION AND EVOLUTION IN A CHANGING SOCIAL PROGRAM. John C. Merriam. Proc. Amer. Philos. Soc., Philadelphia, vol.73, no.5, pp.351-370, May, 1934.

WINTER FEEDING - IS IT REALLY NECESSARY? Helen Merritts. Pennsylvania Game News, Harrisburg, vol.15, no.2, pp.12, 31, May, 1944.

BIG GAME - WINTER RANGE. J. Paul Miller. Outdoor America, Madison, vol.8, no. 5, pp.28-29, Apr.-June, 1943.

NON-GOVERNMENTAL CONSERVATION AGENCIES. Paul Miller. Pennsylvania Game News, Harrisburg, vol.12, no.6, pp.12-13, 31, Sep., 1941.

AERIAL SURVEY OF UPLAND GAME. W.L. Miller. N. Dakota Outdoors, Grand Forks, vol.8, no.9, p.11, Mar., 1946.

BIG-GAME RESOURCE. G. E. Mitchell. Trans. N. Amer. Wildl. Conf., vol.14, pp.538-543, 1949.

DETERMINATION OF CARRYING CAPACITY ON WILDLIFE AREAS. G. E. Mitchell. Trans. 6th N. Amer. Wildl. Conf., Washington, D.C., pp.140-148, 1941.

STATUS OF GAME MANAGEMENT. G. E. Mitchell. Oregon Outdoors, Oswego, vol.4, no.11, pp.10-11, illus., Nov., 1947.

STEWARDSHIP OF WILD GAME. G. E. Mitchell. Oregon Outdoors, Oswego, vol.4, no.5, pp.8-10, 18, 21, illus., May, 1947.

GAME RESERVES AND NATIONAL PARKS. Peter Chalmers Mitchell. Indian Wild Life, Agra, vol.4, no.3, pp.120-130, July-Sep., 1939.

(Reply of W. L. McAtee to) VALUE OF PREY-INDIVIDUAL ANALYSIS OF STOMACH CONTENTS OF PREDATORY ANIMALS, Carl O. Mohr. Jour. Mamm., vol. 17, no.2, pp.193-194, May, 1936.

IMPORTANCE OF NATURAL CONDITIONS IN NATIONAL PARKS. Barrington Moore. Hunting and Conservation, the book of the Boone and Crockett Club, pp.340-355, New Haven, Yale Univ. Press., 1925.

FARMERS FORGET THEIR FUR CROPS. George C. Moore. Alabama Conservation, Montgomery, vol.14, no.11, pp.5, 13, May, 1943.

BIG GAME ON PUBLIC LANDS. Frank Morgan. Colorado Conserv. Comments, Denver, vol.8, no.2, pp.19-20, June 15, 1945.

CLOSED SEASONS FOR BIG GAME - ARE THEY BENEFICIAL? R. C. Morris. Jour. Bombay Nat. Hist. Soc., vol.39, no.3, pp.621, Sep. 25, 1937.

WILD LIFE PRESERVATION. R. C. Morris. Indian Wild Life, Agra, vol.4, no.4, pp. 163-174, 176, illus., Oct.-Nov.-Dec., 1939.

HISTORY OF GAME MANAGEMENT. James N. Morton. Pennsylvania Game News, vol. 8, no.1, pp.12-14, Apr., 1937.

WILDLIFE CONSERVATION AND THE BIBLE. James N. Morton. Pennsylvania Game News, Harrisburg, vol.12, no.6, pp.10-11, 31, Sep., 1941.

BIG GAME RANGE. O. J. Murie. Trans. Amer. Game Conf., vol.18, pp.253-255, (1931) 1932.

ON THE PROTECTION OF BIRDS AND MAMMALS IN AMERICA AND EUROPE. Nagamichi Mroda. Bull. Japan Soc. Preserving Beautiful Scenery Historic Nat. Monuments, vol.4, no.3, pp.188-199, Mar. 1, 1929.

CONSERVATION VI. (AN ADDRESS BEFORE THE MEMBERS OF THE RYE GARDEN CLUB APRIL 23, 1940) Robert Cushman Murphy. Bull. Garden Club Amer., pp.34-53, Mar., 1941.

CONSERVATION FOR EVERYBODY. Robert Cushman Murphy. School Nature League Bull., New York, ser.no.12, bull.no.7, pp.1-4, Mar., 1942.

S.O.S. FOR A CONTINENT. Robert Cushman Murphy. Nat. Hist., New York, vol.43, no.3, illus. folded map of North America, Mar., 1939.

CONGRESS ADVANCES WILD-LIFE CONSERVATION. E. W. Nelson. Nat. Parks Bull., no. 43, pp.7-9, Mar., 24, 1925.

CONSERVATION OF GAME IN THE NATIONAL FORESTS AND NATIONAL PARKS. E. W. Nelson. Amer. Forestry, pp.139-145, figs., Mar., 1917.

CONSERVATION OF MARINE MAMMALS. E. W. Nelson. Science, n.s., vol.58, pp.135-136, Aug. 24, 1923.

FEDERAL AND STATE GAME PRESERVES. E. W. Nelson. Bull. Amer. Game Protective Assoc., New York, vol.9, no.2, pp.6-8, illus., Apr., 1920.

MAKING THE GAME LAST. E. W. Nelson. Outers' Recreation, vol.63, pp.182-186, 248-250, Sep., 1920.

PRACTICAL GAME ADMINISTRATION. E.W. Nelson. Bull. Amer. Game Protective Assoc., vol.14, pp.5-6, Apr., 1925.

STUDY OF CONSERVATION. Curtis L. Newcombe. Jour. Higher Education, vol.16, no.6, pp.299-306, June, 1945.

TOUCH ME NOT. Arnold Nicholson. Country Gentleman, vol.107, no.11, pp.20-21, 72-73, Nov., 1937.

TIMBER-GRAZING-GAME. A SUGGESTED COMBINED PROGRAM FOR UNCULTIVATED LANDS. L. T. Nieland. Agric. Extension Serv., Univ. Florida, Gainesville, Bull.127, pp.19, figs.4, Dec., 1945.

WILDLIFE RESTORATION AND THE AMERICAN TRAPPERS ASSOCIATION. R.S. Oakes. Trans. N. Amer. Wildl. Conf., vol.2, pp. 531-535, 1937.

ORGANIZATIONS AND OFFICIALS CONCERNED WITH WILDLIFE PROTECTION: 1942. Harry C. Oberholser. U.S.Dept. Interior, Fish and Wildl. Serv., Circ.no.5, pp.25, Apr., 1943.

CONSERVATION ON CONSERVATION. Jack O'Connor. Arizona Wildlife and Sportsman, Phoenix, vol.1, no.11, pp.2, 4-5, 8, Feb., 1940.

WINTER RANGE AS A LIMITING FACTOR IN BIG GAME MANAGEMENT. Orange A. Olsen. Bull. Univ. Idaho, vol.33, no.22, (Bull. School Forestry, no.8) pp.20-22, Dec., 1938.

CONSERVATION OF WILDLIFE. Fairfield Osborn. Animal Kingdom, New York, vol. 49, no.1, pp.31-34, Feb. 21, 1946.

CONSERVATION - THE CORE OF OUR DEMOCRACY. Fairfield Osborn. Trans. 13th N. Amer. Wildl. Conf., Washington, pp.160-163, 1948.

CAN WE SAVE THE MAMMALS? Henry Fairfield Osborn, Harold Elmer Anthony. Nat.Hist., vol.22, no.5, pp.388-405, 1922.

WHAT IS OR SHOULD BE THE STATUS OF WILDLIFE AS A FACTOR IN DRAINAGE AND RECLAMATION PLANNING? J. S. Page, S. B. Locke, S. H. McCrory, G. W. Grebe. Trans. 3rd N. Amer. Wildl. Conf., pp.109-125, 1938.

UNVANISHING WILDLIFE. C. M. Palmer, Jr. Conservation, Washington, D.C., vol.6, no. 4, pp.26-28, July-Aug., 1940.

SEVEN KEYS TO WILD LIFE CONSERVATION. E. Laurence Palmer. Amer. Biol. Teacher, Farmville, vol.6, no.5, pp.57-64, Dec., 1943.

FLUCTUATING GAME POPULATIONS AND THE SPORTSMAN. Ralph S. Palmer. Proc. 1948 Northeast Game Conf., Boston, pp.117-120, 1948.

NATIONAL RESERVATIONS FOR THE PROTECTION OF WILD LIFE. T. S. Palmer. U.S. Dept. Agric., Bur. Biol. Sur., Circ. no.87, pp.32, figs.5, Oct. 5, 1912.

PROGRESS OF GAME PROTECTION IN 1908. T. S. Palmer. Yearbook, U.S. Dept. Agric., 1908, pp.580-590, 1909.

REPORT OF THE COMMITTEE CONSERVATION OF LAND MAMMALS. T. S. Palmer, Lee R. Dice, Edward A. Preble. Jour. Mamm., vol.9, no.4, pp.352-354, Nov., 1928.

FEDERAL AID IN WILDLIFE RESTORATION. GENERAL INFORMATION. R. M. Rutherford. U.S. Dept. Interior, Fish and Widlife Serv., Regulatory Announcement, no.18, pp.12, Dec., 1946.

PROBLEMS RESULTING FROM CREATION OF REFUGES FOR BIG GAME. Barry C. Park. Trans. 8th N. Amer. Wildl. Conf., Washington, D.C., pp.339-346, 1943.

WHAT IS THE AIM OF GAME MANAGEMENT? E. L. Perry, Jour. Forestry, Washington, vol.28, no.5, pp.632-636, May, 1930.

VIEWPOINTS ON THE ANALYSIS OF OPEN SEASON SEX AND AGE RATIOS. George A. Petrides. Trans. 14th N. Amer. Wildl. Conf., Washington, pp.391-410, 1949.

CONSERVATION OF BIG GAME. John C. Phillips. N. Amer. Big Game, book of the Boone and Crockett Club, compiled by the Committee on Records of N. Amer. Big Game. Charles Scribners Sons, New York, pp.35-52, 1939.

CONSERVATION OF OUR MAMMALS AND BIRDS. John C. Phillips. Harvard Graduates' Mag., pp.36-52, Sep., 1921.

FIRST FIVE YEARS. John C. Phillips, Harold J. Coolidge. Amer. Committee for International Wild Life Protection, pp.15, Dec., 1934.

WHERE WILD CREATURES LOSE THEIR FEAR OF MAN: A SMALL NATURE RESERVE IN A PRIVATE GARDEN. Oliver G. Pike. Illus. London News, vol.215, no. 5766, pp.614-615, illus., Oct. 22, 1949.

WILDLIFE CONSERVATION AS AFFECTED BY AMERICAN INDIAN AND CAUCASIAN CONCEPTS. Clifford C. Presnall. Jour. Mamm., vol.24, no.4, pp.458-464, Nov. 17, 1943.

WILDLIFE PROGRAM OF THE NATIONAL PARK SERVICE. C. C. Presnall. Virginia Wildlife, Blacksburg, vol.1, no.12, pp.2-3, 8, Aug., 1938.

MARSH-BLASTING AS A WILDLIFE MANAGEMENT TECHNIQUE. Maurice W. Provost. Jour. Wildl. Mgt., Menasha, vol.12, no.4, pp.350-387, Oct., 1948.

NATIONAL PARK WILDLIFE RANGES. Harold M. Ratcliff, Lowell Sumner. Trans. 10th N. Amer. Wildl. Conf., pp.246-250, 1945.

RELATIONSHIP OF PREDATORY CONTROL AND BIG-GAME PROBLEM AREAS. Allen C. Randle. Trans. N. Amer. Wildl. Conf., vol.8, pp.329-331, 1943.

FEDERAL GAME CONSERVATION WORK. P. G. Redington. Parks and Recreation, vol. 15, no.10, pp.659-662, figs., June, 1932.

LET'S MANAGE FUR BEARERS. Jack D. Remington. Colo. Cons., vol.3, no.1, pp. 24-26, Jan.-Feb., 1954.

PREDATOR CONTROL AND WILDLIFE MANAGEMENT. William E. Riter. Trans. 6th N. Amer. Wildl. Conf., Washington, D.C., pp.294-299, 1941.

FUNCTION AND OPERATION OF BIG-GAME CHECK STATIONS IN COLORADO. Glenn E. Rogers. Jour. Wildl. Mgt., vol.17, no.3, pp.256-267, July, 1953.

A FARMER LOOKS AT WILDLIFE MANAGEMENT. Hartwell E. Roper. Pennsylvania Game News, Harrisburg, vol.16, no.9, pp. 4-5, 25, Dec., 1945.

HANDLING OUR BIG GAME HERDS. W. M. Rush. Trans. 20th Amer. Game Conf., 1934, Amer. Game Assoc., New York, pp. 130-144, 1934.

WILDLIFE MANAGEMENT AND OUR BIG GAME ANIMALS. W. M. Rush. Nature Mag., Washington, D.C., vol.33, no.1, pp.29-36, illus., Jan., 1940.

YOSEMITE MUSEUM AND THE CONSERVATION OF WILD LIFE. C. P. Russell. Yosemite Nature Notes, vol.8, pp.63-67, June, 1929.

ELEVEN YEARS OF WILDLIFE RESTORATION. R. M. Rutherford. Virginia Wildlife, Richmond, vol.11, no.2, pp.4-7, 26, illus., Feb., 1950.

WILDLIFE MANAGEMENT ON PUBLIC LANDS AN OPPORTUNITY, NOT A PROBLEM. Allen S. Peck. Trans. 8th N. Amer. Wildl. Conf., Washington, D.C., pp.67-72, 1943.

(THE PAN AMERICAN LEAGUE FOR THE PROTECTION OF NATURE.) La liga Pan Americana para la protección de la naturaleza. Hugo Salomon. El Hornero, vol.4, no.2, pp.191-194, Oct., 1928.

CONSERVATION BRIEFS. II. MAMMALS. Colin Campbell Sanborn. Field Mus. News, Chicago, vol.14, no.3, p.7, Mar., 1943.

RESOLUTIONS BY THE FUR RESOURCES MANAGEMENT SECTION. S. M. Schiele. Trans. N. Amer. Wildl. Conf., vol.2, pp.523-525, 1937.

IS IT RIGHT TO PROTECT THE FEMALE OF THE SPECIES AT THE COST OF THE MALE? Otto Schierbeck. Canadian Field Nat., vol.43, no.1, pp.6-9, Jan., 1929.

REGULATED WILDLIFE MANAGEMENT AREAS ON THE NATIONAL FORESTS IN THE SOUTH AND SOUTHEAST. E. A. Schilling. Trans. 8th N. Amer. Wildl. Conf., Washington, D.C., pp.102-109, 1943.

GAME DIVISION PROGRAM. P. W. Schneider. Oregon State Game Comm. Bull., Portland, vol.3, no.5, pp.1, 6-8, illus., May, 1948.

(PROTECTION OF NATURE AS A NATIONAL AND INTERNATIONAL CULTURAL TASK.) Naturschutz als voelkische und internationale Kulturaufgabe. Walther Schoenichen. Jena, Verlag von Gustav Fisher, pp.viii-458, figs.120, pls.68, 1942. (Mammals, pp.331-405.)

DOMESTIC LIVESTOCK ON FEDERAL LANDS. John W. Scott. Outdoor American, vol.8, no.5, pp.26-28, Apr.-May-June, 1943.

COOPERATION IN FISH AND WILDLIFE MANAGEMENT. Thomas G. Scott. Iowa Conservationist, Des Moines, vol.6, no.11, pp.179, 182, Nov. 15, 1947.

FOREST SERVICE POLICY IN GAME MANAGEMENT. H. L. Shantz. California Fish and Game, vol.23, no.1, pp.77-84, Jan., 1937.

NECESSARY CONCEPTS IN BIG GAME MANAGEMENT. H. L. Schantz. Utah Juniper, vol.11, pp.5-7, 1940.

RESPONSIBILITIES AND LIMITATIONS IN REMOVING GAME SURPLUSES ON NATIONAL FOREST AREAS. H. L. Schantz. Trans. 6th N. Amer. Wildl. Conf., Washington, D.C., pp.368-377, 1941.

HOW BEST TO PLAN FOR WILDLIFE IN LAND MANAGEMENT. H. L. Schantz, I. T. Bode, Seth Gordon. Trans. 3rd N. Amer. Wildl. Conf., pp.16-30, 1938.

WILDLIFE AND THE FORESTS. Robert W. Shaw. Wildlife in North Carolina, Raleigh, vol.12, no.6, pp.8-10, illus., Oct., 1948.

TALK ON PRESERVATION OF WILD LIFE. E. O. Shebeare. Indian Wild Life, vol.2, no.2, pp.287-290, Apr.-June, 1937.

NATIONAL WILD LIFE RESERVATIONS. H.P. Sheldon. U.S. Dept. Agric., Misc. Publ. no.51, pp.9, figs.2, issued Sep., 1929; revised Mar., 1930.

FENCING NATURAL AREAS. V. E. Shelford. Ecology, vol.31, no.2, pp.288-290, illus., Apr., 1950.

NATURE SANCTUARY IDEA. V. E. Shelford. Audubon Mag., Harrisburg, vol.43, no.6, pp.503-510, illus., Nov.-Dec., 1941.

BIG GAME MANAGEMENT. Ernest E. Shepard. Hunting & Fishing in Canada, Montreal, vol.13, no.4, pp.10-11, 1947.

GROWTH OF SOUND IDEAS IN GAME MANAGEMENT. Ward Shepard. Amer. Forestry, vol.28, pp.613-616, figs.7, Oct., 1922.

WILDLIFE MANAGEMENT HANDBOOK FOR FOREST OFFICERS- REGION 5. S. B. Show, A. G. Brenneis, F. P. Cronemiller, R. L. Dering, Ivan Sack, D. M. Traugh. Oakland, Calif. Forest Service, U.S. Dept. Agric., pp.243, figs.8, 1947.

WILDLIFE MANAGEMENT ON THE NATIONAL FORESTS. F. A. Silox. Proc. N. Amer. Wildl. Conf., pp.255-259, 1936.

IS THERE A PLACE FOR STOCKING IN GAME MANAGEMENT? J. V. Skiff. Trans. 13th N. Amer. Wildl. Conf., Washington, pp.215-227, 1948.

PROTECT FUR-BEARERS. Glen A. Smith. Big Horn (Missoula, Montana), vol.3, no.2, p.7, May, 1926.

(Review by Don W. Hayne of) ESTIMATING GAME FROM LICENSE REPORTS. William J. Sondrini. Jour. Wildl. Mgt., Ithaca, N.Y., vol.15, no.3, pp.325-326, July, 1951.

STOCKING VERSUS ENVIRONMENTAL IMPROVEMENT FOR WILDLIFE. Melvin O. Steen. N. Dakota Outdoors, Bismarck, vol. 11, no.3, pp.4-5, 14, Sep., 1948.

GAME PRESERVATION IN WARTIME FACING A DIFFICULT SITUATION. Martin Stephens. Field, London, vol.174, no.4532, p.885, Nov. 4, 1939.

RANCH MANAGEMENT. Ronald Stephenson. Fur of Canada, Winnipeg, vol.13, no.8, pp. 15-17, May, 1948.

SOME PROBLEMS IN RANCH MANAGEMENT. Ronald Stephenson. Nat. Fur News, Denver, vol.20, no.6, pp.12, 26-27, July, 1948.

CONSERVATION AT THE CROSSROADS. Aaron Sternfield. Hunting & Fishing, Philadelphia, vol.26, no.5, p.25, May, 1949.

BASIC WILDLIFE CONSERVATION. Ross O. Stevens. Jour. Elisha Mitchell Sci. Soc., Chapel Hill, vol.59, no.2, pp.209-213, Dec., 1943.

TALK ABOUT WILDLIFE FOR HUNTERS, FISHERMAN AND NATURE LOVERS. Ross O. Stevens. Bynum Printing Co., Raleigh, N.C., pp.229, 1944.

PRESERVING OF WILD LIFE. J.S.Stevenson-Hamilton. Field, London, vol.154, p.169, Aug. 3, 1929.

THE STOCKMAN: HIS IMPORTANCE IN MANAGEMENT OF LAND AND BIG GAME. L. A. Stoddart. Trans. N. Amer. Wildl. Conf., vol.15, pp.83-93, 1950.

SUMMARY AND RECOMMENDATIONS FROM THE TECHNICAL SESSIONS. Tracy I. Storer. Trans. 8th N. Amer. Wildl. Conf., Washington, pp.79-86, 1943.

BIOLOGY OF WILDERNESS PROTECTION. E. Lowell Sumner. Bull. Audubon Soc. New Hampshire, p.6, 1943.

NEED FOR A MORE SERIOUS EFFORT TO RESCUE A FEW FRAGMENTS OF VANISHING NATURE. F. B. Sumner. Sci. Monthly, pp.236-248, Mar., 1920.

RESPONSIBILITY OF THE BIOLOGIST IN THE MATTER OF PRESERVING NATURAL CONDITIONS. F. B. Sumner. Science, Lancaster, vol.54, no.1385, pp.39-48, July 15, 1921.

BIG GAME AND GOVERNMENT. T. Surber. Conservation Volunteer, St. Paul, vol.1, no. 3, pp.48-50, Dec., 1940.

WILDLIFE MANAGEMENT AND ECOLOGY. Fustav Swanson. Sci. Monthly, Lancaster, vol.72, no.4, pp.230-232, Apr., 1951.

ECONOMIC BASIS CONSERVATION TRENDS. Ernest F. Swift. Wisconsin Conserv. Bull., Madison, vol.14, no.4, pp.7-9, Apr., 1949.

SOME CRITERIA FOR DETERMINING PROPER FORAGE UTILIZATION BY BIG GAME ON WINTER RANGES. Lloyd W. Swift. Jour. Mamm., vol.22, no.1, pp. 47-53, Feb., 1941.

PREDATORS - HUMAN AND WILD. P. A. Taverner. Conservation, Washington, D.C., vol.6, no.2, pp.38-40, Mar.-Apr., 1940.

SCIENTIFIC ADVICE FOR WILD LIFE CONSERVATIONISTS. P. A. Taverner. Canadian Field-Nat., vol.40, pp.105-106, May 14, 1926.

CONSERVATION AND WAR. W. P. Taylor. Nature Mag., Washington, D.C., vol.37, no.1, pp.40-43, illus., Jan., 1944.

CONSERVATION IS NOT INHERITED. W.P. Taylor. Trans. 9th N. Amer. Wildl. Conf., Washington, pp.358-361, 1944.

CONSERVATION OF THE NATIVE FAUNA. W. P. Taylor. Scientific Monthly, vol.3, no.4, pp.399-409, Oct., 1916.

FARMER-SPORTSMAN, A PARTNERSHIP FOR WILDLIFE RESTORATION. W. P. Taylor. Trans. 4th N. Amer. Wildl. Conf., Washington, D.C., pp.155-162, 1939.

HOW CAN WE SECURE THIS THING CALLED CONSERVATION? W. P. Taylor. Oklahoma Game & Fish News, Oklahoma City, vol.4, no.12, pp.9-10, Dec., 1948.

MUSEUM OF NATURAL HISTORY AND THE CONSERVATION OF GAME. W. P. Taylor. Proc. Amer. Assoc. Mus., vol. 9, pp.96-103, 1915.

THE NEED FOR NATURAL AREAS. W.P. Taylor. Ecology, vol.15, no.3, pp.328-329, July, 1934.

WHAT CAN MY SPORTSMAN'S CLUB DO? W. P. Taylor. Louisiana Conservationist, New Orleans, vol.2, no.6, pp.16-18, 22, Feb., 1950.

WILDLIFE MANAGEMENT DEMONSTRATION ON A COUNTYWIDE BASIS. W. P. Taylor. Trans. 2nd N. Amer. Wildl. Conf., St. Louis, pp.47-55, Mar. 1-4, 1937.

LET'S BRING WILDLIFE BACK TO THE WOODS. John K. Terres. Audubon Mag., New York, vol.48, no.5, pp.294-300, illus., Sep.-Oct., 1946.

NATIONAL PARKS AND WILDERNESS USE. Ben H. Thompson. Fauna Natl. Parks U.S., Dept. Interior, Fauna ser. no.2, pp.47-55, figs.17-18, 1935.

(THE NETHERLANDS COMMITTEE FOR THE INTERNATIONAL PRESERVATION OF NATURE.) Nederlandsche Commissie voor Internationale Natuurbescherming. P. G. von Tienhoven. Mededeelingen, Amsterdam, no.10, pp.77, illus., 1935.

TIMBER AND GAME. Harold Titus. Pennsylvania Game News, Harrisburg, vol.16, no.6, pp.7-9, 28, illus., Sep., 1945.

INTERNATIONAL AGREEMENTS ON CONSERVATION OF MARINE RESOURCES. Jozo Tomasevich. Food Research Inst., Commodity Policy Studies no.1, Stanford, Univ. Press, pp.xi-297, charts 11, maps 3, 1943.

MANY FACTORS DETERMINE OWNERSHIP OF WILDLIFE. Mandt Torrison. West Va. Conservation, Charleston, vol.7, no.10, pp.17-20, Jan., 1944.

OWNERSHIP OF WILDLIFE. Mandt Torrison. Wyoming Wild Life, Cheyenne, vol. 9, no.3, pp.24-28, Mar., 1944.

WILD ANIMAL OWNERSHIP. WHEN IS IT LEGALLY YOURS? Mandt Torrison. Conservation Volunteer, St. Paul, vol.6, no.31, pp.1-5, Apr., 1943; Ohio Conserv. Bull., Columbus, vol.7, no.8, pp.12-13, Aug., 1943.

BOONE AND CROCKETT CLUB REPORT OF THE GAME PRESERVATION COMMITTEE 1915. Charles H. Townsend. Pp.62, 1915.

WILDLIFE MANAGEMENT; UPLAND GAME AND GENERAL PRINCIPLES. Reuben Edwin Trippensee. McGraw-Hill Book Co., New York, pp.479, illus., 1948.

(Review by Durward L. Allen of) WILDLIFE MANAGEMENT, UPLAND GAME AND GENERAL PRINCIPLES. Reuben Edwin Trippensee. Jour. Mamm., vol.30, no.3, pp.321-322, Aug. 17, 1949.

WILDLIFE MANAGEMENT. VOL. II. FUR BEARERS, WATER-FOWL, AND FISH. Reuben Edwin Trippensee. McGraw-Hill Co., New York, pp.572, illus., 1953.

(Review by A. de Vos of) WILDLIFE MANAGEMENT, FUR BEARERS, WATER-FOWL, AND FISH. R.E. Trippensee. Jour.Mamm., vol.36, no.1, pp.148-149, Feb. 25, 1955.

PRESERVATION OF WILD LIFE. L. A. Turley. Univ. Oklahoma Bull., Norman, n.s., no.322 (Univ. Studies, no.21), pp. 35-42, Dec. 1, 1925.

FUR BIOLOGIST. Reed Twitchell. Missouri Conservationist, Jefferson City, vol.10, no.1, pp.4-7, illus., Jan., 1949.

REPORT OF THE PRESIDENT'S COMMITTEE ON WILD LIFE RESTORATION. U.S. Department of Agriculture, pp.1-27, pl. Exihibits A-F, 1934.

AVAILABILITY OF SURPLUS BIG-GAME ANIMALS ON NATIONAL WILDLIFE REFUGES. U.S. Fish and Wildlife Service, Leafl. no.341, pp.1-6, Sep., 1952.

DISTANCE FROM WATER AS A FACTOR IN GRAZING CAPACITY OF RANGELAND. K. A. Valentine. Jour. Forestry, vol.45, no.10, pp.749-754, Oct., 1947.

EXCERPTS FROM THE ADDRESS BY GEORGE VARGAS, RENO, NEVADA. Colorado Conserv. Comments, Denver, vol.7, no.2, pp.9-11, June 15, 1944.

CAMP AS A WILD LIFE SANCTUARY. William G. Vinal. Nature Mag., vol.11, pp.174-176, illus., Mar., 1928.

WILDLIFE ASPECTS OF RANGE REHABILITATION. Charles T. Vorhies. Hoofs and Horns, vol.5, no.8, pp.6-7; vol.5, no.9, pp.10-11, Jan.-Feb., 1936.

CORRELATION BETWEEN GAME AND FOREST MANAGEMENT. A. de Vos. Sylva, Toronto, vol.5, no.3, pp.28-34, illus., May-June, 1949.

CONTEST FOR WESTERN PUBLIC GAME FIELDS. J. V. K. Wagar. Jour. Forestry, vol.45, no.5, pp.323-328, May, 1947; Trans. N. Amer. Wildl. Conf., vol.12, pp.165-174, 1947.

WILD LIFE CONSERVATION. Frederic C. Walcott. 71st Congr., 3rd Session, Senate, Report no.1329, pp.19, Jan. 21, 1931.

GETTING PUBLIC SUPPORT FOR MAMMAL PROTECTION. Ernest P. Walker. Jour. Mamm., vol.9, no.3, pp.195-200, Aug., 1928; Fur Jour., vol.2, no.7, pp.28-29, 47-48, illus., Aug., 1928.

WILD LIFE PROTECTION - AN URGENT PROBLEM. Ernest P. Walker. Smiths. Rep. for 1930, publ.3089, pp.327-346, pls.4, figs.13, 1931.

CONSERVATION OF GAME AND FUR-BEARING ANIMALS. Henry B. Ward. Science, n.s., vol.53, p.288, Mar. 25, 1921.

WAR AND WILDLIFE. J. D. U. Ward. Conservation, Washington, D.C., vol.6, no.5, pp.3-6, Sep.-Oct., 1940.

FORESTS AND FOREST WILDLIFE IN THE POSTWAR ERA. Lyle F. Watts. Trans. 11th N. Amer. Wildl. Conf., Washington, pp.36-42, 1946.

RECREATIONAL RESOURCES OF FEDERAL LANDS. William P. Wharton. Report of the joint committee on recreational survey of federal lands of the American Forestry Assoc. and the National Parks Assoc. to the National Conference on Outdoor Recreation. Pp.141, illus., 1928.

FOREST AND GAME MANAGEMENT. H.N. Wheeler. Kentucky Sportsman, Somerset, vol.2, no.3, pp.6-7, Feb., 1940.

WILD LIFE CONSERVATION AND FOREST ZOOLOGY. Alvin G. Whitney. Suppl. to Forestry Issue, Michigan Alumnus of Univ. Michigan, pp.4, illus., Apr.21, 1928. (Reprinted in Parks and Recreation, vol.11, pp. 424-429, Aug., 1928.)

CONSERVATION OF THE GREAT MARINE VERTEBRATES: IMMINENT DESTRUCTION OF THE WEALTH OF THE SEAS. G. R. Wieland. Popular Sci. Monthly, pp.425-430, May, 1908.

YOU CAN KILL'EM WITH KINDNESS. James Wilson, Alice Wilson. Pennsylvania Game News, Harrisburg, vol.14, no.11, pp.8-9, 23-25, illus., Feb., 1944.

PRACTICE OF WILDLIFE CONSERVATION. L. W. Wing. Wiley, New York, pp.412, 1951.

MEN AND MAMMALS IN JOINT OCCUPATION OF NATIONAL PARKS. George M. Wright. Fauna, Nat'l Parks, U.S. Dept. Interior, ser.no.2, pp.13-29, figs.5-9, 1935.

CRIPPLE KILL! Wyoming Game and Fish Commission. Wyo. Wild Life, vol.16, no.12, pp.12-15, illus., Dec., 1952.

(INTERNATIONAL BENEFIT FROM A MEASURE OF FAUNA PROTECTION.) Beneficio internacional de una medida de proteccion faunistica. José Yepes. Rev. Argentina Zoogeogr., Buenos Aires, vol.2, no.3, pp. 147-152, Dec. 21, 1942.

SURVEY AND EVALUATION OF BIG GAME EXCLOSURES IN UTAH. Stanford Young. M.S. thesis, Utah State Agr. Coll., 1955.

CARRYING CAPACITY OF BIG GAME RANGE. Vernon A. Young. Jour. Wildl. Mgt., vol.2, no.3, pp.131-134, July, 1938.

ANIMALS AND AIR RAIDS. Conservation, Washington, D.C., vol.6, no.6, p.19, Nov.-Dec., 1940.

BIG GAME INCREASING. Bull. Massachusetts Audubon Soc., Boston, vol.28, no.4, p.122, May, 1944.

BIRD REFUGES AND BIG-GAME PRESERVES ADMINISTERED BY THE BUREAU OF BIOLOGICAL SURVEY. Wildlife Research and Management Leaflet BS-16, Bur. Biol.Surv., U.S. Dept. Agric., pp.7, map, Aug., 1935.

CIVILIAN CONSERVATION CAMPS RESOLUTION. Jour. Mamm., vol.16, no.3, p.239, Aug., 1935.

COOPERATIVE WILDLIFE-MANAGEMENT RESEARCH, 1938. U.S. Bur. Biol. Surv. Widlife Research and Management Leaflet BS-129, Washington, D.C., pp.4, tbls.3, Mar., 1939.

EMERGENCY CONSERVATION WORKS. Jour. Mamm., vol.17, no.3, pp.297-298, Aug., 1936.

FUR ANIMAL CONSERVATION AND RESTORATION FROM THE 1941 ANNUAL REPORT OF THE DIRECTOR OF THE FISH AND WILDLIFE SERVICE TO THE SEC'Y OF THE INTERIOR. Amer. Fur Breeder, Duluth, vol.14, no.11, pp.22-24, May, 1942.

FUR BEARERS BEST MANAGED AS ONE GROUP. Mich. Cons. vol.8, no.2, pp.10, Oct., 1938.

GAME IN YOUR FOREST. Outdoor Georgia, Atlanta, vol.11, no.11, pp.6, 12, June, 1943.

GAME RANGE PROBLEM WHEN WINTER COMES. Colorado Conserv. Comments, Denver, vol.10, no.13, pp.10-13, 16-18, illus., Mar., 1950.

INTERNATIONAL AGREEMENTS ON CONSERVATION OF MARINE RESOURCES, WITH SPECIAL REFERENCE TO THE NORTH PACIFIC FOOD RESEARCH INSTITUTE. Stanford Univ., California, pp.xi-297, 1942.

INTERNATIONAL OFFICE FOR THE PROTECTION OF NATURE. Jour. Mamm., vol. 16, no.3, p.254, Aug., 1935.

INTERNATIONAL OFFICE FOR THE PROTECTION OF NATURE, ITS ORIGIN, ITS PROGRAMME, ITS ORGANIZATION. Publ. International office for the protection of nature. Brussels, 1931.

INTERNATIONAL WILD LIFE PROTECTION COMMITTEE RESOLUTION. Jour. Mamm., vol.16, no.3, pp.240-241, Aug., 1935.

NATIONALISM OR INTERNATIONALISM IN WILD LIFE CONSERVATION. Indian Wild Life, vol.2, no.4, pp.379-397, Oct.-Dec., 1937.

NATURE RESERVES. Nature, London, vol. 151, no.3843, pp.707-709, June 26, 1943.

REPORT OF COMMITTEE ON THE CONSERVATION OF LAND MAMMALS. Jour. Mamm., vol.16, no.3, pp.237-238, Aug., 1935.

SMALL WILDLIFE SANCTUARIES. Nature Mag., Washington, vol.38, no.1, p.33, Jan., 1945.

SURVEY OF DATA RECEIVED FROM THE DUTCH INDIES. Special Publication of the American Committee for International Wild Life Protection, no.8, pp.24-73, 1936.

WILDLIFE AND THE LAND. A STORY OF REGENERATION. Publ. Special U.S. Senate Comm. Conservation Wildlife Resources, 75th Congr., 1st Sess., pp.90, 1937.

WILD LIFE PROBLEM OF THE NATIONAL PARK SYSTEM. Science, Lancaster, n.s., vol.74, no.1926, p.540, Nov. 27, 1931.

WILDLIFE RESTORATION AND CONSERVATION. Proceedings of the North American Wildlife Conference called by President Franklin D. Roosevelt. 74th Congress, 2nd Session, pp.675, pls.77, 1936.

CONTROL, MAMMAL

DEFENSIVE CONTROL OF RODENTS AND RABBITS. Philip F. Allan. Jour. Wildl.Mgt., Menasha, vol.6, no.2, pp.122-132, Apr., 1942.

WORK OF THE BIOLOGICAL SURVEY RELATING TO FUR BEARING ANIMALS. Frank G. Ashbrook. Fins, Feathers and Fur, no.33, pp.74-75, Mar., 1923.

TRAPPING VERSUS NIGHT HUNTING FOR CONTROLLING RACCOONS AND OPOSSUMS WITHIN SANCTUARIES. Thomas Z. Atkeson, David C. Hulse. Jour. Wildl. Mgt., Ithaca, vol.17, no.2, pp.159-162, Apr., 1953.

WHO SHALL CONTROL OUR WILD LIFE? Lester Bagley. Wyoming Wild Life, Cheyenne, vol.8, no.11, pp.1-10, illus., Nov., 1943.

DIRECTIONS FOR FIELD WORK OF THE ASSISTANTS OF THE BIOLOGICAL SURVEY. Vernon Bailey. U.S. Dept. Agric., Biol. Surv., pp.1-10, May 27, 1912.

COOPERATIVE CAMPAIGNS FOR THE CONTROL OF GROUND SQUIRRELS, PRAIRIE-DOGS, AND JACK RABBITS. W. B. Bell. Yearbook U.S. Dept. Agric., no.724, pp.1-11, pls.1-3, 1917.

"VERMIN" CONTROL IN GAME CONSERVATION. Frank D. Blair. Fins, Feathers and Fur, no.56, pp.22, 24-25, 31, 33-34, Feb., 1928.

NUISANCE WILDLIFE CONTROL. Ben O. Bradley. New York State Cons., vol.2, no.4, pp.6-7, Feb.-Mar., 1948.

DESTRUCTION OF GROUND VERMIN BY TRAPPING. John Butler. Game and Gun, vol.4, pp.573-574, illus., Nov., 1927.

EXPERIMENTS ON TOXICITY OF DDT TO WILDLIFE. Don R. Coburn. Jour. Wildl. Mgt., Menasha, vol.10, no.3, pp.208-216, July, 1946.

DDT: ITS EFFECT ON FISH AND WILDLIFE. Clarence Cottam, Elmer Higgins. U.S. Dept. Interior, Fish and Wildlife Serv., Washington, Circ.11, pp.1-14, 1946.

EFFECTS OF DDT ON WILDLIFE IN A MISSISSIPPI RIVER BOTTOM WOODLAND. Leo K. Couch. Trans. 11th N. Amer. Wildl. Conf., Washington, pp.323-329, 1946.

WILD LIFE CONSERVATION AND CONTROL IN WYOMING UNDER THE LEADERSHIP OF THE UNITED STATES BIOLOGICAL SURVEY. Albert M. Day, Almer P. Nelson. Pp.32, illus., June, 1929.

POISON AND ECOLOGY. Lee R. Dice. Bird-Lore, vol.49, no.1, pp.12-17, Jan.-Feb., 1938.

CONTROL OF POCKET GOPHERS AND MOLES IN CALIFORNIA. Joseph Dixon. California Agric. Extension Service, circ. 29, pp.1-16, illus., Mar., 1929.

FUR BEARERS CAUGHT IN TRAPS SET FOR PREDATORY ANIMALS. Joseph S. Dixon. Jour. Mamm., vol.11, no.3, pp. 373-377, Aug., 1930.

(Comments by E.A. Goldman on) FUR BEARERS CAUGHT IN TRAPS SET FOR PREDATORY ANIMALS. J.S. Dixon. Jour. Mamm., vol.11, no.3, p.377, Aug., 1930.

COMMON PESTS. HOW TO CONTROL SOME OF THE PESTS THAT AFFECT MAN'S HEALTH, HAPPINESS AND WELFARE. Rennie W. Doane. Charles C. Thomas, Springfield, Illinois, pp.viii-384 (-13), figs.215, Aug., 1931.

CONTROL OF SMALL ANIMALS IN HOMES AND GARDENS. W. Robert Eadie, W. J. Hamilton, Jr. State College Agric., Ithaca, Cornell Ext. Bull.729, pp.1-20, illus., Nov., 1947.

CONTROL OF SMALL ANIMALS IN HOMES AND GARDENS. W. Robert Eadie, W. J. Hamilton, Jr. Cornell Ext. Bull. no.729, pp.20, figs.12, Oct., 1948.

ANIMAL CONTROL IN FIELD, FARM AND FOREST. W. Robert Eadie. Macmillan Co., New York, pp.vii-257, 1954.

(Review by Antoon de Vos of) ANIMAL CONTROL IN FIELD, FARM AND FOREST. W. Robert Eadie. Jour. Mamm., vol.35, no.4, pp.604-605, Nov. 29, 1954.

POISON FOR OUR WILD LIFE. Mrs. C. N. Edge. Emergency Conservation Committee, New York, pp.4, May, 1931.

FINISHING THE MAMMALS. Rosalie Edge. Emergency Conservation Committee, New York, no.59, pp.1-24, illus., Oct., 1936.

UNITED STATES BUREAU OF DESTRUCTION AND EXTERMINATION. MISNAMED AND PERVERTED "BIOLOGICAL SURVEY" Rosalie Edge. Emergency Conservation Committee Publication, pp.32, Sep., 1934.

EFFECT OF PREDATOR CONTROL ON RUFFED GROUSE POPULATIONS IN NEW YORK. Frank C. Edminster. Jour. Wildl. Mgt., Menasha, vol.3, no.4, pp.345-352, Oct., 1939.

RESEARCH STUDIES IN THE CONTROL OF DESTRUCTIVE MAMMALS. F. E. Garlough. U.S. Dept. Agric., Wildlife Research and Management Leaflet BS-91, pp.12, figs.3, May, 1937.

RESEARCH STUDIES IN THE CONTROL OF DESTRUCTIVE MAMMALS. F. E. Garlough. Trans. N. Amer. Wildl. Conf., vol.2, pp.303-310, 1937.

CONTROL OF INJURIOUS MAMMALS. E.A. Goldman. Science, n.s., vol.75, no.1942, pp.309-311, Mar. 18, 1932.

EFFECT OF DDT ON ANIMAL LIFE OF BULL'S ISLAND, SOUTH CAROLINA. Phil. Goodrum, W. P. Baldwin, John W. Aldrich. Jour. Wildl. Mgt., Menasha, vol.13, no.1, pp.1-10, Jan., 1949.

WHAT THE BIOLOGICAL SURVEY IS DOING TO CONSERVE WILD LIFE IN NEW MEXICO. A. E. Gray. New Mexico Conservationist, vol.1, no.3, pp.4-5, 27, illus., Mar., 1928.

WHOLESALE POISONING OF WILD ANIMAL LIFE. J. Grinnell. The Condor, vol.33, no.3, pp.131-132, May-June, 1931.

THE POISONER AGAIN. A REPLY TO W.C. HENDERSON'S DEFENSE OF THE BIOLOGICAL SURVEY IN THE DECEMBER ISSUE OF OUTDOOR LIFE. E. Raymond Hall. Outdoor Life, vol.67, no.4, pp.26-27, 82-84, figs.4, Apr., 1931; no.5, pp.28-29, 62-63, figs.4, May, 1931.

FIELD-MOUSE AND RABBIT CONTROL IN NEW YORK ORCHARDS. W. J. Hamilton, Jr. Cornell Univ., Ext. Bull. 338, pp.23, Sep., 1935.

RESOLUTION OPPOSING THE POISONING OF PREDATORY MAMMALS AND RODENTS. R. T. Hatt. Jour. Mamm., vol.13, no.3, p.288, Aug., 1932.

BIOLOGICAL PRINCIPLES IN THE CONTROL OF DESTRUCTIVE ANIMALS. Martin A. C. Hinton. Proc. Linn. Soc. London, Session 144, 1931, Pt. IV, pp.111-126, June 6, 1932.

DESTRUCTION OF OUR BIRDS AND MAMMALS. William T. Hornaday. New York Zool. Soc., 2nd annual report, pp.77-126, Mar. 15, 1898.

WILDLIFE CONTROL - DEPREDATIONS ON SEEDINGS REQUIRE PROTECTIVE ACTION. Walter E. Howard. Western Livestock Jour., Los Angeles, vol.29, no.27, pp.92-94, Apr. 15, 1951.

ALL ABOUT FERRETS AND RATS. Adolph Isaacsen. New York, pp.66, illus., 1886; 2d ed., New York, A. Isaacsen, pp.67, illus., 1890. (Complete history of ferrets, rats, and rat extermination, from personal experiences and study.)

RESOLUTION ON DESTRUCTION OF VERMIN AND PREDATORY ANIMALS. Hartley H. T. Jackson. Science, vol.59, no.1538, p.548, June 20, 1924.

CONTROL OF PREDATORY ANIMALS. W.M. Jardine. Letter from the Secretary of Agric. transmitting report on investigations made by the Department of Agriculture as to the feasibility of a ten-year cooperative program for the control of predatory animals within the United States. 70th Congress, 2nd Session, House Doc. no.496, pp.1-17, Jan. 3, 1929.

ANOTHER VIEWPOINT ON "VERMIN". J. P. Jensen. Fins, Feathers and Fur, no. 56, pp.23, 26, 35, Feb., 1928.

CONTROL OF MAMMALS INJURIOUS TO AGRICULTURE IN KANSAS. George E. Johnson. Kansas State Agric. College, Agric. Exper. Sta., circ.120, pp.1-10, Dec., 1925.

USE OF POISONS FOR DESTROYING NOXIOUS MAMMALS. David E. Lantz. Yearbook U.S. Dept. Agric., 1908, pp.421-432, 1909.

CONTROL OF PREDATORY ANIMALS. Scott Leavitt. Hearing before the Committee on Agriculture, House of Representatives, 71st Congress, 2nd Session on H.R. 9599, Serial O, pp.1-100, Apr. 29, 30, and May 1, 1930.

FACTS CONCERNING THE USE OF THALLIUM IN CALIFORNIA TO POISON RODENTS-ITS DESTRUCTIVENESS TO GAME BIRDS, SONG BIRDS AND OTHER VALUABLE WILD LIFE. Jean M. Lindsdale. The Condor, vol. 33, no.3, pp.92-106, figs.20, May-June, 1931.

FURTHER FACTS CONCERNING LOSSES TO WILD ANIMAL LIFE THROUGH PEST CONTROL IN CALIFORNIA. Jean M. Linsdale. The Condor, vol.34, no.3, pp.121-135, May-June, 1932.

INSECTICIDES VS. WILDLIFE. Joseph P. Linduska. Trans. 13th N. Amer. Wildl. Conf., Washington, pp.121-128, 1948.

EFFECTS OF DDT AND OTHER INSECTICIDES ON FISH AND WILDLIFE. SUMMARY OF INVESTIGATIONS DURING 1947. Joseph P. Linduska, Eugene W. Surber. Fish and Wildlife Service Circular, U.S. Dept. Interior, no.15, pp.19, 1948.

NOTE. (POISONING OPERATIONS). M.W. Lyon, Jr. Amer. Midland Nat., vol.12, no.11, p.504, Sep., 1931.

EFFECT OF DDT ON MAMMALS. R. E. Mackie. Ontario Dept. Lands and Forests, Div. Research Biol. Bull. no.2, pp.63-70, 1949.

POISON! Harry McGuire. Outdoor Life, Denver, Colo., vol.66, no.2, p.9, Aug., 1930.

WHO IS RIGHT ABOUT POISONING. Harry McGuire. Outdoor Life, vol.70, no.6, pp. 24-27, Dec., 1932

LETTER TO DR. M. W. LYON IN REGARD TO USE OF POISON. C. Hart Merriam. Jour. Mamm., vol.13, no.1, pp.97-98, Feb., 1932.

SHALL WE PROTECT THE KILLERS? C.B. Miller. Field and Stream, New York, vol.50 no.9, pp.40-41, 96-97, illus., Jan., 1946.

VALUE OF PREY-INDIVIDUAL ANALYSIS OF STOMACH CONTENTS OF PREDATORY MAMMALS. Carl O. Mohr. Jour. Mamm., vol.16, no.4, pp.323-324, Nov., 1935.

VALUE OF PREY-INDIVIDUAL ANALYSIS OF STOMACH CONTENTS OF PREDATORY ANIMALS. (Reply to W. L. McAtee.) Carl O. Mohr. Jour. Mamm., vol.17, no.2, p. 194, May, 1936.

ANALYSIS OF BIG GAME DAMAGE CONTROL METHODS. T. B. Murray. Proc. Ann. Conf. W. Assn. State Game and Fish. Comm. vol.30, pp.51-52, 1950.

WILL DDT KILL WILDLIFE? William W. Neely. Field and Stream, New York, vol. 62, no.12, pp.62-161, illus., Apr., 1948.

REPORT OF CHIEF OF BUREAU OF BIOLOGICAL SURVEY. E. W. Nelson. Ann. Rep., U.S. Dept. Agric., Washington, D.C., pp.16, 1917.

REPORT OF CHIEF OF BUREAU OF BIOLOGICAL SURVEY. E. W. Nelson. Ann. Rep., U.S. Dept. Agric., Washington, D.C., pp.36, 1920.

EXTERMINATION OF NOXIOUS ANIMALS BY BOUNTIES. T. S. Palmer. Yearbook, U.S. Dept. Agric., Washington, D.C., pp.55-68, 1896.

POISONING BIRDS AND MAMMALS. T.Gilbert Pearson. Bird-Lore, pp.362-364, Sep. Oct., 1931.

POISON AFIELD. Wayland Potter. Hunting & Fishing, Philadelphia, vol.26, no.8, pp.18-21, illus., Aug., 1949.

ARE WE OVER-CONTROLLING PREDATORS? Richard Pough. Conservation, Amer.Forestry Assoc., Washington, D.C., vol.5, no.3, pp.17-19, May-June, 1939.

POLICIES AND PHILOSOPHIES OF PREDATOR AND RODENT CONTROL. Clifford C. Presnall. Trans. 14th N. Amer. Wildl.Conf., Washington, pp.586-592, 1949.

UNITED STATES BIOLOGICAL SURVEY. DESTRUCTION, NOT SCIENTIFIC INVESTIGATION AND CONSERVATION, NOW ITS CHIEF ACTIVITY. Davis Quinn. Emergency Conservation Committee, New York, pp.23, May, 1930.

INFORMATION FOR THE GUIDANCE OF FIELD MEN COOPERATORS OF THE BUREAU OF BIOLOGICAL SURVEY ENGAGED IN THE CONTROL OF INJURIOUS RODENTS AND PREDATORY ANIMALS. Paul G. Redington, S. P. Young. Misc. Publ. 115, U.S.Dept. Agric., Washington, D. C., pp.8, Apr., 1931.

UNITED STATES BUREAU OF BIOLOGICAL SURVEY. Paul G. Redington. Scientific Monthly, pp.289-306, figs.24, Oct., 1933.

DESTRUCTION OF "VERMIN". Albert M. Reese. Science, Lancaster, n.s., vol.82, no.2138, pp.593-594, Dec. 20, 1935; Scientific Monthly, vol.45, pp.349-353, Oct., 1937.

CONTROL OF BIG GAME DEPREDATIONS ON AGRICULTURE. O. L. Resner. Washington State Game Bull., Seattle, vol.1, no.1, pp.5-6, illus., Aug., 1949; Proc.Ann. Conf. W. Assn. State Game and Fish Comm. vol.29, pp.96-97, 1949.

POISON FOR ANIMAL FRIENDS. W. J. Schoonmaker. Nat. Humane Rev., Albany, vol.34, no.3, pp.16-17, Mar., 1946.

BIOLOGICAL CONTROL OF RODENTS AND PREDATORS. V. E. Shelford. Sci. Monthly, Lancaster, vol.55, no.4, (whole no.325), pp.331-341, illus., Oct., 1942.

CONTROL OF NUISANCE WILD ANIMALS AND BIRDS. Charles Shick. Cooperative Extension Service, Michigan State Coll., East Lansing, and Game Division, Michigan Dept. Conserv., Lansing, Information Circ. no.93, pp.19, mimeo., Apr. 26, 1955.

FIELD OBSERVATIONS OF BIOLOGICAL SURVEY POISONING. Jordan K. Smith. Outdoor Life, Denver, Colorado, vol.66, no.2, pp.38-39, Aug., 1930.

THE UNIVERSAL DIRECTORY FOR TAKING ALIVE AND DESTROYING RATS, AND ALL OTHER KINDS OF FOUR-FOOTED AND WINGED VERMIN, IN A METHOD HITHERTO UNATTEMPTED: CALCULATED FOR THE USE OF THE GENTLEMAN, THE FARMER, AND THE WARRENER. Robert Smith. London, pp.iv-218, pl.vi, 1768; 4th ed. London, J. Walker, pp.viii-150, fold. pl.v, 1812.

CULTURAL METHODS AND OTHER PRACTICES USED IN THE CONTROL OF INJURIOUS WILDLIFE. Donald A. Spencer. Trans. 3rd N. Amer. Wildl. Conf., pp.699-704, 1938.

CULTURAL AND OTHER METHODS FOR THE CONTROL OF INJURIOUS WILDLIFE. Donald A. Spencer. U.S. Biol. Surv. Wildl. Research & Mgt. Leaflet BS-115, pp.1-6, June, 1938.

COMMENTS ON POISON OPERATIONS AGAINST PREDATORY MAMMALS AND RODENTS. Witmer Stone. The Auk, vol. 48, no.3, pp.477-479, July, 1931.

CALCULATING POISON BAIT MIXTURES. Tracy I. Storer. Jour. Wildl. Mgt., Menasha, vol.10, no.2, pp.177-180, Apr., 1946.

DDT AND WILDLIFE. Tracy I. Storer. Jour. Wildl. Mgt., Menasha, vol.10, no.3, pp. 181-183, July, 1946.

RODENTS AND CONSERVATION. Charles T. Vorhies. Nature Mag., vol.28, no.6, pp.363-365, 379, Dec., 1936.

OPPOSE FEDERAL BUREAU CONTROL OF WILDLIFE. New Mexico Mag., Albuquerque, vol.21, no.8, p.28, Aug., 1943.

AMMUNITION NOW AVAILABLE FOR CONTROL OF PREDATORS. Science News Letter, Washington, D.C., vol.44, no.11, p. 175, Sep. 11, 1943.

INFORMATION FOR THE GUIDANCE OF FIELDMEN AND COOPERATORS OF THE FISH AND WILDLIFE SERVICE ENGAGED IN THE CONTROL OF PREDATORY ANIMALS AND INJURIOUS RODENTS. U.S. Dept. Interior, Fish and Wildlife Service, Widlife Circ.5, pp.1-7, July, 1940.

NEW HOPE FOR THE BIOLOGICAL SURVEY. Publ. National Anti-Steel-Trap League, Inc., Washington, D.C., pp.31, Nov., 1939.

WIPING OUT WILD LIFE. Outdoor Life , vol. 68, no.3, p.36, Sep., 1931.

## DICTIONARIES, ENCYCLOPEDIAS, MANUALS

A DICTIONARY OF BIOLOGY. M. Abercrombie, C. J. Hickman, L. M. Johnson. Penguin Books, Baltimore, rev. ed., pp.251, 1957.

DICTIONARY OF FUR NAMES. Bridgewater M. Arnold. Nat. Assoc. Fur Industry, Yearbook, pp.39-47, Sep., 1925.

DICTIONARY OF BIOLOGICAL EQUIVALENTS GERMAN-ENGLISH. Ernst Artschwager. The Wilkins-Williams Co., 1930.

(Review of) FRENCH ENCYCLOPEDIA. VOL. V. LIVING THINGS: PLANTS AND ANIMALS.) Encyclopédie Francaise. Tome V. Les êtres vivants: Plantes et Animaux. E. Bourdelle. Librairie Larousse, Mammalia, Paris, vol.2, no.3, pp.158-160, Sep., 1938.

(MANUAL OF MAMMALOGY.) Manual de Mastozoologia. Angel Cabrera. Privately printed, pp.440, figs.176, illus., 1922.

MANUAL OF MAMMALOGY. E. Lendell Cockrum. Burgess Publishing Co., Minneapolis, Minn., pp.175, illus., 1955.

MANUAL FOR SMALL MUSEUMS. Laurence Vail Coleman. Putnam, New York & London, pp.i-xiv, 1-395, pls.1-32, 1927.

MAMMALS. A MANUAL OF CONSERVATION FOR MISSOURI TEACHERS, NO.6. Everett F. Evans. Jefferson City, Mo., Missouri conservation commission, 1941.

3001 QUESTIONS AND ANSWERS; CONTAINING MUCH VALUABLE INFORMATION FOR HUNTERS, TRAPPERS AND OUTDOOR PEOPLE IN GENERAL AND COULD PROPERLY BE CALLED AN ENCYCLOPEDIA OF USEFUL INFORMATION. Arthur Robert Harding. Columbus, Ohio, pp.395, 1913.

(Review by William P. Harris, Jr. of) ANIMAL ENCYCLOPAEDIA. Leo Wender. New York, Oxford Univ. Press, pp.266, 1949; Jour. Mamm., vol.31, no.1, pp.102-103, Feb. 21, 1950.

HENDERSON'S DICTIONARY OF SCIENTIFIC TERMS. I. F. Henderson, W. D. Henderson. (7th ed. rev. and enlarged by Dr. J. H. Kenneth). D. Van Nostrand Co., Inc., Princeton, N.J., pp.600.

A SOURCE-BOOK OF BIOLOGICAL NAMES AND TERMS. Edmund C. Jaeger. Charles C. Thomas, Springfield, Ill., pp.xxvi-256, illus., 1944; Pp.35-317, 1955.

ANIMAL DICTIONARY. Ina Belle Maddox. McAllen. Tex., pp.11, 1951.

(ENCYCLOPEDIA OF THE NATURAL SCIENCES.)Encyklopeadie der Naturwissenschaften. Paul Matschie. Enthalt: Handwoerterbuch der Zoologie, Anthropologie und Ethnologie, Abt.1, Lief.71, (1897) to Abt.1, Lief.77, (1900) Breslau: Verlag von Eduard Trewendt.

HANDBOOK OF BIOLOGICAL DATA, ed. by William S. Spector. National Research Council. Washington, Nat. Res. Council, pp.36-584, 1956.

HANDLIST OF AMERICAN NATURALISTS, BASED ON THE DICTIONARY OF AMERICAN BIOGRAPHY. Paul H. Oehser. Amer. Nat., vol.72, pp.534-546, Nov.-Dec., 1938.

NEW COMPLETE RUSSIAN-ENGLISH DICTIONARY. (NEW ORTHOGRAPHY.) Louis Segal. Percy Lund, Humphries & Co. Ltd., London, reprinted 4th ed., pp.i-xiv-1016, Feb., 1958.

DATES OF CHARLES D'ORBIGNY'S DICTIONNAIRE UNIVERSEL D'HISTOIRE NATURELLE, 1839-1849. X. Davies Sherborn, T. S. Palmer. Ann. and Mag. Nat. Hist., London, ser.7, vol.3, pp.350-352, Apr., 1899.

ON THE DATES OF THE 'ENCYCLOPEDIE METHODIQUE'. C. Davies Sherborn, B. B. Woodward. Proc. Zool. Soc. London, pt.3, pp.582-584, Oct. 2, 1893.

THE CENTURY CYCLOPEDIA OF NAMES. Benjamin E. Smith. 1894. (Vol.1.)

THE CENTURY DICTIONARY AND CYCLOPEDIA. Benjamin E. Smith. The Century Dictionary Supplement,vols. 11 and 12.

TARAHUMARA-ENGLISH, ENGLISH-TARAHUMARA DICTIONARY, AND AN INTRODUCTION TO TARAHUMARA GRAMMAR. I. Thord-Gray. Univ. Miami Press, Coral Gables, pp.1170, 1955.

LABORATORY MANUAL FOR EMBRYOLOGY. Theodore W. Torrey. Dept. Zool. Indiana Univ., Bloomington, pp.100, 1946.

ANIMAL ENCYCLOPAEDIA, WITH LATIN INDEX. Leo Wender. Oxford Univ. Press, New York, pp.266, illus., American ed. 1949.

INTRODUCTION TO THE LITERATURE OF VERTEBRATE ZOOLOGY, BASED CHIEFLY ON THE TITLES IN THE BLACKER LIBRARY OF ZOOLOGY, THE EMMA SHEARER WOOD LIBRARY OF ORNITHOLOGY, THE BIBLIOTHECA OSLERIANA AND OTHER LIBRARIES OF McGILL UNIVERSITY, MONTREAL. Casey A. Wood. London, Oxford Univ. Press, pp.xix-643, 1931.

MAMMALS AND BIRDS, A SELECTION OF ARTICLES FROM THE NEW 14th ED. OF THE ENCYCLOPEDIA BRITANNICA. Paul Bransom. Charles Livingston Bull. New York, Encyclopedia Britannica, Inc., pp.xxp., 1 1.,199, col.front., illus., plates (part col.), 1933. (Britannica booklet no.3.)

MANUAL OF AMERICAN AND EUROPEAN MAMMALS, REPRODUCED IN NATURAL COLORS WITH THEIR COMMON AND SCIENTIFIC NAMES. New York and London, Funk & Wagnalls Co., 1923.

## DISEASES AND PARASITES

EFFECTS ON MAMMALS OF DDT USED IN FOREST INSECT CONTROL IN THE NORTHERN ROCKY MOUNTAINS. Lowell Adams. USDA, N. Rocky Mt. Forest and Range Exp. Sta., Res. Note 56, pp.3, Nov. 21, 1947.

EFFECTS ON FISH, BIRDS, AND MAMMALS OF DDT USED IN THE CONTROL OF FOREST INSECTS IN IDAHO AND WYOMING. Lowell Adams, Mitchell G. Havanan, Neil W. Hosley, David W. Johnston. Jour. Wildl. Mgt., Menasha, vol.13, no.3, pp.245-254, July, 1949.

FUNGUS DISEASES OF ANIMALS. G. C. Ainswoth. Nature, London, vol.166, no. 4222, pp.547-549, Sep. 30, 1950.

PARASITES AND PARASITIC DISEASES OF DOMESTIC ANIMALS IN THE HAWAIIAN ISLANDS. Joseph E. Alicata. Pacific Sci., Honolulu, vol.1, no.2, pp.69-84, Apr., 1947.

ON THE EFFECTS OF DISEASE AND SENILITY AS ILLUSTRATED IN THE BONES AND TEETH OF MAMMALS. Harrison Allen. Science, N.S., vol.5, no.112, pp. 289-294, Feb. 19, 1897.

SCREWWORM MENACE. Ralph H. Allen, Jr. Alabama Conservation, Montgomery, vol.22, nos.6-7, pp.11, 16, illus., Dec., 1950; Jan., 1951.

ETHYL ACETATE-CARBON TETRACHLORIDE MIXTURE. E. A. Back, R. T. Cotton. Jour. Econ. Entomology, vol.17, no.6, p.663, Dec., 1924.

NEWLY RECOMMENDED FUMIGANT, ETHYL ACETATE, IN COMBINATION WITH CARBON TETRACHLORIDE. E. A. Back, R. T. Cotton. Jour. Econ. Entomology, vol.18, pp.302-307, Apr., 1925.

THE ROLE OF FUNCTIONAL ACTIVITY IN THE PRODUCTION OF MAMMARY CARCINOMA. H. I. Bagg. Amer. Nat., vol.60, no.668, pp.234-239, 1926.

(MAGGOTS AS WOUND PARASITES IN DOMESTIC ANIMALS IN SOUTHERN SERBIA.) Fliegenmaden als Wundschmarotzer bei den Haustieren in Suedserbien. N.Baranoff, J. Jezic. Zeitschr.f.Parasitenkunde, vol.1, pp.416-422, figs.4, Oct. 27, 1928.

SOME WILDLIFE DISEASES IN THE EASTERN UNITED STATES. J. F. Bell, W. S. Chalgren. Jour. Wildl. Mgt., Menasha, vol. 7, no.3, pp.270-278, pl.1, July, 1943.

EFFECTS ON WILDLIFE OF DDT USED FOR CONTROL OF DUTCH ELM DISEASE. Allen H. Benton. Jour. Wildl. Mgt., Menasha, vol.15, no.1, pp.20-27, Jan., 1951.

PRELIMINARY NOTE ON TRICHINOSIS INVESTIGATIONS IN ALASKA. P. J. Brandly, Robert Rausch. Arctic, Ottawa, vol.3, no.2, pp.105-107, Aug., 1950.

(PATHOLOGICAL CONDITIONS ON THE BONES OF PREHISTORIC MAMMALS.) Pathologische Befunde an Knochen Vorzeitlicher Saeugetiere. R. Breuer. Palaeobiologica, Vienna & Leipzig, Jahrg.4, vol.4, nos.6-7, pp.352-355, pls.32-35, 1931.

SUSCEPTIBILITY OF ANIMALS TO ENDEMIC TYPHUS FEVER. George D. Brigham. Publ. Health Reports, Washington, D.C., vol.52, no.21, pp.660-662, May 21, 1937.

NOTE ON TRICHINOSIS IN ANIMALS OF THE CANADIAN NORTHWEST TERRITORIES. Malcolm Brown, and others. Canadian Jour. Public Health, Toronto, vol.40, no.1, pp.20-21, Jan., 1949.

INTERNAL PARASITES OF LAND MAMMALS IN SCOTLAND. W. M. Cameron. Proc. Roy. Physical Soc., vol.22, pt.3, pp.133-154,June, 1933.

MORPHOLOGY, TAXONOMY, AND LIFE HISTORY OF METORCHIS CONJUNCTUS (COBBOLD, 1860). T. W. M. Cameron.Can. J. Res., Sec. D, vol.22, no.1, pp.6-16, Feb., 1944.

PARASITES CARRIED BY WILD ANIMALS OF IMPORTANCE TO MAN AND DOMESTIC ANIMALS. T. W. M. Cameron. Conv. Internat.Assn.Game, Fish and Cons.Comm., vol.28, pp.79-83, 1935.

WILD MEAT IS GOOD MEAT. Arthur H. Carhart. Field and Stream, New York, vol. 52, no.7, pp.48-49, 117-118, Nov., 1947.

SOME PARASITES OF BIRDS AND MAMMALS FROM CANNA. Robert Carrick. Scottish Nat., Edinburgh, no.235, pp.23-24, Jan.-Feb., 1939.

BUCCAL FOOD IMPACTION IN WHITE-TAILED DEER AND ACTINOMYCES NECROPHORUS IN BIG GAME. Jules S. Cass. Jour. Wildl. Mgt., Menasha, vol. 11, no.1, pp.91-94, pl.8, Jan., 1947.

BOTFLIES AND GAME. A. B. Champlain. Pennsyivania Game News, Harrisburg, vol. 12, no.6, p.29, Sep., 1941.

STUDY OF STRIGEIDS FROM MICHIGAN MAMMALS, WITH COMMENTS ON THE CLASSIFICATION OF MAMMALIAN STRIGEIDS. Asa C. Chandler, Robert Rausch. Trans. Am. Micros. Soc. vol.65, no.4, pp.328-337, Oct., 1946.

EXPERIMENTAL EFFORTS TO TRANSFER MONKEY MALARIA TO MAN. Herbert C. Clark, Lawrence H. Dunn. Amer. Jour. Tropical Med., vol.11, no.1, pp.1-10, Jan., 1931.

EXPERIMENTAL STUDIES ON CHAGAS' DISEASE IN PANAMA. Herbert C. Clark, Lawrence H. Dunn. Amer. Jour. Tropical Med., vol.12, no.1, pp.49-77, Jan., 1932.

TRICHINOSIS IN THE ARCTIC: REVIEW. Frank H. Connell. Arctic, Jour. Arctic Inst. North Amer., vol.2, no.2, pp.98-107, figs. 3, Sep., 1949.

DISEASE AND PARASITES OF BIG GAME MAMMALS OF WESTERN CANADA. I.McT. Cowan. Rep. Proc. 5th Ann. B. C. Game Cons., pp.37-64, illus., 1951.

REPORT UPON SOME DISEASES AND PARASITES OF GAME BIRDS AND GAME AND FUR-BEARING MAMMALS IN BRITISH COLUMBIA. I.McT. Cowan. Rept. Provincial Game Comm., 1941, Victoria, B.C., pp.6, 1942.

METAZOAN PARASITES FROM ZULULAND. H. H. Curson. South African Jour. Nat. Hist., vol.6, pp.181-187, Apr., 1928.

(ON THE GENERA PROTOTAPIRELLA, TRIPALMARIA, AND TRICAUDALIA.) Sur les genres Prototapirella, Tripalmaria et Tricaudalia. Aristides Marques Da Cunha, Julio Muniz. Comptes Rendus des Seances de la Soc. de Biol., vol.97, pp.1088-1090, figs.5, Oct. 21, 1927.

(PARASITIC CILIATES OF BRAZILIAN MAMMALS.) Cilies parasites de mammiferes du Bresil. Aristides Marques Da Cunha, Julio Muniz. Comptes Rendus des Seances de la Soc. de Biol., vol.97, pp.825-827, Aug. 26, 1927.

ORNITHODOROS PARKERI: DISTRIBUTION AND HOST DATA; SPONTANEOUS INFECTION WITH RELAPSING FEVER SPIROCHETES. Gordon E. Davis. Pub. Health Rep., vol.54, no.29, pp.1345-1349, July 21, 1939.

PREDATORS AND RODENTS ARE FACTORS IN THE SPREAD OF DISEASE. Albert M. Day, J. E. Shillinger. USDA, Ybk. Agr., pp.284-286, 1935.

DISTRIBUTION OF QUINACRINE IN DOGS AND IN RABBITS. E. H. Dearborn. Trop. Disease Bull., London, vol.45, no.5, p. 397, May, 1948.

TRIATOMA HEIDEMANNI AS A POSSIBLE VECTOR OF RELAPSING FEVER. Thelma de Shazo. Amer. Jour. Med. Tech., vol.9, no.3, pp.75-81, May, 1943.

STUDIES UPON LEPROSY. I. TRANSMISSION OF HUMAN LEPROSY TO THE WHITE MOUSE. H. C. De Souza-Araujo. Instituto Oswaldo Cruz (Rio de Janeiro), das Memorias, no.8, pp.123-127, pls.2, June 22, 1929.

BANG'S DISEASE ( A COMMITTEE REPORT ). C. R. Donham, and others. Jour. Amer. Vet. Med. Assoc., New York, vol.95, pp.606-611, Nov., 1939.

SOME NOTES ON THE USE OF THALLIUM TORPEDOES. R. E. Doty. Hawaiian Planters' Rec., vol.37, no.2, pp.96-97, 1933.

USE OF CORN OIL FOR THALLIUM WHEAT TORPEDOES. R. E. Doty. Hawaiian Planters' Rec., vol.36, no.2, pp.117-125, figs.3, 1932.

NOTES ON RELAPSING FEVER IN PANAMA WITH SPECIAL REFERENCE TO ANIMAL HOSTS. Lawrence H. Dunn, Herbert C. Clark. Amer. Jour. Tropical Med., vol. 13, no.2, pp.201-209, Mar., 1933.

ABDOMINAL PREGNANCY IN ANIMALS, WITH AN ACCOUNT OF A CASE OF MULTIPLE ECTOPIC GESTATION IN A RABBIT. Nellie B. Eales. Jour. Anat., vol.67, pt.1, pp.108-117, Oct., 1932.

SURVEY OF THE ECTOPARASITES OF CERTAIN MAMMALS IN OKLAHOMA. Leslie L. Ellis, Jr. Ecology, Durham, vol.36, no.1, pp.12-18, illus., Jan., 1955.

PARASITES FROM RODENTS AND SHREWS IN THE OUTER HEBRIDES. Charles Elton. Entom. Monthly Mag., vol.72, no.254, pp. 31-34, Feb., 1936.

HISTOPLASMOSIS: ANIMAL RESERVOIRS AND OTHER SOURCES IN NATURE OF THE PATHOGENIC FUNGUS, HISTOPLASMA. C. W. Emmons. Amer. Jour. Public Health, Albany, vol.40, no.4, pp.436-440, Apr., 1950.

HISTOPLASMOSIS IN ANIMALS. C. W. Emmons. Trans. New York Acad. Sci., ser.2, vol.2, no.7, pp.248-254, May, 1949.

HISTOPLASMOSIS. PROVED OCCURRENCE OF INAPPARENT INFECTION IN DOGS, CATS AND OTHER ANIMALS. C. W. Emmons, and others. Amer. Jour. Hyg., vol. 61, no.1, pp.40-44, Jan., 1955.

HISTOPLASMOSIS IN RATS AND SKUNKS IN GEORGIA. C. W. Emmons, H. B. Morlan, E.L. Hill. U.S. Public Health Repts., Washington, vol.64, no.45, pp.1423-1430, illus., Nov. 11, 1949.

EFFECTS OF DDT MOSQUITO LARVICIDING ON WILDLIFE. PT. 2. EFFECTS OF ROUTINE AIRPLANE LARVICIDING ON BIRD AND MAMMAL POPULATIONS. Arnold B. Erickson. U.S. Pub. Health Repts., Washington, vol.62, no.35, pp.1254-1262, Aug. 29, 1947.

NEW MITES OF THE PARASITIC GENUS HAEMOGAMASUS BERLESE. H.E. Ewing. Proc. Biol. Soc. Washington, vol.38, pp. 137-144, Nov. 13, 1925.

SECOND INTRODUCED RAT MITE BECOMES ANNOYING TO MAN. H. E. Ewing. Proc. Helminthol. Soc. Washington, vol.9, no.2, pp.74-75, July, 1942.

SOME PECULIAR RELATIONSHIPS BETWEEN ECTOPARASITES AND THEIR HOSTS. H.E. Ewing. Amer. Nat., vol.67, no.711, pp.365-373, July-Aug., 1933.

SOME PARASITIC PROTOZOA FOUND IN SOUTH AFRICA. H. B. Fanthom. VIII.South African Jour. Sci., vol.22, pp.346-354, Nov., 1925.

ANIMAL PARASITES OF WILD AND DOMESTIC MAMMALS AND THEIR RELATIONSHIP TO HUMAN WELFARE. Ernest Carroll Faust. Scientific Monthly, vol.32, no.3, pp. 228-234, Mar., 1931.

REPORT UPON A COLLECTION OF INSECT ECTOPARASITES FROM AUSTRALIAN AND TASMANIAN MAMMALS. G. F. Ferris. Amer. Mus.Nov., no.110, pp.4, figs.5, Apr. 21, 1924.

CHRONIC ARTHRITIS IN WILD MAMMALS. Herbert Fox. Trans. Amer. Philos. Soc., Philadelphia, n.s., vol.31, pt.2, pp.73-148, pls.12, Feb., 1939.

DISEASE IN CAPTIVE WILD MAMMALS AND BIRDS. Herbert Fox. Philadelphia, London, and Chicago; J. B. Lippincott Co., vol. 8, pp.665-vii, figs.87, 1923.

NOTES ON ECTOPARASITES FROM VENEZUELA (SIPHONAPTERA AND ACARINA). Irving Fox. Zoologica, New York, vol.32, pt.3, nos.13-17, pp.117-119, Nov. 12, 1947.

(PECULIARITIES OF THE ARISAL AND SPREAD OF TROPICAL ANIMAL PLAGUES.) Besonderheiten der Entstehung und Verbreitung tropischer Tierseuchen. W. Frei. Acta Tropica, Basel, vol.3, no.1, pp.1-28, 1946. (In German, with English and French summaries.)

INFECTION AND IMMUNIZATION OF LABORATORY ANIMALS WITH RICKETTSIA PROWAZEKII OF REDUCED PATHOGENICITY, STRAIN E. E. F. Perez Gallardo, J. P. Fox. Amer. Jour. Hygiene, Lancaster, vol.48, no.1, pp.6-21, July, 1948.

POSSIBILITIES OF SECONDARY POISONING OF BIRDS AND MAMMALS. F. E. Garlough, Justus C. Ward. Science, n.s., vol.75, no. 1943, pp.335-337, Mar., 25, 1932.

PARASITISM AND ITS EFFECT ON FUR ANIMALS (CONTINUED). F.X.Gassner. Amer. Fur Breeder, Duluth, vol.17, no.1, pp.20, 22, July, 1944; no.2, pp.32, 34, 36, 38, Aug., 1944.

WILDLIFE EFFECTS OF DDT DUST USED FOR TICK CONTROL ON A TEXAS PRAIRIE. John L. George, William H. Stickel. Amer. Midland Nat., Notre Dame, vol.42, no.1, pp.228-237, July, 1949.

VIRUS INFECTION OF THE MAMMALIAN FETUS. Ernest W. Goodpasture. Science, Lancaster , n.s., vol.95, no.2468, pp. 391-396, Apr. 17, 1942.

CAUSE OF CANCER IN FUR-BEARERS IS NOT KNOWN. J. R. Gorham, E. R. Quortrup. Amer. Nat. Fur & Market Jour., Wausau, vol.27, no.4, p.13, Nov., 1948.

CHASTEK PARALYSIS FROM FISH DIETS. R. G. Green. Amer. Fur Breeder, Duluth, vol.13, no.9, p.20, Mar., 1941.

FEEDING ROUGH FISH TO FUR ANIMALS. HOW A DISEASE RIDDLE WAS SOLVED. R.G. Green. Conservation Volunteer, St. Paul, vol.3, no.15, pp.14-18, Cec., 1941.

PROGRESS REPORT OF WILD LIFE DISEASE STUDIES FOR 1933. R. G. Green, J. E.Shillinger. Trans. 20th Amer. Game Conf., 1934, Amer. Game Assoc., New York, pp.288-297, 1934.

PROGRESS REPORT OF WILD LIFE DISEASE STUDIES FOR 1934. R. G. Green, J. E.Shillinger. Trans. 21st Amer. Game Conf., 1935, Amer. Game Assoc., New York, pp.397-401, 1935.

PROGRESS REPORT OF WILD LIFE DISEASE STUDIES FOR 1935. R. G. Green, J. E. Shillinger. Proc. North Amer. Wildl. Conf., Washington, D.C., pp.469-471, Feb. 3-7, 1936.

RELATION OF DISEASE TO WILD LIFE CYCLES. R. G. Green, J. E. Shillinger. Trans. 19th Amer. Game Conf., 1932, Amer. Game Assoc., New York, pp.432-436, 1933.

EPIZOOTIC FUR ENCEPHALITIS. Green, Ziegler, Dewey, Shillinger. I-II-III. Amer. Fur Breeder, vol.4, no.5, pp.4-8, Nov.1931; vol.4, no.6, pp.4-8, Dec., 1931; vol.4, no. 8, pp.20-22, Feb., 1932.

DIPTEROUS LARVAE PARASITIC ON ANIMALS AND MAN AND SOME DIPTEROUS LARVAE CAUSING MYASIS IN MAN. Charles T. Greene. Trans. Amer. Entomological Soc., vol.82, pp.17-34, June 22, 1956.

CYST-FORMING PROTOZOA IN REINDEER AND CARIBOU, AND A SARCOSPORIDIAN PARASITE OF THE SEAL (PHOCA RICHARDI.) Seymour Hadwen. Jour. Amer. Vet. Med. Ass., vol.61, n.s., vol.14, no.4, pp.374-382, figs.1-8, July, 1922.

INFECTIOUS DISEASE OF DOMESTIC ANIMALS. William Arthur Hagan, Dorsey William Bruner. Comstock Publ. Co., Ithaca, pp.xxx-920, illus., 1951. (Second edition.)

PARASITE CONTROL IN ANIMALS. Maurice C. Hall. Outdoor America, vol.9, no.12, pp.16-17, 46, fig., July, 1931.

DIOCTOPHYMA RENALE (GOEZE, 1782), A STUDY OF THE MIGRATION ROUTES TO THE KIDNEYS OF MAMMALS AND RESULTANT PATHOLOGY. Carl W. Hallberg. Ph.D. thesis, U. Mich., 1952.

BIBLIOGRAPHY OF REFERENCES TO DISEASES OF WILD MAMMALS AND BIRDS. Patricia O'Connor Halloran. Amer. Jour. Veterinary Research, vol.16, no.61, part 2, pp.465, 1955.

MALAYSIAN PARASITES - XXXIII. THE HOSTS. J. L. Harrison. Studies from the Institute for Medical Research, Federation of Malaya, vol.28, pp.409-426, 1957.

ECTOPARASITES OCCURRING ON MAMMALS IN THE VICINITY OF FORT HOOD, TEXAS. Robert A. Hedeen. Tex. Jour. Sci., vol.5, no.1, pp.125-129, Mar., 1953.

TRICHOMONADS FROM THE VAGINA OF THE MONKEY, FROM THE MOUTH OF THE CAT AND MAN, AND FROM THE INTESTINE OF THE MONKEY, OPPOSSUM AND PRAIRIE DOG. R. Hegner, H. Ratcliffe. Jour. Parasitology, vol. 14, pp.27-35, illus., 1927.

SOME INTESTINAL AMOEBAE AND FLAGELLATES FROM THE CHIMPANZEE, THREE-TOED SLOTH, SHEEP AND GUINEA-PIG. R. Hegner, E. Schumaker. Jour. Parasitology, vol.15, pp.31-37, fig.1, Sep., 1928.

GIARDIA AND CHILOMASTIX FROM MONKEYS, GIARDIA FROM THE WILD CAT, AND BOLANTIDIUM FROM THE SHEEP. Robert W. Hegner. Jour. Parasitology, vol. 11, pp.75-78, figs.4, Dec., 1924.

(ON THE HEALING OF BONE FRACTURES IN FREE-LIVING ANIMALS.) Ueber Heilung von Knochenbruechen bei frei lebenden Tieren. Otto von Heinzerling. Zool. Anzeiger, Leipzig, vol.140, no.1-2, pp.49-57, figs. 4, Oct., 15, 1942.

EXPERIMENTAL TRANSMISSION OF LYMPHOGRANULOMA VENEREUM VIRUS THROUGH THE PLACENTA. Hugo Hellendall. Proc. Soc. Exper. Biol and Med., Utica, vol.41, no.1, pp.140-141, Oct., 1942.

OBSERVATIONS ON COCCIDIA OF SMALL MAMMALS IN CALIFORNIA, WITH DESCRIPTIONS OF SEVEN NEW SPECIES. Dora Priaulx Henry. Univ. Calif. Publ. Zool., vol.37, no.11, pp.279-290, pls.17, 18, Apr. 23, 1932.

HIPPOBOSCID FLIES AS PARASITES OF GAME ANIMALS IN CALIFORNIA. Carlton M. Herman. California Fish and Game, San Francisco, vol.31, no.1, pp.16-25, illus., Jan., 1945.

PARASITES OBTAINED FROM ANIMALS IN THE COLLECTION OF THE NEW YORK ZOOLOGICAL PARK DURING 1938. Calton M. Herman. Zoologica, New York, vol.24, pt.4, nos.27-31, pp.481-485, tbls.2, Dec. 22, 1939. (Mammalia, pp.482-483.)

DISEASE INVESTIGATIONS ON MAMMALS AND BIRDS BY THE CALIFORNIA DIVISION OF FISH AND GAME. Carlton M. Herman, Merton N. Rosen. California Fish & Game, San Francisco, vol.35, no.3, pp.193-199, July, 1949.

PARASITES OF FUR ANIMALS. C. A.Herrick. American Fur Breeder, Duluth, vol. 20, no.3, pp.30, 32, 34, Sep., 1947; Fur of Canada, Winnipeg, vol.13, no.1, pp.29-30, Oct., 1947; Natl. Fur News, Denver, vol.19, no.10, pp.18, 52-53, Nov., 1947.

ECTOPARASITES FROM MAMMALS AND BIRDS ON A QUAIL PRESERVE. B. G. Hightower, V. W. Lehman, R. B. Eads. Jour. Mamm., vol.34, no.2, pp.268-271, May 14, 1953.

SELF-REPAIR. John Eric Hill. Nat. Hist., New York, vol.55, no.7, p.337, illus., Sep., 1946.

WILDLIFE AND DISEASE. C. W. Hobley. Jour. Soc. Preservation Fauna Empire, Hertford, n.s., pt.xvi, pp.16-28, 1932.

HOST-PARASITE-DISEASE RELATIONSHIP IN A MAMMALIAN COMMUNITY IN THE CENTRAL COAST RANGE OF CALIFORNIA. R. Holdenried, F. C. Evans, D. S. Longanecker. Ecological Monographs, Durham, vol.21, pp.1-18, Jan., 1951.

FAUNAL EXPLORATION AS A BASIC APPROACH FOR STUDYING INFECTIONS COMMON TO MAN AND ANIMALS. Harry Hoogstraal. East African Medical Jour., vol.33, no.11, pp.417-424, Nov., 1956.

THE EFFECT OF THALLIUM ON PLANT GROWTH. E. E. Horn, Justus C. Ward, James C. Munch, F. C. Garlough. Science, n.s., vol.80, no.2068, pp.167-168, Aug. 17, 1934.

HYDROCEPHALUS IN LOWER ANIMALS. CONGENITAL OCCURRENCE IN A CALF AND AN ALBINO RAT. Joseph William Houck. Anat. Rec., vol.45, no.1, pp.83-106, figs.6, 1930.

ECOLOGY OF DERMACENTOR ALBIPICTUS (PACKARD). Darill E. Howell. Proc. Sixth Pac. Sci. Cong., vol.4, pp.439-458, 1940.

SOME MAMMALIAN ECTOPARASITES. Douglass H. Hubbard. Jour. Mamm., vol. 22, no.2, pp.202-203, May 14, 1941.

RICKETTSIALPOX- A NEWLY RECOGNIZED RICKETTSIAL DISEASE. IV. ISOLATION OF A RICKETTSIA APPARENTLY IDENTICAL WITH CAUSATIVE AGENT OF RICKETTSIALPOX FROM ALLODERMANYSSUS SANGUINEUS, A RODENT MITE. Robert J. Huebner, William L. Jellison, Charles Pomerantz. Public Health Reports, vol.61, no.47, pp.1677-1682, Nov. 22, 1946.

(CRISTA SAGITTALIS, A REMARKABLE CULTURE.) Crista sagittalis, en merkelig dannelse. Chr. Hysing-Dahl. Saertrykk av Fauna, nr.2.

(METHODICALLY FIGHTING DISEASE IN ZOO ANIMALS AND PROTECTING THEM AGAINST DISEASE.) Metodische Krankheits-Bekaempfung und -Verhuetung bei Zootieren. E. Jacob. Zool. Garten, n.F., vol. 19, no.5, pp.243-248, 1952.

ANOPLURA FROM MAMMALS OF THE PRIBILOF ISLANDS. William L. Jellison. Jour. Parasit. vol.38, no.3, pp.274-275, June, 1952.

HAPLOMYCOSIS IN MONTANA RABBITS, RODENTS, AND CARNIVORES. William L. Jellison. U.S. Publ. Health Repts., Washington, vol.65, no.33, pp.1057-1063, Aug. 18, 1950.

RELATIVE VALUES OF MAN, MOUSE, AND DOMESTIC FOWL AS EXPERIMENTAL HOSTS FOR THE BED-BUG, CIMEX LECTULARIUS L. C. G. Johnson. Proc. Soc. London, Abstracts, vol.107, ser.C., no.3, pp. 8-9, Mar. 2, 1937.

AFFECTIVE-RESPIRATORY FACTORS IN CATATONIA. E. J. Kempf. Med. Jour. Record, pp.1-15, Feb. 19, 1930.

SPECIES AND INCIDENCE OF DIPTEROUS LARVAE CONCERNED IN WOUND MYIASIS. E. F. Knipling, H. T. Rainwater. Jour. Parasitology, vol.23, no.5, pp.451-455, Oct., 1937.

(SPIROCHETES IN MAMMALS.) Spirochaeten in Saeugetieren. Ingo Krumbiegel. Zeitschrift f. Saeugetierkunde, vol.3, pp.49-54, June 11, 1928.

(ON TWO INTERESTING BONE FRACTURES.) Ueber zwei interessante Knochenbrueche. Friedrich Kuhlhorn. Anat. Anz., Jena, vol. 85, nos.22-24, pp.401-442, figs.2, Feb.15, 1938.

ON THE ROLE OF MAMMALS IN THE EPIDEMIOLOGY OF TICKBORNE ENCEPHALITIS OF USSURI DISTRICT. A. P. Kusiakin. Zool. Jour. USSR, Moscow, vol.21, no.3, pp.69-87, tbls.2, 1942.(English summary.)

BLOOD PARASITES OF MAMMALS IN NEW ZEALAND. Marshall Laird. Zool. Publ. Victoria Univ. College, Wellington, no.9, pp.1-14, illus., 1951.

GAME DISEASE IN FINLAND 1924-43. Teppo Lampio. Suomen Riista, Helsinki, no.1, pp.93-142, figs.17, 1946.

ANIMAL DISEASE AND HUMAN WELFARE. G. La Page. Nature, London, vol.160, no. 4059, pp.237-238, Aug. 16, 1947.

TUBERCULOSIS OF VOLES AND SHREWS. G. La Page. Nature, London, vol.160, no. 4072, p.687, Nov. 15, 1947.

NEW ORGANISM RESEMBLING P. TULARENSIS ISOLATED FROM WATER. C. L. Larson, W. Wicht, W. L. Jellison. Public Health Rep., vol.70, no.3, pp.253-258, Mar., 1955.

PLACE OF PARASITOLOGY IN THE PROGRAM OF CONSERVATION. George R. La Rue. Michigan Acad. Sci., Arts and Letters, 34th and 35th Ann. Rept., pp.70-82, 1933.

SOME NEW PILICOLOUS MITES FROM SOUTH AFRICAN MAMMALS. R. F. Lawrence. Parasitology, London, vol. 39, nos.1-2, pp.39-42, illus., July, 1948.

PRELIMINARY STUDIES ON PARASITES OF UPLAND GAME BIRDS AND FURBEARING MAMMALS OF ILLINOIS. W. Henry Leigh. Illinois Nat. Hist. Surv. Bull., Urbana, vol.21, art.5, pp.183-194, illus., Aug., 1940.

PRELIMINARY NOTE ON BILHARZIA MARGREBOWIEI, A NEW PARASITE OF RUMINANTS AND POSSIBLY OF MAN IN NORTHERN RHODESIA. P. L. Leroux. Jour. Helminthology, vol.11, no.1, pp.57-62, Jan., 1933.

MYIASIS IN WILD ANIMALS IN SOUTHWESTERN TEXAS. Arthur W. Lindquist. Jour. Econ. Entom., vol.30, no.5, pp.735-740, figs.2, Oct., 1937.

(REVISION OF THE GENUS HYMENOLEPIS WEINLAND.) Revision del genero Hymenolepis Weinland. Carlos Rodriguez Lopez-Neyra. III. Rev. Iberica Parasitologia, Madrid, vol.2, nos.2-3, pp.213-256, pls. 5-7, Apr.-July, 1942.

NAMING OF ANIMAL PARASITES. Marcus W. Lyon, Jr. Jour. Amer. Med. Assoc., vol.76, p.813, Mar. 19, 1921.

FILARIA BANCROFTI IN THE DISTRICT OF COLUMBIA. Marcus W. Lyon, Jr. Science, n.s., vol.43, no.1117, p.762, May 26, 1916.

FILARIASIS. REPORT OF TWO CASES IN THE DISTRICT OF COLUMBIA, AND ANALYSIS OF THE CASES REPORTED FOR EASTERN NORTH AMERICA. Marcus W. Lyon, Jr.Jour. Amer. Med. Assoc., vol. 68, pp.118-119, Jan. 13, 1917.

THALLIUM POISONING. Marcus W. Lyon, Jr. Science, n.s., vol.75, no.1945, pp.381-382, Apr. 8, 1932.

THE RÔLE OF VERTEBRATES IN THE CONTROL OF INSECT PESTS. W. L. McAtee. Smithsonian Rep., 1925, pp.415-437, pls.7, 1926.

COMINGS AND GOINGS OF EPIDEMICS. George W. McCoy. Jour. Washington Acad. Sci., vol.26, no.3, pp.87-99, Mar. 15, 1936.

SOME ECTOPARASITES, EXCLUDING IXODOIDEA, OF DELAWARE MAMMALS. Donald MacCreary. Jour. Econ. Ent., vol. 38, no.1, pp.126-127, Feb., 1945.

SALMONELLA INFECTION. A.M. McDermid. American Fur Breeder, Duluth, vol.20, no.6, pp.48, 50-51, Dec., 1947.

EVIDENCE OF THE PRESENCE OF EQUINE ENCEPHALOMYELITIC VIRUS IN PHILIPPINE ANIMALS. Don L. Mace, R. L. Ott, F. S. Cortez. Bull. U.S. Army Med. Dept., Washington, vol.9, no.6, pp.504-507, June, 1949.

INHERITANCE OF RESISTANCE AND SUSCEPTIBILITY TO INFECTIOUS ABORTION. Miguel Manresa. Jour. Infectious Diseases, vol.51, pp.30-71, figs.16, July-Aug., 1932.

LIST OF THE PARASITES RECORDED FROM SEA MAMMALS CAUGHT OFF THE WEST COAST OF NORTH AMERICA. L. Margolis. Jour. Fish. Res. Bd. Can. vol.11, pp.267-283, 1954.

ZOONOSES IN THE SOUTH. J. D. Martin. Public Health Repts., U.S. Public Health Service, Washington, vol.72, no.3, pp.210-216, Mar., 1957.

POPULATION STUDIES OF THE EUROPEAN SPRUCE SAWFLY (GILPINIA HERCYNIAE HTG.). R. Martineau. Forestry Chronicle, Toronto, vol.19, no.2, pp.87-107, illus., June, 1943.

PARASITES AND THE AID THEY GIVE IN PROBLEMS OF TAXONOMY, GEOGRAPHICAL DISTRIBUTION, AND PALEOGRAPHY. Maynard M. Metcalf. Smithsonian Misc. Coll., vol.81, no.8, pp.1-36, figs.4, Feb. 28, 1929.

DISEASES OF WILD LIFE TRANSMISSIBLE TO MAN. K. F. Meyer. California Fish and Game, vol.18, no.3, pp.203-207, July, 1932.

CANINE, MURINE, AND HUMAN LEPTOSPIROSIS IN CALIFORNIA. K. F. Meyer, B. Eddie, B. Anderson-Stewart. Proc. Soc. Exper. Biol. and Med., New York, vol.38, no.1, pp.17-19, Feb., 1938.

INFECTIOUS DISEASE IN NATIVE WILD ANIMALS OF THE COLUMBIA BASIN, WASHINGTON. Norman G. Miller, Charles H. Drake. Northwest Science, vol.28, no.4, pp.135-156, Nov., 1954.

CALCULI AND OTHER STONES FOUND IN MAMMALS. Charles Milton, Joseph M. Axelrod. Jour. Mamm., vol.32, no.2, pp. 139-154, May, 1951.

BOTULISM IN THE MOUSE, MINK, AND FERRET WITH SPECIAL REFERENCE TO SUSCEPTIBILITY AND PATHOLOGICAL ALTERATIONS. T.Moll, C.A. Brandly. Amer. Jour. Vet. Res., vol.12, no.45, pp.355-363, illus., Oct., 1951.

PALEOPATHOLOGY: AN INTRODUCTION TO THE STUDY OF ANCIENT EVIDENCES OF DISEASE. Roy L. Moody. Univ. of Ill. Press, Urbana, Ill., pp.567, pls.117, figs. 49, 1923.

HOST RELATIONSHIPS AND SEASONAL ABUNDANCE OF SOME SOUTHWEST GEORGIA ECTOPARASITES. H. B. Morlan. Amer. Midl. Nat., vol.48, no.1, pp.74-93, July, 1952.

SEROLOGICAL SURVEY FOR MURINE TYPHUS INFECTION IN SOUTHWEST GEORGIA ANIMALS. H. B. Morlan, B. L. Hill, Joseph H. Schubert. Pub. Health Rep., vol. 65, no.2, pp.57-63, Jan. 13, 1950.

GENUS MESOCESTOIDES IN MAMMALS. PT. 1. Justus F. Mueller. Zool. Jahrbuecher (Systematik), vol.55, pp.403-418, figs.2, Sep. 12, 1928.

CONTRIBUTIONS TO THE DYNAMICS OF THE PARASITOLOGICAL FAUNA OF MAMMALS. S. P. Naumov. Zool. Jour. USSR, Moscow, vol.23, no.4, pp.181-188, figs.6, 1944.

STRUCTURE AND DIVISION OF CHILOMASTIX INTESTINALIS KUCZYUSKI, WITH NOTES ON SIMILAR FORMS IN MAN, AND OTHER VERTEBRATES. Dashu Nie. Jour. Morphol., Philadelphia, vol.82, no.3, pp. 287-329, pls.1-5, May, 1948.

(IDENTIFICATION OF THE TOXOPLASMAS OF BIRDS AND MAMMALS.) Identidade dos toxoplasmas de aves e de mamiferos. P. Nobrega, J. Reis. Arq. Inst. Biol. Dept. Defesa Sanitaria Agric., Sao Paulo, vol.13, pp. 21-28, fig.1, pls.3-6, 1942. (In Portuguese, with English summary.)

(SPIROCHETOSES OF WILD ANIMALS.) Spirochétoses des animaux sauvages. J. Nouvel. Mammalia, Paris, vol.18, no.1, pp.112-123, Mar., 1954.

(SPIROCHETOSES OF WILD ANIMALS.) Les Spirochetoses des Animaux Sauvages (Part II). J. Nouvel. Mammalia, vol.18, no.3, pp.277-286, Sep., 1954.

CASES OF NECROBACILLOSIS IN ARTIODACTILA AND MACROPUS IN THE MOSCOW ZOOLOGICAL GARDENS. B. M. Olivkov, O. A. Nossova. Proc. Moscow Zool. Park, vol.1, pp.322-335, 1940. (In Russian with a resume in English.)

RESERVOIR HOSTS OF CHAGAS' DISEASE IN THE STATE OF TEXAS. A. Packchanian. Amer. Jour. Trop. Med., vol.22, no.6, pp.623-631, Nov., 1942.

(THE PALEOPATHOLOGY AT THE MUSEUM OF TOULOUSE.) La paleopathologie au Museum de Toulouse. L. Pales. Bull. Soc. Hist. Nat. Toulouse, vol.61, pp.135-155, figs.14, 1931.

ANIMAL DISEASES. C. M. Palmer, Jr. Pennsylvania Game News, New Cumberland, vol.10, no.6, pp.14-15, illus., Sep., 1939.

DISEASE A SERIOUS WILDLIFE PROBLEM. C. M. Palmer, Jr. Virginia Wildlife, Blacksburg, vol.2, no.11, pp.2-3, July, 1939.

ECOLOGY OF THE ECTOPARASITES OF NIGERIAN RODENTS AND INSECTIVORES. A. S. Pearse. Jour. Mamm., Baltimore, vol.10, no.3, pp.229-238, Aug. 10, 1929.

GRANULOSA CELL TUMORS IN FEMALE RATS AND RABBITS. B. M. Peckham, R. R. Greene, M. E. Jeffries. Science, Lancaster, vol.107, no.2778, pp.319-320, Mar. 26, 1948.

PARASITIC PROBLEM. Lawrence R. Penner. Zoonooz, Zool. Soc. San Diego, vol.13, no. 2, p.7, Feb., 1941.

GAME AND DISEASE. A. Blayney Percival. Jour. East Africa and Uganda Nat. Hist. Soc., no.13, pp.302-315, Nov., 1918.

(INTESTINAL PROTOZOANS OF VERTEBRATES OBSERVED IN SALOBRA.) Protozoarios intestinais de vertebrados observados em Salobra. C. Pereira, W. F. de Almeida. Mem. Inst. Oswaldo Cruz, Rio de Janeiro, vol.36, no.3, pp.321-324, Nov., 1941.

REPORT ON THE DEATHS WHICH OCCURRED IN THE ZOOLOGICAL GARDENS DURING 1913, TOGETHER WITH A LIST OF THE BLOOD-PARASITES FOUND DURING THE YEAR. H. G. Plimmer. Proc. Zool. Soc. London, pp.181-190, Mar., 1914.

REPORT ON THE DEATHS WHICH OCCURRED IN THE ZOOLOGICAL GARDENS DURING 1914, TOGETHER WITH A LIST OF THE BLOOD-PARASITES FOUND DURING THE YEAR. H. G. Plimmer. Proc. Zool. Soc. London, pp.123-130, Mar., 1915.

PREVENTION AND CURE OF FUR ANIMAL DISEASES. George C. Poppensick. Black Fox Mag., New York, vol.32, no.7, pp.22, 33-37, Nov., 1948; Fur of Canada, Winnipeg, vol.14, no.3, pp.3-4, 36, Dec., 1948; Amer. Nat. Fur & Market Jour., Wausau, vol.27, no.7, pp.5-6, 27, 30, Feb., 1949.

REPORT OF THE HONORARY PARASITOLOGIST FOR 1943. Annie Porter. Proc. Zool. Soc. London, vol.114, pt.3, pp.319-321, Dec., 1944.

(OBSERVATIONS OF SOME CASES OF SICKNESS IN ANIMALS OF THE SCHOENBRUNN ZOO.) Beobachtungen ueber einige Faelle von Erkrankungen unter den Tieren des Schoenbrunner Tiergartens. Theodor Purmann. Zool. Garten, Leipzig, n.F., vol.2, nos. 7-9, pp.205-220, figs.1-12, Jan., 1930.

BOTULISM IS MENACE TO FUR FARMERS. E. R. Quortup. Amer. Nat. Fur and Market Jour., Wausau, vol.23, no.2, pp.9-10, Sep., 1944.

REVISION OF THE FUR MITES MYOBIIDAE (ACARINA). Charles D. Radford. Bull. Mus. Nat. Hist. Nat., Paris, ser.2, vol.20, no. 5, pp.458-464, Sep., 1948.

ECTOPARASITIC SURVEY OF MAMMALS FROM LAVACA COUNTY, TEXAS. Neal M. Randolph, R. B. Eads. Ann. Ent. Soc. Am., vol.39, no.4, pp.597-601, Dec., 1946.

REVIEW OF MYXOMATOSIS IN AUSTRALIA, 1950-1955. F. N. Ratcliffe. Jour. Australia Inst. Agric. Sci., vol.21, no.3, pp. 130-133, Sep., 1955.

ANIMAL-BORNE DISEASES IN ALASKA AND THEIR PUBLIC HEALTH SIGNIFICANCE. Robert Rausch. Proc. XVth Internat. Vet. Congress, Stockholm, vol.8, pp.254-259, 1954.

SUMMARY OF CURRENT INFORMATION ON SOME ANIMAL-BORNE DISEASES IN ALASKA. Robert Rausch. Science in Alaska 1952, Proceedings 3d Alaskan Science Conference, Alaska Div. AAAS., pp.144-147, Sep., 1954.

(MEDICAL AND CLIMATOLOGICAL FINDINGS IN THE POLAR SEA.) Medicinisch-klimatologische Erfahrungen im Eismeer. Bernhard Rawitz. Deutsche Med. Wochenschrift, Leipzig, Jahrg. 26, no.13, pp.215-217, Mar. 29, 1900.

RESISTANCE TO DISEASE. Casper L. Redfield. New York Med. Jour., vol.119, no.13, (whole no.2104), pp.524-544, Mar. 29, 1919.

GERMFREE VERTEBRATES: PRESENT STATUS. J. A. Reyniers. New York Acad. of Sci., vol.78, pp.1-400.

FUR ANIMAL PARASITES. William A. Riley. Amer. Fur Breeder, vol.2, no.1, p.9, July, 1929.

HOW TO DETECT THE PARASITES OF FUR-BEARING ANIMALS. William A. Riley, Reed O. Christenson. Amer. Fur Breeder, vol.4, no.1, pp.4-8, July, 1931.

TRICHINOSIS IN ARCTIC ANIMALS. Hans Roth. Nature, London, vol.163, no.4151, pp.805-806, May 21, 1949.

PRELIMINARY SURVEY OF THE INSECT ECTOPARASITES OF THE MAMMALS OF ALABAMA. Orren L. Royal. Master's thesis, Univ. Ala., 1952.

NOTES ON DISEASES IN WILD GAME MAMMALS. W. M. Rush. Jour. Mamm., vol.8, no.2, pp.163-165, May, 1927.

WHEN ANIMALS GET SICK. William Rush. Amer. Forests, Washington, vol.52, no.1, pp.24-26, 48, illus., Jan., 1946.

BRUCELLOSIS ABSENT IN WYOMING GAME. J. F. Ryff. Wyo. Wild Life, vol.15, no.9, pp.13, 38, Sep., 1951.

(DENTAL AND ORAL PATHOLOGICAL CASES IN THE CAPTIVE WILD ANIMALS OF THE ZOO OF BUENOS AIRES.) Casos de patologia dental y oral en animales salvajes en cautividad en el Jardin Zoológico de la ciudad de Buenos Aires. Enrique J. Saporiti. Revista "Diana", Buenos Aires, nos.171-172, pp.8 (reprint), 1954.

PARASITES COMMON TO ANIMALS AND MAN. Benjamin Schwarz. Ann Rep. Smithsonian Inst., Publication 4232, pp.419-431, 1956.

TWO CASES OF PERITONEAL NEOPLASM (ENDOTHELIOMA). H. Harold Scott. Proc. Zool. Soc. London, pt.3, pp.511-518, pls. 6, Sep., 1927.

INFLUENCE OF WILD ANIMALS IN THE DISSEMINATION OF DISEASE OF LIVESTOCK IN AUSTRALIA. H. R. Seddon. Proc. Roy. Soc. Queensland, Brisbane, 1942, vol.54, pp.1-12, June 8, 1943.

NEW SUBFAMILY OF BEETLES PARASITIC ON MAMMALS. Charles H. Seevers. Zool. Ser. Field Mus. Nat. Hist., vol.28, no.3, pp.155-172, pls.10-12, Mar. 17, 1944.

REVISION OF THE TRIBE AMBLYOPHININI: STAPHYLINID BEETLES PARASITIC ON MAMMALS. Charles H. Seevers. Fieldiana: Zoology, Chicago Nat. Hist. Mus., vol.37, pp.211-264, illus., June 19, 1955. (List of mammalian hosts, pp.261-262.)

SOME PARASITES OF OREGON WILDLIFE. J. N. Shaw. Oregon Agric. Expt. Sta. Corvallis, Tech. Bull. 11, pp.1-16, illus., May, 1947.

DISEASE AS A FACTOR IN GAME FLUCTUATION. J. E. Shillinger. U.S. Dept. Agric. Wildlife Research & Management Leaflet BS-99, pp.3, Dec., 1937.

DISEASES OF FUR ANIMALS. J. E. Shillinger. Farmers' Bulletin, no.1777, pp.22, figs.7, July, 1937.

DISEASES OF FUR ANIMALS. J. E. Shillinger. USDI, Cons. Bull. 20, pp.23, 1942.

DISEASES OF FUR ANIMALS. J. E. Shillinger. USDA, Ykb. Agr. 1942: pp.1232-1238, 1943.

INFECTIOUS DISEASES AS A CAUSE OF LOSS IN WILDLIFE. J. E. Shillinger. Wildlife Research and Management Leaflet BS-9, Bur. Biol. Surv., pp.4, May, 1935.

SARCOSPORIDIOSIS A PROTOZOAN DISEASE OF WILDLIFE. J. E. Shillinger, P. W. Wetmore. Trans. 3rd North Amer. Wildl. Conf., pp.898-901, 1938.

MAMMAL DISTRIBUTION IN RELATION TO DISEASE. E. Allen Shippee. Symposium on ecology of disease transmission in native animals, Univ. Utah, pp.33-43, figs.8, 1955.

FEDERAL EFFORT TO PROMOTE THE SCIENCE OF VETERINARY MEDICINE. R. W. Shufeldt. Med. Record, New York, vol.94, no.6, (whole no.2492), pp.237-239, figs.4, Aug. 10, 1918.

FORTHCOMING BULLETINS FROM OFFICE OF THE SURGEON GENERAL OF THE ARMY. R. W. Shufeldt. Amer. Med. Philadelphia, vol.12, no.11, pp.743-750, figs.5, Nov., 1917.

TYPES OF MAMMALS. WITH NOTES ON HYBRIDS, DISEASES, ALBINISM, AND OTHER CONDITIONS EQUALLY APPLICABLE TO MAN. R. W. Shufeldt. Med. Record, reprints paged 1-23, figs.5, Jan. 29, 1921.

INFECTIOUS DISEASES OF FUR BEARING ANIMALS. Heinz A. Siedentopf. Natl. Fur News, Denver, vol.19, no.9, pp.16, 54-55, Oct., 1947; Fur of Canada, Winnipeg, vol. 13, no.1, pp.3, 34, Oct., 1947; American Fur Breeder, Duluth, vol.20, no.5, pp.62, 64, 66, Nov., 1947.

GLOBAL EPIDEMIOLOGY. A GEOGRAPHY OF DISEASE AND SANITATION. James Stevens Simmons, Tom F. Whayne, Gaylord West Anderson, Harold Maclachan Horack. J. B. Lippincott Co., Philadelphia, pp.xxvi-504, Sep., 1944.

MOST ANCIENT EVIDENCE OF DISEASE AMONG SOUTH AMERICAN MAMMALS. George Gaylord Simpson. Amer. Mus. Novitates, no.543, pp.4, figs.3, June 20, 1932.

SEMLIKI FOREST VIRUS. II. IMMUNOLOGICAL STUDIES WITH SPECIFIC ANTIVIRAL SERA AND SERA FROM HUMANS AND WILD ANIMALS. K. C. Smithburn, A. F. Mahaffy, A. J. Haddow. Jour. Immunology, Baltimore, vol.49, no.3, pp.159-173, Sep., 1944.

REPORT ON THE AVAILABLE EVIDENCE SHOWING THE RELATION OF GAME TO THE SPREAD OF TSETSE FLY BORNE DISEASES IN AFRICA. Richard P. Strong, J. C. Bequaert, L. R. Cleveland. Special Publ. Amer. Comm. Internat. Wildl. Protection, Cambridge, vol.1, no.1, pp.1-46, 1931.

RICKETS IN MONKEYS, LIONS, BEARS AND BIRDS. J. Bland Sutton. Jour. Compar. Med. and Surg., vol.10, no.1, pp.1-29, figs.29, Jan., 1888.

INCIDENCE OF DIPTERAN PARASITOSIS IN POPULATIONS OF SMALL MAMMALS. Frederick H. Test, Avery R. Test. Jour. Mamm., vol.24, no.4, pp.506-508, Nov. 17, 1943.

IMPORTANCE OF DISEASE IN WILD ANIMALS. A. D. Thomas, W. O. Neitz. South African Jour. Sci., vol.30, pp.419-425, Oct., 1933.

PARASITES OF BRITISH BIRDS AND MAMMALS. IV. RECORDS OF MAMMAL PARASITES. Gordon B. Thompson. Entom. Monthly Mag., vol.71, pp.214-219, Sep.-Oct., 1935.

PARASITES OF BRITISH BIRDS AND MAMMALS. VI. SOME PARASITES OF THE RED DEER AND WILD CAT. Gordon B. Thompson. Scottish Nat., Edinburgh, no.219, pp.75-78, May-June, 1936.

ECTOPARASITES FROM MAMMALS AT CAMP LEJEUNE, NORTH CAROLINA. Ted Tibbetts. Jour. Econ. Ent., vol.46, no.3, p.530, June, 1953.

(NOTE ON THE MARINE ACARIENS COLLECTED BY DR. F. DELFIN IN THE CALDERA BAY.) Note sur les Acariens marins recueills par M. Le Dr. F. Delfin dans la Baie de Caldera. E. L. Trouessart. Actas Soc. Cientifica Chili, vol.6, pp.61-62, 1896.

STUDIES OF ACARI. VI. PARASITIC MITES FROM MAMMALIAN HOSTS OBTAINED IN CEYLON. F.A. Turk. Parasitol., Cambridge, vol.40, nos.1-2, pp.63-76, Jan., 1950.

COMPARATIVE STUDY OF GRAHAMELLAE, HAEMOBARTONELLAE, AND EPERYTHROZOA IN SMALL MAMMALS. Ernest Edward Tyzzer. Proc. Amer. Philos. Soc., Philadelphia, vol.85, no.4, pp.359-398, figs.24, June 8, 1942.

(CUTANEOUS TUBERCULOSIS OF THE AXIS DEER (AXIS AXIS ERXLEB.) AND THE TIGER (FELIS TIGRIS L.).) Tuberculose cutanée du cerf axis (Axis axis (Erxleb)) et du tigre (Felis tigris L.). Ach. Urbain, J. Nouvel. Bull. Acad. Véterinaire France, Paris, vol.20, no.1, pp.38-40, Jan., 1947.

PEDIGREE OF CONGENITAL DISLOCATION OF LENSES. C. H. Usher. Biometrika, vol.16, parts III and IV., pp.273-282, Dec., 1924.

ACANTHOCEPHALA OF NORTH AMERICAN MAMMALS. Harley J. Van Cleave. Ill. Biol. Monog., vol.23, nos.1-2, pp.x-179, illus., 1953.

ON SOME FILARIAE PARASITIC IN SURINAM MAMMALS, WITH THE DESCRIPTION OF FILARIOPSIS ASPER N.G., N. SP. P. H. Van Thiel. Parasitology, vol.18, pp.128-136, figs.17, Jan. 22, 1926.

THE DISEASES OF WILD ANIMALS. Jean Vilain. ("Revue Zoologique".) Popular Sci. Monthly, vol.16, no.1, pp.11-13, 1879.

INFLUENCE OF CIVILIZATION ON HUMAN ZOO-PARASITIC DISEASES. Henry B. Ward. Proc. 7th. Internat. Zool. Congress, pp.7, 1909.

PRESENT LINES OF ATTACK ON ANIMAL PARASITOLOGY. Henry B. Ward. Science, n.s., vol.59, pp.305-310, Apr. 4, 1924.

(CONTRIBUTION TO DENTAL PATHOLOGY.) Beitraege zur Pathologie der Zaehne. C. Wedl, M. Heider. Verlag Central-Vereines Deutscher Zahnaerzte, pp.16.

MORPHOLOGY OF THE INTESTINAL TRICHOMONAD FLAGELLATES IN MAN AND OF SIMILAR FORMS IN MONKEYS, CATS, DOGS, AND RATS. D. H. Wenrich. Jour. Morph., Philadelphia, vol.74, no.1, pp.189-211, illus., Jan., 1944.

CONTRIBUTION TO THE BIOLOGY OF ORNITHODORUS HERMSI WHEELER HERMS AND MEYER. Charles M. Wheeler. Jour. Parasitol., Lancaster, vol.29, no.1, pp.33-41, figs.2, Feb., 1943.

(VITAMINS AND DEFICIENCY DISEASES.) Ueber Vitamine und Mangelkrankheiten. Ed. Wiedemann. Zool. Garten, N.F., Leipzig, vol.10, nos.1-2, pp.41-50, May, 1938.

SOME MAMMALIAN ECTOPARASITES FROM WEST VIRGINIA. L. Wayne Wilson. Jour. Mamm., vol.24, no.1, p.102, Feb. 20, 1943.

OBSERVATIONS ON VECTORS OF CHAGAS' DISEASE IN THE UNITED STATES. I. CALIFORNIA. Sherwin F. Wood. Bull. Southern California Acad. Sci., Los Angeles, vol.41, pt.2, pp.61-69, May-Aug., 1942.

OBSERVATIONS ON VECTORS OF CHAGAS' DISEASE IN THE UNITED STATES. II. ARIZONA. Sherwin F. Wood. Amer. Jour. Tropical Med., Baltimore, vol.23, no.3, pp.315-320, May, 1943.

ONE ANIMAL DISEASE TRANSMISSIBLE TO HUMANS. Harry R. Woodward. Yellowstone Nat. Notes, vol.10, nos.1-2, pp.7-8, Jan-Feb., 1933.

OBSERVATIONS ON ECTOPARASITES OF SOME SMALL MAMMALS IN EVERGLADES NATIONAL PARK AND HILLSBOROUGH COUNTY, FLORIDA. C. Brooke Worth. Jour. Parasitol., Lancaster, vol.36, no.4, pp.326-335, illus., Aug., 1950.

INTESTINAL DISEASES VERSUS RANCH TECHNIQUE. R. W. Wuestenberg. Amer. Fur Breeder, Duluth, vol.18, no.3, pp.54, 56, Sep., 1945.

(Reviw by George B. Wislocki of) DISEASE IN CAPTIVE WILD MAMMALS AND BIRDS. INCIDENCE, DESCRIPTION, COMPARISON. Herbert Fox. Jour. Mamm., vol.5, no.2, pp.136-137, May, 1924.

MYIASIS IN MAN AND ANIMALS IN AFRICA. F. Zumpt. S.A. Journal of Clinical Sci., vol. 2, no.1, pp.38-69, illus., Mar., 1951.

## DISEASES AND PARASITES -- DISTEMPER

COMBATING DISTEMPER IN PRINCE EDWARD ISLAND. Geo. C. Bishop. Nat. Fur News, Denver, vol.19, no.6, pp.14, 30-31, illus., July, 1947; Fur of Canada, Winnipeg, vol.12, no.10, pp.38-39, July, 1947.

DISTEMPER IN FUR BEARING ANIMALS. F. X. Gassner. Fur of Canada, Winnipeg, vol.9, no.11, pp.4-7, Aug., 1944;National Fur News, Denver, vol.16, no.7, pp.6, 24-25, 27, illus., Aug., 1944.

COMPARATIVE STUDY OF DISTEMPER INCLUSIONS. R. G. Green, C. A. Evans. Amer. Jour. Hyg., Baltimore, vol.29, no. 2, sec. B, pp.73-87, figs.4, Mar., 1939.

DISTEMPER IN FUR BEARING ANIMALS. Dr. Kirk. Fur of Canada, Winnipeg, vol.9, no.6, pp.3, 10-11, Mar., 1944.

INCLUSION BODIES IN DISTEMPER. Louis Wipf. Natl. Fur News, vol.12, no.4, p.4, May 1940.

DISTEMPER IN FUR BEARING ANIMALS. National Fur News, Denver, vol.16, no.5, pp.8-9, 12-13, June, 1944.

## DISEASES AND PARASITES -- FLEAS

CONTRIBUTIONS FROM THE LOS ANGELES MUSEUM-CHANNEL ISLANDS BIOLOGICAL SURVEY. NO. 20. THREE NEW FLEAS (SIPHONAPTERA). G. F. Augustson. Bull. S. Calif. Acad. Sci., vol.40, no.2, pp.101-107, May-Aug., 1941.

FLEA GENUS THRASSIS AND SYLVATIC PLAGUE, WITH THE DESCRIPTION OF T. BRENNANI N. SP. G. F. Augustson. Jour. Parasitology, vol.30, no.4, pp.237-240, Aug., 1944.

SOME NEW CALIFORNIA SIPHONAPTERA. G. F. Augustson. Bull. S. Calif. Acad. Sci., vol.40, no.3, pp.140-146, Sep.-Dec., 1941.

THE FLEAS (SIPHONAPTERA) OF ALBERTA, WITH A LIST OF THE KNOWN VECTORS OF SYLVATIC PLAGUE. John H. Brown. Ann. Entomol. Soc. America, Columbus, vol.57, no.2, pp.207-213, June, 1944.

PLAGUE INFECTION IN FLEAS FROM MONTEREY COUNTY, AND THE LAKE TAHOE REGION, CALIFORNIA. C. R. Eskey, K. F. Meyer. Public Health Rep., U.S. Treasury Dept., vol.51, no.44, p. 1505, 1936.

ON THE RELATIONSHIP OF SOME MAMMAL FLEAS TO THEIR HOSTS. F. C. Evans, R. B. Freeman. Annals Entom. Soc. Amer., vol.43, no.3, pp.320-333, Sep., 1950.

FLEAS OF EASTERN UNITED STATES. Irving Fox. Iowa State College Press, Ames, pp.191, pls.31, Feb., 1940.

FLEAS OF WESTERN NORTH AMERICA: THEIR RELATION TO THE PUBLIC HEALTH. C. Andresen Hubbard. Iowa State College Press, Ames, pp.1-535, pls.5, text fig.235, 1947.

(Review by R. B. Eads of) FLEAS OF WESTERN NORTH AMERICA. C. Andresen Hubbard. Jour. Mamm., vol.28, no.4, p.410, Nov. 26, 1947.

TEN PAPERS ON WESTERN FLEAS. C. Andresen Hubbard. Pac. Univ. Bull., vol. 37, nos.1-10, p.55, Mar. 1940 to May, 1941.

SIPHONAPTERA HOST DISTRIBUTION OF THE GENUS OPISOCROSTIS JORDAN. William L. Jellison. Trans. Amer. Microscop. Soc., vol.66, no.1, pp.64-69, Jan., 1947.

SIPHONAPTERA COLLECTED DURING A VISIT TO THE EASTERN UNITED STATES OF NORTH AMERICA IN 1927. Karl Jordan. Novitates Zoologicae, vol.34, pp.178-188, illus., Feb., 1928.

LIST OF FLEAS (SIPHONAPTERA) COLLECTED AT TAMA, IOWA. C. R. Joyce, Gaines W. Eddy. Iowa State College Jour. Sci., Ames, vol.18, no.2, pp.209-215, Jan., 1944.

ROLE OF THE INFECTED AND THE INFECTIVE FLEA IN THE SPREAD OF SYLVATIC PLAGUE. K. F. Meyer. Vierteljahrschrift Naturf. Gesell. Zuerich, vol.83, no. 30, pp.160-169, 1938.

NEW NORTH AMERICAN FLEAS. Robert Traub. Field Mus. Nat. Hist., Zool. Ser. 29, no.15, pp.211-220, Dec., 1944.

## DISEASES AND PARASITES -- FOOT AND MOUTH DISEASE

HOOF AND MOUTH DISEASE. I. B. Boughton. Trans. N. A. Wildl. Conf., vol.12, pp.520-523, 1947.

REPORT ON FAUNAL SURVEYS OF FOOT-AND-MOUTH AREAS IN 1934-1935. Charles Elton. Prog. Rep. Foot-and-Mouth Dis. Res. Comm. 5 (Appendix 5), pp.379-386, 1937.

(THE INSTIGATOR OF FOOT AND MOUTH DISEASE.) Der Maul- und Klauenseuche-Erreger. H. Stauffachen. Rev. Suisse de Zool., vol.34, pp.207-216, figs.8, 1927.

ORIGIN OF FOOT-AND-MOUTH DISEASE. H. M. Woodcock. Nature, vol.113, p.165, Feb. 2, 1924.

FOOT AND MOUTH DISEASE. THE SEARCH FOR THE CARRIER AND THE NEED FOR AN ANTIDOTE. Field, vol.170, no.4330, pp. 1346-1348, Nov. 20, 1937.

FOOT-AND-MOUTH DISEASE IN WILDLIFE. Jour. Amer. Vet. Med. Assoc., Chicago, vol.112, no.854, p.337, May, 1948.

## DISEASES AND PARASITES -- HYDATID DISEASE

OCCURRENCE OF THE GRANULAR TAPEWORM ECHINOCOCCUS GRANULOSUS IN WILD GAME IN NORTH AMERICA. Ian McT. Cowan. Jour. Wildl. Mgt., Menasha, vol.12, no.1, pp.105-106, Jan., 1948

HYDATID DISEASE(ECHINOCOCCUS GRANULOSUS)IN SASKATCHEWAN BIG GAME. T. A. Harper, R.A.Ruttan, W.A.Benson. Trans. 20th N. A. Wildl. Conf. pp.198-208, illus., 1955.

IMPORTANCE OF SYLVATIC HYDATID DISEASE. Thomas B. Magath. Jour. Amer. Vet. Med. Assoc., vol.125, no.932, pp. 411-414, Nov., 1954.

HYDATID DISEASE IN BOREAL REGIONS. Robert Rausch. Arctic, Jour. Arctic Inst. North Amer., Ottawa, vol.5, no.3, pp.157-174, illus., Oct., 1952.

HYDATID DISEASE (ECHINOCOCCOSIS) IN ALASKA AND THE IMPORTANCE OF RODENT INTERMEDIATE HOSTS. Robert Rausch, Everett L. Schiller. Science, vol. 113, no.2925, pp.57-58, Jan. 19, 1951.

MAINTENANCE OF ECHINOCOCCUS IN THE UNITED STATES. W. A. Riley. Jour. Amer. Vet. Med. Assoc., vol.95, no.449, pp.170-172, Aug., 1939.

NEED FOR DATA RELATIVE TO THE OCCURRENCE OF HYDATIDS AND OF ECHINOCOCCUS GRANULOSUS IN WILDLIFE. W. A. Riley. Jour. Wildl. Mgt., Menasha, vol.3, no.3, pp.255-257, July, 1939.

STUDIES ON THE HELMINTH FAUNA OF ALASKA. XIX. AN EXPERIMENTAL STUDY ON BLOWFLY (PHORMIA REGINA) TRANSMISSION OF HYDATID DISEASE. E. L. Schiller. Exp. Parasit. vol.3, no.2, pp.161-166, illus., Mar., 1954.

DISTRIBUTION AND INCIDENCE OF ECHINOCOCCUS GRANULOSUS IN MAN AND OTHER ANIMALS WITH SPECIAL REFERENCE TO CANADA. Gordon K. Sweatman. Can. Jour. Public Health, vol.43, pp.480-486, maps, Nov., 1952.

ECHINOCOCCOSIS ON ST. LAWRENCE ISLAND, ALASKA. Lyell J. Thomas, and others. Science, vol.120, no.3131, pp.1102-1103, Dec. 31, 1954.

## DISEASES AND PARASITES -- LICE

ON THE TAXONOMY, BIOLOGY, AND DISTRIBUTION OF THE BITING LICE OF THE FAMILY GYROPIDAE. H. E. Ewing. Proc. U.S. Nat. Mus., vol.63, art.20, pp.1-42, pl.1, Mar. 4, 1924.

ANOPLURA OF THE CANADIAN ARCTIC EXPEDITION, 1913-1918. G. F. Ferris. Rep. Canadian Arctic Exped. 1913-1918, vol.3, part D, p.11d, Sep. 12, 1919.

CONCERNING LICE. G. F. Ferris. Jour. Mamm., vol.3, no.1, pp.16-18, Feb., 1922.

HOST-ASSOCIATIONS OF THE LICE OF MAMMALS. G. H. E. Hopkins. Proc. Zool. Soc. London, vol.119, pt.2, pp.387-604, Aug. 17, 1949.

ANOPLURA AND MALLOPHAGA INFESTING MAMMALS OF IOWA. Charles R. Joyce. Ph. D. thesis, Iowa State Coll., 1952.

PARASITES OF BRITISH BIRDS AND MAMMALS. IX. A BIBLIOGRAPHY OF THE PAPERS CONTAINING RECORDS OF MALLOPHAGA (BITING LICE) FROM BIRDS AND

MAMMALS. Gordon B. Thompson. Entom. Monthly Mag., vol.72, no.259, pp.159-161, July, 1936.

EVOLUTION AND HOST-RELATIONSHIPS OF THE SUCKING LICE OF THE FERUNGULATA. J. E. Webb. Proc. Zool. Soc. London, vol.119, pt.1, pp.133-188, figs.149, May 16, 1949.

SPIRACLE STRUCTURE AS A GUIDE TO THE PHYLOGENETIC RELATIONSHIPS OF THE ANOPLURA (BITING AND SUCKING LICE), WITH NOTES ON THE AFFINITIES OF THE MAMMALIAN HOSTS. J. E. Webb. Proc. Zool. Soc. London, vol.116, pt.1, pp. 49-119, figs.216, May, 1946.

LICE ON HIBERNATING AND NON HIBERNATING MAMMALS. F. H. Wilson. Jour. Mamm., vol.18, no.3, pp.361-362, Aug. 14, 1937.

DISEASES AND PARASITES -- PLAGUE

SYLVATIC PLAGUE IN PARK COUNTY, COLORADO. D. H. Ecke, C. W. Johnson. Trans. 15th North Amer. Wildl. Conf., Washington, pp.191-197, 1950.

PLAGUE IN COLORADO AND TEXAS. D.H. Ecke, C. W. Johnson, V. I. Miles, M. J. Wilcomb. Public Health Monog., no.6, p. 54, 1952.

ON THE IMPORTANCE OF PREDATORY BIRDS IN THE EPIDEMIOLOGY OF PLAGUE. A. N. Egorov. Rev. Microbiol., Epidemiol. & Parasitol. (Rev. Microbiol.), Saratov, vol. 12, no.2, pp.133-134, 1933. (In Russian with English summary.)

PLAGUE AND THE REGULATION OF NUMBERS IN WILD ANIMALS. C. S. Elton. Jour. Hygiene, vol.24, pp.138-163, Oct. 12, 1925.

PLAGUE IN THE UNITED STATES. Brock C. Hampton. Pub. Health Rep., vol.55, no.26, pp.1143-1158, June 28, 1940.

ANTI-PLAGUE MEASURES IN TACOMA, WASHINGTON. James M. Hundley, Kaarlo W. Nasi. U.S. Publ. Health Repts., Washington, vol.59, no.38, pp.1239-1255, illus., Sep. 22, 1944.

CONTROL OF PLAGUE. Leo Kartman. California Vector News, State Dept. Public Health, Berkeley, vol.3, no.12, pp.62-67, Dec., 1956.

RELATIVE SIGNIFICANCE OF DIFFERENT MAMMALS IN PLAGUE EPIZOOTICS AND IN THE ARISING OF HUMAN PLAGUE CASES IN THE MONGOL-TRANSBAIKALIAN ENDEMIC FOCUS. V. V. Kucheruk. Zool. Jour. USSR, Moscow, vol.24, no.5, pp.309-320, figs.2, tbls.5, 1945. (English summary.)

MAMMALS AND PLAGUE DISTRIBUTION IN THE UNITED STATES. Willard H. Lahnum. U.S. Naval Med. Bull., Washington, vol.46, no.5, pp.782-785, May, 1946.

FURTHER NOTE ON NATURAL AND EXPERIMENTAL PLAGUE IN TARBAGANS. Wu Lien-Ter, G. L. Tuck. Jour. Hygiene, Cambridge, vol.22, pp.329-334, 1924.

PLAGUE CONTROL WITH DDT AND "1080". Atilio Macchiavello. Amer. Jour. Pub.Health, vol.36, no.8, pp.842-854, Aug., 1946.

NATURAL HISTORY OF PLAGUE AND PSITTACOSIS. Karl F. Meyer. Public Health Repts., U.S.Public Health Service, Washington, vol.72, no.8, pp.705-717, Aug., 1957.

PLAGUE PROBLEMS IN SOUTH AFRICA. W. A. Murray. So. African Jour. Nat. Hist., vol. 6, no.4, pp.308-314, June, 1929.

PLAGUE IN JAVA, 1910-1912. N. H. Swellengrebel. Hygiene, London, vol.48, no.2, pp.135-145, Oct., 1950.

PLAGUE - FIELD SURVEYS IN WESTERN UNITED STATES DURING TEN YEARS (1936-1945). N. E. Wayson. U.S. Publ. Health Repts., Washington, vol.62, no.22, pp.780-791, May 30, 1947.

PLAGUE INFECTION IN CALIFORNIA. U.S. Public Health Repts., Washington, D.C., vol.58, no.41, pp.1528-1529, Oct. 8, 1943.

PLAGUE INFECTION IN NYE COUNTY, NEVADA, AND LEA COUNTY, NEW MEXICO. U.S. Publ. Health Repts., Washington, vol.65, no.11, p.378, Mar. 17, 1950.

PLAGUE INFECTION REPORTED IN THE UNITED STATES DURING 1942. U.S. Publ. Health Repts., vol.58, no.16, pp.640-645, Apr. 16, 1943.

PLAGUE INFECTION REPORTED IN THE UNITED STATES DURING 1943. U.S. Publ. Health Repts., vol.59, no.28, pp.911-915, July 14, 1944.

POSITIVE PLAGUE AND TULAREMIA SPECIMENS REPORTED IN CANADA DURING 1942. U.S. Publ. Health Repts., vol.58, no.16, p.646, Apr. 16, 1943.

DISEASES AND PARASITES -- RABIES

OBSERVATIONS ON RABIES. G. H. Adlam. Can. Jour. Compar. Med. & Vet. Sci., vol. 17, no.10, pp.418-421, illus., Oct., 1953.

RABIES - A PUBLIC HEALTH PROBLEM OF INCREASING IMPORTANCE. J. Robert Anderson. Virginia Wildl., Richmond, vol. 11, no.8, pp.18-22, illus., Aug., 1950.

RABIES CONTROL IN ALBERTA. E. E. Ballantyne, J. G. O'Donoghue. Jour. Amer. Vet. Med. Assoc., vol.125, no.931, pp. 316-326, illus., Oct., 1954.

RABIES, A TENNESSEE PROBLEM. Charles T. Caraway, Albert E. Hyder. Tenn. Cons., vol.21, no.3, pp.20-22, Mar., 1955.

WILDLIFE RABIES CONTROL PROGRAM IN NEW YORK. Ralph Colson, Warren H. McKeon. Proc. 8th Ann. N. E. Wildl. Conf., Jackson's Mill, W. Va., pp.1-6, Apr. 1-4, 1952.

RABIES (IN NEW YORK STATE). Ralph Colson, W. S. Stone, D. J. Dean. New York State Cons., vol.9, no.5, pp.8-12, illus., Apr.-May, 1955.

CONTROL OF RABIES. REPORT BY THE COMMITTEE ON PUBLIC HEALTH RELATIONS OF THE NEW YORK ACADEMY OF MEDICINE. E. H. L. Corwin, Lois Stice. Pub. Health Rep., vol.62, no.34, pp.1215-1237, Aug. 22, 1947.

WILDLIFE RABIES IN TEXAS - A PRELIMINARY REPORT. R. B. Eads, J. S. Wiseman, J. E. Grimes, G. C. Menzies. Public Health Repts., U.S. Public Health Service, Washington, vol.70, no.10, pp.995-1000, Oct., 1955.

RABIES PROBLEM (IN FLORIDA). Florida Game and Fresh Water Fish Commission. Fla. Wildl. , vol.8, no.12, pp.24-25, 40, illus., May, 1955.

ONLY ONE STATE AHEAD OF KENTUCKY IN OCCURRENCE OF RABIES. Larry R. Gale. Ky. Happy Hunting Ground, vol.11, no.5, pp.30-31, illus., Sep., 1955.

RABIES IN THE WILD. H. T. Gier. Jour. Wildl. Mgt., Menasha, vol.12, no.2, pp. 142-153, April, 1948.

THE 1951-1952 OUTBREAK OF RABIES IN NORTH DAKOTA. C. R. Grondahl. Bimonthly Bull., N. Dak. Agr. Exp. Sta., vol.15, no. 4, pp.139-145, maps & graph., Mar.-Apr., 1953.

RABIES IN IOWA. Stanley L. Hendricks, H. U. Garrett. Jour. Amer. Vet. Med. Assoc., vol.122, no.915, pp.474-478, graphs & map, June, 1953.

RABIES IN WISCONSIN. Ruth L. Hine. Wis. Cons. Bull., vol.20, no.7, pp.25-28, figs.2, July, 1955.

RABIES IN VIRGINIA AND ITS RELATION TO WILDLIFE. John C. Jones. Va. Wildl., vol.15, no.4, pp.8-10, 12, Apr., 1954.

STATUS OF RABIES IN THE MIDDLE ATLANTIC STATES OF VIRGINIA, WEST VIRGINIA, MARYLAND, DELAWARE, AND THE DISTRICT OF COLUMBIA FOR THE FISCAL YEAR 1953-1954. John C. Jones. Md. Cons., vol.32, no.4, pp.6-11, illus., July, 1955.

PRACTICAL PROBLEMS IN RABIES CONTROL. Hilary Koprowski, et al. Public Health Repts., U.S. Public Health Serv., Washington, vol.70, no.6, pp.564-569, June, 1955.

(CONTROL OF WILD-ANIMAL VECTORS OF RABIES ALONG THE MEXICAN-AMERICAN BORDER.) Control de los animales silvestres vectores de rabia a lo largo de la frontera Mexicano-Estadounidense. Clifford C. Presnall. Bol. Oficina Sanitaria Panamericana, vol.43, no.2, pp.159-161, Aug., 1957. (With English summary.)

WILDLIFE RABIES CONTROL. Clifford C. Presnall. Public Health Repts., U.S. Public Health Service, Washington, vol.70, no.12, pp.1216-1217, Dec., 1955.

MAMMALS CONCERNED IN THE BUBONIC PLAGUE AND RABIES PROBLEM IN SOUTH AFRICA. Austin Roberts. South African Jour. Sci., Johannesburg, vol.32, pp.414-460, Nov., 1935.

REPORT OF THE COMMITTEE ON RABIES. H. W. Schoening, et al. Proc. Ann. Meeting U.S. Livestock Sanitary Assoc., vol.50, pp.39-42, 1946.

OUTBREAK OF RABIES IN NORTH WEST CANADA, 1951-1952. V. E. F. Solman. Arctic Cir., vol.5, no.5, pp.57, 1952.

RABIES PROBLEMS AND CONTROL, A NATION WIDE PROGRAM. James H. Steele, Ernest S. Tierkel. U.S. Public Health Repts., Washington, vol.64, no.25, pp.785-796, June 24, 1949.

WHAT ABOUT RABIES? Daniel O. Trainer, Jr. Wisconsin Conservation Bull., vol.22, no.9, pp.15-18, map, Sep., 1957.

PARALYTIC RABIES INVESTIGATION. REPORT OF ZOOLOGIST FOR HALF YEAR ENDING 31st DECEMBER, 1934. F. W. Urich. Council Paper no.75 of 1935, Trinidad and Tobago, pp.3-6, 1935.

EPIZOOTIC OF RABIES IN INTERIOR ALASKA 1945-1947. Ralph B. Williams. Can. Jour. Compar. Med., vol.13, no.6, pp.136-143, map, 1949.

(RABIES IN THE WILD ANIMALS OF STATE OF TEXAS.) La rabia en los animales silvestres del estado de Texas. Kenneth S. Young, J.V. Irons. Bol. de la Offic. Sanit., vol.35, no.4, pp.410-417, Oct., 1953.

RABIES IN THE WILD. Stanley P. Young. American Forests, Washington, vol.56, no. 8, pp.26-30, 42, Aug., 1950.

RABIES IN THE UNITED STATES IN 1954. Jour. Amer. Vet. Med. Assoc., vol.127, no.942, p.240, map, Sep., 1955.

DISEASES AND PARASITES -- SCRUB TYPHUS

STUDIES ON TSUTSUGAMUSHI DISEASE (SCRUB TYPHUS, MITEBORNE TYPHUS) IN NEW GUINEA AND ADJACENT ISLANDS: EPIDEMIOLOGY, CLINICAL OBSERVATIONS, AND ETIOLOGY IN THE DOBADURA AREA. Francis G. Blake, Kenneth F. Maxcy, Joseph F. Sadusk, Jr., Glen M. Kohls, E. John Bell. Amer. Jour. Hygiene, Baltimore, vol.41, no.3, pp.243-373, figs.32, pls.3, May, 1945. (Mammals, pp.265-274.)

TROMBICULA FLETCHERI WOMERSLEY AND HEASLIP 1943, A VECTOR OF TSUTSUGAMUSHI DISEASE (SCRUB TYPHUS) IN NEW GUINEA. Francis G. Blake, Kenneth F. Maxcy, Joseph F. Sadusk, Jr., Glen M. Kohls, E. John Bell. Science, Lancaster, n.s., vol.102, no.2638, pp.61-64, July 20, 1945.

TSUTSUGAMUSHI DISEASE. EPIDEMIOLOGY AND METHODS OF SURVEY AND CONTROL. David H. Johnson, George W. Wharton. U.S. Naval Medical Bull., Washington, vol.46, no.3, pp.459-472, illus., Mar., 1946.

STUDIES ON TSUTSUGAMISHI DISEASE (SCRUB TYPHUS, MITE-BORNE TYPHUS) IN NEW GUINEA AND ADJACENT ISLANDS: FURTHER OBSERVATIONS ON EPIDEMIOLOGY AND ETIOLOGY. Glen M. Kohls, Charles A. Armbrust, Edwin N. Irons, Cornelius B. Philip. Amer. Jour. Hygiene, Baltimore, vol.41, no.3, pp.374-396, May, 1945.

OBSERVATIONS ON TSUTSUGAMUSHI DISEASE (SCRUB TYPHUS) IN ASSAM AND

BURMA. Thomas T. Mackie, Gordon E. Davis, Henry S. Fuller, John A. Knapp, Maurice L. Steinacker, Kenneth E. Stager, Robert Traub, William L. Jellison, Dick D. Millspaugh, Robert C. Austrian, E. John Bell, Glen M. Kohlis, Wei Hsi, James A. V.Girsham. Amer. Jour. Hygiene, Baltimore, vol.43, no.3, pp.195-218, figs.4, May, 1946.

OBSERVATIONS ON TSUTSUGAMUSHI DISEASE (MITE-BORNE OR SCRUB TYPHUS) IN NORTHWEST HONSHU ISLAND, JAPAN, IN THE FALL OF 1945. I. EPIDEMIOLOGICAL AND ECOLOGICAL DATA. Cornelius B. Philip. Amer. Jour. Hygiene, Baltimore, vol.46, no.1, pp.45-59, figs.8, July, 1947.

OBSERVATIONS ON TSUTSUGAMUSHI DISEASE (MITE-BORNE OR SCRUB TYPHUS) IN NORTHWEST HONSHU ISLAND, JAPAN, IN THE FALL OF 1945. II. SYSTEMATIC COMMENT ON THE JAPANESE VOLE-MITES. Cornelius B. Philip. Amer. Jour. Hygiene, Baltimore, vol.46, no.1, pp.60-65, July, 1947.

STUDIES ON TSUTSUGAMUSHI DISEASE (SCRUB TYPHUS, MITE-BORNE TYPHUS) IN NEW GUINEA AND ADJACENT ISLANDS. TSUTSUGAMUSHI DISEASE WITH HIGH ENDEMICITY ON A SMALL SOUTH SEA ISLAND. Cornelius B. Philip, Glen M. Kohls. Amer. Jour. Hygiene, vol.42, no.2, pp.195-203, figs.4, Sep., 1945.

TSUTSUGAMUSHI DISEASE (SCRUB OR MITE-BORNE TYPHUS) IN THE PHILIPPINE ISLANDS DURING AMERICAN REOCCUPATION IN 1944-1945. II. OBSERVATIONS ON TROMBICULID MITES. Cornelius B. Philip, Theodore E. Woodward. Jour. Parasitology, Baltimore, vol.32, no.5, pp.502-513, Oct., 1946.

REVIEW OF FIELD INVESTIGATIONS CONCERNING THE MAMMAL RESERVOIRS OF SCRUB TYPHUS IN THE NEW GUINEA AREA. Ellis Troughton. Commonwealth of Australia, Council for Scientific and Industrial Research, Tropical Scientific Section, Melbourne, Report T.S.S. 2, pp.1-14, July, 1945.

## DISEASES AND PARASITES -- SPOTTED FEVER

DISTRIBUTIONAL STUDIES OF PARASITIC ARTHROPODS IN UTAH, DETERMINED AS ACTUAL AND POTENTIAL VECTORS OF ROCKY MOUNTAIN SPOTTED FEVER AND PLAGUE WITH NOTES ON VECTOR-HOST RELATIONSHIPS. D. Elden Beck. Brigham Young U. Sci. Bull., Biol. Ser., vol.1, no. 1, p.64, illus., Mar., 1955.

SOME COMMON MAMMALS OF WESTERN MONTANA IN RELATION TO AGRICULTURE AND SPOTTED FEVER. Clarence Birdseye. Washington, Govt. Print. Off., pp.46, illus., 1912.

ROCKY MOUNTAIN SPOTTED-FEVER MYSTERY. WHO WAS THE KILLER OF BITTER ROOT VALLEY? MEDICAL MEN TURNED DETECTIVES TO FIND OUT. Ruth Brecher, Edward Brecher. Sci. Illus., New York, vol.1, no.2, pp.60-61, illus., May, 1946.

MAMMALS OF BITTERROOT VALLEY, MONTANA, IN THEIR RELATION TO SPOTTED FEVER. Henry W. Henshaw, Clarence Birdseye. Washington, Govt. Print. Off., pp.24, illus., 1911.

SPOTTED FEVER AND OTHER ALBERTAN TICKS. John H. Brown. Canadian Jour. Res. Ottawa, sec.D, vol.22, no.2, pp.36-51, illus., Apr., 1944.

## DISEASES AND PARASITES -- TICKS

HOSTS OF CERTAIN NEW YORK TICKS. George Anastos. Psyche, Boston, vol.54, no.3, pp.178-180, Sep., 1947.

TROBICULA CYNOS EWING, 1937, AND THREE RELATED NEW SPECIES (ACARINA: TROMBICULIDAE). James M. Brennan. Wasmann Jour. Biol., vol.10, no.1, pp.55-65, illus., Spring, 1952.

TWO NEW SPECIES OF TROMBICULA: T. MONTANENSIS AND T. APLODONTIAE (ACARINA, TROBICULIDAE) FROM NORTHWESTERN UNITED STATES. James M. Brennan. Jour. Parasitology, vol.32, no.5, pp.441-444, Oct., 1946.

IXODES NEOTOMAE, NEW SPECIES FROM CALIFORNIA (ACARINA: IXODIDAE). R.A. Cooley. Pan-Pac. Ent., vol.20, no.1, pp.7-12, Jan., 1944.

ARGASIDAE OF NORTH AMERICA, CENTRAL AMERICA AND CUBA. R. A. Cooley, Glen M. Kohls. Univ. Press, Notre Dame, Ind., pp.1-152, pls.14, figs.57.

GENUS IXODES IN NORTH AMERICA. R.A. Cooley, Glen M. Kohls. Superintendent of Documents, U.S. Govt. Printing Off., Washington, D.C., Nat. Inst. Health Bull.no.184, pp.246, text-figs.87.

(Review by William L. Jellison of) GENUS IXODES IN NORTH AMERICA, R. A. Cooley, Glen M. Kohls. Jour. Mamm., vol.27, no.4, p.399, Nov. 25, 1946.

IXODES CALIFORNICUS BANKS 1904, IXODES PACIFICUS N. SP., AND IXODES CONEPATI N. SP. R. A. Cooley, Glen M. Kohls. Pan-Pac. Ent., vol.19, no.4, pp. 139-147, Oct., 1943.

THREE NEW SPECIES OF ORNITHODOROS (ACARINA: IXODOIDEA). R. A. Cooley, Glen M. Kohls. Pub. Health Rep., vol.56, no.12, pp.587-594, Mar. 21, 1941.

TICKS - A MENACE TO ANIMAL LIFE. C. H. Curran. Nat. Hist., New York, vol. 54, no.5, pp.212-215, illus., May, 1945.

ORNITHODOROS PARKERI COOLEY; OBSERVATIONS ON THE BIOLOGY OF THIS TICK. Gordon E. Davis. Jour. Parasitology, vol.27, no.5, pp.425-433, Oct., 1941.

TICKS AND RELAPSING FEVER IN THE UNITED STATES. Gordon E. Davis. Pub. Health Rep., vol.55, no.51, pp.2347-2350, Dec. 20, 1940.

ACARI AS AGENTS TRANSMITTING TYPHUS IN INDIA, AUSTRALASIA AND THE FAR EAST. Susan Finnegan. British Mus. (Nat. Hist.), London, Economic Ser., no.16, pp.78, figs.49, 1945.

SEASONAL ABUNDANCE OF THE TICK DERMACENTOR PARUMAPERTUS. Calvin Fremling, Allan Gastfriend. Ecol. vol.36, no.1, pp.162-163, graphs., Jan., 1955.

WILDLIFE EFFECTS OF DDT DUST USED FOR TICK CONTROL ON A TEXAS PRAIRIE. John L. George, William H. Stickel. Amer. Midland Nat., Notre Dame, vol.42, no.1, pp.228-237, July, 1949.

SYNONYMY, HOSTS, AND TYPE MATERIAL OF GUNTHERIA BIPYGALIS (GUNTHER) (ACARINA: TROMBIDIIDAE). Carl E. M. Gunther. Proc. Linnean Soc. New South Wales, Sydney, vol.66, nos.295-296, pts. 3-4, p.155, 1941.

ON SOME NEW OR LITTLE-KNOWN SPECIES OF ACARI. Stanley Hirst. Proc. Zool. Soc. London, pp.971-1000, Dec., 1923.

NOTES ON EGYPTIAN TICKS (IXODOIDEA). I. GENUS ARGAS (ARGASIDAE) IN THE CAIRO AREA. Harry Hoogstraal. Proc.Egyptian Acad. Sci., Cairo, vol.7, pp.114-127, pls.1-3, 1952.

TICKS (IXODOIDEA) OF THE MALAGASY FAUNAL REGION (EXCEPTING THE SEYCHELLES). Harry Hoogstraal. Bull. Mus. Comp. Zool., Cambridge, vol.3, no.2, pp.37-113, Dec., 1953.

TICK-HOST ANEMIA: A SECONDARY ANEMIA INDUCED BY DERMACENTOR ANDERSONI STILES. Wm. L. Jellison. Jour. Parasitology, vol.24, no.2, pp.143-154, Apr., 1938.

MAMMAL HOST RECORDS OF ACARINA AND INSECTA FROM THE VICINITY OF HAMILTON, ONTARIO. W. W. Judd. Jour. Mamm., vol.31, no.3, pp.357-358, Aug. 21, 1950.

MAMMAL HOST RECORDS OF ACARINA AND INSECTA FROM THE VICINITY OF LONDON, ONTARIO. W. W. Judd. Jour. Mamm., vol.34, no.1, pp.137-139, Feb. 19, 1953.

SOME RECORDS OF ECTOPARASITIC ACARINA AND INSECTA FROM MAMMALS IN ONTARIO. W. W. Judd. Jour. Parasit., vol.40, no.4, pp.483-484, Aug., 1954.

TICKS OF DELAWARE WITH SPECIAL REFERENCE TO DERMACENTOR VARIABILIS (SAY) VECTOR OF ROCKY MOUNTAIN SPOTTED FEVER. Donald MacCreary. Bull. Delaware Agric. Expt. Sta., Newark, no.252, pp.1-22, illus., Jan., 1945.

PART PLAYED BY ALTERNATIVE HOSTS IN MAINTAINING THE TICK POPULATION OF HILL PASTURES. John Macleod. Jour. Anim. Ecol., vol.3, no.2, pp.161-164, Nov., 1934.

ARACHNIDS FOUND ON NIGERIAN RODENTS AND INSECTIVORES. A. S. Pearse. Jour. E. Mitchell Sci. Soc., vol.43, pp. 171-180, July, 1928.

TICKS AS VECTORS OF ANIMAL DISEASES. Cornelius B. Philip. Canadian Entomologist, London, Ont., vol.71, no.3, pp.55-65, Mar., 1939.

BIOLOGY OF IXODES MURIS BISHOPP AND SMITH (IXODIDAE). Carroll N. Smith. Ann. Ent. Soc. Am., vol.37, no.2, pp.221-234, June, 1944.

(NOTES ON TICKS OF DOMESTIC ANIMALS IN PORTUGUESE EAST AFRICA.) Notas sobre as carracas dos animais domesticos na Africa Oriental Portuguesa. Gertrud Theiler. Mocambique, Documentario Trimestral, Lourenco, Marques, no.33, pp.51-120, figs. 49, Mar., 1943.

OBSERVATIONS ON THE INCIDENCE OF TICKS ON KENYA MAMMALS. Neal A. Weber. Entomological News, vol.59, no. 9, pp.235-242, Nov., 1948.

## DISEASES AND PARASITES -- TRYPANOSOMES

EQUINE TRYPANOSOMIASIS - "MURRINA" OR "DERRENGADERA". SOME NOTES ON THE DISEASE IN PANAMA. Herbert C. Clark, Timothy L. Casserly, I.O. Gladish. Amer. Vet. Med. Assoc., vol.83, no.3, n.s., 36, pp.358-389, Sep., 1933.

ANIMAL SUSCEPTIBILITY TO TRYPANOSOMA HIPPICUM, THE EQUINE TRYPANOSOME OF PANAMA WITH SPECIAL REFERENCE TO CATTLE AS AN UNHARMED HOST AND PROBABLE RESERVOIR OF IMPORTANCE. Herbert C. Clark, Lawrence H. Dunn. Amer. Jour. Trop. Med., vol.13, no. 3, pp.273-281, fig.1, May, 1933.

STUDIES ON THE TRYPANOSOMES OF SOME CALIFORNIA MAMMALS. Betty Schuck Davis. Univ. California Publ. Zool., vol.57, no.3, pp.145-250, illus., Oct. 17, 1952.

(NOTES ON THE BEHAVIOUR OF TRYPANOSOMA EQUINUM IN LABORATORY ANIMALS.) Notas sobre o comportamento do "Trypanosoma equinum" em animais de laboratoria. Gisela R. Jansen. Rev. Brasileira Biol., Rio de Janeiro, vol.2, no.2, pp.247-253, figs.3, June, 1942.

(CONTRIBUTION TO THE STUDY OF AMERICAN TRYPANOSOMIASIS.) Contribuicao ao estudo da tripanosomiase americana. Bichat de Almeida Rodrigues, Gervásio de Brito Melo. Mem. Inst. Oswaldo Cruz, Rio de Janeiro, vol.37, no.1, pp.77-90, pls.1-2, Mar., 1942.

ADDITIONAL OBSERVATIONS ON TRYPANOSOMA CRUZI CHAGAS, FROM ARIZONA IN INSECTS, RODENTS, AND EXPERIMENTALLY INFECTED ANIMALS. Sherwin F. Wood. Amer. Jour. Tropical Med., Baltimore, vol.29, no.1, pp.43-55, pl.1, Jan., 1949.

## DISEASES AND PARASITES -- TULAREMIA

TULAREMIA. I. H. Alexander. Pennsylvania Game News, Harrisburg, vol.15, no.2, pp. 3, 28, May, 1944.

TAKE TULAREMIA VERY SERIOUSLY. B.F. Austin. Alabama Conserv., Montgomery, vol. 15, no.9, pp.7, 13, Mar., 1944.

TULAREMIA, AN ANIMAL-BORNE DISEASE. W. B. Bell, J. E. Shillinger. Bureau Biol.

Surv., Wildl. Res. & Mgt. Leaflet BS-5, pp.3, Apr., 1935.

SUSCEPTIBILITY OF FUR-BEARING ANIMALS AND GAME BIRDS TO TULARAEMIA. John H. Brown. Canadian Field-Nat., Sutton West, vol.58, no.2, pp.55-60, Mar.-Apr., 1944.

DOGS AND OTHER MAMMALS AS HOSTS OF TULAREMIA AND OF VECTOR TICKS IN ARKANSAS. Ernest L. Calhoun, Carl O. Mohr. Amer. Jour. Hygiene, vol.63, no. 2, pp.127-135, Mar., 1956.

TULAREMIA. John L. Cull. Rod and Gun in Canada, Montreal, vol.48, no.8, pp.30-31, Jan., 1947.

HISTORY OF TULARAEMIA. Edward Francis. (De Lamar Lectures, John Hopkins Univ. School Hygiene, Baltimore, Md., 1926-1927), pp.94-115, 1927.

OCCURRENCE OF TULARAEMIA IN NATURE AS A DISEASE OF MAN. Edward Francis. U.S. Public Health Service, Hygienic Lab., Bull. no.130, pp.1-8, Mar., 1922.

(TULAREMIA.) Tulaeramie. Edward Francis. Handb. der pathogenen Mikroorganismen, Jena, vol.6, no.16, pp.207-242, figs.21, pls.1-2, 1928.

TULAREMIA. Edward Françis. Scientific Monthly, vol.38, pp.476-479, July, 1934.

TULAREMIA. HOW TO PREVENT AND CONTROL IT. Edward Francis. Illinois Dept. Public Health, Educ. Health, Springfield, cir.no.31, pp.12, illus., 1927.

NEBRASKA'S GASTRONOMIC UNDERWORLD. Paul T. Gilbert. Outdoor Nebraska, Lincoln, vol.22, no.1, pp.14-17, illus., Spring, 1944.

TULAREMIA AND THE SPORTSMAN. E.W. Given. Pennsylvania Game News, vol.9, no. 7, pp.8-9, 30, illus., Oct., 1938.

TULAREMIA IN FUR BEARERS. John R. Gorham. Fur of Canada, Winnipeg, vol.14, no.12, p.7, Sep., 1949; Black Fox Mag. & Modern Mink Breeder, New York, vol.33, no.6, pp.16, 38, illus., Oct., 1949; Nat. Fur News, Denver, vol.21, no.12, p.6, Jan., 1950.

VIRULENCE OF TULAREMIA AS RELATED TO ANIMAL AND ORTHROPOD HOSTS. R.G. Green. Amer. Jour. Hygiene, Baltimore, vol. 38, no.3, pp.282-292, Nov., 1943.

TULAREMIA GEOGRAPHICAL DISTRIBUTION OF "DEERFLY FEVER" AND THE BITING FLY, CHRYSOPS DISCALIS WILLISTON. W. L. Jellison. U.S. Public Health Repts., Washington, vol.65, no. 41, pp.1321-1329, Oct. 13, 1950.

RODENTS, RABBITS AND TULAREMIA IN NORTH AMERICA: SOME ZOOLOGICAL AND EPIDEMIOLOGICAL CONSIDERATIONS. W. L. Jellison, R. R. Parker. Amer. Jour. Tropical Med., Baltimore, vol.25, no.4, pp.349-362, maps 5, July, 1945.

TICKS AND DISEASE WITH SPECIAL REFERENCE TO SPOTTED FEVER AND TULAREMIA IN EASTERN STATES. R. Matheson. Cornell Veterinarian, Ithaca, vol.50, pp.167-177, Apr., 1940.

REVIEW OF TULAREMIA IN BRITISH COLUMBIA, WITH SPECIAL REFERENCE TO A RECENT HUMAN CASE. T. K. Moilliet. Can. Ent. vol.68, no.6, pp.121-124, June, 1936.

TULAREMIA IN WISCONSIN. Banner Bill Morgan. Trans. Wisconsin Acad. Sci., Arts & Letters, vol.39, pp.1-19, 1949.

SURVEY OF PASTEURELLA TULARENSIS INFECTION IN THE ANIMALS OF THE JACKSON HOLE AREA. Mitsuru Nakamura. Zoologica, New York, vol.35, pt.2, no.9, pp.129-131, Aug., 1950.

ON CERTAIN REGULARITIES IN DISTRIBUTION OF TULAREMIA IN THE USSR. N. Nekipelov. Zool. Jour. USSR, Moscow, vol. 23, no.5, pp.275-279, 1944. ( English summary.)

HOW'S YOUR TULAREMIA I. Q.? Clay Shoenfeld. Sports Afield, Minneapolis, vol. 118, no.4, pp.56-57, 93, illus., Oct., 1947.

CULTIVATION OF PASTEURELLA TULARENSIS IN A LIQUID MEDIUM. Edward A. Steinhaus, R. R. Parker, Max T. McKee. Publ. Health Repts., Washington, D.C., vol.59, no.3, pp.78-79, Jan. 21, 1944.

TULAREMIA, TICKS AND TEXAS. R. D. Turk. Texas Game and Fish, Austin, vol.6, no.5, pp.11, 17, Apr., 1948.

TULAREMIA. A. Vol'fertz. Rev.Microbiol. Epidemiol. & Parasitol.(Rev.Microbiol.), Saratov, vol.14, pp.183-197, 1935. (In Russian.)

TULAREMIA IN FUR-BEARING ANIMALS. Fritz Volkmar. American Fur Breeder, vol.5, no.4, pp.11-13, Oct., 1932.

TULAREMIA, AN ANIMAL-BORNE DISEASE. U.S. Dept. Interior, Fish & Wildl. Service, Wildl. Leaflet 271, pp.4, June, 1948.

TULAREMIA - "RABBIT FEVER". Wyoming Wild Life, Cheyenne, vol.5, no.6, pp.1-2, 16, June, 1940.

## DISEASES AND PARASITES -- WORMS

NOTES ON SOME PARASITIC NEMATODES. H. A. Baylis. Ann. and Mag. Nat. Hist., London, ser.11, vol.11, no.84, pp.793-804, (Dec., 1944) Apr. 12, 1945.

ON A COLLECTION OF CESTODES AND NEMATODES FROM SMALL MAMMALS IN TANGANYIKA TERRITORY. H. A. Baylis. Ann. and Mag. Nat. Hist., London, ser.10, vol.13, no.75, pp.338-353, Mar., 1934.

PRELIMINARY DESCRIPTIONS OF THREE NEW PARASITIC NEMATODES. H. A. Baylis, R. Daubney. Ann. and Mag. Nat. Hist., ser. 9, vol.11, pp.333-335, Mar., 1923.

REPORT ON A COLLECTION OF PARASITIC NEMATODES, MAINLY FROM EGYPT. C. L. Boulenger. Parasitology, vol.18, pp.86-100, figs.28, Jan. 22, 1926.

MAMMALIAN TREMATODES. II. THREE FLUKES FROM SMALL MAMMALS. Elon E. Byrd, Robert J. Reiber. Jour. Tennessee Acad. Sci., Nashville, vol.17, no.1, pp. 143-148, pl.1, Jan., 1942.

SPECIFIC STATUS OF MONILIFORMIS (ACANTHOCEPHALA) OF TEXAS RATS, AND A REVIEW OF THE SPECIES OF THIS GENUS IN THE WESTERN HEMISPHERE. Asa C. Chandler. Jour. Parasitology, vol.27, no.3, pp.241-244, June, 1941.

NEW CESTODE, OOCHORISTICA PENNSYLVANICA AND SOME NEW OR RARE HELMINTH HOST RECORDS FROM PENNSYLVANIA MAMMALS. Asa C. Chandler, Dorothy M. Melvin. Jour. Parasitol., Lancaster, vol.37, no.1, pp.106-109, Feb., 1951.

TREMATODA AND CESTODA. A. R.Cooper. Rep. Canadian Arctic Exped. 1913-1918, vol. 9, part G-H, pp.1-27, pls.2, Ottawa, Feb. 4, 1921.

MORPHOLOGICAL AND BIOLOGICAL STUDIES ON CERTAIN STRIGEID TREMATODES OF MAMMALS. Ashton C. Cuckler. PhD thesis, Univ. Minn., 1942.

NOTE ON THE MEMBERS OF THE NEMATODE GENUS TRICHOSTRONGYLUS OCCURRING IN RODENTS AND LAGOMORPHS, WITH DESCRIPTIONS OF TWO NEW SPECIES. G. Dikmans. Jour. Wash. Acad. Sci., vol.27, no.5, pp.203-209, May 15, 1937.

TWO NEW NEMATODES FROM RODENTS. G. Dikmans. Proc. Helminth. Soc. Wash., vol.6, no.1, pp.1-4, Jan., 1939.

GENUS AELUROSTRONGYLUS CAMERON, 1927 (NEMATODA: METASTRONGYLIDAE), AND ITS RELATIVES; WITH DESCRIPTIONS OF PARAFILAROIDES, GEN. NOV., AND ANGIOSTRONGYLUS GUBERNACULATUS, SP. NOV. Ellsworth C. Dougherty. Proc. Helminth. Soc. Wash., vol.13, no.1, pp. 16-26, Jan., 1946.

GENUS PROTOSTRONGYLUS KAMENSKII, 1905 (NEMATODA: METASTRONGYLIDAE), AND ITS RELATIVES: PRELIMINARY NOTE. Ellsworth C. Dougherty. Jour. Parasitology, vol.32, no.1, pp.7-16, Feb., 1946.

NOTES ON NEMATODES FROM THE LUNGS AND FRONTAL SINUSES OF NEW YORK FUR-BEARERS. Frans C. Goble, Arthur H. Cook. Jour. Parasitol., Lancaster, vol.28, no.6, pp.451-455, map 1, Dec., 1942.

NOTES ON RELATIONSHIPS OF PARASITIC FLATWORMS TO BIRDS AND MAMMALS. John E. Guberlet. Murrelet (Seattle), vol.11, no.1, pp.15-17, Jan., 1930.

NEMATODE PARASITES OF MAMMALS OF THE ORDERS RODENTIA, LAGOMORPHA, AND HYRACOIDEA. Maurice C. Hall. U.S. Nat. Mus. Proc., Washington, vol.50, pp. 1-258, illus., 1916.

TWO NEW GENERA OF NEMATODES, WITH A NOTE ON A NEGLECTED NEMATODE STRUCTURE. Maurice C. Hall. Proc. U.S. Nat. Mus., vol.59, pp.541-546, Oct., 1921.

EYE WORM (THELAZIA CALIFORNIENSIS) INFECTION IN DEER IN CALIFORNIA. Carlton M. Herman. Calif. Fish and Game, vol.30, no.1, pp.58-59, Jan., 1944.

STUDIES ON FILAROID NEMATODES OF THE PORCUPINE AND SNOWSHOE HARE IN MINNESOTA. Paul R. Highby. PhD thesis, Univ. Minn., 1942.

PHYSIOLOGY AND CULTIVATION IN ARTIFICIAL MEDIA OF NEMATODES PARASITIC IN THE ALIMENTARY TRACT OF ANIMALS. A. D. Hobson. Parasitol., London, vol.38, no.4, pp.183-227, Feb., 1948.

NOTES ON THE HELMINTHS OF MAMMALS IN THE MOUNTAIN LAKE REGION. Harry Lee Holloway. Ann Arbor, Univ. Microfilms, Publication no.17, 612, 1957.

NEMATODES FROM AUSTRALIAN MARINE MAMMALS. T. Harvey Johnston, Patricia M. Mawson. Records South Australian Mus., Adelaide, vol.6, no.4, pp.429-434, figs. 10, Feb. 28, 1941.

OBSERVATIONS ON THE ROUTE OF MIGRATION OF THE COMMON LIVER FLUKE, FASCIOLA HEPATICA, IN THE DEFINITIVE HOST. Wendell H. Krull, R. Scott Jackson. Jour. Washington Acad. Sci., vol.33, no.3, pp.79-82, Mar. 15, 1943.

SURVEY OF THE HELMINTH PARASITES OF SMALL MAMMALS IN THE VICINITY OF MANHATTAN, KANSAS. Thomas J. Landis. Master's thesis, Kans. State Coll., 1952.

NEMATODE PARASITES OF MAMMALS. Gervase W. McClure. Zoologica (Sci.Contrib. New York Zool. Soc.), vol.15, no.3, pp.49-60, July 23, 1934.

OBSERVATIONS ON THE NEMATODE GENUS NEMATODIRUS, WITH DESCRIPTIONS OF NEW SPECIES. Henry G. May. Proc. U.S. Nat. Mus., vol.58, pp.577-588, pls.29-35, Dec., 1920.

CESTODES OF MAMMALS. Frederick J. Miggitt. London. Jena Frommannsche Buchdruckerei (H.Pohle), pp.282, 1924.

SECOND SPECIES OF THE NEMATODE GENUS ACANTHOXYURUS. H. O. Monnig. 17th report Director Veterinary Services and Animal Industry, Union South Africa, pp. 269-272, figs.4, Aug., 1931.

STUDIES ON THE BIONOMICS AND CONTROL OF THE BURSATE NEMATODES OF HORSES AND SHEEP. I. THE EFFECT OF URINE ON THE EGGS AND LARVAE IN THE FECES. I. W. Parnell. Canadian Jour. Res., vol.10, no.5, pp.532-538, May, 1934.

STATUS OF UROTREMA SHILLINGERI PRICE, 1931 (TREMATODA: UROTREMATIDAE). L. R. Penner. Trans. Amer. Micros. Soc., vol.60, no.3, pp.359-364, July, 1941.

NEW HELMINTH PARASITES FROM CENTRAL AMERICAN MAMMALS. Emmett W. Price. Proc. U.S. Nat. Mus., vol.73, art. 4, pp.1-7, pls.1-2, 1928.

SYNOPSIS OF THE TREMATODE FAMILY SCHISTOSOMIDAE WITH DESCRIPTIONS OF NEW GENERA AND SPECIES. Emmett W. Price. Proc. U.S. Nat. Mus., vol.75, art. 18, pp.1-39, pls.1-15, 1929.

TREMATODE PARASITES OF MARINE MAMMALS. Emmett W. Price. U.S. Nat. Mus.

Proc., Washington, vol.81, art.13, p.68, pl. 12 on 6 l, 1933.

ECOLOGY OF THE HELMINTH PARASITES OF SMALL MAMMALS COLLECTED FROM NORTHRUP CANYON, UPPER GRAND COULEE, WASHINGTON. John S. Rankin, Jr. Murrelet, Seattle, vol.26, no.1, pp.11-14, (Jan.-Apr.) Apr. 25, 1945.

HELMINTH PARASITES OF BIRDS AND MAMMALS IN WESTERN MASSACHUSETTS. John S. Rankin, Jr. Amer. Midland Nat., Notre Dame, vol.35, no.3, pp.756-768, May, 1946.

SYNOPSIS OF THE TREMATODE FAMILY HETEROPHYIDAE WITH DESCRIPTION OF A NEW GENUS AND FIVE NEW SPECIES. Brayton Howard Ransom. Proc. U.S. Nat. Mus., vol.57, pp.527-573, 1920.

BIOTIC INTERRELATIONSHIPS OF HELMINTH PARASITISM. Robert Rausch. Publ. Health Repts., Washington, vol.66, no.29, pp.928-934, July 20, 1951.

STUDIES ON THE HELMINTH FAUNA OF ALASKA. XXIV. ECHINOCOCCUS SIBIRICENSIS N. SP., FROM ST. LAWRENCE ISLAND. Robert Rausch, Everett L. Schiller. Jour. Parasit., vol.40, no.6, pp.659-662, illus., Dec., 1954.

OCCURRENCE OF LARVAE OF TRICHINELLA SPIRALIS IN ALASKAN MAMMALS. Robert Rausch, B. B. Babero, R. V. Rausch, E. L. Schiller. Jour. Parasitol., vol.42, no.3, pp.259-271, June 1956.

STUDIES ON NORTH AMERICAN HELMINTHS OF THE GENUS CAPILLARIA ZEDER, 1800 (NEMATODA): I. CAPPILLARIDS FROM MAMMALS. Clark P. Read. Jour. Parasitol., Lancaster, vol.35, no.3, pp.223-227, June, 1949.

STUDIES ON NORTH AMERICAN HELMINTHS OF THE GENUS CAPILLARIA ZEDER, 1800 (NEMATODA): II. ADDITIONAL CAPILLARIDS FROM MAMMALS WITH KEYS TO THE NORTH AMERICAN MAMMALIAN SPECIES. Clark P. Read. Jour. Parasitol., Lancaster, vol.35, no.3, pp.231-239, June, 1949.

SOME NEMATODES FROM MAMMALS OF REELFOOT LAKE IN TENNESSEE. Robert J. Reiber, Elon E. Byrd. Jour. Tennessee Acad. Sci., Nashville, vol.17, no.1, pp. 78-89, pls.4, Jan., 1942.

FLUKES IN MINK AND OTHER FUR BEARERS. Dr. Wm A. Riley. Amer. Fur Breeder, vol.11, no.8, p.22, Feb., 1930.

ON THE PROBABLE ORIGIN, HOMOLOGIES AND DEVELOPMENT OF THE FLUKES OF CETACEANS AND SIRENIANS. John A. Ryder. Amer. Nat., vol.19, no.5, pp.515-519, 1885.

NEW LIVER FLUKE FROM A MONKEY AND NEW PARASITIC ROUNDWORMS FROM VARIOUS AFRICAN ANIMALS. J. H. Sandground. Proc. U.S. Nat. Mus., vol.75, art.12, pp.1-11, pls.1-2, 1929.

SOME NEW CESTODE AND NEMATODE PARASITES FROM TANGANYIKA TERRITORY. J. H. Sandground. Proc. Boston Soc. Nat. Hist., vol.39, no.4, pp.131-150, illus., 1928.

PARASITIC NEMATODES FROM CHINA. Benjamin Schwartz. Proc. U.S. Nat. Mus., vol. 68, art.13, pp.1-10, Feb., 1926.

TWO NEW NEMATODES OF THE FAMILY STRONGYLIDAE, PARASITIC IN THE INTESTINES OF MAMMALS. Benjamin Schwartz. Proc. U.S. Nat. Mus., vol.73, art.2, pp. 1-5, pls.1-2, 1928.

PLATYHELMINTHS FROM FUR BEARERS IN THE WICHITA MOUNTAINS WILDLIFE REFUGE, WITH ESPECIAL REFERENCE TO OOCHORISTICA SPP. J. Teague Self, T. J. McKnight. Amer. Midland Nat., vol.43, no. 1, pp.58-61, Jan., 1950.

(NEMATODES IN MAMMALS.) Nematoden in Saeugetieren. C. Sprehn. Zeitschr. f. Saeugetierkunde, vol.2, no.1, pp.38-67, Oct. 15, 1927.

REVIEW OF CANADIAN HELMINTHOLOGY. I. PRESENT STATUS OF KNOWLEDGE OF THE HELMINTH PARASITES OF DOMESTICATED AND SEMIDOMESTICATED MAMMALS AND ECONOMICALLY IMPORTANT BIRDS IN CANADA, AS DETERMINED FROM WORK PUBLISHED PRIOR TO 1933. W.E. Swales. Canadian Jour. Research, vol.8, no.5, pp.468-477, May, 1933.

REVIEW OF CANADIAN HELMINTHOLOGY. II. ADDITIONS TO PART I, AS DETERMINED FROM A STUDY OF PARASITIC HELMINTHS COLLECTED IN CANADA. W.E. Swales. Canadian Jour. Res., vol.8, no.5, pp.478-482, May, 1933.

CONTRIBUTION TO THE KNOWLEDGE OF THE HELMINTH FAUNA OF FUKIEN. PT. 1. AVIAN, REPTILIAN AND MAMMALIAN TREMATODES. C. C. Tang. Peking Nat. Hist. Bull., Peking, vol.15, pt.4, pp.299-316, pls.4, June, 1941.

ON THE CESTODE PARASITES FROM MAMMALIAN HOSTS WHICH DIED IN THE GARDENS OF THE ZOOLOGICAL SOCIETY OF LONDON DURING THE YEARS 1919-1921; WITH A DESCRIPTION OF A NEW SPECIES OF CYCLORCHIDA. G.M. Vevers. Proc. Zool. Soc. London, 1922, pt.4, pp.921-928, Feb., 1923.

ON THE PARASITIC NEMATODA COLLECTED FROM MAMMALIAN HOSTS WHICH DIED IN THE GARDENS OF THE ZOOLOGICAL SOCIETY OF LONDON DURING THE YEARS 1919-1921; WITH A DESCRIPTION OF THREE NEW GENERA AND THREE NEW SPECIES. G.M. Vevers. Proc. Zool. Soc. London, 1922, pt.4, pp. 901-919, Feb., 1923.

LIFE HISTORY CYCLES OF THE GIANT KIDNEY WORM, DIOCTOPHYMA RENALE (NEMATODA), OF MAN AND MANY OTHER MAMMALS. Arthur E. Woodhead. Trans. Amer. Micros. Soc., vol.69, no.1, pp.21-46, pls.6, Jan., 1950.

## DISEASES AND PARASITES -- YELLOW FEVER

(A BIOLOGICAL STATION FOR THE STUDY OF MOSQUITOES AND WILD ANIMALS RELATED TO THE YELLOW FEVER.) Una estacao biologica para estudo dos mosquitos e dos outros animaes silvestres relacionados com a febre amarela. Henrique de Beaurepaire Aragao. Mem. Inst. Oswaldo Cruz, Rio de Janeiro, vol.38, fasc. 1, pp.21-37, figs.7, 1943.

LABORATORY STUDIES OF THE SAIMIRI-HAEMAGOGUS CYCLE OF JUNGLE YELLOW FEVER. Marston Bates, Manuel Roca-Garcia. Amer. Jour. Trop. Medicine, Baltimore, vol.25, no.3, pp.203-216, figs. 2, May, 1945.

MAMMALIAN HOST IN YELLOW FEVER. John C. Bugher. In "Yellow Fever," edited by George K. Strode, McGraw-Hill Book Co., New York, pp.299-425, illus., 1951.

PROGRESS OF SYLVAN YELLOW FEVER WAVE IN CENTRAL AMERICA: NICARAGUA AND HONDURAS. Norman W. Elton. Amer. Jour. Public Health, Albany, vol.42, no.12, pp.1527-1534, Dec., 1952.

YELLOW FEVER IMMUNE BODIES IN THE BLOOD OF AFRICAN ANIMALS. G. M. Fintlay, and others. Trans. Royal Soc. Trop. Medicine & Hygiene, vol.29, no.4, pp.419-424, Jan., 1936.

MAMMALOGY IN AN EPIDEMIOLOGICAL STUDY OF JUNGLE YELLOW FEVER IN BRAZIL. Raymond M. Gilmore. Jour. Mamm., Baltimore, vol.24, no.2, pp.144-162, figs.4, pls.2, May, 1943.

## DISTRIBUTION see GEOGRAPHICAL DISTRIBUTION

## DOMESTICATION

(OUTLINE OF A HISTORY OF THE ORIGIN OF DOMESTIC ANIMALS.) Grundzuege einer Stammes-Geschichte der Haustiere. O. Antonius. Jena, Fischer, pp.337, figs.144, 1922.

(SUB-FOSSIL DOMESTIC HORSES AND OXEN.) Chevaux et boeufs domestiques sub-fossiles. Gaston Astre. Bull. Soc. Hist. Nat. Toulouse, vol.75, pp.227-232, Dec. 30, 1940.

DOGS, CATS AND OTHER PETS. William O. Bates. London and New York, Butterick Publishing Co., Ltd., pp.56, illus., 1896; Metropolitan pamphlet series, vol.IX, no.1.

WILD ANIMAL PETS. Belle J. Benchley. San Diego Zoonooz, vol.21, no.8, pp.3-7, illus., Aug., 1948.

WILD ANIMAL PETS. Belle J. Benchley. Zoonooz, Zool. Soc. San Diego, vol.12, no.7, pp.4, 6, July, 1940.

NATURALIZATION OF ANIMALS, WITH SPECIAL REFERENCE TO SOUTH AFRICA. R. Bigalke. S. African Jour. Sci., Johannesburg, vol.33, pp.44-63, Mar., 1937.

PROBLEM OF THE ORIGIN OF DOMESTIC ANIMALS. S. Bogoliubsky. Trudy Lab. Genet., Akad. Nauk, Leningrad, USSR, vol.1, pp.13-54, figs.7, tbl.1, 1933.

PROBLEM OF EVOLUTIONARY MORPHOLOGY OF THE DOMESTIC ANIMALS. S. Bogoliubsky. Bull. Acad. Sci. USSR, cl. sci. math. et nat., ser. biol. Moscow, nos.2-3, pp.317-374, figs.27, 1936. (In Russian, with English summary.)

CONTRIBUTION TO THE INVESTIGATION OF DOMESTIC ANIMALS IN USSR FROM THE POINT OF VIEW OF NATURAL HISTORY AND ESPECIALLY OF OSTEOLOGY. A. H. Brauner. Trudy Lab. Genet., Akad. Nauk, Leningrad, USSR, vol.1, pp.109-156, 1933.

DOMESTIC ANIMALS. Daniel Jay Browne. U.S. Patent Office, Report, Agriculture, 1853, pp.1-58, Washington, 1854.

ARCHEOLOGY AND THE DOMESTICATION OF ANIMALS IN THE OLD WORLD. Robert H. Dyson, Jr. Amer. Anthropologist, vol.55, no.5, pt.1, pp.661-673, Dec., 1953.

WILD ANIMAL PETS. William Finley, Irene Finley. Charles Scribner's Sons, vol.8, pp. XIV-311, pls.47, Apr., 1928.

(Review by Hartley H. T. Jackson of ) WILD ANIMAL PETS, William Finley, Irene Finley. Jour. Mamm., vol.9, no.3, pp.257-258, Aug., 1928.

DOMESTICATED ANIMALS OF SHANG AND THEIR SACRIFICE. H. E. Gibson. Jour. N. China Roy. Asiat. Soc. 1938, Shanghai, vol. 68, pp.9-22, figs.30, 1939.

STORY OF DOMESTIC ANIMALS IN AMERICA. NEARLY ALL THE ANIMALS VITAL TO THE GROWTH OF THIS CONTINENT FROM THE SHEEP TO JEFFERSON DAVIS'S CAMEL CORPS, WERE IMPORTATIONS. George G. Goodwin. Natural History, New York, vol.38, no.5, pp.403-407, Dec., 1936.

MY STRANGE PETS OF THE YUKON. Jean Gordon. Alaska Sportsman, Ketchikan, vol.9, no.1, pp.8-9; 28-30, no.2, pp.12-13, 18, 21-24, illus., Jan.- Feb., 1943.

PART OF PALEOZOOLOGY IN THE STUDY OF THE ORIGIN OF DOMESTIC ANIMALS. V. I. Gromova. Trudy Lab. Genet., Akad. Nauk, Leningrad, USSR, vol.1, pp.55-62, 1933.

PERUVIAN PETS. Hilda Hempl Heller. Nat. Hist., vol.24, pp.479-493, figs.14, July-Aug., 1924.

(NATURAL RACE HISTORY OF DOMESTIC MAMMALS.) Natuerliche Rassengeschichte der Haussaeugetiere. Max Hilzheimer. Berlin, Walter de Gruyter and Co., 1926.

DOMESTICATION OF ANIMALS. Walter Hough. Scientific Monthly, vol.39, pp. 144-150, Aug., 1934.

(METHODS AND PROBLEMS OF SEMEN TRANSMISSION WITH DOMESTIC MAMMALS.) Methode und Probleme der Samenuebertragung bei Haussaeugetieren. J. Huhn. Zeitschr. f. Saeugetierk., Berlin, vol.22, nos.3-4, pp.136-150, 1957.

DISTRIBUTION OF DOMESTIC ANIMALS. Ellsworth Huntington. Econ. Geog., vol. 1, no.2, pp.143-172, July (Aug.), 1925.

DERIVATION OF THE EUROPEAN DOMESTIC ANIMALS. Konrad Keller. Smiths. Inst., Annual Rep., 1912, Washington, pp. 483-491, 1913. (Translated from "Verhandlungen des VIII. Internationalen zoologenkongresses in Graz", Aug. 15-20, 1910, pp. 356-365, Jena, 1912.)

THE DOMESTIC ANIMALS OF MONGOLIA. A REVIEW. D. Kislovsky. Jour. Heredity, vol.29, no.1, pp.27-32, figs.10-13, Jan., 1938.

(DOMESTIC ANIMAL AND MAN.) Haustier und Mensch. Berthold Klatt. Richard Hermes Verlag, Hamburg, pp.1-95, figs. 33, 1948.

(MENDELISM, DOMESTICATION, AND CRANIOLOGY.) Mendelismus, Domestikation und Kraniologie. Berthold Klatt. Archiv f. Anthrop., n.F., vol.18, nos. 3-4, pp.225-250, text figs.4, 1921.

(ON SOUTH AMERICAN DOMESTIC ANIMALS (I).) Ueber suedamerikanische Haustiere I. Hans Krieg. Zool. Garten, n.f., vol.1, pp.273-284, pls.1-7, 1929.

PARASITIC ANIMALS AND THE WORLD'S FOOD. G. Lapage. Endeavour, London, vol.7, no.25, pp.27-31, Jan., 1948.

(DOMESTICATED ANIMALS OF PRE-COLUMBIAN AMERICA.) Los animales domesticos de la America precolombiana. Richard E. Latcham. Publ. Mus. Etnol. y Antrop de Chile, vol.3, pp.1-199, 1922.

(PRINCIPLES OF BREEDING DOMESTIC ANIMALS.) Principes de l'elevage des animaux domestiques. James Law. Bull. Soc. Roy. Linneenne, Bruxelles, pp.1-21, 1874.

CAUSE OF DOMESTICATION. W. L. McAtee. Science, Lancaster, n.s., vol.96, no.2488, p.231, Sep. 4, 1942.

(THE ESSENCE OF DOMESTICATION.) Vom Wesen der Domestikation. Hans Nachtsheim. Der Biologe, vol.7, no.10, pp.321-329, Oct., 1938.

(OLD PERUVIAN DOMESTIC ANIMALS.) Ueber alt-peruanische Hausthiere. A. Nehring. Congr. Internat. Americanistes, Compte-Rendu 7th Sess, Berlin, 1888, pp. 308-321, pl.3, 1890.

DOMESTIC MAMMALS. E. Laurence Palmer. Nature Magazine, Washington, D.C., vol.32, no.10, pp.565-572, illus., Dec., 1939.

(ON THE PROBLEM OF THE REGISTRATION OF ANIMAL STOCKS.) Zur Frage der Tierbestands-Registriering. H. B. Peters. Zool.Garten, n.f., Leipzig, vol.6, nos.7-9, pp.192-196, Oct., 1933.

BOOK OF WILD PETS. Clifford B. Moore. Boston, pp.565, photos 214, drawings 128, 1954.

(ON THE HISTORY OF THE OLDEST DOMESTIC ANIMALS.) Zur Geschichte der aeltesten Haustiere. August Otto. Breslau, pp.78, 1889.

BREEDING AND IMPROVEMENT OF FARM ANIMALS. Victor Arthur Rice, Frederick Newcomb Andrews. McGraw-Hill Co., New York, pp.787, illus., 1951. (Fourth edition.)

(CONTRIBUTION TO KNOWLEDGE OF THE DOMESTIC ANIMALS OF THE PEAT BOGS OF THE GARDA.) Contributo alla conoscenza degli animali domestici delle torbiere del Garda. Alfredo Riedel. Mem. Mus. Civico Storia Nat. Verona, vol.5, pp.61-88, pls.1-7, Dec. 15, 1955.

FROM DOGS TO HORSES AMONG THE WESTERN INDIAN TRIBES. F. G. Roe. Trans. Roy. Soc. Canada, Ottawa, sec.2, ser.3, vol.33, pp.209-275, May, 1939.

COMMENSALISM AND DOMESTICATION. Ernst Schwarz. Amer. Naturalist, Lancaster, Pa., vol.73, no.746, pp.270-278, May-June, 1939.

(ON THE PRESENCE OF DWARF BOVINES NEAR BERLIN AROUND 1810 AND ON A REMARKABLE CHARACTERISTIC OF THE MACEDONIAN HORSE.) Ueber das Vorkommen von Zwergrindern bei Berlin um 1810 und ueber eine merkwuerdige Eigentuemlichkeit mazedonischer Pferde. Paul Schulze. Sitz.-ber. u. Abhandl. Naturforsch. Gesellschaft Rostock (3), vol.2, pp.5-8, pl.1, (1927-29) 1930.

(MAN'S UNSUCCESSFUL DOMESTIC ANIMAL BREEDING.) Zu Grunde gegangene Haustierzuchten des Menschen. E. Stechow. Zool. Anzeiger, Supplement band, vol.1, pp.173-177, 1925.

ECONOMIC UTILIZATION OF WILDLIFE THROUGH PARTIAL, OR COMPLETE DOMESTICATION. Vilhjalmur Stefansson. Trans. 14th North Amer. Wildlife Conf., Washington, pp.31-35, 1949.

NATURALIZED ANIMALS AND PLANTS. Geo. M. Thomson. New Zealand Jour. of Sci. and Tech., vol.6, pp.223-231, Dec., 1923.

TAME OR FAMILIAR? Frank Thone. Science News Letter, Washington, D.C., vol.50, no.4, p.62, July 27, 1946.

(MAMMALS THAT CAN BE ACCLIMATIZED OR DOMESTICATED IN FRANCE OR THE FRENCH COLONIES.) Les mammiferes a acclimater ou a domestiquer en France ou dans les Colonies Francaises. E. L. Trouessart. Bull. Soc. Nat. Acclimat.France, Paris, pp.1-22, 1899-1900.

PART OF SOVIET SCIENCE IN STUDYING THE PROBLEM OF THE ORIGIN OF DOMESTIC ANIMALS. N.I. Vavilov. Trudy Lab. Genet., Akad. Nauk, Leningrad, USSR, vol.1, pp.5-12, 1933.

SCIENTIFIC PROCESSES FOR THE IMPROVEMENT OF FARM ANIMALS. L.M. Winters. Sci. Monthly, Lancaster, vol. 69, no.3, pp.197-200, figs.3, Sep., 1949.

DOMESTICATION OF ANIMALS. Clark Wissler. Nat. Hist., New York, vol.54, no.5, pp.200-206, illus., May, 1945.

(RACE CONCEPT IN ITS GENETIC AND HISTORICAL SIGNIFICANCE AS REGARDS OUR DOMESTIC ANIMALS.) Der Rassenbegriff fuer unsere Haustiere in genetischer und historischer Bedeutung. Chr. Wriedt. Zeitschr. f. Ind. Abstammungs- u. Vererbungslehre, vol.46, pp.208-228, figs. 20, 1928.

DOMESTICATED ANIMALS INHABITING DESERT AREAS. Norman C. Wright. In Biology of Deserts edited by J. L. Cloudsley-Thompson, Inst. of Biology, London, pp.168-172, 1954.

GI PETS - SOME ARE ALIENS. Outdoor Indiana, Indianapolis, vol.12, no.4, pp. 2-3, illus., May-June, 1945.

SOME MAMMALS TAMED BY MAN. Mus. News, Univ. S. Dakota, Vermillion, vol. 10, no.4, Jan., 1949.

THEY WORK FOR A LIVING. Jr. Nat. Hist. Mag., New York, vol.7, no.9, pp.4-7, illus., Nov., 1942.

## ECOLOGY

JUNGLE DROUGHT. W. G. Adam. Country Life, London, vol.72, no.1872, pp.636-638, photos 5, Dec. 3, 1932.

ECOLOGICAL CONDITIONS IN NATIONAL FORESTS AND NATIONAL PARKS. Charles C. Adams. Sci. Monthly, vol.20, pp.561-593, illus., June, 1925.

GUIDE TO THE STUDY OF ANIMAL ECOLOGY. Charles C. Adams. Macmillan Co., pp.xii-183, 1913.

NOTE FOR SOCIAL-MINDED ECOLOGISTS AND GEOGRAPHERS. Charles C. Adams. Ecology, vol.19, no.3, pp.500-502, July, 1938.

OUTLINE OF THE RELATIONS OF ANIMALS TO THEIR INLAND ENVIRONMENTS. Charles C. Adams. Smiths. Inst., Annual Rep., 1917, Washington, pp.515-542, 1919. (Reprinted from the Bull. of the Ill. State Lab. of Nat. Hist., vol.11, pp.1-32, 1915.)

PATTERN OF WILDLIFE DISTRIBUTION FITS THE SOIL PATTERN. Wm. A. Albrecht. Missouri Conservationist, Jefferson City, vol.4, no.3, pp.1-3, 16, June, 1943; N. Dakota Outdoors, Bismarck, vol.7, no.7, pp.12-14, Jan., 1945.

PRINCIPLES OF ANIMAL ECOLOGY. W.C. Allee, Alfred E. Emerson, Orlando Park, Thomas Park, Karl P. Schmidt. W.B. Saunders, Philadelphia and London, pp.xii-837, illus., Oct., 1949.

IMPORTANCE OF ECOLOGY IN THE INTERPRETATION OF FOSSIL FAUNAS. Frank Collins Baker. Ecology, vol.2, pp. 277-280, Oct., 1921. (Jan. 20, 1922.)

ROLE OF ICE IN THE DISTRIBUTION OF MAMMALS. A. W. F. Banfield. Jour. Mamm., vol.35, no.1, pp.104-107, Feb. 10, 1954.

ENVIRONMENTAL ANALYSIS OF FOREST EDGES IN RELATION TO WILDLIFE. Frank B. Barick. Trans. 10th Amer. Wildl. Conf., Washington, pp.126-136, 1945.

ECOLOGICAL RELATIONSHIPS BETWEEN THE WOODCHUCK, MARMOTA M. MONAX, AND THE COTTONTAIL, SYLVILAGUS FLORIDANUS MEARNSII: THEIR LIFE HISTORY AND MANAGEMENT. John D. Beule. MS thesis, Pa. State Coll., 1940.

SOME OBSERVED EFFECTS OF STREAM-VALLEY FLOODING ON MAMMALIAN POPULATIONS IN EASTERN OKLAHOMA. W. Frank Blair. Jour. Mamm., vol.20, no.3, pp.304-306, Aug. 14, 1939.

COMPARISON OF THE ANIMAL COMMUNITIES OF CONIFEROUS AND DECIDUOUS FORESTS. Irving H. Blake. Illinois Biol. Mon., vol.10, no.4, pp.7-147, pls. 1-16, tbls.25, Oct., 1926.

FURTHER STUDIES ON DECIDUOUS FOREST ANIMAL COMMUNITIES. Irving H. Blake. Ecology, vol.12, no.3, pp.508-527, July, 1931.

PROBLEMS OF ANIMAL ECOLOGY. F.S. Bodenheimer. London, Oxford Univ.Press, 1938.

(A FIGHT BETWEEN GIANTS.) En kamp mellen giganter. Karl Borg. Svensk Jakt, Stockholm, vol.86, no.10, p.257, Oct. 17, 1948.

(ROLE OF SPRING FLOODS IN THE ECOLOGY OF MAMMALS.) Rol vesennego pavodka v ekologii mlekoputayuschix poimennex biotopov. L. P. Borodin. Zool. Journ., Akad. Nauk USSR, Moscow, vol.30, no.6, pp.607-615, 1951.

(CLASSIFICATION AND CHARACTERISTICS OF THE PRINCIPAL TYPES OF SOCIAL GROUPINGS IN WILD VERTEBRATES.) Classification et caracteristiques des principaux types de groupements sociaux chez les Vertébrés sauvages. F. Bourliere. In Structure et physiologie des sociétés animals, Paris, pp.71-79, Mar., 1950 (1952).

SOME BIOLOGICAL EFFECTS OF DITCHING TIDEWATER MARSHES. Warren S. Bourn, Clarence Cottam. Res. Rept., U.S. Fish and Wildl. Service, Washington, no.19, pp. 30, illus., maps 7, 1950.

FIRE AND ITS EFFECT ON WILD LIFE. Lee P. Brown. Jour. Mamm., vol.4, no.3, pp.195-196, Aug., 1923.

FIGHTS BETWEEN INDIAN WILD ANIMALS. R. G. Burton. Field, London, vol.150, p. 395, Sep. 8, 1927.

WILD ANIMALS AND FIRE. R. G. Burton. Field, London, vol.151, p.338, Feb. 23, 1928.

RECORD OF FRUITS AND SEEDS DISPERSED BY MAMMALS AND BIRDS FROM THE SINGIDA DISTRICT OF TANGANYIKA TERRITORY. B. D. Burtt. Jour. Ecol., vol. 17, no.2, pp.351-355, Aug., 1929.

SOME RACCOON AND GROUNDHOG RELATIONSHIPS. Robert T. Butterfield. Jour. Wildl. Mgt., Ithaca, vol.18, no.4, pp.433-437, Oct., 1954.

(AN INTERESTING BIOLOGICAL LAW: ECOLOGICAL INCOMPATIBILITY.) La incompatibilidad ecológica una ley biológica interesante. Angel Cabrera. Anales Soc. Cient. Argentina, Buenos Aires, vol. 114, pp.243-260, 1932.

WILDLIFE AND MAN. G. Clifford Carl. Victoria Nat., vol.1, no.1, pp.5-6, 1944.

TEMPERATURE AS AN ECOLOGICAL FACTOR IN ANIMALS. Royal N. Chapman. Amer. Nat., vol.62, pp.298-310, July, 1928.

ECOLOGY, EVOLUTION, AND DISTRIBUTION OF THE VERTEBRATES. Austin H. Clark. Ann. Rept. Smiths. Inst., Washington, 1952, publ.4111, pp.283-303, 1953.

RELATION OF SMALL MAMMALS TO AVAILABILITY OF NORTHERN WHITE CEDAR FOR DEER BROWSE. Eldon R. Clark. MS thesis, Univ. Maine, 1942.

INTERESTING CORN SHOCK FAUNA. C. H. D. Clarke. Canadian Field-Nat., Ottawa, vol.53, no.4, p.60, Apr. 15, 1939.

SOME VARIATIONS IN GROUPING AND DOMINANCE PATTERNS AMONG BIRDS AND MAMMALS. N. E. Collias. Zoologica, New York, vol.35, pt.2, pp.97-119, illus., Aug. 1, 1950.

RELATIONSHIPS OF SOIL AND WILDLIFE. Bill Crawford. Wildlife and the Soil, Circ. Missouri Conserv. Comm., no.134, pp. 10-18, illus., Aug., 1949.

SOME SPECIFIC RELATIONSHIPS BETWEEN SOILS AND WILDLIFE. Bill Crawford. Jour. Wildl. Mgt., Menasha, vol.14, no.2, pp. 115-123, Apr., 1950.

INTERSPECIFIC COMPETITION. A. C. Crombile. Jour. Animal Ecol., London, vol. 16, no.1, pp.44-73, illus., May, 1947.

WILDLIFE RELATIONSHIPS TO SOIL TYPES. Arthur H. Denney. Trans. 9th N. Amer. Wildl. Conf., Washington, pp.316-323, fig.1, 1944.

BIOTIC AREAS AND ECOLOGIC HABITATS AS UNITS FOR THE STATEMENT OF ANIMAL AND PLANT DISTRIBUTION. Lee R. Dice. Science, vol.55, no.1422, pp.4, Mar. 31, 1922.

DISTRIBUTION AND ROLE OF MAMMALS IN CLIMAX COMMUNITIES. Lee R. Dice Carnegie Inst. of Washington, Yearbook no. 24(1925), pp.339-340, 1926.

LIFE ZONES AND MAMMALIAN DISTRIBUTION. Lee R. Dice. Jour. Mamm., vol.4, no.1, pp.39-47, Feb., 1923.

NATURAL COMMUNITIES. Lee R. Dice. Ann Arbor, Univ. of Michigan Press, X plus 547 pp., illus., 1952.

OCCURRENCE OF TWO SUBSPECIES OF THE SAME SPECIES IN THE SAME AREA. Lee R. Dice. Jour. Mamm., vol.12, no.3, pp.210-213, Aug., 1931.

RELATION OF MAMMALIAN DISTRIBUTION TO VEGETATION TYPES. Lee R. Dice. Scientific Monthly, vol.33, pp. 312-317, Oct., 1931.

WHAT IS ECOLOGY? Lee R. Dice. Sci. Monthly, Lancaster, vol.80, no.6, pp. 346-351, June, 1955.

EVIDENCE OF INTERRELATION BETWEEN FOX AND CARIBOU. Donald R. Dickey. Jour. Mamm., vol.4, no.2, pp.121-122, May, 1923.

STRANGE ANIMAL FRIENDSHIPS. Frank J. Dobie. Nature Mag., Washington, vol. 38, no.1, pp.9-12, illus., Jan., 1945; S. Dakota Cons. Digest, Pierre, vol.12, no. 2, pp.2-3, 15, Feb., 1945.

(Review by W. Robert Eadie of) NATURAL COMMUNITIES, Lee R. Dice. Jour. Mamm., vol.34, no.2, pp.272-274, May 14, 1953.

EFFECT OF REFORESTATION ON GAME. Frank C. Edminster. Trans. 21st Amer. Game Conf, 1935, Amer. Game Assoc., New York, pp.313-318, 1935.

FIRE - FISH AND WILDLIFE. Bob Elliot. Hunting and Fishing, Philadelphia, vol.25, no.2, pp.48-49, Feb., 1948.

EFFECT OF STORM ON ANIMALS. B.C. Ellison. Jour. Bombay Nat. Hist. Soc., vol.28, p.1126, Dec. 20, 1922.

ANIMAL ECOLOGY. Charles Elton. London, Sidwick and Jackson Ltd., pp.xxi-207, pls.8, 1927; New York, Macmillan Co., pp.xxx-209, figs.13, 1939.

ECOLOGY OF INVASIONS BY ANIMALS AND PLANTS. Charles Elton. Oxford Univ., pp.181, illus., 1958.

INDIVIDUALS AND COMMUNITIES - A BIOLOGIST'S VIEW. Francis C. Evans. Michigan Alumnus Quarterly Review, vol. 58, no.21, pp.297-299, Aug. 9, 1952.

SOME OBSERVATIONS RELATIVE TO METEOROLOGICAL INFLUENCES. J. D. Figgins. Proc. Colorado Mus. Nat Hist., vol.5, no.2, pp.13-21, July 20, 1925.

ANIMALS AND BIRDS IN AIR RAIDS. James Fisher. Field, London, vol.177, no.4594, p.60, Jan. 11, 1941.

TWENTY-FOUR HOUR RHYTHMS OF MAMMALS IN A COLD ENVIRONMENT. G. E. Folk, Jr. American Naturalist, vol.91, no. 858, pp.153-166, May-June, 1957.

FOREST NEIGHBORS. Robert H. Forbes. Living Wilderness, Washington, vol.11, no.16, pp.25-28, illus., Mar., 1946.

MAMMALIA IN THE STEPPE BIOCENOSE. A. N. Formosov. Ecology, vol.9, no.4, pp.449-460, Oct., 1928.

SNOW COVERING AS AN ENVIRONMENT FACTOR AND ITS IMPORTANCE IN THE ECOLOGY OF MAMMALS AND BIRDS. A. N. Formosov. Bull. Soc. Nat. Moscow, sect. biol. n.s., vol.48, no.4, pp.60-69, 1939. (In English, with Russian resume.)

PINCH PERIOD. Charles Friley. Michigan Conserv., Lansing, vol.23, no.1, pp.29-30, Jan., 1954.

CARDINAL PRINCIPLES OF ECOLOGY. W. F. Ganong. Science, n.s., vol.19, no.482, pp.493-498, Mar. 25, 1904.

DEER-ELK-BEAR INVESTIGATIONS. Paul F. Gilbert. Quart. Prog. Rept. Colorado Dept. Game & Fish, Denver, pp.55-84, illus., Apr., 1950.

THE LAND AND WILDLIFE. Edward H. Graham. Oxford Univ. Press, New York City, pp.232, illus., 1947.

REDWOOD FORESTS, A WILDLIFE HABITAT. Hilda Wood Grinnell. Audubon Nat. Bull., New York, vol.19, no.2, pp.1-4, illus., Oct., 1948.

PRESENCE AND ABSENCE OF ANIMALS. Joseph Grinnell. Univ. Cal. Chronicle, pp.427-450, Oct., 1928.

DEVELOPMENT OF ECOLOGY AND ITS RELATIONSHIP TO PALEONTOLOGY. Gordon Gunter. Texas Jour. Sci., vol.5, no.2, pp.137-147, June, 1953.

HISTORIC FOREST FIRES OF AMERICA. John D. Guthrie. Amer. Forests, Washington, D.C., vol.49, no.6, pp.290-294, 316-317, illus., June, 1943.

SMALL MAMMALS TRAPPED BY PLANTS. W. J. Hamilton, Jr. Jour. Mamm., vol. 20, no.1, p.110, Feb. 14, 1939.

WHERE DO ANIMALS GO IN WINTER-TIME? W. J. Hamilton, Jr. Animal Kingdom, New York Zool. Soc., vol.58, no.6, pp. 170-175, illus., Dec., 1955.

PREDATORS, RODENTS AND SOIL. Ross Hardy. Wyoming Wild Life, Cheyenne, vol. 10, no.4, pp.29-30, illus., Apr., 1946.

LIVESTOCK AND BIG GAME ON NATIONAL FORESTS. E. S. Haskell. Natl. Wool Grower, vol.36, no.8, pp.12-13, 52, Aug., 1946.

WHEN WINTER COMES TO THE MAMMAL WORLD. Robert T. Hatt. Natural History, vol.31, no.5, pp.519-529, illus., Sep.-Oct., 1931.

SMALL MAMMAL RELATIONSHIPS IN AN EPHEDRA COMMUNITY. Albert C. Hawbecker. Jour. Mamm., vol.32, no.1, pp.50-60, pls.2, Feb. 15, 1951.

REACTIONS OF ANIMALS TO CHANGES IN PHYSICAL ENVIRONMENT. I. ANIMAL AND EARTHQUAKE. H. V. Hentig. Jour. Comp. Psychol., vol.3, pp.61-71, 1923.

GAME AND PREDATORS ON A GAME PRESERVE. Robert J. Higgins. Game Breeder and Sportsman, New York, vol. 51, no.9, p.100, Nov.-Dec., 1946.

SOME WILDLIFE-FOREST RELATIONSHIPS. E. E. Horn. Trans. 3rd N. Amer. Wildl. Conf., pp.376-380, 1938.

INTERRELATIONS OF RODENTS AND OTHER WILDLIFE OF THE RANGE. E.E. Horn, H. S. Fitch. San Joaquin Experimental Range, Univ. Calif. Coll. Agirc., Agric. Exper. Sta., Bull.663, pp.96-129, illus., Apr., 1942.

OUTLINE FOR AN ECOLOGICAL LIFE HISTORY OF POCKET GOPHERS AND OTHER FOSSORIAL MAMMALS. Walter E. Howard, Lloyd G. Ingles. Ecology, Lancaster, vol.32, no.3, pp.537-544, July, 1951.

APPARENTLY NEUTRAL RELATIONS OF WEASEL AND SQUIRREL. William Johnston Howard. Jour. Mamm., vol.16, no.4, pp. 322-323, Nov., 1935.

POPULATIONS AND HOME RANGES OF SMALL MAMMALS ON AN OVERGROWN FIELD. Joseph C. Howell. Jour. Mamm., vol.35, no.2, pp.177-186, diagrams, May, 1954.

BEHAVIOUR OF SAMBHUR IN THE PRESENCE OF WILD DOGS. T. R. Hubback. Jour. Bombay Nat. Hist. Soc., vol.41, no. 1, p.172, 1939.

ABUNDANCE OF DESERT ANIMALS INDICATED BY CAPTURE IN FRESH ROAD TAR. Carl L. Hubbs, Boyd W. Walker. Ecology, vol.28, no.4, pp.464-466, Oct., 1947.

BATTLE OF MATILIJA CANYON (SANTE BARBARA FOREST, CALIF.). Wallace Hutchinson. Amer. Forests, vol.39, no.1, pp.3-4, 26, Jan.1933.

RODENTS, RABBITS, AND GRASSLAND. E. R. Kalmbach. Grass, Yearbook of Agric., Washington, pp.248-256, 1948.

RELATIONSHIP OF FUR-BEARERS TO OTHER WILDLIFE. George H. Kelker. Bull. Univ. Idaho, vol.33, no.22, (Bull. School Forestry, no.8), pp.80-82, Dec., 1938.

STUDY OF MERRIAM'S TEMPERATURE LAWS. S. Charles Kendeigh. Wilson Bull., vol.44, no.3, pp.129-143, figs.2, 1932.

MAMMAL RELATIONSHIPS TO UPLAND GAME AND OTHER WILDLIFE. E.V. Komarek. Trans. 2nd N. Amer. Wildl. Conf., pp.561-569, 1937.

ROLE OF SOME BIRDS AND MAMMALS IN SEED GERMINATION. Laurits Krefting, Eugene I. Roe. Ecol. Monographs, Durham, vol.19, no.3, pp.269-286, July, 1949.

WILD ANIMALS AND THE LAND. F. Howard Lancum. Crosby Lockwood and Son, Ltd., London, pp.126, pls.29, 1947.

WILD ANIMALS AND THE LAND. F. Howard Lancum. Bull. Ministry Agric. & Fisheries, London, no.150, pp.60, illus., 1951.

(DOCUMENTS ON THE ETHOLOGY OF THE MAMMALS.) Documents pour l'ethologie des mammifères. F. Lataste. Bordeaux, pp.659, 1887. Reprinted from Actes Soc. Linn. Bordeaux, Vols. 40, 41, 43.

ECOLOGICAL NICHES FOR WARM-BLOODED VERTEBRATE ANIMALS. Jean M. Linsdale. Wasmann Jour. Biol., vol. 15, no.1, pp.107-122, Spring, 1957.

ENVIRONMENTAL RESPONSES OF VERTEBRATES IN THE GREAT BASIN. Jean M. Linsdale. Amer. Midland Nat., Notre Dame, vol.19, no.1, pp.1-206, figs.12, Jan., 1938.

INSECT INHABITANTS OF BIRDS AND MAMMAL NESTS. E. Gorton Linsley. Jour. Wildl. Mgt., Menasha, vol.7, no.4, p.423, Oct., 1943.

DRAMAS OF THE WILD. Leo A. Luttringer, Jr. Penna. Game News, New Cumberland, vol.10, no.5, pp.12-15, illus., Aug. 1939.

EFFECTS OF STORMS ON WILDLIFE. H. Elliott McClure. Nature Notes, Peoria, vol.9, nos.3-4, pp.43-45, Mar.-Apr., 1942.

WILDLIFE CAN TAKE IT. Ken Martin. Wyoming Wild Life, Cheyenne, vol.11, no.5, p.26, May, 1947.

ONE OF THE POSSIBLE APPLICATIONS OF THE ECOLOGICAL PRINCIPLE OF BERGMAN. V. E. Martino. Zapiski Russkago Nauchnago Inst. Belgrade, no.12, pp. 95-97, 1935. ( In Bulgarian, with English summary.)

DEER VS. WILDCAT. D. A. Miller. Yosemite Nature Notes, vol.25, no.2, p.56, Feb., 1946.

INSTANCE OF LOCAL TEMPERATURE CONTROL OF THE DISTRIBUTION OF MAMMALS. Gerrit S. Miller, Jr. Science, n.s., vol.8, no.201, pp.615-618, Nov. 4, 1898.

CURIOUS COMPANIONSHIP BETWEEN PANTHER AND WILD BOAR. J.Monteath. Jour. Bombay Nat. Hist. Soc., vol.39, no.1, pp.157-158, Dec., 1936.

PREY CHASES PREDATOR. George C. Moore. Jour. Mamm., vol.22, no.2, p. 198, May 14, 1941.

LIGHT PENETRATION IN RELATION TO SMALL MAMMAL ABUNDANCE. Archie S. Mossman. Jour. Mamm., vol.36, no.4, pp.564-566, fig.1, Dec. 14, 1955.

WILDLIFE PREPARES FOR WINTER. W.O. Nagel. Missouri Conservationist, Jefferson City, vol.5, no.1, pp.4-5, 14-15, illus., Jan., 1944.

TRANSITION ZONES. J. T. Nichols. Science, n.s., vol.58, pp.153-155, Aug. 31, 1923.

EFFECT OF RODENTS, RABBITS, AND CATTLE ON TWO VEGETATION TYPES IN SEMIDESERT RANGE LAND. J. J. Norris. Bull. New Mexico Agric. Expt. Sta., no.353, p.23, illus., Jan., 1950.

BATTLE OF WITS. William Nyquist. Yellowstone Nat. Notes, Yellowstone Park, vol.18, nos.3-4, pp.16-17, Mar.-Apr., 1941.

FUNDAMENTALS OF ECOLOGY. Eugene P. Odum. W. B. Saunders, Philadelphia, pp.443, illus., 1953.

DUEL IN THE DEEP WOODS. Dale O'Hara. Forest and Outdoors, Montreal, vol.6, no. 3, p.96, Mar., 1940.

OBSERVATIONS CONCERNING THE FUTURE OF ECOLOGY. Orlando Park. Ecology, Lancaster, vol.26, no.1, pp.1-9, Jan., 1945.

EFFECTS OF BURNING-OVER AND RAKING-OFF LITTER ON CERTAIN SOIL ANIMALS IN THE DUKE FOREST. A. S. Pearse. Amer. Midland Nat., Notre Dame, vol.29, no.2, pp.406-424, Mar., 1943.

EFFECTS OF ENVIRONMENT ON ANIMALS. A. S. Pearse. Amer. Nat., vol.56, pp.144-158, Apr., 1922.

LIFE ZONES, BIOMES, OR LIFE FORMS? Roger T. Peterson. Audubon Mag., Harrisburg, vol.44, no.1, pp.21-36, illus., Jan.-Feb., 1942.

RELATIONS OF HEDGEROWS IN WINTER TO WILDLIFE IN CENTRAL NEW YORK. George A. Petrides. Jour. Wildl. Mgt., Menasha, vol.6, no.4, pp.261-280, pls. 21-22, Oct., 1942.

NATURAL REPLACEMENT OF WEED HOSTS OF THE BEET LEAFHOPPER AS AFFECTED BY RODENTS. R. L. Piemeisel. USDA, Cir.739, p.48, Dec., 1945.

WILD LIFE PREPARES FOR WINTER. Frances Pitt. Field, London, vol.162, no.4218, p.1095, illus., Oct. 28, 1933.

WEATHER AND WILD LIFE. Earl L. Poole. Frontiers, Philadelphia, vol.2, no. 4, pp.111-114, illus., Apr., 1938.

ON "SAVSSATS": A CROWDING OF ARCTIC ANIMALS AT HOLES IN THE SEA ICE. Morten P. Porsild. Geogr. Rev., New York, vol.6, no.3, pp.215-228, figs.7, Sep., 1918.

WILDLIFE COMMUNITY. Richard H. Pough. Audubon Mag., New York, vol.46, no.3, pp.160-166, illus., May-June, 1944.

FORESTRY IN RELATION TO GAME. George D. Pratt. Amer. Forests and Forest Life, vol.35, pp.323-326, illus., June, 1929.

APPLIED ECOLOGY OF PREDATION ON LIVESTOCK RANGES. C. C. Presnall. Jour. Mamm., vol.29, no.2, pp.155-161, illus., May 14, 1948.

PORCUPINE DAMAGE TO BIGHORN SHEEP. Alvert Van S. Pulling. Jour. Wildl. Mgt., Menasha, vol.9, no.4, p.329, Oct., 1945.

COMPARISON OF OVERWINTERING POPULATIONS OF SMALL MAMMALS IN A NORTHERN CONIFEROUS FOREST FOR TWO CONSECUTIVE YEARS. Don C. Quimby. Jour. Mamm., vol.25, no.1, pp. 86-87, Feb., 1944.

MOLE SHREWS VERSUS MOLE MICE. Samuel N. Rhoads. The American Friend, pp.62-63, Jan. 21, 1897.

FACTORS IN WILDLIFE POPULATIONS. William Marshall Rush. Amer. Forests, Washington, D.C., vol.47, no.10, pp. 473-475, Oct., 1941.

(ECOLOGICAL FACTORS IN THE DAILY CYCLE OF ACTIVITY IN SOME SMALL MAMMALS.) Les factures ecologiques du cycle journalier d'activite chez quelques petits mammiferes francais. Saint Girons. Mammalia, Paris, vol.21, no.3, pp.197-209, Sep., 1957.

TEAMWORK IN NATURE. Ivan T.Sanderson. Nature Mag., Washington, D.C., vol.37, no.6, pp.302-304, 333, illus., June-July, 1944.

A MINK-MUSKRAT INCIDENT. Edmund J. Sawyer. Murrelet, Seattle, vol.27, no.1, pp. 2-3, illus., Apr. 30, 1946.

BURROW ASSOCIATIONS OF SMALL MAMMALS. Theo H. Scheffer. Murrelet, Seattle, vol.26, no.2, pp.24-26, May-Aug. (Aug. 10), 1945.

OUTLINE FOR ECOLOGICAL LIFE HISTORY STUDIES OF MARINE MAMMALS. Victor B. Scheffer. Ecology, New York, vol.33, no.2, pp.287-296, Apr., 1952.

EFFECTS OF A SEVERE SNOW AND ICE STORM ON GAME POPULATIONS IN TENNESSEE. Vincent Schultz. Jour. Tennessee Acad. Sci., vol.29, no.1, pp.24-35, Jan., 1954.

BIG GAME AND LIVESTOCK ON THE WESTERN RANGE. H. E. Schwan. 10th Trans. N. Amer. Wildl. Conf., pp.219-224, 1945.

STRANGE ANIMAL FRIENDSHIPS. D.Seth-Smith. Field, London, vol.163, no.4240, p.687, illus., Mar. 31, 1934.

LABORATORY AND FIELD ECOLOGY. THE RESPONSES OF ANIMALS AS INDICATORS OF CORRECT WORKING METHODS. Victor E. Shelford. Williams and Wilkins Co., Baltimore, pp.12-608, figs.219, bibliogr., 1929.

PRAIRIES AGAIN. B. Shimek. Science, n.s., vol.68, pp.321-323, Oct. 5, 1928.

APPROACH TO THE PALEOECOLOGY OF MAMMALS. J. Arnold Shotwell. Ecology, Durham, vol.36, no.2, pp.327-337, illus., Apr., 1955.

ON THE INFLUENCE OF CLIMATIC VARIATIONS OF RECENT DECADES OF GAME ECONOMY. Lauri Siivonen. Fennia, pp.77, illus., 1952.

RELATIONSHIP OF FOREST WILD LIFE TO PINE REPRODUCTION. Clarence F. Smith. Jour. Wildl. Mgt., Menasha, vol. 7, no.1, pp.124-125, Jan., 1943.

FRIENDSHIP BETWEEN FOX AND CARIBOU. H. A. P. Smith. Jour. Mamm., vol.4, no.2, pp.122-123, May, 1923.

ANIMAL COMMUNITIES OF A DECIDUOUS FOREST SUCCESSION. V. G. Smith. Ecology, vol.9, no.4, pp.479-500, figs.4, Oct., 1928.

BATTLE ROYAL BETWEEN TIGERS AND AN ELEPHANT. E. A. Smythies. Jour. Bombay Nat. Hist. Soc., vol.41, no.3, pp.654-655, Apr., 1940.

(Review by Dana Paul Snyder of) PRINCIPLES OF ANIMAL ECOLOGY, W. C. Alee, Alfred E. Emerson, Orlando Park, Thomas Park, Karl P. Schmidt. Jour. Mamm., vol.31, no. 3, pp.365-367, Aug. 21, 1950.

(MAMMALS AND THE SURROUNDING WORLD.) Saeugetiere und Umwelt. Alexander Sokolowsky. Zeitschr. f. Saeugetierk., vol.2, no.2, pp.29-38, Oct. 15, 1928.

ANIMALS AS MODIFIED BY ENVIRONMENT. J. B. Steere. The Popular Sci. Monthly, vol. 33, pp.243-249, June 1888.

OBSERVATIONS ON THE EFFECT OF FLOOD ON ANIMALS. Lucille F. Stickel. Ecology, Durham, vol.29, no.4, pp.505-506, Oct., 1948.

BIG GAME-RANGE LIVESTOCK COMPETITION ON WESTERN RANGES. L. A. Stoddart, D. I. Rasmussen. 10th Trans. N. Amer. Wildl. Conf., pp.251-256, 1945.

ORGANISM AND ITS ENVIRONMENT. F.B. Sumner. Sci. Monthly, vol.14, no.3, pp. 223-233, Mar., 1922.

SOME BIOLOGICAL PROBLEMS OF OUR SOUTHWESTERN DESERTS. F. B. Sumner. Ecology, vol.6, pp.352-371, Oct., 1925.

STABILITY OF SUBSPECIFIC CHARACTERS UNDER CHANGED CONDITIONS OF ENVIRONMENT. F. B. Sumner. Amer. Nat., vol.58, pp.481-505, tbls.8, Nov.-Dec., 1924.

HOW ANIMAL HABITATS HAVE CHANGED. T. Surber. Conserv. Volunteer, St. Paul, vol.1, no.6, pp. 4-9, Mar., 1941.

OUTLINES FOR STUDY OF MAMMALIAN ECOLOGY AND LIFE HISTORIES. Walter P. Taylor. USDI, F & WS, Wildl. Leaflet 304, p.26, Apr., 1948.

RELATION OF ANIMALS TO WEATHER AND CLIMATE. Walter P. Taylor. Jour. Mamm., vol.8, no.1, pp.75-76, Feb., 1927.

SIGNIFICANCE OF EXTREME OR INTERMITTENT CONDITIONS IN DISTRIBUTION OF SPECIES AND MANAGEMENT OF NATURAL RESOURCES, WITH A RESTATEMENT OF LIEBIG'S LAW OF MINIMUM. Walter P. Taylor. Ecology, vol.15, no.3, pp.374-379, Oct., 1934.

SIGNIFICANCE OF THE BIOTIC COMMUNITY IN ECOLOGICAL STUDIES. Walter P. Taylor. Quart. Review Biol., vol.10, no.3, pp.291-307, Sep., 1935.

SOME ANIMAL ASPECTS OF REFORESTATION AND EROSION CONTROL. Walter P. Taylor. Jour. Forestry, vol.32, no.1, pp.8-10, Jan., 1934.

SOME ANIMAL RELATIONS TO SOILS. Walter P. Taylor. Ecology, vol.16, no.2, pp.127-136, Apr., 1935.

SOME EFFECTS OF ANIMALS ON PLANTS. Walter P. Taylor. Sci. Monthly, vol.43, no.3, pp.262-271, Sep., 1936.

RESPONSES OF SMALL MAMMAL POPULATIONS TO LOGGING OF DOUGLAS-FIR. Lloyd Tevis, Jr. Jour. Mamm., vol.37, no. 2, pp.189-196, June 9, 1956.

RACCOON, SQUIRREL, RABBIT AND OPOSSUM POPULATION IN A 56-ACRE OAK-MAPLE WOODS. Rex M. Thomson. Master's thesis, Univ. Ill., 1952.

EFFECTS OF CERTAIN ANIMALS THAT LIVE IN SOILS. James Thorp. Sci. Monthly, Lancaster, vol.68, no.3, pp.180-191, Mar., 1949.

DEPENDENCE OF SOILS ON ANIMAL LIFE. William R. Van Dersal. Natl. Assoc. Audubon Soc., New York, pp.7, 1937.

TEMPERATURE AND LIFE. Henry de Varigny. Smiths. Inst., Annual Rep., 1890, Washington, pp.407-428, 1891. (Translated from the Revue des deux mondes, May 1, 1889, vol.XCIII, pp.176-201.)

DROUTH MEASUREMENTS AND THE EFFECT OF THE 1936 DROUTH ON WILD LIFE. Douglas Wade. Trans. 3rd N. Amer. Wildl. Conf., pp.558-569, 1938.

FUR, FISH, AND GAME - SOME SUGGESTED RELATIONSHIPS. Douglas Wade. Trans. 6th N. Amer. Wildl. Conf., Washington, D.C., pp.314-320, 1941.

HARE V. STOAT. W. Ward. Northwestern Nat., Arbroath, vol.11, no.3, p.265, illus., Sep., 1936.

SOME ASPECTS OF THE ADAPTATION OF LIVING ORGANISMS TO THEIR ENVIRONMENT. Henry Sloane Halcro Wardlaw. Smiths. Inst., Annual Rep. 1931, Washington, pp.389-411, 1932. (Reprinted from the Proceedings of the Linnean Soc. of New S. Wales, vol.55, pt.1, no.227, Apr. 15, 1930.)

ANALYSIS OF SMALL MAMMAL POPULATIONS IN THE DECIDUOUS FOREST BIOME. Ralph Martin Wetzel. Ann Arbor, Univ. Microfilms, Publication no.1564, 1950.

OBSERVATIONS ON THE BEHAVIOR OF ANIMALS DURING THE TOTAL SOLAR ECLIPSE OF AUGUST 31, 1932. William Morton Wheeler, Clinton V. Maccoy, Ludlow Griscom, Glover M. Allen, Harold J. Coolidge, Jr. Proc. Amer. Acad. Arts and Sci., Boston, vol.70, no.2, pp.33-70, Mar., 1935.

EFFECT OF FOREST FIRES ON WILDLIFE. George O. White. Missouri Wildlife, Springfield, vol.1, no.7, p.6, Feb., 1939.

A HAPPY COMMUNITY. A STUDY OF ANIMAL RELATIONS ON A WILD LIFE SANCTUARY. H. M. Wight. Nature Mag., vol.22, no.2, pp.75-78, 88-90, illus., Aug., 1933.

MARSH RACCOON AS A COMPETITOR OF THE MUSKRAT. Norman Wilder, Henry Cofer, Robert Beck. Del. Bd. Game and Fish Comm., pp.6, June, 1951.

AREA AND NUMBER OF SPECIES. C. B. Williams. Nature, London, vol.152, no. 3853, pp.264-267, Sep. 4, 1943.

INFLUENCE OF THE GRAND COULEE DEVELOPMENT ON BIRDS AND MAMMALS. Leonard Wing. Northwest Science, Cheney, vol.16, no.2, pp.33-35, May, 1942.

PRINCIPLES OF GENERAL ECOLOGY. Angus M. Woodbury. Blakiston, New York, VIII plus 503 pp., figs.167, 1954.

NOTES ON THE EFFECTS OF DROUGHT ON ANIMAL POPULATION IN WESTERN KANSAS. L. D. Wooster. Trans. Kansas Acad. Sci., vol.38, pp.351-352, 1935.

COAL-STRIPPED LAND AS A MAMMAL HABITAT, WITH SPECIAL REFERENCE TO FUR ANIMALS. Lee E. Yeager. Amer. Midland Nat., Notre Dame, vol. 27, no.3, pp.613-635, figs.8, May (July), 1942.

SOME EFFECTS OF FLOODING AND WATERFOWL CONCENTRATION ON MAMMALS OF A REFUGE AREA IN CENTRAL ILLINOIS. Lee E. Yeager, Harry G. Anderson. Amer. Midland Nat., Notre Dame, vol. 31, no.1, pp.159-181, figs.2, Jan., 1944.

WATER LEVELS IN RELATION TO FUR BEARERS AND WATERFOWL IN CENTRAL WISCONSIN. F. R. Zimmerman. Wisconsin Conserv. Bull., Madison, vol.8, no.1, pp. 23-26, illus., Jan., 1943.

(SYMBIOSIS BETWEEN THE MAMMALS AND BIRDS OF THE PRIMITIVE FOREST.) Symbiose zwischen Urwaldsaeugern und -voegeln. Ernst A. Zwilling. Saeugetierk. Mitteil., vol.1, no.3, p.125, July 1, 1953.

BEAR AND BULL MOOSE IN BATTLE TO THE DEATH. Rod & Gun in Canada, Montreal, vol.50, no.8, p.5, Jan., 1949.

MAMMALS AND MAN. Nature, London, vol.147, no.3721, p.236, Feb. 22, 1941.

MAMMALS AND MAN. Nature, London, vol.147, no.3724, p.325, Mar. 15, 1941.

ONE IMPRESSIVE WAY NATURE TAKES CARE OF SURPLUS GAME ANIMALS. North Dakota Outdoors, Grand Forks, vol. 8, no.6, p.7, illus., Dec., 1945.

OPOSSUMS MOB CAT. Forest & Bird, Wellington, New Zealand, no.102, p.7, Nov., 1951.

ECONOMIC IMPORTANCE

ECONOMIC AND SOCIAL IMPORTANCE OF ANIMALS IN FORESTRY WITH SPECIAL REFERENCE TO WILD LIFE. Charles C. Adams. Roosevelt Wild Life Bull., vol.3, no.4, pp.509-676, pls.20-21, 1927.

IMPORTANCE OF PRESERVING WILDERNESS CONDITIONS. Charles C. Adams. New York State Mus. Bull.279, pp.37-46, pls., 1929.

RELATION OF WILD LIFE TO THE PUBLIC IN NATIONAL AND STATE PARKS. Charles C. Adams. Proc. Second Nat. Conf. State Parks, 1922, pp.129-147, 1923.

PERFUME, THE BUSINESS OF ILLUSION. Lonnelle Aikman. Nat. Geogr. Mag., Washington, vol.99, no.4, pp.536-538, 543, 547, illus., Apr., 1951.

(Review by Hartley H.T. Jackson of) FUR-FARMING FOR PROFIT. Frank G. Ashbrook. OUR WILD ANIMALS. Edwin Lincoln Moseley. Jour. Mamm., vol.9, no.2, pp. 157, 159, May 9, 1928.

RAISING SMALL ANIMALS FOR PLEASURE AND PROFIT. Frank G. Ashbrook. New York, and London: D. Van Nostrand Co., 8 vo., pp. VIII plus 260, text figs.152, Nov., 1951.

(Review by Hartley H.T. Jackson of) RAISING SMALL ANIMALS FOR PLEASURE AND PROFIT. Frank G. Ashbrook. Jour. Mamm., vol.33, no.3, p.400, Aug. 19, 1952.

ECONOMICS OF GAME. Lester Bagley. Wyoming Wild Life, Cheyenne, vol.13, no.1, pp.16-19, Jan., 1949.

WILDLIFE ALLIES HELP TO HOLD OUR WORLD IN BALANCE. James L. Baillie, Jr. Forest & Outdoors Montreal, vol.12, pp.45-46, 1947.

WAR AND WILD LIFE. D. R. Barton. Indian Wild Life, Agra, vol.4, no.4, pp.175-184, 186, Oct.-Dec., 1939; Conservation, Amer. Forestry Assn., Washington, D.C., vol.5, no.6, pp.23-26, Nov.-Dec., 1939.

WILDLIFE DIVIDEND. Devereux Butcher. Nat. Parks Mag., Washington, D.C., vol. 16, no.71, p.3, Oct.-Dec., 1942.

SHEEP AND SAGE CHICKENS. Arthur H. Carhart. Nat. Wool Grower, Salt Lake City, vol.32, no.1, pp.23-25, Jan., 1942.

DOMESTIC STOCK AND WILD LIFE. R. E. Clark. Outdoor Life, vol.68, no.4, pp.14-15, 45-46, figs.4, Oct., 1931.

WILDLIFE, A RESOURCE OF THE RANGE. R. J. Costley, and others. Grass; Ybk. Agr., pp.243-248, 1948.

WAR AND WILDLIFE. W. E. Crouch. Wisconsin Conserv. Bull., Madison, vol. 7, no.6, pp.10-12, June, 1942.

WARTIME USES OF WILDLIFE PRODUCTS. Albert M. Day. Trans. 8th N. Amer. Wildl. Conf., Washington, D.C., pp.45-54, 1943.

WILDLIFE CONTRIBUTIONS TO THE WAR. Albert M. Day. Amer. Forests, Washington, D.C., vol.49, no.7, pp.327-330, 366-368, July, 1943.

SEED-EATING MAMMALS IN RELATION TO REFORESTATION. Ned Dearborn. U.S. Dept. Agr., Bur. Biol. Surv. Circ. no.78, pp.5, figs.3, Apr. 4, 1911.

VERMIN. Guy Dollman. Nat. Hist. Mag., London, vol.5, no.40, pp.345-361, illus., Oct., 1936.

GAME AND FUR BELONG TO ALL THE PEOPLE. Frank Dufresne. Alaska Sportsman, Ketchikan, vol.10, no.4, pp.16-18, 21, illus., Apr., 1944.

WILDLIFE - AN ESSENTIAL RESOURCE. P. F. English. Trans. 8th N. Amer. Wildlife Conf., Washington, D.C., pp.187-190, 1943.

ON THE SOCIAL POTENTIALITIES OF WILDLIFE MANAGEMENT. Paul L. Errington. Jour. Wildl. Mgt., Menasha, vol. 4, no.4, pp.451-452, Oct., 1940.

A QUESTION OF VALUES. Paul L. Errington. Jour. Wildl. Mgt., Menasha, vol.11, no.3, pp.267-272, July, 1947.

WHAT HAS THE WAR DONE TO WILDLIFE? Fred Everett. Field and Stream, New York, vol.50, no.3, pp.18-19, 65-68, July, 1945.

CARE AND BREEDING OF LABORATORY ANIMALS. Edmund J. Farris (Editor). Wiley, N.Y., pp.xvi-515, illus., 1950.

POSSIBLE IMPORTANCE OF OTHER VERTEBRATES IN SARDINE INVESTIGATIONS. Francis E. Felin, John C. Marr. Trans. 16th N. Amer. Wildl. Conf., Washington, pp.431-436, 1951.

ECONOMIC VALUE OF PREDACEOUS BIRDS AND MAMMALS. A. K. Fisher. Yearbook Dept. Agric. for 1908, pp.187-194, pls.1-3, 1909.

(THE QUESTION OF IVORY.) La question de l'ivoire. Victor Forbin. La Nature, Paris, no.3139, pp.222-223, fig.1, July 1, 1947.

ON THE UTILIZATION OF THE FAUNA OF TERRESTRIAL VERTEBRATES AND SOME PROBLEMS OF ITS RECONSTRUCTION. A.N. Formosov. Zoologicheskii Zhurnal, Moscow, vol.16, no.3, pp.407-442, 1937.

BEAR AND SQUIRREL DAMAGE TO YOUNG REDWOOD. Emanuel Fritz. Jour. Forestry, vol.49, no.9, pp.651-652, Sep., 1951.

WILDLIFE IN NEW WORLD ECONOMY. Ira N. Gabrielson. Proc. 8th Amer. Sci. Congr., Washington, D.C., vol.5, pp.263-271, 1942.

(NATURAL HISTORY OF MAMMALS, THEIR HABITS AND CONNECTION WITH THE ARTS, COMMERCE, AND AGRICULTURE.) Histoire naturelle des mammifères, avec l'indication de leurs moeurs, et de leurs rapports avec les arts, le commerce et l'agriculture. Paul Gervais. Paris, L. Curmer, 2 v., col.front., illus., plates (part col.), 1854-1855.

MAMMALS WHICH DAMAGE FOREST PLANTATIONS. V. P. Grechkin. (English translation of Russian zoological literature. Trans.250) from Lesn. Khoz., no.1, pp. 54-57, 1950. Transl. by J. D. Jackson, 1953.

PELTS AND PREDATORS. R. F. Gregg. Colorado Conservation, vol.3, no.2, pp. 26-28, Mar.-Apr., 1954.

WHY WE NEED WILD BIRDS AND MAMMALS. J. Grinnell. Sci. Monthly, vol.41, pp.553-556, Dec., 1935.

WILD ANIMAL LIFE AS A PRODUCT AND AS A NECESSITY OF NATIONAL FORESTS. J. Grinnell. Jour. Forestry, vol.22, no.8, pp.837-845, Dec., 1924.

ANIMAL LIFE AS AN ASSET OF NATIONAL PARKS. J. Grinnell, Tracy I. Storer. Science, n.s., vol.44, no.1133, pp.375-380, Sep. 15, 1916.

THOSE LITTLE MAMMALS. W. J. Hamilton, Jr. N.Y. State Cons., vol.1, no.6, pp.16-17, June-July, 1947.

WHAT IS VERMIN? W. J. Hamilton, Jr. Fur-Fish-Game, vol.57, no.5, pp.52-54, fig.1, May, 1933.

ANIMALS ARE A RESOURCE TOO. Ross Hardy. Utah Educational Review, Salt Lake City, pp.165-167, Mar., 1947.

ANIMAL FIBERS USED IN BRUSHES. Thora M. Hardy, John I. Hardy. Circ. U.S. Dept. Agr., Washington, no.802, pp.15, Jan., 1949.

MARKET FOR MARINE ANIMAL OILS IN THE UNITED STATES. Roger W. Harrison. Investigational Reports no.7, Bureau of Fisheries, U.S. Dept. Commerce, pp.78, figs.17, 1932.

(LET'S PROTECT NATURE! SHE WILL REWARD US.) Protégeons la Nature. Elle rendra. J. P. Harroy. Inst. Parcs Nat. Congo Belge, Brussels, pp.97, pls.15, 1946.

NO MORE WILDERNESS. Sherman S. Hayden. Aubudon Mag., New York., vol. 46, no.1, pp.30-35, Jan.-Feb., 1944.

ECONOMIC MAMMALOGY. Junius Henderson, Elberta L. Craig. C.C. Thomas, Springfield, Ill., and Baltimore, Md., pp. 397, 1932.

(Review by Jean M. Linsdale of) ECONOMIC MAMMALOGY. Junius Henderson, Elberta L. Craig. Jour. Mamm., vol.15, no.1, pp.73-74, Feb., 1934.

(HARMFUL AND HELPFUL ANIMALS IN AREAS OF FIELD-PROTECTING CULTIVATION.) Vrednyye i poleznyye zveri rayonov polezashchitnykh nasazhdeniy. Vladimir Georgievich Heptner. Moscow, Moscow Univ. Press, 1950.

EXISTENCE OF WILDLIFE AS SOMETHING TO EXPECT TOO OFTEN TAKEN FOR GRANTED. C. Graham Hixon. Alabama Cons., Montgomery, vol.16, no.12, pp.6, 12, 14, illus., June, 1945.

WHAT CAN FOREST WILDLIFE CONTRIBUTE TO THE WAR PROGRAM? N. W. Hosley, and others. Jour. Forestry, Washington, D.C., vol.42, no.5, pp.361-363, May, 1944.

WILDLIFE DEPREDATIONS ON BROADCAST SEEDINGS OF BURNED BRUSHLANDS. Walter E. Howard. Jour. Range Mgt., vol.3, no.4, pp.291-298, Oct., 1950.

REPORT OF THE COMMITTEE ON ECONOMIC MAMMALOGY. Charles E. Johnson. Jour. Mamm., vol.14, no.3, pp.266-268, Aug., 1933.

HOUSING OF LABORATORY ANIMALS. J. I. M. Jones, E.C. Wood. Jour. Hyg., Cambridge, vol.47, no.2, pp.190-196, pls. 7-8, June, 1949.

WILDLIFE HELPS WIN THE WAR. V.E. Joslin. Conservation Volunteer, St. Paul, vol.5, no.29, pp.4-6, Feb., 1943.

ON THE HUNTING AND UTILIZATION OF SEA ANIMALS AND SHARKS IN THE FAR EAST. A. G. Kaganowsky (Editor). Bull. Pacific Sci. Inst. Fisheries and Oceanography, vol.10, pp.1-115, 1937. (In Russian with English summaries after each chapter.)

SOME MATERIAL ON THE QUESTION OF THE EXPLOITATION OF MARINE MAMMALS. I. I. Kharkov. Bull. Pacific Sci. Inst. Fisheries & Oceanography, Vladivostok, vol.10, pp.59-103, 1937. (In Russian with English summary.)

EFFECT OF SIMULATED SNOWSHOE HARE AND DEER DAMAGE ON PLANTED CONIFERS IN THE LAKE STATES. Laurits W. Krefting. Jour. Wildl. Mgt., Ithaca, vol.17, no.4, pp.487-494, Oct., 1953.

WILD ANIMALS AND AGRICULTURE. F.H. Lancum. Jour. Minister Agr., London, vol. 52, pp.228-231, 276-278, 331, 371-373, 422-424, 464-467, 520-522, 563-566, 1945-1946.

STRANGE USES FOR ANIMALS. Frank W. Lane. Nat. Hist., New York, vol.55, no. 9, pp.412-414, 434, illus., Nov., 1946.

FAMOUS IVORY TREASURES OF A NEGRO KING. Herbert Lang. Amer. Mus. Jour., New York, vol.18, no.7, pp.527-552, illus., 1918.

WILDERNESS AND CULTURE. A. Leopold. Sierra Club Bull., San Francisco, vol.42, no.6, pp.33-37, June, 1957.

WILDERNESS VALUES. A. Leopold. Living Wilderness, Washington, D.C., vol.7, no. 7, pp.24-25, Mar., 1942.

WILDLIFE IN AMERICAN CULTURE. A. Leopold. Jour. Wildl. Mgt., Menasha, vol. 7, no.1, pp.1-6, Jan., 1943.

WILDLIFE VALUES. Harrison F. Lewis. Trans. 14th N. Amer. Wildl. Conf., Washington, pp.16-21, 1949.

CHARACTERISTICS OF FUR ANIMAL GREASE AND ITS USE IN MEDICINE. S.V. Labochev. Zool. Jour. USSR, Moscow, vol.22, no.3, pp.174-177, tbls.3, 1943. (With English summary.)

BEAUTIFUL BASKETS FROM UGLU HIDES. Ruel McDaniel. Amer. Forests and Forest Life, vol.35, no.1, pp.44-45, illus., Jan., 1929.

(POCKET BOOK OF ANIMAL PESTS IN FIELD, GARDEN, STOREHOUSE, HOUSE, FRUIT CULTURE, AND VINEYARD.) Taschenbuch der Tierischen Schaedlinge in Feld, Garten, Speicher, Haus, im Obstbau und im Weinberg. F.W. Maier-Bode. Munich, J.F. Schreiber, pp.163, pls.38, 1924.

(USEFUL MAMMALS OF THE GERMAN COLONIES.) Nutzbare Saeugetiere der deutschen Kolonien. Paul Matschie. Verhandlung Deutschen Kolonialkongresses, pp.136-147, 1903.

A "VERMIN" RECORD. H. G. Maurice. Jour. Soc. Preservation Fauna Empire, Hertford, n.s., pt.45, pp.17-18, Aug., 1942.

LONG CHANCES IN THE ANIMAL DEALER'S GAME. Charles Mayer. Asia, vol.21, pp.154-159, 168, Feb., 1921.

CIRCULAR ON THE ECONOMIC RELATIONS OF MAMMALS. Clinton Hart Merriam. 2d ed, Washington, Gov't Print.Off., U.S. Dept. of Agr., Div. of Economic Ornithology and Mammalogy, circular 3, pp.3, 1886.

GAME AND WILD-FUR PRODUCTION AND UTILIZATION ON AGRICULTURAL LAND. J.Paul Miller, Burewell B.Powell. U.S. Dept. Agric., Circ. no.636, pp.58, figs.12, Jan., 1942.

(ON THE PRINCIPLES OF THE AESTHETIC EVALUATION OF MAMMALS.) Ueber die Grundlagen der aesthetischen Beurteilung der Saeugetiere. K. von Mobius. Sitzungsberichte der Akad. Wissenschaften zu Berlin, XIV, pp.164-182, Mar. 22, 1900.

WILD ANIMAL DAMAGE TO SEED AND SEEDLINGS ON CUT-OVER DOUGLAS FIR LANDS OF OREGON AND WASHINGTON. A. W. Moore. U.S. Dept. Agriculture Technical Bull. no.706, Wasnington, pp.1-28, figs.14, June, 1940.

WILDLIFE IN THE FARM PROGRAM. James N. Morton. Pennsylvania Game News, vol.9, no.2, pp.4-6; no.3, pp. 4-7, 32, May and June, 1938.

INCOME POSSIBILITIES FROM A SMALL ARTIFICIAL POND IN EASTERN CONNECTICUT. A.E. Moss. Jour. Wildl. Mgt., Menasha, vol.6, no.2, pp.141-146, Apr., 1942.

WILDERNESS AND WILDLIFE. Olaus J. Murie. The Living Wilderness, vol.3, no.3, p.5, Dec., 1937.

VANDALS OF THE NIGHT. J. Laurens Nicholes. Pasadena, Calif., Publications, Press, pp.118, pls.4, 1948.

FROST AND RABBITS AS WELL AS DEER DESTROY TREE SEEDLINGS. C.E. Ostrom. USDA, Allegheny Forest Exp. Sta., Tech. Note 33, p.2, 1942.

DECISION OF THE SUPREME COURT OF THE UNITED STATES ON THE SALE OF IMPORTED GAME. T.S. Palmer. U.S. Dept. Agric., Bureau Biol. Surv., Circ. no.67, pp.1-12, Dec. 9, 1908.

GAME AS A NATIONAL RESOURCE. T.S. Palmer. U.S. Dept. Agric., Bull.1049, pp. 1-48, Mar. 14, 1922.

(INVESTIGATIONS OF FOSSIL FINDS AND PRIMITIVE PEOPLES AS REGARDS THEIR VALUE FOR PRACTICAL MEDICINE AND DENTISTRY.) Untersuchungen an fossilen Funden und primitiven Voelkern in ihrer Auswertung fuer die praktische Medizine und Zahnheilkunde. Fr. Proell. Forsch. und Fortschritte, vol.8, no.28, pp.360-361, Oct. 1, 1932.

ANIMALS AND PERFUMES. W. P. Pycraft. Illus. London News, vol.187, no.5044, p. 1126, illus., Dec. 21, 1935.

OUTLINE OF ECONOMIC ZOOLOGY. Albert M. Reese. Blakiston Co., Philadelphia, 4th ed., pp.xii-359, figs.191, 1942.

WILDLIFE A FOREST RESOURCE. Paul H. Roberts, J.H. Stone. (In A national plan for American Forestry) Senate Doc. no.12, 73d Congress, 1st Session, Washington, D.C., pp.489-525, 1933.

LESSONS FROM PAST FOREST PLANTINGS IN THE LAKE STATES. P. O. Rudolf. USDA, Lake States Forest Exp. Sta., pp.6, Aug., 1936.

RODENTS AND MOLES AS PESTS IN BULB PLANTINGS. Theo H. Scheffer, F. E. Garlough. U.S. Dept. Agric., circular no. 381, pp.16, figs.9, Feb., 1936.

(VERTEBRATE ANIMALS USEFUL OR HARMFUL TO AGRICULTURE OF BELGIUM.) Sur les animaux vertebrés de la Belgique, utiles on nuisibles a l'agriculture. Edm. Selys-Longchamps. Bruxelles, ser.2, vol.12, no.12, pp.418-453, 1861.

EXTERMINATION OF MAMMALS. THEIR ECONOMIC VALUE; AND THEIR GREAT IMPORTANCE TO MAN THROUGH THE STUDY OF THEIR COMPARATIVE ANATOMY. R.W. Shufeldt. Med. Rec., New York, vol.99, no.19, (whole no.2635), pp. 777-782, May 7, 1921.

HUNTING AND GAME ECONOMY. Lauri Siivonen. Suomi, pp.503-513, illus., 1952.

CHINA'S IVORY CARVING INDUSTRY. Arthur De Carle Sowerby. The China Jour., Shanghai, vol.25, no.3, pp.151-154, photos, Sep., 1936.

THE IVORY PRODUCING ANIMALS. Arthur De Carle Sowerby. China Jour., vol.25, no. 3, pp.160-169, illus., Sep., 1936.

HOW TO MAKE A PROFIT IN RANCH MANAGEMENT. Ronald G. Stephenson. Black Fox Mag., New York, vol.32, no.1, pp.12, 27, May, 1948.

UTILIZATION OF THE SKIN OF AQUATIC ANIMALS. Charles H. Stevenson. Rep. of the Commission, U.S. Commission of Fish and Fisheries, part xxviii for the year ending June 30, 1902.

ROLE OF VERTEBRATE PALEONTOLOGY IN PETROLEUM EXPLORATION. R.A. Stirton. Earth Science Digest, vol.6, no.3, pp.31-32, Nov., 1952.

BIOLOGY OF WILDERNESS PROTECTION. E. Lowell Sumner. Sierra Club Bull., San Francisco, vol.27, no.4, pp.14-22, Aug., 1942.

BIOLOGIST AND THE WAR. Walter P. Taylor. Audubon Mag., New York, vol.45, no.2, pp.71-76, Mar.-Apr., 1943.

SOME ANIMAL ASPECTS OF REFORESTATION AND EROSION CONTROL. Walter P. Taylor. Jour. of Forestry, vol.32, no.1, pp.8-10, Jan., 1934.

WILDLIFE AND THE FARM INDUSTRY. Walter P. Taylor. Rept. Kansas State Bd. Agric., Topeka, vol.64, no.266, pp.21-29, Apr., 1945.

TIMBER AND GAME - TWIN CROPS. Harold Titus. Pennsylvania Game News, Harrisburg, vol.16, no.7, pp.8-9, 26-27, illus., Oct., 1945; Trans. 10th N. Amer. Wildl. Conf., Washington, pp. 146-163, illus., 1945.

AGRICULTURE DAMAGES. R.L.Turpin. Conv. Internat. Assn. Game, Fish and Cons. Comm., 39: pp.87-91, 1949.

"PESTS" AND AGRICULTURE. John G. Tyler. The Condor, vol.33, no.6, pp. 258-259, Nov.-Dec., 1931.

(USEFUL VERTEBRATES AND THE DAMAGES DONE TO THE AGRICULTURE OF THE COUNTRY.) Los animales vertebrados utiles y los dañinos á la agricultura del pais. Francisco del Valle Atiles. Puerto-Rico, Impr. del "Boletin mercantil," pp. 47, 1887.

WHAT ABOUT PAYING OUR DEBT TO NATURE? Dan A. Wallace. Conserv. Volunteer, St. Paul, vol.11, no.60, pp.21-23, Jan.-Feb., 1948.

WAR AND WILDLIFE. J.D.U. Ward. Nature Mag., Washington, D.C., vol. 33, no.7, pp.385-390, illus., Aug.-Sep., 1940.

IVORY: ITS VARIETIES AND IMITATIONS. R. Webster. Gemmologist, London, vol.13, no.154, pp.45-47, May,1944; no.155, pp.51-54, June 1944; no.156, pp.57-59, July, 1944; vol.14, no.157, pp.4-5, Aug., 1944; no.158, pp.9-11, Sep., 1944; no.159, pp.16-17, Oct., 1944; no.160, pp.19-21, Nov., 1944; no.161, pp.28-29, Dec., 1944; no.162, pp.31-32, Jan., 1945; no.163, pp.39-41, Feb., 1945; no.164, pp.46-47, Mar., 1945; no.165, pp. 52-53, Apr., 1945; no.166, pp.56-59, May, 1945; no.167, pp.64-65, June 1945; no.168, pp.67-69, July, 1945; vol.15, no.169, pp. 2-3, Aug., 1945.

(ON THE TRAPPING AND SELLING OF ANIMALS.) Ueber Tierfang und Tierhandel. Ludwig Zukowsky. Kleintier und Pelztier, Leipzig, Jahrg.10, no.7, pp.101-104, figs.3, Apr. 1, 1934.

ANIMALS FOR SHOW AND PLEASURE IN ANCIENT ROME. Published by Manchester Univ. Press, 1937.

DEER-CHASING DOG ON TROLLEY WIRE STOPS CROP DAMAGE. Maryland Conservationist, Baltimore, vol.19, no.4, p.7, Fall, 1942.

LIVING SOURCES OF LUXURY WRAPS: FOX, MINK, CHINCHILLA, AND BEAVER. Illus. London News, vol.214, no.5731, p. 234, Feb. 19, 1949.

MANY VISITORS VIEW GAME FARM'S WILDLIFE. West Virginia Conservation, Charleston, vol.8, no.6, pp.8, 21, Sep., 1944.

THE PESTS OF THE FARM; BEING AN ACCOUNT OF THE VARIOUS DEPREDATING ANIMALS, BIRDS AND INSECTS WHICH ANNOY THE AMERICAN FARMER. WITH DIRECTIONS FOR THEIR DESTRUCTION. WITH ILLUSTRATIONS ON WOOD. New York, C.M. Saxton & Co., pp.135, illus., 1855.

RABBIT OR DEER DAMAGE? Forest Res. Dig., pp.10-12, Dec., 1935.

SIZE OF STOCK IN RELATION TO ANIMAL INJURY. Forest Res. Dig., pp.1-2, Feb., 1935.

SPECIAL ARTICLES. A QUESTION OF VALUES. Jour. Wildl. Mgt., Menasha, vol.11, no.3, pp.267-272, July, 1947.

WHAT WE OWE TO WILD LIFE. SURVEY OF THE EMPIRE'S BIG GAME TODAY. Field, London, vol.162, no.4204, pp.226-227, July 22, 1933.

## EDUCATION AND TEXTBOOKS

VERTEBRATE ZOOLOGY. G.R. de Beer. New York, Macmillan Co., vol.8, pp.xx-505, text figs.185, 1928.

VERTEBRATE ZOOLOGY. G.R. de Beer. Sidgwick & Jackson Ltd., London, pp.xv-435, Sep., 1951.

ZOOLOGY FOR HIGH SCHOOLS. J.F. Calvert, J.H. Cameron. 12mo., pp.viii-344, illus., Toronto: Educational Book Co., Oct., 1928.

ELEMENTS OF GENERAL ZOOLOGY. William J. Dakin. New York, Oxford Univ. Press, American Branch, vol.8, pp.xvi-496, text figs.252, 1927.

WILDLIFE CONSERVATION TEACHING PROGRAM. William B. Davis. Trans. 8th N. Amer. Wildl. Conf., Washington, pp. 198-205, 1943.

CLASSROOM TEACHER. IDENTIFICATION-APPRECIATION SCIENCE SECTION. MAMMALS. Lee R. Dice. Classroom Teacher, Chicago, vol.9, pp.241-320, illus., 1927.

EDUCATION AND WILDLIFE CONSERVATION. Ira N. Gabrielson. Trans. 10th N. Amer. Wildl. Conf., Washington, pp.203-209, 1945.

SOURCE OF STUDY MATERIAL FOR THE COUNTRY MAMMALOGIST. W. J. Hamilton, Jr. Science, n.s., vol.76, no.1959, p.55, July 15, 1932.

SOURCES OF MAMMALIAN STUDY MATERIAL. Irving E. Hampe. Maryland Nat., Baltimore, vol.18, no.3, p.50, Summer, 1948.

(ZOOLOGY TEXTBOOK.) Lehrbuch der Zoologie. Richard Hertwig. Jena, G. Fischer, pp.iv-588, illus., 1892.

WILDLIFE IS PART OF OUR SCHOOL. Edith L. Johnson. Audubon Mag., New York, vol.49, no.6, pp.340, 344, illus., Nov.-Dec., 1947.

TEACHING OF ANATOMY. William Keiller. Philadelphia Med. Jour., special no. on Med. Education, pp.8, Sep. 1, 1900.

(IMPORTANCE OF SCHOOL AND UNIVERSITY AS REGARDS THE ZOOLOGICAL GARDEN.) Die Bedeutung von Schule und Universitaet fuer den Zoologischen Garten. R. Lehmensick. Zool. Garten, n.F., Leipzig, vol.7, nos.10-12, pp.286-289, Feb., 1935.

INTRODUCTION TO ZOOLOGY. Zeno Payne Metcalf. C.C. Thomas, Springfield, Ill., pp.xix-425, text figs.184, Oct., 1932.

OUTLINE OF GENERAL ZOOLOGY. Horatio Hackett Newmann. Macmillan Co., New York, pp.xvi-480, figs.179, July, 1924.

TEACHING GEOGRAPHY THROUGH THE STUDY OF MAMMAL DISTRIBUTION. E. Laurence Palmer, Edna Drill. Cornell Rural School Leaflet, vol.33, no.1, pp. 4-49, Sep., 1939.

TEXT-BOOK OF ZOOLOGY. Thomas Jeffery Parker. 2d ed., London, Macmillan and Co., Ltd., vol.2, illus. (part col.), 1910.

EDUCATIONAL VALUE OF NATURE-STUDY. C.F. Curtis Riley. School and Society, vol. 21, no.542, pp.1-28 (of reprint), May 16, 1925.

ELEMENTS OF MAMMALOGY. W.S.W. Ruschenberger. Grigg & Elliot, Philadelphia, pp.151, pls.5, 1945.

MAMMALIA, RECENT AND EXTINCT; AN ELEMENTARY TREATISE FOR THE USE OF PUBLIC SCHOOLS OF NEW SOUTH WALES. Alexander Walker Scott. Sydney, T. Richards, Government Printer, pp.xii, 141, vii, 1873.

SCIENCE OF BIOLOGY. George G. Scott. Thomas Y. Crowell Co., New York, vol. 8, pp.xii-617, text figs.355, 1925.

GENERAL ZOOLOGY. George M. Shaw. Vol.1, pt.1, 1800; vol.1, pt.2, 1800; vol. 2, pt.1, 1801; vol.2, pt.2, 1801.

GENERAL ZOOLOGY. Tracy I. Storer. McGraw-Hill, pp.xii plud 798, illus., 1943.

OUTLINE OF ZOOLOGY. J. Arthur Thomas. Seventh Ed., New York, Oxford Univ. Press, American Branch, pp.i-xxii, 1-8, 1-421, 1921.

PHYLOGENETIC INTERPRETATIONS IN THE TEACHING OF COMPARATIVE VERTEBRATE ANATOMY. Theodore W. Torrey. Turtox News, Chicago, vol.25, no.11, pp. 222-223, Nov., 1947.

EDUCATION AND EMPLOYMENT IN THE FISH AND WILDLIFE FIELD. David B. Turner. Trans. 11th N. Amer. Wildl. Conf., Washington, pp.93-96, 1946.

EDUCATION FOR THE VETERINARY PROFESSION. Nature, London, vol.153, no.3871, pp.35-38, Jan. 8, 1944.

## EMBRYOLOGY

EMBRYONIC DEVELOPMENT OF THE OVARY AND TESTIS OF THE MAMMALS. Bennet Mills Allen. Chicago, Ill., pp.58, illus., pl.vii, 1903. Plates printed on both sides. Thesis Ph. D., Univ. of Chicago, 1903. Reprinted from the American Jour. of Anatomy, vol.3, no.2, pp.89-146, 1903.

PARTHENOGENESIS AND POLYPLOIDY IN MAMMALIAN DEVELOPMENT. R.A. Beatty. Cambridge, Univ. Press, pp.xi-132, pls., diagr., (Cambridge Monographs in Experimental Biology no.7), 1957.

CONTRIBUTION TO EMBRYOLOGY. Carnegie Institution, Washington, vol.15, pp.iii-139, pls., 1923.

INDUCTION OF MAMMARY DUCTS. Alan Deakin. Nature, London, vol.3467, no.137, pp.619-620, Apr. 11, 1936.

(EMBRYOLOGICAL RESEARCH ON THE KIDNEY OF MAMMALS.) Ricerche Embriologische Sul Rene Dei Mammiferi. Carlo Emery. Mem. Cl. di Sci. Fis. Mat. e Nat., Reale Accademia dei Lincei, ser. 3a, vol.15, pp.3-12, pl.1, Rome, 1883.

(ON THE DESTRUCTION OF CELLS DURING NORMAL DEVELOPMENT IN VERTEBRATES.) Ueber Untergang von Zellen waehrend der normalen Entwicklung bei Wirbeltieren. M. Ernst. Zeitschrift f. Anat. Entwicklungsgeschichte, vol.79, pp.228-262, illus., May 5, 1926.

(NOTES ON THE EMBRYOLOGY OF MAMMALS.) Remarques pour l'embryologie des mammiferes. Serge Frechkop. Bull. Mus. Roy. Hist. Nat. Belgique, vol.17, no.69, pp.1-6, figs.5, Nov., 1941

CHEMICAL INDUCTION OF POLYPLOID BREEDS OF MAMMALS. Goesta Per Engelbert Haeggqvist. Stockholm, Almqvist & Wiksells boktr., pp.11, pl., diagr., 1950.

DEVELOPMENT AND FATE OF THE CORPUS LUTEUM IN THE VERTEBRATE SERIES. R.J. Harrison. Biol. Rev., London, vol.23, no.3, pp.296-331, July, 1948.

ON THE PROBLEM OF "PARTHENOGENESIS" IN THE MAMMALIAN OVARY. Otto F. Kampmeier. Amer. Jour. Anat., vol.43, pp.45-76, figs.11, 1929.

(ON THE COMPARATIVE HISTOLOGY AND EMBRYOLOGY OF THE SUPRARENAL CAPSULE OF MAMMALS AND MAN.) Zur vergleichenden Histologie und Embryologie der Nebenniere der Saeuger und des Menschen. S. Kohno. Zeitschr. f. Anat. und Entwicklungsgesch., vol.77, pp.419-480, figs.29, Oct. 31, 1925.

ALTERNATE GENERATION AND PARTHENOGENESIS IN THE ANIMAL KINGDOM. LECTURE DELIVERED BEFORE THE VIENNA SOCIETY FOR THE DIFFUSION OF SCIENTIFIC KNOWLEDGE. Georg Andreas Kornhuber. Smiths. Inst., Annual Rep., 1871, Washington, pp.235-247, 1873.

COURSE OF THE WOLFFIAN TUBULES IN MAMMALIAN EMBRYOS. Frederic T. Lewis. Amer. Jour. Anat., vol.26, pp. 423-435, Jan. 15, 1920.

PARTHENOGENETIC DEVELOPMENT OF OVA IN THE MAMMALIAN OVARY AND THE ORIGIN OF OVARIAN TERATOMATA AND CHORIO-EPITHELIOMATA. Leo Loeb. Jour. Amer. Med. Assoc., vol.56, pp.1327-1328, May 6, 1911.

HARVARD EMBYOLOGICAL COLLECTION. Charles Sedgwick Minot. Jour. Med. Res., Boston, vol.13, n.s., vol.8, no.5, pp.499-522, Aug., 1905.

IMPLANTATION OF THE HUMAN OVUM IN THE UTERUS. Charles Sedgwick Minot. Trans. Amer. Gynecological Society, pp.8, 1904.

SEGMENTATION OF THE OVUM, WITH ESPECIAL REFERENCE TO THE MAMMALIA. Charles Sedgwick Minot. Amer. Nat., Boston, vol.23, no.270, pp.463-481, figs.1-10; no.273, pp.753-769, figs. 11-20, June, Sep., 1889.

STUDY OF MAMMALIAN EMBRYOLOGY. Charles Sedgwick Minot. Amer. Nat., Boston, vol.34, no.408, pp.913-941, figs. 11, Dec., 1900.

POLYEMBRYONY IN ANIMALS. J.T. Patterson. Quart. Rev. Biol., vol.2, pp.399-426, figs.48, Sep., 1927.

FIFTH AORTIC ARCH OF MAMMALIAN EMBRYOS; THE NATURE OF THE LAST PHARYNGEAL EVAGINATION. Frank Reagan. Amer. Jour. Anat., Philadelphia, vol.12, no.4, pp.493-514, figs.16, pls.3, Jan., 1912.

EARLIEST BLOOD VESSELS OF THE MAMMALIAN EMBRYO, STUDIED BY MEANS OF THE INJECTION METHOD. Franklin P. Reagen. Univ. California Publ. Zool., vol.28, no.19, pp.361-364, Feb., 1926.

(EMBRYOGENESIS OF THE SKELETON OF THE MAMMAL EXTREMITIES.) Die Embryogenese des Extremitatenskelettes der Saeugetiere. Ein Beitrag zur Frage der Entwicklung der Tetrapodengliedmassen. Elisabeth Charlotte Schmidt-Ehrenberg. Rev. Suisse Zool., Geneva, vol.49, no.1, pp.33-131, figs.37, pl.1, Feb., 1942.

DEVELOPMENT OF THE ATRIOVENTRICULAR NODE, BUNDLE OF HIS, AND SINOATRIAL NODE IN THE CALF; WITH

A DESCRIPTION OF A THIRD EMBRYONIC NODE-LIKE STRUCTURE. Ralph F. Shaner. Anat. Rec., vol.44, pp.85-100, figs.22, 1929.

FATE OF THE DUCT OF CUVIER IN MAN AND CERTAIN OTHER MAMMALS. M.A.H. Siddiqi, R.V. Sing. Proc. Nat. Acad. Sci. India, vol.8, pt.3, pp.68-70, figs.6, Aug., 1938.

(CRITICAL REMARKS ON THE TRIPLOBLAST THEORY.) Kritische Bemerkungen zur Dreikeimblaettertheorie. Fritz Strauss. Verhandl. Schweizer.Naturforsch. Gesell., pp.134-135, 1944.

(IMPLANTATION OF THE EMBRYO, THE EARLY PHASE OF PLACENTATION AND MENSTRUATION, IN THE LIGHT OF COMPARATIVE EMBRYOLOGICAL KNOWLEDGE.) Die Implantation des Keimes, die Fruehphase der Placentation und die Menstruation im Licht vergleichend-embryologischer Erfahrungen. Fritz Strauss. Paul Haupt, Bern, pp.72, pls.12, 1944.

(NEW VIEWPOINTS ON THE STRUCTURE AND FUNCTION OF THE PLACENTA.) Neue Gesichtspunkte ueber Bau und Leistung der Placenta. Fritz Strauss. Mitteil. Naturf. Gesell. Bern, n.F., vol. 15, (Siztungsber.), pp.vii-viii, 1957.

DEVELOPMENT OF THE EGG AS SEEN BY THE EMBRYOLOGIST. George L. Streeter. Sci. Monthly, pp.495-506, figs. 7, June, 1931.

USE OF CEREBRAL ANAEMIA IN EXPERIMENTAL EMBRYOLOGICAL STUDIES UPON MAMMALS. E.A. Swenson. Anat. Record, vol.30, pp.147-152, May 25, 1925.

(HERR HANS VIRCHOW REPORTS ON HIS EMBRYOLOGICAL AND ANGIOLOGICAL FINDINGS REGARDING NORTH AMERICAN VERTEBRATES.) Herr Hans Virchow teilte einige embryologische und angiologische Erfahrungen ueber nordamerikanische Wirbeltiere mit. Hans Virchow. Gesell. natur. Freunde, Berlin, pp.33-44, Jan., 1894.

ORGANIZERS IN MAMMALIAN DEVELOPMENT. C.H. Waddington. Nature, London, vol.138, no.3481, p.125, July 18, 1936.

NOTE ON THE ORIGIN AND HISTOGENESIS OF THE MESONEPHRIC DUCT IN MAMMALS. Ernst Weinberg. Anat. Rec., vol. 41, pp.373-386, Feb. 25, 1929.

RECAPITULATION THEORY OR BIOGENETIC LAW IN EMBRYOLOGY. H.V. Wilson. Amer. Nat., Lancaster, vol.75, pp.20-30, Jan.-Feb., 1941.

GENESIS OF SOMATIC MOTOR FUNCTION IN MAMMALIAN EMBRYOS: SYNTHESIZING ARTICLE. William F. Windle. Physiol. Zool., Chicago, vol.17, no.3, pp.247-260, July, 1944.

ENCLYCLOPEDIAS see DICTIONARIES, ENCYCLOPEDIAS, MANUALS

ENDOCRINOLOGY see PHYSIOLOGY -- ENDOCRINOLOGY

## EVOLUTION

INFLUENCE OF PHYSICAL CONDITIONS IN THE GENESIS OF SPECIES. Joel Asaph Allen. Smiths. Inst., Annual Rep., 1905, Washington, pp.375-402, 1906. (Reprinted, with note and bracketed additions by the author, from the Radical Review, vol.I, pp.108-140, 1877.

SPECIALIZATION AND EVOLUTION. Dean Amadon. Amer. Nat., Lancaster, vol.77, no.769, pp.133-141, Mar.-Apr., 1943.

(ON THE EVOLUTION OF THE TEETH OF MAMMALS.) Sur l'évolution des dents des Mammifères. Florentino Ameghino. Boletin Acad. Nac. de. Cien. de Cordoba, Buenos Aires, vol.14, nos.3-4, pp.381-517 (3-139), 1896.

ON SOME SIMILARITIES IN THE EVOLUTION OF THE DENTITION IN THE SIRENIA AND PROBOSCIDEA. C.W. Andrews. Ann. and Mag. Nat. Hist., ser.9, vol.13, pp.304-309, Mar., 1924.

CONTRIBUTION TO THE THEORY OF EVOLUTION BY NATURAL SELECTION. Joshua L. Bailey. Amer. Nat., Lancaster, vol.75, no.758, pp.213-230, tbls.4, May-June, 1941.

DEVELOPMENT OF FUNCTION IN THE MAMMALIAN ORGANISM. Joseph Barcroft. Roy. Inst. Great Britain, Special Afternoon Lecture, pp.13, May 20, 1941.

EVOLUTION OF FUNCTION IN THE MAMMALIAN ORGANISM. Joseph Barcroft. Nature, London, vol.147, no.3738, pp.762-765, June 21, 1941.

ZOOLOGICAL GOD. Edward H. Berry. The Saturday Review of Literature, New York, pp.52-53, Aug. 15, 1930.

EVOLUTIONARY SIGNIFICANCE OF GEOGRAPHIC VARIATION IN POPULATION DENSITY. W. Frank Blair. Texas Jour. Sci., vol.3, no.1, pp.53-57, Mar. 30, 1951.

(HOW DID MAMMALS ORIGINATE?) Wo sind die Saeugetiere entstanden?Caesar R. Boettger. Sitz. Ges. naturforsch. Freunde, pp.24-30, Mar. 15, 1938.

(CAN THE FORM OF HORNS BE TRACED BACK, AND CAN A DEVELOPMENT DIRECTION BE THEREBY BROUGHT TO LIGHT.) Lassen sich die Gehoernformen von einander ableiten und ist dabei eine Entwicklungsrichtung zu erkennen? Hans von Boetticher. Zeitschr. Saeugetierk., Berlin, vol.18, no.2, p.136, Sep. 28, 1952.

PRESENT OUTLOOK ON DESCENT. F.O. Bower. Nature, vol.113, pp.356-358, Mar. 8, 1924.

PROGRESSIVE CLINES. F.W. Braestrup. Nature, London, vol.156, no.3959, pp.337-338, Sep. 15, 1945.

CROONIAN LECTURE: ON THE ORIGIN OF MAMMALS. Pl.1-7. R. Broom. Roy. Soc. of London, Philos. trans., vol.206, ser. B, pp.1-48, 1914-1915.

EVOLUTION AS THE PALAEONTOLOGIST SEES IT. R. Broom. S. African Jour. Sci., Johannesburg, vol.29, pp.54-71, Oct., 1932.

EVOLUTION - IS THERE INTELLIGENCE BEHIND IT? R. Broom. S. African Jour.Sci., vol.30, pp.1-19, Oct., 1933.

MAMMAL-LIKE REPTILES OF SOUTH AFRICA AND THE ORIGIN OF MAMMALS. R. Broom. London, H.F. & G. Witherby, pp.xvi-376, figs.111, 1932.

ON RECENT DISCOVERIES THROWING LIGHT ON THE ORIGIN OF THE MAMMAL-LIKE REPTILES. R. Broom. Ann. Transvaal Mus., vol.2, pt.2, pp.253-255, fig.1, Oct. 31, 1938.

ON SOME RECENT NEW LIGHT ON THE ORIGIN OF MAMMALS. R. Broom. Proc. Linnean Soc. N.S.W., vol.54, pt.5, pp. 688-694, 1929.

EVOLUTION OF CARNASSIAL DENTITIONS IN THE MAMMALIA. P.M. Butler. Proc. Zool. Soc. London, vol.116, part 2, pp.198-220, figs.13, Nov., 1946.

THEORY OF THE EVOLUTION OF MAMMALIAN MOLAR TEETH. P.M. Butler. Amer. Jour. Sci., New Haven, vol.239, no.6, pp.421-450, figs.10, June, 1941.

NOTES ON THE EVOLUTION OF THE MAMMAL-LIKE REPTILES. Frank Byrne. Trans. Kansas Acad. Sci. Topeka, vol. 43, pp.291-296, fig.1, 1940.

ANIMAL EVOLUTION. G.S. Carter. Sidzwick & Jackson, Ltd., London, pp.xv-368, illus., 1951.

SPECIATION, DEFENSE MECHANISMS IN PLANTS AND ANIMALS. BIOLOGICAL BASIS OF SOCIAL PROBLEMS. REGENERATION. Symposia Biologica. Jaques Cattell, editor. The Jaques Cattell Press, Lancaster, Pa., vol.2, pp.1-270, 1941.

(Translation by Gerrit S. Miller, Jr. of) PARASITISM AND SYMBIOSIS IN THEIR RELATION TO THE PROBLEM OF EVOLUTION. Maurice Caullery. Annual Rep. Smiths. Inst. for 1920, pp.399-409, May 16, 1922.

(ON THE SLOWNESS OF THE EVOLUTION OF THE CONTINENTAL MAMMALIAN FAUNA.) Observations sur la lenteur d'Evolution des faunes de Mammiféres continentales. P. Teilhard de Chardin. Palaeobiologica, Vienna & Leipzig, vol.1, pp.55-60, 1928.

ANIMAL EVOLUTION. Austin Clark. Proc. Nat. Acad. Sci., vol.8, no.7, pp.219-225, July, 1922.

ANIMAL EVOLUTION. Austin H. Clark. Quart. Rev. Biol., vol.3, pp.523-541, Dec., 1928.

HORSES, DOGS AND CATS. Austin H. Clark. Science, n.s., vol.70, pp.37-38, July 12, 1929.

ONTOGENY OF A GENUS. Austin H.Clark. Amer. Nat., vol.45, pp.372-374, June, 1911.

ANCESTORS OF THE EUTHERIA. W.E. Le Gros Clark. Nature, London, vol.144, no.3648, p.600, Sep. 30, 1939.

EVOLUTION OF THE VERTEBRATES. Edwin H. Colbert. John Wiley and Sons, New York, pp.XIII-479, figs.122, 1955.

PROGRESSIVE ADAPTIONS AS SEEN IN THE FOSSIL RECORD. Edwin H. Colbert. Genetics, Paleontology and Evolution, Princeton Univ. Press, pp.390-402, 1949.

TRIUMPH OF THE MAMMALS. Edwin H. Colbert. Guide leaflet series of the American Mus. of Nat. Hist., no.112, illus., 1942. Issued under the direction of the Committee on popular publications. Reprinted from Nat.Hist., vol.XLIX, no.5, and vol.L, no.1, May and June, 1942.

EVOLUTIONARY SIGNIFICANCE OF SPECIES. O.F. Cook. Smiths. Rep. for 1904, publ.1620, pp.397-412, 1905.

EVIDENCE FOR EVOLUTION IN THE HISTORY OF THE EXTINCT MAMMALIA. E.D. Cope. Proceedings of the American Assoc. for the advancement of Sci., vol.XXXII, Minneapolis meeting, Aug., 1883, Salem, Mass., Printed at the Salem press, pp.19, 1883.

PRIMARY FACTORS OF ORGANIC EVOLUTION. E.D. Cope. Chicago, Open Court Pub. Co., pp.16-532, 1896.

BACTERIAL GROWTH CURVE AND THE HISTORY OF SPECIES. A. Steven Corbet. Nature, London, vol.131, no.3298, pp.61-62, figs.1, Jan. 14, 1933.

ADAPTIVE EVOLUTION, WITH SPECIAL REFERENCE TO METAMORPHOSIS AND SEX-LIMITED CHARACTERS. J.T. Cunningham. Proc. Linn. Soc. London, 142nd sess., pp.165-186, Jan., 1931.

LAW OF INFILTRATION IN FORE-BRAIN EVOLUTION. R.A. Dart. Acta Zoologica, vol.6, pp.223-252, figs.8, 1925.

MECHANISM OF ORGANIC EVOLUTION. Charles B. Davenport. Washington Acad. Sci., vol.20, no.14, pp.317-331, figs.4, Aug. 19, 1930.

(ON CONVERGENT AND PARALLEL EVOLUTION.) A propos des evolutions convergentes et paralleles. Ed. Dechambre. Mammalia, Paris, vol.15, no.4, pp.175-183, Dec., 1951.

(Review by C. B. Davenport of) SPECIES AND VARITIES, THEIR ORIGIN BY MUTATION. Hugo de Vries. Science, n.s., vol. 22, no.560, pp.369-372, Sep. 22, 1905.

THEORETICAL EFFECTIVENESS OF ADVERSE SELECTION. Lee R. Dice. Contrib. Lab. Vert. Genetics, Univ. Michigan, Ann Arbor, no.14, pp.6, June, 1940.

PROBLEM OF SPECIES IN VIEW OF THE ORIGIN OF SOME NEW FORMS IN MICE. N. Dobrovolskaia-Zavadskaia. Biol. Reviews and Biol. Proc. Cambridge Philos. Soc., vol.4, no.4, pp.327-351, pls.8-11, Oct., 1929.

ATTEMPT TO EXHIBIT DIAGRAMMATICALLY THE SEVERAL STAGES OF EVOLUTION OF THE MAMMALIA. G.E. Dobson.

Rep. British Assn. Adv. Sci., no.54, pp. 768-769, pl.9, 1884.

EVOLUTION, GENETICS, AND MAN. T. Dobzhansky. John Wiley and Sons, Inc., New York, pp.398, illus., 1955.

GENETICS AND MACRO EVOLUTION. A REVIEW (OF "TEMPO AND MODE IN EVOLUTION," BY G. G. SIMPSON, 1944). T. Dobzhansky. Jour. Heredity, Washington, vol.36, no.4, pp.113-115, Apr., 1945.

SURVIVAL OF SPECIFIC CHARACTERS. Emmett Reid Dunn. Copeia, no.2, pp.85-98, July 16, 1935.

FORAMEN OVALE. Tilly Edinger, David B. Kitts. Evolution, Lancaster, vol.8, no.4, pp.389-404, figs.4, Dec., 1954.

(ON THE EVOLUTION AND NOMENCLATURE OF SPECIES.) Ueber Art-Wandlung und Art-Benennung. K. Ehrenberg. Biologia Gener., vol.4, nos.6-8, pp.695-712, 1928.

(ON ORTHOGENESIS AND THE WEAKNESS OF DARWINIAN SELECTION IN THE FORMATION OF SPECIES.) Ueber bestimmt gerichtete Entwicklung (Orthogenesis) und ueber Ohnmacht der Darwin'schen Zuchtwahl bei der Artbildung. G.H. Theodor Eimer. Compte-Rendu Seances 3me Congress internat. Zool., Leyden, pp.145-169, Sep. 16-21, 1895.

EVOLUTION OF THE HUMAN FOOT, WITH ESPECIAL REFERENCE TO THE JOINTS. Herbert Elftman, John Manter. Jour. Anat., Cambridge, vol.70, pt.1, pp.56-67, figs.6, Oct., 1935.

MORPHOLOGY AND FUNCTIONAL EVOLUTION OF THE ATLASAXIS COMPLEX FROM FISH TO MAMMALS. Francis Gaynor Evans. Ann. New York Acad. Sci., vol.39, art.2, pp.29-104, figs.15, July 13, 1939.

SPECIES PROBLEM. Knut Faegri. Nature, London, vol.136, no.3450, pp.954-955, Dec. 14, 1935.

EVOLUTION OF THE UNGULATE MAMMALS. Herman LeRoy Fairchild. Proc. Rochester Acad. Sci., vol.11, pp.206-209, June, 1894.

(SIGNIFICANCE OF RACE CONCEPT.) Die Bedeutung des Rassebegriffes. Ernst Feige. Naturwiss., vol.17, no.34, pp. 719-724, figs.8, Sep. 13, 1929.

NATURAL SELECTION. E.B. Ford. Nature, London, vol.138, no.3503, pp.1053-1054, Dec. 19, 1936.

(ON THE EVOLUTION OF THE DENTITION OF MAMMALS.) Sur l'evolution de la dentition des mammiferes. Serge Frechkop. Soc. Roy. Zool. Belgique, Bruxelles, vol.6, pp. 38-56, figs.13, 1935.

(REMARKS ON THE EVOLUTION OF THE MOLARS IN THE MAMMALS.) Remarques sur l'évolution des dents molaires chez les mammifères, par E. Patte. Serge Frechkop. Questions Sci. Louvain, pp.177-180, July 20, 1935.

(COMPARATIVE EVOLUTION OF UPPER MOLARS IN PRIMATES AND PRIMITIVE INSECTIVORES.) L'evolution comparée des molaires supérieures chez les primates et les insectivores primitifs. Madeleine Friant. Comptes Rendus Acad. Sci., Paris, vol.198, no.18, pp.1622-1624, Apr.30, 1934.

(MORPHOLOGICAL EVOLUTION OF THE DENTITION OF PLACENTAL MAMMALS.) L'évolution morphologique de la dentition chez les mammifères placentaires. Madeleine Friant. Mensuels Soc. Nat. Luxembourgeois, n.s., ann. 29, pp.45-57, figs.12, 1935.

(RESEARCH ON THE EVOLUTION OF THE DENTITION OF PLACENTAL MAMMALS STARTING FROM THE BEGINNING OF THE TERTIARY PERIOD.) Expose de recherches sur l'évolution de la dentition des Mammifères placentaires a partir du début des temps tertaires. M. Friant. Bull. Soc. Fribourgeoise Sci. nat. C.R., 1924-35 et 1935-36, Fribourg, vol.33, pp.124-130, 1937.

SIGNIFICANCE OF DIVERGENCE OF THE FIRST DIGIT IN THE PRIMITIVE MAMMALIAN FOOT. James William Gidley. Jour. Washington Acad. Sci., vol.9, pp. 273-280, May 19, 1919.

DOCTRINE OF DARWIN. Theodore Gill. Proc. Biol. Soc. Washington, vol.1, pp. 47-55, 1882.

ALBERT GAUDRY AND THE EVOLUTION OF THE ANIMAL KINGDOM. Philippe Glangeaud. Smiths. Inst., Annual Rep., 1909, Washington, pp.417-429, 1910. Translated from Rev. générale des sciences pures et appliquées, Paris, 20th year, no. 6, Mar. 30, 1909.

DARWINIAN INTERPRETATIONS. E.S. Goodrich. Eugenics Rev., vol.19, pp.114-115, July, 1927.

GENERAL FUNCTION OF THE GALL BLADDER FROM THE EVOLUTIONARY STANDPOINT. Frank W. Gorham, Andrew Conway Ivy. Field Mus. Nat. Hist, Chicago, zool. ser., vol.22, no.3, pp.159-213, June 21, 1938.

ZOOLOGY SINCE DARWIN. Ludwig von Graff. Smiths. Inst., Annual Rep., 1895, Washington, pp.477-491, pl.XXVII, 1896. Translated from original, "Die Zoologie seit Darwin," Graz, 1896.

BASIC PATENTS IN EVOLUTION. I, II, III. W.K. Gregory. Scientific American, pp.112-113, 200-202, 286-288, figs.18, Aug.-Sep.-Oct., 1930.

BASIC PATENTS IN NATURE. W.K. Gregory. Science, n.s., vol.78, no.2034, pp.561-566, Dec. 22, 1933.

CERTAIN CRITICAL STAGES IN THE EVOLUTION OF THE VERTEBRATE JAWS. W.K. Gregory. Jour. Orthodontia, Oral Surg. and Radiography, St. Louis. vol.17, no.12, pp. 1138-1148, figs.6, Dec., 1931.

EARLIEST KNOWN FOSSIL STAGES IN THE EVOLUTION OF THE ORAL CAVITY AND JAWS. W.K. Gregory. Amer. Jour. Orthodontics and Oral Surgery, St. Louis, vol.29, no.5, pp.1-24, figs.22, May, 1943.

EVOLUTION EMERGING. W.K. Gregory. Macmillan Co., New York, vol.I, pp.1-736, text; vol.II, pp.1-1013, illus., 1951.

(Review by R.A. Stirton of) EVOLUTION EMERGING. W.K. Gregory. Jour. Mamm., vol.33, no.2, pp.261-262, May 16, 1952.

EVOLUTION OF ORTHODONTY. W.K. Gregory, Dental Cosmos, pp.11, figs.9, May, 1918.

EVOLUTION OF THE HUMAN FACE. ESPECIALLY THE STORY OF THE EVOLUTION FROM FISH TO MAN, OF THE LACRYMAL BONE AS ONE OF THE BONES AROUND THE EYE SOCKET. W.K. Gregory. Nat. Hist., vol.19, nos. 4-5, pp.421-425, illus., 1919.

FACT AND THEORIES OF EVOLUTION, WITH SPECIAL REFERENCE TO THE ORIGIN OF MAN. W. K. Gregory. Dental Cosmos, pp.1-19 (of reprint), Mar., 1920. (Lecture delivered before the annual meeting of the Eastern Assoc. of Graduates of the Angle School of Orthodontia, New York City, May 5 and 6, 1919.)

HALF CENTURY OF TRITUBERCULY; THE COPE-OSBORN THEORY OF DENTAL EVOLUTION WITH A REVISED SUMMARY OF MOLAR EVOLUTION FROM FISH TO MAN. W.K. Gregory. Proc. Amer. Philos. Soc., vol.73, no.4, pp.169-317, figs.71, Apr., 1934.

NEW ANTHROPOGENY: TWENTY-FIVE STAGES OF VERTEBRATE EVOLUTION, FROM SILURIAN CHORDATE TO MAN. W.K. Gregory. Science, vol.77, no.1985, pp.29-40, Jan. 13, 1933.

ON DESIGN IN NATURE. W.K. Gregory. Yale Rev., pp.12, Jan., 1924.

ON THE EVOLUTION OF THE SKULLS OF VERTEBRATES WITH SPECIAL REFERENCE TO HERITABLE CHANGES IN PROPORTIONAL DIAMETERS (ANISOMERISM). W.K. Gregory. Proc. Nat. Acad. Sci., vol.21, no.1, pp.1-8, figs.3, Jan., 1935.

ON THE MEANING AND LIMITS OF IRREVERSIBILITY OF EVOLUTION. W.K. Gregory, Amer. Naturalist, vol.70, pp. 517-528, Dec., 1936.

OUR FACE FROM FISH TO MAN. W.K. Gregory. New York, G.P. Putnam's Sons, vol.8, pp.xl.- 295, pl.1, text figs.118, Apr., 1929.

PELVIS FROM FISH TO MAN: A STUDY IN PALEOMORPHOLOGY. W.K. Gregory. Amer. Naturalist, vol.69, pp.193-210, figs. 12, May-June, 1935.

POLYSOMERISM AND ANISOMERISM IN CRANIAL AND DENTAL EVOLUTION AMONG VERTEBRATES. W.K. Gregory. Proc. Nat. Acad. Sci., Washington, D.C., vol.20, no.1, pp.1-9, Jan., 1934.

REDUPLICATION IN EVOLUTION. W.K. Gregory. Quart. Rev. Biol., Baltimore, vol.10, no.3, pp.272-290, figs.12, Sep., 1935.

(Review by Ned Hollister of) REVIEW OF THE EVOLUTION OF THE LACRYMAL BONE OF VERTEBRATES WITH SPECIAL REFERENCE TO THAT OF MAMMALS. W.K. Gregory. Jour. Mamm., vol.2, no.2, pp.118-119, May 2, 1921.

ROLES OF MOTILE LARVAE AND FIXED ADULTS IN THE ORIGIN OF THE VERTEBRATES. W.K. Gregory. Quart. Review Biol., Baltimore, vol.21, no.4, pp.348-364, figs.12, Dec., 1946.

STUDIES IN COMPARATIVE MYOLOGY AND OSTEOLOGY; NO.IV. A REVIEW OF THE EVOLUTION OF THE LACRYMAL BONE OF VERTEBRATES WITH SPECIAL REFERENCE TO THAT OF MAMMALS. W.K. Gregory. Bull. Amer. Mus. Nat. Hist., vol.42, art.2, pp.95-263, figs.196, pl.17, Dec. 4, 1920.

TRANSFORMATION OF ORGANIC DESIGNS: A REVIEW OF THE ORIGIN AND DEPLOYMENT OF THE EARLIER VERTEBRATES. W.K. Gregory. Biol. Reviews, Cambridge Philos. Soc., vol.11, no.3, pp.311-344, July, 1936.

'WILLISTON'S LAW' RELATING TO THE EVOLUTION OF SKULL BONES IN THE VERTEBRATES. W.K. Gregory. Amer. Jour. Phys. Anthrop., vol.20, no.2, pp.123-152, figs.4, July-Sep., 1935.

GEOGRAPHY AND EVOLUTION. Joseph Grinnell. Ecology, vol.5, no.3, pp.225-229, July, 1924.

ON THE DIFFERENT TYPES OF VARIATION OF CHARACTERS IN THE EVOLUTION OF ANIMALS. Vera Gromova. Comptes Rendus (Doklady) Acad. Sci. USSR, Moscow, vol.54, no.5, pp.441-444, Nov. 20, 1946.

DIVERGENT EVOLUTION THROUGH CUMULATIVE SEGREGATION. John Thomas Gulick. Smiths. Inst., Annual Rep., 1891, Washington, pp.269-336, tbls., 1893. (From the Jour. of Zool. of the Linnean Soc., vol. xx, pp.189-274, 1888.)

EVOLUTION OF EPIPHYSES AND OF ENDOCHONDRAL BONE. R. Wheeler Haines. Biol. Rev. Cambridge Philos. Soc., vol.17, no.4, pp.267-292, figs. 10, Oct., 1942.

NATURAL SELECTION. J.B.S. Haldane. Nature, London, vol.138, no.3503, p.1053, Dec. 19, 1936.

EVOLUTION OF MAMMALS, INCLUDING MODERN MAN. James Coffee Harris. Cave Spring, Ga., pp.43, illus., diagrs., 1934.

(PIONEERS OF THE MAMMAL FAMILY.) Die Pioniere des Saeugetier-Stammes. E. Henning. Natur und Museum, Frankfurt a.M., vol.57, no.5, pp.201-209, figs.8, May, 1927.

IRREVERSIBLE DIFFERENTIATION AND ORTHOGENESIS. C.J. Herrick. Science, n.s., vol.51, no.1330, pp.621-625, June 25, 1920.

HABIT AND ENVIRONMENT AS MAKERS OF SPECIES. Martin A.C. Hinton. Eugenics Rev., vol.19, pp.109-113, July, 1927.

FORGOTTEN EVOLUTIONIST. S.J. Holmes. Science, n.s., vol.77, no.1985, pp.48-49, Jan. 13, 1933.

RECAPITULATION AND ITS SUPPOSED CAUSES. S.J. Holmes. Quart. Rev. Biol., Baltimore, vol.19, no.4, pp.319-331, Dec., 1944.

MAMMALIAN EVOLUTION IN THE QUATERNARY OF SOUTHERN AND EASTERN ASIA. D.A. Hooijer. Evolution, Lancaster, vol.3, no.2, pp.125-128, June, 1949.

STUDY OF SUBSPECIFIC ADVANCE IN THE QUATERNARY. D.A. Hooijer. Evolution, Lancaster, vol.4, no.4, pp.360-361, Dec., 1950.

WAGES OF BIOLOGICAL SIN. Earnest Albert Hooton. Atlantic Monthly, vol.164, no.4, pp.435-445, Oct., 1939.

ORGANIC EVOLUTION. ITS PROBLEMS AND PERPLEXITIES. Ales Hrdlicka. Science, vol.71, no.1835, pp.230-233, Feb. 28, 1930.

CONCEPTS OF HOMOLOGY AND ANALOGY. Carl L. Hubbs. Amer. Nat., Lancaster, vol.78, pp.289-307, July-Aug., 1944.

EVOLUTION OF FACIAL MUSCULATURE AND CUTANEOUS FIELD OF TRIGEMINUS. Pt. I. Ernst Huber. Quart.Rev.Biol., vol.5, no.2, pp.133-188, figs.26, June, 1930; Pt. II. vol.5, no.4, pp.389-437, figs. 27-46, Dec., 1930.

EVOLUTION OF FACIAL MUSCULATURE AND FACIAL EXPRESSION. Ernst Huber. Baltimore, Johns Hopkins Press, pp.xii-184, figs.28, 1931.

(Review by C. Tate Regan of) EVOLUTION OF FACIAL MUSCULATURE AND FACIAL EXPRESSION. Ernst Huber. Ann. & Mag. Nat. Hist., ser.10, vol.8, no.47, pp.557-559, Nov., 1931.

EVOLUTION, THE MODERN SYNTHESIS. J. Huxley. London and New York, numerous English editions and one American edition. 1943.

EVOLUTIONARY PROCESS (pp.1-23). In Evolution as a process. J. Huxley, editor. George Allen and Unwin, London, pp.8-367, 1954.

SPECIES AND EVOLUTION. J. Huxley. Endeavor, London, vol.5, no.17, pp.3-12, figs.1-9, Jan., 1946.

INTERPRETERS OF GENESIS AND THE INTERPRETERS OF NATURE. T.S. Huxley. Popular Sci. Monthly, vol.28, pp.449-460, Feb., 1886.

(ATLAS OF BRAINS OF MAMMALS OF THE REPUBLIC OF ARGENTINA; ANATOMICAL, HISTOLOGICAL, AND BIOLOGICAL COMPARATIVE STUDIES OF THE EVOLUTION OF THE CEREBRAL HEMISPHERES AND CORTEX.) Atlas del cerebro de los mamiferos de la Republica Argentina; estudios anatomicos, histologicos y biologicos comparados, sobre la evolucion de los hemisferios y de la corteza cerebral. Christfried Jakob. Presentado al Congreso cientifico internacional americano de 1910 y publicado con fondos del mismo congreso. Buenos Aires, Imprenta de G. Kraft, pp.102, 1913.

DISCUSSION. SYSTEMATICS AND THE ORIGIN OF SPECIES, FROM THE VIEWPOINT OF A ZOOLOGIST. Glenn L. Jepsen. Amer. Jour. Sci., New Haven, vol.241, pp.521-528, Aug., 1943.

SELECTION, "ORTHOGENESIS" AND THE FOSSIL RECORD. Glenn L. Jepson. Proc. Amer. Philos. Soc., Philadelphia, vol.93, no.6, pp.479-500, Dec., 1949.

GENETICS, PALEONTOLOGY AND EVOLUTION. Glenn L. Jepsen, Kenneth W. Cooper. Princeton Univ. Bicentennial Conf., ser.2, conf.3, pp.1-37, illus., 1948.

GENETICS, PALEONTOLOGY AND EVOLUTION. Glenn L. Jepsen, George Gaylord Simpson, Ernst Mayr, editors. Princeton Univ. Press, pp.xiv-474, illus., 1949.

ISOLATION WITH SEGREGATION AS A FACTOR IN ORGANIC EVOLUTION. David Starr Jordan. Smiths. Inst., Annual Rep., 1925, Washington, pp.321-326, 1926.

ORIGIN OF THE MAMMALS. J.S. Kingsley. Science, n.s., vol.14, no.345, pp.193-205, figs.A-E, Aug. 9, 1901.

(Review of) FORMENKREIS THEORY AND THE PROGRESS OF THE ORGANIC WORLD. O.Kleinschmidt. Translated by F.C.R. Jourdain. H.F. and G. Witherby, London, pp.192; Jour. Bombay Nat. Hist. Soc., vol. 41, no.1, pp.163, 1939.

DESINTEGRATION AND DESINTEGRATIVE FACTORS IN THE PROCESS OF EVOLUTION. Ch.S. Koshtojanz. Zool. Jour. USSR, Moscow, vol.22, no.3, pp.131-137, 1943. (English summary.)

DIRECT ACTION OF ENVIRONMENT AND EVOLUTION. Petr Aleksieevich Kropotkin. Smiths. Inst., Annual Rep., 1918, Washington, pp.400-427, 1820.

(ORIGIN OF MAMMALS.) Ursprung der Saeugetiere. Emil Kuhn-Schnyder. Vierteljahrsschrift Naturforsch. Gesell. Zuerich, IC (1954), pp.165-197, illus., Sep. 30, 1954.

BUT IF IT BE A FOSSIL! Francis P. LeBuffe. America, vol.46, pp.158-159, Nov. 21, 1931.

"GOD" AND SOME SCIENTISTS. Francis P. LeBuffe. America, N.Y., pp.1-32, 1931.

MISGUIDED EVOLUTIONISTS. Francis P. LeBuffe. America, pp.1-24, 1931.

SO THIS IS EVOLUTION! Francis P. Le Buffe. 1st printing, pp.32, America, 1931.

GENESIS OF SEX. Joseph Le Conte. Popular Sci. Monthly, pp.167-179, fig.1, Dec., 1879.

ON TIME AND SURVIVAL. A.Starker Leopold. Pacific Discovery, California Acad. Sci., San Francisco, vol.1, no.6, pp.28-29, Nov.-Dec., 1948.

REVIEW OF OSBORN'S "EVOLUTION OF MAMMALIAN MOLAR TEETH TO AND FROM THE TRIANGULAR TYPE". Richard S. Lull. Science, n.s., vol.27, no.687, pp.341-342, Feb. 28, 1908.

FURTHER EVIDENCE FOR THE LAMARCKIAN THEORY OF THE CAUSE OF EVOLUTION. E.W. MacBride. Nature, London, vol.143, no.3614, pp.205-206, Feb. 4, 1939.

DARWINISM REPROVED AND REFUTED. Louis Mackall. Washington City, pp.1-25, 1873.

ORGANIC EVOLUTION: DARWINIAN AND DE VRIESIAN. Nottidge Charles Macnamara. Smiths. Inst., Annual Rep., 1911, Washington, pp.363-378, 1912.

(EVOLUTION OF THE WRIST OF MAMMALS.) Voprosi evolutsii kisti mlykopitayushchikh. S.F. Manzii. Zool. Zhurnal, Moscow, vol.32, no.4, pp.756-765, 1953.

(THEORETICAL-CRITICAL REMARKS ON THE THEORY OF VARIATION.) Theoretisch-kritische Bemerkungen zur Variationslehre. W. Marinelli. Biologia Generalis, Vienna, Bd.4, Lief.1-2, pp.103-130, 1928.

ANTI-EVOLUTION: GIRARDEAU VERSUS WOODROW. James L. Martin. Memphis, Tenn., pp.1-16, Aug. 25, 1888.

CREATION BY EVOLUTION. Francis Mason. Macmillan Co., New York, pp.vii-xx-1-392, figs., 1928. (Contributions by 26 authors.)

(THE EVOLUTION OF THE CHROMOSOMAL FORMULA IN THE VERTEBRATES.) L'évolution de la formula chromosomiale chez les Vertebres. R. Matthey. Experientia, Basel, vol.1, no.2, pp.50-56, May 15, 1945; vol.1, no.3, pp.78-86, June 15, 1945.

CLIMATE AND EVOLUTION. W.D.Matthew. Second edition, revised and enlarged.Special Publ. New York Acad. Sci., vol.1, pp.xii-223, figs.33, June 15, 1939.

PATTERN OF EVOLUTION. CRITICISM OF DOCTOR AUSTIN CLARK'S THESIS. W.D. Matthew. Scientific American, New York, pp.192-196, Sep., 1930.

TIME RATIOS IN THE EVOLUTION OF MAMMALIAN PHYLA. CONTRIBUTION TO THE PROBLEM OF THE AGE OF THE EARTH. W.D. Matthew. Science, Lancaster, vol.40, no.1024, pp.232-235, Aug. 14, 1914.

ON THE SYSTEM OF CORRELATIVE VARIATIONS OF FORM, FUNCTION AND ENVIRONMENT IN THE EVOLUTION OF ANIMALS. B.S. Matveiev. Zool.Jour. USSR, Moscow, vol.24, no.1, pp.1-22, chart 1, 1945. (English summary.)

CHANGE OF GENETIC ENVIRONMENT AND EVOLUTION (pp.157-180). In Evolution as a Process, ed. by Julian Huxley. E.Mayr. George Allen and Unwin, London, pp.8-367, 1954.

SYSTEMATICS AND THE ORIGIN OF SPECIES FROM THE VIEWPOINT OF A ZOOLOGIST. E. Mayr. Columbia Univ. Press, New York, Columbia Biol. Ser., no.13, pp. x-334, figs.29, 1942.

LECTURES UPON EVOLUTION AND ANIMAL DISTRIBUTION. (MAN'S ORIGIN AND THE METHOD OF HIS EVOLUTION. Pp.111-131.) (MAN'S FUTURE; CAN HE CONTROL IT? Pp.132-151.) (ANIMAL DISTRIBUTION AND ANCIENT DISTRIBUTION ROUTES. Pp. 152-183.) Maynard M. Metcalf. Univ. of Buffalo Studies, vol.2, no.4, pp.111-183, figs.26, Dec., 1922.

ECOLOGIC FACTORS THAT ACCELERATE FORMATION OF RACES AND SPECIES OF TERRESTRIAL VERTEBRATES. Alden H. Miller. Evolution, vol.10, no.3, pp.262-277, Sep., 1956.

HABITAT SELECTION AMONG HIGHER VERTEBRATES AND ITS RELATION TO INTRASPECIFIC VARIATION. Alden H. Miller. Amer. Nat., Lancaster, vol.76, no.762, pp.25-35, Jan.-Feb., 1942.

WHAT AMERICAN ZOOLOGISTS HAVE DONE FOR EVOLUTION. Edward S. Morse. Popular Sci. Monthly, vol.31, no.6, pp. 804-813, Oct., 1887.

SPECIAL CREATION AND EVOLUTION. AN EXPOSITION OF THE OPENING CHAPTERS OF MR. HERBERT SPENCER'S "PRINCIPLES OF BIOLOGY," PART III. Constance C. W. Naden. Birmingham Nat. Hist. and Microscop. Soc., Sociol. Sect., pp.15, 1885.

ON TYPICAL SELECTION, AS A MEANS OF REMOVING THE DIFFICULTIES ATTENDING THE DOCTRINE OF THE ORIGIN OF SPECIES OF NATURAL SELECTION. E. Vansittart Neale. Proc. Zool. Soc. London, pt.29, pp.1-11, 1861.

EVOLUTION, GENETICS AND EUGENICS. H.H. Newman. Chicago, 3rd ed. pp.644, 1932.

RE SPECIATION WITHOUT CLIMATIC CHANGE OR GEOGRAPHIC ISOLATION. J. T. Nichols. Science, n.s., vol.67, pp.346-347, Mar. 30, 1928.

WHAT PRODUCES SPECIES? RECENT LABORATORY AND FIELD WORK GIVE A SOLUTION TO A PROBLEM OF LONG STANDING. G. Kingsley Noble. Nat. Hist., New York, vol.30, no.1, pp.60-70, illus., Jan-Feb., 1930.

HEREDITY AND EVOLUTION. Francis Nopesa. Proc. Zool. Soc. London, pp. 633-665, illus., July, 1926.

ORIGIN OF MAMMALS BASED UPON CRANIAL MORPHOLOGY OF THE THERAPSID SUBORDERS. Everett C. Olson. Geol. Soc. America, Baltimore, Special papers no.55, pp.xi-136, figs. 27, June, 1944.

EVOLUTION OF MAMMALIAN MOLAR TEETH TO AND FROM THE TRIANGULAR TYPE. Henry Fairfield Osborn. Macmillan Co., London, pp.250, illus., 1907.

EVOLUTION OF THE AMBLYPODA. PART I. TALIGRADA AND PANTODONTA. Henry Fairfield Osborn. Bull. Amer. Mus. Nat. Hist., New York, vol.10, art.11, pp.169-218, figs.29, June 3, 1898.

HOMOPLASY AS A LAW OF LATENT OR POTENTIAL HOMOLOGY. Henry Fairfield Osborn. Amer. Nat., Boston, vol.36, no. 424, pp.259-271, figs.6, Apr., 1902.

LAW OF ADAPTIVE RADIATION. Henry Fairfield Osborn. Amer. Nat., Boston, vol.36, no.425, pp.353-363, figs.4, May, 1902.

NEW CONCEPT OF EVOLUTION BASED UPON RESEARCHES ON THE TITANOTHERES AND THE PROBOSCIDEANS.

Henry Fairfield Osborn. Science, n.s., vol.74, no.1927, pp.557-559, Dec. 4, 1931.

NINE PRINCIPLES OF EVOLUTION REVEALED BY PALEONTOLOGY. Henry Fairfield Osborn. American Naturalist, vol.66, no.702, pp.52-60, Jan.-Feb., 1932.

ORIGIN OF SINGLE CHARACTERS AS OBSERVED IN FOSSIL AND LIVING ANIMALS AND PLANTS. Henry Fairfield Osborn. Amer. Nat., Lancaster, vol.49, no.580, pp.193-240, figs.10, Apr., 1915.

ORIGIN OF SPECIES, 1859-1925. Henry Fairfield Osborn. Sci. Monthly, Lancaster, vol.22, pp.185-192, Mar., 1926.

ORIGIN OF SPECIES. II. DISTINCTIONS BETWEEN RECTIGRADATIONS AND ALLOMETRONS. Henry Fairfield Osborn. Proc. Nat. Acad. Sci., Washington, D.C., vol. 11, no.12, pp.749-752, Dec., 1925.

ORIGIN OF SPECIES. V. SPECIATION AND MUTATION. Henry Fairfield Osborn. Amer. Nat., vol.41, no.672, pp.5-42, 1927.

ORIGIN OF SPECIES AS REVEALED BY VERTEBRATE PALAEONTOLOGY. Henry Fairfield Osborn. Nature, London, vol.115, no.2902, pp.925-926; no.2903, pp.961-963, June 13, 20, 1925.

PRESENT PROBLEMS IN EVOLUTION AND HEREDITY. Henry Fairfield Osborn. Smiths. Inst., Annual Rep., 1892, Washington, pp. 313-374, tbl., diagrs., 1893.

RECENT REVIVALS OF DARWINISM. Henry Fairfield Osborn. Science, n.s., vol.77, no.1991, pp.199-202, Feb. 24, 1933.

THE RISE OF THE MAMMALIA IN NORTH AMERICA. Henry Fairfield Osborn. Studies Biol. Lab. Columbia Coll., Zoology, Boston, vol.1, no.2, pp.45, illus., 1893.

OBSERVATIONS ON THE ORIGIN OF THE PAIRED LIMBS OF VERTEBRATES. Raymond C. Osburn. Amer. Jour. Anat., vol.7, no.2, pp.171-194, pls.5, Aug. 1, 1907.

NINE LECTURES ON MAMMALIAN DESCENT. (ANNOUNCEMENT OF LECTURE SERIES.) W. K. Parker. Roy. Coll. Surgeons England, p.1, 1884.

ON MAMMALIAN DESCENT (BEING) THE HUNTERIAN LECTURES FOR 1884. W.K. Parker. London, pp.229, illus., 1885.

ON THE EVOLUTION OF THE MAMMALIAN PALATE. F. R. Parrington, T.S. Westoll. Philos. Trans. Roy. Soc. London, vol.230, no.571, pp.305-355, illus., June, 1940.

(REMARKS ON THE EVOLUTION OF MOLARS IN MAMMALS. THE PALEONTOLOGY AND GREAT PROBLEMS OF GENERAL BIOLOGY.) Remarques sur l'évolution des dents molaires chez les mammiferes. La Paléontologie et les grands problemes de la biologie generale. Etienne Patte. Actualites scientifiques et industrielles, no.176, Paris, Herman & Cie, pp.49, figs.6, 1934.

EARLY CRETACEOUS MAMMALS AND THE EVOLUTION OF MAMMALIAN MOLAR TEETH. Bryan Patterson. Fieldiana, Geol., Chicago, vol.13, no.1, pp.1-105, illus., Dec. 28, 1956.

EVOLUTION AND MORTALITY. Raymond Pearl. Quart. Rev. Biol., vol.3, pp.271-280, June, 1928.

HISTORIC DEVELOPMENT OF THE EVOLUTIONARY IDEA. Branislav Petrinievics. Smiths. Inst., Annual Rep., 1921, Washington, pp.325-334, 1922. Translated from L'évolution universelle, Paris, 1921.

(LAW OF NONCORRELATIVE EVOLUTION.) La loi de l'évolution non correlative. Branislav Petronievics. Rev. Gen. Sci., Paris, vol.30, pp. 3-10, Apr., 1919.

ON THE LAW OF IRREVERSIBLE EVOLUTION. Branislav Petronievics. Ann. Rep. Smiths. Inst., 1918, pp.429-440, 1920.

ON THE DIFFICULTIES ENCOUNTERED IN THE EVOLUTION OF AIR-BREATHING VERTEBRATES. F.H. Pike. Science, n.s., vol.59, pp.402-403, May 2, 1924.

(THE ADVENT OF THE MAMMALS.) L'apparition des mammiféres. Jean Piveteau. Mammalia, Paris, vol.10, nos.1-2, pp.18-29, figs.11, Mar.-June, 1947.

(THE ORIGIN OF MAMMALS.) L'origine des mammiferes. Jean Piveteau. Mammalia, Paris, vol.1, no.5, pp.189-204, figs.12, Sep., 1937.

EMERGENT EVOLUTION. W.P. Pycraft. Illus. London News, vol.192, no.5135, p.125, figs.3, Jan. 22, 1938.

PUZZLES OF EVOLUTION. W.P. Pycraft. Illus. London News, vol.195, no.5236, p.340, illus., Aug. 26, 1939.

SOME NEW ASPECTS OF EVOLUTION. W. P. Pycraft. Trans. Norfolk and Norwich Nat. Soc., vol.14, pt.1, pp.1-30, pls.4, (1935) 1936.

ICE AGE AND MAMMAL SPECIATION IN NORTH AMERICA. A.L. Rand. Arctic, Montreal, vol.7, no.1, pp.31-35, June, 1954.

POSSIBLE SELECTIVE MECHANISM IN THE EVOLUTION OF THE VERTEBRATE HEART. W.D.L. Ride. Proc. Zool. Soc. London, vol.123, pt.4, pp.753-755, Feb. 10, 1954.

PRINCIPLE OF EVOLUTION OF NERVOUS FUNCTION. Walther Riese. Jour. Nervous and Mental Disease, Chicago, vol.98, no. 3, pp.255-266, Sep., 1943.

CONVERGENCE IN ANIMALS PAST AND PRESENT-UNRELATED SPECIES WITH SIMILAR TRENDS. Elmer S. Riggs. Field Mus. News, Chicago, vol.11, no.9, p.5, Sep., 1940.

(RESEARCH ON SANGUINE GROUPS AND THE PROBLEM OF SPECIES.) Le recherches sur les groupes sanguins et le probleme de l'espece. P. Rode. Archiv. Mus. Nat. d'Hist. Nat., Paris, ser.6, vol.12, pp.497-503, June, 1935.

REPLY TO "FALLACIES OF EVOLUTION". George J. Romanes. Popular Science Monthly, pp.101-114, 1879.

TIME SERIES AND TRENDS IN ANIMAL EVOLUTION. Alfred Sherwood Romer. Genetics, Paleontology, and Evolution, Princeton Univ. Press, pp.103-120, 1949.

USE AND DISUSE. W.E. Rotzell. Hahnemannian Monthly, Philadelphia, vol.31, no.11, pp.721-726, Nov., 1896.

ON THE DEVELOPMENT OF THE CETACEA, TOGETHER WITH A CONSIDERATION OF THE PROBABLE HOMOLOGIES OF THE FLUKES OF CETACEANS AND SIRENIANS. John A. Ryder. Rep. U.S. Comm. Fish and Fisheries, Washington, D.C., 1885, pt.13, appendix D, pp.427-488, pls.3, figs.3, 1887.

FACTORS OF EVOLUTION. I.I. Schmalhausen. Translated by Isadore Dordick and edited by Theodosius Dobzyhansky. Blakiston, Philadelphia, pp.xiv-427, illus., 1949.

(MAMMALS IN THEIR RELATIONSHIP TO ANTIQUITY.) Die Saeugethiere in ihrem Verhaeltniss zur Vorwelt. Eduard Oskar Schmidt. E.A. Brockhaus, Leipzig, pp. xii-280, illus., 1884.

COROLLARY AND COMMENTARY FOR "CLIMATE AND EVOLUTION." Karl P. Schmidt. Amer. Midland Nat., Notre Dame, vol.30, no.1, pp.241-253, July, 1943.

OUR FRIENDLY ANIMALS AND WHENCE THEY CAME. Karl P. Schmidt. Illustrated by Walter Alois Weber. M.A.Donohue and Co., Chicago, pp.54, col.illus.12, many vignettes, 4to, boards.

EVOLUTION OF CLIMATIC ADAPTATION IN HOMEOTHERMS. P.F. Scholander. Evolution, Lancaster, vol.9, no.1, pp.15-26, illus., Mar., 1955.

STUDIES ON THE EVOLUTION OF HUMAN TEETH. Adolph H. Schultz. Dental Cosmos for Oct.-Nov., 1925, pp.1-24 (of reprint), Nov., 1925.

LAWS OF MAMMALIAN EVOLUTION. W.B. Scott. Sci. Monthly, vol.43, pp.421-429, Nov., 1936.

ORIGIN OF THE MAMMALIAN FAUNAS OF NORTH AND SOUTH AMERICA. W.B. Scott. Palaeobiologica, Vienna, vol.1, pp.253-262, 1928.

EVOLUTIONARY FORCE OF A WIDE RANGE. Ernest Thompson Seton. Jour. Mamm., vol. 3, no.5, pp.167-169, Aug., 1922.

EVOLUTION OF THE MAMMALIAN EAR DRUM AND TYMPANIC CAVITY. C.C.D. Shute. Jour. Anat., Cambridge, England, vol.90, no.2, pp.261-281, Apr., 1956.

CRITIQUE OF A NEW THEORY OF MAMMALIAN DENTAL EVOLUTION. George Gaylord Simpson. Jour. Dental Research, vol.13, no.4, pp.261-272, Aug., 1933.

EVOLUTION UP TO DATE. A REVIEW. George Gaylord Simpson. Jour. Heredity, Baltimore, vol.41, no.4, pp.110-112, Apr., 1950.

EVOLUTIONARY DETERMINISM AND THE FOSSIL RECORD. George Gaylord Simpson. Sci. Monthly, Lancaster, vol.71, no.4, pp.262-267, Oct., 1950.

MAJOR FEATURES OF EVOLUTION. George Gaylord Simpson. Columbia Univ. Press, New York City, pp.XX-434, figs.52, tbls.28, 1953.

MEANING OF EVOLUTION. George Gaylord Simpson. Yale Univ. Press, New Haven, pp.xv-364, figs.38, 1949.

ORIGIN OF MAMMALIAN FAUNAS AS ILLUSTRATED BY THAT OF FLORIDA. George Gaylord Simpson. American Naturalist, vol. 65, no.698, pp.258-276, May-June, 1931.

PATTERNS OF PHYLETIC EVOLUTION. George Gaylord Simpson. Bull. Geolog. Soc., Amer., vol.48, pp.303-314, figs.7, Mar. 1, 1937.

PRE-CRETACEOUS EVOLUTION OF MAMMALIAN LOWER MOLARS. George Gaylord Simpson. Abstract. Bull. Geol. Soc. Amer., vol.37, p.238, Mar., 1926.

RISE OF THE MAMMALS; AFTER DOMINATING THE WORLD FOR MILLIONS OF YEARS THE DINOSAURS COME TO AN ABRUPT END AND THE MEEK INHERIT THE EARTH. George Gaylord Simpson. New York, illus., 1942. (Guide leaflet series of the American Mus. of Nat. Hist., no.110.) Reprinted from Nat. Hist., vol.49, Feb. and Apr., 1942.

ROLE OF THE INDIVIDUAL IN EVOLUTION. George Gaylord Simpson. Jour. Washington Acad. Sci., vol.31, no.1, pp.1-20, Jan. 15, 1941.

SPECIES CONCEPT. George Gaylord Simpson. Evolution, Lancaster, vol.5, no.4, pp.285-298, Dec., 1951.

TEMPO AND MODE IN EVOLUTION. George Gaylord Simpson. Trans. New York Acad. Sci., ser.2, vol.8, no.2, pp.45-60, Dec., 1945.

(ON THE ORIGIN OF THE MAMMALS (MAMMALIA).) Ueber den Ursprung der Saeugetiere (Mammalia). V. Sixta. Zool Anzeiger, Leipzig, vol.28, nos.19-20, pp.671-678, Mar. 28, 1905.

EVOLUTIONARY TENDENCIES IN THE JAWS. G. Elliot Smith. Internat. Jour. Orthodontia, Oral Surgery and Radiogr., St. Louis, vol.18, no.9, pp.918-926, figs.3, Sep., 1932.

FACTORS OF ORGANIC EVOLUTION. Herbert Spencer. Popular Science Monthly, pp.54-63, May, 1886.

ON THE EVOLUTION OF THE FAMILY. Herbert Spencer. Popular Science Monthly, pp.129-142, June, 1877.

ISOLATION VERSUS NATURAL SELECTION. Leonhard Stejneger, Auk, vol.23, no.3, pp. 265-270, July, 1906.

OBSERVATIONS ON EVOLUTIONARY RATES IN HYPSODONTY. R.A. Stirton. Evolution, New York, vol.1, nos.1-2, pp.32-41, figs.9, Mar.-June, 1947.

PRESENCE OF A FACTORIAL BASIS FOR CHARACTERS LOST IN EVOLUTION: THE ATAVISTIC REAPPEARANCE OF DIGITS IN MAMMALS. Charles R. Stockard. Amer.

Jour. Anat., vol.45, no.3, pp.345-378, figs.6, 1930.

IS EVOLUTION A CONTINUOUS OR DISCONTINUOUS PROCESS? Francis B.Sumner. Sci. Monthly, vol.29, pp.72-78, July, 1929.

STABILITY OF SUBSPECIFIC CHARACTERS UNDER CHANGED CONDITIONS OF ENVIRONMENT. F.B. Sumner. Amer. Nat., vol.58, pp.481-505, Nov., 1924.

WHERE DOES ADAPTATION COME IN? Francis B. Sumner. Amer.Nat., Lancaster, vol.76, no.766, pp.433-444, Sep.-Oct., 1942.

HOMOLOGY, ANALOGY AND PLASIS. John Tait. Quart. Rev. Biol. vol.3, pp. 151-173, June, 1928.

BRAIN FROM FISH TO MAN. A SERIES OF CULMINATING PHASES IN EVOLUTION. Frederick Tilney. Sci. Monthly, vol.45, no.4, pp.289-306, figs.1-16, Oct., 1937; no.5, pp.415-426, figs.17-22, Nov., 1937.

PROBLEM OF DEGENERACY. Alfred Frank Tredgold. Smiths. Inst., Annual Rep., 1918, Washington, pp.547-562, 1920. Reprinted from the Quarterly Review, July, 1917.

(ON THE ORIGIN OF MAMMALS.) Sur l'origine des Mammiferes. Jean Viret. Bull. Soc. Linneenne Lyon, 7e Année, no.7, pp.211-212, Sep., 1938.

EVOLUTION AT THE POPULATION LEVEL WITH SPECIAL REFERENCE TO GAME ANIMALS AND PRACTICAL GAME MANAGEMENT. Paavo Voipio. Riistatieteellisia Julkaisuja, Papers on Game Research, Helsinki, no.5, pp.176, illus., 1950.

EVIDENCE OF EVOLUTION. Hugo De Vries. Science, n.s., vol.20, no.508, pp.395-401, Sep. 23, 1904.

(SIGNIFICANCE OF FLEAS AS REGARDS THE QUESTION OF THE GENESIS OF MAMMAL FAUNA.) Die Bedeutung der Floehe fuer die Frage nach der Genises der Saeugetierfauna. J. Wagner. Zoogeographica, vol.1, no.2, pp.263-268, figs. 1, map, July, 1932.

METHOD OF ORGANIC EVOLUTION. Alfred Russel Wallace. Smiths. Inst., Annual Rep., 1894, Washington, pp.413-435, 1896. (From the Fortnightly Review, Feb. and Mar., 1895, vol.XVII, new series, nos.138, 139, 1895.)

STUDIES ON THE EVOLUTION OF THE PELVIS OF MAN AND OTHER PRIMATES. Harriet Cutler Waterman. Bull. Amer. Mus. Nat. Hist., New York, vol.58, pp.585-642, figs.10, pl.22, Dec. 7, 1929.

ADAPTATION. D.M.S. Watson. Nature, vol.124, pp.231-234, Aug. 10, 1929.

EVOLUTION OF THE MAMMALIAN EAR. D.M.S. Watson. Evolution, Lancaster, vol.7, no.2, pp.159-177, illus., June, 1953.

POLAR CLIMATE IN TIME THE MAJOR FACTOR IN THE EVOLUTION OF PLANTS AND ANIMALS. G.R. Wieland. Amer. Jour. Sci., vol.16, pp.401-430, Dec., 1903.

SURVIVAL OF THE FITTEST. Henry Smith Williams. R.M. McBride & Co., New York, pp.xxix-321, col.front., illus., pls., 1932.

DARWIN AND "DARWINISM". Sir Bertram C.A. Windle. Paulist Press, New York, pp.55, 1912.

PORCUPINES, PALEOGEOGRAPHY AND PARALLELISM. Albert E. Wood. Evolution, Lancaster, vol.4, no.1, pp.87-98, figs.2, Mar., 1950.

TEMPO AND MODE IN EVOLUTION: A CRITICAL REVIEW. Sewall Wright. Ecology, Brooklyn, vol.26, no.4, pp. 415-419, Oct., 1945.

NATURAL SELECTION BEFORE THE "ORIGIN OF SPECIES". Conway Zirkle. Proc. Amer. Philos. Soc., Philadelphia, vol.84, no.1, pp.71-123, Apr. 25, 1941.

EVOLUTION IN REVERSE: EXTINCT ANIMALS BROUGHT BACK TO LIFE AT THE MUNICH ZOO. Illus. London News, vol. 214, no.5735, p.381, illus., Mar. 19, 1949.

## EXPEDITIONS

VOYAGE ROUND THE WORLD IN THREE YEARS (1740-44). G. Anson. Compiled by R. Walter, London, John and Paul Knapton, pp.34-417, 1748.

VOYAGE OF THE WHALBERG. T.S. Bandegee. Zoe, vol.5, no.2, pp.20-28, 1900.

ARCTURUS ADVENTURE. C.W. Beebe. Putnam's Sons, New York, pp.20-439, many pls., 1926.

EXPEDITIONS. T.D.A. Cockerell. Science, vol.78, no.2026, pp.384-385, Oct. 27, 1933.

WILKES EXPLORING EXPEDITION OF THE UNITED STATES NAVY, 1838-1842; AND SYMPOSIUM ON AMERICAN POLAR EXPLORATION. Edwin G. Conklin, and others. Proc. Amer. Philos. Soc., Lancaster, vol. 82, no.5, pp.519-950, June 29, 1940.

NEW VOYAGE ROUND THE WORLD... WITH AN INTRODUCTION BY SIR ALBERT GRAY. W. Dampier. London, Adam and Charles Black, pp.42-376, 1697 (1937).

ZOOLOGY OF THE VOYAGE OF H. M. S. BEAGLE, UNDER THE COMMAND OF CAPTAIN FITZROY, R. N., DURING THE YEARS 1832 TO 1836. Charles Robert Darwin. Smith, Elder and Co., London, vol.5, pl. 166, 1839-43; Part I. FOSSIL MAMMALIA, 2p.l., iii-iv, iv, 111 p., xxxii pl., 1840; Part II. MAMMALIA, ix, 2 p., l., v, 97 p., 35 pl., 1839; Part III. BIRDS, 4 p. l., ii, 156, 8, p., 50 pl., 1841; Part IV. FISH, xv, l, 172 p., 29 pl., 1842; Part V. REPTILES, 3 p. l., v-vi, 51, 1 p., pl.20, 1843.

(MAMMAL AND REPTILE ACQUISITIONS OF THE AUSTRIAN NATURE RESEARCHERS DURING THE WORLD VOYAGE OF HIS MAJESTY'S FRIGATE "NOVARA".) Ausbeute der oesterreichischen Naturforscher an Saeugetieren und Reptilien waehrend der Weltumsegelung Sr. Majestaet Fregatte Novara. L. J. Fitzinger. Sitzungsbericht Akad. Wissensch., Vienna, vol.42, pp.383-416.

VOYAGE ROUND THE WORLD, IN H. B. M. SLOOP, "RESOLUTION," COMMANDED BY CAPT. JAMES COOK, DURING THE YEARS 1772, 73, 74 AND 75. G. Forster. London, vols.2, 1777.

ZOOLOGICAL NOTES FROM THE VOYAGE OF PETER MUNDY, 1655-56. SEA ELEPHANT ON ST. HELENA; WHALE AT GREENWICH. F.C. Fraser. Proc. Linn. Soc. London, sess.147, pt.2, pp.33-37, pl.2, May 10, 1935.

BERING'S VOYAGE. AN ACCOUNT OF THE EFFORTS OF THE RUSSIANS TO DETERMINE THE RELATION OF ASIA AND AMERICA. Frank Alfred Golder. New York, in 2 volumes, 1925.

MAMMALIA OF THE VOYAGE OF THE EREBUS AND TERROR . J.E. Gray. London, pp.53, pl., 1844-45.

ZOOLOGY OF THE VOYAGE OF THE H. M. S. SULPHUR DURING 1836-42. J. E. Gray. Mammalia, London, pp.36, pl.18, 184[illegible]

(GENERAL INSTRUCTIONS TO NATURALIST EXPLORERS.) Instrucciones generales a los Exploradores Naturalistas. A.L. Herrera. Mexico City, Imprenta de la Direccion de Estudios Biologicos, pp. 1-41, 1922.

(ZOOLOGICAL AND COMPARATIVE ANATOMY OBSERVATIONS. VOYAGE OF HUMBOLDT AND BONPLAUD. PART II.) Recueil d'observations de Zoologie et d'Anatomie comparée. Voyage de Humboldt et Bonplaud. Deuxième partie. A. de Humboldt, A. Bonplaud. Paris, vol.1, pp.1-368, vol.2, pp.1-64, pls.34, (1811) 1812.

DATES OF PUBLICATION OF "VERHANDELINGEN OVER DE NATUURLIJKE GESCHIEDENIS DER NEDERLANDSCHE OVERZEESCHE BEZITTINGEN". A.M. Husson, L.B. Holthuis. Zool. Mededelingen, vol.34, pp. 17-24, 1955.

(THE CHIROPTERS, INSECTIVORES, AND MURINES OF THE SEMON JOURNEY FOR THE PURPOSE OF INVESTIGATION.) Die Chiropteren, Insectivoren und Muriden der Semon'schen Forschungsreise. Paul Matschie. Jenaische Denkschr., vol.8, (Semon, Zoolog. Forschungsreisen, vol.5,) pp.773-778, Verlag von Gustav Fischer in Jena, 1903.

(MAMMALS OF THE HAMBURG MAGALHAENS JOURNEY FOR THE PURPOSE OF COLLECTING SPECIMENS.) Saeugetiere der Hamburger Magalhaensischen Sammelreise. Paul Matschie. Ergebnisse der Hamburger Magalhaensischen Sammelreise, Lfg.3, pp.1-30, pl.1, 1898.

LAST CRUISE OF THE "OLIVER CROMWELL", 1779. Louis F. Middlebrook. Publ. Marine Hist. Assoc., Inc., Mystic, Conn., vol.1, no.3, pp.41-52, illus., Aug. 25, 1931.

LAWS OF OLERON OR THE JUDGEMENTS OF THE SEA, A. D. 1375. Louis F. Middlebrook. Publ. Marine Hist. Assoc., Inc., Mystic, Conn., vol.1, no.10, pp.171-183, illus., Apr. 22, 1935. (From Black Book of the Admiralty - Reprinted 1871.)

ROUND THE WORLD WITH "GALATHEA." H. Mielche. William Hodge, London, p. 241, 1953.

EXPLORATIONS IN AUSTRALIA AND CHINA. Gerrit S. Miller, Jr. Smiths. Miscel. Coll., vol.74, no.5, pp.41-42, fig.46, May 8, 1923.

NARRATIVE OF FOUR VOYAGES...FROM THE YEAR 1822 TO 1831. B. Morrell. J. and J. Harper, New York, p.492, 1832.

LOGBOOK FOR GRACE. Robert Cushman Murphy. Macmillan Co., New York, vol. 8, pp.X-270, text figs. and map, 1947.

DISCOVERY OF AN UNKNOWN CONTINENT. Henry Fairfield Osborn. Nat. Hist., vol.24, pp.133-149, figs.11, Mar.-Apr., 1924.

JAMES SIMPSON-ROOSEVELT EXPEDITION OF THE FIELD MUSEUM OF NATURAL HISTORY. Wilfred H. Osgood. Science, n.s., vol.61, pp.461-462, May 1, 1925.

UNITED STATES EXPLORING EXPEDITION. DURING THE YEARS 1838, 1839, 1840, 1841, 1842. UNDER THE COMMAND OF CHARLES WILKES, U. S. N. VOL. VIII. Titian Ramsey Peale. United States exploring expedition, by authority of Congress.

JOURNAL AT SEA. 1845. John T. Perkins. Publ. Marine Hist. Assoc., Inc., Mystic, Conn., vol.1, no.8, pp.119-151, illus., Feb. 10, 1934. (From the original copy owned by Mrs. Grosvenor Ely.)

(EXPEDITION REPORTS.) Expeditionsnachrichten. H. Pohle. Zeitschrift f. Saeugetierkunde, vol.3, pp.308, June 11, 1928.

(CENTENARY CELEBRATION - WILKES EXPLORING EXPEDITION OF THE UNITED STATES NAVY. 1838-1842) and (SYMPOSIUM ON AMERICAN POLAR EXPLORATION. FEBRUARY 23, 24, 1940). Proc. of the American Philosophical Society, vol. 82, no.5, June 29, 1940.

(EXCURSION OF THE DISCOVERIES OF THE ASTROLABE, EXECUTED BY ORDER OF THE KING DURING THE YEARS 1826-27-28-29.) Voyage de decouvertes de l'Astrolabe execute par ordre du Roi, pendant les années 1826-27-28-29. Quoy & Gaimard. Zoologie, in J. Dumont d'Urville, vol.I, pp.i-1-5-268, pls.1-28, 1830.

ZOOLOGY OF THE VOYAGE OF H. M. S. EREBUS & TERROR ... DURING THE YEARS 1839 TO 1843. Sir John Richardson. Pt. I., London, Longman, Brown, Green, and Longmans, 1844.

ZOOLOGY OF THE VOYAGE OF H. M. S. HERALD... DURING THE YEARS 1845-51. Sir John Richardson. Ed. by Professor Edward Forbes, F.R.S. Fossil mammals. Reeve and Co., London, vi, 100 p., xv double pl., 1852.

ZOOLOGY OF THE VOYAGE OF H. M. S. HERALD... DURING THE YEARS 1845-51. Sir John Richardson. Ed. by Professor Edward Forbes, F.R.S. Vertebrals, including fossil mammals. L.Reeve, London, 3 p. l, vi-xi, 171, 1 p., xxxiii pl., 1854.

(ZOOLOGICAL OBSERVATION.) Obeservations zoologiques. H. Schlegel. II Ned. Tijdschr. Dierk., vol.3, pp.249-258; III Ned. Tijdschr. Dierk., vol.3, pp.325-358, 1866.

ZOOLOGICAL CONTRIBUTION OF THE LEWIS AND CLARK EXPEDITION. Henry W. Setzer. Jour. Washington Acad. Sci., vol.44, no.11, pp.356-357, Nov., 1954.

SCARRIT EXPEDITIONS OF THE AMERICAN MUSEUM OF NATURAL HISTORY, 1930-34. George Gaylord Simpson. Science, n.s., vol.80, no.2070, pp.207-208, Aug. 31, 1934.

THIRD SCARRIT EXPEDITION OF THE AMERICAN MUSEUM OF NATURAL HISTORY. George Gaylord Simpson. Science, n.s., vol.83, no.2140, pp.13-14, Jan. 3, 1936.

LAND MAMMALS OF THE VOYAGE OF THE "CHALLENGER." Oldfield Thomas. Natural Science, vol.7, no.41, pp.73-74, July, 1895.

VOYAGE OF THE DISCOVERY. D'Arcy W. Thompson. Nature, London, vol.140, no. 3543, pp.529-532, figs.2, Sep. 25, 1937.

(MAMMALS OF THE MISSION TO THE EQUATOR, ACCORDING TO THE COLLECTIONS OF DR. RIVET.) Mammiferes de la Mission de L'Équateur, D'Apres les collections formees par Le Dr. Rivet. E.L. Trouessart. Controle Sci. Acad. Sci.1899-1906, Paris, vol.9, pp.A.1-A.31, pls.8, 1911.

ZOOLOGY OF THE VOYAGE OF H.M.S. BEAGLE, UNDER THE COMMAND OF CAPTAIN FITZROY, DURING THE YEARS 1832 TO 1836. George R. Waterhouse. London, pp.1-100, pls.35, 1838.

(WORK ON BIRDS AND MAMMALS COLLECTED ON THE EXPEDITION.) Bearbeitung der auf der Expedition gesammelten Voegel und Saeugetiere. Aus der Kaiserlich-Koeniglichen Hof-und Staatsdruckerei, pp.139, illus., pl.IV, fold.map., 1917.

EXPERIMENTAL BIOLOGY

PARTHENOGENESIS AND POLYPLOIDY IN MAMMALIAN DEVELOPMENT. R.A.Beatty. Cambridge Monographs in Experimental Biology, Cambridge Univ. Press, vol.7, pp.1-132, pls.2, 1957.

EXPERIMENTAL STUDIES ON THE MOVEMENT OF THE MAMMALIAN TONGUE. G.A. Bennett, R.C. Hutchinson. Anat.Rec., Philadelphia, vol.94, no.1, pp.57-83, pls. 5, Jan., 1946.

(AN OPPOSITE-DIRECTED MUTATION AND MODIFICATION, EFFECTED THROUGH ONE AND THE SAME AGENT (ALCOHOL).) Ueber eine entgegengesetzt gerichtete Mutation und Modifikation, bewirkt durch eine- und dasselbe Agens (Alkohol). A. Bluhm. Biol. Zentralblatt, vol.50, pp.102-113, 1930.

(METHODICS OF THE INTRA-UTERINE OPERATION ON THE SURVIVING MAMMAL FETUS.) Die Methodik der intrauterinen Operation am ueberlebenden Saeugetierfoetus. Ernst Bors. Archiv f. Entwicklungsmechanik, vol.105, pp.655-666, figs.4, Aug. 25, 1925.

(RESEARCH ON THE ACTION OF THYMONUCLEINIC ACID DURING OOGENESIS IN VARIOUS SPECIES OF ANIMALS.) Recherches sur le comportement de l'acide thymonucleinique au course de l'oogenèse chez diverses especes animals. J.Brachet. Archives de Biologie, vol.39, pp.677-697, pl.1, 1929.

REVIEW OF ANIMAL EXPERIMENTATION IN INFECTIOUS HEPATITIS AND SERUM HEPATITIS. James W. Colbert. Yale Jour. Biol. Med., New Haven, vol.21, no.4, pp.335-343, Mar., 1949.

(EXPERIMENTAL CONTRIBUTION TO DEMONSTRATION OF CUTANEOUS RESPIRATION OF MAMMALS.) Contributo sperimentale alla dimostrazione della resprazione cutanea dei mammiferi. Giovanni Domini. Rivista Sci. Nat. "Natura," vol.19, pp.5-8, 1928.

A CYTOLOGICAL STUDY OF THE REGENERATION OF GASTRIC GLANDS FOLLOWING THE EXPERIMENTAL REMOVAL OF LARGE AREAS OF MUCOSA. Arthur Newton Ferguson. Amer. Jour. Anat., vol.42, pp. 403-441, illus., Nov. 15, 1928.

(EXPERIMENTAL HYPERFEMINIZATION AND ITS INFLUENCE ON THE SEX OF FUTURE GENERATIONS.) Experimentelle Hyperfeminierung und ihr Einfluss auf das Geschlecht der Nachkommenschaft. D. Gostimirovic. Biol. Zentralblatt, vol.49, pp. 24-28, 1929.

(FURTHER COMMUNICATIONS ON THE RESULT OF EXPERIMENTAL HYPERFEMINIZATION, II (PRELIMINARY COMMUNICATION.) Weitere Mitteilungen ueber das Ergebniss der experimentellen Hyperfeminierung II, vorlaeufige Mitteilung. D. Gostimirovic. Biol. Zentralblatt, vol. 50, pp.599-608, 1930.

FIELD TESTS OF THEORIES CONCERNING DISTRIBUTIONAL CONTROL. Joseph Grinnell. Amer. Naturalist, vol.51, pp.115-128, Feb., 1917.

CONTROLLABLE SOURCE OF MITOSES IN MAMMALS. Robert T. Hance. Trans. Amer. Micro. Soc., vol.46, pp.66-68, illus., Jan., 1927.

ROLE OF HUMORAL ANTAGONISM IN HETEROPLASTIC TRANSPLANTATION IN MAMMALS. Morgan Harris. Jour. Exper. Zool., Philadelphia, vol.93, no.1, pp.131-145, June, 1943.

(ON THE EFFECT OF VARIOUS MATERIALS ON THE ISOLATED MAMMAL HEART.) Ueber die Einwirkung verschiedener Stoffe auf das isolirte Saeugethierherz. Karl Hedbom. Skandinavischen Archiv f. Physiologie, Leipzig, vol.8, pp.169-222, pls.3, 1898.

RESUSCITATION WITH CARBON DIOXIDE. Yandell Henderson. Science, vol.83, no. 2157, pp.399-402, May 1, 1936.

EXPERIMENTAL CHEMOTHERAPY OF FILARIASIS. II. EFFECT OF PIPERAZINE DERIVATIVES AGAINST NATURALLY ACQUIRED FILARIAL INFECTIONS IN COTTON RATS AND CATS. R.I. Hewitt, E. White, W.S. Wallace, H.W. Stewart, S. Kushner. Jour. Lab. and Clin. Med., St. Louis, vol.32, no.11, pp.1304-1313, 1947.

PHRENIC NEURECTOMY AND PERITONEAL ABSORPTION. G.M. Higgins, M.G.Beaver, W.S. Lemon. Amer. Jour. Anat., vol.45, pp.137-158, figs.8, Jan. 15, 1930.

DEVELOPMENT AND FUNCTION OF VOLUNTARY AND CARDIAC MUSCLE IN EMBRYOS WITHOUT NERVES. Davenport Hooker. Jour. Exper. Zool., Philadelphia, vol.2, no.2, pp.159-186, figs.7, pl.1, Aug., 1911.

(ON THE SIGNIFICANCE OF EXPERIMENTAL METHOD IN FACIAL INVESTIGATION, WITH OBSERVATIONS ON THE PHYLOGENIC DEVELOPMENT OF FACIAL MUSCULATURE IN THE VERTEBRATES.) Ueber die Bedeutung der experimentellen Methode in der Facialisforschung, nebst Betrachtungen ueber die phylogenetische Entwicklung der Facialismuskulatur in der Vertebraten-Reihe. Ernst Huber. Anat. Anzeiger, Jena, vol.58, pp.177-205, 1924.

COD-LIVER OIL FOR "SNUFFLES" IN RABBITS AND PNEUMONIA IN GUINEA-PIGS. Heman L. Ibsen. Science, n.s., vol.66, pp.509-510, Nov. 25, 1927.

(TYPES OF ARTIFICIAL SKULL DEFORMATION.) Die Arten der Kuenstlichen Schaedeldeformation. J. Imbelloni. Anthropos, vol. 25, pp.801-830, figs.5-14, pls.1-12, 1930.

RELATIVE VALUES OF MAN, MOUSE, AND DOMESTIC FOWLS AS EXPERIMENTAL HOSTS FOR THE BED-BUG, CIMEZ LECTULARIUS L. C.G.Johnson. Proc. Zool. Soc. London, vol.107, ser.A, Gen. and Exper., pt.1, pp.107-126, tbls.16, Apr., 1937.

(CONTRIBUTION TO THE PROBLEM OF EXPERIMENTAL HYPERFEMINIZATION.) Beitrag zur Frage des experimentellen Hyperfeminismus. W. Kolmer. Zeitschr. f. vergleich. Physiologie, vol.9, pp.520-522, Apr. 16, 1929.

(SELECTION OF ANIMAL SPECIES ACCORDING TO MENDEL'S LAWS AND DURABLE MODIFICATIONS OBTAINED BY REPEATED VACCINATION.) Selection d'especes animales a characteres selon les lois mendéliennes et modifications durables obtenues par des vaccinations repetees. E. Lesné, G. Dreyfus-Sée. Comptes Rendus Séances Soc. Biol., Paris, vol.98, pp.922-924, Apr. 17, 1928.

PATHOLOGY OF EXPERIMENTAL POISONING IN CATS, RABBITS, AND RATS WITH 2, 2 BIS-PARACHLORPHENYL-1, 1, 1 TRICHLORETHANE. R.D. Lillie, M.I. Smith. U.S. Publ. Health Repts., Washington, D.C., vol.59, no.30, pp. 979-984, July 28, 1944.

(FURTHER INVESTIGATIONS ON THE ARTIFICIAL GENERATION OF THE MATERNAL PLACENTA AND ON THE MECHANICS OF THE SEXUAL CYCLE OF THE FEMALE MAMMAL ORGANISM.) Weitere Untersuchungen ueber die kuenstliche Erzeugung der muetterlichen Placenta und ueber die Mechanik des sexuellen Zyklus des weiblichen Saeugetier-organismus. Leo von Loeb. Separatabdruck aus Zentralblatt f. Physiologie, Bd.XXIV, no. 6, pp.1-5, 1910.

REACTION OF THE UTERINE MUCOSA TOWARDS FOREIGN BODIES INTRODUCED INTO THE UTERINE CAVITY. Leo von Loeb. Proc. Soc. Exper. Biol. and Med., vol.8, pp.90-91, 1910.

CELL ORGANS DURING KERATINIZATION IN NORMAL AND MALIGNANT GROWTH. R.J. Ludford. Quart. Jour. Micro. Sci., vol.69, pp.27-57, pl.2-4, figs.9, Dec., 1924.

INFLUENCE OF CALCIUM AND BARIUM ON THE FLOW OF URINE. John Bruce MacCallum. Univ. Calif. Publ. Physiol., vol.1, no.10, pp.81-82, Jan. 15, 1904.

INFLUENCE OF SALINE PURGATIVES ON LOOPS OF INTESTINE REMOVED FROM THE BODY. John Bruce MacCallum. Univ. Calif. Publ. Physiol., vol.1, no.13, pp. 115-123, Mar. 25, 1904.

ON THE LOCAL APPLICATION OF SOLUTIONS OF SALINE PURGATIVES TO THE PERITONEAL SURFACES OF THE INTESTINE. John Bruce MacCallum. Univ. Calif. Publ. Physiol., vol.1, no.21, pp.187-197, July 10, 1904.

SECRETION OF SUGAR INTO THE INTESTINE CAUSED BY INTRAVENOUS SALINE INFUSIONS. John Bruce MacCallum. Univ. Calif. Publ. Physiol., vol.1, no.14, pp. 125-137, Mar. 30, 1904.

THIRD REPORT ON A LAMARCKIAN EXPERIMENT. Wm. McDougall, J.B. Rhine. The British Jour. of Psychology, vol.24, pt.2, pp.213-235, Oct., 1933.

EXPERIMENTAL ATTEMPTS TO MODIFY THE SEX RATIO IN RABBITS AND PIGS. Hugh C. McPhee. Jour. Heredity, Washington, D.C., vol.33, no.12, pp.429-433, Dec., 1942.

TRANSFERENCE OF SECONDARY SEXUAL CHARACTERS OF MAMMALS FROM MALES TO FEMALES. C.I. Forsyth Major. Geol. Mag., London, n.s., decade 4, vol.8, pp. 241-245, June, 1901.

(ON THE SPEED OF OXYDOREDUCTION PROCESSES PRODUCED BY MAMMAL CELLS (NORMAL ADULT TISSUES).) Sur la vitesse des processus d'oxydoreduction produits par les cellules de mammiferes (tissus normaux adultes). P. Mauriac, E. Aubertin, E. Aubel. Comptes Rendus Séances Soc. Biol. Paris, vol.98, pp.959-960, Apr. 17, 1928.

PATHOLOGIC CHANGES IN ANIMALS EXPOSED TO A COMMERCIAL CHLORINATED DIPHENYL. J.W. Miller. U.S. Publ. Health Repts., Washington, vol.59, no.33, pp.1085-1093, pl.1, Aug. 18, 1944.

PRODUCTION OF ARTIFICIAL HERMAPHRODITES IN MAMMALS. Carl R. Moore.

Science, n.s., vol.52, pp.179-182, Aug. 20, 1920.

STUDY AT HIGH ALTITUDE OF REPRODUCTION, GROWTH, SEXUAL MATURITY, AND ORGAN WEIGHTS. Carl R. Moore, Dorothy Price. Jour. Exper. Zool., Philadelphia, vol. 108, no.2, pp.171-216, July, 1948.

NOTES ON THE APPLICATION OF EXPERIMENTAL METHODS UPON MAMMALIAN EMBRYOS. J.S. Nicholas. Anat. Rec., vol. 31, pp.385-394, Dec. 25, 1925.

INFLUENCE OF ALCOHOL ON DURATION OF LIFE. Raymond Pearl. Proc. Nat. Acad. Sci., Washington, D.C., vol.10, no.6, pp.231-237, June, 1924.

(EXPERIMENTAL DETERMINATION OF SEX IN MAMMALS.) La determination experimental du sexe chez les mammiferes. F. Petter. Mammalia, Paris, vol.14, no.3, pp.49-77, Sep., 1950.

EFFECT OF PITRESSIN AND PITOCIN ON OXYGEN CONSUMPTION OF EXCISED TISSUE. Morris H. Pincus. Proc. Soc.Exper. Biol. & Med., vol.30, pp.1171-1174, 1933.

LIPO-GEL REACTION EXERTED BY FOLLICULAR FLUID UPON SPERMATOZOA AND ITS SIGNIFICANCE (LILLIE'S REACTION). G.T. Popa. Biol.Bull., vol.52, pp. 223-237, Apr., 1927.

DETERMINATION OF HAIR PIGMENTS. II. TRANSPLANTATION OF HAIR PIGMENTS. Sheldon C. Reed. Jour. Exper. Zool., Philadelphia, vol.79, no.3, pp.331-336, 1938.

ALCOHOL AS A FOOD. Curt P. Richter. Quart. Jour. Studies on Alcohol, New Haven, vol.1, no.4, pp.650-662, figs.7, Mar., 1941.

EFFECT OF CEREBRAL ANEMIA UPON BLOOD PRESSURE AND RESPIRATION. F. Roberts. Jour. Physiol., vol.59, pp. 100-120, Oct., 1924.

(STRUGGLE AGAINST AGING.) Der Kampf gegen das Altern. Peter Schmidt. Die Umschau in Wissenschaft und Technik, Frankfurt a.M., vol.31, pp.765-770, figs.1-6, Sep., 1927.

EXPERIMENTAL MODIFICATION OF THE GERM-PLASM AND ITS BEARING ON THE INHERITANCE OF ACUIRED CHARACTERS. Charles R. Stockard. Proc. Amer. Philos. Soc., vol.62, no.5, pp.311-326, tbls.3, figs. 2, Nov., 1923.

EXPERIMENTAL TRANSMISSION OF YELLOW FEVER TO LABORATORY ANIMALS. Adrian Stokes, Johannes H. Bauer, N.Paul Hudson. Amer. Jour. Trop. Medicine, vol. 8, no.2, pp.103-164, figs.28, Mar., 1928.

EFFECT OF THYROPARATHYROIDECTOMY ON BODY ACTIVITIES. O.O. Stoland, Homer L. Bryant. Proc. Oklahoma Acad. Sci., vol. 5, 1925, pp.51-58, Mar., 1926.

EXPERIMENTAL STUDY OF THE INFLUENCE OF PELAGE PIGMENTATION ON METABOLIC RATE AND ITS POSSIBLE RELATIONSHIP TO BODY TEMPERATURE CONTROL AND ECOLOGICAL DISTRIBUTION. Donald E. Stullken, William A. Hiestand. Ecology, Durham, vol.34, no. 3, pp.610-613, illus., July, 1953.

VALUE TO MANKIND OF HUMANELY CONDUCTED EXPERIMENTS UPON LIVING ANIMALS. Francis B. Sumner. Bull. Scripps Inst. Biol. Research, La Jolla, no.6, pp.1-27, Oct. 5, 1918.

EXPERIMENTAL POLIOMYELITIS. 2. FAILURE TO TRANSMIT THE DISEASE TO JERBOA MICE (NOTOMYS MITCHELLI), RATS (RATTUS NORVEGICUS) AND PHALANGERS (TRICHOSURUS VULPECULA). Charles Swan. Australian Jour. Exper. Biol. and Med. Sci., Adelaide, vol.20, pt.1, pp.31-32, Mar., 1942.

(B C G VACCINE APPLIED TO WILD ANIMALS.) Le vaccin BCG applique aux animaux sauvages. Achille Urbain, P. Bullier. Archiv. Mus. Nat. d'Hist. Nat., Paris, ser.6, vol.12, pp.313-316, (vol. du Tricentenaire, vol.1), June, 1935.

(ACTION OF INJECTIONS OF FOLLICULAR LIQUID ON THE MAMMARY GLAND.) Action des injections de liquide folliculaire sur la glande mammaire. P. Vintemberger. Archives de Biologie, vol.35, pp.125-154, pl.6, Oct., 1925.

NUTRITIONAL ANEMIA ON WHOLE MILK DIETS AND ITS CORRECTION WITH THE ASH OF BEEF LIVER. J. Waddell, C.A. Elvehjem, H.Steenbock, E.B. Hart. Science, n.s., vol.67, pp.139-140, Feb. 3, 1928.

TRANSPLANTATION OF FETAL TISSUES BETWEEN RABBITS AND RATS. A. J. Waterman. Proc. Nat. Acad. Sci., Washington, vol.21, no.12, pp.635-637, Dec., 1935.

NERVE REUNION WITH SLEEVES OF FROZEN-DRIED ARTERY IN RABBITS, CATS AND MONKEYS. Paul Weiss. Proc. Soc. Exper. Biol. and Med., New York, vol. 54, no.3, pp.274-277, Dec., 1943.

GRAFTING OF ANIMAL TISSUES. G. M. Wyburn, P. Bacsich. Endeavour, London, vol.7, no.28, pp.165-169, figs.7, Oct., 1948.

EXTINCTION AND EXTERMINATION see POPULATION DYNAMICS -- EXTINCTION AND EXTERMINATION

FLEAS see DISEASES AND PARASITES -- FLEAS

## FOOD HABITS

CONSUMPTION OF PONDEROSA PINE SEED BY SMALL MAMMALS. Lowell Adams. Res. Note Northern Rocky Mountain Forest & Range Expt. Sta., Missoula, no.80, pp.4, Mar., 1950.

CRANE-FLIES OF NEW YORK, PART II. C.P. Alexander. Mem.38, Agric. Exp. Sta., Cornell Univ., p.721, June, 1920.

SOURCES OF WATER SUPPLY FOR DESERT ANIMALS. Vernon Bailey. Sci. Monthly, vol. 17, no.1, pp.66-86, figs.18, July, 1923.

FOOD HABITS STUDY OF GAME ANIMALS. Theodore C. Baker, Chester Anderson, William Crump. Wyo. Wild Life, vol.17, no. 11, pp.24-31, illus., Nov., 1953.

OVERGRAZING. Elliot S. Barker. Conv. Internat. Assn. Game, Fish and Cons.Comm., vol.28, pp.28-30, 1935.

WINTER FOOD PRODUCTIVITY OF AGRICULTURAL LAND FOR SEED-EATING BIRDS AND MAMMALS. Philip S. Baumgras. Jour. Wildl. Mgt., Menasha, vol.7, no.1, pp.13-18, Jan., 1943.

GRASSHOPPER POISON AND WILDLIFE. Watson E. Beed. Amer. Wildlife, vol.26, no.4, pp.53-64, illus., July-Aug., 1937.

PREDACEOUS ENEMIES OF ANTS. J. Bequaert. Bull. Amer. Mus. Nat. Hist., vol.45, pp.271-331, Oct. 19, 1922.

SMALL MAMMALS AS PREDATORS OF SAWFLIES. C.H. Buckner. Can. Ent., vol.87, no.3, pp.121-123, Mar., 1955.

PLIMSOLL LINE IN WHITE CEDARS. John B. Burnham. Jour. Mamm., vol.9, no.1, pp.43-47, Feb., 1928.

MAN: VEGETARIAN OR CARNIVORE? Maurice Burton. Illus. London News, vol. 214, no.5728, pp.146-147, Jan. 29, 1949.

WILD ANIMALS AND WATER. R. G. Burton. Field, London, vol.156, no.4045, p.20, July 5, 1939.

BROWSE UTILIZATION STUDY OF BIG GAME WINTER RANGES WITHIN THE FLATHEAD FOREST OF THE CONTINENTAL MANAGEMENT UNIT. Robert Casebeer, Merle Rognrud. (Cover title: Browse utilization study / Winter 1948-1949 / Western Montana.) Mont. Fish & Game Comm., Wildl. Restoration Div., pp.iv-29, Jan., 1950.

FOOD OF ARCTIC BIRDS AND MAMMALS COLLECTED BY THE BARTLETT EXPEDITIONS OF 1931, 1932, AND 1933. Clarence Cottam. Jour. Washington Acad. Sci., vol. 26, no.4, pp.166-177, Apr. 15, 1936.

FOOD HABITS OF SOME ARCTIC BIRDS AND MAMMALS. Clarence Cottam, Harold C. Hanson. Field Mus. Nat. Hist., Zool. ser., vol.20, no.31, pp.405-426, June 14, 1938.

ANIMALS THAT EAT PONDEROSA PINE SEED. James D. Curtis. Jour. Wildl. Mgt., Menasha, vol.12, no.3, pp.327-328, July, 1948.

DEER FOOD PRODUCED BY ICE STORM. James D. Curtis. Jour. Wildl. Mgt., vol. 9, no.3, pp.257-258, July, 1945.

POTASSIUM HYDROXIDE (KOH) AS AN AID IN FOOD HABITS RESEARCH. Walter W. Dalquest. California Fish and Game, San Francisco, vol.28, no.2, pp.125-126, Apr., 1942.

EARTHWORMS IN THE WINTER DIET OF THE OPPOSUM AND RACCOONS. Ralph W. Dexter. Jour. Mamm., vol 32, no.4, p.464, Nov. 19, 1951.

ENDOGONE AS ANIMAL FOOD. William W. Diehl. Science, Lancaster, n.s., vol.90, no.2341, p.442, Nov. 10, 1939.

FOOD PREDILECTIONS OF PREDATORY AND FURBEARING MAMMALS. Joseph Dixon. Jour. Mamm., vol.6, no.1, pp.34-46, figs.10, pl.4, Feb., 1925.

WATERING PATTERNS OF SOME DESERT GAME ANIMALS. James B. Elder. Jour. Wildl. Mgt., vol.20, no.4, pp.368-378, Oct., 1956.

SEASONAL ACCEPTANCE OF BAIT BY SMALL MAMMALS. Henry S. Fitch. Jour. Mamm., vol.35, no.1, pp.39-47, Feb. 10, 1954.

INFLUENCE OF SMALL MAMMALS AND OTHER FACTORS UPON THE LARCH SAWFLY SURVIVAL. S.A. Graham. Jour. Econ. Entomol., vol.21, pp.301-310, Apr., 1928.

MATERIALS ON THE FEEDING OF CERTAIN GAME ANIMALS OF THE TARTAR REPUBLIC. N.D. Grigorjev, V.P. Teplov, V.I. Tikhvinsky. Raboty Volzhsko-Kamskoi Krajevoi Promyslovoi Biologicheskoi Stantsii (Works of Volga-Kama Region Ind.Biol. Sta.), Kazan, no.1, pp.91-125, fig.1, 1931. (In Russian with Tartar summary.)

ON CERTAIN SMALL TERRESTRIAL MAMMALS THAT ARE ALLEGED TO FISH WITH THE TAIL. E.W. Gudger. Amer. Midland Nat., vol.50, no.1, pp.189-201, July, 1953.

FOOD OF SMALL FOREST MAMMALS IN EASTERN UNITED STATES. W.J.Hamilton, Jr. Jour. Mamm., Baltimore, vol.22, no.3, pp.250-263, Aug. 14, 1941.

FOOD OF SOME SMALL MAMMMALS FROM THE GASPE PENINSULA, P.Q. W.J.Hamilton, Jr., W.J.Hamilton, III. Canadian Field-Nat., vol.68, no.3, pp.108-109, July-Sep., 1954.

NATURAL FOOD OF SOME RATS AND OTHER MAMMALS. J.L. Harrison. Bull. Raffles Mus., Singapore, no.25, pp.157-165, Dec., 1954.

(DISREGARDED MYCOPHAGY OF CERTAIN MAMMALS.) Mycophagie méconnue de certains mammifères. H.Heim de Balsac. Revue de Mycologie, vol.16, pp.238-241, 1951.

WILDLIFE'S TOLL OF A FOOD PATCH OF CORN. George O. Hendrickson, Clifford Schlesselman. Jour. Mamm., vol.18, no.2, pp.236-237, May 14, 1937.

MEAT SUPPLY. John Eric Hill. Nat. Hist., New York, vol.55, no.9, p.435, illus., Nov., 1946.

RATIONING. John Eric Hill. Nat. Hist., New York, vol.51, no.2, p.75, illus., Feb., 1943.

SELECTION BY CERTAIN SMALL MAMMALS OF DEAD, PARASITIZED, AND HEALTHY PREPUPAE OF THE EUROPEAN PINE SAWFLY, NEODIPRION SERTIFER. C.S. Holling. Canad. Jour. Sci., Ottawa, vol.33, no.6, pp.404-419, illus., Dec., 1955.

BROWSE UTILIZATION STUDIES ON THE POCATELLO WINTER BIG GAME RANGE. Leonard W. Hoskins. M.S. thesis, Univ. Idaho, p.85, 1952.

WINTER BROWSE ON THE POCATELLO BIG GAME RANGE IN SOUTHEASTERN IDAHO. Leonard W. Hoskins. Jour. Wildl. Mgt., vol.19, no.2, pp.215-225, Apr., 1955.

GALL-STONES AND BEZOARS. G. Evelyn Hutchinson. Amer. Scientist, Burlington, vol.39, no.4, pp.718-719, Oct., 1951.

WHO TRIMS THE CREOSOTE BUSHES? Edmund C. Jaeger. Jour. Mamm., vol. 29, no.2, pp.187-188, May 14, 1948.

GENERAL SUMMARY OF THE FOOD OF MISSOURI PREDATORY AND GAME ANIMALS. Leroy J. Korschgen. Missouri Conserv. Comm., Jefferson City, pp.61, July, 1952.

(AROMATIC FODDER SUPPLEMENTS FOR DEMANDING UNGULATES.) Wuerzige Futterzusaetze fuer anspruchsvolle Huftiere. I. Krumbiegel. Zool. Garten, n.F., Leipzig, vol.6, nos.4-6, pp.129-130, July, 1933.

WATER-LIKE SURFACES ATTRACT VOLANT DESERT ANIMALS. Philip H. Krutzsch. Ecology, Lancaster, vol.29, no.3, pp.391-392, July, 1948.

FOODS OF FUR ANIMALS OF THE PATUXENT RESEARCH REFUGE, MARYLAND. Leonard M. Llewellyn, Francis M. Uhler. Amer. Midland Nat., Notre Dame, vol.48, no.1, pp.193-203, July, 1952.

UTILIZATION OF RUSSIAN THISTLE BY WILDLIFE. W.S. Long. Jour. Wildl. Mgt., Menasha, vol.5, no.2, pp.136-138, Apr., 1941.

EFFECTIVENESS IN NATURE OF THE SO-CALLED PROTECTIVE ADAPTATIONS IN THE ANIMAL KINGDOM, CHIEFLY AS ILLUSTRATED BY THE FOOD HABITS OF NEARCTIC BIRDS. W.L. McAtee. Smiths. Misc. Coll., Washington, D.C., vol.85, no.7, Publ.3125, pp.201, Mar. 15, 1932.

PRELIMINARY STUDY OF THE UPPER SELWAY RIVER BIG GAME WINTER RANGE WITH SPECIAL REFERENCE TO BROWSE UTILIZATION. Clay Y. McCulloch, Jr. M.S. thesis, Univ. Idaho, p.107, 1952.

UTILIZATION OF WINTER BROWSE ON WILDERNESS BIG GAME RANGE. Clay Y. McCulloch, Jr. Jour. Wildl. Mgt., Ithaca, vol.19, no.2, pp.206-215, Apr., 1955.

IDENTIFICATION OF PLANT ITEMS IN FOOD STUDIES. A.C. Martin. Trans. 3rd. N. Amer. Wildl. Conf., pp.805-806, 1938.

FOOD HABITS OF YOSEMITE MAMMALS AS INDICATED BY THEIR TEETH. Pt. 1. Richard G. Miller. Yosemite Nature Notes, vol.24, no.2, pp.33-36, illus., Feb., 1945.

FOOD HABITS OF YOSEMITE MAMMALS AS INDICATED BY THEIR TEETH. Pt. 3. MOLES AND SHREWS (INSECTIVORA), BATS (CHIROPTERA). Richard G. Miller. Yosemite Nature Notes, Yosemite, vol. 24, no.4, pp.54-56, Apr., 1945.

FOOD HABITS OF YOSEMITE MAMMALS AS INDICATED BY THEIR TEETH. Pt. 4, EVEN-TOED HOOFED MAMMALS(ARTIODACTYLA), HARES, RABBITS, AND PIKAS (LAGOMORPHA). Richard G. Miller. Yosemite Nature Notes, Yosemite, vol.24, no. 5, pp.62-64, May, 1945.

DIFFERENTIATION BY SMALL MAMMAL PREDATORS BETWEEN SOUND AND EMPTY COCOONS OF THE EUROPEAN SPRUCE SAWFLY. R.F. Morris. Canadian Entomologist, Ottawa, vol.81, no.5, pp.114-120, illus., May, 1949.

PRELIMINARY NOTES ON THE NATURAL CONTROL OF THE EUROPEAN SPRUCE SAWFLY BY SMALL MAMMALS. R. F. Morris. Can. Ent., vol.74, no.11, pp.197-202, Nov., 1942.

OBSERVATIONS ON FOOD CONSUMPTION AND PREFERENCE IN FOUR ALASKAN MAMMALS. Peter R. Morrison, William J. Teitz. Arctic, Jour. Arctic Inst. North America, Ottawa, vol.6, no.1, pp.52-57, Mar., 1953.

NATURE'S SANITARY CORPS. W. O. Nagel. Wyoming Wild Life, Cheyenne, vol.8, no. 10, pp.12-14, Oct., 1943.

TABLE IN THE WILDERNESS. W.O. Nagel. Missouri Conservationist, Jefferson City, vol.11, no.10, pp.4-5, 12-13, illus., Oct., 1950.

REPRODUCTION STUDY OF NORTHERN WHITE CEDAR. Thomas C. Nelson. Michigan Dept. Conserv., Lansing, pp. ix-100, illus., 1951.

WHERE DO DEER AND RABBITS FEED? C.E. Ostrom. Pennsylvania Game News, vol.7, no.7, pp.15, 30, Nov.-Dec., 1937.

QUESTION OF TASTE. Arthur Newton Pack. Nature Mag., vol.13, pp.147-151, illus., Mar., 1929.

FOOD REQUIREMENTS OF SOME ALASKAN GAME MAMMALS. L. J. Palmer. Jour. Mamm., vol.25, no.1, pp.49-54, Feb., 1944.

YIELD AND PERSISTENCE OF WILDLIFE FOOD PLANTS. Barry C. Park. Jour. Wildl. Mgt., Menasha, vol.6, no.2, pp.118-121, Apr., 1942.

PLANT PATHOLOGY IN RELATION TO NORTHEASTERN FOREST WILDLIFE COVER. John Pearce, Perley Spaulding. Jour. Wildl. Mgt., Menasha, vol.6, no.3, pp.194-202, pl.14, July, 1942.

LICHENS - THEIR BIOLOGICAL AND ECONOMIC SIGNIFICANCE. George A. Perez-Llano. Botanical Review, Lancaster, vol.10, no.1, pp.1-65, Jan., 1944.

CLASSIFICATION OF THE LEGUMINOUS FRUITS ACCORDING TO THEIR ECOLOGICAL AND MORPHOLOGICAL PROPERTIES. L. van der Pijl. Proc. Kon. Nederlandse Akad. Wetensch., ser.C, vol.59, no.3, pp.301-313, 1956. (Dissemination by bats and other mammals, pp.304-305.)

COYOTES CAN'T WIN AGAINST RODENTS. Clifford C. Presnall. Nat. Wool Grower, vol.43, no.6, pp.22-23, June, 1953.

EARTH-EATING AND SALT-LICKING IN INDIA. K.S. Rahda. Jour. Bombay Nat. Hist. Soc., vol.40, no.4, pp.724-726, May, 1939.

COACTIONS OF BEAVER AND MOOSE ON A JOINT FOOD SUPPLY IN THE BUFFALO RIVER MEADOWS AND SURROUNDING AREA IN JACKSON HOLE, WYOMING. Ward J. Rudersdorf. M.S. thesis, Utah State Agr. Coll., 1953.

SECRET KILLERS. Archibald Rutledge. Pennsylvania Game News, Harrisburg, vol. 17, no.5, pp.6-7, illus., Aug., 1946.

GEOGRAPHY OF MAST FEEDING. Earl B. Shaw. Econ. Georg., vol.16, no.3, pp.233-249, July, 1940.

REPORT ON COOPERATIVE QUAIL INVESTIGATION: 1925-1926. Herbert L. Stoddard. Pp.62, pls.5, Nov. 2, 1926. (Relation of mammals to quail, pp.32-37.)

FOOD HABITS RESEARCH. B.P. Stollberg. Wisconsin Wildl. Res., Wis. Conserv. Dept., Madison, Quart. Prog. Repts., vol.7, no.1, pp.25-32, Apr., 1948.

UNUSUAL FEEDING HABIT OF WOODCHUCK AND COTTONTAIL. Walter Robert Sylvester. Jour. Mamm., vol.24, no.4, pp.499-500, Nov. 17, 1943.

ON THE FEEDING OF AQUATIC ANIMALS. V.I. Tikhvinsky. Raboty Volzhsko-Kamskoi Krajevoi Promyslovoi Biologicheskoi Stantsii (Works of Volga-Kama Region Industrial Biological Station), Kasan, no.1, pp.169-202, 1931. (In Russian with Tartar summary.)

(SOME FINDINGS OF HAIR BALL INVESTIGATIONS.) Einige Ergebnisse von Gewoelluntersuchungen. O. Uttendorfer. Zeitschr.f. Saeugetierkunde, Berlin, vol.7, nos.1-6, pp.259-261, Dec. 15, 1932.

UTILIZATION OF OAKS BY BIRDS AND MAMMALS. William R. Van Dersal. Jour. Wildl. Mgt., Menasha, vol.4, no.4, pp.404-428, Oct., 1940.

UTILIZATION OF WOODY PLANTS AS FOOD BY WILDLIFE. William R. Van Dersal. Trans. 3rd N. Amer. Wildl. Conf., pp.768-775, 1938.

WATER REQUIREMENTS OF DESERT ANIMALS IN THE SOUTHWEST. Charles T. Vorhies. Univ. Arizona, Tucson, Tech. Bull. no.107, pp.487-525, pls.4, June, 1945.

GAME FOOD PLANTS. S.A. Wilde. Wisc. Conserv. Bull., Madison, vol.11, no.5, pp.18-20, May, 1946.

FOOD OF SEA OTTERS AND HARBOR SEALS AT AMCHITKA ISLAND. Ford Wilke. Jour. Wildl. Mgt., vol.21, no. 2, pp.241-242, Apr., 1957.

NOTES ON THE FOOD OF FUR SEAL, SEA-LION, AND HARBOR PORPOISE. Ford Wilke, Karl W. Kenyon. Jour. Wildl. Mgt., Ithaca, vol.16, no.3, pp.396-397, July, 1952.

FOOD HABITS OF FURBEARERS OF THE UPLAND POST OAK REGION IN TEXAS. John E. Wood. Jour. Mamm., vol.35, no.3, pp.406-415, Aug. 20, 1954.

BEZOAR STONES. Chronicles of Pharmacy, London, vol.2, pp.15-19, 1910.

ABOUT BEZOARS. Nature Mag., Washington, D.C., vol.35, no.9, p.449, Nov., 1942.

NATURE'S SANITARY CORPS. Ohio Conserv. Bull., Columbus, vol.8, no.5, pp.16-17, May, 1944.

PREDATORY MAMMALS AND GAME BIRDS. Nature, London, vol.132, no.3344, p.866, Dec. 2, 1933.

ZOO VICTORY GARDENS HELP FEED THE ANIMALS. Science News Letter, Washington, D.C., vol.45, no.19, p.297, May 6, 1944.

## FOOD SOURCES, MAMMALS AS

INCREASED USE OF GAME AS A FOOD. Frank G. Ashbrook. Pennsylvania Game News, Harrisburg, vol.15, no.8, pp.7, 28, Nov., 1944.

TEXAS OVERLOOKING FLESH OF FUR BEARING ANIMAL AS TASTY TIDBIT WHEN PROPERLY PREPARED. Rollin H. Baker. Texas Game, Fish & Oyster Comm., vol.5, no.6, pp.4-5, 7, June 1942.

ACHIEVEMENT AND EARLY CONSEQUENCES OF FOOD-PRODUCTION: A CONSIDERATION OF ARCHEOLOGICAL AND NATURAL-HISTORICAL EVIDENCE. Robert J. Braidwood, Charles A. Reed. Cold Spring Harbor Symposia on Quantitative Biology, vol.22, pp.22-31, 1957.

FOOD ANIMALS OF THE PERUVIAN HIGHLANDS. George F. Eaton. XXI Congrès International des Américanistes, Session de Goeteborg 20-26, 1924, pp. 61-67, 1925.

MEAT OF SOME WILD MAMMALS AND BIRDS AS AN ADDITIONAL FOOD RESOURCE. A.N. Formozov. Zool Jour. USSR, Moscow, vol.21, nos.1-2, pp.3-9, tbl.1, 1942. (English summary.)

GOOD EATING FROM WOODS AND FIELDS. 2ND REVISION. R.G. Hill. Ext. Bull. Mich. State College, East Lansing, no.252, pp.24, illus., June, 1947.

ANIMAL DIET OF EARLY MAN. Marcus Ward Lyon, Jr. Science, n.s., vol.44, no. 1134, pp.426-427, Sep. 22, 1916.

MAMMALS EATEN BY INDIANS, OWLS, AND SPANIARDS IN THE COAST REGION OF THE DOMINICAN REPUBLIC. Gerrit S. Miller, Jr. Smiths. Misc. Coll., vol.82, no.5, publ.3030, pp.1-16, pls.2, Dec. 11, 1929.

SAVE MEAT -- IT IS VALUABLE. D. I. Rasmussen. USDI, F&WS, Wildl. Leaflet 246, p.5, Oct., 1943.

"MAKANAN MALAYU". SOME OF THE FOODS IN COMMON USE AMONG THE NATIVES OF BORNEO AND CELEBES. H. C. Raven. Nat. Hist., New York, vol.34, no. 2, pp.176-182, illus., Mar.-Apr., 1934.

FOSSILS

(ESSENCE, TASKS, AND GOALS OF PALEOBIOLOGY.) Wesen, Aufgaben und Ziele der Palaeobiologie. O. Abel. Der Biologie, Muenchen, Jahrg.1, no.12, pp.259-263, Sep., 1932.

(PRINCIPLES OF THE PALEOBIOLOGY OF VERTEBRATES.) Grundzuege der Palaeobiologie der Wirbeltiere. O. Abel. Stuttgart, 1912.

CAMPING IN A PREHISTORIC FOREST. H. E. Anthony. Nat. Hist., vol.30, no.4, pp. 367-376, illus., July-Aug., 1930.

WAY OF A FOSSIL HUNTER. D.R. Barton. Nat. Hist., New York, vol.47, no.3, pp. 172-176, photo, Mar., 1941.

ANIMAL REMAINS. D. M. A. Bate.(In) P. L.O. Guy, and Robert M. Engberg, Megiddo Tombs, Oriental Inst. Publ., Univ.Chicago, vol.33, pp.209-213, figs.204-206, 1938.

RECONSTRUCTION OF PREHISTORIC ANIMALS. Herman T. Beck. Los Angeles County Mus. Quarterly, vol.2, no.2, pp.17-19, illus., Apr., 1942.

ON THE REMNANTS OF THE QUATERNARY MAMMALS. E.I. Beljaeva. Bull. Soc. Nat. Moscow, n.s., vol.47, (sect.geol., vol.17, no.6,) pp.85-89, 1939. (In Russian with English summary.)

(DENTAL NOMENCLATURE OF THE LITOPTERNA.) Nomenclatura dentaria de los "Litopterna." Alejandro F.Bordas. Physis, Rev. Soc. Argentina Cienc. Nat., Buenos Aires, vol.12, no.44, p.365, June 30, 1938.

ON THE STRUCTURE OF THE MAMMAL-LIKE REPTILES OF THE SUB-ORDER GORGONOPSIA. R. Broom. Philos. Trans. Roy. Soc. London, (B), vol.218, pp.345-371, figs.2, pls.27-34, Aug. 20, 1930.

JEFFERSON'S CONTRIBUTION TO PALEONTOLOGY. Roland W. Brown. Jour. Washington Acad. Sci., vol.33, no.9, pp.257-259, Sep. 15, 1943.

OBSERVATIONS UPON THE BRAIN CASTS OF TERTIARY MAMMALS. Adam Todd Bruce. Princeton, N.J., pp.36-45, pl., 1883. (Contributions from the E.M.Mus. of geology and archaeology of Princeton Coll., bulletin no.3.)

PLEISTOCENE REBORN. Hulbert Burroughs. Nature Mag., Washington, D.C., vol.31, no.6, pp.329-332, June-July, 1938.

TRENDS AND DEVELOPMENTS IN VERTEBRATE PALEONTOLOGY. Charles L. Camp. Bull. Geol. Soc. Amer., Baltimore, vol.57, no.6, pp.541-545, June, 1946.

METHODS IN PALEONTOLOGY. Charles L. Camp, G. Dallas Hanna. Univ. Calif. Press., Berkeley, pp.153, figs.56, 1937.

DILEMMA OF THE PALEONTOLOGIST. E.C. Case. Contrib. Mus. Paleontol.Univ. Michigan, Ann Arbor, vol.9, no.5, pp.173-215, Nov. 6, 1951.

(OSTEOGRAPHY AND OSTEOMETRY OF THE GENERA TYPOTHERIODON AND TYPOTHERIUM.) Osteografia y osteometria comparada de los generos Typotheriodon y Typotherium. Noemi V. Cattoi. Buenos Aires, Republica Argentina, (Universidad de Buenos Aires) pp.119, (3), pl.XXVIII, 1943.

CERTAIN POSSIBILITIES IN THE FIELD STUDY OF VERTEBRATE FOSSILS. John Clark. Jour. Paleont, Menasha, Wisc., vol.13, no.1, pp.137-139, Jan., 1939.

CIRCUS WITHOUT SPECTATORS. Edwin H. Colbert. Nat. Hist., New York, vol. 49, no.5, pp.248-252, illus., May, 1942.

DISTRIBUTIONAL AND PHYLOGENETIC STUDIES OF INDIAN FOSSIL MAMMALS. Edwin H. Colbert. New York, N.Y., 2p. 1., 20, 15, 16, 24, 15 p., illus., (incl. maps) 1935. (Contributions from the Department of Geology of Columbia Univ., vol.XLV, no.7) thesis Ph.D., Columbia Univ., 1935. American Mus. novitates nos.796, 797, 798, 799, 800.

MIGRATIONS OF CENOZOIC MAMMALS. Edwin H. Colbert. Trans. New York Acad. Sci., ser.2, vol.1, no.6, pp.89-94, Apr., 1939.

PLEISTOCENE MAMMALS OF NORTH AMERICA AND THEIR RELATIONS TO EURASIAN FORMS. Edwin H. Colbert. Early Man, J.B. Lippincott Co., Philadelphia, pp.173-184, pls.11-12, figs.25, tbls., 1937.

HUNTING IN THE LAND OF LONG AGO. Joseph P. Connolly. South Dakota Conservationist, Pierre, pp.1-3, 12, figs.3, Aug., 1940.

(RECONSTITUTION OF EXTINGUISHED ANIMALS. THE REGRESSIVE METHOD: "THE RETURN TO THE ANCESTORS.") La reconstitution des animaux éteints. La methode régressive: "Le retour a l'ancetre". Paul Cordier-Goni. Mammalia, Paris, vol. 17, no.4, pp.354-359, Dec., 1953.

BONES FOR THE ARCHAEOLOGIST. I. W. Cornwall. Macmillan Co., New York, pp. 257, illus., 1956.

(THE SUCCESSIVE FAUNAS OF LAND MAMMALS ON THE AMERICAN CONTINENT.) As sucessivas faunas de mamiferos terrestres no continente americano. Carlos de Paula Couto. Rio de Janeiro, Oficina Grafica da Universidade do Brasil, pp.159, illus., 1952.

FOSSIL MAMMALIAN REMAINS. Warren R. Dawson. Proc. Zool. Soc. London, part 2, pp.793-796, July, 1925.

(MAMMALIA EXKL. HOMINIDAE.) Mammalia exkl. Hominidae. W.O. Dietrich. Fortschr. der Palaeont., Berlin, vol.2, pp. 322-363, 1939.

(ON RECONSTRUCTIONS OF FOSSIL MAMMALS.) Ueber Rekronstruktionen fossiler Saeugetiere. W.O. Dietrich. Zeitschr. f. Saeugetierkunde, vol.2, pp.177-186, Apr. 29, 1929.

VERTEBRATE PALEONTOLOGIST AT WORK. John A. Dorr. Carnegie Mag., Pittsburgh, vol.26, no.2, pp.62-65, Feb., 1952.

VERTEBRATE FOSSILS FROM THE MINA ERUPCION. George F. Eaton. Amer. Jour. Sci., ser.5, vol.6, pp.229-238, figs.9, Sep., 1923.

(AIMS AND RESULTS OF PALEONEUROLOGY.) Objets et résultats de la paléoneurologie. Tilly Edinger. Ann.Paleontologie, vol.42, pp.97-116, 1956.

(MAMMAL REMAINS FROM THE MIRE OF LAKE BALATON.) Mammaltierreste aus dem Balatonsee-Schlamm.J. Ehik. Arb. Ungarisch. biol. Forschungs-Inst., Tihany, vol.7, pp.17-18, 1934.(In Hungarian, with German summary.)

(EXCURSIONS IN THE FIELD OF PALEONTOLOGY. CONTRIBUTION TO THE THEME: PHOTOGRAPHY AND SCIENCE.) Kurt Ehrenberg. Photographie und Forschung, no.7, pp.202-215, figs.17, June, 1936.

(FURTHER INVESTIGATIONS OF DISEASE MANIFESTATIONS IN PREHISTORIC ANIMALS AND RESULTS THEREOF.) Neuere Untersuchungen ueber Krankheitserscheinungen bei vorzeitlichen Tieren und ihre Ergebnisse. Kurt Ehrenberg. Medizinische Klinik, Berlin, Jahrg. 1931, no.5, pp.8, 1931.

(FOX-OR DEVIL-HOLES NEAR EGGENBURG (LOWER DANUBE).) Die Fuchs- oder Teufelslucken bei Eggenburg Niederdonau. Kurt Ehrenberg, Otto Sickenberg, Angela Stifft-Gottlieb. Abhandl. Zool.-Bot. Gesell. Vienna, vol.17, no.1, pp.1-130, pls.1-18, 1938. (Hyaena spelaea,pp. 24-130, pls.5-18.)

ARCHAELOGICAL OBSERVATIONS ON THE PROBLEM OF POST-GLACIAL EXTINCTION. Loren C. Eiseley. American Antiquity, vol.8, no.3, pp.209-217, Jan., 1943

AGE OF MAMMALS. Carroll Lane Fenton. Girard, Kan., Haldeman-Julius Co., pp.64, illus., 1923.

(HISTORY OF MAMMALS IN THE QUATERNARY PERIOD.) Istoriia fauny mlekopitaiushchikh v chetvertichnom periode. K.K. Flerov. Moscow University Press, Moscow, pp.37, (chiefly illus.) 1955.

SOME STRANGE INTERPRETATIONS OF EARLY DISCOVERED FOSSILS. H. O. Fletcher. Australian Mus. Mag., Sydney, vol.9, no.1, pp.27-31, illus., Mar. 1, 1946.

EARLY MAN AND FOSSIL BISON. Richard G. Forbis. Science, Lancaster, vol.123, no.319, pp.327-328, Feb. 24, 1956.

BIG GAME OF THE PLEISTOCENE. Childs Frick. North American Big Game. A book of the Boone and Crockett Club, compiled by the Committee on Records of North American Big Game. Charles Scribners Sons., New York, pp.1-14, 1939.

CHILDS FRICK TERTIARY-QUARTERNARY EXPLORATIONS, 1928. Childs Frick. Nat. Hist., New York, vol.29, no.1, pp.106-108, Jan.-Feb., 1929.

(Review by P. Rode of) (MANUAL OF GENERAL PREHISTORY.) Manuel de préhistory génerale. Raymond Furon. Mammalia, Paris, vol.3, nos.3-4, p.133, Sep.-Dec., 1939.

(CLIMATE OF THE HUNGARIAN MOUSTERIAN AS MIRRORED BY ITS FAUNA.) Das Klima des ungarischen Mousterien im Spiegel seiner Fauna. Stefan von Gaal. Ann. Hist. Nat. Mus. Nat. Hungarici, Budapest, pars mineral, geol. et palaeontol, vol.34, pp.31-55, 1941.

THE TILLODONTIA: AN EARLY TERTIARY ORDER OF MAMMALS. C. Lewis Gazin. Smiths. Misc. Coll. Washington, vol.121, no.10, pp.1-110, illus., June 23, 1953.

(DESCRIPTION OF SOME FOSSIL SEAL AND CETACEAN BONES.) Description de Quelques Ossements Fossiles de Phoques et de Cetacés. Paul Gervais. Mem. Acad. Sci. Montpellier, vol.2, pp.1-8, 1851.

NOTES ON THE FOSSIL MAMMALIAN GENUS PTILODUS, WITH DESCRIPTIONS OF NEW SPECIES. James W. Gidley. U.S. Nat. Mus. Proceedings, Washington, 1909, vol.36, pp.611-626, illus., pl.70, June 19, 1909.

NOTICE OF A NEW PALEOCENE MAMMAL, A POSSIBLE RELATIVE OF THE TITANOTHERES. James W. Gidley. Proc. U.S. Nat. Mus., vol.52, no.2187, pp.431-435, Feb. 23, 1917.

(MAMMALS IN ZOOLOGICAL, ANATOMICAL, AND PALEONTOLOGICAL ASPECTS, COMPREHENSIVELY REPRESENTED.) Die Saeugethiere in zoologischer, anatomischer und palaeontologischer Beziehung umfassend dargestellt. C.G. Giebel. A.Abel, Leipzig, pp.xii-1108, 1855.

IDENTIFICATION AND VALUE OF MAMMAL BONES FROM ARCHEOLOGIC EXCAVATIONS. Raymond M. Gilmore. Jour. Mamm., Baltimore, vol.30, no.2, pp.163-169, May 23, 1949.

FACILITATE COOPERATION IN THE IDENTIFICATION OF MAMMAL BONES FROM ARCHAEOLOGICAL SITES. Raymond M. Gilmore. Amer. Antiquity, Menasha, vol.12, no.1, pp.49-50, July, 1946.

GLOSSARY OF FOSSIL MAMMALIA FOR THE USE OF STUDENTS OF PALAEONTOLOGY. John Ellard Gore. Roorkee, Thomason Coll. Press, pp.51, 1874.

REVISION OF THE TERTIARY MULTITUBERCULATA. Walter Granger, George G. Simpson. Bull. Amer. Mus. Nat.Hist., vol.56, art.9, pp.601-676, figs.1-43, Feb. 21, 1929.

DR. MERRIAM'S CONTRIBUTIONS TO THE DEVELOPMENT OF VERTEBRATE PALEONTOLOGY ON THE PACIFIC COAST. W.K. Gregory. Sci. Monthly, vol.42, no.4, pp. 377-380, fig., Apr., 1936.

GENETICS VERSUS PALEONTOLOGY. W.K. Gregory. Amer. Nat., vol.51, no.610, pp. 622-635, Oct., 1917.

REVIEW OF WILLIAM DILLER MATTHEW'S CONTRIBUTIONS TO MAMMALIAN PALAEONTOLOGY. W.K. Gregory. Amer. Mus. Nov., no.473, pp.1-23, May 14, 1931.

SECOND REPORT OF THE COMMITTEE ON THE NOMENCLATURE OF THE CRANIAL ELEMENTS IN THE PERMIAN TETRAPODA. W.K. Gregory. Bull. Geol. Soc. of Amer., vol.28, pp.973-986, Dec. 19, 1917.

SUPRA-SPECIFIC VARIATION IN NATURE AND IN CLASSIFICATION. FEW EXAMPLES FROM MAMMALIAN PALEONTOLOGY. W.K. Gregory. Amer. Naturalist, vol.71, pp.268-276, figs.5, May-June, 1937.

FURTHER NOTES ON THE MOLARS OF HESPEROPITHECUS AND OF PITHECANTHROPUS. W.K. Gregory, Milo Hellman. Bull. Amer. Mus. Nat. Hist., vol.48, pp.509-530, figs.15, Dec.4, 1923.

(SOME FEATURES OF THE PRESERVATION OF SOFT MAMMAL BONES FROM FLUVIAL DEPOSITS AS AN INDICATION OF THEIR GEOLOGICAL AGE.) Nekotorie osobennosti sokhrannosti kostei melkikh mlekopitayushchikh iz ruslovogo allyuviya kak pokazateli ikh geologicheskogo vozrasta. I.M. Gromov. Trudi Zool. Inst. Akad. Nauk USSR, vol.22, pp.100-111, 1957.

CHARACTERISTIC MAMMALS OF THE EARLY PLEISTOCENE. O.P. Hay. Jour. Washington Acad. Sci., vol.18, pp.421-430, Sep. 19, 1928.

CHARACTERISTICS OF SUNDRY FOSSIL VERTEBRATES. O.P. Hay. Pan-Amer. Geol., vol.39, pp.101-120, pls.3, figs.2, Mar., 1923.

DESCRIPTIONS OF SPECIES OF PLEISTOCENE VERTEBRATA, TYPES OR SPECIMENS OF MOST OF WHICH ARE PRESERVED IN THE UNITED STATES NATIONAL MUSEUM. O.P. Hay. Proc. U.S. Nat. Mus., vol.59, pp.599-642, pls.116-124, Oct. 13, 1921.

NOTES ON SPECIES OF ICHTHYODECTES, INCLUDING THE NEW SPECIES I. CRUENTUS, AND ON THE RELATED AND HEREIN ESTABLISHED GENUS GILLICUS. O.P. Hay. American Jour. Sci., vol.VI, pp.226-232, figs.1-5, 1898.

ON SOME RECENT EXCURSIONS INTO PLEISTOCENE GEOLOGY AND PALEONTOLOGY. O.P. Hay. Jour. Washington Acad. Sci., vol.19, no.21, pp.463-469, Dec. 19, 1929.

ON THE CORRELATION OF CERTAIN PLEISTOCENE DEPOSITS AND THEIR FOSSILS. O.P. Hay. Jour. Washington Acad. Sci., vol.15, no.11, pp.239-246, June 4, 1925.

ON THE RELATIVE AGES OF CERTAIN PLEISTOCENE DEPOSITS. O.P. Hay. Amer. Jour. Sci., vol.47, pp.361-375, May, 1919.

RECOGNITION OF PLEISTOCENE FAUNAS. O.P. Hay. Smiths. Misc. Coll., vol.59, no.20, publ. 2139, pp.16, figs.10, Aug. 17, 1912.

WHERE DO THE LANCE CREEK ("CERATOPS") BEDS BELONG, IN THE CRETACEOUS OR IN THE TERTIARY? O.P. Hay. Proc. Indiana Acad. Sci., 25th Anniv. Meet., pp.1-27, 1909.

(CONTRIBUTION TO KNOWLEDGE OF FOSSIL MAMMALS.) Beitrage zur Kenntniss fossiler Saeugethiere. Reinhold Friedrich Hensel. Berlin, pp.(659)-704, pls. XV-XVI, 1856.

(ANIMAL BONES OF RERIK.) Tierknochen von Rerik. Max Hilzheimer. Zeitschr. f. Saeugetierkunde, Berlin, vol.13, pp.164-171, pl.29, Sep. 1, 1939.

THEY GAVE LIFE TO BONES. Clayton Hoagland. Sci. Monthly, Lancaster, vol. 56, no.2, whole no.329, pp.114-133, illus., Feb., 1943.

APPENDIX ON THE CORRELATION OF CERTAIN TERTIARY DEPOSITS OF INDIA AND EUROPE. Tindell A. Hopwood. Records Geol. Surv. India, Calcutta, vol.73, pt.4, pp.472-478, 1938.

FOSSIL MAMMALS AND PLEISTOCENE CORRELATION. Tindell A. Hopwood. Proc. Geol. Assoc., London, vol.51, pt.1, pp. 79-88, Mar. 29, 1940.

BACK OF HISTORY. William Howells. Doubleday and Co., Inc. Garden City, N.Y., pp.384, illus., 1954.

TAR TRAP TREASURE. Blackmer Humphrey. Nat. Hist., New York, vol.59, no.3, pp. 120-127, illus., Mar., 1950.

STUDIES ON HETEROGONIC GROWTH. (IV) THE BIMODAL CEPHALIC HORN OF XYLOTRUPES GIDEON. Julian S. Huxley. Jour. Genetics., Cambridge, vol.18, no.1, pp.45-53, figs.1-2, Mar., 1927.

LIFE THROUGH THE AGES. Charles R. Knight. Alfred A. Knopf, New York, pp. 66, illus., 1946.

ON DOCODONTA, A NEW ORDER OF JURASSIC MAMMALIA. M. Kretzoi. Ann. Mus. Nat. Hungarici, Budapest, vol.39, no.6, pp.108-111, figs.2, 1946.

SKELETON TALKS. BONES OF SKELETON GIVE AMAZING DATA... TELL AGE, RACE, SEX, STATURE, AND SO ON... STUDY IS IMPORTANT IN ANTHROPOLOGY, ARCHEOLOGY, AND CRIMINOLOGY. Wilton Marion Krogman. Scientific American, vol.159, no. 2, pp.61-64, photos 9, Aug., 1938.

GEOLOGY OF THE FISSURE-FILLING "HOLWELL 2;" THE AGE-DETERMINATION OF THE MAMMALIAN TEETH THEREIN; AND A REPORT ON THE TECHNIQUE EMPLOYED WHEN COLLECTING THE TEETH OF EOZOSTRODON AND THE MICROCLEPIDAE. Walter G. Kuhne. Proc. Zool. Soc. London, vol.116, nos.3-4, pp.729-733, Feb. 28, 1947.

LIASSIC THERAPSID OLIGOKYPHUS. WITH TWELVE STEREOSCOPIC PLATES AND SIXTY-SIX FIGURES IN THE TEXT. Walter G. Kuhne. London, printed by order of the Trustees of the British Museum, pp.x-149, illus., pls.12, 1956.

AGE GROUPS IN FOSSIL MAMMALS, A PRELIMINARY REPORT. Bjoern Kurten. Helsingfors, pp.6, diagrs., 1953.

DESCRIPTION OF SOME REMAINS OF EXTINCT MAMMALIA. Joseph Leidy. Jour. Acad. Nat. Sci. Philadelphia, ser. 2, vol.3, pp.166-171, pls.15-17, 1856.

REMARKS ON SAUROCEPHALUS AND ITS ALLIES. Joseph Leidy. Trans. Amer. Philos. Soc., vol.11, pp.9-13, 1857.

(BONE REMAINS OF BURENRAIN NEAR SISSACH.) Knochenreste vom Burenrain bei Sissach. Franz Leuthardt. Naturforschende gesellschaft Baselland, Taetigkeitsbericht, Liestal, no.10, 1933-5, pp. 146-154, 1936.

NEW SIWALIK CORRELATION. G. Edward Lewis. Amer. Jour. Sci., vol.33, pp.191-204, figs.2, Mar., 1937.

HOW MAN BEGAN TO UNDERSTAND FOSSILS. Willy Ley. Frontiers, Philadelphia, vol.10, no.1, pp.8-9, 30-32, illus., Oct., 1945.

MONUMENTS TO THE PAST. Willy Ley. Fauna, Philadelphia, vol.4, no.3, pp.66-71, illus., Sep., 1942.

TWO NEW MIOCENE ENTELODONTS. Frederic B. Loomis. Jour. Mamm., vol. 13, no.4, pp.358-362, Nov., 1932.

ANIMALS OF THE PAST. F.A. Lucas. McClure, Phillips & Co., 1901.

PUBLICATIONS IN VERTEBRATE PALAEONTOLOGY. J. Lucas. Publ. Amer. Mus. Nat. Hist., New York, pp.44, Dec. 30, 1938.

(SCIENTIFIC MEMORIES.) Memorias scientificas. Peter Wilhelm Lund. Bello Horizonte, Edicões Apóllo, pp.vii-286, 1935.

SCIENTIFIC ZOOLOGICAL PUBLICATIONS OF THE AMERICAN MUSEUM: SUMMARY OF WORK ON FOSSIL MAMMALS. Frank E. Lutz. Nat. Hist., vol.19, no.6, pp.731-733, Dec., 1919.

CAVERN OF THE THREE BROTHERS (ARIEGE). George Grant Mac Curdy. Science, n.s., vol.41, no.1065, pp. 782-783, May 28, 1915.

DINOCERATA. A MONOGRAPH OF AN EXTINCT ORDER OF GIGANTIC MAMMALS. O.C. Marsh. Washington, Govt. Print.Off., pp.xviii-243, illus., pl.LVI, (U.S. Geological Survey, Monographs. vol.X) 1886.

NEW MIOCENE MAMMAL. O.C. Marsh. Amer. Jour. Sci., New Haven, ser.3, vol. 47, no.147, p.409, illus., May, 1894.

NEW ORDER OF EOCENE MAMMALS. O.C. Marsh. Amer. Jour. Sci. & Arts, vol.9, Mar., 1875.

NOTICE OF NEW TERTIARY MAMMALS. O.C. Marsh. Amer. Jour. Arts & Sci., vol.7, pp.531-534, May, 1874.

NOTICE OF NEW TERTIARY MAMMALS. O.C. Marsh. Amer. Jour. Sci., ser.3, vol.9, no.51, pp.239-250, Mar., 1875.

ON SOME CHARACTERS OF THE GENUS CORYPHODON OWEN. O.C. Marsh. Amer. Jour. Sci. & Arts., New Haven, vol.11, pp.425-428, figs.2, May, 1876.

PRINCIPAL CHARACTERS OF THE DINOCERATA. Pt.1. O. C. Marsh. Amer. Jour. Sci. & Arts, New Haven, vol.11, pp.163-168, figs.1, pls.6, Feb., 1876.

FOUR NOTES ON FOSSIL MAMMALIA. H. Matsumoto. Jour. Geol. Soc. Japan, Tokyo, vol.40, no.479, p.550, July 20, 1933. (In Japanese.)

COLLECTION OF FOSSIL VERTEBRATES. W.D. Matthew. Amer. Mus. Jour., New York, vol.3, no.5, (Guide Leaflet no.12) pp.32, illus., Oct., 1903.

EARLY DAYS OF FOSSIL HUNTING IN THE HIGH PLAINS. W.D. Matthew. Nat. Hist., vol.26, pp.449-454, Sep.-Oct., 1926.

EVIDENCE OF THE PALEOCENE VERTEBRATE FAUNA ON THE CRETACEOUS-TERTIARY PROBLEM. W.D. Matthew. Bull. Geol. Soc. Amer., Washington, D.C., vol.25, no.3, pp.381-402, Sep. 15, 1914.

FOSSIL BONES IN THE ROCK. W. D. Matthew. Nat. Hist., New York, vol.23, no.4, pp.358-369, illus., July-Aug., 1923.

FOSSIL VERTEBRATES AND THE CRETACEOUS-TERTIARY PROBLEM. W.D. Matthew. Amer. Jour. Sci., New Haven, ser.5, vol.2, pp.209-227, Oct., 1921.

NOTE ON THE CERNAYSIAN MAMMAL FAUNA. W.D. Matthew. Amer. Jour.Sci., New Haven, vol.1, art.39, pp.509-511, June, 1921.

RANGE AND LIMITATIONS OF SPECIES AS SEEN IN FOSSIL MAMMAL FAUNAS. W.D. Matthew. Bull. Geol. Soc. Amer., Washington, D.C., vol.41, no.2, pp.271-274, June 30, 1930.

RECENT PROGRESS AND TRENDS IN VERTEBRATE PALEONTOLOGY. W.D. Matthew. Bull. Geol. Soc. Amer., vol. 34, pp.401-418, Sep. 30, 1923.

RECENT PROGRESS AND TRENDS IN VERTEBRATE PALEONTOLOGY. W.D. Matthew. Smiths. Rept., 1923, Publ.no. 2769, pp.273-289, 1925.

REVISION OF THE LOWER EOCENE WASATCH AND WIND RIVER FAUNAS. PART II, ORDER CONDYLARTHRA, FAMILY HYPSODONTIDAE. W. D. Matthew. Bull. Amer. Mus. Nat. Hist., vol.34, art.9, pp.311-328, figs.10, May 29, 1915.

REVISION OF THE LOWER EOCENE WASATCH AND WIND RIVER FAUNAS. PART IV. ENTELONYCHIA, PRIMATES, INSECTIVORA (PART). W. D. Matthew. Bull. Amer. Mus. Nat. Hist., New York, vol.34, art.14, pp.429-483, figs.52, pl. 15, Sep. 24, 1915.

VALUE OF PALEONTOLOGY. W. D. Matthew. Nat. Hist., vol.25, pp.166-168, Mar.-Apr. (May), 1925.

WHY PALAEONTOLOGY? W.D. Matthew. Nat. Hist., vol.21, pp.639-641, Nov.-Dec., 1921.

FAMILY DEINODONTIDAE, WITH A NOTICE OF A NEW GENUS FROM THE CRETACEOUS OF ALBERTA. W.D. Matthew, Barnum Brown. Bull. Amer. Mus. Nat. Hist., New York, vol.46, art.6, pp.367-385, fig. 1, May 31, 1922.

FAUNA OF THE HOULDJIN GRAVELS. W.D. Matthew, Walter Granger. Amer. Mus. Novit., vol.97, pp.1-6, figs.1-6, Dec. 18, 1923.

NEW GENERA OF PALEOCENE MAMMALS. W.D. Matthew, Walter Granger. Amer. Mus. Novitates, New York, no.13, pp.7, Sep.6, 1921.

FIELD MEETING AT SWANSCOMBE, KENT. SATURDAY, MARCH 25TH, 1939. K. P. Oakley. Proc. Geol. Assoc., London, vol. 50, pt.3, pp.357-361, Sep. 29, 1939.

FOSSIL MAMMAL WITH UNBORN TWINS. Cleophas C. O'Harra. Science, vol.71, no.1839, pp.341-342, Mar. 28, 1930.

AGE OF MAMMALS IN EUROPE, ASIA AND NORTH AMERICA. Henry Fairfield Osborn. New York, Macmillan Co., pp. xvii-635, illus., maps, (1910) 1921.

CORRELATION OF THE CENOZOIC THROUGH ITS MAMMALIAN LIFE. Henry Fairfield Osborn. Jour. Geol., vol.18, no.3, pp.201-215, figs.4, Apr.-May, 1910.

EIGHTEEN PRINCIPLES OF ADAPTATION IN ALLOIOMETRONS AND ARISTOGENES. Henry Fairfield Osborn. Palaeobiologica, Vienna, vol.6, pp.273-302, figs.12, tbls. 3, 1938.

FOSSIL MAMMALS OF THE UPPER CRETACEOUS BEDS. Henry Fairfield Osborn. Bull. Amer. Mus. Nat. Hist., New York, vol.5, art.17, pp.311-330, figs.4, pls.7-8, Dec. 15, 1893.

NEW VERTEBRATES OF THE MID-CRETACEOUS. Henry Fairfield Osborn. Science, n.s., Lancaster, vol.16, no. 408, pp.673-676, Oct. 24, 1902.

PALEONTOLOGY VERSUS GENETICS. Henry Fairfield Osborn. Science, vol. 72, no.1853, pp.1-3, July 4, 1930.

PUBLICATION STANDARDS IN VERTEBRATE PALAEONTOLOGY. Henry Fairfield Osborn. Proc. Biol. Soc. Washington, vol.36, pp.1-6, Feb. 3, 1923.

RECENT ZOOPALEONTOLOGY. REMARKABLE NEW MAMMAL FROM JAPAN. ITS RELATIONSHIP TO THE CALIFORNIAN GENUS DESMOSTYLUS MARSH. Henry Fairfield Osborn. Science, n.s., vol.XVI, no.409, pp.713-715, Oct. 31, 1902.

RECENT ZOOPALEONTOLOGY. TRIASSIC ICHTHYOSAURS FROM CALIFORNIA AND NEVADA. Henry Fairfield Osborn. Science, n.s, vol.XVI, no.410, pp.749-752, Nov. 7, 1902.

REPLY TO PROFESSOR O. C. MARSH'S "NOTE ON MESOZOIC MAMMALIA." Henry Fairfield Osborn. Amer. Nat., Boston, vol.25, no.297, pp.775-783, Sep., 1891.

REVIEW OF THE PLEISTOCENE OF EUROPE, ASIA AND NORTHERN AFRICA. Henry Fairfield Osborn. Ann. New York Acad. Sci., vol.26, pp.215-315, figs.20, July 30, 1915.

SKULL OF BATHYOPSIS, WIND RIVER UINTATHERE. Henry Fairfield Osborn. Bull. Amer. Mus. Nat. Hist., New York, vol.32, art.22, pp.417-420, figs.4, pls. 44-46, Sep. 2, 1913.

AN UPPER PLIOCENE CAVE. Henry Fairfield Osborn. Science, Lancaster, n.s, vol.17, no.425, p.312, Feb. 20, 1903.

ELEPHANT ENAMEL METHOD OF MEASURING PLEISTOCENE TIME. ALSO STAGES IN THE SUCCESSION OF FOSSIL MAN AND STONE AGE INDUSTRIES. Henry Fairfield Osborn, Edwin H. Colbert. Proc. Amer. Philos. Soc., vol.70, no.2, pp.187-191, 1931.

MARINE MAMMALS. Earl Leroy Packard. Washington, D.C., Carnegie Institution of Washington, 2 p. l., 136 p., illus., pl., fold. map., 1934.

ON THE CYNODONT GENUS GALESAURUS, WITH NOTE ON THE FUNCTIONAL SIGNIFICANCE OF THE CHANGES IN THE EVOLUTION OF THE THERIODENT SKULL. F. R. Parrington. Ann. and Mag. Nat. Hist., London, ser.10, vol.13, no.73, pp.38-67, figs.9, pl.1, Jan., 1934.

ANIMAL REMAINS. Bryan Patterson. (In) H. H. von der Osten, The Alisher Hueyuek Seasons of 1930-32, pt.3, Oriental Inst. Publ., vol. 30, pp.294-309, figs.247-254, 1938.

AUDITORY REGION OF AN UPPER PLIOCENE TYPOTHERID. Bryan Patterson. Geol. Series Field Mus. Nat. Hist., Publ. 331, vol.6, no.5, pp.83-89, figs.7-9, Dec. 31, 1934.

AUDITORY REGION OF THE TOXODONTIA. Bryan Patterson. Field Mus. Nat. Hist., Geol. ser., publ.305, vol.6, no.1, pp.2-27, figs. 5, Jan., 1932.

COLLECTING FOSSIL VERTEBRATES. Bryan Patterson. Chicago Nat., vol.3, no.1, pp.3-10, 1940.

CONTRIBUTION TO THE OSTEOLOGY OF TITANOIDES AND THE RELATIONSHIPS OF THE AMBLYPODA. Bryan Patterson. Proc. Amer. Philos. Soc., vol.73, no.2, pp.71-101, figs.13, pls.2, Nov. 29, 1933.

CRANIAL CHARACTERS OF HOMALODOTHERIUM. Bryan Patterson. Geol. Series Field Mus. Nat. Hist., Publ. 333, vol.6, no.7, pp.113-117, figs.23, Dec.31, 1934.

EARLY CRETACEOUS MAMMALS AND THE EVOLUTION OF MAMMALIAN MOLAR TEETH. Bryan Patterson. Chicago, Nat. Hist. Mus., no.809, pp.105, illus., 1956.

INTERNAL STRUCTURE OF THE EAR IN SOME NOTOUNGULATES. Bryan Patterson. Geol. Ser. Field Mus. Nat. Hist., vol.6, no.15, pp.199-227, figs.44-54, Oct. 31, 1936.

(NOTES ON THE SKULL OF A YOUNG SPECIMEN OF MESOTHERIUM CRISTATUM.) Notas acerca del craneo de un ejemplar juvenil de Mesotherium cristatum. Bryan Patterson. Rev. Mus. Municipal Ciencias Nat. y Tradic. Mar del Plata, vol.1, ent.1, pp.71-78, illus., Dec., 1952.

SECOND CONTRIBUTION TO THE OSTEOLOGY AND AFFINITIES OF THE PALEOCENE AMBLYPOD TITANOIDES. Bryan Patterson. Proc. Amer. Philos. Soc., Philadelphia, vol.75, no.2, pp.143-162, figs.6, June, 1935.

SOME NOTOUNGULATE BRAINCASTS. Bryan Patterson. Geol. Ser., Field Mus. Nat. Hist., vol.6, no.19, pp.273-301, figs.75-80, Dec. 28, 1937.

UPPER PREMOLAR-MOLAR STRUCTURE IN THE NOTOUNGULATA WITH NOTES ON TAXONOMY. Bryan Patterson. Geol. Series Field Mus. Nat. Hist., Publ.332, vol.6, no.6, pp.91-111, figs.10-22, Dec. 31, 1934.

(SUCCESSIVE FAUNAS OF LAND MAMMALS ON THE AMERICAN CONTINENT.) As sucessivas faunas de mamiferos terrestres no continente americano. Carlos de Paula Couto. Rio de Janeiro, Oficina Gráfica da Universidade do Brasil, pp.159, illus., 1952.

NOTE ON ROOT-DIVISION IN THE MOLAR TEETH OF TRITYLODON. Branislav Petronievics. Ann. and Mag. Nat. Hist., ser.9, vol.10, pp.216-217, Aug., 1922.

APPLICATION OF THE EUROPEAN TIME SCALE TO THE UPPER TERTIARY OF NORTH AMERICA. Guy E. Pilgrim. Geol. Mag., London, vol.77, pp.1-27, Jan.-Feb., 1940.

(FIRST PLACENTAL MAMMALS.) Les premiers mammiferes placentaires. Jean Piveteau. La Terre et la Vie (Revue d'Hist. Nat.), vol.1, no.5, pp.314-315, illus., June, 1931.

(OLDEST KNOWN MAMMAL.) Le plus ancien mammifere connu. Jean Piveteau. La Terre et la Vie (Revue d'Hist.Nat.), vol.1, no.1, pp.57-58, fig.1, Feb., 1931.

(ENVIRONMENT, ADJUSTMENT AND CONTINUANCE IN THE LIGHT OF GEOLOGICAL TRANSMISSION.) Umwelt, Anpassung und Beharrung im Lichte erdgeschichtlicher Ueberlieferung. Joseph Felix Pompecky. Rede zum Antritt des Rektorats der Friedrich-Wilhelms-Universitaet zu Berlin, p.24, Oct. 15, 1925.

PROBLEMS OF ARMATURE. W.P. Pycraft. Illus. London News, vol.195, no.5250, p. 820, illus., Dec. 2, 1939.

ANIMALS ON THE MARCH. William Maxwell Reed. New York, Harcourt, Brace and Co., pp.xvi-335, illus., 1937.

(NEW DESCRIPTIVE DATA ON CHAPALMATHERIUM NOVUM AMEGH.) Nuevos datos descriptivos sobre Chapalmatherium novum Amegh. Osvaldo A. Reig. Rev. Mus. Municipal Ciencias Nat. y Tradic. Mar del Plata, vol.1, ent.1, pp.105-117, illus., Dec., 1952.

AFFINITIES OF PLAGIAULAX (MULTITUBERCULATA). W. D. L. Ride. Proc. Zool. Soc. London, vol.128, pt.3, pp. 397-402, June 6, 1957.

(BRIEF PALEONTOLOGICAL COMMUNICATIONS.) Kleine Palaeontologische Mitteilungen. Otto Roger. Augsburg Nat. Ver. Ber., pp.93-118, pls.3, 1885.

EURYPTERID INFLUENCE ON VERTEBRATE HISTORY. Alfred S. Romer. Science, Lancaster, n.s., vol.78, no.2015, pp.114-117, Aug. 11, 1933.

GEOLOGY, 1888-1938. VERTEBRATE PALEONTOLOGY. Alfred S. Romer. Geol. Soc. Amer., 50th Anniversary Vol., pp.105-135, June, 1941.

VERTEBRATE PALEONTOLOGY. Alfred S. Romer. Univ. of Chicago, second Edition, pp.687, pls.377, tbls.4, 1945.

(ASSUMED RELATIONSHIP OF ARGYROLAGUS WITH THE TYPOTHERIA.) La supuesta Afinidad de Argyrolagus. Carlos Rusconi. Bol. Acad. Nac. Cienc. Córdoba, Buenos Aires, vol.33, pp.173-182, figs.12, 1936.

(STATE OF PRESERVATION OF FOSSIL BONES IN CAVE DEPOSITIONS.) Der Erhaltungszustand fossiler Knochen in Hoehlenablagerungen. Josef Schadler. Palaeobiologica, vol.2, nos.4-5, pp. 283-286. 1929.

FIRST MAMMALS. William E. Scheele. Cleveland, World Pub. Co., pp.128, illus., 1955.

HOW OLD IS THE PLEISTOCENE? James A. B. Scherer. Science, vol.71, no.1849, pp.585-586, June 6, 1930.

MAMMALIA IN THEIR RELATION TO PRIMEVAL TIMES. Eduard Oskar Schmidt. New York, D. Appleton and Co., pp.xii-308, illus., 1886.

(SOME INTERESTING MAMMALIAN FOSSILS FROM OSTERGOTLAND.) Några intressanta daggdjursfossil fran Ostergotland. Harold Schoett, Orvar Isberg. Fauna och Flore, Stockholm, pt.2, pp.50-67, illus., 1931.

EAR BONES OF NOTOTHERIA AND ALLIED ANIMALS. H. H. Scott, Clive E. Lord. Papers & Proc. Royal Soc. Tasmania for 1924, pp.1-7, Mar. 4, 1925.

ASTRAPOTHERIA. William Berryman Scott. Proc. Amer. Philos. Soc., vol.77, no.3, pp.309-393, pls.9, Mar., 1937.

HISTORY OF LAND MAMMALS IN THE WESTERN HEMISPHERE. William Berryman Scott. Macmillan Co., second Edition revised, pp.I-XIV, 1-786, figs.420, 1937.

SOME MEMORIES OF A PALAEONTOLOGIST. William Berryman Scott. Princeton Univ. Press, pp.(7)-336, 1939.

(Review by A.S. Woodward of) SOME MEMORIES OF A PALAEONTOLOGIST. William Berryman Scott. Nature, London, vol.145, no.3665, p.121, Jan. 27, 1940.

ON THE MESOZOIC MAMMALIA. R. W. Shufeldt. West Amer. Sci., San Diego, vol.5, no.3, (whole no.41) pp.20-22, Nov., 1888.

FREQUENCY OF VERTEBRATE FOSSILS IN RIVER DEPOSITS. Ellis W. Shuler. Science, n.s., vol.77, no.1998, pp.368-369, Apr. 14, 1933.

(MAMMAL FAUNA OF THE FOX- OR DEVIL-HOLES NEAR EGGENBURG.) Die Saeugetierfauna der Fuchs- oder Teufelslucken bei Eggenburg. O. Sickenberg. Verh.zool.-bot. Ges. Wien, vol. 83, Ber. Sekt. f. Palaeont. u. Abstam, pp.31-38, Dec. 31, 1933.

ANIMAL FROM A LOST WORLD. George Gaylord Simpson. Nat. Hist., New York, vol.36, no.4, pp.316-318, illus., Nov., 1935.

ARE DROMATHERIUM AND MICROCONODON MAMMALS? George Gaylord Simpson. Science, Lancaster, n.s., vol.63, no.1639, pp.548-549, May 28, 1926.

BEGINNING OF THE AGE OF MAMMALS. George Gaylord Simpson. Biol.Reviews, vol.12, no.1, pp.1-47, figs.11, Jan., 1937.

BRAINCASTS OF PHENACODUS, NOTOSTYLOPS, AND RHYPHODON. George Gaylord Simpson. Amer. Mus. Novitates, New York, no.622, pp.19, figs.3, May 23, 1933.

BRAINCASTS OF TWO TYPOTHERES AND A LITOPTERN. George Gaylord Simpson. Amer. Mus. Novitates, no.629, pp.18, figs.3, June 3, 1933.

CENSUS OF PLAEOCENE MAMMALS. George Gaylord Simpson. Amer. Mus. Nov., no.848, pp.15, May 15, 1936.

DATA ON THE RELATIONSHIPS OF LOCAL AND CONTINENTAL MAMMALIAN FAUNAS. George Gaylord Simpson. Jour. Paleontol., vol.10, no.5, pp.410-414, figs.2, July, 1936.

EAR REGION AND THE FORAMINA OF THE CYNODONT SKULL. George Gaylord Simpson. Amer. Jour. Sci., vol.26, pp.285-294, figs.5, Sep., 1933.

FIRST MAMMALS. George Gaylord Simpson. Quart. Review Biol., vol.10, no.2, pp.154-180, figs.19, June, 1935.

GLOSSARY AND CORRELATION CHARTS OF NORTH AMERICAN TERTIARY MAMMAL-BEARING FORMATIONS. George Gaylord Simpson. Bull. Amer. Mus. Nat. Hist., New York, vol.67, art.3, pp.79-121, figs.8, Nov. 25, 1933.

HOW FOSSILS ARE COLLECTED. George Gaylord Simpson. Natural History, New York, vol.39, no.5, pp.329-333, May, 1937.

MEEK INHERIT THE EARTH. RISE OF THE MAMMALS: ADAPTABILITY AND INTELLIGENCE VS.SLUGGISHNESS AND BRAWN. George Gaylord Simpson. Nat. Hist., New York, vol.49, no.2, pp.98-103, illus., Feb., 1942.

MESOZOIC MAMMALIA. 2. TINDON AND ITS ALLIES. George Gaylord Simpson. Amer. Jour. Sci., vol.10, pp.451-470, figs.9, Nov., 1925.

MESOZOIC MAMMALIA. 3. PRELIMINARY COMPARISON OF JURASSIC MAMMALS EXCEPT MULTITUBERCULATES. George Gaylord Simpson. Amer. Jour. Sci., vol. 10, no.60, pp.559-569, illus., Dec., 1925.

MESOZOIC MAMMALIA. 4. MULTITUBERCULATES AS LIVING ANIMALS. George Gaylord Simpson. Amer. Jour. Sci., vol. 2, p.280, pp.228-250, figs.8, Mar., 1926.

MESOZOIC MAMMALIA. 5. DROMATHERIUM AND MICROCONODON. George Gaylord Simpson. Amer. Jour. Sci., vol.12, no.68, pp.87-108, 1926.

MESOZOIC MAMMALIA. 9. BRAIN OF JURASSIC MAMMALS. George Gaylord Simpson. Amer. Jour. Sci., vol.14, no. 82, pp.259-268, 1927.

MESOZOIC MAMMALIA. 10. TRIASSIC MAMMALS. George Gaylord Simpson. Amer. Jour. Sci., vol.15, no.86, pp.154-167, figs. 1-3, Feb., 1928.

MESOZOIC MAMMALIA. 11.BRANCATHERULUM TENDAGURENSE DIETRICH. George Gaylord Simpson. Amer. Jour. Sci., vol.15, no.88, pp.303-308, figs.2, Apr., 1928.

MESOZOIC MAMMALIA. 12. INTERNAL MANDIBULAR GROOVE OF JURASSIC MAMMALS. George Gaylord Simpson. Amer. Jour. Sci., vol.15, no.90, pp.461-470, figs. 1-7, June, 1928.

MOUNTED SKELETON AND RESTORATION OF AN EARLY PALEOCENE MAMMAL. George Gaylord Simpson. Amer. Mus. Novitates, New York, no.1155, pp.7, figs. 6, Dec. 31, 1941.

MOUNTED SKELETONS OF EOHIPPUS, MERYCHIPPUS, AND HESPEROSIREN. George Gaylord Simpson. Amer. Mus. Novitates, no.587, pp.7, figs.3, Dec. 15, 1932.

NEW JURASSIC MAMMAL. George Gaylord Simpson. Amer. Mus. Novitates, no.943, pp.1-6, fig.1, Sep. 13, 1937.

NEW PALEOCENE UINTATHERE AND MOLAR EVOLUTION IN THE AMBLYPODA. George Gaylord Simpson. Amer. Mus. Nov., no.387, pp.1-9, figs.9, Nov. 27, 1929.

PALEOBIOLOGY OF JURASSIC MAMMALS. George Gaylord Simpson. Palaeobiologica, Vienna, vol.5, pp.127-158, figs.6, 1933.

REVIEW OF A NEW DISCOVERY OF TRIASSIC ANIMALS. George Gaylord Simpson. Amer. Jour. Sci., New Haven, ser.5, vol.35, no. 206, pp.144-146, Feb. 1938.

SKULL STRUCTURE OF THE MULTITUBERCULATA. George Gaylord Simpson. Bull. Amer. Mus. Nat. Hist., vol.73, art.8, pp. 727-763, figs.9, Oct. 8, 1937.

SPECIMEN OF THE UPPER CRETACEOUS MULTITUBERCULATE MENISCOESSUS. George Gaylord Simpson. Amer. Mus.Nov., New York, no.825, pp.4, figs.2, Mar. 14, 1936.

STRUCTURE AND AFFINITIES OF TRIGONOSTYLOPS. George Gaylord Simpson. Amer. Mus. Novitates, New York, no. 608, pp.28, figs.10, Apr. 11, 1933.

STRUCTURE OF A PRIMITIVE NOTOUNGULATE CRANIUM. George Gaylord Simpson. Amer. Mus. Nov., no.824, pp.31, figs.11, Mar. 13, 1936.

SUPER-SPECIFIC VARIATION IN NATURE AND IN CLASSIFICATION FROM THE VIEWPOINT OF PALEONTOLOGY.George Gaylord Simpson. Amer. Nat., vol.71, no.734, pp. 236-267, figs.10, May-June, 1937.

TATLIODON, NEW GENUS, TO REPLACE TANAODON SIMPSON NON KIRK. George Gaylord Simpson. Amer. Jour. Sci., vol. 14, no.79, p.71, 1927.

TRENDS IN RESEACH AND THE JOURNAL OF PALEONTOLOGY. George Gaylord Simpson. Jour. Paleontol., Menasha, vol. 24, no.4, pp.498-499, July, 1950.

HIND LIMB MUSCULATURE AND HABITS OF A PALEOCENE MULTITUBERCULATE. George Gaylord Simpson. Amer. Mus. Nov., no.333, pp.1-19, Nov. 1, 1928.

(IMPORTANCE OF STATISTICAL VARIATION INVESTIGATIONS AS REGARDS MAMMALOGICAL PALEONTOLOGY.) Bedeutung variationsstatistischer Untersuchungen fuer die Saeugetier-Palaeontologie. W. Soergel. Neues Jahrb. f.Mineral., Geol., Paleont., Suppl., vol.63, B, pp.349-450.

CRITICAL REVIEW OF THE MINT CANYON MAMMALIAN FAUNA AND ITS CORRELATIVE SIGNIFICANCE. R. A. Stirton. Amer. Jour. Sci., vol.26, pp.569-576, Dec., 1933.

PRINCIPLES IN CORRELATION AND THEIR APPLICATION TO LATER CENOZOIC HOLARCTIC CONTINENTAL MAMMALIAN FAUNAS. R.A. Stirton. Internat. Geol. Congress, Rept. 18th Session, Great Britain, 1948, part 11, pp.74-84, 1951.

(METHODOLOGY IN PALEONTOLOGY.) Methodologisches zur Palaeontologie. E. Stromer. Palaeont. Zeitschr., Berlin, vol. 17, nos.1-2, pp.21-27, Aug. 20, 1935.

(NOTEWORTHY GAPS IN THE KNOWLEDGE OF MESOZOIC AND TERTIARY TERRESTRIAL VERTEBRATES AND THOSE INHABITING FRESH WATER.) Beachtenswerte Luecken in der Kenntnis mesozoischer und tertitaerer Land und Suesswasser bewohnender Wirbeltiere. E. Stromer. Centralblatt f. Mineral., etc., Jahrg. 1931, Abt. B, no.6, pp.288-296, 1931.

CORRELATION OF SOME MIOCENE AND PLIOCENE MAMMALIAN ASSEMBLAGES IN NORTH AMERICA AND ASIA WITH A DISCUSSION OF THE MIO-PLIOCENE BOUNDARY. P. Teilhard De Chardin, R.A. Stirton. Univ. Calif. Publ. Bull. Dept. Geol. Sci., vol.23, no.8, pp.277-290, Dec. 7, 1934.

MENISCOTHERIUM RUBUSTUM SP. NOV., AND A DISCUSSION OF MYRACOPS SOCIALIS MARSH. Malcolm Rutherford Thorpe. Amer. Jour. Sci., ser.5, vol. 27, no.162, pp.401-409, figs.6, June, 1934.

(REMARKS ON MAMMAL REMAINS FROM THE JURASSIC CONGLOMERATION OF BIESENDORF.) Bemerkungen zu einem Saeugerrest aus der Juranagelfluh von Biesendorf (Amt Engen). Heinz Tobien. Jahresb. und Mitteil. Oberrheinischen geol. Vereins, Stuttgart, n.F., vol.24, Jahrg.1935, pp. 132-136, figs.2, Apr., 1935.

MARINE MAMMALS (SYMPOSIUM ON TEN YEAR'S PROGRESS IN VERTEBRATE PALAEONTOLOGY). Frederick W. True. Bull. Geol. Soc. America, vol.23, pp. 197-200, 1912.

(Review by W.D. Matthew of) (PRINCIPLES OF PALEONTOLOGY) Grundzuege der Palaeontologie. K.A. von Zittel. Science, n.s., vol.58, pp.107-109, Aug. 10, 1923.

(PRINCIPLES OF PALEONTOLOGY. PART II) VERTEBRATA (NEWLY TREATED BY F. BROILI AND MAX SCHLOSSER.) Grundzuege der Palaeontologie, II Abt., Vertebrata Neugearbeitet von F. Broili und Max Schlosser. K. A. von Zittel. R. Oldenbourg, Munich and Berlin, 1923.

PALEONTOLOGIC SKETCHES. PT. 1. PREHISTORIC FAUNA OF FLORIDA. PT. 2. THE EVOLUTION OF THE TEETH. Arthur Frederic Wark. Florida Nat., vol.2, pp.1-8, illus., 1928.

VERTEBRATE PALAEONTOLOGY. D.M.S. Watson. Nature, London, vol.156, no.3956, p.225, Aug. 25, 1945.

(Review by Remington Kellogg of)RECENT VERTEBRATE CARCASSES AND THEIR PALEOBIOLOGICAL SIGNIFICANCE. Rezente Wirbeltierleichen und ihre palaeobiologische Bedeutung. Johannes Weigelt. Jour. Mamm., vol.9, no.2, pp.159-160, May, 1928.

TYPES OF THE FOSSIL MAMMALS DESCRIBED AS AQUILA ANTIQUA AND AQUILA FEROX. Alexander Wetmore. Jour. Mamm., vol.15, no.3, p.251, Aug., 1934.

(RECENT VERTEBRATE CARCASSES AND THEIR PALEOBIOLOGICAL IMPORTANCE.) Rezente wirbeltierleichen und ihre palaobiologische Bedeutung. Johannes Wiegelt. Leipzig, published by Max Weg, vol.8, pp.XVI, pls.227, figs.28, Dec., 1927.

CONDYLARTH GENUS ELLIPSODON. Robert W. Wilson. Univ. Kansas Publ., Mus. Nat. Hist., vol.9, no.5, pp.105-116, illus., May 19, 1956.

PLEISTOCENE MAMMALIAN FAUNA FROM THE CARPINTERIA ASPHALT. Robert W. Wilson. Contrib. to Palaeont., Carnegie Inst. Washington, Publ.440, pp.59-76, Nov. 15, 1933.

(FOSSILS OF CAVE FAUNA II. CATALOGUE OF FOSSILS, I:ANIMALS.) Fauna fossilis cavernarum II. Fossilium Catalogus, I: Animalia. B. Wolf. Editus a W.Quenstedt, 's-Gravenhage, pt.89, pp.193-208, June 3, 1939.

PROBLEM OF THE UINTATHERIUM MOLARS. Horace Elmer Wood. Bull. Amer. Mus. Nat. Hist., vol.48, pp.599-604, figs.4, Dec. 11, 1923.

SOME EARLY TERTIARY RHINOCEROSES AND HYRACODONTS. Horace Elmer Wood. Bull. Amer. Paleontology, vol.13, no.50, pp.1-89, pls.1-7, figs.1-40, Dec. 3, 1927.

EARLY MAN AND THE ASSOCIATED FAUNAS IN THE OLD WORLD. A. S. Woodward. Science, n.s., vol.78, no. 2014, pp.89-92, Aug. 4, 1933.

VERTEBRATE PALEONTOLOGY. A. S. Woodward. Cambridge Univ. Press.

GANODONTA AND THEIR RELATIONSHIP TO THE EDENTATA. J. L. Wortman. Bull. Amer. Mus. Nat. Hist., vol.9, art.6, pp. 59-110, figs.36, Mar. 22, 1897.

PSITTACOTHERIUM, A MEMBER OF A NEW AND PRIMITIVE SUBORDER OF THE EDENTATA. J.L. Wortman. Bull. Amer. Mus. Nat. Hist., vol.8, art.16, pp.259-262, Nov. 30, 1896.

STUDIES OF EOCENE MAMMALIA IN THE MARSH COLLECTION, PEABODY MUSEUM. J. L. Wortman. New Haven, Conn., 2 pts. in 1 v., illus., pl.,1902-04.

(CHRONOLOGY OF THE PLEISTOCENE.) Die Chronologie des Pleistozaens. F. E. Zeuner. Bull. Acad. Sci. math. et nat. Acad. Roy. Serbe, Belgrade, ser.B, sci. nat., no.4, pp.1-79, 1938.

TIME AND THE BIOLOGIST. F.E.Zeuner. Discovery, London, vol.7, no.8, pp.242-249, figs.13, Aug., 1946.

## FUR-BEARERS AND THE FUR INDUSTRY

RELATION OF THE ROOSEVELT WILD LIFE STATION TO THE FUR INDUSTRY. Charles C. Adams. Nat. Assoc. Fur Industry, Yearbook, 1925, pp.52-54, Sep., 1925.

MARSH MANAGEMENT FOR FUR PRODUCTION. D. J. Allan. Trans. 7th N. Amer. Wildl. Conf., Washington, D.C., pp.263-271, 1942.

FARMS AND FUR BEARERS. Philip F. Allan. Virginia Wildlife, Richmond, vol. 8, no.1, pp.8-9, 22; no.2, pp.10-11, 18-20; no.3, pp.14-16, illus., Jan., Feb., Mar., 1947.

FUR BEARERS FIGHT AXIS. Philip F. Allan. U.S. Dept. Agric., Soil Conserv., Washington, D.C., vol.9, no.5, pp.106-108, 117, Nov., 1943.

FUR FROM FARM LANDS. Philip F. Allan. Soil Conserv., Washington, D.C., vol.9, nos.11-12, pp.256-261, 283-286, illus., May-June, 1944.

IS FUR FARMING A SAFE INVESTMENT? Walter Alwyn-Schmidt. Black Fox Mag., New York, vol.32, no.7, pp.19-20, 41-42, Nov., 1948.

DESTRUCTION OF WILD LIFE FOR FUR. Betty Ardron. Indian Wild Life, vol.1, no.2, pp.65-66, Aug., 1936.

BREEDING OF FUR ANIMALS. F. G. Ashbrook. U.S. Dept. Agric., Yearbook, separate no.1603, pp.1379-1395, figs.7, 1937.

FUR-AN IMPORTANT WILDLIFE CROP. F. G. Ashbrook. Nat. Fur News, Denver, vol.20, no.3, pp.15, 25; no.4, pp.20-24, Apr., May, 1948; Iowa Conservationist, Des Moines, vol.7, no.10, pp.73, 79, illus., Oct. 15, 1948; Trans. 13th N.Amer. Wildl. Conf., pp.465-474, 1948.

FUR AN IMPORTANT WILDLIFE RESOURCE. F. G. Ashbrook. Texas Game & Fish, Austin, vol.7, no.1, pp.17, 23, Dec., 1948.

FUR ANIMALS-A VALUABLE NATURAL RESOURCE. F. G. Ashbrook. Chicago Naturalist, vol.6, no.4, pp.79-83, Dec., 1943.

FUR FARMING. F. G. Ashbrook. Farm Jour., vol.48, no.10, p.72, Oct.,1924.

FUR FARMING-A PROFITABLE WILDLIFE BUSINESS. F. G. Ashbrook. Trans. 11th N. Amer. Wildl. Conf., Washington, pp. 505-510, 1946; Nat. Fur News, Denver, vol.17, no.3, pp.9-19, Apr., 1946; Fur of Canada, Winnipeg, vol.11, no.7, pp. 10-12, Apr., 1946.

FUR FARMING FOR PROFIT. F. G.Ashbrook. New York, Macmillan Co., vol.8, pp.XXIII-300, text figs.127, Mar. 27,1928.

FUR FARMING FOR PROFIT. F. G. Ashbrook. New York, Orange Judd Publishing Co., Inc., vol.8, pp.429, text figs.166, Jan. 30, 1948.

(Review by Hartley H.T. Jackson of) FUR FARMING FOR PROFIT. F. G. Ashbrook. Jour. Mamm., vol.29, no.3, p.304, Aug. 31, 1948.

FUR ANIMALS, THEIR IMPORTANCE AND VALUE TO THE FARMER. F. G.Ashbrook. Black Fox Mag., New York, vol.31, no.12, pp.16, 26, Apr., 1948.

FUR FARMING UNDER WAR CONDITIONS. F. G. Ashbrook. Nat. Fur News, Denver, vol.16, no.2, pp.4, 20, Mar., 1944.

CONSERVATION AND THE MOLT CYCLE. F. G. Ashbrook. Jour. Tech. Assoc. Fur Industry, Brooklyn, vol.5, no.2, pp.39-47, June, 1934.

FUR FARMING IN PERSPECTIVE. F. G. Ashbrook. Amer. Fur Breeder, vol.9, no.8, pp.4, 6, Feb., 1937.

FUR RESOURCES - THE STEPCHILD OF CONSERVATION. F. G. Ashbrook. U.S. Dept. Agric., Wildlife Research and Management Leaflet BS-25, pp.4, Dec., 1935.

FUR TRADE AND THE FUR SUPPLY. F.G. Ashbrook. Jour. Mamm., vol.3, no.1, pp. 1-7, Feb., 1922.

FURS GLAMOROUS AND PRACTICAL, FUR BUYING MYSTERY REMOVED. F.G. Ashbrook. Van Nostrand. pp.xiv-88, illus., 1954.

NEED FOR RESEARCH IN FUR ANIMAL PRODUCTION. F. G. Ashbrook. Jour. Wildl. Mgt., Menasha, vol.5, no.2, pp. 139-140, Apr., 1941.

ORGANIZATION-A FUNDAMENTAL OF SUCCESS IN FUR FARMING. F. G. Ashbrook. Fur of Canada, Winnipeg, vol.9, no. 10, pp.12-13, July, 1944; National Fur News, Denver, vol.16, no.7, pp.7, 30, Aug.,1944.

PRELIMINARY STUDY OF THE STATISTICAL DATA ON FUR RESOURCES AND THE FUR TRADE. F. G. Ashbrook, Horace J. McMullen. Nat. Asso. Fur Industry Yearbook, 1925, pp.5-34, Sep., 1925.

PREVENTING WASTE OF FUR TRAPPING WHEN PELTS ARE NOT PRIME. F. G. Ashbrook. Trans. 3rd N. Amer. Wildl. Conf., pp.511-514, 1938.

PRODUCTION AND CONSERVATION OF FUR ANIMALS. F. G. Ashbrook. Game Breeder, vol.22, pp.337-343, Nov., 1928.

PROGRESS IN FUR FARMING. F. G. Ashbrook. Amer. Fur Breeder, vol.11, no.7, pp. 22-24, Jan., 1930.

RECOMMENDATIONS TO BEGINNERS IN FUR FARMING. F. G. Ashbrook. U.S. Dept. Agric. Leaflet no.27, pp.1-6, Nov., 1928; Game and Fish Conservationist, Richmond, Va., vol.9, no.1, pp.9-10, June, 1929.

STORY OF FUR FARMING. F. G. Ashbrook. Nat. Fur News, Denver, vol.20, no.10, pp. 30-31, 94-95, Nov., 1948.

TRAPPING LAWS AND THE FUR SUPPLY. F. G. Ashbrook. Jour. Mamm., vol.6, no. 3, pp.168-173, Aug., 1925.

WORK OF THE UNITED STATES DEPARTMENT OF AGRICULTURE RELATING TO FUR-BEARING ANIMALS. F.A. Ashbrook. Fur Trade Yearbook, vol.1, no.1, pp.43-50, 1924.

SAVING FUR ANIMALS IN FLOOD TIME. Stanley C. Asthur. Fur Jour., vol.1, no.5, pp.8, 9, 20, 38, 43, illus., Sep.,1927.

FUR; A PRACTICAL TREATISE. Max Bachrach. Rev. ed., Prentice-Hall, pp.672, 1946.

(WHAT IS NECESSARY IN THE NEW BREEDING YEAR?) Was ist im neuen Zuchtjahr notwendig? H. Bahlcke. Deutsche Pelztierzuechter, Munich, vol.14, no.3, pp.49-51, Feb.1, 1939.

PREPARATION OF PELTS FROM ALABAMA FUR ANIMALS. Fred S. Barkalow. Jour. Alabama Acad. Sci., vol.10, pt.2, p.27, June, 1938.

PROGRESS AT THE U. S. FUR ANIMAL EXPERIMENTAL STATION. Charles F. Bassett. Fur of Canada, Winnipeg, vol. 10, no.1, p.22, Apr., 1945; Nat. Fur News, Denver, vol.17, no.5, pp.9, 12, 20, 24, June, 1945.

DO FUR BEARERS EFFECT UPLAND BIRDS IN WINTER? Watson E. Beed. Trans. 3rd N. Amer. Wildl. Conf., pp.508-510, 1938.

(REARING FUR ANIMALS.) L'elevage des animaux a fourrure. Henry Beetz. Quebec, pp.106, illus., Jan. - Feb., 1945.

NEED FOR FUR FARM RESEARCH. Wm. P. Bender. Nat. Fur News, Denver, vol.17, no.7, pp.8, 20-21, Aug., 1946.

FEEDING FOR PRODUCTION. G.W.Berry. National Fur News, Denver, vol.16, no.5, p.16, June, 1944.

TRAPPING THRILL OF BOYHOOD, IS ALMOST A MILLION DOLLAR BUSINESS. R.M. Berry. Iowa Cons., vol.1, no.9, pp.1-3, Oct., 1942.

(INTERNATIONAL EXPOSITION OF FUR ANIMALS.) L'exposition internationale des animaux a fourrure. E. Bourdelle. Revue d'Histoire Naturelle, Pt. 1, A.Mammiferes, Paris, vol.11, no.1, pp.38-39, Jan., 1930.

FOOD FOR THOUGHT. E. Rendle Bowness. Fur of Canada, Winnipeg, vol.13, no.8, pp. 10-12, May, 1948.

(FROM THE FUR KINGDOM. VOL. I) HISTORY OF FURRIERY. VOL. II) NATURAL HISTORY OF FUR-BEARING ANIMALS.) Aus dem Reiche der Pelze. Bd. I. Geschichte des Rauchwarenhandels. Bd. II. Naturgeschichte der Pelztiere. Emil Brass. Berlin, Apr., 1911.

HOUSE DIVIDED AGAINST ITSELF. OPINION REGARDING THE PRESENT AND FUTURE STATUS OF THE AMERICAN FUR INDUSTRY IN ITS RELATIONS WITH GOVERNMENT. W.J. Brett. Fur of Canada, Winnipeg, vol.9, no.9, p.5, June, 1944.

TRAGEDY OF THE AMERICAN FUR BEARERS. W. J. Brett. Fur Trade Review, pp.13-16, Oct., 1935.

EFFECT OF THE WAR ON FUR FARMING. G. E. Broyles. Trans. 8th N. Amer. Wildl. Conf., Washington, D.C., pp.318-322,1943.

ROMANCE OF AMERICAN FURS. Wanda Burnett. Nat. Geogr. Mag., Washington, vol.93, no.3, pp.379-402, illus., Mar., 1948.

GENETICS AND FUR BREEDING. Leonard Butler. American Nat. Fur & Market Jour., Wausau, vol.27, no.10, pp.5-6, May,1949.

SEASONAL AND NUTRITIONAL STUDIES ON ANIMAL PELTRIES. Joseph Caspe, F. G. Ashbrook, Chas. E. Kellogg. Jour. Tech. Assoc. Fur Industry, vol.v, no.2, pp.70-82, June, 1934.

VETERINARY PROBLEMS OF THE FUR RANCH. T. T. Chaddock. American Fur Breeder, Duluth, vol.20, no.7, p.64, Jan., 1948.

TRAPPING FARM FUR-BEARERS. Walter S. Chansler. Outdoorsman, Chicago, vol. 89, no.5, whole no.528, pp.53-54, Sep.-Oct., 1947.

FACING FACTS IN FUR FARMING. Noble Clark. Nat. Fur News, Denver, vol.18, no. 8, pp.15, 31, 50, Sep., 1946.

WHY STUDY THE FOOD OF FUR ANIMALS? Clarence Cottam, A.L. Nelson. Trans. 3rd N. Amer. Wildl. Conf., pp.527-530, 1938.

REGISTERED TRAPLINES. V.Crichton. Sylva, Toronto, vol.4, no.2, pp.3-15, illus., 1948.

NOTE CONCERNING FUR FARMING. Norman Criddle. Canadian Field-Nat., vol.41, no.6, pp.137-138, Sep., 1927.

WAR, THE 20 PERCENT TAX, AND THE FUR BUSINESS. A.H. Crow. Nat. Fur News, Denver, vol.17, no.3, pp.6, 21, Apr., 1945.

BEGINNING OF THE FUR FARMING INDUSTRY. Charles Dalton. Amer. Fur Breeder, vol.2, no.2, pp.10-12, Aug., 1929.

(SYSTEMATIC SURVEY OF FUR-BEARING ANIMALS.) Systematische Uebersicht der Pelztiere. Heinrich Dathe. Der Rauchwarenmarkt, Leipzig, nos.3-4, pp.3-40, 1944.

FUR SITUATION. N. Dearborn. Jour. Mamm., vol.1, no.3, pp.144-145, May, 1920.

MAINTENANCE OF THE FUR SUPPLY. N. Dearborn. U.S. Dept. Agric. Circ.135, pp.1-12, pls.1-9, Nov., 1920.

TRAPPING ON THE FARM. N. Dearborn. Yearbook Dept. of Agric., 1919, pp.451-484, figs.1-23, 1920.

FUR FARMING TODAY-AND TOMORROW. Michael Dederer. Nat. Fur News, Denver, vol.17, no.10, pp.9, 50, 53-55, Nov., 1945.

HISTORY OF THE FUR INDUSTRY. Michael Dederer. Fur of Canada, Winnipeg, vol.14, no.2, pp.3-4, 34-35, Nov., 1948.

IF I WERE A FUR FARMER. Michael Dederer. Natl. Fur News, Denver, vol. 19, no.11, pp.15, 34-36, 46-47, Dec., 1947.

REVIEW OF FUR FARMING PROBLEMS. Michael Dederer. Natl. Fur News, Denver, vol.16, no.10, pp.6, 34-36, 38, 40-41, Nov., 1944.

ARTIFICIAL DISTRIBUTION OF FUR-BEARING MAMMALS. Joseph Dixon. Jour. Mamm., vol.10, no.4, pp.358-359, Nov., 1929.

HOME DRESSING OF FURS AND SKINS. Joseph Dixon. Forest & Stream, pp.308-309, figs.3, July, 1917.

SPERM STUDIES AS A GUIDE IN FUR-ANIMAL BREEDING PRACTICE. Robert K. Enders. USDA, Biol. Survey, Wildl. Leaflet 138, p.3, June 1939; Amer. Fur Breeder, Duluth, vol.14, no.4, pp.40-41, Oct., 1941; vol.15, no.7, pp.20-21, Jan., 1943.

PRE-BIRTH PERIOD IN FUR-BEARING ANIMALS. Robert K. Enders, Oliver P. Pearson. Science, Lancaster, n.s., vol. 98, no.2552, pp.10-11, Nov. 26, 1943.

FUR REFUGE EXPERIMENTS PAY OUT. Paul L. Errington. Iowa Conservationist, Des Moines, vol.4, no.10, pp.175-176, Oct. 15, 1945.

FARM FUR AND PROFIT. Edson Fichter. Outdoor Nebraska, Lincoln, vol.20, no.4, pp.6, 20, Nov., 1942.

PLATFORM OF THE AMERICAN TRAPPERS' ASSOCIATION. Irving M. Genfan. Proc. N. Amer. Wildl. Conf., pp.632-637, 1936.

ECONOMIC IMPORTANCE OF THE FUR INDUSTRY. G. Donald Gibbons. Trans. N. Amer. Wildl. Conf., vol.12, pp.139-146, 1947.

DISINFECTANTS ON FUR FARM. J. R. Gorham. Fur of Canada, Winnipeg, vol. 14, no.8, p.12, May, 1949.

HOW TO USE DISINFECTANTS ON FUR FARM. J.R. Gorham. Black Fox Mag., New York, vol.33, no.2, pp.9, 21, June, 1949.

RED LEADING OF EQUIPMENT MAY CAUSE POISONING. J. R. Gorham. Amer. Nat. Fur & Market Jour., Wausau, vol.27, no.8, pp.8, 14, Mar., 1949.

COMMENTS ON THE PAPERS ON THE FUR INDUSTRY PROGRAM. Samuel A. Graham. Trans. 10th N. Amer. Wildl. Conf., Washington, pp.98-101, 1945.

INTEGRATION OF FUR AND TIMBER PRODUCTION. Samuel A. Graham. Trans. 7th N. Amer. Wildl. Conf., Washington, D.C., pp.456-462, 1942.

IT IS POOR ECONOMY TO TAKE FURS ANY TIME EXCEPT WHEN THEY ARE PRIME. William C. Grimm. S. Dakota Conservation Digest, Pierre, vol.9, no. 12, pp.1, 14, Dec., 1942.

PROBLEM OF THE FURRING SEASON. Clarence S. Grubbs. Fur of Canada, Winnipeg, vol.11, no.1, pp.28-29, Oct., 1945.

(LIST OF PERIODICALS AND MAGAZINES PERTAINING TO THE PRODUCTION AND SALE OF FURS.) Foerteckning oever tidskrifter och tidningar roerande produktionen och handeln med paelsskinn. Astrid Guilletmot. Saertryck ur Vara Paelsdjur, no. 14, pp.3, 1951.

DISCUSSION ON FUR-ANIMAL BREEDING. C.K. Gunn. Amer. Nat. Fur & Market Jour., Wausau, vol.27, no.11, pp.16-17, 72, June, 1949.

FUR FARMING INDUSTRY. C.K. Gunn. Fur of Canada, Winnipeg, vol.11, no.10, pp.16, 18, July, 1946.

HOW GENETICS ASSISTS THE FUR ANIMAL BREEDER. C.K. Gunn. Amer. Fur Breeder, Duluth, vol.19, no.3, pp.66, 68-71, illus., Sep., 1946; Fur of Canada, Winnipeg, vol.12, no.1, pp.41-42, 44, Oct., 1946.

FUR AND THE PUBLIC DOMAIN. E. Raymond Hall. Trapper and Sportsman, vol.1, no.1, pp.12-14, Jan., 1938.

FUR BEARERS AND THE WAR. E.Raymond Hall. Trans. 7th N. Amer. Wildl. Conf., Washington, D.C., pp.472-480, 1942.

OUR FUR-BEARERS - A VANISHING NATIONAL RESOURCE. EACH YEAR SEES A DECREASE IN THE NUMBER OF PELTS TAKEN, AND THE SITUATION CALLS FOR QUICK AND INTELLIGENT ACTION. W. J. Hamilton, Jr. Bull. New York Zool. Soc., vol.41, no.3, pp.94-101, illus., May-June, 1938.

PRIMENESS, CONDITION AND FUR VALUES. W. J. Hamilton, Jr., David B. Cook. Trans. 11th N. Amer. Wildl. Conf., Washington, pp. 162-167, fig.1, 1946; Virginia Wildlife, Richmond, vol.8, no.2, pp.4-6, illus., Feb., 1947.

DR. HANSON GIVES PROBABLE RESULTS OF CROSS BREEDING. Karl B. Hanson. Amer. Fur Breeder, vol.4, no.1, p.22, July, 1931.

AMATEUR TRAPPER, AND TRAP-MAKER'S GUIDE. Stanley Harding. New York, Dick & Fitzgerald, vi, (7)-134 pp., illus., 1875.

OUR PRESENT FEEDING PROBLEMS. G.R. Hartsough. Fur of Canada, Winnipeg, vol. 11, no.11, pp.24-25, Aug., 1946.

WHEN YOU BUY FURS. Leon A. Hausman. Pa. Game News, vol.22, no.9, pp.36-39, illus., Dec., 1951.

SKINNING, FLESHING AND STRETCHING FURS. Elmer Hemminghaus. Fur-Fish-Game (Harding's Mag.), Columbus, vol.79, no.12, pp.40-41, illus., Dec., 1945.

GIVE YOUR FURS A BREAK. Baird Hershey. Texas Game and Fish, Austin, vol.5, no.1, pp.8, 18, 22, illus., Dec., 1946.

FUR TRADE AND WILD ANIMALS. William T. Hornaday. Zool. Soc. Bull., vol.24, pp. 29-52, figs.21, Mar., 1921; Wisconsin Conservationist, vol.3, no.2, pp.5-6, May, 1921.

HOW TO PELT. H.C. Hudson. Amer. Fur Breeder, vol.11, no.5, p.4, Nov., 1929.

FUR FARMING AND GAME RAISING, OLD IDEAS. Hartley H.T. Jackson. Jour. Mamm., vol.11, no.3, pp.432-433, Aug., 1930.

FROZEN STORAGE FOR FUR FARMS. F.H. Kaup. American Fur Breeder, Duluth, vol.15, no.2, pp.8-11, Aug., 1942.

WHAT VALUE IN OUR FUR-BEARERS? Chester E. Kebbe. Oregon State Game Comm. Bull., Portland, vol.5, no.11, pp. 1, 6-7, illus., Nov., 1950.

FEDERAL FUR ANIMAL RESEARCH PROGRAM. Charles E. Kellogg. Amer. Fur Breeder, Duluth, vol.13, no.8, pp.22-24, Feb., 1941.

FEEDING FISH TO FUR ANIMALS. Charles E. Kellogg. Amer. Fur Breeder, Duluth, vol. 15, no.9, pp.16-19, Mar., 1943.

FUR FARMING POSSIBILITIES. Charles E. Kellogg. Leaflet U.S. Dept. Agr., Washington, no.267, pp.9, illus., Jan., 1950.

GENETICS APPLIED TO FUR ANIMAL BREEDING. Charles E. Kellogg. Fur of Canada, Winnipeg, vol.11, no.7, pp.3, 5-7, Apr., 1946; Nat. Fur News, Denver, vol.17, no.4, pp.10-11, 20, 25-27, 29-30, May, 1946.

HISTORICAL REVIEW OF FEDERAL FUR FARMING. Charles E. Kellogg. Amer. Nat. Fur & Market Jour., Wausau, vol.27, no.11, pp.1-10, 82, June, 1949.

HISTORY OF FEDERAL RESEARCH, AND SOME ACHIEVEMENTS. Charles E. Kellogg. Black Fox Mag. & Modern Mink Breeder, New York, vol.33, no.3, pp.8, 30; no.4, pp.15, 26, July, Aug., 1949.

REVIEW OF TECHNICAL LITERATURE ON FEDERAL FUR-FARMING RESEARCH. Charles E. Kellogg. Fur of Canada, Winnipeg, vol.16, no.7, pp.5-6, Apr., 1951.

SEASONAL AND NUTRITIONAL STUDIES ON ANIMAL PELTRIES. Charles E.Kellogg, Joseph Caspe, Frank G. Ashbrook. Jour. Tech. Assoc. Fur Industry, vol.v, no.2, pp.70-82, June, 1934.

FALLACIES THAT MAY PROVE COSTLY TO THE FUR FARMER. Arnold H. Kennedy. Fur of Canada, Winnipeg, vol.11, no.11, pp. 12-14, Aug., 1946.

WATCH YOUR FEED TO AVOID BOTULINUS POISONING. Arnold H. Kennedy. Black Fox Mag., New York, vol.32, no.7, pp.25, 40, Nov., 1948.

FUR-FARMING POSSIBILITIES. H.J. LaDue. Fins, Feathers, and Fur, no.18, pp.12-14, June, 1919.

FUTURE OF THE NORTHWEST'S FUR SUPPLY. H.J. LaDue. Fins, Feathers, and Fur, no.28, pp.1-2, Dec., 1921.

INBREEDING NECESSARY FOR FUTURE PROGRESS IN FUR FARMING. H.J. Ladue. Amer. Fur Breeder, vol.4, no.8, pp.8-13, Feb., 1932.

SULFONAMIDES IN FUR ANIMAL WORK. Peter H. Langer. Natl. Fur News, Denver, vol.20, no.1, pp.17, 38, Feb., 1948.

USE AND MISUSE OF DRUGS IN FUR ANIMAL WORK. Peter H. Langer. Amer. Fur Breeder, Duluth, vol.20, no.5, pp.26-28, 30, 32, 34, Nov., 1947.

FURRY DIVIDENDS. D.W. Lay. Texas Game and Fish, vol.3, no.10, p.8, 9, 20, illus., Sep., 1945.

MANAGEMENT OF FUR-BEARING ANIMALS ON TEXAS FARMS AND RANCHES. D. W. Lay. Bull. Texas Game, Fish & Oyster Comm., no.19, pp.3-8, May, 1940.

SOME ASPECTS OF ADMINISTRATION OF THE FUR RESOURCES. D.W. Lay. Trans. N. Amer. Wildl. Conf., vol.8, pp.308-310, 1943.

DISCUSSION OF THE REQUIREMENTS OF A BALANCED DIET. Carl W. Lindow. Black Fox Mag & Modern Mink Breeder, New York, vol.32, no.12, pp.15, 21, 22, Apr., 1949.

FEED NEEDS OF FUR RANCHERS. Carl W. Lindow. Amer. Fur Breeder, Duluth, vol.21, no.9, pp.24-28, Mar., 1949.

FUR RANCHER MUST PROVIDE COMPLETE RATION. Carl W. Lindow. Amer. Nat. Fur & Market Jour., Wausau, vol.27, no.9, pp. 7-8, 15, Apr., 1949.

TIME TO SUM UP. PART 2. Neil M. Lindsey. Fur-Fish-Game (Harding's Mag.), Columbus, vol.83, no.5, pp.10-11, 28-29, May, 1946.

TIME TO SUM UP. PART 3. Neil M. Lindsey. Fur-Fish-Game (Harding's Mag.), Columbus, vol.84, no.6, pp.14-15, 45, illus., June, 1946.

PROPER PELT PREPARATION PAYS. David Loffman. Amer. Fur Breeder, Duluth, vol. 23, no.5, pp.13, 54, Nov., 1950.

FUR QUALITY COMES FIRST. Arthur MacArthur. Amer. Fur Breeder, Duluth, vol.21, no. 12, pp.6, 8, 10, June, 1949.

FUR FARMING. J.M.D. Mackenzie. Jour. Bombay Nat. Hist. Soc., vol.36, no.4, pp.988-992, Dec. 15, 1933.

ECONOMIES OF THE FUR TRADE. Alexander T. Macleod. Trans. 10th N. Amer. Wildl. Conf., Washington, pp.94-97, 1945.

TRADING IN RAW FURS. Alexander T. Macleod. Trans. 11th N. Amer. Wildl.Conf., Washington, pp.458-464, 1946.

TRAPPING - THE CRAFT AND SCIENCE OF CATCHING FURBEARING ANIMALS. Harold McCracken, Harry Van Cleve. A.S.Barnes and Co., Inc., New York, pp.196, illus., 1947.

NOTES ON FUR-BEARERS. William H. Marshall. Bull. Univ. Idaho, vol.33, no. 22, (Bull. School Forestry, no.8), pp.82-85, Dec., 1938.

FUR FOR PROFIT. Herbert Mezger. Black Fox Mag., New York, vol.32, no.4, pp. 13, 32-33, 34-35, Aug., 1948; Nat. Fur News, Denver, vol.20, no.8, pp.15, 24-26, Sep., 1948.

COLLECTION OF FURS. D.C. Mills. Jour. Home Economics, vol.18, pp.691-696, Dec., 1926.

INTERNATIONAL FUR TRADE. D.C.Mills. Jour. Home Economics, vol.18, pp.623-626, Nov., 1926.

PREPARATION OF FURS: FUR DRESSING. D.C. Mills. Jour. Home Economics, vol. 19, pp.16-19, Jan., 1927.

PREPARATION OF FURS: FUR DYEING. D.C. Mills. Jour. Home Economics, vol. 19, pp.75-77, Feb., 1927.

FURS FROM FARM AND RANCH. Levi L. Mohler. Outdoor Nebraska, Lincoln, vol. 21, no.4, p.17, Jan., 1944.

FUR BEARING ANIMALS ADD TO FARM INCOME. James N. Morton. Pennsylvania Game News, vol.9, no.4, pp.14, 32, July, 1938.

FUR--A WILD CROP OF GREAT VALUE. W.O. Nagel. Mo. Cons., vol.6, no.12, pp.4-5, 10, Dec., 1945.

FUR BEARERS—NEGLECTED SOURCE OF FOREST REVENUE. Earl C. O'Roke. Trans. 7th N. Amer. Wildl. Conf., Washington, D.C., pp.451-456, 1942.

IN VIVO OR IN VITRO-THE ANIMAL OR THE TEST TUBE. George L. Ott. Fur of Canada, Winnipeg, vol.13, no.4, pp.24-25, Jan., 1948; Amer. Fur Breeder, Duluth, vol. 20, no.6, pp.44, 46, Dec., 1947; Natl. Fur News, Denver, vol.20, no.1, pp.22, 24, Feb., 1948.

VACCINATION IS LIKE TAKING OUT INSURANCE POLICY. George L. Ott. Amer. Nat. Fur & Market Jour. Wausau, vol.27, no.6, pp.17, 25, Jan., 1949.

BUILDING OUR FUR RESOURCES. E.L. Paynter. Fur of Canada, Winnipeg, pp.3-4, Jan., 1948.

CAREFULLY CONSIDER YOUR MATING PROBLEMS. Katherine E. Penn. Black Fox Mag. & Modern Mink Breeder, New York, vol.32, no.11, pp.18, 28, Mar., 1949.

MARCH PROBLEMS ON THE FUR FARM. Katherine E. Penn. Fur of Canada, Winnipeg, vol.14, no.5, p.9, Feb., 1949.

FUR MARKET. Abe Permack. National Fur News, Denver, vol.20, no.2, pp.13, 34-35, Mar., 1948.

PRACTICAL RESEARCH ON THE FUR FARM. David W. Peterson. Fur of Canada, Winnipeg, vol.11, no.8, pp.18-19, May, 1946; Nat. Fur News, Denver, vol.17, no. 4, pp.9, 18-19, May, 1946.

DETERMINATION OF SEX AND AGE RATIOS IN FUR ANIMALS. George A. Petrides. Amer. Midland Nat., vol.43, no.2, pp.355-382, Mar., 1950.

ARTIFICIAL AIDS IN PRODUCING A FARM FUR CROP. Emmett B. Polderboer. Jour. Wildl. Mgt., Menasha, vol.6, no.3, pp. 208-209, July, 1942.

SOME INTERESTING FUR ANIMALS. Edward A. Preble. Nature Mag., Washington, D.C., vol.33, no.10, pp.577-580, figs.8, Dec., 1940.

TRAPPING HINTS. Hector D. Prine. Outdoorsman, Chicago, vol.86, no.2, whole no.507, p.45, Mar.-Apr., 1944.

ANNUAL FUR PRICE LIST. J. Rashky & Co. St. Louis, Mo., p.4, 1888.

(USING ROTAN IN PROCESSING THE SKINS OF SMALL MAMMALS.) Verwendung von Rotan beim Anfertigen von Kleinsaeugerbaelgen. Edwin Reinwaldt. Saeugetierk. Mitteil., vol.5, no.4, p.169, Dec. 1, 1957.

FEED REQUIREMENTS. W. Roberts. Black Fox Mag., New York, vol.32, no.10, pp.11-13, 24-26, Feb., 1949.

ROLE OF PROTEINS IN FURBEARING ANIMAL FEEDING. W. Roberts. Amer. Nat. Fur & Market Jour. Wausau, vol.27, no.8, pp.7, 26-27, 29-30, Mar., 1949.

(THE FLAYING AND TREATMENT OF FUR-BEARING ANIMALS.) Turkisriistan nylkeminen ja kaesittely. J. F. Ruotsalainen. Suomen Riista, Suomen Riistanhoito-Saatio, Riistantutkimuslaitos (Finnish Foundation for Game Preservation, Game Research Inst.), Helsinki, vol.1, pp.157-170, figs.8, 1946. (In Finnish, with English summary.)

(HANDBOOK ON FUR ANIMALS.) Pelsdyrboken. Handbok i opdrett av pelsdyr. Sigvald Salvesen. 12 mo. paper, pp.144, illus., Oslo, J.W. Cappelens Forlag, Apr., 1928.

PICTORIAL ENCYCLOPEDIA OF FURS. Arthur Samet. Carey Press, New York, pp.474, illus., 1950.

TO THE FUR BREEDERS OF THE UNITED STATES. Arthur Sampson. Nat. Fur News, Denver, vol.15, no.9, pp.12-13, 23, Oct., 1943.

OUR DEBT TO THE FUR BEARER. W. E. Sanderson. Nature Mag., vol.12, pp.357-361, illus., Dec., 1928.

FUR TRAPPING METHODS. S.V.Sedlak. Pennsylvania Game News, Harrisburg, vol. 14, no.8, pp.13, 27, illus., Nov., 1943.

PRACTICAL FUR FARMING. Ernest Thompson Seton. Field and Stream, pt.1, vol.18, Mar., 1914; pt.2, vol.18, Apr., 1914; pt.3, vol.18, May, 1914; pt.4, vol.18, July, 1914; pt.5, vol.18, Aug., 1914; pt.6, vol.18, Nov., 1914; pt.7, vol.19, Jan., 1915.

MAKING SURE OF THE FUR HARVEST. Phil Shackleton. Forest & Outdoors, Montreal, vol.13, p.112, 1947.

GENETICS AND PLANNED BREEDING. R. M. Shackelford. Nat. Fur News, Denver, vol.19, no.11, pp.14, 44-45, 50-51, Dec., 1947; Amer. Fur Breeder, Duluth, vol.20, no.8, pp.44-46, 48, 50, 52, Feb., 1948.

GENETICS AND PLANNED BREEDING. R.M. Shackelford. Natl. Fur News, Denver, vol. 19, no.11, pp.14, 44-45, 50-51, Dec., 1947.

MECHANICS OF INBREEDING. R.M. Shackelford. Amer. Nat. Fur & Market Jour., Wausau, vol.27, no.12, pp.6-8, July, 1949.

RELATION OF GENETICS TO PLANNED BREEDING. R.M. Shackelford. Nat. Fur News, Denver, vol.19, no.4, pp.8-9, 14-15, 26-27, illus., May, 1947; Fur of Canada, Winnipeg, vol.12, no.9, pp.31-33, illus., June, 1947.

INTERNATIONAL FUR FARM PRODUCTION FIGURES. Willard B. Sheldon. Amer. Fur Breeder, Duluth, vol.21, no.4, pp.62, 64, 66, 68, Oct., 1948.

FUR TRADING-OLDEST OF INDUSTRIES. J.J. Shomon. Virginia Wildl., Richmond, vol.10, no.2, pp.5-7, 21, illus., Feb., 1949.

PELTING AND PREPARING PELTS FOR MARKET. Joseph S. Sterling. Amer. Fur Breeder, vol.11, no.6, pp.20-22, Dec., 1929.

(FUR FARMING IN THE PAST, PRESENT, AND FUTURE.) Pelztierzucht in Vergangenheit, Gegenwart und Zukunft. W. Stichel. Zeitschr. f. Saeugetierk., Berlin, vol.6, no.2, pp.66-69, Dec. 15, 1931.

FUR FARM SANITATION AND TREATING SUGGESTIONS. F. S. Swale. Amer. Fur Breeder, vol.4, no.4, pp.6-8, Oct., 1931.

FUR-BEARING MAMMALS: AN UNAPPRECIATED NATURAL RESOURCE. Walter P. Taylor. Science, n.s., vol.37, no.952, pp.485-487, Mar. 28, 1913.

WAR AND TRAPPING. Raymond Thompson. Fur-Fish-Game (Harding's Mag.), Columbus, vol.79, no.2, pp.10-11, 21, Feb., 1945.

ANIMAL RECORDS. Hugh F. Travis. Fur of Canada, Winnipeg, vol.14, no.11, pp.8-9, Aug., 1949.

FUR PRODUCTIVITY OF SUBMARGINAL FARMLAND. Francis M. Uhler. Jour. Wildl. Mgt., Ithaca, N.Y., vol.16, no.1, pp.79-86, Jan., 1952.

OUR FUR BEARERS AND THEIR CONSERVATION. Harry Van Cleve. Trans. N.Amer. Wildl. Conf., vol.2, pp.539-541, 1937.

PELTING EQUIPMENT AND HOW TO SKIN, FLESH, STRETCH, AND DRY PELTS. Harry Van Cleve. Trans. 10th N. Amer. Wildl. Conf., Washington, pp.86-90, 1945.

FUR-A NEGLECTED RESOURCE? Douglas E. Wade. U.S. Dept. Interior, Fish and Wildlife Service, Pittman-Robertson Quart., vol.1, no.2, pp.120-124, Apr., 1941.

FUR, FISH, AND GAME--SOME SUGGESTED RELATIONSHIPS. Douglas E. Wade. Trans. N. Amer. Wildl. Conf., vol.6, pp.314-319, 1941.

UNWRITTEN CHAPTER OF THE FUR-TRADE. W.S. Wallace. Trans. Roy. Soc. Canada, Ottawa, sec.2, ser.3, vol.33, pp.1-8, May, 1939.

FUR-BEARING ANIMALS. Bruno Walimeyer. Georg. Kurt Schauer, Frankfurt am Main, pp.xii-215, illus.78, maps 5, 1951.

HURRICANE DAMAGE TO FUR INDUSTRY. F.J. Webert. Louisiana Conservationist, vol.8, no.12, pp.10-13, 20-21, Nov., 1956.

DETERMINATION OF THE MATING CYCLE. Leon F. Whitney. Amer. Fur Breeder, vol.11, no.6, pp.12-14, Dec., 1929.

ARTIFICIAL INSEMINATION. L.M. Winters. American Fur Breeder, Duluth, vol.11, no.3, pp.16, 18, Sep., 1938.

NATURALLY SUSTAINED YIELD IN A FUR CROP IN MISSISSIPPI. Lee E. Yeager. Jour. Wildl. Mgt., vol.1, nos.1-2, pp.28-36, July, 1937.

WETLAND IS FUR COUNTRY. Lee E. Yeager. Distrib. by the Natl. Wildl. Fed. in cooperation with US F&WS , pp.1-12, illus., 1954.

LITTLE KNOWN FACTS ABOUT FUR. Stanley P. Young. Amer. Forests, Washington, D.C., vol.49, no.4, pp.166-167, 189-190, illus., Apr., 1943.

DIRECTORY OF THE FUR TRADE...1923-1924. Mrs. Julian C. Austrian Corp., New York, pp.384, illus., 1923.

FRIEND'S TRAPPER'S GUIDE. Denver, Colo., Chicago, C. Friend & Co., Inc., pp.36, illus., 1913.

FURBEARERS OFFER A PROFIT TO FARMERS. Mo. Cons., vol.3, no.2, pp.1-7, Dec., 1940.

WHERE WILD ANIMALS ARE BRED FOR THEIR PELTS: AMERICAN FUR RANCHES. Illus. London News, vol.214, no.5731, p. 235, Feb. 19, 1949.

WILD FUR CATCH DECREASING. Texas Game & Fish, Austin, vol.7, no.3, p.11, Feb., 1949.

GAME AND FUR LAWS

ABSTRACT OF FUR LAWS, 1945-1946. Frank G. Ashbrook. USDI, F&WS, Wildl. Leaflet 279, pp.48, Oct., 1945.

ABSTRACT OF FUR LAWS, 1946-1947. Frank G. Ashbrook. USDI, F&WS, Wildl. Leaflet 291, pp.47, Oct., 1946.

ABSTRACT OF FUR LAWS, 1952-1953. Frank G. Ashbrook. USDI, F&WS, Wildl. Leafl. 343, pp.43, Oct., 1952.

ABSTRACT OF FUR LAWS, 1953-1954. Frank G. Ashbrook. USDI, F&WS, Wildl. Leafl. 347, pp.41, Oct., 1953.

ABSTRACT OF FUR LAWS, 1954-1955. Frank G. Ashbrook. USDI, F&WS, Wildl. Leafl. 363, pp.39, Oct., 1954.

LAWS RELATING TO FUR ANIMALS FOR THE SEASON 1924-1925. Frank G. Ashbrook, Frank L. Earnshaw. U.S. Dept. Agric., Farmers Bull.1445, pp.22, Sep., 1924.

FUR LAWS FOR THE SEASON 1926-1927. Frank G. Ashbrook, Frank L. Earnshaw. U.S.Dept.Agric., Farmers Bull.1515, pp.28, Sep., 1926.

FUR LAWS FOR THE SEASON 1927-1928. Frank G. Ashbrook, Frank L. Earnshaw. U.S. Dept. Agric., Farmers Bull. 1552, pp.28, Nov., 1927.

FACTORS TO CONSIDER IN TRAPPING REGULATIONS. Arthur H. Cook. N.Y. State Cons. Dept., Fish & Wildl. Inf. Bull.1, pp.4, 1948.

THOSE HUNTING AND TRAPPING REGULATIONS. L.A. Davenport. Michigan Conserv., Lansing, vol.17, no.12, pp.3, 12-13, fig.1, Dec., 1948.

GAME LAWS FOR THE SEASON 1926-1927. Talbott Denmead, Frank L. Earnshaw. U.S. Dept. Agric., Farmer's Bull. 1505, pp.45, Aug., 1926.

LAWS AND REGULATIONS ISSUED DURING THE YEARS 1930-1934. J.M. Kenya Derscheid. Revue Internationale de Legislation pour la Protection de la Nature, Bruxelles, pp. 9, 1932.

GAME LAWS FOR ... 1927-1928. Frank L. Earnshaw. U.S. Dept. Agric., Farmers Bull.1550, pp.46, Aug., 1927.

GAME LAWS FOR THE SEASON 1930-1931. SUMMARY OF THE PROVISIONS OF FEDERAL, STATE, AND PROVINCIAL STATUTES. Frank L. Earnshaw, Frank G. Grimes. Farmers Bull. 1647, U.S. Dept. Agric., pp.46, Sep., 1930.

LAWS RELATING TO FUR ANIMALS FOR THE SEASON 1925-1926. Frank L. Earnshaw, Frank G. Ashbrook. U.S. Dept. Agric., Farmers Bull. 1469, pp.27, Sep., 1925.

FUR LAWS FOR THE SEASON 1928-1929. Frank L. Earnshaw, Frank G. Grimes. U.S. Dept. Agric., Farmers Bull. 1576, pp.29, Oct., 1928.

FUR LAWS FOR THE SEASON 1929-1930. Frank L. Earnshaw, Frank G. Grimes. U.S. Dept. Agric., Farmers Bull. 1618, pp.30, Oct., 1929.

REGULATIONS RELATING TO MIGRATORY BIRDS AND CERTAIN GAME ANIMALS:1938. Ira N. Gabrielson. U.S. Dept. Agric., Serv. & Reg. Announce., BS-92, pp.12, Aug., 1938.

UGANDA. LAWS AND REGULATIONS ISSUED DURING THE YEARS 1930-1934. Tordis Graim. Internat. Review Legislation for Protection of Nature, Brussels, pp.12, 1933.

FUR LAWS FOR THE SEASON 1927-1928. Frank G. Grimes, Frank L. Earnshaw, Frank G. Ashbrook. U.S. Dept. Agric., Farmers Bull. 1552, pp.28, Oct., 1927.

FUR LAWS FOR THE SEASON 1930-1931. Frank G. Grimes. U.S. Dept. Agric., Farmers Bull.1648, pp.30, Oct., 1930.

ABSTRACT OF FUR LAWS. 1935-1936. Frank G. Grimes. U.S. Dept. Agric., Wildl. Res. and Mgt. Leaflet BS-23, pp.29, Nov., 1935.

ABSTRACT OF FUR LAWS. 1936-1937. Frank G. Grimes. U.S.Dept., Agric., Wildl. Res. and Mgt. Leaflet, BS-97, pp.31, Oct., 1937.

ABSTRACT OF FUR LAWS, 1937-1938. Frank G. Grimes. U.S. Dept. Agric., Wildl. Res. and Mgt. Leaflet, BS-97, pp.31, Oct., 1937.

ABSTRACT OF FUR LAWS, 1938-1939. Frank G. Grimes. U.S. Dept. Agric., Wildl. Res. and Mgt. Leaflet BS-118, pp.35, Sep., 1938.

ABSTRACT OF FUR LAWS. 1939-1940. Frank G. Grimes. U.S. Dept. Interior, Bur. Biol. Surv., Wildl. Leaflet BS-147, pp.37, Oct., 1939.

ABSTRACT OF FUR LAWS. 1940-1941. Frank G. Grimes. USDI, F&WS, Wildl. Leaflet 174, pp.39, Oct., 1940.

GAME, FUR AND FISH LAWS; BOOK OF VALUABLE INFORMATION FOR HUNTERS, TRAPPERS AND ANGLERS, CONTAINING LAWS OF UNITED STATES AND CANADA. Arthur Robert Harding. Columbus, O., A.R. Harding, pp.127, 1913.

LAWS RELATING TO FUR-BEARING ANIMALS, 1915. SUMMARY OF LAWS IN THE UNITED STATES AND CANADA RELATING TO TRAPPING, PROTECTION, PROPAGATION, AND BOUNTIES. David E. Lantz. U.S. Dept. Agric., Farmers Bull. 706, pp.24, Feb.23, 1916.

LAWS RELATING TO FUR-BEARING ANIMALS, 1916. SUMMARY OF LAWS IN THE UNITED STATES AND CANADA RELATING TO TRAPPING, PROTECTION, PROPAGATION, AND BOUNTIES. David E. Lantz. U.S. Dept. Agric., Farmers Bull. 783, pp.28, Oct. 19, 1916.

LAWS RELATING TO FUR-BEARING ANIMALS, 1917. SUMMARY OF LAWS IN THE UNITED STATES AND CANADA RELATING TO TRAPPING OPEN SEASONS, PROPAGATION, AND BOUNTIES. David E. Lantz. U.S. Dept. Agric., Farmers Bull. 911, pp.32, Oct., 1917; Mammalia, vol.90, no.3837.

GAME LAWS FOR 1919. SUMMARY OF THE PROVISIONS OF FEDERAL, STATE, AND PROVINCIAL STATUTES. Geo. A. Lawyer, Frank L. Earnshaw. U.S. Dept. Agric., Farmers Bull.1077, pp.80, Aug., 1919.

GAME LAWS FOR 1921. SUMMARY OF FEDERAL, STATE, AND PROVINCIAL STATUTES. Geo. A. Lawyer, Frank L. Earnshaw. U.S. Dept. Agric., Farmers Bull. 1235, pp.80, Aug., 1921.

GAME LAWS FOR THE SEASON 1923-1924. SUMMARY OF FEDERAL, STATE, AND PROVINCIAL STATUTES. Geo. A. Lawyer, Frank L. Earnshaw. U.S. Dept. Agric., Farmers Bull. 1375, pp.70, Sep., 1923.

GAME LAWS FOR THE SEASON 1924-1925. SUMMARY OF FEDERAL, STATE, AND PROVINCIAL STATUTES. Geo. A. Lawyer, Frank L. Earnshaw. U.S. Dept. Agric., Farmers Bull. 1444, pp.38, Aug., 1924.

GAME LAWS FOR THE SEASON 1925-1926. Geo. A. Lawyer, Frank L. Earnshaw. U.S. Dept. Agric., Farmers Bull. 1466, pp. 46, Aug., 1925.

LAWS RELATING TO FUR-BEARING ANIMALS, 1921. SUMMARY OF LAWS IN THE UNITED STATES, CANADA, AND NEWFOUNDLAND, RELATING TO TRAPPING, OPEN SEASONS, PROPAGATION, AND BOUNTIES. Geo. A. Lawyer, Frank L. Earnshaw. U.S. Dept. Agric., Farmers Bull. 1238, pp.30, Sep., 1921.

LAWS RELATING TO FUR ANIMALS. Geo. A. Lawyer, Frank L. Earnshaw. U.S. Dept. Agric., Farmers Bull. 1293, pp.30, Aug., 1922.

LAWS RELATING TO FUR ANIMALS FOR THE SEASON 1923-1924. Geo. A. Lawyer, Frank L. Earnshaw. U.S. Dept. Agric., Farmers Bull.1387, pp.33, Nov., 1923.

DIGEST OF GAME LAWS FOR 1901. T.S. Palmer, H.W. Olds. U.S. Dept. Agric., Div. Biol. Surv., Bull. 16, pp.152, pls.8, 1901.

GAME LAWS FOR 1906. T.S. Palmer, R.W. Williams, Jr. U.S. Dept. Agric., Farmers Bull. 265, pp.54, figs.2, 1906.

INFORMATION CONCERNING GAME: SEASONS, SHIPMENT, AND SALE. T.S.Palmer, H.W. Olds. U.S. Dept. Agric., Div.Biol. Surv., Circ.31, pp.20, Oct. 25, 1900.

LAWS REGULATING THE TRANSPORTATION AND SALE OF GAME. T.S. Palmer, H.W. Olds. U.S. Dept. Agric., Div.Biol. Surv., Bull.14, pp.89, pls.9, 1900.

FUR LAWS FOR THE SEASON 1931-1932. H.P. Sheldon, Frank G. Grimes. U.S. Dept. Agric., Farmers Bull. 1685, pp.30, Nov., 1931.

GAME LAWS FOR THE SEASON 1931-1932. SUMMARY OF FEDERAL, STATE, AND PROVINCIAL STATUTES. H.P.Sheldon, Frank G. Grimes. U.S. Dept. Agric., Farmers Bull. 1684, pp.52, Sep., 1931.

GAME LAWS FOR THE SEASON 1934-1935. SUMMARY OF FEDERAL, STATE, AND PROVINCIAL STATUTES. H.P.Sheldon, Frank G. Grimes. U.S. Dept. Agric., Farmers Bull. 1742, pp.37, Oct., 1934.

GAME LAWS FOR THE SEASON 1935-1936. SUMMARY OF FEDERAL, STATE, AND PROVINCIAL STATUTES. H.P.Sheldon, Frank G. Grimes. U.S. Dept. Agric., Farmers Bull.1755, pp.38, Oct., 1935.

GAME LAWS FOR THE SEASON 1936-1937. SUMMARY OF FEDERAL, STATE, AND PROVINCIAL STATUTES. H.P.Sheldon, Frank G. Grimes. U.S. Dept. Agric., Farmers Bull. 1766, pp.38, Oct., 1936.

ABSTRACT OF FUR LAWS, 1941-1942. USDI, F&WS, Wildl. Leaflet 199, pp.40, Sep., 1941.

ABSTRACT OF FUR LAWS, 1942-1943. USDI, F&WS, Wildl. Leaflet 226, pp.43, Nov., 1942.

GENETICS see HEREDITY

GEOGRAPHICAL DISTRIBUTION

SHIFTING OF MAMMALIAN FAUNAS, AS SHOWN BY THE PLEISTOCENE REMAINS OF ILLINOIS. L. A. Adams. Trans.Ill. State Acad. Sci., vol.16, pp.140-144, 1923.

GEOGRAPHICAL DISTRIBUTION OF THE MAMMALIA, CONSIDERED IN RELATION TO THE PRINCIPAL ONTOLOGICAL REGIONS OF THE EARTH, AND THE LAWS THAT GOVERN THE DISTRIBUTION OF ANIMAL LIFE. Joel Asaph Allen. U.S. Geological and Geographical Survey of the Territories, Bull. Govt. Print. Off., Washington, vol.4, no.2, art.xv, pp.313-377, 1878.

DISTRIBUTION AND ABUNDANCE OF ANIMALS. H.G. Andrewartha, L.C. Birch. Univ. Chicago Press, pp.782, 1954.

ROLE OF ICE IN THE DISTRIBUTION OF MAMMALS. A. W. F. Banfield. Jour.Mamm., vol.35, no.1, pp.104-107, Feb., 1954.

(Review by Wilfred H. Osgood of) ATLAS OF ZOOGEOGRAPHY. J. G. Bartholomew, W. Eagle Clark, Percy H. Grimshaw. Science, Lancaster, n.s., vol.34, no.874, pp.411-412, Sep. 29, 1911.

DISTRIBUTION OF MARINE MAMMALS. G. Baur. Science, n.s., vol.5, pp.956-957, 1897.

(CAUSES OF THE ICE AGE.) Die Ursachen der Eiszeit. K. Beurlen. Natur and Mus., vol.57, no.10, pp.449-467, figs.16, Oct., 1927.

ROLE OF WEATHER IN DETERMINING THE DISTRIBUTION AND ABUNDANCE OF ANIMALS. L.C. Birch. Cold Spring Harbor Symposia on Quantitative Biology, vol.22, pp.203-218, 1957.

PALAEOGEOGRAPHY AND POLAR SHIFT. STUDY OF HYPOTHETICAL PROJECTIONS.

Davidson Black. Bull. Geol. Soc. China, vol.10, pp.106-157, figs.26, 1931.

(WHERE DID THE MAMMALS ORIGINATE?) Wo sind die Saeugetiere entstanden? Caesar R. Boettger. Sitz. Ber. Ges. naturforsch. Freunde, Berlin, pp.24-30, Mar. 15, 1938.

REMARKS ON FAUNAL EXCHANGE THROUGH THE SAHARA. F.W.Braestrup. Vidensk. Medd. fra Dansk naturh. Foren., Copenhagen, vol.110, pp.1-15, fig.1, Nov., 1947.

SOME COMMENTS UPON H.C. RAVEN'S PAPER: "WALLACE'S LINE AND THE DISTRIBUTION OF INDO-AUSTRALIAN MAMMALS." L.D.Brongersma. Archiv. Neerlandaises Zool., vol.2, nos.2-3, pp.240-256, Dec. 21, 1936.

(AZARA AS A ZOOGEOGRAPHER THROUGH HIS WRITINGS ON QUADRUPEDS.) Azara como zoogeografo a traves de sus escritos sobre cuadrupedos. Angel Cabrera. Gaea, Anal. Soc. Argentina Estud. Geograf., Buenos Aires, vol.7, no.1, pp.73-79, 1943.

ICE AGE WINTER RESORT. DRIVEN SOUTH IN A SPECTACULAR POPULATION MOVEMENT BY RELENTLESS GLACIERS THAT DESCENDED UPON NORTH AMERICA, THE ANIMALS DISCOVERED FLORIDA'S WARM HAVEN A MILLION YEARS AGO. Edwin H.Colbert. Nat. Hist., New York, vol.50, no.1, pp. 16-21, illus., June, 1942.

(PRINCIPLES OF AN ECOLOGICAL ZOOGEOGRAPHY.) Grundlagen einer oekologischen Tiergeographie. Friedrich Dahl. Gustav Fischer, Jena, part 1, pp.113, figs. 11, maps 2, 1921; part 2, pp.122, 1923.

ZOOGEOGRAPHY: THE GEOGRAPHICAL DISTRIBUTION OF ANIMALS. Philip J. Darlington, Jr. John Wiley & Sons, New York, pp.xiii-675, 1957. (Mammals, pp. 320-410.)

(INSULAR FAUNA.) Le Faune Insulari. I. De Stefani. L'Universo, Florence, Anno 10, no.4, pp.24, illus., Apr., 1929.

(ANIMAL WORLD IN THE ICE AGE.) Die Tierwelt im Eiszeitalter. W.O.Dietrich. Brandenburgische Jahrbuecher, no.8, pp. 45-50, figs.7, 1938.

ON SOME PECULARITIES IN THE GEOGRAPHICAL DISTRIBUTION AND IN THE HABITS OF CERTAIN MAMMALS INHABITING CONTINENTAL AND OCEANIC ISLANDS. G.E. Dobson. Ann.& Mag.Nat. Hist. London, ser.5, vol.2, pp.153-159, Sep., 1884.

TERTIARY MAMMALS AND CONTINENTAL DRIFT. Alex L. Du Toit. Amer. Jour. Sci., New Haven, vol.242, no.3, pp.145-163, Mar., 1944.

GLACIAL-THEORIES IN THE LIGHT OF BIOLOGICAL INVESTIGATION. J.Ehik. Ann. Mus. Hung., Budapest, vol.18, pp. 89-110, figs.7, 1921.

ZOOGEOGRAPHY OF THE SEA. S.Ekman. London, Sidgwick and Jackson, pp.14-417, 1953.

(DISTINGUISHED WORK ON GEOPALEONTOLOGY BY CARLOS RUSCONI.) La destacada obra geopaleontologica de don Carlos Rusconi. Mario A. Fontana. Revista Soc. "Amigos de la Arqueologia," Montevideo, vol.6, pp.1-28, 1933.

(ON MAPS OF THE GEOGRAPHICAL DISTRIBUTION OF GAME ANIMALS.) Ueber Karten geographischer Verbreitung von Jagdtieren. A.N. Formosov. Zoologitscheskij Jour. (vormals "Revue Zool. Russe"), Moscow, vol.12, pt.4, pp.110-116, 1933. (In Russian, with German summary.)

GREAT ICE AGE, AND ITS RELATION TO THE ANTIQUITY OF MAN. James Geikie. New York, pp.545, pl.16, 1874.

(ANIMAL LIFE ON THE SURFACE OF THE CONTINENTS.) La vie des animaux à la surface des continents. L. Germain. Paris, Felix Alcau, pp.iii-260, maps, 1924.

PRINCIPLES OF ZOOGEOGRAPHY. Theodore Gill. Proc. Biol. Soc., Washington, vol.2, 1882-84, pp.39, 1884.

SOUTHERN RECORDS FOR ARCTIC MAMMALS AND A NORTHERN RECORD FOR ALFARO'S RICE RAT. G.G. Goodwin, Jour. Mamm., 35:258, 1954.

BARRIERS TO DISTRIBUTION AS REGARDS BIRDS AND MAMMALS. J. Grinnell. Amer. Naturalist, vol.48, pp.248-254, Apr., 1914.

GENERAL ZOOGEOGRAPHY. V.G.Heptner. Gosudarstvennae Izdatelstvo Biol.i.Med. Lit., pp.548, 1936. (In Russian.)

DISTRIBUTION OF ANIMALS. R. Hesse, W.C. Allee, K.P. Schmidt.Encyclopaedia Britannica, pp.11, pls.5, 1948.

ECOLOGICAL ANIMAL GEOGRAPHY. R. Hesse, W.C. Allee, K.P. Schmidt. John Wiley & Sons, Inc., New York, pp.597, figs.135, Apr., 1937; 2nd ed., New York, Wiley, pp.xiii-715.

EARTH-MOVEMENTS, ICE AGES, AND FAUNAS. A. Tindell Hopwood. Geol. Mag., London, vol.73, no.862, pp.185-188, Apr., 1936.

AGENCIES WHICH GOVERN THE DISTRIBUTION OF LIFE. A. Brazier Howell. Amer. Nat., vol.56, pp.428-438, Sep.-Oct., 1922.

THEORIES OF DISTRIBUTION-A CRITIQUE. A. Brazier Howell. Ecology, vol.5, pp.51-53, Jan., 1924.

(SURVEY OF THE MAMMALS ACCORDING TO THEIR WORLD DISTRIBUTION.) Ueberblick der Saeugethiere nach ihrer Vertheilung ueber die Welttheile. J.C.W.Illiger. Abhandl. Physik.Klasse der Koeniglich-Preuss. Akad. Wissensch., pp.39-159, 1804-1811.

(BIOGEOGRAPHICAL HISTORY OF AMERICA AND WEGENER'S THEORY.) L'histoire biogeographique de l'Amérique et le théorie de Wegener. L. Joleaud. Jour.Soc. Américanistes Paris, vol.16, pp.325-360, 1924.

(ICE AGE IN THE LIGHT OF BIOLOGY.) Die Eiszeit im Lichte der Biologie.Theodor Kormos. Palaeobiologica, vol.5, pp.251-274, 1933.

(ORIGIN AND PRIMITIVE DISTRIBUTION OF TERTIARY MAMMALS.) Origine et répartition primitive des Mammiferes tertiaires. R. Lavocat. Mammalia, Paris, vol.19, no.2, pp.302-308, June, 1955.

(MORPHOLOGICAL-GEOGRAPHICAL GROUPING OF MAMMALS.) Morphologisch-geographische formenreihen bei den Saeugetieren. Wilhelm Leche. Lund, C.W. K. Gleerup, pp.76, illus., 1921.

FAUNAL CONNECTIONS BETWEEN EUROPE AND NORTH AMERICA. Carl H. Lindroth. Univ. of Lund, Sweden, pp.344, illus., 1957.

MOVEMENTS AND CHANGES OF AREA AT THE CLIMATIC LIMIT OF TERRESTRIAL ANIMAL SPECIES. Carl H. Lindroth. Bertil Hanstroem, Zoological Papers in Honour of his Sixty-fifth Birthday, Zoological Institute, Lund, Sweden, pp.226-230, 1956.

GEOGRAPHICAL HISTORY OF MAMMALS. Richard Lydekker. Univ. Press, Cambridge, pp.400, illus., 1896.

VERTICAL DISTRIBUTION OF ANIMALS. Marcus W. Lyon, Jr. Sci.Amer., vol.110, p.432, May 23, 1914.

ZOOGEOGRAPHIC POSITION OF THE MOUNTAINOUS RIDGE OF BISTRA. V.E. Martino. Zapiski Russkgo Nauchnago Inst. Belgrade, issue 10, pp.81-91, fig.1, tbl., 1934.

(GEOGRAPHICAL QUESTIONS FROM MAMMALOGY.) Geographische Fragen aus der Saeugetierkunde. Paul Matschie. Verhandl. Gesell. Erdk. Berlin, Bd.23, Heft 4-5, pp. 245-256, pl.1, May 2, 1896.

RANGE AND LIMITATIONS OF SPECIES AS SEEN IN FOSSIL MAMMAL FAUNAS. W.D. Matthew. Bull. Geol. Soc.America, vol.41, pp.271-274, June 30, 1930;Abstract, op.cit., vol.41, pp.210-211.

WALLACE'S LINE IN THE LIGHT OF RECENT ZOOGEOGRAPHIC STUDIES. Ernst Mayr. Quart. Rev. Biol., Baltimore, vol. 19, no.1, pp.1-14, Mar., 1944.

LAWS OF TEMPERATURE CONTROL OF THE GEOGRAPHIC DISTRIBUTION OF TERRESTRIAL ANIMALS AND PLANTS. C. Hart. Merriam. Nat. Geographic Mag., vol.6, pp.179-238, pls.10-14, Dec. 29, 1894.

(ON THE GEOGRAPHICAL DISTRIBUTION OF MAMMALS.) Ueber die geographische Vertheilung der Saeugethiere. J. Minding. Berlin, pp.104, 1829.

THE LAND VERTEBRATES OF PEMBA, ZANZIBAR, AND MAFIA; ZOOGEOGRAPHICAL STUDY. R.E. Moreau, R.H.W.Pakenham. Proc. Zool. Soc. London, ser.A, vol. 110, pts.3 and 4, 1940, pp.97-128, Mar. 18, 1941.

PRESENT STATUS OF STUDIES OF FAUNAL DISTRIBUTION WITH REFERENCE TO OCEANIC ISLANDS. E.P. Mumford. Proc. 6th Pacific Sci. Congr., Berkeley, vol.4, pp.241-248, 1940.

GEOGRAPHICAL DISTRIBUTION OF MAMMALS. Andrew Murray. London, pp.420, illus., 1866.

ANIMAL GEOGRAPHY; FAUNAS OF THE NATURAL REGIONS OF THE GLOBE. Marion Isabel Newbigin. Oxford Clarendon Press, pp.238, illus., 1913.

DISTRIBUTION OF MARINE MAMMALS. A. E. Ortmann. Science, n.s., vol.5, pp. 957-958, 1897.

OWEN ON DISTRIBUTION. Sir Richard Owen. London, 8, 8, 6p., illus., 1859.

(THE PHYSICAL CAUSES OF GLACIAL PERIODS.) Les causes physiques des périodes glaciaires. Benard C.Pontois. Riviera Scientifique, 14th year, no.2, pp.25-39, 1927.

WALLACE'S LINE AND THE DISTRIBUTION OF INDO-AUSTRALIAN MAMMALS. Henry C. Raven. Bull. Amer. Mus. Nat. Hist., vol.68, art.4, pp.ii-179-293, maps 10, Apr. 5, 1935.

ANIMAL CLASSIFICATION AND DISTRIBUTION. Douglas M. Reid. Philadelphia, J.B. Lippincott Co., pp.XV-51, 12 mo, 1925.

WALLACE'S LINE AND THE DISTRIBUTION OF MAMMALS. James Ritchie.Nature, London, vol.136, no.3435, pp.325-326, 1935.

ON THE EVOLUTION AND RADIATION OF MAMMALIAN FAUNAE. Ernst Schufaz. Acta Zoologica, vol.5, pp.393-423, 1924.

GEOGRAPHICAL DISTRIBUTION OF MAMMALS. P.L. Sclater. Sci. Lectures for the People, Manchester, ser.6, no.5, pp.67-84, 1874.

ON THE DISTRIBUTION OF MARINE MAMMALS. P.L. Sclater. Science, n.s., vol.5, pp.956-957, 1897; Proc. Zool. Soc.London 1897, pp.349-359, 1898.

GEOGRAPHY OF MAMMALS. W.L.Sclater. London, pp.335, illus., fold.maps, 1899.

GEOGRAPHY OF MAMMALS. No.I. INTRODUCTORY. W.L. Sclater. Geogr. Jour., London, vol.3, no.2, pp.95-105, map, Feb., 1894.

GEOGRAPHY OF MAMMALS. No.IV. THE ETHIOPIAN REGION. W.L. Sclater. Geogr. Jour., London, vol.7, no.3, pp.282-296, map., Mar., 1896.

GEOLOGICAL CLIMATES. W.B. Scott. Bull. Geol. Soc. Amer., vol.37, pp.261-278, Mar., 1926.

ANTARCTICA AS A FAUNAL MIGRATION ROUTE. George Gaylord Simpson. Proc. Sixth Pacific Science Congress, 1939, Geophysics and Geology, pp.755-768, 1941.

EVOLUTION AND GEOGRAPHY. ESSAY ON HISTORICAL BIOGEOGRAPHY WITH SPECIAL REFERENCE TO MAMMALS. George Gaylord Simpson. Condon Lectures, Oregon State System Higher Education, Eugene, pp.7-64, illus., 1953.

GREAT ANIMAL INVASION. George Gaylord Simpson. Nat. Hist., New York, vol.49, no.4, pp.206-211, 236, Apr., 1942.

MAMMALS AND LAND BRIDGES. George Gaylord Simpson. Jour. Washington Acad.

Sci., vol.30, no.4, pp.137-163, figs.6, Apr. 15, 1940.

MAMMALS AND THE NATURE OF CONTINENTS. George Gaylord Simpson. Amer. Jour. Sci., New Haven, vol.241, no.1, pp.1-31, Jan., 1943.

RANGE AS A ZOOLOGICAL CHARACTER. George Gaylord Simpson. Amer. Jour. Sci., New Haven, vol.239, no.11, pp.785-804, Nov., 1941.

TERTIARY LAND BRIDGES. George Gaylord Simpson. Trans. New York Acad. Sci., ser. 2, vol.8, no.8, pp.255-258, June, 1946.

(REMARKS ON THE NORTHERN CENTER OF ORIGIN OF NONMARINE VERTEBRATES.) Bemerkungen ueber das nordische Entstehungszentrum nichtmariner Wirbeltiere. Ernst Stromer. Palaeont. Zeitschr., Berlin, vol.17, nos.1-2, pp.9-20, Aug. 20, 1935.

SUMMARY OF THE MAMMALIAN FAUNAE OF EASTERN ASIA AND THE INTERRELATIONSHIPS OF CONTINENTS SINCE THE MESOZOIC. F. Takai. Japanese Jour.Geol. & Geogr., vol.22, pp.169-205, 1952.

(PRINCIPLES, MEANS, AND OBJECTS OF ECOLOGICAL DOMESTIC-ANIMAL GEOGRAPHY.) Grundlagen, Wege und Ziele der oekologischen Haustiergeographie. Stefan Taussig. Zeitschr. f. Zuechtung, Reihe B: Tierzuechtung und Auechtungsbiologie einschliesslich Tierernaehrung, Bd.xxv, Heft 1 und 2, mit 11 Abbildungen und 3 farbigen Karten, 1932.

(ZOOGEOGRAPHICAL DISTRIBUTION.) La Distribution Geographique des Animaux. E.L. Trouessart. Gaston Doin, Paris, pp. 1-332, i-xii, figs.14, maps, 1922.

(BIOGEOGRAPHICAL HISTORY OF AMERICA AND WEGENER'S THEORY.) L'histoire biogeographique de l'Amerique et la theorie de Wegener. L. Voleaud. Jour. Soc. Americanistes Paris, vol.16, pp.325-360, 1924.

HELODERMA SUSPECTUM, AUTOMOBILE TOURISTS AND ANIMAL DISTRIBUTION. Charles T. Vorhies. Science, n.s., vol.68, pp.182-183, Aug. 24, 1928.

(GEOGRAPHICAL DISTRIBUTION OF MAMMALS.) Die geographische Verbreitung der Saeugethiere. Johann A. Wagner. Abhandlungen d. II. Cl. d. Ak. d. Wiss. IV.Bd. Abth.I., pp.244, maps 9, 1844-1846.

AGE AND AREA: STUDY IN GEOGRAPHICAL DISTRIBUTION AND ORIGIN OF SPECIES. J.C. Willis. Univ. Press, Cambridge, pp.1-x, 1-259, maps, diagrams, 1922.

(ZOOGEOGRAPHY.) Zoogeografia. Angel Cabrera Y Jose Yepes. Capitulo Geogr. Republica Argentina, Buenos Aires, vol. 8, pp.347-483, illus., 1947.

(CONTRIBUTIONS TO THE ZOOGEOGRAPHY OF THE NORTHERN POLAR BASIN IN CONNECTION WITH THE QUESTION OF ITS PALEOGEOGRAPHIC PAST.) Beitraege zur Zoogeographie des Noerdlichen Polarbasins im zusammenhang mit der Frage ueber dessen Palaeogeographische Vergangenheit. L. Zenkewitsch. Zologitscheskij Journal (vormals"Revue Zool.Russe"), Moscow, vol. 12, pt.4, pp.17-34, 1933. (In Russian, with German summary.)

(GEOGRAPHICAL HISTORY OF MAN AND QUADRUPEDS.) Geographische Geschichte des Menschen und der vierfussigen Thiere. Eberhard August Wilhelm von Zimmerman. Baende 1, 2 and 3, Leipzig, 1778-1783.

GESTATION see REPRODUCTIVE BIOLOGY

GROWTH see PHYSIOLOGY -- GROWTH

GUIDE TO MUSEUMS see MUSEUMS -- CATALOGS, COLLECTIONS, GUIDES

GUIDES TO ZOOS see ZOOS

HABITS see BEHAVIOR; FOOD HABITS; PSYCHOLOGY, ANIMAL

HEMATOLOGY see ANATOMY -- HEMATOLOGY, CIRCULATORY SYSTEM

HEREDITY

CONCEPT OF RACE IN THE HUMAN SPECIES IN THE LIGHT OF GENETICS. M.F. Ashley-Montagu. Jour. Heredity, Washington, D.C., vol.32, no.8, pp. 243-247, Aug., 1941.

VARIABILITY IN WILD AND INBRED MAMMALIAN POPULATIONS. Robert S. Bader. Quart. Jour. Florida Acad. Sci., vol.19, no.1, pp.14-34, Mar., 1956.

SEXUAL PHOTOPERIODICITY. INFLUENCE OF VARYING QUANTITIES AND QUALITIES OF LIGHT ON SEXUAL ACTIVITY IN PLANTS AND ANIMALS AN EXAMPLE OF THE INTERACTION OF GENETIC AND ENVIRONMENTAL FACTORS IN CONDITIONING THE EXPRESSION OF CHARACTERS. T.Hume Bissonette. Jour.Heredity, vol.27, no.5, pp.170-180, figs.4, May, 1936.

CRITERIA FOR SPECIES AND THEIR SUBDIVISIONS FROM THE POINT OF VIEW OF GENETICS. W. Frank Blair. Ann. New York Acad. Sci., vol.44, art.2, pp.179-188, June 8, 1943.

FACTORS AFFECTING GENE EXCHANGE BETWEEN POPULATIONS IN THE PEROMYSCUS MANICULATUS GROUP. W.Frank Blair. Texas Jour Sci., vol.5, no.1, pp.17-33, Mar., 1953.

QUANTITATIVE CHARACTERS IN RECIPROCAL HYBRIDS. R.A. Brink. Amer. Nat., vol.69, no.722, pp.278-285, May-June, 1935.

ARE THE VARIOUS PARTS OF THE BODY GENETICALLY INDEPENDENT IN SIZE? W. E. Castle. Proc. Nat. Acad. Sci., vol. 10, pp.181-182, May, 1924.

COLOR VARIETIES OF THE RABBIT AND OF OTHER RODENTS, THEIR ORIGIN AND INHERITANCE. W. E. Castle. Science, n.s., vol.26, no.661, pp.287-291, Aug. 30, 1907.

CONTINUATION OF EXPERIMENTAL STUDIES OF HEREDITY IN SMALL MAMMALS. W.E. Castle. Carnegie Inst. of Washington, Year Book 22, p.279, 1924.

CONTINUATION OF EXPERIMENTAL STUDIES OF HEREDITY IN SMALL MAMMALS. W.E. Castle. Carnegie Inst. of Washington, Year Book, no.24, pp.276-278, Dec., 1925.

DOES THE INHERITANCE OF DIFFERENCES IN GENERAL SIZE DEPEND UPON GENERAL OR SPECIAL SIZE FACTORS? W. E. Castle. Proc. Nat. Acad. Sci., vol.10, no.1, pp.19-23, Jan., 1924.

DOMINANT AND RECESSIVE BLACK IN MAMMALS. W. E. Castle. Jour. Heredity, Baltimore, vol.42, no.1, pp.48-49, Jan.-Feb., 1951.

HEREDITY IN RABBITS AND GUINEA-PIGS. W. E. Castle. Bibliographia Genetica ('s-Gravenhage, Martinus Nijhoff), vol.1, pp. 419-458, illus., 1925.

MAMMALIAN GENETICS. W. E. Castle. Harvard Univ. Press, Cambridge, Mass., pp.169, figs.131, 1940.

SIZE INHERITANCE. W. E. Castle. Amer. Nat., Lancaster, vol.75, no.760, pp.488-498, Sep.-Oct., 1941.

TEST OF SEX CONTROL BY MODIFICATION OF THE ACID-ALKALINE BALANCE. Leon J. Cole, Emanuel Waletzky, Max Shackelford. Jour. Heredity, Washington, D.C., vol.31, no.12, pp.501-502, Dec., 1940.

LINKAGE RELATIONS IN ANIMALS. W.A. Craft. Proc. Oklahoma Acad. Sci., vol.5, 1925, pp.97-99, Mar., 1926. (Abstract.)

(GENOTYPIC OBSERVATIONS.) Genotypische Betrachtungen. G. Dahlberg. Zeitschrift f. induktive Abstammungs u. Vererbungslehre, vol.53, pp.133-148, figs.2, 1930.

POSSIBILITY OF INCOMPLETE SEX LINKAGE IN MAMMALS. C.D. Darlington, J.B. S. Haldane, P.Ch.Koller. Nature, London, vol.133, no.3359, p.417, Mar. 17, 1934.

DETERMINATION OF DOMINANCE IN MENDELIAN INHERITANCE. C.B.Davenport. Proc. Amer. Philos. Soc., vol.47, pp.59-63, fig.1, Apr. 25, 1908.

IMPERFECTION OF DOMINANCE AND SOME OF ITS CONSEQUENCES. C.B. Davenport. Amer.Nat., vol.44, pp.129-135, Mar., 1910.

LIGHT THROWN BY GENETICS ON EVOLUTION AND DEVELOPMENT. C.B. Davenport. Scientific Monthly, vol.30, pp.307-314, Apr., 1930.

(CAN INDIVIDUAL CALLOSITIES BECOME HEREDITARY?) Les callosites individuelles peuvent-elles devenir hereditaires? Ed. Dechambre. Mammalia, Paris, vol.17, no. 2, pp.89-95, June, 1953.

(GENETICS AND RACES.) Genetica razas. Jorge Dennler. Anal. Soc. Cien. Argentina, Buenos Aires, vol.134, pt.3, pp.171-182, Sep., 1942.

ARE RACIAL AND SPECIFIC CHARACTERS NON-MENDELIAN? T. Dobzhansky. Jour. Mamm., vol.15, no.1, pp.1-3, Feb., 1934.

GENETICS AND THE ORIGIN OF SPECIES. T. Dobzhansky. Columbia Biol. Ser. no.11, pp.364, figs.22, tbls.22, 1937.

McDOUGALL'S EXPERIMENTS ON THE INHERITANCE OF ACQUIRED HABITS. G.C. Drew. Nature, London, vol.143, no.3614, pp.188-191, Feb. 4, 1939.

GENETIC MONSTERS. L.C. Dunn. Sci. American, New York, vol.182, no.6, pp. 16-19, illus., June, 1950.

TWO DECADES OF GENETIC PROGRESS. Edward Murray East. Smiths. Inst., Annual Rep., 1922, Washington, pp.285-295, 1924. (Reprinted with change of title, from Jour. of Heredity, May, 1922.)

GENETIC STUDIES ON ECTOPIA LENTIS. PEDIGREE OF SIMPLE ECTOPIA OF THE LENS. Harold F. Falls, C.W.Cotterman. Archives Ophthalmol., New York, vol.30, pp.610-620, pp.7, figs.2, Nov., 1943.

(NOTES ON AN ORIGINAL SCHEME OF SPERMATOGENESIS IN MAMMALS.) Note sur un schema original de la spermatogenese chez les mammiferes. Ch. L. Faure. Bull. Soc. Hist. Nat. Toulouse, vol.50, pp.205-209, fig.1, 1922.

NEW HOPE IN HEREDITY. Martin H. Fischer. Unpopular Rev., London, vol. 11, no.22, pp.320-339, Apr.-June, 1919.

MENDELIAN GENES AND RATES OF DEVELOPMENT IN GAMMARUS CHEVREUXI. E.B. Ford, J.S. Huxley. Brit. Jour. Exper. Biol., London, vol.5, no.2, pp.112-134, figs.1-20, pl.1, Dec., 1927.

INTRODUCTION TO THE LAWS OF VARIATION AND HEREDITY. WITH A FOREWORD AND SUMMARY (IN CHINESE), BY WONG WEN HAO. A.B.D. Fortuyn. Paper, Peking, Commercial Press, pp.104, illus., 1927.

CHROMOSOME NUMBERS IN MAMMALS AND MAN. R. Ruggles Gates. Science, Lancaster, n.s., vol.96, no.2493, pp.336-337, Oct. 9, 1942.

HUMAN HEREDITY IN RELATION TO ANIMAL GENETICS. R. Ruggles Gates. Amer. Nat., Lancaster, vol.80, no.786, pp.68-84, Jan. 1, 1946.

MAUPERTIUS AND THE BEGINNINGS OF GENETICS. Bentley Glass. Quart. Rev. Biol., Baltimore, vol.22, no.3, pp.196-210, illus., Sep., 1947.

BIOLOGICAL SIGNIFICANCE OF INHERITED VARIATIONS. 1. TYPES OF SCAPULAE. William Washington Graves. Saint Louis Univ. School of Medicine, pp.3, 1939.

GENETIC LINKAGE IN SIZE INHERITANCE-A REPLY. C.V. Green. Amer. Nat., vol.66, no.702, pp.87-91, Jan.-Feb., 1932. (Reply to W.E.Castle.)

HEREDITARY ABSENCE OF THE INCISOR TEETH. R.O. Greep. Jour. Heredity, Washington, D.C., vol.32, no.11, pp.397-398, figs.2, Nov., 1941.

GENES IN MAMMALIAN DEVELOPMENT. H. Gruenberg. Inaugural Lecture, Univ. College, London, pp.1-17, 1957.

INHERITANCE OF FUR CHARACTERS. C.K. Gunn. American Fur Breeder, Duluth, vol.13, no.3, pp.6, 8-9, Sep., 1940.

SOMA AND GERM. M.F. Guyer. Amer. Nat., vol.59, no.661, pp.97-114, Mar.-Apr., 1925.

COMPARATIVE GENETICS OF COLOUR IN RODENTS AND CARNIVORA. J.B.S. Haldane. Biol. Reviews, vol.2, no.3, pp. 199-212, 1927.

INHERITANCE OF ACCESSORY MAMMAE. Carl Hartman. Science, n.s., vol.64, p. 249, Sep. 10, 1926.

REVIEW OF THE CHROMOSOME NUMBERS IN THE METAZOA. PART 2. Ethel Browne Harvey. Jour. Morphology, vol.34, no.1, pp.1-67, June 20 (July), 1920.

MAMMALIAN CHROMOSOMES IN VITRO. III. ON SOMATIC ANEUPLOIDY. T.C. Hsu, C.M. Pomerat. Jour. Morphology, vol.93, no.2, pp.301-330, illus., 1953.

HEREDITY AS A FACTOR IN CRANIAL AND FACIAL DEVELOPMENT. Byron O. Hughes. Amer. Jour. Orthodontics and Oral Surgery, St. Louis, vol.28, no.6, Orthodontics, pp.357-360, June, 1942.

GENETIC PURITY IN ANIMAL COLONIES. F.B. Hutt. Ann. New York Acad. Sci., vol.46, art.1, pp.5-21, June 15, 1945.

ANTIGENS, ANTIBODIES AND GENES. M. R. Irwin. Biol. Reviews, London, vol.21, no.3, pp.93-100, July, 1946.

HETEROCHROMOSOMES IN MAMMALS. H.E. Jordan. Proc. Soc. Exper. Biol. & Medicine, vol.10, no.1, pp.20-21, Oct. 16, 1912.

INHERITANCE OF SKIN COLOR. H. E. Jordan. Science, Lancaster, n.s., vol. 36, no.918, pp.151-152, Aug. 2, 1912.

ADAPTATION AND INHERITANCE IN THE LIGHT OF MODERN EXPERIMENTAL INVESTIGATION. Paul Kammerer. Smiths. Inst., Annual Rep., 1912, Washington, pp. 421-441, pls.8, 1913. (Translated from Himmel und Erde, Berlin, pp.385-395, June 1911; pp.443-457, July, 1911.)

NOTE ON THE OCCURRENCE AND INHERITANCE OF PIGMENTED WOOL. R.B. Kelley, H.E.B. Shaw. Jour. Council Sci. and Industrial Research, Melbourne, vol.15, no.1, pp.1-3, Feb., 1942.

GENETICS APPLIES TO FUR ANIMAL BREEDING. Chas. E. Kellogg. American Fur Breeder, Duluth, vol.19, no.1, pp.6-20, July, 1946.

INTRODUCTION TO GENETIC STATISTICS. Oscar Kempthorne. John Wiley & Sons, Inc., N.Y., pp.XVII-545, 1957.

(MENDELISM, DOMESTICATION, AND CRANIOLOGY.) Mendelismus Domestikation und Kraniologie. Berthold Klatt. Archiv. f. Anthropologie, n.F., vol.18, pp.225-250, figs.4, 1921.

CHROMOSOME BEHAVIOR IN THE MALE FERRET AND MOLE DURING ANOESTRUS. P.C. Koller. Proc. Roy. Soc. London, ser. B., no.822, vol.121, pp.192-206, figs.1-11, pls.3-4, Nov. 2, 1936.

ON MOSAIC INHERITANCE IN MAMMALS. Taku Komai. Amer. Naturalist, Lancaster, vol.85, no.824, pp.333-334, 1951.

SOME GENETIC TARGETS FOR FUR BREEDER TO SHOOT AT. Harry J. LaDue. Amer. Fur Breeder, vol.1, no.10, pp.4, 6-9, illus., vol.1, no.11, pp.6-7, 1929.

GENETIC BASIS OF SELECTION. I. Michael Lerner. Univ. of Calif., Berkeley, pp.298, 1958.

LETHAL AND SUBLETHAL CHARACTERS IN FARM ANIMALS. A CHECK-LIST AND PROPOSED NUMBERING SYSTEM. I. Michael Lerner. Jour. Heredity, Washington, vol.35, no.7, pp.219-224, July, 1944.

OPPORTUNITIES FOR RESEARCH IN MAMMALIAN GENETICS. C.C. Little. Sci. Monthly, vol.26, pp.521-534, June, 1928.

OPPORTUNITIES FOR RESEARCH IN MAMMALIAN GENETICS. C.C. Little. Sigma Xi Quart., vol.16, no.1, pp.16-35, Mar., 1928.

RESULTS OF IN-BREEDING IN THE ABSENCE OF GENETICAL CONTROL AND SELECTION OF ANIMALS. K.M. Liutikov. Problems of Animal Husbandry, Moscow, no.3, pp.15-44, figs.2, 1936. (In Russian.)

HEREDITARY CASE OF CONGENITAL ABSENCE OF ONE KIDNEY. Marcus W. Lyon Jr. Anat. Rec., vol.13, no.5, pp.303-304, fig.1, Oct., 1917.

MECHANISM OF HEREDITY IN RELATION TO THE THEORY OF NATURAL SELECTION. W. L. McAtee. Ohio Jour. Sci., Columbus, vol.43, no.3, pp.117-120, May, 1943.

SPERMATOGENESIS OF DOMESTIC MAMMALS. III. SPERMATOGENESIS OF THE MOUSE AND OF THE RABBIT. Kiyoshi Masui. Jour. College Agric., Imperial Univ., Tokyo, vol.8, pp.207-252, pls.4-10, Mar. 30, 1923.

(NEW CONTRIBUTION TO STUDY OF HETERO-CHROMOSOMES IN MAMMALS, AND SINGULARLY IN RODENTS.) Contribution nouvelle a l'etude des heterochromosomes chez les mammiferes, et singulierement chez rongeurs. Robert Matthey. Jour. Genetics, vol.36, no.1, pp.73-102, figs.6, pls.3-7, May, 1938.

(PROBLEM OF HETERO-CHROMOSOMES IN MAMMALS.) Le probleme des heterochromosomes chez les mammiferes. Robert Matthey. Archiv. Biol., Liege, vol.47, fasc.3, pp.319-383, figs.9, pls.10-14, 1936.

IS MUTATION A FACTOR IN THE EVOLUTION OF HIGHER VERTEBRATES? C. Hart Merriam. Science, New York, n.s., vol. 23, no.581, pp.241-257, Feb. 16, 1906.

DETERMINATE MUTATION. Maynard M. Metcalf. Science, n.s., vol.21, no.531, pp.355-356, Mar. 3, 1905.

(ON LETHAL FACTORS, WITH CONSIDERATION OF THEIR BEHAVIOR IN DOMESTIC ANIMALS AND MAN.) Ueber Letalfaktoren, mit Beruecksichtigung ihres Verhaltens bei Haustieren und Menschen. O.L. Mohr. Zeitschrift f. induktive Abstammungs- und Vererbungslehre, vol.41, pp.59-109, illus., 1926.

NOTE ON CERTAIN MENDELIAN RATIOS. Larry Moore, Clyde E. Keeler. Jour. Heredity, Baltimore, vol.38, no.12, p.380, Dec., 1947.

HERITABLE VARIATIONS, THEIR PRODUCTION BY X RAYS AND THEIR RELATION TO EVOLUTION. Hermann Joseph Muller. Smiths. Inst., Annual Rep., 1929, Washington, pp.345-362, 1930.

PRIMARILY UNADAPTIVE VARIANTS. John Treadwell Nichols. Amer. Nat., Lancaster, vol.50, no.597, pp.565-574, Sep., 1916.

NEW LIST OF THE CHROMOSOME NUMBERS IN VERTEBRATA (MARCH 1937). Kan Oguma, Sajiro Makino. Jour. Faculty Sci., Hokaido Imp. Univ., Sapporo, ser.6 (Zool.), vol.5, no.4, pp.297-356, tbls.7, June, 1937. (Mammalia, pp.318-330.)

RECTIGRADATIONS AND ALLOMETRONS IN RELATION TO THE CONCEPTIONS OF THE "MUTATIONS OF WAAGEN," OF SPECIES, GENERA, AND PHYLA. Henry Fairfield Osborn. Bull. Geol. Soc. Amer., Washington, D.C., vol.25, no.3, pp.411-416, Sep. 15, 1914.

CHROMOSOME NUMBERS IN MAMMALS. Theophilus S. Painter. Science, n.s., vol. 61, pp.423-424, Apr. 17, 1925.

FURTHER OBSERVATIONS ON THE SEX CHROMOSOMES OF MAMMALS. Theophilus S. Painter. Science, n.s., vol.58, pp.247-248, Sep. 28, 1923.

THE Y-CHROMOSOME IN MAMMALS. Theophilus S. Painter. Science, n.s., vol. 53, no.1378, pp.503-504, May 27, 1921.

GENETICS AND BREEDING. Raymond Pearl. Science, Lancaster, n.s., vol.37, no.954, pp.539-546, Apr.11, 1913.

DETERMINATION OF HAIR PIGMENTS. III. PROOF THAT EXPRESSION OF THE BLACK-AND-TAN GENE IS DEPENDENT UPON TISSUE ORGANIZATION. Sheldon C. Reed. Jour. Exper. Zool., Philadelphia, vol.79, no.3, pp.337-346, 1938.

WEISMANN'S THEORY OF HEREDITY. George John Romanes. Smiths. Inst., Annual Rep., 1890, Washington, pp.433-446, 1891.

SYMPOSIUM ON 25 YEARS OF PROGRESS IN MAMMALIAN GENETICS AND CANCER, HELD AT THE JACKSON MEMORIAL LABORATORY, BAR HARBOR, MAINE, JUNE, 1954. Elizabeth Shull Russell. Jour. National Cancer Inst., vol.15, no.3, pp. 551-851, illus., Dec., 1954.

(PALEONTOLOGY, PHYLOGENY, AND GENETICS.) Palaeontologie, Entwicklungslehre und Genetik. Otto H. Schindewolf. Kritik und Synthese, Gebrueder Borntraeger, Berlin, pp. v-108, Figs.34, 1936.

"JAPANESE" PATTERN IN WILD MAMMALS. Ernst Schwarz. Proc. Zool. Soc. London, vol.107, ser.A., Gen. and Exper., pt.1, p.127, pl.1, Apr., 1937.

SEASONAL PATTERN AND GENIC BALANCE. Ernst Schwarz. Auk, Cambridge, vol.58, pp. 233-235, Apr., 1941.

INHERITANCE OF THE BLOOD GROUPS. Laurence H. Snider. Genetics, vol.9, no.5, pp.465-475, Sep., 1924.

BEYOND THE GENE. T.M. Sonneborn. Amer. Sci., New Haven, vol.37, no.1, pp.33-59, Jan., 1949.

WEISMANNISM ONCE MORE. Herbert Spencer. Contemporary Review, London, vol.66, pp.592-608, 1894.

(Review by W.E. Castle of) GENETIC AND ENDOCRINE BASIS FOR DIFFERENCES IN FORM AND BEHAVIOR. Charles R. Stockard. Jour. Heredity, Washington, D.C., vol.33, no.7, pp.249-252, July, 1942.

ON THE INHERITANCE OF CRANIAL ANOMALIES. Percy Stocks. Biometrika, vol.16, parts III and IV, pp.406-410, Dec., 1924.

GEOGRAPHIC VARIATION AND MENDELIAN INHERITANCE. F.B. Sumner. Jour. Exper. Zool., vol.30, no.3, pp.369-402, figs.7, tbls., Apr., 1920.

MODERN CONCEPTIONS OF HEREDITY AND GENETIC STUDIES AT THE SCRIPPS INSTITUTION. F.B. Sumner. Bull. Scripps Inst. Biol. Res. Univ. Cal., no.3, pp.24, Oct., 19, 1917.

PARTIAL GENETIC INDEPENDENCE IN SIZE OF THE VARIOUS PARTS OF THE BODY. F.B. Sumner. Proc. Nat. Acad. Sci., vol.10, pp.178-180, May, 1924.

SIZE-FACTORS AND SIZE-INHERITANCE. F.B. Sumner. Proc. Nat. Acad. Sci., vol. 9, pp.391-397, Nov., 1923.

SOME FACTS RELEVANT TO A DISCUSSION OF THE ORIGIN AND INHERITANCE OF SPECIFIC CHARACTERS. F.B. Sumner. Amer. Nat., vol.57, pp.238-254, May-June, 1923.

TAXONOMIC DISTINCTIONS VIEWED IN THE LIGHT OF GENETICS. F.B. Sumner. Amer. Nat., vol.68, no.715, pp.137-149, Mar.-Apr., 1934.

BILATERAL ASYMMETRY IN ITS RELATIONS TO CERTAIN PROBLEMS OF GENETICS. F.B. Sumner, R.R. Huestis. Genetics, vol.6, pp.445-485, figs.5, Sep., 1921.

TRENDS IN THE EVOLUTION OF MAMMALIAN CHROMOSOMES. Phillip V. Tobias. S. African Jour. Sci., vol.50, no.5, pp.134-140, Dec., 1953.

ON HEREDITY. Sir William Turner. Smiths. Inst., Annual Rep., 1889, Washington, pp.

541-554, 1890. (Report of the British Assoc., vol. LIX, pp.756-771.)

NON-INHERITANCE OF THE EFFECTS OF TRAINING. E.M. Vicari. Science, n.s., vol.59, p.303, Mar. 28, 1924.

SUBSPECIFIC BOUNDARIES AND GENODYNAMICS OF POPULATIONS IN MAMMALS AND BIRDS. Paavo Voipio. Ann. Zool., Soc. Zool. Bot. Fennica "Vanamo", vol.15, no.4, pp.1-32, 1952.

WHAT GENETICISTS KNOW ABOUT HOW HEREDITY WORKS. Patricia Wentz. Black Fox Mag., New York, vol.33, no.2, pp. 6-7, 16, 22, June, 1949; Fur of Canada, Winnipeg, vol.14, no.11, pp. 14-15, Aug., 1949.

MUTATION THEORY OF PROFESSOR DE VRIES. Charles Abiathan White. Smiths. Inst., Annual Rep., 1901, Washington, pp. 631-640, 1902.

VACUOLATION A FACTOR IN THE DIVISION OF ANIMAL CELLS. H.V. Wilson. Science, Lancaster, n.s., vol.88, no. 2289, p.435, Nov. 11, 1938.

GENETIC ASPECTS OF GROOMING, A SOCIALLY IMPORTANT BEHAVIOR PATTERN. Robert M. Yerkes. Jour. Social Philos., vol.4, pp.3-25, 1933.

COMPARATIVE STUDY OF THE CYTOPLASMIC COMPONENTS DURING THE OOGENESIS OF DOG, CAT, AND RABBIT. I. Zlotnik. Proc. Roy. Soc. Edinburgh, London, vol.63, pt.2, no.13, pp.200-212, pls.3, figs.4, Dec. 18, 1948.

MAMMALIAN LETHAL CHARACTERS. Jour. Mamm., vol.15, no.4, pp.313-315, Nov., 1934.

SMALL MAMMAL POPULATION OF A HARDWOOD FOREST IN NORTHERN MICHIGAN. Contrib. Lab. Vertebrate Genetics, Univ. Michigan, Ann. Arbor, no.17, pp.10, Nov., 1941.

STERILIZATION OF DEGENERATES AND CRIMINALS CONSIDERED FROM THE STANDPOINT OF GENETICS. Eugenics Rev., London, vol.11, no.1, pp.1-6, Apr., 1919.

HIBERNATION see PHYSIOLOGY -- HIBERNATION

## HOME RANGES AND TERRITORIALITY

TECHNIQUES FOR THE STUDY OF MAMMAL POPULATIONS. W. Frank Blair. Jour. Mamm., vol.22, no.2, pp.148-157, May, 1941.

TERRITORIAL BEHAVIOR AND POPULATIONS OF SOME SMALL MAMMALS IN SOUTHERN MICHIGAN. W.H. Burt. Mus. Zool., Univ. Michigan, Misc. Publ., no. 45, pp.1-58, pls.2, 1940.

TERRITORIALITY. W.H. Burt. Jour. Mamm., Baltimore, vol.30, no.1, pp.25-27, Feb. 14, 1949.

TERRITORIALITY AND HOME RANGE CONCEPTS AS APPLIED TO MAMMALS. W.H. Burt. Jour. Mamm., vol.24, no.3, pp.346-352, fig.1, Aug. 17, 1943.

CALCULATION OF HOME RANGE AND DENSITY OF SMALL MAMMALS. John B. Calhoun. U.S. Dept. of Health, Education, and Welfare, Public Health Service, Washington, no.592, Public Health Monograph no.55, pp.v-24, illus., 1958.

TECHNIQUE FOR INVESTIGATING THE DISTANCE PARAMETER OF HOME RANGE. John B. Calhoun. Jour. Mamm., vol.36, no. 1, pp.45-52, graphs, Feb., 1955.

ANALYSIS OF HOME RANGE FROM RECAPTURE DATA. David E. Davis. Jour. Mamm., vol.34, no.3, pp.352-359, Aug., 1953.

ANIMAL'S HOME IS ITS CASTLE. David E. Davis. Sci. Monthly, Lancaster, vol. 69, no.4, pp.249-253, Oct., 1949.

HOME RANGE OF SOME BRAZILIAN MAMMALS. David E. Davis. Jour. Mamm., vol.26, no.2, pp.119-127, fig.1, July 15, 1945.

WINTER HOME RANGES OF SOME SMALL ILLINOIS MAMMALS. Clarence J. Goodnight, E.J. Koestner. Jour. Tennessee Acad. Sci., Nashville, vol.17, no.3, pp.276-279, fig.1, July, 1942.

CALCULATION OF SIZE OF HOME RANGE. D.W. Hayne. Jour. Mamm., vol.30, no.1, pp.1-18, figs.2, Feb. 4, 1949; vol.31, pp. 26-39, 1950.

(MAMMAL TERRITORIES AND THEIR MARKING.) Saeugetier-Territorien und ihre Markierung. H. Hediger. Bijdragen tot de Dierkunde, vol.28, pp.172-184, 1949.

POPULATIONS AND HOME RANGES OF SMALL MAMMALS ON AN OVERGROWN FIELD. Joseph C. Howell. Jour. Mamm., vol.35, no.2, pp.177-186, May 26, 1954.

HOME RANGE. Aldo Leopold. Wisconsin Conserv. Bull., Madison, vol.8, no.9, pp.23-24, Sep., 1943.

WAYS OF MARKING THE TERRITORY AMONG GAME ANIMALS. R. Rainesalo. Suomen Riista, vol.7, pp.48-51, illus., 1952. (In Finnish with English summary.)

COMPARISON OF CERTAIN METHODS OF MEASURING RANGES OF SMALL MAMMALS. Lucille F. Stickel. Jour. Mamm., vol.35, no.1, pp.1-15, Feb. 10, 1954.

## HUNTING

SPORT AND TRAVEL IN INDIA AND CENTRAL AMERICA. A.G. Bagot. London, Chapman & Hall, ld., pp.viii-371, 1897.

NORTH FOR BIG GAME. E.C. Boyer. The Beaver, Winnipeg, Outfit 270, no.4, pp. 6-9, illus., Mar., 1940.

NATIONAL COLLECTION OF HEADS AND HORNS. William Bridges. Bull. New York Zool. Soc., vol.38, no.2, pp.39-51, illus., Mar.-Apr., 1935.

CONTROLLED HUNTING PAYS WHEN SPORTSMEN CARRY THE BALL. J. G. Burr. Texas Game and Fish, Austin, vol. 5, no.1, pp.4, 24-25, illus., Dec., 1946.

BUZZACOTT'S MASTERPIECE; OR, THE COMPLETE HUNTERS', TRAPPERS' AND CAMPERS' LIBRARY OF VALUABLE INFORMATION. Francis Henry Buzzacott. Milwaukee, Wis., McMains & Meyer, pp.544, illus.(incl.port.), 1913.

GETTING THE BIG GAME. J.B. Caldwell. Alaska Sportsman, Ketchikan, vol.11, no.4, pp.14-15, 24-27, illus., Apr., 1945.

HUNTING IS SERIOUS BUSINESS THIS YEAR. Charles Callison. Missouri Conservationist, Jefferson City, vol.4, no.9, pp.4-5, illus., Dec., 1943.

GAME TRAILS FROM ALASKA TO AFRICA. R.R.M. Carpenter. Privately printed, pp. xiii-180-56, Sep., 1944.

SCORING BIG GAME TROPHIES. NEW SYSTEM OF MEASURING: WITH ESPECIALLY DESIGNED CHARTS TO CODIFY THESE MEASUREMENTS AND AUTOMATICALLY ARRIVE AT A SCORING WHICH WILL REFLECT THE RELATIVE EXCELLENCE OF OUR BIG GAME TROPHIES. James L. Clark. Privately publ., New York., pp.29, illus., 1945.

TRAILS OF THE HUNTED. James L. Clark. Boston, Little, Brown and Co., vol.8, pp. XIII-309, illus.47, 1928.

WHEN HE LAYS HIS EARS BACK, LOOK OUT! Tom E. Clarke. Alaska Sportsman, Ketchikan, vol.8, no.6, pp.14-17, 25-32, illus., June, 1947.

CARCLEW'S FIRST KADIR CUP. A PIG-STICKING MEMORY THAT CANNOT FADE. J. Scott Cockburn. Field, London, vol.164, no.4275, pp.1300-1301, illus., Dec. 1, 1934.

ONE CROWDED HOUR. Brooke Dolan II. Frontiers, Philadelphia, vol.6, no.2, pp. 40-43, illus., Dec., 1941.

CATALOGUE OF THE SELOUS COLLECTION OF BIG GAME IN THE BRITISH MUSEUM (NATURAL HISTORY). J. G. Dollman. British Mus.(Nat.Hist.), Dept. of Zoology, London, printed by order of the Trustees, pp.vii-112, 1921.

GAME ANIMALS OF THE EMPIRE. J.G. Dollman. British Mus.(Nat.Hist.), pp.1-82, pls.1-10, 1932.

BIG GAME AND BIG LIFE. J. Morewood Dowsett. London, John Bale, Sons and Danielson, Ltd., pp.xii-242, many pls., 1926.

(SOMETHING THAT WE HUNTERS UNFORTUNATELY DO NOT KNOW.) Etwas, was wir Jaeger leider nicht wissen. O. Frhr. von Dungern-Oberau. Deutsche Jagd, Berlin, nos.35-36, pp.321-322, Dec. 6, 1940.

KILLER BEARS AND MOOSE. Byron M. Fisher. Rod and Gun in Canada, Montreal, vol.49, no.10, pp.8, 29-31, Mar., 1948.

EATING OF TROPHIES. Grancel Fitz. North American Big Game. Book of the Boone and Crockett Club, compiled by the Committee on Records of N. American Big Game. Charles Scribner's Sons, New York, pp.63-111, 1939.

TAKING CARE OF BIG GAME TROPHY. James D. Gay. Wyoming Wild Life, Cheyenne, vol.12, no.8, pp.16-20, illus., Sep., 1948.

VANISHED GAME OF YESTERDAY. Madison Grant. Reprint from the Boone and Crockett Club book "Hunting Trails on Three Continents." Derrydale Press, Inc., New York, pp.22, figs.2, 1933.

WHY CONTROL HUNTS? Grits Gresham. Ariz. Wildl. Sportsman, vol.23, no.8, pp. 14-19, 73, illus., Aug., 1952.

HUNTING AT HIGH ALTITUDES. George Bird Grinnell. The Book of the Boone and Crockett Club, New York & London, Harper & Brothers, pp.511, pls., 1913.

SPORT ON LAND AND WATER, RECOLLECTIONS OF FRANK GRAY GRISWOLD. Frank Gray Griswold. Norwood, Mass., Priv. print., the Plimpton Press, pp.163, pls., 1913.

CLEAN KILLS ON BIG GAME. Bob Hagel. Fur-Fish-Game (Harding's Mag.), Columbus, vol.79, no.2, pp.10-11, 33, Feb., 1946.

BIG GAME OF THE WORLD AND ITS TROPHIES. Theodor Haltenorth, Werner Trense. Bayarischer Landwirtschaftsverlag GMBH, Bonn-Munich-Vienna, pp.XII-436, figs.264, color pls.12, maps.6, 1956. (In German, with English and French descriptions of the illus.)

(GAME ZOOLOGY--ALSO FOR NON-HUNTERS.) Jagdzoologie--auch fuer Nichtjaeger. H. Hediger. Reinhardt, pp.212, illus., 1951. (Switzerland.)

STORY OF AN OUTING. Alonzo Barton Hepburn. New York & London, Harper & Brothers, pp.107, illus., pl., 1913.

SHEEP AND BEAR TRAILS. WITH AN INTRODUCTION BY ROBERT A. BARTLETT. John P. Holman. New York, Frank Walters, Grand Central Palace, vol.8, pp.XVI, pls. 211, frontispiece, 23 plates in text, 1933.

BIG GAME BY PROXY. Bud Jackson. Outdoorsman, Chicago, vol.87, no.3, (whole no.514), pp.16-17, 50-51, illus., May-June, 1945.

RECORD GAME HEADS. George B. Johnson. Virginia Wildlife, Blacksburg, vol.3, no.2, p.2, Oct., 1939.

RECORD AND NEAR RECORD HEADS OF THE LAST SEASON. Coloman Jonas. Western Sportsman, Denver, vol.7, no.5, pp.6-7, 20, illus., Oct., 1941.

(ON THE POSSESSION OF HUNTING DISTRICTS WITH BIRDS AND MAMMALS AS POPULATION AND ECOLOGIC FACTOR.) Ueber den Revierbesitz bei Voegeln und Saeugetieren als populationsoekologischer Faktor. Olavi Kalela. Ann. Zool., Soc. Zool. Bot. Fennicae "Vanamo", vol.16, no.2, pp.48, 1954.

TROPHIES OF THE CHASE. SURVEY OF THE PRESENT EXHIBITS IN THE NATIONAL COLLECTION OF HEADS AND HORNS. Claude W. Leister. Bull. New York Zool. Soc., vol.38, no.2, pp.53-65, illus., Mar.-Apr., 1935.

GREAT AND SMALL GAME OF EUROPE WESTERN AND NORTHERN ASIA AND AMERICA, THEIR DISTRIBUTION, HABITS, AND STRUCTURE. Richard Lydekker. 1901.

(ON HUNTERS, EXHIBITION (SHOW).) Vladimir Martino. Lovtsa, nos.3-4, pp. 1-3, Mar.-Apr., 1938. (Bulgarian.)

(ON HUNTERS, EXHIBITION (SHOW).) Vladimir Martino. Lovtsa, nos.9-10, pp.2, photos 2, Sep.-Oct., 1938. (Bulgarian.)

FIELD BOOK; OR, SPORTS AND PASTIMES OF THE UNITED KINGDOM; COMP. FROM THE BEST AUTHORITIES, ANCIENT AND MODERN. William Hamilton Maxwell. London, E. Wilson, pp.viii-616, illus., 1833.

RECOLLECTIONS OF MY FIFTY YEARS HUNTING AND FISHING. Wm. B. Mershon. Boston, Stratford Co., pp.259, illus., 1923.

BREATH FROM THE VELDT. John Guille Millais. New and rev. ed., London, H. Sotheran and Co., pp.x-345, illus., pls., 1899.

BIG GAME HUNTING. G.S. Miller, Jr. The World is Yours, Smiths. Inst. Radio Program, pp.3 (not numbered), Aug. 2, 1936.

MEASURE THOSE GAME HEADS. Jack O'Connor. Arizona Wildlife and Sportsman, Phoenix, vol.1, no.3, p.6, Mar., 1939.

TROPHIES OF BIG GAME AT LEIPZIG. Eric Parker. Field, London, vol.155, no. 4043, p.920, June 21, 1930.

FROM BURMA TO AFRICA. CONTRASTS IN SEARCH OF BIG GAME WITH RIFLE AND CAMERA. E.H. Peacock. Field, London, vol.164, no.4267, pp.798-799, illus., Oct. 6, 1934.

SPORTSMAN'S SCRAPBOOK. John C. Phillips. Boston, Houghton Mifflin Co., vol.8, pp.212, illus., Oct., 1928.

BIG GAME SHOOTING. Clive Phillipps-Wolley. 2d ed., London, Longmans, Green and Co., vol.2, illus., pls., 1895.

REGULATED HUNTING ON THE PISGAH. C.E. Rachford. Amer. Forests, vol.39, no.3, pp.99-102, Mar., 1933.

USE OF CONTROLLED HUNTING IN THE SELWAY IN 1937. Jess Robertson, A.B. Hatch. Bull. Univ. Idaho, vol.33, no.22, (Bull. School Forestry, no.8), pp.29-30, Dec., 1938.

HUNTING IN MANY LANDS. Theodore Roosevelt, George Bird Grinnell. Book of the Boone and Crockett Club, 1895.

MOST DANGEROUS ANIMAL TO HUNT. Archibald Rutledge. Sports Afield, Minneapolis, vol.117, no.2, pp.22-23, 68-70, illus., Feb., 1947.

INDIAN METHODS OF HUNTING. WAS THE EARLY-DAY INDIAN A CONSERVATIONIST? Hugh L. Scott. Field and Stream, no.4, pp. 32-33, 61, Aug., 1929.

CONTROLLED HUNTING. Walter E. Scott. Texas Game & Fish, Austin, vol.6, no.10, pp.4, 21, Sep., 1948.

METHODS OF CONTROLLED PUBLIC HUNTING IN THE UNITES STATES AND CANADA. Walter E. Scott. Jour. Wildl. Mgt., vol.12, no.3, pp.236-240, July, 1948.

BONANZA FROM THE MARSHES. Joseph J. Shomon. Hunting and Fishing, Philadelphia, vol.25, no.3, pp.44-45, illus., Mar., 1948.

(Review by M. Klemm of) (PRINCIPLES OF THE SCIENCE OF HUNTING.) Grundlagen der Jagdkunde. Solovev. Zeitschr.f. Saugetierk., vol.5, no.1, pp.37-39, Aug. 8, 1930.

SPORTSMAN'S MISCELLANY. Arthur de Carle Sowerby. TME Tienstsin Press, Ltd., Tientsin, pp.226, illus., 1917.

SPORTING DICTIONARY AND RURAL REPOSITORY OF GENERAL INFORMATION UPON EVERY SUBJECT APPERTAINING TO THE SPORTS OF THE FIELD. William Taplin. London, Vernor and Hood, vol.2, pls., 1803.

HUNTING SKETCHES. Anthony Trollope. London, Chapman and Hall, pp.115, 1865.

RECORDS OF BIG GAME CONTAINING AN ACCOUNT OF THEIR DISTRIBUTION, DESCRIPTION OF SPECIES, LENGTHS, AND WEIGHTS, MEASUREMENTS OF HORNS AND FIELD NOTES FOR THE USE OF SPORTSMEN AND NATURALISTS. Rowland Ward. 1896.

RECORDS OF BIG GAME. 6th Edition. Rowland Ward. 1910.

ROWLAND WARD'S RECORDS OF BIG GAME: AFRICAN AND ASIATIC SECTIONS, GIVING THE DISTRIBUTION, CHARACTERISTICS, DIMENSIONS, WEIGHTS, AND HORN & TUSK MEASUREMENTS. 10th Edition. Rowland Ward. Edited by Guy Dollman, J.B. Burlace. London, Rowland Ward, Ltd., pp.xiii-408, illus., 1935.

HOW TO HUNT AND FISH. Aaron A. Warford. New York, F. Tousey, pp. 60, 1882.

HUNTING BIG GAME. Townsend Whelen. Military Service Publ. Co., Harrisburg, vols.2, 1946. (Vol.1, Africa and Asia, vol.2, The Americas.)

(ABOVE AND UNDER THE EARTH.) Ueber und unter der Erde. K. Wockenfusz. Deutsche Jagd, Berlin, nos.46-47, pp.621-623, illus., Feb. 16, 1940.

(FOR THE HUNTER OF WILD ANIMALS.) Okhotniku o zveriakh. Nikolai Anatol'evich Zvorykin. Moscow, Military Publishing House, pp.213, illus., 1953.

HUNTING, SHOOTING AND FISHING: A SPORTING MISCELLANY. WITH ANECDOTIC CHAPTERS ABOUT HORSES AND DOGS. New York, Scribner, Welford & Armstrong, pp.iv-317, illus., pls., 1877.

LIFE IN THE BACK-WOODS: A GUIDE TO THE SUCCESSFUL HUNTING AND TRAPPING OF ALL KINDS OF ANIMALS. New York, F.M. Reed, pp.28, 1875.

MEASURING HUNTING TROPHIES. (From the Boone and Crocket Club's "N. American Big Game"). Wyoming Wild Life, Cheyenne, vol.4, no.12, pp.10-13, illus., Dec., 1939.

NORTH AMERICAN TROPHY RECORDS. Wyoming Wild Life, Cheyenne, vol.4, no.12, pp.14-17, Dec., 1939.

(WHEN THE FULL MOON SHINES.) Wenn der Vollmond scheint. Deutsche Jagd, Berlin, nos.40-41, pp.563-564, Jan. 5, 1940.

## HYBRIDS

INTERBREEDING OF NATURAL POPULATIONS OF VERTEBRATES. W. Frank Blair. Amer. Nat., Lancaster, vol.85, no.820, pp.9-30, Jan.-Feb., 1951.

HYBRIDS AND INTERGRADES. Emmet R. Dunn. Copelia, no.1, pp.1-4, Apr. 10, 1937.

SOME OBSERVATIONS RELATIVE TO HYBRIDS AND INTERGRADATION. J.D. Figgins. Proc. Colorado Mus. Nat. Hist., vol.5, no.1, pp.3-10, June 19, 1925.

HYBRIDS. T. Gill. Amer. Naturalist, vol. 6, p.3, 1872.

(HYBRIDIZATION CLAIMED BY THE AUSTRALIANS.) Preteso ibridismo degli Australiani. V. Giuffrida-Ruggeri. Rend. R. Accad. Sci. Fis. et Matem. Napoli, ser. 3a, vol.25, pp.6, 1919.

MAMMALIAN HYBRIDS. CHECK-LIST WITH BIBLIOGRAPHY. Annie P. Gray. Commonwealth Bur. Anim. Breeding & Genetics Tech. Commun. no.10, p.144, 1954.

(HYBRIDIZATION IN MAMMALS.) Bastardierung bei Saeugetieren. H. Heck. Der Naturforscher, Berlin, vol.9, nos.1-2, pp. 18-20, pls.4-5, Apr.-May, 1932.

DISTANT HYBRIDIZATION OF ANIMALS-PRESENT STATUS AND FUTURE PROSPECTS. I.I. Lus. Bull. Acad. Sci., USSR, Cl.Sci.Math. et Nat., ser. Biol., Moscow, no.4, pp.776-852, figs.22, folded map, 1938. (In Russian, with English summary.)

(HYBRIDIZATION IN MAMMALS.) L'hybridation chez les mammifères. Francis Petter. Naturalia, Paris, no.18, pp.17-20, illus., Mar., 1955.

TYPES OF MAMMALS. WITH NOTES ON HYBRIDS DISEASES, ALBINISM AND OTHER CONDITIONS EQUALLY APPLICABLE TO MAN. R.W. Shufeldt. Med. Record, New York, vol.99, no.5, (whole no.2621), pp.180-186, figs.5, Jan. 29, 1921.

HYDATID DISEASE see DISEASES AND PARASITES -- HYDATID DISEASE

ILLUSTRATIONS see PHOTOGRAPHY AND PICTORIAL REPRESENTATION

## INTRODUCTIONS

EFFECT OF THE INTRODUCTION OF EXOTIC ANIMAL FORMS. R.M. Anderson. Proc. 5th Pacific Science Congress, Victoria and Vancouver, B.C., 1933, Univ. Toronto Press, pp.769-778, 1934.

(THE TRANSPORTATION OF WILD ANIMALS.) Le transport des animaux sauvages. Paul Bullier. Naturalia, Paris, no.18, pp.7-12, illus., Mar., 1955.

IMPORTATIONS OF LIVE BIRDS AND ANIMALS. Talbott Denmead. Pennsylvania Game News, Harrisburg, vol.15, no.12, pp.10, 31, Mar., 1945.

EVALUATION OF WILDLIFE IMPORTATIONS. Herbert W. Levi. Sci. Monthly, Lancaster, vol.74, no.6, pp.315-322, illus., June, 1952.

DANGER OF INTRODUCING NOXIOUS ANIMALS AND BIRDS. T.S. Palmer. Yearbook U.S. Dept. Agric., Washington, D.C., pp.87-110, figs.6, pls.8, 1898.

MAIN PRINCIPLES UNDERLYING METHODS FOR INCREASING THE SUPPLIES OF FUR-BEARING ANIMALS BY INTRODUCING THEM INTO NEW AREAS. L.V. Shaposhnikov. Trans. Cent. Lab. Game Indus., no.5, pp. 129-138, 1941.

INTRODUCED MAMMALS AND THEIR INFLUENCE ON NATIVE BIOTA. Antoon de Vos, Richard H. Manville, Richard C. van Gelder. Zoologica, New York Zool. Soc., vol.41, pt.4, pp.163-194, Dec. 31, 1956.

INTERSTATE TRANSPLANTS OF MAMMALS (RESOLUTION). Jour. Mamm., vol.16, no.3, p.240, Aug., 1935.

JAWS see ANATOMY -- SKULL, JAWS, TEETH

LABORATORY DEVICES see APPARATUS (CAGES, LABORATORY DEVICES, ETC.)

LAWS (FUR AND GAME) see GAME AND FUR LAWS

LEGEND AND BIBLICAL REFERENCE see MAMMALS IN LITERATURE AND FOLKLORE

LICE see DISEASES AND PARASITES -- LICE

## LIFE SPAN

AGE OF ANIMALS. Hari Narayan G. Acharya. Jour. Bombay Nat. Hist. Soc., vol.35, no.4, pp.884-885, July 15, 1932.

COMPARISON OF AGE CHANGES IN SALIVARY GLANDS OF MAN AND OF THE RAT. Warren Andrew. Jour. Gerontology, Springfield, vol.7, no.2, pp.178-190, illus., Apr., 1952.

COMPARATIVE CHRONOLOGIC AGE IN MAN AND OTHER MAMMALS. Sydney A. Asdell. Jour. Gerontology, Springfield, Ill., vol.1, no.2, pp.224-236, Apr., 1946.

LONGEVITY OF WILD ANIMALS IN CAPTIVITY. R. Biglake. South African Jour. Nat. Hist., vol.6, no.4, pp.297-302, June, 1929.

POPULATION DENSITY, LIFE SPAN, AND MORTALITY RATES OF SMALL MAMMALS IN THE BLUEGRASS MEADOW AND BLUEGRASS FIELD ASSOCIATIONS OF SOUTHERN MICHIGAN. W.F. Blair. Amer. Midl. Nature, vol.40, pp.395-419, 1948.

(LONGEVITY OF MAMMALS IN THE MENAGERIE OF THE NATIONAL MUSEUM OF NATURAL HISTORY.) La longévite des Mammiferes a la ménagerie du Museum national d'Histoire naturelle. E. Bourdelle, A. Mouquet. Bull. Mus. Nat. Hist. Nat., Paris, vol.2, no.5, pp.488-497, June, 1930.

(THE LONGEVITY OF SMALL WILD MAMMALS.) La longevite des petits mammiferes sauvages. Francois Bourliere. Mammalia, Paris, vol.11, no.3, pp.111-115(Sep., 1947), 1948.

PATRIARCHS IN THE ZOOLOGICAL PARK. CENSUS OF SOME OF THE OLDER INHABITANTS. William Bridges. Bull. New York Zool. Soc., vol.38, no.3, pp.89-98, illus., May-June, 1935.

LONGEVITY OF MAMMALS IN PHILADELPHIA GARDEN. C. Emerson Brown. Parks and Recreation, vol.9, pp.361-363, Feb., 1926. (Reprinted from Jour. Mamm., vol. 6, no.4, pp.264-267, Nov., 1925.)

LONGEVITY IN ANIMALS. Maurice Burton. Illus. London News, vol.213, no.5703, pp. 164-166, illus., Aug. 7, 1948.

PROBLEMS OF AGEING. E.V. Cowdry. Waverly Press, Inc., Baltimore, pp.758, figs.121, Jan., 1939; Williams & Wilkins Co., Baltimore, 2d ed., pp.xxxvi-936, figs.129, Sep., 1942.

LIFE TABLES FOR NATURAL POPULATIONS OF ANIMALS. Edward S. Deever, Jr. Quart. Rev. Biol., Baltimore, vol.22, no.4, pp.283-314, Dec., 1947.

DURATION OF LIFE OF SOME INDIAN MAMMALS. Cedric Dover. Jour. Bombay Nat. Hist. Soc., vol.36, no.1, pp.244-256, Nov. 15, 1932.

OLD AGE PENSIONERS. Certrude H. Duetz. Fauna, Philadelphia, vol.1, no.4, pp.59-63, illus., Dec., 1939.

ANIMAL LIFE SPANS. Stanley S. Flower. Fauna, Quart. Publ. Zool. Soc. Philadelphia, vol.1, no.4, pp.64-68, illus., Dec., 1939.

CONTRIBUTIONS TO OUR KNOWLEDGE OF THE DURATION OF LIFE IN VERTEBRATE ANIMALS. Stanley S. Flower. Proc. Zool. Soc. London for 1931, pt.1, pp.145-234, Apr. 14, 1931.

AGE DETERMINATION IN MAMMALS. Charles P. Gandal. Trans. N.Y. Acad. Sci., (Ser.2) vol.16, no.6, pp.312-314, Apr., 1954.

OLD AGE IN MAMMALS. John Eric Hill. Nat. Hist., New York, vol.50, no.4, p. 211, illus., Nov., 1942.

(CONTRIBUTION TO THE PROBLEM OF OLD AGE.) Beitraege zum Altersproblem. D. Kotsovsky. Biol. Zentralblatt, vol.49, pp.764-767, figs.2, 1929.

(NEW TABLE OF ANIMAL LONGEVITY.) Nouveau tableau du règne animal. René Primevère Lesson. Mammiferes, Paris, A. Bertrand, pp.204, 1842.

LONGEVITY OF SOME MICHIGAN FARM GAME MAMMALS. J.P. Linduska. Jour. Mamm., vol.28, no.2, pp.126-129, May 19, 1947.

(LIFE SPAN OF SOME ANIMALS IN ZOOLOGICAL GARDENS.) Lebensdauer einiger Tiere in Zoologischen Gaerten. Erna Mohr. Zool. Garten, Leipzig, n.F., vol.18, nos. 1-2, p.60, 1951.

DURATION OF LIFE OF SOME INDIAN MAMMALS. TIGERS. R.C. Morris. Jour. Bombay Nat. Hist. Soc., vol.36, no.1, pp.250-252, Nov. 15, 1932.

ANIMAL METHUSELAHS. WHICH ANIMALS LIVE THE LONGEST? Barclay Moon Newman. Scientific American, New York, vol.164, no. 1, pp.7-10, Jan., 1941.

NOTE REGARDING THE RELATION OF AGE TO FECUNDITY. Raymond Pearl. Science, n.s., vol.37, no.945, pp.226-228, Feb. 7, 1913.

(SOME REMARKABLE CASES OF NATURAL MUMMIFICATION IN MAMMALS.) Einige bemerkenswerte Faelle natuerlicher Mumifikation bei Saeugetieren. Nicolaus Peters. Zool. Garten, Leipzig, n.F., vol.5, nos. 1-3, pp.15-33, figs.1-12, June, 1932.

(CORRELATION BETWEEN LONGEVITY AND FECUNDITY IN DIFFERENT MAMMALIAN SPECIES.) Sur la correlation entre la durée de la vie et la fécondité chez différentes espèces de mammiferes. S.A. Severtsova. Bull. Acad. Sci. USSR, ser.7, cl.Sci.phys.-math., Leningrad, 1930, no. 9, pp.931-950, 1930. (In Russian.)

LIFE SPAN OF ANIMALS. Alexander Sprunt. Sci. Digest, Chicago, vol.6, no.2, pp.81-84, Aug., 1939.

(BODY SIZE AND LIFE SPAN IN ANIMALS.) Koerpergroesse und Lebensdauer der Tiere. Istvan Szabo. Zool. Anzeiger, vol.74, pp. 39-53, Oct. 20, 1927.

(LONGEVITY OF ANIMALS AND PLANTS FROM THE VIEWPOINT OF PHYLOGENETIC DEVELOPMENT.) Lebensdauer der Tiere und Pflanzen vom Gesichtspunkt der phylogenetischen Entwicklung. Istvan Szabo. Zool. Anzeiger, vol.62, pp.289-304, May 5, 1925.

(ADVANCED AGE OF VARIOUS ANIMALS IN THE DUSSELDORF ZOOLOGICAL GARDEN.) Hohes Alter verschiedener Tiere im Duesseldorfer Zoologischen Garten. Rudolf Weber. Zool. Garten, vol.14, no.4, pp.208-210, illus., 1942.

(TWO INTERESTING VERTEBRATE MUMMIES.) Zwei interessante Wirbeltiermumien. J.V. Zelizko. Paleont. Zeitschr., Berlin, vol.14, nos.1-2, pp.122-126, figs.2, May 31, 1932.

AGE OF ANIMALS. Discovery, Cambridge, England, n.s., vol.3, no.24, p.144, Mar., 1940.

ANIMAL MUMMIES. Field Mus. News, Chicago, vol.12, no.5, p.5, May, 1941.

LOCOMOTION see PHYSIOLOGY -- LOCOMOTION

MAMMALOGY

COOPERATION FOR LIFE HISTORY WORK. C.C. Adams, V. Bailey, W.P. Taylor. Jour. Mamm., vol.5, no.4, p.274, Nov., 1929.

(SHORT DESCRIPTIONS OF MAMMALS.) Magdir le-yonkim. Bath-Sheba Aharoni. Jerusalem, pp.52, 1941/42.

ROE-DEER AND NARWHALS.) Ayalah w'tahash (Cervus capreolus et Monodon monoceros). Israel Aharoni. Tarbiz, Jerusalem, vol.8, no.34, pp.319-339, illus., 1937. (Text mostly in Hebrew.)

SOME OLD BOOKS. Glover M. Allen. Bull. Boston Soc. Nat. Hist., no.43, pp.10-12, Apr., 1927.

WILD ANIMALS I HAVE KNOWN. J.A. Allen. Amer. Nat., vol.33, pp.666-668, Aug., 1899.

(FOREST ZOOLOGY. I. MAMMALS AND MAMMAL TRAVELS.) Forstzoologie. 1. Saeugethiere nebst Anhand: Saeugethierfaehrten. Bernard Althum. Berlin, pp.409, figs.120, pls.5, 1876.

ANIMALS OF AMERICA, "MAMMALS OF AMERICA". H.E. Anthony. Garden City, N.Y., Garden City Publishing Co., Inc., pp.xxiii-335, illus. (incl.maps), col.pls., diagrs., 1937.

LIVES OF GAME ANIMALS. REVIEW OF VOLUME 1. H.E. Anthony. Nat. Hist., vol.25, no.6, pp.579-582, Nov.-Dec., 1925 (Jan., 1926). (Review of Seton's Lives of game animals, vol.1.)

FURRY FRIENDS. Frank G. Ashbrook. Racine, Wis., pp.20, col.illus., 1930.

(OF THE CONSTANTS OF NATURE. CLASS MAMMALIA.) Sur les constantes de la nature. Classe des mammifères. Charles Babbage. Brussels, Impr. de M. Hayez, pp. 9, 1853. (In English.)

DWELLERS IN THE DESERT. Vernon Bailey. Nature Mag., vol.23, no.2, pp.63-68, illus., Feb., 1934.

THE WORLD WE LIVE IN: PART VI. THE AGE OF MAMMALS. Lincoln Barnett. Life, vol.35, no.6, pp.88-109, illus., Oct. 19, 1953.

NOTE ON VARIATION IN THE WEASEL AND HEDGEHOG. G.E.H. Barrett-Hamilton. Ann. & Mag. Nat. Hist., ser.7, vol.6, pp.243-246, Aug., 1900.

(MAMMALS.) Mammiferi. Oscar de Beaux. Boll. Mus. Zool. e Anat. Compar. Univ. Torino, vol.46, ser.3, no.86, pp.23, tbls., 1937-38.

MAMMALIA. Frank Evers Beddard. London, Macmillan and Co., Ltd., New York, Macmillan Co., pp.xii-605, illus., 1902.

GENERAL HISTORY OF BIRDS AND QUADRUPEDS, WITH 128 ENGRAVINGS. Thomas Bewick. Philadelphia, R. Desilver, pt.1, pp. 70, pt.2, pp.142, pls., 1824.

DESERT DWELLERS. John L. Blackford. Nat. Hist., New York, vol.53, no.1, pp. 24-27, illus., Jan., 1944.

HOW TO KNOW THE MAMMALS. Ernest S. Booth. William C. Brown Co., Dubuque, Iowa, pp.206, figs.415, 1949.

ANIMAL AND ITS ENVIRONMENT. TEXT-BOOK OF THE NATURAL HISTORY OF ANIMALS. L.A. Borradaile. Oxford Univ. Press, American Branch, New York, vol. 8, pp.vi-399, col.pls.4, figs.426, 1923.

(NEW DATA FROM THE LIFE OF THE WOLF AND WILD HOG.) Neues aus dem Leben des Wolfes und Wildschweines. E. Botezat. Bul. Fac. Ştiinte, Cernăuti, vol. 5, no.1, pp.158-168, 1931.

(LIFE AND HABITS OF MAMMALS.) Vie et moeurs des mammiferes. F. Bourliere. Payot, Paris, pp.249, 1951.

(Review by W.J. Hamilton, Jr. of) (LIFE AND HABITS OF MAMMALS.) Vie et moeurs des mammiferes. F. Bourliere. Jour. Mamm., vol.32, no.4, p.478, Nov. 19, 1951.

NATURAL HISTORY OF MAMMALS. F. Bourliere. Published by Alfred A. Knopf, Inc., New York, pp.363, illus., 1954. (Translated from the French by H. M. Parshley.)

(Review by W. Robert Eadie of) NATURAL HISTORY OF MAMMALS. F. Bourliere. Jour. Mamm., vol.35, no.4, p.603, Nov. 29, 1954.

MAMMALS OF THE WORLD. THEIR LIFE AND HABITS. F. Bourliere. Published by Alfred A. Knopf, Inc., New York, pp.223, illus., 1955.

(Review by Robert W. Eadie of) MAMMALS OF THE WORLD. THEIR LIFE AND HABITS. F. Bourliere. Jour. Mamm., vol.37, no.1, pp.133-134, Feb. 28, 1956.

DESERT DWELLERS. George M. Bradt. Nat. Hist., New York, vol.56, no.3, pp. 120-125, illus., Mar., 1947.

MAMMALS AND BIRDS. Paul Bransom. New York, Charles Livingston Bull, Encyclopeadia Britannica, 14th Ed., p. 199, illus., 1933. (Britannica Booklet no.3.)

(Review by Edward G. Huey of) CHILD'S STORY OF THE ANIMAL WORLD. Howell A. Brazier. Jour. Mamm., vol.17, no.1, p.69, Feb., 1936.

THE ANIMALS OF THE WORLD. MAMMALIA. BREHM'S LIFE OF ANIMALS, A COMPLETE NATURAL HISTORY FOR POPULAR HOME INSTRUCTION AND FOR THE USE OF SCHOOLS. Copiously illustrated with wood cuts and color-plates. Brought down and especially adapted for the use of English readers. Tr. from the 3d German ed. as edited by Prof.Dr.Pechuel-Loesche and Dr. William Haacke, and rev. and abridged by Prof.Richard Schmidtlein. Chicago, A.N. Marquis & Co., pp.608, col.front, illus., col.pls.4, 1911.

(WILD ANIMALS, SELECTION FROM THE FIRST EDITIONS OF BREHM'S ANIMAL LIFE, BY DR. WALTHER KAHLE.) Wildtiere, Auswahl aus den ersten Auflagen von Brehms Tierleben, von Dr. Walther Kahle. A. Brehm. Leipzig, Bibliographisches Inst., pp.393, ill.34, tbl.28, pls., 1924.

(Review by Robert M. Erkes of) BREHM'S NATURAL HISTORY OF ANIMALS. A. Brehm. Jour. Comp. Psych., vol.4, pp. 347-348, 1924.

WILD ANIMALS OF THE WORLD. William Bridges. Garden City Publ. Co., Garden City, New York, pp.272, illus., 1948.

(STUDY OF SMALL MAMMALS.) De studie van kleine Zoodieren. F.H. van Brink. Levende Natuur, vol.34, no.9, pp.308-311, Jan. 1, 1930.

MY ANIMAL FRIENDS. C.Emerson Brown. Doubleday, Doran & Co., Inc., Garden City, New York, pp.262, illus., 1932.

NOTES ON A FEW MICE, RABBITS AND OTHER ANIMALS. Lee P. Brown. Jour. Mamm., vol.4, no.4, pp.258-260, Nov., 1923.

SQUIRRELS AND OTHER FUR-BEARERS. J. Burroughs. Boston, vol.8, pp.149, 1900.

RABBITS OR CHUCKS? Lysle Burtch. Pennsylvania Game News, Harrisburg, vol.19, no.6, p.28, Sep., 1948.

ADAPTATIONS FOR LIFE AMONG THE TREES: DIVERSITY OF FORM OF ARBOREAL ANIMALS. Maurice Burton. Illus. London News, vol.219, no.5880, pp.1076-1077, illus., Dec. 29, 1951.

ANIMALS ON PARADE. Maurice Burton. Elsevier Publ. Co., Ltd., London, vols. 2, 1949.

YOUNG ANIMALS'FIRST GLIMPSE OF LIFE. Maurice Burton. Illus. London News, vol.234, no.6250, Mar. 21, 1959.

ANIMAL LIFE IN DESERTS. STUDY OF THE FAUNA IN RELATION TO THE ENVIRONMENT. P.A. Buxton. London, Edward Arnold and Co., pp.176, figs.43, 1923.

(WILD ANIMALS.) Los animales salvajes. Angel Cabrera. Madrid, Espasa-Calpe, s.a., pp.93, illus., pl.6, 1932.

GENERA MAMMALIUM. MONOTREMATA, MARSUPIALIA. Angel Cabrera. Madrid, Museo Nacional de Ciencias Naturales, pp.1-177, pls.1-19, col.figs., 1919.

(Review by G.S.Miller of) GENERA MAMMALIUM. MONOTREMATA, MARSUPIALIA. Angel Cabrera. Jour. Mamm., vol.1, no.3, pp.148-149, 1920.

MEETING THE MAMMALS. Victor H. Cahalane. MacMillan Co., New York, pp.ix-133, illus., 1943.

MAMMALOGY AND ORNITHOLOGY. John Cassin. Philadelphia, C. Sherman & Son, pp.viii-466, illus., atlas, col.pl.53, 1858.

MAMMALS OF THE LAND, AIR AND SEA. E. Burnahm Chamberlain. Nature Mag., vol.17, no.5, pp.309-312, figs.9, May, 1931.

JUNGLE IN SUNLIGHT AND SHADOW. F.W. Champion. Chatto and Windus, London, pp.xvi-270, pls.95, 1933.

WHALES, GRIZZLIES, AND WOLVES. Campbell Church. Sportsman, Boston, vol.13, no.2, pp.35-47, illus., Feb., 1933.

SOME USEFUL ANIMALS. Ella Rodman Church. Philadelphia, Presbyterian Board of Publication and Sabbath-School Work, pp.366, illus., 1888.

CABINET OF QUADRUPEDS. John Church. London, Printed for Darton and Harvey, vol. 2, pl.84, 1805.

ANIMALS ALIVE. A.H. Clark. New York, D.Van Nostrand Co., pp.426, illus., 1948.

NOCTURNAL ANIMALS. A.H. Clark. Jour. Washington Acad. Sci., vol.4, no.6, pp. 139-142, Mar. 19, 1914.

GIANTS OF THE ANIMAL KINGDOM. Edwin H. Colbert. Nat. Hist., New York, vol.58, no.9, pp.418-423, 430-431, illus., Nov., 1949.

WILDERNESS MAGIC. Donald M. Cole. Field and Stream, New York, vol.48, no. 7, pp.36-38, 63, illus., Nov., 1943.

NATURAL HISTORY OF QUADRUPEDS. John Lee Comstock. New York, Pratt, Woodford & Co., pp.73, illus., fold.pl., 1848.

MAMMALS OF OTHER LANDS. Charles J. Cornish, and others. New York, Univ. Society Inc., pp.v-354, illus., pls., 1917.

LOVABLE BEASTS. Harper Cory. Ivor Nicholson & Watson, Ltd., London, pp. xiv-119, figs.65, 1932.

HOUSEHOLD BOOK OF NATURE. Hugh Craig. New York, Johnson & Bailey, pp. 800, col.pl.64, 1897.

LITTLE BEASTS OF FIELD AND WOOD. William Everett Cram. Boston, Small, Maynard and Co., pp.xx-261, pls., 1899.

ANIMAL KINGDOM. Cuvier. Carvill, N. Y., pp.532, 1932. (Translated from the French and abridged by H. M'Murtrie.)

HOW TO SEE BEASTS. E.F. Daglish. New York, W.Morrow & Co., pp.127, illus., pls., 1933.

LIFE STORY OF BEASTS. E.F.Daglish. New York, pp.219, illus., 1931.

REPRIMANDS FROM WILDLIFE. Byron W. Dalrymple. Sports Afield, Minneapolis, vol.119, no.2, pp.58, 74, illus., Feb., 1948.

(NATURAL HISTORY OF ANIMALS.) Histoire naturelle des animaux. Louis Jean Marie Daubenton. Paris, Chez Panckoucke, 1782.

(MAMMALS.) Mammifères. P.L.Dekeyser, A. Villiers. Conferência Internacional dos Africanistas Ocidentais, Lisbon, vol.3, pp.73-91, Aug., 1951.

WHO'S WHO IN THE ZOO. Ralph De Sola. New York, Halcyon House, pp.211, illus., 1937.

NATURE, THE OVERSEER. Alan Devoe. Audubon Mag., New York, vol.45, no.5, pp.270-276, Sep.-Oct., 1943.

WINTER WATCHING. Alan Devoe. Audubon Mag., New York, vol.47, no.1, sec.1, pp. 2-8, illus., Jan.-Feb., 1945.

REAL BOOK ABOUT AMAZING ANIMALS. Alice Dickinson. Garden City, New York, Garden City Books, pp.191, illus., 1951.

(MAMMALS IN THE "ZOOLOGICAL TREATISE".) Les mammifères dans le "Traité de Zoologie". Jean Dorst. Mammalia, Paris, vol.20, no.1, pp.83-87, Mar., 1956.

PIKA AND PRAIRIE DOG. Stuart C.Downing. Canadian Nature, Toronto, vol.11, no.2, pp. 36-37, illus., Mar.-Apr., 1949.

WOLVERINE AND DEER. Stuart C.Downing. Canadian Nature, Toronto, vol.10, no.3, pp. 96-97, illus., May-June, 1948.

OUR ANIMAL FRIENDS AND FOES. William Atherton DuPuy. Philadelphia, John C. Winston Co., pp.274, illus., 1925.

PAWS, HOOFS, AND FLIPPERS. Olive Lydia Earle. New York, Morrow, pp.192, illus., 1954.

OUR GREAT OUTDOORS: MAMMALS. C.W. G.Eifrig. Chicago, Rand McNally and Co., vol.8, pp.xiii, pls.257, text figs.177, col. pls.2, July, 1928.

SUBTERRANEAN MAMMALS OF THE WORLD. J.R.Ellerman. Trans. Roy. Soc. South Africa, vol.35, no.1, pp.11-20, Aug., 1956.

LIST OF MAMMALS FROM SOMALI-LAND. (REMARKS UPON TWO SPECIES OF DEER OF THE GENUS CERVUS FROM THE PHILIPPINE ARCHIPELAGO.) D.G. Elliot. Field Col. Mus. Publ.19, Zool.ser. vol.I, no.5, pp.109-155, pls.16-38, June, 1897.

WILD ANIMAL SHOW. Mildred J.Erickson. Amer. Forests, Washington, vol.54, no.8, pp.356-358, illus., Aug., 1948.

MAMMALS. Everett F. Evans. Missouri Conserv. Comm., Jefferson City, Manual Conserv. for Missouri Teachers, no.6, pp.1-29, 1941.

(WILD AND DOMESTIC ANIMALS.) Wildtiere und Haustiere. Otto Fehringer. Kosmos, Stuttgart, pp.79, figs.17, 1936.

(WORLD OF MAMMALS.) Welt der Saeugetiere. Otto Fehringer. Munich, Droemer, pp.431, illus., maps, 1953.

NATURAL HISTORY OF BRITISH AND FOREIGN QUADRUPEDS. James H.Fennell. London, J. Thomas, pp.xv-556, illus., 1841.

(CHIROPTERA AND INSECTIVORA.) Chirotteri ed insettivori. E. Festa. Milano, Ruwenzori ralazione scientifiche, vol.1, pp.14, illus., Oct., 1907.

(LIFE AND HABITS OF ANIMALS. THE MAMMALS.) Vita o costumi degli animali. I mammiferi. 4th Ed. Louis Figuier. Milano, Fratelli Treves, pp.xi-654, illus., pls., 1882.

MAMMALIA. Louis Figuier. London, Chapman and Hall, pp.xi-606, illus., 1870.

(POPULAR SCIENTIFIC NATURAL HISTORY OF THE MAMMALS IN THEIR MAIN FORMS.) Wissenschaftlich-populaere Naturgeschichte der Saeugethiere in ihren saemtlichen Hauptformen. Leop. Jos. Fitzinger. Vienna, vols. I-VI, 1860-1861.

LIFE IN THE DESERT AT NIGHT. Richard B. Freeman. Nature Notes, Peoria, vol.9, nos.3-4, pp.33-37, Mar.-Apr., 1942.

MAMMALOGY. Herbert Friedmann. Jour. Washington Acad. Sci., vol.34, no.5, May 15, 1944.

IN ALL SEASONS. Bill Geagan. Outdoorsman, Chicago, vol.86, no.1, whole no.506, pp.8-9, 41-42, illus., Jan.-Feb., 1944.

RODENTS, MARSUPIALS, AND VERMIN. P. Gennadius. Athens, pp.139, figs.6, 1916. (Greek text.)

(NATURAL HISTORY OF MAMMALS WITH ORIGINAL COLOR FIGURES DRAWN FROM LIVING ANIMALS.) Histoire naturelle des mammifères, avec des figures originales, coloriées, dessinées d'Apres des animaux vivans. E. Geoffroy Saint-Hiliare, Frederic Cuvier. Paris, vols.1-7, 1824-1842.

(COURSE OF THE NATURAL HISTORY OF MAMMALS.) Cours de l'histoire naturelle des mammiferes. E. Geoffroy Saint-Hilaire. Paris, pp.665, pl., 1829.

(THE QUADRUPEDS.) Die Vierfuessler. Richard Hans Wilhelm Ferdinand Gerlach. Hamburg, Claassen, pp.383, illus., 1951.

(NATURAL HISTORY OF MAMMALS: VOL. I. PRIMATES, CHIROPTERS, INSECTIVORES AND RODENTS.) Histoire Naturelles des Mammiferes. Vol.1. Primates, Cheiropteres, Insectivores et Rongeurs. Paul Gervais. 1854.

(NATURAL HISTORY OF MAMMALS, WITH INDICATION OF THEIR HABITS AND THEIR RELATIONSHIPS WITH ARTS, COMMERCE, AND AGRICULTURE.) Histoire naturelle des mammiferes, avec l'indication de leurs moeurs, et de leurs rapports avec les arts, le commerce et l'agriculture. Paul Gervais. Paris, L.Curmer, vol.2, illus., pls., 1854-55.

(MICROMAMMALS.) Micromammiferi. A. Ghidini. Boll. del Nat. Anno 26, no.5-7, pp.8, illus., 1906.

(Review by John Squire of) ENCHANTED TRAILS. Christopher Gibson Bart. DESERT

JOURNEYS. Geoffrey Rawson. Illus. London News, vol.213, no.5718, p.568, illus., Nov. 20, 1948.

MAMMALS IN ZOOLOGICAL, ANATOMICAL, AND PALEONTOLOGICAL REFERENCE, COMPREHENSIVELY REPRESENTED.) Die Saeugethiere in zoologischer, anatomischer und palaeontologischer Beziehung umfassend dargestellt. C.G.Andreas Giebel. Leipzig, A.Abel, pp.xii-1108, 1855.

(NATURAL HISTORY OF THE ANIMAL KINGDOM.) Naturgeschichte des Thierreichs. Vol.I. MAMMALS. C.G.Andreas Giebel. Leipzig, pp.522, illus., 1859.

STANDARD NATURAL HISTORY. MAMMALS. Theodore Gill. Boston, vol.5, pp. 46-67, 1886.

ON THE CHARACTERISTICS OF THE PRIMARY GROUPS OF THE CLASS OF MAMMALS. Theodore Gill. Amer. Assoc. Adv. Sci., Cambridge, vol.20, pp.284-306, 1871.

(NATURAL HISTORY OF THE ANIMAL KINGDOM FOR HIGHER SCHOOLS.) Naturgeschichte des Thierreichs fuer hoehere Schulen. J. Gistel. Stuttgart, pp.16-216+4, pls.32, 1848.

SOME PERTINENT WILDLIFE FACTS. Phil Goodrum. Texas Game, Fish, and Oyster Comm., Monthly Bull., Austin, vol.3, no.1, pp.1-2, Dec., 1939.

NATURAL HISTORY. MAMMALIA. P.H. Gosse. London, Soc. for Promoting Christian Knowledge, pp.vi-302, illus., 1848.

(MAMMALS.) Mammifères. Pierre-P. Grassé. (In) Traité de zoologie (Zoological Treatise.) Paris, Masson et Cie, vol.17, (2pts.) pp. 2300, figs.2106, 1955.

ORDERS OF MAMMALS. William King Gregory. New York, The Trustees, pp.v-524, illus., 1910. (Bull. of the Amer.Mus. of Nat. Hist., vol.XXVII, 1910.)

VARIATION AMONG INSULAR MAMMALS OF GEORGIA STRAIT, BRITISH COLUMBIA. E. Raymond Hall. Amer. Nat., vol.72, no. 742, pp.453-463, figs.2, Sep.-Oct., 1938.

MAMMAL LIFE OF THE FOREST FLOOR. UNDER THE CARPET OF LEAVES LIES A WHOLE LITTLE WORLD INHABITED BY SHREWS AND MOLES AND MICE. W.J. Hamilton, Jr. Bull. New York Zool. Soc., vol.43, no.6, pp.171-180, figs.12, Nov.-Dec., 1940.

NATURE SPREADS A VARIED TABLE. Wm. J. Hamilton, Jr. Animal Kingdom, New York Zool. Soc., vol.58, no.4, pp.98-103, illus., July-Aug., 1955.

SMALL MAMMALS AND THE FOREST. Wm. J. Hamilton, David B. Cook. Trans. 10th N. Amer. Wildl. Conf., Washington, pp.137-139, 1945; Jour. Forestry, Washington, vol. 38, no.6, pp.468-473, June, 1940.

MUSEUM NOTES: MAMMALS. Francis Harper. Bull. Bost. Soc. Nat. Hist., no. 49, pp.18-19, Oct., 1928.

NOTES ON MAMMALS. Herbert M.W.Haven. Maine Nat., vol.7, no.4, p.160, Dec., 1927.

PARADE OF THE ANIMAL KINGDOM. Robert Hegner, Jane Z. Hegner. New York, Macmillan Co., pp.vi-675, illus., 1936. (Mammals, pp.515-664.)

(MAMMALOGICAL NOTES.) Mammalogische Notizen. R. Hensel. Archiv. Naturg., vol.45, pp.198-210, 1879.

(REMARKS ON THE BIOLOGY OF SOME MAMMALS.) Bemerkungen zur Biologie einiger Saeugetiere. Erich Hesse. Zeitschr. f. Saeugetierk., vol.1, no.1, pp.47-58, Aug. 31, 1926.

(MAMMALOGY AND ARCHAEOLOGY.) Saeugetierkunde und Archaeologie. Max Hilzheimer. Zeitschr. f. Saeugetierk., vol.1, no.2, pp.140-169, illus., Dec.24, 1926.

(REMAINING LARGE MAMMALS.) Die uebrigen Grossaeugetiere. Max Hilzheimer. Zeitschr. f. Saeugetierk., vol.11, pp.316-317, Mar. 13, 1936.

MAMMALS OF MAMMOTH, MONO COUNTY, CALIFORNIA. A. Brazier Howell. Jour. Mamm., vol.5, no.1, pp.25-36, Feb., 1924.

DOCTOR GOES WILD. Vance Hoyt. Nature Mag., Washington, vol.38, no.9, pp.482-498, illus., Nov., 1945.

(ZOOLOGICAL VARIATIONS.) Variations zoologiques. V.A. Huard. Le Naturaliste Canadien, vol.54, no.4, pp.73-76, Oct., 1927.

RACIAL AND INDIVIDUAL VARIATION IN ANIMALS, ESPECIALLY FISHES. Carl L. Hubbs. Amer. Nat., vol.68, no.715, pp.115-128, Mar.-Apr., 1934.

(Review by A. Brazier Howell of) CHILD'S STORY OF THE ANIMAL WORLD. Edward G. Huey. Jour. Mamm., vol.17, no.1, p. 69, Feb., 1936.

LEMMINGS AND LYNXES. G.Everlyn Hutchinson. Amer. Scientist, Burlington, vol.37, no.4, pp.614, 616, 618, Oct., 1949.

ADDITIONAL MAMMAL NOTES. T.van Hyning. Proc. Iowa Acad. Sci., Des Moines, vol.20, pp.311-312, 1914.

LIFE OF ANIMALS: MAMMALS. Ernest Ingersoll. New York, Macmillan, pp.xi-555, illus., col.pl., 1906.

(Footnote to: THE WORD MAMMALOGIST, C.W.G.Eifrig.) Hartley H.T. Jackson. Jour. Mamm., vol.10, no.4, Nov. 4, 1929.

(SHORT COMMUNICATIONS ON MAMMALS.) Kleine Mitteilungen ueber Saeugetiere. A. Jacobi. Abhandl. Ber. Kon. Zoll.Anthrop. Ethno. Mus. Dresden, vol.12, pp.3-13, 1911.

NATURE'S "JITTERBUGS". Ellsworth Jaeger. Nature Mag., Washington, D.C., vol.33, no. 7, pp.395-397, illus., Aug.-Sep., 1940.

(VERTEBRATES, SURVEY OF FOSSIL AND LIVING FORMS.) Wirbeltiere, eine uebersicht ueber die Fossilen und lebenden Formen. Otto Max Johannes Jaekel. Berlin, Gebrueder Borntraeger, pp.viii-252, illus., 1911.

STALKING WILD LIFE THROUGH THE MAILS. Raymond E. Janssen. Nat.Notes, Peoria, vol.7, no.10, pp.219-223, Oct., 1940.

NATURALIST'S LIBRARY. MAMMALIA. William Jardine. Edinburgh, W.H.Lizars, vol.13, illus., pl.(part col.), 1833-42.

ELEPHANTS AND RHINOS. H. Jeffreys. Field, London, vol.162, no.4206, p.379, Aug. 5, 1933.

NATURAL HISTORY. ANIMALS. George Jennison. London, A.& C. Black, Ltd., pp.xv-343, illus., col.pls., 1927.

STORY OF ANIMALS; MAMMALS AROUND THE WORLD. Gaylord Johnson. Irvington-on-Hudson, N.Y., Harvey House, pp.120, illus., 1958.

ANIMAL FAMILIES AND WHERE THEY LIVE. Arnrid Johnston. London, Country Life, Ltd., pp.28 (not numbered), pls. 24, 1939.

(DESERT LIFE.) La Vie dans les déserts. D.N. Kachkarov, E.P. Korovine. French edition by Th. Monod. Paris, Payot, pp. 361, pls.32, figs.63, 1942.

IT'S ALL VERY CONFUSING. E.L.Keithan. Alaska Sportsman, Ketchikan, vol.10, no.7, pp.18-20, illus., July, 1944.

(ON THE IMPOSSIBILITY OF ANIMAL LIFE WITHOUT MICROBES.) Sur l'impossibilité de la vie animale sans microbes. J. Kiantitzine. Archives de Biologie, vol.37, pp. 397-406, Sep. 20, 1927.

DESERT ANIMALS. Rita Kissin. Philadelphia, David McKay Co., pp.26, illus., 1947.

ANIMALS OF THE WORLD FOR YOUNG PEOPLE. Charles Robert Knight. New York, Stokes Co., pp.250, illus., col. pls.40, 1908.

FOUR-FOOTED KINGS OF WESTERN ROCK CASTLE. Hamilton M. Laing. Nature Mag., vol.30, no.5, pp.269-272, illus., Nov., 1937.

ANIMAL WONDERLAND. Frank W.Lane. London, Country Life, Ltd., pp.232, pls. 80, 1948.

ZOOLOGICAL MISCELLANY. MAMMALOGY. F.W. Langdon. Jour. Cincinnati Soc. Nat. Hist., vol.4, pp.336-337, Dec., 1881.

PRESENT DAY MAMMALS. Claude W. Leister. New York Zoological Soc., pp. 74, illus., 1931.

(MAMMALOGICAL MANUAL. OR NATURAL HISTORY OF MAMMALS.) Manuel de mammalogie, ou histoire naturelle des mammiferes. R.P. Lesson. Paris, Roret, pp.441, 1827.

(ZOOLOGICAL FRAGMENTS.) Zoologische Bruchstuecke. Friedrich Sigismund Leuckart. Part I. Helmstadt, pp.viii-70, pls.2, 1819; Part II. Helmstadt, pp.viii-130, pls.6, 1841; Part III. Freiburg, pp.iii-60, pls.2, 1842.

ANIMAL WORLD. Lorna Lewis. London, Paul Elek Pub., Ltd., (Life and Leisure series no.7), pp.142, 1949.

LUNGFISH, THE DODO, AND THE UNICORN. Willy Ley. Viking Press, New York, pp.361, illus., 1948.

ANIMALS ARE MY HOBBY. Gertrude Davies Lintz. Robert M.McBride & Co., New York, pp.301, illus., 1942.

MOTHER NATURE: STUDY OF ANIMAL LIFE AND DEATH. Wm.J. Long. New York and London, Harper and Bros., pp. vii-330, pls.8, 1923.

ODD EXPERIENCES WITH ANIMALS. J. Alden Loring. Nature Mag., Washington, vol.42, no.2, pp.73-75, 98, illus., Feb., 1949.

(STUDIES OF SMALL MAMMALS.) Studien an Kleinsaeugern. Hans Luettschwagen. Verhandl. Deutschen Zoologen in Mainz, 1949 (Zool. Anzeiger, 14 Supplementband), Leipzig, pp.315-330, 1950.

GREAT AND SMALL GAME OF EUROPE, WESTERN AND NORTHERN ASIA AND AMERICA; THEIR DISTRIBUTION, HABITS, AND STRUCTURE. R. Lydekker. London, R. Ward, Ltd., pp.xx-445, illus.75, col. pls.8, 1901.

HAND-BOOK TO THE MARSUPIALIA AND MONOTREMATA. R. Lydekker. London, Lloyd's Nat. Hist., pp.320, illus., 1896.

MOSTLY MAMMALS, ZOOLOGICAL ESSAYS. R. Lydekker. London, Hutchinson & Co., pp.383, pls., 1903.

INTRODUCTION TO THE STUDY OF MAMMALS, LIVING AND EXTINCT. R.Lydekker, W.H. Flower. 1891.

ON FOREST-BED MAMMALS. C. I. Forsyth Major. Proc. Zool. Soc. London for 1908, pp.630-634, Oct., 1908.

GENERAL INTRODUCTION TO THE NATURAL HISTORY OF MAMMIFEROUS ANIMALS, WITH A PARTICULAR VIEW OF THE PHYSICAL HISTORY OF MAN, AND THE MORE CLOSELY ALLIED GENERA OF THE ORDER QUADRUMANA, OR MONKEYS. W.C. Linnaeus Martin. London, Wright and Co., pp.545, illus., pls. 12, 1841.

MAKING FRIENDS WITH WILDLIFE. Karl Howard L. Maslowski. Audubon Mag., New York, vol.49, no.6, pp.355-365, illus., Nov.-Dec., 1947.

(MAMMALS.) Saeugethiere. Paul Matschie. Hamburg, pp.29, col.pl.1, 1898.

ANIMALS OF THE WORLD. J. Walker McSpadden. Garden City Publ. Co., New York, pp.354, illus., 1947.

MAN AND THE ZEBRA. J.I. Menzies. Nature, London, vol.169, no.4294, pp. 275-276, Feb. 16, 1952.

TYPE SPECIMENS IN NATURAL HISTORY. C. Hart Merriam. Science, New York, n.s., vol.5, no.123, pp.731-732, May 7, 1897.

(INSECTIVORES AND GALEOPITHECUS-GEOLOGICALLY OLD FORMS.) Insectivoren und Galeopithecus geologisch alte Formen. C. Meyer. Neues Jahrb. Mineral., Stuttgart, vol.2, pp.229-230, 1885.

LIFE HISTORY STUDIES OF ANIMALS. Louis Compton Miall. Smiths. Inst., Annual Rep., 1897, Washington, pp. 483-506, 1898.

MAMMALS AND HOW THEY ARE STUDIED. WARMBLOODED VERTEBRATES, PART 2. Gerrit S. Miller, James W. Gidley. Smiths. Sci. Ser., vol.9, pp.171-389, figs.25, pls. 70-124, Dec. 17, 1931.

(MAMMALS.) Mammifères. Alphonse Milne-Edwards. Paris, pp.32, pl.8, 1890. (France-Marine et de l'instruction publique, Ministeres de la Mission scientifique du Cap Horn, 1882-83; Zoologie, vol.6.)

(RESEARCH ON THE NATURAL HISTORY OF MAMMALS.) Recherches pour servir a l'histoire naturelle des mammiferes. Henri Milne-Edwards. Paris, vol.2, atlas, 1868-1874.

HOOFED MAMMALS OF THE WORLD. Ugo Mochi, T. Donald Carter. Scribner's, New York, pp.14 (not numbered), pls.40, 1953.

DESCENT TO THE UNDERWORLD. Charles E.Mohr. Fauna, Philadelphia, vol.7, no.1, pp.2-10, illus., Mar., 1945.

NATURAL HISTORY READINGS. Book 1. MAMMALS. Book 2. BIRDS. John Monteith. New York and Chicago, Franklin Pub.Co., vols.1-2, illus., 1899.

SAIGA ANTELOPE AND LONG-HAIRED TIGER. William J. Morden. Nat. Hist., vol.30, no.5, pp.538-551, Sep.-Oct., 1930.

(Review by A.H.Howell of) FIELD BOOK OF ANIMALS IN WINTER. Ann Haven Morgan. Jour. Mamm., vol.20, no.4, p. 509, Nov., 1939.

OPEN BOOK OF WILDLIFE. INTRODUCTION TO NATURE STUDY. Richard Morse. Adam & Charles Black, London, pp.240, col.pls.15, half-tone photographs 50, figs., 1941.

NOTES ON THE MARKHORE AND THE CHIMPANZEE. James Murie. Proc.Zool. Soc. London, pp.35, 1866.

HUMOROUS TALES OF THE WOODS. Clyde Newkirk. Boston, Mass., National Sportsman, Inc., pp.46, illus., 1913.

ALL ABOUT ANIMALS, FOR OLD AND YOUNG, POPULAR, INTERESTING AND AMUSING. Geo. Newnes. London, pp.240, illus.

WILD ANIMAL FRIENDS. B. Nicholas. London, Lutterworth, pp.104, 1946.

(GIANTS OF THE BUSH AND FOREST.) Géants de la brouse et de la fôret. Joseph Oberthur. Paris, Durel, pp.172, illus., pls., 1946.

STUDYING MAMMALS AS A HOBBY. Charles M. Oehler. Nat. Hist. Hobbies, Cincinnati Mus. Nat. Hist., Misc. Publ. no.3, pp.23-24, Apr., 1942.

RARITY OF THE DEEP. Robert T. Orr. Pacific Discovery, San Francisco, vol.3, no.6, pp.13-15, illus., Dec., 1950.

(VON BUFFON'S NATURAL HISTORY OF QUADRUPEDS.) Herrn von Bueffon's Naturgeschichte der vierfuessigen Thiere. Bernhard Christian Otto. Bd.19, 1792.

CIRCUS AND ZOO. E. Laurence Palmer. Nature Mag., Washington, D.C., vol.34, no.10, pp.557-564, illus., Dec., 1941.

DESERTED DESERTS? E. Laurence Palmer. Nature Mag., Washington, D.C., vol.34, no.2, pp.85-92, illus., Feb., 1941.

FIELDBOOK OF MAMMALS; UNIT IN A SERIES OF AIDS TO CONSERVATION. E. Laurence Palmer. 1st Ed. New York, Dutton, pp.321, illus., 1957.

ANIMALS WE KNOW. Bertha Morris Parker. Evanston, Ill., New York City, Row, Peterson and Co., pp.35, col.illus., 1944.

MAMMALIA AND ORNITHOLOGY. Titan Ramsey Peale. Philadelphia, C.Sherman, pp.xxv-338, illus., 1848.

HISTORY OF QUADRUPEDS, 3d Ed. Thomas Pennant. London, Printed for B.& J. White, vol.2, pls., 1793.

ANIMAL FACES. R. Marlin Perkins. Foster and Stewart, Buffalo, N.Y., pp.93, illus., 1944.

WHO KNOWS ALL THE ANSWERS? MANY FACTS AWAIT DISCOVERY-PERHAPS YOU WILL FIND THE ANSWERS IN YOUR OWN BACK YARD. George A. Petrides. Audubon Mag., New York, vol.45, no.4, pp.215-221, illus., July-Aug., 1943.

ANIMALS IN ACTION. G.Pickwell. New York, 1940.

(STUDY OF WILD MAMMALS IN THE BELGIAN CONGO IN COMING YEARS.) L'etude des mammifères sauvages au Congo Belge dans les prochaines annees. P.Pirlot. Folia Scientifica Africae Centralis, Bukavu, vol.1, no.4, pp.3-6, Dec., 1955.

WHAT ANIMAL IS IT? Anna Pistorius. Wilcox and Follett Co., Chicago, New York, and Toronto, pp.27, illus., 1947.

MAMMALIA SECTION FROM C.T. REGAN'S "NATURAL HISTORY," R.I.Pocock. London, n.d., vol.8, pp.276, col.pls.8, photographs 350.

ZOOLOGICAL CONTRADICTION. Charles G. Poole. Monthly Bull. Dept. Agric. Calif., vol.18, no.5, pp.316-318, figs.2, May, 1929.

(WORLD OF MAMMALS.) Swiat ssaków. Roman Poplewski. Lvov-Warsaw, Ksiaznica-atlas, pp.303, illus., 1937.

WILD BEASTS; STUDY OF THE CHARACTERS AND HABITS OF THE ELEPHANT, LION, LEOPARD, PANTHER, JAGUAR, TIGER, PUMA, WOLF, AND GRIZZLY BEAR. John Hampden Porter. New York, C. Scribner's Sons, pp.ix-380, pl.8, 1894; 1903.

LETTERS ON SEVERAL ZOOLOGICAL SUBJECTS. R. Ker Porter. Proc. Zool. Soc. London, pt.1, p.114, 1833.

(MAMMALOGICAL NEWS.) Notices Mammalogiques. M. Pucheran. Extrait Revue et Magasin Zool., no.4, pp.37, pl.25, 1856.

WOLVES, EAGLES, AND SEALS. William Putvin. Alaska Sportsman, Ketchikan, vol. 6, no.1, pp.12, 23-25, Jan., 1940.

HIGH-JUMPERS AND GREAT WALKERS. W.P. Pycraft. Illus. London News, vol. 194, no.5206, p.129, figs.3, Jan. 28, 1939.

WILD "TAIL TWISTERS." W.P.Pycraft. Illus. London News, vol.193, no.5185, p. 416, figs.3, Sep. 3, 1938.

NOTES ON THE DERBYAN ELAND, THE AFRICAN ELEPHANT AND THE GORILLA. W. Winwood Reade. Proc. Zool. Soc. London, pt.31, pp.169-173, pl.xxii, 1863.

(ANIMAL KINGDOM.) Regnum animale. H.G.L. Reichenbach. Lipsiae, pt.1, pp. 50, pl.78, 1836.

(DEFINITIVE NATURAL HISTORY OF THE FATHERLAND AND FOREIGN COUNTRIES. THE MAMMALS.) Die vollstaendigste Naturgeschichte des In- und Auslandes. Die Saeugethiere. H.G. Ludwig Reichenbach. Vol. III, 1845; Vol.II, 1846.

LETTER RELATING TO POTAMOCHOERUS PORCUS AND PTERONURA SANDBACHII. J. Reinhardt. Proc. Zool. Soc. London, pp.55-58, 1869.

NATURAL HISTORY OF QUADRUPEDS. James Rennie. New York, Harper & Bros., pp.viii-324, illus., 1840.

REPRINT OF ORD'S ZOOLOGY. Samuel N. Rhoads. Abridged edition, privately printed, pp.291-320 and 1-51, Oct., 1894.

ANIMALS; POPULAR NATURAL HISTORY OF WILD BEASTS. Wallace de Groot Cecil Rice. Chicago, H.S.Stone & Co., pp.xxii-313, pls., 1901.

OF WHALES AND MEN. R.B. Robertson. New York, Alfred A. Knopf, pp.xii-300, 1954.

(SMALL ATLAS OF MAMMALS. I. MONOTREMATA, MARSUPIALIA, EDENTATA, RODENTIA.) Petit atlas des mammifères. Fascicule I. Monotrèmes, marsupiaux, édentes rongeurs. Paul Rode. Editions N. Boubée & Cie., Paris, pp.47, pls.12, 1942.

(SMALL ATLAS OF MAMMALS. IV. INSECTIVORES, PRIMATES.) Petit atlas des mammiferes. Fascicule IV. Insectivores, primates. Paul Rode. Editions N. Boubée & Cie., Paris, pp.81, figs.12, pls.12, 1944.

OUR OLDEST LIVING MAMMAL. Philip S. Rose. Sports Afield, Minneapolis, vol. 117, no.2, pp.24-25, 100-103, illus., Feb., 1947.

MAMMALOGY: NATURAL HISTORY OF MAMMIFEROUS ANIMALS. W.S.W. Ruschenberger. Philadelphia, Turner & Fisher, pp.151, 1842.

SENTINELS OF THE WILD. Archibald Rutledge. Field and Stream, New York, vol.48, no.10, pp.26-27, 85, illus., Feb., 1944.

ANIMAL TREASURE. Ivan T.Sanderson. New York, The Viking Press, pp.325, illus., 1937.

(Review by H.E. Anthony of) ANIMAL TREASURE. Ivan T. Sanderson, New York, The Viking Press, pp.7-325, illus., 1937. Nat. Hist., New York, vol.41, no. 4, pp.305-306, Apr., 1938.

IN REFUTATION OF MR. A. LOVERIDGE ON "ANIMAL TREASURE." Ivan T.Sanderson. Sci. Monthly, Lancaster, vol.50, no.5, pp.448-454, May, 1940.

(Reply to criticisms of) ANIMAL TREASURE. Ivan T. Sanderson. Nature, London, vol. 143, no.3622, pp.563-564, Apr. 1, 1939.

ANIMALS NOBODY KNOWS. Ivan T. Sanderson. New York, The Viking Press, pp.77, illus., 1940.

LITTLE KNOWN MAMMALS. Ivan T.Sanderson. Prepared with the cooperation of the National Audubon Society, Garden City, N.Y., N.Doubleday, pp.56, illus., 1956.

LIVING MAMMALS OF THE WORLD IN COLOR; TREASURY OF REAL LIFE, NATURAL-COLOR PHOTOGRAPHS AND COMPLETE UP-TO-DATE, ACCURATE DESCRIPTION OF 189 MAMMALS. BASED ON LIVING MAMMALS OF THE WORLD. Ivan T. Sanderson. Garden City, N.Y., Hanover House, pp.160, illus., 1958.

SPRING IN THE BURROWS. T.H.Scheffer. Nature Mag., vol.3, pp.289-290, 296, figs.5, May, 1924.

CURIOUS CAT. Jacqueline Schermerhorn. San Diego Zoonooz, vol.17, no.12, pp.3-4, illus., Dec., 1944.

(MONOGRAPHS ON THE MAMMALS.) Monographien der Saeugethiere. Heinrich Rudolf Schinz. Zuerich, pp.53, pls.54, 1848.

(NATURAL HISTORY AND PICTURES OF MAMMALS. DRAWN UP ACCORDING TO THE LATEST SYSTEMS FOR GENERAL USE, AND WITH ATTENTION GIVEN FOR THE INSTRUCTION OF YOUTH.) Naturgeschichte und Abbildungen der Saeugethiere. Nach den neuesten Systemen zum gemeinnuetzigen Gebrauche entworfen, und mit Beruecksichtigung fuer den Unterricht der Jugend. Heinrich Rudolf Schinz. Zuerich, Brodtmanns Lithographischer Kunstanstalt, pp.vi-417, atlas, col.pl., 1824.

LIVING PREHISTORIC ANIMALS. ULTRA-CONSERVATIVES FROM THE AGE OF REPTILES THAT STRUGGLE FOR SURVIVAL IN A CHANGING MODERN WORLD. Erich Maren Schlaikjer. Nat. Hist., New York, vol.39, pp.124-135, illus., Feb., 1937.

(MAMMALS IN ILLUSTRATIONS FROM NATURE AND WITH DESCRIPTIONS.) Saeugethiere in Abbildungen nach der Natur und mit Beschreibungen. Johann Christian Daniel Schreber. Leipzig, T.O. Weigel, pp.810, col.pls.51, 1855.

(NATURAL HISTORY OF THE ANIMAL KINGDOM.) Naturgeschichte des Tierreichs. J.F. Schreiber. Esslingen, vols.1-3, col. pls., 1869.

LORDS OF THE WILD. Samuel Scoville. New York, William Morrow and Co., pp. 246, pls.4, 1928.

NATURAL HISTORY, BIRDS AND MAMMALS. David Seth-Smith. London, Jenkins, pp.198, illus., 1949.

(Review by Edward A. Preble of) GAME ANIMALS AND THE LIVES THEY LIVE. E. T. Seton. Jour. Mamm., vol.12, no.1, pp.83-84, Feb., 1931.

FOR A METHODIC STUDY OF LIFE-HISTORIES OF MAMMALS. E.T. Seton. Jour. Mamm., vol.1, no.2, pp.67-69, Feb., 1920.

LIVES OF GAME ANIMALS. E.T. Seton. New York, Doubleday & Co., Inc., vols.4, illus., 1925-1928.

LIVES OF GAME ANIMALS. (EXCERPTS.) E.T. Seton. Nat. Hist., vol.25, no.6, pp. 583-592, Nov.-Dec., 1925 (Jan., 1926.)

FRIENDS OF THE FOREST, OBSERVATIONS OF WILD ANIMAL LIFE. Frank North Shankland. New York, Saalfield Publishing Co., pp.92, illus., col.pls., 1932.

LIFE HISTORY PROBLEM AND A MEANS FOR ITS SOLUTION. William T. Shaw. Jour. Mamm., vol.6, no.3, pp.157-162, pls.3, Aug., 1925.

(Review by T.Barbour of) WILD BEASTS TODAY. Harold J. Shepstone. Science, n.s., vol.76, no.1978, pp.490-491, Nov. 25, 1932.

ON THE DATES OF THE PARTS, PLATES, AND TEXT OF SCHREBER'S "SAEUGETHIERE" (MAMMALS). C. Davies Sherborn. Proc. Zool. Soc. London, pt.4, pp.587-592, Apr. 1, 1892.

MAMMALOGICAL NOTICES. J.H. Slack. Proc. Acad. Nat. Sci. Phila., pp.1-5, Mar., 1867.

INTRODUCTION TO THE MAMMALIA, CHIEFLY WITH REFERENCE TO THE PRINCIPAL FAMILIES NOT DESCRIBED AT LENGTH IN THE FORMER VOLUMES. Charles Hamilton Smith. Edinburgh, W.H. Lizars, pp.313, col.pls.31, 1842.

MAMMALIA. INTRODUCTION TO MAMMALIA. Charles Hamilton Smith. Edinburgh, W.H. Lizars, pp.313, col.pls.31, 1858. (Reprint of 1842 work.)

ANIMAL TALES FROM THE HILLS. Dorothy E. Snyder. Bull. Massachusetts Audubon Soc. Boston, vol.28, no.4, pp.124-126, illus., May, 1944.

NOTES ON RATTUS RATTUS JALORENSIS AND R. R. ROQUEI, AND ON SOME FRUGIVOROUS BATS. H.J.V.Sody. Treubia, Buitenzorg, vol.17, no.4, pp.403-405, Apr., 1940.

NOCTURNAL ANIMALS. H.N.Southern. Sci. American, New York, vol.193, no.4, pp.88-98, illus., Oct., 1955.

DINGO IS A DOG BUT KOALA IS NOT A BEAR. David G. Stead. Mid-Pacific Mag., vol.49, no.4, pp.270-274, fig.1, Oct.-Dec., 1936.

ANIMAL LIFE IN THE BALANCE OF NATURE. Traby I. Storer. (In) Changes in California's Plants, Animals and Topography (within memory of living men), Commonwealth, San Francisco, pt.2, vol.12, no.19 (Trans.Commonwealth Club of California, vol.30, no.7), pp. 279-290, illus., May 12, 1936.

MAMMALS THAT EAT INSECTS. SHREWS, MOLES, AND BATS. Thaddeus Surber. Conservation Volunteer, St. Paul, vol.9, no.53, pp. 20-24, illus., July-Aug., 1946.

ON THE NATURAL HISTORY AND CLASSIFICATION OF QUADRUPEDS. William Swainson. London, Printed for Longman, Rees, Orme, Brown, Green & Longman, pp.viii-397, illus., 1835.

BASIC IMPORTANCE OF LIFE HISTORY STUDIES. Walter P. Taylor. Jour. Mamm., vol.5, no.1, pp.44-48, Feb., 1924.

OUTLINES FOR STUDIES OF MAMMALIAN LIFE HISTORIES. Walter P. Taylor. Misc. Publ.86, U.S. Dept. Agric., pp.12, Oct., 1930.

SUGGESTIONS FOR FIELD STUDIES OF MAMMALIAN LIFE-HISTORIES. Walter P. Taylor. U.S. Dept. Agric., Dept. Circ., no.59, pp.1-8, Sep., 1919.

BYWAYS TO ADVENTURE. GUIDE TO NATURE HOBBIES. Edwin Way Teale. Dodd, Mead & Co., New York, pp.x-222, illus., 1942.

(MAMMALOGY MONOGRAPHS.) Monographies de mammalogie. Coenraad Jacob Temminck. Paris & Leiden, vol.2, pl., 1827-41.

NOTES ON SOME UNGULATE MAMMALS. Oldfield Thomas. Proc. Zool. Soc. London, pp.384-389, June, 1891.

NOTES ON VARIOUS AMERICAN MAMMALS. Oldfield Thomas. Ann. & Mag. Nat. Hist. (7), vol.2, no.10, pp.318-320, Oct., 1898.

BEARS AND MEN. Frank Thone. Science News Letter, Washington, D.C., vol.44, no.18, p.287, Oct. 30, 1943.

(GENERAL ZOOLOGY, MAN AND MAMMAL.) Allgemeine Zoologie, Mensch und Saeugetheire. Friedrich Tiedemann. Zoologie, Landshut, vol.1, pp.610, 1808.

MAMMALIA. SYLLABUS OF A COURSE OF FIVE LECTURES. Henry William Marett Tims. London, Printed for the London County Council, pp.7, 1912.

HISTORIE OF FOURE-FOOTED BEASTS. Edward Topsell. London, W.Iaggard, pp. 757, illus., pl., 1607.

FRIEND AND FOE FROM FIELD AND FOREST; NATURAL HISTORY OF THE MAMMALIA. Mrs. Grace Townsend. Chicago, Philadelphia, L.P.Miller & Co., pp.549, illus., col.pls.8, 1890.

(MAMMALS.) Mammifères 1892-1893. E.L. Trouessart. L'Annuaire Geolegique Univ., Paris, vol.10, pp.677-729, 1893; vol.5, pp. 915-970, 1888.

(ALPINE ANIMAL LIFE.) Thierleben der Alpenwelt. Dr.Friedrich von Tschudi. Leipzig, pp.xv-590, illus., 1865.

WILD BROTHER. William Lyman Underwood. Boston, Atlantic Monthly Press, 12mo., pp. 1-xi, 1-140, pls.39, 1921.

STRANGE ANIMALS AND THEIR STORIES. (ANIMALS IN ARMOR. LAND OF MARSUPIALS. TOPSYTURVY CREATURES. BEHEMOTHS OF SCRIPTURE. GIANTS WHO TOOK TO THE SEA. CAMELS OF THE ANDES. STRANGEST ANIMAL OF ALL.) Alpheus Hyatt Verrill. Boston, L.C.Page & Co., pp.xiv-235, illus., pl.vi, 1939.

(MAMMALS. ORIGINAL FRENCH EDITION.) Les Mammiferes. Edition francaise originale. Karl Christoph Vogt. Paris, G. Masson, Editeur, pp.xxvii-548, illus., 1884.

NATURAL HISTORY OF ANIMALS (CLASS MAMMALIA-ANIMALS WHICH SUCKLE THEIR YOUNG), IN WORD AND PICTURE. Karl Christoph Vogt. London, Blackie & Son, Ltd., vols.2, illus., pl.xl.

SOME SUGGESTIONS FOR SMALL-MAMMAL STUDIES IN MISSOURI. Douglas E. Wade. Proc. Missouri Acad. Sci., Columbia, vol.7, no.4, whole no.24, p.94, Jan. 25, 1942. (Abstract.)

(MAMMALS IN ILLUSTRATIONS FROM NATURE AND WITH DESCRIPTIONS. A SUMMARY OF THE LATEST DISCOVERIES TREATED IN THE FIELD OF MAMMALOGY.) Saeugethiere in Abbildungen nach der Natur und mit Beschreibungen. Eine Zusammenstellung der Neuesten Entdeckungen auf dem Gebiet der Saeugethierkunde bearbeitet. Johann Andreas Wagner. 1856.

NATURAL HISTORY OF THE MAMMALIA. G.R. Waterhouse, London, H. Bailliere, vols.2, illus., pls.45, 1846-48.

(MAMMALS. INTRODUCTION TO THE ANATOMY AND SYSTEMATICS OF RECENT AND FOSSIL MAMMALIA.) Saugethiere. Einfuehrung in die Anatomie und Systematik der recenten und fossilen Mammalia. Max Wilhelm Carl Weber. Jena, G. Fischer, pp.xi-866, illus., 1904.

(THE MAMMALS.) Die Saeugetiere. Max Wilhelm Carl Weber. Jena, 2nd ed., vol.1, pp.xv-444, Morphology, with H.M.de Burlet, 1927; vol.2, pp.xxiv-898, Systematics, with O.Abel, 1928.

(STRUGGLE FOR EXISTENCE IN THE NORTHERN WILDERNESS.) Kampf ums Dasein in nordischer Wildnis. Stig Wesslen. Naturforscher, vol.13, no.3, pp.88-90, pls. 6, June, 1936.

BOOK OF THE ANIMAL KINGDOM. MAMMALS. William Percival Westell. London, J.M. Dent & Sons, Ltd; New York, E. P. Dutton & Co., pp.xix-379, col.front, pls. (partly col.), 1910.

WARM-BLOODED VERTEBRATES: PART I. BIRDS. Alexander Wetmore. PART II. MAMMALS. Gerrit S. Miller, Jr., James W. Gidley. New York, Smiths. Inst. series, pp.389, illus., pls.124, 1943. (Smiths. Scientific series, vol.9.)

(ZOOLOGICAL OBSERVATIONS.) Zoologische Beobachtungen. Otto Wettstein-Westersheim. Spelaeologisches Jahrbuch, vol.4, pp.66-68, 1923.

OUR ANIMAL FRIENDS OF THE WILD. James W. Whilt. Shenandoah, Ia., World Publishing Co., pp.63, illus., 1927.

CALL OF THE WILDS AND THE FARM. Neal S. Whisenhunt. Published by the author, Jennings, Louisiana, pp.106, illus., 1925.

ON A FOETAL MANATEE AND CETECEAN, WITH REMARKS UPON THE AFFINITIES AND ANCESTRY OF THE SIRENIA. Burt G. Wilder. Amer. Jour. Sci. & Arts, vol.10, pp.10, pl.8, Aug., 1875.

(NATURAL HISTORY CONVERSATIONS.) Unterhaltungen aus der Naturgeschichte. Gottlieb Tobias Wilhelm. Augsburg, in der M. Engelbrechtischen Kunsthandlung, vols. 2, col.pls.64, 1792.

LIVING WORLD. Samuel H. Williams. New York, Macmillan Co., pp.xxii-704, figs. 240 (Mammals, pp.471-535), 1937.

SOME FACTS AND FICTIONS OF ZOOLOGY. Andrew Wilson. Popular Science Monthly, vol.17, pp.96-109, May, 1880.

NATURAL HISTORY OF QUADRUPEDS AND WHALES; BEING THE ARTICLE "MAMMALIA," FROM THE SEVENTH EDITION OF THE ENCYCLOPAEDIA BRITANNICA. James Wilson. Edinburgh, A. and C. Black, pp.192, pls.17, illus., 1837.

HALLMARKS OF MANKIND. Frederic Wood-Jones. Williams & Wilkins Co., Baltimore, pp.86, illus., 1948.

LIFE OF MAMMALS. J.Z. Young. Oxford Univ. Press, New York, pp.xv-820, illus., Jan., 1957.

LIFE OF VERTEBRATES. J.Z. Young. London, Oxford Univ. Press, pp.776, 1950.

(Review by William P. Harris, Jr. of) LIFE OF VERTEBRATES. J.Z. Young. Jour. Mamm., vol.32, no.3, pp.371-372, Aug. 23, 1951.

MICE, MEN, AND ELEPHANTS. BOOK ABOUT THE MAMMALS. Herbert S. Zim. Harcourt, Brace and Co., New York, pp. 215, 1942.

CHEAPEST TRACTOR. A.E.Zischka. Canadian Geogr. Jour., Ottawa, vol.17, no.3, pp.142-145, illus., Sep., 1938.

CAMBRIDGE NATURAL HISTORY. New York, vol.10, illus., maps, 1895-1909.

CITIZENS OF THE JUNGLE. Animal Kingdom, New York, vol.45, no.6, pp.138-141, illus., Nov.-Dec., 1942.

COYOTE-ANTELOPE CHASE. S.Dakota Conserv. Digest, Pierre, vol.17, no.7, p.15, illus., July, 1950.

FROM THE WORLD'S SCRAPBOOK. Illus. London News, vol.211, no.5669, p.670, illus., Dec. 13, 1947.

ITEMS FROM THE WORLD'S SCRAPBOOK. THREE TIGERS BAGGED IN TEN MINUTES IN THE JUNGLE; CIRCUS ELEPHANT ON THE EIFFEL TOWER. Illus. London News, vol.213, no.5700, p.77, illus., July 17, 1948.

(MAMMALOGICAL NOTES.) Notes de mammalogie, no.1. Shanghai, Universite l'Aurore, Musée Heude, illus., pls., maps, 1943.

MAMMALS. Animal Kingdom, New York, vol.47, no.2, pp.29-32, illus., Mar.-Apr., 1944.

NATURAL HISTORY OF QUADRUPEDS, AND CETACEOUS ANIMALS. Bungay, Brightly and Co., vol.1, pp.xxxi-471, pls. 1-69; vol.2, pp.44, pls.69-120, 1811.

PAPERS ON MAMMALOGY. Published in Honor of Wilfred Hudson Osgood. Field Mus. of Nat. Hist., Chicago, Zoological series, vol.27, pp.397, illus., pls.12, Dec. 8, 1941.

(SMALL MAMMAL ATLAS. II. UNGULATES.) Petit atlas des mammiferes. Fascicule II. Ongulés. Editions N.Boubée & Cie., Paris, pp.61, pls.12, figs.18, 1942.

SOME GENERAL NOTES ON NATURAL HISTORY. MAMMALS. Proc. Isle of Wight Nat. Hist. and Archaeol. Soc., Newport, vol.3, pt.5, p.340, June, 1943.

THOSE PECULIAR ANTEATERS. Our Dumb Animals, Norwood, vol.81, no.8, p.9, illus., Aug., 1948.

WHO'S WHO IN THE ZOO; NATURAL HISTORY OF MAMMALS. Prepared by Workers of the WPA Federal Writers' Project in the City of New York. Sponsored by the Guilds' Committee for Federal Writers' Publications, Inc., New York, Halcyon House, pp.211, illus., 1937.

## MAMMALS IN LITERATURE AND FOLKLORE

(NEW POINTS OF VIEW ABOUT BIBLICAL AND TALMUDICAL ZOOLOGY.) Vues nouvelles sur la Zoologie Biblique et Talmudique. I. Aharoni. Revue Études Sémitiques, Paris, pp.32-41, 1938.

ON SOME ANIMALS MENTIONED IN THE BIBLE. I. Aharoni. Osiris, Brugis, vol.5, pp.461-478, 1938.

THE HORN OF THE UNICORN. John Tyler Bonner. Sci. Amer., New York, vol.184, no.3, pp.42-43, illus., Mar., 1951.

ANIMALS OF THE BIBLE. Hal Borland. Frontiers, Philadelphia, vol.6, no.2, pp. 35-39, illus., Dec., 1941.

BURGESS ANIMAL BOOK FOR CHILDREN. Thornton W. Burgess. Boston, Little,Brown, and Co., pp.i-xvii, 1-363, Nov., 1920.

ANIMALS OF THE BIBLE. J. Rodger Darling. Fauna, Philadelphia, vol.8, no.4, pp.114-117, illus., Dec., 1946.

BOOK OF ANIMAL LIFE. Mrs. Alice Mary Dicken. Boston, Little, Brown and Co., pp. xii-315, illus., pls., 1937.

PANGOLIN AND SAMBAR: CURIOUS BELIEF. M.J. Dickins, S.H. Prater, C.McCann. Jour. Bombay Nat. Hist. Soc., vol.40, no.2, p. 322, Sep., 1938.

ARTIFICIAL PRODUCTION OF THE FABULOUS UNICORN. MODERN INTERPRETATION OF AN ANCIENT MYTH. W. Franklin Dove. Sci. Monthly, vol.42, no.5, pp.431-436, figs.4, May, 1936.

HOOFS AND CLAWS; OR, MRS. BURTON'S POLICY. Sidney Dyer. Philadelphia, American Baptist Publication Society, pp.363, illus., pls., 1875

101 ANIMALS OF THE BIBLE. Brayton Eddy. Animal Kingdom, New York, vol.51, no.6, pp.169-173, illus., Nov.-Dec., 1948.

MAMMALS. Charles Lincoln Edwards. Los Angeles, Calif., Hesperian Press, pp.93, illus., 1932.

MAMMALS. Charles William Gustave Eifrig. New York, Chicago, Rand, McNally & Co., pp.xiii-257, illus., col.pl., 1928.

INDIAN MYTHOLOGY AND EXTINCT FOSSIL VERTEBRATES. Loren C. Eiseley. Amer. Anthropol., Menasha, n.s., vol.47, no.2, pp.318-320, Apr.-June, 1945.

MEN, MASTODONS, AND MYTH. Loren C. Eiseley. Sci. Monthly, Lancaster, vol.62, no.6, pp.517-524, June, 1946.

BELIEFS, CUSTOMS, AND FOLK-TALES OF THE BEHRANG-VALLEY SENOI. Leon H.M. Evans. Jour. Fed. Malay States Mus., Singapore, vol.7, pt.4, pp.193-209, June, 1918.

THIS LITTLE PIG WENT TO JAIL. Ronald Flamm. Fauna, Philadelphia, vol.5, no.1, pp.20-21, illus., Mar., 1943.

BOOK OF QUADRUPEDS, FOR YOUTH, EMBRACING DESCRIPTIONS OF THE MOST INTERESTING AND REMARKABLE QUADRUPEDS IN ALL COUNTRIES, WITH PARTICULAR NOTICES OF THOSE OF AMERICA. Samuel Griswold Goodrich. New York, P. Hill, pp.324, illus., 1832.

FIRST BOOK OF TROPICAL MAMMALS. Helen Hoke. New York, F.Watts, pp.62, illus., 1958.

HALF HOURS WITH THE MAMMALS. Charles Frederick Holder. New York, Cincinnati American Book Co., pp.253, illus., 1907.

CHILD'S STORY OF THE ANIMAL WORLD. Edward G. Huey. New York, Reynal and Hitchcock, pp.355, illus., Nov., 1935.

(Review by Francis Petter of) (MAMMOTHS AND MEN FROM CAVERNS.) Mammouths et hommes des cavernes. Dr. Gromier. Mammalia, Paris, vol.15, no.3, p.103, Sep., 1951.

BEASTS OF HERALDRY. John Eric Hill. Nat. Hist., New York, vol.49, no.4, p. 223, illus., Apr., 1942.

(SOME REMAINS OF ANIMAL SACRIFICES IN SICHEM.) Einige Reste tierischer Aufopfer aus Sichem. Max Hilzheimer. Zeitschrift f. Saeugetierk., vol.4, no.2, pp. 125-128, Aug. 6, 1929.

RED BOOK OF ANIMAL STORIES. Andrew Lang. New York, Longmans, Green, and Co., pp.379, illus., pls., 1899.

(LEGEND OF THE UNICORNS.) La legende del'unicorne. Willi Ley. La Terre et la Vie, 8 annee, no.6, pp.177-185, illus., Nov.-Dec., 1938.

UNICORN—MYTH OR MAN-MADE. Willy Ley. Frontiers, Philadelphia, vol.4, no.2, pp.50-54, figs.4, Dec., 1939.

UNICORN AND HIS HORN. Frederic A. Lucas. Nat. Hist., vol.20, pp.532-535, Dec., 1920.

ANIMALS OF THE BIBLE. Roderick Macdonald. Bull. Zool. Soc. Philadelphia, vol. 10, no.4, pp.4, Oct.-Nov., 1935.

PAVILAND CAVE, THE "RED LADY," THE DELUGE, AND WILLIAM BUCKLAND. F.J. North. Ann. Sci., London, vol.5, no. 2, pp.91-128, figs.2, Dec., 1942.

SIBERIAN MAN AND MAMMOTH. E. W. Pfizenmayer. Blackie and Son Ltd., London and Glasgow, pp.xii-256, illus., 1939.

(HORNED ASS, HORNED SWINE, AND HORNED HYENA IN CLASSICAL ANTIQUITY.) Gehoernte Esel, gehoernte Schweine, und gehoernte Hyaenen im klassischen Altertum. Heinrich Prell. Zeitschr. Saugetierk., Berlin, vol.19, nos.1-2, pp.108-116, July 30, 1954.

CONCERNING UNICORNS. W.H.Ridell. Antiquity, Quart. Rev. Archaeol., Gloucester, no.76, pp.194-202, pls.2, Dec., 1945.

ANIMAL TALES; AN ANTHOLOGY OF ANIMAL LITERATURE OF ALL COUNTRIES. Ivan T. Sanderson. New York, Alfred A. Knopf, pp.xviii-512-xiv, illus., 1946.

(WILD ANIMALS ON OLD ORIENTAL SEALS.) Tiere der Wildbahn auf altorientalischen Siegeln. Hartmut Schmoekel. Zool. Garten, Leipzig, vol.23, nos. 1-3, pp.136-145, illus., 1957.

LEGENDS OF ANIMALS. W.J. Schoonmaker. Nat. Humane Rev., Mount Morris, vol.29, no.11, pp.10-11, Nov., 1941.

WILD ANIMALS I HAVE KNOWN, AND 200 DRAWINGS. Ernest Thompson Seton. New York, C. Scribner's Sons, pp.359, illus., pls., 1898.

ABOMINABLE SNOWMAN. William L. Straus, Jr. Science, vol.123, no.3206, pp. 1024-1025, June 8, 1956.

(CONTRIBUTION FROM ANTIQUITY TO MAMMALOGY.) Beitraege aus den Alten zur Saeugethierkunde. F.L. Walther. Neue Ann. Wetteranischen Gesells., vol.1, no.2, pp.247-312, 1819.

FIRST BOOK OF MAMMALS. Margaret Williamson. New York, F. Watts, pp.62, illus., 1957.

(Review by Gerrit S. Miller, Jr. of) SIGN OF THE PROPHET JONAH AND ITS MODERN CONFIRMATIONS. Ambrose John Wilson. Jour. Mamm., Baltimore, vol.9, no.2, pp. 16-161, May 9, 1928.

GOLDEN BOOK OF ANIMALS. New York, Simon and Schuster, pp.96, illus., 1958

NATURALIST'S OWN BOOK; COMPRISING DESCRIPTIONS AND AUTHENTIC ANECDOTES OF QUADRUPEDS; SCIENTIFICALLY ARRANGED ACCORDING TO THE SYSTEM OF CUVIER. Philadelphia, Key & Biddle, pp.xvi, 17-400, illus., 1835.

MANUALS see DICTIONARIES, ENCYCLOPEDIAS, MANUALS

## MARINE AND AQUATIC MAMMALS

GENEALOGICAL HISTORY OF THE MARINE MAMMALS. Othenio Abel. Smiths. Inst., Annual Rep., 1907, Washington, pp.473-496, illus., 1908.

PRESENT STATUS OF THE MARINE MAMMALS. George C.L. Bertram. Jour. Soc. Preserv. Fauna Empire, n.s., part 61, pp. 10-14, illus., Mar., 1950.

(MARINE MAMMALS.) Mamiferos marinos. Angel Cabrera. Espasa-Calpe, S.A., Madrid & Barcelona, pp.94, figs.25, 1929.

DISTRIBUTION OF MARINE MAMMALS. T. Gill. Science, n.s., vol.5, no.129, pp. 955-956, 1897.

MAMMALIAN LIFE IN HIGH LATITUDES. Robert W. Gray. Nature, London, vol.124, no.3119, p.228, Aug. 10, 1929.

ANIMAL PHYLA KNOWN TO CONTAIN POISONOUS MARINE ANIMALS. Bruce W. Halstead. Venoms, Publ. no.44, Amer. Assoc. Adv. Sci., Washington, pp.9-27, 1956.

AQUATIC MAMMALS. THEIR ADAPTATIONS TO LIFE IN THE WATER. A. Brazier Howell. Springfield,Ill., Baltimore, Md., Charles C. Thomas, pp.XII-338, illus. 53, 1930.

(Review by Remington Kellogg of) AQUATIC MAMMALS. THEIR ADAPTATIONS TO LIFE IN THE WATER. A. Brazier Howell. Jour. Mamm., vol.11, no.2, pp.241-242, May, 1930.

FURTHER NOTE ON AQUATIC MAMMALS. A. Brazier Howell. Jour. Mamm., vol.11, no.3, p.432, Aug., 1930.

PROBLEMS RELATED TO MARINE MAMMALS. Remington Kellogg. Bull. Arctic Inst. N. Amer., Montreal, no.1, pp.43-44, Mar., 1946.

SEA OTTER--PAST AND PRESENT. M.F. Murphy. Nature Mag., vol.32, no.8, pp. 425-428, Oct., 1939.

EARLY TERRORS OF THE DEEP. Elsie A. Parry. Nature Mag., Washington, D.C., vol.36, no.9, pp.487-490, 500, Nov., 1943.

ON THE DISTRIBUTION OF MARINE MAMMALIA. P.L. Sclater. Zoologist, London, ser.4, vol.1, no.671, pp.217-228, May 15, 1897; Proc. Zool. Soc. London, pt.2, pp. 349-359, pls.24, Aug.1, 1897.

INFLUENCE OF MAN ON MARINE LIFE. C.M. Yonge. Endeavor, London, vol.6, no.21, pp.3-10, figs.7, Jan., 1947.

## MARKING AND RINGING

MARKING WILD ANIMALS FOR IDENTIFICATION. Frank G. Ashbrook. U.S. Dept.

Agric., Bureau of Biol. Survey, Wildl. Res. and Mgt. Leaflet BS-57, pp.3, fig.1, 1936.

RINGING TECHNIQUE FOR SMALL MAMMALS. Dennis Chitty. Jour. Animal Ecol., London, vol.6, no.1, pp.36-53, figs.5, tbls.10, May, 1937.

TECHNIQUE FOR MARKING MAMMALS. Arthur H. Cook. Jour. Mamm., vol.24, no.1, pp.45-47, fig.1, Feb. 20, 1943.

PLASTIC COLLARS WITH PATTERNS OF REFLECTIVE TAPE FOR MARKING NOCTURNAL MAMMALS. E.H.M.Ealey, G.M. Dunnet. C.S.I.R.O. Wildl. Res., Commonwealth Scientific & Industrial Res. Organization, Melbourne, vol.1, no.1, pp. 59-62, Sep., 1956.

TECHNIQUES FOR CAPTURE AND MARKING OF MAMMALS. Richard H. Manville. Jour. Mamm., vol.30, no.1, pp.27-33, Feb., 1949.

APPARATUS FOR MARKING WILD ANIMALS WITH COLORED DYES. James Moffitt. Jour. Wildl. Mgt., Menasha, vol. 6, no.4, pp.312-318, Oct., 1942.

COLLAR FOR IDENTIFICATION OF BIG GAME. Donald R. Progulske. Jour. Wildl. Mgt., vol.21, no.2, pp.251-252, illus., Apr., 1957.

USES OF MARKING ANIMALS IN ECOLOGICAL STUDIES: MARKING OF MAMMALS; STANDARD METHODS AND NEW DEVELOPMENTS. Richard D. Taber. Ecology, vol.37, no.4, pp.681-685, Oct., 1956.

TWO MARKING DEVICES FOR LARGE LAND MAMMALS. Richard D. Taber, Antoon de Vos, Margaret Altmann. Jour. Wildl. Mgt., vol.20, no.4, pp.464-465, Oct., 1956.

NEW TYPE OF BIRD AND MAMMAL MARKER. R.E. Trippensee. Jour. Wildl. Mgt., Menasha, vol.5, no.1, pp.120-124, illus., Jan., 1941.

MEASUREMENTS see ANATOMY -- WEIGHTS AND MEASUREMENTS

METHODS AND TECHNIQUES see TECHNIQUES AND METHODS

## MIGRATIONS AND MOVEMENTS

PERIODICAL EMIGRATIONS OF MAMMALS. A.W. Anthony. Jour. Mamm., vol.4, no.1, pp.60-61, Feb., 1923.

INDUCED EMIGRATIONS AMONG SMALL MAMMALS. John B. Calhoun, William L. Webb. Science, vol.117, no.3040, pp.358-360, graphs, Apr. 3, 1953.

MIGRATIONS OF MARINE MAMMALS. Robert Clarke. Norsk Hvalfangst-Tidende (Norwegian Whaling Gazette), vol.46, no. 11, pp.609-630, Nov., 1957.

ORIGIN OF THE FAUNA OF THE GREATER ANTILLES, WITH DISCUSSION OF DISPERSAL OF ANIMALS OVER WATER AND THROUGH THE AIR. P.J. Darlington, Jr. Quart. Rev. Biol. vol.13, no.3, pp.274-300, Sep., 1938.

STORY OF MIGRATION. E.A.P. Ennion. Oxford Univ. Press, Toronto, pp.100, illus., 1947.

WANDERING OF ANIMALS. Hans Friedrich Gadow. Cambridge (Eng.) Univ. Press, New York, G.P. Putnam's Sons, pp.vi-150, maps 17, 1913.

MIGRATION OF VERTEBRATE ANIMALS. J. Gray. Endeavour, London, vol.5, no.19, pp.83-89, figs.4, July, 1946.

USE OF A ROAD BY MAMMALS. Albert C. Hawbecker. Jour. Mamm., vol.25, no.2, p.196, May 26, 1945.

ARTIFACT TRANSPORT BY MIGRATORY ANIMALS AND OTHER MEANS. Robert F. Heizer. Amer. Antiquity, Menasha, vol.9, no.4, pp.395-400, fig.32, Apr., 1944.

(MIGRATIONS OF MAMMALS.) Wanderungen der Saeugetiere. Max Hilzheimer. Ergebnisse der Biol., vol.5, pp.219-289, 1929.

SURFACE WANDERINGS OF FOSSORIAL MAMMALS. A. Brazier Howell. Jour. Mamm., vol.3, no.1, pp.19-22, Feb. 8, 1922.

MAMMALIAN INVASION VIA THE HIGHWAY. Laurence M. Huey. Jour. Mamm., vol.22, no.4, pp.383-385, Nov. 14, 1941.

(CONSIDERATIONS ON THE MIGRATION OF THE WILD MAMMALS.) Considérations sur les migrations des Mammifères Sauvages. A. Jeannin. Mammalia, Paris, vol.9, nos.3-4, pp.69-89, Sep.-Dec., 1945.

(MIGRATIONS OF AMERICAN AND AFRICAN MAMMALS ACROSS THE ATLANTIC REGIONS DURING THE NEOCENE.) Les migrations des mammifères Americaines et Africains a travers les regions Atlantiques pendant les temps Neogenes. L. Joleaud. Revue generale des Science, Paris, vol.30, pp.704-713, figs. (maps) 1-9, Dec. 30, 1919.

(Review by G.S.Miller of) (MIGRATIONS OF AMERICAN AND AFRICAN MAMMALS ACROSS THE ATLANTIC REGIONS DURING THE NEOCENE.) Les migrations des mammiferes Américains et Africains a travers les regions Atlantiques pendant les temps Neogenes. L. Joleaud. Jour. Mamm., vol.1, no.4, pp.190-191, May, 1920.

SEA-ICE AND MIGRATIONS OF SOME MAMMALS. A.A. Kirpitchinkov. Zool. Jour., Moscow, vol.17, no.2, pp.273-279, 1938. (In Russian, with English summary.)

DISPERSAL OF LAND ANIMALS. W.D. Matthew. Scientia, Bologna (3), vol.48, pp.33-42, July, 1930.

MIGRATION OF MAMMALS. L. Harrison Matthews. Discovery, vol.15, no.5, pp. 202-206, figs.4, May, 1954; Ann. Rept. Smiths. Inst., Washington, 1954, publ. 4199, pp.277-284, illus., 1955.

STANDARD AND ADAPTIVE SPECIALIZATION IN RELATION TO MIGRATION AND DISTRIBUTION. John T. Nichols. Canadian Field-Nat., vol.40, pp.169-171, Dec. 24, 1926.

SOURCE OF ANIMALS MOVING INTO A DEPOPULATED AREA. Lucille F. Stickel. Jour. Mamm., vol.27, no.4, pp.301-307, figs.2, Nov. 25, 1946.

ANIMAL MIGRATION--PERIODIC-RESPONSE THEORY. Angus M. Woodbury. Auk, Lancaster, vol.58, no.4, pp.463-505, Oct., 1941.

NOTES OF A MID-WINTER WANDERER IN YOSEMITE VALLEY. George H. Wright. Yosemite Nature Notes, vol.8, pp.4-5, Jan., 1929.

## MORTALITY

SOME AUTOPSY FINDINGS IN FUR ANIMALS. W.H. Armstrong. Amer. Fur Breeder, Duluth, vol.13, no.7, pp.28-30, Jan., 1941.

TOLL OF ANIMAL LIFE EXACTED BY MODERN CIVILIZATION. C.M. Beadnell. Proc. Zool. Soc. London, vol.107, ser.A., Gen. and Exper., pt.2, pp.173-182, tbls. 2, July, 1937.

PERIODIC DIE-OFF IN CERTAIN HERBIVOROUS MAMMALS AND BIRDS. F. W. Braestrup. Science, Lancaster, n.s., vol. 92, no.2390, pp.354-355, Oct. 18, 1940.

PRENATAL MORTALITY IN MAMMALS. F.W. Rogers Brambell. Biol. Rev., London, vol.23, no.4, pp.370-407, Oct., 1948.

PRENATAL MORTALITY. F. W. Rogers Brambell, Ivor H. Mills. Nature, London, vol.153, no.3888, p.558, May 6, 1944.

MORTALITY OF WILDLIFE ON A TEXAS HIGHWAY. William B. Davis. Jour. Wildl. Mgt., Menasha, vol.4, no.1, pp.90-91, tbl.1, Jan., 1940.

PROBLEM OF WILDLIFE DESTRUCTION BY AUTOMOBILE TRAFFIC. L.M. Dickerson. Jour. Wildl. Mgt., Menasha, vol.3, no.2, pp.104-116, Apr., 1939.

QUESTION OF WILDLIFE DESTRUCTION BY THE AUTOMOBILE. W.A. Dreyer. Science, vol.82, no.2132, pp.439-440, Nov. 8, 1935.

AUTOPSIES REVEAL CAUSES OF DEATH AMONG ZOO ANIMALS. Dorothy Foss. Chicago Nat. Hist. Mus. Bull., vol.18, no.3, p.4, Mar., 1947.

WILDLIFE KILL ON HIGHWAYS OF STATE INCREASES. Larry R. Gale. Kentucky Happy Hunting Ground, Frankfort, vol.6, no.3, pp.5, 7, May, 1950.

FOREST FIRES ARE KILLING OUR GAME. Arthur Grahame. Pennsylvania Game News, Harrisburg, vol.11, no.1, pp.11-13, Apr., 1940.

REPORT ON DEATHS OCCURRING IN THE SOCIETY'S GARDENS DURING THE YEAR 1932. A.E. Hamerton. Proc. Zool. Soc. London for 1933, pt.2, pp.451-482, pls.3, June, 1933.

REPORT ON THE DEATHS OCCURRING IN THE SOCIETY'S GARDENS DURING THE YEAR 1936. A.E. Hamerton. Proc. Zool. Soc. London for 1937, ser.B. vol.107, pt. 3, pp.443-474, pls.1-3, Sep., 1937.

REVIEW OF MORTALITY RATES AND REPORT ON THE DEATHS OCCURRING IN THE SOCIETY'S GARDENS DURING THE YEAR 1938. A.E. Hamerton. Proc. Zool. Soc. London, vol.109, ser.B, pts.3-4, pp.281-327, Dec., 1939.

REPORT ON DEATHS OCCURRING IN THE SOCIETY'S GARDENS DURING THE YEAR 1941. A.E. Hamerton. Proc. Zool. Soc. London, vol.112, ser.B, pts.3-4, pp.120-136, Feb., 1943.

REPORT ON THE DEATHS OCCURRING IN THE SOCIETY'S GARDENS DURING 1943. A.E. Hamerton. Proc. Zool. Soc. London, vol.114, pt.3, pp.307-318, Dec., 1944.

REPORT ON THE DEATHS OCCURRING IN THE SOCIETY'S GARDENS DURING THE YEAR 1944. A.E. Hamerton. Proc. Zool. Soc. London, vol.115, pts.3-4, pp.371-384, Feb., 1946.

HIGHWAY MORTALITY OF WILDLIFE IN SOUTHERN MICHIGAN. Arnold O. Haugen. Jour. Mamm., vol.25, no.2, pp.177-184, May 25, 1944.

KILLING OF ANIMALS UPON HIGHWAYS. Max Henrici. Cardinal, Sewickley, vol.5, no.8, p.196, July, 1942.

BIRDS AND ANIMALS KILLED BY FOREST FIRES. Jack Horton. Murrelet, Seattle, vol. 11, no.1, p.22, Jan., 1930.

DESTRUCTION OF WILD LIFE IN THE MATILJA FIRE. W.I. Hutchinson. California Fish and Game, vol.19, no.2, pp. 126-128, figs.45-46, Apr., 1933.

COMPARATIVE STUDY OF THE BIRTH MORTALITY IN THE ALBINO RAT AND IN MAN. Helen Dean King. Anat. Record, vol. 20, pp.321-354, Mar. 20, 1921.

(Review by Hartley H.T. Jackson of) COMPARATIVE STUDY OF THE BIRTH MORTALITY IN THE ALBINO RAT AND IN MAN. Helen Dean King. Jour. Mamm., vol.2, no.4, p. 242, Nov., 1921.

REPORT OF THE DEATHS WHICH OCCURRED IN THE SOCIETY'S GARDENS DURING 1921. N.S. Lucas. Proc. Zool. Soc. London, 1922, pp.281-283, June, 1922.

HIGHWAY MORTALITY IN NORTHERN MICHIGAN. Richard H. Manville. Jour. Mamm., vol.30, no.3, pp.311-312, Aug. 17, 1949.

DEADLY EFFECT OF FOREST FIRES ON FUR-BEARERS. David C. Mills. Parks and Recreation, vol.7, no.6, pp.636-638, July-Aug., 1924.

ANIMAL MORTALITY ON THREE MILES OF YORKSHIRE ROADS. W. Pickles. Jour. Anim. Ecol., London, vol.11, no.1, pp. 37-43, May, 1942.

REPORT ON THE DEATHS OCCURRRING IN THE SOCIETY'S GARDENS DURING THE YEAR 1925. H. Harold Scott. Proc. Zool. Soc. London, 1926, pp.231-244, Apr. 29, 1926.

REPORT ON THE DEATHS OCCURRING IN THE SOCIETY'S GARDENS DURING THE YEAR 1926. H. Harold Scott. Proc. Zool. Soc. London, 1927, pt.1, pp.173-198, Apr. 6, 1927.

REPORT OF DEATHS OCCURRING IN THE SOCIETY'S GARDENS DURING THE YEAR 1927. H. Harold Scott. Proc. Zool. Soc. London, 1928, pt.1, pp.81-119, Apr., 1928.

WILDLIFE MORTALITY ON IOWA HIGHWAYS. Thomas G. Scott. Amer. Midland Nat., Notre Dame, vol.20, no.3, pp.527-539, Nov., 1938.

WILD LIFE AND THE MOTOR CAR. Ernest Thompson Seton. Jour. Mamm., vol.2, no. 4, p.240, Nov., 1921.

NEW FACTOR IN THE DESTRUCTION OF MAMMALS. A.R. Shadle. Zeitschr. f. Saeugetierk., Berlin, vol.6, no.2, pp.70-77, Dec. 15, 1931.

POST-MORTEM EXAMINATIONS OF WILD BIRDS AND MAMMALS. J.E. Shillinger, William Rush. U.S. Dept. Agric., Miscel. Publ. no.270, pp.15, figs.6, May, 1937.

NOTES ON MAMMAL MORTALITY ON HIGHWAYS. James M. Sprague. Jour. Mamm., Baltimore, vol.20, no.1, pp. 110-111, Feb. 14, 1939.

FOREST FIRES DESTROY GAME. Charles G. Stivers. California Fish and Game, vol. 6, no.1, pp.36-37, Jan., 1920.

AUTOMOBILES AND ANIMAL MORTALITY. Dayton Stoner. Science, n.s., vol.69, pp. 670-671, June 28, 1929.

HIGHWAY MORTALITY AMONG MAMMALS. Dayton Stoner. Science, vol.81, no.2104, pp. 401-402, Apr. 26, 1935.

TOLL OF THE AUTOMOBILE. Dayton Stoner. Science, n.s., vol.61, pp.56-57, Jan. 16, 1925.

WILDLIFE CASUALTIES ON THE HIGHWAYS. Dayton Stoner. Wilson Bull., vol. 48, no.4, pp.276-283, Dec., 1936.

(REPORT ON THE MORTALITY AND NATALITY REGISTERED AT THE BOIS DE VINCENNES ZOOLOGICAL PARK IN 1945.) Rapport sur la mortalité et la natalité enregistrées au Parc Zoologique de Bois de Vincennes en 1945. Ach. Urbain, J. Nouvel, P. Bullier. Bull. Mus. Nat. Hist. Nat., Paris, ser.2, vol.18, no.2, pp.146-157, Feb., 1946.

(REPORT ON THE MORTALITY AND NATALITY REGISTERED AT THE BOIS DE VINCENNES ZOOLOGICAL PARK IN 1948.) Rapport sur la mortalite et la natalité enregistreés au Parc Zoologique du Bois de Vincennes pendant l'année 1948. Ach. Urbain, J. Nouvel, P. Bullier, J. Rinjard. Bull. Mus. Nat. Hist. Nat., Paris, ser.2, vol.21, no. 2, pp.178-193, Mar., 1949.

(REPORT ON THE MORTALITY AND NATALITY REGISTERED AT THE BOIS DE VINCENNES ZOOLOGICAL PARK DURING THE YEAR 1950.) Rapport sur la mortalité et la natalité enregistrees au Parc Zoologique du Bois de Vincennes pendant l'année 1950. Ach. Urbain, J. Nouvel, P. Bullier, J. Rinjard. Bull. Mus. Nat. Hist. Nat., Paris, ser.2, vol.23, no.2, pp.157-172, Mar., 1951.

CASUALTIES AMONG ANIMALS ON MOUNTAIN ROADS. Edward R. Warren. Science, n.s., vol.83, no.2140, p.14, Jan. 3, 1936.

HIGHWAY TOLL OF WILDLIFE. Virginia Widl., Richmond, vol.6, no.1, p.17, Fall-Winter, 1942.

PASSING OF TWO ZOO FAVORITES. Fauna, Philadelphia, vol.5, no.2, pp.60-61, illus., June, 1943.

## MUSEUMS

MUSEUM WORK IN CALIFORNIA. Clinton G. Abbott. Nature Mag., vol.12, pp.244, 269, illus., Oct., 1928.

DEPARTMENT OF MAMMALS, AMERICAN MUSEUM. H.E. Anthony. Nat. Hist., vol. 22, pp.532-542, figs.9, Dec., 1922.

SUPPLY AND DEMAND. G. Arnold. South African Jour. Nat. Hist., vol.5, pp.9-11, Dec., 1925.

REPORTS OF PROGRESS OF THE NEBRASKA STATE MUSEUM. Erwin H. Barbour. Bull. Nebraska State Mus., Lincoln, vol.2, no.1, pp.1-16, figs.4, Dec., 1938.

("GIOCOMO DORIA" CIVIC MUSEUM OF NATURAL HISTORY IN GENOA.) Il Museo Civico di Storia Naturale "Giocomo Doria" in Genova. Oscar de Beaux. Atti. Soc. Sci. e Lett. Genova, vol.5, fasc.3, pp.1-4, 1940.

(REPORT ON THE "ACTIVITY" OF THE G. DORIA CIVIC MUSEUM OF NATURAL HISTORY DURING THE YEAR 1936.) Relazione sull 'attivita' del Museo Civico di Storia Naturale G. Doria, durante l'anno 1936. Oscar de Beaux. Annali del Museo Civico Naturale di Genova, vol.59, pp.28-50, July, 1937.

(NATURAL SCIENCES INSTITUTE OF HIS MAJESTY, THE KING OF BULGARIA.) Naturwissenschaftlichen Institute seiner Majestaet des Koenigs der Bulgaren. Iw Buresch. Mitteilungen Koenigl. Naturwissenschaft Inst. in Sofia, Bulgarien, vol. 1, pp.1-16, illus., 1928.

DEVELOPMENT OF THE MODERN MUSEUM IDEA. E.C. Chubb. South African Jour. Nat. Hist., vol.5, pp.11-19, Dec., 1925.

PROGRAMME OF FIELD WORK OF NATIONAL MUSEUM OF CANADA, 1927. W.H. Collins. Canadian Field-Nat., vol. 41, no.6, pp.133-135, Sep., 1927.

MUSEUMS THAT PHOTOGRAPH NATURE. J.D. Figgins. Municipal Facts, Denver, vol.4, nos.4-5, pp.9-13, Apr.-May, 1921.

MUSEUMS AND THEIR EDUCATIONAL VALUE. F.W. Fitzsimons. S. African Jour. Nat. Hist., vol.5, pp.20-22, Dec., 1925.

HISTORY AND DESCRIPTION OF THE ROYAL MUSEUM OF NATURAL HISTORY (PARIS). Joseph Philippe Francois. L.T. Cellott, Paris, pp.237-609, 1823.

MUSEUM CONSCIENCE. Joseph Grinnell. Museum Work, vol.4, pp.62-63, Mar., 1922.

(HISTORY OF THE EXECUTIVE BOARD OF BIOLOGIC STUDIES.) Historia de la Direccion de Estudiós Biológicos. A. L. Herrera. Bol. Dir. Estud. Biol., vol.3, no.3, pp.53-63, May, 1926.

(NATIONAL MUSEUM OF NATURAL HISTORY. ITS HISTORY, ITS PRESENT STATE.) Le Muséum National d'Histoire naturelle. Son histoire-son état actuel. Pt.1, Historique Géneral. Paul Lemoine. Archiv. Mus. Nat. d'Hist. Nat., Paris, ser.6, vol.12, pp.3-79, figs.18, June, 1935.

MUSEUM METHODS. Wm. Libbey. Fourth Ann. Rpt. E.M. Museum of Geology and Archaeology, pp.24, June, 1885.

NOTES ON THE SCIENTIFIC MUSEUMS OF EUROPE. W.D. Matthew. Nat. Hist., New York, vol.21, no.2, pp.185-190, Mar.-Apr., 1921.

MAMMALOGY AND THE SMITHSONIAN INSTITUTION. Gerrit Smith Miller. Smiths. Inst., Ann. Rept., 1928, Washington, pp. 391-411, pl.3, 1929.

(MUSEUM OF NATURAL HISTORY OF PARIS: CLASSIFICATION OF MAMMALS.) Museum d'Histoire Naturelle de Paris: La classification des mammiferes. Alphonse Milne-Edwards. Nat. Hist., vol.71, 1872.

(REPORT CONCERNING THE ROYAL MUSEUM OF NATURAL HISTORY AT LEIDEN (1 SEP. 1927 - 1 SEP. 1928).) Verslag omtrent 's Rijks Museum van Natuurlijke Historie te Leiden (1 Sep. 1927 - 1 Sep. 1928). E. D. van Oort. Leiden, 1928.

(MARINE MUSEUM OF BIARRITZ.) Le Musée de la mer de Biarritz. Lucien Perruche. La Nature, Paris, no.3045, pp.167-171, figs.10, Mar. 15, 1939.

MODERN MUSEUM METHODS. S.H. Prater. Jour. Bombay Nat. Hist. Soc., vol.33, no. 1, pp.149-162, pls.7, Sep. 30, 1928.

NOTES ON A VISIT TO CERTAIN MUSEUMS IN GREAT BRITAIN. WITH SPECIAL RELATION TO THE PRINCE OF WALES' MUSEUM, BOMBAY. S.H. Prater. Jour. Bombay Nat. Hist. Soc., vol.29, pp.456-465, pl.1, Aug. 25, 1923.

PRINCIPLES AND EXTENT OF THE EDUCATIONAL SERVICE RENDERED TO THE SCHOOLS BY MUSEUMS IN AMERICA. S.H. Prater. Jour. Bombay Nat. Hist. Soc., vol. 32, pp.169-182, pls.4, Aug. 1, 1927.

DOCUMENTS RELATIVE TO ITS ORIGIN AND HISTORY. William Jones Rhees. Smithsonian Institution, vol.1, 1835-1887, vol.2, 1887-1899.

UNIVERSITY MUSEUM OF ZOOLOGY AND CULTURAL PROGRESS. A. Richards. Chronicles of Oklahoma, Oklahoma City, vol.20, no.3, pp.265-272, Sep., 1942.

MUSEUMS, HIGHER VERTEBRATE ZOOLOGY AND THEIR RELATIONSHIP TO HUMAN AFFAIRS. Austin Roberts. Carnegie Visitors' reports, Pretoria, pp.68, 1935.

DEVELOPMENT OF MUSEUM TAXIDERMY. John Rowley. Part I. Museum Graphic (Los Angeles), vol.1, no.4, pp.121-134, illus., Mar., 1927; part 2. Museum Graphic, vol.1, no.5, pp.193-206, illus., May, 1927.

PROPOSED AFRICAN MAMMAL HALL FOR LOS ANGELES MUSEUM. John Rowley. Museum Graphic (Los Angeles Museum), vol.1, no.2, pp.43-50, illus., Nov., 1926.

SYSTEMATIC ZOOLOGY IN MUSEUMS. Alexander G. Ruthven. Univ. Bull., Univ. Michigan, vol.24, no.14, pp.30-35, Sep. 30, 1922.

ARMY MEDICAL MUSEUMS. R.W. Shufeldt. Med. Record, New York, vol.92, no.16, whole no.2450, pp.663-665, figs.5, Oct. 20, 1917.

CASE HISTORY OF A SCIENTIFIC NEWS STORY. George Gaylord Simpson. Science, Lancaster, n.s., vol.92, no.2381, pp.148-150, Aug. 16, 1940.

FIRST NATURAL HISTORY MUSEUM IN AMERICA. George Gaylord Simpson. Science, Lancaster, n.s., vol.96, no. 2490, pp.261-263, Sep. 18, 1942.

EUROPEAN MUSEUMS. Huron H. Smith. Milwaukee Public Mus., Yearbook, vol.5, 1925, pp.135-157, illus., Mar. 10, 1927.

(OUR ZOOLOGICAL MUSEUM.) Ons Zoologische Museum. H.J.V. Sody. Nederlandsche-Indische Jager, Buitenzorg, p.1, Nov., 1939.

REPORT OF THE REPRESENTATIVE OF THE SMITHSONIAN INSTITUTION AND NATIONAL MUSEUM. F.W. True. Report (of Board of Management) on the United States Government Exhibit at the Tennessee Centennial Exposition, Nashville, pp. 99-121, pls.27-34, 1897.

REPORT ON THE EXHIBIT OF THE UNITED STATES NATIONAL MUSEUM AT THE PAN-AMERICAN EXPOSITION, BUFFALO, NEW YORK, 1901. F.W. True, W.H. Holmes, G.P. Merrill. Report U.S. Nat. Mus., 1901, pp.177-231, pls.1-72, 1903.

REPORT ON THE TENNESSEE CENTENNIAL EXPOSITION, NASHVILLE, TENN. 1897. F.W. True. Appendix 8, Ann. Rept. Board of Regents Smiths. Inst. for the year ending June 30, 1898, pp.90-100, 1900.

EDINBURGH CONFERENCE, 1901. THE PUBLIC MUSEUMS IN EDINBURGH. William Turner. The Museums Jour., London, vol. 1, pp.7-25, 1902.

MARVELS IN OUR MUSEUMS: NATURE IS FULL OF SURPRISES. Martha Weinman. Collier's, Springfield, pp.62-67, illus., June 24, 1955.

EXPLORING FIELD MUSEUM. Field Mus. Nat. Hist., Chicago, pp.88 (not numbered), illus., 1942.

HALL OF NORTH AMERICAN MAMMALS OF THE AMERICAN MUSEUM OF NATURAL

HISTORY. Science, Lancaster, n.s., vol. 95, no.2466, p.348, Apr. 3, 1942.

MUSEUMS - CATALOGS, COLLECTIONS, GUIDES

(PALEOBIOLOGICAL COLLECTIONS OF THE PALEONTOLOGICAL AND PALEOBIOLOGICAL INSTITUTE OF THE UNIVERSITY OF VIENNA.) Palaeobiologische Sammlungen des Palaeontologischen und Palaeobiologischen Institutes der Universitaet Wien. Othenio Abel. Palaeobiologica, vol.2, nos.4-5, pp.270-282, 1929.

TYPE SPECIMENS OF MAMMALS IN THE MUSEUM OF COMPARATIVE ZOÖLOGY. Glover M. Allen. Bull. Mus. Comp.Zool. at Harvard College, vol.71, no.4, pp.231-289, Jan., 1931.

VISITORS' GUIDE TO THE COLLECTION OF MAMMALS IN THE AMERICAN MUSEUM OF NATURAL HISTORY, NEW YORK CITY. J.A. Allen. New York, pp.89, 1892.

GLIMPSES INTO THE HALL OF OCEAN LIFE. H.E. Anthony. Natural Hist., New York, vol.33, no.4, pp.365-380, figs., July-Aug., 1933.

GRAND TOUR OF NORTH AMERICA. H.E. Anthony. Nat. Hist., New York, vol.49, no. 4, pp.189-205, illus., Apr., 1942. (American Museum Nat.History's new Hall of North American Mammals.)

NEW HALL OF NORTH AMERICAN MAMMALS BRINGS THE WILDLIFE OF OUR CONTINENT TO NEW YORK CITY. H.E. Anthony. New York, pp.16, illus., 1942. (American Museum of Nat. Hist., Guide Leaflet series no.111.)

SOUTHERN ASIA IN THE AMERICAN MUSEUM. H.E. Anthony. Nat. Hist., vol.30, no.6, pp.577-592, illus., Nov.-Dec., 1930.

SOME NOTEWORTHY ACCESSIONS TO THE NATIONAL MUSEUM MAMMAL COLLECTION. Alexander William Francis Banfield. Ottawa, pp.2, 1960.(Canada, Nat. Museum, Ottawa, Nat. Hist. papers, no.6.)

BRITISH MUSEUM (NATURAL HISTORY). GUIDE TO THE EXHIBITION GALLERIES OF GEOLOGY AND PALEONTOLOGY. F.A. Bather. London, British Museum, pp.64, 1923.

CATALOGUE OF THE GEOLOGICAL MUSEUM. VERTEBRATA. MAMMALIA. RHINOCERATIDAE. GENUS EPIACERATHERIUM ABEL. E.Beliajeva. Trudy Geologischeskogo Muzeia Akademii Nauk SSSR (Tran. Mus. Geol. Acad. Sci. USSR), vol. 6, pp.179-193, 1930.

CATALOGUE OF THE MAMMALIA IN THE MUSEUM, ASIATIC SOCIETY. E. Blyth. Calcutta, vol.8, pp.200, 1863.

CATALOGUE OF THE ANATOMICAL & ZOOLOGICAL MUSEUM OF JOSHUA BROOKES.. WHICH WILL BE SOLD AT AUCTION ... ON MONDAY, THE 14th DAY OF JULY, 1828. J. Brookes. London, pp.76, 1828.

(TYPE CONCEPT IN ZOOLOGY, AND THE TYPES OF MAMMALS IN THE MUSEUM OF NATURAL SCIENCES.) El concepto de tipo en Zoologia y los tipos de mamiferos del Museo de Ciencias Naturales. Angel Cabrera. Trabajos Mus. Cienc.Nat., Madrid, no.3, pp.1-32, 1912.

CATALOGUE OF THE TYPE AND FIGURED SPECIMENS OF VERTEBRATE FOSSILS IN THE MUSEUM OF PALEONTOLOGY, UNIVERSITY OF MICHIGAN. E.C.Case. Contrib. Mus. Paleontol. Univ. Michigan, Ann Arbor, vol.6, no.10, pp.319-336, Apr. 15, 1947. (Fossil mammals, pp.334-335.)

(MAMMALS FROM THE NATURAL HISTORY MUSEUM OF LONG-JUMEAU.) Les pièces mammalogiques de musee d'histoire naturelle de Longjumeau. F. Cathelin. Mammalia, Paris, vol.1, no.3, pp.117-121, Mar., 1937.

FOSSIL MAMMALS AT THE COLORADO MUSEUM OF NATURAL HISTORY.T.D. A.Cockerell. Sci. Monthly, vol.17, pp. 271-278, figs.7, Sep., 1923.

FOSSIL MAMMALS FROM BURMA IN THE AMERICAN MUSEUM OF NATURAL HISTORY. Edwin H. Colbert. Bull. Amer.Mus. Nat. Hist., vol.74, art.6, pp.255-430, figs.64, tbls., Oct. 14, 1938.

SOME FOSSIL MAMMALS IN THE SOUTH AFRICAN MUSEUM COLLECTION. H.B. S. Cooke. Ann. South African Mus., vol. 42, pt.3, pp.161-168, illus., Jan., 1955.

NOTES ON SOME MAMMALS IN THE BRITISH COLUMBIA PROVINCIAL MUSEUM WITH A LIST OF THE TYPE SPECIMENS OF NORTH AMERICAN RECENT MAMMALS IN THE MUSEUM. Ian McTaggart Cowan. Canadian Field-Nat., vol.50, no.9, pp.145-148, Dec. 3, 1936.

CATALOGUE OF THE SELOUS COLLECTION OF BIG GAME IN THE BRITISH MUSEUM (NATURAL HISTORY). J.G. Dollman. London, British Museum, pp. i-vii, 1-112, portrait, 1921.

SOME RECORD AND OTHER FINE UNGULATE HEADS IN THE MUSEUM COLLECTION. Guy Dollman. Nat.Hist. Mag., London, vol.2, no.12, pp.136-142, pls.4, Oct., 1929.

(MOUNTED SPECIMENS OF EXTINCT MAMMALS IN THE COLLECTIONS OF THE MUSEUM.) Notice sur les spécimens naturalisés de mamiféres eteints existant dans les collections du Museum. Jean Dorst. Bull. Mus. Nat. Hist. Nat., Paris, ser.2, vol.24, no.1, pp.63-78, 1952.

IN TRUST FOR THE FUTURE. MUSEUM RESEARCH COLLECTION, WHAT AND WHY? J. Kenneth Doutt. Pennsylvania Game News, Harrisburg, vol.17, no.1, pp.8-9, 27, illus., Apr., 1946.

LIST OF TYPES OF MAMMALS IN THE COLLECTION OF THE CARNEGIE MUSEUM ON APRIL 2, 1934. J. Kenneth Doutt. Ann. Carnegie Mus., vol.22, nos.3-4, pp.317-321, Apr. 2, 1934.

MAMMAL COLLECTIONS OF NORTH AMERICA. J.Kenneth Doutt, A.Brazier Howell, W.B. Davis. Jour. Mamm., vol. 26, no.3, pp.231-272, Aug., 1945.

HISTORY OF ZOOLOGY AT THE UNIVERSITY OF CALIFORNIA, BERKELEY. Richard M. Eakin. Bios, Mt.Vernon, Iowa, vol.27, no.2, pp.67-92, illus., May, 1956.

CATALOGUE OF THE COLLECTION OF MAMMALS IN THE FIELD COLUMBIAN MUSEUM. D.G. Elliott. Field Columbian Mus., publ. no.115, Zool. ser., vol.8, pp.694, figs.92, 1907.

ON SUNDRY COLLECTIONS OF MAMMALS. D.G. Elliot. Chicago, pp.67-82, pl.vi-xiii, 1896. (Field Columbian Mus., Publication 11, Zoological series, vol.1, no.3.)

AMERICAN MUSEUM OF NATURAL HISTORY, NEW YORK. VISITORS' GUIDE TO THE COLLECTION OF MAMMALS IN THE AMERICAN MUSEUM OF NATURAL HISTORY. L.S. Forster. New York, printed for the Museum, pp.52, illus., 1885.

(CATALOG OF MAMMALS OF THE NATIONAL MUSEUM OF NATURAL HISTORY.) Catalogue des mammiféres du Museum National d'Histoire Naturelle. Etienne Geoffroy St.Hilaire. Paris, pp. 272, 1803.

(SYSTEMATIC CATALOG OF THE MAMMAL, BIRD, AND ANNEXED COLLECTIONS.) Catalogue methodique de la collection des mammiféres, de la collection des oiseaux et des collections annexes. Isidore Geoffroy St.Hilaire. Paris, Gide et Baudry, pp.96, 1851.

BIRD AND MAMMAL TYPE SPECIMENS FORMERLY IN THE RAFFLES MUSEUM COLLECTIONS. C.A. Gibson-Hill. Bull. Raffles Mus., Singapore, no.19, pp.133-198, Jan., 1949.

MAMMAL TYPE SPECIMENS FORMERLY IN THE RAFFLES MUSEUM SINGAPORE. C.A. Gibson-Hill. Jour. Mamm., vol.29, no.1, pp.66-67, Feb. 13, 1948.

CATALOGUE OF COLLECTIONS TO ILLUSTRATE THE ANIMAL RESOURCES AND THE FISHERIES OF U. S. G.Brown Goode. Bull. U.S. Nat. Mus., no.14, pp.351, 1879.

CATALOGUE OF TYPE SPECIMENS OF RECENT MAMMALS IN THE AMERICAN MUSEUM OF NATURAL HISTORY.George G. Goodwin. Bull. Amer. Mus. Nat.Hist., New York, vol.102, art.3, pp.207-412, Aug. 31, 1953.

CATALOGUE OF CARNIVOROUS, PACHYDERMATOUS, AND EDENTATA MAMMALIA IN THE BRITISH MUSEUM. J. E. Gray. London, Printed by order of the Trustees, pp.vii-398, illus., 1869.

CATALOGUE OF THE SEALS AND WHALES IN THE BRITISH MUSEUM. (2nd Ed.) J.E. Gray. Brit. Mus. (Nat. Hist.), London, pp. vii-402, illus., 1866.

CATALOGUE ON THE SPECIMENS OF MAMMALIA IN THE COLLECTION OF THE BRITISH MUSEUM. (PART 1, CETACEA; PART 2, SEALS). J.E.Gray. Binder's title: Gray, Catalogue Cetacea and Seals, 1850.

DESCRIPTION OF SOME NEW OR LITTLE KNOWN MAMMALIA, PRINCIPALLY IN THE BRITISH MUSEUM COLLECTION. J.E. Gray. Mag. Nat. Hist., n.s., vol.1, pp.577-587, 1837.

HAND-LIST OF THE EDENTATE, THICK-SKINNED AND RUMINANT MAMMALS IN THE BRITISH MUSEUM. J.E. Gray. London, Printed by order of the Trustees, pp.vii-176, pls.42, 1873.

LIST OF THE OSTEOLOGICAL SPECIMENS IN THE COLLECTION OF THE BRITISH MUSEUM. J.E. Gray. Publ. Brit. Mus. (Nat. Hist.) London, pp.1-147, 1847.

LIST OF THE SPECIMENS OF MAMMALIA IN THE COLLECTION OF THE BRITISH MUSEUM. J.E. Gray. London, Brit.Mus., pp.28-216, 1843.

SEALS (part 2, pp.5-48). In Catalogue of the Specimens of Mammalia in the Colletions of the British Museum. J. E.Gray. London, Brit. Mus., 3 parts, 1850.

SUPPLEMENT TO THE CATALOGUE OF SEALS AND WHALES IN THE BRITISH MUSEUM. J.E. Gray. London, Brit.Mus., pp.103, 1871.

REPORT ON SOME OF THE ADDITIONS TO THE COLLECTIONS OF MAMMALIA IN THE BRITISH MUSEUM. Albert Guenther. Proceedings of the Zoological Society of London, pp.735-751, pl., 1876.

CATALOGUE OF THE UNGULATE MAMMALS IN THE BRITISH MUSEUM OF NATURAL HISTORY. Sidney Harmer. Vol. V. Perissodactyla, Hyracoidae, Proboscidae with addenda to the earlier volumes. London, pp.207, illus., 1916.

NEW HABITAT GROUPS OF MAMMALS. Francis Harper. Bull. Boston Soc. Nat. Hist., no.40, pp.7-9, illus., July, 1926.

GUIDE TO THE HALL OF BIOLOGY OF MAMMALS IN THE AMERICAN MUSEUM OF NATURAL HISTORY. Robert T. Hatt. New York, Museum Press, pp.49, illus., 1933. (Guide Leaflet series no.76.)

ON SEVERAL NEW RODENTS IN THE ALBANY MUSEUM. John Hewitt. Records Albany Mus., vol.3, pt.5, pp.430-440, pls.26-27, July 31, 1927.

(SAALBURG MUSEUM'S ANIMAL REMAINS FROM THE ROMAN ERA.) Im Saalburg Museum aufbewahrten Tierreste aus roemischer Zeit. Max Hilzheimer. Saalburg-jahrbuch, vol.5, pp.100-158, 1924.

GUIDE TO THE FOSSIL MAMMALS IN THE BRITISH MUSEUM (NATURAL HISTORY). A.T. Hopwood. Publ. British Museum, London, pp.1-84, figs.72, pls.3, 1934.

CATALOGUE OF THE MAMMALIA IN THE MUSEUM OF THE HON. EAST-INDIA COMPANY. Thomas Horsfield. London, Printed by J. & H. Cox, pp.vi-212, 1851.

HABITAT GROUPS AT THE FAIRBANKS MUSEUM. Inez Addie Howe. Museum Work, vol.3, pp.125-127, Jan., 1921.

(OSTEOLOGICAL CATALOG OF MAMMALS.) Catalogue ostéologique des mammiferes. F.A. Jentink. Mus. Hist. nat. Pays-Bas, vol.9, pp.1-360, pls.i-xii, 1887.

(SYSTEMATIC CATALOG OF MAMMALS (RODENTS, INSECTIVORES, CHIROPTERS, EDENTATES, AND MARSUPIALS).) Catalogue systématique des mammifères (Rongeurs, Insectivores, Cheiroptères, Édentés et Marsupiaux). F.A. Jentink. Mus. Hist. nat. Pays-Bas, vol.12, pp.1-280, 1888.

(TRINIL COLLECTION OF PROF. DUBOIS.) De Trinil-collectie van Prof.Dubois. A.D. de Jongh. Tijdschr.kon.Nederl.Aardr.Gen., Leiden, 2de ser., vol.48, no.2, pp.350-353, Mar., 1931.

PULO CONDORE GROUP AND ITS MAMMALS. C. Boden Kloss. Jour. Nat. Hist. Soc. Siam, vol.4, pp.73-83, Mar., 1921.

(STATE ZOOLOGICAL COLLECTION OF MUNICH.) Zoologische Staatssammlung Muenchen. Hans Krieg. Fuehrer, pp.145-189, 1934.

(LIST OF THE DUPLICATES OF THE ZOOLOGICAL MUSEUM OF THE IMPERIAL UNIVERSITY OF BERLIN, WITH A DESCRIPTION OF PREVIOUSLY UNKNOWN SPECIES OF MAMMALS, BIRDS, AMPHIBIANS, AND FISHES.) Verzeichnis der Doubletten des zoologischen Museums der Koenigl. Universitaet zu Berlin, nebst Beschreibung vieler bisher unbekannten Arten von Saeugethieren, Voegel, Amphibien und Fischen. H. Lichtenstein. Berlin, pp.118, 1823.

AMERICAN MUSEUM OF NATURAL HISTORY, NEW YORK. GUIDE TO THE HALL OF MAMMALS. Frederic A. Lucas. New York, pp.16, illus., 1926. (Guide Leaflet no.57.)

CATALOGUE OF THE FOSSIL MAMMALIA IN THE BRITISH MUSEUM (NATURAL HISTORY.) Richard Lydekker. London, Printed by order of the Trustees, vol.5, illus., 1885-87.

GUIDE TO THE DOMESTICATED ANIMALS (OTHER THAN HORSES) EXHIBITED IN THE CENTRAL AND NORTH HALLS OF THE BRITISH MUSEUM. Richard Lydekker. 1st Ed. 1908. 2nd Ed. 1912.

GUIDE TO THE GREAT GAME ANIMALS (UNGULATA) IN THE DEPARTMENT OF ZOOLOGY, BRITISH MUSEUM (NATURAL HISTORY). Richard Lydekker. London, pp.93, illus., 1907.

CATALOGUE OF THE TYPE SPECIMENS OF MAMMALS IN THE U.S. NATIONAL MUSEUM, INCLUDING THE BIOLOGICAL SURVEY COLLECTION. Marcus Ward Lyon, W.H. Osgood. Bulletin no.62, pp. 1-325, Jan. 28, 1909.

NEWS ABOUT COLLECTIONS. V.Martino. Lovtsa, nos.11-12, pp.2, illus., Nov.-Dec., 1937

(NEWLY ACQUIRED MAMMALS OF THE NATURAL HISTORY MUSEUM OF LUEBECK.) Neue erworbene Saeugetiere des Naturhistorischen Museums in Luebeck. Paul Matschie. Mitteil. Geograph. Gesell. u.Naturh. Mus. Luebeck, ser.2, Hft.7-8, pp.129-134, 1894.

MAMMALS AND MAN, HANDBOOK TO A TEMPORARY EXHIBITION NOVEMBER, 1940 TO APRIL, 1941. Colin Matheson. Cardiff, Pub. by the Nat. Mus. of Wales and by the Press Board of the Univ. of Wales, pp.22, 1940.

FOSSIL CARNIVORES, MARSUPIALS AND SMALL MAMMALS IN THE AMERICAN MUSEUM OF NATURAL HISTORY. GUIDE LEAFLET TO THE COLLECTIONS IN THE DEPARTMENT OF VERTEBRATE PALAEONTOLOGY. W.D. Matthew. New York, Museum, pp.41, illus., pls., 1905. (Guide Leaflet no.17.)

HALL OF FOSSIL VERTEBRATES. W.D. Matthew. Amer. Mus. Jour., New York, vol.2, no.1, pp.19, illus., Jan., 1902.(Guide Leaflet no.3.)

CATALOGUE OF TYPE SPECIMENS OF MAMMALS IN THE NATURAL HISTORY MUSEUM OF STANFORD UNIVERSITY. William V. Mayer. Proc. California Zool. Club, Stanford Univ., vol.1, no.6, pp. 29-32, 1949.

MAMMAL COLLECTION OF THE NATURAL HISTORY MUSEUM OF STANFORD UNIVERSITY. William V. Mayer. Jour. Mamm., vol.29, no.3, p.301, Aug. 31, 1948.

(LIST OF MAMMAL TYPES OF THE SENCKENBERG MUSEUM.) Verzeichnis der Saeugetier-typen des Senckenbergischen Museums. Robert Mertens. Senckenbergiana, Frankfurt, vol.7, nos.1-2, pp.18-37, Feb. 12, 1925.

CONTRIBUTIONS TO THE SCIENTIFIC COLLECTIONS OF THE MUSEUM OF VERTEBRATE ZOOLOGY OF THE UNIVERSITY OF CALIFORNIA JULY 1, 1945 TO DECEMBER 31, 1950. Alden H. Miller. Univ. of California, pp.8, 1951.

HORNIMAN MUSEUM AND LIBRARY, FOREST HILL, S.E. 23. HANDBOOK TO THE CASES ILLUSTRATING THE EVOLUTION OF ANIMALS. H.N. Milligan.Publ. by London County Council, pp.71, illus., 1928.

(MAMMAL TYPES IN THE ZOOLOGICAL MUSEUM OF HALLE-ON-THE-SAALE.) Saeugetiertypen im Zoologischen Museum Halle an der Saale. Erna Mohr. Zeitschr. f. Naturwissenschaften, Halle a. s., vol. 94, pp.215-226, 1941.

WILD LIFE VISTAS ALONG CENTRAL PARK. Russel Owen. New York Times Mag., New York, p.19, illus., Mar. 29, 1942.

SCIENTIFIC AND DESCRIPTIVE CATALOGUE OF PEALE'S MUSEUM. C. W. Peale, A.M.F.J. Beauvois. Philadelphia, Printed by S.H. Smith, pp.44, 1796.

CATALOG OF THE TYPE SPECIMENS OF MAMMALS IN THE UNITED STATES NATIONAL MUSEUM, INCLUDING THE BIOLOGICAL SURVEY'S COLLECTION. A.J. Poole, Viola S.Schantz. Bull. U.S. Nat. Mus.178, pp.14-705, 1942.

(Review of) CATALOG OF THE TYPE SPECIMENS OF MAMMALS IN THE UNITED STATES NATIONAL MUSEUM, INCLUDING THE BIOLOGICAL SURVEY'S COLLECTIONS. A.J. Poole, Viola S. Schantz. Mammalia, Paris, vol.10, no.1, pp.66, Mar., 1946.

CATALOGUE OF THE MAMMALS IN THE BARNUM MUSEUM OF TUFTS COLLEGE. A.E. Preble. Sci. Ser. Tufts College Studies, no.8, pp.437-443, June, 1904.

MAMMAL COLLECTION AT BOSTON UNIVERSITY. Ralph B. Priddy. Jour. Mamm., vol.28, no.2, p.205, May 19, 1947.

(REPORT ON THE WURTTEMBERG NATURAL-HISTORY COLLECTION IN STUTTGART. ZOOLOGICAL DEPARTMENT.) Bericht der Wuertt. Naturaliensammlung in Stuttgart. Zoologische Abteilung. Rauther. Jahresheft Ver. Vaterl. Naturkunde Wuerttemberg, Jahrg.85, pp.14-23, figs.4, 1929.

(NEW VERTEBRATES OF THE BERLIN ZOOLOGICAL MUSEUM.) Neue Wirbelthiere des Zoologischen Museums in Berlin. Ant. Reichenow. Zool. Anzeiger, Leipzig, no.255, pp.369-372, July 11, 1887.

JEFFERSON'S GIFT OF FOSSILS TO THE MUSEUM OF NATURAL HISTORY IN PARIS. Howard C. Rice, Jr. Proc. Amer. Philos. Soc., Philadelphia, vol.95, no.6, pp.597-627, illus., Dec. 21, 1951.

FIELD MUSEUM EXHIBITS WORLD'S ONLY ARTICULATED SKELETON OF ASTRAPOTHERIUM. Elmer S. Riggs. Field Mus. Notes, vol.6, no.7, p.3, fig., July, 1935.

COLLECTION OF MAMMALS IN THE TRANSVAAL MUSEUM REGISTERED UP TO 31st MARCH, 1913, WITH DESCRIPTIONS OF NEW SPECIES. Austin Roberts. Annals Transvaal Mus., Pretoria, vol.4, no.2, pp.65-109, figs.6-11, Oct., 1913.

FOURTH SUPPLEMENTARY LIST OF MAMMALS IN THE COLLECTION OF THE TRANSVAAL MUSEUM. Austin Roberts. Annals Transvaal Mus., Pretoria, vol.5, no.4, pp.263-278, May 16, 1917.

SUPPLEMENT TO LIST OF MAMMALS IN THE TRANSVAAL MUSEUM. Austin Roberts. Annals Transvaal Museum, Pretoria, vol.4, no.2, pp.108-109, fig. 12, Oct., 1913.

COLLECTING LARGE MAMMALS FOR MUSEUM EXHIBITION. Robert H. Rockwell. Nat. Hist., vol.27, pp.583-587, illus., Dec., 1927 (Mar., 1928.)

UNGULATE MAMMALS COLLECTED BY CAPTAIN ANGUS BUCHANAN. Lord Rothschild. Nov. Zool., vol.28, pp.75-77, May, 1921.

(CATALOGUE OF THE DEPARTMENT OF ANTHROPOLOGY OF THE JUAN C. MOYANO MUSEUM.) Catalogo del Departmento de Anthropologia del Museo Juan C.Moyano. Carlos Rusconi. Rev. Junta Estudios Hist. Mendoza, vol.13, no.3, pp.15 (361-375), Dec. 31, 1938.

(TERATOLOGICAL MATERIAL IN THE MENDOZA MUSEUM.) Material teratologico en el Museo de Mendoza. Carlos Rusconi. Rev. Mus. Hist. Nat. Mendoza, vol.3, entr.2, pp.95-137, figs.36, June 30, 1949.

CATALOGUE OF TYPE SPECIMENS OF MAMMALS IN CHICAGO NATURAL HISTORY MUSEUM. Colin Campbell Sanborn. Fieldiana, Zool., Chicago, vol.32, no.4, pp.209-293, pl.1, Aug. 28, 1947.

BIOLOGICAL SURVEY MAMMAL COLLECTION. Viola S. Schantz. U.S. Dept. Interior, Bur. Biol. Surv., Wildlife Leaflet BS-153, pp.5, figs.3, Feb., 1940.

PRELIMINARY ACCOUNT OF THE FOSSIL MAMMALS FROM THE WHITE RIVER FORMATION CONTAINED IN THE MUSEUM OF COMPARATIVE ZOOLOGY. William Berryman Scott. Bull. Mus. Comp. Zool., vol.13, pp.151-171, pls.2, 1886-1888.

EXHIBITION SERIES OF BIRDS AND MAMMALS IN THE UNITED STATES NATIONAL MUSEUM. R.W. Shufeldt. Museum Work, vol.3, pp.178-185, Mar., 1921.

CATALOGUE OF THE MESOZOIC MAMMALIA IN THE GEOLOGICAL DEPARTMENT OF THE BRITISH MUSEUM. George Gaylord Simpson. British Mus. Nat. Hist., London, pp.x-215, pls.12, figs.56, 1928.

(NOTES ON THE OLDEST MAMMALS IN THE COLLECTION OF ROTH.) Notas sobre los mamiferos mas antiguos de la Coleccion Roth. George Gaylord Simpson. Inst. Mus. Univ. Nac. La Plata, vol.2, pp.63-94, figs.3, 1936.

GUIDE TO THE GROUPS OF MAMMALS. J.J. Simpson. Amgueddfa Genedlaethol Cymru, Nat. Mus. Wales, Cardiff, pp.24, illus., 1925.

CHINA'S NATURAL HISTORY. GUIDE TO THE SHANGHAI MUSEUM (R.A.S.) Arthur de Carle Sowerby. Publ. Roy. Asiatic Soc., North China Branch, pp.v-108, illus., 1936. (Mammals, pp.41-64.)

(MAMMALOGICAL MONOGRAPHS, OR DESCRIPTION OF SOME MAMMAL GENERA WHOSE SPECIES HAVE BEEN OBSERVED IN THE VARIOUS EUROPEAN MUSEUMS.) Monographies de mammalogie, ou Description de quelques genres de mammifères, dont les especes ont ete observées dans les differens musées de l'Europe. C. J.Temminck. Paris, G.Dufour et E.d'Ocagne, vol.2, pls., 1827-41.

(CATALOGUE OF THE MONOTREMES AND MARSUPIALS IN THE COLLECTIONS OF THE ZOOLOGICAL MUSEUM OF COIMBRA.) Catalogue des Monotremes et Marsupiaux existants dans les Collections du Museum Zoologique de Coimbra. António Armando Themido. Memorias E Estudos Do Museu Zoologico Da Universidad De Coimbra, Serie I, no.35, pp.1-8, 1929.

(CATALOGUE OF THE OSTEOLOGIC COLLECTIONS OF THE ZOOLOGIC MUSEUM OF COIMBRA.) Catalogue des Collections Ostéologiques du Muséum Zoologique de Coimbra. António Armando Themido. Mem. e Estudos Mus. Zool. Univ. Coimbra, ser.1, no.53, pp.5-27, 1931.

(CATALOG OF THE UNGULATES AND SIRENIANS IN THE COLLECTIONS OF THE ZOOLOGIC MUSEUM OF COIMBRA.) Catalogue des Ongulés et Siréniens existants dans les Collections du Muséum Zoologique de Coimbra. António Armando Themido. Memórias E Estudos Do Museu Zoologico Da Univ. De Coimbra. ser.1.-N 49. Imprensa Da Univ. Coimbra, pp.1-22, 1931.

CATALOGUE OF THE MARSUPIALIA AND MONOTREMATA IN THE COLLECTION OF THE BRITISH MUSEUM (NATURAL HISTORY). Oldfield Thomas. London, pp. iii-xiii, 1-401, figs.6, pls.i-xxviii, 1888.

HISTORY OF THE COLLECTIONS CONTAINED IN THE NATURAL HISTORY DEPARTMENT OF THE BRITISH MUSEUM. I. MAMMALS. Oldfield Thomas. Publ. Brit. Mus., vol.2, pp.3-66, 1906.

NEW BATS AND RODENTS IN THE BRITISH MUSEUM COLLECTION. Oldfield Thomas. Ann. & Mag. Nat. Hist. (8), vol.2, no.10, pp.370-375, Oct., 1908.

ON THE MAMMALS PRESENTED BY ALLAN O. HUME, ESQ., C.B., TO THE NATURAL HISTORY MUSEUM. Oldfield Thomas. Proc. Zool. Soc., London, pp.54-79, pls.5-6, Jan. 19, 1886.

ON THE PROBABLE IDENTITY OF CERTAIN SPECIMENS, FORMERLY IN THE LIDTH DE JEUDE COLLECTION , AND NOW IN THE BRITISH MUSEUM, WITH THOSE FIGURED BY ALBERTA SEBA IN HIS "THESAURUS" OF 1734. Oldfield Thomas. Proc. Zool. Soc., London, no.22, pp.309-318, May 3, 1882.

TYPES OF THE MAMMALS DESCRIBED BY M. FERNAND LATASTE. Oldfield Thomas. Ann. and Mag. Nat. Hist., ser. 9, vol.4, pp.350-354, Nov., 1919.

(SYSTEMATIC AND SYNONYMIC CATALOGUE OF LIVING AND EXTINCT MAMMALS.) Catalogue systématique, synonymique et géographique des mammifères vivante et fossiles. E.L. Troussart. Paris, pts.4, 1879-1885.

CATALOGUE OF THE AQUATIC MAMMALS EXHIBITED BY THE U. S. NAT. MUSEUM (AT GREAT INTERNATIONAL FISHERIES EXHIBITION, LONDON, 1883.) Frederick W. True. Smiths. Inst., Special Publ., no. 562, pp.1-22, 1884.

CATALOGUE OF THE AQUATIC MAMMALS EXHIBITED BY THE UNITED STATES NATIONAL MUSEUM. Frederick W. True. Washington, Govt. Print. Off., pp.22, 1884. (Bull. U.S. Nat. Mus., no.27, pp.623-644.)

GUIDE TO A COLLECTION ILLUSTRATING THE FAMILIES OF MAMMALS, EXHIBITED IN THE OHIO VALLEY CENTENNIAL EXPOSITION IN 1888 BY THE U. S. NATIONAL MUSEUM. Frederick W. True. Proc. U.S. Nat. Mus., vol.11, Appendix pp.1-26, 1888.

MARINE MAMMALS OF THE ANATOMICAL MUSEUM OF THE UNIVERSITY OF EDINBURGH. PART 1. CETACEA. PART 2. SIRENIA. PART 3. PINNIPEDIA. William Turner. London, Macmillan, pp.15-207, pls.17, 1912.

(MAMMALS OF THE LIVE COLLECTIONS OF THE NATIONAL MUSEUM OF NATURAL HISTORY.) Les mammifères des collections vivantes du Museum National d'Histoire Naturelle. E.Dechambre Urbain, M. A. Pasquier. Mammalia, Paris, vol.2, no.3, pp.148-156, Sep., 1938.

CATALOGUE OF SCHOOL SERIES OF SKELETONS. Henry A. Ward. Privately printed, Rochester, N.Y., pp.1-39, illus., 1881.

CATALOGUE OF SPECIMENS OF COMPARATIVE OSTEOLOGY. Henry L. Ward. Privately printed, Rochester, N.Y., pp.84, Aug., 1877.

CATALOGUE OF SPECIMENS OF COMPARATIVE OSTEOLOGY FOR SALE. Henry A. Ward. Privately printed, Rochester, N.Y., pp.53, Sep., 1880.

CATALOGUE OF THE COLLEGE SERIES OF CASTS OF FOSSILS, FROM THE PRINCIPAL MUSEUMS OF EUROPE AND AMERICA, WITH SHORT DESCRIPTIONS AND ILLUSTRATIONS. Henry A. Ward. Privately printed, Rochester, N.Y., pp. 136, figs., 1870. (Mammals, pp.1-28)

CATALOGUE OF THE MAMMALIA PRESERVED IN THE MUSEUM OF THE ZOOLOGICAL SOCIETY OF LONDON. G.R. Waterhouse. London, Ed.2, pp.68, 1838.

CHARACTERS OF A NEW GALAGO (G. ALLENI) AND A NEW PTEROMYS (P. HORSFIELDII), IN THE SOCIETY'S COLLECTION. G.R. Waterhouse. Proc. Zool. Soc., London, pt.5, p.87, 1837.

ON TWO SPECIES OF MAMMALIA, FROM THE SOCIETY'S COLLECTION, BELONGING TO THE GENERA GERBILLUS AND HERPESTES. G. R. Waterhouse. Proc. Zool. Soc., London, pt.6, p.55, 1838.

(FURTHER REMARKS OF DR. WEIGOLD ON THE COLLECTED MAMMALS.) Weitere Bemerkungen Dr. Weigolds zu den gesammelten Saeugetieren. H. Weigold. In Zool. Ergeb. Walter Stotzner's Exped. Szetschivan, etc., Teil 3. From Ber. d. Mus. Tierk. Volkerk. Dresden., no.2, vol.xvi, pp.71-76, 1924.

EIGHT HISTORIC FOSSIL MAMMAL SPECIMENS IN THE MUSEUM OF COMPARATIVE ZOOLOGY. Horace Elmer Wood. Cambridge, Mass., pp.110, illus., pl., tbls., 1960. (Harvard Univ. Mus. of Comparative Zoology, Bulletin, vol.123, no.3.)

ALBUM OF THE GROUPS IN THE VERNAY-FAUNTHORPE HALL OF SOUTH ASIATIC MAMMALS OF THE AMERICAN MUSEUM OF NATURAL HISTORY. New York, Amer. Mus. of Nat. Hist., Printed by Rembrandt Gravure Co., pp.53, illus., 1930.

BIOLOGICAL SURVEY MAMMAL COLLECTION. COMPILED IN THE SECTION OF WILDLIFE SURVEYS. DIVISION OF WILDLIFE RESEARCH. U.S. Bureau of Biological Survey, Washington, D.C., pp. 4, pl., 1940. (Wildlife Leaflet BS-153, Feb., 1940.

BIOLOGICAL SURVEY MAMMAL COLLECTION. U.S. Dept. Interior, Fish and Wildl. Serv., Wildlife Leaflet 211, pp.5, figs.3, Feb., 1942.

CATALOGUE OF THE BONES OF MAMMALIA IN THE COLLECTION OF THE BRITISH MUSEUM. British Mus. Nat. Hist., Dept. of Zoology, London, Printed by order of the Trustees, pp.296, 1862.

CATALOGUE OF THE SPECIMENS OF MAMMALIA IN THE COLLECTION OF THE BRITISH MUSEUM. PART III. UNGULATA FURCIPEDA. British Mus. (Nat. Hist.) Dept. of Zoology, London, pp.xvi-286, pls., 1852.

CATALOGUE OF THE UNGULATE MAMMALS IN THE BRITISH MUSEUM (NATURAL HISTORY). British Mus. (Nat.Hist.) Dept. of Zoology, London, vol.5, 1913-1916.

DESCRIPTIVE AND ILLUSTRATED CATALOGUE OF THE FOSSIL ORGANIC REMAINS OF MAMMALIA AND AVES CONTAINED IN THE MUSEUM OF THE ROYAL COLLEGE OF SURGEONS OF ENGLAND. London, Royal College of Surgeons of England, Printed by R. and J.E.Taylor, pp.391, pl.10, 1845.

GUIDE TO THE DOMESTICATED ANIMALS (OTHER THAN HORSES) EXHIBITED IN THE CENTRAL AND NORTH HALLS OF THE BRITISH MUSEUM (NATURAL HISTORY). 2d Ed. British Mus. (Nat.Hist.) Dept. of Zoology, London, Printed by order of the Trustees, pp.vi-56, illus., pls., 1912.

GUIDE TO THE FOSSIL MAMMALS AND BIRDS IN THE DEPARTMENT OF GEOLOGY AND PALAEONTOLOGY IN THE BRITISH MUSEUM(NATURAL HISTORY). British Mus. (Nat.Hist.) Dept. of Geology, 7th Ed., London, Printed by order of the Trustees, pp.xii-103, illus., tbl., 1896; 10th Ed., pp.96, illus., fold.tbl., 1923.

GUIDE TO THE FOSSIL MAMMALS IN THE BRITISH MUSEUM (NATURAL HISTORY). British Mus. (Nat.Hist.) Dept. of Geology, London, Printed by order of the Trustees, pp.84, pls.3, text-figs.72, 1934.

GUIDE TO THE GALLERIES OF MAMMALIA IN THE DEPARTMENT OF ZOOLOGY OF THE BRITISH MUSEUM(NATURAL HISTORY). British Mus. (Nat. Hist.) Dept. of Zoology, London, the Trustees, pp.126, illus., fold.plan.4, 1902.

GUIDE TO THE GALLERIES OF MAMMALIA (MAMMALIAN, OSTEOLOGICAL, CETACEAN) IN THE DEPARTMENT OF ZOOLOGY OF THE BRITISH MUSEUM (NATURAL HISTORY). British Mus. (Nat. Hist.) Dept. of Zoology, London, the Trustees, pp.125, illus., fold.plan., 1885; 4th Ed., pp.126, illus., 2 plans on fold.pl., 1892; 5th Ed., pp.126, illus., 2 plans on fold. pl., 1894.

GUIDE TO THE GALLERIES OF MAMMALS IN THE DEPARTMENT OF ZOOLOGY OF THE BRITISH MUSEUM (NATURAL HISTORY). British Mus. (Nat. Hist.) Dept. of Zoology, the Trustees, pp.123, illus., pl.3, 1921. (10th Ed.)

GUIDE TO THE GALLERIES OF MAMMALS (OTHER THAN UNGULATES) IN THE DEPARTMENT OF ZOOLOGY OF THE BRITISH MUSEUM (NATURAL HISTORY). British Mus. (Nat. Hist.) Dept. of Zoology, the Trustees, 8th Ed., pp. 101, illus., fold.plan., 1906.

GUIDE TO THE GROUPS OF MAMMALS. Cardiff, Wales. National Mus. of Wales, pp.24, pl.iv, 1925.

GUIDE TO THE SPECIMENS OF GREAT GAME ANIMALS (UNGULATA) EXHIBITED IN THE DEPARTMENT OF ZOOLOGY, BRITISH MUSEUM (NATURAL HISTORY). 2d Ed., British Mus. (Nat.Hist.) Dept. of Zoology, the Trustees, pp.x-95, illus., pls., 1913.

(LIST OF MAMMALS IN THE MUSEUM OF THE SOCIETY OF NATURAL HISTORY IN HANOVER.) Verzeichnis der im Museum der Naturhistorischen Gesellschaft zu Hannover vorhandenen Saeugetiere. Hannover, Druck von W. Riemschneider, pp.30, 1897.

LIST OF SKELETONS AND CRANIA IN THE SECTION OF COMPARATIVE ANATOMY OF THE U. S. ARMY MEDICAL MUSEUM. Army Med. Mus., Washington, D.C., pp.1-46, notes, 1876.

(MAMMAL COLLECTION OF THE PARIS MUSEUM OF NATIONAL HISTORY.) Collection de mammiferes du Museum d'Histoire naturelle de Paris. Paris, Museum of Nat. Hist., pl.54, 1829.

WHERE SCIENCE, ART AND ADVENTURE JOIN. Oil-Power, New York, vol.13, no.6, pp.4-12, illus., June, 1938. (Mammal habitat groups in the American Museum.)

MUSEUMS -- TAXIDERMY AND EXHIBITION see SPECIMENS -- COLLECTION, PREPARATION, PRESERVATION

MYOLOGY see ANATOMY -- MYOLOGY

## NATURAL HISTORY

APPARENTLY OVERLOOKED SOURCE BOOK OF BIOLOGICAL HISTORY. Gordon Alexander. Science, vol.61, pp.285-286, Mar. 13, 1925.

EDWARD TYSON, M.D., F.R.S., 1650-1708, AND THE RISE OF HUMAN AND COMPARATIVE ANATOMY IN ENGLAND. STUDY IN THE HISTORY OF SCIENCE. M.F. Ashley Montagu. Mem. Amer. Philos. Soc., Philadelphia, vol.20, pp.xxix-488, figs.56, 1943.

WHY A NATURALIST? Vernon Bailey. National Nature News, vol.1, no.27, pp. 1, 6, 7, illus., Sep. 27, 1937.

NATURALIST'S SCRAPBOOK. Thomas Barbour. Harvard Univ. Press, pp.x-218, illus.

THE WORLD WE LIVE IN. Lincoln Barnett. Part X. THE ARCTIC BARRENS. Life, vol. 36, no.23, pp.90-115, illus., June 7, 1954; Part XI. THE RAIN FOREST. Life, vol.37, no.12, pp.76-102, illus., Sep. 20, 1954; Part XII. THE WOODS OF HOME. Life, vol.37, no.19, pp.78-100, illus., Nov. 8, 1954.

MY LIFE IN A MAN MADE JUNGLE. Belle J. Benchley. Publ. Faber and Faber, London, 1942.

(POWER, BEAUTY, AND MYSTERIES OF NATURE.) Kraft, Schoenheit und Geheimnisse der Natur. Wilhelm Boelsche. Natur u. Volk, Frankfurt a.M., vol.68, no.10, pp.476-479, Oct. 1, 1938.

NATURE ANALOGIES. W.B. Crow. Scientia, Bologna, vol.58, pp.157-171, Sep. 1, 1935.

THRILLS OF A NATURALIST'S QUEST. Raymond L. Ditmars. Macmillan Co., New York, pp.xii-268, frontispiece, figs. 48, 1932.

ANCIENT NATURAL HISTORY LORE. C.R. Eastman. Science, n.s., Lancaster, vol. 20, no.506, pp.347-348, Sep. 9, 1904.

CAMP-FIRES OF A NATURALIST. C. E. Edwards. New York, mo.12, pp.304, illus. 13, 1893.

OF MEN AND MARSHES. Paul L. Errington. Macmillan Co., New York, pp.ix-150, illus. 22, Nov. 26, 1957.

GREAT MOTHER EARTH. Attilio Gatti. Chas. Scribner's Sons, New York, pp.vii-xvi, 19-335, illus., 1937. (Original edition, London, pp.295, 1936.)

(GENERAL HANDBOOK AND MANUAL OF NATURAL SCIENCE. VOL. I.) Gemeinnuetziges Hand- und Hilfsbuch der Naturgeschichte, Erster Band. C.W.L. Gloger. Breslau, pp.167-174, 1842.

BEGINNING OF AMERICAN SCIENCE. THE THIRD CENTURY. G. Brown Goode. Proc. Biol. Soc. Washington, vol.4, pp.9-94, Jan. 22, 1887.

CATALOGUE OF PAPERS CONCERNING THE DATES OF PUBLICATION OF NATURAL HISTORY BOOKS. Francis J. Griffin. 1st supplement Jour. Soc. Bibliogr. Nat. Hist., London, vol.2, pp.1-17, 1943.

JOSEPH GRINNELL'S PHILOSOPHY OF NATURE. Joseph Grinnell. Univ. California Press, Berkeley, pp.vi-238, illus., incl. 2 color pls., 1943.

GROWTH OF BIOLOGY IN THE NINETEENTH CENTURY. Oskar Hertwig. Smiths. Inst., Annual Rep., 1900, Washington, pp.461-478, 1901.

ADVANCE OF SCIENCE IN THE LAST HALF CENTURY. Thomas Henry Huxley. Smiths. Inst., Annual Rep., 1887, Washington, pp.57-98, 1889.

CENTURY OF PROGRESS IN SMITHSONIAN BIOLOGY. Remington Kellogg. Science, Lancaster, vol.104, no.2693, pp.132-141, Aug. 9, 1946.

GROWTH OF BIOLOGY. William A. Locy. New York, Henry Holt and Co., vol.8, pp. 481, illus., 1925.

FIRST CHAPTER IN NATURAL HISTORY; BEING THE INTRODUCTION TO CHAMPLIN'S YOUNG FOLKS' CYCLOPAEDIA OF NATURAL HISTORY. F.A. Lucas. Amer. Mus. Nat. Hist., Guide Leaflet, no.51, pp.1-20, Apr., 1920.

SOME MISTAKES OF SCIENTISTS. F.A. Lucas. Nat. Hist., vol.28, no.2, pp.169-174, 1928.

ROYAL NATURAL HISTORY. VOL. 1, 2. Richard Lydekker.

(Review by C. Hart Merriam of) ROYAL NATURAL HISTORY. Richard Lydekker. Science, New York, vol.1, no.14, pp. 387-389, Apr. 5, 1895.

WHEN LOST IN THE NORTH: I. LOST IN THE WOODS; II. LOST IN THE ARCTIC. Dan McCowan, E.J. Gall. Beaver, Winnipeg, outfit 275, pp.36-42, illus., June, 1944.

APPRAISAL OF NATURAL HISTORY. M. Maldonado-Koerdell. Chicago Naturalist, vol.8, no.3, pp.49-53, Nov., 1945.

EVOLUTION OF THE SCIENTIFIC INVESTIGATOR. Simon Newcomb. Smiths. Inst., Annual Rep., 1904, Washington, pp.221-233, 1905.

HANDLIST OF AMERICAN NATURALISTS, BASED ON THE DICTIONARY OF AMERICAN BIOGRAPHY. Paul H. Oehser. Amer. Nat., vol.72, pp.534-546, Nov.-Dec., 1938.

FIELDBOOK OF NATURAL HISTORY. E. Laurence Palmer. New York, McGraw-Hill Book Co., pp.664, illus., 1949.

STANDARD NATURAL HISTORY. W.P. Pycraft. London, Warne & Co., Ltd., Mammals, pp.45-942, col.pls.12, figs. over 900, 1931.

(FROM THE "ICE AGE ANIMAL PRESERVE.") Aus dem "Eiszeitlichen Wildgehege". Richard Rein. Naturforscher, vol. 13, no.8, pp.277-280, pls.16, figs.4, Nov., 1936.

A MODEL OF NATURE. Arthur William Ruecker. Smiths. Inst., Annual Rep., 1901, Washington, pp.171-191, 1902.

WHAT IS A NATURALIST? A STUDY IN NATURAL HISTORY. Karl P. Schmidt. Chicago Nat., vol.6, no.3, pp.51-63, illus., Nov., 1943.

LIFE; ITS NATURE, ORIGIN AND MAINTENANCE. Edward Albert Sharpey-Schafer. Smiths. Inst., Annual Rep., 1912, Washington, pp.493-525, 1913.

ON THE DATES OF THE NATURAL HISTORY PORTION OF SAVIGNY'S 'DESCRIPTION DE L'EGYPTE'. C. Davies Sherborn. Proc. Zool. Soc. London, pt.1, pp.285-288, June 1, 1897.

NATURE BY DAY. Arthur R. Thompson. London, Ivor Nicholson and Watson, pp. xi-162, 1932.

(MAN AND THE EARTH.) El hombre y la tierra. Guillermo Vogt. Biblioteca Enciclopedica Popular, Mexico, vol.32, pp.1-95, 1944.

EVERYDAY LIFE IN ANCIENT TIMES. National Geographic Society, pp.232, illus.

ILLUSTRATED LIBRARY OF THE NATURAL SCIENCES. New York, Simon and Schuster, vols.1-4, pictures more than 3, 000.

NEUROLOGY see ANATOMY -- NEUROLOGY

## NOMENCLATURE

MAMMAL NAMES PROPOSED BY OKEN IN HIS "LEHRBUCH DER ZOOLOGIE." J.A. Allen. Bull. Amer. Mus. Nat. Hist., vol.16, pp.373-379, Oct. 11, 1902.

NOMENCLATORIAL NOTES ON AMERICAN MAMMALS. J.A. Allen. Bull. Amer. Mus. Nat. Hist., vol.16, pp.159-168, July 1, 1902.

NOMENCLATORIAL NOTES ON CERTAIN NORTH AMERICAN MAMMALS. J.A. Allen. Bull. Amer. Mus. Nat. Hist., vol.10, pp.449-461, Nov. 10, 1898.

NOTE ON THE NAMES OF A FEW SOUTH AMERICAN MAMMALS. J.A. Allen. Proc. Biol. Soc. Washington, vol.14, pp.183-185, Dec. 12, 1901.

ON THE NAMES OF MAMMALS GIVEN BY KERR IN HIS "ANIMAL KINGDOM," PUBLISHED IN 1792. J.A. Allen. Bull. Amer. Mus. Nat. Hist., vol.7, pp.179-192, June 20, 1895.

ZIMMERMAN'S 'ZOOLOGIAE GEOGRAPHICAE' AND 'GEOGRAPHISCHE GESCHICHTE' CONSIDERED IN THEIR RELATION TO MAMMALIAN NOMENCLATURE. J.A. Allen. Bull. Amer. Mus. Nat. Hist., vol. 16, pp.13-22, Feb. 1, 1902.

ENDORSEMENT OF THE USE OF GENERIC NAMES AS COMMON NOUNS. C.D. Beers. Science, Lancaster, n.s., vol.96, no.2496, pp.403-404, Oct. 30, 1942.

(NOTES ON THE NAMES OF SOME MAMMALS.) Notas sobre los nombres de algunos mamiferos. Carlos Berg. Mus. Nac. Buenos Aires, vol.1, no.7, pp.260-263, Oct. 9, 1900.

(NOTES ON THE NAMES OF SOME SOUTH AMERICAN MAMMALS.) Notas sobre los Nombres de algunos mamiferos Sudamericanos. Carlos Berg. Com. Mus. Nac., Buenos Aires, vol.1, no.6, pp.219-222, May 23, 1900.

GENDER OF SCIENTIFIC NAMES IN ZOOLOGY. Richard E. Blackwelder. Jour. Washington Acad. Sci., Menasha, vol.31, no.4, pp.135-140, tbls.2, Apr. 15, 1941.

FAMILY NAMES. J. Chester Bradley. Science, n.s., vol.68, pp.102-104, Aug. 3, 1928.

USE OF PARENTHESES IN ZOOLOGICAL NOMENCLATURE. Arthur N. Bragg. Science, Lancaster, n.s., vol.89, no.2321, p.583, June 23, 1939.

CHANGES IN THE NOMENCLATURE OF MICHIGAN MAMMALS. William Henry Burt. Occas. Papers Mus. Zool., Univ. Michigan, Ann Arbor, no.481, pp.9, Nov.10, 1943.

REMARK ON FAMILY NAMES. Thos. L. Casey. Science, n.s., vol.52, pp.491-492, Nov. 19, 1920.

LIST OF THE NAMES PROPOSED FOR GENERA AND SUBGENERA OF RECENT MAMMALS FROM THE PUBLICATION OF T. S. PALMER'S 'INDEX GENERUM MAMMALIUM' 1904 TO THE END OF 1951. L.R. Conisbee. British Mus. (Nat. Hist.), London, pp.109, Sep. 7, 1953.

STABILITY IN GENERIC NOMENCLATURE. O.F. Cook. Science, n.s., vol.8, no.189, pp.186-190, Aug. 12, 1898.

TERMS RELATING TO GENERIC TYPES. O.F. Cook. American Naturalist, vol.48, pp.308-314, May, 1914.

(NOMENCLATURE DECISIONS OF THE INTERNATIONAL ZOOLOGICAL CONGRESS OF COPENHAGEN.) Decisions de nomenclature au Congres international de Zoologie de Copenhague. Jean Dorst. Mammalia, Paris, vol.18, no.2, pp.219-220, June, 1954.

(SCIENTIFIC NAMES OF SOME MAMMALS.) Propos des noms scientifiques de quelques Mammifères. Jean Dorst. Mammalia, Paris, vol.19, no.3, pp.429-430, Sep., 1955.

TERMINOLOGY OF MICROGEOGRAPHIC RACES IN MAMMALS. J. Kenneth Doutt. Systematic Zoology, vol.4, no.4, pp.179-185, Dec., 1955.

(ON SPECIES CHANGE AND NOMENCLATURE.) Ueber Art-Wandlung und Art-Benennung. Kurt Ehrenberg. Biologia Generalis, Vienna and Leipzig, vol.4, pts.6-8, pp.695-712, pls.23, 1928.

NOMENCLATURAL EFFICIENCY. E.P. Felt. Science, n.s., vol.65, pp.489-491, May 20, 1927.

SCIENCE AND SCIENTIFIC NAMES. E.P. Felt, S.C. Bishop. Amer. Nat., vol.60, no.668, pp.275-281, 1926.

UNOFFICAL INTERPRETATION OF THE INTERNATIONAL RULES OF ZOOLOGICAL NOMENCLATURE. W.I. Follett. Issued with the cooperation of the California Acad. of Sci. and the Society of Systematic Zoology, pp.5-99, Sep., 1955, (not published.)

TERMINOLOGY OF TYPES. D.L. Frizzell. Amer. Midl. Nat., vol.14, pp.637-668, 1933.

SOME FUNDAMENTALS OF NOMENCLATURE. Edward L. Greene. Science, n.s., pp.13-16, Jan. 3, 1896.

NOMENCLATURE AND TYPE LOCALITIES OF CERTAIN OLD WORLD MAMMALS. Francis Harper. Jour.Mamm., vol.21, no.2, pp.191-203, May 14, 1940.

(SOME CONSIDERATIONS ON NOMENCLATURE.) Einige nomenklatorische Betrachtungen. Ernst Hartert. Zool. Anz., vol.28, no.4, pp.154-158, Oct. 7, 1904.

NAMES OF MAMMALS DATED FROM FRISCH, 1775, AND ZIMMERMANN, 1777. Philip Hershkovitz. Jour. Mamm., vol.29, no.3, pp.272-277, Aug. 31, 1948.

STATUS OF NAMES CREDITED TO OKEN, 1816. Philip Hershkovitz. Jour. Mamm., vol.30, no.3, pp.289-301, Aug. 17, 1949.

TECHNICAL NAMES OF THE AFRICAN MUISHOND (GENUS ZORILLA) AND THE COLOMBIAN HOG-NOSED SKUNK (GENUS CONEPATUS). Philip Hershkovitz. Proc. Biol. Soc. Washington, vol.62, pp.13-16, Mar. 17, 1949.

INTERNATIONAL ZOOLOGY AND THE INTERNATIONAL CODE. Ned Hollister. Science, n.s., vol.48, no.1227, pp.12-13, July 5, 1918.

SOURCE-BOOK OF BIOLOGICAL NAMES AND TERMS. E.C. Jaeger. Springfield, Ill., Charles C. Thomas, pp.35-317, 1955.

NEW NAMES FOR MAMMALS PROPOSED BY BOROWSKI IN 1780 AND 1781. Remington Kellogg. Proc. Biol. Soc. Washington, vol.45, pp.147-148, Sep. 9, 1932.

ARE CORRECTIONS TO THE ORIGINAL SPELLING OF GENERIC NAMES ADVANTAGEOUS? J. Brooks Knight. Jour. Sci., New Haven, vol.239, no.4, pp.312-315, Apr., 1941.

NEW NAMES FOR MAMMALS. M. Kretzoi. Ann. Hist. Nat. Mus. Nat. Hungarici, Budapest, vol.40, no.6, pp.285-287, 1947.

(PREOCCUPIED MAMMAL NAMES AND THOSE TO BE REPLACED BY OLDER NAMES.) Praeokkupierte und durch ältere zu ersetzende Saeugetiernamen. M Kretzoi. Sonderabdruck aus Foldtani Koziony, vol.72, pp.345-349, 1942.

(WHAT IS BINOMIAL NOMENCLATURE?) Was ist binaere Nomenklatur? Einar Loennberg. Zool. Anzeiger, vol.44, no.7, pp. 332-336, May 26, 1914.

FAMILY AND SUBFAMILY NAMES IN ZOOLOGY. M.W. Lyon, Jr. Science, n.s., vol.52, pp.291-292, Sep. 24, 1920.

THE "ONE-LETTER" RULE FOR GENERIC NAMES IN ZOOLOGY. W.L. McAtee. Amer. Nat., vol.55, pp.89-96, Feb., 1921.

SELECTION OF FAMILY NAMES IN ZOOLOGY. W.L. McAtee. Jour. Washington Acad. Sci., vol.11, pp.230-235, May 19, 1921.

USE OF GENERIC NAMES AS COMMON NOUNS. S.O. Mast. Science, Lancaster, n.s, vol.96, no.2489, p.252, Sep. 11, 1942.

(TERNARY NOMENCLATURE.) Ternaere Nomenclature.) Paul Matschie. Sitz.-Ber. Gesell. Naturf. Freunde, Berlin, no.9, pp. 216-220, Nov. 20, 1900.

PREOCCUPIED NAMES. W.D. Matthew. Jour. Mamm., Baltimore, vol.10, no.2, p.171, May 9, 1929.

NEW NAMES FOR SPERMOPHILUS BREVICAUDUS, CANIS PALLIDUS AND SOREX CAUDATUS MERRIAM. C. Hart Merriam. Science, n.s., Lancaster, vol. 8, no.205, p.782, Dec. 2, 1898.

WHY SHOULD EVERY SPECIMEN BE NAMED? C. Hart Merriam. Jour. Mamm., vol.1, no.1, pp.41-42, Nov., 1919.

HOW THE TAXONOMIST NAMES THE ANIMALS. Z.P. Metcalf. Sci. Monthly, vol.45, no.6, pp.513-523, Dec., 1937.

GENERIC NAMES GIVEN BY FRISCH IN 1775. Gerrit S. Miller, Jr. Ann. and Mag. Nat. Hist., ser.7, vol.16, pp.461-464, Oct., 1905.

SUGGESTIONS AS TO NOMENCLATURE. Gerrit S. Miller, Jr. Science, n.s., no.16, pp.114-115, July 18, 1902.

SCIENTIFIC NAMES OF LATIN AND GREEK DERIVATION. Walter Miller. Proc. Calif. Acad. Sci., ser.3, Zool., vol.1, no.3, pp.115-143, Apr. 10, 1897.

ERRONEOUS EMENDATION OF GENERIC NAMES. Raymond C. Moore, J. Marvin Weller, J. Brookes Knight. Jour. Paleontol., Menasha, vol.16, no.2, pp.250-261, Mar., 1942.

NOMENCLATOR ZOOLOGICUS. LIST OF THE NAMES OF GENERA AND SUBGENERA IN ZOOLOGY FROM THE TENTH EDITION OF LINNAEUS 1758 TO THE END OF 1935. Sheffield A. Neave. Zool Soc. London, vol. 1 (A-C), pp.xiv-958, 1939.

NOMENCLATURE OF FAMILIES AND SUBFAMILIES IN ZOOLOGY. Harry C. Oberholser. Science, n.s, vol.52, pp.142-147, Aug. 13, 1920.

HOMONYMS AND NOMENCLATORS. Paul H. Oehser. Amer. Midland Nat., vol.16, no.6, pp.962-963, Nov., 1935.

NAMES OF SOME SOUTH AMERICAN MAMMALS. Wilfred H. Osgood. Jour. Mamm., Baltimore, vol.1, no.1, pp.33-36, Nov. 28, 1919.

NOTES ON NOMENCLATURE OF SOUTH AMERICAN MAMMALS. Wilfred H. Osgood. Jour. Mamm., Baltimore, vol.2, no.1, pp. 39-40, Feb. 10, 1921.

OUTWORN NOMENCLATURAL PRACTICE. Wilfred H. Osgood. Science, n.s., vol.89, no.2297, pp.9-11, Jan. 6, 1939.

SOME UNRECOGNIZED AND MISAPPLIED NAMES OF AMERICAN MAMMALS. Wilfred H. Osgood. Proc.Biol.Soc.Washington, vol. 20, pp.43-52, Apr. 18, 1907.

INDEX GENERUM MAMMALIUM: A LIST OF THE GENERA AND FAMILIES OF MAMMALS. T.S. Palmer. U.S. Dept. Agric., Div. Biol. Surv., N.A.Fauna no.23, Gov't. Print.Off., Washington, 1904.

NOTES ON THE NOMENCLATURE OF FOUR GENERA OF TROPICAL AMERICAN MAMMALS. T.S. Palmer. Proc.Biol. Soc. Washington, vol.11, pp.173-174, June 9, 1897.

SOME NEW GENERIC NAMES OF MAMMALS. T.S. Palmer. Science, Lancaster, n.s., vol.17, no.439, p.873, May 29, 1903.

ZOOLOGICAL NAMES. PRELIMINARY LIST OF PHYLA, CLASSES, ORDERS, ETC., OF ANIMALS. A.S. Pearse. (Prepared for A.A.A.S., Section F, Committee on Nomenclature.) Mimeographed, pp.12, May 10, 1934.

ZOOLOGICAL NAMES. SECOND PRELIMINARY LIST OF PHYLA, CLASSES, ORDERS, SUBORDERS OF ANIMALS. A. S. Pearse. (Prepared for A.A.A.S., Section F, Committee on Nomenclature.) Mimeographed, pp.14, Feb. 10, 1935.

ZOOLOGICAL NAMES. LIST OF PHYLA, CLASSES, AND ORDERS. A.S. Pearse. (Prepared for A.A.A.S., Section F, Amer. Assoc.Adv.Sci.) Mimeographed, pp.12, Apr. 1, 1936.

(SUPPLEMENT TO C.D. SHERBORN'S INDEX ANIMALIUM.) Supplement zu C.D.Sherborns Index Animalium. Franz Poche. Festschrift zum 60 Geburtstage von Prof. Dr. Embrik Strand, vol.5, pp.477-615, Feb. 28, 1939.

SOME PROPOSED CHANGES IN THE NOMENCLATURE OF THE AMERICAN MAMMALIA. Samuel N. Rhoads. American Naturalist, pp.523-526, June, 1894.

NOMENCLATURE OF SUPERGENERIC NAMES. S.A. Rohwer. Jour. Washington Acad. Sci., vol.11, pp.106-109, Mar. 4, 1921.

STABILITY OF FAMILY NAMES: SOME PRINCIPLES AND PROBLEMS. Curtis W. Sabrosky. Amer. Nat., Lancaster, vol. 81, pp.153-160, Mar.-Apr., 1947.

RENAMING PRIMARY HOMONYMS AFTER GENERIC REALLOCATION. Hubert G. Schenk, A. Myra Keen. Jour.Paleontol., Menasha, vol.16, no.6, pp.779-780, Nov., 1942.

NOMENCLATOR ZOOLOGICUS. Samuel H. Scudder. U.S. Nat. Mus. Bull.19, 1882.

INDEX ANIMALIUM. 1801-1850. Carolo Davies Sherborn. London, Printed by order of the Trustees of the British Museum. Part 3. INDEX ANNS-BAIL., pp.385-640, Nov., 1923, Part 4. INDEX BAIL-BYZOS, pp.641-943, May, 1924; Part 5. INDEX C-CEYL, pp.945-1196, Oct., 1924; Part 6. INDEX CEYL-CONCOLOR, pp.1197-1452, Jan., 1925; Part 7. INDEX CONCOLOR-CZIZEKI, pp. 1453-1771, June, 1925; Part 8. INDEX DAAKAR-DORSALIS, pp.1773-2008, Nov., 1925; Part 9. INDEX DORSALIS-EURYSTOMUS, pp.2009-2248, Feb., 1926; Part 10. INDEX EURYSTOMUS-FUNEREUS, pp.2249-2568, June, 1926; Part 11. INDEX FUNEREUS-GYZEHENSIS, pp.2569-2880, Nov., 1926; Part 12. INDEX HAANI-IMPLICATUS, pp. 2881-3126, Mar., 1927; Part 13. INDEX IMPLICATUS-LAMINELLA, pp.3137-3392, July, 1927; Part 14. INDEX LAMINELLA-LYZZIA, pp.3393-3746, Dec., 1927; Part 15. INDEX M-A-MELANOPHYSA, pp.3747-3970, May, 1928; Part 16. INDEX MELANOPHYSA-MUNCHISSONI, pp.3971-4194, Aug., 1928; Part 17. INDEX MUNDANYX, pp.4195-4450, Nov., 1928; Part 18. INDEX O-NIGRUM-PALLENS, pp.4451-4690, Mar., 1929; Part 19. INDEX PALLENS-PHYLLOCHOREIA, pp.4691-4930, June, 1929; Part 20. INDEX PHYLLOCHROMA-PRATINCOLA, pp.4931-5138, Oct., 1929; Part 21. INDEX PRATINCOLA-PYXIS, pp.5139-5348, Dec., 1929; Part 22. INDEX QUACHA-RYZO, pp.5349-5702, June, 1930; Part 23. INDEX S-LITTERA-SERRATUS, pp.5703-5910, Sep., 1930; Part 24. INDEX SERRATUS-SQUAMOSUS, pp.5911-6118, Dec., 1930; Part 25. INDEX SQUAMOSUS-SZENT, pp.6119-6358, Mar., 1931; Part 26. INDEX T-TRICHOSCELIA, pp.6359-6582, June, 1931; Part 27. INDEX TRICHOSCELIS-VARIEGATUS, pp.6583-6806, Oct., 1931; Part 28. INDEX VARIEGATUS ZIZYPHINUS, pp.6807-7056, Feb., 1932; Part 29. EPILOGUE, ADDITIONS TO BIBLIOGRAPHY, ADDITIONS AND CORRECTIONS, INDEX TO TRIVIALIA UNDER GENERA, pp.1-208, June, 1932; Part 30. INDEX TO TRIVIALIA UNDER GENERA, (ATHERINA-DIA), pp.209-416, Aug., 1932; Part 31. INDEX TO TRIVIALIA UNDER GENERA, (DIABASIS (COL.)-LYURUS), pp.417-654, Nov., 1932; Part 32. INDEX TO TRIVIALIA UNDER GENERA(MABOUYA-PRIONOPS), pp.655-878, Apr., 1933; Part 33. INDEX TO TRIVIALIA UNDER GENERA, (PRIONOPUS-ZYXOMMA; ADDENDA: ACETOSAE-VOLTZI), pp.879-1098, July, 1933.

FOR AND AGAINST UNIFORM ENDINGS IN ZOOLOGICAL NOMENCLATURE. George Gaylord Simpson. Systematic Zoology, vol.1, no.1, pp.20-23, Spring, 1952.

CHAPTER IN THE HISTORY OF ZOOLOGICAL NOMENCLATURE. Leonhard Stejneger. Smiths. Misc.Coll., vol.77, no.1, pp.1-21, Aug. 30, 1924.

FUTURE OF ZOOLOGICAL NOMENCLATURE, WITH AN APPENDIX: HISTORY OF RULES RE DESIGNATION OF GENOTYPES. C.W. Stiles. Trans. 4th Internat. Congr. Entomol., Ithaca, pp.622-645, 1928.

INTERNATIONAL CODE OF ZOOLOGICAL NOMENCLATURE AS APPLIED TO MEDICINE. C.W. Stiles. Treas. Dept., Publ. Health and Marine-Hosp. Serv.U.S.Washington, D.C., Hygienic Lab. Bull.no.24, pp.50, Sep., 1905.

INTERNATIONAL RULES OF ZOOLOGICAL NOMENCLATURE. C.W.Stiles. Proc.Biol. Soc. Washington, vol.39, pp.75-103, July 29, 1926.

IS AN INTERNATIONAL ZOOLOGICAL NOMENCLATURE PRACTICABLE? C.W. Stiles. Science, vol.73, no.1892, pp.349-354, Apr. 3, 1931.

NOTICE TO ZOOLOGISTS OF GENERIC NAMES TO BE INSERTED IN THE OFFICIAL LIST. C.W. Stiles. Science, n.s., vol.60, pp.384-385, Oct. 24, 1924.

OPINIONS RENDERED BY THE INTERNATIONAL COMMISSION ON ZOOLOGICAL

NOMENCLATURE. C.W. Stiles. Smiths. Misc. Coll., vol.73, no.6, pp.26, (publ. 3016), June 8, 1929.

PROPOSED AMENDMENTS: INTERNATIONAL RULES OF ZOOLOGICAL NOMENCLATURE. C.W. Stiles. Entomol. News, Philadelphia, vol.40, no.10, pp.329-333, Dec., 1929.

REPORT OF THE INTERNATIONAL COMMISSION ON ZOOLOGICAL NOMENCLATURE. C.W. Stiles. Atti Dell'XI Congresso Internationale di Zoologia, Padova, 1930, pp.84-92, 1931.

REPORT ON RULES OF ZOOLOGICAL NOMENCLATURE TO BE SUBMITTED TO THE FOURTH INTERNATIONAL ZOOLOGICAL CONGRESS AT CAMBRIDGE BY THE INTERNATIONAL COMMISSION FOR ZOOLOGICAL NOMENCLATURE. C.W.Stiles. Leipzig, pp.30, 1898.

UNDERLYING FACTORS IN THE CONFUSION IN ZOOLOGICAL NOMENCLATURE WITH A DEFINITE PRACTICAL SUGGESTION FOR THE FUTURE. C.W. Stiles. Science, n.s., vol.65, pp.194-199, Feb. 25, 1927.

WHAT CONSTITUTES PUBLICATION?C. W. Stiles. Science, n.s., vol.67, pp.471-478, May 11, 1928.

(MISCELLANEOUS ZOOLOGICAL AND PALEONTOLOGICAL NOMENCLATURE I-II.) Miscellanea nomenclatorica zoologica et paleontologica I-II. E. Strand. Archiv.f. Naturgeschichte, vol.92, Abt. A., heft 8, pp.30-75, 1928.

ANALYSIS OF THE MAMMALIAN GENERIC NAMES GIVEN IN DR. C. W. L. GLOGER'S 'NATURGESCHICHTE' (1841). Oldfield Thomas. Ann. & Mag. Nat. Hist. (6), vol. 15, no.86, pp.189-193, Feb., 1895.

GENERIC NAMES MYRMECOPHAGA AND DIDELPHIS. Oldfield Thomas. American Naturalist, vol.35, no.410, pp.143-145, Feb., 1901.

GENERIC NAMES OF THE PACCARIES, NORTHERN FUR-SEAL, AND SEA LEOPARD. Oldfield Thomas. Proc. Biol.Soc. Washington, vol.15, pp.153-154, June 20, 1902.

NOMINA CONSERVANDA IN MAMMALIA. Oldfield Thomas. Proc. Zool.Soc. London, pp.345-348, July 9, 1924.

ON THE GENERIC NAMES NOTOPHORUS, ALCES, DAMA, AND CEPHALOTES. Oldfield Thomas. Proc. Biol. Soc., Washington, vol.15, pp.197-198, Oct. 10, 1902.

ZOOLOGICAL NAMES SIMIA, S. SATYRUS AND PITHECUS AND THEIR POSSIBLE SUPPRESSION. Oldfield Thomas, M.A.C. Hinton. Nature, London, vol.118, no.2968, p.411, Sep. 18, 1926.

GENERIC NAMES GIVEN BY FRISCH IN 1775. Oldfield Thomas, G.S. Miller. Ann. & Mag. Nat. Hist. (7), vol.16, no.94, pp.461-464, Oct., 1905.

INDEX TO THE OPINIONS RENDERED BY THE INTERNATIONAL COMMISSION ON ZOOLOGICAL NOMENCLATURE. Harley J. Van Cleave. Amer. Midland Nat., Notre Dame, vol.30, no.1, pp.223-240, July, 1943.

NOMENCLATURE QUESTION. Lester F. Ward. Bull. Torrey Botanical Club, vol.22, no.7, pp.308-329, folded tbls.2, July, 1895.

INDEX ZOOLOGICUS. (Alphabetical list of names of genera and subgenera proposed for use in zoology as recorded in the "Zoological Record" 1880-1900, together with other names not included in the "Nomenclator Zoologicus" of S.H. Scudder.) Charles Owen Waterhouse. Edited by David Sharp. 1902.

INDEX ZOOLOGICUS NO. II.(Alphabetical list of names of genera and subgenera proposed for use in zoology as recorded in the "Zoological Record" vols.38-47 inclusive (1901-1910) and the zoology volumes of the "International Catalogue of Scientific Literature" annual issues 1-10, together with other names not included in previous nomenclators). Charles Owen Waterhouse. Edited by David Sharp. 1912.

INDEX GENERUM MAMMALIUM, ORIGINAL MANUSCRIPT. Frederick Herschel Waterhouse. Pp.158, 1894.

APPLICATION OF THE LAW OF PRIORITY. Hugh Watson. Ann. and Mag. Nat. Hist., ser.9, vol.14, pp.328-337, Sep., 1924.

PRIORITY IN FAMILY, ORDER AND HIGHER GROUP NAMES. Horace E. Wood. Science, n.s., vol.72, no.1861, pp.219-220, Aug.29, 1930.

INTERNATIONAL COMMISSION ON ZOOLOGICAL NOMENCLATURE. Opinions rendered by the International Commission on Zoological Nomenclature. Opinions 68 to 77. Smiths. Misc. Coll., vol.73, no. 1, pp.1-73, Jan. 31, 1922; Opinions 91 to 97. Smiths. Misc. Coll., vol.73, no.4, pp.1-30, Oct. 8, 1926; Opinions 98 to 104. Smiths. Misc. Coll., vol.73, no.5, pp. 1-28, Sep. 19, 1928; Opinions 105 to 114. Smiths. Misc. Coll., vol.73, no.6, pp. 1-26, June 8, 1929.

NUTRITION see PHYSIOLOGY -- NUTRITION

ORIENTATION see VOCALIZATIONS AND ORIENTATION

ORIGINS see EVOLUTION

PALEONTOLOGY see FOSSILS

PARASITES see DISEASES AND PARASITES

PELAGE see ANATOMY -- PELAGE, SKIN, COLORATION

## PHOTOGRAPHY AND PICTORIAL REPRESENTATION

ANIMAL DRAWINGS, NO. 1. Walter Addison. Bull. New York Zool. Soc., vol.43, no.5, pp.8, Sep.-Oct., 1940.

MARTIN JOHNSON AND HIS EXPEDITION TO LAKE PARADISE. A CULMINATING CHAPTER IN THE HISTORY OF WILDLIFE PHOTOGRAPHY, WITH A SURVEY OF SOME OF THE EARLIER STAGES IN THE DEVELOPMENT OF ITS TECHNIQUE. Carl E. Akeley. Nat. Hist., vol.24, pp. 285-296, illus., May-June, 1924.

ANIMAL FIGURES IN THE MAYA CODICES. Glover M. Allen, Alfred M. Tozzer. Peabody Mus. Amer. Arch. & Eth., Harvard Univ., vol.4, no.3, pp.283-372, pls.1-39, Feb., 1910.

DESCRIPTIVE AND PICTORIAL ILLUSTRATIONS OF THE WILD ANIMALS MENTIONED IN NATURAL HISTORY. George F. Bailey. New York, S.Booth, pp.48, illus., 1870.

STONE-AGE ART OF SCANDINAVIA: A GREAT FIND IN ROCK-CARVINGS IN NORWAY. Johs Boe. Illus. London News, vol.181, no.4887, pp.986-987, illus., Dec. 17, 1932.

CONVENIENT METHOD OF PHOTOGRAPHING SMALL MAMMALS. R.M. Bond. Jour. Mamm., vol.23, no.2, pp.183-186, pls.2, May 14, 1942.

DRAWINGS BY GEORGE GIBBS IN THE FAR NORTHWEST, 1849-1851. David I.Bushnell, Jr. Smiths. Misc. Coll., vol.97, no.8, (publ.3485), pp.1-28, figs.5, pls.1-8, Dec. 30, 1938.

WEST AFRICAN FAUNA PHOTOGRAPHED BY A COLLECTOR FOR THE ZOO. G.S. Cansdale. Illus. London News, vol.211, no. 5654, pp.244 - 245, illus., Aug. 30, 1947.

CAMERA TRAPPING A NOVEL DEVICE FOR WILD ANIMAL PHOTOGRAPHY. Henry R. Carey. Jour. Mamm., vol.7, no.4, pp. 278-281, pls.7, Nov., 1926.

NATURE PHOTOGRAPHY. N.R. Casillo. Pennsylvania Game News, Harrisburg, vol. 17, no.1, pp.10-11, 28, illus., Apr., 1946.

THIRTY-SIX ANIMALS, DRAWN FROM NATURE, AND ENGRAVED IN AQUATINTA. Chales Catton. London, printed for the Author, and sold by I. and J. Taylor; New Haven, Conn., H. Howe, pp.38, pl.36, 1825.

JUNGLE IN SUNLIGHT AND SHADOW. F.W. Champion. New York, pp.270, pls.95, 1934.

BLOODLESS QUEST. John Coleman, Jr. Sportsman, vol.5, no.3, pp.40-42, illus., Mar., 1929.

MUSEUM PHOTOGRAPHY. Charles H. Coles. Complete Photographer, Chicago, vol.7, issue 41, pp.2642-2655, illus., Oct. 30, 1942.

NATURALIST AT NIGHT. Blair Coursen. Turtox News, Chicago, vol.35, no.8, pp. 176-182, Aug., 1957.

(PLASTIC X-RAY PHOTOGRAPHS.) Plastische Roentgenbilder. Philip Creswick, R.I.Browne. Die Umschau, Frankfurt a. M., Jahrg.37, no.44, pp.860-861, figs. 4, Oct. 28, 1933.

WILD ANIMALS AND THE CAMERA. Walter Pfeffer Dando. London, Jarrold & Sons, pp.xx-179, pls., 1911.

(DEVELOPMENT OF MAMMAL SKIN DRAWINGS.) Sur l'évolution des dessins tégumentaires mammaliens. E.G.Dehaut. Bull. Mus. Nat. Hist. Nat., Paris, ser.2, vol.15, no.2, pp.75-78, figs.2, Feb., 1943.

PHOTOGRAMS OF SMALL BONES AND SKULLS. Ernest C. Driver. Science, Lancaster, vol.107, no.2783, p.451, illus., Apr. 30, 1948.

ART AND ANIMALS. A. Radclyffe Dugmore. Nat. Hist., vol.32, no.3, pp.229-243, fig. 22, May-June, 1932.

HOW I PHOTOGRAPHED CANADIAN BIG GAME. A. Radclyffe Dugmore. Animal & Zoo Mag., London, vol.5, no.12, pp. 4-7, illus., May, 1941.

(WHY ARE THINGS VERY DIFFICULT FOR OUR HUNTING-ANIMAL PAINTERS AND SCULPTORS?) Warum haben es unsere Jagtiermaler und -plastiker sehr schwer. Otto Frhr. von Dungern-Oberbau. Deutsche Jagd, Berlin, nos.15-16, pp.137-138, illus., July 19, 1940.

AS THE CAMERA SEES THEM. Sam Dunton. New York, Animal Kingdom, vol.52, no.2, pp.48-53, illus., Mar.-Apr., 1949.

ZOO NEWS IN PICTURES. Sam Dunton. Animal Kingdom, New York Zool. Soc., vol.59, no.6, pp.175-177, Nov., 1956. (Markhor, Hippo, Walrus.)

ZOO NEWS IN PICTURES. Sam Dunton. Animal Kingdom, New York Zool. Soc., vol.60, no.1, pp.15-17, illus., Feb., 1957. (Wapiti, Tenrec, Chimpanzee.)

FLASH! SEEING THE UNSEEN BY ULTRA HIGHSPEED PHOTOGRAPHY. Harold E. Edgerton, James R. Killian, Jr. Boston, Hale, Cushman and Flint, pp.203, illus., Oct., 1939.

EYE, FILM, AND CAMERA IN COLOR PHOTOGRAPHY. Ralph M. Evans. Eastman Kodak Co. Pp.410, 1959.

ANIMAL DRAWINGS NO. 2. Roberta Everett. Bull. New York Zool. Soc., vol.44, no.1, pls.7, Jan.-Feb., 1941.

CAMERA HUNTING IN THE NORTHLAND. William L. Finley. Nature Mag., vol.9, pp.73-78, 159-164, 211-217, 291-296, illus., Feb. to May, 1927.

PICTURING WILDLIFE IN THE NATIONAL PARKS. William L. Finley. Nat. Parks Mag., Washington, D.C., vol.16, no.71, pp.17-21, illus., Oct.-Dec., 1942.

FILMING MUSK-OXEN AND ARCTIC FOXES. Richard Finnie. Nature Mag., Washington,

D.C., vol.32, no.6, pp.309-312, illus., June-July, 1939.

ZOO PHOTOGRAPHY. Arthur H. Fisher. Complete Photographer, Chicago, vol.9, issue 54, pp.3522-3528, illus., Mar. 10, 1943.

GREAT DISCOVERY OF PREHISTORIC ART: SOME 2500 ROCK-DRAWINGS AND PAINTINGS FOUND IN THE FEZZAN DESERT--A VAST PICTURE CHRONICLE OF PRIMITIVE MAN AND CONTEMPORARY ANIMALS. Leo Frobenius. Illus. London News, vol.181, no.4883, pp.798-801, illus., Nov. 19, 1932.

FROM ROCK TO CANVAS. HOW THE SCIENTIFIC ARTIST BRINGS A PREHISTORIC ANIMAL TO LIFE. John C. Germann. Nat. Hist., New York, vol.51, no.4, pp.166-175, illus., Apr., 1943.

DOMESTIC ANIMALS IN ROCK ART. E. Goodall. Trans. Rhodesia Sci. Assoc., Bulawayo, vol.41, pp.57-62, figs.4, 1946.

NIGHT MOVIES OF WILD ANIMALS. Kenneth Gordon. Murrelet, Seattle, vol.21, no.3, pp.62-64, Sep.-Dec., 1940.

THIRTY YEARS OF NATURE PHOTOGRAPHY. PERSONAL RECORD OF TWO OBSERVERS. Seton Gordon. Cassel & Co. Ltd., pp.xi-100, pls.108, 1936.

CAMERA TRAPPING IN THE SNOW. Tappan Gregory. Jour. Mamm., vol.10, no.2, pp. 142-148, pls.13-14, May, 1929.

EYES IN THE NIGHT. Tappan Gregory. Thomas Y. Crowell Co., New York, vol. 8, pp.xi-243, illus., 1939.

FLASHES OF WILDLIFE. Tappan Gregory. Outdoor America, vol.1, n.s., no.8, pp. 4-5, 9, illus., June, 1936.

FLASHLIGHTS OF COTTONTAILS AND A CHIPMUNK. Tappan Gregory. Jour. Mamm., vol.11, no.2, pp.201-204, pl.10, May, 1930.

FLASHLIGHTS OF SMALL MAMMALS. Tappan Gregory. Jour. Mamm., vol.6, no.4, pp.232-236, pls.2, Nov., 1925.

RANDOM FLASHLIGHTS. Tappan Gregory. Jour. Mamm., vol.8, no.1, pp.45-47, pl. 7, Feb., 1927.

SOME FLASHLIGHTS OF NEW MEXICO MAMMALS. Tappan Gregory. Jour.Mamm., vol.8, no.4, pp.285-289, pls.5, Nov., 1927.

PHOTOGRAPHS OF SOME MAMMALS, BIRDS AND REPTILES NOW OR RECENTLY LIVING IN THE ZOOLOGICAL GARDEN. Newton H. Hartman. Annual Rep. Zool. Soc. Philadelphia, 1931, pp.3-27, illus., 1931.

(ANIMAL REPRESENTATIONS. THE MAMMALS. VOL. 2. WALL PICTURES.) Tierdarstellungen. Die Saeugetiere. Vol. 2. Die Wandbilder. Oskar Heinroth, Max Hilzheimer. Das Grabdenkmal des Koenig S'a hu-re. Wiss. Veroeffentl. d. Deutsch. Orient.-Gesell., Leipzig, vol.26, pp.167-184, pls.1, 3, 17, 31, 55, 56, 1913.

SHOOT THEM WITH A CAMERA. Frederick W. Hollender. Alaska Sportsman, Ketchikan, vol.9, no.6, pp.12-13, 26, illus., June, 1943.

WILD LIFE PHOTOGRAPHY IN THE MALAYAN JUNGLE. Theodore Hubback. Jour. Bombay Nat. Hist. Soc., vol.41, no.1, pp.48-63, pls.8, 1939.

CAMERA SAFARIS. Martin Johnson. Nat. Hist., New York, vol.37, no.1, pp.46-62, illus., Jan., 1936.

PICTURING AFRICA. Martin Johnson. Nat. Hist., vol.27, pp.539-560, illus., Dec., 1927 (Mar., 1928).

WINGS OVER AFRICA. ACCOUNT OF A PHOTOGRAPHIC EXPEDITION THAT TRAVELED BY AIRPLANE THROUGH 60,000 MILES OF AFRICAN SKY. Martin Johnson. Nat. Hist., New York, vol.34, no.7, pp.597-611, illus., Nov., 1934.

BIG GAME PHOTOGRAPHY. Cherry Kearton. Field, London, vol.154, no.4007, p.543, Oct. 12, 1929.

STALKING BIG GAME WITH A CAMERA. Cherry Kearton. Field, London, vol.154, no.4002, pp.357-358, Sep. 7, 1929.

ANIMAL STARS OF "THE YEARLING." Jean Kent. Nature Mag., Washington, vol. 39, no.9, pp.465-468, illus., Nov., 1946.

PHOTOGRAPHIC STUDIES. G.E. Kirkpatrick. San Diego Zoonooz, vol.17, no. 10, pp.4-5, illus., Nov., 1944.

(ON A PHOTOGRAPH FROM THE ZOOLOGICAL GARDEN.) Zum Lichtbild aus den Zoologischen Garten. Josef Klintz. Zool. Garten n.F., Leipzig, vol.7, nos. 7-9, pp.213-216, Nov., 1934.

HUNTING WITH A CAMERA. EXHIBITION OF PHOTOGRAPHS OF MAMMALS AT THE AMERICAN MUSEUM. Herbert Lang. Nat. Hist., vol.22, pp.224-234, pls.9, May-June, 1922.

PHOTOGRAPHS OF AFRICAN MAMMALS. Herbert Lang. Nature Mag., vol.16, no.5, pp.314-315, figs.6, Nov., 1930.

NEW REVIEW OF THE WESTERN EUROPEAN GROUP OF QUATERNARY CAVE ART. P.A. Leason. Proc. Prehistoric Soc., Cambridge, n.s., vol.5, pt.1, pp.51-60, figs.4, 1939.

DRAWINGS BY A FIELD ARTIST. W.R. Leigh. Nat. Hist., New York, vol.57, no.3, pp.120-125, illus., Mar., 1948.

PAINTING THE BACKGROUNDS FOR THE AFRICAN HALL GROUPS. W.R. Leigh. Nat. Hist., vol.27, pp.575-582, illus., Dec., 1927 (Mar., 1928).

(REPRESENTATION OF NEW OR LITTLE KNOWN MAMMALS IN PICTURES AND DESCRIPTIONS OF 65 SPECIES IN 50 LITHOGRAPH COLOR PLATES AFTER THE ORIGINALS OF THE ZOOLOGICAL MUSEUM OF THE UNIVERSITY OF BERLIN.) Darstellung neuer oder wenig Bekannter Saeugethiere in Abbildungen und Beschreibungen von fuenf und sechzig Arten auf fuenfzig colorirten Steindruecktafeln nach den Originalen des Zoologischen Museums der Universitaet zu Berlin. H. Lichtenstein. 2 Parts, 1827-34.

HUNTING WITH A CAMERA. Dan McCowan. Beaver, Winnipeg, outfit 279, pp.22-25, illus., June, 1948.

(PICTURES OF THE ANIMAL WORLD.) Lebensbilder aus der Tierwelt. H. Meerwarth, K. Soffel. Leipzig, vols.6, 1910-11.

ILLUSTRATIONS ON THE STANDARD NATURAL HISTORY: WITH ELLIOTT COUES. C.Hart Merriam. Science, n.s., vol.25, pp.682-684, June 21, 1895.

PHOTOGRAPHY AT THE ZOO. Mark Mooney, Jr. The Camera, Philadelphia, vol.58, no.6, pp.399-404, June, 1939.

DRAWINGS BY THE SUDANESE ARTISTS OF SEVEN THOUSAND YEARS AGO. NEOLITHIC ROCK-DRAWINGS FROM THE POTHOLES OF THE NILE. Oliver H. Myers. Illus. London News, vol.213, no.5717, pp. 556-557, illus., Nov. 13, 1948.

HOW TO HUNT WITH A CAMERA. William Nesbit. New York, E.P. Dutton and Co., pp.337, illus., 1926.

FRIEZE OF BEASTS MADE 12,000 B.C.: FIRST PREHISTORIC ROCK DRAWINGS THAT HAVE BEEN FOUND IN PALESTINE. René Neuville. Illus. London News, vol. 181, no.4881, pp.730-731, illus., Nov. 5, 1932.

WILD ANIMALS PHOTOGRAPHED AND DESCRIBED. John Fortuné Nott. London, S. Low, Marston, Searle, & Rivington, pp.xi-568, illus., pls., 1886.

PHOTOGRAPHING YOSEMITE BIRDS AND SMALL MAMMALS IN COLOR. Lloyd P. Parratt. Yosemite Nat.Notes, Yosemite, vol.20, no.5, pp.38-40, May, 1941.

SHETLAND PIRATES AND OTHER WILD LIFE STUDIES. Francis Pitt. London, A. Allen and Unwin, Ltd., pp.248, pls. 16, 1923.

RECENTLY-FOUND TREASURES OF ONE OF THE WORLD'S FIRST AND GREATEST EMPIRES: ACHAEMENID GOLD OBJECTS. Arthur Upham Pope. Illus. London News, vol.213, no.5700, pp.57-59, illus., July 17, 1948.

CAMERA IN PLACE OF RIFLE. A.W. Redfern. Jour. Soc. Preservation Fauna of the Empire, Hertford, n.s., pt.37, pp.22-26, pls.3, Aug., 1939.

WHO--ME? (KOALA, FOX, HAMSTER, LEMUR, TIGER.) Russel Roberts and others. Nat. Hist., New York, vol.53, no.1, pp.44-47, photographs, Jan., 1944.

(SMALL ATLAS OF MAMMALS.) Petit atlas des mammifères. Paul Rode. Paris, N. Boubee & Co., vol.4, illus.(incl.map), col.pls., diagrs., 1942-44.

SMALL ANIMAL PHOTO-CAGE. W.M. Rush. Nature Mag., vol.20, no.5, p.198, illus., Nov., 1932.

WITH A CAMERA IN THE ANTARCTIC. A. Saunders. Photographic Jour., vol.78, pp.164-173, illus., Apr., 1938.

(MAMMALS IN ILLUSTRATIONS FROM NATURE, WITH DESCRIPTIONS.) Die Saeugethiere in Abbildungen nach der Natur, mit Beschreibungen. J.C.D. von Schreber. Leipzig, 7 parts, col.pls., 1774-1846.

HUNTING WILDLIFE WITH YOUR CAMERA. C.W. Schwartz. Popular Photography, Chicago, vol.10, no.6, pp.34-35, 88-89, illus., June, 1942.

PHOTOGRAPHING SMALL MAMMALS. C.W. Schwartz. Yosemite Nat. Notes, Stockton, vol.18, no.8, pp.92-93, Aug., 1939.

NIMROD WITH A KODAK. THERE ARE NO GAME LAWS FOR HIM; HE MAY GO FORTH AT ALL SEASONS AND ON THE SABBATH. Joseph Seabury. The Sportsman, Boston, Mass., pp.79-80, illus., June, 1930.

ON PHOTOGRAPHIC CAGES. Ernest Thompson Seton. Jour. Mamm., vol.5, no.4, pp.269-270, Nov., 1924.

HIDE AND SQUEAK!--IF YOU WANT TO GET GOOD ANIMAL PHOTOGRAPHS. H. H. Sheldon. Nat. Hist., New York, vol. 48, no.1, pp.50-51, illus., June, 1941.

PATTERN FOR WILD LIFE. H.H. Sheldon. Amer. Annual Photography, Boston, vol.58, pp.85-93, figs.7, 1943.

FLSHLIGHT STORY OF AN ALBINO PORCUPINE AND OF A CUNNING BUT UNFORTUNATE COON. George Shiras, 3rd. Nat. Geo. Mag., Washington, D.C., vol. 22, no.6, pp.572-596, illus., June, 1911.

HUNTING WILD LIFE WITH CAMERA AND FLASHLIGHT. RECORD OF 65 YEARS' VISITS TO THE WOODS AND WATERS OF NORTH AMERICA. VOL. 1. LAKE SUPERIOR REGION. VOL. 2. WILD LIFE OF COASTS, ISLANDS, AND MOUNTAINS. George Shiras, 3rd. 1936.

(PICTURES OF ANIMALS.) Mao p'I shou t'u shuo. Chên-huang Shou. The Science Publishing Corporation, Peking, pp.142, illus., 1958.

HOW DOST THOU PORTRAY THE SIMURGH? INTRODUCING THE STORY OF ANIMAL ART THROUGH THE AGES. George Gaylord Simpson. Nat. Hist., New York, vol.47, no. 2, pp.86-96, illus., Feb., 1941.

MODERN NOAH'S ARK. R.G. Skerrett. Compressed Air, New York, vol.50, no.7, pp.185-187, illus., July, 1945.

SIX PICTURES. Lorene Squire. Beaver Winnipeg, outfit 269, no.1, pp.34-39, illus., June, 1938.

CAMERA STALKING. C.H. Stockley. Jour. Soc. Preservation Fauna of Empire, Hertford, n.s., pt.33, pp.20-25, photos 2, Mar., 1938.

MEASUREMENT AND PHOTOGRAPHY OF SPECIMENS OF BIG GAME. C.H. Stockley. Jour. Bombay Nat. Hist. Soc., vol.29, pp. 209-213, fig.1, pls.3, Apr. 20, 1923.

WILDLIFE GALLERY. DICK GROSSENHEIDER'S MAMMAL DRAWINGS. George

Miksch Sutton. Audubon Mag., New York, vol.44, no.3, pp.146-149, illus., May-June, 1942.

SOME SIERRAN CHIPMUNKS. WITH NOTES ON PHOTOGRAPHY OF SMALL MAMMALS BY JOSEPH DIXON. H.S. Swath. Mus.Vert. Zool. Univ. Calif., pp.401-413, pls.223-225, 1919.

(ANIMAL PICTURE CLASSIFICATION.) Pu ju lei tung wu t'u chien. Pang-chieh T'an. Science Publishing Corporation, Peking, pp.191, illus., 1955.

AMERICAN SKETCHBOOKS OF A FRENCH NATURALIST 1816-1837. DESCRIPTION OF THE CHARLES ALEXANDER LESUEUR COLLECTION WITH A BRIEF ACCOUNT OF THE ARTIST. R.W.G. Vail. Proc.Amer. Antiq. Soc. Boston, vol.48, pt.1, n.s., pp. 49-155, sketches 7, photo, Apr. 20, 1938.

HUNTING WITH BRUSH AND GUN. Roger B. Whitman. Country Life, vol.40, no.5, pp.34-39, 5 half-tones and 4 col.pls., Sep., 1921.

SHORT ACCOUNT OF ZOOLOGICAL ILLUSTRATION. Walter J. Wildering. Animal Kingdom, New York, vol.47, no.3, pp.70-77, illus., May-June, 1944.

PHOTOGRAPHS OF MULE DEER AND AFRICAN LIONS. J.C. Williams. Nat. Hist., New York, vol.52, no.3, pp.102-103, Oct., 1943.

ANIMAL KINGDOM. Illustrated Catalogue of an Exhibition of Manuscript Illuminations, Book Illustrations, Drawings, Cylinder Seals, and Bindings. Pierpont Morgan Library, New York, pp.70, pls.10, 1940.

ANIMALS AND BIRDS ON ROMAN COINS. South Australian Naturalist, Adelaide, vol. 24, no.3, pp.7-9, figs.29, Apr., 1947.

BEASTS AND MONTHERS BRILLIANTLY PORTRAYED IN BYZANTINE MOSAICS. Illus. London News, vol.210, no.5640, p.539, illus., May 24, 1947.

BORNEO. A Photographic Album ( set of three). Editors, Georg Mueller & Co., Munich, Germany, 1926.

CATALOGUE OF THE JONES COLLECTION. PT. 3. PAINTINGS AND MINIATURES. London, Victoria & Albert Museum, pp.xii-148, pl.59, 1923.

CHINESE ANIMAL PORTRAITURE. Illus. London News, vol.210, no.5637, p.470, illus., May 3, 1947.

COLOR PLATES TO CUVIER'S MAMMALS. London, vol.8, pls.75, 1837.

FAMOUS DRAWINGS FROM HOLKHAM. Illus. London News, vol.213, no.5700, p. 79, illus., July 17, 1948.

THE FINEST EXAMPLE OF AURIGNACIAN DRAWING; NEWLY DISCOVERED IN LA COLOMBIÈRE ROCK-SHELTER. Illus. London News, vol.214, no.5740, pp.542-543, illus., Apr. 23, 1949.

GREAT DISCOVERY OF PREHISTORIC ART:MORE REVELATIONS FROM THE FEZZAN ROCKS. BIG-GAME STUDIES BY AFRICAN "PRIMITIVES": ELEPHANT; GIRAFFE; BUFFALO; AND RHINOCEROS. Illus. London News, vol.181, no.4884, pp. 860-861, illus., Nov. 26, 1932.

ILLUSTRATIONS OF ANIMALS. Made Under the Direction of the Society for Promoting Christian Knowledge. London, (n.d.), col.pls.

MASTERPIECES RECALLING VANISHED EMPIRES. IRANIAN ART OF SEVERAL GREAT EPOCHS. Illus. London News, vol.213, no.5705, pp.214, 215, illus., Aug. 21, 1948.

SEE NATURE THROUGH THE CAMERA'S EYE. Nat. Hist., New York, vol.51, no.1, pp.48-49, illus., Jan., 1943.

SEEING NATURE THROUGH THE CAMERA'S EYE. Nat. Hist., New York, vol. 52, no.3, pp.100-102, illus., Oct., 1943.

SPEAKING OF PICTURES: HOUSE CATS (AND DOGS) MAKE STRANGE ADOPTIONS. Life, New York, vol.27, no.4, pp.10-12, illus., July 25, 1949.

STUBBS, THE GREAT ANIMAL PAINTER. Illus. London News, vol.219, no.5856, p. 73, illus., July 14, 1951.

WILD LIFE IN THE CAMERA'S EYE. Illus. London News, vol.216, no.5786, pp.381, 383, illus., Mar. 11, 1950.

## PHYLOGENY

(PALEOBIOLOGY AND PHYLOGENY.) Palaeobiologie und Stammesgeschichte. O. Abel. Jena, 1929.

(OUTLINE OF A PHYLOGENY OF DOMESTIC ANIMALS.) Grundzuege einer Stammesgeschichte der Haustiere. Otto Antonius. Verlag von Gustav Fischer, Jena, illus., 1924.

PRECIPITINS AND PHYLOGENY IN ANIMALS. Alan Boyden. Amer. Nat., vol.68, no.719, pp.516-536, Nov., 1934.

ON THE PHYLOGENESIS OF THE MAMMARY GLANDS AND TACTILE HAIRS.) Ueber die Phylogenese der Milchdruesen und der Tasthaare. Ivar Broman. Anat. Anzeiger, vol.59, pp.132-138, Jan. 6, 1925.

HAIR IN ITS RELATIONS TO QUESTIONS OF HOMOLOGY AND PHYLOGENY. C.H. Danforth. Amer. Jour. Anat., vol.36, pp. 47-68, fig.1, Sep. 15, 1925.

(THE THEORY OF FOETALIZATION AND THE FORMATION OF RACES OF DOGS AND PIGS.) La théorie de la foetalisation et la formation des races de chiens et de porcs. Ed Dechambre. Mammalia, Paris, vol.13, no.4, pp.129-137, Dec., 1949.

ON THE PHYLOGENY OF HAIR. Hans Ellias, Seymour Bortner. Amer. Mus. Novitates, vol.1820, pp.1-15, Mar. 29, 1957.

THE TORSION OF THE HUMERUS: A PHYLOGENETIC SURVEY FROM FISH TO MAN. F.Gaynor Evans, Vernon E. Krahl. Amer. Jour. Anat., Philadelphia, vol.76, no.3, pp.303-337, figs.5, May, 1945.

(DISTRIBUTION OF DOMESTIC ANIMALS AND PHYLOGENY.) Haustierverbreitung und Stammesgeschichte. Ernst Feige. Fortschr. Landwirtschaft, Berlin, Jahrg.3, no.16, pp.721-724, Aug. 15, 1928.

(ON THE PHYLOGENESIS OF THE PLACENTA.) Zur Phylogenese der Placenta. O. Grosser. Anat. Anzeiger, vol.68, pp. 297-300, 1929.

ANALYSIS OF SOME PHYLOGENETIC TERMS, WITH ATTEMPTS AT REDEFINITION. Otto Haas, George Gaylord Simpson. Proc. Amer. Philos. Soc., Philadelphia, vol.90, no.5, pp.319-349, Dec., 1946.

PHYLOGENETIC ARRANGEMENT OF THE MUSCULAR SYSTEM. A. Brazier Howell. Anat. Record, vol.66, no.3, pp.295-316, Oct., 1936.

PHYLOGENY OF THE DISTAL MUSCULATURE OF THE PECTORAL APPENDAGE. A. Brazier Howell. Jour. Morphology, vol. 60, no.1, pp.287-315, figs.2, Dec., 1936.

(Review by H.E. Jordan of) EARLY ONTOGENETIC PHENOMENA IN MAMMALS AND THEIR BEARINGS ON OUR INTERPRETATION OF THE PHYLOGENY OF VERTEBRATES. Hubrecht. Anat. Record, Philadelphia, vol.3, no.7, pp.440-444, July, 1909.

(FORAMEN SPINOSUM AS A PHYLOGENETIC MONUMENT.) Das Foramen spinosum als ein phylogenetisches Merkmal. K.Jazuta. Anat. Anzeiger, vol.70, nos.8-10, pp.212-213, Aug. 14, 1930.

PHYLOGENETIC TREES. Glenn L. Jepsen. Trans. New York Acad. Sci., ser.2, vol.6, no.3, pp.81-92, Jan., 1944.

DESCENT AND RACE BIOLOGY OF FURRED ANIMALS. Ivar Johansson. Fur of Canada, Winnipeg, vol.12, no.1, pp.12, 14, 16, Oct., 1946.

(ON THE DEVELOPMENTAL HISTORY OF THE DENTAL SYSTEM OF THE MAMMALS, A CONTRIBUTION TO THE PHYLOGENY OF THIS ANIMAL GROUP.) Zur Entwicklungsgeschichte des Zahnsystems der Saeugethiere, zugleich ein Beitrag zur Stammesgeschichte dieser Thiergruppe. Wilhelm Leche. Stuttgart, E.Naegele, vol.3, illus., pl.25 (part col.), 1895-1907.

ON THE PHYLOGENY OF HORSES, DOGS AND CATS. W.D. Matthew. Science, n.s., vol.69, pp.494-496, May 10, 1929.

(NOTES ON THE MORPHOLOGY AND PHYLOGENY OF THE VERTEBRATES.) Notizen zur Morphologie und Stammesgeschichte der Wirbeltiere. A. Naef. Biol. Zentralblatt, vol.46, pp.205-212, figs.3, 1926.

RELATIVE GROWTH AND VERTEBRATE PHYLOGENY. Fred J. Phleger, Jr. Amer. Jour. Sci., New Haven, vol.238, no.9, pp. 643-662, figs.6, Sep., 1940.

(ATTEMPT AT A PHYLOGENY OF THE MAMMALIAN DENTITION.) Versuch einer Phylogenie des Saeugethier-Gebisses. Inaugural-Dissertation Univ. Jena, pp.59, 1883.

## PHYSIOLOGY

QUANTITATIVE RELATIONS IN THE PHYSIOLOGICAL CONSTITUTION OF MAMMALS. E.F. Adolph. Science, Lancaster, vol.109, no.2841, pp.579-585, figs.4, June 10, 1949.

COMPARATIVE STUDY OF THE OLFACTORY AND TRIGEMINAL REFLEXES ELICITED BY VARIOUS VAPORS IN DIFFERENT MAMMALS. William F. Allen. Proc. Washington Acad. Sci., vol.26, no. 11, pp.466-473, figs.2, Nov. 15, 1936.

METABOLISM OF CINCHONINE IN DOGS AND IN MAN. J.C. Andrews, W.E. Cornatzer. Trop. Disease Bull., London, vol.45, no.5, pp.396-397, May, 1948.

ABOUT MICE AND MAN; AN INTRODUCTION TO MAMMALIAN BIOLOGY. Frederick R. Avis. Portland, Me., J.W. Walch, pp.194, illus.(part col.), 1957.

(DEVELOPMENT OF YOUNG MAMMALS AND VARIATIONS OF TEMPERATURES; STUDY OF THE INFLUENCE OF NOXIOUS APPLICATIONS.) Développement des jeunes mammifères et variations de températures; étude des influences nocives-applications. Marius Baccino. Paris, Maloine, pp.175, illus., tbls., diagrs., 1937.

FORMATION OF UREA IN THE MAMMALIAN BODY WITHOUT PARTICIPATION OF ARGINASE. S.J. Bach, S. Williamson. Nature, London, vol.150, no.3811, pp.575-577, Nov. 14, 1942.

(PLEURAL PRESSURE IN MAMMALS.) La pression pleurale chez les mammiferes. Louis Emile Francois Baillet. Montpellier, Imprimerie de la manufacture de la Charite, pp.166, illus., diagrs., 1935.

MICROBIAL SYNTHESIS AND AUTOLYSIS IN THE DIGESTIVE TRACT OF HERBIVORA. Frank Baker. Nature, London, vol.149, no. 3786, pp.582-583, May 23, 1942.

COMPARATIVE BIOLOGIC-ANATOMICAL RESEARCHES ON MASTICATION IN SOME MAMMALS. G. Becht. Proc. Kon. Nederlandse Akad. Wetensch., ser.C, vol.56, no.4, pp.508-527, Sep.-Oct., 1953.

SURFACE TEMPERATURE OF THE ELEPHANT, RHINOCEROS, AND HIPPOPOTAMUS. Francis G. Bennedict, Edward L. Fox, Marion L. Baker. Amer. Jour.Physiol., Memphis, vol.56, no.3, pp.464-474, figs. 6, July, 1921.

RESPIRATION AND METABOLISM. (In) Comparative Animal Physiology, C.L. Prosser, ed. Philadelphia, W.B.Saunders, chap.8, pp.209-289, 1950.

MODIFICATION OF MAMMALIAN SEXUAL CYCLES. V. THE AVENUE OF RECEPTION OF SEXUALLY STIMULATING LIGHT. Thomas Hume Bissonnette. Jour. Comp. Psychol., Baltimore, vol.22, no.1, pp.93-103, Aug., 1936.

SEXUAL PHOTOPERIODICITY. Thomas Hume Bissonnette. Quart. Review Biol., vol. 11, no.4, pp.371-386, Dec., 1936.

PROBLEMS OF PHYSIOLOGY AND ECOLOGY OF DESERT ANIMALS. F.S.Bodenheimer. (In) Biology of Deserts, edited by J.L.Cloudsley-Thompson, Inst. of Biology, London, pp.162-167, 1954.

(TAIL FUNCTIONS IN VERTEBRATES. A CONTRIBUTION TO THE COMPARATIVE BIOLOGY AND PSYCHOLOGY OF THE VERTEBRATES.) Schwanzfunktionen bei Wirbeltieren. Ein Beitrag zur vergleichenden Biologie und Psychologie der Wirbeltiere. Peter Bopp. Rev. Suisse Zool., vol.61, no.3, pp.83-151, illus., Mar., 1954.

(ADAPTATIONS TO AQUATIC LIFE IN MAMMALS.) Les adaptations a la vie aquatique chez les mammiferes. Francois Bourliere. La Nature, no.3233, pp.321-326, Sep., 1954.

BLOOD VOLUME IN MAMMALS. J.D. Burke. Physiological Zoology, Chicago, vol.27, no.1, pp.1-20, Jan., 1954.

OXYGEN CAPACITY IN MAMMALS. J.D. Burke. Physiol. Zoology, Chicago, vol. 26, no.3, pp.259-265, July, 1953.

GROWTH OF THE HAIR. Herman B.Chase. Physiol. Rev., Washington, vol.34, no.1, pp.113-126, Jan., 1954.

WATER EXCHANGES OF SOME SMALL MAMMALS. Robert M. Chew. PhD thesis, Univ. Ill., 1948; Ecological Monographs, Durham, vol.21, pp.215-225, figs.4, July, 1951.

EFFECT OF POPULATION SIZE ON THE WEIGHTS OF THE REPRODUCTIVE ORGANS OF WHITE MICE. John J.Christian. Naval Med. Res. Inst., Res. Rep., vol. 13, pp.81-88, graphs., Mar., 1955.

RELATION OF THE ADRENAL CORTEX TO POPULATION SIZE IN RODENTS.John J. Christian. Sc.D. thesis, Johns Hopkins School of Hyg. & Public Health, pp.124, May, 1954.

REDUCTION OF ADRENAL WEIGHT IN RODENTS BY REDUCING POPULATION SIZE. John J. Christian, David E.Davis. Trans. 20th N. Amer. Wildl. Conf., pp. 177-189, graphs, 1955.

NERVOUS AND VASCULAR RELATIONS OF THE PINEAL GLAND. W.E.Le Gros Clark. Jour. Anat., Cambridge, vol.77, pt.4, pp.471-492, figs.8, pls.2, July, 1940.

PHYSIOLOGICAL ONTOGENY. I. THE PRESENT STATUS OF THE PROBLEM. Alfred E. Cohn, Henry A. Murray, Jr. Quart. Rev. Biol., vol.2, pp.469-493, Dec., 1927.

NOTE ON THE PHYSIOLOGY OF THE MAMMALIAN EPIDIDYMIS AND SPERMATOZOON. Lawrence Collery. Dublin, Hodges, pp.213-223, 1944.

OESTRUS, OVULATION AND MENSTRUATION. George W. Corner. Physiol. Rev., vol.3, pp.457-482, 1923.

ABNORMAL SEXUALITY IN ANIMALS. II. PHYSIOLOGICAL. F.A.E. Crew. Quart. Rev. Biol., vol.2, no.2, pp.249-266, illus., June, 1927.

MANUAL FOR LABORATORY WORK IN MAMMALIAN PHYSIOLOGY. Fred Edmund D'Amour. Chicago, Univ. of Chicago Press, vol.1, 1948.

LIVER VITAMIN A RESERVES OF SOME BRITISH WILD ANIMALS. A.W. Davies, Alastair N. Worden. Proc. Zool. Soc.London, vol.123, pt.4, pp.739-746, Feb. 10, 1954.

CONDUCTING SYSTEM OF THE VERTEBRATE HEART. Francis Davies, Eric T.B. Francis. Biol. Rev. Cambridge Philos.Soc., vol.21, no.4, pp.173-188, Oct., 1946.

BODY TEMPERATURES OF SOME CENTRAL AMERICAN MAMMALS. David E. Davis. Jour. Mamm., vol.17, no.2, pp.165-166, tabls.

(RELATIONS BETWEEN PHYSIOLOGICAL AND MORPHOLOGICAL ADAPTATION IN SOME WILD AND DOMESTIC ANIMALS.) Relations entre l'adaptation physiologique et la morphologie chez quelques mammiferes domestiques et sauvages. Ed Dechambre. Mem. Mus. Nat. Hist. Nat., Paris, nov. ser., vol.26, no.4, pp.75-241, 1948.

PHYSIOLOGY OF THE PARATHYROID GLANDS. Lester R. Dragstedt. Physiol. Rev., vol.7, pp.499-530, Oct.. 1927.

PHYSIOLOGY OF DOMESTIC ANIMALS (6th ed.). H.H.Dukes. Comstock Publ. Co., Ithaca, N.Y., pp.xii-817, illus., 1947.

TEMPERATURE AND THE GROWTH OF HAIR. Paul Eaton, Mary Wright Eaton. Science, n.s., vol.86, no.2233, p.354, Oct. 15, 1937.

(BODY TEMPERATURES IN TROPIC BATS AND ARMADILLOS.) Koerpertemperaturen bei tropischen Fledermaeuse und Schuppentieren. M. Eisentraut. Saeugetierk. Mitteil., Stuttgart, vol.4, no.2, pp.64-67, Apr. 1, 1956.

(TEMPERATURE FLUCTUATIONS IN THE LOWER MAMMALS.) Temperaturschwankungen bei niederen Saeugetieren. M. Eisentraut. Zeitschr. Saeugetierk., vol.21, nos. 1-2, pp.49-52, 1956.

FORCES AND ENERGY CHANGES IN THE LEG DURING WALKING. Herbert Elftman. Amer. Jour. Physiol., Memphis, vol.125, no.2, pp.339-356, figs.9, tbl.1, Feb., 1939.

FUNCTION OF MUSCLES IN LOCOMOTION. Herbert Elftman. Amer. Jour. Physiol., Memphis, vol.125, no.2, pp.357-366, figs. 4, Feb., 1939.

BODY TEMPERATURES OF SOME CENTRAL AMERICAN MAMMALS. Robert K. Enders, David E. Davis. Jour. Mamm., vol.17, no. 2, pp.165-166, tbls., May, 1936.

HEAT REGULATION AND METABOLISM IN SOME TROPICAL MAMMALS AND BIRDS. P.S. Enger. Acta.Physiol.Scand., Stockholm, vol.40, nos.2-3, pp.161-168, Oct., 1957.

STUDIES ON THE PHYSIOLOGY OF THE PLAIN MUSCLE. II. OXYGEN USAGE OF PLAIN MUSCLE, AND ITS RELATION TO TONUS. C. Lovatt Evans. Jour. Physiol., vol.58, pp.22-32, Oct., 1923.

STUDIES ON THE PHYSIOLOGY OF THE PLAIN MUSCLE. I. EFFECT OF ALTERATION OF THE HYDROGEN ION CONCENTRATION ON THE TONE AND CONTRACTIONS OF PLAIN MUSCLE. C. Lovatt Evans, S.W.F. Underhill. Jour. Physiol., vol.58, pp.1-14, 1923.

EFFECT OF LOW ENVIRONMENTAL TEMPERATURE ON THE COMPOSITION OF DEPOT FAT IN RELATION TO HIBERNATION. D.W. Fawcett, C.P. Lyman. Jour. Physiol., Cambridge, England, vol. 126, no.2, pp.235-247, Nov., 1954.

WATER BALANCE IN MARINE MAMMALS. E.S. Fetcher, Jr. Quart. Rev. Biol., Baltimore, vol.14, no.4, pp.451-459, Dec., 1939.

THE BODILY ELECTRIACL POTENTIAL CHANGES ASSOCIATED WITH OVULATION AND EARLY PREGNANCY.Glen Finch, R. M. Yerkes, James H. Elder. Proc. Soc. Exper. Biol. & Med., New York, vol.37, pp.560-563, figs.2, 1937.

TISSUE DISTRIBUTION AND ELIMINATION OF DDD AND DDT FOLLOWING ORAL ADMINISTRATION TO DOGS AND RATS. J.K. Finnegan, H.B. Haag, P.S. Larson. Proc. Soc. Exp. Biol. Med., Utica, vol. 72, no.2, pp.357-360, Nov., 1949.

(FURTHER INVESTIGATION OF THE GOALS OF ANIMAL TRADE.) Weitere Untersuchung der Ziele der tierischen Handlung. W.Fischel. Zeitschr. f. vergleich. Physiologie, vol.11, pp.523-548, figs.6, Feb. 25, 1930.

(ON THE IMPORTANCE OF MEMORY FOR THE GOALS OF THE ANIMAL TRADE.) Ueber die Bedeutung der Erinnerung fuer die Ziele der tierischen Handlung. W. Fischel. Zeitschr. f. vergleich. Physiologie, vol.9, pp.636-664, figs.5, June 4, 1929.

RESPIRATORY QUOTIENT OF THE MAMMARY GLAND. S.J. Folley, T.H.French. Science, Lancaster, n.s., vol.161, no.4102, pp.933-934, June 12, 1948.

COMPARATIVE STUDY OF THE OXYGEN DISSOCIATION OF MAMMALIAN HEMOGLOBIN. C.W. Foreman. Jour. Cell. & Comp. Physiol., Philadelphia, vol.44, no. 3, pp.421-429, Dec., 1954.

SOME OBSERVATIONS ON COMPARATIVE CONSTITUTION IN MAN AND THE LOWER MAMMALS. Herbert Fox. Proc. Amer. Philos. Soc., vol.68, no.1, pp.27-51, 1929.

HEAT DEATH TEMPERATURES AND NORMAL BODY TEMPERATURES OF BIRDS AND MAMMALS. F.D. Fuller, W.A. Hiestand. Turtox News, Chicago, vol.25, no.8, pp.148-149, Aug., 1947.

(HOMEOTHERMY.) L'homéothermie. J.Giaja. Paris, Actualites scient.industr., no.576, pp.70, 1938.

DIVISION OF THE COMMON MAMMALS INTO TWO GROUPS ACCORDING TO THE CONCENTRATION OF FRUCTOSE IN THE BLOOD OF THE FOETUS. R.F.W. Goodwin. Jour. Physiol., London, vol.132, no. 1, pp.146-156, Apr., 1956.

GENERAL FUNCTION OF THE GALL BLADDER FROM THE EVOLUTIONARY STANDPOINT. Frank Gorham, Andrew Conway Ivy. Field Mus. Nat. Hist., Zool. ser., vol.22, no.3, publ.417, pp.159-213, tbls.16, June 21, 1938.

INFLUENCE OF FOLLICULIN ON BONE METABOLISM, STUDIED BY MEANS OF RADIOPHOSPHORUS. J.Govaerts, M.J. Dallemagne. Nature, London, vol.161, no.4103, p.977, June 19, 1948.

AIR CONDITIONING IN NATURE. SHOWING HOW OUR NASAL CHAMBER IS EQUIPPED TO CLEANSE AND TEMPER THE AIR WE BREATHE, BUT LESS EFFECTIVELY THAN IN SOME ANIMALS. William K. Gregory. Natural History, vol. 38, no.5, pp.382-384, figs.5, Dec., 1936.

PHYSIOLOGICAL THERMODYNAMICS OF ARCTIC ANIMALS. D.R. Griffin. Science in Alaska, Proc.Second Alaskan Science Conf., 1951, pp.93-97, 1953.

ACCLIMATIZATION TO HIGH ALTITUDES. J.S. Haldane. Physiol. Rev., vol.7, pp. 363-384, fig.1, July, 1927.

ADAPTATIONS OF MAMMALS TO HIGH ALTITUDES. F.G. Hall. Jour. Mamm., vol.18, no.4, pp.468-472, figs.2, tbls.2, Nov., 1937.

COMPARATIVE PHYSIOLOGY IN HIGH ALTITUDES. F.G. Hall, D.B. Dill, E.S. Guzman Barron. Jour. Cell. Comp. Physiol., vol.8, pp.301-313, 1936.

INFRARED EMISSIVITIES OF SOME ARCTIC FAUNA. H.T. Hammel. Jour.Mamm., vol.37, no.3, pp.375-378, Sep. 11, 1956.

DOSES OF HISTAMINE PRODUCING MINIMAL AND MAXIMAL GASTRIC SECRETORY RESPONSES IN DOG AND MAN. M.E.Hanson, M.I. Grossman, A.C. Ivy. Amer. Jour.Physiol., Baltimore, vol.153, no.2, pp.242-258, May 1, 1948.

EXERCISE AND TEMPERATURE REGULATION IN LEMMINGS AND RABBITS. J. S. Hart, O.Heroux. Canadian Jour.Biochem. & Physiol., Ottawa, vol.33, no.3, pp.428-425, May, 1955.

DEVELOPMENT OF THE EGG AS SEEN BY THE PHYSIOLOGIST. Carl G. Hartman. Scientific Monthly, vol.33, pp.17-27, figs. 20, July, 1931.

PHYSIOLOGY OF OVULATION. Carl G. Hartman. Trans. New York Acad. Sci., ser.2, vol.1, no.8, pp.126-128, June, 1939.

GASPING PATTERNS OF THE ISOLATED RESPIRATORY CENTERS OF BIRDS AND MAMMALS DURING ANOXIA, THEIR PHYLOGENETIC SIGNIFICANCE AND IMPLICATION IN HIBERNATION. W.A. Hiestand, F.W. Stemler, J.E. Wiebers. Physiol. Zoology, Chicago, vol.26, no.2, pp.167-172, Apr., 1953.

HEARTBEATS. John Eric Hill. Nat. Hist., New York, vol.56, no.4, p.187, Apr., 1947.

ATRICHIA IN MAMMALS. W.C. Osman Hill. Proc. Zool. Soc. London, vol.128, no.1, pp.145-147, Feb. 14, 1957.

(EXPERIMENTAL STUDIES ON THE RELATION BETWEEN BODY TEMPERATURE AND LEUCOCYTE LEVEL.) Etudes expérimentales sur la relation entre la température du corps et le taux leucocytaire. Gustaf Hoglund. Comptes Rendus des Séances de la Soc. de Biol., vol.97, pp.1165-1167, Oct. 28, 1927.

ADAPTATION IN CAUDAL MUSCULATURE. Ruth A. Holzapfel. Proc. Oklahoma Acad. Sci., vol.5, 1925, pp.66-70, Mar., 1926.

ACTION OF THE HEART AND CIRCULATION DURING DIVING. Laurence Irving. Trans. New York Acad. Sci., ser.2, vol. 5, no.1, pp.11-16, Oct. 12, 1942.

CLIMATIC ADAPTATION IN ARCTIC AND TROPIC ANIMALS. Laurence Irving. Public Health Repts., Washington, vol.66, no.29, pp.939-941, July 20, 1951.

INSENSITIVITY OF DIVING ANIMALS TO $CO_2$. Laurence Irving. Amer. Jour. Physiol., Baltimore, vol.124, no.3, pp.729-734, Dec., 1938.

ON THE ABILITY OF WARM-BLOODED ANIMALS TO SURVIVE WITHOUT BREATHING. Laurence Irving. Scientific Monthly, vol.38, pp.422-428, May, 1934.

RESPIRATION IN DIVING MAMMALS. Laurence Irving. Physiol. Rev., Baltimore, vol. 19, no.1, pp.112-134, Jan., 1939.

STUDIES ON PHYSIOLOGICAL ADAPTATION TO COLD IN ARCTIC MAMMALS. Laurence Irving. Science in Alaska, Proc. Second Alaskan Science Conf., 1951, pp.113-117, 1953.

METABOLISM OF SOME ALASKAN ANIMALS IN WINTER AND SUMMER. Laurence Irving, Hildur Krog, Mildred Monson. Physiological Zoology, vol.28, no.3, pp.173-185, July, 1955.

TEMPERATURE OF SKIN IN THE ARCTIC AS A REGULATOR OF HEAT. Laurence Irving, John Krog. Jour. Applied Physiol., vol.7, no.4, pp.355-364, Jan., 1955.

ON THE MELTING POINTS OF ANIMAL FATS IN COLD CLIMATES. Laurence Irving, Knut Schmidt-Nielsen, Norman S.B. Abrahamsen. Physiological Zoology, vol.30, no.2, pp.93-105, Apr., 1957.

NATURE OF THE ABNORMALLY RAPID INCREASE IN WEIGHT UPON REFEEDING AFTER A PERIOD OF GROWTH SUPPRESSION. C.M. Jackson. Amer. Jour. Anat., Philadelphia, vol.64, no.1, pp.41-58, Jan. 15, 1939.

SOME READAPTATIONS OF THE MAMMALIAN PES IN RESPONSE TO ARBOREAL HABITS. F. Wood Jones. Proc. Zool. Soc. London, vol.123, pt.1, pp.33-41, June 10, 1953.

INVESTIGATIONS, CHEMICAL AND PHYSIOLOGICAL, RELATIVE TO CERTAIN AMERICAN VERTEBRATA. Joseph Jones. Smiths. Inst., Washington, pp.137, illus., 1856.

BODY TEMPERATURES OF SMALL MAMMALS. S. Charles Kendeigh. Jour. Mamm., vol.26, no.1, pp.86-87, Feb. 23, 1945.

HYPOXIA AND TEMPERATURE REGULATION OF MICE, DOGS, AND MAN. F.J. Kotte, J. S. Phalen, C. B. Taylor, M. B. Vischer, G.T. Evans. Amer. Jour. Physiol., Baltimore, vol.153, no.1, pp.10-15, Apr.1, 1948.

UREA SYNTHESIS IN MAMMALIAN LIVER. H.A. Krebs. Nature, London, vol.151, no. 3818, p.23, Jan. 2, 1943.

STRUCTURE, FUNCTION AND PATTERN IN BIOLOGY AND ANTHROPOLOGY. A.L. Kroeber. Sci. Monthly, Lancaster, vol.56, no.2, whole no.329, pp.105-113, Feb., 1943.

(TETANUS AND TONUS OF THE SKELETAL MUSCLES OF VERTEBRATES AND MAN.) Tetanus und Tonus der quergestreifte Skelettmuskeln der Wirbeltiere und des Menschen. Paul Krueger. Leipzig, Geest & Portig, pp. 431, illus., 1952.

(ON THE CATALYTIC EFFECT OF THE BLOOD OF VARIOUS VERTEBRATES.) Ueber die Katalytische Wirkung des Blutes verschiedener Wirbel-Tiere. F. von Krueger, H. Schuhknecht. Zeitschr. f. Vergleichende Physiologie, vol.8, pp.635-657, fig.1, Dec. 4, 1928.

VASCULAR DILATATION CAUSED BY THE SYMPATHETIC AND THE COURSE OF VASO-MOTOR NERVES. J.N. Langley. Jour. Physiol., vol.58, pp.70-73, 1923.

STUDY OF THE INNERVATION OF THE TONGUE MUSCULATURE WITH PARTICULAR REFERENCE TO THE PROPRIOCEPTIVE MECHANISM. O.R. Langworthy. Jour. Comp. Neur., vol.36, pp.273-298, pls.2, Feb. 15, 1924.

(INITIAL ORIENTATION OF THE POSTERIOR MEMBER OF VERTEBRATES.) Orientation initiale du membre postérieur des Vertébrés. Fernand Lataste. Comptes Rendus Séances Soc. Biol., vol.90, pp. 1010-1012, 1924.

PHYSIOLOGY OF SLEEP. R. Legendre. Smiths. Inst., Annual Rep., 1911, Washington, pp.587-610, 1912.

(LAW OF METABOLISM REDUCTION AND ITS SIGNIFICANCE.) Gesetz der Stoffwechselreduktion und seine Bedeutung. Guenther Lehmann. Handbuch der Zoologie, Berlin, vol.8, pt.5, no.5, pp.1-32, 1956.

(BIOMETRICAL RESEARCH ON THE CARDIAC FREQUENCY AND THE SYSTOLIC INDEX IN EMOTIONAL STATES.) Recherches biometriques sur la fréquence cardiaque et l'indice systolique dans les états affectifs. M. Liberson, W. Liberson. Contrib. Inst. Biol. Univ. Montréal, no.9, pp.21-43, figs. 12, 1941.

(BIOMETRIC RESEARCH ON INDIVIDUAL ELECTROENCEPHALOGRAMS.) Recherches biométriques sur les électroencephalogrammes individuels. W. Lieberson. Contrib. Inst. Biol. Univ. Montréal, no.9, pp.1-19, figs.4, 1941.

CONTROL OF SWIMMING POSITION BY MECHANICAL FACTORS AND PROPRIOCEPTION. John H. Lochhead. Quart. Rev. Biol., Baltimore, vol.17, no.1, pp.12-30, figs.9, Mar., 1942.

ON THE CONSTANCY OF THE BASAL METABOLISM. Graham Lusk, E.F. Du Bois. Jour. Physiol., vol.59, pp.213-216, Oct., 1924.

SIGNIFICANCE OF THE GALL BLADDER. Philip D. McMaster. Proc. Amer. Philos. Soc., vol.62, pp.185-189, 1923.

CHANGES IN THE GOLGI APPARATUS OF THE GASTRIC GLAND CELLS IN RELATION TO ACTIVITY. Wen-Chao Ma, R.K. S. Lim, An-Ch'Ang Liu. Chinese Jour. Physiol., vol.1, pp.305-330, illus., 1927.

HEAT RADIATION OF DOMESTIC ANIMALS DURING SEVERE COLD WEATHER. G. Allen Mail, Harlow B. Mills. Jour. Mamm., vol.17, no.3, pp.282-283, Aug., 1936.

(ON THE POSTMORTAL EXCITABILITY OF THE STRIATE MUSCLES OF WARM-BLOODED ANIMALS.) Ueber die postmortale Erregbarkeit quergestreifter Warmblutmuskeln. Ernst Mangold. Inaugural-Dissertation, Univ. Jena, pp.1-17, 1903

(EFFECT OF COLD ON AMAZON MAMMALS.) Efecto del fro en mamiferos amazónicos. F. Guillermo Mann. Investig. Zool. Chilenas, Univ. Chile, vol.3, nos. 8-10, p.155, Oct. 25, 1957.

REACTIONS TO GREAT ENVIRONMENTAL HEAT IN ANIMALS. Frank Marsh. (In) Biology of deserts, edited by J.L. Cloudsley-Thompson, Inst. of Biology, London, pp.188-192, 1954.

FUNCTIONS OF THE PYRAMIDAL TRACTS. Clyde Marshall. Quart. Rev. Biol., vol.11, no.1, pp.35-56, figs.7, Mar., 1936.

(ON THE INFLUENCE OF MOUNTAIN CLIMATE ON MAMMALS.) Ueber den Einfluss des Bergsklima auf die Saeugetiere. A. Maskovcev. Travaux Lab. Morph. Evolutive, Acad. Sci. USSR, Moscow and Leningrad, vol.2, livr.3, pp.5-30, 1935. (In Russian.)

ON ADAPTATION TO LACTATION IN MAMMALS. B.S. Matveiev. Zool. Jour. USSR, Moscow, vol.21, no.3, pp.47-68, figs.11, tbls.4, 1942. (With English summary.)

METABOLIC WATER AND DESSICATION. Kenneth Mellanby. Nature, London, vol. 150, no.3792, p.21, July 4, 1942.

PHAGOCYTOSIS IN A MAMMALIAN OVARY. Maynard M. Metcalf. Biol. Bull., Boston, vol.2, no.6, pp.338-339, June, 1901.

(MICROSCOPIC INVESTIGATIONS ON THE COURSE OF THE DIGESTION OF MEAT AND CHICKEN EGG WHITE IN THE STOMACH OF DIFFERENT ANIMALS.) Mikroskopische Untersuchungen ueber den Verlauf der Verdauung von Fleisch und Huehnereiweiss im Magen verschiedener Tiere. H. Meyer. Zeitschr. f. Vergleich. Physiologie, vol.10, pp.712-750, figs.8, 1929.

INFLUENCE OF ENVIRONMENTAL TEMPERATURES ON WARM-BLOODED ANIMALS. Clarence A. Mills. Ann. New York Acad. Sci., vol.46, art.1, pp.97-113, June 15, 1945.

HEAT RADIATION OF DOMESTIC ANIMALS DURING SEVERE COLD WEATHER. Harlow B. Mills. Jour. Mamm., vol.17, no.3, pp. 282-283, Aug., 1936.

ADAPTATIONS OF ANIMALS TO CLIMATIC EXTREMES: A REVIEW. A.D. Moore. Wilson Bull., Ann Arbor, vol.63, no.4, pp.358-362, Dec., 1951.

METABOLISM OF A VERY SMALL MAMMAL. Peter R. Morrison, Oliver P. Pearson. Science, Lancaster, n.s., vol.104, no.2700, pp.287-289, Sep. 27, 1946.

WEIGHT AND BODY TEMPERATURE IN MAMMALS. Peter R. Morrison, Fred A. Ryser. Science, Lancaster, vol.116, no. 3009, pp.231-232, Aug. 29, 1952.

ELECTRIC TRANSPORT OF FLUID ACROSS MAMMALIAN SEROUS MEMBRANES. Stuart Mudd. Science, n.s., vol.60, pp.527-528, Dec. 5, 1924.

(PHYSIOLOGY OF MAN AND MAMMALS.) Physiologie des Menschen und der Saeugethiere. Immanuel Munk. Berlin, Hirschwald, 4. Aufl., pp.633, 1897.

(ON THE DEVELOPMENT PHYSIOLOGY OF THE EYE. II) COMPARATIVE CHRONOMETRICAL AND ECOLOGICAL STUDIES OF THE RETINA OF CARNIVORES AND UNGULATES.) Zur Entwicklungsphysiologie des Auges. II) Vergleichend chronometrische und oekologische Studien an der Retina der Carnivoren und Ungulaten. E. Murr. Biol. Zentralblatt, vol.49, pp.346-379, figs. 15, 1929.

PHYSIOLOGY OF OVARIAN ACTIVITY. A.S. Parkes. Biol. Rev. and Biol. Proc. Cambridge Philos. Soc., vol.3, pp.208-260, July, 1928.

(ATTEMPT AT AN ECOLOGIC APPRAISAL OF THE EFFECT OF HUNGER ON ANIMAL ORGANISMS.) Opyt ekologicheskoi otsenki deistviia golodaniia na organizm jivotnex. V.N. Pavlinin, S.S. Schwartz. Zool. Jurnal, Akad. Nauk USSR, Moscow, vol.30, no.6, pp.620-628, 1951.

METABOLISM AND BIOENERGETICS. Oliver P. Pearson. Scientific Monthly, vol.66, no. 2, Feb., 1948.

METABOLISM OF SMALL MAMMALS, WITH REMARKS ON THE LOWER LIMIT OF MAMMALIAN SIZE. Oliver P. Pearson. Science, Lancaster, vol.108, no.2793, p.44, fig.1, July 9, 1948.

RATE OF METABOLISM OF SOME SMALL MAMMALS. Oliver P. Pearson. Ecology, vol.28, no.2, pp.127-145, Apr., 1947.

(RESISTANCE OF LOWER VERTEBRATES TO DIVERSE POISONS AND THEIR CONSEQUENCES.) Résistance des vertébrés inferieurs aux divers poisons et ses conséquences. M. Phisalix. Revue d'Histoire Naturelle, Pt. 1, A. Mammiferes, Paris, vol.11, no.2, pp.72-80, Feb., 1930.

(ON THE PHYSIOLOGY OF LOSS OF TEETH.) Ueber den physiologischen

Zahnausfall. Hermann Pohle. Sitz.Ber. Gesell.Naturf. Freunde, pp.115-122, figs.2, 1921.

(PHYSIOLOGY OF MARINE ANIMALS.) Physiologie des animaux marins. Paul Portier. Flammarion, pp.252, figs.42, 1938.

(Review by Robert Didier of) (PHYSIOLOGY OF MARINE ANIMALS.) Physiologie des animaux marins. Paul Portier. Bibliotheque Philos. Sci., vol.1, pp.252, figs.42, 1938; Mammalia, Paris, vol.3, no.1, p.40, 1939.

WATER. C.L. Prosser. (In) Comparative Animal Physiology, ed. Philadelphia, W.B. Saunders, chap.2, pp.6-74, 1950.

OBSERVATIONS ON THE BIOCLIMATE OF SOME TAIGA MAMMALS. William O. Pruitt, Jr. Arctic, vol.10, no.3, pp. 131-138, 1957.

HANDS AND FEET: SERVANTS OF THE BRAIN. W.P. Pycraft. Illus. London News, vol.189, no.5087, p.666, figs.2, Oct. 17, 1936.

TASTE AND SOLUBILITY OF TOXIC COMPOUNDS IN POISONING OF RATS AND MAN. Curt P. Richter. Jour. Comp. & Physiol. Psychol., Baltimore, vol.43, no. 5, pp.358-374, illus., Oct., 1950.

HAND AND FOOT PATTERNS OF LOW ELECTRICAL SKIN RESISTANCE: THEIR ANATOMICAL AND NEUROLOGICAL SIGNIFICANCE. Curt P. Richter, Bettye G. Woodruff, Billie C. Eaton. Jour. Neurophysiol., Springfield, vol.6, pp.417-424, 1943.

ON THE ISOLATION OF OOCYTASE, THE FERTILIZING AND CYTOLYSING SUBSTANCE IN MAMMALIAN BLOOD SERA. T. Brailsford Robertson. Univ. Calif. Pub. Phys., vol.4, no.11, pp.95-102, Mar. 19, 1912.

HEAT TOLERANCES OF AUSTRALIAN MONOTREMES AND MARSUPIALS. K.W. Robinson. Australian Jour. Biol. Sci., vol.7, no.3, pp.348-360, Aug., 1954.

REACTION TO HOT ATMOSPHERES OF VARIOUS SPECIES OF AUSTRALIAN MARSUPIAL AND PLACENTAL ANIMALS. K.W. Robinson, P.R. Morrison. Jour. Cellular & Comp. Physiol., Philadelphia, vol.29, no.3, pp.445-478, June, 1957.

WARM-BLOODEDNESS. Simon Rodbard. Sci. Monthly, Lancaster, vol.77, no.3, pp.137-142, illus.. Sep., 1953.

WEIGHT AND BODY TEMPERATURE IN MAMMALS. Simon Rodbard. Science, Lancaster, vol.117, no.3036, pp.256-257, Mar. 6, 1953.

ACCLIMATION OF FURBEARING ANIMALS IN USSR. L.B. Schaposchnikov. Zool. Jour., Moscow, vol.17, no.5, pp. 939-960, 1938. (In Russian.)

ANIMALS AND ARID CONDITIONS: PHYSIOLOGICAL ASPECTS OF PRODUCTIVITY AND MANAGEMENT. Knut Schmidt-Nielsen. Future of Arid Lands, Amer. Assoc. Adv. Sci., Washington, pp.368-382, 1956.

HEAT REGULATION IN SMALL AND LARGE DESERT MAMMALS. Knut Schmidt-Nielsen. (In) Biology of Deserts, edited by J.L. Cloudsley-Thompson, Inst. of Biology, London, pp. 182-187, 1954.

WATER ECONOMY OF DESERT MAMMALS. Knut Schmidt-Nielsen. Sci. Monthly, Lancaster, vol.69, no.3, pp.180-185, figs.2, Sep., 1949.

SALT EXCRETION IN DESERT MAMMALS. Knut Schmidt-Nielsen, Bodil Schmidt-Nielsen. Amer. Jour. Physiol., Baltimore, vol. 154, no.1, pp.163-166, July 1, 1948.

EVOLUTION OF CLIMATIC ADAPTATION IN HOMEOTHERMS. P.F. Scholander. Evolution, vol.9, pp.15-26, 1955.

EXPERIMENTAL INVESTIGATIONS ON THE RESPIRATORY FUNCTION IN DIVING MAMMALS AND BIRDS. P.F. Scholander. Oslo, Hvalradets Skrifter, Sci. Res. Marine Biol. Res., no.22, pp.131, figs.88, 1940.

ADAPTATION TO COLD IN ARCTIC AND TROPICAL MAMMALS AND BIRDS IN RELATION TO BODY TEMPERATURE, INSULATION, AND BASAL METABOLIC RATE. P.F. Scholander, Raymond Hock, Vladimir Walthers, Laurence Irving. Biol. Bull., Lancaster, vol.99, no.2, pp.259-271, illus., Oct., 1950.

HEAT REGULATION IN SOME ARCTIC AND TROPICAL MAMMALS AND BIRDS. P.F. Scholander, Raymond Hock, Vladimir Walthers, Fred Johnson, Laurence Irving. Biol. Bull., Lancaster, vol.99, no.2, pp.237-258, illus., Oct., 1950.

BODY INSULATION OF SOME ARCTIC AND TROPICAL MAMMALS AND BIRDS. P.F. Scholander, Vladimir Walthers, Raymond Hock, Laurence Irving. Biol. Bull., Lancaster, vol.99, no.2, pp.225-236, illus., Oct., 1950.

(RESPIRATORY CENTER OF MAMMALS AND THE REGULATION OF ITS ACTIVITY.) Dykhatel'nyi tsentr mlekopitaiushchikh zhivotnykh i reguliatsiia ego deiatel'nosti. M. Sergievskii. Moscow, Medgiz, pp. 394, 1950.

AUTOTOMY OF THE TAIL IN MAMMALS. Vincent Serventy. Western Australian Nat., Perth, vol.5, no.4, pp.92-93, May 29, 1956.

MEASURING THE INTENSITY OF THE STRUGGLE FOR EXISTENCE AND THE DEGREE OF ADAPTABILITY OF ANIMALS. S.A. Sewertzoff. Comptes Rendus (Doklady) Acad. Sci. USSR, Moscow, n.s., vol.32, no.3, pp.219-222, 1941.

OBSERVATIONS ON THE 'SUSTAINED PRESSOR PRINCIPLE' IN DIFFERENT ANIMAL SPECIES. R.E. Shipley, O.M. Helmer. Amer. Jour. Physiol., Baltimore, vol.153, no.2, pp. 341-347, May 1, 1948.

CHANGES IN ELASTICITY OF MAMMALIAN MUSCLE UNDERGOING RIGOR MORTIS. E.C. Bate Smith. Jour. Physiology, London, vol.96, no.2, pp.176-193, figs.6, tbls.3, 1939.

QUANTITATIVE RELATIONS BETWEEN LIVER MITOCHONDRIA METABOLISM AND TOTAL BODY WEIGHT IN MAMMALS. Robert Emrie Smith. New York, Acad. of Sci., vol.62, art.17, pp.403-421, 1956.

SEMLIKI FOREST VIRUS. II. IMMUNOLOGICAL STUDIES WITH SPECIFIC ANTIVIRAL SERA AND SERA FROM HUMANS AND WILD ANIMALS. K.C. Smithburn, A.F. Mahaffy, A.J. Haddow. Jour. Immunology, Baltimore, vol.49, no.3, pp.159-173, Sep., 1944.

THE CONCEPT OF NERVE-MUSCLE SPECIFICITY. William L. Straus, Jr. Biological Reviews, Cambridge, vol.21, no.2, pp.75-91, Apr., 1946.

DORSAL AORTIC PLEXUS: FACTOR IN THE DEVELOPMENT OF BODY WALL DRAINAGE IN THE RABBIT. Leon H. Strong. Univ. Calif. Publ. Zool., vol.29, no.13, pp.305-319, figs.4, 1927.

EFFECTS OF ENVIRONMENTAL TEMPERATURE ON OXYGEN CONSUMPTION IN ARCTIC AND TEMPERATE-ZONE MAMMALS. Bernard J. Sullivan, Joseph T. Mullen. Physiological Zool., Chicago, vol.27, no.1, pp.21-28, Jan., 1954.

PHYSIOLOGICAL EFFECTS OF TROPICAL CLIMATE. E.S. Sundstroem. Physiol. Rev., vol.7, pp.320-362, Apr., 1927.

RELATION OF WATER TO DORMANCY IN MAMMALS. Arthur Svihla. Murrelet, Seattle, vol.22, no.1, pp.15-18, Jan.-Apr., 1941.

ANIMAL AS A PRIME MOVER. Robert Henry Thurston. Smith. Inst., Annual Rep., 1896, Washington, pp.297-338, 1898.

RECORD OF METABOLISM IMPRINTED ON THE SKELETON. T. Wingate Todd. Amer. Jour. Orthodontics and Oral Surgery, St. Louis, vol.24, no.9, pp.811-826, figs. 12, Sep., 1938.

STOMACH AS AN ORGAN OF SOCIAL ADJUSTMENT. T. Wingate Todd. Sci. Monthly, Lancaster, vol.43, pp.341-345, Oct., 1936.

STOMACH'S RESPONSE TO THE MENU. T. Eingate Todd, W.M. Kuenzel. Reprint from Proc. Inter-State Post-Graduate Medical Assembly of North America, pp. 11, figs.11, Oct., 1935.

(WARMTH BALANCE, GEOGRAPHICAL DISTRIBUTION, BIOTOPE, AND ACCLIMATIZATION.) Warmehaushalt, geographische Verbreitung, Biotop und Akklimatisation. Herbert Ullrich. Zool. Garten, Leipzig, n.F., vol.17, nos.1-5, pp.74-84, 1950.

TOTAL AND TISSUE RESPIRATION IN RELATION TO BODY WEIGHT: COMPARISON OF THE KELP CRAB WITH OTHER CRUSTACEANS AND WITH MAMMALS. F. W. Weymouth, J.M. Crismon, V.E. Hall, H.S. Belding, John Field, 2d. Physiological Zool., Chicago, vol.17, no.1, pp.50-71, Jan., 1944.

(SPECIFICITIES OF CELL PERMEABILITY AND PHYLOGENIC RELATIONSHIP.) Spezifitaeten der Zellpermeabilitaet und stammesgeschichtliche Verwandtschaft. W. Wilbrandt, H. Mislin, F. Strauss. Zeitschr. Vergleich. Physiol., vol.37, pp.211-220, illus., 1955.

PHYSIOLOGY PRACTICUMS. EXPLICIT DIRECTIONS FOR EXAMINING PORTIONS OF THE CAT, AND THE HEART, EYE, AND BRAIN OF THE SHEEP, AS AN AID IN THE STUDY OF ELEMENTARY PHYSIOLOGY. Burt G. Wilder. Privately printed, 2nd edition, pp.74, figs.30, 1895.

LOCATION OF THE TESTES AND BODY TEMPERATURE IN MAMMALS. George B. Wislocki. Quart. Review Biol., Baltimore, vol.8, no.4, pp.385-396, Dec., 1933.

LIVER VITAMIN A RESERVES OF SOME BRITISH WILD ANIMALS. Alastair N. Worden. Proc. Zool. Soc. London, vol. 123, pt.4, pp.739-746, Feb. 10, 1954.

(BIOLOGICAL INVESTIGATIONS OF THE HEALING OF FRACTURES IN MAMMALS.) Histologische Untersuchungen ueber die Heilung von Knochenbrueche bei Saeugern. Hermann Wurmback. Zeitschr. Wiss. Zoologie, vol.132, pp.200-256, figs.11, pls.2, Sep., 1928.

(ATTEMPT AT A PHYSIOLOGICAL INTERPRETATION OF THE HYPERTROPHY OF THE TYMPANIC BULLAE OF SAHARA MAMMALS.) Essai d'une interpretation physiologique de l'hypertrophie des bulles tympaniques des mammiferes Sahariens. Edoardo Zavattari. Mammalia, Paris, vol.2, no.4, pp.173-176, Dec., 1938.

METABOLISM OF SMALL MAMMALS, WITH REMARKS ON THE LOWER LIMIT OF MAMMALIAN SIZE. Science, Lancaster, vol.108, no.2793, p.44, July 9, 1948.

## PHYSIOLOGY -- ENDOCRINOLOGY

OVARIAN FOLLICULAR HORMONE: STUDY OF VARIATION IN PIG, COW, AND HUMAN OVARIES. E. Allen. Soc. Exper. Biol. and Med. Proc., vol.23, pp.383-387, 1926.

OVARIAN AND PLACENTAL HORMONES. E. Allen, E.A. Doisy. Physiol. Rev., vol.7, pp.600-650, Oct., 1927.

OVARIAN HORMONE: PRELIMINARY REPORT ON ITS LOCALIZATION, EXTRACTION, PARTIAL PURIFICATION, AND ACTION IN TEST ANIMALS. E. Allen, E.A. Doisy. Jour. Amer. Med. Assoc., vol.81, pp.819-821, 1923.

EARLY DEVELOPMENT OF THE MEMBRANOUS LABYRINTH IN MAMMALIAN EMBRYOS, WITH SPECIAL REFERENCE TO THE ENDOLYMPHATIC DUCT AND THE UTICULO-ENDOLYMPHATIC DUCT. Barry J. Anson. Anat. Rec., Philadelphia, vol.59, no.1, pp.15-25, figs.33, 1933.

HORMONES AND BEHAVIOR: A SURVEY OF INTERRELATIONSHIPS BETWEEN ENDOCRINE SECRETIONS AND PATTERNS OF OVERT RESPONSE. Frank A. Beach. Harper & Brothers, New York, pp.xiv-368, 1948.

PITUITARY BODY IN GIANT ANIMALS FOSSIL AND LIVING: A SURVEY AND A

SUGGESTION. Tilly Edinger. Quart. Rev. Biol., Baltimore, vol.17, no.1, pp.31-45, figs.2, Mar., 1942.

THE ROLE OF THE ANTERIOR PITUITARY IN COMPENSATORY OVARIAN HYPERTROPHY. Earl T. Engle. Ant. Rec., vol. 37, pp.275-286, Jan. 25, 1928.

RELATION OF SEX HORMONES TO PIGMENTATION AND TO TESTIS DESCENT IN THE OPOSSUM AND GROUND SQUIRREL. Miriam Posner Finkel. Amer. Jour. Anat., Philadelphia, vol.76, no.1, pp. 93-151, figs.1-7, pls.1-3, Jan., 1945.

CYTOLOGICAL CRITERIA OF MAMMALIAN ENDOCRINE ACTIVITY. C. L. Foster. Nature, London, vol.150, no. 3801, pp.279-282, Sep. 5, 1942.

METABOLIC CHANGES FOLLOWING THE INTRAVENOUS INJECTION OF POSTERIOR PITUITARY EXTRACTS AND THEIR CORRELATION WITH THE WELL-KNOWN PHARMACODYNAMIC ACTIONS OF THE DRUGS. E.M.K. Geiling, A.M.DeLawder. Bull. Johns Hopkins Hospital, vol.51, no. 1, pp.1-26, fig.1, July, 1932.

SITE OF FORMATION OF THE POSTERIOR LOBE HORMONES. E.M.K. Geiling, F.K. Oldham. Trans. Assoc. Amer.Physicians, vol.52, pp.1-5 (p.132), 1937.

CARDIOVASCULAR AND METABOLIC REACTIONS OF MAN TO THE INTRAMUSCULAR INJECTION OF POSTERIOR PITUITARY LIQUID (PITUITRIN), PITRESSIN AND PITOCIN. Arthur Grollman, E. M. K. Geiling. Jour. Pharm. & Exper. Therap., vol.46, no.4, pp.447-460, fig.1, Dec., 1932.

DELAYED IMPLANTATION AND DISCONTINUOUS DEVELOPMENT IN THE MAMMALS. G.W.D. Hamlett. Quart. Rev. Biol., vol.10, no.4, pp.432-447, Dec., 1935.

FOLLICLE-STIMULATING EFFECT OF PIG ANTERIOR LOBE ON THE MONKEY OVARY. Carl G. Hartman, R.R. Squier. Anat. Record, vol.50, no.3, pp.267-272, figs.2, pl.1, Sep., 1931.

FUNCTIONS OF THE ENDOCRINE ORGANS. R.G. Hoskins. Sci. Monthly, vol.18, no.3, pp.257-273, Mar., 1924.

THE COMPARATIVE PHYSIOLOGY OF REPRODUCTION AND THE EFFECTS OF SEX HORMONES IN VERTEBRATES. I. Chester Jones, P. Eckstein. Memoirs of the Society for Endocrinology of New York, Cambridge Univ. Press, pp.253, illus.

OVARIAN SECRETION AND TUMOR INCIDENCE. Leo Loeb. Science, n.s., vol.67, p.104, Jan. 27, 1928.

EFFECT OF TESTICULAR HORMONE ON THE FORMATION OF SEMINAL FRUCTOSE. T. Mann, Ursula Parsons. Nature, London, vol.160, no.4061, p.294, Aug. 30, 1947.

OESTRUS PRODUCING HORMONES. G.F. Marrian, A. Butenhandt. Nature, London, vol.128, no.3225, p.305, Aug. 22, 1931; Science, vol.74, no.1926, p.547, Nov. 27, 1931.

GONAD HORMONES AND SEX DIFFERENTIATION. Carl R. Moore. Amer. Nat., Lancaster, vol.78, no.775, pp.97-130, Mar.-Apr., 1944.

BEHAVIOR AND ENDOCRINE REGULATORS OF THE INTERNAL ENVIRONMENT. Curt P. Richter. Endocrinology, Los Angeles, vol.28, no.2, pp.193-195, Feb., 1941.

THE INTERNAL ENVIRONMENT AND BEHAVIOR. PART V. INTERNAL SECRETIONS. Curt P. Richter. Amer. Jour. Psychiatry, Baltimore, vol.97, no.4, pp.878-893, figs.11, Jan., 1941.

SOME NEW OBSERVATIONS BEARING ON THE EFFECT OF HYPERTHYROIDISM ON GENITAL STRUCTURE AND FUNCTION. Kenneth M. Richter. Jour. Morphol., Philadelphia, vol.74, no.3, pp.375-394, pls.4, May, 1944.

ENDOCRINE REGULATION OF REPRODUCTION. Oscar Riddle. Endocrinology, vol.13, no.4, pp.311-319, figs.3, July-Aug., 1929.

CYCLE OF RESPONSIVITY OF CASTRATED ALBINO MICE AND OF HUMAN BEINGS TO OESTRONE INJECTION. E.V. Shute. Nature, London, no.3613, p.161, Jan. 28, 1939.

FURTHER INVESTIGATIONS CONCERNING THE INFLUENCE OF ESTROGEN ON SKELETAL TISSUES. Martin Silberberg, Ruth Silberberg. Amer. Jour. Anat., Philadelphia, vol.69, no.2, pp.295-331, illus., Sep. 15, 1941.

GENERAL ENDOCRINOLOGY. C. Donnell Turner. Philadelphia, W.B. Saunders Co., pp.xi-553, figs.171, 1955.

ORGANIZERS IN MAMMALIAN DEVELOPMENT. C.H. Waddington. Nature, London, vol.138, no.3481, p.125, July 18, 1936.

ROLE OF ESTROGEN IN MAMMARY GLAND DEVELOPMENT AND LACTATION. S. M. Walker. Proc. Louisiana Acad. Sci., Baton Rouge, vol.6, pp.59-62, Feb. 15, 1942.

ANIMAL ENDOCRINES IN RELATION TO SEXUAL BEHAVIOR. William C. Young. Ann. New York Acad. Sci., vol.47, art.5, pp.609-616, May 9, 1947.

GLANDULAR STATUS OF BROWN MULTIOCULAR ADIPOSE TISSUE. Endocrinology, vol.6, pp.760-770, Nov., 1922.

(MOTHER INSTINCT THROUGH HORMONES.) Mutterinstinkt durch Hormone. Kosmos, Stuttgart, vol.29, no.5, p.182, illus., May, 1932.

## PHYSIOLOGY -- GROWTH

(GROWTH.) Wachstum. Ludwig von Bertalanffy. Handbuch der Zoologie, Berlin, Bd. 8, Teil 4, no.6, (Lieferung 10) pp.1-68, May, 1957.

COMPARISON OF GROWTH CURVES OF MAN AND OTHER ANIMALS. Samuel Brody. Science, n.s., vol.67, pp.43-46, Jan. 13, 1928.

GROWTH AND DEVELOPMENT. Robert B. DePugh. Jour. Canine Genetics, Soc. Advancement Canine Genetics, Independence, Missouri, pp.7-31, Sep., 1956.

ALLOMETRIC GROWTH: ONTOGENETIC AND PHYLOGENETIC SIGNIFICANCE OF DIFFERENTIAL RATES OF GROWTH. A.H. Hersh. Growth, Third Growth Symposium, Menasha, vol.5, pp.113-145, figs. 4, 1941.

THE EXISTENCE AND IMPORTANCE OF GROWTH-GRADIENTS. J.S. Huxley. Biol. Zentralblatt, Leipzig, vol.49, no.8, pp.490-493, 1929.

(MECHANICAL CONDITIONALITY IN THE DEVELOPMENT OF ORGANISMS.) Mechanische Bedingtheit in der Entwicklung der Organismen. Hans Krieg. Naturwissenschaften, Berlin, Jahrg.25, no.47, pp.757-762, figs.6, 1937.

(ROTATION OF THE PELVIS DURING THE DEVELOPMENT OF THE MAMMALS.) Die Drehung des Beckens waehrend der Entwicklung der Saeugetiere. Anton Kriesselbach. Zeitschr. f. Saeugetierkunde, Berlin, vol.9, nos.1-3, pp.387-391, figs.2, pl. 17a, Dec. 30, 1934.

GROWTH AND SEXUAL MATURITY IN AQUATIC MAMMALS. R.M. Laws. Nature, London, vol.178, no.4526, pp. 193-194, July 28, 1956.

(ON THE SIGNIFICANCE OF OXYGEN AS REGARDS THE GROWTH OF MAMMALIAN TISSUE.) Ueber die Bedeutung des Sauerstoffs fuer das Wachstum der Gewebe von Saeugetieren. Leo Loeb, M.S.Fleisher. Biochem. Zeitschr., vol.36, nos.2-4, pp. 98-113, 1911.

DOES THE AMOUNT OF FOOD CONSUMED INFLUENCE THE GROWTH OF AN ANIMAL? H.H. Mitchell. Science, n.s., vol. 66, pp.596-600, Dec. 16, 1927; vol.68, pp.82-84, July 27, 1928.

(EXPERIMENTS ON GROWTH IN MAMMALS (RODENTS). PART I. GENERAL, COURSE OF EXTERNAL GROWTH.) Untersuchungen ueber das Wachstum bei Saeugetieren (Nagern). I. Teil: Allgemeines, aeusserer Wachstumverlauf. K. Saller. Archiv f. Entwicklungsmechanik, vol.3, pp.453-592, figs.19, Oct.28, 1927.

ON GROWTH AND FORM. D'Arcy Wentworth Thompson. MacMillan Co., New York, new ed., pp.1116, figs.554, pls.2, 1943.

DIFFERENTIAL SKELETAL MATURATION IN RELATION TO SEX, RACE, VARIABILITY AND DISEASE. T. Wingate Todd. Child Development, vol.2, no.1, pp.49-65, figs. 7, Mar., 1931.

HOW ANIMALS DEVELOP. Conrad Hal Waddington. London, George Allen and Unwin Ldt., pp.128, figs.30, 1935.

(ON THE REVERSIBILITY OF DEVELOPMENT.) Ueber Umkehrbarkeit der Entwicklung. Franz Weidenreich. Palaeontologische Zeitschr., Berlin, vol.13, no.3, pp.177-186, Sep. 15, 1931.

## PHYSIOLOGY -- HIBERNATION

HIBERNATION--THE LONG SLEEP. W.J. Breckenridge. Conservation Volunteer, St. Paul, vol.5, no.30, pp.37-40, Mar., 1943.

(EXPERIMENTAL CONTRIBUTION TO THE PHYSIOLOGY OF HIBERNATION.) Experimenteller Beitrag zur Physiologie des Winterschlafes. F. Bruman. Zeitschr. f. Vergleich.Physiologie, vol.10, pp.419-430, figs.5, Oct. 25, 1929.

RECENT KNOWLEDGE ON HIBERNATION. Maurice Burton. Illus. London News, vol. 216, no.5778, p.64, illus., Jan. 14, 1950.

RATE OF ACTION OF INSULIN IN ARTIFICIALLY COOLED MAMMALS. INSULIN AND THE MECHANISM OF HIBERNATION. Gordon James Cassidy. Amer. Jour. of Physiology, vol.73, no.2, pp.413-428, tbls., diagrs., July, 1925.

CHARACTERISTICS OF THE HIBERNATING HEART. A.R. Dawe, P.R. Morrison. Amer. Heart Jour., St. Louis, vol.49, no. 3, pp.367-384, Mar., 1955.

THEY SLEEP THE WINTER AWAY. Donald W. Douglass. Michigan Conserv., Lansing, vol.23, no.6, pp.22-23, illus., Nov., 1954.

(HIBERNATION IN THE ANIMAL WORLD.) Ueberwinterung im Tierreich. M. Eisentraut. Der Naturforscher, Jahrg.11, no.10, pp.337-343, figs.10, Jan., 1935.

(AWAKENING OF HIBERNATING ANIMALS.) Le réveil des hibernants. M. Fontaine. Naturalia, Paris, no.18, pp.29-34, illus., Mar., 1955.

HIBERNATION AND THE ENDOCRINES. Mark A. Foster, R.C. Foster, R.K. Meyer. Endocrinology, Los Angeles, vol. 24, no.5, pp.603-612, May, 1939.

WINTER SLEEP. ANIMALS THAT HIBERNATE. W.J. Hamilton, Jr. School Nat. League Bull., New York, ser.17, no.6, pp.1-4, Feb., 1947.

(WINTER SLEEP.) Winterschlaf. K. Herter. Handbuch der Zoologie, vol.8, no.4, pt.4, pp.1-60, illus., 1956.

WINTER SLEEP. John Eric Hill. Nat.Hist., New York, vol.50, no.5, p.247, illus., Dec., 1942.

HIBERNATION IN MAMMALS. George E. Johnson. Quart. Rev. Biol., vol.6, pp. 439-461, Dec., 1931.

(HIBERNAL LETHARGY OF MAMMALS AND ITS GENESIS.) La léthargie hibernale des mammiferes et sa genese. C. Kayser. Mammalia, Paris, vol.14, no.4, pp.105-125, pl.1, Dec., 1950.

(HIBERNAL SLEEP.) Le sommeil hibernal. C. Kayser. Biol. Rev., vol.25, pp.255-282, 1950.

(Review by P. Rode of) (RESPIRATORY EXCHANGES IN HIBERNATORS.) Les echanges respiratoires des hibernants. C. Kayser. Mammalia, Paris, vol.9, nos.3-4, pp.103-104, Sep.-Dec., 1945.

PHYSIOLOGY OF MAMMALIAN HIBERNATION. Barbara Ruth Landau. University Microfilms, Ann Arbor, Mich., Publication no.19, 107, 1956.

(HIBERNATING SMALL MAMMALS IN THE BUILDINGS OF A VILLAGE OF THE ERZGEBIRGE.) In Gebaeuden eines Erzgebirges Dorfes ueberwinternde Kleinsaeuger. Richard Lange. Zeitschr. f. Saeugetierk., Berlin, vol.20, nos.2-3, pp.187-189, Aug. 3, 1955.

ACTIVITY, FOOD CONSUMPTION AND HOARDING IN HIBERNATORS. C.P. Lyman. Jour. Mamm., vol.35, no.4, pp.545-552, Nov. 29, 1954.

HIBERNATION. C.P. Lyman, P.O. Chatfield. Sci. Amer., New York, vol.183, no.6, pp. 18-21, illus., Dec., 1950.

PHYSIOLOGY OF HIBERNATION IN MAMMALS. C.P. Lyman, P.O. Chatfield. Physiol. Reviews, Washington, vol.35, no.2, pp.403-425, Apr., 1955.

INTERNATIONAL SYMPOSIUM ON NATURAL MAMMALIAN HIBERNATION. Proceedings, Dedham, Mass., May, 1959. Edited by C.P. Lyman, A.R. Dawe, Cambridge, Mass., pp.549, illus., diagrs., tbls., 1960. (Harvard Univ., Mus. of Comparative Zoology, Bulletin, vol.124.)

HIBERNATION OF ANIMALS. L. Harrison Matthews. Discovery, vol.15, no.10, pp. 437-442, Nov., 1954.

HIBERNATION OF MAMMALS. L. Harrison Matthews. Ann. Rept. Smiths. Inst., Washington, 1955, pp.407-417, pls.1-2, 1956.

IN WINTER QUARTERS. NATURE'S REMEDY FOR FOOD PROBLEMS. Frances Pitt. Field, London, vol.164, no.4271, p.1026, illus., Nov. 3, 1934.

THEORIES OF HIBERNATION. Andrew Theodore Rasmussen. Amer. Nat., vol. 50, no.593, pp.609-625, Oct., 1916.

SERUM MAGNESIUM CHANGES IN HIBERNATION. M.L. Riedesel, G.E. Folk. Nature, London, vol.177, no.4510, p.668, Apr. 7, 1956.

(ON THE MECHANISM OF LETHARGY IN HIBERNATING MAMMALS.) Sul meccanismo del letargo dei mammiferi ibernanti. Alberto Salmon. Riv. Biol., Peruglia-Venezia, vol. 12, fasc.1-2, pp.80-92, Jan.-Apr., 1930.

(WINTER SLEEP.) Vintersovn. Knut Schmidt-Nielsen. Naturens Verden, Kobenhavn, vol. 25, no.8, pp.350-367, figs.7, 1941.

CALENDAR OF DISAPPEARANCE AND EMERGENCE OF SOME HIBERNATING MAMMALS AT WELLS RIVER, VERMONT. Wendell P. Smith. Jour. Mamm., vol.12, no.1, pp.78-79, Feb., 1931.

RELATION OF WATER TO DORMANCY IN AESTIVATING AND HIBERNATING MAMMALS. Arthur Svihla. Science in Alaska, Proc. Second Alaskan Science Conf., 1951, p.124, 1953.

"NOW I LAY ME." Frank Thone. Science News Letter, Washington, D.C., vol.42, no.17, p.269, Oct. 24, 1942.

(HIBERNATION OF OUR MAMMALS.) De Winterslaap van onze Zoogdieren. G. H. Waage. Natuurhist, Mammblad, Limburg, vol.15, no.10, pp.124-125, 1926.

STUDY OF LACTATE AND PYRUVATE LEVLES DURING HIBERNATION AND COLD EXPOSURE. Abstract. M.L. Zimny. Anat. Rec., Philadelphia, vol.121, no.2, p.385, Feb., 1955.

BIG SLEEPERS OF THE ANIMAL WORLD. Science Illus., Louisville, vol.2, no.3, pp.38-39, illus., Mar., 1947.

## PHYSIOLOGY -- LOCOMOTION

SPEED--HUMANITY BEATEN ONLY BY AN 818-MILES-PER-HOUR FLY! CHART SHOWING MAN OUTSTRIPPING BEASTS, BIRDS, AND FISH, THANKS TO HIS INVENTION OF MACHINERY. Roy Chapman Andrews. Illus. London News, vol.192, no. 5150, pp.18-19, Jan. 1, 1938.

WINGS WIN. SHOWING THAT NEITHER FINS, FEET, WHEELS NOR PROPELLER-DRIVEN AIRPLANES CAN COMPETE WITH NATURE'S TINY SPEED CHAMPION, CEPHENOMYIA. Roy Chapman Andrews. Nat. Hist., New York, vol.40, no.3, pp.559-565, illus., Oct., 1937.

SOME ASPECTS OF THE MECHANICS OF MAMMALIAN LOCOMOTION. O.R. Barclay. Jour. Exper. Biol., Cambridge, England, vol.30, no.1, pp.116-120, Mar., 1953.

SPEED OF MAMMALS. Nicholas Biddle. Pa. Game News, vol.8, no.5, p.19, Aug., 1937.

LOCOMOTION IN MAMMALS. C.W. Brazenor. Victorian Nat., Melbourne, vol.57, no. 8, pp.143-146, Dec., 1940.

MUSCLE AND MOVEMENT. Maurice Burton. Illus. London News, vol.216, no.5799, pp. 908-909, illus., June 10, 1950.

SPEED ON LAND. Maurice Burton. Illus. London News, vol.211, no.5668, pp.642, 644, 645, illus., Dec. 6, 1947.

HOW ANIMALS RUN. SOME INTERESTING LAWS GOVERNING ANIMAL LOCOMOTION, AND AN AMERICAN MUSEUM EXHIBIT THAT ILLUSTRATES HOW CERTAIN BONES FUNCTION DURING SPEEDY ACTION. S. Harmsted Chubb. Nat. Hist., New York, vol. 29, no.5, pp.543-551, illus., Sep.-Oct., 1929.

SPEED OF SOME WILD MAMMALS. Clarence Cottam, Cecil S. Williams. Jour. Mamm., vol.24, no.2, pp.262-263, May, 1943.

(JUVENILE LOCOMOTION IN MAN AND MAMMALS.) La locomocion juvenil en el hombre y en los mamiferos. Paul Magne de la Croix. Anat. Soc. Cient. Argentina, vol.116, no.6, pp.281-285, figs.1-3, Dec., 1933.

(MORPHOLOGY OF THE MAMMALIAN TAIL IN RELATION TO LOCOMOTION.) La morphologie de la queue des mammiferes dans ses rapports avec la locomotion. M. Dor. Paris, pp.184, pls.8, 1937.

(Review by P. Rode of) (MORPHOLOGY OF THE MAMMALIAN TAIL IN RELATION TO LOCOMOTION.) La morphologie de la queue des mammifères dans ses rapports avec la locomotion. M. Dor. Mammalia, Paris, vol.1, no.6, pp.263-264, Dec., 1937.

HOW ANIMALS MOVE. James Gray. New York, Cambridge Univ. Press, pp.114, figs. 52, pls.15.

(Review by James N. Layne of) HOW ANIMALS MOVE. James Gray. Jour. Mamm., vol.35, no.3, pp.464-465, Aug. 20, 1954.

ENVIRONMENT AND LOCOMOTION IN MAMMALS. William K. Gregory. Nat. Hist., New York, vol.51, no.5, pp.222-227, 244, illus., May, 1943.

SPEEDY ANIMALS. John Eric Hill. Nat. Hist., New York, vol.54, no.8, p.359, Oct., 1945.

SPEED IN ANIMALS--THEIR SPECIALIZATION FOR RUNNING AND LEAPING. A. Brazier Howell. Univ. Chicago Press, pp. 270, figs.55, Aug., 1944.

SPEED OF GAME BIRDS, FISH AND MAMMALS. Frank W. Lane. Field, London, vol. 175, no.4551, pp.414-416, Mar. 16, 1940.

SOME SPEEDS OF SMALL MAMMALS. James N. Layne, Allen H. Benton. Jour. Mamm., vol.35, no.1, pp.103-104, Feb. 10, 1954.

SPEED IN THE WILD. Harry Livingston. S. Dakota Conservation Digest, Pierre, vol. 9, no.2, p.17, illus., Feb., 1942.

RUNNING SPEEDS OF SKUNK AND EUROPEAN HARE. D.A. MacLulich. Canadian Field-Nat., vol.50, no.5, p.92, May, 1936.

EVOLUTION OF LOCOMOTION IN MAMMALS. P. Magne de la Croix. Jour. Mamm., vol.17, no.1, pp.51-54, figs.12, Feb., 1936.

(PARALLEL BETWEEN THE LOCOMOTIVE EVOLUTION OF VERTEBRATES AND ARTICULATES.) Parallèle entre l'evolution locomotrice des vertebres et celle des articulés. P. Magne de la Croix. Anales Soc. Cient. Argentina, Buenos Aires, vol. 114, pt.3, pp.143-146, Sep., 1932.

COMPARATIVE LOCOMOTION OF DIFFERENT ANIMALS. Etienne Jules Marey. Smiths. Inst., Annual Rep., 1893, Washington, pp. 501-504, pl.xxiii-xxv, 1894.

ANIMALS IN MOTION. Eadweard Muybridge. Dover Publications, Inc., New York, pp.440, pls.183, figs.21, illus., Nov. 10, 1957.

SOME LOCOMOTORY ADAPTATIONS IN MAMMALS. J. Maynard Smith, R.J.G. Savage. Jour. Linnean Soc. London, vol. 42, no.288, pp.603-622, Jan., 1956.

SPEED OF PREDATOR AND PREY. Clarence A. Sooter. Jour. Mamm., vol.24, no.1, pp.102-103, Feb. 20, 1943.

## PHYSIOLOGY -- NUTRITION

NUTRITIONAL KNOWLEDGE SHORT CUT. Earl L. Atwood. Jour. Wildl. Mgt., Menasha, vol.12, no.1, pp.1-8, Jan., 1948.

MICROBIAL FACTORS IN THE DIGESTIVE ASSIMILATION OF STARCH AND CELLULOSE IN HERBIVORA. Frank Baker. Nature, London, vol.150, no.3808, pp. 479-481, Oct. 24, 1942.

NUTRITIONAL STUDIES ON CALIFORNIA BIG GAME. Harold D. Bissell. Proc. 32nd Ann. Conf. Western Assn. State Game & Fish Comm., Glacier Nat. Park, Mont., June 15-17, 1952, pp.178-184, 1953.

GOOD NUTRITION, ITS IMPORTANCE AND PRACTICAL VALUE. E. Rendle Bowness. Black Fox Mag., New York, vol.32, no.1, pp.10, 22; no.2, pp.15, 27-28; no.3, pp.12, 20, May, June, July, 1948.

IMPORTANCE, PRACTICAL VALUE OF GOOD NUTRITION. E. Rendle Bowness. Amer. Nat. Fur & Market Jour., Wausau, vol.27, no.1, pp.9, 25, 29-30; no.2, pp. 12, 33, 37-38, Aug., Sep., 1948.

SOME OBSERVATIONS ON FUR ANIMAL NUTRITION. E. Rendle Bowness. Fur of Canada, Winnipeg, vol.12, no.11, pp.3-4, Aug., 1947; Natl. Fur News, Denver, vol. 19, no.9, pp.26-27, 56-57, Oct., 1947; American Fur Breeder, Duluth, vol.20, no.3, pp.68, 70, 72, 74, 76, 78, Sep., 1947.

NUTRITION OF FUR BEARING ANIMALS. Dr. Branion. Fur of Canada, Winnipeg, vol. 11, no.10, pp.12, 14, July, 1946.

DIFFERENCES IN NUTRITIVE VALUES OF WINTER GAME FOODS. Paul L. Errington. Proc. N. Amer. Wildl. Conf., Feb. 3-7, 1936 (Senate Comm. Print, 74th Cong., 2nd Sess.), pp.1-4, (356-360), 1936.

STUDIES ON NUTRITION OF MAMMALS. Hans Honigmann. Part 1. Proc. Zool. Soc. London for 1936, pt.2, pp.517-530, July, 1936.

STUDIES ON NUTRITION OF MAMMALS. Hans Honigmann. Part 2. Proc. Zool Soc. London for 1937, ser.A, vol.107, pt.4, pp.543-593, fig.1, tabls.39, Jan., 1938.

STUDIES ON NUTRITION OF MAMMALS. Hans Honigmann. Part 3. Proc. Zool. Soc. London, vol.111, ser.A, pts.1-2, pp.1-35, Sep., 1941.

NUTRITION OF FUR ANIMALS. Charles E. Kellogg. Yearbook of Agric., 1939, U.S. Dept. Agric., no.1717, pp.871-892, figs.2, tbls.9, 1940.

(INFLUENCE OF NUTRITION ON THE DEVELOPMENT OF INDIVIDUALS OF THE SAME BROOD DIFFERING AS TO INHERITANCE.) Einfluss der Ernaehrung auf die Entwicklung erblich verschiedener Wurfgeschwister. Hans Nachtsheim. Verhandl. des I. Internat. Kaninchenzuechter-Kongresses, Leipzig, 1930, pp.211-217, 1931.

WARTIME ANIMAL NUTRITION. Patricia O'Connor. News Bull. Staten Id. Zool. Soc., West New Brighton, vol.10, nos. 4, 5, 6, pp.2-3, 4, July-Sep.-Nov., 1943.

CHANGE IN FAT, CARBOHYDRATE AND PROTEIN APPETITE IN VITAMIN B DEFICIENCY. Curt P. Richter, L. Emmett Holt, Jr., Bruno Barelare, Jr., Clarence D.

Hawkes. Amer. Jour. Physiology, vol.124, no.3, pp.596-602, Dec., 1938.

ANIMAL FATS ARE A SOURCE OF FOOD ENERGY. W.L. Roberts. Black Fox Mag. & Modern Mink Breeder, New York, vol.33, no.3, pp.10-11, 17, 20, July, 1949.

IMPORTANCE OF AMINO ACIDS IN NUTRITION. W.L. Roberts. Black Fox Mag. & Modern Mink Breeder, New York, vol.32, no.12, pp.11, 23-24, 26, Apr., 1949.

NUTRITIONAL VALUE OF CARBOHYDRATES. W.L. Roberts. Black Fox Mag. & Modern Mink Breeder, New York, vol.33, no.1, pp.10, 29; no.2, pp.10, 17, May, June, 1949.

FUR ANIMAL NUTRITION IN 1942. Herbert Schaefer. Amer. Fur Breeder, Duluth, vol. 15, no.2, pp.20-24, Aug., 1942.

CHEMICAL CHARACTERISTICS OF NATURAL LICKS USED BY BIG GAME ANIMALS IN WESTERN MONTANA. D.S. Stockstad, Melvin S. Morris, Earl C. Lory. Trans. 18th N. Amer. Wildl.Conf., pp.247-256, illus., 1953.

UTILIZATION OF SUCROSE BY THE MAMMALIAN ORGANISM. Walter W. Wainio. Sci. Rept. Ser., Sugar Research Foundation, Inc., New York, no.12, pp.37, Mar., 1949.

EXPERIMENTS INDICATE "YELLOW FAT" IS OF NUTRITIONAL ORIGIN. C.K. Whitehair, A.E. Schaefer, C.A. Elvehjem. Black Fox Mag. & Modern Mink Breeder, New York, vol.33, no.11, pp.8-9, 21-24, illus., Mar., 1950.

CEREALS AND THEIR PLACE IN FUR ANIMAL NUTRITION. A. L. Wright. Amer. Fur Breeder, Duluth, vol.21, no.12, pp.52-54, June, 1949.

IMPORTANCE OF VITAMINS. A. L. Wright. Amer. Nat. Fur & Market Jour., Wausau, vol.27, no.11, pp.36, 51, 88, June, 1949.

## PHYSIOLOGY -- SENSE ORGANS AND SENSATIONS

EFFECT OF STIMULATION OF THE SENSES OF VISION, HEARING, TASTE, AND SMELL UPON THE SENSIBILITY OF THE ORGANS OF VISION. Frank Allen, Manuel Schwartz. Jour. General Physiology, Baltimore, vol.24, no.1, pp.105-121, figs.7, Sep. 20, 1940.

CONCEPTIONS OF THE STRUCTURE, FUNCTION AND DISEASES OF THE EYE IN THE COLLECTED WORKS OF AMBROISE PARE. Barry J. Anson. Quarterly Bull., Northwestern Univ. Med. School, Chicago, vol. 18, no.3, pp.244-255, figs.2, Fall, 1944.

LOCATION OF THE NASION IN THE LIVING. Montague Francis Ashley-Montagu. Amer. Jour. Phys. Anthrop., vol.20, no.1 and suppl., pp.81-93, fig.1, Apr.-June, 1935.

POWER OF SCENT IN WILD ANIMALS. E.C. Stuart Baker. Jour. Bombay Nat.Hist. Soc., vol.27, pp.112-118, July 1, 1920.

CAN ANIMALS SEE THROUGH GLASS? H. Mortimer Batten. Field, London, vol. 155, no.4040, p.802, May 31, 1930.

(THE OUTER NOSE AS AN ANATOMICAL STRUCTURE.) Die aeussere Nase als anatomische Konstruktion. Hans Boeker. Zeitschrift f. Morphol. u. Anthrop., Stuttgart, vol.34 (Festbd.Eugen Fischer), pp.47-53, figs.5, 1934.

SCENT. R.G. Burton. Jour. Bombay Nat. Hist. Soc., vol.27, p.164, July 1, 1920.

COLOUR AND COLOUR VISION IN ANIMALS. G.S. Carter. Nature, London, vol. 162, no.4120, pp.600-601, Oct. 16, 1948.

(THE DIFFERENTIATION OF THE NICTITATING GLAND AND ITS PHYLETIC SIGNIFICANCE IN INSECTIVORES AND RODENTS.) La differenciation de la glande nyctitante et sa signification phyletique chez les Insectivores et les Rongeurs. G.M. Cei. Mammalia, Paris, vol.11, no.3, pp. 69-100, figs.17, 1948. (Sep., 1947.)

CYCLOPIA IN MAMMALS. Floyd Earle Chidester. Anatomical Record, vol.8, no.6, pp.355-366, illus, June, 1914.

COLOR PERCEPTION IN GAME ANIMALS. James L. Clark. Wyoming Wild Life, Cheyenne, vol.5, no.11, pp.12-13, Nov., 1940.

POWER OF SCENT IN WILD ANIMALS. Hugh Copley. Jour. Bombay Nat. Hist. Soc., vol.28, pp.262-265, Dec. 30, 1921.

EYE AND ITS STRUCTURAL ADAPTATIONS. S.R. Detwiler. Proc. Amer. Philos. Soc., vol.99, no.4, pp.224-238, illus., Aug. 30, 1955.

STUDIES ON THE RETINA. OBSERVATIONS ON THE RODS OF NOCTURNAL MAMMALS. S.R.Detwiler. Jour. Comp. Neur., vol.37, pp.481-488, figs.13, Oct. 15, 1924.

RESONANCE IN THE EXTERNAL AUDITORY MEATUS. N. Fleming. Nature, London, vol. 143, no.3624, pp.642-643, Apr. 15, 1939.

SYSTEMATIC ARRANGEMENT OF FIBRES IN CAPSULA INTERNA, THALAMUS OPTICUS AND PES PEDUNCULI. J.Droogleever Fortuyn. Proc. Kon. Nederl. Akad. Wetensch. Amsterdam, vol.41, no.10, pp.1146-1155, figs.6, Dec., 1938.

(CONTRIBUTIONS TO THE SENSORY PHYSIOLOGY OF THE SKIN.) Beitraege zur Sinnesphysiologie der Haut. Max von Frey. Bericht Math.Phys.Classe K. Saechs. Gesell.Wissensch., Leipzig, pp.166-184, Mar. 4, 1895.

(PROBLEM OF COLOR SENSE IN ANIMALS.) Das Problem des tierischen Farbensinnes. K. von Frisch. Die Naturwissenschaften, Berlin, Heft 24, pp.470-476, June 15, 1923.

(ANATOMICAL PHILOSOPHY.) Philosophie anatomique. Etienne Geoffroy Saint-Hilaire. Paris, J.B. Bailiere, vol.2, atlas, 1818-22.

(HABITUAL CARRIAGE OF THE HEAD AND ITS VESTIBULARY FUNCTION.) Port habituel de la tete et fonction vestibulaire. Louis Girard. Mammalia, Paris, vol. 10, nos.1-2, pp.1-17, figs.7, Mar.-June, 1947.

ISOLATION OF THE MAMMALIAN COLOUR RECEPTORS WITH MICRO-ELECTRODES. Ragnar Granit. Nature, London, vol.155, no. 3946, pp.711-713, June 16, 1945.

(THE SCENT OF GAME.) Det vildas vittring. Claes Grill. Svensk Jakt, Stockholm, vol.78, nos.1, 2, 3, pp.11-15, 70-72, 112-118, Jan., Feb., Mar., 1940.

EARS OF THE WILD. David Gunston. Fauna, Philadelphia, vol.10, no.1, pp.23-24, Mar., 1948.

RECENT ADVANCES IN COLOR VISION. H. Hartridge. Science, Lancaster, vol.108, no.2807, pp.395-404, Oct. 15, 1948.

MAMMALIAN EARS, INSIDE AND OUT. Donald M. Hatfield. Chicago Nat., vol.4, no.3, pp.79-84, illus., Sep., 1941.

HOW NATURE ADAPTS AND DEVELOPS NOSES TO THE NEEDS OF HER CREATURES--QUEER USES FOR QUEER NOSES. Robert T. Hatt. Nat. Hist., New York, vol.29, no.5, pp.497-505, illus., Sep.-Oct., 1929.

EYES IN THE BACK OF THE HEAD. John Eric Hill. Nat. Hist., New York, vol. 56, no.3, p.119, illus., Mar., 1947.

ON THE REPRESENTATIVE OF THE MALLEUS AND THE INCUS OF THE MAMMALIA IN THE OTHER VERTEBRATA. Thomas Henry Huxley. Proc. Zool. Soc. London, pp.391-407, figs.8, 1869.

(INVESTIGATIONS OF THE LENS, THE ZONULA CILIARIS, REFRACTION, AND ACCOMMODATION IN MAMMALS.) Untersuchungen ueber die Linse, die Zonula ciliaris, Refraktion, und Akkomodation von Saeugetieren. H. Kahmann. Zool. Jahrbuecher, Abteil. f. Allg. Zoologie, etc., vol.48, pp.509, figs.19, pls.7, Nov. 10, 1930.

FOVEAL TRITANOPIA. S. Karplus. Nature, London, vol.160, no.4071, p.647, Nov. 8, 1947.

COMPARATIVE ANATOMY OF THE TYMPANIC BULLA AND AUDITORY OSSICLES, WITH A NOTE SUGGESTING THEIR FUNCTION. J.A. Keen, C.S. Grobbelaar. Trans. Roy. Soc. S.Africa, Cape Town, vol.28, pt.4, pp.307-329, figs.78, 1941.

VISUAL MECHANISMS. Heinrich Kluver. Biological Symposia, Lancaster, vol.7, pp.viii-322, illus., 1942.

(THEORY OF THE DUBOIS COEFFICIENT OF CEPHALIZATION.) Theorie du coefficient de céphalisation de Dubois. Pierre Le Gallic. Mammalia, Paris, vol.17, no.3, pp.194-207, no.4, pp.322-345, Sep., Dec., 1953.

(HEARING IN MAMMALS.) L'audition chez les mammiferes. J.P. Legouix. Mammalia, Paris, vol.21, no.4, pp.396-404, Dec., 1957.

(STUDY OF HEARING IN MAMMALS WITH HYPERTROPHIED TYMPANIC BULLAE.) Etude de l'audition chez les mammiferes a bulles tympaniques hypertrophiees, J.P. Legouix, F. Petter, A. Wisner. Mammalia, Paris, vol.18, no.3, pp.262-271, figs.5, Sep., 1954. (With English summary.)

(THE VISIBILITY OF ULTRAVIOLET LIGHT AND THE FLUORESCENCE OF THE LENS IN VERTEBRATES. A COMPARATIVE STUDY.) Die Sichtbarkeit ultravioletten Lichtes und die Fluorescenz der Augenlinsen bei Wirbeltieren. Eine vergleichende Studie. Ernst Merker. Zool. Jahrbuecher (Allgemeines), vol.45, pp.535-608, tbls. 6, figs.2, pl.1, 1928.

(ON THE DEVELOPMENTAL PHYSIOLOGY OF THE EYE. I)EXPERIMENTAL INVESTIGATIONS OF THE EFFECT OF LIGHT ON THE GROWTH OF VISUAL CELLS.) Zur Entwicklungs physiologie des Auges. I:Experimentelle Untersuchungen ueber den Einfluss des Lichts auf das Wachstum der Sehzellen. E.Murr. Biol. Zentralblatt, vol.49, pp.156-173, figs.4, 1929.

VISION OF ANIMALS. Kevin O'Day. Victorian Nat., Melbourne, vol.55, no.11, pp.194-196, Mar., 1939.

RELATION OF SMELL, TASTE, AND THE COMMON CHEMICAL SENSE IN VERTEBRATES. George Howard Parker. Jour. Acad. Nat. Sci. Phila., vol.15, pp.221-234, Sep. 7, 1912.

ANIMAL EARS, NATURE'S NEAR MIRACLE. R.O.Peck. Zoonooz, Zool. Soc. San Diego, vol.30, no.3, pp.10-12, illus., Mar., 1957.

(REMARKS ON THE SIGNIFICANCE OF TYMPANIC BULLAE IN MAMMALS.) Remarques sur la signification des bulles tympaniques chez les Mammifères. Francis Petter. Comptes Rendus Acad. Sciences, Paris, vol.237, pp.848-849, Oct. 12, 1953.

MYSTERY OF SCENT. Hugh B.C. Pollard. Eyre and Spottiswoode, London, pp.140, 1937.

(Review by A.L.Arey of) THE RETINA. S.L. Polyak. Anat. Record, Philadelphia, vol.83, no.4, pp.597-601, fig.1, Aug. 25, 1942.

LEND ME YOUR EARS. W.P.Pycraft. Illus. London News, vol.195, no.5235, p.297, illus., Aug. 19, 1939.

SCIENCE THAT IS NOT SCIENCE.(SENSE OF SMELL.) W.P. Pycraft. Illus. London News, vol.181, no.4865, p.80, illus., July 16, 1932.

HOW WE LEARN ABOUT COLOR VISION IN ANIMALS. John V. Quaranta. Animal Kingdom, New York Zool. Soc., vol.57, no.3, pp.71-74, illus., June, 1954.

DEVELOPMENT AND ADULT STRUCTURE OF THE MELLEUS, INCUS AND STAPES. Shafik F. Richany, Theodore H. Bast, Barry J. Anson. Ann. Otology, Rhinology and Laryngology, vol.63, no.2, pp.1-41, illus., June, 1954.

PHENYLTHIOCARBAMIDE TASTE THRESHOLDS OF RATS AND HUMAN BEINGS. Curt P. Richter, Kathryn H. Clisby. Amer. Jour. Physiol., Baltimore, vol.134, no.1, pp.157-164, figs.2, Aug., 1941.

STRUCTURE AND FUNCTION OF THE MAMMALIAN CEREBRAL CORTEX AT THE TIME OF BIRTH. W. Riese. Virginia

Medical Monthly, Richmond, vol.71, pp.134-139, Mar., 1944.

(VOLUNTARY EYE PIGMENTATION IN THE MAMMAL ALBINO.) Willkuerliche Augenpigmentierung beim Saeugetieralbino. W. Schultz. Archiv f. Entwicklungsmechanik, vol.109, pp.287-290, Apr. 11, 1927.

(ON THE MOUSE EYE, ITS ACCOMODATION, AND ON THE EYE OF THE SHREW.) Ueber das Mausauge, seine Akkomodation und ueber das Spitzmausauge. Siegfried Schwarz. Jenaische Zeitschr. f. Naturwiss., Jena, vol.70,(n.F., vol.63), pp.113-158, figs.36, pls.5-6, 1935.

CESIUM IN THE MAMMALIAN RETINA. Gordon H. Scott, Bruce L. Canaga, Jr. Proc. Soc. Exper. Biol. and Med., New York, vol.40, no.2, pp.275-276, Feb., 1939.

COMPARISON OF THE EXTERNAL AND MIDDLE EAR OF MAN AND THE CAT. Thomas B. Spence. Proc. Amer. Soc. Microscopists, 13th Annual Meeting, Detroit, pp.146-164, figs.12, 1890.

STRUCTURE OF THE VERTEBRATE EYE AS AN INDEX OF DEVELOPMENTAL DEFICIENCIES; WITH THE BEARING ON RECENT INHERITANCE STUDIES. Charles R. Stockard. Amer. Nat., vol.58, pp.24-35, Feb., 1924.

COMPARATIVE ANATOMICAL INVESTIGATION OF THE OSSEOUS LABYRINTH (VESTIBULE) IN MAMMALS. B.G. Turkewitsch. Amer. Jour. Anat., vol.57, no. 3, pp.503-539, pls.1-2, Nov. 15, 1935.

(THE EYES AND VISION.) Les yeux et la vision. M.L. Verrier. Mammalia, Paris, vol.2, no.2, pp.105-106, June, 1938.

(THE EYES OF SOME MAMMALS AND THEORIES OF VISION.) Les yeux de quelques mammifères et les théories de la vision. M.L. Verrier. Bull. Biol. France et Belgique, Paris, vol.72, no.3, pp.355-383, figs.20, 1938.

OCCURRENCE OF YELLOW LENSES IN EYES OF DIURNAL SCIURIDAE. Gordon L. Walls. Jour. Mamm., vol.14, no.2, p.182, May, 1933.

PHOTO-MECHANICAL CHANGES IN THE RETINA OF MAMMALS. Gordon L. Walls. Science, n.s., vol.67, pp.655-656, June 29, 1928.

VERTEBRATE EYE AND ITS ADAPTATIVE RADIATION. Gordon L. Walls. Bull. Cranbrook Inst. Sci., Bloomfield Hills, no.19, pp.785, figs.197, pl.1, frontisp., Aug., 1942.

(Review by H.E. Roaf of) VERTEBRATE EYE AND ITS ADAPTIVE RADIATION. Gordon L. Walls. Nature, London, vol. 151, no.3826, p.236, Feb. 27, 1943.

(Review by P. Rode of) VERTEBRATE EYE AND ITS ADAPTIVE RADIATION. Gordon L. Walls. Mammalia, Paris, vol.10, no.1, p.65, Mar., 1946.

ANTERIOR PROCESS AND THE OSSIFICATION OF THE MALLEUS IN MAMMALS. Kamal Wassif. Science, vol.113, no.2937, pp.486-487, Apr. 27, 1951.

STUDIES ON THE STRUCTURE OF THE AUDITORY OSSICLES AND TYMPANIC BONE IN EGYPTIAN INSECTIVORA, CHIROPTERA AND RODENTIA. Kamal Wassif. Bull. Faculty Sci. Fouad I Univ., Cairo, no.27, pp.177-213, figs.20, 1948.

MAMMALIAN MIDDLE EAR. T.S. Westoll. Nature, London, vol.155, no.3926, pp.114-115, illus., Jan. 27, 1945.

NEW LIGHT ON THE MAMMALIAN EAR OSSICLES. T.S. Westoll. Nature, London, vol.154, no.3920, pp.770-771, Dec. 16, 1944.

MAMMALIAN EYE, WITH SPECIAL REFERENCE TO THE FUNDUS APPEARANCES. Casey Wood. Amer. Jour. Ophthalmology, p.28, figs.5, Oct., 1905.

COLOUR SENSE IN WILD ANIMALS. H.A. Wood. Jour. Bombay Nat. Hist. Soc., vol. 39, no.1, p.173, Dec. 1, 1936.

PLAGUE see DISEASES AND PARASITES -- PLAGUE

## POPULATION DYNAMICS

CONFIDENCE LIMITS FOR THE PETERSON OR LINCOLN INDEX USED IN ANIMAL POPULATION STUDIES. Lowell Adams. Jour. Wildl. Mgt., Menasha, vol.15, no.1, pp.13-19, Jan., 1951.

ANIMAL AGGREGATIONS. W.C. Allee. Quart. Rev. Biol. vol.11, no.3, pp.367-398, Sep., 1927.

STUDIES IN ANIMAL AGGREGATIONS: THE RELATION BETWEEN MASS OF ANIMALS AND RESISTANCE TO COLLOIDAL SILVER. W.C. Allee, J. F. Schuett. Biological Bulletin, vol.53, no. 5, pp.301-317, Nov., 1927.

PURPOSES OF MAMMAL POPULATION STUDIES. Durward L. Allen. Jour. Mamm., vol.30, no.1, pp.18-21, Feb. 14, 1949.

FLUCTUATION IN THE POPULATION OF WILD MAMMALS, AND THE RELATIONSHIP OF THIS FLUCTUATION TO CONSERVATION. R.M. Anderson. Canadian Field-Nat., vol.42, pp.189-191, Nov. 1, 1928.

CHANGES IN VERTEBRATE POPULATIONS UNDER CONDITIONS OF DROUGHT. W. Frank Blair. Cold Spring Harbor Symposia on Quantitative Biology, vol.22, pp.273-375, 1957.

POPULATION DYNAMICS OF RODENTS AND OTHER SMALL MAMMALS. W. Frank Blair. Advances in Genetics, New York, vol.5, pp.1-41, 1953.

TECHNIQUES FOR THE STUDY OF MAMMAL POPULATIONS. W. Frank Blair. Jour. Mamm., Baltimore, vol.22, no.2, pp.148-157, figs.2, May 14, 1941.

QUADRAT METHOD OF STUDYING SMALL MAMMAL POPULATIONS. B.P. Bole, Jr. Sci. Publ. Cleveland Mus. Nat Hist., vol. 5, no.4, pp.15-77, figs.3, Dec. 28, 1939.

(COMMENTS ON PERIODIC CHANGES IN NUMBER OF CERTAIN MAMMALS AND BIRDS, WITH AN ATTEMPT AT AN EXPLANATION.) Om periodiske Svingninger i Antal hos visse Pattedyr og Fugle--og et Forsog paa en Forklaring. F.W. Braestrup. Naturens Verden, Copenhagen, Aarg. 24, no. 3, pp.97-108, figs.4, 1940.

RISE AND FALL OF ANIMAL POPULATIONS. Maurice Burton. Illus. London News, vol.219, no.5858, p.148, illus., July 28, 1951.

SOCIAL ASPECTS OF POPULATION DYNAMICS. J.B. Calhoun. Jour. Mamm., vol. 33, pp.139-159, 1952.

ADRENO-PITUITARY SYSTEM AND POPULATION CYCLES IN MAMMALS. J. J. Christian. Jour. Mamm., vol.31, pp.247-259, 1950.

BERNARD ROGAN ROSS TO SPENCER FULLERTON BAIRD. C.H.D. Clarke. Canadian Field-Nat., Ottawa, vol.56, nos.8-9, pp.120-122, Nov.-Dec., 1942.

FLUCTUATIONS IN POPULATIONS. C.H.D. Clarke. Jour. Mamm., Baltimore, vol.30, no.1, pp.21-25, Feb. 14, 1949.

POPULATION PHENOMENA AND COMMON KNOWLEDGE. Lamont C. Cole. Sci. Monthly, Lancaster, vol.67, no.5, pp. 338-345, figs.4, Nov., 1948.

SOME VARIATIONS IN GROUPING AND DOMINANCE PATTERNS AMONG BIRDS AND MAMMALS. N.E. Collias. Zoologica, New York, vol.35, pt.2, no.6, pp.97-119, Aug. 1, 1950.

STUDY OF ANIMAL POPULATIONS. J.R. Dymond. Rod and Gun in Canada, Montreal, vol.40, pp.17-18, 26-27, 1939.

THE "UPS AND DOWNS" OF MAMMALS. FLUCTUATION IN ANIMAL NUMBERS A BASIC PHENOMENON OF NATURE. W. Robert Eadie. Bulletin to the Schools, Univ. State of New York, vol.40, no.6, pp.173-176, Feb., 1954.

PERIODIC FLUCTUATIONS IN THE NUMBERS OF ANIMALS: THEIR CAUSES AND EFFECTS. C.S. Elton. Exper. Biol., Edinburgh, vol.2, pp.119-163, figs.8, Oct., 1924.

FLUCTUATIONS IN WILD ANIMAL POPULATIONS. Charles Elton. Quart. Jour. Forestry, vol.29, no.3, pp.194-198, July, 1935.

FLUCTUATIONS IN WILD LIFE. Charles Elton. Canada's Eastern Arctic, Dept. Interior, Ottawa, pp.62-66, illus., 1935.

RELATIVE ABUNDANCE OF SPECIES AND THE PYRAMID OF NUMBERS. Francis C. Evans. Ecology, New York, vol.31, no. 4, pp.631-632, Oct., 1950.

EXPERIMENTAL STUDIES ON THE DYNAMICS OF POPULATIONS. G.F. Gause. Zool. Jour. USSR, Moscow, vol.24, no.4, pp.215-223, figs.3, tbl.1, 1945. (English summary.)

FLUCTUATION OF GAME IN NUMBERS. E.A. Goldman. Amer. Game, Bull. Amer. Game Protective Assoc., vol.17, pp.59-61, illus., July, 1928.

SMALL GAME CYCLES. Robert G. Green. Minnesota Game and Fish, St. Paul, Conserv. Teaching Aid no.1, pp.28-31, 1940.

EFFECTS OF A WET YEAR ON MAMMALIAN POPULATIONS. Joseph Grinnell. Jour. Mamm., vol.20, no.1, pp.62-64, Feb. 14, 1939.

WINTER REDUCTION OF SMALL MAMMAL POPULATIONS AND ITS PROBABLE SIGNIFICANCE. W.J. Hamilton, Jr. Amer. Nat., Lancaster, vol.76, no.763, pp.216-218, fig.1, Mar.-Apr., 1942.

ANIMAL POPULATIONS AND SUNSPOT CYCLES. Donald M. Hatfield. Chicago Nat., Chicago Acad. Sci., vol.3, no.4, pp.105-110, Dec., 1940.

CYCLES OF ABUNDANCE AND SCARCITY IN CERTAIN MAMMALS AND BIRDS. A.D. Henderson. Jour. Mamm., vol.4, no.4, pp.264-265, Nov., 1923.

SYMPOSIUM ON CYCLES IN ANIMAL POPULATIONS. Oliver H. Hewitt. Jour. Wildl. Mgt., Ithaca, vol.18, no.1, pp.1-112, illus., Jan., 1954.

PERIODIC FLUCTUATIONS IN THE NUMBERS OF SMALL MAMMALS. A. Brazier Howell. Jour. Mamm., vol.4, no.3, pp. 149-155, Aug. 10, 1923.

METHODS OF DETERMINING TRENDS IN BIG GAME NUMBERS AND RANGE CONDITIONS. Gilbert N. Hunter. Trans. 10th N. Amer. Wildl. Conf., Washington, pp.234-241, 1945.

MATAMEK CONFERENCE ON BIOLOGICAL CYCLES. Ellsworth Huntington. Matamek Factory, Canadian Labrador, pp.32, 1932.

ANALYSIS OF AN ANIMAL POPULATION. C.H.N. Jackson. Jour. Anim. Ecol., vol. 8, pp.239-246, 1939.

UPS AND DOWNS OR PERIODIC FLUCTUATIONS IN FUR-BEARING ANIMALS. V.W. Jackson. Amer. Fur Breeder, vol.4, no.2, p.32, Aug., 1931.

FUNDAMENTAL LAWS OF THE DYNAMICS IN MAMMALIAN AND BIRD POPULATIONS. N.I. Kalabukhov. Uspekhi Sovremennoi Biologii, Moscow (Advances in Modern Biology), vol.7, no.3, pp.505-531, figs.10, tbls. 2, 1937. (In Russian.)

ULTIMATE CAUSES OF CYCLIC FLUCTUATIONS IN NUMBERS IN ANIMAL POPULATIONS. Jukka Koskimies. Papers on Game Research, Finnish Game Commission, vol. 15, pp.29, 1955.

ON THE VARIATION AND POPULATION DYNAMICS OF FOSSIL AND RECENT MAMMAL POPULATIONS. Bjorn Kurtén. Acta Zool. Fennica, Soc. Fauna et Flora Fennica, no.76, pp.122, 1953.

POPULATION DYNAMICS--A NEW METHOD IN PALEONTOLOGY. Bjorn Kurtén. Jour. Paleontol., vol.28, pp.286-293, illus., June, 1954.

NATURAL REGULATION OF ANIMAL NUMBERS. David Lack. Oxford Univ. Press, New York, pp.351, illus., Nov., 1954.

ANIMAL CYCLES AND FOOD. J. Burton Lauckhart. Jour. Wildl. Mgt., vol.21, no. 2, pp.230-234, Apr., 1957.

MALTHUSIAN PRINCIPLE IN NATURE. W.L. McAtee. Sci. Monthly, vol.42, no. 5, pp.444-456, May, 1936.

SUNSPOTS AND ABUNDANCE OF ANIMALS. D.A. MacLulich. Jour. Roy. Astron. Soc. Canada, vol.30, no.6, pp.233-246, July-Aug., 1936; Found. for Study of Cycles, Reprint 22, pp.18, 1947.

COMPARATIVE POPULATIONS OF GAME, FUR AND OTHER MAMMALS. Carl O. Mohr. Amer. Midland Nat., Notre Dame, vol.24, no.3, pp.581-584, fig.1, Nov., 1940.

GENERAL QUESTIONS RELATING TO FLUCTUATIONS IN NUMBERS OF MAMMALS AND THE ORGANIZATION OF RESEARCH. S.P. Naumov. (In)Symposium, "Methods for Forecasting Changes in the Numbers of Fur-Bearing Animals and Renewing their Natural Supplies." Trans. Cent. Lab. Game Indus., no.5, pp.7-17, 1941.

ON METHODS FOR STUDYING THE FLUCTUATION IN NUMBERS OF SMALL MAMMALS. S.I. Obolenskij. Zool. Jour. USSR, Moscow, vol.24, no.1, pp.48-58, tbls.3, figs.3, 1945. (English summary.)

FLUCTUATIONS IN SMALL MAMMAL POPULATION. F.L. Osgood. Jour. Mamm., vol.16, no.2, p.156, May, 1935.

SOME REMARKS ON THE SHORT-TERM FLUCTUATIONS IN THE NUMBERS OF NORTHERN BIRDS AND MAMMALS. P. Palmgren. Oikos, vol.1, pp.114-121, 1949.

ON BIOLOGICAL PRINCIPLES AFFECTING POPULATIONS: HUMAN AND OTHER. Raymond Pearl. Amer. Nat., vol.71, no. 732, pp.50-68, Jan.-Feb., 1937.

COMPARISON OF OVERWINTERING POPULATIONS OF SMALL MAMMALS IN A NORTHERN CONIFEROUS FOREST FOR TWO CONSECUTIVE YEARS. Don C. Quimby. Jour. Mamm., vol.25, no.1, pp. 86-87, Feb., 1944.

POPULATION TRENDS OF PREDATORS AND FUR ANIMALS IN 1080 STATION AREAS. Weldon B. Robinson. Jour.Mamm., vol.34, no.2, pp.220-227, 1953.

INCREASE OF HARES (LEPUS EUROPAEUS PALLAS) AT ASHTON WOLD, WITH A NOTE ON THE REPRODUCTION IN NUMBERS OF THE BROWN RAT (RATTUS NORVEGICUS BERKENHOUT). Miriam Rothschild, Harry Marsh. Proc. Zool. Soc. London, vol.127, no.3, pp.441-445, Nov. 29, 1956.

REPLACEMENT-AND-INCREASE RATIO IN SPECIES. Theo. H. Scheffer. Murrelet, vol.14, no.3, pp.51-54, Sep., 1933.

DOES INBREEDING CAUSE THE CYCLE ON GAME ANIMALS? W.E.Scott. Wisconsin Conserv. Bull., Madison, vol.9, no.2, pp. 6-10, Feb., 1944.

(DYNAMICS OF THE ANIMAL POPULATION.) Dinamica de la poblacion animal. S.A. Severtzoff. Edit. Austral. Chile, pp.539, 1947.

ON THE DYNAMICS OF POPULATIONS OF VERTEBRATES. S.A. Severtzoff. Quart. Rev. Biol., vol.9, no.4, pp.409-437, Dec., 1934.

(ON THE PROBLEM OF THE DYNAMICS OF THE HERD IN VERTEBRATES.) Zum Problem der Dynamik der Herde bei den Wirbelthieren. S.A. Severtzoff. Bull.Acad. Sci. USSR, ser.7, Cl. sci. math. et nat., Leningrad, no.7, pp.1005-1046, 1933. (In Russian with German summary.)

NOTES ON POPULATION DYNAMICS OF MICROTUS AND BLARINA WITH A RECORD OF ALBINISM IN BLARINA. Jacob Shapiro. Jour. Wildl. Mgt., vol.14, no. 3, pp.359-360, July, 1950.

DISEASE AS A FACTOR IN GAME FLUCTUATION. J.E. Shillinger. U.S. Dept. Agric. Wildl. Res. and Mgt. Leaflet BS-99, pp.3, Dec., 1937.

STRUCTURE OF SHORT-CYCLE FLUCTUATIONS IN NUMBERS OF MAMMALS AND BIRDS IN THE NORTHERN PARTS OF THE NORTHERN HEMISPHERE. Lauri Siivonen. Papers on Game-Research, Suomen Riistanhoito-Saatio, Helsinki, vol. 1, pp.1-166, illus., 1948.

POPULATION FLUCTUATIONS AND THE LUNAR CYCLE. Lauri Siivonen, Jukka Koskimies. Papers on Game Research, Helsinki, no.14, pp.1-22, illus., 1955.

REPORTED TAKE OF GAME AS AN INDEX TO POPULATION FLUCTUATIONS. J.Victor Skiff. Trans. 3rd N. Amer. Wildl.Conf., pp.576-582, 1938.

NATURAL CONTROL OF ANIMAL POPULATIONS. M.E. Solomon. Jour. Animal Ecol., London, vol.18, no.1, pp.1-35, May, 1949.

ECOLOGICAL REVIEW OF SMALL-MAMMAL OUTBREAKS WITH SPECIAL REFERENCE TO THEIR ASSOCIATION WITH THE FLOWERING OF BAMBOO GRASSES. Ryo Tanaka. Bull. Kochi Women's Univ., Ser. Nat. Sci., vol.5, no.1, pp.20-30, Mar., 1957.

REVISED METHOD FOR ESTIMATING REDUCTION OF NATURAL POPULATIONS EFFECTED BY POISONING. Ryo Tanaka. Japanese Jour. Sanitary Zool., vol.4, no.3, pp.186-193, illus., Mar. 3, 1954.

FLUCTUATION IN ANIMAL POPULATIONS. B.P. Uvarov. Nature, London, vol.153, no. 3872, pp.66-67, Jan. 15, 1944.

(PERIODIC FLUCTATIONS IN NUMBER AND SURVIVAL OF LOCAL ANIMALS.) Jaksoittainen runsaudenvaihtelu ja Paikallisten elainkantojen saily minen. Paavo Voipio. Suomen Riista, Finnish Foundation for Game Preservation, Helsinki, no. 5, pp.144-164, 1950. (In Finnish, with English summary.)

(ON THE POPULATION DYNAMICS OF SMALL MAMMALS IN THE TROPICS AND CAUSES.) Zur Populationsdynamik der Kleinnager in den Tropen und ihre Ursachen. Helmuth O. Wagner. Bonner Zool. Beitraege, Heft 1-2, pp.1-12, 1953.

WILDLIFE CYCLES IN RELATION TO THE SUN. Leonard William Wind. Trans. 21st Amer. Game Conf., 1935, Amer. Game Assoc., New York, pp.345-363, figs.20, 1935.

WILDLIFE IN CYCLES. Leonard Wing. Amer. Forests, vol.43, no.10, pp.496-497, 512-513, illus., Oct., 1937.

ASTRONOMICAL FIGURES OF ANIMAL FECUNDITY: A PICTORIAL ANALYSIS OF SOME MARINE AND TERRESTRIAL POPULATIONS. Illus. London News, vol. 214, no.5748, pp.848-849, illus., June 18, 1949.

BUREAU OF ANIMAL POPULATIONS. Ann. Report, Univ. Oxford, pp.36, 1937-1938.

METHODS FOR FORECASTING CHANGES IN THE NUMBERS OF FUR-BEARING ANIMALS AND RENEWING THEIR NATURAL SUPPLIES. PT. 2. Trans. Cent. Lab. Game Indus., no.5, pp.129-212, 1941.

STUDY OF ANIMAL POPULATIONS. Roy. Ontario Mus. Zool., Bull. no.8, pp.11-16, Nov., 1938

POPULATION DYNAMICS -- ESTIMATES OF NUMBER see CENSUSES, MAMMAL

## POPULATION DYNAMICS -- EXTINCTION AND EXTERMINATION

EXTINCT AND VANISHING MAMMALS OF THE WESTERN HEMISPHERE WITH THE MARINE SPECIES OF ALL THE OCEANS. Glover M. Allen. Amer. Comm. Internat. Wild Life Protection, Special Publ. no.11, pp.xv-620, illus., Dec. 11, 1942.

(EXTINCTION OF PRESENT-DAY ANIMALS. MAN'S RESPONSIBILITY IN THE EPILOGUE OF THE CENOZOIC.) La extincion de las faunas actuales: Responsabilidad del hobre en el epilogo del Cenozoico. Angel Cabrera. Conferencia de extension universitaria pronunciada en la Universidad nacional de La Plata el 25 de junio del ano en curso, pp.22, figs.14, 1936.

WHY DO ANIMALS BECOME EXTINCT? Thedore H. Eaton, Jr. Fauna, Philadelphia, vol.7, no.2, pp.45-47, illus., June, 1945.

FINISHING THE MAMMALS. Rosalie Edge. Emergency Cons. Comm., Pub.7, pp.24, 1936.

FIRE-DRIVE AND THE EXTINCTION OF THE TERMINAL PLEISTOCENE FAUNA. Loren C. Eiseley. Amer. Anthropol., Menasha, n.s., vol.48, no.1, pp.54-59, Jan.-Mar., 1946.

(Review by Charles Elton of) EXTINCT AND VANISHING MAMMALS OF THE WESTERN HEMISPHERE, WITH THE MARINE SPECIES OF ALL THE OCEANS. Glover M. Allen. Jour. Anim. Ecol., London, vol.14, no.2, pp.155-156, Nov., 1945.

EXTINCT AND VANISHING MAMMALS OF THE OLD WORLD. Francis Harper. Amer. Comm. for Internat. Wildl. Protection, Baltimore, Special Publ. no.12, pp.xv-850, figs.67, pl.1, 1945.

"AGE AND AREA" IN RELATION TO EXTINCTION. S.J. Holmes. Science, n.s., vol.61, pp.77-79, Jan. 23, 1925.

DISAPPEARING WILD LIFE. THE LESSON OF THE DODO. Julian S. Huxley. Jour. Soc. Preservation Fauna of Empire, Hertford, n.s., pt.33, pp.25-31, Mar., 1938.

ANIMALS RECENTLY EXTINCT OR THREATENED WITH EXTERMINATION, AS REPRESENTED IN THE COLLECTIONS OF THE U.S. NATIONAL MUSEUM. Frederic A. Lucas. Report Nat. Mus., 1888-89, pp.609-649, pls.95-105, 1891.

EXTINCTION OF SEA MAMMALS. Robert Cushman Murphy. Nat. Hist., vol.23, pp.135-137, Mar.-Apr., 1923.

CAUSES OF EXTINCTION OF MAMMALIA. Henry Fairfield Osborn. Amer. Nat., Boston, vol.40, no.479, pp.769-795, no.480, pp. 829-859, Nov.-Dec., 1906.

EXTINCTION: ITS CAUSES AND RESULTS. James A. Peters. Biologist, vol.32, nos. 1-2, pp.1-8, Aug.-Nov., 1949.

(SOME UNGULATES EXTINCT FOR MILLIONS OF YEARS.) Algunos ungulados extinguidos de hace millones de annos. Carlos Rusconi. Revista Geografica Americana, Buenos Aires, vol.6, pp.164-166, figs.5, 1936.

EXTINCTION OF PLEISTOCENE MAMMALS. W.B. Scott. Bull. Geol. Soc. America, vol.41, no.1, pp.104-105, Mar., 1930.

VANISHED GAME. Henry W. Shoemaker. (In) N. American Big Game. Book of the Boone and Crockett Club, compiled by the Committee on Records of N. American Big Game. New York, Charles Scribner's Sons, pp.15-34, 1939.

EXTINCTION AND EXTERMINATION. I.P. Tolmachoff. Smiths. Rep. for 1929, publ.3044, pp.269-284, Dec. 1, 1930.

EXTINCTION OF WILD LIFE. F.J. Worrall. Our Dumb Animals, Norwood, vol.77, no.6, p.107, illus., June, 1944.

(AFTERTHOUGHTS ON THE CAUSES OF THE MASS DEATH OF RECENT VERTEBRATES.) Nachtraege ueber die Ursachen des Massentodes rezenter Wirbeltiere. J.V. Zelizko. Palaeont. Zeitschr., Berlin, vol.19, pp.350-353, 1937.

(SOME SINGULAR CASES OF THE EXTINCTION OF VERTEBRATES.) Einige sonderbare Faelle vom Untergang der Wirbeltiere. J.V. Zelisko. Zvlastni Otisk z Casopisu "Priroda", Brno, vol.31, no.1, pp.1-4, figs. 2, 1938. (In Polish with German summary.)

## PREY, MAMMALS AS

NOTES ON THE FOOD OF THE HORNED OWL NEAR FALLON, NEVADA. J. R.

Alcorn. Condor, Berkeley. vol.44, no.6, pp.284-285, Nov. 20, 1942.

MANITOBA BIRDS OF PREY, AND THE SMALL MAMMALS DESTROYED BY THEM. George E. Atkinson. Winnipeg, The Stovel Co., pp.16, illus., pl., 1899.

STUDY OF THE WINTER FEEDING HABITS OF THE SHORT-EARED OWL (ASIO FLAMMEUS) IN THE TORONTO REGION. A.W.F. Banfield. Canadian Jour. Research, Ottawa, sect.D, vol.25, no.2, pp.45-65, figs.12, June 4, 1947.

HOME LIFE OF THE BAT FALCON, FALCO ALBIGULARIS ALBIGULARIS DAUDIN. William Beebe. Zoologica, New York Zool. Soc., vol.35, pt.1, no. 4, pp.69-86, Apr. 17, 1950.

GREAT HORNED OWL IN MANITOBA. Ralph D. Bird. Canadian Field-Nat., vol. 43, pp.79-82, Apr., 1929.

MAMMAL REMAINS FROM DETRITUS OF RAPTORIAL BIRDS IN CALIFORNIA. Jack C. von Bloeker. Jour. Mamm., vol. 18, no.3, pp.360-361, Aug. 14, 1937.

OBSERVATIONS ON RAPTORIAL BIRDS IN THE LAVA BEDS--TULE LAKE REGION OF NORTHERN CALIFORNIA. Richard M. Bond. Condor, vol.41, no.2, pp.54-61, Mar., 1939.

FOOD HABITS OF THE BARN OWL IN BRITISH COLUMBIA. I. McT. Cowan. Murrelet, Seattle, vol.23, no.2, pp.48-53, Aug. 14, 1942.

MAMMALS COMPOSE MORE THAN 92 PERCENT OF FOOD OF THE BARN OWL IN TEXAS. Wm.B. Davis. Texas Game, Fish and Oyster Comm., Austin, Monthly Bull., vol.3, no.2, p.6, Jan., 1941.

LEARN FROM THE OWL ABOUT THE SMALL MAMMALS PRESENT IN YOUR COMMUNITY. Ernest C. Driver. Audubon Mag., New York, vol.49, no.1, pp.47-51, illus., Jan.-Feb., 1947.

MAMMAL REMAINS IN OWL PELLETS. Ernest C. Driver. Amer. Midland Nat., Notre Dame, vol.41, no.1, pp.139-142, Jan., 1949.

FOOD HABITS OF BUTEO HAWKS IN NORTH-CENTRAL UNITED STATES. Paul L. Errington, W.J. Breckenridge. Wilson Bull., vol.50, no.2, pp.113-121, June, 1938.

ECOLOGICAL NOTES ON THE PREY SELECTED BY A BARN OWL. Francis C. Evans. Condor, Berkeley, vol.49, no.1, pp.3-9, figs.1-2, Feb. 6, 1947.

NOTE ON THE DIETARY HABITS OF THE BARN OWL. G.L. Foster. Condor, vol.29, p.246, Sep., 1927.

RAPTOR PELLETS AS INDICATORS OF FOOD HABITS. Ben Glading, Daniel F. Tillotson, David M. Selleck. California Fish and Game, San Francisco, vol.29, no.3, pp.92-121, fig.30, July, 1943.

EAGLES' PREY. George Bird Grinnell. Jour. Mamm., vol.10, no.1, p.83, Feb., 1929.

STUDYING OWL PELLETS. C.E. Hope. Canadian Nature, Toronto, vol.6, no.1, pp.22-23, illus., Jan.-Feb., 1944.

KILLING THE TERM, PREDATEE. Carl L. Hubbs. Science, Lancaster, n.s., vol. 89, no.2322, p.605, June 30, 1939.

(ANALYSES OF HAIR BALLS FROM WHITE OWLS.) Analysen von Schleiereulengewoellen. A.M. Husson. Bull. Ligue Luxembourgeoise Prot. Oiseaux, vol.28, ser.3, no.7, pp.101-102, 1948.

SUMMER FOOD FOR BURROWING OWLS IN COSTILLA COUNTY, COLORADO. William M. Longhurst. Condor, Berkeley, vol.44, no.6, pp.281-282, Nov. 20, 1942.

FEEDING HABITS OF BLACK VULTURE. E.A. McIlhenny. Auk, Cambridge, vol. 56, no.4, pp.472-474, Oct., 1939.

VERTEBRATES CAPTURED BY AUSTRALIAN SPIDERS. Keith. C. McKeown. Proc. Roy. Zool. Soc. New South Wales, Sydney, 1942-43, pp.17-30, illus., Aug. 25, 1943.

FOOD AND HABITAT OF THE SPOTTED OWL. Joe T. Marshall, Jr. Condor, Berkeley, vol.44, no.2, pp.66-67, Mar.-Apr., 1942.

NOTES ON THE FOOD HABITS OF CERTAIN RAPTORES IN BRITISH COLUMBIA AND ALBERTA. J.A. Munro. Condor, vol.31, pp.112-116, May, 1929.

CONTENTS OF OWL PELLETS.(Notes and Discussion.) Homer F. Price. Amer. Midland Nat., Notre Dame, vol.28, no.2, pp. 524-525, Sep., 1942.

OWLS, MICE AND MOLES. Samuel N. Rhoads. Forest and Stream, p.1, Aug. 20, 1898.

FOOD HABITS OF NESTING BARN OWLS AND MARSH HAWKS AT DUNE LAKES, CALIFORNIA, AS DETERMINED BY THE "CAGE NEST" METHOD. David M. Selleck, Ben Glading. California Fish and Game, San Francisco, vol.29, no.3, pp.122-131, figs. 31-32, July, 1943.

NOTES ON THE BARN OWLS OF THE SAN FRANCISCO BAY REGION. Clarence F. Smith, Cranson L. Hopkins. Condor, vol. 39, no.5, pp.189-191, Sep.-Oct., 1937.

NOTES ON THE DIET OF THE LONG-EARED OWL. H.L. Stoddard. Year Book of the Public Museum of the City of Milwaukee, 1921, vol.1, pp.66-71, July 20, 1922.

ON THE FOOD OF THE BARN-OWL AND ITS BEARING ON BARN-OWL POPULATION. C.B. Ticehurst. Ibis, ser.13, vol.5, no.2, pp.329-335, Apr., 1935.

BARN OWL IN MICHIGAN--ITS DISTRIBUTION, NATURAL HISTORY AND FOOD HABITS. George J. Wallace. Tech. Bull. Michigan Agric. Exp. Sta., East Lansing, no.208, pp.61, Aug., 1948.

MISTAKING THE HAWK. (Weasel and Microtus eaten by roughleg hawk.) Earl G. Wright. Passenger Pigeon, Madison, vol.7, no.4, p.127, Oct., 1945.

## PSYCHOLOGY, ANIMAL

WHY QUESTION THE REASONING OF ANIMALS? S.F. Aaron. Scientific American, vol.145, no.5, pp.330-332, Nov., 1931.

CAN ANIMALS REASON? BRAINS AND THE BEAST. Frank A. Beach. IV. Nat. Hist., New York, vol.57, no.3, pp.112-116, 137, illus., Mar., 1948.

OF COURSE ANIMALS CAN THINK. Frank A. Beach. Nat. Hist., New York, vol.56, no.3, pp.116-118, Mar., 1947.

DO ANIMALS THINK? W. Reid Blair. Forum, vol.78, pp.253-260, illus., Aug., 1927.

(EXPERIMENTAL INVESTIGATIONS OF THE LEARNING PROCESS. NO. 4: ON THE LABILITY OF HABITS.) Experimentelle Untersuchungen ueber den Lernprozess. Nr.4 (Ueber Labilitaet der Gewohnheit). W.M. Borovski. Zeitschr. f. Vergleich. Physiologie, vol.11, pp.549-564, figs.4, Feb. 25, 1930.

REORIENTATION IN A MULTIPLE-PATH MAZE. Warner Brown. Univ. California Publ. Psychol., Berkeley, vol.5, no.7, pp. 135-160, figs.8, tbls.10, Apr. 27, 1937.

(BRIEF SUPPLEMENT TO "SYMBOLIC ACTS AND THE LIKE IN MAMMALS.) Kleiner Nachtrag zu "Symbolhandlungen und Verwandtes bei Saeugetieren. Heinrich Dathe. Zool. Garten, n.F., Leipzig, vol. 15, nos.1-2, pp.82-84, 1943.

(SOME REMARKS ON THE ORIGIN OF THE EXPRESSION MOVEMENTS OF MAMMALS.) Einige Bemerkungen ueber den Ursprung von Ausdrucksbewegungen bei Saeugetieren. Irenhaus Eibl-Eibesfeldt. Zeitschrift f. Saeugetierk., vol.21, nos.1-2, pp.29-38, 1956.

(MEMORY CAPACITY OF ANIMALS.) Die tierischen Gedaechtnissleistungen. W. Fischel. Biol. Zentralblatt, vol.49, pp. 291-301, 1929.

(SCIENTIFIC ANIMAL PSYCHOLOGY IN THE ZOOLOGICAL GARDEN.) Wissenschaftliche Tierpsychologie im Zoologischen Garten. W. Fischel. Zool. Garten, Leipzig, n.F., vol.2, nos.7-9, pp.165-173, figs.2, Jan., 1930.

(ANIMAL AND HUMAN CHARACTERS.) Tier- und Menschencharakter. Heinrich Frieling. Natur und Kultur, Monatschr.f. Naturforsch. u. Kultur, Muenchen, Jahrg.37, no.1, pp.10-12, Jan., 1940.

PSYCHOLOGY AND PHYSIOLOGY. George Stuart Fullerton. Psychol. Rev., New York, vol.3, no.1, pp.20, Jan., 1896.

PRELIMINARY EXPERIMENTS ON THE CAUSAL FACTORS IN ANIMAL LEARNING. J.A. Gengerelli. Jour. Comp. Psych., vol. 8, pp.435-457, fig.3, Dec., 1928; vol.9, pp.245-274, figs.15, Aug., 1929.

(ON THE PSYCHOLOGY OF LARGE MAMMALS.) Zur Psychologie der Grossaeuger. B. Grzimek. Saeugetierk. Mitteil., Stuttgart, vol.3, no.1, pp.34, Jan. 1, 1955.

(COMPARATIVE ANIMAL AND HUMAN PSYCHIATRY. Vergleichende Tier- und Menschenpsychiatrie. Dr. Hammer. Zeitschrift f. Saeugetierk. Berlin, vol.13, no. 2, pp.192-197, 1939.

(OBSERVATIONS ON ANIMAL PSYCHOLOGY IN THE NATIONAL PARKS OF THE BELGIAN CONGO.) Observations sur la psychologie animale dans les parcs nationaux du Congo Belge. H. Hediger. Brussels, pp. 196, 1951.

STUDIES OF THE PSYCHOLOGY AND BEHAVIOUR OF CAPTIVE ANIMALS IN ZOOS AND CIRCUSES. H. Hediger. London, Butterworth, vol.8, pp.166, pls.16, 1955.

PSYCHOLOGICAL WEAPONS IN ANIMAL FIGHT. R.W.G. Hingston. Character and Personality, Durham, N.C., vol.2, no.1, pp.3-21, figs.6, Sep., 1933.

MINDS AND MANNERS OF WILD ANIMALS. BOOK OF PERSONAL OBSERVATIONS. William T. Hornaday. New York, Charles Scribner's Sons, vol.8, pp.1-328, illus., May, 1922.

(Review by William Beebe of) MINDS AND MANNERS OF WILD ANIMALS. William T. Hornaday. Nat. Hist., vol.23, pp.56-58, Jan.-Feb., 1923.

PSYCHOLOGY OF WILD ANIMALS. William T. Hornaday. N. Dakota Outdoors, Bismarck, vol.1, no.8, pp.16-19, Feb., 1939.

MENTAL AND SPIRITUAL DEVELOPMENT OF ANIMALS; OR, TELEPATHY, THE CLUE TO MANY UNANSWERED QUESTIONS. Leroy Hughbanks. Wellington, Kan., Printed by E.L.Shultz, pp.12, 1914.

HABIT INTERFERENCE IN THE WHITE RAT AND IN HUMAN SUBJECTS. Walter S. Hunter. Jour. Comp. Psychol., vol.2, pp.29-50, Feb. (Mar.), 1922.

FURTHER STUDIES ON THE RELIABILITY OF THE MAZE WITH RATS AND HUMANS. Walter S. Hunter, Randolph Vance. Jour. Comp. Psych., vol.4, pp.431-442, 1924.

WHAT ARE THEY THINKING? Charles R. Knight. Nat. Hist., New York, vol. 41, no. 2, pp.85-89, 148, illus., Feb., 1938.

(CONTRIBUTIONS TO ANIMAL PSYCHOLOGY.) Beitraege zur Tierpsychologie. G.V. Kolosvary. Archiv. f. Naturgesch., vol.92, Heft 8, pp.76-97, figs.14,

(INTRA-INDIVIDUAL VARIATION OF THE PSYCHICAL PHENOMENA OF THE INDIVIDUAL ANIMAL.) Ueber intraindividuelle Variation der psychischen Erscheinungen des Tierindividuums. G. von Kolosvary. Archiv. f. Naturgesch., vol.92, Heft 2, pp.270-280, figs.4, graphs 5, 1927.

(ZOOPSYCHOLOGICAL OBSERVATIONS IN SOUTH AMERICA.) Tierpsychologische Beobachtungen in Suedamerika. Hans Krieg. Veroeffnt. Zool. Staatssamlung, Munich, vol.1, pp.63-96, Jan. 1, 1950.

WIGWAGGING IN THE WILD. MEANING OF THE LANGUAGE OF TAILS. Hamilton M. Laing. Nature Mag., vol.20, no.6, pp.259-262, illus., Dec., 1932.

PSYCHICAL RESEARCH OF THE CENTURY. Andrew Lang. Smiths. Inst., Annual Rep., 1900, Washington, pp.675-681, 1901.

NOTES ON INSTINCT AND INTELLIGENCE IN RATS AND CATS. W.McDougall, K.D. McDougall. Jour. Comp.Psych., vol.7, pp.145-175, illus., 1927.

SCIENCE AND THE RATIONAL ANIMAL. Max Mason. Science, vol.84, no.2169, pp.71-76, July 24, 1936.

NATURE AND DEVELOPMENT OF ANIMAL INTELLIGENCE. Wesley Mills. Macmillan Co., New York, pp.307, 1908.

(JUDGING RELATIONS WITH OBJECTS IN ANIMALS.) Zur Beurteilung des Umgangs mit Gegenstaenden bei Tieren. Fritz Pauli. Biol. Zentralblatt, vol.46, pp.685-686.

WHITE AND TOLMAN ON THE ELIMINATION OF SHORT AND LONG BLIND ALLEYS. Joseph Peterson. Jour. Comp.Psych., vol.4, pp.443-445, 1924.

ANIMAL LEARNING--AN ANCIENT SPECULATION AND A MODERN SCIENCE. John V. Quaranta. Animal Kingdom, New York Zool. Soc., vol.55, no.2, pp.56-59, illus., Mar.-Apr., 1952.

(DO ANIMALS HAVE A CONCIOUSNESS OF DEATH?) Haben Tiere ein Bewusstsein vom Tode? L. Reisinger. Zool. Anzeiger, vol.79, pp.1-4, Oct. 15, 1928.

ANIMAL BEHAVIOR AND INTERNAL DRIVES. Curt P. Richter. Quart. Rev. Biol., vol.2, pp.307-343, illus., Sep., 1927.

CAN ANIMALS THINK? Andrew G.A. Russell. Nat. Hist., New York, vol.55, no.10, pp.478-480, 490-492, illus., Dec., 1946.

STUDIES IN ACTIVITY. IV. RELATION OF ACTIVITY TO MAIZE LEARNING AND TO BRAIN WEIGHT. Mary Shinley. Jour. Comp. Psych., vol.8, pp.187-195, illus., 1928.

DIFFERENTIAL RESPONSE IN ANIMALS TO STIMULI VARYING WITHIN A SINGLE DIMENSION. Kenneth W. Spence. Psychol. Rev., vol.44, no.5, pp.430-444, figs.3, tbls.2, Sep., 1937.

(ON THE PSYCHOLOGY OF LARGE MAMMALS.) Zur Psychologie der Gross-Saeuger. G. Steinbacher. Saeugetierk. Mitteil., Stuttgart, vol.2, no.4, pp.174-176, Oct.1, 1954.

(ON THE QUESTION OF THE ORIGIN OF THE STATES OF SO-CALLED ANIMAL HYPNOSIS.) Zur Frage nach dem Entstehen der Zustaende der sogenannten tierischen Hypnose. J. Ten Cate. Biol. Zentralblatt, vol.28, pp.664-679, 1928.

VALUE OF THE PRELIMINARY PERIOD OF FEEDING IN THE PROBLEM BOX. Carl John Warden. Jour. Comp. Psych., vol.5, pp.365-372, 1925.

YALE LABORATORIES OF COMPARATIVE PSYCHOBIOLOGY. Robert M. Yerkes. Comparative Psychology Monographs, Baltimore, vol.8, no.3, pp.1-33, pls.10, Feb., 1932.

RABIES see DISEASES AND PARASITES -- RABIES

## RELATIONSHIPS

PRECIPITIN REACTION IN THE STUDY OF ANIMAL RELATIONSHIPS. Alan Arthur Boyden. Biol. Bull., vol.50, pp.73-107, Feb., 1926.

(DERIVATIONAL RELATIONSHIPS OF RODENTS (RODENTIA) AND MARSUPIALS (MARSUPIALIA).) Die Stammesverwandtschaft der Nager (Rodentia) mit den Beutelthieren (Marsupialia). A. Fleishmann. Sitz.Ber.K.Preuss Akad.Wiss., Berlin, no. 16, pp.299-305, Mar. 27, 1890.

ON THE RELATIONS OF THE ORDERS OF MAMMALS. Theodore Gill. Amer.Naturalist, vol.4, no.8, pp.502-504, Oct., 1870.

RELATIONS OF THE LEMURS, PRIMATES AND UNGULATES. A.A.W. Hubrecht. Science, n.s., vol.4, no.95, pp.611-612, Oct. 23, 1896.

RESEMBLANCES OF THE ARCHAEOCETI TO THE PINNIPEDIA. R. Kellogg. (In) A Review of the Archaeoceti. Publ.Carneg. Instn.482, pp.15-366, pls.37, 1936.

RELATIONSHIPS OF THE ORDERS OF MAMMALS. William Diller Matthew. Jour. Mamm., vol.24, no.3, pp.304-311, fig.1, Aug. 17, 1943.

(CLOSER RELATIONSHIP BETWEEN MAN AND THE ANTHROPOIDS ON THE BASIS OF MICRO-OSTEOLOGICAL INVESTIGATION, WITH CONSIDERATION OF THE FINER BONE STRUCTURE OF CARNIVORES AND UNGULATES.) Das naehere Verwandtschaftsverhaeltnis zwischen dem Menschen und den Anthropoiden auf Grund mikroosteologischer Untersuchungen auch mit Ruecksicht auf die feinere Knochenstruktur der Carnivoren und Ungulaten. J. Mátyás, M. Szabó. Zeitschr. f. Anat. u. Entwickl. Gesch., vol.97, pp.169-209, figs.5, pls. 17, 1932.

(INTERRELATIONSHIPS OF THE MAMMAL ORDER, WITH SPECIAL CONSIDERATION OF THE MORE CLOSELY RELATED OF THE ANTHROPOIDS.) Die verwandtschaftlichen Beziehungen der Saeugetierordnungen mit besonder Beruecksichtigung der naeheren verwandten der Anthropoideen. J. Mátyás, J. Stiller. Archiv. Zool. Ital., vol.16, pts. 3-4, pp.1169-1229, 1932.

ON A REMARKABLE CASE OF AFFINITY BETWEEN ANIMALS INHABITING GUIANA, W. AFRICA, AND THE MALAY ARCHIPELAGO. Oldfield Thomas. Proc. Zool. Soc., London, pp.415-417, June, 1914.

INTERRELATIONSHIPS OF THE MAMMALIAN GENERA. VOL.1-MONOTREMATA, MARSUPIALIA, INSECTIVORA, CHIROPTERA, EDENTATA. VOL.2-RODENTIA, CARNIVORA, PRIMATES. VOL.3-UNGULATA, CETACEA. Herluf Winge. Translated from Danish by E.Deichmann and G. M. Allen. Illus., pls., Copenhagen, C.A. Reitzel, 1941-1942.

REPORTS, ANNUAL see ANNUAL ZOOLOGICAL REPORTS

## REPRODUCTIVE BIOLOGY

(SOME NOTABLE BREEDING RESULTS IN SCHOENBRUNN IN 1931.) Einige bemerkenswerte Zuchterfolge in Schoenbrunn im Jahre 1931. Otto Antonius. Zool.Garten, Leipzig, n.F., vol.5, nos.4-6, pp.91-97, figs.1-7, Aug., 1932.

PATTERN OF MAMMALIAN REPRODUCTION. S.A. Asdell. Comstock Publ. Co., New York, pp.437, pls.12, diagrs., 1946.

OBSERVATIONS ON THE PENETRATION OF THE SPERM INTO THE MAMMALIAN EGG. C.R. Austin. Australian Jour. Sci. Research, Melbourne, ser.B, vol.4, no.4, pp.581-596, illus., Nov., 1951.

FERTILIZATION IN MAMMALS. C.R. Austin, M.W.H. Bishop. Biol. Rev. Cambridge Phil.Soc., vol.32, no.3, pp.296-348, Aug., 1957.

TRANSFER OF MAMMALIAN OVA BETWEEN SPECIES. R.L.W. Averill, C.E. Adams, L.E.A. Rowson. Nature, London, vol.176, no.4473, pp.167-168, July 23, 1955.

EVOLUTIONARY CHANGES IN THE PHYSIOLOGICAL CONTROL OF MATING BEHAVIOR IN MAMMALS. F.A.Beach. Psychol. Reviews, vol.54, pp.297-315, 1947.

DEVELOPMENT OF THE REPRODUCTIVE DUCTS AND CANALS IN THE FREE-MARTIN WITH COMPARISON OF THE NORMAL. T.H.Bissonnette. Amer. Jour. Anat., vol.33, pp.267-346, pls.8, May 15, 1924.

SEXUAL PERIODICITY. T.H.Bissonnette. Quart. Rev. Biol., vol.11, pp.371-386, 1936.

SEXUAL PHOTOPERIODICITY IN ANIMALS. COMMENTS ON A RECENT DISCUSSION OF THE SUBJECT BY DR. S. ZUCKERMAN. T.H. Bissonnette.Jour. Heredity, Washington, vol.26, no.7, pp. 284-286, July, 1935.

(MAMMAL BIRTHS AT THE MENAGERIE OF THE JARDIN DES PLANTES FROM 1900 TO 1930.) Les naissances de mammifères a la ménagerie du Jardin des Plantes de 1900 a 1930. E. Bourdelle.Bull. Mus. Nat. Hist. Nat., Paris, ser.2, vol. 3, no.6, pp.475-478, June, 1931.

BREEDING DATES OF SMALL MAMMALS AT RALEIGH, NORTH CAROLINA. C.S. Brimley. Jour. Mamm., vol.4, no.4, pp. 263-264, Nov., 1923.

REARING WILD ANIMALS IN CAPTIVITY, AND GESTATION PERIODS. C. Emerson Brown. Jour. Mamm., vol.17, no.1, pp. 10-13, Feb., 1936.

VERTEBRATE SEXUAL CYCLES. W. S. Bullough. John Willey & Sons, New York, pp.viii-117, illus., Dec. 11, 1951.

SEX LIFE OF WILD ANIMALS. A NORTH AMERICAN STUDY. Eugene Burns. Rinehart, pp.xiii-290, 1953.

(REPRODUCTIVE PERIOD AND NUMBER OF FETUSES OF SOME MICROMAMMALS OF THE FAUNA OF FRANCE.) Periode de reproduction et nombre de Foetus de quelques micromammiferes de la Fauna de France. P. Cantuel.Mammalia, Paris, vol.10, nos.3-4, pp.140-144, Sep.-Dec., 1946.

BREEDING NOTES ON A FEW WASHINGTON MAMMALS. Leo K. Couch. Murrelet, vol. 13, no.1, p.25, Jan., 1932.

(SEXUAL CYCLE IN THE FEMALE MAMMAL. STUDY OF THE FOLLICULAR PHASE.) Le cycle sexuel chez la femelle des mammiferes. Etude de la phase folliculair. R. Courrier. Archives de Biologie, vol.34, pp.369-477, pls.9-13, 1924.

SEX RATIO IN MULES AND OTHER HYBRID MAMMALS. W.A. Craft. Quart. Rev. Biol., vol.13, no.1, pp.19-40, Mar., 1938.

ABNORMAL SEXUALITY IN ANIMALS. III. SEX REVERSAL. F. A. E. Crew. Quart. Rev. Biol., vol.2, pp.427-441, figs.2, Sep., 1927.

FUNCTIONAL DEVELOPMENT OF ACCESSORY GLANDS AND SPERMATOGENESIS. D.V. Davies, T. Mann. Nature, London, vol.160, no.4061, p.295, Aug. 30, 1947.

DEVELOPMENT AND VASCULARISATION OF THE CORPUS LUTEUM IN THE MOUSE AND RABBIT. Ruth Deanesly. Proc. Royal Soc. London, ser.B, vol.107, no.B 748, pp. 60-75, pls.6-8, Sep. 3, 1930.

(PROPAGATION, PREGNANCY, AND PARTURITION IN MAMMALS.) Fortpflanzung, Schwangerschaft und Gebaeren der Saeugetiere. F. Doflein. Jena, pp.70, 1920.

(SOME NOTABLE BREEDING RESULTS IN THE ZOOLOGICAL GARDEN OF HANNOVER.) Einige bemerkenswerte Zuchterfolge im Zoologischen Garten Hannover. Carl Eiffert. Zool.Garten, n.F., vol.18, nos.3-4, pp.136-138, 1951.

ON THE ANALYSIS OF PRODUCTIVITY IN POPULATIONS OF HIGHER VERTEBRATES. Paul L. Errington. Jour. Wildl. Mgt., Menasha, vol.6, no.2, pp.165-181, Apr., 1942.

ON THE EXISTENCE OF A HITHERTO UNRECOGNIZED DIETARY FACTOR ESSENTIAL FOR REPRODUCTION. Herbert E. Evans, K. Scott Bishop. Science, n.s., vol.56, pp.650-651, Dec. 8, 1922.

OVOGENESIS AND THE NORMAL FOLLICULAR CYCLE IN ADULT MAMMALIA. Herbert McLean Evans. Berkeley, Calif., Univ. of Calif. Press, pp.224, illus., pls.19-36, tbls., diagrs., 1931.

OVOGENESIS AND FOLLICULAR CYCLE IN ADULT MAMMALIA. Herbert McLean Evans, Olive Swezy. Mem. Univ. Calif., vol.9, no.3, pp.119-188, figs.A-P, pls. 19-36, Dec. 19, 1931.

(DEVELOPMENT OF TYPES IN ANIMAL BREEDING.) Die Typenbildung in der Tierzucht. Ernst Feige. Zeitschr. f.

Ind. Abstammungs. u. Vererbungslehre, vol.50, pp.344-355, figs.4, 1929.

PERIOD OF GESTATION IN SOME AMERICAN MAMMALS. Frank Forrest Gander. Jour. Mamm., vol.9, no.1, p.75, Feb., 1928.

CAROTENOIDS AND REPRODUCTION. T. W. Goodwin. Biol. Reviews, London, vol. 25, no.4, pp.391-413, Oct., 1950.

THE SEASONAL MODIFICATION OF THE TESTES OF VERTEBRATES, WITH SPECIAL REFERENCE TO INTERSTITIAL TISSUE. J.R. Groome. P.Z.S., pt.1, pp. 131-143, figs.4, Mar., 1933.

DEVELOPMENT OF THE SEX CORDS IN THE GONADS OF MAN AND MAMMALS. Peter Gruenwald. Amer. Jour. Anat., Philadelphia, vol.70, no.3, pp.359-389, pls.4, May 15, 1942.

NOTES ON PERIOD OF GESTATIONS. W.J. Hamilton. American Fur Breeders, vol.3, no.6, p.50, 1930.

REPRODUCTIVE RATES OF SOME SMALL MAMMALS. W.J. Hamilton. Jour. Mamm., vol.30, no.3, pp.257-260, Aug., 1949.

FERTILITY IN MAMMALS AND BIRDS. John Hammond. Biol. Reviews Cambridge Philos. Soc., Cambridge, vol.16, no.3, pp.165-190, July, 1941.

BREEDING HABITS AND BREEDING POTENTIALS OF WEST VIRGINIA MAMMALS. C.O. Handley. West Virginia Conserv., Charleston, vol.13, no.11, pp.17, Feb., 1950.

(GOALS AND WAYS OF ANIMAL BREEDING.) Ziele und Wege der Tierzuechtung. Fritz Haring. Zeitschr. f. Saeugetierk., Berlin, vol.19, no.3, pp.117-151, illus., Dec. 31, 1954.

DATA ON THE REPRODUCTION OF SOME MALAYAN MAMMALS. J.L. Harrison. Proc. Zool. Soc. London, vol.125, pt.2, pp.445-460, Aug. 31, 1955.

MATING OF MAMMALS. Carl G. Hartman. Ann. New York Acad. Sci., New York, vol. 46, art.1, pp.23-44, June 15, 1945.

OBSERVATIONS ON THE VIABILITY OF THE MAMMALIAN OVUM. Carl G. Hartman. Amer. Jour. Obstetrics and Gynecology, vol. 7, no.1, pp.4 (reprint), Jan., 1924.

POSSIBLE CASE OF SUPERFETATION? Carl G. Hartman. Jour. Mamm., vol.31, no.1, p.94, Feb. 21, 1950.

OVULATION AND THE TRANSPORT AND VIABILITY OF OVA AND SPERM IN THE FEMALE GENITAL TRACT. Carl G. Hartman. Chapter XIV of "Sex and Internal Secretions," pp.647-733, figs.17, 1932.

SOME EXCESSIVELY LARGE LITTERS OF EGGS LIBERATED AT A SINGLE OVULATION IN MAMMALS. Carl G. Hartman. Jour. Mamm., vol.10, no.3, pp.187-202, pl.15, Aug. 10, 1929.

(CARE OF YOUNG IN MAMMALS.) Brutpflege bei Saeugetieren. H. Hediger. Ciba-Zeitschrift, no.120, pp.4749-4758, 1952.

WILDLIFE NURSERIES. PART 2. Ellis A. Hicks. Iowa Conservationist, Des Moines, vol.5, no.5, pp.33-38, May 15, 1946.

ANIMAL BABY CARRIAGES. John Eric Hill. Nat. Hist., New York, vol.54, no.5, p.198, illus., May, 1945.

X ZONE OF THE SUPRARENAL CORTEX IN RELATION TO GONADAL MATURATION IN MONKEYS AND MICE AND TO EPIPHYSEAL UNIONS IN MONKEYS. Evelyn Howard. Anat. Rec., vol.46, no.2, pp.93-104, 1930.

OBSERVATIONS ON REPRODUCTION IN SOME SMALL MAMMALS OF ARCTIC NORWAY. H.M.D. Hoyte. Jour. Animal Ecol., Cambridge, vol.24, no.2, pp.412-425, Nov., 1955.

MOTHERS OF THE WILDWOOD. Ellworth Jaeger. Canadian Nature, Toronto, vol.5, no.1, pp.14-17, Jan.-Feb., 1943.

DETERMINING FECUNDITY IN MALE SMALL MAMMALS. E.W. Jameson, Jr. Jour. Mamm., vol.31, no.4, pp.433-436, Nov. 21, 1950.

(THE DIVISION OF THE UNFERTILIZED OVULE IN MAMMALS.) La division de l'ovule non feconde chez les mammiferes. J. Janosik. Archives de Biologie, vol.35, pp.117-124, Oct. 15, 1925.

(CONTRIBUTION TO THE HISTOGENESIS OF THE MAMMAL OVARY.) Contribution a l'histogenese de l'ovaire des Mammiferes. F. Jonckheere. Archives de Biologie, vol. 40, pp.357-438, figs.8, pl.3, 1930.

GESTATION PERIODS, A TABLE AND BIBLIOGRAPHY. J.H. Kenneth. Oliver and Boyd, Edinburgh, pp.23, 1943; Commonwealth Bureau Animal Breeding & Genetics, Technical Communication no. 5, Edinburgh (3rd edition), pp.1-39, tbls., 1953.

SIGNIFICANCE OF LITTER-SIZE. David Lack. Animal Ecol., London, vol.17, no.1, pp.45-50, May, 1948.

METABOLIC REGULATOR IN MAMMALIAN SPERMATOZOA. H.A. Lardy, D. Ghosh, G.W.E. Plaut. Science, Lancaster, vol.109, no.2832, pp.365-367, illus., Apr. 8, 1949.

SEX RATIO, FERTILITY AND ANCESTRAL LONGEVITY. Philip S. Lawrence. Quart. Rev. Biol., Baltimore, vol.16, no.1, pp.35-79, Mar., 1941.

ROLE OF BACTERIA IN THE VAGINA WITH SPECIAL REFERENCE TO THE BACTERIAL FLORA OF THE LATERAL VAGINAL CANALS OF THE OPOSSUM DURING THE OESTRUS CYCLE. I.M. Lewis. Trans. Amer. Micro. Soc., vol.44, no.4, pp. 211-215, Oct., 1925.

CYCLIC CHANGES IN THE MAMMALIAN OVARY. Leo Loeb. Proc. Amer. Phil.Soc., vol.50, no.199, pp.228-234, May-June, 1911.

FUNCTION OF THE CORPUS LUTEUM, THE EXPERIMENTAL PRODUCTION OF THE MATERNAL PLACENTA AND THE MECHANISM OF THE SEXUAL CYCLE IN THE FEMALE ORGANISM. Leo Loeb. Medical Record, pp.1-18, June 25, 1910.

(FURTHER INVESTIGATIONS OF THE ARTIFICIAL PRODUCTION OF THE MATERNAL PLACENTA AND OF THE MECHANICS OF THE SEXUAL CYCLE OF THE FEMALE MAMMAL ORGANISM.) Weitere Untersuchungen ueber die kuenstliche Erzeugung der muetterlichen Placenta und ueber die Mechanik des sexuellen Zyklus des weiblichen Saeugetierorganismus. Leo Loeb. Zentralbl. f. Physiol., vol.24, no.6, 1910.

SEX DIFFERENCES IN LENGTH OF GESTATION IN MAMMALS. T. McKeown, B. MacMahon. Jour. Endocrinol., London, vol.13, no.3, pp.309-318, Apr., 1956.

SEXUAL PERIODICITY AND THE CAUSES WHICH DETERMINE IT. F.H.A. Marshall. Philos. Trans. Roy. Soc. London, ser.B., no.539, vol.226, pp.423-456, Dec. 8, 1936.

(WHEN MOTHER LOVE DENIES.) Wenn die Mutterliebe versagt. H. Mattausch. Deutsche Jagd, Berlin, nos.42-43, pp.590-592, Jan. 19, 1940.

BIOLOGY OF THE MAMMALIAN TESTIS AND SCROTUM. Carl R. Moore. Quart. Rev. Biol., vol.1, pp.4-50, figs.8, Jan., 1926.

OVARIAN ACTIVITY IN MAMMALS SUBSEQUENT TO CHEMICAL INJURY OF CORTEX. Carl R. Moore, Hsi Wang. Physiological Zool., Chicago, vol.20, no.3, pp.300-321, pls.1-2, July, 1947.

(ON THE EXPLANATION OF PROLONGED GESTATION IN MAMMALS.) Zur Erklaerung der verlaengerten Tragdauer bei Saeugetieren. E. Murr. Zool. Anzeiger, vol.85, pp.113-129, Oct. 15, 1929.

(ON SOME REGULARITIES OF THE HIBERNAL PROPAGATION OF UNGULATES IN THE WESTERN CAUCASUS MOUNTAINS.) Sur quelques régularités de la propagation hivernale des ongulés dans les montagnes du Caucase Occidental. A.A. Nassimovitch. Bull. Soc. Nat. Moscow, n.s., vol.45, sect. biol., no.1, pp.3-9, 1936. (In Russian with French summary.)

ASPECTS OF TWIN RESEARCH. H.H. Newman. Scientific Monthly, Lancaster, vol.52, no.2, pp.99-112, illus., Feb., 1941.

(MAMMAL REPRODUCTION AT THE ZOOLOGICAL PARK OF THE BOIS DE VINCENNES IN RELATION TO FEEDING.) La reproduction des mammifères au parc zoologique du Bois de Vincennes dans ses rapports avec l'alimentation. J. Nouvel. Mammalia, Paris, vol.16, no.3, pp.160-175, Sep., 1952.

SEASONAL MODIFICATIONS IN TESTES OF VERTEBRATES. R.M. Oslund. Quart. Rev. Biol., vol.3, pp.255-270, June, 1928.

(PECULIAR PROCESSES IN THE REPRODUCTION PHYSIOLOGY OF THE MAMMALS.) Sondervorgaenge in der Fortpflanzungsphysiologie der Saeugetiere. B. Ottow. Saeugetierk. Mitteil., Stuttgart, vol.1, no.4, pp. 154-162, Oct. 1, 1953.

FACTORS GOVERNING THE MAMMALIAN SEX RATIO. A.S. Parkes. Sci. Prog., vol. 18, pp.426-435, 1924.

ON THE CORRELATION BETWEEN THE NUMBER OF MAMMAE OF THE DAM AND SIZE OF LITTER IN MAMMALS. I. INTERRACIAL CORRELATION. Raymond Pearl. Proc. Soc. Exper. Biol. and Med., pp.27-30, 1913.

TABLES FOR CALCULATING COEFFICIENTS OF INBREEDING. Raymond Pearl, John Rice Miner. Ann. Rept. Maine Agric. Exper. Sta., pp.191-202, 1913.

FERTILIZATION IN MAMMALS. Gregory Pincus. Scientific American, New York, vol.184, no.3, pp.44-47, illus., Mar., 1951.

COMPARATIVE BEHAVIOR OF MAMMALIAN EGGS IN VIVO AND IN VITRO. VI. THE MATURATION OF HUMAN OVARIAN OVA. Gregory Pincus, Barbara Saunders. Anat. Record, Philadelphia, vol.75, no.4, pp.537-545, pls.2, tbl.1, Dec. 25, 1939.

NUTRIENTS REQUIRED TO DEVELOP THE FETUS. (Trans. title.) I.S. Popov. Nauch. Agron. Zhur., vol.1, no.3, pp. 205-210, 1924.

NON-UTILIZATION OF LACTIC ACID BY THE LACTATING MAMMARY GLAND. Ross C. Powell, Jr., J.C. Shaw. Science, Lancaster, n.s., vol.96, no.2496, p.403, Oct. 30, 1942.

(ON PROLONGATION OF GESTATION IN MAMMALS.) Ueber die Verlaengerung der Tragzeit bei Saeugetieren. H. Prell. Archiv. Zool. Ital., vol.16, pts.3-4, pp.950-961, 1932.

ANALYSIS OF THE FACTORS INFLUENCING GROWTH AND DEVELOPMENT OF THE MAMMALIAN REPRODUCTIVE TRACT. Dorothy Price. Physiological Zool., Chicago, vol.20, no.3, pp.213-247, July, 1947.

COURTSHIP OF ANIMALS. William Playne Pycraft. New York, H. Holt & Co., pp.318, pls., 1914.

EARLY DEATH OF OVUM IN THE OPOSSUM WITH OBSERVATIONS ON MORIBUND MOUSE EGGS. M.G. Rafferty, C.G. Hartman. Jour. Morphol., Philadelphia, vol. 92, no.3, pp.455-486, May, 1953.

COPULATORY BEHAVIOR OF SMALL MAMMALS. C.E. Reed. Jour. Comp. Psychol., vol.39, pp.185-206, 1946.

CIRCULATORY ADAPTATIONS TO BIRTH. S.R.M. Reynolds. Sci. Monthly, vol.77, no. 4, pp.205-213, illus., Oct., 1953.

PROOFS AND IMPLICATIONS OF COMPLETE SEX-TRANSFORMATION IN ANIMALS. Oscar Riddle. Verhandl. I. Internat. Kongr. f. Sexualforschung Berlin vom 10 bis 16 Oct., 1926, pp.193-218, 1927.

LITTER RECORDS OF SOME MAMMALS OF MEADE COUNTY, KANSAS. George C. Rinker. Trans. Kansas Acad. Sci., Lawrence, vol.45, no.50, pp.376-378, 1942.

(DURATION OF GESTATION IN WILD MAMMALS ACCORDING TO C.E. BROWN. COMPARISON WITH THE FINDINGS OF G. JENNISON.) Les durées de gestation des mammiferes sauvages d'apres C.E.Brown. Comparaison avec les résultats de G.Jennison. P. Rode. Mammalia, Paris, vol.1, pp.26-28, Sep., 1936.

(POLYGAMY OR BREEDING IN PAIRS?) Polygame oder Paarzucht? Julio Rossel. Der Deutsche Pelztierzuechter, Jahrg.1931, Munich, no.15, pp.420-421, fig., Aug.1, 1931.

LIGHT AND SEASONAL REPRODUCTION IN ANIMALS. William Rowan. Biol.Reviews, Cambridge Philos. Soc., vol.13, no.4, pp. 374-402, Oct., 1938.

(FOSTER YOUNG WITH ANIMALS.) Pflegkinder bei Tieren. Bastian Schmid. Kosmos, Stuttgart, vol.29, no.8, pp.284-286, figs. 1-4, Aug., 1932.

PHYSICO-CHEMICAL ANALYSIS OF THE PHYSIOLOGY OF SPERMATOZOA OF MAMMALIA. COMMUNICATION 10. SPERMATOXINE AND QUESTION OF ARTIFICIAL SEX DIFFERENTIATION IN MAMMALIA. V.N. Schreder. Bull. Acad. Sci. USSR, Moscow, biol.ser., 1945, no.4, pp. 404-418, 1945. (In Russian with English summary.)

(UDDER SEEKING IN YOUNG UNGULATES.) Zur Euter-Suche junger Huftiere. Linde Schuller. Saugetierk. Mitteil., vol.5, no.4, p.170, Dec. 1, 1957.

(CONTRIBUTION TO THE PROBLEM OF THE OESTRAL AND BREEDING PERIODS OF MAMMALS IN THE TROPICS.) Ein Beitrag zur Frage der Brunst- und Setzzeiten der Saeugetieren in den Tropen. Ludwig Schuster. Der Zoologische Garten, Leipzig, n.F., vol.2, pts.4-6, pp.114-117, 1929.

ON THE BREEDING OF MAMMALS IN THE GARDENS OF THE ZOOLOGICAL SOCIETY OF LONDON DURING THE PAST TWENTY YEARS. P.L. Sclater. Proc. Zool. Soc. London, pp.623-626, Dec. 10, 1868.

ANIMAL AND HUMAN CHILDREN. J. P. Scott. Children, vol.4, no.5, pp.163-168, 1957.

BIRTH IN UNGULATES. E.J. Slijper. Mammalia, Paris, vol.22, no.1, pp.104-106, Mar., 1958.

SOME REMARKS ON GESTATION IN BIRTH IN CETACEA AND OTHER AQUATIC MAMMALS. E.J. Slijper. Hvalrad. Skr., vol.41, pp.1-62, 1956.

RHYTHMS OF OVOGENESIS BEFORE SEXUAL MATURITY IN THE RAT AND CAT. Mary Elizabeth Sneider. Amer. Jour. Anat., Philadelphia, vol.67, no.3, pp.471-499, pls. 4, Nov. 15, 1940.

(REPRODUCTIVE PERIOD OF JAVANESE MAMMALS.) Voortplantingstijden der Javaansche zoogdieren. H.J.V. Sody. Boschbouwkundig Tijdschrift "Tectona," Buitenzorg, vol.33, pp.23, tbls., Jan., 1940.

REPRODUCTIVE CYCLE, LITTER SIZE, AND LONGEVITY OF SEVERAL SMALL RODENTS. George H.W. Stein. Z.Schaedlingsbekaempfung, vol.42, nos.5-6, p.10, May, 1950.

CONDITIONS AFFECTING THE REPRODUCTIVE POWER IN ANIMALS. James H. Stoller. The Popular Science Monthly, pp. 48-51, Nov., 1889.

WILD ANIMAL PARENTHOOD. Ken Stott, Jr. Nature Mag., Washington, vol.41, no.5, pp.245-247, 270, illus., May, 1948.

(FEMALE GENITAL CYCLE OBSERVED FROM A MATHEMATICAL AND STATISTICAL POINT OF VIEW.) Der weibliche Genitalzyklus, mathematisch-statistisch betrachtet. F. Strauss. Verhandl. Schweizer. Naturforsch. Gesell., pp.152-153, 1948.

(PROBLEM OF THE LOCUS OF FERTILIZATION IN THE MAMMAL EGG.) Das Problem des Befruchtungsortes des Saeugetiereies. F. Strauss. Bull. Schweizerischen Akad. Med. Wissen., vol.10, nos.3-4, pp.239-248, 1954.

A PEDIGREE SYSTEM FOR USE IN BREEDING GUINEA-PIGS AND RABBITS. Frank M. Surface. Annual Rept. Maine Agr. Exper. Sta., pp.306-313, figs.3, 1913.

CHANGING CONCEPT OF OVARIAN RHYTHMS. Olive Swezy. Quart. Rev. Biol., Baltimore, vol.8, no.4, pp.413-433, Dec., 1933.

(ON THE TERMINATION OF OVULATION AND THE OPTIMAL MATING PERIOD IN DOMESTIC ANIMALS.) Ueber den Ovulationstermin und die optimale Begattungszeit bei den Haustieren. J. Tehver. Berliner Tieraerztliche Wochenschrift, Jahrg. 1937, no.27, pp.409-412, July 2, 1937.

(UDDER SEEKING IN YOUNG UNGULATES.) Zur Euter-Suche junger Huftiere. Erhard Thomas. Saeugetierk. Mitteil., Stuttgart, vol.4, no.1, p.31, Jan. 1, 1956.

COMPARATIVE STUDIES ON GONAD DEVELOPMENT IN THE RAT, THE PIG AND IN CATTLE. J.D. Thomson. Proc. Iowa Acad. Sci., Des Moines, vol.49, pp.475-501, pls.3, Sep., 1942.

OESTRUS. Stuart L. Tyson. Science, Lancaster, n.s., vol.74, no.1925, pp.512-513, Nov. 20, 1931.

INBREEDING AMONG WILDLIFE. Hans G. Uhlig. West Virginia Conserv., Charleston, vol.13, no.10, pp.9-10, Jan., 1950.

(OESTRUS, GESTATION, AND ENVIRONMENT.) Brunst, Tragzeit und Umwelt. Herbert Ullrich. Zool. Garten, Leipzig, n.F., vol.20, nos.2-3, pp.153-159, 1953.

(COMPARATIVE STUDIES OF MAMMAL OVULES DURING DIFFERENT PERIODS OF OVOGENESIS.) Etude comparée des ovules des mammiféres aux differentes periodes de l'ovogenèse. O. Van der Stricht. Arch. Biol., vol.32, pp.229-300, pls.10, 1923.

(ON THE PROBLEM OF INBREEDING.) Ueber das Problem der Inzucht. A. von Weinberg. Natur und Museum, Frankfurt a.M., vol.57, no.7, pp.289-311, figs.2, July, 1927.

EFFECTS OF LOW ENVIRONMENTAL TEMPERATURE ON THE REPRODUCTIVE ORGANS OF MALE MAMMALS WITH ANNUAL ASPERMIA. L.J. Wells, Moses Zalesky. Amer. Jour. Anat., Philadelphia, vol.66, no.3, pp.429-447, fig.1, pl.1, May 15, 1940.

LOCATION OF THE TESTES AND BODY TEMPERATURE IN MAMMALS. George B. Wislocki. Quart. Review Biol., vol. 8, no.4, pp.385-396, Dec., 1933.

(CARE OF YOUNG AND NEST BUILDING AMONG MAMMALS.) Brutpflege und Nestbau bei Saeugetieren. W. Wunder. Ergebnisse der Biol., vol.14, pp.280-348, 1937.

OBSERVATIONS AND EXPERIMENTS ON MATING BEHAVIOR IN FEMALE MAMMALS. William C. Young. Quart. Rev. Biol., Baltimore, vol.16, no.2, pp.135-156, June 1941; no.3, pp.311-335, Sep., 1941.

BREEDING SEASONS OF MAMMALS IN CAPTIVITY. S. Zuckerman. Proc. Zool. Soc. London, vol.122, pt.4, pp.827-950, illus., Feb., 1953.

BABIES IN THE ZOO. Animal Kingdom, New York, vol.48, no.5, pp.138-140, illus., Oct. 8, 1945.

REPRODUCTIVE ORGANS see ANATOMY -- REPRODUCTIVE ORGANS AND SEX CELLS

## RESEARCH, MAMMAL

WILDLIFE RESEARCH PROBES INTERRELATIONSHIPS. Harold E. Alexander. Kentucky, Happy Hunting Ground, Frankfort, vol.1, no.4, pp.12-26, July, 1946.

IS WILDLIFE RESEARCH PAYING ITS WAY? I.T. Bode. 13th N. Amer. Wildl. Conf., pp.18-30, 1948.

RESEARCH AND EDUCATION IN THE NATIONAL PARKS. Harold C. Bryant, Wallace W. Atwood. U.S. Dept. Interior, National Park Service, Washington, D.C., pp.vi-66, figs.42, 1932.

FURTHER NEEDS IN WILDLIFE RESEARCH. Clarence Cottam. Jour. Wildl. Mgt., Menasha, vol.13, no.4, pp.333-341, Oct., 1949.

RESEARCH PROBLEMS ON THE UNITED STATES NATIONAL WILDLIFE REFUGES. Clarence Cottam. Trans. 10th N. Amer. Wildl. Conf., Washington, pp.347-353, 1945.

SOME IMPROVEMENTS NEEDED IN WILDLIFE RESEARCH. Clarence Cottam. Jour. Wildl. Mgt., Menasha, vol.11, no.4, pp. 339-347, Oct., 1947.

(REPORTS ON SOME ITALIAN WORKS.) Autoreferate einiger italienischen Arbeiten. Oscar De Beaux. Zeitschr. f. Saeugetierk., vol.3, pp.55-59, June 11, 1928.

REGIONAL RESEARCH STATIONS IN BASIC SCIENCE. Lee R. Dice. Science, vol.103, no.2674, p.403, Mar. 29, 1946.

RESEARCH AT THE WISTAR INSTITUTE, 1905-1925. Henry H. Donaldson. Science, n.s., vol.61, pp.480-483, May 8, 1925.

(TASKS, WAYS, AND RESULTS OF COMPARATIVE SEXUAL-BIOLOGICAL RESEARCH.) Ueber Aufgaben, Wege und Ergebnisse vergleichendsexualbiologischer Forschung. Ulrich Gerhardt. Roux' Archiv. f. Entwicklungsmechanik der Organismen, Berlin, vol.118 (Festschrift f. Hans Spemann, pt.3), pp.11-39, 1929.

RESEARCH NEEDS IN MAMMALOGY. W. J. Hamilton, Jr. Trans. 3rd N. Amer. Wildl. Conf., pp.695-698, 1938.

NEED FOR RESEARCH ON GRASSLANDS. Herbert C. Hanson, C.T. Vorhies. Scientific Monthly, Lancaster, vol.46, pp.230-241, illus., Mar., 1938.

WHY AND HOW RESEARCH? Aldo Leopold. Trans. 13th N. Amer. Wildl. Conf., Washington, pp.44-48, 1948.

STATUS OF WILDLIFE RESEARCH; 1937. W.L. McAtee. U.S. Dept. Agric., Wildl. Research & Management, Leaflet BS-104, pp.30, Feb., 1938.

WORK OF THE DISCOVERY COMMITTEE. N.A. Mackintosh. Proc. Royal Soc. London, ser.A, vol.202, pp.1-16, pls.4, 1950.

(NEWER RESEARCHES IN THE FIELD OF MAMMALOGY.) Neuere Forschungen auf dem Gebiet der Saeugetierkunde. Paul Matschie. Leipzig, Natur und Schule, vol. 1, nos.1-2, pp.51-56, 1902.

LABORATORY OF VERTEBRATE ZOOLOGY AND ITS WORK IN 1932. S.I. Ognev. Sbornik nauchno issledovatel 'skogo inst. Zool. (Abstracts works Zool. Inst. Moscow State Univ.), no.2, pp.38-42, 1935; no.3, pp.77-79, 1936.

REVIEW OF THE WORKS OF LABORATORY OF USEFUL VERTEBRATES. S.I. Ognev. Bull. Nauchnoissledovatel'skogo inst. Zool. Moskovskogo Gosudarstvennogo Universiteta im. M.N. Pokrovskogo (Abstracts works Zool. Inst. Moscow State Univ.) Sektor Nauki Narkomprose RSFSR, Medgiz, pp. 55-57, 1933.

RESEMBLANCES AND CONTRASTS BETWEEN ZOOLOGIC AND PALAEONTOLOGIC RESEARCH IN MAMMALOGY. DESIRABILITY OF UNIFORM STANDARDS AND SYSTEMS IN CLASSIFICATION, IN DESCRIPTION, IN MEASUREMENT, IN REASONING. Henry Fairfield Osborn. Jour. Mamm., vol.2, no.1, pp.1-10, Feb., 1921.

SCIENTIFIC ODYSSEY. REVIEW OF THE WORK OF THE ZOOLOGICAL SOCIETY'S DEPARTMENT OF TROPICAL RESEARCH. Henry Fairfield Osborn. Bull. New York Zool. Soc., vol.44, no.1, pp.3-16, Jan.-Feb., 1941.

PRODUCTS OF THE PITTMAN-ROBERTSON RESEARCH. Robert M. Rutherford. Sports Afield, Minneapolis, vol.118, no.6, pp.50-51, 108-110, illus., Dec., 1947.

TREND OF WILDLIFE RESEARCH. ACCOMPLISHMENTS IN 10 NORTH CENTRAL

STATES. Gustav Swanson. Conservation Volunteer, St. Paul, vol.4, no.23, pp.24-27, Aug., 1942.

BIOLOGICAL STATIONS FOR THE STUDY OF PLANTS AND ANIMALS TOGETHER. Walter P. Taylor. Sci. Monthly, vol.21, pp.390-393, Oct., 1925.

(ABSTRACTS OF SOME RUSSIAN WORKS.) Referate einiger russischen Arbeiten. N.W. Timoféeff-Ressovsky. Zeitschr. f. Saeugetierk., Berlin, vol.7, nos.1-6, pp.37-38, Dec. 15, 1932.

RANDOM SHOTS FROM RESEARCH. (FERRET.) Stanley P. Young. Western Sportsman, Denver, vol.7, no.4, pp.19-21, illus., Sep., 1941.

(GUIDING PRINCIPLES IN INVESTIGATING SMALL MAMMALS OF BRANDENBURG.) Richtlinien fuer die Erforschung maerkischer Kleinsaeuger. K. Zimmermann. Maerkische Tierwelt, Berlin, vol.1, no.4, pp.165-168, Sep. 1, 1935.

REPORT ON THE PROGRESS OF THE DISCOVERY COMMITTEE'S INVESTIGATIONS. Publ. Discovery Comm., Colonial Office, London, pp.52, pls.10, June, 1937.

WORK OF THE DISCOVERY COMMITTEE. FIFTH COMMISSION OF THE R. R. S. DISCOVERY. Nature, London, vol.140, no. 3544, pp.571-572, Oct. 2, 1937.

SCIENTIFIC NAMES see NOMENCLATURE

SCRUB TYPHUS see DISEASES AND PARASITES -- SCRUB TYPHUS

SEALING see WHALING AND SEALING

SENSE ORGANS AND SENSATIONS see PHYSIOLOGY -- SENSE ORGANS AND SENSATIONS

SEX CELLS see ANATOMY -- REPRODUCTIVE ORGANS AND SEX CELLS

SKIN see ANATOMY -- PELAGE, SKIN, COLORATION

SKULL see ANATOMY -- SKULL, JAWS, TEETH

## SOCIETIES AND CONGRESSES, ZOOLOGICAL

(RECORD OF THE LA SALLE NATURAL SCIENCE SOCIETY.) Memoria de la Sociedad de Ciencias Naturales La Salle. A. Mendez. Zoologia, vol.11, no.30, pp. 204-236, illus., Sep.-Dec., 1951.

(MAMMALOGY CONGRESS OF BERKELEY, CALIFORNIA.) Le Congres de Mammalogie de Berkeley (Calif.). P. Rode. Mammalia, Paris, vol.2, no.4, pp.191-192, 1938.

(GERMAN MAMMALOGICAL SOCIETY.) Deutsche Gesellschaft fuer Saeugetierkunde. Hans Rummler. Zeitschr. f. Saeugetierk., vol.10, no.1, pp.119-143, Dec. 31, 1935.

CHARTER, BY-LAWS, AND REGULATIONS OF THE ZOOLOGICAL SOCIETY OF LONDON, INCORPORATED MARCH 27, 1829. Richard Clay and Co., Ltd., Bungay, Suffolk, pp.28, 1940.

SCIENTIFIC CONTRIBUTIONS OF THE NEW YORK ZOOLOGICAL SOCIETY. Zoologica, vol.31, pt.4, nos.10-13, Feb. 21, 1947.

## SPECIMENS -- COLLECTION, PREPARATION, PRESERVATION

AUTOBIOGRAPHY OF A TAXIDERMIST. Carl E. Akeley. World's Work, vol.41, pp. 177-195, figs.24, Dec., 1920.

CLEANING MAMMAL SKELETONS WITH MEAL WORMS. E. Rees Allen, Wilfred T. Neill. Jour. Mamm., vol.31, no.4, p. 464, Nov. 21, 1950.

INSTRUCTIONS FOR PRESERVING ANIMAL SPECIMENS FOR SCIENTIFIC PURPOSES. R.M. Anderson. Nat. Mus. Canada, Ottawa, Special Contrib.43-2, pp.1-34, figs.13, 1943. (Mimeogr.)

METHODS OF COLLECTING AND PRESERVING VERTEBRATE ANIMALS. R.M. Anderson. Nat. Mus. Canada, Ottawa, Bull. 69, pp.v-141, figs.46, 1932; Bull.69, Bio. Ser. no.18, pp.1-162, illus., 1948. (2nd ed., revised.)

(Review by Emmet T. Hooper of) METHODS OF COLLECTING AND PRESERVING VERTEBRATE ANIMALS. R.M. Anderson. (Bull. 69, Biol.Ser.no.18, pp.162, figs.48, Mar. 22, 1949.) Jour. Mamm., vol.31, no.1, p. 102, Feb. 21, 1950.

CAPTURE AND PRESERVATION OF SMALL MAMMALS FOR STUDY. H.E. Anthony. Amer. Mus. Nat. Hist., Guide Leaflet 61, pp.53, illus., Nov., 1925; 3rd ed., 1931.

CAPTURING SMALL MAMMALS FOR STUDY. Vernon Bailey. Jour. Mamm., vol.2, no.2, pp.63-68, May, 1921.

PREPARATION AND CARE OF RAW PELTS IN ALABAMA. F.S. Barkalow. Jour. Alabama Acad. Sci., vol.10, pt.2, p.27, June, 1938.

GAME HEADS--CARE AND PRESERVATION IN THE FIELD. F.S. Barkalow, Jr. Alabama Game and Fish News, Montgomery, vol.11, no.6, pp.3-4, 14, Dec., 1939.

PREPARATION OF PELTS FROM FUR-BEARING ANIMALS. F.S. Barkalow, Jr. Alabama Game and Fish News, vol.10, no.5, pp.4-5, Nov., 1938.

MOUNTING OF HAIRLESS AND SPARSELY HAIRED MAMMALS. Herman T. Beck. Mus. News, Washington, D.C., vol.19, no.12, pp.7-8, Dec. 15, 1941.

METHOD OF PREPARING SKELETONS OF SMALL VERTEBRATES. Rolf L. Bolin. Science, vol.82, no.2132, p.446, Nov., 1935.

CARE OF SKULLS AND SKELETONS OF SMALL ANIMALS. Richard M. Bond. Science, n.s., vol.89, no.2310, p.324, Apr. 7, 1939.

TEMPORARY PRESERVATION OF SMALL MAMMALS IN THE FIELD. Ernest S. Booth. Jour. Mamm., vol.25, no.4, pp.354-358, Dec. 12, 1944.

CLEANING SMALL COLLECTIONS OF SKULLS AND SKELETONS WITH DERMESTID BEETLES. Adrey E. Borell. Jour. Mamm., vol.19, no.1, pp.102-103, Feb. 14, 1938.

EFFECTS OF PRESERVATIVES ON THE FUR COLOR OF MAMMAL SPECIMENS. Walter J. Burns, Jr. Master's thesis, Univ. Idaho, 1952.

(FAST PREPARATION OF OSTEOLOGICAL PIECES.) Préparation rapide de pieces ostéologiques. P. Cantuel. Mammalia, Paris, vol.13, no.3, pp.100-103, Sep., 1949.

PREPARING MAMMAL SKINS IN THE FIELD. Geo. G. Cantwell. Jour. Mamm., vol.11, no.3, pp.324-325, Aug., 1930.

USE OF BAKELITE IN THE PRESERVATION OF FOSSIL MATERIAL. E.C. Case. Science, n.s., vol.61, pp.543-544, May 22, 1925.

PRESERVATION OF MAMMAL SKIN IN THE FIELD. James Lippitt Clark. Jour. Mamm., vol.18, no.1, pp.89-92, Feb. 14, 1937.

SOME PRINCIPLES OF GROUP CONSTRUCTION. Laurence Vail Coleman. Museum Work, vol.3, pp.121-125, Jan., 1921.

HANDBOOK ON PRESERVING MUSEUM SPECIMENS IN THE FIELD. Edward Drane Crabb. Univ. Oklahoma Bull., n.s., no. 268, pp.73, Aug., 1923.

FIVE WAYS OF OBTAINING ANIMALS. Lee S. Crandall. Animal Kingdom, New York, vol.49, no.5, pp.165, 170, illus., Sep.-Oct., 1946

DEEP FREEZER FOR PRESERVING SPECIMENS. Donald H. DeMeules. Jour. Mamm., vol.29, no.2, p.189, May 14, 1948.

PREPARATION OF SCIENTIFIC SPECIMENS OF MAMMALS IN THE FIELD. Lee R. Dice. Univ. Michigan Mus. Zool., Circ. 1, pp.10, fig.1, 1932.

DIRECTIONS FOR THE TANNING AND DRESSING OF FURS. Joseph Dixon. Univ. Calif., College of Agric., Circ.237, pp. 1-5, figs.3, Apr., 1922.

TWO ZOOLOGICAL EXHIBITS. J. Guy Dollman. Proc. Linnean Soc. London, Session 1932-33, pt.2, p.77, Feb. 2, 1933.

WATERPROOFING LABELS FOR WET SPECIMENS. A.A. Doolittle. Science, n.s., vol.61, pp.591-592, June 5, 1925.

COLOR CHANGES IN MAMMAL SKINS DURING PREPARATION. Stuart C. Downing. Jour. Mamm., vol.25, no.2, pp.128-132, July 15, 1945.

CONVENIENT METHOD OF MOUNTING AND STORING THE SKINS OF SMALL MAMMALS. Charles Elton. Jour. Mamm., vol.19, no.2, pp.244-245, May 14, 1938.

RAPID PREPARATION OF TOOTH SECTIONS FOR AGE DETERMINATIONS. H.D. Fisher, B.A. Mackenzie. Jour. Wildl. Mgt., Ithaca, vol.18, no.4, pp.535-537, illus., Oct., 1954.

SAFEGUARDING TYPE SPECIMENS. F.R. Fosberg. Science, Lancaster, Pa., n.s, vol. 89, no.2307, p.245, Mar. 17, 1939.

PREPARATION AND PRESERVATION OF THE BACULUM OF MAMMALS. Charles E. Friley, Jr. Jour. Mamm., vol.28, no. 4, pp.395-397, fig.1, Nov. 26, 1947.

WORLD'S MOST VERSATILE TANNER. Oskar Granstedt, Hobart M. Van Deusen. Leather & Shoes, Chicago, vol.121, no. 23, pp.8-9, 40-42, illus., June 9, 1951.

RAPID METHOD FOR CLEARING AND STAINING SPECIMENS FOR THE DEMONSTRATION OF BONE. Margaret C. Green. Ohio Jour. Sci., Columbus, vol. 52, no.1, pp.31-33, illus., Jan., 1952.

DIRECTIONS FOR PRESERVING SPECIMENS OF LARGE ANIMALS. Joseph Grinnell. Mus. Vert. Zool., Univ. Calif., pp.7, Nov. 20, 1911.

DELETERIOUS EFFECTS OF PRESERVATIVES ON STUDY SPECIMEN OF MAMMALS. E. Raymond Hall. Jour. Mamm., vol.18, no.3, pp.359-360, Aug. 14, 1937.

DERMESTID BEETLES AS AN AID IN CLEANING BONES. E. Raymond Hall, C. Russell Ward. Jour. Mamm., vol.14, no.4, pp.372-374, Nov. 13, 1933.

DESIRABILITY OF RECORDING FULL DATE ON SPECIMEN LABELS. W.J. Hamilton, Jr. Jour. Mamm., vol.19, no.1, p.102, Feb. 14, 1938.

DERMESTID BEETLES FOR CLEANING SKULLS AND SKELETONS IN SMALL QUANTITIES. Ross Hardy. Turtox News, Chicago, vol.23, no.4, pp.69-70, Apr., 1945.

EXPERIMENTS ON THE FADING OF MUSEUM SPECIMENS. Sidney F. Harmer. Museums Jour., vol.21, pp.205-222, pl., Apr., 1922.

TECHNIQUE FOR PREPARING A HAIR COLLECTION FOR FIELD OR LABORATORY USE. Arnold O. Haugen. Jour. Mamm., vol.20, no.2, p.260, May, 1939.

PREPARING GAME AND FISH. J. Larry Hawkes. Alabama Conservation, Montgomery, vol.16, no.6, pp.7, 14, illus., Dec., 1944.

TECHNIQUES OF COLLECTING MICROVERTEBRATE FOSSILS. Claude W. Hibbard. Contrib. Mus. Paleontol. Univ. Michigan, Ann Arbor, vol.8, no.2, pp.7-19, pls.4, Oct. 20, 1949.

CLEANING SKULLS AND SKELETONS: SUPPLEMENTARY NOTE. F.H. Holden. Condor, vol.18, p.231, Nov., 1916.

METHOD OF CLEANING SKULLS AND DISARTICULATED SKELETONS. F.H.

Holden. Condor, vol.16, no.5, pp.239-241, Sep. 15, 1914.

BRIEF DIRECTIONS FOR REMOVING AND PRESERVING THE SKINS OF MAMMALS. William Temple Hornaday. U.S. National Mus., Proceedings, Washington, vol.6, appendix no.22, pp.485-491, illus., 1884.

HOW TO COLLECT MAMMAL SKINS FOR PURPOSES OF STUDY AND FOR MOUNTING. William T. Hornaday. Rep. Smiths. Inst., 1885-86, pt.2, pp.659-670, 1889.

PRESERVATION OF MUSEUM SPECIMENS FROM INSECTS AND THE EFFECTS OF DAMPNESS. Walter Hough. U.S.Nat.Mus., Annual Rep., 1887, Washington, pp.549-558, illus., 1889.

EASY METHOD OF CLEANING SKULLS. A. Brazier Howell. Jour. Mamm., vol.1, no.1, pp.40-41, Nov. 28, 1919.

SUPPLEMENTARY NOTE ON CLEANING SKULLS. A. Brazier Howell. Jour. Mamm., vol.1, no.3, p.145, May, 1920.

PRACTICAL METHOD OF DEGREASING STUDY SKINS. George E. Hudson. Jour. Mamm., vol.16, no.4, pp.329-330, Nov., 1935.

CARE OF MUSEUM SPECIMENS OF RECENT MAMMALS. Hartley H.T. Jackson. Jour. Mamm., vol.7, no.2, pp.113-118, pl.13, May 13, 1926.

METHODS OF COLLECTING CARCASSES. R.A. Johnson. Science, n.s., vol.69, pp. 333-334, Mar. 22, 1929.

INSTRUCTIONS FOR PREPARING MAMMAL SKINS. C. Boden Kloss. Jour. Nat. Hist. Soc. Siam, vol.2, pp.232-246, illus., May, 1917.

MODIFIED TECHNIQUE IN THE PREPARATION OF MAMMAL SKINS. E.J. Koesiner. Jour. Mamm., vol.22, no.3, pp.315-317, pl. 1, Aug. 14, 1941.

MUSEUM AND MICROSCOPIC TECHNIQUE. DRY PRESERVATION OF MUSEUM SPECIMENS: A REVIEW, WITH INTRODUCTION OF SIMPLIFIED TECHNIQUE. Frank M. Kramer. Jour. Technical Methods and Bull. International Assoc. Museums, Ann Arbor-Montreal, no.18, pp.42-50, figs.5, 1938.

PRESERVATION OF SKINS FOR MUSEUM PURPOSES. C.C. Kritzinger. S.African Mus. Assoc. Bull., Natal, vol.3, no.12, pp.351-352, Dec., 1945.

USE OF DERMESTID BEETLES FOR CLEANING MAMMALIAN SKELETONS. E.M.O. Laurie, J.E. Hill. Museums Jour., London, vol.51, no.8, pp.206-207, Nov., 1951.

IMPROVED METHOD FOR PAINTING DISSECTIONS. William W. Looney. Anat.Rec., vol.38, pp.241-243, Apr. 25, 1928.

NOTES ON THE PREPARATION OF ROUGH SKELETONS. Frederic A. Lucas. Proc. U.S. Nat. Museum, no.33, pp.8, figs.12, 1885; Bull. U.S. Nat. Mus., pt.C, no.39, pp.11, figs.12, 1891.

VALUE OF TYPE SPECIMENS AND IMPORTANCE OF THEIR PRESERVATION. O.C. Marsh. Amer. Jour. Sci., vol.6, pp.401-405, Nov., 1898.

SUGGESTIONS AS TO COLLECTING LAND VERTEBRATES ON CORAL ATOLLS. J.T. Marshall, Jr. Atoll Research Bull., Pacific Science Board, Washington, no.17, pp.65-68, May 15, 1953.

BRIEF DIRECTIONS FOR THE MEASUREMENT OF SMALL MAMMALS AND THE PREPARATION OF MUSEUM SKINS. C.Hart. Merriam. U.S. Dept. Agric., Circular 11, pp.4, figs.4, 1889.

DIRECTIONS FOR PREPARING SPECIMENS OF LARGE MAMMALS IN THE FIELD. C. Hart. Merriam. Washington, Govt.Print.Off., U.S.Dept.Agriculture, Biological Survey, Circular 49, pp.4, illus., 1905.

DIRECTIONS FOR PREPARING SPECIMENS OF MAMMALS. Gerrit S. Miller, Jr. Bull. U.S. Nat. Mus., no.39, part N, 3rd ed., pp.1-23, figs.1-6, Feb. 9, 1912; 4th ed., pp.1-24, figs.1-7, Aug. 18, 1914; 5th ed., pp.1-22, Apr. 29, 1925; 6th ed., pp.20, figs.5, Oct. 28, 1932.

DIRECTIONS FOR PREPARING STUDY SPECIMENS OF SMALL MAMMALS. Gerrit S. Miller, Jr. Bull. U.S. Nat. Mus., no. 39, pp.10, fig.1, Aug. 18, 1899; 2nd ed., pp.1-25, figs.1-3, Dec. 27, 1901.

DIRECTIONS FOR SKINNING MAMMALS. Gerrit S. Miller, Jr. P.1, Spring, 1894.

(CAPTURE AND PREPARATION OF SMALL MAMMALS FOR STUDY COLLECTIONS.) Capturo e preparacoa de pequenos mamiferos para colecoes de estudo. João Moojen. Rio de Janeiro, Imprensa nacional, pp.98, illus., 1943.

PRACTICAL TAXIDERMY. WORKING GUIDE. John W. Moyer. Ronald Press, New York, pp. 126, illus., 1953.

HALL OF THE AGE OF MAN IN THE AMERICAN MUSEUM. Henry Fairfield Osborn. Nat. Hist., vol.20, pp.229-246, figs.14, May-June, 1920.

NEW METHODS OF RESTORING EOTITANOPS AND BRONTOTHERIUM. Henry Fairfield Osborn. Bull. Geol. Soc. Amer., Washington, D.C., vol.25, no.3, p.406, fig.1, Sep. 15, 1914.

LABELING LARGE COLLECTIONS OF MAMMALS AND BIRDS. Wilfred H.Osgood. Proc. Amer. Assoc. Museums, Charleston, vol.4, pp.105-111, figs.5, 1910.

WHY IS A TYPE SPECIMEN? Wilfred H. Osgood. Jour. Mamm., vol.9, no.1, pp. 52-56, Feb. 9, 1928.

(ON-THE-SPOT METHOD OF PRESERVING THE BODIES OF SMALL MAMMALS.) Méthode rapide de conservation des cadavres de petits Mammiferes sur les lieux de collecte. F. Petter. Mammalia, Paris, vol. 18, no.4, pp.422-423, Dec., 1954.

PRESERVATION OF MUSEUM OBJECTS IN WAR-TIME. H.J. Plenderleith. Nature, London, vol.152, no.3847, pp.94-97, July 24, 1943.

ISOPROPYL ALCOHOL AS A PRESERVATIVE. Philip H. Pope. Science, n.s., vol. 68, pp.487-489, Nov. 16, 1928.

PREPARING SPECIMENS OF SMALL MAMMALS OTHER THAN BATS. C.Primrose. Jour. Darjeeling Nat. Hist. Soc., vol.12, no.1, pp.17-26, figs.7, June, 1937; no.2, pp.60-69, figs.5, Oct., 1937.

INSTRUCTION FOR THE DIGGING, PREPARING AND MOUNTING OF FOSSIL VERTEBRATES. M.G. Prokhorov. Acad. Sci. USSR, Geol. Mus., Leningrad, pp. 75, figs.6, pls.7, 1929.

METHODS OF PRESERVING BIRDS AND MAMMALS. Kenneth Racey. Murrelet, vol.19, nos.1-2, pp.14-15, Jan.-May, 1938.

GAMONIA: OR, THE ART OF PRESERVING GAME; AND AN IMPROVED METHOD OF MAKING PLANTATIONS AND COVERS, EXPLAINED AND ILLUSTRATED. Lawrence Rawstorne. London, R. Ackermann, pp.208, col.pls., 1837.

(PREPARATION OF OSTEOLOGIC PIECES.) Préparation des pieces osteologiques. Jean Roche. Mammalia, Paris, vol.18, no.4, pp.420-422, Dec., 1954.

(COLLECTING MAMMAL SPECIMENS.) La recolte des échantillons de mammiferes. P. Rode. Mammalia, Paris, vol.1, no.3, pp.122-125, Mar., 1937.

TAXIDERMY AND MUSEUM EXHIBITION. John Rowley. New York and London, D. Appleton and Co., vol.8, pp.331, pl.29, text figs.20, 1925.

(Review by J. Grinnell of) TAXIDERMY AND MUSEUM EXHIBITION. John Rowley. Science, n.s., vol.63, pp.546-548, May 28, 1926.

(Review by Edward A. Preble of) TAXIDERMY AND MUSEUM EXHIBITION. John Rowley. Jour. Mamm., vol.7, no.4, pp.336-337, Nov., 1926.

FLAYING AND TREATMENT OF FUR-BEARING ANIMALS. J.F. Ruotsalainen. Suomen Riista, Helsinki, no.1, pp.157-170, figs.8, 1946.

TIP ON CLEANING SKULLS WITH THE AID OF DERMESTID BEETLES. Victor B.Scheffer. Murrelet, Seattle, vol.21, no.1, p.10, Jan.-Apr., 1940.

OAK BARRELS FOR THE STORAGE OF LARGE ALCOHOLIC SPECIMENS. L.P. Schultz, E.D. Reid. Turtox News, Chicago, vol.17, no.2, pp.2, figs.2, Feb., 1939.

HOW FOSSILS ARE COLLECTED. George Gaylord Simpson. Nat. Hist., vol.39, no. 2, pp.329-334, illus., 1937.

PAPER FOR MUSEUM LABELS. L.J.Spencer. Museums Jour., vol.31, pp.391-393, Dec., 1931.

ELTON'S METHOD OF PREPARING MAMMAL SKINS. Arthur Svihla, Ruth Dowell. Jour. Mamm., vol.20, no.1, p.111, Feb. 14, 1939.

PRESENT LOCATION OF CERTAIN HERPETOLOGICAL AND OTHER SPECIMENS. Edward H. Taylor. Univ. Kansas Sci. Bull., Lawrence, vol.30, pt.1, no. 11, pp.117-187, May 15, 1944.

DIRECTIONS FOR PREPARING SMALL MAMMAL SKINS. Oldfield Thomas. Leaflet, Brit. Mus. Nat. Hist., Feb., 1894.

READY METHOD OF REPAIRING SMALL MAMMAL SKULLS. Oldfield Thomas. Museum Jour. London, vol.25, no.7, pp. 209-210, Jan., 1926.

NEW RECONSTRUCTIONS IN THE YALE PEABODY MUSEUM. Malcom R. Thorpe. Amer. Jour. Sci., ser.5, vol.6, no.32, pp.91-99, figs.6, Aug., 1923.

METHOD FOR CLEANING SKULLS OF SPECIMENS PRESERVED IN ALCOHOL. Luis de la Torre. Jour. Mamm., vol.32, no.2, pp.231-232, May 21, 1951.

PROVISIONAL PLAN FOR A COLLECTION OF MAMMALS TO BE EXHIBITED AT THE WORLD'S INDUSTRIAL AND COTTON CENTENNIAL EXPOSITION OF 1884-85, AT NEW ORLEANS. Frederick William True. U.S. Nat. Mus., Proceedings, Washington, vol.7, appendix no.29, pp. 585-611, 1885.

FROM THE TABLE WITH THE FRINGE ON TOP. Arthur Vance. Frontiers, Philadelphia, vol.10, no.3, pp.66-69, illus., Feb., 1946.

(SUGGESTIONS ON HOW TO PREPARE SPECIMENS IN THE FIELD FOR THE STUDY OF SMALL MAMMALS.) Sugestiones para preparar en el campo ejemplares para estudio de pequenos mamiferos. Bernardo Villa Ramirez. Univ. Nac. Mexico, Inst. Biol., Chapultepec, D.F., Folletos Divulgacion Cien.42, pp. 46, figs.8, 1944.

USEFUL INFORMATION FOR FIELD COLLECTORS IN MEXICO. Bernardo Villa Ramirez. Jour. Mamm., vol.35, no.2, pp.280-281, May 26, 1954.

SOME NOTES ON THE PREPARATION OF MAMMAL SKINS. Alex Walker. Oologist, vol.38, pp.166-170, Dec., 1921.

PRACTICAL METHOD FOR MOUNTING THE BACULA OF SMALL MAMMALS. John A. White. Jour. Mamm., vol.32, no.1, p.125, Feb. 15, 1951.

QUICK METHOD FOR PRESERVING CATS FOR DISSECTION. Horace Elmer Wood. Science, n.s., vol.65, no.1680, p.261, Mar. 11, 1927.

DIRECTIONS FOR PREPARING SKINS OF LARGE MAMMALS FROM THE SIZE OF A WOLF UPWARDS. American Museum of Natural History, New York, pp.4, diagrs.

DIRECTIONS FOR PREPARING SPECIMENS OF LARGE MAMMALS IN THE FIELD. Washington, Govt. Print. Off., U.S.Bureau of Biological Survey, pp.4, illus., (B.S. Doc.102) 1915.

DRESSING AND CARE OF BIG GAME. Sylva, Toronto, vol.3, no.5, pp.41-43, illus., 1947.

HINTS ON REMOVING AND PREPARING SKINS OF MAMMALS. British Mus. Nat.

Hist., London, Printed by Hazell, Watson, & Viney, Ltd., pp.11, illus., 190-?

(INSTRUCTIONS FOR PREPARING MAMMAL SKINS.) Instructions pour préparer les mammifères en peaux. La Terre et La Vie, Annee 4, no.5, pp.297-298, May, 1934.

MOUNTING OF ANIMALS FOR EXHIBITION INVOLVES MANY STEPS AND THE UTMOST CARE. Field Museum News, Chicago, vol. 11, no.1, pp.4-5, figs.4, Jan., 1940.

(MUMMIFICATION, RATHER THAN THE STUFFING, OF ANIMAL CARCASSES.) Mumifizierung der Tierleichen anstatt ihrer Ausstopfung. Anat. Anzeiger, vol.66, pp. 49-64, fig.1, Aug. 15, 1928.

SKINNING AND CURING FURS. Ohio Conserv. Bull., Columbus, vol.7, no.12, p. 14, illus., Dec., 1943.

TAXONOMY

(INTEREST IN CEREBRAL CHARACTERS AS REGARDS THE CLASSIFICATION OF UNGULATES.) De l'intéret des caracteres cerebraux pour la classification des ongules. J. Anthony. Mammalia, Paris, vol.22, no. 1, pp.53-57, Mar., 1958.

ON GENUS AND SPECIES MAKING. Frank Collins Baker. Science, vol.72, no.1854, pp.37-39, July 11, 1930.

AN APOLOGY FOR TAXONOMY. Fred A. Barkley. Biologist, Denver, vol.24, no.2, pp.26-38, Mar., 1943.

SHIFTING DIAGNOSES. F.A. Bather. Palaeobiol., vol.1, no.1, pp.51-54, 1928.

(PENNANT'S SUMMARY OF QUADRUPEDS.) Pennant's Uebersicht der Vierfuessigen Thiere. Johann Matthaus Bechstein. Vol.1, 1799, Vol.2, 1800.

ON THE UNIT OF CLASSIFICATION FOR SYSTEMATIC BIOLOGY. Henry M. Bernard. Proc. Camb. Philos. Soc., vol.11, pt.4, pp.268-280, 1901.

CUVIER'S ANIMAL KINGDOM. (MAMMALIA, BIRDS, AND REPTILES.) Edward Blyth. London, pp.670, illus., 1840.

GENERAL NOTE ON SYSTEMATICS. N.A. Bobrinskii. (English translations of Russian Zoological Literature. Trans. 200a. From Key to the Mammals of the U.S.S.R. by N.A. Bobrinskii, B.A. Kuznetzov, A.P. Kuzyakin, 1944.)

(CONCEPT OF "SUBSPECIES" IN THE ZOOLOGICAL SYSTEM.) Der Begriff der "Untergattung" im zoologischen System. Hans von Boetticher. Zeitschr. f. Saeugetierk., Berlin, vol.17, no.3, pp.146-149, Feb. 19, 1953.

CRITERIA FOR VERTEBRATE SUBSPECIES, SPECIES AND GENERA. Charles M. Bogert, W. Frank Blair, Emmett Reid Dunn, E. Raymond Hall, Carl L. Hubbs, Ernst Mayr, George Gaylord Simpson. Ann. New York Acad. Sci., vol.44, art.2, pp.105-188, June 8, 1943.

NEW SYSTEMATIC ARRANGEMENT OF VERTEBRATED ANIMALS. C.L. Bonaparte. Trans. Linn. Soc. London, vol.18, pp.247-304, 1841.

(VALUE OF THE CRANIAL CAPACITY IN RELATION TO MAMMAL SYSTEMATICS.) La valeur de la capacite cranienne dans ses rapports avec la systématique chez les mammiferes. E. Bourdelle, M. Deziliere. Mammalia, Paris, vol.14, no.4, pp.165-173, Dec., 1950.

ANALYSIS OF THE NATURAL CLASSIFICATIONS OF MAMMALIA, FOR THE USE OF STUDENTS AND TRAVELLERS. T. Edward Bowdich. Paris, pp.115, illus., pls.15, 1821.

SEROLOGY AND ANIMAL SYSTEMATICS. Alan Boyden. Amer. Nat., Lancaster, vol. 77, no.770, pp.234-255, figs.3, May-June, 1943.

USE OF THE TERM ALLOTYPE. J. C. Bradley. Science, n.s., vol.66, p.563, Dec. 9, 1927.

SUBSPECIES CATEGORY IN MAMMALS. William Henry Burt. Systematic Zoology, vol.3, no.3, pp.99-104, Sep., 1954.

GENERA MAMMALIUM. MONOTREMATA, MARSUPIALIA. Angel Cabrera. Museo Nacional de Ciencias Naturales Madrid. Pp. 1-180, pls.19, June 23, 1919.

GENUS IN EVOLUTIONARY TAXONOMY. A.J. Cain. Systematic Zoology, vol.5, no. 3, pp.97-109, Sep., 1956.

MEANING OF BIOLOGICAL CLASSIFICATION. W.T. Calman. Proc. Linn. Soc. London, Session 1934-35, pt.4, pp.145-158, figs.5, 1935.

ON CITING THE TYPES OF NEW GENERA. T.D.A. Cockerell. Science, Lancaster, n.s., vol.36, no.939, p.903, Dec. 27, 1912.

EACH AFTER HIS KIND. Leon J. Cole. Science, Lancaster, n.s., vol.93, nos. 2413, 2414, pp.289-293, 316-319, Mar. 28 and Apr.4, 1941.

(CAPACITY OF THE CRANIUM AND SYSTEMATICS IN URSUS ARCTOS AND RUPICAPRA RUPICAPRA.) Capacite de la boite cranienne et systematique chez Ursus arctos et Rupicapra rupicapra. Marcel A.J. Couturier. Mammalia, Paris, vol.15, no3, pp.73-83, Sep., 1951.

SYNOPSIS OF THE SPECIES OF THE CLASS MAMMALIA. Cuvier. London, vol.8, pp. 391, 1827.

ON THE HIGHER SUBDIVISIONS IN THE CLASSIFICATION OF MAMMALS. James Dwight Dana. New Haven, pp.71, 1863.

PRECISE CRITERION OF SPECIES. A. THE GENERAL METHOD. C.B. Davenport. B. THE CHIEF DIFFERENTIAL AND SPECIFIC VS. INDIVIDUAL CHARACTERS. J. W. Blankenship. Science, n.s., vol.7, no.177, pp.685-695, May 20, 1898.

(IMPORTANCE OF GEOGRAPHIC DISTRIBUTION IN THE SYSTEMATICS OF THE VERTEBRATES.) La importancia de la distribución geográfica en la sistemática de los vertebrados. Jorge G. Dennler. Physis, Buenos Aires, vol.16, no.48, pp.41-53, pls.8, May, 1939.

(SYSTEMATIC STUDY OF THE PENILE BONE OF MAMMALS.) Etude systematique de l'os penien des mammiferes. Robert Didier. Mammalia, Paris, vol.17, no.2, pp.67-74, illus., June, 1953.

RACES AND METHODS OF THEIR STUDY. Theodosius Dobzhansky. Trans. New York Acad. Sci., Lancaster, ser.2, vol.4, no.4, pp.115-123, Feb., 1942.

(SYSTEMATICS AND BIOLOGY OF UNGULATES. (CONFERENCE ON MAMMALIA.) Systematique et biologie des ongules. Colloque organisé par Mammalia. Jean Dorst. Mammalia, Paris, vol.22, no.1, pp.1-8, Mar., 1958.

IN DEFENSE OF THE SUBSPECIES. Stephen D. Durrant. Systematic Zoology, vol. 4, no.4, pp.186-190, Dec., 1955.

(CLASSIFICATION OF MAMMALS.) La classification des mammifères. Milne Alphonse Edwards. Revue Sci. France et de l'Etranger, Paris, ser.2, annee 1, no.53, pp.1245-1250, June 29, 1872.

DESCRIPTIONS OF AN APPARENTLY NEW SPECIES OF MONKEY OF THE GENUS PRESBYTIS FROM SUMATRA, AND OF A BAT OF THE GENUS DERMANURA FROM MEXICO. D.G. Elliot. Proc. Biol. Soc. Washington, vol.19, pp.49-50, May 1, 1906.

DESCRIPTIONS OF APPARENTLY NEW MAMMALS OF THE GENERA OVIBOS, CYNOMYS AND MUSTELA. D. G. Elliot. Proc. Biol. Soc. Washington, vol.18, pp. 135-140, Apr. 18, 1905.

DESCRIPTIONS OF APPARENTLY NEW SPECIES AND SUBSPECIES OF MAMMALS AND A NEW GENERIC NAME PROPOSED. D. G. Elliot. Field Col. Mus. Pub. no. 90, Zool. Ser. vol.3, no.15, pp.263-270, Mar., 1904.

DESCRIPTIONS OF THREE APPARENTLY NEW SPECIES OF MAMMALS. D.G. Elliot. Proc. Biol. Soc. Washington, vol.18, pp. 79-82, Feb. 21, 1905.

DESCRIPTIONS OF TWENTY-SEVEN APPARENTLY NEW SPECIES AND SUBSPECIES OF MAMMALS. D.G. Elliot. Field Col. Mus. Pub. no.87, Zool. Ser. vol.3, no.14, pp.239-261, illus., Dec., 1903.

ON THE GENUS PRESBYTIS ESCH., AND 'LE TARSIER' BUFFON, WITH DESCRIPTIONS OF TWO NEW SPECIES OF TARSIUS. D.G. Elliot. Bull. Amer. Mus. Nat. Hist., New York, vol.28, art.13, pp.151-154, May 27, 1910.

SOME OBSERVATIONS CONCERNING SPECIES AND SUBSPECIES. B.W. Evermann. Science, n.s., vol.11, no.273, pp.451-455, Mar. 23, 1900.

SYLLABUS OF THE MAMMALIA. James Cossar Ewart. Pp.120, pl.83, fold.map.1, 188-.

(SIGNIFICANCE OF THE RACE CONCEPT.) Die Bedeutung des Rassenbegriffes. Ernst Feige. Die Naturwissenschaften, vol.17, no.37, pp.710-724, Sep. 13, 1929.

ON THE ARRANGEMENT OF THE ORDERS AND FAMILIES OF EXISTING MAMMALIA. W.R. Flower. Proc. Zool. Soc. London, pp.177-186, Apr. 17, 1883.

(NOTES ON THE MAMMALS: REMARKS ON THE CLASSIFICATION OF UNGULATES AND THE SYSTEMATIC POSITION OF HYRAXES.) Notes sur les mammiferes. XX. Remarques sur la classification des ongules et sur la position systematique des damans. Serge Frechkop. Bull. Mus. Royal Hist. Nat. Belgique, vol.12, no.37, pp.1-28, figs. 17, Oct., 1936.

(ON THE CLASSIFICATION OF THE UNGULATES.) Sur la classification des Ongules. Serge Frechkop. Mammalia, Paris, vol.1, no.2, pp.37-48, Dec., 1936.

(SOME CRITERIA OF THE SYSTEMATICS OF UNGULATES.) Des criteres de la systematique des ongulés. Serge Frechkop. Mammalia, Paris, vol.22, no.1, pp.12-27, Mar., 1958.

(PENIS BONE IN ZOOLOGICAL CLASSIFICATION.) L'os penien dans la classification zoologique. B. Galli-Valerio. Schweizer Archiv. Tierheilk., Zuerich, vol.74, no.4, pp.193-195, fig.1, Apr., 1932.

(DESCRIPTION OF SOME SPECIES OF SEALS AND CETACEANS.) Description de quelques especes de phoques et de cétacés. Paul Gervais. Ann. Sci. Nat., Paris, Zool., vol.20, pp.281-292, 1853.

(NEW MAMMAL VARIETIES.) Neue Saeugetiervarietaeten. Angelo Chidini. Diana, vol. 30, no.7, p.122, July, 1912.

ARRANGEMENT OF THE FAMILIES OF MAMMALS WITH ANALYTICAL TABLES. Theodore Gill. Smithson. Misc. Coll. no.230, vol.11, pp.6-98, 1872.

NUMBER OF CLASSES OF VERTEBRATES AND THEIR MUTUAL RELATIONS. Theodore Gill. Amer. Jour. Sci. and Arts, vol.6, pp.1-4, Dec., 1873.

ON THE CHARACTERISTICS OF THE PRIMARY GROUPS OF THE CLASS OF MAMMALS. Theodore Gill. Amer. Naturalist, vol.5, p.8, Sep., 1871.

ON THE CHARACTERISTICS OF THE PRIMARY GROUPS OF THE CLASS OF MAMMALS. Theodore Gill. Cambridge, Mass., pp.284-306, 1872. (Proceedings of the American Assoc. for the Advancement of Science, vol.20, 1872.)

ON THE "PRODROMUS METHODI MAMMALIUM" OF STORR. Theodore Gill. Extracted from the Bulletin of the Philosophical Society of Washington, Oct., 1874. Philadelphia, Collins, Printer, 1876.

ON THE RELATIONS OF THE ORDERS OF MAMMALS. Theodore Gill. Salem, Mass., pp.2, 1871. (With his Arrangement of the Families of Mammals, Washington, 1872.)

ON THE STATUS OF ARISTOTLE IN SYSTEMATIC ZOOLOGY. Theodore Gill.

Amer. Naturalist, vol.7, pp.1-6, Aug., 1873.

SYSTEMATIC ZOOLOGY; ITS PROGRESS AND PURPOSE. Theodore Gill. Proc. 7th Intern. Zool. Congr. Boston Meeting, Aug. 19-24, 1907, Cambridge, pp.21, 1910.

ARITHMETICAL DEFINITION OF THE SPECIES, SUBSPECIES AND RACE CONCEPT, WITH A PROPOSAL FOR A MODIFIED NOMENCLATURE. CONTAINING A SIMPLE METHOD FOR THE COMPARISON OF RELATED POPULATIONS. Isaac Ginsburg. Zoologica, New York Zool. Soc., vol. 23, pt.3, pp.253-286, figs.4, Sep. 28, 1938.

DIVERGENCE AND PROBABILITY IN TAXONOMY. Isaac Ginsburg. Zoologica, New York, vol.25, no.2, pt.1, pp.15-31, Mar.18, 1940.

SPECIES AND ITS SUBDIVISIONS. Isaac Ginsburg. Copeia, no.3, pp.184-188, illus., Nov. 19, 1937.

ON THE CLASSIFICATION OF MAMMALIA. Charles Girard. Amer. Assoc. Adv. Sci., pp.319-335, chart, 1851.

DESCRIPTIONS OF SOME NEW SPECIES OF MAMMALIA. J.E. Gray. Proc. Zool. Soc. London, pt.30, pp.261-263, pls.33-35, 1862.

LETTER ON TWO NEW SPECIES OF BATS AND A PORCUPINE (HYSTRIX SUBSPINOSUS, LICHT.) IN THE BRITISH MUSEUM. J. E. Gray. Proc. Zool. Soc. London, pt.11, pp. 20-22, 1843.

MAMMALIA. J.E. Gray. Vol.5, pp.391, 1827. (In) The Animal Kingdom Arranged in Conformity with its Organization, by the Baron G. Cuvier, with Additional Descriptions by Edward Griffith and Others. London, George B. Whittaker, vols.16, 1827-1835.

AN OUTLINE OF AN ATTEMPT AT THE DISPOSITION OF MAMMALIA INTO TRIBES AND FAMILIES, WITH A LIST OF THE GENERA APPARENTLY APPERTAINING TO EACH TRIBE. J.E. Gray. Ann.Phil., n.s., vol.10, pp.337-344, 1825. (Vol.26 of the whole series.)

SPICILEGIA ZOOLOGICA; OR ORIGINAL FIGURES AND SHORT SYSTEMATIC DESCRIPTIONS OF NEW UNFIGURED ANIMALS. J.E. Gray. London, 2 parts (1828 and 1830), each with pls.

LANGUAGE OF TAXONOMY: AN APPLICATION OF SYMBOLIC LOGIC TO THE STUDY OF CLASSIFICATORY SYSTEMS. John R. Gregg. Columbia Univ. Press, New York, pp.70, 1954.

TAXONOMY, LANGUAGE, AND REALITY. John R. Gregg. Amer. Nat., Lancaster, vol. 84, no.819, pp.419-435, Nov.-Dec., 1950.

ORDERS OF MAMMALS. William Gregory. Bull. Amer. Mus. Nat. Hist., vol.27, pp. 3-524, 1910.

SUPRA-SPECIFIC VARIATION IN NATURE AND IN CLASSIFICATION. FEW EXAMPLES FROM MAMMALIAN PALEONTOLOGY. William K. Gregory. Amer. Naturalist, Lancaster, vol.71, no.734, pp.268-276, figs.5, May-June, 1937.

(MODIFICATIONS AND INNOVATIONS RECENTLY PROPOSED IN THE GENERAL CLASSIFICATION OF MAMMALS.) Modificazioni ed innovazioni recentemente proposte nella classificazione generale dei mammiferi. Achille Griffini. Rev. Mensile Sc. Nat. Natura, Pavia, vol.4, pp.59, illus., 1913.

ON THE TAXONOMIC CHARACTERS AFFORDED BY THE MUSCULAR SHEATH OF THE CESOPHAGUS AS REGARDS SAUROPSIDA AND OTHER VERTEBRATA. George Gulliver. Proc. Zool. Soc. London, pp.283-285, 1870.

PROPOSED CLASSIFICATION FOR TYPES OF TWINS IN MAMMALS. Herbert Hahn. Anat. Rec., vol.61, no.1, pp.81-96, figs. 2, Dec. 25, 1934.

CRITERIA FOR VERTEBRATE SUBSPECIES, SPECIES AND GENERA: THE MAMMALS. E. Raymond Hall. Ann. New York Acad.Sci., vol.44, art.2, pp.141-144, June 8, 1943.

(CLASSIFICATION OF THE MAMMALS.) Klassifikation der Saeugetiere. Th. Haltenorth. Handbuch der Zoologie, I (1 and 2), pp.1-40, pls.8.

LOGICAL BASIS OF THE SPECIES CONCEPT. Melville H. Hatch. Amer. Nat., Lancaster, vol.75, no.758, pp.193-212, May-June, 1941.

ON THE STATUS OF PRIVATELY ISSUED PAPERS ON SYSTEMATIC ZOOLOGY. Oliver P. Hay. Proc. Biol. Soc. Washington, vol.37, pp.109-112, May 17, 1924.

TWENTY YEARS OF WORK IN THE FIELD OF SYSTEMATICS AND GEOGRAPHICAL DISTRIBUTION OF MAMMALS. V. Heptner. Zool.Jour., Moscow, vol.16, no.5, pp.902-915, 1937. (In Russian.)

"MAMMALS" IN SYMPOSIUM ON "WHAT KIND OF CHARACTERS DISTINGUISH A SPECIES FROM A SUBDIVISION OF A SPECIES." Ned Hollister. Jour. Washington Acad. Sci., vol.9, p.235, Apr. 19, 1919.

PLAIN STATEMENTS ABOUT RACE. Earnest A. Hooten. Science, vol.83, no.2161, pp. 511-513, May 29, 1936.

BIOMETRIC COMPARISON OF SEVERAL SAMPLES, WITH PARTICULAR REFERENCE TO RACIAL INVESTIGATIONS. Carl L. Hubbs. Amer.Naturalist, vol.76, pp.582-592, Nov.-Dec., 1942.

CRITERIA FOR SUBSPECIES, SPECIES AND GENERA, AS DETERMINED BY RESEARCHES ON FISHES. Carl L. Hubbs. Annals New York Acad. Sci., vol.64, art. 2, pp.109-121, June 8, 1943.

LECTOSYNTYPE, A NEW TERM FOR TYPE SPECIMENS. R.G.S. Hudson. Jour. Paleontol., Menasha, vol.17, no.4, p.410, July, 1943.

CONCEPTION OF A SPECIES. C.C. Hurst. Science, n.s., vol.65, pp.271-273, Mar. 18, 1927.

ON THE EARLY EDITIONS OF LACEPEDE'S "TABLEAUX DES MAMMIFERES ET DES OISEAUX," WITH REMARKS ON TWO HITHERTO OVERLOOKED SPECIES: LORI BENGALENSIS LACEPEDE, 1800, AND ORNITHORYNCHUS NOVAE HOLLANDIAE LACEPEDE, 1800. A.M. Husson, L. B. Holthuis. Zool. Mededel. Rijksmus. Nat. Hist. Leiden, vol.32, no.19, pp.211-219, Dec. 30, 1953.

LACK OF TAXONOMIC TRAINING. Hartley H.T. Jackson. Jour. Mamm., vol.9, no.2, p.179, May, 1928.

(SYSTEMATIC CATALOGUE OF THE MAMMALS: MONKEYS, CARNIVORES, RUMINANTS, PACHYDERMS, SIRENIANS, AND CETACEANS.) Catalogue Systematique des Mammiferes, Singes, Carnivores, Ruminants, Pachydermes, Sirenes et Cétacée. F. A. Jentink. Mus. d'Hist. Nat. des Pays-Bas, vol.XI, 1892.

(SYSTEMATIC CATALOGUE OF THE MAMMALS: RODENTS, INSECTIVORES, CHIROPTERS, EDENTATES, AND MARSUPIALS.) Catalogue Systematique des Mammifères. (Rongeurs, Insectivores, Cheiropteres, Édentés et Marsupiaux.) F.A. Jentink. Mus. d'Hist. Nat. des Pays-Bas, vol.XII, 1888.

HODMEN OF SCIENCE. David Starr Jordan. Science, n.s., vol.62, pp.425-426, Nov. 13, 1925.

(ANIMAL KINGDOM IN ITS PRINCIPAL FORMS; SYSTEMATICALLY DESCRIBED. Thierreich in seinen Hauptformen; Systematisch beschrieben. Dr.J.J. Kaup. Vol.1, 1835.

ANIMAL KINGDOM, OR ZOOLOGICAL SYSTEM, OF THE CELEBRATED SIR CHARLES LINNAEUS. CLASS I. MAMMALIA. Robert Kerr. Edinburgh, pp.644, illus., 1792.

(ON THE LACHRYMAL BONES OF UNGULATES (COMPARATIVE ANATOMICAL CONTRIBUTION TO THE SYSTEMATICS OF RECENT UNGULATA.) Ueber das Traenenbein der Huftiere. Vergleichend-anatomischer Beitrag zur Systematik der rezenten Ungulata. Theodor Knottnerus-Meyer. Archiv. f. Naturgesch., Jahrg.73, vol.1, no.1, pp.1-152, pls.5, 1907.

(THE MAMMALS: FAMILIES AND GENERA, WITH AN APPENDIX ON TOOTH AND BONE STRUCTURE.) Die Saeugethiere nach Familien und Gattungen mit einem Anhang ueber den Zahn- und Knochenbau. Ferdinand Krauss. Stuttgart & Esslingen, pp.104, 1851.

(PRIMER OF ZOOLOGY. VOL. VII. THE TETRAPOD VERTEBRATES, AMPHIBIANS AND REPTILES, FOLLOWED BY A SUMMARY OF THE CLASSIFICATION OF BIRDS AND MAMMALS.) Précis de zoologie. Tome VII. Les vertebrés tetrapodes, amphibiens et reptiles, suivis d'un abgrege de la classification des oiseaux et des mammiferes. Aug. Lameere. Univ. Bruxelles, Recueil Inst. Zool. Torley-Rousseau, vol.9, pp. 357, figs.194, 1942.

(CLASSIFICATION OF UNGULATES ACCORDING TO THEIR ORIGIN AND EVOLUTION.) Classification des ongules d'apres leur origine et leur evolution. R. Lavocat. Mammalia, Paris, vol.22, no.1, pp.28-40, Mar., 1958.

(NEW CLASSIFICATION OF THE ANIMAL KINGDOM. MAMMALS.) Nouveau Tableau Regne Animal. Mammiferes. Rene-Primeverre Lesson. Paris, pp.204, 1842.

(ABRIDGEMENT OF THE NATURAL SYSTEM OF LINNAEUS, HISTORY OF MAMMALS OR QUADRUPEDS AND CETACEANS. CONTAINING 1) FREE TRANSLATION FROM THE TEXT OF LINNAEUS AND GMELIN; 2) EXTRACT OF THE OBSERVATIONS OF BUFFON, BRISSON, PALLAS, AND OTHER CELEBRATED ZOOLOGISTS; 3) COMPARATIVE ANATOMY OF THE PRINCIPAL SPECIES. ALL RELATIVE TO THE MOST CURIOUS AND USEFUL QUADRUPEDS AND CETACEANS.) Abrégé du Systeme de la nature, de Linné, histoire des mammaires ou des quadrupédes et cétacées. Contenant, 1. la traduction libre du texte de Linne et de Gmelin; 2. l'extrait des observations de Buffon, Brisson, Pallas, et autres célèbres zoologistes; 3. l'anatomic comparee des principales especes: le tout relatif aux quadrupedes et aux cetacees les plus curieux et les plus utiles. Carl von Linné. Par m. J.E. Gilibert, Lyon, Chez l'éditeur, pp.497, pls.28, 1805.

SYSTEMA NATURAE. C. Linnaeus. Ed. 10, revised. Stockholm, Laurentii Salvii, vol.1, part 1, p.532, 1758.

(OBSERVATIONS ON THE WORK OF M. LESSON ENTITLED "NEW TABLE OF THE ANIMAL KINGDOM.") Observations sur l'ouvrage de M. Lesson, intitule: Nouveau tableau du Regne animal. Edm. de Selys Longchamps. Revue Zool. Soc. Cuvierienne, 5th année, pp.8, Nov., 1842.

VARIATIONS OR SPECIFIC DISTINCTIONS: WHICH? Richard Swann Lull. Bull. Geol. Soc. Amer., vol.33, pp.599-604, Sep.30, 1922.

THOUGHTS ON SUBSPECIES. W.L. McAtee. Scientific Monthly, Lancaster, vol.53, pp. 368-371, Oct., 1941.

(COMPARABLE VALUE OF THE BRAIN AND METHODS OF DETERMINING THE POSITION OF VERTEBRATES.) Der Komparabilwert des Gehirnes und die Methoden zur Bestimmung der Ranghoehe von Wirbeltieren. Hubert Malthaner. Saeugetierk. Mitteil., Stuttgart, vol.1, no.1, pp.5-8, Jan. 10, 1953.

DESCRIPTION OF A NEW BAT (RHINOLOPHUS LANDERI) FROM FERNANDO PO, AND A NEW HEDGEHOG (ERINACEUS CONCOLOR) FROM TREBIZOND. W. Martin. Proc. Zool. Soc. London, pt.5, p.101, 1837.

ON THE SYSTEMATICS OF GAME (ANIMALS). Vladimir Martino. Lovtsa, nos. 5-6, pp.1-5, illus., tbls., May-June, 1938. (Bulgarian.)

PHYLUM IN ZOOLOGY AND PALEONTOLOGY. W.D. Matthew. Science, n.s., vol.70, pp.142-143, Aug. 9, 1929.

(BONE STRUCTURE AND DIFFERENTIATION OF THE MAMMAL ORDERS.) Knochenbau und Differenzierung der Saeugetierordnungen. Jeno Mátyás. Comptes Rendus XII Congres Internat. Zool. Lisbonne 1935, Lisboa, vol.2, pp.665-674, pl.31, 1936-37.

SYSTEMATICS AND THE ORIGIN OF SPECIES. Ernst Mayr. New York, Columbia Univ. Press, pp.xiv-334, 1942.

METHODS AND PRINCIPLES OF SYSTEMATIC ZOOLOGY. Ernst Mayr, E.Gorton Linsley, Robert L. Usinger. McGraw-Hill Book Co., Inc., New York, pp.328, illus., 1953.

(Review by Robert W. Eadie of) METHODS AND PRINCIPLES OF SYSTEMATIC ZOOLOGY. Ernst Mayr, E.Gorton Linsley, Robert L. Usinger. Jour. Mamm., vol.34, no.4, pp.520-521, Nov.13, 1953.

BRISSON'S GENERA OF MAMMALS, 1762. C. Hart Merriam. Science, n.s., vol.1, no.14, pp.375-376, Apr. 5, 1895.

CRITERIA FOR THE RECOGNITION OF SPECIES AND GENERA. C. Hart Merriam. Jour. Mamm., vol.1, no.1, pp.6-9, Nov., 1919.

SEROLOGICAL EVIDENCE IN DETERMINING TAXONOMIC RELATIONSHIPS OF HIGHER ANIMALS. Max S. Millar, Otis Roy Burket. Jour. Mamm., vol.24, no.4, pp.502-503, Nov. 17, 1943.

PRECISE CRITERION OF SPECIES. Gerrit S. Miller, Jr. Science, n.s., vol.7, no. 181, p.834, July 17, 1898.

(RESEARCH ON THE NATURAL HISTORY OF MAMMALS, INCLUDING SOME CONSIDERATIONS ON THE CLASSIFICATION OF THESE ANIMALS.) Recherches pour servir a l'histoire naturelle des mammifères comprenant des considérations sur la classification de ces Animaux. H. Milne-Edwards, Alphonse Milne-Edwards. 1868-1874.

GENITAL SYSTEM AND THE FETAL MEMBRANES AS CRITERIA FOR MAMMALIAN PHYLOGENY AND TAXONOMY. H. W. Mossman. Jour. Mamm., vol.34, no.3, pp.289-298, Aug. 14, 1953.

ON A NEW GIBBON (HYLOBATES CHOROMANDUS) AND A NEW SPECIES OF COLOBUS (C. LEUCOMEROS). W.Ogilby. Proc. Zool. Soc. London, pt.5, p.68-69, 1837.

PROBLEMS OF TAXONOMY. I. ON THE IMPORTANCE OF MORPHOLOGY IN TAXONOMICAL STUDIES. S.I. Ognev. Zool. Jour. USSR, Moscow, vol.21, no.6, pp.266-281, 1942. (With English summary.)

TAXONOMY PROBLEMS. THE SPECIES PROBLEM IN THE LIGHT OF MODERN DATA. S.I. Ognev. Zool. Jour. USSR, Moscow, vol.23, no.1, pp.1-15, 1944.(With English summary.)

ON THE CHARACTERS, PRINCIPLES OF DIVISION, AND PRIMARY GROUPS OF THE CLASS MAMMALIA. Richard Owen. Amer. Jour. Sci. & Arts, New Haven, ser. 2, vol.25, no.73, pp.7-18; no.74, pp.177-198, figs.6, Jan., Mar., 1858.

ON THE CLASSIFICATION AND GEOGRAPHICAL DISTRIBUTION OF THE MAMMALIA, BEING THE LECTURE ON SIR ROBERT READE'S FOUNDATION, DELIVERED BEFORE THE UNIVERSITY OF CAMBRIDGE, MAY 10, 1859. TO WHICH IS ADDED AN APPENDIX "ON THE GORILLA," AND "ON THE EXTINCTION AND TRANSMUTATION OF SPECIES." Richard Owen. London, J. W. Parker and Son, pp. 103, illus., 1859.

INDEX GENERUM MAMMALIUM: A LIST OF THE GENERA AND FAMILIES OF MAMMALS. Theodore Sherman Palmer. Washington, Gov't Print. Off., Dept. of Agriculture, Division of Biological Survey, North American Fauna no.23, pp.984, 1904.

SYNOPSIS OF QUADRUPEDS. T. Pennant. Chester, pp.25+382, pls.31, 1771.

(ON A NEW GENUS OF CHIROPTERA, AMORPHOCHILUS, FROM PERU, AND ON A CROCIDURA FROM LIBERIA.)Ueber eine neue Gattung von Flederthieren, Amorphochilus, aus Peru und ueber eine Crocidura aus Liberia. W. Peters. Monatsbericht Koen. Wiss. Berlin, pp.184-188, pl., Apr. 26, 1877.

(ON A NEW SPECIES OF CHIROPTER, PROMOPS BONARIENSIS, AND ON LOPHUROMYS, A RODENT GENUS OF WEST AFRICA.) Ueber eine neue Art von Flederthieren, Promops bonariensis und ueber Lophuromys, eine Nagergattung von Westafrika. W. Peters. Auszug Monatsbericht Koen. Wiss. Berlin, pp.232-234, pl., Mar. 16, 1874.

(ON THE NEW SPECIES OF THE MAMMAL GENUS BASSARIS OF CENTRAL AMERICA AND A NEW SQUIRREL SPECIES OF WEST AFRICA.) Ueber eine neue Art der Saeugethiergattung Bassaris aus Centralamerika und eine neue Eichhornart aus Westafrika. W. Peters. Monatsbericht Koen. Wiss. Berlin, pp.704-708, pls.2, Nov. 16, 1874.

(ON THE PERFECTION, ADAPTATION, AND DIFFERENTIATION OF LOWER AND HIGHER ANIMALS.) Ueber Vervollkommung, Anpassung und die Unterscheidung von niederen und hoeheren Tieren. L. Plate. Zool. Jahrb., Jena, vol.45, pp.745-798, 1928.

NUMBER OF FORMS OF RECENT MAMMALS. Arthur J. Poole. Jour. Mamm., vol.7, no.2, pp.134-135, tbl.1, May, 1926; vol.17, no.3, p.282, Aug., 1936.

CONTRIBUTIONS TO A REVISION OF THE NORTH AMERICAN BEAVERS, OTTERS AND FISHERS. Samuel N. Rhoads. Amer. Philos. Soc., n.s., vol.19, pp.417-439, pls.5, 1898.

NEW SUBSPECIES OF THE GRAY FOX AND SAY'S CHIPMUNK. Samuel N. Rhoads. Proc. Acad. Nat. Sciences, Philadelphia, pp.42-44, 1895.

DESCRIPTIONS OF SOME NEW MAMMALS. Austin Roberts. Ann. Trans. Mus., Pretoria, vol.6, part 3, pp.112-115, Apr., 1919.

DESCRIPTIONS OF TWO NEW SPECIES OF A NEW SUBGENUS OF BATS, AND A NEW SPECIES OF MOLERATS. Austin Roberts. Ann. Trans. Mus., Pretoria, vol.6, no.1, pp.4-6, June 28, 1917.

(SYSTEMATIC VALUE OF THE RETINAL VASCULARIZATION OF MAMMALS.) Valeur systématique de la vascularisation retinienne des mammiferes. A. Rochon-Duvigneaud, P. Rode. Mammalia, Paris, vol.7, no.2, pp.56-73, figs.11, June, 1943.

(CONCERNING SIMPSON'S CLASSIFICATION OF MAMMALS.) A propos de la classification des mammiferes de Simpson. P. Rode. Mammalia, Paris, vol.10, no.1, pp.61-64, Mar., 1946.

(USE OF SOME CHARACTERS OF HAIR IN THE SYSTEMATICS OF MAMMALS.) De l'utilisation de quelques caracteres des poils dans la systematique des mammiferes. P. Rode. Bull. Mus. Nat. Hist. Nat., Paris, ser.2, vol.3, no.6, pp.479-486, June, 1931.

PROCEDURE IN TAXONOMY. E. T. Schenk, H. McMasters. Ed.3, enlarged and in part rewritten by A. Myra Keen, S. W. Muller. Stanford Univ. Press, pp.119, 1956.

(SYSTEMATIC LIST OF ALL PRESENTLY KNOWN MAMMALS, OR SYNOPSIS MAMMALIUM AFTER THE CUVIER SYSTEM.) Systematisches Verzeichnis aller bis jetzt bekannten Saeugethiere, oder, Synopsis mammalium nach dem Cuvier'schen System. Heinrich Schinz. Solothurn, vols.2, 1844-1845.

ON THE USE OF FAUNAL LISTS. Ernest Thompson Seton. Proc. Canadian Inst., Toronto, ser.3, vol.7, pp.275-280, 1890.

ON THE DATES OF CUVIER, 'LE REGNE ANIMAL, 'ETC. (DISCIPLES EDITION.) C. Davies Sherborn. Ann. and Mag. Nat. Hist., ser.9, vol.10, pp.555-556, Nov., 1922.

(LINNAEAN AND LAMARCKIAN SYSTEMS.) Systeme et Linne et systeme de Lamarck. B. M. Shittkov. Bull. Soc. Nat. Moscow, Sec. Biol., n.s., vol.49, no.1, pp.17-18, 1940.

ARRANGEMENT ON THE FAMILIES AND THE HIGHER GROUPS OF THE MAMMALIA. R. W. Shufeldt. Nyt Mag. f. Naturvidensk., Christiania, vol.49, no.1, pp.65-80, 1911.

CRITERIA FOR GENERA, SPECIES, AND SUBSPECIES IN ZOOLOGY AND PALEOZOOLOGY. George Gaylord Simpson. Ann. New York Acad. Sci., vol.44, art.2, pp. 145-178, June 8, 1943.

NEOTYPES. George Gaylord Simpson. Amer. Jour. Sci., New Haven, vol.243, pp.680-694, Dec., 1945.

NEW CLASSIFICATION OF MAMMALS. George Gaylord Simpson. Bull. Amer. Mus. Nat. Hist., vol.59, art.5, pp.259-293, Mar. 18, 1931.

(PRESENT TENDENCIES OF THE SYSTEMATICS OF MAMMALS.) Tendances actuelles de la systematique des mammiferes. George Gaylord Simpson. Mammalia, Paris, vol.18, no.4, pp.337-357, Dec., 1954.

PRINCIPLES OF CLASSIFICATION AND A CLASSIFICATION OF MAMMALS. George Gaylord Simpson. Bull. Amer. Mus. Nat. Hist., New York, vol.85, pp.xvi-350, Oct. 5, 1945.

(Review by E. Raymond Hall of) PRINCIPLES OF CLASSIFICATION OF MAMMALS. George Gaylord Simpson. Jour. Mamm., vol.22, no. 3, pp.287-288, Aug., 1946.

(Review by James M. Sprague of)PRINCIPLES OF CLASSIFICATION AND A CLASSIFICATION OF MAMMALS. George Gaylord Simpson. Quart. Rev. Biol., Baltimore, vol.21, no.2, pp.194-195, June, 1946.

SUPER-SPECIFIC VARIATION IN NATURE AND IN CLASSIFICATION. FROM THE VIEW-POINT OF PALEONTOLOGY. George Gaylord Simpson. Amer. Naturalist, vol. 71, pp.236-267, figs.10, May-June, 1937.

TYPES IN MODERN TAXONOMY. George Gaylord Simpson. Amer. Jour. Sci., New Haven, vol.238, pp.413-431, June, 1940.

TAXONOMIC UNIT. T.C. Stephens. Proc. Iowa Acad. Sci., vol.27, 1920, pp.41-50, 1922.

USE AND ABUSE OF THE GENUS. Witmer Stone. Science, n.s., vol.51, pp.427-429, Apr. 30, 1920.

ON THE ZOOLOGICAL STATUS OF TELANTHROPUS CAPENSIS. William L. Straus, Jr. Amer. Jour. Phys. Anthrop., n.s., vol.8, no.4, pp.495-498, Dec., 1950.

ANALYSIS OF A CONCRETE CASE OF INTERGRADATION BETWEEN TWO SUBSPECIES. Francis B. Sumner. Proc. Nat. Acad. Sci. U.S.A., vol.15, pp.110-120, Feb. 15, 1929.

ANALYSIS OF A CONCRETE CASE OF INTERGRADATION BETWEEN TWO SUBSPECIES. II. ADDITIONAL DATA AND INTERPRETATIONS. Francis B. Sumner. Proc. Nat. Acad. Sci. U.S.A., vol.15, pp.481-493, pl.1, June, 1929.

ON THE NATURAL HISTORY AND CLASSIFICATION OF QUADRUPEDS. William Swainson. London, Printed for Longman, Rees, Orme, Brown, Green & Longman, and John Taylor, pp.397, illus., 1935.

TEST OF THE SUBSPECIES. P. A. Taverner. Jour. Mamm., vol.1, no.3, pp.124-127, May, 1920.

(ON THE SYSTEMATIC AND PHYLOGENIC PLACEMENT OF THE GENERA PROMELES AND SEMANTOR.) Ueber die systematische und phylogenetische Stellung der Genera Promeles und Semantor. E. Thenius. S.B. Ost. Akad. Wiss., Abt.1, Band 158, Heft 4, pp.323-335, 1949.

MAMMALS OF THE TENTH EDITION OF LINNAEUS; AN ATTEMPT TO FIX THE TYPES OF THE GENERA AND THE EXACT BASES AND LOCALITIES OF THE SPECIES. Oldfield Thomas. Proc. Zool. Soc. London, pp.120-158, 1911.

NEW ASIATIC AND AUSTRALASIAN BATS AND A NEW BANDICOOT. Oldfield Thomas. Ann. & Mag. Nat. Hist. (8), vol.13, no.76, pp.439-444, Apr., 1894.

NEW BATS AND RODENTS FROM WEST AFRICA, THE MALAY PENINSULA, AND PAPUASIA. Oldfield Thomas. Ann. & Mag. Nat. Hist. (7), vol.14, no.81, pp.196-202, Sep., 1904.

NEW FORMS OF SAIMIRI, ORYZOMYS, PHYLLOTIS, COENDOU, AND CYCLOPES. Oldfield Thomas. Ann. & Mag. Nat. Hist. (7), vol.10, no.57, pp.246-250, Sep., 1902.

NEW GENUS OF OPOSSUMS AND A NEW TUCO-TUCO. Oldfield Thomas. Ann. & Mag. Nat. Hist. (8), vol.9, no.50, pp. 239-241, Feb., 1912.

NEW INSULAR FORMS OF NASUA AND DASYPROCTA. Oldfield Thomas. Ann. & Mag. Nat. Hist. (7), vol.8, no.46, pp. 271-273, Oct., 1901.

NEW SPECIES OF MACROSCELIDES AND GLAUCONYCTERIS. Oldfield Thomas. Ann. & Mag. Nat. Hist. (7), vol.8, no.45, pp.255-257, Sep., 1901.

ON ROBERT KERR'S TRANSLATION OF THE 'SYSTEMA NATURAE' OF LINNAEUS. Oldfield Thomas. Ann. & Mag. Nat. Hist. (5), vol.4, no.23, pp.396-397, Nov., 1879.

SUGGESTIONS FOR THE MORE DEFINITE USE OF THE WORD "TYPE" AND ITS COMPOUNDS, AS DENOTING SPECIMENS OF A GREATER OR LESS DEGREE OF AUTHENTICITY. Oldfield Thomas. Proc. Zool. Soc. London, pp.241-242, Mar. 14, 1893.

TYPES OF THE MAMMALS DESCRIBED BY MR. FERNAND LATASTE. Oldfield Thomas. Ann. & Mag. Nat. Hist. (9), vol.4, no.23, pp.350-354, Nov., 1919.

(CATALOGUE OF MAMMALS LIVING AND FOSSIL.) Catalogus mammalium tam viventium quam fossilium. E. L. Trouessart. Berlin, R. Friedlaender and Sohn, 1905.

(Review by T.S.Palmer of)CATALOGUS MAMMALIUM TAM VIVENTIUM QUAM FOSSILIUM. E.L. Trouessart. Science, Lancaster, n.s, vol.10, no.249, pp.491-495, Oct. 6, 1899.

(DECRIPTION OF NEW MAMMALS FROM AFRICA AND MADAGASCAR.) Description de Mammiféres nouveaux d'Afrique et de Madagascar. E.L. Trouessart. Bull. Mus. d'hist. Nat., Paris, no.7, pp.443-447, Feb., 1907.

(SYSTEMATIC AND GEOGRAPHIC CONSPECTUS OF MAMMALS LIVING AND FOSSIL. SYSTEMATIC, SYNONYMIC, AND GEOGRAPHIC CATALOG OF LIVING AND FOSSIL MAMMALS.) Conspectus systematicus et geographicus mammalium tam viventium quam fossilium. Catalogue systématique, synonymique et géographique des mammiferes vivants et fossiles. E. L. Trouessart. Paris, E.Deyrolle, pp.93, 1879. (Fasc.I.Primates.Simiae, Promisiae, Chiroptera.)

ON CERTAIN MODERN VIEWS CONCERNING THE ORDINAL ARRANGEMENT OF THE HIGHER MAMMALIA. David Tucker. Canadian Jour., n.s., Toronto, vol.9, pp. 154-170, 1864.

INDEX OF THE PELVIC BRIM AS A BASIS OF CLASSIFICATION. William Turner. Jour. Anat. and Physiol., vol.20, pp.125-143, Oct., 1885.

DIFFERENCES IN THE SYSTEMATICS OF PLANTS AND ANIMALS AND THEIR DEPENDENCES ON DIFFERENCES IN STRUCTURE, FUNCTION, AND BEHAVIOUR IN THE TWO GROUPS. W.B. Turrill, and others. Proc. Linnaean Soc. London, 153rd Session (1940-41), pt.3, pp.272-287, Aug. 17, 1942.

GENERAL SYSTEM OF NATURE THROUGH THE THREE GRAND KINGDOMS BY SIR CHARLES LINNE. W. Turton. London, Lackington, Allen and Co., vols.7, 1806.

CHARACTERS OF SOME NEW SPECIES OF THE GENERA MUS AND PHASCOGALE. G.R. Waterhouse. Proc. Zool. Soc. London, pt.5, p.75, 1837.

DESCRIPTION OF A NEW SPECIES OF KANGAROO (MACROPUS BENNETTI) AND A MOUSE (MUS SUBSPINOSUS) FROM THE CAPE OF GOOD HOPE. G.R. Waterhouse. Proc. Zool. Soc. London, pt.5, pp.103-105, 1837.

(THE MAMMALS. VOL. I. AND 2. INTRODUCTION TO THE ANATOMY AND SYSTEMATICS OF RECENT AND FOSSIL MAMMALIA.) Die Saeugetiere, vols. 1 and 2. Einfuehrung in die Anatomie und Systematik der Recenten und Fossilen Mammalia. Max Weber. Jena, Gustav Fischer, 1927-28.

MAXILLARY DIASTEMA AS A CRITERION OF GENERIC DISTINCTION. Franz Weidenreich. Amer. Jour. Phys. Anthropol., Philadelphia, n.s., vol.4, no.2, pp.199-201, June, 1946.

(SYSTEMATICS AND PHYLOGENY OF VERTEBRATES.) Systematik und Stammesgeschichte der Wirbeltiere. Otto von Wettstein. Fortschritte Zool., Jena, vol. 6, pp.98-115, 1942.

(QUANTITATIVE DETERMINATION OF THE GRADATION OF THE MAMMALS.) Zur quantitativen Bestimmung der Rangordnung bei Saeugetieren. Katharina Wirz. Acata Anatomica, vol.9, fasc.1-2, pp.133-196, 1950.

NOTE ON TAXONOMY. Wyoming Wild Life, Cheyenne, vol.12, no.8, pp.27-32, Sep., 1948.

## TECHNIQUES AND METHODS

STAINING MITOCHONDRIA IN FIXED BLOOD SMEAR. Warren Andrew, Henry Johnson. Stain Technology, vol.31, no.1, pp.21-23, illus., Jan., 1956.

(JUSTIFICATION OF THE PRINCIPLES OF THE VESTIBULAR METHOD.)Justification des principes de la methode vestibulaire. J. Anthony. Mammalia, Paris, vol.17, no. 4, pp.275-280, Dec., 1953.

HUMANE METHOD OF KILLING MAMMALS. Vernon Bailey. Jour. Mamm., vol. 17, no.3, pp.283-284, Aug., 1936.

METHOD FOR THE ASSESSMENT OF THE NUTRITIONAL STATUS OF WILD UNGULATES. P.J. Bandy, I.McT.Cowan, W.D. Kitts, A.J. Wood. Canadian Jour. Sci., Ottawa, vol.34, no.1, pp.48-52, illus., Feb., 1956.

HANDLING SMALL MAMMALS. K.R. Barbehenn. Jour. Mamm., vol.35, no.3, p.429, Aug. 20, 1954.

(NEW METHOD OF SEPARATING BONES FROM HAIRBALLS.) Eine neue Methode zur Gewinnung von Knochen aus Gewoellen. Kurt Becker. Zeitschr. f. Saeugetierk., Berlin, vol.22, nos.3-4, pp.242-243, 1957.

PARTIAL BIBLIOGRAPHY OF TECHNIQUES IN MAMMALOGY. Richard G. Beidleman. Rocky Mt. Nat. Assn., pp.i-76, mimeo., 1951.

DECOYING COYOTES AND DEER. Seth B. Benson. Jour. Mamm., vol.29, no.4, pp. 406-409, Dec. 31, 1948.

QUADRAT METHOD OF STUDYING SMALL MAMMAL POPULATIONS. B.P.Bole, Jr. Sci. Publ., Cleveland Mus. Nat. Hist., vol. 5, no.4, pp.15-77, Dec. 28, 1939.

STUDY OF METHODS OF COLOR DETERMINATION. Darl E. Bowers. Systematic Zoology, vol.5, no.4, pp.147-160, 182, Dec., 1956.

ILLUSTRATED FIELD KEY FOR THE IDENTIFICATION OF MAMMAL BONES. George W. Brainerd. Ohio State Archaeolog. and Hist. Quart., Columbus, vol.48, no. 4, pp.324-328, pls.1-7, Oct., 1939.

METHOD FOR VITAL MICROSCOPY OF MAMMALIAN BONE MARROW IN SITU. Per-Ingvar Branemark. Lunds, Univ. Arsskrift, n.F., Avd.2, vol.54, no.2, pp.5-41, 1958.

PARALDEHYDE AS AN AID TO HANDLING MAMMALS. John L. Buckley, Wm.H.Bergstrom. Jour. Wildl. Mgt., Menasha, vol. 15, no.1, pp.112-113, Jan., 1951.

METHOD FOR SELF-CONTROL OF POPULATION GROWTH AMONG MAMMALS LIVING IN THE WILD. John B. Calhoun. Science, Lancaster, vol.109, no.2831, pp.333-335, fig.1, Apr. 1, 1949.

SYSTEM FOR NUMBERING LABORATORY ANIMALS. Emmett B. Carmichael. Science, n.s., vol.87, no.2268, pp.557-558, fig.1, tbl.1, June 17, 1938.

DDT PROTECTS BAIT FROM ANTS. Robert H. Coleman. Jour. Mamm., vol.31, no.2, p.199, May 25, 1950.

TECHNIQUE FOR PREVENTING POST-MORTEM ECTOPARASITE CONTAMINATION. Edwin F. Cook. Jour. Mamm., vol. 35, no.2, pp.266-267, May 26, 1954.

DEVELOPMENT OF A STATEWIDE SYSTEM OF COVER-MAPPING APPLICABLE TO MISSOURI WILDLIFE RANGE. Paul D. Dalke. Jour. Wildl. Mgt., Menasha, vol. 5, no.1, pp.103-107, pl.4, Jan., 1941.

NOTE ON QUANTITATIVE METHODS IN THE OBSERVATION OF BIG GAME IN THE KRUGER NATIONAL PARK. D.H.S.Davis. S. African Jour. Sci., Johannesburg, vol. 36, pp.381-385, folding table, Dec., 1939.

DEEP DIVING AND SUBMARINE OPERATIONS. R.H. Davis. London, Siebe, Gorman and Co., Ed.6, parts 2, 1955.

CALENDAR SYSTEM OF RECORD KEEPING FOR SPORTSMEN. Verne E. Davison. Jour. Wildl. Mgt., Menasha, vol.7, no.2, pp. 129-133, Apr., 1943.

PREPARATIONS OF STAINED DECALCIFIED BONE WHICH RIVAL GROUND SECTIONS. A.B. Dawson. Science, n.s,, vol.66, pp. 399-400, Oct. 28, 1927.

QUANTITATIVE AND EXPERIMENTAL METHODS IN SYSTEMATIC ZOOLOGY. Lee R. Dice. Systematic Zoology, vol. 1, no.3, pp.97-104, Sep., 1952.

SIMPLE METHOD FOR FILING MINIATURE NEGATIVES AND MICROFILM RECORDS IN STRIPS. Lee R. Dice. Science, n.s., vol.89, no.2298, pp.39-40, Jan. 13, 1939.

GRAPHIC METHOD FOR COMPARING SEVERAL SETS OF MEASUREMENTS. Lee R. Dice, Harold J. Leraas. Contrib. Lab. Vert. Genetics, Univ. Michigan, no.3, pp.3, fig.1, June, 1936.

WEIGHING LARGE MAMMALS IN THE FIELD. J. Kenneth Doutt. Jour. Mamm., vol.21, no.1, pp.63-65, fig.1, Feb. 14, 1940.

INVESTIGATION OF A STATISTICAL MEANS OF CALCULATING THE FORM OF THE SKULL OF SOME DOMESTIC MAMMALS OF DRAFT SIZE.(Trans.title) U.Duerst. Zeitschr. f. Tierzuechtung u. Zuechtungsbiol., vol.3, no.3, pp.297-341, illus., 1925.

EFFECTIVE METHOD FOR COLLECTING ECTOPARASITES FROM LIVE ANIMALS AND BIRDS. Lawrence H. Dunn. Psyche, vol.39, nos.1-2, pp.26-29, 1932.

SIMPLE METHOD OF IMMOBILIZING ANIMALS FOR LABORATORY PURPOSES. Lawrence H. Dunn. Amer. Jour. Tropical Medicine, vol.12, no.2, pp.173-178, pl.1, Mar., 1932.

(MATHEMATICAL CLASSIFICATION OF FLUCTUATING BIOLOGICAL RHYTHMS.) Une classification mathématique des rythmes biologiques fluctuants. Henri Durup. Mammalia, Paris, vol.21, no.4, pp.420-429, Dec., 1957.

RAPID PREPARATION OF TOOTH SECTIONS FOR AGE DETERMINATIONS. H.D.Fisher, B.A. Mackenzie. Jour. Wildl. Mgt., vol. 18, no.4, pp.535-537, illus., Oct., 1954.

HINTS ON THE TRANSPORT OF ANIMALS. Stanley Smith Flower. Proc. Zool. Soc. London, pt.2, pp.631-652, July, 1928.

AGE DETERMINATION IN MAMMALS. Charles P. Gandal. Trans. New York Acad. Sci., ser.2, vol.16, no.6, pp.312-314, Apr., 1954.

METHOD OF MEASURING BONE GROWTH IN THE SKULL. N. Giblin, A.Alley. Anat. Record, Philadelphia, vol.53, no.3, pp. 381-387, figs.5, July 25, 1942.

METHODS OF UTILIZING SMALL GAME CROPS DURING WARTIME IN THE SOUTHWEST. Phil Goodrum. Trans. 8th N. Amer. Wildl. Conf., pp.240-247, 1943.

RECORD KEEPING FOR LABORATORY ANIMALS. N.T. Gridgeman. Jour. Hyg., Cambridge, vol.47, no.2, pp.197-201, June, 1949.

FUR STUDY TECHNIQUE. F.N. Hamerstrom, James Blake. Jour. Wildl.Mgt., Menasha, Wisc., vol.3, no.1, pp.54-59, Jan., 1939.

IMPROVED METHOD FOR REVEALING THE SURFACE STRUCTURE OF FUR FIBERS. J.L. Hardy, Thora M. Plitt. U.S. Dept. Interior, Fish and Wildlife Service, Wildlife Circular no.7, pp.10, figs.2, 1940.

SIMPLE TECHNIQUE FOR DEN-USE STUDY. Richard J. Hartesveldt. Jour. Wildl. Mgt., vol.15, no.1, pp.104-105, Jan., 1951.

EXPERIMENTAL CHEMOTHERAPY OF FILARIASIS. I. EXPERIMENTAL METHODS FOR TESTING DRUGS AGAINST NATURALLY ACQUIRED FILARIAL INFECTIONS IN COTTON RATS AND DOGS. R.I. Hewitt, W. S. Wallace, E. White, Y.Subba Row. Jour. Lab. and Clin. Med., St. Louis, vol.32, no.11, pp.1293-1303, 1947.

HUMAN ACTIVITIES AND THE STUDY OF LIFE IN THE SEA. ESSAY ON METHODS OF RESEARCH AND EXPERIMENT. Johan Hjort. Geogr. Review, New York, vol.25, no.4, pp.529-564, figs.10, Oct., 1935.

SELECTION OF FATS BY DERMESTID BEETLES, DERMESTIDAE. Emmet T. Hooper. Jour. Mamm., vol.37, no.1, pp. 125-126, Feb. 28, 1956.

USE DERMESTID BEETLES INSTEAD OF COOKING POTS. Emmet T. Hooper. Jour. Mamm., vol.31, no.1, pp.100-102, Feb. 21, 1950.

ANAESTHETIZING MAMMALS. A.Brazier Howell. Jour. Mamm., vol.18, no.4, p. 513, Nov., 1937.

SIMPLE METHOD OF SAVING SMALL MAMMALS IN THE FIELD. Arthur H. Howell. Jour. Mamm., vol.18, no.1, p.95, Feb. 14, 1937.

METHOD FOR THE FIXATION OF MAMMALIAN CHROMOSOMES IN THE FIELD. W.E. Hoy, Jr., Kalman Berkowitz. Jour. Mamm., vol.12, no.4, pp.397-400, Nov., 1931.

AGE OF THE DOMESTIC ANIMALS. BEING A COMPLETE TREATISE ON THE DENTITION OF THE HORSE, OX, SHEEP, HOG, AND DOG, AND ON THE VARIOUS OTHER MEANS OF DETERMINING THE AGE OF THESE ANIMALS. Rush Shippen Huidekoper. Philadelphia and London, F.A. Davis, pp.217, illus. with 200 engravings, 1891.

INK AND PAPER FOR MUSEUM LABELS. Robert T. Jackson. Proc. Amer. Assoc. Adv. Sci., vol.47, pp.378-379, 1898.

HISTOLOGICAL METHOD FOR THE STUDY OF PIGMENTATION IN MAMMALIAN EPITHELIUM. Beatrice W. Johnson. Amer.Nat., vol.59, no.662, pp.287-288, May-June, 1925.

QUANTITATIVE METHOD IN THE FIELD STUDY OF VERTEBRATE FAUNA AND ANALYSIS OF THE DATA OBTAINED. D.N. Kashkarof. Acta Univ. Asiae Mediae, ser. VIII-a, Zool., fasc.1, pp.1-24, 1927. (In Russian with English summary.)

TECHNOLOGICAL PROCESS OF OBTAINING OILS FROM THE FATS OF MARINE ANIMALS. I.I. Kharkov. Pacific Sci. Inst.Fishery Economics and Oceanography, Moscow, nos.1-2, 1934. (In Russian.)

GRAPHIC METHOD OF SHOWING RELATIONSHIPS. L.M. Klauber. Bull. Zool.Soc. San Diego, no.18, pp.61-76, Sep. 1, 1943.

RAPID AND SIMPLIFIED METHOD FOR REVEALING THE SURFACE PATTERN OF HAIR. C.H. Koonz, E.J. Strandina. Trans. Amer. Micros. Soc., vol.64, no. 1, pp.63-64, Jan., 1945.

METHOD FOR ANALYSING THE WINTER HABITAT PREFERENCES OF FOREST MAMMALS. Jukka Koskimies. Papers on Game Research, Helsinki, vol.8, pp.58-63, 1952.

DECALCIFICATION OF BONE IN ACID FREE SOLUTIONS. B. Kramer, P.G. Shipley. Science, n.s., vol.66, pp.484-485, Nov. 18, 1927.

METHOD OF BLOOD STAINING WHICH REPLACES INJECTIONS. Harry A. Kull. Anat. Record, vol.31, pp.281-284, fig.1, Nov. 25, 1925.

NEW METHOD OF AGE DETERMINATION FOR MAMMALS. R.M. Laws. Nature, vol. 169, no.4310, pp.972-973, illus., June 7, 1952.

(SECOND STUDY ON THE DUBOIS COEFFICIENT THEORY.) Seconde etude sur la theorie du coefficient de Dubois. P.LeGallic. Mammalia, Paris, vol.20, no.1, pp.75-82, Mar., 1956.

SURVIVAL OF ORGANS AND THE "CULTURE" OF LIVING TISSUES. R.Legendre. Smiths. Inst., Annual Rep., 1912, Washington, pp.413-420, pl., 1913.

HOW TO TELL THE AGE OF THE DOMESTIC ANIMALS. A.F.A. Liautard. New York, W.R.Jenkins, pp.33, illus., 1885.

SIMPLE METHOD FOR ESTIMATING THE COAGULATION TIME OF BLOOD. Marcus W. Lyon, Jr. Jour. Amer. Med. Assoc., vol.66, p.891, Mar. 18, 1916.

SIMPLE METHOD TO REPRESENT GRAPHICALLY THE TREND OF VARIATION IN A SMALL NUMBER OF SPECIMENS OF RELATED SPECIES. Marcus W. Lyon, Jr. Science, n.s., vol.27, pp.624-625, Apr.17, 1908.

NEW TECHNIQUES IN HANDLING BIG GAME PROBLEMS IN MONTANA. Lloyd E. McDowell, Dwight S. Stockstad. Proc. 32nd Ann. Conf. Western Assn. State Game & Fish Comm., Glacier Nat.Park, Mont., June 15-17, 1952, pp.210-213, 1953.

TECHNIQUES FOR CAPTURE AND MARKING OF MAMMALS. Richard H. Manville. Jour. Mamm., Baltimore, vol.30, no.1, pp.27-33, Feb. 14, 1949.

CHLORAL HYDRATE NARCOSIS FOR THE LIVE CAPTURE OF MAMMALS. B.J. Marlow. C.S.I.R.O. Wildl. Res., Commonwealth Scientific & Industrial Research Organization, Melbourne, vol.1, no.1, pp.63-65, Sep., 1956.

NEW METHOD OF STUDYING THE MAMMALIAN HEART. H. Newell Martin. Trans. Med. & Chirurg. Faculty State of Maryland, Baltimore, vol.83, pp.192-205, 1881.

RAPID METHOD OF CROSS-SECTIONING MAMMALIAN HAIRS. Harold A. Mathiak. Jour. Wildl. Mgt., vol.2, no.3, pp.162-164, July, 1938.

METHODS OF CORRELATION BY FOSSIL VERTEBRATES. W.D. Matthew. Bull.Geol. Soc. Amer., Washington, D.C., vol.27, no.3, pp.515-524, Sep. 1, 1916.

MEASURING MAMMALS' TAILS. T. C. S. Morrison-Scott. Ann. Mag. Nat. Hist. London, ser.11, vol.3, pp.216-219, figs.3, Feb., 1939.

WEIGHING GAME ANIMALS. Olaus J. Murie. Jour. Mamm., vol.9, no.1, pp.74-75, Feb., 1928.

PROBLEMS OF SMALL MAMMAL SAMPLING. Keith Murray. California Vector News, State Dept. Public Health, vol.4, no.6, pp.35, 39, June, 1957.

WILDLIFE AND HABITATS IN YOUNG COUNTY, TEXAS, BY A NEW METHOD OF SURVEY. Ben Osborn. Jour. Wildl. Mgt., Menasha, vol.7, no.3, pp.241-256, July, 1943.

THE WALTERS "CELLULOID" PROCESS AND ITS RECENT APPLICATIONS. Wilfred H. Osgood. Museums Jour., London, vol. 39, no.4, pp.180-185, pls.27-29, July, 1939.

GRAPHIC REPRESENTATION OF RELATIVE VARIABILITY. Raymond Pearl. Science, n.s., vol.65, pp.237-241, Mar. 11, 1927.

DETERMINATION OF SEX AND AGE RATIOS IN FUR ANIMALS. George A. Petrides. Amer. Midland Nat., Notre Dame, vol.43, no.2, pp.355-382, figs.9, Mar., 1950.

EFFECTIVE DEPILATORY FORMULA FOR USE ON LABORATORY ANIMALS. Isadore Pitesky, Jules H. Last. Science, Lancaster, vol.108, no.2815, p.657, Dec. 10, 1948.

METHOD FOR STAINING THE SCALES OF COARSE HAIRS. Donald S. Po-Chedley. Jour. Mamm., vol.32, no.2, p.232, May 21, 1951.

SUGGESTIONS FOR THE HANDLING OF CERTAIN MAMMALS. Robert Rausch. Jour. Wildl. Mgt., Menasha, vol.11, no.2, p.189, Apr., 1947.

FIELD METHODS FOR COLLECTING MAMMAL ECTOPARASITES. Neil D. Richmond. Jour. Mamm., vol.32, no.1, pp.123-125, Feb. 15, 1951.

TECHNIQUE FOR NIGHT IDENTIFICATION OF ANIMALS. Wilmer C. Richter. Jour. Wildl. Mgt., Ithaca, vol.19, no.1, pp.159-160, illus., Jan., 1955.

USE OF FAECES COUNTS IN STUDIES OF SEVERAL FREE-RANGING MAMMALS IN NEW ZEALAND. Thane Riney. New Zealand Jour. Sci. & Tech., sec.B, vol.38, no.6, pp.507-532, May, 1957.

NEW METHOD FOR ISOLATION AND PURIFICATION OF MAMMALIAN STRIATED MYOFIBRILS. Armin F. Schick, George M. Hass. Science, Lancaster, vol.109, no. 2837, pp.486-487, illus., May 13, 1949.

SIMPLE MICRO-GASOMETRIC METHOD OF ESTIMATING CARBON MONOXIDE IN BLOOD. P.F. Scholander, F.J.W. Roughton. Jour. Industrial Hygiene and Toxicology, Cambridge, vol.24, no.8, pp.218-221, Oct., 1942.

TECHNIQUE OF ANESTHETIZATION AND OF OVARIECTOMY IN THE RAT. W.H. Schultz. Anat. Record, vol.52, no.2, pp. 99-115, Mar. 25, 1932.

FORAGE INVENTORY METHODS, WITH SPECIAL REFERENCE TO BIG GAME RANGES. H.E. Schwan, Lloyd Swift. Trans. 6th N. Amer. Wildl. Conf., Washington, D.C., pp.118-126, 1941.

METHODOLOGY AND TECHNIQUES FOR THE STUDY OF ANIMAL SOCIETIES. J.P. Scott, and others. Ann. New York Acad. Sci., vol.51, art.6, pp.1-122, illus., 1950.

LOCALITY, DATE, AND NAME WITH OBSERVATIONS. Ernest Thompson Seton. Jour. Mamm., vol.1, no.2, p.107, 1920.

ON THE STUDY OF SCATOLOGY. Ernest Thompson Seton. Jour. Mamm., vol.6, no.1, pp.47-49, Feb., 1925.

NOTES ON GRAPHIC BIOMETRIC COMPARISON OF SAMPLES. George Gaylord Simpson. Amer. Nat., Lancaster, vol. 79, pp.95-96, Jan.-Feb., 1945.

SIMPLIFIED SERIAL SECTIONING TECHNIQUE FOR THE STUDY OF FOSSILS. George Gaylord Simpson. Amer. Mus. Novitates, no.634, pp.6, fig.1, June 10, 1933.

STANDARD FREQUENCY DISTRIBUTION METHOD. George Gaylord Simpson, Anne Roe. Amer. Mus. Novitates, New York, no.1190, pp.19, Sep. 30, 1942.

PRACTICAL MODE OF STUDYING THE HEART. W.H. Smith. Physician and Surgeon, Ann Arbor, pp.1-15, 1879.

WATCHING NOCTURNAL ANIMALS BY INFRA RED RADIATION. H.N. Southern, J.S. Watson, Dennis Chitty. Jour. Anim. Ecol., London, vol.15, no.2, pp.198-202 illus., Nov., 1946.

HOW TO CARE FOR YOUR KILL. Gordon Stewart. Texas Game and Fish, Austin, vol.1, no.12, p.9, Nov., 1943.

COLORIMETRIC METHODS IN BIOLOGY. F.B. Sumner. Science, n.s., vol.67, p. 271, Mar. 9, 1928.

LINEAR AND COLORIMETRIC MEASUREMENTS OF SMALL MAMMALS. F. B. Sumner. Jour. Mamm., vol.8, no.3, pp. 177-206, pls.16-19, Aug., 1927.

THEORETICAL JUSTIFICATION OF THE MARK-AND-RELEASE INDEX FOR SMALL MAMMALS. Ryo Tanaka. Bull. Kochi Women's College, Shikoku, Japan, vol.1, pp.38-47, illus., Dec., 1952.

SOME NEW TECHNIQUES--HOOFED MAMMALS. Walter P. Taylor. Trans. N. Amer. Wildl. Conf., vol.12, pp.293-320, 1947.

HOW TO MEASURE AN ANIMAL. Ernest Seton Thompson. Recreation, New York, vol.8, no.4, pp.271-272, figs.7, Apr., 1898.

EFFECT OF MACERATION AND DRYING UPON THE LINEAR DIMENSIONS OF THE GREEN SKULL. T. Wingate Todd. Jour. Anat., vol.57, pp.336-356, July, 1923.

ROENTGENOGRAPHIC APPRAISEMENT OF SKELETAL DIFFERENTIATION. T. Wingate Todd. Child Development, vol.1, no.4, pp.298-310, Dec., 1930.

REVIEW OF NEW TECHNIQUES--FUR BEARERS AND OTHER SMALL MAMMALS. Charles T. Vorhies. Trans. N. Amer. Wildl. Conf., vol.12, pp.324-329, 1947.

METHOD OF NUMBERING LABORATORY RATS. George Walker. Science, vol.82, no.2130, pp.397-398, figs.4, Oct. 25, 1935.

INTENSIVE METHOD OF DETERMINING HUNTER NUMBERS AND ACTIVITIES. Willet N. Wandell. Trans. 11th N. Amer. Wildl. Conf., Washington, pp.373-382, figs.4, 1946.

IDENTIFICATION OF RODENTS AND RABBITS BY THEIR FECAL PELLETS. John Webb. Trans. Kansas Acad. Sci., Topeka, vol.43, pp.479-481, fig.1, 1940.

FIELD AND LABORATORY TECHNIC IN WILDLIFE MANAGEMENT. Howard M. Wight. Univ. Michigan School Forestry, Univ. Mich. Press, pp.107, 1938.

METHOD FOR THE MEASUREMENT OF ACTIVITY OF SMALL ANIMALS. Karl M. Wilbur. Science, n.s., vol.84, no.2177, p.274, Sep. 18, 1936.

SIMPLE METHOD FOR SECTIONING MAMMALIAN HAIRS FOR IDENTIFICATION PURPOSES. Cecil S. Williams. Jour. Mamm., vol.15, no.3, pp.251-252, Aug., 1934.

CONTENTS OF OWL PELLETS AS INDICATORS OF HABITAT PREFERENCES OF SMALL MAMMALS. L.D. Wooster. Trans. Kansas Acad. Sci., vol.39, pp.395-397, 1937.

PREPARATION OF INDUSTRIAL AND MEDICINAL FAT. S.W. Yeskersky, W.N. Podsevalov, A.S. Shibalov. Repts. Astrakhan Volgo-Caspian Sea Sci. Fish. Sta., vol.7, no.4, pp.29-47, 1931. (In Russian.)

HOW TO MAKE SMALL LIGAMENTARY SKELETONS. Ward's Nat. Sci. Bull., Rochester, vol.17, no.1, p.4, Sep., 1943.

TEETH see ANATOMY -- SKULL, JAWS, TEETH

TERRITORIALITY see HOME RANGES AND TERRITORIALITY

TEXTBOOKS see EDUCATION AND TEXTBOOKS

TICKS see DISEASES AND PARASITES -- TICKS

## TRACKS AND TRACKING

CHRISTMAS WALK WITH BIRDS AND BEASTS. A. A. Allen. Amer. Forestry, vol.25, pp.1526-1530, figs.12, Dec., 1919.

COLLECTING TRACKS. Vernon Bailey. Jour. Mamm., vol.4, no.3, p.195, Aug., 1928.

SLEUTH WORK IN THE FIELDS. TRACK READING IN SNOW OR MUD. H. Mortimer Batten. Field, London, vol.164, no.4279, p.1514, illus., Dec. 29, 1934.

ANIMAL TRAILS AND TRAILING. L. W. Brownell. Nature Mag., vol.3, pp.11-16, figs.15, Jan., 1924; Canadian Nature, Toronto, vol.5, no.1, pp.3-5, figs.8, Jan.-Feb., 1943.

ANIMAL TRACKS IN SNOW. R. Clapham. Field, London, vol.151, p.390, illus., Mar. 8, 1928.

ANIMAL TRACKS. Ellsworth Jaeger. Canadian Nat., Toronto, vol.8, no.1, pp. 16-21, illus., Jan., 1946.

HOW TO KNOW FOOTPRINTS. Ellsworth Jaeger. Nat. Hist., New York, vol.44, no. 4, pp.226-232, illus., Nov., 1939.

TRACKS AND TRAILCRAFT. Ellsworth Jaeger. New York, Macmillan Co., pp.381, pls.203, 1948.

(Review by Robert A. McCabe of) TRACKS AND TRAILCRAFT. Ellsworth Jaeger. Jour. Mamm., vol.30, no.3, pp.322-323, Aug. 17, 1949.

TRACKS OUR BOYS MAY SEE. Ellsworth Jaeger. Nature Mag., Washington, D.C., vol.36, no.5, pp.243-246, 276, illus., May, 1943.

WINTER GAME TRAILS. James Kimball. Outdoor Nebraska, Lincoln, vol.21, no.4, pp.19-20, Jan., 1944.

MAMMAL TRACKS AND FACTS. BADGER, BATS. Helen Lawson, Bill Lawson. Ohio Conserv. Bull., Columbus, vol.14, no.4, pp.4-5, illus., Apr., 1950.

MAMMAL TRACKS AND FACTS. BEAVER, BLACK BEAR. Helen Lawson, Bill Lawson. Ohio Conserv. Bull., Columbus, vol.14, no.4, pp.20-21, illus., May, 1950.

ANIMAL TRACKING. George M. Link. (In) Getting at Nature, its Mystery and its Message. Springfield, vol.1, no.2, pp. 4-9, illus., 1940.

FIRST EXPERIENCES IN TRACKING GAME, NO. 1. Denis D. Lyell. Game and Gun, vol. 5, pp.318-321, June, 1928.

ZOOLOGICAL JOTTINGS. ANIMAL SIGNS. H. Elliott McClure. Nature Notes, Peoria, vol.8, no.1, pp.9-12, figs.2, Jan., 1941.

QUANTITATIVE ACCOUNT OF MAMMALS BY THEIR TRACKS. V. Malyshef. Bull. Far Eastern Branch Acad. Sci. USSR, Vladivostok, no.16, pp.177-179, 1936. (In Russian.)

ANIMAL TRACKS. George F. Mason. Morrow, pp.95, 1943.

FIELD GUIDE TO ANIMAL TRACKS. Olaus J. Murie. Peterson Field Guide Series, no. 9, Houghton Mifflin, Boston, pp.374, illus., 1954.

(Review by Robert A. McCabe of) FIELD GUIDE TO ANIMAL TRACKS. Olaus J. Murie. Jour. Mamm., vol.36, no.3, pp. 478-479, Aug. 30, 1955.

HE WHO RUNS MAY BE READ. E. Lawrence Palmer. Nature Mag., Washington, vol.38, no.10, pp.529-536, Dec., 1945.

SIGNS IN THE SNOW. READING TELLTALE TRACKS OF WINTER. Morris L. Paterson. Conservation Volunteer, St. Paul, vol.9, no.51, pp.38-42, illus., Mar.-Apr., 1946.

TRACKS IN THE SNOW. READING THEIR STORY. Chas. Schafer. Michigan Conserv., Lansing, vol.18, no.1, opp.p.36, illus., Jan.-Feb., 1949.

READIN' SIGN. Francis E. Sell. Field and Stream, New York, vol.50, no.8, pp.49, 100-102, illus., Dec., 1945.

TRACKING TECHNIQUE IN THE STUDY OF THE LARGER PREDATORY MAMMALS. A.M. Stebler. Trans. 4th N. Amer. Wildl. Conf., Washington, D.C., pp.203-208, 1939.

TRACK STORIES IN MUD, SAND, AND SNOW. Dorothy A. Treat. School Nature League Bull., New York, ser.16, bull.4, pp.4, Dec., 1945.

LAND OF FOOTPRINTS. ILLUSTRATED FROM PHOTOGRAPHS BY THE AUTHOR AND TWO DRAWINGS BY PHILIP R. GOODWIN. Stewart Edward White. Garden City, N.Y. Doubleday, Page & Co., pp.440, pls., 1912.

AUTOGRAPHS OF WILD ANIMALS. Julia W. Wolfe. Canadian Nature, Toronto, vol. 9, no.3, p.96, May-June, 1947.

ANIMAL TRACKING FOR BOY SCOUTS. HINTS ON ANIMAL TRACKING. Rodney C. Wood. Ottawa, Canadian General Council of the Boy Scouts Assoc., pp.16, illus., Nov., 1924.

ANIMAL TRACKS. Stackpole, pp.64, illus., 1954.

SIGNS IN THE SNOW. Field and Stream, New York, vol.48, no.10, pp.22-23, illus., Feb., 1944.

TRACKS--DO YOU KNOW THEM? Texas Game & Fish, Austin, vol.6, no.11, p.21, Oct., 1948.

## TRAPS AND TRAPPING

BOX TRAP FOR SNOWSHOE HARES AND SMALL RODENTS. C.M. Aldous. Jour. Wildl. Mgt., vol.10, no.1, pp.71-72, Jan., 1946.

INCIDENCE OF CRIPPLING LOSS IN STEEL TRAPPING. Thomas Z. Atkeson. Jour. Wildlife Mgt., vol.20, no.3, pp.323-324, July, 1956.

HUMANE TRAPS--DEVICES FOR CATCHING ANIMALS ALIVE AND UNHURT AND SIMPLE CAGES IN WHICH TO STUDY THEM. Vernon Bailey. Nature Mag., vol.23, no.2, pp.88-91, illus., Feb., 1934.

LIVE TRAPS FOR GAME FARMS. Vernon Bailey. Game Breeder, vol.37, no.1, pp. 2-3, illus.20, Jan., 1933.

TRAPPING ANIMALS ALIVE. Vernon Bailey. Jour. Mamm., vol.13, no.4, pp.337-342, Nov., 1932.

SIMPLE AND EFFECTIVE LIVE TRAP FOR SMALL MAMMALS. W. Frank Blair. Jour. Wildl. Mgt., Menasha, vol.5, no.2, pp.191-193, fig.1, Apr., 1941.

SIMPLE LIVE TRAP FOR SMALL MAMMALS. W.H. Burt. Jour. Mamm., vol.8, no.4, pp.302-304, Nov., 1927.

SHALL THE STEEL TRAP BE OUTLAWED? Henry R. Carey. Sportsman, vol.5, no.2, pp.49-51, illus., Feb., 1929.

NOTES ON SMALL MAMMAL TRAPPING. E.B. Chamberlain, Jr. Bull. S.Carolina Acad. Sci., Columbia, vol.7, pp.21-22, 1941.

PREBAITING SMALL MAMMALS AND NEW DESIGN OF LIVE TRAP. Dennis Chitty, D.A. Kempson. Ecology, vol.30, no.4, pp.536-542, Oct., 1949.

TRAPPING AND FUR MANAGEMENT. Wilson F. Clark. Cornell Univ., Cornell 4-H Club Bull.101, pp.1-43, illus., Oct., 1953.

EFFECTIVENESS OF LIVE TRAPS VERSUS SNAP TRAPS. E. Lendell Cockrum. Jour. Mamm., vol.28, no.2, p.186, May, 1947.

REVIEW AND EVALUATION OF BIG GAME TRAPPING TECHNIQUES. Faye M. Couey. Proc. Ann. Conf. W. Assn. State Game and Fish Comm., vol.29, pp.110-116, 1949.

REGISTERED TRAPLINES. V. Crichton. Sylva, vol.4, no.2, pp.3-15, 1948.

LIVE-TRAP FOR SMALL MAMMALS. L.R. Dice. Jour. Mamm., vol.6, no.3, p.202, Aug., 1925.

TRAPS. PART I. EVOLUTION AND HISTORY. PART II. SEARCH FOR A MORE HUMANE TRAP. Nicholas Drahos. N.Y. State Cons., vol.6, no.1, pp.8-12, vol.6, no.2, pp.24-26, Aug.-Sep., 1951 and Oct.-Nov., 1951.

AUDUBON STEEL-TRAPPING SANCTUARY. Rosalie Edge. Emergency Cons. Comm., N.Y., pp.12, illus., Sep., 1934.

STEEL-TRAPPING BY THE AUDUBON ASSOCIATION. Rosalie Edge. Emergency Conserv. Comm., N.Y., pp.4, Nov. 21, 1933.

HOW EFFICIENT ARE SNAP TRAPS IN TAKING SMALL MAMMALS? R. York Edwards. Jour. Mamm., vol.33, no.4, pp.497-498, Nov., 1952.

FURBEARERS CRY FOR MERCY. Minnie Maddern Fiske. National Parks Mag.,

Washington, vol.21, no.91, pp.24-26, illus., Oct.-Dec., 1947.

NEW STYLE LIVE-TRAP FOR SMALL MAMMALS. Henry S. Fitch. Jour. Mamm., vol.31, no.3, pp.364-365, Aug., 1950.

UTILITY OF BREAK-BACK TRAPS IN POPULATION STUDIES OF SMALL MAMMALS. C.David Fowle, R.Y. Edwards. Jour. Wildl. Mgt., Ithaca, vol.18, no.4, pp.503-508, Oct., 1954.

MODERN INFAMY. Lucy Furman. Nature Mag., Washington, vol.39, no.2, pp.97-99, 108, illus., Feb., 1946.

COMPARISON OF TRAPPING METHODS IN AN ILLINOIS PRAIRIE. Clarence J. Goodnight. E.J.Koestner. Jour.Mamm., vol.23, no.4, pp.435-438, fig.1, Nov. 14, 1942.

(SOME NATIVE AFRICAN TRAPS FOR SMALL MAMMALS.) Quelques pièges indigenes Africains pour petits mammiferes. Marcel Griaule. Mammalia, Paris, vol.4, nos.3-4, pp.94-112, figs.17, Sep.-Dec., 1940.

SELECTIVITY OF MIRROR TRAPS. Roy A. Grizzell, Jr. Jour. Wildl. Mgt., Ithaca, N.Y., vol.16, no.1, pp.114-115, Jan., 1952.

A NON-INJURIOUS ANIMAL TRAP. P. C. Halahan. Field, London, vol.168, no.4381, p.1501, illus., Dec. 12, 1936.

NEW LIVE-TRAP FOR FIELD USE. Robert T. Hatt. Jour. Mamm., vol.6, no.3, pp.178, 181, figs.1, Aug., 1925.

FUR TRAPPING AND MANAGEMENT FOR 4-H CLUBS. Arnold O. Haugen, F.F.Tubbs. Michigan State Coll. Ext. Serv., East Lansing, Club Bull.55, pp.43, figs.24, Nov., 1946.

NEW DEVELOPMENT IN A SMALL MAMMAL TRAP. Paul Hickie. Jour. Mamm., vol.16, no.1, pp.71-73, Feb., 1935.

TRIGGER MECHANISM FOR SMALL MAMMAL LIVE TRAPS. Walter E. Howard. Jour. Mamm., vol.34, no.4, pp.513-514, illus., Nov., 1953.

FURTHER NOTES ON TRAPPING. C.Imrose. Jour. Bombay Nat. Hist. Soc., vol.28, pp. 1129-1130, Dec. 20, 1922.

A SIMPLE "LIVE" TRAP. M.W. Johnson. Science, vol.92, no.2395, p.490, Nov. 22, 1940.

STEEL TRAP. Mrs. Edward La Budde. Wis. Cons. Bull., vol.2, no.5, pp.14-17, May, 1937.

TIPS ON TRAPPING, TAGGING, AND HANDLING SMALL GAME AND FUR ANIMALS. Leonard M. Llewellyn. Proc. N.E. Sect. Widl. Soc., 9th Ann. Conf., Bretton Woods, N.H., Sep. 20-23, 1953, pp.1-27, illus.

TEST OF A METHOD OF SMALL MAMMAL TRAPPING. D.A. MacLulich.Canadian Field-Naturalist, Ottawa, vol.54, no.4, pp.57-58, Apr., 1940.

(TRAP FOR CAPTURING WILD MAMMALS ALIVE.) Trampa para capturar vivos pequeños mamiferos silvestres.F.Guillermo Mann. Biologica, Santiago, fasc.2, pp.139-140, pl., July, 1945.

COMPARISON OF TRAPPING METHODS. R.H. Manville. Jour. Mamm., vol.31, no. 4, pp.377-383, Nov. 21, 1950.

(Review by P.Rode of) (SNARES. STUDY OF CAPTURE INSTRUMENTS USED THROUGHOUT THE WORLD.) Les Pièges. Etude sur les engins de capture utilises dans le monde. E. Merite. Mammalia, Paris, vol.6, nos.3-4, p.127, Sep.-Dec., 1942.

LIVE-TRAPPING STUDY AT O. S. U. Robert H. Mills. Ohio Cons. Bull., vol.6, no.11, pp.20-21, Nov., 1942.

IMPROVEMENTS IN LIVE TRAPPING. A. W. Moore. Jour. Mamm., vol.17, no.4, pp. 372-374, figs.2, Nov., 1936.

NEW LIVE-TRAP FOR SMALL MAMMALS. R.F. Morris. Canadian Field-Nat., Sutton West, vol.57, no.6, pp.113-114, Sep., 1943.

LETHAL TRAP FOR CAPTURING SMALL MAMMALS WITH THEIR ECTOPARASITES. H.P. Nicholson, M.H. Vetter. Jour.Parasitol., Lancaster, vol.36, no.3, pp.235-237, illus., June, 1950.

SNARES AND DEADFALLS. George A. Petrides. Jour. Wildl. Mgt., Menasha, vol. 10, no.3, pp.234-238, July, 1946.

HINTS FOR TRAPPERS. Harold Plasterer. Pennsylvania Game News, Harrisburg, vol. 16, no.4, pp.12-13, 30, illus., July, 1945.

COMPARISON OF CATCH OF TWO SIZES OF SMALL-MAMMAL LIVE TRAPS. Jay C. Quast, Walter E. Howard. Jour.Mamm., vol.34, no.4, pp.514-515, Nov., 1953.

TRAPS AND SNARES. R.U. Sayce. The Montgomeryshire Coll., Trans.Powys-land Club, vol.49, pt.1, pp.37-73, figs.45, 1945.

NOOTKA TRAP FOR SMALL MAMMALS. Victor B. Scheffer. Murrelet, Seattle, vol. 21, no.3, pp.71-72, fig.1, Sep.-Dec., 1940.

BRIEF HISTORY OF THE STEEL TRAP AND ITS USE IN NORTH AMERICA. A.W.Schorger. Trans. Wis. Acad. Sci., Arts & Letters, vol.40, pt.2, pp.171-199, 1951.

HOW TO MAKE A CAT TRAP. James Silver. Leaflet no.50, U.S. Dept. Agric., Bur.Biol. Surv., pp.4, fig.1, Nov., 1929.

ON THE WINTER TRAPPING OF SMALL MAMMALS. J.Dewey Soper. Jour.Mamm., Baltimore, vol.25, no.4, pp.344-353, figs. 5, Nov., 1944.

ANIMAL TRAPS AND SNARES OF THE MAYA INDIANS OF YUCATAN, MEXICO. Morris Steggerda. Amer. Anthropol., Menasha, n.s., vol.46, no.2, pt.1, pp.269-272, pl.1, Apr.-June, 1944.

BAIT FOR SMALL MAMMALS. Lowell E. Swenson. Jour. Mamm., vol.34, no.1, p.137, Feb., 1953.

DIFFERENTIAL RESPONSE TO LIVE TRAPS OF MARKED AND UNMARKED SMALL MAMMALS. Ryo Tanaka. Annot. Zool. Japonenses, Tokyo, vol.29, no.1, pp.44-51, illus., Mar., 1956.

ON THE ANIMAL TRAPS OF AINU TRIBE KEPT IN THE MUSEUM OF HOKKAIDO UNIVERSITY. T.Tsujii. Trans. Mamm. Soc. Japan, no.8, pp.70-71, illus., Feb., 1954. (In Japanese.)

CATCH' EM ALIVE-O! Jour. Bengal Nat. Hist. Soc., Darjeeling, vol.17, no.4, p. 125, illus., 1943.

TULAREMIA see DISEASES AND PARASITES -- TULAREMIA

VERNACULAR NAMES see COMMON NAMES

## VOCALIZATIONS AND ORIENTATION

PRODUCTION OF ULTRASONIC SOUNDS BY LABORATORY RATS AND OTHER MAMMALS. John W. Anderson. Science, vol.119, no.3101, pp.808-809, June 4, 1954.

UNEXPLAINED DIRECTION SENSE OF VERTEBRATES. William J. Beecher. Scientific Monthly, Lancaster, vol.75, no.1, pp.19-25, illus., July, 1952.

ECOLOGICAL BASES OF ORIENTATION. David E. Davis. Proceedings of a Conf. on Orientation in Animals, Office of Naval Research, Washington, pp.183-192, 1954.

SPEECH: ITS FUNCTION AND DEVELOPMENT. Grace A. De Laguna. New Haven, Yale Univ. Press, vol.8, pp.xii, pls.363, 1927.

MARINE MAMMALS OF THE PACIFIC WITH PARTICULAR REFERENCE TO THE PRODUCTION OF UNDERWATER SOUND. Marie Poland Fish. Woods Hole Oceanographic Inst., Tech. Rept., no.8, Office of Naval Research, pp.69(mimeog.), July, 1949.

ORIENTATION OF ANIMALS. Gottfried Fraenkel, Donald L. Gunn. Oxford Univ. Press.

LISTENING IN THE DARK. (Ultrasonic Voices of Bats and Sounds Produced by Bird, Fish, and Whales.) Donald R.Griffin. Yale Univ. Press, New Haven, Conn., 1958.

(ANIMALS THAT I HEARD CALLING, WHISPERING, AND SPEAKING.) Tiere, die ich rufen, raunen und reden hoerte. Wilhelm Juessen. Deutsche Jagd, Berlin, nos.44-45, pp.597-598, Feb. 2, 1940.

ANIMAL SOUNDS AND COMMUNICATION. W.E. Lanyon, W.N. Tavolga (Editors). Amer. Inst. of Biological Sciences, Washington, D.C.

HELLO! DO YOU HEAR ME? E.Laurence Palmer. Nature Mag., Washington, D.C., vol.36, no.2, pp.81-88, illus., Feb., 1943.

(MAKING THE SOUNDS OF ANIMALS UNDERSTANDABLE.) Sichtbarmachung tierischer Laute. B. Schmid. Biol. Zentralblatt, vol.48, pp.513-521, figs.5, 1928.

PSYCHOLOGICAL PROBLEMS IN THE ORIENTATION OF MAMMALS. T. C. Schneirla. Proceedings of a Conf. on Orientation in Animals, Off. of Naval Research, Washington, pp.193-207, 1954.

SURVIVAL VALUE OF VOICE IN SMALL MAMMALS. Hobart M. Smith. Jour.Mamm., vol.25, no.4, p.407, Dec. 12, 1944.

WEIGHTS AND MEASUREMENTS see ANATOMY -- WEIGHTS AND MEASUREMENTS

## WHALING AND SEALING

WHALES AND SEALS AS RESOURCES OF THE SEA. Robert Clarke. Norsk Hvalfangst-Tidende (Norwegian Whaling Gazette), Sandefjord, vol.43, no.9, pp.489-510, Sep., 1954. (In Norwegian and English.)

BIOLOGY AND WHALING IN THE SEAS OF THE FAR EAST. M.M. Sleptov. Food Industry Publ. House, Moscow, pp.64, illus., 1955. (In Russian.)

NOTES ON THE SEAL AND WHALE-FISHERY OF 1881. Thomas Southwell. Proc. Nat. Hist. Soc. Glasgow, pp.215-221, Feb. 28, 1882.

NOTES ON THE SEAL AND WHALE FISHERY OF 1884. Thomas Southwell. Zoologist, London, ser.3, vol.9, no.99, pp.81-88, Mar., 1885.

NOTES ON THE SEAL AND WHALE FISHERY OF 1885. Thomas Southwell. Zoologist, London, pp.98-102, Mar., 1886.

NOTES ON THE SEAL AND WHALE FISHERY OF 1886. Thomas Southwell. Zoologist, London, pp.182-189, May, 1887.

NOTES ON THE SEAL AND WHALE FISHERY OF 1887. Thomas Southwell. Zoologist, London, vol.46 (ser.3, vol.12), no.136, pp.121-128, Apr., 1888.

NOTES ON THE SEAL AND WHALE FISHERY OF 1888. Thomas Southwell. Zoologist, vol.47 (ser.3, vol.13), no. 148, pp.121-126, Apr., 1889.

NOTES ON THE SEAL AND WHALE FISHERY OF 1890. Thomas Southwell. Zoologist, London, vol.49 (ser.3, vol. 15), no.172, pp.121-126, Apr., 1891.

NOTES ON THE SEAL AND WHALE FISHERY OF 1891. Thomas Southwell. Zoologist, London, vol.50 (ser.3, vol. 16), no.183, pp.100-105, Mar., 1892.

NOTES ON THE SEAL AND WHALE FISHERY OF 1892. Thomas Southwell. Zoologist, London, (ser.3, vol.17) no. 195, pp.81-89, Mar., 1893.

NOTES ON THE SEAL AND WHALE FISHERY OF 1894. Thomas Southwell. Zoologist, London, vol.53 (ser.3, vol. 19), no.219, pp.91-95, Mar., 1895.

NOTES ON THE SEAL AND WHALE FISHERY OF 1895. Thomas Southwell. Zoologist, London, vol.54 (ser.3, vol. 20), no.230, pp.41-46, Feb., 1896.

NOTES ON THE SEAL AND WHALE FISHERY OF 1896. Thomas Southwell. Zoologist, London, vol.55 (ser.4, vol. 1), no.668, pp.49-55, 1896.

NOTES ON THE SEAL AND WHALE FISHERY OF 1897. Thomas Southwell. Zoologist, London, vol.56 (ser.4, vol. 2), no.680, pp.69-77, Feb., 1898.

NOTES ON THE SEAL AND WHALE FISHERY OF 1898. Thomas Southwell. Zoologist, London, vol.57 (ser.4, vol. 3), no.693, pp.103-112, Mar., 1899.

NOTES ON THE SEAL AND WHALE FISHERY OF 1899. Thomas Southwell. Zoologist, London, vol.58 (ser.4, vol. 4), no.704, pp.65-73, Feb., 1900.

NOTES ON THE SEAL AND WHALE FISHERY OF 1900. Thomas Southwell. Zoologist, London, vol.59 (ser.4, vol. 5), no.717, pp.81-90, Mar., 1901.

NOTES ON THE SEAL AND WHALE FISHERY OF 1901. Thomas Southwell. Zoologist, London, vol.69 (ser.4, vol. 6), no.728, pp.41-48, Feb., 1902.

NOTES ON THE SEAL AND WHALE FISHERY OF 1902. Thomas Southwell. Zoologist, London, vol.61, (ser.4, vol. 7), no.740, pp.53-58, Feb., 1903.

NOTES ON THE SEAL AND WHALE FISHERY FOR 1903. Thomas Southwell. Zoologist, London, vol.62 (ser.4, vol. 8), no.752, pp.57-65, Feb., 1904.

NOTES ON THE SEAL AND WHALE FISHERY OF 1904. Thomas Southwell. Zoologist, London, vol.63 (ser.4, vol. 9), no.763, pp.22-30, Jan., 1905.

SEA-HUNTERS. Edouard A. Stackpole. J.B. Lippincott Co., New York, pp.510, 1953.

HISTORY OF THE FISHERIES OF NEW SOUTH WALES; WITH A SKETCH OF THE LAWS BY WHICH THEY HAVE BEEN REGULATED. Lindsay G. Thompson. Sydney, pp.1-126, pls.1-4, 1893.

MEMOIRS ON WHALES AND SEALS. William Turner. 1880-1888.

FUR-SEAL, SEA OTTER, AND SALMON FISHERIES. ACTS OF CONGRESS, PRESIDENT'S PROCLAMATIONS, REGULATIONS GOVERNING U. S. VESSELS, ACTS OF PARLIAMENT, ORDERS IN COUNCIL, PERTAINING TO THE FUR-SEAL FISHERIES IN BERING SEA AND NORTH PACIFIC OCEAN, SEA OTTER REGULATIONS, LAWS AS TO SALMON FISHERIES IN ALASKA. U.S. Revenue-Cutter Service. Treasury Dept. Doc. no.1850, Office of Division of Revenue Cutter Service, Washington, Govt. Print. Off., pp.78, 1896.

WILDLIFE CONSERVATION see CONSERVATION, WILDLIFE

WORMS see DISEASES AND PARASITES -- WORMS

## ZOOS

(DEVELOPMENT OF THE COPENHAGEN ZOO FROM 1859 TO THE GIRAFFE ACESSIONS OF 1939.) Werdegang des Kopenhagener Zoos von 1859 bis zur Giraffenanlange 1939. Th. Alving. Zool. Garten, vol.14, nos 1-2, pp.48-54, illus., 1942.

(ZOOLOGICAL GARDEN IN THE MELTING POT, PAST, PRESENT, FUTURE.) Zoologisk Have i Støbeskeen, Fortid, Nutid, Fremtid. Th. Alving. Copenhagen, pp.206, with 303 photographs, 4 maps and plans, 1934.

ZOOLOGICAL GARDENS. Ethan Allen Andrews. I. Scientific Monthly, Lancaster, vol.53, no.1, pp.5-21, illus., July, 1941.

ZOOLOGICAL GARDENS. Ethan Allen Andrews. II. Scientific Monthly, Lancaster, vol.53, no.2, pp.116-132, illus., Aug., 1941.

(REMARKS ON SOME ANIMALS OF THE WEIDHOLZ IMPORTS, 1927 AND 1928.) Bemerkungen ueber einige Tiere der Weidholz-Importe 1927 and 1928. Otto Antonius. Zool. Garten, Leipzig, n.F., vol.1, nos. 10-12, pp.369-390, figs.17, Apr., 1929.

(REMARKS ON THE ANIMALS OF THE WEIDHOLZ IMPORTS OF 1930.) Bemerkungen zu den Tieren des Weidholz-Imports 1930. Otto Antonius. Zool. Garten, Leipzig, n.F., vol.4, nos.6-7, pp.204-222, figs.1-22, July, 1931.

NOTES ON ANIMALS NOW, OR RECENTLY, LIVING IN THE NATIONAL ZOOLOGICAL PARK. A.B. Baker. Smithsonian Misc.Coll., vol.59, no.9, pub.2085, p.4, pl.1, May 17, 1912.

NATIONAL ZOOLOGICAL PARK AND ITS INHABITANTS. Frank Baker. Smithsonian Rep. for 1914, pp.445-478, pls.1-41, 1915.

FROM ANTEATER TO ANT. SOME NOTES FROM THE ZOO. (Photographs of great anteater and aardvark.) Burgees Barnett. Field, London, vol.167, no.4343, p.656, illus., Mar. 21, 1936.

GUIDE BOOK, CHICAGO ZOOLOGICAL PARK. Robert Bean. Chicago Zool. Soc., pp.100, illus., folded map, 1937. (Mammals, pp.20-62.)

DR. BEEBE SURVEYS THE MID-VISTAS OF ZOO LIFE. William Beebe. Animal Kingdom, New York, vol.47, no.2, pp. 37-41, illus., Mar.-Apr., 1944.

OUR ZOO'S FORMER INHABITANTS. William Beebe. Animal Kingdom, New York, vol.46, no.5, pp.111-116, illus., Sep.-Oct., 1943.

ANIMALS AND ZOOS TODAY. R.Bigalke. Cassell and Co., Ltd., London, Toronto, Melbourne and Sydney, vol.8, pp.190, illus., 1939.

(RARE ANIMALS IN THE NEW YORK, WASHINGTON, AND PHILADELPHIA ZOOS.) Les animaux rares dans les zoos de New York, Washington, et Philadelphia. Francois-Edmond Blanc. La Terre et La Vie, vol.7, no. 3, pp.65-75, May-June, 1937.

(MAMMALS OF THE "LIVING GARDEN" OF CAPE FERRAT.) Les mammifères du "Jardin animé" du Cap Ferrat. L.Bognar, E. Bourdelle. La Terrre et la Vie, Paris, no.1, pp.22-27, illus., 1956.

(MAMMALOGICAL AND ORNITHOLOGICAL FAUNA OF THE FRENCH COLONIES AT THE MENAGERIE OF THE MUSEUM OF NATURAL HISTORY(JARDIN DES PLANTES).) La faune mammalogique et ornithologique des colonies Francaises à la menagerie du Muséum d'Historie Naturelle (Jardin des Plantes). E. Bourdelle. La Terre et la Vie (Revue d'Hist.Nat.), vol.2, no.2, pp.107-111, illus., Feb., 1932.

(MAMMALS AND BIRDS FROM FRENCH COLONIES REPRESENTED IN 1931 AT THE MENAGERIE OF THE NATIONAL MUSEUM OF NATURAL HISTORY (JARDIN DES PLANTES).) Mammifères et oiseaux des colonies Francaises represéntes en 1931 a la ménagerie du Museum National d'Histoire Naturelle (Jardin des Plantes). E.Bourdelle. Bull. Mus. Nat. Hist. Nat., Paris, ser.2, vol.3, no.7, pp.586-601, Nov., 1931.

℞ FOR MAN OR BEAST. William Bridges. Animal Kingdom, New York, vol.54, no.2, pp.34-42, illus., Apr., 1951.

RARE, THE STRANGE, AND THE BEAUTIFUL. William Bridges. Animal Kingdom, New York, vol.48, no.5, pp.126-134, illus., Oct. 8, 1945.

NEW HOUSTON ZOO PLANS. C.L.Brock. Parks and Recreation, vol.9, no.4, pp. 408-410, illus., Apr., 1926.

ORNAMENTAL CONCRETE IN HOUSTON ZOO. C.L. Brock. Parks and Recreation, vol.12, pp.173-176, illus., Apr., 1929.

FROM SINGAPORE TO THE ZOO. (Experiences of a collector of live animals.) Frank H. Buck. Asia, vol.22, pp.816-822, 841, 843, Oct., 1922.

SOMETHING IN FAVOR OF ZOOS. Maurice Burton. Illus. London News, vol.216, no. 5787, p.426, illus., Mar. 18, 1950.

VISIT TO THE WHIPSNADE ZOOLOGICAL PARK. R.W. Burton. Jour. Bombay Nat. Hist. Soc., vol.36, no.4, pp.878-883, Dec. 15, 1933.

(ZOOLOGICAL GARDEN OF ROME.) Le Jardin Zoologique de Rome. Monti Della Corte. La Terre et La Vie, Paris, Annee 4e, no.11, pp.612-621, illus., Nov., 1934.

OLD TIMERS IN THE ZOOLOGICAL PARK. Lee S. Crandall. Animal Kingdom, New York, vol.52, no.6, pp.175-177, Dec. 5, 1949.

ZOO-OLOGY. Kenneth Christ. Zoonooz, Zool. Soc. San Diego, vol.12, no.7, p. 5, July, 1940.

(PARK ANIMALS.) Animaux de Parc. J. Delacour. La Terre et la Vie (Revue d'Hist. Nat.), vol.1, no.9, pp.566-571, illus., Oct., 1931.

(ZOOLOGICAL PARK OF WHIPSNADE.) Le Parc Zoologique de Whipsnade. J. Delacour. La Terre et la Vie (Revue d'Hist. Nat.), vol.1, no.8, pp.473-479, illus., Sep., 1931.

GUIDE TO THE NEW YORK ZOOLOGICAL PARK. Raymond L. Ditmars. New York Zool. Soc., pp.xiv-258, illus., 1939.(Mammals, pp.1-104, illus.)

ZOOLOGICAL PARK NOTES. Raymond L. Ditmars. Zool. Soc. Bull., vol.24, pp.115-118, Sep., 1921.

THREE ZOOLOGICAL EXHIBITS. J. Guy Dollman. Proc. Linn. Soc. London, session 147, 1934-35, pt.1, pp.21-23, pl.1, Mar. 6, 1935.

GIANT FOREST HOG EXPECTED AT THE ZOO; AND OTHER SPECIMENS. K.C.Gandar Dower. Illus. London News, vol.189, no. 5083, pp.463, 465, illus., Sep. 19, 1936.

(GUIDE TO THE COPENHAGEN ZOOLOGICAL GARDENS.) Veileder i Zoologisk Have. W. Dreyer. Copenhagen, pp.72, figs., 1921; 1922.

ZOO CELEBRITIES. Sam Dunton. Animal Kingdom, New York, vol.51, no.6, pp.174-179, illus., Nov.-Dec., 1948.

FLYING MAMMALS AT THE ZOO. James Fisher. Field, London, vol.175, no.4566, p.1004, fig.1, June 29, 1940.

MAMMALS. LIST OF THE VERTEBRATED ANIMALS EXHIBITED IN THE GARDENS OF THE ZOOLOGICAL SOCIETY OF LONDON 1828-1927. S.S. Flower. London, vol. 1, pp.11-419, 1929.

NOTES ON EIGHT CONTINENTAL ZOOLOGICAL GARDENS VISITED IN 1929. S.S. Flower. Proc. Zool. Soc. London for 1929, pt.4, pp.659-669, pls.1-2, Feb., 1930.

LIST OF ANIMALS. (2d Ed.) S.S.Flower. Special Report no.5, Zool.Gardens, Giza, near Cairo, Public Works Dept., Gov't. Egypt, Cairo, pp.372, pls.19, 1910.

BABIES OF OUR ZOO ANIMALS. Daniel W. Gates. News Bull. Staten Island Zool. Soc., Inc., vol.8, no.4, pp.3-4, illus., July, 1941.

NATIONAL ZOOLOGICAL PARK OF SCOTLAND. T.H. Gillespie. Zoologische Garten, Leipzig, n.F., vol.10, nos.3-4, pp. 141-147, illus., 1938.

(ZOOLOGICAL GARDENS AND ANIMAL PARKS OF THE RUSSIAN EMPIRE.) Die Zoologischen Garten und Tierparks des russischen Reichs. Heinz Graupner. Zool. Garten, n.F., Leipzig, vol.7, nos.4-6, pp.136-137, Aug., 1934.

CLEANING FROM THE MENAGERIE AND AVIARY AT KNOWSLEY HALL. John Edward Gray. Hoofed Quadrupeds, Knowsley, pp.76, pls.59, 1850.

NOTICE OF AN APE (MACACUS INORNATUS) AND A BUSHBOCK (CEPHALOPHUS BREVICEPS) IN THE GARDENS OF THE SOCIETY. John Edward Gray. Proc. Zool. Soc. London for 1866, pp.202-203, pls.xix-xx, 1866.

FAR-DISTANT ZOOLOGICAL PARKS. THE NATIONAL ZOOLOGICAL GARDENS OF SOUTH AFRICA, AT PRETORIA. A. K. Haagner. Zool. Soc. Bull., vol.24, pp.103-109, figs.17, Sep., 1921.

GUIDE TO THE NATIONAL ZOOLOGICAL GARDENS OF SOUTH AFRICA. A.K. Haagner. Pretoria, pp.1-54, many illus., Oct., 1921.

STOCKING A HOME ZOO. Robert T. Hatt. Nat. Hist., vol.32, no.6, pp.529-538, illus., Nov.-Dec., 1932.

WHY IS A ZOO? CONCERNING THE PLACE OF CAGED ANIMALS IN SOCIETY. Stephen Haweis. Nature Mag., vol.14, no.3, pp.146-150, figs.8, Sep., 1929.

WILD ANIMALS OF THE WORLD; BEING A POPULAR GUIDE TO TARONGA ZOOLOGICAL PARK. Charles Hedley.Pub.by Taronga Zoological Park, Sydney, Australia, pp.128, figs., 1923.

WE PRESENT YACOB, OUR OLDEST AND LARGEST MAMMAL. Edmund Heller. Bull. Wash. Park Zool.Soc., Milwaukee, vol.2, no.I, pp.7-8, photo, Dec., 1931.

SOME RARE AND INTERESTING CARNIVORA AND UNGULATA OF THE MOSCOW ZOOLOGICAL GARDENS. V.G. Heptner. Proc. Moscow Zool. Park, vol.1, pp.45-49, 1940.

ATMOSPHERIC CONDITIONS AT THE ZOOLOGICAL GARDENS, LONDON. Leonard Hill. Proc. Zool. Soc. London, 1924, pp. 333-343, July, 1924.

RECENT ADDITIONS TO THE LONDON ZOO. Edward Hindle. Nature, London, vol.158, no.4018, p.637, Nov. 2, 1946.

ANIMALS IN THE NATIONAL ZOOLOGICAL PARK. N. Hollister. Smiths. Rep. for 1923, pp.291-338, pls.29, June, 1925.

COLLECTIONS OF LIVING ANIMALS FOR THE NATIONAL ZOOLOGICAL PARK. N. Hollister. Smiths. Misc. Coll., vol.72, no.6, pp.59-63, May, 1921.

MODERN MENAGERIE: MORE ABOUT THE NATIONAL ZOOLOGICAL PARK.N.Hollister. Smiths. Inst., Ann. Rep., 1924, pp.249-278, pls.1-18, Oct. 24, 1925.

NATIONAL ZOOLOGICAL PARK: A POPULAR ACCOUNT OF ITS COLLECTIONS. N. Hollister. Smiths. Inst., Ann. Rep., 1917, pp.543-593, pls.1-46, 1919.

NATIONAL ZOOLOGICAL PARK: A POPULAR ACCOUNT OF ITS COLLECTIONS. N. Hollister. Smiths. Inst., Ann. Rep., pp.543-593, Jan., 1920.

POPULAR GUIDE TO THE NATIONAL ZOOLOGICAL PARK. N. Hollister.Smithsonian Inst., pp.1-60, pls.1-46, Oct., 1920.

POPULAR GUIDE TO THE NATIONAL ZOOLOGICAL PARK. Second Edition. N. Hollister. Smiths. Inst., pp.106, map, figs.95, Oct. 13, 1923.

POPULAR OFFICIAL GUIDE TO THE NEW YORK ZOOLOGICAL PARK. William T. Hornaday. N.Y.Zool.Soc., 8th ed., pp.1-113, illus., June 1, 1906.

POPULAR OFFICIAL GUIDE TO THE NEW YORK ZOOLOGICAL PARK. William T. Hornaday. N.Y. Zool.Soc., 12th ed., pp.192, illus., June 1, 1913.

POPULAR OFFICIAL GUIDE TO THE NEW YORK ZOOLOGICAL PARK. William T. Hornaday. N.Y. Zool.Soc., 8th ed., pp.192, maps, illus., Aug., 1923.

WILD-ANIMAL ROUND-UP. William T. Hornaday. New York, Charles Scribner's Sons, pp.372, pls.64, 1925.

EUROPEAN ZOOS--HOW THEY HAVE FARED. Robert G. Hudson, and others. Fauna, Philadelphia, vol.7, no.3, pp. 82-85, illus., Sep., 1945.

SCOTLAND'S ZOO PARK. Robert Hurd. Field, London, vol.158, no.4114, pp.654-655, illus., Oct. 31, 1931.

SIESTA TIME IN THE ZOO. Winifred E. King. San Diego Zoonooz, vol.20, no.8, pp.5-6, illus., Aug., 1947.

(ZOOLOGICAL GARDENS, ANIMAL PARKS, AND PUBLIC AQUARIUMS OF THE WORLD.) Die Zoologischen Gaerten, Tierparks und Schauaquarien der Welt. Hans Kummerloewe, Heinz Graupner. Zool. Garten, n.F., Leipzig, vol.6, nos.10-12, pp.271-275, Dec., 1933.

NEW ANIMALS AGAIN. THREE PRIZES ARRIVE IN A SINGLE SHIPMENT:BAMBOO RATS FROM SIAM, CONEYS AND THE ROOI RHEBOK FROM AFRICA. Claude W. Leister. Bull. New York Zool. Soc., vol. 40, no.4, pp.113-115, figs.3, July-Aug., 1937.

ZOO COMES TO YOU. Burr W. Leyson, Ruth Manecke. Dutton, New York, pp.88, illus., 1954.

(ON REMARKABLE NEW MAMMALS OF THE IMPERIAL ZOOLOGICAL MUSEUM.) Ueber neue merkwuerdige Saeugethiere des Koeniglichen Zoologischen Museums. H. Lichtenstein, W. Peters. Abhandlg.Koenigl. Akad. Wiss. Berlin., 1854, pp.81-101, pls. 3, 1855.

ANIMALS OUTSIDE THE ZOO. Joseph W. Lippincott. Fauna, Philadelphia, vol.3, no.1, pp.12-13, illus., Mar., 1941.

ZOO BABIES. THIS SPRING'S LIST OF NEW ARRIVALS IS THE LARGEST IN SEVERAL YEARS, AND IT INCLUDES A NUMBER OF RARITIES. Claude W. Luister. Animal Kingdom, New York, vol.45, no.3, pp.59-61, illus., May-June, 1942.

EARLY NEW YORKERS LIKED ANIMAL SHOWS. Robert McClung, Gale McClung. Animal Kingdom, New York Zool. Soc., vol.60, no.3, pp.88-93, June, 1957.

BRIEF HISTORY OF THE ZOO. William M. Mann. Scientific Monthly, Lancaster, vol.63, no.5, pp.350-358, illus., Nov., 1946. (National Zoological Park, Washington, D.C.)

(COMMUNICATIONS ON THE MAMMALS OF THE BERLIN ZOOLOGICAL GARDEN AND MUSEUM.) Mittheilungen ueber Saeugethiere des Berliner Zoologischen Gartens und Museums. Paul Matschie. Gesell. Naturf. Freunde, Berlin, no.5, pp.72-74, May 18, 1897.

(NEW MAMMALS FROM THE COLLECTIONS OF MESSRS. ZENKER, NEUMANN, STUHLMANN, AND EMIN.) Neue Saeugetiere aus den Sammlungen der Herren Zenker, Neumann, Stuhlmann, und Emin. Paul Matschie. Sitz.-Ber. Gesell. Naturf. Freunde, Berlin, no.8, pp.194-206, Oct. 16, 1894.

(SOME NEW ACQUISITIONS OF THE BERLIN ZOOLOGICAL GARDEN.) Einige Neuerwerbungen des Berliner Zoologischen Gartens. Paul Matschie. Sitz.-Ber.Gesell. Naturf. Freunde, Berlin, no.10, pp.220-223, Dec. 20, 1892.

(TWO UNGULATES, APPARENTLY NEVER BEFORE DESCRIBED, OF THE BERLIN ZOOLOGICAL GARDEN.) Zwei anscheinend noch nicht beschriebene Hufthiere des Berliner Zoologischen Gartens. Paul Matschie. Sitz-Ber. Gesell. Naturf. Freunde, Berlin, no.9, pp.156-158, Nov. 16, 1897.

OFFICIAL GUIDE TO THE GARDENS OF THE ZOOLOGICAL SOCIETY OF LONDON. P. Chalmers Mitchell. 7th ed. London, pp.96, illus.32, London, 1919.

OFFICIAL GUIDE TO THE GARDENS OF THE ZOOLOGICAL SOCIETY OF LONDON. P. Chalmers Mitchell. 19th ed., pp. 112, illus.52, 1921.

ILLUSTRATED OFFICIAL GUIDE TO THE LONDON ZOOLOGICAL SOCIETY'S GARDENS IN REGENT'S PARK. P. Chalmers Mitchell. 20th ed., pp.112, illus., 1922.

OFFICIAL GUIDE TO THE GARDENS OF THE ZOOLOGICAL SOCIETY OF LONDON. P. Chalmers Mitchell. London, 20th ed., pp.110, illus., 1923.

OFFICIAL GUIDE TO THE GARDENS OF THE ZOOLOGICAL SOCIETY OF LONDON. P. Chalmers Mitchell. 22nd ed., pp.107, illus., 1924.

(ZOOLOGICAL GARDEN OF ODENSE.) Tiergarten in Odense. Erna Mohr. Zool. Garten, n.F., Leipzig, vol.6, nos.4-6, pp.126-129, July, 1933.

FAR-DISTANT PARKS OF ZOOLOGY. I. ZOOLOGICAL PARK OF LIMA, PERU. Robert Cushman Murphy. Zool. Soc. Bull., vol.23, pp.95-100, Sep., 1920.

MONTEZUMA'S ZOO. H.B. Nicholson. Pacific Discovery, California Acad. Sci., vol.8, no.4, pp.3-11, July-Aug., 1955.

MAMMALS OF CIRCUS AND ZOO. Edith A. Pickard. Science Guide for Elementary Schools, vol.3, no.6, pp.1-57, illus., Jan., 1937.

NOTABLE ANIMALS AT THE ZOOLOGICAL GARDENS. R.I. Pocock. Field, London, vol.150, p.612, Oct. 13, 1927.

PRINCE OF WALES'S COLLECTION AT THE ZOOLOGICAL GARDENS. R.I.Pocock. Conquest, London, vol.3, no.33, pp.366-370, figs.8, July, 1922.

COLLECTING FOR A ZOO. A.C. Russell. Nigerian Field, vol.14, no.1, pp.10-19, pls. 10, Jan., 1949.

(ON THE EXISTENCE RIGHT OF ZOOLOGICAL GARDENS.) Vom Daseinsrecht der Zoologischen Gaerten. Karl Max Schneider. Zool. Garten, n.F., Leipzig, vol.8, nos. 7-9, pp.173-179, June, 1936.

(REMARKS ON THE EAST AFRICAN ANIMALS IMPORTED IN 1929 BY CHRISTOPH SCHYLZ.) Bemerkungen ueber die von Christoph Schylz 1929 eingefuehrten ostafrikanischen Tieren. Karl Max Schneider. Zool. Garten, n.F., Leipzig, vol.3, nos. 1-3, pp.19-28, pls.1-16, May, 1930.

(COMPARATIVE BIOLOGICAL MORPHOLOGY AND ZOO KEEPING.) Vergleichende biologische Morphologie und Tiergaertnerei. H. Schreiber. Zool. Garten, n.F., Leipzig, vol.10, nos.3-4, pp.131-139, illus., Sep., 1938.

EXHIBITION OF A LIVING SPECIMEN OF THE PEGUAN TREE SHREW (TUPAIA PEGUANA) AND A SQUIRREL (SCIURUS BLANFORDI). Philip Lutley Sclater.Proc. Zool. Soc. London, p.82, 1875.

NOTICE OF SEVERAL ADDITIONS TO THE MENAGERIE. Philip Lutley Sclater. Proc. Zool. Soc. London, pp.256-257, 1865.

REPORT ON ADDITIONS TO THE SOCIETY'S MENAGERIE DURING THE MONTH OF MAY, AND DESCRIPTION OF CERVUS ALFREDI. Philip Lutley Sclater. Proc. Zool. Soc. London, pp.380-384, figs.2, pl.28, 1870.

STRANGE ARRIVALS AT THE ZOO--TWO PECULIAR PIGS, A GOAT-ANTELOPE, AND SOME "DEVILS." D. Seth-Smith. Field, London, vol.158, no.4115, p.693, illus., Nov. 7, 1931.

WHEN WINTER COMES TO WHIPSNADE. ANIMALS WHICK LIKE THE SNOW. D. Seth-Smith. Field,London, vol.162, no. 4222, pp.1364-1365, illus., Nov. 25, 1933.

CAGE SERVICE. Freeman M. Shelly.Fauna, Philadelphia, vol.1, no.3, pp.46-50, illus., Sep., 1939; Parks and Recreation, Rockford, vol.23, no.2, pp.68-74, illus., Oct., 1939.

CINCINNATI ZOO GUIDE. Sol A. Stephan. Cincinnati Zoological Park Assoc., pp.132, map, illus., 1923.

(ANIMAL PARK OF THE INTERNATIONAL FUR AND HUNTING EXPOSITION OF LEIPZIG, 1930.) Der Tierpark der Internationalen Pelzfach-und Jagdausstellung Leipzig 1930. Dr. W. Stichel. Zeitschr. f. Saeugetierk., vol.8, no.5, pp.228-273, Dec. 20, 1933.

(FROM THE ZOOLOGICAL GARDEN IN LENINGRAD.) Aus dem Zoologischen Garten zu Leningrad. A. Stieren. Zool. Garten, Leipzig, n.F., vol.2, nos.7-9, pp.229-230, Jan., 1930.

(ZOO NEWS FROM RUSSIA.) Tiergartnerisches aus Russland. A. Stieren. Zool. Garten, n.F., Leipzig, vol.6, nos.1-3, p.60, May, 1933.

ZOOLOGICAL PARK IN NEW ZEALAND. Dayton Stoner. Proc. Iowa Acad. Sci., Des Moines, vol.30, pp.143-145, 1923.

CLIPPING HISTORY. Ken Stott, Jr. San Diego Zoonooz, vol.16, no.2, pp.3-4, Feb., 1943.

NEWS FROM THE ZOOS. E.H. Tong, Moira Kelham. Zoo Life, London, vol.10, no.4, pp.120-126, illus., Winter, 1955-1956.

PROVISIONAL PLAN FOR A COLLECTION OF MAMMALS TO BE EXHIBITED AT THE WORLD'S INDUSTRIAL AND COTTON CENTENNIAL EXPOSITION OF 1884-85, AT NEW ORLEANS. Frederick W. True. Proc. U.S. Nat. Museum, vol.7, pp.585-586, 1885. (Also published as Circular 29, U.S.Nat.Mus.)

COMMERCIAL VALUE OF A ZOOLOGICAL GARDEN. George P. Vierheller. Parks and Recreation, vol.9, no.2, pp.176-178, Nov.-Dec., 1925.

SAN DIEGO ZOO'S NEW RESEARCH HOSPITAL. Harry M. Wegeforth. Parks and Recreation, vol.9, pp.565-567, June, 1926.

ANIMAL MODELS. Walter J. Wilwerding. Fauna, Philadelphia, vol.2, no.1, pp.3-7, illus., Mar., 1940.

(NEWS FROM THE ZOOLOGICAL GARDEN OF BERLIN.) Neues aus dem Zoologischen Garten Berlin. F.X.G. Zedtwitz. Zool. Garten, n.F., vol.4, nos.1-2, pp.13-16, figs.1-3, Feb., 1931.

(ON SOME RARE AND PRECIOUS ANIMALS IN CARL HAGENBECK'S ANIMAL PARK.) Ueber einige seltene und kostbare Tiere in Carl Hagenbecks Tierpark. L. Zukowsky. Zool.Beobachter, vol.55, pp.228-234, 1914.

ANIMALS IN THE COLLECTION AS OF JUNE 30, 1933. National Zoological Park, pp.37, mimeogr., 1933.

ANIMALS IN THE NATIONAL ZOOLOGICAL PARK, JUNE 30, 1932. National Zoological Park, pp.12, mimeogr., 1932.

ANIMALS IN THE NATIONAL ZOOLOGICAL PARK, JUNE 30, 1935. National Zoological Park, pp.16, mimeogr., 1935.

BERTRAM MILLS CIRCUS. Illus. London News, vol.219, no.5880, p.1083, illus., Dec. 29, 1951.

"BRING 'EM BACK ALIVE"--AS MOVING PICTURES AND FOR EXHIBITION IN ZOOLOGICAL GARDENS. Illus. London News, vol.181, no.4866, pp.116-117, illus., July 23, 1932.

FIRST FIFTY YEARS OF THE NEW YORK ZOOLOGICAL PARK, AND A LOOK AHEAD. Animal Kingdom, New York, vol.52, no.6, pp.1-28, illus., Dec.5, 1949.

HERE AND THERE. San Diego Zoonooz, vol.19, no.10, p.5, illus., Oct., 1946. (Chinchilla, sloth, hedgehog, wallaby.)

NEW MAMMALS ON EXHIBITION. News Bull. Staten Island Zool. Soc., New York, vol.9, no.3, p.3, illus., May, 1942.

OUR FRIENDS AT THE ZOO. Milwaukee, Wisc., Washington Park Zoological Soc., vol.1, no.1, illus., mimeogr., Dec., 1936.

VALUE OF A MODERN NOAH'S ARK:SOME OF THE ANIMALS WHICH FIGURE IN THE LONDON ZOO'S STOCKTAKING, WITH THEIR PRICES--RANGING FROM A FEW PENCE TO HUNDREDS OF POUNDS. Illus. London News, vol.214, no.2730, pp.212-213, Feb. 12, 1949.

ZOO NEWS. Fauna, Philadelphia, vol.8, no.4, pp.126-127, illus., Dec., 1946.

## SELECTED LIST OF PERIODICALS

Academy of Natural Sciences, Proceedings, Philadelphia, Pa., 1841—.

Africana. African Life Publications, Ltd., Nairobi, Kenya, Africa, 1962—. Incorporates the Journal of East African Wild Life Society. Treats wide variety of African subjects, including mammals and conservation.

African Wild Life. Wild Life Protection Society of South Africa, Johannesburg, South Africa, 1946—. Treats many forms of animal life with emphasis on conservation.

American Midland Naturalist, Notre Dame, Ind., 1909—.

American Museum of Natural History, New York, N. Y.
American Museum Novitates, 1921—.
Bulletin, 1881—.
Natural History, 1900—.
Report, 1869—.

American Naturalist, Boston, Mass., 1867—.

America's First Zoo. Philadelphia Zoological Garden, Philadelphia, Pa., 1949—. Supersedes Fauna.

Anales del Universitie National de Mexico, 1930—.

Animal Kingdom. New York Zoological Society, New York, N.Y., 1912—. Of animals in the wild as well as in the zoo. Non-technical.

Animals. 37 Hertford St., London, W.1., England, Jan. 1963—. Edited by Armand Denis. Profusely illustrated in color, non-technical. Conservation emphasized.

Asiatic Society of Bengal, Calcutta, Journal and Proceedings. 1905—.

Archiv für Naturgeschichte; Zeitschrift für Systematische Zoologie. Akademische Verlagsgesellschaft, Leipzig, Germany, 1932-1944. Illustrated.

Arkiv för Zoologi. Svenska Vetenskaps akademien, Stockholm, Sweden, 1903—. In English, Swedish and German. Illustrated.

Australian Journal of Zoology. Commonwealth Scientific and Industrial Research Organization, Melbourne, Australia, 1953—. Illustrated.

Australian Museum, Records. Sydney, Australia, 1890—.

Australian Museum Magazine. Sydney, Australia, 1921—.

Biological Abstracts. Union of American Biological Societies, Philadelphia, Pa., 1926—.

Biological Society of Washington, Proceedings. 1880—.

Blue-Jay. Yorkton Natural History Society, Yorkton, Saskatchewan, Canada, 1942—.

Bombay Natural History Society, Journal. Bombay, India, 1886—.

Breviora. Museum of Comparative Zoology, Harvard College, Cambridge, Mass., 1952—. Illustrated.

British Museum, Natural History Division, Bulletin. London, England, 1950—.

California Academy of Sciences, Proceedings. San Francisco, Calif., 1854-76; 1888-96; 1907—.

California Fish and Game. California Board of Fish and Game Commissioners, San Francisco, Calif., 1914—.

Canadian Field-Naturalist. Ottawa Field Naturalists' Club, Ottawa, Canada, 1887—.

Canadian Journal of Research, Sec. D—Zoological Sciences. National Research Council of Canada, Ottawa, Canada, 1935—.

China Journal. China Society of Science and Arts; Shanghai Chemical Society, Shanghai, China, 1923—.

Colorado Outdoors. Colorado Game and Fish Dept., Denver, Colo., 1952—.

C.S.I.R.O. Wildlife Research. Wildlife Survey Section, Commonwealth Scientific and Industrial Research Organization, Melbourne, Australia, 1956—. Illustrated.

Cranbrook Institute of Science, Bulletin. Bloomfield Hills, Michigan, 1931—. Occasional articles regarding mammals.

Discovery; the popular journal of knowledge. London, England 1920-40.

East Africa and Uganda Natural History Society, Journal. London, England, 1910—.

Ecological Monographs. Ecological Society of America. Durham, North Carolina, 1931—.

Ecology. Ecological Society of America, Brooklyn, N.Y., 1920—. Supersedes Plant World.

Endeavour; a quarterly review designed to record the progress of the sciences in the service of mankind. Imperial Chemical Industries, London, England, 1942—. Illustrated.

Evolution. Society for the Study of Evolution, Lancaster, Pa., 1947—.

Fauna. Zoological Society of Philadelphia, Pa., 1939-48. Discontinued quarterly. Non-technical, broad zoological coverage. Illustrated.

Field. London, England, 1853—.

Field Museum of Natural History, Zoological Series. Chicago, Ill., 1895—. (See under Fieldiana, 1950—.)

Fieldiana. Zoology Memoirs, Natural History Museum, Chicago, Ill., 1950—.

Florida Academy of Sciences, Proceedings. Gainesville, Fla., 1936—.

Forest and Stream. New York, N.Y., 1873-1930.

Frontiers; a Magazine of Natural History. The Academy of Natural Sciences of Philadelphia, 1936—.

Harvard University, Museum of Comparative Zoology, Bulletin. Cambridge, Mass., 1863—.

Illinois Biological Monographs. University of Illinois, Urbana, Ill., 1914—.

Illustrated London News. London, England, 1842—.

Indiana Academy of Science, Proceedings. Indianapolis, Ind., 1891.

International Zoo News. Zoo-Centrum, Aalten, Netherlands. Mainly news of animals in zoos as submitted by zoos throughout the world. Illustrated.

Journal of Animal Ecology, British Ecological Society, London, England, 1932–.

Journal of Mammalogy. American Society of Mammalogists, Lawrence, Kan., 1919–. Technical publication, formerly published in Baltimore, Md. Officers change occasionally, but usually some key members are in the Division of Mammals, U.S. National Museum, Washington, D.C. Illustrated.

Journal of Wildlife Management. Wildlife Society, Menasha, Wis., 1937–.

Kansas Academy of Science, Transactions. 1872–. Appeared as the Transactions of the Kansas Natural History Society from 1868-71.

Koedoe; journal for scientific research in the national parks of the Union of South Africa. National Parks Board of Trustees, Pretoria, South Africa, 1958–. Text in English or Afrikaans. Illustrated.

Linnean Society of New South Wales, Proceedings. Sydney, Australia, 1875–.

Louisiana Academy of Sciences, Proceedings. 1932–.

Mammalia, morphologie, biologie, systématique des mammifères. Paris, France, 1936–. Text in English and French.

Mammalogical Society of Japan, Journal. Tokyo, Japan, 1952–. Text in Japanese and English.

Murrelet. Pacific Northwest Bird and Mammal Society, Seattle, Wash., 1920–. Treats mammals and birds. Officers and place of publication change.

Musée du Congo Belge, Annales, Zoologie. Tervueren, Belgium, 1898–.

Museum National d'histoire naturelle, Bulletin. Paris, France, 1895–.

National Geographic. National Geographic Society, Washington, D.C., 1889–. Occasional articles and pictures on mammals.

National Museum of Canada, Bulletin. 1913–.

Natural History. American Museum of Natural History, New York, N.Y., 1900–. Published monthly, October through May, bi-monthly, June to September. Non-technical, illustrated, treats of mammals and a wide range of subjects.

Nature. London, England 1869–. Illustrated.

Nature Magazine. Washington, D.C., 1923-1960. This periodical was absorbed by the American Museum of Natural History's publication, Natural History, January, 1960.

New York Zoological Society, Bulletin. New York, N.Y., 1897–. (This publication has been called the News Bulletin and the Zoological Society Bulletin at various times. Animal Kingdom, 1912–[see under that title].)

New Zealand Ecological Society, Proceedings. Wellington, New Zealand, 1952–.

Norsk Hvalfangst-Tidende. Sandefjord, Norway, 1912–. Whales and the whaling industry. Many papers in English as well as Norwegian.

North American Wildlife Conference, Proceedings. Wildlife Management Institute, Washington, D.C., 1936–.

Oryx. Fauna Preservation Society, Hertford, England, 1950–. Illustrated.

Pacific Discovery. California Academy of Sciences, San Francisco, Calif., 1948–. Illustrated monthly, semi-popular.

Pacific Naturalist. Beaudette Foundation for Biological Research, Solvang, Calif., 1958–.

Pacific Science; a quarterly devoted to the biological and physical sciences of the Pacific region. University of Hawaii, Honolulu, Hawaii, 1947–.

Pennsylvania Academy of Science, Proceedings. Harrisburg, Pa., 1924–.

Polar Record, The. Scott Polar Research Institute, Cambridge University Press, England, 1931–.

Priroda. Akademiia nauk, Leningrad, Russia, 1912–.

Queensland Museum, Memoirs. Brisbane, Australia, 1912–. Supersedes Annals, published from 1891-1911.

Raffles Museum and Library, Bulletin. Singapore, Malaya, 1928–. Illustrated.

Revue de Zoologie et de Botanique Africaines. Cercle Zoologique Congolais, Brussels, Belgium, 1911–.

Revue Suisse de Zoologie. Societe Zoologique Suisse, Musee d'Histoire Naturelle, Geneva, Switzerland, 1893–. Illustrated. Summaries in English.

Rijks Museum van Natuurlijke historie, Notes. Leyden, Netherlands, 1879-1914. Superseded by Zoologische mededeelingen, 1915–.

Royal Asiatic Society, of Great Britain and Ireland, Straits Branch, Journal. Singapore, Malaya, 1878-1922. Superseded by Malayan Branch, Journal, 1923–.

San Diego Society of Natural History, Transactions. 1905– (but suspended 1921-25).

Sarawak Museum Journal. Borneo Museum, Kuching, Sarawak, 1911–.

Säugetierkundliche Mitteilungen. Franckh'sche Verlagshandlung, Stuttgart, Germany, 1953–. Illustrated.

Science. Cambridge, Mass., 1883–.

Scottish Naturalist. Edinburgh, Scotland, 1912-1939.

Smithsonian Institution, Washington, D.C. Appendices to the Annual Report to the Board of Regents, 1846–. Miscellaneous Collections, 1862–. U.S. National Museum, Bulletin, 1875–. (See under U.S. National Museum.)

Société nationale d'acclimatation de France, Bulletin. Paris, France, 1854–.

Societas pro Fauna et Flora, Fennica, Helsingfors, Denmark. Acta, 1875–. Memorandum, 1924–.

Société Royale Zoologique de Belgique, Annales. Brussels, Belgium, 1863–.

South Australia Public Library, Museum and Art Gallery, Records. Adelaide, Australia, 1918–.

Southwestern Naturalist. Southwestern Association of Naturalists, Dallas, Tex., 1956–.

Thailand Research Society, Bangkok, Thailand. Journal, 1904–. (Known as the Journal of the Natural History Society of Siam, 1914-25). Natural History Supplement, 1914–.

U.S. National Museum, Washington, D.C. Bulletin, 1875–. Proceedings, 1878–.

University of California Publications in Zoology. Berkeley, Calif., 1902–.

University of Kansas. Museum of Natural History Publications. Lawrence, Kan., 1946–.

University of Michigan. Museum of Zoology, Miscellaneous Publications. Ann Arbor, Mich., 1916–.

Victoria National Museum, Memoirs. Victoria, Australia, 1906–(but suspended 1915-26).

Victorian Naturalist. Field Naturalists' Club of Victoria, Melbourne, Australia, 1884–. Illustrated.

Wild Life Review. Fish and Wildlife Service, Dept. of the Interior, Washington, D.C., 1935–.

Wisconsin Conservation Bulletin. State Conservation Dept., Madison, Wis., 1936–.

Zeitschrift für Säugetierkunde. Im Auftrage der Deutschen Gesellschaft für Säugetierkunde, Berlin, Germany, 1926-1943.

Zoo Life. Zoological Society of London, England, 1946–. Quarterly containing articles on the mammals in the Society's two zoos, as well as in the wild. Well illustrated, non-technical.

Zoologica. New York Zoological Society, New York, N.Y., 1907–. Illustrated. Includes bibliographies.

Zoological Record, London, England 1864–.

Zoological Society of London, Proceedings, 1833–. Transactions, 1835–.

Zoologicheskii Zhurnal. Moscow, Russia, 1916–. Russian, with summaries in English.

Zoologische Garten, Der. Akademische verlags gesellschaft, Leipzig, Germany, 1928–. Text in English, French and German. Illustrated.

Zoologische Jahrbucher. Jena, Germany, 1886–1929, but suspended 1913-1928. Illustrated.

Zoonooz. Zoological Society of San Diego, Calif., 1962–. (Had previously been published under same title, 1926-33.) Articles regarding animals in the zoo and wild. Well illustrated, non-technical.